W9-DEA-722

Sample Hospital Listing:

ANYTOWN, Universal County

⊠ **ANYTOWN HOSPITAL & CLINICS (777777)**, (Formerly Anytown Area Community Hospital and Clinic), 100 South Main Street, Zip 12345–6789; tel. 123/456–7890 **A**9 10] (1)
F10 12 23 24 29 30 31 37 39 49 51 55 57 64 65 66 68 70 71 72 77 78 83 87 88 91 96 97 106 107 110 111 113 124 **P**1 2 3 **S** Universal (7)
County Health System (2) (3)
Primary Contact: Ann M. Generic, Chief Executive Officer
COO: Ann M. Generic
CFO: Michael M. Generic (4)
CMO: Peterl Van Generic, President Medical Staff
CHR: Jerry Generic, Human Resources Director
CNO: Danielle Generic, R.N., Chief Nursing Officer
Web address: www.website.org
Control: Other not–for–profit (including NFP Corporation) **Service:** General (5)
Medical and Surgical

Staffed Beds: 25 **Admissions:** 892 **Census:** 9 **Outpatient Visits:** 44014
Births: 51 **Total Expense ($000):** 19210 **Payroll Expense ($000):** 5864 (6)
Personnel: 182

ANYTOWN, Universal County

⊠ **ANYTOWN HOSPITAL & CLINICS (777777)**, (Formerly Anytown Area Community Hospital and Clinic), 100 South Main Street, Zip 12345–6789; tel. 123/456–7890 **A**9 10

(1) = **Approval Codes**
(2) = **Physician Codes**
(3) = **Health Care System Name**
(4) = **Titles of Chief Administrators**
(5) = **Control and Service Classifications**
(6) = **Utilization Data**
(7) = **Facility Codes**

Hospital, Medicare Provider Number, Address, Telephone, Approval, Facility, and Physician Codes, Health Care System

★ American Hospital Association (AHA) membership
☐ The Joint Commission accreditation
◇ DNV Healthcare Inc. accreditation
○ Healthcare Facilities Accreditation Program
△ Commission on Accreditation of Rehabilitation Facilities (CARF) accreditation

(1) Approval Codes

Reported by the approving bodies specified, as of the dates noted.

1 Accreditation under the hospital program of The Joint Commission (June 2014).
2 Cancer program approved by American College of Surgeons (August 2014).
†3 Approval to participate in residency training, by the Accreditation Council for Graduate Medical Education (April 2014).
†5 Medical school affiliation, reported to the American Medical Association (April 2014).
6 Hospital–controlled professional nursing school, reported by National League for Nursing.
7 Accreditation by Commission on Accreditation of Rehabilitation Facilities (April 2014).

8 Member of Council of Teaching Hospitals of the Association of American Medical Colleges (April 2014).
9 Hospitals contracting or participating in a Plan, reported by the Blue Cross and Blue Shield Association (April 2014).
10 Certified for participation in the Health Insurance for the Aged (Medicare) Program by the Centers for Medicare and Medical Services (February 2014).
11 Healthcare Facilities Accreditation Program (April 2014).

12 Internship approved by American Osteopathic Association (April 2014).
13 Residency approved by American Osteopathic Association (April 2014).
18 Critical Access Hospitals (May 2014).
19 Rural Referral Center (May 2014).
20 Sole Community Provider (May 2014).
21 Accreditation by DNV Healthcare Inc. (April 2014).

Nonreporting indicates that the 2013 Annual Survey questionnaire for the hospital was not received prior to publication.

(2) Physician Codes

Actually available within, and reported by the institution; for definitions, see page A12.

(Alphabetical/Numerical Order)
1 Closed physician–hospital organization (PHO)
2 Equity model
3 Foundation
4 Group practice without walls
5 Independent practice association (IPA)
6 Integrated salary model
7 Management service organization (MSO)
8 Open physician–hospital organization (PHO)

(3) Health Care System Name

The inclusion of the letter ''S'' (1) indicates that the hospital belongs to a health care system and (2) identifies the specific system to which the hospital belongs.

(4) Titles of Chief Administrators

(5) Control and Service Classification
For a list of control and service classifications, see page A13.

Control–The type of organization that is responsible for establishing policy for overall operation of the hospital.

Service–The type of service the hospital provides to the majority of admissions.

(6) Utilization Data

Definitions are based on the American Hospital Association's Hospital Administration Terminology. In completing the survey, hospitals were requested to report data for a full year, in accord with their fiscal year, ending in 2013.

Beds–Number of beds regularly maintained et up and staffed for use) for inpatients as of the close of the reporting period. Excludes newborn bassinets.

Admissions–Number of patients accepted for inpatient service during a 12–month period; does not include newborn.

Census–Average number of inpatients receiving care each day during the 12–month reporting period; does not include newborn.

Outpatient Visits–A visit by a patient who is not lodged in the hospital while receiving medical, dental, or other services. Each appearance of an outpatient in each unit constitutes one visit regardless of the number of diagnostic and/or therapeutic treatments that a patient receives.

Births–Number of infants born in the hospital and accepted for service in a newborn infant bassinet during a 12–month period; excludes stillbirths.

Expense: Expense for a 12–month period; both total expense and payroll components are shown. Payroll expenses include all salaries and wages.

Personnel: Represents personnel situations as they existed at the end of the reporting period; includes full-time equivalents of part–time personnel. Full–time equivalents were calculated on the basis that two part–time persons equal one full–time person.

†Data from the Graduate Medical Education Database, Copyright 2014, American Medical Association, Chicago, Illinois.

Sample Hospital Listing:

ANYTOWN, Universal County

✠ **ANYTOWN HOSPITAL & CLINICS (777777)**, (Formerly Anytown Area Community Hospital and Clinic), 100 South Main Street, Zip 12345–6789; tel. 123/456–7890 **A9** 10] ①

F10 12 23 24 29 30 31 37 39 49 51 55 57 64 65 66 68 70 71 72 77 78 83 87 88 91 96 97 106 107 110 111 113 124 **P**1 2 3 **S** Universal ⑦

County Health System ② ③
Primary Contact: Ann M. Generic, Chief Executive Officer
COO: Ann M. Generic
CFO: Michael M. Generic ④
CMO: Peterl Van Generic, President Medical Staff
CHR: Jerry Generic, Human Resources Director
CNO: Danielle Generic, R.N., Chief Nursing Officer
Web address: www.website.org
Control: Other not–for–profit (including NFP Corporation) **Service:** General Medical and Surgical ⑤

Staffed Beds: 25 **Admissions:** 892 **Census:** 9 **Outpatient Visits:** 44014
Births: 51 **Total Expense ($000):** 19210 **Payroll Expense ($000):** 5864
Personnel: 182

ANYTOWN, Universal County

✠ **ANYTOWN HOSPITAL & CLINICS (777777)**, (Formerly Anytown Area Community Hospital and Clinic), 100 South Main Street, Zip 12345–6789; tel. 123/456–7890 **A9** 10

① = Approval Codes
② = Physician Codes
③ = Health Care System Name
④ = Titles of Chief Administrators
⑤ = Control and Service Classifications
⑥ = Utilization Data
⑦ = Facility Codes

⑥

Hospital, Medicare Provider Number, Address, Telephone, Approval, Facility, and Physician Codes, Health Care System

★ American Hospital Association (AHA) membership
□ The Joint Commission accreditation
◇ DNV Healthcare Inc. accreditation
○ Healthcare Facilities Accreditation Program
△ Commission on Accreditation of Rehabilitation Facilities (CARF) accreditation

---

⑦ Facility Codes

Provided directly by the hospital; for definitions, see page A6.

(Numerical Order)

1. Acute long-term care
2. Adult day care program
3. Airborne infection isolation room
4. Alcoholism-drug abuse or dependency inpatient unit
5. Alcoholism-drug abuse or dependency outpatient unit
6. Alzheimer center
7. Ambulance services
8. Ambulatory surgery center
9. Arthritis treatment center
10. Assisted living
11. Auxiliary
12. Bariatric/weight control services
13. Birthing room-LDR room-LDRP room
14. Blood donor center
15. Breast cancer screening/mammograms
16. Burn care services
17. Cardiac intensive care
18. Adult cardiology services
19. Pediatric cardiology services
20. Adult diagnostic catheterization
21. Pediatric diagnostic catheterization
22. Adult interventional cardiac catheterization
23. Pediatric diagnostic catheterization
24. Adult cardiac surgery
25. Pediatric cardiac surgery
26. Adult cardiac electrophysiology
27. Pediatric cardiac electrophysiology
28. Cardiac rehabilitation
29. Case management
30. Chaplaincy/pastoral care services
31. Chemotherapy
32. Children's wellness program
33. Chiropractic services
34. Community health education
35. Community outreach
36. Complementary and alternative medicine services
37. Computer assisted orthopedic surgery (CAOS)
38. Crisis prevention
39. Dental services
40. Emergency department
41. Pediatric emergency department
42. Satellite emergency department
43. Trauma center (certified)
44. Enabling services
45. Optical colonoscopy
46. Endoscopic ultrasound
47. Ablation of Barrett's esophagus
48. Esophageal impedance study

49. Endoscopic retrograde cholangiopancreatography (ERCP)
50. Enrollment assistance services
51. Extracorporeal shock wave lithotripter (ESWL)
52. Fertility clinic
53. Fitness center
54. Freestanding outpatient care center
55. Genetic testing/counseling
56. Geriatric services
57. Health fair
58. Health research
59. Health screenings
60. Hemodialysis
61. HIV–AIDS services
62. Home health services
63. Hospice program
64. Hospital–based outpatient care center services
65. Immunization program
66. Indigent care clinic
67. Intermediate nursing care
68. Linguistic/translation services
69. Meals on wheels
70. Medical surgical intensive care services
71. Mobile health services
72. Neonatal intensive care
73. Neonatal intermediate care
74. Neurological services
75. Nutrition programs
76. Obstetrics
77. Occupational health services
78. Oncology services
79. Orthopedic services
80. Other special care
81. Outpatient surgery
82. Pain management program
83. Inpatient palliative care unit
84. Palliative care program
85. Patient controlled analgesia (PCA)
86. Patient education center
87. Patient representative services
88. Pediatric intensive care services
89. Pediatric medical–surgical care
90. Physical rehabilitation inpatient services
91. Assistive technology center
92. Electrodiagnostic services
93. Physical rehabilitation outpatient services
94. Prosthetic and orthotic services
95. Robot-assisted walking therapy
96. Simulated rehabilitation environment
97. Primary care department
98. Psychiatric care
99. Psychiatric child–adolescent services
100. Psychiatric consultation–liaison services

101. Psychiatric education services
102. Psychiatric emergency services
103. Psychiatric geriatric services
104. Psychiatric outpatient services
105. Psychiatric partial hospitalization services
106. Psychiatric residential treatment
107. CT scanner
108. Diagnostic radioisotope facility
109. Electron beam computed tomography (EBCT)
110. Full–field digital mammography (FFDM)
111. Magnetic resonance imaging (MRI)
112. Intraoperative magnetic resonance imaging
113. Magnetoencephalography (MEG)
114. Multi–slice spiral computed tomography (MSCT) (<64 slice CT)
115. Multi–slice spiral computed tomography (64 + slice CT)
116. Positron emission tomography (PET)
117. Positron emission tomography/CT (PET/CT)
118. Single photon emission computerized tomography (SPECT)
119. Ultrasound
120. Image–guided radiation therapy (IGRT)
121. Intensity–modulated radiation therapy (IMRT)
122. Proton beam therapy
123. Shaped beam radiation therapy
124. Stereotactic radiosurgery
125. Retirement housing
126. Robotic surgery
127. Rural health clinic
128. Skilled nursing care
129. Sleep center
130. Social work services
131. Sports medicine
132. Support groups
133. Swing bed services
134. Teen outreach services
135. Tobacco treatment/cessation program
136. Bone marrow transplant services
137. Heart transplant
138. Kidney transplant
139. Liver transplant
140. Lung transplant
141. Tissue transplant
142. Other transplant
143. Transportation to health services
144. Urgent care center
145. Virtual colonoscopy
146. Volunteer services department
147. Women's health center/services
148. Wound management services

AHA Guide® to the Health Care Field

2015 Edition

AHA Members $245
Nonmembers $370
AHA Item Number 010015
Telephone ORDERS 1–800–AHA–2626

ISSN 0094–8969
ISBN–13: 978–0–87258–951–3

Contents

C Lists of Health Organizations, Agencies and Providers

D Indexes

† List supplied by The Joint Commission

Acknowledgements and Advisements

Acknowledgements

The AHA Guide® to the Health Care Field is published annually by Health Forum LLC, an affiliate of the American Hospital Association. Contributions are made by Information Systems and Technology, Member Relations, Office of the President, Office of the Secretary, Printing Services Group, AHA Resource Center and the following participants:

Grant Denton	Mary Krzywicki
Dianna Doyle	Andrea Liebig
DeAnn Ellis	Denise Loggins
Joan Finn	Jennifer Pagan
Deanna Frazier	Steve Reczynski
Tan Harris	Christine Remedios
Stella Hines	Jennifer Sikora
Clisby Jackson	Elaine Singh
Danny Jackson	Susan Sheffey
Kimberly Jackson	Gina Wang
Peter Kralovec	Judy Williams

Health Forum LLC acknowledges the cooperation given by many professional groups and government agencies in the health care field, particularly the following: American College of Surgeons; American Medical Association; Blue Cross and Blue Shield Association; Council of Teaching Hospitals of the Association of American Medical Colleges; The Joint Commission; DNV Healthcare Inc.; National League for Nursing Accrediting Commission; Commission on Accreditation of Rehabilitation Facilities; American Osteopathic Association, Centers for Medicare & Medicaid Services; and various offices within the U.S. Department of Health and Human Services.

Advisements

The data published here should be used with the following advisements: The data is based on replies to an annual survey that seeks a variety of information, not all of which is published in this book. The information gathered by the survey includes specific services, but not all of each hospital's services. Therefore, the data does not reflect an exhaustive list of all services offered by all hospitals. For information on the availability of additional data and products, please contact Health Forum LLC at 800/821–2039, or visit our web site.

Health Forum LLC does not assume responsibility for the accuracy of information voluntarily reported by the individual institutions surveyed. **The purpose of this publication is to provide basic data reflecting the delivery of health care in the United States and associated areas, and is not to serve as an official and all inclusive list of services offered by individual hospitals. The information reflected is based on data collected as of May 31, 2014.**

Introduction

An Introduction to AHA Guide®

Welcome, and thank you for purchasing the 2015 edition of *AHA Guide®*. This section is designed to aid you in using the book. While the primary focus of *AHA Guide* is on hospitals, it also contains information on other areas of the health care field, divided across its three major sections:

A. Hospitals

B. Health care systems, networks, and alliances

C. Health care organizations, agencies, and other health care providers

The information contained within this publication was compiled using AHA membership, and the AHA Annual Survey of Hospitals. *AHA Guide* is the leading hospital directory and represents hospitals with or without AHA membership.

Additional information contained in the front of AHA Guide includes:

- A section by section table of contents
- Recognition of the source of data in the *Acknowledgements and Advisements* section
- Information on AHA's history as well as a listing of our awards in *AHA Offices, Officers, Historical Data, and Awards*

Getting Started: The AHA Guide Code Chart

Open the front cover and *AHA Guide* begins with the *2015 AHA Guide Code Chart*. This two page section (front and back) explains how to find and understand the most important elements of each hospital's listing. The chart is specially perforated and is meant to be extracted and used alongside Section A as a resource. The information found on these pages is repeated in the first section, so don't worry about removing the chart.

The *Code Chart* is a very useful tool to have when reading. It allows new users to become familiar with the data, and it aids returning users in understanding the new design and layout of *AHA Guide*. At the top of the chart, there is a sample listing. If you have used this publication before, you will notice the new columnar listing of all hospital entries by city. The city and county names are highlighted in gray, and all hospitals within the city follow. After the hospital name, you will find the address, telephone number, approval, facility and service codes, and health care systems to which the hospital belongs. Following this are the chief administrators and classifications for the hospital. Utilization data for the hospital is found in the box at the bottom of each hospital's entry in *AHA Guide*.

The chart further demonstrates how to understand these important elements:

1. **Approval codes** refer to certifications held by a hospital; they represent information supplied by various national approving and reporting bodies. For example, code A–3 indicates accreditation under one of the programs of the Accreditation Council for Graduate Medical Education, evidence that the hospital has been approved for participation in residency training.

2. **Physician codes** represent the different types of arrangements the hospital participates in with its physicians. In this section, code P-1 signifies a closed physician-hospital organization.

3. **Health Care System names** reference specific health care system headquarters to which the hospital belongs. The presence of a system name indicates that the hospital is a member. If no names are listed, the hospital does not belong to a system.

4. **Titles of Chief Administrators** including the Chief Executive Officer and, when available, other C-Suite officers such as the Chief Financial Officer, Chief Information Officer, Chief Medical Officer, Chief Operating Officer, Chief Human Resources Officer, and Chief Nursing Officer.

5. **Classification** refers to two items in *AHA Guide*. **Control** classification indicates the

---

2015 AHA Guide Code Chart

Sample Hospital Listing:

ANYTOWN, Universal County

⊞ **ANYTOWN HOSPITAL & CLINICS (777777)**, (Formerly Anytown Area Community Hospital and Clinic), 100 South Main Street, Zip 12345-6789; tel. 123/456-7890 **A0** 10 ① ① **F**10 12 23 24 29 30 31 37 39 49 51 55 57 64 65 66 68 70 71 72 77 78 83 87 88 91 96 97 106 107 110 111 113 124 **P**1 2 3 **S**-Universal ⑦
County Health System ② ③
Primary Contact: Ann M. Generic, Chief Executive Officer
COO: Ann M. Generic
CFO: Michael M. Generic ④
CMO: Peterl Van Generic, President Medical Staff
CHR: Jerry Generic, Human Resources Director
CNO: Daniella Generic, R.N., Chief Nursing Officer
Web address: www.website.org
Control: Other not-for-profit (including NFP Corporation) **Service:** General Medical and Surgical ⑤

Staffed Beds: 25 Admissions: 892 Census: 9 Outpatient Visits: 44014 Births: 51 Total Expense ($000): 19210 Payroll Expense ($000): 5864 Personnel: 182 ⑥

ANYTOWN, Universal County

⊞ **ANYTOWN HOSPITAL & CLINICS (777777)**, (Formerly Anytown Area Community Hospital and Clinic), 100 South Main Street, Zip 12345-6789; tel. 123/456-7890 A9 10

① = Approval Codes
② = Physician Codes
③ = Health Care System Name
④ = Titles of Chief Administrators
⑤ = Control and Service Classifications
⑥ = Utilization Data
⑦ = Facility Codes

Hospital, Medicare Provider Number, Address, Telephone, Approval, Facility, and Physician Codes, Health Care System

- American Hospital Association (AHA) membership
- ⊞ The Joint Commission accreditation
- ○ Healthcare Facilities Accreditation Program
- ◇ DNV Healthcare Inc. accreditation
- △ Commission on Accreditation of Rehabilitation Facilities (CARF) accreditation

① **Approval Codes**
Reported by the approving bodies specified, as of the dates noted.

1 Accreditation under the hospital program of the Joint Commission (June 2014).
2 Cancer program approved by American College of Surgeons (August 2014).
†3 Approval to participate in residency training, by the Accreditation Council for Graduate Medical Education (April 2014).
†5 Medical school affiliation, reported to the American Medical Association (April 2014).
6 Hospital-controlled professional nursing school, reported by National League for Nursing.
7 Accreditation by Commission on Accreditation of Rehabilitation Facilities (April 2014).

8 Member of Council of Teaching Hospitals of the Association of American Medical Colleges (April 2014).
9 Hospitals contracting or participating in a Plan, reported by the Blue Cross and Blue Shield Association (April 2014).
10 Certified for participation in the Health Insurance for the Aged (Medicare) Program by the Centers for Medicare and Medical Services (February 2014).
11 Healthcare Facilities Accreditation Program (April 2014).

12 Internship approved by American Osteopathic Association (April 2014).
13 Residency approved by American Osteopathic Association (April 2014).
18 Critical Access Hospitals (May 2014).
19 Rural Referral Center (May 2014).
20 Sole Community Provider (May 2014)
21 Accreditation by DNV Healthcare Inc. (April 2014).

Nonreporting indicates that the 2013 Annual Survey questionnaire for the hospital was not received prior to publication.

② **Physician Codes**
Actually available within, and reported by the institution; for definitions, see page A12.

(Alphabetical/Numerical Order)
1 Closed physician-hospital organization (PHO)
2 Equity model
3 Foundation
4 Group practice without walls
5 Independent practice association (IPA)
6 Integrated salary model
7 Management service organization (MSO)
8 Open physician-hospital organization (PHO)

③ **Health Care System Name**
The inclusion of the letter "S" (1) indicates that the hospital belongs to a health care system and (2) identifies the specific system to which the hospital belongs.

④ **Titles of Chief Administrators**

⑤ **Control and Service Classification**
For a list of control and service classifications, see page A13.

Control—The type of organization that is responsible for establishing policy for overall operation of the hospital.

Service—The type of service the hospital provides to the majority of admissions.

⑥ **Utilization Data**
Definitions are based on the American Hospital Association's Hospital Administration Terminology. In completing the survey, hospitals were requested to report data for a full year, in accord with their fiscal year, ending in 2013.

Beds—Number of beds regularly maintained (set up and staffed for use) for inpatients as of the close of the reporting period. Excludes newborn bassinets.

Admissions—Number of patients accepted for inpatient service during a 12-month period; does not include newborn.

Census—Average number of inpatients receiving care each day during the 12-month reporting period; does not include newborn.

Outpatient Visits—A visit by a patient who is not lodged in the hospital while receiving medical, dental, or other services. Each appearance of an outpatient in each unit constitutes one visit regardless of the number of diagnostic and/or therapeutic treatments that a patient receives.

Births—Number of infants born in the hospital and accepted for service in a newborn infant bassinet during a 12-month period; excludes stillbirths.

Expense: Expense for a 12-month period; both total expense and payroll components are shown. Payroll expenses include all salaries and wages.

Personnel: Represents personnel situations as they existed at the end of the reporting period; includes full-time equivalents of part-time personnel. Full-time equivalents were calculated on the basis that two part-time persons equal one full-time person.

†Data from the Graduate Medical Education Database, Copyright 2014, American Medical Association, Chicago, Illinois.

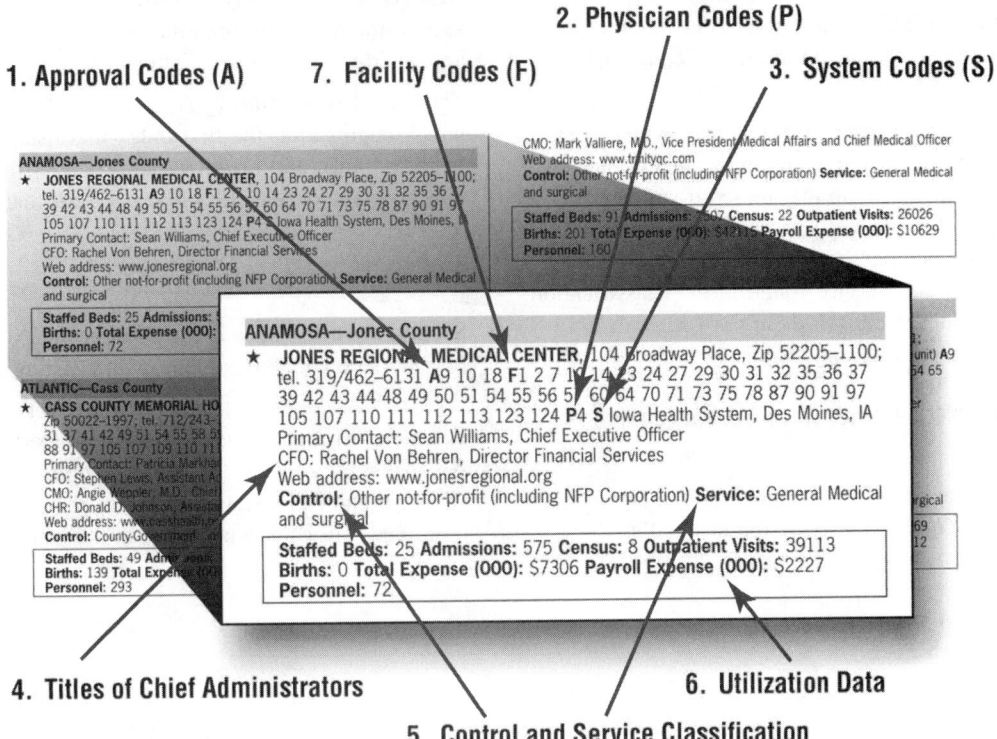

1. Approval Codes (A) **7. Facility Codes (F)** **2. Physician Codes (P)** **3. System Codes (S)**

ANAMOSA—Jones County

★ **JONES REGIONAL MEDICAL CENTER**, 104 Broadway Place, Zip 52205–1100; tel. 319/462–6131 **A**9 10 18 **F**1 2 7 10 14 23 24 27 29 30 31 32 35 36 37 39 42 43 44 48 49 50 51 54 55 56 57 60 64 70 71 73 75 78 87 90 91 97 105 107 110 111 112 113 123 124 **P**4 **S** Iowa Health System, Des Moines, IA
Primary Contact: Sean Williams, Chief Executive Officer
CFO: Rachel Von Behren, Director Financial Services
Web address: www.jonesregional.org
Control: Other not-for-profit (including NFP Corporation) **Service:** General Medical and surgical

Staffed Beds: 25 **Admissions:** 575 **Census:** 8 **Outpatient Visits:** 39113 **Births:** 0 **Total Expense (000):** $7306 **Payroll Expense (000):** $2227 **Personnel:** 72

4. Titles of Chief Administrators **6. Utilization Data**

5. Control and Service Classification

organization that operates the hospital, and **Service** classification refers to the type of service the hospital offers. Previously, this section utilized numerical codes corresponding with a literal value, but the new design of *AHA Guide* bypasses the codes and instead displays the literal classifications for control and service.

- **Control:** In this section, organizations are divided among nonfederal government hospitals, nongovernment not-for-profit hospitals, investor owned for-profit hospitals, and federal government hospitals.
- **Service:** This section displays the primary type of service that a hospital offers. The most common value is general hospital. Among the other services listed in this section are specialties such as psychiatric hospitals or children's hospitals.

6. **Utilization Data** contains the statistics related to the day-to-day and cumulative operation of the hospital. The information included in this section consists of:

- **Beds:** Number of beds regularly maintained.
- **Admissions:** Amount of patients accepted for inpatient services over a 12-month period.

- **Census:** Average number of patients receiving care each day.
- **Outpatient Visits:** Amount of visits by patients not lodged in the hospital while receiving care.
- **Births:** Number of infants born in the hospital and accepted for service in a newborn infant bassinet.
- **Expense:** Includes all expenses (including payroll) that the hospital had over the 12-month period.
- **Personnel:** Represents personnel situations as they existed at the end of the reporting period. In this area, full time equivalency is calculated on the basis that two part-time persons equal one full-time person.

7. **Facility codes** provide a description of the specific services offered by a hospital. Code F-14, for instance, indicates that the hospital contains a Blood Donor Center.

How To Use This Book

Section A begins with the *AHA Guide Hospital Listing Requirements.* This explains the requisite accreditations or characteristics a hospital must meet to be included in *AHA Guide.*

After this there is *An Explanation of the Hospital Listings*. These two pages review the information included in the Code Chart and are a vital resource in identifying the information, symbols, and codes for each hospital's listing.

Next up are the *Annual Survey* definitions, which go into even greater detail in explaining the facility and physician codes. Please note that these are arranged alphabetically and numerically to correspond with the code chart. Also included here are the definitions of the terms for Control and Service found in the Classification section. The listings of *Hospitals in the United States, by State* follow the definitions.

Finding Hospitals & Health Care Professionals in Section A

There are two ways to locate hospitals in the print version of *AHA Guide*. One is by the hospital's geographic classification. In Section A, hospitals are arranged alphabetically by state and then by city. The second method is through the *Hospital Index* that appears directly after the listings.

There is also an *Index of Health Care Professionals* which begins after the first index that lists key people from hospitals and health systems. Look for fold out tabs and tabs on the sides of pages that mark the indices.

AHA Membership Organizations

Section A ends with a description of the AHA Membership categories along with a listing of various AHA Membership organizations.

For more information on Systems, Networks, and Alliances, please read the introduction to Section B. Health organizations, agencies, and providers are described, prior to their listing, at the start of Section C.

AHA Offices, Officers, and Historical Data

Past Presidents/Chairs†

1899	★James S. Knowles	1938	★Robert E. Neff	1978	★Samuel J. Tibbitts
1900	★James S. Knowles	1939	★G. Harvey Agnew, M.D.	1979	W. Daniel Barker
1901	★Charles S. Howell	1940	★Fred G. Carter, M.D.	1980	★Sister Irene Kraus
1902	★J. T. Duryea	1941	★B. W. Black, M.D.	1981	★Bernard J. Lachner
1903	★John Fehrenbatch	1942	★Basil C. MacLean, M.D.	1982	★Stanley R. Nelson
1904	★Daniel D. Test	1943	★James A. Hamilton	1983	Elbert E. Gilbertson
1905	★George H. M. Rowe, M.D.	1944	★Frank J. Walter	1984	Thomas R. Matherlee
1906	★George P. Ludlam	1945	★Donald C. Smelzer, M.D.	1985	★Jack A. Skarupa
1907	★Renwick R. Ross, M.D.	1946	★Peter D. Ward, M.D.	1986	Scott S. Parker
1908	★Sigismund S. Goldwater, M.D.	1947	★John H. Hayes	1987	Donald C. Wegmiller
1909	★John M. Peters, M.D.	1948	★Graham L. Davis	1988	Eugene W. Arnett
1910	★H. B. Howard, M.D.	1949	★Joseph G. Norby	1989	Edward J. Connors
1911	★W. L. Babcock, M.D.	1950	★John N. Hatfield	1990	David A. Reed
1912	★Henry M. Hurd, M.D.	1951	★Charles F. Wilinsky, M.D.	1991	C. Thomas Smith
1913	★F. A. Washburn, M.D.	1952	★Anthony J. J. Rourke, M.D.	1992	D. Kirk Oglesby, Jr.
1914	★Thomas Howell, M.D.	1953	★Edwin L. Crosby, M.D.	1993	Larry L. Mathis
1915	★William O. Mann, M.D.	1954	★Ritz E. Heerman	1994	Carolyn C. Roberts
1916	★Winford H. Smith, M.D.	1955	★Frank R. Bradley	1995	Gail L. Warden
1917	★Robert J. Wilson, M.D.	1956	★Ray E. Brown	1996	Gordon M. Sprenger
1918	★A. B. Ancker, M.D.	1957	★Albert W. Snoke, M.D.	1997	Reginald M. Ballantyne III
1919	★A. R. Warner, M.D.	1958	★Tol Terrell	1998	John G. King
1920	★Joseph B. Howland, M.D.	1959	★Ray Amberg	1999	Fred L. Brown
1921	★Louis B. Baldwin, M.D.	1960	★Russell A. Nelson, M.D.	2000	★Carolyn Boone Lewis
1922	★George O'Hanlon, M.D.	1961	★Frank S. Groner	2001	Gary A. Mecklenburg
1923	★Asa S. Bacon	1962	★Jack Masur, M.D.	2002	Sr. Mary Roch Rocklage, RSM
1924	★Malcolm T. MacEachern, M.D.	1963	★T. Stewart Hamilton, M.D.	2003	Dennis R. Barry
1925	★E. S. Gilmore	1964	★Stanley A. Ferguson	2004	David L. Bernd
1926	★Arthur C. Bachmeyer, M.D.	1965	★Clarence E. Wonnacott	2005	George F. Lynn
1927	★R. G. Brodrick, M.D.	1966	★Philip D. Bonnet, M.D.	January–April 2006	Richard J. Umbdenstock
1928	★Joseph C. Doane, M.D.	1967	★George E. Cartmill	April–December 2006	George F. Lynn
1929	★Louis H. Burlingham, M.D.	1968	★David B. Wilson, M.D.	2007	Kevin E. Lofton
1930	★Christopher G. Parnall, M.D.	1969	★George William Graham, M.D.	2008	William D. Petasnick
1931	★Lewis A. Sexton, M.D.	1970	★Mark Berke	2009	Thomas M. Priselac
1932	★Paul H. Fesler	1971	★Jack A. L. Hahn	2010	Richard P. de Filippi
1933	★George F. Stephens, M.D.	1972	★Stephen M. Morris	2011	John W. Bluford
1934	★Nathaniel W. Faxon, M.D.	1973	★John W. Kauffman	2012	Teri G. Fontenot
1935	★Robert Jolly	1974	★Horace M. Cardwell	2013	Benjamin K. Chu, MD
1936	★Robin C. Buerki, M.D.	1975	Wade Mountz	2014	James H. Hinton
1937	★Claude W. Munger, M.D.	1976	H. Robert Cathcart		
		1977	★John M. Stagl		

Chief Executive Officers

1917–18	★William H. Walsh, M.D.	1943–54	★George Bugbee	1986–91	Carol M. McCarthy, Ph.D., J.D.
1919–24	★Andrew Robert Warner, M.D.	1954–72	★Edwin L. Crosby, M.D.	1991	Jack W. Owen (acting)
1925–27	★William H. Walsh, M.D.	1972	Madison B. Brown, M.D. (acting)	1991–2007	Richard J. Davidson
1928–42	★Bert W. Caldwell, M.D.	1972–86	J. Alexander McMahon	2007	Richard J. Umbdenstock (current)

Distinguished Service Award

The award recognizes significant lifetime contributions and service to health care institutions and associations.

1934	Matthew O. Foley	1964	Russell A. Nelson, M.D.	1991	Carol M. McCarthy, Ph.D., J.D.
1939	Malcolm T. MacEachern, M.D.	1965	Albert W. Snoke, M.D.	1992	David H. Hitt
1940	Sigismund S. Goldwater, M.D.	1966	Frank S. Groner	1993	Edward J. Connors
1941	Frederic A. Washburn, M.D.	1967	Rev. John J. Flanagan, S.J.		Jack W. Owen
1942	Winford H. Smith, M.D.	1968	Stanley W. Martin	1994	George Adams
1943	Arthur C. Bachmeyer, M.D.	1969	T. Stewart Hamilton, M.D.	1995	Scott S. Parker
1944	Rt. Rev. Msgr. Maurice F. Griffin, LL.D.	1970	Charles Patteson Cardwell, Jr.	1996	John A. Russell
1945	Asa S. Bacon	1971	Mark Berke	1997	D. Kirk Oglesby, Jr.
1946	George F. Stephens, M.D.	1972	Stanley A. Ferguson	1998	Henry B. Betts, M.D.
1947	Robin C. Buerki, M.D.	1973	Jack A. L. Hahn	1999	Mitchell T. Rabkin, M.D.
1948	James A. Hamilton	1974	George William Graham, M.D.	2000	Gail L. Warden
1949	Claude W. Munger, M.D.	1975	George E. Cartmill	2001	Gordon M. Sprenger
1950	Nathaniel W. Faxon, M.D.	1976	D. O. McClusky, Jr.	2002	Carolyn Boone Lewis
1951	Bert W. Caldwell, M.D.	1977	Boone Powell	2003	C. Thomas Smith
1952	Fred G. Carter, M.D.	1978	Richard J. Stull	2004	Michael C. Waters
1953	Basil C. MacLean, M.D.	1979	Horace M. Cardwell	2005	John G. King
1954	George Bugbee	1980	Donald W. Cordes	2006	Gary A. Mecklenburg
1955	Joseph G. Norby	1981	Sister Mary Brigh Cassidy		Sr. Mary Roch Rocklage, RSM
1956	Charles F. Wilinsky, M.D.	1982	R. Zach Thomas, Jr.	2007	Richard J. Davidson
1957	John H. Hayes	1983	H. Robert Cathcart	2008	Fred L. Brown
1958	John N. Hatfield	1984	Matthew F. McNulty, Jr., Sc.D.	2009	George F. Lynn
1959	Edwin L. Crosby, M.D.	1985	J. Alexander McMahon	2010	James J. Mongan, M.D.
1960	Oliver G. Pratt	1986	Sister Irene Kraus	2011	Thomas C. Royer, M.D.
1961	E. M. Bluestone, M.D.	1987	W. Daniel Barker	2012	Karen Davis, Ph.D.
1962	Mother Loretto Bernard, S.C., R.N.	1988	Elbert E. Gilbertson	2013	Thomas C. Dolan, Ph.D., FACHE
1963	Ray E. Brown	1989	Donald G. Shropshire	2014	Thomas M. Priselac
		1990	John W. Colloton		

★Deceased
†On June 3, 1972, the House of Delegates changed the title of the chief elected officer to chairman of the Board of Trustees, and the title of president was conferred on the chief executive officer of the Association.

Award of Honor

Awarded to individuals, organizations, or groups to recognize an exemplary contribution to the health and well being of the people through leadership on a major health policy or social initiative.

1966	Senator Lister Hill		Mothers Against Drunk Driving (MADD)		James W. Varnum
1967	Emory W. Morris, D.D.S.	1997	Paul B. Batalden, M.D.	2007	Edward A. Eckenhoff
1971	Special Committee on Provision of Health		Habitat for Humanity International		Stanley F. Hupfeld
	Services (staff also)	1998	John E. Curley, Jr.	2008	Regina M. Benjamin, MD, MBA
1982	Walter J. McNemey		National Civic League		Alfred G. Stubblefield
1989	Ruth M. Rothstein	1999	Joseph Cardinal Bernardin, Literacy Volunteers	2009	The Center to Advance Palliative Care
1990	Joyce C. Clifford, R.N.		of America		Paul B. Hofmann, Dr.PH
1991	Haynes Rice	2000	Institute for Safe Medication Practices	2010	Jack Bovender
1992	Donald W. Dunn	2001	Dennis R. Barry	2011	Cary Medical Center, Caribou, ME
	Ira M. Lane, Jr.	2002	Donald M. Berwick, M.D.	2012	Ronald McDonald House Charities
1993	Elliott C. Roberts, Sr.	2003	Steven A. Schroeder, M.D.		The Schwartz Center for Compassionate
	William A. Spencer, M.D.		Dan S. Wilford		Healthcare
1994	Robert A. Derzon	2004	Ron J. Anderson, M.D.	2013	George C. Halvorson
1995	Russell G. Mawby, Ph.D.		Johnson & Johnson		Reach Out and Read
	John K. Springer	2005	Sr. Mary Jean Ryan	2014	Rhonda Anderson, RN
1996	Stephen J. Hegarty	2006	Jordan J. Cohen, M.D.		Ohio Hospital Association

Justin Ford Kimball Innovators Award

Recognition to individuals or organizations that have made outstanding, innovative contributions to health care financing and/or delivery that improves access or coordination of care.

1958	E. A. van Steenwyk	1973	Herman M. Somers	1994	Donald A. Brennan
1959	George A. Newbury	1974	William H. Ford, Ph.D.	1995	E. George Middleton, Jr.
1960	C. Rufus Rorem, Ph.D.	1975	Earl H. Kammer		Glenn R. Mitchell
1961	James E. Stuart	1976	J. Ed McConnell	1997	Harvey Pettry
1962	Frank Van Dyk	1978	Edwin R. Werner		D. David Sniff
1963	William S. McNary	1979	Robert M. Cunningham, Jr.	1998	Montana Health Research and Education
1964	Frank S. Groner	1981	Maurice J. Norby		Foundation
1965	J. Douglas Colman	1982	Robert E. Rinehimer	1999	Kenneth W. Kizer, M.D.
1967	Walter J. McNemey	1983	John B. Morgan, Jr.	2002	David M. Lawrence, M.D.
1968	John W. Paynter	1984	Joseph F. Duplinsky	2003	Lowell C. Kruse
1970	Edwin L. Crosby, M.D.	1985	David W. Stewart	2006	Spencer Foreman, M.D.
1971	H. Charles Abbott	1988	Ernest W. Saward, M.D.	2009	On Lok
1972	John R. Mannix	1990	James A. Vohs	2012	Thomas S. Nesbitt, M.D.
		1993	John C. Lewin, M.D.		

Board of Trustees Award

Individuals or groups who have made substantial and noteworthy contributions to the work of the American Hospital Association.

1959	Joseph V. Friel	1981	Vernon A. Knutson		Stephen Rogness
	John H. Hayes		John E. Sullivan	2000	Dennis May
1960	Duncan D. Sutphen, Jr.	1982	John Bigelow	2001	Spencer C. Johnson
1963	Eleanor C. Lambertsen, R.N., Ed.D.		Robert W. O'Leary		Michael M. Mitchel
1964	John R. Mannix		Jack W. Owen	2002	Victor L. Campbell
1965	Albert G. Hahn	1984	Howard J. Berman		Joseph A. Parker
	Maurice J. Norby		O. Ray Hurst	2003	J. Richard Gaintner, M.D.
1966	Madison B. Brown, M.D.		James R. Neely		Donald A. Wilson
	Kenneth Williamson	1985	James E. Ferguson	2004	Richard L. Clarke
1967	Alanson W. Wilcox		Cleveland Rodgers		Thelma Traut
1968	E. Dwight Barnett, M.D.	1986	Rex N. Olsen	2005	Merrill Gappmayer
1969	Vane M. Hoge, M.D.	1987	Michael Lesparre		Leo Greenawalt
	Joseph H. McNinch, M.D.	1988	Barbara A. Donaho, R.N.	2006	Robert L. Harman
1972	David F. Drake, Ph.D.	1989	Walter H. MacDonald		Kenneth G. Stella
	Paul W. Earle		Donald R. Newkirk	2007	Deborah Freund, Ph.D.
	Michael Lesparre	1990	William T. Robinson		Michael D. Stephens
	Andrew Pattullo	1992	Jack C. Bills	2008	James R. Castle
1973	Tilden Cummings		Anne Hall Davis	2009	Richard M. Knapp, Ph.D.
	Edmond J. Lanigan	1993	Theodore C. Eickhoff, M.D.	2010	Fred Hessler
1974	James E. Hague		Stephen W. Gamble		John G. O'Brien
	Sister Marybelle		Yoshi Honkawa	2011	Carolyn F. Scanlan
1975	Helen T. Yast	1994	Roger M. Busfield, Jr., Ph.D.		Charlotte S. Yeh, MD
1976	Boynton P. Livingston	1995	Stephen L. Dorn	2012	Larry S. Gage
	James Ludlam		William L. Yates		Larry McAndrews
	Helen McGuire	1996	Leigh E. Morris	2013	Jeffrey D. Selberg
1979	Newton J. Jacobson		John Quigley	2014	Russell D. Harrington, Jr.
	Edward W. Weimer	1998	John D. Leech		Daniel Sisto
1980	Robert B. Hunter, M.D.	1999	Sister Carol Keehan		
	Samuel J. Tibbitts		C. Edward McCauley		

Citation for Meritorious Service

1968	F. R. Knautz		Gordon McLachlan	1983	David M. Kinzer
	Sister Conrad Mary, R.N.	1977	Theodore Cooper, M.D.	1984	Donald L. Custis, M.D.
1971	Hospital Council of Southern California	1979	Norman D. Burkett	1985	John A. D. Cooper, M.D.
1972	College of Misericordia, Dallas, PA		John L. Quigley		Imperial Council of the Ancient Arabic Order of
1973	Madison B. Brown, M.D.		William M. Whelan		the Nobles of the Mystic Shrine for North
	Samuel J. Tibbitts	1980	Sister Grace Marie Hiltz		America
1975	Kenneth B. Babcock, M.D.		Leo J. Gehrig, M.D.	1986	Howard F. Cook
	Sister Mary Maurita Sengelaube	1981	Richard Davi	1987	David H. Hitt
1976	Chaiker Abbis		Pearl S. Fryar		Lucile Packard
	Susan Jenkins	1982	Jorge Brull Nater		

This citation is no longer awarded

AHA NOVA Awards

This award honors effective, collaborative programs focused on improving community health status.

1994
Health Partners of Philadelphi (PA): Albert Einstein Medical Center, Episcopal Hospital, Frankford Hospital, Medical College of Pennsylvania Hospital, St. Christopher's Hospital for Children, Temple University Hospital

Decker Family Development Center: Children's Hospital Medical Center of Akron (OH)
Denver (CO) School–Based Clinics: The Children's Hospital
Basic Health Plan: Dominican Network; Mount Carmel Hospital, Colville, WA; St. Joseph's

Hospital, Chewelah, WA; and Holy Family Hospital, Spokane, WA
HealthLink: Lakes Region General Hospital, Laconia, NH

1995
Bladen Community Care Network: Bladen County Hospital, Elizabethtown, NC
Building a Healthier Community: Community–Kimball Health Care System, Toms River, NJ

Injury Prevention Program: Harlem Hospital Center, New York City, NY
The Community Ministries & Outreach Program: Reaching Out to Our Vickery/Meadow

Neighborhood: Presbyterian Healthcare System, Dallas, TX
"CHOICES": Shriners Hospitals for Crippled Children, Tampa, FL

1996
Lincoln and Sunnyslope: John C. Lincoln Hospital and Health Center, Sunnyslope, AZ
Growing into Life Task Force: Aiken (SC) Regional Medical Centers

People Caring for People: Beatrice (NE) Community Hospital and Health Center
Injury Prevention Center of the Greater Dayton (OH) Area: The Children's Medical Center, Good

Samaritan Hospital and Health Center, Grandview Hospital, Kettering Memorial Hospital, Miami Valley Hospital, and St. Elizabeth Medical Center
Family Road: Hutzel Hospital, Detroit, MI

1997
Health Promotion Schools of Excellence Program: Alliant Health System and Kosair Children's Hospital, Louisville, KY
Health, Outreach, Prevention, and Education (HOPE): Health First Holmes Regional Medical Center, Melbourne, FL

Healthy Community Initiative: Roper Care Alliance, Charleston, SC
Obstetrical Care and Prenatal Counseling Program: St. Alexius Medical Center, Bismarck, ND
HIV/AIDS Neighborhood Service Program: Yale–New Haven Hospital, New Haven, CT

1998
Partners for a Healthier Community: Evergreen Community Health Care, Group Health Cooperative of Puget Sound, Overlake Hospital Medical Center, Providence Health System/Medalia HealthCare, Seattle, WA
Glenwood–Lyndale Community Clinic: Hennepin County Medical Center, Minneapolis, MN

Greater Dallas (TX) Injury Prevention Center: Parkland Health & Hospital System, Children's Medical Center of Dallas, Baylor Health Care System, Methodist Hospitals of Dallas, and Presbyterian Healthcare System
Network of Trust: Phoebe Putney Memorial Hospital, Albany, GA

The Lauderdale Court: A Community Partnership: St. Joseph Hospital and Health Centers, Memphis, TN

1999
Making a Case for Community Health: Middletown (OH) Regional Hospital
The Family Resource Center: Mount Carmel Medical Center, Pittsburgh, KS

The Health Neighborhood Project: St. Patrick Hospital, Missoula, MT
Kids for Health: Washington Regional Medical Center, Fayetteville, AR

Children's Village: Yakima Memorial Hospital, Yakima, WA

2000
Community Healthcare Network: Columbus (GA) Regional Healthcare System
Pasadena County Asthma Project: Huntington Memorial Hospital, Pasadena, CA

Ashe County Health Council "Health Carolinias Task Force": Ashe Memorial Hospital, Jefferson, NC
Caritas–Connection Project: St. Mary's Hospital, Passaic, NJ

Correctional Health Care Program: Baystate Health System, Springfield, MA

2001
J.C. Lewis Health Center: Memorial Health and St. Joseph's Candler Health System, Savannah, GA
Project C.A.R.E.: Mercy Medical Center, Canton, OH

TeenHealthFX.com: Atlantic Health System, Florham Park, NJ

Vista ElderCARE: Vista Health, Waukegan, IL

Western Village Enterprise School: INTEGRIS Health, Oklahoma City, OK

2002
Chester Community Connections: Crozer–Keystone Health System, Springfield, PA
The Hope Street Family Center: California Hospital Medical Center, Los Angeles, CA
Mobile Health Outreach Ministry: St. Vincent's Health System, Jacksonville, FL

Operation Access: Kaiser Foundation Hospitals, Oakland; Sutter Health, Sacramento; San Francisco General Hospital, San Francisco; St. Rose Hospital, Hayward; and Santa Rosa Memorial Hospital, Santa Rosa, CA

Wilmington Health Access for Teens: New Hanover Health Network, Wilmington, NC

2003
C.O.A.C.H. for Kids: Cedars–Sinai Medical Center, Los Angeles, CA
Community Action Network: Trinity Regional Medical Center, Fort Dodge, IA

Hearts N' Health: Glendale Adventist Medical Center, Glendale, CA
Saint Joseph Health Center: Saint Joseph Regional Medical Center, South Bend, IN

St. Mary Medical Center Bensalem Ministries: St. Mary Medical Center, Langhorne, PA

2004
Better Beginnings: Brockton Hospital, Brockton, MA
Buffalo County Community Health Partners: Good Samaritan Health Systems, Kearney, NE

Quad City Health Initiative: Genesis Health System, Davenport, IA and Trinity Regional Health System, Rock Island, IL
Quality of Life in the Truckee Meadows: Washoe Health System, Reno, NV

Solano Coalition for Better Health, Inc.: NorthBay Healthcare Group, Fairfield, CA; Sutter Solano Medical Center, Vallejo, CA; and Kaiser Permanente, Martinez, CA

2005
Children's Health Connection: McKay-Dee Hospital Center, Ogden, UT
Palmetto Health's Vision Health Initiative: Palmetto Health, Columbia, SC

Project Dulce, Whittier Institute for Diabetes: Scripps Health, San Diego, CA
Toledo/Lucas County CareNet: Mercy Health Partners, ProMedica Health System, and Medical

University of Ohio, all of Toledo, OH and St. Luke's Hospital, Maumee, OH
Volunteer Health Advisor (VHA) Program: Cambridge Health Alliance, Cambridge, MA

2006

Healthy Learners, Columbia, SC: Allendale County Hospital, Fairfax, SC; McLeod Medical Center–Dillon, Dillon, SC; Sisters of Charity Providence Hospitals, Columbia, SC; and Self Regional Healthcare, Greenwood, SC

Primary Care Access Network (PCAN): Health Central, Ocoee, FL; Florida Hospital, Winter Park, FL; and Orlando Regional Healthcare, Orlando, FL
ProHealth Care Community Health Outreach Initiative: ProHealth Care, Waukesha, WI

St. Joseph Mobile Health Services: Saint Joseph HealthCare Inc., Lexington, KY
Yonkers Childhood Health Initiative: St. John's Riverside, Yonkers, NY

2007

Medical-Legal Partnership for Children: Boston Medical Center, Boston, MA
NOW (Nutritional Options for Wellness) Program: Spectrum Health, Grand Rapids, MI

Richland Care: Palmetto Health, Columbia, SC
Trauma Nurses Talk Tough: Legacy Health System, Portland, OR

UMass Memorial Medical Center Healthy Youth Development Initiative: UMass Memorial Health Care, Worcester, MA
Youth Health Partnership-Patee Market Youth Dental Clinic: Heartland Health, St. Joseph, MO

2008

Partnership for Community Health: California Pacific Medical Center, San Francisco, CA
Every Child Succeeds: Cincinnati Children's Hospital Medical Center, Cincinnati, OH

Memorial Hermann Health Centers for Schools: Memorial Hermann, Houston, TX
Nutrition Center of Maine: Saint Mary's Health System, Lewiston, ME

***ENERGIZE!* Pediatric Diabetes Intervention Program:** WakeMed Health & Hospitals, Raleigh, NC

2009

Lighten Up 4 Life: Mission Health System, Asheville, NC
Project BRIEF: Jacobi Medical Center and North Central Bronx Hospital, Bronx, NY

Really Awesome Health (RAH) and Wholesome Routines: Duke Raleigh Hospital, Raleigh, NC
Student Success Jobs Program: Brigham and Women's Hospital, Boston, MA

Taos First Steps Program: Holy Cross Hospital, Taos, NM

2010

Community-Based Alternatives to the Emergency Room: Lee Memorial Health System, Fort Meyers, FL
Health-e-Access Telemedicine: University of Rochester Medical Center, Rochester, NY

Healthy Futures: Munson Healthcare System, Traverse City, MI
Healthy San Francisco: San Francisco General Hospital, University of California Medical Center, Chinese Hospital, California Pacific Medical Center,

Saint Francis Memorial Hospital, St. Mary's Medical Center, and Kaiser Permanente, San Francisco, CA
Pediatric Asthma Program: Sinai Health System, Chicago, IL

2011

Emergency Department Consistent Care Program: Providence St. Peter Hospital, Olympia, WA
Integrated Community Nursing Program at Parkview Health: Parkview Health, Fort Wayne, IN

Milwaukee Health Care Partnership: Aurora Health Care, Children's Hospital & Health System, Inc., Columbia St. Mary's, and Froedtert Health, all of Milwaukee, WI, and Wheaton Franciscan Healthcare, Glendale, WI

The Diabetes Collaborative: Northwestern Memorial Hospital, Chicago, IL
Rochester Youth Violence Partnership: University of Rochester Medical Center and Rochester General Health System, Rochester, NY

2012

The Beth Embraces Wellness: An Integrated Approach to Prevention in the Community: Newark Beth Israel Medical Center and Children's Hospital of New Jersey, Newark, NJ

CARE Network: St. Joseph Health Queen of the Valley Medical Center, Napa, CA
Fitness in the City: Boston Children's Hospital, Boston, MA

Puff City: Henry Ford Health System, Detroit, MI
Rural Health Initiative: Shawano Medical Center of ThedaCare, Shawano, WI

2013

Bangor Beacon Community: EMHS, Brewer, ME and St. Joseph Healthcare, Bangor, ME
Chippewa Health Improvement Partnership (CHIP): St. Joseph's Hospital, Chippewa Falls, WI

Core Health Program of Healthier Communities: Spectrum Health, Grand Rapids, MI
Free Preventive Screenings Program: Good Samaritan Hospital, Vincennes, IN

Hope Clinic and Pharmacy: Ephraim McDowell Health, Danville, KY

2014

FirstReach: FirstHealth of the Carolinas, Pinehurst, NC
Children's Hospital Center for Pediatric Medicine Asthma Action Team: Greenville Health System, Greenville, SC

Let's Go!: The Barbara Bush Children's Hospital at Maine Medical Center, Portland, ME
Hearts Beat Back: The Heart of New Ulm (HONU) Project: New Ulm Medical Center, part of Allina Health, New Ulm, MN

Finney County Community Health Coalition: St. Catherine Hospital, Garden City, KS

The Carolyn Boone Lewis Living the Vision Award

Organizations and individuals living AHA's vision of a society of healthy communities where all individuals reach their highest potential for health.

1998	Memorial Healthcare System, Hollywood, FL Baptist Health System, Montgomery, AL	2003	Franklin Memorial Hospital, Farmington, ME	2013	St. Joseph's Hospital Health Center, Syracuse, NY
1999	Robert A. DeVries, Battle Creek, MI Memorial Health System, South Bend, IN	2004	Jamaica Hospital Medical Center, Jamaica, New York		Cheshire Medical Center/Dartmouth–Hitchcock Keene, Keene, NH
2000	Rockingham Memorial Hospital, Harrisonburg, VA	2005	Fairbanks Memorial Hospital, Fairbanks, AK Boston Medical Center, Boston, MA	2014	TPR Collaborative, Maryland
2001	Salina Regional Health Center, Salina, KS	2010	Lehigh Valley Health Network, Allentown, PA		
2002	Health Improvement Collaborative of Greater Cincinnati, Cincinnati, OH	2011	Alaska Native Tribal Health Consortium, Anchorage, AK		

Circle of Life Award

This award celebrates innovation in palliative and end-of-life care.

2000

Improving Care through the End of Life, Franciscan Health System, Gig Harbor, WA

The Hospice of The Florida Suncoast, Largo, FL

Louisiana State Penitentiary Hospice Program, Angola, LA

2001

Department of Pain Medicine and Palliative Care, Beth Israel Medical Center, New York, NY

Palliative CareCenter & Hospice of the North Shore, Evanston , IL

St. Joseph's Manor, Trumbull, CT

Year			
2002 Children's Program of San Diego Hospice and Children's Hospital and Health Center of San Diego, San Diego, CA	Hospice of the Bluegrass, Lexington, KY Project Safe Conduct, Hospice of the Western Reserve and Ireland Cancer Center, Cleveland, OH	**Special Circle of Life Award** Population–based Palliative Care Research Network (PoPCRN), Denver, CO
2003 Hospice & Palliative CareCenter, Winston–Salem, NC	Providence Health System, Portland, OR	University of California Davis Health System, Sacramento, CA
2004 Hope Hospice and Palliative Care, Fort Myers, FL	St. Mary's Healthcare System for Children, Bayside, NY	University of Texas M.D. Anderson Cancer Center Palliative Care, Houston, TX
2005 High Point Regional Health System, High Point, NC	Palliative and End-of-life Care Program, Hoag Memorial Hospital Presbyterian, Newport Beach, CA	Thomas Palliative Care Unit, VCU Massey Cancer Center, Richmond, VA
2006 Continuum Hospice Care, New York, NY	Mercy Supportive Care, St. Joseph Mercy Oakland, Pontiac, MI	Transitions and Life Choices, Fairview Health Services, Minneapolis, MN
2007 UCSF Palliative Care Program, San Francisco, CA	Covenant Hospice, Pensacola, FL	Woodwell: A Program of Presbyterian SeniorCare and Family Hospice and Palliative Care, Oakmont, PA
2008 Children's Hospitals and Clinics of Minnesota, Pain and Palliative Care Program, Minneapolis, MN	Haven Hospice, Gainesville, FL	The Pediatric Advanced Care Team, The Children's Hospital of Philadelphia, Philadelphia, PA
2009 Four Seasons, Flat Rock, NC	Oregon Health and Science University Palliative Medicine & Comfort Care Program, Portland, OR	Wishard Health Services Palliative Care Program, Indianapolis, IN
2010 Department of Veteran Affairs, VA New York/New Jersey Healthcare Network, Brooklyn, NY	Kansas City Hospice & Palliative Care, Kansas City, MO	Snohomish Palliative Partnership, Everett, WA
2011 The Center for Hospice & Palliative Care, Cheektowaga, NY	Gilchrist Hospice Care, Hunt Valley, MD	St. John Providence Health System, Detroit, MI
2012 Haslinger Family Pediatric Palliative Care Center, Akron Children's Hospital, Akron, OH	Calvary Hospital, Bronx, NY	Sharp HealthCare, San Diego, CA
2013 The Denver Hospice and Optio Health Services, Denver, CO	Hertzberg Palliative Care Institute at the Mount Sinai Medical Center, New York, NY	UnityPoint Health, Iowa and Illinois
2014 OACIS/Palliative Medicine, Lehigh Valley Health Network, Allentown, PA	Supportive & Palliative Care, Baylor Health Care System, Dallas, TX	Yakima Valley Memorial Hospital, Yakima, WA

The American Hospital Association–McKesson Quest for Quality Prize
Honoring Leadership and Innovation in Patient Care Quality, Safety, and Commitment

Year			
2002 Missouri Baptist Medical Center, St. Louis, MO	**Finalist:** Fairview Hospital, Greater, Barrington, MA	**Finalist:** Minnesota Children's Hospital and Clinics, Minneapolis, MN
2003 Abington Memorial Hospital, Abington, PA	**Finalist:** Beaumont Hospitals, Royal Oak, MI	**Finalist:** University of Wisconsin Hospital and Clinics, Madison, WI
2004 Sentara Norfolk General Hospital, Norfolk, VA	**Finalist:** The Johns Hopkins Hospital, Baltimore, MD	**Finalist:** Mary Lanning Memorial Hospital, Hastings, NE
2005 North Mississippi Medical Center, Tupelo, MS	**Finalist:** El Camino Hospital, Mountain View, CA	**Finalist:** NewYork-Presbyterian Hospital, New York, NY
2006 Cincinnati Children's Hospital Medical Center, Cincinnati, OH		
2007 Columbus Regional Hospital, Columbus, IN	**Finalist:** Cedars-Sinai Medical Center, Los Angeles, CA	**Finalist:** INTEGRIS Baptist Medical Center, Oklahoma City, OK
2008 Munson Medical Center, Traverse City, MI	**Finalist:** University of Michigan Hospitals & Health Centers, Ann Arbor, MI	
2009 Bronson Methodist Hospital, Kalamazoo, MI	**Finalist:** Beth Israel Deaconess Medical Center, Boston, MA	

2010
McLeod Regional Medical Center, Florence, SC

Finalist: Henry Ford Hospital, Detroit, MI

2011
Memorial Regional Hospital, Hollywood, FL

Finalist: AtlantiCare Regional Medical Center, Atlantic City, NJ

Finalist: Northwestern Memorial Hospital, Chicago, IL

2012
University Hospitals Case Medical Center, Cleveland, OH

Finalist: Lincoln Medical and Mental Health Center, Bronx, NY

Finalist: University of North Carolina Hospitals, Chapel Hill, NC and Life Choices, Fairview Health Services, Minneapolis, MN

2013
Beth Israel Deaconess Medical Center, Boston, MA

Finalist: Franklin Woods Community Hospital, Johnson City, TN

2014
VCU Medical Center, Richmond, VA

Finalist: Carolinas Medical Center-Northeast, Concord, NC

Foster G. McGaw Prize

Honors health delivery organizations that have demonstrated exceptional commitment to community service.

1986	Lutheran Medical Center, Brooklyn, NY	1995	Our Lady of Lourdes Medical Center, Camden, NJ	2004	Henry Ford Health System, Detroit, MI
1987	Copley Hospital, Morrisville, VT			2005	Venice Family Clinic, Venice, CA
	Mount Sinai Hospital, Hartford, CT	1996	St. Mary's Hospital, Rochester, NY	2006	Memorial Healthcare System, Hollywood, FL
1988	MetroHealth System, Cleveland, OH	1997	Bladen County Hospital Rural Health Network, Elizabethtown, NC	2007	Harborview Medical Center, Seattle, WA
1989	Greater Southeast Healthcare System, Washington, DC			2008	St. Mary's Health System, Lewiston, ME
		1998	Allina Health System, Minneapolis, MN	2009	Heartland Health, St. Joseph, MO
1990	Mount Zion Medical Center of The University of California-San Francisco, San Francisco, CA	1999	LAC+USC Healthcare Network, Los Angeles, CA	2010	Allegiance Health, Jackson, MI
1991	Franklin Regional Hospital, Franklin, NH	2000	Kaweah Delta Health Care District, Visalia, CA	2011	Mt. Ascutney Hospital and Health Center, Windsor, VT
1992	Mount Sinai Hospital Medical Center of Chicago, Chicago, IL	2001	Memorial Hospital of South Bend, South Bend, IN	2012	St. Joseph's/Candler Health System, Savannah, GA
1993	The Cambridge Hospital, Cambridge, MA	2002	John C. Lincoln Health Network, Phoenix, AZ	2013	Crozer–Keystone Health System, Delaware County, PA
1994	Parkland Memorial Hospital, Dallas, TX	2003	Phoebe Putney Memorial Hospital, Albany, GA		

Dick Davidson Quality Milestone Award for Allied Association Leadership

The award recognizes state, regional or metropolitan hospital association leadership in improving health care quality.

2011	Michigan Health & Hospital Association South Carolina Hospital Association	2013	Florida Hospital Association Tennessee Hospital Association
2012	Iowa Hospital Association Washington State Hospital Association	2014	Connecticut Hospital Association Wisconsin Hospital Association

AHA Equity of Care Award

The award is presented to hospitals or care systems that are noteworthy leaders and examples to the field in the area of equitable care.

2014 Massachusetts General Hospital, Boston, MA

A

An institution may be listed by the American Hospital Association if it is accredited as a hospital by The Joint Commission, American Osteopathic Association, DNV Healthcare accredited, or Medicare certified as a provider of acute service under Title 18 of the Social Security Act. Membership in the American Hospital Association is not a prerequisite.

If none of the four conditions mentioned above are satisfied, an institution licensed as a hospital by the appropriate state agency may be registered by AHA as a hospital by meeting the following alernative requirements:

Function: The primary function of the institution is to provide patient services, diagnostic and therapeutic, for particular or general medical conditions.

1. The institution shall maintain at least six inpatient beds, which shall be continuously available for the care of patients who are nonrelated and who stay on the average in excess of 24 hours per admission.
2. The institution shall be constructed, equipped, and maintained to ensure the health and safety of patients and to provide uncrowded, sanitary facilities for the treatment of patients.
3. There shall be an identifiable governing authority legally and morally responsible for the conduct of the hospital.
4. There shall be a chief executive to whom the governing authority delegates the continuous responsibility for the operation of the hospital in accordance with established policy.
5. There shall be an organized medical staff of fully licensed physicians* that may include other licensed individuals permitted by law and by the hospital to provide patient care services independently in the hospital. The medical staff shall be accountable to the governing authority for maintaining proper standards of medical care, and it shall be governed by bylaws adopted by said staff and approved by the governing authority.
6. Each patient shall be admitted on the authority of a member of the medical staff who has been granted the privilege to admit patients to inpatient services in accordance with state law and criteria for standards of medical care established by the individual medical staff. Each patient's general medical condition is the responsibility of a qualified physician member of the medical staff. When nonphysician members of the medical staff are granted privileges to admit patients, provision is made for prompt medical evaluation of these patients by a qualified physician. Any graduate of a foreign medical school who is permitted to assume responsibilities for patient care shall possess a valid license to practice medicine, or shall be certified by the Educational Commission for Foreign Medical Graduates, or shall have qualified for and have successfully completed an academic year of supervised clinical training under the direction of a medical school approved by the Liaison Committee on GAT Medical Education.
7. Registered nurse supervision and other nursing services are continuous.
8. A current and complete medical record shall be maintained by the institution for each patient and shall be available for reference.
9. Pharmacy service shall be maintained in the institution and shall be supervised by a registered pharmacist.
10. The institution shall provide patients with food service that meets their nutritional and therapeutic requirements; special diets shall also be available.

---

* Physician–Term used to describe an individual with an M.D. or D.O. degree who is fully licensed to practice medicine in all its phases.

‡ The completed records in general shall contain at least the following: the patient's identifying data and consent forms, medical history, record of physical examination, physicians' progress notes, operative notes, nurses' notes, routine x–ray and laboratory reports, doctors' orders, and final diagnosis.

Types of Hospitals

In addition to meeting these 10 general requirements, hospitals are listed as one of four types of hospitals: general, special, rehabilitation and chronic disease, or psychiatric. The following definitions of function by type of hospital and special requirements are:

General

The primary function of the institution is to provide patient services, diagnostic and therapeutic, for a variety of medical conditions. A general hospital also shall provide:

- diagnostic x–ray services with facilities and staff for a variety of procedures
- clinical laboratory service with facilities and staff for a variety of procedures and with anatomical pathology services regularly and conveniently available
- operating room service with facilities and staff.

Special

The primary function of the institution is to provide diagnostic and treatment services for patients who have specified medical conditions, both surgical and nonsurgical. A special hospital also shall provide:

- such diagnostic and treatment services as may be determined by the Executive Committee of the Board of Trustees of the American Hospital Association to be appropriate for the specified medical conditions for which medical services are provided shall be maintained in the institution with suitable facilities and staff. If such conditions do not normally require diagnostic x–ray service, laboratory service, or operating room service, and if any such services are therefore not maintained in the institution, there shall be written arrangements to make them available to patients requiring them.
- clinical laboratory services capable of providing tissue diagnosis when offering pregacy termination services.

Rehabilitation and Chronic Disease

The primary function of the institution is to provide diagnostic and treatment services to handicapped or disabled individuals requiring restorative and adjustive services. A rehabilitation and chronic disease hospital also shall provide:

- arrangements for diagnostic x–ray services, as required, on a regular and conveniently available basis
- arrangements for clinical laboratory service, as required on a regular and conveniently available basis
- arrangements for operating room service, as required, on a regular and conveniently available basis
- a physical therapy service with suitable facilities and staff in the institution
- an occupational therapy service with suitable facilities and staff in the institution

- arrangements for psychological and social work services on a regular and conveniently available basis
- arrangements for educational and vocational services on a regular and conveniently available basis
- written arrangements with a general hospital for the transfer of patients who require medical, obstetrical, or surgical services not available in the institution.

Psychiatric

The primary function of the institution is to provide diagnostic and treatment services for patients who have psychiatric–related illnesses. A psychiatric hospital also shall provide:

- arrangements for clinical laboratory service, as required, on a regular and conveniently available basis
- arrangements for diagnostic x–ray services, as required on a regular and conveniently available basis
- psychiatric, psychological, and social work service with facilities and staff in the institution
- arrangements for electroencephalograph services, as required, on a regular and conveniently available basis.
- written arrangements with a general hospital for the transfer of patients who require medical, obstetrical, or surgical services not available in the institution.

The American Hospital Association may, at the sole discretion of the Executive Committee of the Board of Trustees, grant, deny, or withdraw the listing of an institution.

---

* Physician–Term used to describe an individual with an M.D. or D.O. degree who is fully licensed to practice medicine in all its phases.

‡ The completed records in general shall contain at least the following: the patient's identifying data and consent forms, medical history, record of physical examination, physicians' progress notes, operative notes, nurses' notes, routine x–ray and laboratory reports, doctors' orders, and final diagnosis.

Explanation of Hospital Listings

Sample Hospital Listing:

ANYTOWN, Universal County

⊞ **ANYTOWN HOSPITAL & CLINICS (777777)**, (Formerly Anytown Area Community Hospital and Clinic), 100 South Main Street, Zip 12345–6789; tel. 123/456–7890 **A**9 10

ANYTOWN, Universal County

⊞ **ANYTOWN HOSPITAL & CLINICS (777777)**, (Formerly Anytown Area Community Hospital and Clinic), 100 South Main Street, Zip 12345–6789; tel. 123/456–7890 **A**9 10] ①

F10 12 23 24 29 30 31 37 39 49 51 55 57 64 65 66 68 70 71 72 77 78 83 87 88 91 96 97 106 107 110 111 113 124 **P**1 2 3 **S** Universal ⑦

County Health System ② ③
Primary Contact: Ann M. Generic, Chief Executive Officer
COO: Ann M. Generic
CFO: Michael M. Generic
CMO: Peterl Van Generic, President Medical Staff ④
CHR: Jerry Generic, Human Resources Director
CNO: Danielle Generic, R.N., Chief Nursing Officer
Web address: www.website.org
Control: Other not–for–profit (including NFP Corporation) **Service:** General Medical and Surgical ⑤

Staffed Beds: 25 **Admissions:** 892 **Census:** 9 **Outpatient Visits:** 44014
Births: 51 **Total Expense ($000):** 19210 **Payroll Expense ($000):** 5864
Personnel: 182 ⑥

① = Approval Codes
② = Physician Codes
③ = Health Care System Name
④ = Titles of Chief Administrators
⑤ = Control and Service Classifications
⑥ = Utilization Data
⑦ = Facility Codes

Hospital, Medicare Provider Number, Address, Telephone, Approval, Facility, and Physician Codes, Health Care System

★ American Hospital Association (AHA) membership
☐ The Joint Commission accreditation   ◇ DNV Healthcare Inc. accreditation
○ Healthcare Facilities Accreditation Program
△ Commission on Accreditation of Rehabilitation Facilities (CARF) accreditation

---

① Approval Codes

Reported by the approving bodies specified, as of the dates noted.

1 Accreditation under the hospital program of The Joint Commission (June 2014).
2 Cancer program approved by American College of Surgeons (August 2014).
†3 Approval to participate in residency training, by the Accreditation Council for Graduate Medical Education (April 2014).
†5 Medical school affiliation, reported to the American Medical Association (April 2014).
6 Hospital–controlled professional nursing school, reported by National League for Nursing.
7 Accreditation by Commission on Accreditation of Rehabilitation Facilities (April 2014).

8 Member of Council of Teaching Hospitals of the Association of American Medical Colleges (April 2014).
9 Hospitals contracting or participating in a Plan, reported by the Blue Cross and Blue Shield Association (April 2014).
10 Certified for participation in the Health Insurance for the Aged (Medicare) Program by the Centers for Medicare and Medical Services (February 2014).
11 Healthcare Facilities Accreditation Program (April 2014).

12 Internship approved by American Osteopathic Association (April 2014).
13 Residency approved by American Osteopathic Association (April 2014).
18 Critical Access Hospitals (May 2014).
19 Rural Referral Center (May 2014).
20 Sole Community Provider (May 2014).
21 Accreditation by DNV Healthcare Inc. (April 2014).

Nonreporting indicates that the 2013 Annual Survey questionnaire for the hospital was not received prior to publication.

② Physician Codes

Actually available within, and reported by the institution; for definitions, see page A12.

(Alphabetical/Numerical Order)

1 Closed physician–hospital organization (PHO)
2 Equity model
3 Foundation

4 Group practice without walls
5 Independent practice association (IPA)
6 Integrated salary model

7 Management service organization (MSO)
8 Open physician–hospital organization (PHO)

③ Health Care System Name

The inclusion of the letter "S" (1) indicates that the hospital belongs to a health care system and (2) identifies the specific system to which the hospital belongs.

④ Titles of Chief Administrators

⑤ Control and Service Classification

For a list of control and service classifications, see page A13.

Control–The type of organization that is responsible for establishing policy for overall operation of the hospital.

Service–The type of service the hospital provides to the majority of admissions.

⑥ Utilization Data

Definitions are based on the American Hospital Association's Hospital Administration Terminology. In completing the survey, hospitals were requested to report data for a full year, in accord with their fiscal year, ending in 2013.

Beds–Number of beds regularly maintained (set up and staffed for use) for inpatients as of the close of the reporting period. Excludes newborn bassinets.

Admissions–Number of patients accepted for inpatient service during a 12–month period; does not include newborn.

Census–Average number of inpatients receiving care each day during the 12–month reporting period; does not include newborn.

Outpatient Visits–A visit by a patient who is not lodged in the hospital while receiving medical, dental, or other services. Each appearance of an outpatient in each unit constitutes one visit regardless of the number of diagnostic and/or therapeutic treatments that a patient receives.

Births–Number of infants born in the hospital and accepted for service in a newborn infant bassinet during a 12–month period; excludes stillbirths.

Expense: Expense for a 12–month period; both total expense and payroll components are shown. Payroll expenses include all salaries and wages.

Personnel: Represents personnel situations as they existed at the end of the reporting period; includes full-time equivalents of part–time personnel. Full–time equivalents were calculated on the basis that two part–time persons equal one full–time person.

---

†Data from the Graduate Medical Education Database, Copyright 2014, American Medical Association, Chicago, Illinois.

Sample Hospital Listing:

ANYTOWN, Universal County

⊞ **ANYTOWN HOSPITAL & CLINICS (777777)**, (Formerly Anytown Area Community Hospital and Clinic), 100 South Main Street, Zip 12345–6789; tel. 123/456–7890 **A9** 10] ①
F10 12 23 24 29 30 31 37 39 49 51 55 57 64 65 66 68 70 71 72 77 78 83 87 88 91 96 97 106 107 110 111 113 124 **P**1 2 3 **S** Universal ⑦
County Health System ② ③
Primary Contact: Ann M. Generic, Chief Executive Officer
COO: Ann M. Generic
CFO: Michael M. Generic ④
CMO: Peterl Van Generic, President Medical Staff
CHR: Jerry Generic, Human Resources Director
CNO: Danielle Generic, R.N., Chief Nursing Officer
Web address: www.website.org
Control: Other not–for–profit (including NFP Corporation) **Service:** General ⑤
Medical and Surgical

Staffed Beds: 25 **Admissions:** 892 **Census:** 9 **Outpatient Visits:** 44014
Births: 51 **Total Expense ($000):** 19210 **Payroll Expense ($000):** 5864
Personnel: 182

ANYTOWN, Universal County

⊞ **ANYTOWN HOSPITAL & CLINICS (777777)**, (Formerly Anytown Area Community Hospital and Clinic), 100 South Main Street, Zip 12345–6789; tel. 123/456–7890 **A9** 10

① = Approval Codes
② = Physician Codes
③ = Health Care System Name
④ = Titles of Chief Administrators
⑤ = Control and Service Classifications
⑥ = Utilization Data
⑦ = Facility Codes

⑥

Hospital, Medicare Provider Number, Address, Telephone, Approval, Facility, and Physician Codes, Health Care System

★ American Hospital Association (AHA) membership
□ The Joint Commission accreditation
◇ DNV Healthcare Inc. accreditation
○ Healthcare Facilities Accreditation Program
△ Commission on Accreditation of Rehabilitation Facilities (CARF) accreditation

---

⑦ Facility Codes

Provided directly by the hospital; for definitions, see page A6.

(Numerical Order)

1. Acute long-term care
2. Adult day care program
3. Airborne infection isolation room
4. Alcoholism-drug abuse or dependency inpatient unit
5. Alcoholism-drug abuse or dependency outpatient unit
6. Alzheimer center
7. Ambulance services
8. Ambulatory surgery center
9. Arthritis treatment center
10. Assisted living
11. Auxiliary
12. Bariatric/weight control services
13. Birthing room-LDR room-LDRP room
14. Blood donor center
15. Breast cancer screening/mammograms
16. Burn care services
17. Cardiac intensive care
18. Adult cardiology services
19. Pediatric cardiology services
20. Adult diagnostic catheterization
21. Pediatric diagnostic catheterization
22. Adult interventional cardiac catheterization
23. Pediatric diagnostic catheterization
24. Adult cardiac surgery
25. Pediatric cardiac surgery
26. Adult cardiac electrophysiology
27. Pediatric cardiac electrophysiology
28. Cardiac rehabilitation
29. Case management
30. Chaplaincy/pastoral care services
31. Chemotherapy
32. Children's wellness program
33. Chiropractic services
34. Community health education
35. Community outreach
36. Complementary and alternative medicine services
37. Computer assisted orthopedic surgery (CAOS)
38. Crisis prevention
39. Dental services
40. Emergency department
41. Pediatric emergency department
42. Satellite emergency department
43. Trauma center (certified)
44. Enabling services
45. Optical colonoscopy
46. Endoscopic ultrasound
47. Ablation of Barrett's esophagus
48. Esophageal impedance study
49. Endoscopic retrograde cholangiopancreatography (ERCP)
50. Enrollment assistance services
51. Extracorporeal shock wave lithotripter (ESWL)
52. Fertility clinic
53. Fitness center
54. Freestanding outpatient care center
55. Genetic testing/counseling
56. Geriatric services
57. Health fair
58. Health research
59. Health screenings
60. Hemodialysis
61. HIV–AIDS services
62. Home health services
63. Hospice program
64. Hospital–based outpatient care center services
65. Immunization program
66. Indigent care clinic
67. Intermediate nursing care
68. Linguistic/translation services
69. Meals on wheels
70. Medical surgical intensive care services
71. Mobile health services
72. Neonatal intensive care
73. Neonatal intermediate care
74. Neurological services
75. Nutrition programs
76. Obstetrics
77. Occupational health services
78. Oncology services
79. Orthopedic services
80. Other special care
81. Outpatient surgery
82. Pain management program
83. Inpatient palliative care unit
84. Palliative care program
85. Patient controlled analgesia (PCA)
86. Patient education center
87. Patient representative services
88. Pediatric intensive care services
89. Pediatric medical–surgical care
90. Physical rehabilitation inpatient services
91. Assistive technology center
92. Electrodiagnostic services
93. Physical rehabilitation outpatient services
94. Prosthetic and orthotic services
95. Robot-assisted walking therapy
96. Simulated rehabilitation environment
97. Primary care department
98. Psychiatric care
99. Psychiatric child–adolescent services
100. Psychiatric consultation–liaison services
101. Psychiatric education services
102. Psychiatric emergency services
103. Psychiatric geriatric services
104. Psychiatric outpatient services
105. Psychiatric partial hospitalization services
106. Psychiatric residential treatment
107. CT scanner
108. Diagnostic radioisotope facility
109. Electron beam computed tomography (EBCT)
110. Full–field digital mammography (FFDM)
111. Magnetic resonance imaging (MRI)
112. Intraoperative magnetic resonance imaging
113. Magnetoencephalography (MEG)
114. Multi–slice spiral computed tomography (MSCT) (<64 slice CT)
115. Multi–slice spiral computed tomography (64 + slice CT)
116. Positron emission tomography (PET)
117. Positron emission tomography/CT (PET/CT)
118. Single photon emission computerized tomography (SPECT)
119. Ultrasound
120. Image–guided radiation therapy (IGRT)
121. Intensity–modulated radiation therapy (IMRT)
122. Proton beam therapy
123. Shaped beam radiation therapy
124. Stereotactic radiosurgery
125. Retirement housing
126. Robotic surgery
127. Rural health clinic
128. Skilled nursing care
129. Sleep center
130. Social work services
131. Sports medicine
132. Support groups
133. Swing bed services
134. Teen outreach services
135. Tobacco treatment/cessation program
136. Bone marrow transplant services
137. Heart transplant
138. Kidney transplant
139. Liver transplant
140. Lung transplant
141. Tissue transplant
142. Other transplant
143. Transportation to health services
144. Urgent care center
145. Virtual colonoscopy
146. Volunteer services department
147. Women's health center/services
148. Wound management services

Annual Survey

Each year, an annual survey of hospitals is conducted by the American Hospital Association through its Health Forum affiliate.

The facilities and services found below are provided by the hospital. For data products reflecting the services provided by a hospital through its health care system, or network or through a formal arrangement with another provider contact Health Forum at 800/821–2039, or visit www.healthforum.com.

The AHA Guide to the Health Care Field does not include all data collected from the 2013 Annual Survey. Requests for purchasing other Annual Survey data should be directed to Health Forum LLC, an affiliate of the American Hospital Association, 155 N. Wacker Drive, Chicago, IL 60606, 800/821–2039.

Definitions of Facility Codes

1. **Acute long–term care.** Provides specialized acute hospital care to medically complex patients who are critically ill, have multisystem complications and/or failure, and require hospitalization averaging 25 days, in a facility offering specialized treatment programs and therapeutic intervention on a 24–hour/7 day a week basis.

2. **Adult day care program.** Program providing supervision, medical and psychological care, and social activities for older adults who live at home or in another family setting, but cannot be alone or prefer to be with others during the day. May include intake assessment, health monitoring, occupational therapy, personal care, noon meal, and transportation services.

3. **Airborne infection isolation room.** A single–occupancy room for patient care where environmental factors are controlled in an effort to minimize the transmission of those infectious agents, usually spread person to person by droplet nuclei associated with coughing and inhalation. Such rooms typically have specific ventilation requirements for controlled ventilation, air pressure and filtration.

4. **Alcoholism–drug abuse or dependency inpatient unit.** Provides diagnosis and therapeutic services to patients with alcoholism or other drug dependencies. Includes care for inpatient/residential treatment for patients whose course of treatment involves more intensive care than provided in an outpatient setting or where patient requires supervised withdrawal.

5. **Alcoholism–drug abuse or dependency outpatient unit.** Organized hospital services that provide medical care and/or rehabilitative treatment services to outpatients for whom the primary diagnosis is alcoholism or other chemical dependency.

6. **Alzheimer center.** Facility that offers care to persons with Alzheimer's disease and their families through an integrated program of clinical services, research, and education.

7. **Ambulance services.** Provision of ambulance services to the ill and injured who require medical attention on a scheduled or unscheduled basis.

8. **Ambulatory surgery center.** Facility that provides care to patients requiring surgery who are admitted and discharged on the same day. Ambulatory surgery centers are distinct from same day surgical units within the hospital outpatient departments for purposes of Medicare payments.

9. **Arthritis treatment center.** Specifically equipped and staffed center for the diagnosis and treatment of arthritis and other joint disorders.

10. **Assisted living.** A special combination of housing, supportive services, personalized assistance and health care designed to respond to the individual needs of those who need help in activities of daily living and instrumental activities of daily living. Supportive services are available, 24 hours a day, to meet scheduled and unscheduled needs, in a way that promotes maximum independence and dignity for each resident and encourages the involvement of a resident's family, neighbor and friends.

11. **Auxiliary.** A volunteer community organization formed to assist the hospital in carrying out its purpose and to serve as a link between the institution and the community.

12. **Bariatric/weight control services.** Bariatrics is the medical practice of weight reduction.

13. **Birthing room–LDR room–LDRP room.** A single room–type of maternity care with a more homelike setting for families than the traditional three–room unit (labor/delivery/recovery) with a separate postpartum area. A birthing room combines labor and delivery in one room. An LDR room accommodates three stages in the birthing process—labor, delivery, and recovery. An LDRP room accommodates all four stages of the birth process—labor, delivery, recovery and postpartum.

14. **Blood donor center.** A facility that performs, or is responsible for the collection, processing, testing or distribution of blood and components.

15. **Breast cancer screening/mammograms.** Mammography screening–the use of breast x–ray to detect unsuspected breast cancer in asymptomatic women. Diagnostic mammography–the x–ray imaging of breast tissue in symptomatic women who are considered to have a substantial likelihood of having breast cancer already.

16. **Burn care services.** Provides care to severely burned patients. Severely burned patients are those with any of the following: 1. Second–degree burns of more than 25% total body surface area for adults or 20% total body surface area for children; 2. Third–degree burns of more than 10% total body surface area; 3. Any severe burns of the hands, face, eyes, ears or feet or; 4. All inhalation injuries, electrical burns, complicated burn injuries involving fractures and other major traumas, and all other poor risk factors.

17. **Cardiac intensive care.** Provides patient care of a more specialized

nature than the usual medical and surgical care, on the basis of physicians' orders and approved nursing care plans. The unit is staffed with specially trained nursing personnel and contains monitoring and specialized support or treatment equipment for patients who, because of heart seizure, open–heart surgery, or other life–threatening conditions, require intensified, comprehensive observation and care. May include myocardial infarction, pulmonary care, and heart transplant units.

18. **Adult cardiology services.** An organized clinical service offering diagnostic and interventional procedures to manage the full range of adult heart conditions.

19. **Pediatric cardiology services.**

20. **Adult diagnostic catheterization.** (also called coronary angiography or coronary arteriography) is used to assist in diagnosing complex heart conditions. Cardiac angiography involves the insertion of a tiny catheter up into the artery in the groin then carefully threading the catheter up into the aorta where the coronary arteries originate. Once the catheter is in place, a dye is injected which allows the cardiologist to see the size, shape and distribution of the coronary arteries. These images are used to diagnose heart disease and to determine, among other things, whether or not surgery is indicated.

21. **Pediatric diagnostic catheterization.** (also called coronary angiography or coronary arteriography) is used to assist in diagnosing complex heart conditions. Cardiac angiography involves the insertion of a tiny catheter up into the artery in the groin then carefully threading the catheter up into the aorta where the coronary arteries originate. Once the catheter is in place, a dye is injected which allows the cardiologist to see the size, shape and distribution of the coronary arteries. These images are used to diagnose heart disease and to determine, among other things, whether or not surgery is indicated.

22. **Adult interventional cardiac catheterization.** Nonsurgical procedure that utilizes the same basic principles as diagnostic catheterization and then uses advanced the techniques to improve the heart's function. It can be less invasive alternative to heart surgery.

23. **Pediatric diagnostic catheterization.** Nonsurgical

procedure that utilizes the same basic principles as diagnostic catheterization and then uses advanced the techniques to improve the heart's function. It can be less invasive alternative to heart surgery.

24. **Adult cardiac surgery.** Includes minimally invasive procedures that include surgery done with only a small incision or no incision at all, such as through a laparoscope or an endoscope and more invasive major surgical procedures that include open chest and open heart surgery.

25. **Pediatric cardiac surgery.** Includes minimally invasive procedures that include surgery done with only a small incision or no incision at all, such as through a laparoscope or an endoscope and more invasive major surgical procedures that include open chest and open heart surgery defibrillator implantation and follow-up.

26. **Adult cardiac electrophysiology.** Evaluation and management of patients with complex rhythm or conduction abnormalities, including diagnostic testing, treatment of arrhythmias by catheter ablation or drug therapy, and pacemaker/defibrillator implantation and follow-up.

27. **Pediatric cardiac electrophysiology.**

28. **Cardiac rehabilitation.** A medically supervised program to help heart patients recover quickly and improve their overall physical and mental functioning. The goal is to reduce risk of another cardiac event or to keep an already present heart condition from getting worse. Cardiac rehabilitation programs include: counseling to patients, an exercise program, helping patients modify risk factors such as smoking and high blood pressure, providing vocational guidance to enable the patient to return to work, supplying information on physical limitations and lending emotional support.

29. **Case management.** A system of assessment, treatment planning, referral and follow–up that ensures the provision of comprehensive and continuous services and the coordination of payment and reimbursement for care.

30. **Chaplaincy/pastoral care services.** A service ministering religious activities and providing pastoral counseling to patients, their families,

and staff of a health care organization.

31. **Chemotherapy.** An organized program for the treatment of cancer by the use of drugs or chemicals.

32. **Children's wellness program.** A program that encourages improved health status and a healthful lifestyle of children through health education, exercise, nutrition and health promotion.

33. **Chiropractic services.** An organized clinical service including spinal manipulation or adjustment and related diagnostic and therapeutic services.

34. **Community health education.** Education that provides health information to individuals and populations as well as support for personal, family and community health decisions with the objective of improving health status.

35. **Community outreach.** A program that systematically interacts with the community to identify those in need of services, alerting persons and their families to the availability of services, locating needed services, and enabling persons to enter the service delivery system.

36. **Complementary and alternative medicine services.** Organized hospital services or formal arrangements to providers that provide care or treatment not based solely on traditional western allopathic medical teachings as instructed in most U.S. medical schools. Includes any of the following; acupuncture, chiropractic, homeopathy, osteopathy, diet and lifestyle changes, herbal medicine, massage therapy, etc.

37. **Computer assisted orthopedic surgery (CAOS).** Orthopedic surgery using computer technology, enabling three–dimensional graphic models to visualize a patient's anatomy.

38. **Crisis prevention** Services provided in order to promote physical and mental well being and the early identification of disease and ill health prior to the onset and recognition of symptoms so as to permit early treatment.

39. **Dental services.** An organized dental service, not necessarily involving special facilities, that provides dental or oral services to inpatients or outpatients.

40. **Emergency department.** Hospital facilities for the provision of

unscheduled outpatient services to patients whose conditions require immediate care. Must be staffed 24 hours a day.

41. **Pediatric emergency department.** Hospital facilities for the provision of unscheduled outpatient services to patients whose conditions require immediate care.

42. **Satellite emergency department.** A facility owned and operated by the hospital but physically separate from the hospital for the provision of unscheduled outpatient services to patients whose conditions require.

43. **Trauma center (certified).** A facility certified to provide emergency and specialized intensive care to critically ill and injured patients.

44. **Enabling services.** A program that is designed to help the patient access health care services by offering any of the following linguistic services, transportation services, and/or referrals to local social services agencies.

45. **Optical colonoscopy.** An examination of the interior of the colon using a long, flexible, lighted tube with a small built-in camera.

46. **Endoscopic ultrasound.** Specially designed endoscope that incorporates an ultrasound transducer used to obtain detailed images of organs in the chest and abdomen. The endoscope can be passed through the mouth or the anus. When combined with needle biopsy the procedure can assist in diagnosis and staging of cancer.

47. **Ablation of Barrett's esophagus.** Premalignant condition that can lead to adenocarcinoma of the esophagus. The non surgical ablation of the premalignant tissue in Barrett's esophagus by the application of thermal energy or light through an endoscope passed from the mouth into the esophagus.

48. **Esophageal impedance study.** A test in which a catheter is placed through the nose into the esophagus to measure whether gas or liquids are passing from the stomach into the esophagus and causing symptoms.

49. **Endoscopic retrograde cholangiopancreatography (ERCP).** A procedure in which a catheter is introduced through an endoscope into the bile ducts and pancreatic ducts. Injection of contrast materials permits detailed x-ray of these structures. The procedure is used diagnostically as

well as therapeutically to relieve obstruction or remove stones

50. **Enrollment assistance services.** A program that provides enrollment assistance for patients who are potentially eligible for public health insurance programs such as Medicaid, State Children's Health Insurance, or local/state indigent care programs. The specific services offered could include explanation of benefits, assist applicants in completing the application and locating all relevant documents, conduct eligibilty interviews, and/or forward applications and documentation to state/local social service or health agency.

51. **Extracorporeal shock wave lithotripter (ESWL).** A medical device used for treating stones in the kidney or urethra. The device disintegrates kidney stones noninvasively through the transmission of acoustic shock waves directed at the stones.

52. **Fertility clinic.** A specialized program set in an infertility center that provides counseling and education as well as advanced reproductive techniques such as: injectable therapy, reproductive surgeries, treatment for endometriosis, male factor infertility, tubal reversals, in vitro fertilization (IVF), donor eggs, and other such services to help patients achieve successful pregnancies.

53. **Fitness center.** Provides exercise, testing, or evaluation programs and fitness activities to the community and hospital employees.

54. **Freestanding outpatient care center.** A facility owned and operated by the hospital, but physically separate from the hospital, that provides various medical treatments on an outpatient basis only. In addition to treating minor illnesses or injuries, the center will stabilize seriously ill or injured patients before transporting them to a hospital. Laboratory and radiology services are usually available.

55. **Genetic testing/counseling** A service equipped with adequate laboratory facilities and directed by a qualified physician to advise parents and prospective parents on potential problems in cases of genetic defects. A genetic test is the analysis of human DNA, RNA, chromosomes, proteins, and certain metabolites in order to detect heritable disease-related genotypes, mutations,

phenotypes, or karyotypes for clinical purposes. Genetic tests can have diverse purposes, including the diagnosis of genetic diseases in newborns, children, and adults; the identification of future health risks; the prediction of drug responses; and the assessment of risks to future children.

56. **Geriatric services.** The branch of medicine dealing with the physiology of aging and the diagnosis and treatment of disease affecting the aged. Services could include: Adult day care program; Alzheimer's diagnostic–assessment services; Comprehensive geriatric assessment; Emergency response system; Geriatric acute care unit; and/or Geriatric clinics.

57. **Health fair.** Community health education events that focus on the prevention of disease and promotion of health through such activities as audiovisual exhibits and free diagnostic services.

58. **Health research.** Organized hospital research program in any of the following areas: basic research, clinical research, community health research, and/or research on innovative health care delivery.

59. **Health screenings.** A preliminary procedure, such as a test or examination to detect the most characteristic sign or signs of a disorder that may require further investigation.

60. **Hemodialysis.** Provision of equipment and personnel for the treatment of renal insufficiency on an inpatient or outpatient basis.

61. **HIV–AIDS services.** Services may include one or more of the following: HIV–AIDS unit (special unit or team designated and equipped specifically for diagnosis, treatment, continuing care planning, and counseling services for HIV–AIDS patients and their families.) General inpatient care for HIV–AIDS (inpatient diagnosis and treatment for human immunodeficiency virus and acquired immunodeficiency syndrome patients, but dedicated unit is not available.) Specialized outpatient program for HIV–AIDS (special outpatient program providing diagnostic, treatment, continuing care planning, and counseling for HIV–AIDS patients and their families.)

62. **Home health services.** Service providing nursing, therapy, and

health–related homemaker or social services in the patient's home.

63. **Hospice program.** A program providing palliative care, chiefly medical relief of pain and supportive services, addressing the emotional, social, financial, and legal needs of terminally ill patients and their families. Care can be provided in a variety of settings, both inpatient and at home.

64. **Hospital–based outpatient care center services.** Organized hospital health care services offered by appointment on an ambulatory basis. Services may include outpatient surgery, examination, diagnosis, and treatment of a variety of medical conditions on a nonemergency basis, and laboratory and other diagnostic testing as ordered by staff or outside physician referral.

65. **Immunization program.** Program that plans, coordinates and conducts immunization services in the community.

66. **Indigent care clinic.** Health care services for uninsured and underinsured persons where care is free of charge or charged on a sliding scale. This would include "free clinics" staffed by volunteer practitioners, but could also be staffed by employees with sponsoring health care organizations subsidizing the cost of service.

67. **Intermediate nursing care.** Provides health–related services (skilled nursing care and social services) to residents with a variety of physical conditions or functional disabilities. These residents do not require the care provided by a hospital or skilled nursing facility, but do need supervision and support services.

68. **Linguistic/translation services.** Services provided by the hospital designed to make health care more accessible to non–English speaking patients and their physicians.

69. **Meals on wheels.** A hospital sponsored program which delivers meals to people, usually the elderly, who are unable to prepare their own meals. Low cost, nutritional meals are delivered to individuals' homes on a regular basis.

70. **Medical surgical intensive care services.** Provides patient care of a more intensive nature than the usual medical and surgical care, on the basis of physicians' orders and approved nursing care plans. These units are staffed with specially trained nursing personnel and contain monitoring and specialized support equipment of patients who, because of shock, trauma, or other life–threatening conditions, require intensified, comprehensive observation and care. Includes mixed intensive care units.

71. **Mobile health services.** Vans and other vehicles used to deliver primary care services.

72. **Neonatal intensive care.** A unit that must be separate from the newborn nursery providing intensive care to all sick infants including those with the very lowest birth weights (less that 1500 grams). NICU has potential for providing mechanical ventilation, neonatal surgery, and special care for the sickest infants born in the hospital or transferred from another institution. A full–time neonatologist serves as director of the NICU.

73. **Neonatal intermediate care.** A unit that must be separate from the normal newborn nursery and that provides intermediate and/or recovery care and some specialized services, including immediate resuscitation, intravenous therapy, and capacity for prolonged oxygen therapy and monitoring.

74. **Neurological services.** Services provided by the hospital dealing with the operative and nonoperative management of disorders of the central, peripheral, and autonomic nervous system.

75. **Nutrition programs.** Those services within a health care facility which are designed to provide inexpensive, nutritionally sound meals to patients.

76. **Obstetrics.** Levels should be designated: (1) unit provides services for uncomplicated maternity and newborn cases; (2) unit provides services for uncomplicated cases, the majority of complicated problems, and special neonatal services; and (3) unit provides services for all serious illnesses and abnormalities and is supervised by a full–time maternal/fetal specialist.

77. **Occupational health services.** Includes services designed to protect the safety of employees from hazards in the work environment.

78. **Oncology services.** Inpatient and outpatient services for patients with cancer, including comprehensive care, support and guidance in addition to patient education and preventiion, chemotherapy, counseling, and other treatment methods.

79. **Orthopedic services.** Services provided for the prevention or correction of injuries or disorders of the skeletal system and associated muscles, joints, and ligaments.

80. **Other special care.** Provides care to patients requiring care more intensive than that provided in the acute area, yet not sufficiently intensive to require admission to an intensive care unit. Patients admitted to the area are usually transferred here from an intensive care unit once their condition has improved. These units are sometimes referred to as definitive observation, step–down, or progressive care units.

81. **Outpatient surgery.** Scheduled surgical services provided to patients who do not remain in the hospital overnight. The surgery may be performed in operating suites also used for inpatient surgery, specially designated surgical suites for outpatient surgery, or procedure rooms within an outpatient care facility.

82. **Pain management program.** A hospital wide formalized program that includes staff education for the management of chronic and acute pain based on guidelines and protocols like those developed by the agency for Health Care Policy Research, etc.

83. **Inpatient palliative care unit.** An inpatient palliative care ward is a physically discreet, inpatient nursing unit where the focus is palliative care. The patient care focus is on symptom relief for complex patients who may be continuing to undergo primary treatment. Care is delivered by palliative medicine specialists.

84. **Palliative care program.** An organized program providing specialized medical care, drugs or therapies for the management of acute or chronic pain and/or the control of symptoms adminstered by specially trained physicians and other clinicians; and supportive care services, such as counseling on advanced directives, spiritual care, and social services, to patients with advanced disease and their families.

85. **Patient controlled analgesia (PCA).** Patient Controlled Analgesia (PCA) is intravenously administered pain medicine under the patient's control. The patient has a button on the end of a cord than can be pushed at will, whenever more pain medicine is desired. This button will only deliver more pain medicine at pre–

determined intervals, as programmed by the doctor's order.

86. **Patient education center.** Written goals and objectives for the patient and/or family related to therapeutic regimens, medical procedures, and self care.

87. **Patient representative services.** Organized hospital services providing personnel through whom patients and staff can seek solutions to institutional problems affecting the delivery of high–quality care and services.

88. **Pediatric intensive care services.** Provides care to pediatric patients that is of a more intensive nature than that usually provided to pediatric patients. The unit is staffed with specially trained personnel and contains monitoring and specialized support equipment for treatment of patients who, because of shock, trauma, or other life–threatening conditions, require intensified, comprehensive observation and care.

89. **Pediatric medical–surgical care.** Provides acute care to pediatric patients on the basis of physicians' orders and approved nursing care plans.

90. **Physical rehabilitation inpatient services.** Provides care encompassing a comprehensive array of restoration services for the disabled and all support services necessary to help patients attain their maximum functional capacity.

91. **Assistive technology center.** A program providing access to specialized hardware and software with adaptations allowing individuals greater independence with mobility, dexterity, or increased communication options.

92. **Electrodiagnostic services.** Diagnostic testing services for nerve and muscle function including services such as nerve conduction studies and needle electromyography.

93. **Physical rehabilitation outpatient services.** Outpatient program providing medical, health–related, therapy, social, and/or vocational services to help disabled persons attain or retain their maximum functional capacity.

94. **Prosthetic and orthotic services.** Services providing comprehensive prosthetic and orthotic evaluation, fitting, and training.

95. **Robot-assisted walking therapy.** A form of physical therapy that uses a robotic device to assist patients who are relearning how to walk.

96. **Simulated rehabilitation environment.** Rehabilitation focused on retraining functional skills in a contextually appropriate environment (simulated home and community settings) or in a traditional setting (gymnasium) using motor learning principles.

97. **Primary care department.** A unit or clinic within the hospital that provides primary care services (e.g. general pediatric care, general internal medicine, family practice and gynecology) through hospital–salaried medical and or nursing staff, focusing on evaluating and diagnosing medical problems and providing medical treatment on an outpatient basis.

98. **Psychiatric care.** Provides acute or long–term care to emotionally disturbed patients, including patients admitted for diagnosis and those admitted for treatment of psychiatric problems, on the basis of physicians' orders and approved nursing care plans. Long–term care may include intensive supervision to the chronically mentally ill, mentally disordered, or other mentally incompetent persons.

99. **Psychiatric child–adolescent services.** Provides care to emotionally disturbed children and adolescents, including those admitted for diagnosis and those admitted for treatment.

100. **Psychiatric consultation–liaison services.** Provides organized psychiatric consultation/liaison services to nonpsychiatric hospital staff and/or department on psychological aspects of medical care that may be generic or specific to individual patients.

101. **Psychiatric education services.** Provides psychiatric educational services to community agencies and workers such as schools, police, courts, public health nurses, welfare agencies, clergy and so forth. The purpose is to expand the mental health knowledge and competence of personnel not working in the mental health field and to promote good mental health through improved understanding, attitudes, and behavioral patterns.

102. **Psychiatric emergency services.** Services or facilities available on a 24–hour basis to provide immediate unscheduled outpatient care, diagnosis, evaluation, crisis intervention, and assistance to persons suffering acute emotional or mental distress.

103. **Psychiatric geriatric services.** Provides care to emotionally disturbed elderly patients, including those admitted for diagnosis and those admitted for treatment.

104. **Psychiatric outpatient services.** Provides medical care, including diagnosis and treatment of psychiatric outpatients.

105. **Psychiatric partial hospitalization services.** Organized hospital services of intensive day/evening outpatient services of three hours or more duration, distinguished from other outpatient visits of one hour.

106. **Psychiatric residential treatment.**

107. **CT scanner.** Computed tomographic scanner for head and whole body scans.

108. **Diagnostic radioisotope facility.** The use of radioactive isotopes (Radiopharmaceutical) as tracers or indicators to detect an abnormal condition or disease.

109. **Electron beam computed tomography (EBCT).** A high tech computed tomography scan used to detect coronary artery disease by measuring coronary calcifications. This imaging procedure uses electron beams which are magnetically steered to produce a visual of the coronary artery and the images are produced faster than conventional CT scans.

110. **Full–field digital mammography (FFDM).** Combines the x–ray generators and tubes used in analog screen–film mammography (SFM) with a detector plate that converts the x–rays into a digital signal.

111. **Magnetic resonance imaging (MRI).** The use of a uniform magnetic field and radio frequencies to study tissue and structure of the body. This procedure enables the visualization of biochemical activity of the cell in vivo without the use of ionizing radiation, radioisotopic substances, or high–frequency sound.

112. **Intraoperative magnetic resonance imaging.** An integrated surgery system which provides an MRI system in an operating room. The system allows for immediate evaluation of the degree to tumor resection while the patient is undergoing a surgical resection. Intraoperative MRI exists when a MRI (low–field or high–field) is placed in the operating theater and is

used during surgical resection without moving the patient from the operating room to the diagnostic imaging suite.

113. **Magnetoencephalography (MEG).** A noninvasive neurophysiological measurement tool used to study magnetic fields generated by neuronal activity of the brain. MEG provides direct information about the dynamics of evoked and spontaneous neural activity and the location of their sources in the brain. The primary uses of MEG include assisting surgeons in localizing the source of epilepsy, sensory mapping and the study of brain function. When it is combined with structural imaging, it is known as magnetic source imaging (MSI).

114. **Multi–slice spiral computed tomography (MSCT) (<64 slice CT).** A specialized computed tomography procedure that provides three–dimensional processing and allows narrower and multiple slices with increased spatial resolution and faster scanning times as compared to a regular computed tomography scan.

115. **Multi–slice spiral computed tomography (64 + slice CT).** Involves the acquisition of volumetric tomographic x–ray absorption data expressed in Hounsfield units using multiple rows of detectors. 64+ systems reconstruct the equivalent of 64 or greater slices to cover the imaged volume.

116. **Positron emission tomography (PET).** A nuclear medicine imaging technology which uses radioactive (positron emitting) isotopes created in a cyclotron or generator and computers to produce composite pictures of the brain and heart at work. PET scanning produces sectional images depicting metabolic activity or blood flow rather than anatomy.

117. **Positron emission tomography/CT (PET/CT).** Provides metabolic functional information for the monitoring of chemotherapy, radiotherapy and surgical planning.

118. **Single photon emission computerized tomography (SPECT).** A nuclear medicine imaging technology that combines existing technology of gamma camera imaging with computed tomographic imaging technology to provide a more precise and clear image.

119. **Ultrasound.** The use of acoustic waves above the range of 20,000 cycles per second to visualize internal body structures.

120. **Image–guided radiation therapy (IGRT).** Automated system for image–guided radiation therapy that enables clinicians to obtain high–resolution x–ray images to pinpoint tumor sites, adjust patient positioning when necessary, and complete a treatment, all within the standard treatment time slot, allowing for more effective cancer treatments.

121. **Intensity–modulated radiation Therapy (IMRT).** A type of three–dimensional radiation therapy, which improves the targeting of treatment delivery in a way that is likely to decrease damage to normal tissues and allows varying intensities diagnosis of genetic diseases in newborns, children, and adults; the identification of future health risks; the prediction of drug responses; and the assessment of risks to future children.

122. **Proton beam therapy.** A form of radiation therapy which administers proton beams. While producing the same biologic effects as x–ray beams, the energy distribution of protons differs from conventional x–ray beams in that they can be more precisely focused in tissue volumes in a three–dimensional pattern resulting in less surrounding tissue damage than conventional radiation therapy permitting administration of higher doses.

123. **Shaped beam radiation therapy.** A precise, non–invasive treatment that involves targeting beams of radiation that mirror the exact size and shape of a tumor at a specific area of a tumor to shrink or destroy cancerous cells. This procedure delivers a therapeutic dose of radiation that conforms precisely to the shape of the tumor, thus minimizing the risk to nearby tissues.

124. **Stereotactic radiosurgery.** Stereotactic radiosurgery (SRS) is a radiotherapy modality that delivers a high dosage of radiation to a discrete treatment area in as few as one treatment session. Includes gamma knife, cyberknife, etc.

125. **Retirement housing.** A facility which provides social activities to senior citizens, usually retired persons, who do not require health care but some short–term skilled nursing care may be provided. A retirement center may furnish housing and may also have acute hospital and long–term care facilities, or it may arrange for acute and long term care through affiliated institutions.

126. **Robotic surgery.** The use of mechanical guidance devices to remotely manipulate surgical instrumentation.

127. **Rural health clinic.** A clinic located in a rural, medically under-served area in the United States that has a separate reimbursement structure from the standard medical office under the Medicare and Medicaid programs.

128. **Skilled nursing care.** Provides non–acute medical and skilled nursing care services, therapy, and social services under the supervision of a licensed registered nurse on a 24–hour basis.

129. **Sleep center.** Specially equipped and staffed center for the diagnosis and treatment of sleep disorders.

130. **Social work services.** Services may include one or more of the following: Organized social work services (services that are properly directed and sufficiently staffed by qualified individuals who provide assistance and counseling to patients and their families in dealing with social, emotional, and environmental problems associated with illness or disability, often in the context of financial or discharge planning coordination.) Outpatient social work services (social work services provided in ambulatory care areas.) Emergency department social work services (social work services provided to emergency department patients by social workers dedicated to the emergency department or on call.)

131. **Sports medicine.** Provision of diagnostic screening and assessment and clinical and rehabilitation services for the prevention and treatment of sports–related injuries.

132. **Support groups.** A hospital sponsored program which allows a group of individuals with the same or similar problems who meet periodically to share experiences, problems, and solutions, in order to support each other.

133. **Swing bed services.** A hospital bed that can be used to provide either acute or long–term care depending on community or patients needs. To be eligible a hospital must have a Medicare provider agreement in place, have fewer than 100 beds, be located in a rural area, not have a 24 hour nursing service waiver in effect, have not been terminated from the

program in the prior two years, and meet various service conditions.

134. **Teen outreach services.** A program focusing on the teenager which encourages an improved health status and a healthful lifestyle including physical, emotional, mental, social, spiritual and economic health through education, exercise, nutrition and health promotion.

135. **Tobacco treatment/cessation program.** Organized hospital services with the purpose of ending tobacco-use habits of patients addicted to tobacco/nicotine.

136.–142. **Transplant services.** The branch of medicine that transfers an organ or tissue from one person to another or from one body part to another to replace a diseased structure or to restore function or to change appearance. Services could include: Bone marrow transplant program (**136. Bone marrow**); heart (**137. Heart transplant**), kidney (**138. Kidney transplant**), liver (**139. Liver transplant**) lung (**140. Lung transplant**), tissue (**141. Tissue transplant**). Please include heart/lung or other multi– transplant surgeries in other (**142. Other Transplant**).

143. **Transportation to health services.** A long–term care support service designed to assist the mobility of the elderly. Some programs offer improved financial access by offering reduced rates and barrier–free buses or vans with ramps and lifts to assist the elderly or handicapped; others offer subsidies for public transport systems or operate mini–bus services exclusively for use by senior citizens.

144. **Urgent care center.** A facility that provides care and treatment for problems that are not life–threatening but require attention over the short term. These units function like emergency rooms but are separate from hospitals with which they may have backup affiliation arrangements.

145. **Virtual colonoscopy.** Noninvasive screening procedure used to visualize, analyze and detect cancerous or potentially cancerous polyps in the colon.

146. **Volunteer services department.** An organized hospital department responsible for coordinating the services of volunteers working within the institution.

147. **Women's center.** An area set aside for coordinated education and treatment services specifically for and promoted by women as provided by this special unit. Services may or may not include obstetrics but include a range of services other than OB.

148. **Wound management services.** Services for patients with chronic wounds and non–healing wounds often resulting from diabetes, poor circulation, improper seating and immunocompromising conditions. The goals are to progress chronic wounds through stages of healing, reduce and eliminate infections, increase physical function to minimize complications from current wounds and prevent future chronic wounds. Wound management services are provided on an inpatient or outpatient basis, depending on the intensity of service needed.

Definitions of Physician Codes

1. **Closed physician–hospital organization (PHO).** A PHO that restricts physician membership to those practitioners who meet criteria for cost effectiveness and/or high quality.

2. **Equity model.** Allows established practitioners to become shareholders in a professional corporation in exchange for tangible and intangible assets of their existing practices.

3. **Foundation.** A corporation, organized either as a hospital affiliate or subsidiary, which purchases both the tangible and intangible assets of one or more medical group practices. Physicians remain in a separate corporate entity but sign a professional services agreement with the foundation.

4. **Group practice without walls.** Hospital sponsors the formation of, or provides capital to physicians to establish, a 'quasi' group to share administrative expenses while remaining independent practitioners.

5. **Independent practice association (IPA).** A legal entity that hold managed care contracts. The IPA then contracts with physicians, usually in solo practice, to provide care either on a fee–for–services or capitated basis. The purpose of an IPA is to assist solo physicians in obtaining managed care contracts.

6. **Integrated salary model.** Physicians are salaried by the hospital or another entity of a health system to provide medical services for primary care and specialty care.

7. **Management services organization (MSO).** A corporation, owned by the hospital or a physician/hospital joint venture, that provides management services to one or more medical group practices. The MSO purchases the tangible assets of the practices and leases them back as part of a full–service management agreement, under which the MSO employs all non–physician staff and provides all supplies/administrative systems for a fee.

8. **Open physician–hospital organization (PHO).** A joint venture between the hospital and all members of the medical staff who wish to participate. The PHO can act as a unified agent in managed care contracting, own a managed care plan, own and operate ambulatory care centers or ancillary services projects, or provide administrative services to physician members.

Control and Service Classifications

Control

Government, nonfederal
State
County
City
City–county
Hospital district or authority

Nongovernment not-for-profit
Church operated
Other

Investor–owned (for–profit)
Individual
Partnership
Corporation

Government, federal
Air Force
Army
Navy
Public Health Service other than 47
Veterans Affairs

Federal other than 41–45, 47–48
Public Health Service Indian Service
Department of Justice

Osteopathic
Church operated
Other not–for–profit
Other
Individual for–profit
Partnership for–profit
Corporation for–profit

Service

General medical and surgical
Hospital unit of an institution
  (prison hospital, college infirmary, etc.)
Hospital unit within a facility for persons
  with intellectual disabilities
Surgical
Psychiatric
Tuberculosis and other respiratory
  diseases
Cancer
Heart

Obstetrics and gynecology
Eye, ear, nose, and throat
Rehabilitation
Orthopedic
Chronic disease
Other specialty
Children's general
Children's hospital unit of an institution
Children's psychiatric
Children's tuberculosis and other
  respiratory diseases
Children's eye, ear, nose, and throat

Children's rehabilitation
Children's orthopedic
Children's chronic disease
Children's other specialty
Intellectual disabilities
Long–Term Acute Care
Alcoholism and other chemical
  dependency
Children's Long–Term Acute Care
Children's Cancer
Children's Heart

Notes

Notes

Notes

Notes

U.S. Hospitals by State

ALABAMA

ALABASTER—Shelby County

☐ **NOLAND HOSPITAL SHELBY (012013)**, 1000 First Street North, 3rd Floor, Zip 35007–8703; tel. 205/620–8641 **A**1 9 10 **F**1 3 26 28 29 30 60 61 75 77 79 84 91 92 103 107 111 119 148 **S** Noland Health Services, Inc., Birmingham, AL
Primary Contact: Laura S. Wills, Administrator
Web address: www.nolandhospitals.com
Control: Other not–for–profit (including NFP Corporation) **Service:** Long–Term Acute Care hospital

> **Staffed Beds:** 52 **Admissions:** 137 **Census:** 11 **Outpatient Visits:** 0 **Births:** 0 **Total Expense ($000):** 4286

☐ **SHELBY BAPTIST MEDICAL CENTER (010016)**, 1000 First Street North, Zip 35007–8703; tel. 205/620–8100 **A**1 9 10 **F**3 8 11 12 13 15 17 18 20 22 24 26 28 29 30 31 34 35 40 43 45 47 48 49 50 57 59 60 64 67 70 72 74 75 76 77 79 81 82 85 87 93 94 103 104 107 108 110 111 114 115 118 119 124 126 127 129 130 131 135 146 147 148 **S** Baptist Health System, Birmingham, AL
Primary Contact: David C. Wilson, President and Chief Executive Officer
CFO: Jennifer Pittman, Chief Financial Officer
CMO: Mark Scofield, M.D., Chief Medical Officer
CIO: Mike Nighman, Facility Coordinator Information Systems
CHR: Cindy Nicholson, Director Human Resources
CNO: Martha Seahorn, R.N., Chief Nurse Office
Web address: www.bhsala.com/shelby/Home.aspx
Control: Church–operated, Nongovernment, not–for profit **Service:** General Medical and Surgical

> **Staffed Beds:** 247 **Admissions:** 11801 **Census:** 144 **Outpatient Visits:** 120979 **Births:** 1111 **Total Expense ($000):** 147587 **Payroll Expense ($000):** 53436 **Personnel:** 947

ALEXANDER CITY—Tallapoosa County

☒ **RUSSELL MEDICAL CENTER (010065)**, 3316 Highway 280, Zip 35010–3369, Mailing Address: P.O. Box 939, Zip 35011–0939; tel. 256/329–7100 **A**1 9 10 19 **F**3 11 13 15 18 20 22 28 29 30 31 32 34 35 36 40 43 45 49 50 51 53 57 59 60 64 67 75 76 77 78 79 80 81 82 85 87 89 93 96 107 108 110 111 114 115 116 117 118 119 121 123 126 129 130 131 132 143 144 146 147 148
Primary Contact: Lother E. Peace, III, President and Chief Executive Officer
CFO: Timothy J. Thornton, Chief Financial Officer
CMO: Michele Goldhagen, M.D., Chief of Staff
CIO: Tommy Spraggins, Director Information Services
CHR: Mary Shockley, Director Human Resources
Web address: www.russellmedcenter.com
Control: Other not–for–profit (including NFP Corporation) **Service:** General Medical and Surgical

> **Staffed Beds:** 69 **Admissions:** 3086 **Census:** 29 **Outpatient Visits:** 89568 **Births:** 455 **Total Expense ($000):** 66150 **Payroll Expense ($000):** 25627 **Personnel:** 467

ANDALUSIA—Covington County

☒ **ANDALUSIA REGIONAL HOSPITAL (010036)**, 849 South Three Notch Street, Zip 36420–5325, Mailing Address: P.O. Box 760, Zip 36420–1214; tel. 334/222–8466, (Nonreporting) **A**1 9 10 **S** LifePoint Hospitals, Inc., Brentwood, TN
Primary Contact: Rebecca Brewer, FACHE, Interim Chief Executive Officer
COO: Melissa Davis, Chief Operating Officer
CFO: Shirley M. Smith, Chief Financial Officer
CIO: Matthew Perry, Director Information Systems
CHR: Kaci Daughtry, Director Human Resources
Web address: www.andalusiaregionalhospital.com
Control: Corporation, Investor–owned, for–profit **Service:** General Medical and Surgical

> **Staffed Beds:** 87

ANNISTON—Calhoun County

☐ **NOLAND HOSPITAL ANNISTON (012011)**, 400 East 10th Street, 4th Floor, Zip 36207–4716; tel. 256/741–6141 **A**1 9 10 **F**1 3 29 148 **S** Noland Health Services, Inc., Birmingham, AL
Primary Contact: Bill Mitchell, Administrator
Web address: www.nolandhealth.com
Control: Other not–for–profit (including NFP Corporation) **Service:** Long–Term Acute Care hospital

> **Staffed Beds:** 38 **Admissions:** 310 **Census:** 24 **Outpatient Visits:** 0 **Births:** 0 **Total Expense ($000):** 8780

☒ **NORTHEAST ALABAMA REGIONAL MEDICAL CENTER (010078)**, 400 East Tenth Street, Zip 36207–4716, Mailing Address: P.O. Box 2208, Zip 36202–2208; tel. 256/235–5121 **A**1 2 9 10 **F**3 8 11 12 13 15 17 18 20 22 24 28 29 30 31 34 35 40 43 44 45 46 47 48 49 50 51 53 54 56 57 59 60 61 64 68 70 74 76 77 78 79 81 82 85 86 87 89 98 102 103 104 105 107 108 110 111 114 115 116 117 119 120 121 123 126 129 130 132 135 146 147 148 **P**6
Primary Contact: Michael Morgan, Interim Chief Executive Officer
COO: Joe Weaver, Chief Operating Officer and Vice President Operations
CFO: Louis A. Bass, Vice President Finance
CMO: David Zinn, M.D., Vice President Medical Affairs
CIO: Pete Furlow, Director Information Technology Services
CHR: Michael S. Simms, Sr., Vice President Human Resources
CNO: Elaine Davis, Chief Nursing Officer and Vice President Patient Services
Web address: www.rmccares.org
Control: Hospital district or authority, Government, nonfederal **Service:** General Medical and Surgical

> **Staffed Beds:** 275 **Admissions:** 12187 **Census:** 153 **Outpatient Visits:** 100624 **Births:** 1341 **Total Expense ($000):** 147402 **Payroll Expense ($000):** 54748

☒ **STRINGFELLOW MEMORIAL HOSPITAL (010038)**, 301 East 18th Street, Zip 36207–3952; tel. 256/235–8900 **A**1 9 10 **F**12 15 18 19 20 22 24 26 29 30 31 34 35 40 43 45 47 48 49 50 51 56 57 59 60 64 65 68 69 70 71 74 75 77 78 79 81 82 85 86 87 93 97 107 108 111 114 119 129 130 131 132 135 141 146 148 **S** Community Health Systems, Inc., Franklin, TN
Primary Contact: Jay Hinesley, Chief Executive Officer
CIO: Peggy Henderson, Director Health Information
CHR: Tamatha Johnson, Director Human Resources
Web address: www.stringfellowhealth.com
Control: Corporation, Investor–owned, for–profit **Service:** General Medical and Surgical

> **Staffed Beds:** 75 **Admissions:** 3445 **Census:** 37 **Outpatient Visits:** 46519 **Births:** 0 **Total Expense ($000):** 41854

ASHLAND—Clay County

★ **CLAY COUNTY HOSPITAL (010073)**, 83825 Highway 9, Zip 36251–7981, Mailing Address: P.O. Box 1270, Zip 36251–1270; tel. 256/354–2131, (Nonreporting) **A**9 10
Primary Contact: Linda U. Jordan, Administrator
COO: Linda U. Jordan, Administrator
CFO: Kerry W. Tomlin, Associate Administrator
CMO: Buddy Smith, M.D., Director Medical Staff
CIO: Brad Strother, Director Information Technology
CHR: Linda T. Smith, Director Human Resources
CNO: Tommie Ann Fisher, R.N., Director of Nursing
Web address: www.claycountyhospital.com
Control: County–Government, nonfederal **Service:** General Medical and Surgical

> **Staffed Beds:** 129

Hospital, Medicare Provider Number, Address, Telephone, Approval, Facility, and Physician Codes, Health Care System

★ American Hospital Association (AHA) membership
☐ The Joint Commission accreditation
◇ DNV Healthcare Inc. accreditation
○ Healthcare Facilities Accreditation Program
△ Commission on Accreditation of Rehabilitation Facilities (CARF) accreditation

AL

ATHENS—Limestone County

☐ **ATHENS–LIMESTONE HOSPITAL (010079)**, 700 West Market Street, Zip 35611–2457, Mailing Address: P.O. Box 999, Zip 35612–0999; tel. 256/233–9292 **A**1 9 10 **F**3 7 8 11 13 15 28 29 34 35 40 45 46 50 51 53 54 56 57 58 59 64 68 70 73 75 76 77 79 81 84 85 86 87 89 93 98 107 108 111 119 129 130 131 132 143 144 146 **S** Huntsville Hospital Health System, Huntsville, AL
Primary Contact: David Pryor, President
COO: Randy Comer, Chief Operating Officer
CFO: Randy Comer, Chief Financial Officer
CMO: Jon Bignault, M.D., Chief of Staff
CIO: Kim Hoback, Supervisor Information Systems
CHR: Rachel Frey, Director Human Resources
CNO: Jan Lenz, Chief Nursing Officer
Web address: www.athenslimestonehospital.com
Control: Hospital district or authority, Government, nonfederal **Service:** General Medical and Surgical

Staffed Beds: 101 **Admissions:** 4076 **Census:** 43 **Outpatient Visits:** 122433 **Births:** 475 **Total Expense ($000):** 63002 **Payroll Expense ($000):** 26426 **Personnel:** 749

ATMORE—Escambia County

★ **ATMORE COMMUNITY HOSPITAL (010169)**, 401 Medical Park Drive, Zip 36502–3091; tel. 251/368–2500 **A**9 10 **F**3 11 15 29 30 40 62 64 70 77 81 85 87 91 93 97 107 111 115 119 127 133 144 146 **S** Baptist Health Care Corporation, Pensacola, FL
Primary Contact: A. William Perkins, Administrator
CFO: Keith Strickling, Chief Financial Officer
CHR: Linda Lowrey, Human Resources Officer
CNO: Ashley Chunn, Director of Nursing
Web address: www.ebaptisthealthcare.org/AtmoreCommunityHospital/
Control: Other not–for–profit (including NFP Corporation) **Service:** General Medical and Surgical

Staffed Beds: 33 **Admissions:** 1369 **Census:** 15 **Outpatient Visits:** 36308 **Births:** 0 **Total Expense ($000):** 17723 **Payroll Expense ($000):** 8684 **Personnel:** 160

BAY MINETTE—Baldwin County

NORTH BALDWIN INFIRMARY (010129), 1815 Hand Avenue, Zip 36507–4110, Mailing Address: P.O. Box 1409, Zip 36507–1409; tel. 251/937–5521 **A**9 10 **F**15 40 53 59 70 76 79 81 93 98 100 101 102 103 104 107 108 119 130 146 **S** Infirmary Health System, Mobile, AL
Primary Contact: Ormand P. Thompson, Administrator
CFO: J. Patrick Murphy, Chief Financial Officer
Web address: www.mobileinfirmary.org
Control: Other not–for–profit (including NFP Corporation) **Service:** General Medical and Surgical

Staffed Beds: 50 **Admissions:** 1915 **Census:** 20 **Outpatient Visits:** 34698 **Births:** 266 **Total Expense ($000):** 24936

BESSEMER—Jefferson County

☐ **MEDICAL WEST (010114)**, 995 Ninth Avenue S.W., Zip 35022–4527; tel. 205/481–7000 **A**1 9 10 **F**3 11 13 15 18 29 30 31 34 40 43 45 49 50 57 59 60 64 68 70 74 75 76 77 78 79 80 81 82 85 86 90 92 93 94 96 98 100 101 102 103 104 107 108 110 111 114 115 118 119 129 130 132 143 146 147 148 **P**6 **S** UAB Health System, Birmingham, AL
Primary Contact: Keith Pennington, President and Chief Executive Officer
COO: Sean Tinney, FACHE, Chief Operating Officer
CFO: Brandon H. Slocum, Senior Vice President and Chief Financial Officer
CMO: Jerry T. McLane, M.D., President Medical Staff
CIO: Bob Duckworth, Director Information Systems
CHR: Gannon Davis, Director Human Resources
CNO: Pamela Spencer Autrey, R.N., Chief Nursing Officer
Web address: www.medicalwesthospital.org
Control: Hospital district or authority, Government, nonfederal **Service:** General Medical and Surgical

Staffed Beds: 236 **Admissions:** 7342 **Census:** 113 **Outpatient Visits:** 196025 **Births:** 534 **Total Expense ($000):** 104601 **Payroll Expense ($000):** 42704 **Personnel:** 968

BIRMINGHAM—Jefferson County

✚ **BIRMINGHAM VETERANS AFFAIRS MEDICAL CENTER**, 700 South 19th Street, Zip 35233–1927; tel. 205/933–8101, (Nonreporting) **A**1 2 3 5 8 **S** Department of Veterans Affairs, Washington, DC
Primary Contact: Thomas C. Smith, III, FACHE, Director
COO: Phyllis J. Smith, Associate Director
CFO: Mary S. Mitchell, Chief Resource Management Services
CMO: William F. Harper, M.D., Chief of Staff
CIO: Antonia Mohamed, Acting Chief Information Officer
CHR: Jacqueline Caron, Chief Human Resources
CNO: Cynthia Cleveland, Ph.D., Associate Director for Patient Care Services and Nurse Executive
Web address: www.birmingham.va.gov/
Control: Veterans Affairs, Government, federal **Service:** General Medical and Surgical

Staffed Beds: 313

✠ **BROOKWOOD MEDICAL CENTER (010139)**, 2010 Brookwood Medical Center Drive, Zip 35209–6875; tel. 205/877–1000 **A**1 2 3 5 10 **F**3 11 12 13 15 17 18 20 22 24 26 28 29 30 31 34 38 40 43 45 56 57 59 60 64 68 70 72 74 75 76 78 79 81 82 85 86 87 90 92 98 100 101 102 103 104 105 107 108 109 110 111 114 115 116 117 119 120 121 122 123 124 126 130 132 135 146 147 148 **S** TENET Healthcare Corporation, Dallas, TX
Primary Contact: Garry L. Gause, President and Chief Executive Officer
COO: Brenda H. Carlisle, R.N., Chief Operating Officer
CFO: Doug Carter, Chief Financial Officer
CMO: Bradley Dennis, M.D., Chief Medical Officer
CIO: Manuel Price, Director Information Systems
CHR: Ronnelle Stewart, SPHR, Chief Human Resources Officer
CNO: Jacquelyn Martinek, R.N., Chief Nursing Officer
Web address: www.bwmc.com
Control: Corporation, Investor–owned, for–profit **Service:** General Medical and Surgical

Staffed Beds: 631 **Admissions:** 25174 **Census:** 363 **Outpatient Visits:** 115032 **Births:** 3862 **Total Expense ($000):** 305094 **Payroll Expense ($000):** 104356 **Personnel:** 1744

✠ **HEALTHSOUTH LAKESHORE REHABILITATION HOSPITAL (013025)**, 3800 Ridgeway Drive, Zip 35209–5599; tel. 205/868–2000 **A**1 9 10 **F**3 29 60 75 77 86 87 90 91 93 94 95 96 130 132 148 **P**8 **S** HEALTHSOUTH Corporation, Birmingham, AL
Primary Contact: Heath Phillips, Administrator and Chief Executive Officer
CFO: Kimberly Thrasher, Controller
CMO: Michael Rosemore, M.D., Medical Director
CHR: Julie Smith, Director Human Resources
CNO: April Cobb, Chief Nursing Officer
Web address: www.healthsouthlakeshorerehab.com
Control: Corporation, Investor–owned, for–profit **Service:** Rehabilitation

Staffed Beds: 100 **Admissions:** 2538 **Census:** 90 **Outpatient Visits:** 11897 **Births:** 0 **Total Expense ($000):** 29113 **Payroll Expense ($000):** 15460 **Personnel:** 328

☐ **HILL CREST BEHAVIORAL HEALTH SERVICES (014000)**, 6869 Fifth Avenue South, Zip 35212–1866; tel. 205/833–9000 **A**1 10 **F**98 99 100 101 102 104 106 **S** Universal Health Services, Inc., King of Prussia, PA
Primary Contact: Steve McCabe, Chief Executive Officer
CFO: Mark Teske, Chief Financial Officer
Web address: www.hillcrestbhs.com
Control: Corporation, Investor–owned, for–profit **Service:** Psychiatric

Staffed Beds: 94 **Admissions:** 1686 **Census:** 64 **Outpatient Visits:** 0 **Births:** 0 **Total Expense ($000):** 19291

☐ **NOLAND HOSPITAL BIRMINGHAM (012009)**, 50 Medical Park East Drive, 8th Floor, Zip 35235; tel. 205/808–5100 **A**1 9 10 **F**1 29 130 148 **S** Noland Health Services, Inc., Birmingham, AL
Primary Contact: Laura S. Wills, Administrator
COO: Sharon Engle, Director Clinical Services
CMO: Mark Middlebrooks, M.D., Medical Director
CHR: Ashley Clark, Coordinator Human Resources
CNO: Rachel Chapman, Nurse Manager
Web address: www.nolandhealth.com
Control: Other not–for–profit (including NFP Corporation) **Service:** Long–Term Acute Care hospital

Staffed Beds: 45 **Admissions:** 340 **Census:** 26 **Outpatient Visits:** 0 **Births:** 0 **Total Expense ($000):** 10282

☐ **PRINCETON BAPTIST MEDICAL CENTER (010103)**, 701 Princeton Avenue S.W., Zip 35211–1303; tel. 205/783–3000 **A**1 2 3 5 9 10 **F**3 11 12 13 15 17 18 20 22 24 26 28 29 30 31 34 35 40 43 45 47 48 49 50 55 56 57 58 59 64 67 70 72 74 75 76 78 79 81 82 83 84 85 87 91 92 93 94 98 103 107 108 110 111 114 115 117 118 119 120 121 123 124 126 129 130 131 132 146 147 148 **S** Baptist Health System, Birmingham, AL
Primary Contact: Betsy Postlethwait, President
COO: Sarah Dudley, Chief Operating Officer
CFO: Beverly Haymon, Chief Financial Officer
Web address: www.bhsala.com
Control: Church–operated, Nongovernment, not–for profit **Service:** General Medical and Surgical

Staffed Beds: 297 **Admissions:** 14081 **Census:** 227 **Outpatient Visits:** 105526 **Births:** 266 **Total Expense ($000):** 203360 **Payroll Expense ($000):** 79182 **Personnel:** 1459

✠ **SELECT SPECIALTY HOSPITAL–BIRMINGHAM (012008)**, 800 Montclair Road, 9th Floor, Zip 35213–1908; tel. 205/599–4600 **A**1 9 10 **F**1 60 77 82 84 103 105 111 115 116 117 118 119 148 **S** Select Medical Corporation, Mechanicsburg, PA
Primary Contact: Andrea White, Chief Executive Officer
CMO: Allan Goldstein, M.D., Medical Director and Chief of Staff
Web address: www.selectspecialtyhospitals.com/company/locations/birmingham.aspx
Control: Corporation, Investor–owned, for–profit **Service:** General Medical and Surgical

Staffed Beds: 38 **Admissions:** 340 **Census:** 27 **Outpatient Visits:** 0 **Births:** 0 **Total Expense ($000):** 13689 **Personnel:** 103

Many Facility Codes have changed. Please refer to the AHA Guide Code Chart.
© 2014 AHA Guide

✠ **ST. VINCENT'S BIRMINGHAM (010056)**, 810 St. Vincent's Drive, Zip 35205–1695, Mailing Address: P.O. Box 12407, Zip 35202–2407; tel. 205/939–7000 **A**1 2 3 5 9 10 **F**3 11 13 15 17 18 20 22 24 26 28 29 30 31 34 35 36 37 40 43 45 50 53 54 57 58 59 60 62 65 66 68 70 72 74 75 76 77 78 79 81 82 84 85 86 87 93 97 107 108 110 111 114 115 119 120 121 123 126 129 130 131 135 146 147 148 **P**8 **S** Ascension Health, Saint Louis, MO
Primary Contact: Andy Davis, President
COO: Andy Davis, Chief Operating Officer
CFO: Wilma Newton, Executive Vice President and Chief Financial Officer
CMO: Gregory L. James, D.O., Chief Medical Officer
CIO: Timothy Stettheimer, Vice President and Chief Information Officer
CHR: Michelle Galipeau, Director Human Resources
Web address: www.stvhs.com
Control: Other not–for–profit (including NFP Corporation) **Service:** General Medical and Surgical

Staffed Beds: 409 **Admissions:** 20069 **Census:** 258 **Outpatient Visits:** 192152 **Births:** 3656 **Total Expense ($000):** 349877 **Payroll Expense ($000):** 97936 **Personnel:** 1891

✠ **ST. VINCENT'S EAST (010011)**, 50 Medical Park East Drive, Zip 35235–9987; tel. 205/838–3000 **A**1 2 3 5 9 10 **F**3 11 12 13 17 18 20 22 24 26 28 29 30 31 34 35 40 43 44 45 48 49 50 53 54 57 58 59 60 64 65 70 72 74 76 77 78 79 81 85 86 87 90 93 94 96 97 98 100 101 102 103 104 105 107 108 111 114 119 121 123 126 129 130 131 132 135 146 **P**8 **S** Ascension Health, Saint Louis, MO
Primary Contact: Michael Korpiel, President and Chief Operating Officer
COO: Andrew Gnann, Vice President Operations
CFO: Jan DiCesare, Vice President Financial Operations
CMO: Frank Malensek, M.D., Chief Medical Officer
CIO: Beverly Golightly, Director Information Technology
CHR: Carol Maietta, Vice President Human Resources and Chief Learning Officer
CNO: Paula McCullough, Chief Nursing Officer
Web address: www.stvhs.com
Control: Other not–for–profit (including NFP Corporation) **Service:** General Medical and Surgical

Staffed Beds: 328 **Admissions:** 15057 **Census:** 230 **Outpatient Visits:** 128566 **Births:** 1074 **Total Expense ($000):** 210436 **Payroll Expense ($000):** 68238 **Personnel:** 1089

✠ **THE CHILDREN'S HOSPITAL OF ALABAMA (013300)**, 1600 Seventh Avenue South, Zip 35233–1785; tel. 205/638–9100 **A**1 3 5 9 10 **F**3 7 8 11 12 16 17 19 21 23 25 27 29 30 31 32 34 35 38 39 40 41 43 46 48 49 50 54 55 57 58 59 60 61 64 65 68 72 74 75 77 78 79 80 81 82 84 85 86 87 88 89 92 93 94 97 98 99 100 101 102 104 107 111 114 115 116 117 118 119 129 130 131 132 134 135 136 137 138 139 142 143 144 146 148
Primary Contact: Wm. Michael Warren, Jr., Chief Executive Officer
COO: Tom Shufflebarger, Chief Operating Officer
CFO: Dawn Walton, Chief Financial Officer
CMO: Crayton A. Fargason, M.D., Medical Director
CIO: Mike McDevitt, Chief Information Officer
CHR: Douglas B. Dean, Chief Human Resources Officer
CNO: Deb Wesley, MSN, Chief Nursing Officer
Web address: www.childrensal.org
Control: Other not–for–profit (including NFP Corporation) **Service:** Children's general

Staffed Beds: 342 **Admissions:** 13993 **Census:** 237 **Outpatient Visits:** 659914 **Total Expense ($000):** 625967 **Payroll Expense ($000):** 224473 **Personnel:** 3848

✠ **TRINITY MEDICAL CENTER (010104)**, 800 Montclair Road, Zip 35213–1984; tel. 205/592–1000 **A**1 2 3 5 9 10 **F**3 11 12 13 15 17 18 20 22 24 26 28 29 30 31 34 35 40 43 45 46 47 48 49 50 51 53 54 57 58 59 64 70 72 73 74 75 76 77 78 79 81 82 84 85 90 93 96 98 99 102 103 106 107 108 109 110 111 114 115 116 117 118 119 120 122 124 126 129 130 131 132 135 146 147 148 **S** Community Health Systems, Inc., Franklin, TN
Primary Contact: Keith Granger, President and Chief Executive Officer
CFO: Julie Soekoro, Chief Financial Officer
CMO: Hugh O'Shields, M.D., President Medical Staff
CIO: Tim Townes, Director Information Systems
CHR: Joel R. Windham, Director Human Resources
CNO: Andy Romine, Chief Nursing Officer
Web address: www.bhsala.com
Control: Corporation, Investor–owned, for–profit **Service:** General Medical and Surgical

Staffed Beds: 379 **Admissions:** 11881 **Census:** 196 **Outpatient Visits:** 303597 **Births:** 570 **Total Expense ($000):** 220091 **Payroll Expense ($000):** 81303 **Personnel:** 1522

UAB HIGHLANDS See University of Alabama Hospital

✠ **UNIVERSITY OF ALABAMA HOSPITAL (010033)**, 619 19th Street South, Zip 35249–1900; tel. 205/934–4011, (Includes UAB HIGHLANDS, 1201 11th Avenue South, Zip 35205–5299; tel. 205/930–7000; Anthony Patterson, Chief Operating Officer) **A**1 2 3 5 8 9 10 **F**3 4 5 6 8 9 11 12 13 15 16 17 18 19 20 21 22 23 24 25 26 27 28 29 30 31 33 34 35 37 38 39 40 43 44 45 46 47 48 49 50 52 53 54 55 56 57 58 59 60 61 62 64 65 66 68 70 71 72 73 74 75 76 77 78 79 81 82 83 84 85 86 87 90 91 92 93 94 95 96 97 98 99 100 101 102 103 104 107 108 110 111 114 115 116 117 118 119 120 121 123 124 126 129 130 131 132 135 136 137 138 139 140 141 142 143 144 145 146 147 148 **P**3 **S** UAB Health System, Birmingham, AL
Primary Contact: Anthony Patterson, Senior Vice President Inpatient Services
CFO: Mary Beth Briscoe, Chief Financial Officer
CMO: Loring Rue, M.D., Senior Vice President, Quality Patient Safety and Clinical Effectiveness
CIO: Joan Hicks, Chief Information Officer
CHR: Alesia Jones, Chief Human Resources Officer
CNO: Terri Lyn Poe, Interim Chief Nursing Officer
Web address: www.uabmedicine.org
Control: State–Government, nonfederal **Service:** General Medical and Surgical

Staffed Beds: 1062 **Admissions:** 71339 **Census:** 931 **Outpatient Visits:** 449155 **Births:** 4087 **Total Expense ($000):** 1211518 **Payroll Expense ($000):** 448379 **Personnel:** 7525

VETERANS AFFAIRS MEDICAL CENTER See Birmingham Veterans Affairs Medical Center

BOAZ—Marshall County

☐ **MARSHALL MEDICAL CENTER SOUTH (010005)**, U.S. Highway 431 North, Zip 35957–0999, Mailing Address: P.O. Box 758, Zip 35957–0758; tel. 256/593–8310 **A**1 9 10 19 **F**3 7 8 11 12 13 15 18 20 22 26 28 29 31 32 34 35 37 40 43 45 46 50 53 54 57 59 64 68 70 74 75 76 78 79 81 85 86 87 93 100 107 108 110 111 114 117 119 121 123 129 130 131 132 135 141 145 146 147 148 **S** Marshall Health System, Guntersville, AL
Primary Contact: John D. Anderson, FACHE, Administrator
CFO: Kathy Nelson, Chief Financial Officer
Web address: www.mmcenters.com//index.php/facilities/marshall_south
Control: Hospital district or authority, Government, nonfederal **Service:** General Medical and Surgical

Staffed Beds: 114 **Admissions:** 5050 **Census:** 50 **Outpatient Visits:** 215416 **Births:** 698 **Total Expense ($000):** 82408 **Payroll Expense ($000):** 28594 **Personnel:** 613

BREWTON—Escambia County

☐ **D. W. MCMILLAN MEMORIAL HOSPITAL (010099)**, 1301 Belleville Avenue, Zip 36426–1306, Mailing Address: P.O. Box 908, Zip 36427–0908; tel. 251/867–8061 **A**1 9 10 **F**3 7 11 13 15 31 34 35 40 45 57 59 62 64 70 75 76 78 79 81 85 86 89 93 100 107 108 111 114 119 127 129 130 131 132 133 135 143 146 **P**6
Primary Contact: Christopher B. Griffin, Chief Executive Officer
CFO: Rick Owens, Chief Financial Officer
CIO: Ian Vickery, Director Information Technology
CHR: Autherine Davis, Director Human Resources
CNO: Bob Ellis, Director of Nursing
Web address: www.dwmmh.org
Control: Hospital district or authority, Government, nonfederal **Service:** General Medical and Surgical

Staffed Beds: 49 **Admissions:** 1882 **Census:** 19 **Outpatient Visits:** 44779 **Births:** 284 **Total Expense ($000):** 25958 **Payroll Expense ($000):** 10319 **Personnel:** 229

BUTLER—Choctaw County

★ **CHOCTAW GENERAL HOSPITAL (011304)**, 401 Vanity Fair Avenue, Zip 36904–3032; tel. 205/459–9100 **A**9 10 18 **F**3 13 29 30 34 35 40 41 80 87 88 89 90 91 93 103 104 107 119 128 133 146 148 **S** Rush Health Systems, Meridian, MS
Primary Contact: J. W. Cowan, Administrator
Web address: www.choctawgeneral.com/cgh/
Control: Other not–for–profit (including NFP Corporation) **Service:** General Medical and Surgical

Staffed Beds: 25 **Admissions:** 312 **Census:** 8 **Outpatient Visits:** 8779 **Births:** 0 **Personnel:** 65

CAMDEN—Wilcox County

J. PAUL JONES HOSPITAL (010102), 317 McWilliams Avenue,
Zip 36726–1610; tel. 334/682–4131 **A**9 10 20 **F**15 29 40 107 119 125
127 133
Primary Contact: Elizabeth M. Kennedy, Administrator
CMO: Willie White, M.D., Director Medical Staff
CIO: Jill Smith, Administrative Coordinator
CHR: Jill Smith, Administrative Coordinator
Control: City–County, Government, nonfederal **Service:** General Medical and
Surgical

Staffed Beds: 21 **Admissions:** 236 **Census:** 2 **Outpatient Visits:** 15149
Births: 0 **Total Expense ($000):** 3892 **Payroll Expense ($000):** 1975
Personnel: 40

CARROLLTON—Pickens County

PICKENS COUNTY MEDICAL CENTER (010109), 241 Robert K. Wilson Drive,
Zip 35447, Mailing Address: P.O. Box 478, Zip 35447–0478;
tel. 205/367–8111, (Nonreporting) **A**9 10 20
Primary Contact: Wayne McElroy, Administrator
CFO: Janice Winters, Controller
CMO: William R. Brooke, M.D., President Medical Staff
CHR: Dottie Wilson, Director Human Resources
Web address: www.dchsystem.com
Control: County–Government, nonfederal **Service:** General Medical and Surgical

Staffed Beds: 52

CENTRE—Cherokee County

CHEROKEE MEDICAL CENTER (010022), 400 Northwood Drive,
Zip 35960–1023; tel. 256/927–5531 **A**1 9 10 **F**3 11 15 29 30 35 40 43 45
48 57 59 64 70 75 77 81 85 87 92 93 96 107 108 114 119 127 129 130
131 133 146 **P**6 **S** Community Health Systems, Inc., Franklin, TN
Primary Contact: Terry Long, Interim Chief Executive Officer
CFO: Zac Allen, CPA, Chief Financial Officer
CHR: Marlene Benefield, Director Human Resources
Web address: www.cherokeemedicalcenter.com
Control: Corporation, Investor–owned, for–profit **Service:** General Medical and
Surgical

Staffed Beds: 45 **Admissions:** 917 **Census:** 12 **Outpatient Visits:** 20227
Births: 0 **Total Expense ($000):** 17108 **Payroll Expense ($000):** 5357
Personnel: 137

CENTREVILLE—Bibb County

BIBB MEDICAL CENTER (010058), 208 Pierson Avenue, Zip 35042–2918;
tel. 205/926–4881 **A**9 10 **F**3 11 15 29 35 40 50 57 59 64 81 93 107 114
119 125 127 130 133 143 144 146
Primary Contact: Joseph Marchant, Administrator
CFO: Heather Desmond, Chief Financial Officer
CMO: John Meigs, Jr., M.D., Chief of Staff
CHR: Kim Hayes, Director Human Resources
Web address: www.bibbmedicalcenter.com
Control: County–Government, nonfederal **Service:** General Medical and Surgical

Staffed Beds: 20 **Admissions:** 251 **Census:** 3 **Outpatient Visits:** 43584
Births: 0 **Total Expense ($000):** 15573 **Payroll Expense ($000):** 7879
Personnel: 198

CHATOM—Washington County

★ **WASHINGTON COUNTY HOSPITAL AND NURSING HOME (011300)**, 14600
St. Stephens Avenue, Zip 36518–9998, Mailing Address: P.O. Box 1299,
Zip 36518–1299; tel. 251/847–2223 **A**9 10 18 **F**15 29 34 40 57 59 64 89
107 114 119 128 133 148 **P**6
Primary Contact: Douglas Tanner, Chief Executive Officer
CFO: Alyson Overstreet, Chief Financial Officer
CMO: Donessa Fraser, M.D., Chief of Staff
CIO: Brady Wright, Information Technology Network Administrator
CHR: Linda Randolph, Director Personnel Services
CNO: Michelle Alford, R.N., Director of Nursing
Web address: www.wchnh.org
Control: County–Government, nonfederal **Service:** General Medical and Surgical

Staffed Beds: 25 **Admissions:** 322 **Census:** 6 **Outpatient Visits:** 11395
Births: 0 **Total Expense ($000):** 6743 **Payroll Expense ($000):** 2854
Personnel: 82

CULLMAN—Cullman County

☐ **CULLMAN REGIONAL MEDICAL CENTER (010035)**, 1912 Alabama Highway
157, Zip 35055, Mailing Address: P.O. Box 1108, Zip 35056–1108;
tel. 256/737–2000 **A**1 9 10 19 20 **F**3 7 11 12 13 15 18 20 22 26 28 29 30
34 35 37 40 43 45 46 49 50 51 53 57 59 62 63 64 70 71 74 75 76 77 79
81 82 83 84 85 86 87 89 93 97 107 108 110 111 114 118 119 121 129
130 131 132 133 134 135 146 147 148
Primary Contact: Cheryl Bailey, R.N., Interim President
CFO: Nesha Donaldson, Chief Financial Officer
CMO: Bill Smith, M.D., Chief of Staff
CIO: Nancy Zavatchen, Director Information Technology
CHR: Toni Geddings, Director Human Resources
CNO: Cheryl Bailey, R.N., Chief Nursing Officer Vice President Patient Care
Services
Web address: www.crmchospital.com
Control: Other not–for–profit (including NFP Corporation) **Service:** General
Medical and Surgical

Staffed Beds: 115 **Admissions:** 6558 **Census:** 64 **Outpatient Visits:** 91950
Births: 751 **Total Expense ($000):** 93554 **Payroll Expense ($000):** 35401
Personnel: 837

DADEVILLE—Tallapoosa County

LAKE MARTIN COMMUNITY HOSPITAL (010052), 201 Mariarden Road,
Zip 36853–6251, Mailing Address: P.O. Box 629, Zip 36853–0629;
tel. 256/825–7821 **A**9 10 **F**11 29 40 45 50 59 62 63 64 65 68 81 82 89 107
111 114 119 127 143
Primary Contact: Michael D. Bruce, Chief Executive Officer
CHR: Karen Treadwell, Director Human Resources
Web address: www.lakemartincommunityhospital.com
Control: Partnership, Investor–owned, for–profit **Service:** General Medical and
Surgical

Staffed Beds: 28 **Admissions:** 746 **Census:** 6 **Outpatient Visits:** 14492
Births: 0 **Total Expense ($000):** 11405

DAPHNE—Baldwin County

★ **EASTPOINTE HOSPITAL (014017)**, 7400 Roper Lane, Zip 36526–5274;
tel. 251/378–6500 **A**9 10 **F**50 98 130 143 **P**6 **S** AltaPointe Health Systems,
Mobile, AL
Primary Contact: Jarett Crum, Administrator
CFO: Kevin Markham, Chief Financial Officer
CMO: Sandra K. Parker, M.D., Chief Medical Officer
CIO: Steve Dolan, Chief Information Officer
CHR: Alicia Donoghue, Director Human Resources
Web address: www.altapointe.org/eastpointe.php
Control: Other not–for–profit (including NFP Corporation) **Service:** Psychiatric

Staffed Beds: 66 **Admissions:** 1465 **Census:** 35 **Outpatient Visits:** 14
Births: 0 **Total Expense ($000):** 8759 **Payroll Expense ($000):** 5141
Personnel: 237

DECATUR—Morgan County

☐ **DECATUR MORGAN HOSPITAL (010085)**, 1201 Seventh Street S.E.,
Zip 35601–3303, Mailing Address: P.O. Box 2239, Zip 35609–2239;
tel. 256/341–2000, (Includes DECATUR MORGAN HOSPITAL PARKWAY CAMPUS,
1874 Beltline Road S.W., Zip 35601–5509, Mailing Address: P.O. Box 2239,
Zip 35609–2239; tel. 256/350–2211; DECATUR MORGAN HOSPITAL–WEST,
2205 Beltline Road S.W., Zip 35601–3687, Mailing Address: P.O. Box 2240,
Zip 35609–2240; tel. 256/306–4000) **A**1 5 9 10 **F**3 6 11 13 15 18 20 28 29
30 31 34 35 38 40 41 43 45 49 50 53 55 56 57 59 60 61 65 68 70 73
74 75 76 77 78 79 81 85 86 87 89 91 92 93 97 98 99 100 101 102 103
104 107 108 110 111 114 119 120 121 123 126 129 130 131 132 134 135
145 146 147 148 **S** Huntsville Hospital Health System, Huntsville, AL
Primary Contact: Nathaniel Richardson, Jr., President
CFO: Kim Shrewsbury, Vice President and Chief Financial Officer
CMO: Allen J. Schmidt, M.D., President, Medical Staff
CIO: Mark Megehee, Vice President and Chief Information Officer
CNO: Anita Walden, Vice President and Chief Nursing Officer
Web address: www.decaturgeneral.org
Control: Hospital district or authority, Government, nonfederal **Service:** General
Medical and Surgical

Staffed Beds: 147 **Admissions:** 7904 **Census:** 91 **Outpatient Visits:** 148989
Births: 797 **Total Expense ($000):** 103102

☐ **NORTH ALABAMA REGIONAL HOSPITAL (014009)**, 4218 Highway 31 South,
Zip 35603–5039; tel. 256/560–2200 **A**1 10 **F**98 102 106 130 132 135
143 **P**6
Primary Contact: Barbara Jackson, Chief Executive Officer
CMO: Marie Glenn, M.D., Clinical Director
CIO: Charles Dufour, Coordinator Information Systems
CHR: Mike Mathis, Manager Personnel
CNO: Beverly Jackson, Acting Director of Nursing
Web address: www.narh.mh.alabama.gov
Control: State–Government, nonfederal **Service:** Psychiatric

Staffed Beds: 74 **Admissions:** 586 **Census:** 74 **Outpatient Visits:** 0 **Births:**
0 **Personnel:** 184

PARKWAY MEDICAL CENTER See Decatur Morgan Hospital Parkway Campus

Many Facility Codes have changed. Please refer to the AHA Guide Code Chart. © 2014 AHA Guide

DEMOPOLIS—Marengo County

BRYAN W. WHITFIELD MEMORIAL HOSPITAL (010112), 105 U.S. Highway 80 East, Zip 36732–3616, Mailing Address: P.O. Box 890, Zip 36732–0890; tel. 334/289–4000, (Nonreporting) **A**9 10 20
Primary Contact: Michael D. Marshall, Administrator and Chief Executive Officer
CFO: Arthur D. Evans, Assistant Administrator
CHR: Danny Smith, Director Human Resources
Web address: www.bwwmh.com
Control: Hospital district or authority, Government, nonfederal **Service:** General Medical and Surgical

> **Staffed Beds:** 99

DOTHAN—Houston County

✠ **FLOWERS HOSPITAL (010055)**, 4370 West Main Street, Zip 36305–4000, Mailing Address: P.O. Box 6907, Zip 36302–6907; tel. 334/793–5000 **A**1 2 9 10 **F**1 3 4 12 13 15 16 17 18 19 20 22 24 26 28 29 31 34 35 40 43 46 48 49 50 51 56 57 59 60 61 64 67 68 70 74 75 76 77 78 79 80 81 82 85 86 87 89 90 92 93 97 98 100 107 108 110 111 114 115 116 117 118 119 126 128 129 132 134 135 146 147 148 **P**6 **S** Community Health Systems, Inc., Franklin, TN
Primary Contact: Suzanne Woods, President and Chief Executive Officer
COO: Barry Moss, Assistant Chief Executive Officer
CFO: Talana Bell, Chief Financial Officer
CIO: Matthew Garrett, Director Information Systems
CHR: Jennifer Odom, Interim Director Human Resources
CNO: Dan L. Cumbie, Chief Nursing Officer
Web address: www.flowershospital.com
Control: Corporation, Investor–owned, for–profit **Service:** General Medical and Surgical

> **Staffed Beds:** 139 **Admissions:** 11296 **Census:** 144 **Outpatient Visits:** 145620 **Births:** 1223 **Total Expense ($000):** 171197 **Payroll Expense ($000):** 59085 **Personnel:** 1247

✠ **HEALTHSOUTH REHABILITATION HOSPITAL (013030)**, 1736 East Main Street, Zip 36301–3040, Mailing Address: P.O. Box 6708, Zip 36302–6708; tel. 334/712–6333 **A**1 9 10 **F**28 29 34 35 56 57 59 64 74 75 77 79 90 91 93 95 96 130 132 **S** HEALTHSOUTH Corporation, Birmingham, AL
Primary Contact: Margaret A. Futch, Chief Executive Officer
CFO: Heath Watson, Controller
CHR: Lydia Christion, Director Human Resources
Web address: www.healthsouthdothan.com
Control: Corporation, Investor–owned, for–profit **Service:** Rehabilitation

> **Staffed Beds:** 43 **Admissions:** 1095 **Census:** 37 **Outpatient Visits:** 1448 **Births:** 0 **Total Expense ($000):** 11827

☐ **LAUREL OAKS BEHAVIORAL HEALTH CENTER (014013)**, 700 East Cottonwood Road, Zip 36301–3644; tel. 334/794–7373 **A**1 9 10 **F**98 99 106 **S** Universal Health Services, Inc., King of Prussia, PA
Primary Contact: Derek Johnson, Chief Executive Officer
CMO: Nelson Handol, M.D., Medical Director
CHR: Lorrie Evans, Director Human Resources
Web address: www.laureloaksbhc.com
Control: Corporation, Investor–owned, for–profit **Service:** Children's hospital psychiatric

> **Staffed Beds:** 38 **Admissions:** 975 **Census:** 34 **Outpatient Visits:** 0 **Births:** 0 **Total Expense ($000):** 11908 **Payroll Expense ($000):** 7168 **Personnel:** 223

☐ **NOLAND HOSPITAL DOTHAN (012010)**, 1108 Ross Clark Circle, 4th Floor, Zip 36301–3022; tel. 334/699–4300 **A**1 9 10 **F**1 29 130 148 **S** Noland Health Services, Inc., Birmingham, AL
Primary Contact: Kaye Burke, Administrator
Web address: www.nolandhealth.com
Control: Other not–for–profit (including NFP Corporation) **Service:** Long–Term Acute Care hospital

> **Staffed Beds:** 35 **Admissions:** 355 **Census:** 27 **Outpatient Visits:** 0 **Births:** 0 **Total Expense ($000):** 10001

✠ **SOUTHEAST ALABAMA MEDICAL CENTER (010001)**, 1108 Ross Clark Circle, Zip 36301–3024, Mailing Address: P.O. Box 6987, Zip 36302–6987; tel. 334/793–8111 **A**1 2 9 10 **F**3 8 12 13 15 18 20 22 24 26 28 29 30 31 32 34 35 37 40 43 44 45 49 50 51 53 54 56 57 59 60 62 63 64 68 70 71 74 75 76 77 78 79 81 82 84 85 86 87 89 92 93 94 98 100 101 102 103 104 105 107 108 110 111 114 115 116 117 118 119 120 121 123 124 126 127 129 130 132 135 146 147 148
Primary Contact: Ronald S. Owen, FACHE, Chief Executive Officer
COO: Charles C. Brannen, Senior Vice President and Chief Operating Officer
CFO: Derek Miller, Senior Vice President and Chief Financial Officer
CMO: Charles Harkness, D.O., Vice President Medical Affairs
CNO: Diane Buntyn, MSN, Vice President Patient Care Services
Web address: www.samc.org
Control: Hospital district or authority, Government, nonfederal **Service:** General Medical and Surgical

> **Staffed Beds:** 420 **Admissions:** 18478 **Census:** 261 **Outpatient Visits:** 113212 **Births:** 1453 **Total Expense ($000):** 273354

ENTERPRISE—Coffee County

✠ **MEDICAL CENTER ENTERPRISE (010049)**, 400 North Edwards Street, Zip 36330–2510; tel. 334/347–0584 **A**1 9 10 **F**3 13 15 29 34 40 45 57 59 70 76 79 81 85 93 107 110 111 114 118 119 130 131 **S** Community Health Systems, Inc., Franklin, TN
Primary Contact: Richard Ellis, Chief Executive Officer
CFO: Greg McGilvray, Chief Financial Officer
CMO: Rick Harrelson, M.D., President Medical Staff
CIO: Stephen Smothers, Director Information Systems
CHR: Toni Kaminski, Director Human Resources
CNO: Bobby Phillips, Chief Nursing Officer
Web address: www.mcehospital.com
Control: Corporation, Investor–owned, for–profit **Service:** General Medical and Surgical

> **Staffed Beds:** 117 **Admissions:** 3573 **Census:** 28 **Outpatient Visits:** 33641 **Births:** 805 **Total Expense ($000):** 41217

EUFAULA—Barbour County

MEDICAL CENTER BARBOUR (010069), 820 West Washington Street, Zip 36027–1899; tel. 334/688–7000 **A**9 10 20 **F**3 11 15 29 30 34 35 40 45 46 50 57 59 64 68 70 81 85 98 103 107 119 127 133 135 146
Primary Contact: Ralph H. Clark, Jr., FACHE, Chief Executive Officer
CFO: Debbie Norton, Chief Financial Officer
CHR: Cindy Griffin, Director Human Resources
CNO: Kathy Wilder, R.N., Chief Clinical Officer
Web address: www.medctrbarbour.org
Control: Hospital district or authority, Government, nonfederal **Service:** General Medical and Surgical

> **Staffed Beds:** 47 **Admissions:** 1492 **Census:** 23 **Outpatient Visits:** 34907 **Births:** 0 **Total Expense ($000):** 15951 **Payroll Expense ($000):** 7265 **Personnel:** 204

EUTAW—Greene County

★ **GREENE COUNTY HEALTH SYSTEM (010051)**, 509 Wilson Avenue, Zip 35462–1099; tel. 205/372–3388 **A**9 10 **F**3 11 40 59 67 93 97 107 119 127 128 143 146 **P**6
Primary Contact: Elmore Patterson, Chief Executive Officer
Web address: www.gcheutaw.com
Control: County–Government, nonfederal **Service:** General Medical and Surgical

> **Staffed Beds:** 20 **Admissions:** 414 **Census:** 4 **Outpatient Visits:** 8559 **Births:** 1 **Total Expense ($000):** 12252 **Payroll Expense ($000):** 4658 **Personnel:** 543

EVERGREEN—Conecuh County

EVERGREEN MEDICAL CENTER (010148), 101 Crestview Avenue, Zip 36401–3333, Mailing Address: P.O. Box 706, Zip 36401–0706; tel. 251/578–2480 **A**9 10 **F**3 29 30 34 35 40 53 57 59 62 81 87 93 97 98 107 114 119 **S** Gilliard Health Services, Montgomery, AL
Primary Contact: William G. McKenzie, Interim Administrator
CFO: Sharon Jones, Chief Financial Officer
CMO: William Farmer, M.D., Chief of Staff
CHR: Tracey Rhodes, Coordinator Human Resources
CNO: Angie Hendrix, Director of Nursing
Web address: www.evergreenmedical.org
Control: Partnership, Investor–owned, for–profit **Service:** General Medical and Surgical

> **Staffed Beds:** 39 **Admissions:** 1806 **Census:** 15 **Births:** 0

Hospital, Medicare Provider Number, Address, Telephone, Approval, Facility, and Physician Codes, Health Care System

★ American Hospital Association (AHA) membership
☐ The Joint Commission accreditation   ◇ DNV Healthcare Inc. accreditation
○ Healthcare Facilities Accreditation Program
△ Commission on Accreditation of Rehabilitation Facilities (CARF) accreditation

FAIRHOPE—Baldwin County

☐ **THOMAS HOSPITAL (010100)**, 750 Morphy Avenue, Zip 36532–1812, Mailing Address: P.O. Box 929, Zip 36533–0929; tel. 251/928–2375 **A**1 9 10 19 **F**3 4 5 8 11 13 14 15 18 20 22 24 26 28 29 30 32 33 34 35 39 40 41 43 45 46 48 49 50 51 53 54 57 58 59 60 61 62 64 65 68 70 73 74 75 76 77 78 79 81 82 85 86 87 89 92 93 97 100 101 104 105 107 108 110 111 113 114 115 117 119 129 130 131 132 134 135 144 146 147 **S** Infirmary Health System, Mobile, AL
Primary Contact: William J. McLaughlin, Administrator
COO: Douglas Garner, Vice President
CMO: Michael McBrearty, M.D., Vice President Medical Affairs
CNO: Julie Rowell, R.N., Chief Nursing Officer
Web address: www.thomashospital.com
Control: Other not–for–profit (including NFP Corporation) **Service:** General Medical and Surgical

Staffed Beds: 136 **Admissions:** 8053 **Census:** 88 **Outpatient Visits:** 113253 **Births:** 1125 **Total Expense ($000):** 114963

FAYETTE—Fayette County

☐ **FAYETTE MEDICAL CENTER (010045)**, 1653 Temple Avenue North, Zip 35555–1314, Mailing Address: P.O. Drawer 710, Zip 35555–0710; tel. 205/932–5966, (Total facility includes 122 beds in nursing home–type unit) **A**1 9 10 **F**3 11 15 28 29 30 34 35 40 43 45 50 57 59 64 68 70 74 75 77 78 79 81 90 93 107 111 114 119 128 130 132 133 **S** DCH Health System, Tuscaloosa, AL
Primary Contact: Donald J. Jones, FACHE, Administrator
CFO: Jeff Huff, Assistant Administrator Finance
CHR: Felicia Solomon–Owens, Director Human Resources
Web address: www.dchsystem.com
Control: Hospital district or authority, Government, nonfederal **Service:** General Medical and Surgical

Staffed Beds: 167 **Admissions:** 1432 **Census:** 127 **Outpatient Visits:** 37196 **Births:** 0

FLORENCE—Lauderdale County

☐ **ELIZA COFFEE MEMORIAL HOSPITAL (010006)**, 205 Marengo Street, Zip 35630–6033, Mailing Address: P.O. Box 818, Zip 35631–0818; tel. 256/768–9191, (Nonreporting) **A**1 9 10 **S** RegionalCare Hospital Partners, Brentwood, TN
Primary Contact: Russell Pigg, Chief Executive Officer
COO: Mike Howard, Associate Administrator
CFO: Steve E. Hobbs, Chief Financial Officer
CMO: Oliver Matthews, M.D., Chief Medical Officer
CIO: William Johnson, Director Information Systems
CHR: Cheryl Lee, Director Human Resources
CNO: Marye Elliott, Chief Nursing Officer
Web address: www.chgroup.org
Control: Hospital district or authority, Government, nonfederal **Service:** General Medical and Surgical

Staffed Beds: 278

FOLEY—Baldwin County

⊞ **SOUTH BALDWIN REGIONAL MEDICAL CENTER (010083)**, 1613 North McKenzie Street, Zip 36535–2299; tel. 251/949–3400 **A**1 9 10 19 **F**3 12 13 15 18 20 28 29 30 31 34 35 38 40 43 45 49 50 51 54 57 59 60 62 64 65 68 70 75 76 77 79 81 82 85 86 87 93 107 108 110 111 114 116 117 118 119 130 131 132 133 134 135 144 146 147 148 **S** Community Health Systems, Inc., Franklin, TN
Primary Contact: Keith Newton, Chief Executive Officer
CFO: Brad Hardcastle, Chief Financial Officer
CMO: Michael Hoffman, M.D., Chief Medical Officer
CHR: Pam Brunson, Director Human Resources
CNO: Margaret Roley, Chief Nursing Officer
Web address: www.southbaldwinrmc.com
Control: Corporation, Investor–owned, for–profit **Service:** General Medical and Surgical

Staffed Beds: 112 **Admissions:** 6438 **Census:** 73 **Outpatient Visits:** 132605 **Births:** 552 **Total Expense ($000):** 71329

FORT PAYNE—Dekalb County

⊞ **DEKALB REGIONAL MEDICAL CENTER (010012)**, 200 Medical Center Drive, Zip 35968–3458, Mailing Address: P.O. Box 680778, Zip 35968–1608; tel. 256/845–3150 **A**1 9 10 20 **F**3 8 12 13 15 18 20 22 26 28 29 35 40 43 45 46 53 56 57 59 70 74 75 76 79 81 82 87 98 103 107 108 110 111 114 119 129 146 147 **S** Community Health Systems, Inc., Franklin, TN
Primary Contact: Corey Ewing, Chief Executive Officer
CFO: Hugh Tobin, Chief Financial Officer
CMO: Anthony Sims, M.D., Chief of Staff
CIO: Joseph Helms, Director Information Systems
CHR: Diane McMichen, Director Human Resources
CNO: Marquita Bailey, Chief Nursing Officer
Web address: www.dekalbregional.com
Control: Corporation, Investor–owned, for–profit **Service:** General Medical and Surgical

Staffed Beds: 115 **Admissions:** 3880 **Census:** 45 **Outpatient Visits:** 59468 **Births:** 671 **Total Expense ($000):** 42933

GADSDEN—Etowah County

⊞ **GADSDEN REGIONAL MEDICAL CENTER (010040)**, 1007 Goodyear Avenue, Zip 35903–1195; tel. 256/494–4000 **A**1 2 9 10 **F**11 13 15 18 20 22 24 27 28 29 30 34 40 56 57 59 60 64 68 70 73 74 76 77 78 79 80 81 89 93 98 102 103 105 107 108 111 112 113 114 115 119 121 130 131 133 146 147 148 **S** Community Health Systems, Inc., Franklin, TN
Primary Contact: Stephen G. Pennington, Chief Executive Officer
COO: Paul Theriot, Chief Operating Officer
CFO: Michael Cotton, Chief Financial Officer
CMO: William Haller, III, M.D., Chief of Staff
CIO: Glenn Phillips, Director Information Systems
CHR: Gale H. Sanders, Director
CNO: Donna Nicholson, Chief Nursing Officer
Web address: www.gadsdenregional.com
Control: Corporation, Investor–owned, for–profit **Service:** General Medical and Surgical

Staffed Beds: 286 **Admissions:** 13393 **Census:** 195 **Outpatient Visits:** 77055 **Births:** 1316 **Total Expense ($000):** 230662 **Payroll Expense ($000):** 53028 **Personnel:** 992

⊞ **HEALTHSOUTH REHABILITATION OF GADSDEN (013032)**, 801 Goodyear Avenue, Zip 35903–1133; tel. 256/439–5000 **A**1 9 10 **F**28 90 93 95 **S** HEALTHSOUTH Corporation, Birmingham, AL
Primary Contact: Kayla Feazell, Chief Executive Officer
COO: Kayla Feazell, Chief Executive Officer
CFO: Lori Norman, Chief Financial Officer
CMO: Diem Yeung, M.D., Medical Director
CIO: Lori Norman, Chief Financial Officer
CHR: Heather Blevins, Director Human Resources
CNO: Barry Eads, Chief Nursing Officer
Web address: www.healthsouthgadsden.com
Control: Corporation, Investor–owned, for–profit **Service:** Rehabilitation

Staffed Beds: 44 **Admissions:** 1060 **Census:** 40 **Outpatient Visits:** 1805 **Births:** 0 **Total Expense ($000):** 10324 **Personnel:** 180

☐ **MOUNTAIN VIEW HOSPITAL (014006)**, 3001 Scenic Highway, Zip 35904–3047, Mailing Address: P.O. Box 8406, Zip 35902–8406; tel. 256/546–9265 **A**1 9 10 **F**2 54 98 99 102 104 105 130 132
Primary Contact: G. Michael Shehi, M.D., Interim Chief Executive Officer
COO: Sara Romano, R.N., Vice President
CFO: Mary Jensen, Controller
CMO: G. Michael Shehi, M.D., Medical Director
CHR: Dave Jensen, Director Human Resources, Performance Improvement and Risk Management
Web address: www.mtnviewhospital.com
Control: Individual, Investor–owned, for–profit **Service:** Psychiatric

Staffed Beds: 68 **Admissions:** 1403 **Census:** 29 **Outpatient Visits:** 23254 **Births:** 0 **Total Expense ($000):** 11935

⊞ **RIVERVIEW REGIONAL MEDICAL CENTER (010046)**, 600 South Third Street, Zip 35901–5399; tel. 256/543–5200 **A**1 9 10 **F**5 8 12 15 17 18 20 22 24 26 29 30 34 37 40 41 45 46 47 48 49 50 51 56 57 59 60 68 69 70 74 75 77 79 81 85 87 91 92 93 94 97 103 107 108 109 110 111 114 115 118 119 120 126 129 130 146 148 **S** Community Health Systems, Inc., Franklin, TN
Primary Contact: James H. Edmondson, Chief Executive Officer
COO: Thomas Roddy, Chief Operating Officer
CIO: Jay Terrell, Manager Management Information Systems
CHR: Leslie Morton, Manager Human Resources
CNO: Tammy Harlow, Chief Nurse Executive
Web address: www.riverviewregional.com
Control: Corporation, Investor–owned, for–profit **Service:** General Medical and Surgical

Staffed Beds: 250 **Admissions:** 5911 **Census:** 99 **Outpatient Visits:** 61468 **Births:** 0 **Total Expense ($000):** 79855 **Payroll Expense ($000):** 24234 **Personnel:** 690

GENEVA—Geneva County

★ **WIREGRASS MEDICAL CENTER (010062)**, 1200 West Maple Avenue, Zip 36340–1694; tel. 334/684–3655, (Total facility includes 96 beds in nursing home–type unit) **A**9 10 **F**29 34 40 45 46 64 70 79 81 93 102 103 107 108 119 128 146
Primary Contact: James F. Heitzenrater, FACHE, Chief Executive Officer
CFO: Gloria McGowan, Chief Financial Officer
CIO: Tom Garske, Director Information Systems
CHR: Pam Phillips, Chief Human Resource Officer
CNO: Craig Cassady, Director of Nursing
Web address: www.alaweb.com/~tgarske
Control: Hospital district or authority, Government, nonfederal **Service:** General Medical and Surgical

Staffed Beds: 163 **Admissions:** 1424 **Census:** 95 **Outpatient Visits:** 11071 **Births:** 0 **Total Expense ($000):** 20903 **Payroll Expense ($000):** 9601 **Personnel:** 283

Many Facility Codes have changed. Please refer to the AHA Guide Code Chart.

© 2014 AHA Guide

GEORGIANA—Butler County

GEORGIANA HOSPITAL (010047), 515 Miranda Street, Zip 36033–4519, Mailing Address: P.O. Box 548, Zip 36033–0548; tel. 334/376–2205, (Nonreporting) **A**9 10
Primary Contact: Harry Cole, Jr., Administrator
Control: Partnership, Investor–owned, for–profit **Service:** General Medical and Surgical

Staffed Beds: 22

GREENSBORO—Hale County

HALE COUNTY HOSPITAL (010095), 508 Green Street, Zip 36744–2316; tel. 334/624–3024 **A**9 10 **F**40
Primary Contact: Thomas O. Lackey, Administrator
Web address: www.halecountyhospital.com
Control: Hospital district or authority, Government, nonfederal **Service:** General Medical and Surgical

Staffed Beds: 20 **Admissions:** 371 **Census:** 3 **Outpatient Visits:** 13607 **Births:** 0 **Total Expense ($000):** 8184

GREENVILLE—Butler County

⊠ **L. V. STABLER MEMORIAL HOSPITAL (010150)**, 29 L. V. Stabler Drive, Zip 36037–3800; tel. 334/382–2671 **A**1 5 9 10 **F**3 15 17 29 35 40 56 57 62 64 81 93 98 103 107 111 119 133 146 147 **S** Community Health Systems, Inc., Franklin, TN
Primary Contact: Connie Nicholas, Interim Chief Executive Officer
COO: Connie Nicholas, Interim Chief Executive Officer
CFO: Vann Windham, Chief Financial Officer
CMO: Norman F. McGowin, III, M.D., Chief of Staff
CIO: Doug Burkett, Manager Information Technology
CHR: Robert Foster, Director Human Resources
CNO: Kimberli Weaver, Chief Nursing Officer
Web address: www.lvstabler.com
Control: Corporation, Investor–owned, for–profit **Service:** General Medical and Surgical

Staffed Beds: 61 **Admissions:** 1459 **Census:** 19 **Outpatient Visits:** 12146 **Births:** 0 **Total Expense ($000):** 18330

GROVE HILL—Clarke County

★ **GROVE HILL MEMORIAL HOSPITAL (010091)**, 295 South Jackson Street, Zip 36451–3231, Mailing Address: P.O. Box 935, Zip 36451–0935; tel. 251/275–3191 **A**9 10 **F**3 11 13 15 28 29 30 32 34 35 40 43 56 57 59 64 66 75 76 81 86 87 89 97 98 101 103 104 107 114 119 127 129 132 135 146
Primary Contact: Emily Steadham, Administrator
CFO: Elaine Averett, Chief Financial Officer
CMO: Eniola Fagbongbe, M.D., Chief Medical Staff
CIO: Aaron Harrell, Director
CHR: Aubrey Sheffield, Administrative Assistant Human Resources and Public Relations
CNO: Karen Coleman, Director of Nursing
Web address: www.grovehillmemorial.org
Control: City–Government, nonfederal **Service:** General Medical and Surgical

Staffed Beds: 33 **Admissions:** 1397 **Census:** 17 **Outpatient Visits:** 23395 **Births:** 230 **Total Expense ($000):** 14707

GUNTERSVILLE—Marshall County

MARSHALL MEDICAL CENTER NORTH (010010), 8000 Alabama Highway 69, Zip 35976; tel. 256/753–8000 **A**5 9 10 **F**3 8 11 12 13 15 26 28 29 32 34 35 37 38 40 43 45 49 50 51 53 54 57 59 64 68 70 74 75 76 79 81 82 85 86 87 93 99 100 102 103 104 107 108 110 111 114 117 119 130 131 132 133 135 141 146 147 **S** Marshall Health System, Guntersville, AL
Primary Contact: Cheryl M. Hays, FACHE, Administrator
COO: Cheryl M. Hays, FACHE, Administrator
CFO: Kathy Nelson, Chief Financial Officer
CIO: Kim Bunch, Director Information Technology
CHR: Jeff Stone, Director Human Resources
CNO: Kathy Woodruff, R.N., Chief Nursing Officer
Web address: www.mmcenters.com
Control: Hospital district or authority, Government, nonfederal **Service:** General Medical and Surgical

Staffed Beds: 90 **Admissions:** 4478 **Census:** 52 **Outpatient Visits:** 136322 **Births:** 326 **Total Expense ($000):** 58315 **Payroll Expense ($000):** 21382 **Personnel:** 398

HALEYVILLE—Winston County

⊠ **LAKELAND COMMUNITY HOSPITAL (010125)**, Highway 195 East, Zip 35565–9536, Mailing Address: P.O. Box 780, Zip 35565–0780; tel. 205/486–5213 **A**1 9 10 **F**3 15 29 30 34 40 43 62 70 77 81 93 98 103 107 110 115 119 130 131 133 146 **S** LifePoint Hospitals, Inc., Brentwood, TN
Primary Contact: Cynthia Nichols, R.N., MSN, Chief Executive Officer
CFO: Penny Westmoreland, Chief Financial Officer
Web address: www.lakelandcommunityhospital.com/
Control: Corporation, Investor–owned, for–profit **Service:** General Medical and Surgical

Staffed Beds: 56 **Admissions:** 1767 **Census:** 21 **Outpatient Visits:** 9803 **Births:** 0 **Total Expense ($000):** 12866

HAMILTON—Marion County

⊠ **MARION REGIONAL MEDICAL CENTER (010044)**, 1256 Military Street South, Zip 35570–5003; tel. 205/921–6200 **A**1 9 10 **F**40 53 57 59 77 81 93 107 111 119 133 **S** North Mississippi Health Services, Inc., Tupelo, MS
Primary Contact: Tanya Brasher, Administrator
CMO: Jarred Sartain, M.D., President Medical Staff
CHR: Anne Lawler, Director Human Resources
CNO: Jennifer Cagle, Director of Nursing
Web address: www.nmhs.net
Control: Other not–for–profit (including NFP Corporation) **Service:** General Medical and Surgical

Staffed Beds: 36 **Admissions:** 803 **Census:** 8 **Outpatient Visits:** 20851 **Births:** 0 **Total Expense ($000):** 21818

HUNTSVILLE—Madison County

BEHAVIORAL HEALTHCARE CENTER AT HUNTSVILLE (014018), 5315 Millennium Drive N.W., Zip 35806–2458; tel. 256/964–6700, (Nonreporting) **A**10 **S** Tennessee Health Management, Parsons, TN
Primary Contact: Bradley Moss, Administrator
Web address: www.tnhealthmanagement.com/bhc/huntsville
Control: Corporation, Investor–owned, for–profit **Service:** Psychiatric

Staffed Beds: 20

⊠ **CRESTWOOD MEDICAL CENTER (010131)**, One Hospital Drive, Zip 35801–3403; tel. 256/429–4000 **A**1 5 9 10 **F**3 5 11 12 13 15 17 18 20 22 29 30 31 34 35 40 43 45 47 49 50 51 54 56 57 59 60 64 65 68 70 72 74 75 76 77 78 79 81 85 86 87 89 93 97 98 99 100 101 102 103 104 105 107 108 110 111 114 115 119 126 129 130 131 132 146 147 148 **S** Community Health Systems, Inc., Franklin, TN
Primary Contact: Pamela Hudson, M.D., Chief Executive Officer
COO: Bobby Ginn, Chief Operating Officer
CFO: Sherry J. Jones, Chief Financial Officer
CHR: Elyria Sinclair, Director Human Resources
CNO: Martha Delaney Walls, R.N., Chief Nursing Officer
Web address: www.crestwoodmedcenter.com
Control: Corporation, Investor–owned, for–profit **Service:** General Medical and Surgical

Staffed Beds: 150 **Admissions:** 9608 **Census:** 102 **Outpatient Visits:** 101608 **Births:** 696 **Total Expense ($000):** 141010 **Payroll Expense ($000):** 46399 **Personnel:** 918

⊠ **HEALTHSOUTH REHABILITATION HOSPITAL OF NORTH ALABAMA (013029)**, 107 Governors Drive S.W., Zip 35801–4326; tel. 256/535–2300 **A**1 9 10 **F**3 29 30 90 93 95 130 **S** HEALTHSOUTH Corporation, Birmingham, AL
Primary Contact: Douglas H. Beverly, Chief Executive Officer
Web address: www.healthsouthhuntsville.com
Control: Corporation, Investor–owned, for–profit **Service:** Rehabilitation

Staffed Beds: 70 **Admissions:** 1789 **Census:** 66 **Outpatient Visits:** 1027 **Births:** 0 **Total Expense ($000):** 18732

Hospital, Medicare Provider Number, Address, Telephone, Approval, Facility, and Physician Codes, Health Care System

★ American Hospital Association (AHA) membership
☐ The Joint Commission accreditation
◇ DNV Healthcare Inc. accreditation
○ Healthcare Facilities Accreditation Program
△ Commission on Accreditation of Rehabilitation Facilities (CARF) accreditation

AL

HUNTSVILLE HOSPITAL (010039), 101 Sivley Road S.W., Zip 35801–4470; tel. 256/265–1000, (Includes HUNTSVILLE HOSPITAL FOR WOMEN AND CHILDREN, 911 Big Cove Road S.E., Zip 35801–3784; tel. 256/265–1000; MADISON HOSPITAL, 8375 Highway 72 West, Madison, Zip 35758–9573; tel. 256/265–2012; Mary Lynne Wright, R.N., President) **A**1 2 3 5 10 **F**5 7 8 12 13 14 15 17 18 19 20 21 22 23 24 25 26 28 29 30 31 35 37 38 39 40 41 43 48 49 50 51 53 54 56 57 59 60 63 64 68 70 71 72 73 76 78 79 80 81 82 84 85 88 89 93 96 98 99 100 101 102 103 104 105 107 108 109 110 111 114 115 116 117 118 119 126 129 130 132 134 142 145 146 147 148 **S** Huntsville Hospital Health System, Huntsville, AL
Primary Contact: David S. Spillers, Chief Executive Officer
COO: Jeff Samz, Chief Operating Officer
CFO: Kelli Powers, Chief Financial Officer
CMO: Robert Chappell, M.D., Chief Medical Officer and Chief Quality Officer
CIO: Rick Corn, Chief Information Officer
CHR: Andrea P. Rosler, Vice President Human Resources
CNO: Karol Jones, Chief Nursing Officer
Web address: www.huntsvillehospital.org
Control: Hospital district or authority, Government, nonfederal **Service:** General Medical and Surgical

Staffed Beds: 876 **Admissions:** 42317 **Census:** 571 **Outpatient Visits:** 749346 **Births:** 5161 **Total Expense ($000):** 734465 **Payroll Expense ($000):** 294038 **Personnel:** 6355

JACKSON—Clarke County

JACKSON MEDICAL CENTER (010128), 220 Hospital Drive, Zip 36545–2459, Mailing Address: P.O. Box 428, Zip 36545–0428; tel. 251/246–9021 **A**9 10 **F**3 11 15 29 34 40 45 57 59 62 76 81 85 89 107 108 111 115 119 133 134 144 **S** Gilliard Health Services, Montgomery, AL
Primary Contact: Amy Gibson, Chief Executive Officer
COO: Jennifer M. Ryland, R.N., Chief Administrative Officer
CFO: Amy Gibson, Chief Executive Officer
CHR: Kathy Jones, Director Human Resources
Web address: www.jacksonmedicalcenter.org
Control: Partnership, Investor–owned, for–profit **Service:** General Medical and Surgical

Staffed Beds: 26 **Admissions:** 622 **Census:** 7 **Outpatient Visits:** 14066 **Total Expense ($000):** 8836

JACKSONVILLE—Calhoun County

RMC JACKSONVILLE (010146), 1701 Pelham Road South, Zip 36265–3399, Mailing Address: P.O. Box 999, Zip 36265–0999; tel. 256/435–4970 **A**1 9 10 **F**3 4 5 11 13 15 29 30 34 35 40 42 45 48 50 51 56 57 59 64 65 68 69 76 79 81 82 85 93 98 103 107 108 111 114 119 120 129 135 146
Primary Contact: Joe Weaver, Vice President Operations
COO: Carlos Farmer, R.N., Director Clinical Operations
CFO: Robbin Curlee, Controller
CMO: Rey Gavino, M.D., Chief of Staff
CIO: Richard Maust, Chief Information Officer
CHR: Doug Scott, Director Human Resources
CNO: Jean Ann McMurrey, R.N., Chief Nursing Officer
Web address: www.jmchealth.com
Control: Hospital district or authority, Government, nonfederal **Service:** General Medical and Surgical

Staffed Beds: 70 **Admissions:** 1840 **Census:** 24 **Outpatient Visits:** 54693 **Births:** 342 **Total Expense ($000):** 23635 **Payroll Expense ($000):** 9615 **Personnel:** 191

JASPER—Walker County

WALKER BAPTIST MEDICAL CENTER (010089), 3400 Highway 78 East, Zip 35501–8907, Mailing Address: P.O. Box 3547, Zip 35502–3547; tel. 205/387–4000 **A**1 9 10 20 **F**3 8 11 13 15 18 20 22 26 29 30 31 34 35 40 41 43 45 47 50 56 57 59 64 67 68 70 74 75 76 77 78 79 81 82 85 87 94 96 97 98 100 101 102 103 104 107 108 110 111 115 119 126 130 132 146 147 148 **S** Baptist Health System, Birmingham, AL
Primary Contact: Robert Phillips, Administrator
CFO: John Langlois, Chief Financial Officer
CIO: Kenny Horton, Director Information Systems
CHR: Pat Morrow, Director Human Resources
CNO: Robbie Hindman, Vice President Patient Care Services and Chief Nursing Officer
Web address: www.bhsala.com/home_walker.cfm?id=41
Control: Church–operated, Nongovernment, not–for profit **Service:** General Medical and Surgical

Staffed Beds: 236 **Admissions:** 7321 **Census:** 88 **Outpatient Visits:** 75454 **Births:** 759 **Total Expense ($000):** 88411 **Payroll Expense ($000):** 28799 **Personnel:** 582

LUVERNE—Crenshaw County

BEACON CHILDREN'S HOSPITAL (014015), 150 Hospital Drive, Zip 36049; tel. 334/335–5040, (Nonreporting) **A**1 9 10
Primary Contact: Bradley Eisemann, Administrator
Web address: www.beaconchildrenshospital.com
Control: Other not–for–profit (including NFP Corporation) **Service:** Psychiatric

Staffed Beds: 24

CRENSHAW COMMUNITY HOSPITAL (010008), 101 Hospital Circle, Zip 36049–7344; tel. 334/335–3374, (Nonreporting) **A**9 10
Primary Contact: Bradley Eisemann, Administrator
COO: Victoria Lawrenson, Chief Operating Officer
CMO: Charles Tompkins, M.D., Chief of Staff
CHR: Patricia Jarry, Manager Human Resources
Control: Corporation, Investor–owned, for–profit **Service:** General Medical and Surgical

Staffed Beds: 49

MADISON—Madison County

BRADFORD HEALTH SERVICES AT HUNTSVILLE, 1600 Browns Ferry Road, Zip 35758–9601, Mailing Address: P.O. Box 1488, Zip 35758–0176; tel. 256/461–7272, (Nonreporting) **S** Bradford Health Services, Birmingham, AL
Primary Contact: Bob Hinds, Executive Director
Web address: www.bradfordhealth.com
Control: Corporation, Investor–owned, for–profit **Service:** Alcoholism and other chemical dependency

Staffed Beds: 84

MOBILE—Mobile County

BAYPOINTE BEHAVIORAL HEALTH (014014), 5800 Southland Drive, Zip 36693–3313; tel. 251/661–0153 **A**9 10 **F**98 99 **S** AltaPointe Health Systems, Mobile, AL
Primary Contact: Heather Joseph, Administrator
Web address: www.altapointe.org
Control: Other not–for–profit (including NFP Corporation) **Service:** Children's hospital psychiatric

Staffed Beds: 60 **Admissions:** 881 **Census:** 20 **Outpatient Visits:** 0 **Births:** 0 **Total Expense ($000):** 4669 **Payroll Expense ($000):** 2400 **Personnel:** 101

INFIRMARY LONG TERM ACUTE CARE HOSPITAL (012006), 5 Mobile Infirmary Circle, Zip 36607–3513, Mailing Address: P.O. Box 2226, Zip 36652–2226; tel. 251/660–5239 **A**1 9 10 **F**1 29 30 56 59 75 82 84 86 91 103 119 132 148 **S** Infirmary Health System, Mobile, AL
Primary Contact: Susanne Marmande, Administrator
Web address: www.theinfirmary.com/
Control: Corporation, Investor–owned, for–profit **Service:** General Medical and Surgical

Staffed Beds: 38 **Admissions:** 314 **Census:** 23 **Outpatient Visits:** 0 **Births:** 0 **Total Expense ($000):** 9775

△ **MOBILE INFIRMARY MEDICAL CENTER (010113)**, 5 Mobile Infirmary Drive North, Zip 36607–3513, Mailing Address: P.O. Box 2144, Zip 36652–2144; tel. 251/435–2400, (Includes ROTARY REHABILITATION HOSPITAL, 5 Mobile Infirmary Circle, Zip 36607, Mailing Address: P.O. Box 2144, Zip 36652; tel. 334/431–3400) **A**1 2 3 5 7 9 10 **F**1 3 8 11 12 13 15 17 18 20 22 24 26 29 30 34 35 40 41 43 45 46 47 48 49 50 51 52 53 54 56 57 59 60 64 68 70 74 75 76 77 78 79 80 81 82 85 86 87 89 90 91 92 93 96 98 102 103 107 108 110 111 114 115 118 119 120 121 124 126 129 130 131 132 145 146 147 148 **S** Infirmary Health System, Mobile, AL
Primary Contact: Kenneth C. Brewington, M.D., Administrator
CFO: Joe Denton, Executive Vice President and Chief Financial Officer
CIO: Eddy Stephens, Vice President Information Technology
CHR: Sheila Young, Vice President Human Resources
CNO: Suzanne C. Bird, R.N., Chief Nursing Officer
Web address: www.mobileinfirmary.org
Control: Other not–for–profit (including NFP Corporation) **Service:** General Medical and Surgical

Staffed Beds: 510 **Admissions:** 27991 **Census:** 418 **Outpatient Visits:** 216170 **Births:** 1078 **Total Expense ($000):** 331067

✠ **PROVIDENCE HOSPITAL (010090)**, 6801 Airport Boulevard, Zip 36608–3785, Mailing Address: P.O. Box 850429, Zip 36685–0429; tel. 251/633–1000 **A**1 2 3 5 9 10 **F**3 11 13 15 17 18 20 22 24 26 28 29 30 31 34 35 40 44 45 49 50 51 53 54 55 57 58 59 60 61 64 65 68 70 73 74 75 76 77 78 79 80 81 82 83 84 85 86 87 89 92 93 96 102 107 108 110 111 114 115 117 119 120 121 124 126 129 130 131 132 135 142 146 148 **P**5 6 **S** Ascension Health, Saint Louis, MO
Primary Contact: Clark P. Christianson, President and Chief Executive Officer
COO: Todd S. Kennedy, Executive Vice President and Chief Operating Officer
CFO: C. Susan Cornejo, Senior Vice President Finance and Chief Financial Officer
CMO: William M. Lightfoot, M.D., Vice President Medical Services
CIO: Kathy Ross, Chief Information Officer
CHR: Christopher Cockrell, Executive Director Human Resources
CNO: Peter Lindquist, Vice President and Chief Nursing Officer
Web address: www.providencehospital.org
Control: Church–operated, Nongovernment, not–for profit **Service:** General Medical and Surgical

Staffed Beds: 349 **Admissions:** 14271 **Census:** 206 **Outpatient Visits:** 141714 **Births:** 1664 **Total Expense ($000):** 194730 **Payroll Expense ($000):** 67056 **Personnel:** 1594

ROTARY REHABILITATION HOSPITAL See Mobile Infirmary Medical Center

Many Facility Codes have changed. Please refer to the AHA Guide Code Chart.

© 2014 AHA Guide

☐ **SPRINGHILL MEMORIAL HOSPITAL (010144)**, 3719 Dauphin Street, Zip 36608–1798, Mailing Address: P.O. Box 8246, Zip 36689–0246; tel. 251/344–9630 **A**1 9 10 **F**11 13 15 17 18 20 22 24 26 28 29 30 31 34 40 46 47 49 50 51 57 60 70 74 75 76 77 78 79 81 82 85 86 87 88 89 93 107 110 111 115 118 119 126 127 129 130 132 146 147 148
Primary Contact: Jeffery M. St. Clair, President and Chief Executive Officer
COO: Jeffery M. St Clair, President and Chief Executive Officer
CFO: Jan Grigsby, Vice President and Chief Financial Officer
CMO: Liston Jones, M.D., Medical Director
CIO: Mark Kilborn, Director Information Systems
CHR: Daniela Batchelor, Director Human Resources
CNO: Paul Read, R.N., Vice President and Chief Nursing Officer
Web address: www.springhillmemorial.com
Control: Corporation, Investor–owned, for–profit **Service:** General Medical and Surgical

Staffed Beds: 192 **Admissions:** 9633 **Census:** 132 **Outpatient Visits:** 161064 **Births:** 616 **Total Expense ($000):** 132434 **Payroll Expense ($000):** 41923 **Personnel:** 1048

⊠ **UNIVERSITY OF SOUTH ALABAMA CHILDREN'S AND WOMEN'S HOSPITAL (013301)**, (Childrens and Womens), 1700 Center Street, Zip 36604–3301; tel. 251/415–1000 **A**1 3 5 9 10 **F**3 7 11 13 15 21 27 29 30 31 40 48 49 52 55 58 59 64 72 73 74 75 76 77 78 79 81 85 86 87 88 89 93 107 111 114 119 130 143 146 147 **S** University of South Alabama Hospitals, Mobile, AL
Primary Contact: Owen Bailey, Administrator
CFO: William B. Bush, CPA, Chief Financial Officer
CIO: Mark Lauteren, Chief Information Officer
CHR: Janice Rehm, Manager Human Resources
CNO: Carol Druckenmiller, R.N., Assistant Administrator and Chief Nursing Officer
Web address: www.usahealthsystem.com/usacwh
Control: State–Government, nonfederal **Service:** Other specialty

Staffed Beds: 198 **Admissions:** 9355 **Census:** 161 **Outpatient Visits:** 64631 **Births:** 2757 **Total Expense ($000):** 116041 **Payroll Expense ($000):** 48499 **Personnel:** 1076

⊠ **UNIVERSITY OF SOUTH ALABAMA MEDICAL CENTER (010087)**, 2451 Fillingim Street, Zip 36617–2293; tel. 251/471–7000 **A**1 2 3 5 8 9 10 **F**3 11 16 17 18 20 22 24 26 29 31 34 40 43 46 49 57 58 59 60 61 64 70 74 78 79 81 85 87 107 108 111 114 115 119 130 146 148 **S** University of South Alabama Hospitals, Mobile, AL
Primary Contact: A. Elizabeth Anderson, Administrator
CFO: William B. Bush, CPA, Chief Financial Officer
CIO: Mark Lauteren, Chief Information Officer
CHR: Anita Shirah, Director Human Resources
CNO: Lisa Mestas, Chief Nursing Officer and Assistant Administrator Clinical Services
Web address: www.usahealthsystem.com/usamc
Control: State–Government, nonfederal **Service:** General Medical and Surgical

Staffed Beds: 132 **Admissions:** 6961 **Census:** 113 **Outpatient Visits:** 52463 **Births:** 1 **Total Expense ($000):** 158332 **Payroll Expense ($000):** 72559 **Personnel:** 1335

MONROEVILLE—Monroe County

⊠ **MONROE COUNTY HOSPITAL (010120)**, 2016 South Alabama Avenue, Zip 36460–3044, Mailing Address: P.O. Box 886, Zip 36461–0886; tel. 251/575–3111, (Nonreporting) **A**1 9 10 20
Primary Contact: Jeffrey M. Brannon, Chief Executive Officer
CFO: Wes Nall, Chief Financial Officer
CMO: David Stallworth, M.D., Chief of Staff
CIO: Jody Falkenberry, Director Information Systems
CHR: Tara Nowling, Director Human Resources
CNO: Barbara Harned, R.N., Chief Nursing Officer
Web address: www.mchcare.com
Control: Hospital district or authority, Government, nonfederal **Service:** General Medical and Surgical

Staffed Beds: 62

MONTGOMERY—Montgomery County

☐ **BAPTIST MEDICAL CENTER EAST (010149)**, 400 Taylor Road, Zip 36117–3512, Mailing Address: P.O. Box 241267, Zip 36124–1267; tel. 334/277–8330 **A**1 9 10 **F**3 11 12 13 15 19 20 30 34 35 40 44 45 47 49 50 56 57 63 64 68 70 72 73 75 76 77 79 81 82 85 86 89 90 93 94 107 108 111 114 115 119 126 129 130 132 135 146 147 **S** Baptist Health, Montgomery, AL
Primary Contact: Jeff G. Rains, Chief Executive Officer
CFO: Katrina Belt, Chief Financial Officer
CHR: Kay Bennett, Vice President Human Resources
CNO: Kathy Gaston, Chief Nursing Officer
Web address: www.baptistfirst.org
Control: Hospital district or authority, Government, nonfederal **Service:** General Medical and Surgical

Staffed Beds: 183 **Admissions:** 9860 **Census:** 114 **Outpatient Visits:** 85838 **Births:** 3370 **Total Expense ($000):** 98885 **Payroll Expense ($000):** 38869 **Personnel:** 808

☐ **BAPTIST MEDICAL CENTER SOUTH (010023)**, 2105 East South Boulevard, Zip 36116–2409, Mailing Address: Box 11010, Zip 36111–0010; tel. 334/288–2100 **A**1 3 5 9 10 **F**3 5 11 12 13 15 17 18 20 22 24 26 28 29 30 31 34 35 40 44 45 47 49 50 56 57 58 59 60 61 63 64 68 70 72 74 75 76 78 79 81 82 84 85 86 87 89 90 93 94 98 100 101 102 103 104 105 107 108 110 111 114 115 116 117 118 119 126 129 130 131 132 135 146 147 148 **S** Baptist Health, Montgomery, AL
Primary Contact: J. Peter Selman, Chief Executive Officer
CFO: Melissa Johnson, Chief Financial Officer
CMO: Donovan Kendrick, M.D., Chief Medical Officer
CIO: Steve Miller, Director Information Systems
CHR: Kay Bennett, System Director Human Resources
CNO: Karen McCaa, R.N., Vice President Patient Care Services and Chief Nursing Officer
Web address: www.baptistfirst.org
Control: Hospital district or authority, Government, nonfederal **Service:** General Medical and Surgical

Staffed Beds: 387 **Admissions:** 18638 **Census:** 251 **Outpatient Visits:** 244136 **Births:** 793 **Total Expense ($000):** 365265 **Payroll Expense ($000):** 92770 **Personnel:** 1830

⊠ **CENTRAL ALABAMA VETERANS HEALTH CARE SYSTEM**, 215 Perry Hill Road, Zip 36109–3798; tel. 334/272–4670, (Includes MONTGOMERY DIVISION, 215 Perry Hill Road, tel. 334/272–4670; TUSKEGEE DIVISION, 2400 Hospital Road, Tuskegee, Zip 36083–5001; tel. 334/727–0550), (Total facility includes 58 beds in nursing home–type unit) **A**1 3 **F**3 5 18 29 30 34 35 38 39 40 45 50 53 56 57 59 61 62 63 64 65 68 70 75 77 79 80 81 82 84 85 86 87 90 91 92 93 94 96 97 98 100 101 102 103 104 105 106 107 108 111 114 115 116 117 119 128 130 132 135 143 146 147 148 **S** Department of Veterans Affairs, Washington, DC
Primary Contact: James R. Talton, MS, FACHE, Director
CFO: Debra Nicholson, Manager Finance
CMO: Cliff Robinson, M.D., Chief of Staff
CIO: Rhoda Tyson, Chief Information Officer
CHR: Janice Hardy, Chief Human Resource Management Service
Web address: www.centralalabama.va.gov/
Control: Veterans Affairs, Government, federal **Service:** General Medical and Surgical

Staffed Beds: 245 **Admissions:** 2371 **Census:** 191 **Outpatient Visits:** 406795 **Births:** 0 **Total Expense ($000):** 239083 **Payroll Expense ($000):** 109056 **Personnel:** 1519

⊠ **HEALTHSOUTH REHABILITATION HOSPITAL OF MONTGOMERY (013028)**, 4465 Narrow Lane Road, Zip 36116–2900; tel. 334/284–7700 **A**1 9 10 **F**3 9 28 29 34 35 54 56 57 59 64 74 75 77 86 90 93 95 130 131 132 143 146 148 **P**5 **S** HEALTHSOUTH Corporation, Birmingham, AL
Primary Contact: Linda Wade, Chief Executive Officer
CFO: Heath Watson, Controller
CMO: Jeffrey Eng, M.D., Medical Director
CIO: Anidra Billingslea, Health Insurance Management
CHR: Kim McDaniel, Director Human Resources
CNO: Lee Anne Montgomery, R.N., Chief Nursing Officer
Web address: www.healthsouthmontgomery.com
Control: Corporation, Investor–owned, for–profit **Service:** Rehabilitation

Staffed Beds: 70 **Admissions:** 1769 **Census:** 63 **Outpatient Visits:** 4895 **Births:** 0 **Total Expense ($000):** 17765 **Payroll Expense ($000):** 10375 **Personnel:** 181

Hospital, Medicare Provider Number, Address, Telephone, Approval, Facility, and Physician Codes, Health Care System

★ American Hospital Association (AHA) membership
☐ The Joint Commission accreditation
◇ DNV Healthcare Inc. accreditation
○ Healthcare Facilities Accreditation Program
△ Commission on Accreditation of Rehabilitation Facilities (CARF) accreditation

✠ **JACKSON HOSPITAL AND CLINIC (010024)**, 1725 Pine Street,
Zip 36106–1117; tel. 334/293–8000 **A**1 9 10 **F**13 15 17 18 20 22 24 26 29
30 31 34 40 45 46 49 5⁷ 59 64 68 70 74 76 77 78 79 81 82 84 85 86 87
89 107 108 111 114 116 117 118 119 126 130 131 135 144 146 147 **P**6
Primary Contact: Joe B. Riley, President and Chief Executive Officer
COO: Michael James, Chief Operations Officer
CFO: Paul Peiffer, Chief Financial Officer and Vice President
CHR: Gilbert Darrington, Director Human Resources
CNO: Sharon A. Goodison, R.N., Chief Nursing Officer
Web address: www.jackson.org
Control: Other not–for–profit (including NFP Corporation) **Service:** General
Medical and Surgical

Staffed Beds: 251 **Admissions:** 12383 **Census:** 165 **Outpatient Visits:** 148650 **Births:** 1332 **Total Expense ($000):** 167909 **Payroll Expense ($000):** 62421 **Personnel:** 1305	

LONG TERM CARE HOSPITAL See Noland Hospital Montgomery

MONTGOMERY DIVISION See Central Alabama Veterans Health Care System

☐ **NOLAND HOSPITAL MONTGOMERY (012007)**, 1725 Pine Street, 5 North,
Zip 36106–1109; tel. 334/240–0532 **A**1 9 10 **F**1 29 130 148 **S** Noland Health
Services, Inc., Birmingham, AL
Primary Contact: Susan E. Legg, Interim Administrator
Web address: www.nolandhealth.com
Control: Other not–for–profit (including NFP Corporation) **Service:** Long–Term
Acute Care hospital

Staffed Beds: 65 **Admissions:** 418 **Census:** 27 **Outpatient Visits:** 0 **Births:** 0 **Total Expense ($000):** 10665	

MOULTON—Lawrence County

☐ **LAWRENCE MEDICAL CENTER (010059)**, 202 Hospital Street,
Zip 35650–1218, Mailing Address: P.O. Box 39, Zip 35650–0039;
tel. 256/974–2200 **A**1 9 10 **F**3 15 28 29 30 34 35 40 45 46 47 50 54 56 57
59 62 64 65 66 68 70 75 81 85 86 87 93 97 107 108 111 114 118 119 127
130 132 135 146 147 **S** Huntsville Hospital Health System, Huntsville, AL
Primary Contact: Kyle Buchanan, Chief Executive Officer
CFO: Jim Crawford, Chief Financial Officer
CIO: Jeremy Duncan, Director Information Systems
CHR: Diane K. Secor, Director Human Resources
CNO: Sherry Jolley, Chief Clinical Officer
Web address: www.lawrencemedicalcenter.com
Control: County–Government, nonfederal **Service:** General Medical and Surgical

Staffed Beds: 43 **Admissions:** 917 **Census:** 11 **Outpatient Visits:** 27032 **Births:** 0	

MUSCLE SHOALS—Colbert County

☐ **SHOALS HOSPITAL (010157)**, 201 Avalon Avenue, Zip 35661–2805, Mailing
Address: P.O. Box 3359, Zip 35662–3359; tel. 256/386–1600, (Nonreporting)
A1 9 10 **S** RegionalCare Hospital Partners, Brentwood, TN
Primary Contact: Jeff Jennings, FACHE, Chief Executive Officer
CFO: Steve E. Hobbs, Chief Financial Officer
CMO: Terry TRUE, M.D., Chief of Staff
CIO: William Johnson, Director Information Systems
CHR: Nancy Bowling, Director Human Resources
CNO: Denida A. Cox, Chief Nursing Officer
Web address: www.shoalshospital.com
Control: Hospital district or authority, Government, nonfederal **Service:** General
Medical and Surgical

Staffed Beds: 131	

NORTHPORT—Tuscaloosa County

NORTHPORT MEDICAL CENTER (010145), 2700 Hospital Drive,
Zip 35476–3360; tel. 205/333–4500 **A**5 **F**3 11 13 15 29 30 34 35 40 42 45
56 57 58 59 61 64 68 70 72 74 75 76 79 81 82 85 86 87 90 93 96 98 100
101 102 103 104 107 108 110 111 114 119 129 130 131 132 135 146 147
148 **S** DCH Health System, Tuscaloosa, AL
Primary Contact: Luke Standeffer, Administrator
CFO: Nina Dusang, Chief Financial Officer
CMO: Kenneth Aldridge, M.D., Vice President Medical Affairs
CIO: Kim Ligon, Director Information Services
CHR: Peggy Sease, Vice President Human Resources
CNO: Lorraine Yehlen, R.N., Chief Nursing Officer
Web address: www.dchsystem.com
Control: Hospital district or authority, Government, nonfederal **Service:** General
Medical and Surgical

Staffed Beds: 196 **Admissions:** 8092 **Census:** 116 **Outpatient Visits:** 95477 **Births:** 1408 **Total Expense ($000):** 62722	

ONEONTA—Blount County

✠ **ST. VINCENT'S BLOUNT (010050)**, 150 Gilbreath, Zip 35121–2827, Mailing
Address: P.O. Box 1000, Zip 35121–0013; tel. 205/274–3000 **A**1 9 10 **F**3 11
15 18 29 30 34 40 43 45 57 59 64 65 70 75 77 79 81 82 85 93 97
107 108 110 119 135 **P**8 **S** Ascension Health, Saint Louis, MO
Primary Contact: Evan Ray, President
CFO: David Cauble, Chief Financial Officer
CMO: David R. Wilson, M.D., Chief of Staff
CIO: Timothy Stettheimer, Regional Chief Information Officer
CHR: Carol Maietta, Vice President and Talent Resource Officer Human Resources
and Learning
CNO: Paula McCullough, VP Patient Care Services
Web address: www.stvhs.com
Control: Other not–for–profit (including NFP Corporation) **Service:** General
Medical and Surgical

Staffed Beds: 40 **Admissions:** 1087 **Census:** 12 **Outpatient Visits:** 36430 **Births:** 0 **Total Expense ($000):** 19832 **Payroll Expense ($000):** 6678 **Personnel:** 133	

OPELIKA—Lee County

✠ **EAST ALABAMA MEDICAL CENTER (010029)**, 2000 Pepperell Parkway,
Zip 36801–5452; tel. 334/749–3411, (Total facility includes 113 beds in nursing
home–type unit) **A**1 2 9 10 19 **F**3 7 10 11 13 15 17 18 20 22 24 26 28 29 30
31 32 34 40 43 45 50 51 53 54 56 57 59 64 65 71 64 68 70 74 75 76 77
78 79 81 82 84 85 86 89 93 98 99 100 102 103 104 107 108 110 111 114
115 117 118 119 120 121 123 125 126 128 129 130 131 132 135 146 148
Primary Contact: Terry W. Andrus, President
COO: Laura D. Grill, R.N., Executive Vice President and Administrator
CFO: Sam Price, Executive Vice President Finance/Chief Financial Officer
CMO: Michael Lisenby, M.D., Vice President and Chief Medical Officer
CIO: Tommy Chittom, Vice President Information Services
CHR: Susan Johnston, Director Human Resources
Web address: www.eamc.org
Control: Hospital district or authority, Government, nonfederal **Service:** General
Medical and Surgical

Staffed Beds: 371 **Admissions:** 13626 **Census:** 263 **Outpatient Visits:** 125426 **Births:** 1543 **Total Expense ($000):** 233852	

OPP—Covington County

★ **MIZELL MEMORIAL HOSPITAL (010007)**, 702 Main Street, Zip 36467–1626,
Mailing Address: P.O. Box 1010, Zip 36467–1010; tel. 334/493–3541,
(Nonreporting) **A**9 10
Primary Contact: Jana Wyatt, Chief Executive Officer
CFO: Amy Bess, Chief Financial Officer
CIO: Elizabeth Cook, Chief Information Officer
CHR: Dianne Morrison, Director Human Resources
CNO: Steven Skeen, R.N., Chief Nursing Officer
Web address: www.mizellmh.com
Control: Other not–for–profit (including NFP Corporation) **Service:** General
Medical and Surgical

Staffed Beds: 58	

OZARK—Dale County

DALE MEDICAL CENTER (010021), 126 Hospital Avenue, Zip 36360–2080;
tel. 334/774–2601 **A**9 10 **F**8 11 13 15 17 29 40 51 53 54 57 59 62 63 70
75 76 77 81 85 86 89 93 98 103 107 108 111 118 119 144 147
Primary Contact: Vernon Johnson, Administrator
CFO: Brad Hull, Chief Financial Officer
CMO: Steve Brandt, M.D., Chief of Staff
CHR: Sheila Dunn, Assistant Administrator Human Resources
Web address: www.dalemedical.org
Control: Corporation, Investor–owned, for–profit **Service:** General Medical and
Surgical

Staffed Beds: 75 **Admissions:** 2115 **Census:** 33 **Outpatient Visits:** 45037 **Births:** 0 **Total Expense ($000):** 31411	

PELL CITY—St. Clair County

✠ **ST. VINCENT'S ST. CLAIR (010130)**, 7063 Veterans Parkway,
Zip 35125–1499; tel. 205/814–2105 **A**1 9 10 **F**3 11 15 29 30 34 35 40 43
50 57 59 64 66 68 70 74 75 77 78 79 81 86 87 93 107 111 119 130 135
146 148 **P**8 **S** Ascension Health, Saint Louis, MO
Primary Contact: Evan Ray, President
CFO: Jason Lynn, Director Finance
Web address: www.stvhs.com
Control: Other not–for–profit (including NFP Corporation) **Service:** General
Medical and Surgical

Staffed Beds: 40 **Admissions:** 2186 **Census:** 26 **Outpatient Visits:** 43691 **Births:** 0 **Total Expense ($000):** 25243 **Payroll Expense ($000):** 8994 **Personnel:** 188	

PHENIX CITY—Russell County

JACK HUGHSTON MEMORIAL HOSPITAL (010168), 4401 Riverchase Drive, Zip 36867–7483; tel. 334/732–3000 **A**9 10 **F**3 29 40 70 79 81 107 111 115 119 131
Primary Contact: Mark A. Baker, Chief Executive Officer
COO: Rachel H. Crenshaw, Chief Operating Officer
CFO: Angela Hodzeda, Chief Financial Officer
CMO: Lamar Carden, M.D., Chief Medical Officer
CHR: Lana Thomas–Folds, System Director Human Resources
CNO: Sylvia Thomas, Chief Nursing Officer
Web address: www.jackhughstonmemorialhospital.com
Control: Corporation, Investor–owned, for–profit **Service:** General Medical and Surgical

Staffed Beds: 35 **Admissions:** 2494 **Census:** 23 **Outpatient Visits:** 25095 **Births:** 0 **Total Expense ($000):** 42454 **Payroll Expense ($000):** 12839 **Personnel:** 272

✠ **REGIONAL REHABILITATION HOSPITAL (013033)**, 3715 Highway 280/431 North, Zip 36867; tel. 334/732–2200 **A**1 9 10 **F**3 29 30 90 93 95 132 **S** HEALTHSOUTH Corporation, Birmingham, AL
Primary Contact: Jill Jordan, Chief Executive Officer
CFO: Bobby Edmondson, Controller
CMO: Nitin Desei, M.D., Medical Director
CIO: Jacki Cuevas, Director Health Information Services
CHR: Cindy Glynn, Director Human Resources
CNO: Wendy Lee, Chief Nursing Officer
Web address: www.regionalrehabhospital.com
Control: Partnership, Investor–owned, for–profit **Service:** Rehabilitation

Staffed Beds: 48 **Admissions:** 1122 **Census:** 43 **Outpatient Visits:** 4039 **Births:** 0 **Total Expense ($000):** 13484

PRATTVILLE—Autauga County

☐ **PRATTVILLE BAPTIST HOSPITAL (010108)**, 124 South Memorial Drive, Zip 36067–3619, Mailing Address: P.O. Box 681630, Zip 36068–1638; tel. 334/365–0651 **A**1 9 10 **F**3 11 12 15 29 30 34 35 40 44 45 50 56 57 59 63 64 68 70 75 81 82 84 85 86 87 107 111 114 129 132 146 **S** Baptist Health, Montgomery, AL
Primary Contact: Ginger Henry, Chief Executive Officer
CFO: LaDonna McDaniel, Financial Manager
CIO: B. Blaine Brown, Vice President and General Counsel
CHR: Kymberli Skipper, Manager Human Resources
Web address: www.baptistfirst.org/facilities/prattville–baptist–hospital/default.aspx
Control: Hospital district or authority, Government, nonfederal **Service:** General Medical and Surgical

Staffed Beds: 50 **Admissions:** 2469 **Census:** 27 **Outpatient Visits:** 63552 **Births:** 0 **Total Expense ($000):** 31504 **Payroll Expense ($000):** 11267 **Personnel:** 233

RED BAY—Franklin County

★ **RED BAY HOSPITAL (011302)**, 211 Hospital Road, Zip 35582–3858, Mailing Address: P.O. Box 490, Zip 35582–0490; tel. 256/356–9532 **A**9 10 18 **F**15 29 30 34 35 39 40 45 53 56 57 59 64 65 68 75 77 81 86 87 93 107 119 127 128 130 131 133 135 143 146 147 **S** Huntsville Hospital Health System, Huntsville, AL
Primary Contact: Glen M. Jones, Administrator
CFO: Samuel A. Strickland, Chief Financial Officer
CMO: Raynard Fabianke, M.D., Chief of Staff
CHR: Amy Leigh Bishop, Director Human Resources
Web address: www.redbayhospital.com
Control: Hospital district or authority, Government, nonfederal **Service:** General Medical and Surgical

Staffed Beds: 25 **Admissions:** 385 **Census:** 8 **Outpatient Visits:** 12137 **Births:** 0 **Total Expense ($000):** 7341 **Personnel:** 89

RUSSELLVILLE—Franklin County

✠ **RUSSELLVILLE HOSPITAL (010158)**, 15155 Highway 43, Zip 35653–1975, Mailing Address: P.O. Box 1089, Zip 35653–1089; tel. 256/332–1611 **A**1 9 10 **F**3 8 13 14 15 20 29 34 37 40 45 47 48 50 56 57 59 62 68 70 76 77 79 81 82 85 87 93 107 108 110 111 115 119 130 133 146 **S** LifePoint Hospitals, Inc., Brentwood, TN
Primary Contact: Christine R. Stewart, FACHE, Chief Executive Officer
CFO: Penny Westmoreland, Chief Financial Officer
CHR: Stephen Proctor, Director of Human Resources/Risk
CNO: Belinda Johnson, R.N., Chief Nursing Officer/Chief Clinical Officer
Web address: www.russellvillehospital.com
Control: Partnership, Investor–owned, for–profit **Service:** General Medical and Surgical

Staffed Beds: 92 **Admissions:** 2231 **Census:** 23 **Outpatient Visits:** 17380 **Births:** 0 **Total Expense ($000):** 20394

SCOTTSBORO—Jackson County

☐ **HIGHLANDS MEDICAL CENTER (010061)**, 380 Woods Cove Road, Zip 35768–2428, Mailing Address: P.O. Box 1050, Zip 35768–1050; tel. 256/259–4444, (Nonreporting) **A**1 5 9 10 20
Primary Contact: Kim Bryant, Chief Executive Officer
CFO: Dan Newell, Chief Financial Officer
CIO: Doug Newby, Chief Information Officer
CHR: Susanna S. Sivley, Chief Personnel Officer
Web address: www.highlandsmedcenter.com
Control: Hospital district or authority, Government, nonfederal **Service:** General Medical and Surgical

Staffed Beds: 92

SELMA—Dallas County

✠ **VAUGHAN REGIONAL MEDICAL CENTER (010118)**, 1015 Medical Center Parkway, Zip 36701–6352; tel. 334/418–4100, (Nonreporting) **A**1 3 5 9 10 19 20 **S** LifePoint Hospitals, Inc., Brentwood, TN
Primary Contact: David R. Sirk, Chief Executive Officer
COO: Debbie Pace, Chief Operating Officer
CFO: Kelly Penton, Chief Financial Officer
CMO: Walid Freij, M.D., Chief of Staff
CIO: Matthew McHugh, Director Information Services
CHR: Dionne Williams, Director Human Resources
CNO: Genesia L. Rucker, MSN, Chief Nursing Officer
Web address: www.vaughanregional.com
Control: Corporation, Investor–owned, for–profit **Service:** General Medical and Surgical

Staffed Beds: 149

SHEFFIELD—Colbert County

✠ **HELEN KELLER HOSPITAL (010019)**, 1300 South Montgomery Avenue, Zip 35660–6334, Mailing Address: P.O. Box 610, Zip 35660–0610; tel. 256/386–4196, (Nonreporting) **A**1 9 10 **S** Huntsville Hospital Health System, Huntsville, AL
Primary Contact: W. Douglas Arnold, President and Chief Executive Officer
COO: Paul Storey, Chief Operating Officer
CFO: Morris S. Strickland, Chief Financial Officer
CHR: Pam Bryant, Director Human Resources
Web address: www.helenkeller.com
Control: Hospital district or authority, Government, nonfederal **Service:** General Medical and Surgical

Staffed Beds: 159

SYLACAUGA—Talladega County

☐ **COOSA VALLEY MEDICAL CENTER (010164)**, 315 West Hickory Street, Zip 35150–2996; tel. 256/401–4000, (Nonreporting) **A**1 9 10
Primary Contact: Glenn C. Sisk, President
CFO: Janice Brown, Chief Financial Officer
CIO: Sandra Murchison, Director Medical Records
CHR: Christy Knowles, Chief Human Resources Officer
Web address: www.cvhealth.net
Control: Other not–for–profit (including NFP Corporation) **Service:** General Medical and Surgical

Staffed Beds: 101

TALLADEGA—Talladega County

☐ **CITIZENS BAPTIST MEDICAL CENTER (010101)**, 604 Stone Avenue, Zip 35160–2217, Mailing Address: P.O. Box 978, Zip 35161–0978; tel. 256/362–8111 **A**1 9 10 19 **F**3 11 13 15 29 30 34 35 40 49 50 53 57 59 60 62 64 65 67 70 74 75 76 79 81 82 86 93 98 103 107 108 110 111 112 114 118 119 129 131 132 135 146 148 **S** Baptist Health System, Birmingham, AL
Primary Contact: Joel Taylor, Administrator
CFO: Zach Abercrombie, Chief Financial Officer
CHR: Sandra Willis, Manager Human Resources
Web address: www.bhsala.com/home_citizens.cfm?id=38
Control: Church–operated, Nongovernment, not–for profit **Service:** General Medical and Surgical

Staffed Beds: 116 **Admissions:** 2935 **Census:** 30 **Births:** 316 **Total Expense ($000):** 33954 **Payroll Expense ($000):** 15949 **Personnel:** 293

Hospital, Medicare Provider Number, Address, Telephone, Approval, Facility, and Physician Codes, Health Care System

★ American Hospital Association (AHA) membership
☐ The Joint Commission accreditation
◇ DNV Healthcare Inc. accreditation
○ Healthcare Facilities Accreditation Program
△ Commission on Accreditation of Rehabilitation Facilities (CARF) accreditation

TALLASSEE—Elmore County

★ **COMMUNITY HOSPITAL (010034)**, 805 Friendship Road, Zip 36078–1234; tel. 334/283–6541, (Nonreporting) **A**9 10
Primary Contact: Jennie R. Rhinehart, Administrator and Chief Executive Officer
Web address: www.chal.org
Control: Other not–for–profit (including NFP Corporation) **Service:** General Medical and Surgical

Staffed Beds: 69

TROY—Pike County

☐ **TROY REGIONAL MEDICAL CENTER (010126)**, 1330 Highway 231 South, Zip 36081–3058; tel. 334/670–5000, (Nonreporting) **A**1 9 10
Primary Contact: Teresa G. Grimes, Chief Executive Officer
CFO: Janet Smith, Chief Financial Officer
CMO: Paul Dulaney, Chief of Staff
CIO: Blake Thomason, Director Information Systems
CHR: Beth Nissen, Director Human Resources
CNO: Amy Minor, Chief Nursing Officer
Web address: www.troymedicalcenter.com
Control: Corporation, Investor–owned, for–profit **Service:** General Medical and Surgical

Staffed Beds: 78

TUSCALOOSA—Tuscaloosa County

☐ **BRYCE HOSPITAL (014007)**, 200 University Boulevard, Zip 35401–1294; tel. 205/759–0799, (Nonreporting) **A**1 3 5 10
Primary Contact: Roxanna Bender, Interim Administrator
CFO: Wendell Summerville, Chief Financial Officer
CMO: Cynthia Moore Sledge, M.D., Medical Director
CIO: Ronene Howell, Director Health Information Management
CHR: Jim Elliott, Director Human Resources
Control: State–Government, nonfederal **Service:** Psychiatric

Staffed Beds: 820

☐ **DCH REGIONAL MEDICAL CENTER (010092)**, 809 University Boulevard East, Zip 35401–2029; tel. 205/759–7111 **A**1 2 3 5 9 10 20 **F**3 11 12 13 15 17 18 20 22 24 26 28 29 30 31 35 38 40 43 45 48 49 50 51 57 59 60 61 62 64 66 68 70 72 74 75 76 77 78 79 81 82 86 87 88 89 90 93 94 96 98 100 101 102 103 104 105 106 107 108 110 111 114 115 116 117 118 119 121 126 129 130 131 132 146 147 148 **P**8 **S** DCH Health System, Tuscaloosa, AL
Primary Contact: William H. Cassels, Administrator
CFO: Nina Dusang, Vice President Finance and Chief Financial Officer
CMO: Kenneth Aldridge, M.D., Vice President Medical Affairs
CIO: Kim Ligon, Director Information Services
CHR: Peggy Sease, Vice President Human Resources
CNO: Lorraine Yehlen, R.N., Vice President Patient Care Services
Web address: www.dchsystem.com
Control: Hospital district or authority, Government, nonfederal **Service:** General Medical and Surgical

Staffed Beds: 684 Admissions: 31544 Census: 461 Outpatient Visits: 440489 Births: 3244 Total Expense ($000): 430129 Payroll Expense ($000): 195618 Personnel: 3735

☐ **MARY S HARPER GERIATRIC PSYCHIATRY CENTER (014012)**, 200 University Boulevard, Zip 35401–1250; tel. 205/759–0900, (Nonreporting) **A**1 10
Primary Contact: Beverly White, MS, Facility Director
CFO: Sarah Mitchell, Director Finance
CMO: Robin Barton Lariscy, M.D., Medical Director
CIO: Sarah Mitchell, Director Finance
CHR: Jim Elliott, Director Human Resources
Web address: www.mh.alabama.gov
Control: Corporation, Investor–owned, for–profit **Service:** Psychiatric

Staffed Beds: 96

☐ **NOLAND HOSPITAL TUSCALOOSA (012012)**, 809 University Boulevard E, 4th Floor, Zip 35401–2029; tel. 205/759–7241 **A**1 9 10 **F**1 29 130 148 **S** Noland Health Services, Inc., Birmingham, AL
Primary Contact: Dale Jones, Administrator
Web address: www.nolandhealth.com
Control: Other not–for–profit (including NFP Corporation) **Service:** Long–Term Acute Care hospital

Staffed Beds: 32 Admissions: 306 Census: 23 Outpatient Visits: 0 Births: 0 Total Expense ($000): 8890

☐ **TAYLOR HARDIN SECURE MEDICAL FACILITY (014011)**, 1301 Jack Warner Parkway, Zip 35404–1060; tel. 205/556–7060, (Nonreporting) **A**1 10
Primary Contact: Shelia Taylor, Director
Web address: www.mh.alabama.gov/
Control: Corporation, Investor–owned, for–profit **Service:** Psychiatric

Staffed Beds: 114

⊞ **TUSCALOOSA VETERANS AFFAIRS MEDICAL CENTER**, 3701 Loop Road East, Zip 35404–5015; tel. 205/554–2000, (Nonreporting) **A**1 **S** Department of Veterans Affairs, Washington, DC
Primary Contact: Maria Andrews, MS, Director
COO: Gary D. Trende, FACHE, Associate Director
CFO: Angelia Stevenson, Manager Finance
CMO: Mark Nissenbaum, M.D., Chief of Staff
Web address: www.tuscaloosa.va.gov
Control: Veterans Affairs, Government, federal **Service:** Psychiatric

Staffed Beds: 381

TUSKEGEE—Macon County

TUSKEGEE DIVISION See Central Alabama Veterans Health Care System, Montgomery

UNION SPRINGS—Bullock County

BULLOCK COUNTY HOSPITAL (010110), 102 West Conecuh Avenue, Zip 36089–1303; tel. 334/738–2140, (Nonreporting) **A**9 10 20
Primary Contact: Jacques Jarry, Administrator
COO: Victoria Lawrenson, Chief Operating Officer
CMO: Maria Bernardo, M.D., Chief of Staff
Control: Corporation, Investor–owned, for–profit **Service:** General Medical and Surgical

Staffed Beds: 41

VALLEY—Chambers County

☐ **EAST ALABAMA MEDICAL CENTER–LANIER (010025)**, 4800 48th Street, Zip 36854–3666; tel. 334/756–9180, (Total facility includes 103 beds in nursing home–type unit) **A**1 9 10 19 **F**3 11 13 15 18 20 22 28 29 30 34 40 41 43 45 46 47 48 49 57 59 62 64 68 70 74 76 77 79 81 85 86 87 89 93 100 102 107 108 110 111 115 118 119 124 128 129 130 132 133 135 146 147
Primary Contact: Carey M. Owen, Chief Executive Officer
CFO: Tommy Lane, Assistant Vice President, Finance and Operations
CIO: Linde Lashley, Manager Information Management
CHR: Clara Pitts, Director Human Resources
CNO: Eve Milner, R.N., Assistant Vice President, Clinical Services
Web address: www.lanierhospital.com
Control: Other not–for–profit (including NFP Corporation) **Service:** General Medical and Surgical

Staffed Beds: 188 Admissions: 2796 Census: 124 Outpatient Visits: 33438 Births: 394

WARRIOR—Jefferson County

BRADFORD HEALTH SERVICES AT WARRIOR LODGE, 1189 Allbritt Road, Zip 35180, Mailing Address: P.O. Box 129, Zip 35180–0129; tel. 205/647–1945, (Nonreporting) **S** Bradford Health Services, Birmingham, AL
Primary Contact: Roy M. Ramsey, Executive Director
Web address: www.bradfordhealth.com
Control: Corporation, Investor–owned, for–profit **Service:** Alcoholism and other chemical dependency

Staffed Beds: 100

WEDOWEE—Randolph County

WEDOWEE HOSPITAL (010032), 209 North Main Street, Zip 36278–7428, Mailing Address: P.O. Box 307, Zip 36278–0307; tel. 256/357–2111, (Nonreporting) **A**9 10
Primary Contact: Michael D. Alexander, MS, Interim Chief Executive Officer
Web address: www.wedoweehospital.org/
Control: County–Government, nonfederal **Service:** General Medical and Surgical

Staffed Beds: 28

WETUMPKA—Elmore County

ELMORE COMMUNITY HOSPITAL (010097), 500 Hospital Drive, Zip 36092–1625, Mailing Address: P.O. Box 130, Zip 36092–0003; tel. 334/567–4311 **A**9 10 **F**3 4 11 29 40 45 57 59 62 70 81 82 97 107 111 114 119 143 144
Primary Contact: Gordon Faulk, Administrator
CFO: Mike Bruce, Chief Financial Officer
CHR: Cindy Futral, Director Human Resources
Web address: www.elmorehospital.com/
Control: Partnership, Investor–owned, for–profit **Service:** General Medical and Surgical

Staffed Beds: 49 Admissions: 891 Census: 10 Outpatient Visits: 33258 Births: 0 Total Expense ($000): 14792

Many Facility Codes have changed. Please refer to the AHA Guide Code Chart. © 2014 AHA Guide

WINFIELD—Marion County

☒ **NORTHWEST MEDICAL CENTER (010086)**, 1530 U.S. Highway 43,
Zip 35594–5056; tel. 205/487–7000 **A**1 9 10 **F**3 8 15 18 29 34 35 40 50 53
56 57 59 64 68 70 79 81 85 90 98 103 107 108 110 111 114 119 127 130
132 133 135 **S** LifePoint Hospitals, Inc., Brentwood, TN
Primary Contact: Robert Henger, Interim Chief Executive Officer
CFO: James Gory, Chief Financial Officer
CMO: Gary Fowler, M.D., Chief of Staff Family Practice
Web address: www.northwestmedcenter.com
Control: Corporation, Investor–owned, for–profit **Service:** General Medical and
Surgical

Staffed Beds: 66 **Admissions:** 1842 **Census:** 23 **Outpatient Visits:** 35313
Births: 0 **Total Expense ($000):** 23070

YORK—Sumter County

HILL HOSPITAL OF SUMTER COUNTY (010138), 751 Derby Drive,
Zip 36925–2121; tel. 205/392–5263 **A**9 10 **F**33 40 57 58 62 107 119
Primary Contact: Loretta Wilson, Administrator
CFO: Joyce Wedgeworth, Financial Clerk
CMO: Gary Walton, M.D., Chief Medical Officer
CNO: Cynthia Brown, Director of Nursing
Control: Other not–for–profit (including NFP Corporation) **Service:** General
Medical and Surgical

Staffed Beds: 33 **Admissions:** 641 **Census:** 4 **Outpatient Visits:** 6278
Births: 0 **Total Expense ($000):** 9436

Hospital, Medicare Provider Number, Address, Telephone, Approval, Facility, and Physician Codes, Health Care System

★ American Hospital Association (AHA) membership
☐ The Joint Commission accreditation ◇ DNV Healthcare Inc. accreditation
○ Healthcare Facilities Accreditation Program
△ Commission on Accreditation of Rehabilitation Facilities (CARF) accreditation

ALASKA

ANCHORAGE—Anchorage Division

✠ **ALASKA NATIVE MEDICAL CENTER (020026)**, 4315 Diplomacy Drive, Zip 99508–5926; tel. 907/563–2662, (Nonreporting) **A**1 3 5 10
Primary Contact: Roald Helgesen, Chief Executive Officer
CMO: Paul Franke, M.D., Chief Medical Officer
CHR: Sonya Conant, Senior Director Human Resources
Web address: www.anmc.org
Control: Other not–for–profit (including NFP Corporation) **Service:** General Medical and Surgical

Staffed Beds: 138

☐ **ALASKA PSYCHIATRIC INSTITUTE (024002)**, 3700 Piper Street, Zip 99508–4677; tel. 907/269–7100 **A**1 10 **F**98 99 100 103
Primary Contact: Melissa Ring, Ph.D., M.D., Chief Executive Officer
COO: Ron Hale, Administrator
CFO: Tina Williams, Chief Financial Officer
CIO: Stephen Schneider, Manager Information Services
CHR: Jason Goodenbery, Administrative Assistant III
CNO: Sharon Bergstedt, Director of Nursing
Web address: www.hss.state.ak.us/dbh/API/
Control: State–Government, nonfederal **Service:** Psychiatric

Staffed Beds: 80 **Admissions:** 1670 **Census:** 57 **Outpatient Visits:** 0 **Births:** 0 **Total Expense ($000):** 30011 **Payroll Expense ($000):** 16104 **Personnel:** 270

✠ **ALASKA REGIONAL HOSPITAL (020017)**, 2801 Debarr Road, Zip 99508–2997, Mailing Address: P.O. Box 143889, Zip 99514–3889; tel. 907/264–1754, (Nonreporting) **A**1 2 9 10 **S** HCA, Nashville, TN
Primary Contact: Julie Taylor, FACHE, Chief Executive Officer
COO: Victor Rosenbaum, Chief Operating Officer
CFO: Lynn Kennington, Chief Financial Officer
CMO: David Cadogan, Chief Medical Officer
CIO: Gene Kaplanis, Director Information Technology
CHR: Tammy Kaminski, Director Human Resources
CNO: Linda Doughty, Chief Nursing Officer
Web address: www.alaskaregional.com
Control: Corporation, Investor–owned, for–profit **Service:** General Medical and Surgical

Staffed Beds: 132

✠ **NORTH STAR BEHAVIORAL HEALTH SYSTEM (024001)**, 2530 DeBarr Circle, Zip 99508–2948; tel. 907/258–7575, (Includes NORTH STAR BEHAVIORAL HEALTH, 1650 South Bragaw, Zip 99508–3467; tel. 907/258–7575) **A**1 5 9 10 **F**98 99 106 130 **S** Universal Health Services, Inc., King of Prussia, PA
Primary Contact: Andrew Mayo, M.D., Chief Executive Officer and Managing Director
CFO: Alan Barnes, Chief Financial Officer
CMO: Ruth Dukoff, M.D., Medical Director
CIO: Brian O'Connell, Director Information Services
CHR: Sabrina Ben, Director Human Resources
CNO: Brandy Proctor, Director of Nursing
Web address: www.northstarbehavioral.com
Control: Corporation, Investor–owned, for–profit **Service:** Children's hospital psychiatric

Staffed Beds: 200 **Admissions:** 1142 **Census:** 175 **Outpatient Visits:** 0 **Births:** 0 **Total Expense ($000):** 29618 **Payroll Expense ($000):** 17257 **Personnel:** 268

✠ **PROVIDENCE ALASKA MEDICAL CENTER (020001)**, 3200 Providence Drive, Zip 99508–4615, Mailing Address: P.O. Box 196604, Zip 99519–6604; tel. 907/562–2211, (Includes CHILDREN'S HOSPITAL AT PROVIDENCE, 3200 Providence Drive, Zip 99508; tel. 907/212–3130), (Nonreporting) **A**1 2 9 10 13 **S** Providence Health & Services, Renton, WA
Primary Contact: Bruce Lamoureux, Vice President and Chief Executive Officer
CFO: Anthony Dorsch, Chief Financial Officer
CMO: Roy Davis, Chief Medical Officer
CIO: Stephanie Morton, Chief Information Officer
CHR: Scott Jungwirth, Chief Human Resources Officer
Web address: www.providence.org/alaska/pamc/default.htm
Control: Church–operated, Nongovernment, not–for profit **Service:** General Medical and Surgical

Staffed Beds: 368

✠ **ST. ELIAS SPECIALTY HOSPITAL (022001)**, 4800 Cordova Street, Zip 99503–7218; tel. 907/561–3333, (Nonreporting) **A**1 9 10
Primary Contact: Sharon H. Kurz, Ph.D., Chief Executive Officer
Web address: www.st–eliashospital.com
Control: Other not–for–profit (including NFP Corporation) **Service:** Long–Term Acute Care hospital

Staffed Beds: 45

BARROW—North Slope Division

✠ **SAMUEL SIMMONDS MEMORIAL HOSPITAL (021312)**, 7000 Uulu Street, Zip 99723, Mailing Address: P.O. Box 29, Zip 99723–0029; tel. 907/852–4611 **A**1 9 10 18 **F**29 30 38 39 40 68 76 89 93 97 107 110 119 130
Primary Contact: Jeffrey Prater, Chief Executive Officer
CMO: Devon Allen, M.D., Chief of Medical Staff
CNO: Donna Patterson, Director of Nursing
Web address: www.arcticslope.org
Control: Other not–for–profit (including NFP Corporation) **Service:** General Medical and Surgical

Staffed Beds: 14 **Admissions:** 215 **Census:** 2 **Outpatient Visits:** 34799 **Births:** 23

BETHEL—Bethel Division

✠ **YUKON–KUSKOKWIM DELTA REGIONAL HOSPITAL (020018)**, 700 Chief Eddie Hoffman Highway, Zip 99559–3000, Mailing Address: P.O. Box 528, Zip 99559–0528; tel. 907/543–6300, (Nonreporting) **A**1 10
Primary Contact: Gene Peltola, President and Chief Executive Officer
CFO: Vanetta Van Cleave, Chief Financial Officer
CIO: William Pearch, Chief Information Officer
Web address: www.ykhc.org
Control: Other not–for–profit (including NFP Corporation) **Service:** General Medical and Surgical

Staffed Beds: 37

CORDOVA—Valdez–Cordova Division

★ **CORDOVA COMMUNITY MEDICAL CENTER (021307)**, 602 Chase Avenue, Zip 99574, Mailing Address: P.O. Box 160, Zip 99574–0160; tel. 907/424–8000, (Nonreporting) **A**9 10 18
Primary Contact: Theresa Carte, Ph.D., Administrator and Chief Executive Officer
CFO: Tiffany G. Varnadoe, Director Finance
CMO: James Dudley, M.D., Medical Director
CHR: Tim James, Coordinator Human Resources
Web address: www.cdvcmc.com
Control: City–Government, nonfederal **Service:** General Medical and Surgical

Staffed Beds: 23

DILLINGHAM—Dillingham Division

✠ **BRISTOL BAY AREA HEALTH CORPORATION (021309)**, 6000 Kanakanak Road, Zip 99576, Mailing Address: P.O. Box 130, Zip 99576–0130; tel. 907/842–5201, (Nonreporting) **A**1 5 9 10 18
Primary Contact: Robert J. Clark, President and Chief Executive Officer
COO: Lucrecia Scotford, Executive Vice President and Chief Operations Officer
CFO: David Morgan, Vice President and Chief Financial Officer
CMO: Arnold Loera, M.D., Clinical Director
CIO: Bill Wilcox, Chief Information Technology Officer
CHR: John Davis, Chief Human Resources Officer
CNO: Starla Fox, Manager Nursing Services Division
Web address: www.bbahc.org
Control: Other not–for–profit (including NFP Corporation) **Service:** General Medical and Surgical

Staffed Beds: 15

ELMENDORF AFB—Anchorage Division

✠ **U. S. AIR FORCE REGIONAL HOSPITAL**, 5955 Zeamer Avenue, Zip 99506–3702; tel. 907/580–3006, (Nonreporting) **A**1 5 **S** Department of the Air Force, Washington, DC
Primary Contact: Colonel Scott Suckow, Commander
COO: Colonel Rebecca Seese, Chief Operating Officer
CFO: Major Felicia Burks, Chief Financial Officer
CMO: Colonel Marriner Oldham, M.D., Chief Medical Officer
CIO: Major Phillip Oliphant, Chief Information Officer
CHR: Mark Clark, Human Resources Liaison
Web address: www.elmendorf.af.mil/
Control: Air Force, Government, federal **Service:** General Medical and Surgical

Staffed Beds: 64

Many Facility Codes have changed. Please refer to the AHA Guide Code Chart. © 2014 AHA Guide

FAIRBANKS—Fairbanks North Star Division

☒ **FAIRBANKS MEMORIAL HOSPITAL (020012)**, 1650 Cowles Street, Zip 99701–5998; tel. 907/452–8181, (Total facility includes 90 beds in nursing home–type unit) **A**1 2 9 10 19 20 **F**3 13 15 18 20 22 28 29 30 34 35 40 45 48 50 51 57 60 62 63 64 67 68 70 74 75 77 78 79 81 82 85 86 87 89 93 96 98 100 101 103 107 108 110 111 114 115 119 120 121 126 128 129 130 132 146 148 **S** Banner Health, Phoenix, AZ
Primary Contact: Michael K. Powers, FACHE, Chief Executive Officer
CFO: Jim Lynch, Chief Financial Officer
CMO: Gregory Johnson, D.D.S., Medical Director
CIO: Carl J. Kegley, System Director Information Technology
CHR: Carol Barnett, Chief Human Resources Officer
CNO: Gena Edmiston, R.N., Chief Nursing Officer
Web address: www.bannerhealth.com/locations/alaska/fairbanks+memorial+Hospital
Control: Other not–for–profit (including NFP Corporation) **Service:** General Medical and Surgical

Staffed Beds: 217 **Admissions:** 5137 **Census:** 128 **Outpatient Visits:** 314245 **Births:** 1164 **Total Expense ($000):** 209350 **Payroll Expense ($000):** 81309 **Personnel:** 998

FORT WAINWRIGHT—Fairbanks North Star Division

☒ **BASSETT ARMY COMMUNITY HOSPITAL**, 1060 Gaffney Road, Box 7400, Zip 99703–5001, Mailing Address: 1060 Gaffney Road, Box 7440, Zip 99703–5001; tel. 907/361–4000, (Nonreporting) **A**1 **S** Department of the Army, Office of the Surgeon General, Falls Church, VA
Primary Contact: Timothy Bergeron, Deputy Commander, Administration
CMO: Colonel Leo Bennett, M.D., Deputy Commander Clinical Services
CHR: Terri Morefield, Deputy Chief Human Resources Division
Web address: www.alaska.amedd.army.mil
Control: Army, Government, federal **Service:** General Medical and Surgical

Staffed Beds: 24

HOMER—Kenai Peninsula Division

★ **SOUTH PENINSULA HOSPITAL (021313)**, 4300 Bartlett Street, Zip 99603–7000; tel. 907/235–8101, (Total facility includes 28 beds in nursing home–type unit) **A**9 10 18 **F**3 11 13 15 29 30 31 34 35 40 45 50 51 56 59 62 64 67 68 70 75 76 77 78 79 81 85 87 93 94 97 107 110 111 115 119 128 129 130 133 146 148 **P**8
Primary Contact: Robert F. Letson, FACHE, Chief Executive Officer
CFO: Lori Meyer, Interim Chief Financial Officer
CMO: Hal Smith, M.D., Chief of Staff
CIO: Jim Bartilson, Manager Information Systems
CHR: Cindy H. Brinkerhoff, Director Human Resources
CNO: Shara Sutherlin, R.N., Director Patient Care Services
Web address: www.sphosp.com
Control: Hospital district or authority, Government, nonfederal **Service:** General Medical and Surgical

Staffed Beds: 50 **Admissions:** 870 **Census:** 33 **Outpatient Visits:** 46231 **Births:** 122 **Total Expense ($000):** 49342 **Payroll Expense ($000):** 21551 **Personnel:** 317

JUNEAU—Juneau Division

☒ **BARTLETT REGIONAL HOSPITAL (020008)**, 3260 Hospital Drive, Zip 99801–7808; tel. 907/796–8900 **A**1 9 10 20 **F**4 5 13 15 28 29 30 31 34 40 43 57 59 70 76 77 81 85 86 91 93 98 99 100 102 104 105 107 108 110 111 114 115 119 120 129 130 135 148 **P**6
Primary Contact: Charles E. Bill, Chief Executive Officer
CFO: Alan Germany, Interim Chief Financial Officer
CMO: Amy Dressel, M.D., Chief of Staff
CIO: Martha Palicka, Interim Manager Information Systems
CHR: Mila Cosgrove, Manager Human Resources
CNO: William Gardner, Chief Nursing Officer
Web address: www.bartletthospital.org
Control: City–Government, nonfederal **Service:** General Medical and Surgical

Staffed Beds: 45 **Admissions:** 2152 **Census:** 25 **Outpatient Visits:** 44336 **Births:** 379 **Total Expense ($000):** 85817 **Payroll Expense ($000):** 33660 **Personnel:** 404

KETCHIKAN—Ketchikan Gateway Division

★ ◇ **PEACEHEALTH KETCHIKAN MEDICAL CENTER (021311)**, 3100 Tongass Avenue, Zip 99901–5746; tel. 907/225–5171, (Total facility includes 25 beds in nursing home–type unit) **A**9 10 18 21 **F**15 18 30 31 34 40 43 45 46 53 57 59 62 63 64 65 68 75 76 77 79 81 84 85 93 94 100 104 107 108 110 111 115 118 128 129 130 131 146 147 148 **P**6 **S** PeaceHealth, Vancouver, WA
Primary Contact: Ken Tonjes, Interim Chief Administrative Officer
CFO: Ken Tonjes, Chief Financial Officer
CMO: Peter Rice, M.D., Medical Director
CIO: Tim Walker, Manager Information Services
CHR: Lanetta Lundberg, Vice President Culture and People
Web address: www.peacehealth.org
Control: Church–operated, Nongovernment, not–for profit **Service:** General Medical and Surgical

Staffed Beds: 50 **Admissions:** 1366 **Census:** 30 **Outpatient Visits:** 34846 **Births:** 223 **Total Expense ($000):** 61824 **Payroll Expense ($000):** 27145 **Personnel:** 409

KODIAK—Kodiak Island Division

☒ **PROVIDENCE KODIAK ISLAND MEDICAL CENTER (021306)**, 1915 East Rezanof Drive, Zip 99615–6602; tel. 907/486–3281, (Total facility includes 19 beds in nursing home–type unit) **A**1 9 10 18 **F**3 11 12 13 15 29 30 31 32 34 35 38 40 44 45 46 50 59 63 64 66 67 68 70 75 76 77 78 79 81 84 85 87 90 92 93 98 99 100 101 102 103 104 105 107 110 111 114 119 128 129 130 132 133 146 148 **S** Providence Health & Services, Renton, WA
Primary Contact: Donald J. Rush, Chief Executive Officer
COO: Brenda Zawacki, Chief Operating Manager
CFO: Timothy Hocum, Chief Financial Officer
CMO: Steve Smith, M.D., Chief of Staff
CIO: David Johnson, Manager Information Services
CNO: LeeAnn Horn, Chief Nurse Executive
Web address: www.providence.org
Control: Other not–for–profit (including NFP Corporation) **Service:** General Medical and Surgical

Staffed Beds: 25 **Admissions:** 736 **Census:** 22 **Outpatient Visits:** 23731 **Births:** 173 **Total Expense ($000):** 35091 **Payroll Expense ($000):** 17860 **Personnel:** 253

KOTZEBUE—Northwest Arctic Division

☐ **MANIILAQ HEALTH CENTER (021310)**, 436 5th Avenue, Zip 99752–0043, Mailing Address: P.O. Box 43, Zip 99752–0043; tel. 907/442–7344, (Total facility includes 4 beds in nursing home–type unit) **A**1 5 9 10 18 **F**3 13 29 34 39 40 41 45 46 50 57 59 65 69 75 76 80 107 119 128 130 135 147
Primary Contact: Paul Hansen, Administrator
COO: Timothy Schuerch, President and Chief Executive Officer
CFO: Lucy Nelson, Director Finance, Vice President
CMO: Patricia Clancy, M.D., Director Medical Services
CIO: Eugene Smith, Chief Information Officer
CHR: Gerty Gallaham, Director Human Resources
CNO: Donna K. Biagioni, R.N., Director of Nursing
Web address: www.maniilaq.org
Control: PHS, Indian Service, Government, federal **Service:** General Medical and Surgical

Staffed Beds: 17 **Admissions:** 682 **Census:** 6 **Births:** 47

NOME—Nome Division

☒ **NORTON SOUND REGIONAL HOSPITAL (021308)**, Bering Straits, Zip 99762, Mailing Address: P.O. Box 966, Zip 99762–0966; tel. 907/443–3311, (Nonreporting) **A**1 5 9 10 18
Primary Contact: Angela Gorn, Vice President
COO: Roy Agloinga, Chief Administrative Officer
CMO: David Head, M.D., Chief Medical Staff
CIO: Dan Bailey, Director Information Systems
CHR: Tiffany Martinson, Director Human Resources
Web address: www.nortonsoundhealth.org
Control: Other not–for–profit (including NFP Corporation) **Service:** General Medical and Surgical

Staffed Beds: 36

Hospital, Medicare Provider Number, Address, Telephone, Approval, Facility, and Physician Codes, Health Care System

★ American Hospital Association (AHA) membership
☐ The Joint Commission accreditation
◇ DNV Healthcare Inc. accreditation
○ Healthcare Facilities Accreditation Program
△ Commission on Accreditation of Rehabilitation Facilities (CARF) accreditation

AK

PALMER—Matanuska–Susitna Division

✠ **MAT–SU REGIONAL MEDICAL CENTER (020006)**, 2500 South Woodworth Loop, Zip 99645–8984, Mailing Address: P.O. Box 1687, Zip 99645–1687; tel. 907/861–6000 **A**1 9 10 20 **F**3 8 13 15 18 19 20 22 26 28 29 30 31 34 35 39 40 45 46 47 50 51 54 57 59 64 65 68 70 74 75 76 77 78 79 81 85 86 87 93 97 99 107 108 110 111 114 115 119 124 126 128 129 130 132 133 135 144 146 148 **P**5 6 **S** Community Health Systems, Inc., Franklin, TN
Primary Contact: John R. Lee, Chief Executive Officer
CMO: Christopher Sahlstrom, M.D., Chief of Staff
CIO: Bryan Meurer, Director Information Systems
CHR: Cathy Babuscio, Director Human Resources
CNO: Emily Stevens, Chief Nursing Officer
Web address: www.matsuregional.com
Control: Partnership, Investor–owned, for–profit **Service:** General Medical and Surgical

> **Staffed Beds:** 74 **Admissions:** 4415 **Census:** 42 **Outpatient Visits:** 82404
> **Births:** 736 **Total Expense ($000):** 106524 **Payroll Expense ($000):** 42325
> **Personnel:** 447

PETERSBURG—Wrangell–Petersburg Division

★ **PETERSBURG MEDICAL CENTER (021304)**, 103 Fram Street, Zip 99833, Mailing Address: Box 589, Zip 99833–0589; tel. 907/772–4291, (Total facility includes 15 beds in nursing home–type unit) **A**9 10 18 **F**15 31 34 40 45 57 59 62 64 67 79 81 84 85 93 97 107 114 119 133 146 148
Primary Contact: Elizabeth Woodyard, R.N., MSN, Chief Executive Officer
CFO: Leon Walsh, Chief Financial Officer
CHR: Cynthia Newman, Manager Human Resources
CNO: Jennifer Bryner, Chief Nursing Officer
Web address: www.pmc–health.com
Control: City–County, Government, nonfederal **Service:** General Medical and Surgical

> **Staffed Beds:** 27 **Admissions:** 158 **Census:** 21 **Outpatient Visits:** 9395
> **Births:** 1 **Total Expense ($000):** 12948 **Payroll Expense ($000):** 6131
> **Personnel:** 99

SEWARD—Kenai Peninsula Division

★ **PROVIDENCE SEWARD MEDICAL CENTER (021302)**, 417 First Avenue, Zip 99664, Mailing Address: P.O. Box 365, Zip 99664–0365; tel. 907/224–5205, (Total facility includes 40 beds in nursing home–type unit) **A**9 10 18 **F**3 29 30 40 43 64 93 107 114 119 128 133 146 148 **S** Providence Health & Services, Renton, WA
Primary Contact: Joseph Fong, Administrator
Web address: www.providence.org
Control: Church–operated, Nongovernment, not–for profit **Service:** General Medical and Surgical

> **Staffed Beds:** 46 **Admissions:** 116 **Census:** 36 **Outpatient Visits:** 28428
> **Births:** 1 **Total Expense ($000):** 16113 **Payroll Expense ($000):** 9217

SITKA—Sitka Division

✠ **SEARHC MT. EDGECUMBE HOSPITAL (020027)**, 222 Tongass Drive, Zip 99835–9416; tel. 907/966–2411 **A**1 5 9 10 **F**3 5 8 13 15 28 29 30 34 39 40 43 44 45 46 50 53 54 58 59 61 64 65 66 70 74 75 76 81 87 93 97 99 104 107 110 111 119 130 131 132 **P**6
Primary Contact: Daniel P. Neumeister, Administrator
COO: Daniel P. Neumeister, Chief Operating Officer
CFO: Barbara Searls, Chief Financial Officer
CMO: Elliot Bruhl, M.D., Medical Director
CIO: Bob Cita, Director Information Services
CHR: Alicia Gassman, Director Human Resources
CNO: Brad Langdorf, R.N., Chief Nursing Officer
Web address: www.searhc.org
Control: Other not–for–profit (including NFP Corporation) **Service:** General Medical and Surgical

> **Staffed Beds:** 27 **Admissions:** 994 **Census:** 9 **Outpatient Visits:** 20453
> **Births:** 64

★ **SITKA COMMUNITY HOSPITAL (021303)**, 209 Moller Avenue, Zip 99835–7142; tel. 907/747–3241, (Nonreporting) **A**9 10 18
Primary Contact: Hugh R. Hallgren, Chief Executive Officer
CFO: Lee W. Bennett, Chief Financial Officer
CHR: Kelley Fink, Coordinator Human Resources
Web address: www.sitkahospital.org
Control: City–Government, nonfederal **Service:** General Medical and Surgical

> **Staffed Beds:** 27

SOLDOTNA—Kenai Peninsula Division

✠ **CENTRAL PENINSULA GENERAL HOSPITAL (020024)**, 250 Hospital Place, Zip 99669–6999; tel. 907/714–4404, (Total facility includes 58 beds in nursing home–type unit) **A**1 9 10 20 **F**3 4 5 11 13 15 28 29 30 31 34 35 36 38 40 45 46 47 48 49 53 57 59 65 68 70 74 75 76 77 78 79 81 82 84 85 86 87 93 97 99 100 102 103 104 105 106 107 108 111 114 119 128 129 130 131 132 133 134 135 145 146 147 148 **P**1
Primary Contact: Richard Davis, Chief Executive Officer
COO: Matt Dammeyer, Ph.D., Chief Operating Officer
CFO: Shaun Keef, Chief Financial Officer
CMO: Gregg Motonaga, M.D., Chief of Staff
CIO: Bryan Downs, Director Information Systems
CHR: John Dodd, Vice President Human Resources
Web address: www.cpgh.org
Control: Other not–for–profit (including NFP Corporation) **Service:** General Medical and Surgical

> **Staffed Beds:** 117 **Admissions:** 2951 **Census:** 76 **Outpatient Visits:** 84606
> **Births:** 459 **Total Expense ($000):** 111425 **Payroll Expense ($000):** 49283
> **Personnel:** 651

VALDEZ—Valdez–Cordova Division

★ **PROVIDENCE VALDEZ MEDICAL CENTER (021301)**, 911 Meals Avenue, Zip 99686–0550, Mailing Address: P.O. Box 550, Zip 99686–0550; tel. 907/835–2249, (Nonreporting) **A**9 10 18 **S** Providence Health & Services, Renton, WA
Primary Contact: Barbara Bigelow, Administrator
CFO: Jeremy O'Neil, Manager Finance
CMO: John Cullen, M.D., Chief of Staff and Medical Director Long Term Care
CHR: Maureen Radotich, Director Human Resources
Web address: www.providence.org/alaska
Control: City–Government, nonfederal **Service:** General Medical and Surgical

> **Staffed Beds:** 21

WRANGELL—Wrangell–Petersburg Division

★ **WRANGELL MEDICAL CENTER (021305)**, First Avenue & Bennett Street, Zip 99929, Mailing Address: P.O. Box 1081, Zip 99929–1081; tel. 907/874–7000, (Total facility includes 12 beds in nursing home–type unit) **A**9 10 18 **F**3 11 15 29 31 34 35 40 50 57 59 64 65 67 68 75 81 85 86 93 102 107 110 114 119 130 133 148
Primary Contact: Marla I. Sanger, R.N., Chief Executive Officer
CFO: Dana Strong, Chief Financial Officer
CIO: Cathy Gross, Director Health Information Management Systems
Web address: www.wrangellmedicalcenter.com
Control: City–County, Government, nonfederal **Service:** General Medical and Surgical

> **Staffed Beds:** 22 **Admissions:** 157 **Census:** 14 **Outpatient Visits:** 11538
> **Births:** 0 **Total Expense ($000):** 9502 **Payroll Expense ($000):** 3412
> **Personnel:** 56

Many Facility Codes have changed. Please refer to the AHA Guide Code Chart. © 2014 AHA Guide

ARIZONA

APACHE JUNCTION—Pinal County

☒ **BANNER GOLDFIELD MEDICAL CENTER (030134)**, 2050 West Southern Avenue, Zip 85120–7305; tel. 480/733–3300 **A**1 10 **F**3 13 18 29 30 34 36 40 41 44 45 47 49 50 61 68 70 75 77 79 81 82 85 86 87 91 92 100 102 107 111 114 119 130 132 135 136 141 142 145 146 147 148 **S** Banner Health, Phoenix, AZ
Primary Contact: Julie Nunley, R.N., Chief Executive Officer
CFO: Tracy French, Chief Financial Officer
CMO: Devin Minior, M.D., Interim Chief Medical Officer
CHR: Janine Polito, Chief Human Resources Officer
CNO: Terri Paulus, Chief Nursing Officer
Web address: www.bannerhealth.com/Locations/Arizona/Banner+Goldfield+Medical+Center/_Welcome+to+Banner+Goldfield.htm
Control: Other not–for–profit (including NFP Corporation) **Service:** General Medical and Surgical

Staffed Beds: 30 **Admissions:** 242 **Census:** 2 **Total Expense ($000):** 9258 **Payroll Expense ($000):** 4876 **Personnel:** 103

BENSON—Cochise County

BENSON HOSPITAL (031301), 450 South Ocotillo Street, Zip 85602–6403, Mailing Address: P.O. Box 2290, Zip 85602–2290; tel. 520/586–2261 **A**9 10 18 **F**3 11 29 30 34 40 43 50 57 59 64 75 77 87 107 114 119 132 133 146 148
Primary Contact: Richard Polheber, Chief Executive Officer
CFO: Ken Goranson, Chief Financial Officer
CIO: Rob Roberts, Director Information Technology
CHR: Isabel Dominguez, Director Human Resources
Web address: www.bensonhospital.org
Control: Other not–for–profit (including NFP Corporation) **Service:** General Medical and Surgical

Staffed Beds: 22 **Admissions:** 342 **Census:** 3 **Outpatient Visits:** 14878 **Births:** 2 **Total Expense ($000):** 12856 **Payroll Expense ($000):** 6090 **Personnel:** 126

BISBEE—Cochise County

★ **COPPER QUEEN COMMUNITY HOSPITAL (031312)**, 101 Cole Avenue, Zip 85603–1399; tel. 520/432–5383 **A**9 10 18 **F**3 11 15 18 29 40 43 45 46 62 74 75 77 81 85 107 110 114 119 127 130 133 135 147
Primary Contact: James J. Dickson, Administrator and Chief Executive Officer
CFO: James Ehasz, Chief Financial Officer
CMO: Heidi Lodge, Chief of Staff
CIO: David Chmura, Manager Management Information Systems
CHR: Virginia Martinez, Manager Human Resources
CNO: Linda Morin, Director of Nursing
Web address: www.cqch.org
Control: Other not–for–profit (including NFP Corporation) **Service:** General Medical and Surgical

Staffed Beds: 14 **Admissions:** 368 **Census:** 4 **Outpatient Visits:** 36039 **Births:** 0 **Total Expense ($000):** 20618 **Payroll Expense ($000):** 10789 **Personnel:** 161

BULLHEAD CITY—Mohave County

☒ **WESTERN ARIZONA REGIONAL MEDICAL CENTER (030101)**, 2735 Silver Creek Road, Zip 86442–8303; tel. 928/763–2273, (Nonreporting) **A**1 9 10 19 **S** Community Health Systems, Inc., Franklin, TN
Primary Contact: Alex Villa, Chief Executive Officer
Web address: www.warmc.com
Control: Corporation, Investor–owned, for–profit **Service:** General Medical and Surgical

Staffed Beds: 139

CASA GRANDE—Pinal County

★ ◇ **BANNER CASA GRANDE MEDICAL CENTER (030016)**, 1800 East Florence Boulevard, Zip 85122–5399; tel. 520/381–6300 **A**9 10 21 **F**11 13 15 18 20 22 28 29 30 31 34 40 45 46 49 50 57 59 60 68 70 74 75 76 78 79 81 85 87 89 93 98 103 107 108 110 111 112 115 116 117 118 119 129 130 132 144 146 147 148
Primary Contact: Rona Curphy, President and Chief Executive Officer
CFO: Karen Francis, Chief Financial Officer
CMO: Richard Stubbs, M.D., Vice President Medical Affairs
CIO: Walter Chisenski, Director Information Technology
CHR: Carol D'Souza, Director Human Resources
CNO: Cheryse Austin, Vice President Patient Care Services and Chief Nursing Officer
Web address: www.casagrandehospital.com
Control: Other not–for–profit (including NFP Corporation) **Service:** General Medical and Surgical

Staffed Beds: 187 **Admissions:** 7680 **Census:** 88 **Births:** 721 **Total Expense ($000):** 110895 **Payroll Expense ($000):** 50093 **Personnel:** 750

CHANDLER—Maricopa County

☐ **ARIZONA ORTHOPEDIC SURGICAL HOSPITAL (030112)**, 2905 West Warner Road, Zip 85224–1674; tel. 480/603–9000 **A**1 9 10 **F**8 29 64 79 81 85 111 **S** United Surgical Partners International, Addison, TX
Primary Contact: Duane Scholer, Chief Executive Officer
Web address: www.azosh.com
Control: Corporation, Investor–owned, for–profit **Service:** Orthopedic

Staffed Beds: 24 **Admissions:** 797 **Census:** 6 **Births:** 0 **Total Expense ($000):** 20011 **Payroll Expense ($000):** 5420 **Personnel:** 73

☒ **CHANDLER REGIONAL MEDICAL CENTER (030036)**, 1955 West Frye Road, Zip 85224–6282; tel. 480/728–3000 **A**1 9 10 19 **F**3 8 11 13 15 17 18 20 22 24 26 28 29 30 31 32 34 35 37 40 41 42 44 45 46 47 48 49 50 51 54 57 58 59 60 63 64 65 66 68 70 71 72 73 74 75 76 77 78 79 81 82 84 85 86 87 93 96 100 103 107 108 110 111 114 115 119 126 130 131 132 135 143 144 146 147 148 **P**6 **S** Dignity Health, San Francisco, CA
Primary Contact: Tim Bricker, President and Chief Executive Officer
COO: Peter Menor, Vice President Operations
CFO: Mark Kem, Vice President Finance and Chief Financial Officer
CMO: Terry J. Happel, M.D., Vice President and Chief Medical Officer
CHR: Renea Brunke, Vice President Human Resources
CNO: Peg Smith, Vice President and Chief Nursing Officer
Web address: www.chandlerregional.com
Control: Other not–for–profit (including NFP Corporation) **Service:** General Medical and Surgical

Staffed Beds: 243 **Admissions:** 17978 **Census:** 187 **Outpatient Visits:** 161416 **Births:** 3691 **Total Expense ($000):** 298698 **Payroll Expense ($000):** 123569 **Personnel:** 1671

CHINLE—Apache County

☒ **CHINLE COMPREHENSIVE HEALTH CARE FACILITY (030084)**, Highway 191, Zip 86503, Mailing Address: P.O. Drawer PH, Zip 86503–8000; tel. 928/674–7011, (Nonreporting) **A**1 9 10 **S** U. S. Indian Health Service, Rockville, MD
Primary Contact: Ronald Tso, Chief Executive Officer
COO: Shirley Lewis, Administrative Officer
CFO: Philene Tyler, Chief Finance Officer
CMO: Kevin Rand, M.D., Clinical Director
CIO: Perry Francis, Supervisory Information Technology Specialist
CHR: Lorraine Smith, Supervisory Human Resource Specialist
CNO: Patricia Gorman, Chief Nurse Executive
Web address: www.ihs.gov
Control: PHS, Indian Service, Government, federal **Service:** General Medical and Surgical

Staffed Beds: 60

Hospital, Medicare Provider Number, Address, Telephone, Approval, Facility, and Physician Codes, Health Care System

★ American Hospital Association (AHA) membership
☐ The Joint Commission accreditation   ◇ DNV Healthcare Inc. accreditation

○ Healthcare Facilities Accreditation Program
△ Commission on Accreditation of Rehabilitation Facilities (CARF) accreditation

AZ

COTTONWOOD—Yavapai County

★ ◇ **VERDE VALLEY MEDICAL CENTER (030007)**, 269 South Candy Lane, Zip 86326–4170; tel. 928/639–6000 **A**9 10 13 20 21 **F**3 8 11 13 15 18 19 20 22 28 29 30 31 32 34 35 36 40 44 46 47 48 49 50 53 57 59 60 64 68 70 74 75 76 77 78 79 81 82 85 86 87 89 93 98 100 101 102 103 107 108 110 111 114 115 118 119 120 121 123 129 130 131 132 135 143 145 146 147 148 **S** Northern Arizona Healthcare, Flagstaff, AZ
Primary Contact: Barbara Dember, President and Chief Executive Officer
CFO: Gregory Kuzma, Vice President and Chief Financial Officer
CMO: Harry Alberti, M.D., Chief Medical Officer and Vice President Medical Affairs
CIO: Marilynn Black, Chief Information Officer
CHR: Lori L. Jackson, Director Human Resources
CNO: Jennifer Brewer, R.N., Chief Nursing Officer and Vice President Nursing Services
Web address: www.nahealth.com
Control: Other not–for–profit (including NFP Corporation) **Service:** General Medical and Surgical

Staffed Beds: 110 **Admissions:** 4487 **Census:** 50 **Outpatient Visits:** 96982 **Births:** 597 **Total Expense ($000):** 130830 **Payroll Expense ($000):** 50750 **Personnel:** 674

DOUGLAS—Cochise County

SOUTHEAST ARIZONA MEDICAL CENTER (031303), 2174 Oak Avenue, Zip 85607–6003; tel. 520/364–7931, (Nonreporting) **A**9 10 18
Primary Contact: Annie Benson, Chief Executive Officer
CFO: Alvin Chilton, Chief Financial Officer
CMO: Christopher Spooner, M.D., Chief of Staff
CIO: Ann Bliss, Manager Computer Services
CHR: Roberta Berry, Manager Human Resources
Web address: www.samcdouglas.org
Control: Other not–for–profit (including NFP Corporation) **Service:** General Medical and Surgical

Staffed Beds: 25

FLAGSTAFF—Coconino County

★ ◇ **FLAGSTAFF MEDICAL CENTER (030023)**, 1200 North Beaver Street, Zip 86001–3118; tel. 928/779–3366 **A**9 10 19 20 21 **F**3 5 7 8 11 12 13 15 17 18 20 22 24 26 28 29 30 31 32 34 35 36 37 40 43 44 45 49 50 53 54 57 58 59 60 61 64 68 70 72 74 75 76 77 78 79 81 82 84 85 86 87 88 89 93 98 99 100 101 102 103 104 105 107 108 111 114 115 116 117 118 119 120 121 123 126 130 131 132 135 145 146 147 148 **S** Northern Arizona Healthcare, Flagstaff, AZ
Primary Contact: Irwin Bloom, President and Chief Executive Officer
CFO: Gregory Kuzma, Vice President and Chief Financial Officer
CMO: Steven Lewis, M.D., Senior Vice President and Chief Medical Officer
CIO: John Schofield, Chief Information Officer
CHR: Patricia Crofford, Vice President Human Resources
Web address: www.flagstaffmedicalcenter.com
Control: Other not–for–profit (including NFP Corporation) **Service:** General Medical and Surgical

Staffed Beds: 267 **Admissions:** 13751 **Census:** 170 **Outpatient Visits:** 67590 **Births:** 1287 **Total Expense ($000):** 318500 **Payroll Expense ($000):** 117760 **Personnel:** 1590

☐ **GUIDANCE CENTER (034023)**, 2187 North Vickey Street, Zip 86004–6121; tel. 928/527–1899, (Nonreporting) **A**1 10
Primary Contact: Karissa Nisted, Interim Chief Executive Officer
Web address: www.tgcaz.org
Control: Other not–for–profit (including NFP Corporation) **Service:** Psychiatric

Staffed Beds: 10

FLORENCE—Pinal County

◇ **FLORENCE HOSPITAL AT ANTHEM (030132)**, 4545 North Hunt Highway, Zip 85132–6937; tel. 520/868–3333, (Nonreporting) **A**10 21
Primary Contact: Arthur M. Doloresco, Chief Executive Officer
CFO: T. Patrick Clune, Chief Financial Officer
CNO: Kimberly Fawley, Chief Nursing Officer
Web address: www.fhanthem.com
Control: Partnership, Investor–owned, for–profit **Service:** General Medical and Surgical

Staffed Beds: 36

FORT DEFIANCE—Apache County

★ **TSEHOOTSOOI MEDICAL CENTER (030071)**, Highway 12 & Bonito Drive, Zip 86504, Mailing Address: P.O. Box 649, Zip 86504–0649; tel. 928/729–8000, (Nonreporting) **A**10 **S** U. S. Indian Health Service, Rockville, MD
Primary Contact: Leland Leonard, Ph.D., Chief Executive Officer
COO: Valonia Hardy, Chief Healthy Living Officer
CFO: Rachel Sorrell, Chief Financial Officer
CMO: Michael Tutt, M.D., Chief Medical Officer
CIO: Virgil Chavez, Director Information Technology
CHR: Vivian Santistevan, Chief Human Resources
CNO: Tori Davidson, R.N., Chief Nursing Officer
Web address: www.fdihb.org
Control: PHS, Indian Service, Government, federal **Service:** General Medical and Surgical

Staffed Beds: 39

FORT MOHAVE—Mohave County

⊞ **VALLEY VIEW MEDICAL CENTER (030117)**, 5330 South Highway 95, Zip 86426–9225; tel. 928/788–2273, (Nonreporting) **A**1 9 10 **S** LifePoint Hospitals, Inc., Brentwood, TN
Primary Contact: Richard G. Carter, Chief Executive Officer
CHR: Susan L. Scharles, Director Human Resources
Web address: www.valleyviewmedicalcenter.net
Control: Corporation, Investor–owned, for–profit **Service:** Other specialty

Staffed Beds: 66

GANADO—Apache County

⊞ **SAGE MEMORIAL HOSPITAL (031309)**, Highway 264, Zip 86505, Mailing Address: P.O. Box 457, Zip 86505–0457; tel. 928/755–4500 **A**1 9 10 18 **F**1 5 7 11 18 29 32 34 35 39 40 50 53 54 57 59 62 64 65 68 75 100 101 104 107 119 127 133 134 144
Primary Contact: Christi J. El–Meligi, R.N., Chief Executive Officer
COO: Netrisha Dalgai, Director of Operations
CFO: Michael Katigbak, Chief Financial Officer
CMO: Jeremy Wray, D.O., Medical Director
CIO: Michael Katigbak, Director Computer Services
CHR: Gary Pahe, Manager Human Resources
CNO: Ernasha McIntosh, Interim Director of Nursing
Web address: www.sagememorial.org
Control: Other not–for–profit (including NFP Corporation) **Service:** General Medical and Surgical

Staffed Beds: 25 **Admissions:** 381 **Census:** 5 **Total Expense ($000):** 32058 **Payroll Expense ($000):** 10281

GILBERT—Maricopa County

⊞ **BANNER GATEWAY MEDICAL CENTER (030122)**, 1900 North Higley Road, Zip 85234–1604; tel. 480/543–2000 **A**1 9 10 **F**3 12 13 15 29 30 31 34 35 36 40 45 46 47 48 49 50 54 55 57 58 59 60 64 68 70 75 76 77 78 79 80 81 82 84 85 86 87 92 97 100 107 108 109 110 111 114 115 116 117 118 119 120 121 123 124 126 130 131 132 133 135 136 146 147 148 **S** Banner Health, Phoenix, AZ
Primary Contact: Todd S. Werner, Chief Executive Officer
CFO: Claire Agnew, Chief Financial Officer
CMO: David Edwards, M.D., Chief Medical Officer
CHR: Amber R. Kovacs, Chief Human Resources Officer
Web address: www.bannerhealth.com/Locations/Arizona/Banner+Gateway+Medical+Center/
Control: Other not–for–profit (including NFP Corporation) **Service:** General Medical and Surgical

Staffed Beds: 177 **Admissions:** 13607 **Census:** 127 **Births:** 4141 **Personnel:** 1380

GILBERT HOSPITAL (030120), 5656 South Power Road, Zip 85295–8487; tel. 480/984–2000 **A**9 10 **F**3 29 34 40 41 45 49 50 59 70 79 81 82 87 107 108 111 114 119
Primary Contact: Bryan J. Hargis, FACHE, Chief Executive Officer
CFO: Dennis E. Rutherford, CPA, Chief Financial Officer
CMO: Timothy Johns, M.D., Chief Medical Officer
CIO: Michelle Cianfrani, Director Information Technology
CNO: Marla Meggars, R.N., Chief Nursing Officer
Web address: www.gilberter.com
Control: Corporation, Investor–owned, for–profit **Service:** General Medical and Surgical

Staffed Beds: 19 **Admissions:** 680 **Census:** 6

Many Facility Codes have changed. Please refer to the AHA Guide Code Chart. © 2014 AHA Guide

⊠ **MERCY GILBERT MEDICAL CENTER (030119)**, 3555 South Val Vista Road, Zip 85297–7323; tel. 480/728–8000 **A**1 9 10 19 **F**3 8 11 13 15 18 20 22 26 28 29 30 31 32 34 35 37 38 40 41 42 44 45 46 47 48 49 50 51 57 58 59 60 63 64 65 66 68 70 73 74 75 76 77 78 79 81 82 83 84 85 86 87 96 99 100 101 102 103 107 108 110 111 114 115 119 126 129 130 132 135 144 145 146 148 **P**6 **S** Dignity Health, San Francisco, CA
Primary Contact: Tim Bricker, President and Chief Executive Officer
COO: Jane E. Hanson, R.N., Chief Operating Officer
CFO: Chuck Sowers, Vice President Finance and Chief Financial Officer
CMO: Phil Fracica, M.D., Vice President and Chief Medical Officer
CIO: Larissa Spraker, Vice President Business Development and Chief Strategy Officer
CHR: Anita Harger, Director Human Resources
CNO: Julie Hoffman, Vice President Patient Care Services and Chief Nursing Officer
Web address: www.mercygilbert.org
Control: Other not–for–profit (including NFP Corporation) **Service:** General Medical and Surgical

Staffed Beds: 212 **Admissions:** 12992 **Census:** 125 **Outpatient Visits:** 90839 **Births:** 2877 **Total Expense ($000):** 206568 **Payroll Expense ($000):** 80582 **Personnel:** 1139

GLENDALE—Maricopa County

⊠ **ARROWHEAD HOSPITAL (030094)**, 18701 North 67th Avenue, Zip 85308–7100; tel. 623/561–1000 **A**1 9 10 **F**3 11 13 15 17 18 20 22 24 26 28 29 30 31 34 35 37 40 41 42 44 47 48 49 57 59 64 70 72 74 75 76 77 78 79 81 85 87 107 108 110 111 113 118 119 130 146 148 **S** TENET Healthcare Corporation, Dallas, TX
Primary Contact: Frank L. Molinaro, Chief Executive Officer
CMO: Patrick Smith, M.D., Chief Medical Officer
CHR: Sharon M. Chadwick, Director Human Resources
Web address: www.arrowheadhospital.com
Control: Corporation, Investor–owned, for–profit **Service:** General Medical and Surgical

Staffed Beds: 234 **Admissions:** 11299 **Census:** 111 **Births:** 3049 **Total Expense ($000):** 133273 **Payroll Expense ($000):** 60570

☐ **AURORA PHOENIX HOSPITAL (034024)**, 6015 West Peoria Avenue, Zip 85302–1213; tel. 623/344–4400 **A**1 9 10 **F**4 5 29 50 68 87 98 99 100 101 103 104 105 130 133 **S** Aurora Behavioral Health Care, Corona, CA
Primary Contact: Bruce Waldo, Chief Executive Officer
CFO: Rebekah Francis, JD, Chief Financial Officer
CHR: Vicki Thomsen, Director Human Resources
CNO: Lori Milus, R.N., Director of Nursing
Web address: www.aurorabehavioral.com
Control: Corporation, Investor–owned, for–profit **Service:** Psychiatric

Staffed Beds: 90 **Admissions:** 3738 **Census:** 76 **Births:** 0

⊠ **BANNER THUNDERBIRD MEDICAL CENTER (030089)**, 5555 West Thunderbird Road, Zip 85306–4696; tel. 602/865–5555, (Includes BANNER BEHAVIORAL HEALTH CENTER–THUNDERBIRD CAMPUS, 5555 West Thunderbird Road, Zip 85306; tel. 602/588–5555) **A**1 9 10 **F**3 5 13 15 17 18 19 20 22 24 26 28 29 30 31 34 35 36 37 38 40 41 43 44 45 46 49 50 51 59 60 61 64 68 70 72 73 74 75 76 77 78 79 80 81 82 85 86 87 88 89 90 91 92 93 94 96 98 100 101 102 104 105 107 108 110 111 114 115 116 117 118 119 120 121 123 124 126 130 131 132 134 135 145 146 147 148 **S** Banner Health, Phoenix, AZ
Primary Contact: Thomas C. Dickson, Chief Executive Officer
CFO: Richard Miller, Administrator Finance
CMO: Kathryn Perkins, M.D., Chief Medical Officer
CHR: Laura Witt, Administrator Human Resources
Web address: www.bannerhealth.com/Locations/Arizona/Banner+Thunderbird+Medical+Center/
Control: Other not–for–profit (including NFP Corporation) **Service:** General Medical and Surgical

Staffed Beds: 476 **Admissions:** 32651 **Census:** 378 **Births:** 5123 **Total Expense ($000):** 419925 **Payroll Expense ($000):** 154528 **Personnel:** 2640

⊠ **HEALTHSOUTH VALLEY OF THE SUN REHABILITATION HOSPITAL (033032)**, 13460 North 67th Avenue, Zip 85304–1042; tel. 623/878–8800 **A**1 9 10 **F**29 62 64 75 90 93 132 **S** HEALTHSOUTH Corporation, Birmingham, AL
Primary Contact: Beth Bacher, Chief Executive Officer
CFO: Kathryn Haney, Controller
CMO: Michael Kravetz, M.D., Medical Director
CHR: Danette Garcia, Director Human Resources
CNO: Kathy Rupp, R.N., Chief Nursing Officer
Web address: www.healthsouthvalleyofthesun.com
Control: Corporation, Investor–owned, for–profit **Service:** Rehabilitation

Staffed Beds: 75 **Admissions:** 1323 **Census:** 50 **Outpatient Visits:** 13283 **Births:** 0 **Total Expense ($000):** 20397 **Payroll Expense ($000):** 11673 **Personnel:** 157

GLOBE—Gila County

COBRE VALLEY COMMUNITY HOSPITAL See Cobre Valley Regional Medical Center

★ **COBRE VALLEY REGIONAL MEDICAL CENTER (031314)**, 5880 South Hospital Drive, Zip 85501–9454; tel. 928/425–3261 **A**9 10 18 **F**3 11 12 13 15 18 29 30 34 35 40 43 45 46 49 51 57 59 64 70 74 75 76 78 79 81 82 87 92 93 97 107 108 110 111 115 117 118 119 127 128 129 130 133 135 146 147 148 **P**5 **S** HealthTech Management Services, Brentwood, TN
Primary Contact: Neal Jensen, Chief Executive Officer
CFO: James R. Childers, Chief Financial Officer
CIO: Sharon Bennett, Manager Information Systems
CHR: Rita Murphy, Director Human Resources
Web address: www.cvrmc.org
Control: Other not–for–profit (including NFP Corporation) **Service:** General Medical and Surgical

Staffed Beds: 25 **Admissions:** 1757 **Census:** 16 **Outpatient Visits:** 49705 **Births:** 286 **Total Expense ($000):** 36471 **Payroll Expense ($000):** 15949 **Personnel:** 245

GOODYEAR—Maricopa County

⊠ **WEST VALLEY HOSPITAL (030110)**, 13677 West McDowell Road, Zip 85395–2635; tel. 623/882–1500, (Nonreporting) **A**1 9 10 **S** TENET Healthcare Corporation, Dallas, TX
Primary Contact: Stan V. Holm, FACHE, Chief Executive Officer
CFO: Richard Franco, Chief Financial Officer
CMO: Ron Kenneth, M.D., Chief Medical Officer
Web address: www.wvhospital.com
Control: Corporation, Investor–owned, for–profit **Service:** General Medical and Surgical

Staffed Beds: 106

☐ **WESTERN REGIONAL MEDICAL CENTER (030127)**, 14200 West Celebrate Life way, Zip 85338–3005; tel. 623/207–3000, (Nonreporting) **A**1 **S** Cancer Treatment Centers of America, Schaumburg, IL
Primary Contact: Matthew McGuire, President and Chief Executive Officer
Web address: www.cancercenter.com/western–hospital.cfm
Control: Corporation, Investor–owned, for–profit **Service:** Cancer

Staffed Beds: 24

KEAMS CANYON—Navajo County

⊠ **HOPI HEALTH CARE CENTER (031305)**, Highway 264 Mile Marker 388, Zip 86042, Mailing Address: P.O. Box 4000, Polacca, Zip 86042–4000; tel. 928/737–6000, (Nonreporting) **A**1 10 18 **S** U. S. Indian Health Service, Rockville, MD
Primary Contact: De Alva Honahnie, Chief Executive Officer
COO: Leonard H. Lopez, Chief Operating Officer
CFO: Dorothy Sulu, Budget Analyst
CMO: Darren Vicenti, M.D., Clinical Director
CHR: Trudy Begay, Human Resources Specialist
CNO: Melissa Wyaco, Chief Nurse Executive
Web address: www.ihs.gov/index.asp
Control: PHS, Indian Service, Government, federal **Service:** General Medical and Surgical

Staffed Beds: 15

KINGMAN—Mohave County

★ ◇ **KINGMAN REGIONAL MEDICAL CENTER (030055)**, 3269 Stockton Hill Road, Zip 86409–3691; tel. 928/757–2101 **A**9 10 13 19 20 21 **F**3 11 13 15 17 18 22 24 28 29 30 31 34 35 40 42 43 49 51 53 57 59 60 62 63 64 70 74 75 76 77 78 79 81 82 84 85 86 87 89 90 93 97 104 105 107 108 110 111 114 115 116 117 118 119 121 123 127 129 130 132 135 143 144 146 147 148 **P**6 7
Primary Contact: Brian Turney, Chief Executive Officer
COO: Ryan Kennedy, Chief Operating Officer
CFO: Timothy D. Blanchard, Chief Financial Officer
CMO: Thomas Gaughan, M.D., Chief Medical Officer
CIO: Robert (Bob) Sarnecki, Chief Information Officer
CHR: Heather N. Crowl, Chief Human Resources Officer
CNO: Kimberly Miyauchi, R.N., Chief Nursing Officer
Web address: www.azkrmc.com
Control: Hospital district or authority, Government, nonfederal **Service:** General Medical and Surgical

Staffed Beds: 180 **Admissions:** 9204 **Census:** 116 **Outpatient Visits:** 385163 **Births:** 690 **Total Expense ($000):** 224503 **Payroll Expense ($000):** 96512 **Personnel:** 1562

Hospital, Medicare Provider Number, Address, Telephone, Approval, Facility, and Physician Codes, Health Care System

★ American Hospital Association (AHA) membership
☐ The Joint Commission accreditation   ◇ DNV Healthcare Inc. accreditation
○ Healthcare Facilities Accreditation Program
△ Commission on Accreditation of Rehabilitation Facilities (CARF) accreditation

LAKE HAVASU CITY—Mohave County

✠ **HAVASU REGIONAL MEDICAL CENTER (030069)**, 101 Civic Center Lane, Zip 86403–5683; tel. 928/855–8185, (Nonreporting) **A**1 9 10 19 20 **S** LifePoint Hospitals, Inc., Brentwood, TN
Primary Contact: F. Dana Ellerbe, Chief Executive Officer
CFO: Christopher Flores, Chief Financial Officer
CMO: Michael Rosen, M.D., Chief Medical Officer
CIO: Linda Toy, Director Information Systems
CNO: Julie Bowman, Chief Nursing Officer
Web address: www.havasuregional.com
Control: Corporation, Investor–owned, for–profit **Service:** General Medical and Surgical

Staffed Beds: 138

LAKESIDE—Navajo County

☐ **CCC AT PINEVIEW HOSPITAL (034027)**, 1920 West Commerce Drive, Zip 85929; tel. 928/368–4110, (Nonreporting) **A**1 9 10
Primary Contact: Michelle Witt, Administrator
Web address: www.ccc–az.org
Control: Other not–for–profit (including NFP Corporation) **Service:** Psychiatric

Staffed Beds: 16

MESA—Maricopa County

☐ **ARIZONA SPINE AND JOINT HOSPITAL (030107)**, 4620 East Baseline Road, Zip 85206–4624; tel. 480/832–4770 **A**1 9 10 **F**3 29 79 81 82 85 131 **S** National Surgical Hospitals, Chicago, IL
Primary Contact: Chris Hill, Chief Executive Officer
CHR: Diane Hearne, Director Human Resources
CNO: Stacy Hayes, R.N., Chief Nursing Officer
Web address: www.azspineandjoint.com
Control: Corporation, Investor–owned, for–profit **Service:** Orthopedic

Staffed Beds: 23 Admissions: 751 Census: 4 Births: 0

✠ **BANNER BAYWOOD MEDICAL CENTER (030088)**, 6644 East Baywood Avenue, Zip 85206–1797; tel. 480/321–2000 **A**1 9 10 **F**3 13 15 18 29 30 31 34 36 37 40 41 44 45 47 48 49 50 51 56 57 59 60 61 64 68 70 74 75 76 77 78 79 80 81 82 84 85 86 87 90 91 92 94 96 100 102 103 107 108 110 111 113 114 118 119 126 129 130 132 135 136 146 147 148 **P**8 **S** Banner Health, Phoenix, AZ
Primary Contact: Laura Robertson, R.N., Chief Executive Officer
CFO: Stanley Adams, Chief Financial Officer
CMO: Larry Spratling, M.D., Chief Medical Officer
CIO: Janice Hoppe, Vice President Information Technology System
CHR: Pam Cannon, Chief Human Resources Officer
CNO: Cynthia Helmich, R.N., Chief Nursing Officer
Web address: www.bannerhealth.com/locations/Arizona/banner+baywood+medical+center
Control: Other not–for–profit (including NFP Corporation) **Service:** General Medical and Surgical

Staffed Beds: 388 Admissions: 19385 Census: 231 Births: 721 Total Expense ($000): 227925 Payroll Expense ($000): 86240 Personnel: 1525

BANNER CHILDREN'S HOSPITAL See Cardon Children's Medical Center

✠ **BANNER DESERT MEDICAL CENTER (030065)**, 1400 South Dobson Road, Zip 85202–4707; tel. 480/412–3000, (Includes CARDON CHILDREN'S MEDICAL CENTER, 1400 South Dobson Road, tel. 480/412–3000; Rhonda Anderson, R.N., FACHE, Chief Executive Officer; SAMARITAN BEHAVIORAL HEALTH CENTER–DESERT SAMARITAN MEDICAL CENTER, 2225 West Southern Avenue, Zip 85202; tel. 602/464–4000) **A**1 3 5 9 10 **F**3 13 18 19 20 21 22 23 24 25 26 27 28 29 30 31 32 34 36 37 40 41 44 45 46 47 48 49 50 51 57 58 59 60 61 64 68 70 72 74 75 76 77 78 81 84 85 86 87 88 89 91 92 93 96 100 102 107 108 111 114 115 117 118 119 121 123 124 126 129 130 131 132 135 146 148 **S** Banner Health, Phoenix, AZ
Primary Contact: Robert Gould, Chief Executive Officer
CFO: Clifford Loader, Chief Financial Officer
CMO: Marjorie Bessel, M.D., Chief Medical Officer
CIO: Stacey Hinkle, Director Information Technology
CHR: Kevin McVeigh, Chief Human Resources Officer
Web address: www.bannerhealth.com/Locations/Arizona/Banner+Desert+Medical+Center
Control: Other not–for–profit (including NFP Corporation) **Service:** General Medical and Surgical

Staffed Beds: 549 Admissions: 33894 Census: 383 Births: 5022 Total Expense ($000): 497023 Payroll Expense ($000): 177076 Personnel: 3000

✠ **BANNER HEART HOSPITAL (030105)**, 6750 East Baywood Avenue, Zip 85206–1749; tel. 480/854–5000 **A**1 9 10 **F**3 17 18 20 22 24 26 28 29 30 34 36 44 45 50 51 56 57 59 60 61 64 68 74 75 77 78 81 82 84 85 86 87 92 94 100 103 113 119 126 130 132 135 146 147 148 **S** Banner Health, Phoenix, AZ
Primary Contact: Laura Robertson, R.N., Chief Executive Officer
CFO: Stanley Adams, Chief Financial Officer
CMO: Mark Starling, M.D., Chief Medical Officer
CIO: Janice Hoppe, Vice President, Information Technology System
CHR: Pam Cannon, Chief Human Resources Officer
CNO: Cynthia Helmich, R.N., Chief Nursing Officer
Web address: www.bannerhealth.com/Locations/Arizona/Banner+Heart+Hospital/
Control: Other not–for–profit (including NFP Corporation) **Service:** Heart

Staffed Beds: 111 Admissions: 5500 Census: 58 Births: 0 Total Expense ($000): 100075 Payroll Expense ($000): 25063 Personnel: 408

CARDON CHILDREN'S MEDICAL CENTER See Banner Desert Medical Center

✠ **HEALTHSOUTH EAST VALLEY REHABILITATION HOSPITAL (033037)**, 5652 East Baseline Road, Zip 85206–4713; tel. 480/567–0350 **A**1 9 10 **F**28 29 64 74 75 77 79 82 90 91 93 94 95 96 130 132 148 **S** HEALTHSOUTH Corporation, Birmingham, AL
Primary Contact: Larry Niemann, Chief Executive Officer
CMO: Martin Yee, M.D., Medical Director
CHR: Nancy Pickler, Director of Human Resources
CNO: Hope Dunn, Chief Nursing Officer
Web address: www.healthsoutheastvalley.com
Control: Corporation, Investor–owned, for–profit **Service:** Rehabilitation

Staffed Beds: 60 Admissions: 1147 Census: 43 Outpatient Visits: 4391 Births: 0 Personnel: 153

★ ◇ **MOUNTAIN VISTA MEDICAL CENTER (030121)**, 1301 South Crismon Road, Zip 85209–3767; tel. 480/358–6100, (Nonreporting) **A**9 10 21 **S** IASIS Healthcare, Franklin, TN
Primary Contact: Anthony Marinello, Chief Executive Officer
CNO: Bill Southwick, R.N., Chief Nursing Officer
Web address: www.mvmedicalcenter.com
Control: Corporation, Investor–owned, for–profit **Service:** General Medical and Surgical

Staffed Beds: 172

PROMISE HOSPITAL OF PHOENIX (032006), 433 East 6th Street, Zip 85203–7104; tel. 480/427–3000, (Nonreporting) **A**10 **S** Promise Healthcare, Boca Raton, FL
Primary Contact: Scott Floden, Chief Executive Officer
COO: Wendy Larson, Chief Clinical Officer
CFO: Theo Clark, Director Financial Services
CMO: Syed Shahryar, M.D., Medical Director
CHR: Christie Brea, Manager Human Resources
Web address: www.promise–phoenix.com
Control: Corporation, Investor–owned, for–profit **Service:** Long–Term Acute Care hospital

Staffed Beds: 40

RESTORA HOSPITAL OF MESA (032007), 215 South Power Road, Zip 85206–5235; tel. 480/985–6992, (Nonreporting) **A**10 **S** Restora Healthcare, Alpharetta, GA
Primary Contact: Judith Schiros, Chief Executive Officer
Web address: www.restorahealthcare.com
Control: Corporation, Investor–owned, for–profit **Service:** Long–Term Acute Care hospital

Staffed Beds: 120

SAMARITAN BEHAVIORAL HEALTH CENTER–DESERT SAMARITAN MEDICAL CENTER See Banner Desert Medical Center

TRILLIUM SPECIALTY HOSPITAL–EAST VALLEY See Restora Hospital of Mesa

NOGALES—Santa Cruz County

✠ **CARONDELET HOLY CROSS HOSPITAL (031313)**, 1171 West Target Range Road, Zip 85621–2415; tel. 520/285–3000 **A**1 9 10 18 **F**11 13 29 30 32 34 35 40 50 51 56 57 59 60 63 64 68 70 75 76 77 79 81 84 86 87 89 93 102 107 111 119 130 132 133 134 135 146 **S** Ascension Health, Saint Louis, MO
Primary Contact: Debbie Knapheide, MSN, Site Administrator, Chief Nursing Officer and Chief Operating Officer
COO: Debbie Knapheide, MSN, Site Administrator, Chief Nursing Officer and Chief Operating Officer
CFO: Alan Strauss, Chief Financial Officer
CMO: Roy Farrell, M.D., Chief Medical Officer
CHR: Igor Shegolev, Interim Director
CNO: Debbie Knapheide, MSN, Site Administrator, Chief Nursing Officer and Chief Operating Officer
Web address: www.carondelet.org
Control: Church–operated, Nongovernment, not–for profit **Service:** General Medical and Surgical

Staffed Beds: 25 Admissions: 1337 Census: 8 Outpatient Visits: 34937 Births: 726 Total Expense ($000): 23040 Payroll Expense ($000): 9507 Personnel: 145

AZ

ORO VALLEY—Pima County

⊞ **ORO VALLEY HOSPITAL (030114)**, 1551 East Tangerine Road,
Zip 85755–6213; tel. 520/901–3500 **A**1 9 10 **F**3 15 17 18 20 22 27 29 30
34 35 40 48 49 50 51 59 60 70 74 79 81 85 87 90 91 93 107 108 110 111
114 115 119 129 144 146 147 **S** Community Health Systems, Inc., Franklin, TN
Primary Contact: Jae Dale, Chief Executive Officer
CFO: Mark Hoffman, Chief Financial Officer
CMO: Paul Bejarino, M.D., Chief of Staff
Web address: www.nmcorovalley.com
Control: Corporation, Investor–owned, for–profit **Service:** General Medical and
Surgical

Staffed Beds: 144 **Admissions:** 5198 **Census:** 53 **Total Expense ($000):**
89318 **Payroll Expense ($000):** 37529 **Personnel:** 579

PAGE—Coconino County

⊞ **PAGE HOSPITAL (031304)**, 501 North Navajo Drive, Zip 86040, Mailing
Address: P.O. Box 1447, Zip 86040–1447; tel. 928/645–2424 **A**1 9 10 18 **F**3
8 11 13 15 29 30 31 34 35 36 39 40 41 43 45 54 57 59 64 68 70 75 76 77
79 81 82 85 86 87 93 107 111 114 119 129 130 133 135 146 148 **S** Banner
Health, Phoenix, AZ
Primary Contact: Sandy Haryasz, R.N., Chief Executive Officer
CFO: Darcy Robertson, Chief Financial Officer
CMO: Thomas Wood, M.D., Chief Medical Officer
CIO: Paul Caldwell, Facility Coordinator Information Technology Customer
Relations
CHR: Ed Franklin, Chief Human Resources Officer
CNO: Susan Eubanks, Chief Nursing Officer
Web address: www.bannerhealth.com/Locations/Arizona/Page+Hospital
Control: Other not–for–profit (including NFP Corporation) **Service:** General
Medical and Surgical

Staffed Beds: 25 **Admissions:** 501 **Census:** 3 **Births:** 202 **Total Expense**
($000): 11959 **Payroll Expense ($000):** 5342 **Personnel:** 94

PARKER—La Paz County

LA PAZ REGIONAL HOSPITAL (031317), 1200 West Mohave Road,
Zip 85344–6349; tel. 928/669–9201 **A**9 10 18 20 **F**3 11 15 18 20 22 26 28
29 34 35 39 40 45 46 50 51 53 57 59 65 66 68 70 75 78 79 81 82 85 87
90 93 97 102 107 110 111 114 115 119 127 130 132 133 135 144
146 148
Primary Contact: M. Victoria Clark, Chief Executive Officer
CFO: Steve Stewart, Chief Financial Officer
CMO: Jack Dunn, M.D., Chief of Staff
CHR: Regina M. Martinez, Director Human Resources
CNO: Bonnie Viloria, Chief Nursing Officer
Web address: www.lapazhospital.org
Control: Other not–for–profit (including NFP Corporation) **Service:** General
Medical and Surgical

Staffed Beds: 25 **Admissions:** 569 **Census:** 6 **Outpatient Visits:** 27539
Births: 0 **Total Expense ($000):** 22599 **Payroll Expense ($000):** 9315
Personnel: 180

⊞ **U. S. PUBLIC HEALTH SERVICE INDIAN HOSPITAL (031307)**, 12033 Agency
Road, Zip 85344–7718; tel. 928/669–2137, (Nonreporting) **A**1 9 10 18 **S** U. S.
Indian Health Service, Rockville, MD
Primary Contact: Dee Hutchison, Chief Executive Officer
CFO: Robin Tahbo, Financial Management Officer
CMO: Laurence Norick, M.D., Clinical Director
CIO: JayLynn Saavedra, Chief Information Officer
Web address: www.ihs.gov
Control: Public Health Service, Government, federal **Service:** General Medical
and Surgical

Staffed Beds: 20

PAYSON—Gila County

⊞ **PAYSON REGIONAL MEDICAL CENTER (030033)**, 807 South Ponderosa
Street, Zip 85541–5599; tel. 928/474–3222 **A**1 9 10 20 **F**13 15 18 29 30 35
37 40 51 70 75 76 77 78 79 81 82 85 86 87 91 93 96 97 107 110 111 113
119 132 146 147 148 **S** Community Health Systems, Inc., Franklin, TN
Primary Contact: Lance Porter, Chief Executive Officer
CFO: Peter Finelli, Chief Financial Officer
CMO: John Vandruff, M.D., Chief of Staff
CIO: Nick Vandermeer, Director Information Systems
CHR: Shawn M. Thomas, Director Human Resources
CNO: Hart Hintze, Chief Nursing Officer
Web address: www.paysonhospital.com
Control: Corporation, Investor–owned, for–profit **Service:** General Medical and
Surgical

Staffed Beds: 39 **Admissions:** 2034 **Census:** 16 **Births:** 154

PEORIA—Maricopa County

KINDRED HOSPITAL ARIZONA–NORTHWEST PHOENIX See Kindred Hospital
Arizona–Phoenix, Phoenix

PHOENIX—Maricopa County

☐ **ARIZONA STATE HOSPITAL (034021)**, 2500 East Van Buren Street,
Zip 85008–6079; tel. 602/244–1331 **A**1 10 **F**3 29 30 39 53 57 59 65 68 75
77 94 98 130 135 143 146 **P**6
Primary Contact: Ann M. Froio, Interim Chief Executive Officer
COO: Donna Noriega, Chief Operating Officer
CFO: Donna Noriega, Chief Operating Officer
CMO: Steve Dingle, M.D., Chief Medical Officer
CIO: Bruce Randolph, Chief Information Technology
CHR: Jeanine Decker, Manager Human Resources
Web address: www.hs.state.az.us
Control: State–Government, nonfederal **Service:** Psychiatric

Staffed Beds: 299 **Admissions:** 64 **Census:** 237 **Outpatient Visits:** 0 **Births:**
0 **Total Expense ($000):** 55242 **Payroll Expense ($000):** 27553
Personnel: 465

⊞ **BANNER ESTRELLA MEDICAL CENTER (030115)**, 9201 West Thomas Road,
Zip 85037–3332; tel. 623/327–4000 **A**1 9 10 **F**3 5 13 18 20 22 24 28 29 30
31 34 35 36 37 38 40 41 44 45 46 49 50 51 57 58 59 60 61 64 68 70 74
75 76 77 78 79 80 81 82 85 86 87 91 92 94 96 102 107 108 111 114 115
119 126 130 131 132 135 144 145 146 147 148 **S** Banner Health,
Phoenix, AZ
Primary Contact: Debra J. Krmpotic, R.N., Chief Executive Officer
COO: Gary Foster, R.N., Assistant Administrator
CFO: Dean Shepardson, Chief Financial Officer
CMO: Timothy Ranney, M.D., Chief Medical Officer
CHR: JoAnn Odell, Chief People Resource Officer
CNO: Nancy Adamson, R.N., Chief Nursing Officer
Web address: www.bannerhealth.com/Locations/Arizona/Banner+Estrella+
Medical+Center/
Control: Other not–for–profit (including NFP Corporation) **Service:** General
Medical and Surgical

Staffed Beds: 213 **Admissions:** 16442 **Census:** 156 **Births:** 4129 **Total**
Expense ($000): 216261 **Payroll Expense ($000):** 79960 **Personnel:** 1347

⊞ △ **BANNER GOOD SAMARITAN MEDICAL CENTER (030002)**, 1111 East
McDowell Road, Zip 85006–2666, Mailing Address: P.O. Box 2989,
Zip 85062–2989; tel. 602/239–2000 **A**1 2 3 5 7 8 9 10 **F**3 13 15 17 18 20
22 24 26 28 29 30 31 34 36 37 38 39 40 43 44 45 46 47 49 50 51 52 53
55 57 58 59 60 61 64 66 68 70 72 74 75 76 77 78 79 80 81 82 84 85 86
87 90 91 92 93 94 96 97 98 100 101 102 104 107 108 110 111 115 116
117 118 119 120 121 123 124 126 130 131 132 135 138 139 141 142 145
146 147 148 **S** Banner Health, Phoenix, AZ
Primary Contact: Steve Narang, M.D., Chief Executive Officer
CFO: Kathy Kotin, Chief Financial Officer
CMO: Paul Stander, M.D., Chief Medical Officer
CIO: Michael S. Warden, Senior Vice President Information Technology
CHR: Michael Fleming, Chief People Officer
Web address: www.bannerhealth.com/Locations/Arizona/Banner+Good+
Samaritan+Medical+Center
Control: Other not–for–profit (including NFP Corporation) **Service:** General
Medical and Surgical

Staffed Beds: 685 **Admissions:** 32104 **Census:** 437 **Births:** 5855 **Total**
Expense ($000): 658817 **Payroll Expense ($000):** 225656 **Personnel:**
3771

HAVEN SENIOR HORIZONS (034020), 1201 South 7th Avenue, Suite 200,
Zip 85007–4076; tel. 623/236–2000 **A**10 **F**42 56 68 98 100 101 102 103 **P**5
S Haven Behavioral Healthcare, Nashville, TN
Primary Contact: Kathy Shaw, Chief Executive Officer
CHR: Erin McEldowney, Manager Human Resources
CNO: Char Ralstin, Director of Nursing
Web address: www.havenbehavioral.com
Control: Corporation, Investor–owned, for–profit **Service:** Psychiatric

Staffed Beds: 30 **Admissions:** 741 **Census:** 25 **Outpatient Visits:** 0 **Births:**
0

Hospital, Medicare Provider Number, Address, Telephone, Approval, Facility, and Physician Codes, Health Care System

★ American Hospital Association (AHA) membership
☐ The Joint Commission accreditation
◇ DNV Healthcare Inc. accreditation
○ Healthcare Facilities Accreditation Program
△ Commission on Accreditation of Rehabilitation Facilities (CARF) accreditation

AZ

★ ○ ◇ **JOHN C. LINCOLN DEER VALLEY HOSPITAL (030092)**, 19829 North 27th Avenue, Zip 85027–4002; tel. 623/879–6100 **A**9 10 11 21 **F**3 8 15 17 18 20 22 24 26 28 29 31 34 35 40 41 43 45 46 49 50 54 55 57 58 59 60 64 70 74 75 77 78 79 81 85 87 89 92 107 108 111 114 115 118 119 126 130 132 145 146 147 148 **S** John C. Lincoln Health Network, Phoenix, AZ
Primary Contact: John L. Harrington, Jr., FACHE, Chief Executive Officer
CMO: Mary Ann Turley, D.O., Medical Director
CHR: Frank L. Cummins, Vice President Human Resources
CNO: Jessica Rivas, R.N., Vice President and Chief Nursing Officer
Web address: www.jcl.com
Control: Other not–for–profit (including NFP Corporation) **Service:** General Medical and Surgical

Staffed Beds: 204 **Admissions:** 12821 **Census:** 126 **Outpatient Visits:** 128327 **Births:** 0

★ **JOHN C. LINCOLN NORTH MOUNTAIN HOSPITAL (030014)**, 250 East Dunlap Avenue, Zip 85020–2825; tel. 602/943–2381 **A**9 10 **F**3 11 15 17 18 20 22 24 26 28 29 30 31 34 37 40 43 45 46 47 49 50 53 54 57 58 59 60 64 68 70 74 75 77 78 79 81 85 92 107 108 111 114 115 118 119 126 130 132 135 145 146 147 148 **S** John C. Lincoln Health Network, Phoenix, AZ
Primary Contact: Margaret Elizabeth Griffin, Chief Executive Officer
CFO: Todd La Porte, Chief Financial Officer
CMO: Christopher Shearer, M.D., Chief Medical Officer
CHR: Carol Henderson, Senior Vice President, Chief Talent Officer
CNO: Jelden Arcilla, R.N., Vice President and Chief Nursing Officer
Web address: www.jcl.com
Control: Other not–for–profit (including NFP Corporation) **Service:** General Medical and Surgical

Staffed Beds: 262 **Admissions:** 15957 **Census:** 196 **Outpatient Visits:** 93348 **Births:** 0

⊠ **KINDRED HOSPITAL ARIZONA–PHOENIX (032000)**, 40 East Indianola Avenue, Zip 85012–2059; tel. 602/280–7000, (Includes KINDRED HOSPITAL ARIZONA–NORTHWEST PHOENIX, 13216 North Plaza Del Rio Boulevard, Peoria, Zip 85381–4907; tel. 623/974–5463; Karen Shammas, Chief Executive Officer) **A**1 10 **F**1 3 17 29 30 40 47 60 75 85 119 148 **S** Kindred Healthcare, Louisville, KY
Primary Contact: Heidi Miller, Chief Executive Officer
Web address: www.khphoenix.com/
Control: Corporation, Investor–owned, for–profit **Service:** General Medical and Surgical

Staffed Beds: 58 **Admissions:** 234 **Census:** 24 **Births:** 0 **Total Expense ($000):** 19530 **Payroll Expense ($000):** 8945

LOS NINOS HOSPITAL (033301), 2303 East Thomas Road, Zip 85016–7827; tel. 602/954–7311, (Nonreporting) **A**10
Primary Contact: William Timmons, Chief Executive Officer
Web address: www.losninoshospital.com
Control: Other not–for–profit (including NFP Corporation) **Service:** Children's other specialty

Staffed Beds: 15

★ ◇ **MARICOPA INTEGRATED HEALTH SYSTEM (030022)**, 2601 East Roosevelt Street, Zip 85008–4956; tel. 602/344–5011, (Includes ARIZONA CHILDREN'S CENTER, 2601 East Roosevelt Street, Zip 85008–4973; tel. 602/344–5051) **A**3 5 8 9 10 21 **F**3 13 15 16 17 18 20 22 26 28 29 30 31 32 34 39 40 41 42 43 45 46 47 48 49 51 53 54 57 58 59 60 61 64 66 68 70 72 73 76 77 78 79 81 85 86 87 88 89 93 94 97 98 103 104 105 107 108 110 111 114 115 116 117 118 119 130 135 144 146 147 148 **P**1
Primary Contact: Stephen A. Purves, FACHE, President and Chief Executive Officer
COO: William F. Vanaskie, Executive Vice President and Chief Operating Officer
CFO: Michael Ayres, Senior Vice President and Chief Financial Officer
CMO: Robert Fromm, M.D., Chief Medical Officer
CIO: Kelly Summers, Chief Information Officer
CHR: Marshall Jones, Senior Vice President Human Resources
CNO: Sherry Stotler, R.N., Chief Nursing Officer
Web address: www.mihs.org
Control: Hospital district or authority, Government, nonfederal **Service:** General Medical and Surgical

Staffed Beds: 522 **Admissions:** 17295 **Census:** 367 **Outpatient Visits:** 390123 **Births:** 2522 **Total Expense ($000):** 509532 **Payroll Expense ($000):** 230296

⊠ **MARYVALE HOSPITAL MEDICAL CENTER (030001)**, 5102 West Campbell Avenue, Zip 85031–1799; tel. 623/848–5000 **A**1 9 10 **F**3 13 18 20 22 26 29 34 35 40 45 49 59 68 70 73 74 75 76 81 86 107 108 111 119 130 146 147 **S** TENET Healthcare Corporation, Dallas, TX
Primary Contact: Crystal Hamilton, R.N., Chief Executive Officer
CFO: Julie Hastings–Smith, Chief Financial Officer
CHR: Erin Gonzalez, Director Human Resources and Education
CNO: Scott Morey, Chief Nursing Officer
Web address: www.maryvalehospital.com
Control: Corporation, Investor–owned, for–profit **Service:** General Medical and Surgical

Staffed Beds: 100 **Admissions:** 4781 **Census:** 49 **Outpatient Visits:** 52973 **Births:** 442 **Total Expense ($000):** 51593 **Payroll Expense ($000):** 27515 **Personnel:** 367

⊠ **MAYO CLINIC HOSPITAL (030103)**, 5777 East Mayo Boulevard, Zip 85054–4502; tel. 480/515–6296 **A**1 2 3 5 8 9 10 **F**3 6 8 9 12 15 17 18 20 22 24 26 28 29 30 31 33 34 35 36 37 39 40 45 46 47 48 49 50 51 54 55 56 58 59 60 61 64 68 70 74 75 77 78 79 80 81 82 84 85 86 87 90 92 93 96 97 100 103 104 107 108 110 111 112 114 115 116 117 118 119 120 121 123 124 126 129 130 131 135 136 137 138 139 141 142 145 146 147 148 **P**6 **S** Mayo Clinic, Rochester, MN
Primary Contact: Ann M. Meyers, Hospital Administrator
COO: Kevin Paige, Chair, Practice Operations
CFO: Jeffrey R. Froisland, Chief Financial Officer
CMO: Jeff T. Mueller, M.D., Chief Medical Officer, Medical Director
CIO: Amy Z. Vrabel, Chief Information Officer
CHR: Nichelle A. Baker, Chair Human Resources
CNO: Teresa Connolly, MSN, Chief Nursing Officer
Web address: www.mayoclinic.org/arizona/
Control: Other not–for–profit (including NFP Corporation) **Service:** General Medical and Surgical

Staffed Beds: 268 **Admissions:** 12147 **Census:** 168 **Outpatient Visits:** 45444 **Births:** 0 **Total Expense ($000):** 394787 **Payroll Expense ($000):** 123267 **Personnel:** 3707

☐ **OASIS HOSPITAL (030131)**, 750 North 40th Street, Zip 85008–6486; tel. 602/797–7700, (Nonreporting) **A**1 9 10
Primary Contact: James Flinn, JD, FACHE, Chief Executive Officer
Web address: www.oasishospital.com
Control: Partnership, Investor–owned, for–profit **Service:** Orthopedic

Staffed Beds: 64

⊠ **PARADISE VALLEY HOSPITAL (030083)**, 3929 East Bell Road, Zip 85032–2196; tel. 602/923–5000, (Nonreporting) **A**1 9 10 **S** TENET Healthcare Corporation, Dallas, TX
Primary Contact: David Tupponce, M.D., Interim Chief Executive Officer
CFO: Jeffrey Zyla, Chief Financial Officer
CMO: David Tupponce, Chief Medical Officer
CHR: Erin Gonzalez, Director Human Resources
CNO: Vicki Lynn Huber, R.N., Chief Nursing Officer
Web address: www.paradisevalleyhospital.com
Control: Corporation, Investor–owned, for–profit **Service:** General Medical and Surgical

Staffed Beds: 142

★ **PHOENIX BAPTIST HOSPITAL (030030)**, 2000 West Bethany Home Road, Zip 85015–2443; tel. 602/249-0212, (Includes ARIZONA HEART HOSPITAL, 1930 East Thomas Road, Zip 85016; tel. 602/532–1000; Danny L. Jones, Jr., FACHE, Chief Executive Officer), (Nonreporting) **A**3 5 9 10 **S** TENET Healthcare Corporation, Dallas, TX
Primary Contact: Danny L. Jones, Jr., FACHE, Chief Executive Officer
COO: Chris Bird, Chief Operating Officer
CFO: Leanne Krush, Chief Financial Officer
CMO: Lynnette Watkins, M.D., Chief Medical Officer
CHR: Lois Dopler, Interim Director Human Resources
CNO: Lorna Maxson, R.N., Chief Nursing Officer
Web address: www.phoenixbaptisthospital.com
Control: Corporation, Investor–owned, for–profit **Service:** General Medical and Surgical

Staffed Beds: 215

⊠ **PHOENIX CHILDREN'S HOSPITAL (033302)**, 1919 East Thomas Road, Zip 85016–7710; tel. 602/546–1000 **A**1 3 5 9 10 **F**3 8 11 15 17 19 21 23 25 27 29 30 31 32 34 35 37 38 39 40 41 42 43 44 46 48 49 50 54 55 57 58 59 60 61 64 65 66 68 71 72 73 74 75 77 78 79 81 82 84 85 86 87 88 89 91 92 93 94 96 97 98 99 100 101 102 104 105 107 108 111 113 114 115 116 117 118 119 129 130 131 132 134 135 136 138 144 146 148 **P**6
Primary Contact: Robert L. Meyer, President and Chief Executive Officer
COO: Betsy Kuzas, Executive Vice President and Chief Operating Officer
CFO: Craig L. McKnight, Senior Vice President and Chief Financial Officer
CMO: Murray Pollack, M.D., Vice President and Chief Medical Officer
CIO: David Higginson, Senior Vice President and Chief Information Officer
CHR: Thomas Diederich, Senior Vice President Human Resources
CNO: Pam Carlson, Senior Vice President and Chief Nursing Officer
Web address: www.phoenixchildrens.com
Control: Other not–for–profit (including NFP Corporation) **Service:** Children's general

Staffed Beds: 363 **Admissions:** 12857 **Census:** 208 **Outpatient Visits:** 216121 **Births:** 0 **Total Expense ($000):** 626869 **Payroll Expense ($000):** 254026 **Personnel:** 3012

⊠ **PHOENIX VETERANS AFFAIRS HEALTH CARE SYSTEM**, 650 East Indian School Road, Zip 85012–1892; tel. 602/277–5551, (Nonreporting) **A**1 2 3 9 **S** Department of Veterans Affairs, Washington, DC
Primary Contact: Steven W. Young, Interim Director
CFO: Christine Hollingsworth, Chief Financial Officer
CMO: Raymond Chung, M.D., Chief of Staff
Web address: www.phoenix.va.gov/
Control: Veterans Affairs, Government, federal **Service:** General Medical and Surgical

Staffed Beds: 197

Many Facility Codes have changed. Please refer to the AHA Guide Code Chart. © 2014 AHA Guide

✠ **SELECT SPECIALTY HOSPITAL–PHOENIX (032001)**, 350 West Thomas Road, 3rd Floor Main, Zip 85013–4409; tel. 602/406–6802, (Nonreporting) **A**1 10 **S** Select Medical Corporation, Mechanicsburg, PA
Primary Contact: Sharon Anthony, Chief Executive Officer
Web address: www.selectspecialtyhospitals.com/company/locations/phoenix.aspx
Control: Corporation, Investor–owned, for–profit **Service:** Long–Term Acute Care hospital

Staffed Beds: 48

SELECT SPECIALTY HOSPITAL–PHOENIX DOWNTOWN See Select Specialty Hospital–Scottsdale, Scottsdale

✠ △ **ST. JOSEPH'S HOSPITAL AND MEDICAL CENTER (030024)**, 350 West Thomas Road, Zip 85013–4496, Mailing Address: P.O. Box 2071, Zip 85001–2071; tel. 602/406–3000, (Includes CHILDREN'S HEALTH CENTER, 350 West Thomas Road, Zip 85013–4409) **A**1 2 3 5 7 8 9 10 19 **F**3 6 11 12 13 15 17 18 20 22 24 25 29 30 31 34 35 40 43 45 46 47 48 49 51 53 55 56 57 58 59 64 66 68 70 71 72 73 74 75 76 77 78 79 81 82 83 84 85 86 87 90 91 92 93 94 96 97 100 101 102 103 104 107 108 110 111 114 115 118 119 121 123 124 126 130 131 140 141 146 147 148 **P**5 6 **S** Dignity Health, San Francisco, CA
Primary Contact: Patty White, R.N., MS, President
CFO: John Peters, Chief Financial Officer
CHR: Maureen Sterbach, Vice President Human Resources
CNO: Julie Ward, Chief Nursing Officer
Web address: www.stjosephs–phx.org
Control: Other not–for–profit (including NFP Corporation) **Service:** General Medical and Surgical

Staffed Beds: 586 Admissions: 30222 Census: 403 Outpatient Visits: 472684 Births: 4708 Total Expense ($000): 888665 Payroll Expense ($000): 350540 Personnel: 4265

☐ **ST. LUKE'S BEHAVIORAL HEALTH CENTER (034013)**, 1800 East Van Buren, Zip 85006–3742; tel. 602/251–8546, (Nonreporting) **A**1 9 10 **S** IASIS Healthcare, Franklin, TN
Primary Contact: Gregory L. Jahn, R.N., Chief Executive Officer
CFO: Ruby Majhail, Chief Financial Officer
CMO: Mario Tafur, M.D., Chief of Staff
CIO: Chris Ulrey, Director Management Information Systems
CHR: Amy M. Howell, Director Human Resources
Web address: www.iasishealthcare.com
Control: Corporation, Investor–owned, for–profit **Service:** Psychiatric

Staffed Beds: 85

★ ◇ **ST. LUKE'S MEDICAL CENTER (030037)**, 1800 East Van Buren Street, Zip 85006–3742; tel. 602/251–8100, (Includes TEMPE ST. LUKE'S HOSPITAL, 1500 South Mill Avenue, Tempe, Zip 85281–6699; tel. 480/784–5510; Dale Larson, Administrator), (Nonreporting) **A**9 10 21 **S** IASIS Healthcare, Franklin, TN
Primary Contact: Edward W. Myers, Chief Executive Officer
CFO: Ken Walsh, Chief Financial Officer
CHR: Trinise Thompson, Director Human Resources
Web address: www.stlukesmedcenter.com
Control: Corporation, Investor–owned, for–profit **Service:** General Medical and Surgical

Staffed Beds: 225

☐ **THE SURGICAL HOSPITAL OF PHOENIX (030108)**, 6501 North 19th Avenue, Zip 85015–1646; tel. 602/795–6020 **A**1 9 10 **F**12 29 45 49 70 81 107 111 114 119
Primary Contact: Karen Bonamase, R.N., Chief Executive Officer
CFO: Marcus Losada, Controller
CMO: Christopher A. Yeung, M.D., Chief of Staff
CHR: Deby Tooker, Director Human Resources
CNO: Deborah Roberts, R.N., Chief Nursing Officer
Web address: www.sshaz.com
Control: Corporation, Investor–owned, for–profit **Service:** Surgical

Staffed Beds: 33 Admissions: 1281 Census: 6 Births: 0 Total Expense ($000): 22541 Payroll Expense ($000): 6513 Personnel: 97

✠ **U. S. PUBLIC HEALTH SERVICE PHOENIX INDIAN MEDICAL CENTER (030078)**, 4212 North 16th Street, Zip 85016–5389; tel. 602/263–1200, (Nonreporting) **A**1 5 9 10 **S** U. S. Indian Health Service, Rockville, MD
Primary Contact: John Molina, M.D., JD, Chief Executive Officer
CFO: Geraldine Harney, Chief Financial Officer
CMO: Dave Civic, M.D., Associate Director Clinical Services
CIO: Vina Montour, Director Information Technology
CHR: Betty Weston, Chief Human Resources Officer
Web address: www.ihs.gov
Control: PHS, Indian Service, Government, federal **Service:** General Medical and Surgical

Staffed Beds: 127

☐ **VALLEY HOSPITAL PHOENIX (034026)**, 3550 East Pinchot Avenue, Zip 85018–7434; tel. 602/957–4000, (Nonreporting) **A**1 9 10 **S** Universal Health Services, Inc., King of Prussia, PA
Primary Contact: Michelle David, Chief Executive Officer
Web address: www.valleyhospital–phoenix.com
Control: Corporation, Investor–owned, for–profit **Service:** Psychiatric

Staffed Beds: 122

PRESCOTT—Yavapai County

✠ **NORTHERN ARIZONA VETERANS AFFAIRS HEALTH CARE SYSTEM**, 500 Highway 89 North, Zip 86313–5000; tel. 928/445–4860, (Nonreporting) **A**1 9 **S** Department of Veterans Affairs, Washington, DC
Primary Contact: Donna K. Jacobs, FACHE, Director
COO: James Belmont, Associate Director
CFO: Ame Callahan, Acting Manager Resource Management Service
CMO: A. Panneer Selvam, M.D., Chief of Staff
CIO: Scott McCrimmon, Manager Information Technology
CHR: Jane Lewerke, Manager Human Resources
CNO: Marianne Locke, R.N., Associate Director Patient Care Services
Web address: www.prescott.va.gov/
Control: Veterans Affairs, Government, federal **Service:** General Medical and Surgical

Staffed Beds: 151

★ **YAVAPAI REGIONAL MEDICAL CENTER (030012)**, 1003 Willow Creek Road, Zip 86301–1668; tel. 928/445–2700 **A**9 10 **F**3 11 15 17 18 20 22 24 28 29 30 31 32 34 35 40 45 46 50 53 54 57 59 60 64 68 70 74 75 77 78 79 81 82 84 85 86 87 91 93 107 108 111 114 118 119 130 131 132 135 146 148 **P**6
Primary Contact: John Amos, President and Chief Executive Officer
COO: Larry P. Burns, Jr., Chief Operating Officer
CFO: Brian Hoefle, Chief Financial Officer
CMO: Joseph Goldberger, M.D., Chief Medical Officer
CHR: Mark Timm, Director Human Resources
CNO: Diane Drexler, R.N., Chief Nursing Officer
Web address: www.yrmc.org
Control: Other not–for–profit (including NFP Corporation) **Service:** General Medical and Surgical

Staffed Beds: 134 Admissions: 6998 Census: 70 Outpatient Visits: 73441 Births: 0 Total Expense ($000): 167304 Payroll Expense ($000): 62244 Personnel: 955

PRESCOTT VALLEY—Yavapai County

☐ **MOUNTAIN VALLEY REGIONAL REHABILITATION HOSPITAL (033036)**, 3700 North Windsong Drive, Zip 86314–1253; tel. 928/759–8800, (Nonreporting) **A**1 9 10 **S** Ernest Health, Inc., Albuquerque, NM
Primary Contact: Judy Baum, Chief Executive Officer
Web address: www.mvrrh.ernesthealth.com
Control: Corporation, Investor–owned, for–profit **Service:** Rehabilitation

Staffed Beds: 16

WINDHAVEN PSYCHIATRIC HOSPITAL (034025), 3347 North Windsong Drive, Zip 86314–2283; tel. 928/445–5211 **A**9 10 **F**29 98 99 100 **P**6
Primary Contact: Larry D. Green, Jr., Chief Executive Officer
COO: Pamela Pierce, Chief Operating Officer
CFO: Doug Oliver, Chief Financial Officer
CMO: Lisa Parsons, M.D., Chief Medical Officer
CHR: Pamela Pierce, Chief Human Resource
Web address: www.wygc.org
Control: Other not–for–profit (including NFP Corporation) **Service:** Psychiatric

Staffed Beds: 16 Admissions: 758 Census: 14 Outpatient Visits: 0 Births: 0 Total Expense ($000): 3775 Payroll Expense ($000): 2035 Personnel: 31

★ **YAVAPAI REGIONAL MEDICAL CENTER – EAST (030118)**, 7700 East Florentine Road, Zip 86314–2245; tel. 928/445–2700 **A**9 10 **F**3 11 13 15 29 30 31 40 68 70 72 75 76 77 78 81 84 85 86 87 89 93 107 108 111 114 116 117 118 119 130 146 147 148
Primary Contact: John Amos, Chief Executive Officer
CFO: Brian Hoefle, Chief Financial Officer
CMO: Joseph Goldberger, M.D., Chief Medical Officer
CHR: Mark Timm, Director Human Resources
CNO: Diane Drexler, R.N., Chief Nursing Officer
Web address: www.yrmc.org
Control: Other not–for–profit (including NFP Corporation) **Service:** General Medical and Surgical

Staffed Beds: 72 Admissions: 4185 Census: 31 Outpatient Visits: 47459 Births: 1039 Total Expense ($000): 49784 Payroll Expense ($000): 24466 Personnel: 416

Hospital, Medicare Provider Number, Address, Telephone, Approval, Facility, and Physician Codes, Health Care System

★ American Hospital Association (AHA) membership
☐ The Joint Commission accreditation ◇ DNV Healthcare Inc. accreditation
○ Healthcare Facilities Accreditation Program
△ Commission on Accreditation of Rehabilitation Facilities (CARF) accreditation

AZ

SACATON—Pinal County

☒ **HUHUKAM MEMORIAL HOSPITAL (031308)**, 483 West Seed Farm Road, Zip 85147, Mailing Address: P.O. Box 38, Zip 85147–0001; tel. 602/528–1200, (Nonreporting) **A**1 9 10 18
Primary Contact: Richard Narcia, Chief Executive Officer
COO: Pamela Thompson, Chief Operations Officer
CMO: Noel Habib, M.D., Chief Medical Officer
CHR: Michael Freeman, Director Human Resources
Web address: www.grhc.org
Control: Other not-for-profit (including NFP Corporation) **Service:** General Medical and Surgical

Staffed Beds: 12

SAFFORD—Graham County

★ **MT. GRAHAM REGIONAL MEDICAL CENTER (030068)**, 1600 20th Avenue, Zip 85546–4097; tel. 928/348–4000 **A**9 10 20 **F**3 11 13 15 18 26 29 30 34 35 40 43 45 46 48 49 50 53 57 59 62 63 64 65 66 70 75 76 79 81 85 87 93 97 107 110 111 114 119 127 129 130 133 134 135 143 145 **P**6
Primary Contact: Mark E. Marchetti, Chief Executive Officer
CFO: Keith Bryce, Chief Financial Officer
CIO: Keith Bryce, Chief Financial Officer
CHR: Irvan Wick Lewis, Vice President Human Resources and Clinic Management
CNO: Lori Burress, Chief Nursing Officer
Web address: www.mtgraham.org
Control: Hospital district or authority, Government, nonfederal **Service:** General Medical and Surgical

Staffed Beds: 49 Admissions: 1902 Census: 11 Outpatient Visits: 156077 Births: 601 Total Expense ($000): 55487 Payroll Expense ($000): 24499 Personnel: 389

SAN CARLOS—Gila County

☒ **U. S. PUBLIC HEALTH SERVICE INDIAN HOSPITAL (030077)**, 238 Cibeque Circle, Zip 85550, Mailing Address: P.O. Box 208, Zip 85550–0208; tel. 928/475–2371, (Nonreporting) **A**1 10 **S** U. S. Indian Health Service, Rockville, MD
Primary Contact: Robert Harry, M.D., Chief Executive Officer
CFO: Vivie Hosteenez, Chief Financial Officer
CMO: Douglas Brinkerhoff, M.D., Clinical Director
CIO: Nimmy Mathews, Acting Director Quality Management
CHR: Shirley M. Boni, Administrative Officer
Web address: www.ihs.gov
Control: PHS, Indian Service, Government, federal **Service:** General Medical and Surgical

Staffed Beds: 8

SAN TAN VALLEY—Pinal County

☒ **BANNER IRONWOOD MEDICAL CENTER (030130)**, 37000 North Gantzel Road, Zip 85140–7303; tel. 480/394–4000 **A**1 9 10 **F**3 13 18 29 30 34 36 40 41 43 44 45 47 49 50 61 68 75 76 77 79 80 81 82 85 86 87 92 97 100 102 107 111 114 119 130 132 135 136 141 142 145 146 147 148 **S** Banner Health, Phoenix, AZ
Primary Contact: Julie Nunley, R.N., Chief Executive Officer
CFO: Tracy French, Chief Financial Officer
CMO: Darren West, M.D., Interim Chief Medical Officer
CHR: Janine Polito, Chief Human Resources Officer
CNO: Terri Paulus, Chief Nursing Officer
Web address: www.bannerhealth.com/Locations/Arizona/Banner+Ironwood/
Control: Other not-for-profit (including NFP Corporation) **Service:** General Medical and Surgical

Staffed Beds: 53 Admissions: 2516 Census: 19 Outpatient Visits: 30112 Births: 1030 Total Expense ($000): 57492 Payroll Expense ($000): 16770 Personnel: 290

SCOTTSDALE—Maricopa County

☒ **BANNER BEHAVIORAL HEALTH HOSPITAL – SCOTTSDALE (034004)**, 7575 East Earll Drive, Zip 85251–6915; tel. 480/941–7500 **A**1 9 10 **F**5 29 30 34 35 36 38 44 50 57 68 75 86 87 98 99 101 102 104 105 106 130 132 134 135 146 **P**5 **S** Banner Health, Phoenix, AZ
Primary Contact: Cherie Martin, R.N., MSN, FACHE, Chief Executive Officer
CFO: Michael A. Cimino, Jr., Chief Financial Officer
CMO: Clifford Zeller, M.D., Chief Medical Officer
CHR: Kevin McVeigh, Interim Chief Human Resources Officer
CNO: Cherri Anderson, Chief Nursing Officer
Web address: www.bannerhealth.com/Locations/Arizona/Banner+Behavioral+Health
Control: Other not-for-profit (including NFP Corporation) **Service:** Psychiatric

Staffed Beds: 95 Admissions: 4149 Census: 84 Births: 0 Total Expense ($000): 30966 Payroll Expense ($000): 15646 Personnel: 281

★ ◇ **FREEDOM PAIN HOSPITAL**, (Pain Specialty), 17500 North Perimeter Drive, Zip 85255–7808; tel. 480/586–2300 **A**21 **F**29 33 34 36 58 64 80 81 82 85 87
Primary Contact: Duane Bernard, President, Chief Financial Officer and Chief Operating Officer
COO: Duane Bernard, President, Chief Financial Officer and Chief Operating Officer
CFO: Duane Bernard, President, Chief Financial Officer and Chief Operating Officer
CMO: Natalie Shand, M.D., Vice President Integrative Medicine and Chief Medical Officer
CIO: Milad Najjar, Information Technology
CHR: Samantha Mendez, Human Resources
CNO: Jani Manseau, Vice President Operations and Chief Nursing Officer
Web address: www.freedompainhospital.com
Control: Corporation, Investor-owned, for-profit **Service:** Other specialty

Staffed Beds: 12 Admissions: 27 Census: 1 Outpatient Visits: 1661 Births: 0 Total Expense ($000): 9696 Payroll Expense ($000): 2245

☒ **HEALTHSOUTH SCOTTSDALE REHABILITATION HOSPITAL (033025)**, 9630 East Shea Boulevard, Zip 85260–6267; tel. 480/551–5400, (Nonreporting) **A**1 9 10 **S** HEALTHSOUTH Corporation, Birmingham, AL
Primary Contact: Timothy T. Poore, Chief Executive Officer
CFO: Lisa Barrick, Controller
CMO: Keith W. Cunningham, M.D., Medical Director
CHR: Mary Beth Giczi, Director Human Resources
CNO: Diane M. Caruso, MSN, Chief Nursing Officer
Web address: www.healthsouthscottsdale.com
Control: Corporation, Investor-owned, for-profit **Service:** Rehabilitation

Staffed Beds: 60

★ ◇ **SCOTTSDALE HEALTHCARE REHABILITATION HOSPITAL (033038)**, 8850 East Pima Center Parkway, Zip 85258–4619; tel. 480/800–3900, (Nonreporting) **A**10 11 **S** Select National Corporation, Mechanicsburg, PA
Primary Contact: Kelly Silberschlag, Chief Executive Officer
Web address: www.scottsdale–rehab.com/
Control: Partnership, Investor-owned, for-profit **Service:** Rehabilitation

Staffed Beds: 50

★ ◇ **SCOTTSDALE HEALTHCARE SHEA MEDICAL CENTER (030087)**, 9003 East Shea Boulevard, Zip 85260–6771; tel. 480/323–3000, (Nonreporting) **A**2 3 5 9 10 21 **S** Scottsdale Healthcare, Scottsdale, AZ
Primary Contact: Gary E. Baker, Senior Vice President and Chief Executive Officer
CFO: Todd La Porte, Senior Vice President and Chief Financial Officer
CMO: James Burke, M.D., Senior Vice President and Chief Medical Officer
CIO: James R. Cramer, Vice President and Chief Information Officer
CHR: Carol Henderson, Senior Vice President and Chief Talent Officer
CNO: Joanne T. Clavelle, R.N., Senior Vice President and Chief Clinical Officer
Web address: www.shc.org
Control: Other not-for-profit (including NFP Corporation) **Service:** General Medical and Surgical

Staffed Beds: 409

★ ◇ **SCOTTSDALE HEALTHCARE THOMPSON PEAK HOSPITAL (030123)**, 7400 East Thompson Peak Parkway, Zip 85255–4109; tel. 480/324–7000, (Nonreporting) **A**9 10 21 **S** Scottsdale Healthcare, Scottsdale, AZ
Primary Contact: Kimberly Post, R.N., Vice President and Administrator
CFO: Todd La Porte, Chief Financial Officer
CMO: James Burke, M.D., Senior Vice President and Chief Medical Officer
CIO: James R. Cramer, Chief Information Officer
CHR: Carol Henderson, Vice President Human Resources
Web address: www.shc.org
Control: Other not-for-profit (including NFP Corporation) **Service:** General Medical and Surgical

Staffed Beds: 64

★ ◇ **SCOTTSDALE HEALTHCARE–OSBORN MEDICAL CENTER (030038)**, 7400 East Osborn Road, Zip 85251–6403; tel. 480/882–4000, (Nonreporting) **A**2 3 5 8 9 10 21 **S** Scottsdale Healthcare, Scottsdale, AZ
Primary Contact: Gary E. Baker, Senior Vice President and Administrator
CFO: Todd La Porte, Senior Vice President and Chief Financial Officer
CMO: James Burke, M.D., Senior Vice President and Chief Medical Officer
CIO: James R. Cramer, Vice President and Chief Information Officer
CHR: Carol Henderson, Vice President Human Resources
Web address: www.shc.org
Control: Other not-for-profit (including NFP Corporation) **Service:** General Medical and Surgical

Staffed Beds: 347

☒ **SELECT SPECIALTY HOSPITAL–SCOTTSDALE (032005)**, 7400 East Osborn Road, 3 West, Zip 85251–6432; tel. 480/882–4360, (Includes SELECT SPECIALTY HOSPITAL–PHOENIX DOWNTOWN, 1012 East Wiletta Street, 4th Floor, Phoenix, Zip 85006; tel. 602/239–6134; Sharon Anthony, Market Administrator), (Nonreporting) **A**1 10 **S** Select Medical Corporation, Mechanicsburg, PA
Primary Contact: Anthony Martino, Chief Executive Officer
Web address: www.selectspecialtyhospitals.com/company/locations/scottsdale.aspx
Control: Corporation, Investor-owned, for-profit **Service:** Long–Term Acute Care hospital

Staffed Beds: 62

SELLS—Pima County

☒ **U. S. PUBLIC HEALTH SERVICE INDIAN HOSPITAL–SELLS (030074)**,
Highway 86 & Topawa Road, Zip 85634, Mailing Address: P.O. Box 548,
Zip 85634–0548; tel. 520/383–7251, (Nonreporting) **A**1 9 10 **S** U. S. Indian
Health Service, Rockville, MD
Primary Contact: Priscilla Whitethorne, Chief Executive Officer
COO: Diane Shanley, Deputy Service Unit Director
CFO: Vivian Draper, Chief Financial Officer
CMO: Peter Ziegler, M.D., Acting Chief Medical Officer
CIO: Karen Wade, Chief Information Officer
CNO: Donna Hobbs, Nurse Executive
Web address: www.ihs.gov
Control: PHS, Indian Service, Government, federal **Service:** General Medical and
Surgical

Staffed Beds: 12

SHOW LOW—Navajo County

★ **SUMMIT HEALTHCARE REGIONAL MEDICAL CENTER (030062)**, 2200 East
Show Low Lake Road, Zip 85901–7800; tel. 928/537–4375, (Nonreporting) **A**9
10 20
Primary Contact: Ronald L. McArthur, Chief Executive Officer
COO: Doug Gilchrist, Chief Operating Officer
CFO: Kurt Loveless, Chief Financial Officer
CMO: Jeffrey Northup, D.O., Chief Medical Officer
CIO: Kent McQuillan, Chief Information Officer
CHR: Connie Kakavas, Chief Human Resources Officer
CNO: Cynthia Ebert, R.N., Chief Nursing Officer
Web address: www.summithealthcare.net
Control: Other not–for–profit (including NFP Corporation) **Service:** General
Medical and Surgical

Staffed Beds: 78

SIERRA VISTA—Cochise County

☒ **SIERRA VISTA REGIONAL HEALTH CENTER (030043)**, 300 El Camino Real,
Zip 85635–2899; tel. 520/458–4641 **A**1 9 10 13 20 **F**3 11 13 15 18 20 22
27 28 29 30 34 35 40 41 45 46 48 49 50 51 57 60 63 64 70 73 75 76 77
79 81 82 85 86 89 93 107 111 114 115 118 119 127 130 145 146 148
S RegionalCare Hospital Partners, Brentwood, TN
Primary Contact: Dean French, M.D., Chief Executive Officer
COO: Bruce J. Norton, Senior Vice President and Chief Operating Officer
CFO: Steve Calabrese, Vice President and Chief Financial Officer
CMO: Steven Mehta, M.D., Chief Medical Officer
CIO: Jorge Moreno, Director Information Technology Operations
CHR: Traci Meyer, Director Human Resources and Public Relations Officer
CNO: Cynthia Lewis, Chief Nursing Officer
Web address: www.svrhc.org
Control: Other not–for–profit (including NFP Corporation) **Service:** General
Medical and Surgical

Staffed Beds: 83 **Admissions:** 3790 **Census:** 30 **Births:** 878 **Personnel:** 601

SPRINGERVILLE—Apache County

WHITE MOUNTAIN REGIONAL MEDICAL CENTER (031315), 118 South
Mountain Avenue, Zip 85938–5104; tel. 928/333–4368, (Nonreporting) **A**9
10 18
Primary Contact: James Robertson, Chief Executive Officer
CFO: James Hamblin, Chief Financial Officer
CMO: Scott Hamblin, M.D., President Medical Staff
Web address: www.wmrmc.com
Control: Other not–for–profit (including NFP Corporation) **Service:** General
Medical and Surgical

Staffed Beds: 20

SUN CITY—Maricopa County

☒ **BANNER BOSWELL MEDICAL CENTER (030061)**, 10401 West Thunderbird
Boulevard, Zip 85351–3004, Mailing Address: P.O. Box 1690, Zip 85372–1690;
tel. 623/832–4000, (Total facility includes 71 beds in nursing home–type unit) **A**1
2 9 10 **F**2 3 11 15 17 18 20 22 24 26 28 29 30 31 34 35 37 40 44 45 47
49 50 53 56 57 58 59 60 61 64 65 69 70 74 75 78 79 81 84 85 86 87 90
91 92 93 94 96 107 108 110 111 114 115 117 118 119 124 126 128 130
132 135 136 141 143 145 146 147 148 **S** Banner Health, Phoenix, AZ
Primary Contact: David Cheney, Chief Executive Officer
CFO: Jeremy Williams, Chief Financial Officer
CMO: Kathryn Perkins, M.D., Chief Medical Officer
CHR: Brenda Dietrich, Chief Human Resources Officer
CNO: Cathy Townsend, Chief Nursing Officer
Web address: www.bannerhealth.com/Locations/Arizona/Banner+Boswell+
Medical+Center
Control: Other not–for–profit (including NFP Corporation) **Service:** General
Medical and Surgical

Staffed Beds: 441 **Admissions:** 20993 **Census:** 336 **Births:** 0 **Total
Expense ($000):** 260940 **Payroll Expense ($000):** 99725 **Personnel:** 1746

RESTORA HOSPITAL OF SUN CITY (032008), 13818 North Thunderbird
Boulevard, Zip 85351–2574; tel. 623/977–1325, (Nonreporting) **A**10 **S** Restora
Healthcare, Alpharetta, GA
Primary Contact: Gregory Sassman, Interim Chief Executive Officer
Web address: www.restorahealthcare.com
Control: Corporation, Investor–owned, for–profit **Service:** Long–Term Acute Care
hospital

Staffed Beds: 120

TRILLIUM SPECIALTY HOSPITAL–WEST VALLEY See Restora Hospital of Sun
City

SUN CITY WEST—Maricopa County

☒ **BANNER DEL E. WEBB MEDICAL CENTER (030093)**, 14502 West Meeker
Boulevard, Zip 85375–5299, Mailing Address: P.O. Box 5169, Zip 85376–5169;
tel. 623/214–4000 **A**1 9 10 **F**3 5 8 9 13 15 18 20 22 28 29 30 31 34 36 37
39 40 41 44 45 46 47 48 49 50 51 56 57 58 59 60 61 64 65 68 70 74 75
76 77 78 79 80 81 82 84 85 86 87 90 91 92 93 94 96 98 100 102 103 104
105 107 108 110 111 114 115 118 119 126 130 131 132 135 145 146 147
148 **P**1 8 **S** Banner Health, Phoenix, AZ
Primary Contact: Debbie Flores, Chief Executive Officer
CMO: Michel Dagher, D.O., Vice President and Chief Medical Officer
CIO: David Runt, Chief Information Officer
Web address: www.bannerhealth.com/Locations/Arizona/Banner+Del+Webb+
Medical+Center/
Control: Other not–for–profit (including NFP Corporation) **Service:** General
Medical and Surgical

Staffed Beds: 373 **Admissions:** 16138 **Census:** 194 **Outpatient Visits:**
106656 **Births:** 1687 **Total Expense ($000):** 232441 **Payroll Expense
($000):** 84904 **Personnel:** 1445

TEMPE—Maricopa County

☐ **AURORA TEMPE HOSPITAL (034028)**, 6350 South Maple Street,
Zip 85283–2857; tel. 480/345–5400, (Nonreporting) **A**1 9 10 **S** Aurora
Behavioral Health Care, Corona, CA
Primary Contact: Bruce Waldo, Chief Executive Officer
CFO: Rebekah Francis, JD, Chief Financial Officer
CMO: Jason Friday, M.D., Medical Director
CHR: Vicki Thomsen, Director Human Resources
Web address: www.auroraarizona.com
Control: Partnership, Investor–owned, for–profit **Service:** Psychiatric

Staffed Beds: 70

AZ

TUBA CITY—Coconino County

⊞ **TUBA CITY REGIONAL HEALTH CARE CORPORATION (030073)**, 167 Main Street, Zip 86045–0611, Mailing Address: P.O. Box 600, Zip 86045–0600; tel. 928/283–2501 **A**1 3 9 10 **F**3 5 8 9 11 13 14 15 18 26 27 28 29 30 31 32 34 35 36 38 39 40 41 43 44 45 46 47 48 50 52 53 54 55 56 57 58 59 60 61 62 63 64 65 66 68 70 71 74 75 76 77 79 80 81 82 83 84 85 86 87 89 90 91 92 93 94 95 96 97 99 100 101 102 103 104 107 108 110 111 114 115 119 124 127 128 130 131 132 133 134 135 141 142 143 144 145 146 147 148 **P**1 6 7
Primary Contact: Joseph T. Engelken, Chief Executive Officer
COO: Lynette Bonar, Chief Support Services
CFO: Clifford Lee Olsson, Chief Financial Officer
CMO: Alan Spacone, M.D., Chief Medical Officer
CHR: John S. Pemberton, Director Human Resources
Web address: www.tchealth.org
Control: Other not–for–profit (including NFP Corporation) **Service:** General Medical and Surgical

| Staffed Beds: 73 Admissions: 2442 Census: 28 Outpatient Visits: 776354 Births: 450 Total Expense ($000): 143919 Payroll Expense ($000): 73733 Personnel: 1028 |

TUCSON—Pima County

⊞ **CARONDELET ST. JOSEPH'S HOSPITAL (030011)**, 350 North Wilmot Road, Zip 85711–2678; tel. 520/873–3000 **A**1 9 10 **F**3 5 11 12 13 18 20 22 28 29 30 31 34 35 38 40 44 45 46 47 49 50 57 59 60 61 64 68 69 70 72 74 75 76 77 78 79 81 82 83 84 85 86 87 90 92 93 98 100 101 102 103 104 105 107 108 114 115 118 119 126 129 130 132 135 145 146 147 148 **S** Ascension Health, Saint Louis, MO
Primary Contact: Tony Fonze, President and Chief Executive Officer
CFO: Alan Strauss, Chief Financial Officer
CMO: Donald Denmark, M.D., Chief Medical Officer
CIO: Sally Zambrello, Chief Information Officer
CHR: Igor Shegolev, Vice President Human Resources
CNO: Robin Conklin, R.N., Chief Nursing Officer
Web address: www.carondelet.org
Control: Church–operated, Nongovernment, not–for profit **Service:** General Medical and Surgical

| Staffed Beds: 486 Admissions: 16414 Census: 216 Outpatient Visits: 144429 Births: 2537 Total Expense ($000): 247813 Payroll Expense ($000): 90143 Personnel: 1429 |

⊞ **CARONDELET ST. MARY'S HOSPITAL (030010)**, 1601 West St. Mary's Road, Zip 85745–2682; tel. 520/872–3000 **A**1 3 9 10 **F**3 5 11 15 17 18 20 22 24 26 28 29 30 31 34 38 40 44 45 46 47 49 50 51 56 57 58 59 60 61 63 64 68 69 70 74 77 78 79 81 82 84 85 87 90 92 93 96 98 100 101 102 103 107 108 110 111 114 115 118 119 129 130 132 146 148 **S** Ascension Health, Saint Louis, MO
Primary Contact: Amy Beiter, M.D., President and Chief Executive Officer
CMO: Donald Denmark, M.D., Chief Medical Officer
Web address: www.carondelet.org
Control: Church–operated, Nongovernment, not–for profit **Service:** General Medical and Surgical

| Staffed Beds: 262 Admissions: 11125 Census: 142 Outpatient Visits: 186699 Births: 0 Total Expense ($000): 187411 Payroll Expense ($000): 69626 Personnel: 1131 |

☐ **CORNERSTONE HOSPITAL OF SOUTHEAST ARIZONA (032004)**, 7220 East Rosewood Drive, Zip 85710–1350; tel. 520/546–4595 **A**1 10 **F**1 29 30 75 77 82 84 85 90 **S** Cornerstone Healthcare Group, Dallas, TX
Primary Contact: Louise Cassidy, Chief Executive Officer
CFO: Kurt Schultz, Group Chief Financial Officer
CMO: Haroon Haque, M.D., Medical Director
CIO: Adam Davis, Director Information Technology
CHR: Debra Ramage, Director Human Resources and Payroll
CNO: Robert Labowitz, Chief Nursing Officer
Web address: www.chghospitals.com
Control: Corporation, Investor–owned, for–profit **Service:** Long–Term Acute Care hospital

| Staffed Beds: 34 Admissions: 283 Census: 19 |

⊞ **HEALTHSOUTH REHABILITATION HOSPITAL OF SOUTHERN ARIZONA (033029)**, 1921 West Hospital Drive, Zip 85704–7806; tel. 520/742–2800 **A**1 9 10 **F**3 29 34 59 64 69 90 93 95 96 130 131 132 143 148 **S** HEALTHSOUTH Corporation, Birmingham, AL
Primary Contact: Robert C. Honeycutt, FACHE, Chief Executive Officer
CFO: Kaleigh Hotchkiss, Controller
CMO: Susan Bulen, M.D., Medical Director
CHR: Neil Cullen, Director Human Resources
CNO: Annette Barr, Chief Nursing Officer
Web address: www.healthsouthsouthernarizona.com
Control: Corporation, Investor–owned, for–profit **Service:** Rehabilitation

| Staffed Beds: 60 Admissions: 1096 Census: 37 Outpatient Visits: 3055 Births: 0 Total Expense ($000): 15401 Payroll Expense ($000): 7836 Personnel: 136 |

⊞ **HEALTHSOUTH REHABILITATION INSTITUTE OF TUCSON (033028)**, 2650 North Wyatt Drive, Zip 85712–6108; tel. 520/325–1300 **A**1 9 10 **F**29 34 35 62 90 93 96 130 132 **S** HEALTHSOUTH Corporation, Birmingham, AL
Primary Contact: Jeffrey Christensen, Chief Executive Officer
CFO: Mary Donovan, Controller
CMO: Jon Larson, M.D., Medical Director
CHR: Dawn Mosier, Director Human Resources
Web address: www.rehabinstituteoftucson.com
Control: Corporation, Investor–owned, for–profit **Service:** Rehabilitation

| Staffed Beds: 80 Admissions: 1490 Census: 52 Outpatient Visits: 0 Births: 0 Total Expense ($000): 18686 Payroll Expense ($000): 10580 Personnel: 183 |

⊞ **KINDRED HOSPITAL–TUCSON (032002)**, 355 North Wilmot Road, Zip 85711–2601; tel. 520/584–4500, (Nonreporting) **A**1 10 **S** Kindred Healthcare, Louisville, KY
Primary Contact: Marc Lemon, Chief Executive Officer
CFO: Lynn Myers, Controller
CMO: Sunil Natrajan, M.D., Medical Director
CNO: Annette Lindeman, Chief Clinical Officer
Web address: www.khtucson.com
Control: Corporation, Investor–owned, for–profit **Service:** Long–Term Acute Care hospital

| Staffed Beds: 51 |

⊞ **NORTHWEST MEDICAL CENTER (030085)**, 6200 North La Cholla Boulevard, Zip 85741–3599; tel. 520/742–9000 **A**1 3 5 9 10 **F**3 8 12 13 15 17 18 19 20 22 24 26 28 29 30 31 34 35 37 40 49 53 57 59 68 70 72 74 75 76 78 79 81 85 91 93 102 107 108 110 111 113 114 118 119 126 130 135 144 146 147 148 **S** Community Health Systems, Inc., Franklin, TN
Primary Contact: Kevin Stockton, Chief Executive Officer
CFO: Ronald Patrick, Chief Financial Officer
CIO: David Bullock, Director Information Services
CNO: Kay Stubbs, Chief Nursing Officer
Web address: www.northwestmedicalcenter.com
Control: Corporation, Investor–owned, for–profit **Service:** General Medical and Surgical

| Staffed Beds: 270 Admissions: 17645 Census: 166 Births: 2799 Total Expense ($000): 264337 Payroll Expense ($000): 113309 Personnel: 1690 |

☐ **PALO VERDE MENTAL HEALTH SERVICES**, 2695 North Craycroft, Zip 85712–2244, Mailing Address: P.O. Box 40030, Zip 85717–0030; tel. 520/322–2888, (Nonreporting) **A**1 9 **S** Universal Health Services, Inc., King of Prussia, PA
Primary Contact: P. Jay Frayser, Chief Executive Officer
CFO: Richard N. England, Chief Financial Officer
Web address: www.paloverdebh.com/
Control: Other not–for–profit (including NFP Corporation) **Service:** Psychiatric

| Staffed Beds: 48 |

☐ **SIERRA TUCSON**, 39580 South Lago Del Oro Parkway, Zip 85739–9637; tel. 520/624–4000 **A**1 5 **F**4 29 33 35 36 53 75 80 82 98 106 118 135 **P**6 **S** CRC Health Group, Inc., Cupertino, CA
Primary Contact: Stephen P. Fahey, Executive Director
COO: Stephen P. Fahey, Executive Director
CFO: Amy Fritton, Controller
CMO: Jerome Lerner, M.D., Medical Director
CHR: Betty Dickens, Director Human Resources
CNO: Sue Menzie, R.N., Director Patient Care
Web address: www.sierratucson.com
Control: Corporation, Investor–owned, for–profit **Service:** Psychiatric

| Staffed Beds: 139 Admissions: 1109 Census: 90 Outpatient Visits: 0 Births: 0 |

☐ **SONORA BEHAVIORAL HEALTH HOSPITAL (034022)**, 6050 North Corona Road, #3, Zip 85704–1096; tel. 520/469–8700 **A**1 3 9 10 **F**5 29 98 99 100 103 104 143 **P**5 **S** Acadia Healthcare Company, Inc., Franklin, TN
Primary Contact: Edeli Kinsala, Chief Executive Officer
CMO: Steven Bupp, M.D., Medical Director
CHR: Ciria Soto, Director Human Resources
CNO: Angel Payne, Clinical Director, Director of Nursing
Control: Corporation, Investor–owned, for–profit **Service:** Psychiatric

| Staffed Beds: 72 Admissions: 2583 Census: 59 Outpatient Visits: 2545 Births: 0 Total Expense ($000): 16391 Payroll Expense ($000): 9507 Personnel: 154 |

Many Facility Codes have changed. Please refer to the AHA Guide Code Chart. © 2014 AHA Guide

✠ △ **SOUTHERN ARIZONA VETERANS AFFAIRS HEALTH CARE SYSTEM**,
3601 South 6th Avenue, Zip 85723–0002; tel. 520/792–1450, (Nonreporting)
A1 3 5 7 9 **S** Department of Veterans Affairs, Washington, DC
Primary Contact: Jonathan H. Gardner, FACHE, Director
CFO: Larry Korn, Manager Finance
CMO: Jayendra H. Shah, M.D., Chief Medical Officer
CIO: John Walston, Chief Information Officer
CHR: Patrice Craig, Manager Human Resources
Web address: www.tucson.va.gov
Control: Veterans Affairs, Government, federal **Service:** General Medical and
Surgical

Staffed Beds: 285

TMC FOR CHILDREN See TMC Healthcare

★ **TMC HEALTHCARE (030006)**, 5301 East Grant Road, Zip 85712–2874;
tel. 520/327–5461, (Includes TMC FOR CHILDREN, 5301 East Grant Road,
Zip 85712–2805; tel. 520/327–5461) **A**3 5 8 9 10 **F**3 11 12 13 15 17 18 20
22 24 26 28 29 30 31 32 34 35 37 40 41 43 45 46 47 48 49 50 51 53 57
58 59 60 62 63 64 65 68 72 74 75 76 79 81 82 84 85 87 88 89 98 100
102 107 108 110 111 113 114 115 119 126 129 130 132 134 143 146
148 **P**6
Primary Contact: Judy F. Rich, President and Chief Executive Officer
COO: David R. Ressler, Senior Vice President and Chief Operations Officer
CFO: Stephen Bush, Chief Financial Officer
CMO: Rick Anderson, M.D., Senior Vice President and Chief Medical Officer
CIO: Frank Marini, Vice President and Chief Information Officer
CHR: Richard W. Lawley, Vice President Human Resources
CNO: Elizabeth Maish, R.N., Vice President and Chief Nursing Officer
Web address: www.tmcaz.com
Control: Other not–for–profit (including NFP Corporation) **Service:** General
Medical and Surgical

Staffed Beds: 591 **Admissions:** 30654 **Census:** 351 **Outpatient Visits:**
147876 **Births:** 5602 **Total Expense ($000):** 419401 **Payroll Expense**
($000): 169728 **Personnel:** 2912

☐ **UNIVERSITY OF ARIZONA MEDICAL CENTER – SOUTH CAMPUS (030111)**,
2800 East Ajo Way, Zip 85713–6289; tel. 520/874–2000 **A**1 5 6 9 10 **F**3 11
12 15 18 20 22 26 29 30 34 35 36 38 40 43 44 50 51 54 55 56 57 58 59
61 64 65 68 70 74 75 77 79 81 82 85 87 93 97 98 100 101 102 103 104
107 110 111 114 115 119 127 130 131 135 145 146 147 148 **P**4
Primary Contact: Sarah Frost, Administrator
COO: Sarah Frost, Administrator and Chief Operating Officer
CFO: Misty Hansen, Chief Financial Officer
CMO: John Kettelle, M.D., Chief Medical Officer
CIO: Dan Critchley, Chief Information Officer
CHR: John Marques, Vice President Chief Human Resources Officer
CNO: Victoria D. Began, R.N., Chief Nursing Officer
Web address: www.uahealth.com
Control: Other not–for–profit (including NFP Corporation) **Service:** General
Medical and Surgical

Staffed Beds: 161 **Admissions:** 7249 **Census:** 110 **Outpatient Visits:**
206776 **Births:** 0 **Total Expense ($000):** 137169 **Payroll Expense ($000):**
50660 **Personnel:** 978

✠ **UNIVERSITY OF ARIZONA MEDICAL CENTER – UNIVERSITY CAMPUS**
(030064), 1501 North Campbell Avenue, Zip 85724–5128; tel. 520/694–0111,
(Includes DIAMOND CHILDREN'S HOSPITAL, 1501 North Campbell Avenue,
Zip 85724–0001; tel. 520/694–0111) **A**1 3 5 8 9 10 **F**3 8 11 12 13 17 18 19
20 21 22 23 24 25 26 27 28 29 30 31 32 34 35 36 37 38 40 41 43 44 45
46 47 48 49 50 53 54 57 58 59 60 61 62 64 67 68 69 70 72 74 75 76 77
78 79 81 84 85 86 87 88 89 92 93 97 100 101 102 107 108 111 114 115
116 117 118 119 120 121 123 124 126 129 130 132 135 136 137 138 139
140 141 142 145 146 147 148 **P**4 6
Primary Contact: Karen Mlawsky, Chief Executive Officer
COO: Sarah Frost, Chief Operating Officer and Administrator, University of Arizona
Medical Center – South Campus
CFO: Misty Hansen, Chief Financial Officer
CMO: Andreas Theodorou, Chief Medical Officer
CIO: Dan Critchley, Chief Information Officer
CHR: John Marques, Vice President Human Resources
CNO: Victoria D. Began, R.N., Chief Nursing Officer, Vice President Patient
Services
Web address: www.uahealth.com
Control: Other not–for–profit (including NFP Corporation) **Service:** General
Medical and Surgical

Staffed Beds: 479 **Admissions:** 23082 **Census:** 362 **Outpatient Visits:**
479259 **Births:** 1882 **Total Expense ($000):** 644405 **Payroll Expense**
($000): 212667 **Personnel:** 3710

WHITERIVER—Navajo County

☐ **U. S. PUBLIC HEALTH SERVICE INDIAN HOSPITAL–WHITERIVER (030113)**,
200 West Hospital Drive, Zip 85941–0860, Mailing Address: State Route 73, Box
860, Zip 85941–0860; tel. 928/338–4911 **A**1 10 **F**3 8 13 29 32 34 35 36 38
39 40 44 45 46 50 53 54 56 57 59 61 64 65 66 68 75 76 78 79 81 82 84
85 86 87 89 91 93 94 97 100 101 104 107 111 114 119 130 131 132 135
144 146 147 148 **S** U. S. Indian Health Service, Rockville, MD
Primary Contact: Michelle Martinez, Chief Executive Officer
COO: Brian Campbell, Director Professional Services
CFO: Desdemona Leslie, Finance Officer
CMO: John Umhau, M.D., Clinical Director
CIO: Russell Barker, Information Officer
CHR: Lena Fasthorse, Supervisor Human Resource
CNO: Jana Towne, Nurse Executive
Web address: www.ihs.gov
Control: PHS, Indian Service, Government, federal **Service:** General Medical and
Surgical

Staffed Beds: 39 **Admissions:** 1245 **Census:** 15

WICKENBURG—Maricopa County

★ **WICKENBURG COMMUNITY HOSPITAL (031300)**, 520 Rose Lane,
Zip 85390–1447; tel. 928/684–5421 **A**9 10 18 **F**11 15 34 40 53 57 59 63 65
90 93 107 110 111 115 117 119 127 133 146 148
Primary Contact: James Tavary, Chief Executive Officer
CFO: Ron Smith, Chief Financial Officer
CMO: Dennis Barraco, D.O., Medical Director
CIO: Michael McKay, Manager Information Systems
CNO: Linda Brockwell, R.N., Chief Nursing Officer
Web address: www.wickenburgcommunityhospital.com
Control: Other not–for–profit (including NFP Corporation) **Service:** General
Medical and Surgical

Staffed Beds: 19 **Admissions:** 488 **Census:** 6 **Births:** 0 **Total Expense**
($000): 20206 **Payroll Expense ($000):** 8693 **Personnel:** 153

WILLCOX—Cochise County

★ **NORTHERN COCHISE COMMUNITY HOSPITAL (031302)**, 901 West Rex Allen
Drive, Zip 85643–1009; tel. 520/384–3541, (Total facility includes 24 beds in
nursing home–type unit) **A**9 10 18 **F**29 34 35 40 43 56 57 59 64 65 77 90 93
107 110 111 115 119 127 128 133 143 146
Primary Contact: Roland Knox, Chief Executive Officer
CMO: Hisham Hamam, M.D., Chief of Staff
CIO: Dennis Drury, Director Information Technology
CNO: Pam Noland, Director Nursing
Web address: www.ncch.com
Control: Hospital district or authority, Government, nonfederal **Service:** General
Medical and Surgical

Staffed Beds: 48 **Admissions:** 464 **Census:** 17 **Outpatient Visits:** 16243
Births: 0 **Total Expense ($000):** 17913 **Payroll Expense ($000):** 8626
Personnel: 163

WINSLOW—Navajo County

★ **LITTLE COLORADO MEDICAL CENTER (031311)**, 1501 Williamson Avenue,
Zip 86047–2797; tel. 928/289–4691 **A**9 10 18 **F**29 34 40 50 65 79 81 107
127 130 133
Primary Contact: Jeffrey J. Hamblen, Chief Executive Officer
CFO: Randy Glassman, Chief Financial Officer
CMO: Perry Mitchell, M.D., Chief of Staff
CHR: Nina L. Ferguson, Director Human Resources
Web address: www.lcmcwmh.org
Control: Other not–for–profit (including NFP Corporation) **Service:** General
Medical and Surgical

Staffed Beds: 25 **Admissions:** 1276 **Census:** 9 **Births:** 189 **Total Expense**
($000): 25906 **Payroll Expense ($000):** 11224 **Personnel:** 189

Hospital, Medicare Provider Number, Address, Telephone, Approval, Facility, and Physician Codes, Health Care System

★ American Hospital Association (AHA) membership
☐ The Joint Commission accreditation   ◇ DNV Healthcare Inc. accreditation
○ Healthcare Facilities Accreditation Program
△ Commission on Accreditation of Rehabilitation Facilities (CARF) accreditation

YUMA—Yuma County

★ **YUMA REGIONAL MEDICAL CENTER (030013)**, 2400 South Avenue A,
Zip 85364–7170; tel. 928/344–2000 **A**2 9 10 19 20 **F**3 8 11 12 13 15 18 20
22 24 26 28 29 30 31 32 34 35 38 39 40 41 45 46 47 48 49 50 54 56 57
58 59 64 65 68 70 72 74 75 76 77 78 79 81 82 83 84 85 86 87 89 93 97
100 104 107 108 109 110 111 114 115 116 117 118 119 120 121 122 123
124 130 132 146 147 148 **P**7
Primary Contact: Pat Walz, President and Chief Executive Officer
CFO: David Willie, Chief Financial Officer
CMO: Carl Myers, M.D., Vice President Medical Affairs and Chief Medical Officer
CIO: Gene Shaw, Chief Information Officer
CHR: Sharon R. Gardner, Vice President Human Resources
CNO: Deborah Carver, R.N., Vice President Patient Care Services
Web address: www.yumaregional.org
Control: Other not–for–profit (including NFP Corporation) **Service:** General
Medical and Surgical

Staffed Beds: 406 **Admissions:** 16560 **Census:** 183 **Outpatient Visits:**
168888 **Births:** 3349 **Total Expense ($000):** 304891 **Payroll Expense
($000):** 116242 **Personnel:** 1615

✠ **YUMA REHABILITATION HOSPITAL (033034)**, 901 West 24th Street,
Zip 85364–6384; tel. 928/726–5000, (Nonreporting) **A**1 9 10 **S** HEALTHSOUTH
Corporation, Birmingham, AL
Primary Contact: Joshua Bowie, Chief Executive Officer
CFO: Larry Barclift, Chief Financial Officer
CMO: Rinely Aguiar–Olsen, M.D., Medical Director
CHR: Linda Woen, Director Human Resources
CNO: Kristin Parra, Chief Nursing Officer
Web address: www.yumarehabhospital.com
Control: Corporation, Investor–owned, for–profit **Service:** Rehabilitation

Staffed Beds: 41

Many Facility Codes have changed. Please refer to the AHA Guide Code Chart.

ARKANSAS

ARKADELPHIA—Clark County

☒ **BAPTIST HEALTH MEDICAL CENTER–ARKADELPHIA (041321)**, 3050 Twin Rivers Drive, Zip 71923–4299; tel. 870/245–2622 **A**1 9 10 18 **F**3 11 13 15 29 30 34 40 43 57 59 61 62 63 64 65 68 69 70 81 93 107 110 111 114 119 127 129 130 133 135 146 **S** Baptist Health, Little Rock, AR
Primary Contact: John Bowen, Assistant Vice President and Administrator
CFO: Robert C. Roberts, Vice President and Chief Financial Officer
CMO: Eddie Phillips, M.D., Chief Medical Officer
CIO: David House, Vice President and Chief Information Officer
CHR: Anthony Kendall, Vice President Human Resources
Web address: www.baptist-health.com/locations/accesspoint.aspx?accessPointID=187
Control: Other not–for–profit (including NFP Corporation) **Service:** General Medical and Surgical

Staffed Beds: 25 **Admissions:** 1239 **Census:** 13 **Outpatient Visits:** 27295 **Births:** 370 **Total Expense ($000):** 19450 **Payroll Expense ($000):** 8133 **Personnel:** 146

ASHDOWN—Little River County

★ **LITTLE RIVER MEMORIAL HOSPITAL (041320)**, 451 West Locke Street, Zip 71822–3325; tel. 870/898–5011, (Nonreporting) **A**9 10 18
Primary Contact: James Dowell, Administrator and Chief Executive Officer
CFO: Jackie Rainey, Chief Financial Officer
CIO: Mitchell Jones, Director Information Technology
CHR: Vicki Keener, Administrative Assistant and Director Human Resources
CNO: Cynthia Metzger, Chief Nursing and Operations Officer
Control: County–Government, nonfederal **Service:** General Medical and Surgical

Staffed Beds: 25

BARLING—Sebastian County

☐ **VALLEY BEHAVIORAL HEALTH SYSTEM (044006)**, 10301 Mayo Drive, Zip 72923–1660; tel. 479/494–5700 **A**1 9 10 **F**38 98 99 100 101 102 103 104 105 106 130 **P**6 **S** Acadia Healthcare Company, Inc., Franklin, TN
Primary Contact: Holli Baker, Chief Executive Officer
CFO: Paul D. Ervin, Chief Financial Officer
CMO: Richard Livingston, M.D., Medical Director
CHR: Patricia J. Moore, Director Human Resource
Web address: www.valleybehavioral.com
Control: Corporation, Investor–owned, for–profit **Service:** Psychiatric

Staffed Beds: 75 **Admissions:** 1700 **Census:** 60 **Outpatient Visits:** 8000 **Births:** 0 **Personnel:** 154

BATESVILLE—Independence County

★ **WHITE RIVER MEDICAL CENTER (040119)**, 1710 Harrison Street, Zip 72501–7303, Mailing Address: P.O. Box 2197, Zip 72503–2197; tel. 870/262–1200, (Total facility includes 11 beds in nursing home–type unit) **A**9 10 19 20 **F**3 8 11 12 13 15 17 20 22 28 29 30 31 34 35 38 40 43 44 45 48 50 51 56 57 59 60 64 68 70 74 75 77 78 79 81 82 85 86 87 90 93 98 100 101 103 104 107 108 110 111 114 115 119 121 126 127 128 129 130 131 132 135 144 146 147 148 **P**6 **S** White River Health System, Batesville, AR
Primary Contact: Gary Bebow, FACHE, Administrator and Chief Executive Officer
COO: Tammy Gavin, Assistant Administrator and Chief Operating Officer
CFO: Jana Richardson, Chief Financial Officer
CMO: Doug Bernard, M.D., Chief Medical Officer
CIO: Gary Paxson, Chief Information Officer
CHR: Gary McDonald, Associate Administrator Human Resources
CNO: Dede Strecker, Chief Nursing Officer
Web address: www.whiteriverhealthsystem.com
Control: Other not–for–profit (including NFP Corporation) **Service:** General Medical and Surgical

Staffed Beds: 210 **Admissions:** 8039 **Census:** 116 **Outpatient Visits:** 217948 **Births:** 740 **Total Expense ($000):** 153651 **Payroll Expense ($000):** 56908 **Personnel:** 1131

BENTON—Saline County

☐ **RIVENDELL BEHAVIORAL HEALTH SERVICES OF ARKANSAS (044007)**, 100 Rivendell Drive, Zip 72019–9100; tel. 501/316–1255 **A**1 9 10 **F**29 38 59 75 87 98 99 100 101 102 105 106 130 132 **P**5 **S** Universal Health Services, Inc., King of Prussia, PA
Primary Contact: Dwight A. Lacy, Chief Executive Officer
CFO: Mike Rainbolt, Chief Financial Officer
Web address: www.rivendellofarkansas.com
Control: Corporation, Investor–owned, for–profit **Service:** Psychiatric

Staffed Beds: 77 **Admissions:** 2303 **Census:** 67 **Outpatient Visits:** 23 **Births:** 0 **Total Expense ($000):** 10396 **Payroll Expense ($000):** 5699 **Personnel:** 128

★ **SALINE MEMORIAL HOSPITAL (040084)**, 1 Medical Park Drive, Zip 72015–3354; tel. 501/776–6000 **A**9 10 **F**3 7 11 12 13 15 17 18 20 22 29 30 34 35 40 41 43 50 57 59 62 63 64 70 74 75 76 77 79 81 84 85 87 89 90 91 93 96 98 107 108 110 111 114 115 118 119 129 130 131 132 135 144 146 148 **P**8
Primary Contact: Bob Trautman, Chief Executive Officer
COO: Carla Robertson, Chief Operating Officer and Chief Financial Officer
CFO: Carla Robertson, Chief Operating Officer and Chief Financial Officer
CIO: Andy Dick, Director Information Services
CHR: Carol Matthews, Director Human Resources
CNO: Debbie Burrow, R.N., Chief Nursing Officer
Web address: www.salinememorial.org
Control: Other not–for–profit (including NFP Corporation) **Service:** General Medical and Surgical

Staffed Beds: 113 **Admissions:** 5673 **Census:** 72 **Outpatient Visits:** 73002 **Births:** 560 **Total Expense ($000):** 80571 **Payroll Expense ($000):** 39144 **Personnel:** 602

BERRYVILLE—Carroll County

☒ **MERCY HOSPITAL BERRYVILLE (041329)**, 214 Carter Street, Zip 72616–4303; tel. 870/423–3355 **A**1 9 10 18 **F**3 11 15 28 29 30 31 34 35 40 43 45 46 48 50 57 59 61 64 75 77 78 79 81 85 93 107 108 114 119 129 130 131 132 133 146 148 **P**6 **S** Mercy Health, Chesterfield, MO
Primary Contact: Kristy Estrem, FACHE, President
CFO: Sherry Clouse Day, Vice President Finance
CHR: Taya James, Director
CNO: Michele Gann, Vice President Patient Services
Web address: www.mercy.net/berryvillear
Control: Church–operated, Nongovernment, not–for profit **Service:** General Medical and Surgical

Staffed Beds: 25 **Admissions:** 814 **Census:** 8 **Outpatient Visits:** 28746 **Births:** 0 **Total Expense ($000):** 16303 **Payroll Expense ($000):** 8082 **Personnel:** 176

BLYTHEVILLE—Mississippi County

☐ **GREAT RIVER MEDICAL CENTER (040069)**, 1520 North Division Street, Zip 72315–1448, Mailing Address: P.O. Box 108, Zip 72316–0108; tel. 870/838–7300 **A**1 9 10 19 20 **F**11 13 15 28 29 34 45 46 53 57 59 64 68 70 75 76 79 81 89 93 97 107 108 111 114 119 120 130 135 146 147 **P**7 **S** Mississippi County Hospital System, Blytheville, AR
Primary Contact: Ralph E. Beaty, Chief Executive Officer
COO: Chris Raymer, R.N., Chief Operating Officer and Chief Nursing Officer
CFO: Randy Nichols, Chief Financial Officer
CMO: Sia Shahriari, M.D., Chief of Staff
CIO: Tammy Bratcher, System Information Technology Director
CHR: Cheri Blurton, Director Human Resources, HIPAA Privacy Officer
CNO: Chris Raymer, R.N., Chief Operating Officer and Chief Nursing Officer
Web address: www.mchsys.org
Control: County–Government, nonfederal **Service:** General Medical and Surgical

Staffed Beds: 73 **Admissions:** 1862 **Census:** 14 **Outpatient Visits:** 29257 **Births:** 421 **Personnel:** 239

Hospital, Medicare Provider Number, Address, Telephone, Approval, Facility, and Physician Codes, Health Care System

★ American Hospital Association (AHA) membership
☐ The Joint Commission accreditation
◇ DNV Healthcare Inc. accreditation
○ Healthcare Facilities Accreditation Program
△ Commission on Accreditation of Rehabilitation Facilities (CARF) accreditation

AR

BOONEVILLE—Logan County

BOONEVILLE COMMUNITY HOSPITAL (041318), 880 West Main Street, Zip 72927–3443, Mailing Address: P.O. Box 290, Zip 72927–0290; tel. 479/675–2800 **A**9 10 18 **F**3 8 11 14 15 18 26 27 29 30 34 40 41 43 45 57 59 62 65 68 81 87 92 97 107 127 133 146
Primary Contact: David Hill, Regional Administrator
CFO: J. Stuart Lisko, Regional Director Operations, Critical Access Hospital Operations
CMO: Michael Miranda, Chief of Staff
CHR: Doris Whitaker, Vice President and Manager
CNO: Candace Bollinger, Director of Nursing
Web address: www.mercy.net
Control: Other not–for–profit (including NFP Corporation) **Service:** General Medical and Surgical

Staffed Beds: 25 **Admissions:** 374 **Census:** 4 **Outpatient Visits:** 14809 **Births:** 0 **Total Expense ($000):** 9526 **Payroll Expense ($000):** 3902 **Personnel:** 78

CALICO ROCK— County

COMMUNITY MEDICAL CENTER OF IZARD COUNTY (041306), 61 Grasse Street, Zip 72519, Mailing Address: P.O. Box 438, Zip 72519–0438; tel. 870/297–3726 **A**9 10 18 **F**3 11 15 29 30 34 35 40 43 45 47 57 64 81 93 107 111 119 127 128 130 133 146
Primary Contact: Kim Skidmore, Administrator
CMO: Bethany Knight, M.D., Chief of Staff
Web address: www.cmcofic.org
Control: Other not–for–profit (including NFP Corporation) **Service:** General Medical and Surgical

Staffed Beds: 25 **Admissions:** 524 **Census:** 6 **Outpatient Visits:** 3454 **Births:** 0 **Total Expense ($000):** 7273 **Payroll Expense ($000):** 3211 **Personnel:** 72

CAMDEN—Ouachita County

★ **OUACHITA COUNTY MEDICAL CENTER (040050)**, 638 California Avenue S.W., Zip 71701–4699, Mailing Address: P.O. Box 797, Zip 71711–0797; tel. 870/836–1000 **A**9 10 20 **F**3 4 5 7 8 11 13 15 29 31 34 40 41 43 46 48 49 56 57 59 62 63 64 65 68 69 70 75 76 77 78 81 85 87 89 93 98 100 102 103 107 108 111 114 115 119 127 129 130 132 133 135 146 148 **P**8
Primary Contact: Peggy L. Abbott, President and Chief Executive Officer
CFO: Robert Anders, Chief Financial Officer
CIO: Kenny Frachiseur, Chief Information Officer
CHR: Mary Bridges, Director Human Resources
CNO: Diane Isaacs, Director of Nursing
Web address: www.ouachitamedcenter.com
Control: Other not–for–profit (including NFP Corporation) **Service:** General Medical and Surgical

Staffed Beds: 65 **Admissions:** 2104 **Census:** 18 **Outpatient Visits:** 31018 **Births:** 220 **Total Expense ($000):** 33644 **Payroll Expense ($000):** 15597 **Personnel:** 397

OUACHITA MEDICAL CENTER See Ouachita County Medical Center

CLARKSVILLE—Johnson County

★ **JOHNSON REGIONAL MEDICAL CENTER (040002)**, 1100 East Poplar Street, Zip 72830–4419, Mailing Address: P.O. Box 738, Zip 72830–0738; tel. 479/754–5454 **A**5 9 10 **F**3 7 11 13 15 29 34 35 40 43 45 50 56 57 59 62 64 68 70 75 76 77 79 81 85 90 91 92 93 96 98 103 104 107 108 110 111 114 118 119 129 130 132 147 148
Primary Contact: Larry Morse, Chief Executive Officer and Administrator
COO: Larry Morse, Chief Executive Officer and Administrator
CFO: Edward Anderson, Chief Financial Officer
CIO: Deb Bjorgum, Manager Data Processing
CHR: Maribel Baker, Director Human Resources
CNO: Terri Stumbaugh, R.N., Director Patient Care Services
Web address: www.jrmc.com
Control: Other not–for–profit (including NFP Corporation) **Service:** General Medical and Surgical

Staffed Beds: 80 **Admissions:** 2430 **Census:** 28 **Outpatient Visits:** 38167 **Births:** 419 **Total Expense ($000):** 31647 **Payroll Expense ($000):** 14511 **Personnel:** 339

CLINTON—Van Buren County

OZARK HEALTH MEDICAL CENTER (041313), Highway 65 South, Zip 72031–9045, Mailing Address: P.O. Box 206, Zip 72031–0206; tel. 501/745–7000, (Nonreporting) **A**10 18
Primary Contact: David Deaton, Chief Executive Officer
CFO: Mike Deaton, Chief Financial Officer
CMO: Steve Schoettle, M.D., Chief Medical Staff
CHR: Sally Cassell, Manager Human Resources
CNO: Edna Prosser, Chief Nursing Officer
Web address: www.ozarkhealthinc.com
Control: Other not–for–profit (including NFP Corporation) **Service:** General Medical and Surgical

Staffed Beds: 157

CONWAY—Faulkner County

✉ **CONWAY REGIONAL MEDICAL CENTER (040029)**, 2302 College Avenue, Zip 72034–6297; tel. 501/329–3831 **A**1 9 10 **F**3 8 11 13 15 17 18 20 22 24 28 29 30 31 35 40 43 45 49 50 51 53 56 57 59 60 62 64 70 74 75 76 77 78 79 81 84 85 87 89 93 103 107 108 110 111 115 117 119 120 127 130 131 132 146 147 148 **P**8
Primary Contact: James M. Lambert, FACHE, President and Chief Executive Officer
COO: Alan Finley, Chief Operating Officer
CFO: Steven P. Rose, Chief Financial Officer
CMO: Stephen Hudson, M.D., Chief of Staff
CHR: Richard Tyler, Corporate Director Human Resources
CNO: Jacquelyn Wilkerson, R.N., Chief Nursing Officer
Web address: www.conwayregional.org
Control: Other not–for–profit (including NFP Corporation) **Service:** General Medical and Surgical

Staffed Beds: 154 **Admissions:** 7871 **Census:** 85 **Outpatient Visits:** 106921 **Births:** 1827 **Total Expense ($000):** 130843 **Payroll Expense ($000):** 48161 **Personnel:** 1060

CONWAY REGIONAL REHAB HOSPITAL (043033), 2210 Robinson Street, Zip 72034–4943; tel. 501/932–3500 **A**9 10 **F**29 90 91 148 **P**1
Primary Contact: Sherry Gann, Administrator
Web address: www.conwayregional.org
Control: Hospital district or authority, Government, nonfederal **Service:** Rehabilitation

Staffed Beds: 26 **Admissions:** 409 **Census:** 14 **Outpatient Visits:** 0 **Births:** 0 **Total Expense ($000):** 4769 **Payroll Expense ($000):** 1407 **Personnel:** 46

CROSSETT—Ashley County

★ **ASHLEY COUNTY MEDICAL CENTER (041323)**, 1015 Unity Road, Zip 71635–9443, Mailing Address: P.O. Box 400, Zip 71635–0400; tel. 870/364–4111 **A**9 10 18 **F**3 11 13 15 18 29 30 31 34 35 40 45 50 53 56 57 59 62 64 68 70 75 76 77 78 79 81 85 93 98 100 103 104 105 107 108 110 111 115 119 127 129 130 132 133 148
Primary Contact: Phillip K. Gilmore, FACHE, Chief Executive Officer
CFO: Bill Couch, Chief Financial Officer
CMO: Brad Walsh, M.D., Chief of Staff
CIO: Dan Austin, Manager Data Processing
CHR: Shirley White, Director Human Resources
CNO: Emily Bendinelli, Director of Nurses
Web address: www.acmconline.org
Control: Other not–for–profit (including NFP Corporation) **Service:** General Medical and Surgical

Staffed Beds: 33 **Admissions:** 1172 **Census:** 16 **Outpatient Visits:** 78405 **Births:** 167 **Total Expense ($000):** 24258 **Payroll Expense ($000):** 11529 **Personnel:** 201

DANVILLE—Yell County

★ **CHAMBERS MEMORIAL HOSPITAL (040011)**, Highway 10 at Detroit, Zip 72833, Mailing Address: P.O. Box 639, Zip 72833–0639; tel. 479/495–2241 **A**9 10 20 **F**3 11 29 34 35 40 43 45 57 59 62 81 93 97 107 114 119 128 130 133
Primary Contact: Michael Scott Peek, Chief Executive Officer
CMO: John Westwood, M.D., Chief of Staff
CIO: Ken Masters, Director Information Technology
CHR: Stacey Lane, Executive Assistant Human Resources
CNO: Joeann Bowerman, Director of Nursing Services
Web address: www.chambershospital.com
Control: Other not–for–profit (including NFP Corporation) **Service:** General Medical and Surgical

Staffed Beds: 41 **Admissions:** 2093 **Census:** 15 **Outpatient Visits:** 24010 **Births:** 0 **Total Expense ($000):** 18497 **Payroll Expense ($000):** 8556 **Personnel:** 197

DARDANELLE—Yell County

RIVER VALLEY MEDICAL CENTER (041302), 200 North Third Street, Zip 72834–3802, Mailing Address: P.O. Box 578, Zip 72834–0578; tel. 479/229–4677, (Nonreporting) **A**9 10 18 **S** Allegiance Health Management, Shreveport, LA
Primary Contact: Christopher L. Bariola, Chief Executive Officer
CMO: William P. Scott, M.D., Chief of Staff
CHR: Kathy Hastin, Administrative Assistant Human Resources
Control: Corporation, Investor–owned, for–profit **Service:** General Medical and Surgical

Staffed Beds: 35

Many Facility Codes have changed. Please refer to the AHA Guide Code Chart. © 2014 AHA Guide

DE QUEEN—Sevier County

DE QUEEN MEDICAL CENTER (041319), 1306 Collin Raye Drive, Zip 71832–2502; tel. 870/584–4111 **A**9 10 18 **F**3 11 15 29 40 57 59 75 77 90 93 107 114 119 129 133 146 148
Primary Contact: Jeremy Icenhower, Administrator and Chief Executive Officer
CFO: Vicky Kelly, Chief Financial Officer
CMO: Jason Lofton, M.D., Medical Director
CIO: David Harris, Director Information Systems
CHR: Ramona Driver, Director Human Resources
CNO: Kristy Richardson, Director of Nursing
Web address: www.dequeenhospital.com
Control: Corporation, Investor–owned, for–profit **Service:** General Medical and Surgical

Staffed Beds: 35 Admissions: 704 Census: 14 Outpatient Visits: 73093 Births: 0 Personnel: 163

DE WITT—Arkansas County

★ **DEWITT HOSPITAL (041314)**, Highway 1 and Madison Street, Zip 72042–9481, Mailing Address: P.O. Box 32, Zip 72042–0032; tel. 870/946–3571, (Total facility includes 60 beds in nursing home–type unit) **A**9 10 18 **F**3 7 11 29 34 35 40 57 59 62 64 107 119 127 128 133 143 145 **P**6
Primary Contact: Darren Caldwell, Chief Executive Officer
CMO: Stan Burleson, M.D., Chief Medical Staff
CIO: Jonathan Fuchs, Chief Information Officer
CHR: Hannah Hackney, Director Accounting and Human Resources
CNO: Rosie Killion, R.N., Chief Nursing Officer
Web address: www.dhnh.org
Control: Other not–for–profit (including NFP Corporation) **Service:** General Medical and Surgical

Staffed Beds: 85 Admissions: 389 Census: 51 Outpatient Visits: 8865 Births: 0 Total Expense ($000): 9177 Payroll Expense ($000): 4828 Personnel: 160

DUMAS—Desha County

DELTA MEMORIAL HOSPITAL (041326), 811 South Highway 65, Zip 71639–3006, Mailing Address: P.O. Box 887, Zip 71639–0887; tel. 870/382–4303 **A**9 10 18 **F**3 11 13 15 29 34 35 40 45 50 55 57 59 62 64 68 75 76 77 78 81 86 87 93 97 107 114 119 120 127 128 130 133 134 135 148 **P**6
Primary Contact: Darren Caldwell, Chief Executive Officer
CFO: Cris Bolin, Chief Executive Officer
CMO: Thomas Lewellen, D.O., Chief of Staff
CIO: Chris McTigrit, Manager Information Technology
CHR: Doris Fortenberry, Coordinator Human Resources
Web address: www.deltamem.org
Control: Other not–for–profit (including NFP Corporation) **Service:** General Medical and Surgical

Staffed Beds: 25 Admissions: 871 Census: 8 Outpatient Visits: 34604 Births: 91 Total Expense ($000): 13416 Payroll Expense ($000): 6274 Personnel: 144

EL DORADO—Union County

⊞ **MEDICAL CENTER OF SOUTH ARKANSAS (040088)**, 700 West Grove Street, Zip 71730–4416; tel. 870/863–2000 **A**1 9 10 19 20 **F**3 11 13 15 17 18 20 22 24 26 28 29 31 34 35 40 43 45 50 56 57 59 64 70 73 75 76 78 79 80 81 82 85 89 90 93 107 108 110 111 114 115 119 130 146 147 148 **P**7 8 **S** Community Health Systems, Inc., Franklin, TN
Primary Contact: Kyle Swift, Chief Executive Officer
COO: Ross Korkmas, Assistant Chief Executive Officer
CFO: Dale Maddox, Chief Financial Officer
CMO: Ken Gati, M.D., Chief of Staff
CIO: Rob Robison, Director Information Technology
CHR: LaKeitha Davis, Director Human Resources
CNO: Keitha Griffith, Chief Nursing Officer
Web address: www.themedcenter.net
Control: Corporation, Investor–owned, for–profit **Service:** General Medical and Surgical

Staffed Beds: 120 Admissions: 4510 Census: 45 Outpatient Visits: 53083 Births: 604 Total Expense ($000): 68026 Payroll Expense ($000): 23462 Personnel: 483

EUREKA SPRINGS—Carroll County

EUREKA SPRINGS HOSPITAL (041304), 24 Norris Street, Zip 72632–3541; tel. 479/253–7400 **A**9 10 18 **F**3 11 15 29 30 34 35 40 43 44 45 50 57 59 64 75 77 81 85 86 87 90 93 104 107 128 130 131 132 133 146
S Allegiance Health Management, Shreveport, LA
Primary Contact: Christopher L. Bariola, Chief Executive Officer
CFO: Sondra Wear, Director Financial Services
CMO: Gregory Kresse, M.D., Chairman Medical Staff
CIO: Drew Wood, Director Information Technology
CHR: Jodi Smith, Administrative Assistant Human Resources
CNO: Vicki Andert, Chief Nursing Officer
Web address: www.eurekaspringshospital.com
Control: Corporation, Investor–owned, for–profit **Service:** General Medical and Surgical

Staffed Beds: 15 Admissions: 334 Census: 5 Outpatient Visits: 6270 Births: 0 Total Expense ($000): 7085 Payroll Expense ($000): 2851 Personnel: 83

FAYETTEVILLE—Washington County

⊞ **HEALTHSOUTH REHABILITATION HOSPITAL (043032)**, 153 East Monte Painter Drive, Zip 72703–4002; tel. 479/444–2200 **A**1 9 10 **F**3 29 34 57 59 64 75 77 79 90 91 92 93 94 95 96 **P**8 **S** HEALTHSOUTH Corporation, Birmingham, AL
Primary Contact: Jack C. Mitchell, FACHE, Chief Executive Officer
CFO: Robbi Hudson, Chief Financial Officer
CMO: Marty Hurlbut, M.D., Medical Director
CHR: Missy Cole, Director Human Resources
CNO: Miriam Irvin, CNO
Web address: www.healthsouthfayetteville.com
Control: Corporation, Investor–owned, for–profit **Service:** Rehabilitation

Staffed Beds: 60 Admissions: 1353 Census: 48 Outpatient Visits: 5984 Births: 0 Total Expense ($000): 13106 Payroll Expense ($000): 7573 Personnel: 154

○ **PHYSICIANS' SPECIALTY HOSPITAL (040152)**, 3873 North Parkview Drive, Zip 72703, Mailing Address: 3875 North Parkview Drive, Zip 72703; tel. 479/571–7070 **A**9 10 11 **F**3 12 29 40 45 51 79 81 82 85 107 111 114 119 131 **P**2
Primary Contact: Russ Greene, Chief Executive Officer
CFO: Rhonda McCabe, Chief Financial Officer
CIO: Walter Beadle, Chief Information Officer
CHR: Deborah Austin, Chief People Officer
CNO: Kelley Oliver, R.N., Chief Nursing Officer
Web address: www.pshfay.com
Control: Corporation, Investor–owned, for–profit **Service:** Surgical

Staffed Beds: 21 Admissions: 1067 Census: 5 Outpatient Visits: 7741 Births: 0 Total Expense ($000): 30261 Payroll Expense ($000): 8943 Personnel: 215

★ **REGENCY HOSPITAL OF NORTHWEST ARKANSAS (042009)**, 1125 North College Avenue, Zip 72703–1908; tel. 479/338–2360, (Includes REGENCY HOSPITAL OF NORTHWEST ARKANSAS – SPRINGDALE, 609 West Maple Avenue, 6th Floor, Springdale, Zip 72764; tel. 479/757–2600; Jerry Alexander, Chief Executive Officer) **A**9 10 **F**1 75 85 86 87 **S** Select Medical Corporation, Mechanicsburg, PA
Primary Contact: Jerry Alexander, Chief Executive Officer
COO: Ruth Jones, Chief Operating Officer
CMO: Gary Templeton, M.D., Medical Director
CHR: Melissa Ross–Cole, Director Human Resources
Web address: www.regencyhospital.com
Control: Corporation, Investor–owned, for–profit **Service:** Long–Term Acute Care hospital

Staffed Beds: 50 Admissions: 391 Census: 30 Outpatient Visits: 0 Births: 0 Total Expense ($000): 16160 Payroll Expense ($000): 6372 Personnel: 122

□ **SPRINGWOODS BEHAVIORAL HEALTH HOSPITAL (044019)**, 1955 West Truckers Drive, Zip 72704–5637; tel. 479/973–6000 **A**1 9 10 **F**5 34 38 56 57 98 99 100 101 103 104 105 106 130 132 134 **P**6
Primary Contact: Lee Christenson, Chief Executive Officer
Web address: www.springwoodsbehavioral.com
Control: Corporation, Investor–owned, for–profit **Service:** Psychiatric

Staffed Beds: 80 Admissions: 2147 Census: 44 Outpatient Visits: 700 Births: 0 Total Expense ($000): 12626 Payroll Expense ($000): 4885 Personnel: 168

Hospital, Medicare Provider Number, Address, Telephone, Approval, Facility, and Physician Codes, Health Care System

★ American Hospital Association (AHA) membership
□ The Joint Commission accreditation   ◇ DNV Healthcare Inc. accreditation
○ Healthcare Facilities Accreditation Program
△ Commission on Accreditation of Rehabilitation Facilities (CARF) accreditation

☐ **VANTAGE POINT OF NORTHWEST ARKANSAS (044004)**, 4253 North Crossover Road, Zip 72703–4596; tel. 479/521–5731 **A**1 9 10 **F**5 87 98 99 100 101 102 103 104 106 130 132 **P**6 **S** Acadia Healthcare Company, Inc., Franklin, TN
Primary Contact: Connie Borengasser, Chief Executive Officer
CFO: Ben Winbery, Chief Financial Officer
CMO: Norman Snyder, M.D., Medical Director
CIO: Margaret Brown, Director Medical Records
CHR: Rebecca Lencho, Director Human Resources
CNO: Robyn Sims, Director of Nursing
Web address: www.vantagepointnwa.com
Control: Corporation, Investor–owned, for–profit **Service:** Psychiatric

Staffed Beds: 92 **Admissions:** 2116 **Census:** 82 **Outpatient Visits:** 135503 **Births:** 0 **Total Expense ($000):** 22604 **Payroll Expense ($000):** 14185 **Personnel:** 293

✠ **VETERANS HEALTH CARE SYSTEM OF THE OZARKS**, 1100 North College Avenue, Zip 72703–1944; tel. 479/443–4301, (Nonreporting) **A**1 2 5 **S** Department of Veterans Affairs, Washington, DC
Primary Contact: Mark A. Enderele, M.D., Director
COO: Doris B. Cassidy, Associate Director
CMO: Bonnie Baker, M.D., Chief Medical Services
CIO: Michael Gracie, Chief Information Officer
CHR: Kathryn L. Barker, Chief Human Resources Management
Web address: www.fayettevillear.va.gov
Control: Veterans Affairs, Government, federal **Service:** General Medical and Surgical

Staffed Beds: 72

✠ **WASHINGTON REGIONAL MEDICAL CENTER (040004)**, 3215 North Hills Boulevard, Zip 72703–4424; tel. 479/463–1000 **A**1 9 10 **F**3 9 11 12 13 14 17 18 20 22 24 26 28 29 30 31 34 35 39 40 43 45 46 47 48 49 50 51 53 54 56 57 58 59 60 61 62 63 64 68 70 72 73 74 75 76 77 78 79 81 82 84 85 86 87 89 92 93 97 100 102 107 110 111 114 115 118 119 126 129 130 131 132 135 146 147 148 **P**6 8
Primary Contact: William L. Bradley, President and Chief Executive Officer
CFO: Dan Eckels, Chief Financial Officer
CMO: David Ratcliff, M.D., Chief Medical Affairs
CIO: Becky Magee, Chief Information Officer
CHR: Steve Percival, Director Human Resources
CNO: Beverly Williams, Chief Nursing Officer
Web address: www.wregional.com
Control: Other not–for–profit (including NFP Corporation) **Service:** General Medical and Surgical

Staffed Beds: 270 **Admissions:** 12221 **Census:** 137 **Outpatient Visits:** 143927 **Births:** 1108 **Total Expense ($000):** 191789 **Payroll Expense ($000):** 72823 **Personnel:** 1850

FORDYCE—Dallas County

★ **DALLAS COUNTY MEDICAL CENTER (041317)**, 201 Clifton Street, Zip 71742–3099; tel. 870/352–6300 **A**9 10 18 **F**11 29 30 34 35 59 64 81 91 93 103 107 127 129 130 133
Primary Contact: John R. Tucker, FACHE, Administrator and Chief Executive Officer
CFO: Billie Launius, Director Business Finance
CMO: Michael Payne, M.D., Chief of Staff
CHR: Audrey Allen, Coordinator Benefits
CNO: Hollie Raney, Director of Nursing
Web address: www.dallascountymedicalcenter.com
Control: County–Government, nonfederal **Service:** General Medical and Surgical

Staffed Beds: 22 **Admissions:** 343 **Census:** 3 **Outpatient Visits:** 23509 **Births:** 0 **Total Expense ($000):** 8672 **Payroll Expense ($000):** 3209 **Personnel:** 77

FORREST CITY—St. Francis County

✠ **FORREST CITY MEDICAL CENTER (040019)**, 1601 Newcastle Road, Zip 72335–2218; tel. 870/261–0000 **A**1 9 10 20 **F**3 7 11 13 15 29 40 45 50 57 59 70 76 81 85 93 103 107 108 111 114 118 119 130 133 145 146 **P**6 **S** Community Health Systems, Inc., Franklin, TN
Primary Contact: Kevin Decker, Chief Executive Officer
CFO: Mark Henke, Chief Financial Officer
CMO: James Meredith, M.D., Chief of Staff
CIO: Scott Miller, Director Information Services
CHR: Sherry McLaughlin, Director Human Resources
CNO: Rhonda Nelson, Chief Nursing Officer
Web address: www.forrestcitymedicalcenter.com
Control: Corporation, Investor–owned, for–profit **Service:** General Medical and Surgical

Staffed Beds: 39 **Admissions:** 2253 **Census:** 21 **Outpatient Visits:** 34240 **Births:** 786 **Total Expense ($000):** 27178 **Payroll Expense ($000):** 8541 **Personnel:** 169

FORT SMITH—Sebastian County

✠ **ADVANCE CARE HOSPITAL OF FORT SMITH (042008)**, 7301 Rogers Avenue, 4th Floor, Zip 72903–4100; tel. 479/314–4900 **A**1 9 10 **F**1 3 29 30 68 75 77 82 84 85 91 130 148 **S** Dubuis Health System, Houston, TX
Primary Contact: Keith Rogers, Interim Administrator
CFO: Paul Veillon, CPA, Chief Financial Officer
Web address: www.dubuis.org/AdvanceCareHospitalofFortSmith
Control: Church–operated, Nongovernment, not–for profit **Service:** Long–Term Acute Care hospital

Staffed Beds: 25 **Admissions:** 243 **Census:** 18 **Outpatient Visits:** 0 **Births:** 0 **Total Expense ($000):** 7986 **Payroll Expense ($000):** 3035 **Personnel:** 57

✠ **HEALTHSOUTH REHABILITATION HOSPITAL OF FORT SMITH (043028)**, 1401 South J Street, Zip 72901–5155; tel. 479/785–3300 **A**1 9 10 **F**28 29 34 35 77 90 91 93 94 95 96 129 130 131 132 **S** HEALTHSOUTH Corporation, Birmingham, AL
Primary Contact: Dawn Watts, Chief Executive Officer
CFO: Brenda Forbes, Controller
CMO: Cygnet Schroeder, D.O., Medical Director
CIO: Donna England, Director Medical Records
CHR: S. Janette Daniels, Director Human Resources
CNO: Jacqueline Floyd, Chief Nursing Officer
Web address: www.healthsouthfortsmith.com
Control: Corporation, Investor–owned, for–profit **Service:** Rehabilitation

Staffed Beds: 60 **Admissions:** 1349 **Census:** 42 **Outpatient Visits:** 6264 **Births:** 0 **Total Expense ($000):** 13460 **Payroll Expense ($000):** 7213 **Personnel:** 131

✠ **MERCY HOSPITAL FORT SMITH (040062)**, 7301 Rogers Avenue, Zip 72903–4189, Mailing Address: P.O. Box 17000, Zip 72917–7000; tel. 479/314–6000 **A**1 2 5 9 10 **F**3 11 12 13 15 17 18 20 22 24 26 28 29 30 31 32 34 35 36 38 40 42 43 44 45 49 50 53 56 57 58 59 61 62 63 64 65 68 70 71 72 73 74 75 76 77 78 79 81 82 83 84 85 86 87 89 90 92 93 95 96 102 107 108 110 111 114 115 119 120 121 123 124 126 129 130 134 135 143 146 147 148 **P**6 8 **S** Mercy Health, Chesterfield, MO
Primary Contact: Ryan Gehrig, President
COO: Brent Hubbard, Chief Operating Officer
CFO: Greta Wilcher, Senior Vice President and Chief Financial Officer
CMO: David Hunton, M.D., Chief Medical Officer
CHR: Bryan Brown, Executive Director
CNO: Marianne Rataj, R.N., Chief Nursing Officer
Web address: www.mercy.net/fortsmithar
Control: Church–operated, Nongovernment, not–for profit **Service:** General Medical and Surgical

Staffed Beds: 374 **Admissions:** 13423 **Census:** 181 **Outpatient Visits:** 155352 **Births:** 1803 **Total Expense ($000):** 222260 **Payroll Expense ($000):** 66364 **Personnel:** 1515

✠ **SELECT SPECIALTY HOSPITAL–FORT SMITH (042006)**, 1001 Towson Avenue, 6 Central, Zip 72901–4921; tel. 479/441–3960 **A**1 9 10 **F**1 3 29 34 45 46 56 57 74 75 78 79 94 148 **S** Select Medical Corporation, Mechanicsburg, PA
Primary Contact: Cindy McLain, Chief Executive Officer
Web address: www.selectspecialtyhospitals.com/company/locations/fortsmith.aspx
Control: Corporation, Investor–owned, for–profit **Service:** Long–Term Acute Care hospital

Staffed Beds: 34 **Admissions:** 443 **Census:** 31 **Outpatient Visits:** 0 **Births:** 0 **Total Expense ($000):** 13380 **Payroll Expense ($000):** 4638 **Personnel:** 81

✠ **SPARKS REGIONAL MEDICAL CENTER (040055)**, 100 Towson Avenue, Zip 72901–2632, Mailing Address: P.O. Box 2406, Zip 72917–7006; tel. 479/441–4000 **A**1 5 6 9 10 **F**3 8 12 13 15 17 18 20 22 24 26 28 29 30 31 34 35 40 45 46 47 48 49 50 51 53 54 56 58 59 60 62 64 67 70 72 74 75 76 77 78 79 81 82 85 86 89 93 97 98 103 107 108 109 110 111 112 113 114 115 117 119 120 121 122 124 126 127 129 130 144 146 147 148 **P**8 **S** Community Health Systems, Inc., Franklin, TN
Primary Contact: Daniel E. McKay, Chief Executive Officer
COO: Jeremy Drinkwitz, Chief Operating Officer
CFO: Richard Boone, Chief Financial Officer
CMO: Katherine Irish–Clardy, M.D., Chief Medical Officer
CIO: Tom Sallis, Director Information Systems
CHR: Robert Freeman, Director Human Resources
CNO: Cindy Slaydon, Chief Nursing Executive
Web address: www.sparks.org
Control: Corporation, Investor–owned, for–profit **Service:** General Medical and Surgical

Staffed Beds: 303 **Admissions:** 16080 **Census:** 221 **Outpatient Visits:** 164022 **Births:** 1101 **Total Expense ($000):** 222233 **Payroll Expense ($000):** 67210 **Personnel:** 1654

Many Facility Codes have changed. Please refer to the AHA Guide Code Chart. © 2014 AHA Guide

GRAVETTE—Benton County

OZARKS COMMUNITY HOSPITAL (041331), 1101 Jackson Street S.W., Zip 72736–9121; tel. 479/787–5291 **A**9 10 18 **F**3 29 40 44 45 50 56 59 64 65 75 82 85 87 89 93 96 100 103 104 107 111 114 119 128 129 130 133 143 **P**6
Primary Contact: Paul Taylor, Administrator
Web address: www.ochonline.com/
Control: Corporation, Investor–owned, for–profit **Service:** General Medical and Surgical

Staffed Beds: 25 **Admissions:** 688 **Census:** 10 **Outpatient Visits:** 34935 **Births:** 0 **Total Expense ($000):** 12491 **Payroll Expense ($000):** 5787 **Personnel:** 187

HARRISON—Boone County

★ **NORTH ARKANSAS REGIONAL MEDICAL CENTER (040017)**, 620 North Main Street, Zip 72601–2911; tel. 870/414–4000 **A**9 10 19 20 **F**3 7 11 13 15 17 18 24 28 29 30 31 34 35 39 40 41 43 45 57 59 62 63 64 65 68 70 73 75 76 77 78 79 81 83 84 85 86 89 92 93 97 98 102 103 107 108 110 111 114 115 118 119 120 121 123 127 129 130 131 132 144 146 147 148 **P**8
Primary Contact: Vincent Leist, President and Chief Executive Officer
COO: Richard McBryde, Senior Vice President and Chief Operating Officer
CFO: Debbie Henry, Vice President Financial Services
CIO: William J. Bogle, Director Information Systems
CHR: Linda Dickey Melton, Vice President Human Resources
CNO: Sammie Cribbs, Vice President Patient Care Services
Web address: www.narmc.com
Control: Other not–for–profit (including NFP Corporation) **Service:** General Medical and Surgical

Staffed Beds: 127 **Admissions:** 4368 **Census:** 39 **Outpatient Visits:** 127489 **Births:** 761 **Total Expense ($000):** 73668 **Payroll Expense ($000):** 29860 **Personnel:** 728

HEBER SPRINGS—Cleburne County

☒ **BAPTIST HEALTH MEDICAL CENTER–HEBER SPRINGS (041312)**, 1800 Bypass Road, Zip 72543–9135; tel. 501/887–3000 **A**1 9 10 18 **F**3 8 11 15 28 29 30 31 34 35 36 40 43 45 48 50 51 57 59 64 68 74 75 77 78 79 81 85 93 102 107 110 111 115 116 117 119 127 129 131 132 133 134 135 143 146 **S** Baptist Health, Little Rock, AR
Primary Contact: Edward L. Lacy, FACHE, Vice President and Administrator
Web address: www.baptist-health.com/maps–directions/bhmc–heber–springs
Control: Other not–for–profit (including NFP Corporation) **Service:** General Medical and Surgical

Staffed Beds: 25 **Admissions:** 766 **Census:** 7 **Outpatient Visits:** 30365 **Births:** 0 **Total Expense ($000):** 18489 **Payroll Expense ($000):** 6063 **Personnel:** 135

HELENA—Phillips County

☒ **HELENA REGIONAL MEDICAL CENTER (040085)**, 1801 Martin Luther King Drive, Zip 72342, Mailing Address: P.O. Box 788, Zip 72342–0788; tel. 870/338–5800 **A**1 9 10 20 **F**3 11 13 15 28 29 34 40 43 50 59 62 70 74 75 76 79 81 86 87 89 90 91 93 97 107 108 111 114 119 130 132 133 135 145 146 147 148 **S** Community Health Systems, Inc., Franklin, TN
Primary Contact: Buddy Daniels, Chief Executive Officer
CFO: Amy Rice, Chief Financial Officer
CIO: Robert White, Director Information Technology
CHR: Juril Fonzie, Director Human Resources
CNO: Jodi Love, R.N., Chief Nursing Officer
Web address: www.helenarmc.com
Control: Corporation, Investor–owned, for–profit **Service:** General Medical and Surgical

Staffed Beds: 105 **Admissions:** 1738 **Census:** 13 **Outpatient Visits:** 23666 **Births:** 159 **Total Expense ($000):** 28610 **Payroll Expense ($000):** 8601 **Personnel:** 146

HOPE—Hempstead County

◇ **WADLEY REGIONAL MEDICAL CENTER AT HOPE (040153)**, 2001 South Main Street, Zip 71801–8194; tel. 870/722–3800 **A**9 10 21 **F**3 11 15 18 29 35 40 56 57 59 64 70 86 93 98 103 107 111 114 119 127 130 **S** IASIS Healthcare, Franklin, TN
Primary Contact: Thomas D. Gilbert, FACHE, Chief Executive Officer
CFO: Bonny Sorensen, Chief Financial Officer
CIO: Matt Kesterson, Director Information Services
CHR: Debby Butler, Director Human Resources
CNO: Shelly Strayhorn, R.N., Chief Nursing Officer
Web address: www.wadleyhealthathope.com
Control: Corporation, Investor–owned, for–profit **Service:** General Medical and Surgical

Staffed Beds: 79 **Admissions:** 1210 **Census:** 18 **Outpatient Visits:** 25187 **Births:** 0 **Total Expense ($000):** 13394 **Payroll Expense ($000):** 6170 **Personnel:** 136

HOT SPRINGS—Garland County

□ **NATIONAL PARK MEDICAL CENTER (040078)**, 1910 Malvern Avenue, Zip 71901–7799; tel. 501/321–1000 **A**1 9 10 19 **F**3 11 13 15 17 18 20 22 24 28 29 30 31 34 35 40 45 46 47 49 56 57 59 62 64 70 73 74 75 76 78 79 81 85 87 89 90 93 98 103 107 108 110 111 114 119 124 128 129 130 131 132 143 146 147 148 **P**1 **S** Capella Healthcare, Franklin, TN
Primary Contact: Jerry D. Mabry, FACHE, Chief Executive Officer
COO: Brian Bell, Associate Administrator and Chief Operating Officer
CFO: Robbie Pettey, Chief Financial Officer
CMO: David Desoto, M.D., Chief of Staff
CIO: Thomas Elmore, Director Information System
CHR: Sandra Culliver, Director Human Resources
Web address: www.nationalparkmedical.com
Control: Corporation, Investor–owned, for–profit **Service:** General Medical and Surgical

Staffed Beds: 193 **Admissions:** 6459 **Census:** 95 **Outpatient Visits:** 53731 **Births:** 545 **Total Expense ($000):** 69568 **Payroll Expense ($000):** 25673 **Personnel:** 552

HOT SPRINGS NATIONAL PARK—Garland County

☒ **ADVANCE CARE HOSPITAL OF HOT SPRINGS (042004)**, 300 Werner Street, 3rd Floor East, Zip 71913–6406; tel. 501/609–4300 **A**1 9 10 **F**1 3 29 30 45 68 77 79 85 87 118 130 135 148 **S** Dubuis Health System, Houston, TX
Primary Contact: Keith Rogers, Administrator
CFO: Paul Veillon, CPA, Chief Financial Officer
CIO: David Cook, Manager Information Systems
Web address: www.dubuis.org/AdvanceCareHospitalofHotSprings
Control: Church–operated, Nongovernment, not–for profit **Service:** Long–Term Acute Care hospital

Staffed Beds: 26 **Admissions:** 184 **Census:** 13 **Outpatient Visits:** 0 **Births:** 0 **Total Expense ($000):** 5987 **Payroll Expense ($000):** 2189 **Personnel:** 48

★ **LEVI HOSPITAL (040132)**, 300 Prospect Avenue, Zip 71901–4097; tel. 501/624–1281 **A**9 10 **F**40 57 59 64 93 98 102 103 104 107 130 131 132
Primary Contact: Patrick G. McCabe, Jr., FACHE, President and Chief Executive Officer
CFO: Charles Oswalt, Vice President, Chief Financial Officer and Compliance Officer
CMO: P. Ross Bandy, M.D., Chief Medical Officer and Chief of Staff
CIO: Charles Oswalt, Vice President, Chief Financial Officer and Compliance Officer
CHR: Susan Kramer, Director of Human Resources
CNO: Steven Boyd, R.N., Nurse Executive
Web address: www.levihospital.com
Control: Other not–for–profit (including NFP Corporation) **Service:** Psychiatric

Staffed Beds: 50 **Admissions:** 1284 **Census:** 19 **Outpatient Visits:** 17409 **Births:** 0 **Total Expense ($000):** 7854 **Payroll Expense ($000):** 4421 **Personnel:** 104

Hospital, Medicare Provider Number, Address, Telephone, Approval, Facility, and Physician Codes, Health Care System

★ American Hospital Association (AHA) membership
□ The Joint Commission accreditation   ◇ DNV Healthcare Inc. accreditation
○ Healthcare Facilities Accreditation Program
△ Commission on Accreditation of Rehabilitation Facilities (CARF) accreditation

AR

MERCY HOSPITAL HOT SPRINGS (040026), 300 Werner Street, Zip 71913–6406, Mailing Address: P.O. Box 29001, Zip 71903–9001; tel. 501/622–1000, (Includes HEALTHPARK HOSPITAL, 1636 Higdon Ferry Road, Zip 71913; tel. 501/520–2000) **A**1 2 9 10 19 **F**3 11 12 13 15 17 18 20 22 24 26 28 29 30 31 34 35 37 38 40 43 49 50 56 57 59 62 64 65 66 68 69 70 71 74 75 76 77 78 79 81 84 85 86 87 89 90 92 93 98 103 107 108 110 111 112 114 115 116 117 118 119 120 121 124 126 129 130 132 134 135 146 147 148 **P**6 **S** Mercy Health, Chesterfield, MO
Primary Contact: Kim Day, Interim President
COO: Andrew Runge, Chief Operating Officer
CFO: Sarah Bradley, Vice President Finance
CIO: Bill Perry, Director Information Systems
Web address: www.saintjosephs.com
Control: Church–operated, Nongovernment, not–for profit **Service:** General Medical and Surgical

Staffed Beds: 282 **Admissions:** 12220 **Census:** 163 **Outpatient Visits:** 165910 **Births:** 939 **Total Expense ($000):** 177930 **Payroll Expense ($000):** 64996 **Personnel:** 1271

JACKSONVILLE—Pulaski County

ALLEGIANCE SPECIALTY HOSPITAL OF LITTLE ROCK See Cornerstone Hospital of North Little Rock

CORNERSTONE HOSPITAL OF NORTH LITTLE ROCK (042010), 1400 Braden Street, Zip 72076–3721; tel. 501/985–7026 **A**9 10 **F**1 3 18 29 59 65 75 148 **S** Cornerstone Healthcare Group, Dallas, TX
Primary Contact: Steve Patterson, Chief Executive Officer
CNO: Joy Miller, Chief Nursing Officer
Web address: www.chghospitals.com/littlerock/
Control: Corporation, Investor–owned, for–profit **Service:** Long–Term Acute Care hospital

Staffed Beds: 40 **Admissions:** 277 **Census:** 19 **Outpatient Visits:** 0 **Births:** 0 **Total Expense ($000):** 8518 **Payroll Expense ($000):** 3899 **Personnel:** 57

NORTH METRO MEDICAL CENTER (040074), 1400 West Braden Street, Zip 72076–3788; tel. 501/985–7000 **A**9 10 **F**3 11 12 15 17 29 34 35 40 43 50 56 57 59 62 64 68 70 79 80 81 85 103 104 107 108 110 111 115 118 119 129 130 132 146 148 **P**8 **S** Allegiance Health Management, Shreveport, LA
Primary Contact: Cindy Stafford, Chief Executive Officer
CFO: Lynn Muller, Chief Financial Officer
CMO: Ann Layton, M.D., Chief of Staff
CHR: Jane Rockwell, Director Support Services
Web address: www.northmetromed.com
Control: Corporation, Investor–owned, for–profit **Service:** General Medical and Surgical

Staffed Beds: 73 **Admissions:** 1462 **Census:** 29 **Outpatient Visits:** 54718 **Births:** 0 **Total Expense ($000):** 29140 **Payroll Expense ($000):** 13746 **Personnel:** 282

JONESBORO—Craighead County

HEALTHSOUTH REHABILITATION HOSPITAL OF JONESBORO (043029), 1201 Fleming Avenue, Zip 72401–4311, Mailing Address: P.O. Box 1680, Zip 72403–1680; tel. 870/932–0440, (Nonreporting) **A**1 9 10 **S** HEALTHSOUTH Corporation, Birmingham, AL
Primary Contact: Donna Harris, Chief Executive Officer
CFO: Allan Jones, Controller
CMO: Terence Braden, III, D.O., Medical Director
CHR: Tammy Barley, Director, Human Resources
Web address: www.healthsouthjonesboro.com
Control: Corporation, Investor–owned, for–profit **Service:** Rehabilitation

Staffed Beds: 67

NEA BAPTIST MEMORIAL HOSPITAL (040118), 4800 East Johnson Avenue, Zip 72401–8413; tel. 870/936–1000 **A**1 9 10 **F**3 11 12 13 17 18 20 22 24 28 29 30 31 34 39 40 45 46 48 49 57 59 60 74 75 76 77 78 79 81 82 84 85 86 87 89 93 107 108 111 115 118 119 124 130 135 146 148 **P**8 **S** Baptist Memorial Health Care Corporation, Memphis, TN
Primary Contact: Brad Parsons, FACHE, Administrator and Chief Executive Officer
CFO: Kyle Sanders, Chief Financial Officer
CMO: Stephen Woodruff, M.D., Chief Medical Officer
CIO: Terry Crider, Information Technology Site Manager
CHR: James Keller, Director Human Resources
CNO: Paula Grimes, R.N., Chief Nursing Officer
Web address: www.neabaptist.com
Control: Other not–for–profit (including NFP Corporation) **Service:** General Medical and Surgical

Staffed Beds: 100 **Admissions:** 6714 **Census:** 71 **Outpatient Visits:** 44448 **Births:** 801 **Total Expense ($000):** 93900 **Payroll Expense ($000):** 33731 **Personnel:** 717

ST. BERNARDS MEDICAL CENTER (040020), 225 East Jackson Avenue, Zip 72401–3119; tel. 870/207–4100, (Total facility includes 26 beds in nursing home–type unit) **A**1 9 10 19 **F**2 3 5 11 12 13 15 17 18 20 22 24 29 30 31 32 34 35 37 38 40 43 45 46 48 49 50 51 53 54 55 56 57 58 59 60 61 62 63 64 68 69 70 71 72 74 75 76 77 78 79 81 82 84 85 86 87 89 92 93 96 98 99 100 101 102 103 104 105 107 108 110 111 114 115 116 117 119 120 121 123 124 126 128 129 130 131 132 135 136 141 144 145 146 147 148 **P**6 8
Primary Contact: Chris B. Barber, FACHE, President and Chief Executive Officer
COO: Michael K. Givens, FACHE, Administrator
CFO: Harry Hutchison, Vice President Fiscal Services
CMO: Shane Speights, M.D., Vice President Medical Affairs
CIO: Mark Odom, Chief Information Officer
CHR: Jacque Hurd, Vice President Human Resources
CNO: Susan Greenwood, R.N., Vice President and Chief Nursing Officer
Web address: www.stbernards.info
Control: Church–operated, Nongovernment, not–for profit **Service:** General Medical and Surgical

Staffed Beds: 380 **Admissions:** 17108 **Census:** 195 **Outpatient Visits:** 235587 **Births:** 1329 **Total Expense ($000):** 253280 **Payroll Expense ($000):** 85355 **Personnel:** 1935

LAKE VILLAGE—Chicot County

★ **CHICOT MEMORIAL MEDICAL CENTER (041328)**, 2729 Highway 65 and 82 South, Zip 71653; tel. 870/265–5351 **A**9 10 18 **F**3 7 11 13 15 18 29 34 35 36 40 43 45 50 53 57 59 62 64 71 75 77 81 82 85 87 93 107 111 114 119 130 132 133 146 148
Primary Contact: David Mantz, Chief Executive Officer
CFO: Vicki Allen, Chief Financial Officer
CMO: Michael Bradley Mayfield, M.D., Chief of Staff
CIO: David Andrews, Manager Information Systems
CHR: Bobbie Ivey, Director Human Resources
CNO: Eric Selby, R.N., Chief Nursing Officer
Web address: www.chicotmemorial.com
Control: Other not–for–profit (including NFP Corporation) **Service:** General Medical and Surgical

Staffed Beds: 25 **Admissions:** 1065 **Census:** 11 **Outpatient Visits:** 19235 **Births:** 105 **Total Expense ($000):** 16257 **Payroll Expense ($000):** 7581 **Personnel:** 142

SOUTHEAST REHABILITATION HOSPITAL (043034), 2729–A Highway 65 and 82 South, Zip 71653; tel. 870/265–4333 **A**10 **F**3 90
Primary Contact: Stacy Noble, Administrator
Web address: www.lakevillageclinic.com/southeast–rehabilitation–hospital.html
Control: Partnership, Investor–owned, for–profit **Service:** Rehabilitation

Staffed Beds: 15 **Admissions:** 195 **Census:** 6 **Outpatient Visits:** 0 **Births:** 0 **Total Expense ($000):** 3547 **Payroll Expense ($000):** 2277 **Personnel:** 49

LITTLE ROCK—Pulaski County

ARKANSAS CHILDREN'S HOSPITAL (043300), 1 Children's Way, Zip 72202–3500; tel. 501/364–1100 **A**1 3 5 8 9 10 **F**3 7 8 9 11 12 16 17 19 21 23 25 27 28 29 30 31 32 34 35 38 39 40 41 43 45 46 48 50 53 55 57 58 59 60 61 64 68 71 72 73 74 75 77 78 79 80 81 82 84 85 86 87 88 89 90 91 93 94 97 99 100 102 107 108 111 114 115 116 117 118 119 126 129 130 131 132 135 136 137 138 143 146 **P**1
Primary Contact: Marcella Doderer, FACHE, President and Chief Executive Officer
COO: David Berry, Senior Vice President and Chief Operating Officer
CFO: Gena Wingfield, Senior Vice President and Chief Financial Officer
CMO: Jay Deshpande, M.D., Chief Quality Officer and Chief Medical Officer
CIO: Darrell Leonhardt, Senior Vice President Information Systems
CHR: Andree Trosclair, Vice President Human Resources
Web address: www.archildrens.org
Control: Other not–for–profit (including NFP Corporation) **Service:** Children's general

Staffed Beds: 338 **Admissions:** 14845 **Census:** 222 **Outpatient Visits:** 343993 **Births:** 0 **Total Expense ($000):** 481478 **Payroll Expense ($000):** 203821 **Personnel:** 3644

ARKANSAS HEART HOSPITAL (040134), 1701 South Shackleford Road, Zip 72211–4335; tel. 501/219–7000 **A**1 3 5 9 10 **F**3 11 17 18 20 22 24 26 29 30 34 35 40 57 58 59 64 70 74 75 81 85 86 102 107 111 114 119 127 129 130 132 148
Primary Contact: Bruce Murphy, M.D., President and Chief Executive Officer
CHR: Brent Davis, Human Resources Team Leader
Web address: www.arheart.com
Control: Partnership, Investor–owned, for–profit **Service:** Heart

Staffed Beds: 112 **Admissions:** 6212 **Census:** 57 **Outpatient Visits:** 29716 **Births:** 0 **Total Expense ($000):** 121442 **Payroll Expense ($000):** 34839 **Personnel:** 718

ARKANSAS STATE HOSPITAL (044011), 305 South Palm Street, Zip 72205–5432; tel. 501/686–9000 **A**1 3 5 9 10 **F**3 29 30 53 98 99 103 143 **P**6
Primary Contact: Steve Henson, Chief Executive Officer
CFO: Gary W. Hollis, Comptroller
CMO: Steven Dornon, M.D., Medical Director
CIO: Tina Grissom, Chief Information Technology Officer
CHR: Donna Sadler, Director Human Resources
CNO: James Scoggins, Director of Nursing
Web address: www.state.ar.us/dhs/dmhs
Control: State–Government, nonfederal **Service:** Psychiatric

Staffed Beds: 222 **Admissions:** 657 **Census:** 202 **Outpatient Visits:** 0 **Births:** 0 **Total Expense ($000):** 54375 **Payroll Expense ($000):** 25253 **Personnel:** 605

★ **BAPTIST HEALTH EXTENDED CARE HOSPITAL (042012)**, 9601 Interstate 630, Exit 7, 10th Floor, Zip 72205–7202; tel. 501/202–1070 **A**9 10 **F**1 3 29 31 77 87 130 148 **S** Baptist Health, Little Rock, AR
Primary Contact: Mike Perkins, Vice President and Administrator
CFO: Robert C. Roberts, Vice President
CIO: David House, Vice President
CHR: Anthony Kendall, Vice President Human Resources
CNO: Diane Smith, Chief Nursing Officer
Web address: www.baptist–health.com/maps–directions/bh_extended_care/default.aspx
Control: Other not–for–profit (including NFP Corporation) **Service:** Long–Term Acute Care hospital

Staffed Beds: 37 **Admissions:** 297 **Census:** 23 **Outpatient Visits:** 0 **Births:** 0 **Total Expense ($000):** 11923 **Payroll Expense ($000):** 4491 **Personnel:** 87

☒ **BAPTIST HEALTH MEDICAL CENTER–LITTLE ROCK (040114)**, 9601 Interstate 630, Exit 7, Zip 72205–7299; tel. 501/202–2000 **A**1 3 5 6 9 10 **F**3 4 5 7 8 11 12 13 15 17 18 20 22 24 26 28 29 30 31 32 34 35 36 37 38 40 43 44 45 49 50 54 56 57 58 59 60 61 62 64 65 67 68 70 72 73 74 75 76 77 78 79 81 82 84 85 86 87 89 93 98 99 100 101 102 103 104 107 108 110 111 114 118 119 126 128 129 130 131 132 134 135 137 138 143 144 146 147 148 **S** Baptist Health, Little Rock, AR
Primary Contact: Greg Crain, Vice President and Administrator
CFO: Robert C. Roberts, Senior Vice President Financial Services
CMO: Anthony Bennett, M.D., Chief Clinical Affairs
CIO: David House, Vice President and Chief Information Officer
CHR: Anthony Kendall, Vice President Human Resources
CNO: Jill Massiet, R.N., Vice President Patient Care
Web address: www.baptist–health.org/maps–directions/bhmc–lr
Control: Other not–for–profit (including NFP Corporation) **Service:** General Medical and Surgical

Staffed Beds: 688 **Admissions:** 28692 **Census:** 434 **Outpatient Visits:** 145990 **Births:** 3223 **Total Expense ($000):** 428638 **Payroll Expense ($000):** 137364 **Personnel:** 2497

☒ △ **BAPTIST HEALTH REHABILITATION INSTITUTE (043026)**, 9601 Interstate 630, Exit 7, Zip 72205–7202; tel. 501/202–7000 **A**1 3 5 7 9 10 **F**29 30 35 50 53 64 75 79 81 86 87 90 91 93 95 96 130 132 143 **S** Baptist Health, Little Rock, AR
Primary Contact: Lee Gentry, FACHE, Vice President and Administrator
CFO: Robert C. Roberts, Senior Vice President
CIO: David House, Vice President and Chief Information Officer
CHR: Anthony Kendall, Vice President Human Resources
Web address: www.baptist–health.com/locations/accesspoint.aspx?accessPointID=202
Control: Other not–for–profit (including NFP Corporation) **Service:** Rehabilitation

Staffed Beds: 100 **Admissions:** 1429 **Census:** 50 **Outpatient Visits:** 128710 **Births:** 0 **Total Expense ($000):** 28984 **Payroll Expense ($000):** 13442 **Personnel:** 258

☒ △ **CENTRAL ARKANSAS VETERANS HEALTHCARE SYSTEM**, 4300 West Seventh Street, Zip 72205–5446; tel. 501/257–1000, (Includes NORTH LITTLE ROCK DIVISION, 2200 Fort Roots Drive, North Little Rock, Zip 72114–1706; tel. 501/661–1202), (Nonreporting) **A**1 2 3 5 7 8 **S** Department of Veterans Affairs, Washington, DC
Primary Contact: Michael R. Winn, Director
CFO: Colonel Nate Todd, Chief Financial Officer
CMO: Margie Scott, M.D., Chief of Staff
CIO: Jim Hall, Acting Chief Information Officer
CHR: Richard Nelson, Chief of Human Resources Management Services
Web address: www.littlerock.va.gov/
Control: Veterans Affairs, Government, federal **Service:** General Medical and Surgical

Staffed Beds: 386

☒ **PINNACLE POINTE HOSPITAL (044013)**, 11501 Financial Center Parkway, Zip 72211–3715; tel. 501/223–3322 **A**1 9 10 **F**29 34 98 99 100 101 102 104 105 106 130 **S** Universal Health Services, Inc., King of Prussia, PA
Primary Contact: John McNally, Chief Executive Officer
CFO: Gina Dailey, Chief Financial Officer
CMO: Ben Nimmo, M.D., Medical Director
CIO: James L. Howe, Director Human Resources
CHR: James L. Howe, Director Human Resources
CNO: Bobby Alexander, Chief Nursing Officer
Web address: www.pinnaclepointehospital.com
Control: Corporation, Investor–owned, for–profit **Service:** Children's hospital psychiatric

Staffed Beds: 124 **Admissions:** 2485 **Census:** 108 **Outpatient Visits:** 348588 **Births:** 0 **Total Expense ($000):** 16482 **Payroll Expense ($000):** 9838 **Personnel:** 217

☒ **ST. VINCENT INFIRMARY MEDICAL CENTER (040007)**, Two St. Vincent Circle, Zip 72205–5499; tel. 501/552–3000 **A**1 3 9 10 **F**3 11 13 17 18 20 22 24 26 27 28 29 30 31 34 35 37 40 43 44 45 48 49 50 51 53 54 56 57 58 59 60 61 64 68 70 72 74 75 76 77 78 79 80 81 82 83 84 85 86 87 91 92 93 96 97 98 100 101 102 107 108 109 110 111 112 114 115 116 117 118 119 124 126 129 130 132 135 143 146 147 148 **P**1 6 7 **S** Catholic Health Initiatives, Englewood, CO
Primary Contact: Chad S. Aduddell, President
COO: Chad S. Aduddell, President
CFO: Mark J. McGinnis, Executive Vice President and Chief Financial Officer
CMO: Thomas H. Cummins, M.D., Senior Vice President and Chief Medical Officer
CHR: Tim Osterholm, Senior Vice President and Chief People Officer
CNO: Brenda Baird, Senior Vice President and Chief Nursing Officer
Web address: www.chistvincent.com/
Control: Church–operated, Nongovernment, not–for profit **Service:** General Medical and Surgical

Staffed Beds: 447 **Admissions:** 20145 **Census:** 279 **Outpatient Visits:** 147739 **Births:** 1567 **Total Expense ($000):** 362736 **Payroll Expense ($000):** 136371 **Personnel:** 1857

☒ **UAMS MEDICAL CENTER (040016)**, 4301 West Markham Street, Zip 72205–7101; tel. 501/686–7000 **A**1 3 5 8 9 10 13 **F**3 11 12 13 14 15 17 18 20 22 24 26 29 30 31 34 40 43 44 45 46 47 48 49 50 52 53 54 55 56 57 58 59 60 61 64 66 67 68 70 71 72 73 74 75 76 77 78 79 81 82 84 85 86 87 91 92 93 94 96 97 98 99 100 101 102 103 104 107 108 110 111 114 115 116 117 118 119 120 121 123 124 126 129 130 131 132 136 138 139 141 142 145 146 147 148 **P**6
Primary Contact: Roxane A. Townsend, M.D., Chief Executive Officer
COO: Melissa Fontaine, Chief Operating Officer
CFO: William Bowes, Chief Financial Officer
CMO: Nicholas P. Lang, M.D., Chief Medical Officer
CIO: David L. Miller, Chief Information Officer
CHR: Jeff Risinger, Director Human Resources
CNO: Mary Helen Forrest, R.N., Chief Nursing Officer
Web address: www.uams.edu/medcenter
Control: State–Government, nonfederal **Service:** General Medical and Surgical

Staffed Beds: 453 **Admissions:** 22679 **Census:** 373 **Outpatient Visits:** 443761 **Births:** 2945 **Total Expense ($000):** 579073 **Payroll Expense ($000):** 189007 **Personnel:** 3641

MAGNOLIA—Columbia County

★ **MAGNOLIA REGIONAL MEDICAL CENTER (040067)**, 101 Hospital Drive, Zip 71753–2415, Mailing Address: P.O. Box 629, Zip 71754–0629; tel. 870/235–3000 **A**9 10 20 **F**3 11 13 15 29 31 34 35 40 43 57 59 62 64 70 75 76 77 81 86 87 91 93 97 107 108 110 111 115 119 129 130 132 133 146 147 148
Primary Contact: Margaret M. West, MS, Chief Executive Officer
CMO: John Alexander, Jr., M.D., Chief of Staff
CHR: Shawnee Hicks, Director Human Resources
Web address: www.magnoliahospital.org
Control: City–Government, nonfederal **Service:** General Medical and Surgical

Staffed Beds: 45 **Admissions:** 1611 **Census:** 12 **Outpatient Visits:** 31689 **Births:** 216 **Total Expense ($000):** 22819 **Payroll Expense ($000):** 10871 **Personnel:** 240

AR

MALVERN—Hot Spring County

★ **BAPTIST HEALTH MEDICAL CENTER–HOT SPRING COUNTY (040076)**, 1001 Schneider Drive, Zip 72104–4811; tel. 501/332–1000 **A**9 10 **F**3 11 15 17 18 29 34 40 43 45 57 59 62 70 72 73 75 81 89 98 106 107 110 111 115 119 129 130 146 148 **S** Baptist Health, Little Rock, AR
Primary Contact: Sheila Williams, Vice President and Administrator
CMO: Allen Gerber, M.D., Chief of Staff
CHR: Kelli Hopkins, Director Human Resources
CNO: Dee Schall, Chief Nursing Officer
Web address: www.https://www.baptist–health.org
Control: Other not–for–profit (including NFP Corporation) **Service:** General Medical and Surgical

Staffed Beds: 72 Admissions: 2210 Census: 24 Outpatient Visits: 32295 Births: 0 Total Expense ($000): 20739 Payroll Expense ($000): 10322 Personnel: 300

MAUMELLE—Pulaski County

☐ **METHODIST BEHAVIORAL HOSPITAL OF ARKANSAS (044017)**, 1601 Murphy Drive, Zip 72113–6187; tel. 501/803–3388 **A**1 9 10 **F**30 32 38 50 54 64 75 86 87 98 99 102 104 106 130 **P**1
Primary Contact: Andy Altom, Chief Executive Officer
Web address: www.umch.org
Control: Other not–for–profit (including NFP Corporation) **Service:** Children's hospital psychiatric

Staffed Beds: 60 Admissions: 1302 Census: 54 Outpatient Visits: 84229 Births: 0 Total Expense ($000): 15746 Payroll Expense ($000): 7478 Personnel: 132

MCGEHEE—Desha County

★ **MCGEHEE–DESHA COUNTY HOSPITAL (041308)**, 900 South Third, Zip 71654–2562, Mailing Address: P.O. Box 351, Zip 71654–0351; tel. 870/222–5600 **A**9 10 18 **F**3 11 29 40 45 57 59 62 64 68 107 111 119 132 133 135 146 148
Primary Contact: John E. Heard, Chief Executive Officer
CFO: Teresa Morgan, Chief Financial Officer
CMO: James Young, M.D., Chief of Staff
CIO: Shaun Perry, Chief Information Officer
CNO: Sarah Calvert, Chief Nursing Officer
Control: Other not–for–profit (including NFP Corporation) **Service:** General Medical and Surgical

Staffed Beds: 25 Admissions: 287 Census: 3 Outpatient Visits: 6935 Births: 0 Total Expense ($000): 8982 Payroll Expense ($000): 4220 Personnel: 103

MENA—Polk County

★ **MENA REGIONAL HEALTH SYSTEM (040015)**, 311 North Morrow Street, Zip 71953–2516; tel. 479/394–6100 **A**9 10 20 **F**3 11 13 15 29 30 31 32 34 35 40 43 45 49 50 54 56 57 59 64 68 70 75 76 77 78 79 81 86 87 90 91 93 96 98 100 101 103 104 107 108 111 114 115 118 119 129 130 131 133 144 146 147 **P**8
Primary Contact: Tim Bowen, Chief Executive Officer
COO: Richard A. Billingsley, MSN, Chief Operating Officer and Chief Nursing Officer
CMO: Thomas Sullivan, M.D., Chief of Staff
CIO: Nicholas Dunn, Director Information Systems
CHR: Amy Jarman, Director Human Resources
CNO: Richard A. Billingsley, MSN, Chief Operating Officer and Chief Nursing Officer
Web address: www.menaregional.com
Control: City–Government, nonfederal **Service:** General Medical and Surgical

Staffed Beds: 65 Admissions: 1671 Census: 21 Outpatient Visits: 25702 Births: 335 Total Expense ($000): 26385 Payroll Expense ($000): 13139 Personnel: 247

MONTICELLO—Drew County

DREW MEMORIAL HOSPITAL (040051), 778 Scogin Drive, Zip 71655–5729; tel. 870/367–2411 **A**9 10 20 **F**11 13 15 29 30 31 34 35 40 43 45 57 59 62 64 68 70 75 76 77 78 81 82 86 87 91 93 96 103 107 110 111 115 119 128 129 130 132 133 147 148 **P**6
Primary Contact: Ronald K. Rooney, FACHE, Interim Chief Executive Officer
CFO: Shannon Clark, Chief Financial Officer
CMO: Jeffery Reinhart, M.D., Chief of Staff
CIO: Rusty Bryant, Director Information Technology
CHR: Keith Van Dee, Director Human Resources
CNO: Linda Orrell, Interim Chief Nursing Officer
Web address: www.drewmemorial.org
Control: Other not–for–profit (including NFP Corporation) **Service:** General Medical and Surgical

Staffed Beds: 49 Admissions: 2454 Census: 19 Outpatient Visits: 20172 Births: 305 Total Expense ($000): 26361 Payroll Expense ($000): 11180 Personnel: 260

MORRILTON—Conway County

ST. ANTHONY'S MEDICAL CENTER See St. Vincent Morrilton

★ **ST. VINCENT MORRILTON (041324)**, 4 Hospital Drive, Zip 72110–4510; tel. 501/977–2300 **A**9 10 18 **F**2 3 11 15 28 29 30 34 35 40 50 56 57 59 62 64 70 77 79 81 85 87 93 97 107 110 111 112 114 119 127 130 131 132 133 135 143 146 **P**6 **S** Catholic Health Initiatives, Englewood, CO
Primary Contact: Leslie Arnold, Chief Executive Officer and Administrator
CFO: Amanda George, Assistant Controller
CMO: Charles Howard, M.D., Chief of Staff
CHR: Tammy Smith, Director Human Resources
Web address: www.stanthonysmorrilton.com/
Control: Church–operated, Nongovernment, not–for profit **Service:** General Medical and Surgical

Staffed Beds: 25 Admissions: 734 Census: 8 Outpatient Visits: 28124 Births: 0 Total Expense ($000): 15051 Payroll Expense ($000): 6127 Personnel: 111

MOUNTAIN HOME—Baxter County

★ **BAXTER REGIONAL MEDICAL CENTER (040027)**, 624 Hospital Drive, Zip 72653–2955; tel. 870/508–1000 **A**9 10 19 20 **F**7 11 13 15 17 18 20 22 24 28 29 30 31 40 41 43 45 46 47 49 53 57 59 62 63 64 70 71 76 77 78 79 81 82 84 85 86 87 90 93 98 103 104 107 108 111 114 115 119 124 126 127 129 130 132 135 146 147 148 **P**6 8
Primary Contact: Ron Peterson, FACHE, President and Chief Executive Officer
COO: Rudy Darling, Chief Operating Officer
CFO: Ivan Holleman, Chief Financial Officer
CHR: Karen Adams, Vice President Human Resources
CNO: Cathleen Hamel, MS, Vice President and Chief Nursing Officer
Web address: www.baxterregional.org
Control: Other not–for–profit (including NFP Corporation) **Service:** General Medical and Surgical

Staffed Beds: 209 Admissions: 8987 Census: 103 Outpatient Visits: 98943 Births: 626 Total Expense ($000): 153916 Payroll Expense ($000): 60890 Personnel: 1244

MOUNTAIN VIEW—Stone County

★ **STONE COUNTY MEDICAL CENTER (041310)**, 2106 East Main Street, Zip 72560–6439, Mailing Address: P.O. Box 510, Zip 72560–0510; tel. 870/269–4361 **A**9 10 18 **F**3 8 11 15 29 34 35 40 43 57 59 64 79 81 91 93 107 111 114 119 128 133 146 147 148 **S** White River Health System, Batesville, AR
Primary Contact: Stanley Townsend, Chief Executive Officer
CFO: Jana Richardson, Chief Financial Officer
CIO: Gary Paxson, Associate Administrator Information Systems
CHR: Gary McDonald, Associate Administrator Human Resources
CNO: Diana Shelden, Chief Nursing Officer
Web address: www.whiterivenhealthsystem.com
Control: Other not–for–profit (including NFP Corporation) **Service:** General Medical and Surgical

Staffed Beds: 25 Admissions: 866 Census: 9 Outpatient Visits: 19542 Births: 1 Total Expense ($000): 14154 Payroll Expense ($000): 5194 Personnel: 109

NASHVILLE—Howard County

★ **HOWARD MEMORIAL HOSPITAL (041311)**, 130 Medical Circle, Zip 71852–8606; tel. 870/845–4400 **A**9 10 18 **F**3 11 15 29 30 34 35 39 40 43 45 50 53 57 64 65 70 77 81 85 87 93 102 107 108 110 119 133 146
Primary Contact: Debra J. Wright, R.N., Chief Executive Officer
CFO: William J. Craig, Chief Financial Officer
CMO: John Hearnsberger, M.D., Chief of Staff
CHR: Gayla Lacefield, Director Human Resources
CNO: Alesha Danielle Collins, Chief Nursing Officer
Web address: www.howardmemorial.com
Control: Other not–for–profit (including NFP Corporation) **Service:** General Medical and Surgical

Staffed Beds: 20 Admissions: 553 Census: 6 Outpatient Visits: 27892 Births: 0 Total Expense ($000): 14018 Payroll Expense ($000): 5831 Personnel: 127

AR

NEWPORT—Jackson County

☒ **HARRIS HOSPITAL (040080)**, 1205 McLain Street, Zip 72112–3533; tel. 870/523–8911 **A**1 9 10 20 **F**3 11 13 15 17 18 19 29 30 34 35 38 40 43 50 56 57 59 64 65 70 73 75 76 77 79 81 85 87 89 93 98 102 103 105 107 111 114 119 133 135 146 147 **P**6 **S** Community Health Systems, Inc., Franklin, TN
Primary Contact: Robert Rupp, Chief Executive Officer
CFO: Misty Gates, Chief Financial Officer
CMO: Jabez Jackson, M.D., Chief of Staff
CHR: Margaret Gates, Chief Human Resources
CNO: Judy Haney, Chief Nursing Officer
Web address: www.harrishospital.com
Control: Corporation, Investor–owned, for–profit **Service:** General Medical and Surgical

Staffed Beds: 104 **Admissions:** 1935 **Census:** 19 **Outpatient Visits:** 37988 **Births:** 363 **Total Expense ($000):** 31247 **Payroll Expense ($000):** 9415 **Personnel:** 185	

NORTH LITTLE ROCK—Pulaski County

☐ **ARKANSAS SURGICAL HOSPITAL (040147)**, 5201 North Shore Drive, Zip 72118–5312; tel. 501/748–8000 **A**1 9 10 **F**3 29 35 40 74 75 79 81 82 85 87 107 111 114 119 131 146
Primary Contact: Carrie Helm, Chief Executive Officer
CFO: Charles Powell, Chief Financial Officer
CMO: Kenneth A. Martin, M.D., Chief of Staff
CIO: Scott Davis, Manager Information Technology
CHR: Tina Albright, Vice President Human Resources and Consumer Advocacy
CNO: Judy Jones, Chief Clinical Officer
Web address: www.ArkSurgicalHospital.com
Control: Corporation, Investor–owned, for–profit **Service:** General Medical and Surgical

Staffed Beds: 51 **Admissions:** 3457 **Census:** 21 **Outpatient Visits:** 18489 **Births:** 0 **Total Expense ($000):** 45210 **Payroll Expense ($000):** 11859 **Personnel:** 217	

☒ △ **BAPTIST HEALTH MEDICAL CENTER – NORTH LITTLE ROCK (040036)**, 3333 Springhill Drive, Zip 72117–2922; tel. 501/202–3000 **A**1 3 7 9 10 **F**3 8 11 13 15 17 18 20 22 24 26 28 29 30 31 37 38 40 43 45 46 47 49 50 53 54 56 59 60 64 65 70 72 73 76 77 78 79 81 85 86 87 89 90 93 94 107 108 110 111 114 116 117 118 119 124 126 129 130 132 135 144 146 147 148 **S** Baptist Health, Little Rock, AR
Primary Contact: Harrison M. Dean, FACHE, Senior Vice President and Administrator
CFO: Robert C. Roberts, Senior Vice President Financial Services
CMO: Eddie Phillips, M.D., Chief Medical Affairs
CIO: David House, Vice President and Chief Information Officer
CHR: Anthony Kendall, Vice President Human Resources
CNO: Kathy Martin, Vice President Patient Care
Web address: www.baptist–health.com/locations/accesspoint.aspx?accessPointID=190
Control: Other not–for–profit (including NFP Corporation) **Service:** General Medical and Surgical

Staffed Beds: 225 **Admissions:** 12197 **Census:** 131 **Outpatient Visits:** 121750 **Births:** 1512 **Total Expense ($000):** 162617 **Payroll Expense ($000):** 56567 **Personnel:** 999	

NORTH LITTLE ROCK DIVISION See Central Arkansas Veterans Healthcare System, Little Rock

☐ **THE BRIDGEWAY (044005)**, 21 Bridgeway Road, Zip 72113–9516; tel. 501/771–1500 **A**1 9 10 **F**4 5 98 99 104 105 106 **P**5 **S** Universal Health Services, Inc., King of Prussia, PA
Primary Contact: Jason Miller, Interim Chief Executive Officer
COO: Jason Miller, Chief Operating Officer
CFO: Fred Woods, Chief Financial Officer
CMO: Philip L. Mizell, M.D., Medical Director
CHR: Neely Robison, Director Human Resources
CNO: Sherrie James, R.N., Director of Nursing
Web address: www.thebridgeway.com
Control: Corporation, Investor–owned, for–profit **Service:** Psychiatric

Staffed Beds: 103 **Admissions:** 4218 **Census:** 85 **Outpatient Visits:** 10341 **Births:** 0 **Total Expense ($000):** 16963 **Payroll Expense ($000):** 8179 **Personnel:** 155	

OSCEOLA—Mississippi County

☐ **SOUTH MISSISSIPPI COUNTY REGIONAL MEDICAL CENTER (041316)**, 611 West Lee Avenue, Zip 72370–3001, Mailing Address: P.O. Box 108, Zip 72370; tel. 870/563–7000 **A**1 9 10 18 **F**29 40 50 57 59 68 75 81 93 107 114 130 133 146 **S** Mississippi County Hospital System, Blytheville, AR
Primary Contact: Ralph E. Beaty, Chief Executive Officer
COO: Chris Raymer, R.N., Chief Operating Officer and Chief Nursing Officer
CFO: Randy Nichols, Chief Financial Officer
CMO: Pratapji Thakor, M.D., Chief of Staff
CIO: Tammy Bratcher, Director Information Technology
CHR: Cheri Blurton, Director Human Resources
CNO: Chris Raymer, R.N., Chief Operating Officer and Chief Nursing Officer
Web address: www.mchsys.com
Control: County–Government, nonfederal **Service:** General Medical and Surgical

Staffed Beds: 25 **Admissions:** 597 **Census:** 6 **Births:** 0 **Personnel:** 70	

OZARK—Franklin County

★ **MERCY HOSPITAL OZARK (041303)**, 801 West River Street, Zip 72949–3023; tel. 479/667–4138 **A**9 10 18 **F**3 18 20 22 24 26 28 34 35 40 43 45 57 59 64 68 81 85 107 119 133 **P**6 8 **S** Mercy Health, Chesterfield, MO
Primary Contact: Teresa Williams, R.N., Interim Administrator
COO: Brent Hubbard, Chief Operating Officer
CMO: John Lachowsky, M.D., Chief Medical Officer
CIO: Tiana Bolduc, Chief Information Officer
Web address: www.mercy.net/northwestarar/practice/mercy–hospital–ozark
Control: Church–operated, Nongovernment, not–for profit **Service:** General Medical and Surgical

Staffed Beds: 25 **Admissions:** 338 **Census:** 4 **Outpatient Visits:** 11676 **Births:** 0 **Total Expense ($000):** 9560 **Payroll Expense ($000):** 3628 **Personnel:** 51	

PARAGOULD—Greene County

☒ △ **ARKANSAS METHODIST MEDICAL CENTER (040039)**, 900 West Kingshighway, Zip 72450–5942, Mailing Address: P.O. Box 339, Zip 72451–0339; tel. 870/239–7000 **A**1 7 9 10 19 **F**3 7 10 11 13 15 18 20 22 28 29 32 34 35 39 40 43 45 49 50 51 53 54 57 59 62 64 68 70 75 76 78 79 81 85 86 87 89 90 93 97 107 108 110 111 114 115 119 125 129 130 131 132 133 135 146 147 148 **P**6 8
Primary Contact: Barry L. Davis, FACHE, President and Chief Executive Officer
CFO: Brad Bloemer, Vice President Finance and Chief Financial Officer
CMO: David Quinn, M.D., Chief of Staff
CIO: Mardy Holmes, Director Information Technology
CHR: Kevin Thielemier, Director Human Resources
CNO: Lana R. Williams, Chief Nursing Officer
Web address: www.arkansasmethodist.org
Control: Other not–for–profit (including NFP Corporation) **Service:** General Medical and Surgical

Staffed Beds: 125 **Admissions:** 4423 **Census:** 58 **Outpatient Visits:** 114887 **Births:** 518 **Total Expense ($000):** 58749 **Payroll Expense ($000):** 25991 **Personnel:** 541	

PARIS—Logan County

★ **MERCY HOSPITAL PARIS (041300)**, 500 East Academy, Zip 72855–4040; tel. 479/963–6101 **A**9 10 18 **F**3 35 40 43 45 57 59 64 68 81 85 107 119 133 **P**6 8 **S** Mercy Health, Chesterfield, MO
Primary Contact: Sharon D. Sorey, R.N., Regional Administrator
COO: Brent Hubbard, Chief Operating Officer
Web address: www.mercy.net/fortsmithar
Control: Church–operated, Nongovernment, not–for profit **Service:** General Medical and Surgical

Staffed Beds: 16 **Admissions:** 182 **Census:** 2 **Outpatient Visits:** 12120 **Births:** 0 **Total Expense ($000):** 7616 **Payroll Expense ($000):** 3189 **Personnel:** 46	

PIGGOTT—Clay County

★ **PIGGOTT COMMUNITY HOSPITAL (041330)**, 1206 Gordon Duckworth Drive, Zip 72454–1911; tel. 870/598–3881 **A**9 10 18 **F**7 15 18 29 34 35 40 43 57 59 62 64 77 81 93 107 111 114 119 127 129 130 133 143 146 148
Primary Contact: James L. Magee, Executive Director
CFO: Linda Ort, Chief Financial Officer
Web address: www.piggottcommunityhospital.com
Control: City–Government, nonfederal **Service:** General Medical and Surgical

Staffed Beds: 25 **Admissions:** 849 **Census:** 13 **Outpatient Visits:** 11917 **Births:** 0 **Total Expense ($000):** 14501 **Payroll Expense ($000):** 7443 **Personnel:** 201	

Hospital, Medicare Provider Number, Address, Telephone, Approval, Facility, and Physician Codes, Health Care System

★ American Hospital Association (AHA) membership
☐ The Joint Commission accreditation
◇ DNV Healthcare Inc. accreditation
○ Healthcare Facilities Accreditation Program
△ Commission on Accreditation of Rehabilitation Facilities (CARF) accreditation

AR

PINE BLUFF—Jefferson County

ARKANSAS DEPARTMENT OF CORRECTION HOSPITAL, 7500 Correctional Circle, Zip 71603–1438; tel. 870/267–6999, (Nonreporting) **A**3 5
Primary Contact: Roland Anderson, M.D., Medical Director
Control: State–Government, nonfederal **Service:** Hospital unit of an institution (prison hospital, college infirmary, etc.)

> Staffed Beds: 27

★ △ **JEFFERSON REGIONAL MEDICAL CENTER (040071)**, 1600 West 40th Avenue, Zip 71603–6301; tel. 870/541–7100 **A**3 5 **F**3 8 11 13 15 17 18 20 22 24 28 29 30 31 34 35 40 43 45 46 48 49 50 51 53 54 56 57 59 60 61 64 65 70 72 73 74 75 76 77 78 79 81 85 86 87 89 90 96 97 98 100 101 102 103 107 108 110 111 114 115 116 118 119 124 128 130 131 132 135 143 144 145 146 147 148 **P**7
Primary Contact: Walter E. Johnson, Jr., President and Chief Executive Officer
COO: Brian N. Thomas, Senior Vice President and Chief Operating Officer
CFO: Bryan G. Jackson, Vice President and Chief Financial Officer
CMO: John Lytle, M.D., Chief of Staff
CIO: Patrick Neece, Chief Information Officer
CHR: M Daryl Scott, Assistant Vice President
CNO: Louise Hickman, R.N., Vice President of Patient Care Services
Web address: www.jrmc.org
Control: Other not–for–profit (including NFP Corporation) **Service:** General Medical and Surgical

> Staffed Beds: 333 Admissions: 9216 Census: 146 Outpatient Visits: 203053 Births: 1023 Total Expense ($000): 179928 Payroll Expense ($000): 78359 Personnel: 1400

POCAHONTAS—Randolph County

FIVE RIVERS MEDICAL CENTER (040047), 2801 Medical Center Drive, Zip 72455–9436; tel. 870/892–6000 **A**9 10 20 **F**3 11 18 29 40 43 45 47 50 57 59 62 70 79 81 85 93 98 103 107 111 113 115 119 130 133 146 148
Primary Contact: Luther J. Lewis, FACHE, Chief Executive Officer
CFO: Joey Radcliff, Chief Financial Officer
CHR: Alvin Taylor, Chief Human Resources
CNO: Mandy Dollins, R.N., Chief Nursing Officer
Web address: www.fiveriversmedicalcenter.com
Control: Other not–for–profit (including NFP Corporation) **Service:** General Medical and Surgical

> Staffed Beds: 46 Admissions: 796 Census: 12 Outpatient Visits: 19507 Births: 0 Total Expense ($000): 16498 Payroll Expense ($000): 7911 Personnel: 129

ROGERS—Benton County

⊞ **MERCY HOSPITAL ROGERS (040010)**, 2710 Rife Medical Lane, Zip 72758–1452; tel. 479/338–8000 **A**1 9 10 **F**3 8 11 13 15 17 18 20 22 24 28 29 30 40 43 45 46 49 57 59 62 64 70 72 75 76 77 79 81 82 84 86 87 89 93 107 108 110 111 115 118 119 129 130 131 135 146 148 **P**6 **S** Mercy Health, Chesterfield, MO
Primary Contact: Eric Pianalto, President
COO: Brenda Chase, Chief Operating Officer
CFO: Benny Stover, Vice President Finance
CMO: Chris Johnson, M.D., Chief of Staff
CHR: Rick Barclay, Vice President Support Services
CNO: Michele Diedrich, R.N., Chief Nursing Officer
Web address: www.mercyhealthnwa.smhs.com
Control: Church–operated, Nongovernment, not–for profit **Service:** General Medical and Surgical

> Staffed Beds: 147 Admissions: 10980 Census: 88 Outpatient Visits: 190838 Births: 1327 Total Expense ($000): 142139 Payroll Expense ($000): 43805 Personnel: 963

RUSSELLVILLE—Pope County

☐ **SAINT MARY'S REGIONAL MEDICAL CENTER (040041)**, 1808 West Main Street, Zip 72801–2724; tel. 479/968–2841 **A**1 9 10 19 **F**3 11 13 15 18 20 22 29 31 34 35 40 43 45 50 51 53 54 56 57 59 64 68 70 74 75 76 78 79 81 85 86 87 89 90 93 98 107 108 110 111 114 118 119 120 121 127 129 130 131 132 146 147 148 **S** Capella Healthcare, Franklin, TN
Primary Contact: Donald J. Frederic, FACHE, Chief Executive Officer
COO: Mike McCoy, Chief Operating Officer
CFO: Wendell VanEs, Chief Financial Officer
CMO: Doug Kerin, M.D., Chief of Staff
CHR: Connie Gragg, Director Human Resources
CNO: Pat Torrico, R.N., Chief Nursing Officer
Web address: www.saintmarysregional.com
Control: Corporation, Investor–owned, for–profit **Service:** General Medical and Surgical

> Staffed Beds: 151 Admissions: 5907 Census: 69 Outpatient Visits: 76202 Births: 920 Total Expense ($000): 72983 Payroll Expense ($000): 23369 Personnel: 491

SALEM—Fulton County

FULTON COUNTY HOSPITAL (041322), 679 North Main Street, Zip 72576–9451, Mailing Address: P.O. Box 517, Zip 72576–0517; tel. 870/895–2691 **A**9 10 18 **F**3 7 28 29 34 40 43 57 59 75 107 119 133 146
Primary Contact: Charles Willett, Administrator and Chief Executive Officer
Web address: www.fultoncountyhospital.org
Control: County–Government, nonfederal **Service:** General Medical and Surgical

> Staffed Beds: 25 Admissions: 1016 Census: 12 Outpatient Visits: 15159 Births: 0 Total Expense ($000): 8757 Payroll Expense ($000): 3496 Personnel: 114

SEARCY—White County

ADVANCED CARE HOSPITAL OF WHITE COUNTY (042011), 1200 South Main Street, Zip 72143–7321; tel. 501/278–3155 **A**9 10 **F**1 3 17 29 30 68 70 75 89 91 130 148
Primary Contact: Terri L. Parsons, Administrator
CMO: Miguel Aguinaga, M.D., Medical Director
CNO: Kathy DeVore, R.N., Director Patient Services
Web address: www.advancedcarehospital.com
Control: Other not–for–profit (including NFP Corporation) **Service:** Long–Term Acute Care hospital

> Staffed Beds: 27 Admissions: 181 Census: 14 Outpatient Visits: 0 Births: 0 Total Expense ($000): 6848 Payroll Expense ($000): 2834 Personnel: 52

★ **WHITE COUNTY MEDICAL CENTER (040014)**, 3214 East Race Avenue, Zip 72143–4810; tel. 501/268–6121, (Includes WHITE COUNTY MEDICAL CENTER – SOUTH CAMPUS, 1200 South Main Street, Zip 72143–7397; tel. 501/278–3100) **A**9 10 19 20 **F**1 3 11 12 13 17 18 20 22 24 28 29 30 31 34 35 39 40 43 45 51 54 57 59 61 62 64 68 70 74 75 76 77 78 79 81 86 87 89 90 93 98 100 102 103 105 107 108 111 115 119 126 129 130 131 132 134 135 145 146 147 148 **P**2 6
Primary Contact: Raymond W. Montgomery, II, FACHE, President and Chief Executive Officer
CFO: Stuart Hill, Vice President and Treasurer
CMO: John Henderson, M.D., Chief Medical Officer
CIO: Kevin Hoofman, Director Management Information
CHR: Pamela G. Williams, Director Human Resources
CNO: Peggy Turner, Assistant Vice President and Director of Nursing
Web address: www.wcmc.org
Control: Other not–for–profit (including NFP Corporation) **Service:** General Medical and Surgical

> Staffed Beds: 286 Admissions: 11941 Census: 151 Outpatient Visits: 90279 Births: 1224 Total Expense ($000): 175492 Payroll Expense ($000): 78163 Personnel: 1233

SHERWOOD—Pulaski County

★ **ST. VINCENT MEDICAL CENTER–NORTH (040137)**, 2215 Wildwood Avenue, Zip 72120–5089; tel. 501/552–7100 **A**9 10 **F**3 11 15 18 20 22 26 29 35 40 43 44 45 50 64 70 74 79 81 85 87 107 110 111 112 115 118 119 146 **S** Catholic Health Initiatives, Englewood, CO
Primary Contact: David R. Fox, Administrator and Chief Executive Officer
CMO: David Hall, M.D., Senior Vice President and Chief Medical Officer
CIO: Tommye Billing, Vice President and Chief Information Officer
CHR: Margaret Nixon, Director Human Resources
Web address: www.stvincenthealth.com
Control: Church–operated, Nongovernment, not–for profit **Service:** General Medical and Surgical

> Staffed Beds: 58 Admissions: 1758 Census: 17 Outpatient Visits: 26117 Births: 0 Total Expense ($000): 25923 Payroll Expense ($000): 8694 Personnel: 136

⊞ **ST. VINCENT REHABILITATION HOSPITAL (043031)**, 2201 Wildwood Avenue, Zip 72120–5074, Mailing Address: P.O. Box 6930, Zip 72124–6930; tel. 501/834–1800 **A**1 9 10 **F**29 35 50 90 91 93 95 96 130 132 143 148 **S** HEALTHSOUTH Corporation, Birmingham, AL
Primary Contact: Lisa Watson, Chief Executive Officer
CFO: Stacy Shilling, Controller
CMO: Kevin J. Collins, M.D., Medical Director
CNO: Shannon Moreno–Cook, Chief Nursing Officer
Web address: www.stvincenthealth.com/svrehabhospital/index.html
Control: Corporation, Investor–owned, for–profit **Service:** Rehabilitation

> Staffed Beds: 60 Admissions: 1556 Census: 51 Outpatient Visits: 6213 Births: 0 Total Expense ($000): 21421 Payroll Expense ($000): 10239 Personnel: 174

Many Facility Codes have changed. Please refer to the AHA Guide Code Chart. © 2014 AHA Guide

SILOAM SPRINGS—Benton County

✠ **SILOAM SPRINGS REGIONAL HOSPITAL (040001)**, 603 North Progress Avenue, Zip 72761–4352; tel. 479/524–4141 **A**1 9 10 **F**3 8 11 13 15 18 28 29 30 34 35 40 43 45 50 57 59 68 70 73 76 77 79 81 85 87 93 97 107 108 110 111 115 119 129 130 131 141 143 146 147 148 **P**1 7 **S** Community Health Systems, Inc., Franklin, TN
Primary Contact: Kevin J. Clement, Chief Executive Officer
CFO: James E. Little, Chief Financial Officer
CMO: Hunt Cooper, M.D., Chief of Staff
CHR: Carmen Burasco, Director Human Resources
Web address: www.ssrh.net/Pages/home.aspx
Control: Corporation, Investor–owned, for–profit **Service:** General Medical and Surgical

Staffed Beds: 54 **Admissions:** 2211 **Census:** 17 **Outpatient Visits:** 30161
Births: 569 **Total Expense ($000):** 25934 **Payroll Expense ($000):** 11105
Personnel: 267

SPRINGDALE—Washington County

✠ **NORTHWEST MEDICAL CENTER – SPRINGDALE (040022)**, 609 West Maple Avenue, Zip 72764–5394, Mailing Address: P.O. Box 47, Zip 72765–0047; tel. 479/751–5711, (Includes NORTHWEST MEDICAL CENTER – BENTONVILLE, 3000 Medical Center Parkway, Bentonville, Zip 72712; tel. 479/553–1000, Benjamin Casmer, Chief Operating Officer; WILLOW CREEK WOMEN'S HOSPITAL, 4301 Greathouse Springs Road, Johnson, Zip 72741–0544, Mailing Address: P.O. Box 544, Zip 72741–0544; tel. 479/684–3000; Debbie A. Crandall, Administrative Director) **A**1 3 9 10 **F**3 8 11 12 13 14 15 17 18 20 22 24 26 28 29 30 34 35 36 40 43 45 46 47 48 49 50 51 56 59 60 61 64 68 70 71 72 74 75 77 78 79 80 81 85 86 87 90 91 92 93 98 102 107 108 110 111 114 115 118 119 124 126 129 130 131 135 144 146 147 148 **P**5 8 **S** Community Health Systems, Inc., Franklin, TN
Primary Contact: Sharif Omar, Chief Executive Officer
CFO: Steve Flader, Chief Financial Officer
CMO: Robert Petrino, M.D., Chief of Staff
CIO: Paul DeMay, Chief Information Officer
Web address: www.northwesthealth.com
Control: Corporation, Investor–owned, for–profit **Service:** General Medical and Surgical

Staffed Beds: 346 **Admissions:** 16323 **Census:** 170 **Outpatient Visits:** 170416 **Births:** 3784 **Total Expense ($000):** 216831 **Payroll Expense ($000):** 77320 **Personnel:** 1374

STUTTGART—Arkansas County

★ **BAPTIST HEALTH MEDICAL CENTER–STUTTGART (040072)**, North Buerkle Road, Zip 72160–3420, Mailing Address: P.O. Box 1905, Zip 72160–1905; tel. 870/673–3511 **A**9 10 **F**3 11 13 15 18 29 30 34 35 39 40 43 53 57 59 64 68 70 75 76 78 79 81 85 87 93 97 107 110 111 114 119 127 128 129 130 133 135 146 148 **S** Baptist Health, Little Rock, AR
Primary Contact: Terry L. Amstutz, FACHE, Vice President and Administrator
CMO: Christopher Morgan, M.D., Chief of Staff
CIO: Warren Horton, Information Technologist
CNO: Susan Williams, R.N., Chief Nursing Officer
Web address: www.baptist-health.org/maps-directions/bhmc-stuttgart/default.aspx
Control: Other not–for–profit (including NFP Corporation) **Service:** General Medical and Surgical

Staffed Beds: 49 **Admissions:** 1560 **Census:** 14 **Outpatient Visits:** 25746
Births: 206 **Total Expense ($000):** 24738 **Payroll Expense ($000):** 9100
Personnel: 212

TEXARKANA—Miller County

☐ **RIVERVIEW BEHAVIORAL HEALTH (044020)**, 701 Arkansas Boulevard, Zip 71854–2105; tel. 870/772–5028 **A**1 9 10 **F**34 38 54 87 98 99 101 102 103 104 105 130 143 **S** Acadia Healthcare Company, Inc., Franklin, TN
Primary Contact: Michael A. Truman, Chief Executive Officer
CFO: Fred Lewis, Chief Financial Officer
CMO: John Gary Tharp, M.D., Medical Director
CHR: Roberta Bachman, Director Human Resources
CNO: Crystal Chambliss, Director of Nursing
Web address: www.riverviewbehavioralhealth.com
Control: Corporation, Investor–owned, for–profit **Service:** Psychiatric

Staffed Beds: 62 **Admissions:** 707 **Census:** 35 **Outpatient Visits:** 0 **Births:** 0 **Total Expense ($000):** 13188 **Payroll Expense ($000):** 7393 **Personnel:** 86

VAN BUREN—Crawford County

✠ **SUMMIT MEDICAL CENTER (040018)**, East Main and South 20th Streets, Zip 72956–5715, Mailing Address: P.O. Box 409, Zip 72957–0409; tel. 479/474–3401 **A**1 9 10 **F**3 8 11 12 15 18 29 30 34 35 40 43 45 48 49 50 51 56 57 58 59 64 65 68 70 74 75 77 79 81 82 85 86 87 93 97 100 107 108 110 111 114 119 130 131 132 135 144 146 **P**6 **S** Community Health Systems, Inc., Franklin, TN
Primary Contact: Daniel E. McKay, Chief Executive Officer
CHR: James Ford, Director Human Resources
CNO: Shelly L. Weilenman, R.N., Administrator and Chief Nursing Executive
Web address: www.summitmedicalcenter.net
Control: Corporation, Investor–owned, for–profit **Service:** General Medical and Surgical

Staffed Beds: 103 **Admissions:** 1727 **Census:** 15 **Outpatient Visits:** 35749
Births: 0 **Total Expense ($000):** 21248 **Payroll Expense ($000):** 7515
Personnel: 188

WALDRON—Scott County

★ **MERCY HOSPITAL WALDRON (041305)**, 1341 West 6th Street, Zip 72958–7642; tel. 479/637–4135 **A**9 10 18 **F**3 35 40 43 45 57 59 64 65 68 81 85 107 119 127 133 **P**6 8 **S** Mercy Health, Chesterfield, MO
Primary Contact: Dorothy O'Bar, R.N., Regional Administrator
COO: Brent Hubbard, Chief Operating Officer
CFO: Greta Wilcher, Senior Vice President and Chief Financial Officer
CMO: Nathan Bennett, M.D., Chief Medical Officer
CNO: Dorothy O'Bar, R.N., Regional Administrator
Web address: www.stedwardmercy.com
Control: Church–operated, Nongovernment, not–for profit **Service:** General Medical and Surgical

Staffed Beds: 24 **Admissions:** 340 **Census:** 4 **Outpatient Visits:** 26773
Births: 0 **Total Expense ($000):** 10196 **Payroll Expense ($000):** 3897
Personnel: 39

WALNUT RIDGE—Lawrence County

✠ **LAWRENCE MEMORIAL HOSPITAL (041309)**, 1309 West Main, Zip 72476–1430, Mailing Address: P.O. Box 839, Zip 72476–0839; tel. 870/886–1200, (Includes LAWRENCE HALL NURSING HOME), (Total facility includes 179 beds in nursing home–type unit) **A**1 9 10 18 **F**3 11 15 28 29 32 34 35 40 45 46 47 57 59 84 85 97 107 111 114 119 127 128 129 130 133 135 146
Primary Contact: George S. Fray, Interim President
COO: Junior Briner, Chief Operating Officer
CFO: Vanessa Wagner, Chief Financial Officer
CMO: Kevin Diamond, M.D., Chief of Staff
CHR: Donna Carter, Director Human Resources
CNO: Rosalind Casillas, Director of Nursing
Web address: www.lawrencehealth.net
Control: County–Government, nonfederal **Service:** General Medical and Surgical

Staffed Beds: 204 **Admissions:** 1173 **Census:** 173 **Outpatient Visits:** 23487
Births: 0 **Total Expense ($000):** 19690 **Payroll Expense ($000):** 10160
Personnel: 321

WARREN—Bradley County

★ **BRADLEY COUNTY MEDICAL CENTER (041327)**, 404 South Bradley Street, Zip 71671–3493; tel. 870/226–3731 **A**9 10 18 **F**3 11 13 15 29 30 34 40 45 49 50 56 57 59 62 68 76 77 81 87 89 93 98 103 104 107 108 111 115 118 119 129 130 131 132 133 147 **P**6
Primary Contact: Rex Jones, Chief Executive Officer
CFO: Brandon Gorman, Controller
CMO: Joe H. Wharton, M.D., Chief of Staff
CHR: Angela Lochridge, Director Human Resources
CNO: Tiffany Holland, Chief Nursing Officer
Web address: www.bradleycountymedicalcenter.com
Control: Other not–for–profit (including NFP Corporation) **Service:** General Medical and Surgical

Staffed Beds: 33 **Admissions:** 1446 **Census:** 15 **Outpatient Visits:** 46720
Births: 160 **Total Expense ($000):** 20904 **Payroll Expense ($000):** 8685
Personnel: 206

Hospital, Medicare Provider Number, Address, Telephone, Approval, Facility, and Physician Codes, Health Care System

★ American Hospital Association (AHA) membership
☐ The Joint Commission accreditation
◇ DNV Healthcare Inc. accreditation
○ Healthcare Facilities Accreditation Program
△ Commission on Accreditation of Rehabilitation Facilities (CARF) accreditation

WYNNE—Cross County

✠ **CROSSRIDGE COMMUNITY HOSPITAL (041307)**, 310 South Falls Boulevard,
Zip 72396–3013, Mailing Address: P.O. Box 590, Zip 72396–0590;
tel. 870/238–3300 **A**1 9 10 18 **F**3 11 15 28 34 35 40 43 50 57 59 62 64 68
69 75 77 81 93 107 110 111 114 119 130 133 135 146
Primary Contact: Gary R. Sparks, Administrator
COO: Bryan Mattes, Associate Administrator
CFO: Janice Morris, Accountant
CIO: Gail Copeland, Director Management Information Systems
CHR: Bertha Ragle, Director Personnel
CNO: Amelia Davis, Director of Nursing
Control: Church–operated, Nongovernment, not–for profit **Service:** General
Medical and Surgical

Staffed Beds: 15 **Admissions:** 656 **Census:** 7 **Outpatient Visits:** 17508
Births: 0 **Total Expense ($000):** 13508 **Payroll Expense ($000):** 5487
Personnel: 132

Many Facility Codes have changed. Please refer to the AHA Guide Code Chart.

CALIFORNIA

ALAMEDA—Alameda County

☒ **ALAMEDA HOSPITAL (050211)**, 2070 Clinton Avenue, Zip 94501–4397;
tel. 510/522–3700, (Nonreporting) **A**1 9 10
Primary Contact: Deborah E. Stebbins, FACHE, Chief Executive Officer
CFO: Robert C. Anderson, Interim Chief Financial Officer
CMO: Aika Sharma, M.D., President Medical Staff
CIO: Robert Lundy-Paine, Director Information Systems
CHR: Phyllis Weiss, Director Human Resources
Web address: www.alamedahospital.org
Control: Hospital district or authority, Government, nonfederal **Service:** General
Medical and Surgical

Staffed Beds: 131

ALHAMBRA—Los Angeles County

☐ **ALHAMBRA HOSPITAL MEDICAL CENTER (050281)**, 100 South Raymond
Avenue, Zip 91801–3199, Mailing Address: P.O. Box 510, Zip 91802–2510;
tel. 626/570–1606 **A**1 9 10 **F**1 2 3 18 28 29 31 34 35 40 45 46 49 50 51 56
57 59 60 64 70 74 75 77 78 79 80 81 85 86 87 90 92 93 107 108 115 119
130 143 146 **S** AHMC & Healthcare, Inc., Alhambra, CA
Primary Contact: Iris Lai, Chief Executive Officer
CFO: Linda Marsh, Vice President Financial Services and Chief Financial Officer
CMO: Stephen Chen, M.D., Chief Medicare
CIO: Johnson Legaspi, Director Information Systems
CHR: Elizabeth Sabandit, Director Human Resources
CNO: Eleanor Martinez, Chief Nursing Officer
Web address: www.alhambrahospital.com
Control: Partnership, Investor–owned, for–profit **Service:** General Medical and
Surgical

Staffed Beds: 144 **Admissions:** 4174 **Census:** 79 **Outpatient Visits:** 24193
Births: 0 **Total Expense ($000):** 88631

ALTURAS—Modoc County

MODOC MEDICAL CENTER (051330), 228 West Mcdowell Avenue,
Zip 96101–3934; tel. 530/233–5131, (Total facility includes 71 beds in nursing
home–type unit) **A**9 10 18 **F**7 29 34 35 40 46 57 65 81 93 114 119 127 128
130 133 146 **P**5
Primary Contact: Kevin Kramer, Chief Executive Officer
CMO: Ed Richert, M.D., Chief of Staff
CHR: Diane Hagelthorn, Human Resources Generalist
Web address: www.modocmedicalcenter.org
Control: Hospital district or authority, Government, nonfederal **Service:** General
Medical and Surgical

Staffed Beds: 87 **Admissions:** 353 **Census:** 42 **Outpatient Visits:** 10826
Births: 0 **Total Expense ($000):** 14262 **Payroll Expense ($000):** 5612
Personnel: 135

ANAHEIM—Orange County

☐ **AHMC ANAHEIM REGIONAL MEDICAL CENTER (050226)**, 1111 West La
Palma Avenue, Zip 92801–2881; tel. 714/774–1450, (Nonreporting) **A**1 9 10
S AHMC & Healthcare, Inc., Alhambra, CA
Primary Contact: Patrick A. Petre, Chief Executive Officer
COO: Deborah G. Webber, Chief Operating Officer
CFO: Michael Chung, Chief Financial Officer
CMO: Amitabh Prakash, M.D., Chief Medical Officer
CIO: Jeff DesRoches, Manager Information Systems
CHR: Kathy Doi, Executive Director Human Resources
CNO: Phyllis Snyder, Chief Nursing Officer
Web address: www.anaheimregionalmc.com
Control: Other not–for–profit (including NFP Corporation) **Service:** General
Medical and Surgical

Staffed Beds: 223

ANAHEIM MEDICAL CENTER See Kaiser Permanente Orange County Anaheim
Medical Center

★ **KAISER PERMANENTE ORANGE COUNTY ANAHEIM MEDICAL CENTER
(050609)**, 3430 East La Palma Avenue, Zip 92806–2020; tel. 714/644–2000,
(Includes ORANGE COUNTY IRVINE MEDICAL CENTER, 6640 Alton Parkway, Irvine,
Zip 92618; tel. 949/932–5000) **A**3 5 10 **F**3 13 14 15 17 18 19 20 29 30 31
35 37 40 44 45 46 47 48 49 50 59 61 62 63 64 65 68 70 72 74 75 76 78
79 80 81 82 84 85 87 89 92 93 100 107 108 111 114 115 119 130 135
143 146 148 **S** Kaiser Foundation Hospitals, Oakland, CA
Primary Contact: Julie K. Miller–Phipps, Senior Vice President and Executive
Director
COO: Margie Harrier, Medical Center Chief Operations Officer
CFO: Marcus Hoffman, Area Chief Financial Officer
CMO: Nancy Gin, M.D., Area Associate Medical Director
CIO: James Brady, Area Information Officer
CHR: Jocelyn A. Herrera, Director Human Resources
CNO: Karolynne Johnson, R.N., Chief Nurse Executive, Anaheim Medical Center
Web address: www.kp.org
Control: Other not–for–profit (including NFP Corporation) **Service:** General
Medical and Surgical

Staffed Beds: 436 **Admissions:** 24388 **Census:** 258 **Outpatient Visits:**
351262 **Births:** 5592 **Personnel:** 2493

☐ **WEST ANAHEIM MEDICAL CENTER (050426)**, 3033 West Orange Avenue,
Zip 92804–3156; tel. 714/827–3000 **A**1 5 10 **F**3 11 15 17 18 20 22 24 29
40 45 49 70 79 81 85 98 103 105 107 108 111 114 119 128 130 146
S Prime Healthcare Services, Ontario, CA
Primary Contact: Virgis Narbutas, Chief Executive Officer
CFO: Alan H. Smith, Chief Financial Officer
CMO: Hassan Alkhouli, M.D., Chief Medical Officer
CIO: Vic Mahan, Director Information Technology
CHR: Stephanie Sioson, Director Human Resources
CNO: Virginia Edward, R.N., Administrator and Chief Nursing Officer
Web address: www.westanaheimmedctr.com
Control: Partnership, Investor–owned, for–profit **Service:** General Medical and
Surgical

Staffed Beds: 219 **Admissions:** 5898 **Census:** 85 **Outpatient Visits:** 65158
Births: 0 **Total Expense ($000):** 96655

☐ **WESTERN MEDICAL CENTER ANAHEIM (050744)**, 1025 South Anaheim
Boulevard, Zip 92805–5806; tel. 714/533–6220, (Nonreporting) **A**1 9 10
S Integrated Healthcare, Santa Ana, CA
Primary Contact: Suzanne Richards, R.N., M.P.H., Chief Executive Officer
CMO: Harmohinder Gogia, M.D., Chief Medical Officer
CIO: Nova Stewart, Chief Information Officer
Web address: www.westernmedanaheim.com
Control: Corporation, Investor–owned, for–profit **Service:** General Medical and
Surgical

Staffed Beds: 188

ANTIOCH—Contra Costa County

☒ **KAISER PERMANENTE ANTIOCH MEDICAL CENTER (050760)**, 4501 Sand
Creek Road, Zip 94531–8687; tel. 925/813–6500 **A**1 10 **F**3 5 9 13 15 18 29
30 31 32 34 35 36 38 40 45 49 50 54 56 57 59 60 61 63 64 65 68 70 72
74 75 77 78 79 81 82 83 84 85 86 87 91 92 93 94 96 97 99 100 101 102
103 104 107 108 109 110 111 112 115 116 119 130 132 134 135 141 144
146 147 148 **S** Kaiser Foundation Hospitals, Oakland, CA
Primary Contact: Colleen McKeown, Senior Vice President
COO: Linda Krystof, Interim Chief Operating Officer
CFO: Brian Yamada, Interim Area Finance Officer
CIO: To Tsang, Interim Area Information Officer
CHR: Evert Hendrix, Area Human Resources Leader
CNO: Linda Krystof, Chief Nursing Officer
Web address: www.https://health.kaiserpermanente.org/wps/portal/facility/
100382
Control: Other not–for–profit (including NFP Corporation) **Service:** General
Medical and Surgical

Staffed Beds: 150 **Admissions:** 7865 **Census:** 73 **Births:** 1500 **Personnel:**
1079

Hospital, Medicare Provider Number, Address, Telephone, Approval, Facility, and Physician Codes, Health Care System

★ American Hospital Association (AHA) membership
☐ The Joint Commission accreditation   ◇ DNV Healthcare Inc. accreditation

○ Healthcare Facilities Accreditation Program
△ Commission on Accreditation of Rehabilitation Facilities (CARF) accreditation

☒ **SUTTER DELTA MEDICAL CENTER (050523)**, 3901 Lone Tree Way,
Zip 94509–6253; tel. 925/779–7200 **A**1 9 10 **F**3 8 11 13 15 18 20 22 26 29
30 31 34 35 40 41 45 47 49 50 51 57 59 60 65 66 68 70 72 74 76 77 78
79 81 82 84 85 89 93 96 107 108 110 111 114 115 119 130 132 146 147
148 **S** Sutter Health, Sacramento, CA
Primary Contact: Gary D. Rapaport, Chief Executive Officer
COO: Susan C. Bumatay, R.N., Assistant Administrator
CFO: Julie Peterson, Chief Financial Officer
CMO: Bobby Glickman, M.D., Chief of Staff
CIO: Kathy Frederickson, Information Systems Site Lead
CHR: Christine Green, Administrative Director Human Resources
CNO: Dori Stevens, Chief Nursing Officer
Web address: www.sutterdelta.org
Control: Other not–for–profit (including NFP Corporation) **Service:** General
Medical and Surgical

Staffed Beds: 136 **Admissions:** 7545 **Census:** 75 **Outpatient Visits:** 79412
Births: 976 **Total Expense ($000):** 172802 **Payroll Expense ($000):** 58133
Personnel: 770

APPLE VALLEY—San Bernardino County

★ ○ **ST. MARY MEDICAL CENTER (050300)**, 18300 Highway 18,
Zip 92307–2206, Mailing Address: P.O. Box 7025, Zip 92307–0725;
tel. 760/242–2311 **A**2 9 10 11 **F**8 11 13 15 18 20 22 24 26 28 29 30 34 35
40 45 46 50 57 59 60 64 65 68 70 71 72 75 76 77 78 79 81 82 83 84 85
86 87 89 93 107 108 111 115 119 126 127 130 132 135 143 146 148 **P**3 5
S St. Joseph Health, Irvine, CA
Primary Contact: Alan H. Garrett, Chief Executive Officer
COO: Kelly Linden, Senior Vice President, Chief Operating Officer
CFO: Tracey Fernandez, Chief Financial Officer
CMO: Dennis Haghighat, M.D., Vice President Medical Affairs
CIO: Doug Kleine, IT Director
CHR: Joseph Turco, Director Human Resources
CNO: Marilyn Drone, R.N., Vice President, CNO
Web address: www.stmaryapplevalley.com/
Control: Church–operated, Nongovernment, not–for profit **Service:** General
Medical and Surgical

Staffed Beds: 208 **Admissions:** 16629 **Census:** 174 **Outpatient Visits:**
141739 **Births:** 2570 **Total Expense ($000):** 265718 **Payroll Expense
($000):** 92189 **Personnel:** 1555

ARCADIA—Los Angeles County

☒ **METHODIST HOSPITAL OF SOUTHERN CALIFORNIA (050238)**, 300 West
Huntington Drive, Zip 91007–3473, Mailing Address: P.O. Box 60016,
Zip 91066–6016; tel. 626/898–8000, (Total facility includes 26 beds in nursing
home–type unit) **A**1 2 9 10 **F**3 12 13 14 15 17 18 20 22 24 26 28 29 30 31
34 35 37 38 40 45 46 48 49 50 51 55 56 57 58 59 60 64 65 68 70 72 73
74 75 76 77 78 79 81 82 84 85 86 87 90 92 94 100 102 107 108 111 114
115 117 119 120 121 123 128 130 132 135 146 147 148
Primary Contact: Dan F. Ausman, President and Chief Executive Officer
COO: Steven A. Sisto, Senior Vice President and Chief Operating Officer
CFO: William E. Grigg, Senior Vice President and Chief Financial Officer
CHR: William Budzinski, Vice President Human Resources
Web address: www.methodisthospital.org
Control: Other not–for–profit (including NFP Corporation) **Service:** General
Medical and Surgical

Staffed Beds: 335 **Admissions:** 16620 **Census:** 209 **Outpatient Visits:**
65890 **Births:** 1823 **Total Expense ($000):** 272077 **Payroll Expense
($000):** 115729 **Personnel:** 1677

ARCATA—Humboldt County

○ **MAD RIVER COMMUNITY HOSPITAL (050028)**, 3800 Janes Road,
Zip 95521–4788, Mailing Address: P.O. Box 1115, Zip 95518–1115;
tel. 707/822–3621, (Nonreporting) **A**9 10 11
Primary Contact: Douglas A. Shaw, Chief Executive Officer
COO: Steve Engle, Chief Operations Officer
CFO: Michael Young, Chief Financial Officer
CMO: Ronald Berman, M.D., Chief of Staff
CIO: Steve Engle, Chief Operations Officer
CHR: Peggy Shea, Human Resources Lead
CNO: Ken Terpening, Chief Nursing Officer
Web address: www.madriverhospital.com
Control: Corporation, Investor–owned, for–profit **Service:** General Medical and
Surgical

Staffed Beds: 68

ARROYO GRANDE—San Luis Obispo County

☒ **ARROYO GRANDE COMMUNITY HOSPITAL (050016)**, 345 South Halcyon
Road, Zip 93420–3899; tel. 805/489–4261, (Total facility includes 14 beds in
nursing home–type unit) **A**1 9 10 **F**8 11 15 29 30 34 35 37 39 40 50 51 54 57
59 64 68 70 75 77 78 79 81 84 87 90 93 94 96 100 107 108 109 110 111
114 117 118 119 129 130 132 146 148 **S** Dignity Health, San Francisco, CA
Primary Contact: Kenneth Dalebout, Administrator and Chief Executive Officer
CHR: Ami Padilla, Director Human Resources
Web address: www.arroyograndehospital.org
Control: Other not–for–profit (including NFP Corporation) **Service:** General
Medical and Surgical

Staffed Beds: 67 **Admissions:** 2632 **Census:** 33 **Outpatient Visits:** 63249
Births: 0 **Total Expense ($000):** 70173 **Payroll Expense ($000):** 23422
Personnel: 299

ATASCADERO—San Luis Obispo County

☐ **ATASCADERO STATE HOSPITAL**, 10333 El Camino Real, Zip 93422–5808,
Mailing Address: P.O. Box 7001, Zip 93423–7001; tel. 805/468–2000 **A**1 **F**34
39 53 57 59 75 77 82 86 87 98 103 130 132 144 146 **P**1
Primary Contact: Linda Persons, Executive Director
COO: David Landrum, Chief Police Services
CFO: Janie Pagnini, Administrator Accounting
CMO: David Fennell, M.D., Acting Medical Director
CIO: James Grover, Manager Data Processing
CHR: Elizabeth Andres, Director Human Resources
CNO: Liz Souza, Coordinator Nursing Services
Web address: www.dmh.ca.gov/statehospitals/atascadero
Control: State–Government, nonfederal **Service:** Psychiatric

Staffed Beds: 1275 **Admissions:** 1145 **Census:** 1041 **Births:** 0 **Total
Expense ($000):** 201777 **Payroll Expense ($000):** 130504 **Personnel:**
1932

AUBURN—Placer County

☒ **SUTTER AUBURN FAITH HOSPITAL (050498)**, 11815 Education Street,
Zip 95602–2410; tel. 530/888–4500 **A**1 2 9 10 **F**3 8 11 12 15 17 18 20 28
29 30 31 34 35 37 39 44 45 47 49 50 57 58 59 62 63 64 68 70 74 75 78
79 81 85 86 87 92 93 107 108 110 111 114 119 130 132 135 145 146 147
148 **S** Sutter Health, Sacramento, CA
Primary Contact: Mitchell J. Hanna, Chief Executive Officer
CFO: Gary Hubschman, Administrative Director Finance
CMO: John Mesic, M.D., Chief Medical Officer
CIO: Tom Ream, Regional Chief Information Officer
CHR: Yvette Martinez, Director Human Resources
CNO: Gina Temple, Chief Nurse Executive
Web address: www.sutterhealth.org
Control: Other not–for–profit (including NFP Corporation) **Service:** General
Medical and Surgical

Staffed Beds: 72 **Admissions:** 3784 **Census:** 34 **Outpatient Visits:** 98219
Births: 0 **Total Expense ($000):** 107843 **Payroll Expense ($000):** 35005
Personnel: 405

AVALON—Los Angeles County

★ **CATALINA ISLAND MEDICAL CENTER (051307)**, 100 Falls Canyon Road,
Zip 90704, Mailing Address: P.O. Box 1563, Zip 90704–1563;
tel. 310/510–0700, (Nonreporting) **A**9 10 18
Primary Contact: John P. Friel, Chief Executive Officer
CFO: John Lovrich, Chief Financial Officer
CMO: Monte Mellon, M.D., Chief of Staff
CIO: Richard Kleinman, R.N., Manager Medical Informatics
CHR: Krista Steuter, Director Human Resources
CNO: Nancy Mattis, Chief Patient Care Services
Web address: www.catalinaislandmedicalcenter.org
Control: Other not–for–profit (including NFP Corporation) **Service:** General
Medical and Surgical

Staffed Beds: 12

BAKERSFIELD—Kern County

☐ **BAKERSFIELD HEART HOSPITAL (050724)**, 3001 Sillect Avenue,
Zip 93308–6337; tel. 661/316–6000 **A**1 10 **F**17 18 20 22 24 26 29 30 34 40
46 57 59 74 81 107 111 115 119 147
Primary Contact: David Veillette, President
CFO: Barbara Jo Wolff, Chief Financial Officer
CMO: Brijesh Bhambi, M.D., Chief Medical Officer
CIO: Peter Mayer, Director Information Systems
CHR: Linda Hansen, Director Human Resources
CNO: Marilyn Mahugh, Vice President Clinical Services
Web address: www.bakersfieldhearthospital.com
Control: Partnership, Investor–owned, for–profit **Service:** General Medical and
Surgical

Staffed Beds: 47 **Admissions:** 3863 **Census:** 44 **Outpatient Visits:** 12408
Births: 0 **Total Expense ($000):** 74458

Many Facility Codes have changed. Please refer to the AHA Guide Code Chart.

CA

✠ **BAKERSFIELD MEMORIAL HOSPITAL (050036)**, 420 34th Street,
Zip 93301–2237; tel. 661/327–1792, (Nonreporting) **A**1 9 10 **S** Dignity Health,
San Francisco, CA
Primary Contact: Jon Van Boening, President and Chief Executive Officer and
Senior Vice President Operations Dignity Health Central Va
COO: Bruce Peters, Vice President and Chief Operating Officer
CFO: Jesica Hanson, Vice President and Chief Financial Officer
CMO: Rodney Mark Root, D.O., Vice President Medical Affairs
CHR: Sheri Comaianni, Vice President Human Resources
Web address: www.bakersfieldmemorial.org
Control: Other not–for–profit (including NFP Corporation) **Service:** General
Medical and Surgical

Staffed Beds: 255

☐ **GOOD SAMARITAN HOSPITAL (050257)**, 901 Olive Drive, Zip 93308–4144,
Mailing Address: P.O. Box 85002, Zip 93380–5002; tel. 661/399–4461,
(Nonreporting) **A**1 9 10
Primary Contact: Tim Kollars, Chief Executive Officer
COO: Noel Cabezzas, Chief Operating Officer
CFO: Vicki Nguyen, Chief Financial Officer
CMO: Ronnie Claiborne, M.D., Chief Medical Officer
CIO: Anand Manohara, Associate Administrator
CHR: Milissa Newton, Supervisor Human Resources
Control: Partnership, Investor–owned, for–profit **Service:** General Medical and
Surgical

Staffed Beds: 29

✠ **HEALTHSOUTH BAKERSFIELD REHABILITATION HOSPITAL (053031)**, 5001
Commerce Drive, Zip 93309–0689; tel. 661/323–5500 **A**1 9 10 **F**3 28 29 35
59 64 77 82 90 91 92 93 95 96 148 **S** HEALTHSOUTH Corporation,
Birmingham, AL
Primary Contact: Martha Samora, R.N., Chief Executive Officer
CFO: Robert Mosesian, Controller
CMO: Chris Yoon, M.D., Medical Director
CIO: Tara DeMontgorency, Director Business Deveiopment
CHR: Tami Holden, Director Human Resources
Web address: www.healthsouthbakersfield.com
Control: Corporation, Investor–owned, for–profit **Service:** Rehabilitation

Staffed Beds: 66 **Admissions:** 1793 **Census:** 57 **Births:** 0 **Total Expense**
($000): 19139

☐ **KERN MEDICAL CENTER (050315)**, 1700 Mount Vernon Avenue,
Zip 93306–4018; tel. 661/326–2000 **A**1 2 3 5 8 9 10 **F**2 3 11 15 20 29 31
34 40 44 45 49 50 51 54 57 58 59 61 62 64 66 68 70 72 73 74 75 76 78
79 81 85 87 89 92 93 94 97 98 106 107 108 111 114 115 119 130 146
147 **P**6
Primary Contact: John Nilon, Interim Chief Executive Officer
CMO: Eugene Kercher, M.D., Chief Medical Officer
CIO: Bill Fawns, Interim Manager Information Systems
CHR: Steve O'Connor, Manager Human Resources
Web address: www.kernmedicalcenter.com
Control: County–Government, nonfederal **Service:** General Medical and Surgical

Staffed Beds: 188 **Admissions:** 11096 **Census:** 136 **Outpatient Visits:**
143729 **Total Expense ($000):** 296105

✠ **MERCY HOSPITALS OF BAKERSFIELD (050295)**, 2215 Truxtun Avenue,
Zip 93301–3698, Mailing Address: P.O. Box 119, Zip 93302–0119;
tel. 661/632–5000, (Includes MERCY SOUTHWEST HOSPITAL, 400 Old River
Road, Zip 93311; tel. 661/663–6000) **A**1 2 9 10 **F**11 12 13 15 29 30 34 35
40 50 57 59 60 62 64 70 72 74 75 76 78 79 81 82 84 86 87 93 107 111
114 118 119 121 123 130 131 146 147 148 **S** Dignity Health, San
Francisco, CA
Primary Contact: Jon Van Boening, Interim President and Chief Executive Officer
CFO: Rodney Winegarner, Chief Financial Officer
CIO: Jeff Vague, Regional Manager Information Systems
CHR: Jay King, Vice President Human Resources
Web address: www.mercybakersfield.org
Control: Church–operated, Nongovernment, not–for profit **Service:** General
Medical and Surgical

Staffed Beds: 222 **Admissions:** 11938 **Census:** 127 **Outpatient Visits:**
135997 **Total Expense ($000):** 257399

✠ **SAN JOAQUIN COMMUNITY HOSPITAL (050455)**, 2615 Chester Avenue,
Zip 93301–2014, Mailing Address: P.O. Box 2615, Zip 93303–2615;
tel. 661/395–3000 **A**1 9 10 **F**3 8 11 12 13 15 16 18 20 22 24 26 28 29 30
31 34 35 40 45 47 49 54 57 59 62 64 65 68 70 71 72 74 75 76 77 78 79
81 84 85 86 87 91 94 107 108 110 111 114 115 116 117 118 119 120 121
123 124 126 130 132 135 146 148 **P**3 7 **S** Adventist Health, Roseville, CA
Primary Contact: Douglas Duffield, President and Chief Executive Officer
CFO: Brent Soper, Chief Financial Officer
CHR: Marlene Kreidler, Executive Director Human Resources
Web address: www.sanjoaquinhospital.org
Control: Church–operated, Nongovernment, not–for profit **Service:** General
Medical and Surgical

Staffed Beds: 255 **Admissions:** 17910 **Census:** 200 **Outpatient Visits:**
162968 **Births:** 3063 **Total Expense ($000):** 336015 **Payroll Expense**
($000): 123659 **Personnel:** 1920

BALDWIN PARK—Los Angeles County

BALDWIN PARK MEDICAL CENTER See Kaiser Permanente Baldwin Park
Medical Center

✠ **KAISER PERMANENTE BALDWIN PARK MEDICAL CENTER (050723)**, 1011
Baldwin Park Boulevard, Zip 91706–5806; tel. 626/851–1011 **A**1 10 **F**3 8 13
15 18 29 30 31 34 35 40 41 49 56 57 58 59 60 61 62 63 64 65 68 70 72
74 75 76 77 78 79 81 82 84 85 86 87 93 94 107 111 119 130 146 147 148
S Kaiser Foundation Hospitals, Oakland, CA
Primary Contact: Margaret H. Pierce, Executive Director
COO: Payman Roshan, Chief Operating Officer
CFO: Rebecca Wheeler, Director Finance
CMO: John Bigley, M.D., Medical Director
CIO: Linda C. Salazar, Information Technology Leader
CNO: Michelle Nowicki, R.N., Chief Nurse Executive
Web address: www.kp.org
Control: Other not–for–profit (including NFP Corporation) **Service:** General
Medical and Surgical

Staffed Beds: 254 **Admissions:** 12596 **Census:** 101 **Outpatient Visits:**
347759

★ **KINDRED HOSPITAL–BALDWIN PARK (052045)**, 14148 Francisquito Avenue,
Zip 91706–6120; tel. 626/388–2700 **A**9 10 **F**1 29 45 60 84 107 111 119 130
148 **S** Kindred Healthcare, Louisville, KY
Primary Contact: Swenda Moreh, Chief Executive Officer
COO: Dina Garrow, Chief Nursing Officer and Chief Operating Officer
CFO: Christine Saltonstall, Chief Financial Officer
CMO: Anil Gupta, M.D., Chief of Staff
CHR: Antoinette Bibal, Director Human Resources
CNO: Dina Garrow, Chief Nursing Officer and Chief Operating Officer
Web address: www.khbaldwinpark.com
Control: Corporation, Investor–owned, for–profit **Service:** Long–Term Acute Care
hospital

Staffed Beds: 91 **Admissions:** 966 **Census:** 74 **Outpatient Visits:** 0 **Births:**
0 **Total Expense ($000):** 33165 **Payroll Expense ($000):** 17529
Personnel: 247

VISTA SPECIALTY HOSPITAL OF SAN GABRIEL VALLEY See Kindred
Hospital–Baldwin Park

BANNING—Riverside County

✠ **SAN GORGONIO MEMORIAL HOSPITAL (050054)**, 600 North Highland
Springs Avenue, Zip 92220–3046; tel. 951/845–1121 **A**1 9 10 **F**3 8 11 13 15
18 28 29 30 34 35 40 45 56 57 64 70 76 79 81 82 85 87 93 104 107 108
110 115 119 130 146 147 148
Primary Contact: Mark S. Turner, Chief Executive Officer
CFO: David Recupero, Chief Financial Officer
CMO: Richard Sheldon, M.D., Vice President Medical Affairs
CIO: Linda Palmer, Coordinator Medical Records
CHR: Lynn M. Gomez, Executive Director Human Resources
CNO: Pat Brown, R.N., Chief Nursing Officer
Web address: www.sgmh.org
Control: Hospital district or authority, Government, nonfederal **Service:** General
Medical and Surgical

Staffed Beds: 71 **Admissions:** 3280 **Census:** 35 **Outpatient Visits:** 42135
Births: 504 **Total Expense ($000):** 55980 **Payroll Expense ($000):** 23718
Personnel: 329

CA

Hospital, Medicare Provider Number, Address, Telephone, Approval, Facility, and Physician Codes, Health Care System

★ American Hospital Association (AHA) membership
☐ The Joint Commission accreditation ◇ DNV Healthcare Inc. accreditation
○ Healthcare Facilities Accreditation Program
△ Commission on Accreditation of Rehabilitation Facilities (CARF) accreditation

CA

BARSTOW—San Bernardino County

✠ **BARSTOW COMMUNITY HOSPITAL (050298)**, 820 East Mountain View Street, Zip 92311–3004; tel. 760/256–1761 **A**1 9 10 20 **F**3 8 11 13 15 29 35 40 70 76 79 81 107 108 111 114 119 **P**8 **S** Community Health Systems, Inc., Franklin, TN
Primary Contact: Steven Foster, Chief Executive Officer
CFO: Carrie Howell, Chief Financial Officer
CIO: Scott Bullock, Director Information Systems
CNO: Donna M. Smith, Chief Nursing Officer
Web address: www.barstowhospital.com
Control: Corporation, Investor–owned, for–profit **Service:** General Medical and Surgical

Staffed Beds: 30 Admissions: 2417 Census: 19 Outpatient Visits: 33903
Total Expense ($000): 36391

BERKELEY—Alameda County

✠ △ **ALTA BATES SUMMIT MEDICAL CENTER (050305)**, 2450 Ashby Avenue, Zip 94705–2067; tel. 510/204–4444, (Includes ALTA BATES MEDICAL CENTER–HERRICK CAMPUS, 2001 Dwight Way, Zip 94704; tel. 510/204–4444) **A**1 3 5 7 9 10 **F**3 5 8 11 13 15 17 18 20 22 26 28 29 30 31 34 35 36 37 45 46 47 49 55 56 57 58 59 60 61 64 68 70 72 74 75 76 77 78 79 81 82 84 85 87 90 93 98 99 100 103 104 105 107 108 110 111 114 116 117 118 119 120 121 123 124 130 132 135 136 146 147 148 **S** Sutter Health, Sacramento, CA
Primary Contact: Charles Prosper, Chief Executive Officer
CFO: Robert Petrina, Chief Financial Officer
CMO: John Gentile, M.D., Vice President Medical Affairs
Web address: www.altabates.com
Control: Other not–for–profit (including NFP Corporation) **Service:** General Medical and Surgical

Staffed Beds: 441 Admissions: 19306 Census: 284 Outpatient Visits:
176085 Births: 7071 Total Expense ($000): 686698 Payroll Expense ($000): 184498 Personnel: 1931

BIG BEAR LAKE—San Bernardino County

★ **BEAR VALLEY COMMUNITY HOSPITAL (050618)**, 41870 Garstin Drive, Zip 92315, Mailing Address: P.O. Box 1649, Zip 92315–1649; tel. 909/866–6501, (Total facility includes 21 beds in nursing home–type unit) **A**9 10 20 **F**3 15 29 33 34 35 39 40 50 54 56 57 59 64 81 82 93 97 107 119 128 129 133 146
Primary Contact: Raymond T. Hino, Chief Executive Officer
COO: Scott Rogers, Chief Operating Officer
CFO: Marcus Armstrong, Chief Financial Officer
CMO: Michael Norman, M.D., Chief Medical Staff
CHR: Kathy Norris, Director Human Resources
CNO: Mary Norman, R.N., Chief Nursing Officer
Web address: www.bvchd.com
Control: Hospital district or authority, Government, nonfederal **Service:** General Medical and Surgical

Staffed Beds: 30 Admissions: 166 Census: 20 Outpatient Visits: 35791
Births: 4 Total Expense ($000): 20116 Payroll Expense ($000): 10384 Personnel: 157

BISHOP—Inyo County

✠ **NORTHERN INYO HOSPITAL (051324)**, 150 Pioneer Lane, Zip 93514–2599; tel. 760/873–5811 **A**1 9 10 18 **F**3 11 13 15 31 34 40 45 46 47 64 68 70 76 77 79 81 85 89 93 107 108 111 127 130 133
Primary Contact: Victoria Alexander–Lane, Chief Executive Officer
COO: Leon Freis, Chief Operating Officer
CMO: Thomas Boo, M.D., Chief of Staff
CIO: Adam Taylor, Manager Information Technology
CHR: Georgan L. Stottlemyre, Director Human Resources
CNO: Kathy Decker, Interim Chief Nursing Officer
Web address: www.nih.org
Control: Hospital district or authority, Government, nonfederal **Service:** General Medical and Surgical

Staffed Beds: 25 Admissions: 836 Census: 6 Outpatient Visits: 68303
Total Expense ($000): 64025

BLYTHE—Riverside County

PALO VERDE HOSPITAL (050423), 250 North First Street, Zip 92225–1702; tel. 760/922–4115 **A**9 10 20 **F**29 40 45 46 70 76 81 107 118
Primary Contact: Sandra J. Anaya, R.N., Chief Executive Officer
CFO: Christa Ronde, Assistant Chief Financial Officer
CMO: Hossain Sahlolbei, M.D., Chief of Staff
CIO: Jerome Learson, Manager Information Technology and Chief Security Officer
CHR: Myrna Davis, Manager Human Resources
CNO: Nena Foreman, Chief Nursing Officer
Web address: www.paloverdehospital.org
Control: Hospital district or authority, Government, nonfederal **Service:** General Medical and Surgical

Staffed Beds: 51 Admissions: 1086 Census: 10 Outpatient Visits: 17520
Total Expense ($000): 27391

BRAWLEY—Imperial County

★ ◇ **PIONEERS MEMORIAL HEALTHCARE DISTRICT (050342)**, 207 West Legion Road, Zip 92227–7780; tel. 760/351–3333 **A**9 10 21 **F**3 11 13 15 18 29 30 31 34 35 40 43 45 49 51 56 57 59 64 65 70 73 74 75 76 77 78 79 81 85 86 89 93 97 107 108 110 111 115 119 127 130 144 146 147
Primary Contact: Larry Lewis, Chief Executive Officer
COO: Stephen J. Campbell, Chief Operating Officer
CFO: Roger Armstrong, Interim Chief Financial Officer
CMO: Travis Calvin, Jr., M.D., Chief of Staff
CIO: Kathleen S. McKernan, Director Information Systems
CHR: Julie Cunningham, Associate Administrator and Chief Human Resources Officer
Web address: www.pmhd.org
Control: Hospital district or authority, Government, nonfederal **Service:** General Medical and Surgical

Staffed Beds: 107 Admissions: 5512 Census: 45 Outpatient Visits: 99266
Births: 1733 Total Expense ($000): 97832 Payroll Expense ($000): 39751 Personnel: 703

BREA—Orange County

✠ **KINDRED HOSPITAL–BREA (052039)**, 875 North Brea Boulevard, Zip 92821–2699; tel. 714/529–6842, (Nonreporting) **A**1 9 10 **S** Kindred Healthcare, Louisville, KY
Primary Contact: Diane Zeoli, Chief Executive Officer
COO: Denise Jenkins, Chief Clinical Officer
CFO: John Browne, Assistant Administrator Finance
CMO: Jyotika Wali, M.D., Chief of Staff
Web address: www.kindredhospitalbrea.com/
Control: Corporation, Investor–owned, for–profit **Service:** Long–Term Acute Care hospital

Staffed Beds: 48

BURBANK—Los Angeles County

✠ △ **PROVIDENCE SAINT JOSEPH MEDICAL CENTER (050235)**, 501 South Buena Vista Street, Zip 91505–4866; tel. 818/843–5111, (Nonreporting) **A**1 2 7 9 10 **S** Providence Health & Services, Renton, WA
Primary Contact: Michael A. Rembis, FACHE, Chief Executive Officer
COO: David Emter, Chief Operating Officer
CFO: Glenn Bales, Chief Financial Officer
CMO: Nick Testa, M.D., Chief Medical Officer
CIO: Anne Marie Brody, Director Information Systems Customer Service
CHR: LaDonna Najieb, Service Area Director Human Resources
CNO: Valarie Fleming, R.N., Chief Nursing Officer
Web address: www.providence.org
Control: Church–operated, Nongovernment, not–for profit **Service:** General Medical and Surgical

Staffed Beds: 488

BURLINGAME—San Mateo County

✠ **MILLS–PENINSULA HEALTH SERVICES (050007)**, 1501 Trousdale Drive, Zip 94010–3282; tel. 650/696–5400, (Includes MILLS HOSPITAL, 100 South San Mateo Drive, San Mateo, Zip 94401; tel. 415/696–4400; PENINSULA HOSPITAL, 1783 El Camino Real, Zip 94010–3205; tel. 650/696–5400), (Total facility includes 62 beds in nursing home–type unit) **A**1 9 10 **F**2 3 4 5 6 8 9 11 12 13 15 17 18 20 22 24 26 28 29 30 31 34 35 36 37 38 40 45 46 47 48 49 51 53 54 55 56 57 58 59 60 64 65 66 68 72 74 75 76 77 78 79 81 84 85 86 87 91 93 94 97 98 99 100 101 102 103 104 105 107 108 110 111 114 115 118 119 121 123 124 126 128 130 132 134 135 146 147 148 **S** Sutter Health, Sacramento, CA
Primary Contact: Robert W. Merwin, Chief Executive Officer
CFO: Iftikhar Hussain, Chief Financial Officer
CMO: Michael K. Wood, M.D., Chief Medical Officer
CIO: Michael Reandeau, Chief Information Officer
CHR: Debbie Goodin, Vice President Human Resources
Web address: www.mills–peninsula.org
Control: Other not–for–profit (including NFP Corporation) **Service:** General Medical and Surgical

Staffed Beds: 320 Admissions: 14089 Census: 160 Outpatient Visits:
324087 Births: 1960 Total Expense ($000): 485942 Payroll Expense ($000): 143408 Personnel: 1575

CAMARILLO—Ventura County

✠ **ST. JOHN'S PLEASANT VALLEY HOSPITAL (050616)**, 2309 Antonio Avenue, Zip 93010–1414; tel. 805/389–5800, (Nonreporting) **A**1 9 10 **S** Dignity Health, San Francisco, CA
COO: Kim A. Wilson, R.N., Chief Operating Officer
CFO: Robert D. Wardwell, Chief Financial Officer
CMO: Eugene Fussell, M.D., Chief Medical Officer
CIO: Jeff Perry, Director Information Technology
CHR: Ed Gonzales, Vice President Human Resources
CNO: Raye Burkhardt, Chief Nursing Officer
Web address: www.stjohnshealth.org
Control: Other not–for–profit (including NFP Corporation) **Service:** General Medical and Surgical

Staffed Beds: 127

Many Facility Codes have changed. Please refer to the AHA Guide Code Chart. © 2014 AHA Guide

CAMP PENDLETON—San Diego County

✠ **NAVAL HOSPITAL CAMP PENDLETON**, Santa Margarita Road, Building H100,
Zip 92055–5191, Mailing Address: P.O. Box 555191, Zip 92055–5191;
tel. 760/725–1304, (Nonreporting) **A**1 3 5 **S** Bureau of Medicine and Surgery,
Department of the Navy, Washington, DC
Primary Contact: Captain Mark A. Kobelja, MC, USN, Commanding Officer
CFO: Commander Gordon Blighton, Director Resource Management
CMO: Lynn Bailey, M.D., Director Primary Care and Medical Services
CIO: Gabe Vallido, Chief Information Officer
CHR: Lieutenant Jet Ramos, Head Staff Administration
Web address: www.cpen.med.navy.mil/
Control: Navy, Government, federal **Service:** General Medical and Surgical

Staffed Beds: 72

CANOGA PARK—Los Angeles County, See Los Angeles

CARMICHAEL—Sacramento County

✠ **MERCY SAN JUAN MEDICAL CENTER (050516)**, 6501 Coyle Avenue,
Zip 95608–0306, Mailing Address: P.O. Box 479, Zip 95609–0479;
tel. 916/537–5000 **A**1 2 3 5 9 10 **F**3 8 11 12 13 17 18 20 22 24 26 28 29
30 31 34 35 37 40 43 45 47 48 49 51 58 59 62 63 64 66 68 70 72 74 75
76 77 78 79 81 82 83 84 85 89 92 93 107 108 111 114 115 118 119 126
129 130 132 135 146 148 **S** Dignity Health, San Francisco, CA
Primary Contact: Brian K. Ivie, President
COO: Paul R. Luehrs, Chief Operating Officer
CFO: Robert Pascuzzi, Chief Financial Officer
CMO: Mark Owens, M.D., Vice President Medical Affairs
CHR: Donna Utley, Vice President Human Resources
Web address: www.mercysanjuan.org
Control: Church–operated, Nongovernment, not–for profit **Service:** General
Medical and Surgical

Staffed Beds: 359 **Admissions:** 24455 **Census:** 267 **Outpatient Visits:**
189777 **Total Expense ($000):** 537396

CASTRO VALLEY—Alameda County

✠ **EDEN MEDICAL CENTER (050488)**, 20103 Lake Chabot Road,
Zip 94546–5305; tel. 510/537–1234 **A**1 2 9 10 **F**3 11 13 15 29 30 31 34 35
38 40 43 46 49 50 51 53 56 57 58 59 60 65 68 70 74 75 76 77 78 79 81
84 85 87 93 100 101 102 107 108 110 111 114 117 118 119 120 121 130
132 135 144 146 147 148 **S** Sutter Health, Sacramento, CA
Primary Contact: George Bischalaney, President and Chief Executive Officer
Web address: www.edenmedcenter.org
Control: Other not–for–profit (including NFP Corporation) **Service:** General
Medical and Surgical

Staffed Beds: 130 **Admissions:** 8550 **Census:** 95 **Outpatient Visits:** 66350
Births: 1250 **Total Expense ($000):** 281000 **Payroll Expense ($000):**
91305 **Personnel:** 897

CEDARVILLE—Modoc County

SURPRISE VALLEY HEALTH CARE DISTRICT (051308), 741 North Main
Street, Zip 96104, Mailing Address: P.O. Box 246, Zip 96104–0246;
tel. 530/279–6111, (Nonreporting) **A**9 10 18
Primary Contact: Wanda Grove, Administrator
CFO: Renae Sweet, Chief Financial Officer
CMO: Chuck Colas, M.D., Medical Director
CHR: William Bostic, Administrative Assistant Human Resources
Web address: www.svhospital.org/
Control: Hospital district or authority, Government, nonfederal **Service:** General
Medical and Surgical

Staffed Beds: 4

CERRITOS—Los Angeles County

☐ **COLLEGE HOSPITAL CERRITOS (054055)**, 10802 College Place,
Zip 90703–1579; tel. 562/924–9581, (Nonreporting) **A**1 9 10 **S** College Health
Enterprises, Santa Fe Springs, CA
Primary Contact: Stephen Witt, President and Chief Executive Officer
CFO: Roderick Bell, Chief Financial Officer
CHR: Holly Risha, Administrative Director Human Resources
Web address: www.collegehospitals.com
Control: Corporation, Investor–owned, for–profit **Service:** Psychiatric

Staffed Beds: 157

CHESTER—Plumas County

★ **SENECA HEALTHCARE DISTRICT (051327)**, 130 Brentwood Drive,
Zip 96020–0737, Mailing Address: P.O. Box 737, Zip 96020–0737;
tel. 530/258–2151, (Total facility includes 16 beds in nursing home–type unit) **A**9
10 18 **F**34 35 40 46 54 57 59 65 66 68 75 79 81 82 85 93 97 107 108 111
114 119 127 128 131 133 135 146 148
Primary Contact: Linda S. Wagner, MSN, FACHE, Chief Executive Officer
CFO: Carlene Slusher, Director Finance
CMO: Dana Ware, M.D., Chief of Staff
CIO: Elizabeth Steffen, Director Information Technology
CHR: Marie Stuersel, Director Human Resources
CNO: Teresa L. Whitfield, R.N., Chief Nursing Officer
Web address: www.senecahospital.org
Control: Hospital district or authority, Government, nonfederal **Service:** General
Medical and Surgical

Staffed Beds: 26 **Admissions:** 204 **Census:** 17 **Outpatient Visits:** 28552
Births: 0

CHICO—Butte County

✠ **ENLOE MEDICAL CENTER (050039)**, 1531 Esplanade, Zip 95926–3386;
tel. 530/332–7300, (Includes ENLOE MEDICAL CENTER–COHASSET, 560
Cohasset Road, Zip 95926; tel. 530/332–7300), (Nonreporting) **A**1 9 10
Primary Contact: Michael C. Wiltermood, President and Chief Executive Officer
CMO: Forrest Olson, M.D., Chief Medical Officer
CHR: Carol Linscheid, Vice President Human Resources
Web address: www.enloe.org
Control: Other not–for–profit (including NFP Corporation) **Service:** General
Medical and Surgical

Staffed Beds: 263

CHINO—San Bernardino County

☐ **CANYON RIDGE HOSPITAL (054111)**, 5353 G Street, Zip 91710–5250;
tel. 909/590–3700 **A**1 9 10 **F**5 38 98 99 100 101 102 104 105 **S** Universal
Health Services, Inc., King of Prussia, PA
Primary Contact: Jeff McDonald, Chief Executive Officer
CFO: Burt Harris, Chief Financial Officer
CMO: Mir Ali–Khan, M.D., Medical Director
CIO: Maria Patterson, Manager Health Information Management
CHR: Ericca Lopez, Director Human Resources
Web address: www.canyonridgehospital.com
Control: Corporation, Investor–owned, for–profit **Service:** Psychiatric

Staffed Beds: 106 **Admissions:** 5748 **Census:** 85 **Outpatient Visits:** 11336
Births: 0 **Total Expense ($000):** 21205

★ ○ **CHINO VALLEY MEDICAL CENTER (050586)**, 5451 Walnut Avenue,
Zip 91710–2672; tel. 909/464–8600, (Nonreporting) **A**10 11 12 13 **S** Prime
Healthcare Services, Ontario, CA
Primary Contact: James M. Lally, D.O., President and Chief Medical Officer
CFO: Gregory Brentano, Chief Financial Officer
CIO: Vic Mahan, Chief Information Officer
Web address: www.cvmc.com
Control: Corporation, Investor–owned, for–profit **Service:** General Medical and
Surgical

Staffed Beds: 112

CHULA VISTA—San Diego County

SCRIPPS MERCY HOSPITAL CHULA VISTA See Scripps Mercy Hospital, San
Diego

✠ **SHARP CHULA VISTA MEDICAL CENTER (050222)**, 751 Medical Center
Court, Zip 91911–6699, Mailing Address: P.O. Box 1297, Zip 91912–1297;
tel. 619/502–5800, (Total facility includes 100 beds in nursing home–type unit)
A1 2 9 10 **F**8 11 12 13 15 18 20 22 24 26 28 29 30 31 34 35 40 46 47 49
51 53 54 57 59 60 63 64 65 70 72 75 76 77 78 79 81 82 85 86 87 93 107
108 110 111 114 115 118 119 120 121 123 124 126 128 130 132 143 146
147 148 **P**5 **S** Sharp HealthCare, San Diego, CA
Primary Contact: Pablo Velez, Chief Executive Officer
CMO: Lynn Welling, M.D., Chief Medical Officer
CHR: Zoe Gardner, Manager Human Resources
Web address: www.sharp.com
Control: Other not–for–profit (including NFP Corporation) **Service:** General
Medical and Surgical

Staffed Beds: 343 **Admissions:** 14606 **Census:** 268 **Outpatient Visits:**
109107 **Births:** 2704 **Total Expense ($000):** 305957 **Payroll Expense
($000):** 125190 **Personnel:** 1473

Hospital, Medicare Provider Number, Address, Telephone, Approval, Facility, and Physician Codes, Health Care System

★ American Hospital Association (AHA) membership
☐ The Joint Commission accreditation ◇ DNV Healthcare Inc. accreditation
○ Healthcare Facilities Accreditation Program
△ Commission on Accreditation of Rehabilitation Facilities (CARF) accreditation

CLEARLAKE—Lake County

✠ **ST. HELENA HOSPITAL CLEAR LAKE (051317)**, 15630 18th Avenue, Zip 95422–9336, Mailing Address: P.O. Box 6710, Zip 95422; tel. 707/994–6486 **A**1 9 10 18 **F**18 34 40 45 50 57 62 70 76 81 87 93 97 107 108 110 111 113 116 118 127 130 133 134 143 144 **P**3 **S** Adventist Health, Roseville, CA
Primary Contact: David Santos, President and Chief Executive Officer
COO: David Santos, President Chief Executive Officer
CFO: Buck McDonald, Chief Financial Officer
CMO: Marc Shapiro, M.D., Chief Medical Officer
CIO: Joshua Cowan, Chief Information Officer
CHR: Audrey Barrall, Director Human Resources
CNO: Colleen Assavapisitkul, Chief Nursing Officer
Web address: www.adventisthealth.org
Control: Church–operated, Nongovernment, not–for profit **Service:** General Medical and Surgical

Staffed Beds: 25 **Admissions:** 1368 **Census:** 14 **Outpatient Visits:** 149712 **Births:** 190 **Total Expense ($000):** 67464 **Payroll Expense ($000):** 23778 **Personnel:** 356

CLOVIS—Fresno County

☐ **CLOVIS COMMUNITY MEDICAL CENTER (050492)**, 2755 Herndon Avenue, Zip 93611–6801; tel. 559/324–4000, (Nonreporting) **A**1 9 10 **S** Community Medical Centers, Fresno, CA
Primary Contact: Craig Castro, Chief Executive Officer
CFO: Tracy Kiritani, Vice President and Chief Financial Officer
CIO: George Vasquez, Chief Technology Officer
CHR: Ginny Burdick, Senior Vice President and Chief Human Resources Officer
Web address: www.communitymedical.org
Control: Other not–for–profit (including NFP Corporation) **Service:** General Medical and Surgical

Staffed Beds: 109

COALINGA—Fresno County

COALINGA REGIONAL MEDICAL CENTER (050397), 1191 Phelps Avenue, Zip 93210–9636; tel. 559/935–6400, (Total facility includes 99 beds in nursing home–type unit) **A**9 10 20 **F**15 32 35 40 41 50 57 59 65 66 68 89 90 93 102 107 110 115 119 127 128 130 143 148
Primary Contact: Sharon A. Spurgeon, Chief Executive Officer
CFO: Sandra Earls, Chief Financial Officer
CMO: Lymar Bik, M.D., Medical Director
CIO: Chris Burrage, Manager Information Technology
CHR: Lucia Lopez, Manager Human Resources
CNO: Betty Hull, R.N., Chief Nursing Officer
Web address: www.coalingamedicalcenter.com
Control: Hospital district or authority, Government, nonfederal **Service:** General Medical and Surgical

Staffed Beds: 123 **Admissions:** 338 **Census:** 75 **Outpatient Visits:** 27119 **Births:** 0 **Total Expense ($000):** 22042

COLTON—San Bernardino County

○ **ARROWHEAD REGIONAL MEDICAL CENTER (050245)**, 400 North Pepper Avenue, Zip 92324–1819; tel. 909/580–1000 **A**2 3 5 9 10 11 12 13 **F**3 8 13 15 16 18 20 22 28 29 30 31 32 34 35 36 39 40 43 45 47 49 50 51 52 54 55 56 57 60 64 66 68 70 72 74 75 76 77 78 79 81 82 84 85 86 87 89 91 92 93 97 98 100 101 102 107 108 110 111 114 115 116 118 119 120 121 130 132 135 146 147 148 **P**5
Primary Contact: William T. Foley, M.D., Administrator
COO: Maureen A. Malone, Chief Operating Officer
CFO: Frank Arambula, Chief Financial Officer
CMO: Richard Pitts, D.O., Medical Director
CIO: Felix Ekpo, Interim Manager Information Systems
CHR: Victor Tordesillas, Director Human Resources
CNO: Michelle Sayre, R.N., Chief Nursing Officer
Web address: www.arrowheadmedcenter.org
Control: County–Government, nonfederal **Service:** General Medical and Surgical

Staffed Beds: 436 **Admissions:** 23997 **Census:** 336 **Outpatient Visits:** 320686 **Births:** 2567 **Total Expense ($000):** 516531 **Payroll Expense ($000):** 170082 **Personnel:** 2812

COLUSA—Colusa County

☐ **COLUSA REGIONAL MEDICAL CENTER (050434)**, 199 East Webster Street, Zip 95932–2954; tel. 530/458–5821, (Total facility includes 6 beds in nursing home–type unit) **A**1 9 10 20 **F**29 30 35 40 53 54 57 59 62 64 65 68 70 75 76 77 81 84 85 107 119 128 129 130 133 144 146
Primary Contact: Walter G. Beck, Chief Executive Officer
CFO: Tish Miller, Chief Financial Officer
CMO: Gregory Burt, M.D., Chief of Staff
CIO: Rachel Betke–Mena, Director Health Information Management
CHR: Dierdre Athenais, Director Human Resources
Web address: www.colusamedicalcenter.org
Control: Other not–for–profit (including NFP Corporation) **Service:** General Medical and Surgical

Staffed Beds: 30 **Admissions:** 900 **Census:** 10 **Outpatient Visits:** 45130 **Total Expense ($000):** 20190

CONCORD—Contra Costa County

✠ **JOHN MUIR BEHAVIORAL HEALTH CENTER (054131)**, 2740 Grant Street, Zip 94520–2265; tel. 925/674–4100 **A**1 9 10 **F**4 5 64 98 99 100 103 104 105 130 **S** John Muir Health, Walnut Creek, CA
Primary Contact: Cindy Bolter, Chief Nursing and Operations Officer
CFO: Michael Moody, Senior Vice President and Chief Financial Officer
CMO: Nagui Achamallah, M.D., Chief of Staff
CIO: Eric Saff, Senior Vice President and Chief Information Officer
CHR: Alice A. Villanueva, Senior Vice President Human Resources
CNO: Cindy Bolter, Chief Nursing and Operations Officer
Web address: www.johnmuirhealth.com
Control: Other not–for–profit (including NFP Corporation) **Service:** Psychiatric

Staffed Beds: 73 **Admissions:** 2800 **Census:** 52 **Outpatient Visits:** 16872 **Births:** 0

✠ **JOHN MUIR MEDICAL CENTER, CONCORD (050496)**, 2540 East Street, Zip 94520–1906; tel. 925/682–8200 **A**1 9 10 **F**3 12 15 17 18 20 22 24 26 28 29 30 31 34 37 40 44 45 46 47 48 49 50 54 56 57 58 59 64 70 74 75 78 79 80 81 82 84 85 86 87 93 107 108 110 114 115 118 119 120 121 123 126 130 132 135 141 143 145 146 148 **P**3 5 **S** John Muir Health, Walnut Creek, CA
Primary Contact: Michael S. Thomas, President and Chief Administrative Officer
COO: Michael S. Thomas, President and Chief Administrative Officer
CFO: Michael Moody, Chief Financial Officer
CMO: John Ganey, M.D., Chief of Staff
CIO: Jim Wesley, Interim Senior Vice President and Chief Information Officer
CHR: Lisa Foust, Senior Vice President Human Resources
CNO: Donna Brackley, R.N., Senior Vice President Patient Care Services
Web address: www.johnmuirhealth.com
Control: Other not–for–profit (including NFP Corporation) **Service:** General Medical and Surgical

Staffed Beds: 183 **Admissions:** 9378 **Census:** 110 **Outpatient Visits:** 188944 **Births:** 0 **Total Expense ($000):** 372504 **Payroll Expense ($000):** 139870 **Personnel:** 1039

CORONA—Riverside County

☐ **CORONA REGIONAL MEDICAL CENTER (050329)**, 800 South Main Street, Zip 92882–3400; tel. 951/737–4343, (Includes CORONA REGIONAL MEDICAL CENTER–REHABILITATION, 730 Magnolia Avenue, Zip 92879; tel. 951/736–7200), (Nonreporting) **A**1 9 10 **S** Universal Health Services, Inc., King of Prussia, PA
Primary Contact: Mark Utter, Chief Executive Officer
CFO: Becky Cheng, Chief Financial Officer
CMO: Michael Molinari, M.D., Chief of Staff
CIO: Tura Heckler, Director Information Systems
CHR: Ruth Battles, Administrative Director Human Resources
Web address: www.coronaregional.com
Control: Corporation, Investor–owned, for–profit **Service:** General Medical and Surgical

Staffed Beds: 240

CORONADO—San Diego County

✠ **SHARP CORONADO HOSPITAL AND HEALTHCARE CENTER (050234)**, 250 Prospect Place, Zip 92118–1999; tel. 619/522–3600, (Total facility includes 122 beds in nursing home–type unit) **A**1 9 10 **F**3 11 15 29 30 34 35 36 37 40 45 53 57 59 60 64 65 68 69 70 74 75 77 79 81 82 85 86 87 93 107 111 114 119 128 130 135 146 148 **S** Sharp HealthCare, San Diego, CA
Primary Contact: Susan Stone, R.N., Ph.D., Senior Vice President and Chief Executive Officer
Web address: www.sharp.com
Control: Other not–for–profit (including NFP Corporation) **Service:** General Medical and Surgical

Staffed Beds: 181 **Admissions:** 2700 **Census:** 122 **Outpatient Visits:** 53761 **Births:** 0 **Total Expense ($000):** 78355 **Payroll Expense ($000):** 35154 **Personnel:** 431

COSTA MESA—Orange County

☐ **COLLEGE HOSPITAL COSTA MESA (050543)**, 301 Victoria Street, Zip 92627–7131; tel. 949/642–2734, (Nonreporting) **A**1 9 10 **S** College Health Enterprises, Santa Fe Springs, CA
Primary Contact: Susan L. Taylor, Chief Executive Officer
CFO: Dale Bracy, Chief Financial Officer
CMO: Michael Schwartz, M.D., Chief of Staff
CIO: Eladio Aldana, Manager Information Systems
CHR: Sharon DuBruyne, Director Human Resources
Web address: www.collegehospitals.com/cosHome
Control: Corporation, Investor–owned, for–profit **Service:** Psychiatric

Staffed Beds: 122

COVINA—Los Angeles County

☐ **AURORA CHARTER OAK HOSPITAL (054069)**, 1161 East Covina Boulevard, Zip 91724–1599; tel. 626/966–1632, (Nonreporting) **A**1 9 10 **S** Aurora Behavioral Health Care, Corona, CA
Primary Contact: Todd A. Smith, Chief Executive Officer
COO: Sheila Cordova, Director Clinical Services and Chief Operating Officer
CMO: Adib Bitar, M.D., Medical Director
CHR: Christine de la Paz, Director Human Resources
Web address: www.aurorabehavioral.com
Control: Corporation, Investor–owned, for–profit **Service:** Psychiatric

Staffed Beds: 95

★ **CITRUS VALLEY MEDICAL CENTER–INTER COMMUNITY CAMPUS (050382)**, 210 West San Bernadino Road, Zip 91723–1515, Mailing Address: P.O. Box 6108, Zip 91722–5108; tel. 626/331–7331, (Includes CITRUS VALLEY MEDICAL CENTER–INTER–COMMUNITY CAMPUS, 210 West San Bernardino Road, Mailing Address: P.O. Box 6108, Zip 91722–5108; tel. 626/331–7331; CITRUS VALLEY MEDICAL CENTER–QUEEN OF THE VALLEY CAMPUS, 1115 South Sunset Avenue, West Covina, Zip 91790–3940, Mailing Address: P.O. Box 1980, Zip 91793–1980; tel. 626/962–4011) **A**9 10 **F**3 7 8 11 13 15 17 18 20 22 24 25 26 27 28 29 30 31 32 34 35 40 41 44 45 46 47 49 50 51 55 56 57 59 64 65 68 69 70 71 72 74 75 76 77 78 79 80 81 82 83 84 85 86 87 89 90 92 93 96 98 102 103 105 107 108 110 114 115 118 119 120 121 124 126 128 129 130 131 132 135 143 146 147 148 **S** Citrus Valley Health Partners, Covina, CA
Primary Contact: Robert H. Curry, President and Chief Executive Officer
CFO: Roger Sharma, Chief Financial Officer
CIO: Pavel Bindra, M.D., Chief Medical Officer and Chief Information Officer
CHR: Paul Heredia, Chief Human Resources Officer
CNO: Diana Lugo–Zenner, R.N., Chief Nursing Officer
Web address: www.cvhp.org
Control: Other not–for–profit (including NFP Corporation) **Service:** General Medical and Surgical

Staffed Beds: 326 **Admissions:** 25303 **Census:** 287 **Outpatient Visits:** 153246 **Births:** 4100 **Total Expense ($000):** 357028 **Payroll Expense ($000):** 119378 **Personnel:** 1590

CRESCENT CITY—Del Norte County

⊠ **SUTTER COAST HOSPITAL (050417)**, 800 East Washington Boulevard, Zip 95531–8359; tel. 707/464–8511 **A**1 9 10 20 **F**3 8 11 13 15 29 30 34 35 40 43 45 46 47 48 51 54 57 59 62 68 70 75 76 79 81 82 84 85 87 93 97 107 108 110 111 114 118 119 127 130 132 135 144 146 148 **S** Sutter Health, Sacramento, CA
Primary Contact: Mitchell J. Hanna, Interim Chief Executive Officer
Web address: www.sutterhealth.org
Control: Other not–for–profit (including NFP Corporation) **Service:** General Medical and Surgical

Staffed Beds: 49 **Admissions:** 2279 **Census:** 20 **Outpatient Visits:** 41255 **Births:** 341 **Total Expense ($000):** 66405 **Payroll Expense ($000):** 22091 **Personnel:** 373

CULVER CITY—Los Angeles County

◇ **SOUTHERN CALIFORNIA HOSPITAL AT CULVER CITY (050752)**, 3828 Delmas Terrace, Zip 90232–6806; tel. 310/836–7000, (Nonreporting) **A**9 10 21
Primary Contact: Barbara Schneider, R.N., Chief Executive Officer
CFO: Vincent Rubin, Chief Financial Officer
CMO: Martha Sonnenberg, M.D., Chief of Staff
CIO: Carrie Bonar, Chief Information Officer
CHR: Betty J. Harris, Director Human Resources
Web address: www.sch–culvercity.com
Control: Corporation, Investor–owned, for–profit **Service:** General Medical and Surgical

Staffed Beds: 420

DALY CITY—San Mateo County

⊠ **SETON MEDICAL CENTER (050289)**, 1900 Sullivan Avenue, Zip 94015–2229; tel. 650/992–4000, (Total facility includes 116 beds in nursing home–type unit) **A**1 2 9 10 **F**3 8 17 18 20 22 24 26 28 29 30 31 34 35 40 45 46 49 53 54 57 59 60 64 65 66 68 70 71 72 74 75 77 78 79 81 82 84 87 93 107 110 111 114 115 116 117 118 119 120 121 123 124 128 130 133 135 146 147 148 **P**3 **S** Daughters of Charity Health System, Los Altos Hills, CA
Primary Contact: Joanne E. Allen, President and Chief Executive Officer
COO: Stephanie Mearns, Vice President Patient Care Services and Chief Nurse Executive
CFO: Richard Wood, Chief Financial Officer
CMO: David Goldschmid, M.D., President Medical Staff
CHR: Patricia White, Vice President Human Resources
Web address: www.setonmedicalcenter.org
Control: Church–operated, Nongovernment, not–for profit **Service:** General Medical and Surgical

Staffed Beds: 423 **Admissions:** 6873 **Census:** 236 **Outpatient Visits:** 192702 **Births:** 601 **Total Expense ($000):** 303344 **Payroll Expense ($000):** 132380 **Personnel:** 1060

DAVIS—Yolo County

⊠ **SUTTER DAVIS HOSPITAL (050537)**, 2000 Sutter Place, Zip 95616–6201, Mailing Address: P.O. Box 1617, Zip 95617–1617; tel. 530/756–6440 **A**1 3 5 9 10 **F**3 8 11 13 15 18 19 28 29 31 40 47 48 49 57 70 75 78 79 81 85 86 107 108 114 119 124 146 **S** Sutter Health, Sacramento, CA
Primary Contact: Janet Wagner, R.N., Chief Executive Officer
CFO: Allison Viramoutes, Chief Financial Officer
CMO: Deven Merchant, M.D., Chief Medical Executive
CHR: Don Hartman, Director Human Resources
CNO: Myrna Chang, Chief Nursing Executive
Web address: www.sutterhealth.org
Control: Other not–for–profit (including NFP Corporation) **Service:** General Medical and Surgical

Staffed Beds: 48 **Admissions:** 3373 **Census:** 23 **Outpatient Visits:** 41692 **Births:** 1408 **Total Expense ($000):** 80226 **Payroll Expense ($000):** 26304 **Personnel:** 328

DELANO—Kern County

○ **DELANO REGIONAL MEDICAL CENTER (050608)**, 1401 Garces Highway, Zip 93215–3690, Mailing Address: P.O. Box 460, Zip 93216–0460; tel. 661/725–4800, (Nonreporting) **A**9 10 11
Primary Contact: Bahram Ghaffari, President
CFO: Bahram Ghaffari, President
CIO: Sandy Bakich, Director Information Management
CHR: Del Garbanzos, Director Human Resources
Web address: www.drmc.com
Control: Other not–for–profit (including NFP Corporation) **Service:** General Medical and Surgical

Staffed Beds: 100

DOWNEY—Los Angeles County

★ ◇ **DOWNEY REGIONAL MEDICAL CENTER (050393)**, 11500 Brookshire Avenue, Zip 90241–4917; tel. 562/904–5000 **A**9 10 12 13 21 **F**3 8 11 13 15 17 18 22 24 29 30 31 34 35 38 40 45 47 49 56 57 64 72 76 77 78 79 81 85 89 91 92 93 107 108 109 110 111 115 119 130 146 **P**3 5
Primary Contact: James R. West, President and Chief Executive Officer
COO: Robert Fuller, Executive Vice President and Chief Operating Officer
CFO: Ed King, Chief Financial Officer
CIO: Nick Pappas, Chief Information Officer
CHR: Carole Everhart, Administrative Director Human Resources
CNO: Heather Conwell, Chief Nursing Officer
Web address: www.drmci.org
Control: Other not–for–profit (including NFP Corporation) **Service:** General Medical and Surgical

Staffed Beds: 199 **Admissions:** 11037 **Census:** 121 **Outpatient Visits:** 93334 **Births:** 1324 **Total Expense ($000):** 179064 **Payroll Expense ($000):** 73334 **Personnel:** 1033

⊠ **KAISER PERMANENTE DOWNEY MEDICAL CENTER (050139)**, 9333 Imperial Highway, Zip 90242–2812; tel. 562/657–9000 **A**1 10 **F**3 8 13 15 18 19 29 30 31 35 38 40 45 46 49 51 58 60 64 65 68 70 72 74 75 76 78 79 81 82 83 84 85 87 88 89 92 100 107 110 111 114 115 119 126 130 132 146 148 **S** Kaiser Foundation Hospitals, Oakland, CA
Primary Contact: James Branchick, R.N., MS, Executive Director
CNO: Patricia J. Clausen, R.N., Chief Nurse Executive
Web address: www.kaiserpermanente.org
Control: Other not–for–profit (including NFP Corporation) **Service:** General Medical and Surgical

Staffed Beds: 342 **Admissions:** 17836 **Census:** 161 **Outpatient Visits:** 183100

CA

Hospital, Medicare Provider Number, Address, Telephone, Approval, Facility, and Physician Codes, Health Care System

★ American Hospital Association (AHA) membership
☐ The Joint Commission accreditation   ◇ DNV Healthcare Inc. accreditation

○ Healthcare Facilities Accreditation Program
△ Commission on Accreditation of Rehabilitation Facilities (CARF) accreditation

☐ △ **RANCHO LOS AMIGOS NATIONAL REHABILITATION CENTER (050717)**, 7601 East Imperial Highway, Zip 90242–3496; tel. 562/401–7111, (Nonreporting) **A**1 3 5 7 9 10 **S** Los Angeles County–Department of Health Services, Los Angeles, CA
Primary Contact: Jorge Orozco, Chief Executive Officer
COO: Benjamin Ovando, Chief Operations Officer
CFO: Robin Bayus, Chief Financial Officer
CMO: Mindy Aisen, M.D., Chief Medical Officer
CIO: Francis Tang, Chief Information Officer
CHR: Elizabeth Jacobi, Associate Director Human Resources
CNO: Aries Limbaga, R.N., Chief Nursing Officer
Web address: www.rancho.org
Control: County–Government, nonfederal **Service:** Rehabilitation

Staffed Beds: 207

DUARTE—Los Angeles County

⊞ **CITY OF HOPE'S HELFORD CLINICAL RESEARCH HOSPITAL (050146)**, 1500 East Duarte Road, Zip 91010–3012; tel. 626/256–4673 **A**1 2 3 5 8 9 10 **F**3 8 11 14 15 18 26 29 30 31 32 34 35 36 38 44 45 46 47 49 50 55 56 57 58 59 61 63 64 68 70 74 75 77 78 79 80 81 82 84 85 86 87 88 89 92 93 96 99 100 101 102 103 104 107 108 110 111 114 115 116 117 118 119 120 121 123 124 126 130 132 134 135 136 141 142 144 145 146 147 148 **P**3
Primary Contact: Robert Stone, President and Chief Executive Officer
COO: Marty Sargeant, Chief Operating Officer
CFO: Gary F. Conner, Chief Financial Officer
CMO: Alexandra Levine, M.D., Chief Medical Officer
CIO: Paul Conocenti, Chief Information Officer
CHR: Stephanie Neuvirth, Chief Human Resource and Diversity Officer
Web address: www.cityofhope.org
Control: Other not–for–profit (including NFP Corporation) **Service:** Cancer

Staffed Beds: 186 Admissions: 5997 Census: 164 Outpatient Visits: 189642 Births: 0 Total Expense ($000): 684310 Payroll Expense ($000): 234381 Personnel: 3041

EL CENTRO—Imperial County

⊞ **EL CENTRO REGIONAL MEDICAL CENTER (050045)**, 1415 Ross Avenue, Zip 92243–4398; tel. 760/339–7100 **A**1 9 10 **F**3 11 13 15 18 26 29 30 31 34 40 43 45 46 47 48 49 50 51 54 57 59 60 64 66 70 74 75 76 78 79 81 82 85 86 87 89 93 97 107 108 110 111 114 115 116 117 119 126 127 130 131 145 146 147 148
Primary Contact: Tomas Virgen, R.N., Interim Administrator and Chief Executive Officer
COO: Tomas Virgen, R.N., Chief Operating Officer
CFO: Kathleen Farmer, Assistant Administrator Finance and Chief Financial Officer
CIO: John Gaede, Director Information Systems
CHR: Bill Moore, Chief Human Resources
Web address: www.ecrmc.org
Control: City–Government, nonfederal **Service:** General Medical and Surgical

Staffed Beds: 161 Admissions: 6297 Census: 67 Outpatient Visits: 186696 Births: 1147 Total Expense ($000): 123250 Payroll Expense ($000): 46034 Personnel: 823

ELDRIDGE—Sonoma County

SONOMA DEVELOPMENTAL CENTER (050547), 15000 Arnold Drive, Zip 95431–8900, Mailing Address: P.O. Box 1493, Zip 95431–1493; tel. 707/938–6000, (Nonreporting) **A**10
Primary Contact: Karen Faria, Executive Director
COO: Karen Clark, Director Administrative Services
CMO: Carol Castillo, Medical Director
CHR: Brenda Dukes, Director Human Resources
Web address: www.dds.ca.gov/sonoma
Control: State–Government, nonfederal **Service:** Institution for mental retardation

Staffed Beds: 546

ENCINITAS—San Diego County

⊞ △ **SCRIPPS MEMORIAL HOSPITAL–ENCINITAS (050503)**, 354 Santa Fe Drive, Zip 92024–5182, Mailing Address: P.O. Box 230817, Zip 92023–0817; tel. 760/633–6501 **A**1 2 7 9 10 **F**3 8 11 13 14 15 18 20 26 29 31 34 35 40 44 49 54 57 58 59 64 65 69 70 74 75 76 77 78 79 81 82 84 85 86 87 90 91 92 93 94 96 102 107 108 111 114 115 119 130 132 146 148 **P**3 5 **S** Scripps Health, San Diego, CA
Primary Contact: Chris D. Van Gorder, FACHE, President and Chief Executive Officer
COO: Rebecca Cofinas, Vice President and Chief Operating Executive Operations
CFO: Sharon Creal, Vice President Financial Operations
CHR: Cara Williams, Director Human Resources
Web address: www.scripps.org
Control: Other not–for–profit (including NFP Corporation) **Service:** General Medical and Surgical

Staffed Beds: 158 Admissions: 9404 Census: 109 Outpatient Visits: 67714 Births: 1706 Total Expense ($000): 214357 Payroll Expense ($000): 82420 Personnel: 1011

ENCINO—Los Angeles County, See Los Angeles

ESCONDIDO—San Diego County

⊞ △ **PALOMAR MEDICAL CENTER (050115)**, 2185 West Citracado Parkway, Zip 92029–4159; tel. 760/739–3000, (Total facility includes 86 beds in nursing home–type unit) **A**1 7 9 10 **F**3 11 12 13 15 17 18 20 22 24 26 28 29 31 40 42 43 45 46 47 50 51 62 64 68 70 74 75 76 77 78 79 81 84 85 86 87 90 93 96 97 98 100 102 103 104 105 107 108 111 112 114 115 119 120 121 123 124 126 128 129 130 131 146 147 148 **P**3 4 5 **S** Palomar Health, Escondido, CA
Primary Contact: Lorie K. Shoemaker, R.N., MSN, Interim Chief Administrative Officer
CMO: Duane Buringrud, M.D., Chief Medical and Quality Officer
CIO: Prudence August, Chief Information Officer
CHR: Brenda C. Turner, Chief Human Resources Officer
CNO: Lorie K. Shoemaker, R.N., Chief Nursing Officer
Web address: www.palomarhealth.org
Control: Hospital district or authority, Government, nonfederal **Service:** General Medical and Surgical

Staffed Beds: 345 Admissions: 21642 Census: 315 Outpatient Visits: 114112 Births: 3369 Total Expense ($000): 447038 Payroll Expense ($000): 171636 Personnel: 2077

EUREKA—Humboldt County

HUMBOLDT COUNTY MENTAL HEALTH (054124), 720 Wood Street, Zip 95501–4413; tel. 707/268–2900 **A**10 **F**38 40 98 99 100 101 102 103
Primary Contact: Jet L. DeKruse, Administrator
CMO: Harpreet Duggal, M.D., Medical Director, Department of Health and Human Services
CNO: Sherry Gallagher, Director Nursing, Department of Health and Human Services
Web address: www.https://co.humboldt.ca.us/hhs/mhb/
Control: County–Government, nonfederal **Service:** Psychiatric

Staffed Beds: 16 Admissions: 630 Census: 9 Outpatient Visits: 0 Births: 0 Total Expense ($000): 4518 Payroll Expense ($000): 2761 Personnel: 53

★ ○ **ST. JOSEPH HOSPITAL (050006)**, 2700 Dolbeer Street, Zip 95501–4799; tel. 707/445–8121, (Includes GENERAL HOSPITAL, 2200 Harrison Avenue, Zip 95501–3299; tel. 707/445–5111) **A**2 9 10 11 19 **F**3 8 11 12 13 15 17 18 20 22 24 26 28 29 30 31 35 39 40 45 46 47 48 49 53 54 62 63 64 68 70 72 74 75 76 78 79 81 82 84 85 86 87 90 93 96 107 108 110 111 114 115 118 119 120 121 123 124 129 130 131 146 148 **P**5 **S** St. Joseph Health, Irvine, CA
Primary Contact: David O'Brien, M.D., President
CFO: Mich Riccioni, Chief Financial Officer
CMO: Mathew Miller, M.D., Vice President and Chief Medical Officer
CIO: Wendy Thorpe, Area Director Information Systems
CHR: Linda Cook, Vice President Human Resources
CNO: Carol Reeder, R.N., Chief Nursing Officer
Web address: www.stjosepheureka.org
Control: Church–operated, Nongovernment, not–for profit **Service:** General Medical and Surgical

Staffed Beds: 153 Admissions: 6279 Census: 78 Outpatient Visits: 171660 Births: 574 Total Expense ($000): 185790 Payroll Expense ($000): 53610 Personnel: 955

FAIRFIELD—Solano County

⊞ **NORTHBAY MEDICAL CENTER (050367)**, 1200 B. Gale Wilson Boulevard, Zip 94533–3587; tel. 707/646–5000, (Includes NORTHBAY VACAVALLEY HOSPITAL, 1000 Nut Tree Road, Vacaville, Zip 95687–4100; tel. 707/624–7000) **A**1 2 5 9 10 **F**2 3 6 8 11 13 17 18 19 20 22 24 26 28 29 30 31 32 35 36 40 41 43 44 46 49 50 51 54 56 59 62 63 64 65 70 72 73 74 75 76 77 78 79 80 81 82 84 85 87 89 92 93 94 96 97 100 104 107 114 115 118 119 121 130 131 132 146 147 148 **P**3
Primary Contact: Deborah Sugiyama, President
CFO: Arthur E. DeNio, Vice President and Chief Financial Officer
CIO: Paul Alcala, Vice President and Chief Information Officer
CHR: Ken McCollum, Vice President, Human Resources
CNO: Kathleen Richerson, R.N., Vice President and Chief Nursing Officer
Web address: www.northbay.org
Control: Other not–for–profit (including NFP Corporation) **Service:** General Medical and Surgical

Staffed Beds: 170 Admissions: 8826 Census: 101 Outpatient Visits: 227507 Births: 1368 Total Expense ($000): 378159 Payroll Expense ($000): 163286 Personnel: 1295

FALL RIVER MILLS—Shasta County

★ **MAYERS MEMORIAL HOSPITAL DISTRICT (051305)**, 43563 Highway 299 East, Zip 96028–0459, Mailing Address: P.O. Box 459, Zip 96028–0459; tel. 530/336–5511, (Total facility includes 87 beds in nursing home–type unit) **A**9 10 18 **F**13 40 45 56 57 59 63 64 76 81 85 93 107 114 119 128 130 132 133 146
Primary Contact: Matthew Rees, Chief Executive Officer
CFO: Travis Lakey, Chief Financial Officer
CMO: Dan Dahle, Chief of Staff
CIO: Chris Broadway, Manager Information Technology
CHR: Julie Thompson, Manager Personnel and Payroll
CNO: Sherry Wilson, R.N., Chief Nursing Officer
Web address: www.mayersmemorial.com
Control: Hospital district or authority, Government, nonfederal **Service:** General Medical and Surgical

Staffed Beds: 104 **Admissions:** 508 **Census:** 80 **Outpatient Visits:** 15650 **Births:** 60 **Total Expense ($000):** 21481 **Payroll Expense ($000):** 9101 **Personnel:** 208

FALLBROOK—San Diego County

✠ **FALLBROOK HOSPITAL (050435)**, 624 East Elder Street, Zip 92028–3099; tel. 760/728–1191, (Nonreporting) **A**1 9 10 20 **S** Community Health Systems, Inc., Franklin, TN
Primary Contact: Kirkpatrick Conley, Chief Executive Officer
Web address: www.fallbrookhospital.com
Control: Hospital district or authority, Government, nonfederal **Service:** General Medical and Surgical

Staffed Beds: 86

FOLSOM—Sacramento County

✠ **MERCY HOSPITAL OF FOLSOM (050414)**, 1650 Creekside Drive, Zip 95630–3400; tel. 916/983–7400 **A**1 5 9 10 **F**3 8 11 12 13 29 30 34 35 36 37 39 40 49 57 59 60 64 66 68 70 74 75 77 79 81 82 84 85 86 93 107 108 114 115 118 119 130 132 146 147 148 **P**3 4 5 **S** Dignity Health, San Francisco, CA
Primary Contact: Michael R. Ricks, President
CFO: Robin Rogness, Vice President and Chief Financial Officer
CHR: Amy Mantell, Vice President Human Resources
Web address: www.mercyfolsom.org
Control: Church–operated, Nongovernment, not–for profit **Service:** General Medical and Surgical

Staffed Beds: 106 **Admissions:** 5953 **Census:** 51 **Outpatient Visits:** 51097 **Births:** 904 **Total Expense ($000):** 145437 **Payroll Expense ($000):** 59514 **Personnel:** 479

✠ **VIBRA HOSPITAL OF SACRAMENTO (052033)**, 330 Montrose Drive, Zip 95630–2720; tel. 916/351–9151, (Nonreporting) **A**1 9 10 **S** Vibra Healthcare, Mechanicsburg, PA
Primary Contact: Janet Biedron, R.N., Chief Executive Officer
CFO: Bruce MacNeill, Chief Financial Officer
CMO: Alan Cubre, M.D., Medical Director
CHR: Michael G. Fanselau, District Director Human Resources
Web address: www.vhsacramento.com
Control: Corporation, Investor–owned, for–profit **Service:** Long–Term Acute Care hospital

Staffed Beds: 37

FONTANA—San Bernardino County

✠ **KAISER PERMANENTE FONTANA MEDICAL CENTER (050140)**, 9961 Sierra Avenue, Zip 92335–6794; tel. 909/427–5000 **A**1 3 5 10 **F**3 4 13 15 18 20 28 29 30 31 35 40 41 44 45 46 48 49 50 57 58 60 62 63 64 65 68 70 72 73 74 75 76 77 78 79 81 82 84 85 86 87 88 89 100 102 107 108 111 114 115 117 119 130 132 135 141 145 146 148 **S** Kaiser Foundation Hospitals, Oakland, CA
Primary Contact: Greg Christian, Executive Director
COO: Ray Hahn, Chief Operating Officer
CFO: Donald P. Bernard, Chief Financial Officer
CMO: David Quam, M.D., Area Medical Director
CIO: David Young, M.D., Area Information Officer
CHR: Kimberly Labiaga, Human Resources Leader
CNO: Toni Andersen, R.N., Chief Nurse Executive
Web address: www.kaiserpermanente.org
Control: Other not–for–profit (including NFP Corporation) **Service:** General Medical and Surgical

Staffed Beds: 334 **Admissions:** 18296 **Census:** 218 **Outpatient Visits:** 95994 **Births:** 3486 **Personnel:** 2591

FORT BRAGG—Mendocino County

✠ **MENDOCINO COAST DISTRICT HOSPITAL (051325)**, 700 River Drive, Zip 95437–5495; tel. 707/961–1234, (Nonreporting) **A**1 9 10 18
Primary Contact: Wayne Allen, Interim Chief Executive Officer
CFO: Wayne Allen, Chief Financial Officer
CMO: John Kermen, D.O., Chief Medical Staff
CIO: Jeff Edwards, Manager Information Services
CHR: Scott Kidd, Director Human Resources
CNO: Bonnie Kittner, R.N., Chief Nursing Officer
Web address: www.mcdh.org
Control: Hospital district or authority, Government, nonfederal **Service:** General Medical and Surgical

Staffed Beds: 25

FORT IRWIN—San Bernardino County

✠ **WEED ARMY COMMUNITY HOSPITAL**, Inner Loop Road and 4th Street, Building 166, Zip 92310–5065, Mailing Address: P.O. Box 105109, Zip 92310–5109; tel. 760/380–3108, (Nonreporting) **A**1 **S** Department of the Army, Office of the Surgeon General, Falls Church, VA
Primary Contact: Colonel Cheryl Taylor–Whitehead, Commander
CIO: Michael Haenelt, Chief Information Management
Web address: www.irwin.amedd.army.mil
Control: Army, Government, federal **Service:** General Medical and Surgical

Staffed Beds: 27

FORTUNA—Humboldt County

★ **REDWOOD MEMORIAL HOSPITAL (051318)**, 3300 Renner Drive, Zip 95540–3198; tel. 707/725–3361 **A**2 9 10 18 **F**3 11 13 15 17 18 29 30 34 35 39 40 45 50 53 56 57 59 63 64 68 70 75 76 77 79 81 82 84 85 86 88 93 107 110 114 119 130 131 132 133 146 **P**5 **S** St. Joseph Health, Irvine, CA
Primary Contact: David O'Brien, M.D., President
COO: Joseph J. Rogers, Vice President and Chief Operating Officer
CFO: Andrew Rybolt, Vice President and Chief Financial Officer
CHR: Bob Sampson, Vice President Human Resources
Web address: www.redwoodmemorial.org/
Control: Church–operated, Nongovernment, not–for profit **Service:** General Medical and Surgical

Staffed Beds: 25 **Admissions:** 1613 **Census:** 15 **Outpatient Visits:** 44276 **Births:** 392 **Total Expense ($000):** 37088 **Payroll Expense ($000):** 13170 **Personnel:** 167

FOUNTAIN VALLEY—Orange County

✠ **FOUNTAIN VALLEY REGIONAL HOSPITAL AND MEDICAL CENTER (050570)**, 17100 Euclid Street, Zip 92708–4043; tel. 714/966–7200, (Nonreporting) **A**1 2 5 9 10 **S** TENET Healthcare Corporation, Dallas, TX
Primary Contact: B. Joseph Badalian, Chief Executive Officer
CFO: Ken Jordan, Chief Financial Officer
CMO: E. V. Sunderrajan, M.D., Chief of Staff
CIO: Freddie Sanchez, Director Information Systems
CHR: Tim Howard, Chief Human Resources Officer
CNO: Mary Botticella, R.N., Chief Nursing Officer
Web address: www.fountainvalleyhospital.com
Control: Corporation, Investor–owned, for–profit **Service:** General Medical and Surgical

Staffed Beds: 242

✠ **ORANGE COAST MEMORIAL MEDICAL CENTER (050678)**, 9920 Talbert Avenue, Zip 92708–5115; tel. 714/378–7000 **A**1 2 9 10 **F**3 11 12 13 15 18 20 22 24 26 28 29 30 31 34 35 38 40 44 45 46 47 48 49 50 51 53 55 56 57 58 59 64 65 68 70 72 74 75 76 77 78 79 81 82 84 85 86 87 93 107 108 110 111 114 115 116 117 118 119 124 126 130 131 132 135 143 145 146 147 **P**3 5 **S** MemorialCare, Fountain Valley, CA
Primary Contact: Marcia Manker, Chief Executive Officer
COO: Emily Randle, Vice President Operations
CFO: Steve McNamara, Chief Financial Officer
CIO: Scott Raymond, Director Information Systems
CHR: Michelle Gutierrez, Executive Director Human Resources
CNO: Dale Vital, Chief Nursing Officer
Web address: www.memorialcare.org
Control: Other not–for–profit (including NFP Corporation) **Service:** General Medical and Surgical

Staffed Beds: 218 **Admissions:** 12905 **Census:** 127 **Outpatient Visits:** 74017 **Births:** 1686 **Total Expense ($000):** 256109 **Payroll Expense ($000):** 69735 **Personnel:** 1105

Hospital, Medicare Provider Number, Address, Telephone, Approval, Facility, and Physician Codes, Health Care System

★ American Hospital Association (AHA) membership
☐ The Joint Commission accreditation   ◇ DNV Healthcare Inc. accreditation

○ Healthcare Facilities Accreditation Program
△ Commission on Accreditation of Rehabilitation Facilities (CARF) accreditation

---

FREMONT—Alameda County

☒ **FREMONT HOSPITAL (054110)**, 39001 Sundale Drive, Zip 94538–2005; tel. 510/796–1100 **A**1 9 10 **F**3 5 29 30 38 68 98 99 100 101 102 103 104 105 130 132 135 143 **S** Universal Health Services, Inc., King of Prussia, PA
Primary Contact: John C. Cooper, Chief Executive Officer
CMO: Vikas Duvvuri, M.D., Medical Director
CHR: Tom Piz, Director Human Resources
Web address: www.fremonthospital.com
Control: Corporation, Investor–owned, for–profit **Service:** Psychiatric

> **Staffed Beds:** 96 **Admissions:** 3957 **Census:** 86 **Outpatient Visits:** 13076 **Births:** 0 **Total Expense ($000):** 20987 **Payroll Expense ($000):** 13994

☒ **WASHINGTON HOSPITAL HEALTHCARE SYSTEM (050195)**, 2000 Mowry Avenue, Zip 94538–1746; tel. 510/797–1111 **A**1 2 9 10 **F**3 8 13 15 17 18 20 22 24 26 28 29 30 31 34 35 36 37 38 39 40 45 49 50 55 57 58 59 60 65 70 71 74 75 76 77 78 79 81 84 85 86 87 89 93 102 107 108 110 115 118 119 120 121 124 126 130 132 133 144 146 147 148 **P**3 5 7
Primary Contact: Nancy D. Farber, Chief Executive Officer
COO: Edward J. Fayen, Associate Administrator Operations and Support
CFO: Chris Henry, Associate Administrator and Chief Financial Officer
CMO: Albert Brooks, M.D., Chief Medical Staff Services
CIO: Robert Thorwald, Chief Information Officer
CHR: Bryant Welch, Chief Human Resources
CNO: Stephanie Williams, R.N., Chief Nursing Officer
Web address: www.whhs.com
Control: Hospital district or authority, Government, nonfederal **Service:** General Medical and Surgical

> **Staffed Beds:** 269 **Admissions:** 11493 **Census:** 158 **Total Expense ($000):** 425225

FRENCH CAMP—San Joaquin County

☐ **SAN JOAQUIN GENERAL HOSPITAL (050167)**, 500 West Hospital Road, Zip 95231–9693, Mailing Address: P.O. Box 1020, Stockton, Zip 95201–3120; tel. 209/468–6000 **A**1 3 5 10 **F**3 11 13 15 20 29 30 31 32 34 35 39 40 45 49 50 54 56 59 60 61 64 65 66 68 70 72 74 75 76 77 78 79 81 82 85 87 89 93 97 100 107 108 115 119 129 130 143 146 147
Primary Contact: David K. Culberson, Chief Executive Officer
CFO: Ron Kreutner, Chief Financial Officer
CMO: Sheela Kapre, M.D., Chief Medical Officer
CIO: Don Johnston, Chief Information Officer
CHR: Lisa M. Lopez, Director Human Resources
CNO: Erlinda Bolor, R.N., Chief Nursing Officer
Web address: www.sjgeneral.org/
Control: County–Government, nonfederal **Service:** General Medical and Surgical

> **Staffed Beds:** 110 **Admissions:** 8661 **Census:** 102 **Outpatient Visits:** 169007 **Total Expense ($000):** 226266

FRESNO—Fresno County

COMMUNITY BEHAVIORAL HEALTH CENTER, 7171 North Cedar Avenue, Zip 93720–3311; tel. 559/449–8000 **A**9 **F**29 87 98 102 130 **S** Community Medical Centers, Fresno, CA
Primary Contact: Jack Chubb, Chief Executive Officer
COO: Craig Wagoner, Chief Operating Officer
CFO: Stephen Walter, Senior Vice President and Chief Financial Officer
CMO: Tom Utecht, M.D., Senior Vice President and Chief Quality Officer
CIO: George Vasquez, Vice President Information Services
CHR: Ginny Burdick, Vice President Human Resources
CNO: Karen Buckley, R.N., Chief Nursing Officer
Web address: www.communitymedical.org
Control: Other not–for–profit (including NFP Corporation) **Service:** Psychiatric

> **Staffed Beds:** 61 **Admissions:** 3601 **Census:** 50 **Outpatient Visits:** 0 **Births:** 0 **Total Expense ($000):** 13843 **Payroll Expense ($000):** 8748 **Personnel:** 117

☐ **COMMUNITY REGIONAL MEDICAL CENTER (050060)**, 2823 Fresno Street, Zip 93721–1324, Mailing Address: P.O. Box 1232, Zip 93715–1232; tel. 559/459–6000, (Total facility includes 106 beds in nursing home–type unit) **A**1 2 5 8 9 10 **F**3 7 11 13 15 16 17 18 20 22 24 26 29 30 31 34 35 37 39 40 43 44 45 46 47 48 49 50 51 54 55 56 57 58 59 60 61 62 64 65 66 68 70 72 74 75 76 77 78 79 81 82 83 84 85 86 87 89 90 93 97 98 100 101 102 103 104 105 106 107 108 109 110 111 112 113 114 115 118 119 120 121 122 124 126 128 130 132 135 143 145 146 147 148 **P**5 **S** Community Medical Centers, Fresno, CA
Primary Contact: John M. Chubb, Chief Executive Officer
COO: Patrick W. Rafferty, Executive Vice President and Chief Operating Officer
CFO: Stephen Walter, Senior Vice President and Chief Financial Officer
CMO: Tom Utecht, M.D., Chief Quality Officer
CIO: Craig Castro, Chief Information Officer
CHR: Ginny Burdick, Vice President Human Resources
Web address: www.communitymedical.org
Control: Other not–for–profit (including NFP Corporation) **Service:** General Medical and Surgical

> **Staffed Beds:** 808 **Admissions:** 38832 **Census:** 655 **Outpatient Visits:** 348909 **Births:** 6061 **Total Expense ($000):** 871869 **Payroll Expense ($000):** 314032 **Personnel:** 3814

☐ **FRESNO HEART AND SURGICAL HOSPITAL (050732)**, 15 East Audubon Drive, Zip 93720–1542; tel. 559/433–8000, (Nonreporting) **A**1 9 10 **S** Community Medical Centers, Fresno, CA
Primary Contact: Wanda Holderman, R.N., Chief Executive Officer
CFO: Ben Armfield, Chief Financial Officer
CMO: Tom Utecht, M.D., Corporate Chief Quality Officer
CIO: George Vasquez, Corporate Chief Information Officer
CHR: Julie Adair, Interim Corporate Chief Human Resources Officer
CNO: Heather Rodriguez, Chief Nursing Officer
Web address: www.fresnoheartandsurgical.org
Control: Corporation, Investor–owned, for–profit **Service:** Heart

> **Staffed Beds:** 60

FRESNO MEDICAL CENTER See Kaiser Permanente Fresno Medical Center

☐ **FRESNO SURGICAL HOSPITAL (050708)**, 6125 North Fresno Street, Zip 93710–5207; tel. 559/431–8000, (Nonreporting) **A**1 9 10
Primary Contact: Kristine Kassahn, Chief Executive Officer
CFO: Bruce Cecil, Chief Financial Officer
CMO: Bruce Witmer, M.D., Medical Director
CHR: Laura Patillo, Manager Human Resources
Web address: www.fresnosurgicalhospital.com
Control: Partnership, Investor–owned, for–profit **Service:** General Medical and Surgical

> **Staffed Beds:** 16

☒ **KAISER PERMANENTE FRESNO MEDICAL CENTER (050710)**, 7300 North Fresno Street, Zip 93720–2942; tel. 559/448–4500, (Nonreporting) **A**1 10 **S** Kaiser Foundation Hospitals, Oakland, CA
Primary Contact: Jeffrey A. Collins, M.D., Senior Vice President and Area Manager
CFO: Richard Alves, Chief Financial Officer
CMO: Varouj Altebarmakian, M.D., Physician in Chief
CIO: Brad Bain, Information Systems Leader
Web address: www.kaiserpermanente.org
Control: Other not–for–profit (including NFP Corporation) **Service:** General Medical and Surgical

> **Staffed Beds:** 169

☒ **SAINT AGNES MEDICAL CENTER (050093)**, 1303 East Herndon Avenue, Zip 93720–3397; tel. 559/450–3000 **A**1 2 9 10 **F**3 8 11 13 15 17 18 20 22 24 26 28 29 30 31 34 35 37 40 44 45 46 47 49 50 51 55 56 57 58 59 61 64 66 70 74 75 76 77 78 79 81 82 84 85 86 87 91 92 93 94 95 96 97 102 107 108 110 111 112 113 114 115 116 117 118 119 120 121 123 124 126 130 132 135 146 147 148 **P**1 5 **S** Catholic Health East / Trinity Health, Livonia, MI
Primary Contact: Nancy Hollingsworth, R.N., MSN, President and Chief Executive Officer
COO: Mark T. Bateman, Interim Chief Operating Officer
CFO: Phil Robinson, Chief Financial Officer
CMO: Stephen Soldo, M.D., Chief Medical Officer
CIO: Irfan Ali, Director Information Services
CHR: Stacy Vaillancourt, Vice President Marketing, Communications, Advocacy and Human Resources
CNO: Lori Wightman, R.N., Chief Nursing Officer
Web address: www.samc.com
Control: Church–operated, Nongovernment, not–for profit **Service:** General Medical and Surgical

> **Staffed Beds:** 436 **Admissions:** 24390 **Census:** 255 **Outpatient Visits:** 323821 **Births:** 3771 **Total Expense ($000):** 455549 **Payroll Expense ($000):** 151705 **Personnel:** 1894

☒ △ **SAN JOAQUIN VALLEY REHABILITATION HOSPITAL (053032)**, 7173 North Sharon Avenue, Zip 93720–3329; tel. 559/436–3600 **A**1 7 9 10 **F**29 30 53 54 57 64 74 75 77 79 82 90 93 94 130 131 **S** Vibra Healthcare, Mechanicsburg, PA
Primary Contact: Mary Jo Jacobson, Chief Executive Officer
CFO: Margaret Casarez, Chief Financial Officer
CMO: Michael Azevedo, M.D., Medical Director
CIO: Christi Rolff, Director Business Development
CHR: Jennifer Morrow, Director Human Resources
Web address: www.sanjoaquinrehab.com
Control: Corporation, Investor–owned, for–profit **Service:** Rehabilitation

> **Staffed Beds:** 62 **Admissions:** 1630 **Census:** 50 **Outpatient Visits:** 32885 **Births:** 0 **Total Expense ($000):** 23410

☒ **VETERANS AFFAIRS CENTRAL CALIFORNIA HEALTH CARE SYSTEM**, 2615 East Clinton Avenue, Zip 93703–2223; tel. 559/225–6100, (Nonreporting) **A**1 3 5 **S** Department of Veterans Affairs, Washington, DC
Primary Contact: Wessel Meyer, M.D., Acting Director
CFO: Matthew Whetton, Chief Business Administration
CMO: Wessel Meyer, M.D., Chief of Staff
CIO: William Harris, Chief Information Resources Management
CHR: Sandra Stein, Chief Human Resources Management
Web address: www.fresno.va.gov/
Control: Veterans Affairs, Government, federal **Service:** General Medical and Surgical

> **Staffed Beds:** 54

CA

FULLERTON—Orange County

☒ △ **ST. JUDE MEDICAL CENTER (050168)**, 101 East Valencia Mesa Drive, Zip 92835–3875; tel. 714/992–3000 **A**1 2 5 7 9 10 **F**2 3 8 9 11 12 13 15 18 20 22 24 26 28 29 30 31 32 34 35 36 39 40 44 45 46 47 48 49 50 51 53 54 55 56 57 58 59 60 61 62 63 64 65 66 68 70 71 72 74 75 76 77 78 79 81 82 83 84 85 86 87 90 91 92 93 95 96 97 100 107 108 109 110 111 114 115 116 117 118 119 120 121 123 124 126 128 129 130 131 132 134 135 143 146 147 148 **P**3 5 **S** St. Joseph Health, Irvine, CA
Primary Contact: Lee Penrose, President and Chief Executive Officer
COO: Brian Helleland, Executive Vice President and Chief Operating Officer
CFO: Ed Salvador, Chief Financial Officer
CIO: Ryan Olsen, Vice President of Operations
CHR: Mark Jablonski, Vice President Mission Integration
CNO: Linda Jenkins, R.N., Vice President Patient Care Services
Web address: www.stjudemedicalcenter.org
Control: Church–operated, Nongovernment, not–for profit **Service:** General Medical and Surgical

Staffed Beds: 369 **Admissions:** 14804 **Census:** 195 **Outpatient Visits:** 242921 **Births:** 1931 **Total Expense ($000):** 450249 **Payroll Expense ($000):** 140813 **Personnel:** 1812

GARBERVILLE—Humboldt County

JEROLD PHELPS COMMUNITY HOSPITAL (051309), 733 Cedar Street, Zip 95542–3292; tel. 707/923–3921, (Nonreporting) **A**9 10 18
Primary Contact: Harry Jasper, Administrator
COO: Kent Scown, Director Operations and Information Services
CFO: Harry Jasper, Chief Financial Officer
CMO: Marcin Matuszkiewicz, M.D., Chief of Staff and Medical Director
CIO: Kent Scown, Director Operations and Information Services
CHR: Dee Way, Director Human Resources
CNO: Sarah Beach, Director of Nursing
Web address: www.shchd.org
Control: Hospital district or authority, Government, nonfederal **Service:** General Medical and Surgical

Staffed Beds: 16

GARDEN GROVE—Orange County

☐ **GARDEN GROVE HOSPITAL AND MEDICAL CENTER (050230)**, 12601 Garden Grove Boulevard, Zip 92843–1959; tel. 714/537–5160 **A**1 9 10 **F**3 15 17 18 29 30 40 45 49 51 64 72 76 79 81 85 107 108 111 114 119 130 146 **S** Prime Healthcare Services, Ontario, CA
Primary Contact: Virgis Narbutas, Chief Executive Officer
CFO: Alan H. Smith, Chief Financial Officer
CMO: Hassan Alkhouli, M.D., Chief Medical Officer
CIO: Adam Morquecho, Director Information Systems
CHR: Stephanie Sioson, Director Human Resources
CNO: Sofia Abrina, Administrator and Chief Nursing Officer
Web address: www.gardengrovehospital.com
Control: Corporation, Investor–owned, for–profit **Service:** General Medical and Surgical

Staffed Beds: 167 **Admissions:** 6017 **Census:** 63 **Outpatient Visits:** 35450 **Total Expense ($000):** 89552

GARDENA—Los Angeles County

★ **KINDRED HOSPITAL SOUTH BAY (052050)**, 1246 West 155th Street, Zip 90247–4062; tel. 310/323–5330, (Nonreporting) **A**9 10 **S** Kindred Healthcare, Louisville, KY
Primary Contact: Lourene Money, R.N., Interim Chief Executive Officer
COO: Michael Grubb, Chief Operating Officer and Chief Financial Officer
CFO: Michael Grubb, Chief Operating Officer and Chief Financial Officer
CHR: Michelle Parra, Director Human Resources
Web address: www.khsouthbay.com/
Control: Corporation, Investor–owned, for–profit **Service:** Long–Term Acute Care hospital

Staffed Beds: 84

☐ **MEMORIAL HOSPITAL OF GARDENA (050468)**, 1145 West Redondo Beach Boulevard, Zip 90247–3528; tel. 310/532–4200, (Nonreporting) **A**1 9 10 **S** Avanti Hospitals, El Segundo, CA
Primary Contact: Araceli Lonergan, Chief Executive Officer
CFO: Daniel R. Heckathorne, Chief Financial Officer
CMO: Nosratian Farshao, M.D., Chief Medical Staff
CHR: Matthew Kempiak, Director Human Resources and Administrative Services
CNO: Glenda Luce, Chief Nursing Officer
Web address: www.mhglax.com/
Control: Corporation, Investor–owned, for–profit **Service:** General Medical and Surgical

Staffed Beds: 172

VISTA HOSPITAL OF SOUTH BAY See Kindred Hospital South Bay

GILROY—Santa Clara County

☒ **SAINT LOUISE REGIONAL HOSPITAL (050688)**, 9400 No Name Uno, Zip 95020–3528; tel. 408/848–2000 **A**1 9 10 **F**3 11 13 15 17 29 30 31 34 35 37 40 41 45 46 47 59 60 64 68 69 70 75 76 78 79 81 82 85 107 108 111 114 118 130 132 135 143 144 146 148 **S** Daughters of Charity Health System, Los Altos Hills, CA
Primary Contact: James F. Dover, FACHE, President and CEO
COO: Carol Furgurson, Chief Operating Officer
CFO: Nicole Thomson, Chief Financial Officer
CIO: Dick Hutsell, Vice President Information Technology Services
CHR: Lin Velasquez, Vice President Human Resources
CNO: Marilyn Gerrior, R.N., Chief Nursing Executive
Web address: www.dochs.org
Control: Church–operated, Nongovernment, not–for profit **Service:** General Medical and Surgical

Staffed Beds: 93 **Admissions:** 2868 **Census:** 29 **Outpatient Visits:** 22845 **Births:** 546

GLENDALE—Los Angeles County

☒ **GLENDALE ADVENTIST MEDICAL CENTER (050239)**, 1509 Wilson Terrace, Zip 91206–4098; tel. 818/409–8000 **A**1 2 3 5 9 10 **F**3 5 6 8 9 13 14 15 17 18 20 22 24 26 29 30 31 34 35 37 40 47 48 49 51 53 56 57 58 59 62 64 65 68 70 72 74 75 76 77 78 79 81 82 83 84 85 87 90 92 93 96 98 102 103 104 105 106 107 108 110 111 114 115 117 118 119 121 124 126 129 130 131 132 135 146 147 148 **P**3 7 **S** Adventist Health, Roseville, CA
Primary Contact: Kevin A. Roberts, FACHE, President and Chief Executive Officer
COO: Warren Tetz, Senior Vice President and Chief Operating Officer
CFO: Kelly Turner, Senior Vice President Finance and Chief Financial Officer
CMO: Arby Nahapetian, M.D., Vice President Medical Affairs and Quality
CIO: Sharon Correa, Vice President and Chief Information Officer
CHR: Susan Crabtree, Director Human Resources
CNO: Judy Blair, Senior Vice President Clinical Services and Chief Nursing Officer
Web address: www.glendaleadventist.com
Control: Church–operated, Nongovernment, not–for profit **Service:** General Medical and Surgical

Staffed Beds: 462 **Admissions:** 20074 **Census:** 286 **Outpatient Visits:** 264993 **Births:** 2401 **Total Expense ($000):** 397775 **Payroll Expense ($000):** 139112 **Personnel:** 1979

☒ **GLENDALE MEMORIAL HOSPITAL AND HEALTH CENTER (050058)**, 1420 South Central Avenue, Zip 91204–2594; tel. 818/502–1900 **A**1 9 10 **F**12 14 15 17 18 20 22 24 26 28 29 30 31 34 35 40 45 46 47 49 51 53 58 64 68 70 72 74 75 76 78 79 81 84 85 90 92 93 98 100 101 102 107 108 110 111 114 115 119 120 128 130 131 132 144 147 148 **S** Dignity Health, San Francisco, CA
Primary Contact: Jack Ivie, President
CFO: Rebecca Cheng, Chief Financial Officer
CIO: Brian Gregor, Manager Information Technology Operations
CHR: Nga Nguyen, Manager Human Resources and Organizational Development
CNO: Claire H. Hanks, R.N., Vice President and Chief Nursing Officer
Web address: www.glendalememorial.com
Control: Other not–for–profit (including NFP Corporation) **Service:** General Medical and Surgical

Staffed Beds: 334 **Admissions:** 10014 **Census:** 133 **Outpatient Visits:** 102619 **Births:** 1989 **Total Expense ($000):** 233559 **Payroll Expense ($000):** 89607 **Personnel:** 1020

★ ◇ **USC VERDUGO HILLS HOSPITAL (050124)**, 1812 Verdugo Boulevard, Zip 91208–1409; tel. 818/790–7100, (Nonreporting) **A**9 10 21
Primary Contact: Debbie Walsh, MSN, Chief Executive Officer
COO: Paul M. Czajka, Chief Operating Officer
CFO: Mark Overeem, Chief Financial Officer
CMO: Donald Larsen, M.D., Chief Medical Officer
CHR: Eva Herberger, Administrator Human Resources
CNO: Janet Brooks, Chief Nursing Officer
Web address: www.uscvhh.org
Control: Other not–for–profit (including NFP Corporation) **Service:** General Medical and Surgical

Staffed Beds: 158

GLENDORA—Los Angeles County

○ **EAST VALLEY HOSPITAL MEDICAL CENTER (050205)**, 150 West Route 66, Zip 91740–6207; tel. 626/852–5000, (Nonreporting) **A**9 10 11
Primary Contact: C. Joseph Chang, President and Chief Executive Officer
CIO: Wayne Giddings, Manager Management Information Systems
CHR: Kim Bui, Director Human Resources
Control: Other not–for–profit (including NFP Corporation) **Service:** General Medical and Surgical

Staffed Beds: 118

Hospital, Medicare Provider Number, Address, Telephone, Approval, Facility, and Physician Codes, Health Care System

★ American Hospital Association (AHA) membership
☐ The Joint Commission accreditation   ◇ DNV Healthcare Inc. accreditation
○ Healthcare Facilities Accreditation Program
△ Commission on Accreditation of Rehabilitation Facilities (CARF) accreditation

✠ **FOOTHILL PRESBYTERIAN HOSPITAL (050597)**, 250 South Grand Avenue, Zip 91741–4218; tel. 626/963–8411 **A**1 9 10 **F**3 7 11 13 15 17 18 29 30 31 34 35 40 41 44 45 49 50 51 60 64 68 70 74 75 76 77 78 79 81 85 86 87 107 108 114 119 130 131 143 146 **S** Citrus Valley Health Partners, Covina, CA
Primary Contact: Robert H. Curry, President and Chief Executive Officer
COO: Elvia Foulke, Executive Vice President and Chief Operating Officer
CMO: John DiMare, M.D., Medical Director
CIO: David McCobb, Chief Information Officer
Web address: www.cvhp.org/Our_Facilities/Foothill_Presbyterian.aspx
Control: Other not–for–profit (including NFP Corporation) **Service:** Obstetrics and gynecology

Staffed Beds: 75 **Admissions:** 4971 **Census:** 49 **Outpatient Visits:** 54911 **Births:** 866 **Total Expense ($000):** 71395 **Payroll Expense ($000):** 28346 **Personnel:** 363

GRANADA HILLS—Los Angeles County, See Los Angeles

GRASS VALLEY—Nevada County

✠ **SIERRA NEVADA MEMORIAL HOSPITAL (050150)**, 155 Glasson Way, Zip 95945–5723, Mailing Address: P.O. Box 1029, Zip 95945–1029; tel. 530/274–6000, (Nonreporting) **A**1 2 9 10 19 **S** Dignity Health, San Francisco, CA
Primary Contact: Katherine A. Medeiros, President and Chief Executive Officer
CFO: Carolyn Canady, Chief Financial Officer
CMO: Brian Evans, M.D., Chief of Medicine
CHR: Terri Labriola, Human Resources Officer
CNO: Jill McWilliams, Chief Nursing Officer
Web address: www.snmh.org
Control: Other not–for–profit (including NFP Corporation) **Service:** General Medical and Surgical

Staffed Beds: 121

GREENBRAE—Marin County

✠ **MARIN GENERAL HOSPITAL (050360)**, 250 Bon Air Road, Zip 94904–1784, Mailing Address: P.O. Box 8010, San Rafael, Zip 94912–8010; tel. 415/925–7000 **A**1 2 10 **F**3 8 13 15 18 20 22 24 26 28 29 30 31 34 35 36 37 40 43 45 47 49 57 58 59 60 68 70 72 74 75 76 77 78 79 81 84 85 86 87 89 93 98 100 104 105 107 108 110 111 114 115 116 117 118 119 120 121 123 124 126 130 132 141 146 148 **P**3 4 5
Primary Contact: Lee Domanico, Chief Executive Officer
CFO: David W. Cox, Chief Financial Officer
CMO: Joel Sklar, M.D., Chief Medical Officer
CIO: Mark Zielazinski, Chief Information and Technology Integration Officer
CHR: Linda Lang, Chief Human Resources Officer
Web address: www.maringeneral.org
Control: Other not–for–profit (including NFP Corporation) **Service:** General Medical and Surgical

Staffed Beds: 173 **Admissions:** 9497 **Census:** 111 **Outpatient Visits:** 169545 **Births:** 1345 **Total Expense ($000):** 310565 **Payroll Expense ($000):** 120069 **Personnel:** 1128

GRIDLEY—Butte County

★ ◇ **ORCHARD HOSPITAL (051311)**, 240 Spruce Street, Zip 95948–2216, Mailing Address: P.O. Box 97, Zip 95948–0097; tel. 530/846–5671 **A**9 10 18 21 **F**11 15 18 29 30 34 35 36 40 45 49 50 54 59 64 65 68 70 71 75 77 79 81 93 97 107 110 111 114 119 128 130 133 146 148
Primary Contact: Jim Opdahl, Interim Chief Executive Officer
COO: Tracy Atkins, Chief Operating and Nursing Officer
CMO: Henry Starkes, M.D., Medical Director
CIO: Ryan Quist, Administrative Assistant
CNO: Tracy Atkins, Chief Operating and Nursing Officer
Web address: www.bgmh.us.com/
Control: Other not–for–profit (including NFP Corporation) **Service:** General Medical and Surgical

Staffed Beds: 45 **Admissions:** 649 **Census:** 26 **Outpatient Visits:** 44025 **Births:** 0 **Total Expense ($000):** 22449

HANFORD—Kings County

✠ **ADVENTIST MEDICAL CENTER – HANFORD (050121)**, 115 Mall Drive, Zip 93230–3513; tel. 559/582–9000, (Includes ADVENTIST MEDICAL CENTER–SELMA, 1141 Rose Avenue, Selma, Zip 93662–3241; tel. 559/891–1000; Richard L. Rawson, President and Chief Executive Officer) **A**1 10 **F**3 8 13 14 15 20 22 29 30 34 35 40 56 57 59 68 70 76 79 81 93 106 107 111 119 130 146 147 148 **S** Adventist Health, Roseville, CA
Primary Contact: Wayne Ferch, President and Chief Executive Officer
CIO: Michael Aubry, Director Information Systems
Web address: www.adventisthealthcv.com/hospital_newhanfordhospital.aspx
Control: Church–operated, Nongovernment, not–for profit **Service:** General Medical and Surgical

Staffed Beds: 199 **Admissions:** 9890 **Census:** 114 **Outpatient Visits:** 211639 **Births:** 770 **Total Expense ($000):** 207403 **Payroll Expense ($000):** 80729 **Personnel:** 1587

✠ **CENTRAL VALLEY GENERAL HOSPITAL (050196)**, 1025 North Douty Street, Zip 93230–3722, Mailing Address: P.O. Box 480, Zip 93232–2113; tel. 559/583–2100 **A**1 9 10 **F**8 13 18 19 29 34 39 50 54 57 59 64 65 76 87 97 107 109 110 111 114 119 129 130 135 144 146 147 **S** Adventist Health, Roseville, CA
Primary Contact: Wayne Ferch, President and Chief Executive Officer
Web address: www.hanfordhealth.com
Control: Church–operated, Nongovernment, not–for profit **Service:** General Medical and Surgical

Staffed Beds: 49 **Admissions:** 2113 **Census:** 11 **Outpatient Visits:** 413225 **Births:** 1976 **Total Expense ($000):** 94608 **Payroll Expense ($000):** 32190 **Personnel:** 791

HARBOR CITY—Los Angeles County, See Los Angeles

HAWAIIAN GARDENS—Los Angeles County

◇ **TRI–CITY REGIONAL MEDICAL CENTER (050575)**, 21530 South Pioneer Boulevard, Zip 90716–2608; tel. 562/860–0401 **A**9 10 21 **F**3 12 15 17 29 34 35 40 57 64 70 81 93 107 110 111 114 119 126 130 143 148
Primary Contact: James Sherman, President and Chief Executive Officer
CMO: Derek Dobalian, M.D., Chief of Staff
CIO: Anthony Carrasco, Director Information Systems
CHR: Jillian Guerra, Chief Human Resources Officer
CNO: Juliet Miranda, Chief Nursing Officer
Web address: www.tri–cityrmc.org
Control: Other not–for–profit (including NFP Corporation) **Service:** General Medical and Surgical

Staffed Beds: 107 **Admissions:** 3130 **Census:** 43 **Outpatient Visits:** 15051 **Births:** 0 **Total Expense ($000):** 63161

HAYWARD—Alameda County

HAYWARD MEDICAL CENTER See Kaiser Permanente Hayward Medical Center

✠ **KAISER PERMANENTE HAYWARD MEDICAL CENTER (050512)**, 27400 Hesperian Boulevard, Zip 94545–4299; tel. 510/784–4000, (Includes FREMONT MEDICAL CENTER, 39400 Paseo Padre Parkway, Fremont, Zip 94538–2310; tel. 510/248–3000; Denise Vincenzi, Administrator), (Nonreporting) **A**1 3 5 10 **S** Kaiser Foundation Hospitals, Oakland, CA
Primary Contact: Thomas S. Hanenburg, Senior Vice President
COO: Debbie Hemker, Chief Operating Officer
Web address: www.kaiserpermanente.org
Control: Other not–for–profit (including NFP Corporation) **Service:** General Medical and Surgical

Staffed Beds: 208

ST. ROSE HOSPITAL (050002), 27200 Calaroga Avenue, Zip 94545–4383; tel. 510/264–4000 **A**9 10 **F**3 11 12 13 14 15 17 18 20 22 29 30 31 34 35 40 44 46 49 50 51 57 59 62 63 64 65 68 70 75 76 77 78 79 81 82 84 87 93 107 108 110 114 119 130 132 135 144 147 148
Primary Contact: Lex Reddy, President and Chief Executive Officer
CFO: Michael Taylor, Vice President Financial Services and Chief Financial Officer
CMO: Charles S. Feldstein, M.D., Vice President Medical Affairs
CHR: John Davini, Vice President
Web address: www.srhca.org
Control: Church–operated, Nongovernment, not–for profit **Service:** General Medical and Surgical

Staffed Beds: 150 **Admissions:** 6131 **Census:** 73 **Total Expense ($000):** 132284

HEALDSBURG—Sonoma County

◇ **HEALDSBURG DISTRICT HOSPITAL (051321)**, 1375 University Avenue, Zip 95448–3382; tel. 707/431–6500, (Nonreporting) **A**9 10 18 21
Primary Contact: Nancy Schmid, Chief Executive Officer
COO: Regina Novello, R.N., Chief Operating Officer
CFO: John S. Parigi, II, Interim Chief Financial Officer
CMO: Judy Widger, M.D., Chief of Staff
CIO: Steven Hansen, Director Information Technology
CHR: Kristina Holloway, Chief Human Resources Officer
CNO: Susan G. Spoelma, MSN, Chief Nursing Officer
Web address: www.nschd.org
Control: Hospital district or authority, Government, nonfederal **Service:** General Medical and Surgical

Staffed Beds: 24

Many Facility Codes have changed. Please refer to the AHA Guide Code Chart. © 2014 AHA Guide

HEMET—Riverside County

☐ **HEMET VALLEY MEDICAL CENTER (050390)**, 1117 East Devonshire Avenue, Zip 92543–3083; tel. 951/652–2811 **A**1 9 10 **F**3 4 13 15 17 18 20 22 26 29 30 31 34 35 39 40 45 46 49 50 51 56 57 60 64 68 70 74 75 76 77 78 79 80 81 82 85 87 92 93 97 99 100 107 108 111 114 119 121 128 130 132 146 148 **S** Physicians for Healthy Hospitals, Hemet, CA
Primary Contact: Joel Bergenfeld, Chief Executive Officer
CFO: John R. Collins, Chief Financial Officer
CHR: Michele Bird, Chief Human Resources Officer
CNO: Elizabeth C. Gardner, R.N., Chief Nursing Officer
Web address: www.physiciansforhealthyhospitals.com
Control: Corporation, Investor–owned, for–profit **Service:** General Medical and Surgical

Staffed Beds: 238 **Admissions:** 10867 **Census:** 131 **Outpatient Visits:** 49916 **Births:** 1311 **Total Expense ($000):** 122432 **Payroll Expense ($000):** 42298 **Personnel:** 675

HOLLISTER—San Benito County

⊠ **HAZEL HAWKINS MEMORIAL HOSPITAL (050296)**, 911 Sunset Drive, Zip 95023–5695; tel. 831/637–5711, (Includes WILLIAM AND INEZ MABIE SKILLED NURSING FACILITY, 911 Sunset Drive, Zip 95023; tel. 408/637–5711), (Total facility includes 98 beds in nursing home–type unit) **A**1 9 10 **F**3 8 11 13 15 29 31 34 35 40 45 50 51 57 59 62 66 68 70 76 79 81 83 84 85 93 97 107 111 115 119 127 128 129 130 131 132 146 147
Primary Contact: Ken Underwood, Chief Executive Officer
CFO: Mark Robinson, Associate Administrator and Chief Financial Officer
CIO: Julio Gil, Manager Information Services
CHR: Ysidro Gallardo, Associate Administrator Human Resources
Web address: www.hazelhawkins.com
Control: Hospital district or authority, Government, nonfederal **Service:** General Medical and Surgical

Staffed Beds: 122 **Admissions:** 2528 **Census:** 116 **Outpatient Visits:** 134996 **Births:** 446 **Total Expense ($000):** 87839 **Payroll Expense ($000):** 34537 **Personnel:** 477

HOLLYWOOD—Los Angeles County, See Los Angeles

HUNTINGTON BEACH—Orange County

☐ **HUNTINGTON BEACH HOSPITAL (050526)**, 17772 Beach Boulevard, Zip 92647–6896; tel. 714/843–5000 **A**1 10 **F**3 11 15 17 18 20 22 29 40 45 49 64 70 79 81 85 98 103 105 107 108 111 114 119 130 146 **S** Prime Healthcare Services, Ontario, CA
Primary Contact: Virgis Narbutas, Chief Executive Officer
CFO: Alan H. Smith, Chief Financial Officer
CMO: Hassan Alkhouli, M.D., Medical Director
CIO: Adam Morquecho, Director Information Technology
CHR: Stephanie Sioson, Director Human Resources
CNO: Sofia Abrina, Administrator and Chief Nursing Officer
Web address: www.hbhospital.com
Control: Other not–for–profit (including NFP Corporation) **Service:** General Medical and Surgical

Staffed Beds: 131 **Admissions:** 3681 **Census:** 53 **Outpatient Visits:** 29968 **Births:** 0 **Total Expense ($000):** 54443

HUNTINGTON PARK—Los Angeles County

COMMUNITY AND MISSION HOSPITALS OF HUNTINGTON PARK See Community Hospital of Huntington Park

○ **COMMUNITY HOSPITAL OF HUNTINGTON PARK (050091)**, 2623 East Slauson Avenue, Zip 90255–2926; tel. 323/583–1931 **A**10 11 **F**3 29 40 41 49 70 79 81 89 107 108 119 130 148 **S** Avanti Hospitals, El Segundo, CA
Primary Contact: Hector Hernandez, M.D., Chief Executive Officer
CFO: Cheryl Tong, Corporate Chief Financial Officer
CMO: Jose Rivas, M.D., Chief of Staff
CIO: Jason Cervantes, Corporate Chief Information Officer
CHR: Paul Celuch, Corporate Human Resources Director
CNO: Lisa Jacobson, Director of Nursing
Web address: www.chhplax.com
Control: Corporation, Investor–owned, for–profit **Service:** General Medical and Surgical

Staffed Beds: 81 **Admissions:** 4028 **Census:** 39 **Outpatient Visits:** 38235 **Births:** 0

INDIO—Riverside County

⊠ **JOHN F. KENNEDY MEMORIAL HOSPITAL (050534)**, 47111 Monroe Street, Zip 92201–6799; tel. 760/347–6191 **A**1 9 10 **F**3 8 18 20 29 30 34 35 37 40 46 47 48 49 50 54 56 57 59 68 70 74 76 78 79 81 85 87 89 97 107 108 111 118 119 126 130 146 148 **S** TENET Healthcare Corporation, Dallas, TX
Primary Contact: Gary Honts, Interim Chief Executive Officer
COO: Parrish Scarboro, Chief Operating Officer
Web address: www.jfkmemorialhosp.com
Control: Corporation, Investor–owned, for–profit **Service:** General Medical and Surgical

Staffed Beds: 109 **Admissions:** 8204 **Census:** 68 **Outpatient Visits:** 52040 **Births:** 2186 **Total Expense ($000):** 106595 **Payroll Expense ($000):** 50344 **Personnel:** 627

INGLEWOOD—Los Angeles County

☐ **CENTINELA HOSPITAL MEDICAL CENTER (050739)**, 555 East Hardy Street, Zip 90301–4011, Mailing Address: P.O. Box 720, Zip 90312–6720; tel. 310/673–4660 **A**1 10 **F**8 11 13 17 18 20 22 24 26 28 29 30 34 40 41 42 45 46 47 48 49 57 59 60 68 70 72 74 75 76 77 79 81 82 84 85 87 90 93 107 108 109 111 112 115 117 119 128 130 135 143 146 147 148 **S** Prime Healthcare Services, Ontario, CA
Primary Contact: Linda Bradley, Chief Executive Officer
CFO: Paul Sennett, Chief Financial Officer
CMO: Paryus Patel, M.D., Chief Medical Officer
CIO: Martin Cordova, Director Information Services
CHR: George Akopyan, Director Human Resources
CNO: Mohammad Abdelnaser, Chief Nursing Officer
Web address: www.centinelamed.com
Control: Corporation, Investor–owned, for–profit **Service:** General Medical and Surgical

Staffed Beds: 353 **Admissions:** 18118 **Census:** 196 **Outpatient Visits:** 60517 **Total Expense ($000):** 233322

IRVINE—Orange County

◇ **HOAG ORTHOPEDIC INSTITUTE (050769)**, 16250 Sand Canyon Avenue, Zip 92618–3714; tel. 949/517–3149, (Nonreporting) **A**5 21
Primary Contact: Deressa Reid, Interim Chief Executive Officer
Web address: www.hoag.org/Locations/Pages/HoagHospOrthoInstitute.aspx
Control: Other not–for–profit (including NFP Corporation) **Service:** Orthopedic

Staffed Beds: 20

ORANGE COUNTY IRVINE MEDICAL CENTER See Kaiser Permanente Orange County Anaheim Medical Center, Anaheim

JACKSON—Amador County

⊠ **SUTTER AMADOR HOSPITAL (050014)**, 200 Mission Boulevard, Zip 95642–2564; tel. 209/223–7500 **A**1 5 9 10 **F**29 34 35 46 47 49 54 59 64 65 70 75 76 77 78 79 81 84 85 87 93 102 107 108 110 111 115 119 129 130 132 146 148 **S** Sutter Health, Sacramento, CA
Primary Contact: Anne Platt, Chief Executive Officer
CFO: Brett Moore, CPA, Assistant Administrator Finance
CMO: Ron Hood, M.D., Chief of Staff
CIO: Joy Bailey, Director Information Technology
CHR: Beverly Revels, Director Human Resources
CNO: Nikki Allen, Patient Care Executive
Web address: www.sutteramador.org
Control: Other not–for–profit (including NFP Corporation) **Service:** General Medical and Surgical

Staffed Beds: 52 **Admissions:** 2440 **Census:** 23 **Outpatient Visits:** 41031 **Births:** 303 **Total Expense ($000):** 60080 **Payroll Expense ($000):** 20164 **Personnel:** 183

JOSHUA TREE—San Bernardino County

⊠ **HI-DESERT MEDICAL CENTER (050279)**, 6601 White Feather Road, Zip 92252–6607; tel. 760/366–3711, (Total facility includes 120 beds in nursing home–type unit) **A**1 9 10 20 **F**3 8 11 13 15 18 29 30 34 35 40 45 46 50 54 57 59 62 63 64 65 66 68 70 71 74 77 79 81 82 93 94 97 104 107 108 111 115 119 127 128 130 135 146 148 **P**5
Primary Contact: Robert C. Tyk, Chief Executive Officer
COO: Judith J. Austin, MSN, Chief Nursing Officer and Chief Operating Officer
CMO: Sumit Mahajan, M.D., Chief Medical Staff
CHR: Barbara Staresinic, Director Human Resources
CNO: Judith J. Austin, MSN, Chief Nursing Officer and Chief Operating Officer
Web address: www.hdmc.org
Control: Hospital district or authority, Government, nonfederal **Service:** General Medical and Surgical

Staffed Beds: 179 **Admissions:** 3640 **Census:** 139 **Outpatient Visits:** 110437 **Births:** 460 **Total Expense ($000):** 60737 **Payroll Expense ($000):** 26214 **Personnel:** 431

CA

KENTFIELD—Marin County

⊞ **KENTFIELD REHABILITATION AND SPECIALTY HOSPITAL (052043)**, 1125 Sir Francis Drake Boulevard, Zip 94904–1455; tel. 415/456–9680 **A**1 9 10 **F**1 11 29 30 54 59 60 64 65 74 75 77 79 82 92 93 94 97 130 148 **S** Vibra Healthcare, Mechanicsburg, PA
Primary Contact: Ann Gors, Chief Executive Officer
CFO: Stephanie Lawrence, Chief Financial Officer
CMO: Curtis Roebken, M.D., Chief Medical Staff
CHR: Julene English, Director Human Resources
Web address: www.kentfieldrehab.com
Control: Corporation, Investor–owned, for–profit **Service:** Long–Term Acute Care hospital

Staffed Beds: 48 Admissions: 442 Census: 45 Outpatient Visits: 15763 Births: 0 Total Expense ($000): 28687

KING CITY—Monterey County

☐ **MEE MEMORIAL HOSPITAL (050189)**, 300 Canal Street, Zip 93930–3431; tel. 831/385–6000, (Nonreporting) **A**1 5 9 10 20
Primary Contact: Lex Smith, Chief Executive Officer
CFO: Gary L. Wangsmo, Chief Financial Officer
CMO: Schindelheim Roy, M.D., Chief of Staff
CIO: Mike McNamara, Chief Information Officer
CHR: Karen Wong, Chief Human Resources Officer
Web address: www.meememorial.com
Control: Other not–for–profit (including NFP Corporation) **Service:** General Medical and Surgical

Staffed Beds: 119

LA JOLLA—San Diego County

⊞ **SCRIPPS GREEN HOSPITAL (050424)**, 10666 North Torrey Pines Road, Zip 92037–1093; tel. 858/455–9100 **A**1 2 8 9 10 **F**3 8 11 12 14 15 17 18 20 22 24 26 28 29 30 31 34 35 36 37 44 45 46 47 49 50 51 54 57 58 59 61 64 68 70 74 75 77 78 79 80 81 82 84 85 86 87 93 107 108 110 111 113 114 115 118 119 120 121 123 124 126 130 131 132 136 138 139 141 142 146 148 **P**3 **S** Scripps Health, San Diego, CA
Primary Contact: Robin Brown, Chief Executive, Senior Vice President
CFO: Richard Rothberger, Corporate Executive Vice President and Chief Financial Officer
CMO: James LaBelle, M.D., Chief Medical Officer
CIO: Patric Thomas, Corporate Vice President Information Services
CHR: Victor Buzachero, Corporate Senior Vice President for Innovation, Human Resources and Performance Management
Web address: www.scrippshealth.org
Control: Other not–for–profit (including NFP Corporation) **Service:** General Medical and Surgical

Staffed Beds: 173 Admissions: 10027 Census: 104 Outpatient Visits: 84988 Births: 0 Total Expense ($000): 309842 Payroll Expense ($000): 98842 Personnel: 1296

⊞ **SCRIPPS MEMORIAL HOSPITAL–LA JOLLA (050324)**, 9888 Genesee Avenue, Zip 92037–1200, Mailing Address: P.O. Box 28, Zip 92038–0028; tel. 858/626–4123 **A**1 2 3 5 9 10 **F**3 4 5 8 11 12 13 14 15 17 18 20 22 24 26 28 29 30 31 34 35 40 43 44 45 46 48 49 51 53 54 57 58 59 64 65 68 70 74 75 76 77 78 79 81 82 84 85 86 87 91 92 93 94 99 100 101 102 103 104 107 108 110 111 114 115 116 117 118 119 124 126 130 132 141 142 145 146 147 148 **P**3 5 **S** Scripps Health, San Diego, CA
Primary Contact: Gary G. Fybel, Chief Executive, Senior Vice President
COO: Cindy Steckel, Vice President Chief Nurse and Operations Executive
CFO: Linda Honaker, Vice President Financial Operations
CMO: James LaBelle, M.D., Chief Medical Officer
CHR: Michelle Horton, Senior Director Human Resources Services
CNO: Cindy Steckel, Vice President Chief Nurse and Operations Executive
Web address: www.scripps.org/locations/hospitals__scripps–memorial–hospital–la–jolla
Control: Other not–for–profit (including NFP Corporation) **Service:** General Medical and Surgical

Staffed Beds: 285 Admissions: 16311 Census: 200 Outpatient Visits: 96820 Births: 3820 Total Expense ($000): 426789 Payroll Expense ($000): 150786 Personnel: 1943

LA MESA—San Diego County

☐ **ALVARADO PARKWAY INSTITUTE BEHAVIORAL HEALTH SYSTEM (054075)**, 7050 Parkway Drive, Zip 91942–1535; tel. 619/465–4411 **A**1 9 10 **F**4 5 29 34 35 38 50 59 64 68 75 82 87 98 100 101 102 103 104 105 130 135
Primary Contact: Patrick C. Ziemer, Chief Executive Officer
CFO: Chad Engbrecht, Chief Financial Officer
CMO: Saleem Ishaque, M.D., Executive Medical Director
CNO: Bonnie Asada, Director of Nursing
Web address: www.apibhs.com
Control: Corporation, Investor–owned, for–profit **Service:** Psychiatric

Staffed Beds: 66 Admissions: 2446 Census: 60 Births: 0 Total Expense ($000): 22539

⊞ △ **SHARP GROSSMONT HOSPITAL (050026)**, 5555 Grossmont Center Drive, Zip 91942–3019, Mailing Address: P.O. Box 158, Zip 91944–0158; tel. 619/740–6000, (Total facility includes 30 beds in nursing home–type unit) **A**1 2 7 9 10 **F**3 8 11 13 15 17 18 20 22 24 26 28 29 30 31 34 35 38 40 44 45 46 47 48 49 50 54 55 56 57 58 59 60 61 62 63 64 65 68 70 72 74 75 76 77 78 79 80 81 82 83 84 85 86 87 90 91 92 93 94 96 97 98 99 100 101 102 103 104 105 107 108 109 110 111 114 115 116 117 118 119 120 121 123 124 126 128 129 130 132 135 143 145 146 147 148 **S** Sharp HealthCare, San Diego, CA
Primary Contact: Michele T. Tarbet, Chief Executive Officer
COO: Maryann Cone, Chief Operating Officer
CFO: Kari Cornicelli, Chief Financial Officer
CMO: Michael Murphy, M.D., Chief Medical Officer
CIO: Kenneth Lawonn, Senior Vice President and Chief Information Officer
CHR: George Holtz, Director Human Resources
CNO: Dale E. Beatty, MSN, Chief Nursing Officer
Web address: www.sharp.com
Control: Other not–for–profit (including NFP Corporation) **Service:** General Medical and Surgical

Staffed Beds: 499 Admissions: 28574 Census: 338 Outpatient Visits: 302923 Births: 3772 Total Expense ($000): 578370 Payroll Expense ($000): 236687 Personnel: 2749

LA MIRADA—Los Angeles County

⊞ **KINDRED HOSPITAL–LA MIRADA (052038)**, 14900 East Imperial Highway, Zip 90638–2172; tel. 562/944–1900, (Includes KINDRED HOSPITAL SAN GABRIEL VALLEY, 845 North Lark Ellen Avenue, West Covina, Zip 91791–1069; tel. 626/339–5451; Eleyce Winn, Chief Executive Officer; KINDRED HOSPITAL SANTA ANA, 1901 North College Avenue, Santa Ana, Zip 92706–2334; tel. 714/564–7800; Victor Carrasco, Chief Executive Officer), (Nonreporting) **A**1 9 10 **S** Kindred Healthcare, Louisville, KY
Primary Contact: April Myers, Administrator
CFO: Rishab Punjabi, Chief Financial Officer
CMO: Prakash Chandra Patel, M.D., Chief of Staff
CHR: Susan Bergquist, Human Resources Generalist
CNO: Esperanza Sanchez, Chief Clinical Officer
Web address: www.kindredlamirada.com/
Control: Corporation, Investor–owned, for–profit **Service:** Long–Term Acute Care hospital

Staffed Beds: 216

LA PALMA—Orange County

☐ **LA PALMA INTERCOMMUNITY HOSPITAL (050580)**, 7901 Walker Street, Zip 90623–1764; tel. 714/670–7400 **A**1 10 **F**3 11 13 15 17 18 20 22 29 35 40 41 45 49 59 69 70 76 79 81 85 98 103 104 105 107 108 111 114 119 130 146 147 148 **S** Prime Healthcare Services, Ontario, CA
Primary Contact: Virgis Narbutas, Chief Executive Officer
CFO: Alan H. Smith, Chief Financial Officer
CMO: Sami Shoukair, M.D., Chief Medical Officer
CIO: Vic Mahan, Director Information Technology
CHR: Stephanie Sioson, Director Human Resources
CNO: Hilda Manzo–Luna, Chief Nursing Officer
Web address: www.lapalmaintercommunityhospital.com
Control: Other not–for–profit (including NFP Corporation) **Service:** General Medical and Surgical

Staffed Beds: 141 Admissions: 3614 Census: 50 Outpatient Visits: 22382 Total Expense ($000): 52956

LAGUNA HILLS—Orange County

⊞ **SADDLEBACK MEMORIAL MEDICAL CENTER (050603)**, 24451 Health Center Drive, Zip 92653–3689; tel. 949/837–4500, (Includes SADDLEBACK MEMORIAL MEDICAL CENTER – SAN CLEMENTE CAMPUS, 654 Camino De Los Mares, San Clemente, Zip 92673–2827; tel. 949/496–1122) **A**1 2 5 9 10 **F**3 11 12 13 14 15 18 20 22 24 26 28 29 30 31 34 35 36 38 40 44 45 49 50 51 53 54 55 56 57 58 59 62 63 64 65 68 70 72 74 75 76 77 78 79 81 82 84 85 86 87 93 94 96 100 107 108 110 111 114 115 116 117 118 119 120 121 123 126 130 132 135 141 142 143 145 146 147 148 **P**3 5 7 **S** MemorialCare, Fountain Valley, CA
Primary Contact: Steve Geidt, Chief Executive Officer
COO: Cheryl Jacob, Chief Operating Officer
CFO: Adolfo Chanez, Vice President Finance and Chief Financial Officer
CMO: Ernest Hayward, M.D., Chief of Staff
CIO: J. Scott Joslyn, Senior Vice President and Chief Information Officer
CHR: Kayce H. Hudson, Executive Director Human Resources
CNO: Kathy Dawson, R.N., Chief Nursing Officer
Web address: www.memorialcare.org
Control: Other not–for–profit (including NFP Corporation) **Service:** General Medical and Surgical

Staffed Beds: 313 Admissions: 15586 Census: 164 Outpatient Visits: 296798 Births: 2568 Total Expense ($000): 337574 Payroll Expense ($000): 114318 Personnel: 1518

Many Facility Codes have changed. Please refer to the AHA Guide Code Chart.

LAKE ARROWHEAD—San Bernardino County

✠ **SAN BERNARDINO MOUNTAINS COMMUNITY HOSPITAL DISTRICT (051312)**, 29101 Hospital Road, Zip 92352–9706, Mailing Address: P.O. Box 70, Zip 92352–0070; tel. 909/336–3651, (Total facility includes 20 beds in nursing home–type unit) **A**1 9 10 18 **F**11 29 30 31 34 35 39 40 45 50 57 64 65 66 68 69 71 75 79 81 85 86 87 99 104 107 114 119 127 128 130 133 146 148
Primary Contact: Charles Harrison, Chief Executive Officer
COO: Terry Pena, Chief Operating Officer and Chief Nursing Officer
CFO: Yvonne Waggener, Chief Financial Officer
CMO: Lawrence Walker, M.D., Chief of Staff
CIO: Patrick Miller, Technology Coordinator
CHR: Julie Atwood, Director Human Resources
CNO: Terry Pena, Chief Nursing Officer and Chief Nursing Officer
Web address: www.mchcares.com
Control: Hospital district or authority, Government, nonfederal **Service:** General Medical and Surgical

> **Staffed Beds:** 37 **Admissions:** 295 **Census:** 23 **Outpatient Visits:** 25291 **Births:** 0 **Total Expense ($000):** 16665

LAKE ISABELLA—Kern County

KERN VALLEY HEALTHCARE DISTRICT (051314), 6412 Laurel Avenue, Zip 93240–9529, Mailing Address: P.O. Box 1628, Zip 93240–1628; tel. 760/379–2681, (Total facility includes 74 beds in nursing home–type unit) **A**9 10 18 **F**11 29 30 34 35 40 45 57 59 64 70 77 81 93 103 107 114 119 127 128 130 133 146
Primary Contact: Timothy McGlew, Chief Executive Officer
CFO: Chester Beedle, Chief Financial Officer
CMO: Gary A. Finstad, M.D., Chief of Staff
CIO: Paul Quinn, Information Systems Manager
CHR: Debra Hoffman, Manager Human Resources
CNO: Mark Gordon, Chief Nursing Officer
Web address: www.kvhd.org
Control: Hospital district or authority, Government, nonfederal **Service:** Long–Term Acute Care hospital

> **Staffed Beds:** 99 **Admissions:** 849 **Census:** 59 **Outpatient Visits:** 16049 **Births:** 0 **Total Expense ($000):** 21312 **Payroll Expense ($000):** 9299

LAKEPORT—Lake County

✠ **SUTTER LAKESIDE HOSPITAL (051329)**, 5176 Hill Road East, Zip 95453–6300; tel. 707/262–5000 **A**1 9 10 18 **F**3 8 11 13 15 18 29 30 34 35 36 40 43 45 46 51 54 56 57 59 61 64 65 66 68 70 71 74 75 76 77 79 81 82 85 86 87 91 93 97 107 110 111 114 116 118 119 127 130 131 133 135 146 147 148 **S** Sutter Health, Sacramento, CA
Primary Contact: Siri Nelson, Chief Administrative Officer
CFO: Linnea Humble, Director of Finance
CMO: Diane Pege, M.D., Vice President Medical Affairs
CIO: Jack Buell, Director Information Services
CHR: Brenda DeRamus, Manager Human Resources
CNO: Teresa Campbell, R.N., Chief Nursing Executive
Web address: www.sutterlakeside.org
Control: Other not–for–profit (including NFP Corporation) **Service:** General Medical and Surgical

> **Staffed Beds:** 25 **Admissions:** 2036 **Census:** 19 **Outpatient Visits:** 75187 **Births:** 335 **Total Expense ($000):** 65266 **Payroll Expense ($000):** 21814 **Personnel:** 280

LAKEWOOD—Los Angeles County

✠ **LAKEWOOD REGIONAL MEDICAL CENTER (050581)**, 3700 East South Street, Zip 90712–1498, Mailing Address: P.O. Box 6070, Zip 90714–6070; tel. 562/531–2550 **A**1 9 10 **F**3 11 15 17 18 20 22 24 26 29 30 34 35 38 40 45 49 50 51 57 59 64 68 70 74 75 77 81 85 87 93 107 108 109 111 115 118 119 120 130 132 143 146 148 **S** TENET Healthcare Corporation, Dallas, TX
Primary Contact: Ronald J. Galonsky, Chief Executive Officer
CFO: Eric Delgado, Chief Financial Officer
CMO: Ronald L. Kaufman, M.D., Chief Medical Officer
CIO: Pat Pierce, Director Information Systems
CHR: Mary Okuhara, Director Human Resources
CNO: Terri Newton, Chief Nursing Officer
Web address: www.lakewoodregional.com
Control: Corporation, Investor–owned, for–profit **Service:** General Medical and Surgical

> **Staffed Beds:** 153 **Admissions:** 8174 **Census:** 104 **Outpatient Visits:** 58377 **Births:** 0 **Total Expense ($000):** 140229 **Payroll Expense ($000):** 63308 **Personnel:** 718

LANCASTER—Los Angeles County

✠ **ANTELOPE VALLEY HOSPITAL (050056)**, 1600 West Avenue J, Zip 93534–2894; tel. 661/949–5000, (Nonreporting) **A**1 9 10
Primary Contact: Dennis M. Knox, Chief Executive Officer
CFO: Paul Brydon, Chief Financial Officer
CMO: Radha Krishnan, M.D., Chief Medical Officer
CIO: Dale Lepper, Interim Chief Information Officer
CHR: George Leisher, Chief Human Resources Officer
CNO: Jack J. Burke, MS, Chief Operating Officer and Chief Nursing Officer
Web address: www.avhospital.org
Control: Hospital district or authority, Government, nonfederal **Service:** General Medical and Surgical

> **Staffed Beds:** 368

LEMOORE—Kings County

✠ **NAVAL HOSPITAL LEMOORE**, 937 Franklin Avenue, Zip 93246–0001; tel. 559/998–4481, (Nonreporting) **A**1 **S** Bureau of Medicine and Surgery, Department of the Navy, Washington, DC
Primary Contact: Captain Cynthia J. Gantt, Commanding Officer
CFO: Thomas M. Brui, Director Resource Management
CMO: Scott Cota, M.D., Director Medical Services
CIO: Victor Dela Torre, Command Legal Officer
CHR: Billy Newman, Department Head
Web address: www.med.navy.mil/sites/nhlem/Pages/index.aspx
Control: Navy, Government, federal **Service:** General Medical and Surgical

> **Staffed Beds:** 16

LIVERMORE—Alameda County

VALLEY MEMORIAL See ValleyCare Medical Center, Pleasanton

VETERANS AFFAIRS PALO ALTO HEALTH CARE SYSTEM, LIVERMORE DIVISION See Veterans Affairs Palo Alto Health Care System, Palo Alto

LODI—San Joaquin County

✠ **LODI MEMORIAL HOSPITAL (050336)**, 975 South Fairmont Avenue, Zip 95240–5179, Mailing Address: P.O. Box 3004, Zip 95241–1908; tel. 209/334–3411, (Includes LODI MEMORIAL HOSPITAL WEST, 800 South Lower Sacramento Road, Zip 95242; tel. 209/333–0211), (Nonreporting) **A**1 9 10
Primary Contact: Joseph P. Harrington, President and Chief Executive Officer
COO: Mark Sey, Vice President and Chief Administrative Officer
CFO: Terry Deak, Chief Financial Officer
CHR: Mark T. Wallace, Director Human Resources
CNO: Debbie Moreno, Chief Nursing Officer
Web address: www.lodihealth.org
Control: Other not–for–profit (including NFP Corporation) **Service:** General Medical and Surgical

> **Staffed Beds:** 103

LOMA LINDA—San Bernardino County

LOMA LINDA UNIVERSITY CHILDREN'S HOSPITAL See Loma Linda University Medical Center

LOMA LINDA UNIVERSITY HEART & SURGICAL HOSPITAL See Loma Linda University Medical Center

✠ △ **LOMA LINDA UNIVERSITY MEDICAL CENTER (050327)**, 11234 Anderson Street, Zip 92354–2804, Mailing Address: P.O. Box 2000, Zip 92354–0200; tel. 909/558–4000, (Includes LOMA LINDA UNIVERSITY CHILDREN'S HOSPITAL, 11234 Anderson Street, tel. 909/558–8000; LOMA LINDA UNIVERSITY EAST CAMPUS HOSPITAL, 25333 Barton Road, Zip 92354–3053; tel. 909/558–6000; LOMA LINDA UNIVERSITY HEART & SURGICAL HOSPITAL, 26780 Barton Road, Zip 92354; tel. 909/583–2900) **A**1 2 3 5 7 8 9 10 **F**2 3 8 11 12 13 15 17 18 19 20 21 22 23 24 25 26 27 28 29 30 31 32 34 35 37 40 41 43 45 46 47 48 49 50 54 57 59 60 62 64 65 68 70 72 74 75 76 77 78 79 81 82 84 85 86 87 88 89 90 91 92 93 94 107 108 110 111 112 114 115 116 117 118 119 120 121 122 123 124 126 129 130 132 134 136 137 138 139 141 142 143 144 146 147 148 **P**3 **S** Loma Linda University Adventist Health Sciences Center, Loma Linda, CA
Primary Contact: Kerry Heinrich, Interim Chief Executive Officer
CFO: Steve Mohr, Senior Vice President Finance and Chief Financial Officer
CMO: H. Roger Hadley, M.D., Vice President, Medical Affairs
CIO: Mark Zirkelbach, Chief Information Officer
CHR: Della G. Stange, Executive Director, People Services
CNO: Judith Storfjell, Ph.D., Senior Vice President and Chief Nursing Officer
Web address: www.llumc.edu
Control: Other not–for–profit (including NFP Corporation) **Service:** General Medical and Surgical

> **Staffed Beds:** 829 **Admissions:** 30867 **Census:** 538 **Outpatient Visits:** 638187 **Births:** 2691 **Total Expense ($000):** 1165015 **Payroll Expense ($000):** 418649 **Personnel:** 7109

CA

CA

✠ △ **VETERANS AFFAIRS LOMA LINDA HEALTHCARE SYSTEM**, 11201 Benton Street, Zip 92357–1000; tel. 909/825–7084, (Total facility includes 110 beds in nursing home–type unit) **A**1 2 3 5 7 8 **F**2 3 5 8 12 15 18 20 22 26 28 29 30 31 33 35 36 38 39 40 45 46 47 48 49 50 51 55 56 57 58 59 60 61 62 63 64 65 68 70 74 75 77 78 79 80 81 82 84 85 86 87 92 93 94 97 98 100 102 103 104 107 108 110 111 114 115 117 118 119 127 128 129 130 132 135 143 145 146 147 148 **S** Department of Veterans Affairs, Washington, DC
Primary Contact: Barbara Fallen, FACHE, Director
COO: Shane Elliott, Associate Director Administration
CFO: Ron Pitts, Chief Financial Officer
CMO: Dwight Evans, M.D., Chief of Staff
CIO: Doug Wirthgen, Facility Chief Information Officer
CHR: Eugene Wylie, Chief Human Resources Officer
CNO: Anne Gillespie, R.N., Associate Director Patient Care and Nursing Services
Web address: www.lomalinda.va.gov
Control: Veterans Affairs, Government, federal **Service:** General Medical and Surgical

Staffed Beds: 268 **Admissions:** 8694 **Census:** 193 **Outpatient Visits:** 741881 **Births:** 0

LOMPOC—Santa Barbara County

★ **LOMPOC VALLEY MEDICAL CENTER (050110)**, 1515 East Ocean Avenue, Zip 93436–7092, Mailing Address: P.O. Box 1058, Zip 93438–1058; tel. 805/737–3300, (Total facility includes 110 beds in nursing home–type unit) **A**9 10 **F**3 11 13 15 18 19 29 34 40 43 45 64 70 75 76 77 79 81 85 93 107 108 110 111 114 116 117 118 119 128 129 130 135 146 148
Primary Contact: James J. Raggio, Chief Executive Officer
COO: Naishadh Buch, Chief Operating Officer
CFO: Robert M. Baden, Chief Financial Officer
CMO: Randall Michel, M.D., Chief of Staff
CIO: Jim White, Chief Information Officer
CHR: Edwin R. Braxton, Director Human Resources
CNO: Jayne Scalise, R.N., Chief Nursing Executive
Web address: www.lompocvmc.com
Control: Hospital district or authority, Government, nonfederal **Service:** General Medical and Surgical

Staffed Beds: 170 **Admissions:** 2265 **Census:** 125 **Outpatient Visits:** 62097 **Births:** 451 **Total Expense ($000):** 65162 **Payroll Expense ($000):** 25416 **Personnel:** 397

LONE PINE—Inyo County

★ **SOUTHERN INYO HEALTHCARE DISTRICT (051302)**, 501 East Locust Street, Zip 93545–1009, Mailing Address: P.O. Box 1009, Zip 93545–1009; tel. 760/876–5501, (Nonreporting) **A**9 10 18
Primary Contact: Lee Barron, Chief Executive Officer
CFO: Lee Barron, Chief Executive Officer
CIO: Patricia M. Murray, Information Officer
CHR: Ashley Williams, Manager Human Resources
Web address: www.sihd.org
Control: Hospital district or authority, Government, nonfederal **Service:** General Medical and Surgical

Staffed Beds: 4

LONG BEACH—Los Angeles County

☐ **COMMUNITY HOSPITAL OF LONG BEACH (050727)**, 1720 Termino Avenue, Zip 90804–2104; tel. 562/498–1000 **A**1 9 10 **F**3 11 12 14 18 26 28 29 30 31 34 35 38 40 45 46 50 54 56 57 59 64 65 68 70 71 75 77 79 81 82 85 86 87 93 98 100 101 102 103 104 105 107 108 111 114 119 130 132 135 146 148 **S** MemorialCare, Fountain Valley, CA
Primary Contact: Diana Hendel, PharmD, Chief Executive Officer
COO: Diane DeWalsche, R.N., Chief Operating Officer
CMO: Dennis Parmer, M.D., Chief Medical Staff
CIO: Robert Klingseis, Manager Information Systems
CHR: Valene J. Martin, Administrative Director Human Resources
Web address: www.chlb.org
Control: Other not–for–profit (including NFP Corporation) **Service:** General Medical and Surgical

Staffed Beds: 148 **Admissions:** 4468 **Census:** 53 **Outpatient Visits:** 25820 **Births:** 0 **Total Expense ($000):** 54357 **Payroll Expense ($000):** 23455 **Personnel:** 395

✠ △ **LONG BEACH MEMORIAL MEDICAL CENTER (050485)**, 2801 Atlantic Avenue, Zip 90806–1701, Mailing Address: P.O. Box 1428, Zip 90801–1428; tel. 562/933–2000 **A**1 2 3 5 7 8 9 10 **F**3 4 5 11 15 17 18 20 22 24 26 28 29 30 31 34 35 36 37 38 39 40 43 44 45 47 48 49 50 52 53 55 56 57 58 59 61 63 64 65 68 70 74 75 77 78 79 81 82 84 85 86 87 90 93 96 97 107 108 110 111 114 115 116 117 118 119 120 121 123 124 126 129 130 131 132 135 141 142 143 144 146 147 148 **P**3 4 5 **S** MemorialCare, Fountain Valley, CA
Primary Contact: Diana Hendel, PharmD, Chief Executive Officer
COO: Tamra Kaplan, Chief Operating Officer
CFO: John Bishop, Chief Financial Officer
CMO: Susan Melvin, D.O., Chief Medical Officer
CIO: Danny Asaoka, Executive Director Information Systems
CHR: Myra Gregorian, Vice President Human Resources
CNO: Judith A. Fix, R.N., Senior Vice President and Chief Nursing Officer
Web address: www.memorialcare.org/LongBeach
Control: Other not–for–profit (including NFP Corporation) **Service:** General Medical and Surgical

Staffed Beds: 420 **Admissions:** 21424 **Census:** 271 **Outpatient Visits:** 137612 **Births:** 0 **Total Expense ($000):** 474606 **Payroll Expense ($000):** 151120 **Personnel:** 3174

☐ **MILLER CHILDREN'S HOSPITAL LONG BEACH (053309)**, 2801 Atlantic Avenue, Zip 90806–1701; tel. 562/933–5437 **A**1 2 9 10 **F**3 11 12 13 14 15 19 21 23 25 27 29 30 31 32 34 35 36 37 38 40 41 43 44 45 47 48 49 50 52 53 54 55 57 58 59 61 64 65 66 68 72 74 75 76 77 78 79 81 82 84 85 86 87 88 89 93 96 97 99 100 101 102 104 107 108 111 114 115 116 117 118 119 120 121 123 124 126 129 130 132 134 135 141 142 143 144 146 147 148 **P**5 **S** MemorialCare, Fountain Valley, CA
Primary Contact: Diana Hendel, PharmD, Chief Executive Officer
Web address: www.memorialcare.org
Control: Other not–for–profit (including NFP Corporation) **Service:** Children's general

Staffed Beds: 373 **Admissions:** 16385 **Census:** 228 **Outpatient Visits:** 129813 **Births:** 5667 **Total Expense ($000):** 464833 **Payroll Expense ($000):** 143211 **Personnel:** 1260

◇ **PACIFIC HOSPITAL OF LONG BEACH (050277)**, 2776 Pacific Avenue, Zip 90806–2699, Mailing Address: P.O. Box 1268, Zip 90801–1268; tel. 562/595–1911, (Nonreporting) **A**9 10 12 13 21
Primary Contact: Michael D. Drobot, Chief Executive Officer
COO: Jennifer Ensminger, Chief Operating Officer
CFO: Jim Canedo, Chief Financial Officer
CMO: Luke Watson, M.D., Chief of Staff
CIO: Rohan Corea, Director Healthcare Information Technology
CHR: Ann Mattia Schiller, Vice President Human Resources
CNO: Kathryn McLaughlin, Vice President and Chief Nursing Officer
Web address: www.phlb.org
Control: Other not–for–profit (including NFP Corporation) **Service:** General Medical and Surgical

Staffed Beds: 184

✠ **ST. MARY MEDICAL CENTER (050191)**, 1050 Linden Avenue, Zip 90813–3321, Mailing Address: P.O. Box 887, Zip 90801–0887; tel. 562/491–9000 **A**1 2 3 5 9 10 **F**3 8 12 13 15 17 18 19 20 22 24 26 28 29 30 31 34 35 38 39 40 43 45 46 47 48 49 50 54 55 56 57 58 59 60 61 64 65 66 68 70 71 74 75 76 77 78 79 80 81 82 84 85 86 87 89 90 93 97 107 108 110 111 113 114 117 118 119 120 121 125 130 143 145 146 147 148 **S** Dignity Health, San Francisco, CA
Primary Contact: Thomas A. Salerno, President and Chief Executive Officer
COO: Gail Daly, Chief Nursing Officer and Chief Operating Officer
CFO: Harold Way, Chief Financial Officer
CMO: Andrew Burg, M.D., Chief of Staff
CIO: Rich Patla, Site Director
CHR: Bob Bokern, Director Human Resources
CNO: Gail Daly, Chief Nursing Officer and Chief Operating Officer
Web address: www.stmarymedicalcenter.org
Control: Other not–for–profit (including NFP Corporation) **Service:** General Medical and Surgical

Staffed Beds: 131 **Admissions:** 10706 **Census:** 130 **Outpatient Visits:** 120664 **Births:** 2584 **Total Expense ($000):** 237292 **Payroll Expense ($000):** 98263 **Personnel:** 1057

✠ △ **VETERANS AFFAIRS LONG BEACH HEALTHCARE SYSTEM**, 5901 East 7th Street, Zip 90822–5201; tel. 562/826–8000, (Nonreporting) **A**1 2 3 5 7 8 **S** Department of Veterans Affairs, Washington, DC
Primary Contact: Michael W. Fisher, Executive Director
COO: Anthony DeFrancesco, Associate Director
CFO: Michael J. Rupert, Chief Financial Officer
CMO: Sandor Szabo, M.D., Chief of Staff
CIO: Rodney Sagmit, Chief Information Management
CHR: Mary E. McCartan, Manager Human Resources
Web address: www.longbeach.va.gov/
Control: Veterans Affairs, Government, federal **Service:** General Medical and Surgical

Staffed Beds: 237

LOS ALAMITOS—Orange County

⊠ **LOS ALAMITOS MEDICAL CENTER (050551)**, 3751 Katella Avenue,
Zip 90720–3164; tel. 562/598–1311 **A**1 9 10 **F**3 8 11 13 15 17 18 20 22 28
29 31 34 35 40 41 44 45 49 50 51 54 55 56 57 59 64 65 66 68 70 75 76
77 78 79 81 82 85 86 87 98 103 107 108 109 110 111 112 114 115 117
119 120 121 124 126 130 132 142 143 146 148 **P**2 3 5 **S** TENET Healthcare
Corporation, Dallas, TX
Primary Contact: Kent G. Clayton, Chief Executive Officer
CFO: Dave Vickers, Chief Financial Officer
CIO: Sally Andrada, Chief Information Officer
CHR: Angie Driscoll, Director Human Resources
Web address: www.losalamitosmedctr.com
Control: Corporation, Investor–owned, for–profit **Service:** General Medical and
Surgical

Staffed Beds: 167 **Admissions:** 9645 **Census:** 114 **Outpatient Visits:** 83892
Births: 1398 **Total Expense ($000):** 152946 **Payroll Expense ($000):**
71135 **Personnel:** 880

LOS ANGELES—Los Angeles County

(Mailing Addresses - Canoga Park, Encino, Granada Hills, Harbor City,
Hollywood, Mission Hills, North Hollywood, Northridge, Panorama City,
San Pedro, Sepulveda, Sherman Oaks, Sun Valley, Sylmar, Tarzana, Van
Nuys, West Hills, West Los Angeles, Woodland Hills)

⊠ **BARLOW RESPIRATORY HOSPITAL (052031)**, 2000 Stadium Way,
Zip 90026–2696; tel. 213/250–4200 **A**1 9 10 **F**1 29 30 45 64 65 75 93 130
132 148
Primary Contact: Margaret W. Crane, Chief Executive Officer
COO: Alex Villarruz, Chief Operating Officer
CFO: Edward Engesser, Chief Financial Officer and Chief Information Officer
CMO: David Nelson, M.D., Medical Director
CIO: Edward Engesser, Chief Financial Officer and Chief Information Officer
CHR: Rashawn Woods, Vice President Human Resources
CNO: Gladys D'Souza, Chief Nursing Officer
Web address: www.barlow2000.org
Control: Other not–for–profit (including NFP Corporation) **Service:** Long–Term
Acute Care hospital

Staffed Beds: 105 **Admissions:** 759 **Census:** 69 **Outpatient Visits:** 15
Births: 0 **Total Expense ($000):** 50347 **Payroll Expense ($000):** 21846
Personnel: 293

⊠ **CALIFORNIA HOSPITAL MEDICAL CENTER (050149)**, 1401 South Grand
Avenue, Zip 90015–3010; tel. 213/748–2411, (Total facility includes 31 beds in
nursing home–type unit) **A**1 3 5 9 10 **F**3 11 17 29 30 31 34 35 40 43 45 49
51 53 57 59 64 70 72 78 79 81 84 102 107 108 111 114 119 121 128 130
132 135 143 146 147 **S** Dignity Health, San Francisco, CA
Primary Contact: Margaret R. Peterson, Ph.D., R.N., President
COO: Harold Newton, Chief Operating Officer
CFO: Rebecca Cheng, Chief Financial Officer
CMO: Joseph Nussbaum, M.D., Chief of Staff
CIO: Rich Patla, Director Information Technology
CHR: Lisa Guzman, Director Human Resources
CNO: Patricia Stone, R.N., Chief Nursing Officer
Web address: www.chmcla.org
Control: Other not–for–profit (including NFP Corporation) **Service:** General
Medical and Surgical

Staffed Beds: 318 **Admissions:** 17338 **Census:** 189 **Outpatient Visits:**
87049 **Births:** 4445 **Total Expense ($000):** 333375 **Payroll Expense
($000):** 128893 **Personnel:** 1358

⊠ △ **CEDARS–SINAI MEDICAL CENTER (050625)**, 8700 Beverly Boulevard,
Zip 90048–1865, Mailing Address: Box 48750, Zip 90048–0750;
tel. 310/423–5000 **A**1 2 3 5 7 8 9 10 **F**3 5 6 8 9 11 12 13 14 15 17 18 19
20 21 22 23 24 25 26 27 28 29 30 31 32 33 34 35 36 37 38 39 40 43 44
45 46 47 48 49 50 51 52 53 54 55 56 57 58 59 60 61 64 65 66 68 69 70
71 72 74 75 76 77 78 79 81 82 83 84 85 86 87 88 89 90 91 92 93 96 97
100 102 107 108 109 110 111 112 113 114 115 116 117 118 119 120 121
122 123 124 126 130 131 132 133 134 135 136 137 138 139 140 141 142
145 146 147 148 **P**3 5 8
Primary Contact: Thomas M. Priselac, President and Chief Executive Officer
COO: Mark R. Gavens, Senior Vice President Clinical Care Services and Chief
Operating Officer
CFO: Edward M. Prunchunas, Senior Vice President and Chief Financial Officer
CMO: Michael L. Langberg, M.D., Senior Vice President Medical Affairs and Chief
Medical Officer
CIO: Darren Dworkin, Senior Vice President and Chief Information Officer
CHR: Jeanne Flores, Senior Vice President Human Resources and Organizational
Development
CNO: Linda Burnes Bolton, R.N., Vice President and Chief Nursing Officer
Web address: www.cedars–sinai.edu
Control: Other not–for–profit (including NFP Corporation) **Service:** General
Medical and Surgical

Staffed Beds: 881 **Admissions:** 49752 **Census:** 689 **Outpatient Visits:**
715574 **Births:** 6908 **Total Expense ($000):** 2363629 **Payroll Expense
($000):** 897605 **Personnel:** 10915

⊠ **CHILDREN'S HOSPITAL LOS ANGELES (053302)**, 4650 Sunset Boulevard,
Zip 90027–6062, Mailing Address: P.O. Box 27980, Zip 90027–0980;
tel. 323/660–2450 **A**1 3 5 9 10 **F**3 5 8 14 17 19 21 23 25 27 29 30 31 32
34 35 36 38 39 40 41 43 44 45 46 49 50 51 54 55 57 58 59 60 61 64 68
71 72 74 75 77 78 79 80 81 82 84 85 86 87 88 89 90 93 99 100 104 107
108 111 114 115 116 117 118 119 120 121 129 130 131 132 134 135 136
137 138 139 140 141 146 148
Primary Contact: Richard D. Cordova, FACHE, President and Chief Executive
Officer
COO: Rodney Hanners, Senior Vice President and Chief Operating Officer
CFO: Lannie Tonnu, Senior Vice President and Chief Financial Officer
CMO: Brent Polk, M.D., Chair Department of Pediatrics and Vice President
Academic Affairs
CIO: Marty Miller, Vice President and Chief Information Officer
CNO: Mary Dee Hacker, R.N., Vice President, Patient Care Services and Chief
Nursing Officer
Web address: www.chla.org
Control: Other not–for–profit (including NFP Corporation) **Service:** Children's
general

Staffed Beds: 347 **Admissions:** 13822 **Census:** 282 **Outpatient Visits:**
318966 **Births:** 0 **Total Expense ($000):** 811422 **Payroll Expense ($000):**
338746 **Personnel:** 4663

☐ **EAST LOS ANGELES DOCTORS HOSPITAL (050641)**, 4060 Whittier
Boulevard, Zip 90023–2526; tel. 323/268–5514 **A**1 9 10 **F**1 3 7 8 13 17 29
30 35 40 41 76 77 79 80 81 82 89 91 93 107 119 130 148 **S** Avanti
Hospitals, El Segundo, CA
Primary Contact: Araceli Lonergan, Chief Executive Officer
CFO: Daniel R. Heckathorne, System Chief Financial Officer
CMO: Michael Austerlitz, M.D., Chief of Staff
CIO: Jason Cervantes, Chief Information Officer
CHR: Paul Celuch, Chief Human Resource Officer
CNO: Nadine A. Mariotti, R.N., Chief Nursing Officer
Web address: www.elalax.com
Control: Partnership, Investor–owned, for–profit **Service:** General Medical and
Surgical

Staffed Beds: 127 **Admissions:** 4171 **Census:** 68 **Outpatient Visits:** 20690
Births: 756 **Total Expense ($000):** 81344 **Payroll Expense ($000):** 23704
Personnel: 391

☐ **ENCINO HOSPITAL MEDICAL CENTER (050158)**, 16237 Ventura Boulevard,
Encino, Zip 91436–2272; tel. 818/995–5000, (Total facility includes 26 beds in
nursing home–type unit) **A**1 10 **F**17 29 35 38 40 49 51 57 70 75 77 78 79 81
98 103 107 118 119 128 130 146 **S** Prime Healthcare Services, Ontario, CA
Primary Contact: Bockhi Park, Chief Executive Officer
CFO: Kanner Tillman, Chief Financial Officer
CMO: Muhammad Anwar, M.D., Chief Medical Officer
CIO: Edward Barrera, Director Communications
CHR: Barbara Back, Manager Human Resources
CNO: Vilma L. Dinham, R.N., Chief Nursing Officer
Web address: www.encinomed.com
Control: Other not–for–profit (including NFP Corporation) **Service:** General
Medical and Surgical

Staffed Beds: 56 **Admissions:** 2223 **Census:** 86 **Outpatient Visits:** 10574
Births: 0 **Total Expense ($000):** 51550 **Payroll Expense ($000):** 20288
Personnel: 291

Hospital, Medicare Provider Number, Address, Telephone, Approval, Facility, and Physician Codes, Health Care System

★ American Hospital Association (AHA) membership
☐ The Joint Commission accreditation
◇ DNV Healthcare Inc. accreditation
○ Healthcare Facilities Accreditation Program
△ Commission on Accreditation of Rehabilitation Facilities (CARF) accreditation

CA

○ **GATEWAYS HOSPITAL AND MENTAL HEALTH CENTER (054028)**, 1891 Effie Street, Zip 90026–1793; tel. 323/644–2000 **A**10 11 **F**29 35 77 98 99 100 101 104 106 130 **P**6
Primary Contact: Mara Pelsman, Chief Executive Officer
COO: Jeff Emery, Chief Financial Officer and Chief Operating Officer
CFO: Jeff Emery, Chief Financial Officer and Chief Operating Officer
CMO: Mark Hantoot, M.D., Medical Director
CIO: Jeff Emery, Chief Financial Officer and Chief Operating Officer
CHR: Melanie Van Heusen, Director Human Resources
Web address: www.gatewayshospital.org
Control: Other not-for-profit (including NFP Corporation) **Service:** Psychiatric

Staffed Beds: 55 **Admissions:** 991 **Census:** 36 **Outpatient Visits:** 115156 **Births:** 0 **Total Expense ($000):** 27151 **Payroll Expense ($000):** 14322 **Personnel:** 305

GENERAL HOSPITAL See LAC/University of Southern California Medical Center

☐ **GOOD SAMARITAN HOSPITAL (050471)**, 1225 Wilshire Boulevard, Zip 90017–2395; tel. 213/977–2121 **A**1 2 3 5 9 10 **F**3 7 8 9 11 13 14 15 17 18 20 22 24 26 28 29 30 31 34 35 36 37 40 45 46 47 48 49 50 51 53 56 57 58 59 60 61 64 65 68 70 72 74 76 77 78 79 81 85 86 87 93 107 108 110 111 114 115 117 118 119 120 121 123 124 126 129 130 132 143 144 145 146 148 **P**5
Primary Contact: Andrew B. Leeka, President and Chief Executive Officer
COO: Dan C. McLaughlin, Vice President Professional Services
CFO: Alan Ino, Chief Financial Officer
CMO: Andrew Fishmann, M.D., Chairman, Medical Staff
CIO: Dean Campbell, Vice President Information Services and Chief Information Officer
CHR: Lexie Schuster, Vice President Human Resources
CNO: Margaret Pfeiffer, R.N., Vice President Patient Care Services
Web address: www.goodsam.org
Control: Other not-for-profit (including NFP Corporation) **Service:** General Medical and Surgical

Staffed Beds: 374 **Admissions:** 13117 **Census:** 164 **Outpatient Visits:** 81112 **Births:** 3942 **Total Expense ($000):** 277818 **Payroll Expense ($000):** 112266 **Personnel:** 1279

⊞ **HOLLYWOOD PRESBYTERIAN MEDICAL CENTER (050063)**, 1300 North Vermont Avenue, Zip 90027–6306; tel. 323/913–4914 **A**1 9 10 **F**3 8 13 15 17 18 20 22 24 26 29 30 31 34 40 45 49 50 56 57 58 59 60 61 64 68 70 72 74 75 76 77 78 79 80 81 85 87 89 90 92 93 96 107 108 111 115 119 130 132 146 147 148 **P**3 5
Primary Contact: Kenneth I. Rivers, President and Chief Executive Officer
COO: Allen Stefanek, Chief Operating Officer
CFO: Allen Stefanek, Chief Financial Officer
CMO: John Gentile, M.D., Chief Medical Officer
CIO: Steve Giles, Chief Information Officer
CHR: Norma Braun, Vice President Human Resources
CNO: Julieta M. Padilla, Chief Nursing Officer
Web address: www.hollywoodpresbyterian.com
Control: Partnership, Investor-owned, for-profit **Service:** General Medical and Surgical

Staffed Beds: 434 **Admissions:** 13517 **Census:** 232 **Outpatient Visits:** 55188 **Births:** 3728 **Total Expense ($000):** 239041 **Payroll Expense ($000):** 91841 **Personnel:** 1168

KAISER FOUNDATION MENTAL HEALTH CENTER See Kaiser Permanente Los Angeles Medical Center

⊞ **KAISER PERMANENTE LOS ANGELES MEDICAL CENTER (050138)**, 4867 Sunset Boulevard, Zip 90027–5961; tel. 323/783–4011, (Includes KAISER FOUNDATION MENTAL HEALTH CENTER, 765 West College Street, Zip 90012; tel. 213/580–7200) **A**1 3 5 8 10 **F**3 5 8 13 15 17 18 19 20 21 22 23 24 26 28 29 30 31 35 36 38 40 44 45 46 47 49 50 54 55 56 57 58 59 60 61 62 63 64 65 66 68 70 72 73 74 75 76 78 79 80 81 82 83 84 85 86 87 88 89 92 93 94 97 98 99 100 101 102 103 104 105 106 107 108 109 110 111 113 114 115 118 119 120 121 122 123 124 126 129 130 131 132 135 144 146 147 148 **P**6 **S** Kaiser Foundation Hospitals, Oakland, CA
Primary Contact: Mark E. Costa, Executive Director
COO: Derek Berz, Chief Operating Officer
CFO: Brad Malsed, Area Chief Finance Officer
CMO: Michael Tome, M.D., Medical Director
CIO: David Strickland, Area Information Officer
CHR: Paul J. Martin, Director Human Resources
CNO: Debra Grant, R.N., Chief Nursing Officer
Web address: www.kaiserpermanente.org
Control: Other not-for-profit (including NFP Corporation) **Service:** General Medical and Surgical

Staffed Beds: 464 **Admissions:** 23269 **Census:** 313 **Outpatient Visits:** 2314858 **Births:** 2475 **Personnel:** 5942

⊞ **KAISER PERMANENTE PANORAMA CITY MEDICAL CENTER (050137)**, 13652 Cantara Street, Panorama City, Zip 91402–5497; tel. 818/375–2000 **A**1 3 5 10 **F**6 13 14 15 18 29 30 31 32 34 35 38 40 44 45 46 47 48 49 50 52 54 55 56 57 59 60 61 62 63 64 65 68 70 72 74 75 76 77 78 79 81 82 83 84 85 86 87 93 97 99 100 101 102 103 104 107 108 110 111 130 131 132 134 135 144 146 147 148 **S** Kaiser Foundation Hospitals, Oakland, CA
Primary Contact: Dennis C. Benton, Executive Director
COO: Barbara C. Zelinski, Chief Operating Officer
CFO: Karla Valle–Smith, Area Chief Finance Officer
CMO: Mary L. Wilson, M.D., Area Medical Director
CIO: Earle Johnson, Area Information Officer
CHR: Carole L. Erken, Human Resources Leader
CNO: Carolyn D. Pontius, R.N., Chief Nurse Executive
Web address: www.kaiserpermanente.org
Control: Other not-for-profit (including NFP Corporation) **Service:** General Medical and Surgical

Staffed Beds: 194 **Admissions:** 10823 **Census:** 131 **Births:** 2002

⊞ **KAISER PERMANENTE SOUTH BAY MEDICAL CENTER (050411)**, 25825 Vermont Avenue, Harbor City, Zip 90710–3599; tel. 310/325–5111 **A**1 10 **F**3 12 13 15 17 18 29 30 31 34 35 40 44 45 46 47 48 49 50 57 58 59 60 61 64 65 68 70 72 74 75 76 78 79 81 82 84 85 86 87 88 94 100 107 108 110 111 114 115 118 119 130 135 146 147 148 **P**6 **S** Kaiser Foundation Hospitals, Oakland, CA
Primary Contact: Lesley A. Wille, Administrator and Executive Director
Web address: www.kaiserpermanente.org
Control: Other not-for-profit (including NFP Corporation) **Service:** General Medical and Surgical

Staffed Beds: 229 **Admissions:** 12375 **Census:** 125 **Outpatient Visits:** 68000 **Births:** 2123 **Personnel:** 969

⊞ **KAISER PERMANENTE WEST LOS ANGELES MEDICAL CENTER (050561)**, 6041 Cadillac Avenue, Zip 90034–1700; tel. 323/857–2201 **A**1 3 5 10 **F**3 12 13 14 15 29 30 31 34 35 40 45 46 47 48 49 50 55 56 59 60 61 64 65 68 70 72 74 75 78 79 81 82 84 85 86 87 97 107 108 110 111 114 115 116 117 119 126 130 132 135 141 146 147 148 **P**6 **S** Kaiser Foundation Hospitals, Oakland, CA
Primary Contact: Georgina R. Garcia, R.N., Executive Director
CFO: Alice H. Issai, Business Strategy and Finance Leader
CMO: Fred Alexander, M.D., Medical Director
CIO: Gregory M. Sincock, Information Technology Leader
Web address: www.kaiserpermanente.org
Control: Other not-for-profit (including NFP Corporation) **Service:** General Medical and Surgical

Staffed Beds: 199 **Admissions:** 13337 **Census:** 107 **Outpatient Visits:** 72191 **Births:** 1835 **Total Expense ($000):** 1044977 **Payroll Expense ($000):** 103168 **Personnel:** 1105

⊞ **KAISER PERMANENTE WOODLAND HILLS MEDICAL CENTER (050677)**, 5601 DeSoto Avenue, Woodland Hills, Zip 91367–6798; tel. 818/719–2000 **A**1 3 5 10 **F**3 13 14 15 17 18 29 30 31 34 40 41 45 48 49 50 51 55 56 57 60 61 64 65 68 70 72 73 74 75 76 77 78 79 81 82 84 85 86 87 89 92 93 100 102 103 107 108 111 116 119 124 130 132 141 143 144 146 147 148 **P**6 **S** Kaiser Foundation Hospitals, Oakland, CA
Primary Contact: Michael C. Carter, Executive Director
COO: Richard Trogman, FACHE, Chief Operating Officer
CFO: Marilou Cheung, Assistant Administrator Finance
CMO: Shirley Suda, M.D., Area Medical Director
CIO: David Snow, Area Information Officer
CHR: Cathy Cousineau, Director Human Resources
CNO: Nancy Tankel, R.N., Chief Nurse Executive
Web address: www.kaiserpermanente.org
Control: Other not-for-profit (including NFP Corporation) **Service:** General Medical and Surgical

Staffed Beds: 175 **Admissions:** 12564 **Census:** 121 **Outpatient Visits:** 43540 **Births:** 1651 **Personnel:** 1477

⊞ **KECK HOSPITAL OF USC (050696)**, 1500 San Pablo Street, Zip 90033–5313; tel. 323/442–8500 **A**1 3 5 8 9 10 **F**3 8 9 11 12 15 17 18 20 22 24 26 28 29 30 31 34 35 36 37 38 39 45 46 47 48 49 50 51 53 54 55 56 57 58 59 60 61 64 65 68 70 74 75 77 78 79 81 82 84 85 86 87 90 92 93 94 96 97 98 100 101 104 105 107 108 110 111 114 115 116 117 118 119 120 121 123 124 126 129 130 131 132 135 136 137 138 139 140 141 142 143 145 146 147 148 **P**1
Primary Contact: Scott Evans, PharmD, Chief Executive Officer
CFO: Robert Allen, Chief Financial Officer
CMO: Donald Larsen, M.D., Chief Medical Officer
CIO: Mark Amey, Chief Information Officer
CHR: Matthew McElrath, Chief Human Resources Officer
Web address: www.keckhospitalofusc.org
Control: Other not-for-profit (including NFP Corporation) **Service:** General Medical and Surgical

Staffed Beds: 250 **Admissions:** 10078 **Census:** 208 **Outpatient Visits:** 308802 **Births:** 0 **Total Expense ($000):** 612026 **Payroll Expense ($000):** 195246 **Personnel:** 2553

Many Facility Codes have changed. Please refer to the AHA Guide Code Chart. © 2014 AHA Guide

KEDREN COMMUNITY MENTAL HEALTH CENTER (054083), 4211 South Avalon Boulevard, Zip 90011–5699; tel. 323/233–0425 **A**10 **F**29 30 31 35 64 68 99 100 101 104 105
Primary Contact: John H. Griffith, Ph.D., President & Chief Executive Officer
COO: Madeline Valencerina, Chief Operating Officer
CFO: Rizwan A. Uraizee, Chief Financial Officer
CMO: Frank L. Williams, Executive Vice President/ Medical Director
CNO: Essie Adams, Director of Nursing
Web address: www.kedrenmentalhealth.com
Control: State–Government, nonfederal **Service:** Psychiatric

Staffed Beds: 72 **Admissions:** 1066 **Census:** 70 **Outpatient Visits:** 124156
Births: 0 **Total Expense ($000):** 32013 **Payroll Expense ($000):** 18538
Personnel: 384

✸ **KINDRED HOSPITAL–LOS ANGELES (052032)**, 5525 West Slauson Avenue, Zip 90056–1067; tel. 310/642–0325, (Nonreporting) **A**1 9 10 **S** Kindred Healthcare, Louisville, KY
Primary Contact: Phillip R. Wolfe, Administrator
CFO: Charles Natcher, Chief Financial Officer
Web address: www.kindredhospitalla.com/
Control: Corporation, Investor–owned, for–profit **Service:** Long–Term Acute Care hospital

Staffed Beds: 81

☐ **LAC–OLIVE VIEW–UCLA MEDICAL CENTER (050040)**, 14445 Olive View Drive, Sylmar, Zip 91342–1438; tel. 818/364–1555, (Nonreporting) **A**1 3 5 10 **S** Los Angeles County–Department of Health Services, Los Angeles, CA
Primary Contact: Carolyn F. Rhee, Chief Executive Officer
COO: Ernest Espinoza, Interim Chief Operating Officer
CFO: Anthony Gray, Chief Financial Officer
CMO: William Loos, M.D., Chief Medical Officer
CIO: Melvin Brewster, Chief Information Officer
CHR: Thomas Beggane, Manager Human Resources
Web address: www.ladhs.org
Control: County–Government, nonfederal **Service:** General Medical and Surgical

Staffed Beds: 238

☐ **LAC/UNIVERSITY OF SOUTHERN CALIFORNIA MEDICAL CENTER (050373)**, 1200 North State Street, Zip 90033–1029; tel. 323/226–2622, (Includes GENERAL HOSPITAL, 1200 North State Street, Zip 90033; WOMEN'S AND CHILDREN'S HOSPITAL, 1240 North Mission Road, Zip 90033) **A**1 2 3 5 8 9 10 **F**7 13 14 15 16 17 18 19 20 21 22 23 24 25 26 27 28 29 30 31 34 35 36 38 39 40 41 43 44 45 46 47 48 49 50 51 53 54 55 56 57 58 59 60 61 63 64 65 66 68 69 70 71 72 74 75 76 77 78 79 80 81 82 83 84 85 86 87 88 89 91 92 93 94 97 98 99 100 101 102 103 104 105 107 108 109 110 111 112 113 115 116 117 119 121 122 123 124 129 130 131 133 134 135 144 145 146 147 148 **P**6 **S** Los Angeles County–Department of Health Services, Los Angeles, CA
Primary Contact: Dan Castillo, Chief Executive Officer
COO: Henry Ornelas, Chief Operating Officer
CFO: Mark Corbet, Interim Chief Financial Officer
CMO: Hal F. Yee, Jr., M.D., Interim Chief Medical Officer
CIO: Oscar Austelli, Chief Information Officer
CHR: Elizabeth Jacobi, Human Resources Director
CNO: Isabel Milan, R.N., Chief Nursing Officer
Web address: www.lacusc.org
Control: County–Government, nonfederal **Service:** General Medical and Surgical

Staffed Beds: 664 **Admissions:** 30700 **Census:** 547 **Outpatient Visits:** 569796 **Births:** 1018 **Total Expense ($000):** 1287147 **Payroll Expense ($000):** 494204

◇ **LOS ANGELES COMMUNITY HOSPITAL AT LOS ANGELES (050663)**, 4081 East Olympic Boulevard, Zip 90023–3330; tel. 323/267–0477, (Includes LOS ANGELES COMMUNITY HOSPITAL OF NORWALK, 13222 Bloomfield Avenue, Norwalk, Zip 90650; tel. 562/863–4763), (Nonreporting) **A**10 21 **S** Alta Healthcare System, Los Angeles, CA
Primary Contact: Omar Ramirez, Chief Executive Officer
CFO: Johnnette Chong, Chief Financial Officer
Control: Corporation, Investor–owned, for–profit **Service:** General Medical and Surgical

Staffed Beds: 180

LOS ANGELES COUNTY CENTRAL JAIL HOSPITAL, 441 Bauchet Street, Zip 90012–2906; tel. 213/473–6100, (Nonreporting)
Primary Contact: Tom Flaherty, Assistant Administrator
Control: County–Government, nonfederal **Service:** Hospital unit of an institution (prison hospital, college infimary, etc.)

Staffed Beds: 190

LOS ANGELES MEDICAL CENTER See Kaiser Permanente Los Angeles Medical Center

☐ **MIRACLE MILE MEDICAL CENTER (050751)**, 6000 San Vicente Boulevard, Zip 90036–4404; tel. 323/930–1040, (Nonreporting) **A**1 9 10
Primary Contact: Gil Tepper, M.D., Chief Executive Officer
COO: Liz Cheever, Administrator
CFO: Bert Roberts, Controller
CMO: Gil Tepper, M.D., Chief of Staff
CIO: Jonathan Lindell, Director Information Technology
CHR: Liz Cheever, Administrator
CNO: Melody Bradley, Chief Nursing Officer
Web address: www.miraclemilemedicalcenter.com
Control: Individual, Investor–owned, for–profit **Service:** General Medical and Surgical

Staffed Beds: 17

☐ **MISSION COMMUNITY HOSPITAL (050704)**, 14850 Roscoe Boulevard, Panorama City, Zip 91402–4677; tel. 818/787–2222, (Nonreporting) **A**1 9 10
Primary Contact: James Theiring, Chief Executive Officer
CFO: Vincenzo Variale, Chief Financial Officer
CMO: Glenn Marshak, M.D., Chief of Staff
CIO: Dustin Fennell, Director Information Systems
CHR: Carolyn Fish, Director Human Resources
CNO: Gwendolyn Dianne Wagner, R.N., Chief Nursing Officer
Web address: www.mchonline.org
Control: Other not–for–profit (including NFP Corporation) **Service:** General Medical and Surgical

Staffed Beds: 145

MOTION PICTURE AND TELEVISION FUND HOSPITAL AND RESIDENTIAL SERVICES (050552), 23388 Mulholland Drive, Woodland Hills, Zip 91364–2792; tel. 818/876–1888, (Nonreporting) **A**9 10
Primary Contact: Bob Beitcher, Chief Executive Officer
COO: David Asplund, Chief Operating Officer
CFO: Frank Guarrera, Executive Vice President and Chief Financial Officer
CHR: Nancy Rubin, Vice President Human Resources
Web address: www.mptvfund.org
Control: Other not–for–profit (including NFP Corporation) **Service:** General Medical and Surgical

Staffed Beds: 20

✸ △ **NORTHRIDGE HOSPITAL MEDICAL CENTER (050116)**, 18300 Roscoe Boulevard, Northridge, Zip 91328–4167; tel. 818/885–8500 **A**1 2 3 5 7 9 10 19 **F**1 2 3 5 8 11 12 13 14 15 17 18 20 22 24 26 28 29 30 31 34 35 38 40 41 43 48 49 56 57 58 59 60 61 64 68 70 72 74 75 76 77 78 79 81 82 84 85 86 87 88 89 90 93 97 98 99 100 101 102 103 104 105 107 108 110 111 114 117 118 119 121 124 126 129 130 132 134 146 147 148 **S** Dignity Health, San Francisco, CA
Primary Contact: Saliba Salo, President
CFO: Michael Taylor, Vice President Finance
CHR: Susan Paulsen, Director Human Resources
CNO: Mary Jane Jones, R.N., Vice President Nursing Operations
Web address: www.northridgehospital.org
Control: Other not–for–profit (including NFP Corporation) **Service:** General Medical and Surgical

Staffed Beds: 371 **Admissions:** 15509 **Census:** 192 **Outpatient Visits:** 61943 **Births:** 1518 **Total Expense ($000):** 347874 **Payroll Expense ($000):** 142098 **Personnel:** 1648

◇ **OLYMPIA MEDICAL CENTER (050742)**, 5900 West Olympic Boulevard, Zip 90036–4671; tel. 310/657–5900 **A**9 10 21 **F**3 6 8 15 17 29 31 34 35 40 45 46 47 49 56 57 58 59 64 70 74 75 77 78 79 81 82 85 86 87 93 100 103 104 107 111 115 119 130 131 132 143 146
Primary Contact: John A. Calderone, Ph.D., Chief Executive Officer
CFO: Matthew Williams, R.N., Chief Financial Officer
CMO: James Peace, M.D., Chief of Staff
CIO: Fritz Campbell, Director Information Systems
CHR: Judy Snyder, Director Human Resources
CNO: Karen Knueven, Chief Nursing Officer
Web address: www.olympiamc.com
Control: Partnership, Investor–owned, for–profit **Service:** General Medical and Surgical

Staffed Beds: 204 **Admissions:** 6060 **Census:** 80 **Outpatient Visits:** 36308 **Births:** 0 **Total Expense ($000):** 103970 **Payroll Expense ($000):** 43720 **Personnel:** 666

CA

CA

☐ **PACIFIC ALLIANCE MEDICAL CENTER (050018)**, 531 West College Street, Zip 90012–2385; tel. 213/624–8411, (Nonreporting) **A**1 9 10
Primary Contact: John R. Edwards, Administrator and Chief Executive Officer
CFO: Allan Shubin, Chief Financial Officer
CIO: John D. Brown, Director Information Systems
Web address: www.pamc.net
Control: Partnership, Investor–owned, for–profit **Service:** General Medical and Surgical

Staffed Beds: 138

☐ **PACIFICA HOSPITAL OF THE VALLEY (050378)**, 9449 San Fernando Road, Sun Valley, Zip 91352–1489; tel. 818/767–3310, (Nonreporting) **A**1 9 10
Primary Contact: Ayman Mousa, R.N., Ph.D., Chief Executive Officer
COO: Daniel Santos, Director Ancillary Services
CFO: Eileen Fisler, Chief Financial Officer
CMO: Joseph Eipe, M.D., Chief Medical Officer
CIO: Mubashir Hashmi, Chief Information Officer
CHR: Patti Alonzo, Manager Human Resources
CNO: Janet B. Latto, Chief Nursing Officer and Disaster Officer
Web address: www.pacificahospital.com
Control: Corporation, Investor–owned, for–profit **Service:** General Medical and Surgical

Staffed Beds: 231

PANORAMA CITY MEDICAL CENTER See Kaiser Permanente Panorama City Medical Center

PROMISE HOSPITAL OF EAST LOS ANGELES (052046), 443 South Soto Street, Zip 90033–4398; tel. 323/261–1181 **A**9 10 **F**3 29 30 31 35 36 42 56 57 59 60 61 63 65 68 70 74 75 77 78 79 82 84 85 86 87 91 92 100 101 103 107 108 119 143 148 **P**1 **S** Promise Healthcare, Boca Raton, FL
Primary Contact: Michael D. Kerr, Chief Executive Officer
Web address: www.promiseeastla.com
Control: Corporation, Investor–owned, for–profit **Service:** Long–Term Acute Care hospital

Staffed Beds: 36 **Admissions:** 318 **Census:** 24 **Outpatient Visits:** 0 **Births:** 0 **Total Expense ($000):** 65000

✠ △ **PROVIDENCE HOLY CROSS MEDICAL CENTER (050278)**, 15031 Rinaldi Street, Mission Hills, Zip 91345–1207; tel. 818/365–8051, (Total facility includes 48 beds in nursing home–type unit) **A**1 2 7 9 10 **F**3 11 13 15 17 18 20 22 24 26 29 30 31 32 34 35 40 43 44 45 50 54 57 59 64 68 70 72 73 74 75 76 77 78 79 81 82 84 86 87 90 93 96 107 108 110 111 114 115 116 117 118 119 126 128 130 131 132 135 146 147 148 **S** Providence Health & Services, Renton, WA
Primary Contact: Bernard Klein, M.D., Chief Executive Officer
CFO: Dave Mast, Chief Financial Officer
CHR: Lori Curry, Regional Chief Human Resources Officer
CNO: Ann Dechairo–Marino, R.N., Chief Nursing Officer
Web address: www.https://california.providence.org/holy–cross/Pages/default.aspx
Control: Church–operated, Nongovernment, not–for profit **Service:** General Medical and Surgical

Staffed Beds: 264 **Admissions:** 16162 **Census:** 242

✠ △ **PROVIDENCE LITTLE COMPANY OF MARY MEDICAL CENTER SAN PEDRO (050078)**, 1300 West Seventh Street, San Pedro, Zip 90732–3505; tel. 310/832–3311 **A**1 7 9 10 **F**2 3 4 5 11 13 14 15 18 29 30 32 34 35 40 44 45 49 50 51 57 59 60 65 66 68 70 71 74 75 77 78 79 81 82 85 86 87 90 92 93 94 96 98 100 101 102 103 104 107 108 110 111 119 120 123 128 130 132 133 135 145 146 **S** Providence Health & Services, Renton, WA
Primary Contact: Elizabeth Dunne, Interim Chief Executive Officer
COO: Carlos W. Priestley, Chief Operating Officer
CFO: Elizabeth Zuanich, Chief Financial Officer
CMO: Herbert Webb, M.D., Chief Medical Officer
CIO: Rachel Sanchez, Director Information Systems
CHR: Andreas Viggers, Director Human Resources
Web address: www.https://california.providence.org/san–pedro
Control: Other not–for–profit (including NFP Corporation) **Service:** General Medical and Surgical

Staffed Beds: 327 **Admissions:** 6821 **Census:** 190 **Outpatient Visits:** 62051 **Births:** 621 **Total Expense ($000):** 176020 **Payroll Expense ($000):** 65088 **Personnel:** 751

✠ **PROVIDENCE TARZANA MEDICAL CENTER (050761)**, 18321 Clark Street, Tarzana, Zip 91356–3521; tel. 818/881–0800 **A**1 9 10 **F**11 13 14 15 17 18 20 22 24 26 28 29 30 31 34 35 37 39 40 41 46 47 49 51 56 57 59 60 63 65 70 72 74 75 76 77 78 79 81 82 83 84 85 87 89 93 107 108 110 111 114 115 116 117 118 119 130 132 135 146 147 148 **S** Providence Health & Services, Renton, WA
Primary Contact: Dale Surowitz, Chief Executive
COO: Phyllis Bushart, R.N., Chief Operating Officer
CFO: Ted Wang, Chief Financial Officer
CIO: Alex Nury, Chief Information Officer
CHR: Wendy Regal, Director Human Resources
CNO: Neil Christopher R. Apeles, MSN, Chief Nursing Officer
Web address: www.providence.org/tarzana
Control: Other not–for–profit (including NFP Corporation) **Service:** General Medical and Surgical

Staffed Beds: 245 **Admissions:** 13997 **Census:** 171 **Outpatient Visits:** 42919

✠ **RONALD REAGAN UNIVERSITY OF CALIFORNIA LOS ANGELES MEDICAL CENTER (050262)**, 757 Westwood Plaza, Zip 90095–8358; tel. 310/825–9111, (Includes MATTEL CHILDREN'S HOSPITAL, 10833 Le Conte Avenue, Zip 90024; tel. 310/825–9111) **A**1 3 5 8 9 10 **F**3 6 7 8 9 11 12 13 14 15 17 18 19 20 21 22 23 24 25 26 27 28 29 30 31 32 34 35 36 40 41 43 44 45 46 47 48 49 50 51 52 54 55 56 57 58 59 61 62 64 65 66 68 70 71 72 74 75 76 77 78 79 81 82 83 84 85 86 87 88 89 90 92 93 94 96 97 102 107 108 110 111 112 113 114 115 116 117 118 119 120 121 123 124 126 129 130 131 132 135 136 137 138 140 141 142 143 145 146 147 148 **P**6 **S** University of California–Systemwide Administration, Oakland, CA
Primary Contact: David Feinberg, M.D., Chief Executive Officer
CFO: Paul Staton, Chief Financial Officer
CMO: J. Thomas Rosenthal, M.D., Chief Medical Officer
CIO: Virginia McFerran, Chief Information Officer
CHR: Mark Speare, Senior Associate Director Human Resources
CNO: Heidi M. Crooks, R.N., Senior Associate Director, Outpatient and Patient Care Services
Web address: www.uclahealth.org
Control: State–Government, nonfederal **Service:** General Medical and Surgical

Staffed Beds: 466 **Admissions:** 23222 **Census:** 448 **Outpatient Visits:** 736692 **Births:** 1936 **Total Expense ($000):** 1410580 **Payroll Expense ($000):** 544840 **Personnel:** 7350

○ **SHERMAN OAKS HOSPITAL (050755)**, 4929 Van Nuys Boulevard, Sherman Oaks, Zip 91403–1777; tel. 818/981–7111 **A**10 11 **F**17 20 29 31 34 35 38 40 56 57 59 61 64 70 75 77 78 79 81 82 85 98 103 104 105 107 108 118 119 130 131 132 146 148 **S** Prime Healthcare Services, Ontario, CA
Primary Contact: Bockhi Park, Chief Executive Officer
CFO: Daniel Leon, Chief Financial Officer
CMO: Michael Malamed, M.D., Chief of Staff
Web address: www.shermanoakshospital.com
Control: Other not–for–profit (including NFP Corporation) **Service:** General Medical and Surgical

Staffed Beds: 77 **Admissions:** 4610 **Census:** 74 **Outpatient Visits:** 29132 **Births:** 0

✠ **SHRINERS HOSPITALS FOR CHILDREN–LOS ANGELES (053310)**, 3160 Geneva Street, Zip 90020–1199; tel. 213/388–3151 **A**1 3 5 9 10 **F**3 8 11 29 32 34 35 57 58 59 64 65 68 75 79 81 82 86 87 89 91 93 94 107 119 130 134 141 142 143 146 148 **S** Shriners Hospitals for Children, Tampa, FL
Primary Contact: Sidney M. Ono, Administrator
CFO: David Burkitt, Director Fiscal Services
CMO: Hugh Watts, M.D., Chief of Staff
CIO: Mark Garrett, Chief Information Officer
Web address: www.shrinershospitalsforchildren.org/Hospitals/Locations/Losangeles.aspx
Control: Other not–for–profit (including NFP Corporation) **Service:** Children's general

Staffed Beds: 30 **Admissions:** 351 **Census:** 2 **Outpatient Visits:** 11786 **Births:** 0 **Total Expense ($000):** 33325 **Payroll Expense ($000):** 13468 **Personnel:** 177

☐ **SILVER LAKE MEDICAL CENTER (050763)**, 1711 West Temple Street, Zip 90026–5421; tel. 213/989–6100, (Includes SILVER LAKE MEDICAL CENTER–INGLESIDE HOSPITAL, 7500 East Hellman Avenue, Rosemead, Zip 91770; tel. 626/288–1160), (Nonreporting) **A**1 10 **S** Success Healthcare, Boca Raton, FL
Primary Contact: Brent A. Cope, Chief Executive Officer
CFO: John Cowles, Chief Financial Officer
CMO: Louis Acosta, M.D., Chief of Staff
CIO: Scott Musack, Chief Information Officer
CHR: Sylvia Cloud, Director Human Resources
Web address: www.silverlakemc.com
Control: Corporation, Investor–owned, for–profit **Service:** General Medical and Surgical

Staffed Beds: 150

Many Facility Codes have changed. Please refer to the AHA Guide Code Chart. © 2014 AHA Guide

◇ **SOUTHERN CALIFORNIA HOSPITAL AT HOLLYWOOD (050135)**, 6245 De Longpre Avenue, Zip 90028–9001; tel. 323/462–2271, (Includes SOUTHERN CALIFORNIA HOSPITAL AT VAN NUYS, 14433 Emelita Street, Van Nuys, Zip 91401; tel. 818/787–1511), (Nonreporting) **A**10 21 **S** Alta Healthcare System, Los Angeles, CA
Primary Contact: Bruce P. Grimshaw, Chief Executive Officer
Web address: www.hollywoodcommunityhospital.org/
Control: Corporation, Investor–owned, for–profit **Service:** General Medical and Surgical

Staffed Beds: 45

SOUTHERN CALIFORNIA HOSPITAL AT VAN NUYS See Southern California Hospital at Hollywood

⊠ **ST. VINCENT MEDICAL CENTER (050502)**, 2131 West Third Street, Zip 90057–1901, Mailing Address: P.O. Box 57992, Zip 90057–0992; tel. 213/484–7111, (Total facility includes 27 beds in nursing home–type unit) **A**1 9 10 **F**3 11 15 17 18 20 22 24 26 29 30 31 34 35 36 40 45 47 49 50 54 57 58 59 60 63 64 65 68 69 70 71 74 75 77 78 79 80 81 82 85 87 91 93 96 107 108 110 111 118 119 120 121 125 128 130 136 138 142 143 146 148 **P**5 **S** Daughters of Charity Health System, Los Altos Hills, CA
Primary Contact: Catherine Fickes, R.N., President and Chief Executive Officer
CFO: Michael Garko, Chief Financial Officer
CMO: Brian Kahn, M.D., Chief of Staff
CIO: Dan Robbins, Information Technology and Account Executive
CHR: Christine Carson, Vice President Human Resources
CNO: Judy McCurdy, R.N., Vice President and Chief Nursing Officer
Web address: www.stvincentmedicalcenter.com
Control: Church–operated, Nongovernment, not–for profit **Service:** General Medical and Surgical

Staffed Beds: 271 **Admissions:** 8215 **Census:** 131 **Outpatient Visits:** 94286 **Births:** 0 **Total Expense ($000):** 229408 **Payroll Expense ($000):** 78965 **Personnel:** 1035

⊠ **STEWART & LYNDA RESNICK NEUROPSYCHIATRIC HOSPITAL AT UCLA (054009)**, 760 Westwood Plaza, Zip 90095–8353; tel. 310/825–9989 **A**1 3 5 9 10 **F**3 5 6 29 30 35 40 42 43 55 56 64 68 77 86 87 98 99 100 101 102 103 104 105 130 132 134 147 **P**1 **S** University of California–Systemwide Administration, Oakland, CA
Primary Contact: Peter Whybrow, M.D., Chief Executive Officer
COO: Ruth Irwin, Associate Director Clinical Operations
CHR: Cindy Cohen, Director Human Resources
Web address: www.semel.ucla.edu/resnick
Control: State–Government, nonfederal **Service:** Psychiatric

Staffed Beds: 74 **Admissions:** 2006 **Census:** 68 **Outpatient Visits:** 18189 **Births:** 0 **Total Expense ($000):** 49674 **Payroll Expense ($000):** 29840 **Personnel:** 323

☐ **TEMPLE COMMUNITY HOSPITAL (050111)**, 235 North Hoover Street, Zip 90004–3672; tel. 213/382–7252, (Nonreporting) **A**1 9 10
Primary Contact: Herbert G. Needman, President and Chief Executive Officer
CFO: John Skelton, Director Finance
CMO: Assa Weinberg, M.D., Chief of Staff
CIO: Diane Adams, Director Business Services
CHR: Leslie Beasley, Director Human Resources
Web address: www.templecommunityhospital.com
Control: Corporation, Investor–owned, for–profit **Service:** General Medical and Surgical

Staffed Beds: 130

⊠ **UNIVERSITY OF SOUTHERN CALIFORNIA–NORRIS CANCER HOSPITAL (050660)**, 1441 Eastlake Avenue, Zip 90089–0112; tel. 323/865–3000 **A**1 2 3 5 9 11 15 29 30 31 34 35 36 38 39 45 46 47 48 49 50 54 55 56 57 58 59 60 61 64 65 68 70 74 75 77 78 79 81 82 84 85 86 87 92 93 94 100 101 104 107 108 110 111 114 115 118 119 120 121 123 124 130 132 135 136 143 145 146 147 148 **P**1
Primary Contact: Scott Evans, PharmD, Chief Executive Officer
COO: Tarek Salaway, Chief Operating Officer
CFO: Robert Allen, Chief Financial Officer
CMO: Stephanie Hall, M.D., Medical Director
CIO: Joshua Lee, Chief Information Officer
CHR: Matthew McElrath, Chief Human Resources Officer
CNO: Annette Sy, R.N., Chief Nursing Officer
Web address: www.uscnorriscancerhospital.org
Control: Other not–for–profit (including NFP Corporation) **Service:** Cancer

Staffed Beds: 60 **Admissions:** 526 **Census:** 13 **Outpatient Visits:** 99109 **Births:** 0 **Total Expense ($000):** 113176 **Payroll Expense ($000):** 26591 **Personnel:** 432

USC UNIVERSITY HOSPITAL See Keck Hospital of USC

★ ◇ **VALLEY PRESBYTERIAN HOSPITAL (050126)**, 15107 Vanowen Street, Van Nuys, Zip 91405–4597; tel. 818/782–6600 **A**9 10 21 **F**3 13 18 20 22 24 28 29 31 34 35 40 44 45 46 49 50 53 57 59 64 65 70 72 74 75 76 77 78 79 81 85 86 87 88 89 90 96 107 108 109 114 115 119 122 123 130 145 146 147 148 **P**5
Primary Contact: Gustavo A. Valdespino, President and Chief Executive Officer
COO: Gayathri S. Jith, M.P.H., Senior Vice President Strategy and Operations
CFO: Lori Cardle, Senior Vice President, Chief Financial Officer
CIO: Jeff Allport, Vice President, Chief Information Officer
CHR: Jonathan Wu, Vice President Human Resources
CNO: Lori Burnell, R.N., Senior Vice President and Chief Nursing Officer
Web address: www.valleypres.org
Control: Other not–for–profit (including NFP Corporation) **Service:** General Medical and Surgical

Staffed Beds: 350 **Admissions:** 15612 **Census:** 186 **Outpatient Visits:** 108565 **Births:** 3711 **Total Expense ($000):** 306479 **Payroll Expense ($000):** 110344 **Personnel:** 1433

★ △ **VETERANS AFFAIRS GREATER LOS ANGELES HEALTHCARE SYSTEM**, 11301 Wilshire Boulevard, Zip 90073–1003; tel. 310/478–3711, (Nonreporting) **A**5 7 8 **S** Department of Veterans Affairs, Washington, DC
Primary Contact: Donna M. Beiter, R.N., MSN, Director
COO: Lynn Carrier, Associate Director Administration and Support
CFO: Olivia Ortiz–Bitner, Acting Chief Financial Officer
CMO: Dennis Schaberg, M.D., Chief Medicine
CIO: Eugene Archey, Chief Information Technology
CHR: Harold Goings, Chief Human Resources
Web address: www.losangeles.va.gov/
Control: Veterans Affairs, Government, federal **Service:** General Medical and Surgical

Staffed Beds: 1087

⊠ **WEST HILLS HOSPITAL AND MEDICAL CENTER (050481)**, 7300 Medical Center Drive, West Hills, Zip 91307–1900; tel. 818/676–4000 **A**1 9 10 **F**3 11 12 13 14 15 17 18 20 22 24 26 28 29 31 34 35 40 45 46 47 48 49 51 54 56 57 59 60 64 66 68 70 72 75 76 77 78 79 81 82 85 86 87 91 93 107 108 109 110 111 113 114 118 119 130 132 143 144 145 146 147 148 **S** HCA, Nashville, TN
Primary Contact: Douglas Long, President and Chief Executive Officer
COO: Omar Chughtai, Vice President and Chief Operating Officer
CFO: Tony Lopez, Vice President and Chief Financial Officer
CMO: Ron Chitayat, M.D., Chief Medical Staff
CIO: Tony Lopez, Chief Financial Officer
CHR: Edward Battista, Vice President Human Resources
CNO: Janet Brooks, R.N., Vice President and Chief Nursing Officer
Web address: www.westhillshospital.com
Control: Corporation, Investor–owned, for–profit **Service:** General Medical and Surgical

Staffed Beds: 225 **Admissions:** 8111 **Census:** 114 **Total Expense ($000):** 171297

WEST LOS ANGELES MEDICAL CENTER See Kaiser Permanente West Los Angeles Medical Center

⊠ **WHITE MEMORIAL MEDICAL CENTER (050103)**, 1720 Cesar Chavez Avenue, Zip 90033–2414; tel. 323/268–5000, (Total facility includes 27 beds in nursing home–type unit) **A**1 2 3 5 9 10 **F**3 11 13 15 17 18 19 20 22 24 26 27 28 29 30 31 34 35 40 45 46 47 48 49 50 51 53 57 58 59 64 68 70 72 74 75 76 78 79 81 82 84 85 86 87 88 89 90 91 92 93 96 98 99 102 103 107 108 109 110 111 114 115 116 117 118 119 120 121 123 128 130 131 132 146 147 148 **P**1 4 7 **S** Adventist Health, Roseville, CA
Primary Contact: Beth D. Zachary, FACHE, President and Chief Executive Officer
CFO: John Raffoul, Senior Vice President Finance
CIO: Ralf Weissenberger, Director Information Systems
CHR: Natasha Milatovich, Association Vice President Human Resources
Web address: www.whitememorial.com
Control: Church–operated, Nongovernment, not–for profit **Service:** General Medical and Surgical

Staffed Beds: 353 **Admissions:** 20151 **Census:** 246 **Outpatient Visits:** 70497 **Births:** 4053 **Total Expense ($000):** 339316 **Payroll Expense ($000):** 124483 **Personnel:** 1644

WOMEN'S AND CHILDREN'S HOSPITAL See LAC/University of Southern California Medical Center

WOODLAND HILLS MEDICAL CENTER See Kaiser Permanente Woodland Hills Medical Center

---

Hospital, Medicare Provider Number, Address, Telephone, Approval, Facility, and Physician Codes, Health Care System

★ American Hospital Association (AHA) membership
☐ The Joint Commission accreditation
◇ DNV Healthcare Inc. accreditation
○ Healthcare Facilities Accreditation Program
△ Commission on Accreditation of Rehabilitation Facilities (CARF) accreditation

---

CA

LOS BANOS—Merced County

⊠ **MEMORIAL HOSPITAL LOS BANOS (050528)**, 520 West I Street,
Zip 93635–3498; tel. 209/826–0591 **A**1 9 10 20 **F**3 11 13 15 18 29 30 34
35 40 45 46 49 50 57 59 64 66 68 70 75 81 85 107 108 110 111 115 119
127 130 132 135 146 **S** Sutter Health, Sacramento, CA
Primary Contact: Asit Gokli, M.D., Chief Executive Officer
CFO: Timothy J. Noakes, Chief Financial Officer
CHR: Shawn Garcia, Manager Human Resources
CNO: Kristie Marion, Chief Nurse Executive
Web address: www.memoriallosbanos.org/
Control: Other not–for–profit (including NFP Corporation) **Service:** General
Medical and Surgical

> **Staffed Beds:** 46 **Admissions:** 1377 **Census:** 10 **Outpatient Visits:** 52389
> **Births:** 732 **Total Expense ($000):** 43261 **Payroll Expense ($000):** 13716
> **Personnel:** 208

LYNWOOD—Los Angeles County

⊠ **ST. FRANCIS MEDICAL CENTER (050104)**, 3630 East Imperial Highway,
Zip 90262–2636; tel. 310/900–8900, (Nonreporting) **A**1 9 10 **S** Daughters of
Charity Health System, Los Altos Hills, CA
Primary Contact: Gerald T. Kozai, President and Chief Executive Officer
COO: Kurt Weinmeister, Chief Operating Officer
CFO: Nancy Wilson, Senior Vice President and Chief Financial Officer
CIO: Judi Binderman, Chief Information Technology Officer and Chief Medical
Informatics Officer
CHR: Laura Kato, Vice President Human Resources
CNO: Mary Lynne Knighten, R.N., Chief Nursing Officer and Vice President Patient
Care Services
Web address: www.dochs.org
Control: Church–operated, Nongovernment, not–for profit **Service:** General
Medical and Surgical

> **Staffed Beds:** 323

MADERA—Madera County

☐ △ **CHILDREN'S HOSPITAL CENTRAL CALIFORNIA (053300)**, 9300 Valley
Children's Place, Zip 93636–8761; tel. 559/353–3000 **A**1 3 5 7 9 10 **F**3 8 9 11
19 21 23 25 27 28 29 30 31 32 34 35 38 40 41 44 46 48 50 54 55 57 58
59 60 61 62 64 65 68 72 73 74 75 77 78 79 81 82 84 85 86 87 88 89 90
93 94 97 107 108 111 114 115 119 127 129 130 131 132 134 143 146
147 148
Primary Contact: Todd Suntrapak, President and Chief Executive Officer
CFO: Michele Waldron, Senior Vice President and Chief Financial Officer
CMO: David Christensen, M.D., Senior Vice President Medical Affairs and Chief
Medical Officer
CHR: Nat Ponticello, Vice President Human Resources
CNO: Beverly P. Hayden–Pugh, R.N., Vice President and Chief Nursing Officer
Web address: www.childrenscentralcal.org
Control: Other not–for–profit (including NFP Corporation) **Service:** Children's
general

> **Staffed Beds:** 340 **Admissions:** 12850 **Census:** 209 **Outpatient Visits:**
> 236383 **Births:** 0 **Total Expense ($000):** 432698 **Payroll Expense ($000):**
> 169765 **Personnel:** 1984

○ **MADERA COMMUNITY HOSPITAL (050568)**, 1250 East Almond Avenue,
Zip 93637–5696, Mailing Address: P.O. Box 1328, Zip 93639–1328;
tel. 559/675–5501 **A**9 10 11 19 **F**3 13 29 30 34 35 40 45 46 47 48 49 54
59 62 64 65 70 74 75 76 77 79 81 82 107 108 110 111 114 119 127 132
146 147 148 **P**5
Primary Contact: Evan J. Rayner, Chief Executive Officer
COO: Karen Paolmelli, Chief Operating Officer
CFO: Mark Foote, Chief Financial Officer
CIO: Darla Rigg, Interim Director, Information Systems
CHR: Christine M. Watts–Johnson, Assistant Vice President
CNO: Meri Combs, R.N., Vice President and Chief Nursing Officer
Web address: www.maderahospital.org
Control: Other not–for–profit (including NFP Corporation) **Service:** General
Medical and Surgical

> **Staffed Beds:** 106 **Admissions:** 4570 **Census:** 56 **Outpatient Visits:** 148127
> **Births:** 1568 **Total Expense ($000):** 86361 **Payroll Expense ($000):** 35029
> **Personnel:** 782

MAMMOTH LAKES—Mono County

◇ **MAMMOTH HOSPITAL (051303)**, 85 Sierra Park Road, Zip 93546–2073,
Mailing Address: P.O. Box 660, Zip 93546–0660; tel. 760/934–3311 **A**9 10 18
21 **F**3 11 13 15 18 29 31 34 35 39 40 45 46 50 53 57 59 64 65 68 70 74
75 76 77 78 79 81 82 85 93 97 99 104 107 110 111 114 119 127 131 132
146 147
Primary Contact: Gary Myers, Chief Executive Officer
CFO: Melanie Van Winkle, Chief Financial Officer
CMO: Tomi Bortolazzo, M.D., Chief of Staff
CIO: Mark Lind, Director Information Technology
CHR: Jeff Byberg, Manager Human Resources
CNO: Kathleen Alo, R.N., Chief Nursing Officer
Web address: www.mammothhospital.com
Control: Hospital district or authority, Government, nonfederal **Service:** General
Medical and Surgical

> **Staffed Beds:** 17 **Admissions:** 635 **Census:** 4 **Outpatient Visits:** 9885
> **Births:** 110 **Total Expense ($000):** 57637 **Payroll Expense ($000):** 17304
> **Personnel:** 259

MANTECA—San Joaquin County

⊠ **DOCTORS HOSPITAL OF MANTECA (050118)**, 1205 East North Street,
Zip 95336–4900; tel. 209/823–3111 **A**1 9 10 **F**3 11 12 13 15 29 31 34 35
40 45 49 50 51 75 76 78 79 81 85 102 107 108 110 111 115 116 117 118
119 130 132 146 147 148 **S** TENET Healthcare Corporation, Dallas, TX
Primary Contact: Nicholas R. Tejeda, FACHE, Chief Executive Officer
COO: Carmen Silva, R.N., Chief Operating Officer
CFO: Tracy Roman, Chief Financial Officer
CHR: Traci Holzer, Chief Human Resources Officer
CNO: Patricia R. Gooch, MSN, Chief Nursing Officer
Web address: www.doctorsmanteca.com
Control: Corporation, Investor–owned, for–profit **Service:** General Medical and
Surgical

> **Staffed Beds:** 73 **Admissions:** 3525 **Census:** 38 **Outpatient Visits:** 57106
> **Births:** 708 **Total Expense ($000):** 67484 **Payroll Expense ($000):** 35108
> **Personnel:** 387

⊠ **KAISER PERMANENTE MANTECA MEDICAL CENTER (050748)**, 1777 West
Yosemite Avenue, Zip 95337–5187; tel. 209/825–3500, (Includes MODESTO
MEDICAL CENTER, 4601 Dale Road, Modesto, Zip 95356–9718;
tel. 209/735–5000; Corwin N. Harper, Administrator) **A**1 10 **F**3 13 15 17 20 29
30 31 39 40 50 64 70 72 73 74 75 76 77 78 79 81 82 84 85 86 87 89 93
100 107 108 110 111 114 115 119 128 130 146 148 **P**3 **S** Kaiser Foundation
Hospitals, Oakland, CA
Primary Contact: Corwin N. Harper, Senior Vice President and Area Manager
COO: Corwin N. Harper, Senior Vice President and Area Manager
CFO: Debra L. Brown, Area Financial Officer
CMO: Moses D. Elam, M.D., Physician–in–Chief
CIO: Tom J. Osteen, Director Area Technology
CHR: Pat McKeldin, Human Resource Business Partner
Web address: www.kaiserpermanente.org
Control: Other not–for–profit (including NFP Corporation) **Service:** General
Medical and Surgical

> **Staffed Beds:** 239 **Admissions:** 9298 **Census:** 89 **Outpatient Visits:** 68751
> **Births:** 2376 **Personnel:** 2027

MARINA DEL REY—Los Angeles County

☐ **MARINA DEL REY HOSPITAL (050740)**, 4650 Lincoln Boulevard,
Zip 90292–6306; tel. 310/823–8911, (Nonreporting) **A**1 9 10
Primary Contact: Sean Fowler, Chief Executive Officer
COO: Phyllis Buchart, Chief Operating Officer
CFO: Stephen A. Hargett, Senior Vice President and Chief Financial Officer
Web address: www.marinahospital.com
Control: Corporation, Investor–owned, for–profit **Service:** General Medical and
Surgical

> **Staffed Beds:** 40

MARIPOSA—Mariposa County

★ **JOHN C. FREMONT HEALTHCARE DISTRICT (051304)**, 5189 Hospital Road,
Zip 95338–9524, Mailing Address: P.O. Box 216, Zip 95338–0216;
tel. 209/966–3631, (Nonreporting) **A**9 10 18
Primary Contact: Alan MacPhee, Chief Executive Officer
CFO: Matthew Robichaux, Chief Financial Officer
CMO: Joseph E.C. Rogers, M.D., Chief of Staff
CIO: Phil Blas, Chief Information Officer
CNO: Theresa Loya, R.N., Chief Nursing Officer
Web address: www.jcf–hospital.com
Control: Hospital district or authority, Government, nonfederal **Service:** General
Medical and Surgical

> **Staffed Beds:** 34

Many Facility Codes have changed. Please refer to the AHA Guide Code Chart. © 2014 AHA Guide

CA

MARTINEZ—Contra Costa County

⊞ **CONTRA COSTA REGIONAL MEDICAL CENTER (050276)**, 2500 Alhambra Avenue, Zip 94553–3156; tel. 925/370–5000 **A**1 2 10 **F**3 11 13 15 18 30 31 36 39 40 41 44 45 49 50 51 52 54 56 58 59 61 62 64 65 66 68 70 71 72 73 74 75 76 77 78 79 81 82 84 85 86 87 92 93 96 97 98 100 102 103 104 107 108 109 110 111 114 119 130 132 143 146 147 148 **P**6
Primary Contact: Anna M. Roth, R.N., MS, M.P.H., Chief Executive Officer
COO: Timothy Thompson–Cook, Chief Operating Officer
CFO: Patrick Godley, Chief Financial Officer
CMO: David Goldstein, M.D., Chief Medical Officer
CNO: Jaspreet Benepal, Chief Nursing Officer
Web address: www.cchealth.org/medical_center/
Control: County–Government, nonfederal **Service:** General Medical and Surgical

Staffed Beds: 112 **Admissions:** 8886 **Census:** 111 **Outpatient Visits:** 389166 **Births:** 1960 **Total Expense ($000):** 470257 **Payroll Expense ($000):** 153631 **Personnel:** 1761

KAISER FOUNDATION HOSPITAL See Kaiser Permanente Walnut Creek Medical Center, Walnut Creek

MARYSVILLE—Yuba County

★ **FREMONT–RIDEOUT HEALTH GROUP (050133)**, 726 Fourth Street, Zip 95901–5600; tel. 530/749–4300, (Includes FREMONT MEDICAL CENTER, 970 Plumas Street, Yuba City, Zip 95991–4087; tel. 530/751–4000) **A**9 10 20 **F**3 8 13 15 17 18 19 20 22 24 28 29 30 31 40 43 45 47 49 54 59 61 64 68 70 72 74 76 77 78 79 81 82 85 89 93 94 96 97 107 110 111 114 115 117 119 120 121 123 124 130 147 148 **P**3
Primary Contact: Robert Chason, Interim Chief Executive Officer
CMO: Robert Plass, M.D., Chief Medical Officer
CIO: Tarun Ghosh, Chief Information Officer
CHR: Tresha Moreland, Vice President Human Resources
Web address: www.frhg.org
Control: Other not–for–profit (including NFP Corporation) **Service:** General Medical and Surgical

Staffed Beds: 233 **Admissions:** 12456 **Census:** 140 **Outpatient Visits:** 155587 **Births:** 2041 **Total Expense ($000):** 288036 **Payroll Expense ($000):** 84332 **Personnel:** 1198

MENLO PARK—San Mateo County

⊞ **MENLO PARK SURGICAL HOSPITAL (050754)**, 570 Willow Road, Zip 94025–2617; tel. 650/324–8500 **A**1 5 9 10 **F**18 35 64 68 79 81 82 85 **S** Sutter Health, Sacramento, CA
Primary Contact: Kathleen Palange, R.N., Chief Administrative Officer
CMO: Andrew Gutow, M.D., Medical Director
CNO: Marjorie Eckford, Chief Nursing Officer
Web address: www.pamf.org/mpsh
Control: Other not–for–profit (including NFP Corporation) **Service:** General Medical and Surgical

Staffed Beds: 12 **Admissions:** 246 **Census:** 1 **Outpatient Visits:** 2947 **Births:** 0 **Total Expense ($000):** 13669 **Payroll Expense ($000):** 4055 **Personnel:** 40

MERCED—Merced County

⊞ **MERCY MEDICAL CENTER MERCED (050444)**, 333 Mercy Avenue, Zip 95340–8319; tel. 209/564–5000, (Includes MERCY MEDICAL CENTER MERCED–DOMINICAN CAMPUS, 2740 M Street, Zip 95340–2880; tel. 209/384–6444; David S. Dunham, President) **A**1 3 5 9 10 19 **F**3 13 15 18 20 26 28 29 30 34 35 39 40 41 42 45 49 50 57 59 62 64 65 66 68 74 75 76 77 79 81 84 85 86 87 93 96 97 107 108 110 111 115 119 127 130 132 146 148 **P**3 **S** Dignity Health, San Francisco, CA
Primary Contact: David S. Dunham, President
COO: Charles Kassis, Chief Operating Officer
CFO: Michael Strasser, Vice President and Chief Financial Officer
CMO: Robert Streeter, M.D., Vice President Medical Affairs
CIO: Daniel Andresen, Chief information Officer
CHR: Julie Rocha, Vice President Human Resources
CNO: Greg Rouleau, Vice President Nursing
Web address: www.mercymercedcares.org
Control: Church–operated, Nongovernment, not–for profit **Service:** General Medical and Surgical

Staffed Beds: 186 **Admissions:** 10152 **Census:** 114 **Outpatient Visits:** 212537 **Births:** 794 **Total Expense ($000):** 245597 **Payroll Expense ($000):** 91338 **Personnel:** 1137

MISSION HILLS—Los Angeles County, See Los Angeles

MISSION VIEJO—Orange County

☐ **CHILDREN'S HOSPITAL AT MISSION (053306)**, 27700 Medical Center Road, Zip 92691–6426; tel. 949/364–1400 **A**1 9 10 **F**3 11 36 72 74 79 81 85 88 89 146
Primary Contact: Kimberly C. Cripe, President and Chief Executive Officer
COO: Matthew S. Gerlach, Chief Operating Officer
CFO: Kerri Ruppert Schiller, Senior Vice President and Chief Financial Officer
CMO: Maria Minon, M.D., Vice President Medical Affairs and Chief Medical Officer
CIO: Mark Headland, Chief Information Officer
CHR: Mamoon Syed, Vice President Human Resources
CNO: Melanie Patterson, R.N., Vice President Patient Care Services and Chief Nursing Officer
Web address: www.choc.org
Control: Other not–for–profit (including NFP Corporation) **Service:** Children's general

Staffed Beds: 54 **Admissions:** 1863 **Census:** 21 **Outpatient Visits:** 22779 **Births:** 0 **Total Expense ($000):** 47141 **Payroll Expense ($000):** 7990 **Personnel:** 92

⊞ △ **MISSION HOSPITAL (050567)**, 27700 Medical Center Road, Zip 92691–6474; tel. 949/364–1400, (Includes MISSION HOSPITAL LAGUNA BEACH, 31872 Coast Highway, Laguna Beach, Zip 92651–6775; tel. 949/499–1311) **A**1 2 7 9 10 **F**3 4 5 8 11 13 14 15 17 18 20 22 24 26 28 29 30 31 34 35 36 40 43 44 45 46 47 48 49 50 53 54 57 58 59 64 65 66 68 70 74 75 76 77 78 79 80 81 82 84 85 86 87 90 92 93 96 98 100 101 104 105 107 108 110 111 114 115 116 117 118 119 120 121 123 126 129 130 131 132 134 135 141 143 145 146 147 148 **P**3 5 **S** St. Joseph Health, Irvine, CA
Primary Contact: Kenneth McFarland, President and Chief Executive Officer
COO: Michael D. Beck, Vice President Operations
CFO: Eileen Haubl, Senior Vice President and Chief Financial Officer
CMO: Linda Sieglen, M.D., Chief Medical Officer
CIO: Bill Russell, Senior Chief Information Officer
CHR: Terri Covert, Vice President Human Resources
CNO: Linda Johnson, R.N., Chief Clinical Officer
Web address: www.mission4health.com
Control: Church–operated, Nongovernment, not–for profit **Service:** General Medical and Surgical

Staffed Beds: 232 **Admissions:** 19850 **Census:** 232 **Outpatient Visits:** 185606 **Births:** 2825 **Total Expense ($000):** 430083 **Payroll Expense ($000):** 134390 **Personnel:** 1775

MODESTO—Stanislaus County

★ ◇ **CENTRAL VALLEY SPECIALTY HOSPITAL (052055)**, 730 17th Street, Zip 95354–1209; tel. 209/248–7700, (Nonreporting) **A**21
Primary Contact: Gia Smith, Chief Executive Officer
Control: Partnership, Investor–owned, for–profit **Service:** Long–Term Acute Care hospital

Staffed Beds: 100

⊞ **DOCTORS MEDICAL CENTER (050464)**, 1441 Florida Avenue, Zip 95350–4418, Mailing Address: P.O. Box 4138, Zip 95352–4138; tel. 209/578–1211 **A**1 2 9 10 **F**3 13 17 18 20 22 24 26 28 29 31 35 40 41 43 45 46 48 49 50 51 55 57 59 60 65 70 72 74 75 76 77 78 79 80 81 85 89 98 102 103 107 108 109 110 111 112 113 114 115 116 117 118 119 126 130 132 146 147 **S** TENET Healthcare Corporation, Dallas, TX
Primary Contact: Warren J. Kirk, Chief Executive Officer
COO: Mike King, Chief Operating Officer
CFO: Greg Berry, Chief Financial Officer
CIO: Debbie Fuller, Director Health Information Systems and Chief Information Officer
CHR: Michele Bava, Director Human Resources
CNO: Lani Dickinson, R.N., Chief Nursing Officer
Web address: www.dmc–modesto.com
Control: Corporation, Investor–owned, for–profit **Service:** General Medical and Surgical

Staffed Beds: 455 **Admissions:** 23520 **Census:** 335 **Outpatient Visits:** 133194 **Births:** 3917 **Total Expense ($000):** 400656 **Payroll Expense ($000):** 188071 **Personnel:** 1899

Hospital, Medicare Provider Number, Address, Telephone, Approval, Facility, and Physician Codes, Health Care System

★ American Hospital Association (AHA) membership
☐ The Joint Commission accreditation
◇ DNV Healthcare Inc. accreditation
◯ Healthcare Facilities Accreditation Program
△ Commission on Accreditation of Rehabilitation Facilities (CARF) accreditation

CA

✠ **MEMORIAL MEDICAL CENTER (050557)**, 1700 Coffee Road,
Zip 95355–2869, Mailing Address: P.O. Box 942, Zip 95353–0942;
tel. 209/526–4500, (Includes MEMORIAL MEDICAL CENTER, 1700 Coffee Road,
Zip 95355, Mailing Address: Box 942, Zip 95353; tel. 209/526–4500) **A**1 2 9
10 **F**3 8 11 12 13 15 17 18 20 22 24 28 29 30 31 34 35 40 43 45 46 47 48
49 50 51 57 59 60 62 64 66 68 70 73 74 75 76 77 78 79 81 82 84 85 86
87 89 107 108 111 114 115 118 119 120 121 124 130 146 148 **S** Sutter
Health, Sacramento, CA
Primary Contact: Daryn J. Kumar, Chief Executive Officer
COO: Steve Mitchell, Chief Operating Officer
CFO: Eric Dalton, Chief Financial Officer
CIO: Patrick Anderson, Chief Information Officer
CHR: Paula Rafala, Director, Human Resources
CNO: Sandra Proctor, R.N., Chief Nurse Executive
Web address: www.memorialmedicalcenter.org
Control: Other not–for–profit (including NFP Corporation) **Service:** General
Medical and Surgical

Staffed Beds: 423 **Admissions:** 17307 **Census:** 225 **Outpatient Visits:** 91564 **Births:** 1852 **Total Expense ($000):** 488759 **Payroll Expense ($000):** 155458 **Personnel:** 2023

MODESTO MEDICAL CENTER See Kaiser Permanente Manteca Medical Center,
Manteca

STANISLAUS SURGICAL HOSPITAL (050726), 1421 Oakdale Road,
Zip 95355–3356; tel. 209/572–2700 **A**5 9 10 **F**3 15 45 46 47 51 81 82 85
91 93 107 110 111 114 119 145 148
Primary Contact: Douglas V. Johnson, Chief Executive Officer
CFO: Richard Hart, Chief Financial Officer
CMO: Wesley Kinzie, M.D., Chief of Staff
CIO: Richard Hart, Chief Financial Officer
CHR: Tyson Hubbard, Director Human Resources
CNO: Susan Gonzalez, Director of Clinical Services
Web address: www.stanislaussurgical.com
Control: Corporation, Investor–owned, for–profit **Service:** Surgical

Staffed Beds: 23 **Admissions:** 700 **Census:** 5 **Outpatient Visits:** 29355 **Births:** 0 **Total Expense ($000):** 32592 **Payroll Expense ($000):** 8784 **Personnel:** 173

MONROVIA—Los Angeles County

○ **MONROVIA MEMORIAL HOSPITAL (052054)**, 323 South Heliotrope Avenue,
Zip 91016–2914; tel. 626/408–9800, (Nonreporting) **A**9 10 11
Primary Contact: Ron Kupferstein, Chief Executive Officer
Web address: www.monroviamemorial.com
Control: Partnership, Investor–owned, for–profit **Service:** Long–Term Acute Care
hospital

Staffed Beds: 49

MONTCLAIR—San Bernardino County

☐ **MONTCLAIR HOSPITAL MEDICAL CENTER (050758)**, 5000 San Bernardino
Street, Zip 91763–2326; tel. 909/625–5411 **A**1 10 **F**29 40 76 81 107 148
S Prime Healthcare Services, Ontario, CA
Primary Contact: Gregory Brentano, Chief Executive Officer
CFO: Robert Bonner, Chief Financial Officer
CMO: Joseph Hourany, Chief Medical Officer
CNO: Gail Aviado, Chief Nursing Officer
Web address: www.montclair–hospital.com
Control: Other not–for–profit (including NFP Corporation) **Service:** General
Medical and Surgical

Staffed Beds: 102 **Admissions:** 3735 **Census:** 32 **Outpatient Visits:** 21063

MONTEBELLO—Los Angeles County

◇ **BEVERLY HOSPITAL (050350)**, 309 West Beverly Boulevard, Zip 90640–4308;
tel. 323/726–1222, (Nonreporting) **A**9 10 21
Primary Contact: Alice Cheng, Interim President and Chief Executive Officer
CFO: Larry Pugh, Vice President and Chief Financial Officer
CIO: Mark Turner, Director Information Systems
CHR: John Barnes, Administrative Director Human Resources
CNO: Kathy Wojno, Vice President Nursing Services and Chief Nursing Officer
Web address: www.beverly.org
Control: Other not–for–profit (including NFP Corporation) **Service:** General
Medical and Surgical

Staffed Beds: 102

MONTEREY—Monterey County

✠ **COMMUNITY HOSPITAL OF THE MONTEREY PENINSULA (050145)**, 23625
Holman Highway, Zip 93940–5902, Mailing Address: Box 'HH', Zip 93942–6032;
tel. 831/624–5311, (Total facility includes 28 beds in nursing home–type unit) **A**1
2 9 10 **F**3 5 11 12 13 14 15 17 18 20 22 24 26 28 29 30 31 34 35 37 40
44 45 46 47 48 49 50 51 53 54 57 58 59 60 61 62 63 64 68 70 73 74 75
76 77 78 79 81 82 83 84 85 86 87 89 90 91 92 93 94 96 98 99 100 101
102 103 104 105 107 110 111 114 115 116 117 118 119 120 121 123 124
128 129 130 132 134 135 145 146 148
Primary Contact: Steven J. Packer, M.D., President and Chief Executive Officer
CFO: Laura Zehm, Vice President and Chief Financial Officer
CMO: Anthony D. Chavis, M.D., Vice President Enterprise Medical Officer,
Community Hospital Foundation
Web address: www.chomp.org
Control: Other not–for–profit (including NFP Corporation) **Service:** General
Medical and Surgical

Staffed Beds: 248 **Admissions:** 11775 **Census:** 159 **Outpatient Visits:** 281892 **Births:** 1212 **Total Expense ($000):** 421951 **Payroll Expense ($000):** 143713 **Personnel:** 1668

MONTEREY PARK—Los Angeles County

☐ **GARFIELD MEDICAL CENTER (050737)**, 525 North Garfield Avenue,
Zip 91754–1205; tel. 626/573–2222 **A**1 9 10 12 13 **F**3 11 13 15 17 18 20
22 24 26 28 29 31 34 35 40 44 45 49 50 56 57 59 60 64 67 68 70 72 74
75 76 77 78 79 81 82 85 86 87 90 91 92 93 107 108 118 119 130 132 143 146
147 148 **P**5 **S** AHMC & Healthcare, Inc., Alhambra, CA
Primary Contact: David J. Batista, Chief Executive Officer
COO: David J. Batista, Chief Operating Officer
CFO: Steve Maekawa, Chief Financial Officer
CMO: Terry Lee, M.D., Chief of Staff
CIO: Ann Curnutt, Director Information Systems
CHR: Rebecca R. Ricartti, Interim Director Human Resources
CNO: Shirley Tang, R.N., Chief Nursing Officer
Web address: www.garfieldmedicalcenter.com
Control: Partnership, Investor–owned, for–profit **Service:** General Medical and
Surgical

Staffed Beds: 210 **Admissions:** 12869 **Census:** 151 **Outpatient Visits:** 25682 **Births:** 4465

☐ **MONTEREY PARK HOSPITAL (050736)**, 900 South Atlantic Boulevard,
Zip 91754–4780; tel. 626/570–9000 **A**1 9 10 **F**3 15 29 34 35 40 49 50 57
59 60 70 75 76 81 86 87 89 107 113 114 119 130 142 143 146 **S** AHMC &
Healthcare, Inc., Alhambra, CA
Primary Contact: Philip A. Cohen, Chief Executive Officer
COO: Ericka Smith, Chief Operating Officer
CFO: Daniel Song, Chief Financial Officer
CMO: Azucena Porral, M.D., Chief of Staff
CIO: Angelica Ching, Director Information Systems
CNO: Evelyn Ku, Chief Nursing Officer
Web address: www.montereyparkhosp.com
Control: Partnership, Investor–owned, for–profit **Service:** General Medical and
Surgical

Staffed Beds: 101 **Admissions:** 4676 **Census:** 43 **Outpatient Visits:** 19804 **Births:** 1495 **Total Expense ($000):** 69893 **Payroll Expense ($000):** 20412 **Personnel:** 295

MORENO VALLEY—Riverside County

✠ **KAISER PERMANENTE MORENO VALLEY MEDICAL CENTER (050765)**,
27300 Iris Avenue, Zip 92555–4800; tel. 951/243–0811 **A**1 10 **F**3 13 17 29
30 35 40 44 45 46 49 50 59 60 64 65 68 70 75 76 77 79 81 84 85 87 97
100 102 107 108 109 111 115 119 130 135 146 148 **S** Kaiser Foundation
Hospitals, Oakland, CA
Primary Contact: Corey A. Seale, Administrator
Control: Other not–for–profit (including NFP Corporation) **Service:** General
Medical and Surgical

Staffed Beds: 71 **Admissions:** 4216 **Census:** 37 **Outpatient Visits:** 36625 **Births:** 1058 **Personnel:** 210

✠ **RIVERSIDE COUNTY REGIONAL MEDICAL CENTER (050292)**, 26520 Cactus
Avenue, Zip 92555–3911; tel. 951/486–4000 **A**1 3 5 10 12 13 **F**3 8 11 13 15
29 30 31 32 35 39 40 43 44 46 47 49 50 56 57 58 59 64 65 66 68 70 71
72 74 75 76 77 78 79 81 82 85 87 88 89 93 94 97 98 99 100 101 102 103
104 107 108 111 114 118 119 130 135 143 146 147 148
Primary Contact: Lowell W. Johnson, LFACHE, Chief Executive Officer
CFO: Christopher Hans, Chief Financial Officer
CMO: Arnold Tabuenca, M.D., Medical Director
CNO: Judi Nightingale, R.N., Chief Nursing Officer
Web address: www.rcrmc.org
Control: County–Government, nonfederal **Service:** General Medical and Surgical

Staffed Beds: 439 **Admissions:** 22131 **Census:** 329 **Outpatient Visits:** 286121 **Births:** 2442 **Total Expense ($000):** 458800 **Payroll Expense ($000):** 188192 **Personnel:** 2625

MOUNT SHASTA—Siskiyou County

✠ **MERCY MEDICAL CENTER MOUNT SHASTA (051319)**, 914 Pine Street, Zip 96067–2143; tel. 530/926–6111 **A**1 9 10 18 **F**3 11 13 15 29 30 35 40 43 50 53 56 57 59 62 63 64 68 70 75 76 77 79 81 82 84 89 93 107 108 110 111 114 118 119 121 127 130 131 132 133 143 146 148 **S** Dignity Health, San Francisco, CA
Primary Contact: Kenneth E. S. Platou, President
CFO: Gina Anderson, Chief Financial Officer
CMO: Dan Purtzer, M.D., Chief of Staff
CHR: Michelle Michl, Director Human Resources
CNO: Sherie Ambrose, Vice President Patient Care Services
Web address: www.mercymtshasta.org
Control: Other not–for–profit (including NFP Corporation) **Service:** General Medical and Surgical

Staffed Beds: 33 **Admissions:** 1096 **Census:** 8 **Outpatient Visits:** 57911 **Births:** 163 **Total Expense ($000):** 48964 **Payroll Expense ($000):** 20489 **Personnel:** 213

MOUNTAIN VIEW—Santa Clara County

✠ **EL CAMINO HOSPITAL (050308)**, 2500 Grant Road, Zip 94040–4302, Mailing Address: P.O. Box 7025, Zip 94039–7025; tel. 650/940–7000, (Includes EL CAMINO HOSPITAL LOS GATOS, 815 Pollard Road, Los Gatos, Zip 95032–1438; tel. 408/378–6131) **A**1 2 9 10 **F**3 5 11 12 13 15 17 18 20 22 24 26 28 29 30 31 34 35 40 45 46 49 50 51 54 55 56 57 58 59 60 64 65 70 72 74 75 76 77 78 79 81 82 84 85 86 87 89 90 93 98 101 102 103 104 105 107 108 110 111 114 115 116 117 118 119 120 121 123 124 126 129 130 132 135 143 146 147
Primary Contact: Tomi S. Ryba, President and Chief Executive Officer
COO: Mike Zdeblick, Chief Operating Officer
CFO: Iftikhar Hussain, Chief Financial Officer
CMO: Eric Pifer, M.D., Chief Medical Officer
CIO: Greg Walton, Chief Information Officer
CHR: Kathryn M. Fisk, Chief Human Resources Officer
CNO: Cheryl Reinking, R.N., Chief Nursing Officer
Web address: www.elcaminohospital.org
Control: Hospital district or authority, Government, nonfederal **Service:** General Medical and Surgical

Staffed Beds: 420 **Admissions:** 19220 **Census:** 240 **Outpatient Visits:** 250113 **Births:** 5227 **Total Expense ($000):** 632313 **Payroll Expense ($000):** 276997 **Personnel:** 1549

MURRIETA—Riverside County

☐ **LOMA LINDA UNIVERSITY MEDICAL CENTER–MURRIETA (050770)**, 28062 Baxter Road, Zip 92563–1401; tel. 951/290–4000 **A**1 9 10 **F**3 12 13 15 18 20 22 24 28 29 30 31 34 35 37 40 45 46 49 56 57 59 60 64 65 68 70 74 75 76 77 78 79 81 85 87 91 93 100 107 108 109 110 111 114 115 116 117 119 120 121 123 126 130 131 141 144 146 148 **P**8 **S** Loma Linda University Adventist Health Sciences Center, Loma Linda, CA
Primary Contact: Richard L. Rawson, Chief Executive Officer
COO: Richard M. Tibbits, Vice President and Chief Operating Officer
CFO: James Uli, Chief Financial Officer
CMO: Jeff Conner, M.D., Chief Medical Staff
Web address: www.llumcmurrieta.org
Control: Church–operated, Nongovernment, not–for profit **Service:** General Medical and Surgical

Staffed Beds: 106 **Admissions:** 8721 **Census:** 79 **Outpatient Visits:** 21584 **Births:** 1035 **Total Expense ($000):** 196438 **Payroll Expense ($000):** 53141

SOUTHWEST HEALTHCARE SYSTEM (050701), 25500 Medical Center Drive, Zip 92562–5965; tel. 951/696–6000, (Includes INLAND VALLEY MEDICAL CENTER, 36485 Inland Valley Drive, Wildomar, Zip 92595–9700; tel. 951/677–1111; RANCHO SPRINGS MEDICAL CENTER, 25500 Medical Center Drive, tel. 951/696–6000) **A**9 10 **F**11 12 13 15 18 20 29 30 34 35 37 40 43 45 50 51 60 70 76 78 79 81 85 87 107 111 115 116 117 126 130 146 148 **S** Universal Health Services, Inc., King of Prussia, PA
Primary Contact: Bradley D. Neet, FACHE, Chief Executive Officer
COO: Jared Giles, Chief Operating Officer
CFO: Jon Zilkow, Chief Financial Officer
CMO: Yara Gorski, M.D., Chief of Staff
CIO: Jeffrey Upcraft, Director Information Services
CHR: Laura Culbertson, Director Human Resources
CNO: Melissa Burns, Chief Nursing Officer, Inland Valley Medical Center
Web address: www.swhealthcaresystem.com/
Control: Corporation, Investor–owned, for–profit **Service:** General Medical and Surgical

Staffed Beds: 252 **Admissions:** 14894 **Census:** 148 **Outpatient Visits:** 87896 **Births:** 3163 **Total Expense ($000):** 209218 **Payroll Expense ($000):** 96086 **Personnel:** 1140

NAPA—Napa County

☐ **NAPA STATE HOSPITAL (054122)**, 2100 Napa–Vallejo Highway, Zip 94558–6293; tel. 707/253–5000 **A**1 3 5 10 **F**30 39 53 56 59 61 67 68 77 86 98 103 128 130 132 135 146 **P**6
Primary Contact: Dolly Matteucci, Executive Director
COO: Dolly Matteucci, Executive Director
Web address: www.dmh.ca.gov
Control: State–Government, nonfederal **Service:** Psychiatric

Staffed Beds: 1318 **Admissions:** 649 **Census:** 1184 **Outpatient Visits:** 0 **Births:** 0 **Total Expense ($000):** 243700 **Payroll Expense ($000):** 159933 **Personnel:** 2188

✠ **QUEEN OF THE VALLEY MEDICAL CENTER (050009)**, 1000 Trancas Street, Zip 94558–2340, Mailing Address: P.O. Box 2340, Zip 94558–0688; tel. 707/252–4411 **A**1 2 9 10 **F**3 8 11 13 15 17 18 20 22 24 26 28 29 30 31 32 34 35 36 39 40 43 44 45 46 47 48 49 50 51 53 57 59 60 61 64 68 70 72 74 75 76 77 78 79 81 82 84 85 86 87 89 90 91 92 93 97 102 107 108 110 111 114 115 116 117 118 119 120 121 123 124 126 130 132 135 146 148 **S** St. Joseph Health, Irvine, CA
Primary Contact: Walt Mickens, FACHE, President and Chief Executive Officer
COO: Vincent Morgese, M.D., Executive Vice President, Chief Operating Officer and Chief Medical Officer
CFO: Mich Riccioni, Vice President and Chief Financial Officer, Northern California Region
CMO: Vincent Morgese, M.D., Executive Vice President, Chief Operating Officer and Chief Medical Officer
CHR: Robert A. Eisen, Vice President Human Resources, Northern California Region
Web address: www.thequeen.org
Control: Church–operated, Nongovernment, not–for profit **Service:** General Medical and Surgical

Staffed Beds: 174 **Admissions:** 7154 **Census:** 89 **Outpatient Visits:** 185690 **Births:** 795 **Total Expense ($000):** 252460 **Payroll Expense ($000):** 88001

NATIONAL CITY—San Diego County

☐ △ **PARADISE VALLEY HOSPITAL (050024)**, 2400 East Fourth Street, Zip 91950–2099; tel. 619/470–4321, (Includes BAYVIEW BEHAVIORAL HEALTH CAMPUS, 330 Moss Street, Chula Vista, Zip 91911–2005; tel. 619/426–6311; George Lewis, Executive Director), (Nonreporting) **A**1 7 9 10 **S** Prime Healthcare Services, Ontario, CA
Primary Contact: Neerav Jadeja, Administrator
CFO: Janet L. Caceres, Chief Financial Officer
CMO: Genaro Fernandez, M.D., Chief of Staff
CIO: Amanda Kaems, Manager Information Systems
CHR: Lorraine Villegas, Manager Human Resources
Web address: www.paradisevalleyhospital.org
Control: Corporation, Investor–owned, for–profit **Service:** General Medical and Surgical

Staffed Beds: 205

NEEDLES—San Bernardino County

★ **COLORADO RIVER MEDICAL CENTER (051323)**, 1401 Bailey Avenue, Zip 92363–3198; tel. 760/326–7100 **A**9 10 18 **F**1 3 4 16 17 29 30 34 35 40 45 50 53 57 59 65 67 68 70 72 73 77 79 80 81 87 88 89 90 98 102 107 114 119 128 130 145 146 148 **P**4
Primary Contact: Steve Lopez, Chief Executive Officer
COO: Knaya Tabora, Chief Operating Officer and Chief Nursing Officer
CFO: Steve Lopez, Chief Executive Officer
CMO: Robert Strecker, M.D., Chief of Staff
CIO: Ron Chieffo, Chief Information Officer
CHR: Pam Barrett, Human Resources Director
CNO: Knaya Tabora, Chief Operating Officer and Chief Nursing Officer
Web address: www.crmccares.com
Control: Other not–for–profit (including NFP Corporation) **Service:** General Medical and Surgical

Staffed Beds: 25 **Admissions:** 580 **Census:** 5 **Outpatient Visits:** 8820 **Births:** 0 **Total Expense ($000):** 9111 **Payroll Expense ($000):** 4002 **Personnel:** 83

NEWPORT BEACH—Orange County

★ ◇ **HOAG MEMORIAL HOSPITAL PRESBYTERIAN (050224)**, One Hoag Drive, Zip 92663–4120, Mailing Address: P.O. Box 6100, Zip 92658–6100; tel. 949/764–4624, (Includes HOAG HOSPITAL IRVINE, 16200 Sand Canyon Avenue, Irvine, Zip 92618–3714; tel. 949/764–8240) **A**9 10 21 **F**3 4 11 13 14 15 17 18 20 22 24 26 28 29 30 31 34 35 36 37 40 44 45 46 47 48 49 50 51 54 55 57 58 59 60 64 68 70 71 72 74 75 76 77 78 79 81 82 84 85 86 87 92 93 96 100 102 103 107 108 110 111 115 116 117 118 119 120 121 123 124 129 130 132 135 141 143 145 146 147 148
Primary Contact: Robert Braithwaite, President and Chief Executive Officer
CFO: Jennifer C. Mitzner, Senior Vice President Finance and Chief Financial Officer
CMO: Jack Cox, M.D., Senior Vice President and Chief Quality Officer
CIO: Tim Moore, R.N., Senior Vice President and Chief Information Officer
CHR: Jan L. Blue, Vice President Human Resources
CNO: Richard A. Martin, MSN, Senior Vice President and Chief Nursing Officer
Web address: www.hoaghospital.org
Control: Other not–for–profit (including NFP Corporation) **Service:** General Medical and Surgical

Staffed Beds: 558 **Admissions:** 23669 **Census:** 281 **Outpatient Visits:** 374447 **Births:** 6024 **Total Expense ($000):** 812324 **Payroll Expense ($000):** 295815

NEWPORT BAY HOSPITAL (054135), 1501 East 16th Street, Zip 92663–5924; tel. 949/650–9750 **A**10 **F**35 98 100 101 103 130 148
Primary Contact: James E. Parkhurst, President and Chief Executive Officer
COO: Garry Hardwick, R.N., Chief Operating Officer
CFO: Rocky Gentner, Chief Financial Officer
CMO: Jason Kellogg, M.D., Chief of Staff
CIO: Nina Swenson, Director Business Services
CHR: Phyllis Parkhurst, Vice President Support Services
Web address: www.newportbayhospital.com
Control: Corporation, Investor–owned, for–profit **Service:** Psychiatric

Staffed Beds: 34 **Admissions:** 816 **Census:** 30 **Outpatient Visits:** 0 **Births:** 0

NORTH HOLLYWOOD—Los Angeles County, See Los Angeles

NORTHRIDGE—Los Angeles County, See Los Angeles

NORWALK—Los Angeles County

COAST PLAZA DOCTORS HOSPITAL See Coast Plaza Hospital

☐ **COAST PLAZA HOSPITAL (050771)**, 13100 Studebaker Road, Zip 90650–2500; tel. 562/868–3751, (Nonreporting) **A**1 10 **S** Avanti Hospitals, El Segundo, CA
Primary Contact: Richard Rowe, PharmD, Chief Executive Officer
CFO: Mihi Lee, Chief Financial Officer
CMO: Galal S. Gough, M.D., Chief of Staff
CIO: Linda K. Roman, Administrator
Web address: www.coastplaza.com
Control: Partnership, Investor–owned, for–profit **Service:** General Medical and Surgical

Staffed Beds: 123

LOS ANGELES COMMUNITY HOSPITAL OF NORWALK See Los Angeles Community Hospital at Los Angeles, Los Angeles

☐ **METROPOLITAN STATE HOSPITAL (054133)**, 11401 Bloomfield Avenue, Zip 90650–2015; tel. 562/863–7011, (Nonreporting) **A**1 10
Primary Contact: Michael Barsom, M.D., Executive Director
CFO: Maybelle Manlangit, Senior Accounting Officer
CIO: Paul Mello, Manager Data Processing
CHR: Jorge Banuedos, Director Human Resources
Web address: www.dmh.ca.gov
Control: State–Government, nonfederal **Service:** Psychiatric

Staffed Beds: 657

NOVATO—Marin County

✠ **NOVATO COMMUNITY HOSPITAL (050131)**, 180 Rowland Way, Zip 94945–5009, Mailing Address: P.O. Box 1108, Zip 94948–1108; tel. 415/209–1300 **A**1 9 10 **F**3 15 18 26 29 30 31 34 40 45 49 50 51 54 56 59 64 68 70 74 75 77 78 79 81 84 85 87 93 107 108 111 115 119 130 131 132 134 143 144 146 148 **S** Sutter Health, Sacramento, CA
Primary Contact: Brian Alexander, Chief Administrative Officer
CMO: Barbara Nylund, M.D., Chief of Staff
CIO: Kathryn Graham, Director Communications and Community Relations
CHR: Diana G. Johnson, Acting Chief Human Resources Officer
Web address: www.novatocommunity.sutterhealth.org
Control: Other not–for–profit (including NFP Corporation) **Service:** General Medical and Surgical

Staffed Beds: 40 **Admissions:** 1615 **Census:** 14 **Outpatient Visits:** 78561 **Births:** 0 **Total Expense ($000):** 63779 **Payroll Expense ($000):** 20267 **Personnel:** 228

OAKDALE—Stanislaus County

✠ **OAK VALLEY HOSPITAL DISTRICT (050067)**, 350 South Oak Street, Zip 95361–3519; tel. 209/847–3011, (Nonreporting) **A**1 5 9 10
Primary Contact: John McCormick, President and Chief Executive Officer
CFO: Alberto Diaz, Chief Financial Officer
CMO: Lee Horwitz, M.D., Chief of Staff
CIO: Sherry Peral, Manager Information Systems
CHR: Brian Beck, Vice President Human Resources
CNO: Joann L. Saporito, R.N., Vice President Nursing Services
Web address: www.ovhd.com
Control: Hospital district or authority, Government, nonfederal **Service:** General Medical and Surgical

Staffed Beds: 150

OAKLAND—Alameda County

✠ **ALAMEDA COUNTY MEDICAL CENTER (050320)**, 1411 East 31st Street, Zip 94602–1018; tel. 510/437–4800, (Includes ALAMEDA COUNTY MEDICAL CENTER–FAIRMONT CAMPUS, 15400 Foothill Boulevard, San Leandro, Zip 94578–1009; tel. 510/895–4200; James E. T. Jackson, M.P.H., Chief Administrative Officer) **A**1 3 5 10 **F**3 5 11 13 15 18 20 22 24 28 29 30 31 32 34 35 36 38 39 40 43 44 46 49 50 54 56 57 58 59 60 61 65 66 68 70 71 73 74 75 76 77 78 79 81 82 84 85 86 87 90 91 93 96 97 98 104 105 107 111 115 119 128 130 132 135 142 143 146 147 148 **P**4 **S** Alameda Health System, San Leandro, CA
Primary Contact: Wright L. Lassiter, III, Chief Executive Officer
CFO: Marion Schales, Chief Financial Officer
CMO: Sang–ick Chang, M.D., Chief Medical Officer
CHR: Jeanette L. Louden Corbett, Chief Human Resources Officer
Web address: www.alamedahealthsystem.org
Control: Hospital district or authority, Government, nonfederal **Service:** General Medical and Surgical

Staffed Beds: 384 **Admissions:** 14301 **Census:** 313 **Outpatient Visits:** 399872 **Births:** 1149 **Total Expense ($000):** 516795 **Payroll Expense ($000):** 268326 **Personnel:** 2417

✠ **ALTA BATES SUMMIT MEDICAL CENTER – SUMMIT CAMPUS (050043)**, 350 Hawthorne Avenue, Zip 94609–3100; tel. 510/655–4000, (Total facility includes 71 beds in nursing home–type unit) **A**1 2 9 10 **F**3 8 11 12 15 17 18 20 22 24 26 29 30 31 34 35 36 40 45 46 47 49 56 57 58 59 60 61 64 68 70 74 75 77 78 79 81 82 84 85 86 87 97 107 108 111 115 116 117 118 119 120 121 122 123 126 128 130 135 136 146 148 **S** Sutter Health, Sacramento, CA
Primary Contact: Charles Prosper, Chief Executive Officer
CMO: John Gentile, M.D., Vice President Medical Affairs
CHR: Mark Beiting, Vice President Human Resources
Web address: www.altabatessummit.com
Control: Other not–for–profit (including NFP Corporation) **Service:** General Medical and Surgical

Staffed Beds: 382 **Admissions:** 11952 **Census:** 166 **Outpatient Visits:** 129091 **Births:** 0 **Total Expense ($000):** 387526 **Payroll Expense ($000):** 122882 **Personnel:** 1412

☐ **CHILDREN'S HOSPITAL AND RESEARCH CENTER OAKLAND (053301)**, 747 52nd Street, Zip 94609–1859; tel. 510/428–3000 **A**1 3 5 9 10 **F**3 19 21 23 25 29 30 31 32 33 34 35 36 38 40 41 43 45 46 48 50 54 55 57 58 59 61 64 65 66 68 72 74 75 77 78 79 81 82 83 84 86 87 88 89 90 93 97 99 100 101 102 104 107 108 111 114 118 119 127 129 130 131 132 134 136 143 146 148 **P**3 5
Primary Contact: Bertram Lubin, M.D., President and Chief Executive Officer
CFO: Doug Myers, Senior Vice President and Chief Financial Officer
CIO: Don Livsey, Vice President and Chief Information Officer
Web address: www.childrenshospitaloakland.org
Control: Other not–for–profit (including NFP Corporation) **Service:** Children's general

Staffed Beds: 190 **Admissions:** 10298 **Census:** 131 **Outpatient Visits:** 238590 **Births:** 0 **Total Expense ($000):** 506029 **Payroll Expense ($000):** 192912 **Personnel:** 2217

✠ **KAISER PERMANENTE OAKLAND MEDICAL CENTER (050075)**, 3600 Broadway, Zip 94611–5693; tel. 510/752–1000, (Includes KAISER PERMANENTE RICHMOND MEDICAL CENTER, 901 Nevin Avenue, Richmond, Zip 94801–2555; tel. 510/307–1500) **A**1 3 5 8 10 **F**3 7 11 12 13 15 18 19 29 30 31 34 35 36 38 40 41 44 45 46 49 50 51 55 56 57 58 59 60 61 62 63 64 65 68 70 72 74 75 76 77 78 79 80 81 82 83 84 85 86 87 88 89 93 94 97 99 100 107 110 111 112 115 119 129 130 131 132 135 144 146 147 148 **S** Kaiser Foundation Hospitals, Oakland, CA
Primary Contact: Odette Bolano, R.N., Senior Vice President and Area Manager
CFO: Dennis Morris, Area Finance Officer
CMO: John Loftus, M.D., Chief of Staff
CIO: Johnny Law, Area Information Officer
CHR: Rick Mead, Human Resources Leader
CNO: Charlene Boyer, Chief Nursing Officer
Web address: www.kaiserpermanente.org
Control: Other not–for–profit (including NFP Corporation) **Service:** General Medical and Surgical

Staffed Beds: 267 **Admissions:** 16538 **Census:** 167

OAKLAND MEDICAL CENTER See Kaiser Permanente Oakland Medical Center

Many Facility Codes have changed. Please refer to the AHA Guide Code Chart. © 2014 AHA Guide

CA

☐ **TELECARE HERITAGE PSYCHIATRIC HEALTH CENTER (054146)**, 2633 East 27th Street, Zip 94601–1912; tel. 510/535–5115, (Nonreporting) **A**1 9 10
Primary Contact: Anne L. Bakar, President and Chief Executive Officer
Web address: www.tbhcare.com/
Control: Partnership, Investor–owned, for–profit **Service:** Psychiatric

Staffed Beds: 26

OCEANSIDE—San Diego County

✠ **TRI–CITY MEDICAL CENTER (050128)**, 4002 Vista Way, Zip 92056–4593; tel. 760/724–8411 **A**1 2 3 5 9 10 **F**1 3 4 11 13 14 15 16 17 18 20 22 24 26 28 29 30 31 34 35 37 38 40 45 46 47 49 50 51 53 57 58 59 62 63 64 65 67 68 70 72 73 74 75 76 77 78 79 80 81 82 85 86 87 88 89 90 93 96 98 100 101 102 103 104 105 107 108 110 111 114 115 117 118 119 126 128 130 132 133 135 143 146 147 148
Primary Contact: Timothy M. Moran, Chief Executive Officer
COO: Casey Fatch, Chief Operating Officer
CFO: Steve Dietlin, Chief Financial Officer
CMO: Scott Worman, Chief of Staff
CIO: Kim Cook, Interim Clinical Applications Services Manager
CHR: Esther Beverly, Vice President Human Resources
CNO: Sharon A. Schultz, MSN, Chief Nurse Executive and Vice President
Web address: www.tricitymed.org
Control: Hospital district or authority, Government, nonfederal **Service:** General Medical and Surgical

Staffed Beds: 330 **Admissions:** 15409 **Census:** 188 **Outpatient Visits:** 173332 **Births:** 2645 **Total Expense ($000):** 322843 **Payroll Expense ($000):** 149454 **Personnel:** 1526

ONTARIO—San Bernardino County

★ **KAISER PERMANENTE ONTARIO MEDICAL CENTER (050140)**, 2295 South Vineyard Avenue, Zip 91761–7925; tel. 909/724–5000 **F**3 8 11 13 15 18 28 29 30 31 35 40 41 44 45 46 48 49 50 57 58 59 60 62 63 65 68 70 73 74 75 76 77 78 79 81 82 84 85 86 87 100 102 107 108 110 111 114 115 117 118 119 130 132 135 141 145 146 148 **S** Kaiser Foundation Hospitals, Oakland, CA
Primary Contact: Greg Christian, Executive Director
COO: Lloyd Duplechan, Chief Operating Officer
CFO: Donald P. Bernard, Area Chief Finance Officer
CMO: David Quam, M.D., Area Medical Director
CIO: David Young, M.D., Area Information Officer
CHR: Kimberly Labiaga, Human Resources Director
CNO: Yvonne Roddy–Sturm, R.N., Chief Nurse Executive
Web address: www.kp.org
Control: Other not–for–profit (including NFP Corporation) **Service:** General Medical and Surgical

Staffed Beds: 176 **Admissions:** 9252 **Census:** 101 **Outpatient Visits:** 49924 **Births:** 1910 **Personnel:** 985

✠ **KINDRED HOSPITAL–ONTARIO (052037)**, 550 North Monterey Avenue, Zip 91764–3399; tel. 909/391–0333, (Nonreporting) **A**1 9 10 **S** Kindred Healthcare, Louisville, KY
Primary Contact: Robin Rapp, MS, R.N., Chief Executive Officer
CFO: Omar Oregel, Controller
CMO: Marc Lynch, D.O., Chief of Staff
CHR: Laurel Scharber, Administrative Assistant and Coordinator Human Resources
CNO: Holly Ramos, R.N., Chief Clinical Officer
Web address: www.khontario.com/
Control: Corporation, Investor–owned, for–profit **Service:** Long–Term Acute Care hospital

Staffed Beds: 91

ORANGE—Orange County

☐ **CHAPMAN MEDICAL CENTER (050745)**, 2601 East Chapman Avenue, Zip 92869–3296; tel. 714/633–0011, (Nonreporting) **A**1 9 10 **S** Integrated Healthcare, Santa Ana, CA
Primary Contact: Don Kreitz, Chief Executive Officer
COO: Ada Yeh, R.N., Chief Operating Officer and Chief Nursing Officer
CFO: Robert Heinemeier, Chief Financial Officer
CMO: Steven Duckor, M.D., Chief of Staff
CIO: Sri Yarramsetti, Chief Information Officer
CHR: JoAnne Suehs, Manager Human Resources
CNO: Ada Yeh, R.N., Vice President Operations and Chief Nursing Officer
Web address: www.chapmanmedicalcenter.com
Control: Corporation, Investor–owned, for–profit **Service:** General Medical and Surgical

Staffed Beds: 100

☐ **CHILDREN'S HOSPITAL OF ORANGE COUNTY (053304)**, 1201 West La Veta Avenue, Zip 92868–4203, Mailing Address: PO Box 5700, Zip 92863–5700; tel. 714/997–3000 **A**1 3 5 9 10 **F**3 14 17 19 21 23 25 27 29 30 31 32 34 35 40 41 50 55 57 58 59 61 64 65 66 68 71 72 74 75 77 78 79 81 85 86 87 88 89 91 92 93 97 104 107 111 113 114 115 116 117 118 119 120 121 123 126 129 130 132 134 136 146 **P**5
Primary Contact: Kimberly C. Cripe, President and Chief Executive Officer
COO: Matthew S. Gerlach, Chief Operating Officer
CFO: Kerri Ruppert Schiller, Senior Vice President and Chief Financial Officer
CMO: Maria Minon, M.D., Vice President Medical Affairs and Chief Medical Officer
CIO: Mark Headland, Chief Information Officer
CHR: Mamoon Syed, Vice President Human Resources
CNO: Melanie Patterson, R.N., Vice President Patient Care Services and Chief Nursing Officer
Web address: www.choc.org
Control: Other not–for–profit (including NFP Corporation) **Service:** Children's general

Staffed Beds: 279 **Admissions:** 11476 **Census:** 159 **Outpatient Visits:** 200277 **Births:** 0 **Total Expense ($000):** 526327 **Payroll Expense ($000):** 141582 **Personnel:** 2352

◇ **HEALTHBRIDGE CHILDREN'S HOSPITAL (053308)**, 393 South Tustin Street, Zip 92866–2501; tel. 714/289–2400 **A**9 10 21 **F**3 29 64 65 75 77 90 93 128 130 132 146 148 **S** Nexus Health Systems, Houston, TX
Primary Contact: Brian Cotter, Chief Executive Officer
Web address: www.HealthBridgeOrange.com
Control: Partnership, Investor–owned, for–profit **Service:** Children's rehabilitation

Staffed Beds: 27 **Admissions:** 150 **Census:** 20 **Outpatient Visits:** 134 **Births:** 0 **Total Expense ($000):** 9630 **Payroll Expense ($000):** 5286 **Personnel:** 129

✠ **ST. JOSEPH HOSPITAL (050069)**, 1100 West Stewart Drive, Zip 92868–3849, Mailing Address: P.O. Box 5600, Zip 92863–5600; tel. 714/633–9111 **A**1 2 5 9 10 **F**3 5 8 12 13 14 15 17 18 19 20 21 22 23 25 27 28 29 30 31 34 35 37 39 40 41 45 46 47 49 50 51 54 55 57 58 59 60 64 65 66 68 69 70 71 74 75 76 77 78 79 80 81 82 84 85 86 87 91 92 93 98 100 102 104 105 107 108 109 110 111 113 114 115 116 117 118 119 120 121 123 124 126 129 130 131 132 135 138 141 146 147 148 **P**3 5 **S** St. Joseph Health, Irvine, CA
Primary Contact: Steven C. Moreau, President and Chief Executive Officer
COO: Jeremy Zoch, Executive Vice President and Chief Operating Officer
CFO: Kristi Liberatore, Vice President and Chief Financial Officer
CMO: Raymond Casciari, M.D., Chief Medical Officer
CIO: Jeremy Zoch, Executive Vice President and Chief Operating Officer
CHR: Mary P. Leahy, Vice President Human Resources
CNO: Katie Skelton, MSN, Vice President Nursing and Chief Nursing Officer
Web address: www.sjo.org
Control: Other not–for–profit (including NFP Corporation) **Service:** General Medical and Surgical

Staffed Beds: 379 **Admissions:** 20150 **Census:** 213 **Outpatient Visits:** 290357 **Births:** 4835 **Total Expense ($000):** 621720 **Payroll Expense ($000):** 187810 **Personnel:** 2624

✠ **UC IRVINE MEDICAL CENTER (050348)**, 101 The City Drive South, Zip 92868–3298; tel. 714/456–6011 **A**1 2 3 5 8 9 10 **F**3 6 8 9 11 12 13 14 15 16 17 18 20 22 24 26 28 29 30 31 34 35 36 43 44 45 46 47 48 49 50 51 53 54 55 56 57 58 59 60 61 64 65 66 68 70 71 72 74 75 76 77 78 79 80 81 82 84 85 86 87 90 91 92 93 96 97 98 99 100 101 102 104 105 107 108 110 111 112 114 115 116 117 118 119 120 121 123 124 126 130 132 134 135 138 141 142 145 146 147 148 **P**6 **S** University of California–Systemwide Administration, Oakland, CA
Primary Contact: Terry A. Belmont, Chief Executive Officer
COO: Alice H. Issai, Chief Operating Officer
CFO: Morris J. Frieling, Chief Financial Officer
CMO: Doug Merill, M.D., Chief Medical Officer
CIO: Scott Cebula, Interim Chief Information Officer
CHR: Susi Takeuchi, Chief Human Resources Officer
CNO: Karen A. Grimley, R.N., Chief Nursing Officer
Web address: www.ucihealth.com
Control: State–Government, nonfederal **Service:** General Medical and Surgical

Staffed Beds: 409 **Admissions:** 19312 **Census:** 301 **Outpatient Visits:** 561021 **Births:** 1472 **Total Expense ($000):** 749092 **Payroll Expense ($000):** 323892 **Personnel:** 4363

Hospital, Medicare Provider Number, Address, Telephone, Approval, Facility, and Physician Codes, Health Care System

★ American Hospital Association (AHA) membership
☐ The Joint Commission accreditation
◇ DNV Healthcare Inc. accreditation
○ Healthcare Facilities Accreditation Program
△ Commission on Accreditation of Rehabilitation Facilities (CARF) accreditation

CA

OROVILLE—Butte County

OROVILLE HOSPITAL (050030), 2767 Olive Highway, Zip 95966–6118; tel. 530/533–8500 **A**9 10 **F**3 11 13 15 18 26 28 29 30 31 32 33 34 35 38 39 40 41 43 44 45 46 47 49 50 51 54 56 57 59 60 61 62 64 65 66 68 70 74 75 76 78 79 81 82 84 85 86 87 93 94 96 97 107 108 110 111 115 116 117 118 119 120 121 123 124 126 127 129 130 132 144 146 147 148
Primary Contact: Robert J. Wentz, President and Chief Executive Officer
COO: Scott Chapple, Chief Operating Officer
CFO: Ashok Khanchandani, Chief Financial Officer
CMO: Mathew N. Fine, M.D., Chief Medical Officer
CIO: Denise LeFevre, Chief Information Officer
CHR: Scott Chapple, Chief Operating Officer
CNO: Carol Speer–Smith, R.N., Chief Nursing Officer
Web address: www.orovillehospital.com
Control: Other not–for–profit (including NFP Corporation) **Service:** General Medical and Surgical

Staffed Beds: 133 **Admissions:** 10851 **Census:** 119 **Outpatient Visits:** 300899 **Births:** 425 **Total Expense ($000):** 191193 **Payroll Expense ($000):** 79294 **Personnel:** 1130

OXNARD—Ventura County

☒ **ST. JOHN'S REGIONAL MEDICAL CENTER (050082)**, 1600 North Rose Avenue, Zip 93030–3723; tel. 805/988–2500 **A**1 2 9 10 **F**3 8 11 12 13 14 15 17 18 20 22 24 26 28 29 30 31 34 35 36 39 40 42 45 47 48 49 50 51 54 56 57 58 59 60 61 62 63 64 65 66 68 70 71 72 74 75 76 77 78 79 81 82 83 84 85 86 87 90 91 92 93 96 97 107 108 109 110 111 112 113 114 115 119 120 121 122 124 126 130 132 134 135 146 147 148 **P**3 5 7 **S** Dignity Health, San Francisco, CA
Primary Contact: Charles Cova, Interim Chief Executive Officer
COO: Kim A. Wilson, R.N., Chief Operating Officer
CFO: Robert D. Wardwell, Chief Financial Officer
CMO: Eugene Fussell, M.D., Chief Medical Officer
CIO: Jeff Perry, Director Information Technology
CHR: Ed Gonzales, Vice President Human Resources
CNO: Gudrun Moll, R.N., Chief Nursing Officer
Web address: www.stjohnshealth.org
Control: Other not–for–profit (including NFP Corporation) **Service:** General Medical and Surgical

Staffed Beds: 139 **Admissions:** 10998 **Census:** 139 **Outpatient Visits:** 80491 **Births:** 2445 **Total Expense ($000):** 257262 **Payroll Expense ($000):** 106038

PALM SPRINGS—Riverside County

☒ **DESERT REGIONAL MEDICAL CENTER (050243)**, 1150 North Indian Canyon Drive, Zip 92262–4872, Mailing Address: P.O. Box 2739, Zip 92263–2739; tel. 760/323–6511, (Total facility includes 30 beds in nursing home–type unit) **A**1 2 9 10 **F**3 12 13 14 15 17 18 20 22 24 26 28 29 30 31 34 35 40 43 45 46 47 48 49 50 51 52 53 54 55 56 57 58 59 60 61 62 64 65 68 70 72 74 75 76 77 78 79 81 82 84 85 86 87 89 90 92 93 94 100 102 107 108 109 110 111 114 115 116 117 119 120 124 126 128 130 131 132 144 146 147 148 **S** TENET Healthcare Corporation, Dallas, TX
Primary Contact: Carolyn W. Caldwell, Chief Executive Officer
COO: Jeffrey Patterson, Chief Operating Officer
CFO: Richard Phillips, Chief Financial Officer
CMO: Charles Andeson, Chief Medical Officer
CIO: Robert Klingseis, Director Information Systems
CHR: Frederick K. Owusu, Chief Human Resources Officer
CNO: Mary Anne McCrea, Chief Nursing Officer
Web address: www.desertmedctr.com
Control: Individual, Investor–owned, for–profit **Service:** General Medical and Surgical

Staffed Beds: 387 **Admissions:** 18081 **Census:** 217 **Outpatient Visits:** 151071 **Births:** 3262 **Total Expense ($000):** 297801 **Payroll Expense ($000):** 142693 **Personnel:** 1646

PALMDALE—Los Angeles County

☐ **PALMDALE REGIONAL MEDICAL CENTER (050204)**, 38600 Medical Center Drive, Zip 93551–4483; tel. 661/382–5000 **A**1 9 10 **F**3 8 11 12 18 20 22 24 26 29 30 40 45 46 47 49 50 51 64 68 70 74 77 79 81 85 87 93 107 108 111 114 115 119 130 141 146 148 **S** Universal Health Services, Inc., King of Prussia, PA
Primary Contact: Richard Allen, Chief Executive Officer
COO: Karen Faulis, Chief Operating Officer
CFO: Kurt Broten, Chief Financial Officer
CIO: Roy Singleton, Director Computer Information Systems
CHR: Karen Hickling, Director Human Resources
CNO: Pat McClendon, MSN, Chief Nursing Officer
Web address: www.palmdaleregional.com
Control: Corporation, Investor–owned, for–profit **Service:** General Medical and Surgical

Staffed Beds: 157 **Admissions:** 7977 **Census:** 95 **Births:** 0

PALO ALTO—Santa Clara County

☒ **LUCILE SALTER PACKARD CHILDREN'S HOSPITAL AT STANFORD (053305)**, 725 Welch Road, Zip 94304–1614; tel. 650/497–8000 **A**1 3 5 9 10 **F**3 7 11 12 13 15 17 19 25 27 28 29 30 31 32 34 35 36 38 43 44 45 46 47 48 49 50 54 55 57 58 59 60 61 62 64 65 66 68 71 72 73 74 75 76 77 78 79 80 81 82 84 85 86 87 88 89 91 92 93 96 97 99 100 101 104 107 111 115 119 124 126 129 130 131 132 134 136 137 138 139 140 141 142 144 145 146 148 **P**3 **S** Stanford Health Care, Palo Alto, CA
Primary Contact: Christopher G. Dawes, President and Chief Executive Officer
COO: Anne McCune, Chief Operating Officer
CMO: Kenneth Cox, M.D., Chief Medical Officer
CIO: James McCaughey, Chief Strategy Officer
CHR: Greg Souza, Vice President Human Resources
CNO: Susan Costello, Chief Nursing Officer
Web address: www.stanfordchildrens.org
Control: Other not–for–profit (including NFP Corporation) **Service:** Children's general

Staffed Beds: 302 **Admissions:** 12866 **Census:** 228 **Outpatient Visits:** 297430 **Births:** 4136 **Total Expense ($000):** 812604 **Payroll Expense ($000):** 272077 **Personnel:** 2673

☒ **STANFORD HOSPITAL AND CLINICS (050441)**, 300 Pasteur Drive, Suite H3200, Zip 94304–2203; tel. 650/723–4000 **A**1 3 5 8 9 10 **F**3 5 6 7 8 9 11 12 14 15 17 18 20 21 22 23 24 26 27 28 29 30 31 33 34 35 36 37 38 39 40 41 43 44 45 46 47 48 49 50 52 54 55 56 57 58 59 60 61 63 64 65 66 67 68 70 74 75 77 78 79 81 82 84 85 86 87 91 92 93 94 97 98 100 101 102 103 104 107 108 110 111 114 115 116 117 118 119 120 121 123 124 126 129 130 131 132 135 136 137 138 139 140 141 142 143 144 145 146 147 148 **P**3 6 **S** Stanford Health Care, Palo Alto, CA
Primary Contact: Amir Dan Rubin, President and Chief Executive Officer
COO: James Hereford, Chief Operating Officer
CFO: Daniel Morrissette, Chief Financial Officer
CMO: Norman Rizk, M.D., Chief Medical Officer
CIO: Pravene Nath, Chief Information Officer
CHR: Kety Duron, Vice President Human Resources
CNO: Nancy Lee, R.N., Vice President Patient Care Services and Chief Nursing Officer
Web address: www.stanfordhospital.com/
Control: Other not–for–profit (including NFP Corporation) **Service:** General Medical and Surgical

Staffed Beds: 477 **Admissions:** 25573 **Census:** 385 **Outpatient Visits:** 1066497 **Births:** 0 **Total Expense ($000):** 2273540 **Payroll Expense ($000):** 694965 **Personnel:** 7681

☒ △ **VETERANS AFFAIRS PALO ALTO HEALTH CARE SYSTEM**, 3801 Miranda Avenue, Zip 94304–1207; tel. 650/493–5000, (Includes PALO ALTO DIVISION, 3801 Miranda Avenue, tel. 650/493–5000; VETERANS AFFAIRS PALO ALTO HEALTH CARE SYSTEM, LIVERMORE DIVISION, 4951 Arroyo Road, tel. 510/447–2560), (Nonreporting) **A**1 2 3 5 7 **S** Department of Veterans Affairs, Washington, DC
Primary Contact: Elizabeth Joyce Freeman, FACHE, Director
CFO: Mel Niese, Chief Fiscal Service
CMO: Lawrence Leung, M.D., Chief of Staff
CIO: Doug Wirthgen, Chief Information Officer
CHR: Lori Peery, Chief Human Resource Management Services
Web address: www.paloalto.va.gov/
Control: Veterans Affairs, Government, federal **Service:** General Medical and Surgical

Staffed Beds: 473

PANORAMA CITY—Los Angeles County, See Los Angeles

PARADISE—Butte County

☒ **FEATHER RIVER HOSPITAL (050225)**, 5974 Pentz Road, Zip 95969–5593; tel. 530/877–9361, (Nonreporting) **A**1 2 9 10 **S** Adventist Health, Roseville, CA
Primary Contact: Kevin R. Erich, President and Chief Executive Officer
CFO: Dan Gordon, Chief Financial Officer
CMO: Anthony Nasr, M.D., Chief Medical Staff
CIO: Dan Gordon, Chief Financial Officer
CHR: Denton Gruzensky, Director Human Resources
Web address: www.frhosp.org
Control: Church–operated, Nongovernment, not–for profit **Service:** General Medical and Surgical

Staffed Beds: 54

PARAMOUNT—Los Angeles County

☐ **PROMISE HOSPITAL OF EAST LOS ANGELES, SUBURBAN MEDICAL CENTER CAMPUS**, 16453 South Colorado Avenue, Zip 90723–5000; tel. 562/531–3110, (Nonreporting) **A**1 9 **S** Promise Healthcare, Boca Raton, FL
Primary Contact: Michael D. Kerr, Chief Executive Officer
CIO: Fred Snyder, Vice President Information Technology
CHR: Denise Livingston, Director Human Resources
CNO: Jodi Hein, R.N., Chief Clinical Officer
Web address: www.promiseeastla.com
Control: Corporation, Investor–owned, for–profit **Service:** General Medical and Surgical

Staffed Beds: 182

Many Facility Codes have changed. Please refer to the AHA Guide Code Chart. © 2014 AHA Guide

PASADENA—Los Angeles County

☐ **AURORA LAS ENCINAS HOSPITAL (054078)**, 2900 East Del Mar Boulevard, Zip 91107–4399; tel. 626/795–9901, (Nonreporting) **A**1 9 10 **S** Aurora Behavioral Health Care, Corona, CA
Primary Contact: Gerard Conway, Chief Executive Officer
CMO: Daniel Suzuki, M.D., Medical Director
CIO: Eric Kim, Chief Information Officer
CHR: Veronica Herrera, Director Human Resources
Web address: www.lasencinashospital.com
Control: Corporation, Investor–owned, for–profit **Service:** Psychiatric

Staffed Beds: 138

✠ **HUNTINGTON MEMORIAL HOSPITAL (050438)**, 100 West California Boulevard, Zip 91105–3097, Mailing Address: P.O. Box 7013, Zip 91109–7013; tel. 626/397–5000 **A**1 2 3 5 9 10 **F**3 4 5 8 11 12 13 14 15 18 20 22 24 26 28 29 30 31 34 35 37 40 41 43 44 45 46 47 48 49 50 51 53 56 58 59 60 61 63 64 65 66 68 70 72 74 75 76 77 78 79 81 82 84 86 87 88 89 90 92 93 97 98 100 101 102 103 104 105 106 107 108 111 114 115 118 119 120 121 123 126 129 130 132 146 147 148 **P**3 5 7
Primary Contact: Stephen A. Ralph, President and Chief Executive Officer
COO: James S. Noble, Executive Vice President, Chief Operating Officer and Chief Financial Officer
CFO: James S. Noble, Executive Vice President, Chief Operating Officer and Chief Financial Officer
CMO: Paula Verrette, M.D., Vice President Quality and Performance Improvement and Chief Medical Officer
CIO: Debbie Tafoya, Vice President and Chief Information Officer
CHR: Debbie Ortega, Chief Human Resource Officer and Vice President Administrative Services
CNO: Gloria Sanchez–Rico, Chief Nursing Officer and Vice President
Web address: www.huntingtonhospital.com
Control: Other not–for–profit (including NFP Corporation) **Service:** General Medical and Surgical

Staffed Beds: 556 **Admissions:** 25963 **Census:** 333 **Outpatient Visits:** 149734 **Births:** 3366 **Total Expense ($000):** 535495 **Payroll Expense ($000):** 190694 **Personnel:** 2890

PATTON—San Bernardino County

☐ **PATTON STATE HOSPITAL**, 3102 East Highland Avenue, Zip 92369–7813; tel. 909/425–7000 **A**1 **F**3 29 30 39 53 57 58 59 61 65 74 75 77 86 87 98 100 101 103 130 132 135 143 146 **P**1
Primary Contact: Harry Oreol, Acting Chief Executive Officer
CFO: Kathleen Gamble, Fiscal Officer
CMO: George Christison, M.D., Medical Director
CIO: Cindy Barrett, Administrative Assistant
CHR: Nancy Varela, Director Human Resources
Web address: www.dmh.cahwnet.gov/statehospitals/patton
Control: State–Government, nonfederal **Service:** Psychiatric

Staffed Beds: 1528 **Admissions:** 1036 **Census:** 1506 **Births:** 0 **Total Expense ($000):** 285071 **Payroll Expense ($000):** 178114 **Personnel:** 2304

PERRIS—Riverside County

★ ○ **KINDRED HOSPITAL RIVERSIDE (052052)**, 2224 Medical Center Drive, Zip 92571–2638; tel. 951/436–3535 **A**9 10 11 **F**1 3 17 29 39 45 48 49 50 56 74 75 77 84 85 87 92 94 103 107 108 119 130 148 **S** Kindred Healthcare, Louisville, KY
Primary Contact: James Linhares, Chief Executive Officer
COO: Guay Khim Fugate, Chief Operations Officer
CFO: John Browne, Senior Chief Financial Officer
CHR: Tom Wright, Director Human Resources
Web address: www.khriverside.com
Control: Partnership, Investor–owned, for–profit **Service:** Long–Term Acute Care hospital

Staffed Beds: 40 **Admissions:** 429 **Census:** 33 **Outpatient Visits:** 0 **Births:** 0 **Total Expense ($000):** 21623

PETALUMA—Sonoma County

✠ **PETALUMA VALLEY HOSPITAL (050136)**, 400 North McDowell Boulevard, Zip 94954–2366; tel. 707/778–1111 **A**1 9 10 **F**3 11 13 15 29 30 34 35 40 44 45 46 49 50 51 57 60 63 64 68 69 70 75 76 77 78 79 81 82 84 85 86 87 92 93 97 107 108 110 111 115 119 130 146 148 **S** St. Joseph Health, Irvine, CA
Primary Contact: Todd Salnas, President
COO: David Ziolkowski, Chief Operating Officer
CFO: Mich Riccioni, Chief Financial Officer
CIO: Patrick Wylie, Director Information Systems
Web address: www.stjosephhealth.org/About–Us/Facilities/Petaluma–Valley–Hospital.aspx
Control: Other not–for–profit (including NFP Corporation) **Service:** General Medical and Surgical

Staffed Beds: 27 **Admissions:** 2658 **Census:** 24 **Outpatient Visits:** 58751 **Births:** 423 **Total Expense ($000):** 83713 **Payroll Expense ($000):** 28354 **Personnel:** 308

PLACENTIA—Orange County

✠ **PLACENTIA–LINDA HOSPITAL (050589)**, 1301 North Rose Drive, Zip 92870–3899; tel. 714/993–2000 **A**1 9 10 **F**3 11 12 15 17 29 30 31 34 40 45 46 47 48 49 57 59 65 70 75 79 81 82 85 87 93 107 108 111 118 119 130 131 132 135 144 145 146 148 **P**3 5 **S** TENET Healthcare Corporation, Dallas, TX
Primary Contact: Dwayne Richardson, Interim Chief Executive Officer
COO: Dwayne Richardson, Chief Operating Officer
CFO: Charles Natcher, Chief Financial Officer
CIO: Edwin Delos Santos, Director Information Systems
CHR: Diane Worthington, Director Human Resources
CNO: Judy Chabot, R.N., Chief Nursing Officer
Web address: www.placentialinda.com
Control: Corporation, Investor–owned, for–profit **Service:** General Medical and Surgical

Staffed Beds: 114 **Admissions:** 3537 **Census:** 32 **Outpatient Visits:** 56913 **Births:** 0 **Total Expense ($000):** 52456 **Payroll Expense ($000):** 29122 **Personnel:** 378

PLACERVILLE—El Dorado County

✠ **MARSHALL MEDICAL CENTER (050254)**, 1100 Marshall Way, Zip 95667–5722; tel. 530/622–1441, (Nonreporting) **A**1 2 9 10
Primary Contact: James Whipple, Chief Executive Officer
CFO: Laurie Eldridge, Chief Financial Officer
CMO: Rene Orona, M.D., Chief of Staff
CIO: Mike Jones, Director Information Services
CHR: Scott Comer, Director Administrative Services
Web address: www.marshallmedical.org
Control: Other not–for–profit (including NFP Corporation) **Service:** General Medical and Surgical

Staffed Beds: 105

PLEASANTON—Alameda County

✠ **VALLEYCARE MEDICAL CENTER (050283)**, 5555 West Las Positas Boulevard, Zip 94588–4000; tel. 925/847–3000, (Includes VALLEY MEMORIAL, 1111 East Stanley Boulevard, Livermore, Zip 94550–4115; tel. 925/447–7000), (Nonreporting) **A**1 2 9 10
Primary Contact: Scott Gregerson, President and Chief Executive Officer
COO: Cindy Noonan, Chief Operating Officer
CMO: Dat Nguyen, M.D., Chief of Staff
CIO: Bob Woods, Chief Information Officer
CHR: Chris Faber, Human Resources Analyst
Web address: www.valleycare.com
Control: Other not–for–profit (including NFP Corporation) **Service:** General Medical and Surgical

Staffed Beds: 183

CA

CA

POMONA—Los Angeles County

✠ △ **CASA COLINA HOSPITAL FOR REHABILITATIVE MEDICINE (053027)**, 255 East Bonita Avenue, Zip 91767–1923, Mailing Address: P.O. Box 6001, Zip 91769–6001; tel. 909/596–7733 **A**1 7 9 10 **F**3 29 30 34 35 44 53 54 56 58 59 64 74 75 79 86 87 90 91 92 93 95 96 97 107 110 111 115 119 130 131 132 134 146 148
Primary Contact: Felice L. Loverso, Ph.D., President and Chief Executive Officer
CFO: David Morony, Chief Financial Officer
CMO: Christopher Chalian, M.D., Medical Director
CIO: Ross Lesins, Chief Information Officer
CHR: Karen Du Pont, Chief Human Resource Officer
CNO: Kathryn Johnson, Chief Nursing Officer
Web address: www.casacolina.org
Control: Other not-for-profit (including NFP Corporation) **Service:** Rehabilitation

Staffed Beds: 68 **Admissions:** 1387 **Census:** 59 **Outpatient Visits:** 77165 **Births:** 0 **Total Expense ($000):** 40146 **Payroll Expense ($000):** 23488 **Personnel:** 534

LANTERMAN DEVELOPMENTAL CENTER (050545), 3530 Pomona Boulevard, Zip 91768–3238, Mailing Address: P.O. Box 100, Zip 91769–0100; tel. 909/444–7200, (Nonreporting) **A**10
Primary Contact: Judi Murray, Facility Director
COO: Donna Tuzzolino, Director Administrative Services
CFO: Rosie Flores–Ramirez, Director Fiscal Services
CMO: Hao Nguyen, M.D., Medical Director
CIO: George Oliva, Associate Information Systems Analyst
CHR: Estela Contreras, Director Human Resources
CNO: Tess Caisip, Coordinator of Nursing Services
Web address: www.dds.ca.gov
Control: State–Government, nonfederal **Service:** Hospital unit within an institution for the mentally retarded

Staffed Beds: 481

✠ **POMONA VALLEY HOSPITAL MEDICAL CENTER (050231)**, 1798 North Garey Avenue, Zip 91767–2918; tel. 909/865–9500 **A**1 2 3 5 10 **F**3 11 13 15 17 18 20 22 24 26 28 29 30 31 34 35 40 41 45 46 47 49 50 51 53 54 55 57 58 59 60 61 63 64 68 69 70 72 74 75 76 77 78 79 81 84 85 89 92 93 107 108 110 111 114 115 116 117 118 119 120 121 123 124 126 129 130 131 132 135 144 145 146 147 148 **P**7
Primary Contact: Richard E. Yochum, President and Chief Executive Officer
CFO: Michael Nelson, Executive Vice President and Chief Financial Officer
CMO: Kenneth Nakamoto, M.D., Vice President Medical Affairs
CIO: Kent Hoyos, Chief Information Officer
CHR: Ray Inge, Vice President Human Resources
CNO: Darlene Scafiddi, R.N., Vice President Nursing and Patient Care Services
Web address: www.pvhmc.org
Control: Other not-for-profit (including NFP Corporation) **Service:** General Medical and Surgical

Staffed Beds: 399 **Admissions:** 20349 **Census:** 255 **Outpatient Visits:** 484231 **Births:** 6492 **Total Expense ($000):** 479870 **Payroll Expense ($000):** 212222 **Personnel:** 2369

PORTERVILLE—Tulare County

PORTERVILLE DEVELOPMENTAL CENTER (050546), (Development Disabilities), 26501 Avenue 140, Zip 93257–9109, Mailing Address: P.O. Box 2000, Zip 93258–2000; tel. 559/782–2222 **A**10 **F**3 39 57 65 67 77 119 128 130 143 146 148
Primary Contact: Theresa Billeci, Executive Director
COO: Betty Davis, Director Administrative Services
CFO: Karen Warren, Fiscal Officer
CMO: Joseph Mendoza, M.D., Medical Director
CIO: Vincent Chandler, Director Information Services
CHR: Shawna Gregg, Director Human Resources
CNO: Tom Shelton, Coordinator of Nursing Services
Web address: www.pdc.dds.ca.gov/
Control: State–Government, nonfederal **Service:** Other specialty

Staffed Beds: 484 **Admissions:** 38 **Census:** 98 **Outpatient Visits:** 0 **Births:** 0 **Total Expense ($000):** 146191 **Payroll Expense ($000):** 79087 **Personnel:** 1244

☐ **SIERRA VIEW DISTRICT HOSPITAL (050261)**, 465 West Putnam Avenue, Zip 93257–3320; tel. 559/784–1110, (Total facility includes 35 beds in nursing home–type unit) **A**1 9 10 **F**3 13 15 29 30 31 34 35 40 42 45 47 49 54 57 59 60 65 68 70 75 76 78 79 81 85 87 89 93 107 108 110 111 115 119 121 123 130 132 135 146 147 148
Primary Contact: Donna J. Hefner, R.N., President and Chief Executive Officer
CFO: John Chivers, Senior Vice President Finance
CHR: Sharon Brown, Vice President Human Resources
Web address: www.sierra–view.com
Control: Hospital district or authority, Government, nonfederal **Service:** General Medical and Surgical

Staffed Beds: 156 **Admissions:** 6692 **Census:** 106 **Outpatient Visits:** 145616 **Births:** 1693 **Total Expense ($000):** 131114 **Payroll Expense ($000):** 48485 **Personnel:** 846

PORTOLA—Plumas County

EASTERN PLUMAS HEALTH CARE (051300), 500 First Avenue, Zip 96122–9406; tel. 530/832–6500, (Nonreporting) **A**9 10 18
Primary Contact: Thomas P. Hayes, Chief Executive Officer
CFO: Jeri Nelson, Chief Financial Officer
CMO: Eric Bugna, M.D., Chief of Staff
CHR: Cathy Conant, Chief Human Resources and Personnel
Web address: www.ephc.org
Control: Hospital district or authority, Government, nonfederal **Service:** General Medical and Surgical

Staffed Beds: 10

POWAY—San Diego County

✠ **POMERADO HOSPITAL (050636)**, 15615 Pomerado Road, Zip 92064–2460; tel. 858/613–4000, (Total facility includes 129 beds in nursing home–type unit) **A**1 9 10 **F**3 11 12 13 14 18 20 29 30 31 34 35 36 38 40 45 46 47 50 51 54 55 56 57 58 59 62 64 65 68 70 72 74 75 76 77 78 79 81 82 84 85 87 97 98 100 101 102 103 107 110 111 119 120 128 130 131 132 133 143 144 146 147 148 **P**3 **S** Palomar Health, Escondido, CA
Primary Contact: David A. Tam, M.D., FACHE, Chief Administrative Officer
CIO: Steven Tanaka, Chief Information Officer
CHR: Brenda C. Turner, Chief Human Resources Officer
Web address: www.pph.org
Control: Hospital district or authority, Government, nonfederal **Service:** General Medical and Surgical

Staffed Beds: 203 **Admissions:** 6856 **Census:** 185 **Outpatient Visits:** 72931 **Births:** 1200 **Total Expense ($000):** 149860 **Payroll Expense ($000):** 60800 **Personnel:** 546

QUINCY—Plumas County

☐ **PLUMAS DISTRICT HOSPITAL (051326)**, 1065 Bucks Lake Road, Zip 95971–9599; tel. 530/283–2121 **A**1 9 10 18 **F**3 7 13 15 18 19 30 32 39 40 45 57 61 64 68 75 79 81 82 85 107 111 114 119 127
Primary Contact: Douglas L. Lafferty, Chief Executive Officer
CMO: Vincent Frantz, M.D., Chief of Staff
CIO: Brenda Compton, Manager Information Technology
CHR: Denise Harding, Director Human Resources
Web address: www.pdh.org
Control: Hospital district or authority, Government, nonfederal **Service:** General Medical and Surgical

Staffed Beds: 25 **Admissions:** 473 **Census:** 3 **Total Expense ($000):** 20282

RANCHO CUCAMONGA—San Bernardino County

★ ○ **KINDRED HOSPITAL RANCHO (052049)**, 10841 White Oak Avenue, Zip 91730–3811; tel. 909/581–6400 **A**9 10 11 **F**3 29 30 34 35 45 46 60 64 68 70 74 75 77 79 81 82 84 85 87 107 111 119 130 148 **S** Kindred Healthcare, Louisville, KY
Primary Contact: Jody Knox, Administrator
Web address: www.khrancho.com
Control: Corporation, Investor–owned, for-profit **Service:** Long–Term Acute Care hospital

Staffed Beds: 55 **Admissions:** 761 **Census:** 47 **Births:** 0

RANCHO MIRAGE—Riverside County

✠ △ **EISENHOWER MEDICAL CENTER (050573)**, 39000 Bob Hope Drive, Zip 92270–3221; tel. 760/340–3911 **A**1 2 3 5 7 9 10 **F**2 3 9 11 12 15 17 18 20 22 24 26 28 29 30 31 34 35 37 40 41 45 47 49 50 53 54 56 57 58 59 60 61 64 65 68 70 74 75 77 78 79 81 82 84 85 86 87 89 90 93 96 97 98 100 101 102 103 107 108 109 110 111 112 114 115 116 117 119 120 121 123 124 126 129 130 131 132 135 144 145 146 147 148 **P**3
Primary Contact: G. Aubrey Serfling, President and Chief Executive Officer
COO: Martin Massiello, Executive Vice President and Chief Operating Officer
CFO: Ken Wheat, Senior Vice President and Chief Financial Officer
CMO: Alan Williamson, M.D., Chief Medical Officer
CIO: David Perez, Vice President and Chief Information Officer
CHR: Liz Guignier, Vice President Human Resources
CNO: Ann R. Mostofi, MSN, Vice President Patient Care and Chief Nursing Officer
Web address: www.emc.org
Control: Other not-for-profit (including NFP Corporation) **Service:** General Medical and Surgical

Staffed Beds: 380 **Admissions:** 19148 **Census:** 221 **Outpatient Visits:** 564868 **Births:** 0 **Total Expense ($000):** 525021 **Payroll Expense ($000):** 166359 **Personnel:** 2489

RED BLUFF—Tehama County

✠ **ST. ELIZABETH COMMUNITY HOSPITAL (050042)**, 2550 Sister Mary Columba Drive, Zip 96080–4397; tel. 530/529–8000 **A**1 9 10 20 **F**3 7 8 11 13 15 29 30 32 34 35 40 43 45 51 54 62 63 64 68 70 75 76 81 82 84 85 89 93 107 108 110 111 114 119 130 131 132 133 145 146 148 **P**3 **S** Dignity Health, San Francisco, CA
Primary Contact: G. Todd Smith, President
CFO: Gina Anderson, Chief Financial Officer
CMO: James DeSoto, M.D., Vice President Medical Affairs
CIO: Henry Niessink, Senior Manager Information Technology Systems
CHR: Denise Little, Director Human Resources
Web address: www.mercy.org
Control: Church–operated, Nongovernment, not–for profit **Service:** General Medical and Surgical

> **Staffed Beds:** 65 **Admissions:** 3023 **Census:** 22 **Outpatient Visits:** 66735 **Births:** 699 **Total Expense ($000):** 73471 **Payroll Expense ($000):** 33359 **Personnel:** 368

REDDING—Shasta County

✠ **MERCY MEDICAL CENTER REDDING (050280)**, 2175 Rosaline Avenue, Zip 96001–2549, Mailing Address: P.O. Box 496009, Zip 96049–6009; tel. 530/225–6000 **A**1 2 3 5 9 10 **F**2 3 7 11 13 15 17 18 20 22 24 28 29 30 31 34 35 37 40 43 45 46 47 48 49 50 54 57 59 61 62 63 64 66 68 70 72 75 76 77 78 79 81 82 84 85 89 91 97 107 108 111 114 115 118 119 126 130 132 135 143 144 145 146 147 148 **S** Dignity Health, San Francisco, CA
Primary Contact: Mark Korth, President
COO: Patrick Varga, Chief Operating Officer
CFO: Kimberly Miranda, Regional Vice President Finance and Chief Financial Officer
CMO: James DeSoto, M.D., Vice President Medical Affairs
CIO: Henry Niessink, Regional Director Information Technology Services
CHR: Stephan Hosler, Vice President Human Resources
CNO: Kimberly Shaw, Vice President Patient Care and Chief Nursing Executive
Web address: www.mercy.org
Control: Church–operated, Nongovernment, not–for profit **Service:** General Medical and Surgical

> **Staffed Beds:** 267 **Admissions:** 12917 **Census:** 156 **Outpatient Visits:** 137846 **Births:** 1999 **Total Expense ($000):** 359932 **Payroll Expense ($000):** 133481 **Personnel:** 1414

NORTHERN CALIFORNIA REHABILITATION HOSPITAL See Vibra Hospital of Northern California

PATIENTS' HOSPITAL OF REDDING (050697), 2900 Eureka Way, Zip 96001–0220; tel. 530/225–8700 **A**9 10 **F**81 82 85
Primary Contact: Shari Lejsek, Administrator
CFO: Kim Needles, Manager Business Office
CMO: James Tate, M.D., Chief of Staff
CIO: Kim Cameron, Manager Health Information Services
CHR: Brenda Meline, Manager Human Resources
CNO: Diane Rieke, Director Patient Care Services
Web address: www.patientshospital.com
Control: Individual, Investor–owned, for–profit **Service:** General Medical and Surgical

> **Staffed Beds:** 10 **Admissions:** 229 **Census:** 1 **Outpatient Visits:** 2145 **Births:** 0

✠ **SHASTA REGIONAL MEDICAL CENTER (050764)**, 1100 Butte Street, Zip 96001–0853, Mailing Address: P.O. Box 496072, Zip 96049–6072; tel. 530/244–5400 **A**1 5 9 10 **F**3 11 17 18 20 22 24 26 28 29 30 34 40 43 45 49 50 51 57 59 65 70 74 75 77 79 81 84 85 86 89 107 108 111 115 119 132 146 148 **S** Prime Healthcare Services, Ontario, CA
Primary Contact: Cynthia Gordon, R.N., Chief Executive Officer
COO: Becky Levy, Chief Operating Officer
CFO: Becky Levy, Chief Financial Officer
CMO: Marcia McCampbell, M.D., Chief Medical Officer
CIO: Tony VanBoekel, Director Information Systems
CHR: Andrew Torge, Director Human Resources
CNO: Leslie Woodson, R.N., Chief Nursing Officer
Web address: www.shastaregional.com
Control: Corporation, Investor–owned, for–profit **Service:** General Medical and Surgical

> **Staffed Beds:** 120 **Admissions:** 7124 **Census:** 78 **Outpatient Visits:** 57658 **Births:** 0 **Total Expense ($000):** 127959

✠ **VIBRA HOSPITAL OF NORTHERN CALIFORNIA (052047)**, 2801 Eureka Way, Zip 96001–0222; tel. 530/246–9000, (Total facility includes 32 beds in nursing home–type unit) **A**1 9 10 **F**1 29 30 64 77 93 119 128 130 148 **S** Vibra Healthcare, Mechanicsburg, PA
Primary Contact: Chris Jones, Chief Executive Officer
COO: Lisa Stevens, Chief Clinical Officer and Chief Operating Officer
CFO: Rebecca Andrews, Chief Financial Officer
CMO: Nanda Kumar, M.D., Chief of Staff
CIO: Mark Cardenas, Director Plant Operations
CHR: Wendy Tempest, Director Human Resources
Web address: www.norcalrehab.com
Control: Corporation, Investor–owned, for–profit **Service:** Long–Term Acute Care hospital

> **Staffed Beds:** 88 **Admissions:** 1226 **Census:** 76 **Outpatient Visits:** 2930 **Births:** 0 **Total Expense ($000):** 32555 **Payroll Expense ($000):** 14947 **Personnel:** 242

REDLANDS—San Bernardino County

✠ **LOMA LINDA UNIVERSITY BEHAVIORAL MEDICINE CENTER (054093)**, 1710 Barton Road, Zip 92373–5304; tel. 909/558–9200 **A**1 5 9 10 **F**4 5 29 34 35 57 87 98 99 100 101 102 103 104 105 130 132 **S** Loma Linda University Adventist Health Sciences Center, Loma Linda, CA
Primary Contact: Jill Pollock, Administrator
COO: Ruthita J. Fike, Chief Executive Officer
CFO: Steve Mohr, Senior Vice President Finance and Chief Financial Officer
CMO: William Murdoch, M.D., Medical Director
CIO: Mark Zirkelback, Chief Information Officer
CHR: Mark Hubbard, Vice President Risk Management
CNO: Norie Lee Reyes Bencito, ACA–AC, R.N., R.N., Director of Nursing
Web address: www.llu.edu
Control: Other not–for–profit (including NFP Corporation) **Service:** Psychiatric

> **Staffed Beds:** 89 **Admissions:** 4249 **Census:** 72 **Outpatient Visits:** 34188 **Births:** 0 **Total Expense ($000):** 32573 **Payroll Expense ($000):** 15128 **Personnel:** 255

✠ **REDLANDS COMMUNITY HOSPITAL (050272)**, 350 Terracina Boulevard, Zip 92373–4897, Mailing Address: P.O. Box 3391, Zip 92373–0742; tel. 909/335–5500, (Nonreporting) **A**1 9 10
Primary Contact: James R. Holmes, President and Chief Executive Officer
Web address: www.redlandshospital.org
Control: Other not–for–profit (including NFP Corporation) **Service:** General Medical and Surgical

> **Staffed Beds:** 172

REDWOOD CITY—San Mateo County

✠ **KAISER PERMANENTE REDWOOD CITY MEDICAL CENTER (050541)**, 1150 Veterans Boulevard, Zip 94063–2087; tel. 650/299–2000 **A**1 3 5 10 **F**3 8 13 15 18 20 22 26 28 29 30 31 32 34 35 36 40 44 45 49 50 51 53 54 55 56 57 58 59 64 65 68 70 73 74 75 76 77 78 79 80 81 82 84 85 86 87 91 92 93 94 95 96 97 99 100 101 103 104 107 108 110 111 114 115 119 129 130 131 132 134 135 146 147 148 **P**6 **S** Kaiser Foundation Hospitals, Oakland, CA
Primary Contact: Frank T. Beirne, FACHE, Senior Vice President and Area Manager
COO: Maureen O'Brien, Chief Operating Officer
CFO: Tim O'Connor, Area Finance Officer
CMO: James O'Donnell, Physician in Chief
CHR: Sharon Barncord, Business Partner Human Resources
CNO: Barbara E. Van Amburg, R.N., Chief Nursing Officer
Web address: www.kaiserpermanente.org
Control: Other not–for–profit (including NFP Corporation) **Service:** General Medical and Surgical

> **Staffed Beds:** 213 **Admissions:** 7597 **Census:** 85 **Outpatient Visits:** 524663 **Births:** 1471 **Personnel:** 1398

CA

Hospital, Medicare Provider Number, Address, Telephone, Approval, Facility, and Physician Codes, Health Care System

★ American Hospital Association (AHA) membership
☐ The Joint Commission accreditation
◇ DNV Healthcare Inc. accreditation
○ Healthcare Facilities Accreditation Program
△ Commission on Accreditation of Rehabilitation Facilities (CARF) accreditation

---

CA

✠ **SEQUOIA HOSPITAL (050197)**, 170 Alameda De Las Pulgas, Zip 94062–2799; tel. 650/369–5811 **A**1 9 10 **F**11 12 13 15 18 20 22 24 26 28 29 30 31 32 34 35 37 40 45 46 49 50 53 57 59 60 64 68 70 74 75 76 77 78 79 81 84 86 87 92 93 94 107 108 110 111 114 115 118 119 120 121 123 126 129 130 132 135 146 147 148 **P**3 **S** Dignity Health, San Francisco, CA
Primary Contact: Glenna L. Vaskelis, President and Senior Vice President Operations Dignity Health Bay Area Service Area
COO: Sherie C. Hickman, Vice President Operations and Chief Operating Officer
CFO: Gratia Barton, Chief Financial Officer
CMO: Christopher Dunn, M.D., Vice President Medical Affairs
CIO: Gracie O'Brien, Chief Information Officer
CHR: Linde Cheema, Vice President Human Resources
CNO: Sherry Eldridge, Vice President Patient Care Services and Chief Nurse Executive
Web address: www.sequoiahospital.org
Control: Other not–for–profit (including NFP Corporation) **Service:** General Medical and Surgical

Staffed Beds: 128 Admissions: 5964 Census: 63 Outpatient Visits: 104957 Births: 1576 Total Expense ($000): 223915 Payroll Expense ($000): 84496 Personnel: 689

REEDLEY—Fresno County

★ ◇ **ADVENTIST MEDICAL CENTER–REEDLEY (050192)**, 372 West Cypress Avenue, Zip 93654–2199; tel. 559/638–8155 **A**9 10 21 **F**13 15 29 30 40 45 50 64 76 77 81 87 107 110 111 114 119 127 133 135 **S** Adventist Health, Roseville, CA
Primary Contact: Wayne Ferch, President and Chief Executive Officer
CFO: Teresa Jacques, Interim Chief Financial Officer
CMO: Todd Spencer, M.D., Chief Medical Staff
CIO: Valerie Alvarez, Executive Assistant
CHR: Ramona Alvarado, Interim Manager Human Resources
Web address: www.skdh.org
Control: Church–operated, Nongovernment, not–for profit **Service:** General Medical and Surgical

Staffed Beds: 49 Admissions: 2081 Census: 12 Outpatient Visits: 138588 Births: 1185 Total Expense ($000): 43683 Payroll Expense ($000): 16293 Personnel: 370

RESEDA—Los Angeles County

☐ **JOYCE EISENBERG–KEEFER MEDICAL CENTER (054147)**, 7150 Tampa Avenue, Zip 91335–3700; tel. 818/774–3000, (Nonreporting) **A**1 10
Primary Contact: Ilana Grossman, Administrator
CNO: Haya Berci, Executive Director of Nursing
Web address: www.jha.org
Control: Other not–for–profit (including NFP Corporation) **Service:** Psychiatric

Staffed Beds: 10

RICHMOND—Contra Costa County

KAISER PERMANENTE RICHMOND MEDICAL CENTER See Kaiser Permanente Oakland Medical Center, Oakland

RIDGECREST—Kern County

★ ◇ **RIDGECREST REGIONAL HOSPITAL (051333)**, 1081 North China Lake Boulevard, Zip 93555–3130; tel. 760/446–3551, (Total facility includes 26 beds in nursing home–type unit) **A**9 10 18 21 **F**1 3 4 8 11 13 15 16 17 18 28 29 30 32 34 35 40 41 43 45 50 56 57 59 62 63 64 66 67 68 70 72 73 75 76 77 79 80 81 84 85 87 88 89 90 93 97 98 104 107 108 110 111 114 115 119 127 128 129 130 131 133 134 144 146 147 148
Primary Contact: James A. Suver, FACHE, Chief Executive Officer
CFO: Lois Johnson, Administrator Fiscal Services
CMO: Victoria Schauf, M.D., Chief of Staff
CIO: Randy Ferguson, Chief Information Officer
CHR: Dave Shary, Administrator Human Resources
Web address: www.rrh.org
Control: Other not–for–profit (including NFP Corporation) **Service:** General Medical and Surgical

Staffed Beds: 51 Admissions: 1857 Census: 22 Outpatient Visits: 123324 Births: 446 Total Expense ($000): 79978 Payroll Expense ($000): 27875 Personnel: 572

RIVERSIDE—Riverside County

✠ **KAISER PERMANENTE RIVERSIDE MEDICAL CENTER (050686)**, 10800 Magnolia Avenue, Zip 92505–3000; tel. 951/353–2000 **A**1 3 5 10 **F**3 13 15 17 28 29 30 31 35 40 44 45 46 48 49 50 51 59 60 62 63 64 65 68 70 72 74 75 76 77 78 79 81 82 84 85 86 87 89 92 93 97 100 102 107 108 109 110 111 114 115 117 118 119 130 144 146 147 148 **S** Kaiser Foundation Hospitals, Oakland, CA
Primary Contact: Vita M. Willett, Administrator and Executive Director
CFO: Lorna Curtis, Chief Financial Officer
CMO: Richard Rajatatnam, M.D., Area Medical Director
CIO: Alfred T. Velasquez, Area Information Officer
CHR: Wendy Sander, Director Human Resources
CNO: Kim E. Hadden, R.N., Chief Nurse Executive
Web address: www.kaiserpermanente.org
Control: Other not–for–profit (including NFP Corporation) **Service:** General Medical and Surgical

Staffed Beds: 226 Admissions: 12177 Census: 133 Outpatient Visits: 150279 Births: 2933 Personnel: 614

PACIFIC GROVE HOSPITAL (054130), 5900 Brockton Avenue, Zip 92506–1862; tel. 951/275–8400 **A**9 10 **F**5 98 103 104 105 130 **P**1 **S** Acadia Healthcare Company, Inc., Franklin, TN
Primary Contact: Amrita Rai, Administrator
Web address: www.pacificgrovehospital.com
Control: Corporation, Investor–owned, for–profit **Service:** Psychiatric

Staffed Beds: 50 Admissions: 973 Census: 14 Births: 0

☐ **PARKVIEW COMMUNITY HOSPITAL MEDICAL CENTER (050102)**, 3865 Jackson Street, Zip 92503–3998; tel. 951/688–2211 **A**1 9 10 **F**1 3 8 12 13 15 29 34 35 40 45 46 50 57 59 60 62 64 68 70 72 76 77 79 81 84 85 86 87 89 107 108 111 114 115 119 130 132 146 147 148
Primary Contact: Steven Popkin, Chief Executive Officer
COO: Robert Brown, Chief Operating Officer
CFO: Patti Lepe, Chief Financial Officer
CMO: Dong Kim, M.D., Chief of Staff
CIO: John Ciccarelli, Director Information Technology
CHR: Lizette O. Norton, Vice President Human Resources
CNO: Thomas Santos, R.N., Chief Nursing Officer and Director Quality Services
Web address: www.pchmc.org
Control: Other not–for–profit (including NFP Corporation) **Service:** General Medical and Surgical

Staffed Beds: 193 Admissions: 8998 Census: 106 Outpatient Visits: 72041 Births: 1858 Total Expense ($000): 145932 Payroll Expense ($000): 55749 Personnel: 1048

RIVERSIDE CENTER FOR BEHAVIORAL MEDICINE See Pacific Grove Hospital

✠ **RIVERSIDE COMMUNITY HOSPITAL (050022)**, 4445 Magnolia Avenue, Zip 92501–4199, Mailing Address: P.O. Box 1669, Zip 92502–1669; tel. 951/788–3000, (Nonreporting) **A**1 2 5 9 10 **S** HCA, Nashville, TN
Primary Contact: Patrick D. Brilliant, President and Chief Executive Officer
COO: Daniel Bowers, Chief Operating Officer
CFO: Russell T. Young, Chief Financial Officer
CMO: Lawrence Clark, M.D., President Medical Staff
CIO: Cae Swanger, Chief Information Officer
CHR: Nathan Bigler, Vice President Human Relations
CNO: Francine Paschall, R.N., Chief Nursing Officer
Web address: www.riversidecommunityhospital.com
Control: Corporation, Investor–owned, for–profit **Service:** General Medical and Surgical

Staffed Beds: 373

RIVERSIDE MEDICAL CENTER See Kaiser Permanente Riverside Medical Center

ROSEMEAD—Los Angeles County

☐ **BHC ALHAMBRA HOSPITAL (054032)**, 4619 North Rosemead Boulevard, Zip 91770–1478, Mailing Address: P.O. Box 369, Zip 91770–0369; tel. 626/286–1191 **A**1 9 10 **F**98 99 104 105 **S** Universal Health Services, Inc., King of Prussia, PA
Primary Contact: Peggy Minnick, R.N., Chief Executive Officer
CFO: Michelle Jackson, Chief Financial Officer
CMO: Wakelin McNeel, M.D., Medical Director
CIO: Debbie Irvin, Director Health Information Management
CHR: Venus Taylor, Director Human Resources
Web address: www.bhcalhambra.com
Control: Corporation, Investor–owned, for–profit **Service:** Psychiatric

Staffed Beds: 97 Admissions: 5232 Census: 83 Births: 0

SILVER LAKE MEDICAL CENTER–INGLESIDE HOSPITAL See Silver Lake Medical Center, Los Angeles

Many Facility Codes have changed. Please refer to the AHA Guide Code Chart. © 2014 AHA Guide

ROSEVILLE—Placer County

⊠ **KAISER PERMANENTE ROSEVILLE MEDICAL CENTER (050772)**, 1600 Eureka Road, Zip 95661–3027; tel. 916/784–4000, (Nonreporting) **A**1 10 **S** Kaiser Foundation Hospitals, Oakland, CA
Primary Contact: Edward S. Glavis, Senior Vice President and Area Manager
Web address: www.kp.org
Control: Other not–for–profit (including NFP Corporation) **Service:** General Medical and Surgical

Staffed Beds: 340

⊠ **SUTTER ROSEVILLE MEDICAL CENTER (050309)**, One Medical Plaza, Zip 95661–3037; tel. 916/781–1000 **A**1 2 5 9 10 **F**3 8 12 13 15 19 21 28 29 30 31 34 35 40 43 45 46 50 58 59 60 63 64 65 68 70 72 74 75 78 79 81 82 84 85 89 90 93 94 96 107 108 109 111 114 116 119 126 130 131 132 141 146 147 148 **S** Sutter Health, Sacramento, CA
Primary Contact: Patrick R. Brady, Chief Executive Officer
COO: Dionne Miller, Chief Operating Officer
CFO: Gary Hubschman, Administrative Director Finance
CMO: Stuart Bostrom, M.D., Director Medical Affairs
CIO: Nancy Turner, Director Communications
CHR: Lynda Dasaro, Director Human Resources
CNO: Barbara J. Nelson, Ph.D., Chief Nursing Executive
Web address: www.sutterroseville.org
Control: Other not–for–profit (including NFP Corporation) **Service:** General Medical and Surgical

Staffed Beds: 328 **Admissions:** 19676 **Census:** 243 **Outpatient Visits:** 172802 **Births:** 3039 **Total Expense ($000):** 419183 **Payroll Expense ($000):** 133805 **Personnel:** 2100

SACRAMENTO—Sacramento County

☐ **HERITAGE OAKS HOSPITAL (054104)**, 4250 Auburn Boulevard, Zip 95841–4164; tel. 916/489–3336 **A**1 3 5 9 10 **F**2 3 5 38 64 87 98 99 100 101 102 103 104 105 130 **P**8 **S** Universal Health Services, Inc., King of Prussia, PA
Primary Contact: Shawn Silva, Chief Executive Officer
CFO: Art Wong, Chief Financial Officer
CMO: Joseph Sison, M.D., Medical Director
CHR: Lisa Myers, Director Human Resources
Web address: www.heritageoakshospital.com
Control: Corporation, Investor–owned, for–profit **Service:** Psychiatric

Staffed Beds: 120 **Admissions:** 4153 **Census:** 103 **Outpatient Visits:** 16128 **Births:** 0 **Total Expense ($000):** 20785 **Payroll Expense ($000):** 12224 **Personnel:** 225

⊠ **KAISER PERMANENTE SACRAMENTO MEDICAL CENTER (050425)**, 2025 Morse Avenue, Zip 95825–2100; tel. 916/973–5000 **A**1 3 5 10 **F**3 8 15 17 18 20 29 30 34 35 40 41 44 45 46 48 49 50 51 56 57 60 64 65 68 70 74 75 77 78 79 81 82 84 85 102 107 108 111 114 115 119 120 129 130 146 148 **S** Kaiser Foundation Hospitals, Oakland, CA
Primary Contact: Ronald Groepper, Senior Vice President and Area Manager
CFO: Jim Eldridge, Area Financial Officer
CMO: Chris Palkowski, M.D., Physician in Chief
CIO: Philip Fasano, Chief Information Officer
CHR: Gay Westfall, Senior Vice President Human Resources
Web address: www.kp.org
Control: Other not–for–profit (including NFP Corporation) **Service:** General Medical and Surgical

Staffed Beds: 287 **Admissions:** 9841 **Census:** 119 **Outpatient Visits:** 221015 **Births:** 2

⊠ **KAISER PERMANENTE SOUTH SACRAMENTO MEDICAL CENTER (050674)**, 6600 Bruceville Road, Zip 95823–4691; tel. 916/688–2430 **A**1 3 5 10 **F**3 8 12 13 15 20 22 29 30 31 34 35 40 43 44 45 49 50 58 59 61 62 63 64 65 68 70 73 74 75 76 77 78 79 81 82 84 85 86 87 93 96 97 100 104 107 108 109 110 111 114 115 119 126 129 130 131 134 135 144 146 147 148 **S** Kaiser Foundation Hospitals, Oakland, CA
Primary Contact: Patricia M. Rodriguez, Senior Vice President and Area Manager
CIO: Kathleen McKenna, Public Affairs Leader
Web address: www.kp.org
Control: Other not–for–profit (including NFP Corporation) **Service:** General Medical and Surgical

Staffed Beds: 181 **Admissions:** 13397 **Census:** 123 **Outpatient Visits:** 99806 **Births:** 2352 **Personnel:** 1353

⊠ △ **MERCY GENERAL HOSPITAL (050017)**, 4001 J Street, Zip 95819–3600; tel. 916/453–4545, (Total facility includes 38 beds in nursing home–type unit) **A**1 2 3 5 7 9 10 **F**3 8 11 13 15 17 18 20 22 24 26 28 29 30 31 34 35 36 37 38 39 40 44 45 46 47 48 49 50 51 53 56 57 58 59 63 64 66 68 70 74 75 76 77 78 79 81 82 84 85 86 87 90 91 93 94 96 99 100 107 108 109 111 114 115 119 124 126 128 130 131 132 135 143 145 146 **P**3 5 **S** Dignity Health, San Francisco, CA
Primary Contact: Edmundo Castaneda, President
COO: Patricia Monczewski, Chief Operating Officer
CFO: Ronald Kroll, Chief Financial Officer
CMO: Robert Wiebe, M.D., Chief Medical Officer
CHR: Cyndi Kirch, Vice President Human Resources
Web address: www.mercygeneral.org
Control: Other not–for–profit (including NFP Corporation) **Service:** General Medical and Surgical

Staffed Beds: 286 **Admissions:** 16370 **Census:** 193 **Outpatient Visits:** 207944 **Births:** 2121 **Total Expense ($000):** 486899 **Payroll Expense ($000):** 180431 **Personnel:** 1303

⊠ **METHODIST HOSPITAL OF SACRAMENTO (050590)**, 7500 Hospital Drive, Zip 95823–5477; tel. 916/423–3000, (Total facility includes 166 beds in nursing home–type unit) **A**1 9 10 **F**3 8 11 12 13 17 29 30 34 35 37 39 40 41 47 49 50 59 60 61 64 68 70 73 74 75 76 77 79 81 84 85 86 87 93 96 97 107 108 111 116 117 118 119 126 128 130 131 132 143 146 147 148 **P**5 **S** Dignity Health, San Francisco, CA
Primary Contact: Eugene Bassett, President and Chief Executive Officer
COO: Anita J. Kennedy, Vice President Operations
CFO: Bonnie Jenkins, Chief Financial Officer
CMO: Amir Sweha, M.D., Vice President Medical Administration
CHR: Cyndi Kirch, Vice President Human Resources
CNO: Martina Evans–Harrison, R.N., Chief Nurse Executive
Web address: www.methodistsacramento.org
Control: Other not–for–profit (including NFP Corporation) **Service:** General Medical and Surgical

Staffed Beds: 325 **Admissions:** 9882 **Census:** 248 **Outpatient Visits:** 70025 **Births:** 1812 **Total Expense ($000):** 250916 **Payroll Expense ($000):** 105412 **Personnel:** 878

☐ **SHRINERS HOSPITALS FOR CHILDREN–NORTHERN CALIFORNIA (053311)**, 2425 Stockton Boulevard, Zip 95817–2215; tel. 916/453–2000, (Nonreporting) **A**1 3 5 9 10 **S** Shriners Hospitals for Children, Tampa, FL
Primary Contact: Margaret Bryan, Administrator
COO: Margaret Bryan, Administrator
CFO: William Dalby, Director Fiscal Services
CIO: John Bevel, Manager Information Systems
CHR: Deborah Rubens, Director Human Resources
Web address: www.shrinershospitalsforchildren.org/Hospitals/Locations/NorthernCalifornia.aspx
Control: Other not–for–profit (including NFP Corporation) **Service:** Children's general

Staffed Beds: 70

☐ **SIERRA VISTA HOSPITAL (054087)**, 8001 Bruceville Road, Zip 95823–2329; tel. 916/288–0300 **A**1 9 10 **F**35 50 98 99 100 101 102 103 104 105 130 **S** Universal Health Services, Inc., King of Prussia, PA
Primary Contact: Mike Zauner, Chief Executive Officer
CFO: Nicole Sinclair, Chief Financial Officer
CMO: Okechukwu Nwangburuka, M.D., Medical Director
CIO: Ixel Morell, Director Business Development
CNO: Gwen Hubbard, Director of Nursing
Web address: www.sierravistahospital.com
Control: Corporation, Investor–owned, for–profit **Service:** Psychiatric

Staffed Beds: 120 **Admissions:** 5767 **Census:** 103 **Outpatient Visits:** 6470 **Births:** 0 **Personnel:** 287

SOUTH SACRAMENTO MEDICAL CENTER See Kaiser Permanente South Sacramento Medical Center

⊠ **SUTTER CENTER FOR PSYCHIATRY (054096)**, 7700 Folsom Boulevard, Zip 95826–2608; tel. 916/386–3000 **A**1 9 10 **F**29 30 34 35 68 98 99 100 101 104 105 130 132 133 134 **S** Sutter Health, Sacramento, CA
Primary Contact: John W. Boyd, PsyD, Chief Administrative Officer
CFO: Pamela Ansley, Director Finance
CMO: Cindy Thygeson, M.D., Director Medical Affairs
CHR: Kristin Daniels, Manager Human Resources
Web address: www.sutterpsychiatry.org
Control: Other not–for–profit (including NFP Corporation) **Service:** Psychiatric

Staffed Beds: 71 **Admissions:** 2883 **Census:** 52 **Outpatient Visits:** 4086 **Births:** 0 **Total Expense ($000):** 22078 **Payroll Expense ($000):** 11304 **Personnel:** 168

CA

Hospital, Medicare Provider Number, Address, Telephone, Approval, Facility, and Physician Codes, Health Care System

★ American Hospital Association (AHA) membership
☐ The Joint Commission accreditation
◇ DNV Healthcare Inc. accreditation
○ Healthcare Facilities Accreditation Program
△ Commission on Accreditation of Rehabilitation Facilities (CARF) accreditation

CA

☒ **SUTTER MEDICAL CENTER, SACRAMENTO (050108)**, 5151 F Street, Zip 95819–3295; tel. 916/454–3333, (Includes SUTTER CHILDREN'S CENTER, 5151 F. Street, Zip 95819–3223; tel. 800/478–8837; SUTTER GENERAL HOSPITAL, 2801 L Street, Zip 95816; tel. 916/454–2222), (Total facility includes 100 beds in nursing home–type unit) **A**1 2 3 5 9 10 **F**3 11 12 15 17 18 19 20 21 22 23 24 25 26 27 28 29 30 31 34 35 36 37 40 45 46 49 52 55 56 58 59 61 63 64 68 70 72 74 75 76 77 78 79 81 84 85 86 87 88 89 93 102 107 108 110 111 114 115 119 124 126 128 129 130 132 134 136 137 146 147 148 **S** Sutter Health, Sacramento, CA
Primary Contact: Carrie Owen–Plietz, Chief Executive Officer
COO: Faraaz Yousuf, Chief Operating Officer
CFO: Richard SooHoo, Chief Financial Officer
CMO: Muhammed Afzal, M.D., Chief of Staff
CIO: Jim Mills, Regional Director Information Technology
CHR: Colleen Peschel, Director Human Resources
CNO: Marchelle M. McGriff, Chief Nursing Executive
Web address: www.sutterhealth.org
Control: Other not–for–profit (including NFP Corporation) **Service:** General Medical and Surgical

> **Staffed Beds:** 620 **Admissions:** 30043 **Census:** 434 **Outpatient Visits:** 196891 **Births:** 5549 **Total Expense ($000):** 821085 **Payroll Expense ($000):** 252681 **Personnel:** 3747

☒ **UNIVERSITY OF CALIFORNIA, DAVIS MEDICAL CENTER (050599)**, 2315 Stockton Boulevard, Zip 95817–2282; tel. 916/734–2011, (Includes UNIVERSITY OF CALIFORNIA DAVIS CHILDREN'S HOSPITAL, 2315 Stockton Boulevard, Zip 95817–2201; tel. 800/282–3284) **A**1 2 3 5 8 9 10 **F**3 6 8 9 11 12 13 15 16 17 18 19 20 21 22 23 24 25 26 27 28 29 30 31 32 34 35 36 37 38 39 40 41 43 44 45 46 47 48 49 50 51 53 54 55 56 57 58 59 60 61 62 63 64 65 66 68 70 71 72 73 74 75 76 77 78 79 81 82 84 85 86 87 88 89 90 91 92 93 94 96 97 99 100 101 102 103 104 107 108 110 111 114 115 116 117 118 119 120 121 123 124 126 129 130 131 132 134 135 136 138 141 142 143 144 145 146 147 148 **P**6 **S** University of California–Systemwide Administration, Oakland, CA
Primary Contact: Ann Madden Rice, Chief Executive Officer
COO: Vincent Johnson, Chief Operating Officer
CFO: Timothy Maurice, Chief Financial Officer
CMO: J. Douglas Kirk, M.D., Chief Medical Officer
CIO: Michael N. Minear, Chief Information Officer
CHR: Stephen Chilcott, Associate Director Human Resources
CNO: Carol Robinson, R.N., Chief Patient Care Services Officer
Web address: www.ucdmc.ucdavis.edu
Control: Other not–for–profit (including NFP Corporation) **Service:** General Medical and Surgical

> **Staffed Beds:** 581 **Admissions:** 32654 **Census:** 473 **Outpatient Visits:** 1207624 **Births:** 1907 **Total Expense ($000):** 1411695 **Payroll Expense ($000):** 637564 **Personnel:** 7414

SAINT HELENA—Napa County

☒ **ST. HELENA HOSPITAL NAPA VALLEY (050013)**, 10 Woodland Road, Zip 94574–9554; tel. 707/963–3611 **A**1 9 10 **F**3 4 5 8 15 17 18 20 22 24 26 28 29 30 31 34 35 36 37 40 42 47 50 51 53 57 58 59 60 62 64 65 70 74 75 76 77 78 79 81 82 84 85 86 87 92 97 98 99 100 101 102 104 105 107 108 110 111 115 117 119 120 121 126 129 130 131 135 146 147 148 **P**3 **S** Adventist Health, Roseville, CA
Primary Contact: Steven Herber, M.D., FACS, President and Chief Executive Officer
CFO: Carlton Jacobson, Vice President
CMO: Steven Herber, M.D., President and Chief Executive Officer
CIO: Todd Peterson, Director Information Systems
CHR: Stacy Nelson, II, Director Human Resources
CNO: Nia Lendaris, Regional Vice President Patient Care
Web address: www.sthelenahospital.org
Control: Church–operated, Nongovernment, not–for profit **Service:** General Medical and Surgical

> **Staffed Beds:** 116 **Admissions:** 5386 **Census:** 62 **Outpatient Visits:** 90503 **Births:** 226 **Total Expense ($000):** 180013 **Payroll Expense ($000):** 56552 **Personnel:** 879

SALINAS—Monterey County

☒ **NATIVIDAD MEDICAL CENTER (050248)**, 1441 Constitution Boulevard, Zip 93906–3100, Mailing Address: P.O. Box 81611, Zip 93912–1611; tel. 831/647–7611 **A**1 3 5 9 10 **F**3 11 12 13 15 18 29 30 34 35 37 40 45 46 47 48 49 50 51 57 59 61 64 68 70 72 74 75 76 78 79 81 82 84 85 86 87 89 90 92 96 97 98 107 108 111 114 118 119 130 133 146 147 148 **P**6
Primary Contact: Kelly O'Keefe, Interim Chief Executive Officer
CMO: Gary Gray, D.O., Chief Medical Officer
CIO: Kirk Larson, Chief Information Officer
CHR: Janine Bouyea, Director Human Resources
Web address: www.natividad.com
Control: County–Government, nonfederal **Service:** General Medical and Surgical

> **Staffed Beds:** 141 **Admissions:** 7995 **Census:** 94 **Outpatient Visits:** 163495 **Births:** 2626 **Total Expense ($000):** 176723 **Payroll Expense ($000):** 58028 **Personnel:** 826

☒ **SALINAS VALLEY MEMORIAL HEALTHCARE SYSTEM (050334)**, 450 East Romie Lane, Zip 93901–4098; tel. 831/757–4333 **A**1 2 9 10 **F**3 13 15 17 18 19 20 22 24 26 28 29 31 34 35 37 40 45 46 49 57 58 59 64 68 70 72 74 75 76 77 78 79 81 84 85 87 89 107 108 110 111 115 118 119 126 129 130 146 148
Primary Contact: Pete Delgado, President and Chief Executive Officer
COO: James Griffith, Chief Operating Officer
CFO: Augustine Lopez, Chief Financial Officer
CMO: Allen Radner, M.D., Chief Medical Officer
CIO: Audrey Parks, Senior Administrative Director Information Technology
CHR: Michelle B. Childs, Senior Administrative Director Human Resources
CNO: Christie Gonder, Chief Nursing Officer
Web address: www.svmh.com
Control: Hospital district or authority, Government, nonfederal **Service:** General Medical and Surgical

> **Staffed Beds:** 185 **Admissions:** 10303 **Census:** 125 **Outpatient Visits:** 107156 **Births:** 1732 **Total Expense ($000):** 306677 **Payroll Expense ($000):** 142507 **Personnel:** 1080

SAN ANDREAS—Calaveras County

☒ **MARK TWAIN MEDICAL CENTER (051332)**, 768 Mountain Ranch Road, Zip 95249–9998; tel. 209/754–3521 **A**1 9 10 18 **F**3 8 11 12 15 18 28 29 30 31 33 34 35 36 38 40 41 44 45 46 47 48 49 50 53 54 56 57 59 64 65 66 68 70 75 77 78 79 81 82 83 84 85 86 87 92 93 96 97 99 102 104 107 108 110 111 114 117 119 127 130 131 132 133 144 145 146 147 148 **P**6 **S** Dignity Health, San Francisco, CA
Primary Contact: Craig J. Marks, FACHE, President
CFO: Jacob Lewis, Chief Financial Officer
CHR: Nancy Vargas, Director Human Resources
Web address: www.marktwainhospital.com
Control: Other not–for–profit (including NFP Corporation) **Service:** General Medical and Surgical

> **Staffed Beds:** 25 **Admissions:** 1302 **Census:** 12 **Outpatient Visits:** 72710 **Births:** 0 **Total Expense ($000):** 53278 **Payroll Expense ($000):** 21954 **Personnel:** 245

SAN BERNARDINO—San Bernardino County

☒ △ **BALLARD REHABILITATION HOSPITAL (053037)**, 1760 West 16th Street, Zip 92411–1160; tel. 909/473–1200 **A**1 7 9 10 **F**29 34 35 50 64 79 90 93 96 130 132 135 148 **S** Vibra Healthcare, Mechanicsburg, PA
Primary Contact: Mary Miles Hunt, Chief Executive Officer
COO: Mary Miles Hunt, Chief Executive Officer
CFO: Jonathan Silver, Chief Financial Officer
CMO: Van Chen, M.D., Medical Director
CNO: Chris Bauman, Director of Nursing
Web address: www.ballardrehab.com
Control: Corporation, Investor–owned, for–profit **Service:** Rehabilitation

> **Staffed Beds:** 45 **Admissions:** 1139 **Census:** 42 **Outpatient Visits:** 6542 **Births:** 0 **Total Expense ($000):** 20225 **Payroll Expense ($000):** 10378 **Personnel:** 162

☒ **COMMUNITY HOSPITAL OF SAN BERNARDINO (050089)**, 1805 Medical Center Drive, Zip 92411–1214; tel. 909/887–6333, (Total facility includes 122 beds in nursing home–type unit) **A**1 9 10 **F**8 11 13 15 20 28 29 30 31 32 34 35 40 45 46 47 48 49 50 57 59 60 62 65 68 70 72 74 75 76 77 79 81 82 86 87 89 94 98 100 101 104 107 108 111 119 128 130 132 135 146 147 148 **S** Dignity Health, San Francisco, CA
Primary Contact: June Collison, President
CFO: Ed Sorenson, Vice President Finance and Chief Financial Officer
CIO: Robert Redden, Site Director Information Technology
CHR: Denice C. Findlay, Director Human Resources
Web address: www.chsb.org
Control: Other not–for–profit (including NFP Corporation) **Service:** General Medical and Surgical

> **Staffed Beds:** 364 **Admissions:** 11541 **Census:** 246 **Outpatient Visits:** 93292 **Births:** 3005 **Total Expense ($000):** 214820 **Payroll Expense ($000):** 96540 **Personnel:** 1154

☒ **ST. BERNARDINE MEDICAL CENTER (050129)**, 2101 North Waterman Avenue, Zip 92404–4855; tel. 909/883–8711, (Nonreporting) **A**1 2 9 10 **S** Dignity Health, San Francisco, CA
Primary Contact: Steven R. Barron, President
CFO: Darryl VandenBosch, Vice President and Chief Financial Officer
CMO: Betty Daniels, M.D., Chief of Staff
CIO: James Croker, Director Information Systems
CHR: Dee Webb, Vice President Human Resources
Web address: www.stbernardinemedicalcenter.com
Control: Other not–for–profit (including NFP Corporation) **Service:** General Medical and Surgical

> **Staffed Beds:** 250

Many Facility Codes have changed. Please refer to the AHA Guide Code Chart. © 2014 AHA Guide

CA

SAN DIEGO—San Diego County

☒ **ALVARADO HOSPITAL MEDICAL CENTER (050757)**, 6655 Alvarado Road,
Zip 92120–5208; tel. 619/287–3270 **A**1 2 9 10 **F**3 7 12 15 17 18 20 22 24
26 28 29 31 34 35 36 40 46 53 55 56 59 60 61 64 65 68 70 74 75 77 78
79 80 81 82 84 86 87 90 93 96 107 108 111 114 115 118 119 129 130
132 146 148 **S** Prime Healthcare Services, Ontario, CA
Primary Contact: Robin Gomez, R.N., MSN, Administrator
CFO: Brian Kleven, Chief Financial Officer
CMO: Larry Emdur, D.O., Chief Medical Officer
CIO: Wayne Bartlett, Director Information Systems
CHR: Sara Turner, Director Human Resources
CNO: Peggy Jezsu, Chief Nursing Officer
Web address: www.alvaradohospital.com
Control: Corporation, Investor–owned, for–profit **Service:** General Medical and
Surgical

Staffed Beds: 83 **Admissions:** 6702 **Census:** 82 **Outpatient Visits:** 41860
Births: 0 **Total Expense ($000):** 152505

☐ **AURORA SAN DIEGO HOSPITAL (054095)**, 11878 Avenue of Industry,
Zip 92128–3490; tel. 858/487–3200 **A**1 9 10 **F**4 5 34 35 82 98 99 101 102
103 104 105 130 132 **S** Aurora Behavioral Health Care, Corona, CA
Primary Contact: James S. Plummer, Chief Executive Officer
COO: Barbara Kennison, Director Clinical Services
CFO: Gene Fantano, Chief Financial Officer
CMO: Thomas Flanagan, M.D., Medical Director
CIO: Alain Azcona, Director Business Development
CHR: Susan Haas, Director Human Resources
Web address: www.sandiego.aurorabehavioral.com/
Control: Individual, Investor–owned, for–profit **Service:** Psychiatric

Staffed Beds: 80 **Admissions:** 3632 **Census:** 67 **Outpatient Visits:** 1085
Births: 0 **Personnel:** 221

☒ **KAISER PERMANENTE SAN DIEGO MEDICAL CENTER (050515)**, 4647 Zion
Avenue, Zip 92120–2507; tel. 619/528–5000 **A**1 3 5 10 **F**3 8 13 14 15 29 30
31 40 41 45 46 47 48 49 50 51 54 55 56 58 59 60 61 62 63 64 65 68 70
71 72 74 75 77 78 79 81 82 83 84 85 86 87 97 100 102 103 104 107 108
111 114 115 117 118 119 130 131 132 144 146 148 **S** Kaiser Foundation
Hospitals, Oakland, CA
Primary Contact: E. Jane Finley, Senior Vice President and Executive Director
CFO: Lynette Seid, Area Chief Financial Officer
CMO: Paul E. Bernstein, M.D., Area Medical Director
CIO: Matthew T. Ebaugh, Area Information Officer
CHR: Cherie L. Sampson, Director Human Resources
Web address: www.kaiserpermanente.org
Control: Other not–for–profit (including NFP Corporation) **Service:** General
Medical and Surgical

Staffed Beds: 414 **Admissions:** 30793 **Census:** 282 **Outpatient Visits:**
177887 **Births:** 4562 **Personnel:** 3136

☒ **KINDRED HOSPITAL–SAN DIEGO (052036)**, 1940 El Cajon Boulevard,
Zip 92104–1096; tel. 619/543–4500 **A**1 9 10 **F**1 3 18 29 70 107 119
S Kindred Healthcare, Louisville, KY
Primary Contact: Cathryn Branch, R.N., Chief Executive Officer
CMO: Davies Wong, M.D., Medical Director
CHR: Jody Dewen Moore, District Director Human Resources
CNO: Maureen Bodine, Chief Clinical Officer
Web address: www.kindredsandiego.com
Control: Corporation, Investor–owned, for–profit **Service:** Long–Term Acute Care
hospital

Staffed Beds: 70 **Admissions:** 633 **Census:** 50 **Outpatient Visits:** 0 **Births:**
0 **Total Expense ($000):** 30239

☒ **NAVAL MEDICAL CENTER SAN DIEGO**, 34800 Bob Wilson Drive,
Zip 92134–5000; tel. 619/532–6400, (Nonreporting) **A**1 2 3 5 **S** Bureau of
Medicine and Surgery, Department of the Navy, Washington, DC
Primary Contact: Rear Admiral Bruce Gillingham, Commander
CFO: Captain O. G. Haugen, Director Resources
CIO: Lieutenant D. V. Gonzales, Head Information Technology Management
Web address: www.med.navy.mil/sites/nmcsd/Pages/default.aspx
Control: Navy, Government, federal **Service:** General Medical and Surgical

Staffed Beds: 285

☐ **PROMISE HOSPITAL OF SAN DIEGO (052051)**, 5550 University Avenue,
Zip 92105–2307; tel. 619/582–3800, (Nonreporting) **A**1 9 10 **S** Promise
Healthcare, Boca Raton, FL
Primary Contact: Chuck Smith, Interim Chief Executive Officer
CFO: Kevin Ohler, Director of Finance
CMO: Larry Emdur, D.O., Chief of Staff
CIO: Jim Wilson, Vice President Information Technology
CHR: Kathleen Greene, Director Human Resources
CNO: Kevin Wood, Interim Chief Clinical Officer
Web address: www.promisesandiego.com
Control: Corporation, Investor–owned, for–profit **Service:** Long–Term Acute Care
hospital

Staffed Beds: 100

☒ **RADY CHILDREN'S HOSPITAL – SAN DIEGO (053303)**, 3020 Childrens Way,
Zip 92123–4223; tel. 858/576–1700, (Total facility includes 43 beds in nursing
home–type unit) **A**1 3 5 9 10 **F**1 3 4 7 8 9 10 11 12 16 17 19 20 21 22 23 24
25 26 27 28 29 30 31 32 34 35 36 38 39 40 41 43 45 46 47 48 50 54 55
57 58 59 60 62 63 64 65 67 68 70 72 73 74 75 77 78 79 80 81 82 83 84
85 86 87 88 89 90 91 92 93 94 98 99 100 101 102 104 105 106 107 108
111 114 115 118 119 122 124 128 129 130 131 132 133 134 135 136 137
138 139 141 143 144 145 146 148 **P**3 5
Primary Contact: Donald Kearns, M.D., Acting President
COO: Meg Norton, Executive Vice President and Chief Administrative Officer
CFO: Roger Roux, Chief Financial Officer
CMO: Irvin A. Kaufman, M.D., Chief Medical Officer
CIO: Albert Oriol, Vice President Information Management and Chief Information
Officer
CHR: Mamoon Syed, Vice President Human Resources
CNO: Mary Fagan, MSN, Chief Nursing Officer
Web address: www.rchsd.org
Control: Other not–for–profit (including NFP Corporation) **Service:** Children's
general

Staffed Beds: 377 **Admissions:** 17650 **Census:** 235 **Outpatient Visits:**
289719 **Births:** 0 **Total Expense ($000):** 739829 **Payroll Expense ($000):**
268226 **Personnel:** 3714

RADY CHILDREN'S HOSPITAL AND HEALTH CENTER See Rady Children's
Hospital – San Diego

☐ **SAN DIEGO COUNTY PSYCHIATRIC HOSPITAL (054114)**, 3853 Rosecrans
Street, Zip 92110–3115, Mailing Address: P.O. Box 85524, Zip 92186–5524;
tel. 619/692–8211, (Nonreporting) **A**1 10
Primary Contact: Izabela Karmach, R.N., Administrator
COO: Izabela Karmach, R.N., Administrator
CFO: Raul J. Loyo–Rodriguez, Administrative Analyst III
CMO: Michael Krelstein, M.D., Medical Director
CIO: Linda Cannon, Chief Medical Records Services
CHR: Francisco Puentes, Human Resource Officer
Web address: www.sdcounty.ca.gov
Control: County–Government, nonfederal **Service:** Psychiatric

Staffed Beds: 357

SAN DIEGO MEDICAL CENTER See Kaiser Permanente San Diego Medical
Center

☒ **SCRIPPS MERCY HOSPITAL (050077)**, 4077 Fifth Avenue, Zip 92103–2105;
tel. 619/294–8111, (Includes SCRIPPS MERCY HOSPITAL CHULA VISTA, 435 H
Street, Chula Vista, Zip 91912–6617, Mailing Address: P.O. Box 1537,
Zip 91910–1537; tel. 619/691–7000) **A**1 2 3 5 9 10 **F**3 8 11 12 13 14 15 17
18 20 22 24 26 28 29 30 31 32 34 35 39 40 43 44 45 46 49 50 51 54 56
57 58 59 61 64 65 66 68 70 73 74 75 76 77 78 79 81 82 83 84 85 86 87
92 93 97 98 100 101 102 103 104 105 107 108 110 111 114 115 118 119
126 129 130 132 134 135 141 146 147 148 **P**5 **S** Scripps Health, San
Diego, CA
Primary Contact: Thomas A. Gammiere, Chief Executive, Senior Vice President
CFO: Edward Turk, Vice President Finance
CMO: Davis Cracroft, M.D., Senior Director Medical Affairs
CIO: Drexel DeFord, Chief Information Officer
Web address: www.scrippshealth.org
Control: Other not–for–profit (including NFP Corporation) **Service:** General
Medical and Surgical

Staffed Beds: 436 **Admissions:** 33331 **Census:** 418 **Outpatient Visits:**
166815 **Births:** 3777 **Total Expense ($000):** 657178 **Payroll Expense
($000):** 252042 **Personnel:** 3254

Hospital, Medicare Provider Number, Address, Telephone, Approval, Facility, and Physician Codes, Health Care System

★ American Hospital Association (AHA) membership
☐ The Joint Commission accreditation   ◇ DNV Healthcare Inc. accreditation
○ Healthcare Facilities Accreditation Program
△ Commission on Accreditation of Rehabilitation Facilities (CARF) accreditation

✠ △ **SHARP MEMORIAL HOSPITAL (050100)**, 7901 Frost Street,
Zip 92123–2701; tel. 858/939–3400 **A**1 2 7 9 10 **F**3 8 11 12 15 18 20 22 24
26 28 29 30 31 33 34 35 36 40 43 44 45 46 49 55 56 57 58 59 60 62 64
65 68 70 74 75 77 78 79 81 82 84 85 86 87 90 91 93 94 96 97 107 108
110 114 115 119 120 121 123 124 126 129 130 131 132 135 137 138 142
143 145 146 148 **S** Sharp HealthCare, San Diego, CA
Primary Contact: Tim Smith, Senior Vice President and Chief Executive Officer
COO: Janie Kramer, Chief Operating Officer
CFO: Bernie Thibodeau, Interim Chief Financial Officer
CMO: Geoffrey Stiles, M.D., Chief Medical Officer
CIO: Kenneth Lawonn, Senior Vice President and Chief Information Officer
CHR: Connie Duquette, Director Human Resources
CNO: Pamela Wells, R.N., Chief Nursing Officer
Web address: www.sharp.com
Control: Other not–for–profit (including NFP Corporation) **Service:** General
Medical and Surgical

> **Staffed Beds:** 382 **Admissions:** 19230 **Census:** 260 **Outpatient Visits:**
> 365194 **Births:** 0 **Total Expense ($000):** 625647 **Payroll Expense ($000):**
> 230176 **Personnel:** 3100

✠ **SHARP MESA VISTA HOSPITAL (054145)**, 7850 Vista Hill Avenue,
Zip 92123–2717; tel. 858/278–4110, (Includes SHARP MCDONALD CENTER,
7989 Linda Vista Road, Zip 92111–5106; tel. 858/637–6920) **A**1 9 10 **F**4 5 29
35 40 43 56 58 64 87 98 99 100 101 102 103 104 105 130 132 135 143
146 **S** Sharp HealthCare, San Diego, CA
Primary Contact: Kathi Lencioni, Senior Vice President and Chief Executive Officer
CFO: Kevin Thompson, Chief Financial Officer
CMO: Michael Plopper, M.D., Chief Medical Officer
CIO: Kenneth Lawonn, Senior Vice President Information Systems
CHR: Carlisle Lewis, III, Senior Vice President Legal and Human Resources
CNO: Cheryl Odell, R.N., Chief Nursing Officer
Web address: www.sharp.com
Control: Other not–for–profit (including NFP Corporation) **Service:** Psychiatric

> **Staffed Beds:** 163 **Admissions:** 6124 **Census:** 122 **Outpatient Visits:** 92506
> **Births:** 0 **Total Expense ($000):** 67546 **Payroll Expense ($000):** 39276
> **Personnel:** 536

✠ **UC SAN DIEGO HEALTH SYSTEM (050025)**, 200 West Arbor Drive,
Zip 92103–9000; tel. 619/543–6222 **A**1 2 3 5 8 9 10 **F**3 6 9 11 12 13 15 16
17 18 20 22 24 26 29 30 31 34 36 37 40 43 44 45 46 47 48 49 50 51 54
55 56 57 58 59 60 61 64 65 66 68 70 72 73 74 75 76 77 78 79 80 81 82
84 85 86 87 91 92 93 97 98 99 100 101 102 103 107 108 109 110 111
113 114 115 117 118 119 120 121 123 124 126 129 130 131 132 136 137
138 139 140 141 142 145 146 147 148 **P**1 **S** University of
California–Systemwide Administration, Oakland, CA
Primary Contact: Paul S. Viviano, Chief Executive Officer
COO: Margarita Baggett, MSN, Interim Chief Operating Officer
CFO: Lori Donaldson, Chief Financial Officer
CMO: Angela Scioscia, M.D., Chief Medical Officer
CIO: Ed Babakanian, Chief Information Officer
CHR: William J. Murin, Chief Human Resources Officer
CNO: Margarita Baggett, MSN, Chief Nursing Officer
Web address: www.health.ucsd.edu
Control: State–Government, nonfederal **Service:** General Medical and Surgical

> **Staffed Beds:** 524 **Admissions:** 27674 **Census:** 427 **Outpatient Visits:**
> 682310 **Births:** 2446 **Total Expense ($000):** 1003085 **Payroll Expense**
> **($000):** 387263 **Personnel:** 5341

UNIVERSITY OF CALIFORNIA SAN DIEGO MEDICAL CENTER See UC San
Diego Health System

✠ △ **VETERANS AFFAIRS SAN DIEGO HEALTHCARE SYSTEM**, 3350 LaJolla
Village Drive, Zip 92161–0002; tel. 858/552–8585, (Total facility includes 39
beds in nursing home–type unit) **A**1 3 5 7 8 **F**1 3 4 5 12 15 18 20 22 24 26 29
30 34 35 36 37 38 39 40 44 45 46 47 48 49 50 54 55 56 57 58 59 60 61
62 63 64 65 68 71 74 75 77 79 80 81 82 83 84 85 86 87 90 91 92 93 94
95 96 97 98 100 101 102 103 104 105 106 107 110 111 114 115 116 117
118 119 126 129 130 132 135 143 144 145 146 147 148 **S** Department of
Veterans Affairs, Washington, DC
Primary Contact: Jeffrey T. Gering, FACHE, Director
COO: Cynthia Abair, Associate Director
CFO: Ronald Larson, Chief Financial Officer
CMO: Robert M. Smith, M.D., Chief of Staff
CIO: Ruey Keller, Acting Chief Information Officer
CHR: Stephanie Wright, Director Human Resources Management
Web address: www.sandiego.va.gov
Control: Veterans Affairs, Government, federal **Service:** General Medical and
Surgical

> **Staffed Beds:** 216 **Admissions:** 7800 **Census:** 150 **Outpatient Visits:**
> 822512 **Births:** 0 **Total Expense ($000):** 625907 **Payroll Expense ($000):**
> 254645 **Personnel:** 2898

✠ **VIBRA HOSPITAL OF SAN DIEGO (052044)**, 555 Washington Street,
Zip 92103–2294; tel. 619/260–8300, (Nonreporting) **A**1 9 10 **S** Vibra
Healthcare, Mechanicsburg, PA
Primary Contact: Natalie Germuska, R.N., MSN, Chief Executive Officer
COO: Tim Clark, Chief Operating Officer and Chief Clinical Officer
CFO: Mike Gonzales, Chief Financial Officer
CMO: John Fox, M.D., Chief Medical Officer
CHR: Tamia Khalique, Director Human Resources
Web address: www.vhsandiego.com/
Control: Corporation, Investor–owned, for–profit **Service:** Long–Term Acute Care
hospital

> **Staffed Beds:** 57

SAN DIMAS—Los Angeles County

☐ **SAN DIMAS COMMUNITY HOSPITAL (050588)**, 1350 West Covina Boulevard,
Zip 91773–3219; tel. 909/599–6811 **A**1 9 10 **F**3 8 13 15 29 30 40 45 46 49
50 70 79 81 85 107 108 110 115 119 130 146 148 **S** Prime Healthcare
Services, Ontario, CA
Primary Contact: Kevan Metcalfe, Chief Executive Officer
CFO: Robert Bonner, Chief Financial Officer
CMO: Zuhair Yahya, M.D., Chief Medical Officer
CIO: Jason Beckett, Director Information Services
Web address: www.sandimashospital.com/
Control: Corporation, Investor–owned, for–profit **Service:** General Medical and
Surgical

> **Staffed Beds:** 101 **Admissions:** 4074 **Census:** 38 **Outpatient Visits:** 21706
> **Births:** 410 **Total Expense ($000):** 53352 **Payroll Expense ($000):** 18763
> **Personnel:** 419

SAN FRANCISCO—San Francisco County

✠ △ **CALIFORNIA PACIFIC MEDICAL CENTER (050047)**, 2333 Buchanan
Street, Zip 94115–1925, Mailing Address: P.O. Box 7999, Zip 94120–7999;
tel. 415/600–6000, (Includes CALIFORNIA PACIFIC MEDICAL CENTER–DAVIES
CAMPUS, Castro and Duboce Streets, Zip 94114; tel. 415/565–6000), (Total
facility includes 94 beds in nursing home–type unit) **A**1 2 3 5 7 8 9 10 **F**2 6 7 8
12 13 15 17 18 19 20 22 24 26 27 28 29 30 31 32 34 35 36 38 39 40 41
46 51 52 55 56 57 58 59 60 61 63 65 68 70 72 74 75 76 77 78 79 81 82
84 85 86 87 88 89 90 93 96 97 98 101 102 104 107 108 110 111 114 115
117 118 119 121 126 128 130 132 133 135 136 137 138 139 141 142 143
144 145 146 147 148 **S** Sutter Health, Sacramento, CA
Primary Contact: Warren S. Browner, M.D., M.P.H., Chief Executive Officer
CFO: John Gates, Vice President Finance and Chief Financial Officer
CMO: Allan Pont, M.D., Vice President Medical Affairs
CIO: Craig Vercruysse, Chief Information Officer
CNO: Diana M. Karner, R.N., Chief Nursing Officer
Web address: www.cpmc.org
Control: Other not–for–profit (including NFP Corporation) **Service:** General
Medical and Surgical

> **Staffed Beds:** 724 **Admissions:** 25942 **Census:** 392 **Outpatient Visits:**
> 447099 **Births:** 5160 **Total Expense ($000):** 1116383 **Payroll Expense**
> **($000):** 346776 **Personnel:** 3886

✠ **CHINESE HOSPITAL (050407)**, 845 Jackson Street, Zip 94133–4899;
tel. 415/982–2400 **A**1 9 10 **F**3 11 15 18 29 30 31 34 35 40 45 47 49 50 57
59 60 64 65 70 75 77 78 79 81 86 87 97 107 108 110 115 118 119 130
132 135 145 146 147
Primary Contact: Brenda Yee, R.N., MSN, Chief Executive Officer
COO: Linda Schumacher, Chief Operating Officer
CFO: Thomas Bolger, Chief Financial Officer
CMO: William Chung, M.D., Chief of Staff
CIO: Abel Lai, Manager Information Systems
CHR: Lydia Mahr–CHan, Director Human Resources
CNO: Peggy Cmiel, R.N., Chief Nursing Officer
Web address: www.chinesehospital–sf.org
Control: Other not–for–profit (including NFP Corporation) **Service:** General
Medical and Surgical

> **Staffed Beds:** 30 **Admissions:** 1890 **Census:** 31 **Outpatient Visits:** 68392
> **Births:** 0 **Total Expense ($000):** 65103 **Payroll Expense ($000):** 30283
> **Personnel:** 272

JEWISH HOME OF SAN FRANCISCO (054089), 302 Silver Avenue,
Zip 94112–1510; tel. 415/334–2500, (Nonreporting) **A**10
Primary Contact: Daniel R. Ruth, President and Chief Executive Officer
COO: Kevin Ward, Chief Operating Officer
CFO: Victor E. Meinke, Chief Financial Officer
CNO: Edwin Cabigao, Chief Nursing Officer
Web address: www.jhsf.org
Control: Other not–for–profit (including NFP Corporation) **Service:** Psychiatric

> **Staffed Beds:** 12

CA

✠ **KAISER PERMANENTE SAN FRANCISCO MEDICAL CENTER (050076),** 2425 Geary Boulevard, Zip 94115–3358; tel. 415/833–2000 **A**1 3 5 10 **F**3 8 13 15 17 18 19 20 21 22 23 24 26 28 29 30 31 32 33 35 40 41 44 45 46 49 50 52 60 61 62 64 65 66 68 70 72 74 75 76 77 78 79 81 82 84 85 86 87 89 100 107 108 111 119 130 141 146 **P**2 **S** Kaiser Foundation Hospitals, Oakland, CA
Primary Contact: Christine Robisch, Senior Vice President and Area Manager
COO: Helen Archer–Duste, Chief Operating Officer
CFO: Alex Khoo, Interim Area Finance Officer
CMO: Robert Mithun, M.D., Physician in Chief
CIO: Peti Arunamata, Interim Area Director Information Technology
CHR: Diane J. Easterwood, Human Resources Business Partner
Web address: www.kaiserpermanente.org
Control: Other not–for–profit (including NFP Corporation) **Service:** General Medical and Surgical

Staffed Beds: 215 **Admissions:** 11516 **Census:** 150 **Outpatient Visits:** 53083 **Births:** 2701 **Personnel:** 2197

★ **LAGUNA HONDA HOSPITAL AND REHABILITATION CENTER (050668),** (GACH with Distinct Part SNF Services), 375 Laguna Honda Boulevard, Zip 94116–1499; tel. 415/759–2300, (Total facility includes 769 beds in nursing home–type unit) **A**10 **F**3 29 30 53 56 61 63 64 65 74 75 77 82 83 84 90 92 93 94 100 103 104 127 128 130 132 135 146 148
Primary Contact: Mivic Hirose, Executive Administrator
COO: Michael R. Llewellyn, Chief Operating Officer
CFO: Tess Navarro, Chief Financial Officer
CMO: Colleen Riley, M.D., Medical Director
CIO: Pat Skala, Chief Information Officer
CHR: Willie Ramirez, Manager Labor Relations
Web address: www.lagunahonda.org/
Control: City–County, Government, nonfederal **Service:** Other specialty

Staffed Beds: 780 **Admissions:** 988 **Census:** 756 **Births:** 0

✠ △ **SAINT FRANCIS MEMORIAL HOSPITAL (050152),** 900 Hyde Street, Zip 94109–4899, Mailing Address: P.O. Box 7726, Zip 94120–7726; tel. 415/353–6000, (Nonreporting) **A**1 2 7 9 10 **S** Dignity Health, San Francisco, CA
Primary Contact: Hugh Vincent, M.D., Interim Chief Executive Officer
CFO: Alan Fox, Chief Financial Officer
CHR: Richard Mead, Senior Director Human Resources
Web address: www.saintfrancismemorial.org
Control: Other not–for–profit (including NFP Corporation) **Service:** General Medical and Surgical

Staffed Beds: 239

✠ **SAN FRANCISCO GENERAL HOSPITAL AND TRAUMA CENTER (050228),** 1001 Potrero Avenue, Zip 94110–3594; tel. 415/206–8000 **A**1 2 3 5 8 10 **F**3 13 15 17 18 20 22 29 30 34 35 36 38 39 40 43 44 45 46 47 48 49 50 57 58 59 60 61 64 65 68 70 71 72 74 75 76 77 78 79 81 82 83 84 86 87 89 92 93 94 97 98 99 100 102 105 107 108 110 111 119 128 129 130 131 132 135 144 146 147 148
Primary Contact: Sue Currin, R.N., MS, Chief Executive Officer
COO: Sharon McCole–Wicher, R.N., Chief Nursing Officer
CFO: Valerie Inouye, Chief Financial Officer
CMO: John Luce, M.D., Chief Medical Officer
CIO: Pat Skala, Chief Information Officer
Web address: www.sfdph.org
Control: City–County, Government, nonfederal **Service:** General Medical and Surgical

Staffed Beds: 441 **Admissions:** 16158 **Census:** 349 **Outpatient Visits:** 592678 **Births:** 1145 **Total Expense ($000):** 674691 **Payroll Expense ($000):** 419132

SAN FRANCISCO MEDICAL CENTER See Kaiser Permanente San Francisco Medical Center

✠ **SAN FRANCISO VETERANS AFFAIRS MEDICAL CENTER,** 4150 Clement Street, Zip 94121–1545; tel. 415/221–4810, (Total facility includes 120 beds in nursing home–type unit) **A**1 2 3 5 **F**3 5 8 12 17 18 20 22 24 26 28 29 30 31 34 35 37 38 39 40 45 46 47 48 49 50 54 56 57 58 59 60 61 62 63 64 65 70 74 75 77 78 79 81 82 83 84 86 87 92 93 94 97 98 100 101 102 103 104 105 106 107 108 109 111 112 114 115 116 117 118 119 126 127 128 129 130 132 135 143 144 145 146 147 148 **P**1 **S** Department of Veterans Affairs, Washington, DC
Primary Contact: Bonnie S. Graham, Director
COO: Ezra R. Safdie, Associate Director
CFO: Brian Kelly, Acting Chief Fiscal Service
CIO: Judith A. Ringler, Chief Information Resources Management
CHR: Terrence Vail, Acting Chief Human Resources Management Services
Web address: www.sanfrancisco.va.gov/
Control: Veterans Affairs, Government, federal **Service:** General Medical and Surgical

Staffed Beds: 244 **Admissions:** 5512 **Census:** 192 **Outpatient Visits:** 614770 **Births:** 0 **Total Expense ($000):** 574841 **Payroll Expense ($000):** 220662 **Personnel:** 2992

✠ **ST. LUKE'S HOSPITAL (050055),** 3555 Cesar Chavez Street, Zip 94110–4403; tel. 415/600–6000, (Total facility includes 19 beds in nursing home–type unit) **A**1 5 10 **F**8 13 18 20 29 30 34 35 40 55 63 66 67 68 70 72 75 76 77 78 79 81 82 85 87 89 93 97 100 107 108 110 111 114 118 119 128 130 143 146 147 148 **S** Sutter Health, Sacramento, CA
Primary Contact: Warren S. Browner, M.D., M.P.H., Chief Executive Officer
COO: Rick Stevens, Chief Administrative Officer
CFO: John Gates, Chief Financial Officer
CMO: Jerome Franz, M.D., Chief Medical Staff
CIO: Rob Seide, Manager Marketing and Communications
CHR: Linda Isaacs, Vice President Human Resources
Web address: www.stlukes–sf.org
Control: Other not–for–profit (including NFP Corporation) **Service:** General Medical and Surgical

Staffed Beds: 174 **Admissions:** 3886 **Census:** 87 **Outpatient Visits:** 78822 **Births:** 954 **Total Expense ($000):** 166459 **Payroll Expense ($000):** 46685 **Personnel:** 525

✠ **ST. MARY'S MEDICAL CENTER (050457),** 450 Stanyan Street, Zip 94117–1079; tel. 415/668–1000, (Nonreporting) **A**1 2 3 5 9 10 **S** Dignity Health, San Francisco, CA
Primary Contact: Anna Cheung, President
COO: Deborah Kolhede, Vice President and Chief Operating Officer
CFO: Eric Brettner, Vice President and Chief Financial Officer
CMO: Francis Charlton, Jr., M.D., Chief Medical Staff
CHR: Barbara Morrissett, Vice President Human Resources
CNO: Barbara Eusebio, R.N., Vice President, Chief Nurse Executive
Web address: www.stmarysmedicalcenter.com
Control: Other not–for–profit (including NFP Corporation) **Service:** General Medical and Surgical

Staffed Beds: 232

✠ **UCSF MEDICAL CENTER (050454),** 500 Parnassus Avenue, Zip 94143–0296, Mailing Address: 500 Parnassus Avenue, Box 0296, Zip 94143–0296; tel. 415/476–1000, (Includes UCSF BENIOFF CHILDREN'S HOSPITAL, 500 Parnassus Avenue, Zip 94143–2203, Mailing Address: 505 Parnassus Avenue, Zip 94143–2203; tel. 888/689–8273) **A**1 2 3 5 8 9 10 **F**3 6 7 8 9 10 11 13 14 15 17 18 19 20 21 22 23 24 25 26 27 29 30 31 32 33 34 35 36 37 39 40 41 43 44 45 46 47 48 49 50 51 52 53 54 55 56 57 58 59 60 61 62 63 64 65 66 68 70 72 74 75 76 77 78 79 81 82 83 84 85 86 87 88 89 92 93 94 95 96 97 99 100 101 102 103 104 105 107 108 109 110 111 112 113 114 115 116 117 118 119 120 121 123 124 126 129 130 131 132 134 135 136 137 138 139 140 141 142 144 145 146 147 148 **P**6 **S** University of California–Systemwide Administration, Oakland, CA
Primary Contact: Mark R. Laret, Chief Executive Officer
COO: Ken M. Jones, Chief Operating Officer
CFO: Barrie Strickland, Chief Financial Officer
CMO: Josh Adler, M.D., Chief Medical Officer
CIO: Joe Bergfort, Chief Information Officer
CHR: David Odato, Chief Administrative and Chief Human Resources Officer
CNO: Sheila Antrum, R.N., Chief Nursing Officer, Director Patient Care Services
Web address: www.ucsfhealth.org
Control: Other not–for–profit (including NFP Corporation) **Service:** General Medical and Surgical

Staffed Beds: 650 **Admissions:** 28440 **Census:** 485 **Outpatient Visits:** 979297 **Births:** 1914 **Total Expense ($000):** 2057676 **Payroll Expense ($000):** 772994 **Personnel:** 6852

VETERANS AFFAIRS MEDICAL CENTER See San Francisco Veterans Affairs Medical Center

---

Hospital, Medicare Provider Number, Address, Telephone, Approval, Facility, and Physician Codes, Health Care System

★ American Hospital Association (AHA) membership
☐ The Joint Commission accreditation ◇ DNV Healthcare Inc. accreditation

◯ Healthcare Facilities Accreditation Program
△ Commission on Accreditation of Rehabilitation Facilities (CARF) accreditation

CA

SAN GABRIEL—Los Angeles County

☐ **SAN GABRIEL VALLEY MEDICAL CENTER (050132)**, 438 West Las Tunas Drive, Zip 91776–1216, Mailing Address: P.O. Box 1507, Zip 91778–1507; tel. 626/289–5454 **A**1 9 10 **F**3 13 15 18 29 31 34 35 36 40 44 45 49 50 56 57 59 64 68 70 72 74 75 76 77 78 79 81 84 85 86 87 98 102 103 107 108 115 119 120 128 130 143 146 147 148 **S** AHMC & Healthcare, Inc., Alhambra, CA
Primary Contact: Howard Ternes, Chief Executive Officer
COO: Karen Price–Gharzeddine, R.N., Chief Nursing Officer and Chief Operating Officer
CFO: Andrew Grim, Chief Financial Officer
CIO: Bernie Sauer, Director Information Technology
CHR: Victor Voisard, Director Human Resources
CNO: Karen Price–Gharzeddine, R.N., Chief Operating Officer and Chief Nursing Officer
Web address: www.sgvmc.org
Control: Partnership, Investor–owned, for–profit **Service:** General Medical and Surgical

Staffed Beds: 273 **Admissions:** 9737 **Census:** 163 **Outpatient Visits:** 28791 **Births:** 2858 **Total Expense ($000):** 142066 **Payroll Expense ($000):** 66001 **Personnel:** 751

SAN JOSE—Santa Clara County

✠ **GOOD SAMARITAN HOSPITAL (050380)**, 2425 Samaritan Drive, Zip 95124–3997, Mailing Address: P.O. Box 240002, Zip 95154–2402; tel. 408/559–2011 **A**1 2 9 10 **F**2 3 5 8 11 12 13 15 17 18 19 20 21 22 23 24 25 26 27 28 29 30 31 34 35 37 38 40 44 45 46 47 48 49 50 54 57 58 59 60 63 64 68 70 72 74 75 76 77 78 79 81 82 83 84 85 86 87 88 89 90 93 96 98 101 102 104 105 107 108 110 111 114 115 116 117 118 119 120 121 123 124 126 130 132 146 147 148 **S** HCA, Nashville, TN
Primary Contact: Paul Beaupre, M.D., Chief Executive Officer
COO: Jordan Herget, Chief Operating Officer
CFO: Lana Arad, Chief Financial Officer
CMO: Bruce Wilbur, M.D., Chief Medical Officer
CIO: Darrell O'Dell, Director Information Services
CHR: Edward Battista, Vice President Human Resources
CNO: Darina Kavanagh, R.N., Chief Nursing Officer
Web address: www.goodsamsanjose.com
Control: Corporation, Investor–owned, for–profit **Service:** General Medical and Surgical

Staffed Beds: 376 **Admissions:** 16303 **Census:** 215 **Outpatient Visits:** 133335 **Births:** 3573 **Total Expense ($000):** 324908 **Payroll Expense ($000):** 178562 **Personnel:** 989

✠ **KAISER PERMANENTE SAN JOSE MEDICAL CENTER (050604)**, 250 Hospital Parkway, Zip 95119–1199; tel. 408/972–7000 **A**1 10 **F**3 8 13 17 18 20 22 29 30 31 35 40 46 49 51 56 68 70 72 73 74 76 78 79 81 82 84 85 87 89 104 107 108 110 111 114 115 119 130 141 146 148 **S** Kaiser Foundation Hospitals, Oakland, CA
Primary Contact: Irene Chavez, Senior Vice President and Area Manager
COO: Irene Chavez, Senior Vice President and Area Manager
CFO: Stephen L. Kalsman, Area Finance Officer
CMO: Raj Bhandari, M.D., Physician–in–Chief
CIO: Greg Tuck, Area Information Officer
CHR: Susan Franzella, Human Resource Business Partner
CNO: Theresa R. Nero, R.N., Chief Nursing Officer
Web address: www.kaiserpermanente.org
Control: Other not–for–profit (including NFP Corporation) **Service:** General Medical and Surgical

Staffed Beds: 217 **Admissions:** 13156 **Census:** 126 **Outpatient Visits:** 179061 **Births:** 2041 **Personnel:** 1911

✠ **O'CONNOR HOSPITAL (050153)**, 2105 Forest Avenue, Zip 95128–1471; tel. 408/947–2500 **A**1 2 9 10 **F**1 3 8 11 13 15 18 19 20 22 24 26 28 29 30 31 34 35 37 40 44 46 48 49 50 53 54 57 59 60 64 66 68 70 72 74 75 76 77 78 79 81 84 85 86 87 89 93 97 100 107 108 110 111 114 116 117 118 119 121 123 128 130 131 132 135 146 147 148 **S** Daughters of Charity Health System, Los Altos Hills, CA
Primary Contact: James F. Dover, FACHE, President and CEO
CFO: David W. Carroll, Chief Financial Officer
CMO: George Block, M.D., Chief Medical Officer
CIO: Richard Hutsell, Vice President and Chief Information Officer, Daughters of Charity Health System
CHR: Julie Hatcher, Vice President Human Resources
Web address: www.oconnorhospital.org
Control: Other not–for–profit (including NFP Corporation) **Service:** General Medical and Surgical

Staffed Beds: 202 **Admissions:** 11655 **Census:** 143 **Outpatient Visits:** 157654 **Births:** 3241 **Total Expense ($000):** 321223 **Payroll Expense ($000):** 143074 **Personnel:** 937

✠ **REGIONAL MEDICAL CENTER OF SAN JOSE (050125)**, 225 North Jackson Avenue, Zip 95116–1603; tel. 408/259–5000, (Nonreporting) **A**1 9 10 **S** HCA, Nashville, TN
Primary Contact: Michael T. Johnson, Chief Executive Officer
COO: Brian J. Knecht, Chief Operating Officer
CFO: Raju Iyer, Chief Financial Officer
CMO: William Scott, M.D., Vice President Medical Affairs
CIO: Shirley Joyal, Director Information Systems
CHR: Nancy Clark, Vice President Human Resources
Web address: www.regionalmedicalsanjose.com
Control: Partnership, Investor–owned, for–profit **Service:** General Medical and Surgical

Staffed Beds: 193

SAN JOSE MEDICAL CENTER See Kaiser Permanente San Jose Medical Center

☐ △ **SANTA CLARA VALLEY MEDICAL CENTER (050038)**, 751 South Bascom Avenue, Zip 95128–2699; tel. 408/885–5000 **A**1 3 5 7 9 10 **F**3 5 9 12 13 15 16 17 18 19 20 21 22 23 24 25 26 27 28 29 30 31 32 34 35 39 40 43 45 46 47 48 49 50 51 52 55 56 58 59 60 61 64 65 66 68 70 71 72 73 74 75 76 77 78 79 80 81 82 83 84 85 86 87 88 89 90 92 93 97 98 99 100 101 102 103 104 107 108 109 110 111 112 114 115 116 117 118 119 120 121 122 123 124 129 130 131 132 134 135 143 144 146 147 148 **P**6
Primary Contact: Paul E. Lorenz, Chief Executive Officer
COO: Benita McLarin, Chief Operating Officer
CMO: Jeffrey Arnold, M.D., Chief Medical Officer
CIO: Lee Herrmann, Chief Healthcare Technology Officer
CHR: David Manson, Manager Human Resources
CNO: Trudy Johnson, R.N., Chief Nursing Officer
Web address: www.scvmed.org
Control: County–Government, nonfederal **Service:** General Medical and Surgical

Staffed Beds: 330 **Admissions:** 22185 **Census:** 322 **Outpatient Visits:** 866561 **Births:** 3896 **Total Expense ($000):** 1139019 **Payroll Expense ($000):** 438516

SAN LEANDRO—Alameda County

ALAMEDA COUNTY MEDICAL CENTER–FAIRMONT CAMPUS See Alameda County Medical Center, Oakland

✠ **KINDRED HOSPITAL–SAN FRANCISCO BAY AREA (052034)**, 2800 Benedict Drive, Zip 94577–6840; tel. 510/357–8300 **A**1 9 10 **F**1 107 **S** Kindred Healthcare, Louisville, KY
Primary Contact: Ed Kelly, Chief Executive Officer
CFO: Ziba Aflak, Chief Financial Officer
CHR: Erin Greene, Coordinator Human Resources
CNO: Emily Gard, Chief Clinical Officer
Web address: www.kindredhospitalsfba.com
Control: Corporation, Investor–owned, for–profit **Service:** Long–Term Acute Care hospital

Staffed Beds: 99 **Admissions:** 520 **Census:** 53 **Outpatient Visits:** 0 **Births:** 0

SAN LEANDRO HOSPITAL (050773), 13855 East 14th Street, Zip 94578–2600; tel. 510/357–6500, (Nonreporting) **A**10 **S** Alameda Health System, San Leandro, CA
Primary Contact: James E. T. Jackson, M.P.H., Chief Administrative Officer
Web address: www.sanleandrohospital.org
Control: Other not–for–profit (including NFP Corporation) **Service:** General Medical and Surgical

Staffed Beds: 80

☐ **WILLOW ROCK CENTER (054149)**, 2050 Fairmont Drive, Zip 94578–1001; tel. 510/895–5502 **A**1 10 **F**29 34 57 98 99 101
Primary Contact: John Adams, Administrator
Web address: www.tbhcare.com
Control: Individual, Investor–owned, for–profit **Service:** Children's hospital psychiatric

Staffed Beds: 16 **Admissions:** 577 **Census:** 10 **Outpatient Visits:** 0 **Births:** 0 **Total Expense ($000):** 5314 **Payroll Expense ($000):** 2289 **Personnel:** 46

SAN LUIS OBISPO—San Luis Obispo County

CALIFORNIA MENS COLONY HOSPITAL, Highway 1, Zip 93409–8101, Mailing Address: P.O. Box 8101, Zip 93403–8101; tel. 805/547–7913, (Nonreporting)
Primary Contact: Martha Wallace, Administrator
CFO: William Cook, Associate Warden Business Service
CIO: Terry Knight, Public Information Officer and Administrative Assistant
Web address: www.yaca.ca.gov/visitors/fac_prison_cmc.html
Control: State–Government, nonfederal **Service:** Hospital unit of an institution (prison hospital, college infirmary, etc.)

Staffed Beds: 39

✠ **FRENCH HOSPITAL MEDICAL CENTER (050232)**, 1911 Johnson Avenue, Zip 93401–4197; tel. 805/543–5353 **A**1 2 9 10 **F**8 11 15 18 20 22 24 28 29 30 34 35 40 46 50 53 54 57 59 64 68 70 75 76 77 78 79 81 84 85 86 87 89 97 100 107 108 110 111 114 115 119 124 130 132 134 146 147 148 **S** Dignity Health, San Francisco, CA
Primary Contact: Alan Iftiniuk, Chief Executive Officer
COO: Carla A. Adams, Chief Nursing Officer and Chief Operating Officer
CFO: Sue Andersen, Chief Financial Officer
CMO: Scott Smelser, M.D., Chief of Staff
CIO: Cyndi Lang, Director Information Services
CHR: Barry Nateman, Manager Human Resources
CNO: Carla A. Adams, Chief Nursing Officer and Chief Operating Officer
Web address: www.frenchmedicalcenter.org
Control: Other not–for–profit (including NFP Corporation) **Service:** General Medical and Surgical

Staffed Beds: 112 **Admissions:** 4235 **Census:** 39 **Outpatient Visits:** 73306 **Births:** 588 **Total Expense ($000):** 96981 **Payroll Expense ($000):** 35678 **Personnel:** 391

✠ **SIERRA VISTA REGIONAL MEDICAL CENTER (050506)**, 1010 Murray Avenue, Zip 93405–1806, Mailing Address: P.O. Box 1367, Zip 93406–1367; tel. 805/546–7600 **A**1 2 9 10 19 **F**3 15 17 18 20 29 30 31 34 38 40 45 46 49 50 51 57 59 64 65 68 70 72 73 74 75 76 77 78 79 80 81 84 85 86 89 100 107 108 110 111 114 115 119 126 130 131 132 145 146 147 148 **S** TENET Healthcare Corporation, Dallas, TX
Primary Contact: Joseph DeSchryver, Chief Executive Officer
COO: Ike MMeje, Chief Operating Officer
CFO: Rollie Pirkl, Chief Financial Officer
CIO: Robert Leonard, Director Information Services
CHR: Kristin Flynn, Chief Human Resources Officer
CNO: Nicki E. Edwards, Ph.D., Interim Chief Nursing Officer
Web address: www.sierravistaregional.com
Control: Corporation, Investor–owned, for–profit **Service:** General Medical and Surgical

Staffed Beds: 164 **Admissions:** 5346 **Census:** 63 **Outpatient Visits:** 43223 **Births:** 1284 **Total Expense ($000):** 109231 **Payroll Expense ($000):** 50163 **Personnel:** 629

SAN MATEO—San Mateo County

MILLS HOSPITAL See Mills–Peninsula Health Services, Burlingame

☐ **SAN MATEO MEDICAL CENTER (050113)**, 222 West 39th Avenue, Zip 94403–4398; tel. 650/573–2222, (Total facility includes 28 beds in nursing home–type unit) **A**1 3 5 9 10 **F**1 3 15 18 19 29 30 31 32 39 40 45 47 49 51 54 56 59 60 61 64 65 66 68 69 70 71 74 75 78 79 81 82 84 85 87 89 90 93 97 98 100 101 102 103 104 105 107 115 119 128 130 134 146 147 148 **P**8
Primary Contact: Susan P. Ehrlich, M.D., Chief Executive Officer
COO: John Thomas, Chief Operating Officer
CFO: David S. McGrew, Chief Financial Officer
CMO: Chester Kunnappilly, M.D., Chief Medical Officer and Chief Quality Officer
CIO: Michael Aratow, M.D., Chief Information Officer
CHR: Angela Gonzales, Manager Human Resources
CNO: Joan G. Spicer, R.N., Chief Nursing Officer
Web address: www.sanmateomedicalcenter.org
Control: County–Government, nonfederal **Service:** General Medical and Surgical

Staffed Beds: 73 **Admissions:** 3700 **Census:** 91 **Outpatient Visits:** 518648 **Births:** 0 **Total Expense ($000):** 245955 **Payroll Expense ($000):** 88561 **Personnel:** 1103

SAN PABLO—Contra Costa County

☐ **DOCTORS MEDICAL CENTER (050079)**, 2000 Vale Road, Zip 94806–3808; tel. 510/970–5000 **A**1 2 9 10 **F**3 8 11 15 18 22 24 26 28 29 30 31 34 35 40 45 46 49 50 54 57 59 60 64 68 70 74 75 78 79 81 85 86 87 93 94 107 119 120 129 130 132 146 147 148
Primary Contact: Dawn M. Gideon, Interim Chief Executive Officer
COO: Kathy White, R.N., Interim Chief Operating Officer
CFO: James Boatman, Chief Financial Officer
CMO: Richard Stern, M.D., President Medical Staff
CIO: Phyllis Moore, Director Information Systems and Data Center
CHR: John Hardy, Vice President Human Resources
CNO: Bobbie Ellerston, Interim Chief Nursing Officer
Web address: www.doctorsmedicalcenter.org
Control: Hospital district or authority, Government, nonfederal **Service:** General Medical and Surgical

Staffed Beds: 100 **Admissions:** 5510 **Census:** 67 **Outpatient Visits:** 72270 **Births:** 0 **Total Expense ($000):** 147142 **Payroll Expense ($000):** 56457

SAN PEDRO—Los Angeles County, See Los Angeles

SAN RAFAEL—Marin County

✠ **KAISER PERMANENTE SAN RAFAEL MEDICAL CENTER (050510)**, 99 Montecillo Road, Zip 94903–3397; tel. 415/444–2000 **A**1 10 **F**3 8 15 20 29 30 31 35 40 43 45 46 47 48 49 50 56 59 61 62 64 65 68 70 79 81 84 85 86 87 93 107 108 110 111 114 118 119 130 146 **S** Kaiser Foundation Hospitals, Oakland, CA
Primary Contact: Judy Coffey, Senior Vice President and Area Manager
COO: Tony Fiorello, R.N., Chief Operating and Chief Nursing Officer
CFO: John Groesbeck, Area Finance Officer
CMO: Gary Mizono, M.D., Physician–in–Chief
CIO: Stanley Dobrawa, Area Technology Director
CHR: Rudy Collins, Human Resources Business Partner
CNO: Tony Fiorello, R.N., Chief Operating and Chief Nursing Officer
Web address: www.kaiserpermanente.org
Control: Other not–for–profit (including NFP Corporation) **Service:** General Medical and Surgical

Staffed Beds: 116 **Admissions:** 4792 **Census:** 51 **Outpatient Visits:** 29703 **Births:** 0 **Personnel:** 1114

SAN RAMON—Contra Costa County

✠ **SAN RAMON REGIONAL MEDICAL CENTER (050689)**, 6001 Norris Canyon Road, Zip 94583–5400; tel. 925/275–9200 **A**1 9 10 **F**3 8 11 13 15 17 18 20 22 24 26 28 29 30 31 34 35 37 40 45 46 47 48 49 53 57 59 64 70 72 75 76 77 78 79 81 85 86 87 89 93 107 108 110 118 119 126 130 131 132 146 147 148 **S** TENET Healthcare Corporation, Dallas, TX
Primary Contact: Gary Sloan, Chief Executive Officer
CFO: Beenu Chadha, Chief Financial Officer
CMO: Erik Gracer, M.D., Chief of Staff
CIO: Asa Mandale, Interim Director Information Systems and Telecommunications
CHR: Dennis Mills, Director Human Resources
CNO: Pam Pshea, R.N., Chief Nursing Officer
Web address: www.sanramonmedctr.com
Control: Corporation, Investor–owned, for–profit **Service:** General Medical and Surgical

Staffed Beds: 123 **Admissions:** 4296 **Census:** 45 **Outpatient Visits:** 72238 **Births:** 724 **Total Expense ($000):** 123934 **Payroll Expense ($000):** 59039 **Personnel:** 566

SANTA ANA—Orange County

☐ **COASTAL COMMUNITIES HOSPITAL (050747)**, 2701 South Bristol Street, Zip 92704–6278; tel. 714/754–5454 **A**1 9 10 **F**1 3 4 7 8 13 14 17 29 30 34 35 40 50 56 57 60 64 65 67 68 70 75 76 77 79 81 82 86 87 89 90 93 98 101 103 104 105 107 111 119 128 130 143 146 147 **S** Integrated Healthcare, Santa Ana, CA
Primary Contact: Luke Tharasri, Chief Executive Officer
CFO: Robert Heinemeier, Chief Financial Officer
CHR: Debby Riester, Manager Human Resources
Web address: www.coastalcommhospital.com
Control: Corporation, Investor–owned, for–profit **Service:** General Medical and Surgical

Staffed Beds: 178 **Admissions:** 3577 **Census:** 89 **Outpatient Visits:** 32030 **Total Expense ($000):** 59513

☐ **WESTERN MEDICAL CENTER–SANTA ANA (050746)**, 1001 North Tustin Avenue, Zip 92705–3577; tel. 714/835–3555, (Nonreporting) **A**1 3 5 9 10 **S** Integrated Healthcare, Santa Ana, CA
Primary Contact: Daniel Brothman, Chief Executive Officer
COO: Doug Norris, Administrator and Chief Operating Officer
CFO: Kathy Hammack, Chief Financial Officer
CMO: Seifolah Esfandiari, M.D., Chief of Staff
CIO: Nova Stewart, Chief Information Officer
CHR: Milas H. Kennington, Vice President, Human Resources
CNO: Patricia Rives, R.N., Chief Nursing Officer
Web address: www.westernmedicalcenter.com
Control: Corporation, Investor–owned, for–profit **Service:** General Medical and Surgical

Staffed Beds: 282

SANTA BARBARA—Santa Barbara County

COTTAGE REHABILITATION HOSPITAL See Santa Barbara Cottage Hospital

CA

Hospital, Medicare Provider Number, Address, Telephone, Approval, Facility, and Physician Codes, Health Care System

★ American Hospital Association (AHA) membership
☐ The Joint Commission accreditation
◇ DNV Healthcare Inc. accreditation
◯ Healthcare Facilities Accreditation Program
△ Commission on Accreditation of Rehabilitation Facilities (CARF) accreditation

CA

✠ **GOLETA VALLEY COTTAGE HOSPITAL (050357)**, 351 South Patterson Avenue, Zip 93111–2496, Mailing Address: Box 6306, Zip 93160–6306; tel. 805/967–3411 **A**1 9 10 **F**8 11 12 15 29 40 65 68 70 79 81 107 110 114 119 124 130 148 **S** Cottage Health System, Santa Barbara, CA
Primary Contact: Ronald C. Werft, President and Chief Executive Officer
COO: Steven A. Fellows, Executive Vice President and Chief Operating Officer
CFO: Joan Bricher, Senior Vice President Finance and Chief Financial Officer
CMO: Edmund Wroblewski, M.D., Vice President Medical Affairs and Chief Medical Officer
CIO: Alberto Kywi, Chief Information Officer
CHR: Patrice Ryan, Vice President Human Resources
Web address: www.sbch.org
Control: Other not–for–profit (including NFP Corporation) **Service:** General Medical and Surgical

Staffed Beds: 80 **Admissions:** 1553 **Census:** 40 **Outpatient Visits:** 37838 **Births:** 0 **Total Expense ($000):** 63661 **Payroll Expense ($000):** 24413 **Personnel:** 281

✠ △ **SANTA BARBARA COTTAGE HOSPITAL (050396)**, 400 West Pueblo Street, Zip 93105–4390, Mailing Address: P.O. Box 689, Zip 93102–0689; tel. 805/682–7111, (Includes COTTAGE CHILDREN'S HOSPITAL, 400 West Pueblo Street, Zip 93105–4353; tel. 877/247–3260; COTTAGE REHABILITATION HOSPITAL, 2415 De la Vina Street, Zip 93105–3819; tel. 805/687–7444; Melinda Staveley, President and Chief Executive Officer) **A**1 2 3 5 7 9 10 **F**3 4 5 8 11 12 13 15 17 18 20 22 24 26 28 29 30 31 34 35 40 43 46 50 53 54 57 58 59 60 64 65 68 70 72 74 75 76 78 79 81 84 86 88 89 90 91 92 93 96 98 100 102 103 104 106 107 110 111 114 115 117 119 126 130 132 135 146 148 **S** Cottage Health System, Santa Barbara, CA
Primary Contact: Ronald C. Werft, President and Chief Executive Officer
COO: Steven A. Fellows, Executive Vice President and Chief Operating Officer
CFO: Joan Bricher, Senior Vice President Finance and Chief Financial Officer
CMO: Edmund Wroblewski, M.D., Vice President Medical Affairs and Chief Medical Officer
CIO: Alberto Kywi, Chief Information Officer
CHR: Patrice Ryan, Vice President Human Resources
CNO: Herb J. Geary, R.N., Vice President Patient Care Services and Chief Nursing Officer
Web address: www.cottagehealthsystem.org
Control: Other not–for–profit (including NFP Corporation) **Service:** General Medical and Surgical

Staffed Beds: 351 **Admissions:** 18204 **Census:** 228 **Outpatient Visits:** 127893 **Births:** 2349 **Total Expense ($000):** 523577 **Payroll Expense ($000):** 171568 **Personnel:** 2159

SANTA BARBARA COUNTY PSYCHIATRIC HEALTH FACILITY (054125), 315 Camino Del Remedio, Zip 93110–1332; tel. 805/681–5244 **A**10 **F**75 87 98 130 132 133 143
Primary Contact: Takashi Wada, Interim Director
CFO: Michael C. Evans, Chief Executive Officer and Deputy Director of Finance and Administration
CMO: Ole Behrendtsen, M.D., Medical Director
CIO: Dana Fahey, Manager Management Information Systems
CHR: Elena Molelus, Manager Human Resources
Web address: www.countyofsb.org
Control: County–Government, nonfederal **Service:** Psychiatric

Staffed Beds: 16 **Admissions:** 569 **Census:** 14 **Outpatient Visits:** 0 **Births:** 0

SANTA CLARA—Santa Clara County

✠ **KAISER PERMANENTE SANTA CLARA MEDICAL CENTER (050071)**, 700 Lawrence Expressway, Zip 95051–5173; tel. 408/851–1000 **A**1 2 3 5 10 **F**3 5 8 11 12 13 15 17 18 19 20 21 22 23 24 26 28 29 31 32 34 35 36 38 40 41 44 45 48 49 50 51 52 53 54 55 56 57 58 59 60 62 63 64 65 68 70 71 72 74 75 77 78 79 81 82 83 84 85 86 87 88 91 92 93 94 96 97 99 100 101 104 107 108 109 110 111 114 115 116 117 118 119 120 121 123 124 126 129 130 131 132 134 135 144 146 147 148 **P**3 **S** Kaiser Foundation Hospitals, Oakland, CA
Primary Contact: Christopher L. Boyd, Senior Vice President and Area Manager
COO: Pamela Lindemoen, Chief Operating Officer
CFO: Sean Fitzpatrick, Area Finance Officer
CMO: Susan Smarr, M.D., Physician–in–Chief
CIO: Scott May, Area Director Technology
CHR: Robert Hyde, Human Resources Business Partner
CNO: Anne M. Goldfisher, R.N., Chief Nursing Officer
Web address: www.kaiserpermanente.org
Control: Other not–for–profit (including NFP Corporation) **Service:** General Medical and Surgical

Staffed Beds: 327 **Admissions:** 20967 **Census:** 244 **Outpatient Visits:** 1459966 **Births:** 4358 **Personnel:** 3020

SANTA CRUZ—Santa Cruz County

✠ **DOMINICAN HOSPITAL (050242)**, 1555 Soquel Drive, Zip 95065–1794; tel. 831/462–7700 **A**1 2 9 10 **F**3 7 8 10 11 13 15 17 18 20 22 24 26 28 29 30 31 34 35 37 40 45 46 53 57 59 60 62 64 65 66 68 70 71 72 74 75 76 77 78 79 81 82 83 84 85 86 87 89 90 91 92 93 95 98 102 105 107 111 112 114 115 116 117 119 126 128 130 146 147 148 **S** Dignity Health, San Francisco, CA
Primary Contact: Nanette Mickiewicz, M.D., President
COO: Chris Wernke, Chief Operating Officer
CFO: Rick Harron, Chief Financial Officer
CMO: Freddie Weinstein, M.D., Chief Medical Officer
CIO: Lee Vanderpool, Vice President
CHR: Vicki Miranda, Vice President Human Resources
Web address: www.dominicanhospital.org
Control: Other not–for–profit (including NFP Corporation) **Service:** General Medical and Surgical

Staffed Beds: 275 **Admissions:** 12345 **Census:** 166 **Outpatient Visits:** 198147 **Births:** 858 **Total Expense ($000):** 360040 **Payroll Expense ($000):** 154194 **Personnel:** 1118

✠ **SUTTER MATERNITY AND SURGERY CENTER OF SANTA CRUZ (050714)**, 2900 Chanticleer Avenue, Zip 95065–1816; tel. 831/477–2200 **A**1 9 10 **F**3 13 34 45 57 79 81 85 119 126 132 146 **S** Sutter Health, Sacramento, CA
Primary Contact: Stephen Gray, Chief Administrative Officer
CFO: Bonnie Liang, Divisional Finance Officer
CMO: Joseph Fabry, D.O., Chief of Staff
CIO: Michael Reandeau, Regional Chief Information Officer
CHR: Harley Neumann, Ph.D., Regional Vice President Human Resources
CNO: Sherri Stout–Torres, R.N., Chief Nursing Executive
Web address: www.suttermatsurg.org
Control: Other not–for–profit (including NFP Corporation) **Service:** General Medical and Surgical

Staffed Beds: 30 **Admissions:** 1445 **Census:** 10 **Outpatient Visits:** 10895 **Births:** 924 **Total Expense ($000):** 55030 **Payroll Expense ($000):** 16242 **Personnel:** 202

SANTA MARIA—Santa Barbara County

✠ **MARIAN REGIONAL MEDICAL CENTER (050107)**, 1400 East Church Street, Zip 93454–5906; tel. 805/739–3000, (Total facility includes 95 beds in nursing home–type unit) **A**1 2 9 10 **F**3 8 11 12 13 15 17 18 20 22 24 28 29 30 31 34 35 36 37 39 40 46 49 50 53 54 56 57 58 59 60 62 63 64 65 66 68 69 72 74 75 76 77 78 79 81 82 84 85 86 87 89 93 97 100 107 108 110 111 114 115 116 117 118 119 126 127 128 129 130 132 134 135 143 146 147 148 **S** Dignity Health, San Francisco, CA
Primary Contact: Charles J. Cova, President and Chief Executive Officer
COO: Kerin Mase, R.N., Chief Operating Officer and Chief Nursing Officer
CFO: Sue Andersen, Chief Financial Officer
CMO: Chuck Merrill, M.D., Vice President Medical Affairs
CIO: Patricia Haase, Director Information Technology and Communications
CHR: Jay King, Vice President Human Resources
CNO: Kerin Mase, R.N., Chief Operating Officer and Chief Nursing Officer
Web address: www.marianmedicalcenter.org
Control: Church–operated, Nongovernment, not–for profit **Service:** General Medical and Surgical

Staffed Beds: 286 **Admissions:** 10823 **Census:** 190 **Outpatient Visits:** 206598 **Births:** 2852 **Total Expense ($000):** 280233 **Payroll Expense ($000):** 106883 **Personnel:** 1246

SANTA MONICA—Los Angeles County

✠ **SAINT JOHN'S HEALTH CENTER (050290)**, 2121 Santa Monica Boulevard, Zip 90404–2091; tel. 310/829–5511 **A**1 2 9 10 **F**8 11 13 15 18 20 22 24 26 29 30 34 35 40 46 49 58 70 72 74 75 76 78 79 81 82 83 84 93 97 107 108 109 111 112 114 115 119 121 124 126 130 131 **S** Providence Health & Services, Renton, WA
Primary Contact: Marcel C. Loh, FACHE, Chief Executive Officer
COO: Kenneth L. Meehan, Interim Chief Operating Officer
CFO: Michelle Mok, Chief Financial Officer
CIO: Martha Ponce, Director Information Technologies and Telecommunications
CHR: Steven Sharrer, Vice President Human Resources
CNO: Dawna Hendel, R.N., Chief Nursing Officer and Vice President Patient Care Services
Web address: www.newstjohns.org/home.aspx
Control: Church–operated, Nongovernment, not–for profit **Service:** General Medical and Surgical

Staffed Beds: 234 **Admissions:** 11944 **Census:** 139 **Outpatient Visits:** 209945 **Total Expense ($000):** 300292

⊞ **SANTA MONICA–UCLA MEDICAL CENTER AND ORTHOPAEDIC HOSPITAL (050112)**, 1250 16th Street, Zip 90404–1249; tel. 310/319–4000 **A**1 3 5 9 10 **F**3 8 9 11 12 13 15 18 20 22 24 26 27 29 30 31 34 35 37 40 41 45 46 47 48 49 50 52 54 55 56 57 58 59 64 65 68 70 72 74 75 76 78 79 81 82 84 85 86 87 89 93 96 97 102 107 108 110 111 114 115 116 117 118 119 130 131 143 145 146 147 **P**6 **S** University of California–Systemwide Administration, Oakland, CA
Primary Contact: Paul Watkins, Chief Administrative Officer
COO: Posie Carpenter, R.N., Chief Administrative Officer
CFO: Paul Staton, Chief Financial Officer
CMO: James Atkinson, M.D., Medical Director
CIO: Virginia McFerran, Chief Information Officer
CHR: Mark Speare, Senior Associate Director Patient Relations and Human Resources
Web address: www.healthcare.ucla.edu
Control: State–Government, nonfederal **Service:** General Medical and Surgical

> **Staffed Beds:** 266 **Admissions:** 16100 **Census:** 215 **Outpatient Visits:** 177432 **Births:** 1492 **Total Expense ($000):** 377028 **Payroll Expense ($000):** 144890 **Personnel:** 1656

SANTA ROSA—Sonoma County

⊞ **KAISER PERMANENTE SANTA ROSA MEDICAL CENTER (050690)**, 401 Bicentennial Way, Zip 95403–2192; tel. 707/571–4000 **A**1 10 **F**3 8 13 15 30 31 40 44 45 60 62 64 68 70 72 76 78 79 81 83 85 89 100 107 108 110 111 114 115 119 130 146 **S** Kaiser Foundation Hospitals, Oakland, CA
Primary Contact: Judy Coffey, Senior Vice President and Area Manager
COO: Susan Janvrin, R.N., Chief Operating and Chief Nursing Officer
CFO: John Groesbeck, Area Finance Officer
CMO: Kirk Pappas, M.D., Physician–in–Chief
CIO: Stanley Dobrawa, Area Technology Director
CHR: Rudy Collins, Human Resources Business Partner
CNO: Susan Janvrin, R.N., Chief Operating and Chief Nursing Officer
Web address: www.kaiserpermanente.org
Control: Other not–for–profit (including NFP Corporation) **Service:** General Medical and Surgical

> **Staffed Beds:** 117 **Admissions:** 7961 **Census:** 78 **Outpatient Visits:** 54852 **Births:** 1889 **Personnel:** 1631

⊞ **SANTA ROSA MEMORIAL HOSPITAL (050174)**, 1165 Montgomery Drive, Zip 95405–4897, Mailing Address: P.O. Box 522, Zip 95402–0522; tel. 707/546–3210 **A**1 2 9 10 **F**3 8 11 12 13 15 18 20 22 24 26 28 29 30 31 34 35 39 40 43 44 45 46 47 48 49 51 54 56 58 59 60 64 65 66 68 70 71 72 74 75 76 77 78 79 81 82 84 85 86 87 89 90 92 93 102 104 105 107 108 111 115 119 130 143 144 146 148 **S** St. Joseph Health, Irvine, CA
Primary Contact: Todd Salnas, President
COO: David Ziolkowski, Chief Operating Officer
CFO: Mich Riccioni, Chief Financial Officer
CMO: Richard Carvolth, M.D., Chief Medical Officer
CIO: Terri Oliver, Interim Executive Director Information Systems
CHR: Robert A. Eisen, Vice President Human Resources
CNO: Tiffany Oliver, Chief Nursing Officer
Web address: www.stjosephhealth.org
Control: Other not–for–profit (including NFP Corporation) **Service:** General Medical and Surgical

> **Staffed Beds:** 272 **Admissions:** 12638 **Census:** 158 **Outpatient Visits:** 168836 **Births:** 903 **Total Expense ($000):** 371940 **Payroll Expense ($000):** 103967 **Personnel:** 1215

⊞ **SUTTER MEDICAL CENTER OF SANTA ROSA, CHANATE CAMPUS (050291)**, 3325 Chanate Road, Zip 95404–1707; tel. 707/576–4000, (Includes WARRACK CAMPUS, 2449 Summerfield Road, Zip 95405–7815; tel. 707/576–4200) **A**1 3 5 9 10 **F**3 8 11 12 13 15 18 20 22 24 26 29 31 34 35 36 39 40 49 50 51 56 59 60 61 64 65 68 70 72 74 75 76 77 78 79 81 82 84 85 87 107 108 111 119 130 146 148 **S** Sutter Health, Sacramento, CA
Primary Contact: Mike Purvis, Chief Administrative Officer
CFO: Avery Schlesenberg, Chief Financial Officer
CMO: Robert Heckey, M.D., Chief of Staff
CHR: Steve Morales, Director Human Resources
Web address: www.sutterhealth.org
Control: Other not–for–profit (including NFP Corporation) **Service:** General Medical and Surgical

> **Staffed Beds:** 116 **Admissions:** 6205 **Census:** 65 **Outpatient Visits:** 48971 **Births:** 1592 **Total Expense ($000):** 170922 **Payroll Expense ($000):** 60160 **Personnel:** 482

SEPULVEDA—Los Angeles County, See Los Angeles

SHERMAN OAKS—Los Angeles County, See Los Angeles

SIMI VALLEY—Ventura County

⊞ **SIMI VALLEY HOSPITAL AND HEALTH CARE SERVICES (050236)**, 2975 North Sycamore Drive, Zip 93065–1277; tel. 805/955–6000 **A**1 2 9 10 **F**8 15 28 29 30 31 34 35 40 45 46 49 57 59 60 62 64 72 76 78 81 93 107 108 111 112 114 119 146 147 **P**3 **S** Adventist Health, Roseville, CA
Primary Contact: Kim S. Milstien, President and Chief Executive Officer
CFO: Jon Giese, Vice President and Chief Financial Officer
CMO: John Dingilian, M.D., Chief Medical Officer
CIO: Bridget Nakamura, Director Information Systems
CHR: Sandra Werner, Director Human Resources
CNO: Caroline Esparza, Senior Vice President and Chief Nurse Executive
Web address: www.simivalleyhospital.com
Control: Church–operated, Nongovernment, not–for profit **Service:** General Medical and Surgical

> **Staffed Beds:** 144 **Admissions:** 5142 **Census:** 60 **Outpatient Visits:** 78811 **Births:** 607 **Total Expense ($000):** 117399 **Payroll Expense ($000):** 48764 **Personnel:** 665

SOLVANG—Santa Barbara County

⊞ **SANTA YNEZ VALLEY COTTAGE HOSPITAL (051331)**, 2050 Viborg Road, Zip 93463–2295; tel. 805/688–6431 **A**1 9 10 18 **F**15 28 40 57 68 81 85 107 111 114 119 143 146 **S** Cottage Health System, Santa Barbara, CA
Primary Contact: Ronald C. Werft, President and Chief Executive Officer
COO: Steven A. Fellows, Executive Vice President and Chief Operating Officer
CFO: Joan Bricher, Senior Vice President Finance and Chief Financial Officer
CMO: Edmund Wroblewski, M.D., Vice President Medical Affairs and Chief Medical Officer
CIO: Alberto Kywi, Chief Information Officer
CHR: Patrice Ryan, Vice President Human Resources
Web address: www.cottagehealthsystem.org
Control: Other not–for–profit (including NFP Corporation) **Service:** General Medical and Surgical

> **Staffed Beds:** 11 **Admissions:** 176 **Census:** 2 **Outpatient Visits:** 16611 **Births:** 0 **Total Expense ($000):** 13744 **Payroll Expense ($000):** 6085 **Personnel:** 63

SONOMA—Sonoma County

⊞ **SONOMA VALLEY HOSPITAL (050090)**, 347 Andrieux Street, Zip 95476–6811, Mailing Address: P.O. Box 600, Zip 95476–0600; tel. 707/935–5000, (Nonreporting) **A**1 9 10
Primary Contact: Kelly Mather, Chief Executive Officer
CFO: Richard Reid, Chief Financial Officer
CMO: Robert Cohen, M.D., Chief Medical Officer
CIO: Fe Sendaydiego, Director Information Systems
CHR: Paula M. Davis, Chief Human Resources Officer
CNO: Leslie Lovejoy, R.N., Chief Nursing and Quality Officer
Web address: www.svh.com
Control: Hospital district or authority, Government, nonfederal **Service:** General Medical and Surgical

> **Staffed Beds:** 38

SONORA—Tuolumne County

⊞ **SONORA REGIONAL MEDICAL CENTER (050335)**, 1000 Greenley Road, Zip 95370–4819; tel. 209/536–5000, (Total facility includes 68 beds in nursing home–type unit) **A**1 9 10 19 20 **F**3 8 11 13 15 17 18 20 28 29 30 31 34 35 39 40 45 49 53 54 56 57 59 62 63 64 70 71 75 76 77 78 79 81 84 85 86 87 92 93 97 107 108 110 111 114 115 118 119 120 121 122 123 127 128 130 131 132 133 135 143 144 146 148 **P**6 **S** Adventist Health, Roseville, CA
Primary Contact: Andrew Jahn, President and Chief Executive Officer
CFO: Greg McCulloch, CPA, Vice President of Finance and Chief Financial Officer
CMO: Ed Clinite, D.O., Chief of Staff
CIO: Bruce Chan, Director Business Planning and Marketing
CHR: Rick A. Dodds, Vice President Human Resources
CNO: Julie Kline, Senior Vice President Patient Services
Web address: www.sonoramedicalcenter.org/
Control: Church–operated, Nongovernment, not–for profit **Service:** General Medical and Surgical

> **Staffed Beds:** 152 **Admissions:** 4937 **Census:** 119 **Outpatient Visits:** 269716 **Births:** 536 **Total Expense ($000):** 196687 **Payroll Expense ($000):** 72495 **Personnel:** 1043

CA

Hospital, Medicare Provider Number, Address, Telephone, Approval, Facility, and Physician Codes, Health Care System

★ American Hospital Association (AHA) membership
☐ The Joint Commission accreditation
◇ DNV Healthcare Inc. accreditation
○ Healthcare Facilities Accreditation Program
△ Commission on Accreditation of Rehabilitation Facilities (CARF) accreditation

© 2014 AHA Guide   *Many Facility Codes have changed. Please refer to the AHA Guide Code Chart.*   Hospitals **A95**

SOUTH EL MONTE—Los Angeles County

☐ **GREATER EL MONTE COMMUNITY HOSPITAL (050738)**, 1701 Santa Anita Avenue, Zip 91733–3411; tel. 626/579–7777 **A**1 9 10 **F**3 13 17 18 19 29 34 35 40 49 56 57 59 65 68 70 76 81 87 89 93 107 119 128 130 143 146 **S** AHMC & Healthcare, Inc., Alhambra, CA
Primary Contact: Stanley Toy, Jr., M.D., Chief Executive Officer
COO: Jose Ortega, Chief Operating Officer
CFO: Michael Chung, Chief Financial Officer
CMO: Dilip Patel, M.D., Chief of Staff
CIO: Jay Geldhof, Director Information Systems
CHR: Jason Jaquez, Director Human Resources
CNO: Evelyn Calubaquib, Chief Nursing Officer
Web address: www.greaterelmonte.com
Control: Hospital district or authority, Government, nonfederal **Service:** General Medical and Surgical

Staffed Beds: 117 **Admissions:** 3951 **Census:** 46 **Outpatient Visits:** 18336
Births: 566 **Total Expense ($000):** 57313 **Payroll Expense ($000):** 18902
Personnel: 304

SOUTH LAKE TAHOE—El Dorado County

✠ **BARTON MEMORIAL HOSPITAL (050352)**, 2170 South Avenue, Zip 96150–7026, Mailing Address: P.O. Box 9578, Zip 96158–9578; tel. 530/541–3420, (Total facility includes 48 beds in nursing home–type unit) **A**1 9 10 20 **F**3 8 11 13 15 18 29 30 32 34 35 38 40 44 47 48 50 54 57 59 62 63 64 65 66 68 70 75 76 77 79 81 82 83 84 85 86 87 89 90 92 93 94 96 97 99 100 104 107 109 110 111 112 113 114 115 116 117 118 119 121 122 123 124 126 127 128 129 130 131 132 133 135 143 144 146 147 148
Primary Contact: John G. Williams, President and Chief Executive Officer
COO: Kathy Cocking, R.N., Vice President Operations
CFO: Richard P. Derby, Vice President Finance
CMO: Clint Purvance, M.D., Chief Medical Officer
CHR: LeAnne Kankel, Vice President Human Relations
Web address: www.bartonhealth.org
Control: Other not–for–profit (including NFP Corporation) **Service:** General Medical and Surgical

Staffed Beds: 111 **Admissions:** 2302 **Census:** 64 **Outpatient Visits:** 73210
Births: 292 **Total Expense ($000):** 99093 **Payroll Expense ($000):** 41787
Personnel: 733

SOUTH SAN FRANCISCO—San Mateo County

✠ **KAISER PERMANENTE SOUTH SAN FRANCISCO (050070)**, 1200 El Camino Real, Zip 94080–3208; tel. 650/742–2000 **A**1 10 **F**3 5 8 12 15 18 29 30 31 32 34 35 36 40 45 46 47 48 49 50 51 53 54 55 56 57 58 59 64 65 68 70 74 75 77 78 79 81 82 84 85 86 87 91 92 93 94 95 96 97 99 100 101 103 104 107 108 110 111 114 115 118 119 120 121 123 124 129 130 131 132 135 146 147 148 **P**6 **S** Kaiser Foundation Hospitals, Oakland, CA
Primary Contact: Frank T. Beirne, FACHE, Senior Vice President and Area Manager
CFO: Mark Okashima, Area Finance Officer
CMO: Michelle Caughey, M.D., Physician In Chief
CIO: Angel Shew, Director Area Technology
CHR: Sharon Barncord, Human Resource Business Partner
Web address: www.kaiserpermanente.org
Control: Other not–for–profit (including NFP Corporation) **Service:** General Medical and Surgical

Staffed Beds: 120 **Admissions:** 5220 **Census:** 53 **Outpatient Visits:** 712505
Births: 0 **Personnel:** 1207

STOCKTON—San Joaquin County

☐ **DAMERON HOSPITAL (050122)**, 525 West Acacia Street, Zip 95203–2484; tel. 209/944–5550 **A**1 9 10 **F**12 13 17 18 20 22 24 26 29 30 34 35 40 45 59 70 72 75 76 77 79 81 82 89 93 107 115 119 144 146 147 148
Primary Contact: Lorraine P. Auerbach, FACHE, President and Chief Executive Officer
COO: Michael Glasberg, Senior Vice President, Chief Operating Officer
CFO: Elizabeth R. Propp, Vice President Finance and Chief Financial Officer
CMO: Bradley Reinke, M.D., Vice President Medical Affairs and Chief Medical Officer
CIO: David Kerrins, Vice President Information Services and Chief Information Officer
CHR: Tresha Moreland, Regional Vice President Human Resources
CNO: Janine Hawkins, R.N., Vice President Patient Care Services and Chief Nursing Officer
Web address: www.dameronhospital.org
Control: Other not–for–profit (including NFP Corporation) **Service:** General Medical and Surgical

Staffed Beds: 202 **Admissions:** 8062 **Census:** 84 **Outpatient Visits:** 106468
Total Expense ($000): 169291

✠ **ST. JOSEPH'S BEHAVIORAL HEALTH CENTER (054123)**, 2510 North California Street, Zip 95204–5568; tel. 209/461–2000 **A**1 9 10 **F**5 29 38 68 98 100 101 103 104 105 130 132 143 146 **S** Dignity Health, San Francisco, CA
Primary Contact: Paul Rains, R.N., MSN, President
CFO: Doreen Hartmann, Chief Financial Officer
CMO: David Robinson, D.O., Medical Director
CHR: Nancy Vargas, Chief Human Resources
CNO: Benny Lee Lucas, Jr., Chief Nursing Executive
Web address: www.stjosephscanhelp.org
Control: Church–operated, Nongovernment, not–for profit **Service:** Psychiatric

Staffed Beds: 35 **Admissions:** 1787 **Census:** 32 **Outpatient Visits:** 8647
Births: 0 **Total Expense ($000):** 14810 **Payroll Expense ($000):** 8528
Personnel: 113

✠ **ST. JOSEPH'S MEDICAL CENTER (050084)**, 1800 North California Street, Zip 95204–6019, Mailing Address: P.O. Box 213008, Zip 95213–9008; tel. 209/943–2000, (Nonreporting) **A**1 2 9 10 19 **S** Dignity Health, San Francisco, CA
Primary Contact: Donald J. Wiley, President and Chief Executive Officer
COO: Michael R. Ricks, Chief Operating Officer
CFO: Nikki Ochoa, Interim Chief Financial Officer
CMO: Susan McDonald, M.D., Vice President
CIO: Randall Gamino, Director Perot Site
CHR: Nancy Vargas, Vice President Human Resources
Web address: www.stjosephsCARES.org
Control: Church–operated, Nongovernment, not–for profit **Service:** General Medical and Surgical

Staffed Beds: 273

SUN CITY—Riverside County

☐ **MENIFEE VALLEY MEDICAL CENTER (050684)**, 28400 McCall Boulevard, Zip 92585–9537; tel. 951/679–8888 **A**1 9 10 **F**11 12 14 15 29 30 31 34 35 40 45 46 47 49 50 51 57 59 70 78 79 81 82 107 108 114 119 130 **S** Physicians for Healthy Hospitals, Hemet, CA
Primary Contact: Joel Bergenfeld, Chief Hospital Executive Officer
CHR: Michele Bird, Chief Human Resources Officer
Web address: www.valleyhealthsystem.com
Control: Partnership, Investor–owned, for–profit **Service:** General Medical and Surgical

Staffed Beds: 74 **Admissions:** 3110 **Census:** 35 **Births:** 0

SUN VALLEY—Los Angeles County, See Los Angeles

SUSANVILLE—Lassen County

✠ **BANNER LASSEN MEDICAL CENTER (051320)**, 1800 Spring Ridge Drive, Zip 96130–6100; tel. 530/252–2000 **A**1 9 10 18 **F**3 8 11 13 15 29 31 35 40 45 68 76 81 93 107 108 110 111 114 119 129 130 146 147 148 **S** Banner Health, Phoenix, AZ
Primary Contact: Catherine S. Harshbarger, R.N., Chief Executive Officer
CFO: Jon R. McMillan, Chief Financial Officer
CMO: Hal Meadows, M.D., Chief Medical Officer
CHR: Roberto Martinez, Chief Human Resources Officer
CNO: Kathy H. Virgil–Belding, Chief Nursing Officer
Web address: www.bannerhealth.com/Locations/California/Banner+Lassen+Medical+Center
Control: Other not–for–profit (including NFP Corporation) **Service:** General Medical and Surgical

Staffed Beds: 25 **Admissions:** 1172 **Census:** 11 **Outpatient Visits:** 31178
Births: 224 **Total Expense ($000):** 30435 **Payroll Expense ($000):** 12595
Personnel: 180

SYLMAR—Los Angeles County, See Los Angeles

TARZANA—Los Angeles County, See Los Angeles

TEHACHAPI—Kern County

★ ◇ **TEHACHAPI VALLEY HEALTHCARE DISTRICT (051301)**, 115 West E Street, Zip 93561–1607, Mailing Address: P.O. Box 1900, Zip 93581–1900; tel. 661/823–3000 **A**9 10 18 21 **F**29 40 54 57 59 64 65 66 68 82 93 107 119 127 130 132 133
Primary Contact: Eugene Suksi, Interim Chief Executive Officer
CFO: Chester Beedle, Interim Chief Financial Officer
CMO: Susan Cribbs, D.O., Chief of Staff
CIO: Dusty Colvard, Manager Information Technology
CHR: Susan Nelson–Jones, Director Human Resources
CNO: Juliana Kay Kirby, R.N., Chief Nursing Officer
Web address: www.tvhd.org
Control: Hospital district or authority, Government, nonfederal **Service:** General Medical and Surgical

Staffed Beds: 24 **Admissions:** 106 **Census:** 1 **Outpatient Visits:** 37921
Births: 3 **Total Expense ($000):** 18927 **Payroll Expense ($000):** 8910
Personnel: 216

Many Facility Codes have changed. Please refer to the AHA Guide Code Chart.

CA

TEMPLETON—San Luis Obispo County

⊞ **TWIN CITIES COMMUNITY HOSPITAL (050633)**, 1100 Las Tablas Road, Zip 93465–9796; tel. 805/434–3500 **A**1 9 10 **F**3 13 15 29 30 31 34 35 37 38 40 45 46 55 57 59 60 64 65 68 70 74 75 77 78 79 81 82 84 85 107 111 114 115 119 130 132 144 146 147 **S** TENET Healthcare Corporation, Dallas, TX
Primary Contact: Mark P. Lisa, FACHE, Chief Executive Officer
COO: Mike Lane, Chief Operating Officer
CFO: Paul Posmoga, Chief Financial Officer
CIO: Don Wheeler, Director Information Systems
CHR: Eloise Rendon, Director Human Resources
CNO: Carol Howland, Chief Nursing Officer
Web address: www.twincitieshospital.com
Control: Corporation, Investor–owned, for–profit **Service:** General Medical and Surgical

Staffed Beds: 122 **Admissions:** 4843 **Census:** 50 **Outpatient Visits:** 43429 **Births:** 699 **Total Expense ($000):** 75930 **Payroll Expense ($000):** 30290 **Personnel:** 397

THOUSAND OAKS—Ventura County

⊞ **LOS ROBLES HOSPITAL AND MEDICAL CENTER (050549)**, 215 West Janss Road, Zip 91360–1899; tel. 805/497–2727, (Total facility includes 42 beds in nursing home–type unit) **A**1 2 9 10 **F**3 8 13 15 17 18 19 20 22 24 26 28 29 31 34 35 40 41 43 46 47 48 49 54 57 59 64 65 69 70 72 74 75 76 77 78 79 81 82 84 85 87 89 90 93 107 108 110 111 114 119 126 128 130 131 132 135 146 147 148 **S** HCA, Nashville, TN
Primary Contact: Natalie Mussi, Chief Executive Officer
CMO: Hannah Grossman, M.D., Chief Medical Officer
CIO: Alex Bryer, Director Information Management
CHR: Patrick Guy, Vice President Human Resources
CNO: Cynthia J. Johnson, R.N., Chief Nursing Officer
Web address: www.losrobleshospital.com
Control: Corporation, Investor–owned, for–profit **Service:** General Medical and Surgical

Staffed Beds: 334 **Admissions:** 15481 **Census:** 226 **Outpatient Visits:** 86852 **Births:** 1912 **Total Expense ($000):** 325753 **Payroll Expense ($000):** 124829

THOUSAND OAKS SURGICAL HOSPITAL (050749), 401 Rolling Oaks Drive, Zip 91361–1050; tel. 805/777–7750, (Nonreporting) **A**9 10
Primary Contact: Gregory R. Angle, Chief Executive Officer
CFO: Craig Corley, Chief Financial Officer
CMO: Steven Bansbach, M.D., Medical Director
CIO: Michael Lashley, Network Administrator
CHR: Jean Callahan, Manager Human Resources
Web address: www.toshospital.com
Control: Partnership, Investor–owned, for–profit **Service:** General Medical and Surgical

Staffed Beds: 17

TORRANCE—Los Angeles County

☐ **DEL AMO HOSPITAL (054053)**, 23700 Camino Del Sol, Zip 90505–5000; tel. 310/530–1151, (Nonreporting) **A**1 9 10 **S** Universal Health Services, Inc., King of Prussia, PA
Primary Contact: Lisa K. Montes, Chief Executive Officer
Web address: www.delamohospital.com
Control: Corporation, Investor–owned, for–profit **Service:** Psychiatric

Staffed Beds: 70

☐ **HARBOR–UCLA MEDICAL CENTER (050376)**, 1000 West Carson Street, Zip 90502–2059; tel. 310/222–2345 **A**1 2 3 5 8 10 **F**3 11 12 13 14 15 17 18 19 20 22 24 25 26 29 30 31 32 34 35 39 40 41 43 44 45 46 47 48 49 52 55 56 57 59 60 61 64 66 68 70 72 74 76 77 78 79 81 82 84 85 87 88 89 93 97 98 100 101 102 107 108 110 114 115 116 118 119 120 129 130 131 132 134 135 138 141 144 146 147 148 **P**3 **S** Los Angeles County–Department of Health Services, Los Angeles, CA
Primary Contact: Delvecchio Finley, Chief Executive Officer
COO: Kimberly McKenzie, R.N., Chief Nursing Officer and Chief Operations Officer
CFO: Jody Nakasuji, Chief Financial Officer
CMO: Timothy Van Natta, M.D., Chief Medical Officer
CIO: Sandy Mungovan, Chief Information Officer
CHR: Karyl Smith, Director Human Resources
CNO: Kimberly McKenzie, R.N., Chief Nursing Officer and Chief Operations Officer
Web address: www.humc.edu
Control: County–Government, nonfederal **Service:** General Medical and Surgical

Staffed Beds: 389 **Admissions:** 19990 **Census:** 322 **Outpatient Visits:** 411532 **Births:** 797 **Total Expense ($000):** 744911 **Payroll Expense ($000):** 286845 **Personnel:** 3744

⊞ **PROVIDENCE LITTLE COMPANY OF MARY MEDICAL CENTER – TORRANCE (050353)**, 4101 Torrance Boulevard, Zip 90503–4664; tel. 310/540–7676, (Total facility includes 77 beds in nursing home–type unit) **A**1 2 9 10 **F**3 8 11 13 14 15 18 19 20 22 24 26 28 29 30 31 34 35 40 41 44 45 46 49 51 57 59 60 62 64 68 70 72 74 75 76 77 78 79 81 82 84 85 86 87 89 91 92 93 107 108 110 111 114 115 116 117 118 119 120 121 123 126 128 130 132 133 143 144 145 146 147 148 **S** Providence Health & Services, Renton, WA
Primary Contact: Elizabeth Dunne, Chief Executive
CFO: Elizabeth Zuanich, Chief Financial Officer
CMO: Laurence Eason, M.D., Chief Medical Officer
Web address: www.lcmweb.org
Control: Other not–for–profit (including NFP Corporation) **Service:** General Medical and Surgical

Staffed Beds: 359 **Admissions:** 19837 **Census:** 248 **Outpatient Visits:** 232675 **Births:** 2670 **Total Expense ($000):** 325202 **Payroll Expense ($000):** 125051 **Personnel:** 1593

⊞ **TORRANCE MEMORIAL MEDICAL CENTER (050351)**, 3330 Lomita Boulevard, Zip 90505–5073; tel. 310/325–9110 **A**1 2 9 10 **F**3 5 8 11 12 13 14 15 16 17 18 20 22 24 26 28 29 30 31 34 35 36 37 40 41 46 47 49 50 51 54 57 58 59 60 62 63 64 70 72 74 75 76 77 78 79 81 82 83 84 85 86 87 89 91 93 96 107 108 109 110 111 114 115 116 117 118 119 120 121 123 126 128 129 130 132 134 135 143 144 145 146 147 148
Primary Contact: Craig Leach, President and Chief Executive Officer
CFO: Bill Larson, Chief Financial Officer
CMO: John McNamara, M.D., Chief Medical Officer
CIO: Bernadette Reid, Chief Information Officer
CHR: Lois Michael, Vice President Human Resources
Web address: www.torrancememorial.org
Control: Other not–for–profit (including NFP Corporation) **Service:** General Medical and Surgical

Staffed Beds: 377 **Admissions:** 22904 **Census:** 261 **Outpatient Visits:** 312580 **Births:** 3057 **Total Expense ($000):** 469136 **Payroll Expense ($000):** 176697 **Personnel:** 2709

TRACY—San Joaquin County

⊞ **SUTTER TRACY COMMUNITY HOSPITAL (050313)**, 1420 North Tracy Boulevard, Zip 95376–3497; tel. 209/835–1500 **A**1 9 10 **F**3 11 13 15 18 29 30 31 34 35 39 45 46 49 50 54 57 59 60 64 68 70 74 75 76 77 78 79 81 82 85 86 87 93 107 108 110 111 115 119 124 130 132 135 146 148 **S** Sutter Health, Sacramento, CA
Primary Contact: David M. Thompson, Chief Executive Officer
COO: Doug Archer, Assistant Administrator
CFO: Eric Dalton, Chief Financial Officer
CIO: Catherine M. Larsen, Director Marketing
CHR: Melanie Wallace, Manager Human Resources
Web address: www.suttertracy.org
Control: Other not–for–profit (including NFP Corporation) **Service:** General Medical and Surgical

Staffed Beds: 81 **Admissions:** 3606 **Census:** 31 **Outpatient Visits:** 72217 **Births:** 627 **Total Expense ($000):** 93686 **Payroll Expense ($000):** 32059 **Personnel:** 432

TRAVIS AFB—Solano County

⊞ **DAVID GRANT USAF MEDICAL CENTER**, 101 Bodin Circle, Zip 94535–1809; tel. 707/423–7300, (Nonreporting) **A**1 3 5 **S** Department of the Air Force, Washington, DC
Primary Contact: Colonel Brian T. Hayes, Commander
CFO: Major Jonathan Richards, Chief Financial Officer
CMO: Colonel Chris Scharenbrock, M.D., Chief Medical Staff
Web address: www.travis.af.mil/units/dgmc/index.asp
Control: Air Force, Government, federal **Service:** General Medical and Surgical

Staffed Beds: 110

TRUCKEE—Nevada County

TAHOE FOREST HOSPITAL DISTRICT (051328), 10121 Pine Avenue, Zip 96161–4856, Mailing Address: P.O. Box 759, Zip 96160–0759; tel. 530/587–6011, (Nonreporting) **A**2 5 9 10 18 **S** Tahoe Forest Health System, Truckee, CA
Primary Contact: Robert A. Schapper, Chief Executive Officer
CFO: Crystal Betts, Chief Financial Officer
CMO: Richard Ganong, M.D., Chief of Staff
CIO: Mark Griffiths, Chief Systems Innovation Officer
CHR: Marcie Mortensson, Chief Human Resources Officer
Web address: www.tfhd.com
Control: Hospital district or authority, Government, nonfederal **Service:** General Medical and Surgical

Staffed Beds: 25

Hospital, Medicare Provider Number, Address, Telephone, Approval, Facility, and Physician Codes, Health Care System

★ American Hospital Association (AHA) membership
☐ The Joint Commission accreditation
◇ DNV Healthcare Inc. accreditation
◯ Healthcare Facilities Accreditation Program
△ Commission on Accreditation of Rehabilitation Facilities (CARF) accreditation

CA

TULARE—Tulare County

☒ ◇ **TULARE REGIONAL MEDICAL CENTER (050359)**, 869 North Cherry Street, Zip 93274–2287; tel. 559/688–0821 **A**1 9 10 21 **F**3 11 13 15 20 26 29 34 35 40 45 46 47 48 49 50 53 56 57 59 60 62 64 65 66 68 70 71 73 74 75 76 77 79 81 85 86 89 93 97 107 108 110 111 118 119 126 127 129 130 131 132 135 146 147 148
Primary Contact: Anthony K. Jones, M.D., Chief Restructuring Officer and Chief Executive Officer
CFO: Michael Bernstein, Chief Financial Officer
CMO: Pradeep Kamboj, M.D., Chief Medical Staff
CIO: Jim Peelgren, Chief Information Officer
CHR: John Barbadian, Vice President Human Resources
CNO: Patricia Mathewson, Chief Nursing Officer
Web address: www.tulareregional.org
Control: Hospital district or authority, Government, nonfederal **Service:** General Medical and Surgical

Staffed Beds: 103 **Admissions:** 4727 **Census:** 50 **Outpatient Visits:** 112727 **Births:** 1238 **Personnel:** 357

TURLOCK—Stanislaus County

☒ **EMANUEL MEDICAL CENTER (050179)**, 825 Delbon Avenue, Zip 95382–2016, Mailing Address: P.O. Box 819005, Zip 95381–9005; tel. 209/667–4200, (Total facility includes 155 beds in nursing home–type unit) **A**1 2 9 10 **F**3 8 10 11 15 18 20 22 24 26 29 30 31 34 35 39 40 47 48 49 54 59 60 64 68 70 73 75 76 77 78 79 81 89 93 97 107 108 110 111 114 115 118 119 120 121 123 127 128 130 132 146 147 148
Primary Contact: Susan C. Micheletti, Chief Executive Officer
CFO: David Neapolitan, Chief Financial Officer
CHR: Terry Gray, Vice President Human Resources
CNO: Constance Fairchilds, R.N., Vice President Patient Care Services
Web address: www.emanuelmed.org
Control: Church–operated, Nongovernment, not–for profit **Service:** General Medical and Surgical

Staffed Beds: 354 **Admissions:** 9777 **Census:** 242 **Outpatient Visits:** 85782 **Births:** 1338 **Total Expense ($000):** 199369 **Payroll Expense ($000):** 69606 **Personnel:** 1043

TUSTIN—Orange County

☒ **HEALTHSOUTH TUSTIN REHABILITATION HOSPITAL (053034)**, 14851 Yorba Street, Zip 92780–2925; tel. 714/832–9200 **A**1 9 10 **F**29 34 57 60 74 75 77 82 90 94 130 132 **S** HEALTHSOUTH Corporation, Birmingham, AL
Primary Contact: Diana C. Hanyak, Chief Executive Officer
CFO: Paula Redmond, Controller
CMO: Rodric Bell, M.D., Medical Director
CHR: JoAnn Roiz, PHR, Director Human Resources
Web address: www.tustinrehab.com
Control: Corporation, Investor–owned, for–profit **Service:** Rehabilitation

Staffed Beds: 48 **Admissions:** 1344 **Census:** 42 **Outpatient Visits:** 0 **Births:** 0 **Total Expense ($000):** 19666

NEWPORT SPECIALTY HOSPITAL (052053), 14662 Newport Avenue, Zip 92780–6064; tel. 714/838–9600, (Nonreporting) **A**9 10
Primary Contact: Richard Luna, President and Chief Executive Officer
COO: Kara Bourne, R.N., Chief Nursing Officer and Chief Operating Officer
CIO: Darla Kennedy, Chief Information Officer
CHR: Aprille Major, Director Human Resources
Web address: www.newportspecialtyhospital.com/
Control: Corporation, Investor–owned, for–profit **Service:** Long–Term Acute Care hospital

Staffed Beds: 42

TWENTYNINE PALMS—San Bernardino County

☒ **ROBERT E. BUSH NAVAL HOSPITAL**, 1145 Sturgis Road, Zip 92278, Mailing Address: Box 788250, MCAGCC, Zip 92278–8250; tel. 760/830–2190, (Nonreporting) **A**1 **S** Bureau of Medicine and Surgery, Department of the Navy, Washington, DC
Primary Contact: Captain Jay C. Sourbeer, Commanding Officer
CFO: Lieutenant Commander Amy Sulog, Comptroller
CMO: Commander Michael E. Cardenas, M.D., Director Medical Services
CHR: Virginia Ward, Human Resources Officer
CNO: Captain Sandra Mason, Director Nursing Services and Senior Nurse Executive
Web address: www.med.navy.mil/sites/nhtp/Pages/default.aspx
Control: Navy, Government, federal **Service:** General Medical and Surgical

Staffed Beds: 29

UKIAH—Mendocino County

☒ **UKIAH VALLEY MEDICAL CENTER (050301)**, 275 Hospital Drive, Zip 95482–4531; tel. 707/462–3111 **A**1 5 9 10 20 **F**3 8 11 12 13 15 18 29 30 31 32 34 35 38 40 44 45 46 48 49 50 51 54 57 59 60 64 65 68 70 72 75 76 77 78 79 81 82 84 85 86 87 93 94 97 107 108 110 111 114 115 116 117 118 119 127 130 131 132 135 144 146 147 148 **S** Adventist Health, Roseville, CA
Primary Contact: Gwen Matthews, R.N., MSN, Chief Executive Officer
CIO: David Eastman, Site Director
CHR: Rebecca Ryan, Interim Director Human Resources and Employee Health
Web address: www.adventisthealth.org
Control: Church–operated, Nongovernment, not–for profit **Service:** General Medical and Surgical

Staffed Beds: 48 **Admissions:** 3844 **Census:** 32 **Outpatient Visits:** 217809 **Births:** 815 **Total Expense ($000):** 106504 **Payroll Expense ($000):** 39125 **Personnel:** 536

UPLAND—San Bernardino County

☒ **SAN ANTONIO COMMUNITY HOSPITAL (050099)**, 999 San Bernardino Road, Zip 91786–4920, Mailing Address: Box 5001, Zip 91785–5001; tel. 909/985–2811 **A**1 2 9 10 **F**3 8 11 13 15 17 18 20 22 24 26 28 29 31 35 38 40 45 46 49 50 54 57 59 60 61 64 65 69 70 72 74 75 76 77 78 79 80 81 82 83 84 85 86 87 89 91 92 93 94 107 108 110 111 114 115 118 119 121 123 124 130 132 146 147 148
Primary Contact: Harris F. Koenig, President and Chief Executive Officer
CFO: Wah Chung Hsu, Senior Vice President Finance
CMO: Jay Shah, M.D., President Medical Staff
CIO: Kamel Pandya, Director Information Services
CHR: Lynn Kelly, Vice President Human Resources
CNO: Liz Aragon, R.N., Vice President, Chief Nursing Officer
Web address: www.sach.org
Control: Other not–for–profit (including NFP Corporation) **Service:** General Medical and Surgical

Staffed Beds: 279 **Admissions:** 15575 **Census:** 147 **Outpatient Visits:** 218528 **Births:** 2166 **Total Expense ($000):** 265272 **Payroll Expense ($000):** 112643 **Personnel:** 1572

VACAVILLE—Solano County

CALIFORNIA MEDICAL FACILITY, 1600 California Drive, Zip 95687; tel. 707/448–6841, (Nonreporting)
Primary Contact: Mary Lou Dunlap, Correctional Health Services Administrator
CMO: Raymond Andreasen, M.D., Chief Medical Officer–Inpatient
Web address: www.cya.ca.gov/visitors/fac_prison_cmf.html
Control: State–Government, nonfederal **Service:** Hospital unit of an institution (prison hospital, college infimary, etc.)

Staffed Beds: 215

☒ **KAISER PERMANENTE VACAVILLE MEDICAL CENTER (050767)**, 1 Quality Drive, Zip 95688–9494; tel. 707/624–4000 **A**1 10 **F**3 13 15 20 22 29 30 31 34 35 40 43 44 45 46 47 48 49 50 51 57 58 59 60 61 62 63 64 65 68 70 74 75 76 77 78 79 81 82 84 85 87 97 107 108 110 111 114 115 118 119 130 132 135 141 142 146 147 148 **S** Kaiser Foundation Hospitals, Oakland, CA
Primary Contact: Max Villalobos, Senior Vice President
Web address: www.kp.org
Control: Other not–for–profit (including NFP Corporation) **Service:** General Medical and Surgical

Staffed Beds: 140 **Admissions:** 4446 **Census:** 49 **Births:** 110 **Personnel:** 858

NORTHBAY VACAVALLEY HOSPITAL See NorthBay Medical Center, Fairfield

VALENCIA—Los Angeles County

☒ **HENRY MAYO NEWHALL MEMORIAL HOSPITAL (050624)**, 23845 McBean Parkway, Zip 91355–2083; tel. 661/253–8000 **A**1 2 9 10 **F**3 7 8 9 11 15 17 18 20 22 24 26 28 29 30 31 34 35 38 40 41 42 43 45 49 50 54 55 57 59 60 64 70 72 74 76 77 78 79 81 82 84 85 86 87 90 93 94 98 99 100 101 102 103 104 105 107 108 109 110 114 115 118 119 130 132 135 146 147 148 **P**3
Primary Contact: Roger E. Seaver, President and Chief Executive Officer
COO: John V. Schleif, Senior Vice President and Chief Operating Officer
CFO: C. R. Hudson, Senior Vice President and Chief Financial Officer
CMO: Richard Frankenstein, M.D., Vice President and Chief Medical Officer
CIO: Cindy Peterson, Vice President and Chief Information Officer
CHR: Mark Puleo, Vice President and Chief Human Resources Officer
CNO: Larry R. Kidd, R.N., Vice President and Chief Nursing Officer
Web address: www.henrymayo.com
Control: Other not–for–profit (including NFP Corporation) **Service:** General Medical and Surgical

Staffed Beds: 238 **Admissions:** 12415 **Census:** 149 **Outpatient Visits:** 92470 **Births:** 1156 **Total Expense ($000):** 238353 **Payroll Expense ($000):** 76453 **Personnel:** 1336

VALLEJO—Solano County

☒ △ **KAISER PERMANENTE VALLEJO MEDICAL CENTER (050073)**, 975 Sereno Drive, Zip 94589–2441; tel. 707/651–1000 **A**1 7 10 **F**3 5 13 15 20 22 29 30 31 34 35 36 40 44 45 46 47 48 49 50 51 57 58 59 61 62 63 64 65 68 70 73 74 75 76 77 78 79 81 82 84 85 87 90 91 92 93 94 97 107 108 110 111 114 115 116 117 118 119 129 130 132 135 141 142 144 146 147 148 **S** Kaiser Foundation Hospitals, Oakland, CA
Primary Contact: Corwin N. Harper, Senior Vice President and Area Manager
COO: Karen Grisnak, R.N., Chief Operating Officer and Assistant Administrator Quality Services
CFO: Joseph D'Angina, Area Finance Officer
CMO: Steven Stricker, M.D., Physician in Chief
CIO: Gale Austin-Moore, Director Area Technology
CHR: Sherri Stegge, Director Human Resources
Web address: www.kaiserpermanente.org
Control: Other not-for-profit (including NFP Corporation) **Service:** General Medical and Surgical

Staffed Beds: 248 **Admissions:** 9150 **Census:** 102 **Births:** 2243 **Personnel:** 1903

☒ **ST. HELENA HOSPITAL–CENTER FOR BEHAVIORAL HEALTH (054074)**, 525 Oregon Street, Zip 94590–3201; tel. 707/648–2200 **A**1 9 10 **F**29 30 50 64 65 68 98 99 104 105 130 146 **S** Adventist Health, Roseville, CA
Primary Contact: Patricia Williams, Regional VP for Behavioral Medicine and Population Health
CFO: Edward A. McDonald, Chief Financial Officer
Web address: www.sthelenahospitals.org/location/center-for-behavioral-health
Control: Other not-for-profit (including NFP Corporation) **Service:** Psychiatric

Staffed Beds: 61 **Admissions:** 2380 **Census:** 55 **Outpatient Visits:** 5203 **Births:** 0 **Total Expense ($000):** 20736 **Payroll Expense ($000):** 10585 **Personnel:** 155

☒ **SUTTER SOLANO MEDICAL CENTER (050101)**, 300 Hospital Drive, Zip 94589–2574, Mailing Address: P.O. Box 3189, Zip 94590–0669; tel. 707/554–4444 **A**1 2 9 10 **F**3 8 11 13 15 18 26 29 30 31 34 35 40 45 49 50 51 55 57 59 64 68 70 74 75 76 77 78 79 81 84 85 86 87 100 107 108 110 111 114 118 119 120 121 123 124 130 132 146 **S** Sutter Health, Sacramento, CA
Primary Contact: Theresa Glubka, Chief Executive Officer
CFO: Cynthia van Hoff, Chief Financial Officer
CHR: Jean Willhite, Director Human Resources
Web address: www.suttersolano.org
Control: Other not-for-profit (including NFP Corporation) **Service:** General Medical and Surgical

Staffed Beds: 102 **Admissions:** 4552 **Census:** 49 **Outpatient Visits:** 61825 **Births:** 653 **Total Expense ($000):** 131719 **Payroll Expense ($000):** 43777 **Personnel:** 463

VAN NUYS—Los Angeles County, See Los Angeles

VENTURA—Ventura County

☐ **AURORA VISTA DEL MAR HOSPITAL (054077)**, 801 Seneca Street, Zip 93001–1411; tel. 805/653–6434, (Nonreporting) **A**1 9 10 **S** Aurora Behavioral Health Care, Corona, CA
Primary Contact: Mayla Krebsbach, Chief Executive Officer
COO: Sherri Block, Chief Operating Officer
CFO: Steve Ruths, M.D., Medical Director
Web address: www.vistadelmarhospital.com
Control: Corporation, Investor-owned, for-profit **Service:** Psychiatric

Staffed Beds: 87

★ ◇ **COMMUNITY MEMORIAL HEALTH SYSTEM (050394)**, 147 North Brent Street, Zip 93003–2809; tel. 805/652–5011, (Includes COMMUNITY MEMORIAL HOSPITAL, 147 North Brent Street, Zip 93003–2854; tel. 805/652–5011; OJAI VALLEY COMMUNITY HOSPITAL, 1306 Maricopa Highway, Ojai, Zip 93023–3163; tel. 805/646–1401; Haady Lashkari, Chief Administrative Officer), (Total facility includes 66 beds in nursing home–type unit) **A**2 9 10 21 **F**3 8 11 12 13 15 17 18 19 20 22 24 26 28 29 30 31 32 34 35 40 45 46 47 48 49 53 54 57 59 64 65 66 68 70 71 72 74 75 77 78 79 81 82 83 84 85 86 97 99 100 101 104 107 108 110 111 115 118 119 126 127 128 130 131 132 144 145 146 147 148 **P**4 7
Primary Contact: Gary Wilde, President and Chief Executive Officer
COO: Adam Thunell, Chief Operating Officer and Vice President Operations
CFO: David Glyer, Vice President Finance
CMO: Stanley Frochtzwajg, M.D., Chief Medical Officer
CIO: Ron Sandifer, Chief Information Officer
CHR: Diany Klein, Vice President Human Resources
Web address: www.cmhshealth.org
Control: Other not-for-profit (including NFP Corporation) **Service:** General Medical and Surgical

Staffed Beds: 296 **Admissions:** 14899 **Census:** 133 **Outpatient Visits:** 449723 **Births:** 2591

☐ **VENTURA COUNTY MEDICAL CENTER (050159)**, 3291 Loma Vista Road, Zip 93003–3099; tel. 805/652–6000, (Nonreporting) **A**1 9 10
Primary Contact: Cyndie Cole, R.N., MSN, Administrator
CMO: Bryan Wong, M.D., Medical Director
CIO: Terry Theobald, Chief Information Officer
CHR: Tim Rhyne, Personnel Officer
CNO: Susan Scott, Chief Nurse Executive
Web address: www.vchca.org
Control: County–Government, nonfederal **Service:** General Medical and Surgical

Staffed Beds: 160

VICTORVILLE—San Bernardino County

★ ○ **DESERT VALLEY HOSPITAL (050709)**, 16850 Bear Valley Road, Zip 92395–5795; tel. 760/241–8000 **A**9 10 11 **F**3 13 15 18 20 22 24 26 29 30 31 34 35 37 38 40 45 46 47 48 49 50 51 56 57 58 59 61 64 65 68 70 79 81 82 85 107 108 111 114 115 119 126 129 130 135 144 146 148 **S** Prime Healthcare Services, Ontario, CA
Primary Contact: Fred Hunter, R.N., Chief Executive Officer
COO: Luis Leon, Chief Operating Officer
CFO: Martin Mansukhani, Chief Financial Officer
CIO: Sreekant Gotti, Director Information Systems
CNO: Patrick Reinhard, R.N., Chief Nursing Officer
Web address: www.dvmc.com
Control: Corporation, Investor–owned, for–profit **Service:** General Medical and Surgical

Staffed Beds: 110 **Admissions:** 9297 **Census:** 87 **Outpatient Visits:** 77847 **Births:** 801 **Total Expense ($000):** 100950 **Payroll Expense ($000):** 37642 **Personnel:** 688

○ **VICTOR VALLEY GLOBAL MEDICAL CENTER (050517)**, 15248 Eleventh Street, Zip 92395–3704; tel. 760/245–8691, (Nonreporting) **A**9 10 11
Primary Contact: Suzanne Richards, R.N., M.P.H., Chief Executive Officer
COO: Doreen Dann, R.N., Chief Operating Officer
CIO: Joe Archer, Chief Information Officer
CHR: Cesar Lugo, Director Human Resources
Web address: www.vvch.org
Control: Other not–for–profit (including NFP Corporation) **Service:** General Medical and Surgical

Staffed Beds: 115

VISALIA—Tulare County

☒ △ **KAWEAH DELTA MEDICAL CENTER (050057)**, 400 West Mineral King Boulevard, Zip 93291–6263; tel. 559/624–2000, (Includes SOUTH CAMPUS, 1633 South Court Street, Zip 93277; tel. 559/624–6090), (Total facility includes 61 beds in nursing home–type unit) **A**1 7 9 10 **F**3 13 15 17 18 20 22 24 26 28 29 30 31 34 35 40 41 43 45 49 50 51 53 54 56 57 59 60 62 63 64 65 68 70 73 74 75 76 77 78 79 81 82 84 85 87 89 90 93 97 98 99 100 101 102 103 104 107 108 110 111 114 116 117 118 119 123 124 126 127 128 129 130 131 132 134 135 144 146 147 148 **P**7
Primary Contact: Lindsay K. Mann, Chief Executive Officer
COO: Thomas J. Rayner, Senior Vice President and Chief Operating Officer
CFO: Gary Herbst, Senior Vice President and Chief Financial Officer
CMO: James Paskert, M.D., Vice President Chief Medical and Quality Officer
CIO: Mike Mistretta, Vice President and Chief Information Officer
CHR: Debbie Wood, Vice President Human Resources
CNO: Linda Pruett, R.N., Vice President Chief Nursing Officer
Web address: www.kaweahdelta.org
Control: Hospital district or authority, Government, nonfederal **Service:** General Medical and Surgical

Staffed Beds: 421 **Admissions:** 22494 **Census:** 351 **Outpatient Visits:** 633640 **Births:** 4166 **Total Expense ($000):** 434699 **Payroll Expense ($000):** 186137 **Personnel:** 3327

CA

Hospital, Medicare Provider Number, Address, Telephone, Approval, Facility, and Physician Codes, Health Care System

★ American Hospital Association (AHA) membership
☐ The Joint Commission accreditation   ◇ DNV Healthcare Inc. accreditation
○ Healthcare Facilities Accreditation Program
△ Commission on Accreditation of Rehabilitation Facilities (CARF) accreditation

CA

WALNUT CREEK—Contra Costa County

☒ △ **JOHN MUIR MEDICAL CENTER, WALNUT CREEK (050180)**, 1601 Ygnacio Valley Road, Zip 94598–3194; tel. 925/939–3000 **A**1 2 7 9 10 **F**1 3 4 11 13 15 16 17 18 20 22 24 26 28 29 30 31 34 35 37 39 40 43 44 45 46 47 49 50 54 56 57 58 59 60 62 64 65 67 68 70 72 73 74 75 76 77 78 79 80 81 82 84 85 86 87 88 89 90 93 96 98 100 102 107 108 110 118 119 120 121 123 124 126 128 130 131 132 135 141 145 146 147 148 **P**3 5 **S** John Muir Health, Walnut Creek, CA
Primary Contact: Jane Willemsen, Chief Administrative Officer
COO: Raymond Nassief, Senior Vice President Operations and Clinical Transformation
CFO: Michael Moody, Senior Vice President and Chief Financial Officer
CMO: Irving Pike, M.D., Chief Medical Officer
CIO: Jim Wesley, Interim Chief Information Officer
CHR: Alice A. Villanueva, Senior Vice President Human Resources
CNO: Debra Pendergast, Senior Vice President Patient Care Services and Chief Nursing Officer
Web address: www.jmmdhs.com/index.php/jmmdhs_jmmc.html
Control: Other not–for–profit (including NFP Corporation) **Service:** General Medical and Surgical

> **Staffed Beds:** 367 **Admissions:** 17891 **Census:** 231 **Outpatient Visits:** 315426 **Births:** 2826 **Total Expense ($000):** 746893 **Payroll Expense ($000):** 272494 **Personnel:** 2032

☒ **KAISER PERMANENTE WALNUT CREEK MEDICAL CENTER (050072)**, 1425 South Main Street, Zip 94596–5300; tel. 925/295–4000, (Includes KAISER FOUNDATION HOSPITAL, 200 Muir Road, Martinez, Zip 94553–4696; tel. 510/372–1000) **A**1 3 5 10 **F**3 8 9 13 15 18 29 30 31 32 34 35 36 38 40 45 49 50 54 56 57 59 60 61 62 63 64 65 68 70 72 74 75 76 77 78 79 81 82 83 84 85 86 87 89 91 92 93 94 96 97 99 100 101 102 103 104 107 108 110 111 114 115 116 117 118 119 126 130 132 134 135 144 146 147 148 **S** Kaiser Foundation Hospitals, Oakland, CA
Primary Contact: Colleen McKeown, Senior Vice President and Area Manager
CFO: Yakesun Wing, Business Strategy and Finance Leader
CIO: Kevin Wheeler, Information Technology Leader
Web address: www.kaiserpermanente.org
Control: Other not–for–profit (including NFP Corporation) **Service:** General Medical and Surgical

> **Staffed Beds:** 233 **Admissions:** 14608 **Census:** 169 **Births:** 3623 **Personnel:** 1974

WATSONVILLE—Santa Cruz County

☒ **WATSONVILLE COMMUNITY HOSPITAL (050194)**, 75 Nielson Street, Zip 95076–2468; tel. 831/724–4741 **A**1 9 10 **F**3 11 13 15 18 20 29 34 35 40 45 49 50 51 57 60 64 68 70 72 74 76 77 79 81 87 89 93 97 107 111 115 119 130 144 146 148 **S** Community Health Systems, Inc., Franklin, TN
Primary Contact: Audra Earle, FACHE, Chief Executive Officer
CFO: Dennis T. Bynum, Interim Chief Financial Officer
CMO: Robert Weber, M.D., Chief Medical Staff
CIO: Sergio Nell, Director Information Systems
CHR: Jeri Gilbert, Director Human Resources
Web address: www.watsonvillehospital.com
Control: Corporation, Investor–owned, for–profit **Service:** General Medical and Surgical

> **Staffed Beds:** 106 **Admissions:** 4542 **Census:** 48 **Outpatient Visits:** 65179 **Births:** 1305 **Total Expense ($000):** 111066 **Payroll Expense ($000):** 67027

WEAVERVILLE—Trinity County

TRINITY HOSPITAL (051315), 60 Easter Avenue, Zip 96093, Mailing Address: P.O. Box 1229, Zip 96093–1229; tel. 530/623–5541, (Total facility includes 26 beds in nursing home–type unit) **A**9 10 18 **F**3 11 29 30 34 40 45 57 62 64 81 107 114 119 127 128 130 133
Primary Contact: Stanley C. Oppegard, Chief Executive Officer
CFO: Kathy Walker, Chief Financial Officer
CMO: Donald Krouse, M.D., Chief of Staff
CIO: Jennifer Van Matre, Director Finance
CHR: Heidi Corrigan, Manager Human Resources
CNO: Judy Nordlund, R.N., Chief Nursing Officer
Web address: www.mcmedical.org
Control: Hospital district or authority, Government, nonfederal **Service:** General Medical and Surgical

> **Staffed Beds:** 47 **Admissions:** 426 **Census:** 24 **Outpatient Visits:** 31562 **Births:** 0 **Total Expense ($000):** 13984 **Payroll Expense ($000):** 5068 **Personnel:** 131

WEST COVINA—Los Angeles County

☐ **DOCTORS HOSPITAL OF WEST COVINA (050096)**, 725 South Orange Avenue, Zip 91790–2614; tel. 626/338–8481, (Total facility includes 24 beds in nursing home–type unit) **A**1 9 10 **F**3 29 46 81 85 104 105 128 130
Primary Contact: Gerald H. Wallman, Administrator
CFO: Kami Horvat, Chief Financial Officer
CMO: Nashat Ateia, M.D., Chief of Staff
CHR: Lourdes Meza, Coordinator Human Resources
CNO: Rita Lawrence, Director of Nursing
Control: Corporation, Investor–owned, for–profit **Service:** General Medical and Surgical

> **Staffed Beds:** 51 **Admissions:** 132 **Census:** 22 **Births:** 0

WEST HILLS—Los Angeles County, See Los Angeles

WEST LOS ANGELES—Los Angeles County, See Los Angeles

WESTMINSTER—Orange County

☒ **KINDRED HOSPITAL–WESTMINSTER (052035)**, 200 Hospital Circle, Zip 92683–3910; tel. 714/893–4541, (Nonreporting) **A**1 9 10 **S** Kindred Healthcare, Louisville, KY
Primary Contact: Brooke Saunders, Administrator
CFO: Dale Wagner, Chief Financial Officer
Web address: www.khwestminster.com/
Control: Corporation, Investor–owned, for–profit **Service:** Long–Term Acute Care hospital

> **Staffed Beds:** 109

WHITTIER—Los Angeles County

☒ **PRESBYTERIAN INTERCOMMUNITY HEALTH HOSPITAL (050169)**, 12401 Washington Boulevard, Zip 90602–1099; tel. 562/698–0811, (Total facility includes 35 beds in nursing home–type unit) **A**1 2 9 10 **F**3 11 13 14 15 17 18 20 22 24 26 28 29 30 31 34 35 36 37 40 45 46 49 50 51 54 55 56 57 58 59 60 61 62 63 64 65 66 68 69 70 71 72 74 75 76 77 78 79 81 84 85 86 87 89 90 92 93 96 107 108 110 111 114 115 116 117 118 119 120 121 123 124 128 130 131 132 135 143 145 146 147 148 **P**3 5
Primary Contact: James R. West, President and Chief Executive Officer
CFO: Mitchell T. Thomas, Chief Financial Officer
CMO: Rosalio J. Lopez, M.D., Senior Vice President and Chief Medical Officer
CIO: Peggy Chulack, Chief Administrative Officer and Chief Information Officer
CHR: Lon Orey, Vice President Human Resources
Web address: www.whittierpres.com
Control: Other not–for–profit (including NFP Corporation) **Service:** General Medical and Surgical

> **Staffed Beds:** 548 **Admissions:** 19714 **Census:** 242 **Outpatient Visits:** 247067 **Births:** 4033 **Total Expense ($000):** 456149 **Payroll Expense ($000):** 170319 **Personnel:** 2804

☐ **WHITTIER HOSPITAL MEDICAL CENTER (050735)**, 9080 Colima Road, Zip 90605–1600; tel. 562/945–3561, (Nonreporting) **A**1 9 10 **S** AHMC & Healthcare, Inc., Alhambra, CA
Primary Contact: Richard Castro, Chief Executive Officer
COO: Mary Anne Monje, Chief Financial Officer and Chief Operating Officer
CFO: Mary Anne Monje, Chief Financial Officer and Chief Operating Officer
CMO: Martha Dispoto, R.N., Chief Nursing Officer
CIO: Jay Geldhof, Director Information Systems
CHR: Martha Salado, Interim Director Human Resources
Web address: www.whittierhospital.com
Control: Corporation, Investor–owned, for–profit **Service:** General Medical and Surgical

> **Staffed Beds:** 81

WILLITS—Mendocino County

☒ **FRANK R. HOWARD MEMORIAL HOSPITAL (051310)**, One Madrone Street, Zip 95490–4298; tel. 707/459–6801 **A**1 9 10 18 **F**11 15 29 30 34 35 40 57 59 68 70 75 79 81 93 107 110 111 115 119 131 132 133 135 146 147 148 **S** Adventist Health, Roseville, CA
Primary Contact: Rick Bockmann, Chief Executive Officer
CFO: Brandon Parker, Vice President Finance and Chief Financial Officer
CMO: Kimberly Faucher, M.D., Chief Medical Officer
CHR: Darcy De Leon, Director Human Resources
CNO: Karen M. Scott, Vice President Patient Care
Web address: www.howardhospital.com
Control: Church–operated, Nongovernment, not–for profit **Service:** General Medical and Surgical

> **Staffed Beds:** 25 **Admissions:** 1471 **Census:** 16 **Outpatient Visits:** 34994 **Births:** 1 **Total Expense ($000):** 41781 **Payroll Expense ($000):** 17228 **Personnel:** 211

WILLOWS—Glenn County

GLENN MEDICAL CENTER (051306), 1133 West Sycamore Street,
Zip 95988–2745; tel. 530/934–1800, (Nonreporting) **A**9 10 18
Primary Contact: Woody J. Laughnan, Jr., Administrator
CFO: Gary Pea, Chief Financial Officer
CMO: Mark Garrison, Chief of Staff
CHR: Deborah McMillan, Director Human Resources
CNO: Veena Vangari, R.N., Chief Nursing Officer
Web address: www.glennmed.org
Control: Other not–for–profit (including NFP Corporation) **Service:** General
Medical and Surgical

Staffed Beds: 15

WOODLAND—Yolo County

⌧ **WOODLAND HEALTHCARE (050127)**, 1325 Cottonwood Street,
Zip 95695–5199; tel. 530/662–3961, (Nonreporting) **A**1 5 9 10 **S** Dignity
Health, San Francisco, CA
Primary Contact: H. Kevin Vaziri, President
Web address: www.woodlandhealthcare.org
Control: Other not–for–profit (including NFP Corporation) **Service:** General
Medical and Surgical

Staffed Beds: 111

WOODLAND HILLS—Los Angeles County, See Los Angeles

YREKA—Siskiyou County

☐ **FAIRCHILD MEDICAL CENTER (051316)**, 444 Bruce Street, Zip 96097–3450;
tel. 530/842–4121 **A**1 9 10 18 **F**3 11 13 15 30 35 40 43 45 50 57 59 64 70
75 76 79 81 86 87 89 93 107 108 114 118 119 127 129 130 132 133
146 148
Primary Contact: Jonathon Andrus, Chief Executive Officer
CFO: Kelly Martin, Chief Financial Officer
CMO: David Della Lana, M.D., Chief of Staff
CIO: Joan Munson, Manager Information Systems
CHR: Joann Sarmento, Manager Human Resources
CNO: Kathy Shelvock, R.N., Assistant Administrator Patient Care Services
Web address: www.fairchildmed.org
Control: Other not–for–profit (including NFP Corporation) **Service:** General
Medical and Surgical

Staffed Beds: 25 **Admissions:** 1745 **Census:** 14 **Outpatient Visits:** 93471
Total Expense ($000): 55992

YUBA CITY—Sutter County

FREMONT MEDICAL CENTER See Fremont–Rideout Health Group, Marysville

☐ **SUTTER SURGICAL HOSPITAL – NORTH VALLEY (050766)**, 455 Plumas
Boulevard, Zip 95991–5074; tel. 530/749–5700 **A**1 9 10 **F**3 26 29 30 34 37
57 64 68 74 79 81 85 86 111 146
Primary Contact: Renee Schroyer, Chief Executive Officer
CHR: Michelle Guina, Manager Human Resources
CNO: David Cooke, Chief Nursing Officer
Web address: www.sshnv.org
Control: Corporation, Investor–owned, for–profit **Service:** Surgical

Staffed Beds: 14 **Admissions:** 590 **Census:** 4 **Outpatient Visits:** 4706
Births: 0 **Total Expense ($000):** 20392 **Payroll Expense ($000):** 5244
Personnel: 76

COLORADO

ALAMOSA—Alamosa County

★ **SAN LUIS VALLEY HEALTH (060008)**, 106 Blanca Avenue, Zip 81101–2393; tel. 719/589–2511 **A**9 10 20 **F**3 7 11 13 15 29 30 31 33 40 43 53 70 75 76 77 78 79 81 85 93 107 111 114 119 129 130 131 146 147 148 **P**6 **S** San Luis Valley Health, Alamosa, CO
Primary Contact: Konnie Martin, Chief Executive Officer
COO: Patti Thompson, Chief Operating Officer
CFO: Shane Mortensen, Chief Financial Officer
CMO: Gregory McAuliffe, M.D., Chief Medical Officer
CIO: Chuck Laufle, Director of Information Services
CHR: Mandy Lee Crockett, Director Human Resources
Web address: www.slvrmc.org
Control: Other not-for-profit (including NFP Corporation) **Service:** General Medical and Surgical

Staffed Beds: 44 **Admissions:** 2011 **Census:** 16 **Outpatient Visits:** 97448 **Births:** 438 **Total Expense ($000):** 57785 **Payroll Expense ($000):** 28393 **Personnel:** 566

ASPEN—Pitkin County

⊞ **ASPEN VALLEY HOSPITAL DISTRICT (061324)**, 401 Castle Creek Road, Zip 81611–1159; tel. 970/925–1120 **A**1 9 10 18 **F**3 7 8 10 13 15 18 28 29 31 34 40 43 57 59 64 68 70 75 76 77 78 79 81 82 85 86 87 89 93 94 107 108 110 111 115 118 119 131 132 133 135 144 146 148
Primary Contact: Daniel J. Bonk, Chief Executive Officer
CFO: Terry Collins, Chief Financial Officer
CMO: J. Christopher Beck, D.O., President Medical Staff
CIO: Ginny Dyche, Director Community Relations
CHR: Alicia Miller, Director Human Resources
CNO: Elaine Gerson, Chief Clinical Officer and General Counsel
Web address: www.avhaspen.org
Control: Hospital district or authority, Government, nonfederal **Service:** General Medical and Surgical

Staffed Beds: 25 **Admissions:** 1153 **Census:** 7 **Outpatient Visits:** 34094 **Births:** 202 **Total Expense ($000):** 63038 **Payroll Expense ($000):** 25687 **Personnel:** 354

AURORA—Adams County

⊞ **CHILDREN'S HOSPITAL COLORADO (063301)**, 13123 East 16th Avenue, Zip 80045–7106; tel. 720/777–1234, (Includes CHILDREN'S HOSPITAL OF COLORADO AT MEMORIAL, 1400 East Boulder Street, Colorado Springs, Zip 80909–5533; tel. 719/365–5000) **A**1 3 5 9 10 **F**3 11 12 13 14 17 19 21 23 25 27 28 29 30 31 32 34 35 36 38 39 40 41 42 43 44 45 46 48 49 50 53 54 55 58 59 60 61 64 65 66 68 71 72 74 75 76 77 78 79 80 81 82 84 85 86 87 88 89 91 92 93 95 96 97 98 99 100 101 102 104 105 107 108 111 113 114 115 116 117 119 126 129 130 131 132 134 136 137 138 139 141 144 145 146 147 148 **P**8
Primary Contact: James E. Shmerling, Chief Executive Officer
COO: Jena Hausmann, President and Chief Operating Officer
CFO: Jeff Harrington, Chief Financial Officer
CMO: Joan Bothner, M.D., Chief Medical Officer
CIO: Mary Anne Leach, Vice President and Chief Information Officer
CHR: Nita Mosby Henry, Vice President Human Resources
CNO: Kelly Marie Johnson, R.N., Senior Vice President Patience Care Services and Chief Nursing Officer
Web address: www.thechildrenshospital.org
Control: Other not-for-profit (including NFP Corporation) **Service:** Children's general

Staffed Beds: 454 **Admissions:** 17646 **Census:** 296 **Outpatient Visits:** 631433 **Births:** 65 **Total Expense ($000):** 816886 **Payroll Expense ($000):** 341326 **Personnel:** 4869

⊞ **KINDRED HOSPITAL–AURORA (062013)**, 700 Potomac Street 2nd Floor, Zip 80011–6844; tel. 720/857–8333, (Nonreporting) **A**1 9 10 **S** Kindred Healthcare, Louisville, KY
Primary Contact: David Kowalski, Chief Executive Officer
CMO: Eric Yaeger, M.D., Chief Medical Officer
CHR: Becky Small, Chief Human Resources Officer
CNO: Paul Green, Chief Clinical Officer
Web address: www.khaurora.com/
Control: Corporation, Investor–owned, for–profit **Service:** Long–Term Acute Care hospital

Staffed Beds: 37

⊞ **MEDICAL CENTER OF AURORA (060100)**, 1501 South Potomac Street, Zip 80012–5411; tel. 303/695–2600, (Includes MEDICAL CENTER OF AURORA NORTH, 700 Potomac Street, Zip 80011–6792; tel. 303/363–7200; SOUTH CAMPUS, 1501 South Potomac, Zip 80012; tel. 303/695–2600) **A**1 2 9 10 **F**3 8 11 13 15 17 18 20 22 24 26 28 29 30 31 34 35 37 39 40 42 43 45 46 47 48 49 53 54 56 57 59 63 64 68 70 72 74 75 76 77 78 79 81 82 84 85 86 87 89 92 98 103 107 108 110 111 114 115 117 118 119 126 129 130 132 135 146 147 148 **P**6 8 **S** HCA, Nashville, TN
Primary Contact: Richard A. Hammett, Chief Executive Officer
COO: Mary Berrigan, Chief Operating Officer
CFO: Bryce DeHaven, Chief Financial Officer
CMO: Dianne McCallister, M.D., Chief Medical Officer
Web address: www.auroramed.com
Control: Corporation, Investor–owned, for–profit **Service:** General Medical and Surgical

Staffed Beds: 303 **Admissions:** 14768 **Census:** 203

⊞ △ **SPALDING REHABILITATION HOSPITAL (063027)**, 900 Potomac Steet, Zip 80011–6716; tel. 303/367–1166, (Nonreporting) **A**1 7 10 **S** HCA, Nashville, TN
Primary Contact: Kristen DeHart, Interim Administrator
COO: Debbie Petersen, R.N., Chief Operating Officer and Chief Nursing Officer
CFO: Joyce Webber, Chief Financial Officer
CHR: Donna Greeley, Director Human Resources
CNO: Debbie Petersen, R.N., Chief Operating Officer and Chief Nursing Officer
Web address: www.spaldingrehab.com
Control: Partnership, Investor–owned, for–profit **Service:** Rehabilitation

Staffed Beds: 40

⊞ **UNIVERSITY OF COLORADO HOSPITAL (060024)**, 12605 East 16th Avenue, Zip 80045–2545; tel. 720/848–0000 **A**1 2 3 5 8 9 10 **F**3 4 5 6 8 9 11 12 13 15 16 17 18 20 22 24 26 28 29 30 31 33 34 35 36 37 38 40 43 44 45 46 47 48 49 50 52 53 54 55 56 57 58 59 60 61 64 65 68 70 71 72 74 75 76 77 78 79 81 82 84 85 86 87 90 91 92 93 94 96 97 100 101 102 103 104 107 108 110 111 113 114 115 117 118 119 120 121 123 124 126 130 131 132 134 135 136 137 138 139 140 141 142 146 147 148
Primary Contact: John P. Harney, President and Chief Executive Officer
CFO: Anthony C. DeFurio, Vice President and Chief Financial Officer
CMO: Greg Stiegmann, M.D., Vice President Clinical Affairs
CIO: Steve Hess, Vice President Information Services and Chief Information Officer
Web address: www.uch.edu
Control: Hospital district or authority, Government, nonfederal **Service:** General Medical and Surgical

Staffed Beds: 563 **Admissions:** 25811 **Census:** 407 **Outpatient Visits:** 862196 **Births:** 2750 **Total Expense ($000):** 908861 **Payroll Expense ($000):** 316363 **Personnel:** 4855

BOULDER—Boulder County

⊞ △ **BOULDER COMMUNITY HOSPITAL (060027)**, 1100 Balsam Avenue, Zip 80304–3496, Mailing Address: P.O. Box 9019, Zip 80301–9019; tel. 303/440–2273, (Includes BOULDER COMMUNITY FOOTHILLS HOSPITAL, 4747 Arapahoe Avenue, Zip 80303–1133, Mailing Address: P.O. Box 9047, Zip 80301–9047; tel. 720/854–7000) **A**1 2 3 5 7 9 10 **F**11 13 17 18 19 20 22 24 25 26 28 29 30 34 37 40 43 46 50 53 54 57 59 60 62 64 68 70 72 74 75 76 77 78 79 81 82 87 89 90 97 98 107 111 116 119 124 126 129 130 131 144 146 147 148 **P**4 5
Primary Contact: David P. Gehant, President and Chief Executive Officer
CFO: Bill Munson, Vice President and Chief Financial Officer
CNO: Jacqueline M. Attlesey–Pries, R.N., Chief Nursing Officer, Vice President
Web address: www.bch.org
Control: Other not-for-profit (including NFP Corporation) **Service:** General Medical and Surgical

Staffed Beds: 178 **Admissions:** 8690 **Census:** 103 **Outpatient Visits:** 423740 **Births:** 1212 **Total Expense ($000):** 308687 **Payroll Expense ($000):** 125871 **Personnel:** 1777

Many Facility Codes have changed. Please refer to the AHA Guide Code Chart. © 2014 AHA Guide

BRIGHTON—Adams County

⊞ **PLATTE VALLEY MEDICAL CENTER (060004)**, 1600 Prairie Center Parkway,
Zip 80601–4006; tel. 303/498–1600 **A**1 5 9 10 **F**3 7 13 15 18 20 22 26 28
29 30 31 35 40 43 45 49 57 68 70 72 74 75 76 77 78 79 81 85 87 89 90
92 93 107 108 110 111 115 119 130 132 135 146 147 148
Primary Contact: John R. Hicks, President and Chief Executive Officer
COO: Kurt Gensert, R.N., Vice President Operations
CFO: Harold Dupper, Chief Financial Officer
CMO: Kirk Quackenbush, M.D., Chief of Staff
CIO: Darrell Messersmith, Director Information Systems
CHR: Jackie J. Dunkin, Director Human Resources
Web address: www.pvmc.org
Control: Other not–for–profit (including NFP Corporation) **Service:** General
Medical and Surgical

Staffed Beds: 70 **Admissions:** 3186 **Census:** 25 **Outpatient Visits:** 66945
Births: 951 **Total Expense ($000):** 91943 **Payroll Expense ($000):** 31951
Personnel: 500

BRUSH—Morgan County

★ **EAST MORGAN COUNTY HOSPITAL (061303)**, 2400 West Edison Street,
Zip 80723–1640; tel. 970/842–6200 **A**9 10 18 **F**3 11 15 28 29 34 35 40 43
45 50 53 57 59 64 68 70 75 77 79 81 85 87 93 107 115 119 127 130 132
133 148 **P**6 **S** Banner Health, Phoenix, AZ
Primary Contact: Linda Thorpe, Chief Executive Officer
CFO: Thomas Loff, Chief Financial Officer
CMO: Lawrence Schoelkopf, M.D., Chief Medical Officer
CIO: Michael S. Warden, Senior Vice President and Chief Information Officer
CHR: Gracie Ramos, Human Resource Generalist
CNO: Roberta Bean, R.N., Interim Chief Nursing Officer
Web address: www.emchbrush.com
Control: Other not–for–profit (including NFP Corporation) **Service:** General
Medical and Surgical

Staffed Beds: 17 **Admissions:** 482 **Census:** 5 **Births:** 0 **Total Expense
($000):** 22739 **Payroll Expense ($000):** 10878 **Personnel:** 169

BURLINGTON—Kit Carson County

★ **KIT CARSON COUNTY HEALTH SERVICE DISTRICT (061313)**, 286 16th
Street, Zip 80807–1697; tel. 719/346–5311 **A**9 10 18 **F**3 13 15 29 31 34 35
40 43 45 47 48 57 62 63 64 68 75 76 78 79 81 84 93 107 108 110 111
115 119 127 130 133 135 148
Primary Contact: Donald Wade, Chief Executive Officer
CMO: Bong Pham, Chief Medical Officer
CIO: Paul Velasco, IT Manager
CHR: Robin Konecne, Manager Human Resources
CNO: Kandi Kuper, Chief Nursing Officer
Web address: www.kccmh.org
Control: Hospital district or authority, Government, nonfederal **Service:** General
Medical and Surgical

Staffed Beds: 19 **Admissions:** 348 **Census:** 5 **Outpatient Visits:** 12189
Births: 56 **Total Expense ($000):** 13417 **Payroll Expense ($000):** 5657
Personnel: 109

CANON CITY—Fremont County

⊞ **ST. THOMAS MORE HOSPITAL (060016)**, 1338 Phay Avenue,
Zip 81212–2302; tel. 719/285–2000 **A**1 9 10 20 **F**3 8 11 12 13 14 15 29 30
34 35 40 43 51 53 57 59 64 66 69 70 75 76 77 79 81 82 85 86 87 89 93
97 107 108 110 111 119 127 128 129 131 132 133 135 146 147 148
S Catholic Health Initiatives, Englewood, CO
Primary Contact: Sheri Trahern, CPA, FACHE, Chief Executive Officer
CFO: Gwenyth Howard, Vice President Finance
CMO: Victoria King, M.D., Chief Medical Officer
CIO: Jillian Maes, Director Marketing and Public Relations
CHR: Janet Reedy, Manager Human Resources
CNO: Marcia L. DePriest, R.N., Chief Nursing Officer
Web address: www.stmhospital.org
Control: Church–operated, Nongovernment, not–for profit **Service:** General
Medical and Surgical

Staffed Beds: 55 **Admissions:** 1682 **Census:** 18 **Outpatient Visits:** 40623
Births: 219 **Total Expense ($000):** 39644 **Payroll Expense ($000):** 16370
Personnel: 394

CASTLE ROCK—Douglas County

⊞ **CASTLE ROCK ADVENTIST HOSPITAL (060125)**, 2350 Meadows Boulevard,
Zip 80109–8405; tel. 720/455–5000, (Nonreporting) **A**1 **S** Adventist Health
System Sunbelt Health Care Corporation, Altamonte Springs, FL
Primary Contact: Todd Folkenberg, Chief Executive Officer
CFO: Jeremy Pittman, Chief Financial Officer
Web address: www.castlerockhospital.org
Control: Other not–for–profit (including NFP Corporation) **Service:** General
Medical and Surgical

Staffed Beds: 50

CHEYENNE WELLS—Cheyenne County

★ **KEEFE MEMORIAL HOSPITAL (060043)**, 602 North 6th Street West,
Zip 80810, Mailing Address: P.O. Box 578, Zip 80810–0578; tel. 719/767–5661
A9 10 20 **F**1 3 15 29 34 35 36 40 43 45 57 59 64 65 68 89 90 93 97 107
108 110 114 119 127 128 133 147 **P**6
Primary Contact: Virginia Hallagin, Chief Executive Officer
CFO: Brenda Nauman, Controller
CMO: Christopher Williams, M.D., Chief of Staff
CIO: Jeanne Moffat, Manager Information Technology
CHR: Erica Kern, Director Human Resources
CNO: Sue Kern, Director of Nursing
Web address: www.keefememorial.com
Control: County–Government, nonfederal **Service:** General Medical and Surgical

Staffed Beds: 11 **Admissions:** 65 **Census:** 1 **Outpatient Visits:** 3555 **Births:**
0 **Total Expense ($000):** 4486 **Payroll Expense ($000):** 2198 **Personnel:**
50

COLORADO SPRINGS—El Paso County

☐ **CEDAR SPRINGS HOSPITAL (064009)**, 2135 Southgate Road,
Zip 80906–2693; tel. 719/633–4114, (Nonreporting) **A**1 9 10 **S** Universal Health
Services, Inc., King of Prussia, PA
Primary Contact: A. Elaine Crnkovic, Chief Executive Officer
CFO: Cynthia D. Deboer, Chief Financial Officer
CMO: Larry Shores, M.D., Executive Medical Director
CHR: Jessica McCoy, Director Human Resources
CNO: Jodi Mattson, Director of Nursing
Web address: www.cedarspringsbhs.com
Control: Corporation, Investor–owned, for–profit **Service:** Psychiatric

Staffed Beds: 110

⊞ **HEALTHSOUTH REHABILITATION HOSPITAL OF COLORADO SPRINGS
(063030)**, 325 Parkside Drive, Zip 80910–3134; tel. 719/630–8000 **A**1 10
F29 30 54 62 64 100 132 **S** HEALTHSOUTH Corporation, Birmingham, AL
Primary Contact: Stephen Schaefer, Chief Executive Officer
CFO: Pat Penrod, Controller
CHR: Diana Crepeau, Director Human Resources
Web address: www.healthsouthcoloradosprings.com
Control: Corporation, Investor–owned, for–profit **Service:** Rehabilitation

Staffed Beds: 56 **Admissions:** 1021 **Census:** 36 **Outpatient Visits:** 11299
Births: 0 **Total Expense ($000):** 15725 **Payroll Expense ($000):** 8539
Personnel: 135

⊞ △ **MEMORIAL HOSPITAL (060022)**, 1400 East Boulder Street,
Zip 80909–5599; tel. 719/365–9888 **A**1 2 7 9 10 **F**3 8 11 12 13 15 18 19 20
21 22 23 24 26 27 28 29 30 31 34 35 36 40 41 43 44 45 46 48 49 54 55
57 58 59 64 68 70 72 74 76 77 78 79 81 82 84 85 86 87 88 90 92 93 94
96 97 107 108 109 110 111 114 115 116 117 118 119 120 121 123 124
126 129 130 132 135 141 144 146 148 **P**6 8 **S** University of Colorado Health,
Fort Collins, CO
Primary Contact: George E. Hayes, FACHE, President and Chief Executive Officer
COO: Colette C. Martin, Chief Operating Officer
CFO: Dan Rieber, Interim Chief Financial Officer
CMO: Patrick O. Faricy, M.D., Chief Medical Officer
CHR: Jeffrey Johnson, Vice President
CNO: Michelle Smith, R.N., Chief Clinical Officer
Web address: www.memorialhealthsystem.com
Control: Other not–for–profit (including NFP Corporation) **Service:** General
Medical and Surgical

Staffed Beds: 448 **Admissions:** 14741 **Census:** 169 **Outpatient Visits:**
381963 **Births:** 3290 **Total Expense ($000):** 421308 **Payroll Expense
($000):** 166199 **Personnel:** 2735

☐ **PEAK VIEW BEHAVIORAL HEALTH (064026)**, 7353 Sisters Grove,
Zip 80923–2615; tel. 719/444–8484, (Nonreporting) **A**1 9 10 **S** Strategic
Behavioral Health, LLC, Memphis, TN
Primary Contact: Lana Currance, R.N., MSN, Chief Executive Officer
Web address: www.strategicbh.com/peakview.html
Control: Corporation, Investor–owned, for–profit **Service:** Psychiatric

Staffed Beds: 24

CO

Hospital, Medicare Provider Number, Address, Telephone, Approval, Facility, and Physician Codes, Health Care System

★ American Hospital Association (AHA) membership
☐ The Joint Commission accreditation ◇ DNV Healthcare Inc. accreditation
○ Healthcare Facilities Accreditation Program
△ Commission on Accreditation of Rehabilitation Facilities (CARF) accreditation

✠ △ **PENROSE–ST. FRANCIS HEALTH SERVICES (060031)**, 2222 North
Nevada Avenue, Zip 80907–6799, Mailing Address: P.O. Box 7021,
Zip 80933–7021; tel. 719/776–5000; (Includes PENROSE HOSPITAL, 2215
North Cascade Avenue, Zip 80907, Mailing Address: P.O. Box 7021,
Zip 80933–7021; tel. 719/776–5000; ST. FRANCIS MEDICAL CENTER, 6001
East Woodmen Road, Zip 80923–2601; tel. 719/776–5000) **A**1 2 7 9 10 19 **F**3
5 11 12 13 14 15 17 18 20 22 24 26 28 29 30 31 34 35 36 38 39 40 41 42
43 44 45 46 47 48 49 50 52 53 54 55 56 57 58 59 61 62 64 65 68 70 71
72 74 75 76 77 78 79 81 82 84 85 86 87 88 89 90 91 93 96 97 99 100 101
102 103 107 108 110 114 115 118 119 120 121 123 124 126 127 129 130
131 132 135 144 146 147 148 **P**5 **S** Catholic Health Initiatives, Englewood, CO
Primary Contact: Margaret D. Sabin, President and Chief Executive Officer
COO: Andrea C. Coleman, Chief Operating Officer
CIO: Tanya Bell, Public Information Officer
CHR: James Humphrey, Vice President Talent Resources and Human Resources
for South Side Operating Group
Web address: www.penrosestfrancis.org
Control: Church–operated, Nongovernment, not–for profit **Service:** General
Medical and Surgical

Staffed Beds: 371 **Admissions:** 21967 **Census:** 242 **Outpatient Visits:**
156012 **Births:** 2670 **Total Expense ($000):** 387865 **Payroll Expense**
($000): 125230

✠ **SELECT LONG TERM CARE HOSPITAL – COLORADO SPRINGS (062016)**,
6001 East Woodmen Road, 6th Floor, Zip 80923–2601; tel. 719/571–6000,
(Nonreporting) **A**1 9 10 **S** Select Medical Corporation, Mechanicsburg, PA
Primary Contact: Kent Helwig, Chief Executive Officer
CMO: Dave Call, M.D., Medical Director
CHR: Lisa Gayler, Director Human Resources
CNO: Cathrine Viccellio, Chief Nursing Officer
Web address: www.selectmedical.com
Control: Corporation, Investor–owned, for–profit **Service:** Long–Term Acute Care
hospital

Staffed Beds: 30

CORTEZ—Montezuma County

★ ◇ **SOUTHWEST MEMORIAL HOSPITAL (061327)**, 1311 North Mildred Road,
Zip 81321–2299; tel. 970/565–6666 **A**9 10 18 21 **F**3 7 11 13 15 28 29 31
34 35 40 47 48 50 54 59 64 65 70 75 76 79 81 82 85 86 87 93 94 97 107
108 110 111 115 119 127 129 130 131 132 133 135 146 147 148 **P**1
Primary Contact: Liz Sellers, R.N., MSN, Interim Chief Executive Officer
CFO: John Nadone, Chief Financial Officer
CIO: David Cabana, Director Management Information Systems
CHR: Jim Bob Wynes, Director Human Resources
CNO: Liz Sellers, R.N., Chief Nursing Officer
Web address: www.swhealth.org
Control: Other not–for–profit (including NFP Corporation) **Service:** General
Medical and Surgical

Staffed Beds: 25 **Admissions:** 1150 **Census:** 10 **Outpatient Visits:** 45338
Births: 191 **Total Expense ($000):** 50418 **Payroll Expense ($000):** 21084
Personnel: 306

CRAIG—Moffat County

✠ **MEMORIAL HOSPITAL AT CRAIG (061314)**, 750 Hospital Loop,
Zip 81625–8750; tel. 970/824–9411 **A**1 9 10 18 **F**3 7 11 13 15 29 31 32 34
35 40 43 45 49 50 51 57 59 68 70 75 76 77 78 79 81 85 86 87 91 93 97
102 107 108 110 111 112 114 119 129 130 131 132 133 135 146 147 148
S QHR, Brentwood, TN
Primary Contact: John Rossfeld, Interim Chief Executive Officer
CFO: Tim Howard, Interim Chief Financial Officer
CMO: Scott Ellis, D.O., Chief of Staff
CIO: Jennifer Riley, Chief Organizational Excellence
CHR: Jill Spencer, Chief Human Resources
CNO: Kimberly White, R.N., Chief of Nursing
Web address: www.thememorialhospital.com
Control: County–Government, nonfederal **Service:** General Medical and Surgical

Staffed Beds: 25 **Admissions:** 559 **Census:** 5 **Outpatient Visits:** 23057
Births: 121 **Total Expense ($000):** 34469 **Payroll Expense ($000):** 12350
Personnel: 245

DEL NORTE—Rio Grande County

★ **RIO GRANDE HOSPITAL (061301)**, 310 County Road 14, Zip 81132–8758;
tel. 719/657–2510 **A**9 10 18 **F**34 40 43 57 65 81 93 107 111 115 119 127
129 133 **P**6
Primary Contact: Arlene Harms, Chief Executive Officer
CFO: Greg Porter, Chief Financial Officer
CMO: Heidi E. Helgeson, M.D., Chief Medical Officer
CIO: Yael DeFaye, Director, Information Technology
CHR: Paula Warner–Pacheco, Chief Human Resources
CNO: Beverly Martinez, Director of Nursing
Web address: www.rio–grande–hospital.org/
Control: Other not–for–profit (including NFP Corporation) **Service:** General
Medical and Surgical

Staffed Beds: 17 **Admissions:** 320 **Census:** 3 **Outpatient Visits:** 35300
Births: 0 **Total Expense ($000):** 12839 **Payroll Expense ($000):** 6013
Personnel: 109

DELTA—Delta County

✠ **DELTA COUNTY MEMORIAL HOSPITAL (060071)**, 1501 East 3rd Street,
Zip 81416–2815, Mailing Address: P.O. Box 10100, Zip 81416–0008;
tel. 970/874–7681 **A**1 9 10 **F**3 11 13 15 28 29 30 31 34 40 43 45 50 57 59
62 70 75 76 77 78 79 81 85 87 93 107 108 110 111 114 115 119 124 127
129 146 147 148 **P**5 8
Primary Contact: Jason Cleckler, Chief Executive Officer
CFO: Bev Carlson, Chief Financial Officer
CMO: John P. Knutson, M.D., Chief Medical Staff
CIO: Mitch Van Scoyk, Manager Information Systems
CHR: Larry Vincent, Director Human Resources
Web address: www.deltahospital.org
Control: Hospital district or authority, Government, nonfederal **Service:** General
Medical and Surgical

Staffed Beds: 49 **Admissions:** 1761 **Census:** 14 **Outpatient Visits:** 86994
Births: 253 **Total Expense ($000):** 63961 **Payroll Expense ($000):** 23819
Personnel: 416

DENVER—Denver, Adams and Arapaho Coun Counties

✠ **COLORADO ACUTE LONG TERM HOSPITAL (062012)**, 1690 North Meade
Street, Zip 80204–1552; tel. 303/264–6900, (Nonreporting) **A**1 9 10 **S** LifeCare
Management Services, Plano, TX
Primary Contact: Craig Bailey, MS, Administrator
Web address: www.lifecare–hospitals.com/hospital/colorado
Control: Corporation, Investor–owned, for–profit **Service:** Long–Term Acute Care
hospital

Staffed Beds: 63

☐ **COLORADO MENTAL HEALTH INSTITUTE AT FORT LOGAN (064003)**, 3520
West Oxford Avenue, Zip 80236–3197; tel. 303/761–0220, (Nonreporting) **A**1 3
5 10
Primary Contact: Elizabeth M. Stillman, Acting Director
CFO: Bob Fries, Director Fiscal Services
CIO: Billie Busby, Assistant Director
Web address: www.cdhs.state.co.us/cmhifl
Control: State–Government, nonfederal **Service:** Psychiatric

Staffed Beds: 297

✠ **DENVER HEALTH (060011)**, 777 Bannock Street, Zip 80204–4507;
tel. 303/436–6000 **A**1 3 5 9 10 **F**3 5 7 8 11 12 13 15 18 19 20 22 26 28 29
30 31 32 34 35 37 38 39 40 41 42 43 44 45 46 49 50 52 53 54 55 56 57
58 59 60 61 64 65 66 68 70 71 72 74 75 76 77 78 79 80 81 82 84 85 86
87 88 89 90 92 93 94 97 98 99 100 102 103 104 107 108 110 111 114
115 118 119 127 129 130 131 132 134 135 143 144 146 147 148 **P**6
Primary Contact: Arthur A. Gonzalez, Dr.PH, FACHE, Chief Executive Officer
COO: Stephanie Thomas, Chief Operating Officer
CFO: Peg Burnette, Chief Financial Officer
CMO: Thomas MacKenzie, M.D., Medical Director, Chief of Clinical Operations
CIO: Jeff Pelot, Interim Chief Information Officer
CHR: Greg Rossman, Chief Human Resource Officer
CNO: Kathy Boyle, R.N., Chief Nursing Officer
Web address: www.denverhealth.org
Control: Hospital district or authority, Government, nonfederal **Service:** General
Medical and Surgical

Staffed Beds: 421 **Admissions:** 20866 **Census:** 281 **Outpatient Visits:**
824773 **Births:** 3192 **Total Expense ($000):** 822631 **Payroll Expense**
($000): 367222 **Personnel:** 5028

✠ **EXEMPLA SAINT JOSEPH HOSPITAL (060028)**, 1835 Franklin Street,
Zip 80218–1126; tel. 303/837–7111 **A**1 3 5 9 10 **F**3 8 11 12 13 18 20 22
24 28 29 30 31 34 35 37 40 43 45 46 49 50 55 58 60 63 64 66 68 70
71 72 74 75 76 77 78 79 81 82 84 85 87 93 107 108 110 111 114 115 116
117 119 120 121 123 124 126 130 145 146 **P**6 7 **S** SCL Health System,
Denver, CO
Primary Contact: Bain J. Farris, President and Chief Executive Officer
COO: Barbara A. Jahn, Chief Operating Officer
CFO: Buzz Binder, Vice President Finance
CMO: Shawn Dufford, M.D., Vice President Medical Affairs and Chief Medical
Officer
CHR: William R. Gould, Vice President Human Resources
CNO: Mary Shepler, R.N., Vice President and Chief Nursing Officer
Web address: www.exempla.org
Control: Other not–for–profit (including NFP Corporation) **Service:** General
Medical and Surgical

Staffed Beds: 369 **Admissions:** 18353 **Census:** 232 **Outpatient Visits:**
219521 **Births:** 3944 **Total Expense ($000):** 434261 **Payroll Expense**
($000): 149477 **Personnel:** 2185

✠ **KINDRED HOSPITAL–DENVER (062009)**, 1920 High Street, Zip 80218–1213;
tel. 303/320–5871, (Nonreporting) **A**1 9 10 **S** Kindred Healthcare, Louisville, KY
Primary Contact: Harvey Ross, Chief Executive Officer
CFO: Tim Stecker, Chief Financial Officer
CMO: Eric Yaeger, M.D., Medical Director
Web address: www.kh–denver.com
Control: Corporation, Investor–owned, for–profit **Service:** Long–Term Acute Care
hospital

Staffed Beds: 68

CO

Many Facility Codes have changed. Please refer to the AHA Guide Code Chart. © 2014 AHA Guide

NATIONAL JEWISH HEALTH (060107), (AllerCardio Resp Rheum ID GI), 1400 Jackson Street, Zip 80206–2762; tel. 303/388–4461 **A**1 3 5 9 10 **F**3 9 11 12 18 20 28 29 30 31 32 34 35 36 44 45 46 47 48 50 54 55 57 58 59 61 64 65 66 68 74 75 77 78 84 86 87 89 90 93 96 97 98 99 100 101 104 107 108 111 114 115 116 117 118 119 127 129 130 132 134 135 143 145 146 **P**6
Primary Contact: Michael Salem, M.D., President and Chief Executive Officer
COO: Ron Berge, Executive Vice President and Chief Operating Officer
CFO: Christine Forkner, Executive Vice President and Chief Financial Officer
CMO: Gary Cott, M.D., Executive Vice President Medical and Clinical Services
CIO: Lots Pook, Chief Information Officer
CHR: Sarah Taylor, Chief Human Resources
CNO: Jeff Downing, R.N., Chief Nursing Officer
Web address: www.njhealth.org
Control: Other not–for–profit (including NFP Corporation) **Service:** Other specialty

Staffed Beds: 46 **Admissions:** 66 **Census:** 1 **Outpatient Visits:** 88094 **Births:** 0 **Total Expense ($000):** 206500 **Payroll Expense ($000):** 109241 **Personnel:** 1491

PORTER ADVENTIST HOSPITAL (060064), 2525 South Downing Street, Zip 80210–5876; tel. 303/778–1955 **A**1 2 9 10 **F**3 4 5 8 11 15 17 18 20 22 24 26 28 29 30 31 34 35 36 37 40 45 46 47 48 49 50 53 54 55 56 57 58 59 60 64 65 68 70 74 75 77 78 79 81 82 83 84 85 86 87 90 91 92 93 94 96 97 98 100 101 102 103 104 105 106 107 108 109 110 111 112 114 115 116 117 118 119 120 121 122 123 124 126 129 130 131 132 135 138 139 141 142 146 147 148 **P**6 **S** Adventist Health System Sunbelt Health Care Corporation, Altamonte Springs, FL
Primary Contact: Randall L. Haffner, Ph.D., Chief Executive Officer
CFO: Andrew Gaasch, Chief Financial Officer
CHR: Oz Muller, Director Human Resources
CNO: Sharon H. Pappas, Ph.D., Chief Nursing Officer
Web address: www.centura.org
Control: Church–operated, Nongovernment, not–for profit **Service:** General Medical and Surgical

Staffed Beds: 250 **Admissions:** 10532 **Census:** 140 **Outpatient Visits:** 65403 **Births:** 0 **Total Expense ($000):** 238175 **Payroll Expense ($000):** 79156 **Personnel:** 1227

△ **PRESBYTERIAN–ST. LUKE'S MEDICAL CENTER (060014)**, 1719 East 19th Avenue, Zip 80218–1281; tel. 303/839–6000, (Includes ROCKY MOUNTAIN HOSPITAL FOR CHILDREN, 1719 East 19th Avenue, Zip 80218–1235; tel. 720/754–1000) **A**1 2 3 5 7 9 10 **F**3 8 9 11 12 13 14 15 18 19 20 21 22 23 24 25 26 28 29 30 31 34 35 37 40 41 43 44 45 46 47 48 49 50 51 54 55 56 57 58 59 60 61 63 64 65 66 68 70 72 73 74 75 76 78 79 80 81 82 83 84 85 86 87 88 89 93 96 97 107 108 110 111 112 114 115 116 117 119 120 121 123 124 126 127 129 130 131 132 134 136 138 145 146 147 148 **P**2 3 4 6 **S** HCA, Nashville, TN
Primary Contact: Madeleine Roberson, Chief Executive Officer
COO: Rebecca Stallworth, Chief Operating Officer
CFO: Kevin Corcoran, Chief Financial Officer
CMO: Reginald Washington, M.D., Chief Medical Officer
CIO: Don Laughlin, Director Information Services
CHR: Keri Moore, Vice President Human Resources and Support Services
CNO: Margaret Scheaffel, R.N., Chief Nursing Officer
Web address: www.pslmc.com
Control: Corporation, Investor–owned, for–profit **Service:** General Medical and Surgical

Staffed Beds: 399 **Admissions:** 11371 **Census:** 209 **Outpatient Visits:** 74397 **Births:** 1551

ROSE MEDICAL CENTER (060032), 4567 East Ninth Avenue, Zip 80220–3941; tel. 303/320–2121 **A**1 2 3 5 9 10 **F**3 8 11 12 15 18 20 22 24 26 28 29 30 31 34 35 48 50 53 54 55 58 59 60 61 64 68 70 72 74 75 76 77 78 79 81 82 84 85 86 87 89 91 92 93 94 97 100 101 102 107 108 110 111 112 114 115 116 117 118 119 120 121 122 123 126 129 130 131 132 135 143 146 147 148 **P**6 8 **S** HCA, Nashville, TN
Primary Contact: Kenneth H. Feiler, Chief Executive Officer
COO: Ryan Tobin, Chief Operating Officer
CFO: Jac Connelly, Chief Financial Officer
CMO: Andrew Ziller, M.D., Chief Medical Officer
CIO: Dave Trevathan, Director Information Systems
CHR: Clarence McDavid, Vice President Human Resources
CNO: Lynne Wagner, R.N., Chief Nursing Officer
Web address: www.rosebabies.com
Control: Individual, Investor–owned, for–profit **Service:** General Medical and Surgical

Staffed Beds: 262 **Admissions:** 12587 **Census:** 135 **Outpatient Visits:** 55824 **Total Expense ($000):** 232831 **Payroll Expense ($000):** 83418

SELECT SPECIALTY HOSPITAL DENVER SOUTH See Select Specialty Hospital–Denver

SELECT SPECIALTY HOSPITAL–DENVER (062015), 1719 East 19th Avenue, 5B, Zip 80218–1235; tel. 303/563–3700, (Includes SELECT SPECIALTY HOSPITAL DENVER SOUTH, 2525 South Downing Street, 3 South, Zip 80210–5817; tel. 303/715–7373), (Nonreporting) **A**1 9 10 **S** Select Medical Corporation, Mechanicsburg, PA
Primary Contact: George Welton, Chief Executive Officer
Web address: www.selectspecialtyhospitals.com/company/locations/denver.aspx
Control: Corporation, Investor–owned, for–profit **Service:** Long–Term Acute Care hospital

Staffed Beds: 65

△ **VETERANS AFFAIRS EASTERN COLORADO HEALTH CARE SYSTEM**, 1055 Clermont Street, Zip 80220–3877; tel. 303/399–8020, (Total facility includes 100 beds in nursing home–type unit) **A**1 3 5 7 **F**3 18 20 22 24 26 29 30 31 35 36 38 39 40 44 45 46 47 48 49 50 53 54 55 56 57 58 59 60 61 62 63 64 65 68 70 74 75 77 78 79 80 81 82 83 84 85 87 90 91 92 93 94 95 96 97 98 100 101 102 103 104 105 106 107 108 111 114 115 119 126 127 128 129 130 132 135 144 146 147 148 **S** Department of Veterans Affairs, Washington, DC
Primary Contact: Lynette A. Roff, Director
CFO: Eliott R. Vanderstek, Chief Fiscal Service
CMO: Ellen Mangione, M.D., Chief of Staff
CIO: Don Huckaby, Chief Information Management Service
CHR: Lorene Connel, Chief Human Resources Management Service
Web address: www.denver.va.gov/
Control: Veterans Affairs, Government, federal **Service:** General Medical and Surgical

Staffed Beds: 271 **Admissions:** 5432 **Census:** 97 **Outpatient Visits:** 847827 **Births:** 0 **Total Expense ($000):** 591451 **Payroll Expense ($000):** 259162 **Personnel:** 2293

DURANGO—La Plata County

ANIMAS SURGICAL HOSPITAL (060117), 575 Rivergate Lane, Zip 81301–7487; tel. 970/247–3537, (Nonreporting) **A**9 10
Primary Contact: Brett Gosney, Chief Executive Officer
Web address: www.animassurgical.com/index.htm
Control: Corporation, Investor–owned, for–profit **Service:** Surgical

Staffed Beds: 12

MERCY REGIONAL MEDICAL CENTER (060013), 1010 Three Springs Boulevard, Zip 81301–8296; tel. 970/247–4311 **A**1 2 9 10 20 **F**11 13 15 17 18 20 22 24 26 27 28 29 30 31 35 36 40 42 43 45 49 50 59 60 61 66 70 72 73 76 78 79 81 84 85 87 89 94 96 97 107 111 115 119 127 129 130 131 132 133 135 146 147 148 **P**6 **S** Catholic Health Initiatives, Englewood, CO
Primary Contact: Thomas Gessel, FACHE, President and Chief Executive Officer
COO: Will McConnell, Ph.D., Vice President Operations – Outreach Strategy and Centura Health Physicians Group Administrator Southwest
CFO: Jane Strobel, Vice President and Chief Financial Officer
CMO: Bill Plauth, M.D., Vice President Operations and Chief Medical Officer
CIO: Neil Stock, Director Technology and Facilities
CHR: Cathy Roberts, Vice President Mission Integration Human Resources
CNO: Nancy Hoyt, R.N., Vice President Operations/Clinical and Chief Nursing Officer
Web address: www.mercydurango.org
Control: Church–operated, Nongovernment, not–for profit **Service:** General Medical and Surgical

Staffed Beds: 82 **Admissions:** 4206 **Census:** 38 **Outpatient Visits:** 94105 **Births:** 864 **Total Expense ($000):** 105900 **Payroll Expense ($000):** 35843 **Personnel:** 846

EADS—Kiowa County

★ **WEISBROD MEMORIAL COUNTY HOSPITAL (061300)**, 1208 Luther Street, Zip 81036, Mailing Address: P.O. Box 817, Zip 81036–0817; tel. 719/438–5401 **A**9 10 18 **F**7 34 40 57 59 64 93 127 129 133 135 143
Primary Contact: Tristen Sheridan, Administrator
CFO: Shannon Dixon, Manager Business Office
CMO: Jeff Waggoner, M.D., Chief of Staff
CHR: Shannon Dixon, Manager Business Office
CNO: Connie Richardson, Director of Nursing
Web address: www.kchd.org
Control: Hospital district or authority, Government, nonfederal **Service:** General Medical and Surgical

Staffed Beds: 25 **Admissions:** 38 **Census:** 1 **Outpatient Visits:** 8290 **Births:** 0

CO

Hospital, Medicare Provider Number, Address, Telephone, Approval, Facility, and Physician Codes, Health Care System

★ American Hospital Association (AHA) membership
□ The Joint Commission accreditation
◇ DNV Healthcare Inc. accreditation
○ Healthcare Facilities Accreditation Program
△ Commission on Accreditation of Rehabilitation Facilities (CARF) accreditation

CO

ENGLEWOOD—Arapahoe County

✠ **CRAIG HOSPITAL (062011)**, 3425 South Clarkson Street, Zip 80113–2899; tel. 303/789–8000 **A**1 3 5 9 10 **F**29 30 34 35 36 44 50 53 58 64 68 74 75 77 81 86 87 90 91 93 95 96 97 104 130 132 146 148
Primary Contact: Michael L. Fordyce, President and Chief Executive Officer
COO: Dana Polonsky, Vice President of Clinical Services
CFO: Julie Keegan, Vice President Finance
CMO: Thomas E. Balazy, M.D., Medical Director
CIO: Chris Watkins, Director of Information Technology
CHR: Stacy L. Abel, Director Human Resources
CNO: Diane Reinhard, R.N., Vice President of Patient Care Services
Web address: www.craighospital.org
Control: Other not–for–profit (including NFP Corporation) **Service:** Rehabilitation

Staffed Beds: 85 **Admissions:** 505 **Census:** 73 **Outpatient Visits:** 4136
Births: 0 **Total Expense ($000):** 72554 **Payroll Expense ($000):** 35094
Personnel: 652

✠ **SWEDISH MEDICAL CENTER (060034)**, 501 East Hampden Avenue, Zip 80113–2702; tel. 303/788–5000 **A**1 2 3 5 9 10 **F**3 7 8 11 12 13 15 18 20 22 24 26 29 30 31 34 35 38 39 40 42 43 44 45 47 48 49 50 53 55 57 58 59 60 64 66 68 70 72 73 74 75 76 77 78 79 81 82 84 85 86 87 88 89 90 92 97 102 107 108 109 111 114 115 116 117 118 119 120 121 122 123 124 126 129 130 131 132 146 147 148 **P**8 **S** HCA, Nashville, TN
Primary Contact: Mary M. White, Chief Executive Officer
COO: Daniel Miller, Chief Operating Officer
CFO: Kathy Ashenfelter, Chief Financial Officer
CMO: Paul Hancock, M.D., Chief Medical Officer
CIO: Jeff Schnoor, Director Information Systems
CHR: Lisa Morris, Vice President Human Resources
CNO: Shari Chavez, Chief Nursing Officer
Web address: www.swedishhospital.com
Control: Partnership, Investor–owned, for–profit **Service:** General Medical and Surgical

Staffed Beds: 354 **Admissions:** 20240 **Census:** 263 **Outpatient Visits:** 110797 **Births:** 2137 **Personnel:** 1600

ESTES PARK—Larimer County

★ **ESTES PARK MEDICAL CENTER (061312)**, 555 Prospect Avenue, Zip 80517–6312, Mailing Address: P.O. Box 2740, Zip 80517–2740; tel. 970/586–2317, (Total facility includes 45 beds in nursing home–type unit) **A**9 10 18 **F**3 7 8 13 15 18 29 30 31 34 35 40 43 45 56 57 59 62 63 64 75 76 77 78 79 81 82 85 91 93 97 107 110 113 119 128 130 131 132 133 143 146 148
Primary Contact: Brian J. Herwig, Chief Executive Officer
CFO: Sam Radke, Vice President of Finance
CMO: Chris Daley, M.D., Chief of Staff
CIO: Gary Hall, Vice President of Information Technology
CHR: Robert Stansel, Vice President of Human Resources
Web address: www.epmedcenter.com
Control: Hospital district or authority, Government, nonfederal **Service:** General Medical and Surgical

Staffed Beds: 58 **Admissions:** 585 **Census:** 41

FORT CARSON—El Paso County

✠ **EVANS U. S. ARMY COMMUNITY HOSPITAL**, 1650 Cochrane Circle, Building 7500, Zip 80913–4613; tel. 719/526–7200, (Nonreporting) **A**1 9 **S** Department of the Army, Office of the Surgeon General, Falls Church, VA
Primary Contact: Colonel Dennis P. LeMaster, Commander
CFO: Major Bradley Robinson, Chief Financial Officer
CHR: Lieutenant Colonel Lory Gurr, Chief Human Resources Division
Web address: www.evans.amedd.army.mil
Control: Army, Government, federal **Service:** General Medical and Surgical

Staffed Beds: 57

FORT COLLINS—Larimer County

✠ **POUDRE VALLEY HOSPITAL (060010)**, 1024 South Lemay Avenue, Zip 80524–3998; tel. 970/495–7000, (Includes MOUNTAIN CREST HOSPITAL, 4601 Corbett Drive, Zip 80525; tel. 970/270–4800) **A**1 2 9 10 19 **F**3 5 7 11 12 13 14 15 18 20 22 28 29 30 31 32 34 35 38 39 40 43 44 45 46 47 48 49 50 53 54 55 57 58 59 60 61 64 65 66 68 69 70 72 73 74 75 76 77 78 79 80 81 82 84 85 86 87 89 92 93 98 99 100 101 102 103 104 105 106 107 108 110 111 114 115 118 119 120 121 123 124 126 129 130 131 132 134 135 143 146 147 148 **P**5 6 **S** University of Colorado Health, Fort Collins, CO
Primary Contact: Kevin L. Unger, FACHE, President and Chief Executive Officer
CFO: Stephanie Doughty, Chief Financial Officer
CMO: William Neff, M.D., Chief Medical Officer
CIO: Fernando Pedroza, Vice President Information Technology
CHR: Anjanette Mosebar, Director Human Resources
CNO: Donna D. Poduska, MS, Chief Nursing Officer
Web address: www.uchealth.org
Control: Other not–for–profit (including NFP Corporation) **Service:** General Medical and Surgical

Staffed Beds: 226 **Admissions:** 13131 **Census:** 131 **Outpatient Visits:** 515208 **Births:** 2394 **Total Expense ($000):** 398065 **Payroll Expense ($000):** 143477 **Personnel:** 1630

FORT MORGAN—Morgan County

✠ **COLORADO PLAINS MEDICAL CENTER (060044)**, 1000 Lincoln Street, Zip 80701–3298; tel. 970/867–3391 **A**1 9 10 20 **F**3 11 13 15 28 29 31 34 35 40 43 44 45 48 50 51 53 56 57 59 62 64 70 75 76 77 79 81 86 87 97 98 100 101 103 105 107 108 110 111 114 119 129 130 131 133 146 147 148 **P**6 **S** LifePoint Hospitals, Inc., Brentwood, TN
Primary Contact: Michael N. Patterson, Chief Executive Officer
CFO: Christina Patton, Chief Financial Officer
CHR: Janet Brinkman, Director Human Resources
CNO: Sonya Bass, MS, Chief Nursing Officer
Web address: www.coloradoplainsmedicalcenter.com
Control: Corporation, Investor–owned, for–profit **Service:** General Medical and Surgical

Staffed Beds: 50 **Admissions:** 1610 **Census:** 20 **Outpatient Visits:** 37317
Births: 422 **Total Expense ($000):** 39485 **Payroll Expense ($000):** 19483
Personnel: 219

FRISCO—Summit County

✠ **ST. ANTHONY SUMMIT MEDICAL CENTER (060118)**, 340 Peak One Drive, Zip 80443, Mailing Address: P.O. Box 738, Zip 80443–0738; tel. 970/668–3300 **A**1 9 10 **F**3 34 40 42 43 45 57 59 68 70 75 76 77 79 81 82 84 85 97 107 110 111 119 129 130 132 144 146 147 **S** Catholic Health Initiatives, Englewood, CO
Primary Contact: Paul J. Chodkowski, Chief Executive Officer
COO: Mary L. Henrikson, Chief Nursing Officer and Chief Operating Officer
CFO: David Thompson, Chief Financial Officer
CMO: Alan Dulit, M.D., Chief Medical Officer
CHR: Dana Laverdiere, Director Human Resources
CNO: Mary L. Henrikson, Chief Nursing Officer and Chief Operating Officer
Web address: www.summitmedicalcenter.org
Control: Church–operated, Nongovernment, not–for profit **Service:** General Medical and Surgical

Staffed Beds: 34 **Admissions:** 1176 **Census:** 9 **Outpatient Visits:** 20367
Births: 329 **Total Expense ($000):** 43787 **Payroll Expense ($000):** 13729
Personnel: 197

FRUITA—Mesa County

★ **FAMILY HEALTH WEST (061302)**, 300 West Ottley Avenue, Zip 81521–2118, Mailing Address: P.O. Box 130, Zip 81521–0130; tel. 970/858–9871, (Total facility includes 120 beds in nursing home–type unit) **A**9 10 18 **F**3 6 9 10 29 34 35 36 39 40 41 45 50 56 59 64 65 66 68 74 75 79 81 82 85 86 87 90 93 100 107 111 114 119 128 130 132 133 135 143 144 146 148 **P**6
Primary Contact: Mark J. Francis, President, Chief Executive Officer and Hospital Administrator
CFO: Jason McCormick, Vice President Finance and Chief Financial Officer
CMO: Christopher Wibblesman, M.D., Chief of Staff
CIO: Patrick Yount, Director Information Services
CHR: Kelly Murphy, Director Human Resources
CNO: Lori Henderson, Chief Nursing Officer, Vice President Clinical
Web address: www.fhw.org
Control: Other not–for–profit (including NFP Corporation) **Service:** General Medical and Surgical

Staffed Beds: 136 **Admissions:** 533 **Census:** 110 **Outpatient Visits:** 9329
Births: 0 **Total Expense ($000):** 23361 **Payroll Expense ($000):** 9312
Personnel: 559

GLENWOOD SPRINGS—Garfield County

✠ **VALLEY VIEW HOSPITAL (060075)**, 1906 Blake Avenue, Zip 81601–4259; tel. 970/945–6535 **A**1 9 10 20 **F**3 4 11 13 14 15 18 20 22 28 29 30 31 34 35 36 40 43 45 49 50 51 55 57 58 59 64 65 68 69 70 74 75 76 77 78 81 82 85 86 87 93 96 97 99 104 107 108 110 111 114 115 116 117 118 119 120 121 123 124 126 129 130 131 132 135 145 146 147 148
Primary Contact: Gary L. Brewer, Chief Executive Officer
COO: Dewane Pace, Executive Director Ancillary Departments
CFO: Larry L. Dupper, Chief Financial Officer
CMO: Al Saiiman, M.D., Chief Medical Officer
CIO: Richard S. Escue, Director Information Technology
CHR: Daniel Biggs, Director Human Resources
CNO: Sandra Hurley, MS, Chief Nursing Officer
Web address: www.vvh.org
Control: Other not–for–profit (including NFP Corporation) **Service:** General Medical and Surgical

Staffed Beds: 56 **Admissions:** 2533 **Census:** 27 **Outpatient Visits:** 98107
Births: 672 **Total Expense ($000):** 147557 **Payroll Expense ($000):** 62939
Personnel: 755

Many Facility Codes have changed. Please refer to the AHA Guide Code Chart. © 2014 AHA Guide

GRAND JUNCTION—Mesa County

✠ ○ **COMMUNITY HOSPITAL (060054)**, 2021 North 12th Street,
Zip 81501–2999; tel. 970/242–0920 **A**1 9 10 11 **F**3 8 12 15 29 30 34 35 40
47 48 49 50 57 59 62 64 70 75 77 79 81 85 86 87 93 97 107 108 110 111
114 115 119 129 130 131 132 144 146 147 148 **P**8 **S** QHR, Brentwood, TN
Primary Contact: Chris Thomas, FACHE, President and Chief Executive Officer
CMO: Donald Nicolay, M.D., Chief Medical Officer
CIO: Mike Kansgen, Director Information Services
CNO: Kristin Gundt, Chief Nursing Officer
Web address: www.yourcommunityhospital.com
Control: Other not–for–profit (including NFP Corporation) **Service:** General
Medical and Surgical

Staffed Beds: 42 **Admissions:** 1409 **Census:** 13 **Births:** 0

✠ **GRAND JUNCTION VETERANS AFFAIRS MEDICAL CENTER**, 2121 North
Avenue, Zip 81501–6428; tel. 970/242–0731, (Nonreporting) **A**1 **S** Department
of Veterans Affairs, Washington, DC
Primary Contact: Terry S. Atienza, Director
COO: Patricia A. Hitt, Associate Director
CFO: Laquita Gruver, Fiscal Officer
CMO: William R. Berryman, M.D., Chief of Staff
CIO: Craig Frerichs, Chief Information Technology Service
CHR: William Chester, Manager Human Resources
Web address: www.grandjunction.va.gov/
Control: Veterans Affairs, Government, federal **Service:** General Medical and
Surgical

Staffed Beds: 23

✠ **ST. MARY'S HOSPITAL AND REGIONAL MEDICAL CENTER (060023)**, 2635
North 7th Street, Zip 81501–8209, Mailing Address: P.O. Box 1628,
Zip 81502–1628; tel. 970/298–2273 **A**1 2 3 10 19 20 **F**3 7 12 13 14 15 17
18 20 22 24 26 28 29 30 31 34 35 37 40 43 44 45 49 50 51 53 54 55 57
58 59 61 64 67 68 69 70 72 74 75 76 77 78 79 81 82 85 86 87 89 90 91
93 96 97 100 102 107 108 109 110 111 114 115 116 117 119 121 123
124 126 129 130 131 132 135 143 145 146 147 148 **P**6 **S** SCL Health
System, Denver, CO
Primary Contact: Michael J. McBride, FACHE, President and Chief Executive
Officer
COO: Reza Kaleel, Executive Vice President and Chief Operating Officer
CFO: Terri Chinn, Vice President Finance
CIO: John Bullard, Director Information Technology
CHR: Judy White House, Vice President Human Resources
CNO: Shelley Peterson, R.N., Vice President Patient Services and Chief Nursing
Officer
Web address: www.stmarygj.com
Control: Church–operated, Nongovernment, not–for profit **Service:** General
Medical and Surgical

Staffed Beds: 346 **Admissions:** 12581 **Census:** 166 **Births:** 2191 **Total
Expense ($000):** 332060 **Payroll Expense ($000):** 124692 **Personnel:**
1743

VETERANS AFFAIRS MEDICAL CENTER See Grand Junction Veterans Affairs
Medical Center

WEST SPRINGS HOSPITAL (064023), 515 28 3/4 Road, Zip 81501–5016;
tel. 970/263–4918, (Nonreporting) **A**9 10
Primary Contact: Sharon Raggio, President and Chief Executive Officer
CNO: LaCinda Kelleher, Director of Nursing
Web address: www.cwrmhc.org
Control: Other not–for–profit (including NFP Corporation) **Service:** Psychiatric

Staffed Beds: 32

GREELEY—Weld County

✠ **NORTH COLORADO MEDICAL CENTER (060001)**, 1801 16th Street,
Zip 80631–5154; tel. 970/352–4121 **A**1 2 9 10 **F**3 7 8 11 12 13 14 15 18 20
22 24 26 28 29 30 31 34 35 38 40 42 43 46 49 50 51 53 54 55 56 57 58
59 60 61 62 63 64 65 68 70 73 74 75 76 77 79 80 81 82 84 85 86 87
89 93 97 99 104 107 108 110 111 114 115 116 117 118 119 120 121 123
126 127 129 130 131 132 133 135 141 143 144 146 147 148 **P**6 **S** Banner
Health, Phoenix, AZ
Primary Contact: Richard O. Sutton, Chief Executive Officer
COO: Wendy Sparks, Chief Operating Officer
CFO: Mary McCabe, Chief Financial Officer
CMO: Sheldon Stadnyk, M.D., Chief Medical Officer
CHR: Jeannie Gallagher, Chief Human Resource Officer
CNO: Tiffany Erin Hettinger, Associate Chief Nursing Officer
Web address: www.ncmcgreeley.com
Control: Other not–for–profit (including NFP Corporation) **Service:** General
Medical and Surgical

Staffed Beds: 238 **Admissions:** 12677 **Census:** 127 **Births:** 1902 **Total
Expense ($000):** 326353 **Payroll Expense ($000):** 97058 **Personnel:** 1722

GUNNISON—Gunnison County

✠ **GUNNISON VALLEY HOSPITAL (061320)**, 711 North Taylor Street,
Zip 81230–2296; tel. 970/641–1456, (Total facility includes 56 beds in nursing
home–type unit) **A**1 9 10 18 **F**3 7 11 13 15 28 29 30 31 34 35 40 43 45 56
57 59 64 68 70 76 77 78 79 81 85 87 93 97 107 110 111 114 119 128 129
132 133 133 146 147 148
Primary Contact: Robert J. Santilli, Chief Executive Officer
CFO: James P. Barbuat, Chief Financial Officer
CIO: Trevor Smith, Chief Management Information Services
CHR: Christina Lovelace, Director Human Resources
CNO: Audrey Cortez, Chief Nursing Officer
Web address: www.gvh–colorado.org
Control: County-Government, nonfederal **Service:** General Medical and Surgical

Staffed Beds: 80 **Admissions:** 488 **Census:** 45 **Outpatient Visits:** 34641
Births: 112 **Total Expense ($000):** 32205 **Payroll Expense ($000):** 11096
Personnel: 176

HAXTUN—Phillips County

★ **HAXTUN HOSPITAL DISTRICT (061304)**, 235 West Fletcher Street,
Zip 80731–2737; tel. 970/774–6123, (Nonreporting) **A**9 10 18
Primary Contact: Don Burris, Chief Executive Officer
CFO: Sandra Lambrecht, Chief Financial Officer
CMO: Lila Statz, M.D., Chief of Staff
CHR: Brenda Lechman, Director Human Resources
Web address: www.haxtunhealth.org
Control: Hospital district or authority, Government, nonfederal **Service:** General
Medical and Surgical

Staffed Beds: 25

HOLYOKE—Phillips County

★ **MELISSA MEMORIAL HOSPITAL (061305)**, 1001 East Johnson Street,
Zip 80734–1854; tel. 970/854–2241 **A**9 10 18 **F**3 7 15 28 29 34 35 40 43
45 50 57 59 64 68 75 77 81 84 85 93 97 107 110 111 114 119 127 129
133 146 148 **P**6
Primary Contact: John J. Aycub, FACHE, Chief Executive Officer
CFO: Gregory J. Was, CPA, Chief Financial Officer
CMO: Dennis Jelden, M.D., Chief of Staff
CHR: Sharon Greenman, Director Human Resources
CNO: Claudia Powell, R.N., Director of Nursing
Web address: www.melissamemorial.org
Control: Hospital district or authority, Government, nonfederal **Service:** General
Medical and Surgical

Staffed Beds: 15 **Admissions:** 215 **Census:** 3 **Outpatient Visits:** 10076
Births: 0 **Total Expense ($000):** 10945 **Payroll Expense ($000):** 4258
Personnel: 90

HUGO—Lincoln County

LINCOLN COMMUNITY HOSPITAL AND NURSING HOME (061306), 111 6th
Street, Zip 80821–0248, Mailing Address: P.O. Box 248, Zip 80821–0248;
tel. 719/743–2421, (Nonreporting) **A**9 10 18
Primary Contact: Monica Wilkins, Chief Executive Officer
CMO: Mark Olson, M.D., Chief of Staff
CIO: Michael Gaskins, Director Information Technology
Web address: www.lincolncommunityhospitalandnursinghome.com
Control: County–Government, nonfederal **Service:** General Medical and Surgical

Staffed Beds: 50

JOHNSTOWN—Larimer County

□ **NORTHERN COLORADO LONG TERM ACUTE HOSPITAL (062017)**, 4401
Union Street, Zip 80534; tel. 970/619–3663, (Nonreporting) **A**1 9 10 **S** Ernest
Health, Inc., Albuquerque, NM
Primary Contact: Dawn Morrissey, Chief Operating Officer
Web address: www.ncltah.ernesthealth.com/
Control: Partnership, Investor–owned, for–profit **Service:** Long–Term Acute Care
hospital

Staffed Beds: 40

Hospital, Medicare Provider Number, Address, Telephone, Approval, Facility, and Physician Codes, Health Care System

★ American Hospital Association (AHA) membership
□ The Joint Commission accreditation ◇ DNV Healthcare Inc. accreditation
○ Healthcare Facilities Accreditation Program
△ Commission on Accreditation of Rehabilitation Facilities (CARF) accreditation

CO

✠ **NORTHERN COLORADO REHABILITATION HOSPITAL (063033)**, 4401 Union Street, Zip 80534–2800; tel. 970/619–3400 **A**1 10 **F**29 90 91 92 93 96 119 132 **S** Ernest Health, Inc., Albuquerque, NM
Primary Contact: Elizabeth Bullard, Chief Operating Officer
CFO: Ken R. Derrington, Chief Financial Officer
CMO: Indria S. Lanig, M.D., Medical Director
CHR: Jill Scanlon, Director Human Resources
CNO: Rhonda Carolus, Director of Nursing Operations
Web address: www.ncrh.ernesthealth.com
Control: Corporation, Investor–owned, for–profit **Service:** Rehabilitation

Staffed Beds: 40 **Admissions:** 882 **Census:** 34 **Births:** 0 **Total Expense ($000):** 16007 **Payroll Expense ($000):** 6330

JULESBURG—Sedgwick County

SEDGWICK COUNTY HEALTH CENTER (061310), 900 Cedar Street, Zip 80737–1199; tel. 970/474–3323, (Total facility includes 52 beds in nursing home–type unit) **A**9 10 18 **F**10 13 15 31 32 34 40 45 53 56 57 59 64 65 66 67 76 81 89 107 110 111 114 119 127 128 133
Primary Contact: David Garnas, Chief Executive Officer
COO: David Garnas, Chief Executive Officer
CFO: Karla Dunker, Director Finance
CMO: Donald Regier, M.D., Chief Medical Officer
CHR: Sonja Bell, Coordinator Human Resources
Control: County–Government, nonfederal **Service:** General Medical and Surgical

Staffed Beds: 61 **Admissions:** 138 **Census:** 48 **Outpatient Visits:** 13425 **Births:** 21 **Total Expense ($000):** 8888 **Payroll Expense ($000):** 4256 **Personnel:** 89

KREMMLING—Grand County

★ **MIDDLE PARK MEDICAL CENTER–KREMMLING (061318)**, 214 South Fourth Street, Zip 80459, Mailing Address: P.O. Box 399, Zip 80459–0399; tel. 970/724–3442, (Nonreporting) **A**9 10 18
Primary Contact: Trampas Hutches, Interim Chief Executive Officer
COO: Trampas Hutches, Chief Operating Officer
CFO: Brendan Gale, Chief Financial Officer
CMO: Jason Stuerman, M.D., Chief of Staff
CIO: Michelle Balleck, Director Public Relations
CHR: Jason Bryan, Director Human Resources
CNO: Carmen Covington, Chief Nursing Officer
Web address: www.mpmc.org
Control: Hospital district or authority, Government, nonfederal **Service:** General Medical and Surgical

Staffed Beds: 19

LA JARA—Conejos County

★ **SAN LUIS VALLEY HEALTH CONEJOS COUNTY HOSPITAL (061308)**, 19021 U.S. Highway 285, Zip 81140–0639, Mailing Address: P.O. Box 639, Zip 81140–0639; tel. 719/274–5121 **A**9 10 18 **F**3 29 40 43 54 56 59 64 70 87 93 97 107 114 119 127 128 133 **S** San Luis Valley Health, Alamosa, CO
Primary Contact: Kelly Gallegos, Administrator
CFO: Shane Mortensen, Chief Financial Officer
CMO: Gregory McAuliffe, M.D., Chief Medical Officer
CIO: Kathy Rogers, Vice President Marketing
CHR: Mandy Lee Crockett, Director Human Resources
CNO: Tandra Dunn, Director of Nursing
Web address: www.sanluisvalleyhealth.org/locations/conejos–county–hospital
Control: Other not–for–profit (including NFP Corporation) **Service:** General Medical and Surgical

Staffed Beds: 17 **Admissions:** 173 **Census:** 2

LA JUNTA—Otero County

✠ **ARKANSAS VALLEY REGIONAL MEDICAL CENTER (060036)**, 1100 Carson Avenue, Zip 81050–2799; tel. 719/383–6000, (Total facility includes 99 beds in nursing home–type unit) **A**1 9 10 20 **F**3 8 11 13 15 29 31 34 35 40 43 45 57 59 64 67 68 70 75 76 77 78 79 81 84 85 86 87 89 93 97 107 108 110 111 115 118 119 128 129 130 132 145 147 148 **P**6 **S** QHR, Brentwood, TN
Primary Contact: Lynn Crowell, Chief Executive Officer
CFO: Janette Bender, Chief Financial Officer
CMO: Michael Morley, M.D., Chief of Staff
CIO: Annette Cook, Application Support Specialist
CHR: Leigh Fitzpatrick, Director Human Resources
Web address: www.avrmc.org
Control: Other not–for–profit (including NFP Corporation) **Service:** General Medical and Surgical

Staffed Beds: 163 **Admissions:** 2450 **Census:** 85

LAFAYETTE—Boulder County

✠ **EXEMPLA GOOD SAMARITAN MEDICAL CENTER (060116)**, 200 Exempla Circle, Zip 80026–3370; tel. 303/689–4000 **A**1 9 10 **F**3 11 12 13 15 18 20 22 24 28 29 30 31 34 35 36 40 43 45 46 49 51 55 57 59 60 63 64 68 70 72 74 75 76 77 78 79 80 81 84 85 86 87 91 92 93 94 100 102 107 108 110 111 114 115 119 126 130 132 143 145 146 147 148 **P**6 **S** SCL Health System, Denver, CO
Primary Contact: David Hamm, President and Chief Executive Officer
COO: Beth Forsyth, Chief Operating Officer
CFO: John Higgins, Vice President and Chief Financial Officer
CMO: Todd Mydler, M.D., Vice President and Chief Medical Officer
CHR: Amy Pacey, Vice President Human Resources
CNO: Susan Kerschen, MS, Vice President and Chief Nursing Officer
Web address: www.exempla.org
Control: Other not–for–profit (including NFP Corporation) **Service:** General Medical and Surgical

Staffed Beds: 192 **Admissions:** 12198 **Census:** 135 **Outpatient Visits:** 102430 **Births:** 2328 **Total Expense ($000):** 234848 **Payroll Expense ($000):** 78224 **Personnel:** 1185

LAKEWOOD—Jefferson County

☐ **ORTHOCOLORADO HOSPITAL (060124)**, 11650 West 2nd Place, Zip 80228–1527; tel. 720/321–5000, (Nonreporting) **A**1 5 9
Primary Contact: Jude Torchia, Chief Executive Officer
Web address: www.orthocolorado.org
Control: Partnership, Investor–owned, for–profit **Service:** Orthopedic

Staffed Beds: 48

✠ **ST. ANTHONY HOSPITAL (060015)**, 11600 West Second Place, Zip 80228–1527; tel. 720/321–0000 **A**1 2 3 5 9 10 **F**3 7 11 12 17 18 20 22 24 26 28 29 30 31 34 35 36 40 43 45 46 47 48 49 50 53 56 57 59 64 65 68 70 74 75 76 77 78 79 81 82 84 85 87 90 92 93 96 97 102 107 108 111 114 115 116 117 118 119 120 121 123 124 126 129 130 132 133 134 135 146 147 148 **S** Catholic Health Initiatives, Englewood, CO
Primary Contact: Jeffrey Brickman, FACHE, President and Chief Executive Officer
COO: Patrick Green, Chief Operating Officer
CFO: David Thompson, Chief Financial Officer
CMO: Christopher Ott, M.D., Chief Medical Officer
CIO: Dana Moore, Senior Vice President Information Services
CHR: Michelle Fornier–Johnson, Group Vice President Human Resources
CNO: Kay J. Miller, MS, Chief Nursing Officer
Web address: www.stanthonyhosp.org
Control: Church–operated, Nongovernment, not–for profit **Service:** General Medical and Surgical

Staffed Beds: 224 **Admissions:** 10656 **Census:** 160 **Outpatient Visits:** 75576 **Births:** 0 **Total Expense ($000):** 311253 **Payroll Expense ($000):** 83817 **Personnel:** 1406

LAMAR—Prowers County

★ **PROWERS MEDICAL CENTER (061323)**, 401 Kendall Drive, Zip 81052–3993; tel. 719/336–4343 **A**9 10 18 **F**3 11 13 15 18 28 29 31 34 35 40 45 50 56 57 59 62 64 65 66 68 78 81 85 86 93 97 107 111 119 127 130 133 146 147 148 **P**3 6 **S** QHR, Brentwood, TN
Primary Contact: Craig Loveless, Chief Executive Officer
COO: Karen Bryant, Chief Support Services Officer
CFO: Audrey Kane, Interim Chief Financial Officer
CMO: Barry Portner, M.D., Chief of Staff
CIO: Jason Spano, Manager Information Technology
CHR: Karen Bryant, Chief Support Services Officer
Web address: www.prowersmedical.com
Control: Hospital district or authority, Government, nonfederal **Service:** General Medical and Surgical

Staffed Beds: 25 **Admissions:** 654 **Census:** 5 **Outpatient Visits:** 37081 **Births:** 162 **Total Expense ($000):** 22345 **Payroll Expense ($000):** 10205 **Personnel:** 220

LEADVILLE—Lake County

★ **ST. VINCENT GENERAL HOSPITAL DISTRICT (061319)**, 822 West 4th Street, Zip 80461–3897; tel. 719/486–0230, (Nonreporting) **A**9 10 18 **S** QHR, Brentwood, TN
Primary Contact: Joyce Beck, Chief Executive Officer
CFO: Ric Eisenring, Chief Financial Officer
CMO: Gary Petry, M.D., Chief of Staff
CHR: Cheryl Snider, Director Human Resources
CNO: Von Kilpatrick, Chief Nursing Officer
Web address: www.svghd.org
Control: Hospital district or authority, Government, nonfederal **Service:** General Medical and Surgical

Staffed Beds: 25

Many Facility Codes have changed. Please refer to the AHA Guide Code Chart. © 2014 AHA Guide

LITTLETON—Jefferson County

FEDERAL CORRECTIONAL INSTITUTE HOSPITAL, 9595 West Quincy Street, Zip 80123–1159; tel. 303/985–1566, (Nonreporting)
Primary Contact: Mike Hudson, Administrator
Control: Department of Justice, Government, federal **Service:** Hospital unit of an institution (prison hospital, college infimary, etc.)

Staffed Beds: 6

✠ **HEALTHSOUTH REHABILITATION HOSPITAL OF DENVER (063034)**, 1001 West Mineral Avenue, Zip 80120–4507; tel. 303/334–1100 **A**1 10 **F**28 29 60 74 77 90 91 130 132 143 148 **P**5 **S** HEALTHSOUTH Corporation, Birmingham, AL
Primary Contact: David H. Shefte, Chief Executive Officer
CFO: Liz Freudenberg, Chief Financial Officer
CMO: Jill Castro, M.D., Medical Director
CHR: Sarah Thomas, Director of Human Resources
CNO: Carol Anne Banville, Chief Nursing Officer
Web address: www.healthsouthdenver.com
Control: Partnership, Investor–owned, for–profit **Service:** Rehabilitation

Staffed Beds: 28 **Admissions:** 482 **Census:** 17 **Outpatient Visits:** 0 **Births:** 0 **Total Expense ($000):** 7379 **Payroll Expense ($000):** 4358 **Personnel:** 76

☐ **HIGHLANDS BEHAVIORAL HEALTH SYSTEM (064024)**, 8565 South Poplar Way, Zip 80130–3602; tel. 720/348–2800, (Nonreporting) **A**1 9 10 **S** Universal Health Services, Inc., King of Prussia, PA
Primary Contact: Paul Sexton, Chief Executive Officer
Web address: www.highlandsbhs.com
Control: Corporation, Investor–owned, for–profit **Service:** Psychiatric

Staffed Beds: 86

✠ **LITTLETON ADVENTIST HOSPITAL (060113)**, 7700 South Broadway Street, Zip 80122–2628; tel. 303/730–8900 **A**1 2 9 10 **F**3 11 13 15 17 18 20 22 29 30 31 34 35 36 37 40 41 42 43 45 46 47 48 49 53 54 55 57 59 64 68 70 72 74 75 76 77 78 79 81 82 83 84 85 87 89 92 93 97 107 108 110 111 114 115 116 117 118 119 126 129 130 131 132 135 146 147 148 **P**6 **S** Adventist Health System Sunbelt Health Care Corporation, Altamonte Springs, FL
Primary Contact: Brett Spenst, Chief Executive Officer
COO: Geoff Lawton, Vice President Operations
CFO: Cheryl Curry, Chief Financial Officer
CMO: Lawrence Wood, M.D., Chief Medical Officer
CHR: Rita K. Arthur, Director Human Resources
CNO: Rhonda Ward, R.N., Chief Nursing Officer
Web address: www.centura.org
Control: Church–operated, Nongovernment, not–for profit **Service:** General Medical and Surgical

Staffed Beds: 201 **Admissions:** 9268 **Census:** 105 **Outpatient Visits:** 84463 **Births:** 1619 **Total Expense ($000):** 201893 **Payroll Expense ($000):** 63851 **Personnel:** 946

LONE TREE—Douglas County

✠ **SKY RIDGE MEDICAL CENTER (060112)**, 10101 Ridge Gate Parkway, Zip 80124–5522; tel. 720/225–1000 **A**1 2 9 10 **F**3 8 12 13 15 17 18 20 22 24 28 29 30 31 34 35 36 37 40 41 43 45 46 47 48 49 54 57 59 64 70 72 73 74 75 76 77 78 79 81 82 84 85 86 87 89 93 97 107 108 111 114 115 119 120 121 123 126 129 130 131 132 135 146 147 148 **P**3 6 8 **S** HCA, Nashville, TN
Primary Contact: Maureen Tarrant, Chief Executive Officer
COO: Susan Hicks, Chief Operating Officer
CFO: Craig Sammons, Chief Financial Officer
CMO: David Markenson, M.D., Chief Medical Officer
CIO: Evan Tice, Director Information Technology and Systems
CHR: Jim Ritchey, Director Human Resources
CNO: Marian Savitsky, R.N., Chief Nursing Officer
Web address: www.skyridgemedcenter.com
Control: Corporation, Investor–owned, for–profit **Service:** General Medical and Surgical

Staffed Beds: 177 **Admissions:** 13643 **Census:** 132 **Outpatient Visits:** 91845 **Births:** 3602 **Personnel:** 1087

LONGMONT—Boulder County

✠ **LONGMONT UNITED HOSPITAL (060003)**, 1950 West Mountain View Avenue, Zip 80501–3162, Mailing Address: P.O. Box 1659, Zip 80502–1659; tel. 303/651–5111, (Total facility includes 15 beds in nursing home–type unit) **A**1 2 9 10 **F**2 3 11 13 15 18 20 22 28 29 30 31 34 35 36 37 39 40 43 44 45 47 48 49 50 53 54 56 57 59 61 64 68 70 73 74 75 76 77 78 79 81 82 84 85 86 87 89 92 93 107 108 110 111 114 115 118 119 121 123 126 128 129 130 131 132 135 146 148 **P**6
Primary Contact: Mitchell C. Carson, President and Chief Executive Officer
CFO: Neil W. Bertrand, Chief Financial Officer
CMO: Amy Johnson, M.D., Chief of Staff
CIO: Michael Jefferies, Vice President Information Systems
CHR: Warren Laughlin, Vice President Human Resources
CNO: Nancy Driscoll, R.N., Chief Nursing Officer
Web address: www.luhcares.org
Control: Other not–for–profit (including NFP Corporation) **Service:** General Medical and Surgical

Staffed Beds: 146 **Admissions:** 7576 **Census:** 88 **Outpatient Visits:** 131345 **Births:** 1057 **Total Expense ($000):** 174393 **Payroll Expense ($000):** 70230 **Personnel:** 1075

LOUISVILLE—Boulder County

✠ **AVISTA ADVENTIST HOSPITAL (060103)**, 100 Health Park Drive, Zip 80027–9583; tel. 303/673–1000 **A**1 9 10 **F**3 8 11 13 15 17 18 20 22 29 30 31 34 40 43 44 45 47 48 49 50 59 60 62 63 64 68 70 72 74 75 76 77 78 79 81 82 85 86 87 89 93 107 108 111 114 115 119 129 130 131 132 135 146 147 148 **P**4 6 **S** Adventist Health System Sunbelt Health Care Corporation, Altamonte Springs, FL
Primary Contact: Dennis Barts, Chief Executive Officer
CFO: Brent Davis, Chief Financial Officer
CMO: David Ehrenberger, M.D., Chief Medical Officer
CHR: Robert Stansel, Director Human Resources
CNO: Lesley Radocy, R.N., Chief Nursing Officer
Web address: www.avistahospital.org
Control: Church–operated, Nongovernment, not–for profit **Service:** General Medical and Surgical

Staffed Beds: 114 **Admissions:** 4435 **Census:** 41 **Outpatient Visits:** 44227 **Births:** 2046 **Total Expense ($000):** 81180 **Payroll Expense ($000):** 33315 **Personnel:** 462

☐ **CENTENNIAL PEAKS HOSPITAL (064007)**, 2255 South 88th Street, Zip 80027–9716; tel. 303/673–9990, (Nonreporting) **A**1 9 10 **S** Universal Health Services, Inc., King of Prussia, PA
Primary Contact: Elicia Bunch, Chief Executive Officer
COO: Lisa Strub, Director Clinical Services
CFO: Tim Ryan, Director Finance
CMO: Konoy Mandal, M.D., Medical Director
CHR: Suzanne Martinez, Director Human Resources
CNO: Bob Williams, Director of Nursing
Web address: www.centennialpeaks.com
Control: Other not–for–profit (including NFP Corporation) **Service:** Psychiatric

Staffed Beds: 72

LOVELAND—Larimer County

✠ **MCKEE MEDICAL CENTER (060030)**, 2000 Boise Avenue, Zip 80538–4281; tel. 970/669–4640 **A**1 2 9 10 **F**2 3 8 11 12 13 15 18 20 22 28 29 30 31 34 35 38 40 43 46 49 50 54 56 57 59 60 62 64 68 70 74 75 77 78 79 80 81 82 85 86 87 93 97 104 107 108 110 111 114 115 119 121 123 126 129 130 132 133 134 135 144 146 147 148 **P**6 **S** Banner Health, Phoenix, AZ
Primary Contact: Michelle L. Joy, Chief Operating Officer
COO: Michelle L. Joy, Chief Operating Officer
CFO: Lori Sehrt, Chief Financial Officer
CMO: Bert Honea, M.D., Medical Director
CIO: Steve Rains, Director Information Services
CHR: Jeannie Gallagher, jeanie.gallagher@bannerhealth.com
CNO: Kelly Sturler, Chief Nursing Officer
Web address: www.mckeeloveland.com
Control: Other not–for–profit (including NFP Corporation) **Service:** General Medical and Surgical

Staffed Beds: 105 **Admissions:** 4876 **Census:** 38 **Outpatient Visits:** 90645 **Births:** 812 **Total Expense ($000):** 121343 **Payroll Expense ($000):** 37590 **Personnel:** 632

CO

Hospital, Medicare Provider Number, Address, Telephone, Approval, Facility, and Physician Codes, Health Care System

★ American Hospital Association (AHA) membership
☐ The Joint Commission accreditation   ◇ DNV Healthcare Inc. accreditation
○ Healthcare Facilities Accreditation Program
△ Commission on Accreditation of Rehabilitation Facilities (CARF) accreditation

CO

⊞ **MEDICAL CENTER OF THE ROCKIES (060119)**, 2500 Rocky Mountain
Avenue, Zip 80538–9004; tel. 970/624–2500 **A**1 9 10 **F**3 8 11 13 14 15 17
18 20 22 24 26 28 29 30 31 32 34 35 38 39 40 42 43 44 45 47 49 50 54
55 57 58 59 60 61 64 65 68 70 74 75 76 77 78 79 80 81 82 84 85 86 87
89 90 92 93 96 100 107 108 110 111 114 115 118 119 126 129 130 131
132 134 135 143 146 147 148 **P**5 6 **S** University of Colorado Health, Fort
Collins, CO
Primary Contact: Kevin L. Unger, FACHE, President and Chief Executive Officer
CFO: Stephanie Doughty, Chief Financial Officer
CMO: William Neff, M.D., Chief Medical Officer
CIO: Steve Hess, Vice President & Chief Information Officer
Web address: www.medctrrockies.org
Control: Other not–for–profit (including NFP Corporation) **Service:** General
Medical and Surgical

> **Staffed Beds:** 166 **Admissions:** 8616 **Census:** 99 **Outpatient Visits:** 170583
> **Births:** 704 **Total Expense ($000):** 276081 **Payroll Expense ($000):** 83385
> **Personnel:** 928

MEEKER—Rio Blanco County

★ **PIONEERS MEDICAL CENTER (061325)**, 345 Cleveland Street,
Zip 81641–3238; tel. 970/878–5047, (Includes WALBRIDGE MEMORIAL
CONVALESCENT WING), (Total facility includes 30 beds in nursing home–type
unit) **A**9 10 18 **F**8 15 29 32 34 35 40 50 53 57 59 62 64 65 69 75 77 81 82
85 93 97 107 127 128 133 135 143 148 **P**6 **S** QHR, Brentwood, TN
Primary Contact: Kenneth Harman, Chief Executive Officer
COO: Drew Varland, Chief Nursing Officer and Chief Operating Officer
CFO: James W. Worrell, Chief Financial Officer
CMO: Albert Krueger, M.D., Chief of Staff
CIO: Curtis Cooper, Manager Information Systems
CHR: Twyla Jensen, Director Human Resources
Web address: www.pioneershospital.org
Control: Hospital district or authority, Government, nonfederal **Service:** General
Medical and Surgical

> **Staffed Beds:** 40 **Admissions:** 127 **Census:** 25 **Outpatient Visits:** 10243
> **Births:** 0 **Total Expense ($000):** 13178 **Payroll Expense ($000):** 6540
> **Personnel:** 108

MONTROSE—Montrose County

⊞ **MONTROSE MEMORIAL HOSPITAL (060006)**, 800 South Third Street,
Zip 81401–4212; tel. 970/249–2211 **A**1 9 10 20 **F**3 12 13 15 17 18 20 22
28 29 30 31 34 35 40 43 45 46 51 57 66 70 73 74 75 76 78 79 80 81 82
85 88 89 90 93 107 108 110 111 115 119 126 127 129 130 131 146 **P**5 8
S QHR, Brentwood, TN
Primary Contact: Mary E. Snyder, Interim Chief Executive Officer
COO: Mary E. Snyder, Chief Operations Officer
CFO: Stephan A. Wilson, Chief Financial Officer
CMO: Richard Shannon, M.D., Chief of Staff
CIO: Carlos Lovera, Director Information Systems
CHR: Kathy McKie, Director Human Resources
Web address: www.montrosehospital.com
Control: Other not–for–profit (including NFP Corporation) **Service:** General
Medical and Surgical

> **Staffed Beds:** 69 **Admissions:** 2891 **Census:** 28 **Outpatient Visits:** 96515

PAGOSA SPRINGS—Archuleta County

PAGOSA SPRINGS MEDICAL CENTER (061328), 95 South Pagosa Boulevard,
Zip 81147–8329; tel. 970/731–3700, (Nonreporting) **A**9 10 18
Primary Contact: Bradley Cochennet, Chief Executive Officer
Control: Other not–for–profit (including NFP Corporation) **Service:** General
Medical and Surgical

> **Staffed Beds:** 11

PARKER—Douglas County

⊞ **PARKER ADVENTIST HOSPITAL (060114)**, 9395 Crown Crest Boulevard,
Zip 80138–8573; tel. 303/269–4000 **A**1 2 9 10 **F**3 11 12 13 15 20 22 29 30
31 34 35 36 38 40 43 45 46 49 50 54 55 57 59 64 70 72 73 74 75 76 77
78 79 81 82 83 84 85 87 93 96 97 107 110 111 114 115 116 117 119 126
129 130 131 135 146 147 148 **P**6 **S** Adventist Health System Sunbelt Health
Care Corporation, Altamonte Springs, FL
Primary Contact: Morre Dean, Chief Executive Officer
CFO: Andrew Gaasch, Chief Financial Officer
Web address: www.parkerhospital.org
Control: Church–operated, Nongovernment, not–for profit **Service:** General
Medical and Surgical

> **Staffed Beds:** 143 **Admissions:** 7322 **Census:** 75 **Outpatient Visits:** 59229
> **Births:** 1630 **Total Expense ($000):** 145058 **Payroll Expense ($000):**
> 48999 **Personnel:** 733

PUEBLO—Pueblo County

☐ **COLORADO MENTAL HEALTH INSTITUTE AT PUEBLO (060115)**, 1600 West
24th Street, Zip 81003–1499; tel. 719/546–4000, (Nonreporting) **A**1 3 5 10
Primary Contact: John R. DeQuardo, M.D., Superintendent
CFO: Jim Duff, Chief Financial Officer
CMO: Al Singleton, M.D., Chief Psychiatry and Chief Medical Staff
CIO: Eunice Wolther, Public Information Officer
CHR: Mary Young, Director Human Resources
Web address: www.cdhs.state.co.us/cmhip
Control: State–Government, nonfederal **Service:** Psychiatric

> **Staffed Beds:** 514

☐ **HAVEN BEHAVIORAL WAR HEROES HOSPITAL (064025)**, 1008 Minnequa
Avenue, Suite 6100, Zip 81004–3733; tel. 719/546–6000, (Nonreporting) **A**1 10
S Haven Behavioral Healthcare, Nashville, TN
Primary Contact: Carrin Harper, M.D., Chief Executive Officer
Control: Corporation, Investor–owned, for–profit **Service:** Psychiatric

> **Staffed Beds:** 20

⊞ △ **PARKVIEW MEDICAL CENTER (060020)**, 400 West 16th Street,
Zip 81003–2781; tel. 719/584–4000, (Total facility includes 20 beds in nursing
home–type unit) **A**1 7 9 10 **F**2 3 4 5 8 11 13 15 18 20 22 24 28 29 30 31 34
35 37 38 40 42 43 45 46 49 50 51 53 56 57 58 59 62 64 70 73 74 75 76
78 79 81 82 84 85 86 87 89 90 93 94 95 96 97 98 99 100 101 102 103
104 105 107 108 111 114 115 116 119 128 129 130 132 135 141 146 147
148 **P**6 8
Primary Contact: Michael T. Baxter, Chief Executive Officer
COO: Robert P. Thames, Chief Operating Officer
CFO: Leslie Barnes, Chief Financial Officer
CMO: Steve Nafziger, M.D., Vice President Medical Affairs
CIO: Steve Shirley, Chief Information Officer
CHR: Darrin Smith, Vice President Human Resources
CNO: Linda Flores, R.N., Vice President Nursing Services
Web address: www.parkviewmc.org
Control: Other not–for–profit (including NFP Corporation) **Service:** General
Medical and Surgical

> **Staffed Beds:** 370 **Admissions:** 13579 **Census:** 224 **Outpatient Visits:**
> 206032 **Births:** 1435 **Total Expense ($000):** 257090 **Payroll Expense**
> **($000):** 107708 **Personnel:** 2077

⊞ **ST. MARY–CORWIN MEDICAL CENTER (060012)**, 1008 Minnequa Avenue,
Zip 81004–3798; tel. 719/557–4000 **A**1 2 9 10 12 13 **F**3 13 15 18 20 22 26
28 29 30 31 34 35 40 43 45 47 48 49 50 51 53 55 57 58 59 64 68 70 72
73 75 76 78 79 81 82 84 85 86 87 89 90 107 108 110 111 114 115 117
119 120 121 123 124 126 129 130 131 132 135 146 147 148 **P**6 **S** Catholic
Health Initiatives, Englewood, CO
Primary Contact: Brian Moore, President and Chief Executive Officer
COO: Michael Cafasso, Vice President Operations
CFO: Vanessa Kochevar, Chief Financial Officer
CMO: Charles Raye, M.D., Chief Medical Officer
CHR: Timea Kennedy, Director Human Resources
CNO: Donna Fisher, MS, Chief Nursing Officer
Web address: www.centura.org
Control: Church–operated, Nongovernment, not–for profit **Service:** General
Medical and Surgical

> **Staffed Beds:** 153 **Admissions:** 6272 **Census:** 74 **Outpatient Visits:** 86088
> **Births:** 568 **Total Expense ($000):** 143995 **Payroll Expense ($000):** 53322
> **Personnel:** 860

RANGELY—Rio Blanco County

★ **RANGELY DISTRICT HOSPITAL (061307)**, 225 Eagle Crest Drive,
Zip 81648–2104; tel. 970/675–5011, (Total facility includes 10 beds in nursing
home–type unit) **A**9 10 18 **F**1 3 7 10 15 33 34 35 40 43 45 50 57 59 62 64
65 67 68 69 91 93 97 104 107 111 114 115 119 128 133 144 148
Primary Contact: Nick Goshe, Chief Executive Officer
CFO: Jim Dillon, Chief Financial Officer
CMO: S. Kathleen Rieves, M.D., Chief Medical Officer
CHR: Cynthia S. Stults, Executive Assistant and Human Resources Director
CNO: Sharma Vaughn, Chief Nursing Officer
Web address: www.rangelyhospital.com
Control: Hospital district or authority, Government, nonfederal **Service:**
Long–Term Acute Care hospital

> **Staffed Beds:** 25 **Admissions:** 72 **Census:** 11 **Births:** 0 **Total Expense**
> **($000):** 18981 **Payroll Expense ($000):** 6829

RIFLE—Garfield County

★ **GRAND RIVER HOSPITAL DISTRICT (061317)**, 501 Airport Road,
Zip 81650–8510, Mailing Address: P.O. Box 912, Zip 81650–0912;
tel. 970/625–1510, (Total facility includes 57 beds in nursing home–type unit) **A**9
10 18 **F**3 11 12 15 29 34 35 39 40 41 43 45 50 55 57 59 64 68 69 75 77
79 81 85 87 93 96 97 107 108 110 111 112 114 118 119 127 128 129 130
131 132 133 144 145 146 148 **P**6
Primary Contact: James Coombs, Chief Executive Officer
COO: Bill Noel, Chief Operating Officer
CMO: Gary Meyer, M.D., Chief of Staff
CIO: Diana Murray, Director Information Systems
CHR: Dawn Hodges, Director Human Resources
CNO: Erin Muck, Chief Nursing Officer
Web address: www.grhd.org
Control: Hospital district or authority, Government, nonfederal **Service:** General
Medical and Surgical

> **Staffed Beds:** 70 **Admissions:** 554 **Census:** 49 **Outpatient Visits:** 58040
> **Births:** 1 **Total Expense ($000):** 51614 **Payroll Expense ($000):** 25571
> **Personnel:** 394

SALIDA—Chaffee County

★ **HEART OF THE ROCKIES REGIONAL MEDICAL CENTER (061322)**, 1000
Rush Drive, Zip 81201–9627, Mailing Address: P.O. Box 429, Zip 81201–0429;
tel. 719/530–2200 **A**9 10 18 **F**3 5 11 13 15 28 29 31 34 35 39 40 43 45 50
54 57 64 68 70 74 75 76 77 78 79 81 82 85 89 93 97 99 104 107 110 111
114 117 119 127 129 130 131 133 135 146 147 148
Primary Contact: Robert A. Morasko, Chief Executive Officer
CFO: Lesley Fagerberg, Vice President Fiscal Services
CMO: James Wigington, M.D., Chief of Staff
CIO: Andy Waldbart, Department Manager
CHR: Barbara J. Abel, Vice President Human Resources
CNO: Linda Johnson, R.N., Vice President of Nursing
Web address: www.hrrmc.com
Control: Hospital district or authority, Government, nonfederal **Service:** General
Medical and Surgical

> **Staffed Beds:** 25 **Admissions:** 1055 **Census:** 11 **Outpatient Visits:** 53123
> **Births:** 130 **Total Expense ($000):** 40617 **Payroll Expense ($000):** 17321
> **Personnel:** 271

SPRINGFIELD—Baca County

★ **SOUTHEAST COLORADO HOSPITAL DISTRICT (061311)**, 373 East Tenth
Avenue, Zip 81073–1699; tel. 719/523–4501, (Total facility includes 56 beds in
nursing home–type unit) **A**9 10 18 **F**3 6 7 11 29 34 35 40 42 45 50 56 57 62
63 66 68 81 93 97 107 127 133 147 148 **P**6
Primary Contact: Jerry Jasper, Chief Executive Officer and Administrator
CFO: Dorothy Burke, Chief Financial Officer
CMO: Jerry Flynn, M.D., Chief of Staff
CIO: Chris Westphal, Chief Information Technology Officer
CHR: Sherrilyn Turner, Director Human Resources
Web address: www.sechosp.org
Control: Hospital district or authority, Government, nonfederal **Service:** General
Medical and Surgical

> **Staffed Beds:** 79 **Admissions:** 204 **Census:** 46 **Outpatient Visits:** 39041
> **Births:** 0 **Total Expense ($000):** 11860 **Payroll Expense ($000):** 5551
> **Personnel:** 108

STEAMBOAT SPRINGS—Routt County

⊠ **YAMPA VALLEY MEDICAL CENTER (060049)**, 1024 Central Park Drive,
Zip 80487–8813; tel. 970/879–1322, (Total facility includes 59 beds in nursing
home–type unit) **A**1 2 9 10 20 **F**3 13 15 18 28 29 30 31 34 35 36 40 43 45
46 48 49 50 51 57 64 68 70 73 75 76 77 78 79 81 82 84 85 86 87 93 107
110 111 115 119 128 129 130 131 132 133 135 143 146 147
Primary Contact: Frank May, Chief Executive Officer
COO: David Garner, Chief Operating Officer
CFO: Robert Flake, Chief Financial Officer
CMO: Larry Bookman, D.O., Chief Medical Officer
CIO: Mark Clark, Vice President Information Services
CHR: Soniya Fidler, Chief Human Resources Officer
CNO: Marie Timlin, R.N., Chief Nursing Officer
Web address: www.yvmc.org
Control: Other not–for–profit (including NFP Corporation) **Service:** General
Medical and Surgical

> **Staffed Beds:** 98 **Admissions:** 1592 **Census:** 68 **Outpatient Visits:** 61712
> **Births:** 307 **Total Expense ($000):** 76730 **Payroll Expense ($000):** 27105
> **Personnel:** 359

STERLING—Logan County

⊠ **STERLING REGIONAL MEDCENTER (060076)**, 615 Fairhurst Street,
Zip 80751–4523; tel. 970/522–0122 **A**1 9 10 20 **F**13 15 18 28 29 30 31 34
35 36 40 43 45 50 51 57 59 64 68 69 70 75 76 77 78 79 81 85 87 93 94
97 107 108 109 110 111 114 115 119 127 129 130 131 146 148 **P**6
S Banner Health, Phoenix, AZ
Primary Contact: Julie Klein, Chief Executive Officer
CFO: Pamela Stieb, Chief Financial Officer
CMO: Jeff Bacon, D.O., Medical Director
CHR: Cynda Eklund, Chief Human Resources Officer
CNO: Wade Alan Tyrrell, RN, Chief Nursing Officer
Web address: www.bannerhealth.com/Locations/Colorado/Sterling+Regional+
MedCenter
Control: Other not–for–profit (including NFP Corporation) **Service:** General
Medical and Surgical

> **Staffed Beds:** 25 **Admissions:** 1275 **Census:** 10 **Births:** 230 **Total Expense
> ($000):** 40210 **Payroll Expense ($000):** 14924 **Personnel:** 253

THORNTON—Adams County

⊠ **NORTH SUBURBAN MEDICAL CENTER (060065)**, 9191 Grant Street,
Zip 80229–4341; tel. 303/451–7800 **A**1 9 10 **F**3 11 12 13 15 18 20 22 29
30 35 40 43 45 59 60 64 68 70 72 74 75 78 79 81 84 85 87 89 107
108 111 115 119 129 130 132 135 146 **S** HCA, Nashville, TN
Primary Contact: Jennifer Alderfer, Chief Executive Officer
CFO: Deborah Hart, Chief Financial Officer
CIO: Jeff Schnoor, Director Information Technology and Systems
CHR: Suzanne Kelley, Director Human Resources
CNO: Erica Rossitto, R.N., Chief Nursing Officer
Web address: www.northsuburban.com
Control: Corporation, Investor–owned, for–profit **Service:** General Medical and
Surgical

> **Staffed Beds:** 115 **Admissions:** 6883 **Census:** 72

⊠ **VIBRA HOSPITAL OF DENVER (062014)**, 8451 Pearl Street, Zip 80229–4804;
tel. 303/288–3000, (Nonreporting) **A**1 9 10 **S** Vibra Healthcare,
Mechanicsburg, PA
Primary Contact: Craig L. Johnson, FACHE, Resource Chief Executive Officer
CMO: John Buckley, M.D., President Medical Staff
CHR: Lorna Fulton, Director Human Resources
Web address: www.vhdenver.com
Control: Corporation, Investor–owned, for–profit **Service:** Long–Term Acute Care
hospital

> **Staffed Beds:** 71

TRINIDAD—Las Animas County

★ **MT. SAN RAFAEL HOSPITAL (061321)**, 410 Benedicta Avenue,
Zip 81082–2093; tel. 719/846–9213 **A**9 10 18 **F**3 15 28 34 40 45 46 50 65
75 81 82 85 89 93 94 96 97 107 111 114 119 127 129 133 146 147 148
Primary Contact: Robert Quist, Chief Executive Officer
CFO: David W. Rollins, Chief Financial Officer
CMO: Thomas Goodell, M.D., Chief of Staff
CIO: Michael Archuleta, Chief Information Technology Officer
CHR: Tammy Rogers, Director Human Resources
CNO: Denise C. Clark, R.N., Chief Clinical Officer
Web address: www.msrhc.org
Control: Other not–for–profit (including NFP Corporation) **Service:** General
Medical and Surgical

> **Staffed Beds:** 18 **Admissions:** 809 **Census:** 10 **Outpatient Visits:** 36995
> **Births:** 0 **Total Expense ($000):** 23442 **Payroll Expense ($000):** 11184
> **Personnel:** 203

VAIL—Eagle County

⊠ **VAIL VALLEY MEDICAL CENTER (060096)**, 181 West Meadow Drive,
Zip 81657–5242, Mailing Address: P.O. Box 40000, Zip 81658–7520;
tel. 970/476–2451, (Nonreporting) **A**1 9 10 20
Primary Contact: Doris Kirchner, Chief Executive Officer
CFO: Charles Crevling, Senior Vice President and Chief Financial Officer
CMO: Barry Hammaker, M.D., Chief Medical Officer and Chief Clinical Officer
CIO: Brian Foster, Chief Information Officer
CHR: Rick Smith, Senior Vice President Human Resources and Chief
Administrative Officer
CNO: Sheila Sherman, Vice President Patient Care Services
Web address: www.vvmc.com
Control: Other not–for–profit (including NFP Corporation) **Service:** General
Medical and Surgical

> **Staffed Beds:** 58

CO

WALSENBURG—Huerfano County

★ **SPANISH PEAKS REGIONAL HEALTH CENTER (061316)**, 23500 U.S.
Highway 160, Zip 81089–9524; tel. 719/738–5100 **A**9 10 18 **F**11 28 34 35 39
40 43 45 50 57 59 64 79 81 82 85 93 97 107 110 111 115 119 127 129
131 133 147 148 **P**6
Primary Contact: Todd Oberheu, Chief Executive Officer
CFO: Richard L. Corradino, Chief Financial Officer
CMO: Thomas Hoffeld, M.D., Chief of Staff
CHR: Tony Marostica, Director Human Resources
CNO: Darlene Colt, R.N., Chief Nursing Officer
Web address: www.sprhc.org
Control: Hospital district or authority, Government, nonfederal **Service:** General
Medical and Surgical

Staffed Beds: 20 **Admissions:** 226 **Census:** 2 **Outpatient Visits:** 36411 **Births:** 0 **Total Expense ($000):** 13977 **Payroll Expense ($000):** 7559 **Personnel:** 126	

WESTMINSTER—Jefferson County

CLEO WALLACE CENTERS HOSPITAL, 8405 Church Ranch Boulevard,
Zip 80021–3918; tel. 303/466–7391, (Nonreporting) **A**9
Primary Contact: Michael J. Montgomery, President and Chief Executive Officer
CFO: Jonelle A. Roberts, Chief Financial Officer
Web address: www.devereux.org
Control: Other not-for-profit (including NFP Corporation) **Service:** Children's
hospital psychiatric

Staffed Beds: 61	

⊠ **ST. ANTHONY NORTH HOSPITAL (060104)**, 2551 West 84th Avenue,
Zip 80031–3807; tel. 303/426–2151 **A**1 9 10 **F**3 11 13 15 18 20 22 26 28
29 30 31 34 35 36 40 42 43 45 46 49 54 57 60 63 64 65 68 70 72 74 75
76 77 78 79 81 82 84 85 87 92 93 97 102 107 108 110 114 115 119 130
146 147 148 **S** Catholic Health Initiatives, Englewood, CO
Primary Contact: Carole Peet, R.N., MSN, President and Chief Executive Officer
CFO: Alison Mizer, Chief Financial Officer
CIO: Dana Moore, Senior Vice President Information Services
CHR: Robert Archibold, Director, Human Resources
CNO: Carol A. Butler, R.N., VP Patient Care Services & Operations
Web address: www.stanthonynorth.org
Control: Church-operated, Nongovernment, not-for profit **Service:** General
Medical and Surgical

Staffed Beds: 122 **Admissions:** 5903 **Census:** 63 **Outpatient Visits:** 56282 **Births:** 801 **Total Expense ($000):** 104057 **Payroll Expense ($000):** 39476 **Personnel:** 731	

WHEAT RIDGE—Jefferson County

⊠ **LUTHERAN MEDICAL CENTER (060009)**, 8300 West 38th Avenue,
Zip 80033–6005; tel. 303/425–4500, (Includes EXEMPLA WEST PINES, 3400
Lutheran Parkway, Zip 80033; tel. 303/467–4000), (Total facility includes 121
beds in nursing home–type unit) **A**1 2 9 10 **F**4 5 10 11 13 15 18 20 22 24 26
28 29 30 31 33 34 35 36 40 43 45 47 48 49 50 54 55 58 59 60 62 63 64
67 68 70 72 74 75 76 77 78 79 81 84 85 86 87 94 98 100 101 102 103
104 105 107 108 110 111 114 115 119 120 121 123 124 125 126 128 129
130 132 146 147 148 **P**6 **S** SCL Health System, Denver, CO
Primary Contact: Grant Wicklund, President and Chief Executive Officer
COO: Peggy Cain Price, Vice President and Chief Operating Officer
CFO: Karen Scremin, Vice President Finance
CMO: Christina Johnson, M.D., Vice President and Chief Clinical and Quality Officer
CHR: Scott Day, Vice President Human Resources
CNO: Geraldine Towndrow, R.N., Vice President and Chief Nursing Officer
Web address: www.exempla.org
Control: Other not-for-profit (including NFP Corporation) **Service:** General
Medical and Surgical

Staffed Beds: 475 **Admissions:** 12145 **Census:** 330 **Outpatient Visits:** 190436 **Births:** 2739 **Total Expense ($000):** 323691 **Payroll Expense ($000):** 112925 **Personnel:** 1809	

WOODLAND PARK—Teller County

◇ **PIKES PEAK REGIONAL HOSPITAL (061326)**, 16420 West Highway 24,
Zip 80863; tel. 719/687–9999 **A**9 10 18 21 **F**3 15 29 30 34 40 41 43 45 50
57 59 64 65 68 75 77 79 80 81 85 87 93 97 107 110 111 114 119 129 131
133 146 148 **P**6 **S** IASIS Healthcare, Franklin, TN
Primary Contact: Terry Buckner, Chief Executive Officer
CFO: Kimberly Monvesky, Chief Financial Officer
CMO: Kurt Wever, M.D., Chief of Staff
CHR: Arianne Randolph, Director Human Resources
CNO: Rodney Bice, R.N., Chief Nursing Officer
Web address: www.pprmc.org
Control: Corporation, Investor-owned, for-profit **Service:** General Medical and
Surgical

Staffed Beds: 15 **Admissions:** 515 **Census:** 4 **Outpatient Visits:** 25625 **Births:** 0 **Total Expense ($000):** 17488 **Payroll Expense ($000):** 6531 **Personnel:** 123	

WRAY—Yuma County

WRAY COMMUNITY DISTRICT HOSPITAL (061309), 1017 West 7th Street,
Zip 80758–1420; tel. 970/332–4811, (Nonreporting) **A**9 10 18
Primary Contact: Edward Finley, Administrator
CFO: Jennie Sullivan, Director Finance
CMO: Monte Uyemura, M.D., Chief of Staff
Web address: www.wcdh.org
Control: Hospital district or authority, Government, nonfederal **Service:** General
Medical and Surgical

Staffed Beds: 16	

YUMA—Yuma County

★ **YUMA DISTRICT HOSPITAL (061315)**, 1000 West 8th Avenue,
Zip 80759–2641; tel. 970/848–5405 **A**9 10 18 **F**3 11 13 15 28 29 30 31 34
35 36 40 43 44 50 53 57 59 62 64 65 68 74 75 76 77 78 79 81 82 87 93
97 99 101 102 103 104 107 111 115 119 127 130 133 148 **P**6
Primary Contact: John Gardner, Chief Executive Officer
CFO: Cathy Wolff, Vice President Financial Services and Chief Financial Officer
CMO: John Wolz, M.D., Chief Medical Staff
CIO: Jason Hawley, Manager Information Services
CHR: Gini Adams, Director Employee and Public Relations
CNO: Beth Saxton, R.N., Vice President Patient Care Services
Web address: www.yumahospital.org
Control: Hospital district or authority, Government, nonfederal **Service:** General
Medical and Surgical

Staffed Beds: 12 **Admissions:** 229 **Census:** 2 **Outpatient Visits:** 43337 **Births:** 0 **Total Expense ($000):** 21113 **Payroll Expense ($000):** 8917 **Personnel:** 122	

CO

Many Facility Codes have changed. Please refer to the AHA Guide Code Chart.

© 2014 AHA Guide

CONNECTICUT

BETHLEHEM—Litchfield County

WELLSPRING FOUNDATION, 21 Arch Bridge Road, Zip 06751–1612, Mailing Address: P.O. Box 370, Zip 06751–0370; tel. 203/266–7235, (Nonreporting) **A**9
Primary Contact: Richard E. Beauvais, Ph.D., Chief Executive Officer
CFO: Richard E. Beauvais, Ph.D., Chief Executive Officer
Web address: www.wellspring.org
Control: Other not–for–profit (including NFP Corporation) **Service:** Psychiatric

Staffed Beds: 36

BRANFORD—New Haven County

☐ **THE CONNECTICUT HOSPICE (070038)**, 100 Double Beach Road, Zip 06405–4909; tel. 203/315–7500, (Nonreporting) **A**1 10
Primary Contact: Rosemary Johnson Hurzeler, President and Chief Executive Officer
Web address: www.hospice.com
Control: Other not–for–profit (including NFP Corporation) **Service:** Other specialty

Staffed Beds: 52

BRIDGEPORT—Fairfield County

✠ **BRIDGEPORT HOSPITAL (070010)**, 267 Grant Street, Zip 06610–2805, Mailing Address: P.O. Box 5000, Zip 06610–0120; tel. 203/384–3000 **A**1 2 3 5 6 8 9 10 **F**3 5 6 8 11 12 13 14 15 16 18 19 20 22 24 26 28 29 30 31 32 34 35 36 38 39 40 41 43 44 45 46 47 48 49 50 51 52 54 55 56 57 58 59 61 64 65 66 68 70 74 75 76 77 78 79 80 81 82 84 85 86 87 90 93 96 97 98 99 100 101 102 103 104 105 107 108 110 111 114 117 118 119 120 121 123 124 126 129 130 131 132 134 135 144 145 146 147 148 **P**3 **S** Yale New Haven Health System, New Haven, CT
Primary Contact: William M. Jennings, President and Chief Executive Officer
COO: Norman G. Roth, Executive Vice President and Chief Operating Officer
CFO: Patrick McCabe, Senior Vice President Finance and Chief Financial Officer
CMO: Michael Ivy, M.D., Senior Vice President for Medical Affairs and Chief Medical Officer
CIO: Daniel Barchi, Senior Vice President, Technical Services and Chief Information Officer
CHR: Melissa Turner, Senior Vice President Human Resources
CNO: MaryEllen Kosturko, R.N., Senior Vice President Patient Care Operations and Chief Nursing Officer
Web address: www.bridgeporthospital.org
Control: Other not–for–profit (including NFP Corporation) **Service:** General Medical and Surgical

Staffed Beds: 330 Admissions: 16380 Census: 254 Outpatient Visits: 294185 Births: 2262 Total Expense ($000): 409234 Payroll Expense ($000): 147977 Personnel: 2118

SOUTHWEST CONNECTICUT MENTAL HEALTH SYSTEM (074012), 1635 Central Avenue, Zip 06610–2717; tel. 203/551–7400 **A**9 10 **F**5 29 35 38 50 59 98 100 101 102 104 130 132 **S** Connecticut Department of Mental Health and Addiction Services, Hartford, CT
Primary Contact: Daniel Wartenberg, PsyD, M.P.H., Chief Executive Officer
COO: Cindy Perjon, Associate Director
CFO: Scott Courtemanche, Chief Financial Officer
CMO: Stephen R. Atkins, M.D., Medical Director
CIO: Bernetta Witcher–Boateng, Director Quality Improvement Services and Compliance
CHR: Paula DeBarros, Director Human Resources
Web address: www.ct.gov/dmhas/cwp/view.asp?a=2946&q=378936
Control: State–Government, nonfederal **Service:** Psychiatric

Staffed Beds: 62 Admissions: 76 Census: 61 Births: 0

✠ **ST. VINCENT'S MEDICAL CENTER (070028)**, 2800 Main Street, Zip 06606–4292; tel. 203/576–5454, (Includes ST. VINCENT'S BEHAVIORAL HEALTH, 47 Long Lots Road, Westport, Zip 06880–3800; tel. 203/221–8813; Margaret Hardy, R.N., MS, Vice President and Executive Director) **A**1 2 3 5 9 10 **F**3 4 5 8 12 13 16 17 18 20 22 24 26 28 29 30 31 33 34 35 36 38 40 43 44 45 46 47 48 49 50 53 54 55 56 57 58 59 60 61 63 64 65 66 68 70 71 74 75 76 77 78 79 80 81 82 83 84 85 86 87 90 91 92 93 96 97 98 99 100 101 102 103 104 105 106 107 108 110 111 114 115 117 118 119 120 121 123 124 126 130 132 134 143 144 145 146 147 148 **P**1 **S** Ascension Health, Saint Louis, MO
Primary Contact: Stuart G. Marcus, M.D., FACS, President and Chief Executive Officer
COO: Dale G. Danowski, R.N., Senior Vice President Chief Operating Officer and Chief Nursing Officer
CFO: John Gleckler, Chief Financial Officer
CMO: Larry Schek, M.D., Senior Vice President Chief Medical Director and Vice President Cardiology
CIO: Rick McCarthy, Chief Information Officer
CHR: Wayne Rustin, Vice President, Chief Human Resources Officer
CNO: Dale G. Danowski, R.N., Senior Vice President Chief Operating Officer and Chief Nursing Officer
Web address: www.stvincents.org
Control: Other not–for–profit (including NFP Corporation) **Service:** General Medical and Surgical

Staffed Beds: 416 Admissions: 19368 Census: 321 Outpatient Visits: 550366 Births: 1015 Total Expense ($000): 416504 Payroll Expense ($000): 190390 Personnel: 2306

BRISTOL—Hartford County

✠ **BRISTOL HOSPITAL (070029)**, Brewster Road, Zip 06011, Mailing Address: P.O. Box 977, Zip 06011–0977; tel. 860/585–3000, (Nonreporting) **A**1 2 5 9 10
Primary Contact: Kurt A. Barwis, FACHE, President and Chief Executive Officer
COO: Marc D. Edelman, Vice President Operations
CFO: Peter Freytag, Senior Vice President Finance and Chief Financial Officer
CMO: Leonard Banco, M.D., Senior Vice President and Chief Medical Officer
CIO: David Rackliffe, Assistant Vice President Information Services
CHR: Jeanine Reckdenwald, Vice President Human Resources and Support Services
Web address: www.bristolhospital.org
Control: Other not–for–profit (including NFP Corporation) **Service:** General Medical and Surgical

Staffed Beds: 115

DANBURY—Fairfield County

✠ **DANBURY HOSPITAL (070033)**, 24 Hospital Avenue, Zip 06810–6099; tel. 203/739–7000 **A**1 2 3 5 8 9 10 **F**3 5 8 9 12 13 14 15 17 18 20 22 24 26 28 29 30 31 32 34 35 36 37 38 39 40 43 44 45 46 47 48 49 50 51 54 55 56 57 58 59 61 64 65 66 68 70 72 74 75 76 77 78 79 81 82 83 84 85 86 87 89 90 91 92 93 94 96 97 98 99 100 101 102 103 104 105 107 108 109 110 111 112 114 115 116 117 118 119 120 121 123 124 126 129 130 131 132 134 135 144 145 146 147 148 **P**6 8 **S** Western Connecticut Health Network, Danbury, CT
Primary Contact: John M. Murphy, M.D., President and Chief Executive Officer
COO: Michael Daglio, Chief Operating Officer
CFO: Steven Rosenberg, Chief Financial Officer
CMO: Matthew Miller, M.D., Vice President Medical Affairs
CIO: Kathleen DeMatteo, Chief Information Officer
CHR: Phyllis F. Zappala, Senior Vice President
CNO: Moreen Donahue, R.N., Chief Nursing Executive
Web address: www.danburyhospital.org
Control: Other not–for–profit (including NFP Corporation) **Service:** General Medical and Surgical

Staffed Beds: 336 Admissions: 16808 Census: 239 Outpatient Visits: 425298 Births: 2004 Total Expense ($000): 497161 Payroll Expense ($000): 191371 Personnel: 2362

DERBY—New Haven County

GRIFFIN HOSPITAL (070031), 130 Division Street, Zip 06418–1326;
tel. 203/735–7421 **A**1 2 9 10 **F**3 5 8 12 13 15 18 28 29 30 34 35 36 38 40
45 49 50 51 53 56 57 58 59 64 65 68 70 71 74 75 76 77 78 79 81 82 84
85 86 87 93 94 96 97 98 99 100 101 102 103 104 105 107 108 110 111
114 116 117 118 119 120 121 129 130 132 134 135 144 146 147 148
Primary Contact: Patrick Charmel, President and Chief Executive Officer
CMO: Kenneth V. Schwartz, M.D., Medical Director
CIO: George Tomas, Director Information Services
CHR: Steve Mordecai, Director Human Resources
CNO: Barbara J. Stumpo, R.N., Vice President Patient Care Services
Web address: www.griffinhealth.org
Control: Other not–for–profit (including NFP Corporation) **Service:** General
Medical and Surgical

> **Staffed Beds: 111 Admissions: 6555 Census: 81 Outpatient Visits: 192984**
> **Births: 622 Total Expense ($000): 129750 Payroll Expense ($000): 53238**
> **Personnel: 866**

FARMINGTON—Hartford County

**UNIVERSITY OF CONNECTICUT HEALTH CENTER, JOHN DEMPSEY
HOSPITAL (070036)**, 263 Farmington Avenue, Zip 06032–1941;
tel. 860/679–2000 **A**1 2 3 5 8 9 10 12 13 **F**3 5 6 7 8 9 11 13 15 18 20 22
24 26 29 30 31 34 35 36 37 38 39 40 44 45 46 47 48 49 50 51 52 54 55
56 57 58 59 60 61 63 64 65 66 68 70 74 75 76 77 78 79 81 82 83 85
86 87 91 92 93 94 97 98 99 100 101 102 103 104 105 107 108 110 111
114 115 117 118 119 120 121 123 124 126 127 129 130 131 132 133 134
135 143 144 145 146 147 148 **P**6
Primary Contact: Anne Diamond, JD, Interim Chief Executive Officer
COO: Anne Diamond, JD, Chief Operating Officer
CFO: John Biancamano, Chief Financial Officer
CMO: Richard Simon, M.D., Chief of Staff
CIO: Sandra Armstrong, Chief Information Officer
CHR: Carolle Andrews, Interim Chief Human Resources Officer
CNO: Ellen Leone, R.N., Chief Nursing Officer
Web address: www.uchc.edu
Control: State–Government, nonfederal **Service:** General Medical and Surgical

> **Staffed Beds: 174 Admissions: 8033 Census: 107 Outpatient Visits:**
> **279665 Births: 439 Total Expense ($000): 312451 Payroll Expense**
> **($000): 110137 Personnel: 1478**

GREENWICH—Fairfield County

GREENWICH HOSPITAL (070018), 5 Perryridge Road, Zip 06830–4697;
tel. 203/863–3000 **A**1 2 3 5 9 10 **F**3 5 8 11 12 13 14 15 18 20 22 26 28 29
30 31 32 34 35 36 37 38 39 40 44 45 46 47 48 49 50 51 52 53 54 55 56
57 58 59 61 63 64 65 66 68 70 72 74 75 76 77 78 79 80 81 82 84 85 86
87 89 93 96 97 99 100 101 102 103 104 107 108 109 110 111 114 115
116 117 118 119 120 121 123 124 126 129 130 131 132 134 135 146 147
148 **P**2 3 5 **S** Yale New Haven Health System, New Haven, CT
Primary Contact: Frank A. Corvino, President and Chief Executive Officer
COO: Quinton J. Friesen, Executive Vice President and Chief Operating Officer
CFO: Eugene Colucci, Vice President Finance
CMO: A. Michael Marino, M.D., Senior Vice President Medical Administration
Web address: www.greenhosp.org
Control: Other not–for–profit (including NFP Corporation) **Service:** General
Medical and Surgical

> **Staffed Beds: 174 Admissions: 10516 Census: 128 Outpatient Visits:**
> **296673 Births: 2204 Total Expense ($000): 311015 Payroll Expense**
> **($000): 111450 Personnel: 1501**

HARTFORD—Hartford County

CONNECTICUT CHILDREN'S MEDICAL CENTER (073300), 282 Washington
Street, Zip 06106–3322; tel. 860/545–9000, (Nonreporting) **A**1 3 5 9 10
Primary Contact: Martin J. Gavin, President and Chief Executive Officer
CFO: Gerald J. Boisvert, Vice President and Chief Financial Officer
CMO: Paul Dworkin, M.D., Physician–in–Chief
CIO: Kelly R. Styles, Vice President and Chief Information Officer
CHR: Elizabeth Rudden, Vice President Human Resources
Web address: www.ccmckids.org
Control: Other not–for–profit (including NFP Corporation) **Service:** Children's
general

> **Staffed Beds: 147**

HARTFORD HOSPITAL (070025), 80 Seymour Street, Zip 06102–8000,
Mailing Address: P.O. Box 5037, Zip 06102–5037; tel. 860/545–5000, (Includes
INSTITUTE OF LIVING, 400 Washington Street, Zip 06106–3392;
tel. 860/545–7000), (Total facility includes 104 beds in nursing home–type unit)
A1 2 3 5 7 8 9 10 11 12 13 **F**2 15 17 18 20 22 24 26 28 29
30 31 34 35 36 37 38 39 40 43 44 45 46 47 48 49 50 51 52 53 54 55 56
57 58 59 60 61 63 64 65 66 68 70 71 74 75 76 77 78 79 80 81 82 83 84
85 86 87 91 92 93 94 96 97 98 99 100 101 102 103 104 105 106 107 108
110 111 114 115 116 117 118 119 120 121 123 124 125 126 128 129 130
131 132 135 137 138 139 141 145 146 147 148 **P**6 8 **S** Hartford HealthCare,
Hartford, CT
Primary Contact: Stuart Markowitz, M.D., President
CMO: Stuart Markowitz, M.D., Chief Medical Officer
CIO: Stephan O'Neill, Vice President Information Services
CHR: Richard McAloon, Vice President Human Resources
Web address: www.harthosp.org
Control: Other not–for–profit (including NFP Corporation) **Service:** General
Medical and Surgical

> **Staffed Beds: 817 Admissions: 38617 Census: 716 Outpatient Visits:**
> **213964 Births: 3587 Total Expense ($000): 1089262 Payroll Expense**
> **($000): 477251 Personnel: 5827**

MOUNT SINAI REHABILITATION HOSPITAL (073025), 490 Blue Hills Avenue,
Zip 06112–1513; tel. 860/714–3500 **A**1 10 **F**29 30 34 54 58 59 64 68 74 75
82 90 91 92 93 94 95 96 130 131 132 **P**8 **S** Saint Francis Care, Inc.,
Hartford, CT
Primary Contact: Christopher M. Dadlez, President and Chief Executive Officer
Web address: www.stfranciscare.org
Control: Other not–for–profit (including NFP Corporation) **Service:** Rehabilitation

> **Staffed Beds: 30 Admissions: 685 Census: 26 Outpatient Visits: 35496**
> **Births: 0 Total Expense ($000): 26682 Payroll Expense ($000): 11693**
> **Personnel: 211**

SAINT FRANCIS HOSPITAL AND MEDICAL CENTER (070002), 114
Woodland Street, Zip 06105–1208; tel. 860/714–4000 **A**1 2 3 5 8 9 10 **F**3 8
11 12 13 15 17 18 20 22 24 26 28 29 30 31 34 35 36 38 39 40 43 45 46
47 48 49 50 53 54 55 56 57 58 59 61 64 65 66 68 70 72 73 74 75 76 77
78 79 81 82 84 85 87 91 92 93 94 95 96 97 98 99 100 101 102 103 104
107 111 115 117 118 119 120 121 123 124 126 129 130 131 132 134 135
144 145 146 147 148 **P**8 **S** Saint Francis Care, Inc., Hartford, CT
Primary Contact: Christopher M. Dadlez, President and Chief Executive Officer
COO: Kathleen M. Roche, R.N., Executive Vice President and Chief Operating
Officer
CFO: John N. Giamalis, Senior Vice President and Chief Financial Officer
CMO: Rolf W. Knoll, M.D., Senior Vice President and Chief Medical Officer
CIO: Linda Shanley, Vice President and Chief Information Officer
CHR: Dawn L. Bryant, Senior Vice President and Chief Human Resource Officer
Web address: www.saintfranciscare.com
Control: Church–operated, Nongovernment, not–for profit **Service:** General
Medical and Surgical

> **Staffed Beds: 612 Admissions: 29685 Census: 419 Outpatient Visits:**
> **284843 Births: 2941 Total Expense ($000): 666257 Payroll Expense**
> **($000): 252559 Personnel: 4802**

MANCHESTER—Hartford County

MANCHESTER MEMORIAL HOSPITAL (070027), 71 Haynes Street,
Zip 06040–4188; tel. 860/646–1222 **A**1 2 5 9 10 **F**3 4 5 11 13 15 18 24 28
29 30 31 34 35 36 38 39 40 42 45 47 49 50 51 56 57 58 59 61 63 64 65
70 72 74 75 76 77 78 79 80 81 84 85 86 87 89 93 98 99 100 101 102 103
104 105 107 108 110 111 114 116 118 119 124 126 128 129 130 131 132
134 135 141 142 146 148 **P**1 5 6 **S** Eastern Connecticut Health Network,
Manchester, CT
Primary Contact: Peter J. Karl, President and Chief Executive Officer
CFO: Michael D. Veillette, Senior Vice President and Chief Financial Officer
CMO: Joel R. Reich, M.D., Senior Vice President Medical Affairs
CIO: James Weeks, Interim Chief Information Officer
CHR: Deborah Gogliettino, Senior Vice President Human Resources
CNO: Mary Powers, MSN, Senior Vice President Patient Care Services
Web address: www.echn.org
Control: Other not–for–profit (including NFP Corporation) **Service:** General
Medical and Surgical

> **Staffed Beds: 156 Admissions: 8114 Census: 118 Outpatient Visits:**
> **293754 Births: 1226 Total Expense ($000): 188335 Payroll Expense**
> **($000): 83909 Personnel: 1077**

Many Facility Codes have changed. Please refer to the AHA Guide Code Chart. © 2014 AHA Guide

CT

MANSFIELD CENTER—Tolland County

☒ **NATCHAUG HOSPITAL (074008)**, 189 Storrs Road, Zip 06250–1683;
tel. 860/456–1311 **A**1 9 10 **F**5 98 99 100 104 105 106 **S** Hartford HealthCare,
Hartford, CT
Primary Contact: Stephen W. Larcen, Ph.D., President and CEO
COO: David Klein, Ph.D., Vice President Operations, Behavioral Health Network
CFO: Paul V. Maloney, Vice President Finance, Behavioral Health Network
CMO: Deborah Weidner, M.D., Medical Director
CIO: Mark Olson, Interim Chief Information Officer, Behavioral Health Network
CHR: Janet Keown, Vice President Human Resources, Behavioral Health Network
CNO: Justin Sleeper, Vice President Clinical Operations, Behavioral Health Network
Web address: www.natchaug.org
Control: Other not–for–profit (including NFP Corporation) **Service:** Psychiatric

Staffed Beds: 57 **Admissions:** 2049 **Census:** 52 **Outpatient Visits:** 58037
Births: 0 **Total Expense ($000):** 48232 **Payroll Expense ($000):** 29329
Personnel: 427

MERIDEN—New Haven County

☒ **MIDSTATE MEDICAL CENTER (070017)**, 435 Lewis Avenue, Zip 06451–2101;
tel. 203/694–8200 **A**1 2 9 10 **F**3 11 12 13 15 18 28 29 30 31 34 35 36 38
39 40 44 45 46 47 48 49 50 51 53 54 56 57 59 61 63 64 68 70 74 75 76
78 79 81 82 84 85 86 87 97 98 102 107 108 110 111 114 115 117 118
119 120 121 123 124 126 129 130 131 132 144 145 146 147 148 **P**3 5
S Hartford HealthCare, Hartford, CT
Primary Contact: Lucille A. Janatka, President and CEO
CMO: Kenneth R. Kurz, M.D., Chief of Staff
CIO: Jennifer Comerford, Manager Information Services
CHR: Ken Cesca, Vice President Human Resources
Web address: www.midstatemedical.org
Control: Other not–for–profit (including NFP Corporation) **Service:** General
Medical and Surgical

Staffed Beds: 129 **Admissions:** 8922 **Census:** 109 **Outpatient Visits:**
177356 **Births:** 906 **Total Expense ($000):** 210520 **Payroll Expense
($000):** 75258 **Personnel:** 1052

MIDDLETOWN—Middlesex County

☐ **ALBERT J. SOLNIT PSYCHIATRIC CENTER – SOUTH CAMPUS**, 915 River
Road, Zip 06457–3921, Mailing Address: P.O. Box 2792, Zip 06457–9292;
tel. 860/704–4000, (Nonreporting) **A**1 3 5
Primary Contact: Michelle Sarofin, Superintendent
CFO: Connie Tessarzik, Business Manager
CMO: Lesley Siegel, M.D., Medical Director
CIO: Andrew J A Kass, M.D., Assistant Superintendent
Web address: www.ct.gov/
Control: State–Government, nonfederal **Service:** Children's hospital psychiatric

Staffed Beds: 102

☐ **CONNECTICUT VALLEY HOSPITAL (074003)**, Eastern Drive,
Zip 06457–3947, Mailing Address: P.O. Box 351, Zip 06457–3947;
tel. 860/262–5000, (Includes WHITING FORENSIC DIVISION OF CONNECTICUT
VALLEY HOSPITAL, O'Brien Drive, Zip 06457, Mailing Address: Box 70,
Zip 06457–3942; tel. 203/344–2541) **A**1 3 5 9 10 **F**3 4 29 30 36 39 50 53
57 65 68 75 77 98 101 103 106 130 **S** Connecticut Department of Mental
Health and Addiction Services, Hartford, CT
Primary Contact: Helene M. Vartelas, Chief Executive Officer
COO: John D'Evano, Chief Operating Officer
CFO: Michael Schuberth, Director, Fiscal Services and Plant Operations
CMO: Thomas Pisano, M.D., Chief Professional Services
CIO: Kathryn Connelly, Manager Information Technology
CHR: Cheryl Thompson, Facility Director Human Resources
CNO: Jerilynn Lamb–Pagone, Nurse Executive
Web address: www.ct.gov/dmhas/cwp/view.asp?a=3519&q=416778
Control: State–Government, nonfederal **Service:** Psychiatric

Staffed Beds: 596 **Admissions:** 3563 **Census:** 568 **Outpatient Visits:** 0
Births: 0 **Total Expense ($000):** 164315 **Payroll Expense ($000):** 133564
Personnel: 1473

☒ **MIDDLESEX HOSPITAL (070020)**, 28 Crescent Street, Zip 06457–3650;
tel. 860/358–6000 **A**1 2 3 5 9 10 **F**3 5 12 13 15 18 20 22 24 28 29 30 31
32 34 35 36 38 40 42 45 46 47 49 50 51 54 55 57 58 59 60 62 63 64 65
68 70 74 75 76 77 78 79 81 83 84 85 86 87 89 92 93 94 97 98 99 100
101 102 103 104 105 107 108 110 111 114 115 116 117 118 119 120 121
123 124 126 129 130 131 132 134 135 145 146 147 148 **P**6
Primary Contact: Vincent G. Capece, Jr., President and Chief Executive Officer
CFO: Susan Martin, Vice President Finance
CMO: Arthur V. McDowell, III, M.D., Vice President Clinical Affairs
CIO: Ludwig Johnson, Vice President Information Technology
CHR: Gregory Nokes, Vice President Human Resources
CNO: Jacquelyn Calamari, MSN, Vice President and Chief Nursing Officer
Web address: www.middlesexhospital.org
Control: Other not–for–profit (including NFP Corporation) **Service:** General
Medical and Surgical

Staffed Beds: 237 **Admissions:** 14080 **Census:** 164 **Outpatient Visits:**
1406201 **Births:** 1078 **Total Expense ($000):** 342279 **Payroll Expense
($000):** 164393 **Personnel:** 1760

WHITING FORENSIC DIVISION OF CONNECTICUT VALLEY HOSPITAL See
Connecticut Valley Hospital

MILFORD—New Haven County

☒ **MILFORD HOSPITAL (070019)**, 300 Seaside Avenue, Zip 06460–4603;
tel. 203/876–4000 **A**1 9 10 **F**3 8 11 13 15 29 32 34 35 37 38 40 45 46 49
50 54 57 58 59 63 64 68 70 74 75 76 78 79 81 82 85 87 89 102 107 108
111 114 118 119 126 130 132 135 144 146
Primary Contact: Joseph Pelaccia, President and Chief Executive Officer
COO: Lloyd Friedman, M.D., Vice President Medical Affairs and Chief Operating
Officer
CFO: Joseph Pelaccia, President and Chief Executive Officer
CMO: Lloyd Friedman, M.D., Vice President Medical Affairs and Chief Operating
Officer
CIO: Marilyn Christensen, Director Information Technology
CHR: Jeffrey Komornik, Director Human Resources
CNO: Beverly Lyon, R.N., Vice President Nursing
Web address: www.milfordhospital.org
Control: Other not–for–profit (including NFP Corporation) **Service:** General
Medical and Surgical

Staffed Beds: 42 **Admissions:** 3256 **Census:** 37 **Outpatient Visits:** 60897
Births: 94 **Total Expense ($000):** 80716 **Payroll Expense ($000):** 37819
Personnel: 541

NEW BRITAIN—Hartford County

☒ △ **HOSPITAL FOR SPECIAL CARE (072004)**, 2150 Corbin Avenue,
Zip 06053–2298; tel. 860/223–2761 **A**1 3 5 7 10 **F**1 3 11 29 30 35 39 53 56
64 89 90 91 92 93 96 119 130 131 132 135 146 148
Primary Contact: John J. Votto, D.O., President and Chief Executive Officer
CFO: Laurie A. Whelan, Senior Vice President Finance and Chief Financial Officer
CMO: Paul Scalise, M.D., Chief Pulmonary Medicine and Internal Medicine
CIO: Stan Jankowski, Vice President and Chief Information Officer
CHR: Judi Trczinski, Vice President and Chief Human Resources Officer
Web address: www.hfsc.org
Control: Other not–for–profit (including NFP Corporation) **Service:** Long–Term
Acute Care hospital

Staffed Beds: 226 **Admissions:** 604 **Census:** 198 **Outpatient Visits:** 20845
Births: 0 **Total Expense ($000):** 89680 **Payroll Expense ($000):** 66171
Personnel: 747

☒ **THE HOSPITAL OF CENTRAL CONNECTICUT (070035)**, 100 Grand Street,
Zip 06052–2017, Mailing Address: P.O. Box 100, Zip 06052–2017;
tel. 860/224–5011, (Includes BRADLEY MEMORIAL, 81 Meriden Avenue,
Southington, Zip 06489–3297; tel. 860/276–5000; NEW BRITAIN GENERAL, 100
Grand Street, Mailing Address: P.O. Box 100, Zip 06050–0100;
tel. 860/224–5011) **A**1 2 3 5 8 9 10 **F**3 11 12 13 15 18 20 22 28 29 30 31
34 35 38 40 44 45 49 50 51 53 54 57 58 59 60 61 64 65 66 68 70 72 74
75 76 77 78 79 81 84 85 86 87 89 93 97 98 99 100 101 102 103 104 105
107 108 110 111 114 115 117 118 119 120 121 123 124 126 129 130 132
135 142 144 146 147 148 **P**6 **S** Hartford HealthCare, Hartford, CT
Primary Contact: Lucille A. Janatka, President and CEO
CFO: Brian Rogoz, Vice President Finance and Treasurer
CIO: Frank Pinto, Chief Information Officer
CHR: Elizabeth A. Lynch, Vice President Human Resources
Web address: www.thocc.org
Control: Other not–for–profit (including NFP Corporation) **Service:** General
Medical and Surgical

Staffed Beds: 184 **Admissions:** 16301 **Census:** 192 **Outpatient Visits:**
407308 **Births:** 1567 **Total Expense ($000):** 374270 **Payroll Expense
($000):** 168707 **Personnel:** 1858

CT

Hospital, Medicare Provider Number, Address, Telephone, Approval, Facility, and Physician Codes, Health Care System

★ American Hospital Association (AHA) membership
☐ The Joint Commission accreditation   ◇ DNV Healthcare Inc. accreditation
○ Healthcare Facilities Accreditation Program
△ Commission on Accreditation of Rehabilitation Facilities (CARF) accreditation

NEW CANAAN—Fairfield County

☐ **SILVER HILL HOSPITAL (074014)**, 208 Valley Road, Zip 06840–3899;
tel. 203/966–3561, (Nonreporting) **A**1 9 10
Primary Contact: Sigurd H. Ackerman, M.D., President and Chief Executive Officer
COO: Elizabeth Moore, Chief Operating Officer
CFO: Ruurd Leegstra, Chief Financial Officer
CMO: Sigurd H. Ackerman, M.D., President and Chief Executive Officer
CIO: Maria Klinga, Director Management Information Systems
CHR: Rich Juliana, Director Human Resources
Web address: www.silverhillhospital.org
Control: Other not-for-profit (including NFP Corporation) **Service:** Psychiatric

Staffed Beds: 60

NEW HAVEN—New Haven County

☐ **CONNECTICUT MENTAL HEALTH CENTER (074011)**, 34 Park Street,
Zip 06519–1109, Mailing Address: P.O. Box 1842, Zip 06508–1842;
tel. 203/974–7144 **A**1 3 5 9 10 **F**5 29 30 57 58 75 87 98 99 103 104 130
132 146 **S** Connecticut Department of Mental Health and Addiction Services,
Hartford, CT
Primary Contact: Michael Sernyak, M.D., Director
COO: Robert Cole, Chief Operating Officer
CFO: Robert Cole, Chief Operating Officer
CMO: Jeanne Steines, D.O., Medical Director
CIO: Paul Moore, Chief Information Officer
CHR: Carolyn Wallace, Director Human Resources
Web address: www.ct.gov/dmhas/cwp/view.asp?a=2906&q=334596
Control: State–Government, nonfederal **Service:** Psychiatric

Staffed Beds: 32 **Admissions:** 219 **Census:** 25 **Outpatient Visits:** 73264
Births: 0

HOSPITAL OF SAINT RAPHAEL See Yale–New Haven Hospital–Saint Raphael
Campus

☒ **YALE–NEW HAVEN HOSPITAL (070022)**, 20 York Street, Zip 06510–3202;
tel. 203/688–4242, (Includes YALE–NEW HAVEN CHILDREN'S HOSPITAL, 1 Park
Street, Zip 06504–8901; tel. 203/688–4242; YALE–NEW HAVEN
HOSPITAL–SAINT RAPHAEL CAMPUS, 1450 Chapel Street, Zip 06511–4405;
tel. 203/789–3000; Christopher M. O'Connor, President and Chief Executive
Officer; YALE–NEW HAVEN PSYCHIATRIC HOSPITAL, 184 Liberty Street,
Zip 06519–1625; tel. 203/688–9704; Paul Haeberle, Executive Director), (Total
facility includes 108 beds in nursing home–type unit) **A**1 2 3 5 8 9 10 **F**3 5 6 8
9 11 12 13 14 15 17 18 19 20 21 22 23 24 25 26 27 28 29 30 31 32 34 35
36 37 38 39 40 41 42 43 44 45 46 47 48 49 50 51 52 53 54 55 56 57 58
59 61 64 65 66 68 70 71 72 73 74 75 78 79 80 81 82 84 85 86 87
88 89 90 91 92 93 94 96 97 98 99 100 101 102 103 104 105 107 108 109
110 111 112 114 115 116 117 118 119 120 121 123 124 126 128 129 130
131 132 134 135 136 137 138 139 141 142 143 144 145 146 147 148 **P**2
3 5 6 **S** Yale New Haven Health System, New Haven, CT
Primary Contact: Marna P. Borgstrom, Chief Executive Officer
COO: Richard D'Aquila, President and Chief Operating Officer
CFO: James Staten, Senior Vice President Finance
CMO: Peter N. Herbert, M.D., Senior Vice President Medical Affairs and Chief of
Staff
CIO: Daniel Barchi, Senior Vice President Information Systems and Chief
Information Officer
CHR: Kevin A. Myatt, Senior Vice President Human Resources
CNO: Patricia Sue Fitzsimons, R.N., Senior Vice President Patient Services
Web address: www.ynhh.org
Control: Other not-for-profit (including NFP Corporation) **Service:** General
Medical and Surgical

Staffed Beds: 1612 **Admissions:** 74942 **Census:** 1202 **Outpatient Visits:**
1087751 **Births:** 6168 **Total Expense ($000):** 2236083 **Payroll Expense**
($000): 780282 **Personnel:** 10732

NEW LONDON—New London County

☒ △ **LAWRENCE + MEMORIAL HOSPITAL (070007)**, 365 Montauk Avenue,
Zip 06320–4769; tel. 860/442–0711, (Nonreporting) **A**1 2 7 9 10 **S** L+M
Healthcare, New London, CT
Primary Contact: Bruce D. Cummings, President and Chief Executive Officer
COO: Daniel Rissi, M.D., Vice President, Chief Medical and Clinical Operations
Officer
CFO: Lugene A. Inzana, Vice President and Chief Financial and Support Services
Officer
CMO: Daniel Rissi, M.D., Chief Medical and Clinical Operations
CIO: Kimberly Kalajainen, Vice President and Chief Information Officer
CHR: Donna Epps, Vice President and Chief Human Resources Officer
CNO: Lauren Williams, R.N., Vice President of Professional Services and Chief
Nursing Officer
Web address: www.lmhospital.org
Control: Other not-for-profit (including NFP Corporation) **Service:** General
Medical and Surgical

Staffed Beds: 252

NEW MILFORD—Litchfield County

☒ ○ **NEW MILFORD HOSPITAL (070015)**, 21 Elm Street, Zip 06776–2993;
tel. 860/355–2611 **A**1 2 5 9 10 11 19 **F**3 15 28 29 30 31 34 35 36 38 40 45
46 47 48 49 50 51 53 57 59 64 65 68 70 74 75 78 79 81 84 85 86 87 89
104 105 107 108 109 110 111 115 119 120 121 122 123 124 129 130 132
134 135 145 146 147 148 **S** Western Connecticut Health Network, Danbury, CT
Primary Contact: Thomas Koobatian, M.D., Executive Director and Chief of Staff
CFO: Steven Rosenberg, Senior Vice President, Chief Financial Officer and
Treasurer
CMO: Thomas Koobatian, M.D., Executive Director and Chief of Staff
CIO: Peter Courtway, Chief Information Officer
CHR: Phyllis F. Zappala, Senior Vice President Human Resources
Web address: www.newmilfordhospital.org
Control: Other not-for-profit (including NFP Corporation) **Service:** General
Medical and Surgical

Staffed Beds: 59 **Admissions:** 1769 **Census:** 19 **Outpatient Visits:** 60293
Births: 55 **Total Expense ($000):** 72962 **Payroll Expense ($000):** 28966
Personnel: 360

NORWALK—Fairfield County

☒ △ **NORWALK HOSPITAL (070034)**, 34 Maple Street, Zip 06850–3894;
tel. 203/852–2000 **A**1 2 3 5 7 9 10 **F**3 5 7 8 11 12 13 15 17 18 20 22 26 28
29 30 31 34 35 36 39 40 43 44 45 46 47 48 49 50 51 53 54 55 57 58 59
64 65 66 68 70 71 72 74 75 76 77 78 79 80 81 82 84 85 87 89 90 91 93
96 98 100 101 102 103 104 105 107 108 110 111 114 115 117 118 119
120 121 123 124 126 129 130 131 132 135 145 146 148 **P**6
Primary Contact: Daniel J. DeBarba, Jr., President and Chief Executive Officer
CFO: Michael Kruzick, Acting Chief Financial Officer
CMO: Michael Marks, M.D., Chief of Staff
CHR: Anthony Aceto, Vice President Human Resources
Web address: www.norwalkhospital.org
Control: Other not-for-profit (including NFP Corporation) **Service:** General
Medical and Surgical

Staffed Beds: 313 **Admissions:** 11721 **Census:** 154 **Outpatient Visits:**
261165 **Births:** 1459 **Total Expense ($000):** 338981 **Payroll Expense**
($000): 138383 **Personnel:** 1649

NORWICH—New London County

☒ **THE WILLIAM W. BACKUS HOSPITAL (070024)**, 326 Washington Street,
Zip 06360–2740; tel. 860/889–8331 **A**1 2 3 5 9 10 **F**3 9 11 12 13 15 18 20
26 28 29 30 31 34 35 36 40 42 43 45 46 49 50 51 54 57 58 59 61 62 63
64 65 70 71 74 75 76 78 79 81 82 84 85 86 87 89 92 93 97 98 100 101
102 103 104 105 107 108 110 111 114 115 116 117 118 119 120 121 126
130 132 133 134 135 144 145 146 147 148 **S** Hartford HealthCare,
Hartford, CT
Primary Contact: David A. Whitehead, President and CEO
COO: Cary Trantalis, R.N., Regional Vice President Operations
CFO: Daniel E. Lohr, Regional Vice President Finance
CMO: Robert Sidman, M.D., Medical Director
CIO: Pamela M. Muccilli, Regional Director Management Information Systems
CHR: Theresa L. Buss, Regional Vice President, Human Resources
CNO: Mary Anne Bylone, R.N., Regional Vice President Patient Care Services
Web address: www.backushospital.org
Control: Other not-for-profit (including NFP Corporation) **Service:** General
Medical and Surgical

Staffed Beds: 184 **Admissions:** 10573 **Census:** 128 **Outpatient Visits:**
460916 **Births:** 861 **Total Expense ($000):** 250413 **Payroll Expense**
($000): 117253 **Personnel:** 1386

PUTNAM—Windham County

☒ **DAY KIMBALL HOSPITAL (070003)**, 320 Pomfret Street, Zip 06260–1836,
Mailing Address: P.O. Box 6001, Zip 06260–0901; tel. 860/928–6541 **A**1 9 10
F3 8 13 15 17 18 28 29 30 31 34 35 36 38 40 45 50 54 56 58 59 62 63 64
65 68 70 73 75 76 77 78 79 81 84 85 87 89 90 93 98 99 100 102 103 104
107 108 109 110 111 115 116 117 118 119 129 130 132 145 146 147 148
Primary Contact: Robert E. Smanik, FACHE, President and Chief Executive Officer
COO: Donald St. Onge, Chief Operating Officer
CFO: Douglas Glazier, Interim Chief Financial Officer
CMO: John Graham, M.D., Vice President Medical Affairs
CIO: Odile Romanick, Chief information Officer
CHR: John Miller, Director Human Resources
CNO: Donald St. Onge, Chief Operating Officer
Web address: www.daykimball.org
Control: Other not-for-profit (including NFP Corporation) **Service:** General
Medical and Surgical

Staffed Beds: 65 **Admissions:** 3777 **Census:** 45 **Births:** 574 **Total Expense**
($000): 110625 **Payroll Expense ($000):** 47682 **Personnel:** 745

CT

ROCKY HILL—Hartford County

VETERANS HOME AND HOSPITAL (072006), 287 West Street,
Zip 06067–3501; tel. 860/616–3703, (Nonreporting) **A**10
Primary Contact: Margaret Concannon, Administrator
CFO: Gregory J. Gioia, Chief Fiscal and Administrative Services
CMO: Michael M. Cebrik, M.D., Director Medical Staff
Web address: www.state.ct.us/ctva/
Control: State–Government, nonfederal **Service:** Long–Term Acute Care hospital

Staffed Beds: 215

SHARON—Litchfield County

☐ **SHARON HOSPITAL (070004)**, 50 Hospital Hill Road, Zip 06069–2096, Mailing
Address: P.O. Box 789, Zip 06069–0789; tel. 860/364–4000, (Nonreporting) **A**1
9 10 20 **S** RegionalCare Health Partners, Brentwood, TN
Primary Contact: Kim Lumia, President and Chief Executive Officer
CFO: Carolyn Allen, Chief Financial Officer
CMO: Michael Parker, M.D., Chief of Staff
CHR: Kathleen Berlinghoff, Director Human Resources
Web address: www.sharonhospital.com
Control: Corporation, Investor–owned, for–profit **Service:** General Medical and
Surgical

Staffed Beds: 78

SOMERS—Tolland County

CONNECTICUT DEPARTMENT OF CORRECTION'S HOSPITAL, 100 Bilton
Road, Zip 06071–1059, Mailing Address: P.O. Box 100, Zip 06071–0100;
tel. 860/749–8391, (Nonreporting)
Primary Contact: Edward A. Blanchette, M.D., Director
Control: State–Government, nonfederal **Service:** Hospital unit of an institution
(prison hospital, college infirmary, etc.)

Staffed Beds: 29

SOUTHINGTON—Hartford County

BRADLEY MEMORIAL See The Hospital of Central Connecticut, New Britain

STAFFORD SPRINGS—Tolland County

☐ **JOHNSON MEMORIAL HOSPITAL (070008)**, 201 Chestnut Hill Road,
Zip 06076–4005; tel. 860/684–4251 **A**1 2 9 10 **F**3 8 11 13 15 18 28 29 30
31 34 35 40 45 50 54 57 59 60 64 68 70 75 76 78 81 84 85 92 93 94 97
98 100 102 105 106 107 111 114 119 129 130 131 135 146 148 **P**5
Primary Contact: Stuart E. Rosenberg, President and Chief Executive Officer
CFO: John Grish, Chief Financial Officer
CMO: Ian Tucker, M.D., Vice President Medical Affairs
CHR: Donna M. Megliola, Assistant Vice President
CNO: Patricia Jagoe, Assistant Vice President Patient Care
Web address: www.jmmc.com
Control: Other not–for–profit (including NFP Corporation) **Service:** General
Medical and Surgical

**Staffed Beds: 88 Admissions: 2925 Census: 42 Outpatient Visits: 83239
Total Expense ($000): 63331 Payroll Expense ($000): 26864 Personnel:
387**

STAMFORD—Fairfield County

✠ **STAMFORD HOSPITAL (070006)**, 30 Shelburne Road, Zip 06902–3628,
Mailing Address: P.O. Box 9317, Zip 06904–9317; tel. 203/276–1000 **A**1 2 3 5
8 9 10 **F**3 8 11 12 13 15 17 18 19 20 22 24 26 28 29 30 31 32 34 35 36
37 38 40 41 43 44 45 46 47 48 49 50 52 53 54 55 58 59 60 61 64
65 66 68 70 71 72 73 74 75 76 77 78 79 81 82 84 85 86 87 89 90 91 92
93 95 96 97 98 100 101 102 103 104 107 108 110 111 114 115 116 117
118 119 120 121 123 124 126 129 130 131 132 135 144 145 146 147 148
P4 6
Primary Contact: Brian G. Grissler, President and Chief Executive Officer
COO: Kathleen A. Silard, R.N., Executive Vice President Operations and Chief
Operating Officer
CFO: Kevin Gage, Chief Financial Officer
CMO: Sharon Kiely, M.D., Senior Vice President Medical Affairs and Chief Medical
Officer
CIO: David Taylor, Vice President Information Systems and Chief Information
Officer
CHR: Elaine Guglielmo, Vice President Human Resources and Organizational
Development
CNO: Ellen M. Komar, R.N., Vice President Patient Care Services
Web address: www.stamhealth.org
Control: Other not–for–profit (including NFP Corporation) **Service:** General
Medical and Surgical

**Staffed Beds: 305 Admissions: 12786 Census: 181 Outpatient Visits:
436054 Births: 2085 Total Expense ($000): 453666 Payroll Expense
($000): 184582 Personnel: 2043**

TORRINGTON—Litchfield County

✠ **THE CHARLOTTE HUNGERFORD HOSPITAL (070011)**, 540 Litchfield Street,
Zip 06790–6679, Mailing Address: P.O. Box 988, Zip 06790–0988;
tel. 860/496–6666 **A**1 2 9 10 **F**13 15 18 28 29 30 31 32 34 35 38 40 42 45
47 48 49 50 51 57 59 60 63 64 68 70 74 75 76 78 79 80 81 82 83 85 87
89 93 94 97 98 99 100 102 104 105 108 110 115 116 118 119 120 121
123 129 130 131 132 135 144 145 146 148 **P**6
Primary Contact: Daniel J. McIntyre, President and Chief Executive Officer
CFO: Susan Schapp, Vice President Finance and Treasurer
CMO: Mark Prete, M.D., Vice President Medical Affairs
CHR: R. James Elliott, Vice President Human Resources
Web address: www.charlottehungerford.org
Control: Other not–for–profit (including NFP Corporation) **Service:** General
Medical and Surgical

**Staffed Beds: 72 Admissions: 6097 Census: 70 Outpatient Visits: 275240
Births: 465 Total Expense ($000): 124900 Payroll Expense ($000): 58472
Personnel: 648**

VERNON—Tolland County

✠ **ROCKVILLE GENERAL HOSPITAL (070012)**, 31 Union Street, Vernon
Rockville, Zip 06066–3160; tel. 860/872–0501 **A**1 10 **F**3 11 15 18 24 28 29
30 34 35 36 38 39 40 42 44 45 47 49 50 51 54 56 57 59 61 63 64 65 66
70 72 74 75 77 78 79 80 81 82 84 85 86 87 89 90 93 97 98 107 108 110
111 114 118 119 124 128 130 131 132 135 141 142 144 146 147 148 **P**1
5 6 **S** Eastern Connecticut Health Network, Manchester, CT
Primary Contact: Peter J. Karl, President and Chief Executive Officer
CFO: Michael D. Veillette, Senior Vice President and Chief Financial Officer
CMO: Joel R. Reich, M.D., Senior Vice President Medical Affairs
CIO: James Weeks, Interim Chief Information Officer
CHR: Deborah Gogliettino, Senior Vice President Human Resources
CNO: Mary Powers, MSN, Senior Vice President Patient Care Services
Web address: www.echn.org
Control: Other not–for–profit (including NFP Corporation) **Service:** General
Medical and Surgical

**Staffed Beds: 47 Admissions: 2581 Census: 34 Outpatient Visits: 113901
Births: 0 Total Expense ($000): 71670 Payroll Expense ($000): 31510
Personnel: 316**

WALLINGFORD—New Haven County

☐ △ **GAYLORD HOSPITAL (072003)**, Gaylord Farm Road, Zip 06492–7048,
Mailing Address: P.O. Box 400, Zip 06492–7048; tel. 203/284–2800 **A**1 5 7 10
F1 29 30 53 54 60 63 64 75 82 84 87 91 93 94 95 96 107 114 119 129
130 131 146 148
Primary Contact: George M. Kyriacou, President and Chief Executive Officer
CFO: Art Tedesco, Interim Chief Financial Officer
CMO: Stephen Holland, M.D., Vice President Chief Medical Officer and Medical
Director
CIO: Gerry Maroney, Chief Information Officer and Security Officer
CHR: Wally G. Harper, Vice President Human Resources
CNO: Virginia Staubach, R.N., Chief Nursing Officer and Senior Director of Nursing
Services
Web address: www.gaylord.org
Control: Other not–for–profit (including NFP Corporation) **Service:** Long–Term
Acute Care hospital

**Staffed Beds: 128 Admissions: 1507 Census: 114 Outpatient Visits: 56133
Births: 0 Total Expense ($000): 75811 Payroll Expense ($000): 40092
Personnel: 476**

★ **MASONICARE HEALTH CENTER (070039)**, 22 Masonic Avenue,
Zip 06492–3048, Mailing Address: P.O. Box 70, Zip 06492–7001;
tel. 203/679–5900, (Nonreporting) **A**3 5 6 10
Primary Contact: Stephen B. McPherson, President
COO: Jon–Paul Venoit, Chief Operating Officer
CFO: Raymond Scott Thelen, Vice President and Chief Financial Officer
CMO: Ronald Schwartz, M.D., Medical Director
CIO: Michael Nichols, Chief Information Officer
CHR: Edward Dooling, Vice President, Human Resources
CNO: Patti Russell, Vice President Nursing
Web address: www.masonicare.org
Control: Other not–for–profit (including NFP Corporation) **Service:** Other specialty

Staffed Beds: 65

CT

Hospital, Medicare Provider Number, Address, Telephone, Approval, Facility, and Physician Codes, Health Care System

★ American Hospital Association (AHA) membership
☐ The Joint Commission accreditation   ◇ DNV Healthcare Inc. accreditation
○ Healthcare Facilities Accreditation Program
△ Commission on Accreditation of Rehabilitation Facilities (CARF) accreditation

WATERBURY—New Haven County

SAINT MARY'S HOSPITAL (070016), 56 Franklin Street, Zip 06706–1281;
tel. 203/709–6000 **A**1 2 3 5 9 10 **F**3 5 8 11 12 13 15 17 18 20 22 24 28 29
30 31 32 34 35 36 37 39 40 41 43 45 49 50 53 54 57 59 64 70 72 74 75
76 77 78 79 80 81 85 87 93 96 98 100 102 104 107 108 110 111 114 115
118 119 126 129 130 132 135 144 146 147 **P**6
Primary Contact: Chad W. Wable, President and Chief Executive Officer
COO: Charles Flinn, Vice President, Chief Operating Officer
CFO: Ralph W. Becker, Vice President, Chief Financial Officer
CMO: Steven E. Schneider, M.D., Chief Medical Officer
CIO: Michael Novak, Vice President, Operations and Chief Information Officer
CHR: M. Clark Kearney, Vice President Human Resources
CNO: Elizabeth Bozzuto, R.N., Chief Nursing Officer and Vice President
Web address: www.stmh.org
Control: Church–operated, Nongovernment, not–for profit **Service:** General
Medical and Surgical

Staffed Beds: 168 **Admissions:** 11691 **Census:** 137 **Outpatient Visits:**
228443 **Births:** 984 **Total Expense ($000):** 255204 **Payroll Expense
($000):** 108933 **Personnel:** 1457

WATERBURY HOSPITAL (070005), 64 Robbins Street, Zip 06708–2600;
tel. 203/573–6000 **A**1 2 3 5 9 10 19 **F**3 5 9 12 13 15 17 18 20 22 24 28 29
30 34 35 38 40 43 44 45 47 49 50 51 53 55 57 59 61 64 68 70 72 73 74
75 76 78 79 81 82 84 85 87 96 97 98 99 100 101 102 103 104 105 107
108 111 115 119 129 130 131 132 145 146 148
Primary Contact: Darlene Stromstad, FACHE, President and Chief Executive
Officer
CFO: Colleen M. Scott, Vice President Finance
CMO: David Puzzuto, M.D., Vice President Medical Affairs and Chief Medical
Officer
CIO: Michael J. Cemeno, Chief Information Officer
CHR: Diane Woolley, Vice President Human Resources
CNO: Sandra Ladarola, Chief Nursing Officer
Web address: www.waterburyhospital.org
Control: Other not–for–profit (including NFP Corporation) **Service:** General
Medical and Surgical

Staffed Beds: 176 **Admissions:** 10843 **Census:** 145 **Outpatient Visits:**
206349 **Births:** 1171 **Total Expense ($000):** 213171 **Payroll Expense
($000):** 84495 **Personnel:** 1063

WEST HARTFORD—Hartford County

★ **THE HOSPITAL AT HEBREW HEALTH CARE (070040)**, 1 Abrahms Boulevard,
Zip 06117–1525; tel. 860/523–3800 **A**10 **F**11 29 30 34 35 56 64 65 84 87
93 98 103 128 130 132 146 148
Primary Contact: Bonnie B. Gauthier, President and Chief Executive Officer
COO: Kathy Mon, Vice President Operations
CFO: David Houle, Executive Vice President and Chief Financial Officer
CMO: Henry Schneiderman, M.D., Vice President Medical Services and Physician
in Chief
CHR: Carmella Ross, Manager Human Resources
Web address: www.hebrewhealthcare.org
Control: Other not–for–profit (including NFP Corporation) **Service:** Chronic
disease

Staffed Beds: 322 **Admissions:** 847 **Census:** 256 **Outpatient Visits:** 1146
Births: 0 **Total Expense ($000):** 32420 **Payroll Expense ($000):** 17851
Personnel: 387

WEST HAVEN—New Haven County

VETERANS AFFAIRS CONNECTICUT HEALTHCARE SYSTEM, 950 Campbell
Avenue, Zip 06516–2770; tel. 203/932–5711, (Includes WEST HAVEN DIVISION,
950 Campbell Avenue, Zip 06516–2700; tel. 203/932–5711), (Nonreporting) **A**1
2 3 5 8 **S** Department of Veterans Affairs, Washington, DC
Primary Contact: Gerald F. Culliton, Medical Center Director
CFO: Joseph LaMadeleine, Chief Financial Officer
CMO: Michael Ebert, M.D., Chief of Staff
CIO: Joseph Erdos, M.D., Chief Information Officer
CHR: Mark Bain, Chief Human Resources
Web address: www.connecticut.va.gov
Control: Veterans Affairs, Government, federal **Service:** General Medical and
Surgical

Staffed Beds: 160

WESTPORT—Fairfield County

ST. VINCENT'S BEHAVIORAL HEALTH See St. Vincent's Medical Center,
Bridgeport

WILLIMANTIC—Windham County

WINDHAM COMMUNITY MEMORIAL HOSPITAL See Windham Hospital

WINDHAM HOSPITAL (070021), 112 Mansfield Avenue, Zip 06226–2040;
tel. 860/456–9116 **A**1 5 9 10 19 **F**3 8 11 12 13 14 15 17 18 28 29 30 31 32
34 35 36 40 45 48 50 51 54 56 57 59 60 61 63 64 65 66 68 69 70 74 75
76 77 78 79 81 82 83 84 85 86 87 89 93 94 100 102 107 108 110 111 115
116 117 118 119 129 130 131 132 **134** 135 144 146 147 148 **P**8 **S** Hartford
HealthCare, Hartford, CT
Primary Contact: David A. Whitehead, President and CEO
COO: Cary Trantalis, R.N., Chief Operating Officer, East Region
CFO: Daniel E. Lohr, Regional Vice President Finance
CMO: Nadia Nashid, M.D., Chief of Staff
CHR: Theresa L. Buss, Regional Vice President Human Resources
CNO: Mary Anne Bylone, R.N., Regional Vice President, Patient Care Services
Web address: www.windhamhospital.org
Control: Other not–for–profit (including NFP Corporation) **Service:** General
Medical and Surgical

Staffed Beds: 79 **Admissions:** 3786 **Census:** 45 **Outpatient Visits:** 120084
Births: 382 **Total Expense ($000):** 91368 **Payroll Expense ($000):** 41730
Personnel: 528

Many Facility Codes have changed. Please refer to the AHA Guide Code Chart. © 2014 AHA Guide

DELAWARE

DOVER—Kent County

⊠ △ **BAYHEALTH MEDICAL CENTER (080004)**, 640 South State Street, Zip 19901–3530; tel. 302/674–4700, (Includes BAYHEALTH MEDICAL CENTER AT KENT GENERAL, 640 South State Street, Zip 19901–3597; BAYHEALTH MEDICAL CENTER, MILFORD MEMORIAL HOSPITAL, 21 West Clarke Avenue, Milford, Zip 19963–1840, Mailing Address: P.O. Box 199, Zip 19963–0199; tel. 302/430–5738; Michael Ashton, Administrator) **A**1 2 5 7 9 10 **F**3 8 11 12 13 15 17 18 20 22 24 26 28 29 30 31 32 34 35 38 40 41 42 43 44 45 47 48 49 50 51 53 54 55 57 58 59 60 61 62 64 67 68 70 72 73 74 75 76 77 78 79 81 82 84 85 86 87 89 90 93 94 98 99 100 101 102 103 104 107 108 110 111 114 115 117 118 119 120 121 123 124 126 129 130 131 132 134 135 144 146 147 148
Primary Contact: Terry Murphy, President and Chief Executive Officer
COO: Deborah Watson, Senior Vice President and Chief Operating Officer
CFO: Mike Tretina, Senior Vice President and Chief Financial Officer
CMO: Gary M. Siegelman, M.D., Senior Vice President and Chief Medical Officer
CIO: Michael J. Metzing, Vice President Corporate Services
CHR: Shana Ross, Vice President Human Resources
CNO: Bonnie I. Perratto, MSN, Senior Vice President, Chief Nurse Executive
Web address: www.bayhealth.org
Control: Other not–for–profit (including NFP Corporation) **Service:** General Medical and Surgical

Staffed Beds: 326 **Admissions:** 18235 **Census:** 261 **Outpatient Visits:** 553696 **Births:** 2226 **Total Expense ($000):** 432187 **Payroll Expense ($000):** 200176 **Personnel:** 2874

☐ **DOVER BEHAVIORAL HEALTH SYSTEM (084004)**, 725 Horsepond Road, Zip 19901–7232; tel. 302/741–0140, (Nonreporting) **A**1 9 10 **S** Universal Health Services, Inc., King of Prussia, PA
Primary Contact: Jean–Charles Constant, Administrator
Web address: www.doverbehavioral.com
Control: Corporation, Investor–owned, for–profit **Service:** Psychiatric

Staffed Beds: 52

LEWES—Sussex County

⊠ **BEEBE HEALTHCARE (080007)**, 424 Savannah Road, Zip 19958–1462; tel. 302/645–3300 **A**1 2 6 9 10 **F**2 3 8 11 12 13 15 17 18 20 22 24 26 28 29 30 31 32 34 35 36 38 40 43 49 50 51 54 55 56 57 58 59 60 61 62 64 65 68 70 74 75 76 77 78 79 80 81 83 84 85 87 89 93 97 100 107 108 110 111 114 115 116 117 118 119 120 121 123 124 130 132 134 143 146 147 148 **P**4
Primary Contact: Jeffrey M. Fried, FACHE, President and Chief Executive Officer
CFO: Paul Pernice, Vice President Finance
CMO: Jeffrey Hawtof, M.D., Vice President Medical Operations and Informatics
CIO: Michael Maksymow, Vice President Information Systems
CHR: Catherine Halen, Vice President Human Resources
CNO: Steve Rhone, R.N., Vice President Patient Care Services
Web address: www.beebemed.org
Control: Other not–for–profit (including NFP Corporation) **Service:** General Medical and Surgical

Staffed Beds: 155 **Admissions:** 9151 **Census:** 102 **Outpatient Visits:** 492659 **Births:** 887 **Total Expense ($000):** 258398 **Payroll Expense ($000):** 95577 **Personnel:** 1695

MILFORD—Sussex County

BAYHEALTH MEDICAL CENTER, MILFORD MEMORIAL HOSPITAL See Bayhealth Medical Center, Dover

NEW CASTLE—New Castle County

☐ **DELAWARE PSYCHIATRIC CENTER (084001)**, 1901 North Dupont Highway, Zip 19720–1199; tel. 302/255–2700 **A**1 3 5 10 **F**30 34 39 58 59 65 68 75 86 87 98 100 101 103 106 130 132 135 143 146 **P**1
Primary Contact: Kevin Ann Huckshorn, R.N., MSN, Director
CIO: James Nau, Manager Computer and Applications Support
Web address: www.dhss.delaware.gov
Control: State–Government, nonfederal **Service:** Psychiatric

Staffed Beds: 189 **Admissions:** 443 **Census:** 137 **Outpatient Visits:** 0 **Births:** 0 **Total Expense ($000):** 33019 **Payroll Expense ($000):** 18658 **Personnel:** 511

☐ **MEADOW WOOD BEHAVIORAL HEALTH SYSTEM (084003)**, 575 South Dupont Highway, Zip 19720–4606; tel. 302/328–3330, (Nonreporting) **A**1 9 10 **S** Acadia Healthcare Company, Inc., Franklin, TN
Primary Contact: Bill A. Mason, Chief Executive Officer
CFO: Maria Valdenegro, Chief Financial Officer
Web address: www.meadowwoodhospital.com
Control: Corporation, Investor–owned, for–profit **Service:** Psychiatric

Staffed Beds: 53

NEWARK—New Castle County

⊠ **CHRISTIANA CARE HEALTH SYSTEM (080001)**, 4755 Ogletown–Stanton Road, Zip 19718–0002, Mailing Address: P.O. Box 6001, Zip 19714–6001; tel. 302/733–1000, (Includes CHRISTIANA HOSPITAL, 201 South Broom Street, Wilmington, Zip 19805, Mailing Address: P.O. Box 2653, Zip 19805; tel. 302/658–6711; WILMINGTON HOSPITAL, 501 West 14th Street, Wilmington, Zip 19801, Mailing Address: Box 1668, Zip 19899; tel. 302/733–1000) **A**1 2 3 5 8 9 10 12 13 **F**2 3 6 7 8 11 12 13 15 17 18 20 22 24 26 28 29 30 31 32 34 35 36 37 38 39 40 42 43 44 45 46 47 48 49 50 53 54 55 56 57 58 59 60 61 62 64 65 66 68 70 72 74 75 76 77 78 79 80 81 82 84 85 86 87 88 89 90 92 93 94 96 97 98 99 100 101 102 103 104 105 107 108 110 111 114 115 116 117 118 119 120 121 123 124 126 129 130 131 132 134 135 136 138 143 145 146 147 148 **P**6 **S** Christiana Care Health System, Wilmington, DE
Primary Contact: Robert J. Laskowski, M.D., President and Chief Executive Officer
COO: Gary W. Ferguson, Executive Vice President and Chief Operating Officer
CFO: Thomas L. Corrigan, Senior Vice President Finance, Managed Care and Chief Financial Officer
CMO: Janice E. Nevin, M.D., Chief Medical Officer
CIO: Randall Gaboriault, Chief Information Officer
CHR: Audrey C. Van Luven, Senior Vice President and Chief Human Resources Officer
CNO: Diane P. Talarek, R.N., Chief Nursing Officer
Web address: www.christianacare.org
Control: Other not–for–profit (including NFP Corporation) **Service:** General Medical and Surgical

Staffed Beds: 1011 **Admissions:** 53621 **Census:** 752 **Outpatient Visits:** 541171 **Births:** 6346 **Total Expense ($000):** 1360866 **Payroll Expense ($000):** 644522 **Personnel:** 9181

☐ **ROCKFORD CENTER (084002)**, 100 Rockford Drive, Zip 19713–2121; tel. 302/996–5480 **A**1 9 10 **F**98 99 103 104 105 **P**6 8 **S** Universal Health Services, Inc., King of Prussia, PA
Primary Contact: John F. McKenna, Chief Executive Officer and Managing Director
COO: Shawn Walsh, Chief Operating Officer
CFO: Kumar Purohit, Chief Financial Officer
CHR: Jessi Jeppi, Director Human Resources
Web address: www.rockfordcenter.com
Control: Corporation, Investor–owned, for–profit **Service:** Psychiatric

Staffed Beds: 118 **Admissions:** 4499 **Census:** 120 **Outpatient Visits:** 16336 **Births:** 0 **Total Expense ($000):** 25078 **Payroll Expense ($000):** 11906 **Personnel:** 231

SEAFORD—Sussex County

⊠ **NANTICOKE MEMORIAL HOSPITAL (080006)**, 801 Middleford Road, Zip 19973–3636; tel. 302/629–6611 **A**1 2 9 10 19 **F**3 8 11 13 15 17 18 20 22 28 29 30 31 32 34 35 40 43 47 48 49 50 51 57 59 64 65 68 70 74 75 77 79 81 85 86 87 93 107 108 109 110 111 114 115 117 119 120 121 123 124 129 130 132 135 146 147 148
Primary Contact: Steven A. Rose, R.N., President and Chief Executive Officer
COO: Penny Short, R.N., Chief Operating Officer
CFO: Denise Jester, Chief Financial Officer
CMO: Robert Ferber, M.D., Chief Clinical Innovation Officer
CIO: Susan Godesky, Director Information Technology
CHR: Barbara A. Hendricks, Vice President, Human Resources
CNO: Lori L. Lee, Assistant Vice President Nursing
Web address: www.nanticoke.org
Control: Other not–for–profit (including NFP Corporation) **Service:** General Medical and Surgical

Staffed Beds: 98 **Admissions:** 5287 **Census:** 55 **Outpatient Visits:** 119732 **Births:** 825 **Total Expense ($000):** 108258 **Payroll Expense ($000):** 40169 **Personnel:** 770

DE

Hospital, Medicare Provider Number, Address, Telephone, Approval, Facility, and Physician Codes, Health Care System

★ American Hospital Association (AHA) membership
☐ The Joint Commission accreditation   ◇ DNV Healthcare Inc. accreditation
○ Healthcare Facilities Accreditation Program
△ Commission on Accreditation of Rehabilitation Facilities (CARF) accreditation

WILMINGTON—New Castle County

⊞ △ **ALFRED I. DUPONT HOSPITAL FOR CHILDREN (083300)**, 1600 Rockland Road, Zip 19803–3616, Mailing Address: Box 269, Zip 19899–0269; tel. 302/651–4000 **A**1 3 5 7 10 **F**3 7 8 9 11 12 17 19 21 23 25 27 28 29 30 31 32 34 35 39 40 41 42 43 45 48 50 53 54 55 57 58 59 60 61 63 64 65 67 68 72 73 74 75 78 79 81 82 84 85 86 87 88 89 90 91 92 93 94 97 99 100 101 102 104 107 111 114 115 118 119 126 127 129 130 131 132 134 136 137 138 139 143 144 146 148 **S** Nemours, Jacksonville, FL
Primary Contact: Roy Proujansky, M.D., Chief Executive Officer
COO: Paul D. Kempinski, Chief Operating Officer
CFO: William N. Britton, Associate Administrator Finance
CMO: Brent R. King, Chief Medical Officer and Chief Physician
CIO: Ann Altoe, Senior Director Information Systems and Security Officer
Web address: www.nemours.org
Control: Other not–for–profit (including NFP Corporation) **Service:** Children's general

Staffed Beds: 195 **Admissions:** 8742 **Census:** 123 **Outpatient Visits:** 178000 **Births:** 0 **Total Expense ($000):** 349707 **Payroll Expense ($000):** 120081 **Personnel:** 2031

CHRISTIANA HOSPITAL See Christiana Care Health System, Newark

⊞ **SELECT SPECIALTY HOSPITAL–WILMINGTON (082000)**, 701 North Clayton Street, 5th Floor, Zip 19805–3948; tel. 302/421–4545 **A**1 10 **F**1 29 30 130 148 **S** Select Medical Corporation, Mechanicsburg, PA
Primary Contact: Sharon Rosetti, R.N., Chief Executive Officer
CFO: David Huffman, Vice President and Controller
CMO: Hummayun Ismail, M.D., Medical Director
CHR: Barbara A. Foster, Regional Human Resources Director
Web address: www.selectspecialtyhospitals.com/company/locations/wilmington.aspx
Control: Corporation, Investor–owned, for–profit **Service:** Long–Term Acute Care hospital

Staffed Beds: 35 **Admissions:** 321 **Census:** 26 **Outpatient Visits:** 0 **Births:** 0 **Personnel:** 105

⊞ **ST. FRANCIS HOSPITAL (080003)**, Seventh and Clayton Streets, Zip 19805–0500, Mailing Address: P.O. Box 2500, Zip 19805–0500; tel. 302/421–4100, (Nonreporting) **A**1 2 3 5 9 10 **S** Catholic Health East / Trinity Health, Livonia, MI
Primary Contact: Brian E. Dietz, FACHE, Interim President and Chief Executive officer
CIO: Paul W. Rowe, Director Information Technology
CHR: Charlene J. Wilson, Vice President Human Resources
Web address: www.stfrancishealthcare.org
Control: Other not–for–profit (including NFP Corporation) **Service:** General Medical and Surgical

Staffed Beds: 214

⊞ **VETERANS AFFAIRS MEDICAL CENTER**, 1601 Kirkwood Highway, Zip 19805–4989; tel. 302/994–2511, (Nonreporting) **A**1 2 3 5 8 **S** Department of Veterans Affairs, Washington, DC
Primary Contact: Robin C. Aube–Warren, Director
CFO: Mary Ann Kozel, Chief Fiscal
CMO: Enrique Guttin, M.D., Chief of Staff
CIO: Scott Vlars, Chief Information Technology Services
CHR: Louis McCloskey, Chief Human Resources
Web address: www.va.gov/wilmington
Control: Veterans Affairs, Government, federal **Service:** General Medical and Surgical

Staffed Beds: 60

WILMINGTON HOSPITAL See Christiana Care Health System, Newark

DISTRICT OF COLUMBIA

WASHINGTON—District Of Columbia County

☒ **CHILDREN'S NATIONAL MEDICAL CENTER (093300)**, 111 Michigan Avenue N.W., Zip 20010–2916; tel. 202/476–5000 **A**1 3 5 8 9 10 **F**3 5 7 8 11 12 14 17 18 19 21 23 25 27 29 30 31 32 34 35 36 38 39 40 41 42 43 44 45 46 48 49 50 51 54 55 57 58 59 60 61 64 65 66 68 71 72 74 75 77 78 79 81 82 83 84 85 86 87 88 89 92 93 94 96 97 98 99 100 102 104 107 111 112 115 116 117 118 119 126 129 130 131 132 134 136 137 138 141 142 146 148 **P**6
Primary Contact: Kurt Newman, M.D., President and Chief Executive Officer
COO: Kathleen Gorman, MSN, Executive Vice President Patient Care Services and Chief Operating Officer
CFO: Douglas Myers, Executive Vice President and Chief Financial Officer
CMO: Mark L. Batshaw, M.D., Physician–in–Chief, Executive Vice President and Chief Academic Officer
CIO: Brian Jacobs, M.D., Vice President Chief Information Officer and Chief Medical Information Officer
CHR: Darryl Varnado, Executive Vice President and Chief People Officer
CNO: Linda Talley, MS, Vice President and Chief Nursing Officer
Web address: www.childrensnational.org
Control: Other not–for–profit (including NFP Corporation) **Service:** Children's general

Staffed Beds: 303 **Admissions:** 15139 **Census:** 247 **Outpatient Visits:** 480231 **Births:** 0 **Total Expense ($000):** 724744 **Payroll Expense ($000):** 342794 **Personnel:** 5638

☒ △ **GEORGE WASHINGTON UNIVERSITY HOSPITAL (090001)**, 900 23rd Street N.W., Zip 20037–2342; tel. 202/715–4000 **A**1 2 3 5 7 8 9 10 **F**3 7 8 11 12 13 15 17 18 20 22 24 26 29 30 31 33 34 35 36 37 39 40 43 44 45 46 47 48 49 50 52 55 56 57 58 59 61 63 64 68 70 71 72 74 75 76 77 78 79 81 82 83 84 85 86 87 90 92 93 94 95 96 97 98 100 101 102 104 107 108 109 110 111 112 113 114 115 116 117 118 119 120 121 123 126 129 130 131 132 136 141 146 147 148 **S** Universal Health Services, Inc., King of Prussia, PA
Primary Contact: Barry A. Wolfman, Chief Executive Officer and Managing Director
COO: Kimberly Russo, Chief Operating Officer
CFO: Richard Davis, Chief Financial Officer
CMO: Gary Little, M.D., Medical Director
CIO: Louis Duhe, Senior Director Information Technology
CHR: Erin Fagan, Manager Human Resources
CNO: Jennifer Kirby, R.N., Chief Nursing Officer
Web address: www.gwhospital.com
Control: Partnership, Investor–owned, for–profit **Service:** General Medical and Surgical

Staffed Beds: 363 **Admissions:** 18334 **Census:** 251 **Outpatient Visits:** 179168 **Births:** 2406 **Total Expense ($000):** 333487 **Payroll Expense ($000):** 134500 **Personnel:** 1794

GEORGETOWN UNIVERSITY HOSPITAL See MedStar Georgetown University Hospital

☒ **HOWARD UNIVERSITY HOSPITAL (090003)**, 2041 Georgia Avenue N.W., Zip 20060–0002; tel. 202/865–6100 **A**1 2 3 5 8 9 10 **F**3 8 12 13 15 17 18 24 26 29 30 31 32 34 35 36 38 39 40 41 43 44 45 46 50 54 55 56 57 58 59 60 61 64 65 66 68 70 71 72 73 74 75 76 77 78 79 81 82 85 86 87 89 93 97 98 99 100 101 102 103 104 107 108 110 111 114 115 118 119 123 124 129 130 132 146 147 148 **P**4
Primary Contact: Wayne A. I. Frederick, Interim Chief Executive Officer
COO: Paul Mullings, Chief Operating Officer
CMO: Thomas E. Gaiter, M.D., Chief Medical Officer
CIO: Bernie Galla, Interim Director Management Information Systems
CHR: Anthony Jacks, Director Human Resources
Web address: www.huhealthcare.com
Control: Other not–for–profit (including NFP Corporation) **Service:** General Medical and Surgical

Staffed Beds: 241 **Admissions:** 9641 **Census:** 130 **Outpatient Visits:** 185092 **Births:** 735 **Total Expense ($000):** 304157 **Payroll Expense ($000):** 120854 **Personnel:** 1996

☒ **MEDSTAR GEORGETOWN UNIVERSITY HOSPITAL (090004)**, 3800 Reservoir Road N.W., Zip 20007–2197; tel. 202/444–2000 **A**1 2 3 5 8 9 10 **F**3 9 11 13 15 18 20 26 28 29 30 31 32 34 35 37 40 44 45 46 47 48 49 50 51 55 57 58 59 60 61 64 65 66 68 70 71 72 73 74 75 76 77 78 79 80 81 82 84 85 86 87 88 89 92 93 97 98 99 100 102 103 104 105 107 108 110 111 114 115 116 117 118 119 120 121 123 124 126 129 130 131 132 134 136 138 139 142 145 146 147 148 **P**6 **S** MedStar Health, Columbia, MD
Primary Contact: Richard L. Goldberg, M.D., President
COO: Michael Sachtleben, Chief Operating Officer
CFO: Paul Warda, Chief Financial Officer
CMO: Lisa Boyle, M.D., Vice President Medical Affairs and Medical Director
CIO: Catherine Szenczy, Senior Vice President and Chief Information Officer
CHR: Mary Jo Schweickhardt, Vice President Human Resources
CNO: Eileen Brennan Ferrell, R.N., Vice President and Chief Nursing Officer
Web address: www.georgetownuniversityhospital.org
Control: Other not–for–profit (including NFP Corporation) **Service:** General Medical and Surgical

Staffed Beds: 396 **Admissions:** 16852 **Census:** 313 **Outpatient Visits:** 777591 **Births:** 1087 **Total Expense ($000):** 791183 **Payroll Expense ($000):** 365730 **Personnel:** 4435

☒ △ **MEDSTAR NATIONAL REHABILITATION HOSPITAL (093025)**, 102 Irving Street N.W., Zip 20010–2949; tel. 202/877–1000 **A**1 3 5 7 9 10 **F**3 9 18 28 29 30 34 35 52 54 58 60 64 68 74 75 79 82 86 90 91 92 93 94 95 96 98 119 129 130 131 132 146 148 **P**6 **S** MedStar Health, Columbia, MD
Primary Contact: John D. Rockwood, President
CFO: Michael Boemmel, Vice President and Chief Financial Officer
CMO: Michael R. Yochelson, M.D., Vice President and Medical Director
CHR: Pamela Ashby, Vice President Human Resources
CNO: Rosemary C. Welch, R.N., Vice President and Chief Nursing Officer
Web address: www.medstarnrh.org
Control: Other not–for–profit (including NFP Corporation) **Service:** Rehabilitation

Staffed Beds: 137 **Admissions:** 2118 **Census:** 100 **Outpatient Visits:** 232960 **Births:** 0 **Total Expense ($000):** 98367 **Payroll Expense ($000):** 55397 **Personnel:** 1131

☒ **MEDSTAR WASHINGTON HOSPITAL CENTER (090011)**, 110 Irving Street N.W., Zip 20010–3017; tel. 202/877–7000 **A**1 2 3 5 8 9 10 **F**3 5 9 12 13 14 15 16 17 18 20 22 24 26 28 29 30 31 32 34 35 36 37 38 39 40 43 44 45 46 47 48 49 50 54 55 56 57 58 59 60 61 64 65 66 68 70 71 72 73 74 75 76 77 78 79 80 81 82 84 85 86 87 92 97 98 100 101 102 103 104 105 107 108 109 110 111 112 114 115 116 117 118 119 120 121 123 124 126 130 131 132 133 134 135 137 138 139 141 142 143 144 146 147 148 **P**1 **S** MedStar Health, Columbia, MD
Primary Contact: John Sullivan, President
COO: Catherine Monge, Senior Vice President Operations
CFO: Deana Stout, Interim Chief Financial Officer
CMO: Gregory J. Argyros, M.D., Interim Vice President Medical Affairs
CIO: Joe Brothman, Vice President Information Systems
CHR: James P. Hill, Senior Vice President Administrative Services
CNO: Susan E. Eckert, R.N., Senior Vice President and Chief Nursing Officer
Web address: www.whcenter.org
Control: Other not–for–profit (including NFP Corporation) **Service:** General Medical and Surgical

Staffed Beds: 769 **Admissions:** 38695 **Census:** 617 **Outpatient Visits:** 398058 **Births:** 3717 **Total Expense ($000):** 1066915 **Payroll Expense ($000):** 502314 **Personnel:** 5668

NATIONAL REHABILITATION HOSPITAL See MedStar National Rehabilitation Hospital

☒ **PROVIDENCE HOSPITAL (090006)**, 1150 Varnum Street N.E., Zip 20017–2104; tel. 202/269–7000, (Total facility includes 252 beds in nursing home–type unit) **A**1 2 3 5 9 10 **F**3 4 5 12 13 15 17 20 26 29 30 31 34 35 40 42 43 45 46 49 50 53 54 56 57 59 61 64 65 66 68 69 70 72 74 75 76 77 78 79 81 82 83 84 85 86 87 91 92 93 94 95 96 97 98 102 103 104 105 106 107 108 111 112 114 118 119 126 128 129 130 131 132 134 135 143 146 147 148 **S** Ascension Health, Saint Louis, MO
Primary Contact: Amy E. Freeman, President and Chief Executive Officer
CFO: Rick Talento, Senior Vice President and Chief Financial Officer
CMO: Raymond L. Cox, M.D., Chief Medical Officer
CIO: Alan Wyman, Chief Information Officer
CHR: Matt Lasecki, Interim Vice President Human Resources
CNO: Thedosia Munford, Senior Vice President and Chief Nursing Officer
Web address: www.provhosp.org
Control: Other not–for–profit (including NFP Corporation) **Service:** General Medical and Surgical

Staffed Beds: 541 **Admissions:** 12270 **Census:** 385 **Births:** 1873

DC

Hospital, Medicare Provider Number, Address, Telephone, Approval, Facility, and Physician Codes, Health Care System

★ American Hospital Association (AHA) membership
☐ The Joint Commission accreditation
◇ DNV Healthcare Inc. accreditation
◯ Healthcare Facilities Accreditation Program
△ Commission on Accreditation of Rehabilitation Facilities (CARF) accreditation

☐ **PSYCHIATRIC INSTITUTE OF WASHINGTON (094004)**, 4228 Wisconsin Avenue N.W., Zip 20016–2138; tel. 202/885–5600, (Nonreporting) **A**1 5 9 10
Primary Contact: Charles J. Baumgardner, President and Chief Executive Officer
COO: Carol Desjeunes, Vice President and Chief Operating Officer
CFO: Aarti Subramanian, Vice President and Chief Financial Officer
CMO: Howard Hoffman, M.D., Medical Director
CIO: Ray Santina, Director Information Systems
CHR: Dawn Hatterer–Hoag, Director Human Resources
Web address: www.psychinstitute.com
Control: Corporation, Investor–owned, for–profit **Service:** Psychiatric

Staffed Beds: 104

☒ **SIBLEY MEMORIAL HOSPITAL (090005)**, 5255 Loughboro Road N.W., Zip 20016–2633; tel. 202/537–4000, (Total facility includes 45 beds in nursing home–type unit) **A**1 3 5 9 10 **F**3 6 8 10 12 13 14 15 17 18 20 22 29 30 31 34 35 40 46 47 48 51 53 55 56 57 59 60 62 64 65 68 70 73 74 75 76 77 78 79 81 82 84 85 86 87 92 93 96 98 100 102 103 105 107 108 109 110 111 114 117 119 120 121 123 124 126 128 129 130 131 132 135 141 145 146 147 148 **S** Johns Hopkins Health System, Baltimore, MD
Primary Contact: Richard O. Davis, Ph.D., President
COO: Sanjay K. Saha, Chief Operating Officer
CFO: Marty Basso, Chief Financial Officer
CMO: M. Therese McDonnell, M.D., Interim Vice President Patient Safety, Quality and Medical Affairs
CIO: Christopher T. Timbers, Chief Information Officer
CHR: Queenie C. Plater, Vice President and Chief Human Resources Officer
CNO: Lynn Meuer, Interim Chief Nursing Officer
Web address: www.sibley.org
Control: Other not–for–profit (including NFP Corporation) **Service:** General Medical and Surgical

Staffed Beds: 246 Admissions: 11558 Census: 158 Outpatient Visits: 93405 Births: 3437 Total Expense ($000): 234109 Payroll Expense ($000): 106128 Personnel: 1533

☐ **SPECIALTY HOSPITAL OF WASHINGTON (092002)**, 700 Constitution Avenue N.E., Zip 20002–6058; tel. 202/546–5700, (Nonreporting) **A**1 10 **S** Specialty Hospitals of America, LLC, Portsmouth, NH
Primary Contact: Susan P. Bailey, R.N., Chief Executive Officer
CFO: Ed Clark, Vice President Finance
CMO: Manisha Singal, M.D., Medical Director
CHR: Margaret A. Fisher, Executive Director Human Resources
Web address: www.specialtyhospitalofwashington.com
Control: Corporation, Investor–owned, for–profit **Service:** Long–Term Acute Care hospital

Staffed Beds: 177

☐ **SPECIALTY HOSPITAL OF WASHINGTON–HADLEY (092003)**, 4601 Martin Luther King Jr. Avenue, S.W., Zip 20032–1131; tel. 202/574–5700, (Nonreporting) **A**1 10 **S** Specialty Hospitals of America, LLC, Portsmouth, NH
Primary Contact: Cathy Borris–Hale, Chief Executive Officer
CFO: Ronald Davis, Chief Financial Officer
CMO: Samir Al–Khouri, M.D., Medical Director
CHR: Bing Lechoco, Director Human Resources
Control: Corporation, Investor–owned, for–profit **Service:** Long–Term Acute Care hospital

Staffed Beds: 82

★ **ST. ELIZABETHS HOSPITAL (094001)**, 1100 Alabama Avenue S.E., Zip 20032–4540; tel. 202/562–4000 **A**3 5 10 **F**30 39 56 59 65 74 75 86 91 98 99 103 130 135 146 148
Primary Contact: Patrick J. Canavan, PsyD, Chief Executive Officer
CFO: James V. Jackson, Budget Director
CMO: Bernard Arons, M.D., Director Medical Affairs
CHR: Lorraine Green, MSN, Chief Human Resources Officer
CNO: Clotilde Vidoni–Clark, R.N., Chief Nurse Executive
Web address: www.dmh.dc.gov
Control: City–Government, nonfederal **Service:** Psychiatric

Staffed Beds: 292 Admissions: 400 Census: 270 Outpatient Visits: 0 Births: 0

☒ △ **THE HSC PEDIATRIC CENTER**, 1731 Bunker Hill Road N.E., Zip 20017–3096; tel. 202/832–4400 **A**1 7 9 **F**3 12 29 30 32 34 35 39 50 54 57 58 64 65 68 71 75 80 83 84 86 87 90 91 93 94 95 96 130 132 133 143 146 148 **P**8
Primary Contact: John Mathewson, Interim Chief Operating Officer
COO: John Mathewson, Interim Chief Operating Officer
CFO: Nancy J. Southers, Vice President and Chief Financial Officer
CMO: Robert Blake, M.D., Chief Medical Officer
CHR: Lynne Hostetter, Vice President Human Resources
CNO: Debbie C. Holson, R.N., Vice President Patient Care Services and Chief Nursing Officer
Web address: www.hscpediatriccenter.org/
Control: Other not–for–profit (including NFP Corporation) **Service:** Children's chronic disease

Staffed Beds: 118 Admissions: 330 Census: 46 Outpatient Visits: 9585 Births: 0 Total Expense ($000): 40435 Payroll Expense ($000): 16441 Personnel: 300

☒ **UNITED MEDICAL CENTER (090008)**, 1310 Southern Avenue S.E., Zip 20032–4623; tel. 202/574–6000, (Total facility includes 120 beds in nursing home–type unit) **A**1 9 10 **F**3 13 15 18 20 22 29 30 34 35 40 45 50 57 59 60 61 64 65 68 70 74 75 76 77 79 81 85 87 91 93 96 97 98 100 102 107 108 110 111 114 119 130 146 147 148
Primary Contact: David R. Small, FACHE, Chief Executive Officer
COO: Pamela Lee, Executive Vice President Operations and Chief Quality Officer
CFO: Michael Davis, Vice President Finance and Chief Financial Officer
CMO: Cyril Allen, M.D., Chief Medical Officer
CIO: John Wilcox, Interim Chief Information Officer
CHR: Jackie Johnson, Executive Vice President Human Resources
CNO: Maribel Torres, Executive Vice President Patient Care Services and Chief Nursing Officer
Web address: www.united–medicalcenter.com
Control: State–Government, nonfederal **Service:** General Medical and Surgical

Staffed Beds: 354 Admissions: 5597 Census: 207 Outpatient Visits: 79108 Births: 463 Total Expense ($000): 101640 Payroll Expense ($000): 50727 Personnel: 661

VETERANS AFFAIRS MEDICAL CENTER See Washington DC Veterans Affairs Medical Center

☒ △ **WASHINGTON DC VETERANS AFFAIRS MEDICAL CENTER**, 50 Irving Street N.W., Zip 20422–0002; tel. 202/745–8000, (Nonreporting) **A**1 2 3 5 7 9 **S** Department of Veterans Affairs, Washington, DC
Primary Contact: Brian A. Hawkins, Director
CFO: Frank Filosa, Fiscal Manager
CIO: Amanda Graves, Chief Information Systems
Web address: www.washingtondc.va.gov/
Control: Veterans Affairs, Government, federal **Service:** General Medical and Surgical

Staffed Beds: 291

WASHINGTON HOSPITAL CENTER See MedStar Washington Hospital Center

DC

Many Facility Codes have changed. Please refer to the AHA Guide Code Chart. © 2014 AHA Guide

FLORIDA

ALTAMONTE SPRINGS—Seminole County

FLORIDA HOSPITAL–ALTAMONTE See Florida Hospital, Orlando

APALACHICOLA—Franklin County

GEORGE E. WEEMS MEMORIAL HOSPITAL (101305), 135 Avenue G.,
Zip 32320–1613, Mailing Address: P.O. Box 580, Zip 32329–0580;
tel. 850/653–8853 **A**9 10 18 **F**7 29 30 35 40 45 50 54 57 75 107 114 128
133 135 144
Primary Contact: Ray Brownsworth, Chief Executive Officer
CFO: James Robinson, Chief Financial Officer
CIO: Dennis Peterson, Chief Information Officer
CHR: Ginny Grimer, Director Human Resources
Web address: www.weemsmemorial.com
Control: Partnership, Investor–owned, for–profit **Service:** General Medical and
Surgical

Staffed Beds: 25 **Admissions:** 279 **Census:** 2 **Births:** 0 **Total Expense
($000):** 7633 **Payroll Expense ($000):** 3533

APOPKA—Orange County

FLORIDA HOSPITAL–APOPKA See Florida Hospital, Orlando

ARCADIA—Desoto County

☐ **DESOTO MEMORIAL HOSPITAL (100175)**, 900 North Robert Avenue,
Zip 34266–8712, Mailing Address: P.O. Box 2180, Zip 34265–2180;
tel. 863/494–3535, (Nonreporting) **A**1 9 10 20
Primary Contact: Vincent A. Sica, President and Chief Executive Officer
CFO: Dan Hogan, Chief Financial Officer
CMO: Steven Mishkind, M.D., Chief of Staff
CIO: Kristen Spahr, Director of Marketing
CHR: Lois Hilton, Director Human Resources
CNO: Joseph La Cava, Chief Nursing Officer and Director Of Anesthesia
Web address: www.dmh.org
Control: Other not–for–profit (including NFP Corporation) **Service:** General
Medical and Surgical

Staffed Beds: 49

ATLANTIS—Palm Beach County

⊞ **JFK MEDICAL CENTER (100080)**, 5301 South Congress Avenue,
Zip 33462–1197; tel. 561/965–7300, (Nonreporting) **A**1 2 3 5 9 10 **S** HCA,
Nashville, TN
Primary Contact: Gina Melby, Chief Executive Officer
CFO: Jim Leamon, Chief Financial Officer
CIO: Jane Stewart, Director Information Services
CHR: Trudy Bromley, Vice President Human Resources
Web address: www.jfkmc.com
Control: Corporation, Investor–owned, for–profit **Service:** General Medical and
Surgical

Staffed Beds: 424

AVENTURA—Miami–Dade County

⊞ **AVENTURA HOSPITAL AND MEDICAL CENTER (100131)**, 20900 Biscayne
Boulevard, Zip 33180–1407; tel. 305/682–7000, (Nonreporting) **A**1 2 9 10
S HCA, Nashville, TN
Primary Contact: Dianne Goldenberg, Chief Executive Officer
COO: Lorna Kernizan, Chief Operating Officer
CFO: Alisa Bert, Chief Financial Officer
CMO: Martin Grossman, Chief of Staff
CHR: Denver Hopkins, Director of Human Resources
CNO: Karen Bibbo, R.N., Chief Nursing Officer
Web address: www.aventurahospital.com
Control: Corporation, Investor–owned, for–profit **Service:** General Medical and
Surgical

Staffed Beds: 359

BARTOW—Polk County

⊞ **BARTOW REGIONAL MEDICAL CENTER (100121)**, 2200 Osprey Boulevard,
Zip 33830–3308, Mailing Address: P.O. Box 1050, Zip 33831–1050;
tel. 863/533–8111, (Nonreporting) **A**1 9 10 **S** Community Health Systems, Inc.,
Franklin, TN
Primary Contact: Philip Minden, Chief Executive Officer
CFO: Michael Boscia, Chief Financial Officer
CMO: Stuart Patterson, M.D., Chief of Staff
CIO: Vilakon Champavannarath, Director Information Systems
CHR: Marie Horton, Director Associate Relations
Web address: www.bartowregional.com
Control: Corporation, Investor–owned, for–profit **Service:** General Medical and
Surgical

Staffed Beds: 72

BAY PINES—Pinellas County

⊞ △ **BAY PINES VETERANS AFFAIRS MEDICAL CENTER**, 10000 Bay Pines
Boulevard, Zip 33744–8200, Mailing Address: P.O. Box 5005, Zip 33744–5005;
tel. 727/398–6661, (Total facility includes 112 beds in nursing home–type unit)
A1 2 3 5 7 9 **F**3 4 5 8 12 15 18 20 22 26 28 29 30 31 36 38 39 40 45 46
47 49 51 53 54 56 57 58 59 60 61 62 63 64 65 68 70 74 75 77 78 79 81
82 83 84 85 86 87 90 91 93 94 97 98 102 103 104 105 106 107 108 110
111 114 115 116 117 118 119 120 121 123 128 129 130 131 132 135 143
144 146 147 148 **P**6 **S** Department of Veterans Affairs, Washington, DC
Primary Contact: Suzanne M. Klinker, Director
COO: Kris Brown, Associate Director
CFO: Jeanine Ergle, Chief Financial Officer
CMO: George F. Van Buskirk, M.D., Chief of Staff
CIO: John Williams, Chief Information Officer
CHR: Paula Buchele, Chief Human Resources
Web address: www.baypines.va.gov/
Control: Veterans Affairs, Government, federal **Service:** General Medical and
Surgical

Staffed Beds: 396 **Admissions:** 11968 **Census:** 301 **Outpatient Visits:**
1306854 **Births:** 0 **Total Expense ($000):** 631381 **Payroll Expense ($000):**
237838 **Personnel:** 3414

BELLE GLADE—Palm Beach County

GLADES GENERAL HOSPITAL See Lakeside Medical Center

⊞ **LAKESIDE MEDICAL CENTER (100130)**, 39200 Hooker Highway,
Zip 33430–5368; tel. 561/996–6571 **A**1 9 10 **F**3 11 13 15 29 34 35 40 50
56 57 68 70 76 80 81 85 87 89 91 92 93 107 108 109 110 111 114 119
130 135 143 146
Primary Contact: Thomas J. Leach, Administrator
COO: Darcy Davis, Chief Financial Officer
CFO: Darcy Davis, Chief Financial Officer
CMO: Ron Wiewora, M.D., Chief Medical Officer
CIO: Rick Roche, Director Human Resources and Information Systems
CHR: Rick Roche, Director Human Resources and Information Systems
Web address: www.lakesidemedical.org
Control: Hospital district or authority, Government, nonfederal **Service:** General
Medical and Surgical

Staffed Beds: 70 **Admissions:** 3035 **Census:** 29 **Outpatient Visits:** 32661
Births: 500 **Total Expense ($000):** 41509 **Payroll Expense ($000):** 17226
Personnel: 368

BLOUNTSTOWN—Calhoun County

★ **CALHOUN–LIBERTY HOSPITAL (101304)**, 20370 N.E. Burns Avenue,
Zip 32424–1045, Mailing Address: P.O. Box 419, Zip 32424–0419;
tel. 850/674–5411 **A**9 10 18 **F**3 7 15 29 34 40 45 50 54 57 59 97 107 110
114 119 127 128 133 135 **P**6
Primary Contact: Phillip Hill, Chief Executive Officer
CFO: Nathan Ebersole, Controller
CIO: Michael Flowers, Director Information Management
CHR: Lynn Pitts, Director Human Resources
CNO: Debra Summers, Chief Nursing Officer
Web address: www.calhounlibertyhospital.com
Control: Other not–for–profit (including NFP Corporation) **Service:** General
Medical and Surgical

Staffed Beds: 25 **Admissions:** 689 **Census:** 16 **Outpatient Visits:** 22882
Births: 1 **Total Expense ($000):** 10247 **Payroll Expense ($000):** 5404
Personnel: 146

FL

Hospital, Medicare Provider Number, Address, Telephone, Approval, Facility, and Physician Codes, Health Care System

★ American Hospital Association (AHA) membership
☐ The Joint Commission accreditation   ◇ DNV Healthcare Inc. accreditation
○ Healthcare Facilities Accreditation Program
△ Commission on Accreditation of Rehabilitation Facilities (CARF) accreditation

BOCA RATON—Palm Beach County

BOCA RATON COMMUNITY HOSPITAL See Boca Raton Regional Hospital

☐ **BOCA RATON REGIONAL HOSPITAL (100168)**, 800 Meadows Road,
Zip 33486–2368; tel. 561/955–7100 **A**1 2 5 9 10 **F**3 8 11 12 13 15 17 18 20
22 24 26 28 29 30 31 34 35 36 37 40 44 45 46 47 48 49 50 51 53 54 55
56 57 58 59 60 61 62 64 68 70 71 72 74 75 76 77 78 79 81 82 84 85 86
87 91 92 93 94 96 97 100 102 103 107 108 109 110 111 112 114 115 116
117 118 119 120 121 123 124 126 130 131 132 135 144 145 146 147
148 **P**6
Primary Contact: Jerry J. Fedele, President and Chief Executive Officer
COO: Karen Poole, Chief Operating Officer
CFO: Dawn Jauersack, Vice President and Chief Financial Officer
CMO: Charles Posternack, M.D., Vice President
CIO: Robin Hildwein, Chief Information Officer
CHR: Mindy Raymond, Vice President Human Resources
CNO: Melissa Durbin, R.N., Chief Nursing Officer
Web address: www.brrh.com
Control: Other not–for–profit (including NFP Corporation) **Service:** General
Medical and Surgical

> **Staffed Beds:** 393 **Admissions:** 15745 **Census:** 198 **Outpatient Visits:**
> 334143 **Births:** 1927 **Total Expense ($000):** 346156 **Payroll Expense
> ($000):** 128597 **Personnel:** 1958

✠ **WEST BOCA MEDICAL CENTER (100268)**, 21644 State Road 7,
Zip 33428–1899; tel. 561/488–8000 **A**1 5 9 10 **F**8 13 15 18 19 29 31 35 39
40 41 49 54 57 64 70 72 74 76 79 80 81 85 86 88 89 90 93 107 108 109
110 111 114 115 117 118 119 126 129 130 131 147 148 **P**4 5 **S** TENET
Healthcare Corporation, Dallas, TX
Primary Contact: Mitchell S. Feldman, Chief Executive Officer
COO: Laura A. Cillo, Chief Operating Officer
CFO: Brook Thomas, Chief Financial Officer
CMO: Jack L. Harari, M.D., Chief Medical Officer
CIO: Lauren McCauley, Marketing Director
CHR: Stephanie Sherman, Chief Human Resources Officer
CNO: Ruth Schwarzkopf, R.N., Chief Nursing Officer
Web address: www.westbocamedctr.com
Control: Corporation, Investor–owned, for–profit **Service:** General Medical and
Surgical

> **Staffed Beds:** 195 **Admissions:** 10112 **Census:** 117 **Outpatient Visits:**
> 69699 **Births:** 2080 **Total Expense ($000):** 112963 **Payroll Expense
> ($000):** 45549 **Personnel:** 618

BONIFAY—Holmes County

☐ **DOCTORS MEMORIAL HOSPITAL (101307)**, 2600 Hospital Drive,
Zip 32425–4264, Mailing Address: P.O. Box 188, Zip 32425–0188;
tel. 850/547–8000 **A**1 9 10 18 **F**3 11 15 29 30 40 45 50 57 59 64 70 77 81
90 93 107 110 114 119 131 133 146 148
Primary Contact: Joann Baker, Administrator
CFO: Celia F. Ward, Controller and Chief Financial Officer
CMO: Leisa Bailey, M.D., Chief of Staff
CIO: Rohan Anderson, Chief Information Officer
CHR: Christy Booth, Chief Human Resources Officer
CNO: Karla Rockwell, Director of Nursing
Web address: www.doctorsmemorial.org
Control: Hospital district or authority, Government, nonfederal **Service:** General
Medical and Surgical

> **Staffed Beds:** 20 **Admissions:** 874 **Census:** 9 **Outpatient Visits:** 16321
> **Births:** 0 **Total Expense ($000):** 13277 **Payroll Expense ($000):** 5314
> **Personnel:** 134

BOYNTON BEACH—Palm Beach County

☐ **BETHESDA HOSPITAL EAST (100002)**, 2815 South Seacrest Boulevard,
Zip 33435–7995; tel. 561/737–7733 **A**1 5 9 10 **F**3 8 12 13 15 17 18 20 22
24 26 28 29 30 31 34 35 40 41 45 46 49 50 51 56 58 60 61 64 68 70 72
74 75 76 77 78 79 81 86 87 88 89 90 93 94 96 107 110 111 114 115 119
120 121 123 124 126 129 130 131 132 133 143 146 148
Primary Contact: Roger L. Kirk, President and Chief Executive Officer
COO: Gary Nordmark, Administrator and Vice President Operations
CFO: Joanne Aquilina, Vice President Finance and Chief Financial Officer
CMO: Albert Biehl, M.D., Vice President Medical Affairs
CIO: Leslie Albright, Vice President Information Systems
CHR: Regina Bellway, Vice President Human Resources
CNO: Geralyn Lunsford, R.N., Administration and Vice President Patient Services
Web address: www.bethesdaweb.com
Control: Other not–for–profit (including NFP Corporation) **Service:** General
Medical and Surgical

> **Staffed Beds:** 481 **Admissions:** 20307 **Census:** 293 **Outpatient Visits:**
> 236306 **Births:** 2978 **Total Expense ($000):** 270760 **Payroll Expense
> ($000):** 103663 **Personnel:** 1803

BRADENTON—Manatee County

✠ △ **BLAKE MEDICAL CENTER (100213)**, 2020 59th Street West,
Zip 34209–4669; tel. 941/792–6611, (Nonreporting) **A**1 2 7 9 10 **S** HCA,
Nashville, TN
Primary Contact: Daniel J. Friedrich, III, Chief Executive Officer
COO: Valerie L. Powell–Stafford, Chief Operating Officer
CMO: Kirk Cianciolo, D.O., Chief Medical Officer
CIO: Shannon Piatkowski, Director Information Technology
CHR: Veronica Lequeux, Vice President Human Resources
Web address: www.blakemedicalcenter.com
Control: Corporation, Investor–owned, for–profit **Service:** General Medical and
Surgical

> **Staffed Beds:** 294

☐ **LAKEWOOD RANCH MEDICAL CENTER (100299)**, 8330 Lakewood Ranch
Boulevard, Zip 34202–5174; tel. 941/782–2100, (Nonreporting) **A**1 9 10
S Universal Health Services, Inc., King of Prussia, PA
Primary Contact: Linda S. Widra, FACHE, Ph.D., R.N., Interim Chief Executive
Officer
COO: Linda S. Widra, FACHE, Chief Operating Officer
CFO: Gerald Christine, Chief Financial Officer
CHR: Trish Morales, Director Human Resources
Web address: www.lakewoodranchmedicalcenter.com
Control: Corporation, Investor–owned, for–profit **Service:** General Medical and
Surgical

> **Staffed Beds:** 120

MANATEE GLENS HOSPITAL AND ADDICTION CENTER (104040),
(Substance Abuse Mental Health and Addictions), 2020 26th Avenue East,
Zip 34208–7753, Mailing Address: P.O. Box 9478, Zip 34206–9478;
tel. 941/782–4600 **A**9 10 **F**4 5 38 44 50 61 98 99 100 101 102 103 104
132 134 135
Primary Contact: Mary Ruiz, Chief Executive Officer
COO: Deborah Kostroun, Chief Operating Officer
CFO: Sean Gingras, CPA, Chief Financial Officer
CMO: Ranjay Halder, M.D., Chief Medical Director
CIO: Heidi L. Blair, Vice President Administration
CHR: Colleen O'Connor, Director Human Resources
Web address: www.manateeglens.org
Control: Other not–for–profit (including NFP Corporation) **Service:** Other specialty

> **Staffed Beds:** 78 **Admissions:** 3877 **Census:** 68 **Outpatient Visits:** 0 **Births:**
> 0 **Total Expense ($000):** 10099 **Payroll Expense ($000):** 4332 **Personnel:**
> 203

☐ **MANATEE MEMORIAL HOSPITAL (100035)**, 206 Second Street East,
Zip 34208–1000; tel. 941/746–5111, (Nonreporting) **A**1 2 5 9 10 **S** Universal
Health Services, Inc., King of Prussia, PA
Primary Contact: Kevin DiLallo, Chief Executive Officer
CFO: Mark A. Tierney, Chief Financial Officer
CMO: Linda Christmann, M.D., Chief of Staff
CIO: Troy Beaubien, Director Information Services
CHR: Sheree Threewits, Director Human Resources
CNO: Darlette Tice, Chief Nursing Officer
Web address: www.manateememorial.com
Control: Partnership, Investor–owned, for–profit **Service:** General Medical and
Surgical

> **Staffed Beds:** 319

MANATEE PALMS YOUTH SERVICES, 4480 51st Street West,
Zip 34210–2855; tel. 941/792–2222, (Nonreporting) **A**9 **S** Universal Health
Services, Inc., King of Prussia, PA
Primary Contact: Kerry Knott, Chief Executive Officer
CFO: Linda Weymouth, Chief Financial Officer
CMO: Jaime Barker, M.D., Medical Director
Web address: www.mpys.com
Control: Corporation, Investor–owned, for–profit **Service:** Children's hospital
psychiatric

> **Staffed Beds:** 60

BRANDON—Hillsborough County

✠ **BRANDON REGIONAL HOSPITAL (100243)**, 119 Oakfield Drive,
Zip 33511–5779; tel. 813/681–5551, (Nonreporting) **A**1 5 9 10 **S** HCA,
Nashville, TN
Primary Contact: Bland Eng, Chief Executive Officer
COO: Janice Balzano, Chief Operating Officer
CFO: Michael T. Terrell, Chief Financial Officer
CMO: Joseph C. Corcoran, Chief Medical Officer
CIO: Aaron Fountain, Chief Information Officer
CHR: Doug Goodman, Vice President Human Resources
CNO: Chris Taramasco, R.N., Chief Nursing Officer
Web address: www.brandonhospital.com
Control: Corporation, Investor–owned, for–profit **Service:** General Medical and
Surgical

> **Staffed Beds:** 407

BROOKSVILLE—Hernando County

✠ **BAYFRONT HEALTH BROOKSVILLE (100071)**, 17240 Cortez Boulevard, Zip 34601–8921, Mailing Address: P.O. Box 37, Zip 34605–0037; tel. 352/796–5111, (Includes BAYFRONT HEALTH SPRING HILL, 10461 Quality Drive, Spring Hill, Zip 34609–9634; tel. 352/688–8200; Patrick Maloney, Market Chief Executive Officer), (Nonreporting) **A**1 9 10 **S** Community Health Systems, Inc., Franklin, TN
Primary Contact: Kenneth R. Wicker, Chief Executive Officer
COO: Scott Hartsell, Chief Operating Officer
CFO: Matthew Seagroves, Chief Financial Officer
CMO: Mohammad A. Joud, M.D., Chief of Staff
CIO: Lee Burch, Director Management Information Systems
CHR: Claudia L. Jack, Director Associate Relations
Web address: www.brooksvilleregionalhospital.org
Control: Corporation, Investor–owned, for–profit **Service:** General Medical and Surgical

> **Staffed Beds:** 91

✠ **HEALTHSOUTH REHABILITATION HOSPITAL OF SPRING HILL (103042)**, 12440 Cortez Boulevard, Zip 34613–2628; tel. 352/592–4250 **A**1 9 10 **F**3 28 29 34 57 62 64 74 79 82 90 93 95 96 132 **S** HEALTHSOUTH Corporation, Birmingham, AL
Primary Contact: Lori Bedard, Chief Executive Officer
CFO: Kimberly Lunt, Controller
CMO: Mira Zelin, D.O., Medical Director
CIO: Myra Merillo, Supervisor Health Information Management
CHR: Mary Salamanca, Director Human Resources
CNO: Edwin Montanez, R.N., Chief Nursing Officer
Web address: www.healthsouthspringhill.com
Control: Corporation, Investor–owned, for–profit **Service:** Rehabilitation

> **Staffed Beds:** 80 **Admissions:** 1581 **Census:** 65 **Outpatient Visits:** 8810 **Births:** 0 **Total Expense ($000):** 19779 **Payroll Expense ($000):** 12216

✠ **OAK HILL HOSPITAL (100264)**, 11375 Cortez Boulevard, Zip 34613–5409; tel. 352/596–6632 **A**1 2 9 10 **F**3 11 15 17 18 20 22 24 26 29 30 31 34 35 40 41 45 46 48 49 50 51 56 57 59 64 70 74 75 77 78 79 81 85 87 89 93 107 108 110 111 114 115 118 119 126 130 131 132 146 147 148 **S** HCA, Nashville, TN
Primary Contact: Mickey Smith, Chief Executive Officer
COO: Sonia I. Gonzalez, R.N., Chief Operating Officer
CFO: Chance Phillips, Chief Financial Officer
CMO: Ganesh Chari, M.D., Chief of Staff
CIO: Cindy Peters, Chief Information Officer
CHR: Charles Snider, Vice President Human Resources
CNO: Leanne Salazar, Chief Nursing Officer
Web address: www.oakhillhospital.com
Control: Corporation, Investor–owned, for–profit **Service:** General Medical and Surgical

> **Staffed Beds:** 262 **Admissions:** 13896 **Census:** 164 **Outpatient Visits:** 77171 **Births:** 0 **Total Expense ($000):** 148104 **Payroll Expense ($000):** 53792 **Personnel:** 947

☐ **SPRINGBROOK HOSPITAL (104057)**, 7007 Grove Road, Zip 34609–8610; tel. 352/596–4306, (Nonreporting) **A**1 9 10
Primary Contact: James E. O'Shea, Administrator
Web address: www.springbrookhospital.org/
Control: Other not–for–profit (including NFP Corporation) **Service:** Psychiatric

> **Staffed Beds:** 50

CAPE CORAL—Lee County

★ ◇ **CAPE CORAL HOSPITAL (100244)**, 636 Del Prado Boulevard, Zip 33990–2695; tel. 239/424–2000 **A**9 10 21 **F**3 11 13 14 15 17 18 20 22 28 29 30 31 34 40 45 46 48 50 51 52 53 57 59 60 65 66 68 70 74 75 76 79 81 82 84 85 86 87 89 93 94 97 107 110 111 115 119 129 130 132 135 146 147 148 **S** Lee Memorial Health System, Fort Myers, FL
Primary Contact: James R. Nathan, President and Chief Executive Officer
COO: Lawrence Antonucci, M.D., Chief Operating Officer
CFO: Mike German, Chief Financial Officer
CMO: Mark Greenberg, M.D., Chief Medical Officer
CIO: Mike Smith, Chief Information Officer
CHR: Jon C. Cecil, Chief Human Resource Officer
Web address: www.leememorial.org
Control: Hospital district or authority, Government, nonfederal **Service:** General Medical and Surgical

> **Staffed Beds:** 291 **Admissions:** 14622 **Census:** 170 **Outpatient Visits:** 233594 **Births:** 1362

CELEBRATION—Osceola County

FLORIDA HOSPITAL CELEBRATION HEALTH See Florida Hospital, Orlando

CHATTAHOOCHEE—Gadsden County

FLORIDA STATE HOSPITAL (104000), U.S. Highway 90 East, Zip 32324–1000, Mailing Address: P.O. Box 1000, Zip 32324–1000; tel. 850/663–7536, (Nonreporting) **A**10
Primary Contact: Diane R. James, Administrator
CFO: Denise Smith, Director Financial Services
Web address: www.dcf.state.fl.us/institutions/fsh
Control: State–Government, nonfederal **Service:** Psychiatric

> **Staffed Beds:** 987

CHIPLEY—Washington County

☐ **NORTHWEST FLORIDA COMMUNITY HOSPITAL (101308)**, 1360 Brickyard Road, Zip 32428–6303, Mailing Address: P.O. Box 889, Zip 32428–0889; tel. 850/638–1610, (Total facility includes 34 beds in nursing home–type unit) **A**1 9 10 18 **F**3 11 15 18 29 30 34 35 40 45 57 59 62 68 81 82 85 93 104 107 111 114 119 127 128 129 130 131 133 135 146 148 **S** Alliant Management Services, Louisville, KY
Primary Contact: Mark E. Bush, Chief Executive Officer
COO: Janet Kinney, Chief Operating Officer
CFO: Marcey Black, Chief Financial Officer
CHR: Shelia Schiefelbein, Coordinator Human Resources
CNO: Joan Beard, Chief Nursing Officer
Web address: www.nfch.org
Control: Corporation, Investor–owned, for–profit **Service:** General Medical and Surgical

> **Staffed Beds:** 59 **Admissions:** 818 **Census:** 42 **Outpatient Visits:** 52905 **Births:** 0

CLEARWATER—Pinellas County

✠ **MORTON PLANT HOSPITAL (100127)**, 300 Pinellas Street, Zip 33756–3804, Mailing Address: P.O. Box 210, Zip 33757–0210; tel. 727/462–7000, (Total facility includes 120 beds in nursing home–type unit) **A**1 2 3 5 9 10 **F**3 5 6 11 13 15 17 18 20 22 24 26 28 29 30 31 34 35 37 38 40 42 45 46 48 49 50 51 53 54 55 57 58 59 60 61 62 64 65 66 68 70 72 74 75 76 77 78 79 80 81 82 84 85 86 87 98 99 100 101 102 103 104 107 108 109 110 111 114 115 116 117 118 119 120 121 123 124 126 128 129 130 131 132 143 144 145 146 147 148 **P**6 7 **S** Morton Plant Mease Health Care, Clearwater, FL
Primary Contact: N. Kristopher Hoce, President
CFO: Carl Tremonti, Chief Financial Officer
CMO: Jeff Jensen, M.D., Vice President, Medical Affairs
CHR: Sharon Collotta, Director Human Resources
CNO: Lisa Johnson, R.N., Chief Nursing Executive
Web address: www.mortonplant.com
Control: Other not–for–profit (including NFP Corporation) **Service:** General Medical and Surgical

> **Staffed Beds:** 662 **Admissions:** 25007 **Census:** 415 **Outpatient Visits:** 105032 **Births:** 2313 **Total Expense ($000):** 404216 **Payroll Expense ($000):** 132091 **Personnel:** 2436

☐ **WINDMOOR HEALTHCARE OF CLEARWATER (104017)**, 11300 U.S. 19 North, Zip 33764; tel. 727/541–2646, (Nonreporting) **A**1 9 10 **S** Universal Health Services, Inc., King of Prussia, PA
Primary Contact: Wendy Merson, Chief Executive Officer
Web address: www.windmoor.com
Control: Corporation, Investor–owned, for–profit **Service:** Psychiatric

> **Staffed Beds:** 100

CLERMONT—Lake County

☐ **SOUTH LAKE HOSPITAL (100051)**, 1900 Don Wickham Drive, Zip 34711–1979; tel. 352/394–4071 **A**1 9 10 **F**3 8 11 13 15 18 20 22 26 29 30 31 32 34 35 37 40 45 46 47 48 49 50 51 53 54 57 59 60 62 64 66 68 70 74 75 76 77 78 79 81 82 85 86 87 89 92 93 107 108 110 111 114 115 116 117 119 124 126 127 130 131 132 135 145 146 147 148 **P**6 **S** Orlando Health, Orlando, FL
Primary Contact: John Moore, President
COO: Paul Johns, Chief Operating Officer
CFO: Lance Sewell, Chief Financial Officer
CHR: Sue Brown, Administrator Human Resources
CNO: Linda Walton, R.N., Chief Nursing Officer
Web address: www.southlakehospital.com
Control: Hospital district or authority, Government, nonfederal **Service:** General Medical and Surgical

> **Staffed Beds:** 122 **Admissions:** 7316 **Census:** 80 **Outpatient Visits:** 96928 **Births:** 532 **Total Expense ($000):** 128356 **Payroll Expense ($000):** 51810 **Personnel:** 958

Hospital, Medicare Provider Number, Address, Telephone, Approval, Facility, and Physician Codes, Health Care System

★ American Hospital Association (AHA) membership
☐ The Joint Commission accreditation ◇ DNV Healthcare Inc. accreditation
○ Healthcare Facilities Accreditation Program
△ Commission on Accreditation of Rehabilitation Facilities (CARF) accreditation

CLEWISTON—Hendry County

✠ **HENDRY REGIONAL MEDICAL CENTER (101309)**, 524 West Sagamore Avenue, Zip 33440–3514; tel. 863/902–3000 **A**1 9 10 18 **F**3 11 15 18 29 34 35 40 45 50 57 59 64 65 68 70 75 77 79 81 82 85 93 97 107 110 111 114 119 127 130 133 135 146 **P**6 **S** QHR, Brentwood, TN
Primary Contact: R. D. Williams, Chief Executive Officer
CFO: John Beltz, Chief Financial Officer
CMO: Karim Kaki, M.D., Chief Medical Director
CIO: Leon Hoover, Director Information Systems
CHR: Lisa Miller, Director Human Resources
CNO: Sandra E. Viall, MSN, Chief Nursing Officer
Web address: www.hendryregional.org
Control: Hospital district or authority, Government, nonfederal **Service:** General Medical and Surgical

Staffed Beds: 25 **Admissions:** 829 **Census:** 7 **Outpatient Visits:** 37982 **Births:** 0 **Total Expense ($000):** 28240 **Payroll Expense ($000):** 11979 **Personnel:** 208

COCOA BEACH—Brevard County

✠ **HEALTH FIRST CAPE CANAVERAL HOSPITAL (100177)**, 701 West Cocoa Beach Causeway, Zip 32931–5595, Mailing Address: P.O. Box 320069, Zip 32932–0069; tel. 321/799–7111 **A**1 9 10 **F**3 11 13 15 18 20 22 26 29 30 31 34 35 40 43 44 45 46 47 48 49 51 54 56 57 59 60 62 64 65 68 70 74 75 76 78 79 81 82 85 86 87 91 92 93 103 107 108 110 111 114 115 116 117 119 124 129 130 132 143 146 147 **P**6 7 **S** Health First, Inc., Rockledge, FL
Primary Contact: J. Stuart Mitchell, III, Interim Chief Executive Officer
CFO: Joseph G. Felkner, Senior Vice President Finance and Chief Financial Officer
CMO: Jeffrey Stalnaker, M.D., Vice President, Medical Affairs
CIO: Lori Delone, Senior Vice President Support Services and Chief Information Officer
CHR: Paula B. Just, Vice President Human Resources
CNO: Connie Bradley, R.N., Chief Nursing Officer
Web address: www.health–first.org
Control: Other not–for–profit (including NFP Corporation) **Service:** General Medical and Surgical

Staffed Beds: 145 **Admissions:** 6337 **Census:** 70 **Outpatient Visits:** 107414 **Births:** 695 **Total Expense ($000):** 87371 **Payroll Expense ($000):** 38746 **Personnel:** 439

CORAL GABLES—Miami–Dade County

✠ **BAPTIST HEALTH SOUTH FLORIDA, DOCTORS HOSPITAL (100296)**, 5000 University Drive, Zip 33146–2094; tel. 786/308–3000 **A**1 9 10 **F**3 11 18 29 30 31 34 35 37 40 45 47 49 53 57 58 59 60 63 64 68 70 74 75 77 78 79 81 82 84 85 86 87 93 94 100 102 107 108 110 111 114 115 119 124 126 130 131 132 135 143 146 148 **S** Baptist Health South Florida, Coral Gables, FL
Primary Contact: Nelson Lazo, Chief Executive Officer
CFO: Maria J. Yanez, Chief Financial Officer
Web address: www.baptisthealth.net
Control: Other not–for–profit (including NFP Corporation) **Service:** General Medical and Surgical

Staffed Beds: 146 **Admissions:** 6060 **Census:** 86 **Outpatient Visits:** 64104 **Births:** 0 **Total Expense ($000):** 172669 **Payroll Expense ($000):** 54826 **Personnel:** 864

✠ **CORAL GABLES HOSPITAL (100183)**, 3100 Douglas Road, Zip 33134–6914; tel. 305/445–8461, (Nonreporting) **A**1 9 10 **S** TENET Healthcare Corporation, Dallas, TX
Primary Contact: Jeffrey M. Welch, Chief Executive Officer
COO: Cristina Jimenez, Chief Operating Officer
CFO: Henry Capote, Interim Chief Financial Officer
CMO: Pedro Friarte, Director of Physician Services
CIO: Mercy Hermosa, Director of Information System
CHR: Ana Paguaga, Director of Human Resources
CNO: David O'Brien, Chief Nursing Officer
Web address: www.coralgableshospital.com
Control: Corporation, Investor–owned, for–profit **Service:** General Medical and Surgical

Staffed Beds: 256

CORAL SPRINGS—Broward County

✠ **BROWARD HEALTH CORAL SPRINGS (100276)**, 3000 Coral Hills Drive, Zip 33065–4108; tel. 954/344–3000 **A**1 9 10 **F**3 11 12 13 15 17 20 29 31 34 35 40 41 48 51 55 57 58 59 61 63 64 66 70 72 74 75 76 77 78 79 80 81 82 84 85 86 87 88 89 93 96 107 108 111 114 115 118 119 126 129 130 131 132 143 146 147 148 **S** Broward Health, Fort Lauderdale, FL
Primary Contact: Drew Grossman, Chief Executive Officer
COO: Kimberley Graham, R.N., Chief Nursing Officer and Chief Operating Officer
CFO: Arthur Wallace, Chief Financial Officer
CMO: Azeem Sachedina, M.D., Chief of Staff
CHR: Eileen O'Brien, Director Human Resources
CNO: Kimberley Graham, R.N., Chief Nursing Officer and Chief Operating Officer
Web address: www.browardhealth.org
Control: Hospital district or authority, Government, nonfederal **Service:** General Medical and Surgical

Staffed Beds: 182 **Admissions:** 12827 **Census:** 137 **Outpatient Visits:** 128277 **Births:** 2303 **Total Expense ($000):** 140182 **Payroll Expense ($000):** 59419 **Personnel:** 940

CRESTVIEW—Okaloosa County

✠ **NORTH OKALOOSA MEDICAL CENTER (100122)**, 151 Redstone Avenue S.E., Zip 32539–6026; tel. 850/689–8100 **A**1 9 10 **F**3 8 11 13 15 18 20 22 28 29 30 34 35 40 48 49 50 51 53 54 57 59 64 70 75 79 81 85 86 87 93 97 107 108 110 111 114 115 116 117 119 127 129 130 131 146 147 148 **S** Community Health Systems, Inc., Franklin, TN
Primary Contact: David W. Fuller, Chief Executive Officer
COO: Heath Evans, Assistant Chief Executive Officer
CFO: Jim Andrews, Chief Financial Officer
CMO: Michael Foley, M.D., Chief Medical Officer
CIO: Jenny Zeitler, Network Administrator
CHR: Melody M. Miller–Collette, Director Human Resources
CNO: Nina Perez, R.N., Chief Nursing Officer
Web address: www.northokaloosa.com
Control: Corporation, Investor–owned, for–profit **Service:** General Medical and Surgical

Staffed Beds: 110 **Admissions:** 5785 **Census:** 57 **Outpatient Visits:** 80111 **Births:** 529 **Personnel:** 614

CRYSTAL RIVER—Citrus County

✠ **SEVEN RIVERS REGIONAL MEDICAL CENTER (100249)**, 6201 North Suncoast Boulevard, Zip 34428–6712; tel. 352/795–6560 **A**1 9 10 **F**3 8 13 15 18 20 22 29 30 34 40 45 49 59 70 74 75 76 77 78 79 81 90 93 97 107 111 114 115 118 119 126 130 132 146 147 148 **S** Community Health Systems, Inc., Franklin, TN
Primary Contact: Joyce A. Brancato, Chief Executive Officer
COO: DeAnna Beverly, Chief Operating Officer
CHR: Joann Mramor, Director Human Resources
CNO: Cynthia Heitzman, R.N., Chief Nursing Officer
Web address: www.srrmc.com
Control: Corporation, Investor–owned, for–profit **Service:** General Medical and Surgical

Staffed Beds: 128 **Admissions:** 7090 **Census:** 81 **Births:** 245

CUTLER BAY—Miami–Dade County

HEALTHSOUTH REHABILITATION HOSPITAL See HEALTHSOUTH Rehabilitation Hospital of Miami

✠ **HEALTHSOUTH REHABILITATION HOSPITAL OF MIAMI (103038)**, 20601 Old Cutler Road, Zip 33189–2400; tel. 305/251–3800 **A**1 9 10 **F**3 29 77 86 90 91 96 130 132 135 148 **S** HEALTHSOUTH Corporation, Birmingham, AL
Primary Contact: Elizabeth L. Izquierdo, CPA, Chief Executive Officer
CFO: Reyna Hernandez, Chief Financial Officer
CIO: Miguel Cruz, Medical Staff Credentialing Coordinator
CHR: Susan Riley, Director Human Resources
CNO: Ellen Romanowski, Chief Nursing Officer
Web address: www.healthsouthmiami.com
Control: Corporation, Investor–owned, for–profit **Service:** Rehabilitation

Staffed Beds: 60 **Admissions:** 1316 **Census:** 43 **Outpatient Visits:** 0 **Births:** 0 **Total Expense ($000):** 16204 **Payroll Expense ($000):** 7922 **Personnel:** 147

DADE CITY—Pasco County

✠ **BAYFRONT HEALTH DADE CITY (100211)**, 13100 Fort King Road, Zip 33525–5294; tel. 352/521–1100, (Nonreporting) **A**1 9 10 **S** Community Health Systems, Inc., Franklin, TN
Primary Contact: Shauna McKinnon, Chief Executive Officer
CFO: Linda Stockton, Chief Financial Officer
CMO: Petros Tsambiras, M.D., Chief of Staff
CIO: Cheryl Kaufman, Director Health Information Management
CHR: Tabatha Wallace, Director Human Resources
Web address: www.pascoregionalmc.com
Control: Corporation, Investor–owned, for–profit **Service:** General Medical and Surgical

Staffed Beds: 120

FL

Many Facility Codes have changed. Please refer to the AHA Guide Code Chart. © 2014 AHA Guide

DAVENPORT—Polk County

✠ **HEART OF FLORIDA REGIONAL MEDICAL CENTER (100137)**, 40100 Highway 27, Zip 33837–5906; tel. 863/422–4971, (Nonreporting) **A**1 9 10 **S** Community Health Systems, Inc., Franklin. TN
Primary Contact: Ann Barnhart, Chief Executive Officer
CFO: Tonja Mosley, Chief Financial Officer
CMO: Claudio Manubens, M.D., Chief of Staff
CIO: Louis Jones, Director Management Information Systems
CHR: Joan Ailard, Director Human Resources
CNO: Dottie Mileto, Chief Nursing Officer
Web address: www.heartofflorida.com
Control: Corporation, Investor–owned, for–profit **Service:** General Medical and Surgical

Staffed Beds: 194

DAYTONA BEACH—Volusia County

✠ **FLORIDA HOSPITAL MEMORIAL MEDICAL CENTER (100068)**, 301 Memorial Medical Parkway, Zip 32117–5167; tel. 386/676–6000, (Includes FLORIDA HOSPITAL–OCEANSIDE, 264 South Atlantic Avenue, Ormond Beach, Zip 32176–8192; tel. 386/672–4161) **A**1 2 9 10 **F**2 3 11 12 13 15 17 18 20 22 24 26 28 29 30 31 32 34 35 40 42 45 46 47 54 57 58 59 68 70 74 75 76 77 78 79 81 82 86 87 90 91 92 93 97 100 107 108 109 110 111 112 114 116 117 119 120 121 123 124 130 131 132 135 144 146 147 148 **P**6 **S** Adventist Health System Sunbelt Health Care Corporation, Altamonte Springs, FL
Primary Contact: Daryl Tol, Chief Executive Officer
COO: Darlinda Copeland, Chief Operating Officer
CFO: Debora Thomas, Chief Financial Officer
CMO: Ron Jimenez, M.D., Chief Medical Officer
CHR: Opal R. Howard, Executive Director Human Resources
CNO: Michele Goeb–Burkett, R.N., Chief Nursing Officer
Web address: www.floridahospitalmemorial.org
Control: Church–operated, Nongovernment, not–for profit **Service:** General Medical and Surgical

Staffed Beds: 211 **Admissions:** 13351 **Census:** 181 **Outpatient Visits:** 120575 **Births:** 1388 **Total Expense ($000):** 239965 **Payroll Expense ($000):** 87032 **Personnel:** 1705

✠ **HALIFAX HEALTH MEDICAL CENTER OF DAYTONA BEACH (100017)**, 303 North Clyde Morris Boulevard, Zip 32114–2700; tel. 386/254–4000, (Includes HALIFAX BEHAVIORAL SERVICES, 841 Jimmy Ann Drive, Zip 32117–4599; tel. 904/274–5333; HALIFAX HEALTH MEDICAL CENTER OF PORT ORANGE, 1041 Dunlawton Avenue, Port Orange, Zip 32127; tel. 386/322–4700; Ann Martorano, Chief Operatiang Officer) **A**1 2 3 5 9 10 **F**3 11 12 13 17 18 20 22 24 26 28 29 30 31 40 42 43 45 46 47 49 53 55 60 65 70 72 76 77 78 79 81 85 86 87 88 89 93 97 98 99 100 101 102 103 107 108 111 114 115 118 119 120 121 123 124 126 130 131 132 135 138 146 147 148
Primary Contact: Jeff Feasel, Chief Executive Officer
COO: Ann Martorano, Chief Operating Officer
CFO: Eric Peburn, Chief Financial Officer
CMO: Donald Stoner, M.D., Chief Medical Officer
CIO: Tom Stafford, Chief Information Officer
CHR: Kimberly Fulcher, Chief Human Resources Officer
Web address: www.halifax.org
Control: Hospital district or authority, Government, nonfederal **Service:** General Medical and Surgical

Staffed Beds: 678 **Admissions:** 22321 **Census:** 328 **Outpatient Visits:** 253158 **Births:** 1957 **Total Expense ($000):** 426660 **Payroll Expense ($000):** 177818 **Personnel:** 3185

DEERFIELD BEACH—Broward County

✠ △ **BROWARD HEALTH NORTH (100086)**, 201 East Sample Road, Zip 33064–3502; tel. 954/941–8300 **A**1 2 7 10 **F**3 6 11 15 17 18 20 28 29 30 31 34 35 37 40 43 45 46 49 51 55 57 58 59 60 61 64 66 68 70 74 75 77 78 79 80 81 82 83 84 85 86 87 90 92 93 94 96 100 107 108 110 111 114 115 117 118 119 120 121 123 124 129 130 131 132 143 145 146 148 **S** Broward Health, Fort Lauderdale, FL
Primary Contact: Pauline Grant, FACHE, Chief Executive Officer
COO: Kevin Fusco, Chief Operating Officer
CFO: Robert Bugg, Chief Financial Officer
CMO: Darren Hoffberger, D.O., Chief of Staff
CIO: Doris Crain, Vice President and Chief Information Officer
CHR: Grace King, Regional Director Human Resources
CNO: Bettiann S. Ruditz, Chief Nursing Officer
Web address: www.browardhealth.org
Control: Hospital district or authority, Government, nonfederal **Service:** General Medical and Surgical

Staffed Beds: 334 **Admissions:** 13254 **Census:** 203 **Outpatient Visits:** 108758 **Births:** 0 **Total Expense ($000):** 211815 **Payroll Expense ($000):** 79792 **Personnel:** 1249

DEFUNIAK SPRINGS—Walton County

HEALTHMARK REGIONAL MEDICAL CENTER (100081), 4413 U.S. Highway 331 South, Zip 32435–6307; tel. 850/951–4500 **A**9 10 **F**3 40 45 62 64 65 70 75 81 87 93 94 97 107 111 114 115 119 127 133 143 146 **P**6
Primary Contact: James H. Thompson, Ph.D., FACHE, Owner and Chief Executive Officer
COO: Gerald C. Beard, Chief Operating Officer
CFO: Jim Brewer, M.P.H., Chief Financial Officer
CMO: Edward Tenewitz, M.D., Chief of Staff
CIO: Ray Downs, Senior Staff Accountant
CHR: Debra Tiller, Director Personnel and Administrative Secretary
Web address: www.healthmarkregional.com
Control: Individual, Investor–owned, for–profit **Service:** General Medical and Surgical

Staffed Beds: 50 **Admissions:** 940 **Census:** 11 **Outpatient Visits:** 19642 **Births:** 0 **Total Expense ($000):** 10683 **Payroll Expense ($000):** 4968 **Personnel:** 119

DELAND—Volusia County

✠ **FLORIDA HOSPITAL DELAND (100045)**, 701 West Plymouth Avenue, Zip 32720–3236; tel. 386/943–4522 **A**1 9 10 **F**3 4 13 15 18 20 22 26 28 29 30 31 34 35 37 38 40 45 46 47 48 49 50 54 55 56 57 58 59 60 64 70 74 75 76 77 78 79 80 81 84 85 86 87 93 97 98 100 102 107 108 109 110 111 112 114 115 116 117 119 120 124 126 129 130 131 132 135 146 147 **S** Adventist Health System Sunbelt Health Care Corporation, Altamonte Springs, FL
Primary Contact: Timothy W. Cook, President and CEO
COO: Hector M. De Jesus, Chief Operating Officer
CFO: Nigel Hinds, Chief Financial Officer
CMO: Samuel Edwards, M.D., Chief of Staff
CIO: Kevin Piper, Director Information Systems
CHR: Stefanie Audet, Director Human Resources
CNO: Patricia Ann Stark, R.N., CNO
Web address: www.fhdeland.org
Control: Other not–for–profit (including NFP Corporation) **Service:** General Medical and Surgical

Staffed Beds: 156 **Admissions:** 8830 **Census:** 93 **Outpatient Visits:** 117706 **Births:** 583 **Total Expense ($000):** 113990 **Payroll Expense ($000):** 44747 **Personnel:** 737

DELRAY BEACH—Palm Beach County

✠ **DELRAY MEDICAL CENTER (100258)**, 5352 Linton Boulevard, Zip 33484–6580; tel. 561/498–4440, (Includes FAIR OAKS PAVILION, 5440 Linton Boulevard, Zip 33484–6578; tel. 561/495–1000; PINECREST REHABILITATION HOSPITAL, 5360 Linton Boulevard, Zip 33484–6538; tel. 561/495–0400) **A**1 9 10 **F**3 4 11 12 15 17 18 20 22 24 26 29 31 34 35 37 38 40 41 43 45 46 47 49 50 56 57 58 59 60 64 65 67 70 74 75 77 78 79 80 81 82 84 85 87 90 91 93 94 96 98 100 101 102 103 104 107 108 111 114 115 118 119 126 129 130 131 132 133 135 143 144 146 147 148 **S** TENET Healthcare Corporation, Dallas, TX
Primary Contact: Mark Bryan, Chief Executive Officer
CMO: Anthony Dardano, M.D., Chief Medical Officer
CIO: Robens Rosena, Director Information Systems
CHR: Shannon Wills, Director Human Resources
Web address: www.delraymedicalctr.com
Control: Corporation, Investor–owned, for–profit **Service:** General Medical and Surgical

Staffed Beds: 493 **Admissions:** 17968 **Census:** 267 **Births:** 0 **Total Expense ($000):** 239672 **Payroll Expense ($000):** 84325

DUNEDIN—Pinellas County

☐ **BAYCARE ALLIANT HOSPITAL (102021)**, 601 Main Street, Zip 34698–5848; tel. 727/736–9999 **A**1 9 10 **F**1 3 28 29 130 148
Primary Contact: Jacqueline Arocho, Administrator
CFO: John Proni, CPA, Manager Finance
CMO: Leonard Dunn, M.D., Chief Medical Officer
CHR: Darlene Shelton, Coordinator Team Resources
CNO: Karen Duffy, R.N., Director Patient Care Services
Web address: www.baycare.org
Control: Other not–for–profit (including NFP Corporation) **Service:** Long–Term Acute Care hospital

Staffed Beds: 38 **Admissions:** 383 **Census:** 29 **Outpatient Visits:** 0 **Births:** 0 **Total Expense ($000):** 16748 **Payroll Expense ($000):** 6026 **Personnel:** 99

Hospital, Medicare Provider Number, Address, Telephone, Approval, Facility, and Physician Codes, Health Care System

★ American Hospital Association (AHA) membership
☐ The Joint Commission accreditation
◇ DNV Healthcare Inc. accreditation
◯ Healthcare Facilities Accreditation Program
△ Commission on Accreditation of Rehabilitation Facilities (CARF) accreditation

FL

☐ **MEASE DUNEDIN HOSPITAL (100043)**, 601 Main Street, Zip 34698–5891, Mailing Address: P.O. Box 760, Zip 34697–0760; tel. 727/733–1111 **A**1 9 10 **F**3 12 15 17 18 26 29 30 31 34 37 40 44 49 59 60 62 68 70 75 78 79 81 84 85 86 87 107 108 110 111 114 118 119 130 132 145 146 **P**6 7 **S** Morton Plant Mease Health Care, Clearwater, FL
Primary Contact: Lou Galdieri, R.N., President
CFO: Carl Tremonti, Chief Financial Officer
CMO: Donald Pocock, M.D., Chief Medical Officer
CHR: Sharon Collotta, Director Human Resources
Web address: www.mpmhealth.com
Control: Other not–for–profit (including NFP Corporation) **Service:** General Medical and Surgical

Staffed Beds: 124 **Admissions:** 4602 **Census:** 57 **Outpatient Visits:** 32403 **Births:** 0 **Total Expense ($000):** 67497 **Payroll Expense ($000):** 26720 **Personnel:** 388	

EGLIN AFB—Okaloosa County

✠ **U. S. AIR FORCE REGIONAL HOSPITAL**, 307 Boatner Road, Suite 114, Zip 32542–1282; tel. 850/883–8221, (Nonreporting) **A**1 3 5 **S** Department of the Air Force, Washington, DC
Primary Contact: Colonel Gianna Zeh, Commander
Web address: www.eglin.af.mil
Control: Air Force, Government, federal **Service:** General Medical and Surgical

Staffed Beds: 57

ENGLEWOOD—Sarasota County

✠ **ENGLEWOOD COMMUNITY HOSPITAL (100267)**, 700 Medical Boulevard, Zip 34223–3978; tel. 941/475–6571, (Nonreporting) **A**1 9 10 **S** HCA, Nashville, TN
Primary Contact: Dale Alward, Chief Executive Officer
COO: Alex Chang, Chief Operating Officer
CMO: Eric Pressman, D.O., Chair Department of Medicine
CHR: Tony Welch, Vice President, Human Resources
CNO: Kathleen Pace, MSN, Chief Nursing Officer
Web address: www.englewoodcommunityhospital.com
Control: Corporation, Investor–owned, for–profit **Service:** General Medical and Surgical

Staffed Beds: 100

FERNANDINA BEACH—Nassau County

✠ **BAPTIST MEDICAL CENTER NASSAU (100140)**, 1250 South 18th Street, Zip 32034–3098; tel. 904/321–3500 **A**1 9 10 **F**3 11 13 15 18 26 29 30 34 35 40 45 49 64 70 74 76 79 81 82 85 92 93 102 107 108 110 111 114 115 119 124 129 132 146 148 **S** Baptist Health, Jacksonville, FL
Primary Contact: Stephen Lee, FACHE, President
COO: Patricia K. Hausauer, Director Finance
CFO: Patricia K. Hausauer, Director Finance
CHR: Jodi Atkins, Human Resources Specialist
CNO: Barbara S. Gingher, R.N., Assistant Administrator for Patient Care Services
Web address: www.baptistjax.com/locations/baptist–medical–center–nassau
Control: Other not–for–profit (including NFP Corporation) **Service:** General Medical and Surgical

Staffed Beds: 52 **Admissions:** 3195 **Census:** 29 **Outpatient Visits:** 66175 **Births:** 559 **Total Expense ($000):** 48479 **Payroll Expense ($000):** 17050 **Personnel:** 338	

FORT LAUDERDALE—Broward County

☐ **ATLANTIC SHORES HOSPITAL (104065)**, 4545 North Federal Highway, Zip 33308–5274; tel. 954/771–2711, (Nonreporting) **A**1 9 10 **S** Universal Health Services, Inc., King of Prussia, PA
Primary Contact: Manuel R. Llano, Chief Executive Officer
COO: Karin Carol, Chief Operating Officer
Web address: www.atlanticshoreshospital.com
Control: Corporation, Investor–owned, for–profit **Service:** Psychiatric

Staffed Beds: 72

✠ **BROWARD HEALTH IMPERIAL POINT (100200)**, 6401 North Federal Highway, Zip 33308–1495; tel. 954/776–8500 **A**1 9 10 **F**3 11 12 15 20 29 31 34 35 40 45 51 53 55 57 58 59 61 63 64 66 68 70 74 75 77 78 79 80 81 82 84 85 86 87 93 98 100 102 104 105 107 108 111 114 115 118 119 126 129 130 131 132 143 146 147 148 **S** Broward Health, Fort Lauderdale, FL
Primary Contact: Alice Taylor, R.N., MSN, Chief Executive Officer
COO: Sandra Todd–Atkinson, Chief Operating Officer and Chief Nursing Officer
CFO: Susan Newton, Chief Financial Officer
CHR: Carl McDonald, Regional Director Human Resources
CNO: Sandra Todd–Atkinson, Chief Operating Officer and Chief Nursing Officer
Web address: www.browardhealth.org
Control: Hospital district or authority, Government, nonfederal **Service:** General Medical and Surgical

Staffed Beds: 180 **Admissions:** 8334 **Census:** 100 **Outpatient Visits:** 82390 **Births:** 0 **Total Expense ($000):** 103459 **Payroll Expense ($000):** 41840 **Personnel:** 682	

✠ **BROWARD HEALTH MEDICAL CENTER (100039)**, 1600 South Andrews Avenue, Zip 33316–2510; tel. 954/355–4400, (Includes CHRIS EVERT CHILDRENS HOSPITAL, 1600 South Andrews Avenue, tel. 954/355–4400; Calvin E. Glidewell, Jr., Chief Executive Officer) **A**1 2 5 9 10 12 13 **F**3 11 13 15 17 18 20 22 24 26 28 29 30 31 34 35 40 41 43 45 48 49 51 53 57 59 60 61 62 63 64 65 66 68 70 71 72 73 74 75 76 77 78 79 80 81 82 83 84 85 87 88 89 93 94 98 100 102 105 107 108 110 111 114 115 116 117 119 120 121 126 129 130 139 146 147 **S** Broward Health, Fort Lauderdale, FL
Primary Contact: Calvin E. Glidewell, Jr., Chief Executive Officer
CFO: Alexander Fernandez, Chief Financial Officer
CMO: Rajiv Chokshi, M.D., Chief of Staff
CIO: Doris Crain, Vice President Information Services
CHR: Dionne Wong, Vice President and Chief Human Resources Officer
Web address: www.browardhealth.org
Control: Hospital district or authority, Government, nonfederal **Service:** General Medical and Surgical

Staffed Beds: 625 **Admissions:** 28420 **Census:** 423 **Outpatient Visits:** 259414 **Births:** 3394 **Total Expense ($000):** 442541 **Payroll Expense ($000):** 175775 **Personnel:** 3008	

FLORIDA MEDICAL CENTER See North Shore Medical Center, Florida Medical Center Campus

☐ **FORT LAUDERDALE HOSPITAL (104026)**, 1601 East Las Olas Boulevard, Zip 33301–2393; tel. 954/463–4321, (Nonreporting) **A**1 9 10 **S** Universal Health Services, Inc., King of Prussia, PA
Primary Contact: Manuel R. Llano, Chief Executive Officer
CFO: Gina Lee, Chief Financial Officer
Web address: www.fortlauderdalehospital.org
Control: Corporation, Investor–owned, for–profit **Service:** Psychiatric

Staffed Beds: 100

✠ **HOLY CROSS HOSPITAL (100073)**, 4725 North Federal Highway, Zip 33308–4668, Mailing Address: P.O. Box 23460, Zip 33307–3460; tel. 954/771–8000, (Data for 180 days) **A**1 2 9 10 **F**3 8 11 12 13 15 17 18 20 22 24 26 28 29 30 34 35 37 38 40 44 45 46 47 49 50 51 53 54 55 56 57 58 59 62 64 65 66 67 68 70 71 72 74 75 76 77 78 79 81 82 83 84 85 86 87 90 92 93 97 107 108 110 111 114 115 116 117 118 119 121 124 126 129 130 131 132 144 146 147 148 **P**6 **S** Catholic Health East / Trinity Health, Livonia, MI
Primary Contact: Patrick Taylor, M.D., President and Chief Executive Officer
COO: Luisa Gutman, Senior Vice President and Chief Operating Officer
CFO: Linda Wilford, CPA, Senior Vice President and Chief Financial Officer
CMO: Kenneth Homer, M.D., Chief Medical Officer
CIO: Jeff Smith, Chief Information Officer
CNO: Taren Ruggiero, R.N., Vice President and Chief Nursing Officer
Web address: www.holy–cross.com
Control: Other not–for–profit (including NFP Corporation) **Service:** General Medical and Surgical

Staffed Beds: 559 **Admissions:** 8635 **Census:** 235 **Outpatient Visits:** 124548 **Births:** 646 **Total Expense ($000):** 154535 **Payroll Expense ($000):** 53680 **Personnel:** 2586	

IMPERIAL POINT MEDICAL CENTER See Broward Health Imperial Point

✠ **KINDRED HOSPITAL SOUTH FLORIDA–FORT LAUDERDALE (102010)**, 1516 East Las Olas Boulevard, Zip 33301–2399; tel. 954/764–8900, (Includes KINDRED HOSPITAL SOUTH FLORIDA–CORAL GABLES, 5190 S.W. Eighth Street, Coral Gables, Zip 33134–2495; tel. 305/445–1364; Charles Doten, Chief Executive Officer; KINDRED HOSPITAL SOUTH FLORIDA–HOLLYWOOD, 1859 Van Buren Street, Hollywood, Zip 33020–5127; tel. 954/920–9000; Craig A. Hoover, Administrator), (Nonreporting) **A**1 9 10 **S** Kindred Healthcare, Louisville, KY
Primary Contact: Theodore L. Welding, Administrator
CFO: Dean Card, Chief Financial Officer
Web address: www.khfortlauderdale.com/
Control: Corporation, Investor–owned, for–profit **Service:** Long–Term Acute Care hospital

Staffed Beds: 123

✠ **NORTH SHORE MEDICAL CENTER, FLORIDA MEDICAL CENTER CAMPUS (100210)**, 5000 West Oakland Park Boulevard, Zip 33313–1585; tel. 954/735–6000, (Nonreporting) **A**1 9 10 **S** TENET Healthcare Corporation, Dallas, TX
Primary Contact: Gabrielle Finley–Hazle, Chief Executive Officer
Web address: www.fmc–campus.com
Control: Partnership, Investor–owned, for–profit **Service:** General Medical and Surgical

Staffed Beds: 459

FORT MYERS—Lee County

CHILDREN'S HOSPITAL OF SOUTHWEST FLORIDA See Lee Memorial Hospital

Many Facility Codes have changed. Please refer to the AHA Guide Code Chart. © 2014 AHA Guide

★ ◇ **GULF COAST MEDICAL CENTER (100220)**, 13681 Doctor's Way,
Zip 33912–4300; tel. 239/343–1000 **A**9 10 21 **F**3 11 13 17 18 20 22 24 26
28 29 30 40 45 46 49 60 64 70 74 76 77 79 80 81 84 91 93 107 108 111
115 118 119 130 138 146 **S** Lee Memorial Health System, Fort Myers, FL
Primary Contact: James R. Nathan, President and Chief Executive Officer
COO: Lawrence Antonucci, M.D., Chief Operating Officer
CFO: Mike German, Chief Financial Officer
CMO: Mark Greenberg, M.D., Medical Director
CIO: Mike Smith, Chief Information Officer
CHR: Jon C. Cecil, Chief Human Resource Officer
CNO: Donna Giannuzzi, R.N., Chief Patient Care Officer
Web address: www.leememorial.org
Control: Hospital district or authority, Government, nonfederal **Service:** General
Medical and Surgical

Staffed Beds: 349 **Admissions:** 21774 **Census:** 272 **Outpatient Visits:** 59501 **Births:** 1581

★ △ ◇ **LEE MEMORIAL HOSPITAL (100012)**, 2776 Cleveland Avenue,
Zip 33901–5855, Mailing Address: P.O. Box 2218, Zip 33902–2218;
tel. 239/332–1111, (Includes CHILDREN'S HOSPITAL OF SOUTHWEST FLORIDA,
9981 South HealthPark Drive, Zip 33908; tel. 239/433–7799; HEALTHPARK
MEDICAL CENTER, 9981 South HealthPark Drive, Zip 33908; tel. 239/433–7799;
THE REHABILITATION HOSPITAL, 2776 Cleveland Avenue, Zip 33901;
tel. 239/332–1111), (Total facility includes 112 beds in nursing home–type unit)
A2 7 9 10 21 **F**3 11 13 14 15 17 18 19 20 21 22 24 26 28 29 30 31 32 34
35 38 40 41 43 45 48 50 51 53 54 56 57 58 59 61 62 64 65 68 70 72 73
74 75 76 77 78 79 80 81 82 84 85 86 87 88 89 90 93 94 97 100 102 103
104 105 106 107 108 110 111 113 114 115 116 117 119 126 128 129 130
131 132 134 135 146 147 148 **S** Lee Memorial Health System, Fort Myers, FL
Primary Contact: James R. Nathan, President and Chief Executive Officer
COO: Lawrence Antonucci, M.D., Chief Operating Officer
CFO: Mike German, Chief Financial Officer
CMO: Chuck Krivenko, M.D., Chief Medical Officer, Clinical and Quality Services
CIO: Mike Smith, Chief Information Officer
CHR: Jon C. Cecil, Chief Human Resource Officer
CNO: Donna Giannuzzi, R.N., Chief Nursing Officer
Web address: www.leememorial.org
Control: Hospital district or authority, Government, nonfederal **Service:** General
Medical and Surgical

Staffed Beds: 835 **Admissions:** 38167 **Census:** 611 **Outpatient Visits:** 160177 **Births:** 3447

☐ ◇ **PARK ROYAL HOSPITAL (104074)**, 9241 Park Royal Drive,
Zip 33908–9204; tel. 239/985–2700 **A**1 9 10 21 **F**4 5 29 98 102 103 104
S Acadia Healthcare Company, Inc., Franklin, TN
Primary Contact: Michael K. Evans, Chief Executive Officer
CFO: Amy Ciampa, Chief Financial Officer
CHR: Robert Raynor, Human Resources Director
Web address: www.ParkRoyalHospital.com
Control: Corporation, Investor–owned, for–profit **Service:** Psychiatric

Staffed Beds: 103 **Admissions:** 2237 **Census:** 64 **Births:** 0

FORT PIERCE—St. Lucie County

☒ **LAWNWOOD REGIONAL MEDICAL CENTER & HEART INSTITUTE (100246)**,
1700 South 23rd Street, Zip 34950–4803; tel. 772/461–4000, (Includes
LAWNWOOD PAVILION, 1860 North Lawnwood Circle, Zip 34950, Mailing
Address: P.O. Box 1540, Zip 34954–1540; tel. 361/466–1500), (Nonreporting)
A1 9 10 **S** HCA, Nashville, TN
Primary Contact: Greg Lowe, Chief Executive Officer
CFO: Robert Dunwoody, Chief Financial Officer
CIO: Eric Castle, Director Information Services
CHR: Pam Burchell, Director Human Resources
Web address: www.lawnwoodmed.com
Control: Corporation, Investor–owned, for–profit **Service:** General Medical and
Surgical

Staffed Beds: 331

FORT WALTON BEACH—Okaloosa County

☒ **FORT WALTON BEACH MEDICAL CENTER (100223)**, 1000 Mar–Walt Drive,
Zip 32547–6795; tel. 850/862–1111, (Nonreporting) **A**1 2 9 10 **S** HCA,
Nashville, TN
Primary Contact: Mitchell P. Mongell, FACHE, Chief Executive Officer
COO: Jeremy Gray, Chief Operating Officer
CFO: Jeffrey Steve Moore, Chief Financial Officer
CMO: Colonel Tama Van Decar, M.D., Chief Medical Officer
CIO: Amy Caldeira, Director Information Technology and Systems
CHR: Julia Truman, Vice President Human Resources
CNO: Holly McGucken, R.N., Chief Nursing Officer
Web address: www.fwbmc.com
Control: Corporation, Investor–owned, for–profit **Service:** General Medical and
Surgical

Staffed Beds: 257

GAINESVILLE—Alachua County

☒ **MALCOM RANDALL VETERANS AFFAIRS MEDICAL CENTER**, 1601 S.W.
Archer Road, Zip 32608–1197; tel. 352/376–1611, (Nonreporting) **A**1 3 5
S Department of Veterans Affairs, Washington, DC
Primary Contact: Thomas Wisnieski, FACHE, Director
COO: Thomas Sutton, Associate Director
CFO: Jim Taylor, Chief Business Office
CMO: Brad Bender, M.D., Chief of Staff
CIO: Deborah Michel–Ogborn, Chief Information Resource Management
CHR: Michelle Manderino, Chief Human Resources
Web address: www.northflorida.va.gov/
Control: Veterans Affairs, Government, federal **Service:** General Medical and
Surgical

Staffed Beds: 222

☒ **NORTH FLORIDA REGIONAL MEDICAL CENTER (100204)**, 6500 Newberry
Road, Zip 32605–4392, Mailing Address: P.O. Box 147006, Zip 32614–7006;
tel. 352/333–4000 **A**1 2 9 10 **F**3 12 13 15 17 18 20 22 24 26 28 29 30 31
34 35 37 40 42 45 46 48 49 50 51 55 56 57 59 60 64 70 72 74 75 76 77
78 79 80 81 85 86 87 89 107 108 109 110 111 113 114 115 116 117 118
119 120 121 123 124 126 129 130 132 135 145 146 147 148 **S** HCA,
Nashville, TN
Primary Contact: Ward Boston, III, Chief Executive Officer
COO: Thibaut vanMarcke, Chief Operating Officer
CFO: Jay St Pierre, Chief Financial Officer
CMO: Ann Weber, M.D., Chief Medical Officer
CIO: Eric Strand, Director Information Services
CHR: Brenda Cox, Assistant Vice President Human Resources
CNO: Scarlott Mueller, Chief Nursing Officer
Web address: www.nfrmc.com
Control: Corporation, Investor–owned, for–profit **Service:** General Medical and
Surgical

Staffed Beds: 445 **Admissions:** 26971 **Census:** 279 **Outpatient Visits:** 140978 **Births:** 2759 **Total Expense ($000):** 341547 **Payroll Expense ($000):** 85705 **Personnel:** 1426

☒ **SELECT SPECIALTY HOSPITAL–GAINESVILLE (102022)**, 2708 S.W. Archer
Road, Zip 32608–1316; tel. 352/337–3240, (Nonreporting) **A**1 9 10 **S** Select
Medical Corporation, Mechanicsburg, PA
Primary Contact: Cheryl Hayes, Chief Executive Officer
Web address: www.selectspecialtyhospitals.com/company/locations/gainesville.
aspx
Control: Corporation, Investor–owned, for–profit **Service:** Long–Term Acute Care
hospital

Staffed Beds: 44

SHANDS REHAB HOSPITAL See UF Health Shands Hospital

Hospital, Medicare Provider Number, Address, Telephone, Approval, Facility, and Physician Codes, Health Care System

★ American Hospital Association (AHA) membership
☐ The Joint Commission accreditation ◇ DNV Healthcare Inc. accreditation
○ Healthcare Facilities Accreditation Program
△ Commission on Accreditation of Rehabilitation Facilities (CARF) accreditation

✠ △ **UF HEALTH SHANDS HOSPITAL (100113)**, 1600 S.W. Archer Road, Zip 32610–3003, Mailing Address: P.O. Box 100326, Zip 32610–0326; tel. 352/265–0111, (Includes SHANDS CANCER HOSPITAL, 1515 S.W. Archer Road, Zip 32608–1134; tel. 352/265–0111; SHANDS HOSPITAL FOR CHILDREN, 1600 S.W. Archer Road, Mailing Address: P.O. Box 100335, Zip 32610–0335; tel. 352/265–0111; SHANDS REHAB HOSPITAL, 4101 N.W. 89th Boulevard, Zip 32606–3813; tel. 352/265–5499; Marina T. Cecchini, Administrator; SHANDS VISTA, 4101 N.W. 89th Boulevard, Zip 32606, Mailing Address: P.O. Box 24059, Zip 32602; tel. 352/265–5491; Marina T. Cecchini, Administrator) **A**1 2 3 5 7 8 9 10 **F**2 3 4 5 6 7 8 9 11 12 13 15 16 17 18 19 20 21 22 23 24 25 26 27 29 30 31 32 34 35 36 37 38 39 40 41 43 44 45 46 47 48 49 50 51 52 53 54 55 56 57 58 59 60 61 62 64 65 66 68 69 70 72 73 74 75 76 77 78 79 80 81 82 84 85 86 87 88 89 90 91 93 94 96 97 98 99 100 101 102 103 104 105 107 108 109 110 111 114 115 116 117 118 119 120 121 123 124 126 129 130 131 132 134 135 136 137 138 139 140 141 142 143 144 145 146 147 148 **P**6 **S** UF Health Shands, Gainesville, FL
Primary Contact: Edward Jimenez, Interim Chief Executive Officer
CFO: William J. Robinson, Senior Vice President and Treasurer
CMO: Timothy C. Flynn, M.D., Chief of Staff
CIO: Kari Cassel, Senior Vice President and Chief Information Officer
CHR: Janet L. Christie, Senior Vice President Human Resources
Web address: www.shands.org
Control: Other not–for–profit (including NFP Corporation) **Service:** General Medical and Surgical

Staffed Beds: 952 **Admissions:** 41950 **Census:** 755 **Outpatient Visits:** 854097 **Births:** 2825 **Total Expense ($000):** 1055680 **Payroll Expense ($000):** 390866 **Personnel:** 7507

GRACEVILLE—Jackson County

CAMPBELLTON GRACEVILLE HOSPITAL (101302), 5429 College Drive, Zip 32440–1897; tel. 850/263–4431 **A**9 10 18 **F**3 28 29 30 34 35 40 54 59 63 64 65 67 77 83 84 94 97 107 119 127 128 130 133 135 148
Primary Contact: Jimmy Rigsby, Chief Executive Officer
CFO: Dena Cooper, Chief Financial Officer
CMO: Steve Davis, M.D., Chief Medical Officer
CHR: Judy Austin, Director Human Resources
Web address: www.pahn.org/cgh.cfm
Control: Hospital district or authority, Government, nonfederal **Service:** General Medical and Surgical

Staffed Beds: 25 **Admissions:** 145 **Census:** 1 **Births:** 0 **Total Expense ($000):** 8203 **Payroll Expense ($000):** 4514

GREEN COVE SPRINGS—Clay County

✠ **KINDRED HOSPITAL NORTH FLORIDA (102015)**, 801 Oak Street, Zip 32043–4317; tel. 904/284–9230 **A**1 9 10 **F**1 18 28 29 30 31 46 84 107 119 **S** Kindred Healthcare, Louisville, KY
Primary Contact: Susan Drago, Chief Executive Officer
CFO: Steve Hart, Controller
CMO: Lionel J. Gatien, D.O., Chief of Staff
CIO: Rick Chapman, Chief Information Officer
CNO: Susan Drago, R.N., Chief Clinical Officer
Web address: www.khnorthflorida.com
Control: Corporation, Investor–owned, for–profit **Service:** Long–Term Acute Care hospital

Staffed Beds: 80 **Admissions:** 616 **Census:** 56 **Outpatient Visits:** 0 **Births:** 0 **Total Expense ($000):** 31093 **Payroll Expense ($000):** 10479 **Personnel:** 269

GULF BREEZE—Santa Rosa County

✠ **GULF BREEZE HOSPITAL (100266)**, 1110 Gulf Breeze Parkway, Zip 32561–4884; tel. 850/934–2000 **A**1 9 10 **F**3 8 11 15 20 26 29 30 31 40 44 45 46 50 54 57 59 64 68 70 71 74 75 78 79 81 82 84 85 86 91 93 107 108 110 111 114 119 120 121 123 130 131 132 143 146 147 148 **S** Baptist Health Care Corporation, Pensacola, FL
Primary Contact: Scott Raynes, Senior Vice President, Gulf Breeze Market Segment
CFO: Kerry Vermillion, Senior Vice President Finance and Chief Financial Officer
Web address: www.ebaptisthealthcare.org/GulfBreezeHospital/
Control: Other not–for–profit (including NFP Corporation) **Service:** General Medical and Surgical

Staffed Beds: 77 **Admissions:** 4076 **Census:** 41 **Outpatient Visits:** 112806 **Births:** 0 **Total Expense ($000):** 83197 **Payroll Expense ($000):** 23948 **Personnel:** 437

HIALEAH—Miami–Dade County

✠ **HIALEAH HOSPITAL (100053)**, 651 East 25th Street, Zip 33013–3878; tel. 305/693–6100 **A**1 9 10 **F**3 12 13 14 15 18 24 29 31 34 40 41 49 56 57 59 60 61 68 70 72 74 76 77 79 81 82 85 93 107 111 115 119 126 129 130 132 147 148 **S** TENET Healthcare Corporation, Dallas, TX
Primary Contact: Ben A. Rodriguez, Chief Executive Officer
COO: Patrick Downes, Chief Operating Officer
CFO: Arthur West, Chief Financial Officer
CMO: Orlando Garcia, M.D., Chief Medical Officer
CHR: Yamila Herrera, Director Human Resources
CNO: Lourdes Camps, R.N., Chief Nursing Officer
Web address: www.hialeahhosp.com
Control: Corporation, Investor–owned, for–profit **Service:** General Medical and Surgical

Staffed Beds: 160 **Admissions:** 11417 **Census:** 144 **Outpatient Visits:** 37011 **Births:** 1295 **Personnel:** 563

☐ **PALM SPRINGS GENERAL HOSPITAL (100050)**, 1475 West 49th Street, Zip 33012–3275, Mailing Address: P.O. Box 2804, Zip 33012–2804; tel. 305/558–2500, (Nonreporting) **A**1 10
Primary Contact: Nicholas T. Smith, Chief Executive Officer
CFO: Tony Milian, Chief Financial Officer
CHR: Lourdes Anton, Director Human Resources
Web address: www.psghosp.com
Control: Corporation, Investor–owned, for–profit **Service:** General Medical and Surgical

Staffed Beds: 190

✠ **PALMETTO GENERAL HOSPITAL (100187)**, 2001 West 68th Street, Zip 33016–1898; tel. 305/823–5000, (Nonreporting) **A**1 9 10 12 13 **S** TENET Healthcare Corporation, Dallas, TX
Primary Contact: Ana J. Mederos, Chief Executive Officer
COO: Georgina Diaz, Chief Operating Officer
CFO: Oscar Vicente, Chief Financial Officer
CMO: Eloy Roman, M.D., Chief of Staff
CHR: Ana Gonzalez–Fajardo, Human Resources Director
Web address: www.palmettogeneral.com
Control: Corporation, Investor–owned, for–profit **Service:** General Medical and Surgical

Staffed Beds: 360

SOUTHERN WINDS HOSPITAL See Westchester General Hospital, Miami

HOLLYWOOD—Broward County

HOLLYWOOD PAVILION (104015), 1201 North 37th Avenue, Zip 33021–5498; tel. 954/962–1355, (Nonreporting) **A**9 10
Primary Contact: Karen Kallen–Zury, Chief Executive Officer
COO: Christopher Gabel, Chief Operating Officer
CFO: Rocky Davidson, Chief Financial Officer
CHR: Len Alpert, Director Human Resources
Web address: www.hollywoodpavilion.com
Control: Corporation, Investor–owned, for–profit **Service:** Psychiatric

Staffed Beds: 46

✠ △ **MEMORIAL REGIONAL HOSPITAL (100038)**, 3501 Johnson Street, Zip 33021–5421; tel. 954/987–2000 **A**1 2 3 5 7 9 10 **F**3 4 5 7 8 11 12 13 15 16 17 18 19 20 21 22 23 24 25 26 27 28 29 30 31 32 34 35 36 37 38 39 40 41 43 44 45 46 47 49 50 51 53 54 55 56 57 58 59 60 61 62 64 65 66 67 68 70 71 72 73 74 75 76 77 78 79 80 81 82 84 85 87 88 89 90 91 93 96 97 98 99 100 101 102 103 104 105 107 108 110 111 114 115 118 119 120 121 122 123 126 130 131 132 134 135 137 145 146 147 148 **S** Memorial Healthcare System, Hollywood, FL
Primary Contact: Zeff Ross, FACHE, Senior Vice President and Chief Executive Officer
CFO: David Smith, Chief Financial Officer
CMO: Stanley Marks, M.D., Chief Medical Officer
CIO: Forest Blanton, Administrator Process Engineering
CHR: Ray Kendrick, Chief Human Resources Officer
CNO: Maggie Hansen, R.N., Chief Nursing Officer
Web address: www.mhs.net
Control: Hospital district or authority, Government, nonfederal **Service:** General Medical and Surgical

Staffed Beds: 757 **Admissions:** 30594 **Census:** 469 **Outpatient Visits:** 380661 **Births:** 4608 **Total Expense ($000):** 658523 **Payroll Expense ($000):** 254847 **Personnel:** 4031

Many Facility Codes have changed. Please refer to the AHA Guide Code Chart. © 2014 AHA Guide

FL

★ △ **MEMORIAL REGIONAL HOSPITAL SOUTH**, 3600 Washington Street, Zip 33021–8216; tel. 954/966–4500, (Includes JOE DIMAGGIO CHILDREN'S HOSPITAL, 1000 Joe DiMaggio Drive, Zip 33021–5426; tel. 954/987–2000; Chantal Leconte, Chief Executive Officer), (Nonreporting) **A**7 9 **S** Memorial Healthcare System, Hollywood, FL
Primary Contact: Douglas Zaren, FACHE, Administrator
CFO: Veronica Bautista, Chief Financial Officer
CHR: Vivian Sandler, Director Human Resources
Web address: www.memorialregionalsouth.com
Control: Hospital district or authority, Government, nonfederal **Service:** General Medical and Surgical

Staffed Beds: 324

☐ **SOUTH FLORIDA STATE HOSPITAL (104001)**, 800 East Cypress Drive, Zip 33025–4543; tel. 954/392–3000, (Nonreporting) **A**1 10
Primary Contact: Lee Packer, Administrator
Web address: www.geocarellc.com/Locations/SouthFloridaStateHospital
Control: State-Government, nonfederal **Service:** Psychiatric

Staffed Beds: 355

HOMESTEAD—Miami–Dade County

☒ **BAPTIST HEALTH SOUTH FLORIDA, HOMESTEAD HOSPITAL (100125)**, 975 Baptist Way, Zip 33033–7600; tel. 786/243–8000 **A**1 9 10 **F**3 11 13 15 18 29 30 31 34 35 40 41 45 47 49 50 51 53 57 58 59 60 61 63 64 68 70 74 75 76 78 79 81 82 84 85 86 87 89 93 102 107 108 110 111 114 115 119 129 130 131 132 134 135 145 146 147 148 **S** Baptist Health South Florida, Coral Gables, FL
Primary Contact: William M. Duquette, Chief Executive Officer
COO: Kenneth R. Spell, Vice President Operations
CFO: Erik Long, Controller
CMO: Steven Fletcher, M.D., Chief of Staff
CIO: Mimi Taylor, Corporate Vice President Information Technology
CHR: Corey Heller, Corporate Vice President and Chief Human Resources Officer
CNO: Nancy Gail Gordon, R.N., CNO and VP of Nursing
Web address: www.baptisthealth.net
Control: Other not–for–profit (including NFP Corporation) **Service:** General Medical and Surgical

Staffed Beds: 142 **Admissions:** 9794 **Census:** 90 **Outpatient Visits:** 124624 **Births:** 1542 **Total Expense ($000):** 195839 **Payroll Expense ($000):** 69227 **Personnel:** 1044

HUDSON—Pasco County

☒ **REGIONAL MEDICAL CENTER BAYONET POINT (100256)**, 14000 Fivay Road, Zip 34667–7199; tel. 727/869–5400, (Nonreporting) **A**1 2 9 10 **S** HCA, Nashville, TN
Primary Contact: Shayne George, Chief Executive Officer
COO: Shalin Shah, Chief Operating Officer
CFO: Thomas Lawhorne, Chief Financial Officer
CMO: Joseph Pino, M.D., Chief Medical Officer
CIO: Mike Wilms, Director Information Systems
CHR: Geoffrey A. Washburn, Vice President
CNO: Tanya Simpson, Chief Nursing Officer
Web address: www.rmchealth.com
Control: Corporation, Investor–owned, for–profit **Service:** General Medical and Surgical

Staffed Beds: 290

INVERNESS—Citrus County

☒ **CITRUS MEMORIAL HEALTH SYSTEM (100023)**, 502 West Highland Boulevard, Zip 34452–4754; tel. 352/726–1551 **A**1 9 10 19 **F**8 11 15 18 20 22 24 28 29 30 31 34 35 40 44 45 46 47 48 49 50 54 57 59 60 61 62 64 68 70 75 76 77 78 79 81 85 86 89 93 97 107 108 110 111 114 115 118 119 129 130 132 135 144 146 147 148 **P**6
Primary Contact: Ralph A. Aleman, President and Chief Executive Officer
CFO: Mark Williams, Chief Financial Officer
CMO: C. Toumbis, M.D., Chief of Staff
CIO: Nick Brooks, Director of Information Systems
CHR: Lee Glotzback, Director Human Resources
CNO: Linda M. McCarthy, R.N., VP/ Chief Nursing Officer
Web address: www.citrusmh.com
Control: Other not–for–profit (including NFP Corporation) **Service:** General Medical and Surgical

Staffed Beds: 198 **Admissions:** 10305 **Census:** 121 **Outpatient Visits:** 183495 **Births:** 614 **Total Expense ($000):** 152980 **Payroll Expense ($000):** 59058 **Personnel:** 1094

JACKSONVILLE—Duval County

☒ **BAPTIST MEDICAL CENTER JACKSONVILLE (100088)**, 800 Prudential Drive, Zip 32207–8202; tel. 904/202–2000, (Includes BAPTIST MEDICAL CENTER SOUTH, 14550 St. Augustine Road, Zip 32258–2160; tel. 904/821–6000; Ronald G. Robinson, Administrator; WOLFSON CHILDREN'S HOSPITAL, 800 Prudential Drive, Zip 32207; tel. 904/202–8000; Michael D. Aubin, President) **A**1 2 3 5 9 10 **F**3 5 6 8 11 12 13 15 17 18 19 20 21 22 23 24 25 26 27 28 30 31 32 34 35 36 37 38 39 40 41 42 45 46 47 48 49 50 51 53 55 56 57 58 59 60 61 62 64 68 70 72 73 74 75 76 78 79 80 81 82 83 85 87 88 89 92 93 94 98 99 100 101 102 103 104 105 107 108 109 110 111 112 113 114 115 116 117 118 119 120 121 123 124 126 129 130 132 134 135 136 146 147 148 **P**6 **S** Baptist Health, Jacksonville, FL
Primary Contact: Michael A. Mayo, FACHE, President
COO: John F. Wilbanks, FACHE, Chief Operating Officer
CFO: Scott Wooten, Senior Vice President and Chief Financial Officer
CMO: Keith L. Stein, M.D., Senior Vice President Medical Affairs and Chief Medical Officer
CIO: Roland Garcia, Senior Vice President and Chief Information Officer
CHR: M. Beth Mehaffey, Vice President Human Resources
Web address: www.e–baptisthealth.com
Control: Other not–for–profit (including NFP Corporation) **Service:** General Medical and Surgical

Staffed Beds: 878 **Admissions:** 42773 **Census:** 564 **Outpatient Visits:** 450290 **Births:** 4150 **Total Expense ($000):** 752233 **Payroll Expense ($000):** 256393 **Personnel:** 5691

☒ △ **BROOKS REHABILITATION HOSPITAL (103039)**, 3599 University Boulevard South, Zip 32216–4252; tel. 904/345–7600 **A**1 7 9 10 **F**10 29 30 54 62 64 90 91 93 95 96 130 132 146
Primary Contact: Douglas Baer, Chief Executive Officer
COO: Michael Spigel, Executive Vice President & Chief Operating Officer
CFO: Douglas Baer, Chief Executive Officer
CMO: Trevor Paris, M.D., Medical Director
CIO: Karen Green, Chief Information Officer
CHR: Karen Gallagher, Vice President Human Resources and Learning
CNO: Joanne Hoertz, Vice President of Nursing
Web address: www.brookshealth.org
Control: Other not–for–profit (including NFP Corporation) **Service:** Rehabilitation

Staffed Beds: 140 **Admissions:** 3144 **Census:** 129 **Outpatient Visits:** 239731 **Births:** 0 **Total Expense ($000):** 72629 **Payroll Expense ($000):** 28542 **Personnel:** 416

☒ **MAYO CLINIC JACKSONVILLE (100151)**, 4500 San Pablo Road South, Zip 32224–1865; tel. 904/953–2000 **A**1 2 3 5 8 9 10 **F**3 6 8 9 11 12 14 15 17 18 20 22 24 26 28 29 30 31 34 35 37 40 45 46 47 48 49 50 51 54 55 56 57 58 59 60 61 63 64 65 68 70 74 75 77 78 79 80 81 82 84 85 86 87 91 92 93 96 97 100 104 105 107 108 110 111 112 114 115 116 117 118 119 120 121 123 124 126 129 130 131 132 135 136 137 138 139 140 141 142 145 146 148 **P**6 **S** Mayo Clinic, Rochester, MN
Primary Contact: William C. Rupp, M.D., Chief Executive Officer
COO: Hilary G. Mathews, MS, Administrator
CFO: Mary Hoffman, Chief Financial Officer
CMO: Nancy Dawson, M.D., Medical Director
CIO: John Crooks, Chairman Information Services
CHR: Daniel Tomlinson, Chair Human Resources
CNO: Debra Harrison, MS, Chief Nursing Officer
Web address: www.mayoclinic.org/jacksonville/
Control: Other not–for–profit (including NFP Corporation) **Service:** General Medical and Surgical

Staffed Beds: 249 **Admissions:** 13035 **Census:** 171 **Outpatient Visits:** 46329 **Births:** 0 **Total Expense ($000):** 362447 **Payroll Expense ($000):** 77638 **Personnel:** 2165

☒ **MEMORIAL HOSPITAL JACKSONVILLE (100179)**, 3625 University Boulevard South, Zip 32216–4207, Mailing Address: P.O. Box 16325, Zip 32245–6325; tel. 904/399–6111 **A**1 2 9 10 **F**3 4 11 12 13 15 17 18 20 22 28 29 30 31 32 34 35 38 40 41 42 45 51 52 53 54 55 57 58 59 64 65 70 72 74 75 77 78 79 81 82 84 87 97 98 100 101 102 103 104 105 107 111 126 130 143 146 147 148 **S** HCA, Nashville, TN
Primary Contact: James F. O'Loughlin, President and Chief Executive Officer
COO: Bobby McCullough, Chief Operating Officer
CFO: Andy Miller, Chief Financial Officer
CMO: Aaron West, M.D., Chief Medical Officer
CIO: Lance Penton, Director, Information Services
CHR: Stuart Thompson, Vice President Human Resources
CNO: Suzanne Woods, Senior Vice President of Nursing
Web address: www.memorialhospitaljax.com
Control: Corporation, Investor–owned, for–profit **Service:** General Medical and Surgical

Staffed Beds: 418 **Admissions:** 21726 **Census:** 288 **Births:** 1571 **Total Expense ($000):** 288222 **Payroll Expense ($000):** 93608

FL

Hospital, Medicare Provider Number, Address, Telephone, Approval, Facility, and Physician Codes, Health Care System

★ American Hospital Association (AHA) membership
☐ The Joint Commission accreditation
◇ DNV Healthcare Inc. accreditation
◯ Healthcare Facilities Accreditation Program
△ Commission on Accreditation of Rehabilitation Facilities (CARF) accreditation

✠ **NAVAL HOSPITAL JACKSONVILLE**, 2080 Child Street, Zip 32214–5000;
tel. 904/542–7300, (Nonreporting) **A**1 3 5 **S** Bureau of Medicine and Surgery,
Department of the Navy, Washington, DC
Primary Contact: Commander Darryl Green, Director Administration
CFO: Lieutenant Commander Michael Gregonis, Comptroller
CMO: Captain Christopher Quarles, M.D., Director Medical Services
CIO: Mike Haytaian, Head Director Information Resources Management
CHR: Captain Ruby Tennyson, Director Administration
Web address: www.med.navy.mil/SITES/NAVALHOSPITALJAX/Pages/default.aspx
Control: Navy, Government, federal **Service:** General Medical and Surgical

Staffed Beds: 64

☐ **RIVER POINT BEHAVIORAL HEALTH (104016)**, 6300 Beach Boulevard,
Zip 32216–2782; tel. 904/724–9202, (Nonreporting) **A**1 9 10 **S** Universal Health
Services, Inc., King of Prussia, PA
Primary Contact: Gayle Eckerd, Chief Executive Officer
CFO: Jenni Stackhouse, Chief Financial Officer
CIO: Bill Willis, Director Information Technology
CHR: Cathy Calhoun, Director Human Resources
Web address: www.riverpointbehavioral.com
Control: Corporation, Investor–owned, for–profit **Service:** Psychiatric

Staffed Beds: 92

✠ **SPECIALTY HOSPITAL JACKSONVILLE (102012)**, 4901 Richard Street,
Zip 32207–7328; tel. 904/737–3120 **A**1 9 10 **F**1 18 29 60 75 85 119 130
148 **S** HCA, Nashville, TN
Primary Contact: Barbara McCarthy, Chief Executive Officer
CFO: Joshua Szostek, Chief Financial Officer
CMO: Wendell H. Williams, Jr., M.D., Medical Director
CIO: Lance Penton, Director, Information Services
CHR: Lisa Ayala, R.N., Director Human Resources
Web address: www.specialtyhospitaljax.com
Control: Corporation, Investor–owned, for–profit **Service:** Long–Term Acute Care
hospital

Staffed Beds: 62 Admissions: 784 Census: 55 Outpatient Visits: 0 Births:
0 Personnel: 202

✠ **ST. VINCENT'S MEDICAL CENTER RIVERSIDE (100040)**, 1 Shircliff Way,
Zip 32204–4748, Mailing Address: P.O. Box 2982, Zip 32203–2982;
tel. 904/308–7300 **A**1 2 3 5 9 10 13 **F**3 7 11 12 13 15 17 18 20 22 24 26
28 29 30 31 34 35 36 38 40 44 45 46 47 48 49 50 53 54 55 56 57 58
59 60 61 64 65 66 68 70 71 72 74 75 76 78 79 81 82 84 85 86 87 91 93
94 96 97 107 108 110 111 114 115 117 118 119 120 121 123 124 126
130 131 132 133 135 143 144 145 146 147 148 **S** Ascension Health, Saint
Louis, MO
Primary Contact: Moody L. Chisholm, President & Chief Executive Officer
COO: Donnie Romine, Chief Operating Officer
CFO: Kimberly Hodgkinson, Chief Financial Officer
CIO: Ann Carey, Vice President and Chief Information Officer
CHR: Janice G. Lipsky, R.N., System Vice President Human Resources and
Organizational Development
CNO: Gail P. Green, R.N., Chief Nursing Officer
Web address: www.jaxhealth.com
Control: Church–operated, Nongovernment, not–for profit **Service:** General
Medical and Surgical

Staffed Beds: 528 Admissions: 26270 Census: 347 Outpatient Visits:
147358 Births: 1714 Total Expense ($000): 414086 Payroll Expense
($000): 133272 Personnel: 2261

✠ **ST. VINCENT'S MEDICAL CENTER SOUTHSIDE (100307)**, 4201 Belfort Road,
Zip 32216–1431; tel. 904/296–3700 **A**1 3 5 9 10 **F**3 12 13 15 18 20 22 26
29 30 31 34 35 37 40 44 45 47 49 51 57 59 60 64 65 70 72 74 75 76 78
79 81 82 85 86 87 93 96 107 108 110 111 114 115 116 124 126 128 129 130
131 132 143 146 147 148 **S** Ascension Health, Saint Louis, MO
Primary Contact: Moody L. Chisholm, President and Chief Executive Officer
COO: Kyle Sanders, Chief Operating Officer
CFO: Kimberly Hodgkinson, Chief Financial Officer
CIO: Beth Fagin, Manager Information Systems
CHR: Edwina Coulliette, Manager Human Resources
CNO: Lorraine Keith, FACHE, Chief Nursing Officer
Web address: www.jaxhealth.com
Control: Church–operated, Nongovernment, not–for profit **Service:** General
Medical and Surgical

Staffed Beds: 288 Admissions: 12637 Census: 152 Outpatient Visits:
40099 Births: 1432 Total Expense ($000): 164063 Payroll Expense
($000): 49465 Personnel: 765

✠ **UF HEALTH JACKSONVILLE (100001)**, 655 West Eighth Street,
Zip 32209–6595; tel. 904/244–0411, (Total facility includes 56 beds in nursing
home–type unit) **A**1 2 3 5 8 9 10 **F**3 5 8 11 12 13 15 17 18 19 20 22 24 25
26 28 29 30 31 32 33 34 35 36 37 38 39 40 41 43 44 45 46 47 49 50 51
52 53 54 56 57 58 59 60 61 62 64 65 66 68 70 71 72 73 74 75 76 77 78
79 80 81 82 84 85 86 87 88 89 92 93 94 96 97 98 99 100 101 102 103
104 105 107 108 109 110 111 114 115 116 117 118 119 120 121 123 124
126 128 129 130 131 132 134 135 141 145 146 147 148 **S** UF Health
Shands, Gainesville, FL
Primary Contact: Russell Armistead, Chief Executive Officer
COO: Greg Miller, Senior Vice President Operations
CFO: Mike Gleason, Vice President and Chief Financial Officer
CMO: David Vukich, M.D., Senior Vice President, Chief Medical Officer and Chief
Quality Officer
CIO: Kari Cassel, Senior Vice President and Chief Information Officer
CHR: Lesli Ward, Vice President Human Resources
CNO: Patrice I. Jones, R.N., Vice President and Chief Nursing Officer
Web address: www.ufhealthjax.org/
Control: Other not–for–profit (including NFP Corporation) **Service:** General
Medical and Surgical

Staffed Beds: 620 Admissions: 24001 Census: 426 Outpatient Visits:
425717 Births: 2879 Total Expense ($000): 529423 Payroll Expense
($000): 189555 Personnel: 3120

☐ **WEKIVA SPRINGS CENTER FOR WOMEN (104069)**, 3947 Salisbury Road,
Zip 32216–6115; tel. 904/296–3533, (Nonreporting) **A**1 9 10 **S** Universal Health
Services, Inc., King of Prussia, PA
Primary Contact: Gayle Eckerd, Chief Executive Officer
Web address: www.wekivacenter.com
Control: Other not–for–profit (including NFP Corporation) **Service:** Psychiatric

Staffed Beds: 60

✠ **BAPTIST MEDICAL CENTER BEACHES (100117)**, 1350 13th Avenue South,
Zip 32250–3205; tel. 904/627–2900 **A**1 9 10 **F**3 8 11 13 15 18 20 28 29 30
31 36 40 43 45 49 50 53 54 57 59 61 64 74 75 76 77 78 79 80 81 82 85
86 93 107 108 110 111 114 115 118 119 129 130 146 147 148 **S** Baptist
Health, Jacksonville, FL
Primary Contact: Joseph M. Mitrick, FACHE, President
COO: John F. Wilbanks, FACHE, Chief Operating Officer
CFO: Scott Wooten, Senior Vice President and Chief Financial Officer
CMO: Keith L. Stein, M.D., Chief Medical Officer
CIO: Roland Garcia, Senior Vice President and Chief Information Officer
CHR: Dana Voiselle, Director Human Resources
Web address: www.community.e–baptisthealth.com/bmc/beaches/index.html
Control: Other not–for–profit (including NFP Corporation) **Service:** General
Medical and Surgical

Staffed Beds: 136 Admissions: 7355 Census: 80 Outpatient Visits: 91637
Births: 1155 Total Expense ($000): 100220 Payroll Expense ($000):
34504 Personnel: 673

★ **JAY HOSPITAL (100048)**, 14114 South Alabama Street, Zip 32565–1219;
tel. 850/675–8000 **A**9 10 **F**3 11 15 18 29 30 34 35 40 45 46 48 49 50 57
59 64 75 77 81 82 85 93 107 114 119 130 132 133 135 146 147 **S** Baptist
Health Care Corporation, Pensacola, FL
Primary Contact: Michael T. Hutchins, Administrator
CFO: Keith Strickling, Chief Accountant
CMO: Mark Elder, D.O., Chief of Staff
CHR: Linda Lowery, Manager Human Resources
CNO: Patsy Jackson, Director of Nursing
Web address: www.bhcpns.org/jayhospital/
Control: Other not–for–profit (including NFP Corporation) **Service:** General
Medical and Surgical

Staffed Beds: 49 Admissions: 582 Census: 8 Outpatient Visits: 21234
Births: 0 Total Expense ($000): 10755 Payroll Expense ($000): 4656
Personnel: 96

✠ **JUPITER MEDICAL CENTER (100253)**, 1210 South Old Dixie Highway,
Zip 33458–7299; tel. 561/747–2234 **A**1 2 9 10 **F**3 8 11 12 13 15 18 20 28
29 30 31 34 35 36 37 40 47 48 49 50 53 54 55 57 58 59 66 70 71 74 75
76 77 78 79 80 81 82 84 85 86 87 93 107 108 109 110 111 114 115 116
117 118 119 120 121 123 126 129 130 132 135 143 144 146 147 148 **P**6
Primary Contact: John D. Couris, President and Chief Executive Officer
CFO: Dale E. Hocking, Chief Financial Officer
CIO: Tom Crawford, Chief Information Officer
CHR: Peter Gloggner, Chief Human Resources Officer
Web address: www.jupitermed.com
Control: Other not–for–profit (including NFP Corporation) **Service:** General
Medical and Surgical

Staffed Beds: 163 Admissions: 10252 Census: 123 Outpatient Visits:
132910 Births: 1135 Total Expense ($000): 176699 Payroll Expense
($000): 69641 Personnel: 1207

KEY WEST—Monroe County

☒ **LOWER KEYS MEDICAL CENTER (100150)**, 5900 College Road, Zip 33040–4396, Mailing Address: P.O. Box 9107, Zip 33041–9107; tel. 305/294–5531, (Includes DE POO HOSPITAL, 1200 Kennedy Drive, Zip 33041; tel. 305/294–4692), (Nonreporting) **A**1 9 10 19 20 **S** Community Health Systems, Inc., Franklin, TN
Primary Contact: Nicki L. Will–Mowery, Ph.D., Chief Executive Officer
COO: Meylan Love–Watler, Chief Operating Officer
CFO: Dale Guffey, Chief Financial Officer
CMO: Jerome Covington, M.D., Chief Medical Officer
CIO: Les Jackson, Manager Information Systems
CHR: Donald Canalejo, Director Human Resources
Web address: www.lkmc.com
Control: Corporation, Investor–owned, for–profit **Service:** General Medical and Surgical

Staffed Beds: 90

KISSIMMEE—Osceola County

FLORIDA HOSPITAL KISSIMMEE See Florida Hospital, Orlando

☒ **OSCEOLA REGIONAL MEDICAL CENTER (100110)**, 700 West Oak Street, Zip 34741–4996; tel. 407/846–2266, (Nonreporting) **A**1 2 5 9 10 **S** HCA, Nashville, TN
Primary Contact: Robert M. Krieger, Chief Executive Officer
CFO: Glenn Romig, Chief Financial Officer
CMO: Aida Sanchez–Jimenez, M.D., Chief Medical Officer
CHR: Sylvia Lollis, Director Human Resources
CNO: Sonya Quintana, R.N., Chief Nursing Officer
Web address: www.osceolaregional.com
Control: Corporation, Investor–owned, for–profit **Service:** General Medical and Surgical

Staffed Beds: 235

☒ **POINCIANA MEDICAL CENTER (100320)**, 325 Cypress Parkway, Zip 34758; tel. 407/530–2000, (Nonreporting) **A**1 10 **S** HCA, Nashville, TN
Primary Contact: Joanna J. Conley, FACHE, Chief Executive Officer
Web address: www.poincianamedicalcenter.com
Control: Corporation, Investor–owned, for–profit **Service:** General Medical and Surgical

Staffed Beds: 24

LAKE BUTLER—Union County

LAKE BUTLER HOSPITAL HAND SURGERY CENTER (101303), 850 East Main Street, Zip 32054–1353, Mailing Address: P.O. Box 748, Zip 32054–0748; tel. 386/496–2323 **A**9 10 18 **F**29 40 54 64 77 81 93 97 127 130 133 135
Primary Contact: Pamela B. Howard, R.N., Chief Executive Officer, Administrator and Risk Manager
COO: Jennifer Thomas, Chief Operating Officer and Director of Public Relations
CFO: Paula Webb, Chief Financial Officer and Compliance Officer
CMO: Cynthia Larimer, M.D., Chief of Staff
CIO: Diane Cason, Chief Information Officer, Controller and Director Human Resources
CNO: Mandy Dicks, Director of Nursing
Web address: www.lakebutlerhospital.com
Control: Corporation, Investor–owned, for–profit **Service:** General Medical and Surgical

Staffed Beds: 25 **Admissions:** 81 **Census:** 1 **Births:** 0 **Total Expense ($000):** 9760 **Payroll Expense ($000):** 6419

RECEPTION AND MEDICAL CENTER, State Road 231 South, Zip 32054, Mailing Address: P.O. Box 628, Zip 32054–0628; tel. 386/496–6000, (Nonreporting)
Primary Contact: Rhonda Almanza, Administrator
Web address: www.dc.state.fl.us
Control: State–Government, nonfederal **Service:** Hospital unit of an institution (prison hospital, college infimary, etc.)

Staffed Beds: 133

LAKE CITY—Columbia County

☒ **LAKE CITY MEDICAL CENTER (100156)**, 340 N.W. Commerce Drive, Zip 32055–4709; tel. 386/719–9000, (Nonreporting) **A**1 9 10 **S** HCA, Nashville, TN
Primary Contact: Mark Robinson, FACHE, Chief Executive Officer
COO: Jennifer B. Adams, Chief Operating Officer and Chief Financial Officer
CFO: Jennifer B. Adams, Chief Operating Officer and Chief Financial Officer
CMO: Miguel Tepedino, M.D., Chief Medicine
CIO: Taylor Dickerson, Chief Information Officer
CHR: Steve Gordon, Director Human Resources
Web address: www.lakecitymedical.com
Control: Corporation, Investor–owned, for–profit **Service:** General Medical and Surgical

Staffed Beds: 67

★ **LAKE CITY VETERANS AFFAIRS MEDICAL CENTER**, 619 South Marion Avenue, Zip 32025–5898; tel. 386/755–3016, (Nonreporting) **S** Department of Veterans Affairs, Washington, DC
Primary Contact: Thomas Wisnieski, FACHE, Director
CIO: James Hudson, Assistant Chief Information Resource Management
Web address: www.northflorida.va.gov/
Control: Veterans Affairs, Government, federal **Service:** General Medical and Surgical

Staffed Beds: 180

☒ **SHANDS LAKE SHORE REGIONAL MEDICAL CENTER (100102)**, 368 N.E. Franklin Street, Zip 32055–3047; tel. 386/292–8000, (Nonreporting) **A**1 9 10 **S** Community Health Systems, Inc., Franklin, TN
Primary Contact: Rhonda Kay Sherrod, R.N., MSN, Administrator
CMO: Ricardo Rosato, M.D., President Medical Staff
CHR: Janice Jackson, Director Human Resources
Web address: www.shandslakeshore.com
Control: Partnership, Investor–owned, for–profit **Service:** General Medical and Surgical

Staffed Beds: 85

VETERANS AFFAIRS MEDICAL CENTER See Lake City Veterans Affairs Medical Center

LAKE WALES—Polk County

☒ **LAKE WALES MEDICAL CENTER (100099)**, 410 South 11th Street, Zip 33853–4256; tel. 863/676–1433 **A**1 9 10 **F**3 11 15 18 20 29 30 34 35 40 45 46 49 50 57 59 64 70 74 75 79 81 82 85 86 87 89 91 92 93 94 96 107 108 110 111 114 115 119 124 129 131 132 146 147 148 **S** Community Health Systems, Inc., Franklin, TN
Primary Contact: Andrew Howard, Interim Chief Executive Officer
CFO: Danny Warren, Chief Financial Officer
CMO: Sunil Nihalani, M.D., Chief Medical Staff
CIO: Erwin Jaropillo, Director Information Systems
CHR: Renee Latterner, Director Human Resources
CNO: Lee Clack, R.N., Chief Nursing Officer
Web address: www.lakewalesmedicalcenter.com
Control: Corporation, Investor–owned, for–profit **Service:** General Medical and Surgical

Staffed Beds: 131 **Admissions:** 4600 **Census:** 56 **Outpatient Visits:** 45135 **Births:** 0 **Total Expense ($000):** 50669 **Payroll Expense ($000):** 21887 **Personnel:** 451

LAKE WORTH—Palm Beach County

☒ **SELECT SPECIALTY HOSPITAL–PALM BEACH (102023)**, 3060 Melaleuca Lane, Zip 33461–5174; tel. 561/357–7200, (Nonreporting) **A**1 9 10 **S** Select Medical Corporation, Mechanicsburg, PA
Primary Contact: Larry Melby, Chief Executive Officer
Web address: www.selectspecialtyhospitals.com/company/locations/palmbeach.aspx
Control: Corporation, Investor–owned, for–profit **Service:** Long–Term Acute Care hospital

Staffed Beds: 60

FL

Hospital, Medicare Provider Number, Address, Telephone, Approval, Facility, and Physician Codes, Health Care System

★ American Hospital Association (AHA) membership
☐ The Joint Commission accreditation   ◇ DNV Healthcare Inc. accreditation
○ Healthcare Facilities Accreditation Program
△ Commission on Accreditation of Rehabilitation Facilities (CARF) accreditation

LAKELAND—Polk County

LAKELAND REGIONAL MEDICAL CENTER (100157), 1324 Lakeland Hills Boulevard, Zip 33805–4543; tel. 863/687–1100 **A**1 2 3 5 9 10 **F**3 4 11 13 17 18 20 22 24 26 28 29 30 31 34 37 38 40 41 43 44 45 46 47 49 51 55 56 57 58 59 60 61 64 65 66 70 71 72 74 75 76 77 78 79 80 81 82 83 84 85 86 87 88 89 93 98 99 100 101 102 103 104 107 108 109 110 111 114 115 118 119 120 121 123 124 126 130 132 135 143 144 146 147 148 **P**6
Primary Contact: Mack Reavis, M.D., President and Chief Medical Officer
CFO: Evan Jones, Chief Financial Officer
CMO: Mack Reavis, M.D., President and Chief Medical Officer
CIO: Elizabeth Kerns, Chief Information Officer
CHR: Amy C. Barry, Senior Vice President and Chief Human Resources Officer
Web address: www.lrmc.com
Control: Other not–for–profit (including NFP Corporation) **Service:** General Medical and Surgical

Staffed Beds: 755 Admissions: 38983 Census: 492 Outpatient Visits: 235921 Births: 3252 Total Expense ($000): 530016 Payroll Expense ($000): 215716 Personnel: 4063

LAND O'LAKES—Pasco County

FLORIDA HOSPITAL AT CONNERTON LONG TERM ACUTE CARE (102026), 9441 Health Center Drive, Zip 34637–5837; tel. 813/903–3701 **A**1 9 10 **F**1 3 4 16 17 29 30 34 67 70 72 73 80 88 89 90 98 119 128 146 148 **S** Adventist Health System Sunbelt Health Care Corporation, Altamonte Springs, FL
Primary Contact: Brian Adams, President and Chief Executive Officer
COO: Debora Martoccio, R.N., Chief Operating Officer
CMO: Sharad Patel, M.D., Medical Director
CNO: Rafael Padilla, R.N., Chief Nursing Officer
Web address: www.elevatinghealthcare.org
Control: Church–operated, Nongovernment, not–for profit **Service:** Long–Term Acute Care hospital

Staffed Beds: 50 Admissions: 681 Census: 48 Outpatient Visits: 0 Births: 0 Total Expense ($000): 22454 Payroll Expense ($000): 9822 Personnel: 173

LARGO—Pinellas County

HEALTHSOUTH REHABILITATION HOSPITAL (103037), 901 North Clearwater–Largo Road, Zip 33770–4126; tel. 727/586–2999, (Nonreporting) **A**1 9 10 **S** HEALTHSOUTH Corporation, Birmingham, AL
Primary Contact: Tripp Smith, Chief Executive Officer
CFO: Judith Johnson, Controller
CMO: Richard A. Liles, M.D., Medical Director
CHR: Jackie Chalk, Director Human Resources
CNO: Pattie Brenner, R.N., Chief Nursing Officer
Web address: www.healthsouthlargo.com
Control: Corporation, Investor–owned, for–profit **Service:** Rehabilitation

Staffed Beds: 70

LARGO MEDICAL CENTER (100248), 201 14th Street S.W., Zip 33770–3133, Mailing Address: P.O. Box 2905, Zip 33779–2905; tel. 727/588–5200, (Includes LARGO MEDICAL CENTER – INDIAN ROCKS, 2025 Indian Rocks Road, Zip 33774–1096, Mailing Address: P.O. Box 2025, Zip 33779–2025; tel. 727/581–9474), (Nonreporting) **A**1 2 5 9 10 12 13 **S** HCA, Nashville, TN
Primary Contact: Anthony M. Degina, President and Chief Executive Officer
COO: Mark Miller, FACHE, Chief Operating Officer
CFO: Robert E. Billings, Chief Financial Officer
CMO: David Weiland, M.D., Chief Medical Officer
CIO: David Saly, Director, Information Services
CNO: Brenda Simpson, R.N., Chief Nursing Officer
Web address: www.largomedical.com
Control: Corporation, Investor–owned, for–profit **Service:** General Medical and Surgical

Staffed Beds: 243

LAUDERDALE LAKES—Broward County

ST. ANTHONY'S REHABILITATION HOSPITAL (103027), 3485 N.W. 30th Street, Zip 33311–1890; tel. 954/739–6233 **A**1 7 9 10 **F**28 29 30 34 35 60 64 68 74 79 90 91 93 94 95 96 130 131 132 148 **S** Catholic Health Services, Lauderdale Lakes, FL
Primary Contact: Joseph M. Catania, Chief Executive Officer
Web address: www.catholichealthservices.org
Control: Church–operated, Nongovernment, not–for profit **Service:** Rehabilitation

Staffed Beds: 26 Admissions: 518 Census: 19 Outpatient Visits: 1644 Births: 0 Total Expense ($000): 8442 Payroll Expense ($000): 4024 Personnel: 67

LEESBURG—Lake County

LEESBURG REGIONAL MEDICAL CENTER (100084), 600 East Dixie Avenue, Zip 34748–5999; tel. 352/323–5762 **A**1 2 7 9 10 **F**3 8 11 13 15 17 18 20 22 24 26 28 29 30 31 34 49 53 54 57 59 64 66 68 70 74 75 76 77 78 79 81 82 85 87 89 90 91 93 96 107 108 110 111 114 115 119 120 130 132 135 144 146 147 148 **P**6 **S** Central Florida Health Alliance, Leesburg, FL
Primary Contact: Donald G. Henderson, FACHE, President and Chief Executive Officer
COO: Saad Ehtisham, R.N., Vice President and Chief Operating Officer
CFO: Diane P. Harden, Chief Financial Officer
CIO: David Steele, Vice President Information Technology
CHR: Amie Richason, Vice President Human Resources
CNO: Jeri Keel, Vice President Chief Clinical Officer
Web address: www.cfhalliance.org
Control: Other not–for–profit (including NFP Corporation) **Service:** General Medical and Surgical

Staffed Beds: 316 Admissions: 16514 Census: 214 Outpatient Visits: 67393 Births: 1440 Total Expense ($000): 214040 Payroll Expense ($000): 81814 Personnel: 1454

LIFESTREAM BEHAVIORAL CENTER (104018), 2020 Tally Road, Zip 34748–3426, Mailing Address: P.O. Box 491000, Zip 34749–1000; tel. 352/315–7500 **A**9 10 **F**4 5 29 34 35 50 56 57 59 66 68 87 98 99 101 102 103 104 106 130 132 **P**1
Primary Contact: Jonathan M. Cherry, President and Chief Executive Officer
COO: Howard Weiner, Senior Vice President Administrative Services
CFO: Carol Dozier, Chief Financial Officer
CMO: T. J. Valente, M.D., Medical Director
CHR: Ben Hargrove, Human Resources Director
Web address: www.lsbc.net
Control: Other not–for–profit (including NFP Corporation) **Service:** Psychiatric

Staffed Beds: 46 Admissions: 1985 Census: 38 Outpatient Visits: 37123 Births: 0 Personnel: 87

LEHIGH ACRES—Lee County

LEHIGH REGIONAL MEDICAL CENTER (100107), 1500 Lee Boulevard, Zip 33936–4835; tel. 239/369–2101, (Nonreporting) **A**1 10 **S** Community Health Systems, Inc., Franklin, TN
Primary Contact: Joanie Jeannette, MSN, Chief Executive Officer
COO: Harlo McCall, Chief Operating Officer
CFO: Osman Gruhonjic, Chief Financial Officer
CMO: Joe Lemmons, D.O., Chief of Staff
CIO: Jeff Hampton, Director Information Systems
CHR: Mary Gray, Director Human Resources
CNO: Julie G. Banker, R.N., Chief Nursing Officer
Web address: www.lehighregional.com
Control: Corporation, Investor–owned, for–profit **Service:** General Medical and Surgical

Staffed Beds: 88

LIVE OAK—Suwannee County

SHANDS LIVE OAK REGIONAL MEDICAL CENTER (101301), 1100 S.W. 11th Street, Zip 32064–3608; tel. 386/362–0800 **A**1 9 10 18 **F**15 18 29 34 35 40 41 45 50 54 56 57 59 64 68 75 81 91 92 93 97 102 107 108 110 111 119 127 135 146 147 **S** Community Health Systems, Inc., Franklin, TN
Primary Contact: Rhonda Kay Sherrod, R.N., MSN, Interim Chief Executive Officer
CFO: Mihn Dang–Do, Chief Financial Officer
CMO: Andrew C. Bass, M.D., Medical Director
CIO: Scott Thompson, Market Management Information System Director
CHR: Angela Altman, Market Human Resources Director
CNO: Jana Rolerson, Chief Nursing Officer
Web address: www.shandsliveoak.com/
Control: Corporation, Investor–owned, for–profit **Service:** General Medical and Surgical

Staffed Beds: 25 Admissions: 1338 Census: 15 Outpatient Visits: 40996 Births: 0

LOXAHATCHEE—Palm Beach County

PALMS WEST HOSPITAL (100269), 13001 Southern Boulevard, Zip 33470–9203; tel. 561/798–3300 **A**1 9 10 12 13 **F**3 8 13 15 18 19 20 22 29 30 31 34 35 39 40 41 45 46 49 50 51 56 60 63 64 68 70 74 75 76 77 78 79 80 81 82 84 85 87 88 89 93 107 108 110 111 114 115 119 124 126 130 131 142 146 147 148 **S** HCA, Nashville, TN
Primary Contact: Eric Goldman, Chief Executive Officer
COO: Madeline Nava, Chief Operating Officer
CFO: Steven Burroughs, Chief Financial Officer
CIO: Martha Stinson, Director of Information Technology
CHR: Marcy Mills–Mathews, Director Human Resources
CNO: Silvia Stradi, Chief Nursing Officer
Web address: www.palmswesthospital.com
Control: Corporation, Investor–owned, for–profit **Service:** General Medical and Surgical

Staffed Beds: 204 Admissions: 12113 Census: 133 Outpatient Visits: 73943 Births: 1246 Total Expense ($000): 135086 Payroll Expense ($000): 50516 Personnel: 519

Many Facility Codes have changed. Please refer to the AHA Guide Code Chart. © 2014 AHA Guide

FL

MACCLENNY—Baker County

ED FRASER MEMORIAL HOSPITAL AND BAKER COMMUNITY HEALTH CENTER (100134), 159 North Third Street, Zip 32063–2103, Mailing Address: P.O. Box 484, Zip 32063–0484; tel. 904/259–3151, (Nonreporting) **A**9 10 20
Primary Contact: Dennis R. Markos, Chief Executive Officer
CFO: W. Steve Dudley, CPA, Chief Financial Officer
CMO: Mark Hardin, M.D., Medical Director
CIO: Ernie Waller, Director Information Technology
CHR: Stacey Conner, Director Personnel
CNO: Valerie Markos, Chief Nursing Officer
Web address: www.bcmedsvcs.com
Control: Other not-for-profit (including NFP Corporation) **Service:** General Medical and Surgical

Staffed Beds: 68

MADISON—Madison County

MADISON COUNTY MEMORIAL HOSPITAL (101311), 224 N.W. Crane Avenue, Zip 32340–2561; tel. 850/973–2271, (Nonreporting) **A**9 10 18
Primary Contact: David Abercrombie, Chief Executive Officer
COO: Tammy Stevens, Chief Operating Officer
CFO: Patrick Halfhill, Chief Financial Officer
CMO: Brett Perkins, M.D., Chief Medical Staff
CIO: Patrick Stiff, Coordinator Information Technology
CHR: Cindi Burnett, Chief Human Resources Officer
Web address: www.mcmh.us/
Control: Other not-for-profit (including NFP Corporation) **Service:** General Medical and Surgical

Staffed Beds: 25

MARATHON—Monroe County

FISHERMEN'S HOSPITAL (101312), 3301 Overseas Highway, Zip 33050–2329; tel. 305/743–5533 **A**1 9 10 18 **F**3 11 15 17 18 29 34 35 40 45 46 50 51 57 59 64 68 70 75 79 81 82 85 91 93 107 108 110 111 114 119 124 130 133 141 146 **P**8 **S** QHR, Brentwood, TN
Primary Contact: Hal W. Leftwich, FACHE, Chief Executive Officer
COO: Lynn Mauck, R.N., Chief Operating Officer and Chief Nursing Officer
CFO: Scott Merkle, Chief Financial Officer
CMO: Ronald Samess, M.D., Chief of Staff
CIO: Joe Brake, Director Information Services
CHR: Michele Teller, Director Human Resources
CNO: Lynn Mauck, R.N., Chief Operating Officer and Chief Nursing Officer
Web address: www.fishermenshospital.org
Control: Other not-for-profit (including NFP Corporation) **Service:** General Medical and Surgical

Staffed Beds: 25 **Admissions:** 599 **Census:** 5 **Outpatient Visits:** 10427 **Births:** 0 **Total Expense ($000):** 24708 **Payroll Expense ($000):** 10710 **Personnel:** 197

MARGATE—Broward County

NORTHWEST MEDICAL CENTER (100189), 2801 North State Road 7, Zip 33063–5727; tel. 954/974–0400 **A**1 9 10 **F**3 8 11 12 13 15 17 18 22 24 26 29 31 34 35 40 41 44 45 46 47 49 50 53 56 57 59 60 61 63 64 65 68 70 73 74 75 76 77 78 79 80 81 82 83 85 86 87 89 93 107 108 110 111 114 115 117 118 119 126 129 130 131 132 135 146 147 148 **S** HCA, Nashville, TN
Primary Contact: Mark Rader, FACHE, Chief Executive Officer
COO: Erica Gulrich, Chief Operating Officer
CFO: Ananda Rampat, Chief Financial Officer
CMO: Jose Martinez, M.D., Chief Medical Officer
CIO: David Irizarri, Director Information Technology
CHR: Lynda Bryan, Vice President Human Resources
CNO: Sandra Emeott, R.N., Chief Nursing Officer
Web address: www.northwestmed.com
Control: Corporation, Investor-owned, for-profit **Service:** General Medical and Surgical

Staffed Beds: 223 **Admissions:** 14107 **Census:** 145 **Births:** 1498 **Total Expense ($000):** 159226 **Payroll Expense ($000):** 47007

MARIANNA—Jackson County

JACKSON HOSPITAL (100142), 4250 Hospital Drive, Zip 32446–1917, Mailing Address: P.O. Box 1608, Zip 32447–5608; tel. 850/526–2200 **A**1 9 10 20 **F**3 7 11 13 15 18 29 30 31 34 35 40 45 49 50 52 53 57 70 75 76 78 79 81 85 86 87 89 97 107 108 110 111 114 119 127 130 132 133 135 144 146 147 **S** QHR, Brentwood, TN
Primary Contact: Larry Meese, Chief Executive Officer
CFO: Kevin Rovito, Chief Financial Officer
CMO: Doyle Bosse, M.D., Chief Medical Officer
CIO: Beth Medlock, Manager Information Technology
CHR: Brooke G. Donaldson, Assistant Administrator Human Resources
CNO: Robbin K. Catt, Chief Nursing Officer
Web address: www.jacksonhosp.com
Control: Hospital district or authority, Government, nonfederal **Service:** General Medical and Surgical

Staffed Beds: 68 **Admissions:** 3014 **Census:** 37 **Outpatient Visits:** 27784 **Births:** 476 **Total Expense ($000):** 46896 **Payroll Expense ($000):** 20952 **Personnel:** 460

MELBOURNE—Brevard County

CIRCLES OF CARE (104024), 400 East Sheridan Road, Zip 32901–3184; tel. 321/722–5200, (Nonreporting) **A**1 9 10
Primary Contact: James B. Whitaker, President
CFO: David L. Feldman, Executive Vice President and Treasurer
CMO: Jose Alvarez, M.D., Chief Medical Staff
CHR: Linda Brannon, Vice President Human Resources
Web address: www.circlesofcare.org
Control: Other not-for-profit (including NFP Corporation) **Service:** Psychiatric

Staffed Beds: 134

DEVEREUX HOSPITAL AND CHILDREN'S CENTER OF FLORIDA, 8000 Devereux Drive, Zip 32940–7907; tel. 321/242–9100, (Nonreporting) **S** Devereux, Villanova, PA
Primary Contact: Steven Murphy, Executive Director
COO: Eva Horner, Assistant Executive Director Operations
CFO: Kelly Messer, Director Administrative Services
CMO: Emilio Roig, M.D., Network Medical Director
CIO: Diana Deitrick, Director Information Services
CHR: Tim Dillion, Vice President of Human Resources
Web address: www.devereux.org
Control: Other not-for-profit (including NFP Corporation) **Service:** Children's hospital psychiatric

Staffed Beds: 100

HEALTH FIRST HOLMES REGIONAL MEDICAL CENTER (100019), 1350 South Hickory Street, Zip 32901–3224; tel. 321/434–7000 **A**1 5 9 10 **F**3 7 11 13 15 17 18 20 22 24 26 29 30 31 34 35 40 43 45 46 47 48 49 56 57 59 60 65 68 70 72 73 74 75 76 77 78 79 81 82 83 84 85 87 89 91 92 93 100 107 108 110 111 114 115 116 117 118 119 124 126 129 130 132 146 147 148 **P**6 7 **S** Health First, Inc., Rockledge, FL
Primary Contact: Sean Gregory, President
CFO: Joseph G. Felkner, Executive Vice President, Finance and Chief Financial Officer
CMO: Joseph Albert Gurri, Vice President of Medical Affairs
CIO: Dustin Leek, Vice President of Enterprise Technical Services
CHR: Paula B. Just, Chief Human Resources Officer
CNO: Kelly Breedlove, Vice President of Nursing
Web address: www.health-first.org
Control: Other not-for-profit (including NFP Corporation) **Service:** General Medical and Surgical

Staffed Beds: 514 **Admissions:** 26611 **Census:** 375 **Outpatient Visits:** 216945 **Births:** 2572 **Total Expense ($000):** 369551 **Payroll Expense ($000):** 148769 **Personnel:** 1744

HEALTH FIRST PALM BAY HOSPITAL (100316), 1425 Malabar Road N.E., Zip 32907–2506; tel. 321/434–8000 **A**10 **F**3 11 15 18 20 29 30 34 40 43 45 49 51 53 57 59 60 65 68 70 74 75 79 81 84 85 87 91 92 93 107 108 110 111 114 115 118 119 130 132 143 145 146 **P**6 7 **S** Health First, Inc., Rockledge, FL
Primary Contact: J. Stuart Mitchell, III, Interim President
COO: Judy Gizinski, Chief Operating Officer
CFO: Joseph G. Felkner, Executive Vice President and Chief Financial Officer
CMO: Scott Gettings, M.D., Senior Vice President and Chief Medical Affairs
CIO: Lori Delone, Senior Vice President Information Technology
CHR: Paula B. Just, Chief Human Resources Officer
CNO: Connie Bradley, R.N., Senior Vice President Nursing and Chief Nursing Officer
Web address: www.health–first.org/hospitals_services/pbch/index.cfm
Control: Other not–for–profit (including NFP Corporation) **Service:** General Medical and Surgical

Staffed Beds: 119 **Admissions:** 5861 **Census:** 76 **Outpatient Visits:** 74207 **Births:** 0 **Total Expense ($000):** 70029 **Payroll Expense ($000):** 31861 **Personnel:** 323

☐ **HEALTH FIRST VIERA HOSPITAL (100315)**, 8745 North Wickham Road, Zip 32940–5997; tel. 321/434–9164 **A**1 9 10 **F**3 11 12 15 18 20 22 26 29 30 31 34 35 38 40 44 45 46 47 48 49 50 51 55 56 57 59 60 64 68 70 74 75 77 78 79 81 82 85 86 87 93 94 97 107 108 110 111 115 116 117 119 124 126 132 145 146 148 **P**6 **S** Health First, Inc., Rockledge, FL
Primary Contact: J. Stuart Mitchell, III, Interim President
COO: Deborah Angerami, Chief Operating Officer
CFO: Joseph G. Felkner, Executive Vice President and Chief Financial Officer
CMO: Scott Gettings, M.D., Senior Vice President and Chief Medical Officer
CIO: Lori Delone, Senior Vice President and Chief Information Officer
CHR: Paula B. Just, Chief Human Resources Officer
CNO: Connie Bradley, R.N., Senior Vice President and Chief Nursing Officer
Web address: www.vierahospital.org
Control: Other not–for–profit (including NFP Corporation) **Service:** General Medical and Surgical

Staffed Beds: 84 **Admissions:** 3587 **Census:** 39 **Outpatient Visits:** 49715 **Births:** 0 **Total Expense ($000):** 75188 **Payroll Expense ($000):** 25170 **Personnel:** 296

✚ **HEALTHSOUTH SEA PINES REHABILITATION HOSPITAL (103034)**, 101 East Florida Avenue, Zip 32901–8301; tel. 321/984–4600 **A**1 9 10 **F**29 34 59 62 64 68 79 82 86 87 91 93 94 95 96 130 132 148 **S** HEALTHSOUTH Corporation, Birmingham, AL
Primary Contact: Denise B. McGrath, Chief Executive Officer
CFO: Dana Edwards, Chief Financial Officer
CMO: Juan Lebron, M.D., Medical Director
CHR: James L. Henry, Director Human Resources
CNO: Corinne Romano, R.N., Chief Nursing Officer
Web address: www.healthsouthseapines.com
Control: Corporation, Investor–owned, for–profit **Service:** Rehabilitation

Staffed Beds: 90 **Admissions:** 1439 **Census:** 58 **Outpatient Visits:** 4800 **Births:** 0 **Total Expense ($000):** 15733 **Payroll Expense ($000):** 11335 **Personnel:** 180

✚ **KINDRED HOSPITAL MELBOURNE (102027)**, 765 West Nasa Boulevard, Zip 32901–1815; tel. 321/733–5725 **A**1 5 9 **F**1 3 17 29 70 107 114 148 **S** Kindred Healthcare, Louisville, KY
Primary Contact: Joyce Baldrica, Chief Executive Officer
Web address: www.khmelbourne.com
Control: Corporation, Investor–owned, for–profit **Service:** Long–Term Acute Care hospital

Staffed Beds: 60 **Admissions:** 450 **Census:** 31 **Outpatient Visits:** 0 **Births:** 0 **Total Expense ($000):** 19139 **Payroll Expense ($000):** 6958 **Personnel:** 117

✚ **WUESTHOFF MEDICAL CENTER – MELBOURNE (100291)**, 250 North Wickham Road, Zip 32935–8625; tel. 321/752–1200 **A**1 9 10 **F**3 11 12 13 15 18 20 22 29 30 38 40 49 50 51 57 59 60 64 68 70 74 75 76 77 79 80 81 85 87 89 93 102 107 108 111 114 115 116 117 119 126 130 131 132 135 144 146 147 148 **S** Community Health Systems, Inc., Franklin, TN
Primary Contact: Richard Frank, Chief Executive Officer
CFO: Steve Bender, Chief Financial Officer
Web address: www.wuesthoff.com/locations/wuesthoff–medical–center–melbourne
Control: Corporation, Investor–owned, for–profit **Service:** General Medical and Surgical

Staffed Beds: 119 **Admissions:** 4574 **Census:** 61 **Births:** 236 **Total Expense ($000):** 72251 **Payroll Expense ($000):** 21985

MIAMI—Miami–Dade County

✚ △ **BAPTIST HEALTH SOUTH FLORIDA, BAPTIST HOSPITAL OF MIAMI (100008)**, 8900 North Kendall Drive, Zip 33176–2197; tel. 786/596–1960, (Includes BAPTIST CHILDREN'S HOSPITAL, 8900 North Kendall Drive, Zip 33176–2118; tel. 786/596–1960) **A**1 2 3 5 7 9 10 **F**3 8 11 13 15 17 18 19 20 22 24 26 28 29 30 31 32 34 35 40 41 45 46 47 49 50 51 53 54 55 56 57 58 59 60 61 62 63 64 66 68 70 72 73 74 75 76 77 78 79 81 82 84 85 86 87 88 89 90 91 92 93 96 100 102 107 108 109 110 111 114 115 116 117 118 119 120 121 123 124 126 129 130 132 135 144 145 146 147 148 **S** Baptist Health South Florida, Coral Gables, FL
Primary Contact: Albert Boulenger, Chief Executive Officer
COO: Randall Lee, Vice President and Chief Operating Officer
CFO: Ralph E. Lawson, Executive Vice President and Chief Financial Officer
CMO: Mark J. Hauser, M.D., Chief Medical Officer
CIO: Mimi Taylor, Corporate Vice President Information Technology
CHR: Corey Heller, Corporate Vice President and Chief Human Resources Officer
Web address: www.baptisthealth.net
Control: Other not–for–profit (including NFP Corporation) **Service:** General Medical and Surgical

Staffed Beds: 672 **Admissions:** 34021 **Census:** 483 **Outpatient Visits:** 372014 **Births:** 4383 **Total Expense ($000):** 762631 **Payroll Expense ($000):** 261070 **Personnel:** 3979

✚ **BAPTIST HEALTH SOUTH FLORIDA, SOUTH MIAMI HOSPITAL (100154)**, 6200 S.W. 73rd Street, Zip 33143–4679; tel. 786/662–4000 **A**1 9 10 **F**3 5 11 12 13 15 17 18 20 22 24 26 28 29 30 31 34 35 36 40 46 48 49 50 51 52 53 54 57 58 59 60 61 64 68 70 72 74 75 76 77 78 79 81 82 84 85 86 87 93 107 108 110 111 114 115 116 117 118 119 120 121 123 124 126 129 130 132 135 144 146 147 148 **S** Baptist Health South Florida, Coral Gables, FL
Primary Contact: Lincoln S. Mendez, Chief Executive Officer
COO: Jeanette Stone, Vice President Operations
CFO: Berta Rufat, Controller
CMO: Jeremy Tabak, M.D., President Medical Staff
CIO: Mimi Taylor, Vice President Information Technology
CHR: Diana Montenegro, Director Human Resources
CNO: Kathy Sparger, R.N., Chief Nursing Officer
Web address: www.baptisthealth.net
Control: Other not–for–profit (including NFP Corporation) **Service:** General Medical and Surgical

Staffed Beds: 364 **Admissions:** 15457 **Census:** 210 **Outpatient Visits:** 260627 **Births:** 4324 **Total Expense ($000):** 431828 **Payroll Expense ($000):** 147461 **Personnel:** 2190

✚ **BAPTIST HEALTH SOUTH FLORIDA, WEST KENDALL BAPTIST HOSPITAL (100314)**, 9555 S.W. 162nd Avenue, Zip 33196–6408; tel. 786/467–2000 **A**1 10 **F**3 13 18 19 29 30 31 34 35 40 41 45 49 50 51 53 57 58 59 60 63 64 68 70 74 75 76 78 79 81 82 84 85 86 87 93 100 102 107 108 109 111 114 115 119 130 131 132 135 146 147 148 **S** Baptist Health South Florida, Coral Gables, FL
Primary Contact: Javier Hernandez–Lichtl, Chief Executive Officer
CFO: Odalys Remigio, Assistant Vice President, Finance
CMO: Juan–Carlos Verdeja, M.D., President of Medical Staff
CHR: Hilde Zamora de Aguero, Human Resources Site Director
CNO: Denise H. Harris, R.N., Chief Nursing Officer
Web address: www.baptisthealth.net/en/facilities/West–Kendall–Baptist–Hospital/Pages/default.aspx
Control: Other not–for–profit (including NFP Corporation) **Service:** General Medical and Surgical

Staffed Beds: 133 **Admissions:** 5752 **Census:** 64 **Outpatient Visits:** 61105 **Births:** 728 **Total Expense ($000):** 158300 **Payroll Expense ($000):** 52184 **Personnel:** 846

✚ **BASCOM PALMER EYE INSTITUTE–ANNE BATES LEACH EYE HOSPITAL (100240)**, 900 N.W. 17th Street, Zip 33136–1199, Mailing Address: Box 016880, Zip 33101–6880; tel. 305/326–6000 **A**1 3 5 9 10 **F**8 34 40 44 50 55 57 58 59 64 66 68 71 74 78 79 81 86 87 92 93 94 107 108 111 119 129 130 141 144 146 **P**6 **S** University of Miami Health System, Miami, FL
Primary Contact: Michael B. Gittelman, Administrator
COO: Charles Pappas, M.D., Chief Operating Officer
CFO: Harry Rohrer, Chief Financial Officer
CMO: Eduardo Alfonso, M.D., Chairman Ophthalmology
CHR: Paul Hudgins, Associate Vice President Human Resources
Web address: www.bascompalmer.org
Control: Other not–for–profit (including NFP Corporation) **Service:** Eye, ear, nose, and throat

Staffed Beds: 56 **Admissions:** 57 **Census:** 1 **Outpatient Visits:** 226901 **Births:** 0 **Total Expense ($000):** 95734 **Payroll Expense ($000):** 27923 **Personnel:** 621

HIGHLAND PARK HOSPITAL See Jackson Health System

FL

☐ △ **JACKSON HEALTH SYSTEM (100022)**, 1611 N.W. 12th Avenue, Zip 33136–1005; tel. 305/585–1111, (Includes HIGHLAND PARK HOSPITAL, 1695 N.W. Ninth Avenue, Zip 33136; tel. 305/355–8234; HOLTZ CHILDREN'S HOSPITAL, 1611 N.W. 12th Avenue, tel. 305/585–5437; Daniel Armstrong, Chief Administrative Officer; JACKSON MEMORIAL HOSPITAL, 1611 N.W. 12th Avenue, Zip 33136; tel. 305/585–6661; Alex Contreras–Soto, Senior Vice President and Chief Administrative Officer; JACKSON NORTH MEDICAL CENTER, 160 N.W. 170th Street, North Miami Beach, Zip 33169–5576; tel. 305/651–1100; Sandy Sears, Senior Vice President and Chief Administrative Officer; JACKSON SOUTH COMMUNITY HOSPITAL, 9333 S.W. 152nd Street, Zip 33157–1780; tel. 305/251–2500; Martha Garcia, Senior Vice President and Chief Administrative Officer), (Total facility includes 343 beds in nursing home–type unit) **A**1 3 5 7 8 9 10 **F**1 3 4 5 8 11 12 13 15 16 17 18 19 20 21 22 23 24 25 26 27 28 29 30 31 34 35 38 39 40 41 43 44 45 49 50 54 55 56 57 58 59 60 61 64 65 66 67 68 70 71 72 74 75 76 77 78 79 80 81 82 83 84 85 86 87 88 89 90 93 94 96 97 98 99 100 101 102 103 104 106 107 108 109 110 111 114 115 116 117 118 119 120 121 123 126 128 130 132 135 136 137 138 139 140 141 142 146 147 148 **P**6
Primary Contact: Carlos A. Migoya, President and Chief Executive Officer
COO: Don S. Steigman, Chief Operating Officer
CFO: Mark T. Knight, Executive Vice President and Chief Financial Officer
CMO: Michael K. Butler, M.D., Executive Vice President and Chief Medical Officer
CIO: Fernando Martinez, Vice President and Chief Information Officer
CHR: Trummell Valdera, Senior Vice President and Chief Human Resources Officer
Web address: www.um–jmh.org
Control: County–Government, nonfederal **Service:** General Medical and Surgical

Staffed Beds: 1939 Admissions: 58275 Census: 1091 Outpatient Visits: 334622 Births: 6028 Total Expense ($000): 1513235 Payroll Expense ($000): 689984 Personnel: 8910

JACKSON SOUTH COMMUNITY HOSPITAL See Jackson Health System

☒ **KENDALL REGIONAL MEDICAL CENTER (100209)**, 11750 Bird Road, Zip 33175–3530; tel. 305/223–3000, (Nonreporting) **A**1 9 10 **S** HCA, Nashville, TN
Primary Contact: Scott A. Cihak, Chief Executive Officer
COO: Elizabeth Durrence, Chief Operating Officer
CFO: Scott Herndon, Chief Financial Officer
CIO: Francis Tezanos, Director Information Technology and Services
CHR: Knicole S. White, Director Human Resources
CNO: Wendy Stuart, Chief Nursing Officer
Web address: www.kendallmed.com
Control: Partnership, Investor–owned, for–profit **Service:** General Medical and Surgical

Staffed Beds: 300

☒ **MIAMI CHILDREN'S HOSPITAL (103301)**, 3100 S.W. 62nd Avenue, Zip 33155–3009; tel. 305/666–6511 **A**1 2 3 5 8 9 10 12 13 **F**1 3 4 7 8 9 16 17 18 19 20 21 22 23 24 25 27 29 30 31 32 34 35 36 38 39 40 41 42 43 44 45 46 50 53 54 55 57 58 59 60 61 64 65 66 67 68 70 71 72 73 74 75 76 77 78 79 80 81 82 85 86 87 88 89 90 93 97 98 99 100 101 102 104 105 106 107 108 111 114 115 116 117 118 119 120 127 128 129 130 131 132 134 136 143 144 146 **P**6 7
Primary Contact: M. Narendra Kini, M.D., President and Chief Executive Officer
COO: Martha McGill, Executive Vice President and Chief Operating Officer
CFO: Timothy L. Birkenstock, Chief Financial Officer
CMO: Deise Granado–Villar, M.D., Chief Medical Officer and Senior Vice President Medical Affairs
CIO: Edward Martinez, Chief Information Officer
CHR: Michael S. Kushner, Senior Vice President and Chief Talent Officer
CNO: Jacqueline Gonzalez, Senior Vice President and Chief Nursing Officer
Web address: www.mch.com
Control: Other not–for–profit (including NFP Corporation) **Service:** Children's general

Staffed Beds: 272 Admissions: 11272 Census: 173 Outpatient Visits: 445902 Births: 0 Total Expense ($000): 490430 Payroll Expense ($000): 234338 Personnel: 3191

☐ **MIAMI JEWISH HOME AND HOSPITAL FOR AGED (100277)**, 5200 N.E. Second Avenue, Zip 33137–2706; tel. 305/751–8626, (Nonreporting) **A**1 3 5 10
Primary Contact: Jeffrey P. Freimark, Chief Executive Officer
CFO: Lisa Jo Desmarteau, Chief Financial Officer
CMO: Brian Kiedrowski, M.D., Chief Medical Director
CHR: Larry McDonald, Director Human Resources
Web address: www.mjhha.org
Control: Other not–for–profit (including NFP Corporation) **Service:** General Medical and Surgical

Staffed Beds: 32

☒ △ **MIAMI VETERANS AFFAIRS HEALTHCARE SYSTEM**, 1201 N.W. 16th Street, Zip 33125–1624; tel. 305/575–7000, (Nonreporting) **A**1 3 5 7
S Department of Veterans Affairs, Washington, DC
Primary Contact: Paul M. Russo, FACHE, Director
CFO: Albert Tucker, Chief Financial Officer
CMO: Vincent DeGennaro, M.D., Chief of Staff
CIO: Anthony Brooks, Chief Information Officer
CHR: Loyman Marin, Chief Human Resources
CNO: Marcia C. Lysaght, R.N., Associate Director Patient Care Services
Web address: www.miami.va.gov/
Control: Veterans Affairs, Government, federal **Service:** General Medical and Surgical

Staffed Beds: 401

☒ **NORTH SHORE MEDICAL CENTER (100029)**, 1100 N.W. 95th Street, Zip 33150–2098; tel. 305/835–6000, (Nonreporting) **A**1 9 10 **S** TENET Healthcare Corporation, Dallas, TX
Primary Contact: Manuel Linares, Chief Executive Officer
COO: Shana Crittenden, Chief Operating Officer
CFO: Howard Brown, Chief Financial Officer
CMO: Marcia Bierman, M.D., Chief of Staff
CIO: Luis Estrada, Director Multifacility Information Systems
CHR: Carmen Gomez, Director Human Resources
CNO: Patrick Beaver, Chief Nursing Officer
Web address: www.northshoremedical.com
Control: Corporation, Investor–owned, for–profit **Service:** General Medical and Surgical

Staffed Beds: 357

☒ **SELECT SPECIALTY HOSPITAL–MIAMI (102001)**, 955 N.W. 3rd Street, Zip 33128–1274; tel. 305/416–5700, (Nonreporting) **A**1 9 10 **S** Select Medical Corporation, Mechanicsburg, PA
Primary Contact: Dionisio Bencomo, Chief Executive Officer
Web address: www.selectspecialtyhospitals.com/company/locations/miami.aspx
Control: Corporation, Investor–owned, for–profit **Service:** Long–Term Acute Care hospital

Staffed Beds: 40

☐ **SISTER EMMANUEL HOSPITAL (102016)**, 3663 South Miami Avenue, Zip 33133–4253; tel. 305/285–2939, (Nonreporting) **A**1 9 10
Primary Contact: Shed Boren, Administrator and Chief Executive Officer
CFO: Miguel Vasquez, Chief Financial Officer
CMO: Hugo Gonzalez, M.D., Chief Medical Officer
CIO: Macarena Restrepo, Manager Business Office
CHR: Kathy Mainieri, Human Resource Specialist
Web address: www.sisteremmanuelhospital.org/
Control: Church–operated, Nongovernment, not–for profit **Service:** Long–Term Acute Care hospital

Staffed Beds: 29

☒ **UNIVERSITY OF MIAMI HOSPITAL (100009)**, 1400 N.W. 12th Avenue, Zip 33136–1003; tel. 305/325–5511 **A**1 2 3 5 9 10 **F**3 8 11 12 15 17 18 20 22 24 26 29 30 31 34 35 36 38 39 40 42 44 45 46 47 48 49 50 51 54 57 58 59 63 64 66 68 70 71 74 75 77 78 79 80 81 82 84 85 86 87 90 92 93 97 98 100 102 105 107 108 109 110 111 113 114 115 117 118 119 120 121 123 124 126 130 131 135 141 146 148 **S** University of Miami Health System, Miami, FL
Primary Contact: David Zambrana, R.N., Chief Executive Officer
CFO: Harry Rohrer, Chief Financial Officer
CMO: Francisco Kerdel, M.D., President Medical Staff
CIO: Craig Scott, Interim Director Management Information Systems
CHR: Errol Douglas, Director Human Resources
Web address: www.umiamihospital.com
Control: Other not–for–profit (including NFP Corporation) **Service:** General Medical and Surgical

Staffed Beds: 516 Admissions: 21094 Census: 328 Outpatient Visits: 138049 Births: 0 Total Expense ($000): 365419 Payroll Expense ($000): 111977 Personnel: 1954

FL

✠ **UNIVERSITY OF MIAMI HOSPITAL AND CLINICS (100079)**, 1475 N.W. 12th Avenue, Zip 33136–1002; tel. 305/243–4000 **A**1 2 3 5 9 10 **F**3 9 11 12 14 15 18 19 29 30 31 32 34 35 36 38 44 45 46 47 48 49 50 52 54 55 57 58 59 61 64 65 68 70 74 75 77 78 79 80 81 82 84 85 86 87 91 92 93 97 99 100 101 103 104 107 108 110 111 114 115 117 118 119 120 121 123 124 126 130 132 135 136 141 145 146 147 148 **P**6 **S** University of Miami Health System, Miami, FL
Primary Contact: Richard R. Ballard, Chief Executive Officer and Administrator
COO: Joseph B. Natoli, Senior Vice President Business and Finance and Chief Financial Officer
CFO: Harry Rohrer, Chief Financial Officer
CMO: W. Jarrad Goodwin, M.D., Director
CHR: Paul Hudgins, Associate Vice President Human Resources
Web address: www.uhealthsystem.com
Control: Other not–for–profit (including NFP Corporation) **Service:** General Medical and Surgical

> **Staffed Beds:** 40 **Admissions:** 1576 **Census:** 30 **Outpatient Visits:** 357061 **Births:** 0 **Total Expense ($000):** 299456 **Payroll Expense ($000):** 58565 **Personnel:** 1106

VETERANS AFFAIRS MEDICAL CENTER See Miami Veterans Affairs Healthcare System

✠ △ **WEST GABLES REHABILITATION HOSPITAL (103036)**, 2525 S.W. 75th Avenue, Zip 33155–2800; tel. 305/262–6800 **A**1 7 9 10 **F**7 29 90 91 93 148 **S** Select Medical Corporation, Mechanicsburg, PA
Primary Contact: Walter Concepcion, Chief Executive Officer
CFO: Sara Reohr, Regional Controller
CMO: Jose L. Vargas, M.D., Medical Director
CHR: Barbara Etchason, HR Manager
CNO: Constance Hughes, Director of Nursing
Web address: www.westgablesrehabhospital.com/
Control: Corporation, Investor–owned, for–profit **Service:** Rehabilitation

> **Staffed Beds:** 60 **Admissions:** 1442 **Census:** 49 **Outpatient Visits:** 18075 **Births:** 0 **Total Expense ($000):** 20725 **Payroll Expense ($000):** 10117

○ **WESTCHESTER GENERAL HOSPITAL (100284)**, 2500 S.W. 75th Avenue, Zip 33155–2805; tel. 305/264–5252, (Includes SOUTHERN WINDS HOSPITAL, 4225 West 20th Street, Hialeah, Zip 33012–5835; tel. 305/558–9700) **A**9 10 11 12 13 **F**3 15 18 29 31 40 45 49 56 65 70 74 75 77 78 79 81 85 87 98 99 100 102 103 107 108 110 114 115 119 130
Primary Contact: Gilda Baldwin, Chief Executive Officer
CFO: Joel Snook, Chief Financial Officer
CMO: Rogelio Zaldivar, M.D., Medical Director
CHR: Alicia Lund, Director Human Resources
Web address: www.westchesterhospital.com
Control: Corporation, Investor–owned, for–profit **Service:** General Medical and Surgical

> **Staffed Beds:** 197 **Admissions:** 9046 **Census:** 140 **Outpatient Visits:** 31548 **Births:** 0 **Total Expense ($000):** 68027 **Payroll Expense ($000):** 33875 **Personnel:** 638

MIAMI BEACH—Dade County

MIAMI HEART CAMPUS AT MOUNT SINAI MEDICAL CENTER See Mount Sinai Medical Center

☐ △ **MOUNT SINAI MEDICAL CENTER (100034)**, 4300 Alton Road, Zip 33140–2948; tel. 305/674–2121, (Includes MIAMI HEART CAMPUS AT MOUNT SINAI MEDICAL CENTER, 4701 North Meridian Avenue, Zip 33140–2910; tel. 305/672–1111) **A**1 2 3 5 7 8 9 10 13 **F**1 3 4 6 8 13 14 15 16 17 18 20 22 24 26 28 29 30 31 34 35 37 39 40 42 43 44 45 46 47 49 51 53 54 55 56 57 58 59 60 61 62 64 65 66 67 70 71 72 73 74 75 76 77 78 79 80 81 82 83 84 85 86 87 88 89 90 91 92 93 96 97 98 100 101 102 103 104 107 108 110 111 112 114 115 118 119 120 121 123 124 126 128 129 130 131 132 135 143 145 146 147 148
Primary Contact: Steven D. Sonenreich, President and Chief Executive Officer
COO: Angel Pallin, Senior Vice President of Operations
CFO: Alex A. Mendez, Executive Vice President of Operations and Chief Financial Officer
CMO: Robert Goldszer, M.D., Senior Vice President and Chief Medical Officer
CIO: Tom Gillette, Senior Vice President and Chief Information Officer
CHR: Georgia McLean, Director Human Resources
Web address: www.msmc.com
Control: Other not–for–profit (including NFP Corporation) **Service:** General Medical and Surgical

> **Staffed Beds:** 608 **Admissions:** 22742 **Census:** 373 **Outpatient Visits:** 180837 **Births:** 2710 **Total Expense ($000):** 412822 **Payroll Expense ($000):** 165014 **Personnel:** 3394

MIDDLEBURG—Clay County

ST. VINCENT'S MEDICAL CENTER CLAY COUNTY (100321), 1670 St. Vincent's Way, Zip 32068–8427, Mailing Address: 1580 Branan Field Road, Zip 32068–8427; tel. 904/602–1000, (Nonreporting)
Primary Contact: Blain Claypool, Chief Executive Officer
Web address: www.jaxhealth.com/
Control: Church–operated, Nongovernment, not–for profit **Service:** General Medical and Surgical

> **Staffed Beds:** 64

MILTON—Santa Rosa County

✠ **SANTA ROSA MEDICAL CENTER (100124)**, 6002 Berryhill Road, Zip 32570–5062; tel. 850/626–7762 **A**1 9 10 **F**3 11 13 15 18 20 29 30 34 35 40 45 49 54 57 59 64 65 74 75 76 77 79 81 85 87 97 107 108 111 115 119 126 129 130 132 135 144 146 147 148 **S** Community Health Systems, Inc., Franklin, TN
Primary Contact: Phillip L. Wright, FACHE, Chief Executive Officer
CFO: Jared Whipkey, Chief Financial Officer
CIO: Rick Payne, Director Information Systems
CHR: Christopher Foreman, Director Human Resources
CNO: Trish Davis, Chief Nursing Officer
Web address: www.santarosamedicalcenter.org
Control: Corporation, Investor–owned, for–profit **Service:** General Medical and Surgical

> **Staffed Beds:** 68 **Admissions:** 3947 **Census:** 37 **Outpatient Visits:** 69857 **Births:** 406 **Total Expense ($000):** 51136 **Payroll Expense ($000):** 15600 **Personnel:** 378

WEST FLORIDA COMMUNITY CARE CENTER (104027), 5500 Stewart Street, Zip 32570–4304; tel. 850/983–5500 **A**10 **F**29 30 98 106 130 132 143
Primary Contact: Carmen Paroby, Administrator
Control: Other not–for–profit (including NFP Corporation) **Service:** Psychiatric

> **Staffed Beds:** 80 **Admissions:** 221 **Census:** 79 **Outpatient Visits:** 0 **Births:** 0

MIRAMAR—Broward County

✠ **MEMORIAL HOSPITAL MIRAMAR (100285)**, 1901 S.W. 172nd Avenue, Zip 33029–5592; tel. 954/538–5000 **A**1 9 10 **F**3 13 15 29 30 40 41 45 49 50 57 59 61 64 68 70 72 74 75 76 78 79 81 82 85 86 87 91 93 107 108 110 111 114 115 118 119 126 130 131 132 145 146 147 **S** Memorial Healthcare System, Hollywood, FL
Primary Contact: Leah A. Carpenter, Administrator and Chief Executive Officer
CFO: Judy Sada, Chief Financial Officer
CMO: Stanley Marks, M.D., Chief Medical Officer
CIO: Forest Blanton, Senior VP and Chief Information Officer
CHR: Ray Kendrick, Chief Human Resources Officer
CNO: Denise Reynolds, Chief Nursing Officer
Web address: www.mhs.net
Control: Hospital district or authority, Government, nonfederal **Service:** General Medical and Surgical

> **Staffed Beds:** 178 **Admissions:** 8858 **Census:** 88 **Outpatient Visits:** 120640 **Births:** 3069 **Total Expense ($000):** 123667 **Payroll Expense ($000):** 57214 **Personnel:** 796

MIRAMAR BEACH—Walton County

✠ **SACRED HEART HOSPITAL ON THE EMERALD COAST (100292)**, 7800 Highway 98 West, Zip 32550; tel. 850/278–3000 **A**1 9 10 **F**3 11 13 15 18 20 22 26 28 29 30 31 34 35 36 40 44 49 50 51 53 57 58 59 60 64 68 70 74 75 76 78 79 81 82 84 85 86 87 93 96 107 108 110 111 114 115 118 119 121 123 124 130 132 135 146 147 148 **P**7 **S** Ascension Health, Saint Louis, MO
Primary Contact: Roger L. Hall, President
CMO: Gary M. Pablo, M.D., Chief Medical Officer
Web address: www.sacredheartemerald.org
Control: Other not–for–profit (including NFP Corporation) **Service:** General Medical and Surgical

> **Staffed Beds:** 58 **Admissions:** 4479 **Census:** 37 **Outpatient Visits:** 75724 **Births:** 926 **Total Expense ($000):** 80297 **Payroll Expense ($000):** 25480 **Personnel:** 367

NAPLES—Collier County

✠ △ **NCH DOWNTOWN NAPLES HOSPITAL (100018)**, 350 Seventh Street North, Zip 34102–5754, Mailing Address: P.O. Box 413029, Zip 34101–3029; tel. 239/624–4000, (Includes NCH NORTH NAPLES HOSPITAL, 11190 Health Park Boulevard, Zip 34110–5729, Mailing Address: 11190 Health Park Boulevard, Zip 34110–5729; tel. 239/552–7000) **A**1 2 7 9 10 **F**3 11 13 14 18 20 22 24 26 28 29 30 31 34 37 40 41 45 47 49 50 53 55 57 59 64 68 70 72 74 75 76 77 78 79 81 84 85 86 87 88 89 90 92 93 95 96 98 100 102 103 107 108 111 114 115 119 126 130 146 147 148
Primary Contact: Allen S. Weiss, M.D., President and Chief Executive Officer
COO: Phillip C. Dutcher, Chief Operating Officer
CFO: Mike Stephens, Chief Financial Officer
CMO: Doug Ardion, M.D., Chief Medical Officer
CHR: John McGirl, Chief Human Resources Officer
CNO: Michele Thoman, R.N., Chief Nursing Officer
Web address: www.nchmd.org
Control: Other not–for–profit (including NFP Corporation) **Service:** General Medical and Surgical

> **Staffed Beds:** 716 **Admissions:** 30451 **Census:** 376 **Outpatient Visits:** 276070 **Births:** 2954 **Total Expense ($000):** 382941 **Payroll Expense ($000):** 145468 **Personnel:** 2616

Many Facility Codes have changed. Please refer to the AHA Guide Code Chart. © 2014 AHA Guide

⊠ **PHYSICIANS REGIONAL – PINE RIDGE (100286)**, 6101 Pine Ridge Road, Zip 34119–3900; tel. 239/348–4000, (Includes PHYSICIANS REGIONAL, 8300 Collier Boulevard, Zip 34114; tel. 239/354–6000; C. Scott Campbell, Market Chief Executive Officer), (Nonreporting) **A**1 9 10 **S** Community Health Systems, Inc., Franklin, TN
Primary Contact: C. Scott Campbell, Market Chief Executive Officer
COO: Susan Takacs, Market Chief Operating Officer
CFO: Ken Warriner, Market Chief Financial Officer
CHR: Jill Gaffoli, Director Human Resources
CNO: Judy C. Paull, R.N., Market Chief Nursing Executive
Web address: www.physiciansregional.com
Control: Corporation, Investor–owned, for–profit **Service:** General Medical and Surgical

Staffed Beds: 70

☐ **WILLOUGH HEALTHCARE SYSTEM (104063)**, 9001 Tamiami Trail East, Zip 34113–3304; tel. 239/775–4500, (Nonreporting) **A**1 9 10
Primary Contact: James E. O'Shea, Administrator
CFO: Steve Baldwin, Vice President Finance
Web address: www.thewilloughatnaples.com/
Control: Corporation, Investor–owned, for–profit **Service:** Psychiatric

Staffed Beds: 80

NEW PORT RICHEY—Pasco County

⊠ △ **MORTON PLANT NORTH BAY HOSPITAL (100063)**, 6600 Madison Street, Zip 34652–1900; tel. 727/754–9222 **A**1 7 9 10 **F**3 11 18 20 22 29 30 31 34 35 40 44 45 47 48 49 50 57 58 59 64 68 70 74 75 77 78 79 81 84 85 86 87 90 93 96 98 99 100 102 107 108 109 111 114 115 118 119 129 130 132 135 136 143 146 148 **P**6 7 **S** Morton Plant Mease Health Care, Clearwater, FL
Primary Contact: Michael Yungmann, President
CFO: Carl Tremonti, Chief Financial Officer
CMO: Donald Pocock, M.D., Chief Medical Officer
CHR: Sharon Collotta, Director Team Resources
CNO: Lisa Johnson, R.N., Chief Nursing Executive
Web address: www.mpmhealth.com
Control: Other not–for–profit (including NFP Corporation) **Service:** General Medical and Surgical

Staffed Beds: 226 **Admissions:** 10642 **Census:** 145 **Outpatient Visits:** 33419 **Births:** 0 **Total Expense ($000):** 101643 **Payroll Expense ($000):** 42134 **Personnel:** 611

NEW SMYRNA BEACH—Volusia County

⊠ **BERT FISH MEDICAL CENTER (100014)**, 401 Palmetto Street, Zip 32168–7399; tel. 386/424–5000 **A**1 9 10 **F**3 11 15 18 20 22 28 29 30 33 34 40 45 46 49 50 57 59 60 66 68 70 74 78 79 81 84 93 107 108 110 111 114 115 119 120 121 135 148 **P**5
Primary Contact: Steven W. Harrell, FACHE, Interim Chief Executive Officer
COO: Steven W. Harrell, FACHE, Chief Operating Officer
CFO: Al W. Allred, Chief Financial Officer
CMO: Eric Lo, M.D., Chief Medical Staff
CIO: Calvin Patrick, II, Director Information Services
CHR: Nancy K. Evolga, Executive Director Human Resources
CNO: Linda G. Breum, R.N., Chief Nursing Officer
Web address: www.bertfish.com
Control: Hospital district or authority, Government, nonfederal **Service:** General Medical and Surgical

Staffed Beds: 85 **Admissions:** 3679 **Census:** 44 **Outpatient Visits:** 125641 **Births:** 0 **Total Expense ($000):** 86864 **Payroll Expense ($000):** 32512 **Personnel:** 626

NICEVILLE—Okaloosa County

⊠ **TWIN CITIES HOSPITAL (100054)**, 2190 Highway 85 North, Zip 32578–1045; tel. 850/678–4131 **A**1 9 10 **F**3 29 34 35 45 50 59 70 75 79 81 82 85 93 107 108 110 111 115 119 124 147 **S** HCA, Nashville, TN
Primary Contact: David Whalen, Chief Executive Officer
CFO: Mark Day, Chief Financial Officer
CHR: Cyndi Ronca, Director Human Resources
Web address: www.tchealthcare.com
Control: Corporation, Investor–owned, for–profit **Service:** General Medical and Surgical

Staffed Beds: 38 **Admissions:** 1790 **Census:** 18 **Outpatient Visits:** 38672 **Births:** 0 **Total Expense ($000):** 34943 **Payroll Expense ($000):** 12088 **Personnel:** 161

NORTH MIAMI—Miami–Dade County

☐ △ **ST. CATHERINE'S REHABILITATION HOSPITAL (103026)**, 1050 N.E. 125th Street, Zip 33161–5881; tel. 305/357–1735, (Nonreporting) **A**1 7 9 10 **S** Catholic Health Services, Lauderdale Lakes, FL
Primary Contact: Jaime Gonzalez, Administrator
COO: Jim Ball, Chief Operating Officer
CFO: Mary Jo Frick, Director Finance
CMO: Miriam Feliz, M.D., Medical Director
Web address: www.catholichealthservices.org
Control: Other not–for–profit (including NFP Corporation) **Service:** Rehabilitation

Staffed Beds: 60

NORTH MIAMI BEACH—Dade County

JACKSON NORTH MEDICAL CENTER See Jackson Health System, Miami

OCALA—Marion County

⊠ **HEALTHSOUTH REHABILITATION HOSPITAL OF OCALA (103043)**, 2275 S.W. 22nd Lane, Zip 34471–7710; tel. 352/282–4000 **A**1 **F**3 16 18 29 34 35 57 60 74 82 90 95 96 128 132 143 148 **S** HEALTHSOUTH Corporation, Birmingham, AL
Primary Contact: Ellen Witterstaeter, FACHE, Chief Executive Officer
CFO: Sammy King, Controller
CMO: Amy Clunn, M.D., Medical Director
CHR: Tracy Sapp, Director Human Resources
CNO: Wendy Milam, Chief Nursing Officer
Web address: www.healthsouthocala.com
Control: Corporation, Investor–owned, for–profit **Service:** Rehabilitation

Staffed Beds: 40 **Admissions:** 2922 **Census:** 33 **Births:** 0

⊠ **KINDRED HOSPITAL OCALA (102019)**, 1500 S.W. 1st Avenue, Zip 34471–6504; tel. 352/369–0513, (Nonreporting) **A**1 9 10 **S** Kindred Healthcare, Louisville, KY
Primary Contact: Merlene Bhoorasingh, Administrator
CFO: Dean Cocchi, Chief Financial Officer
Web address: www.kindredocala.com/
Control: Corporation, Investor–owned, for–profit **Service:** Long–Term Acute Care hospital

Staffed Beds: 31

⊠ **MUNROE REGIONAL MEDICAL CENTER (100062)**, 1500 S.W. 1st Avenue, Zip 34471–6504, Mailing Address: P.O. Box 6000, Zip 34478–6000; tel. 352/351–7200, (Nonreporting) **A**1 3 5 9 10 **S** HCA, Nashville, TN
Primary Contact: Richard Mutarelli, Interim Chief Executive Officer
COO: Philoron A. Wright, II, FACHE, Chief Operating Officer
CFO: Eric LaChance, Chief Financial Officer
CMO: Lon McPherson, M.D., Senior Vice President Medical Affairs and Chief Quality Officer
CIO: Carl Candullo, Chief Information Officer
CNO: Pamela W. Michell, R.N., Vice President, Chief Nursing Officer
Web address: www.munroeregional.com
Control: Corporation, Investor–owned, for–profit **Service:** General Medical and Surgical

Staffed Beds: 370

⊠ **OCALA REGIONAL MEDICAL CENTER (100212)**, 1431 S.W. First Avenue, Zip 34471–6500, Mailing Address: P.O. Box 2200, Zip 34478–2200; tel. 352/401–1000, (Includes WEST MARION COMMUNITY HOSPITAL, 4600 S.W. 46th Court, Zip 34474; tel. 352/291–3000), (Nonreporting) **A**1 2 9 10 **S** HCA, Nashville, TN
Primary Contact: Randy McVay, Chief Executive Officer
CMO: Art Osberg, M.D., Chief Medical Officer
CIO: Brandon Holbert, Director, Information Services
CHR: Wayne Nielsen, Director Human Resources
Web address: www.ocalaregional.com
Control: Corporation, Investor–owned, for–profit **Service:** General Medical and Surgical

Staffed Beds: 270

THE CENTERS (104068), 5664 S.W. 60th Avenue, Zip 34474–5677; tel. 352/291–5500 **A**9 10 **F**4 29 98 99 100 101 102 103 104 130
Primary Contact: Timothy Cowart, Interim Chief Executive Officer
Web address: www.thecenters.us
Control: Other not–for–profit (including NFP Corporation) **Service:** Psychiatric

Staffed Beds: 61 **Admissions:** 6283 **Census:** 47 **Outpatient Visits:** 1996 **Births:** 0 **Total Expense ($000):** 8479 **Payroll Expense ($000):** 4723

FL

Hospital, Medicare Provider Number, Address, Telephone, Approval, Facility, and Physician Codes, Health Care System

★ American Hospital Association (AHA) membership
☐ The Joint Commission accreditation
◇ DNV Healthcare Inc. accreditation
○ Healthcare Facilities Accreditation Program
△ Commission on Accreditation of Rehabilitation Facilities (CARF) accreditation

THE VINES (104071), 3130 S.W. 27th Avenue, Zip 34471–4306; tel. 352/671–3130 **A**9 10 **F**4 98 99 101 102 103 104 105 106 **S** Universal Health Services, Inc., King of Prussia, PA
Primary Contact: Stephen Quintyne, Chief Executive Officer
Web address: www.thevineshospital.com
Control: Corporation, Investor–owned, for–profit **Service:** Psychiatric

Staffed Beds: 64 **Admissions:** 2121 **Census:** 64 **Births:** 0 **Total Expense ($000):** 10005 **Payroll Expense ($000):** 5541

OCOEE—Orange County

☒ **HEALTH CENTRAL HOSPITAL (100030)**, 10000 West Colonial Drive, Zip 34761–3499; tel. 407/296–1000, (Total facility includes 228 beds in nursing home–type unit) **A**1 9 10 **F**3 8 11 12 13 15 17 18 20 22 26 28 29 30 34 35 37 40 45 49 50 51 57 59 60 70 73 74 76 79 81 85 86 87 89 93 97 107 108 110 111 115 118 119 128 129 130 132 144 146 148 **P**6 **S** Orlando Health, Orlando, FL
Primary Contact: Gregory P. Ohe, President
COO: Rick Smith, Chief Operating Officer
CFO: Michael E. Mueller, Chief Financial Officer
CMO: James Barton Rodier, M.D., Chief Quality Officer
CIO: John M. Sills, Chief Information Officer
CHR: Nancy Dinon, Vice President Human Resources
CNO: Christina McGuirk, Chief Nursing Officer
Web address: www.healthcentral.org
Control: Other not–for–profit (including NFP Corporation) **Service:** General Medical and Surgical

Staffed Beds: 399 **Admissions:** 12473 **Census:** 345 **Outpatient Visits:** 110850 **Births:** 765 **Total Expense ($000):** 172783 **Payroll Expense ($000):** 72509 **Personnel:** 1170

OKEECHOBEE—Okeechobee County

☒ **RAULERSON HOSPITAL (100252)**, 1796 Highway 441 North, Zip 34972–1918, Mailing Address: P.O. Box 1307, Zip 34973–1307; tel. 863/763–2151, (Nonreporting) **A**1 9 10 20 **S** HCA, Nashville, TN
Primary Contact: Robert H. Lee, President
CFO: Heather Garvey, Chief Financial Officer
CMO: Mohammad Riaz, M.D., Chief of Staff
CIO: Doug Schneider, Director Information Systems
CHR: Janis Stevens, Director Human Resources
Web address: www.raulersonhospital.com
Control: Corporation, Investor–owned, for–profit **Service:** General Medical and Surgical

Staffed Beds: 100

ORANGE CITY—Volusia County

☒ **FLORIDA HOSPITAL FISH MEMORIAL (100072)**, 1055 Saxon Boulevard, Zip 32763–8468; tel. 386/917–5000 **A**1 9 10 **F**1 3 4 11 15 16 17 20 28 29 30 31 34 35 37 40 45 48 49 59 64 67 70 72 73 74 75 76 77 78 79 80 81 82 85 87 88 89 90 91 92 93 98 100 104 107 108 110 111 114 115 116 117 118 119 120 121 128 129 130 132 135 144 146 147 148 **P**8 **S** Adventist Health System Sunbelt Health Care Corporation, Altamonte Springs, FL
Primary Contact: Ed Noseworthy, President and Chief Executive Officer
COO: Danielle Johnson, Chief Operating Officer
CFO: Eric Osterly, Chief Financial Officer
CMO: Leighton Smith, M.D., Chief Medical Officer
CHR: Bonne S. Macpherson, Director Human Resources
CNO: Jennifer Shull, R.N., Chief Nursing Officer
Web address: www.fhfishmemorial.org
Control: Church–operated, Nongovernment, not–for profit **Service:** General Medical and Surgical

Staffed Beds: 175 **Admissions:** 8121 **Census:** 97 **Outpatient Visits:** 88810 **Births:** 1 **Total Expense ($000):** 122189 **Payroll Expense ($000):** 45167 **Personnel:** 777

ORANGE PARK—Clay County

☒ **ORANGE PARK MEDICAL CENTER (100226)**, 2001 Kingsley Avenue, Zip 32073–5156; tel. 904/639–8500 **A**1 2 9 10 **F**3 8 11 15 17 18 20 22 24 26 28 29 30 31 34 35 40 45 46 48 49 50 60 67 68 70 72 74 76 77 79 81 84 85 87 93 94 97 98 100 101 102 103 104 107 108 110 111 114 115 118 119 126 131 132 135 146 147 148 **S** HCA, Nashville, TN
Primary Contact: Chad Patrick, President and Chief Executive Officer
COO: Christopher J. Mosley, Chief Operating Officer
CFO: Fred Ashworth, Chief Financial Officer
CMO: Lawrence Coots, M.D., Chief Medical Officer
CHR: Chris Marlin, Director Human Resources
CNO: Kathy Hester, Chief Nursing Officer
Web address: www.opmedical.com
Control: Corporation, Investor–owned, for–profit **Service:** General Medical and Surgical

Staffed Beds: 297 **Admissions:** 17649 **Census:** 210 **Births:** 2155 **Total Expense ($000):** 206270 **Payroll Expense ($000):** 66268

ORLANDO—Orange County

ARNOLD PALMER CHILDREN'S HOSPITAL See Orlando Regional Medical Center

☐ **CENTRAL FLORIDA BEHAVIORAL HOSPITAL (104072)**, 6601 Central Florida Parkway, Zip 32821–8064; tel. 407/370–0111 **A**1 5 9 10 **F**98 99 101 102 103 105 130 **S** Universal Health Services, Inc., King of Prussia, PA
Primary Contact: Vickie Lewis, Chief Executive Officer
CFO: Marsha Burick, Chief Financial Officer
Web address: www.centralfloridabehavioral.com
Control: Corporation, Investor–owned, for–profit **Service:** Psychiatric

Staffed Beds: 126 **Admissions:** 5221 **Census:** 102 **Outpatient Visits:** 0 **Births:** 0

☒ △ ◇ **FLORIDA HOSPITAL (100007)**, 601 East Rollins Street, Zip 32803–1248; tel. 407/303–6611, (Includes FLORIDA HOSPITAL CELEBRATION HEALTH, 400 Clebration Place, Celebration, Zip 34747; tel. 407/303–4000; Monica Reed, M.D., Administrator; FLORIDA HOSPITAL EAST ORLANDO, 7727 Lake Underhill Drive, Zip 32822; tel. 407/277–8110; FLORIDA HOSPITAL FOR CHILDREN–WALT DISNEY PAVILION, 601 East Rollins Street, tel. 407/303–9732; Lars D. Houmann, President; FLORIDA HOSPITAL KISSIMMEE, 2450 North Orange Blossom Trai, Kissimmee, Zip 34741; tel. 407/846–4343; William Haupt, Administrator; FLORIDA HOSPITAL–ALTAMONTE, 601 East Altamonte Drive, Altamonte Springs, Zip 32701; tel. 407/830–4321; Rob Fulbright, Administrator; FLORIDA HOSPITAL–APOPKA, 201 North Park Avenue, Apopka, Zip 32703; tel. 407/889–2566; Verbelee Neilsen Swanson, Administrator; WINTER PARK MEMOR!AL HOSPITAL, 200 North Lakemont Avenue, Winter Park, Zip 32792–3273; tel. 407/646–7000; Ken Bradley, Administrator) **A**1 2 3 5 7 8 9 10 21 **F**3 6 7 9 11 12 13 15 17 18 19 20 21 22 23 24 25 26 27 28 29 30 31 32 34 35 36 37 38 39 40 41 44 45 46 47 48 49 50 51 53 54 55 56 57 58 59 60 61 62 64 65 66 68 70 71 72 73 74 75 76 77 78 79 80 81 82 84 85 86 87 88 89 90 91 92 93 94 96 97 98 100 101 102 103 104 107 108 110 111 112 113 114 115 116 117 118 119 120 121 123 124 126 129 130 131 132 134 135 136 137 138 139 140 141 142 145 146 147 148 **P**1 6 **S** Adventist Health System Sunbelt Health Care Corporation, Altamonte Springs, FL
Primary Contact: Lars D. Houmann, President
COO: Brian Paradis, Chief Operating Officer
CFO: Eddie Soler, Chief Financial Officer
CMO: David Moorhead, M.D., Chief Medical Officer
CHR: Sheryl Dodds, Chief Clinical Officer
Web address: www.flhosp.org
Control: Other not–for–profit (including NFP Corporation) **Service:** General Medical and Surgical

Staffed Beds: 2396 **Admissions:** 133221 **Census:** 1800 **Outpatient Visits:** 1025759 **Births:** 10220 **Total Expense ($000):** 3396260 **Payroll Expense ($000):** 908146 **Personnel:** 17083

LAKESIDE BEHAVIORAL HEALTHCARE–PRINCETON PLAZA (104067), 1800 Mercy Drive, Zip 32808–5646; tel. 407/875–3700, (Nonreporting) **A**5 9 10
Primary Contact: Jerry Kassab, President and Chief Executive Officer
Web address: www.lakesidecares.org
Control: Other not–for–profit (including NFP Corporation) **Service:** Psychiatric

Staffed Beds: 54

☒ **NEMOURS CHILDREN'S HOSPITAL (103304)**, (Specialized pediatric services), 13535 Nemours Parkway, Zip 32827–7402; tel. 407/567–4000 **A**1 9 10 **F**29 30 31 32 34 35 39 40 41 45 48 50 53 54 55 57 58 59 60 64 65 68 72 74 75 77 78 79 81 82 86 87 88 89 91 92 93 94 96 97 99 100 101 102 107 108 111 115 118 119 129 130 131 132 143 144 146 **S** Nemours, Jacksonville, FL
Primary Contact: Roger A. Oxendale, Chief Executive Officer
CMO: Lane Donnelly, M.D., Chief Medical Officer
CNO: Barbara Meeks, MSN, Chief Nurse Executive
Web address: www.nemours.org
Control: Other not–for–profit (including NFP Corporation) **Service:** Children's other specialty

Staffed Beds: 100 **Admissions:** 2028 **Census:** 22 **Outpatient Visits:** 20186 **Births:** 0 **Personnel:** 421

Many Facility Codes have changed. Please refer to the AHA Guide Code Chart. © 2014 AHA Guide

✖ **ORLANDO REGIONAL MEDICAL CENTER (100006)**, 1414 Kuhl Avenue, Zip 32806–2093; tel. 407/841–5111, (Includes ARNOLD PALMER CHILDREN'S HOSPITAL, 92 West Miller Street, Zip 32806; tel. 407/649–6960; Kathy Swanson, President; ORLANDO REGIONAL–LUCERNE, 818 Main Lane, Zip 32801–3727; tel. 321/841–4200; WINNIE PALMER HOSPITAL FOR WOMEN AND BABIES, 83 West Miller Street, Zip 32806; tel. 321/843–2201; Kathy Swanson, President) **A**1 2 3 5 8 9 10 **F**3 4 5 8 11 12 13 15 16 17 18 19 20 21 22 23 24 25 26 27 28 29 30 31 34 35 36 37 40 41 43 44 45 46 48 49 50 51 55 57 58 59 61 62 64 68 70 71 72 73 74 75 76 77 78 79 80 81 82 84 85 86 87 88 89 90 91 92 93 94 96 97 98 99 100 101 102 103 104 107 108 110 111 114 115 116 117 118 119 120 121 123 124 126 129 130 131 132 134 135 146 147 148 **P**6 **S** Orlando Health, Orlando, FL
Primary Contact: Mark A. Jones, President
CFO: Paul Goldstein, Vice President Finance and Chief Financial Officer
CMO: Timothy Bullard, M.D., Chief of Staff
CIO: Rick Schooler, Vice President and Chief Information Officer
CHR: Nancy Dinon, Vice President Human Resources
Web address: www.orhs.org
Control: Other not–for–profit (including NFP Corporation) **Service:** General Medical and Surgical

Staffed Beds: 1168 **Admissions:** 76061 **Census:** 1036 **Outpatient Visits:** 798718 **Births:** 13659 **Total Expense ($000):** 1467803 **Payroll Expense ($000):** 599438 **Personnel:** 10593

✖ **SELECT SPECIALTY HOSPITAL–ORLANDO (102003)**, 2250 Bedford Road, Zip 32803–1443; tel. 407/303–7869, (Includes SELECT SPECIALTY HOSPITAL–ORLANDO SOUTH, 5579 South Orange Avenue, Zip 32809–3493; tel. 407/241–4800), (Nonreporting) **A**1 9 10 **S** Select Medical Corporation, Mechanicsburg, PA
Primary Contact: Nellie Castroman, Chief Executive Officer
COO: James Whitacre, Chief Operating Officer
Web address: www.selectspecialtyhospitals.com/company/locations/orlando.aspx
Control: Corporation, Investor–owned, for–profit **Service:** Long–Term Acute Care hospital

Staffed Beds: 75

SELECT SPECIALTY HOSPITAL–ORLANDO SOUTH See Select Specialty Hospital–Orlando

WINNIE PALMER HOSPITAL FOR WOMEN AND BABIES See Orlando Regional Medical Center

OXFORD—Sumter County

PROMISE HOSPITAL OF FLORIDA AT THE VILLAGES (102028), 5050 County Road, Zip 34484; tel. 352/689–6400 **A**10 **F**1 18 26 28 29 30 31 34 57 84 90 98 130 **P**5 **S** Promise Healthcare, Boca Raton, FL
Primary Contact: Hoyt Ross, Chief Executive Officer
CNO: Janice M. McCoy, MS, Chief Clinical Officer
Web address: www.promise-villages.com
Control: Corporation, Investor–owned, for–profit **Service:** Long–Term Acute Care hospital

Staffed Beds: 40 **Admissions:** 240 **Census:** 21 **Outpatient Visits:** 0 **Births:** 0 **Personnel:** 164

PALATKA—Putnam County

✖ **PUTNAM COMMUNITY MEDICAL CENTER (100232)**, Highway 20 West, Zip 32177–8118, Mailing Address: P.O. Box 778, Zip 32178–0778; tel. 386/328–5711 **A**1 9 10 19 **F**3 11 13 15 18 20 22 28 29 30 34 35 40 45 46 50 51 54 57 59 60 64 70 74 75 76 77 79 81 85 87 93 107 108 110 111 114 115 119 129 130 133 135 146 147 148 **S** LifePoint Hospitals, Inc., Brentwood, TN
Primary Contact: Michael Clark, Interim Chief Executive Officer
CFO: Debra Noyes, Chief Financial Officer
CMO: Joseph Stillword, Chief of Staff
CIO: Yvette A. Jones, HIM Director
CHR: John Schneider, Human Resources Director
CNO: Carol Negoshian, MSN, Chief Nursing Officer
Web address: www.pcmcfl.com
Control: Corporation, Investor–owned, for–profit **Service:** General Medical and Surgical

Staffed Beds: 99 **Admissions:** 4846 **Census:** 87 **Births:** 425 **Total Expense ($000):** 68169 **Payroll Expense ($000):** 23053

PALM BEACH GARDENS—Palm Beach County

✖ **PALM BEACH GARDENS MEDICAL CENTER (100176)**, 3360 Burns Road, Zip 33410–4323; tel. 561/622–1411, (Nonreporting) **A**1 9 10 **S** TENET Healthcare Corporation, Dallas, TX
Primary Contact: Larry Coomes, Chief Executive Officer
CFO: Judi Stimson–Rusin, Chief Financial Officer
CIO: James Vega, Director Information Systems
CHR: Kevin Caracciolo, Chief Human Resources Officer
Web address: www.pbgmc.com
Control: Corporation, Investor–owned, for–profit **Service:** General Medical and Surgical

Staffed Beds: 199

PALM COAST—Flagler County

✖ **FLORIDA HOSPITAL–FLAGLER (100118)**, 60 Memorial Medical Parkway, Zip 32164–5980; tel. 386/586–2000 **A**1 2 9 10 **F**11 15 18 20 22 28 29 30 31 34 35 40 45 46 47 49 50 51 54 57 59 60 62 63 64 68 70 74 75 77 78 79 81 85 86 87 93 97 107 108 110 111 114 115 117 119 120 121 123 124 126 130 132 135 144 146 147 **P**6 **S** Adventist Health System Sunbelt Health Care Corporation, Altamonte Springs, FL
Primary Contact: Kenneth R. Mattison, Chief Executive Officer
CFO: Valerie Ziesmer, Chief Financial Officer
CMO: John Walsh, M.D., Chief Medical Officer
CHR: Joshua I. Champion, Director
CNO: Ellen Lenkevich, R.N., Vice President and Chief Nursing Officer
Web address: www.floridahospitalflagler.com/
Control: Church–operated, Nongovernment, not–for profit **Service:** General Medical and Surgical

Staffed Beds: 99 **Admissions:** 6879 **Census:** 81 **Outpatient Visits:** 104092 **Births:** 0 **Total Expense ($000):** 139972 **Payroll Expense ($000):** 59840 **Personnel:** 792

PANAMA CITY—Bay County

✖ **BAY MEDICAL CENTER SACRED HEART (100026)**, 615 North Bonita Avenue, Zip 32401–3600, Mailing Address: P.O. Box 59515, Zip 32412–0515; tel. 850/769–1511, (Nonreporting) **A**1 2 9 10 **S** LHP Hospital Group, Plano, TX
Primary Contact: Barry L. Keel, Chief Executive Officer
CFO: Warren Ladner, Chief Financial Officer
CHR: Donna Baird, Vice President Corporate Services
Web address: www.baymedical.org
Control: Hospital district or authority, Government, nonfederal **Service:** General Medical and Surgical

Staffed Beds: 362

☐ **EMERALD COAST BEHAVIORAL HOSPITAL (104073)**, 1940 Harrison Avenue, Zip 32405–4542; tel. 850/763–0017 **A**1 9 10 **F**98 99 100 101 102 103 104 105 **S** Universal Health Services, Inc., King of Prussia, PA
Primary Contact: Tim Bedford, Chief Executive Officer
Web address: www.emeraldcoastbehavioral.com
Control: Corporation, Investor–owned, for–profit **Service:** Psychiatric

Staffed Beds: 86 **Admissions:** 2601 **Census:** 65 **Outpatient Visits:** 0 **Births:** 0 **Total Expense ($000):** 12328 **Payroll Expense ($000):** 6446

✖ **GULF COAST REGIONAL MEDICAL CENTER (100242)**, 449 West 23rd Street, Zip 32405–4593, Mailing Address: P.O. Box 15309, Zip 32406–5309; tel. 850/769–8341 **A**1 2 9 10 **F**3 8 12 13 15 20 22 26 29 30 31 34 35 37 39 40 41 46 47 48 49 51 54 56 57 59 60 64 68 70 72 74 75 76 77 78 79 80 81 85 86 87 89 93 107 108 109 111 114 116 117 118 119 126 130 131 132 135 144 146 147 148 **S** HCA, Nashville, TN
Primary Contact: Carlton Ulmer, Chief Executive Officer
COO: Holly Jackson, Chief Operating Officer
CFO: Laurie Haynes, Chief Financial Officer
CHR: Tracy McGlon, Director Human Resources
CNO: Mary Reval, R.N., Chief Nursing Officer
Web address: www.egulfcoastmedical.com
Control: Corporation, Investor–owned, for–profit **Service:** General Medical and Surgical

Staffed Beds: 176 **Admissions:** 11017 **Census:** 108 **Births:** 2376 **Total Expense ($000):** 135128 **Payroll Expense ($000):** 40164

FL

Hospital, Medicare Provider Number, Address, Telephone, Approval, Facility, and Physician Codes, Health Care System
★ American Hospital Association (AHA) membership   ◯ Healthcare Facilities Accreditation Program ☐ The Joint Commission accreditation   ◇ DNV Healthcare Inc. accreditation   △ Commission on Accreditation of Rehabilitation Facilities (CARF) accreditation

HEALTHSOUTH EMERALD COAST REHABILITATION HOSPITAL (103040), 1847 Florida Avenue, Zip 32405–4640; tel. 850/914–8600 **A**1 9 10 **F**3 28 29 34 57 59 68 75 77 85 86 87 90 91 95 96 130 131 132 148 **S** HEALTHSOUTH Corporation, Birmingham, AL
Primary Contact: Tony N. Bennett, Chief Executive Officer
CFO: Bradley Tilghman, Controller
CMO: Michael Hennigan, M.D., Medical Director
CHR: Traci Powell, Director Human Resources
Web address: www.healthsouthpanamacity.com
Control: Corporation, Investor–owned, for–profit **Service:** Rehabilitation

Staffed Beds: 75 Admissions: 1529 Census: 55 Outpatient Visits: 0 Births: 0 Total Expense ($000): 18231 Payroll Expense ($000): 9834 Personnel: 202

SELECT SPECIALTY HOSPITAL--PANAMA CITY (102017), 615 North Bonita Avenue, 3rd Floor, Zip 32401–3623; tel. 850/767–3180 **A**1 9 10 **F**1 3 29 148 **S** Select Medical Corporation, Mechanicsburg, PA
Primary Contact: Randal S. Hamilton, Chief Executive Officer
CMO: Amir Manzoor, M.D., Medical Director
Web address: www.selectspecialtyhospitals.com/company/locations/panamacity.aspx
Control: Corporation, Investor–owned, for–profit **Service:** Long–Term Acute Care hospital

Staffed Beds: 30 Admissions: 393 Census: 26 Outpatient Visits: 0 Births: 0 Total Expense ($000): 10141 Payroll Expense ($000): 5347 Personnel: 101

PEMBROKE PINES—Broward County

MEMORIAL HOSPITAL PEMBROKE (100230), 7800 Sheridan Street, Zip 33024–2536; tel. 954/883–8482 **A**1 9 10 **F**3 8 12 17 29 30 40 45 46 47 48 49 50 51 59 60 64 70 79 81 82 83 85 86 87 107 111 114 115 119 129 130 132 144 146 148 **S** Memorial Healthcare System, Hollywood, FL
Primary Contact: Keith W. Gallagher, FACHE, Administrator and Chief Executive Officer
CFO: Joseph Stuczynski, Assistant Administrator Finance and Support
CMO: Stanley Marks, M.D., Chief Medical Officer
CIO: Forest Blanton, Chief Information Officer
CNO: Judy Frum, R.N., Chief Nursing Officer
Web address: www.memorialpembroke.com/
Control: Hospital district or authority, Government, nonfederal **Service:** General Medical and Surgical

Staffed Beds: 149 Admissions: 5394 Census: 63 Births: 0 Total Expense ($000): 118404 Payroll Expense ($000): 53426

MEMORIAL HOSPITAL WEST (100281), 703 North Flamingo Road, Zip 33028–1014; tel. 954/436–5000 **A**1 9 10 **F**3 12 13 15 17 18 20 22 26 28 29 30 31 34 35 36 40 41 45 46 47 49 51 53 55 56 57 59 60 61 64 68 70 72 74 75 76 78 79 81 82 85 87 91 92 93 107 108 110 111 114 115 118 119 120 121 126 130 131 132 136 145 146 147 148 **S** Memorial Healthcare System, Hollywood, FL
Primary Contact: C. Kennon Hetlage, FACHE, Administrator and Chief Executive Officer
CFO: Walter Bussell, Chief Financial Officer
CMO: Eric Freling, M.D., Director Medical Staff Affairs
CIO: Forest Blanton, Chief Information Officer
CHR: Maria Naranjo, Director Human Resources
CNO: Grisel Fernandez-Bravo, R.N., Chief Nursing Officer
Web address: www.mhs.net
Control: Hospital district or authority, Government, nonfederal **Service:** General Medical and Surgical

Staffed Beds: 384 Admissions: 20830 Census: 252 Outpatient Visits: 275889 Births: 4191 Total Expense ($000): 337533 Payroll Expense ($000): 131092 Personnel: 1876

PENSACOLA—Escambia County

BAPTIST HOSPITAL (100093), 1000 West Moreno, Zip 32501–2316, Mailing Address: P.O. Box 17500, Zip 32522–7500; tel. 850/434–4011 **A**1 2 9 10 **F**3 7 8 11 12 13 15 17 18 19 20 22 24 26 28 29 30 31 34 35 37 40 43 45 46 47 48 49 50 51 52 54 55 56 57 58 59 60 61 62 63 64 67 70 71 74 75 76 77 78 79 80 81 82 84 85 86 87 92 93 97 98 99 100 101 102 103 104 107 108 110 111 114 115 116 117 118 119 120 121 123 124 126 129 130 131 132 135 144 146 147 148 **P**4 6 **S** Baptist Health Care Corporation, Pensacola, FL
Primary Contact: Scott Raynes, Interim Administrator
CFO: Sharon Nobles, Interim Chief Financial Officer
CMO: Mike Oleksyk, M.D., Vice President and Chief Medical Officer
CIO: Steven Sarros, Vice President and Chief Information Officer
CHR: Darlene Stone, Vice President Human Resources
CNO: Cynde Gamache, R.N., Vice President and Chief Nursing Officer
Web address: www.ebaptisthealthcare.org
Control: Other not–for–profit (including NFP Corporation) **Service:** General Medical and Surgical

Staffed Beds: 339 Admissions: 17625 Census: 213 Outpatient Visits: 260304 Births: 938 Total Expense ($000): 253497 Payroll Expense ($000): 84608 Personnel: 1502

NAVAL HOSPITAL PENSACOLA, 6000 West Highway 98, Zip 32512–0003; tel. 850/505–6413 **A**1 3 5 **F**3 5 13 15 18 29 30 32 33 34 35 38 39 40 45 49 50 51 53 54 55 57 58 59 64 65 68 70 74 75 76 77 79 81 85 86 87 92 93 97 100 101 102 104 107 108 110 111 114 115 118 119 124 129 130 131 135 146 147 148 **S** Bureau of Medicine and Surgery, Department of the Navy, Washington, DC
Primary Contact: Commander Devin Morrison, Director Administration
COO: Commander Devin Morrison, Director for Administration
CMO: Commander Carolyn Rice, M.D., Director Medical Services
CIO: Lieutenant Commander William Berg, Chief Information Officer
CHR: Commander Devin Morrison, Director for Administration
CNO: Captain Amy Tarbay, Director Nursing Services
Web address: www.med.navy.mil/sites/pcola/Pages/default.aspx
Control: Navy, Government, federal **Service:** General Medical and Surgical

Staffed Beds: 28 Admissions: 2120 Census: 14 Outpatient Visits: 581929 Births: 458 Total Expense ($000): 120806 Payroll Expense ($000): 28458 Personnel: 1989

REHABILITATION INSTITUTE OF WEST FLORIDA See West Florida Hospital

SACRED HEART HOSPITAL OF PENSACOLA (100025), 5151 North Ninth Avenue, Zip 32504–8795, Mailing Address: P.O. Box 2700, Zip 32513–2700; tel. 850/416–7000 **A**1 2 3 5 **F**3 5 13 15 18 29 30 32 33 34 35 40 41 43 45 46 47 48 49 50 54 55 57 58 59 60 61 65 66 70 71 72 73 74 75 76 77 78 79 81 82 84 85 87 88 89 90 92 93 96 97 107 108 110 111 112 114 116 117 119 120 124 126 128 130 131 132 135 144 145 146 147 148 **S** Ascension Health, Saint Louis, MO
Primary Contact: Henry Stovall, President
CFO: C. Susan Cornejo, Chief Financial Officer
CMO: Stephanie J. Duggan, M.D., Vice President and Chief Medical Officer
CIO: Kathy Ross, Chief Information Officer
CHR: Carol Whittington, Chief Human Resources Officer
CNO: Amy Wilson, Vice President and Chief Nursing Officer
Web address: www.sacred–heart.org
Control: Other not–for–profit (including NFP Corporation) **Service:** General Medical and Surgical

Staffed Beds: 560 Admissions: 23313 Census: 265 Births: 3863 Total Expense ($000): 372482 Payroll Expense ($000): 119049

SELECT SPECIALTY HOSPITAL–PENSACOLA (102024), 7000 Cobble Creek Drive, Zip 32504–8638; tel. 850/473–4800, (Nonreporting) **A**1 9 10 **S** Select Medical Corporation, Mechanicsburg, PA
Primary Contact: David Goodson, Chief Executive Officer
CMO: John Bray, M.D., Medical Director
Web address: www.selectspecialtyhospitals.com/company/locations/pensacola.aspx
Control: Corporation, Investor–owned, for–profit **Service:** Long–Term Acute Care hospital

Staffed Beds: 54

WEST FLORIDA HOSPITAL (100231), 8383 North Davis Highway, Zip 32514–6088; tel. 850/494–4000, (Includes REHABILITATION INSTITUTE OF WEST FLORIDA, 8383 North Davis Highway, Zip 32514, Mailing Address: P.O. Box 18900, Zip 32523; tel. 850/494–6000; THE PAVILION, 8383 North Davis Highway, Zip 32523, Mailing Address: P.O. Box 18900, Zip 32523; tel. 904/494–5000), (Nonreporting) **A**1 2 9 10 **S** HCA, Nashville, TN
Primary Contact: Brian Baumgardner, Chief Executive Officer
COO: Kenneth C. Donahey, Chief Operating Officer
CFO: Randy Butler, Chief Financial Officer
CMO: Terry Stallings, M.D., Chief Medical Officer
CIO: Jeff Amerson, Director Information System
CHR: Wanda Salley, Vice President Human Resources
CNO: Karen White-Trevino, Chief Nursing Officer
Web address: www.westfloridahospital.com
Control: Corporation, Investor–owned, for–profit **Service:** General Medical and Surgical

Staffed Beds: 339

PERRY—Taylor County

★ **DOCTOR'S MEMORIAL HOSPITAL (100106)**, 333 North Byron Butler Parkway, Zip 32347–2300; tel. 850/584–0800 **A**9 10 20 **F**3 7 11 15 29 30 34 35 40 45 50 57 59 62 70 81 85 89 93 107 110 111 114 119 127 129 132 133 146 **P**6
Primary Contact: Geri Forbes, Chief Executive Officer
CMO: Ron Emerick, M.D., Chief of Staff
CHR: Sarah Brus, Director Human Resources
CNO: Mary Lescher, Chief Clinical Officer
Web address: www.doctorsmemorial.com
Control: Other not–for–profit (including NFP Corporation) **Service:** General Medical and Surgical

Staffed Beds: 45 Admissions: 985 Census: 9 Births: 4 Total Expense ($000): 27611 Payroll Expense ($000): 12297

Many Facility Codes have changed. Please refer to the AHA Guide Code Chart. © 2014 AHA Guide

FL

PLANT CITY—Hillsborough County

✠ **SOUTH FLORIDA BAPTIST HOSPITAL (100132)**, 301 North Alexander Street,
Zip 33563–4303, Mailing Address: Drawer H, Zip 33564–9058;
tel. 813/757–1200 **A**1 9 10 **F**3 11 12 13 15 18 20 22 28 29 30 31 34 35 40
44 45 47 48 49 51 57 59 64 67 68 70 71 74 75 76 77 78 79 81 85 86 87
89 93 94 107 108 110 111 114 115 117 118 119 126 131 132 135 146
148 **P**6 7 **S** Catholic Health East / Trinity Health, Livonia, MI
Primary Contact: Karen Kerr, R.N., Interim President and Chief Executive Officer
COO: Stephen A. Nierman, Chief Operating Officer
CFO: Cathy Yoder, Chief Financial Officer
CMO: Mark Vaaler, M.D., Chief Medical Officer
CHR: Juanita Radford, Coordinator Team Resource
Web address: www.sjbhealth.org
Control: Other not-for-profit (including NFP Corporation) **Service:** General
Medical and Surgical

Staffed Beds: 125 **Admissions:** 5856 **Census:** 62 **Outpatient Visits:** 54416 **Births:** 479 **Total Expense ($000):** 83646 **Payroll Expense ($000):** 34498 **Personnel:** 486	

PLANTATION—Broward County

✠ **PLANTATION GENERAL HOSPITAL (100167)**, 401 N.W. 42nd Avenue,
Zip 33317–2882; tel. 954/587–5010, (Includes MERCY HOSPITAL – A CAMPUS
OF PLANTATION GENERAL HOSPITAL, 3663 South Miami Avenue, Miami,
Zip 33133–4237; tel. 305/854–4400; Barbara Simmons, R.N., Chief Executive
Officer), (Nonreporting) **A**1 2 9 10 **S** HCA, Nashville, TN
Primary Contact: Randy Gross, Chief Executive Officer
COO: Kristen Lindenboom, Chief Operating Officer
CFO: Irfan Mirza, Chief Financial Officer
CIO: Mia McGlynn, Director Management Information Systems
CHR: Jennifer Allen, Vice President Human Resources
Web address: www.plantationgeneral.com
Control: Corporation, Investor-owned, for-profit **Service:** General Medical and
Surgical

Staffed Beds: 264

✠ **WESTSIDE REGIONAL MEDICAL CENTER (100228)**, 8201 West Broward
Boulevard, Zip 33324–2701; tel. 954/473–6600 **A**1 9 10 **F**3 8 11 15 17 18 20
22 24 26 29 30 31 34 35 40 44 45 48 49 50 57 59 60 68 70 74 75 77 78
79 80 81 82 85 86 87 93 107 108 110 111 114 115 117 119 126 129 130
131 132 145 146 148 **S** HCA, Nashville, TN
Primary Contact: Lee B. Chaykin, Chief Executive Officer
COO: Shana Sappington-Crittenden, Chief Operating Officer
CFO: Kevin Corcoran, Chief Financial Officer
CMO: Brian Weinstein, M.D., Chief of Staff
CIO: Andres Blanco, Director Management Information Systems
CHR: Maria Rivera, Director Human Resources
Web address: www.westsideregional.com
Control: Corporation, Investor-owned, for-profit **Service:** General Medical and
Surgical

Staffed Beds: 215 **Admissions:** 13518 **Census:** 163 **Outpatient Visits:** 56936 **Births:** 0 **Total Expense ($000):** 135045 **Payroll Expense ($000):** 54824 **Personnel:** 736

PORT CHARLOTTE—Charlotte County

✠ **BAYFRONT HEALTH PORT CHARLOTTE (100077)**, 2500 Harbor Boulevard,
Zip 33952–5000; tel. 941/766–4122, (Nonreporting) **A**1 9 10 **S** Community
Health Systems, Inc., Franklin, TN
Primary Contact: Richard H. Satcher, Market Chief Executive Officer
COO: Drew Emery, Chief Operating Officer
CFO: Cheryl Tibbett, Chief Financial Officer
CMO: Thomas Noone, M.D., Chief Medical Officer
CHR: Karen Gardiner, Human Resources Director
CNO: Hollie Vaughan, Interim Chief Nursing Officer
Web address: www.bayfrontcharlotte.com
Control: Corporation, Investor-owned, for-profit **Service:** General Medical and
Surgical

Staffed Beds: 296

✠ △ **FAWCETT MEMORIAL HOSPITAL (100236)**, 21298 Olean Boulevard,
Zip 33952–6765; tel. 941/629–1181 **A**1 2 7 9 10 **F**3 8 15 18 20 22 26 29 30
31 34 35 40 45 46 47 48 49 51 57 59 64 70 74 75 77 78 79 81 85 86 87
90 91 93 96 107 108 110 111 114 119 131 132 146 147 148 **S** HCA,
Nashville, TN
Primary Contact: Thomas J. Rice, FACHE, President and Chief Executive Officer
CFO: Phillip Baker, Vice President and Chief Financial Officer
CHR: Tony Welch, Vice President Human Resources
CNO: Kathleen Pace, MSN, Vice President and Chief Nursing Officer
Web address: www.fawcetthospital.com
Control: Corporation, Investor-owned, for-profit **Service:** General Medical and
Surgical

Staffed Beds: 238 **Admissions:** 11003 **Census:** 144 **Births:** 0 **Total Expense ($000):** 133466 **Payroll Expense ($000):** 44959

PORT ST. JOE—Gulf County

✠ **SACRED HEART HOSPITAL ON THE GULF (100313)**, 3801 East Highway 98,
Zip 32456–5318; tel. 850/229–5600 **A**1 9 10 **F**1 3 4 11 15 16 17 29 30 31
34 35 40 44 45 48 50 54 57 59 64 67 68 70 72 73 76 79 80 81 85 88 89
90 93 98 107 110 111 114 119 128 130 131 133 146 147 **P**7 **S** Ascension
Health, Saint Louis, MO
Primary Contact: Roger L. Hall, President
CNO: Katherine L. Chastain, R.N., Chief Nursing Officer
Web address: www.sacred-heart.org/gulf/
Control: Other not-for-profit (including NFP Corporation) **Service:** General
Medical and Surgical

Staffed Beds: 19 **Admissions:** 533 **Census:** 5 **Outpatient Visits:** 16821 **Births:** 0 **Total Expense ($000):** 18332 **Payroll Expense ($000):** 6024 **Personnel:** 82

PORT ST. LUCIE—St. Lucie County

☐ **PORT ST. LUCIE HOSPITAL (104070)**, 2550 S.E. Walton Road,
Zip 34952–7168; tel. 772/335–0400 **A**1 9 10 **F**4 5 34 98 101 102 103 104
105 130 132 135 143
Primary Contact: John Sannuto, Chief Executive Officer
Web address: www.portstluciehospitalinc.com
Control: Other not-for-profit (including NFP Corporation) **Service:** Psychiatric

Staffed Beds: 75 **Admissions:** 1777 **Census:** 69 **Births:** 0 **Total Expense ($000):** 16044 **Payroll Expense ($000):** 5715

✠ **ST. LUCIE MEDICAL CENTER (100260)**, 1800 S.E. Tiffany Avenue,
Zip 34952–7521; tel. 772/335–4000, (Nonreporting) **A**1 2 9 10 13 **S** HCA,
Nashville, TN
Primary Contact: Jay Finnegan, Chief Executive Officer
COO: Calvin Thomas, IV, Chief Operating Officer
CFO: Kevin Keeling, Chief Financial Officer
Web address: www.stluciemed.com
Control: Corporation, Investor-owned, for-profit **Service:** General Medical and
Surgical

Staffed Beds: 194

PUNTA GORDA—Charlotte County

✠ **BAYFRONT HEALTH PUNTA GORDA (100047)**, 809 East Marion Avenue,
Zip 33950–3819, Mailing Address: P.O. Box 51–1328, Zip 33951–1328;
tel. 941/639–3131 **A**1 9 10 **F**3 17 18 28 29 30 31 34 35 36 38 39 40 44 45
50 53 54 56 57 59 64 68 70 74 75 77 78 79 81 85 86 87 93 94 98 100
101 102 103 107 108 110 111 115 118 119 126 130 131 132 135 146 148
S Community Health Systems, Inc., Franklin, TN
Primary Contact: Brandon Downey, Chief Executive Officer
Web address: www.charlotteregional.com
Control: Corporation, Investor-owned, for-profit **Service:** General Medical and
Surgical

Staffed Beds: 208 **Admissions:** 5525 **Census:** 87 **Births:** 0 **Total Expense ($000):** 69332 **Payroll Expense ($000):** 23238

RIVIERA BEACH—Palm Beach County

✠ **KINDRED HOSPITAL THE PALM BEACHES (102025)**, 5555 West Blue Heron
Boulevard, Zip 33418–7813; tel. 561/840–0754 **A**1 9 10 **F**1 3 18 29 30 45 48
70 74 75 77 79 82 84 85 91 97 100 107 114 145 148 **S** Kindred Healthcare,
Louisville, KY
Primary Contact: Timothy Page, Chief Executive Officer
Web address: www.khthepalmbeaches.com/
Control: Corporation, Investor-owned, for-profit **Service:** Long-Term Acute Care
hospital

Staffed Beds: 70 **Admissions:** 514 **Census:** 36 **Outpatient Visits:** 0 **Births:** 0 **Total Expense ($000):** 21266 **Payroll Expense ($000):** 8331

FL

Hospital, Medicare Provider Number, Address, Telephone, Approval, Facility, and Physician Codes, Health Care System	
★ American Hospital Association (AHA) membership	◯ Healthcare Facilities Accreditation Program
☐ The Joint Commission accreditation ◇ DNV Healthcare Inc. accreditation	△ Commission on Accreditation of Rehabilitation Facilities (CARF) accreditation

ROCKLEDGE—Brevard County

✠ **WUESTHOFF MEDICAL CENTER – ROCKLEDGE (100092)**, 110 Longwood Avenue, Zip 32955–2887, Mailing Address: P.O. Box 565002, Mail Stop 1, Zip 32956–5002; tel. 321/636–2211 **A**1 2 9 10 **F**3 11 13 15 17 18 20 22 24 26 28 29 30 31 34 40 49 50 51 54 56 57 58 59 60 61 62 64 68 70 72 74 75 76 77 78 79 80 81 82 84 85 86 87 89 92 93 98 100 101 102 103 107 108 111 114 115 119 126 129 130 131 132 135 144 146 147 148 **S** Community Health Systems, Inc., Franklin, TN
Primary Contact: Timothy J. Cerullo, Chief Executive Officer
CFO: Richard Haun, Chief Financial Officer
CMO: Vinay Mehindru, M.D., Medical Director
CIO: David Barnhart, Director Information Systems
CHR: Marchita H. Marino, Vice President Human Resources
Web address: www.wuesthoff.org
Control: Corporation, Investor–owned, for–profit **Service:** General Medical and Surgical

Staffed Beds: 298 **Admissions:** 12315 **Census:** 159 **Births:** 544 **Total Expense ($000):** 147297 **Payroll Expense ($000):** 50374

SAFETY HARBOR—Pinellas County

☐ **MEASE COUNTRYSIDE HOSPITAL (100265)**, 3231 McMullen–Booth Road, Zip 34695–6607, Mailing Address: P.O. Box 1098, Zip 34695–1098; tel. 727/725–6222 **A**1 2 9 10 **F**3 8 13 15 17 18 20 22 26 28 29 30 31 34 35 37 40 41 44 46 49 51 53 59 60 62 64 68 70 72 73 75 76 77 78 79 81 84 85 86 87 89 107 108 109 111 114 115 116 117 118 119 126 129 130 131 132 145 146 147 148 **P**6 7 **S** Morton Plant Mease Health Care, Clearwater, FL
Primary Contact: Lou Galdieri, R.N., President
CFO: Carl Tremonti, Chief Financial Officer
CMO: Donald Pocock, M.D., Chief Medical Officer
CHR: Sharon Collotta, Director Human Resources
Web address: www.mpmhealth.com
Control: Other not–for–profit (including NFP Corporation) **Service:** General Medical and Surgical

Staffed Beds: 293 **Admissions:** 15832 **Census:** 195 **Outpatient Visits:** 112433 **Births:** 2162 **Total Expense ($000):** 210954 **Payroll Expense ($000):** 79564 **Personnel:** 1208

SAINT AUGUSTINE—St. Johns County

☐ **FLAGLER HOSPITAL (100090)**, 400 Health Park Boulevard, Zip 32086–5784; tel. 904/819–5155 **A**1 2 9 10 20 **F**1 3 5 8 11 12 13 14 15 18 20 22 24 28 29 30 31 34 35 38 40 45 49 56 57 58 59 60 65 67 70 72 73 74 75 76 78 79 80 81 82 85 86 87 89 90 93 98 100 101 102 104 105 106 107 108 110 111 114 115 119 120 126 128 129 130 131 132 135 146
Primary Contact: Joseph S. Gordy, President
COO: Jason P. Barrett, Chief Operating Officer
CFO: Lynda I. Kirker, Chief Financial Officer
CMO: Douglas Dew, M.D., President Medical Staff
CIO: Bill Rieger, Chief Information Officer
CHR: Jeff Hurley, Vice President Human Resources
Web address: www.flaglerhospital.org
Control: Other not–for–profit (including NFP Corporation) **Service:** General Medical and Surgical

Staffed Beds: 318 **Admissions:** 12900 **Census:** 161 **Births:** 1290 **Total Expense ($000):** 205592 **Payroll Expense ($000):** 75974

SAINT CLOUD—Osceola County

✠ **ST. CLOUD REGIONAL MEDICAL CENTER (100302)**, 2906 17th Street, Zip 34769–6099; tel. 407/892–2135 **A**1 9 10 **F**3 15 18 29 30 34 35 40 45 46 49 51 57 59 70 74 75 77 78 79 81 82 85 86 87 91 93 94 96 97 107 108 110 111 115 119 146 **S** Community Health Systems, Inc., Franklin, TN
Primary Contact: Brent Burish, Chief Executive Officer
CFO: Jordan Ohman, Chief Financial Officer
CMO: Scott Wurm, M.D., Chief Medical Officer
CIO: James Devlin, Director Information Systems
CHR: Bethany Meadows, Director Human Resources
CNO: Inna Makievsky, FACHE, Chief Nursing Officer
Web address: www.stcloudregional.com
Control: Corporation, Investor–owned, for–profit **Service:** General Medical and Surgical

Staffed Beds: 84 **Admissions:** 3981 **Census:** 45 **Births:** 0 **Total Expense ($000):** 43222 **Payroll Expense ($000):** 16560

SAINT PETERSBURG—Pinellas County

✠ **ALL CHILDREN'S HOSPITAL JOHNS HOPKINS MEDICINE (103300)**, 501 6th Avenue South, Zip 33701–4634; tel. 727/898–7451 **A**1 3 5 8 9 10 **F**3 11 17 18 19 20 21 22 23 24 25 26 27 29 30 31 32 34 35 36 37 39 40 41 43 44 45 46 47 48 49 50 54 55 57 58 59 60 61 64 65 68 72 73 74 75 77 78 79 81 82 84 85 86 87 88 89 92 93 96 97 99 100 107 111 114 115 116 118 119 129 130 131 132 134 135 136 137 141 142 143 144 146 148 **S** Johns Hopkins Health System, Baltimore, MD
Primary Contact: Jonathan M. Ellen, M.D., President
CFO: Nancy Templin, Vice President Finance and Chief Financial Officer
CMO: Michael Epstein, M.D., Senior Vice President Medical Affairs
CIO: Cal Popovich, Vice President Information Technology
CHR: Jay Kuhns, Vice President Human Resources
Web address: www.allkids.org
Control: Other not–for–profit (including NFP Corporation) **Service:** Children's general

Staffed Beds: 259 **Admissions:** 8325 **Census:** 192 **Outpatient Visits:** 353283 **Births:** 0 **Total Expense ($000):** 373961 **Payroll Expense ($000):** 152789 **Personnel:** 2662

✠ **BAYFRONT HEALTH ST. PETERSBURG (100032)**, 701 Sixth Street South, Zip 33701–4891; tel. 727/823–1234, (Nonreporting) **A**1 3 5 9 10 **S** Community Health Systems, Inc., Franklin, TN
Primary Contact: Kathryn Gillette, President and Chief Executive Officer
COO: Lavah Lowe, Executive Vice President and Chief Operating Officer
CFO: Eric Smith, Chief Financial Officer
CIO: Kevin Murphy, Director, Information Technology Services
CHR: Jim Reames, Director Human Resources
CNO: Karen Long, R.N., Vice President Nursing
Web address: www.bayfrontstpete.com
Control: Corporation, Investor–owned, for–profit **Service:** General Medical and Surgical

Staffed Beds: 382

✠ **EDWARD WHITE HOSPITAL (100239)**, 2323 Ninth Avenue North, Zip 33713–6898, Mailing Address: P.O. Box 12018, Zip 33733–2018; tel. 727/323–1111, (Nonreporting) **A**1 9 10 **S** HCA, Nashville, TN
Primary Contact: Sharon Hayes, Chief Executive Officer
CFO: Drew Strauch, Chief Financial Officer
CMO: Clinton Davis, M.D., Chief of Staff
CIO: Charles Fribbley, Director Information Services
CHR: Sam Veltri, Vice President Human Resources
CNO: Pat Willie, R.N., Chief Nursing Officer
Web address: www.edwardwhitehospital.com
Control: Corporation, Investor–owned, for–profit **Service:** General Medical and Surgical

Staffed Beds: 110

✠ **NORTHSIDE HOSPITAL (100238)**, 6000 49th Street North, Zip 33709–2145; tel. 727/521–4411 **A**1 9 10 12 13 **F**3 17 18 20 22 24 26 28 29 30 31 34 35 40 45 49 50 51 53 56 57 58 59 60 64 65 70 74 75 77 78 79 81 85 92 93 107 108 111 114 115 118 119 135 146 **S** HCA, Nashville, TN
Primary Contact: Dia Nichols, Chief Executive Officer
COO: Jayme Chancellor, Chief Operating Officer
CFO: Gary Searls, Chief Financial Officer
CMO: Ira Siegman, M.D., Chief Medical Officer
CIO: Kirk Hendrick, Director Information Systems
CHR: Maggie Miklos, Director Human Resources
CNO: Wendy Lincoln, Chief Nursing Officer
Web address: www.northsidehospital.com
Control: Corporation, Investor–owned, for–profit **Service:** General Medical and Surgical

Staffed Beds: 227 **Admissions:** 9324 **Census:** 115 **Outpatient Visits:** 42984 **Births:** 0 **Total Expense ($000):** 117534 **Payroll Expense ($000):** 44212 **Personnel:** 596

★ ◇ **PALMS OF PASADENA HOSPITAL (100126)**, 1501 Pasadena Avenue South, Zip 33707–3798; tel. 727/381–1000, (Nonreporting) **A**9 10 21 **S** HCA, Nashville, TN
Primary Contact: Sharon Hayes, Interim Chief Executive Officer
CFO: James B. Gilbert, Chief Financial Officer
CMO: George Hutter, M.D., Chief of Staff
CIO: Danny Waters, Director, Information Services
CHR: Karen Casteel, Director Human Resources
CNO: Andrea Clyne, R.N., Chief Nursing Officer
Web address: www.palmspasadena.com
Control: Corporation, Investor–owned, for–profit **Service:** General Medical and Surgical

Staffed Beds: 307

Many Facility Codes have changed. Please refer to the AHA Guide Code Chart. © 2014 AHA Guide

FL

✠ **ST. ANTHONY'S HOSPITAL (100067)**, 1200 Seventh Avenue North,
Zip 33705–1388, Mailing Address: P.O. Box 12588, Zip 33733–2588;
tel. 727/825–1100, (Total facility includes 28 beds in nursing home–type unit) **A**1
2 5 9 10 **F**3 11 12 15 17 18 20 22 26 28 29 30 31 34 35 40 44 45 46 49
51 57 59 60 64 68 70 74 75 77 78 79 81 84 85 86 87 93 98 100 102 103
107 108 110 111 114 115 117 118 119 121 123 124 126 128 129 130 131
132 135 146 148 **P**6 7 **S** Catholic Health East / Trinity Health, Livonia, MI
Primary Contact: William G. Ulbricht, President
COO: Ronald J. Colaguori, Vice President Operations
CFO: Carl Tremonti, Chief Financial Officer
CMO: James McClintic, M.D., Vice President Medical Affairs
CIO: Tim Thompson, Vice President Information Services
CHR: James S. Bacon, Director Team Resources
Web address: www.stanthonys.com/
Control: Other not–for–profit (including NFP Corporation) **Service:** General
Medical and Surgical

> **Staffed Beds:** 344 **Admissions:** 15830 **Census:** 243 **Outpatient Visits:**
> 80870 **Births:** 0 **Total Expense ($000):** 206886 **Payroll Expense ($000):**
> 87023 **Personnel:** 1348

✠ **ST. PETERSBURG GENERAL HOSPITAL (100180)**, 6500 38th Avenue North,
Zip 33710–1629; tel. 727/384–1414, (Nonreporting) **A**1 2 9 10 12 13 **S** HCA,
Nashville, TN
Primary Contact: Robert B. Conroy, Jr., Chief Executive Officer
COO: Stephanie McNulty, Chief Operating Officer
CFO: Andrew Smith, CFO
CHR: Guy Samuel, Director Human Resources
CNO: JoAnne Cattell, Chief Nursing Officer
Web address: www.stpetegeneral.com
Control: Corporation, Investor–owned, for–profit **Service:** General Medical and
Surgical

> **Staffed Beds:** 219

SANFORD—Seminole County

✠ **CENTRAL FLORIDA REGIONAL HOSPITAL (100161)**, 1401 West Seminole
Boulevard, Zip 32771–6764; tel. 407/321–4500, (Nonreporting) **A**1 9 10 **S** HCA,
Nashville, TN
Primary Contact: Wendy H. Brandon, Chief Executive Officer
COO: Glenn Carney, Chief Operating Officer
CFO: Richard Read, Chief Financial Officer
CIO: Jerry Ballard, Director Information Systems
CHR: Linda V. Smith, Vice President Human Resources
CNO: Maria Calloway, R.N., Chief Nursing Officer
Web address: www.centralfloridaregional.com
Control: Corporation, Investor–owned, for–profit **Service:** General Medical and
Surgical

> **Staffed Beds:** 226

SARASOTA--Sarasota County

✠ **COMPLEX CARE HOSPITAL AT RIDGELAKE (102018)**, 6150 Edgelake Drive,
Zip 34240–8803; tel. 941/342–3000 **A**1 10 **F**1 29 91 148 **S** LifeCare
Management Services, Plano, TX
Primary Contact: Danny R. Edwards, Administrator
CFO: Leah Drabant, Director of Finance
CMO: Craig Harcup, M.D., Hospital Medical Director
CHR: Jennifer Sparks, Human Resources Generalist
CNO: Timothy Mitchell, R.N., Chief Nursing Officer
Web address: www.lifecare–hospitals.com/hospital.php?id=23
Control: Corporation, Investor–owned, for–profit **Service:** Long–Term Acute Care
hospital

> **Staffed Beds:** 40 **Admissions:** 459 **Census:** 33 **Outpatient Visits:** 0 **Births:**
> 0 **Total Expense ($000):** 18779 **Payroll Expense ($000):** 8148 **Personnel:**
> 191

✠ **DOCTORS HOSPITAL OF SARASOTA (100166)**, 5731 Bee Ridge Road,
Zip 34233–5056; tel. 941/342–1100, (Nonreporting) **A**1 2 9 10 **S** HCA,
Nashville, TN
Primary Contact: Robert C. Meade, Chief Executive Officer
CFO: Charles Schwaner, III, Chief Financial Officer
CMO: Thomas Trinchetto, M.D., Chief Medical Officer
CHR: Theresa Levering, Director Human Resources
CNO: Kathy Mitchell, R.N., Chief Nursing Officer
Web address: www.doctorsofsarasota.com
Control: Corporation, Investor–owned, for–profit **Service:** General Medical and
Surgical

> **Staffed Beds:** 168

✠ △ **HEALTHSOUTH REHABILITATION HOSPITAL OF SARASOTA (103031)**,
6400 Edgelake Drive, Zip 34240–8813; tel. 941/921–8600, (Nonreporting) **A**1 7
9 10 **S** HEALTHSOUTH Corporation, Birmingham, AL
Primary Contact: Marcus Braz, Chief Executive Officer
CFO: Barbara Bierut, Chief Financial Officer
CMO: Alexander De Jesus, M.D., Medical Director
CHR: Brenda Benner, Director Human Resources
CNO: Jacqueline Juenger, R.N., Chief Nursing Officer
Web address: www.healthsouthsarasota.com
Control: Corporation, Investor–owned, for–profit **Service:** Rehabilitation

> **Staffed Beds:** 86

HEALTHSOUTH RIDGELAKE HOSPITAL See Complex Care Hospital at
Ridgelake

☐ △ **SARASOTA MEMORIAL HEALTH CARE SYSTEM (100087)**, 1700 South
Tamiami Trail, Zip 34239–3555; tel. 941/917–9000 **A**1 2 3 5 7 9 10 **F**3 6 7 8
11 12 13 15 17 18 20 22 24 26 28 29 30 31 32 34 35 36 37 38 39 40 42
44 45 46 47 48 49 50 51 53 54 55 56 57 58 59 60 64 66 68 70 72 73 74
75 76 77 78 79 80 81 82 84 85 86 87 89 90 91 93 95 96 98 99 100 101
102 103 105 107 108 110 111 114 115 116 117 118 119 124 126 129 130
131 132 135 143 144 145 146 147 148
Primary Contact: David Verinder, Interim Chief Executive Officer
COO: David Verinder, Chief Operating Officer
CFO: Bill Woeltjen, Chief Financial Officer
CMO: Steve Taylor, M.D., Chief Medical Officer
CIO: Denis Baker, Chief Information Officer
CHR: Laurie Bennett, Director Human Resources
CNO: Jan Mauck, R.N., Chief Nursing Officer
Web address: www.smh.com
Control: Hospital district or authority, Government, nonfederal **Service:** General
Medical and Surgical

> **Staffed Beds:** 645 **Admissions:** 25576 **Census:** 326 **Outpatient Visits:**
> 528731 **Births:** 2974 **Total Expense ($000):** 461300 **Payroll Expense
> ($000):** 177289 **Personnel:** 3672

SEBASTIAN—Indian River County

✠ **SEBASTIAN RIVER MEDICAL CENTER (100217)**, 13695 North U.S. Highway
1, Zip 32958–3230, Mailing Address: Box 780838, Zip 32978–0838;
tel. 772/589–3186, (Total facility includes 31 beds in nursing home–type unit) **A**1
9 10 **F**11 12 15 18 20 22 28 29 31 34 40 41 45 46 49 50 51 57 59 60 62
63 64 65 68 70 74 75 77 78 79 81 83 84 85 86 87 89 90 91 92 93 107
110 111 114 115 116 119 126 129 130 132 133 145 146 148 **P**8
S Community Health Systems, Inc., Franklin, TN
Primary Contact: Kelly Enriquez, Chief Executive Officer
CFO: John McEachern, Controller
CMO: Ralph Geiger, M.D., Chief of Staff
CHR: Kam Storey, Director Human Resources
Web address: www.sebastianrivermedical.com
Control: Corporation, Investor–owned, for–profit **Service:** General Medical and
Surgical

> **Staffed Beds:** 140 **Admissions:** 4500 **Census:** 60 **Outpatient Visits:** 17300
> **Births:** 0

SEBRING—Highlands County

✠ **FLORIDA HOSPITAL HEARTLAND MEDICAL CENTER (100109)**, 4200 Sun'n
Lake Boulevard, Zip 33872–1986, Mailing Address: P.O. Box 9400,
Zip 33871–9400; tel. 863/314–4466 **A**1 9 10 19 **F**8 11 13 15 18 20 22 24
28 29 30 34 35 37 40 44 45 49 50 51 53 54 57 59 60 62 64 70 75 79 81
82 86 87 89 98 100 101 103 104 107 108 110 111 114 118 119 127 129
130 132 133 134 146 147 148 **P**6 **S** Adventist Health System Sunbelt Health
Care Corporation, Altamonte Springs, FL
Primary Contact: Eric Stevens, Chief Executive Officer
CFO: Rosalie Oliver, Chief Financial Officer
CMO: Jorge F. Gonzalez, M.D., Chief Medical Officer
CHR: Anthony Stahl, Vice President
CNO: Gloria N. Santos, R.N., Chief Nursing Officer
Web address: www.fhheartland.org/
Control: Church–operated, Nongovernment, not–for profit **Service:** General
Medical and Surgical

> **Staffed Beds:** 214 **Admissions:** 11525 **Census:** 152 **Outpatient Visits:**
> 154947 **Births:** 739 **Total Expense ($000):** 172437 **Payroll Expense
> ($000):** 75716 **Personnel:** 1365

Hospital, Medicare Provider Number, Address, Telephone, Approval, Facility, and Physician Codes, Health Care System

★ American Hospital Association (AHA) membership
☐ The Joint Commission accreditation
◇ DNV Healthcare Inc. accreditation
○ Healthcare Facilities Accreditation Program
△ Commission on Accreditation of Rehabilitation Facilities (CARF) accreditation

FL

✠ **HIGHLANDS REGIONAL MEDICAL CENTER (100049)**, 3600 South Highlands Avenue, Zip 33870–5495, Mailing Address: Drawer 2066, Zip 33871–2066; tel. 863/471–5800 **A**1 9 10 19 **F**3 11 13 18 20 22 29 34 40 45 49 50 51 57 59 64 70 76 79 81 85 87 93 97 107 108 110 114 119 124 129 146 **S** Community Health Systems, Inc., Franklin, TN
Primary Contact: Joseph Bernard, Chief Executive Officer
COO: Robert Palussek, Chief Operating Officer
CFO: Vicki DeRenzis, Chief Financial Officer
CMO: Roger Arumugam, M.D., Chief Medical Officer
CIO: Nate Johnson, Chief Information Officer
CHR: John D. Ware, Human Resources Director
CNO: Adam Kless, Chief Nursing Officer
Web address: www.highlandsregional.com
Control: Corporation, Investor–owned, for–profit **Service:** General Medical and Surgical

Staffed Beds: 116 **Admissions:** 4092 **Census:** 47 **Births:** 360 **Total Expense ($000):** 59884 **Payroll Expense ($000):** 17742

SOUTH MIAMI—Miami–Dade County

☐ **LARKIN COMMUNITY HOSPITAL (100181)**, 7031 S.W. 62nd Avenue, Zip 33143–4781; tel. 305/284–7500 **A**1 9 10 13 **F**3 8 11 15 18 29 31 34 35 39 40 45 46 49 50 51 56 57 58 59 62 64 65 70 74 75 78 79 81 82 85 86 87 96 97 98 102 103 104 105 107 108 111 114 117 118 119 124 126 129 130 135 143 148
Primary Contact: Sandra Sosa–Guerrero, Chief Executive Officer
COO: George J. Michel, Chief Operating Officer
CFO: Edgar Castillo, Chief Financial Officer
CMO: Mario Almeida–Suarez, M.D., Chief of Staff
CIO: Orlando Suarez, Manager Information Technology
CHR: Deshire Pena, Assistant Director Administrator
CNO: Manuel Fernandez, Vice President Nursing
Web address: www.larkinhospital.com
Control: Individual, Investor–owned, for–profit **Service:** General Medical and Surgical

Staffed Beds: 146 **Admissions:** 6127 **Census:** 83 **Outpatient Visits:** 13043 **Births:** 0 **Total Expense ($000):** 75687 **Payroll Expense ($000):** 34869 **Personnel:** 670

STARKE—Bradford County

SHANDS STARKE See Shands Starke Regional Medical Center

✠ **SHANDS STARKE REGIONAL MEDICAL CENTER (101310)**, 922 East Call Street, Zip 32091–3699; tel. 904/368–2300 **A**1 9 10 18 **F**3 11 15 29 30 34 35 40 44 45 50 57 59 64 68 75 77 81 85 93 97 107 111 114 119 127 129 131 132 135 **P**6 **S** Community Health Systems, Inc., Franklin, TN
Primary Contact: Rhonda Kay Sherrod, R.N., MSN, Interim Chief Executive Officer
Web address: www.shands.org
Control: Partnership, Investor–owned, for–profit **Service:** General Medical and Surgical

Staffed Beds: 25 **Admissions:** 1535 **Census:** 14 **Births:** 0 **Total Expense ($000):** 26625 **Payroll Expense ($000):** 10918

STUART—Martin County

✠ **HEALTHSOUTH REHABILITATION HOSPITAL AT MARTIN HEALTH (103044)**, 5850 S.E. Community Drive, Zip 34997–6420; tel. 772/324–3500, (Data for 210 days) **A**1 10 **F**3 28 29 34 35 57 75 77 86 87 90 91 95 96 100 130 132 148 **P**8 **S** HEALTHSOUTH Corporation, Birmingham, AL
Primary Contact: Kevin R. Conn, Interim Chief Executive Officer
CFO: Dawn Salas, Controller
CMO: Stephen L. Chastain, M.D., Chief Medical Officer
CHR: Annette DiPiero, Human Resource Director
CNO: Jimmy Dascani, Chief Nursing Officer
Web address: www.healthsouthmartin.com
Control: Corporation, Investor–owned, for–profit **Service:** Rehabilitation

Staffed Beds: 34 **Admissions:** 470 **Census:** 28 **Outpatient Visits:** 0 **Births:** 0 **Total Expense ($000):** 9066 **Payroll Expense ($000):** 4818

✠ **MARTIN HEALTH SYSTEM (100044)**, 200 S.E. Hospital Avenue, Zip 34994–2346, Mailing Address: P.O. Box 9010, Zip 34995–9010; tel. 772/287–5200, (Includes MARTIN MEMORIAL HOSPITAL SOUTH, 2100 S.E. Salerno Road, Zip 34997; tel. 772/223–2300) **A**1 2 9 10 **F**3 8 11 12 13 15 17 18 20 22 24 26 28 29 30 31 35 36 37 40 42 45 46 47 49 50 51 53 55 60 64 68 70 72 74 75 76 77 78 79 81 82 85 86 87 90 91 93 94 95 107 108 110 111 114 115 116 117 118 119 120 121 123 124 126 129 130 132 143 144 146 **P**6
Primary Contact: Mark E. Robitaille, President and Chief Executive Officer
COO: Robert L. Lord, JD, Senior Vice President and Chief Operating Officer
CFO: Chuck Cleaver, Vice President and Chief Financial Officer
CMO: Michael Skehan, M.D., Senior Vice President and Chief Medical Officer
CIO: Edmund Collins, Chief Information Officer
CHR: Angie L. Metcalf, Vice President and Chief Human Resource Officer
CNO: Donna Herrin Griffith, FACHE, Senior Vice President and Chief Patient Care Officer
Web address: www.mmhs.com
Control: Other not–for–profit (including NFP Corporation) **Service:** General Medical and Surgical

Staffed Beds: 321 **Admissions:** 16614 **Census:** 204 **Outpatient Visits:** 99745 **Births:** 1343 **Total Expense ($000):** 297008 **Payroll Expense ($000):** 126850 **Personnel:** 2500

SUN CITY CENTER—Hillsborough County

✠ **SOUTH BAY HOSPITAL (100259)**, 4016 Sun City Center Boulevard, Zip 33573–5298; tel. 813/634–3301 **A**1 9 10 **F**3 15 18 29 30 31 34 35 37 40 45 49 50 57 59 64 68 70 74 75 77 78 79 81 82 85 86 87 93 107 108 110 111 114 118 119 132 146 148 **S** HCA, Nashville, TN
Primary Contact: Sharon L. Roush, Chief Executive Officer
COO: Gary Malaer, Chief Operating Officer
CFO: Shawn Gregory, Chief Financial Officer
CIO: Danny Waters, Director Information Technology and Systems
CHR: Megan Dean, Director Human Resources
CNO: Terrie Jefferson, R.N., Chief Nursing Officer
Web address: www.southbayhospital.com
Control: Corporation, Investor–owned, for–profit **Service:** General Medical and Surgical

Staffed Beds: 112 **Admissions:** 7387 **Census:** 90 **Outpatient Visits:** 32394 **Births:** 0 **Total Expense ($000):** 63867 **Payroll Expense ($000):** 24898 **Personnel:** 293

SUNRISE—Broward County

✠ **HEALTHSOUTH SUNRISE REHABILITATION HOSPITAL (103028)**, 4399 North Nob Hill Road, Zip 33351–5899; tel. 954/749–0300 **A**1 10 **F**3 29 62 82 90 91 93 95 96 132 148 **S** HEALTHSOUTH Corporation, Birmingham, AL
Primary Contact: Stacy Modlin, Chief Executive Officer
COO: Jay de los Reyes, Chief Operating Officer
CFO: Ruth Goodstein, Controller
CMO: Scott Tannenbaum, M.D., Medical Director
CIO: Angela Manning, Director Health Information Services
CHR: Barbara Dunkiel, Director Human Resources
CNO: Omaira D. Riano, Chief Nursing Officer
Web address: www.healthsouthsunrise.com
Control: Corporation, Investor–owned, for–profit **Service:** Rehabilitation

Staffed Beds: 126 **Admissions:** 2264 **Census:** 88 **Outpatient Visits:** 28550 **Births:** 0 **Total Expense ($000):** 34492 **Payroll Expense ($000):** 17381 **Personnel:** 350

TALLAHASSEE—Leon County

✠ **CAPITAL REGIONAL MEDICAL CENTER (100254)**, 2626 Capital Medical Boulevard, Zip 32308–4499; tel. 850/325–5000, (Nonreporting) **A**1 2 9 10 **S** HCA, Nashville, TN
Primary Contact: Brian Cook, FACHE, Chief Executive Officer
CMO: Steve West, M.D., Chief Medical Officer
CIO: Robert A. Steed, Director Information Systems
CHR: Louise Truitt, Vice President Human Resources
Web address: www.capitalregionalmedicalcenter.com
Control: Individual, Investor–owned, for–profit **Service:** General Medical and Surgical

Staffed Beds: 198

EASTSIDE PSYCHIATRIC HOSPITAL (104059), 2634 Capital Circle N.E., Zip 32308–4106; tel. 850/523–3333, (Nonreporting) **A**9 10
Primary Contact: Jay A. Reeve, President and Chief Executive Officer
COO: Sue Conger, Chief Operating Officer
CFO: Virginia Kelly, Chief Financial Officer
CMO: Ludmila de Faria, M.D., Chief Medical Officer
CIO: Thad Moorer, Chief Information Officer
CHR: Candy Landry, Chief Human Resource Officer
CNO: Judy Goreau, R.N., Director of Nursing
Web address: www.apalacheecenter.org
Control: Other not–for–profit (including NFP Corporation) **Service:** Psychiatric

Staffed Beds: 24

Many Facility Codes have changed. Please refer to the AHA Guide Code Chart. © 2014 AHA Guide

✠ **HEALTHSOUTH REHABILITATION HOSPITAL OF TALLAHASSEE (103033)**, 1675 Riggins Road, Zip 32308–5315; tel. 850/656–4800 **A**1 9 10 **F**29 34 35 56 57 60 64 74 75 77 78 79 82 86 90 93 95 96 130 132 143 146 148 **S** HEALTHSOUTH Corporation, Birmingham, AL
Primary Contact: Dale Neely, Chief Executive Officer
CFO: Jennifer Spooner, Controller
CMO: Robert Rowland, M.D., Medical Director
CIO: Charles O'Keefe, Director Health Information Services
Web address: www.healthsouthtallahassee.com
Control: Corporation, Investor–owned, for–profit **Service:** Rehabilitation

> **Staffed Beds:** 76 **Admissions:** 1182 **Census:** 44 **Births:** 0 **Total Expense ($000):** 15885 **Payroll Expense ($000):** 7389

✠ **SELECT SPECIALTY HOSPITAL–TALLAHASSEE (102020)**, 1554 Surgeons Drive, Zip 32308–4631; tel. 850/219–6800, (Nonreporting) **A**1 9 10 **S** Select Medical Corporation, Mechanicsburg, PA
Primary Contact: Lora Davis, Chief Executive Officer
Web address: www.tallahassee.selectspecialtyhospitals.com/
Control: Corporation, Investor–owned, for–profit **Service:** Long–Term Acute Care hospital

> **Staffed Beds:** 29

✠ **TALLAHASSEE MEMORIAL HEALTHCARE (100135)**, 1300 Miccosukee Road, Zip 32308–5054; tel. 850/431–1155, (Total facility includes 42 beds in nursing home–type unit) **A**1 2 3 5 9 10 **F**2 3 5 6 8 11 12 17 18 19 20 22 24 26 28 29 30 31 34 35 37 40 42 43 45 46 47 49 50 51 53 54 55 56 57 58 59 60 61 62 64 65 68 70 72 73 74 75 76 77 78 79 80 81 82 84 85 86 87 88 89 91 93 96 97 98 99 100 102 103 104 107 108 110 113 114 115 117 118 119 120 121 123 124 126 127 128 129 130 131 132 135 143 144 146 147 148 **P**6
Primary Contact: G. Mark O'Bryant, President and Chief Executive Officer
COO: Jason H. Moore, Vice President and Chief Operating Officer
CFO: William A. Giudice, Vice President and Chief Financial Officer
CMO: Dean Watson, M.D., Chief Medical Officer
CIO: Don Lindsey, Vice President and Chief Information Officer
CHR: Steven W. Adriaanse, Vice President and Chief Human Resources Officer
Web address: www.tmh.org
Control: Other not–for–profit (including NFP Corporation) **Service:** General Medical and Surgical

> **Staffed Beds:** 491 **Admissions:** 26052 **Census:** 356 **Outpatient Visits:** 603290 **Births:** 3713 **Total Expense ($000):** 476236 **Payroll Expense ($000):** 200502 **Personnel:** 3602

TAMARAC—Broward County

✠ **UNIVERSITY HOSPITAL AND MEDICAL CENTER (100224)**, 7201 North University Drive, Zip 33321–2996; tel. 954/721–2200, (Includes UNIVERSITY PAVILION, 7425 North University Drive, Zip 33328; tel. 305/722–9933), (Nonreporting) **A**1 9 10 **S** HCA, Nashville, TN
Primary Contact: Joseph D. Melchiode, Chief Executive Officer
CFO: Aurelio Gonzalez, Chief Financial Officer
CMO: Ran Abrahamy, M.D., Chief of Staff
CIO: Tom Scharff, Director Information Services
Web address: www.uhmchealth.com
Control: Corporation, Investor–owned, for–profit **Service:** General Medical and Surgical

> **Staffed Beds:** 317

TAMPA—Hillsborough County

✠ **FLORIDA HOSPITAL CARROLLWOOD (100069)**, 7171 North Dale Mabry Highway, Zip 33614–2665; tel. 813/932–2222 **A**1 10 **F**3 8 11 15 20 26 29 30 31 34 35 40 44 45 48 49 50 53 54 56 57 58 59 60 61 62 64 65 68 70 74 75 77 78 79 80 81 82 85 86 87 92 93 97 107 111 114 119 130 131 132 143 146 148 **S** Adventist Health System Sunbelt Health Care Corporation, Altamonte Springs, FL
Primary Contact: Joe Johnson, Chief Executive Officer
COO: Mary C. Whillock, R.N., Associate Nursing Officer and Chief Operating Officer
CFO: Marvin A. Kurtz, Chief Financial Officer
Web address: www.elevatinghealthcare.org/locations/carrollwood
Control: Church–operated, Nongovernment, not–for profit **Service:** General Medical and Surgical

> **Staffed Beds:** 90 **Admissions:** 4475 **Census:** 45 **Outpatient Visits:** 58771 **Births:** 0 **Total Expense ($000):** 103644 **Payroll Expense ($000):** 30570 **Personnel:** 469

✠ △ **FLORIDA HOSPITAL TAMPA (100173)**, 3100 East Fletcher Avenue, Zip 33613–4688; tel. 813/971–6000 **A**1 2 3 5 7 10 **F**3 8 11 12 13 15 17 18 20 22 24 26 28 29 30 31 34 35 40 41 44 45 46 47 48 49 50 54 57 58 59 62 64 65 70 72 73 74 75 76 77 78 79 80 81 82 84 85 86 87 88 89 90 91 92 93 96 99 100 107 108 109 110 111 112 114 115 116 117 118 119 120 121 132 136 129 130 132 133 143 144 146 147 148 **P**6 7 **S** Adventist Health System Sunbelt Health Care Corporation, Altamonte Springs, FL
Primary Contact: Brian Adams, President and CEO
COO: Dick Tibbits, Vice President and Chief Operating Officer
CFO: Dima Didenko, Chief Financial Officer
CMO: Brad Bjornstad, M.D., Vice President and Chief Medical Officer
CHR: Dick Tibbits, Vice President and Chief Operating Officer
CNO: Joy B. Solomita, R.N., Vice President and Chief Nursing Officer
Web address: www.floridahospital.com/tampa
Control: Other not–for–profit (including NFP Corporation) **Service:** General Medical and Surgical

> **Staffed Beds:** 369 **Admissions:** 20297 **Census:** 295 **Outpatient Visits:** 130207 **Births:** 1411 **Total Expense ($000):** 311154 **Payroll Expense ($000):** 121195 **Personnel:** 2096

✠ **H. LEE MOFFITT CANCER CENTER AND RESEARCH INSTITUTE (100271)**, 12902 Magnolia Drive, Zip 33612–9497; tel. 813/972–4673 **A**1 2 3 5 9 10 **F**3 8 11 15 26 29 30 31 34 35 36 37 38 44 45 46 47 48 49 50 54 55 56 57 58 59 63 64 68 70 71 74 75 77 78 79 81 82 83 84 85 86 87 91 92 93 96 97 100 101 103 104 107 108 109 110 111 113 114 115 116 117 118 119 120 121 123 124 130 132 134 135 136 141 144 146 147 148 **P**6
Primary Contact: Alan F. List, M.D., President and Chief Executive Officer
COO: John A. Kolosky, Executive Vice President and Chief Operating Officer
CFO: Janene Culumber, Vice President and Chief Financial Officer
CMO: W. Michael Alberts, M.D., Vice President Medical Affairs
CIO: Mark Hulse, Vice President and Chief Information Officer
CHR: Yvette Tremonti, Vice President Human Resources
Web address: www.moffitt.org
Control: Other not–for–profit (including NFP Corporation) **Service:** Cancer

> **Staffed Beds:** 206 **Admissions:** 9373 **Census:** 163 **Outpatient Visits:** 330363 **Births:** 0 **Total Expense ($000):** 771561 **Payroll Expense ($000):** 314106 **Personnel:** 3987

✠ △ **JAMES A. HALEY VETERANS' HOSPITAL**, 13000 Bruce B. Downs Boulevard, Zip 33612–4745; tel. 813/972–2000, (Total facility includes 118 beds in nursing home–type unit) **A**1 3 5 7 8 **F**1 3 5 9 12 15 17 18 20 22 24 26 28 29 30 31 33 36 38 39 40 44 45 48 49 50 51 53 54 55 56 57 58 59 60 61 62 63 64 65 70 71 74 75 77 78 79 80 81 82 83 84 85 86 87 90 91 92 93 94 95 96 97 98 100 101 102 103 104 105 106 107 108 109 110 111 113 114 115 116 117 118 119 120 121 123 127 128 129 130 131 132 135 143 144 146 147 148 **P**1 **S** Department of Veterans Affairs, Washington, DC
Primary Contact: Kathleen R. Fogarty, Director
COO: Roy L. Hawkins, Jr., Deputy Director
CFO: Robert Konkel, Manager Finance
CMO: Edward Cutolo, Jr., M.D., Chief of Staff
CIO: Jose Seymour, Chief Information Resource Management
CHR: Neal C. Hamilton, Chief Human Resources
CNO: Laureen Doloresco, R.N., Associate Director for Patient Care and Nursing Services
Web address: www.tampa.va.gov/
Control: Veterans Affairs, Government, federal **Service:** General Medical and Surgical

> **Staffed Beds:** 566 **Admissions:** 12452 **Census:** 363 **Outpatient Visits:** 1164402 **Births:** 0 **Total Expense ($000):** 795604 **Payroll Expense ($000):** 354518 **Personnel:** 4655

✠ **KINDRED HOSPITAL BAY AREA–TAMPA (102009)**, 4555 South Manhattan Avenue, Zip 33611–2397; tel. 813/839–6341, (Includes KINDRED HOSPITAL–BAY AREA ST. PETERSBURG, 3030 Sixth Street South, Saint Petersburg, Zip 33705–3720; tel. 727/894–8719; Debra Plummer, Chief Executive Officer) **A**1 10 **F**1 3 18 29 34 59 60 70 74 75 85 87 130 148 **S** Kindred Healthcare, Louisville, KY
Primary Contact: Sandra Morgan, Chief Executive Officer
CFO: Frank Billy, Chief Financial Officer
CHR: Melissa Broadnax, Supervisor Human Resources
Web address: www.khtampa.com/
Control: Hospital district or authority, Government, nonfederal **Service:** Long–Term Acute Care hospital

> **Staffed Beds:** 73 **Admissions:** 500 **Census:** 44 **Births:** 0

Hospital, Medicare Provider Number, Address, Telephone, Approval, Facility, and Physician Codes, Health Care System

★ American Hospital Association (AHA) membership
☐ The Joint Commission accreditation   ◇ DNV Healthcare Inc. accreditation
○ Healthcare Facilities Accreditation Program
△ Commission on Accreditation of Rehabilitation Facilities (CARF) accreditation

© 2014 AHA Guide   *Many Facility Codes have changed. Please refer to the AHA Guide Code Chart.*   Hospitals **A147**

FL

✠ **KINDRED HOSPITAL CENTRAL TAMPA (102013)**, 4801 North Howard Avenue, Zip 33603–1411; tel. 813/874–7575, (Nonreporting) **A**1 9 10 **S** Kindred Healthcare, Louisville, KY
Primary Contact: Ralph Seiner, Chief Executive Officer
CFO: John Miner, Chief Financial Officer
Web address: www.kindredcentraltampa.com/
Control: Corporation, Investor–owned, for–profit **Service:** Long–Term Acute Care hospital

Staffed Beds: 102

★ ◇ **MEMORIAL HOSPITAL OF TAMPA (100206)**, 2901 Swann Avenue, Zip 33609–4057; tel. 813/873–6400, (Nonreporting) **A**5 9 10 21 **S** HCA, Nashville, TN
Primary Contact: John J. Mainieri, Chief Executive Officer
CFO: Shelley V. Kolseth, Chief Financial Officer
CIO: John Riton, Director Information Services
Web address: www.memorialhospitaltampa.com
Control: Corporation, Investor–owned, for–profit **Service:** General Medical and Surgical

Staffed Beds: 139

☐ **SHRINERS HOSPITALS FOR CHILDREN–TAMPA (103303)**, 12502 USF Pine Drive, Zip 33612–9499; tel. 813/972–2250 **A**1 3 5 9 10 **F**3 34 35 50 57 64 68 74 77 79 81 85 89 91 93 94 107 131 146 **S** Shriners Hospitals for Children, Tampa, FL
Primary Contact: Jeannette Skinner, R.N., FACHE, Administrator
CFO: Ruth Gregos, Director Finance
CMO: Maureen Maciel, M.D., Chief of Staff
CNO: Beth Demas, Director Public Relations
Web address: www.shrinershospitalsforchildren.org/Hospitals/Locations/Tampa.aspx
Control: Other not–for–profit (including NFP Corporation) **Service:** Children's orthopedic

Staffed Beds: 25 Admissions: 282 Census: 2 Births: 0 Total Expense ($000): 18707 Payroll Expense ($000): 7951

✠ **ST. JOSEPH'S HOSPITAL (100075)**, 3001 West Martin Luther King Jr. Boulevard, Zip 33607–6387, Mailing Address: P.O. Box 4227, Zip 33677–4227; tel. 813/870–4000, (Includes ST. JOSEPH'S CHILDREN'S HOSPITAL OF TAMPA, 3001 Dr. Martin Luther King Jr. Boulevard, Zip 33607; tel. 813/554–8500; ST. JOSEPH'S WOMEN'S HOSPITAL – TAMPA, 3030 West Dr. Martin L. King Boulevard, Zip 33607–6394; tel. 813/872–2950; Kimberly Guy, Chief Operating Officer) **A**1 2 3 5 9 10 **F**3 7 11 12 13 15 17 18 19 20 21 22 23 24 25 26 27 28 29 30 31 33 34 35 37 39 40 41 43 44 45 46 48 49 51 55 57 58 59 64 65 66 68 70 71 72 73 74 75 76 77 78 79 81 82 84 85 86 87 88 89 93 94 98 99 100 101 102 107 108 110 111 114 115 118 119 120 121 123 124 126 127 129 130 131 132 135 145 146 147 148 **P**6 7 **S** Catholic Health East / Trinity Health, Livonia, MI
Primary Contact: Lorraine Lutton, President
CFO: Cathy Yoder, Chief Financial Officer
CMO: Mark Vaaler, M.D., Vice President Medical Staff Affairs
CIO: Lindsey Jarrell, Vice President Information Services
CHR: Pat Teeuwen, Director Team Resources
Web address: www.sjbhealth.org
Control: Other not–for–profit (including NFP Corporation) **Service:** General Medical and Surgical

Staffed Beds: 1006 Admissions: 45799 Census: 590 Outpatient Visits: 233536 Births: 7722 Total Expense ($000): 689157 Payroll Expense ($000): 261099 Personnel: 3824

★ ◇ **TAMPA COMMUNITY HOSPITAL (100255)**, 6001 Webb Road, Zip 33615–3291; tel. 813/888–7060 **A**5 9 10 21 **F**3 4 5 15 18 20 29 40 45 46 47 48 49 70 74 79 81 82 85 92 93 98 102 103 107 110 111 114 115 118 119 126 128 130 146 148 **P**4 5 **S** HCA, Nashville, TN
Primary Contact: Jacob Fisher, Chief Executive Officer
CMO: Patrick Horan, M.D., Chief of Staff
CIO: Larry Mohammed, Director Information Systems
CHR: Judy Miller, Director Human Resources
Web address: www.tampacommunityhospital.com/
Control: Corporation, Investor–owned, for–profit **Service:** General Medical and Surgical

Staffed Beds: 197 Admissions: 1237 Census: 18 Outpatient Visits: 8286 Births: 0 Total Expense ($000): 13855 Payroll Expense ($000): 5342 Personnel: 381

✠ △ **TAMPA GENERAL HOSPITAL (100128)**, 1 Tampa General Circle, Zip 33606–3571, Mailing Address: P.O. Box 1289, Zip 33601–1289; tel. 813/844–7000, (Includes TAMPA GENERAL HOSPITAL CHILDREN'S MEDICAL CENTER, 1 Tampa General Circle, tel. 813/844–7000) **A**1 3 5 7 8 9 10 **F**3 7 8 9 11 12 13 15 16 17 18 19 20 22 24 26 28 29 30 31 32 34 35 36 37 38 40 41 43 44 45 46 47 48 49 50 51 52 53 54 55 56 57 58 59 60 61 64 65 66 68 70 72 73 74 75 76 77 78 79 81 82 83 84 85 86 87 88 89 90 91 92 93 94 96 97 98 100 101 102 103 107 108 109 110 111 114 115 119 120 121 122 123 124 126 129 130 131 132 134 135 137 138 139 140 141 142 143 145 146 147 148 **P**6
Primary Contact: James R. Burkhart, FACHE, President and Chief Executive Officer
COO: Deana Nelson, FACHE, Executive Vice President and Chief Operating Officer
CFO: Steve Short, Executive Vice President Finance and Administration and Chief Financial Officer
CMO: Sally Houston, M.D., Executive Vice President and Chief Medical Officer
CIO: Scott Arnold, Senior Vice President Information Systems
CHR: Chris Roederer, Senior Vice President Human Resources
CNO: Janet Davis, R.N., Senior Vice President and Chief Nursing Officer
Web address: www.tgh.org
Control: Other not–for–profit (including NFP Corporation) **Service:** General Medical and Surgical

Staffed Beds: 1018 Admissions: 45186 Census: 734 Outpatient Visits: 278928 Births: 5246 Total Expense ($000): 986723 Payroll Expense ($000): 366357 Personnel: 6341

TARPON SPRINGS—Pinellas County

✠ **FLORIDA HOSPITAL NORTH PINELLAS (100055)**, 1395 South Pinellas Avenue, Zip 34689–3790; tel. 727/942–5000 **A**1 5 9 10 **F**3 11 13 15 17 18 20 22 26 28 29 30 31 34 35 40 45 46 48 49 50 57 59 64 70 71 75 76 78 79 81 93 94 96 97 107 108 110 111 114 115 117 119 126 128 129 130 131 132 146 147 148 **S** Adventist Health System Sunbelt Health Care Corporation, Altamonte Springs, FL
Primary Contact: Bruce Bergherm, Chief Executive Officer
CFO: Michael Mewhirter, Chief Financial Officer
CMO: Paul Arnold, M.D., Chief of Medical Staff
CIO: Brett Peterson, Director of Information Services
CHR: Vernon Elarbee, Director of Human Resources
CNO: Karen Owensby, R.N., Chief Clinical Officer
Web address: www.fhnorthpinellas.com/
Control: Church–operated, Nongovernment, not–for profit **Service:** General Medical and Surgical

Staffed Beds: 168 Admissions: 4371 Census: 58 Outpatient Visits: 51704 Births: 276 Total Expense ($000): 80113 Payroll Expense ($000): 26843 Personnel: 456

TAVARES—Lake County

✠ **FLORIDA HOSPITAL WATERMAN (100057)**, 1000 Waterman Way, Zip 32778–5266; tel. 352/253–3333 **A**1 2 9 10 **F**3 11 13 15 17 18 20 22 24 26 28 29 30 31 34 35 37 40 45 49 50 53 54 57 59 62 64 66 70 74 75 76 77 79 81 85 89 93 107 108 110 111 114 115 116 117 118 119 120 121 123 132 135 144 146 148 **P**8 **S** Adventist Health System Sunbelt Health Care Corporation, Altamonte Springs, FL
Primary Contact: David Ottati, Chief Executive Officer
COO: Carrie L. Fish, Senior Vice President and Chief Operating Officer
CFO: Frances H. Crunk, Vice President and Chief Financial Officer
CMO: Vinay Mehindru, M.D., Vice President/Chief Medical Officer
CHR: Madge Springer, Director Human Resources
CNO: Patricia R. Dolan, R.N., Vice President/ Chief Nursing Officer
Web address: www.fhwat.org
Control: Church–operated, Nongovernment, not–for profit **Service:** General Medical and Surgical

Staffed Beds: 269 Admissions: 12749 Census: 152 Outpatient Visits: 99817 Births: 523 Total Expense ($000): 186677 Payroll Expense ($000): 67670 Personnel: 1139

TAVERNIER—Monroe County

✠ **BAPTIST HEALTH SOUTH FLORIDA, MARINERS HOSPITAL (101313)**, 91500 Overseas Highway, Zip 33070–2547; tel. 305/434–3000 **A**1 9 10 18 **F**3 11 15 18 28 29 30 31 34 35 40 45 47 50 53 57 59 68 70 74 75 78 79 81 84 85 93 97 102 107 108 110 111 114 115 119 129 130 131 132 133 146 147 148 **P**8 **S** Baptist Health South Florida, Coral Gables, FL
Primary Contact: Rick Freeburg, Chief Executive Officer
CFO: Erik Long, Controller
CIO: Mimi Taylor, Vice President Information Technology
CHR: John Williamson, Human Resources Site Manager
Web address: www.baptisthealth.net/en/facilities/mariners–hospital/Pages/default.aspx
Control: Other not–for–profit (including NFP Corporation) **Service:** General Medical and Surgical

Staffed Beds: 25 Admissions: 597 Census: 6 Outpatient Visits: 20740 Births: 0 Total Expense ($000): 45797 Payroll Expense ($000): 14827 Personnel: 225

FL

Many Facility Codes have changed. Please refer to the AHA Guide Code Chart.   © 2014 AHA Guide

THE VILLAGES—Sumter County

☒ **THE VILLAGES REGIONAL HOSPITAL (100290)**, 1451 El Camino Real, Zip 32159–0041; tel. 352/751–8000 **A**1 9 10 **F**3 8 11 15 18 20 22 28 29 30 31 34 35 40 45 54 57 59 64 70 74 75 77 78 79 81 85 87 93 107 108 111 114 115 118 119 120 121 122 123 124 130 132 144 146 **P**6 **S** Central Florida Health Alliance, Leesburg, FL
Primary Contact: Donald G. Henderson, FACHE, President and Chief Executive Officer
COO: Saad Ehtisham, R.N., Vice President and Chief Operating Officer
CFO: Diane P. Harden, Senior Vice President and Chief Financial Officer
CHR: Amie Richason, Vice President Human Resources
CNO: Mary Jane Curry–Pelyak, R.N., Vice President and Chief Clinical Officer
Web address: www.cfhalliance.org
Control: Other not–for–profit (including NFP Corporation) **Service:** General Medical and Surgical

Staffed Beds: 223 **Admissions:** 11335 **Census:** 163 **Outpatient Visits:** 49658 **Births:** 0 **Total Expense ($000):** 141988 **Payroll Expense ($000):** 54171 **Personnel:** 811

TITUSVILLE—Brevard County

☐ **PARRISH MEDICAL CENTER (100028)**, 951 North Washington Avenue, Zip 32796–2163; tel. 321/268–6111 **A**1 2 9 10 **F**3 11 13 15 18 20 22 28 29 30 34 35 40 45 47 50 51 53 54 56 57 59 60 62 64 68 69 70 74 75 76 77 78 79 80 81 82 83 84 85 86 87 89 92 93 94 107 108 110 111 116 126 129 130 132 134 135 143 144 146 147 148
Primary Contact: George Mikitarian, Jr., Chief Executive Officer
CFO: Timothy K. Skeldon, Senior Vice President and Chief Financial Officer
CMO: Lisa Alexanda, M.D., Vice President Medical Affairs
CIO: William Moore, Chief Information Officer
CHR: Roberta Chaildin, Manager Human Resources
Web address: www.parrishmed.com
Control: Hospital district or authority, Government, nonfederal **Service:** General Medical and Surgical

Staffed Beds: 210 **Admissions:** 6651 **Census:** 77 **Births:** 576 **Total Expense ($000):** 162995 **Payroll Expense ($000):** 62877

TRINITY—Pasco County

COMMUNITY HOSPITAL See Medical Center of Trinity

☒ **MEDICAL CENTER OF TRINITY (100191)**, 9330 State Road 54, Zip 34655–1808; tel. 727/834–4900 **A**1 2 5 10 **F**8 11 13 15 18 20 22 26 29 30 31 34 35 38 40 45 46 47 48 49 57 59 60 67 68 70 74 75 76 77 78 79 80 81 82 84 85 86 87 93 94 98 102 103 107 108 110 111 119 126 130 132 135 146 147 148 **S** HCA, Nashville, TN
Primary Contact: Leigh Massengill, Chief Executive Officer
COO: Kenneth West, Chief Operating Officer
CFO: Michael Wyers, Chief Financial Officer
CMO: Linda Badillo, M.D., Chief of Medical Staff
CIO: Kurt Hornung, Director
CHR: Christena Miano, Human Resources Director
CNO: Nancy Maysilles, R.N., Chief Nursing Officer
Web address: www.medicalcentertrinity.com
Control: Corporation, Investor–owned, for–profit **Service:** General Medical and Surgical

Staffed Beds: 282 **Admissions:** 13421 **Census:** 154 **Births:** 1083 **Total Expense ($000):** 183480 **Payroll Expense ($000):** 56236

VENICE—Sarasota County

☒ **VENICE REGIONAL BAYFRONT HEALTH (100070)**, 540 The Rialto, Zip 34285–2900; tel. 941/485–7711 **A**1 9 10 **F**3 8 11 12 15 17 18 20 22 24 26 28 29 30 31 32 33 34 35 36 37 40 45 46 47 49 50 51 54 56 57 59 60 64 70 74 77 78 79 81 82 87 93 96 107 108 111 114 118 119 126 129 130 144 146 148 **S** Community Health Systems, Inc., Franklin, TN
Primary Contact: Peter Wozniak, MS, R.N., Chief Executive Officer
COO: Kristen Gentry, Chief Operating Officer
CFO: Brian Hess, Chief Financial Officer
CIO: Eloy Rivas, Director of Information Systems
CHR: Faye Peraza, Director Human Resources
CNO: Cathy Carr, MSN, Chief Nursing Officer
Web address: www.veniceregional.com
Control: Corporation, Investor–owned, for–profit **Service:** General Medical and Surgical

Staffed Beds: 312 **Admissions:** 10010 **Census:** 125 **Births:** 0 **Total Expense ($000):** 153508 **Payroll Expense ($000):** 49663

VERO BEACH—Indian River County

☒ **HEALTHSOUTH TREASURE COAST REHABILITATION HOSPITAL (103032)**, 1600 37th Street, Zip 32960–4863; tel. 772/778–2100 **A**1 9 10 **F**12 29 34 90 91 148 **S** HEALTHSOUTH Corporation, Birmingham, AL
Primary Contact: Michael Kissner, Chief Executive Officer
CFO: Kevin Hardy, Chief Financial Officer
CMO: Jimmy Wayne Lockhart, M.D., Medical Director
CHR: Linda Rinehart, Director Human Resources
Web address: www.healthsouthtreasurecoast.com
Control: Corporation, Investor–owned, for–profit **Service:** Rehabilitation

Staffed Beds: 80 **Admissions:** 1397 **Census:** 51 **Outpatient Visits:** 0 **Births:** 0 **Total Expense ($000):** 17617 **Payroll Expense ($000):** 8971 **Personnel:** 167

☒ **INDIAN RIVER MEDICAL CENTER (100105)**, 1000 36th Street, Zip 32960–6592; tel. 772/567–4311 **A**1 2 9 10 **F**3 11 12 13 17 18 20 22 24 26 28 29 30 31 34 35 37 40 44 45 49 50 51 57 58 59 60 61 64 70 74 75 76 77 78 79 80 81 82 83 84 85 86 87 89 92 93 96 97 98 99 100 101 102 103 104 107 108 111 114 115 118 119 120 121 123 126 129 130 131 132 135 144 146 147 148 **P**6
Primary Contact: Jeffrey L. Susi, President and Chief Executive Officer
COO: Steven Salyer, Senior Vice President and Chief Operating Officer
CFO: Greg Gardner, Senior Vice President and Chief Financial Officer
CMO: Charles Mackett, M.D., Senior Vice President and Chief Medical Officer
CIO: William Neil, Vice President and Chief Information Officer
CNO: Lynn Hubbard, R.N., Vice President and Chief Nursing Officer
Web address: www.irmc.cc
Control: Other not–for–profit (including NFP Corporation) **Service:** General Medical and Surgical

Staffed Beds: 249 **Admissions:** 14261 **Census:** 171 **Outpatient Visits:** 130579 **Births:** 1102 **Total Expense ($000):** 195941 **Payroll Expense ($000):** 90354 **Personnel:** 1375

WAUCHULA—Hardee County

☒ **FLORIDA HOSPITAL WAUCHULA (101300)**, 533 West Carlton Street, Zip 33873–3407; tel. 863/773–3101 **A**1 9 10 18 **F**3 40 90 93 107 110 111 127 128 129 130 133 **P**6 **S** Adventist Health System Sunbelt Health Care Corporation, Altamonte Springs, FL
Primary Contact: Denise Grimsley, Administrator
CFO: Rosalie Oliver, Senior Vice President and Chief Financial Officer
CMO: Jorge F. Gonzalez, M.D., Vice President and Chief Nursing Officer
CIO: Jeff McDonald, Information Technology Manager
CHR: Michelle F. Myers, Director Human Resources
CNO: Gloria N. Santos, R.N., Vice President and Chief Nursing Officer
Web address: www.fh.floridahospital.com/heartland/home.aspx
Control: Church–operated, Nongovernment, not–for profit **Service:** General Medical and Surgical

Staffed Beds: 25 **Admissions:** 780 **Census:** 23 **Outpatient Visits:** 153534 **Births:** 0 **Total Expense ($000):** 20522 **Payroll Expense ($000):** 7822 **Personnel:** 111

WESLEY CHAPEL—Pasco County

★ ◇ **FLORIDA HOSPITAL WESLEY CHAPEL (100319)**, 2600 Bruce B. Downs Bouelvard, Zip 33544–9207; tel. 813/929–5000 **A**5 9 10 21 **F**3 11 13 15 18 20 26 29 30 34 35 40 45 51 53 57 59 60 64 70 74 76 77 79 81 86 93 107 108 110 111 115 119 126 131 146 147 **S** Adventist Health System Sunbelt Health Care Corporation, Altamonte Springs, FL
Primary Contact: Denyse Bales–Chubb, Chief Executive Officer
Web address: www.https://www.floridahospital.com/wesley–chapel
Control: Other not–for–profit (including NFP Corporation) **Service:** General Medical and Surgical

Staffed Beds: 83 **Admissions:** 3976 **Census:** 40 **Outpatient Visits:** 40961 **Births:** 403 **Total Expense ($000):** 84099 **Payroll Expense ($000):** 26476 **Personnel:** 512

WEST PALM BEACH—Palm Beach County

☒ **GOOD SAMARITAN MEDICAL CENTER (100287)**, 1309 North Flagler Drive, Zip 33401–3499; tel. 561/655–5511, (Nonreporting) **A**1 2 9 10 **S** TENET Healthcare Corporation, Dallas, TX
Primary Contact: Mark Nosacka, Chief Executive Officer
CFO: Cynthia McCauley, Chief Financial Officer
CIO: Candace Helms, Director Information Services
CHR: Amy Linsin, Chief Human Resources Officer
Web address: www.goodsamaritanmc.com
Control: Corporation, Investor–owned, for–profit **Service:** General Medical and Surgical

Staffed Beds: 174

FL

Hospital, Medicare Provider Number, Address, Telephone, Approval, Facility, and Physician Codes, Health Care System

★ American Hospital Association (AHA) membership
☐ The Joint Commission accreditation ◇ DNV Healthcare Inc. accreditation
○ Healthcare Facilities Accreditation Program
△ Commission on Accreditation of Rehabilitation Facilities (CARF) accreditation

☐ **JEROME GOLDEN CENTER FOR BEHAVIORAL HEALTH, INC. (104008)**, 1041 45th Street, Zip 33407–2494; tel. 561/383–8000, (Nonreporting) **A**1 10
Primary Contact: Linda De Piano, Ph.D., Chief Executive Officer
CFO: Pat Priola, Chief Financial Officer
CMO: Suresh Rajpara, M.D., Chief Medical Officer
CIO: Iris Garcia, Director, Information Services
CHR: Diane B. White, Director Human Resources
Web address: www.goldenctr.org
Control: Other not-for-profit (including NFP Corporation) **Service:** Psychiatric

Staffed Beds: 44

PALM BEACH CHILDREN'S HOSPITAL See St. Mary's Medical Center

✠ △ **ST. MARY'S MEDICAL CENTER (100288)**, 901 45th Street, Zip 33407–2495; tel. 561/844–6300, (Includes PALM BEACH CHILDREN'S HOSPITAL, 901 45th Street, Zip 33407; tel. 561/844–6300) **A**1 5 7 9 10 **F**3 6 8 11 13 15 17 18 19 20 21 23 24 25 29 30 31 34 35 38 39 40 41 43 44 45 47 48 49 50 51 56 57 58 59 60 64 65 68 70 72 73 74 75 76 77 78 79 80 81 85 86 87 88 89 90 92 93 94 96 98 100 101 102 103 107 108 110 111 114 115 119 120 121 123 130 131 132 134 135 146 147 148 **S** TENET Healthcare Corporation, Dallas, TX
Primary Contact: Davide M. Carbone, FACHE, Chief Executive Officer
COO: Joey Bulfin, R.N., Chief Operating Officer
CFO: Tom Schlemmer, Chief Financial Officer
CMO: Jeffrey Davis, D.O., Chief Medical Officer
CIO: Rich Avato, Director
CHR: Thomas J. Piszczatoski, Director Human Resources
CNO: Donna Small, R.N., Chief Nursing Officer
Web address: www.stmarysmc.com
Control: Corporation, Investor-owned, for-profit **Service:** General Medical and Surgical

Staffed Beds: 464 **Admissions:** 17898 **Census:** 286 **Outpatient Visits:** 115393 **Births:** 3429 **Total Expense ($000):** 232074 **Payroll Expense ($000):** 95714 **Personnel:** 1419

VETERANS AFFAIRS MEDICAL CENTER See West Palm Beach Veterans Affairs Medical Center

☐ **WELLINGTON REGIONAL MEDICAL CENTER (100275)**, 10101 Forest Hill Boulevard, Zip 33414–6199; tel. 561/798–8500, (Nonreporting) **A**1 9 10 12 13 **S** Universal Health Services, Inc., King of Prussia, PA
Primary Contact: Robbin Lee, Chief Executive Officer
CFO: Joseph Paul, Chief Financial Officer
CMO: Richard Hays, M.D., Chief of Staff
CIO: Pierre Bergeron, Director Information Services
CHR: Mary Jo Caracciolo, Director Human Resources
CNO: Asenath Cassel, Chief Nursing Officer
Web address: www.wellingtonregional.com
Control: Corporation, Investor-owned, for-profit **Service:** General Medical and Surgical

Staffed Beds: 108

✠ **WEST PALM BEACH VETERANS AFFAIRS MEDICAL CENTER**, 7305 North Military Trail, Zip 33410–6400; tel. 561/422–8262, (Total facility includes 120 beds in nursing home–type unit) **A**1 3 5 9 **F**3 5 7 11 15 18 20 22 29 30 31 33 34 35 36 38 39 40 44 45 47 49 50 51 56 57 59 60 61 62 63 64 65 68 70 71 74 75 77 78 79 81 82 83 84 86 87 91 92 93 94 97 98 100 101 102 104 105 106 107 108 110 111 112 114 115 116 117 119 120 128 129 130 132 133 135 143 146 147 148 **S** Department of Veterans Affairs, Washington, DC
Primary Contact: Charleen R. Szabo, FACHE, Director
CFO: Lori Hancock, Chief Business Officer
CMO: Deepak Mandi, M.D., Chief of Staff
CIO: Karen Gabaldon, Chief Management Information Systems
CHR: David Green, Chief Human Resources
Web address: www.westpalmbeach.va.gov/
Control: Veterans Affairs, Government, federal **Service:** General Medical and Surgical

Staffed Beds: 297 **Admissions:** 7572 **Census:** 175 **Outpatient Visits:** 696618 **Births:** 0 **Total Expense ($000):** 359492 **Payroll Expense ($000):** 168903 **Personnel:** 2560

✠ ○ **WEST PALM HOSPITAL (100234)**, 2201 45th Street, Zip 33407–2047; tel. 561/842–6141 **A**1 9 10 11 12 13 **F**3 29 34 35 40 45 49 57 59 60 70 79 81 82 93 98 99 101 102 103 104 105 107 110 111 119 146 148 **S** HCA, Nashville, TN
Primary Contact: Dana Oaks, Chief Executive Officer
COO: Patrick Chapman, Assistant Vice President Operations
CMO: Paul Seltzer, M.D., Chief of Staff
CIO: Kenneth Vasquez, Associate Director
CHR: Donna Boyle, Director
CNO: Geraldine DeStefano, R.N., Chief Nursing Officer
Web address: www.westpalmhospital.com
Control: Corporation, Investor-owned, for-profit **Service:** General Medical and Surgical

Staffed Beds: 245 **Admissions:** 9609 **Census:** 114 **Outpatient Visits:** 36253 **Births:** 0 **Total Expense ($000):** 77504 **Payroll Expense ($000):** 34669

WESTON—Broward County

✠ **CLEVELAND CLINIC FLORIDA (100289)**, 2950 Cleveland Clinic Boulevard, Zip 33331–3602; tel. 954/659–5000 **A**1 2 3 5 9 10 **F**3 8 9 12 15 17 18 20 22 24 26 28 29 30 31 33 34 35 37 39 40 44 45 47 48 49 50 51 54 55 56 57 58 59 60 61 63 64 65 68 70 74 75 77 78 79 80 81 82 85 86 87 91 92 93 96 97 100 101 107 108 109 110 111 114 115 116 117 119 126 129 130 131 132 135 138 139 141 145 146 147 148 **P**6 **S** Cleveland Clinic Health System, Cleveland, OH
Primary Contact: Wael Barsoum, Interim Chief Executive Officer
CFO: Keith Nilsson, Chief Financial Officer
CMO: Raul Rosenthal, M.D., Interim Chief of Staff
CIO: John Santangelo, Director Information Technology
CHR: Becky Caputo, Interim Director Human Resources
CNO: Kerry Major, R.N., Chief Nursing Officer
Web address: www.clevelandclinic.org/florida
Control: Other not-for-profit (including NFP Corporation) **Service:** General Medical and Surgical

Staffed Beds: 155 **Admissions:** 10117 **Census:** 121 **Outpatient Visits:** 168788 **Births:** 0 **Total Expense ($000):** 183226 **Payroll Expense ($000):** 67936 **Personnel:** 1992

WILLISTON—Levy County

NATURE COAST REGIONAL HOSPITAL See Regional General Hospital
REGIONAL GENERAL HOSPITAL (100322), 125 S.W. Seventh Street, Zip 32696–2403; tel. 352/528–2801, (Nonreporting) **A**9 10
Primary Contact: Davie Lloyd, FACHE, Chief Executive Officer
CFO: Barbara Miller, Manager Business Office
CMO: Jeremie Young, M.D., Chief of Staff
CHR: Karla Dass, Director Human Resources
Web address: www.tricountyhosp.com/
Control: Partnership, Investor-owned, for-profit **Service:** General Medical and Surgical

Staffed Beds: 20

WINTER HAVEN—Polk County

✠ △ **WINTER HAVEN HOSPITAL (100052)**, 200 Avenue F. N.E., Zip 33881–4193; tel. 863/293–1121 **A**1 7 9 10 **F**3 8 11 13 14 15 17 18 20 22 24 26 28 29 30 31 34 36 40 45 49 52 57 58 59 60 64 68 70 72 73 74 75 76 77 78 79 81 82 84 85 86 87 89 90 93 94 98 100 101 102 103 104 107 108 110 111 114 115 118 119 121 123 126 130 132 135 144 146 147 148 **P**6 7
Primary Contact: Stephen A. Nierman, President
COO: David Libby, Vice President Operations
CFO: Tina Solomon, Executive Director Finance
CMO: Donald I. Gale, M.D., Vice President Medical Affairs
CIO: Cal Cole, Director Information Systems
CHR: Andrea K. Williams, Manager, Employee Relations
CNO: Mary Jo Schreiber, R.N., Vice President Patient Services
Web address: www.winterhavenhospital.org
Control: Other not-for-profit (including NFP Corporation) **Service:** General Medical and Surgical

Staffed Beds: 529 **Admissions:** 16196 **Census:** 213 **Outpatient Visits:** 265115 **Births:** 1679 **Total Expense ($000):** 264901 **Payroll Expense ($000):** 128984 **Personnel:** 2166

WINTER PARK—Orange County

WINTER PARK MEMORIAL HOSPITAL See Florida Hospital, Orlando

ZEPHYRHILLS—Pasco County

✠ **FLORIDA HOSPITAL ZEPHYRHILLS (100046)**, 7050 Gall Boulevard, Zip 33541–1399; tel. 813/788–0411 **A**1 5 9 10 **F**3 12 13 14 15 17 18 19 20 22 24 26 28 29 30 31 32 34 35 37 39 40 44 45 46 47 48 49 51 53 54 56 57 59 60 62 63 64 68 70 74 76 77 78 79 81 82 83 86 87 91 92 93 97 107 108 110 111 114 116 119 124 126 129 130 132 133 135 146 147 148 **S** Adventist Health System Sunbelt Health Care Corporation, Altamonte Springs, FL
Primary Contact: Randy Surber, Chief Executive Officer
COO: Donald E. Welch, Chief Operating Officer
CFO: Bill Heinrich, Chief Financial Officer
CMO: Hugar McNamee, D.O., Chief Medical Officer
CIO: Kelley Sasser, Director Information Systems
CHR: Laura Asaftei, Administrative Director
CNO: Gwen Alonso, Chief Nursing Officer
Web address: www.fhzeph.org
Control: Church-operated, Nongovernment, not-for profit **Service:** General Medical and Surgical

Staffed Beds: 139 **Admissions:** 8470 **Census:** 91 **Outpatient Visits:** 124902 **Births:** 389 **Total Expense ($000):** 131156 **Payroll Expense ($000):** 54083 **Personnel:** 882

GEORGIA

ADEL—Cook County

✠ **COOK MEDICAL CENTER–A CAMPUS OF TIFT REGIONAL MEDICAL CENTER (110101)**, 706 North Parrish Avenue, Zip 31620–1511; tel. 229/896–8000, (Total facility includes 95 beds in nursing home–type unit) **A**1 9 10 **F**11 15 29 30 34 35 40 46 56 57 59 64 75 81 86 87 93 97 98 103 107 110 111 118 119 130 133 135 146 147 **S** Tift Regional Health System, Tifton, GA
Primary Contact: Michael L. Purvis, Chief Executive Officer
COO: Kim Wills, Chief Operating Officer
CIO: Barry Medley, Director Information Systems
CHR: Shirley Padgett, Director Human Resources
Web address: www.cookmedicalcenter.com
Control: Hospital district or authority, Government, nonfederal **Service:** General Medical and Surgical

Staffed Beds: 155 **Admissions:** 1007 **Census:** 88 **Outpatient Visits:** 18478 **Births:** 113 **Total Expense ($000):** 17343 **Payroll Expense ($000):** 7556 **Personnel:** 207

ALBANY—Dougherty County

✠ ◇ **PHOEBE PUTNEY MEMORIAL HOSPITAL (110007)**, 417 West Third Avenue, Zip 31701–1943, Mailing Address: P.O. Box 3770, Zip 31706–3770; tel. 229/312–4100, (Includes PHOEBE NORTH, 2000 Palmyra Road, Zip 31701–1528, Mailing Address: P.O. Box 1908, Zip 31702–1908; tel. 229/434–2000) **A**1 2 3 5 9 10 21 **F**3 5 7 11 12 13 15 17 18 20 22 24 26 28 29 30 31 34 35 40 45 46 49 50 51 53 54 56 57 59 60 62 63 64 68 70 72 73 74 75 76 77 78 79 81 82 83 84 85 86 87 89 90 92 93 94 96 97 98 100 101 102 103 104 105 107 108 110 111 114 115 116 117 118 119 120 121 123 124 126 127 129 130 131 132 134 135 136 144 145 146 147 148 **P**1 7 **S** Phoebe Putney Health System, Albany, GA
Primary Contact: Joel Wernick, President and Chief Executive Officer
COO: Joe Austin, Executive Vice President and Chief Operating Officer
CFO: Kerry Loudermilk, Senior Vice President and Chief Financial Officer
CMO: Frank Middleton, M.D., Interim Chief Medical Officer
CIO: Jesse Diaz, Chief Information Officer
CHR: David J. Baranski, Vice President Human Resources
CNO: Laura Shearer, R.N., Senior Vice President and Chief Nursing Officer
Web address: www.phoebeputney.com
Control: Other not–for–profit (including NFP Corporation) **Service:** General Medical and Surgical

Staffed Beds: 526 **Admissions:** 22759 **Census:** 333 **Outpatient Visits:** 1025874 **Births:** 2794 **Total Expense ($000):** 576121 **Payroll Expense ($000):** 184059 **Personnel:** 3103

ALMA—Bacon County

✠ **BACON COUNTY HOSPITAL AND HEALTH SYSTEM (111327)**, 302 South Wayne Street, Zip 31510–2922, Mailing Address: P.O. Drawer 1987, Zip 31510–0987; tel. 912/632–8961, (Nonreporting) **A**1 9 10 18
Primary Contact: Cindy R. Turner, Chief Executive Officer
COO: Cindy R. Turner, Chief Executive Officer
CFO: Kyle Kimmel, Chief Financial Officer
CMO: Lou Ellen Hutcheson, M.D., Chief of Staff
CIO: Neil O'Steen, Director Information Technology
CHR: Kerry Hancock, Director Human Resources
CNO: Deanna Hoff, R.N., Director of Nursing
Web address: www.baconcountyhospital.com
Control: Other not–for–profit (including NFP Corporation) **Service:** General Medical and Surgical

Staffed Beds: 113

AMERICUS—Sumter County

✠ ◇ **PHOEBE SUMTER MEDICAL CENTER (110044)**, 126 Highway 280 West, Zip 31719; tel. 229/924–6011, (Nonreporting) **A**1 9 10 21 **S** Phoebe Putney Health System, Albany, GA
Primary Contact: John Harding, Interim Chief Executive Officer
CMO: Andrew Carlson, M.D., Vice President Medical Staff Services
CIO: Becky Lightner, Director Information Systems
CHR: Deatrice Harris, Supervisor Human Resources and Employment
Web address: www.phoebesumter.org
Control: Other not–for–profit (including NFP Corporation) **Service:** General Medical and Surgical

Staffed Beds: 45

ATHENS—Clarke County

✠ **ATHENS REGIONAL MEDICAL CENTER (110074)**, 1199 Prince Avenue, Zip 30606–2797; tel. 706/475–7000 **A**1 2 9 10 **F**3 8 11 13 15 17 18 20 22 24 26 28 29 30 31 32 34 35 36 40 43 45 46 47 48 49 50 51 54 56 57 58 59 60 61 62 68 70 71 72 73 74 76 77 78 79 80 81 83 84 85 86 87 89 92 93 94 96 100 107 108 110 111 115 116 117 118 119 120 121 123 124 129 130 131 132 135 145 146 147 148
Primary Contact: James G. Thaw, President and Chief Executive Officer
COO: Linda Della Torre, Senior Vice President and Chief Operating Officer
CFO: W. Larry Webb, Senior Vice President and Chief Financial Officer
CMO: Mark J. Costantino, M.D., Interim Chief Medical Officer
CIO: Steve W. Davis, Interim Chief Information Officer
CHR: Kevin Thigpen, Vice President Human Resources
Web address: www.armc.org
Control: Other not–for–profit (including NFP Corporation) **Service:** General Medical and Surgical

Staffed Beds: 341 **Admissions:** 19186 **Census:** 219 **Outpatient Visits:** 315319 **Births:** 2545 **Total Expense ($000):** 356606 **Payroll Expense ($000):** 138502 **Personnel:** 2445

☐ **LANDMARK HOSPITAL OF ATHENS (112017)**, 775 Sunset Drive, Zip 30606–2211; tel. 706/425–1500 **A**1 10 **F**1 3 29 30 45 84 119 130 148 **S** Landmark Hospitals, Cape Girardeau, MO
Primary Contact: Tommy Jackson, Chief Executive Officer
Web address: www.landmarkhospitals.com
Control: Individual, Investor–owned, for–profit **Service:** Long–Term Acute Care hospital

Staffed Beds: 42 **Admissions:** 448 **Census:** 32 **Outpatient Visits:** 0 **Births:** 0 **Personnel:** 126

✠ △ **ST. MARY'S HEALTH CARE SYSTEM (110006)**, 1230 Baxter Street, Zip 30606–3791; tel. 706/389–3000, (Nonreporting) **A**1 7 9 10 **S** Catholic Health East / Trinity Health, Livonia, MI
Primary Contact: Donald McKenna, President and Chief Executive Officer
CFO: Marty Hutson, Chief Financial Officer
CMO: Bruce Middendorf, M.D., Chief Medical Officer
CIO: Kerry Vaughn, Chief Information Officer
CHR: Jeff English, Vice President Human Resources
CNO: Nina Evans, R.N., Vice President and Chief Nursing Officer
Web address: www.stmarysathens.com
Control: Church–operated, Nongovernment, not–for profit **Service:** General Medical and Surgical

Staffed Beds: 165

ATLANTA—Fulton and De Kalb County

☐ **ANCHOR HOSPITAL (114032)**, 5454 Yorktowne Drive, Zip 30349–5317; tel. 770/991–6044, (Nonreporting) **A**1 9 10 **S** Universal Health Services, Inc., King of Prussia, PA
Primary Contact: Margaret P. Collier, Chief Executive Officer and Managing Director
CFO: Pamela Whitehead, Chief Financial Officer
CMO: Shailesh Patel, M.D., Medical Director
CIO: Michael Delpleache, Specialist Information Technology
CHR: Ebuni McFall–Roberts, Director Human Resources
CNO: Kim Butts, System Nurse Executive
Web address: www.anchorhospital.com
Control: Corporation, Investor–owned, for–profit **Service:** Alcoholism and other chemical dependency

Staffed Beds: 111

GA

✠ **ATLANTA MEDICAL CENTER (110115)**, 303 Parkway Drive N.E., Zip 30312–1212; tel. 404/265–4000, (Includes ATLANTA MEDICAL CENTER – SOUTH CAMPUS, 1170 Cleveland Avenue, Zip 30344–3665; tel. 404/466–1170; Daniel Jackson, Chief Administrative Officer) **A**1 3 5 8 9 10 **F**11 12 13 15 17 18 20 22 24 26 28 29 30 31 34 35 36 37 38 40 43 44 45 46 50 53 54 56 57 59 60 61 64 65 66 68 70 72 73 74 75 76 77 78 79 81 84 85 86 87 90 93 96 97 98 100 101 102 103 104 107 108 111 114 118 119 129 130 132 134 144 146 147 148 **P**3 7 8 **S** TENET Healthcare Corporation, Dallas, TX
Primary Contact: Christopher Locke, Interim Chief Executive Officer
COO: Robert Russell, Chief Operating Officer
CFO: Lisa Napier, Chief Financial Officer
CMO: Pano Lamis, Medical Director
CIO: Maryland McCarty, Director Information Systems
CHR: Troy Bond, Chief Human Resources Officer
Web address: www.atlantamedcenter.com
Control: Corporation, Investor–owned, for–profit **Service:** General Medical and Surgical

Staffed Beds: 536 **Admissions:** 18619 **Census:** 287 **Outpatient Visits:** 170770 **Births:** 3227 **Total Expense ($000):** 317529 **Payroll Expense ($000):** 116416 **Personnel:** 1565

☐ △ **CHILDREN'S HEALTHCARE OF ATLANTA (113301)**, 1600 Tullie Circle, N.E., Zip 30329–2303; tel. 404/785–7000, (Includes CHILDREN'S HEALTHCARE OF ATLANTA AT EGLESTON, 1600 Tullie Circle, Zip 30329; tel. 404/325–6000; CHILDREN'S HEALTHCARE OF ATLANTA AT SCOTTISH RITE, 1001 Johnson Ferry Road N.E., Zip 30342–1600; tel. 404/256–5252), (Nonreporting) **A**1 3 5 7 8 9 10
Primary Contact: Donna W. Hyland, President and Chief Executive Officer
COO: Carolyn Kenny, Executive Vice President Clinical Care
CFO: Ruth Fowler, Senior Vice President and Chief Financial Officer
CMO: Daniel Salinas, M.D., Senior Vice President and Chief Medical Officer
CIO: Praveen Chopra, Chief Information and Supply Chain Officer
CHR: Linda Matzigkeit, Senior Vice President Human Resources
Web address: www.choa.org
Control: Other not–for–profit (including NFP Corporation) **Service:** Children's general

Staffed Beds: 496

✠ **EMORY SAINT JOSEPH'S HOSPITAL OF ATLANTA (110082)**, 5665 Peachtree Dunwoody Road N.E., Zip 30342–1701; tel. 678/843–7001 **A**1 2 9 10 **F**3 11 15 17 18 20 22 24 26 28 29 30 31 34 35 37 40 44 45 46 47 49 50 51 53 54 55 57 58 59 60 64 68 70 71 74 75 77 78 79 81 82 84 85 87 93 107 108 110 111 114 115 116 117 118 119 120 121 123 124 126 130 132 135 145 146 147 148 **P**6 **S** Emory Healthcare, Atlanta, GA
Primary Contact: Craig McCoy, Chief Executive Officer
CFO: Kevin Brenan, Chief Financial Officer
CMO: Paul Scheinberg, M.D., Chief of Staff
CIO: Dedra Cantrell, Chief Information Officer
CHR: Audra Farish, Vice President Human Resources
Web address: www.stjosephsatlanta.org
Control: Other not–for–profit (including NFP Corporation) **Service:** General Medical and Surgical

Staffed Beds: 240 **Admissions:** 13148 **Census:** 181 **Outpatient Visits:** 186471 **Births:** 0 **Total Expense ($000):** 308980 **Payroll Expense ($000):** 94404 **Personnel:** 1399

✠ △ **EMORY UNIVERSITY HOSPITAL (110010)**, 1364 Clifton Road N.E., Zip 30322–1102; tel. 404/712–2000, (Includes EMORY UNIVERSITY ORTHOPAEDIC AND SPINE HOSPITAL, 1455 Montreal Road, Tucker, Zip 30084; tel. 404/251–3600; June Conner, R.N., Chief Operating Officer) **A**1 2 3 5 7 8 9 10 **F**3 11 12 15 17 18 20 22 24 26 28 29 30 31 34 35 36 37 38 40 44 45 46 47 48 49 50 55 57 58 59 60 61 64 68 70 74 75 77 78 79 80 81 82 83 84 85 86 87 90 92 93 98 100 101 102 103 104 107 108 110 111 114 115 116 117 118 119 120 121 123 124 126 130 131 132 135 136 137 138 139 140 141 142 145 146 147 148 **P**6 **S** Emory Healthcare, Atlanta, GA
Primary Contact: Robert J. Bachman, Chief Executive Officer
CFO: Greg E. Anderson, Chief Financial Officer, Emory Health System
CMO: Ira Horowitz, M.D., Chief Medical Officer
CIO: Dedra Cantrell, Chief Information Officer
CHR: Mary Beth Allen, Vice President Human Resources
CNO: Nancye R. Feistritzer, Chief Nursing Officer
Web address: www.emoryhealthcare.org
Control: Other not–for–profit (including NFP Corporation) **Service:** General Medical and Surgical

Staffed Beds: 579 **Admissions:** 25302 **Census:** 456 **Outpatient Visits:** 157852 **Births:** 0 **Total Expense ($000):** 725537 **Payroll Expense ($000):** 225394 **Personnel:** 3411

✠ **EMORY UNIVERSITY HOSPITAL MIDTOWN (110078)**, 550 Peachtree Street N.E., Zip 30308–2247; tel. 404/686–4411 **A**1 2 3 5 8 9 10 **F**3 11 12 13 15 17 18 20 22 24 26 28 29 30 31 34 35 36 38 40 44 45 46 49 50 51 52 55 57 58 59 60 61 64 68 70 72 73 74 75 76 77 78 79 80 81 82 83 84 85 86 87 92 93 100 102 104 107 108 110 111 114 115 116 117 118 119 120 121 123 124 126 130 131 132 135 141 146 147 148 **P**6 **S** Emory Healthcare, Atlanta, GA
Primary Contact: Dane C. Peterson, Chief Operating Officer
COO: Dane C. Peterson, Chief Operating Officer
CMO: James P. Steinberg, M.D., Chief Medical Officer
CIO: Dedra Cantrell, Chief Information Officer
CHR: Dallis Howard–Crow, Chief Human Resources Officer
Web address: www.emoryhealthcare.org
Control: Other not–for–profit (including NFP Corporation) **Service:** General Medical and Surgical

Staffed Beds: 431 **Admissions:** 21013 **Census:** 316 **Outpatient Visits:** 178050 **Births:** 3620 **Total Expense ($000):** 539080 **Payroll Expense ($000):** 156447 **Personnel:** 2378

✠ **EMORY WESLEY WOODS GERIATRIC HOSPITAL (110203)**, (Multi–Discrip Geri Hospital), 1821 Clifton Road N.E., Zip 30329–4021; tel. 404/728–6200, (Total facility includes 250 beds in nursing home–type unit) **A**1 3 5 9 10 **F**3 6 11 29 30 34 35 38 39 50 54 56 58 59 60 64 67 68 74 75 86 87 90 93 98 100 101 103 104 105 107 119 128 129 130 132 143 146 148 **P**6 **S** Emory Healthcare, Atlanta, GA
Primary Contact: Jennifer Schuck, Associate Administrator
CMO: Frank Brown, M.D., Chief Medical Officer
CIO: Dedra Cantrell, Chief Information Officer
CHR: Dallis Howard–Crow, Chief Human Resources Officer
CNO: Annette Branan, Chief Nursing Officer, Vice President Patient Care Services
Web address: www.emoryhealthcare.org
Control: Other not–for–profit (including NFP Corporation) **Service:** Other specialty

Staffed Beds: 327 **Admissions:** 1935 **Census:** 191 **Outpatient Visits:** 13365 **Births:** 0 **Total Expense ($000):** 49667 **Payroll Expense ($000):** 24410 **Personnel:** 433

✠ **GRADY MEMORIAL HOSPITAL (110079)**, 80 Jesse Hill Jr. Drive S.E., Zip 30303–3031, Mailing Address: P.O. Box 26189, Zip 30303–0004; tel. 404/616–1000, (Total facility includes 261 beds in nursing home–type unit) **A**1 2 3 5 8 9 10 **F**2 3 7 8 13 15 16 17 18 20 22 24 26 29 30 31 34 35 39 40 43 45 46 50 51 52 53 54 55 56 57 58 59 60 61 62 63 64 65 66 68 70 72 73 74 75 76 77 78 79 80 81 82 84 85 86 87 93 97 98 100 101 102 103 104 105 107 108 109 110 111 112 113 114 115 116 117 118 119 120 121 128 129 130 132 134 135 136 137 138 139 140 141 142 143 144 146 147 148
Primary Contact: John M. Haupert, FACHE, Chief Executive Officer
COO: Christopher R. Mosley, FACHE, Chief Operating Officer
CFO: Mark Meyer, Chief Financial Officer
CMO: Curtis Lewis, M.D., Chief of Staff
CIO: Deborah Cancilla, Chief Information Officer
CHR: Larry A. Callahan, Senior Vice President Human Resources
CNO: Rhonda A. Scott, Ph.D., Chief Nursing Officer and Executive Vice President
Web address: www.gradyhealthsystem.org
Control: Other not–for–profit (including NFP Corporation) **Service:** General Medical and Surgical

Staffed Beds: 872 **Admissions:** 26990 **Census:** 711 **Outpatient Visits:** 621893 **Births:** 2970 **Total Expense ($000):** 762025 **Payroll Expense ($000):** 293437 **Personnel:** 4682

✠ **KINDRED HOSPITAL–ATLANTA (112004)**, 705 Juniper Street N.E., Zip 30308–1307; tel. 404/873–2871 **A**1 9 10 **F**1 3 17 29 30 60 63 70 74 75 82 86 87 128 130 135 148 **S** Kindred Healthcare, Louisville, KY
Primary Contact: Michael Schmitt, M.D., Chief Executive Officer
CFO: Michael Nelson, Chief Financial Officer
CMO: David N. DeRuyter, M.D., President Medical Staff
CHR: Armetria Gibson, Human Resources Generalist
CNO: Annette Harrilson, Chief Clinical Officer
Web address: www.kindredatlanta.com/
Control: Corporation, Investor–owned, for–profit **Service:** Long–Term Acute Care hospital

Staffed Beds: 70 **Admissions:** 531 **Census:** 49 **Births:** 0 **Total Expense ($000):** 19743 **Payroll Expense ($000):** 9657 **Personnel:** 164

✠ **NORTHSIDE HOSPITAL (110161)**, 1000 Johnson Ferry Road N.E., Zip 30342–1611; tel. 404/851–8000 **A**1 2 9 10 **F**3 5 8 11 12 13 15 17 18 20 22 26 28 29 30 31 34 35 37 40 44 45 46 47 48 49 50 54 55 57 58 59 60 64 68 70 71 72 73 74 75 76 77 78 79 80 81 82 84 85 86 87 93 100 104 105 107 108 110 111 114 115 117 118 119 120 121 123 124 126 129 130 132 135 136 145 146 147 148 **S** Northside Healthcare System, Atlanta, GA
Primary Contact: Robert Quattrocchi, President and Chief Executive Officer
CFO: Debbie Mitcham, Chief Financial Officer
CIO: Tina Wakim, Vice President Information
Web address: www.northside.com
Control: Other not–for–profit (including NFP Corporation) **Service:** General Medical and Surgical

Staffed Beds: 567 **Admissions:** 32808 **Census:** 438 **Outpatient Visits:** 608303 **Births:** 14690 **Total Expense ($000):** 1218030 **Payroll Expense ($000):** 365200 **Personnel:** 6453

Many Facility Codes have changed. Please refer to the AHA Guide Code Chart. © 2014 AHA Guide

GA

PEACHFORD BEHAVIORAL HEALTH SYSTEM (114010), 2151 Peachford Road, Zip 30338–6599; tel. 770/455–3200, (Nonreporting) **A**1 9 10 **S** Universal Health Services, Inc., King of Prussia, PA
Primary Contact: Matthew Crouch, Chief Executive Officer and Managing Director
COO: Sharon Stackhouse, Assistant Administrator and Director Risk Management
CFO: April Hughes, Chief Financial Officer
CMO: Asaf Aleem, M.D., Medical Director
CHR: Clay Boyles, Director Human Resources
Web address: www.peachfordhospital.com
Control: Corporation, Investor–owned, for–profit **Service:** Psychiatric

Staffed Beds: 224

PIEDMONT HOSPITAL (110083), 1968 Peachtree Road N.W., Zip 30309–1281; tel. 404/605–5000 **A**1 2 3 5 9 10 **F**3 8 11 12 13 15 17 18 20 22 24 26 28 29 30 31 34 35 40 45 46 47 48 49 50 51 53 54 55 56 57 58 59 60 63 64 65 68 70 72 73 74 75 76 77 78 79 81 82 84 85 86 87 93 107 108 110 111 112 114 115 116 117 118 119 120 121 123 124 126 129 130 131 132 135 137 138 139 142 143 146 147 148 **S** Piedmont Healthcare, Atlanta, GA
Primary Contact: Leslie A. Donahue, President and Chief Executive Officer
COO: Ed Lovern, Chief Operating Officer
CFO: Thomas Arnold, Chief Financial Officer
CMO: Mark Cohen, M.D., Chief Medical Officer
CHR: Rick Springfield, Vice President Human Resources
CNO: Kelly Hulsey, Chief Nursing Officer
Web address: www.piedmonthospital.org
Control: Other not–for–profit (including NFP Corporation) **Service:** General Medical and Surgical

Staffed Beds: 484 Admissions: 25654 Census: 396 Outpatient Visits: 279159 Births: 3462

SAINT JOSEPH'S HOSPITAL OF ATLANTA See Emory Saint Joseph's Hospital of Atlanta

SELECT SPECIALTY HOSPITAL – NORTHEAST ATLANTA (112005), 1821 Clifton Road N.E., 2nd Floor, Zip 30329–4021; tel. 404/728–6200 **A**1 10 **F**1 3 11 29 30 34 50 56 68 74 75 77 82 85 87 **P**6 **S** Select Medical Corporation, Mechanicsburg, PA
Primary Contact: Matthew Paul Pearson, Chief Executive Officer
CFO: Theodore Saunders, Assistant Controller
CMO: Jeffrey Mikell, M.D., Chief Medical Officer
CIO: Vicky Goziah, Software Administrator
CNO: Annette Branan, Chief Nursing Officer and Vice President Patient Care Services
Web address: www.selectspecialtyhospitals.com/
Control: Other not–for–profit (including NFP Corporation) **Service:** Long–Term Acute Care hospital

Staffed Beds: 18 Admissions: 184 Census: 16 Outpatient Visits: 0 Births: 0 Total Expense ($000): 9153 Payroll Expense ($000): 2996 Personnel: 50

SELECT SPECIALTY HOSPITAL–ATLANTA (112009), 550 Peachtree Street N.E., Zip 30308–2247; tel. 404/815–0348, (Nonreporting) **A**1 9 10 **S** Select Medical Corporation, Mechanicsburg, PA
Primary Contact: Dwayne Hooks, Jr., R.N., Chief Executive Officer
Web address: www.selectspecialtyhospitals.com/company/locations/atlanta.aspx
Control: Corporation, Investor–owned, for–profit **Service:** Long–Term Acute Care hospital

Staffed Beds: 30

SHEPHERD CENTER (112003), 2020 Peachtree Road N.W., Zip 30309–1465; tel. 404/352–2020, (Nonreporting) **A**1 3 5 9 10
Primary Contact: Gary R. Ulicny, Ph.D., President and Chief Executive Officer
COO: Sarah Morrison, Vice President Clinical Services
CFO: Stephen B. Holleman, Chief Financial Officer
CMO: Donald P. Leslie, M.D., Medical Director
CIO: Michael L. Jones, Ph.D., Chief Information Officer
CHR: Betsy Fox, Director Human Resources
CNO: Tamara King, R.N., Chief Nurse Executive
Web address: www.shepherd.org
Control: Other not–for–profit (including NFP Corporation) **Service:** Long–Term Acute Care hospital

Staffed Beds: 100

WESLEY WOODS GERIATRIC HOSPITAL OF EMORY UNIVERSITY See Emory Wesley Woods Geriatric Hospital

WESLEY WOODS LONG TERM CARE HOSPITAL See Select Specialty Hospital – Northeast Atlanta

AUGUSTA—Richmond County

△ **CHARLIE NORWOOD VETERANS AFFAIRS MEDICAL CENTER**, 1 Freedom Way, Zip 30904–6285; tel. 706/733–0188, (Nonreporting) **A**1 2 3 5 7 **S** Department of Veterans Affairs, Washington, DC
Primary Contact: Robert U. Hamilton, Director
COO: John D. Stenger, Acting Associate Director
CFO: Earline Corder, Chief Fiscal
CIO: Sandy Williford, Chief Health Information Management and Revenue Administration
CHR: Roger W. Buterbaugh, Chief Human Resources Officer
CNO: Michelle Cox–Henley, R.N., Associate Director for Patient and Nursing Services
Web address: www.augusta.va.gov/
Control: Veterans Affairs, Government, federal **Service:** General Medical and Surgical

Staffed Beds: 338

DOCTORS HOSPITAL (110177), 3651 Wheeler Road, Zip 30909–6426; tel. 706/651–3232, (Nonreporting) **A**1 2 5 9 10 **S** HCA, Nashville, TN
Primary Contact: Douglas Welch, Chief Executive Officer
CIO: Dona Hornung, Director Information and Technology Services
Web address: www.doctors–hospital.net
Control: Corporation, Investor–owned, for–profit **Service:** General Medical and Surgical

Staffed Beds: 242

EAST CENTRAL REGIONAL HOSPITAL (114029), 3405 Mike Padgett Highway, Zip 30906–3897; tel. 706/790–2011, (Includes EAST CENTRAL REGIONAL HOSPITAL, 100 Myrtle Boulevard, Gracewood, Zip 30812–1299; tel. 706/790–2011), (Total facility includes 306 beds in nursing home–type unit) **A**1 5 10 **F**29 34 38 39 59 65 67 75 77 86 87 96 98 101 128 130 132 143 **P**6
Primary Contact: Nan M. Lewis, Administrator
CFO: Candace Walker, Chief Financial Officer
Web address: www.dbhdd.ga.gov
Control: State–Government, nonfederal **Service:** Psychiatric

Staffed Beds: 467 Admissions: 910 Census: 383 Outpatient Visits: 0 Births: 0 Total Expense ($000): 77357 Payroll Expense ($000): 41140 Personnel: 1267

GEORGIA REGENTS MEDICAL CENTER (110034), 1120 15th Street, Zip 30912–0004; tel. 706/721–0211, (Includes CHILDREN'S HOSPITAL OF GEORGIA, 1446 Harper Street, Zip 30912–0012; tel. 706/721–5437) **A**1 2 3 5 8 9 10 13 **F**3 5 6 11 12 13 14 15 17 18 19 20 21 22 23 24 25 26 27 28 29 30 31 32 34 35 36 38 39 40 41 43 44 45 46 48 49 50 51 54 55 56 58 59 60 61 64 65 66 68 70 72 73 74 75 76 77 78 79 80 81 82 84 85 86 87 88 89 91 92 93 94 97 98 99 100 101 102 103 104 107 108 111 113 115 116 117 118 119 120 121 123 124 126 127 129 130 131 132 134 135 136 138 141 142 143 145 146 147 148 **P**3 7
Primary Contact: Peter Buckley, M.D., Interim Chief Executive Officer
COO: Steven Scott, Chief Operating Officer
CFO: Greg Damron, Vice President Finance and Chief Financial Officer
CMO: William Kanto, M.D., Senior Vice President and Chief Medical Officer
CIO: Charles Enicks, Chief Information Officer
CHR: Susan Norton, Vice President Human Resources
CNO: Laura E. Brower, R.N., Chief Nursing Officer
Web address: www.grhealth.org
Control: Other not–for–profit (including NFP Corporation) **Service:** General Medical and Surgical

Staffed Beds: 408 Admissions: 17826 Census: 278 Outpatient Visits: 461127 Births: 1238 Total Expense ($000): 503384 Payroll Expense ($000): 199337

HEALTHSOUTH WALTON REHABILITATION HOSPITAL (113030), 1355 Independence Drive, Zip 30901–1037; tel. 706/724–7746, (Nonreporting) **A**1 5 9 10 **S** HEALTHSOUTH Corporation, Birmingham, AL
Primary Contact: Deborah S. Guthrie, Chief Executive Officer
CMO: Pamela Salazar, M.D., Chief of Staff
CIO: Ann Keller, Supervisor Health Information Management
CHR: Volante Henderson, Director Human Resources
CNO: Lynn Beaulieu, R.N., Chief Nursing Officer
Web address: www.healthsouthwalton.com/
Control: Corporation, Investor–owned, for–profit **Service:** Rehabilitation

Staffed Beds: 58

MEDICAL COLLEGE OF GEORGIA HEALTH See Georgia Regents Medical Center

GA

Hospital, Medicare Provider Number, Address, Telephone, Approval, Facility, and Physician Codes, Health Care System
★ American Hospital Association (AHA) membership
□ The Joint Commission accreditation ◇ DNV Healthcare Inc. accreditation
○ Healthcare Facilities Accreditation Program
△ Commission on Accreditation of Rehabilitation Facilities (CARF) accreditation

⊞ **SELECT SPECIALTY HOSPITAL–AUGUSTA (112013)**, 1537 Walton Way,
Zip 30904–3764; tel. 706/731–1200, (Nonreporting) **A**1 9 10 **S** Select Medical
Corporation, Mechanicsburg, PA
Primary Contact: Curtis L. Roberts, Chief Executive Officer
CHR: Terrie Richardson, Coordinator Human Resources
CNO: Kim Pippin, Chief Nursing Officer
Web address: www.augusta.selectspecialtyhospitals.com
Control: Corporation, Investor–owned, for–profit **Service:** Long–Term Acute Care
hospital

Staffed Beds: 80

⊞ **TRINITY HOSPITAL OF AUGUSTA (110039)**, 2260 Wrightsboro Road,
Zip 30904–4726; tel. 706/481–7000, (Nonreporting) **A**1 5 9 10 **S** Community
Health Systems, Inc., Franklin, TN
Primary Contact: Jason Studley, Chief Executive Officer
CFO: Kevin Cargill, Chief Financial Officer
CMO: Niti Carlson, M.D., Chief of Staff
CIO: Charlotte Choate, Director Information Systems
CHR: Diana Maxson, Director Human Resources
CNO: Megan Freeman, Chief Nursing Officer
Web address: www.trinityofaugusta.com
Control: Corporation, Investor–owned, for–profit **Service:** General Medical and
Surgical

Staffed Beds: 105

⊞ **UNIVERSITY HOSPITAL (110028)**, 1350 Walton Way, Zip 30901–2629;
tel. 706/722–9011 **A**1 2 3 5 9 10 **F**3 12 13 15 17 18 20 22 24 26 28 29 30
31 34 35 37 38 40 41 44 48 49 50 54 56 57 59 60 62 63 64 68 70 72 73
74 75 76 77 78 79 80 81 82 83 84 85 86 87 89 93 97 100 107 108 110
111 114 115 116 118 119 126 129 130 132 134 135 144 146 147 148 **P**8
S University Health Care System, Augusta, GA
Primary Contact: James R. Davis, Chief Executive Officer
CFO: David Belkoski, Executive Vice President and Chief Financial Officer
CMO: William L. Farr, M.D., Chief Medical Officer
CIO: Leslie Clonch, Vice President and Chief Information Officer
CHR: Laurie Ott, Vice President Human Resources and President University Health
Care Foundation
CNO: Lynda Watts, R.N., Vice President Patient Care Services
Web address: www.universityhealth.org
Control: Other not–for–profit (including NFP Corporation) **Service:** General
Medical and Surgical

Staffed Beds: 494 **Admissions:** 21711 **Census:** 302 **Outpatient Visits:**
428897 **Births:** 2901 **Total Expense ($000):** 369313 **Payroll Expense
($000):** 140082 **Personnel:** 2244

VETERANS AFFAIRS MEDICAL CENTER See Charlie Norwood Veterans Affairs
Medical Center

WALTON REHABILITATION HOSPITAL See HEALTHSOUTH Walton Rehabilitation
Hospital

AUSTELL—Cobb County

⊞ △ **WELLSTAR COBB HOSPITAL (110143)**, 3950 Austell Road,
Zip 30106–1121; tel. 770/732–4000 **A**1 3 5 7 9 10 **F**3 4 11 13 15 16 17 18
20 22 26 28 29 30 31 37 38 40 41 44 45 48 49 50 53 54 55 58 59 60 61
62 64 66 68 70 72 73 74 75 76 77 78 79 80 81 82 84 85 86 87 90 93 94
96 98 100 101 102 103 104 105 106 107 108 110 111 114 115 118 119
126 130 132 135 141 146 147 148 **P**5 6 **S** WellStar Health System,
Marietta, GA
Primary Contact: Kem Mullins, FACHE, Senior Vice President and Hospital
President
COO: Kevin Deter, Chief Operating Officer
CFO: Darold Etheridge, Vice President and Chief Financial Officer
CMO: Thomas McNamara, D.O., Vice President Medical Affairs
CIO: Jonathan B. Morris, M.D., Senior Vice President and Chief Information Officer
CHR: Joseph W. Herzberg, Assistant Vice President Human Resources
CNO: Veronica Martin, MSN, Vice President Inpatient Services
Web address: www.wellstar.org
Control: Other not–for–profit (including NFP Corporation) **Service:** General
Medical and Surgical

Staffed Beds: 362 **Admissions:** 20452 **Census:** 269 **Outpatient Visits:**
235431 **Births:** 3595 **Personnel:** 1961

BAINBRIDGE—Decatur County

◇ **MEMORIAL HOSPITAL AND MANOR (110132)**, 1500 East Shotwell Street,
Zip 39819–4256; tel. 229/246–3500, (Nonreporting) **A**9 10 21
Primary Contact: William J. Walker, Jr., Chief Executive Officer
COO: Lee Harris, Assistant Administrator Support Services
CFO: Karen Faircloth, Chief Financial Officer
CMO: Shawn Surratt, M.D., Chief of Staff
CIO: Nelda Moore, Director Data Processing
CHR: Angel Sykes, Director Human Resources
CNO: Cynthia Vickers, R.N., Assistant Administrator for Nursing Services
Web address: www.mh–m.org
Control: Hospital district or authority, Government, nonfederal **Service:** General
Medical and Surgical

Staffed Beds: 80

BAXLEY—Appling County

◇ **APPLING HEALTHCARE SYSTEM (110071)**, 163 East Tollison Street,
Zip 31513–0120; tel. 912/367–9841 **A**9 10 20 21 **F**1 7 8 11 13 15 29 30 40
47 56 60 68 70 75 76 77 80 81 91 98 103 107 111 119 127 133 143 146
147 148
Primary Contact: Peyton A. Smith, Chief Executive Officer
COO: Judy M. Long, R.N., Chief Nursing Officer and Chief Operating Officer
CFO: Raymond J. Leadbetter, Jr., Revenue Cycle Consultant
CMO: Garland Martin, M.D., Chief of Staff
CIO: Gary Gower, Chief Information Officer
CHR: Carla McLendon, Director Human Resources
CNO: Judy M. Long, R.N., Chief Nursing Officer and Chief Operating Officer
Web address: www.appling–hospital.org
Control: County–Government, nonfederal **Service:** General Medical and Surgical

Staffed Beds: 150 **Admissions:** 1173 **Census:** 13

BLAIRSVILLE—Union County

⊞ **UNION GENERAL HOSPITAL (110051)**, 35 Hospital Road, Zip 30512–3139;
tel. 706/745–2111, (Nonreporting) **A**1 9 10 20 **S** Union General Hospital, Inc.,
Blairsville, GA
Primary Contact: Mike Gowder, Chief Executive Officer
COO: Lewis Kelley, Chief Operating Officer
CFO: Stephanie L. Fletcner, CPA, Chief Financial Officer
CMO: Andre Schaeffer, M.D., Chief of Staff
CIO: Mike Johnston, Director Facilities Operations
CHR: Kathy Hood, Administrative Assistant Human Resources
CNO: Julia Barnett, Chief Nursing Officer
Web address: www.uniongeneralhospital.com
Control: Hospital district or authority, Government, nonfederal **Service:** General
Medical and Surgical

Staffed Beds: 195

BLAKELY—Early County

★ ◇ **PIONEER COMMUNITY HOSPITAL OF EARLY (111314)**, 11740
Columbia Street, Zip 39823–2574; tel. 229/723–4241, (Total facility includes
117 beds in nursing home–type unit) **A**9 10 18 21 **F**3 7 29 34 40 45 56 57 59
64 65 77 93 97 98 103 104 107 111 114 119 127 128 129 130 133 135
143 148 **P**6 **S** Pioneer Health Services, Magee, MS
Primary Contact: Allen J. Gamble, Chief Executive Officer
Web address: www.pchearly.com
Control: Corporation, Investor–owned, for–profit **Service:** General Medical and
Surgical

Staffed Beds: 151 **Admissions:** 716 **Census:** 94 **Outpatient Visits:** 13203
Births: 0 **Total Expense ($000):** 20068 **Payroll Expense ($000):** 9490
Personnel: 140

BLUE RIDGE—Fannin County

⊞ **FANNIN REGIONAL HOSPITAL (110189)**, 2855 Old Highway 5,
Zip 30513–6248; tel. 706/632–3711, (Nonreporting) **A**1 9 10 **S** Community
Health Systems, Inc., Franklin, TN
Primary Contact: David S. Sanders, Chief Executive Officer
CFO: Rodney Sisk, Chief Financial Officer
CIO: Timothy Snider, Manager Information Systems
CHR: Terrasina Ensley, Director Human Resources
CNO: Jason L. Jones, R.N., Chief Nursing Officer
Web address: www.fanninregionalhospital.com
Control: Corporation, Investor–owned, for–profit **Service:** General Medical and
Surgical

Staffed Beds: 50

BREMEN—Haralson County

⊞ **HIGGINS GENERAL HOSPITAL (111320)**, 200 Allen Memorial Drive,
Zip 30110–2012; tel. 770/824–2000, (Nonreporting) **A**1 9 10 18 **S** Tanner
Health System, Carrollton, GA
Primary Contact: Michael D. Alexander, MS, Administrator
CIO: Dianne Reed, Director Information Systems
CHR: Vivian C. Barr, Director Human Resources
Web address: www.tanner.org/Main/HigginsGeneralHospitalBremen.aspx
Control: Other not–for–profit (including NFP Corporation) **Service:** General
Medical and Surgical

Staffed Beds: 25

Many Facility Codes have changed. Please refer to the AHA Guide Code Chart.   © 2014 AHA Guide

GA

BRUNSWICK—Glynn County

☒ **SOUTHEAST GEORGIA HEALTH SYSTEM BRUNSWICK CAMPUS (110025)**, 2415 Parkwood Drive, Zip 31520–4722, Mailing Address: P.O. Box 1518, Zip 31521–1518; tel. 912/466–7000, (Total facility includes 220 beds in nursing home–type unit) **A**1 2 9 10 19 20 **F**3 11 12 13 15 17 18 20 22 26 28 29 30 31 34 35 37 40 44 45 46 47 48 49 50 51 54 57 59 64 68 70 71 74 75 76 77 78 79 81 85 86 87 89 91 93 94 96 100 107 108 110 111 114 117 119 120 121 124 126 129 131 132 135 144 146 147 148 **P**5 **S** Southeast Georgia Health System, Brunswick, GA
Primary Contact: Gary R. Colberg, FACHE, President and Chief Executive Officer
CFO: Michael D. Scherneck, Executive Vice President and Chief Financial Officer
CIO: Chuck Bumgardner, Director Information Systems
CHR: Patrick D. Ebri, Ph.D., Vice President, Human Resources
CNO: Elizabeth Gunn, R.N., Vice President, Patient Care Services
Web address: www.sghs.org
Control: Hospital district or authority, Government, nonfederal **Service:** General Medical and Surgical

Staffed Beds: 494 **Admissions:** 12149 **Census:** 375 **Outpatient Visits:** 199501 **Births:** 1336 **Total Expense ($000):** 281806 **Payroll Expense ($000):** 123228 **Personnel:** 1509

CAIRO—Grady County

☒ **GRADY GENERAL HOSPITAL (110121)**, 1155 Fifth Street S.E., Zip 39828–3142, Mailing Address: P.O. Box 360, Zip 39828–0360; tel. 229/377–1150, (Nonreporting) **A**1 9 10 **S** Archbold Medical Center, Thomasville, GA
Primary Contact: Kenneth D. Rhudy, Administrator
COO: LaDon Toole, Administrator
CFO: Skip Hightower, Chief Financial Officer
CIO: Tracy Gray, Chief Information Officer
CHR: Michelle Pledger, Coordinator Human Resources
Web address: www.archbold.org
Control: Hospital district or authority, Government, nonfederal **Service:** General Medical and Surgical

Staffed Beds: 48

CALHOUN—Gordon County

☒ ○ **GORDON HOSPITAL (110023)**, 1035 Red Bud Road, Zip 30701–2082, Mailing Address: P.O. Box 12938, Zip 30703–7013; tel. 706/629–2895 **A**1 2 9 10 11 19 **F**3 7 11 13 15 18 20 29 30 31 34 35 37 40 46 57 59 62 64 70 75 76 77 78 79 81 82 85 86 87 93 107 108 111 115 119 120 121 123 129 130 135 144 146 147 148 **P**1 6 **S** Adventist Health System Sunbelt Health Care Corporation, Altamonte Springs, FL
Primary Contact: Pete M. Weber, President and Chief Executive Officer
COO: Brandon Nudd, Chief Operating Officer
CFO: Cory Reeves, Chief Financial Officer
CMO: Will Theus, M.D., Chief of Staff
CHR: Jeni Hasselbrack, Director Human Resources
CNO: Amy Jordan, R.N., Chief Nursing Officer/Vice President of Nursing
Web address: www.gordonhospital.com
Control: Church–operated, Nongovernment, not–for profit **Service:** General Medical and Surgical

Staffed Beds: 85 **Admissions:** 4278 **Census:** 47 **Outpatient Visits:** 193561 **Births:** 564 **Total Expense ($000):** 95886 **Payroll Expense ($000):** 38636 **Personnel:** 845

CAMILLA—Mitchell County

☒ **MITCHELL COUNTY HOSPITAL (111331)**, 90 East Stephens Street, Zip 31730–1836, Mailing Address: P.O. Box 639, Zip 31730–0639; tel. 229/336–5284, (Nonreporting) **A**1 9 10 18 **S** Archbold Medical Center, Thomasville, GA
Primary Contact: LaDon Toole, Administrator
COO: LaDon Toole, Vice President Network Operations
CFO: Skip Hightower, Senior Vice President and Chief Financial Officer
CMO: Jason Smith, M.D., Chief of Staff
CIO: Tracy Gray, Chief Information Officer
CHR: Vickie County–Teemer, Coordinator Human Resources
CNO: Carla Beasley, Director of Nursing
Web address: www.archbold.org
Control: Hospital district or authority, Government, nonfederal **Service:** General Medical and Surgical

Staffed Beds: 181

CANTON—Cherokee County

☒ **NORTHSIDE HOSPITAL–CHEROKEE (110008)**, 201 Hospital Road, Zip 30114–2408, Mailing Address: P.O. Box 906, Zip 30169–0906; tel. 770/720–5100 **A**1 9 10 **F**3 8 11 12 13 15 18 20 22 26 28 29 30 31 34 35 40 44 45 49 50 54 57 59 60 64 68 70 73 74 75 76 78 79 81 82 85 86 87 93 107 108 110 111 114 119 120 121 123 126 129 130 132 144 146 147 148 **S** Northside Healthcare System, Atlanta, GA
Primary Contact: William M. Hayes, Chief Executive Officer
COO: Mike Patterson, Director of Operations
CFO: Brian Jennette, Chief Financial Officer
CMO: Alexander Kessler, M.D., Chief of Staff
CIO: Bill Dunford, Manager
CHR: Roslyn Roberts, Manager
CNO: Jan Johnson, R.N., Chief Nursing Officer
Web address: www.northside.com
Control: Other not–for–profit (including NFP Corporation) **Service:** General Medical and Surgical

Staffed Beds: 88 **Admissions:** 5088 **Census:** 65 **Outpatient Visits:** 88736 **Births:** 1111 **Total Expense ($000):** 118035 **Payroll Expense ($000):** 49939 **Personnel:** 1042

CARROLLTON—Carroll County

☒ **TANNER MEDICAL CENTER–CARROLLTON (110011)**, 705 Dixie Street, Zip 30117–3818; tel. 770/836–9666, (Nonreporting) **A**1 9 10 **S** Tanner Health System, Carrollton, GA
Primary Contact: Deborah Matthews, Administrator
CHR: Vivian C. Barr, Director Human Resources
Web address: www.tanner.org
Control: Other not–for–profit (including NFP Corporation) **Service:** General Medical and Surgical

Staffed Beds: 201

CARTERSVILLE—Bartow County

☒ **CARTERSVILLE MEDICAL CENTER (110030)**, 960 Joe Frank Harris Parkway, Zip 30120–2129; tel. 770/382–1530, (Nonreporting) **A**1 2 9 10 **S** HCA, Nashville, TN
Primary Contact: Keith Sandlin, Chief Executive Officer
COO: Lori Rakes, Chief Operating Officer
Web address: www.cartersvillemedical.com
Control: Corporation, Investor–owned, for–profit **Service:** General Medical and Surgical

Staffed Beds: 80

CEDARTOWN—Polk County

☒ **POLK MEDICAL CENTER (111330)**, 424 North Main Street, Zip 30125–2698; tel. 770/748–2500 **A**1 10 18 **F**3 15 28 29 30 34 35 40 50 56 57 59 64 68 75 77 93 103 107 108 110 114 119 129 130 132 133 135 143 146 147 148
Primary Contact: Matt Gorman, Administrator
CFO: Rick Sheerin, Chief Financial Officer
CHR: Jeanna Smith, Administrative Assistant and Human Resources Officer
CNO: Charmaine Thomas, R.N., Chief Nursing Officer
Web address: www.polkhospital.org
Control: Hospital district or authority, Government, nonfederal **Service:** General Medical and Surgical

Staffed Beds: 18 **Admissions:** 210 **Census:** 3 **Outpatient Visits:** 30105 **Births:** 0 **Total Expense ($000):** 13338 **Payroll Expense ($000):** 6195 **Personnel:** 87

CHATSWORTH—Murray County

☐ **MURRAY MEDICAL CENTER (110050)**, 707 Old Dalton Ellijay Road, Zip 30705–2060, Mailing Address: P.O. Box 1406, Zip 30705–1406; tel. 706/695–4564 **A**1 9 10 **F**3 7 15 29 40 81 107 111 119 146
Primary Contact: Susan Shook, Interim Chief Executive Officer
CMO: Blaine Minor, M.D., Chief of Staff
CIO: Jose C. Rios, Director Information Services
CHR: Brandy Rymer, Coordinator Human Resources
CNO: Susan Shook, Interim Chief Executive officer
Web address: www.murraymedical.org/
Control: Hospital district or authority, Government, nonfederal **Service:** General Medical and Surgical

Staffed Beds: 33 **Admissions:** 392 **Census:** 3 **Births:** 0 **Total Expense ($000):** 13201 **Payroll Expense ($000):** 5814 **Personnel:** 111

GA

Hospital, Medicare Provider Number, Address, Telephone, Approval, Facility, and Physician Codes, Health Care System

★ American Hospital Association (AHA) membership
☐ The Joint Commission accreditation
◇ DNV Healthcare Inc. accreditation
○ Healthcare Facilities Accreditation Program
△ Commission on Accreditation of Rehabilitation Facilities (CARF) accreditation

CLAXTON—Evans County

⊞ **EVANS MEMORIAL HOSPITAL (110142)**, 200 North River Street,
Zip 30417–1659, Mailing Address: P.O. Box 518, Zip 30417–0518;
tel. 912/739–2611 **A**1 9 10 **F**3 15 34 40 45 53 57 59 68 75 81 93 97 107
108 110 111 115 119 127 130 135 146
Primary Contact: Martha F. Tatum, Chief Executive Officer
CFO: John Wiggins, Chief Financial Officer
CMO: Kyle Parks, Chief of Staff
CIO: Steve Schmidt, Director Information Systems
CHR: Gina Waters, Director Human Resources
CNO: Nikki NeSmith, Chief Nursing Officer
Web address: www.evansmemorialhospital.org
Control: Hospital district or authority, Government, nonfederal **Service:** General
Medical and Surgical

Staffed Beds: 22 **Admissions:** 844 **Census:** 8 **Outpatient Visits:** 30863
Births: 0 **Total Expense ($000):** 15651 **Payroll Expense ($000):** 7881
Personnel: 156

CLAYTON—Rabun County

MOUNTAIN LAKES MEDICAL CENTER (111336), 196 Ridgecrest Circle,
Zip 30525–4111; tel. 706/782–4233 **A**9 10 18 **F**3 8 11 15 18 29 35 40 45
56 64 74 75 77 79 81 82 85 86 87 93 97 102 107 111 114 119 127 129
130 133 148 **P**6
Primary Contact: Kim Ingram, Chief Executive Officer
CFO: Jimmy Norman, Chief Financial Officer
CHR: Charles Harbaugh, Director Human Resources
Web address: www.mountainlakesmedicalcenter.com
Control: Corporation, Investor–owned, for–profit **Service:** General Medical and
Surgical

Staffed Beds: 25 **Admissions:** 442 **Census:** 4 **Outpatient Visits:** 15961
Births: 0 **Personnel:** 69

COCHRAN—Bleckley County

◇ **BLECKLEY MEMORIAL HOSPITAL (111302)**, 145 East Peacock Street,
Zip 31014–7846, Mailing Address: P.O. Box 536, Zip 31014–0536;
tel. 478/934–6211, (Nonreporting) **A**9 10 18 21
Primary Contact: Nikki Paulk, Chief Executive Officer
Control: Hospital district or authority, Government, nonfederal **Service:** General
Medical and Surgical

Staffed Beds: 25

COLQUITT—Miller County

◇ **MILLER COUNTY HOSPITAL (111305)**, 209 North Cuthbert Street,
Zip 39837–3518, Mailing Address: P.O. Box 7, Zip 39837–0007;
tel. 229/758–3305, (Total facility includes 157 beds in nursing home–type unit)
A9 10 18 21 **F**8 29 30 34 38 39 40 44 45 50 57 59 65 66 68 77 81 85 86
87 89 93 97 103 104 107 108 114 119 127 128 129 130 133 135 143 148
Primary Contact: Robin Rau, Chief Executive Officer
CFO: Jill Brown, Chief Financial Officer
CMO: William Swofford, M.D., Chief of Staff
CIO: Keith Lovering, Information Technician
CHR: Karie Spence, Director Human Resources
CNO: Shawn Whittaker, Chief Nursing Officer
Web address: www.millercountyhospital.com
Control: Hospital district or authority, Government, nonfederal **Service:** General
Medical and Surgical

Staffed Beds: 182 **Admissions:** 950 **Census:** 110 **Outpatient Visits:** 32485
Births: 0 **Total Expense ($000):** 19128 **Payroll Expense ($000):** 11876
Personnel: 345

COLUMBUS—Muscogee County

BRADLEY CENTER OF ST. FRANCIS See St. Francis Hospital

⊞ **COLUMBUS SPECIALTY HOSPITAL (112012)**, 710 Center Street, 9th Floor,
Zip 31901–1527; tel. 706/321–6712 **A**1 9 10 **F**1 3 29 30 130 148
Primary Contact: Robert Saulnier, R.N., MSN, Chief Executive Officer
CFO: William Eckstein, Chief Financial Officer
CHR: Myra Whitley, Human Resources Director
CNO: Carol George, Chief Nursing Officer
Web address: www.columbusspecialtyhospital.net
Control: Other not–for–profit (including NFP Corporation) **Service:** Long–Term
Acute Care hospital

Staffed Beds: 33 **Admissions:** 313 **Census:** 22 **Outpatient Visits:** 0 **Births:**
0 **Total Expense ($000):** 12656 **Payroll Expense ($000):** 5028 **Personnel:**
94

⊞ **DOCTORS SPECIALTY HOSPITAL (110186)**, 616 19th Street,
Zip 31901–1528, Mailing Address: P.O. Box 2188, Zip 31902–2188;
tel. 706/494–4262, (Nonreporting) **A**1 9 10 **S** Columbus Regional Healthcare
System, Columbus, GA
Primary Contact: Tamara L. Jackson, R.N., MSN, FACHE, Chief Executive Officer
CMO: Thomas L. Theus, M.D., Chief of Medicine
CIO: Ryan Sanders, Director Information Services
Web address: www.columbusregional.com
Control: Other not–for–profit (including NFP Corporation) **Service:** General
Medical and Surgical

Staffed Beds: 171

HUGHSTON HOSPITAL See Northside Medical Center

⊞ **NORTHSIDE MEDICAL CENTER (110200)**, 100 Frist Court, Zip 31909–3578,
Mailing Address: P.O. Box 7188, Zip 31908–7188; tel. 706/494–2100,
(Nonreporting) **A**1 9 10 **S** Columbus Regional Healthcare System, Columbus, GA
Primary Contact: Tamara L. Jackson, R.N., MSN, FACHE, Chief Executive Officer
COO: Michelle Breitfelder, Chief Operating Officer
CFO: Roland Thacker, Chief Financial Officer
CMO: Lyle Norwood, M.D., Chief of Staff
CIO: Douglas Colburn, Chief Information Officer
CHR: Becky Augustyniak, Director Human Resources
Web address: www.columbusregional.com
Control: Hospital district or authority, Government, nonfederal **Service:**
Orthopedic

Staffed Beds: 100

⊞ **ST. FRANCIS HOSPITAL (110129)**, 2122 Manchester Expressway,
Zip 31904–6878, Mailing Address: P.O. Box 7000, Zip 31908–7000;
tel. 706/596–4000, (Includes BRADLEY CENTER OF ST. FRANCIS, 2000 16th
Avenue, Zip 31906–0308; tel. 706/320–3700) **A**1 3 5 9 10 **F**3 10 11 13 15 17
18 20 22 24 26 28 29 30 31 34 35 40 45 46 49 50 51 53 54 56 57 58 59
60 63 64 70 74 75 76 77 78 79 81 82 85 86 91 92 93 94 98 99 100 101
102 103 104 105 106 107 108 110 111 115 119 126 129 130 131 144 145
146 147 148 **P**6 7
Primary Contact: Robert P. Granger, President and Chief Executive Officer
COO: Kevin Sass, FACHE, Senior Vice President Human Resources, Organization
and Cultural Development
CFO: Matthew Moore, Executive Vice President and Chief Integration Officer
CMO: Bobbi Farber, M.D., Chief Medical Officer
CIO: Chuck Christian, Vice President Chief Information Officer
CHR: E. Rick Lowe, FACHE, Operations Support Risk Management and
Compliance
CNO: Deborah Bostic, MSN, Senior Vice President Hospital Operations and Chief
Nursing Officer
Web address: www.sfhga.com
Control: Other not–for–profit (including NFP Corporation) **Service:** General
Medical and Surgical

Staffed Beds: 326 **Admissions:** 13753 **Census:** 200 **Outpatient Visits:**
149251 **Births:** 204 **Total Expense ($000):** 204217 **Payroll Expense
($000):** 78364 **Personnel:** 2083

⊞ **THE MEDICAL CENTER (110064)**, 710 Center Street, Zip 31901–1527,
Mailing Address: P.O. Box 951, Zip 31902–0951; tel. 706/571–1000,
(Nonreporting) **A**1 2 3 5 9 10 12 13 **S** Columbus Regional Healthcare System,
Columbus, GA
Primary Contact: Ryan Chandler, President and Chief Executive Officer
Web address: www.columbusregional.com
Control: Other not–for–profit (including NFP Corporation) **Service:** General
Medical and Surgical

Staffed Beds: 497

☐ **WEST CENTRAL GEORGIA REGIONAL HOSPITAL (114013)**, 3000 Schatulga
Road, Zip 31907–3117, Mailing Address: P.O. Box 12435, Zip 31917–2435;
tel. 706/568–5000, (Nonreporting) **A**1 10
Primary Contact: John L. Robertson, Administrator
COO: Larmar Cunningham, Chief Operating Officer
CMO: Abiodun Famakinwa, M.D., Acting Clinical Director
CIO: Ron Buchanan, Director Information Services
CHR: Coreg Burns, Human Resources Lead
Web address: www.wcgrh.org
Control: State–Government, nonfederal **Service:** Psychiatric

Staffed Beds: 145

GA

COMMERCE—Jackson County

✠ **NORTHRIDGE MEDICAL CENTER (110040)**, 70 Medical Center Drive,
Zip 30529–1078; tel. 706/335–1000, (Total facility includes 167 beds in nursing
home–type unit) **A**1 9 10 **F**3 11 15 17 18 29 30 33 40 45 46 50 53 63 70 79
81 82 85 89 93 98 103 107 110 111 119 128 130 133 146
Primary Contact: Larry W. Ebert, Jr., Chief Operating Officer and Chief Financial
Officer
CFO: Larry W. Ebert, Jr., Chief Operating Officer and Chief Financial Officer
CMO: Narasimhulu Neelagaru, M.D., Chief of Staff
CNO: Maura Cobb, R.N., Chief Nursing Officer
Web address: www.northridgemc.com
Control: Partnership, Investor–owned, for–profit **Service:** General Medical and
Surgical

> **Staffed Beds:** 257 **Admissions:** 1202 **Census:** 163 **Births:** 0 **Total Expense**
> **($000):** 22692 **Payroll Expense ($000):** 8297 **Personnel:** 203

CONYERS—Rockdale County

✠ **ROCKDALE MEDICAL CENTER (110091)**, 1412 Milstead Avenue N.E.,
Zip 30012–3877; tel. 770/918–3000 **A**1 9 10 **F**3 11 13 15 18 20 28 29 30
34 35 36 40 45 46 47 49 57 59 62 64 68 70 72 74 75 76 79 81 82 85 86
87 92 93 107 108 110 111 114 115 118 119 126 130 131 132 135 145
146 147 148 **S** LifePoint Hospitals, Inc., Brentwood, TN
Primary Contact: Deborah Armstrong, Chief Executive Officer
COO: James Atkins, Chief Operating Officer
CFO: Diane Roth, Chief Financial Officer
CMO: Lisa Gillespie, M.D., Chief Medical Officer
CIO: Gail Waldo, Director Information Technology
CHR: Marianne Freeman, Vice President Human Resources
CNO: Eleanor Post, R.N., Chief Nursing Officer
Web address: www.rockdalemedicalcenter.org
Control: Corporation, Investor–owned, for–profit **Service:** General Medical and
Surgical

> **Staffed Beds:** 157 **Admissions:** 8834 **Census:** 107 **Outpatient Visits:**
> 111695 **Births:** 1860 **Total Expense ($000):** 116005 **Payroll Expense**
> **($000):** 46011 **Personnel:** 772

CORDELE—Crisp County

✠ **CRISP REGIONAL HOSPITAL (110104)**, 902 North Seventh Street,
Zip 31015–3234; tel. 229/276–3100, (Total facility includes 243 beds in nursing
home–type unit) **A**1 9 10 20 **F**3 10 11 13 15 28 29 30 31 34 35 40 43 44 45
48 50 51 54 56 57 58 59 60 61 62 63 64 65 68 70 75 76 77 78 79 81 84
85 86 87 89 90 93 96 97 107 108 110 111 115 125 127 128 129 132 133
135 144 146 147 148 **P**2 8
Primary Contact: Steven Gautney, Chief Executive Officer
COO: Mary Jim Montgomery, R.N., Chief Operating Officer
CFO: Jessica Y. Carter, Chief Financial Officer
CMO: David Kavtaradze, M.D., Chief of Staff
CHR: George M. Laurin, Interim Director Human Resources
CNO: Marsha L. Mulderig, R.N., Chief Nursing Officer
Web address: www.crispregional.org
Control: County–Government, nonfederal **Service:** General Medical and Surgical

> **Staffed Beds:** 316 **Admissions:** 3023 **Census:** 141 **Outpatient Visits:** 94725
> **Births:** 327 **Personnel:** 648

COVINGTON—Newton County

✠ **NEWTON MEDICAL CENTER (110018)**, 5126 Hospital Drive,
Zip 30014–2567; tel. 770/786–7053 **A**1 9 10 **F**7 11 12 13 15 18 20 28 29
30 31 34 35 40 49 59 62 64 70 72 74 75 76 78 79 81 82 85 87 89 93 97
107 108 111 119 130 131 132 141 142 146 147 148
Primary Contact: James F. Weadick, Administrator and Chief Executive Officer
CFO: Troy Brooks, Assistant Administrator Fiscal Services
CMO: Norris Little, Chief of Staff
CIO: Brad Collier, Director
CNO: Patricia A. Waller, R.N., Assistant Administrator Patient Care Services
Web address: www.newtonmedical.com
Control: Other not–for–profit (including NFP Corporation) **Service:** General
Medical and Surgical

> **Staffed Beds:** 101 **Admissions:** 5763 **Census:** 53 **Outpatient Visits:** 244914
> **Births:** 850 **Total Expense ($000):** 80904 **Payroll Expense ($000):** 36623
> **Personnel:** 710

CUMMING—Forsyth County

✠ **NORTHSIDE HOSPITAL–FORSYTH (110005)**, 1200 Northside Forsyth Drive,
Zip 30041–7659; tel. 770/844–3200 **A**1 9 10 **F**3 8 11 12 13 15 18 20 22 26
28 29 30 31 34 35 37 40 44 45 49 50 54 57 59 60 64 68 70 71 73 74 75
76 78 79 81 82 85 86 87 93 107 108 110 111 114 115 117 119 120 121
123 124 126 129 130 132 135 144 146 147 148 **S** Northside Healthcare
System, Atlanta, GA
Primary Contact: Lynn Jackson, Administrator
CFO: Eric Caldwell, Director Finance
Web address: www.northside.com
Control: Other not–for–profit (including NFP Corporation) **Service:** General
Medical and Surgical

> **Staffed Beds:** 228 **Admissions:** 11016 **Census:** 161 **Outpatient Visits:**
> 183358 **Births:** 2478 **Total Expense ($000):** 272217 **Payroll Expense**
> **($000):** 98769 **Personnel:** 1882

CUTHBERT—Randolph County

★ ◇ **SOUTHWEST GEORGIA REGIONAL MEDICAL CENTER (111300)**, 361
Randolph Street, Zip 39840–6127; tel. 229/732–2181, (Nonreporting) **A**9 10
18 21
Primary Contact: Amy Cason, Chief Executive Officer and Chief Nursing Officer
CFO: Brent Rigsby, Chief Financial Officer
CNO: Amy Cason, Chief Executive Officer and Chief Nursing Officer
Web address: www.phoebeputney.com/
Control: Hospital district or authority, Government, nonfederal **Service:** General
Medical and Surgical

> **Staffed Beds:** 105

DAHLONEGA—Lumpkin County

☐ **CHESTATEE REGIONAL HOSPITAL (110187)**, 227 Mountain Drive,
Zip 30533–1606; tel. 706/864–6136 **A**1 9 10 **F**3 15 29 34 49 50 54 56 57
59 64 65 79 81 85 86 87 98 103 105 107 108 110 111 114 119 127 129
130 133 143 146 147 **P**8 **S** Sunlink Health Systems, Atlanta, GA
Primary Contact: Jason Cox, Chief Executive Officer
CFO: Molly Lindquist, Interim Chief Financial Officer
CMO: Richard Wherry, M.D., Chief of Staff
CHR: Barbara Patrick, Director Human Resources
CNO: Barbara Arnau, R.N., Chief Nursing Officer
Web address: www.chestateeregionalhospital.com
Control: Corporation, Investor–owned, for–profit **Service:** General Medical and
Surgical

> **Staffed Beds:** 49 **Admissions:** 1244 **Census:** 13 **Outpatient Visits:** 21433
> **Births:** 150 **Total Expense ($000):** 17022 **Payroll Expense ($000):** 7695
> **Personnel:** 157

DALLAS—Paulding County

✠ **WELLSTAR PAULDING HOSPITAL (110042)**, 600 West Memorial Drive,
Zip 30132–4117; tel. 770/445–4411, (Total facility includes 182 beds in nursing
home–type unit) **A**1 9 10 **F**3 11 15 28 29 30 37 38 40 44 45 50 54 55 59 61
64 68 70 75 77 78 79 81 82 85 86 87 102 107 108 110 111 114 118 119
120 121 123 128 129 130 135 146 **P**5 6 **S** WellStar Health System,
Marietta, GA
Primary Contact: Mark Haney, President
CFO: Marsha Burke, Senior Vice President Financial Services
Web address: www.wellstar.org
Control: Other not–for–profit (including NFP Corporation) **Service:** General
Medical and Surgical

> **Staffed Beds:** 216 **Admissions:** 2179 **Census:** 189 **Outpatient Visits:**
> 102664 **Births:** 0 **Personnel:** 510

GA

DALTON—Whitfield County

⊠ **HAMILTON MEDICAL CENTER (110001)**, 1200 Memorial Drive,
Zip 30720–2529, Mailing Address: P.O. Box 1168, Zip 30722–1168;
tel. 706/272–6000 **A**1 2 9 10 19 **F**3 4 5 8 12 13 15 18 20 22 26 28 29 30
31 34 35 40 43 44 45 46 47 48 49 50 51 53 54 57 59 60 62 63 64 68 70
72 73 74 75 76 77 78 79 81 82 83 84 85 86 87 89 93 96 97 98 100 101
102 103 104 105 107 108 110 111 114 115 116 117 118 119 120 121 123
126 129 130 131 132 135 144 146 147 148
Primary Contact: Jeffrey D. Myers, President and Chief Executive Officer
COO: Sandra D. McKenzie, Executive Vice President and Chief Operating Officer
CFO: Gary L. Howard, Senior VP and Chief Financial Officer
CMO: Stephen G. Rohn, M.D., VP and Chief Medical Officer
CIO: John M. Forrester, Director Information Services
CHR: Jason Hopkins, Director, Human Resources
CNO: Cathy Ferguson, R.N., VP and Chief Nursing Officer
Web address: www.hamiltonhealth.com
Control: Other not–for–profit (including NFP Corporation) **Service:** General
Medical and Surgical

Staffed Beds: 230 **Admissions:** 9281 **Census:** 101 **Outpatient Visits:**
258934 **Births:** 1807 **Personnel:** 1125

DECATUR—Dekalb County

⊠ **ATLANTA VETERANS AFFAIRS MEDICAL CENTER**, 1670 Clairmont Road,
Zip 30033–4004; tel. 404/321–6111, (Nonreporting) **A**1 2 3 5 8 **S** Department
of Veterans Affairs, Washington, DC
Primary Contact: Leslie Wiggins, Director
CFO: Pamela Watkins, Chief Financial Officer
CMO: David Bower, M.D., Chief of Staff
CIO: William Brock, Chief Information Officer
CHR: Zeta Ferguson, Chief Human Resources
CNO: Sandy Leake, MSN, Associate Director, Nursing and Patient Care Services
Web address: www.atlanta.va.gov/
Control: Veterans Affairs, Government, federal **Service:** General Medical and
Surgical

Staffed Beds: 239

☐ **DEKALB MEDICAL AT DOWNTOWN DECATUR (112006)**, 450 North Candler
Street, Zip 30030–2671; tel. 404/501–6700 **A**1 5 9 10 **F**1 3 11 20 29 30 35
50 60 74 75 77 79 82 119 130 146 148 **S** DeKalb Regional Health System,
Decatur, GA
Primary Contact: John Shelton, President and Chief Executive Officer
COO: John Shelton, Executive Vice President and Chief Operating Officer
CMO: David Snyder, M.D., Chief of Staff
CHR: Tom Crawford, Vice President Human Resources
Web address: www.dekalbmedicalcenter.org
Control: Other not–for–profit (including NFP Corporation) **Service:** Long–Term
Acute Care hospital

Staffed Beds: 44 **Admissions:** 347 **Census:** 25 **Outpatient Visits:** 0 **Births:**
0 **Total Expense ($000):** 17284 **Payroll Expense ($000):** 7161 **Personnel:**
200

⊠ **DEKALB MEDICAL AT NORTH DECATUR (110076)**, 2701 North Decatur
Road, Zip 30033–5995; tel. 404/501–1000 **A**1 2 3 9 10 **F**3 11 12 13 15 18
20 21 22 26 28 29 30 31 34 35 36 37 40 48 49 50 53 55 56 57 58 59 60 64
67 70 71 72 73 74 75 76 77 78 79 81 82 85 87 90 93 96 97 98 100 102
105 107 108 111 114 115 117 119 120 121 124 126 129 130 131 132 134
135 146 147 148 **S** DeKalb Regional Health System, Decatur, GA
Primary Contact: John Shelton, President and Chief Executive Officer
COO: Dane Henry, Executive Vice President and Chief Operating Officer
CFO: John Katsianis, Senior Vice President and Chief Financial Officer
CIO: Beth Patino, Chief Information Officer
CHR: LeRoy Walker, Vice President Human Resources
CNO: Susan Breslin, R.N., Vice President Patient Care Services and Chief Nursing
Officer
Web address: www.dekalbmedical.org
Control: Other not–for–profit (including NFP Corporation) **Service:** General
Medical and Surgical

Staffed Beds: 417 **Admissions:** 20392 **Census:** 254 **Outpatient Visits:**
168537 **Births:** 4916 **Total Expense ($000):** 304324 **Payroll Expense
($000):** 107119 **Personnel:** 2500

☐ **GEORGIA REGIONAL HOSPITAL AT ATLANTA (114019)**, 3073 Panthersville
Road, Zip 30034–3828; tel. 404/243–2100, (Nonreporting) **A**1 3 5 10
Primary Contact: Susan Trueblood, Chief Executive Officer
COO: Sonny Slate, Chief Operating Officer
CFO: Reginald Jones, Business Manager
CMO: Emile Risby, M.D., Clinical Director
CIO: Elfie Early, Manager Data Services
CHR: Lorraine Farr, Manager Human Resources
Web address: www.atlantareg.dhr.state.ga.us
Control: State–Government, nonfederal **Service:** Psychiatric

Staffed Beds: 319

VETERANS AFFAIRS MEDICAL CENTER See Atlanta Veterans Affairs Medical
Center

DEMOREST—Habersham County

⊠ **HABERSHAM MEDICAL CENTER (110041)**, 541 Historic Highway 441,
Zip 30535–3118, Mailing Address: P.O. Box 37, Zip 30535–0037;
tel. 706/754–2161, (Nonreporting) **A**1 9 10
Primary Contact: Jerry R. Wise, Chief Executive Officer
COO: Michael Gay, Chief Operating Officer
CFO: Barbara Duncan, Chief Financial Officer
CMO: Terry Greene, M.D., Chief of Staff
CIO: Paul Harris, Manager Information Systems
CHR: Ryan Snow, Interim Director Human Resources
CNO: Janice McKenzie, R.N., Chief Clinical Officer
Web address: www.habershammedical.com/
Control: Hospital district or authority, Government, nonfederal **Service:** General
Medical and Surgical

Staffed Beds: 137

DONALSONVILLE—Seminole County

◇ **DONALSONVILLE HOSPITAL (110194)**, 102 Hospital Circle, Zip 39845–1199;
tel. 229/524–5217, (Total facility includes 75 beds in nursing home–type unit) **A**9
10 21 **F**34 40 45 46 57 59 64 68 76 77 81 87 93 107 108 110 114 119 128
133 147 148
Primary Contact: Charles H. Orrick, Administrator
CFO: James Moody, Chief Financial Officer
CMO: C. O. Walker, M.D., Chief of Staff
CHR: Jo Adams, Director Human Resources
Control: Other not–for–profit (including NFP Corporation) **Service:** General
Medical and Surgical

Staffed Beds: 140 **Admissions:** 1871 **Census:** 82 **Outpatient Visits:** 23538
Births: 238 **Total Expense ($000):** 27598 **Payroll Expense ($000):** 12638
Personnel: 383

DOUGLAS—Coffee County

⊠ **COFFEE REGIONAL MEDICAL CENTER (110089)**, 1101 Ocilla Road,
Zip 31533–2207, Mailing Address: P.O. Box 1287, Zip 31534–1287;
tel. 912/384–1900 **A**1 9 10 20 **F**3 7 8 11 13 15 18 20 28 29 30 31 32 34 35
40 45 47 49 50 51 53 54 56 57 59 61 65 68 70 75 76 77 78 79 81 82 85
86 87 89 97 107 108 110 111 114 115 119 127 130 131 132 135 143 144
146 147 148 **P**8
Primary Contact: George L. Heck, III, President and Chief Executive Officer
CFO: Donald C. Lewis, Jr., Vice President and Chief Financial Officer
CIO: George L. Heck, III, President and Chief Executive Officer
CHR: Laura Bloom, Director Human Resources
Web address: www.coffeeregional.org
Control: Other not–for–profit (including NFP Corporation) **Service:** General
Medical and Surgical

Staffed Beds: 88 **Admissions:** 5084 **Census:** 53 **Outpatient Visits:** 124337
Births: 591 **Total Expense ($000):** 82599 **Payroll Expense ($000):** 49418

DOUGLASVILLE—Douglas County

⊠ **WELLSTAR DOUGLAS HOSPITAL (110184)**, 8954 Hospital Drive,
Zip 30134–2282; tel. 770/949–1500 **A**1 2 9 10 **F**3 11 13 15 20 22 28 29 30
31 37 38 40 44 45 48 49 50 51 54 58 59 60 61 64 66 68 70 74 75 76 77
78 79 81 82 85 86 87 93 94 102 107 108 110 111 114 115 117 118 119
129 130 132 135 146 147 148 **P**5 6 **S** WellStar Health System, Marietta, GA
Primary Contact: Craig A. Owens, President
CFO: Bradley Greene, Chief Financial Officer
CMO: Noel Holtz, M.D., Chief Medical Officer
CHR: Danyale Ziglor, Assistant Director Human Resources
Web address: www.wellstar.org
Control: Other not–for–profit (including NFP Corporation) **Service:** General
Medical and Surgical

Staffed Beds: 102 **Admissions:** 6927 **Census:** 78 **Outpatient Visits:** 134899
Births: 459 **Personnel:** 727

YOUTH VILLAGES INNER HARBOUR CAMPUS, 4685 Dorsett Shoals Road,
Zip 30135–4999; tel. 770/942–2391, (Nonreporting)
Primary Contact: Patrick Lawler, Chief Executive Officer
CFO: J. Steve Lewis, Director Finance
CIO: Laura Sellers, Director Information Systems
CHR: Sherry Kollmeyer, Vice President Human Resources
Web address: www.innerharbour.org
Control: Other not–for–profit (including NFP Corporation) **Service:** Children's
hospital psychiatric

Staffed Beds: 176

DUBLIN—Laurens County

⊠ **CARL VINSON VETERANS AFFAIRS MEDICAL CENTER**, 1826 Veterans Boulevard, Zip 31021–3620; tel. 478/272–1210, (Nonreporting) **A**1 **S** Department of Veterans Affairs, Washington, DC
Primary Contact: John S. Goldman, Director
COO: Gerald M. DeWorth, Associate Director
CFO: Kathy Stephens, Chief Financial Officer
CIO: Mark Cowart, Chief Information Officer
CHR: Kurt Oster, Human Resources Officer
Web address: www.dublin.va.gov/
Control: Veterans Affairs, Government, federal **Service:** General Medical and Surgical

Staffed Beds: 178

⊠ **FAIRVIEW PARK HOSPITAL (110125)**, 200 Industrial Boulevard, Zip 31021–2997, Mailing Address: P.O. Box 1408, Zip 31040–1408; tel. 478/275–2000, (Nonreporting) **A**1 9 10 19 **S** HCA, Nashville, TN
Primary Contact: Donald R. Avery, FACHE, President and Chief Executive Officer
COO: Matthew Steven Hasbrouck, Chief Operating Officer
CFO: Ted Short, Chief Financial Officer
CMO: Jeri Miller, M.D., President Medical Staff
CIO: Marsha Morris, Manager Information Services
CHR: Jeff Bruton, Director Human Resources
CNO: Donna Trickey, R.N., Chief Nursing Officer
Web address: www.fairviewparkhospital.com
Control: Corporation, Investor–owned, for–profit **Service:** General Medical and Surgical

Staffed Beds: 168

DULUTH—De Kalb County

GWINNETT MEDICAL CENTER–DULUTH See Gwinnett Hospital System, Lawrenceville

EAST POINT—Fulton County

⊠ **REGENCY HOSPITAL OF SOUTH ATLANTA (112014)**, 1170 Cleveland Avenue, 4th Floor, Zip 30344–3615; tel. 404/466–6250 **A**1 10 **F**1 18 29 74 77 96 148 **S** Select Medical Corporation, Mechanicsburg, PA
Primary Contact: Yameeka Jones, Chief Executive Officer
Web address: www.regencyhospital.com
Control: Corporation, Investor–owned, for–profit **Service:** Long–Term Acute Care hospital

Staffed Beds: 40 **Admissions:** 261 **Census:** 28 **Births:** 0

EASTMAN—Dodge County

◇ **DODGE COUNTY HOSPITAL (110092)**, 901 Griffin Avenue, Zip 31023–6720, Mailing Address: PO BOX 4309, Zip 31023–4309; tel. 478/374–4000 **A**9 10 21 **F**3 11 13 15 29 30 31 40 45 53 57 59 64 69 70 75 76 79 81 85 86 107 108 110 111 114 119 146 147
Primary Contact: Kevin Bierschenk, Chief Executive Officer
CFO: Jan Hamrick, Chief Financial Officer
CIO: Victor Woodard, Manager Information Technology
CHR: Wendy Selph, Director Human Resources
CNO: Sandra M. Campbell, R.N., Chief Nursing Officer
Web address: www.dodgecountyhospital.com
Control: Hospital district or authority, Government, nonfederal **Service:** General Medical and Surgical

Staffed Beds: 25 **Admissions:** 1495 **Census:** 16 **Outpatient Visits:** 38381 **Births:** 142 **Total Expense ($000):** 18792 **Payroll Expense ($000):** 8591 **Personnel:** 230

EATONTON—Putnam County

☐ **PUTNAM GENERAL HOSPITAL (111313)**, 101 Lake Oconee Parkway, Zip 31024–6054; tel. 706/485–2711 **A**1 9 10 18 **F**3 11 15 28 29 34 35 40 45 51 57 59 64 81 87 93 107 110 111 114 115 119 129 133
Primary Contact: Darrell M. Oglesby, Administrator
CFO: Brenda Jarrett, Chief Financial Officer
CMO: Omar Akhras, M.D., Chief of Staff
CIO: Steven Cason, Chief Information Officer
CHR: Ellen Ellard, Director Human Resources
Web address: www.putnamgeneral.com
Control: Hospital district or authority, Government, nonfederal **Service:** General Medical and Surgical

Staffed Beds: 25 **Admissions:** 726 **Census:** 6 **Outpatient Visits:** 24117 **Births:** 0 **Total Expense ($000):** 13543 **Payroll Expense ($000):** 5481 **Personnel:** 129

ELBERTON—Elbert County

⊠ **ELBERT MEMORIAL HOSPITAL (110026)**, 4 Medical Drive, Zip 30635–1897; tel. 706/283–3151, (Nonreporting) **A**1 9 10
Primary Contact: James Yarborough, FACHE, Chief Executive Officer
CIO: Greg Fields, Director Information Technology
CHR: Georgian Walton, Director Human Resources
CNO: Dede Arnau, R.N., Chief Nursing Officer
Web address: www.emhcare.net
Control: Hospital district or authority, Government, nonfederal **Service:** General Medical and Surgical

Staffed Beds: 42

ELLIJAY—Gilmer County

☐ **NORTH GEORGIA MEDICAL CENTER (110205)**, 1362 South Main Street, Zip 30540–5410, Mailing Address: P.O. Box 2239, Zip 30540–0025; tel. 706/276–4741, (Total facility includes 100 beds in nursing home–type unit) **A**1 9 10 **F**3 11 15 29 30 34 35 36 40 44 45 46 50 57 59 64 65 68 70 75 77 79 81 82 87 90 91 92 93 97 107 108 110 111 114 119 120 125 127 128 129 130 132 133 145 146 **P**6 8 **S** Sunlink Health Systems, Atlanta, GA
Primary Contact: Earl S. Whiteley, FACHE, Chief Executive Officer
COO: Earl S. Whiteley, FACHE, Chief Executive Officer
CFO: Debbie Self, Chief Financial Officer
CMO: Brian Rowan, Chief of Staff
CHR: Mary Beth Ralston, Human Resources Director
CNO: Katie Lancey, Chief Nursing Officer
Web address: www.northgeorgiamedicalcenter.com
Control: Corporation, Investor–owned, for–profit **Service:** General Medical and Surgical

Staffed Beds: 150 **Admissions:** 1122 **Census:** 105 **Births:** 0

FAYETTEVILLE—Fayette County

⊠ **PIEDMONT FAYETTE HOSPITAL (110215)**, 1255 Highway 54 West, Zip 30214–4526; tel. 770/719–7000 **A**1 2 9 10 **F**3 11 13 15 18 20 22 25 26 28 29 30 31 34 35 40 41 45 46 47 48 49 50 51 53 55 57 59 64 70 72 73 74 75 76 77 78 79 81 84 85 87 93 96 107 108 111 114 115 119 121 122 123 124 126 129 130 135 146 147 148 **S** Piedmont Healthcare, Atlanta, GA
Primary Contact: Michael Robertson, Chief Executive Officer
COO: Michael Burnett, Chief Operating Officer
CMO: Frederick Willms, M.D., Vice President Medical Affairs
CHR: Catherine Crisler, Executive Director Human Resources
Web address: www.fayettehospital.org
Control: Other not–for–profit (including NFP Corporation) **Service:** General Medical and Surgical

Staffed Beds: 172 **Admissions:** 12434 **Census:** 141 **Outpatient Visits:** 143572 **Births:** 2448 **Total Expense ($000):** 207354 **Payroll Expense ($000):** 78544 **Personnel:** 1162

FITZGERALD—Ben Hill County

◇ **DORMINY MEDICAL CENTER (110073)**, 200 Perry House Road, Zip 31750–8857, Mailing Address: P.O. Box 1447, Zip 31750–1447; tel. 229/424–7100 **A**9 10 21 **F**3 11 13 15 29 30 31 34 35 40 48 50 56 57 59 63 64 68 70 75 76 77 78 81 82 84 87 89 90 93 107 108 110 111 114 119 127 129 130 132 133 148
Primary Contact: Mel Pyne, Chief Executive Officer
CFO: Paige Wynn, Chief Financial Officer
CMO: Stephen Thombley, M.D., Chief of Staff
CIO: Chris Ward, Director Management Information Systems
CHR: Denise Steverson, Director Human Resources
CNO: Staci Mims, Chief Nursing Officer
Web address: www.dorminymedical.org
Control: Hospital district or authority, Government, nonfederal **Service:** General Medical and Surgical

Staffed Beds: 40 **Admissions:** 1593 **Census:** 15 **Outpatient Visits:** 17229 **Births:** 94 **Total Expense ($000):** 29462 **Payroll Expense ($000):** 9415 **Personnel:** 229

GA

FORSYTH—Monroe County

☐ **MONROE COUNTY HOSPITAL (111318)**, 88 Martin Luther King Jr. Drive, Zip 31029–1682, Mailing Address: P.O. Box 1068, Zip 31029–1068; tel. 478/994–2521 **A**1 9 10 18 **F**3 11 15 29 35 40 57 59 68 75 77 81 107 110 111 114 119 132 133 146 148 **P**1 2 3
Primary Contact: Kay A. Floyd, R.N., Chief Executive Officer
CFO: Marlene McLennan, Controller
CMO: Jeremy Goodwin, M.D., President, Medical Staff
CIO: Donna Hogg, Supervisor Medical Records
CHR: Deborah Flowers, Director Human Resources
CNO: Casey Fleckenstein, Medical and Surgical Nurse Manager
Web address: www.monroehospital.org
Control: Hospital district or authority, Government, nonfederal **Service:** General Medical and Surgical

Staffed Beds: 25 **Admissions:** 493 **Census:** 8 **Outpatient Visits:** 24180 **Births:** 0 **Total Expense ($000):** 10777 **Payroll Expense ($000):** 4269 **Personnel:** 117

FORT BENNING—Muscogee County

☒ **MARTIN ARMY COMMUNITY HOSPITAL**, 7950 Martin Loop, Zip 31905–5648, Mailing Address: 7950 Martin Loop, B9200, Room 010, Zip 31905–5648; tel. 706/544–2516, (Nonreporting) **A**1 3 5 **S** Department of the Army, Office of the Surgeon General, Falls Church, VA
Primary Contact: Colonel Scott B. Avery, Commander
CHR: Major Bernita Hightower, Chief Human Resources
Web address: www.martin.amedd.army.mil
Control: Army, Government, federal **Service:** General Medical and Surgical

Staffed Beds: 57

FORT GORDON—Richmond County

☒ **DWIGHT DAVID EISENHOWER ARMY MEDICAL CENTER**, 300 West Hospital Road, Zip 30905–5741; tel. 706/787–5811, (Nonreporting) **A**1 2 3 5 **S** Department of the Army, Office of the Surgeon General, Falls Church, VA
Primary Contact: Colonel John P. Lamoureux, Commander
CMO: Colonel James M. Baunchalk, Deputy Chief Clinical Services
CIO: Major Joseph A. Ponce, Chief Information Management
CHR: Elizabeth Shelt, Civilian Personnel Officer
Web address: www.ddeamc.amedd.army.mil
Control: Army, Government, federal **Service:** General Medical and Surgical

Staffed Beds: 115

FORT OGLETHORPE—Catoosa County

☐ **HUTCHESON MEDICAL CENTER (110004)**, 100 Gross Crescent Circle, Zip 30742–3669; tel. 706/858–2000, (Nonreporting) **A**1 9 10 **S** Erlanger Health System, Chattanooga, TN
Primary Contact: Farrell Hayes, Interim Chief Executive Officer
COO: Farrell Hayes, Interim Chief Operating Officer
CFO: Farrell Hayes, Chief Financial Officer
CMO: John Nelson, M.D., Chief of Staff
CIO: Ruth Wright, Director Information Services
CHR: Christie Nelson, Director Human Resources
CNO: Cindy Hoggard, Chief Nursing Officer
Web address: www.hutcheson.org
Control: Hospital district or authority, Government, nonfederal **Service:** General Medical and Surgical

Staffed Beds: 185

FORT VALLEY—Peach County

MEDICAL CENTER OF PEACH COUNTY, NAVICENT HEALTH (111310), 601 Blue Bird Boulevard, Zip 31030–4599, Mailing Address: P.O. Box 1799, Zip 31030–1799; tel. 478/825–8691, (Nonreporting) **A**9 10 18 **S** Navicent Health, Macon, GA
Primary Contact: Nancy Peed, Administrator and Chief Executive Officer
CFO: Lisa Urbistondo, Chief Financial Officer
CMO: Crystal Brown, M.D., Medical Director
CNO: Brenda Goodman, Chief Nursing Officer
Web address: www.peachregional.org
Control: Hospital district or authority, Government, nonfederal **Service:** General Medical and Surgical

Staffed Beds: 25

GAINESVILLE—Hall County

★ △ ◇ **NORTHEAST GEORGIA MEDICAL CENTER (110029)**, 743 Spring Street N.E., Zip 30501–3899; tel. 770/219–3553, (Total facility includes 260 beds in nursing home–type unit) **A**2 7 9 10 19 21 **F**3 4 5 7 11 12 13 15 17 18 20 22 24 26 28 29 30 31 34 35 38 39 40 44 45 46 47 48 49 50 51 54 56 57 58 59 60 61 63 64 65 66 68 70 72 73 74 75 76 77 78 79 81 82 85 86 87 89 90 93 98 99 100 101 102 103 104 105 106 107 108 110 111 114 115 116 117 119 120 121 123 124 126 128 129 130 131 132 143 144 146 147 148 **P**6
Primary Contact: Carol H. Burrell, President and Chief Executive Officer
CFO: Tony Herdener, Vice President Systems and Finance
CMO: Jim Bailey, M.D., Chief Medical Officer
CIO: Mark Jennings, Director Information Systems
CNO: Karen Watts, MSN, Vice President of Patient Care and Chief Nursing Officer
Web address: www.nghs.com
Control: Other not–for–profit (including NFP Corporation) **Service:** General Medical and Surgical

Staffed Beds: 513 **Admissions:** 27714 **Census:** 355 **Outpatient Visits:** 351388 **Births:** 3541 **Total Expense ($000):** 546558 **Payroll Expense ($000):** 204578

GRACEWOOD—Richmond County

EAST CENTRAL REGIONAL HOSPITAL See East Central Regional Hospital, Augusta

GREENSBORO—Greene County

☒ **ST. MARY'S GOOD SAMARITAN HOSPITAL (111329)**, 5401 Lake Oconee Parkway, Zip 30642–4232; tel. 706/453–7331 **A**1 9 10 18 **F**3 11 15 26 29 30 34 35 40 45 47 50 51 57 59 64 65 68 74 75 77 81 83 85 87 93 107 110 115 119 129 130 133 147 148 **S** Catholic Health East / Trinity Health, Livonia, MI
Primary Contact: D. Montez Carter, President
CMO: Dave Ringer, M.D., Chief of Staff
CNO: Celia Covington, MSN, Director of Nursing
Web address: www.stmarysgoodsam.org
Control: Church–operated, Nongovernment, not–for profit **Service:** General Medical and Surgical

Staffed Beds: 25 **Admissions:** 548 **Census:** 9 **Outpatient Visits:** 19960 **Births:** 0 **Total Expense ($000):** 13152 **Payroll Expense ($000):** 6258 **Personnel:** 141

GRIFFIN—Spalding County

☒ **SPALDING REGIONAL MEDICAL CENTER (110031)**, 601 South Eighth Street, Zip 30224–4294, Mailing Address: P.O. Drawer V, Zip 30224–1168; tel. 770/228–2721 **A**1 2 9 10 **F**3 7 11 15 18 20 22 29 30 31 34 35 40 49 50 51 53 54 57 59 64 70 73 74 75 76 77 78 79 81 85 87 89 93 107 108 110 111 114 115 119 129 130 131 135 143 146 147 148 **P**8 **S** TENET Healthcare Corporation, Dallas, TX
Primary Contact: John A. Quinn, Chief Executive Officer
COO: Tamara Ison, Chief Operating Officer
CFO: Cameron Pophan, Chief Financial Officer
CMO: Philip Osehobo, M.D., Chief Medical Officer
CIO: Steve Brown, Director Information Systems
CHR: Amanda Remington, Director Human Resources
CNO: Wadra McCullough, Chief Nursing Officer
Web address: www.spaldingregional.com
Control: Corporation, Investor–owned, for–profit **Service:** General Medical and Surgical

Staffed Beds: 160 **Admissions:** 8515 **Census:** 97 **Outpatient Visits:** 97888 **Births:** 917 **Total Expense ($000):** 98241 **Payroll Expense ($000):** 40632 **Personnel:** 675

HAWKINSVILLE—Pulaski County

◇ **TAYLOR REGIONAL HOSPITAL (110135)**, Macon Highway, Zip 31036, Mailing Address: P.O. Box 1297, Zip 31036–7297; tel. 478/783–0200, (Nonreporting) **A**9 10 21
Primary Contact: Dan S. Maddock, President
CFO: Lisa Halliday, Director Accounting Services
CMO: Al Baggett, M.D., Interim Chief of Staff
CIO: Dawn Warnock, Director Medical Records
Web address: www.taylorregional.org
Control: Other not–for–profit (including NFP Corporation) **Service:** General Medical and Surgical

Staffed Beds: 55

HAZLEHURST—Jeff Davis County

☐ **JEFF DAVIS HOSPITAL (111333)**, 1215 South Tallahassee Street, Zip 31539–2921, Mailing Address: P.O. Box 1690, Zip 31539–1690; tel. 912/375–7781, (Nonreporting) **A**1 9 10 18
Primary Contact: Gerald A. Schoendienst, Chief Executive Officer
Web address: www.jeffdavishospital.org/getpage.php?name=2013HF
Control: Hospital district or authority, Government, nonfederal **Service:** General Medical and Surgical

Staffed Beds: 25

Many Facility Codes have changed. Please refer to the AHA Guide Code Chart. © 2014 AHA Guide

GA

HIAWASSEE—Towns County

CHATUGE REGIONAL HOSPITAL AND NURSING HOME (111324), 110 Main Street, Zip 30546–3408, Mailing Address: P.O. Box 509, Zip 30546–0509; tel. 706/896–2222, (Nonreporting) **A**9 10 18 **S** Union General Hospital, Inc., Blairsville, GA
Primary Contact: R. Lewis Kelley, Administrator
CFO: Tim Henry, Accountant
CMO: Robert F. Stahlkuppe, M.D., Chief of Staff
CIO: Walt Stafford, Director Information Technology
CHR: Rita Bradshaw, Director Human Resources
Web address: www.chatugeregionalhospital.org
Control: County–Government, nonfederal **Service:** General Medical and Surgical

Staffed Beds: 137

HINESVILLE—Liberty County

☐ **LIBERTY REGIONAL MEDICAL CENTER (111335)**, 462 Elma G. Miles Parkway, Zip 31313–4000, Mailing Address: P.O. Box 919, Zip 31310–0919; tel. 912/369–9400, (Nonreporting) **A**1 9 10 18
Primary Contact: H. Scott Kroell, Jr., Chief Executive Officer
CFO: Sam Johnson, Chief Financial Officer
Web address: www.libertyregional.org
Control: Hospital district or authority, Government, nonfederal **Service:** General Medical and Surgical

Staffed Beds: 25

⊞ **WINN ARMY COMMUNITY HOSPITAL**, 1061 Harmon Avenue, Zip 31314–5641, Mailing Address: 1061 Harmon Avenue, Suite 2311B, Zip 31314–5641; tel. 912/435–6965 **A**1 3 5 **F**3 7 12 13 15 29 30 32 33 34 35 36 38 39 40 41 44 45 54 57 59 61 64 65 68 71 74 75 76 77 79 81 82 85 87 89 92 93 97 98 100 101 102 104 107 110 111 119 130 132 135 143 146 147 **P**6 **S** Department of the Army, Office of the Surgeon General, Falls Church, VA
Primary Contact: Colonel Kirk W. Eggleston, Commanding Officer
COO: Jose A. Bonilla, Deputy Commander Administration
CMO: Richard Malish, M.D., Deputy Commander Clinical Services
CIO: Arthur N. Kirshner, Chief Information Management
CHR: Major Yvette McCrea, Chief Human Resources
CNO: Colonel Sharon Brown, Deputy Commander Nursing
Web address: www.winn.amedd.army.mil/
Control: Army, Government, federal **Service:** General Medical and Surgical

Staffed Beds: 37 Admissions: 2797 Census: 19 Outpatient Visits: 665635 Births: 1048 Total Expense ($000): 159749 Payroll Expense ($000): 85602 Personnel: 932

HOMERVILLE—Clinch County

★ **CLINCH MEMORIAL HOSPITAL (111308)**, 1050 Valdosta Highway, Zip 31634–9701, Mailing Address: P.O. Box 516, Zip 31634–0516; tel. 912/487–5211 **A**9 10 18 **F**3 7 15 34 40 45 57 59 64 77 91 93 107 110 111 114 119 129 130 133 135 145 146
Primary Contact: Greg Brown, Chief Executive Officer
COO: Greg Brown, Chief Executive Officer
CFO: Sandra Hughes, Chief Financial Officer
CMO: Samuel Cobarrubias, M.D., Chief of Staff
CIO: Shelly Studebaker, Director Management Information Systems
CHR: Shelly Studebaker, Manager Human Resources
CNO: Wayne Lee, Director of Nursing
Web address: www.sgmc.org/healthsystem/clinchmemorial.htm
Control: County–Government, nonfederal **Service:** General Medical and Surgical

Staffed Beds: 25 Admissions: 245 Census: 3 Outpatient Visits: 14369 Births: 0 Total Expense ($000): 10083 Payroll Expense ($000): 3721 Personnel: 109

JACKSON—Butts County

★ **SYLVAN GROVE HOSPITAL (111319)**, 1050 McDonough Road, Zip 30233–1599; tel. 770/775–7861 **A**9 10 18 **F**15 29 34 35 40 50 57 59 68 77 93 107 119 130 133 **S** TENET Healthcare Corporation, Dallas, TX
Primary Contact: John A. Quinn, Chief Executive Officer
CFO: Tamara Ison, Chief Financial Officer
CIO: Steve Brown, Chief Information Officer
CHR: Amanda Remington, Director Human Resources
Web address: www.sylvangrovehospital.com
Control: Corporation, Investor–owned, for–profit **Service:** General Medical and Surgical

Staffed Beds: 24 Admissions: 466 Census: 14 Outpatient Visits: 17388 Births: 0 Total Expense ($000): 8872 Payroll Expense ($000): 4922 Personnel: 73

JASPER—Pickens County

⊞ **PIEDMONT MOUNTAINSIDE HOSPITAL (110225)**, 1266 Highway 515 South, Zip 30143–4872; tel. 706/692–2441 **A**1 9 10 **F**3 13 15 20 28 29 34 35 40 45 46 47 49 57 64 70 76 77 79 81 85 107 108 110 111 114 115 119 129 130 132 135 148 **S** Piedmont Healthcare, Atlanta, GA
Primary Contact: Denise Ray, President and Chief Executive Officer
CFO: Frank R. Powell, Chief Financial Officer
CHR: Connie McLendon, Director Human Resources
CNO: Linda Stead, Chief Nursing Officer
Web address: www.piedmontmountainsidehospital.org
Control: Other not–for–profit (including NFP Corporation) **Service:** General Medical and Surgical

Staffed Beds: 58 Admissions: 2692 Census: 26 Outpatient Visits: 37388 Births: 355 Total Expense ($000): 51515 Payroll Expense ($000): 20801 Personnel: 345

JESUP—Wayne County

☐ **WAYNE MEMORIAL HOSPITAL (110124)**, 865 South First Street, Zip 31545–0210, Mailing Address: P.O. Box 410, Zip 31598–0410; tel. 912/427–6811, (Nonreporting) **A**1 9 10 20
Primary Contact: Joseph P. Ierardi, Chief Executive Officer
CFO: Greg Jones, Chief Financial Officer
CMO: Dan Collipp, M.D., Chief of Staff
CIO: Deborah Six, Coordinator Data Processing
CHR: John McIwain, Director Human Resources
Web address: www.wmhweb.com
Control: County–Government, nonfederal **Service:** General Medical and Surgical

Staffed Beds: 84

JOHNS CREEK—Fulton County

⊞ **EMORY JOHNS CREEK HOSPITAL (110230)**, 6325 Hospital Parkway, Zip 30097–5775; tel. 678/474–7000 **A**1 10 **F**3 11 12 13 15 18 20 22 26 29 30 31 34 35 36 40 45 49 50 51 54 57 59 60 64 68 70 72 73 74 75 76 77 78 79 81 82 85 87 92 93 107 108 110 111 115 116 117 119 126 129 130 131 132 141 146 147 148 **P**6 **S** Emory Healthcare, Atlanta, GA
Primary Contact: Marilyn Margolis, Interim Chief Executive Officer
COO: Laurie Hansen, Associate Administrator
CFO: JoAnn Manning, Chief Financial Officer
CMO: Adedapo Odetoyinbo, M.D., Chief Medical Office
CIO: Brad Foresythe, Director Information Systems
CHR: Jennifer Elizabeth Garber, Vice President Human Resources
CNO: Marilyn Margolis, Chief Nursing Officer
Web address: www.emoryjohnscreek.com
Control: Other not–for–profit (including NFP Corporation) **Service:** General Medical and Surgical

Staffed Beds: 86 Admissions: 5668 Census: 63 Outpatient Visits: 54007 Births: 903 Total Expense ($000): 108184 Payroll Expense ($000): 35573 Personnel: 535

KENNESAW—Cobb County

DEVEREUX GEORGIA TREATMENT NETWORK, 1291 Stanley Road N.W., Zip 30152–4359; tel. 770/427–0147 **F**98 99 106 **S** Devereux, Villanova, PA
Primary Contact: Gwendolyn Skinner, Executive Director
COO: Mary H. Esposito, Assistant Executive Director
CFO: Kathy Goggin, Director Administrative Services
CMO: Yolanda Graham, M.D., Medical Director
CIO: Sam Maguta, Coordinator Information Systems
CHR: Rudie Delien, Director Human Resources
CNO: Debra Sharpton, Director of Nursing
Web address: www.devereuxga.org
Control: Other not–for–profit (including NFP Corporation) **Service:** Children's hospital psychiatric

Staffed Beds: 100 Admissions: 187 Census: 69 Outpatient Visits: 0 Births: 0

GA

Hospital, Medicare Provider Number, Address, Telephone, Approval, Facility, and Physician Codes, Health Care System
★ American Hospital Association (AHA) membership   ○ Healthcare Facilities Accreditation Program
☐ The Joint Commission accreditation   ◇ DNV Healthcare Inc. accreditation   △ Commission on Accreditation of Rehabilitation Facilities (CARF) accreditation

LA GRANGE—Troup County

☒ **WEST GEORGIA HEALTH (110016)**, 1514 Vernon Road, Zip 30240–4199; tel. 706/882–1411, (Total facility includes 260 beds in nursing home–type unit) **A**1 2 9 10 19 **F**3 8 11 12 13 18 20 22 26 28 29 30 31 34 35 40 47 48 49 50 51 54 56 57 58 59 62 63 64 66 68 70 73 74 75 76 77 78 79 80 81 82 84 85 86 89 92 93 96 102 107 108 110 111 114 115 116 117 119 120 121 123 128 129 130 132 135 146 147 148 **P**6
Primary Contact: Gerald N. Fulks, President and Chief Executive Officer
COO: Charis Acree, Senior Vice President
CFO: Paul R. Perrotti, CPA, Chief Financial Officer
CIO: Sonya Christian–Avery, Chief Information Officer
CHR: Tommy Britt, Director Human Resources
Web address: www.wghealth.org/
Control: Other not–for–profit (including NFP Corporation) **Service:** General Medical and Surgical

Staffed Beds: 412 **Admissions:** 7601 **Census:** 314 **Outpatient Visits:** 135914 **Births:** 936 **Total Expense ($000):** 171948 **Payroll Expense ($000):** 64916 **Personnel:** 1294

LAKELAND—Lanier County

☒ **SOUTH GEORGIA MEDICAL CENTER LANIER CAMPUS (111326)**, (Sub–acute), 116 West Thigpen Avenue, Zip 31635–1011; tel. 229/482–3110, (Total facility includes 62 beds in nursing home–type unit) **A**1 9 10 18 **F**3 7 34 35 40 50 53 56 57 59 64 65 68 75 77 93 97 107 111 114 119 128 129 130 133 143 148 **P**6
Primary Contact: Neil W. Ginty, Administrator
CFO: Libby Flemming, Controller and Chief Information Officer
CMO: Bruce Herrington, M.D., Chief Medical Officer
CIO: Libby Flemming, Controller and Chief Information Officer
CHR: Vicki Dinkins, Director Human Resources
Web address: www.sgmc.org
Control: Other not–for–profit (including NFP Corporation) **Service:** Other specialty

Staffed Beds: 87 **Admissions:** 345 **Census:** 68 **Outpatient Visits:** 12030 **Births:** 0 **Total Expense ($000):** 12008 **Payroll Expense ($000):** 5123 **Personnel:** 107

LAVONIA—Franklin County

◇ **TY COBB REGIONAL MEDICAL CENTER (110027)**, 367 Clear Creek Parkway, Zip 30553–4173; tel. 706/356–7800 **A**9 10 21 **F**3 11 13 15 18 29 30 34 35 40 45 46 50 53 57 59 70 75 76 77 81 84 85 87 93 107 108 111 115 119 129 130 146 **S** Ty Cobb Healthcare System, Inc., Royston, GA
Primary Contact: Gregory K. Hearn, Chief Executive Officer
CIO: Tim Vickery, Chief Information Officer
CHR: Lauren Papka, Chief Administrative Officer
CNO: Evelyn Murphy, R.N., Chief Nursing Officer
Web address: www.tycobbhealthcare.org
Control: Other not–for–profit (including NFP Corporation) **Service:** General Medical and Surgical

Staffed Beds: 35 **Admissions:** 1506 **Census:** 15

LAWRENCEVILLE—Gwinnett County

☒ **GWINNETT HOSPITAL SYSTEM (110087)**, 1000 Medical Center Boulevard, Zip 30046–7694, Mailing Address: P.O. Box 348, Zip 30046–0348; tel. 678/312–1000, (Includes GWINNETT MEDICAL CENTER, 1000 Medical Center Boulevard, Zip 30245, Mailing Address: Box 348, Zip 30246; tel. 770/995–4321; Thomas Shepherd, Executive Vice President and Chief Operating Officer; GWINNETT MEDICAL CENTER–DULUTH, 3620 Howell Ferry Road, Duluth, Zip 30096; tel. 678/312–6800), (Total facility includes 89 beds in nursing home–type unit) **A**1 2 9 10 **F**3 8 11 12 13 15 17 18 20 22 24 26 28 29 30 31 34 35 36 37 38 40 41 43 44 45 47 48 49 50 54 55 56 58 59 64 67 68 70 71 72 73 74 75 76 77 78 79 81 82 84 85 86 87 90 93 96 107 108 110 111 114 115 117 118 119 126 128 129 130 131 132 134 135 146 147 148 **P**8
Primary Contact: Philip R. Wolfe, President and Chief Executive Officer
COO: Thomas Shepherd, Executive Vice President and Chief Operating Officer
CFO: Thomas Y. McBride, III, Executive Vice President and Chief Financial Officer
CMO: Alan Bier, M.D., Executive Vice President and Chief Medical Officer
CIO: Patricia A. Lavely, FACHE, Senior Vice President and Chief Information Officer
CHR: Steve Nadeau, Senior Vice President Human Resources
CNO: Carol Danielson, R.N., Senior Vice President and Chief Nursing Officer
Web address: www.gwinnettmedicalcenter.org
Control: Other not–for–profit (including NFP Corporation) **Service:** General Medical and Surgical

Staffed Beds: 542 **Admissions:** 28217 **Census:** 452 **Outpatient Visits:** 351064 **Births:** 4854 **Total Expense ($000):** 556565 **Payroll Expense ($000):** 219922 **Personnel:** 3689

☐ **SUMMITRIDGE HOSPITAL (114004)**, 250 Scenic Highway, Zip 30046–5675; tel. 678/442–5800, (Nonreporting) **A**1 10
Primary Contact: Jeff Pritchard, Chief Executive Officer
Web address: www.summitridgehospital.net
Control: Other not–for–profit (including NFP Corporation) **Service:** Psychiatric

Staffed Beds: 25

LITHONIA—Dekalb County

☐ **DEKALB MEDICAL AT HILLANDALE (110226)**, 2801 DeKalb Medical Parkway, Zip 30058–4996; tel. 404/501–8700 **A**1 9 10 **F**3 11 15 18 29 30 34 35 40 48 49 50 56 57 59 60 70 74 75 77 78 79 81 82 85 93 97 107 108 111 114 119 130 132 146 **S** DeKalb Regional Health System, Decatur, GA
Primary Contact: John Shelton, President and Chief Executive Officer
COO: John Shelton, Chief Operating Officer
CMO: Duane Barclay, D.O., Chief Medical Officer
CIO: Mark Trocino, Chief Information Officer
CHR: Tom Crawford, Vice President Human Resources
Web address: www.dekalbmedical.org
Control: Other not–for–profit (including NFP Corporation) **Service:** General Medical and Surgical

Staffed Beds: 100 **Admissions:** 5394 **Census:** 66 **Outpatient Visits:** 97695 **Births:** 0 **Total Expense ($000):** 72313 **Payroll Expense ($000):** 27493 **Personnel:** 564

LOUISVILLE—Jefferson County

☐ **JEFFERSON HOSPITAL (110100)**, 1067 Peachtree Street, Zip 30434–1599; tel. 478/625–7000 **A**1 9 10 20 **F**11 15 34 40 45 53 54 57 59 63 64 65 66 81 85 89 90 93 97 107 109 114 119 127 129 133 135 **P**6
Primary Contact: James Heitzenrater, Chief Executive Officer
CMO: James Polhill, M.D., Chief Medical Officer
CIO: Dain Overstreet, Manager Information Technology
CHR: Catherine Hall, Manager Human Resources
CNO: Ben Doyle, R.N., Director of Nursing
Web address: www.jeffersonhosp.com
Control: City–County, Government, nonfederal **Service:** General Medical and Surgical

Staffed Beds: 37 **Admissions:** 678 **Census:** 6 **Outpatient Visits:** 69617 **Births:** 1 **Total Expense ($000):** 14057 **Payroll Expense ($000):** 6468 **Personnel:** 124

MACON—Bibb County

☒ **COLISEUM CENTER FOR BEHAVIORAL HEALTH (114015)**, 340 Hospital Drive, Zip 31217–3838; tel. 478/741–1355 **A**1 9 10 **F**3 4 5 29 30 35 38 56 75 98 100 101 102 103 104 105 130 132 **S** HCA, Nashville, TN
Primary Contact: James W. Eyler, FACHE, Chief Executive Officer
Web address: www.coliseumhealthsystem.com
Control: Corporation, Investor–owned, for–profit **Service:** Psychiatric

Staffed Beds: 43 **Admissions:** 1419 **Census:** 27 **Outpatient Visits:** 3366 **Births:** 0 **Personnel:** 89

☒ **COLISEUM MEDICAL CENTERS (110164)**, 350 Hospital Drive, Zip 31217–3871; tel. 478/765–7000, (Nonreporting) **A**1 2 9 10 **S** HCA, Nashville, TN
Primary Contact: Charles G. Briscoe, FACHE, Chief Executive Officer
COO: Todd Dixon, R.N., Chief Operating Officer
CFO: Heath King, Chief Financial Officer
CMO: Michael Thornsberry, M.D., Chief Medical Officer
CIO: Joan Morstad, Director Information Systems
CHR: Laura Booras, Vice President Human Resources
CNO: Candice R. Carroll, Chief Nursing Officer
Web address: www.coliseumhealthsystem.com
Control: Corporation, Investor–owned, for–profit **Service:** General Medical and Surgical

Staffed Beds: 227

☒ **COLISEUM NORTHSIDE HOSPITAL (110201)**, 400 Charter Boulevard, Zip 31210–4853, Mailing Address: P.O. Box 4627, Zip 31208–4627; tel. 478/757–8200, (Nonreporting) **A**1 9 10 **S** HCA, Nashville, TN
Primary Contact: Stephen J. Daugherty, Chief Executive Officer
COO: Todd Dixon, R.N., Chief Operating Officer
CFO: Heath King, Chief Financial Officer
CHR: Laura Booras, Director of Human Resources
CNO: Patricia Derrico, FACHE, Chief Nursing Officer
Web address: www.coliseumhealthsystem.com
Control: Corporation, Investor–owned, for–profit **Service:** General Medical and Surgical

Staffed Beds: 103

GA

★ ◇ **MEDICAL CENTER, NAVICENT HEALTH (110107)**, 777 Hemlock Street, Zip 31201–2155; tel. 478/633–1000, (Includes CHILDREN'S HOSPITAL, 777 Hemlock Street, tel. 478/633–1000) **A**2 3 5 8 9 10 21 **F**3 5 7 8 11 12 13 14 15 17 18 20 22 24 26 28 29 30 31 32 34 35 36 39 40 43 44 45 46 47 48 49 50 51 53 54 56 57 58 59 60 61 62 63 64 65 66 68 70 72 73 74 75 76 77 78 79 81 82 83 84 85 86 87 88 89 92 93 94 97 98 99 100 101 102 103 104 105 107 108 110 111 114 115 119 126 130 132 135 143 144 145 146 147 148 **P**1 **S** Navicent Health, Macon, GA
Primary Contact: Ninfa Saunders, Chief Executive Officer
COO: Tejas Gandhi, Chief Administrative Officer
CFO: Rhonda Perry, Chief Financial Officer
CMO: Fady Wanna, M.D., Chief Clinical Officer and Chief Medical Officer
CIO: William Avenel, Assistant Vice President Information Services
CHR: Bernard J. Price, Assistant Vice President
CNO: Tracey Blalock, Chief Nursing Officer
Web address: www.mccg.org
Control: Other not–for–profit (including NFP Corporation) **Service:** General Medical and Surgical

Staffed Beds: 659 Admissions: 32266 Census: 470 Outpatient Visits: 386679 Births: 2492 Total Expense ($000): 650335 Payroll Expense ($000): 251826 Personnel: 4216

✠ **REGENCY HOSPITAL OF CENTRAL GEORGIA (112016)**, 535 Coliseum Drive, Zip 31217–0104; tel. 478/803–7300, (Nonreporting) **A**1 9 10 **S** Select Medical Corporation, Mechanicsburg, PA
Primary Contact: Michael S. Boggs, Chief Executive Officer
Web address: www.regencyhospital.com
Control: Corporation, Investor–owned, for–profit **Service:** Long–Term Acute Care hospital

Staffed Beds: 34

★ ◇ **REHABILITATION HOSPITAL, NAVICENT HEALTH (113029)**, 3351 Northside Drive, Zip 31210–2587; tel. 478/201–6500 **A**9 10 21 **F**60 68 90 93 132 143 148 **S** Navicent Health, Macon, GA
Primary Contact: Elbert T. McQueen, President and Chief Executive Officer
COO: Darren Pearce, Executive Director
CFO: Beverly Owens, Controller
CMO: Allison Scheetz, M.D., Medical Director
Web address: www.centralgarehab.com
Control: Hospital district or authority, Government, nonfederal **Service:** Rehabilitation

Staffed Beds: 58 Admissions: 977 Census: 38 Outpatient Visits: 11557 Births: 0 Total Expense ($000): 15345 Payroll Expense ($000): 8017 Personnel: 181

MADISON—Morgan County

☐ **MORGAN MEMORIAL HOSPITAL (111304)**, 1077 South Main Street, Zip 30650–2073, Mailing Address: P.O. Box 860, Zip 30650–0860; tel. 706/342–1667 **A**1 9 10 18 **F**29 40 45 79 81 93 107 119 129 133
Primary Contact: Ralph A. Castillo, CPA, Chief Executive Officer
CFO: Kyle Wilkinson, Chief Financial Officer
CMO: Dan Zant, M.D., Chief of Staff
CIO: Patrick Cook, Vice President Support Services
CHR: Sarah Phillips, Manager Human Resources
CNO: Beth O'Neill, Chief Nursing Officer
Web address: www.mmh.org
Control: Hospital district or authority, Government, nonfederal **Service:** General Medical and Surgical

Staffed Beds: 25 Admissions: 472 Census: 18 Outpatient Visits: 13155 Births: 0 Total Expense ($000): 13633 Payroll Expense ($000): 5968

MARIETTA—Cobb County

✠ △ **WELLSTAR KENNESTONE HOSPITAL (110035)**, 677 Church Street, Zip 30060–1148; tel. 770/793–5000 **A**1 2 3 5 7 9 10 **F**3 8 10 11 12 13 15 17 18 20 22 24 26 28 29 30 31 36 37 38 40 41 43 44 45 46 47 48 49 50 53 54 55 58 59 60 61 64 66 68 70 72 73 74 75 76 77 78 79 80 81 82 84 85 86 87 90 93 94 96 100 102 107 108 110 111 114 115 117 118 119 120 121 123 124 125 126 129 130 132 135 141 146 147 148 **P**5 6 **S** WellStar Health System, Marietta, GA
Primary Contact: Dan Woods, President
COO: Monte Wilson, Chief Operating Officer
CFO: Marty Gutkin, Vice President Finance and Chief Financial Officer
CMO: Robert Lubitz, M.D., Vice President of Medical Affairs
CIO: Jonathan B. Morris, M.D., Senior Vice President and Chief Information Officer
CHR: Bobby DeCoux, Assistant Vice President Human Resources
CNO: Laura J. Caramanica, Ph.D., Vice President and Chief Nursing Officer
Web address: www.wellstar.org
Control: Other not–for–profit (including NFP Corporation) **Service:** General Medical and Surgical

Staffed Beds: 588 Admissions: 37072 Census: 480 Outpatient Visits: 450349 Births: 5348 Personnel: 3950

✠ **WELLSTAR WINDY HILL HOSPITAL (112007)**, 2540 Windy Hill Road, Zip 30067–8632; tel. 770/644–1000 **A**1 2 9 10 **F**1 3 5 11 15 29 30 44 45 50 51 58 60 61 64 68 75 77 79 81 85 86 87 93 100 101 107 108 110 111 114 118 119 129 130 135 141 146 148 **P**5 6 **S** WellStar Health System, Marietta, GA
Primary Contact: Lou Little, President
CFO: Marsha Burke, Senior Vice President and Chief Financial Officer
CMO: Larry Haldeman, M.D., Executive Vice President and Chief Medical Officer
CIO: Leigh Cox, Chief Information Officer
Web address: www.wellstar.org
Control: Other not–for–profit (including NFP Corporation) **Service:** Long–Term Acute Care hospital

Staffed Beds: 55 Admissions: 379 Census: 32 Outpatient Visits: 20928 Births: 0 Personnel: 277

METTER—Candler County

☐ **CANDLER COUNTY HOSPITAL (111334)**, 400 Cedar Street, Zip 30439–3338, Mailing Address: P.O. Box 597, Zip 30439–0597; tel. 912/685–5741 **A**1 9 10 18 **F**15 29 35 40 52 56 57 59 70 81 93 103 107 111 114 119 127 133 146
Primary Contact: Stephen C. Shepherd, Chief Executive Officer
Web address: www.candlercountyhospital.com
Control: Hospital district or authority, Government, nonfederal **Service:** General Medical and Surgical

Staffed Beds: 25 Admissions: 754 Census: 7 Births: 0 Total Expense ($000): 16609 Payroll Expense ($000): 9268 Personnel: 207

MILLEDGEVILLE—Baldwin County

CENTRAL STATE HOSPITAL, 620 Broad Street, Zip 31062–0001; tel. 478/445–4128, (Total facility includes 113 beds in nursing home–type unit) **A**9 **F**30 39 57 59 75 86 87 97 98 100 103 107 128 130
Primary Contact: Randall Hines, Interim Administrator
COO: Terry McGee, Chief Operations Officer
CMO: Scott VanSant, M.D., Chief Medical Officer
CIO: Betsy Bradley, Coordinator Performance Improvement
CHR: Myra Holloway, Director Human Resources Management
Web address: www.centralstatehospital.org
Control: State–Government, nonfederal **Service:** Psychiatric

Staffed Beds: 297 Admissions: 83 Census: 296 Outpatient Visits: 0 Births: 0 Total Expense ($000): 85919 Payroll Expense ($000): 35939 Personnel: 999

☐ **OCONEE REGIONAL MEDICAL CENTER (110150)**, 821 North Cobb Street, Zip 31061–2351, Mailing Address: P.O. Box 690, Zip 31059–0690; tel. 478/454–3505, (Total facility includes 15 beds in nursing home–type unit) **A**1 9 10 19 **F**3 11 13 15 28 29 30 31 34 35 37 40 45 46 49 50 53 57 59 64 68 70 75 76 78 79 80 81 82 85 86 87 89 107 108 110 111 114 116 117 119 120 121 123 128 129 132 135 146 147 148 **S** Oconee Regional Health Systems, Milledgeville, GA
Primary Contact: Jean Aycock, President and Chief Executive Officer
CFO: Brenda Qualls, Chief Financial Officer
CHR: Scott Parton, Director Human Resources
CNO: Deborah Block, Vice President Nursing and Chief Nursing Officer
Web address: www.oconeeregional.com
Control: Other not–for–profit (including NFP Corporation) **Service:** General Medical and Surgical

Staffed Beds: 90 Admissions: 3899 Census: 56 Outpatient Visits: 121626 Births: 560 Total Expense ($000): 70332 Payroll Expense ($000): 25590 Personnel: 503

MILLEN—Jenkins County

JENKINS COUNTY HOSPITAL (111311), 931 East Winthrope Avenue, Zip 30442–1839; tel. 478/982–4221 **A**9 10 18 **F**11 15 29 34 40 45 50 57 59 64 65 75 77 79 81 82 90 93 97 107 119 127 133 146
Primary Contact: Robert R. Sellers, Administrator
CFO: Marsha Carroll, Director of Fiscal Services
CIO: Rob Snipes, Chief Information Officer
CHR: Natalie Peterson, Director of Human Resources
CNO: S. Lagina Evans, R.N., Assistant Chief Nursing Officer
Web address: www.optimhealth.com
Control: Corporation, Investor–owned, for–profit **Service:** General Medical and Surgical

Staffed Beds: 25 Admissions: 296 Census: 3 Outpatient Visits: 20547 Births: 0 Total Expense ($000): 8783 Payroll Expense ($000): 4118 Personnel: 60

GA

Hospital, Medicare Provider Number, Address, Telephone, Approval, Facility, and Physician Codes, Health Care System

★ American Hospital Association (AHA) membership
☐ The Joint Commission accreditation   ◇ DNV Healthcare Inc. accreditation

○ Healthcare Facilities Accreditation Program
△ Commission on Accreditation of Rehabilitation Facilities (CARF) accreditation

MONROE—Walton County

⊞ **CLEARVIEW REGIONAL MEDICAL CENTER (110046)**, 2151 West Spring Street, Zip 30655–3115; tel. 770/267–8461 **A**1 9 10 **F**3 11 12 13 15 29 37 40 43 45 46 51 70 76 79 81 82 93 107 108 110 111 115 119 126 129 146 147 **S** Community Health Systems, Inc., Franklin, TN
Primary Contact: James Machado, Chief Executive Officer
COO: Matt Stapleton, Chief Operating Officer
CMO: Kimberly Turner, Chief of Staff
CIO: Ed Stanley, Director Information Systems
CHR: Michele Monsrud, Director Human Resources
CNO: Sharon H. Queen, R.N., Chief Nursing Officer
Control: Corporation, Investor–owned, for–profit **Service:** General Medical and Surgical

Staffed Beds: 77 **Admissions:** 3616 **Census:** 33 **Outpatient Visits:** 44317 **Births:** 325

MONTEZUMA—Macon County

◇ **FLINT RIVER COMMUNITY HOSPITAL (110190)**, 509 Sumter Street, Zip 31063–1733, Mailing Address: P.O. Box 770, Zip 31063–2502; tel. 478/472–3100, (Nonreporting) **A**9 10 21
Primary Contact: Frank Schupp, Chief Executive Officer
CMO: Quincy Jordan, M.D., Chief of Staff
CIO: Shawn Reddick, Director Information Management
CHR: Vicki Stotts, Coordinator Human Resources
CNO: Lee Hughes, R.N., Chief Nursing Officer
Web address: www.flintriverhospital.com/
Control: Corporation, Investor–owned, for–profit **Service:** General Medical and Surgical

Staffed Beds: 49

MONTICELLO—Jasper County

JASPER MEMORIAL HOSPITAL (111303), 898 College Street, Zip 31064–1258; tel. 706/468–6411, (Total facility includes 55 beds in nursing home–type unit) **A**9 10 18 **F**11 18 29 34 40 57 59 65 77 93 97 107 111 119 128 133 146 148 **P**6 **S** Oconee Regional Health Systems, Milledgeville, GA
Primary Contact: Jan Gaston, Administrator
CFO: Stuart Abney, Controller
CHR: Laura Hammonds, Assistant Administrator
CNO: Tammy Honeycutt, R.N., Director of Nursing
Web address: www.jaspermemorialhospital.org
Control: Other not–for–profit (including NFP Corporation) **Service:** General Medical and Surgical

Staffed Beds: 67 **Admissions:** 160 **Census:** 56 **Outpatient Visits:** 10628 **Births:** 0 **Total Expense ($000):** 8911 **Payroll Expense ($000):** 4404 **Personnel:** 118

MOULTRIE—Colquitt County

⊞ ○ **COLQUITT REGIONAL MEDICAL CENTER (110105)**, 3131 South Main Street, Zip 31768–6925, Mailing Address: P.O. Box 40, Zip 31776–0040; tel. 229/985–3420 **A**1 9 10 11 19 20 **F**3 7 11 12 13 15 17 20 29 30 31 32 34 35 39 40 45 47 48 49 56 57 59 60 61 62 63 65 68 70 74 75 76 77 78 79 81 82 85 86 87 89 91 93 97 107 108 110 111 115 119 126 127 129 130 131 132 135 143 144 146 147 148
Primary Contact: James L. Matney, President and Chief Executive Officer
COO: W. Larry Sims, Chief Operating Officer
CFO: Shamb Purohit, Chief Financial Officer
CMO: Andy Wills, Medical Director
CIO: Bill Bishop, Chief Information Officer
CHR: Dawn Johns, Director Human Resources
CNO: Dena Zinker, MSN, Vice President Patient Services
Web address: www.colquittregional.com
Control: Hospital district or authority, Government, nonfederal **Service:** General Medical and Surgical

Staffed Beds: 99 **Admissions:** 4306 **Census:** 48 **Outpatient Visits:** 105462 **Births:** 528 **Total Expense ($000):** 77719 **Payroll Expense ($000):** 31948 **Personnel:** 668

TURNING POINT HOSPITAL (110209), 3015 Veterans Parkway South, Zip 31788–6705, Mailing Address: P.O. Box 1177, Zip 31776–1177; tel. 229/985–4815 **A**9 10 **F**4 5 75 87 98 130 135 143 **P**6 **S** Universal Health Services, Inc., King of Prussia, PA
Primary Contact: Ben Marion, Chief Executive Officer and Managing Director
COO: Judy Payne, R.N., Chief Operating Officer
CFO: Edwin Bennett, Controller
CHR: Jennifer Azar, Director Human Resources
CNO: Faith Connell, Director of Nursing
Web address: www.turningpointcare.com
Control: Corporation, Investor–owned, for–profit **Service:** Alcoholism and other chemical dependency

Staffed Beds: 59 **Admissions:** 3034 **Census:** 42 **Outpatient Visits:** 16966 **Births:** 0 **Total Expense ($000):** 17016 **Payroll Expense ($000):** 9316 **Personnel:** 179

NASHVILLE—Berrien County

⊞ **SOUTH GEORGIA MEDICAL CENTER BERRIEN CAMPUS (110234)**, 1221 East McPherson Avenue, Zip 31639–2326, Mailing Address: P.O. Box 665, Zip 31639–0665; tel. 229/543–7100, (Data for 183 days) **A**1 9 10 **F**3 4 15 29 34 35 38 40 45 50 56 57 59 68 75 77 78 86 87 93 98 103 107 108 110 111 114 115 119 130 133 135 146 147 148
Primary Contact: Neil W. Ginty, Administrator
Web address: www.berrienhospital.com
Control: Hospital district or authority, Government, nonfederal **Service:** General Medical and Surgical

Staffed Beds: 39 **Admissions:** 380 **Census:** 13 **Outpatient Visits:** 12033 **Births:** 0 **Total Expense ($000):** 4268 **Payroll Expense ($000):** 1970 **Personnel:** 91

NEWNAN—Coweta County

⊞ **PIEDMONT NEWNAN HOSPITAL (110229)**, 745 Poplar Road, Zip 30265–1618; tel. 770/400–1000 **A**1 9 10 **F**11 13 15 18 20 28 29 30 31 34 35 40 45 46 49 51 53 57 59 60 64 68 70 74 75 76 78 79 81 84 85 86 87 93 107 108 110 111 114 115 116 117 118 119 120 121 123 126 129 130 132 135 146 148 **S** Piedmont Healthcare, Atlanta, GA
Primary Contact: Michael Robertson, Chief Executive Officer
COO: Nathan Nipper, Vice President and Chief Operating Officer
CFO: John Miles, Chief Financial Officer
CMO: Jeffrey R. Folk, M.D., Vice President Medical Affairs and Chief Medical Officer
CIO: Henry Scott, Executive Director, Technical Services
CHR: Clay Boyles, Executive Director, Human Resources
CNO: Jason Smith, Chief Nursing Officer
Web address: www.piedmontnewnan.org
Control: Other not–for–profit (including NFP Corporation) **Service:** General Medical and Surgical

Staffed Beds: 118 **Admissions:** 6888 **Census:** 76

☐ **SOUTHEASTERN REGIONAL MEDICAL CENTER (110233)**, 600 Parkway North, Zip 30265–8000; tel. 770/400–6000, (Nonreporting) **A**1 10 **S** Cancer Treatment Centers of America, Schaumburg, IL
Primary Contact: Anne Meisner, MSN, President and Chief Executive Officer
COO: David Kent, Chief Operating Officer
CFO: Scott Walker, Chief Financial Officer
CNO: Gloria V. Barnes, MSN, Assistant Vice President Patient Care Services
Web address: www.cancercenter.com/southeastern–hospital.cfm
Control: Corporation, Investor–owned, for–profit **Service:** Cancer

Staffed Beds: 25

OCILLA—Irwin County

⊞ **IRWIN COUNTY HOSPITAL (110130)**, 710 North Irwin Avenue, Zip 31774–5011; tel. 229/468–3800, (Nonreporting) **A**1 9 10
Primary Contact: Sue Spivey, Administrator
CFO: Tami Gray, Chief Financial Officer
CMO: Ashfaq Saiyed, M.D., Medical Director
CHR: Becky Edwards, Manager Human Resources
Web address: www.irwincntyhospital.com
Control: County–Government, nonfederal **Service:** General Medical and Surgical

Staffed Beds: 64

PERRY—Houston County

⊞ **PERRY HOSPITAL (110153)**, 1120 Morningside Drive, Zip 31069–2906; tel. 478/987–3600 **A**1 9 10 **F**3 11 15 18 29 30 34 35 39 40 45 48 50 56 57 58 59 61 68 70 75 79 81 82 85 86 87 89 100 107 110 114 115 119 129 130 131 132 133 134 135 146 147 148 **P**6 **S** Houston Healthcare System, Warner Robins, GA
Primary Contact: David Campbell, Administrator
CFO: Sean Whilden, Chief Financial Officer
CMO: Jefferson Davis, M.D., Medical Director
CIO: Robert Rhodes, Director Information Systems
CHR: Michael O'Hara, Senior Executive Director
CNO: Melinda D. Hartley, R.N., Vice President Patient Care Services
Web address: www.hhc.org
Control: Other not–for–profit (including NFP Corporation) **Service:** General Medical and Surgical

Staffed Beds: 39 **Admissions:** 1572 **Census:** 21 **Outpatient Visits:** 37710 **Births:** 0 **Total Expense ($000):** 24096 **Payroll Expense ($000):** 9904 **Personnel:** 221

GA

Many Facility Codes have changed. Please refer to the AHA Guide Code Chart. © 2014 AHA Guide

QUITMAN—Brooks County

✠ **BROOKS COUNTY HOSPITAL (111332)**, 903 North Court Street,
Zip 31643–1315, Mailing Address: P.O. Box 5000, Zip 31643–5000;
tel. 229/263–4171, (Nonreporting) **A**1 9 10 18 **S** Archbold Medical Center,
Thomasville, GA
Primary Contact: Kenneth D. Rhudy, Chief Executive Officer
CFO: Skip Hightower, Chief Financial Officer
CMO: Michael Sopt, M.D., Chief of Staff
CHR: Janet Eldridge, Director Human Resources and Personnel
CNO: June Furney, R.N., Director of Nursing
Web address: www.archbold.org
Control: Other not–for–profit (including NFP Corporation) **Service:** General
Medical and Surgical

Staffed Beds: 25

REIDSVILLE—Tattnall County

★ **OPTIM MEDICAL CENTER – TATTNALL (111323)**, 247 South Main Street,
Zip 30453–4605; tel. 912/557–1000 **A**9 10 18 **F**3 8 11 15 29 34 35 37 40
45 46 50 54 59 64 74 75 77 79 81 82 85 86 87 90 91 93 94 96 97 107
111 114 119 127 129 130 131 133 146
Primary Contact: Brad Trower, Administrator
Web address: www.tattnallhospital.com
Control: Corporation, Investor–owned, for–profit **Service:** General Medical and
Surgical

Staffed Beds: 25 Admissions: 1169 Census: 8 Outpatient Visits: 26831 Births: 0 Total Expense ($000): 45476 Payroll Expense ($000): 13793 Personnel: 162

RIVERDALE—Clayton County

☐ **RIVERWOODS BEHAVIORAL HEALTH SYSTEM (114035)**, 233 Medical Center
Drive, Zip 30274–2640; tel. 770/991–8500, (Nonreporting) **A**1 5 10 **S** Acadia
Healthcare Company, Inc., Franklin, TN
Primary Contact: Kirk Kureska, Chief Executive Officer
COO: Jenifer Harcourt, Chief Operating Officer
CFO: Tricia Nelson, Chief Financial Officer
CIO: Hema Patel, Director Medical Records
CHR: Tareka Beasley, Director Human Resources
Web address: www.riverwoodsbehavioral.com
Control: Corporation, Investor–owned, for–profit **Service:** Psychiatric

Staffed Beds: 75

☒ **SOUTHERN CRESCENT HOSPITAL FOR SPECIALTY CARE (112015)**, 11
Upper Riverdale Road S.W., 6th Floor, Zip 30274–2615; tel. 770/897–7600 **A**1
10 **F**1 29 30 35 44 75 77 82 84 87 148 **S** Dubuis Health System, Houston, TX
Primary Contact: Jeff Denney, Administrator
Web address: www.christusdubuis.org/SouthernCrescentHospitalforSpecialtyCare
Control: Church–operated, Nongovernment, not–for profit **Service:** Long–Term
Acute Care hospital

Staffed Beds: 30 Admissions: 248 Census: 18 Outpatient Visits: 0 Births: 0 Total Expense ($000): 15279 Payroll Expense ($000): 3890 Personnel: 68

☐ **SOUTHERN REGIONAL MEDICAL CENTER (110165)**, 11 Upper Riverdale
Road S.W., Zip 30274–2615; tel. 770/991–8000, (Nonreporting) **A**1 2 3 5 9 10
Primary Contact: James E. Crissey, President and Chief Executive Officer
COO: Therese O. Sucher, Senior Vice President Operations
CFO: Richard G. Stovall, Senior Vice President Fiscal Services and Chief Financial
Officer
CMO: Willie Cochran, Jr., M.D., Chief of Staff
CIO: Karen Moore, Vice President Information Technology and Chief Information
Officer
CHR: Norma Adams, Director Human Resources
Web address: www.southernregional.org
Control: Other not–for–profit (including NFP Corporation) **Service:** General
Medical and Surgical

Staffed Beds: 274

ROME—Floyd County

✠ **FLOYD MEDICAL CENTER (110054)**, 304 Turner McCall Boulevard,
Zip 30165–5621, Mailing Address: P.O. Box 233, Zip 30162–0233;
tel. 706/509–5000 **A**1 2 3 5 9 10 13 19 **F**3 4 5 6 7 8 9 11 12 13 15 17 18
20 22 26 28 29 30 31 32 34 35 36 37 38 39 40 43 44 45 46 48 49 50 51
53 54 56 57 58 59 61 63 64 65 66 68 70 71 72 74 75 76 77 78 79 81 82
84 85 86 87 88 89 90 93 96 97 98 100 101 102 103 104 107 108 110 111
114 115 118 119 129 130 131 132 134 135 143 144 146 147 148
Primary Contact: Kurt Stuenkel, FACHE, President and Chief Executive Officer
COO: Warren Alston Rigas, Executive Vice President and Chief Operating Officer
CFO: Rick Sheerin, Vice President Fiscal Services
CMO: Joseph Biuso, M.D., Vice President and Chief of Medical Affairs
CIO: Jeff Buda, Chief Information Officer
CHR: Beth Bradford, Director Human Resources
CNO: Sheila Bennett, R.N., Vice President & Chief Nursing Officer
Web address: www.floyd.org
Control: Other not–for–profit (including NFP Corporation) **Service:** General
Medical and Surgical

Staffed Beds: 318 Admissions: 13995 Census: 201 Outpatient Visits: 257633 Births: 2155 Total Expense ($000): 325866 Payroll Expense ($000): 137348 Personnel: 2073

★ **KINDRED HOSPITAL ROME (112010)**, 304 Turner McCall Boulevard,
Zip 30165–5621; tel. 706/378–6800 **A**9 10 **F**1 3 29 75 82 148 **S** Kindred
Healthcare, Louisville, KY
Primary Contact: Chad Lovett, Chief Executive Officer
CFO: Julia Smith, Chief Financial Officer
CMO: Brij Singh, Medical Staff Director
CHR: Holly Murdock, Human Resources Coordinator
CNO: Jennifer Johnstone, Chief Clinical Officer
Web address: www.kindredrome.com
Control: Corporation, Investor–owned, for–profit **Service:** Long–Term Acute Care
hospital

Staffed Beds: 45 Admissions: 477 Census: 33 Outpatient Visits: 0 Births: 0

✠ **REDMOND REGIONAL MEDICAL CENTER (110168)**, 501 Redmond Road,
Zip 30165–1415, Mailing Address: P.O. Box 107001, Zip 30165–7001;
tel. 706/291–0291, (Nonreporting) **A**1 2 9 10 19 **S** HCA, Nashville, TN
Primary Contact: John Quinlivan, Chief Executive Officer
COO: Patrick Trammell, Chief Operating Officer
CFO: Ken Metteauer, Chief Financial Officer
CMO: Julie Coffman Barnes, M.D., Chief Medical Officer
CIO: Brad Treglown, Director Information Systems
CHR: Patsy Adams, Vice President Human Resources
CNO: Lisa Wallace, R.N., Chief Nursing Officer
Web address: www.redmondregional.com
Control: Corporation, Investor–owned, for–profit **Service:** General Medical and
Surgical

Staffed Beds: 230

SPECIALTY HOSPITAL See Kindred Hospital Rome

ROSWELL—Fulton County

✠ **NORTH FULTON REGIONAL HOSPITAL (110198)**, 3000 Hospital Boulevard,
Zip 30076–3899; tel. 770/751–2500, (Nonreporting) **A**1 2 9 10 **S** TENET
Healthcare Corporation, Dallas, TX
Primary Contact: Deborah C. Keel, Chief Executive Officer
COO: Teresa C. Urquhart, Chief Operating Officer
CFO: Lyra Howalt, Chief Financial Officer
CMO: Karim Godamunne, M.D., Chief Medical Officer
CHR: Susan Brown, Chief Human Resources Officer
CNO: Nancy Melcher, Chief Nursing Officer
Web address: www.northfultonregional.com
Control: Corporation, Investor–owned, for–profit **Service:** General Medical and
Surgical

Staffed Beds: 196

GA

Hospital, Medicare Provider Number, Address, Telephone, Approval, Facility, and Physician Codes, Health Care System

★ American Hospital Association (AHA) membership
☐ The Joint Commission accreditation
◇ DNV Healthcare Inc. accreditation
◯ Healthcare Facilities Accreditation Program
△ Commission on Accreditation of Rehabilitation Facilities (CARF) accreditation

SAINT MARYS—Camden County

☒ SOUTHEAST GEORGIA HEALTH SYSTEM CAMDEN CAMPUS (110146), 2000 Dan Proctor Drive, Zip 31558–3810; tel. 912/576–6200 **A**1 9 10 20 **F**3 11 13 15 29 30 31 34 35 40 45 46 47 48 49 50 54 57 59 64 68 70 71 75 77 78 79 81 85 86 87 93 94 96 107 108 110 111 114 119 120 129 130 131 132 146 **P**5 **S** Southeast Georgia Health System, Brunswick, GA
Primary Contact: Howard W. Sepp, Jr., FACHE, Vice President and Administrator
CFO: Michael D. Scherneck, Executive Vice President
CMO: Colonel Thomas C. Whitesell, Jr., MSC, Chief of Staff
CIO: Chuck Bumgardner, Director
CHR: Patrick D. Ebri, Ph.D., Vice President Human Resources
Web address: www.sghs.org
Control: City-County, Government, nonfederal **Service:** General Medical and Surgical

Staffed Beds: 40 **Admissions:** 1921 **Census:** 18 **Outpatient Visits:** 80079 **Births:** 758 **Total Expense ($000):** 38294 **Payroll Expense ($000):** 14327 **Personnel:** 281

SAINT SIMONS ISLAND—Glynn County

☐ SAINT SIMONS BY-THE-SEA HOSPITAL (114016), 2927 Demere Road, Zip 31522–1620; tel. 912/638–1999, (Nonreporting) **A**1 9 10 **S** Universal Health Services, Inc., King of Prussia, PA
Primary Contact: Monica Cook, Interim Chief Executive Officer
CMO: Kim Masters, M.D., Medical Director
CIO: Chisty Mosely, Director Information Management
Web address: www.ssbythesea.com
Control: Corporation, Investor-owned, for-profit **Service:** Psychiatric

Staffed Beds: 101

SANDERSVILLE—Washington County

☐ WASHINGTON COUNTY REGIONAL MEDICAL CENTER (110086), 610 Sparta Road, Zip 31082–1860, Mailing Address: P.O. Box 636, Zip 31082–0636; tel. 478/240–2000, (Nonreporting) **A**1 9 10 20
Primary Contact: Jimmy Childre, Jr., Interim Chief Executive Officer
CFO: Cythia Parker, Fiscal Director
CMO: Robert Wright, M.D., Chief of Staff
CHR: Gayle Prince, Director Human Resources
Web address: www.wcrmc.com
Control: Hospital district or authority, Government, nonfederal **Service:** General Medical and Surgical

Staffed Beds: 116

SAVANNAH—Chatham County

☒ △ CANDLER HOSPITAL (110024), 5353 Reynolds Street, Zip 31405–6015; tel. 912/819–6000, (Total facility includes 11 beds in nursing home–type unit) **A**1 7 9 10 **F**2 3 11 13 15 18 20 29 30 31 32 34 35 36 37 38 39 40 44 45 46 47 48 49 50 53 54 57 58 59 60 61 64 65 68 70 71 73 74 75 76 77 78 80 81 82 84 85 86 87 89 90 93 94 96 107 108 110 111 115 117 118 119 120 121 123 124 126 128 129 130 131 132 135 146 147 148
Primary Contact: Paul P. Hinchey, President and Chief Executive Officer
CFO: Gregory J. Schaack, CPA, Vice President and Chief Financial Officer
CMO: James Scott, M.D., Vice President Medical Affairs
CIO: George Evans, Vice President and Chief Information Officer
CHR: Don Stubbs, Vice President Human Resources
Web address: www.sjchs.org
Control: Church-operated, Nongovernment, not-for profit **Service:** General Medical and Surgical

Staffed Beds: 287 **Admissions:** 12534 **Census:** 199 **Outpatient Visits:** 339378 **Births:** 3021 **Total Expense ($000):** 227407 **Payroll Expense ($000):** 89738 **Personnel:** 1652

☐ COASTAL HARBOR TREATMENT CENTER (114008), 1150 Cornell Avenue, Zip 31406–2702; tel. 912/354–3911, (Nonreporting) **A**1 9 10 **S** Universal Health Services, Inc., King of Prussia, PA
Primary Contact: Ray Heckerman, Chief Executive Officer and Managing Director
COO: Ray Heckerman, Chief Executive Officer and Managing Director
CFO: Brad Lavoie, Chief Financial Officer
CMO: Reemon Bishara, M.D., Medical Director
CHR: Kellie Carlson, Director Human Resources
CNO: Jillisa Thornton, Director of Nursing
Web address: www.coastalharbor.com
Control: Corporation, Investor-owned, for-profit **Service:** Hospital unit within an institution for the mentally retarded

Staffed Beds: 182

GEORGE AND MARIE BACKUS CHILDREN'S HOSPITAL See Memorial Children's Hospital

☐ GEORGIA REGIONAL HOSPITAL AT SAVANNAH (114028), 1915 Eisenhower Drive, Zip 31406–5098; tel. 912/356–2011, (Nonreporting) **A**1 10
Primary Contact: Andy Mannich, Regional Administrator
COO: Thomas F. Kurtz, Jr., Chief Operating Officer
CFO: Janet Edenfield, Director Financial Services
CMO: Donald Manning, M.D., Clinical Director
CHR: Jamekia Powers, Assistant Director Human Resources
Web address: www.garegionalsavannah.com
Control: State-Government, nonfederal **Service:** Psychiatric

Staffed Beds: 105

☒ △ MEMORIAL HEALTH (110036), 4700 Waters Avenue, Zip 31404–6283, Mailing Address: P.O. Box 23089, Zip 31403–3089; tel. 912/350–8000, (Includes MEMORIAL CHILDREN'S HOSPITAL, 4700 Waters Avenue, Zip 31404–6220, Mailing Address: PO Box 23089, Zip 31403–3089; tel. 912/350–1543) **A**1 2 3 5 7 8 10 **F**3 8 11 12 13 14 15 17 18 19 20 22 24 26 28 29 30 31 32 34 35 36 37 39 40 41 43 44 45 46 49 50 52 53 54 55 56 57 58 59 60 61 64 65 66 68 70 71 72 73 74 75 76 77 78 79 80 81 82 83 84 85 86 87 88 89 90 92 93 96 97 98 100 101 102 103 104 107 110 111 115 117 118 119 120 121 122 123 124 126 129 130 131 132 135 143 144 146 147 148 **P**6
Primary Contact: Margaret Gill, Chief Executive Officer
COO: Mary Chatman, Ph.D., Chief Operating Officer
CFO: Laura Dow, Vice President, Finance
CMO: Ramon V. Meguiar, M.D., Chief Medical Officer
CIO: Robert M. Tynan, Chief Information Officer
CHR: Jonathan Small, Vice President, Human Resources
CNO: Mary Chatman, Ph.D., Chief Nursing Officer
Web address: www.memorialhealth.com
Control: Other not-for-profit (including NFP Corporation) **Service:** General Medical and Surgical

Staffed Beds: 529 **Admissions:** 26194 **Census:** 410 **Outpatient Visits:** 246281 **Births:** 2656 **Total Expense ($000):** 451105 **Payroll Expense ($000):** 170050 **Personnel:** 3656

☒ SELECT SPECIALTY HOSPITAL–SAVANNAH (112011), 5353 Reynolds Street, 4 South, Zip 31405–6015; tel. 912/819–7972, (Nonreporting) **A**1 9 10 **S** Select Medical Corporation, Mechanicsburg, PA
Primary Contact: James H. Rogers, FACHE, Chief Executive Officer
Web address: www.selectspecialtyhospitals.com/company/locations/savannah.aspx
Control: Corporation, Investor-owned, for-profit **Service:** Long-Term Acute Care hospital

Staffed Beds: 36

ST. JOSEPH'S CANDLER HOSPITAL See Candler Hospital

☐ △ ST. JOSEPH'S HOSPITAL (110043), 11705 Mercy Boulevard, Zip 31419–1791; tel. 912/819–4100, (Total facility includes 11 beds in nursing home–type unit) **A**1 2 7 9 10 **F**3 11 15 17 18 20 22 24 26 28 29 30 34 35 36 37 38 39 40 41 42 44 45 49 50 56 57 58 59 60 61 65 68 70 74 75 77 79 80 81 82 84 85 86 87 90 93 94 96 107 108 110 114 115 119 126 128 130 131 132 135 146 148
Primary Contact: Paul P. Hinchey, President and Chief Executive Officer
COO: Kyle McCann, Chief Operating Officer
CFO: Gregory J. Schaack, CPA, Vice President and Chief Financial Officer
CMO: James Scott, M.D., Vice President Medical Affairs
CIO: Nolan Henessee, Vice President and Chief Information Officer
CHR: Steve Pound, Vice President Human Resources
CNO: Sherry Danello, MSN, Vice President Patient Care Services
Web address: www.sjchs.org
Control: Church-operated, Nongovernment, not-for profit **Service:** General Medical and Surgical

Staffed Beds: 237 **Admissions:** 11198 **Census:** 173 **Outpatient Visits:** 139381 **Births:** 0 **Total Expense ($000):** 173783 **Payroll Expense ($000):** 63634 **Personnel:** 1193

SMYRNA—Cobb County

☒ EMORY–ADVENTIST HOSPITAL (110183), 3949 South Cobb Drive S.E., Zip 30080–6300; tel. 770/434–0710, (Nonreporting) **A**1 9 10 **S** Adventist Health System Sunbelt Health Care Corporation, Altamonte Springs, FL
Primary Contact: Dennis Kiley, President
COO: Ed Moyer, Chief Operating Officer
CFO: Carol Hazen, Vice President Finance
CHR: Jamie Luce, Director Human Resources
Web address: www.emoryadventist.org
Control: Church-operated, Nongovernment, not-for profit **Service:** General Medical and Surgical

Staffed Beds: 54

Many Facility Codes have changed. Please refer to the AHA Guide Code Chart. © 2014 AHA Guide

✠ **RIDGEVIEW INSTITUTE (114012)**, 3995 South Cobb Drive S.E.,
Zip 30080–6397; tel. 770/434–4567 **A**1 5 9 10 **F**4 29 35 38 75 87 98 99
100 101 103 104 105 130 132 147 **P**8
Primary Contact: Paul Hackman, Chief Executive Officer
CFO: Jerry Magnison, Chief Financial Officer
CMO: Thomas Bradford Johns, M.D., Medical Director
CIO: Lynn Leger, Director Information Systems
CHR: Betty Sonderman, Manager Human Resources
Web address: www.ridgeviewinstitute.com
Control: Other not–for–profit (including NFP Corporation) **Service:** Psychiatric

Staffed Beds: 102 **Admissions:** 4194 **Census:** 66 **Outpatient Visits:** 41584
Births: 0 **Total Expense ($000):** 31611 **Payroll Expense ($000):** 16864
Personnel: 338

SNELLVILLE—Gwinnett County

✠ **EASTSIDE MEDICAL CENTER (110192)**, 1700 Medical Way, Zip 30078–2195;
tel. 770/979–0200 **A**1 2 9 10 **F**3 11 13 15 18 20 22 26 28 29 30 31 34 37
39 40 41 45 49 50 54 56 57 59 64 70 72 73 74 75 76 77 78 79 80 81 82
85 87 90 91 93 94 96 98 101 103 107 108 110 111 112 114 115 118 119
126 129 130 131 132 146 147 148 **S** HCA, Nashville, TN
Primary Contact: Kimberly Ryan, Chief Executive Officer
COO: Callie Andrews, Chief Operating Officer
CMO: Michael O'Neill, M.D., Chief Medical Officer
CIO: Pattie Page, Director Marketing and Public Relations
CHR: Nancy Dwyer, Vice President Human Resources
Web address: www.eastsidemedical.com
Control: Corporation, Investor–owned, for–profit **Service:** General Medical and
Surgical

Staffed Beds: 294 **Admissions:** 10567 **Census:** 152 **Outpatient Visits:**
129727 **Births:** 1473 **Total Expense ($000):** 155506 **Payroll Expense**
($000): 56473 **Personnel:** 940

SPRINGFIELD—Effingham County

✠ **EFFINGHAM HOSPITAL (111306)**, 459 Highway 119 South, Zip 31329–3021,
Mailing Address: P.O. Box 386, Zip 31329–0386; tel. 912/754–6451, (Total
facility includes 105 beds in nursing home–type unit) **A**1 9 10 18 **F**3 6 11 15 18
29 32 34 35 40 43 45 49 50 54 56 57 64 74 77 79 81 85 86 97 107
110 111 114 119 127 128 130 131 132 133 135 146 147 148 **P**6
Primary Contact: Norma J. Morgan, Chief Executive Officer
COO: Tammy Mims, Chief Operating Officer
CMO: James Cornwell, M.D., Chief Medical Staff
CIO: Mary Pizzino, Chief Information Officer
CHR: Vicky Little, Director Human Resources
CNO: Marie Livingstone, R.N., Chief Nursing Officer
Web address: www.effinghamhospital.org
Control: Hospital district or authority, Government, nonfederal **Service:** General
Medical and Surgical

Staffed Beds: 130 **Admissions:** 812 **Census:** 109 **Outpatient Visits:** 53467
Births: 0 **Total Expense ($000):** 35445 **Payroll Expense ($000):** 14375
Personnel: 345

STATESBORO—Bulloch County

✠ **EAST GEORGIA REGIONAL MEDICAL CENTER (110075)**, 1499 Fair Road,
Zip 30458–1683, Mailing Address: P.O. Box 1048, Zip 30459–1048;
tel. 912/486–1000 **A**1 9 10 19 **F**3 11 13 15 18 20 22 26 29 35 37 40 45 46
47 48 49 51 54 57 59 60 64 67 68 70 74 75 76 77 78 79 81 82 85 87 89
93 107 108 110 111 112 114 115 116 117 118 119 126 129 132 145 146
147 148 **P**5 **S** Community Health Systems, Inc., Franklin, TN
Primary Contact: Robert F. Bigley, President and Chief Executive Officer
CFO: Elmer Polite, Chief Financial Officer
CMO: Eric Chand, Chief of Staff
CIO: Conan Stuart, Director Information Services
CHR: Michael Black, Director Human Resources
CNO: Pamela Harrison, R.N., Chief Nursing Officer
Web address: www.eastgeorgiaregional.com
Control: Corporation, Investor–owned, for–profit **Service:** General Medical and
Surgical

Staffed Beds: 149 **Admissions:** 7715 **Census:** 79 **Personnel:** 579

WILLINGWAY HOSPITAL, 311 Jones Mill Road, Zip 30458–4765;
tel. 912/764–6236 **A**9 **F**4 5
Primary Contact: Barbara S. Reid, Chief Executive Officer
CMO: Robert W. Mooney, M.D., Medical Director
Web address: www.willingway.com
Control: Corporation, Investor–owned, for–profit **Service:** Alcoholism and other
chemical dependency

Staffed Beds: 40 **Admissions:** 401 **Census:** 29 **Outpatient Visits:** 6525
Births: 0 **Total Expense ($000):** 7673 **Payroll Expense ($000):** 3760
Personnel: 94

STOCKBRIDGE—Henry County

✠ **HENRY MEDICAL CENTER (110191)**, 1133 Eagle's Landing Parkway,
Zip 30281–5099; tel. 678/604–1000 **A**1 2 9 10 **F**3 8 11 13 15 18 20 22 26
28 29 30 31 34 35 37 40 45 46 49 53 54 57 59 61 64 70 72 74 75 76 77
78 79 81 82 85 86 87 93 100 102 107 108 110 111 114 115 118 119 124
130 132 135 144 146 147 148 **P**3 **S** Piedmont Healthcare, Atlanta, GA
Primary Contact: Charles F. Scott, President and Chief Executive Officer
COO: Jeff Cooper, Chief Operating Officer
CFO: Sherry Henderson, Chief Financial Officer
CMO: Jagdeep Singh, M.D., Chief Medical Officer
CHR: Virgil Holder, Human Resources Business Partner
CNO: Frances Marthone, R.N., Chief Nursing Officer
Web address: www.henrymedical.com
Control: Other not–for–profit (including NFP Corporation) **Service:** General
Medical and Surgical

Staffed Beds: 222 **Admissions:** 12099 **Census:** 150 **Outpatient Visits:**
146195 **Births:** 2087 **Total Expense ($000):** 178024 **Payroll Expense**
($000): 65685 **Personnel:** 1078

SWAINSBORO—Emanuel County

◇ **EMANUEL MEDICAL CENTER (110109)**, 117 Kite Road, Zip 30401–3231,
Mailing Address: P.O. Box 879, Zip 30401–0879; tel. 478/289–1100,
(Nonreporting) **A**9 10 20 21
Primary Contact: Mel Pyne, Chief Executive Officer
CFO: Rhonda Durden, Chief Financial Officer
CMO: Cedric Porter, M.D., President Medical Staff
CIO: Dave Flanders, Director Information Technology Systems
CHR: Ellen Boyd, Director Human Resources
Web address: www.emanuelmedical.org
Control: Hospital district or authority, Government, nonfederal **Service:** General
Medical and Surgical

Staffed Beds: 98

SYLVANIA—Screven County

★ **SCREVEN COUNTY HOSPITAL (111312)**, 215 Mims Road, Zip 30467–2097;
tel. 912/564–7426 **A**9 10 18 **F**3 11 15 29 34 35 40 45 50 59 64 65 75 77
79 81 82 90 93 97 107 119 133 146
Primary Contact: Robert R. Sellers, Administrator
CFO: Marsha Carroll, Director Financial Services
CIO: Rob Snipes, Chief Information Officer
CHR: Natalie Peterson, Human Resources Director
CNO: S. Lagina Evans, R.N., Assistant Chief Nursing Officer
Web address: www.optimhealth.com
Control: Corporation, Investor–owned, for–profit **Service:** General Medical and
Surgical

Staffed Beds: 25 **Admissions:** 297 **Census:** 4 **Outpatient Visits:** 15733
Births: 0 **Total Expense ($000):** 9784 **Payroll Expense ($000):** 5016
Personnel: 71

SYLVESTER—Worth County

★ ◇ **PHOEBE WORTH MEDICAL CENTER (111328)**, 807 South Isabella Street,
Zip 31791–7554, Mailing Address: P.O. Box 545, Zip 31791–0545;
tel. 229/776–6961 **A**9 10 18 21 **F**7 29 34 40 59 64 66 75 93 107 114 119
127 133 146 **P**6 **S** Phoebe Putney Health System, Albany, GA
Primary Contact: Kim Gilman, Chief Executive Officer
CFO: Candace Guarnieri, Chief Financial Officer
CMO: Natu M. Patel, M.D., Chief of Staff
CHR: Clay Jones, Regional Director of Human Resources
Web address: www.phoebeputney.com
Control: Other not–for–profit (including NFP Corporation) **Service:** General
Medical and Surgical

Staffed Beds: 16 **Admissions:** 567 **Census:** 15 **Outpatient Visits:** 15003
Births: 0 **Total Expense ($000):** 16847 **Payroll Expense ($000):** 6888
Personnel: 162

GA

THOMASTON—Upson County

★ ◇ **UPSON REGIONAL MEDICAL CENTER (110002)**, 801 West Gordon Street, Zip 30286–3426, Mailing Address: P.O. Box 1059, Zip 30286–0027; tel. 706/647–8111 **A**9 10 19 20 21 **F**3 11 13 15 28 29 30 31 34 35 36 40 45 46 49 50 57 59 61 64 70 75 76 78 79 80 81 82 85 86 87 89 107 108 110 111 114 115 118 119 124 130 132 133 135 148 **P**6 **S** HealthTech Management Services, Brentwood, TN
Primary Contact: David L. Castleberry, FACHE, Chief Executive Officer
CFO: John Williams, Chief Financial Officer
CIO: Douglas Thompson, Chief Information Officer
CHR: Rich Williams, Director Human Resources
CNO: Marilyn Ray, MSN, Chief Nursing Officer
Web address: www.urmc.org
Control: Other not-for-profit (including NFP Corporation) **Service:** General Medical and Surgical

Staffed Beds: 74 **Admissions:** 3387 **Census:** 33 **Outpatient Visits:** 79566 **Births:** 401 **Total Expense ($000):** 59815 **Payroll Expense ($000):** 23410 **Personnel:** 502

THOMASVILLE—Thomas County

✚ **JOHN D. ARCHBOLD MEMORIAL HOSPITAL (110038)**, 915 Gordon Avenue, Zip 31792–6614, Mailing Address: P.O. Box 1018, Zip 31799–1018; tel. 229/228–2000, (Nonreporting) **A**1 2 9 10 19 **S** Archbold Medical Center, Thomasville, GA
Primary Contact: J. Perry Mustian, President and Chief Executive Officer
CFO: Skip Hightower, Senior Vice President and Chief Financial Officer
CIO: Tracy Gray, Senior Vice President Information Services
CHR: Zach Wheeler, Senior Vice President Human Resources
CNO: Amy Griffin, Vice President Patient Care Services
Web address: www.archbold.org
Control: Other not-for-profit (including NFP Corporation) **Service:** General Medical and Surgical

Staffed Beds: 328

SOUTHWESTERN STATE HOSPITAL (114021), Pine Tree Boulevard, Zip 31792, Mailing Address: P.O. Box 1378, Zip 31799–1378; tel. 229/227–2833, (Nonreporting) **A**10
Primary Contact: Hilary Hoo–You, Regional Administrator
COO: Susie Oates, Assistant Superintendent for Administration
CFO: Charles Barton, Business Manager
CMO: Joseph B. LeRoy, M.D., Clinical Director
CIO: Loma Owens, Data Manager
CHR: Clifton Mitchell, Manager Human Resources
Web address: www.swsh.org
Control: State–Government, nonfederal **Service:** Psychiatric

Staffed Beds: 236

THOMSON—McDuffie County

★ ◇ **UNIVERSITY HOSPITAL MCDUFFIE (110111)**, 521 Hill Street S.W., Zip 30824–2199; tel. 706/595–1411 **A**9 10 21 **F**3 7 11 15 29 30 40 45 50 57 59 64 68 79 81 87 107 110 114 119 129 130 132 146 148 **S** University Health Care System, Augusta, GA
Primary Contact: Sandra I. McVicker, R.N., MSN, President
CFO: Dave Belkoski, Chief Financial Officer
CIO: Lisa Sanderlin, Chief Information Officer
CHR: Belinda H. Campbell, Director Human Resources, Legal Compliance and Risk Management
Web address: www.uh.org
Control: Other not–for–profit (including NFP Corporation) **Service:** General Medical and Surgical

Staffed Beds: 25 **Admissions:** 531 **Census:** 5 **Outpatient Visits:** 30394 **Births:** 0 **Total Expense ($000):** 14468 **Payroll Expense ($000):** 6193 **Personnel:** 82

TIFTON—Tift County

✚ **TIFT REGIONAL MEDICAL CENTER (110095)**, 901 East 18th Street, Zip 31794–3648, Mailing Address: Drawer 747, Zip 31793–0747; tel. 229/382–7120, (Total facility includes 15 beds in nursing home–type unit) **A**1 2 9 10 19 **F**3 8 9 11 12 13 15 18 20 22 26 28 29 31 34 35 40 45 47 49 50 54 57 59 60 63 64 68 70 74 75 76 77 78 79 81 82 84 85 86 87 89 92 93 97 107 108 110 111 114 119 120 121 123 126 127 128 129 130 132 135 143 144 146 147 148 **P**6 **S** Tift Regional Health System, Tifton, GA
Primary Contact: William T. Richardson, President and Chief Executive Officer
COO: Christopher Dorman, Senior Vice President/Chief Operating Officer
CFO: Dennis L. Crum, Senior Vice President and Chief Financial Officer
CMO: William Guest, Senior Vice President and Chief Medical Officer
CIO: Guy McAllister, Vice President and Chief Information Officer
CHR: Ellen Eaton, Vice President Human Resources
CNO: Carol Smith, R.N., Vice President Patient Care and Chief Nursing Officer
Web address: www.tiftregional.com
Control: Hospital district or authority, Government, nonfederal **Service:** General Medical and Surgical

Staffed Beds: 191 **Admissions:** 10346 **Census:** 128 **Outpatient Visits:** 171725 **Births:** 1077 **Total Expense ($000):** 258606 **Payroll Expense ($000):** 98364 **Personnel:** 1777

TOCCOA—Stephens County

✚ **STEPHENS COUNTY HOSPITAL (110032)**, 163 Hospital Drive, Zip 30577–6820; tel. 706/282–4200, (Total facility includes 92 beds in nursing home–type unit) **A**1 9 10 **F**3 7 11 13 15 28 30 34 35 40 51 57 59 60 64 68 70 75 76 77 79 81 85 86 89 93 107 110 111 115 119 125 129 130 146 148
Primary Contact: Edward C. Gambrell, Jr., Administrator
CFO: Jeff Laird, Controller
CHR: Diane Hardeman, Director Personnel
CNO: Faye M. Taylor, R.N., Director of Nursing
Web address: www.stephenscountyhospital.com
Control: Hospital district or authority, Government, nonfederal **Service:** General Medical and Surgical

Staffed Beds: 188 **Admissions:** 2208 **Census:** 110 **Outpatient Visits:** 37362 **Births:** 463 **Total Expense ($000):** 48212 **Payroll Expense ($000):** 22289 **Personnel:** 435

VALDOSTA—Lowndes County

GREENLEAF CENTER (114036), 2209 Pineview Drive, Zip 31602–7316; tel. 229/247–4357, (Nonreporting) **A**10 **S** Acadia Healthcare Company, Inc., Franklin, TN
Primary Contact: Mike Ham, Chief Executive Officer
Web address: www.greenleafcounseling.net
Control: Corporation, Investor–owned, for–profit **Service:** Psychiatric

Staffed Beds: 50

✚ **SOUTH GEORGIA MEDICAL CENTER (110122)**, 2501 North Patterson Street, Zip 31602–1735, Mailing Address: P.O. Box 1727, Zip 31603–1727; tel. 229/333–1000, (Includes SMITH NORTHVIEW HOSPITAL, 4280 North Valdosta Road, Zip 31602, Mailing Address: P.O. Box 10010, Zip 31604; tel. 229/671–2000; Leonard Carter, Campus Administrator) **A**1 2 9 10 19 **F**3 7 8 11 13 15 17 18 19 20 22 24 26 28 29 30 31 32 34 35 37 38 39 40 45 46 47 49 50 51 54 57 59 60 61 64 68 70 71 72 73 74 75 76 77 78 79 81 82 84 85 86 87 89 90 95 96 97 107 108 110 111 113 114 115 117 118 119 120 121 123 124 126 129 130 131 132 134 135 143 144 146 147 148 **P**6
Primary Contact: Randy Sauls, Chief Executive Officer and Administrator
COO: Andrew Flemer, Chief Operating Officer
CFO: Raymond A. Snead, Jr., FACHE, Interim Chief Financial Officer
CMO: Kimberly Megow, M.D., Chief Medical Officer
CIO: Bob Foster, Chief Information Officer
CHR: Johnny Percy Ball, III, Assistant Administrator Human Resources
Web address: www.sgmc.org
Control: Hospital district or authority, Government, nonfederal **Service:** General Medical and Surgical

Staffed Beds: 340 **Admissions:** 15495 **Census:** 200 **Outpatient Visits:** 288568 **Births:** 2169 **Total Expense ($000):** 306213 **Payroll Expense ($000):** 103705 **Personnel:** 2640

VIDALIA—Toombs County

✚ **MEADOWS REGIONAL MEDICAL CENTER (110128)**, One Meadows Parkway, Zip 30474–8759, Mailing Address: P.O. Box 1048, Zip 30475–1048; tel. 912/535–5555 **A**1 9 10 20 **F**11 13 15 18 20 22 29 30 31 34 35 37 40 45 46 47 50 51 53 54 57 59 60 62 64 68 70 74 75 76 77 78 79 81 85 86 87 93 97 107 108 110 111 115 118 119 124 127 129 130 131 132 146 147 148
Primary Contact: Alan Kent, Chief Executive Officer
COO: Shirley Hoskins, Chief Operating Officer
CFO: John Cornell, Vice President Finance
CIO: Charles Bondurant, Chief Information Officer
Web address: www.meadowsregional.org
Control: Other not-for-profit (including NFP Corporation) **Service:** General Medical and Surgical

Staffed Beds: 57 **Admissions:** 4579 **Census:** 44 **Outpatient Visits:** 71689 **Births:** 750 **Total Expense ($000):** 89556 **Payroll Expense ($000):** 30198 **Personnel:** 609

VILLA RICA—Carroll County

✚ **TANNER MEDICAL CENTER–VILLA RICA (110015)**, 601 Dallas Road, Zip 30180–1202, Mailing Address: P.O. Box 638, Zip 30180–0638; tel. 770/456–3000, (Nonreporting) **A**1 9 10 **S** Tanner Health System, Carrollton, GA
Primary Contact: Taylor Powers, Administrator
Web address: www.tanner.org
Control: Other not-for-profit (including NFP Corporation) **Service:** General Medical and Surgical

Staffed Beds: 39

GA

Many Facility Codes have changed. Please refer to the AHA Guide Code Chart. © 2014 AHA Guide

WARM SPRINGS—Meriwether County

☐ **ROOSEVELT WARM SPRINGS LTAC HOSPITAL (112000)**, 6135 Roosevelt Highway, Zip 31830–2757; tel. 706/655–5000 **A**1 10 **F**1 29 30 119 148
Primary Contact: David L. Mork, Jr., FACHE, Chief Executive Officer
CFO: Laura Stokes, Director Financial Services
CMO: W. Burton McDaniel, Jr., M.D., Physician Executive
CHR: Laura Stokes, Director Human Resources
Web address: www.grhealth.org
Control: State–Government, nonfederal **Service:** Long–Term Acute Care hospital

Staffed Beds: 20 **Admissions:** 159 **Census:** 12 **Births:** 0

☐ **ROOSEVELT WARM SPRINGS REHABILITATION AND SPECIALTY HOSPITALS (113028)**, 6135 Roosevelt Highway, Zip 31830–2757, Mailing Address: P.O. Box 280, Zip 31830–0280; tel. 706/655–5515 **A**1 9 10 **F**90 91 107 119 146 148
Primary Contact: David L. Mork, Jr., FACHE, Chief Executive Officer
CFO: Laura Stokes, Director Financial Services
CMO: Burton McDaniel, M.D., Medical Director
CIO: Christen Carter, Director Public Relations
CHR: Laura Stokes, Director Human Resources
Web address: www.rooseveltrehab.org
Control: State–Government, nonfederal **Service:** Rehabilitation

Staffed Beds: 32 **Admissions:** 396 **Census:** 15 **Outpatient Visits:** 0 **Births:** 0

✦ **WARM SPRINGS MEDICAL CENTER (111316)**, 5995 Spring Street, Zip 31830–2149, Mailing Address: P.O. Box 8, Zip 31830–0008; tel. 706/655–3331, (Total facility includes 79 beds in nursing home–type unit) **A**1 9 10 18 **F**3 8 15 29 30 40 45 57 59 75 79 81 93 107 111 114 119 128 130 133 146
Primary Contact: Karen Daniel, Chief Executive Officer
CFO: Patrick Flynn, Chief Financial Officer
CMO: Alan Thompson, M.D., President Medical Staff
CIO: Milo Varnadoe, Director Information Systems
CHR: Theresa Passarelli, Human Resources Generalist
CNO: Lynda Ligon, Chief Nursing Officer
Web address: www.warmspringsmc.org
Control: Hospital district or authority, Government, nonfederal **Service:** General Medical and Surgical

Staffed Beds: 97 **Admissions:** 324 **Census:** 80 **Outpatient Visits:** 18314 **Births:** 0 **Total Expense ($000):** 12242 **Payroll Expense ($000):** 5565 **Personnel:** 122

WARNER ROBINS—Houston County

✦ **HOUSTON MEDICAL CENTER (110069)**, 1601 Watson Boulevard, Zip 31093–3431, Mailing Address: P.O. Box 2886, Zip 31099–2886; tel. 478/922–4281 **A**1 9 10 **F**3 11 13 15 18 20 22 28 29 30 31 34 35 38 39 40 45 48 49 50 51 54 56 57 58 59 60 61 64 68 70 73 75 76 79 81 82 85 86 87 89 98 100 107 108 110 111 114 115 117 118 119 129 130 131 132 134 135 144 146 147 148 **P**6 **S** Houston Healthcare System, Warner Robins, GA
Primary Contact: Cary Martin, Chief Executive Officer
CFO: Sean Whilden, Chief Financial Officer
CIO: George Curtis, Chief Information Officer
CHR: Michael O'Hara, Senior Executive Director Human Resources
Web address: www.hhc.org
Control: Other not–for–profit (including NFP Corporation) **Service:** General Medical and Surgical

Staffed Beds: 237 **Admissions:** 15038 **Census:** 190 **Outpatient Visits:** 239912 **Births:** 2115 **Total Expense ($000):** 205300 **Payroll Expense ($000):** 83336 **Personnel:** 1915

WASHINGTON—Wilkes County

☐ **WILLS MEMORIAL HOSPITAL (111325)**, 120 Gordon Street, Zip 30673–1602, Mailing Address: P.O. Box 370, Zip 30673–0370; tel. 706/678–2151, (Nonreporting) **A**1 9 10 18
Primary Contact: Jane Echols, Chief Executive Officer
CFO: Tracie Burriss, Chief Financial Officer
CMO: Robert J. Williams, M.D., Chief Medical Staff
CIO: Reed Hawkes, Chief Information Officer
CHR: Tom Urban, Director Human Resources
CNO: Ann Harrison, R.N., Director of Nursing
Web address: www.willsmemorialhospital.com
Control: Hospital district or authority, Government, nonfederal **Service:** General Medical and Surgical

Staffed Beds: 25

WAYCROSS—Ware County

✦ **MAYO CLINIC HEALTH SYSTEM IN WAYCROSS (110003)**, 410 Darling Avenue, Zip 31501–6357, Mailing Address: P.O. Box 139, Zip 31502–0139; tel. 912/283–3030, (Nonreporting) **A**1 2 3 5 9 10 19 20 **S** Mayo Clinic, Rochester, MN
Primary Contact: Kenneth Calamia, Chair and Chief Executive Officer
COO: Mary Hoffman, Chief Administrative Officer and Chief Financial Officer
CFO: Mary Hoffman, Chief Administrative Officer and Chief Financial Officer
CIO: Barry Rudd, Chief Information Officer
CHR: Brigitte Churchill, Director of Human Resources
CNO: Holli Sweat, Associate Administrator and Chief Nursing Officer
Web address: www.mayoclinichealthsystem.org
Control: Other not–for–profit (including NFP Corporation) **Service:** General Medical and Surgical

Staffed Beds: 198

WAYNESBORO—Burke County

☐ **BURKE MEDICAL CENTER (110113)**, 351 Liberty Street, Zip 30830–9686; tel. 706/554–4435 **A**1 9 10 **F**11 14 29 30 34 35 45 50 57 68 75 79 81 82 107 110 119 130 133 135 148
Primary Contact: Douglas C. Keir, Interim Chief Executive Officer
CFO: Dianne Stewart, Controller
CHR: Danette Highsmith, Director Human Resources
Web address: www.burkemedical.net
Control: Hospital district or authority, Government, nonfederal **Service:** General Medical and Surgical

Staffed Beds: 40 **Admissions:** 515 **Census:** 4 **Outpatient Visits:** 17484 **Births:** 0 **Total Expense ($000):** 11807 **Payroll Expense ($000):** 3974 **Personnel:** 120

WINDER—Barrow County

✦ **BARROW REGIONAL MEDICAL CENTER (110045)**, 316 North Broad Street, Zip 30680–2150, Mailing Address: P.O. Box 688, Zip 30680–0688; tel. 770/867–3400, (Nonreporting) **A**1 9 10 **S** Community Health Systems, Inc., Franklin, TN
Primary Contact: Chad Hatfield, Chief Executive Officer
CMO: William Lytollis, M.D., Chief of Staff
CIO: Ed Stanley, Director Information Systems
CHR: Tina Jackson, Director Human Resources
Web address: www.barrowregional.com
Control: Corporation, Investor–owned, for–profit **Service:** General Medical and Surgical

Staffed Beds: 56

GA

Hospital, Medicare Provider Number, Address, Telephone, Approval, Facility, and Physician Codes, Health Care System

★ American Hospital Association (AHA) membership
☐ The Joint Commission accreditation ◇ DNV Healthcare Inc. accreditation
○ Healthcare Facilities Accreditation Program
△ Commission on Accreditation of Rehabilitation Facilities (CARF) accreditation

HAWAII

AIEA—Honolulu County

⊞ **PALI MOMI MEDICAL CENTER (120026)**, 98–1079 Moanalua Road,
Zip 96701–4713; tel. 808/486–6000 **A**1 2 5 9 10 **F**3 8 12 15 18 20 22 26 29
30 31 34 35 40 45 46 47 49 50 57 58 59 60 64 65 67 68 69 70 74 75 77
78 79 81 82 83 84 85 86 87 91 92 107 108 110 111 114 115 119 126 130
132 135 142 146 147 148 **P**5 **S** Hawaii Pacific Health, Honolulu, HI
Primary Contact: Jen Chahanovich, Chief Executive Officer
CFO: David Okabe, Executive Vice President, Chief Financial Officer and Treasurer
CMO: James Kakuda, M.D., Chief of Staff
CIO: Steve Robertson, Senior Vice President
CHR: Gail Lerch, R.N., Vice President Human Resources
CNO: Brigitte McKale, MSN, Vice President and Chief Nurse Executive
Web address: www.palimomi.org
Control: Other not–for–profit (including NFP Corporation) **Service:** General
Medical and Surgical

> **Staffed Beds:** 128 **Admissions:** 6581 **Census:** 123 **Outpatient Visits:**
> 157732 **Births:** 0 **Total Expense ($000):** 191025 **Payroll Expense ($000):**
> 72498 **Personnel:** 980

EWA BEACH—Honolulu County

⊞ **KAHI MOHALA BEHAVIORAL HEALTH (124001)**, 91–2301 Old Fort Weaver
Road, Zip 96706–3602; tel. 808/671–8511 **A**1 9 10 **F**29 35 44 68 98 99 100
101 103 104 105 106 127 130 132 133 143 **S** Sutter Health, Sacramento, CA
Primary Contact: Leonard Licina, Chief Executive Officer
CFO: Rose Choy, Chief Financial Officer
CMO: Steven Chaplin, M.D., Medical Director
CHR: Christina Enoka, Director Human Resources and Risk Management
CNO: Diane Bedell, R.N., Director of Nursing
Web address: www.kahimohala.org
Control: Other not–for–profit (including NFP Corporation) **Service:** Psychiatric

> **Staffed Beds:** 76 **Admissions:** 1164 **Census:** 76 **Outpatient Visits:** 3510
> **Births:** 0 **Total Expense ($000):** 22028 **Payroll Expense ($000):** 10323
> **Personnel:** 172

HILO—Hawaii County

⊞ **HILO MEDICAL CENTER (120005)**, 1190 Waianuenue Avenue,
Zip 96720–2089; tel. 808/932–3000, (Total facility includes 112 beds in nursing
home–type unit) **A**1 5 9 10 20 **F**3 11 17 18 20 29 30 31 34 40 43 50 51 57
59 62 67 70 74 75 76 77 78 79 81 85 86 87 93 98 100 101 102 103 107
111 114 119 121 123 128 130 135 146 148 **P**5 6 **S** Hawaii Health Systems
Corporation, Honolulu, HI
Primary Contact: Dan Brinkman, R.N., Interim Chief Executive Officer
COO: Dan Brinkman, R.N., Chief Operating Officer
CFO: Money Atwal, Chief Financial Officer
CMO: Ted Peskin, M.D., Acute Care Medical Director
CIO: Money Atwal, Chief Information Officer
CHR: Holly Ka'Akimaka, Director Human Resources
CNO: Arthur Sampaga, Assistant Director Nursing
Web address: www.hmc.hhsc.org
Control: State–Government, nonfederal **Service:** General Medical and Surgical

> **Staffed Beds:** 276 **Admissions:** 9106 **Census:** 213 **Outpatient Visits:**
> 103680 **Births:** 1139 **Total Expense ($000):** 163006 **Payroll Expense**
> **($000):** 65553 **Personnel:** 1000

HONOKAA—Hawaii County

★ **HALE HO'OLA HAMAKUA (121307)**, 45–547 Plumeria Street,
Zip 96727–6902; tel. 808/932–4100, (Nonreporting) **A**5 9 10 18 **S** Hawaii
Health Systems Corporation, Honolulu, HI
Primary Contact: Teana Kahoohanohano, Interim Administrator
CMO: Bruce Graves, M.D., Chief of Staff
CNO: Faith Olivera, R.N., Interim Director of Nursing
Web address: www.hhh.hhsc.org/
Control: State–Government, nonfederal **Service:** General Medical and Surgical

> **Staffed Beds:** 52

HONOLULU—Honolulu County

⊞ **KAISER PERMANENTE MEDICAL CENTER (120011)**, 3288 Moanalua Road,
Zip 96819–1469; tel. 808/432–0000, (Total facility includes 24 beds in nursing
home–type unit) **A**1 3 5 10 **F**3 4 12 13 15 17 18 19 20 21 22 24 26 29 30 31
32 34 35 36 38 40 41 45 46 47 48 49 50 51 54 55 56 57 58 59 60 61 62
64 65 70 71 72 74 75 76 77 78 79 81 82 83 84 85 86 87 89 92 93 94 97
99 100 101 104 107 108 110 111 115 116 117 119 128 129 130 131 133
134 135 144 146 148 **P**1 **S** Kaiser Foundation Hospitals, Oakland, CA
Primary Contact: Leanne M. Hunstock, R.N., Interim Administrator
CFO: Thomas Risse, Chief Financial Officer and Vice President Business Services
CMO: Keith Ogasawara, M.D., Associate Medical Director and Professional Chief
of Staff
CIO: Brian Yoshii, Vice President Information Technology
CHR: Jean Melnikoff, Vice President Human Resources
CNO: Linda Puu, Chief Nursing Executive
Web address: www.kaiserpermanente.org
Control: Other not–for–profit (including NFP Corporation) **Service:** General
Medical and Surgical

> **Staffed Beds:** 235 **Admissions:** 11075 **Census:** 165 **Outpatient Visits:**
> 59170 **Births:** 1466 **Personnel:** 1560

☐ **KAPIOLANI MEDICAL CENTER FOR WOMEN & CHILDREN (123300)**, 1319
Punahou Street, Zip 96826–1001; tel. 808/983–6000, (Nonreporting) **A**1 2 3 5
9 10 **S** Hawaii Pacific Health, Honolulu, HI
Primary Contact: Martha Smith, Chief Executive Officer
CFO: David Okabe, Senior Vice President, Chief Financial Officer and Treasurer
CIO: Steve Robertson, Vice President
CHR: Gail Lerch, R.N., Vice President
Web address: www.kapiolani.org
Control: Other not–for–profit (including NFP Corporation) **Service:** Children's
general

> **Staffed Beds:** 225

⊞ **KUAKINI MEDICAL CENTER (120007)**, 347 North Kuakini Street,
Zip 96817–2381; tel. 808/536–2236 **A**1 2 3 5 9 10 **F**3 15 17 18 20 22 24 26
28 29 31 34 35 40 45 46 49 57 58 59 60 68 70 74 75 77 78 79 80 81 82
85 86 87 107 108 110 111 114 115 117 118 119 121 129 130 131 132
145 146 147 148 **P**1
Primary Contact: Gary K. Kajiwara, President and Chief Executive Officer
COO: Gregg Oishi, Senior Vice President and Chief Administrative Officer
CFO: Quin Ogawa, Vice President Finance and Chief Financial Officer
CMO: Nobuyuki Miki, M.D., Vice President Medical Services and Chief Medical
Officer
CIO: Gary K. Kajiwara, President and Chief Executive Officer
CHR: Ann N. Choy, Manager Human Resources and Payroll
CNO: Virginia Walker, Vice President Nursing Services and Chief Nursing Officer
Web address: www.kuakini.org
Control: Other not–for–profit (including NFP Corporation) **Service:** General
Medical and Surgical

> **Staffed Beds:** 89 **Admissions:** 6087 **Census:** 115 **Outpatient Visits:** 59907
> **Births:** 0 **Total Expense ($000):** 143646 **Payroll Expense ($000):** 65548
> **Personnel:** 886

★ **LEAHI HOSPITAL (122001)**, 3675 Kilauea Avenue, Zip 96816–2398;
tel. 808/733–8000, (Nonreporting) **A**9 10 **S** Hawaii Health Systems Corporation,
Honolulu, HI
Primary Contact: Reid Kondo, Interim Chief Executive Officer
CFO: Edward Chu, Chief Financial Officer
CMO: Albert Yazawa, M.D., Regional Medical Director
CHR: Russel Higa, JD, Regional Director Human Resources
CNO: Amy Vasunaga, Chief Nurse Executive
Web address: www.hhsc.org
Control: State–Government, nonfederal **Service:** Long–Term Acute Care hospital

> **Staffed Beds:** 188

HI

Many Facility Codes have changed. Please refer to the AHA Guide Code Chart. © 2014 AHA Guide

⊞ **QUEEN'S MEDICAL CENTER (120001)**, 1301 Punchbowl Street, Zip 96813–2499; tel. 808/691–5100, (Total facility includes 27 beds in nursing home–type unit) **A**1 2 3 5 9 10 **F**3 5 11 12 13 15 17 18 20 22 24 26 28 29 31 34 35 37 38 39 40 43 44 45 46 47 48 49 50 51 55 56 57 58 59 60 61 62 63 64 66 68 70 73 74 75 76 77 78 79 81 82 84 85 86 87 93 96 97 98 99 100 101 102 103 104 105 107 108 110 111 115 117 118 119 120 121 124 126 128 129 130 131 132 135 138 139 143 146 147 148 **S** Queen's Health Systems, Honolulu, HI
Primary Contact: Arthur A. Ushijima, FACHE, President
COO: Mark Yamakawa, Chief Operating Officer
CFO: Robert Nobriga, Executive Vice President and Chief Financial Officer
CMO: Leslie Chun, M.D., Vice President Medical Staff and Chief Quality Officer
CIO: Hunter Praywell, Vice President Information Technology and Chief Information Officer
CHR: Nona Tamanaha, Vice President Human Resources
CNO: Cynthia Kamikawa, R.N., Vice President Nursing Emergency Department and Trauma and Chief Nursing Officer
Web address: www.queensmedicalcenter.org
Control: Other not–for–profit (including NFP Corporation) **Service:** General Medical and Surgical

Staffed Beds: 478 **Admissions:** 24048 **Census:** 417 **Outpatient Visits:** 346165 **Births:** 2345 **Total Expense ($000):** 744883 **Payroll Expense ($000):** 306911 **Personnel:** 3442

⊞ **REHABILITATION HOSPITAL OF THE PACIFIC (123025)**, 226 North Kuakini Street, Zip 96817–2488; tel. 808/531–3511 **A**1 9 10 **F**3 11 28 29 34 36 44 54 58 64 68 74 75 77 79 90 91 93 94 95 96 130 131 132 135 143 146 147 148
Primary Contact: Timothy J. Roe, M.D., President and Chief Executive Officer
CFO: Wendy Manuel, Chief Financial Officer
CMO: Jason Chang, M.D., Chief Medical Director
CIO: Scott Morimoto, Director Clinical Informatics
CHR: Faye Miyamoto, Vice President Human Resources
CNO: Amy Parungao, Director of Nursing
Web address: www.rehabhospital.org
Control: Other not–for–profit (including NFP Corporation) **Service:** Rehabilitation

Staffed Beds: 70 **Admissions:** 1521 **Census:** 52 **Outpatient Visits:** 37392 **Births:** 0 **Total Expense ($000):** 37984 **Payroll Expense ($000):** 18595 **Personnel:** 265

☐ **SHRINERS HOSPITALS FOR CHILDREN–HONOLULU (123301)**, 1310 Punahou Street, Zip 96826–1099; tel. 808/941–4466 **A**1 3 5 9 10 **F**3 29 35 39 53 58 64 74 75 77 79 81 85 89 93 94 119 130 132 146 **S** Shriners Hospitals for Children, Tampa, FL
Primary Contact: John R. White, Administrator
CFO: Patricia Miyasawa, CPA, Director Fiscal Service
CMO: Craig Ono, M.D., Chief of Staff
CIO: Gregory A. Wolf, Director Information Systems
CHR: Derek Ito, Director Human Resources
CNO: Andrea Kubota, R.N., Director Patient Care Services
Web address: www.shrinershospitalsforchildren.org/Hospitals/Locations/Honolulu.aspx
Control: Other not–for–profit (including NFP Corporation) **Service:** Children's orthopedic

Staffed Beds: 16 **Admissions:** 221 **Census:** 4 **Outpatient Visits:** 10934 **Births:** 0

☐ **STRAUB CLINIC & HOSPITAL (120022)**, 888 South King Street, Zip 96813–3097; tel. 808/522–4000 **A**1 2 3 5 9 10 **F**3 9 12 15 16 17 18 20 21 22 23 24 26 27 28 29 30 31 34 40 45 47 49 54 56 57 59 64 65 68 70 74 75 77 78 79 81 84 85 86 87 92 93 97 100 104 107 108 110 111 114 118 119 129 130 131 132 135 143 144 145 146 148 **P**6 **S** Hawaii Pacific Health, Honolulu, HI
Primary Contact: Art Gladstone, R.N., Chief Executive Officer
COO: Maureen Flannery, Vice President Clinic Operations
CFO: David Okabe, Executive Vice President, Chief Financial Officer and Treasurer
CMO: Randy Yates, M.D., Chief Medical Officer
CIO: Steve Robertson, Executive Vice President and Chief Information Officer
CHR: Gail Lerch, R.N., Executive Vice President Human Resources
CNO: Patricia Boeckmann, R.N., Vice President Operations and Chief Nursing Officer
Web address: www.straubhealth.org
Control: Other not–for–profit (including NFP Corporation) **Service:** General Medical and Surgical

Staffed Beds: 119 **Admissions:** 7697 **Census:** 124 **Outpatient Visits:** 788098 **Births:** 0 **Total Expense ($000):** 359016 **Payroll Expense ($000):** 161604 **Personnel:** 1512

⊞ **TRIPLER ARMY MEDICAL CENTER**, 1 Jarret White Road, Zip 96859–5001; tel. 808/433–6661 **A**1 2 3 5 **F**3 7 8 12 13 14 15 18 19 20 21 22 23 24 25 26 27 29 30 31 32 33 34 35 36 38 39 40 41 43 44 45 46 47 48 49 50 51 52 53 54 55 56 57 58 59 60 63 64 65 67 68 70 72 74 75 76 77 78 79 81 82 85 86 87 88 89 91 92 93 94 96 97 98 99 100 101 102 103 104 105 106 107 108 110 111 115 116 117 118 119 120 121 123 124 126 127 129 130 131 132 133 134 135 143 144 145 146 147 148 **S** Department of the Army, Office of the Surgeon General, Falls Church, VA
Primary Contact: Brigadier General Dennis D. Doyle, Commanding Officer
COO: Major Elias B. Lozano, Executive Officer
CFO: Lieutenant Colonel Christopher A. Wodarz, Chief, Resource Management Division
CMO: Captain Andrew L. Findlay, Deputy Commander Clinical Services
CIO: Lieutenant Colonel Donna E. Beed, Chief Information Management Division
CHR: Colonel James N. Davidson, Troop Commander
CNO: Colonel Jennifer L. Bedick, Deputy Commander Nursing
Web address: www.tamc.amedd.army.mil
Control: Army, Government, federal **Service:** General Medical and Surgical

Staffed Beds: 194 **Admissions:** 14669 **Census:** 155 **Outpatient Visits:** 808647 **Births:** 2962 **Total Expense ($000):** 512245 **Payroll Expense ($000):** 174541

KAHUKU—Honolulu County

KAHUKU MEDICAL CENTER (121304), 56–117 Pualalea Street, Zip 96731–2052; tel. 808/293–9221, (Nonreporting) **A**9 10 18
Primary Contact: Stephany Vaioleti, Administrator
CFO: Francis Daquioag, Controller
CMO: P. Douglas Nielson, M.D., Chief of Staff
Web address: www.hhsc.org/oahu/kahuku/index.html
Control: Other not–for–profit (including NFP Corporation) **Service:** General Medical and Surgical

Staffed Beds: 11

KAILUA—Honolulu County

⊞ **CASTLE MEDICAL CENTER (120006)**, 640 Ulukahiki Street, Zip 96734–4454; tel. 808/263–5500 **A**1 3 5 9 10 **F**8 12 13 15 18 20 22 24 29 30 31 34 35 40 45 49 51 57 59 64 68 70 71 74 75 76 77 78 79 81 84 93 98 102 107 108 111 115 119 126 130 132 135 146 147 148 **P**6 8 **S** Adventist Health, Roseville, CA
Primary Contact: Kathryn A. Raethel, R.N., M.P.H., President and Chief Executive Officer
CMO: Alan Cheung, M.D., Vice President Medical Affairs
CIO: Brian Rothe, Site Director Information Systems
CHR: Todd Reese, Director Human Resources
CNO: Laura R. Westphal, Vice President Patient Care Services
Web address: www.castlemed.org
Control: Church–operated, Nongovernment, not–for profit **Service:** General Medical and Surgical

Staffed Beds: 160 **Admissions:** 7488 **Census:** 93 **Outpatient Visits:** 109736 **Births:** 1189 **Total Expense ($000):** 137420 **Payroll Expense ($000):** 58557 **Personnel:** 791

KAMUELA—Hawaii County

☐ **NORTH HAWAII COMMUNITY HOSPITAL (120028)**, 67–1125 Mamalahoa Highway, Zip 96743–8496; tel. 808/885–4444 **A**1 5 9 10 20 **F**3 8 13 15 18 26 29 30 31 34 35 36 40 43 46 50 53 57 58 59 62 64 68 70 75 76 77 78 79 81 84 85 93 97 104 107 108 110 111 115 119 130 131 146 147 148 **P**6
Primary Contact: Kenneth D. Graham, FACHE, President
CFO: Marilynn Hata, Vice President Finance and Operations
CMO: Howard Wong, Chief of Staff
CHR: Gary Sirman, Chief Human Resource Officer
Web address: www.nhch.com
Control: Other not–for–profit (including NFP Corporation) **Service:** General Medical and Surgical

Staffed Beds: 33 **Admissions:** 1687 **Census:** 16 **Outpatient Visits:** 59089 **Births:** 492 **Total Expense ($000):** 57997 **Payroll Expense ($000):** 23742 **Personnel:** 324

HI

Hospital, Medicare Provider Number, Address, Telephone, Approval, Facility, and Physician Codes, Health Care System

★ American Hospital Association (AHA) membership
☐ The Joint Commission accreditation   ◇ DNV Healthcare Inc. accreditation
○ Healthcare Facilities Accreditation Program
△ Commission on Accreditation of Rehabilitation Facilities (CARF) accreditation

KANEOHE—Honolulu County

☐ **HAWAII STATE HOSPITAL**, 45–710 Keaahala Road, Zip 96744–3597;
tel. 808/236–8237 **A**1 3 5 **F**34 39 59 75 77 98 101 102 103 105 106 130
132 135 143 146
Primary Contact: Mark Fridovich, Ph.D., Administrator
COO: William T. Elliott, Associate Administrator Administrative and Support
Services
CFO: Anthony Fraiola, Business Manager
CMO: James Westphal, M.D., Medical Director
CIO: John Jansen, Management Information Specialist
CHR: Karen Hara, Personnel Management Specialist
CNO: Leona Guest, Chief Nursing Unit
Web address: www.hshweb.health.state.hi.us
Control: State–Government, nonfederal **Service:** Psychiatric

> **Staffed Beds:** 178 **Admissions:** 333 **Census:** 190 **Outpatient Visits:** 0
> **Births:** 0 **Total Expense ($000):** 67763 **Payroll Expense ($000):** 35468
> **Personnel:** 588

KAPAA—Kauai County

★ **SAMUEL MAHELONA MEMORIAL HOSPITAL (121306)**, 4800 Kawaihau Road,
Zip 96746–1971; tel. 808/822–4961, (Nonreporting) **A**9 10 18 **S** Hawaii Health
Systems Corporation, Honolulu, HI
Primary Contact: Scott McFarland, Interim Regional Chief Executive Officer
CFO: Michael Perel, Regional Chief Financial Officer
CMO: Gerald Tomory, M.D., Regional Medical Director
CIO: Sandra McMaster, Regional Chief Information Officer
CHR: Lani Aranio, Regional Director Human Resources
Web address: www.smmh.hhsc.org
Control: State–Government, nonfederal **Service:** General Medical and Surgical

> **Staffed Beds:** 80

KAUNAKAKAI—Maui County

⊞ **MOLOKAI GENERAL HOSPITAL (121303)**, 280 Home Olu Place,
Zip 96748–0408, Mailing Address: P.O. Box 408, Zip 96748–0408;
tel. 808/553–5331, (Total facility includes 2 beds in nursing home–type unit) **A**1
5 9 10 18 **F**3 4 15 16 17 29 34 35 40 41 44 50 57 59 63 64 65 66 68 69
70 72 73 75 76 77 78 80 82 84 87 88 89 90 91 93 97 98 107 110 115 119
127 128 130 132 133 134 135 147 148 **P**6 **S** Queen's Health Systems,
Honolulu, HI
Primary Contact: Janice Kalanihuia, President
CFO: Zessica L. Apiki, Accountant
CMO: William Thomas, Jr., M.D., Medical Director Clinical and Internal Affairs
CIO: Sampson Wescoatt, Manager Information Technology
CHR: Alicia Teves, Coordinator Human Resources
Web address: www.queens.org
Control: Other not–for–profit (including NFP Corporation) **Service:** General
Medical and Surgical

> **Staffed Beds:** 15 **Admissions:** 104 **Census:** 3 **Outpatient Visits:** 29521
> **Births:** 17 **Total Expense ($000):** 12314 **Payroll Expense ($000):** 4500
> **Personnel:** 75

KEALAKEKUA—Hawaii County

⊞ **KONA COMMUNITY HOSPITAL (120019)**, 79–1019 Haukapila Street,
Zip 96750–7920; tel. 808/322–9311, (Nonreporting) **A**1 5 9 10 20 **S** Hawaii
Health Systems Corporation, Honolulu, HI
Primary Contact: Jay E. Kreuzer, FACHE, Chief Executive Officer
CFO: Dean Herzog, Chief Financial Officer
CMO: Kathleen Rokavec, M.D., Medical Director
CHR: Kathryn Salomon, Director Human Resources
CNO: Patricia Kalua, Chief Nurse Executive
Web address: www.kch.hhsc.org
Control: Other not–for–profit (including NFP Corporation) **Service:** General
Medical and Surgical

> **Staffed Beds:** 54

KOHALA—Hawaii County

★ **KOHALA HOSPITAL (121302)**, 54–383 Hospital Road, Zip 96755, Mailing
Address: P.O. Box 10, Kapaau, Zip 96755–0010; tel. 808/889–6211,
(Nonreporting) **A**9 10 18 **S** Hawaii Health Systems Corporation, Honolulu, HI
Primary Contact: Eugene Amar, Jr., Administrator
CMO: Silvia Sonnenschein, M.D., Chief of Staff
Web address: www.koh.hhsc.org
Control: State–Government, nonfederal **Service:** General Medical and Surgical

> **Staffed Beds:** 26

KULA—Maui County

★ **KULA HOSPITAL (121308)**, 100 Keokea Place, Zip 96790–7450;
tel. 808/878–1221, (Nonreporting) **A**5 9 10 18 **S** Hawaii Health Systems
Corporation, Honolulu, HI
Primary Contact: Nick Hughey, Administrator
CFO: Nerissa Garrity, Chief Financial Officer
CMO: Nicole Apoliona, M.D., Medical Director
Web address: www.hhsc.org
Control: State–Government, nonfederal **Service:** General Medical and Surgical

> **Staffed Beds:** 6

LANAI CITY—Maui County

★ **LANAI COMMUNITY HOSPITAL (121305)**, 628 Seventh Street,
Zip 96763–0650, Mailing Address: P.O. Box 630650, Zip 96763–0650;
tel. 808/565–8450, (Nonreporting) **A**9 10 18 **S** Hawaii Health Systems
Corporation, Honolulu, HI
Primary Contact: Nick Hughey, Administrator
Web address: www.lch.hhsc.org
Control: Other not–for–profit (including NFP Corporation) **Service:** General
Medical and Surgical

> **Staffed Beds:** 14

LIHUE—Kauai County

☐ **WILCOX MEMORIAL HOSPITAL (120014)**, 3–3420 Kuhio Highway,
Zip 96766–1099; tel. 808/245–1100 **A**1 5 9 10 20 **F**3 13 15 18 28 29 30 31
34 35 40 43 46 47 48 49 50 57 59 60 64 68 70 74 75 76 77 78 79 81 84
85 91 93 97 102 107 108 110 111 114 115 119 130 133 135 146 147 148
S Hawaii Pacific Health, Honolulu, HI
Primary Contact: Kathy Clark, R.N., President and Chief Executive Officer
CFO: David Okabe, Executive Vice President, Chief Financial Officer and Treasurer
CMO: Craig Netzer, M.D., President Medical Staff
CIO: Steve Robertson, Executive Vice President Revenue Cycle Management and
Chief Information Officer
CNO: Mary Ann England, Chief Nurse Executive
Web address: www.wilcoxhealth.org
Control: Other not–for–profit (including NFP Corporation) **Service:** General
Medical and Surgical

> **Staffed Beds:** 65 **Admissions:** 3378 **Census:** 40 **Outpatient Visits:** 80016
> **Births:** 509 **Total Expense ($000):** 85956 **Payroll Expense ($000):** 29705
> **Personnel:** 424

PAHALA—Hawaii County

★ **KAU HOSPITAL (121301)**, 1 Kamani Street, Zip 96777, Mailing Address: P.O.
Box 40, Zip 96777–0040; tel. 808/928–2050, (Total facility includes 16 beds in
nursing home–type unit) **A**9 10 18 **F**40 127 128 133 146 **S** Hawaii Health
Systems Corporation, Honolulu, HI
Primary Contact: Merilyn Harris, Administrator
CFO: Money Atwal, Chief Financial Officer
CMO: Clifford Field, M.D., Medical Director
Web address: www.hhsc.org
Control: State–Government, nonfederal **Service:** General Medical and Surgical

> **Staffed Beds:** 21 **Admissions:** 12 **Census:** 13 **Outpatient Visits:** 2237
> **Births:** 0 **Total Expense ($000):** 7110 **Payroll Expense ($000):** 4731

WAHIAWA—Honolulu County

⊞ **WAHIAWA GENERAL HOSPITAL (120004)**, 128 Lehua Street,
Zip 96786–2036; tel. 808/621–8411, (Total facility includes 93 beds in nursing
home–type unit) **A**1 3 5 9 10 **F**1 3 4 8 11 15 16 17 29 31 40 56 62 67 70 72
73 75 76 77 78 79 80 85 86 87 88 89 90 93 96 98 103 107 108 109
110 115 119 128 130 132 145 146 147 148 **P**8
Primary Contact: R. Don Olden, Chief Executive Officer
COO: R. Don Olden, Chief Executive Officer
CMO: Manuel Abundo, M.D., Chief of Staff
CIO: Jason Fujinaka, Manager Information System
CHR: Rosalyn Perez, Director Human Resources
CNO: Susan Ohlson, Ph.D., Director of Nursing–Acute
Web address: www.wahiawageneral.org
Control: Other not–for–profit (including NFP Corporation) **Service:** General
Medical and Surgical

> **Staffed Beds:** 160 **Admissions:** 3291 **Census:** 136 **Outpatient Visits:** 31839
> **Births:** 0 **Total Expense ($000):** 60517 **Payroll Expense ($000):** 28272
> **Personnel:** 432

WAILUKU—Maui County

⊞ **MAUI MEMORIAL MEDICAL CENTER (120002)**, 221 Mahalani Street,
Zip 96793–2581; tel. 808/244–9056, (Nonreporting) **A**1 5 9 10 20 **S** Hawaii
Health Systems Corporation, Honolulu, HI
Primary Contact: Wesley Lo, Regional Chief Executive Officer
CIO: Dana Mendoza, Chief Information Officer
Web address: www.mmmc.hhsc.org
Control: State–Government, nonfederal **Service:** General Medical and Surgical

> **Staffed Beds:** 213

HI

Many Facility Codes have changed. Please refer to the AHA Guide Code Chart. © 2014 AHA Guide

⊠ **KAUAI VETERANS MEMORIAL HOSPITAL (121300)**, Waimea Canyon Road,
Zip 96796, Mailing Address: P.O. Box 337, Zip 96796–0337;
tel. 808/338–9431, (Total facility includes 20 beds in nursing home–type unit) **A**1
9 10 18 **F**1 11 13 15 17 40 67 70 76 79 81 89 93 107 110 111 114 119
128 130 133 147 **S** Hawaii Health Systems Corporation, Honolulu, HI
Primary Contact: Scott McFarland, Interim Regional Chief Executive Officer
CFO: Michael Perel, Regional Chief Financial Officer
CMO: Gerald Tomory, M.D., Regional Medical Director
CIO: Sandra McMaster, Regional Chief Information Officer
CHR: Solette Perry, Regional Director Human Resources
Web address: www.kvmh.hhsc.org
Control: State–Government, nonfederal **Service:** General Medical and Surgical

Staffed Beds: 45 **Admissions:** 849 **Census:** 27 **Outpatient Visits:** 8550
Births: 264 **Total Expense ($000):** 46403 **Payroll Expense ($000):** 36746
Personnel: 276

HI

IDAHO

AMERICAN FALLS—Power County

★ **POWER COUNTY HOSPITAL DISTRICT (131304)**, 510 Roosevelt Road,
Zip 83211–1362, Mailing Address: P.O. Box 420, Zip 83211–0420;
tel. 208/226–3200, (Nonreporting) **A**9 10 18
Primary Contact: Dallas Clinger, Administrator
COO: Rock Roy, Professional Services Director
CFO: Jeremy Claunch, Chief Financial Officer
CMO: Bret Timmons, D.O., Chief Medical Staff
CIO: Mindy Earl, Health Information Manager
CHR: Norma Hartley, Director Human Resources
CNO: Daniel Kuta, R.N., Director of Nursing
Web address: www.pchd.net
Control: Hospital district or authority, Government, nonfederal **Service:** General
Medical and Surgical

Staffed Beds: 10

ARCO—Butte County

LOST RIVERS MEDICAL CENTER (131324), 551 Highland Drive,
Zip 83213–9771, Mailing Address: P.O. Box 145, Zip 83213–0145;
tel. 208/527–8206, (Nonreporting) **A**9 10 18
Primary Contact: Brad Huerta, Chief Executive Officer and Administrator
CFO: Jon Smith, Chief Financial Officer
CMO: Jeffrey Haskell, M.D., Chief Medical Staff
CHR: Tina Akins, Director Human Resources
CNO: Geri Cammack, R.N., Director of Nursing
Web address: www.lostriversmedical.com
Control: Hospital district or authority, Government, nonfederal **Service:** General
Medical and Surgical

Staffed Beds: 43

BLACKFOOT—Bingham County

⊞ **BINGHAM MEMORIAL HOSPITAL (131325)**, 98 Poplar Street,
Zip 83221–1799; tel. 208/785–4100, (Total facility includes 70 beds in nursing
home–type unit) **A**1 9 10 18 **F**2 3 12 13 15 18 20 26 29 34 35 37 39 40 45
47 50 55 56 57 58 59 64 68 70 74 76 77 79 81 82 85 86 87 93 97 107
108 109 110 111 115 119 127 128 129 130 131 132 133 134 135 144 146
147 148
Primary Contact: Louis D. Kraml, FACHE, Chief Executive Officer
COO: Dan Cochran, Chief Operating Officer
CFO: Jeff Daniels, Chief Financial Officer
CIO: Robert Weis, Director Information Systems
CHR: Tara Preston, Director Human Resources
CNO: Carolyn Hansen, Chief Nursing Officer
Web address: www.binghammemorial.org
Control: Other not–for–profit (including NFP Corporation) **Service:** General
Medical and Surgical

Staffed Beds: 95 **Admissions:** 2075 **Census:** 61 **Outpatient Visits:** 52377
Births: 350 **Total Expense ($000):** 84004 **Payroll Expense ($000):** 36555
Personnel: 577

MOUNTAIN RIVER BIRTHING AND SURGERY CENTER (130067), 350 North
Meridian Street, Zip 83221–1625; tel. 208/782–0300 **A**9 10 **F**3 79 81 85 86
87 107 130 135 148
Primary Contact: Louis D. Kraml, FACHE, Chief Executive Officer
COO: Dan Cochran, Chief Operating Officer
CFO: Jeff Daniels, Chief Financial Officer
CIO: Robert Weis, Director Information Technology
CHR: Tara Preston, Director Human Resources
CNO: Nathan Buck, R.N., Nursing Manager
Web address: www.binghammemorial.org
Control: Corporation, Investor–owned, for–profit **Service:** Surgical

Staffed Beds: 8 **Admissions:** 124 **Census:** 1 **Outpatient Visits:** 6116 **Births:**
0 **Total Expense ($000):** 6074 **Payroll Expense ($000):** 820 **Personnel:** 20

☐ **STATE HOSPITAL SOUTH (134010)**, 700 East Alice Street, Zip 83221–4925,
Mailing Address: P.O. Box 400, Zip 83221–0400; tel. 208/785–1200,
(Nonreporting) **A**1 10
Primary Contact: Tracey Sessions, Administrator
COO: Greg Horton, Director Support Services
CFO: Eric Price, Financial Specialist, Senior
CMO: Kelly Palmer, D.O., Medical Director
CIO: Julie Sutton, Director Performance Improvement
CHR: Sheryl Donnelly, Human Resources Specialist
CNO: Randy Walker, Director Nursing Services
Web address: www.healthandwelfare.idaho.gov
Control: State–Government, nonfederal **Service:** Psychiatric

Staffed Beds: 77

BOISE—Ada County

BOISE BEHAVIORAL HEALTH HOSPITAL See Safe Haven Hospital of Treasure
Valley

⊞ **BOISE VETERANS AFFAIRS MEDICAL CENTER**, 500 West Fort Street,
Zip 83702–4598; tel. 208/422–1000, (Total facility includes 24 beds in nursing
home–type unit) **A**1 3 5 9 **F**1 2 3 4 5 8 9 10 12 16 29 30 31 34 35 38 39 40
43 45 46 47 50 53 54 56 57 58 59 60 61 62 63 64 65 66 67 68 71 74 75
77 78 79 80 81 82 83 84 85 86 87 90 91 92 93 94 96 97 98 100 101 102
103 104 105 106 107 108 111 112 119 120 121 122 123 124 127 128 129
130 132 133 135 143 144 145 146 147 148 **S** Department of Veterans Affairs,
Washington, DC
Primary Contact: David P. Wood, FACHE, Director
CFO: Ron Blanton, Chief Fiscal Services
CMO: Paul Lambert, M.D., Chief of Staff
CHR: Randy Turner, Chief Human Resource Management Services
Web address: www.boise.va.gov/
Control: Veterans Affairs, Government, federal **Service:** General Medical and
Surgical

Staffed Beds: 85 **Admissions:** 3373 **Census:** 64 **Outpatient Visits:** 318117
Births: 0 **Total Expense ($000):** 195000 **Payroll Expense ($000):** 112000
Personnel: 1036

★ △ **ELKS REHAB HOSPITAL (133025)**, 600 North Robbins Road,
Zip 83702–4565, Mailing Address: P.O. Box 1100, Zip 83701–1100;
tel. 208/489–4444, (Nonreporting) **A**5 7 10
Primary Contact: Joseph P. Caroselli, Chief Executive Officer
COO: Melissa Honsinger, Chief Operating Officer
CFO: Doug Lewis, Chief Financial Officer
CMO: Lee Kornfield, M.D., Medical Director
CIO: Scott Pyrah, Director Information Systems
CHR: Jim Atkins, Director Employee Services
Web address: www.idahoelksrehab.org
Control: Other not–for–profit (including NFP Corporation) **Service:** Rehabilitation

Staffed Beds: 31

IDAHO ELKS REHABILITATION HOSPITAL See Elks Rehab Hospital

☐ **INTERMOUNTAIN HOSPITAL (134002)**, 303 North Allumbaugh Street,
Zip 83704–9208; tel. 208/377–8400, (Nonreporting) **A**1 9 10 **S** Universal Health
Services, Inc., King of Prussia, PA
Primary Contact: Jeffrey F. Morrell, Chief Executive Officer
CMO: Harry Silsby, M.D., Medical Director
CHR: Angela Billingsley, Director Human Resources
Web address: www.intermountainhospital.com
Control: Corporation, Investor–owned, for–profit **Service:** Psychiatric

Staffed Beds: 140

SAFE HAVEN HOSPITAL OF TREASURE VALLEY (134009), 8050 Northview
Street, Zip 83704–7126; tel. 208/327–0504, (Nonreporting) **A**5 9 10 **S** Safe
Haven Health Care, Pocatello, ID
Primary Contact: Scott Proctor, Chief Executive Officer
CMO: David Kent, M.D., Chief Medical Officer
CIO: Debra Alexander, Chief Information Officer
CHR: Kathy Cady, Coordinator Human Resources, Accounts Payable and Payroll
Web address: www.boisepsychhospital.com
Control: Corporation, Investor–owned, for–profit **Service:** Psychiatric

Staffed Beds: 22

☐ **SOUTHWEST IDAHO ADVANCED CARE HOSPITAL (132003)**, 6651 West
Franklin Road, Zip 83709–0914; tel. 208/376–5700, (Nonreporting) **A**1 9 10
S Ernest Health, Inc., Albuquerque, NM
Primary Contact: Nolan Hoffer, Chief Executive Officer
Web address: www.siach.ernesthealth.com/
Control: Corporation, Investor–owned, for–profit **Service:** Long–Term Acute Care
hospital

Staffed Beds: 40

ID

Many Facility Codes have changed. Please refer to the AHA Guide Code Chart.
© 2014 AHA Guide

✠ **ST. LUKE'S REGIONAL MEDICAL CENTER (130006)**, 190 East Bannock Street, Zip 83712–6241; tel. 208/381–2222, (Includes ST. LUKE'S CHILDREN'S HOSPITAL, 190 East Bannock Street, tel. 208/381–1200; ST. LUKE'S MERIDIAN MEDICAL CENTER, 520 South Eagle Road, Meridian, Zip 83642; tel. 208/706–5000) **A**1 2 3 5 9 10 **F**7 8 11 12 13 15 17 18 19 20 21 22 23 24 25 26 27 28 29 30 31 32 34 35 36 37 40 41 46 47 48 49 53 54 56 57 59 61 62 63 64 68 69 70 71 72 74 75 76 77 78 79 81 82 84 86 87 88 89 107 108 110 111 114 115 117 119 126 127 129 130 131 132 134 136 144 146 147 **P**6 8 **S** St. Luke's Health System, Boise, ID
Primary Contact: Kathy D. Moore, Chief Executive Officer
CFO: Jeff Taylor, Vice President Finance
CMO: Bart Hill, M.D., Chief Medical Officer
CIO: Marc Chasin, M.D., Chief Information Officer
CHR: Maureen O'Keeffe, Vice President and Chief Human Resource Officer
CNO: Cynthia Gearhard, Chief Nursing Officer
Web address: www.stlukesonline.org/boise
Control: Other not-for-profit (including NFP Corporation) **Service:** General Medical and Surgical

Staffed Beds: 583 **Admissions:** 28218 **Census:** 304 **Outpatient Visits:** 1360937 **Births:** 5170 **Total Expense ($000):** 1123935 **Payroll Expense ($000):** 456233 **Personnel:** 8163

☐ **TREASURE VALLEY HOSPITAL (130063)**, 8800 West Emerald Street, Zip 83704–8205; tel. 208/373–5000, (Nonreporting) **A**1 9 10
Primary Contact: Nick Genna, Administrator
CMO: Jeffrey Hessing, M.D., Medical Director
CHR: Kathleen Phelps, Director Human Resources
Web address: www.treasurevalleyhospital.com
Control: Corporation, Investor–owned, for–profit **Service:** General Medical and Surgical

Staffed Beds: 9

VETERANS AFFAIRS MEDICAL CENTER See Boise Veterans Affairs Medical Center

★ **BOUNDARY COMMUNITY HOSPITAL (131301)**, 6640 Kaniksu Street, Zip 83805–7532; tel. 208/267–3141, (Includes BOUNDARY COUNTY NURSING HOME), (Total facility includes 32 beds in nursing home–type unit) **A**9 10 18 **F**3 11 15 35 40 45 50 57 59 65 75 77 81 85 87 93 107 110 111 114 119 128 130 133 143 146 148
Primary Contact: Craig A. Johnson, Chief Executive Officer
CFO: Jordan Leigh, Chief Financial Officer
CHR: Ann Coughlin, Director Human Resources
CNO: Tari Yourzek, Chief Nursing Officer
Web address: www.boundaryhospital.org
Control: County–Government, nonfederal **Service:** General Medical and Surgical

Staffed Beds: 52 **Admissions:** 168 **Census:** 33 **Outpatient Visits:** 22437 **Births:** 0 **Total Expense ($000):** 11054 **Payroll Expense ($000):** 6173 **Personnel:** 157

✠ **CASSIA REGIONAL MEDICAL CENTER (131326)**, 1501 Hiland Avenue, Zip 83318–2688; tel. 208/678–4444 **A**1 9 10 18 **F**3 7 8 11 13 15 18 28 29 30 34 35 38 40 41 50 57 59 64 68 70 74 75 76 77 79 81 82 85 86 93 97 107 108 110 111 114 119 129 130 131 132 146 147 148 **P**6 **S** Intermountain Healthcare, Inc., Salt Lake City, UT
Primary Contact: Rod Barton, Administrator
CFO: Mark Christensen, Director, Finance
CIO: Carie Call, Computer Support
CHR: Keri Perrigot, Director Human Resources
CNO: Michele Pond-Bell, R.N., Nurse Administrator
Web address: www.cassiaregional.org
Control: Other not–for–profit (including NFP Corporation) **Service:** General Medical and Surgical

Staffed Beds: 25 **Admissions:** 1644 **Census:** 13 **Outpatient Visits:** 103971 **Births:** 678 **Total Expense ($000):** 43202 **Payroll Expense ($000):** 17899 **Personnel:** 327

✠ **WEST VALLEY MEDICAL CENTER (130014)**, 1717 Arlington, Zip 83605–4802; tel. 208/459–4641, (Nonreporting) **A**1 9 10 **S** HCA, Nashville, TN
Primary Contact: Elizabeth Hunsicker, Chief Executive Officer
COO: Jennifer Opsut, Interim Chief Operating Officer
CFO: Kate Fowler, Chief Financial Officer
CMO: Richard Augustus, M.D., Chief Medical Officer
CIO: Jason Martinez, Director Information Technology
CHR: Senta Cornelius, Director Human Resources
CNO: Edith E. Irving, R.N., Chief Nursing Officer
Web address: www.westvalleymedctr.com
Control: Corporation, Investor–owned, for–profit **Service:** General Medical and Surgical

Staffed Beds: 122

★ **CASCADE MEDICAL CENTER (131308)**, 402 Lake Cascade Parkway, Zip 83611–7702, Mailing Address: P.O. Box 1330, Zip 83611–1330; tel. 208/382–4242 **A**9 10 18 **F**11 29 32 34 40 45 53 59 64 65 67 87 89 93 97 102 107 114 127 128 130 131 133 135 147 **P**6
Primary Contact: Virgil Boss, Chief Executive Officer
CFO: Penny Lancaster, Controller
CMO: Mikael Bedeli, M.D., Medical Director
CNO: Teri Coombs, R.N., Director Nursing Services
Web address: www.cascademedicalcenter.net
Control: Hospital district or authority, Government, nonfederal **Service:** General Medical and Surgical

Staffed Beds: 10 **Admissions:** 24 **Census:** 1 **Outpatient Visits:** 6997 **Births:** 0 **Total Expense ($000):** 3186 **Payroll Expense ($000):** 1846 **Personnel:** 28

★ ◇ **KOOTENAI HEALTH (130049)**, 2003 Kootenai Health Way, Zip 83814–2677; tel. 208/625–4000, (Includes KOOTENAI BEHAVIORAL HEALTH, 2301 North Ironwood Place, Zip 83814–2650; tel. 208/625–4800) **A**2 9 10 19 21 **F**2 3 4 5 6 8 9 11 12 13 15 17 18 20 22 24 26 28 29 30 31 32 34 35 37 39 40 41 43 44 45 46 47 48 49 50 51 53 54 55 56 57 58 59 60 63 64 65 68 70 71 72 73 74 75 76 77 78 79 81 82 83 84 85 86 87 89 90 91 92 93 96 97 98 99 100 101 102 103 104 107 108 110 111 114 115 116 117 118 119 120 121 123 124 126 127 129 130 131 132 134 135 143 144 146 148 **P**6
Primary Contact: Jon Ness, Chief Executive Officer
COO: Jeremy Evans, Vice President Operations
CFO: Kimberly Webb, Chief Financial Officer
CMO: Walter Fairfax, M.D., Chief Medical Officer
CHR: Daniel Klocko, Vice President Human Resources
CNO: Joan M. Simon, R.N., Chief Nursing Officer
Web address: www.kh.org
Control: Hospital district or authority, Government, nonfederal **Service:** General Medical and Surgical

Staffed Beds: 254 **Admissions:** 12899 **Census:** 160 **Outpatient Visits:** 363718 **Births:** 1615 **Total Expense ($000):** 313781 **Payroll Expense ($000):** 140965 **Personnel:** 1923

★ **ST. MARY'S HOSPITAL (131321)**, Lewiston and North Streets, Zip 83522–9750, Mailing Address: P.O. Box 137, Zip 83522–0137; tel. 208/962–3251, (Nonreporting) **A**9 10 18 **S** Essentia Health, Duluth, MN
Primary Contact: Patrick J. Branco, President
COO: Sharon J. Moriarty, Chief Operating Officer
CFO: Lenne Bonner, Chief Financial Officer
CMO: Jack Secrest, M.D., Chief Medical Officer
CHR: Debbie Schumacher, Manager Human Resource
Web address: www.smh–cvhc.org/getpage.php?name=index
Control: Other not–for–profit (including NFP Corporation) **Service:** General Medical and Surgical

Staffed Beds: 28

ID

DRIGGS—Teton County

★ **TETON VALLEY HEALTH CARE (131313)**, 120 East Howard Street, Zip 83422–5112; tel. 208/354–2383, (Nonreporting) **A**9 10 18
Primary Contact: Keith Gnagey, Chief Executive Officer
CFO: Traci Prenot, Chief Financial Officer
CMO: Nathan Levanger, M.D., Chief of Staff
CHR: Dory Harris, Director Human Resource
CNO: Angela Booker, Director of Nursing Services
Web address: www.tvhcare.org
Control: County–Government, nonfederal **Service:** General Medical and Surgical

Staffed Beds: 13

EMMETT—Gem County

WALTER KNOX MEMORIAL HOSPITAL (131318), 1202 East Locust Street, Zip 83617–2715; tel. 208/365–3561, (Nonreporting) **A**9 10 18
Primary Contact: Wade C. Johnson, MS, FACHE, Chief Executive Officer
CHR: Susan Vahlberg, Director Employee and Community Relations
Web address: www.wkmh.org
Control: County–Government, nonfederal **Service:** General Medical and Surgical

Staffed Beds: 16

GOODING—Gooding County

★ **NORTH CANYON MEDICAL CENTER (131302)**, 267 North Canyon Drive, Zip 83330–5500; tel. 208/934–4433, (Nonreporting) **A**9 10 18 **S** St. Luke's Health System, Boise, ID
Primary Contact: Tim Powers, Chief Executive Officer
CFO: Tim Powers, Chief Executive Officer
CMO: Mark Spencer, D.O., Chief of Staff
CIO: Paul Castronova, Chief Information Officer
CHR: Sara Otto, Director Human Resources
CNO: Karin Frodin–White, Chief Nursing Officer
Web address: www.ncm–c.org
Control: Other not–for–profit (including NFP Corporation) **Service:** General Medical and Surgical

Staffed Beds: 14

GRANGEVILLE—Idaho County

★ **SYRINGA HOSPITAL AND CLINICS (131315)**, 607 West Main Street, Zip 83530–1396; tel. 208/983–1700 **A**9 10 18 **F**7 13 29 30 40 50 59 63 76 81 93 107 119 127 133
Primary Contact: Joseph Cladouhos, Chief Executive Officer
CFO: Betty A. Watson, Chief Financial Officer
CMO: Daniel Griffis, M.D., Chief Medical Officer
CIO: Darla Whitley, Manager Health Information Technology
CHR: Katy Eimers, Human Resources Officer
CNO: Cindy Daly, R.N., Director of Nursing
Web address: www.syringahospital.org
Control: Hospital district or authority, Government, nonfederal **Service:** General Medical and Surgical

Staffed Beds: 14 **Admissions:** 400 **Census:** 4 **Outpatient Visits:** 15000 **Births:** 32 **Total Expense ($000):** 12781 **Payroll Expense ($000):** 6168

IDAHO FALLS—Bonneville County

⊞ **EASTERN IDAHO REGIONAL MEDICAL CENTER (130018)**, 3100 Channing Way, Zip 83404–7533, Mailing Address: P.O. Box 2077, Zip 83403–2077; tel. 208/529–6111, (Total facility includes 16 beds in nursing home–type unit) **A**1 2 9 10 19 **F**3 7 11 12 13 15 18 20 21 22 23 24 28 29 30 31 34 35 36 39 40 43 44 46 49 50 51 53 57 59 64 65 67 68 70 72 74 75 76 77 78 79 81 82 85 86 87 88 89 90 91 92 93 98 99 100 102 106 107 108 111 114 115 118 119 120 121 123 128 130 131 132 135 146 147 148 **S** HCA, Nashville, TN
Primary Contact: Douglas Crabtree, Chief Executive Officer
COO: Sandee Moore, Chief Operating Officer
CFO: Jeffrey D. Baiocco, Chief Financial Officer
CMO: Todd Williams, M.D., President Medical Staff
CHR: Wendy Andersen, Director Human Resources
CNO: Kathleen Nelson, R.N., Chief Nursing Officer
Web address: www.eirmc.com
Control: Corporation, Investor–owned, for–profit **Service:** General Medical and Surgical

Staffed Beds: 309 **Admissions:** 12029 **Census:** 184

MOUNTAIN VIEW HOSPITAL (130065), 2325 Coronado Street, Zip 83404–7407; tel. 208/557–2700, (Nonreporting) **A**9 10
Primary Contact: James Adamson, Chief Executive Officer
COO: Peter Fabrick, Vice President Clinical Operations
CHR: Eilene Horne, Manager Human Resources
Web address: www.mountainviewhospital.org
Control: Corporation, Investor–owned, for–profit **Service:** General Medical and Surgical

Staffed Beds: 22

JEROME—Jerome County

★ **ST. LUKE'S JEROME (131310)**, 709 North Lincoln Street, Zip 83338–1851, Mailing Address: 709 North Lincoln Avenue, Zip 83338–1851; tel. 208/324–4301 **A**9 10 18 **F**7 13 15 29 30 32 34 39 40 56 57 59 64 65 68 77 79 81 86 87 97 107 111 119 127 133 146 147 **P**6 **S** St. Luke's Health System, Boise, ID
Primary Contact: James L. Angle, FACHE, Chief Executive Officer
CMO: Elizabeth Sugden, M.D., Chief Medical Officer
CHR: Mark Stevens, Director Human Resources
CNO: Jill Howell, Clinical Director and Chief Nursing Officer
Web address: www.stlukesonline.org/jerome/
Control: Other not–for–profit (including NFP Corporation) **Service:** General Medical and Surgical

Staffed Beds: 25 **Admissions:** 532 **Census:** 7 **Outpatient Visits:** 48776 **Births:** 186 **Total Expense ($000):** 17053 **Payroll Expense ($000):** 9547 **Personnel:** 190

KELLOGG—Shoshone County

◇ **SHOSHONE MEDICAL CENTER (131314)**, 25 Jacobs Gulch, Zip 83837–2023; tel. 208/784–1221, (Nonreporting) **A**9 10 18 21
Primary Contact: Gary Moore, Chief Executive Officer
CFO: Jerry Brantz, Chief Financial Officer
CMO: Thomas Heston, M.D., Chief of Staff
CIO: John Wohlman, Manager Information Systems
CHR: Dana Hemphill, Manager Human Resources
CNO: Beth Bates, Chief Nursing Officer
Web address: www.shoshonehealth.com
Control: Hospital district or authority, Government, nonfederal **Service:** General Medical and Surgical

Staffed Beds: 25

KETCHUM—Blaine County

⊞ **ST. LUKE'S WOOD RIVER MEDICAL CENTER (131323)**, 100 Hospital Drive, Zip 83340, Mailing Address: P.O. Box 100, Zip 83340–0100; tel. 208/727–8800 **A**1 9 10 18 **F**3 7 8 11 13 15 29 30 31 34 35 36 37 39 40 43 45 50 54 57 59 62 64 68 74 75 76 79 81 82 85 86 87 91 93 97 104 107 108 110 111 114 115 119 126 130 131 132 133 134 135 141 143 145 146 147 148 **P**6 8 **S** St. Luke's Health System, Boise, ID
Primary Contact: Cody Langbehn, Chief Executive Officer
CNO: Suzanne Miller, R.N., Senior Director Patient Care Services and Nursing
Web address: www.slrmc.org
Control: Other not–for–profit (including NFP Corporation) **Service:** General Medical and Surgical

Staffed Beds: 25 **Admissions:** 1061 **Census:** 8 **Outpatient Visits:** 78110 **Births:** 217 **Total Expense ($000):** 52517 **Payroll Expense ($000):** 24205 **Personnel:** 337

LEWISTON—Nez Perce County

⊞ **ST. JOSEPH REGIONAL MEDICAL CENTER (130003)**, 415 Sixth Street, Zip 83501–2431; tel. 208/743–2511 **A**1 2 9 10 19 20 **F**8 11 13 15 18 20 22 30 31 34 35 38 40 41 43 45 46 50 53 54 57 58 59 63 64 68 69 70 71 74 75 76 77 79 81 83 84 86 87 89 91 92 93 94 97 98 100 101 102 103 104 106 107 108 110 111 114 115 116 117 118 119 120 121 124 129 130 132 133 135 144 146 **P**6 **S** Ascension Health, Saint Louis, MO
Primary Contact: Michael T. Rooney, M.D., Interim President and Chief Executive Officer
CFO: Thomas Safley, Chief Financial Officer
CMO: Michael T. Rooney, M.D., Chief of Staff
CHR: Brenda J. Forge, Vice President Human Resources
CNO: Alan Abbott, Vice President Patient Care Services
Web address: www.sjrmc.org
Control: Church–operated, Nongovernment, not–for profit **Service:** General Medical and Surgical

Staffed Beds: 119 **Admissions:** 5040 **Census:** 58 **Outpatient Visits:** 117421 **Births:** 793 **Total Expense ($000):** 132066 **Payroll Expense ($000):** 52762 **Personnel:** 783

MALAD CITY—Oneida County

ONEIDA COUNTY HOSPITAL (131303), 150 North 200 West, Zip 83252–1239, Mailing Address: Box 126, Zip 83252–0126; tel. 208/766–2231, (Nonreporting) **A**10 18
Primary Contact: John Williams, Administrator and Chief Executive Officer
CFO: Cindy Howard, Director Financial Services
CHR: Kathy Hubbard, Manager Human Resources
Web address: www.oneidahospital.com
Control: County–Government, nonfederal **Service:** General Medical and Surgical

Staffed Beds: 11

Many Facility Codes have changed. Please refer to the AHA Guide Code Chart. © 2014 AHA Guide

MCCALL—Valley County

★ **ST. LUKE'S MCCALL (131312)**, 1000 State Street, Zip 83638–3704;
tel. 208/634–2221 **A**5 9 10 18 **F**3 8 9 11 15 30 32 34 35 36 38 40 45 46 50
57 59 64 68 79 81 85 86 87 93 97 107 115 119 130 132 133 134 135 146
P6 8 **S** St. Luke's Health System, Boise, ID
Primary Contact: Michael A. Fenello, Chief Executive Officer
CFO: Matt Groenig, Vice President Finance
Web address: www.mccallhosp.org
Control: Other not–for–profit (including NFP Corporation) **Service:** General
Medical and Surgical

Staffed Beds: 15 **Admissions:** 458 **Census:** 3 **Outpatient Visits:** 40293
Births: 78 **Total Expense ($000):** 23118 **Payroll Expense ($000):** 12259
Personnel: 214

MERIDIAN—Ada County

ST. LUKE'S MERIDIAN MEDICAL CENTER See St. Luke's Regional Medical
Center, Boise

⊞ **VIBRA HOSPITAL OF BOISE (132002)**, 2131 South Bonito Way,
Zip 83642–1659; tel. 877/801–2244, (Nonreporting) **A**1 10 **S** Vibra Healthcare,
Mechanicsburg, PA
Primary Contact: Randall J. Evaro, Chief Executive Officer
Web address: www.vhboise.com
Control: Corporation, Investor–owned, for–profit **Service:** Long–Term Acute Care
hospital

Staffed Beds: 60

MONTPELIER—Bear Lake County

★ **BEAR LAKE MEMORIAL HOSPITAL (131316)**, 164 South Fifth Street,
Zip 83254–1597; tel. 208/847–1630, (Total facility includes 36 beds in nursing
home–type unit) **A**9 10 18 **F**2 3 5 10 11 12 18 34 35 37 39 40 45 50 53 56
57 59 60 62 68 70 75 79 81 85 86 87 93 97 101 105 107 114 119 120 126
127 128 129 130 133 135 146 **P**6
Primary Contact: Rodney D. Jacobson, Administrator
Web address: www.blmhospital.com
Control: County–Government, nonfederal **Service:** General Medical and Surgical

Staffed Beds: 57 **Admissions:** 449 **Census:** 35 **Births:** 68 **Total Expense
($000):** 19446 **Payroll Expense ($000):** 9404 **Personnel:** 204

MOSCOW—Latah County

⊞ **GRITMAN MEDICAL CENTER (131327)**, 700 South Main Street,
Zip 83843–3056; tel. 208/882–4511 **A**1 9 10 18 **F**3 8 11 13 15 19 28 29 34
35 36 37 40 45 46 49 51 53 54 56 57 59 60 64 65 70 75 76 77 79 81 82
84 85 86 87 89 93 96 107 108 110 111 113 114 119 127 129 130 131 132
135 143 146 147 148 **S** QHR, Brentwood, TN
Primary Contact: Kara Besst, President and Chief Executive Officer
CFO: Preston Becker, Chief Financial Officer
CMO: Dustin Worth, M.D., Chief Medical Staff
CIO: Kane Francetich, Chief Information Officer
CHR: Dennis Cockrell, Director Human Resources
CNO: Sheryl M. Washburn, MSN, Chief Nursing Officer
Web address: www.gritman.org
Control: Other not–for–profit (including NFP Corporation) **Service:** General
Medical and Surgical

Staffed Beds: 25 **Admissions:** 1465 **Census:** 11 **Outpatient Visits:** 58860
Births: 339 **Total Expense ($000):** 43191 **Payroll Expense ($000):** 19587
Personnel: 332

MOUNTAIN HOME—Elmore County

★ **ST. LUKE'S ELMORE (131311)**, 895 North Sixth East Street, Zip 83647–2207,
Mailing Address: P.O. Box 1270, Zip 83647–1270; tel. 208/587–8401, (Total
facility includes 38 beds in nursing home–type unit) **A**9 10 18 **F**3 7 11 13 29 30
34 35 40 45 57 64 75 76 77 81 89 107 111 114 119 127 128 129 130 133
146 **S** St. Luke's Health System, Boise, ID
Primary Contact: Gregory L. Maurer, Administrator
COO: Betty Van Gheluwe, Chief Operating Officer
CFO: Tricia Senger, Chief Financial Officer
CMO: Karl Olson, M.D., Chief of Staff
CNO: Debbie Plemmons, MSN, Chief Nursing Officer
Web address: www.elmoremedicalcenter.org
Control: Other not–for–profit (including NFP Corporation) **Service:** General
Medical and Surgical

Staffed Beds: 57 **Admissions:** 788 **Census:** 27 **Outpatient Visits:** 45807
Births: 111 **Total Expense ($000):** 25622 **Payroll Expense ($000):** 9569
Personnel: 223

MOUNTAIN HOME AFB—Elmore County

⊞ **U. S. AIR FORCE CLINIC**, 90 Hope Drive, Building 600, Zip 83648–1057;
tel. 208/828–7610, (Nonreporting) **A**1 9 **S** Department of the Air Force,
Washington, DC
Primary Contact: Lieutenant Colonel Gregory W. Carson, Administrator
CFO: Robert Magnuson, Business Operations Flight Chief
CIO: Richard Broemeling, Information Systems Flight Commander
Control: Air Force, Government, federal **Service:** General Medical and Surgical

Staffed Beds: 10

NAMPA—Canyon County

MERCY MEDICAL CENTER See Saint Alphonsus Medical Center – Nampa

⊞ **SAINT ALPHONSUS MEDICAL CENTER – NAMPA (130013)**, 1512 12th
Avenue Road, Zip 83686–6008; tel. 208/463–5000 **A**1 9 10 **F**3 11 12 13 15
18 20 22 28 29 30 31 34 35 37 40 42 44 49 50 53 54 55 57 59 64 67 68
69 70 72 73 75 76 77 78 79 80 81 82 84 85 86 87 89 93 96 107 108 110
111 114 115 118 119 126 129 130 132 133 135 141 143 145 146 147 148
S Catholic Health East / Trinity Health, Livonia, MI
Primary Contact: Karl Keeler, Chief Executive Officer
COO: Phil Harrop, Executive Director Operations
CFO: Lannie Checketts, Interim Assistant Chief Financial Officer
CMO: Dustan Hughes, M.D., Vice President Medical Affairs
CIO: Daniel Wright, Director Information Technology
CHR: Stefanie Thiel, Senior Human Resources Business Partner
CNO: Clint L. Child, R.N., Chief Nursing Officer
Web address: www.mercynampa.org
Control: Church–operated, Nongovernment, not–for profit **Service:** General
Medical and Surgical

Staffed Beds: 142 **Admissions:** 5350 **Census:** 45 **Outpatient Visits:** 97256
Births: 1048 **Total Expense ($000):** 87465 **Payroll Expense ($000):** 33250
Personnel: 691

OROFINO—Clearwater County

★ **CLEARWATER VALLEY HOSPITAL AND CLINICS (131320)**, 301 Cedar,
Zip 83544–9029; tel. 208/476–4555, (Nonreporting) **A**9 10 18 **S** Essentia
Health, Duluth, MN
Primary Contact: Patrick J. Branco, President
COO: Larry Barker, Chief Operating Officer
CFO: Lenne Bonner, Chief Financial Officer
Web address: www.smh–cvhc.org
Control: Other not–for–profit (including NFP Corporation) **Service:** General
Medical and Surgical

Staffed Beds: 23

STATE HOSPITAL NORTH, 300 Hospital Drive, Zip 83544–9034;
tel. 208/476–4511, (Nonreporting)
Primary Contact: Debra Manfull, Interim Chief Executive Officer
CMO: Karla Eisele, M.D., Clinical Director
CIO: James Sarbacher, Chief Information Officer
CHR: Heather Vandenbark, Human Resources Specialist
Web address: www.healthandwelfare.idaho.gov
Control: State–Government, nonfederal **Service:** Psychiatric

Staffed Beds: 60

POCATELLO—Bannock County

⊞ **PORTNEUF MEDICAL CENTER (130028)**, 777 Hospital Way,
Zip 83201–5175; tel. 208/239–1000 **A**1 2 3 5 9 10 20 **F**3 7 11 12 13 14 15
17 18 19 20 22 24 28 29 31 34 35 37 39 40 44 45 46 47 48 49 50 54 56
57 58 59 61 64 65 68 70 71 72 74 75 76 77 78 79 80 81 82 85 86 87 88
89 90 92 93 96 97 98 100 101 102 103 104 107 108 109 110 111 114 115
118 119 120 121 123 124 126 129 130 131 132 135 143 144 146 147 **P**2
S LHP Hospital Group, Plano, TX
Primary Contact: Daniel Ordyna, Chief Executive Officer
COO: Don Wadle, Vice President Clinical and Support Services
CFO: John Abreu, Vice President and Chief Financial Officer
CHR: Don Wadle, Interim Director Human Resources
CNO: Natalie R. Smith, R.N., Vice President Patient Care Services and Chief
Nursing Officer
Web address: www.portmed.org
Control: Corporation, Investor–owned, for–profit **Service:** General Medical and
Surgical

Staffed Beds: 175 **Admissions:** 8652 **Census:** 95 **Outpatient Visits:** 216566
Births: 1462 **Total Expense ($000):** 202474 **Payroll Expense ($000):**
73709 **Personnel:** 1055

ID

Hospital, Medicare Provider Number, Address, Telephone, Approval, Facility, and Physician Codes, Health Care System

★ American Hospital Association (AHA) membership
□ The Joint Commission accreditation ◇ DNV Healthcare Inc. accreditation

○ Healthcare Facilities Accreditation Program
△ Commission on Accreditation of Rehabilitation Facilities (CARF) accreditation

SAFE HAVEN HOSPITAL OF POCATELLO (134011), 1200 Hospital Way, Zip 83201–2708; tel. 208/232–2570, (Total facility includes 75 beds in nursing home–type unit) **A**10 **F**56 98 103 128 130 143 **P**6 **S** Safe Haven Health Care, Pocatello, ID
Primary Contact: Josiah Dahlstrom, Administrator
Web address: www.safehavenhealthcare.org/safehaven_hospital/index.html
Control: Corporation, Investor–owned, for–profit **Service:** Psychiatric

Staffed Beds: 87 **Admissions:** 422 **Census:** 76 **Outpatient Visits:** 0 **Births:** 0

POST FALLS—Kootenai County

☐ **NORTHERN IDAHO ADVANCED CARE HOSPITAL (132001)**, 600 North Cecil Road, Zip 83854–6200; tel. 208/262–2800, (Nonreporting) **A**1 9 10 **S** Ernest Health, Inc., Albuquerque, NM
Primary Contact: Maria Godley, R.N., Chief Executive Officer
Web address: www.niach.ernesthealth.com
Control: Corporation, Investor–owned, for–profit **Service:** Long–Term Acute Care hospital

Staffed Beds: 40

☐ **NORTHWEST SPECIALTY HOSPITAL (130066)**, 1593 East Polston Avenue, Zip 83854–5326; tel. 208/262–2300, (Nonreporting) **A**1 9 10 **S** National Surgical Hospitals, Chicago, IL
Primary Contact: Vaughn Ward, Chief Executive Officer
CFO: Rick Rasmussen, Chief Financial Officer
CIO: Craig McIntosh, Chief Information Officer
CHR: Gina Schneider, Director Human Resources
CNO: Christi Nance, R.N., Chief Nursing Officer
Web address: www.northwestspecialtyhospital.com
Control: Corporation, Investor–owned, for–profit **Service:** Surgical

Staffed Beds: 34

PRESTON—Franklin County

★ **FRANKLIN COUNTY MEDICAL CENTER (131322)**, 44 North First East Street, Zip 83263–1399; tel. 208/852–0137, (Nonreporting) **A**9 10 18
Primary Contact: Michael G. Andrus, Administrator and Chief Executive Officer
CFO: Paul Smart, CPA, Chief Financial Officer
CHR: Courtney Dursteler, Chief Human Resources Officer
CNO: Patrica Bowles, R.N., Chief Nursing Officer
Web address: www.fcmc.org
Control: County–Government, nonfederal **Service:** General Medical and Surgical

Staffed Beds: 65

REXBURG—Madison County

★ ◇ **MADISON MEMORIAL HOSPITAL (130025)**, 450 East Main Street, Zip 83440–2048, Mailing Address: P.O. Box 310, Zip 83440–0310; tel. 208/359–6900 **A**9 10 21 **F**3 8 11 13 15 29 30 31 32 34 35 40 41 45 49 59 60 65 66 68 70 72 75 76 77 78 79 81 82 85 86 87 89 91 93 96 107 108 111 115 118 119 130 146 147 148 **P**8
Primary Contact: Rachel Ann Gonzales, MSN, R.N., Chief Executive Officer
COO: Audrey Fletcher, Chief Operating Officer
CFO: Troy Christensen, Chief Financial Officer
CMO: Doug Cottrel, M.D., Chief Medical Officer
CNO: Robert Kendrick, Chief Nursing Officer
Web address: www.madisonhospital.org
Control: County–Government, nonfederal **Service:** General Medical and Surgical

Staffed Beds: 69 **Admissions:** 4221 **Census:** 21 **Outpatient Visits:** 29055 **Births:** 1470 **Total Expense ($000):** 43800 **Payroll Expense ($000):** 19769 **Personnel:** 402

RUPERT—Minidoka County

★ **MINIDOKA MEMORIAL HOSPITAL (131319)**, 1224 Eighth Street, Zip 83350–1599; tel. 208/436–0481, (Total facility includes 46 beds in nursing home–type unit) **A**9 10 18 **F**3 7 11 15 18 29 30 34 35 37 40 45 50 56 57 59 62 63 64 65 68 70 75 77 79 81 83 84 85 86 87 97 107 108 111 114 119 127 128 130 131 132 133 134 143 146 147 148 **P**1 3 5
Primary Contact: Carl Hanson, Administrator
COO: Joel Rogers, Chief Operating Officer
CFO: Jason Gibbons, Chief Financial Officer
CMO: Brian Muir, Chief of Staff
CIO: Nick Martin, Chief Information Officer
CHR: Tammy Hanks, Director Human Resources
CNO: Marcia Drage, R.N., Chief Nursing Officer
Web address: www.minidokamemorial.com
Control: County–Government, nonfederal **Service:** General Medical and Surgical

Staffed Beds: 72 **Admissions:** 516 **Census:** 47 **Outpatient Visits:** 16108 **Births:** 0 **Total Expense ($000):** 21819 **Payroll Expense ($000):** 9513 **Personnel:** 201

MINIDOKA MEMORIAL HOSPITAL AND EXTENDED CARE FACILITY See Minidoka Memorial Hospital

SAINT MARIES—Benewah County

★ **BENEWAH COMMUNITY HOSPITAL (131317)**, 229 South Seventh Street, Zip 83861–1803; tel. 208/245–5551 **A**9 10 18 **F**8 13 29 30 31 34 35 40 45 57 59 64 75 76 78 79 81 82 84 85 92 93 97 99 100 101 103 104 107 111 114 119 127 129 131 133 135 146 **P**6
Primary Contact: Brenda Parnell, Chief Executive Officer
CFO: Lori Stoltz, Chief Financial Officer
CMO: Terry Davenport, D.O., Chief of Staff
CHR: Marlana Barden, Director Human Resources
CNO: Jim Broyles, Director of Nursing
Web address: www.bchmed.org
Control: County–Government, nonfederal **Service:** General Medical and Surgical

Staffed Beds: 19 **Admissions:** 350 **Census:** 3

SALMON—Lemhi County

★ **STEELE MEMORIAL MEDICAL CENTER (131305)**, 203 South Daisy Street, Zip 83467–4709; tel. 208/756–5600 **A**9 10 18 **F**3 11 13 15 28 29 31 34 35 40 45 55 57 59 64 65 66 68 75 76 77 78 79 81 82 85 86 87 90 93 97 104 107 111 115 119 127 129 131 132 133 135 145 146 148 **P**6 **S** QHR, Brentwood, TN
Primary Contact: Jeff Hill, Chief Executive Officer
COO: Abner King, Chief Operating Officer
CFO: Gregory Hexem, Chief Financial Officer
CMO: Richard Natelson, M.D., Chief of Staff
CHR: Libby Brittain, Director Human Resources
CNO: Stephanie Orr, R.N., Chief Nursing Officer
Web address: www.steelemh.org
Control: County–Government, nonfederal **Service:** General Medical and Surgical

Staffed Beds: 18 **Admissions:** 404 **Census:** 3 **Outpatient Visits:** 28115 **Births:** 44 **Total Expense ($000):** 16693 **Payroll Expense ($000):** 6668 **Personnel:** 113

SANDPOINT—Bonner County

⊠ **BONNER GENERAL HOSPITAL (131328)**, 520 North Third Avenue, Zip 83864–1507; tel. 208/263–1441 **A**1 9 10 18 **F**3 11 13 15 17 22 26 28 29 30 34 35 40 45 46 47 48 54 57 59 62 63 64 68 75 76 77 79 81 85 86 87 93 102 107 108 110 111 114 118 119 130 131 132 142 144 146
Primary Contact: Sheryl Rickard, Chief Executive Officer
CIO: Bob Hess, Chief Information Officer
CHR: Brad Waterbury, Director Human Resources
CNO: Linda Rammler, R.N., Chief Nursing Officer
Web address: www.bonnergeneral.org/index.php
Control: Other not–for–profit (including NFP Corporation) **Service:** General Medical and Surgical

Staffed Beds: 25 **Admissions:** 1541 **Census:** 12 **Outpatient Visits:** 56614 **Births:** 344 **Total Expense ($000):** 43051 **Payroll Expense ($000):** 17753 **Personnel:** 297

SODA SPRINGS—Caribou County

★ **CARIBOU MEMORIAL HOSPITAL AND LIVING CENTER (131309)**, 300 South Third West, Zip 83276–1598; tel. 208/547–3341, (Total facility includes 30 beds in nursing home–type unit) **A**9 10 18 **F**11 34 40 56 57 59 70 76 81 107 127 128 130 133 148
Primary Contact: John L. Hoopes, Chief Executive Officer
CFO: Jon Smith, Chief Financial Officer
CMO: John K. Franson, M.D., Chief Medical Staff
CIO: Johnathan Inskeep, Chief Information Officer
CHR: Michael D. Peck, Assistant Administrator
CNO: Brenda Bergholm, MSN, Chief Nursing Officer
Web address: www.cariboumemorial.org
Control: County–Government, nonfederal **Service:** General Medical and Surgical

Staffed Beds: 55 **Admissions:** 296 **Census:** 22 **Outpatient Visits:** 11846 **Births:** 29 **Total Expense ($000):** 11817

TWIN FALLS—Twin Falls County

⊠ **ST. LUKE'S MAGIC VALLEY MEDICAL CENTER (130002)**, 801 Pole Line Road West, Zip 83301–5810, Mailing Address: P.O. Box 409, Zip 83303–0409; tel. 208/814–1000 **A**1 2 5 9 10 19 20 **F**3 4 5 7 8 11 13 15 18 20 22 29 30 31 35 40 57 62 63 68 70 72 76 77 78 79 81 85 87 89 90 93 96 98 107 110 111 114 119 130 146 **P**6 8 **S** St. Luke's Health System, Boise, ID
Primary Contact: James L. Angle, FACHE, Regional Chief Executive Officer
CFO: Joshua Custer, Director Finance
CIO: Melissa Capps, Site Leader Information Technology
CHR: Mark Stevens, Senior Director Human Resources
CNO: Amy Bearden, R.N., Vice President Patient Care Services and Chief Nursing Officer
Web address: www.stlukesonline.org
Control: Other not–for–profit (including NFP Corporation) **Service:** General Medical and Surgical

Staffed Beds: 224 **Admissions:** 10222 **Census:** 105 **Outpatient Visits:** 604359 **Births:** 1729 **Total Expense ($000):** 260707 **Payroll Expense ($000):** 86334 **Personnel:** 2441

ID

Many Facility Codes have changed. Please refer to the AHA Guide Code Chart. © 2014 AHA Guide

★ ◇ **WEISER MEMORIAL HOSPITAL (131307)**, 645 East Fifth Street,
Zip 83672–2202; tel. 208/549–0370, (Nonreporting) **A**9 10 18 21 **S** St. Luke's
Health System, Boise, ID
Primary Contact: Tom Murphy, Chief Executive Officer
CFO: Nate Coburn, Chief Financial Officer
CMO: Bryan L. Drake, D.O., Chief of Staff
CHR: Terri Kautz, Manager Human Resources
CNO: Reuben J. DeKastle, Chief Nursing Officer
Web address: www.weisermemorialhospital.org
Control: Hospital district or authority, Government, nonfederal **Service:** General
Medical and Surgical

Staffed Beds: 25

Hospital, Medicare Provider Number, Address, Telephone, Approval, Facility, and Physician Codes, Health Care System

★ American Hospital Association (AHA) membership
□ The Joint Commission accreditation   ◇ DNV Healthcare Inc. accreditation
○ Healthcare Facilities Accreditation Program
△ Commission on Accreditation of Rehabilitation Facilities (CARF) accreditation

ILLINOIS

ALEDO—Mercer County

★ **GENESIS MEDICAL CENTER–ALEDO (141304)**, 409 N.W. Ninth Avenue,
Zip 61231–1296; tel. 309/582–9100 **A**9 10 18 **F**3 11 15 29 30 34 35 40 45
50 54 56 57 59 64 75 77 79 81 82 85 87 93 94 97 107 108 114 119 127
128 130 131 133 144 146 147 **P**6 **S** Genesis Health System, Davenport, IA
Primary Contact: Ted Rogalski, Administrator
CFO: Mark G. Rogers, Chief Financial Officer
CMO: Kristen Wurzburger, M.D., Chief of Staff
CIO: Robert Frieden, Vice President Information Systems
CHR: Megan Clark, Coordinator Human Resources
CNO: Heidi Hess, Chief Nursing Officer
Web address: www.genesishealth.com
Control: Other not–for–profit (including NFP Corporation) **Service:** General
Medical and Surgical

Staffed Beds: 22 **Admissions:** 141 **Census:** 2 **Outpatient Visits:** 4710
Births: 0 **Total Expense ($000):** 5252 **Payroll Expense ($000):** 2187
Personnel: 99

ALTON—Madison County

✠ **ALTON MEMORIAL HOSPITAL (140002)**, One Memorial Drive,
Zip 62002–6722; tel. 618/463–7311, (Total facility includes 62 beds in nursing
home–type unit) **A**1 9 10 **F**3 4 5 7 11 13 15 18 20 22 29 30 31 34 35 38 39 40
45 46 49 50 56 57 59 64 69 70 74 75 76 77 78 79 81 85 86 87 89 92 93
96 98 103 104 107 108 110 111 114 115 116 117 118 119 120 121 123
128 129 130 131 132 146 148 **S** BJC HealthCare, Saint Louis, MO
Primary Contact: David A. Braasch, President
COO: Brad Goacher, Vice President Administration
CFO: Susan Koesterer, Regional Director Finance
CMO: Sebastian Rueckert, M.D., Vice President and Chief Medical Officer
CIO: David Weiss, Vice President Information System
CHR: Bryan Hartwick, Vice President Human Resources
CNO: Debra Turpin, R.N., Vice President Patient Care Services and Chief Nursing
Officer
Web address: www.altonmemorialhospital.org
Control: Other not–for–profit (including NFP Corporation) **Service:** General
Medical and Surgical

Staffed Beds: 253 **Admissions:** 7785 **Census:** 151 **Outpatient Visits:**
136642 **Births:** 697 **Total Expense ($000):** 128475 **Payroll Expense**
($000): 46542 **Personnel:** 730

☐ **ALTON MENTAL HEALTH CENTER (144016)**, 4500 College Avenue,
Zip 62002–5099; tel. 618/474–3800, (Nonreporting) **A**1 10 **S** Division of Mental
Health, Department of Human Services, Springfield, IL
Primary Contact: Brian E. Thomas, Administrator
CFO: Susan Shobe, Director Administration and Support Services
CMO: Claudia Kachigion, M.D., Medical Director
Control: State–Government, nonfederal **Service:** Psychiatric

Staffed Beds: 165

✠ **SAINT ANTHONY'S HEALTH CENTER (140052)**, 1 Saint Anthony's Way,
Zip 62002–4579, Mailing Address: PO Box 340, Zip 62002–0340;
tel. 618/465–2571, (Includes SAINT CLARE'S HOSPITAL, 915 East Fifth Street,
Zip 62002–6434; tel. 618/463–5151), (Total facility includes 30 beds in nursing
home–type unit) **A**1 2 9 10 **F**2 3 5 10 11 13 15 18 20 22 29 30 31 32 34 35
37 38 39 40 41 44 45 46 47 48 49 50 51 53 56 57 58 59 60 61 62 63 64
65 68 69 70 74 75 76 77 78 79 81 82 84 85 86 87 89 90 91 92 93 95 96
99 100 101 102 103 104 107 108 110 111 114 115 116 117 118 119 120
121 123 128 129 130 131 132 134 135 146 147 148 **P**6
Primary Contact: Sister M. Mikela Meidl, Chief Executive Officer
COO: Sister M. Anselma, Chief Operating Officer
CFO: Mike Nelson, Chief Financial Officer
CMO: Larry Burch, M.D., Vice President Medical Affairs
CIO: Sister M. Anselma, Chief Operating Officer
CHR: Sister M. Anselma, Chief Operating Officer
CNO: Deborah L. Birk, Ph.D., Vice President Patient Care Services
Web address: www.sahc.org
Control: Church–operated, Nongovernment, not–for profit **Service:** General
Medical and Surgical

Staffed Beds: 203 **Admissions:** 4010 **Census:** 56 **Outpatient Visits:** 119389
Births: 310 **Total Expense ($000):** 76428 **Payroll Expense ($000):** 28574
Personnel: 605

ANNA—Union County

☐ **CHOATE MENTAL HEALTH CENTER (144038)**, 1000 North Main Street,
Zip 62906–1699; tel. 618/833–5161, (Nonreporting) **A**1 10 **S** Division of Mental
Health, Department of Human Services, Springfield, IL
Primary Contact: Elaine Ray, Administrator
COO: Elaine Ray, Administrator
CMO: John Larcas, M.D., Acting Medical Director
CIO: Cindy Flamm, Manager Quality
CHR: Tammy Tellor, Acting Director Human Resources
Control: State–Government, nonfederal **Service:** Psychiatric

Staffed Beds: 79

✠ **UNION COUNTY HOSPITAL (141342)**, 517 North Main Street,
Zip 62906–1696; tel. 618/833–4511, (Total facility includes 22 beds in nursing
home–type unit) **A**1 9 10 18 **F**3 11 15 28 29 30 34 35 40 45 49 50 57 59 64
68 75 77 81 85 87 93 97 107 110 114 119 127 130 133 146 148 **P**6
S Community Health Systems, Inc., Franklin, TN
Primary Contact: James R. Farris, FACHE, Chief Executive Officer
CFO: Terry Paligo, Chief Financial Officer
CMO: Tamer Aiti, M.D., Chief of Staff
CIO: John Hegger, Director Information Systems
CHR: Tammy Samuels, Director Human Resources
CNO: Melanie Koch, R.N., Chief Nursing Officer
Web address: www.unioncountyhospital.com
Control: Corporation, Investor–owned, for–profit **Service:** General Medical and
Surgical

Staffed Beds: 47 **Admissions:** 637 **Census:** 22 **Outpatient Visits:** 35105
Births: 2 **Total Expense ($000):** 18923 **Payroll Expense ($000):** 8346

ARLINGTON HEIGHTS—Cook County

✠ **NORTHWEST COMMUNITY HOSPITAL (140252)**, 800 West Central Road,
Zip 60005–2392; tel. 847/618–1000 **A**1 2 9 10 **F**3 5 13 15 17 18 20 22 24
26 28 29 30 31 32 34 35 37 38 39 40 41 43 44 45 46 47 49 50 54 55 56
57 59 61 62 63 64 65 68 70 71 72 73 74 75 76 77 78 79 81 82 84 85 86
87 89 92 93 94 96 98 99 100 101 102 103 104 105 106 107 108 110 111
114 115 116 117 118 119 120 121 123 124 126 129 130 131 132 135 144
145 146 147 148 **P**8
Primary Contact: Stephen Scogna, President and Chief Executive Officer
COO: Michael Hartke, Executive Vice President, Chief Operating Officer
CFO: Marsha Liu, Executive Vice President and Chief Financial Officer
CMO: Eric Benink, M.D., Chief Medical Officer
CIO: Glen Malan, Vice President Information Technology and Chief Information
Officer
CHR: Ann M. Patrick, Vice President Human Resources
CNO: Kimberly Nagy, R.N., Executive Vice President, Patient Services and Chief
Nursing Officer
Web address: www.nch.org
Control: Other not–for–profit (including NFP Corporation) **Service:** General
Medical and Surgical

Staffed Beds: 358 **Admissions:** 27360 **Census:** 224 **Outpatient Visits:**
350672 **Births:** 2869 **Total Expense ($000):** 418192 **Payroll Expense**
($000): 177709 **Personnel:** 3205

AURORA—Du Page and Kane Counties

✠ **PRESENCE MERCY MEDICAL CENTER (140174)**, 1325 North Highland
Avenue, Zip 60506–1449; tel. 630/859–2222 **A**1 2 9 10 **F**3 5 12 13 15 18 20
22 24 26 28 29 30 31 34 35 36 38 40 43 45 46 49 56 57 59 61 65 68 70
73 75 76 77 78 79 81 82 85 86 87 93 97 98 99 100 101 102 103 104 105
107 111 114 115 119 125 126 130 132 135 144 146 147 **P**5 **S** Presence
Health, Chicago, IL
Primary Contact: Michael L. Brown, Regional President and Chief Executive Officer
COO: Mary Vonderau, Vice President Strategy and Operations
Web address: www.provena.org/mercy/
Control: Other not–for–profit (including NFP Corporation) **Service:** General
Medical and Surgical

Staffed Beds: 123 **Admissions:** 9238 **Census:** 117 **Outpatient Visits:**
254424 **Births:** 433 **Total Expense ($000):** 180974 **Payroll Expense**
($000): 51715 **Personnel:** 788

PROVENA MERCY MEDICAL CENTER See Presence Mercy Medical Center

Many Facility Codes have changed. Please refer to the AHA Guide Code Chart. © 2014 AHA Guide

IL

✠ △ **RUSH–COPLEY MEDICAL CENTER (140029)**, 2000 Ogden Avenue, Zip 60504–7222; tel. 630/978–6200 **A**1 2 3 5 7 9 10 **F**3 7 9 13 15 17 18 19 20 22 24 26 28 29 30 31 32 34 35 36 37 38 39 40 42 43 44 45 46 47 49 50 51 52 53 54 55 56 57 58 59 60 61 62 64 65 66 68 70 72 73 74 75 76 77 78 79 81 82 84 85 86 87 89 90 92 93 96 97 107 108 110 111 114 115 117 118 119 120 121 123 130 131 132 134 135 143 144 145 146 147 148 **P**6 **S** Rush University Medical Center, Chicago, IL
Primary Contact: Barry C. Finn, President and Chief Executive Officer
COO: John A. Diederich, Senior Vice President Operations and Chief Operating Officer
CFO: Brenda VanWyhe, Senior Vice President Finance and Chief Financial Officer
CMO: Steve B. Lowenthal, M.D., Senior Vice President Medical Affairs and Chief Medical Officer
CIO: Dennis DeMasie, Vice President Information Systems and Chief Information Officer
CNO: Mary Shilkaitis, Vice President Patient Care and Chief Nursing Officer
Web address: www.rushcopley.com
Control: Other not–for–profit (including NFP Corporation) **Service:** General Medical and Surgical

Staffed Beds: 210 **Admissions:** 13287 **Census:** 155 **Outpatient Visits:** 215967 **Births:** 3326 **Total Expense ($000):** 260873 **Payroll Expense ($000):** 105226 **Personnel:** 1595

BARRINGTON—Lake County

★ ◇ **ADVOCATE GOOD SHEPHERD HOSPITAL (140291)**, 450 West Highway 22, Zip 60010–1919; tel. 847/381–0123 **A**2 9 10 21 **F**3 11 12 13 15 17 18 19 20 22 24 26 28 29 30 31 34 35 36 37 40 43 45 46 47 48 49 54 57 59 63 64 65 68 70 74 75 76 77 78 79 81 82 84 87 89 91 92 93 94 97 100 101 102 103 104 105 107 110 111 114 115 118 119 120 121 123 126 129 130 132 135 146 **P**8 **S** Advocate Health Care, Downers Grove, IL
Primary Contact: Karen A. Lambert, President
COO: Michael Ploszek, Vice President Physician Strategy and Clinical Operations
CFO: George Teufel, Vice President Finance
CMO: Barry Rosen, M.D., Vice President Medical Management
CIO: Chuck Malik, Director Information Systems
CHR: Jason Spigner, Vice President Human Resources
CNO: Marianne D. Araujo, R.N., Vice President Nursing and Chief Nurse Executive
Web address: www.advocatehealth.com/gshp/
Control: Church–operated, Nongovernment, not–for profit **Service:** General Medical and Surgical

Staffed Beds: 169 **Admissions:** 8835 **Census:** 93 **Outpatient Visits:** 229739 **Births:** 1382 **Total Expense ($000):** 220166 **Payroll Expense ($000):** 73965 **Personnel:** 785

BELLEVILLE—St. Clair County

★ ○ **MEMORIAL HOSPITAL (140185)**, 4500 Memorial Drive, Zip 62226–5399; tel. 618/233–7750, (Total facility includes 70 beds in nursing home–type unit) **A**9 10 11 **F**3 11 13 15 18 20 22 24 26 28 29 30 31 34 37 39 40 45 46 49 51 53 54 57 59 60 62 64 70 71 74 75 76 77 79 81 82 84 85 86 87 89 92 93 94 96 107 108 110 111 112 114 115 118 119 126 128 129 130 131 132 135 145 146 147 148 **P**6 8
Primary Contact: Mark J. Turner, President and Chief Executive Officer
COO: Michael T. McManus, Chief Operating Officer
CFO: Amy Thomas, Vice President Finance
CMO: William Casperson, M.D., Vice President Medical Affairs
CIO: Jennifer Meinkoth, Chief Information Officer
CHR: John C. Ziegler, FACHE, Vice President Human Resources
CNO: Nancy R. Weston, R.N., Vice President Nursing Services
Web address: www.memhosp.com
Control: Other not–for–profit (including NFP Corporation) **Service:** General Medical and Surgical

Staffed Beds: 345 **Admissions:** 16388 **Census:** 238 **Outpatient Visits:** 315101 **Births:** 1579 **Total Expense ($000):** 257360 **Payroll Expense ($000):** 98663 **Personnel:** 2076

✠ △ **ST. ELIZABETH'S HOSPITAL (140187)**, 211 South Third Street, Zip 62220–1998; tel. 618/234–2120 **A**1 3 5 7 9 10 **F**3 4 5 11 13 15 18 20 22 24 26 28 29 30 35 39 40 45 46 49 50 53 54 56 57 59 60 64 65 68 70 74 75 77 78 79 81 82 85 86 87 90 93 97 98 100 101 102 103 104 105 107 108 111 115 116 117 118 119 121 124 129 130 131 132 135 144 146 147 148 **P**6 8 **S** Hospital Sisters Health System, Springfield, IL
Primary Contact: Maryann Reese, R.N., FACHE, President and Chief Executive Officer
CFO: David Nosacka, Chief Financial Officer
CMO: Shelly Harkins, M.D., Chief Medical Officer
CIO: Leslee Martin, Manager Information Technology
CHR: Jason T. Snow, Director People Services
CNO: Shelley Harris, MSN, Chief Nursing Officer
Web address: www.steliz.org
Control: Church–operated, Nongovernment, not–for profit **Service:** General Medical and Surgical

Staffed Beds: 260 **Admissions:** 10429 **Census:** 116 **Outpatient Visits:** 161310 **Births:** 901 **Total Expense ($000):** 163745 **Payroll Expense ($000):** 53070 **Personnel:** 1074

BENTON—Franklin County

★ **FRANKLIN HOSPITAL DISTRICT (141321)**, 201 Bailey Lane, Zip 62812–1969; tel. 618/439–3161 **A**9 10 18 **F**11 15 29 30 34 35 40 45 56 57 59 66 75 77 81 93 97 107 114 119 127 132 133 **P**6
Primary Contact: Hervey E. Davis, Chief Executive Officer
COO: Michael J. Budnick, FACHE, Chief Operating Officer
CMO: David Hartman, M.D., Chief of Staff
CIO: David Williams, Director Information Technology
CHR: Nancy Seibert, Director Human Resources
CNO: Terri Hermann, R.N., Chief Nursing Officer
Web address: www.franklinhospital.net
Control: Hospital district or authority, Government, nonfederal **Service:** General Medical and Surgical

Staffed Beds: 25 **Admissions:** 301 **Census:** 2 **Outpatient Visits:** 13336 **Births:** 0 **Total Expense ($000):** 14348 **Payroll Expense ($000):** 7257 **Personnel:** 165

BERWYN—Cook County

✠ **MACNEAL HOSPITAL (140054)**, 3249 South Oak Park Avenue, Zip 60402–0715; tel. 708/783–9100 **A**1 2 3 5 8 9 10 13 **F**3 5 13 15 18 19 20 22 24 26 28 29 30 31 34 35 37 40 43 45 46 47 49 50 54 56 57 58 59 64 65 68 70 73 74 75 76 77 78 79 81 82 84 85 86 87 89 92 93 96 97 98 100 101 102 103 104 105 107 108 110 111 114 119 121 126 130 131 132 141 146 147 148 **P**5 6 8 **S** TENET Healthcare Corporation, Dallas, TX
Primary Contact: J. Scott Steiner, Chief Executive Officer
CFO: Michael A. Lawrence, Chief Financial Officer
CMO: Charles Bareis, M.D., Medical Director
CIO: Peyman Zand, Interim Chief Information Officer, Chicago Market
CHR: Richard Dodsworth, Vice President Human Resources
CNO: Kathleen Benjamin, R.N., Chief Nursing Officer
Web address: www.macneal.com
Control: Corporation, Investor–owned, for–profit **Service:** General Medical and Surgical

Staffed Beds: 371 **Admissions:** 16727 **Census:** 219 **Outpatient Visits:** 198589 **Births:** 1753 **Total Expense ($000):** 224871 **Payroll Expense ($000):** 99654 **Personnel:** 1907

BLOOMINGTON—Mclean County

✠ **OSF ST. JOSEPH MEDICAL CENTER (140162)**, 2200 East Washington Street, Zip 61701–4323; tel. 309/662–3311, (Total facility includes 12 beds in nursing home–type unit) **A**1 2 9 10 **F**3 11 12 13 15 18 20 22 24 28 29 30 31 34 35 37 40 43 45 49 50 51 54 57 59 60 61 64 65 66 68 70 74 75 76 77 78 79 81 82 84 85 86 87 89 92 93 96 97 107 108 110 111 114 115 118 119 127 128 130 131 132 135 144 146 147 148 **P**6 **S** OSF Healthcare System, Peoria, IL
Primary Contact: Chad Boore, President and Chief Executive Officer
CFO: John R. Zell, Chief Financial Officer
CMO: Paul E. Pedersen, M.D., Vice President and Chief Medical Officer
CHR: Sue A. Herriott, Director Human Resources
CNO: Deborah S. Smith, R.N., Vice President, Chief Nursing Officer
Web address: www.osfstjoseph.org
Control: Church–operated, Nongovernment, not–for profit **Service:** General Medical and Surgical

Staffed Beds: 149 **Admissions:** 6875 **Census:** 72 **Outpatient Visits:** 358192 **Births:** 891 **Total Expense ($000):** 153346 **Payroll Expense ($000):** 54585 **Personnel:** 887

IL

BLUE ISLAND—Cook County

✠ **METROSOUTH MEDICAL CENTER (140118)**, 12935 South Gregory Street, Zip 60406–2470; tel. 708/597–2000 **A**1 9 10 **F**3 13 15 18 20 22 24 26 28 29 30 31 34 35 40 43 47 49 50 53 56 59 60 62 63 70 72 74 75 76 78 79 81 82 83 84 85 87 93 96 97 98 102 103 107 108 110 111 114 115 118 119 126 129 130 135 141 142 146 147 148 **S** Community Health Systems, Inc., Franklin, TN
Primary Contact: Brian Sinotte, Chief Executive Officer
COO: Barbara Fideli, Chief Operating Officer, Non–clinical Services
CFO: Pamela Cassara, Chief Financial Officer
CIO: Bashirat Hahn, Chief Information Officer
CHR: Russell Hale, Director Human Resources
CNO: Kathleen Hartman, Chief Nursing Officer
Web address: www.metrosouthmedicalcenter.com
Control: Corporation, Investor–owned, for–profit **Service:** General Medical and Surgical

> **Staffed Beds:** 285 **Admissions:** 9679 **Census:** 99 **Outpatient Visits:** 44016 **Births:** 1562 **Total Expense ($000):** 131358 **Payroll Expense ($000):** 75189 **Personnel:** 800

BOLINGBROOK—Will County

✠ **ADVENTIST BOLINGBROOK HOSPITAL (140304)**, 500 Remington Boulevard, Zip 60440–4906; tel. 630/312–5000 **A**1 9 10 **F**3 12 13 15 18 20 22 28 29 30 31 34 35 37 40 43 45 46 47 49 50 51 52 54 56 57 58 59 60 61 64 65 66 68 70 73 74 75 76 78 79 81 82 85 86 87 92 93 96 107 108 110 111 114 115 119 129 130 131 132 145 146 147 148 **P**7 8 **S** Adventist Health System Sunbelt Health Care Corporation, Altamonte Springs, FL
Primary Contact: Rick Mace, Chief Executive Officer
CFO: Mike Murrill, Vice President and Chief Financial Officer
CMO: Richard Carroll, M.D., Chief Medical officer
CIO: John McLendon, Senior Vice President and Chief Information Officer
CHR: Gerald Staley, Director Human Resources
CNO: Jolene Albaugh, R.N., Vice President and Chief Nursing Officer
Web address: www.keepingyouwell.com/abh/
Control: Church–operated, Nongovernment, not–for profit **Service:** General Medical and Surgical

> **Staffed Beds:** 148 **Admissions:** 5417 **Census:** 53 **Outpatient Visits:** 84402 **Births:** 915 **Total Expense ($000):** 106969 **Payroll Expense ($000):** 34106 **Personnel:** 511

BREESE—Clinton County

✠ **ST. JOSEPH'S HOSPITAL (140145)**, 9515 Holy Cross Lane, Zip 62230–3618; tel. 618/526–4511 **A**1 9 10 **F**3 11 13 15 28 29 30 32 34 35 40 43 50 53 56 57 59 68 70 79 81 85 93 103 107 108 110 111 115 118 119 124 127 129 130 131 132 134 135 144 146 148 **S** Hospital Sisters Health System, Springfield, IL
Primary Contact: Paulette Evans, R.N., MSN, Interim President and Chief Executive Officer
CFO: John Jeffries, Director Finance
CHR: Robert J. Otrembiak, Director Human Resources
CNO: Paulette Evans, R.N., Chief Nursing Officer
Web address: www.stjoebreese.com
Control: Church–operated, Nongovernment, not–for profit **Service:** General Medical and Surgical

> **Staffed Beds:** 60 **Admissions:** 1433 **Census:** 10 **Outpatient Visits:** 94486 **Births:** 512 **Total Expense ($000):** 43338 **Payroll Expense ($000):** 15081 **Personnel:** 316

CANTON—Fulton County

✠ **GRAHAM HOSPITAL (140001)**, 210 West Walnut Street, Zip 61520–2497; tel. 309/647–5240, (Total facility includes 38 beds in nursing home–type unit) **A**1 6 9 10 20 **F**3 11 13 15 26 28 29 30 40 45 50 53 54 57 59 62 63 64 65 67 70 75 76 77 79 81 82 85 87 89 91 93 97 107 108 110 111 114 115 119 124 127 128 129 130 131 132 135 143 144 145 146 **P**3
Primary Contact: Robert G. Senneff, FACHE, President and Chief Executive Officer
CFO: Eric Franz, Vice President, Finance and Chief Financial Officer
CHR: Canise A. McComb, Director Human Resources
CNO: Teresa L. McConkey, MSN, Vice President Nursing and Chief Nursing Officer
Web address: www.grahamhospital.org
Control: Other not–for–profit (including NFP Corporation) **Service:** General Medical and Surgical

> **Staffed Beds:** 87 **Admissions:** 2524 **Census:** 51 **Outpatient Visits:** 189799 **Births:** 269 **Total Expense ($000):** 70134 **Payroll Expense ($000):** 28867 **Personnel:** 569

CARBONDALE—Jackson County

✠ **MEMORIAL HOSPITAL OF CARBONDALE (140164)**, 405 West Jackson Street, Zip 62901–1467, Mailing Address: P.O. Box 10000, Zip 62902–9000; tel. 618/549–0721 **A**1 2 3 5 9 10 **F**3 11 13 18 20 22 24 26 28 29 30 31 34 35 40 45 46 48 49 54 56 57 59 64 68 70 72 74 75 76 77 78 79 81 82 83 84 85 86 87 89 107 108 111 114 115 119 120 121 126 130 131 132 135 145 146 147 **P**1 **S** Southern Illinois Hospital Services, Carbondale, IL
Primary Contact: Bart Millstead, Administrator
CFO: Michael Kasser, Vice President Chief Financial Officer and Treasurer
CMO: Marci Moore–Connelly, M.D., Vice President Chief Medical Officer
CIO: David Holland, Vice President Chief Innovation Officer
CHR: Pamela S. Henderson, Vice President Human Resources
CNO: Julie Firman, R.N., Vice President and Chief Nursing Officer
Web address: www.sih.net
Control: Other not–for–profit (including NFP Corporation) **Service:** General Medical and Surgical

> **Staffed Beds:** 159 **Admissions:** 10547 **Census:** 93 **Outpatient Visits:** 116413 **Births:** 2020 **Total Expense ($000):** 209059 **Payroll Expense ($000):** 55536 **Personnel:** 936

CARLINVILLE—Macoupin County

★ **CARLINVILLE AREA HOSPITAL (141347)**, 20733 North Broad Street, Zip 62626–1499; tel. 217/854–3141 **A**9 10 18 **F**11 15 28 29 34 35 40 45 64 77 79 81 91 93 107 110 115 129 133 **P**6 **S** HealthTech Management Services, Brentwood, TN
Primary Contact: Kenneth G. Reid, President and Chief Executive Officer
CFO: Mike Brown, Chief Financial Officer
CMO: Kate Williams, M.D., President, Medical Staff
CIO: Jerod Cottingham, Director Information Systems
CHR: Tracy Koster, Director Human Resources
CNO: Sara McPeak, Chief Nursing Officer
Web address: www.cahcare.com
Control: Other not–for–profit (including NFP Corporation) **Service:** General Medical and Surgical

> **Staffed Beds:** 25 **Admissions:** 616 **Census:** 8 **Outpatient Visits:** 22028 **Births:** 0 **Total Expense ($000):** 18413 **Payroll Expense ($000):** 6560 **Personnel:** 144

CARROLLTON—Greene County

THOMAS H. BOYD MEMORIAL HOSPITAL (141300), 800 School Street, Zip 62016–1498; tel. 217/942–6946, (Includes REISCH MEMORIAL NURSING HOME), (Nonreporting) **A**9 10 18
Primary Contact: Deborah Campbell, Administrator
CHR: Lisa Eldridge, Human Resources Officer
Control: Other not–for–profit (including NFP Corporation) **Service:** General Medical and Surgical

> **Staffed Beds:** 65

CARTHAGE—Hancock County

☐ **MEMORIAL HOSPITAL (141305)**, 1454 North County Road 2050, Zip 62321–3551, Mailing Address: P.O. Box 160, Zip 62321–0160; tel. 217/357–8500 **A**1 9 10 18 **F**3 11 13 15 29 30 31 34 35 36 40 45 56 57 59 64 75 76 80 81 82 85 87 103 107 108 110 115 119 125 127 128 129 130 132 133 144 146
Primary Contact: Ada Bair, Chief Executive Officer
COO: Florine Dixon, Chief Operating Officer
CFO: Teresa Smith, Chief Financial Officer
CIO: Syndi Horn, Director Information Systems
CHR: Dan Smith, Director Human Resources
Web address: www.mhtlc.org
Control: Other not–for–profit (including NFP Corporation) **Service:** General Medical and Surgical

> **Staffed Beds:** 18 **Admissions:** 611 **Census:** 7 **Outpatient Visits:** 17921 **Births:** 112 **Total Expense ($000):** 20457 **Payroll Expense ($000):** 8007 **Personnel:** 175

CENTRALIA—Marion County

✠ **ST. MARY'S HOSPITAL (140034)**, 400 North Pleasant Avenue, Zip 62801–3056; tel. 618/436–8000 **A**1 2 9 10 **F**3 5 11 13 15 18 20 26 28 29 30 31 32 34 35 37 38 40 44 45 46 50 54 57 59 61 64 68 70 73 74 75 76 77 78 79 80 81 82 84 85 86 87 89 90 91 92 93 94 98 99 100 101 102 103 104 105 107 108 110 111 114 118 119 120 121 129 130 131 132 135 146 147 148 **P**6 8 **S** SSM Health, Saint Louis, MO
Primary Contact: Bruce Merrell, FACHE, President
COO: Mark A. Clark, Vice President Operations
CFO: Kay Tinsley, Vice President Finance
CMO: Rajendra Shroff, M.D., Administrative Medical Director
CIO: Ralph Caudill, Director Information Systems
CHR: Thomas W. Blythe, Vice President Human Resources
Web address: www.smgsi.com
Control: Church–operated, Nongovernment, not–for profit **Service:** General Medical and Surgical

> **Staffed Beds:** 113 **Admissions:** 5573 **Census:** 58 **Outpatient Visits:** 200716 **Births:** 340 **Total Expense ($000):** 98717 **Payroll Expense ($000):** 36013 **Personnel:** 787

Many Facility Codes have changed. Please refer to the AHA Guide Code Chart.

CENTREVILLE—St. Clair County

☐ **TOUCHETTE REGIONAL HOSPITALS (140077)**, 5900 Bond Avenue, Zip 62207–2326; tel. 618/332–3060 **A**1 9 10 **F**3 11 13 15 18 29 31 40 45 47 50 54 55 62 64 68 70 73 75 76 78 79 81 85 87 89 92 98 99 101 102 104 105 107 108 110 114 119 125 130 135 143 144 146 148 **P**6
Primary Contact: Larry W. McCulley, President and Chief Executive Officer
COO: Tom Mikkelson, M.D., Interim Chief Operating Officer
CFO: John Majchrzak, Chief Financial Officer
CMO: Tom Mikkelson, M.D., Vice President Medical Affairs
Web address: www.touchette.org
Control: Other not–for–profit (including NFP Corporation) **Service:** General Medical and Surgical

Staffed Beds: 119 **Admissions:** 2540 **Census:** 26 **Outpatient Visits:** 53151 **Births:** 280 **Total Expense ($000):** 55972 **Payroll Expense ($000):** 26313 **Personnel:** 489

CHAMPAIGN—Champaign County

☐ **THE PAVILION (144029)**, 809 West Church Street, Zip 61820–3399; tel. 217/373–1700, (Nonreporting) **A**1 9 10 **S** Universal Health Services, Inc., King of Prussia, PA
Primary Contact: Joseph Sheehy, Chief Executive Officer and Managing Director
CFO: Edith Frasca, Controller and Chief Financial Officer
Web address: www.pavilionhospital.com
Control: Corporation, Investor–owned, for–profit **Service:** Psychiatric

Staffed Beds: 46

CHESTER—Randolph County

☐ **CHESTER MENTAL HEALTH CENTER**, Chester Road, Zip 62233–0031, Mailing Address: Box 31, Zip 62233–0031; tel. 618/826–4571 **A**1 **F**29 30 39 86 98 106 130 **P**6 **S** Division of Mental Health, Department of Human Services, Springfield, IL
Primary Contact: Leah Hammel, Acting Administrator
CFO: Sarah Imhoff, Business Administrator
CMO: Maitra Rupa, M.D., Acting Medical Director
CIO: Anthony Young, Information Services Specialist
CHR: Kim Holsapple, Human Resource Specialist
CNO: Jennifer Klingeman, Director of Nursing
Control: State–Government, nonfederal **Service:** Psychiatric

Staffed Beds: 245 **Admissions:** 257 **Census:** 239 **Outpatient Visits:** 0 **Births:** 0 **Total Expense ($000):** 33198 **Payroll Expense ($000):** 27513 **Personnel:** 394

☐ **MEMORIAL HOSPITAL (141338)**, 1900 State Street, Zip 62233–1116, Mailing Address: P.O. Box 609, Zip 62233–0609; tel. 618/826–4581, (Nonreporting) **A**1 9 10 18
Primary Contact: Brett Bollmann, Administrator
CFO: Gail Miesner, Chief Financial Officer
CMO: Alan Liefer, M.D., President Medical Staff
CIO: Becky Bunselmeyer, Director Information Services
CHR: May Rose, Director Human Resources
Web address: www.mhchester.com
Control: Hospital district or authority, Government, nonfederal **Service:** General Medical and Surgical

Staffed Beds: 25

CHICAGO—Cook County

ADVOCATE BETHANY HOSPITAL See RML Specialty Hospital

🗷 **ADVOCATE ILLINOIS MASONIC MEDICAL CENTER (140182)**, 836 West Wellington Avenue, Zip 60657–5147; tel. 773/975–1600 **A**1 2 3 5 8 9 10 12 13 **F**3 5 13 15 17 18 19 20 22 24 26 28 29 30 31 32 33 34 35 36 38 39 40 43 44 45 46 47 48 49 50 53 54 55 56 57 58 59 60 61 64 66 68 70 71 72 73 74 75 76 77 78 79 81 82 84 85 86 87 89 90 92 93 96 97 98 99 100 101 102 103 104 107 108 110 111 115 117 118 119 120 121 123 124 126 130 131 132 134 135 141 143 146 147 148 **P**6 8 **S** Advocate Health Care, Downers Grove, IL
Primary Contact: Susan Nordstrom Lopez, President
CFO: Jack Gilbert, Vice President Finance and Support Services
CMO: Robert Zadylak, M.D., Vice President Medical Management
CIO: John Alban, Director Information Systems
CHR: Katie Bata, Vice President Human Resources
CNO: Donna J. King, R.N., Vice President Clinical Operations and Chief Nursing Executive
Web address: www.advocatehealth.com/masonic
Control: Other not–for–profit (including NFP Corporation) **Service:** General Medical and Surgical

Staffed Beds: 328 **Admissions:** 14529 **Census:** 198 **Outpatient Visits:** 175086 **Births:** 2656 **Total Expense ($000):** 322693 **Payroll Expense ($000):** 135351 **Personnel:** 2173

★ ◇ **ADVOCATE TRINITY HOSPITAL (140048)**, 2320 East 93rd Street, Zip 60617–3983; tel. 773/967–2000 **A**9 10 21 **F**1 3 4 11 13 15 16 17 18 20 22 24 26 28 29 30 31 34 35 40 45 49 50 56 57 58 59 60 61 65 67 68 70 72 73 74 75 76 77 78 79 80 81 82 84 87 88 89 90 92 93 98 107 108 110 111 114 115 119 126 128 129 130 132 146 148 **P**5 8 **S** Advocate Health Care, Downers Grove, IL
Primary Contact: Michelle Gaskill, R.N., President
CFO: Maureen Morrison, Vice President Financial Services
CMO: Dianna Grant, M.D., Vice President Medical Management
CIO: Bonita Brown–Roberts, Director Information Systems
CHR: Daylashunta Randolph, Senior Vice President Human Resources
CNO: Jacquelyn Whitten, R.N., Chief Nurse Executive and Vice President Nursing
Web address: www.advocatehealth.com/trinity
Control: Other not–for–profit (including NFP Corporation) **Service:** General Medical and Surgical

Staffed Beds: 188 **Admissions:** 11104 **Census:** 111 **Outpatient Visits:** 76550 **Births:** 1171 **Total Expense ($000):** 155998 **Payroll Expense ($000):** 57757 **Personnel:** 917

🗷 **ANN & ROBERT H. LURIE CHILDREN'S HOSPITAL OF CHICAGO (143300)**, 225 East Chicago Avenue, Zip 60611–2991; tel. 312/227–4000 **A**1 2 3 5 8 9 10 **F**3 8 9 11 12 17 18 19 21 23 25 27 29 30 31 32 34 35 36 37 38 39 40 41 43 44 45 46 48 49 50 51 54 55 57 58 59 60 61 63 64 65 68 72 74 75 78 79 81 82 84 85 86 87 88 89 91 92 93 94 96 97 98 99 100 101 102 104 105 107 108 111 113 115 116 117 118 119 124 126 129 130 131 132 134 136 137 138 139 141 142 144 146 148
Primary Contact: Patrick M. Magoon, President and Chief Executive Officer
COO: Gordon B. Bass, Chief Operating Officer
CFO: Paula Noble, Chief Financial Officer and Treasurer
CMO: Michael Kelleher, Chief Medical Officer
CIO: Stan Krok, Chief Information Officer
CHR: Barbara Bowman, Chief Human Resource Officer
Web address: www.luriechildrens.org
Control: Other not–for–profit (including NFP Corporation) **Service:** Children's general

Staffed Beds: 288 **Admissions:** 11573 **Census:** 191 **Outpatient Visits:** 511271 **Births:** 0 **Total Expense ($000):** 629308 **Payroll Expense ($000):** 259833 **Personnel:** 4422

☐ **AURORA CHICAGO LAKESHORE HOSPITAL (144005)**, 4840 North Marine Drive, Zip 60640–4296; tel. 773/878–9700, (Nonreporting) **A**1 3 5 9 10 **S** Aurora Behavioral Health Care, Corona, CA
Primary Contact: C. Alan Eaks, Chief Executive Officer
CFO: Carol Peart, Chief Financial Officer
CMO: Peter Nierman, M.D., Chief Medical Officer
CHR: Johanne Jeanty, Director Human Resources
CNO: Beth Jelesky, Director of Nursing and Director Clinical Services
Web address: www.chicagolakeshorehospital.com
Control: Corporation, Investor–owned, for–profit **Service:** Psychiatric

Staffed Beds: 108

BERNARD MITCHELL HOSPITAL See University of Chicago Medical Center

CHICAGO LYING–IN HOSPITAL See University of Chicago Medical Center

☐ **CHICAGO–READ MENTAL HEALTH CENTER (144010)**, 4200 North Oak Park Avenue, Zip 60634–1457; tel. 773/794–4000, (Nonreporting) **A**1 10 **S** Division of Mental Health, Department of Human Services, Springfield, IL
Primary Contact: Thomas Simpatico, M.D., Facility Director and Network System Manager
Control: State–Government, nonfederal **Service:** Psychiatric

Staffed Beds: 200

CHILDREN'S MEMORIAL HOSPITAL See Ann & Robert H. Lurie Children's Hospital of Chicago

☐ **GARFIELD PARK HOSPITAL (144039)**, 520 North Ridgeway Avenue, Zip 60624–1232; tel. 773/265–3700, (Nonreporting) **A**1 10 **S** Universal Health Services, Inc., King of Prussia, PA
Primary Contact: Kathe Dellacecca, Chief Executive Officer
CFO: Patricia Ellison, Chief Financial Officer
CMO: Tina Mahera, M.D., Chief Medical Officer
CHR: Janice Clark, Manager Human Resources
Web address: www.garfieldparkhospital.com
Control: Corporation, Investor–owned, for–profit **Service:** Children's hospital psychiatric

Staffed Beds: 88

IL

☐ **HARTGROVE HOSPITAL (144026)**, 5730 West Roosevelt Road, Zip 60644–1580; tel. 773/413–1700, (Nonreporting) **A**1 10 **S** Universal Health Services, Inc., King of Prussia, PA
Primary Contact: Steven Airhart, Chief Executive Officer
CFO: Srbo Nikolic, Chief Financial Officer
CMO: Johnny Williamson, M.D., Chief Medical Officer
CHR: Anthony Rivera, Director Human Resources
CNO: Jody Bhambra, Chief Nursing Officer
Web address: www.hartgrovehospital.com
Control: Corporation, Investor–owned, for–profit **Service:** Psychiatric

Staffed Beds: 128

★ ○ **HOLY CROSS HOSPITAL (140133)**, 2701 West 68th Street, Zip 60629–1882; tel. 773/884–9000 **A**9 10 11 **F**4 5 13 15 18 20 22 28 29 30 31 34 35 38 40 41 44 45 50 51 54 57 58 59 60 61 64 65 66 67 68 70 74 75 76 77 78 79 81 82 83 84 85 86 87 90 91 92 93 97 107 108 109 110 111 114 115 119 120 121 130 132 135 146 147 148 **S** Sinai Health System, Chicago, IL
Primary Contact: Lori Pacura, R.N., MSN, Senior Vice President
COO: Paul M. Teodo, Chief Operating Officer
CFO: Loren Chandler, Interim, Vice President and Chief Financial Officer
CMO: Catherine Kallal, M.D., Chief Medical Officer
CIO: Ken Slawkowski, Interim Director Information Systems
CHR: Doris Gutierrez, Director Human Resources
CNO: Katherine Loeb, R.N., Interim Vice President, Patient Care Services
Web address: www.holycrosshospital.org
Control: Other not–for–profit (including NFP Corporation) **Service:** General Medical and Surgical

Staffed Beds: 213 **Admissions:** 8750 **Census:** 107 **Outpatient Visits:** 58905 **Births:** 392 **Total Expense ($000):** 99963 **Payroll Expense ($000):** 50354 **Personnel:** 722

☐ **JACKSON PARK HOSPITAL AND MEDICAL CENTER (140177)**, 7531 Stony Island Avenue, Zip 60649–3993; tel. 773/947–7500 **A**1 9 10 **F**2 3 5 13 15 18 29 30 31 32 34 35 38 40 45 50 56 59 61 63 64 65 66 68 70 74 75 76 77 78 79 81 82 84 85 87 93 97 98 100 101 102 104 105 107 108 110 115 119 130 132 135 143 144 147 148
Primary Contact: William Dorsey, M.D., Board Chairman and Chief Executive Officer
COO: Randall Smith, Executive Vice President
CFO: Nelson Vasquez, Vice President Finance
CMO: Bangalore Murthy, M.D., Director Medical Staff
CIO: Thomas Pankow, Chief Information Officer
CHR: Tracey Jones, Director Human Resources
Web address: www.jacksonparkhospital.org
Control: Other not–for–profit (including NFP Corporation) **Service:** General Medical and Surgical

Staffed Beds: 118 **Admissions:** 8861 **Census:** 102 **Outpatient Visits:** 49126 **Births:** 307 **Total Expense ($000):** 90734 **Payroll Expense ($000):** 40843 **Personnel:** 607

✠ △ **JESSE BROWN VETERANS AFFAIRS MEDICAL CENTER**, 820 South Damen, Zip 60612–3776; tel. 312/569–8387, (Total facility includes 22 beds in nursing home–type unit) **A**1 3 5 7 8 **F**2 3 5 8 10 11 12 14 15 17 18 20 22 24 26 28 29 30 31 34 35 38 39 40 44 45 46 47 50 53 54 57 58 59 60 61 62 63 64 65 68 70 71 74 75 77 78 79 80 81 82 84 85 86 87 93 94 97 98 100 101 102 104 105 106 107 111 119 126 127 129 130 132 133 135 143 144 146 147 148 **S** Department of Veterans Affairs, Washington, DC
Primary Contact: Ann R. Brown, FACHE, Director
COO: Michelle Blakely, Associate Director
CFO: Kalpana Mehta, Chief Fiscal Services
CMO: Wendy W. Brown, M.D., Chief of Staff
CIO: Howard Loewenstein, Chief Information Resource Management Services
CHR: Wayne Davis, Manager Human Resources
Web address: www.chicago.va.gov/
Control: Veterans Affairs, Government, federal **Service:** General Medical and Surgical

Staffed Beds: 198 **Admissions:** 8349 **Census:** 164 **Outpatient Visits:** 934565 **Births:** 0 **Personnel:** 3008

✠ **JOHN H. STROGER JR. HOSPITAL OF COOK COUNTY (140124)**, 1969 West Ogden Avenue, Zip 60612–3714; tel. 312/864–6000 **A**1 2 3 5 8 9 10 13 **F**3 5 11 13 15 16 17 18 19 20 22 24 29 30 31 35 36 38 39 40 41 42 43 44 45 46 47 48 49 51 52 54 55 56 58 59 60 61 64 65 68 70 72 74 75 76 77 78 79 81 82 84 85 86 87 88 89 91 92 93 94 97 99 100 101 102 103 104 107 108 110 111 114 115 118 119 121 123 129 130 132 134 135 146 147 148 **P**6 **S** Cook County Health and Hospitals System, Chicago, IL
Primary Contact: W. Peter Daniels, Chief Operating Officer
CFO: John R. Morales, Chief Financial Officer
CMO: Claudia Fegan, M.D., Chief Medical Officer
CIO: Bala Hota, Interim Chief Information Officer
CHR: Paris I. Partee, Associate Administrator and Director Human Resources
CNO: Antoinette Williams, Chief Nursing Officer
Web address: www.cookcountyhealth.net
Control: County–Government, nonfederal **Service:** General Medical and Surgical

Staffed Beds: 460 **Admissions:** 22558 **Census:** 294 **Outpatient Visits:** 827943 **Births:** 798 **Total Expense ($000):** 918361 **Payroll Expense ($000):** 414932 **Personnel:** 5420

JOHNSTON R. BOWMAN HEALTH CENTER See Rush University Medical Center

KINDRED CHICAGO LAKESHORE See Kindred Chicago–Central Hospital

✠ **KINDRED CHICAGO–CENTRAL HOSPITAL (142009)**, 4058 West Melrose Street, Zip 60641–4797; tel. 773/736–7000, (Includes KINDRED CHICAGO LAKESHORE, 6130 North Sheridan Road, Zip 60660; tel. 773/381–1222; Diane Otteman, Chief Executive Officer; KINDRED HOSPITAL CHICAGO NORTH, 2544 West Montrose Avenue, Zip 60618–1589; tel. 773/267–2622; Larry Foster, R.N., MSN, Chief Executive Officer), (Nonreporting) **A**1 9 10 **S** Kindred Healthcare, Louisville, KY
Primary Contact: Bruce Carey, Chief Executive Officer
COO: Joanne Garcia, Chief Operating Officer
CFO: Mary Treacy Shiff, Chief Financial Officer
Web address: www.khchicagocentral.com
Control: Corporation, Investor–owned, for–profit **Service:** Long–Term Acute Care hospital

Staffed Beds: 187

KINDRED HOSPITAL CHICAGO NORTH See Kindred Chicago–Central Hospital

✠ **LA RABIDA CHILDREN'S HOSPITAL (143301)**, 6501 South Promontory Drive, Zip 60649–1003; tel. 773/363–6700 **A**1 3 5 9 10 **F**3 12 19 28 29 30 32 34 35 38 40 41 50 57 58 59 64 65 74 75 77 79 82 85 86 87 89 91 93 96 97 99 100 102 104 130 132 134 143 144 146 148 **P**6
Primary Contact: Brenda J. Wolf, President and Chief Executive Officer
CFO: Mark Renfree, Chief Financial Officer
CMO: Dilek Bishku, M.D., Vice President Medical Affairs
CIO: Timothy Diamond, Chief Information Officer
CHR: Frances Lefkow, Director Human Resources
Web address: www.larabida.org
Control: Other not–for–profit (including NFP Corporation) **Service:** Children's chronic disease

Staffed Beds: 49 **Admissions:** 683 **Census:** 17 **Outpatient Visits:** 30137 **Births:** 0 **Total Expense ($000):** 47336 **Payroll Expense ($000):** 21394 **Personnel:** 441

☐ **LORETTO HOSPITAL (140083)**, 645 South Central Avenue, Zip 60644–5059; tel. 773/626–4300 **A**1 10 **F**2 3 4 5 15 18 29 30 31 34 35 38 40 44 45 50 54 57 59 60 61 64 65 68 70 74 75 78 79 81 85 86 87 89 92 93 98 102 103 104 105 106 107 108 115 119 130 132 143 146 147 148
Primary Contact: Sonia Mehta, M.D., Chief Executive Officer and Chief Medical Officer
CFO: John Valles, Senior Vice President and Chief Financial Officer
CMO: Sonia Mehta, M.D., Chief Executive Officer and Chief Medical Officer
CIO: Suresh Krishnan, Vice President and Chief Information Officer
CHR: Amy Coleman, Director Human Resources
CNO: James M. Renneker, MSN, Vice President and Chief Nursing Officer
Web address: www.lorettohospital.org
Control: Other not–for–profit (including NFP Corporation) **Service:** General Medical and Surgical

Staffed Beds: 176 **Admissions:** 4183 **Census:** 63 **Outpatient Visits:** 33212 **Births:** 0 **Total Expense ($000):** 60110 **Payroll Expense ($000):** 28660 **Personnel:** 483

✠ **LOUIS A. WEISS MEMORIAL HOSPITAL (140082)**, 4646 North Marine Drive, Zip 60640–5759; tel. 773/878–8700 **A**1 2 3 5 9 10 **F**3 8 9 15 18 20 22 24 28 29 31 34 35 36 37 40 44 45 49 56 57 58 59 62 64 65 66 68 70 74 75 77 78 79 81 82 84 85 86 87 90 92 93 96 97 98 100 101 102 103 107 108 110 111 114 118 119 121 126 129 130 131 132 135 141 143 146 148 **P**5 6 8 **S** TENET Healthcare Corporation, Dallas, TX
Primary Contact: Anthony Tedeschi, M.D., M.P.H., Chief Executive Officer and Chief Medical Officer
CFO: Jeffrey L. Meigs, Chief Financial Officer
CMO: Anthony Tedeschi, M.D., Chief Executive Officer and Chief Medical Officer
CIO: Thomas Crawford, Chicago Market Chief Information Officer
CHR: Keoni Nader, Director Human Resources
Web address: www.weisshospital.com
Control: Corporation, investor–owned, for–profit **Service:** General Medical and Surgical

Staffed Beds: 184 **Admissions:** 5925 **Census:** 87 **Outpatient Visits:** 72134 **Births:** 0 **Total Expense ($000):** 121021 **Payroll Expense ($000):** 45879 **Personnel:** 691

Many Facility Codes have changed. Please refer to the AHA Guide Code Chart. © 2014 AHA Guide

IL

★ ○ **MERCY HOSPITAL AND MEDICAL CENTER (140158)**, 2525 South Michigan Avenue, Zip 60616–2333; tel. 312/567–2000 **A**2 3 5 9 10 11 **F**3 5 12 13 15 17 18 20 22 24 26 28 29 30 31 32 34 35 40 44 45 46 49 50 51 52 53 54 55 56 57 58 59 61 64 65 66 70 73 74 76 77 78 79 81 82 85 86 87 89 90 92 93 96 97 98 99 100 101 102 103 104 105 107 108 110 111 114 115 117 118 119 121 123 124 126 130 131 132 133 134 135 143 144 145 146 147 148 **P**5 6 **S** Catholic Health East / Trinity Health, Livonia, MI
Primary Contact: Carol L. Schneider, President and Chief Executive Officer
COO: Richard Cerceo, Executive Vice President and Chief Operating Officer
CFO: Eric Krueger, Chief Financial Officer
CMO: Michael McDonnell, M.D., Chief Medical Officer
CIO: John Romeo, Chief Information Officer
CHR: Nancy L. Hill–Davis, Vice President Human Resources and Risk Management
CNO: Carla Campbell, R.N., Chief Nurse Officer
Web address: www.mercy–chicago.org
Control: Other not–for–profit (including NFP Corporation) **Service:** General Medical and Surgical

Staffed Beds: 189 **Admissions:** 14195 **Census:** 169 **Outpatient Visits:** 374320 **Births:** 2522 **Total Expense ($000):** 238776 **Payroll Expense ($000):** 100248 **Personnel:** 1548

○ **METHODIST HOSPITAL OF CHICAGO (140197)**, 5025 North Paulina Street, Zip 60640–2772; tel. 773/271–9040, (Nonreporting) **A**9 10 11
Primary Contact: Joseph Chandy, Administrator
CFO: Jim Gregory, Controller
Web address: www.bethanymethodist.org
Control: Other not–for–profit (including NFP Corporation) **Service:** General Medical and Surgical

Staffed Beds: 189

⊠ **MOUNT SINAI HOSPITAL (140018)**, California Avenue at 15th Street, Zip 60608–1729; tel. 773/542–2000, (Includes SINAI CHILDREN'S HOSPITAL, California Avenue at 15th Street, Zip 60608; tel. 888/287–4624), (Nonreporting) **A**1 2 3 5 8 9 10 12 13 **S** Sinai Health System, Chicago, IL
Primary Contact: Karen Teitelbaum, President and Chief Executive Officer
CFO: Charles Weis, Chief Financial Officer
CMO: Jack Garon, M.D., Chief Medical Officer
CIO: Richard Dunkin, Vice President and Chief Information Officer
CHR: Andrew Wissel, Director Human Resources
Web address: www.sinai.org
Control: Other not–for–profit (including NFP Corporation) **Service:** General Medical and Surgical

Staffed Beds: 290

⊠ **NORTHWESTERN MEMORIAL HOSPITAL (140281)**, 251 East Huron Street, Zip 60611–2908; tel. 312/926–2000, (Includes PRENTICE WOMEN'S HOSPITAL, 250 East Superior Street, Zip 60611; tel. 312/926–2000; STONE INSTITUTE OF PSYCHIATRY, 320 East Huron Street, Zip 60611; tel. 312/926–2000) **A**1 2 3 5 8 9 10 **F**3 4 5 6 8 9 11 12 13 14 15 17 18 20 22 24 26 28 29 30 31 32 33 34 35 36 37 38 39 40 42 43 44 45 46 47 48 49 50 51 52 53 54 55 56 57 58 59 60 61 62 63 64 65 66 68 70 72 73 74 75 76 77 78 79 80 81 82 83 84 85 86 87 92 93 97 98 99 100 101 102 103 104 105 106 107 108 110 111 114 115 116 117 118 119 120 121 123 124 126 129 130 131 132 134 135 136 137 138 139 141 142 143 144 145 146 147 148 **P**5 6 **S** Northwestern Memorial Healthcare, Chicago, IL
Primary Contact: Dean M. Harrison, President and Chief Executive Officer
CFO: Peter J. McCanna, Executive Vice President Administration and Chief Financial Officer
CMO: Michael G. Ankin, M.D., Vice President Medical Affairs & Chief Medical Officer
CIO: Timothy R. Zoph, Senior Vice President and Chief Information Officer
CHR: Dean Manheimer, Senior Vice President Human Resources
Web address: www.nmh.org
Control: Other not–for–profit (including NFP Corporation) **Service:** General Medical and Surgical

Staffed Beds: 885 **Admissions:** 49397 **Census:** 644 **Outpatient Visits:** 670110 **Births:** 12615 **Total Expense ($000):** 1345210 **Payroll Expense ($000):** 479910 **Personnel:** 6447

☐ **NORWEGIAN AMERICAN HOSPITAL (140206)**, 1044 North Francisco Avenue, Zip 60622–2743; tel. 773/292–8200 **A**1 3 5 6 9 10 **F**5 13 15 18 19 20 22 29 31 32 34 35 36 38 39 40 44 45 46 47 48 49 50 56 57 59 63 64 65 68 70 71 74 75 76 77 78 79 81 82 84 86 87 89 91 92 93 94 96 97 98 100 101 102 103 107 110 111 114 118 119 130 143 146 147 148 **P**8
Primary Contact: Jose R. Sanchez, President and Chief Executive Officer
COO: Abha Agrawal, M.D., Vice President Medical Administration and Chief Operating Officer
CFO: Gary M. Krugel, Chief Financial Officer
CIO: Mariusz Mazek, Chief Information Officer
CHR: Marcia Powers, Vice President Human Resources
CNO: Deborah A. Jasovsky, Ph.D., Chief Nursing Officer
Web address: www.nahospital.org
Control: Other not–for–profit (including NFP Corporation) **Service:** General Medical and Surgical

Staffed Beds: 185 **Admissions:** 6977 **Census:** 91 **Outpatient Visits:** 85047 **Births:** 1234 **Total Expense ($000):** 96060 **Payroll Expense ($000):** 45602 **Personnel:** 729

OUR LADY OF THE RESURRECTION MEDICAL CENTER See Presence Our Lady of the Resurrection Medical Center

PRENTICE WOMEN'S HOSPITAL See Northwestern Memorial Hospital

⊠ **PRESENCE OUR LADY OF THE RESURRECTION MEDICAL CENTER (140251)**, 5645 West Addison Street, Zip 60634–4403; tel. 773/282–7000, (Nonreporting) **A**1 9 10 **S** Presence Health, Chicago, IL
Primary Contact: John D. Baird, Regional President and Chief Executive Officer
COO: Dennis FitzMaurice, Vice President, Professional Services
CFO: Richard Franco, Chief Financial Officer
CMO: David Bordo, M.D., Vice President and Chief Medical Officer
CIO: George Chessum, Senior Vice President and Chief Information Officer
CHR: Ivy McKinley, Regional Human Resources Officer
CNO: Carole Miserendino, MSN, Vice President Patient Care Services and Chief Nursing Officer
Web address: www.presencehealth.org
Control: Church–operated, Nongovernment, not–for profit **Service:** General Medical and Surgical

Staffed Beds: 269

⊠ △ **PRESENCE RESURRECTION MEDICAL CENTER (140117)**, 7435 West Talcott Avenue, Zip 60631-3746; tel. 773/774–8000, (Nonreporting) **A**1 2 3 5 7 9 10 13 **S** Presence Health, Chicago, IL
Primary Contact: John D. Baird, Regional President and Chief Executive Officer
CFO: Richard Franco, Chief Financial Officer
CMO: Stephen Talty, M.D., President Medical Staff
CIO: George Chessum, Senior Vice President Information Systems and Chief Information Officer
CHR: Paul Skiem, Senior Vice President Human Resources
CNO: Carole Miserendino, MSN, Vice President Patient Care Services and Chief Nursing Officer
Web address: www.presencehealth.org
Control: Church–operated, Nongovernment, not–for profit **Service:** General Medical and Surgical

Staffed Beds: 402

⊠ **PRESENCE SAINT JOSEPH HOSPITAL (140224)**, 2900 North Lake Shore Drive, Zip 60657-6274; tel. 773/665–3000, (Nonreporting) **A**1 2 3 5 9 10 **S** Presence Health, Chicago, IL
Primary Contact: Roberta Luskin–Hawk, M.D., President and Chief Executive Officer
CFO: Stanley Kazmierczak, Controller
CMO: M. Todd Grendon, M.D., President Medical Staff
CIO: George Chessum, Senior Vice President Information Systems and Chief Information Officer
CHR: Denise Brown, Vice President Human Resources
Web address: www.reshealth.org
Control: Church–operated, Nongovernment, not–for profit **Service:** General Medical and Surgical

Staffed Beds: 320

IL

Hospital, Medicare Provider Number, Address, Telephone, Approval, Facility, and Physician Codes, Health Care System

★ American Hospital Association (AHA) membership
☐ The Joint Commission accreditation
◇ DNV Healthcare Inc. accreditation
○ Healthcare Facilities Accreditation Program
△ Commission on Accreditation of Rehabilitation Facilities (CARF) accreditation

✠ **PRESENCE SAINTS MARY & ELIZABETH MEDICAL CENTER (140180)**, 2233 West Division Street, Zip 60622–3086; tel. 312/770–2000, (Includes SAINTS MARY & ELIZABETH MEDICAL CENTER, CLAREMONT AVENUE, 1431 North Claremont Avenue, Zip 60622–1791; tel. 773/278–2000; Margaret McDermott, Chief Executive Officer), (Total facility includes 25 beds in nursing home–type unit) **A**1 2 9 10 **F**3 4 5 13 15 17 18 19 20 22 24 26 28 29 30 31 32 34 35 36 40 42 45 47 49 50 51 52 57 58 59 60 64 65 66 68 70 72 74 75 76 77 78 79 81 82 85 86 87 89 90 91 92 93 96 97 98 99 100 101 102 103 104 105 106 107 108 110 111 114 115 116 117 119 120 121 123 126 128 129 130 132 135 143 146 147 148 **P**8 **S** Presence Health, Chicago, IL
Primary Contact: Martin H. Judd, President and Chief Executive Officer
CFO: Kenneth A. Kautzer, Senior Vice President Finance and Treasurer
CIO: Steven Smith, Chief Information Officer
Web address: www.smemc.reshealth.org
Control: Church–operated, Nongovernment, not–for profit **Service:** General Medical and Surgical

Staffed Beds: 476 **Admissions:** 19406 **Census:** 302 **Outpatient Visits:** 176666 **Births:** 1512 **Personnel:** 1999

✠ **PROVIDENT HOSPITAL OF COOK COUNTY (140300)**, 500 East 51st Street, Zip 60615–2494; tel. 312/572–2000 **A**1 3 5 9 10 **F**3 5 8 15 18 29 30 34 35 40 45 50 53 57 59 60 61 64 66 68 78 81 85 87 92 94 104 107 119 130 132 135 143 146 147 **S** Cook County Health and Hospitals System, Chicago, IL
Primary Contact: Thomas J. Dohm, Interim Chief Operating Officer
COO: Michele T. Thompson, Deputy Chief Operating Officer
CFO: Barbara Patterson, Chief Financial Officer
CMO: Aaron Hamb, M.D., Chief Medical Officer
CIO: Donna Hart, Chief Information Officer
Web address: www.ccbhs.org/pages/ProvidentHospitalofCookCounty.htm
Control: County–Government, nonfederal **Service:** General Medical and Surgical

Staffed Beds: 25 **Admissions:** 1409 **Census:** 16 **Outpatient Visits:** 35245 **Births:** 0 **Total Expense ($000):** 61150 **Payroll Expense ($000):** 34059 **Personnel:** 376

✠ **REHABILITATION INSTITUTE OF CHICAGO (143026)**, 345 East Superior Street, Zip 60611–2654; tel. 312/238–1000, (Nonreporting) **A**1 3 5 9 10
Primary Contact: Joanne C. Smith, M.D., President and Chief Executive Officer
COO: Peggy Kirk, Senior Vice President Clinical Operations
CFO: Ed Case, Executive Vice President and Chief Financial Officer
CMO: James Sliwa, M.D., Chief Medical Officer
CIO: Tim McKula, Vice President Information Systems and Chief Information Officer
CHR: Lois Huggins, Chief Human Resources Officer and Senior Vice President Human Resources
Web address: www.ric.org
Control: Other not–for–profit (including NFP Corporation) **Service:** Rehabilitation

Staffed Beds: 182

RESURRECTION MEDICAL CENTER See Presence Resurrection Medical Center

★ **RML SPECIALTY HOSPITAL (142012)**, 3435 West Van Buren Street, Zip 60624–3312; tel. 773/826–6300 **F**1 3 18 29 30 31 45 53 58 74 85 107 114 119 130 146 148
Primary Contact: James R. Prister, President and Chief Executive Officer
COO: Ken Pawola, Chief Operating Officer
CFO: Tom Pater, Vice President Finance and Chief Financial Officer
CMO: Joseph Rosman, M.D., Chief Medical Director
CIO: Julie Ames, Chief Information Officer
CHR: John Landstrom, Vice President Human Resources and Operations
Web address: www.rmlspecialtyhospital.org
Control: Other not–for–profit (including NFP Corporation) **Service:** Long–Term Acute Care hospital

Staffed Beds: 68 **Admissions:** 462 **Census:** 42 **Outpatient Visits:** 20 **Births:** 0 **Total Expense ($000):** 27446 **Payroll Expense ($000):** 14022 **Personnel:** 249

○ **ROSELAND COMMUNITY HOSPITAL (140068)**, 45 West 111th Street, Zip 60628–4294; tel. 773/995–3000, (Nonreporting) **A**9 10 11
Primary Contact: Timothy Egan, Chief Restructuring Officer and President
CMO: Rogelio Cave, M.D., Medical Director
CIO: William Spence, Director
CNO: Winifred Lewis, R.N., Chief Nursing Officer
Web address: www.roselandhospital.org
Control: Other not–for–profit (including NFP Corporation) **Service:** General Medical and Surgical

Staffed Beds: 115

✠ △ **RUSH UNIVERSITY MEDICAL CENTER (140119)**, 1653 West Congress Parkway, Zip 60612–3833; tel. 312/942–5000, (Includes JOHNSTON R. BOWMAN HEALTH CENTER, 700 South Paulina, Zip 60612; tel. 312/942–7000; RUSH CHILDREN'S HOSPITAL, 1653 Wes Congress Parkway, tel. 888/352–7874) **A**1 2 3 5 7 8 9 10 **F**2 3 6 8 9 11 12 13 14 15 17 18 19 20 21 22 23 24 25 26 27 28 29 30 31 32 34 35 36 37 38 39 40 41 43 44 45 46 47 48 49 50 51 52 55 56 57 58 59 60 61 62 63 64 65 66 68 70 72 73 74 75 76 77 78 79 81 82 83 84 85 86 87 88 89 90 91 92 93 94 95 96 97 98 99 100 101 102 103 104 105 107 110 111 114 115 117 118 119 120 121 123 124 125 126 129 130 131 132 134 135 136 137 138 139 141 142 145 146 147 148 **P**8 **S** Rush University Medical Center, Chicago, IL
Primary Contact: Larry J. Goodman, M.D., Chief Executive Officer
COO: Peter W. Butler, President and Chief Operating Officer
CFO: John P. Mordach, Senior Vice President and Chief Financial Officer
CMO: David A. Ansell, M.D., Senior Vice President Clinical Affairs and Chief Medical Officer
CIO: Lac Tran, Senior Vice President Information Services
CHR: Mary Ellen Schopp, Senior Vice President Human Resources
CNO: Cynthia Barginere, MSN, Vice President Clinical Nursing and Chief Nursing Officer
Web address: www.rush.edu
Control: Other not–for–profit (including NFP Corporation) **Service:** General Medical and Surgical

Staffed Beds: 679 **Admissions:** 31839 **Census:** 482 **Outpatient Visits:** 522767 **Births:** 2128 **Total Expense ($000):** 922795 **Payroll Expense ($000):** 292592 **Personnel:** 8296

✠ **SAINT ANTHONY HOSPITAL (140095)**, 2875 West 19th Street, Zip 60623–3596; tel. 773/484–1000 **A**1 3 5 9 10 **F**3 13 15 18 19 29 30 31 32 33 34 35 40 41 44 49 50 51 53 54 57 59 64 65 68 70 74 75 76 77 78 79 81 82 85 86 87 89 93 96 97 98 100 101 102 104 105 107 110 111 115 118 119 130 131 132 143 144 146 147 148 **P**8
Primary Contact: Guy A. Medaglia, President and Chief Executive Officer
CFO: Justin Bynum, Chief Financial Officer
CIO: Mark Jennings, Chief Information Officer
CHR: Malinda Yvonne Carter, Chief Human Resource Manager
CNO: Jill Stemmerman, R.N., Vice President Nursing
Web address: www.sahchicago.org
Control: Church–operated, Nongovernment, not–for profit **Service:** General Medical and Surgical

Staffed Beds: 151 **Admissions:** 6768 **Census:** 83 **Outpatient Visits:** 108200 **Births:** 1804 **Total Expense ($000):** 97021 **Payroll Expense ($000):** 48258 **Personnel:** 869

SAINT JOSEPH HOSPITAL See Presence Saint Joseph Hospital

SAINTS MARY & ELIZABETH MEDICAL CENTER See Presence Saints Mary & Elizabeth Medical Center

✠ △ **SCHWAB REHABILITATION HOSPITAL (143025)**, 1401 South California Avenue, Zip 60608–1858; tel. 773/522–2010, (Nonreporting) **A**1 3 5 7 9 10 **S** Sinai Health System, Chicago, IL
Primary Contact: Alan H. Channing, President and Chief Executive Officer
COO: Karen Teitelbaum, Executive Vice President and Chief Operating Officer
CFO: Charles Weis, Chief Financial Officer
CMO: Karl J. Sandin, M.D., Senior Vice President and Chief Medical Officer
CIO: Peter Ingram, Vice President and Chief Information Officer
CHR: Andrew Wissel, Director Human Resources
Web address: www.schwabrehab.org
Control: Other not–for–profit (including NFP Corporation) **Service:** Rehabilitation

Staffed Beds: 101

☐ **SHRINERS HOSPITALS FOR CHILDREN–CHICAGO (143302)**, 2211 North Oak Park Avenue, Zip 60707–3392; tel. 773/622–5400, (Nonreporting) **A**1 3 5 10 **S** Shriners Hospitals for Children, Tampa, FL
Primary Contact: Mark L. Niederpruem, FACHE, Administrator
CFO: Philip Magid, Director Fiscal Services
CMO: Jeffrey D. Ackman, M.D., Chief of Staff
CIO: Jeffrey Vana, Director Information Services
CHR: James E. Pawlowicz, Director Human Resources
Web address: www.shrinershospitalsforchildren.org/Hospitals/Locations/Chicago.aspx
Control: Other not–for–profit (including NFP Corporation) **Service:** Children's orthopedic

Staffed Beds: 36

○ **SOUTH SHORE HOSPITAL (140181)**, 8012 South Crandon Avenue, Zip 60617–1124; tel. 773/768–0810, (Nonreporting) **A**10 11
Primary Contact: Timothy Caveney, President
CFO: Scott Spencer, Chief Financial Officer
CMO: James Bob Achebe, M.D., President Medical Staff
CIO: Jim Ritchie, Director Management Information Systems
CHR: Roger Rak, Director Human Resources
CNO: Laura Gonzalez, Interim Chief Nurse Executive
Web address: www.southshorehospital.com
Control: Other not–for–profit (including NFP Corporation) **Service:** General Medical and Surgical

Staffed Beds: 125

IL

☐ **ST. BERNARD HOSPITAL AND HEALTH CARE CENTER (140103)**, 326 West 64th Street, Zip 60621–3146; tel. 773/962–3900, (Nonreporting) **A**1 9 10
Primary Contact: Charles Holland, President and Chief Executive Officer
COO: Roland Abellera, Chief Quality Officer and Vice President Clinical Operations
CFO: Guy Alton, Chief Financial Officer
CIO: Guy Alton, Chief Financial Officer
CHR: Donna Dertz, Director Human Resources
CNO: Evelyn Jones, R.N., Vice President Nursing Services
Web address: www.stbernardhospital.com
Control: Church–operated, Nongovernment, not–for profit **Service:** General Medical and Surgical

Staffed Beds: 100

★ ○ **SWEDISH COVENANT HOSPITAL (140114)**, 5145 North California Avenue, Zip 60625–3661; tel. 773/878–8200 **A**2 9 10 11 12 13 **F**3 8 13 15 18 19 20 22 24 26 28 29 30 31 32 34 35 36 38 40 45 46 47 49 50 53 56 57 58 59 60 62 64 68 70 74 75 76 78 79 81 82 84 85 86 87 89 90 92 93 96 97 98 100 101 102 103 104 105 107 108 110 111 114 115 117 118 119 121 123 124 126 128 129 130 131 132 134 135 143 146 147 148 **P**1 5 7
Primary Contact: Mark Newton, President and Chief Executive Officer
COO: Anthony Guaccio, Senior Vice President & Chief Operating Officer
CFO: Thomas J. Garvey, Senior Vice President Operations and Chief Financial Officer
CMO: Derek J. Kelly, M.D., Vice President Transformation and Chief Medical Information Officer
CIO: Karen Sheehan, Vice President and Chief Information Officer
CHR: Anthony Guaccio, Senior Vice President and Chief Operating Officer
CNO: Mary Shehan, R.N., Senior Vice President and Chief Nursing Officer
Web address: www.schosp.org
Control: Church–operated, Nongovernment, not–for profit **Service:** General Medical and Surgical

Staffed Beds: 279 **Admissions:** 14066 **Census:** 199 **Outpatient Visits:** 253588 **Births:** 1814 **Total Expense ($000):** 247686 **Payroll Expense ($000):** 101372 **Personnel:** 1899

○ **THOREK MEMORIAL HOSPITAL (140115)**, 850 West Irving Park Road, Zip 60613–3077; tel. 773/525–6780, (Nonreporting) **A**9 10 11
Primary Contact: Edward Budd, President and Chief Executive Officer
COO: Peter N. Kamberos, Chief Operating Officer
CMO: Ilona Carlos, M.D., President Medical Staff
CIO: Tony Vavarutsos, Director Information Systems
CHR: Brett Wakefield, Director Human Resources
CNO: Mary McCahill, Chief Nursing Officer
Web address: www.thorek.org
Control: Other not–for–profit (including NFP Corporation) **Service:** General Medical and Surgical

Staffed Beds: 134

UNIVERSITY OF CHICAGO COMER CHILDREN'S HOSPITAL See University of Chicago Medical Center

☒ **UNIVERSITY OF CHICAGO MEDICAL CENTER (140088)**, 5841 South Maryland Avenue, Zip 60637–1447; tel. 773/702–1000, (Includes BERNARD MITCHELL HOSPITAL, 950 East 59th Street, Zip 60637; CHICAGO LYING–IN HOSPITAL, 950 East 59th Street, Zip 60637; tel. 312/684–6100; UNIVERSITY OF CHICAGO COMER CHILDREN'S HOSPITAL, 5721 South Maryland Avenue, Zip 60637; tel. 312/702–6168) **A**1 2 3 5 8 9 10 **F**3 5 6 9 11 12 13 14 15 16 17 18 19 20 21 22 23 24 25 26 27 28 29 30 31 32 34 35 36 37 38 40 41 43 44 45 46 47 48 49 50 51 52 54 55 56 57 58 59 60 61 63 64 65 68 70 71 72 73 74 75 76 77 78 79 81 82 83 84 85 86 87 88 89 92 93 97 100 101 102 104 107 108 109 110 111 112 114 115 116 117 118 119 120 121 123 124 126 129 130 131 132 134 135 136 137 138 139 140 141 142 143 144 145 146 147 148 **P**1
Primary Contact: Sharon L. O'Keefe, R.N., President
COO: Jason Keeler, Executive Vice President and Chief Operating Officer
CFO: James Watson, Chief Financial Officer
CMO: Stephen Weber, M.D., Chief Medical Officer
CIO: Eric Yablonka, Vice President and Chief Information Officer
CHR: Robert Hanley, Chief Human Resources Officer
CNO: Debra Albert, MSN, Senior Vice President Patient Care and Chief Nursing Officer
Web address: www.uchospitals.edu
Control: Other not–for–profit (including NFP Corporation) **Service:** General Medical and Surgical

Staffed Beds: 580 **Admissions:** 26089 **Census:** 430 **Outpatient Visits:** 658811 **Births:** 1662 **Total Expense ($000):** 1258610 **Payroll Expense ($000):** 463838 **Personnel:** 7839

☒ △ **UNIVERSITY OF ILLINOIS HOSPITAL & HEALTH SCIENCES SYSTEM (140150)**, 1740 West Taylor Street, Zip 60612–7232; tel. 312/996–7000 **A**1 2 3 5 7 8 9 10 **F**3 12 13 14 15 17 18 19 20 21 22 23 24 25 26 27 28 29 30 31 32 34 35 37 38 39 40 41 45 46 47 48 49 50 52 54 55 56 57 58 59 60 61 64 65 66 68 70 72 73 74 75 76 77 78 79 81 82 84 85 86 87 88 89 90 91 92 93 96 97 98 99 100 101 102 103 104 107 108 110 111 114 115 116 117 118 119 120 121 123 126 129 130 131 132 134 135 136 138 139 141 142 144 145 146 147 148 **P**4
Primary Contact: Bryan Becker, Associate Vice President for Operations and Chief Executive Officer
COO: David Loffing, Chief Operating Officer
CFO: Jeffrey Rooney, Chief Financial Officer
CMO: Bernard Pygon, M.D., Chief Medical Officer
CIO: Audrius Polikaitis, Chief Information Officer
CHR: Mary Jo Smith, Assistant Vice President Human Resources
CNO: Jodi S. Joyce, R.N., Interim Chief Nursing Officer
Web address: www.hospital.uillinois.edu/
Control: State–Government, nonfederal **Service:** General Medical and Surgical

Staffed Beds: 384 **Admissions:** 19306 **Census:** 315 **Outpatient Visits:** 446626 **Births:** 2417 **Total Expense ($000):** 789292 **Payroll Expense ($000):** 286503 **Personnel:** 4342

CHICAGO HEIGHTS—Cook County

ST. JAMES HOSPITAL AND HEALTH CENTERS – CHICAGO HEIGHTS CAMPUS See Franciscan St. James Hospital and Health Centers, Olympia Fields

CLINTON—De Witt County

★ **DR. JOHN WARNER HOSPITAL (141303)**, 422 West White Street, Zip 61727–2272; tel. 217/935–9571 **A**9 10 18 **F**3 7 15 28 29 34 40 45 53 57 59 64 68 70 75 81 82 85 87 93 107 110 127 129 130 132 133 **P**6
Primary Contact: John Winenger, FACHE, Interim Chief Executive Officer
CFO: Donna Wisner, Chief Financial Officer
CMO: Brit Williams, M.D., President Medical Staff
CIO: Larry Schleicher, Manager Information Services
CHR: Sarah Gerke, Manager Human Resources
CNO: Heidi Cook, Chief Nursing Officer
Web address: www.djwhospital.org
Control: City–Government, nonfederal **Service:** General Medical and Surgical

Staffed Beds: 25 **Admissions:** 277 **Census:** 3 **Outpatient Visits:** 16388 **Births:** 0 **Total Expense ($000):** 16154 **Payroll Expense ($000):** 6518 **Personnel:** 141

DANVILLE—Vermilion County

☒ **PRESENCE UNITED SAMARITANS MEDICAL CENTER (140093)**, 812 North Logan, Zip 61832–3788; tel. 217/443–5000 **A**1 2 5 9 10 19 **F**3 8 11 13 15 18 20 28 29 30 31 34 35 40 45 47 49 50 57 59 64 70 74 75 76 77 78 79 81 82 83 85 86 87 89 93 102 107 108 110 111 114 115 118 119 120 121 124 126 129 130 132 134 135 146 147 148 **S** Presence Health, Chicago, IL
Primary Contact: Jared Rogers, M.D., Interim Regional President and Chief Executive Officer
COO: Jennifer Cord, Vice President Operations
CFO: Deborah Schimerowski, Chief Financial Officer
CMO: Carmen Rocco, M.D., Chief Medical Officer
CIO: Paula Keele, Manager Information Systems
CHR: Janet S. Payne, Vice President Human Resources
CNO: Molly Nicholson, R.N., Vice President of Patient Care/Chief Nurse Executive
Web address: www.provena.org/usmc
Control: Church–operated, Nongovernment, not–for profit **Service:** General Medical and Surgical

Staffed Beds: 127 **Admissions:** 6107 **Census:** 55 **Outpatient Visits:** 193129 **Births:** 747 **Total Expense ($000):** 101656 **Payroll Expense ($000):** 33027 **Personnel:** 664

☒ **VETERANS AFFAIRS ILLIANA HEALTH CARE SYSTEM**, 1900 East Main Street, Zip 61832–5198; tel. 217/554–3000, (Nonreporting) **A**1 3 5 9 **S** Department of Veterans Affairs, Washington, DC
Primary Contact: Russell E. Lloyd, Acting Director
COO: Diana Carranza, Associate Director
CFO: Becky Tissier, Chief Fiscal Service
CMO: Khiem Tran, M.D., Acting Chief of Staff
CIO: Sherry Boone, Chief Information Resource Management
CHR: Connie Ohl, Acting Chief Human Resources
Web address: www.danville.va.gov/
Control: Veterans Affairs, Government, federal **Service:** General Medical and Surgical

Staffed Beds: 81

IL

Hospital, Medicare Provider Number, Address, Telephone, Approval, Facility, and Physician Codes, Health Care System

★ American Hospital Association (AHA) membership
☐ The Joint Commission accreditation   ◇ DNV Healthcare Inc. accreditation

○ Healthcare Facilities Accreditation Program
△ Commission on Accreditation of Rehabilitation Facilities (CARF) accreditation

---

DECATUR—Macon County

✠ △ **DECATUR MEMORIAL HOSPITAL (140135)**, 2300 North Edward Street, Zip 62526–4192; tel. 217/876–8121 **A**1 2 3 5 7 9 10 **F**3 11 12 13 14 15 17 18 20 22 24 26 28 29 30 31 34 40 45 46 47 48 49 51 53 54 56 57 58 59 60 61 62 63 64 65 69 70 73 74 75 76 77 78 79 81 82 86 87 89 91 92 93 94 96 107 108 110 111 112 114 115 116 117 118 119 120 121 123 126 129 130 131 132 133 143 144 145 146 147 148 **P**8
Primary Contact: Timothy D. Stone, Jr., Executive Vice President and Administrator
CFO: Al Naqvi, Chief Financial Officer
CMO: Michael Zia, M.D., Vice President Quality Systems and Medical Affairs
CHR: Kevin Horath, Vice President Human Resources
CNO: Linda L. Fahey, R.N., Vice President and Chief Nurse Executive
Web address: www.dmhcares.org
Control: Other not–for–profit (including NFP Corporation) **Service:** General Medical and Surgical

Staffed Beds: 188 **Admissions:** 10941 **Census:** 112 **Outpatient Visits:** 298224 **Births:** 1030 **Total Expense ($000):** 276499 **Payroll Expense ($000):** 109539 **Personnel:** 2101

✠ △ **ST. MARY'S HOSPITAL (140166)**, 1800 East Lake Shore Drive, Zip 62521–3883; tel. 217/464–2966, (Total facility includes 14 beds in nursing home–type unit) **A**1 3 5 7 9 10 **F**2 3 5 11 13 15 18 20 22 28 29 30 31 34 35 40 44 45 50 54 56 57 59 64 66 70 74 76 77 78 79 81 85 86 87 89 90 92 93 96 98 99 100 101 102 103 104 105 107 108 110 111 114 115 117 119 120 121 123 124 128 129 130 131 132 141 142 146 148 **P**7
S Hospital Sisters Health System, Springfield, IL
Primary Contact: Daniel L. Perryman, Chief Executive Officer
CFO: Rebecca Colker, Chief Financial Officer
CHR: Terri Kuhle, Director Human Resources
Web address: www.stmarysdecatur.com
Control: Church–operated, Nongovernment, not–for profit **Service:** General Medical and Surgical

Staffed Beds: 232 **Admissions:** 8238 **Census:** 121 **Outpatient Visits:** 160934 **Births:** 598 **Total Expense ($000):** 132622 **Payroll Expense ($000):** 42171 **Personnel:** 807

DEKALB—DeKalb County

✠ **KISHWAUKEE HOSPITAL (140286)**, 1 Kish Hospital Drive, Zip 60115–9602, Mailing Address: P.O. Box 707, Zip 60115–0707; tel. 815/756–1521 **A**1 2 9 10 **F**3 8 11 13 15 18 20 22 26 28 29 30 31 32 34 35 36 37 40 43 45 46 48 49 57 58 59 60 64 68 70 71 73 74 75 76 77 78 79 81 82 85 86 87 89 93 96 102 104 107 108 110 111 114 115 117 118 119 129 130 131 132 133 135 143 145 146 147 148 **P**8 **S** Kish Health System, DeKalb, IL
Primary Contact: Brad Copple, President
COO: Brad Copple, President
CFO: Loren Foelske, Vice President Finance
CMO: Michael Kulisz, D.O., Chief Medical Officer
CIO: Heath Bell, Chief Information Officer
CHR: Michele McClelland, Vice President Human Resources
CNO: Pamela Duffy, Vice President Patient Care Services and Chief Nursing Officer
Web address: www.kishhospital.org
Control: Other not–for–profit (including NFP Corporation) **Service:** General Medical and Surgical

Staffed Beds: 98 **Admissions:** 5220 **Census:** 53 **Outpatient Visits:** 139848 **Births:** 736 **Total Expense ($000):** 148653 **Payroll Expense ($000):** 42682 **Personnel:** 728

DES PLAINES—Cook County

HOLY FAMILY MEDICAL CENTER See Presence Holy Family Medical Center

✠ **PRESENCE HOLY FAMILY MEDICAL CENTER (142011)**, 100 North River Road, Zip 60016–1255; tel. 847/297–1800, (Nonreporting) **A**1 9 10 **S** Presence Health, Chicago, IL
Primary Contact: John D. Baird, President and Chief Executive Officer
CFO: Donna Pareti, Business Unit Chief Financial Officer
CMO: David Bordo, M.D., Chief Medical Officer
CIO: David Lundal, Senior Vice President Information Systems and Chief Information Officer
CHR: Ivy McKinley, Director Human Resources
CNO: Carole Miserendino, MSN, Chief Nursing Officer
Web address: www.presencehealth.org
Control: Church–operated, Nongovernment, not–for profit **Service:** Long–Term Acute Care hospital

Staffed Beds: 118

DIXON—Lee County

★ **KATHERINE SHAW BETHEA HOSPITAL (140012)**, 403 East First Street, Zip 61021–3187; tel. 815/288–5531 **A**3 5 9 10 **F**3 11 13 15 18 20 22 28 29 30 31 32 34 35 38 39 40 43 44 45 46 47 49 50 54 56 57 59 62 64 65 66 69 70 74 75 77 79 81 85 86 87 91 92 93 94 96 97 98 100 101 102 103 104 107 108 110 111 115 118 119 127 129 130 131 132 135 144 145 146 147 148 **P**6
Primary Contact: David L. Schreiner, FACHE, President and Chief Executive Officer
CFO: Debra Didier, Vice President and Chief Financial Officer
CMO: Tim Appenheimer, M.D., Vice President and Chief Medical Officer
CHR: Suzanne M. Ravlin, Director Human Resources
CNO: Linda Clemen, R.N., Vice President and Chief Nursing Officer
Web address: www.ksbhospital.com
Control: Other not–for–profit (including NFP Corporation) **Service:** General Medical and Surgical

Staffed Beds: 80 **Admissions:** 3831 **Census:** 36 **Outpatient Visits:** 177400 **Births:** 383 **Total Expense ($000):** 127694 **Payroll Expense ($000):** 63007 **Personnel:** 790

DOWNERS GROVE—Dupage County

★ ◇ **ADVOCATE GOOD SAMARITAN HOSPITAL (140288)**, 3815 Highland Avenue, Zip 60515–1590; tel. 630/275–5900, (Nonreporting) **A**2 3 5 9 10 21 **S** Advocate Health Care, Downers Grove, IL
Primary Contact: David Fox, President
COO: Marjorie A. Maurer, MSN, Vice President Operations, Patient Care Services and Chief Nursing Executive
CFO: Mary Treacy–Shiff, Vice President Finance
CMO: Charles Derus, M.D., Vice President Medical Management
CHR: Elizabeth Calby, Vice President Human Resources
CNO: Sandi Churchill, Vice President Business Development and Operations, Professional Services
Web address: www.advocatehealth.com/gsam
Control: Church–operated, Nongovernment, not–for profit **Service:** General Medical and Surgical

Staffed Beds: 319

DU QUOIN—Perry County

✠ **MARSHALL BROWNING HOSPITAL (141331)**, 900 North Washington Street, Zip 62832–1233, Mailing Address: P.O. Box 192, Zip 62832–0192; tel. 618/542–2146 **A**1 9 10 18 **F**3 11 15 28 29 34 35 40 50 59 81 85 93 107 108 110 114 119 125 127 129 131 133
Primary Contact: Edwin A. Gast, Chief Executive Officer
CFO: Brice Harsy, Chief Financial Officer
CIO: William Ralph Bunton, Supervisor Information Technology
CHR: Sarah J. Dickey, Director Human Resources
CNO: Laurie Kellerman, MSN, Chief Nursing Officer
Web address: www.marshallbrowninghospital.com
Control: Other not–for–profit (including NFP Corporation) **Service:** General Medical and Surgical

Staffed Beds: 25 **Admissions:** 712 **Census:** 9 **Outpatient Visits:** 29715 **Births:** 0 **Total Expense ($000):** 16724 **Payroll Expense ($000):** 7145 **Personnel:** 147

EFFINGHAM—Effingham County

✠ **ST. ANTHONY'S MEMORIAL HOSPITAL (140032)**, 503 North Maple Street, Zip 62401–2099; tel. 217/342–2121, (Total facility includes 13 beds in nursing home–type unit) **A**1 2 9 10 19 **F**3 8 11 13 15 18 19 20 28 29 30 31 34 40 45 57 59 60 62 64 68 70 75 76 79 81 82 84 85 89 93 107 108 109 110 111 114 115 118 119 128 129 130 132 146 147 **S** Hospital Sisters Health System, Springfield, IL
Primary Contact: Theresa Rutherford, R.N., MS, FACHE, President and Chief Executive Officer
CFO: Dave Storm, Director Business Support
Web address: www.stanthonyshospital.org
Control: Church–operated, Nongovernment, not–for profit **Service:** General Medical and Surgical

Staffed Beds: 146 **Admissions:** 6143 **Census:** 65 **Outpatient Visits:** 244443 **Births:** 724 **Total Expense ($000):** 101409 **Payroll Expense ($000):** 32491 **Personnel:** 637

ELDORADO—Saline County

FERRELL HOSPITAL (141324), 1201 Pine Street, Zip 62930–1634; tel. 618/273–3361, (Nonreporting) **A**9 10 18
Primary Contact: Donald G. Brown, Interim President and Chief Executive Officer
CFO: Charles Will, Chief Financial Officer
CIO: Brent Volkert, Director Information Technology
CHR: Caleigh Griffin, Vice President Human Resources
CNO: Lisa Anderson, Vice President Nursing
Web address: www.ferrellhosp.org
Control: Other not–for–profit (including NFP Corporation) **Service:** General Medical and Surgical

Staffed Beds: 25

ELGIN—Kane County

⊞ **ADVOCATE SHERMAN HOSPITAL (140030)**, 1425 North Randall Road, Zip 60123–2300; tel. 847/742–9800 **A**1 2 9 10 **F**3 11 13 15 18 19 20 22 24 26 27 28 29 30 31 34 35 38 40 43 45 46 47 48 49 50 55 57 59 64 65 68 70 74 75 76 77 78 79 81 82 85 87 89 92 93 100 107 108 110 111 114 115 118 119 120 121 126 129 130 132 135 144 146 147 148 **P**8 **S** Advocate Health Care, Downers Grove, IL
Primary Contact: Linda Deering, MSN, R.N., President
CMO: Bruce Hyman, M.D., Vice President Clinical Performance
CHR: Melissa O'Neill, Vice President Human Resources
CNO: Judith Balcitis, MS, Vice President, Nursing and Chief Nursing Officer
Web address: www.advocatehealth.com/sherman
Control: Church–operated, Nongovernment, not–for profit **Service:** General Medical and Surgical

Staffed Beds: 255 **Admissions:** 14809 **Census:** 157 **Outpatient Visits:** 297782 **Births:** 2777 **Total Expense ($000):** 273411 **Payroll Expense ($000):** 98318 **Personnel:** 1587

☐ **ELGIN MENTAL HEALTH CENTER (144037)**, 750 South State Street, Zip 60123–7692; tel. 847/742–1040, (Nonreporting) **A**1 5 10 **S** Division of Mental Health, Department of Human Services, Springfield, IL
Primary Contact: Amparo Lopez, Region Executive Director
CFO: Tajudeen Ibrahim, Interim Business Administrator
CMO: Malini Patel, M.D., Medical Director
CIO: Kelly Callahan, Public Information Officer
CHR: Darek Williams, Director Human Resources
Web address: www.dhs.state.il.us
Control: State–Government, nonfederal **Service:** Psychiatric

Staffed Beds: 500

⊞ △ **PRESENCE SAINT JOSEPH HOSPITAL (140217)**, 77 North Airlite Street, Zip 60123–4912; tel. 847/695–3200 **A**1 2 5 7 9 10 **F**5 11 12 15 17 18 20 22 24 26 28 29 30 31 34 35 36 37 38 40 43 44 49 50 53 54 56 57 58 59 60 61 62 63 64 65 68 69 70 74 75 77 78 79 81 82 84 85 86 87 90 93 94 96 97 98 99 100 101 102 103 104 105 107 108 111 114 115 116 117 119 120 121 123 124 130 132 134 135 143 145 146 147 148 **P**5 **S** Presence Health, Chicago, IL
Primary Contact: Michael L. Brown, Regional President and Chief Executive Officer
CFO: Kevin Larkin, Regional Chief Financial Officer
CIO: Trevor O'Malley, Site Manager
CHR: Michael O'Rourke, Regional Human Resources Lead
Web address: www.provena.org
Control: Other not–for–profit (including NFP Corporation) **Service:** General Medical and Surgical

Staffed Beds: 125 **Admissions:** 6998 **Census:** 112 **Outpatient Visits:** 149595 **Births:** 0 **Total Expense ($000):** 141374 **Payroll Expense ($000):** 47519 **Personnel:** 709

PROVENA SAINT JOSEPH HOSPITAL See Presence Saint Joseph Hospital

SHERMAN HOSPITAL See Advocate Sherman Hospital

ELK GROVE VILLAGE—Cook County

⊞ **ALEXIAN BROTHERS MEDICAL CENTER (140258)**, 800 Biesterfield Road, Zip 60007–3397; tel. 847/437–5500, (Includes ALEXIAN BROTHERS WOMEN & CHILDREN'S HOSPITAL, 1555 Barrington Road, Hoffman Estates, Zip 60169–1019; tel. 847/843–2000; ALEXIAN REHABILITATION HOSPITAL, 935 Beisner Road, Zip 60007; tel. 847/640–5600) **A**1 2 3 5 9 10 **F**3 12 13 15 17 18 20 22 24 26 28 29 30 31 34 35 36 37 39 40 41 43 45 46 47 48 49 50 54 55 56 57 59 62 63 64 70 73 74 75 76 78 79 81 82 84 85 86 87 89 90 91 92 93 95 96 107 108 110 111 113 114 115 116 117 119 120 121 123 124 126 129 130 132 135 143 145 146 147 148 **P**6 **S** Ascension Health, Saint Louis, MO
Primary Contact: John P. Werrbach, Chief Executive Officer
Web address: www.alexian.org
Control: Church–operated, Nongovernment, not–for profit **Service:** General Medical and Surgical

Staffed Beds: 375 **Admissions:** 18073 **Census:** 265 **Outpatient Visits:** 410396 **Births:** 1882 **Total Expense ($000):** 398170 **Payroll Expense ($000):** 133609 **Personnel:** 1970

ELMHURST—Dupage County

⊞ **ELMHURST MEMORIAL HOSPITAL (140200)**, 155 East Brush Hill Road, Zip 60126–5658; tel. 331/221–1000 **A**1 2 9 10 **F**3 5 8 13 15 18 19 20 22 24 26 28 29 30 31 34 35 38 40 41 43 44 45 46 47 48 49 50 54 55 57 58 59 62 63 64 65 70 74 75 76 77 78 79 81 82 85 86 87 89 91 92 93 96 97 99 100 101 102 103 104 105 107 108 109 110 111 114 115 117 119 120 121 122 123 126 129 130 131 132 144 146 147 148 **P**3 8 **S** Edward–Elmhurst Healthcare, Naperville, IL
Primary Contact: Mary Lou Mastro, President and Chief Executive Officer
COO: Pamela L. Dunley, R.N., Vice President Chief Nursing Officer and Chief Operating Officer
CFO: Henry Zeisel, Vice President Finance
CMO: Daniel Sullivan, D.O., Chief Medical Officer, Vice President Medical Administration
CIO: Bobbie Byrne, M.D., Vice President Information Systems and Chief Information Officer
CHR: Susan Mitchell, Senior Vice President Human Resources
CNO: Pamela L. Dunley, R.N., Vice President Chief Nursing Officer and Chief Operating Officer
Web address: www.emhc.org
Control: Other not–for–profit (including NFP Corporation) **Service:** General Medical and Surgical

Staffed Beds: 259 **Admissions:** 13173 **Census:** 151 **Outpatient Visits:** 400170 **Births:** 1220 **Total Expense ($000):** 355914 **Payroll Expense ($000):** 132540 **Personnel:** 2464

EUREKA—Woodford County

★ ◇ **ADVOCATE EUREKA HOSPITAL (141309)**, 101 South Major Street, Zip 61530–1246; tel. 309/467–2371 **A**9 10 18 21 **F**3 15 28 29 30 31 34 35 39 40 44 45 50 57 59 64 65 67 68 74 75 77 78 79 81 82 85 86 87 89 90 93 107 108 110 111 114 119 128 129 130 132 133 146 **P**8 **S** Advocate Health Care, Downers Grove, IL
Primary Contact: Colleen Kannaday, FACHE, President
CFO: Aron Klein, Vice President of Finance
CMO: Steven K. Jones, M.D., Medical Director
CIO: David Harper, Director, Site Information Systems
CHR: Antonio Coletta, Vice President Human Resources
CNO: Nancy Allen, R.N., Director, Patient Services and Chief Nursing Executive
Web address: www.advocatehealth.com/eureka/
Control: Church–operated, Nongovernment, not–for profit **Service:** General Medical and Surgical

Staffed Beds: 18 **Admissions:** 301 **Census:** 4 **Outpatient Visits:** 30833 **Births:** 0 **Total Expense ($000):** 14398 **Payroll Expense ($000):** 5433 **Personnel:** 133

EUREKA COMMUNITY HOSPITAL See Advocate Eureka Hospital

EVANSTON—Cook County

⊞ **NORTHSHORE UNIVERSITY HEALTH SYSTEM (140010)**, 2650 Ridge Avenue, Zip 60201–1613; tel. 847/570–2000, (Includes NORTHSHORE EVANSTON HOSPITAL, 2650 Ridge Avenue, Zip 60201–1797; tel. 847/570–2000; Douglas M. Silverstein, President; NORTHSHORE GLENBROOK HOSPITAL, 2100 Pfingsten Road, Glenview, Zip 60025; tel. 847/657–5800; NORTHSHORE HIGHLAND PARK HOSPITAL, 718 Glenview Avenue, Highland Park, Zip 60035–2497; tel. 847/432–8000; NORTHSHORE SKOKIE HOSPITAL, 9600 Gross Point Road, Skokie, Zip 60076–1257; tel. 847/677–9600; Kristen Murtos, FACHE, President) **A**1 2 3 5 8 9 10 **F**3 5 8 9 11 12 13 14 15 18 19 20 22 24 26 28 29 30 31 32 34 35 36 37 38 39 40 43 44 45 46 47 48 49 50 54 55 56 57 58 59 60 61 62 63 64 66 68 70 72 74 75 76 77 78 79 81 82 83 84 85 86 87 88 89 90 92 93 96 97 98 99 100 101 102 103 104 105 107 108 110 111 114 115 116 117 118 119 120 121 123 124 126 129 130 131 132 134 135 136 145 146 147 148 **P**5
Primary Contact: Douglas M. Silverstein, President
COO: J. P. Gallagher, Chief Operating Officer
CFO: Gary Weiss, Chief Financial Officer
CIO: Steven Smith, Chief Information Officer
CHR: Bill Luehrs, Chief Human Resources Officer
CNO: Nancy Semerdjian, R.N., Chief Nursing Officer
Web address: www.northshore.org
Control: Other not–for–profit (including NFP Corporation) **Service:** General Medical and Surgical

Staffed Beds: 697 **Admissions:** 39010 **Census:** 490 **Outpatient Visits:** 2016422 **Births:** 4523 **Total Expense ($000):** 1367855 **Payroll Expense ($000):** 459905 **Personnel:** 5372

IL

Hospital, Medicare Provider Number, Address, Telephone, Approval, Facility, and Physician Codes, Health Care System

★ American Hospital Association (AHA) membership
☐ The Joint Commission accreditation
◇ DNV Healthcare Inc. accreditation
○ Healthcare Facilities Accreditation Program
△ Commission on Accreditation of Rehabilitation Facilities (CARF) accreditation

✠ **PRESENCE SAINT FRANCIS HOSPITAL (140080)**, 355 Ridge Avenue,
Zip 60202–3399; tel. 847/316–4000, (Nonreporting) **A**1 2 3 5 9 10 **S** Presence
Health, Chicago, IL
Primary Contact: Roberta Luskin–Hawk, M.D., Chief Executive Officer
CMO: David DiLoreto, M.D., Executive Vice President and Chief Medical Officer
CIO: George Chessum, Vice President Information Systems
CHR: Paul Skiem, Senior Vice President Human Resources
Web address: www.reshealth.org
Control: Church–operated, Nongovernment, not–for profit **Service:** General
Medical and Surgical

Staffed Beds: 244

SAINT FRANCIS HOSPITAL See Presence Saint Francis Hospital

EVERGREEN PARK—Cook County

☐ **LITTLE COMPANY OF MARY HOSPITAL AND HEALTH CARE CENTERS
(140179)**, 2800 West 95th Street, Zip 60805–2795; tel. 708/422–6200 **A**1 2
9 10 **F**3 5 11 12 13 15 17 18 20 22 26 29 30 31 34 35 36 38 40 41 45 46
47 49 50 54 56 57 59 60 62 63 64 71 73 74 75 76 77 78 79 81 82 83 84
85 86 87 89 92 93 94 98 100 101 102 103 104 105 107 108 110 111 114
115 119 120 121 124 126 129 130 132 135 144 146 147 148 **P**6 7 8
S American Province of Little Company of Mary Sisters, Evergreen Park, IL
Primary Contact: Dennis A. Reilly, President and Chief Executive Officer
COO: Mary Freyer, Chief Operating Officer
CFO: Randy Ruther, Vice President Finance and Chief Financial Officer
CMO: Kent A W Armbruster, M.D., Vice President Medical Affairs
CIO: Darryl Mazzuca, Director Management Information Systems
CHR: Colleen Rohan, Director Human Resources
CNO: Lisa DiMarco, R.N., Vice President Patient Care Service and Chief Nursing
Officer
Web address: www.lcmh.org
Control: Other not–for–profit (including NFP Corporation) **Service:** General
Medical and Surgical

Staffed Beds: 254 Admissions: 12428 Census: 149 Outpatient Visits:
207991 Births: 1179 Total Expense ($000): 187915 Payroll Expense
($000): 83084 Personnel: 1520

FAIRFIELD—Wayne County

✠ **FAIRFIELD MEMORIAL HOSPITAL (141311)**, 303 N.W. 11th Street,
Zip 62837–1203; tel. 618/842–2611 **A**1 9 10 18 **F**3 11 15 18 28 30 31 34
38 40 41 56 57 59 62 64 69 70 75 78 81 87 93 103 104 107 108 111 116
119 127 128 129 130 132 135 145 146 148 **S** Alliant Management Services,
Louisville, KY
Primary Contact: Katherine Bunting, Chief Executive Officer
COO: Dana Shantel Taylor, Director Organizational Development
CFO: Kathy Clayton, Chief Financial Officer
CMO: Wesley Thompson, M.D., President Medical Staff
CIO: Bryan Mitchell, Director Information Systems
CHR: Robert Musoiu, Director Human Resources
CNO: Ann Ignas, R.N., Chief Nurse Executive
Web address: www.fairfieldmemorial.org
Control: Other not–for–profit (including NFP Corporation) **Service:** General
Medical and Surgical

Staffed Beds: 55 Admissions: 943 Census: 27 Outpatient Visits: 38884
Births: 0 Total Expense ($000): 25624 Payroll Expense ($000): 10543
Personnel: 228

FLORA—Clay County

✠ **CLAY COUNTY HOSPITAL (141351)**, 911 Stacy Burk Drive, Zip 62839–3241,
Mailing Address: P.O. Box 280, Zip 62839–0280; tel. 618/662–2131,
(Nonreporting) **A**1 9 10 18 **S** SSM Health, Saint Louis, MO
Primary Contact: Amanda J. Goostree, President
COO: Jamie Veach, Chief Operating Officer
CFO: Mike Hobbs, Chief Financial Officer
CMO: Colleen Murphy, M.D., Chief of Staff
CIO: Phil Bute, Manager Information Technology
CHR: Darla Hout, Director Human Resources and Marketing
Web address: www.claycountyhospital.org
Control: County–Government, nonfederal **Service:** General Medical and Surgical

Staffed Beds: 22

FOREST PARK—Cook County

☐ **RIVEREDGE HOSPITAL (144009)**, 8311 West Roosevelt Road,
Zip 60130–2500; tel. 708/771–7000, (Nonreporting) **A**1 5 9 10 **S** Universal
Health Services, Inc., King of Prussia, PA
Primary Contact: Carey Carlock, Chief Executive Officer
CFO: Michael E. Nelson, Chief Financial Officer
CMO: Lucyna M. Puszkarska, M.D., Medical Director
CIO: Kyle Heinze, Coordinator Information Technology
CHR: Joseph Baw, Director Human Resources
Web address: www.riveredgehospital.com
Control: Corporation, Investor–owned, for–profit **Service:** Psychiatric

Staffed Beds: 224

FREEPORT—Stephenson County

★ **FHN MEMORIAL HOSPITAL (140160)**, 1045 West Stephenson Street,
Zip 61032–4899; tel. 815/599–6000 **A**9 10 19 **F**3 11 13 14 15 18 20 22 28
29 30 31 32 34 38 40 46 47 48 49 50 51 53 57 59 61 63 64 65 68 69 74
75 76 77 78 79 81 82 84 85 86 87 93 97 99 100 101 102 103 104 107 108
109 110 111 114 119 129 130 131 132 135 141 146 **P**6 8
Primary Contact: Michael R. Perry, M.D., President and Chief Executive Officer
COO: Mark Gridley, FACHE, Executive Vice President and Chief Operating Officer
CFO: Michael Clark, Vice President Finance
CMO: Robert D. Geller, M.D., Vice President Medical Affairs
CIO: Mike Willams, Chief Information Officer
CHR: Leonard M. Carter, Vice President Human Resources
CNO: Nancy Cutler, RN, R.N., Vice President Patient Services/CNO
Web address: www.fhn.org
Control: Other not–for–profit (including NFP Corporation) **Service:** General
Medical and Surgical

Staffed Beds: 100 Admissions: 4307 Census: 43 Outpatient Visits: 104966
Births: 365 Total Expense ($000): 97076 Payroll Expense ($000): 29936
Personnel: 508

GALENA—Jo Daviess County

★ **MIDWEST MEDICAL CENTER (141302)**, One Medical Center Drive,
Zip 61036–1697; tel. 815/777–1340, (Nonreporting) **A**9 10 18
Primary Contact: Tracy Bauer, Chief Executive Officer
COO: Steve Busch, Chief Operating Officer
CMO: Grant Westenfelder, M.D., Chief Medical Officer
CHR: Melissa Conley, Director Human Resources
Web address: www.midwestmedicalcenter.org
Control: Corporation, Investor–owned, for–profit **Service:** General Medical and
Surgical

Staffed Beds: 25

GALESBURG—Knox County

✠ **GALESBURG COTTAGE HOSPITAL (140040)**, 695 North Kellogg Street,
Zip 61401–2885; tel. 309/343–8131, (Nonreporting) **A**1 10 19 **S** Community
Health Systems, Inc., Franklin, TN
Primary Contact: Earl J. Tamar, Chief Executive Officer
CFO: Rob Gasaway, Chief Financial Officer
CMO: Mark Davis, M.D., President Medical Staff
CIO: Jeremie Kilgore, Director Information Technology
CHR: Nancy Baird, Director Human Resources
Web address: www.cottagehospital.com
Control: Other not–for–profit (including NFP Corporation) **Service:** General
Medical and Surgical

Staffed Beds: 119

✠ **OSF ST. MARY MEDICAL CENTER (140064)**, 3333 North Seminary Street,
Zip 61401–1299; tel. 309/344–3161 **A**1 9 10 **F**3 11 13 15 18 26 28 29 30
31 34 40 41 43 45 49 50 51 53 56 57 58 59 61 62 63 68 70 74 75 76 77
78 79 81 82 84 85 86 87 89 93 96 97 107 110 111 114 115 117 119 129
130 132 135 145 146 147 **P**6 **S** OSF Healthcare System, Peoria, IL
Primary Contact: Roxanna Crosser, President
COO: Don Shadensack, Vice President Clinical Services
CFO: Curt Lipe, Vice President, Chief Financial Officer
CMO: Mark Meeker, D.O., Medical Staff President
CIO: Becky Lynch, Manager Business Entity Management and Information Systems
CHR: Nichole Hurlbutt, Director Human Resources
CNO: Alice Snyder, Vice President, Chief Nursing Officer
Web address: www.osfstmary.org
Control: Church–operated, Nongovernment, not–for profit **Service:** General
Medical and Surgical

Staffed Beds: 90 Admissions: 3111 Census: 33 Outpatient Visits: 160127
Births: 278 Total Expense ($000): 75476 Payroll Expense ($000): 29111
Personnel: 587

GENESEO—Henry County

✠ **HAMMOND–HENRY HOSPITAL (141319)**, 600 North College Avenue,
Zip 61254–1099; tel. 309/944–4625, (Total facility includes 38 beds in nursing
home–type unit) **A**1 9 10 18 **F**3 8 11 13 15 17 18 19 28 29 34 35 40 44 45
57 59 62 70 75 76 79 81 82 87 88 89 93 107 111 114 119 128 129 130
131 132 133 135 144 146 **P**2 **S** HealthTech Management Services,
Brentwood, TN
Primary Contact: Bradley Solberg, FACHE, Chief Executive Officer
CFO: Jodie Criswell, Vice President Fiscal Services
CIO: Heather Henry, Manager Information Systems
CHR: Hazel Butter, Manager Human Resources
CNO: Laura Domino, R.N., Vice President Patient Care Services
Web address: www.hammondhenry.com
Control: Hospital district or authority, Government, nonfederal **Service:** General
Medical and Surgical

Staffed Beds: 61 Admissions: 1458 Census: 47 Outpatient Visits: 83991
Births: 237 Total Expense ($000): 33974 Payroll Expense ($000): 13037
Personnel: 265

GENEVA—Kane County

⊞ **DELNOR HOSPITAL (140211)**, 300 Randall Road, Zip 60134–4200; tel. 630/208–3000 **A**1 2 9 10 **F**3 12 13 15 18 20 22 26 28 29 30 31 32 34 35 36 39 40 43 44 49 50 53 57 59 64 65 68 70 74 75 76 77 78 79 81 82 85 86 87 89 93 94 96 99 100 101 102 104 107 108 110 111 114 115 118 119 120 121 126 129 130 131 132 135 146 147 148 **S** Cadence Health, Winfield, IL
Primary Contact: Maureen A. Bryant, FACHE, President
CFO: John Orsini, Executive Vice President and Chief Financial Officer
CMO: Mark Daniels, M.D., Vice President Physician Enterprise
CIO: Daniel F. Kinsella, Executive Vice President Information Technology
CHR: Michael Wukitsch, Executive Vice President Human Resources
Web address: www.cadencehealth.org
Control: Other not–for–profit (including NFP Corporation) **Service:** General Medical and Surgical

Staffed Beds: 159 **Admissions:** 7740 **Census:** 79 **Outpatient Visits:** 143473 **Births:** 1517 **Total Expense ($000):** 174898 **Payroll Expense ($000):** 60141 **Personnel:** 1285

GIBSON CITY—Ford County

⊞ **GIBSON AREA HOSPITAL AND HEALTH SERVICES (141317)**, 1120 North Melvin Street, Zip 60936–1477, Mailing Address: P.O. Box 429, Zip 60936–0429; tel. 217/784–4251, (Includes GIBSON COMMUNITY HOSPITAL NURSING HOME), (Total facility includes 42 beds in nursing home–type unit) **A**1 5 9 10 18 **F**3 7 11 13 15 28 29 31 34 35 40 43 44 45 49 50 51 53 56 57 59 63 64 65 67 68 69 70 75 76 77 79 81 82 85 87 93 103 107 108 110 111 115 119 127 128 129 131 132 133 143 146 147 148 **P**6 7 8 **S** Alliant Management Services, Louisville, KY
Primary Contact: Robert C. Schmitt, II, Chief Executive Officer
COO: Robin Rose, R.N., Chief Nursing Officer
CFO: John Jacobson, Chief Financial Officer
CMO: David J. Hagan, M.D., Chief Medical Officer
CHR: Ty Royal, Executive Director of Support Services and Human Resources
CNO: Robin Rose, R.N., Chief Nursing Officer/Chief Operating Officer
Web address: www.gibsonhospital.org
Control: Other not–for–profit (including NFP Corporation) **Service:** General Medical and Surgical

Staffed Beds: 67 **Admissions:** 909 **Census:** 41 **Outpatient Visits:** 95660 **Births:** 164 **Total Expense ($000):** 63226 **Payroll Expense ($000):** 29090 **Personnel:** 563

GLENDALE HEIGHTS—Dupage County

⊞ **ADVENTIST GLENOAKS HOSPITAL (140292)**, 701 Winthrop Avenue, Zip 60139–1403; tel. 630/545–8000 **A**1 9 10 **F**3 11 13 15 17 18 20 22 26 29 30 31 34 35 38 40 43 45 49 57 58 59 61 64 68 70 73 74 75 76 78 79 81 82 85 86 87 92 93 96 97 98 99 100 101 102 103 104 105 107 108 110 111 114 118 119 130 131 132 146 147 148 **P**7 8 **S** Adventist Health System Sunbelt Health Care Corporation, Altamonte Springs, FL
Primary Contact: Bruce C. Christian, Chief Executive Officer
CFO: Eric Moots, Vice President and Chief Financial Officer
CMO: Richard Carroll, M.D., Chief Medical Officer
CIO: Thomas Schoenig, Regional Chief Information Officer
CHR: Donald Russell, Vice President
CNO: Maria Knecht, R.N., Vice President and Chief Nursing Officer
Web address: www.adventistglenoaks.com
Control: Church–operated, Nongovernment, not–for profit **Service:** General Medical and Surgical

Staffed Beds: 140 **Admissions:** 5260 **Census:** 81 **Outpatient Visits:** 35218 **Births:** 454 **Total Expense ($000):** 83119 **Payroll Expense ($000):** 35041 **Personnel:** 544

GLENVIEW—Cook County

NORTHSHORE GLENBROOK HOSPITAL See NorthShore University Health System, Evanston

GRANITE CITY—Madison County

⊞ **GATEWAY REGIONAL MEDICAL CENTER (140125)**, 2100 Madison Avenue, Zip 62040–4799; tel. 618/798–3000 **A**1 9 10 **F**3 8 11 13 15 18 20 22 24 26 28 29 34 35 40 45 49 50 51 54 59 70 74 75 76 77 79 81 85 87 89 90 91 92 93 97 98 99 100 101 102 103 107 108 110 111 114 119 126 128 129 130 132 145 147 148 **P**6 **S** Community Health Systems, Inc., Franklin, TN
Primary Contact: M. Edward Cunningham, Chief Executive Officer
CFO: Ronald Leazer, Chief Financial Officer
CMO: Mike Adams, M.D., Chief Medical Officer
CIO: Dennis Kampwerth, Director Management Information Systems
CHR: J. Ronald Payton, Director Human Resources
Web address: www.gatewayregional.net
Control: Corporation, Investor–owned, for–profit **Service:** General Medical and Surgical

Staffed Beds: 147 **Admissions:** 7050 **Census:** 105 **Outpatient Visits:** 71490 **Births:** 248 **Total Expense ($000):** 129297 **Payroll Expense ($000):** 32993 **Personnel:** 614

GREENVILLE—Bond County

★ ○ **GREENVILLE REGIONAL HOSPITAL (140137)**, 200 Healthcare Drive, Zip 62246–1154; tel. 618/664–1230, (Includes FAIR OAKS), (Total facility includes 108 beds in nursing home–type unit) **A**9 10 11 **F**3 7 11 13 15 28 29 31 34 40 41 45 49 50 56 57 59 64 75 76 78 79 81 85 87 89 91 93 94 97 98 103 104 107 111 115 119 125 127 128 129 130 133 146 **P**6
Primary Contact: Brian Nall, President and Chief Executive Officer
CHR: Vicki Kloeckner, Director Human Resources
CNO: Tammy Lett, R.N., Chief Nursing Officer
Web address: www.greenvilleregionalhospital.com
Control: Other not–for–profit (including NFP Corporation) **Service:** General Medical and Surgical

Staffed Beds: 150 **Admissions:** 1303 **Census:** 39 **Outpatient Visits:** 39099 **Births:** 240 **Total Expense ($000):** 36079 **Payroll Expense ($000):** 16519 **Personnel:** 333

HARRISBURG—Saline County

⊞ **HARRISBURG MEDICAL CENTER (140210)**, 100 Drive Warren Tuttle Drive, Zip 62946–2718, Mailing Address: P.O. Box 428, Zip 62946–0428; tel. 618/253–7671 **A**1 9 10 20 **F**3 8 11 15 28 29 30 31 34 40 45 50 56 57 59 61 62 64 75 77 78 81 85 87 89 91 93 97 98 99 100 101 102 103 104 105 107 108 110 114 118 119 127 129 130 131 133 146
Primary Contact: Rodney Smith, Chief Executive Officer
COO: Danny Lampley, Chief Operating Officer
CFO: John Riley, Chief Financial Officer
CIO: Rick Pyle, Director Information Systems
CHR: Dorene L. Ewell, Director Human Relations Education
CNO: Cindy Ford, R.N., Chief Nursing Officer
Web address: www.harrisburgmc.com
Control: Other not–for–profit (including NFP Corporation) **Service:** General Medical and Surgical

Staffed Beds: 64 **Admissions:** 2386 **Census:** 32 **Outpatient Visits:** 74286 **Births:** 0 **Total Expense ($000):** 44762 **Payroll Expense ($000):** 23312 **Personnel:** 346

HARVARD—Mchenry County

⊞ **MERCY HARVARD HOSPITAL (141335)**, 901 Grant Street, Zip 60033–1898, Mailing Address: P.O. Box 850, Zip 60033–0850; tel. 815/943–5431, (Total facility includes 32 beds in nursing home–type unit) **A**1 9 10 18 **F**3 11 15 28 29 30 35 40 45 46 57 59 64 69 70 75 77 79 81 82 85 87 93 94 96 97 107 108 109 114 119 128 129 130 132 143 146 **P**6 **S** Mercy Health System, Janesville, WI
Primary Contact: Jennifer Hallatt, Chief Operating Officer
CFO: John Cook, Chief Financial Officer
CHR: Heather Niles, Director Human Resources Operations
Web address: www.mercyhealthsystem.org
Control: Other not–for–profit (including NFP Corporation) **Service:** General Medical and Surgical

Staffed Beds: 45 **Admissions:** 570 **Census:** 23 **Outpatient Visits:** 53793 **Births:** 0 **Total Expense ($000):** 21218 **Payroll Expense ($000):** 8277 **Personnel:** 155

IL

HARVEY—Cook County

★ △ ◇ **INGALLS MEMORIAL HOSPITAL (140191)**, One Ingalls Drive, Zip 60426–3591; tel. 708/333–2300 **A**2 7 9 10 21 **F**3 5 8 11 13 15 18 20 22 24 26 28 29 30 31 34 35 36 37 40 42 43 45 46 47 49 50 51 54 56 57 58 59 60 62 63 64 68 70 74 75 76 77 78 79 81 82 84 85 86 87 89 90 92 93 94 97 98 99 101 102 103 104 105 107 108 110 111 113 114 115 116 117 118 119 120 121 123 124 129 130 131 132 135 143 144 146 147 148 **P**8 Primary Contact: Kurt E. Johnson, President and Chief Executive Officer
CFO: Andrew Stefo, Senior Vice President Finance and Chief Financial Officer
CHR: Aletha Ross, Vice President Human Resources
Web address: www.ingallshealthsystem.org
Control: Other not–for–profit (including NFP Corporation) **Service:** General Medical and Surgical

Staffed Beds: 327 **Admissions:** 15338 **Census:** 201 **Outpatient Visits:** 379619 **Births:** 1013 **Total Expense ($000):** 280873 **Payroll Expense ($000):** 99712 **Personnel:** 1654

HAVANA—Mason County

✠ **MASON DISTRICT HOSPITAL (141313)**, 615 North Promenade Street, Zip 62644–1243, Mailing Address: P.O. Box 530, Zip 62644–0530; tel. 309/543–4431 **A**1 9 10 18 **F**7 8 11 15 18 28 29 30 34 35 40 45 49 50 53 54 56 57 59 62 64 65 68 69 75 79 81 93 97 102 103 107 108 110 114 118 119 127 129 130 131 132 133 143 146 **P**6 Primary Contact: Harry Wolin, Administrator and Chief Executive Officer
CFO: Robert J. Stolba, Chief Financial Officer
CMO: Tad A. Yetter, M.D., President Medical Staff
CIO: Aaron Coots, Information Technology Director
CHR: Anne Davis, Director Human Resources
CNO: Rhonda Hine, R.N., Interim Chief Nursing Executive
Web address: www.masondistricthospital.org
Control: Hospital district or authority, Government, nonfederal **Service:** General Medical and Surgical

Staffed Beds: 20 **Admissions:** 276 **Census:** 2 **Outpatient Visits:** 22845 **Births:** 0 **Total Expense ($000):** 22284 **Payroll Expense ($000):** 10557 **Personnel:** 219

HAZEL CREST—Cook County

★ ◇ **ADVOCATE SOUTH SUBURBAN HOSPITAL (140250)**, 17800 South Kedzie Avenue, Zip 60429–0989; tel. 708/799–8000, (Total facility includes 37 beds in nursing home–type unit) **A**2 9 10 21 **F**3 11 13 15 18 20 22 24 26 28 29 30 31 34 35 36 40 45 46 47 49 50 51 53 57 59 60 63 64 68 70 75 76 78 79 81 82 85 87 89 107 108 110 111 114 115 118 119 126 128 129 130 132 145 146 147 148 **P**8 **S** Advocate Health Care, Downers Grove, IL
Primary Contact: Richard Heim, President
COO: Karen Clark, MS, Vice President Operations
CFO: Brian Kelly, Vice President Finance
CIO: Beth Turek, Site Manager Information Systems
CHR: Daylashunta Randolph, Vice President Human Resources
Web address: www.advocatehealth.com/ssub/
Control: Church–operated, Nongovernment, not–for profit **Service:** General Medical and Surgical

Staffed Beds: 250 **Admissions:** 11397 **Census:** 140 **Outpatient Visits:** 120509 **Births:** 1035 **Total Expense ($000):** 195518 **Payroll Expense ($000):** 70689 **Personnel:** 907

HERRIN—Williamson County

☐ **HERRIN HOSPITAL (140011)**, 201 South 14th Street, Zip 62948–3631; tel. 618/942–2171 **A**1 5 9 10 **F**3 11 12 18 28 29 30 34 35 40 45 47 49 50 51 54 56 57 59 60 61 64 68 70 74 75 78 79 81 82 84 85 86 87 90 92 93 100 107 108 111 114 115 119 130 131 132 135 143 146 148 **P**1 **S** Southern Illinois Hospital Services, Carbondale, IL
Primary Contact: Terence Farrell, Vice President and Administrator
CFO: Michael Kasser, Chief Financial Officer
CMO: Michelle Jenkins, M.D., President Medical Staff
CIO: David Holland, Chief Information Officer
CHR: Teresa A. Lovellette, Manager Human Resources
Web address: www.sih.net
Control: Other not–for–profit (including NFP Corporation) **Service:** General Medical and Surgical

Staffed Beds: 114 **Admissions:** 5408 **Census:** 68 **Outpatient Visits:** 122555 **Births:** 0 **Total Expense ($000):** 109574 **Payroll Expense ($000):** 34018 **Personnel:** 646

HIGHLAND—Madison County

✠ **ST. JOSEPH'S HOSPITAL (141336)**, 1515 Main Street, Zip 62249–1656; tel. 618/654–7421 **A**1 9 10 18 **F**8 11 15 26 27 28 29 30 34 35 40 41 44 45 47 49 51 57 59 64 65 68 69 70 71 75 77 79 81 82 84 85 86 87 89 90 93 97 107 108 110 111 114 119 128 129 130 131 132 133 135 143 146 147 **S** Hospital Sisters Health System, Springfield, IL
Primary Contact: Peggy A. Sebastian, MSN, R.N., President and Chief Executive Officer
CFO: James Johnson, Chief Financial Officer
CMO: A. Greg Miranda, D.O., President Medical Staff
Web address: www.stjosephshighland.com
Control: Church–operated, Nongovernment, not–for profit **Service:** General Medical and Surgical

Staffed Beds: 25 **Admissions:** 1040 **Census:** 12 **Outpatient Visits:** 46696 **Births:** 0 **Total Expense ($000):** 25859 **Payroll Expense ($000):** 8873 **Personnel:** 195

HIGHLAND PARK—Lake County

NORTHSHORE HIGHLAND PARK HOSPITAL See NorthShore University Health System, Evanston

HILLSBORO—Montgomery County

✠ **HILLSBORO AREA HOSPITAL (141332)**, 1200 East Tremont Street, Zip 62049–1900; tel. 217/532–6111 **A**1 9 10 18 **F**3 10 15 28 29 30 34 35 40 56 57 59 64 65 75 77 79 81 85 86 87 89 92 93 94 97 107 110 111 115 125 129 130 131 133 135 146 148 **S** HealthTech Management Services, Brentwood, TN
Primary Contact: Rex H. Brown, Chief Executive Officer
CFO: Terri L. Carroll, Vice President Financial Services
CHR: Sharon Clark, Director Human Resources
Web address: www.hillsborohealth.org
Control: Other not–for–profit (including NFP Corporation) **Service:** General Medical and Surgical

Staffed Beds: 25 **Admissions:** 593 **Census:** 8 **Outpatient Visits:** 21772 **Births:** 0 **Total Expense ($000):** 17634 **Payroll Expense ($000):** 6280 **Personnel:** 162

HINES—Cook County

✠ △ **EDWARD HINES, JR. VETERANS AFFAIRS HOSPITAL**, 5000 South Fifth Avenue, Zip 60141–3030, Mailing Address: P.O. Box 5000, Zip 60141–5000; tel. 708/202–8387 **A**1 2 3 5 7 **F**1 3 4 5 6 7 8 9 12 14 15 16 17 18 20 22 24 26 28 29 30 34 35 36 38 39 40 44 45 46 47 48 49 50 54 56 57 58 59 60 61 63 64 65 66 68 70 71 74 75 77 78 79 80 81 82 83 84 86 87 90 91 92 93 94 96 97 98 100 101 102 103 104 105 106 107 108 109 110 111 112 113 115 116 117 119 120 121 122 123 124 126 127 129 130 131 132 135 143 144 146 147 148 **S** Department of Veterans Affairs, Washington, DC
Primary Contact: Joan M. Ricard, R.N., FACHE, Director
COO: Joan M. Ricard, R.N., Director
CFO: Yolanda Martinez, Chief Fiscal Services
CMO: Jack Bulmash, M.D., Chief of Staff
CIO: Robert Tanjuakio, Chief Information Resources Management
Web address: www.hines.va.gov/
Control: Veterans Affairs, Government, federal **Service:** General Medical and Surgical

Staffed Beds: 450 **Admissions:** 10800 **Census:** 466 **Outpatient Visits:** 960000 **Births:** 0 **Total Expense ($000):** 495000 **Payroll Expense ($000):** 230000 **Personnel:** 3087

☐ **JOHN J. MADDEN MENTAL HEALTH CENTER (144028)**, 1200 South First Avenue, Zip 60141–0800; tel. 708/338–7202, (Nonreporting) **A**1 3 5 10 **S** Division of Mental Health, Department of Human Services, Springfield, IL
Primary Contact: Edith Newman, Interim Administrator
CFO: Janice Evans, Chief Financial Officer
Control: State–Government, nonfederal **Service:** Psychiatric

Staffed Beds: 150

VETERANS AFFAIRS EDWARD HINES, JR. HOSPITAL See Edward Hines, Jr. Veterans Affairs Hospital

Many Facility Codes have changed. Please refer to the AHA Guide Code Chart.

© 2014 AHA Guide

IL

HINSDALE—DuPage County

☒ △ **ADVENTIST HINSDALE HOSPITAL (140122)**, 120 North Oak Street,
Zip 60521–3890; tel. 630/856–9000 **A**1 2 3 5 7 9 10 13 **F**3 5 8 11 12 13 14
15 18 20 22 24 26 27 28 29 30 31 34 35 37 38 39 40 43 44 45 47 48 49
52 54 55 56 57 58 59 61 62 63 64 68 70 72 73 74 75 76 78 79 81 82 84
85 86 87 88 89 90 92 93 96 97 98 99 100 101 102 103 104 105 107 108
110 111 114 115 118 119 120 121 123 124 126 129 130 131 132 136 141
146 147 148 **P**7 8 **S** Adventist Health System Sunbelt Health Care Corporation,
Altamonte Springs, FL
Primary Contact: Michael Goebel, Chief Executive Officer
CFO: Rebecca Mathis, Vice President and Chief Financial Officer
CMO: Gary Lipinski, M.D., Regional Vice President and Chief Medical Officer
CIO: Thomas Schoenig, Chief Information Officer
CHR: Donald Russell, Regional Vice President Human Resources
CNO: Shawn O. Tyrrell, R.N., VP/Chief Nursing Officer
Web address: www.keepingyouwell.com
Control: Church–operated, Nongovernment, not–for profit **Service:** General
Medical and Surgical

Staffed Beds: 281 **Admissions:** 12301 **Census:** 149 **Outpatient Visits:**
269021 **Births:** 2009 **Total Expense ($000):** 277318 **Payroll Expense
($000):** 96798 **Personnel:** 1775

☒ **RML SPECIALTY HOSPITAL (142010)**, 5601 South County Line Road,
Zip 60521–4875; tel. 630/286–4000 **A**1 5 9 10 **F**1 3 18 29 30 31 45 53 58
74 85 107 114 119 130 146 148
Primary Contact: James R. Prister, President and Chief Executive Officer
COO: Ken Pawola, Chief Operating Officer
CFO: Tom Pater, Chief Financial Officer
CMO: John Brofman, M.D., Medical Director
CIO: Julie Ames, Chief Information Officer
CHR: John Landstrom, Director Human Resources
CNO: Maura Hopkins, R.N., Chief Nursing Officer
Web address: www.rmlspecialtyhospital.org
Control: Other not–for–profit (including NFP Corporation) **Service:** Long–Term
Acute Care hospital

Staffed Beds: 87 **Admissions:** 877 **Census:** 72 **Outpatient Visits:** 0 **Births:**
0 **Total Expense ($000):** 47434 **Payroll Expense ($000):** 24266
Personnel: 400

HOFFMAN ESTATES—Cook County

☒ **ALEXIAN BROTHERS BEHAVIORAL HEALTH HOSPITAL (144031)**, 1650
Moon Lake Boulevard, Zip 60169–1010; tel. 847/882–1600 **A**1 5 9 10 **F**4 5 29
30 34 35 44 50 56 58 59 65 68 75 77 87 98 99 100 101 102 103 104 105
130 132 146 **S** Ascension Health, Saint Louis, MO
Primary Contact: Clayton Ciha, President and Chief Executive Officer
COO: Christopher Novak, Chief Operating Officer
CFO: David Jones, Chief Financial Officer
CMO: Gregory Teas, M.D., Chief Medical Officer
CIO: Sherrie Russell, Vice President and Chief Information Officer
CNO: Christine Quinlan, MS, Chief Nursing Officer
Web address: www.abbhh.org
Control: Church–operated, Nongovernment, not–for profit **Service:** Psychiatric

Staffed Beds: 141 **Admissions:** 6138 **Census:** 130 **Outpatient Visits:**
155841 **Births:** 0 **Total Expense ($000):** 64538 **Payroll Expense ($000):**
35445 **Personnel:** 560

☒ **ST. ALEXIUS MEDICAL CENTER (140290)**, 1555 Barrington Road,
Zip 60169–1019; tel. 847/843–2000 **A**1 2 3 5 9 10 **F**3 12 13 15 17 18 20 22
26 29 30 31 34 35 37 39 40 41 43 45 46 47 48 49 50 54 55 56 57 59 63
64 70 72 73 74 75 76 77 78 79 81 82 84 85 86 87 88 89 93 107 108 110
111 114 115 119 120 121 123 124 126 130 132 145 146 147 148 **P**6
S Ascension Health, Saint Louis, MO
Primary Contact: Leonard Wilk, President and Chief Executive Officer
CFO: Sherril Vincent, Vice President Finance/CFO, Alexian Brothers Acute Care
Ministries
CMO: Scott Neeley, M.D., Chief Medical Officer
CIO: Sherrie Russell, Chief Information Officer
CHR: Linda Baker, Director Human Resources
CNO: Chris Budzinsky, R.N., Vice President Nursing/CNO Alexian Brothers Acute
Care Ministries
Web address: www.stalexius.org
Control: Church–operated, Nongovernment, not–for profit **Service:** General
Medical and Surgical

Staffed Beds: 261 **Admissions:** 15999 **Census:** 191 **Outpatient Visits:**
229650 **Births:** 3202 **Total Expense ($000):** 277818 **Payroll Expense
($000):** 97283 **Personnel:** 1379

HOOPESTON—Vermilion County

★ ◇ **CARLE HOOPESTON REGIONAL HEALTH CENTER (141316)**, 701 East
Orange Street, Zip 60942–1801; tel. 217/283–5531 **A**9 10 18 21 **F**3 15 29 32
35 40 45 57 59 65 81 85 89 90 93 97 107 110 119 127 128 133 **S** Carle
Foundation, Urbana, IL
Primary Contact: Harry Brockus, Chief Executive Officer
CHR: Melodee Bowers, Director Human Resources
Web address: www.carle.org
Control: Other not–for–profit (including NFP Corporation) **Service:** General
Medical and Surgical

Staffed Beds: 13 **Admissions:** 465 **Census:** 4 **Outpatient Visits:** 9780
Births: 0 **Total Expense ($000):** 29116 **Payroll Expense ($000):** 10423
Personnel: 149

HOPEDALE—Tazewell County

HOPEDALE MEDICAL COMPLEX (141330), 107 Tremont Street,
Zip 61747–7525; tel. 309/449–3321 **A**9 10 18 **F**10 24 28 29 30 31 32 34 35
36 40 49 53 57 59 70 79 81 82 93 97 107 109 110 119 125 128 131 133
145 **P**3
Primary Contact: Alfred N. Rossi, M.D., Chief Executive Officer
COO: Mark F. Rossi, Chief Operating Officer and General Counsel
CHR: Andrea Halley, Director Human Resources
CNO: Timothy Sondag, Senior Nursing Officer
Web address: www.hopedalemc.com
Control: Other not–for–profit (including NFP Corporation) **Service:** General
Medical and Surgical

Staffed Beds: 25 **Admissions:** 503 **Census:** 8 **Births:** 0 **Total Expense
($000):** 22889 **Payroll Expense ($000):** 9104

JACKSONVILLE—Morgan County

☒ **PASSAVANT AREA HOSPITAL (140058)**, 1600 West Walnut Street,
Zip 62650–1136; tel. 217/245–9541, (Total facility includes 15 beds in nursing
home–type unit) **A**1 9 10 19 20 **F**3 8 11 12 13 15 28 29 30 34 35 38 40 45
47 48 55 56 57 59 64 68 69 70 71 75 76 77 79 81 82 85 86 87 89 90
93 96 100 102 104 107 108 111 115 119 128 129 130 131 132 146 148
P4 6
Primary Contact: Douglas L. Rahn, President and Chief Executive Officer
CFO: David Bolen, Vice President and Chief Financial Officer
CMO: Charles Sheaff, M.D., President Medical Staff
CIO: Janie Cook, Director Information Systems
CHR: Jim Bormann, Director Human Resources
CNO: Karen Daum, R.N., Vice President and Chief Nursing Officer
Web address: www.passavanthospital.com
Control: Other not–for–profit (including NFP Corporation) **Service:** General
Medical and Surgical

Staffed Beds: 108 **Admissions:** 3564 **Census:** 41 **Outpatient Visits:** 79913
Births: 353 **Total Expense ($000):** 79440 **Payroll Expense ($000):** 31924
Personnel: 723

JERSEYVILLE—Jersey County

☒ **JERSEY COMMUNITY HOSPITAL (140059)**, 400 Maple Summit Road,
Zip 62052–2028, Mailing Address: P.O. Box 426, Zip 62052–0426;
tel. 618/498–6402 **A**1 9 10 **F**3 7 8 11 12 13 15 28 29 31 34 35 36 40 45 53
57 59 65 68 69 70 74 75 76 77 79 81 85 86 89 93 107 108 110 111 115
119 129 130 131 132 133 134 135 146 147 148
Primary Contact: Jonathan O. Wade, Administrator and Chief Executive Officer
CFO: Beth King, Chief Financial Officer
CMO: Michael McNear, M.D., Chief Medical Officer
CIO: Bob Bray, Chief Information Officer
CHR: Sharon K. Sanford, Director Human Resources
CNO: Julie Smith, R.N., Director of Nursing
Web address: www.jch.org
Control: Hospital district or authority, Government, nonfederal **Service:** General
Medical and Surgical

Staffed Beds: 49 **Admissions:** 1400 **Census:** 10 **Outpatient Visits:** 45309
Births: 164 **Total Expense ($000):** 28899 **Payroll Expense ($000):** 11364
Personnel: 239

IL

JOLIET—Will County

✠ △ **PRESENCE SAINT JOSEPH MEDICAL CENTER (140007)**, 333 North Madison Street, Zip 60435–8200; tel. 815/725–7133 **A**1 2 5 7 9 10 **F**3 5 8 11 12 13 15 17 18 20 22 24 26 28 29 30 31 32 34 35 36 37 38 39 40 41 43 44 45 46 49 50 53 54 56 57 58 59 60 61 64 65 68 70 71 72 74 75 76 77 78 79 80 81 82 84 85 86 87 88 89 90 92 93 96 97 98 99 100 101 102 103 105 107 108 110 111 114 115 118 119 120 121 123 124 126 129 130 131 132 134 135 143 144 145 146 147 **P**8 **S** Presence Health, Chicago, IL
Primary Contact: Beth Hughes, President and Chief Executive Officer
CFO: Melony W. Goodhand, Regional Chief Financial Officer
CMO: David R. Franzblau, M.D., Chief Medical Officer
CIO: Russell Soliman, System Manager Client Services and Management Information Services
Web address: www.provena.org/stjoes
Control: Church–operated, Nongovernment, not–for profit **Service:** General Medical and Surgical

> **Staffed Beds:** 457 **Admissions:** 22784 **Census:** 281 **Outpatient Visits:** 538854 **Births:** 1326 **Total Expense ($000):** 384276 **Payroll Expense ($000):** 128358 **Personnel:** 1977

PROVENA SAINT JOSEPH MEDICAL CENTER See Presence Saint Joseph Medical Center

KANKAKEE—Kankakee County

✠ **PRESENCE ST. MARY'S HOSPITAL (140155)**, 500 West Court Street, Zip 60901–3661; tel. 815/937–2400 **A**1 2 9 10 **F**3 5 11 12 13 15 18 20 22 26 28 29 30 31 32 34 35 36 38 39 40 43 45 48 49 50 53 54 56 57 58 59 60 61 64 65 68 70 74 75 76 77 78 79 81 82 83 84 85 86 87 89 92 93 97 98 99 100 101 102 103 104 105 106 107 108 110 111 114 115 116 119 129 130 131 132 135 143 146 147 148 **S** Presence Health, Chicago, IL
Primary Contact: Beth Hughes, President and Chief Executive Officer
CFO: Melony W. Goodhand, Chief Financial Officer
CMO: Syed Bokhari, M.D., Chief Medical Officer
CIO: Russell Soliman, Director Information Services
CNO: Jacqueline Medland, MS, Regional Chief Nursing Officer
Web address: www.provena.org/stmarys/
Control: Church–operated, Nongovernment, not–for profit **Service:** General Medical and Surgical

> **Staffed Beds:** 155 **Admissions:** 5750 **Census:** 66 **Outpatient Visits:** 202427 **Births:** 444 **Total Expense ($000):** 127990 **Payroll Expense ($000):** 37513 **Personnel:** 685

PROVENA ST. MARY'S HOSPITAL See Presence St. Mary's Hospital

✠ ◇ **RIVERSIDE MEDICAL CENTER (140186)**, 350 North Wall Street, Zip 60901–2901; tel. 815/933–1671 **A**1 2 5 9 10 13 21 **F**3 4 5 6 7 8 9 11 12 13 15 17 18 19 20 22 24 26 28 29 30 31 32 34 35 36 38 39 40 41 43 44 45 46 47 48 49 50 51 54 55 56 57 58 59 61 62 64 65 66 68 70 71 74 75 76 77 78 79 81 82 84 85 86 87 89 90 92 93 96 97 98 99 100 101 102 103 104 105 106 107 108 110 111 114 115 118 119 120 121 123 124 126 127 129 130 131 132 134 135 141 143 145 146 147 148 **P**6
Primary Contact: Phillip M. Kambic, Chief Executive Officer
COO: David Duda, Senior Vice President and Chief Operating Officer
CFO: Bill Douglas, Senior Vice President and Chief Financial Officer
CMO: John Jurica, M.D., Vice President Medical Affairs
CIO: Kyle Hansen, Corporate Director Information Systems
CHR: Becky Hinrichs, Vice President Human Resources
Web address: www.riversidehealthcare.org
Control: Other not–for–profit (including NFP Corporation) **Service:** General Medical and Surgical

> **Staffed Beds:** 325 **Admissions:** 10412 **Census:** 140 **Outpatient Visits:** 375113 **Births:** 1015 **Total Expense ($000):** 232137 **Payroll Expense ($000):** 94565 **Personnel:** 1744

KEWANEE—Henry County

★ **OSF SAINT LUKE MEDICAL CENTER (141325)**, 1051 West South Street, Zip 61443–8354, Mailing Address: P.O. Box 747, Zip 61443–0747; tel. 309/852–7500 **A**9 10 18 **F**3 11 15 18 29 31 32 34 35 36 38 40 45 50 57 59 64 65 66 68 70 75 77 78 79 81 82 85 86 87 92 93 96 97 107 108 110 115 119 127 129 131 132 133 135 146 **P**6 **S** OSF Healthcare System, Peoria, IL
Primary Contact: Lynn Fulton, President
CFO: John Bowser, Vice President, Chief Financial Officer
CIO: Jeremy Johnson, Director of Information Technology
CHR: Renee A. Salisbury, Director Human Resources
CNO: Jennifer Junis, MSN, Vice President Chief Nursing Officer
Web address: www.osfsaintluke.org
Control: Other not–for–profit (including NFP Corporation) **Service:** General Medical and Surgical

> **Staffed Beds:** 25 **Admissions:** 641 **Census:** 6 **Outpatient Visits:** 33761 **Births:** 0 **Total Expense ($000):** 26711 **Payroll Expense ($000):** 9475 **Personnel:** 195

LA GRANGE—Cook County

✠ **ADVENTIST LA GRANGE MEMORIAL HOSPITAL (140065)**, 5101 South Willow Spring Road, Zip 60525–2600; tel. 708/245–9000 **A**1 2 3 5 9 10 13 **F**3 12 13 15 17 18 20 22 24 26 28 29 30 31 34 35 37 39 40 43 44 45 49 50 56 57 58 59 60 61 64 68 70 73 74 75 76 78 79 81 82 85 86 87 89 90 92 96 97 100 107 108 110 111 114 115 118 119 120 121 123 126 129 130 131 132 135 146 147 148 **P**7 8 **S** Adventist Health System Sunbelt Health Care Corporation, Altamonte Springs, FL
Primary Contact: Michael Goebel, Chief Executive Officer
CFO: Rebecca Mathis, Chief Financial Officer
CMO: Gary Lipinski, M.D., Regional Vice President and Chief Medical Officer
CIO: Thomas Schoenig, Chief Information Officer
CHR: Garry Giertuga, Site Manager Human Resources
CNO: Mary S. Murphy, R.N., Regional Chief Nursing Officer
Web address: www.keepingyouwell.com
Control: Church–operated, Nongovernment, not–for profit **Service:** General Medical and Surgical

> **Staffed Beds:** 187 **Admissions:** 7907 **Census:** 96 **Outpatient Visits:** 118582 **Births:** 470 **Total Expense ($000):** 156029 **Payroll Expense ($000):** 55331 **Personnel:** 873

LAKE FOREST—Lake County

LAKE FOREST HOSPITAL See Northwestern Lake Forest Hospital

✠ **NORTHWESTERN LAKE FOREST HOSPITAL (140130)**, 660 North Westmoreland Road, Zip 60045–1696; tel. 847/234–5600, (Total facility includes 74 beds in nursing home–type unit) **A**1 2 3 5 9 10 **F**2 3 8 9 11 13 15 18 20 22 26 28 29 30 31 32 34 35 36 38 40 42 44 45 46 48 49 50 51 53 54 56 57 58 59 62 64 65 70 73 74 75 76 77 78 79 81 82 85 86 87 89 92 93 96 97 107 108 110 111 114 115 116 117 119 120 121 123 128 129 130 131 132 135 146 147 148 **P**8 **S** Northwestern Memorial Healthcare, Chicago, IL
Primary Contact: Thomas J. McAfee, President
CFO: Matthew J. Flynn, Senior Vice President and Chief Financial Officer
CMO: Michael G. Ankin, M.D., Vice President Medical Affairs & Chief Medical Officer
CHR: Marsha Oberrieder, Vice President Operations
CNO: Denise Mageski, MSN, Chief Nurse Executive
Web address: www.lfh.org
Control: Other not–for–profit (including NFP Corporation) **Service:** General Medical and Surgical

> **Staffed Beds:** 189 **Admissions:** 8494 **Census:** 96 **Outpatient Visits:** 192027 **Births:** 1494 **Total Expense ($000):** 233109 **Payroll Expense ($000):** 81014 **Personnel:** 1209

LAWRENCEVILLE—Lawrence County

★ **LAWRENCE COUNTY MEMORIAL HOSPITAL (141344)**, 2200 West State Street, Zip 62439–1852; tel. 618/943–1000 **A**9 10 18 **F**3 11 15 28 29 30 40 75 81 93 107 114 127 130 133 **S** QHR, Brentwood, TN
Primary Contact: Doug Florkowski, Chief Executive Officer
CFO: Larry Spore, Chief Financial Officer
CIO: Gary Theriac, Director Information Technology
CHR: Kim Alldredge, Director Human Resources
CNO: Rita Garvey, Chief Nursing Officer
Web address: www.lcmhosp.org
Control: Other not–for–profit (including NFP Corporation) **Service:** General Medical and Surgical

> **Staffed Beds:** 25 **Admissions:** 699 **Census:** 7 **Outpatient Visits:** 27586 **Births:** 0 **Total Expense ($000):** 12157 **Payroll Expense ($000):** 4792 **Personnel:** 128

LIBERTYVILLE—Lake County

★ ◇ **ADVOCATE CONDELL MEDICAL CENTER (140202)**, 801 South Milwaukee Avenue, Zip 60048–3199; tel. 847/362–2900 **A**2 9 10 21 **F**1 2 3 4 11 12 13 15 16 17 18 19 20 22 24 26 28 29 30 31 32 34 35 36 37 39 40 41 43 44 45 46 47 48 49 50 51 53 54 55 56 57 59 60 64 65 67 68 70 72 73 74 75 76 77 78 79 80 81 82 85 86 87 88 90 92 93 94 96 98 107 108 110 111 114 115 117 118 119 120 121 123 126 128 129 130 131 132 135 144 145 146 147 148 **P**8 **S** Advocate Health Care, Downers Grove, IL
Primary Contact: Dominica Tallarico, President
CFO: David A. Cartwright, Vice President Finance
CMO: Debra Susie–Lattner, M.D., Vice President, Medical Management
CIO: Kathy Fairchild, Director Site Information Systems
CHR: Jason Spigner, Vice President Human Resources
CNO: Mary Hillard, R.N., Vice President Patient Care Services
Web address: www.advocatehealth.com/condell/
Control: Other not–for–profit (including NFP Corporation) **Service:** General Medical and Surgical

> **Staffed Beds:** 277 **Admissions:** 16334 **Census:** 178 **Outpatient Visits:** 207162 **Births:** 2306 **Total Expense ($000):** 279385 **Payroll Expense ($000):** 96727 **Personnel:** 1723

Many Facility Codes have changed. Please refer to the AHA Guide Code Chart. © 2014 AHA Guide

LINCOLN—Logan County

✠ **ABRAHAM LINCOLN MEMORIAL HOSPITAL (141322)**, 200 Stahlhut Drive, Zip 62656–5066; tel. 217/732–2161 **A**1 9 10 18 **F**13 15 28 29 30 34 35 40 57 59 64 71 75 76 77 79 81 82 87 93 107 108 110 111 119 129 130 131 132 133 144 146 **P**5 **S** Memorial Health System, Springfield, IL
Primary Contact: Dolan Dalpoas, President and Chief Executive Officer
COO: Kathleen Vipond, Assistant Administrator and Director
CFO: Andrew Costic, Regional Chief Financial Officer
CMO: Richard Bivin, M.D., President Medical Staff
CIO: Keenan Leesman, Director Information Systems
CHR: Kaylee Tanner, Human Resources Business Partner
Web address: www.almh.org
Control: Other not–for–profit (including NFP Corporation) **Service:** General Medical and Surgical

Staffed Beds: 25 **Admissions:** 1114 **Census:** 10 **Outpatient Visits:** 48814 **Births:** 212 **Total Expense ($000):** 37398 **Payroll Expense ($000):** 13266 **Personnel:** 245

LITCHFIELD—Montgomery County

✠ **ST. FRANCIS HOSPITAL (141350)**, 1215 Franciscan Drive, Zip 62056–1799, Mailing Address: P.O. Box 1215, Zip 62056–0999; tel. 217/324–2191 **A**1 9 10 18 **F**11 13 15 18 28 29 30 34 35 40 44 45 46 50 56 57 59 64 68 70 74 75 76 77 78 79 81 82 85 86 87 92 93 107 111 114 118 119 129 131 132 133 134 135 146 147 **S** Hospital Sisters Health System, Springfield, IL
Primary Contact: David R. Olejniczak, Interim President and Chief Executive Officer
CFO: Diane Lindsay, Chief Financial Officer
Web address: www.stfrancis–litchfield.org
Control: Church–operated, Nongovernment, not–for profit **Service:** General Medical and Surgical

Staffed Beds: 25 **Admissions:** 1294 **Census:** 11 **Outpatient Visits:** 46804 **Births:** 286 **Total Expense ($000):** 29869 **Payroll Expense ($000):** 10716 **Personnel:** 195

MACOMB—Mcdonough County

✠ **MCDONOUGH DISTRICT HOSPITAL (140089)**, 525 East Grant Street, Zip 61455–3318; tel. 309/833–4101, (Total facility includes 16 beds in nursing home–type unit) **A**1 9 10 20 **F**2 3 5 7 11 13 15 28 29 31 34 35 38 40 45 47 48 50 51 54 56 57 59 62 63 64 68 70 75 76 77 78 79 81 82 84 85 86 89 91 93 94 96 97 99 100 101 102 104 107 108 110 115 119 124 127 128 129 130 131 132 135 146 148 **P**8
Primary Contact: Kenneth Boyd, Jr., President and Chief Executive Officer
COO: Lori Moon, R.N., Vice President Clinical Operations/Business Development
CFO: Linda Dace, Vice President Finance
CMO: Christopher Stortzum, M.D., President Medical Staff
CIO: Harlan T. Baker, Department Leader Information Systems
CHR: Sue Dexter, Administrative Department Leader Human Resources
CNO: Wanda Foster, R.N., Vice President Nursing
Web address: www.mdh.org
Control: Hospital district or authority, Government, nonfederal **Service:** General Medical and Surgical

Staffed Beds: 95 **Admissions:** 2264 **Census:** 26 **Outpatient Visits:** 168200 **Births:** 291 **Total Expense ($000):** 64111 **Payroll Expense ($000):** 32241 **Personnel:** 557

MARION—Williamson County

✠ **HEARTLAND REGIONAL MEDICAL CENTER (140184)**, 3333 West DeYoung, Zip 62959–5884; tel. 618/998–7000, (Nonreporting) **A**1 9 10 **S** Community Health Systems, Inc., Franklin, TN
Primary Contact: James Flynn, Chief Executive Officer
CHR: Ed Daech, Director Human Resources
Web address: www.heartlandregional.com
Control: Corporation, Investor–owned, for–profit **Service:** General Medical and Surgical

Staffed Beds: 92

✠ **MARION VETERANS AFFAIRS MEDICAL CENTER**, 2401 West Main Street, Zip 62959–1188; tel. 618/997–5311, (Nonreporting) **A**1 3 5 **S** Department of Veterans Affairs, Washington, DC
Primary Contact: Donald Hutson, Director
COO: Frank Kehus, Associate Director for Operations
CFO: Connie McDonald, Chief Financial Officer
CMO: Michael Ladwig, M.D., Chief of Staff
CIO: Clint Bishop, Program Manager
CHR: Tonya L. Searby, Chief Human Resources
CNO: Rose Burke, Associate Director Patient Care Services
Web address: www.marion.va.gov
Control: Veterans Affairs, Government, federal **Service:** General Medical and Surgical

Staffed Beds: 225

MARYVILLE—Madison County

✠ △ **ANDERSON HOSPITAL (140289)**, 6800 State Route 162, Zip 62062–8500; tel. 618/288–5711 **A**1 7 9 10 **F**3 11 13 15 18 20 22 28 29 30 34 35 40 49 50 57 59 62 70 74 75 76 78 79 81 82 85 90 93 107 110 111 115 118 119 126 129 130 132 144 146 147 148
Primary Contact: Keith Allen Page, President and Chief Executive Officer
CFO: Michael Marshall, Vice President Finance and Chief Financial Officer
CMO: Michael Mulligan, M.D., President Medical Staff
CIO: Michael Ward, Director Information Services
CHR: Robin Steinmann, Administrative Director Human Resources
CNO: Lisa Klaustermeier, R.N., Chief Nursing Officer
Web address: www.andersonhospital.org
Control: Other not–for–profit (including NFP Corporation) **Service:** General Medical and Surgical

Staffed Beds: 154 **Admissions:** 7115 **Census:** 76 **Outpatient Visits:** 175458 **Births:** 1724 **Total Expense ($000):** 113033 **Payroll Expense ($000):** 45963 **Personnel:** 872

MATTOON—Coles County

★ **SARAH BUSH LINCOLN HEALTH CENTER (140189)**, 1000 Health Center Drive, Zip 61938–9253, Mailing Address: P.O. Box 372, Zip 61938–0372; tel. 217/258–2525 **A**9 10 20 **F**3 11 12 13 15 18 20 22 28 29 30 31 32 34 35 36 38 39 40 44 47 48 49 50 54 56 57 59 61 62 63 64 65 66 68 69 70 71 74 75 76 77 78 79 81 82 84 85 86 87 89 93 97 98 99 100 101 102 103 104 105 107 110 111 114 115 117 119 120 121 123 127 129 130 131 132 134 135 144 145 146 147 148 **P**6
Primary Contact: Timothy A. Ols, FACHE, President and Chief Executive Officer
COO: Dennis Pluard, Vice President Operations
CFO: Craig Sheagren, Vice President Finance
CMO: James Hildebrandt, D.O., Vice President Medical Affairs
CIO: Maggie Ratliff, Vice President Information Systems
CHR: Eric Benson, Vice President Human Resources
CNO: Mary Lou Wild, Vice President Patient Care Continuum and Chief Nursing Officer
Web address: www.sarahbush.org
Control: Other not–for–profit (including NFP Corporation) **Service:** General Medical and Surgical

Staffed Beds: 118 **Admissions:** 6628 **Census:** 64 **Outpatient Visits:** 447890 **Births:** 772 **Total Expense ($000):** 195791 **Payroll Expense ($000):** 98365 **Personnel:** 1576

MAYWOOD—Cook County

✠ △ **LOYOLA UNIVERSITY MEDICAL CENTER (140276)**, 2160 South First Avenue, Zip 60153–3328; tel. 708/216–9000, (Includes RONALD MCDONALD CHILDREN'S HOSPITAL, 2160 South 1St. Avenue, tel. 888/584–7888) **A**1 2 3 5 7 8 9 10 **F**3 6 7 8 9 11 12 13 14 15 16 17 18 19 20 21 22 23 24 25 26 27 28 29 30 31 32 33 34 35 36 37 38 39 40 41 43 44 45 46 47 48 49 50 51 54 55 56 57 58 59 60 61 62 63 64 65 66 68 70 71 72 73 74 75 76 77 78 79 80 81 82 84 85 86 87 88 89 90 91 92 93 94 96 97 98 99 100 101 102 103 104 107 108 110 111 113 114 115 116 117 118 119 120 121 123 124 126 129 130 131 132 134 135 136 137 138 139 140 141 142 143 144 145 146 147 148 **P**6 **S** Catholic Health East / Trinity Health, Livonia, MI
Primary Contact: Larry M. Goldberg, President and Chief Executive Officer
CFO: Thomas Honan, Interim Chief Financial Officer
CMO: Robert Cherry, M.D., Chief Medical Officer
CIO: Arthur J. Krumrey, Chief Information Officer
CHR: Vicky Piper, Vice President Human Resources
Web address: www.loyolamedicine.org/Medical_Services/index.cfm
Control: Other not–for–profit (including NFP Corporation) **Service:** General Medical and Surgical

Staffed Beds: 520 **Admissions:** 23572 **Census:** 364 **Outpatient Visits:** 1346082 **Births:** 928 **Total Expense ($000):** 982860 **Payroll Expense ($000):** 493039 **Personnel:** 6074

Hospital, Medicare Provider Number, Address, Telephone, Approval, Facility, and Physician Codes, Health Care System

★ American Hospital Association (AHA) membership
☐ The Joint Commission accreditation   ◇ DNV Healthcare Inc. accreditation
○ Healthcare Facilities Accreditation Program
△ Commission on Accreditation of Rehabilitation Facilities (CARF) accreditation

MCHENRY—Mchenry County

⊞ **CENTEGRA HOSPITAL – MCHENRY (140116)**, 4201 Medical Center Drive, Zip 60050–8409; tel. 815/344–5000 **A**1 2 5 9 10 **F**3 4 11 12 13 15 18 20 22 24 26 28 29 30 31 34 35 37 38 39 40 43 44 49 50 51 54 55 57 58 59 62 64 68 69 70 74 75 76 78 79 81 82 85 86 87 90 92 93 96 100 101 102 107 108 110 111 114 115 117 118 119 120 121 123 126 129 130 131 132 143 146 147 148 **P**4 5 **S** Centegra Health System, Crystal Lake, IL
Primary Contact: Michael S. Eesley, Chief Executive Officer
COO: Jason Sciarro, President and Chief Operating Officer
CFO: David Tomlinson, Executive Vice President Chief Financial Officer and Chief Information Officer
CMO: Irfan Hafiz, Vice President Medical Affairs
CIO: David Tomlinson, Executive Vice President Chief Financial Officer and Chief Information Officer
CHR: Bernadette S. Szczepanski, Vice President, Human Resources Development
Web address: www.centegra.org
Control: Other not–for–profit (including NFP Corporation) **Service:** General Medical and Surgical

> **Staffed Beds:** 173 **Admissions:** 9588 **Census:** 110 **Outpatient Visits:** 131147 **Births:** 742 **Total Expense ($000):** 201949 **Payroll Expense ($000):** 84877 **Personnel:** 1062

MCLEANSBORO—Hamilton County

HAMILTON MEMORIAL HOSPITAL DISTRICT (141326), 611 South Marshall Avenue, Zip 62859–1213, Mailing Address: P.O. Box 429, Mc Leansboro, Zip 62859–0429; tel. 618/643–2361 **A**9 10 18 **F**3 11 15 28 29 40 43 57 81 93 107 108 114 119 127 129 130 133
Primary Contact: Randall W. Dauby, Chief Executive Officer
COO: Bradley Futrell, Chief Operating Officer
CFO: Kent Mitchell, Chief Financial Officer
CIO: Don Darnell, Chief Information Officer
CNO: Patty Blazier, Chief Nursing Officer
Web address: www.hmhospital.org
Control: Hospital district or authority, Government, nonfederal **Service:** General Medical and Surgical

> **Staffed Beds:** 25 **Admissions:** 830 **Census:** 9 **Outpatient Visits:** 30975 **Births:** 0 **Total Expense ($000):** 13651 **Payroll Expense ($000):** 5719 **Personnel:** 135

MELROSE PARK—Cook County

⊞ **GOTTLIEB MEMORIAL HOSPITAL (140008)**, 701 West North Avenue, Zip 60160–1612; tel. 708/681–3200 **A**1 3 5 9 10 **F**2 3 11 12 13 15 18 20 22 24 26 28 29 30 31 34 35 36 39 40 43 44 45 47 49 53 54 56 57 59 60 62 63 64 65 68 70 74 75 76 77 78 79 81 85 86 87 89 92 93 96 97 98 103 107 108 110 111 114 118 119 128 129 130 131 132 143 144 146 147 148 **P**8 **S** Catholic Health East / Trinity Health, Livonia, MI
Primary Contact: Lori Price, President
COO: Ken Fishbain, Chief Operating Officer
CFO: Ellyn Chin, Vice President Finance
CMO: Gerald Luger, M.D., President Medical Staff
CIO: Maurita Adler, Director Information Services
CHR: Brett Wakefield, Vice President Human Resources
Web address: www.gottliebhospital.org
Control: Other not–for–profit (including NFP Corporation) **Service:** General Medical and Surgical

> **Staffed Beds:** 255 **Admissions:** 8106 **Census:** 134 **Outpatient Visits:** 107894 **Births:** 771 **Total Expense ($000):** 135536 **Payroll Expense ($000):** 61410 **Personnel:** 1030

★ ○ **WESTLAKE HOSPITAL (140240)**, 1225 Lake Street, Zip 60160–4000; tel. 708/681–3000, (Nonreporting) **A**3 5 9 10 11 **S** TENET Healthcare Corporation, Dallas, TX
Primary Contact: Patrick Maloney, Chief Executive Officer
COO: Joan Ormsby, Chief Operating Officer
CFO: Gene Smith, Interim Chief Financial Officer
CMO: Robert Chase, M.D., Chief Medical Officer
CHR: Nancy Gunnell, Vice President Human Resources
CNO: Sharon Freyer, R.N., Chief Nursing Officer
Web address: www.wlhospital.com/Home.aspx
Control: Corporation, Investor–owned, for–profit **Service:** General Medical and Surgical

> **Staffed Beds:** 181

MENDOTA—Lasalle County

★ **MENDOTA COMMUNITY HOSPITAL (141310)**, 1401 East 12th Street, Zip 61342–9216; tel. 815/539–7461 **A**9 10 18 **F**3 11 15 28 29 31 34 40 49 57 59 62 65 69 70 77 78 79 81 85 93 107 110 111 115 129 130 133 146 **P**6
Primary Contact: Judy A. Christiansen, R.N., Interim Chief Executive Officer
CFO: Gary Eich, Interim Chief Financial Officer
CMO: Mary Chinn, M.D., President Medical Staff
CIO: Shawn Soliman, Manager Information Services
CHR: Kimberly Kennedy, Manager Human Resources
CNO: Heather Bomstad, R.N., Chief Nursing Officer
Web address: www.mendotahospital.org
Control: Other not–for–profit (including NFP Corporation) **Service:** General Medical and Surgical

> **Staffed Beds:** 25 **Admissions:** 899 **Census:** 11 **Outpatient Visits:** 49959 **Births:** 0 **Total Expense ($000):** 28638 **Payroll Expense ($000):** 14652 **Personnel:** 247

METROPOLIS—Massac County

★ **MASSAC MEMORIAL HOSPITAL (141323)**, 28 Chick Street, Zip 62960–2467, Mailing Address: P.O. Box 850, Zip 62960–0850; tel. 618/524–2176, (Nonreporting) **A**9 10 18
Primary Contact: H. William Hartley, FACHE, Chief Executive Officer
CFO: Jerry Klein, Interim Chief Financial Officer
CHR: Joel Foster, Director Human Resources
CNO: Janet Hester, R.N., Chief Nurse Executive
Web address: www.massachealth.org
Control: Hospital district or authority, Government, nonfederal **Service:** General Medical and Surgical

> **Staffed Beds:** 25

MOLINE—Rock Island County

UNITYPOINT HEALTH – TRINITY MOLINE See UnityPoint Health – Trinity Rock Island, Rock Island

MONMOUTH—Warren County

★ **OSF HOLY FAMILY MEDICAL CENTER (141318)**, 1000 West Harlem Avenue, Zip 61462–1007; tel. 309/734–3141 **A**9 10 18 **F**11 15 28 29 30 34 40 45 46 50 57 59 64 65 68 75 77 81 85 87 93 97 107 110 115 118 119 127 129 130 132 133 135 143 145 146 148 **P**6 **S** OSF Healthcare System, Peoria, IL
Primary Contact: Patricia A. Luker, Chief Executive Officer
CFO: Theresa Springer, Chief Financial Officer
CMO: Frank Lasala, M.D., President Medical Staff
CIO: Lew McCann, Director Management Information Systems
CHR: Jenny Jacobs, Director Human Resources
CNO: Shelley Wiborg, MS, Director of Nursing
Web address: www.osfholyfamily.org
Control: Church–operated, Nongovernment, not–for profit **Service:** General Medical and Surgical

> **Staffed Beds:** 23 **Admissions:** 446 **Census:** 5 **Outpatient Visits:** 73759 **Births:** 0 **Total Expense ($000):** 23446 **Payroll Expense ($000):** 11512 **Personnel:** 202

MONTICELLO—Piatt County

⊞ **KIRBY MEDICAL CENTER (141301)**, 1000 Medical Center Drive, Zip 61856–2116; tel. 217/762–2115, (Nonreporting) **A**1 5 9 10 18
Primary Contact: Steven Tenhouse, FACHE, Chief Executive Officer
CFO: Alexander Nazarian, Chief Financial Officer
CMO: Narain Mandhan, M.D., President Medical Staff
CIO: Kyle Willams, Director Information Technology
CNO: Jennifer Moss, Chief Clinical Officer
Web address: www.kirbyhealth.org
Control: Other not–for–profit (including NFP Corporation) **Service:** General Medical and Surgical

> **Staffed Beds:** 16

MORRIS—Grundy County

★ ○ **MORRIS HOSPITAL & HEALTHCARE CENTERS (140101)**, 150 West High Street, Zip 60450–1497; tel. 815/942–2932 **A**2 9 10 11 **F**3 11 13 15 18 19 20 22 26 28 29 34 35 40 43 47 49 50 54 57 59 64 66 69 70 74 75 76 77 78 79 81 82 85 86 87 89 93 97 102 107 108 110 111 114 115 118 119 120 121 123 130 132 135 143 144 146 **P**6
Primary Contact: Mark B. Steadham, President and Chief Executive Officer
COO: Patrick O'Connor, Chief Operating Officer
CFO: Dean M. Marketti, Vice President Finance
CIO: Dean M. Marketti, Chief Information Officer
CHR: Erin Murphy–Frobish, Vice President Human Resources
CNO: Kimberly A. Landers, MS, Vice President Patient Care Services
Web address: www.morrishospital.org
Control: Other not–for–profit (including NFP Corporation) **Service:** General Medical and Surgical

> **Staffed Beds:** 89 **Admissions:** 3785 **Census:** 37 **Outpatient Visits:** 218723 **Births:** 466 **Total Expense ($000):** 116168 **Payroll Expense ($000):** 49726 **Personnel:** 707

IL

Many Facility Codes have changed. Please refer to the AHA Guide Code Chart. © 2014 AHA Guide

MORRISON—Whiteside County

★ **MORRISON COMMUNITY HOSPITAL (141329)**, 303 North Jackson Street, Zip 61270–3042; tel. 815/772–4003, (Nonreporting) **A**9 10 18
Primary Contact: Pam Pfister, Chief Executive Officer
COO: Pam Pfister, Chief Executive Officer
CFO: Cami Megli, Controller
CMO: Duncan Dinkha, M.D., Chief of Staff
CIO: Pam Pfister, Chief Executive Officer
CHR: Amber L. Temple, Director Human Resources
Web address: www.morrisonhospital.com
Control: Hospital district or authority, Government, nonfederal **Service:** General Medical and Surgical

Staffed Beds: 60

MOUNT CARMEL—Wabash County

⊞ **WABASH GENERAL HOSPITAL (141327)**, 1418 College Drive, Zip 62863–2638; tel. 618/262–8621, (Nonreporting) **A**1 9 10 18 **S** Alliant Management Services, Louisville, KY
Primary Contact: Jay Purvis, Administrator
CFO: Steve McGill, Chief Financial Officer
CMO: Julko Fullop, M.D., Chief of Staff
CIO: Bobby Gage, Director Information Technology
CHR: Bridget Shepard, Director Human Resources
CNO: Tamara Gould, R.N., Director of Nursing
Web address: www.wabashgeneral.com
Control: County-Government, nonfederal **Service:** General Medical and Surgical

Staffed Beds: 25

MOUNT VERNON—Jefferson County

⊞ **CROSSROADS COMMUNITY HOSPITAL (140294)**, 8 Doctors Park Road, Zip 62864–6224; tel. 618/244–5500 **A**1 9 10 **F**3 8 11 12 15 18 29 30 34 35 40 45 46 49 50 53 56 57 59 60 64 68 70 74 75 77 79 81 82 85 93 94 95 96 107 110 111 115 119 126 127 129 135 145 146 147 148 **P**1
S Community Health Systems, Inc., Franklin, TN
Primary Contact: Finny Mathew, Chief Executive Officer
CFO: Eric Jost, Chief Financial Officer
CIO: James Barnes, Director Information Technology
CHR: Jessica Connaway, Director Human Resources
CNO: Sam R. White, Chief Nursing Officer
Web address: www.crossroadscommunityhospital.com
Control: Corporation, Investor-owned, for-profit **Service:** General Medical and Surgical

Staffed Beds: 47 **Admissions:** 1347 **Census:** 13 **Outpatient Visits:** 30801 **Births:** 0 **Total Expense ($000):** 40359 **Payroll Expense ($000):** 16007 **Personnel:** 274

⊞ **GOOD SAMARITAN REGIONAL HEALTH CENTER (140046)**, 605 North 12th Street, Zip 62864–2899; tel. 618/242–4600 **A**1 2 9 10 **F**3 11 13 15 18 20 22 24 26 28 29 30 31 34 35 38 40 44 45 46 50 51 54 56 57 59 61 64 68 70 73 74 75 76 77 78 79 80 81 82 84 85 86 87 89 90 93 94 107 108 110 111 114 115 119 126 130 131 132 135 145 146 147 148 **P**6 8 **S** SSM Health, Saint Louis, MO
Primary Contact: Michael D. Warren, President
COO: Chris Adams, Vice President Operations
CFO: Kay Tinsley, Vice President Fiscal Services
CMO: Daniel Hoffman, M.D., Administrative Medical Director
CIO: Steve Murphy, Director Networks
CHR: Thomas W. Blythe, Regional Vice President Human Resources
Web address: www.smgsi.com
Control: Church-operated, Nongovernment, not-for profit **Service:** General Medical and Surgical

Staffed Beds: 134 **Admissions:** 7054 **Census:** 77 **Outpatient Visits:** 190793 **Births:** 924 **Total Expense ($000):** 159905 **Payroll Expense ($000):** 51393 **Personnel:** 1049

MURPHYSBORO—Jackson County

★ **ST. JOSEPH MEMORIAL HOSPITAL (141334)**, 2 South Hospital Drive, Zip 62966–3333; tel. 618/684–3156 **A**9 10 18 **F**3 11 18 28 29 30 31 34 35 40 45 56 57 59 64 74 75 77 78 79 81 82 85 86 87 93 107 114 119 129 130 132 135 146 148 **P**1 **S** Southern Illinois Hospital Services, Carbondale, IL
Primary Contact: John T. Brothers, R.N., MS, Administrator
CMO: Emily Hanson, M.D., President, Medical Staff
CIO: David Holland, Vice President Information Services
CHR: Kelly Stevens, Manager Human Resources
CNO: Julie Firman, R.N., Chief Nursing Officer
Web address: www.sih.net
Control: Other not-for-profit (including NFP Corporation) **Service:** General Medical and Surgical

Staffed Beds: 25 **Admissions:** 706 **Census:** 6 **Outpatient Visits:** 72755 **Births:** 0 **Total Expense ($000):** 43141 **Payroll Expense ($000):** 12851 **Personnel:** 230

NAPERVILLE—Dupage County

⊞ **EDWARD HOSPITAL (140231)**, 801 South Washington Street, Zip 60540–7499; tel. 630/527–3000 **A**1 2 9 10 **F**3 11 12 13 15 17 18 19 20 22 24 26 27 28 29 30 31 32 34 35 37 39 40 41 42 43 44 45 46 47 48 49 50 54 55 57 58 59 61 64 65 68 70 72 73 74 75 76 77 78 79 81 82 84 85 86 87 88 89 93 96 97 102 107 108 109 110 111 114 115 117 118 119 120 121 123 124 126 129 130 131 132 135 144 146 147 148 **P**1 6
S Edward-Elmhurst Healthcare, Naperville, IL
Primary Contact: Pamela M. Davis, System President and Chief Executive Officer
COO: Marianne Spencer, R.N., Vice President Operations and Chief Operating Officer
CFO: Vincent Pryor, System Executive Vice President and Chief Financial Officer
CMO: Brent Smith, M.D., Chief Medical Officer and Vice President Clinical Integration
CIO: Bobbie Byrne, M.D., Vice President Chief Information Officer
CHR: Susan Mitchell, System Executive Vice President Human Resources
CNO: Patti Ludwig–Beymer, Ph.D., Vice President Chief Nursing Officer
Web address: www.edward.org
Control: Other not-for-profit (including NFP Corporation) **Service:** General Medical and Surgical

Staffed Beds: 311 **Admissions:** 20852 **Census:** 222 **Outpatient Visits:** 493949 **Births:** 3127 **Total Expense ($000):** 470155 **Payroll Expense ($000):** 160243 **Personnel:** 2328

⊞ **LINDEN OAKS HOSPITAL AT EDWARD (144035)**, 852 West Street, Zip 60540–6400; tel. 630/305–5500 **A**1 5 9 10 **F**4 5 29 34 35 38 56 57 59 64 68 75 87 98 99 100 101 103 104 105 106 130 132 134 **P**1 6
S Edward-Elmhurst Healthcare, Naperville, IL
Primary Contact: Gina Sharp, FACHE, President
CFO: Kristen Refness, Chief Financial Officer
CMO: Barry Rabin, M.D., Medical Director
CIO: Hugh Siddiqui, Senior Applications Analyst
CNO: Trish Jones–Bendel, R.N., Chief Nursing Officer
Web address: www.edward.org
Control: Other not-for-profit (including NFP Corporation) **Service:** Psychiatric

Staffed Beds: 108 **Admissions:** 4493 **Census:** 88 **Outpatient Visits:** 50201 **Births:** 0 **Total Expense ($000):** 38446 **Payroll Expense ($000):** 21145 **Personnel:** 384

NASHVILLE--Washington County

⊞ **WASHINGTON COUNTY HOSPITAL (141308)**, 705 South Grand Avenue, Zip 62263–1534; tel. 618/327–8236, (Total facility includes 28 beds in nursing home–type unit) **A**1 9 10 18 **F**28 29 31 34 40 49 57 59 64 65 78 81 85 93 104 107 114 119 127 129 133 145 146 148
Primary Contact: Nancy M. Newby, R.N., Ph.D., FACHE, President and Chief Executive Officer
CFO: Elaine Matzenbacher, Chief Financial Officer
CMO: Alfonso Urdaneta, M.D., President Medical Staff
CIO: Kim Larkin, Chief Information Officer
CHR: David Davenport, Director Human Resources
CNO: Candice Hawley, Chief Nursing Executive
Web address: www.washingtoncountyhospital.org
Control: Hospital district or authority, Government, nonfederal **Service:** General Medical and Surgical

Staffed Beds: 50 **Admissions:** 297 **Census:** 31 **Outpatient Visits:** 31424 **Births:** 0 **Total Expense ($000):** 13160 **Payroll Expense ($000):** 5955 **Personnel:** 140

IL

NEW LENOX—Will County

✠ △ **SILVER CROSS HOSPITAL (140213)**, 1900 Silver Cross Boulevard, Zip 60451–9509; tel. 815/300–1100 **A**1 2 7 9 10 **F**3 5 7 11 12 13 15 18 19 20 22 26 27 28 29 30 31 32 34 35 37 38 40 42 43 44 46 47 48 49 50 53 54 57 59 60 62 64 68 70 74 75 76 77 78 79 81 82 84 85 89 90 92 93 96 98 100 101 102 103 104 105 107 108 110 111 114 115 118 119 126 130 131 132 134 135 146 147 148 **P**1 5 8
Primary Contact: Paul Pawlak, President and Chief Executive Officer
COO: Mary Bakken, Executive Vice President and Chief Operating Officer
CFO: John Krepps, Senior Vice President Finance
CMO: Christopher Udovich, M.D., Chief of Staff
CIO: Kevin Lane, Vice President Information Systems
CHR: Mark Jepson, Vice President
CNO: Peggy Gricus, R.N., Vice President, Patient Care Services and Chief Nursing Officer
Web address: www.silvercross.org
Control: Other not–for–profit (including NFP Corporation) **Service:** General Medical and Surgical

Staffed Beds: 289 **Admissions:** 17497 **Census:** 183 **Outpatient Visits:** 208501 **Births:** 2502 **Total Expense ($000):** 233233 **Payroll Expense ($000):** 95448 **Personnel:** 1439

NORMAL—Mclean County

★ ◇ **ADVOCATE BROMENN MEDICAL CENTER (140127)**, 1304 Franklin Avenue, Zip 61761–3558, Mailing Address: P.O. Box 2850, Bloomington, Zip 61702–2850; tel. 309/454–1400, (Includes BROMENN REGIONAL MEDICAL CENTER, Virginia and Franklin Streets, Zip 61761, Mailing Address: P.O. Box 2850, Bloomington, Zip 61702–2850; tel. 309/454–1400) **A**2 5 10 12 13 21 **F**2 3 4 11 12 13 15 17 18 20 22 24 26 28 29 30 31 32 34 35 38 39 40 43 44 45 49 50 51 54 57 59 64 65 66 68 70 74 75 76 77 78 79 81 82 84 85 86 87 89 90 93 96 97 98 100 101 102 103 107 108 110 111 114 115 118 119 126 130 131 132 135 141 146 147 148 **P**8 **S** Advocate Health Care, Downers Grove, IL
Primary Contact: Colleen Kannaday, FACHE, President
CFO: Aron Klein, Vice President Finance
CMO: James Nevin, M.D., Vice President Medical Management
CHR: Antonio Coletta, Vice President Human Resources
CNO: Laurie Round, R.N., Chief Nurse Executive
Web address: www.bromenn.org
Control: Church–operated, Nongovernment, not–for profit **Service:** General Medical and Surgical

Staffed Beds: 199 **Admissions:** 9468 **Census:** 101 **Outpatient Visits:** 134618 **Births:** 1570 **Total Expense ($000):** 169225 **Payroll Expense ($000):** 55189 **Personnel:** 1055

ADVOCATE BROMENN REGIONAL MEDICAL CENTER See Advocate BroMenn Medical Center

NORTH CHICAGO—Lake County

✠ **CAPTAIN JAMES A. LOVELL FEDERAL HEALTH CARE CENTER**, 3001 Green Bay Road, Zip 60064–3049; tel. 847/688–1900, (Nonreporting) **A**1 3 5 **S** Department of Veterans Affairs, Washington, DC
Primary Contact: Patrick L. Sullivan, FACHE, Director
CFO: Barbara Meadows, Chief Financial Manager
CMO: Tariq Hassan, M.D., Associate Director of Patient Care
CIO: Jonathan Friedman, Public Affairs Officer
CHR: Amy Sanders, Chief Human Resources
CNO: Sarah Fouse, Associate Director of Patient Services
Web address: www.lovell.fhcc.va.gov
Control: Veterans Affairs, Government, federal **Service:** Other specialty

Staffed Beds: 103

NORTHLAKE—Cook County

✠ **KINDRED HOSPITAL CHICAGO–NORTHLAKE (142008)**, 365 East North Avenue, Zip 60164–2628; tel. 708/345–8100 **A**1 9 10 **F**1 3 29 45 77 80 85 91 107 119 130 148 **S** Kindred Healthcare, Louisville, KY
Primary Contact: Beverly Foster, Chief Executive Officer
COO: Sandra Buckhoy, Chief Clinical Officer
CFO: Jay Schweikart, Chief Financial Officer
CMO: Maher Najjar, M.D., Medical Director
Web address: www.kindrednorthlake.com/
Control: Corporation, Investor–owned, for–profit **Service:** Long–Term Acute Care hospital

Staffed Beds: 94 **Admissions:** 639 **Census:** 52 **Outpatient Visits:** 0 **Births:** 0 **Total Expense ($000):** 30050 **Payroll Expense ($000):** 10496 **Personnel:** 161

OAK LAWN—Cook County

★ △ ◇ **ADVOCATE CHRIST MEDICAL CENTER (140208)**, 4440 West 95th Street, Zip 60453–2699; tel. 708/684–8000, (Includes ADVOCATE HOPE CHILDREN'S HOSPITAL, 4440 West 95th Street, Zip 60453–2600; tel. 708/684–8000) **A**2 3 5 7 8 9 10 13 21 **F**3 5 11 13 15 17 18 19 20 21 22 23 24 25 26 27 28 29 30 31 32 34 35 37 38 39 40 41 43 44 45 46 47 48 49 50 51 52 54 55 56 57 58 59 60 61 62 63 64 65 66 68 69 70 71 72 74 75 76 77 78 79 81 82 84 85 86 87 88 89 90 92 93 96 97 98 99 100 101 102 103 104 105 107 108 109 110 111 114 115 118 119 120 121 123 124 126 129 130 131 132 134 135 137 138 143 145 146 147 148 **P**8 **S** Advocate Health Care, Downers Grove, IL
Primary Contact: Kenneth W. Lukhard, President
COO: Michael Wilkins, Chief Operating Officer
CFO: Robert Pekofske, Vice President Finance
CMO: Robert Stein, M.D., Vice President Medical Management
CIO: Brian Banbury, Director Site Information Systems
Web address: www.advocatehealth.com/christ
Control: Other not–for–profit (including NFP Corporation) **Service:** General Medical and Surgical

Staffed Beds: 684 **Admissions:** 39641 **Census:** 549 **Outpatient Visits:** 329533 **Births:** 3686 **Total Expense ($000):** 886420 **Payroll Expense ($000):** 326185 **Personnel:** 4109

OAK PARK—Cook County

✠ **RUSH OAK PARK HOSPITAL (140063)**, 520 South Maple Avenue, Zip 60304–1097; tel. 708/383–9300, (Total facility includes 18 beds in nursing home–type unit) **A**1 3 5 9 10 **F**3 11 15 18 20 22 29 30 34 35 40 45 47 49 50 56 57 59 64 68 70 74 75 77 79 81 82 84 85 87 90 92 93 94 96 107 108 111 114 115 119 128 130 145 146 148 **P**8 **S** Rush University Medical Center, Chicago, IL
Primary Contact: Bruce M. Elegant, President and Chief Executive Officer
COO: James Kaese, Vice President Administration
CFO: Deborah Wilberding, Controller
CMO: Michael R. Silver, M.D., Vice President Medical Affairs
CIO: Dewey Gosnell, Manager
CHR: Cristina Diaz, Director
CNO: Karen Mayer, R.N., VP Patient Care Services
Web address: www.roph.org
Control: Church–operated, Nongovernment, not–for profit **Service:** General Medical and Surgical

Staffed Beds: 108 **Admissions:** 4996 **Census:** 74 **Outpatient Visits:** 97807 **Births:** 0 **Total Expense ($000):** 100735 **Payroll Expense ($000):** 46835 **Personnel:** 802

✠ **WEST SUBURBAN MEDICAL CENTER (140049)**, 3 Erie Court, Zip 60302–2599; tel. 708/383–6200, (Nonreporting) **A**1 2 3 5 9 10 13 **S** TENET Healthcare Corporation, Dallas, TX
Primary Contact: Patrick Maloney, Chief Executive Officer
COO: Joan Ormsby, Vice President
CFO: Gene Smith, Interim Chief Financial Officer
CMO: Robert Chase, M.D., Chief Medical Officer
CHR: Nancy Gunnell, Vice President Human Resources
CNO: Roslyn J. Lennon, R.N., Chief Nursing Officer
Web address: www.westsuburbanmc.com/Home.aspx
Control: Corporation, Investor–owned, for–profit **Service:** General Medical and Surgical

Staffed Beds: 172

OLNEY—Richland County

★ ◯ **RICHLAND MEMORIAL HOSPITAL (140147)**, 800 East Locust Street, Zip 62450–2553; tel. 618/395–2131, (Total facility includes 34 beds in nursing home–type unit) **A**9 10 11 **F**3 7 11 13 15 28 29 31 34 35 40 45 57 59 61 62 63 64 68 69 70 75 76 78 79 81 85 87 89 93 97 98 100 102 103 104 107 108 110 111 115 119 128 129 130 131 132 133 135 143 146 147 **P**6
Primary Contact: David B. Allen, Chief Executive Officer
CFO: Mike Stoverink, Chief Financial Officer
CMO: Robert Nash, M.D., Chief of Staff
CIO: Tim Gillespie, Manager Information Systems
CHR: Jill Van Hyning, Director Human Resources
CNO: Cindy Bailey, R.N., Chief Nursing Officer
Web address: www.richlandmemorial.com
Control: Other not–for–profit (including NFP Corporation) **Service:** General Medical and Surgical

Staffed Beds: 90 **Admissions:** 2525 **Census:** 28 **Outpatient Visits:** 55965 **Births:** 335 **Total Expense ($000):** 43030 **Payroll Expense ($000):** 19871 **Personnel:** 466

Many Facility Codes have changed. Please refer to the AHA Guide Code Chart.
© 2014 AHA Guide

OLYMPIA FIELDS—Cook County

★ ○ **FRANCISCAN ST. JAMES HOSPITAL AND HEALTH CENTERS (140172)**, 20201 South Crawford Avenue, Zip 60461–1010; tel. 708/747–4000, (Includes ST. JAMES HOSPITAL AND HEALTH CENTERS – CHICAGO HEIGHTS CAMPUS, 1423 Chicago Road, Chicago Heights, Zip 60411–3483; tel. 708/756–1000; ST. JAMES HOSPITALS AND HEALTH CENTERS – OLYMPIA FIELDS CAMPUS, 20201 Crawford Avenue, tel. 708/747–4000) **A**2 9 10 11 12 13 **F**12 13 15 18 20 22 24 26 28 29 30 31 35 40 45 46 49 50 53 57 60 62 63 64 66 68 70 75 76 77 78 81 82 84 89 90 91 93 97 107 111 114 115 116 117 119 120 121 124 126 129 130 132 135 143 144 146 148 **P**8 **S** Franciscan Alliance, Mishawaka, IN
Primary Contact: Arnold Kimmel, Chief Executive Officer
CIO: Stephen Maes, Director Information Systems
Web address: www.stjameshhc.org
Control: Church–operated, Nongovernment, not–for profit **Service:** General Medical and Surgical

> **Staffed Beds:** 329 **Admissions:** 16690 **Census:** 188 **Outpatient Visits:** 157518 **Births:** 1058 **Total Expense ($000):** 294689 **Payroll Expense ($000):** 101843 **Personnel:** 1296

ST. JAMES HOSPITAL AND HEALTH CENTERS See Franciscan St. James Hospital and Health Centers

OTTAWA—Lasalle County

✠ **OSF SAINT ELIZABETH MEDICAL CENTER (140110)**, 1100 East Norris Drive, Zip 61350–1687; tel. 815/433–3100 **A**1 9 10 19 **F**3 11 13 15 18 28 29 30 34 35 40 43 45 48 49 53 56 57 59 68 70 75 76 77 79 81 82 84 85 86 87 93 94 98 99 100 101 102 103 104 105 107 108 110 111 115 118 119 130 131 132 135 143 144 146 148 **S** OSF Healthcare System, Peoria, IL
Primary Contact: Robert A. Chaffin, President and Chief Executive Officer
CFO: Dawn Trompeter, Vice President Finance
CMO: Brian S. Rosborough, M.D., Chief Medical Officer
CIO: John Maynard, Director Information Systems
CHR: Robert Gibson, Senior Director Operating Services
CNO: Maeanne Stevens, R.N., Chief Nursing Officer
Web address: www.osfsaintelizabeth.org
Control: Church–operated, Nongovernment, not–for profit **Service:** General Medical and Surgical

> **Staffed Beds:** 90 **Admissions:** 3388 **Census:** 33 **Outpatient Visits:** 166535 **Births:** 247 **Total Expense ($000):** 68734 **Payroll Expense ($000):** 30676 **Personnel:** 505

PALOS HEIGHTS—Cook County

✠ **PALOS COMMUNITY HOSPITAL (140062)**, 12251 South 80th Avenue, Zip 60463–0930; tel. 708/923–4000 **A**1 2 9 10 **F**3 4 5 13 15 17 18 20 22 24 26 28 29 30 31 32 34 35 36 38 40 49 50 54 56 57 59 61 62 63 64 69 70 74 75 76 78 79 81 84 85 87 89 93 98 99 100 102 103 104 105 107 108 110 111 114 115 117 118 119 126 130 132 135 144 146 147 148 **P**6
Primary Contact: Terrence Moisan, M.D., Interim Chief Executive Officer
CFO: Hugh Rose, Vice President Fiscal Management
CIO: Peggy Carroll, Chief Information Officer
CHR: Mary Denisienko, Vice President Human Resources
Web address: www.paloscommunityhospital.org
Control: Other not–for–profit (including NFP Corporation) **Service:** General Medical and Surgical

> **Staffed Beds:** 362 **Admissions:** 17296 **Census:** 217 **Outpatient Visits:** 355429 **Births:** 903 **Total Expense ($000):** 342884 **Payroll Expense ($000):** 161963 **Personnel:** 2151

PANA—Christian County

★ **PANA COMMUNITY HOSPITAL (141341)**, 101 East Ninth Street, Zip 62557–1785; tel. 217/562–2131 **A**9 10 18 **F**3 11 15 28 29 30 31 34 35 40 50 53 56 57 59 62 63 69 75 77 78 81 87 90 93 100 107 114 124 127 130 131 133 147 148 **P**6
Primary Contact: Trina Casner, President and Chief Executive Officer
CFO: James Moon, Chief Financial Officer
CMO: Alan Frigy, M.D., President Medical Staff
CIO: Dianne Bailey, Coordinator Information Systems
CHR: Luann Funk, Administrative Assistant and Manager Human Resources
CNO: Vickie Coen, Chief Clinical Officer and Nurse Executive
Web address: www.panahospital.com
Control: Other not–for–profit (including NFP Corporation) **Service:** General Medical and Surgical

> **Staffed Beds:** 22 **Admissions:** 332 **Census:** 2 **Outpatient Visits:** 47258 **Births:** 0 **Total Expense ($000):** 17247 **Payroll Expense ($000):** 7733 **Personnel:** 148

PARIS—Edgar County

✠ **PARIS COMMUNITY HOSPITAL (141320)**, 721 East Court Street, Zip 61944–2460; tel. 217/465–4141 **A**1 9 10 18 **F**3 15 28 29 30 31 34 35 40 45 50 57 59 64 65 67 69 74 75 77 78 79 81 82 85 86 87 89 90 93 107 108 110 111 114 119 127 128 130 131 132 133 144 146 148 **P**6 **S** Alliant Management Services, Louisville, KY
Primary Contact: Oliver Smith, President and Chief Executive Officer
CFO: Terry Brinkley, Vice President Finance
CIO: Ed Weeks, Manager Information Services
CNO: Susan Livvix, R.N., Vice President Nursing Services
Web address: www.pariscommunityhospital.com
Control: Other not–for–profit (including NFP Corporation) **Service:** General Medical and Surgical

> **Staffed Beds:** 25 **Admissions:** 549 **Census:** 6 **Outpatient Visits:** 82130 **Births:** 0 **Total Expense ($000):** 36045 **Payroll Expense ($000):** 16007 **Personnel:** 222

PARK RIDGE—Cook County

★ △ ◇ **ADVOCATE LUTHERAN GENERAL HOSPITAL (140223)**, 1775 Dempster Street, Zip 60068–1174; tel. 847/723–2210 **A**2 3 5 7 8 9 10 13 21 **F**2 3 5 6 8 9 11 12 13 15 17 18 19 20 21 22 23 24 25 26 27 28 29 30 31 32 34 35 37 38 39 40 41 43 44 45 46 47 48 49 50 53 55 56 57 58 59 60 61 63 64 65 66 68 69 70 72 74 75 76 78 79 80 81 82 84 85 86 87 88 89 90 92 93 94 97 98 99 100 101 102 103 104 105 106 107 108 110 111 112 114 115 116 117 118 119 120 121 123 124 126 129 130 131 132 134 135 136 143 146 147 148 **P**6 8 **S** Advocate Health Care, Downers Grove, IL
Primary Contact: Richard B. Floyd, President
COO: Barbara Weber, Chief Operating Officer
CFO: Jim Kelley, Vice President Finance
CMO: Leo Kelly, M.D., Vice President Medical Management
CIO: Mark Beitzel, Director Information Systems
CHR: Katie Bata, Vice President Human Resources
CNO: Jane Denten, MSN, Vice President Nursing and Chief Nurse Executive
Web address: www.advocatehealth.com/luth/
Control: Other not–for–profit (including NFP Corporation) **Service:** General Medical and Surgical

> **Staffed Beds:** 625 **Admissions:** 28692 **Census:** 402 **Outpatient Visits:** 299669 **Births:** 4438 **Total Expense ($000):** 631870 **Payroll Expense ($000):** 233250 **Personnel:** 3481

PEKIN—Tazewell County

✠ **PEKIN HOSPITAL (140120)**, 600 South 13th Street, Zip 61554–4936; tel. 309/347–1151 **A**1 5 9 10 **F**3 8 11 13 15 18 20 22 28 29 30 31 34 35 40 45 46 47 48 49 50 51 53 57 59 60 62 64 68 69 70 74 75 76 78 79 81 82 85 86 87 89 97 107 108 110 111 115 119 129 130 132 135 144 145 146 147 148 **P**6 **S** QHR, Brentwood, TN
Primary Contact: Bob J. Haley, Chief Executive Officer
CFO: Steve Hall, Chief Financial Officer
CMO: Kathryn Kramer, M.D., President Medical Staff
CHR: Anne Dierker, Vice President Hospital Services
Web address: www.pekinhospital.org
Control: Other not–for–profit (including NFP Corporation) **Service:** General Medical and Surgical

> **Staffed Beds:** 107 **Admissions:** 3450 **Census:** 41 **Outpatient Visits:** 100710 **Births:** 442 **Total Expense ($000):** 62796 **Payroll Expense ($000):** 27665 **Personnel:** 517

PEORIA—Peoria County

GREATER PEORIA SPECIALTY HOSPITAL See Kindred Hospital Peoria

✠ **KINDRED HOSPITAL PEORIA (142013)**, 500 West Romeo B. Garrett Avenue, Zip 61605–2301; tel. 309/680–1500, (Nonreporting) **A**1 9 10 **S** Kindred Healthcare, Louisville, KY
Primary Contact: Ted Paarlberg, Chief Executive Officer
CMO: Michael Peil, M.D., Chief Medical Director
Web address: www.khpeoria.com/
Control: Corporation, Investor–owned, for–profit **Service:** Long–Term Acute Care hospital

> **Staffed Beds:** 50

METHODIST MEDICAL CENTER OF ILLINOIS See UnityPoint Health – Methodist

IL

⊞ △ **OSF SAINT FRANCIS MEDICAL CENTER (140067)**, 530 N.E. Glen Oak
Avenue, Zip 61637–0001; tel. 309/655–2000, (Includes CHILDREN'S HOSPITAL
OF ILLINOIS, 530 N.E. Glen Oak Avenue, tel. 309/655–7171) **A**1 2 3 5 7 8 9 10
F3 8 9 11 12 13 15 17 18 19 20 21 22 23 24 25 26 27 28 29 30 31 32 34
35 37 38 39 40 41 42 43 44 45 46 47 48 49 50 51 52 54 56 57 58 59 60
64 65 66 67 68 69 70 72 73 74 75 76 77 78 79 81 82 83 84 85 86 87 88
89 90 91 92 93 94 96 97 99 100 102 104 105 107 108 110 111 114 115
116 117 118 119 120 121 123 124 126 127 129 130 132 134 138 142 143
144 145 146 147 148 **P**6 **S** OSF Healthcare System, Peoria, IL
Primary Contact: Keith E. Steffen, President and Chief Executive Officer
COO: Susan C. Wozniak, R.N., Senior Vice President and Chief Operating Officer
CFO: Ken Harbaugh, Vice President and Chief Financial Officer
CMO: Tim C. Miller, M.D., Vice President, Chief Medical Officer and Director
Academy Affairs
CHR: Lynn J. Gillespie, Vice President Human Resources and Organizational
Development
Web address: www.osfsaintfrancis.org
Control: Church–operated, Nongovernment, not–for profit **Service:** General
Medical and Surgical

Staffed Beds: 609 **Admissions:** 33534 **Census:** 472 **Outpatient Visits:**
959873 **Births:** 2583 **Total Expense ($000):** 906815 **Payroll Expense
($000):** 333507 **Personnel:** 5243

☐ **PROCTOR HOSPITAL (140013)**, 5409 North Knoxville Avenue,
Zip 61614–5069; tel. 309/691–1000, (Total facility includes 20 beds in nursing
home–type unit) **A**1 3 5 9 10 **F**3 4 5 11 13 15 18 20 22 24 28 29 30 34 40
45 49 51 53 57 59 62 64 65 70 74 75 76 79 81 85 86 87 89 93 98 103
104 105 107 108 110 111 115 118 119 128 129 130 132 135 145 146 148
Primary Contact: Paul E. Macek, President and Chief Executive Officer
CFO: Roger Armstrong, Vice President Finance and Chief Financial Officer
CHR: Linda K. Buck, Vice President Human Resources
Web address: www.proctor.org
Control: Other not–for–profit (including NFP Corporation) **Service:** General
Medical and Surgical

Staffed Beds: 174 **Admissions:** 6211 **Census:** 81 **Outpatient Visits:** 166973
Births: 636 **Total Expense ($000):** 110310 **Payroll Expense ($000):** 37247
Personnel: 871

⊞ **UNITYPOINT HEALTH – METHODIST (140209)**, 221 N.E. Glen Oak Avenue,
Zip 61636–4310; tel. 309/672–5522 **A**1 2 3 5 10 **F**3 8 9 11 12 13 15 17 18
20 22 24 26 28 29 30 31 32 34 35 36 38 40 43 44 45 46 47 48 49 50 53
54 56 57 58 59 60 62 63 64 68 70 74 75 76 77 78 79 81 82 84 85 86 87
89 90 92 93 96 98 99 100 101 102 103 104 105 107 108 110 111 114 115
116 117 118 119 120 121 126 127 129 130 131 132 134 135 136 143 144
145 146 147 148 **P**8 **S** UnityPoint Health, West Des Moines, IA
Primary Contact: Deborah R. Simon, R.N., President and Chief Executive Officer
COO: Keith Knepp, M.D., Executive Vice President and Chief Operating Officer
CFO: Robert Quin, Vice President Finance and Chief Financial Officer
CMO: Gary Knepp, D.O., Vice President Physician Integration and Chief Medical
Officer
CIO: Ryan Walsh, M.D., Chief Medical Information Officer
CHR: Joy Ledbetter, Vice President Employee and Patient Experience and Chief
Human Resources Officer
CNO: Jeanine R. Spain, R.N., Vice President Patient and Support Services and
Chief Nursing Officer
Web address: www.mymethodist.net
Control: Other not–for–profit (including NFP Corporation) **Service:** General
Medical and Surgical

Staffed Beds: 282 **Admissions:** 14784 **Census:** 198 **Outpatient Visits:**
550915 **Births:** 1686 **Total Expense ($000):** 355634 **Payroll Expense
($000):** 140238 **Personnel:** 2131

★ **ILLINOIS VALLEY COMMUNITY HOSPITAL (140234)**, 925 West Street,
Zip 61354–2757; tel. 815/223–3300 **A**9 10 **F**2 3 11 13 15 28 29 30 31 34
35 38 40 45 46 47 48 49 50 51 54 57 59 63 64 65 66 68 69 70 74 75 77
79 81 82 85 87 93 96 97 104 107 110 111 115 118 119 127 129 130 131
132 133 135 143 144 146 147 148 **P**8
Primary Contact: Tommy Hobbs, Chief Executive Officer
COO: Bobby Smith, Vice President Physician Services and Quality
CFO: Stephen Davis, Chief Financial Officer
CMO: Mark Fernandez, M.D., Chief of Staff and President Medical Staff
CIO: Nancy McDonnell, Manager Information Systems
CHR: Mary Beth Herron, Director of Human Resources
CNO: Wilma Hart-Flynn, Ph.D., Vice President Patient Care Services and Chief
Nursing Officer
Web address: www.ivch.org
Control: Other not–for–profit (including NFP Corporation) **Service:** General
Medical and Surgical

Staffed Beds: 56 **Admissions:** 2712 **Census:** 23 **Outpatient Visits:** 151064
Births: 474 **Total Expense ($000):** 72906 **Payroll Expense ($000):** 27027
Personnel: 519

PINCKNEYVILLE—Perry County

★ **PINCKNEYVILLE COMMUNITY HOSPITAL (141307)**, 101 North Walnut Street,
Zip 62274–1099; tel. 618/357–5901 **A**9 10 18 **F**3 15 28 29 31 34 40 43 45
50 53 56 57 78 81 85 93 107 108 110 119 127 130 133 148 **P**6
Primary Contact: Thomas J. Hudgins, FACHE, Administrator and Chief Executive
Officer
CFO: Kara Jo Carson, Chief Financial Officer
CIO: Jeff Roberts, Director Information Technology
CHR: Christie Gajewski, Director Human Resources
CNO: Eva Hopp, Chief Nurse Executive
Web address: www.pvillehosp.org/
Control: Hospital district or authority, Government, nonfederal **Service:** General
Medical and Surgical

Staffed Beds: 25 **Admissions:** 545 **Census:** 7 **Outpatient Visits:** 40271
Births: 0 **Total Expense ($000):** 18279 **Payroll Expense ($000):** 8406
Personnel: 167

PITTSFIELD—Pike County

⊞ **ILLINI COMMUNITY HOSPITAL (141315)**, 640 West Washington Street,
Zip 62363–1350; tel. 217/285–2113 **A**1 9 10 18 **F**3 15 18 19 28 29 30 31
34 40 46 50 53 59 64 65 68 70 75 78 81 82 85 87 89 93 97 107 110 115
119 127 129 130 131 133 146
Primary Contact: Kathy Hull, President and Chief Executive Officer
CFO: Alice Coleman, Blessing Corporate Controller
CMO: Cris Del Rosario, M.D., President Medical Staff
CHR: Becky Myers, Human Resources Specialist
CNO: Holly A. Jones, Administrative Director Nursing Services
Web address: www.illinihospital.org
Control: Other not–for–profit (including NFP Corporation) **Service:** General
Medical and Surgical

Staffed Beds: 21 **Admissions:** 329 **Census:** 3 **Outpatient Visits:** 7285
Births: 0 **Total Expense ($000):** 19986 **Payroll Expense ($000):** 7267
Personnel: 158

PONTIAC—Livingston County

⊞ **OSF SAINT JAMES – JOHN W. ALBRECHT MEDICAL CENTER (140161)**,
2500 West Reynolds, Zip 61764–9774; tel. 815/842–2828 **A**1 9 10 20 **F**3 8 11
13 15 18 28 29 30 32 34 35 40 45 50 56 57 59 64 68 70 75 76 77 79 81
82 84 85 86 87 89 90 91 93 96 97 107 110 111 115 117 118 119 127 128
129 130 131 132 133 135 144 146 147 **P**7 **S** OSF Healthcare System,
Peoria, IL
Primary Contact: David T. Ochs, President and Chief Executive Officer
CFO: Paula Corrigan, Vice President and Chief Financial Officer
CHR: Kenneth Beutke, Vice President Organization Development and Planning
Web address: www.osfsaintjames.org
Control: Church–operated, Nongovernment, not–for profit **Service:** General
Medical and Surgical

Staffed Beds: 42 **Admissions:** 1349 **Census:** 11 **Outpatient Visits:** 187017
Births: 183 **Total Expense ($000):** 65189 **Payroll Expense ($000):** 24639
Personnel: 299

PRINCETON—Bureau County

PERRY MEMORIAL HOSPITAL (141337), 530 Park Avenue East,
Zip 61356–2598; tel. 815/875–2811 **A**9 10 18 **F**3 11 15 26 28 29 30 31 34
35 40 45 47 48 49 56 57 59 64 70 75 77 78 79 81 82 85 86 87 93 107
108 110 111 115 116 117 119 129 130 131 132 133 146 147 **P**8
Primary Contact: Rex D. Conger, FACHE, President and Chief Executive Officer
CFO: Mike Harrell, Chief Financial Officer
CMO: T. Doran, Chief of Staff
CIO: Karen Behrens, Director Technology Services
CHR: Karen Russell, Director Human Resources
Web address: www.perry–memorial.org
Control: City–Government, nonfederal **Service:** General Medical and Surgical

Staffed Beds: 25 **Admissions:** 982 **Census:** 9 **Outpatient Visits:** 52489
Births: 58 **Total Expense ($000):** 34134 **Payroll Expense ($000):** 14913
Personnel: 273

QUINCY—Adams County

☒ △ **BLESSING HOSPITAL (140015)**, Broadway at 11th Street,
Zip 62305–7005, Mailing Address: P.O. Box 7005, Zip 62305–7005;
tel. 217/223–1200, (Includes BLESSING HOSPITAL, Broadway & 14th Street,
Zip 62301, Mailing Address: P.O. Box 7005, Zip 62305–7005;
tel. 217/223–1200), (Total facility includes 20 beds in nursing home–type unit)
A1 2 3 5 7 9 10 13 19 20 **F**3 5 8 11 12 13 15 17 18 20 22 24 26 28 29 30
31 32 34 35 40 43 44 48 49 50 53 56 57 58 59 60 61 62 63 64 66 68 70
73 74 75 76 77 78 79 81 82 84 85 86 87 89 90 94 96 98 99 100 101 102
103 104 107 108 110 111 114 115 118 119 120 121 123 124 126 127 128
129 130 131 132 135 144 146 147 148 **P**8
Primary Contact: Maureen A. Kahn, R.N., President and Chief Executive Officer
COO: Tim Moore, Chief Accounting Officer and Vice President Ancillary Services
and Finance
CFO: Patrick M. Gerveler, Vice President Finance and Chief Financial Officer
CMO: George Liesmann, M.D., Chief Medical Officer
CNO: Jill K. Mason, MS, Chief Nursing Officer
Web address: www.blessinghospital.org
Control: Other not–for–profit (including NFP Corporation) **Service:** General
Medical and Surgical

> **Staffed Beds:** 279 **Admissions:** 13322 **Census:** 165 **Outpatient Visits:**
> 335714 **Births:** 1101 **Total Expense ($000):** 263812 **Payroll Expense**
> **($000):** 105327 **Personnel:** 2047

RED BUD—Randolph County

☒ **RED BUD REGIONAL HOSPITAL (141348)**, 325 Spring Street,
Zip 62278–1105; tel. 618/282–3831, (Nonreporting) **A**1 9 10 18 **S** Community
Health Systems, Inc., Franklin, TN
Primary Contact: Shane Watson, Chief Executive Officer
CFO: Benjamin Wells, Chief Financial Officer
CMO: Julie Kelley, M.D., President Medical Staff
CIO: Nick Behnken, Supervisor Information Technology
CHR: Lori Brooks, Director Human Resources
CNO: Linda Harbison, Chief Nursing Officer
Web address: www.redbudregional.com
Control: Corporation, Investor–owned, for–profit **Service:** General Medical and
Surgical

> **Staffed Beds:** 25

ROBINSON—Crawford County

★ **CRAWFORD MEMORIAL HOSPITAL (141343)**, 1000 North Allen Street,
Zip 62454–1167; tel. 618/544–3131, (Total facility includes 38 beds in nursing
home–type unit) **A**9 10 18 **F**3 11 12 13 15 28 30 31 40 45 53 56 59 62 64 76
77 78 79 80 81 85 93 107 108 111 119 127 128 129 130 132 133 146 147
P6 **S** QHR, Brentwood, TN
Primary Contact: Donald E. Annis, Chief Executive Officer
CFO: Richard Carlson, Chief Financial Officer
CMO: Gregory Kastner, M.D., Chief of Staff
CIO: Tim Richard, IT Coordinator
CHR: Kristi Zane, Chief Human Resources Officer
CNO: Sandra Burtron, MS, Chief Nursing Officer
Web address: www.crawfordmh.org
Control: Hospital district or authority, Government, nonfederal **Service:** General
Medical and Surgical

> **Staffed Beds:** 63 **Admissions:** 1112 **Census:** 32 **Outpatient Visits:** 51242
> **Births:** 198 **Total Expense ($000):** 40094 **Payroll Expense ($000):** 18119
> **Personnel:** 344

ROCHELLE—Ogle County

☒ **ROCHELLE COMMUNITY HOSPITAL (141312)**, 900 North Second Street,
Zip 61068–1764; tel. 815/562–2181 **A**1 9 10 18 **F**3 8 15 29 30 31 34 35 40
41 50 53 57 59 64 68 70 74 75 77 78 81 82 85 86 87 93 97 107 110 115
130 132 133 135 144 146 **P**6
Primary Contact: Mark Batty, Chief Executive Officer
CFO: Lori Gutierrez, Chief Financial Officer
CMO: Jason Popp, Chief of Medical Staff
CIO: Scott Stewart, Manager Information Services
CHR: Laura Cirone, Manager Human Resources
CNO: Jennifer Montgomery, Chief Nursing Officer
Web address: www.rcha.net
Control: Other not–for–profit (including NFP Corporation) **Service:** General
Medical and Surgical

> **Staffed Beds:** 16 **Admissions:** 616 **Census:** 5 **Outpatient Visits:** 36555
> **Births:** 3 **Total Expense ($000):** 27463 **Payroll Expense ($000):** 9451
> **Personnel:** 205

ROCK ISLAND—Rock Island County

☒ △ **UNITYPOINT HEALTH – TRINITY ROCK ISLAND (140280)**, 2701 17th
Street, Zip 61201–5393; tel. 309/779–5000, (Includes UNITYPOINT HEALTH –
TRINITY MOLINE, 500 John Deere Road, Moline, Zip 61265; tel. 309/779–5000),
(Total facility includes 29 beds in nursing home–type unit) **A**1 2 7 9 10 **F**3 5 11
12 13 15 18 20 22 24 26 28 29 30 31 34 35 37 38 40 43 44 45 46 47 48
49 50 57 58 59 63 64 70 74 75 76 78 79 81 82 84 85 86 87 89 90 93 96
98 99 100 101 102 103 104 105 106 107 108 110 114 115 118 119 120
121 123 126 128 129 130 132 134 135 144 146 147 148 **P**6 8 **S** UnityPoint
Health, West Des Moines, IA
Primary Contact: Richard A. Seidler, FACHE, President and Chief Executive Officer
COO: Jay Willsher, Chief Operating Officer
CFO: Greg Pagliuzza, Chief Financial Officer
CMO: Paul McLoone, M.D., Chief Medical Officer
CHR: Cara Fuller, Vice President Human Resources
CNO: Jean B. Doerge, MS, Chief Nursing Officer
Web address: www.trinityqc.com
Control: Other not–for–profit (including NFP Corporation) **Service:** General
Medical and Surgical

> **Staffed Beds:** 343 **Admissions:** 14456 **Census:** 194 **Outpatient Visits:**
> 274605 **Births:** 1459 **Total Expense ($000):** 271275 **Payroll Expense**
> **($000):** 90505 **Personnel:** 2137

ROCKFORD—Winnebago County

☒ **OSF SAINT ANTHONY MEDICAL CENTER (140233)**, 5666 East State Street,
Zip 61108–2425; tel. 815/226–2000 **A**1 2 5 9 10 **F**3 11 12 13 15 16 17 18
20 22 24 26 28 29 30 31 32 34 35 36 37 38 39 40 41 43 44 45 46 49 50
51 53 55 56 57 58 59 64 66 70 73 74 75 76 77 78 79 81 82 84 85 86 87
89 92 93 107 108 110 111 114 115 116 117 118 119 120 121 123 124
129 130 131 132 135 145 146 147 148 **P**6 **S** OSF Healthcare System,
Peoria, IL
Primary Contact: Paula A. Carynski, MS, R.N., President
COO: James Girardy, M.D., Vice President, Chief Surgical Officer
CFO: David Stenerson, Vice President and Chief Financial Officer
CMO: Harneet Bath, M.D., Vice President, Chief Medicine Officer
CIO: Kathy Peterson, Director Information Services
CHR: Karen C. Brown, Vice President Chief Operating Officer
CNO: Colleen Klein, Vice President, Chief Nursing Officer
Web address: www.osfhealth.com
Control: Church–operated, Nongovernment, not–for profit **Service:** General
Medical and Surgical

> **Staffed Beds:** 235 **Admissions:** 10895 **Census:** 133 **Outpatient Visits:**
> 402360 **Births:** 419 **Total Expense ($000):** 348620 **Payroll Expense**
> **($000):** 125455 **Personnel:** 1716

☒ **ROCKFORD MEMORIAL HOSPITAL (140239)**, 2400 North Rockton Avenue,
Zip 61103–3655; tel. 815/971–5000 **A**1 2 5 10 **F**3 11 13 18 19 20 22 24 25
26 27 28 29 30 31 32 34 35 39 40 41 43 44 45 48 49 50 54 55 57 59 63
64 65 68 70 71 72 74 75 76 77 78 79 80 81 82 83 84 85 86 87 88 89 93
97 98 99 100 101 102 103 107 108 111 114 115 118 119 121 123 126
129 130 131 132 135 145 146 147 148 **P**6
Primary Contact: Gary E. Kaatz, President and Chief Executive Officer
COO: Daniel A. Parod, Senior Vice President Hospital and Administrative Affairs
CFO: Henry Seybold, Senior Vice President and Chief Financial Officer
CMO: Kevin Ruggles, M.D., Chief Medical Officer
CIO: Dennis P. L'Heureux, Chief Information Officer
CHR: Heidi Elsbree, Vice President People and Culture
CNO: Susan Schreier, R.N., Chief Nursing Executive
Web address: www.rhsnet.org
Control: Other not–for–profit (including NFP Corporation) **Service:** General
Medical and Surgical

> **Staffed Beds:** 297 **Admissions:** 12532 **Census:** 189 **Outpatient Visits:**
> 275793 **Births:** 1365 **Total Expense ($000):** 284436 **Payroll Expense**
> **($000):** 107917 **Personnel:** 2108

IL

☒ **SWEDISHAMERICAN HOSPITAL (140228)**, 1401 East State Street,
Zip 61104–2315; tel. 815/968–4400 **A**1 2 3 5 9 10 **F**3 13 15 17 18 20 22 24
26 28 29 30 31 34 35 36 37 38 39 40 43 44 45 46 49 50 56 57 58 59 61
64 65 68 70 72 74 75 76 77 78 79 81 82 84 85 86 87 89 92 93 98 99 100
101 102 103 104 105 108 110 111 114 115 117 118 119 121 123 124
129 130 132 146 147 148 **P**6
Primary Contact: William R. Gorski, M.D., President and Chief Executive Officer
COO: Don Daniels, Executive Vice President and Chief Operating Officer
CFO: Don Haring, Vice President Finance and Treasurer
CMO: Michael Born, M.D., Chief Medical Officer and Chief Quality Officer
CIO: Sheryl Johnson, Chief Information Officer
CHR: Jerry Guinane, Vice President Human Resources
CNO: Ann M. Gantzer, Ph.D., Vice President Patient Services and Chief Nursing
Officer
Web address: www.swedishamerican.org
Control: Other not-for-profit (including NFP Corporation) **Service:** General
Medical and Surgical

> **Staffed Beds:** 322 **Admissions:** 15916 **Census:** 180 **Outpatient Visits:**
> 261844 **Births:** 2673 **Total Expense ($000):** 296117 **Payroll Expense**
> **($000):** 109444 **Personnel:** 1917

☒ △ **VAN MATRE HEALTHSOUTH REHABILITATION HOSPITAL (143028)**,
950 South Mulford Road, Zip 61108–4274; tel. 815/381–8500 **A**1 7 9 10 **F**28
29 34 57 64 68 74 75 82 86 90 91 93 95 96 130 131 132 148 **P**5
S HEALTHSOUTH Corporation, Birmingham, AL
Primary Contact: Ken Bowman, Chief Executive Officer
CFO: Mark Lundvall, Controller
CMO: Scott Craig, M.D., Medical Director
CIO: Angela Bergman, Director Health Information Management
CHR: Lisa Vitale, Director Human Resources
CNO: Nancy Miller, R.N., Chief Nursing Officer
Web address: www.healthsouth.com
Control: Partnership, Investor-owned, for-profit **Service:** Rehabilitation

> **Staffed Beds:** 53 **Admissions:** 1384 **Census:** 48 **Outpatient Visits:** 6374
> **Births:** 0 **Total Expense ($000):** 17809 **Payroll Expense ($000):** 9941
> **Personnel:** 139

ROSICLARE—Hardin County

★ **HARDIN COUNTY GENERAL HOSPITAL (141328)**, 6 Ferrell Road, Zip 62982,
Mailing Address: PO BOX 2467, Zip 62982–2467; tel. 618/285–6634,
(Nonreporting) **A**9 10 18
Primary Contact: Roby D. Williams, Administrator
CFO: Janie Parker, Chief Financial Officer
CMO: Marcos N. Sunga, M.D., Chief of Staff
CIO: Brian Casteel, Information Technology Technician
CHR: Joyce Shelby, Manager Human Resources
CNO: Marsha Broadway, Chief Nursing Officer
Web address: www.ilhcgh.org
Control: Other not-for-profit (including NFP Corporation) **Service:** General
Medical and Surgical

> **Staffed Beds:** 25

RUSHVILLE—Schuyler County

★ **SARAH D. CULBERTSON MEMORIAL HOSPITAL (141333)**, 238 South
Congress Street, Zip 62681–1472; tel. 217/322–4321 **A**9 10 18 **F**11 15 18 28
31 33 40 45 57 59 69 77 78 79 81 82 93 96 103 107 110 114 119 125 127
129 132 133 146 148
Primary Contact: Lynn E. Stambaugh, R.N., Chief Executive Officer
CFO: Alan Palo, Chief Financial Officer
CMO: S. K. Kanthilal, M.D., President Medical Staff
CIO: Dan Wise, Manager Information Technology
CNO: Lisa M. Downs, R.N., Chief Nursing Officer
Web address: www.cmhospital.com
Control: Hospital district or authority, Government, nonfederal **Service:** General
Medical and Surgical

> **Staffed Beds:** 22 **Admissions:** 234 **Census:** 2 **Outpatient Visits:** 22195
> **Births:** 0 **Total Expense ($000):** 19664 **Payroll Expense ($000):** 7274
> **Personnel:** 160

SALEM—Marion County

★ **SALEM TOWNSHIP HOSPITAL (141345)**, 1201 Ricker Drive, Zip 62881–4263;
tel. 618/548–3194, (Nonreporting) **A**9 10 18
Primary Contact: Stephanie Hilton–Siebert, President and Chief Executive Officer
CFO: Teresa Stroud, Chief Financial Officer
CMO: Gautam Jha, M.D., Chief of Staff
CIO: Steve Turner, Director Information Technology
CHR: Diane Boswell, Director Human Resources and Marketing
CNO: Kendra Taylor, Director Outpatient Nursing
Web address: www.sthcares.org
Control: City-County, Government, nonfederal **Service:** General Medical and
Surgical

> **Staffed Beds:** 25

SANDWICH—Dekalb County

☒ **VALLEY WEST HOSPITAL (141340)**, 1302 North Main Street,
Zip 60548–2587; tel. 815/786–8484 **A**1 9 10 18 **F**3 11 13 15 18 28 29 30
31 32 34 35 36 40 45 46 49 51 57 58 59 64 68 70 71 75 76 77 78 79 81
82 85 87 89 93 102 104 107 110 115 119 129 130 131 132 135 146 147
S Kish Health System, DeKalb, IL
Primary Contact: Brad Copple, President
COO: David R. Proulx, Assistant Vice President Operations
CFO: Loren Foelske, Vice President Finance
CMO: Michael Kulisz, D.O., Chief Medical Officer
CIO: Heath Bell, Chief Information Officer
CHR: Michele McClelland, Vice President Human Resources
CNO: Pamela Duffy, Vice President Patient Services and CNO
Web address: www.kishhealth.org
Control: Other not-for-profit (including NFP Corporation) **Service:** General
Medical and Surgical

> **Staffed Beds:** 25 **Admissions:** 1150 **Census:** 9 **Outpatient Visits:** 38054
> **Births:** 246 **Total Expense ($000):** 40564 **Payroll Expense ($000):** 11297
> **Personnel:** 191

SHELBYVILLE—Shelby County

★ ◇ **SHELBY MEMORIAL HOSPITAL (140019)**, 200 South Cedar Street,
Zip 62565–1838; tel. 217/774–3961 **A**9 10 20 21 **F**3 15 28 29 40 62 64 81
93 107 108 118 119 127 129 132 133 146 **P**5
Primary Contact: Marilyn Sears, President and Chief Executive Officer
CFO: Phil Miller, Chief Financial Officer
CMO: Urbano Dauz, M.D., President Medical Staff
CIO: Ian Kuhlman, Manager Information Technology
CHR: Amy Koehler, Director Human Resources
CNO: Regina Calvert, Chief Nursing Executive
Web address: www.mysmh.org
Control: Other not-for-profit (including NFP Corporation) **Service:** General
Medical and Surgical

> **Staffed Beds:** 30 **Admissions:** 504 **Census:** 4 **Outpatient Visits:** 25573
> **Births:** 0 **Total Expense ($000):** 16767 **Payroll Expense ($000):** 6874
> **Personnel:** 156

SILVIS—Rock Island County

☒ **GENESIS MEDICAL CENTER, ILLINI CAMPUS (140275)**, 801 Illini Drive,
Zip 61282–1893; tel. 309/281–4000 **A**1 9 10 **F**3 7 11 13 15 18 20 26 28 29
30 31 34 35 38 40 43 44 46 50 53 54 57 59 63 64 68 70 74 75 76 77 78
79 81 82 84 85 86 87 89 97 107 108 110 111 114 119 129 130 131 132
135 146 147 **P**6 **S** Genesis Health System, Davenport, IA
Primary Contact: Kevin Youmans, Interim President
CFO: Mark G. Rogers, Interim Vice President Finance and Chief Financial Officer
CMO: Peter Metcalf, M.D., President Medical Staff
CIO: Robert Frieden, Vice President Information Systems
CHR: Heidi Kahly–McMahon, Vice President Human Resources
Web address: www.genesishealth.com
Control: Other not-for-profit (including NFP Corporation) **Service:** General
Medical and Surgical

> **Staffed Beds:** 101 **Admissions:** 4821 **Census:** 38 **Outpatient Visits:** 102931
> **Births:** 510 **Total Expense ($000):** 76437 **Payroll Expense ($000):** 23787
> **Personnel:** 441

SPARTA—Randolph County

SPARTA COMMUNITY HOSPITAL (141349), 818 East Broadway Street,
Zip 62286–1820, Mailing Address: P.O. Box 297, Zip 62286–0297;
tel. 618/443–2177 **A**9 10 18 **F**3 11 15 28 34 35 40 41 53 54 57 59 62 64
75 77 81 89 93 97 107 115 119 127 130 132 133 143 146 147 **P**5
Primary Contact: Joann Emge, Chief Executive Officer
CFO: Paul Mueller, Chief Financial Officer
CMO: Mark Pruess, M.D., Chief Medical Staff
CIO: Susan Gutjahr, Reimbursement Specialist
CHR: Darla Shawgo, Director Human Resources
CNO: Lori Clinton, Chief Nursing Officer
Web address: www.spartahospital.com
Control: Hospital district or authority, Government, nonfederal **Service:** General
Medical and Surgical

> **Staffed Beds:** 25 **Admissions:** 678 **Census:** 7 **Outpatient Visits:** 37360
> **Births:** 0 **Total Expense ($000):** 26960 **Payroll Expense ($000):** 11478
> **Personnel:** 221

IL

SPRING VALLEY—Bureau County

ST. MARGARET'S HOSPITAL (140143), 600 East First Street,
Zip 61362–1512; tel. 815/664–5311 **A**9 10 **F**3 11 13 15 28 29 30 31 32 34
35 38 40 44 45 46 47 49 53 57 58 59 63 70 74 75 76 77 79 81 82 84 85
87 90 93 96 107 108 110 111 114 118 119 129 130 131 132 133 135 143
144 146 147 148 **P**6 8 **S** Sisters of Mary of the Presentation Health System,
Fargo, ND
Primary Contact: Tim Muntz, President and Chief Executive Officer
CFO: Kim D. Santman, Vice President Finance
CIO: John Sabotta, Director Information Systems
CHR: Lisa R. Blackburn, Director Human Resources
CNO: Mary Vega, R.N., Vice President Nursing
Web address: www.aboutsmh.org
Control: Church–operated, Nongovernment, not–for profit **Service:** General
Medical and Surgical

Staffed Beds: 69 **Admissions:** 2065 **Census:** 20 **Outpatient Visits:** 237577
Births: 267 **Total Expense ($000):** 68685 **Payroll Expense ($000):** 29624
Personnel: 516

SPRINGFIELD—Sangamon County

☐ **ANDREW MCFARLAND MENTAL HEALTH CENTER (144021)**, 901 East
Southwind Road, Zip 62703–5125; tel. 217/786–6994, (Nonreporting) **A**1 3 5
10 **S** Division of Mental Health, Department of Human Services, Springfield, IL
Primary Contact: Karen Schweighart, R.N., MS, Administrator
CFO: Jeff Frey, Business Administrator
CMO: Kasturi Kripakaran, M.D., Medical Director
CIO: Josh Kates, Information Technology Analyst
CNO: Frances Collins, Director of Nursing
Control: State–Government, nonfederal **Service:** Psychiatric

Staffed Beds: 118

KINDRED HOSPITAL SPRINGFIELD See Vibra Hospital of Springfield

☐ **LINCOLN PRAIRIE BEHAVIORAL HEALTH CENTER**, 5230 South Sixth Street,
Zip 62703–5128; tel. 217/585–1180 **A**1 3 5 9 **F**35 38 98 99 100 101 104
105 **P**3 6 **S** Universal Health Services, Inc., King of Prussia, PA
Primary Contact: Mark Littrell, Chief Executive Officer
CFO: Chris Statz, Chief Financial Officer
CMO: Pamela Campbell, M.D., Medical Director
CNO: Renae Hale, Chief Nursing Officer
Web address: www.lincolnprairiebhc.com/
Control: Corporation, Investor–owned, for–profit **Service:** Children's hospital
psychiatric

Staffed Beds: 88 **Admissions:** 1631 **Census:** 61 **Outpatient Visits:** 7322
Births: 0 **Total Expense ($000):** 13468 **Payroll Expense ($000):** 6556
Personnel: 214

✖ △ **MEMORIAL MEDICAL CENTER (140148)**, 701 North First Street,
Zip 62781–0001; tel. 217/788–3000 **A**1 2 3 5 7 8 9 10 **F**3 8 11 12 13 14 15
16 17 18 20 22 24 26 28 29 30 31 32 34 35 36 37 40 43 44 45 46 47 48
49 50 51 54 57 58 59 60 61 63 64 68 69 70 74 75 76 77 78 79 81 82 84
85 86 87 89 90 92 93 96 97 98 100 101 102 103 104 105 107 108 110
111 114 115 116 117 118 119 120 121 124 126 129 130 131 132 134 135
138 141 142 144 145 146 147 148 **P**3 5 **S** Memorial Health System,
Springfield, IL
Primary Contact: Edgar J. Curtis, FACHE, President and Chief Executive Officer
COO: Charles D. Callahan, Ph.D., Executive Vice President and Chief Operating
Officer
CFO: Robert W. Kay, Senior Vice President and Chief Financial Officer
CMO: Rajesh G. Govindaiah, M.D., Chief Medical Officer
CIO: David B. Graham, M.D., Senior Vice President and Chief Information Officer
CHR: Robert F. Scott, Vice President and Chief Human Resources Officer
CNO: Marsha A. Prater, Ph.D., Senior Vice President and Chief Nursing Officer
Web address: www.memorialmedical.com
Control: Other not–for–profit (including NFP Corporation) **Service:** General
Medical and Surgical

Staffed Beds: 473 **Admissions:** 24445 **Census:** 319 **Outpatient Visits:**
486579 **Births:** 1605 **Total Expense ($000):** 548176 **Payroll Expense**
($000): 175196 **Personnel:** 3440

✖ **ST. JOHN'S HOSPITAL (140053)**, 800 East Carpenter Street,
Zip 62769–0002; tel. 217/544–6464, (Includes ST. JOHN'S CHILDREN'S
HOSPITAL, 800 East Carpenter Street, Zip 62769; tel. 217/544–6464), (Total
facility includes 37 beds in nursing home–type unit) **A**1 2 3 5 8 9 10 **F**3 11 12
13 15 17 18 19 20 22 24 26 28 29 30 31 32 34 35 36 37 39 40 43 44 45
46 47 48 49 50 51 53 54 56 57 58 59 60 61 62 63 64 68 70 72 74 75 76
77 78 79 81 82 84 85 86 87 88 89 92 93 94 96 98 100 101 102 103 104
107 108 110 111 114 115 116 117 118 119 120 121 122 123 124 126 128
129 130 131 132 135 145 146 147 148 **S** Hospital Sisters Health System,
Springfield, IL
Primary Contact: Charles Lucore, M.D., President and Chief Executive Officer
COO: David R. Olejniczak, Chief Operating Officer
CFO: Larry Ragel, Chief Financial Officer
CIO: Ryan Leach, Chief Information Officer
CHR: Becky Puclik, Division Chief People Officer
CNO: Sherri Greenwood, Chief Nursing Officer
Web address: www.st–johns.org
Control: Other not–for–profit (including NFP Corporation) **Service:** General
Medical and Surgical

Staffed Beds: 430 **Admissions:** 20552 **Census:** 288 **Outpatient Visits:**
245850 **Births:** 1819 **Total Expense ($000):** 436860 **Payroll Expense**
($000): 138479 **Personnel:** 2551

✖ **VIBRA HOSPITAL OF SPRINGFIELD (142014)**, 701 North Walnut Street,
Zip 62702–4931; tel. 217/528–1217, (Nonreporting) **A**1 9 10 **S** Vibra
Healthcare, Mechanicsburg, PA
Primary Contact: Charles Nordyke, Chief Executive Officer
CNO: Ben Yeboah, Chief Clinical Officer
Web address: www.vibrahealthcare.com
Control: Corporation, Investor–owned, for–profit **Service:** Long–Term Acute Care
hospital

Staffed Beds: 50

STAUNTON—Macoupin County

COMMUNITY MEMORIAL HOSPITAL (141306), 400 Caldwell Street,
Zip 62088–1499; tel. 618/635–2200 **A**9 10 18 **F**3 11 15 28 29 31 34 40 59
64 70 77 78 79 81 82 85 93 107 110 115 119 120 130 132 133 146 **P**6
Primary Contact: Susie Campbell, Chief Executive Officer
CFO: Brian Engelke, Chief Financial Officer
CMO: Joshua Poos, M.D., President Medical Staff
CIO: Cheryl Horner, Supervisor Data Processing
CHR: Marilyn Herbeck, Coordinator Human Resources
CNO: Roberta Brown, Chief Nursing Officer
Web address: www.stauntonhospital.org
Control: Other not–for–profit (including NFP Corporation) **Service:** General
Medical and Surgical

Staffed Beds: 25 **Admissions:** 188 **Census:** 1 **Outpatient Visits:** 24717
Births: 0 **Total Expense ($000):** 13357 **Payroll Expense ($000):** 5537
Personnel: 120

STERLING—Whiteside County

✖ **CGH MEDICAL CENTER (140043)**, 100 East LeFevre Road, Zip 61081–1279;
tel. 815/625–0400 **A**1 9 10 **F**3 7 8 11 13 15 18 20 22 28 29 30 31 34 35 40
45 47 49 50 51 57 59 62 64 68 70 74 76 78 79 81 85 86 87 89 93 97 107
108 110 111 114 115 118 119 124 129 130 132 133 135 145 146 148 **P**6
Primary Contact: Paul Steinke, D.O., President and Chief Executive Officer
COO: Cynthia L. Zander, Vice President and Chief Operating Officer
CFO: Ben Schaab, VP Fiscal Services/ Chief Financial Officer
CMO: Mark Schmelzel, M.D., Vice President and Medical Director
CIO: Randy Davis, Director Information Technology
CHR: Shane Brown, Vice President and Chief Human Resources Officer
CNO: Kristie A. Geil, VP, Chief Nursing Officer
Web address: www.cghmc.com
Control: City–Government, nonfederal **Service:** General Medical and Surgical

Staffed Beds: 99 **Admissions:** 5642 **Census:** 47 **Outpatient Visits:** 361478
Births: 538 **Total Expense ($000):** 190374 **Payroll Expense ($000):** 83771
Personnel: 1244

IL

Hospital, Medicare Provider Number, Address, Telephone, Approval, Facility, and Physician Codes, Health Care System

★ American Hospital Association (AHA) membership
☐ The Joint Commission accreditation ◇ DNV Healthcare Inc. accreditation
○ Healthcare Facilities Accreditation Program
△ Commission on Accreditation of Rehabilitation Facilities (CARF) accreditation

---

STREAMWOOD—Cook County

☐ **STREAMWOOD BEHAVIORAL HEALTH CENTER (144034)**, 1400 East Irving Park Road, Zip 60107–3203; tel. 630/837–9000, (Nonreporting) **A**1 9 10 **S** Universal Health Services, Inc., King of Prussia, PA
Primary Contact: Ron Weglarz, Chief Executive Officer and Managing Director
COO: Ron Weglarz, Chief Executive Officer and Managing Director
CFO: Karen Williams, Chief Financial Officer
CMO: Joseph McNally, M.D., Medical Director
CHR: Michael Isaacs, Director Human Resources
CNO: Olieth Lightbourne, Chief Nursing Officer
Web address: www.streamwoodhospital.com
Control: Corporation, Investor–owned, for–profit **Service:** Children's hospital psychiatric

Staffed Beds: 177

STREATOR—Lasalle County

✠ **ST. MARY'S HOSPITAL (140026)**, 111 Spring Street, Zip 61364–3399; tel. 815/673–2311 **A**1 9 10 **F**3 11 13 15 18 28 29 30 31 34 35 40 41 45 47 50 54 57 59 62 70 75 76 77 78 79 81 82 84 85 87 89 93 107 108 110 111 115 119 130 132 143 146 147 148 **P**8 **S** Hospital Sisters Health System, Springfield, IL
Primary Contact: John T. Flanders, MS, R.N., President and Chief Executive Officer
CFO: Karen S. Clark, Chief Financial Officer
CMO: Maria Granzotti, M.D., Chief Physician Executive, Central Illinois Division
CIO: Georgene Lansford, Director Information Systems
CHR: Beth E. Batdorf, Director People Services
CNO: Diane Genthner, Chief Nursing Officer
Web address: www.stmaryshospital.org
Control: Church–operated, Nongovernment, not–for profit **Service:** General Medical and Surgical

Staffed Beds: 68 **Admissions:** 1846 **Census:** 18 **Outpatient Visits:** 81395 **Births:** 186 **Total Expense ($000):** 31315 **Payroll Expense ($000):** 16037 **Personnel:** 319

SYCAMORE—Dekalb County

✠ **KINDRED HOSPITAL–SYCAMORE (142006)**, 225 Edward Street, Zip 60178–2137; tel. 815/895–2144 **A**1 10 **F**1 3 29 30 45 46 60 63 68 74 78 80 82 84 85 107 114 130 148 **S** Kindred Healthcare, Louisville, KY
Primary Contact: Cindy Smith, Chief Executive Officer
CFO: Jay Schweikart, Chief Financial Officer
CMO: Thomas Liske, M.D., Chief Medical Officer
CHR: Eileen Strachan, Coordinator Human Resources
Web address: www.kindredhospitalsyc.com/
Control: Corporation, Investor–owned, for–profit **Service:** Long–Term Acute Care hospital

Staffed Beds: 69 **Admissions:** 504 **Census:** 38 **Outpatient Visits:** 0 **Births:** 0 **Total Expense ($000):** 22840 **Payroll Expense ($000):** 7233 **Personnel:** 148

TAYLORVILLE—Christian County

✠ **TAYLORVILLE MEMORIAL HOSPITAL (141339)**, 201 East Pleasant Street, Zip 62568–1597; tel. 217/824–3331, (Total facility includes 20 beds in nursing home–type unit) **A**1 5 9 10 18 **F**15 28 29 30 31 34 35 40 45 46 50 57 59 64 75 77 79 81 87 89 93 107 108 110 111 119 128 129 130 131 132 133 144 146 **S** Memorial Health System, Springfield, IL
Primary Contact: Daniel J. Raab, President and Chief Executive Officer
CFO: Andrew Costic, Regional Chief Financial Officer
CHR: Jackie Broaddus, Business Partner
CNO: Tracy Seaton, Director of Nursing
Web address: www.taylorvillememorial.org
Control: Other not–for–profit (including NFP Corporation) **Service:** General Medical and Surgical

Staffed Beds: 45 **Admissions:** 1363 **Census:** 13 **Outpatient Visits:** 36452 **Births:** 0 **Total Expense ($000):** 34807 **Payroll Expense ($000):** 13585 **Personnel:** 285

URBANA—Champaign County

★ △ ◇ **CARLE FOUNDATION HOSPITAL (140091)**, 611 West Park Street, Zip 61801–2595; tel. 217/383–3311 **A**2 3 5 7 9 10 13 21 **F**3 5 7 8 11 12 13 15 17 18 20 22 24 26 28 29 30 31 32 34 35 40 43 44 45 46 47 48 49 50 51 53 56 57 58 59 60 61 62 63 64 65 68 70 72 74 75 76 78 79 80 81 84 85 86 87 89 90 91 93 94 96 107 108 110 111 114 115 116 117 119 126 129 130 131 132 135 145 146 148 **S** Carle Foundation, Urbana, IL
Primary Contact: James C. Leonard, M.D., President and Chief Executive Officer
COO: John Snyder, Executive Vice President and Chief Operating Officer
CFO: Dennis Hesch, Executive Vice President Finance and Chief Financial Officer
CMO: Matthew Gibb, M.D., Executive Vice President and System Chief Medical Officer
CIO: Rick Rinehart, Chief Information Officer
CHR: L. J. Fallon, Executive Vice President, Chief Legal and Human Resources Officer
CNO: Pamela Bigler, R.N., Senior Vice President Chief Nursing Officer
Web address: www.carle.org
Control: Other not–for–profit (including NFP Corporation) **Service:** General Medical and Surgical

Staffed Beds: 345 **Admissions:** 19858 **Census:** 279 **Outpatient Visits:** 784684 **Births:** 2688 **Total Expense ($000):** 412147 **Payroll Expense ($000):** 118716 **Personnel:** 2689

✠ △ **PRESENCE COVENANT MEDICAL CENTER (140113)**, 1400 West Park Street, Zip 61801–2396; tel. 217/337–2000 **A**1 3 5 7 9 10 **F**3 7 13 15 18 20 22 24 26 28 29 30 31 34 35 38 40 41 45 49 50 56 57 59 61 63 64 65 68 70 72 74 75 76 78 79 81 82 83 84 85 89 90 93 98 100 101 102 103 107 108 110 111 114 115 119 126 130 132 135 146 147 148 **S** Presence Health, Chicago, IL
Primary Contact: Jared Rogers, M.D., Interim Regional President and Chief Executive Officer
COO: Jennifer Cord, Assistant Vice President Operations
CFO: Deborah Schimerowski, Vice President Finance and Chief Financial Officer
CMO: Kathleen Collins, M.D., Chief Medical Officer
CIO: Paula Keele, Manager Information Systems
CHR: Janet S. Payne, Vice President Human Resources
CNO: Molly Nicholson, R.N., Chief Nurse Executive
Web address: www.provena.org/covenant
Control: Church–operated, Nongovernment, not–for profit **Service:** General Medical and Surgical

Staffed Beds: 194 **Admissions:** 7386 **Census:** 81 **Outpatient Visits:** 185232 **Births:** 795 **Total Expense ($000):** 133714 **Payroll Expense ($000):** 39284 **Personnel:** 808

VANDALIA—Fayette County

✠ **FAYETTE COUNTY HOSPITAL (141346)**, 650 West Taylor Street, Zip 62471–1296; tel. 618/283–1231, (Total facility includes 85 beds in nursing home–type unit) **A**1 9 10 18 **F**3 7 11 15 28 29 30 34 35 40 45 49 57 59 77 80 81 86 93 107 110 111 112 114 116 117 119 127 128 129 130 132 133 145 146 **P**5 **S** Alliant Management Services, Louisville, KY
Primary Contact: Gregory D. Starnes, Chief Executive Officer
CFO: Pete Fromme, Chief Financial Officer
CMO: Glenn Skow, M.D., Chief of Staff
CIO: Lisa Tessman, Manager Information Technology
CHR: Susan Crawford, Manager Human Resources
CNO: Marci Barth, Chief Nursing Officer
Web address: www.fayettecountyhospital.org
Control: Corporation, Investor–owned, for–profit **Service:** General Medical and Surgical

Staffed Beds: 110 **Admissions:** 933 **Census:** 66 **Outpatient Visits:** 39276 **Births:** 0 **Total Expense ($000):** 22527 **Payroll Expense ($000):** 7839 **Personnel:** 257

WATSEKA—Iroquois County

✠ **IROQUOIS MEMORIAL HOSPITAL AND RESIDENT HOME (140167)**, 200 Fairman Avenue, Zip 60970–1644; tel. 815/432–5841, (Nonreporting) **A**1 9 10 20
Primary Contact: Charles Bohlmann, President and Chief Executive Officer
COO: Christopher Curry, Chief Operating Officer
CMO: Philip Zumwalt, M.D., Chief of Staff
CIO: Tim Smith, Director Information Systems
CHR: Jamie Neumann, Director Human Resources
CNO: Leslie Cottrell, Nurse Lead
Web address: www.iroquoismemorial.com
Control: Other not–for–profit (including NFP Corporation) **Service:** General Medical and Surgical

Staffed Beds: 68

IL

Many Facility Codes have changed. Please refer to the AHA Guide Code Chart. © 2014 AHA Guide

WAUKEGAN—Lake County

⊞ **VISTA MEDICAL CENTER EAST (140084)**, 1324 North Sheridan Road,
Zip 60085–2161; tel. 847/360–3000 **A**1 2 9 10 **F**3 12 13 15 18 20 22 24 26
28 29 30 31 34 35 38 39 40 42 43 44 45 46 47 48 49 50 57 59 68 70 73
74 76 78 79 81 82 84 85 87 89 90 93 100 102 107 108 110 111 114 115
119 126 129 130 132 146 147 148 **P**5 6 **S** Community Health Systems, Inc.,
Franklin, TN
Primary Contact: Barbara J. Martin, R.N., President and Chief Executive Officer
COO: Kim Needham, Assistant Chief Executive Officer
CFO: Pamela German Hill, Chief Financial Officer
CMO: Michael Scheer, M.D., President Medical Staff
CIO: Cathy Adler–Marks, Director Information Technology
CHR: Nancy Alonso, Vice President Human Resources
Web address: www.vistahealth.com
Control: Corporation, Investor–owned, for–profit **Service:** General Medical and
Surgical

> **Staffed Beds:** 190 **Admissions:** 11044 **Census:** 116 **Outpatient Visits:**
> 122556 **Births:** 1248 **Total Expense ($000):** 152495 **Payroll Expense
> ($000):** 52516 **Personnel:** 911

⊞ △ **VISTA MEDICAL CENTER WEST (140033)**, 2615 Washington Street,
Zip 60085–4988; tel. 847/249–3900 **A**1 7 9 10 **F**29 30 34 35 38 40 42 43
50 56 57 59 64 68 77 87 90 96 98 99 101 102 103 104 105 107 119 130
132 135 **P**5 6 **S** Community Health Systems, Inc., Franklin, TN
Primary Contact: Barbara J. Martin, R.N., President and Chief Executive Officer
COO: Kim Needham, Assistant Chief Executive Officer
CFO: Pamela German Hill, Chief Financial Officer
CMO: Wendy Lotts, M.D., President Medical Staff
CIO: Cathy Adler–Marks, Director Information Technology
CHR: Robyn Matsil, Human Resources Director
CNO: Rosetta Speights, R.N., Chief Nursing Officer
Web address: www.vistahealth.com
Control: Corporation, Investor–owned, for–profit **Service:** Psychiatric

> **Staffed Beds:** 67 **Admissions:** 1738 **Census:** 36 **Outpatient Visits:** 20852
> **Births:** 0 **Total Expense ($000):** 17887 **Payroll Expense ($000):** 7427
> **Personnel:** 118

WHEATON—Du Page County

⊞ △ **MARIANJOY REHABILITATION HOSPITAL (143027)**, 26 West 171
Roosevelt Road, Zip 60187–0795, Mailing Address: P.O. Box 795,
Zip 60187–0795; tel. 630/909–8000, (Total facility includes 27 beds in nursing
home–type unit) **A**1 3 5 7 9 10 **F**11 29 30 34 35 36 56 58 64 68 75 82 86 87
90 91 93 94 128 132 143 146 148 **P**6 **S** Wheaton Franciscan Healthcare,
Wheaton, IL
Primary Contact: Kathleen C. Yosko, President and Chief Executive Officer
COO: John Brady, Vice President Physician Services and Organizational Planning
CFO: Michael Hedderman, Senior Vice President Finance and Chief Financial
Officer
CMO: Noel Rao, M.D., Medical Director
CIO: Robert Sinickas, Director Information Services
CHR: Teresa Chapman, Vice President Human Resources
CNO: Kathleen C. Yosko, President and Chief Executive Officer
Web address: www.marianjoy.org
Control: Church–operated, Nongovernment, not–for profit **Service:** Rehabilitation

> **Staffed Beds:** 128 **Admissions:** 2851 **Census:** 88 **Outpatient Visits:** 45304
> **Births:** 0 **Total Expense ($000):** 70197 **Payroll Expense ($000):** 37400
> **Personnel:** 744

WINFIELD—DuPage County

⊞ **CENTRAL DUPAGE HOSPITAL (140242)**, 25 North Winfield Road, Zip 60190;
tel. 630/933–1600, (Includes BEHAVIORAL HEALTH CENTER, 27 West 350 High
Lake Road, tel. 630/653–4000) **A**1 2 5 9 10 **F**3 4 5 8 12 13 15 17 18 19 20
22 24 26 28 29 30 31 34 35 36 37 39 40 41 42 43 44 45 46 47 48 49 50
54 55 57 58 59 64 68 70 72 73 74 75 76 78 79 81 82 84 85 86 87 88 89
91 92 93 94 96 98 99 100 101 102 103 104 105 106 107 108 110 111 112
114 115 116 117 118 119 120 121 122 123 124 126 129 130 132 135 141
142 144 145 146 147 148 **S** Cadence Health, Winfield, IL
Primary Contact: Brian J. Lemon, President
CFO: John Orsini, Executive Vice President and Chief Financial Officer
CMO: Kevin Most, D.O., Vice President Medical Affairs
CIO: Daniel F. Kinsella, Vice President and Chief Information Officer
CHR: Michael Wukitsch, Executive Vice President Human Resources
Web address: www.cdh.org
Control: Other not–for–profit (including NFP Corporation) **Service:** General
Medical and Surgical

> **Staffed Beds:** 364 **Admissions:** 24195 **Census:** 264 **Outpatient Visits:**
> 825800 **Births:** 3041 **Total Expense ($000):** 586918 **Payroll Expense
> ($000):** 194606 **Personnel:** 3233

WOODSTOCK—Mchenry County

⊞ **CENTEGRA HOSPITAL – WOODSTOCK (140176)**, 3701 Doty Road,
Zip 60098–7509, Mailing Address: P.O. Box 1990, Zip 60098–1990;
tel. 815/338–2500, (Total facility includes 25 beds in nursing home–type unit) **A**1
2 9 10 **F**3 4 5 11 12 13 15 18 28 29 30 31 34 35 37 38 39 40 43 44 47 49
50 51 54 57 58 59 64 68 69 70 74 75 76 78 79 81 82 85 86 87 92 93 98
100 101 102 103 105 107 108 110 111 114 118 119 128 129 130 131 132
143 146 147 148 **P**4 5 **S** Centegra Health System, Crystal Lake, IL
Primary Contact: Michael S. Eesley, Chief Executive Officer
COO: Jason Sciarro, President and Chief Operating Officer
CFO: David Tomlinson, Executive Vice President Chief Financial Officer and Chief
Information Officer
CMO: Irfan Hafiz, Vice President Medical Affairs
CIO: David Tomlinson, Senior Vice President, Chief Information Officer
CHR: Bernadette S. Szczepanski, Vice President Human Resources Development
Web address: www.centegra.org
Control: Other not–for–profit (including NFP Corporation) **Service:** General
Medical and Surgical

> **Staffed Beds:** 135 **Admissions:** 7285 **Census:** 82 **Outpatient Visits:** 103914
> **Births:** 827 **Total Expense ($000):** 123681 **Payroll Expense ($000):** 53822
> **Personnel:** 704

ZION—Lake County

☐ **MIDWESTERN REGIONAL MEDICAL CENTER (140100)**, 2520 Elisha Avenue,
Zip 60099–2587; tel. 847/872–4561, (Nonreporting) **A**1 2 3 5 10 **S** Cancer
Treatment Centers of America, Schaumburg, IL
Primary Contact: Scott Jones, Chief Executive Officer
COO: Pete Govorchin, Vice President Operations
CFO: Cecilia Taylor, Chief Financial Officer
CMO: Bradford Tan, M.D., Chief Medical Officer
CIO: Jeff Nickerson, Site Manager Information Systems
CHR: Jacqueline DeRousse, Assistant Vice President Talent
CNO: Jacklynn Lesniak, R.N., Vice President Patient Care Services and Chief
Nursing Officer
Web address: www.cancercenter.com
Control: Corporation, Investor–owned, for–profit **Service:** General Medical and
Surgical

> **Staffed Beds:** 73

IL

Hospital, Medicare Provider Number, Address, Telephone, Approval, Facility, and Physician Codes, Health Care System

★ American Hospital Association (AHA) membership   ○ Healthcare Facilities Accreditation Program
☐ The Joint Commission accreditation   ◇ DNV Healthcare Inc. accreditation   △ Commission on Accreditation of Rehabilitation Facilities (CARF) accreditation

INDIANA

ANDERSON—Madison County

☐ **COMMUNITY HOSPITAL OF ANDERSON AND MADISON COUNTY (150113)**, 1515 North Madison Avenue, Zip 46011–3453; tel. 765/298–4242 **A**1 2 9 10 **F**3 6 10 11 13 15 18 20 22 28 29 30 31 32 34 35 40 44 46 49 50 51 54 56 57 58 59 60 61 64 68 70 74 75 76 77 78 79 81 82 85 86 87 89 93 107 108 109 110 111 114 115 119 120 121 122 123 126 129 130 132 135 143 144 146 147 148 **P**6 **S** Community Health Network, Indianapolis, IN
Primary Contact: Beth S. Tharp, R.N., President and Chief Executive Officer
CFO: John B. Harris, Vice President Finance and Chief Financial Officer
CIO: Joey Hobbs, Chief Information Officer
CHR: Michael Harpe, Vice President Human Resources
CNO: Carol Whitesel, Vice President Patient Care Services and Chief Nursing Officer
Web address: www.communityanderson.com
Control: Other not–for–profit (including NFP Corporation) **Service:** General Medical and Surgical

Staffed Beds: 127 **Admissions:** 5572 **Census:** 56 **Outpatient Visits:** 182899 **Births:** 867 **Total Expense ($000):** 127318 **Payroll Expense ($000):** 55167 **Personnel:** 997

☒ **ST. VINCENT ANDERSON REGIONAL HOSPITAL (150088)**, 2015 Jackson Street, Zip 46016–4339; tel. 765/649–2511 **A**1 2 9 10 **F**3 4 5 8 11 13 14 15 18 20 22 28 29 30 31 32 34 35 36 38 40 44 45 49 50 51 54 56 57 58 59 60 61 62 63 64 65 66 68 70 74 75 76 77 78 79 81 82 84 85 86 87 89 90 92 93 94 96 98 99 100 101 102 103 104 105 106 107 108 110 111 114 116 117 118 119 120 121 123 124 129 130 132 134 135 144 145 146 147 148 **P**6 **S** Ascension Health, Saint Louis, MO
Primary Contact: Thomas J. VanOsdol, President
COO: David Maxwell, Vice President Operations
CFO: Donald L. Apple, Chief Financial Officer
CMO: Gary Brazel, M.D., Chief Medical Officer
CIO: Robert Pope, Information Technology Director and Ministry Liaison
CHR: Glenn C. Fields, Vice President, Human Resources
CNO: Nancy Pitcock, Vice President Nursing and Chief Nursing Officer
Web address: www.stvincent.org/Saint–Johns/Default.aspx
Control: Church–operated, Nongovernment, not–for profit **Service:** General Medical and Surgical

Staffed Beds: 185 **Admissions:** 6882 **Census:** 98 **Outpatient Visits:** 243660 **Births:** 557 **Total Expense ($000):** 196866 **Payroll Expense ($000):** 65822 **Personnel:** 942

ANGOLA—Steuben County

★ **CAMERON MEMORIAL COMMUNITY HOSPITAL (151315)**, 416 East Maumee Street, Zip 46703–2015; tel. 260/665–2141 **A**9 10 18 **F**3 5 10 11 13 15 28 29 30 34 35 38 45 46 47 48 50 54 57 59 62 63 64 65 68 75 76 77 79 81 83 86 87 93 102 107 108 110 111 114 116 117 119 129 130 132 133 144 146 147
Primary Contact: Gregory T. Burns, President and Chief Executive Officer
COO: Connie McCahill, R.N., Chief Operating Officer
CFO: Douglas Bomba, Chief Financial Officer
CMO: Thomas Miller, M.D., Chief Medical Officer
CHR: Nancy Covell, Director Human Resources
CNO: Marcia Michelle Walter, Chief Nursing Officer
Web address: www.cameronmch.com
Control: Other not–for–profit (including NFP Corporation) **Service:** General Medical and Surgical

Staffed Beds: 25 **Admissions:** 1198 **Census:** 10 **Outpatient Visits:** 90412 **Births:** 178 **Total Expense ($000):** 44039 **Payroll Expense ($000):** 15814 **Personnel:** 363

AUBURN—Dekalb County

★ **DEKALB HEALTH (150045)**, 1316 East Seventh Street, Zip 46706–2515, Mailing Address: P.O. Box 542, Zip 46706–0542; tel. 260/925–4600 **A**9 10 **F**3 7 11 13 15 28 29 32 34 35 36 40 45 53 56 57 59 62 63 64 70 73 75 76 77 79 81 82 84 85 86 87 89 93 97 107 108 110 111 114 115 118 119 129 130 132 135 146 147 148 **P**4 6 8
Primary Contact: Fred Price, R.N., President and Chief Executive Officer
CFO: Amy Crouch, Chief Financial Officer
CMO: Emilio Vazquez, M.D., Chief Medical Officer
CIO: Ed Hobbs, Director Information Services
CNO: Donna S. Wisemore, Chief Nursing Officer Vice President, Patient Care Services
Web address: www.dekalbhealth.com
Control: Other not–for–profit (including NFP Corporation) **Service:** General Medical and Surgical

Staffed Beds: 51 **Admissions:** 1965 **Census:** 16 **Outpatient Visits:** 80874 **Births:** 473 **Total Expense ($000):** 59394 **Payroll Expense ($000):** 25452 **Personnel:** 441

NORTHEASTERN CENTER (154050), 1850 Wesley Road, Zip 46706–3653; tel. 260/927–0726, (Nonreporting) **A**10
Primary Contact: Jerry Hollister, Chief Executive Officer
Web address: www.necmh.org
Control: Other not–for–profit (including NFP Corporation) **Service:** Psychiatric

Staffed Beds: 16

AVON—Hendricks County

CLARIAN WEST MEDICAL CENTER See Indiana University Health West Hospital

☒ **INDIANA UNIVERSITY HEALTH WEST HOSPITAL (150158)**, 1111 North Ronald Reagan Parkway, Zip 46123–7085; tel. 317/217–3000 **A**1 2 5 9 10 **F**3 13 15 18 22 26 28 29 30 34 35 40 45 47 48 49 50 51 57 59 64 70 73 74 75 76 77 78 79 81 82 85 86 87 89 93 100 107 110 111 113 114 115 119 120 121 129 130 132 135 146 147 148 **S** Indiana University Health, Indianapolis, IN
Primary Contact: Matthew D. Bailey, FACHE, President and Chief Executive Officer
COO: Judy Coleman, Chief Operating Officer and Chief Financial Officer
CFO: Judy Coleman, Chief Operating Officer and Chief Financial Officer
CMO: Gregory Spurgin, M.D., Chief of Staff
CHR: Lana Funkhouser, Vice President Human Resources
Web address: www.iuhealth.org
Control: Other not–for–profit (including NFP Corporation) **Service:** General Medical and Surgical

Staffed Beds: 127 **Admissions:** 7055 **Census:** 88 **Outpatient Visits:** 156800 **Births:** 1192 **Total Expense ($000):** 132389 **Payroll Expense ($000):** 46091 **Personnel:** 747

BATESVILLE—Franklin County

☒ **MARGARET MARY HEALTH (151329)**, 321 Mitchell Avenue, Zip 47006–8909, Mailing Address: P.O. Box 226, Zip 47006–0226; tel. 812/934–6624 **A**1 2 9 10 18 **F**3 13 15 28 30 31 34 35 36 39 40 45 46 50 54 56 59 62 63 64 65 70 75 76 77 78 79 81 85 86 87 93 107 108 111 114 118 119 121 123 129 130 131 132 135 144 146 148 **P**1
Primary Contact: Timothy L. Putnam, FACHE, President and Chief Executive Officer
CFO: Brian Daeger, Vice President Financial Services
CMO: Andrew Poltrack, M.D., Chief of Staff
CIO: Trisha Prickel, Director Information Systems
CHR: Kimberly Inscho, Vice President Community Relations and Human Resources
Web address: www.mmch.org
Control: Other not–for–profit (including NFP Corporation) **Service:** General Medical and Surgical

Staffed Beds: 25 **Admissions:** 1652 **Census:** 13 **Outpatient Visits:** 155868 **Births:** 426 **Total Expense ($000):** 74211 **Payroll Expense ($000):** 30518 **Personnel:** 445

BEDFORD—Lawrence County

BEDFORD REGIONAL MEDICAL CENTER See Indiana University Health Bedford Hospital

DUNN MEMORIAL HOSPITAL See St. Vincent Dunn Hospital

☒ **INDIANA UNIVERSITY HEALTH BEDFORD HOSPITAL (151328)**, 2900 West 16th Street, Zip 47421–3583; tel. 812/275–1200 **A**1 2 9 10 18 **F**3 7 11 15 18 28 29 30 31 34 35 36 37 38 39 40 41 44 45 46 49 53 57 59 64 65 68 70 71 74 75 78 79 81 82 85 86 87 91 92 93 94 97 102 107 108 110 111 115 118 119 129 130 131 132 133 134 135 144 146 **P**6 **S** Indiana University Health, Indianapolis, IN
Primary Contact: Bradford W. Dykes, President and Chief Executive Officer
CFO: Charles L. Shetler, CPA, Chief Financial Officer
CMO: Joanne F. Smart, M.D., Director of Medical Affairs
CNO: Brenda Davis, R.N., Vice President of Patient Services
Web address: www.iuhealth.org
Control: Other not–for–profit (including NFP Corporation) **Service:** General Medical and Surgical

Staffed Beds: 25 **Admissions:** 1136 **Census:** 13 **Outpatient Visits:** 92419 **Births:** 0 **Total Expense ($000):** 41857 **Payroll Expense ($000):** 18481 **Personnel:** 261

☒ **ST. VINCENT DUNN HOSPITAL (151335)**, 1600 23rd Street,
Zip 47421–4704; tel. 812/275–3331, (Nonreporting) **A**1 9 10 18 **S** Ascension
Health, Saint Louis, MO
Primary Contact: Matt Balla, Chief Executive Officer
CFO: Crystal Plano, Controller
CMO: Deborah W. Craton, M.D., Chief Medical Officer
CIO: Chad Damon, Contractor
CHR: Darci Medlock, Manager Human Resources
CNO: Michelle Dotts–McCool, Chief Nursing Officer
Web address: www.stvincent.org/St-Vincent-Dunn/Default.aspx
Control: Other not–for–profit (including NFP Corporation) **Service:** General
Medical and Surgical

> **Staffed Beds:** 25

BEECH GROVE—Marion County

ST. FRANCIS HOSPITAL AND HEALTH CENTERS – NORTH CAMPUS See
Franciscan St. Francis Health – Beech Grove

BLOOMINGTON—Monroe County

BLOOMINGTON HOSPITAL See Indiana University Health Bloomington Hospital

☐ **BLOOMINGTON MEADOWS HOSPITAL (154041)**, 3600 North Prow Road,
Zip 47404–1616; tel. 812/331–8000 **A**1 9 10 **F**4 98 99 101 102 104 105 106
S Universal Health Services, Inc., King of Prussia, PA
Primary Contact: Jean Scallon, Chief Executive Officer
CFO: Becky T. Nyberg, Chief Financial Officer
CMO: David Gilliam, M.D., Medical Director
CHR: Amanda Shettlesworth, Director Human Resources
CNO: Penny Caswell, Director of Nursing
Web address: www.bloomingtonmeadows.com
Control: Corporation, Investor–owned, for–profit **Service:** Psychiatric

> **Staffed Beds:** 67 **Admissions:** 1249 **Census:** 51 **Outpatient Visits:** 6288
> **Births:** 0 **Total Expense ($000):** 8616 **Payroll Expense ($000):** 5820
> **Personnel:** 140

☒ △ **INDIANA UNIVERSITY HEALTH BLOOMINGTON HOSPITAL (150051)**,
601 West Second Street, Zip 47403–2317, Mailing Address: P.O. Box 1149,
Zip 47402–1149; tel. 812/336–6821 **A**1 2 5 7 9 10 19 **F**3 7 8 11 12 13 15
17 18 19 20 21 22 23 24 25 26 27 28 29 30 31 32 34 35 38 40 45 46 47
48 49 50 53 54 55 57 58 59 60 61 62 63 64 65 68 70 71 74 75 76 77 78
79 81 82 84 85 86 87 89 90 91 92 93 96 97 98 100 101 102 103 104 105
107 108 111 114 115 116 118 119 120 121 123 126 129 130 131 132 135
143 144 146 147 148 **P**6 **S** Indiana University Health, Indianapolis, IN
Primary Contact: Mark E. Moore, President and Chief Executive Officer
CFO: Mike Craig, Chief Financial Officer
CMO: Ken Marshall, M.D., Chief Medical Officer
CIO: Mark W. McMath, Chief Information Officer
CHR: Steven D. Deckard, Vice President Human Resources
Web address: www.iuhealth.org
Control: Other not–for–profit (including NFP Corporation) **Service:** General
Medical and Surgical

> **Staffed Beds:** 292 **Admissions:** 12585 **Census:** 147 **Outpatient Visits:**
> 260057 **Births:** 2031 **Total Expense ($000):** 307971 **Payroll Expense
> ($000):** 125591 **Personnel:** 2148

☒ **MONROE HOSPITAL (150164)**, 4011 South Monroe Medical Park Boulevard,
Zip 47403–8000; tel. 812/825–1111 **A**1 9 10 **F**3 15 18 20 22 29 34 45 46
50 64 65 70 75 79 80 81 85 86 87 91 107 110 111 119 127 146
Primary Contact: James A. Summersett, III, FACHE, Interim Chief Executive Officer
CFO: Dan Urban, Vice President of Finance
CMO: Colin Chang, M.D., Chief of Staff
CIO: Janice Wampler, Chief Information Technology Officer
CHR: Pamela S. Hoffman, Director of Human Resources
CNO: Donetta Breeden, Chief Clinical Officer
Web address: www.monroehospital.com
Control: Corporation, Investor–owned, for–profit **Service:** General Medical and
Surgical

> **Staffed Beds:** 32 **Admissions:** 1230 **Census:** 15 **Outpatient Visits:** 32010
> **Births:** 0 **Total Expense ($000):** 56931 **Payroll Expense ($000):** 11335
> **Personnel:** 201

BLUFFTON—Wells County

☒ **BLUFFTON REGIONAL MEDICAL CENTER (150075)**, 303 South Main Street,
Zip 46714–2503; tel. 260/824–3210, (Total facility includes 13 beds in nursing
home–type unit) **A**1 9 10 **F**3 13 15 18 28 29 30 34 35 40 46 48 50 57 59 65
70 71 74 75 77 79 81 82 85 86 87 91 93 94 96 107 108 110 111 114 119
128 129 130 146 147 148 **S** Community Health Systems, Inc., Franklin, TN
Primary Contact: Aaron Garofola, Chief Executive Officer
COO: Matt Lehn, Chief Operating Officer
CFO: Donald Lovelace, Chief Financial Officer
CMO: Kay Johnson, M.D., Chief of Staff
CNO: Julie Thompson, Chief Nursing Officer
Web address: www.blufftonregional.com
Control: Corporation, Investor–owned, for–profit **Service:** General Medical and
Surgical

> **Staffed Beds:** 79 **Admissions:** 2116 **Census:** 27 **Outpatient Visits:** 56276
> **Births:** 252 **Total Expense ($000):** 35092 **Payroll Expense ($000):** 13238
> **Personnel:** 259

BOONVILLE—Warrick County

☒ **ST. MARY'S WARRICK HOSPITAL (151325)**, 1116 Millis Avenue,
Zip 47601–2204; tel. 812/897–4800 **A**1 9 10 18 **F**1 3 6 11 15 28 29 30 40
45 50 53 56 57 59 64 67 68 79 81 85 87 89 93 98 103 107 111 114 118
119 128 130 132 133 135 146 **S** Ascension Health, Saint Louis, MO
Primary Contact: Kathy J. Hall, Administrator
CFO: Crystal Heaton, Director of Finance
CNO: Karen Waters, Chief Nursing Officer
Web address: www.stmarys.org/warrick
Control: Other not–for–profit (including NFP Corporation) **Service:** General
Medical and Surgical

> **Staffed Beds:** 35 **Admissions:** 919 **Census:** 17 **Outpatient Visits:** 21526
> **Births:** 0 **Total Expense ($000):** 15880 **Payroll Expense ($000):** 6852
> **Personnel:** 128

BRAZIL—Clay County

☒ **ST. VINCENT CLAY HOSPITAL (151309)**, 1206 East National Avenue,
Zip 47834–2797, Mailing Address: P.O. Box 489, Zip 47834–0489;
tel. 812/442–2500 **A**1 9 10 18 **F**3 15 18 29 30 34 35 40 45 50 57 59 65 67
68 75 77 79 81 82 85 86 87 107 108 111 114 119 128 130 131 133 135
146 148 **S** Ascension Health, Saint Louis, MO
Primary Contact: Jerry Laue, Administrator
CFO: Wayne Knight, Director Finance
CMO: Craig Johnson, D.O., Medical Director
CHR: Danielle Abrams, Manager Human Resources, Marketing and Executive
Assistant
CNO: Sandra Haggart, Chief Nursing Officer
Web address: www.stvincent.org
Control: Church–operated, Nongovernment, not–for profit **Service:** General
Medical and Surgical

> **Staffed Beds:** 25 **Admissions:** 723 **Census:** 8 **Outpatient Visits:** 31338
> **Births:** 1 **Total Expense ($000):** 19322 **Payroll Expense ($000):** 6459
> **Personnel:** 87

BREMEN—Marshall County

★ **COMMUNITY HOSPITAL OF BREMEN (151300)**, 1020 High Road,
Zip 46506–1093, Mailing Address: P.O. Box 8, Zip 46506–0008;
tel. 574/546–2211 **A**9 10 18 **F**3 11 13 15 29 34 35 40 45 50 57 59 64 69
75 77 79 81 82 85 93 107 110 111 114 119 128 129 130 132 133 135 146
Primary Contact: David Bailey, FACHE, Chief Executive Officer
CFO: Debra Kipfer, Chief Financial Officer
CMO: Jason Marker, M.D., Chief Medical Officer
CIO: Linda Barrett, Vice President of Information Services
CHR: Patricia Board, Vice President Human Resources
CNO: Sue Bettcher, R.N., Vice President of Nursing Services
Web address: www.bremenhospital.com
Control: Other not–for–profit (including NFP Corporation) **Service:** General
Medical and Surgical

> **Staffed Beds:** 24 **Admissions:** 353 **Census:** 3 **Outpatient Visits:** 26725
> **Births:** 92 **Total Expense ($000):** 15883 **Payroll Expense ($000):** 6145
> **Personnel:** 117

IN

Hospital, Medicare Provider Number, Address, Telephone, Approval, Facility, and Physician Codes, Health Care System

★ American Hospital Association (AHA) membership
☐ The Joint Commission accreditation   ◇ DNV Healthcare Inc. accreditation
○ Healthcare Facilities Accreditation Program
△ Commission on Accreditation of Rehabilitation Facilities (CARF) accreditation

☐ **DOCTORS NEUROMEDICAL HOSPITAL (150180)**, 411 South Whitlock Street, Zip 46506–1626, Mailing Address: P.O. Box 36, Zip 46506–0036; tel. 574/546–3830, (Nonreporting) **A**1 9 10 **S** NeuroPsychiatric Hospitals, Mishawaka, IN
Primary Contact: DeWayne Long, Chief Executive Officer
COO: John M. Day, Chief Operating Officer
CFO: Bernie Hebert, Jr., Chief Financial Officer
CMO: Steven Posar, M.D., Chief of Medicine
CHR: Emyle Kruyer–Collins, Director Human Resources
Web address: www.physicianshospitalsystem.net
Control: Partnership, Investor–owned, for–profit **Service:** Rehabilitation

Staffed Beds: 20

DOCTORS NEUROPSYCHIATRIC HOSPITAL AND RESEARCH INSTITUTE (154058), 417 South Whitlock Street, Zip 46506–1626; tel. 574/546–0330, (Nonreporting) **A**10 **S** NeuroPsychiatric Hospitals, Mishawaka, IN
Primary Contact: Cameron R. Gilbert, Ph.D., President and Chief Executive Officer
Control: **Service:** Psychiatric

Staffed Beds: 20

CARMEL—Hamilton County

CLARIAN NORTH MEDICAL CENTER See Indiana University Health North Hospital

○ **FRANCISCAN ST. FRANCIS HEALTH–CARMEL (150182)**, 12188B North Meridian Street, Zip 46032–4840; tel. 317/705–4500 **A**9 10 11 **F**3 15 29 30 31 35 45 57 59 64 78 79 81 85 94 107 111 115 119 146 **P**7 8 **S** Franciscan Alliance, Mishawaka, IN
Primary Contact: Stephen Wheatley, Chief Executive Officer
Web address: www.franciscanalliance.org/hospitals/carmel/Pages/default.aspx
Control: Church–operated, Nongovernment, not–for profit **Service:** General Medical and Surgical

Staffed Beds: 6 Admissions: 113 Census: 1 Outpatient Visits: 2013 Births: 0 Total Expense ($000): 14965 Payroll Expense ($000): 2554 Personnel: 31

✠ **INDIANA UNIVERSITY HEALTH NORTH HOSPITAL (150161)**, 11700 North Meridian Avenue, Zip 46032–4656; tel. 317/688–2000 **A**1 5 9 10 **F**3 13 15 18 19 20 22 25 29 30 31 34 35 36 37 45 47 49 52 53 55 57 59 60 64 68 70 72 74 75 76 78 79 81 85 87 88 89 93 107 108 110 111 115 119 124 126 129 130 132 135 146 147 148 **S** Indiana University Health, Indianapolis, IN
Primary Contact: Jonathan R. Goble, FACHE, President and Chief Executive Officer
COO: Randall C. Yust, Chief Operating Officer and Chief Financial Officer
CFO: Randall C. Yust, Chief Operating Officer and Chief Financial Officer
CMO: Paul Calkins, M.D., Chief Medical Officer
CIO: Steve Bodenham, Senior Manager Clinical Engineering
CHR: Angela S. Thompson, Vice President Human Resources and Support Services
CNO: Suzanne Del Boccio, MS, Chief Nursing Officer and Vice President Patient Care Services
Web address: www.iuhealth.org
Control: Other not–for–profit (including NFP Corporation) **Service:** General Medical and Surgical

Staffed Beds: 161 Admissions: 6902 Census: 72 Outpatient Visits: 136535 Births: 2211 Total Expense ($000): 181927 Payroll Expense ($000): 58260 Personnel: 896

✠ **ST. VINCENT CARMEL HOSPITAL (150157)**, 13500 North Meridian Street, Zip 46032–1456; tel. 317/582–7000, (Nonreporting) **A**1 9 10 **S** Ascension Health, Saint Louis, MO
Primary Contact: Michael D. Chittenden, President
COO: Daniel LaReau, Executive Director Operations and Information
CFO: Robert A. Bates, Executive Director Finance and Chief Financial Officer
CMO: Steven L. Priddy, M.D., Vice President Physician Affairs and Chief Medical Officer
CIO: Daniel LaReau, Executive Director Operations and Information
CHR: Charles Jeffras, Executive Director Human Resources
CNO: Gwynn Perlich, Vice President of Patient Services and Chief Nursing Officer
Web address: www.stvincent.org
Control: Church–operated, Nongovernment, not–for profit **Service:** General Medical and Surgical

Staffed Beds: 104

CHARLESTOWN—Clark County

☐ **SAINT CATHERINE REGIONAL HOSPITAL (150163)**, 2200 Market Street, Zip 47111–9553, Mailing Address: P.O. Box 9, Zip 47111–0009; tel. 812/256–3301, (Nonreporting) **A**1 9 10
Primary Contact: Merlyn E. Knapp, President and Chief Executive Officer
CMO: Adam French, M.D., Chief Medical Officer
CIO: Kevin McLaughlin, Manager Information Systems
CNO: Virginia Ottersbach, Chief Nursing Officer
Web address: www.saintcatherinehospital.com
Control: Corporation, Investor–owned, for–profit **Service:** General Medical and Surgical

Staffed Beds: 64

CLARKSVILLE—Clark County

○ **KENTUCKIANA MEDICAL CENTER (150176)**, 4601 Medical Plaza Way, Zip 47129–9204; tel. 812/284–6100, (Nonreporting) **A**9 10 11
Primary Contact: Paul Newsom, Chief Operating Officer
Web address: www.kentuckianamedcen.com/
Control: Corporation, Investor–owned, for–profit **Service:** General Medical and Surgical

Staffed Beds: 40

CLINTON—Vermillion County

UNION HOSPITAL CLINTON (151326), 801 South Main Street, Zip 47842–2261; tel. 765/832–2451 **A**1 9 10 18 **F**3 11 15 18 29 30 34 35 40 45 50 57 59 64 65 68 70 75 81 85 86 87 93 97 107 108 110 114 119 130 132 133 146 **P**6
Primary Contact: Terri L. Hill, Vice President and Administrator
COO: Scott L. Teffeteller, President and Chief Executive Officer
CFO: Wayne Hutson, Chief Financial Officer
CIO: Kym Pfrank, Vice President Information Systems
CHR: Sally Zuel, Vice President Human Resources
CNO: Rhonda E. Smith, R.N., Chief Nursing Officer
Web address: www.uhhg.org/wcch/index.html
Control: Other not–for–profit (including NFP Corporation) **Service:** General Medical and Surgical

Staffed Beds: 25 Admissions: 1065 Census: 8 Outpatient Visits: 45732 Births: 0 Total Expense ($000): 21725 Payroll Expense ($000): 9698 Personnel: 143

COLUMBIA CITY—Whitley County

✠ **PARKVIEW WHITLEY HOSPITAL (150101)**, 1260 East State Road 205, Zip 46725–9492; tel. 260/248–9000, (Total facility includes 67 beds in nursing home–type unit) **A**1 9 10 **F**3 5 7 8 13 15 28 29 34 35 38 40 45 50 54 57 59 64 69 70 75 76 79 81 82 85 89 91 93 96 102 107 108 110 111 114 119 125 128 129 132 135 143 144 146 148 **S** Parkview Health, Fort Wayne, IN
Primary Contact: Scott F. Gabriel, President
COO: Scott F. Gabriel, President
CFO: Lisa Peppler, Financial Manager
CMO: Jeffrey Brookes, M.D., Medical Director
CHR: Dianne P. Potter, Manager Human Resources
CNO: Bridget Dolohanty–Johnson, R.N., Vice President Patient Care Services
Web address: www.parkview.com
Control: Other not–for–profit (including NFP Corporation) **Service:** General Medical and Surgical

Staffed Beds: 97 Admissions: 1661 Census: 63 Outpatient Visits: 40467 Births: 300 Total Expense ($000): 43441 Payroll Expense ($000): 13403 Personnel: 259

COLUMBUS—Bartholomew County

★ ○ **COLUMBUS REGIONAL HOSPITAL (150112)**, 2400 East 17th Street, Zip 47201–5360; tel. 812/379–4441 **A**2 9 10 11 19 **F**3 7 11 12 13 15 18 20 22 24 26 28 29 30 31 34 35 38 39 40 45 47 49 50 51 53 57 58 59 64 68 70 73 74 75 76 77 78 79 81 84 85 86 87 89 90 93 98 100 101 102 103 107 108 110 111 113 114 117 118 119 120 121 123 126 129 130 131 132 135 143 146 147 148 **P**3 8
Primary Contact: James Bickel, Chief Executive Officer
CFO: Marlene Weatherwax, Vice President and Chief Financial Officer
CMO: Thomas Sonderman, M.D., Vice President and Chief Medical Officer
CIO: Diana Boyer, Chief Information Officer
CHR: John R. Loya, Vice President Human Resources and Organizational Development
CNO: Pamela Missi, R.N., Vice President and Chief Nursing Officer
Web address: www.crh.org
Control: County–Government, nonfederal **Service:** General Medical and Surgical

Staffed Beds: 198 Admissions: 8949 Census: 94 Outpatient Visits: 222317 Births: 1161 Total Expense ($000): 205909 Payroll Expense ($000): 67723 Personnel: 1486

CONNERSVILLE—Fayette County

○ **FAYETTE REGIONAL HEALTH SYSTEM (150064)**, 1941 Virginia Avenue, Zip 47331–2833; tel. 765/825–5131 **A**9 10 11 **F**3 7 8 11 13 15 18 20 28 29 30 31 34 35 40 45 49 50 53 56 57 59 62 63 64 65 70 74 75 76 77 78 79 81 82 85 89 90 92 93 96 97 98 99 100 103 104 106 107 108 110 111 115 116 117 119 121 129 130 131 132 133 135 144 146 147 **P**6
Primary Contact: Randall White, Chief Executive Officer
CFO: Debra Michalek, Chief Financial Officer
CMO: Mike Rowe, M.D., Chief of Staff
CIO: Andy Merida, Director Management Information Systems
CHR: Rhonda McPherson, Vice President Human Resources
CNO: Beth A. Wampler, R.N., Chief Nursing Officer
Web address: www.fayetteregional.org
Control: Other not–for–profit (including NFP Corporation) **Service:** General Medical and Surgical

Staffed Beds: 75 Admissions: 1741 Census: 38 Outpatient Visits: 88994 Births: 228 Total Expense ($000): 55999 Payroll Expense ($000): 25844 Personnel: 538

IN

CORYDON—Harrison County

★ **HARRISON COUNTY HOSPITAL (151331)**, 1141 Hospital Drive North W., Zip 47112–1774; tel. 812/738–4251, (Nonreporting) **A**9 10 18
Primary Contact: Steven L. Taylor, Chief Executive Officer
CFO: Jeff Davis, Chief Financial Officer
CIO: Chuck Wiley, Manager Information Systems
CHR: Loren Haverstock, Manager Human Resources
CNO: Ruth Donahue, R.N., Chief Nursing Officer
Web address: www.hchin.org
Control: County–Government, nonfederal **Service:** General Medical and Surgical

Staffed Beds: 25

CRAWFORDSVILLE—Montgomery County

○ **FRANCISCAN ST. ELIZABETH HEALTH – CRAWFORDSVILLE (150022)**, 1710 Lafayette Road, Zip 47933–1099; tel. 765/362–2800 **A**9 10 11 **F**3 8 15 28 29 30 40 45 57 64 69 70 75 81 84 85 90 93 103 107 108 110 111 115 119 120 121 123 129 130 132 146 148 **S** Franciscan Alliance, Mishawaka, IN
Primary Contact: Terrance E. Wilson, President and CEO
COO: Terrence Klein, Vice President and Chief Operating Officer
CFO: Keith A. Lauter, Vice President Finance
Web address: www.stclaremedical.org
Control: Church–operated, Nongovernment, not–for profit **Service:** General Medical and Surgical

Staffed Beds: 42 **Admissions:** 1180 **Census:** 13 **Outpatient Visits:** 136962 **Births:** 0 **Total Expense ($000):** 39131 **Payroll Expense ($000):** 10699

ST. CLARE MEDICAL CENTER See Franciscan St. Elizabeth Health – Crawfordsville

CROWN POINT—Lake County

○ **FRANCISCAN ST. ANTHONY HEALTH – CROWN POINT (150126)**, 1201 South Main Street, Zip 46307–8483; tel. 219/738–2100, (Nonreporting) **A**2 5 9 10 11 **S** Franciscan Alliance, Mishawaka, IN
Primary Contact: David Ruskowski, President
CFO: Marc Golan, Chief Financial Officer
CMO: Daniel McCormick, M.D., Vice President Medical Staff Affairs
CIO: Tim Loosemore, Director
CNO: Carol E. Schuster, R.N., Regional Chief Nursing Officer and Vice President Patient Care Services
Web address: www.franciscanalliance.org
Control: Church–operated, Nongovernment, not–for profit **Service:** General Medical and Surgical

Staffed Beds: 254

PINNACLE HOSPITAL (150166), 9301 Connecticut Drive, Zip 46307–7486; tel. 219/756–2100, (Nonreporting) **A**9 10
Primary Contact: Haroon Naz, Chief Executive Officer
Web address: www.pinnaclehealthcare.net
Control: Partnership, Investor–owned, for–profit **Service:** General Medical and Surgical

Staffed Beds: 18

ST. ANTHONY MEDICAL CENTER See Franciscan St. Anthony Health – Crown Point

☒ **VIBRA HOSPITAL OF NORTHWESTERN INDIANA (152028)**, 9509 Georgia Street, Zip 46307–6518; tel. 219/472–2200 **A**1 10 **F**1 29 75 77 85 86 87 130 148 **S** Vibra Healthcare, Mechanicsburg, PA
Primary Contact: Charles Nordyke, Chief Executive Officer
CFO: Douglas Morris, Chief Financial Officer
CMO: Raja Devanathan, M.D., Chief Medical Officer
CNO: Robert Beard, Chief Clinical Officer
Web address: www.vhnwindiana.com/
Control: Corporation, Investor–owned, for–profit **Service:** Long–Term Acute Care hospital

Staffed Beds: 40 **Admissions:** 537 **Census:** 36 **Outpatient Visits:** 0 **Births:** 0 **Total Expense ($000):** 16880 **Payroll Expense ($000):** 7152 **Personnel:** 165

DANVILLE—Hendricks County

★ ○ **HENDRICKS REGIONAL HEALTH (150005)**, 1000 East Main Street, Zip 46122–1948, Mailing Address: P.O. Box 409, Zip 46122–0409; tel. 317/745–4451 **A**2 5 9 10 11 **F**3 8 11 13 15 20 28 29 30 31 32 34 35 40 54 55 56 57 59 60 61 64 66 69 70 73 74 75 76 77 78 79 81 85 86 87 89 93 96 97 107 108 109 110 111 115 117 118 119 120 121 123 129 130 131 132 135 144 146 147 148 **P**6
Primary Contact: Kevin Speer, Chief Executive Officer
CFO: John Komenda, Chief Financial Officer
CMO: John Sparzo, M.D., Vice President Medical Affairs
CIO: Lowell Nicodemus, Director Information Systems
CHR: Gary Lenard, Director Human Resources
Web address: www.hendrickshospital.org
Control: County–Government, nonfederal **Service:** General Medical and Surgical

Staffed Beds: 127 **Admissions:** 5126 **Census:** 51 **Outpatient Visits:** 321907 **Births:** 1140 **Total Expense ($000):** 200637 **Payroll Expense ($000):** 84814 **Personnel:** 1325

DECATUR—Adams County

★ **ADAMS MEMORIAL HOSPITAL (151330)**, 1100 Mercer Avenue, Zip 46733–2303, Mailing Address: P.O. Box 151, Zip 46733–0151; tel. 260/724–2145, (Total facility includes 195 beds in nursing home–type unit) **A**9 10 18 **F**3 5 7 10 13 15 29 31 34 35 38 40 45 47 50 53 57 59 64 65 66 67 68 70 74 75 76 77 79 81 82 84 85 86 87 92 93 96 97 98 99 100 101 102 103 104 105 106 107 108 110 111 115 119 125 128 129 130 131 132 133 135 143 144 145 146 147 148 **P**6
Primary Contact: JoEllen Eidam, Chief Executive Officer
CFO: Dane Wheeler, Chief Financial Officer
CMO: Mark S. Gresla, M.D., Chief of Staff
CIO: Nick Nelson, Director Support Services
CHR: Alison Kukelhan, Manager Human Resources
CNO: Michelle Marie Gough, MSN, RN–B, Chief Nursing Officer
Web address: www.adamshospital.com
Control: County–Government, nonfederal **Service:** General Medical and Surgical

Staffed Beds: 233 **Admissions:** 2256 **Census:** 186 **Outpatient Visits:** 97926 **Births:** 202 **Total Expense ($000):** 86585 **Payroll Expense ($000):** 20127 **Personnel:** 374

DYER—Lake County

FRANCISCAN ST. MARGARET HEALTH – DYER See Franciscan St. Margaret Health – Hammond, Hammond

SAINT MARGARET MERCY HEALTHCARE CENTERS–SOUTH CAMPUS See Franciscan St. Margaret Health – Dyer

EAST CHICAGO—Lake County

☒ **REGENCY HOSPITAL OF NORTHWEST INDIANA (152024)**, 4321 Fir Street, 4th Floor, Zip 46312–3049; tel. 219/392–7790, (Includes REGENCY HOSPITAL OF PORTER COUNTY, 3630 Willow Creek Road, Portage, Zip 46368; tel. 219/364–3800), (Nonreporting) **A**1 10 **S** Select Medical Corporation, Mechanicsburg, PA
Primary Contact: Coleen Zimmerman, Chief Executive Officer
Web address: www.regencyhospital.com/company/locations/indiana–northwest–indiana.aspx
Control: Corporation, Investor–owned, for–profit **Service:** Long–Term Acute Care hospital

Staffed Beds: 25

☐ △ **ST. CATHERINE HOSPITAL (150008)**, 4321 Fir Street, Zip 46312–3097; tel. 219/392–1700 **A**1 5 7 9 10 **F**1 3 5 11 13 15 17 18 20 22 24 26 28 29 30 31 34 35 40 46 49 54 57 58 59 60 61 62 64 68 74 75 76 77 78 79 80 81 82 85 86 87 89 92 98 99 100 101 102 103 104 107 108 110 111 112 115 119 129 130 132 135 144 146 147 148 **P**8 **S** Community Healthcare System, Hammond, IN
Primary Contact: JoAnn Birdzell, Chief Executive Officer and Administrator
COO: Craig Bolda, Chief Operating Officer
CFO: Luis Molina, Chief Financial Officer
CMO: John Griep, M.D., Chief Medical Director
CIO: Gary Weiner, Chief Information Officer
CNO: Paula C. Swenson, R.N., Vice President and Chief Nursing Officer
Web address: www.stcatherinehospital.org
Control: Other not–for–profit (including NFP Corporation) **Service:** General Medical and Surgical

Staffed Beds: 189 **Admissions:** 8634 **Census:** 115 **Outpatient Visits:** 144106 **Births:** 586 **Total Expense ($000):** 160476 **Payroll Expense ($000):** 53470 **Personnel:** 797

IN

Hospital, Medicare Provider Number, Address, Telephone, Approval, Facility, and Physician Codes, Health Care System

★ American Hospital Association (AHA) membership
☐ The Joint Commission accreditation   ◇ DNV Healthcare Inc. accreditation
○ Healthcare Facilities Accreditation Program
△ Commission on Accreditation of Rehabilitation Facilities (CARF) accreditation

ELKHART—Elkhart County

★ ○ △ **ELKHART GENERAL HEALTHCARE SYSTEM (150018)**, 600 East Boulevard, Zip 46514–2499, Mailing Address: P.O. Box 1329, Zip 46515–1329; tel. 574/294–2621 **A**2 5 7 8 10 11 **F**3 5 12 13 15 17 18 20 22 24 26 28 29 30 31 34 35 40 45 46 49 50 57 59 60 64 68 69 70 72 74 75 76 77 78 79 81 82 85 86 87 89 90 91 92 93 99 100 102 104 105 107 108 110 111 114 115 118 119 120 121 123 129 130 132 134 135 146 147 148 **P**6 **S** Beacon Health System, South Bend, IN
Primary Contact: Greg Losasso, President
CFO: Jeff Costello, Chief Financial Officer
CMO: William Buckley, M.D., Chief of Staff
CIO: Steve Huffman, Chief Information Officer
CHR: Steven M. Eller, Vice President Human Resources
CNO: Karra Heggen, R.N., Vice President Nursing
Web address: www.egh.org
Control: Other not–for–profit (including NFP Corporation) **Service:** General Medical and Surgical

Staffed Beds: 260 **Admissions:** 11566 **Census:** 135 **Outpatient Visits:** 489817 **Births:** 1521 **Total Expense ($000):** 269923 **Payroll Expense ($000):** 95210 **Personnel:** 1743

ELWOOD—Madison County

⊞ **ST. VINCENT MERCY HOSPITAL (151308)**, 1331 South A Street, Zip 46036–1942; tel. 765/552–4600 **A**1 2 9 10 18 **F**3 8 11 15 28 29 30 31 34 35 40 44 45 50 53 57 59 64 68 74 75 78 79 81 82 85 86 87 93 107 108 110 111 114 119 129 130 132 133 135 141 146 148 **S** Ascension Health, Saint Louis, MO
Primary Contact: Francis G. Albarano, Administrator
CFO: John Arthur, Chief Financial Officer
CMO: Gary Brazel, M.D., Chief Medical Officer
CHR: Ross Brodhead, Manager Human Resources
CNO: Ann C. Yates, R.N., Director Patient Care and Clinical Services
Web address: www.stvincent.org
Control: Church–operated, Nongovernment, not–for profit **Service:** General Medical and Surgical

Staffed Beds: 25 **Admissions:** 661 **Census:** 7 **Outpatient Visits:** 34974 **Births:** 0 **Total Expense ($000):** 23426 **Payroll Expense ($000):** 8749 **Personnel:** 145

EVANSVILLE—Vanderburgh County

★ ○ **DEACONESS HOSPITAL (150082)**, 600 Mary Street, Zip 47710–1658; tel. 812/450–5000, (Includes DEACONESS CROSS POINTE CENTER, 7200 East Indiana Street, Zip 47715; tel. 812/476–7200; Cheryl Rietman, Chief Administrative Officer) **A**2 3 5 9 10 11 **F**3 5 9 11 12 15 17 18 19 20 22 24 26 29 30 31 32 34 35 36 38 39 40 43 44 45 46 49 50 51 53 54 56 57 58 59 60 61 62 63 64 65 66 68 70 71 74 75 77 78 79 81 82 84 85 86 87 88 89 93 94 96 97 98 99 100 101 102 104 105 107 108 110 111 114 115 116 117 118 119 120 121 123 126 129 130 132 134 135 145 146 148 **P**6 8 **S** Deaconess Health System, Evansville, IN
Primary Contact: Shawn W. McCoy, Chief Administrative Officer
CFO: Cheryl A. Wathen, Interim Chief Financial Officer
CMO: James Porter, M.D., Vice President Medical Affairs
CHR: Larry Pile, Director Human Resources
Web address: www.deaconess.com
Control: Other not–for–profit (including NFP Corporation) **Service:** General Medical and Surgical

Staffed Beds: 489 **Admissions:** 22765 **Census:** 306 **Outpatient Visits:** 570142 **Births:** 0 **Total Expense ($000):** 526761 **Payroll Expense ($000):** 202885 **Personnel:** 3266

EVANSVILLE PSYCHIATRIC CHILDREN CENTER (15J200), 3300 East Morgan Avenue, Zip 47715–2232; tel. 812/477–6436, (Nonreporting) **A**10
Primary Contact: Lottie Cook, Superintendent
COO: Melinda Kendle, Manager Business Office
CMO: Shannon Jones, M.D., Medical Director and Attending Psychiatrist
CIO: David Wirtz, Supervisor Information Technology
CHR: Jennifer Sontz, Director Human Resources
CNO: Elizabeth Angermeier, Director of Nursing
Web address: www.ih.gov
Control: State–Government, nonfederal **Service:** Children's hospital psychiatric

Staffed Beds: 28

☐ **EVANSVILLE STATE HOSPITAL (154056)**, 3400 Lincoln Avenue, Zip 47714–0146; tel. 812/469–6800, (Nonreporting) **A**1 10
Primary Contact: Cathe Fulcher, Superintendent
CFO: Melinda Kendle, Director Fiscal Management
CMO: Melba Briones, M.D., Medical Director
CIO: David Wirtz, Senior LAN Administrator
CHR: Jennifer Sontz, Director Human Resources
Control: State–Government, nonfederal **Service:** Psychiatric

Staffed Beds: 168

⊞ **HEALTHSOUTH DEACONESS REHABILITATION HOSPITAL (153025)**, 4100 Covert Avenue, Zip 47714–5567, Mailing Address: P.O. Box 5349, Zip 47716–5349; tel. 812/476–9983 **A**1 9 10 **F**28 29 64 68 75 87 90 91 93 94 95 96 130 132 143 148 **S** HEALTHSOUTH Corporation, Birmingham, AL
Primary Contact: Barbara Butler, Chief Executive Officer
CFO: Rob Winters, Controller
CMO: Ashok Dhingra, M.D., Executive Medical Director
CIO: Edward Gomez, Manager Information Systems
CHR: Darlene Moog, Director Human Resources
Web address: www.healthsouthdeaconess.com
Control: Corporation, Investor–owned, for–profit **Service:** Rehabilitation

Staffed Beds: 80 **Admissions:** 1740 **Census:** 67 **Outpatient Visits:** 6284 **Births:** 0 **Total Expense ($000):** 20629 **Payroll Expense ($000):** 10934 **Personnel:** 237

⊞ **SELECT SPECIALTY HOSPITAL–EVANSVILLE (152014)**, 400 S.E. 4th Street, Zip 47713–1206; tel. 812/421–2500, (Nonreporting) **A**1 10 **S** Select Medical Corporation, Mechanicsburg, PA
Primary Contact: Mike Carney, Chief Executive Officer
Web address: www.selectspecialtyhospitals.com/company/locations/evansville.aspx
Control: Corporation, Investor–owned, for–profit **Service:** Long–Term Acute Care hospital

Staffed Beds: 60

⊞ △ **ST. MARY'S MEDICAL CENTER OF EVANSVILLE (150100)**, 3700 Washington Avenue, Zip 47714–0541; tel. 812/485–4000 **A**1 2 5 7 9 10 **F**3 8 11 12 13 15 17 18 19 20 22 24 26 28 29 30 31 32 34 35 40 42 43 45 46 47 48 49 50 51 53 54 55 56 57 58 59 60 61 64 65 68 70 71 72 73 74 75 76 77 78 79 80 81 82 83 84 85 86 87 88 89 90 92 93 96 98 100 101 102 107 108 110 111 114 115 116 117 118 119 126 129 130 131 132 134 135 143 144 146 147 148 **P**6 **S** Ascension Health, Saint Louis, MO
Primary Contact: Keith Jewell, President
COO: Gwen L. Sandefur, Executive Vice President and Chief Operating Officer
CFO: John Zabrowski, Chief Financial Officer
CMO: Vernon Maas, M.D., Vice President, Medical Affairs
CIO: Jose Diaz, Director Information Systems
CHR: Marty Mattingly, Chief Human Resources Officer
CNO: Darcy Ellison, R.N., Senior Vice President, Chief Nursing Officer and Inpatient Flow
Web address: www.stmarys.org
Control: Church–operated, Nongovernment, not–for profit **Service:** General Medical and Surgical

Staffed Beds: 436 **Admissions:** 17218 **Census:** 228 **Outpatient Visits:** 354550 **Births:** 1638 **Total Expense ($000):** 392404 **Payroll Expense ($000):** 125880 **Personnel:** 2235

FISHERS—Hamilton County

⊞ **ST. VINCENT FISHERS HOSPITAL (150181)**, 13861 Olio Road, Zip 46037–3487; tel. 317/415–9000, (Nonreporting) **A**1 10 **S** Ascension Health, Saint Louis, MO
Primary Contact: Gary Fammartino, Administrator
CMO: Craig Wilson, Chief Medical Officer
Web address: www.stvincent.org
Control: Other not–for–profit (including NFP Corporation) **Service:** General Medical and Surgical

Staffed Beds: 46

FORT WAYNE—Allen County

⊞ **DUPONT HOSPITAL (150150)**, 2520 East Dupont Road, Zip 46825–1675; tel. 260/416–3000 **A**1 9 10 **F**3 13 15 20 26 29 30 34 35 40 45 49 51 56 57 59 64 65 68 70 72 73 74 75 79 81 82 85 86 87 107 108 111 112 113 114 115 119 124 129 131 132 135 141 145 146 147 148 **P**1 5 **S** Community Health Systems, Inc., Franklin, TN
Primary Contact: Chad Towner, Chief Executive Officer
CFO: Brian Schneider, Chief Financial Officer
CIO: Keith A. Neuman, Chief Information Officer
Web address: www.thedupontdifference.com
Control: Partnership, Investor–owned, for–profit **Service:** General Medical and Surgical

Staffed Beds: 131 **Admissions:** 4416 **Census:** 47 **Outpatient Visits:** 97711 **Births:** 2144 **Total Expense ($000):** 79717 **Payroll Expense ($000):** 29463 **Personnel:** 473

IN

Many Facility Codes have changed. Please refer to the AHA Guide Code Chart.
© 2014 AHA Guide

☒ **LUTHERAN HOSPITAL OF INDIANA (150017)**, 7950 West Jefferson Boulevard, Zip 46804–4140; tel. 260/435–7001 **A**1 2 3 5 9 10 **F**3 7 12 13 15 17 18 19 20 22 24 26 28 29 30 31 32 34 35 39 40 41 43 44 45 46 47 48 49 50 51 54 58 59 60 62 63 64 68 70 72 74 75 76 77 78 79 80 81 82 84 85 86 87 88 89 92 93 96 97 107 108 110 111 112 114 115 116 117 118 119 124 126 129 130 132 137 138 141 143 145 146 147 148 **S** Community Health Systems, Inc., Franklin, TN
Primary Contact: Brian Bauer, Chief Executive Officer
COO: Erica Wehrmeister, Chief Operating Officer
CFO: Cully Chapman, Chief Financial Officer
CMO: Geoffrey Randolph, M.D., Chief Medical Officer
CIO: Keith A. Neuman, Chief Information Officer
CHR: Maria Kurtz, Director Human Resources
CNO: Diane L. Springer, MS, Chief Nursing Officer
Web address: www.lutheranhospital.com
Control: Corporation, Investor–owned, for–profit **Service:** General Medical and Surgical

Staffed Beds: 379 **Admissions:** 18657 **Census:** 251 **Outpatient Visits:** 409814 **Births:** 1013

☒ **ORTHOPAEDIC HOSPITAL OF LUTHERAN HEALTH NETWORK (150168)**, 7952 West Jefferson Boulevard, Zip 46804–4140; tel. 260/435–2999 **A**1 9 10 **F**29 34 35 37 64 77 79 80 81 82 93 94 96 111 131 **P**8 **S** Community Health Systems, Inc., Franklin, TN
Primary Contact: Kenneth Jones, Chief Executive Officer
CFO: Amy Hochstetler, Chief Financial Officer
CMO: Kevin Rahn, President Medical Staff
CIO: Keith A. Neuman, Chief Information Officer
CHR: Maria Kurtz, Director Human Resources
CNO: Marci Hamilton, Chief Nursing Officer
Web address: www.theorthohospital.com
Control: Corporation, Investor–owned, for–profit **Service:** Orthopedic

Staffed Beds: 44 **Admissions:** 2560 **Census:** 17 **Outpatient Visits:** 44162 **Births:** 0 **Total Expense ($000):** 49685 **Payroll Expense ($000):** 11614 **Personnel:** 211

☐ **PARKVIEW ORTHO HOSPITAL (150167)**, 11130 Parkview Circle Drive, Zip 46845–1735; tel. 260/672–5000 **A**1 9 10 **F**3 8 29 30 34 42 45 50 58 65 68 79 81 82 84 85 86 87 90 93 94 96 107 119 141
Primary Contact: Julie Fleck, Chief Operating Officer
Web address: www.parkview.com
Control: Corporation, Investor–owned, for–profit **Service:** Orthopedic

Staffed Beds: 37 **Admissions:** 2041 **Census:** 14 **Outpatient Visits:** 3497 **Births:** 0 **Total Expense ($000):** 48764 **Payroll Expense ($000):** 6693 **Personnel:** 163

★ **PARKVIEW REGIONAL MEDICAL CENTER (150021)**, 11109 Parkview Plaza Drive, Zip 46845–1701; tel. 260/373–4000, (Includes PARKVIEW HOSPITAL RANDALLIA, 2200 Randallia Drive, Zip 46805–4699; tel. 260/373–4000), (Total facility includes 31 beds in nursing home–type unit) **A**9 10 **F**3 5 7 11 13 14 15 17 18 20 22 24 26 28 29 30 31 32 34 35 40 43 44 45 46 49 50 51 53 54 55 57 58 59 60 61 62 63 64 65 68 69 70 72 74 75 76 78 79 81 82 84 85 86 87 88 89 90 92 93 96 98 99 100 101 102 103 104 105 107 108 109 111 114 115 118 119 120 121 123 124 126 128 129 130 131 132 135 141 146 147 148 **S** Parkview Health, Fort Wayne, IN
Primary Contact: Ben Miles, Chief Operating Officer
Web address: www.parkview.com
Control: Other not–for–profit (including NFP Corporation) **Service:** General Medical and Surgical

Staffed Beds: 649 **Admissions:** 32280 **Census:** 466 **Outpatient Visits:** 313413 **Births:** 2963 **Total Expense ($000):** 636880 **Payroll Expense ($000):** 185292 **Personnel:** 3410

☒ △ **REHABILITATION HOSPITAL OF FORT WAYNE (153030)**, 7970 West Jefferson Boulevard, Zip 46804–4140; tel. 260/435–6100 **A**1 7 9 10 **F**29 30 90 93 96 130 132 146 **P**5 **S** Community Health Systems, Inc., Franklin, TN
Primary Contact: Ted Scholten, Chief Operating Officer
COO: Ted Scholten, Chief Operating Officer
CFO: Cully Chapman, Chief Financial Officer
CMO: Heidi Lang, M.D., Chief Medical Officer
CIO: Keith A. Neuman, Chief Information Officer
CHR: Deborah Giardina, Director Human Resources and Medical Staff Services
CNO: Shelley Boxell, R.N., Chief Nursing Officer and Quality Coordinator
Web address: www.rehabhospital.com
Control: Corporation, Investor–owned, for–profit **Service:** Rehabilitation

Staffed Beds: 36 **Admissions:** 553 **Census:** 17 **Outpatient Visits:** 67 **Births:** 0 **Total Expense ($000):** 8910 **Payroll Expense ($000):** 4910 **Personnel:** 85

☒ **SELECT SPECIALTY HOSPITAL–FORT WAYNE (152016)**, 700 Broadway, 7th Floor, Zip 46802–1402; tel. 260/425–3810, (Nonreporting) **A**1 10 **S** Select Medical Corporation, Mechanicsburg, PA
Primary Contact: Robert C. Marquardt, FACHE, Chief Executive Officer
CMO: Yogesh Amin, M.D., Medical Director
CNO: Marielle Lael, R.N., Chief Nursing Officer
Web address: www.fortwayne.selectspecialtyhospitals.com
Control: Corporation, Investor–owned, for–profit **Service:** Long–Term Acute Care hospital

Staffed Beds: 32

☒ **ST. JOSEPH HOSPITAL (150047)**, 700 Broadway, Zip 46802–1493; tel. 260/425–3000, (Total facility includes 20 beds in nursing home–type unit) **A**1 3 5 9 10 **F**3 4 5 13 15 16 17 18 20 22 24 28 29 30 34 35 38 40 45 46 47 49 50 51 53 54 55 56 57 58 59 64 65 68 69 70 72 74 76 77 79 80 81 85 87 92 93 96 98 100 101 102 103 104 105 107 108 110 111 114 115 118 119 128 130 132 142 146 147 148 **P**6 **S** Community Health Systems, Inc., Franklin, TN
Primary Contact: Kenneth Jones, Chief Executive Officer
COO: Jeff Vice, Chief Operating Officer
CFO: Pamela Hess, Chief Financial Officer
CHR: Steve Heggen, Administrative Director Human Resources
Web address: www.stjoehospital.com
Control: Corporation, Investor–owned, for–profit **Service:** General Medical and Surgical

Staffed Beds: 182 **Admissions:** 6296 **Census:** 99 **Outpatient Visits:** 110157 **Births:** 406 **Total Expense ($000):** 94387 **Payroll Expense ($000):** 34369 **Personnel:** 699

☒ **VETERANS AFFAIRS NORTHERN INDIANA HEALTH CARE SYSTEM**, 2121 Lake Avenue, Zip 46805–5100; tel. 260/426–5431, (Includes VETERANS AFFAIRS NORTHERN INDIANA HEALTH CARE SYSTEM–MARION CAMPUS, 1700 East 38th Street, Marion, Zip 46953–4589; tel. 765/674–3321), (Nonreporting) **A**1 **S** Department of Veterans Affairs, Washington, DC
Primary Contact: Denise M. Deitzen, Director
COO: Helen Rhodes, R.N., Associate Director Operations
CFO: Jay H. Vandermark, Chief Financial Officer
CMO: Mark D. Wooten, M.D., Chief of Staff
CIO: David Troyer, Chief Information Officer
CHR: Brian Flynn, Chief Human Resources Officer
Web address: www.northernindiana.va.gov/
Control: Veterans Affairs, Government, federal **Service:** General Medical and Surgical

Staffed Beds: 26

☒ **VIBRA HOSPITAL OF FORT WAYNE (152027)**, 2200 Randallia Drive, Zip 46805–4638; tel. 260/399–2900, (Nonreporting) **A**1 10 **S** Vibra Healthcare, Mechanicsburg, PA
Primary Contact: Kerry Ashment, Chief Executive Officer
Web address: www.vhfortwayne.com
Control: Corporation, Investor–owned, for–profit **Service:** Long–Term Acute Care hospital

Staffed Beds: 50

FRANKFORT—Clinton County

☒ **ST. VINCENT FRANKFORT HOSPITAL (151316)**, 1300 South Jackson Street, Zip 46041–3394, Mailing Address: P.O. Box 669, Zip 46041–0669; tel. 765/656–3000 **A**1 9 10 18 **F**3 11 13 15 28 29 30 31 34 35 40 45 50 57 59 64 65 68 75 76 77 78 79 81 82 85 86 89 90 93 97 107 111 114 119 130 132 133 135 146 148 **S** Ascension Health, Saint Louis, MO
Primary Contact: Thomas Crawford, Administrator
CMO: Stephen Tharp, M.D., Medical Director
CHR: Krista Wright, Director Human Resources
Web address: www.stvincent.org
Control: Church–operated, Nongovernment, not–for profit **Service:** General Medical and Surgical

Staffed Beds: 25 **Admissions:** 858 **Census:** 9 **Outpatient Visits:** 37447 **Births:** 244 **Total Expense ($000):** 23470 **Payroll Expense ($000):** 8404 **Personnel:** 88

IN

Hospital, Medicare Provider Number, Address, Telephone, Approval, Facility, and Physician Codes, Health Care System

★ American Hospital Association (AHA) membership
☐ The Joint Commission accreditation
◇ DNV Healthcare Inc. accreditation
○ Healthcare Facilities Accreditation Program
△ Commission on Accreditation of Rehabilitation Facilities (CARF) accreditation

FRANKLIN—Johnson County

★ ○ **JOHNSON MEMORIAL HOSPITAL (150001)**, 1125 West Jefferson Street, Zip 46131–2140, Mailing Address: P.O. Box 549, Zip 46131–0549; tel. 317/736–3300 **A**5 9 10 11 **F**12 13 15 18 20 28 29 30 31 34 35 36 40 44 45 49 50 54 57 59 62 64 68 70 74 75 76 77 78 79 81 82 85 87 90 93 97 107 108 110 111 114 118 119 129 130 131 132 134 135 144 146 147 148 **P**8
Primary Contact: Larry Heydon, President and Chief Executive Officer
COO: Steve Wohlford, Chief Operating Officer
CFO: Elizabeth A. Hedden, Chief Financial Officer
CMO: John Norris, M.D., Vice President Medical Affairs
CIO: Scott Krodel, Vice President Information Systems
CHR: Judy Ware, Director Human Resources
CNO: Anita M. Keller, R.N., Chief Nursing Officer
Web address: www.johnsonmemorial.org
Control: County–Government, nonfederal **Service:** General Medical and Surgical

Staffed Beds: 101 **Admissions:** 2324 **Census:** 27 **Outpatient Visits:** 140755 **Births:** 368 **Total Expense ($000):** 74725 **Payroll Expense ($000):** 36322 **Personnel:** 642

GARY—Lake County

○ △ **METHODIST HOSPITALS (150002)**, 600 Grant Street, Zip 46402–6099; tel. 219/886–4000, (Includes SOUTHLAKE CAMPUS, 8701 Broadway, Merrillville, Zip 46410; tel. 219/738–5500) **A**2 3 5 7 9 10 11 **F**3 8 11 12 13 15 20 22 24 26 28 29 30 31 32 34 35 37 40 45 47 48 49 50 51 54 55 57 59 62 64 67 70 72 73 74 75 76 77 78 79 81 82 85 86 89 90 93 98 99 100 101 102 103 107 108 110 111 114 115 118 119 120 121 123 124 126 130 132 133 146 147 148 **P**6
Primary Contact: Michael Davenport, M.D., President and Interim Chief Executive Officer
CMO: Charles O. Davidson, M.D., Vice President Medical Affairs
CIO: Shaw Collins, Director Information Technology
CHR: Joyce McGlory, Vice President Human Resources
Web address: www.methodisthospitals.org
Control: Other not–for–profit (including NFP Corporation) **Service:** General Medical and Surgical

Staffed Beds: 505 **Admissions:** 17772 **Census:** 290 **Outpatient Visits:** 261678 **Births:** 1505 **Total Expense ($000):** 310965 **Payroll Expense ($000):** 133510 **Personnel:** 1983

GOSHEN—Elkhart County

GOSHEN GENERAL HOSPITAL See Indiana University Health Goshen Hospital

✠ **INDIANA UNIVERSITY HEALTH GOSHEN HOSPITAL (150026)**, 200 High Park Avenue, Zip 46526–4899, Mailing Address: P.O. Box 139, Zip 46527–0139; tel. 574/533–2141 **A**1 2 9 10 **F**3 11 12 13 15 18 20 22 26 28 29 30 31 32 34 35 36 37 40 44 45 46 47 48 49 50 51 54 56 57 58 59 62 63 64 65 67 68 70 71 74 75 76 77 78 79 80 81 82 84 85 86 87 89 92 93 96 97 102 107 108 110 111 115 116 117 118 119 120 121 123 124 126 127 129 130 131 132 135 145 146 147 148 **P**8 **S** Indiana University Health, Indianapolis, IN
Primary Contact: Randal Christophel, President and Chief Executive Officer
COO: Paulette Brown, Chief Operating Officer
CMO: Randall Cammenga, M.D., Vice President Medical Affairs
CIO: Dolph Voelker, Director Information Services
CHR: Alan Weldy, Vice President Human Resources, Compliance and Legal Services
Web address: www.iuhealth.org
Control: Other not–for–profit (including NFP Corporation) **Service:** General Medical and Surgical

Staffed Beds: 122 **Admissions:** 5707 **Census:** 52 **Outpatient Visits:** 130618 **Births:** 1196 **Total Expense ($000):** 186524 **Payroll Expense ($000):** 61700 **Personnel:** 1224

OAKLAWN PSYCHIATRIC CENTER (154031), 330 Lakeview Drive, Zip 46528–9365, Mailing Address: P.O. Box 809, Zip 46527–0809; tel. 574/533–1234 **A**9 10 **F**4 5 29 30 34 35 38 54 56 98 99 100 101 102 103 104 106 130 146 **P**6
Primary Contact: Laurie N. Nafziger, President and Chief Executive Officer
CFO: Joseph Barkman, Vice President Financial Services
CMO: Daniel Kinsey, M.D., Medical Director
CIO: Jennifer Glick, Manager Clinical Informatics
CHR: Jill Seifer, Vice President Human Resources
CNO: Elaine G. Miller, Director of Nursing
Web address: www.oaklawn.org
Control: Other not–for–profit (including NFP Corporation) **Service:** Psychiatric

Staffed Beds: 16 **Admissions:** 877 **Census:** 14 **Outpatient Visits:** 299453 **Births:** 0 **Total Expense ($000):** 40230 **Payroll Expense ($000):** 24520 **Personnel:** 627

GREENCASTLE—Putnam County

PUTNAM COUNTY HOSPITAL (151333), 1542 Bloomington Street, Zip 46135–2297; tel. 765/653–5121, (Nonreporting) **A**2 9 10 18
Primary Contact: Dennis Weatherford, Chief Executive Officer
CFO: Kevin Fowler, Director Finance
Web address: www.pchosp.org/
Control: County–Government, nonfederal **Service:** General Medical and Surgical

Staffed Beds: 25

GREENFIELD—Hancock County

★ ○ **HANCOCK REGIONAL HOSPITAL (150037)**, 801 North State Street, Zip 46140–1270, Mailing Address: P.O. Box 827, Zip 46140–0827; tel. 317/462–5544 **A**5 9 10 11 **F**3 11 12 13 15 17 18 20 22 28 29 30 31 32 34 35 38 40 44 45 47 48 49 50 53 54 56 57 59 62 63 64 66 68 69 70 74 75 78 79 81 82 83 84 85 86 87 89 90 93 96 98 103 107 110 111 114 115 119 127 129 130 132 134 135 144 146 147 148 **P**2 8
Primary Contact: Steven V. Long, FACHE, President and Chief Executive Officer
CFO: Rick Edwards, Vice President Finance Services
CMO: Michael Fletcher, M.D., President Medical Staff Services
CIO: Jon Miller, Director Accounting and Information Services
CHR: Laura L. Nichols, Director Human Resources
CNO: Sherry Gehring, R.N., Vice President Nursing, Inpatient Care and Chief Nursing Officer
Web address: www.hancockregional.org
Control: County–Government, nonfederal **Service:** General Medical and Surgical

Staffed Beds: 92 **Admissions:** 3100 **Census:** 34 **Outpatient Visits:** 150876 **Births:** 354 **Total Expense ($000):** 93742 **Payroll Expense ($000):** 37901 **Personnel:** 657

GREENSBURG—Decatur County

★ ◇ **DECATUR COUNTY MEMORIAL HOSPITAL (151332)**, 720 North Lincoln Street, Zip 47240–1398; tel. 812/663–4331 **A**2 9 10 18 21 **F**3 7 11 13 15 18 28 29 31 34 40 45 50 54 57 59 62 64 65 68 69 74 75 76 77 78 79 80 81 82 85 86 87 89 92 93 94 96 97 107 108 110 111 115 118 119 129 130 131 132 133 135 145 146 147 148 **P**6
Primary Contact: Linda V. Simmons, President and Chief Executive Officer
COO: David Fry, Vice President of Operations
CFO: Jerry Marks, Vice President Finance
CHR: Amy Lynn Wickens, Executive Director Human Resources
CNO: Diane McKinney, R.N., Vice President Patient Care Service
Web address: www.dcmh.net
Control: County–Government, nonfederal **Service:** General Medical and Surgical

Staffed Beds: 25 **Admissions:** 1219 **Census:** 11 **Outpatient Visits:** 126365 **Births:** 246 **Total Expense ($000):** 48317 **Payroll Expense ($000):** 23772 **Personnel:** 385

GREENWOOD—Johnson County

✠ **KINDRED HOSPITAL INDIANAPOLIS SOUTH (152008)**, 607 Greenwood Springs Drive, Zip 46143–6377; tel. 317/888–8155 **A**1 10 **F**1 3 29 107 119 148 **S** Kindred Healthcare, Louisville, KY
Primary Contact: Matthew Keppler, Market Chief Executive Officer
CFO: William Brenner, Chief Financial Officer
CMO: Steven Samuels, M.D., Medical Director
CNO: Jennifer Stallings, Chief Clinical Officer
Web address: www.khindysouth.com/
Control: Individual, Investor–owned, for–profit **Service:** Long–Term Acute Care hospital

Staffed Beds: 60 **Admissions:** 555 **Census:** 38 **Outpatient Visits:** 0 **Births:** 0

□ **VALLE VISTA HOSPITAL (154024)**, 898 East Main Street, Zip 46143–1400; tel. 317/887–1348 **A**1 9 10 **F**4 5 98 99 100 102 104 105 106 **S** Universal Health Services, Inc., King of Prussia, PA
Primary Contact: Sherri R. Jewett, Chief Executive Officer
CFO: Tim Sides, Chief Financial Officer
CMO: Jennifer Comer, M.D., Medical Director
CIO: Karen Hayden, Director Health Information Services, Performance Improvement and Risk Management
CHR: Ismael Santos, Director Human Resources
Web address: www.vallevistahospital.com
Control: State–Government, nonfederal **Service:** Psychiatric

Staffed Beds: 102 **Admissions:** 2112 **Census:** 54 **Outpatient Visits:** 9966 **Births:** 0 **Total Expense ($000):** 13851 **Payroll Expense ($000):** 6245 **Personnel:** 192

HAMMOND—Lake County

○ △ **FRANCISCAN ST. MARGARET HEALTH – HAMMOND (150004)**, 5454 Hohman Avenue, Zip 46320–1999; tel. 219/933–2074, (Includes FRANCISCAN ST. MARGARET HEALTH – DYER, 24 Joliet Street, Dyer, Zip 46311–1799; tel. 219/865–2141; SAINT MARGARET MERCY HEALTHCARE CENTERS–NORTH CAMPUS, 5454 Hohman Avenue, Zip 46320; tel. 219/932–2300), (Nonreporting) **A**2 5 7 9 10 11 **S** Franciscan Alliance, Mishawaka, IN
Primary Contact: Thomas J. Gryzbek, President
CFO: Jim Lipinski, Chief Financial Officer
Web address: www.smmhc.com
Control: Church–operated, Nongovernment, not–for profit **Service:** General Medical and Surgical

Staffed Beds: 500

Many Facility Codes have changed. Please refer to the AHA Guide Code Chart.

IN

✠ **KINDRED HOSPITAL NORTHWEST INDIANA (152012)**, 5454 Hohman Avenue, 5th Floor, Zip 46320–1931; tel. 219/937–9900, (Nonreporting) **A**1 10 **S** Kindred Healthcare, Louisville, KY
Primary Contact: Frank A. Solare, Chief Executive Officer
Web address: www.khnwindiana.com
Control: Corporation, Investor–owned, for–profit **Service:** Long–Term Acute Care hospital

Staffed Beds: 70

SAINT MARGARET MERCY HEALTHCARE CENTERS See Franciscan St. Margaret Health – Hammond

TRIUMPH HOSPITAL NORTHWEST INDIANA See Kindred Hospital Northwest Indiana

HARTFORD CITY—Blackford County

BLACKFORD COMMUNITY HOSPITAL See Indiana University Health Blackford Hospital

✠ **INDIANA UNIVERSITY HEALTH BLACKFORD HOSPITAL (151302)**, 410 Pilgrim Boulevard, Zip 47348–1897; tel. 765/348–0300 **A**1 9 10 18 **F**3 7 11 15 28 29 34 35 40 44 45 50 57 59 64 75 81 85 93 107 110 114 119 130 132 133 135 143 **S** Indiana University Health, Indianapolis, IN
Primary Contact: Steven J. West, Chief Executive Officer
CFO: Bettie Caldwell, Director Finance
CIO: Steven J. West, Chief Executive Officer
CHR: John Crosbie, Director Support Services
CNO: Kandi Adamson, R.N., Chief Nursing Officer
Web address: www.iuhealth.org
Control: Other not–for–profit (including NFP Corporation) **Service:** General Medical and Surgical

Staffed Beds: 15 Admissions: 495 Census: 7 Outpatient Visits: 37323 Births: 0 Total Expense ($000): 16516 Payroll Expense ($000): 7699 Personnel: 106

HOBART—Lake County

HIND GENERAL HOSPITAL, 101 West 61st Avenue, Zip 46342–6449; tel. 219/947–3030, (Nonreporting)
Primary Contact: Raghu Nayak, Chief Executive Officer
Control: Partnership, Investor–owned, for–profit **Service:** General Medical and Surgical

Staffed Beds: 22

☐ △ **ST. MARY MEDICAL CENTER (150034)**, 1500 South Lake Park Avenue, Zip 46342–6699; tel. 219/942–0551 **A**1 2 7 9 10 **F**3 8 11 12 13 15 18 20 22 24 26 28 29 30 31 34 35 36 38 39 40 45 47 49 50 51 54 57 58 59 60 62 64 65 68 70 74 75 76 77 78 79 80 81 82 85 86 87 89 90 92 93 94 96 107 108 110 111 114 115 117 119 120 121 123 126 129 130 132 134 135 146 147 148 **P**8 **S** Community Healthcare System, Hammond, IN
Primary Contact: Janice L. Ryba, JD, Chief Executive Officer
CFO: Mary Sudicky, Chief Financial Officer
CIO: Gary Weiner, Vice President Information Technology and Chief Information Officer
CHR: Tony Ferracane, Vice President Human Resources
CNO: Tammie R. Jones, R.N., Chief Nursing Officer
Web address: www.comhs.org
Control: Other not–for–profit (including NFP Corporation) **Service:** General Medical and Surgical

Staffed Beds: 195 Admissions: 11428 Census: 159 Outpatient Visits: 169455 Births: 528 Total Expense ($000): 198617 Payroll Expense ($000): 61451 Personnel: 952

HUNTINGTON—Huntington County

✠ **PARKVIEW HUNTINGTON HOSPITAL (150091)**, 2001 Stults Road, Zip 46750–1291; tel. 260/355–3000 **A**1 9 10 **F**3 7 8 13 15 28 29 30 31 32 34 35 36 38 39 40 44 45 46 50 53 56 57 59 64 68 69 70 75 76 77 78 79 81 85 86 87 93 96 97 107 108 111 119 130 131 132 134 135 146 148 **S** Parkview Health, Fort Wayne, IN
Primary Contact: Darlene Garrett, President
COO: Darlene Garrett, President
CMO: Jeffrey Brooks, M.D., Medical Director
CNO: Juli Johnson, R.N., Chief Nursing Officer
Web address: www.parkview.com
Control: Other not–for–profit (including NFP Corporation) **Service:** General Medical and Surgical

Staffed Beds: 36 Admissions: 1894 Census: 16 Outpatient Visits: 38687 Births: 367 Total Expense ($000): 40429 Payroll Expense ($000): 12257 Personnel: 219

INDIANAPOLIS—Marion County

CLARIAN HEALTH PARTNERS See Indiana University Health University Hospital

☐ **COMMUNITY HEART AND VASCULAR HOSPITAL (150154)**, 8075 North Shadeland Avenue, Zip 46250–2693; tel. 317/621–8000 **A**1 10 **F**3 11 17 18 20 22 24 26 28 29 30 34 35 40 55 56 57 58 59 60 63 64 65 68 70 71 74 75 77 80 81 84 85 86 87 91 93 96 107 108 109 115 118 119 130 132 133 144 146 147 148 **P**8 **S** Community Health Network, Indianapolis, IN
Primary Contact: Jason Fahrlander, FACHE, President
COO: Susan Sandberg, R.N., Chief Operating Officer
CFO: Amy Campbell, Chief Financial Officer
CMO: Robert Shoemaker, M.D., Chief of Staff Community Heart and Vascular
CIO: Ron Thieme, Ph.D., Chief Knowledge and Information Officer
CHR: Steve Pearcy, Director Human Resources
CNO: Pamela Hunt, MSN, Vice President of Patient Services and Chief Nursing Executive
Web address: www.ecommunity.com/heart
Control: Other not–for–profit (including NFP Corporation) **Service:** Heart

Staffed Beds: 56 Admissions: 2880 Census: 31 Outpatient Visits: 41997 Births: 0 Total Expense ($000): 94337 Payroll Expense ($000): 22221 Personnel: 286

☐ **COMMUNITY HOSPITAL EAST (150074)**, 1500 North Ritter Avenue, Zip 46219–3095; tel. 317/355–1411 **A**1 2 3 5 9 10 **F**3 11 13 18 20 22 26 28 29 30 31 34 35 38 40 44 45 47 49 50 51 53 56 57 59 60 64 65 68 69 70 73 74 75 76 77 78 79 80 81 85 87 92 96 98 99 100 101 102 103 104 105 106 107 108 110 111 114 115 118 119 120 121 123 129 130 132 144 146 147 148 **P**8 **S** Community Health Network, Indianapolis, IN
Primary Contact: Robin Ledyard, M.D., M.P.H., President
Web address: www.ecommunity.com/east/
Control: Other not–for–profit (including NFP Corporation) **Service:** General Medical and Surgical

Staffed Beds: 243 Admissions: 13259 Census: 160 Outpatient Visits: 296789 Births: 929 Total Expense ($000): 359008 Payroll Expense ($000): 117385 Personnel: 2489

☐ **COMMUNITY HOSPITAL NORTH (150169)**, 7150 Clearvista Drive, Zip 46256–1695; tel. 317/621–6262 **A**1 9 10 **F**3 11 12 13 18 29 30 31 34 35 40 41 45 46 47 48 49 50 52 56 58 59 61 63 64 65 67 69 70 72 74 75 76 77 78 79 81 82 84 85 86 87 88 89 90 91 92 93 96 98 103 107 108 111 115 118 119 120 121 123 126 129 130 132 133 142 144 145 146 147 148 **P**8 **S** Community Health Network, Indianapolis, IN
Primary Contact: Jason Fahrlander, FACHE, President
COO: Susan Sandberg, R.N., Chief Operating Officer
CFO: Amy Campbell, Chief Financial Officer
CMO: Wesley Wong, M.D., Acting Vice President Medical and Academic Affairs
CIO: Ron Thieme, Ph.D., Chief Knowledge and Information Officer
CHR: Steve Pearcy, Director Human Resources
CNO: Cynthia D. Adams, R.N., Network Chief Nursing Officer
Web address: www.ecommunity.com/north
Control: Other not–for–profit (including NFP Corporation) **Service:** General Medical and Surgical

Staffed Beds: 363 Admissions: 16273 Census: 211 Outpatient Visits: 197030 Births: 3584 Total Expense ($000): 289126 Payroll Expense ($000): 83868 Personnel: 998

☐ **COMMUNITY HOSPITAL SOUTH (150128)**, 1402 East County Line Road South, Zip 46227–0963; tel. 317/887–7000 **A**1 9 10 **F**3 11 12 13 15 18 20 22 28 29 30 31 35 37 40 45 46 47 48 49 54 60 64 69 70 73 74 75 76 77 78 79 81 82 84 85 86 89 107 108 110 111 114 115 119 126 129 130 131 146 147 **P**8 **S** Community Health Network, Indianapolis, IN
Primary Contact: Anthony B. Lennen, President
Web address: www.ecommunity.com
Control: Other not–for–profit (including NFP Corporation) **Service:** General Medical and Surgical

Staffed Beds: 158 Admissions: 8572 Census: 84 Outpatient Visits: 129105 Births: 1492 Total Expense ($000): 155042 Payroll Expense ($000): 46701 Personnel: 668

○ **COMMUNITY WESTVIEW HOSPITAL (150129)**, 3630 Guion Road, Zip 46222–1699; tel. 317/924–6661 **A**3 5 9 10 11 12 13 **F**3 9 11 12 15 18 28 29 30 31 34 35 36 40 41 45 49 50 53 56 57 59 60 68 69 74 75 78 79 80 81 82 85 90 92 93 96 97 98 103 107 108 110 111 119 129 130 131 146 147 148 **S** Community Health Network, Indianapolis, IN
Primary Contact: David C. Williams, D.O., President and Chief Executive Officer
COO: Douglas Penley, Chief Operating Officer
CHR: Emily Rogers, Director Human Resources
CNO: Deborah Lee, Chief Nursing Officer
Web address: www.westviewhospital.org
Control: Other not–for–profit (including NFP Corporation) **Service:** General Medical and Surgical

Staffed Beds: 57 Admissions: 1490 Census: 27 Outpatient Visits: 111908 Births: 0 Total Expense ($000): 73144 Payroll Expense ($000): 34326 Personnel: 498

IN

Hospital, Medicare Provider Number, Address, Telephone, Approval, Facility, and Physician Codes, Health Care System

★ American Hospital Association (AHA) membership
☐ The Joint Commission accreditation   ◇ DNV Healthcare Inc. accreditation
○ Healthcare Facilities Accreditation Program
△ Commission on Accreditation of Rehabilitation Facilities (CARF) accreditation

☐ **ESKENAZI HEALTH (150024)**, 720 Eskenazi Avenue, Zip 46202–5166; tel. 317/880–0000 **A**1 3 5 8 9 10 **F**3 5 7 10 12 13 14 15 16 18 19 20 21 22 28 29 30 31 32 34 35 36 38 39 40 43 44 47 48 50 54 55 56 57 59 61 62 64 65 66 68 70 71 72 74 75 76 77 78 79 81 82 84 85 86 87 93 96 97 98 99 100 101 102 103 104 105 106 107 110 111 116 117 118 119 130 132 134 135 143 144 145 146 147 148
Primary Contact: Lisa E. Harris, M.D., Chief Executive Officer and Medical Director
COO: Parveen Chand, Chief Operating Officer
CFO: Dan Sellers, Chief Financial Officer
CMO: Lisa E. Harris, M.D., Chief Executive Officer
CIO: David Shaw, Vice President Information Systems
CHR: Christia Hicks, Vice President Human Resources
CNO: Lee Ann Blue, MSN, Chief Nursing Officer and Executive Vice President Patient Care Services
Web address: www.eskenazihealth.edu
Control: County–Government, nonfederal **Service:** General Medical and Surgical

Staffed Beds: 271 **Admissions:** 15437 **Census:** 203 **Outpatient Visits:** 977401 **Births:** 1849 **Personnel:** 3701

☐ **FAIRBANKS (150179)**, 8102 Clearvista Parkway, Zip 46256–4698; tel. 317/849–8222 **A**1 9 10 **F**4 5 29 30 35 36 75 87 100 105 130 132 135 146 **P**8
Primary Contact: Mark G. Monson, President and Chief Executive Officer
CFO: Barb Elliott, Chief Financial Officer
CMO: Dennis Rhyne, M.D., Acting Medical Director
CIO: Randy Walls, Manager Information Services
CHR: Sharon Baker, Director Support Services
CNO: Jennifer M. Horstman, R.N., Chief Nursing Officer and Chief Information Officer
Web address: www.fairbankscd.org
Control: Other not–for–profit (including NFP Corporation) **Service:** Alcoholism and other chemical dependency

Staffed Beds: 86 **Admissions:** 3471 **Census:** 47 **Outpatient Visits:** 27968 **Births:** 0 **Total Expense ($000):** 19431 **Payroll Expense ($000):** 10037 **Personnel:** 234

○ △ **FRANCISCAN ST. FRANCIS HEALTH – INDIANAPOLIS (150162)**, 8111 South Emerson Avenue, Zip 46237–8601; tel. 317/528–5000 **A**2 7 9 10 11 **F**8 11 12 13 15 17 18 22 24 28 29 30 31 32 34 35 36 40 41 44 48 56 57 60 61 62 63 64 65 66 68 70 72 74 75 76 77 78 79 80 81 82 84 85 86 87 89 90 93 97 107 108 109 110 111 113 115 116 117 118 119 120 121 123 124 126 129 130 131 132 135 144 146 147 148 **S** Franciscan Alliance, Mishawaka, IN
Primary Contact: Robert J. Brody, President and Chief Executive Officer
CFO: Keith A. Lauter, Regional Chief Financial Officer
CMO: Christopher Doehring, M.D., Vice President Medical Affairs
CIO: Barbara Coulter, Director Information Systems
CHR: Corey Baute, Vice President Human Resources
CNO: Susan McRoberts, R.N., Vice President and Chief Nursing Officer
Web address: www.stfrancishospitals.org
Control: Church–operated, Nongovernment, not–for profit **Service:** General Medical and Surgical

Staffed Beds: 455 **Admissions:** 18118 **Census:** 238 **Outpatient Visits:** 530225 **Births:** 2290 **Total Expense ($000):** 571743 **Payroll Expense ($000):** 189144 **Personnel:** 2721

○ **INDIANA ORTHOPAEDIC HOSPITAL (150160)**, 8400 Northwest Boulevard, Zip 46278–1381; tel. 317/956–1000, (Nonreporting) **A**9 10 11
Primary Contact: Jane Keller, R.N., Chief Executive Officer
COO: Stacie Vance, Vice President Clinical Services
CFO: Anthony Gioia, Chief Financial Officer
CMO: Joseph Randolph, M.D., Chairman Medical Executive Committee
CIO: Paul Frey, Director Information Technology Applications
CHR: Kristy Hensley, Director Human Resources
CNO: Stacie Vance, Chief Nursing Officer and Vice President Clinical Services
Web address: www.orthoindy.com
Control: Corporation, Investor–owned, for–profit **Service:** Orthopedic

Staffed Beds: 37

INDIANA UNIVERSITY HEALTH METHODIST HOSPITAL See Indiana University Health University Hospital

⊠ **INDIANA UNIVERSITY HEALTH UNIVERSITY HOSPITAL (150056)**, 550 University Boulevard, Zip 46202–5149, Mailing Address: P.O. Box 1367, Zip 46206–1367; tel. 317/944–5000, (Includes INDIANA UNIVERSITY HEALTH METHODIST HOSPITAL, 1701 North Senate Boulevard, Zip 46202, Mailing Address: 1701 North Senate Bouleverd, Zip 46202; tel. 317/962–2000; Herbert Buchanan, President; INDIANA UNIVERSITY HOSPITAL, 550 North University Boulevard, Zip 46202–5262; tel. 317/274–5000; IU HEALTH SAXONY HOSPITAL, 13000 East 136th Street, Fishers, Zip 46037–9478; tel. 317/678–2000; Jonathan R. Goble, FACHE, Chief Executive Officer; RILEY HOSPITAL FOR CHILDREN AT INDIANA UNIVERSITY HEALTH, 702 Barnhill Drive, Zip 46202–5225; tel. 317/274–5000; Jeff Sperring, M.D., President and Chief Executive Officer) **A**1 2 3 5 8 9 10 **F**3 4 5 6 7 8 9 11 12 13 15 16 17 18 19 20 21 22 23 24 25 26 27 28 29 30 31 32 33 34 35 36 37 38 39 40 41 43 44 45 46 47 48 49 50 51 52 53 54 55 56 57 58 59 60 61 62 63 64 65 68 69 70 71 72 73 74 75 76 77 78 79 81 82 83 84 85 86 87 88 89 91 92 93 94 96 97 98 99 100 101 102 103 104 105 106 107 108 109 110 111 112 113 114 115 116 117 118 119 120 121 122 123 124 126 129 130 131 132 134 135 136 137 138 139 140 141 144 145 146 147 148 **S** Indiana University Health, Indianapolis, IN
Primary Contact: Herbert Buchanan, President
COO: Dennis M. Murphy, Chief Operating Officer
CIO: Richard F. Johnson, Senior Vice President and Chief Information Officer
Web address: www.iuhealth.org
Control: Other not–for–profit (including NFP Corporation) **Service:** General Medical and Surgical

Staffed Beds: 1266 **Admissions:** 51921 **Census:** 911 **Outpatient Visits:** 1147790 **Births:** 3847 **Total Expense ($000):** 2357047 **Payroll Expense ($000):** 802389 **Personnel:** 11910

INDIANA UNIVERSITY HOSPITAL See Indiana University Health University Hospital

⊠ **KINDRED HOSPITAL–INDIANAPOLIS (152007)**, 1700 West 10th Street, Zip 46222–3802; tel. 317/636–4400, (Nonreporting) **A**1 10 **S** Kindred Healthcare, Louisville, KY
Primary Contact: Kristy Walden, R.N., Chief Executive Officer
COO: Angela Lynne Rotert, Chief Clinical Officer
CFO: William Brenner, Chief Financial Officer
CHR: Joe Housh, District Director Human Resources
Web address: www.kindredhospitalindy.com/
Control: Corporation, Investor–owned, for–profit **Service:** Long–Term Acute Care hospital

Staffed Beds: 59

☐ **LARUE D. CARTER MEMORIAL HOSPITAL (154008)**, 2601 Cold Spring Road, Zip 46222–2273; tel. 317/941–4000, (Nonreporting) **A**1 3 5 10
Primary Contact: Eric Heeter, Superintendent
CFO: Michael Logar, Assistant Superintendent
CMO: Beth Pfau, M.D., Chief Medical Officer
CIO: Denton Gross, Director Information Services
CHR: Rebecca Dutton, Director Human Resources
CNO: Todd Rittman, Director of Nursing
Control: State–Government, nonfederal **Service:** Psychiatric

Staffed Beds: 159

METHODIST HOSPITAL See Indiana University Health Methodist Hospital

☐ **OPTIONS BEHAVIORAL HEALTH SYSTEM (154057)**, 5602 Caito Drive, Zip 46226–1346; tel. 317/544–4340, (Nonreporting) **A**1 10 **S** Acadia Healthcare Company, Inc., Franklin, TN
Primary Contact: Rick Bangert, Chief Executive Officer
Web address: www.optionsbehavioralhealthsystem.com/
Control: Corporation, Investor–owned, for–profit **Service:** Psychiatric

Staffed Beds: 42

☐ △ **REHABILITATION HOSPITAL OF INDIANA (153028)**, 4141 Shore Drive, Zip 46254–2607; tel. 317/329–2000 **A**1 3 5 7 9 10 **F**28 29 30 33 54 58 64 75 79 86 87 90 91 92 93 96 130 131 132 146 148 **P**5 **S** Indiana University Health, Indianapolis, IN
Primary Contact: Daniel B. Woloszyn, Chief Executive Officer
COO: Monte Spence, Chief Operating Officer
CFO: Marjorie Basey, Chief Financial Officer
CMO: Flora Hammond, M.D., Chief Medical Affairs
CIO: Gary Skinner, Director Information Technology
CHR: Joni Brown, Director Human Resources
CNO: Debra Cordes, Chief Nursing Officer
Web address: www.rhin.com
Control: Other not–for–profit (including NFP Corporation) **Service:** Rehabilitation

Staffed Beds: 91 **Admissions:** 1344 **Census:** 60 **Outpatient Visits:** 20498 **Births:** 0 **Total Expense ($000):** 38494 **Payroll Expense ($000):** 19334 **Personnel:** 349

IN

Many Facility Codes have changed. Please refer to the AHA Guide Code Chart.   © 2014 AHA Guide

☒ △ **RICHARD L. ROUDEBUSH VETERANS AFFAIRS MEDICAL CENTER**, 1481 West Tenth Street, Zip 46202–2884; tel. 317/554–0000 **A**1 2 3 5 7 8 **F**3 5 18 20 22 24 26 28 29 30 31 33 34 35 36 38 39 40 45 46 49 50 53 54 56 57 58 59 60 61 62 63 64 65 67 70 74 75 77 78 79 80 81 82 83 84 85 86 87 90 91 92 93 94 97 98 100 101 102 103 104 105 107 111 115 117 119 120 121 126 127 129 130 132 135 143 144 146 147 148 **S** Department of Veterans Affairs, Washington, DC
Primary Contact: Thomas Mattice, Director
COO: Jeff Nechanicky, Assistant Director
CFO: Paul Pessagno, Chief Financial Officer
CMO: Ken Klotz, M.D., Chief of Staff
CIO: Steve Stoner, Chief Information Officer
Web address: www.indianapolis.va.gov
Control: Veterans Affairs, Government, federal **Service:** General Medical and Surgical

Staffed Beds: 209 Admissions: 7767 Census: 168 Outpatient Visits: 657637 Births: 0 Total Expense ($000): 442789 Payroll Expense ($000): 200535 Personnel: 2883

RILEY HOSPITAL FOR CHILDREN See Riley Hospital for Children at Indiana University Health

RILEY HOSPITAL FOR CHILDREN AT INDIANA UNIVERSITY HEALTH See Indiana University Health University Hospital

☒ **SELECT SPECIALTY HOSPITAL–INDIANAPOLIS (152013)**, 8060 Knue Road, Zip 46250–1976; tel. 317/783–8985, (Nonreporting) **A**1 10 **S** Select Medical Corporation, Mechanicsburg, PA
Primary Contact: Cheryl G. Gentry, Chief Executive Officer
CHR: Kelly Becker, Administrative Coordinator Human Resources
Web address: www.selectspecialtyhospitals.com/company/locations/indianapolis.aspx
Control: Corporation, Investor–owned, for–profit **Service:** Long–Term Acute Care hospital

Staffed Beds: 45

ST. FRANCIS HOSPITAL AND HEALTH CENTERS – SOUTH CAMPUS See Franciscan St. Francis Health – Indianapolis

★ **ST. VINCENT HEART CENTER (150153)**, 10580 North Meridian Street, Zip 46290–1028; tel. 317/583–5000 **A**9 10 **F**3 18 20 22 24 26 28 29 30 34 35 40 45 46 58 59 75 81 85 86 87 107 111 115 119 129 130 135 148 **P**2 **S** Ascension Health, Saint Louis, MO
Primary Contact: Blake A. Dye, President
COO: Mike Schroyer, Chief Operating Officer
CFO: Becky Jacobson, Vice President Finance
CMO: William Storer, M.D., Medical Director
CIO: Roger Strange, Chief Information Officer
Web address: www.bestheartcare.com/
Control: Partnership, Investor–owned, for–profit **Service:** Heart

Staffed Beds: 107 Admissions: 5210 Census: 58 Outpatient Visits: 10966 Births: 0 Total Expense ($000): 108594 Payroll Expense ($000): 31884 Personnel: 290

☒ **ST. VINCENT INDIANAPOLIS HOSPITAL (150084)**, 2001 West 86th Street, Zip 46260–1991, Mailing Address: P.O. Box 40970, Zip 46240–0970; tel. 317/338–2345, (Includes PEYTON MANNING CHILDREN'S HOSPITAL, 1707 West 86th Street, Zip 46240, Mailing Address: P.O. Box 40407, Zip 46240; tel. 317/415–5500; Anne Coleman, Administrator; PEYTON MANNING CHILDREN'S HOSPITAL AT ST. VINCENT, 2001 West 86th Street, Zip 46260, Mailing Address: P.O. Box 40970, Zip 46240–0970; tel. 317/415–8111; Anne Coleman, Administrator; ST. VINCENT STRESS CENTER, 8401 Harcourt Road, Zip 46260, Mailing Address: P.O. Box 80160, Zip 46280; tel. 317/338–4600; Sheila Mishler, Chief Executive Officer; ST. VINCENT WOMEN'S HOSPITAL, 8111 Township Line Road, Zip 46260–8043; tel. 317/415–8111; Anne Coleman, Administrator) **A**1 2 3 5 8 9 10 **F**2 3 4 5 7 9 11 13 15 17 18 19 20 21 22 23 24 25 26 27 28 29 30 31 32 34 35 37 38 39 40 41 42 43 44 45 46 47 48 49 50 51 53 54 55 56 57 58 59 64 65 66 68 70 71 72 73 74 75 76 78 79 81 82 83 84 85 86 87 88 89 90 91 92 93 94 96 97 98 99 100 101 102 103 104 105 106 107 108 110 111 114 115 116 117 118 119 120 121 123 124 126 129 130 131 132 134 135 137 138 142 143 144 146 147 148 **P**6 **S** Ascension Health, Saint Louis, MO
Primary Contact: Kyle De Fur, FACHE, President
COO: Darcy Burthay, MSN, Chief Nursing Officer and Chief Operating Officer
CFO: Thomas M. Cook, CPA, Chief Financial Officer
CMO: Daniel LeGrand, M.D., Chief Medical Officer
CIO: Brian Peters, Chief Information Officer
CHR: Marty Du Rall, Executive Director Human Resources
CNO: Mary Myers, R.N., Chief Nursing Officer
Web address: www.stvincent.org
Control: Church–operated, Nongovernment, not–for profit **Service:** General Medical and Surgical

Staffed Beds: 921 Admissions: 36352 Census: 569 Outpatient Visits: 944251 Births: 3700 Total Expense ($000): 1047192 Payroll Expense ($000): 384645 Personnel: 4669

☒ **ST. VINCENT SETON SPECIALTY HOSPITAL (152020)**, 8050 Township Line Road, Zip 46260–2478; tel. 317/415–8353 **A**1 9 10 **F**1 29 30 31 35 60 68 75 85 107 114 119 130 148 **P**8 **S** Ascension Health, Saint Louis, MO
Primary Contact: Peter H. Alexander, Administrator
COO: Troy T. Reiff, Corporate Director Operations
CFO: David M. Girten, Corporate Director Financial Services
CMO: Ronald Reisman, M.D., Chief Medical Director
CHR: Terry A. Wignall, Director Human Resources
Web address: www.stvincent.org/
Control: Other not–for–profit (including NFP Corporation) **Service:** Long–Term Acute Care hospital

Staffed Beds: 74 Admissions: 651 Census: 61 Outpatient Visits: 0 Births: 0 Total Expense ($000): 38455 Payroll Expense ($000): 17620 Personnel: 221

WESTVIEW HOSPITAL See Community Westview Hospital

JASPER—Dubois County

☒ **MEMORIAL HOSPITAL AND HEALTH CARE CENTER (150115)**, 800 West Ninth Street, Zip 47546–2516; tel. 812/996–2345, (Total facility includes 20 beds in nursing home–type unit) **A**1 2 9 10 19 **F**3 5 7 8 11 12 13 15 18 20 22 24 26 28 29 30 31 34 35 36 38 40 45 46 47 48 49 51 54 56 57 59 62 64 66 68 70 74 75 76 77 78 79 81 82 84 85 86 87 89 90 93 97 98 100 101 102 103 104 105 107 108 110 111 112 113 114 115 116 117 118 119 120 121 127 128 129 130 131 132 135 143 144 146 147 148 **P**6 **S** American Province of Little Company of Mary Sisters, Evergreen Park, IL
Primary Contact: Raymond W. Snowden, President and Chief Executive Officer
COO: E. Kyle Bennett, Executive Vice President and Chief Operating Officer
CFO: Randall Russell, Vice President and Chief Financial Officer
CMO: Ryan Sherer, M.D., President Medical Staff
CIO: Gary Light, Vice President and Chief Information Officer
CHR: Richard Pea, Director Human Resources
CNO: Tonya Heim, R.N., Vice President Patient Services and Chief Nursing Officer
Web address: www.mhhcc.org
Control: Church–operated, Nongovernment, not–for profit **Service:** General Medical and Surgical

Staffed Beds: 143 Admissions: 5997 Census: 68 Outpatient Visits: 245221 Births: 969 Total Expense ($000): 165774 Payroll Expense ($000): 70354 Personnel: 1188

JEFFERSONVILLE—Clark County

☒ **CLARK MEMORIAL HOSPITAL (150009)**, 1220 Missouri Avenue, Zip 47130–3743, Mailing Address: P.O. Box 69, Zip 47131–0600; tel. 812/282–6631 **A**1 2 3 5 9 10 **F**3 5 11 12 13 15 17 18 20 22 26 28 29 30 31 34 35 38 40 45 46 49 50 53 54 56 57 59 64 65 70 74 75 76 77 78 79 81 82 85 86 87 91 92 97 98 100 101 102 103 104 105 107 108 110 111 114 115 119 124 130 132 135 144 145 146 147 148 **P**6
Primary Contact: Martin Padgett, President and Chief Executive Officer
CFO: Kirk Strack, Vice President and Chief Financial Officer
CMO: William Templeton, III, M.D., Medical Director
CIO: Larry Reverman, Director Information Systems
CHR: Scott Hicks, Vice President
CNO: Kathy Neuner, R.N., Chief Nursing Officer
Web address: www.clarkmemorial.org
Control: County–Government, nonfederal **Service:** General Medical and Surgical

Staffed Beds: 183 Admissions: 13399 Census: 155 Outpatient Visits: 161069 Births: 1514 Total Expense ($000): 143127 Payroll Expense ($000): 72086 Personnel: 1415

☐ **WELLSTONE REGIONAL HOSPITAL (154051)**, 2700 Vissing Park Road, Zip 47130–5989; tel. 812/284–8000 **A**1 9 10 **F**4 5 29 33 34 56 59 71 75 87 98 99 101 103 104 105 130 132 **P**5 **S** Universal Health Services, Inc., King of Prussia, PA
Primary Contact: Greg Stewart, Chief Executive Officer
CFO: Gracia Winsett, Chief Financial Officer
CMO: Asad Ismail, M.D., Medical Director
CIO: Vickie Sommers, Director Business Office
CHR: Tiffany Smith, Director Human Resources
CNO: Sandy Smithers, Director of Nursing
Web address: www.wellstonehospital.com
Control: Corporation, Investor–owned, for–profit **Service:** Psychiatric

Staffed Beds: 100 Admissions: 2852 Census: 68 Outpatient Visits: 7075 Births: 0 Total Expense ($000): 12425 Payroll Expense ($000): 7921 Personnel: 175

IN

Hospital, Medicare Provider Number, Address, Telephone, Approval, Facility, and Physician Codes, Health Care System

★ American Hospital Association (AHA) membership
☐ The Joint Commission accreditation   ◇ DNV Healthcare Inc. accreditation
○ Healthcare Facilities Accreditation Program
△ Commission on Accreditation of Rehabilitation Facilities (CARF) accreditation

KENDALLVILLE—Noble County

✠ **PARKVIEW NOBLE HOSPITAL (150146)**, 401 Sawyer Road, Zip 46755–2568; tel. 260/347–8700 **A**1 9 10 **F**3 7 11 13 15 28 29 34 35 40 45 46 47 50 54 57 59 64 70 74 75 76 79 81 82 85 87 93 94 97 107 108 110 111 114 118 119 129 130 132 135 143 145 146 **S** Parkview Health, Fort Wayne, IN
Primary Contact: Gary W. Adkins, Chief Executive Officer
COO: Gary W. Adkins, Chief Executive Officer
CFO: Michael P. Browning, Chief Financial Officer
CMO: Gerald Warrener, M.D., Chief Medical Officer
CIO: Ron Double, Chief Information Officer
CHR: Bruce Buttermore, Manager Human Resources
CNO: Catherine Byrd, Vice President Patient Services
Web address: www.parkview.com
Control: Other not–for–profit (including NFP Corporation) **Service:** General Medical and Surgical

Staffed Beds: 31 **Admissions:** 1745 **Census:** 16 **Outpatient Visits:** 53077 **Births:** 285 **Total Expense ($000):** 41243 **Payroll Expense ($000):** 12565 **Personnel:** 224

KNOX—Starke County

✠ **INDIANA UNIVERSITY HEALTH STARKE HOSPITAL (150102)**, 102 East Culver Road, Zip 46534–2216, Mailing Address: P.O. Box 339, Zip 46534–0339; tel. 574/772–6231 **A**1 9 10 **F**3 15 18 28 29 30 32 34 35 38 40 45 46 47 49 50 53 57 59 65 68 74 75 77 79 81 85 87 93 94 107 108 110 111 114 115 116 117 119 130 132 133 135 146 148 **S** Indiana University Health, Indianapolis, IN
Primary Contact: Craig Felty, President
CFO: Rosemarie Heise, Vice President Finance
CMO: A. N. Damodaran, M.D., President Medical Staff
CIO: Ashley Norem, Chief Information Systems
CHR: Doug Jesch, Director Human Resources
Web address: www.iuhealth.org/starke/
Control: Other not–for–profit (including NFP Corporation) **Service:** General Medical and Surgical

Staffed Beds: 15 **Admissions:** 1018 **Census:** 9 **Outpatient Visits:** 29466 **Births:** 0 **Total Expense ($000):** 18877 **Payroll Expense ($000):** 6940 **Personnel:** 137

STARKE MEMORIAL HOSPITAL See Indiana University Health Starke Hospital

KOKOMO—Howard County

✠ **COMMUNITY HOWARD REGIONAL HEALTH (150007)**, 3500 South Lafountain Street, Zip 46902–3803, Mailing Address: P.O. Box 9011, Zip 46904–9011; tel. 765/453–0702 **A**1 2 9 10 **F**3 7 8 13 15 17 18 20 22 24 26 28 29 30 31 32 34 35 38 40 45 46 50 53 57 58 59 60 65 66 68 70 71 72 74 75 77 78 79 81 82 85 87 90 96 97 98 99 100 101 102 103 104 105 106 107 108 109 111 115 116 117 119 120 121 123 129 130 131 132 134 135 143 145 146 147 148 **S** Community Health Network, Indianapolis, IN
Primary Contact: Ron Lewis, President and Chief Executive Officer
COO: Theodore Brown, Chief Operating Officer
CFO: Theodore Brown, Vice President Financial Services
CIO: Kevin Purvis, Chief Information Officer
CHR: Michael L. Williams, FACHE, Vice President Human Resources
CNO: Melodi Greene, R.N., Chief Nursing Officer
Web address: www.howardregional.org
Control: Other not–for–profit (including NFP Corporation) **Service:** General Medical and Surgical

Staffed Beds: 168 **Admissions:** 4788 **Census:** 47 **Outpatient Visits:** 230527 **Births:** 430 **Total Expense ($000):** 136219 **Payroll Expense ($000):** 57116 **Personnel:** 861

✠ **COMMUNITY HOWARD SPECIALTY HOSPITAL (153039)**, 829 North Dixon Road, Zip 46901–7709; tel. 765/452–6700 **A**1 9 10 **F**28 29 30 34 53 54 57 64 68 71 77 90 91 93 94 99 129 131 132 **S** Community Health Network, Indianapolis, IN
Primary Contact: Michelle L. Russell, Administrator
CFO: Julie Pena, Director Finance
CMO: Brad Vossberg, M.D., Chief Rehabilitation
CNO: Claudia Jean Lowry, R.N., Director of Nursing
Web address: www.communityhoward.org
Control: Partnership, Investor–owned, for–profit **Service:** Rehabilitation

Staffed Beds: 30 **Admissions:** 568 **Census:** 16 **Outpatient Visits:** 30712 **Births:** 0 **Total Expense ($000):** 12845 **Payroll Expense ($000):** 7207 **Personnel:** 140

HOWARD REGIONAL HEALTH SYSTEM See Community Howard Regional Health

HOWARD REGIONAL HEALTH SYSTEM WEST CAMPUS SPECIALTY HOSPITAL See Community Howard Specialty Hospital

✠ **ST. JOSEPH HOSPITAL & HEALTH CENTER (150010)**, 1907 West Sycamore Street, Zip 46901–4197; tel. 765/452–5611 **A**1 9 10 **F**3 4 5 7 8 13 15 18 20 28 29 30 31 34 35 36 40 44 45 49 50 51 53 55 57 59 64 66 68 69 70 73 74 75 76 77 78 79 81 84 85 86 87 89 90 93 96 98 99 100 101 102 103 104 105 107 108 110 111 115 119 120 121 123 129 130 131 132 135 143 144 145 146 147 **P**6 **S** Ascension Health, Saint Louis, MO
Primary Contact: Kathlene A. Young, MS, FACHE, President and Chief Executive Officer
CFO: Dennis Ressler, Chief Financial Officer
CMO: David L. Williams, M.D., Chief Medical Officer
CIO: Jeffrey Scott, Chief Information Officer
CHR: Cindy Babb, Executive Director Human Resources and Organizational Effectiveness
CNO: Kathleen K. Peoples, R.N., Vice President and Nursing
Web address: www.stvincent.org/stjoseph
Control: Church–operated, Nongovernment, not–for profit **Service:** General Medical and Surgical

Staffed Beds: 137 **Admissions:** 5530 **Census:** 68 **Outpatient Visits:** 169140 **Births:** 825 **Total Expense ($000):** 109339 **Payroll Expense ($000):** 39713 **Personnel:** 691

LA PORTE—Laporte County

✠ **INDIANA UNIVERSITY HEALTH LA PORTE HOSPITAL (150006)**, 1007 Lincolnway, Zip 46350–3201, Mailing Address: P.O. Box 250, Zip 46352–0250; tel. 219/326–1234, (Total facility includes 55 beds in nursing home–type unit) **A**1 2 5 9 10 19 **F**3 8 11 13 15 17 18 20 22 24 26 28 29 30 31 32 34 35 36 38 39 40 45 46 49 50 51 53 54 56 57 58 59 62 63 64 65 66 67 68 70 71 74 75 76 77 79 81 82 84 85 86 87 89 90 93 96 98 100 101 102 103 107 108 110 111 114 115 118 119 126 128 129 130 131 132 135 144 145 146 147 148 **S** Indiana University Health, Indianapolis, IN
Primary Contact: G. Thor Thordarson, President and Chief Executive Officer
COO: Camie Patterson, Chief Operating Officer and Chief Financial Officer
CFO: Camie Patterson, Chief Operating Officer and Chief Financial Officer
CMO: William J. Houston, M.D., Chief Medical Officer
CIO: Earl Adams, Chief Information Officer
CNO: Pauline Arnold, MSN, Chief Nursing and Quality Officer and Vice President Clinical Operations
Web address: www.iuhealth.org
Control: Other not–for–profit (including NFP Corporation) **Service:** General Medical and Surgical

Staffed Beds: 204 **Admissions:** 6122 **Census:** 107 **Outpatient Visits:** 117013 **Births:** 656 **Total Expense ($000):** 160028 **Payroll Expense ($000):** 63278 **Personnel:** 1382

LA PORTE REGIONAL HEALTH SYSTEM See Indiana University Health La Porte Hospital

LAFAYETTE—Tippecanoe County

CLARIAN ARNETT HOSPITAL See Indiana University Health Arnett Hospital

○ **FRANCISCAN ST. ELIZABETH HEALTH – LAFAYETTE CENTRAL (150003)**, 1501 Hartford Street, Zip 47904–2134; tel. 765/423–6011, (Includes LAFAYETTE HOME HOSPITAL, 2400 South Street, Zip 47904–3052; tel. 765/447–6811; ST. ELIZABETH MEDICAL CENTER, 1501 Hartford Street, Zip 47904–2126; tel. 765/423–6011) **A**2 5 6 9 10 11 **F**3 15 28 29 30 31 35 40 63 68 70 74 75 77 78 84 85 94 107 108 110 111 115 119 124 129 130 146 148 **S** Franciscan Alliance, Mishawaka, IN
Primary Contact: Terrance E. Wilson, President and CEO
CFO: Jason Geddes, Chief Financial Officer
CMO: Donald B. Edelen, M.D., Vice President Medical Services and Quality Initiatives
CIO: Lisa K. Decker, Vice President Marketing
CHR: Michelle Duffy, Director Human Resources
Web address: www.ste.org
Control: Church–operated, Nongovernment, not–for profit **Service:** General Medical and Surgical

Staffed Beds: 65 **Admissions:** 3458 **Census:** 42 **Outpatient Visits:** 42186 **Births:** 0 **Total Expense ($000):** 76214 **Payroll Expense ($000):** 30651

○ **FRANCISCAN ST. ELIZABETH HEALTH – LAFAYETTE EAST (150109)**, 1701 South Creasy Lane, Zip 47905–4972; tel. 765/502–4000 **A**10 11 **F**3 11 13 17 18 20 22 24 26 29 30 31 34 35 40 45 46 47 51 62 64 68 70 72 73 74 75 76 77 81 84 85 90 98 107 108 109 110 111 115 118 119 120 121 123 124 126 130 135 146 147 **S** Franciscan Alliance, Mishawaka, IN
Primary Contact: Terrance E. Wilson, President and CEO
Web address: www.ste.org
Control: Church–operated, Nongovernment, not–for profit **Service:** General Medical and Surgical

Staffed Beds: 182 **Admissions:** 7638 **Census:** 79 **Outpatient Visits:** 168744 **Births:** 1961 **Total Expense ($000):** 211385 **Payroll Expense ($000):** 56923

Many Facility Codes have changed. Please refer to the AHA Guide Code Chart. © 2014 AHA Guide

IN

★ ○ **INDIANA UNIVERSITY HEALTH ARNETT HOSPITAL (150173)**, 5165 McCarty Lane, Zip 47905–8764, Mailing Address: P.O. Box 5545, Zip 47903–5545; tel. 765/448–8000 **A**3 5 9 10 11 **F**3 11 12 13 15 18 20 22 24 26 28 29 30 31 34 35 40 45 46 49 50 51 54 57 59 60 64 65 68 69 70 72 74 75 76 77 78 79 80 81 82 85 87 89 93 97 99 107 108 110 111 114 115 116 117 118 119 120 121 126 129 130 131 144 146 147 148 **P**6 **S** Indiana University Health, Indianapolis, IN
Primary Contact: Alfonso W. Gatmaitan, Chief Executive Officer
COO: Brian T. Shockney, FACHE, Chief Operating Officer
CFO: Cara Breidster, Chief Financial Officer
CMO: Jim Bien, M.D., Vice President Quality and Patient Safety
CIO: Rusty McGill, System Director Information Technology
CHR: Koreen H. Kyhnell, Vice President Human Resources
Web address: www.iuhealth.org
Control: Other not–for–profit (including NFP Corporation) **Service:** General Medical and Surgical

Staffed Beds: 201 **Admissions:** 8697 **Census:** 107 **Outpatient Visits:** 76641 **Births:** 1312 **Total Expense ($000):** 347370 **Payroll Expense ($000):** 151565 **Personnel:** 1795

☐ **LAFAYETTE REGIONAL REHABILITATION HOSPITAL (153042)**, 950 Park East Boulevard, Zip 47905–0792; tel. 765/447–4040, (Data for 306 days) **A**1 10 **F**3 29 54 64 75 90 93 130 132 143 148 **P**5 8 **S** Ernest Health, Inc., Albuquerque, NM
Primary Contact: Dennis Schnepp, Chief Executive Officer
Web address: www.lrrh.ernesthealth.com
Control: Corporation, Investor–owned, for–profit **Service:** Rehabilitation

Staffed Beds: 40 **Admissions:** 370 **Census:** 16 **Outpatient Visits:** 257 **Births:** 0 **Total Expense ($000):** 9177 **Payroll Expense ($000):** 3974 **Personnel:** 47

ST. ELIZABETH CENTRAL See Franciscan St. Elizabeth Health – Lafayette Central

☒ **ST. VINCENT SETON SPECIALTY HOSPITAL (152021)**, 1501 Hartford Street, Zip 47904–2134; tel. 765/236–8900 **A**1 10 **F**1 29 30 31 35 60 78 130 **P**8 **S** Ascension Health, Saint Louis, MO
Primary Contact: Peter H. Alexander, Administrator
COO: Troy T. Reiff, Corporate Director Operations
CFO: David M. Girten, Corporate Director Financial Services
CMO: Ronald Reisman, M.D., rireisma@stvincent.org
CHR: Terry A. Wignall, Director Human Resources
Web address: www.stvincent.org
Control: Other not–for–profit (including NFP Corporation) **Service:** Long–Term Acute Care hospital

Staffed Beds: 30 **Admissions:** 212 **Census:** 18 **Outpatient Visits:** 0 **Births:** 0 **Total Expense ($000):** 11556 **Payroll Expense ($000):** 5037 **Personnel:** 40

☐ **SYCAMORE SPRINGS HOSPITAL (154059)**, 833 Park East Boulevard, Zip 47905–0785; tel. 765/743–4400 **A**1 9 10 **F**4 5 98 102 103 104 105
Primary Contact: David Fletcher–Janzen, Chief Executive Officer
CFO: Michael Huth, Chief Financial Officer
CMO: Nizar El Khalili, M.D., Medical Director
CHR: Pam Sichts, Director Human Resources
CNO: Brooke Lavignette, Director of Nursing
Web address: www.sycamorespringshealth.com
Control: Corporation, Investor–owned, for–profit **Service:** Psychiatric

Staffed Beds: 48 **Admissions:** 1106 **Census:** 28 **Outpatient Visits:** 12615 **Births:** 0 **Total Expense ($000):** 8393 **Payroll Expense ($000):** 4204 **Personnel:** 130

LAGRANGE—Lagrange County

☒ **PARKVIEW LAGRANGE HOSPITAL (151323)**, 207 North Townline Road, Zip 46761–1325; tel. 260/463–2143 **A**1 9 10 18 **F**3 7 13 15 17 26 29 30 34 35 40 45 50 51 57 59 63 64 70 75 76 79 81 82 83 84 85 86 87 89 90 93 96 107 108 109 110 111 114 118 119 128 129 130 132 133 143 146 148 **S** Parkview Health, Fort Wayne, IN
Primary Contact: Robert T. Myers, President
CFO: Vickie Stanski, Financial Manager
CMO: Jeffrey Brookes, M.D., Chief Medical Officer
CIO: Ron Double, Chief Information Technology Officer
CHR: Bruce Buttermore, Director Human Resources
Web address: www.parkview.com
Control: Other not–for–profit (including NFP Corporation) **Service:** General Medical and Surgical

Staffed Beds: 25 **Admissions:** 900 **Census:** 10 **Outpatient Visits:** 21843 **Births:** 338 **Total Expense ($000):** 27037 **Payroll Expense ($000):** 8196 **Personnel:** 134

LAWRENCEBURG—Dearborn County

COMMUNITY MENTAL HEALTH CENTER (154011), 285 Bielby Road, Zip 47025–1055; tel. 812/537–1302, (Nonreporting) **A**9 10
Primary Contact: Tom Talbot, Chief Executive Officer
CFO: Georgii Zhirkin, Chief Financial Officer
CMO: Hasan Bakhtier, M.D., Medical Director
CIO: Skip Hudson, Manager Information Technology
CHR: Kelly Stewart, Director of Human Resources
Web address: www.cmhcinc.org
Control: Other not–for–profit (including NFP Corporation) **Service:** Psychiatric

Staffed Beds: 16

★ ○ **DEARBORN COUNTY HOSPITAL (150086)**, 600 Wilson Creek Road, Zip 47025–2751; tel. 812/537–1010 **A**9 10 11 **F**3 11 13 15 20 28 30 34 35 37 40 43 44 45 46 47 49 50 57 59 62 63 64 70 75 76 77 79 81 84 85 86 87 92 93 107 108 110 111 114 116 117 118 119 129 130 131 132 146 148 **P**7
Primary Contact: Roger Howard, President and Chief Executive Officer
CFO: Philip A. Meyer, Vice President, Finance
CHR: Claudia Richardt, Vice President, Human Resources, Community Relations and Marketing
CNO: Angela Scudder, R.N., Vice President Patient Care Services
Web address: www.dch.org
Control: County–Government, nonfederal **Service:** General Medical and Surgical

Staffed Beds: 78 **Admissions:** 4141 **Census:** 44 **Outpatient Visits:** 136787 **Births:** 436 **Total Expense ($000):** 75637 **Payroll Expense ($000):** 31144 **Personnel:** 636

LEBANON—Boone County

☒ **WITHAM MEMORIAL HOSPITAL (150104)**, 2605 North Lebanon Street, Zip 46052–1476, Mailing Address: P.O. Box 1200, Zip 46052–3005; tel. 765/485–8000 **A**1 9 10 **F**3 7 8 13 15 18 20 22 28 29 30 31 34 40 42 45 50 54 56 57 59 60 64 65 68 69 70 75 76 77 79 81 82 83 85 86 87 93 94 97 98 103 107 108 110 111 115 117 118 119 129 130 132 135 141 146 147 148 **P**1
Primary Contact: Raymond V. Ingham, Ph.D., President and Chief Executive Officer
COO: Diane Feder, MSN, Senior Vice President and Chief Operating Officer
CFO: George Pogas, CPA, Senior Vice President and Chief Financial Officer
CMO: Anthony Steele, M.D., Chief Medical Officer
CIO: George Pogas, CPA, Senior Vice President and Chief Financial Officer
CHR: Gary A. Deater, Vice President Administration, Human Resources and Risk Management
CNO: Diane Feder, MSN, Senior Vice President and Chief Operating Officer
Web address: www.witham.org
Control: County–Government, nonfederal **Service:** General Medical and Surgical

Staffed Beds: 52 **Admissions:** 2363 **Census:** 24 **Outpatient Visits:** 125118 **Births:** 450 **Total Expense ($000):** 93437 **Payroll Expense ($000):** 39244 **Personnel:** 585

LINTON—Greene County

☒ **GREENE COUNTY GENERAL HOSPITAL (151317)**, 1185 North 1000 W., Zip 47441–5282; tel. 812/847–2281 **A**1 9 10 18 **F**3 11 13 15 18 30 31 34 35 45 57 59 62 64 65 70 75 76 77 78 79 81 85 86 90 91 93 107 108 110 114 119 130 133 135 146 147 148 **P**6
Primary Contact: Brenda Reetz, R.N., Chief Executive Officer
CFO: April Settles, Chief Financial Officer
CMO: Frederick R. Ridge, Chief of Staff
CIO: Steve Phillips, Information Officer
CNO: Lea Ann Camp, MSN, Chief Nursing Officer
Web address: www.greenecountyhospital.com
Control: County–Government, nonfederal **Service:** General Medical and Surgical

Staffed Beds: 25 **Admissions:** 1108 **Census:** 10 **Outpatient Visits:** 9509 **Births:** 65 **Total Expense ($000):** 29189 **Payroll Expense ($000):** 12083 **Personnel:** 220

LOGANSPORT—Cass County

FOUR COUNTY COUNSELING CENTER (154035), 1015 Michigan Avenue, Zip 46947–1526; tel. 574/722–5151, (Nonreporting) **A**9 10
Primary Contact: C.J. Davis, Chief Executive Officer/ Executive Director
COO: Carrie Cadwell, M.D., Chief Clinical Officer
CFO: Jason Cadwell, Chief Financial Officer
CMO: John Yarling, M.D., Medical Director
CIO: Becky Mulis, Director of Health Information Management Systems
CHR: Steve Curry, Regional Director Human Resources
CNO: Donna Henry, Vice President of Nursing Services
Web address: www.fourcounty.org
Control: Other not–for–profit (including NFP Corporation) **Service:** Psychiatric

Staffed Beds: 15

IN

★ ○ **LOGANSPORT MEMORIAL HOSPITAL (150072)**, 1101 Michigan Avenue, Zip 46947–1528, Mailing Address: P.O. Box 7013, Zip 46947–7013; tel. 574/753–7541 **A**9 10 11 20 **F**3 11 13 15 18 28 29 32 34 35 36 40 44 45 48 49 51 57 59 64 65 68 69 70 75 76 77 78 79 81 85 86 87 93 97 107 108 110 111 114 119 124 129 130 132 133 135 146 147 **P**6
Primary Contact: David J. Berndt, President and Chief Executive Officer
CFO: Julia L. Berndt, Chief Financial Officer
CMO: Charles Montgomery, M.D., Medical Director
CIO: Beth Jump, Chief Information Officer
CHR: Lynda J. Murphy, Vice President Human Resources
Web address: www.logansportmemorial.org
Control: County–Government, nonfederal **Service:** General Medical and Surgical

Staffed Beds: 83 **Admissions:** 1703 **Census:** 15 **Outpatient Visits:** 95707 **Births:** 443 **Total Expense ($000):** 56742 **Payroll Expense ($000):** 26357 **Personnel:** 501

☐ **LOGANSPORT STATE HOSPITAL**, 1098 South State Road 25, Zip 46947–6723; tel. 574/737–3633, (Nonreporting) **A**1
Primary Contact: Robert Clover, Superintendent and Chief Executive Officer
CFO: Misty Moss, Director Business Administration
CMO: Danny Meadows, M.D., Medical Director
CIO: Joe McIntosh, Director Management Information Systems
CHR: Dianne Renner, Director Human Resources
Web address: www.lshonline.org
Control: State–Government, nonfederal **Service:** Psychiatric

Staffed Beds: 396

MADISON—Jefferson County

★ ○ **KING'S DAUGHTERS' HEALTH (150069)**, One Bethany Drive, Zip 47250–3357, Mailing Address: P.O. Box 447, Zip 47250–0447; tel. 812/801–0800 **A**2 9 10 11 19 20 **F**3 7 8 13 15 18 20 22 28 29 30 31 32 34 35 40 42 45 48 49 50 56 57 59 62 63 64 65 68 70 74 75 76 77 78 79 81 82 84 85 86 91 93 94 97 107 108 110 111 115 119 120 121 123 129 130 131 132 134 135 144 145 146 147 148 **P**6
Primary Contact: Carol Dozier, President and Chief Executive Officer
CFO: Steve Meacham, Vice President Finance
CIO: Linda Darnell, Director Management Information Systems
CHR: Susan Poling, Director Human Resources
CNO: Lisa Morgan, R.N., Vice President Patient Services
Web address: www.kdhhs.org
Control: Other not–for–profit (including NFP Corporation) **Service:** General Medical and Surgical

Staffed Beds: 77 **Admissions:** 3651 **Census:** 39 **Outpatient Visits:** 198521 **Births:** 428 **Total Expense ($000):** 117447 **Payroll Expense ($000):** 53274 **Personnel:** 822

☐ **MADISON STATE HOSPITAL (154019)**, 711 Green Road, Zip 47250–2199; tel. 812/265–2611, (Nonreporting) **A**1 10
Primary Contact: Peggy Stephens, M.D., Superintendent and Medical Director
COO: Peggy Stephens, M.D., Superintendent and Medical Director
CFO: Carolyn Copeland, Business Administrator
CMO: Peggy Stephens, M.D., Superintendent and Medical Director
CIO: Ric Martin, Information Specialist
Web address: www.in.gov/fssa/msh
Control: State–Government, nonfederal **Service:** Psychiatric

Staffed Beds: 150

MARION—Grant County

☐ **GRANT–BLACKFORD MENTAL HEALTH CENTER (154021)**, 505 North Wabash Avenue, Zip 46952–2608; tel. 765/662–3971 **A**1 9 10 **F**4 5 34 35 38 50 54 56 57 64 66 86 87 98 99 100 101 102 103 104 105 106 130 132 134 135 143 146
Primary Contact: Paul Kuczora, Chief Executive Officer
Web address: www.cornerstone.org/
Control: Other not–for–profit (including NFP Corporation) **Service:** Psychiatric

Staffed Beds: 16 **Admissions:** 450 **Census:** 6 **Outpatient Visits:** 48785 **Births:** 0 **Total Expense ($000):** 8879 **Payroll Expense ($000):** 5284 **Personnel:** 150

★ ○ **MARION GENERAL HOSPITAL (150011)**, 441 North Wabash Avenue, Zip 46952–2690; tel. 765/660–6000 **A**2 9 10 11 19 20 **F**3 7 8 11 13 15 18 20 22 26 28 29 30 31 34 35 40 41 44 45 50 54 57 58 59 64 66 68 70 74 76 77 78 79 81 82 84 85 86 87 89 90 91 92 93 96 97 107 108 110 111 112 114 115 116 117 118 119 129 130 132 135 145 146 147 148 **P**6
Primary Contact: Paul L. Usher, President and Chief Executive Officer
COO: Bernadine L. Wallace, MSN, Chief Nursing Officer and Chief Operating Officer
CFO: Robyn L. Powell, Chief Financial Officer
CMO: Edward L. Keppler, M.D., Chief Medical Officer
CIO: Emmanuel Ndow, Chief Information Officer
CHR: Karen Jones, Administrative Director Human Resources
Web address: www.mgh.net
Control: Other not–for–profit (including NFP Corporation) **Service:** General Medical and Surgical

Staffed Beds: 115 **Admissions:** 5607 **Census:** 60 **Outpatient Visits:** 224071 **Births:** 749 **Total Expense ($000):** 148876 **Payroll Expense ($000):** 48331 **Personnel:** 1011

VETERANS AFFAIRS NORTHERN INDIANA HEALTH CARE SYSTEM–MARION CAMPUS See Veterans Affairs Northern Indiana Health Care System, Fort Wayne

MARTINSVILLE—Morgan County

✠ **INDIANA UNIVERSITY HEALTH MORGAN HOSPITAL (150038)**, 2209 John R. Wooden Drive, Zip 46151–1840, Mailing Address: P.O. Box 1717, Zip 46151–0717; tel. 765/342–8441 **A**1 2 9 10 **F**3 8 11 15 18 28 29 30 31 32 34 35 40 45 50 55 56 57 59 64 69 70 75 78 79 81 82 84 85 86 93 97 98 103 107 108 110 111 114 116 117 119 120 121 123 129 130 132 144 146 147 148 **P**6 **S** Indiana University Health, Indianapolis, IN
Primary Contact: Doug Puckett, President and Chief Executive Officer
CFO: Scott Andritsch, Vice President and Chief Financial Officer
CMO: Jeffrey Amodeo, M.D., Chief of Staff
CHR: Charlene Hall, Vice President Human Resources and Guest Support Services
CNO: Jason M. King, Vice President Patient Care Services and Chief Nursing Officer
Web address: www.iuhealth.org/morgan/
Control: Other not–for–profit (including NFP Corporation) **Service:** General Medical and Surgical

Staffed Beds: 56 **Admissions:** 1199 **Census:** 16 **Outpatient Visits:** 61931 **Births:** 41 **Total Expense ($000):** 36841 **Payroll Expense ($000):** 15310 **Personnel:** 255

MERRILLVILLE—Lake County

○ **REGIONAL MENTAL HEALTH CENTER (154020)**, 8555 Taft Street, Zip 46410–6123; tel. 219/769–4005, (Nonreporting) **A**9 10
Primary Contact: Robert D. Krumwied, President and Chief Executive Officer
Web address: www.regionalmentalhealth.org/
Control: Corporation, Investor–owned, for–profit **Service:** Psychiatric

Staffed Beds: 16

SOUTHLAKE CAMPUS See Methodist Hospitals, Gary

MICHIGAN CITY—Laporte County

○ **FRANCISCAN ST. ANTHONY HEALTH – MICHIGAN CITY (150015)**, 301 West Homer Street, Zip 46360–4358; tel. 219/879–8511, (Nonreporting) **A**2 9 10 11 19 **S** Franciscan Alliance, Mishawaka, IN
Primary Contact: James Callaghan, III, M.D., President
CFO: Marc Golan, Regional Chief Financial Officer
CIO: Tim Loosemore, Regional Director Information Systems
CHR: John Barrett, Regional Director Human Resources
CNO: Trish Weber, Vice President Operations and Chief Nursing Officer
Web address: www.saintanthonymemorial.org
Control: Church–operated, Nongovernment, not–for profit **Service:** General Medical and Surgical

Staffed Beds: 171

SAINT ANTHONY MEMORIAL See Franciscan St. Anthony Health – Michigan City

MISHAWAKA—St. Joseph County

✠ **KINDRED HOSPITAL OF NORTHERN INDIANA (152018)**, 215 West Fourth Street, Suite 200, Zip 46544–1917; tel. 574/252–2000, (Nonreporting) **A**1 10 **S** Kindred Healthcare, Louisville, KY
Primary Contact: Lori Skora, Chief Executive Officer
CFO: Christy Henrich, Controller
CMO: Shaya Mokfi, M.D., Medical Director and President Medical Staff
CHR: Brenda Schweizer, Coordinator Human Resources
CNO: Suzanne M. Morgan, Chief Clinical Officer
Web address: www.khnorthernindiana.com/
Control: Corporation, Investor–owned, for–profit **Service:** Long–Term Acute Care hospital

Staffed Beds: 32

○ **RIVERCREST SPECIALTY HOSPITAL (152026)**, 1625 East Jefferson Boulevard, Zip 46545–7103; tel. 574/255–1400, (Nonreporting) **A**10 11 **S** NeuroPsychiatric Hospitals, Mishawaka, IN
Primary Contact: Cameron R. Gilbert, Ph.D., President and Chief Executive Officer
Web address: www.physicianshospitalsystem.net/
Control: Partnership, Investor–owned, for–profit **Service:** Long–Term Acute Care hospital

Staffed Beds: 30

IN

Many Facility Codes have changed. Please refer to the AHA Guide Code Chart.   © 2014 AHA Guide

⊠ **SAINT JOSEPH REGIONAL MEDICAL CENTER (150012)**, 5215 Holy Cross Parkway, Zip 46545–1469; tel. 574/335–5000 **A**1 2 9 10 13 **F**13 15 17 18 19 20 21 22 23 24 25 26 28 29 30 31 34 35 39 40 45 46 47 48 49 50 52 54 57 60 66 68 70 71 72 74 75 76 77 78 79 80 81 87 89 90 93 96 107 108 111 115 117 118 119 120 121 123 124 126 127 129 130 131 132 135 144 145 146 147 148 **S** Catholic Health East / Trinity Health, Livonia, MI
Primary Contact: Albert Gutierrez, FACHE, President and Chief Executive Officer
COO: Christopher J. Karam, Chief Operating Officer
CMO: Stephen Anderson, M.D., Chief Medical Officer
CIO: Gary L. Miller, Senior Director Information Systems
CHR: Kurt A. Meyer, Chief Human Resource Officer
CNO: Kenneth C. Hall, R.N., Chief Nursing Officer
Web address: www.sjmed.com
Control: Other not–for–profit (including NFP Corporation) **Service:** General Medical and Surgical

Staffed Beds: 267 **Admissions:** 14683 **Census:** 174 **Outpatient Visits:** 157024 **Births:** 1262 **Total Expense ($000):** 276336 **Payroll Expense ($000):** 75952 **Personnel:** 1273

TRIUMPH OUR LADY OF PEACE HOSPITAL See Kindred Hospital of Northern Indiana

○ **UNITY MEDICAL & SURGICAL HOSPITAL (150177)**, 4455 Edison Lakes Parkway, Zip 46545–1442; tel. 574/968–0867, (Nonreporting) **A**9 10 11
Primary Contact: John M. Day, Chief Executive Officer
COO: Donald Allen, Chief Operating Officer
CFO: Matthew M. Sherwood, Chief Financial Officer
CMO: Viraj Patel, M.D., Chief Medical Officer
CIO: Richard Leighton, Financial Application Analyst
CHR: Emyle Kruyer–Collins, Chief Human Resources Officer
CNO: Sylvia K. Coffing, R.N., Chief Nursing and Compliance Officer
Web address. www.umsh.net
Control: Partnership, Investor–owned, for–profit **Service:** General Medical and Surgical

Staffed Beds: 15

MONTICELLO—White County

★ **INDIANA UNIVERSITY HEALTH WHITE MEMORIAL HOSPITAL (151312)**, 720 South Sixth Street, Zip 47960–8182; tel. 574/583–7111 **A**9 10 18 **F**3 8 11 13 15 29 30 31 34 35 40 45 50 57 59 62 64 75 76 77 78 80 81 85 91 93 107 108 110 111 114 119 129 133 135 146 147 **S** Indiana University Health, Indianapolis, IN
Primary Contact: Stephanie Long, Chief Executive Officer
COO: Mary Minier, Vice President Operations
CMO: Adel Khdour, M.D., Chief Medical Officer
CIO: Michelle Baker, Director Information Systems
CHR: JoEllyn Brockmeyer, Director Human Resources
CNO: Robin S. Smith, Chief Nursing Officer
Web address: www.iuhealth.org/white–memorial
Control: Other not–for–profit (including NFP Corporation) **Service:** General Medical and Surgical

Staffed Beds: 25 **Admissions:** 884 **Census:** 10 **Outpatient Visits:** 32830 **Births:** 163 **Total Expense ($000):** 24875 **Payroll Expense ($000):** 9214 **Personnel:** 166

MOORESVILLE—Morgan County

○ **FRANCISCAN ST. FRANCIS HEALTH – MOORESVILLE (150057)**, 1201 Hadley Road, Zip 46158–1789; tel. 317/831–1160 **A**9 10 11 **F**8 12 13 15 29 30 31 35 37 46 47 49 50 57 58 59 64 70 75 76 77 78 79 80 81 87 91 107 108 109 110 111 116 117 119 120 121 123 124 129 130 144 145 146 147 **P**7 8 **S** Franciscan Alliance, Mishawaka, IN
Primary Contact: Peter J. Murphy, Senior Vice President and Chief Operating Officer
CIO: Barbara Coulter, Director Information Systems
CHR: John Ross, Vice President
Web address: www.franciscanalliance.org/hospitals/mooresville/Pages/default.aspx
Control: Church–operated, Nongovernment, not–for profit **Service:** General Medical and Surgical

Staffed Beds: 115 **Admissions:** 3641 **Census:** 29 **Outpatient Visits:** 124216 **Births:** 256 **Total Expense ($000):** 87592 **Payroll Expense ($000):** 25665 **Personnel:** 364

ST. FRANCIS HOSPITAL–MOORESVILLE See Franciscan St. Francis Health – Mooresville

MUNCIE—Delaware County

○ **AMG SPECIALTY HOSPITAL – MUNCIE (152025)**, 2401 West University Avenue, 8th Floor, Zip 47303–3428; tel. 765/751–5253 **A**10 11 **F**1 3 29 85 100 **P**1
Primary Contact: Rodney Midkiff, Chief Executive Officer
CNO: Tina Riegle, R.N., Chief Clinical Officer
Web address: www.amgmuncie.com/
Control: Corporation, Investor–owned, for–profit **Service:** Long–Term Acute Care hospital

Staffed Beds: 32 **Admissions:** 283 **Census:** 20 **Outpatient Visits:** 0 **Births:** 0 **Total Expense ($000):** 10230 **Payroll Expense ($000):** 3976 **Personnel:** 76

BALL MEMORIAL HOSPITAL See Indiana University Health Ball Memorial Hospital

⊠ △ **INDIANA UNIVERSITY HEALTH BALL MEMORIAL HOSPITAL (150089)**, 2401 University Avenue, Zip 47303–3499; tel. 765/747–3111 **A**1 2 3 5 7 8 9 10 19 **F**3 11 12 13 15 17 18 20 22 24 26 27 28 29 30 31 32 34 35 39 40 41 43 45 49 50 51 53 54 56 57 58 59 60 64 65 66 69 70 72 74 75 76 77 78 79 81 82 83 84 85 86 87 89 90 91 92 93 94 97 99 100 102 107 110 111 114 115 116 117 118 119 120 121 123 124 126 129 130 132 146 147 148 **S** Indiana University Health, Indianapolis, IN
Primary Contact: Michael E. Haley, President and Chief Executive Officer
COO: Lori Luther, Chief Operating Officer and Chief Financial Officer
CFO: Lori Luther, Chief Operating Officer and Chief Financial Officer
CMO: Jeffrey C. Bird, M.D., Chief Medical Officer
CHR: Ann M. McGuire, Vice President Human Resources
CNO: Doreen C. Johnson, FACHE, Chief Nursing Officer
Web address: www.iuhealth.org
Control: Other not–for–profit (including NFP Corporation) **Service:** General Medical and Surgical

Staffed Beds: 344 **Admissions:** 16096 **Census:** 223 **Outpatient Visits:** 311050 **Births:** 1637 **Total Expense ($000):** 313513 **Payroll Expense ($000):** 103481 **Personnel:** 1726

MERIDIAN HEALTH SERVICES (154053), 2401 West University Avenue, Zip 47303–3428; tel. 765/747–3281, (Nonreporting) **A**10
Primary Contact: Hank A. Milius, Chief Executive Officer
CMO: Sarfraz Khan, Medical Director
Web address: www.meridianhs.org
Control: Other not–for–profit (including NFP Corporation) **Service:** Psychiatric

Staffed Beds: 20

RENAISSANCE SPECIALTY HOSPITAL OF CENTRAL INDIANA See AMG Specialty Hospital – Muncie

MUNSTER—Lake County

☐ **COMMUNITY HOSPITAL (150125)**, 901 Macarthur Boulevard, Zip 46321–2959; tel. 219/836–1600 **A**1 2 5 9 10 **F**3 8 11 13 15 17 18 20 22 24 26 28 29 31 34 35 40 45 49 50 51 53 54 57 58 59 60 62 64 68 70 72 73 74 75 76 78 79 80 81 82 85 86 87 89 90 92 93 94 96 107 108 110 111 114 115 117 119 120 121 123 124 126 129 130 132 135 144 146 147 148 **P**6 **S** Community Healthcare System, Hammond, IN
Primary Contact: Donald P. Fesko, Chief Executive Officer and Administrator
CFO: Luis Molina, Vice President Finance and Chief Financial Officer
CMO: Don Henry, M.D., President Medical and Dental Staff
CIO: Gary Weiner, Vice President Information Technology, Chief Information Officer
CHR: Michael Graham, Director Human Resources
CNO: Ronda McKay, MSN, Vice President Patient Care Services, Chief Nursing Officer
Web address: www.comhs.org
Control: Other not–for–profit (including NFP Corporation) **Service:** General Medical and Surgical

Staffed Beds: 457 **Admissions:** 21015 **Census:** 311 **Outpatient Visits:** 360409 **Births:** 1888 **Total Expense ($000):** 426815 **Payroll Expense ($000):** 153352 **Personnel:** 2411

○ **FRANCISCAN HEALTHCARE – MUNSTER (150165)**, 701 Superior Avenue, Zip 46321–4037; tel. 219/924–1300, (Nonreporting) **A**9 10 11 **S** Franciscan Alliance, Mishawaka, IN
Primary Contact: Barbara M. Greene, President
CFO: Harold E. Collins, JD, Chief Financial Officer
CMO: Vijay D. Gupta, M.D., President and Chief Executive Officer
CIO: Steven Krause, Manager Information Technology
Web address: www.franciscanphysicianshospital.org
Control: Partnership, Investor–owned, for–profit **Service:** General Medical and Surgical

Staffed Beds: 32

IN

Hospital, Medicare Provider Number, Address, Telephone, Approval, Facility, and Physician Codes, Health Care System

★ American Hospital Association (AHA) membership
☐ The Joint Commission accreditation
◇ DNV Healthcare Inc. accreditation
○ Healthcare Facilities Accreditation Program
△ Commission on Accreditation of Rehabilitation Facilities (CARF) accreditation

NEW ALBANY—Floyd County

★ ○ **FLOYD MEMORIAL HOSPITAL AND HEALTH SERVICES (150044)**, 1850 State Street, Zip 47150–4997; tel. 812/949–5500, (Total facility includes 266 beds in nursing home–type unit) **A**2 3 5 9 10 11 **F**8 11 12 13 15 17 18 20 22 24 28 29 30 31 34 35 40 43 49 50 56 57 59 62 64 70 71 74 75 76 77 78 79 80 81 82 85 86 87 89 93 100 107 108 110 111 114 115 116 117 118 119 120 121 123 128 129 130 131 132 135 144 146 147 148
Primary Contact: Mark D. Shugarman, President and Chief Executive Officer
COO: Mark Truman, Vice President of Operations
CFO: Ted Miller, Chief Financial Officer
CMO: Daniel J. Eichenberger, M.D., Medical Director
CIO: Brian Cox, Director Information Systems
CHR: Mike Ford, Vice President Human Resources
Web address: www.floydmemorial.com
Control: County–Government, nonfederal **Service:** General Medical and Surgical

Staffed Beds: 477 **Admissions:** 15413 **Census:** 380 **Outpatient Visits:** 428886 **Births:** 995 **Total Expense ($000):** 283399 **Payroll Expense ($000):** 119083 **Personnel:** 2188

☐ **PHYSICIANS' MEDICAL CENTER (150172)**, 4023 Reas Lane, Zip 47150–2228; tel. 812/206–7660, (Nonreporting) **A**1 9 10
Primary Contact: Dennis Medley, Administrator
COO: Dennis Medley, Chief Executive Officer
CFO: Dennis Medley, Chief Executive Officer
CMO: Perry Cassady, M.D., Medical Director
CIO: Mary Arntz, Manager Business Office and Executive Assistant
CHR: Mary Arntz, Manager Business Office and Executive Assistant
CNO: Rob Jones, Chief Nursing Officer
Web address: www.pmcindiana.com
Control: Individual, Investor–owned, for–profit **Service:** General Medical and Surgical

Staffed Beds: 12

⊞ △ **SOUTHERN INDIANA REHABILITATION HOSPITAL (153037)**, 3104 Blackiston Boulevard, Zip 47150–9579; tel. 812/941–8300 **A**1 7 9 10 **F**29 34 35 57 59 74 75 77 79 86 87 90 91 93 96 130 132 135 143 146 **S** Catholic Health Initiatives, Englewood, CO
Primary Contact: Randy L. Napier, President
CFO: Robert Steltenpohl, Vice President
CMO: John C. Shaw, M.D., Medical Director
CHR: Lisa Burris, Director Human Resources
CNO: Suzann Byers, Director of Nursing
Web address: www.sirh.org
Control: Other not–for–profit (including NFP Corporation) **Service:** Rehabilitation

Staffed Beds: 84 **Admissions:** 1312 **Census:** 43 **Outpatient Visits:** 85451 **Births:** 0 **Total Expense ($000):** 56245 **Payroll Expense ($000):** 20931 **Personnel:** 216

NEW CASTLE—Henry County

★ ○ **HENRY COUNTY HOSPITAL (150030)**, 1000 North 16th Street, Zip 47362–4319, Mailing Address: P.O. Box 490, Zip 47362–0490; tel. 765/521–0890, (Nonreporting) **A**9 10 11
Primary Contact: Paul Janssen, President and Chief Executive Officer
COO: Brian K. Ring, Chief Operating Officer
CFO: Darin Brown, Vice President Finance
CMO: Wylie McGlothlin, M.D., Chief Medical Officer
CIO: Mike Spencer, Chief Information Officer
CHR: Deanna Malott, Director Human Resources
CNO: Carrie Williams, R.N., Chief Nursing Officer
Web address: www.hcmhcares.org
Control: County–Government, nonfederal **Service:** General Medical and Surgical

Staffed Beds: 87

NEWBURGH—Warrick County

☐ **BRENTWOOD MEADOWS (154055)**, 4455 Roslin Road, Zip 47630; tel. 812/858–7200, (Nonreporting) **A**1 9 10
Primary Contact: Rosemary Notarantonio, R.N., MSN, Chief Executive Officer
Web address: www.brentwoodmeadows.com
Control: Partnership, Investor–owned, for–profit **Service:** Psychiatric

Staffed Beds: 48

○ **THE HEART HOSPITAL AT DEACONESS GATEWAY (150175)**, 4007 Gateway Boulevard, Zip 47630–8947; tel. 812/842–4784 **A**9 10 11 **F**3 17 18 20 22 24 26 28 29 30 34 35 57 58 59 60 62 63 64 68 81 83 84 85 86 87 107 108 109 111 114 115 116 117 118 119 130 132 **S** Deaconess Health System, Evansville, IN
Primary Contact: Rebecca Malotte, Executive Director and Chief Nursing Officer
COO: Rebecca Malotte, Executive Director and Chief Nursing Officer
CFO: Tracy Silva, Chief Financial Officer
CMO: Lee Wagmeister, M.D., President Medical Staff
CIO: Lisa Hobgood, Chief Information Officer
CHR: Sarah Bryan, Manager Human Resources
CNO: Rebecca Malotte, Executive Director and Chief Nursing Officer
Web address: www.deaconess.com/
Control: Partnership, Investor–owned, for–profit **Service:** Heart

Staffed Beds: 24 **Admissions:** 1576 **Census:** 17 **Outpatient Visits:** 6124 **Births:** 0 **Total Expense ($000):** 37864 **Payroll Expense ($000):** 6454 **Personnel:** 121

★ ○ **THE WOMEN'S HOSPITAL (150149)**, 4199 Gateway Boulevard, Zip 47630–8940; tel. 812/842–4200 **A**9 10 11 **F**3 13 29 30 34 35 36 40 50 53 55 57 59 63 64 65 72 75 76 77 81 84 85 86 87 93 119 126 130 132 134 135 147 **P**6 **S** Deaconess Health System, Evansville, IN
Primary Contact: Christina M. Ryan, R.N., Chief Executive Officer
CFO: Tina Cady, Controller
CIO: Jenny Skelton, System Integration Manager
CHR: Jerri Sue Traylor, Director Human Resources and Community and Employee Wellness
CNO: Christina M. Ryan, R.N., Chief Executive Officer and Chief Nursing Officer
Web address: www.deaconess.com
Control: Partnership, Investor–owned, for–profit **Service:** Obstetrics and gynecology

Staffed Beds: 74 **Admissions:** 3316 **Census:** 45 **Outpatient Visits:** 18455 **Births:** 3104 **Total Expense ($000):** 57792 **Payroll Expense ($000):** 24169 **Personnel:** 440

NOBLESVILLE—Hamilton County

○ △ **RIVERVIEW HOSPITAL (150059)**, 395 Westfield Road, Zip 46060–1425, Mailing Address: P.O. Box 220, Zip 46061–0220; tel. 317/773–0760 **A**2 5 7 9 10 11 **F**3 11 13 15 18 22 24 26 28 29 30 31 34 35 37 40 45 46 49 50 53 54 57 59 60 62 64 65 66 75 77 79 81 82 85 87 91 92 93 97 107 108 109 110 111 114 115 116 117 118 119 120 121 122 123 129 130 131 132 133 135 144 145 146 147 148 **P**2 3 6
Primary Contact: Patricia K. Fox, President and Chief Executive Officer
COO: Lawrence Christman, Chief Financial Officer and Chief Operating Officer
CFO: Brenda Baker, Chief Financial Officer
CMO: John Paris, M.D., Chief Medical Officer
CIO: Brant Bucciarelli, Chief Information Officer
CHR: Ann Kuzee, Executive Director Human Resources
CNO: Joyce Wood, Vice President Organizational Improvement and Chief Nursing Officer
Web address: www.riverview.org
Control: County–Government, nonfederal **Service:** General Medical and Surgical

Staffed Beds: 154 **Admissions:** 4753 **Census:** 72 **Outpatient Visits:** 444554 **Births:** 682 **Total Expense ($000):** 159995 **Payroll Expense ($000):** 64364 **Personnel:** 898

NORTH VERNON—Jennings County

⊞ **ST. VINCENT JENNINGS HOSPITAL (151303)**, 301 Henry Street, Zip 47265–1097; tel. 812/352–4200 **A**1 9 10 18 **F**3 15 29 30 32 34 35 40 44 45 50 56 57 59 64 65 66 77 79 81 85 97 107 111 115 119 132 133 135 144 146 148 **S** Ascension Health, Saint Louis, MO
Primary Contact: Carl W. Risk, II, Administrator
CFO: Joseph Kubala, Chief Financial Officer
CMO: Jennifer Stanley, M.D., Chief Medical Officer
CHR: Kathryn Johnson, Manager Human Resources, Marketing and Public Relations
CNO: Lori Wise, Chief Nursing Officer and Director of Clinical Services
Web address: www.stvincent.org
Control: Other not–for–profit (including NFP Corporation) **Service:** General Medical and Surgical

Staffed Beds: 25 **Admissions:** 445 **Census:** 4 **Outpatient Visits:** 33648 **Births:** 0 **Total Expense ($000):** 16789 **Payroll Expense ($000):** 5932 **Personnel:** 90

PAOLI—Orange County

BLOOMINGTON HOSPITAL OF ORANGE COUNTY See Indiana University Health Paoli Hospital

IN

✠ **INDIANA UNIVERSITY HEALTH PAOLI HOSPITAL (151306)**, 642 West Hospital Road, Zip 47454–9672, Mailing Address: P.O. Box 499, Zip 47454–0499; tel. 812/723–2811 **A**1 9 10 18 **F**3 13 15 29 30 35 40 45 50 57 59 64 76 77 81 84 85 89 93 107 110 111 114 119 129 132 133 135 146 148 **S** Indiana University Health, Indianapolis, IN
Primary Contact: Larry Bailey, Chief Executive Officer
COO: Sonya Zeller, R.N., Vice President, Chief Operating Officer and Chief Nursing Officer
CFO: Sue Brock, Chief Financial Officer
CMO: Matthew B. Main, M.D., Medical Staff President
CHR: Cindy Smale, Director Human Resources
CNO: Sonya Zeller, R.N., Vice President, Chief Operating Officer and Chief Nursing Officer
Web address: www.iuhealth.org/paoli
Control: Other not–for–profit (including NFP Corporation) **Service:** General Medical and Surgical

Staffed Beds: 24 **Admissions:** 502 **Census:** 3 **Outpatient Visits:** 27675 **Births:** 154 **Total Expense ($000):** 20861 **Payroll Expense ($000):** 10281 **Personnel:** 136

PERU—Miami County

✠ **DUKES MEMORIAL HOSPITAL (151318)**, 275 West 12th Street, Zip 46970–1638; tel. 765/472–8000 **A**1 9 10 18 **F**3 7 8 13 15 17 18 28 29 34 35 40 41 50 51 57 59 64 68 69 70 75 76 77 79 81 82 85 87 89 90 93 107 108 110 111 115 118 119 129 130 132 133 135 144 146 147 **P**6 **S** Community Health Systems, Inc., Franklin, TN
Primary Contact: Debra Close, Chief Executive Officer
CFO: Adam Cumbo, Chief Financial Officer
CMO: Neil Stalker, M.D., Chief of Staff
CNO: Beth Daughtery, Chief Nursing Officer
Web address: www.dukesmemorialhosp.com
Control: Corporation, Investor–owned, for–profit **Service:** General Medical and Surgical

Staffed Beds: 25 **Admissions:** 1148 **Census:** 11 **Outpatient Visits:** 38320 **Births:** 208 **Total Expense ($000):** 34320 **Payroll Expense ($000):** 16118

PLYMOUTH—Marshall County

☐ **MICHIANA BEHAVIORAL HEALTH CENTER (154047)**, 1800 North Oak Drive, Zip 46563–3492; tel. 574/936–3784 **A**1 9 10 **F**98 99 105 106 **S** Universal Health Services, Inc., King of Prussia, PA
Primary Contact: Bryan W. Lett, Chief Executive Officer
CFO: Jeff Calvin, Chief Financial Officer
CMO: Robert Raster, M.D., Medical Director
CIO: Bob Kedalis, Director Business Development
CHR: Becky Nowicki, Director Human Resources
Web address: www.michianabhc.com
Control: Corporation, Investor–owned, for–profit **Service:** Psychiatric

Staffed Beds: 75 **Admissions:** 1482 **Census:** 50 **Outpatient Visits:** 0 **Births:** 0 **Total Expense ($000):** 11308 **Payroll Expense ($000):** 5229 **Personnel:** 122

✠ **SAINT JOSEPH REGIONAL MEDICAL CENTER–PLYMOUTH CAMPUS (150076)**, 1915 Lake Avenue, Zip 46563–9366, Mailing Address: P.O. Box 670, Zip 46563–0670; tel. 574/948–4000 **A**1 9 10 **F**13 15 24 29 30 31 34 35 40 45 50 54 57 59 66 68 74 75 76 79 81 87 93 107 108 114 119 120 121 123 124 129 130 132 145 146 **S** Catholic Health East / Trinity Health, Livonia, MI
Primary Contact: Loretta Schmidt, President
COO: Tamara Awald, Chief Nursing Officer and Chief Operating Officer
CFO: Janice Dunn, Chief Financial Officer
CMO: Stephen Anderson, M.D., Chief Medical Officer
CIO: Gary L. Miller, Regional Director Information Systems
CHR: Kurt A. Meyer, Chief Human Resources Officer
CNO: Tamara Awald, Chief Nursing Officer and Chief Operating Officer
Web address: www.sjmed.com
Control: Other not–for–profit (including NFP Corporation) **Service:** General Medical and Surgical

Staffed Beds: 45 **Admissions:** 2165 **Census:** 18 **Outpatient Visits:** 84424 **Births:** 429 **Total Expense ($000):** 41622 **Payroll Expense ($000):** 14295 **Personnel:** 231

PORTLAND—Jay County

✠ **JAY COUNTY HOSPITAL (151320)**, 500 West Votaw Street, Zip 47371–1322; tel. 260/726–7131 **A**1 9 10 18 **F**3 8 11 13 15 28 29 30 32 34 35 40 45 50 57 59 68 70 75 76 77 81 85 86 87 103 107 108 110 111 114 119 129 130 132 133 135 144 146 **P**6 **S** Indiana University Health, Indianapolis, IN
Primary Contact: David W. Hyatt, Chief Executive Officer
CFO: Don Michael, Chief Financial Officer
CIO: Jeff Horn, Coordinator Information Systems
CHR: Jerry Bozell, Administrative Director Human Resources
CNO: Lisa Craiger, Chief Nursing Officer
Web address: www.jaycountyhospital.com
Control: County–Government, nonfederal **Service:** General Medical and Surgical

Staffed Beds: 35 **Admissions:** 947 **Census:** 14 **Outpatient Visits:** 43322 **Births:** 68 **Total Expense ($000):** 34684 **Payroll Expense ($000):** 14256 **Personnel:** 270

PRINCETON—Gibson County

✠ **GIBSON GENERAL HOSPITAL (151319)**, 1808 Sherman Drive, Zip 47670–1043; tel. 812/385–3401, (Total facility includes 45 beds in nursing home–type unit) **A**1 9 10 18 **F**3 5 11 15 28 29 30 31 34 35 38 40 45 54 56 57 59 62 64 68 70 75 77 79 81 89 93 97 99 100 101 102 103 104 107 110 111 115 119 128 129 130 131 132 133 146 148 **P**6 **S** Alliant Management Services, Louisville, KY
Primary Contact: Emmett C. Schuster, President and Chief Executive Officer
CFO: Ron Harrington, Vice President and Chief Financial Officer
CMO: Bruce Brink, Jr., D.O., Chief of Staff
CIO: Ron Harrington, Chief Financial Officer
CHR: D. Deann Hunt, Director Human Resources
CNO: Lori Phillips, Vice President and Chief Nursing Officer
Web address: www.gibsongeneral.com
Control: Other not–for–profit (including NFP Corporation) **Service:** General Medical and Surgical

Staffed Beds: 70 **Admissions:** 721 **Census:** 47 **Outpatient Visits:** 32679 **Births:** 0 **Total Expense ($000):** 24736 **Payroll Expense ($000):** 10752 **Personnel:** 280

RENSSELAER—Jasper County

★ **JASPER COUNTY HOSPITAL (151324)**, 1104 East Grace Street, Zip 47978–3296; tel. 219/866–5141 **A**9 10 18 **F**3 11 13 15 28 29 30 31 34 35 39 40 43 49 50 51 53 54 57 59 62 63 64 65 68 69 70 74 75 76 77 78 79 81 82 85 86 87 93 96 107 108 110 111 114 115 118 119 127 129 130 131 132 133 135 146 148
Primary Contact: Timothy M. Schreeg, President and Chief Executive Officer
CFO: Jeffrey D. Webb, CPA, Chief Financial Officer
CIO: Kirby Reed, Director Information Systems
CHR: Deana Brown, Director Administrative Services
CNO: Stacie Klingler, R.N., Vice President of Patient Services
Web address: www.jchh.com
Control: County–Government, nonfederal **Service:** General Medical and Surgical

Staffed Beds: 25 **Admissions:** 1192 **Census:** 15 **Outpatient Visits:** 100876 **Births:** 80 **Total Expense ($000):** 37544 **Payroll Expense ($000):** 16026 **Personnel:** 353

RICHMOND—Wayne County

★ ○ **REID HOSPITAL AND HEALTH CARE SERVICES (150048)**, 1100 Reid Parkway, Zip 47374–1157; tel. 765/983–3000 **A**2 5 9 10 11 19 20 **F**3 11 13 15 18 20 22 24 26 28 29 30 31 32 34 35 40 43 44 45 47 49 50 51 54 56 57 59 61 63 64 69 70 74 75 76 77 78 79 81 82 83 84 85 86 87 89 90 91 93 96 97 98 100 101 102 103 104 107 108 110 111 114 115 116 117 118 119 120 121 123 126 129 130 131 132 135 144 146 147 148 **P**6 7 8
Primary Contact: Craig C. Kinyon, President
CMO: Thomas Huth, M.D., Vice President Medical Affairs
CIO: Tim Love, Director Information Services
CHR: Scott C. Rauch, Vice President Human Resources
CNO: Kay B. Cartwright, R.N., Vice President and Chief Nursing Officer
Web address: www.reidhosp.com
Control: Other not–for–profit (including NFP Corporation) **Service:** General Medical and Surgical

Staffed Beds: 223 **Admissions:** 10802 **Census:** 141 **Outpatient Visits:** 237538 **Births:** 651 **Total Expense ($000):** 356727 **Payroll Expense ($000):** 138698 **Personnel:** 1980

IN

Hospital, Medicare Provider Number, Address, Telephone, Approval, Facility, and Physician Codes, Health Care System

★ American Hospital Association (AHA) membership
☐ The Joint Commission accreditation ◇ DNV Healthcare Inc. accreditation
○ Healthcare Facilities Accreditation Program
△ Commission on Accreditation of Rehabilitation Facilities (CARF) accreditation

☐ **RICHMOND STATE HOSPITAL (154018)**, 498 N.W. 18th Street,
Zip 47374–2851; tel. 765/966–0511 **A**1 10 **F**29 30 39 68 75 77 87 98 100
101 103 130 132 135 146 **P**6
Primary Contact: Jeffrey Butler, Superintendent
CFO: Dave Shelford, Assistant Superintendent
CMO: Donald Graber, M.D., Medical Director
CIO: Robert Boatman, Director Information Technology
CHR: Sarah Witt, Director Human Resources
Web address: www.richmondstatehospital.org
Control: State–Government, nonfederal **Service:** Psychiatric

Staffed Beds: 213 **Admissions:** 149 **Census:** 203 **Outpatient Visits:** 0
Births: 0 **Total Expense ($000):** 35618 **Payroll Expense ($000):** 17820
Personnel: 438

ROCHESTER—Fulton County

★ **WOODLAWN HOSPITAL (151313)**, 1400 East Ninth Street, Zip 46975–8937;
tel. 574/223–3141 **A**9 10 18 **F**3 11 13 15 29 30 31 34 40 46 56 57 59 63
65 68 69 75 77 78 79 81 82 93 94 97 107 108 111 115 116 119 129 130
132 133 135 143 146 147 148 **P**6
Primary Contact: John L. Alley, Chief Executive Officer
CFO: Dave Cholger, Chief Financial Officer
CHR: Debra J. Lemasters, Director Human Resources
Web address: www.woodlawnhospital.com
Control: County–Government, nonfederal **Service:** General Medical and Surgical

Staffed Beds: 25 **Admissions:** 1156 **Census:** 12 **Outpatient Visits:** 98635
Births: 211 **Total Expense ($000):** 46667 **Payroll Expense ($000):** 21111
Personnel: 358

RUSHVILLE—Rush County

★ **RUSH MEMORIAL HOSPITAL (151304)**, 1300 North Main Street,
Zip 46173–1198, Mailing Address: P.O. Box 608, Zip 46173–0608;
tel. 765/932–4111 **A**9 10 18 **F**3 7 11 15 18 24 28 29 31 35 36 40 46 51 52
57 59 64 65 74 75 77 78 79 81 85 93 97 107 111 114 117 120 121 122
129 130 131 132 133 135 146 147 148 **P**6
Primary Contact: Bradley Smith, President and Chief Executive Officer
COO: Debbie Jones–Browning, Vice President Operations and Physician Services
and Chief Operating Officer
CFO: Karen Meyer, Vice President Finance and Chief Financial Officer
CMO: Daniel Stahl, D.O., Chief of Staff
CIO: Jim Boyer, Vice President Information Technology and Chief Information
Officer
CHR: Dennis Fogle, Vice President of Human Resources
CNO: Gretchen Smith, Vice President Nursing and Compliance and Risk
Web address: www.rushmemorial.com
Control: County–Government, nonfederal **Service:** General Medical and Surgical

Staffed Beds: 25 **Admissions:** 443 **Census:** 4 **Outpatient Visits:** 33317
Births: 0 **Total Expense ($000):** 24079 **Payroll Expense ($000):** 11642
Personnel: 244

SALEM—Washington County

⊞ **ST. VINCENT SALEM HOSPITAL (151314)**, 911 North Shelby Street,
Zip 47167–1694; tel. 812/883–5881 **A**1 9 10 18 **F**3 11 15 28 29 30 32 34
40 45 47 49 57 59 75 77 79 81 82 85 93 104 107 111 114 119 129 130
132 133 148 **P**6 **S** Ascension Health, Saint Louis, MO
Primary Contact: Dana M. Muntz, Chief Executive Officer
CFO: Joseph Kubala, Director Financial and Support Services
CMO: S. E. Kemker, M.D., President Medical Staff
CIO: Jeremy Long, Manager Information Systems
CHR: Val Potter, Director Human Resources
Web address: www.stvincent.org/St-Vincent-Salem/Default.aspx
Control: Other not–for–profit (including NFP Corporation) **Service:** General
Medical and Surgical

Staffed Beds: 25 **Admissions:** 365 **Census:** 4 **Outpatient Visits:** 24095
Births: 0 **Total Expense ($000):** 18111 **Payroll Expense ($000):** 6499
Personnel: 107

SCOTTSBURG—Scott County

⊞ **SCOTT MEMORIAL HOSPITAL (151334)**, 1415 North Gardner Street,
Zip 47170, Mailing Address: Box 430, Zip 47170–0430; tel. 812/752–3456,
(Nonreporting) **A**1 9 10 18 **S** LifePoint Hospitals, Inc., Brentwood, TN
Primary Contact: Michael Everett, Chief Executive Officer
CFO: Angela Doan, Chief Financial Officer
CNO: Dawn Mays, Chief Nursing Officer
Web address: www.scottmemorial.com
Control: County–Government, nonfederal **Service:** General Medical and Surgical

Staffed Beds: 25

SEYMOUR—Jackson County

⊞ **SCHNECK MEDICAL CENTER (150065)**, 411 West Tipton Street,
Zip 47274–2363, Mailing Address: P.O. Box 2349, Zip 47274–5000;
tel. 812/522–2349 **A**1 2 9 10 **F**3 8 12 13 15 18 28 29 30 31 34 35 36 40 45
50 51 56 57 58 59 60 61 62 63 64 68 69 70 74 75 76 77 78 79 81 82 83
84 85 86 87 89 93 104 107 110 111 115 116 118 119 120 121 123 124
126 129 130 131 132 133 135 144 146 147 148 **P**8
Primary Contact: Gary A. Meyer, President and Chief Executive Officer
CFO: Warren Forgey, Executive Vice President and Chief Administrative and
Operations Officer
CIO: Craig Rice, Director Information
CHR: Kathy Covert, Vice President Human Resources
Web address: www.schneckmed.org
Control: County–Government, nonfederal **Service:** General Medical and Surgical

Staffed Beds: 93 **Admissions:** 3366 **Census:** 37 **Outpatient Visits:** 163755
Births: 769 **Total Expense ($000):** 108048 **Payroll Expense ($000):** 45989
Personnel: 779

SHELBYVILLE—Shelby County

★ ○ **MAJOR HOSPITAL (150097)**, 150 West Washington Street,
Zip 46176–1236; tel. 317/392–3211 **A**9 10 11 **F**3 12 13 15 28 29 30 31 34
35 40 50 57 59 62 63 68 70 73 75 77 78 80 81 82 84 85 93 97 107 108
110 111 114 118 119 120 121 123 129 130 132 135 146 147 148 **P**6
Primary Contact: John M. Horner, President and Chief Executive Officer
CFO: Ralph Mercuri, Vice President and Chief Financial Officer
CMO: Douglas S. Carter, M.D., Vice President and Chief Medical Officer
CIO: Dan Van Gundy, Director of Information Technology Systems and Hardware
CHR: Nicki Sparling, Manager Human Resources
CNO: Valerie L. Miller, MSN, Director of Nursing
Web address: www.majorhospital.org
Control: City–County, Government, nonfederal **Service:** General Medical and
Surgical

Staffed Beds: 61 **Admissions:** 2732 **Census:** 27 **Outpatient Visits:** 148897
Births: 343 **Total Expense ($000):** 86543 **Payroll Expense ($000):** 34729

SOUTH BEND—St. Joseph County

⊞ △ **MEMORIAL HOSPITAL OF SOUTH BEND (150058)**, 615 North Michigan
Street, Zip 46601–1033; tel. 574/647–1000, (Includes MEMORIAL CHILDREN'S
HOSPITAL, 615 North Michigan Street, Zip 46601, Mailing Address: 516 North
Michigan Street, Zip 46601; tel. 574/647–1000) **A**1 2 3 5 7 9 10 **F**3 7 8 9 13
15 17 18 19 20 22 24 26 28 29 30 31 35 38 40 43 46 49 50 53 56 59 60
61 64 67 68 70 72 73 74 75 76 77 78 79 81 82 84 85 86 87 88 89 90 92
93 98 99 102 103 107 108 111 114 115 116 117 119 121 124 126 129
130 131 132 134 135 146 147 148 **P**8 **S** Beacon Health System, South
Bend, IN
Primary Contact: Kreg Gruber, President
CFO: Jeff Costello, Chief Financial Officer
CMO: Cheryl Wibbens, M.D., Vice President Medical Staff Affairs
CIO: Steve Huffman, Chief Information Officer
Web address: www.qualityoflife.org
Control: Other not–for–profit (including NFP Corporation) **Service:** General
Medical and Surgical

Staffed Beds: 445 **Admissions:** 19339 **Census:** 253 **Outpatient Visits:**
179979 **Births:** 2401 **Total Expense ($000):** 374039 **Payroll Expense
($000):** 132987 **Personnel:** 2331

SULLIVAN—Sullivan County

★ **SULLIVAN COUNTY COMMUNITY HOSPITAL (151327)**, 2200 North Section
Street, Zip 47882–7523, Mailing Address: P.O. Box 10, Zip 47882–0010;
tel. 812/268–4311 **A**9 10 18 **F**3 8 13 15 28 29 32 34 35 40 44 45 47 48 53
56 57 59 61 62 69 70 75 76 77 78 79 81 86 87 93 97 107 110 111 114
127 129 130 131 133 146 147 148 **P**8 **S** QHR, Brentwood, TN
Primary Contact: Michelle Franklin, Chief Executive Officer
CFO: Alan J. Montella, Assistant Administrator Finance
CMO: Divyesh Purohit, M.D., Chief of Staff
CIO: Hap Beckes, Director Information Systems
CHR: Denise Hart, Director Human Resources
CNO: Lori Resler, R.N., Chief Nurse
Web address: www.schosp.com
Control: County–Government, nonfederal **Service:** General Medical and Surgical

Staffed Beds: 25 **Admissions:** 900 **Census:** 7 **Outpatient Visits:** 70439
Births: 134 **Total Expense ($000):** 22862 **Payroll Expense ($000):** 10022
Personnel: 239

TELL CITY—Perry County

★ **PERRY COUNTY MEMORIAL HOSPITAL (151322)**, 1 Hospital Road,
Zip 47586–2750; tel. 812/547–7011, (Nonreporting) **A**9 10 18 **S** Alliant
Management Services, Louisville, KY
Primary Contact: Joseph A. Stuber, President and Chief Executive Officer
COO: Becky Elder, Vice President Clinical Services
CMO: William Marcrum, M.D., Chief of Staff
CIO: Mark Miller, Director Information Systems
CHR: Sheila Gaynor, Director Human Resources
Web address: www.pchospital.org
Control: County–Government, nonfederal **Service:** General Medical and Surgical

Staffed Beds: 25

Many Facility Codes have changed. Please refer to the AHA Guide Code Chart. © 2014 AHA Guide

TERRE HAUTE—Vigo County

HAMILTON CENTER (154009), 620 Eighth Avenue, Zip 47804–2744;
tel. 812/231–8323 **A**9 10 **F**29 34 38 57 62 66 68 98 100 101 103 104 106
130 132 134 135 **P**6
Primary Contact: Mel Burks, Chief Executive Officer
COO: Robb Johnson, Director Operations
CFO: Renee Utley, Acting Chief Financial Officer
CMO: Ahsan Mahmood, M.D., Chief Medical Officer
CIO: Hans Eilbracht, Chief Information Officer
CHR: Jan Weber, Chief Human Resources Officer
CNO: Brooke Kempt, Corporate Nursing Director
Web address: www.hamiltoncenter.org
Control: Other not–for–profit (including NFP Corporation) **Service:** Psychiatric

Staffed Beds: 16 **Admissions:** 578 **Census:** 14 **Outpatient Visits:** 275881
Births: 0 **Total Expense ($000):** 29232 **Payroll Expense ($000):** 16787
Personnel: 503

☐ **HARSHA BEHAVIORAL CENTER (154054)**, 1420 East Crossing Boulevard,
Zip 47802–5316; tel. 866/644–8880, (Nonreporting) **A**1 9 10
Primary Contact: Roopam Harshawat, Chief Executive Officer
COO: Holly Near, Chief Administrative Officer
CFO: Holly Near, Chief Administrative Officer
CMO: Paras Harshawat, M.D., Medical Director
CNO: Cindy Dowers, Chief Nursing Officer
Web address: www.harshacenter.com
Control: Corporation, Investor–owned, for–profit **Service:** Psychiatric

Staffed Beds: 36

✠ **TERRE HAUTE REGIONAL HOSPITAL (150046)**, 3901 South Seventh Street,
Zip 47802–5709; tel. 812/232–0021 **A**1 2 5 9 10 **F**3 11 13 15 18 20 22 24
26 29 31 34 35 37 40 41 45 46 47 49 57 59 64 65 70 74 76 77 78 79 80
81 82 85 86 89 90 91 92 93 98 102 103 107 108 109 110 111 113 115
119 132 135 144 145 146 147 148 **S** HCA, Nashville, TN
Primary Contact: Mary Ann Conroy, Chief Executive Officer
COO: Tim Prestridge, Chief Operating Officer
CFO: Adam Martin, Chief Financial Officer
CIO: Mike Kuckewich, Director Information Systems
CNO: Angela Ellis, R.N., Chief Nursing Officer
Web address: www.regionalhospital.com
Control: Corporation, Investor–owned, for–profit **Service:** General Medical and
Surgical

Staffed Beds: 208 **Admissions:** 6105 **Census:** 72 **Outpatient Visits:** 50790
Births: 405 **Total Expense ($000):** 106599 **Payroll Expense ($000):** 40500
Personnel: 676

★ ○ △ **UNION HOSPITAL (150023)**, 1606 North Seventh Street,
Zip 47804–2780; tel. 812/238–7000 **A**2 3 5 7 9 10 11 19 **F**3 8 13 15 18 20
22 24 26 28 29 30 31 34 35 36 39 40 45 46 48 49 50 51 53 54 57 59 60
64 68 70 72 73 74 75 76 77 78 79 81 82 85 86 87 89 90 92 93 94 95 96
97 100 107 108 110 111 112 114 115 116 117 118 119 120 121 123 126
127 130 131 132 135 146 147 148 **P**6
Primary Contact: Steve M. Holman, Chief Executive Officer
CFO: Wayne Hutson, Executive Vice President and Chief Financial Officer
CMO: John Bolinger, M.D., Vice President Medical Affairs
CIO: Kym Pfrank, Senior Vice President and Chief Operating Officer
CHR: Sally Zuel, Vice President Human Resources
CNO: Rhonda E. Smith, R.N., Vice President Patient Care Services and Chief
Nursing Officer
Web address: www.uhhg.org
Control: Other not–for–profit (including NFP Corporation) **Service:** General
Medical and Surgical

Staffed Beds: 310 **Admissions:** 15326 **Census:** 207 **Outpatient Visits:**
370231 **Births:** 1811 **Total Expense ($000):** 384842 **Payroll Expense
($000):** 128955 **Personnel:** 1998

TIPTON—Tipton County

✠ **INDIANA UNIVERSITY HEALTH TIPTON HOSPITAL (151311)**, 1000 South
Main Street, Zip 46072–9799; tel. 765/675–8500 **A**1 2 9 10 18 **F**3 8 11 15 17
18 28 29 30 31 34 35 39 40 45 46 47 48 53 57 59 70 74 75 77 78 79 81
82 85 86 87 90 93 107 108 110 111 115 119 128 129 131 132 133 135
146 147 148 **P**8 **S** Indiana University Health, Indianapolis, IN
Primary Contact: Michael Harlowe, President and Chief Executive Officer
CFO: Carrie Springer, Interim Chief Financial Officer and Vice President Finance
CMO: Gaurau Arora, M.D., Chief Medical Officer
CIO: Mike Kessler, Director, Information Services
CHR: Shelly E. Huff, Director Human Resources
CNO: Jo Ellen Scott, R.N., Senior Vice President of Patient Care Services and
Chief Nursing Officer
Web address: www.iuhealth.org
Control: Other not–for–profit (including NFP Corporation) **Service:** General
Medical and Surgical

Staffed Beds: 25 **Admissions:** 1237 **Census:** 14 **Outpatient Visits:** 45587
Births: 0 **Total Expense ($000):** 40313 **Payroll Expense ($000):** 18879
Personnel: 240

TIPTON HOSPITAL See Indiana University Health Tipton Hospital

VALPARAISO—Porter County

✠ **PORTER REGIONAL HOSPITAL (150035)**, 85 East U.S. Highway 6,
Zip 46383–8947; tel. 219/983–8300, (Nonreporting) **A**1 9 10 **S** Community
Health Systems, Inc., Franklin, TN
Primary Contact: Stephen Lunn, Chief Executive Officer
COO: Ashley Dickinson, Chief Operating Officer
CFO: Cheryl A. Harmon, Chief Financial Officer
CMO: Ramireddy K. Tummuru, M.D., Chief Medical Officer
CIO: Robert Richardson, Information Technology Administrator
CHR: Angie Hampton, Director Human Resources
CNO: Taffy J. Arias, R.N., Chief Nursing Officer
Web address: www.porterhealth.com
Control: Corporation, Investor–owned, for–profit **Service:** General Medical and
Surgical

Staffed Beds: 276

PORTER–STARKE SERVICES (154052), 601 Wall Street, Zip 46383–2512;
tel. 219/531–3500 **A**10 **F**5 29 66 68 98 99 101 102 103 104 **P**6
Primary Contact: Rocco Schiralli, President/Chief Executive Officer
CFO: Mary Idstein, Chief Financial Officer
CMO: Anand Popli, Medical Director
Web address: www.porterstarke.org
Control: Other not–for–profit (including NFP Corporation) **Service:** Psychiatric

Staffed Beds: 16 **Admissions:** 692 **Census:** 8 **Outpatient Visits:** 104146
Births: 0 **Total Expense ($000):** 14425 **Payroll Expense ($000):** 8403
Personnel: 188

VINCENNES—Knox County

✠ △ **GOOD SAMARITAN HOSPITAL (150042)**, 520 South Seventh Street,
Zip 47591–1038; tel. 812/882–5220 **A**1 2 7 9 10 19 **F**3 5 8 11 13 15 17 18
20 22 28 29 30 31 32 34 35 38 40 45 46 47 48 49 51 53 54 56 57 58 59
60 63 64 65 66 67 68 70 74 75 76 77 78 79 81 82 84 85 87 89 90 92 93
96 97 98 99 100 101 102 103 104 106 107 108 110 111 115 118 119 120
121 123 127 129 130 131 132 133 134 135 144 145 146 147 148 **P**6
Primary Contact: Robert D. McLin, President and Chief Executive Officer
CFO: Jerry Stump, Chief Financial Officer
CMO: Charles C. Hedde, M.D., Chief Medical Officer
CIO: Marsha Danielsen, Director Information Systems
CHR: Dean Wagoner, Director Human Resources
CNO: Karen S. Haak, R.N., Chief Nursing Officer
Web address: www.gshvin.org/goodsamaritan
Control: County–Government, nonfederal **Service:** General Medical and Surgical

Staffed Beds: 196 **Admissions:** 7098 **Census:** 100 **Outpatient Visits:**
477140 **Births:** 472 **Total Expense ($000):** 200156 **Payroll Expense
($000):** 95788 **Personnel:** 1639

IN

Hospital, Medicare Provider Number, Address, Telephone, Approval, Facility, and Physician Codes, Health Care System

★ American Hospital Association (AHA) membership
☐ The Joint Commission accreditation ◇ DNV Healthcare Inc. accreditation
○ Healthcare Facilities Accreditation Program
△ Commission on Accreditation of Rehabilitation Facilities (CARF) accreditation

WABASH—Wabash County

⊞ **WABASH COUNTY HOSPITAL (151310)**, 710 North East Street,
Zip 46992–1924, Mailing Address: P.O. Box 548, Zip 46992–0548;
tel. 260/563–3131 **A**1 9 10 18 **F**3 11 15 32 34 35 45 47 50 53 57 58 59 62
63 64 65 68 69 75 77 80 81 84 85 86 87 93 97 107 108 111 114 119 124
130 131 132 133 146 147 **S** Alliant Management Services, Louisville, KY
Primary Contact: Marilyn J. Custer–Mitchell, President and Chief Executive Officer
CFO: Jane Bissel, Chief Financial Officer
CMO: Jeff Miller, M.D., Chief of Staff
CIO: David Brinson, Director Information Technology
CHR: Kimberly R. Shininger, Director Human Resources
CNO: Cathy Allyson Wolfe, Chief Nursing Officer
Web address: www.wchospital.com
Control: County–Government, nonfederal **Service:** General Medical and Surgical

> **Staffed Beds:** 25 **Admissions:** 638 **Census:** 6 **Outpatient Visits:** 47018
> **Births:** 0 **Total Expense ($000):** 38723 **Payroll Expense ($000):** 15431
> **Personnel:** 266

WARSAW—Kosciusko County

⊞ **KOSCIUSKO COMMUNITY HOSPITAL (150133)**, 2101 East Dubois Drive,
Zip 46580–3288; tel. 574/267–3200 **A**1 2 9 10 19 **F**3 8 12 13 15 28 29 30
31 32 34 35 40 42 44 50 51 53 57 58 59 64 65 68 70 74 75 76 77 78 79
81 82 85 86 89 90 93 107 108 110 111 114 115 116 117 118 119 120 121
129 130 131 132 144 146 147 148 **P**6 **S** Community Health Systems, Inc.,
Franklin, TN
Primary Contact: Stephen R. Miller, Chief Executive Officer
COO: Andy Guz, Chief Operating Officer
CFO: Douglas J. BeMent, Chief Financial Officer
CMO: Patrick Silveus, M.D., Medical Director
CIO: Tammy Lukens, Director Information
CHR: Joe Jarboe, Director Human Resources
CNO: Kim Finch, Chief Nursing Officer
Web address: www.kch.com
Control: Corporation, Investor–owned, for–profit **Service:** General Medical and
Surgical

> **Staffed Beds:** 72 **Admissions:** 3682 **Census:** 33 **Outpatient Visits:** 99169
> **Births:** 653 **Total Expense ($000):** 65684 **Payroll Expense ($000):** 22994
> **Personnel:** 479

★ **OTIS R. BOWEN CENTER FOR HUMAN SERVICES (154014)**, 850 North
Harrison Street, Zip 46580–3163, Mailing Address: 2621 East Jefferson Street,
Zip 46580–3880; tel. 574/267–7169 **A**9 10 **F**4 5 29 34 35 38 50 66 86 87
98 99 100 101 102 103 104 106 127 130 132 134 135 143 **P**1
Primary Contact: Kurt Carlson, Chief Executive Officer
Web address: www.bowencenter.org
Control: Other not–for–profit (including NFP Corporation) **Service:** Psychiatric

> **Staffed Beds:** 16 **Admissions:** 972 **Census:** 9 **Outpatient Visits:** 460866
> **Births:** 0 **Total Expense ($000):** 37852 **Payroll Expense ($000):** 24314
> **Personnel:** 714

WASHINGTON—Daviess County

⊞ △ **DAVIESS COMMUNITY HOSPITAL (150061)**, 1314 East Walnut Street,
Zip 47501–2860, Mailing Address: P.O. Box 760, Zip 47501–0760;
tel. 812/254–2760, (Nonreporting) **A**1 7 9 10 **S** QHR, Brentwood, TN
Primary Contact: David Bixler, Chief Executive Officer
CMO: Michael Baker, D.O., Chief of Staff
CIO: Richard Meinhart, Manager Information Systems
CHR: Marilyn Richard, Director Human Resources
Web address: www.dchosp.org
Control: County–Government, nonfederal **Service:** General Medical and Surgical

> **Staffed Beds:** 48

WEST LAFAYETTE—Tippecanoe County

★ **RIVER BEND HOSPITAL (154005)**, 2900 North River Road, Zip 47906–3744;
tel. 765/463–2555 **A**9 10 **F**98 102 103
Primary Contact: John R. Walling, President
COO: Tom Gillian, Chief Operating Officer
CFO: Jeff Nagy, Chief Financial Officer
CMO: Richard Rahdert, M.D., Medical Director
CIO: Craig Anderson, Director Management Information Systems
CHR: Jan Shaw, Director Personnel
CNO: Megan Gibson, Nurse Manager
Web address: www.nchsi.com/riverbendhospital.cfm
Control: Other not–for–profit (including NFP Corporation) **Service:** Psychiatric

> **Staffed Beds:** 16 **Admissions:** 831 **Census:** 13 **Outpatient Visits:** 0 **Births:**
> 0

WABASH VALLEY HOSPITAL See River Bend Hospital

WILLIAMSPORT—Warren County

⊞ **ST. VINCENT WILLIAMSPORT HOSPITAL (151307)**, 412 North Monroe
Street, Zip 47993–1049; tel. 765/762–4000 **A**1 9 10 18 **F**3 7 15 29 30 34 35
40 45 50 51 57 59 64 75 77 79 81 85 86 87 93 97 107 111 114 119 127
131 132 133 135 143 146 **P**6 **S** Ascension Health, Saint Louis, MO
Primary Contact: Jane Craigin, Chief Executive Officer
CFO: Janet Merritt, Chief Financial Officer
Web address: www.stvincent.org
Control: Other not–for–profit (including NFP Corporation) **Service:** General
Medical and Surgical

> **Staffed Beds:** 16 **Admissions:** 793 **Census:** 8 **Outpatient Visits:** 72114
> **Births:** 0 **Total Expense ($000):** 19991 **Payroll Expense ($000):** 9638
> **Personnel:** 145

WINAMAC—Pulaski County

★ **PULASKI MEMORIAL HOSPITAL (151305)**, 616 East 13th Street,
Zip 46996–1117, Mailing Address: P.O. Box 279, Zip 46996–0279;
tel. 574/946–2100 **A**9 10 18 **F**1 4 11 13 15 18 28 29 30 31 34 35 40 43 45
50 53 57 59 62 63 64 65 67 68 73 75 76 77 78 79 80 81 82 85 86 87 89
90 91 93 96 97 98 103 107 110 114 119 128 130 131 132 133 135 146 **P**6
Primary Contact: Thomas Barry, Chief Executive Officer
CFO: Gregg Malott, Chief Financial Officer
CMO: Rex Allman, M.D., President Medical Staff
CIO: Jeff Boer, Director Information Technology
CHR: Mark Fenn, Director Human Resources
CNO: Linda Webb, R.N., Chief Nursing Executive
Web address: www.pmhnet.com
Control: County–Government, nonfederal **Service:** General Medical and Surgical

> **Staffed Beds:** 25 **Admissions:** 629 **Census:** 7 **Outpatient Visits:** 23878
> **Births:** 101 **Total Expense ($000):** 21096 **Payroll Expense ($000):** 9858
> **Personnel:** 219

WINCHESTER—Randolph County

⊞ **ST. VINCENT RANDOLPH HOSPITAL (151301)**, 473 Greenville Avenue,
Zip 47394–9436, Mailing Address: P.O. Box 407, Zip 47394–0407;
tel. 765/584–0004 **A**1 9 10 18 **F**3 11 13 15 28 29 30 34 35 40 45 48 50 57
59 64 65 68 75 76 77 79 81 85 86 87 89 93 107 110 111 114 119 124 129
130 131 132 133 135 146 147 148 **S** Ascension Health, Saint Louis, MO
Primary Contact: Francis G. Albarano, Administrator
CFO: John Arthur, Chief Financial Officer
CMO: Daniel Wegg, M.D., Medical Director
CHR: Richard Ross Brodhead, Director Human Resources
CNO: Carla Fouse, Chief Nursing Officer
Web address: www.stvincent.org
Control: Other not–for–profit (including NFP Corporation) **Service:** General
Medical and Surgical

> **Staffed Beds:** 16 **Admissions:** 931 **Census:** 7 **Outpatient Visits:** 43514
> **Births:** 216 **Total Expense ($000):** 24814 **Payroll Expense ($000):** 9665
> **Personnel:** 173

IN

Many Facility Codes have changed. Please refer to the AHA Guide Code Chart. © 2014 AHA Guide

IOWA

ALBIA—Monroe County

★ **MONROE COUNTY HOSPITAL AND CLINICS (161342)**, 6580 165th Street, Zip 52531–8793; tel. 641/932–2134 **A**9 10 18 **F**7 11 15 28 29 31 34 40 45 50 57 59 63 78 81 85 107 110 114 119 127 130 132 133 **P**6
Primary Contact: Todd Willert, Chief Executive Officer
Web address: www.mchalbia.com
Control: County–Government, nonfederal **Service:** General Medical and Surgical

Staffed Beds: 25 **Admissions:** 385 **Census:** 5 **Outpatient Visits:** 48287
Births: 0 **Total Expense ($000):** 16539 **Payroll Expense ($000):** 7047
Personnel: 125

ALGONA—Kossuth County

★ **KOSSUTH REGIONAL HEALTH CENTER (161353)**, 1515 South Phillips Street, Zip 50511–3649; tel. 515/295–2451 **A**9 10 18 **F**11 13 15 17 28 29 30 31 32 34 35 36 40 41 43 50 56 57 59 62 63 64 65 67 68 70 75 76 77 78 81 82 84 86 87 89 90 92 93 97 107 114 119 127 128 129 130 131 132 133 135 146 147 148 **P**8 **S** Catholic Health East / Trinity Health, Livonia, MI
Primary Contact: Scott A. Curtis, Administrator and Chief Executive Officer
CFO: Jason Feucht, Chief Financial Officer
CMO: Michael Lampe, M.D., Chief of Staff
CIO: Nancy Erickson, Administrator Information Systems
CHR: Paula Seely, Manager Human Resources
CNO: Darlene M. Elbert, R.N., Assistant Administrator and Chief Nursing Officer
Web address: www.krhc.com
Control: County–Government, nonfederal **Service:** General Medical and Surgical

Staffed Beds: 23 **Admissions:** 688 **Census:** 9 **Outpatient Visits:** 26529
Births: 104 **Total Expense ($000):** 30237 **Payroll Expense ($000):** 9710
Personnel: 180

AMES—Story County

⊠ △ **MARY GREELEY MEDICAL CENTER (160030)**, 1111 Duff Avenue, Zip 50010–5745; tel. 515/239–2011, (Total facility includes 11 beds in nursing home–type unit) **A**1 2 7 9 10 19 **F**3 7 8 11 12 13 15 17 18 20 22 26 28 29 30 31 34 35 36 37 38 40 43 45 46 49 50 53 55 56 57 58 59 61 62 63 64 65 68 69 70 72 74 75 76 77 78 79 81 82 84 85 86 89 90 92 93 96 98 99 100 101 102 103 104 107 108 110 111 114 115 118 119 120 121 123 124 126 128 129 130 131 132 135 146 148
Primary Contact: Brian Dieter, President and Chief Executive Officer
CFO: Gary Botine, Vice President, Chief Financial Officer
CIO: Scott Carlson, Director
CHR: Betsy V. Schoeller, Director Human Resources and Education
Web address: www.mgmc.org
Control: City–Government, nonfederal **Service:** General Medical and Surgical

Staffed Beds: 192 **Admissions:** 8768 **Census:** 108 **Outpatient Visits:** 165418 **Births:** 1086 **Total Expense ($000):** 160318 **Payroll Expense ($000):** 61802 **Personnel:** 1114

ANAMOSA—Jones County

★ **UNITYPOINT HEALTH – JONES REGIONAL MEDICAL CENTER (161306)**, 1795 Highway 64 East, Zip 52205–2112; tel. 319/462–6131 **A**9 10 18 **F**3 7 11 12 15 28 29 30 31 34 35 38 40 43 45 50 56 57 59 64 68 71 75 81 82 84 85 87 91 93 96 97 99 100 101 102 103 104 107 110 111 114 118 119 130 132 133 135 145 146 148 **P**4 **S** UnityPoint Health, West Des Moines, IA
Primary Contact: Eric Briesemeister, Chief Executive Officer
CFO: Rachel Von Behren, Director Financial Services
CMO: Victor Salas, M.D., President Medical Staff
CHR: Donna Condry, Director Human Resources
Web address: www.jonesregional.org
Control: Other not–for–profit (including NFP Corporation) **Service:** General Medical and Surgical

Staffed Beds: 22 **Admissions:** 494 **Census:** 7 **Outpatient Visits:** 61921
Births: 0 **Total Expense ($000):** 18889 **Payroll Expense ($000):** 6323
Personnel: 127

ATLANTIC—Cass County

★ **CASS COUNTY MEMORIAL HOSPITAL (161376)**, 1501 East Tenth Street, Zip 50022–1997; tel. 712/243–3250 **A**9 10 18 **F**11 13 15 28 29 40 57 59 64 69 70 75 76 77 78 81 82 93 98 99 101 102 103 104 105 107 108 111 119 124 127 129 130 132 133 135 147 148 **P**8
Primary Contact: Todd R. Hudspeth, FACHE, Chief Executive Officer
CMO: James Brown, M.D., Chief of Staff
CIO: Jeff Osegard, Chief Information Officer
CHR: Donald D. Johnson, Assistant Administrator Human Resources
Web address: www.casshealth.org
Control: County–Government, nonfederal **Service:** General Medical and Surgical

Staffed Beds: 33 **Admissions:** 990 **Census:** 12 **Outpatient Visits:** 94889
Births: 139 **Total Expense ($000):** 35379 **Payroll Expense ($000):** 14092
Personnel: 312

AUDUBON—Audubon County

AUDUBON COUNTY MEMORIAL HOSPITAL (161330), 515 Pacific Street, Zip 50025–1056; tel. 712/563–2611 **A**9 10 18 **F**3 11 15 28 31 40 43 45 53 59 64 67 78 79 81 85 90 93 110 119 127 128 133 135
Primary Contact: Thomas G. Smith, Administrator and Chief Executive Officer
CFO: Karen McGuire, Chief Financial Officer
CMO: James Cunningham, D.O., Chief of Staff
CIO: Kelli Burgin, Director Information Technology
CNO: Holly Kjergaard, Chief Nursing Officer
Web address: www.acmhhosp.org
Control: County–Government, nonfederal **Service:** General Medical and Surgical

Staffed Beds: 25 **Admissions:** 133 **Census:** 2 **Outpatient Visits:** 15303
Births: 0 **Total Expense ($000):** 10134 **Payroll Expense ($000):** 4439
Personnel: 86

BELMOND—Wright County

★ ◇ **IOWA SPECIALTY HOSPITAL–BELMOND (161301)**, 403 First Street S.E., Zip 50421–1201; tel. 641/444–3223 **A**9 10 18 21 **F**3 7 11 15 28 29 32 34 35 40 43 45 46 50 53 56 57 59 62 63 64 65 67 68 75 77 79 81 82 85 87 89 92 93 96 97 107 110 111 119 128 129 131 133 135 146 148 **P**6 **S** Iowa Specialty Hospitals, Clarion, IA
Primary Contact: Amy McDaniel, Administrator and Chief Executive Officer
CFO: Greg Polzin, Chief Financial Officer
CMO: Charles B. Brindle, M.D., Chief Medical Staff
Web address: www.iowaspecialtyhospital.com
Control: City–Government, nonfederal **Service:** General Medical and Surgical

Staffed Beds: 22 **Admissions:** 366 **Census:** 5 **Outpatient Visits:** 23572
Births: 0 **Total Expense ($000):** 17246 **Payroll Expense ($000):** 3985
Personnel: 101

BETTENDORF—Scott County

⊠ **UNITYPOINT HEALTH – TRINITY BETTENDORF (160104)**, 4500 Utica Ridge Road, Zip 52722–1626; tel. 563/742–5000 **A**1 9 10 13 **F**3 11 13 15 18 20 22 26 29 30 34 35 37 40 44 45 46 48 50 57 58 59 63 64 70 74 75 76 79 81 82 84 85 86 87 93 96 97 107 108 110 114 119 130 132 135 146 147 148 **P**6 8 **S** UnityPoint Health, West Des Moines, IA
Primary Contact: Richard A. Seidler, FACHE, President and Chief Executive Officer
COO: Jay Willsher, Chief Operating Officer
CFO: Greg Pagliuzza, Chief Financial Officer
CMO: Paul McLoone, M.D., Chief Medical Officer
CHR: Cara Fuller, Vice President Human Resources
CNO: Jean B. Doerge, MS, Chief Nursing Executive
Web address: www.trinityqc.com
Control: Other not–for–profit (including NFP Corporation) **Service:** General Medical and Surgical

Staffed Beds: 76 **Admissions:** 3439 **Census:** 27 **Outpatient Visits:** 45692
Births: 760 **Total Expense ($000):** 60611 **Payroll Expense ($000):** 18684
Personnel: 347

IA

BLOOMFIELD—Davis County

★ **DAVIS COUNTY HOSPITAL (161327)**, 509 North Madison Street, Zip 52537–1271; tel. 641/664–2145, (Total facility includes 32 beds in nursing home–type unit) **A**9 10 18 **F**3 7 11 13 15 29 34 35 40 44 45 50 57 59 63 64 65 67 68 69 75 76 79 81 84 85 86 87 97 107 110 111 114 119 130 132 133 146 **P**6
Primary Contact: Deborah L. Herzberg, R.N., MS, FACHE, Chief Executive Officer
COO: Debbie Scott, Chief Operating Officer
CMO: Sean Brodale, D.O., Chief Medical Staff
CHR: Pam Young, Human Resources Leader
Web address: www.daviscountyhospital.org
Control: County–Government, nonfederal **Service:** General Medical and Surgical

Staffed Beds: 57 **Admissions:** 354 **Census:** 33 **Outpatient Visits:** 25160 **Births:** 27 **Total Expense ($000):** 21125 **Payroll Expense ($000):** 7751 **Personnel:** 161

BOONE—Boone County

★ **BOONE COUNTY HOSPITAL (161372)**, 1015 Union Street, Zip 50036–4821; tel. 515/432–3140, (Total facility includes 14 beds in nursing home–type unit) **A**9 10 18 **F**1 2 4 7 11 13 15 16 17 28 30 31 34 35 40 43 45 50 57 59 62 64 65 67 69 70 72 73 75 76 77 78 79 80 81 82 86 88 89 90 91 93 97 98 107 111 114 119 128 132 133 145 146 147 148 **P**6 **S** QHR, Brentwood, TN
Primary Contact: Joseph S. Smith, Chief Executive Officer
CFO: Joseph Devin, Chief Financial Officer
CMO: Tammara Chance, D.O., Chief of Staff
CIO: Matthew Sabus, Director Information Systems
CHR: Kim Schwartz, Assistant Administrator of Human Resources and Physician Services
Web address: www.boonehospital.com
Control: County–Government, nonfederal **Service:** General Medical and Surgical

Staffed Beds: 39 **Admissions:** 1591 **Census:** 16 **Outpatient Visits:** 59111 **Births:** 151 **Total Expense ($000):** 40887 **Payroll Expense ($000):** 16886 **Personnel:** 337

BRITT—Hancock County

★ **HANCOCK COUNTY HEALTH SYSTEM (161307)**, 532 First Street N.W., Zip 50423–1227; tel. 641/843–5000 **A**9 10 18 **F**3 15 28 29 31 34 35 36 40 43 45 46 53 56 57 59 62 64 65 75 77 81 82 85 93 97 104 107 110 114 119 129 130 131 132 133 135 146 148 **P**1 **S** Catholic Health East / Trinity Health, Livonia, MI
Primary Contact: Vance Jackson, FACHE, Administrator and Chief Executive Officer
CFO: Julie Damm, Chief Financial Officer
CMO: Catherine Butler, M.D., Chief Medical Staff
CIO: Julie Damm, Chief Financial Officer
CHR: Denise Jakoubeck, Director Human Resources
CNO: Laura Zwiefel, Chief Nursing Officer and Assistant Administration
Web address: www.trusthchs.com/hancock–county–health–system
Control: County–Government, nonfederal **Service:** General Medical and Surgical

Staffed Beds: 25 **Admissions:** 460 **Census:** 7 **Outpatient Visits:** 18309 **Births:** 0 **Total Expense ($000):** 16819 **Payroll Expense ($000):** 6099 **Personnel:** 153

CARROLL—Carroll County

★ **ST. ANTHONY REGIONAL HOSPITAL (160005)**, 311 South Clark Street, Zip 51401–3038, Mailing Address: P.O. Box 628, Zip 51401–0628; tel. 712/792–3581, (Total facility includes 79 beds in nursing home–type unit) **A**9 10 20 **F**6 11 13 15 28 29 30 31 34 35 37 38 39 40 43 44 45 46 50 51 56 57 59 60 61 63 64 65 67 68 69 70 74 75 76 77 78 79 81 82 84 85 86 87 89 93 97 98 99 100 101 102 103 104 107 108 110 111 115 118 119 125 127 129 130 131 132 133 134 135 145 146 147 148 **P**6
Primary Contact: Edward H. Smith, Jr., President and Chief Executive Officer
CFO: John Munson, Vice President and Chief Financial Officer
CMO: Thomas Dulaney, M.D., Chief of Staff
CIO: Randy Eischeid, Director Information Systems
CHR: Anna Fitzpatrick, Director Human Resources
CNO: Karen Timm, R.N., Vice President Patient Services
Web address: www.stanthonyhospital.org
Control: Church–operated, Nongovernment, not–for profit **Service:** General Medical and Surgical

Staffed Beds: 155 **Admissions:** 2556 **Census:** 107 **Outpatient Visits:** 97308 **Births:** 331 **Total Expense ($000):** 61704 **Payroll Expense ($000):** 25877 **Personnel:** 531

CEDAR FALLS—Black Hawk County

⊞ **SARTORI MEMORIAL HOSPITAL (160040)**, 515 College Street, Zip 50613–2500; tel. 319/268–3000 **A**1 9 10 **F**3 7 8 11 12 15 29 30 35 40 43 44 46 53 57 59 64 68 70 75 77 79 81 91 93 97 98 103 107 110 111 119 130 131 132 146 **P**1 6 **S** Wheaton Franciscan Healthcare, Wheaton, IL
Primary Contact: Rose Fowler, MS, Administrator
CFO: Michele Panicucci, Chief Financial Officer
CHR: Wayne C. Frangesch, Senior Vice President Human Resources
Web address: www.wheatoniowa.org
Control: Church–operated, Nongovernment, not–for profit **Service:** General Medical and Surgical

Staffed Beds: 50 **Admissions:** 1362 **Census:** 20 **Outpatient Visits:** 41924 **Births:** 0 **Total Expense ($000):** 30216 **Payroll Expense ($000):** 10570 **Personnel:** 182

CEDAR RAPIDS—Linn County

☐ **CONTINUING CARE HOSPITAL AT ST. LUKE'S (162002)**, 1026 A Avenue N.E., 6th Floor, Zip 52402–5036; tel. 319/369–8142 **A**1 10 **F**1 3 29 30 75 84 85 87 148 **S** Dubuis Health System, Houston, TX
Primary Contact: Elly Steffen, Chief Executive Officer and Administrator
CNO: Mary Beth Keuter, Director Patient Care
Web address: www.unitypoint.org/cedarrapids/services–continuing–care–hospital.aspx
Control: Other not–for–profit (including NFP Corporation) **Service:** Long–Term Acute Care hospital

Staffed Beds: 16 **Admissions:** 169 **Census:** 12 **Outpatient Visits:** 0 **Births:** 0 **Total Expense ($000):** 7184 **Payroll Expense ($000):** 2375 **Personnel:** 52

⊞ **MERCY MEDICAL CENTER–CEDAR RAPIDS (160079)**, 701 Tenth Street S.E., Zip 52403–1292; tel. 319/398–6011, (Total facility includes 76 beds in nursing home–type unit) **A**1 2 3 5 9 10 **F**3 5 11 12 15 29 30 31 32 33 34 35 36 38 40 43 44 45 48 49 50 54 55 56 57 59 60 61 62 63 64 65 67 68 70 71 72 74 75 76 77 78 79 81 82 84 85 86 87 88 89 90 91 92 93 94 98 99 100 101 102 103 104 107 108 109 110 111 114 115 116 117 118 119 120 121 123 124 126 128 130 131 132 135 143 145 146 147 148 **P**7 8
Primary Contact: Timothy L. Charles, President and Chief Executive Officer
CFO: Nathan VanGenderen, Executive Vice President and Chief Financial Officer
CMO: Mark Valliere, M.D., Senior Vice President Medical Affairs and Chief Medical Officer
CIO: Jeff Cash, Senior Vice President and Chief Information Officer
CHR: Doug Jontz, Senior Vice President Human Resources
CNO: Mary Brobst, R.N., Senior Vice President Patient Care Services and Chief Nursing Officer
Web address: www.mercycare.org
Control: Church–operated, Nongovernment, not–for profit **Service:** General Medical and Surgical

Staffed Beds: 314 **Admissions:** 11944 **Census:** 194 **Outpatient Visits:** 198561 **Births:** 657 **Total Expense ($000):** 269521 **Payroll Expense ($000):** 101759 **Personnel:** 1922

ST. LUKE'S HOSPITAL See UnityPoint Health – St. Luke's Hospital

⊞ △ **UNITYPOINT HEALTH – ST. LUKE'S HOSPITAL (160045)**, 1026 A Avenue N.E., Zip 52402–3026, Mailing Address: P.O. Box 3026, Zip 52406–3026; tel. 319/369–7211 **A**1 2 3 5 7 9 10 **F**3 5 8 11 12 13 14 15 17 18 19 20 22 24 26 28 29 30 31 32 34 35 36 37 39 40 43 45 46 49 50 54 55 56 57 59 60 61 62 63 64 65 66 70 72 74 75 76 77 78 79 81 82 84 85 86 87 88 89 90 91 92 93 95 96 98 99 100 101 103 104 105 107 108 110 111 114 115 118 119 121 126 130 131 132 134 135 145 146 147 148 **P**4 6 **S** UnityPoint Health, West Des Moines, IA
Primary Contact: Theodore E. Townsend, FACHE, President and Chief Executive Officer
COO: Michelle Niermann, Senior Vice President and Chief Operating Officer
CFO: Milton E. Aunan, II, CPA, Senior Vice President and Chief Financial Officer
CMO: Dustin Arnold, D.O., Vice President and Chief Medical Officer
CHR: Susan L. Slattery, Director Human Resources
CNO: Mary Ann Osborn, R.N., Senior Vice President and Chief Care Coordinator Officer
Web address: www.unitypoint.org
Control: Other not–for–profit (including NFP Corporation) **Service:** General Medical and Surgical

Staffed Beds: 347 **Admissions:** 15954 **Census:** 212 **Outpatient Visits:** 643894 **Births:** 2552 **Total Expense ($000):** 314826 **Payroll Expense ($000):** 120957 **Personnel:** 2303

IA

Many Facility Codes have changed. Please refer to the AHA Guide Code Chart. © 2014 AHA Guide

CENTERVILLE—Appanoose County

★ **MERCY MEDICAL CENTER–CENTERVILLE (161377)**, 1 St. Joseph's Drive,
Zip 52544–8055; tel. 641/437–4111, (Total facility includes 20 beds in nursing
home–type unit) **A**9 10 18 **F**1 3 4 8 11 13 15 16 17 28 29 30 31 34 40 45 46
50 54 57 59 64 67 70 72 73 75 76 77 78 79 80 81 85 86 87 88 89 90 93
97 98 107 110 111 113 115 117 119 127 128 129 130 132 133 135 **P**6
S Catholic Health Initiatives, Englewood, CO
Primary Contact: Clinton J. Christianson, FACHE, President
CHR: Tonya Clawson, Manager Human Resources
CNO: Sherri L. Doggett, Vice President Patient Services
Web address: www.mercycenterville.org
Control: Church–operated, Nongovernment, not–for profit **Service:** General
Medical and Surgical

> **Staffed Beds:** 45 **Admissions:** 754 **Census:** 27 **Outpatient Visits:** 83456
> **Births:** 65 **Total Expense ($000):** 22891 **Payroll Expense ($000):** 9505
> **Personnel:** 188

CHARITON—Lucas County

★ **LUCAS COUNTY HEALTH CENTER (161341)**, 1200 North Seventh Street,
Zip 50049–1258; tel. 641/774–3000 **A**9 10 18 **F**3 5 7 13 15 28 29 31 34 38
40 41 43 44 45 47 50 64 66 68 70 75 76 77 81 85 86 87 89 93 97 104
107 115 119 127 128 130 131 132 133 143 145 146 148
Primary Contact: Veronica Fuhs, Chief Executive Officer
CFO: Larry Brown, Chief Financial Officer
CMO: Christy Manganello, M.D., Chief of Staff
CIO: Terri Black, Network Manager
CHR: Lana Kuball, Director Administrative Services
CNO: JoBeth Lawless, Chief Nursing Officer, Nursing Services and Director
Emergency Management Services
Web address: www.lchcia.com
Control: County–Government, nonfederal **Service:** General Medical and Surgical

> **Staffed Beds:** 25 **Admissions:** 452 **Census:** 5 **Outpatient Visits:** 17562
> **Births:** 65 **Total Expense ($000):** 18085 **Payroll Expense ($000):** 8628
> **Personnel:** 203

CHARLES CITY—Floyd County

FLOYD COUNTY MEDICAL CENTER (161347), 800 Eleventh Street,
Zip 50616–3499; tel. 641/228–6830 **A**9 10 18 **F**3 11 13 15 28 29 31 34 35
40 45 48 57 59 64 69 75 79 81 85 91 93 97 107 115 119 127 130 132 133
146 148 **S** Mayo Clinic, Rochester, MN
Primary Contact: Bill D. Faust, Administrator
CFO: Ronald Timpe, Chief Financial Officer
CHR: Don Nosbisch, Director Human Resources
Web address: www.fcmc.us.com/
Control: County–Government, nonfederal **Service:** General Medical and Surgical

> **Staffed Beds:** 25 **Admissions:** 929 **Census:** 12 **Outpatient Visits:** 54528
> **Births:** 72 **Total Expense ($000):** 22674 **Payroll Expense ($000):** 8342
> **Personnel:** 170

CHEROKEE—Cherokee County

★ **CHEROKEE REGIONAL MEDICAL CENTER (161362)**, 300 Sioux Valley Drive,
Zip 51012–1205; tel. 712/225–5101 **A**9 10 18 **F**7 11 13 15 17 28 29 34 35
40 43 45 53 56 57 59 62 63 64 65 67 68 69 75 76 77 78 81 84 86 87 89
93 96 97 107 111 114 117 119 125 127 128 129 130 131 132 133 135
146 147 148 **P**6
Primary Contact: John M. Comstock, Chief Executive Officer
CFO: Joan Bierman, Vice President Finance
Web address: www.cherokeermc.org
Control: Other not–for–profit (including NFP Corporation) **Service:** General
Medical and Surgical

> **Staffed Beds:** 25 **Admissions:** 1020 **Census:** 10 **Outpatient Visits:** 43791
> **Births:** 158 **Total Expense ($000):** 19929 **Payroll Expense ($000):** 8808
> **Personnel:** 175

☐ **MENTAL HEALTH INSTITUTE (164002)**, 1251 West Cedar Loop,
Zip 51012–1599; tel. 712/225–2594 **A**1 9 10 **F**98 99 100 101 102 104
130 **P**6
Primary Contact: Daniel Gillette, M.D., Clinical Director
CFO: Tony Morris, Business Manager
CMO: Daniel Gillette, M.D., Clinical Director
CHR: Mary Ann Hanson, Director Personnel
Web address: www.dhs.state.ia.us
Control: State–Government, nonfederal **Service:** Psychiatric

> **Staffed Beds:** 37 **Admissions:** 468 **Census:** 29 **Outpatient Visits:** 37 **Births:**
> 0 **Total Expense ($000):** 16661 **Payroll Expense ($000):** 9320 **Personnel:**
> 173

CLARINDA—Page County

★ **CLARINDA REGIONAL HEALTH CENTER (161352)**, 220 Essie Davison Drive,
Zip 51632–2915, Mailing Address: P.O. Box 217, Zip 51632–0217;
tel. 712/542–2176 **A**9 10 18 **F**3 7 11 15 28 29 31 34 36 40 43 50 57 59 64
65 66 69 74 75 77 78 79 81 82 85 86 87 93 97 107 110 111 114 118 119
124 127 128 129 130 132 133 135 143 146 148 **P**3 6
Primary Contact: Christopher R. Stipe, FACHE, Chief Executive Officer
COO: Elaine Otte, Chief Operating Officer
CFO: Melissa Walter, Chief Financial Officer
CMO: Autumn Morales, Chief Medical Staff Officer
CIO: Richard Morgan–Fine, IT Director
CHR: Tammie Driftmier, PHR, Director Human Resources
CNO: Sherrie L. Laubenthal, R.N., Chief Nursing Officer
Web address: www.clarindahealth.com
Control: City–Government, nonfederal **Service:** General Medical and Surgical

> **Staffed Beds:** 25 **Admissions:** 480 **Census:** 4 **Outpatient Visits:** 59385
> **Births:** 0 **Total Expense ($000):** 24961 **Payroll Expense ($000):** 9496
> **Personnel:** 224

MENTAL HEALTH INSTITUTE (164005), 1800 North 16th Street,
Zip 51632–1101; tel. 712/542–2161, (Total facility includes 20 beds in nursing
home–type unit) **A**9 10 **F**67 98 101 103 130 146 **P**6
Primary Contact: Kristine Weitzell, Superintendent
COO: Kristine Weitzell, Superintendent
CFO: Meredith Baker, Business Manager
CMO: Teresa Rosales, M.D., Clinical Director
CIO: Teresa Barlow, Medical Records Administrator
CHR: Sandy Davison, Personnel Assistant
Web address: www.dhs.state.ia.us/
Control: State–Government, nonfederal **Service:** Psychiatric

> **Staffed Beds:** 35 **Admissions:** 282 **Census:** 29 **Outpatient Visits:** 0 **Births:**
> 0 **Total Expense ($000):** 7143 **Payroll Expense ($000):** 5152 **Personnel:**
> 86

CLARION—Wright County

★ ◇ **IOWA SPECIALTY HOSPITAL–CLARION (161302)**, 1316 South Main
Street, Zip 50525–2019; tel. 515/532–2811 **A**9 10 18 21 **F**11 13 15 28 29 31
32 34 35 40 43 45 46 50 56 57 59 63 64 65 68 69 75 76 77 79 81 82 85
86 87 92 93 97 107 110 111 114 119 125 127 129 131 132 133 134 135
146 148 **P**6 **S** Iowa Specialty Hospitals, Clarion, IA
Primary Contact: Steven J. Simonin, Chief Executive Officer
COO: Kirk Rier, Chief Operating Officer
CFO: Greg Polzin, Chief Financial Officer
CMO: Dennis Colby, M.D., Chief of Staff
CHR: Holly Martin, Human Resources Leader
CNO: Abby Young, Chief Nursing Officer
Web address: www.iowaspecialtyhospital.com
Control: City–Government, nonfederal **Service:** General Medical and Surgical

> **Staffed Beds:** 25 **Admissions:** 1331 **Census:** 9 **Outpatient Visits:** 98530
> **Births:** 219 **Total Expense ($000):** 48781 **Payroll Expense ($000):** 18869
> **Personnel:** 339

CLINTON—Clinton County

⊠ **MERCY MEDICAL CENTER–CLINTON (160080)**, 1410 North Fourth Street,
Zip 52732–2940; tel. 563/244–5555, (Includes MERCY SERVICES FOR AGING,
600 14th Avenue North, Zip 52732; tel. 563/244–3888), (Total facility includes
183 beds in nursing home–type unit) **A**1 9 10 19 20 **F**3 11 13 15 18 20 22 28
29 30 31 34 35 36 38 40 44 45 47 49 50 53 56 57 59 60 61 62 63 64 68
70 74 75 76 77 78 79 80 81 82 84 85 87 89 93 98 99 100 101 102 103
107 108 110 115 118 119 121 123 128 129 130 132 146 148 **S** Catholic
Health East / Trinity Health, Livonia, MI
Primary Contact: Sean J. Williams, President and Chief Executive Officer
CFO: Paul Mangin, Vice President Finance
CHR: Shane Buer, Vice President, Human Resources
CNO: Amy Berentes, R.N., Vice President Patient Care Services
Web address: www.mercyclinton.com
Control: Church–operated, Nongovernment, not–for profit **Service:** General
Medical and Surgical

> **Staffed Beds:** 307 **Admissions:** 5597 **Census:** 187 **Outpatient Visits:** 66355
> **Births:** 461 **Total Expense ($000):** 89854 **Payroll Expense ($000):** 37280
> **Personnel:** 794

IA

Hospital, Medicare Provider Number, Address, Telephone, Approval, Facility, and Physician Codes, Health Care System

★ American Hospital Association (AHA) membership
☐ The Joint Commission accreditation   ◇ DNV Healthcare Inc. accreditation
○ Healthcare Facilities Accreditation Program
△ Commission on Accreditation of Rehabilitation Facilities (CARF) accreditation

---

CORALVILLE—Johnson County

IOWA MEDICAL AND CLASSIFICATION CENTER, 2700 Coral Ridge Avenue, Zip 52241–4708, Mailing Address: 2700 Coral Rigde Avenue, Zip 52241; tel. 319/626–2391 **F**29 38 39 59 75 98 101 102 103 105 130 132 143
Primary Contact: Daniel Craig, Warden
Web address: www.oakdaleprison.com/
Control: State–Government, nonfederal **Service:** Psychiatric

> **Staffed Beds:** 24 **Admissions:** 46 **Census:** 17 **Outpatient Visits:** 0 **Births:** 0 **Total Expense ($000):** 2527 **Personnel:** 26

CORNING—Adams County

★ **CHI HEALTH MERCY CORNING (161304)**, 603 Rosary Drive, Zip 50841–1683; tel. 641/322–3121 **A**9 10 18 **F**3 11 15 28 30 31 34 40 43 50 53 56 57 59 64 67 74 75 77 78 79 81 85 97 107 110 114 119 127 128 129 130 133 135 146 147 148 **P**6 **S** Catholic Health Initiatives, Englewood, CO
Primary Contact: Debra Goldsmith, Regional Administrator
CMO: Maen Haddadin, M.D., President Medical Staff
CIO: Kenneth Lawonn, Senior Vice President and Chief Information Officer
CHR: Sandra Lammers, Coordinator Human Resources and Finance
CNO: Jane Carmody, R.N., Vice President and System Chief Nursing Officer
Web address: www.alegent.com
Control: Church–operated, Nongovernment, not–for profit **Service:** General Medical and Surgical

> **Staffed Beds:** 22 **Admissions:** 291 **Census:** 3 **Outpatient Visits:** 63110 **Births:** 0 **Total Expense ($000):** 16704 **Payroll Expense ($000):** 4762 **Personnel:** 130

CORYDON—Wayne County

★ **WAYNE COUNTY HOSPITAL (161358)**, 417 South East Street, Zip 50060–1860, Mailing Address: P.O. Box 305, Zip 50060–0305; tel. 641/872–2260 **A**9 10 18 **F**7 10 13 15 28 29 34 35 39 40 43 51 56 57 59 60 69 70 75 76 77 79 81 85 87 89 91 92 93 97 107 110 114 119 125 127 130 131 132 133 148 **P**6
Primary Contact: Daren Relph, Chief Executive Officer
COO: Michael Thomas, Associate Administrator
CFO: Diane Hook, Chief Financial Officer
CMO: Joel Baker, D.O., Chief Medical Officer
CIO: Laurie Ehrich, Chief Communications Officer
CHR: Dave Carlyle, Director Human Resources
CNO: Sheila Mattly, Chief Nursing Officer
Web address: www.waynecountyhospital.org
Control: County–Government, nonfederal **Service:** General Medical and Surgical

> **Staffed Beds:** 25 **Admissions:** 695 **Census:** 7 **Outpatient Visits:** 20768 **Births:** 148 **Total Expense ($000):** 23568 **Payroll Expense ($000):** 11606 **Personnel:** 223

COUNCIL BLUFFS—Pottawattamie County

⊞ **CHI HEALTH MERCY COUNCIL BLUFFS (160028)**, 800 Mercy Drive, Zip 51503–3128, Mailing Address: P.O. Box 1C, Zip 51502–3001; tel. 712/328–5000 **A**1 9 10 **F**3 5 11 12 13 15 18 20 22 28 29 30 31 34 35 38 39 40 43 44 47 48 49 50 56 57 59 62 64 65 68 70 74 75 76 77 78 79 81 82 84 85 87 89 93 97 98 99 100 101 102 103 104 105 106 107 108 110 111 114 115 119 129 130 132 134 135 143 146 147 148 **P**6 8 **S** Catholic Health Initiatives, Englewood, CO
Primary Contact: Marie E. Knedler, R.N., FACHE, President
CFO: Jeanette Wojtalewicz, Chief Financial Officer
CMO: Joseph Hoagbin, M.D., Chief Quality Officer
CIO: Karun Kapur, Senior Vice President and Chief Information Officer
CHR: Nancy Wallace, Senior Vice President Human Resources
CNO: Jane Carmody, R.N., Vice President and System Chief Nursing Officer
Web address: www.alegent.com/mercy
Control: Church–operated, Nongovernment, not–for profit **Service:** General Medical and Surgical

> **Staffed Beds:** 163 **Admissions:** 7816 **Census:** 85 **Outpatient Visits:** 107547 **Births:** 608 **Total Expense ($000):** 81161 **Payroll Expense ($000):** 34148 **Personnel:** 642

JENNIE EDMUNDSON HOSPITAL See Methodist Jennie Edmundson Hospital

⊞ **METHODIST JENNIE EDMUNDSON HOSPITAL (160047)**, 933 East Pierce Street, Zip 51503–4652, Mailing Address: P.O. Box 2C, Zip 51502–3002; tel. 712/396–6000 **A**1 2 5 9 10 **F**3 11 13 15 18 20 22 26 28 29 30 31 34 35 39 40 43 44 45 47 49 50 57 58 59 61 64 68 70 74 75 76 78 79 81 82 85 86 87 89 92 93 98 100 101 102 103 107 108 110 111 114 115 116 118 119 121 123 129 130 131 132 135 143 145 146 147 148 **S** Nebraska Methodist Health System, Inc., Omaha, NE
Primary Contact: Steven P. Baumert, President and Chief Executive Officer
CFO: Linda K. Burt, Corporate Vice President Finance
CMO: Michael A. Romano, M.D., Vice President Medical Affairs
CIO: Roger Hertz, Vice President
CHR: Holly Huerter, Vice President Human Resources
CNO: Peggy Helget, R.N., Vice President Patient Services and Chief Nursing Officer
Web address: www.bestcare.org
Control: Other not–for–profit (including NFP Corporation) **Service:** General Medical and Surgical

> **Staffed Beds:** 114 **Admissions:** 4849 **Census:** 56 **Outpatient Visits:** 56508 **Births:** 377 **Total Expense ($000):** 86438 **Payroll Expense ($000):** 34441 **Personnel:** 479

CRESCO—Howard County

★ **REGIONAL HEALTH SERVICES OF HOWARD COUNTY (161328)**, 235 Eighth Avenue West, Zip 52136–1098; tel. 563/547–2101 **A**9 10 18 **F**7 11 13 15 18 28 29 34 35 36 40 43 44 50 57 59 62 63 64 65 68 75 76 77 81 82 85 86 87 93 107 110 114 127 128 130 132 133 146 148 **P**8 **S** Catholic Health East / Trinity Health, Livonia, MI
Primary Contact: Robin M. Schluter, Chief Executive Officer
CFO: Brenda Moser, Vice President Finance
CMO: Paul Jensen, M.D., Chief of Staff
CIO: Brenda Moser, Chief Information Officer
CHR: Connie Kuennen, Director Human Resources and Community Relations
CNO: Staci Vrzak, Vice President Patient Care Services
Web address: www.rhshc.com
Control: County–Government, nonfederal **Service:** General Medical and Surgical

> **Staffed Beds:** 20 **Admissions:** 317 **Census:** 4 **Outpatient Visits:** 22058 **Births:** 55 **Total Expense ($000):** 15543 **Payroll Expense ($000):** 5950 **Personnel:** 146

CRESTON—Union County

★ **GREATER REGIONAL MEDICAL CENTER (161365)**, 1700 West Townline Street Suite 3, Zip 50801–1099; tel. 641/782–7091 **A**9 10 18 **F**3 7 11 13 15 28 29 31 34 35 40 43 45 50 56 57 59 63 64 65 66 70 75 76 77 78 79 81 82 84 85 86 93 96 97 107 108 109 110 111 115 119 120 121 122 123 124 125 127 129 130 131 132 133 135 146 148 **P**6 **S** UnityPoint Health, West Des Moines, IA
Primary Contact: Monte Neitzel, Chief Executive Officer
CFO: Matt McCutchan, Chief Financial Officer
CMO: Karen Krogstad, M.D., Chief Medical Officer
CIO: Karla Alford, Chief Information Officer
CHR: Lisa Ross, Human Resources Officer
CNO: Gwen Buck, R.N., Chief Nursing Officer
Web address: www.greaterregional.org
Control: County–Government, nonfederal **Service:** General Medical and Surgical

> **Staffed Beds:** 25 **Admissions:** 759 **Census:** 7 **Outpatient Visits:** 71569 **Births:** 168 **Total Expense ($000):** 43174 **Payroll Expense ($000):** 17940 **Personnel:** 269

DAVENPORT—Scott County

⊞ △ **GENESIS MEDICAL CENTER–DAVENPORT (160033)**, 1227 East Rusholme Street, Zip 52803–2498; tel. 563/421–1000, (Includes GENESIS MEDICAL CENTER–EAST CAMPUS, 1227 East Rusholme Street, Zip 52803; tel. 563/421–1000; GENESIS MEDICAL CENTER–WEST CAMPUS, 1401 West Central Park, Zip 52804–1769; tel. 563/421–1000) **A**1 2 3 5 7 9 10 **F**3 7 11 12 13 15 18 20 22 24 26 28 29 30 31 34 35 37 38 40 43 44 46 49 50 53 54 57 58 59 60 63 64 68 70 72 74 75 77 78 79 80 81 82 84 85 86 87 89 91 92 93 94 96 97 98 100 102 107 110 111 114 115 116 118 119 120 121 123 124 126 129 130 131 132 135 146 147 148 **P**6 **S** Genesis Health System, Davenport, IA
Primary Contact: Wayne A. Diewald, President
CFO: Mark G. Rogers, Interim Vice President Finance and Chief Financial Officer
CMO: Frank Claudy, M.D., Vice President Medical Staff Affairs
CIO: Robert Frieden, Vice President Information Systems
CHR: Heidi Kahly–McMahon, Interim Vice President Human Resources
Web address: www.genesishealth.com
Control: Other not–for–profit (including NFP Corporation) **Service:** General Medical and Surgical

> **Staffed Beds:** 338 **Admissions:** 16789 **Census:** 191 **Outpatient Visits:** 184631 **Births:** 2011 **Total Expense ($000):** 300328 **Payroll Expense ($000):** 86193 **Personnel:** 1600

✠ **SELECT SPECIALTY HOSPITAL–QUAD CITIES (162001)**, 1111 West Kimberly Road, Zip 52806–5711; tel. 563/468–2000 **A**1 10 **F**1 3 29 75 77 85 100 119 130 148 **S** Select Medical Corporation, Mechanicsburg, PA
Primary Contact: Austin B. Cleveland, Chief Executive Officer
Web address: www.selectspecialtyhospitals.com/company/locations/quadcities.aspx
Control: Corporation, Investor–owned, for–profit **Service:** Long–Term Acute Care hospital

Staffed Beds: 50 **Admissions:** 404 **Census:** 31 **Outpatient Visits:** 0 **Births:** 0 **Total Expense ($000):** 15438 **Payroll Expense ($000):** 6653 **Personnel:** 140

DE WITT—Clinton County

✠ **GENESIS MEDICAL CENTER, DEWITT (161313)**, 1118 11th Street, Zip 52742–1296; tel. 563/659–4200, (Total facility includes 75 beds in nursing home–type unit) **A**1 9 10 18 **F**7 11 15 29 30 31 34 35 38 40 43 44 50 53 57 59 64 74 75 77 78 79 81 85 86 87 97 102 107 110 111 114 119 129 130 131 132 133 135 **P**6 **S** Genesis Health System, Davenport, IA
Primary Contact: Curt Coleman, FACHE, Administrator
CMO: Steven Fowler, M.D., President Medical Staff
CHR: Kristin Nicholson, Coordinator Human Resources
CNO: Wanda Haack, MSN, Chief Nursing Officer
Web address: www.genesishealth.com
Control: Other not–for–profit (including NFP Corporation) **Service:** General Medical and Surgical

Staffed Beds: 86 **Admissions:** 237 **Census:** 73 **Outpatient Visits:** 18217 **Births:** 0 **Total Expense ($000):** 17110 **Payroll Expense ($000):** 6785 **Personnel:** 159

DECORAH—Winneshiek County

✠ **WINNESHIEK MEDICAL CENTER (161371)**, 901 Montgomery Street, Zip 52101–2325; tel. 563/382–2911 **A**1 9 10 18 **F**3 7 8 11 13 15 28 29 31 34 35 38 40 43 45 50 56 57 59 61 62 63 64 65 68 69 70 75 76 77 78 79 81 82 86 87 93 97 102 104 107 110 111 114 119 128 129 130 131 132 133 135 144 146 147 148 **S** Mayo Clinic, Rochester, MN
Primary Contact: Lisa Radtke, Interim Chief Administrative Officer
CFO: Lynn Luloff, Chief Financial Officer
CMO: Robert Flinchbaugh, D.O., Chief Medical Officer
CHR: Laurie Bulman, Director Human Resources
CNO: Linda Klimesh, Chief Nursing Officer
Web address: www.winmedical.org
Control: County–Government, nonfederal **Service:** General Medical and Surgical

Staffed Beds: 25 **Admissions:** 1140 **Census:** 12 **Outpatient Visits:** 60371 **Births:** 234 **Total Expense ($000):** 45475 **Payroll Expense ($000):** 16807 **Personnel:** 358

DENISON—Crawford County

★ **CRAWFORD COUNTY MEMORIAL HOSPITAL (161369)**, 100 Medical Parkway, Zip 51442–2299; tel. 712/265–2500 **A**9 10 18 **F**3 7 8 11 13 15 17 28 29 31 34 35 40 45 50 54 56 57 59 64 65 67 68 70 75 76 77 78 79 81 82 85 87 89 93 97 107 110 111 114 119 127 128 133 135 148 **P**6
Primary Contact: Bill Bruce, FACHE, Chief Executive Officer
CFO: Rachel Melby, Controller
CIO: Angie Anderson, Director Information Technology
CNO: Diane Arkfeld, R.N., Vice President, Clinical Nursing
Web address: www.ccmhia.com
Control: County–Government, nonfederal **Service:** General Medical and Surgical

Staffed Beds: 25 **Admissions:** 687 **Census:** 6 **Outpatient Visits:** 39071 **Births:** 119 **Total Expense ($000):** 26760 **Payroll Expense ($000):** 11900 **Personnel:** 211

DES MOINES—Polk County

✠ **BROADLAWNS MEDICAL CENTER (160101)**, 1801 Hickman Road, Zip 50314–1597; tel. 515/282–2200 **A**1 3 5 9 10 **F**2 3 5 11 13 15 18 29 30 31 32 34 35 38 39 40 43 44 45 48 50 52 53 56 57 58 59 64 65 66 68 70 74 75 76 77 78 79 81 82 85 86 87 97 98 99 100 101 102 103 104 105 106 107 111 114 119 129 130 131 132 135 144 146 147 148 **P**6
Primary Contact: Jody J. Jenner, President and Chief Executive Officer
CFO: Al White, CPA, Senior Vice President Business Services
CMO: Vincent Mandracchia, DPM, Chief Medical Officer
CNO: Susan N. Kirstein, R.N., Chief Nursing Officer
Web address: www.broadlawns.org
Control: County–Government, nonfederal **Service:** General Medical and Surgical

Staffed Beds: 95 **Admissions:** 3148 **Census:** 48 **Outpatient Visits:** 214272 **Births:** 288 **Total Expense ($000):** 116473 **Payroll Expense ($000):** 52064 **Personnel:** 855

DES MOINES DIVISION See Veterans Affairs Central Iowa Health Care System

IOWA LUTHERAN HOSPITAL See UnityPoint Health – Des Moines

✠ △ **MERCY MEDICAL CENTER–DES MOINES (160083)**, 1111 6th Avenue, Zip 50314–2611; tel. 515/247–3121, (Includes MERCY FRANKLIN CENTER, 1818 48th Street, Zip 50310; tel. 515/271–6000) **A**1 2 7 9 10 13 **F**3 4 5 6 7 8 9 10 11 13 15 16 17 18 19 20 21 22 23 24 25 26 27 28 29 30 31 32 34 35 36 38 39 40 41 43 44 46 48 49 50 53 54 56 57 58 59 60 61 62 63 64 65 66 68 70 71 72 73 74 75 76 77 78 79 81 82 84 85 86 87 88 89 90 91 92 93 94 96 97 98 99 100 101 102 103 104 105 106 107 108 109 110 111 114 115 116 117 118 119 120 121 123 124 125 126 129 130 131 132 134 135 138 141 142 143 144 145 146 147 148 **P**6 **S** Catholic Health Initiatives, Englewood, CO
Primary Contact: Robert P. Ritz, FACHE, President
COO: Jacqueline C. Frost–Kunnen, R.N., Senior Vice President Operations
CFO: Michael Wegner, Senior Vice President and Chief Financial Officer
CMO: Tommy Ibrahim, Chief Physician Officer
CIO: Cristina Thomas, Vice President and Chief Information Officer
CHR: Kevin Elsberry, Senior Vice President Human Resources
CNO: Mary J. Brown, R.N., Vice President and Chief Nursing Officer
Web address: www.mercydesmoines.org
Control: Church–operated, Nongovernment, not–for profit **Service:** General Medical and Surgical

Staffed Beds: 583 **Admissions:** 28896 **Census:** 407 **Outpatient Visits:** 246152 **Births:** 4861 **Total Expense ($000):** 565578 **Payroll Expense ($000):** 221716 **Personnel:** 3580

★ ◇ **UNITYPOINT HEALTH – DES MOINES (160024)**, 700 East University Avenue, Zip 50316–2392; tel. 515/263–5612, (Total facility includes 12 beds in nursing home–type unit) **A**3 5 9 10 21 **F**3 4 5 8 11 13 15 17 18 20 22 26 28 29 30 34 35 38 39 40 43 44 45 49 50 51 53 56 57 58 59 60 61 64 65 68 70 71 74 75 76 79 81 82 84 85 86 87 93 96 97 98 99 100 101 102 103 104 105 107 108 110 111 114 115 118 119 128 130 132 134 135 146 147 148 **P**6 **S** UnityPoint Health, West Des Moines, IA
Primary Contact: Eric T. Crowell, President and Chief Executive Officer
COO: Eric L. Lothe, Vice President and Administrator
CFO: Joe Corfits, Chief Financial Officer
CMO: Mark Purtle, M.D., Vice President Medical Affairs
CHR: Joyce McDanel, Vice President Human Resources and Education
Web address: www.iowahealth.org
Control: Other not–for–profit (including NFP Corporation) **Service:** General Medical and Surgical

Staffed Beds: 187 **Admissions:** 7513 **Census:** 110 **Outpatient Visits:** 56459 **Births:** 413 **Total Expense ($000):** 109763 **Payroll Expense ($000):** 47205 **Personnel:** 821

★ △ ◇ **UNITYPOINT HEALTH – IOWA METHODIST MEDICAL CENTER (160082)**, 1200 Pleasant Street, Zip 50309–1406; tel. 515/241–6212, (Includes POWELL CONVALESCENT CENTER, 1200 Pleasant, Zip 50309; RAYMOND BLANK MEMORIAL HOSPITAL FOR CHILDREN, Zip 50308; UNITY POINT HEALTH – JOHN STODDARD CANCER CENTER, 1221 Pleasant Street, Zip 50309–1423; tel. 515/241–6212; UNITYPOINT HEALTH – BLANK CHILDREN'S HOSPITAL, 1200 Pleasant Street, tel. 515/241–5437; UNITYPOINT HEALTH – METHODIST WEST HOSPITAL, 1660 60th Street, West Des Moines, Zip 50266–7700; tel. 515/343–1000; YOUNKER MEMORIAL REHABILITATION CENTER, 1200 Pleasant Road, Zip 50308) **A**2 7 8 9 10 21 **F**3 7 8 11 12 13 17 18 20 22 24 26 29 30 31 32 34 35 39 40 41 43 44 45 46 47 49 50 53 54 55 56 57 58 59 60 61 64 65 68 70 71 72 74 75 76 77 78 79 81 82 84 85 86 87 88 89 90 91 92 93 94 96 97 100 107 108 111 114 115 116 117 118 119 120 121 123 124 126 129 130 131 132 134 135 138 146 147 148 **P**6 **S** UnityPoint Health, West Des Moines, IA
Primary Contact: Eric T. Crowell, President and Chief Executive Officer
COO: Steve R. Stephenson, M.D., Executive Vice President and Chief Operating Officer
CFO: Joe Corfits, Senior Vice President Finance
CMO: Mark Purtle, M.D., Vice President Medical Affairs
CHR: Joyce McDanel, Vice President Human Resources and Education
Web address: www.iowahealth.org
Control: Other not–for–profit (including NFP Corporation) **Service:** General Medical and Surgical

Staffed Beds: 478 **Admissions:** 24488 **Census:** 343 **Outpatient Visits:** 265315 **Births:** 4157 **Total Expense ($000):** 507392 **Payroll Expense ($000):** 211638 **Personnel:** 3658

IA

Hospital, Medicare Provider Number, Address, Telephone, Approval, Facility, and Physician Codes, Health Care System

★ American Hospital Association (AHA) membership
□ The Joint Commission accreditation
◇ DNV Healthcare Inc. accreditation
○ Healthcare Facilities Accreditation Program
△ Commission on Accreditation of Rehabilitation Facilities (CARF) accreditation

✠ △ **VETERANS AFFAIRS CENTRAL IOWA HEALTH CARE SYSTEM**, 3600 30th Street, Zip 50310–5753; tel. 515/699–5999, (Includes DES MOINES DIVISION, 3600 30th Street, Zip 50310–5774; tel. 515/699–5999; KNOXVILLE DIVISION, 1515 West Pleasant, Knoxville, Zip 50138–3399; tel. 515/842–3101), (Total facility includes 140 beds in nursing home–type unit) **A**1 3 5 7 9 **F**2 3 5 11 15 18 20 22 28 29 30 31 33 34 35 36 38 39 40 44 45 46 50 53 56 57 59 61 62 63 64 65 66 70 71 74 75 77 78 79 80 81 82 83 84 85 86 87 93 94 97 98 100 101 102 103 104 105 106 107 108 111 114 115 118 119 127 128 129 130 132 135 146 147 148 **S** Department of Veterans Affairs, Washington, DC
Primary Contact: Judith Johnson–Mekota, Director
CMO: Fredrick Bahls, M.D., Chief of Staff
CIO: James Danuser, Chief Information Officer
CHR: Sabrina Owen, Human Resources Officer
Web address: www.centraliowa.va.gov/
Control: Veterans Affairs, Government, federal **Service:** General Medical and Surgical

> **Staffed Beds:** 255 **Admissions:** 2903 **Census:** 155 **Outpatient Visits:** 331409 **Births:** 0 **Total Expense ($000):** 200230 **Payroll Expense ($000):** 125448 **Personnel:** 1494

DUBUQUE—Dubuque County

FINLEY HOSPITAL See UnityPoint Health – Finley Hospital

✠ △ **MERCY MEDICAL CENTER–DUBUQUE (160069)**, 250 Mercy Drive, Zip 52001–7360; tel. 563/589–8000, (Total facility includes 40 beds in nursing home–type unit) **A**1 7 9 10 **F**3 4 5 8 11 13 15 18 20 22 24 26 28 29 30 31 32 34 35 36 38 39 40 43 44 49 50 51 53 64 65 67 70 72 74 75 76 77 78 79 80 81 85 86 87 89 90 91 93 97 98 99 100 101 102 103 104 107 108 111 114 116 119 126 128 129 130 131 132 134 135 143 144 146 147 148 **P**8 **S** Catholic Health East / Trinity Health, Livonia, MI
Primary Contact: Russell M. Knight, President and Chief Executive Officer
CFO: Robert Shafer, Vice President Finance
CIO: Joe Billmeyer, Director, Information Services
CHR: Kathryn Roberts, Director Human Resources
CNO: Kay Takes, R.N., Vice President Patient Care Services and Chief Nursing Officer
Web address: www.mercydubuque.com
Control: Church–operated, Nongovernment, not–for profit **Service:** General Medical and Surgical

> **Staffed Beds:** 272 **Admissions:** 8886 **Census:** 137 **Outpatient Visits:** 41770 **Births:** 857 **Total Expense ($000):** 141849 **Payroll Expense ($000):** 44233 **Personnel:** 994

✠ △ **UNITYPOINT HEALTH – FINLEY HOSPITAL (160117)**, 350 North Grandview Avenue, Zip 52001–6392; tel. 563/582–1881 **A**1 7 9 10 **F**3 11 12 13 15 18 20 22 26 28 29 30 31 34 35 39 40 43 44 45 46 48 49 50 53 56 57 59 60 61 62 64 65 69 70 72 74 75 76 77 78 79 81 82 84 85 86 87 90 93 96 97 98 103 107 108 110 111 115 117 118 119 120 121 123 124 126 129 130 131 132 135 144 146 147 148 **P**1 5 **S** UnityPoint Health, West Des Moines, IA
Primary Contact: David R. Brandon, President and Chief Executive Officer
COO: Chad Wolbers, Chief Operating Officer
CFO: Dan Carpenter, Chief Financial Officer
CMO: Bryan Pechous, M.D., Vice President Medical Affairs
CIO: Tim Loeffelholz, Account Executive Information Technology
CHR: Karla Waldbillig, Director Human Resources
CNO: Diana Batchelor, Chief Nursing Officer
Web address: www.unitypoint.org
Control: Other not–for–profit (including NFP Corporation) **Service:** General Medical and Surgical

> **Staffed Beds:** 109 **Admissions:** 4778 **Census:** 57 **Outpatient Visits:** 85917 **Births:** 670 **Total Expense ($000):** 93803 **Payroll Expense ($000):** 39562 **Personnel:** 736

DYERSVILLE—Dubuque County

★ **MERCY MEDICAL CENTER–DYERSVILLE (161378)**, 1111 Third Street S.W., Zip 52040–1725; tel. 563/875–7101 **A**9 10 18 **F**11 15 34 35 36 39 40 44 50 56 57 59 64 65 75 79 81 85 86 93 119 130 131 132 133 134 135 146 147 **P**8 **S** Catholic Health East / Trinity Health, Livonia, MI
Primary Contact: Russell M. Knight, President and Chief Executive Officer
CFO: Robert Shafer, Vice President Finance
Web address: www.mercydubuque.com/mercy–dyersville
Control: Church–operated, Nongovernment, not–for profit **Service:** General Medical and Surgical

> **Staffed Beds:** 25 **Admissions:** 92 **Census:** 3 **Outpatient Visits:** 3957 **Births:** 0 **Total Expense ($000):** 4855 **Payroll Expense ($000):** 2255 **Personnel:** 53

ELKADER—Clayton County

★ **CENTRAL COMMUNITY HOSPITAL (161319)**, 901 Davidson Street N.W., Zip 52043–9015; tel. 563/245–7000 **A**9 10 18 **F**7 11 15 28 34 35 40 43 50 56 57 59 64 67 68 70 75 81 85 87 89 91 93 107 110 114 119 128 130 132 133 134 146 **S** Catholic Health East / Trinity Health, Livonia, MI
Primary Contact: Frances J. Zichal, Chief Executive Officer
CFO: Patricia Borel, Chief Financial Officer
CIO: Jonathan Holliday, Manager Information Technology
CHR: Angie Gerndt, Human Resources Manager
CNO: Natalie Shea, Chief Nursing Officer
Web address: www.centralcommunityhospital.com
Control: Other not–for–profit (including NFP Corporation) **Service:** General Medical and Surgical

> **Staffed Beds:** 15 **Admissions:** 185 **Census:** 3 **Outpatient Visits:** 7217 **Births:** 0 **Total Expense ($000):** 5835 **Payroll Expense ($000):** 2039 **Personnel:** 57

EMMETSBURG—Palo Alto County

★ **PALO ALTO COUNTY HEALTH SYSTEM (161357)**, 3201 First Street, Zip 50536–2516; tel. 712/852–5500, (Total facility includes 22 beds in nursing home–type unit) **A**9 10 18 **F**3 7 11 13 15 28 29 30 31 34 35 40 43 45 46 50 57 59 62 63 64 65 67 68 69 71 75 76 77 79 81 82 84 85 87 93 107 110 115 119 125 127 129 130 132 133 135 143 146 **S** Catholic Health East / Trinity Health, Livonia, MI
Primary Contact: Desiree Einsweiler, Chief Executive Officer
CFO: Renay Hauswirth, Chief Financial Officer
CMO: Paul Matthews, M.D., President of Medical Staff
CIO: Randy Beaver, Chief Information Officer
CHR: Amy Knoup, Director Human Resources
CNO: JoAnn Higgins, Chief Nursing Officer and Assistant Administrator
Web address: www.pachs.com
Control: County–Government, nonfederal **Service:** General Medical and Surgical

> **Staffed Beds:** 47 **Admissions:** 544 **Census:** 27 **Outpatient Visits:** 22204 **Births:** 100 **Total Expense ($000):** 22793 **Payroll Expense ($000):** 8502 **Personnel:** 179

ESTHERVILLE—Emmet County

★ **AVERA HOLY FAMILY HOSPITAL (161351)**, 826 North Eighth Street, Zip 51334–1598; tel. 712/362–2631 **A**9 10 18 **F**3 11 13 15 28 29 30 31 34 35 40 45 59 63 64 68 69 70 75 76 77 78 79 81 85 87 93 107 114 119 130 132 133 146 **P**4 **S** Avera Health, Sioux Falls, SD
Primary Contact: Dale Hustedt, Administrator
CFO: Shannon Adams, Chief Financial Officer
CMO: Keith Probst, M.D., Chief of Staff
CHR: Janette Jensen, Manager Human Resources
CNO: Cathi Rae Scharnberg, R.N., Vice President Patient Services
Web address: www.avera–holyfamily.org
Control: Church–operated, Nongovernment, not–for profit **Service:** General Medical and Surgical

> **Staffed Beds:** 25 **Admissions:** 831 **Census:** 8 **Outpatient Visits:** 64066 **Births:** 68 **Total Expense ($000):** 22780 **Payroll Expense ($000):** 9377 **Personnel:** 178

FAIRFIELD—Jefferson County

★ **JEFFERSON COUNTY HEALTH CENTER (161364)**, 2000 South Main, Zip 52556–9572, Mailing Address: P.O. Box 588, Zip 52556–0010; tel. 641/472–4111 **A**9 10 18 **F**11 15 28 30 31 34 35 36 40 43 45 57 59 67 68 70 75 77 78 79 81 85 89 93 96 102 107 110 115 119 128 129 133 135 143 146 148 **P**5
Primary Contact: Deborah Cardin, R.N., FACHE, MS, Chief Executive Officer
CFO: Larry Peach, Chief Financial Officer
CHR: Nanette Everly, Manager Human Resources and Administrative Assistant
Web address: www.jeffersoncountyhealthcenter.org
Control: County–Government, nonfederal **Service:** General Medical and Surgical

> **Staffed Beds:** 25 **Admissions:** 959 **Census:** 15 **Outpatient Visits:** 50046 **Births:** 0 **Total Expense ($000):** 27081 **Payroll Expense ($000):** 8771 **Personnel:** 178

FORT DODGE—Webster County

★ ◇ **UNITYPOINT HEALTH – TRINITY REGIONAL MEDICAL CENTER (160016)**, 802 Kenyon Road, Zip 50501–5795; tel. 515/573–3101 **A**2 9 10 19 20 21 **F**3 7 8 11 13 15 18 20 22 24 28 29 30 31 32 34 35 36 40 43 45 47 49 50 53 59 64 68 70 73 75 76 77 78 79 81 82 84 86 87 89 93 102 107 108 110 111 115 118 119 120 121 123 129 130 131 132 135 145 146 148 **P**6 **S** UnityPoint Health, West Des Moines, IA
Primary Contact: Susan K. Thompson, President and Chief Executive Officer
COO: Troy Martens, Chief Operating Officer
CFO: Mike Dewerff, Chief Financial Officer
CHR: Ted W. Vaughn, Director Human Resources
CNO: Debra Shriver, R.N., Chief Nurse Executive
Web address: www.trmc.org
Control: Other not–for–profit (including NFP Corporation) **Service:** General Medical and Surgical

> **Staffed Beds:** 110 **Admissions:** 4003 **Census:** 37 **Outpatient Visits:** 113419 **Births:** 538 **Total Expense ($000):** 91384 **Payroll Expense ($000):** 41315 **Personnel:** 666

IA

Many Facility Codes have changed. Please refer to the AHA Guide Code Chart. © 2014 AHA Guide

FORT MADISON—Lee County

⊠ **FORT MADISON COMMUNITY HOSPITAL (160122)**, 5445 Avenue O,
Zip 52627–9611, Mailing Address: P.O. Box 174, Zip 52627–0174;
tel. 319/372–6530 **A**1 9 10 **F**3 11 13 15 28 29 31 34 40 43 45 50 51 53 57
59 62 64 67 68 70 74 75 76 77 78 79 81 85 86 87 90 91 93 94 96 97 99
100 101 102 103 104 107 108 110 111 115 117 118 119 128 129 130 131
132 133 143 144 146 147 148 **P**6 **S** QHR, Brentwood, TN
Primary Contact: C. James Platt, Chief Executive Officer
CFO: Bradley J. Kokjohn, Chief Financial Officer
CMO: David Wenger–Keller, M.D., Chief of Staff
CIO: Shane Tapper, Director Management Information Systems
CHR: Vicki Kokjohn, Director Employee Relations
CNO: Shelby Dickens, Director, Patient Care Services
Web address: www.fmchosp.com
Control: Other not–for–profit (including NFP Corporation) **Service:** General
Medical and Surgical

> **Staffed Beds:** 50 **Admissions:** 1832 **Census:** 18 **Outpatient Visits:** 99452
> **Births:** 371 **Total Expense ($000):** 52201 **Payroll Expense ($000):** 25308
> **Personnel:** 437

GREENFIELD—Adair County

ADAIR COUNTY MEMORIAL HOSPITAL (161310), 609 S.E. Kent Street,
Zip 50849–9454; tel. 641/743–2123 **A**9 10 18 **F**3 7 11 15 18 28 29 31 34
35 36 40 43 45 48 50 57 59 62 64 65 69 70 75 77 79 81 89 91 93 97 107
108 110 111 114 116 118 119 127 128 129 130 133 148 **P**6
Primary Contact: Angela Mortoza, Administrator
CFO: Kevin Heinzeroth, Chief Financial Officer
CMO: Timothy Piearson, D.O., Chief Medical Officer
CIO: Andy Christie, Chief Information Technology
CHR: Angie Frankl, Director Human Resources
CNO: Cindy K. Peeler, R.N., Chief Nursing Officer
Web address: www.adaircountyhealthsystem.org
Control: County–Government, nonfederal **Service:** General Medical and Surgical

> **Staffed Beds:** 18 **Admissions:** 153 **Census:** 2 **Outpatient Visits:** 12062
> **Births:** 0 **Total Expense ($000):** 10882 **Payroll Expense ($000):** 4046
> **Personnel:** 101

GRINNELL—Poweshiek County

★ **GRINNELL REGIONAL MEDICAL CENTER (160147)**, 210 Fourth Avenue,
Zip 50112–1898; tel. 641/236–2300 **A**9 10 **F**3 11 12 13 15 28 29 30 31 32
34 35 36 37 38 40 43 44 45 46 47 50 53 54 56 57 59 61 62 63 64 65 66
70 75 76 77 78 79 81 84 85 86 87 89 93 97 99 100 101 102 103 104 107
110 111 114 118 119 126 127 129 130 131 132 133 134 135 144 146 147
148 **P**6 7
Primary Contact: Todd C. Linden, President and Chief Executive Officer
CFO: Kyle M. Wilcox, Assistant Vice President Finance
CIO: David L. Ness, Vice President Operations
CHR: Debra S. Nowachek, Director Human Resources
CNO: Doris Rindels, Vice President Operations
Web address: www.grmc.us
Control: Other not–for–profit (including NFP Corporation) **Service:** General
Medical and Surgical

> **Staffed Beds:** 49 **Admissions:** 1457 **Census:** 14 **Outpatient Visits:** 47450
> **Births:** 147 **Total Expense ($000):** 44218 **Payroll Expense ($000):** 20848
> **Personnel:** 369

GRUNDY CENTER—Grundy County

★ **GRUNDY COUNTY MEMORIAL HOSPITAL (161303)**, 201 East J Avenue,
Zip 50638–2096; tel. 319/824–5421, (Total facility includes 55 beds in nursing
home–type unit) **A**9 10 18 **F**15 28 29 34 35 40 43 57 59 63 67 68 75 78 79
81 86 87 93 107 110 111 114 119 128 129 130 131 132 133 135 146 148
S UnityPoint Health, West Des Moines, IA
Primary Contact: Brian Kellar, Chief Executive Officer
COO: Ryan Bingman, Director Operations
CFO: Lisa Zinkula, Chief Financial Officer
CMO: Douglas Cooper, M.D., Chief Medical Officer
CIO: Nicholas Betts, Director Information Technology
CHR: Aaron Wedo, Manager, Human Resources
Web address: www.grundycountyhospital.com
Control: County–Government, nonfederal **Service:** General Medical and Surgical

> **Staffed Beds:** 80 **Admissions:** 359 **Census:** 56 **Outpatient Visits:** 35079
> **Births:** 0 **Total Expense ($000):** 18910 **Payroll Expense ($000):** 7973
> **Personnel:** 142

GUTHRIE CENTER—Guthrie County

★ **GUTHRIE COUNTY HOSPITAL (161314)**, 710 North 12th Street,
Zip 50115–1544; tel. 641/332–2201 **A**9 10 18 **F**11 15 18 28 29 31 34 35 40
43 45 53 56 57 59 64 69 75 77 79 81 85 93 107 110 119 128 130 132 133
143 **S** UnityPoint Health, West Des Moines, IA
Primary Contact: Patrick Peters, Chief Executive Officer
CFO: Melinda Alt, Chief Financial Officer
CMO: Steven Bascom, M.D., Chief Medical Officer
CIO: Jeff Cobb, Information Technologist
CHR: Kimberly Myers, Director Human Resources
Web address: www.guthriecountyhospital.org
Control: County–Government, nonfederal **Service:** General Medical and Surgical

> **Staffed Beds:** 25 **Admissions:** 336 **Census:** 3 **Outpatient Visits:** 37722
> **Births:** 0 **Total Expense ($000):** 14929 **Payroll Expense ($000):** 6536
> **Personnel:** 121

GUTTENBERG—Clayton County

⊠ **GUTTENBERG MUNICIPAL HOSPITAL (161312)**, 200 Main Street,
Zip 52052–9108, Mailing Address: P.O. Box 550, Zip 52052–0550;
tel. 563/252–1121 **A**1 9 10 18 **F**3 7 8 11 13 15 28 34 35 40 43 45 50 53 57
59 64 68 76 81 82 85 89 93 97 102 107 110 111 114 119 127 128 130
132 133 **P**5 6 **S** UnityPoint Health, West Des Moines, IA
Primary Contact: Kimberly A. Gau, FACHE, Chief Executive Officer
CMO: Jeffrey Hoffmann, D.O., Chief Medical Staff
CIO: Ken Kaiser, Director Information Technology
CHR: Leigh Ann Judge, Manager Human Resources
CNO: Kimberley A. Gau, FACHE, Interim Chief Nursing Officer
Web address: www.guttenberghospital.org
Control: City–Government, nonfederal **Service:** General Medical and Surgical

> **Staffed Beds:** 20 **Admissions:** 300 **Census:** 3 **Outpatient Visits:** 22826
> **Births:** 36 **Total Expense ($000):** 11787 **Payroll Expense ($000):** 4779
> **Personnel:** 111

HAMBURG—Fremont County

GEORGE C GRAPE COMMUNITY HOSPITAL (161324), 2959 U.S. Highway
275, Zip 51640–5067; tel. 712/382–1515, (Total facility includes 6 beds in
nursing home–type unit) **A**9 10 18 **F**11 15 18 28 31 34 35 40 43 45 50 53 57
59 62 64 65 68 69 74 75 77 78 79 81 82 85 91 93 107 114 119 128 129
130 131 133 135 148
Primary Contact: Michael O'Neal, Administrator and Chief Executive Officer
CFO: Hilary Christiansen, Chief Financial Officer
CMO: Kelli Woltemath, D.O., Chief Medical Staff
CIO: Craig Wells, Chief Information Officer
CHR: Jackie Wertz, Director Human Resources
CNO: Gloria Mattice, R.N., Director Patient Care
Web address: www.grapehospital.com
Control: Other not–for–profit (including NFP Corporation) **Service:** General
Medical and Surgical

> **Staffed Beds:** 25 **Admissions:** 266 **Census:** 6 **Outpatient Visits:** 19299
> **Births:** 0 **Total Expense ($000):** 9730 **Payroll Expense ($000):** 4305
> **Personnel:** 93

HAMPTON—Franklin County

★ **FRANKLIN GENERAL HOSPITAL (161308)**, 1720 Central Avenue East, Suite
A., Zip 50441–1867; tel. 641/456–5000, (Total facility includes 52 beds in
nursing home–type unit) **A**9 10 18 **F**7 10 11 15 28 30 31 34 40 43 57 59 63
64 65 67 68 75 77 79 81 82 85 86 89 90 93 107 111 114 119 127 128 129
130 131 132 133 135 146 148 **P**8 **S** Catholic Health East / Trinity Health,
Livonia, MI
Primary Contact: Kim Price, Chief Executive Officer
CFO: Bonnie Lettow, Chief Financial Officer
CHR: Victoria Kruse, Manager Human Resources
CNO: Ronda Reimer, R.N., Chief Nursing Officer and Assistant Administrator
Web address: www.franklingeneral.com
Control: County–Government, nonfederal **Service:** General Medical and Surgical

> **Staffed Beds:** 77 **Admissions:** 342 **Census:** 56 **Outpatient Visits:** 17409
> **Births:** 0 **Total Expense ($000):** 17085 **Payroll Expense ($000):** 5858
> **Personnel:** 134

IA

HARLAN—Shelby County

★ **MYRTUE MEDICAL CENTER (161374)**, 1213 Garfield Avenue,
Zip 51537–2057; tel. 712/755–5161 **A**9 10 18 **F**3 5 11 13 15 28 29 31 32
34 35 38 40 43 45 46 50 53 56 57 59 62 63 64 65 68 75 76 77 78 81 85
87 92 93 97 99 101 102 103 104 107 110 114 119 127 129 130 131 132
133 135 146 148 **P**6 8
Primary Contact: Barry Jacobsen, Chief Executive Officer
CFO: Kristy Hansen, Chief Financial Officer
CMO: Scott Markham, D.O., Chief of Staff
CIO: David Sirek, Chief Information Officer
CHR: Donna Christensen–Mores, Director Human Resources
CNO: Karen Buman, Chief Nurse Executive
Web address: www.myrtuemedical.org
Control: County–Government, nonfederal **Service:** General Medical and Surgical

Staffed Beds: 25 **Admissions:** 964 **Census:** 12 **Outpatient Visits:** 91209
Births: 80 **Total Expense ($000):** 32055 **Payroll Expense ($000):** 13284
Personnel: 332

HAWARDEN—Sioux County

★ **HAWARDEN REGIONAL HEALTHCARE (161311)**, 1111 11th Street,
Zip 51023–1999; tel. 712/551–3100 **A**9 10 18 **F**11 15 28 29 31 34 35 40 43
53 59 64 67 69 75 77 80 81 89 90 92 93 107 108 114 127 128 132 133
135 148 **P**3 7 **S** Catholic Health East / Trinity Health, Livonia, MI
Primary Contact: Jayson Pullman, Chief Executive Officer
CFO: Jessica Hughes, Director Finance
CMO: Dale Nystrom, M.D., Chief Medical Officer, Physician
CHR: Maggie Hofer, Human Resources Representative
Web address: www.hawardenregionalhealthcare.com/
Control: City–Government, nonfederal **Service:** General Medical and Surgical

Staffed Beds: 18 **Admissions:** 157 **Census:** 2 **Outpatient Visits:** 17723
Births: 0 **Total Expense ($000):** 6903 **Payroll Expense ($000):** 2356
Personnel: 55

HUMBOLDT—Humboldt County

★ **HUMBOLDT COUNTY MEMORIAL HOSPITAL (161334)**, 1000 North 15th
Street, Zip 50548–1008; tel. 515/332–4200, (Total facility includes 28 beds in
nursing home–type unit) **A**9 10 18 **F**7 8 10 11 12 14 15 28 29 31 32 34 35 40
41 43 45 47 50 51 59 65 69 75 77 78 79 81 82 85 87 91 93 102 107 110 111
114 119 125 130 133 134 **S** UnityPoint Health, West Des Moines, IA
Primary Contact: James Atty, Chief Executive Officer
CFO: Betty Etherington, Chief Financial Officer
CHR: Mary Moritz, Administrator Human Resources
Web address: www.humboldthospital.org
Control: County–Government, nonfederal **Service:** General Medical and Surgical

Staffed Beds: 49 **Admissions:** 272 **Census:** 31 **Outpatient Visits:** 47302
Births: 0 **Total Expense ($000):** 13460 **Payroll Expense ($000):** 5366
Personnel: 108

IDA GROVE—Ida County

★ **HORN MEMORIAL HOSPITAL (161354)**, 701 East Second Street,
Zip 51445–1699; tel. 712/364–3311 **A**9 10 18 **F**11 15 28 29 31 34 40 45 57
59 62 63 64 65 66 68 71 75 77 78 79 81 82 85 89 93 97 107 108 110 111
115 119 127 129 130 131 132 133 135 146 147 148 **P**6
Primary Contact: Christopher Nichols, Chief Executive Officer
CFO: Marcia Fehring, Chief Financial Officer
CIO: Robbie Todd, Director Information Technology
CHR: Lorraine Davis, Vice President Human Resources
CNO: Sharon A. Wellendorf, Chief Nursing Officer
Web address: www.hornmemorialhospital.org
Control: Other not–for–profit (including NFP Corporation) **Service:** General
Medical and Surgical

Staffed Beds: 25 **Admissions:** 545 **Census:** 9 **Outpatient Visits:** 21447
Births: 0 **Total Expense ($000):** 16681 **Payroll Expense ($000):** 7634
Personnel: 156

INDEPENDENCE—Buchanan County

★ **BUCHANAN COUNTY HEALTH CENTER (161335)**, 1600 First Street East,
Zip 50644–3155; tel. 319/332–0999, (Total facility includes 39 beds in nursing
home–type unit) **A**9 10 18 **F**3 11 15 28 29 32 34 35 40 43 45 50 53 56 57 59
64 65 67 70 75 77 79 81 82 86 87 91 93 107 110 111 114 119 125 129
130 131 132 133 135 146 148
Primary Contact: Steve Robert Slessor, Chief Executive Officer
CFO: Ben Stevens, Chief Financial Officer
CHR: Shelby Medina, Chief Administrative Officer
CNO: Rachel Goldenstein, R.N., Chief Nursing Officer
Web address: www.bchealth.info
Control: County–Government, nonfederal **Service:** General Medical and Surgical

Staffed Beds: 58 **Admissions:** 361 **Census:** 37 **Outpatient Visits:** 43298
Births: 0 **Total Expense ($000):** 18968 **Payroll Expense ($000):** 7118
Personnel: 195

☐ **MENTAL HEALTH INSTITUTE (164003)**, 2277 Iowa Avenue, Zip 50644–9106;
tel. 319/334–2583 **A**1 9 10 **F**65 98 99 101 102 106 130 143 146 **P**6
Primary Contact: Bhasker J. Dave, M.D., Superintendent
CFO: Kevin Jimmerson, Business Manager
CMO: Bhasker J. Dave, M.D., Superintendent
Web address: www.dhs.state.ia.us
Control: State–Government, nonfederal **Service:** Psychiatric

Staffed Beds: 75 **Admissions:** 195 **Census:** 46 **Outpatient Visits:** 41 **Births:**
0 **Total Expense ($000):** 23531 **Payroll Expense ($000):** 12765
Personnel: 225

IOWA CITY—Johnson County

✠ **IOWA CITY VETERANS AFFAIRS HEALTH CARE SYSTEM**, 601 Highway 6
West, Zip 52246–2208; tel. 319/338–0581 **A**1 3 5 8 9 **F**3 5 8 11 12 17 18 20
22 24 29 30 31 34 35 38 39 40 43 44 45 46 47 50 51 54 56 57 58 59 60
61 64 70 74 75 78 79 81 82 83 84 85 86 87 91 92 93 94 97 98 100 101
102 103 104 106 **S** Department of Veterans Affairs, Washington, DC
Primary Contact: Dawn Oxley, R.N., Acting Director
COO: Kevin Kosek, Associate Director Operations
CFO: Jennifer Ruppert, Chief Financial Officer
CMO: Richard A. Charlat, Chief of Staff
CIO: Dwight Schuessler, Chief Information Officer
CHR: Dan Helle, Human Resources Officer
CNO: Dawn Oxley, R.N., Associate Director Patient Care Services and Nurse
Executive
Web address: www.iowacity.va.gov/
Control: Veterans Affairs, Government, federal **Service:** General Medical and
Surgical

Staffed Beds: 68 **Admissions:** 3284 **Census:** 49 **Outpatient Visits:** 432046
Births: 0 **Total Expense ($000):** 294658 **Payroll Expense ($000):** 107815
Personnel: 1515

✠ **MERCY IOWA CITY (160029)**, 500 East Market Street, Zip 52245–2689;
tel. 319/339–0300, (Total facility includes 16 beds in nursing home–type unit) **A**1
2 9 10 **F**3 5 8 11 13 15 18 20 22 24 26 28 29 30 31 34 35 38 40 41 43 44
45 48 50 56 57 58 59 62 63 64 65 70 72 73 74 75 76 77 78 79 81 82 85
86 87 89 97 98 100 101 102 103 107 108 110 111 114 115 119 126 128
130 132 135 144 145 146 148 **P**8
Primary Contact: Ronald R. Reed, President and Chief Executive Officer
CFO: Michael G. Heinrich, Executive Vice President and Chief Financial Officer
CMO: Martin Izakovic, M.D., Vice President Medical Staff Affairs and Chief Medical
Officer
CIO: Paul Foelsch, Vice President Information Services and Chief Information
Officer
CHR: Marie Peeters, Director Human Resources
CNO: Cindy L. Penney, R.N., Vice President Nursing
Web address: www.mercyiowacity.org
Control: Church–operated, Nongovernment, not–for profit **Service:** General
Medical and Surgical

Staffed Beds: 234 **Admissions:** 8279 **Census:** 88 **Outpatient Visits:** 334183
Births: 1229 **Total Expense ($000):** 144954 **Payroll Expense ($000):**
60056 **Personnel:** 973

UNIVERSITY HOSPITAL SCHOOL See Center for Disabilities and Development

✠ **UNIVERSITY OF IOWA HOSPITALS AND CLINICS (160058)**, 200 Hawkins
Drive, Zip 52242–1009; tel. 319/356–1616, (Includes CENTER FOR DISABILITIES
AND DEVELOPMENT, 200 Hawkins Drive, Zip 52242; tel. 319/353–6456;
CHEMICAL DEPENDENCY CENTER, 200 Hawkins Drive, Oakdale,
Zip 52242–1007; tel. 319/384–8765; STATE PSYCHIATRIC HOSPITAL, 200
Hawkins Drive, Zip 52242; tel. 319/356–4658; UNIVERSITY OF IOWA CHILDREN'S
HOSPITAL, 200 Hawkins Drive, tel. 319/384–8442) **A**1 2 3 5 8 9 10 **F**3 5 6 7 8
9 11 12 13 14 15 16 17 18 19 20 21 22 23 24 25 26 27 28 29 30 31 32 33
34 35 36 37 38 39 40 41 43 44 45 49 50 51 52 53 54 55 56 57
58 59 60 61 62 63 64 65 66 68 70 72 73 74 75 76 77 78 79 80 81 82 83
84 85 86 87 88 89 90 91 92 93 94 96 97 98 99 100 101 102 103 104 105
107 108 109 110 111 114 115 116 117 118 119 120 121 123 124 126 127
129 130 131 132 135 136 137 138 139 140 141 142 143 144 145 146 147
148 **P**1 7
Primary Contact: Kenneth P. Kates, Chief Executive Officer
COO: Sabi Singh, Co–Chief Operating Officer
CFO: Kenneth Fisher, Associate Vice President Finance and Chief Financial Officer
CMO: Theresa Brennan, M.D., Chief Medical Officer
CIO: Lee Carmen, Associate Vice President Health Care Information Systems
CHR: Jana Wessels, Associate Vice President Human Resources
CNO: Kenneth Rempher, Ph.D., Interim Chief Nursing Officer
Web address: www.uihealthcare.com
Control: State–Government, nonfederal **Service:** General Medical and Surgical

Staffed Beds: 679 **Admissions:** 30344 **Census:** 529 **Outpatient Visits:**
1132798 **Births:** 1939 **Total Expense ($000):** 1093017 **Payroll Expense
($000):** 403853 **Personnel:** 7278

IA

Many Facility Codes have changed. Please refer to the AHA Guide Code Chart. © 2014 AHA Guide

IOWA FALLS—Hardin County

★ **HANSEN FAMILY HOSPITAL (161380)**, 920 South Oak, Zip 50126–9506;
tel. 641/648–4631 **A**9 10 18 **F**11 13 15 28 34 40 43 45 50 53 57 59 64 65
75 76 77 81 82 85 86 87 93 97 100 104 107 110 114 119 133 135 **P**6
S Catholic Health East / Trinity Health, Livonia, MI
Primary Contact: Cherelle Montanye–Ireland, Chief Executive Officer
CFO: Mike White, Chief Financial Officer
CMO: George Pfaltzgraff, Chief Medical Officer
CHR: Cheri Geitz, Director Human Resources
CNO: Katie Rieks, Chief Nursing Officer
Web address: www.hansenfamilyhospital.com
Control: City–Government, nonfederal **Service:** General Medical and Surgical

Staffed Beds: 23 **Admissions:** 656 **Census:** 8 **Outpatient Visits:** 42597
Births: 83 **Total Expense ($000):** 22591 **Payroll Expense ($000):** 9399
Personnel: 215

JEFFERSON—Greene County

★ **GREENE COUNTY MEDICAL CENTER (161325)**, 1000 West Lincolnway,
Zip 50129–1645; tel. 515/386–2114, (Total facility includes 65 beds in nursing
home–type unit) **A**9 10 18 **F**11 13 15 28 29 34 35 36 40 46 56 57 59 62 63
64 65 67 68 75 76 78 79 81 82 85 93 107 114 119 125 128 130 131 132
133 147 **P**5 6 **S** UnityPoint Health, West Des Moines, IA
Primary Contact: Carl P. Behne, Administrator and Chief Executive Officer
CFO: Mark A. VanderLinden, Chief Financial Officer
CMO: Jon Van Der Veer, D.O., Vice President Medical Affairs
CIO: Roger Overby, Executive Director Information Systems
CHR: Cathy Krieger, Human Resources Director
CNO: Katie Heldt, Chief Nursing Officer
Web address: www.gcmchealth.com
Control: County–Government, nonfederal **Service:** General Medical and Surgical

Staffed Beds: 90 **Admissions:** 482 **Census:** 58 **Outpatient Visits:** 27382
Births: 75 **Total Expense ($000):** 22308 **Payroll Expense ($000):** 9801
Personnel: 246

KEOKUK—Lee County

⊠ **KEOKUK AREA HOSPITAL (160008)**, 1600 Morgan Street, Zip 52632–3456;
tel. 319/524–7150 **A**1 9 10 **F**3 11 15 28 29 31 34 35 40 43 45 46 57 59 62
64 68 70 79 81 85 86 87 93 96 107 108 111 114 115 118 119 129 130
131 132 133 146 148 **P**6
Primary Contact: Joseph K. Whiting, FACHE, Interim Chief Executive Officer
CMO: Neville Crenshaw, D.O., Chief of Staff
CIO: Linda Atterberg, Chief Information Officer
CNO: Melanie Kelly, Director of Nursing
Web address: www.keokukhealthsystems.org
Control: Other not–for–profit (including NFP Corporation) **Service:** General
Medical and Surgical

Staffed Beds: 42 **Admissions:** 1411 **Census:** 13 **Outpatient Visits:** 34536
Births: 70 **Total Expense ($000):** 23047 **Payroll Expense ($000):** 9876
Personnel: 271

KEOSAUQUA—Van Buren County

★ **VAN BUREN COUNTY HOSPITAL (161337)**, 304 Franklin Street,
Zip 52565–1164; tel. 319/293–3171 **A**9 10 18 **F**3 7 10 11 13 15 28 29 32
34 35 40 43 45 46 50 56 57 59 64 65 70 75 76 77 81 85 86 87 89 93 97
102 107 110 111 114 119 125 127 128 130 132 133 135 146 147 148 **P**6
Primary Contact: Garen Carpenter, Interim Chief Executive Officer
CFO: Kara McEntee, Chief Financial Officer
CIO: Chris McEntee, Network Specialist
Web address: www.vbch.org
Control: County–Government, nonfederal **Service:** General Medical and Surgical

Staffed Beds: 25 **Admissions:** 381 **Census:** 4 **Outpatient Visits:** 11552
Births: 44 **Total Expense ($000):** 12834 **Payroll Expense ($000):** 6359
Personnel: 146

KNOXVILLE—Marion County

KNOXVILLE DIVISION See Veterans Affairs Central Iowa Health Care System,
Des Moines

★ ◇ **KNOXVILLE HOSPITAL & CLINICS (161355)**, 1002 South Lincoln Street,
Zip 50138–3155; tel. 641/842–2151 **A**9 10 18 21 **F**3 8 11 13 15 28 29 31
34 40 43 45 47 48 49 50 54 57 59 64 65 68 75 76 77 79 81 85 86 93 97
102 107 108 110 111 114 118 119 129 130 132 133 135 146 147 148 **P**6
Primary Contact: Kevin Kincaid, Chief Executive Officer
COO: Christine Buttell, Chief Operating Officer
CFO: Maggie Hamilton–Beyer, Chief Financial Officer
CMO: Daniel Rowley, M.D., Chief of Medical Staff
CIO: Thom Richards, Director Information Technology
CHR: Brian Sims, Director Administrative Services
CNO: Mary Jane Applegate, Chief Nursing Officer
Web address: www.knoxvillehospital.org
Control: Other not–for–profit (including NFP Corporation) **Service:** General
Medical and Surgical

Staffed Beds: 25 **Admissions:** 1217 **Census:** 11 **Outpatient Visits:** 63318
Births: 63 **Total Expense ($000):** 24985 **Payroll Expense ($000):** 10741
Personnel: 196

LAKE CITY—Calhoun County

★ **STEWART MEMORIAL COMMUNITY HOSPITAL (161350)**, 1301 West Main,
Zip 51449–1585; tel. 712/464–3171 **A**9 10 18 **F**7 11 12 13 15 28 29 30 31
34 40 43 45 59 62 63 64 65 69 70 75 76 77 78 79 81 82 86 93 94 107
110 119 127 130 133 135 147 **P**5 6 **S** UnityPoint Health, West Des Moines, IA
Primary Contact: Heather L. Cain, Chief Executive Officer
CFO: Jim Henkenius, Chief Financial Officer
CHR: Bill Albright, Director Human Resources
Web address: www.stewartmemorial.org
Control: Other not–for–profit (including NFP Corporation) **Service:** General
Medical and Surgical

Staffed Beds: 25 **Admissions:** 573 **Census:** 7 **Outpatient Visits:** 49057
Births: 81 **Total Expense ($000):** 30153 **Payroll Expense ($000):** 13114
Personnel: 239

LE MARS—Plymouth County

★ **FLOYD VALLEY HOSPITAL (161368)**, 714 Lincoln Street N.E.,
Zip 51031–3314; tel. 712/546–7871 **A**9 10 18 **F**3 10 11 13 15 28 29 31 32
34 35 40 43 45 50 53 57 59 62 64 65 67 76 78 79 80 81 85 86 87 89 107
110 111 114 119 128 130 132 133 135 146 148 **S** Avera Health, Sioux
Falls, SD
Primary Contact: Michael T. Donlin, FACHE, Administrator
CFO: Daryl Friedenbach, Director Fiscal Services
CMO: Sheila Holcomb, M.D., President Medical Staff
CIO: Jason Uhl, Chief Information Officer
CHR: Mary Helen Gibson, Director Human Resources
CNO: Loretta Myers, MS, Director, Patient Care
Web address: www.floydvalleyhospital.org
Control: City–Government, nonfederal **Service:** General Medical and Surgical

Staffed Beds: 25 **Admissions:** 816 **Census:** 8 **Outpatient Visits:** 51325
Births: 129 **Total Expense ($000):** 33240 **Payroll Expense ($000):** 11241
Personnel: 254

LEON—Decatur County

★ **DECATUR COUNTY HOSPITAL (161340)**, 1405 N.W. Church Street,
Zip 50144–1299; tel. 641/446–4871 **A**9 10 18 **F**3 7 11 15 28 29 31 34 40
57 59 64 67 68 75 78 79 81 85 93 107 111 114 119 128 130 133
Primary Contact: Suzanne Cooner, R.N., MSN, Chief Executive Officer
CFO: Tara Spidle, Chief Financial Officer
CMO: Larry Richard, M.D., Chief Medical Staff
CIO: Daren Steele, Director of Information
CHR: Jo Beth Smith, Chief Support Services and Human Resources
CNO: Andrea Masters, Chief Nursing Officer
Web address: www.decaturcountyhospital.org
Control: County–Government, nonfederal **Service:** General Medical and Surgical

Staffed Beds: 11 **Admissions:** 312 **Census:** 4 **Outpatient Visits:** 12426
Births: 0 **Total Expense ($000):** 10563 **Payroll Expense ($000):** 3566
Personnel: 91

IA

MANCHESTER—Delaware County

★ **REGIONAL MEDICAL CENTER (161343)**, 709 West Main Street, #359, Zip 52057–1526, Mailing Address: P.O. Box 359, Zip 52057–0359; tel. 563/927–3232 **A**9 10 18 **F**3 7 11 13 15 17 28 29 34 35 36 40 43 44 50 53 57 59 61 62 63 64 65 66 68 70 75 76 77 79 81 82 85 86 89 93 94 97 107 108 110 111 114 119 126 127 128 129 130 131 132 133 146 148 **P**6
Primary Contact: Lon D. Butikofer, R.N., Ph.D., Chief Executive Officer
CFO: Danette Kramer, Chief Financial Officer
CIO: Amy Mensen, Chief Administrative Officer
CHR: Amy Mensen, Chief Administrative Officer
CNO: Patricia S. Doyle, R.N., Chief Nursing Officer
Web address: www.regmedctr.org
Control: County–Government, nonfederal **Service:** General Medical and Surgical

> **Staffed Beds:** 25 **Admissions:** 982 **Census:** 9 **Outpatient Visits:** 173859 **Births:** 177 **Total Expense ($000):** 39862 **Payroll Expense ($000):** 19357 **Personnel:** 351

MANNING—Carroll County

★ **MANNING REGIONAL HEALTHCARE CENTER (161332)**, 1550 6th Street, Zip 51455–1093; tel. 712/655–2072, (Total facility includes 56 beds in nursing home–type unit) **A**9 10 18 **F**3 4 5 11 13 15 31 34 35 38 40 43 45 50 56 57 59 64 68 75 76 81 85 89 92 93 97 107 110 114 119 128 130 132 133 146 148 **P**6
Primary Contact: John O'Brien, Chief Executive Officer
CFO: Abbey Stangl, Chief Financial Officer
CMO: Douglas McLaws, D.O., Chief Medical Officer
CIO: Kim C. Jahn, Chief Plant Operations and Chief Information Officer
CHR: Shelli Lorenzen, Director Human Resources
CNO: Amy S. Dawson, Chief Clinical Officer
Web address: www.mrhcia.com
Control: Other not–for–profit (including NFP Corporation) **Service:** General Medical and Surgical

> **Staffed Beds:** 73 **Admissions:** 312 **Census:** 57 **Outpatient Visits:** 7783 **Births:** 30 **Total Expense ($000):** 13009 **Payroll Expense ($000):** 6101 **Personnel:** 149

MAQUOKETA—Jackson County

⊞ **JACKSON COUNTY REGIONAL HEALTH CENTER (161329)**, 700 West Grove Street, Zip 52060–2163; tel. 563/652–2474 **A**1 4 9 10 18 **F**3 7 11 15 28 34 40 43 45 53 59 62 64 65 75 77 81 87 93 107 110 114 119 129 130 132 133 146 **S** Genesis Health System, Davenport, IA
Primary Contact: Curt Coleman, FACHE, Administrator
CFO: Donna Roeder, Chief Financial Officer
CHR: Shannon Langenberg, Director Human Resources
Web address: www.jcrhc.org
Control: County–Government, nonfederal **Service:** General Medical and Surgical

> **Staffed Beds:** 25 **Admissions:** 222 **Census:** 3 **Outpatient Visits:** 19574 **Births:** 0 **Total Expense ($000):** 13001 **Payroll Expense ($000):** 5041 **Personnel:** 114

MARENGO—Iowa County

★ **MARENGO MEMORIAL HOSPITAL, UNITYPOINT HEALTH (161317)**, 300 West May Street, Zip 52301–1261, Mailing Address: P.O. Box 228, Zip 52301–0228; tel. 319/642–5543 **A**9 10 18 **F**3 7 28 29 34 35 38 40 43 45 50 59 64 68 69 75 81 85 96 97 107 114 130 133 143 146 **P**5 6 **S** UnityPoint Health, West Des Moines, IA
Primary Contact: Barry Goettsch, Chief Executive Officer
COO: Mikaela Gehring, Chief Operating Officer
CFO: Matthew Murphy, Chief Financial Officer
CIO: William Grimm, Director, Information Services
CHR: Lesa Waddell, Director Human Resources
CNO: Teresa Sauerbrei, Chief Nursing Officer
Web address: www.marengohospital.org
Control: City–Government, nonfederal **Service:** General Medical and Surgical

> **Staffed Beds:** 25 **Admissions:** 335 **Census:** 11 **Outpatient Visits:** 25194 **Births:** 0 **Total Expense ($000):** 15667 **Payroll Expense ($000):** 6735 **Personnel:** 139

MARSHALLTOWN—Marshall County

★ **MARSHALLTOWN MEDICAL & SURGICAL CENTER (160001)**, 3 South Fourth Avenue, Zip 50158–2998; tel. 641/754–5151, (Total facility includes 15 beds in nursing home–type unit) **A**9 10 19 20 **F**3 7 11 13 15 17 18 20 22 28 29 30 35 39 40 42 43 45 46 50 56 57 59 62 64 65 68 69 70 73 74 75 76 77 79 81 82 85 86 87 89 92 93 94 107 108 111 114 115 116 119 124 129 130 131 133 146 147 148
Primary Contact: John Hughes, FACHE, President and Chief Executive Officer
CFO: Hilary Dolbee, Chief Financial Officer
CMO: Milt Van Gundy, M.D., President Medical Staff
CHR: Jill Petermeier, Senior Executive Human Resources
Web address: www.everydaychampions.org
Control: Other not–for–profit (including NFP Corporation) **Service:** General Medical and Surgical

> **Staffed Beds:** 89 **Admissions:** 2699 **Census:** 24 **Outpatient Visits:** 191277 **Births:** 531 **Total Expense ($000):** 63020 **Payroll Expense ($000):** 30008 **Personnel:** 485

MASON CITY—Cerro Gordo County

⊠ **MERCY MEDICAL CENTER–NORTH IOWA (160064)**, 1000 Fourth Street S.W., Zip 50401–2800; tel. 641/428–7000 **A**1 2 3 5 9 10 13 19 20 **F**3 11 12 13 15 18 20 22 24 26 28 29 30 31 34 35 37 39 40 43 44 45 46 47 48 49 50 54 55 56 57 58 59 60 61 62 63 64 65 68 70 71 72 74 75 76 77 78 79 81 82 84 85 86 87 89 90 91 93 96 97 98 99 100 101 102 103 104 107 108 110 111 113 115 117 118 119 120 121 123 124 125 126 128 129 130 131 132 135 144 145 146 147 148 **P**1 6 **S** Catholic Health East / Trinity Health, Livonia, MI
Primary Contact: Daniel Varnum, President and Chief Executive Officer
COO: Diane Fischels, Senior Vice President and Chief Operating Officer
CFO: Danette Zook, Chief Financial Officer
CMO: Paul Manternach, M.D., Senior Vice President Physician Integration
CIO: Terry Chartier, Director, Information Systems
CHR: Jackie Luecht, Chief Human Resources Officer
CNO: Kim Chamberlin, Vice President Patient Services and Chief Nursing Officer
Web address: www.mercynorthiowa.com
Control: Church–operated, Nongovernment, not–for profit **Service:** General Medical and Surgical

> **Staffed Beds:** 237 **Admissions:** 11846 **Census:** 130 **Outpatient Visits:** 436471 **Births:** 890 **Total Expense ($000):** 311580 **Payroll Expense ($000):** 130175 **Personnel:** 2034

MISSOURI VALLEY—Harrison County

★ **CHI HEALTH MISSOURI VALLEY (161309)**, 631 North Eighth Street, Zip 51555–1102; tel. 712/642–2784 **A**9 10 18 **F**3 11 15 18 28 29 30 31 34 35 39 40 43 45 50 54 59 64 75 77 78 79 81 82 85 93 99 100 102 103 104 107 110 114 119 127 129 133 135 144 146 **P**8 **S** Catholic Health Initiatives, Englewood, CO
Primary Contact: Robert A. Valentine, President
CMO: Daniel Richter, M.D., Chief of Staff
CIO: Ravae Smallwood, IS Coordinator
CHR: Julie Brown, Human Resources Generalist
CNO: Darcy Behrendt, R.N., Vice President, Patient Care Services
Web address: www.alegentcreighton.com/community–memorial
Control: Other not–for–profit (including NFP Corporation) **Service:** General Medical and Surgical

> **Staffed Beds:** 16 **Admissions:** 588 **Census:** 6 **Outpatient Visits:** 42343 **Births:** 0 **Total Expense ($000):** 21496 **Payroll Expense ($000):** 7317 **Personnel:** 176

MOUNT AYR—Ringgold County

RINGGOLD COUNTY HOSPITAL (161373), 504 North Cleveland Street, Zip 50854–2201; tel. 641/464–3226 **A**9 10 18 **F**3 7 15 28 29 31 34 35 38 40 56 57 59 60 64 65 79 81 93 107 111 114 119 133 148 **P**6
Primary Contact: Gordon W. Winkler, Administrator and Chief Executive Officer
CFO: Teresa Roberts, Chief Financial Officer
CIO: Jan Lyons, Regional Director Health Improvement Management
CHR: Mitzi Hymbaugh, Chief Personnel
Web address: www.rchmtayr.org
Control: Hospital district or authority, Government, nonfederal **Service:** General Medical and Surgical

> **Staffed Beds:** 16 **Admissions:** 248 **Census:** 2 **Outpatient Visits:** 20510 **Births:** 0 **Total Expense ($000):** 17453 **Payroll Expense ($000):** 5831 **Personnel:** 103

MOUNT PLEASANT—Henry County

★ **HENRY COUNTY HEALTH CENTER (161356)**, 407 South White Street, Zip 52641–2263; tel. 319/385–3141, (Total facility includes 49 beds in nursing home–type unit) **A**9 10 18 **F**3 7 11 13 15 28 29 31 32 34 35 40 41 43 45 50 57 59 64 65 67 68 70 75 76 77 78 79 81 82 85 86 87 89 93 102 107 108 110 115 118 119 128 129 130 131 132 133 135 143 145 146 **P**6
Primary Contact: Robb Gardner, Chief Executive Officer
CFO: David Muhs, Chief Financial Officer
CMO: Steve Davis, M.D., Chief of Staff
CIO: Steve Stewart, Director Information Technology
CHR: Jim Carson, Director Human Resources
CNO: Jodi Geerts, Chief Nursing Officer
Web address: www.hchc.org
Control: County–Government, nonfederal **Service:** General Medical and Surgical

> **Staffed Beds:** 74 **Admissions:** 714 **Census:** 51 **Outpatient Visits:** 45949 **Births:** 130 **Total Expense ($000):** 31043 **Payroll Expense ($000):** 12688 **Personnel:** 244

Many Facility Codes have changed. Please refer to the AHA Guide Code Chart. © 2014 AHA Guide

IA

MENTAL HEALTH INSTITUTE (164004), 1200 East Washington Street, Zip 52641–1898; tel. 319/385–7231 **A**9 10 **F**4 5 29 75 86 98 100 101 103 130 132 135
Primary Contact: Ron Mullen, Superintendent
CFO: Barb Wheeler, Business Manager
CMO: Russell England, Chief Medical Officer
CHR: Janice Creighton, Human Resources Associate
Web address: www.dhs.state.ia.us
Control: State–Government, nonfederal **Service:** Alcoholism and other chemical dependency

Staffed Beds: 78 **Admissions:** 758 **Census:** 61 **Outpatient Visits:** 266
Births: 0 **Total Expense ($000):** 9038 **Payroll Expense ($000):** 5048
Personnel: 76

MUSCATINE—Muscatine County

⊞ **UNITYPOINT HEALTH – TRINITY MUSCATINE (160013)**, 1518 Mulberry Avenue, Zip 52761–3499; tel. 563/264–9100 **A**1 9 10 20 **F**3 5 11 13 15 28 31 34 38 40 43 45 50 56 57 59 61 64 65 68 69 70 75 76 77 79 81 85 87 89 97 102 107 108 110 111 114 119 124 129 130 131 134 135 147 148 **S** UnityPoint Health, West Des Moines, IA
Primary Contact: James M. Hayes, Chief Executive Officer
CFO: Greg Pagliuzza, Chief Financial Officer
CMO: Manasi Nadkarni, M.D., Vice President Medical Affairs
CIO: Sean Liddell, Manager Regional Service Information Technology
CHR: Karla Blaser, Director Human Resources
CNO: Pam Askew, R.N., Vice President Patient Care Services
Web address: www.unitypoint.org/quadcities/trinity–muscatine.aspx
Control: Other not–for–profit (including NFP Corporation) **Service:** General Medical and Surgical

Staffed Beds: 48 **Admissions:** 1564 **Census:** 12 **Outpatient Visits:** 89863
Births: 359 **Total Expense ($000):** 37605 **Payroll Expense ($000):** 17412
Personnel: 320

NEVADA—Story County

★ **STORY COUNTY MEDICAL CENTER (161333)**, 640 South 19th Street, Zip 50201–2902; tel. 515/382–2111, (Total facility includes 60 beds in nursing home–type unit) **A**9 10 18 **F**3 7 11 28 29 31 32 34 35 36 40 43 50 53 57 59 64 65 68 75 81 85 87 97 107 114 127 130 133 146 148 **P**6 **S** UnityPoint Health, West Des Moines, IA
Primary Contact: Timothy Ahlers, Chief Executive Officer
CFO: Jane Ramthun, Chief Financial Officer
CHR: Kaylee Siebrecht, Director Human Resources
Web address: www.storymedical.org
Control: County–Government, nonfederal **Service:** General Medical and Surgical

Staffed Beds: 77 **Admissions:** 445 **Census:** 59 **Outpatient Visits:** 26872
Births: 0 **Total Expense ($000):** 20215 **Payroll Expense ($000):** 8894
Personnel: 202

NEW HAMPTON—Chickasaw County

★ **MERCY MEDICAL CENTER–NEW HAMPTON (161331)**, 308 North Maple Avenue, Zip 50659–1142; tel. 641/394–4121 **A**9 10 18 **F**3 11 13 15 28 29 34 35 40 43 45 48 56 57 59 64 65 68 74 76 77 79 81 85 93 97 107 110 119 129 131 133 146 148 **P**1 **S** Catholic Health East / Trinity Health, Livonia, MI
Primary Contact: Bruce E. Roesler, FACHE, President and Chief Executive Officer
CFO: Jennifer Rapenske, Manager Financial Services
CMO: Jack Kline, M.D., Chief of Staff
CIO: Terry Chartier, Director, Information Systems
CHR: Jackie Luecht, Director, Human Resources
CNO: Jody Wright, Interim Chief Nursing Officer
Web address: www.mercynewhampton.com
Control: Church–operated, Nongovernment, not–for profit **Service:** General Medical and Surgical

Staffed Beds: 18 **Admissions:** 393 **Census:** 4 **Outpatient Visits:** 18290
Births: 26 **Total Expense ($000):** 15295 **Payroll Expense ($000):** 5471
Personnel: 71

NEWTON—Jasper County

★ ○ **SKIFF MEDICAL CENTER (160032)**, 204 Fourth Avenue East, Zip 50208–3100, Mailing Address: P.O. Box 1006, Zip 50208–1006; tel. 641/792–1273 **A**9 10 11 **F**3 11 13 15 17 28 29 30 31 34 35 36 40 43 44 45 57 59 62 63 64 65 70 75 76 77 78 79 81 82 85 89 90 93 96 102 107 108 110 111 115 118 119 128 130 131 132 133 135 145 146 148 **P**6
Primary Contact: Brett Altman, President and Chief Executive Officer
COO: Brett Altman, Clinical Operations Officer
CIO: Amber Pelzer, Director, Information Services
CHR: Teresa Wermager, Director, Human Resources
CNO: Sheryl Tilus, R.N., Chief Nursing Officer
Web address: www.skiffmed.com
Control: City–Government, nonfederal **Service:** General Medical and Surgical

Staffed Beds: 48 **Admissions:** 1754 **Census:** 24 **Outpatient Visits:** 81447
Births: 179 **Total Expense ($000):** 38058 **Payroll Expense ($000):** 17441
Personnel: 285

OELWEIN—Fayette County

★ **MERCY HOSPITAL OF FRANCISCAN SISTERS (161338)**, 201 Eighth Avenue S.E., Zip 50662–2447; tel. 319/283–6000, (Total facility includes 39 beds in nursing home–type unit) **A**9 10 18 **F**7 11 15 29 30 34 35 40 57 59 69 75 79 81 97 107 110 111 119 127 128 130 132 133 146 **P**1 **S** Wheaton Franciscan Healthcare, Wheaton, IL
Primary Contact: Terri Derflinger, Administrator
CFO: Timothy Huber, Manager Financial Support
CMO: James A. Lehman, M.D., Vice President Medical Affairs
CNO: Phyllis Doulaveris, MSN, Senior Vice President and Chief Nursing Officer
Web address: www.covhealth.com
Control: Church–operated, Nongovernment, not–for profit **Service:** General Medical and Surgical

Staffed Beds: 64 **Admissions:** 316 **Census:** 35 **Outpatient Visits:** 24090
Births: 0 **Total Expense ($000):** 12206 **Payroll Expense ($000):** 5268
Personnel: 95

ONAWA—Monona County

★ **BURGESS HEALTH CENTER (161359)**, 1600 Diamond Street, Zip 51040–1548; tel. 712/423–2311 **A**9 10 18 **F**3 7 11 13 15 28 29 31 32 34 35 40 56 57 59 62 63 64 65 70 75 76 77 78 79 81 82 85 89 93 97 99 100 101 103 104 107 114 119 127 130 132 133 135 146 148 **P**6
Primary Contact: Francis G. Tramp, President
CFO: Shawn Gosch, Chief Financial Officer
CMO: John Garred, Sr., M.D., Chief Medical Officer
CIO: Grady Warner, Director of Information Technology
CHR: Erin Brekke, Director Human Resources
CNO: Patty Sandmann, Senior Director of Nursing
Web address: www.burgesshc.org
Control: Other not–for–profit (including NFP Corporation) **Service:** General Medical and Surgical

Staffed Beds: 25 **Admissions:** 803 **Census:** 8 **Outpatient Visits:** 72440
Births: 55 **Total Expense ($000):** 24081 **Payroll Expense ($000):** 10393
Personnel: 230

ORANGE CITY—Sioux County

★ **ORANGE CITY AREA HEALTH SYSTEM (161360)**, 1000 Lincoln Circle S.E., Zip 51041–1862; tel. 712/737–4984, (Total facility includes 79 beds in nursing home–type unit) **A**9 10 18 **F**7 10 11 13 15 18 28 29 31 34 35 39 40 45 50 53 56 57 59 60 62 63 64 67 68 69 70 75 76 77 78 79 81 82 85 86 87 89 93 97 107 110 111 114 117 119 120 125 127 130 131 132 133 146 147 148 **P**6 **S** Sanford Health, Sioux Falls, SD
Primary Contact: Martin W. Guthmiller, Chief Executive Officer
COO: Daniel P. McCarty, Chief Operating Officer
CFO: Dina Baas, Director Financial Services
CHR: Shari Baker, Director Human Resources
Web address: www.ochealthsystem.org
Control: City–Government, nonfederal **Service:** General Medical and Surgical

Staffed Beds: 104 **Admissions:** 1034 **Census:** 87 **Outpatient Visits:** 71188
Births: 234 **Total Expense ($000):** 39780 **Payroll Expense ($000):** 16778
Personnel: 393

IA

OSAGE—Mitchell County

★ **MITCHELL COUNTY REGIONAL HEALTH CENTER (161323)**, 616 North Eighth Street, Zip 50461–1498; tel. 641/732–6000 **A**9 10 18 **F**7 8 11 15 18 28 29 34 35 40 50 57 59 63 64 65 75 81 85 87 91 93 107 110 114 119 127 128 130 132 133 144 146 **P**8 **S** Catholic Health East / Trinity Health, Livonia, MI
Primary Contact: Shelly Russell, Chief Executive Officer
CFO: Gregory Burkel, Chief Financial Officer
CMO: Jeff Nasstrom, D.O., Chief of Staff
CHR: Jodie Anderson, Director Human Resources
CNO: Shelly Russell, Chief Nursing Officer
Web address: www.mitchellcohospital–clinics.com
Control: County–Government, nonfederal **Service:** General Medical and Surgical

Staffed Beds: 25 **Admissions:** 397 **Census:** 5 **Outpatient Visits:** 56874
Births: 0 **Total Expense ($000):** 18175 **Payroll Expense ($000):** 5945
Personnel: 142

OSCEOLA—Clarke County

★ **CLARKE COUNTY HOSPITAL (161348)**, 800 South Fillmore Street, Zip 50213–1619; tel. 641/342–2184 **A**9 10 18 **F**7 11 15 18 28 29 31 34 35 40 45 50 53 57 59 64 67 68 75 81 89 90 93 94 96 107 111 115 116 117 118 119 128 129 130 133 135 148 **S** UnityPoint Health, West Des Moines, IA
Primary Contact: Brian G. Evans, FACHE, Chief Executive Officer
CFO: Michael Thilges, Chief Financial Officer
CMO: George Fotiadis, M.D., Chief of Staff
CIO: Dennis Blazek, Chief Information Officer
CHR: Kate Emanuel, Director Human Resources
Web address: www.clarkehosp.org
Control: County–Government, nonfederal **Service:** General Medical and Surgical

Staffed Beds: 25 **Admissions:** 332 **Census:** 12 **Outpatient Visits:** 20900
Births: 0 **Total Expense ($000):** 18236 **Payroll Expense ($000):** 6262
Personnel: 146

OSKALOOSA—Mahaska County

✠ **MAHASKA HEALTH PARTNERSHIP (161379)**, 1229 C Avenue East, Zip 52577–4298; tel. 641/672–3100 **A**1 9 10 18 **F**5 7 11 13 15 28 29 30 31 34 35 40 43 45 47 50 54 56 57 59 62 63 64 68 69 70 75 76 77 78 79 81 87 93 97 98 99 100 101 102 103 104 107 110 111 114 119 129 130 133 135 146 148 **P**6
Primary Contact: Jay Christensen, FACHE, Administrator
COO: Erin Baldwin, M.P.H., Chief Operating Officer
CFO: Jon Davis, Chief Financial Officer
CMO: Matt Whitis, Chief Medical Officer
CHR: Jacky Bresnahan, Director Human Resources
Web address: www.mahaskahealth.com
Control: County–Government, nonfederal **Service:** General Medical and Surgical

Staffed Beds: 33 **Admissions:** 1603 **Census:** 18 **Outpatient Visits:** 98068
Births: 183 **Total Expense ($000):** 41017 **Payroll Expense ($000):** 24573
Personnel: 357

OTTUMWA—Wapello County

☐ △ **OTTUMWA REGIONAL HEALTH CENTER (160089)**, 1001 Pennsylvania Avenue, Zip 52501–2186; tel. 641/684–2300 **A**1 2 7 9 10 19 20 **F**3 6 7 8 10 11 13 15 18 20 22 28 29 30 31 34 35 40 41 45 45 47 48 49 51 53 54 56 57 59 60 62 64 72 74 75 76 77 78 79 80 81 82 85 89 90 93 107 108 110 114 115 118 119 120 121 123 125 126 127 129 130 131 135 144 146 147 148 **P**6 **S** RegionalCare Hospital Partners, Brentwood, TN
Primary Contact: Philip J. Noel, III, Chief Executive Officer
CFO: Gene Smith, Interim Vice President and Chief Financial Officer
CMO: Brian Quinn, D.O., Chief Medical Officer
CIO: Scott Garrett, Director of IS
CHR: Kelly Gaul–Houser, Director Human Resources
CNO: Barbara Larson, R.N., Vice President and Chief Nursing Officer
Web address: www.ottumwaregionalhealth.com
Control: Corporation, Investor–owned, for–profit **Service:** General Medical and Surgical

Staffed Beds: 84 **Admissions:** 3329 **Census:** 39 **Outpatient Visits:** 121324
Births: 525 **Total Expense ($000):** 77824 **Payroll Expense ($000):** 26712
Personnel: 492

PELLA—Marion County

✉ **PELLA REGIONAL HEALTH CENTER (161367)**, 404 Jefferson Street, Zip 50219–1257; tel. 641/628–3150, (Total facility includes 63 beds in nursing home–type unit) **A**1 9 10 18 **F**3 11 13 15 18 28 29 30 31 32 34 35 40 43 45 50 51 53 57 59 60 62 63 64 65 66 67 70 74 75 76 77 78 79 81 82 85 86 87 91 93 94 97 102 107 108 110 111 115 119 126 127 128 129 130 131 132 133 144 146 147 148 **P**6
Primary Contact: Robert D. Kroese, FACHE, Chief Executive Officer
COO: Robert D. Kroese, FACHE, Chief Executive Officer
CFO: Ron Wauters, Chief Financial Officer
CIO: Tait Smock, Manager Information Systems
CHR: Teri Lickteig, HR Director
CNO: Yvonne M. O'Brien, MS, Chief of Nursing
Web address: www.pellahealth.org
Control: Other not–for–profit (including NFP Corporation) **Service:** General Medical and Surgical

Staffed Beds: 88 **Admissions:** 1522 **Census:** 65 **Outpatient Visits:** 130200
Births: 410 **Total Expense ($000):** 49049 **Payroll Expense ($000):** 20293
Personnel: 580

PERRY—Dallas County

★ **DALLAS COUNTY HOSPITAL (161322)**, 610 10th Street, Zip 50220–2221; tel. 515/465–3547 **A**9 10 18 **F**10 11 15 18 28 29 31 34 35 39 40 41 43 57 59 65 75 77 78 79 81 82 85 89 90 93 107 110 111 114 116 119 128 129 132 133 146 147 148
Primary Contact: Matt Wille, Chief Executive Officer
CFO: Sandra Christensen, Chief Financial Officer
CMO: Steven Sohn, M.D., President Medical Staff
CHR: Sherry Smith, Manager Human Resources
Web address: www.dallascohospital.org
Control: County–Government, nonfederal **Service:** General Medical and Surgical

Staffed Beds: 18 **Admissions:** 291 **Census:** 4 **Outpatient Visits:** 24875
Births: 1 **Total Expense ($000):** 13998 **Payroll Expense ($000):** 4272
Personnel: 92

POCAHONTAS—Pocahontas County

★ **POCAHONTAS COMMUNITY HOSPITAL (161305)**, 606 N.W. Seventh Street, Zip 50574–1099; tel. 712/335–3501 **A**9 10 18 **F**1 4 7 11 15 16 17 28 29 31 35 40 43 45 59 62 63 64 67 70 72 73 75 77 78 79 80 81 84 88 89 90 93 98 110 119 128 130 132 133 135 146 148 **P**6 **S** UnityPoint Health, West Des Moines, IA
Primary Contact: James D. Roetman, President and Chief Executive Officer
CFO: Lynn Raveling, Chief Financial Officer
CNO: Susie Aden, Director of IP Services
Web address: www.pocahontashospital.org
Control: City–Government, nonfederal **Service:** General Medical and Surgical

Staffed Beds: 20 **Admissions:** 224 **Census:** 2 **Outpatient Visits:** 27745
Births: 0 **Total Expense ($000):** 9638 **Payroll Expense ($000):** 3258
Personnel: 84

PRIMGHAR—O'Brien County

★ **BAUM HARMON MERCY HOSPITAL (161300)**, 255 North Welch Avenue, Zip 51245–7765, Mailing Address: P.O. Box 528, Zip 51245–0528; tel. 712/957–2300 **A**9 10 18 **F**11 15 28 29 30 31 34 35 40 45 53 57 59 64 67 70 75 77 78 81 89 119 127 128 133 135 **P**6 **S** Catholic Health East / Trinity Health, Livonia, MI
Primary Contact: Roger W. Lenz, Interim Chief Executive Officer
CFO: Sue E. McCauley, Director Finance
CMO: Shailesh Desai, M.D., Chief of Staff
Web address: www.baumharmon.org
Control: Church–operated, Nongovernment, not–for profit **Service:** General Medical and Surgical

Staffed Beds: 12 **Admissions:** 117 **Census:** 1 **Outpatient Visits:** 22262
Births: 0 **Total Expense ($000):** 7299 **Payroll Expense ($000):** 3638
Personnel: 70

RED OAK—Montgomery County

★ **MONTGOMERY COUNTY MEMORIAL HOSPITAL (161363)**, 2301 Eastern Avenue, Zip 51566–1300, Mailing Address: P.O. Box 498, Zip 51566–0498; tel. 712/623–7000 **A**9 10 18 **F**3 11 13 15 28 29 31 34 35 40 44 45 50 53 57 59 62 63 64 68 69 70 75 77 78 79 81 82 85 86 87 93 107 110 111 114 118 119 129 130 133 135 146 147 148
Primary Contact: Allen E. Pohren, Administrator
CFO: Rick Leinen, Chief Financial Officer
CMO: Warren Hayes, Chief of Staff
CIO: Ron Kloewer, Chief Information Officer
CHR: Shayla Jennings, Human Resources Director
CNO: Diane McGrew, Chief Nurse Executive
Web address: www.mcmh.org
Control: County–Government, nonfederal **Service:** General Medical and Surgical

Staffed Beds: 25 **Admissions:** 1039 **Census:** 14 **Outpatient Visits:** 42014
Births: 77 **Total Expense ($000):** 28747 **Payroll Expense ($000):** 13021
Personnel: 243

IA

Many Facility Codes have changed. Please refer to the AHA Guide Code Chart.   © 2014 AHA Guide

ROCK RAPIDS—Lyon County

★ **SANFORD HOSPITAL ROCK RAPIDS (161321)**, 801 South Greene Street, Zip 51246–1998; tel. 712/472–2591 **A**9 10 18 **F**11 28 31 34 40 41 45 53 57 59 68 77 81 87 89 97 107 119 127 130 131 133 135 146 **P**6 **S** Sanford Health, Sioux Falls, SD
Primary Contact: Tammy Loosbrock, Chief Executive Officer
CFO: Stanley Knobloch, Chief Financial Officer
CMO: David Springer, M.D., President Medical Staff
CHR: Holly Anderson, Supervisor Human Resources
CNO: Jack Johnson, Chief Nursing Officer
Web address: www.sanfordmerrill.org
Control: Other not–for–profit (including NFP Corporation) **Service:** General Medical and Surgical

Staffed Beds: 14 **Admissions:** 267 **Census:** 3 **Outpatient Visits:** 15191 **Births:** 0 **Total Expense ($000):** 8107 **Payroll Expense ($000):** 3608 **Personnel:** 68

SANFORD MERRILL MEDICAL CENTER See Sanford Hospital Rock Rapids

ROCK VALLEY—Sioux County

★ **HEGG MEMORIAL HEALTH CENTER AVERA (161336)**, 1202 21st Avenue, Zip 51247–1497; tel. 712/476–8000, (Total facility includes 60 beds in nursing home–type unit) **A**9 10 18 **F**3 4 11 13 15 17 28 29 31 34 35 36 40 41 43 45 53 57 59 62 64 67 68 70 73 75 76 77 78 79 81 84 85 89 93 97 107 110 111 114 119 128 130 131 132 133 135 144 147 148 **S** Avera Health, Sioux Falls, SD
Primary Contact: Glenn Zevenbergen, Chief Executive Officer
CFO: Kari Timmer, Chief Financial Officer
CMO: Kevin Post, D.O., Chief Medical Officer
CHR: Tammy Faber, Director Human Resources
CNO: Linda VerSteeg, Director of Nursing
Web address: www.hegghc.org
Control: Other not–for–profit (including NFP Corporation) **Service:** General Medical and Surgical

Staffed Beds: 85 **Admissions:** 316 **Census:** 63 **Outpatient Visits:** 33033 **Births:** 99 **Total Expense ($000):** 16463 **Payroll Expense ($000):** 8188 **Personnel:** 203

SAC CITY—Sac County

★ **LORING HOSPITAL (161370)**, 211 Highland Avenue, Zip 50583–2424; tel. 712/662–7105 **A**9 10 18 **F**3 11 15 28 29 30 31 34 35 40 45 57 59 62 63 64 68 75 78 79 81 86 87 93 107 110 115 119 125 129 130 132 133 146 **S** UnityPoint Health, West Des Moines, IA
Primary Contact: James Beck, Interim President and Chief Executive Officer
CFO: Angie Fischer, Chief Financial Officer
CMO: Les Marczewski, M.D., Chief Medical Officer
CIO: Leah Snyder, Director Health Information Services
CHR: Becky Pontious, Human Resources/Accounting
CNO: Lori Forneris, R.N., Chief Clinical Officer
Web address: www.loringhospital.org
Control: Other not–for–profit (including NFP Corporation) **Service:** General Medical and Surgical

Staffed Beds: 25 **Admissions:** 708 **Census:** 6 **Outpatient Visits:** 22027 **Births:** 0 **Total Expense ($000):** 12787 **Payroll Expense ($000):** 4493 **Personnel:** 95

SHELDON—O'brien County

★ **SANFORD SHELDON MEDICAL CENTER (161381)**, 118 North Seventh Avenue, Zip 51201–1235, Mailing Address: P.O. Box 250, Zip 51201–0250; tel. 712/324–5041, (Total facility includes 70 beds in nursing home–type unit) **A**9 10 18 **F**3 11 13 15 28 29 31 32 34 40 45 50 53 57 59 62 63 64 65 67 68 74 75 76 77 78 79 81 82 84 86 87 91 93 96 97 99 100 101 102 103 104 107 108 110 111 114 119 127 129 130 131 132 133 135 146 148 **P**6 **S** Sanford Health, Sioux Falls, SD
Primary Contact: Richard E. Nordahl, Chief Executive Officer
CFO: Deb Rosburg, Chief Financial Officer
CMO: Amy Badberg, M.D., Physician
CIO: Scott Moffitt, Director Information Systems
CHR: Dianne Wolthuizen, Director Human Resources
CNO: Joni DeKok, Chief Nursing Officer
Web address: www.sanfordsheldon.org
Control: Other not–for–profit (including NFP Corporation) **Service:** General Medical and Surgical

Staffed Beds: 95 **Admissions:** 724 **Census:** 67 **Outpatient Visits:** 95658 **Births:** 133 **Total Expense ($000):** 25269 **Payroll Expense ($000):** 11666 **Personnel:** 243

SHENANDOAH—Page County

★ **SHENANDOAH MEDICAL CENTER (161366)**, 300 Pershing Avenue, Zip 51601–2355; tel. 712/246–1230, (Total facility includes 53 beds in nursing home–type unit) **A**9 10 18 **F**3 10 11 13 15 18 28 29 31 34 36 38 40 41 43 45 50 53 56 57 59 62 63 64 65 67 68 69 70 75 76 77 78 79 81 84 85 87 91 93 104 107 108 110 111 115 117 118 119 127 129 130 131 132 133 135 146 147 148 **P**6
Primary Contact: Karen S. Cole, MS, FACHE, Chief Executive Officer
CFO: Matt Sells, CPA, Chief Financial Officer
CMO: Jerry Schaaf, M.D., Chief Medical Officer
CIO: John Eckmann, Director Information Systems
CHR: Keli Royal, Director Human Resources
CNO: Scott Garland, Chief Nursing Officer
Web address: www.smchospital.com/
Control: Other not–for–profit (including NFP Corporation) **Service:** General Medical and Surgical

Staffed Beds: 78 **Admissions:** 520 **Census:** 49 **Outpatient Visits:** 194367 **Births:** 128 **Total Expense ($000):** 29499 **Payroll Expense ($000):** 14554 **Personnel:** 267

SIBLEY— County

★ **OSCEOLA COMMUNITY HOSPITAL (161345)**, 600 Ninth Avenue North, Zip 51249–1012, Mailing Address: P.O. Box 258, Zip 51249–0258; tel. 712/754–2574 **A**9 10 18 **F**3 8 9 10 11 13 15 17 18 26 28 29 31 32 34 35 36 40 43 45 46 49 53 56 57 59 61 62 64 65 67 68 70 75 76 77 78 79 81 82 83 84 85 86 87 89 93 107 108 110 114 119 125 128 129 130 131 132 133 135 143 144 145 146 147 148 **P**5 **S** Avera Health, Sioux Falls, SD
Primary Contact: Janet H. Dykstra, Chief Executive Officer
CFO: Jerri Palsrok, Manager Business Office
CMO: Gregory J. Kosters, D.O., Chief Medical Officer
CIO: Sherry McElroy, Director Health Information Management
Web address: www.osceolacommunityhospital.org
Control: Other not–for–profit (including NFP Corporation) **Service:** General Medical and Surgical

Staffed Beds: 25 **Admissions:** 336 **Census:** 3 **Outpatient Visits:** 19924 **Births:** 28 **Total Expense ($000):** 11071 **Payroll Expense ($000):** 3375 **Personnel:** 88

SIGOURNEY—Keokuk County

KEOKUK COUNTY HEALTH CENTER (161315), 23019 Highway 149, Zip 52591–8341; tel. 641/622–2720 **A**9 10 18 **F**1 2 3 7 11 12 28 29 30 34 35 38 40 43 45 46 50 56 57 59 63 64 65 67 75 77 82 84 86 87 90 91 93 97 107 128 130 131 132 133 134 135 144 146 148 **P**5 6
Primary Contact: Matthew Ives, Interim Chief Executive Officer and Chief Financial Officer
CFO: Matthew Ives, Interim Chief Executive Officer and Chief Financial Officer
Web address: www.kchc.net
Control: County–Government, nonfederal **Service:** General Medical and Surgical

Staffed Beds: 14 **Admissions:** 141 **Census:** 9 **Outpatient Visits:** 13230 **Births:** 0 **Total Expense ($000):** 9723 **Payroll Expense ($000):** 4266 **Personnel:** 87

SIOUX CENTER—Sioux County

★ **SIOUX CENTER HEALTH (161346)**, 1101 9th Street, S.E., Zip 51250–1398; tel. 712/722–8107, (Total facility includes 69 beds in nursing home–type unit) **A**9 10 18 **F**3 8 10 13 15 17 18 26 28 29 30 31 34 35 40 41 43 45 56 57 59 62 63 64 67 68 74 75 76 77 78 79 81 82 83 84 85 86 87 89 93 97 107 110 111 114 119 125 128 130 131 132 133 135 144 146 147 148 **P**6 **S** Avera Health, Sioux Falls, SD
Primary Contact: Kayleen R. Lee, Chief Executive Officer
CFO: Jackson Schuiteman, Chief Financial Officer
CHR: Theresa Tucker, Human Resources Officer
Web address: www.schospital.org
Control: Other not–for–profit (including NFP Corporation) **Service:** General Medical and Surgical

Staffed Beds: 90 **Admissions:** 544 **Census:** 73 **Outpatient Visits:** 45700 **Births:** 189 **Total Expense ($000):** 28064 **Payroll Expense ($000):** 13208 **Personnel:** 324

IA

Hospital, Medicare Provider Number, Address, Telephone, Approval, Facility, and Physician Codes, Health Care System

★ American Hospital Association (AHA) membership
□ The Joint Commission accreditation
◇ DNV Healthcare Inc. accreditation
○ Healthcare Facilities Accreditation Program
△ Commission on Accreditation of Rehabilitation Facilities (CARF) accreditation

© 2014 AHA Guide   *Many Facility Codes have changed. Please refer to the AHA Guide Code Chart.*   Hospitals **A237**

SIOUX CITY—Woodbury County

⊞ **MERCY MEDICAL CENTER–SIOUX CITY (160153)**, 801 Fifth Street, Zip 51101–1326, Mailing Address: P.O. Box 3168, Zip 51102–3168; tel. 712/279–2010 **A**1 2 3 5 9 10 **F**3 5 11 13 15 17 18 20 22 24 26 28 29 30 31 32 34 35 36 37 38 40 43 44 45 48 49 50 51 55 56 57 59 61 64 65 68 70 71 74 75 76 77 78 79 81 82 84 85 86 87 89 90 92 93 96 97 98 99 100 101 102 103 104 105 107 108 110 111 114 115 118 119 124 126 129 130 132 135 144 146 147 148 **P**6 8 **S** Catholic Health East / Trinity Health, Livonia, MI
Primary Contact: James G. Fitzpatrick, President
CFO: Hugh DePaulis, Interim Vice President and Chief Financial Officer
CMO: Jerome Pierson, Chief Medical Officer
CIO: Steve Larson, M.D., Director Information Systems
CHR: Julie Anfinson, Director Human Resources
CNO: Tracy Larson, MS, Vice President Patient Care Services and Chief Nursing Officer
Web address: www.mercysiouxcity.com
Control: Church–operated, Nongovernment, not–for profit **Service:** General Medical and Surgical

Staffed Beds: 238 **Admissions:** 10284 **Census:** 131 **Outpatient Visits:** 256502 **Births:** 297 **Total Expense ($000):** 195562 **Payroll Expense ($000):** 78274 **Personnel:** 1159

★ ◇ **UNITYPOINT HEALTH – ST. LUKE'S (160146)**, 2720 Stone Park Boulevard, Zip 51104–3734; tel. 712/279–3500 **A**3 5 9 10 21 **F**3 11 13 15 17 18 20 22 26 28 29 30 31 34 35 39 40 43 45 49 50 51 54 56 57 59 60 64 68 70 72 73 74 75 76 77 78 79 81 82 84 85 86 88 89 90 92 93 96 97 98 102 104 107 108 111 114 118 119 126 129 130 131 132 135 142 143 144 145 146 147 **P**6 **S** UnityPoint Health, West Des Moines, IA
Primary Contact: Peter W. Thoreen, FACHE, President and Chief Executive Officer
COO: Lynn Wold, Chief Operation Officer
CFO: James Gobell, Chief Financial Officer
CIO: James Gobell, Chief Financial Officer
CHR: Tammy Hartnett, Employee Relations Manager
CNO: Priscilla Stokes, MS, Vice President Patient Care and Hospital Operations
Web address: www.stlukes.org
Control: Other not–for–profit (including NFP Corporation) **Service:** General Medical and Surgical

Staffed Beds: 151 **Admissions:** 9150 **Census:** 100 **Outpatient Visits:** 68471 **Births:** 1989 **Total Expense ($000):** 136626 **Payroll Expense ($000):** 55537 **Personnel:** 1054

SPENCER—Clay County

★ **SPENCER HOSPITAL (160112)**, 1200 First Avenue East, Suite 1, Zip 51301–4342; tel. 712/264–6111 **A**9 10 **F**3 7 8 11 13 15 28 29 30 31 34 35 39 40 43 45 50 53 54 56 57 59 60 62 63 64 65 69 70 75 76 77 78 79 81 82 84 85 86 87 93 96 97 98 103 107 108 109 111 115 118 119 120 121 123 127 129 130 131 132 133 135 146 147 148 **P**5
Primary Contact: William J. Bumgarner, President
CFO: Mark Gaworski, Vice President Finance, Chief Financial Officer
CMO: Jason Hough, Medical Staff President
CIO: Brenda Marie Tiefenthaler, R.N., Vice President Patient Care and Informatics
CHR: Stephen Duetsch, Vice President Operations and Support
CNO: Brenda Marie Tiefenthaler, R.N., Vice President Patient Care and Informatics
Web address: www.spencerhospital.org
Control: City–Government, nonfederal **Service:** General Medical and Surgical

Staffed Beds: 74 **Admissions:** 2571 **Census:** 28 **Outpatient Visits:** 114657 **Births:** 312 **Total Expense ($000):** 62558 **Payroll Expense ($000):** 21979 **Personnel:** 451

SPIRIT LAKE—Dickinson County

★ **LAKES REGIONAL HEALTHCARE (160124)**, 2301 Highway 71 South, Zip 51360–6810, Mailing Address: P.O. Box AB, Zip 51360–0159; tel. 712/336–1230 **A**9 10 **F**3 7 11 13 15 28 29 30 31 34 35 40 41 43 45 50 57 59 62 63 64 65 69 70 75 76 77 78 79 81 85 89 93 97 107 111 114 119 128 129 130 132 133 143 146 148 **P**6 **S** Avera Health, Sioux Falls, SD
Primary Contact: Jason Harrington, President and Chief Executive Officer
COO: Connie Lange, R.N., Vice President of Patient Care Services
CFO: Steve Alger, Senior Vice President and Chief Financial Officer
CMO: Steven Vander Leest, Chief of Staff
CIO: Brian McShane, IT Manager
CHR: Sarah Roche, Director Human Resources
CNO: Joni K. Mitchell, Vice President Nursing
Web address: www.lakeshealth.org
Control: County–Government, nonfederal **Service:** General Medical and Surgical

Staffed Beds: 30 **Admissions:** 935 **Census:** 10 **Outpatient Visits:** 81080 **Births:** 97 **Total Expense ($000):** 33335 **Payroll Expense ($000):** 11130 **Personnel:** 202

STORM LAKE—Buena Vista County

⊞ **BUENA VISTA REGIONAL MEDICAL CENTER (161375)**, 1525 West Fifth Street, Zip 50588–3027, Mailing Address: P.O. Box 309, Zip 50588–0309; tel. 712/732–4030 **A**1 9 10 18 **F**3 7 8 11 13 15 18 28 29 30 31 34 40 43 45 53 55 56 57 59 63 64 68 70 74 75 76 77 78 79 81 82 84 85 86 87 93 96 98 103 107 108 110 111 115 117 118 119 128 129 130 131 132 133 135 146 147 148 **S** UnityPoint Health, West Des Moines, IA
Primary Contact: Steven Colerick, Chief Executive Officer
CFO: Krista Ketcham, Chief Financial Officer
CMO: Ingrid Franze, Chief Medical Staff
CIO: Brian Granville, Director Information Technology
CHR: Carrie Turnquist, Director Human Resources
CNO: Dawn M. Bach, MS, Chief Clinical Officer
Web address: www.bvrmc.org
Control: County–Government, nonfederal **Service:** General Medical and Surgical

Staffed Beds: 35 **Admissions:** 1317 **Census:** 19 **Outpatient Visits:** 67706 **Births:** 365 **Total Expense ($000):** 40784 **Payroll Expense ($000):** 16701 **Personnel:** 347

SUMNER—Bremer County

★ **COMMUNITY MEMORIAL HOSPITAL (161320)**, 909 West First Street, Zip 50674–1203, Mailing Address: P.O. Box 148, Zip 50674–0148; tel. 563/578–3275 **A**9 10 18 **F**3 11 15 28 29 34 40 45 57 59 64 81 85 86 97 107 114 127 128 129 131 133 135 148 **P**5 6 **S** UnityPoint Health, West Des Moines, IA
Primary Contact: Mary S. Wells, R.N., Chief Executive Officer
CFO: Dawn Everding, Chief Financial Officer
CMO: Jeff Roske, D.O., Chief Medical Staff
CHR: Robin Elliott, Personnel Officer
CNO: Lynne Niemann, Director Nurses and Patient Care
Web address: www.cmhsumner.org
Control: Other not–for–profit (including NFP Corporation) **Service:** General Medical and Surgical

Staffed Beds: 16 **Admissions:** 132 **Census:** 3 **Outpatient Visits:** 11963 **Births:** 0 **Total Expense ($000):** 11462 **Payroll Expense ($000):** 4324 **Personnel:** 81

VINTON—Benton County

★ **VIRGINIA GAY HOSPITAL (161349)**, 502 North Ninth Avenue, Zip 52349–2299; tel. 319/472–6200, (Total facility includes 40 beds in nursing home–type unit) **A**9 10 18 **F**3 15 28 29 34 40 43 45 53 59 62 64 75 77 81 85 86 87 96 97 107 111 114 119 125 127 129 130 131 132 133 143 146 **P**6
Primary Contact: Michael J. Riege, Chief Executive Officer
CFO: Julia Meadows, Chief Financial Officer
CMO: Brian Meeker, D.O., President Medical Staff
CIO: Bernie Markey, Chief Information Officer
CHR: Kim Frank, Chief Human Resources Officer
CNO: Tina M. Eden, Director of Nursing
Web address: www.vghinc.com
Control: Other not–for–profit (including NFP Corporation) **Service:** General Medical and Surgical

Staffed Beds: 65 **Admissions:** 404 **Census:** 44 **Outpatient Visits:** 94970 **Births:** 0 **Total Expense ($000):** 22287 **Payroll Expense ($000):** 11030 **Personnel:** 204

WASHINGTON—Washington County

★ **WASHINGTON COUNTY HOSPITAL AND CLINICS (161344)**, 400 East Polk Street, Zip 52353–1237, Mailing Address: P.O. Box 909, Zip 52353–0909; tel. 319/653–5481, (Total facility includes 43 beds in nursing home–type unit) **A**9 10 18 **F**3 13 15 28 29 34 40 43 45 55 57 59 64 67 68 69 75 76 77 81 82 84 85 86 93 97 107 110 111 114 119 130 132 133 135 146 147 148 **P**6
Primary Contact: Dennis Hunger, Chief Executive Officer
CFO: Steve Sanders, Chief Financial Officer
CMO: Paul Towner, Chief of Staff
CIO: Makyla Maize, Director Information Services
CHR: Tracy Ousey, Director Human Resources
CNO: Barbara Griswold, Chief Nursing Officer
Web address: www.wchc.org
Control: County–Government, nonfederal **Service:** General Medical and Surgical

Staffed Beds: 68 **Admissions:** 1469 **Census:** 49 **Outpatient Visits:** 46000 **Births:** 139 **Total Expense ($000):** 23688 **Payroll Expense ($000):** 10836 **Personnel:** 246

WATERLOO—Black Hawk County

ALLEN MEMORIAL HOSPITAL See UnityPoint Health – Allen Hospital

IA

✈ △ **COVENANT MEDICAL CENTER (160067)**, 3421 West Ninth Street,
Zip 50702–5401; tel. 319/272–8000, (Includes KIMBALL–RIDGE CENTER, 2101
Kimball Avenue, Zip 50702; tel. 319/291–3131) **A**1 3 5 7 9 10 **F**3 4 5 7 11 13
15 18 19 20 22 26 28 29 30 31 33 34 35 40 43 44 46 49 51 53 57 58 59
60 61 62 64 68 70 71 72 74 75 76 77 78 79 81 82 89 90 93 97 98 99 100
104 105 107 108 110 111 114 115 116 118 119 120 127 129 130 131 132
143 144 146 147 148 **P**1 6 **S** Wheaton Franciscan Healthcare, Wheaton, IL
Primary Contact: Jack Dusenbery, President and Chief Executive Officer
COO: Rose Fowler, MS, Vice President Operations
CFO: Michele Panicucci, Senior Vice President and Chief Financial Officer
CMO: James A. Lenman, M.D., Vice President Medical Affairs
CIO: Gregory Smith, Chief Information Officer
CHR: Wayne C. Frangesch, Vice President Human Resources
CNO: Phyllis Doulaveris, MSN, Senior Vice President and Chief Nursing Officer
Web address: www.wheatoniowa.org
Control: Church–operated, Nongovernment, not–for profit **Service:** General
Medical and Surgical

> **Staffed Beds:** 220 **Admissions:** 8781 **Census:** 95 **Outpatient Visits:** 612581
> **Births:** 1492 **Total Expense ($000):** 250844 **Payroll Expense ($000):**
> 114777 **Personnel:** 1752

✈ △ **UNITYPOINT HEALTH – ALLEN HOSPITAL (160110)**, 1825 Logan
Avenue, Zip 50703–1916; tel. 319/235–3941 **A**1 3 5 7 9 10 **F**3 8 11 13 15 18
20 22 24 26 28 29 30 31 34 35 37 40 43 45 46 48 49 50 51 52 54 56 57
59 63 64 66 68 70 72 74 75 77 78 79 81 82 84 85 86 87 88 90 91 92 93
96 97 98 99 100 101 102 103 104 107 108 110 111 114 114 115 118 119 126
127 129 130 132 135 146 147 148 **P**6 8 **S** UnityPoint Health, West Des
Moines, IA
Primary Contact: Pamela K. Delagardelle, President and Chief Executive Officer
COO: Jennifer Friedly, Chief Operating Officer and Vice President
CFO: Renee Rasmussen, Senior Vice President and Chief Financial Officer
CMO: Timothy Horrigan, Chief Medical Officer
CIO: Daniel Norman, Regional Service Manager
CHR: Steven Sesterhenn, Vice President
CNO: Mary Hagen, R.N., VP and Chief Nursing Officer
Web address: www.allenhospital.org
Control: Other not–for–profit (including NFP Corporation) **Service:** General
Medical and Surgical

> **Staffed Beds:** 201 **Admissions:** 10314 **Census:** 108 **Outpatient Visits:**
> 276733 **Births:** 967 **Total Expense ($000):** 203191 **Payroll Expense**
> **($000):** 68809 **Personnel:** 1281

WAUKON—Allamakee County

★ **VETERANS MEMORIAL HOSPITAL (161318)**, 40 First Street S.E.,
Zip 52172–2099; tel. 563/568–3411 **A**9 10 18 **F**7 11 13 15 28 31 34 35 40
45 57 59 62 64 65 75 76 78 79 81 107 119 131 132 133 134 144 146
Primary Contact: Michael D. Myers, Chief Executive Officer
CFO: Scott Knode, Chief Financial Officer
CHR: Erin Berns, Director Human Resources
Web address: www.vmhospital.com
Control: City–Government, nonfederal **Service:** General Medical and Surgical

> **Staffed Beds:** 25 **Admissions:** 728 **Census:** 8 **Outpatient Visits:** 45938
> **Births:** 135 **Total Expense ($000):** 14933 **Payroll Expense ($000):** 6447
> **Personnel:** 145

WAVERLY—Bremer County

✈ **WAVERLY HEALTH CENTER (161339)**, 312 Ninth Street S.W.,
Zip 50677–2999; tel. 319/352–4120 **A**1 9 10 18 **F**3 7 8 11 13 15 28 29 34
35 36 40 43 45 50 57 59 63 64 75 76 77 81 85 86 97 104 107 110 111
114 119 127 130 132 133 134 135 144 146 147 **P**6
Primary Contact: Lisa Bennett, Interim CEO and Chief Financial Officer
CFO: Lisa Bennett, Interim CEO and Chief Financial Officer
CMO: Michael T. Berstler, Chief Medical Officer
CIO: Jerry Tiedt, Director Information Systems
CHR: Angie Tye, Director Human Resources
CNO: Joanne Nathem, MSN, Chief Clinical and Nursing Officer
Web address: www.waverlyhealthcenter.org
Control: City–Government, nonfederal **Service:** General Medical and Surgical

> **Staffed Beds:** 25 **Admissions:** 951 **Census:** 9 **Outpatient Visits:** 106413
> **Births:** 260 **Total Expense ($000):** 49458 **Payroll Expense ($000):** 22829
> **Personnel:** 322

WEBSTER CITY—Hamilton County

HAMILTON HOSPITAL See Van Diest Medical Center

★ **VAN DIEST MEDICAL CENTER (161361)**, 2350 Hospital Drive,
Zip 50595–6600; tel. 515/832–9400 **A**9 10 18 **F**3 7 11 13 15 28 29 35 38
40 43 44 45 59 64 75 76 77 79 81 82 85 86 87 89 93 107 111 115 119
129 130 132 133 135 146 148 **P**6
Primary Contact: Lori Rathbun, Chief Executive Officer
CFO: Alice Heinrichs, CPA, Chief Financial Officer
CMO: Subhosh Sahai, M.D., Chief of Staff
CIO: Dave Dawson, Director Information Services
CNO: Janet Naset–Payne, R.N., Chief Nursing Officer
Web address: www.vandiestmc.org
Control: County–Government, nonfederal **Service:** General Medical and Surgical

> **Staffed Beds:** 25 **Admissions:** 1146 **Census:** 12 **Outpatient Visits:** 19306
> **Births:** 111 **Total Expense ($000):** 15398 **Payroll Expense ($000):** 8397
> **Personnel:** 179

WEST BURLINGTON—Des Moines County

✈ △ **GREAT RIVER MEDICAL CENTER (160057)**, 1221 South Gear Avenue,
Zip 52655–1681; tel. 319/768–1000, (Total facility includes 165 beds in nursing
home–type unit) **A**1 7 9 10 19 **F**3 4 5 7 11 13 15 18 20 22 28 29 30 31 32
34 35 36 38 40 43 48 50 53 57 59 60 62 63 64 67 68 69 70 73 75 76 77
78 79 81 82 84 85 86 87 89 90 91 92 93 96 98 99 100 101 102 103 104
107 108 110 111 114 115 116 117 118 119 121 123 128 129 130 131 132
143 146 147 148 **P**6
Primary Contact: Mark D. Richardson, President and Chief Executive Officer
CFO: Todd J. Sladky, Chief Financial Officer
CMO: John Phillips, Chief of Staff
CIO: Gary Davis, Director Information Systems
CHR: James M. Kammerer, Vice President Support Services
CNO: Teresa Colgan, VP of Nursing
Web address: www.greatrivermedical.org
Control: Other not–for–profit (including NFP Corporation) **Service:** General
Medical and Surgical

> **Staffed Beds:** 378 **Admissions:** 7242 **Census:** 201 **Outpatient Visits:**
> 258350 **Births:** 567 **Total Expense ($000):** 151322 **Payroll Expense**
> **($000):** 62848 **Personnel:** 1221

WEST DES MOINES—Polk County

★ **MERCY MEDICAL CENTER – WEST LAKES**, 1755 59th Place,
Zip 50266–7737; tel. 515/358–8000 **A**9 **F**3 7 11 12 13 15 18 20 22 26 29
30 39 40 41 43 44 50 56 59 61 62 64 65 68 70 75 76 77 78 79 81 85 86
87 93 96 107 108 111 114 118 119 130 132 135 143 146 **S** Catholic Health
Initiatives, Englewood, CO
Primary Contact: Robert P. Ritz, FACHE, President
COO: Sheryl L. Barnes, MSN, Senior Director Clinical Services
Web address: www.mercywestlakes.org/
Control: Church–operated, Nongovernment, not–for profit **Service:** General
Medical and Surgical

> **Staffed Beds:** 74 **Admissions:** 3554 **Census:** 32 **Outpatient Visits:** 21565
> **Births:** 276 **Total Expense ($000):** 45164 **Payroll Expense ($000):** 13405
> **Personnel:** 213

WEST UNION—Fayette County

★ **PALMER LUTHERAN HEALTH CENTER (161316)**, 112 Jefferson Street,
Zip 52175–1022; tel. 563/422–3811 **A**9 10 18 **F**3 8 11 13 15 28 29 30 31
34 40 43 56 57 59 62 63 64 65 68 70 76 77 78 79 81 82 85 86 93 96 107
111 114 119 128 129 130 131 132 133 135 144 146 148
Primary Contact: Steve Stark, Chief Executive Officer
CFO: Joni Gisleson, Director Finance
CMO: Chaudri Rasool, D.O., Chief of Staff
CIO: Kurt Chicken, Director Support Services
CHR: Cheryl Meyer, Director Human Resources
CNO: Kathy Begalske, Chief Nursing Officer
Web address: www.palmerlutheran.org
Control: Other not–for–profit (including NFP Corporation) **Service:** General
Medical and Surgical

> **Staffed Beds:** 25 **Admissions:** 395 **Census:** 5 **Outpatient Visits:** 59817
> **Births:** 87 **Total Expense ($000):** 21794 **Payroll Expense ($000):** 8767
> **Personnel:** 180

IA

Hospital, Medicare Provider Number, Address, Telephone, Approval, Facility, and Physician Codes, Health Care System

★ American Hospital Association (AHA) membership
□ The Joint Commission accreditation ◇ DNV Healthcare Inc. accreditation

○ Healthcare Facilities Accreditation Program
△ Commission on Accreditation of Rehabilitation Facilities (CARF) accreditation

★ **MADISON COUNTY HEALTH CARE SYSTEM (161326)**, 300 West Hutchings Street, Zip 50273–2109; tel. 515/462–2373 **A**9 10 18 **F**3 15 18 28 31 35 37 40 43 45 57 59 63 78 79 81 89 93 97 107 110 114 119 127 128 129 130 131 132 133 135 146 **P**6
Primary Contact: Marcia Hendricks, R.N., FACHE, Chief Executive Officer
COO: Terry E. Simmons, Chief Nursing Officer
CFO: Rebekah Mitchell, Chief Financial Officer
CMO: Amy Kimball, D.O., Chief of Staff
CHR: Jennifer Hannon, Director Human Resources
CNO: Kim Hulbert, R.N., Chief Clinical Officer
Web address: www.madisonhealth.com
Control: County–Government, nonfederal **Service:** General Medical and Surgical

Staffed Beds: 25 **Admissions:** 386 **Census:** 6 **Outpatient Visits:** 60671 **Births:** 0 **Total Expense ($000):** 17774 **Payroll Expense ($000):** 7227 **Personnel:** 157	

IA

Many Facility Codes have changed. Please refer to the AHA Guide Code Chart.

KANSAS

ABILENE—Dickinson County

★ **MEMORIAL HEALTH SYSTEM (171381)**, 511 N.E. Tenth Street,
Zip 67410–2153; tel. 785/263–2100, (Total facility includes 81 beds in nursing home–type unit) **A**9 10 18 **F**3 13 15 18 28 29 31 34 36 40 45 53 57 59 62 63 64 68 69 71 75 77 78 79 81 82 85 87 93 98 103 107 108 110 111 114 119 127 128 130 131 132 133 134 135 143 146 148 **P**6
Primary Contact: Mark A. Miller, FACHE, Chief Executive Officer
COO: Bob Brazil, Chief Operating Officer
CFO: Elgin Glanzer, Chief Financial Officer
CMO: W. L. Short, M.D., Chief Medical Officer
CIO: Blaine Cappel, Director Information Systems
CHR: Bob Brazil, Chief Operating Officer
Web address: www.mhsks.org
Control: Hospital district or authority, Government, nonfederal **Service:** General Medical and Surgical

Staffed Beds: 116 **Admissions:** 867 **Census:** 92 **Outpatient Visits:** 43402
Births: 45 **Total Expense ($000):** 26825 **Payroll Expense ($000):** 13460
Personnel: 344

ANDOVER—Butler County

★ **KANSAS MEDICAL CENTER (170197)**, 1124 West 21st Street,
Zip 67002–5500; tel. 316/300–4000 **A**9 10 **F**3 17 18 20 22 24 29 30 40 49 51 59 60 64 68 70 75 77 79 81 82 85 87 102 107 108 115 119 126 130 131 146 148
Primary Contact: Badr Idbeis, M.D., Chief Executive Officer
COO: Daryl W. Thornton, Chief Operating Officer
CFO: Steven N. Hadley, Chief Financial Officer
CMO: G. Whitney Reader, M.D., Chief Medical Officer
CIO: Mike Buffington, Manager Information Technology
CHR: Norm Nevins, Manager Human Resources
CNO: Janet Kaiser, R.N., Chief Nursing Officer
Web address: www.ksmedcenter.com/
Control: Corporation, Investor–owned, for–profit **Service:** General Medical and Surgical

Staffed Beds: 58 **Admissions:** 2683 **Census:** 28 **Outpatient Visits:** 8587
Births: 1 **Personnel:** 258

ANTHONY—Harper County

★ **ANTHONY MEDICAL CENTER (171346)**, 1101 East Spring Street,
Zip 67003–2122; tel. 620/842–5111 **A**9 10 18 **F**40 48 53 57 64 67 81 93 97 107 119 127 128 133 **P**6
Primary Contact: J. Bryant Anderson, Administrator and Chief Executive Officer
CFO: Lori Allen, Chief Financial Officer
CMO: Sidney Stranathan, D.O., Chief of Staff
CIO: Jim Harbert, Chief Technology Officer
CHR: Kim Barwick, Vice President Human Resources
Control: Hospital district or authority, Government, nonfederal **Service:** General Medical and Surgical

Staffed Beds: 25 **Admissions:** 251 **Census:** 8 **Outpatient Visits:** 21163
Births: 0 **Total Expense ($000):** 7745 **Payroll Expense ($000):** 3797
Personnel: 87

ARKANSAS CITY—Cowley County

★ **SOUTH CENTRAL KANSAS MEDICAL CENTER (170150)**, 6401 Patterson Parkway, Zip 67005–5701, Mailing Address: P.O. Box 1107, Zip 67005–1107; tel. 620/442–2500 **A**9 10 **F**3 11 12 13 15 29 30 34 35 39 40 45 50 52 59 64 68 70 75 76 77 79 81 82 85 87 93 107 108 110 111 115 119 129 132 133 148
Primary Contact: Steven J. Perkins, Chief Executive Officer
CFO: Holly Beaty, Chief Financial Officer
CMO: Kamran Shahzada, M.D., Chief Medical Staff
CHR: Clayton Pappan, Director Human Resources and Marketing
CNO: Patricia Davis, Chief Nursing Officer
Web address: www.sckrmc.org
Control: City–Government, nonfederal **Service:** General Medical and Surgical

Staffed Beds: 37 **Admissions:** 1014 **Census:** 11 **Outpatient Visits:** 23542
Births: 157 **Total Expense ($000):** 18054 **Payroll Expense ($000):** 7471
Personnel: 165

ASHLAND—Clark County

★ **ASHLAND HEALTH CENTER (171304)**, 709 Oak Street, Zip 67831–0188, Mailing Address: P.O. Box 188, Zip 67831–0188; tel. 620/635–2241, (Total facility includes 21 beds in nursing home–type unit) **A**9 10 18 **F**2 30 34 40 53 59 62 64 67 68 85 87 93 107 127 128 133 143 **P**6 **S** Great Plains Health Alliance, Inc., Wichita, KS
Primary Contact: Roger Barnhart, Chief Executive Officer
CFO: Debbie Filson, Chief Financial Officer
CMO: Daniel Shuman, D.O., Chief Medical Officer
CIO: Alan Romans, Director Information Technology
CHR: Debbie Filson, Chief Financial Officer
CNO: Patty Young, R.N., Chief Nursing Officer
Web address: www.ashlandhc.org
Control: Hospital district or authority, Government, nonfederal **Service:** General Medical and Surgical

Staffed Beds: 45 **Admissions:** 115 **Census:** 25 **Outpatient Visits:** 11353
Births: 0 **Total Expense ($000):** 6326 **Payroll Expense ($000):** 3150
Personnel: 79

ATCHISON—Atchison County

★ **ATCHISON HOSPITAL (171382)**, 800 Raven Hill Drive, Zip 66002–9204; tel. 913/367–2131 **A**9 10 18 **F**3 11 12 13 15 28 29 30 31 34 35 40 45 49 50 57 59 62 63 64 65 68 70 75 76 77 79 81 82 85 87 89 92 93 97 107 108 110 111 114 118 119 127 129 130 131 132 133 135 146 147 148 **P**6
Primary Contact: John L. Jacobson, Chief Executive Officer
CFO: Gary R. Foll, Chief Financial Officer
CMO: Scott Rossow, D.O., Chief of Staff
CIO: Michael Gaul, Manager Information Systems
CHR: Pamela K. Sweger, Director Human Resources
CNO: Sandra Leggett, R.N., Chief Nursing Officer
Web address: www.atchisonhospital.org
Control: Other not–for–profit (including NFP Corporation) **Service:** General Medical and Surgical

Staffed Beds: 25 **Admissions:** 1089 **Census:** 10 **Outpatient Visits:** 68584
Births: 144 **Total Expense ($000):** 34943 **Payroll Expense ($000):** 15364
Personnel: 273

ATWOOD—Rawlins County

★ **RAWLINS COUNTY HEALTH CENTER (171307)**, 707 Grant Street,
Zip 67730–1526, Mailing Address: P.O. Box 47, Zip 67730–0047; tel. 785/626–3211 **A**9 10 18 **F**3 28 29 30 34 40 41 45 59 64 65 66 68 75 81 83 85 87 89 93 97 107 114 125 127 128 130 131 132 133 135 148 **P**6 **S** Great Plains Health Alliance, Inc., Wichita, KS
Primary Contact: Sharon K. Cox, FACHE, Chief Executive Officer
CFO: Heather Prideaux, Chief Financial Officer
CNO: Amber Withington, R.N., Chief Nursing Officer
Web address: www.rchc.us
Control: County–Government, nonfederal **Service:** General Medical and Surgical

Staffed Beds: 24 **Admissions:** 290 **Census:** 4 **Outpatient Visits:** 18147
Births: 0 **Total Expense ($000):** 7852 **Payroll Expense ($000):** 3345
Personnel: 72

BELLEVILLE—Republic County

✠ **REPUBLIC COUNTY HOSPITAL (171361)**, 2420 G Street, Zip 66935–2400; tel. 785/527–2254, (Total facility includes 38 beds in nursing home–type unit) **A**1 5 9 10 18 **F**3 13 15 28 29 30 31 35 39 40 45 56 57 64 67 68 75 76 77 78 79 81 85 86 87 89 93 107 108 114 119 128 130 131 133 **S** Great Plains Health Alliance, Inc., Wichita, KS
Primary Contact: Blaine K. Miller, Administrator
CFO: Barry Bottger, Chief Financial Officer
Web address: www.rphospital.org
Control: Other not–for–profit (including NFP Corporation) **Service:** General Medical and Surgical

Staffed Beds: 63 **Admissions:** 906 **Census:** 44 **Outpatient Visits:** 13036
Births: 47 **Total Expense ($000):** 13728 **Payroll Expense ($000):** 6533
Personnel: 161

Hospital, Medicare Provider Number, Address, Telephone, Approval, Facility, and Physician Codes, Health Care System

★ American Hospital Association (AHA) membership
☐ The Joint Commission accreditation ◇ DNV Healthcare Inc. accreditation
○ Healthcare Facilities Accreditation Program
△ Commission on Accreditation of Rehabilitation Facilities (CARF) accreditation

KS

© 2014 AHA Guide   *Many Facility Codes have changed. Please refer to the AHA Guide Code Chart.*   Hospitals **A241**

BELOIT—Mitchell County

★ **MITCHELL COUNTY HOSPITAL HEALTH SYSTEMS (171375)**, 400 West Eighth, Zip 67420–1605, Mailing Address: P.O. Box 399, Zip 67420–0399; tel. 785/738–2266, (Total facility includes 40 beds in nursing home–type unit) **A**9 10 18 **F**3 11 13 15 28 29 31 34 40 43 45 48 50 56 59 62 63 64 68 69 74 76 77 81 82 84 86 87 93 98 103 106 107 111 114 119 128 129 130 132 133 148
Primary Contact: Jeremy Armstrong, FACHE, Chief Executive Officer
CFO: Eldon Koepke, Chief Financial Officer
CIO: Nate Richards, Director Information Technology
CHR: Phyllis Oetting, Director Human Resources
CNO: Jan Kemmerer, Director of Nursing
Web address: www.mchks.com
Control: County–Government, nonfederal **Service:** General Medical and Surgical

Staffed Beds: 75 **Admissions:** 1597 **Census:** 64 **Outpatient Visits:** 13287 **Births:** 96 **Total Expense ($000):** 25157 **Payroll Expense ($000):** 11230 **Personnel:** 263

BURLINGTON—Coffey County

★ **COFFEY COUNTY HOSPITAL (170094)**, 801 North Fourth Street, Zip 66839–2602; tel. 620/364–2121, (Total facility includes 42 beds in nursing home–type unit) **A**5 9 10 20 **F**3 7 10 11 13 15 17 29 30 31 34 40 45 50 57 59 62 64 65 67 68 70 75 76 77 78 79 81 82 85 87 93 107 110 111 114 119 125 127 128 130 132 133 146 **P**6
Primary Contact: Randy L. Lindauer, Ph.D., FACHE, Chief Executive Officer
CFO: Gus Rogers, Chief Financial Officer
CIO: Eric Cole, Director Information Technology
CHR: Theresa Thoele, Director Human Resources
CNO: Melissa Hall, Chief Nursing Officer
Web address: www.coffeyhealth.org
Control: County–Government, nonfederal **Service:** General Medical and Surgical

Staffed Beds: 78 **Admissions:** 879 **Census:** 37 **Outpatient Visits:** 15430 **Births:** 103 **Total Expense ($000):** 23204 **Payroll Expense ($000):** 13171 **Personnel:** 206

CALDWELL—Sumner County

★ **SUMNER COUNTY HOSPITAL DISTRICT ONE (171329)**, 601 South Osage Street, Zip 67022–1654; tel. 620/845–6492 **A**9 10 18 **F**11 40 57 62 75 81 93 107 119 133 **P**5
Primary Contact: Virgil Watson, Administrator
CFO: Jennifer Marcrum, Chief Financial Officer
CMO: Jim Blunk, D.O., Chief Medical Officer
CIO: Trey Watson, Network Administrator
Web address: www.schd1.com
Control: Hospital district or authority, Government, nonfederal **Service:** General Medical and Surgical

Staffed Beds: 15 **Admissions:** 122 **Census:** 2 **Outpatient Visits:** 4441 **Births:** 0 **Total Expense ($000):** 4339 **Payroll Expense ($000):** 1806 **Personnel:** 46

CHANUTE—Neosho County

★ ◇ **NEOSHO MEMORIAL REGIONAL MEDICAL CENTER (171380)**, 629 South Plummer, Zip 66720–1928, Mailing Address: P.O. Box 426, Zip 66720–0426; tel. 620/431–4000 **A**5 9 10 18 21 **F**3 7 11 13 15 28 29 30 34 40 43 50 52 53 57 62 63 64 76 77 79 81 82 85 89 93 107 108 110 111 114 119 128 129 130 133 135 143 146 147 **P**8 **S** QHR, Brentwood, TN
Primary Contact: Dennis Franks, FACHE, Chief Executive Officer
COO: Wendy Brazil, Chief Operating Officer
CFO: Nancy Woodyard, Chief Financial Officer
CMO: Charles Van Houden, M.D., Chief Medical Officer
CIO: Gretchen Keller, Director Health Information
CHR: R. C. Rowan, Director Human Resources
CNO: Jennifer Newton, R.N., Chief Nursing Officer
Web address: www.nmrmc.com
Control: County–Government, nonfederal **Service:** General Medical and Surgical

Staffed Beds: 25 **Admissions:** 1685 **Census:** 18 **Outpatient Visits:** 33934 **Births:** 213 **Total Expense ($000):** 42229 **Payroll Expense ($000):** 18338 **Personnel:** 331

CLAY CENTER—Clay County

★ **CLAY COUNTY MEDICAL CENTER (171371)**, 617 Liberty Street, Zip 67432–1564, Mailing Address: P.O. Box 512, Zip 67432–0512; tel. 785/632–2144 **A**9 10 18 **F**13 15 18 19 28 30 31 40 50 53 55 59 63 64 67 68 70 74 75 76 77 78 79 81 82 84 85 86 87 88 89 93 96 107 108 111 114 119 128 130 132 133 148
Primary Contact: Ron Bender, Chief Executive Officer
COO: Tyce Young, Nurse Informatist
CFO: James Garbarino, Chief Financial Officer
CIO: Jim Seley, Chief Information Officer
CHR: Cindy Rush, Director Human Resources
CNO: Suzanne Ahlberg, Director of Nursing
Web address: www.ccmcks.org
Control: County–Government, nonfederal **Service:** General Medical and Surgical

Staffed Beds: 25 **Admissions:** 733 **Census:** 9 **Outpatient Visits:** 43606 **Births:** 70 **Total Expense ($000):** 16706 **Payroll Expense ($000):** 7489 **Personnel:** 171

COFFEYVILLE—Montgomery County

⌧ **COFFEYVILLE REGIONAL MEDICAL CENTER (170145)**, 1400 West Fourth, Zip 67337–3306; tel. 620/251–1200, (Total facility includes 20 beds in nursing home–type unit) **A**1 2 9 10 **F**3 7 11 13 15 28 29 30 31 34 40 45 46 47 50 57 59 62 64 70 74 75 76 77 78 79 81 82 85 90 93 97 107 108 110 111 112 114 115 117 119 120 121 123 128 130 131 132 135 145 146 147 **P**8
Primary Contact: James R. Chromik, Interim Chief Executive Officer
CFO: Cheryl Batchelor, Chief Financial Officer
CIO: Kris Penco, Director Information Systems
CHR: Becky McCune, Director Human Resources, Community Relations and Education
CNO: Lori Rexwinkle, Chief Nursing Officer
Web address: www.crmcinc.com
Control: Other not–for–profit (including NFP Corporation) **Service:** General Medical and Surgical

Staffed Beds: 88 **Admissions:** 2138 **Census:** 26 **Outpatient Visits:** 52404 **Births:** 228 **Total Expense ($000):** 37528 **Payroll Expense ($000):** 15253 **Personnel:** 317

COLBY—Thomas County

CITIZENS MEDICAL CENTER (171362), 100 East College Drive, Zip 67701–3799; tel. 785/462–7511, (Total facility includes 63 beds in nursing home–type unit) **A**9 10 18 **F**3 11 13 15 28 30 31 34 40 50 64 67 74 76 77 78 79 81 85 86 87 93 97 107 108 110 111 114 119 127 130 133 146 148 **P**6
Primary Contact: Kevan Trenkle, Chief Executive Officer
CFO: Patsy Evans, Chief Financial Officer
CMO: John Dygert, D.O., Chief of Staff
CIO: Rod Williams, Manager Information Systems
CHR: Margaret Kummer, Vice President Human Resources
CNO: Victoria Duffey, Director of Nursing
Web address: www.nwkshealthcare.com
Control: Other not–for–profit (including NFP Corporation) **Service:** General Medical and Surgical

Staffed Beds: 88 **Admissions:** 512 **Census:** 63 **Outpatient Visits:** 12085 **Births:** 134 **Total Expense ($000):** 23960 **Payroll Expense ($000):** 11575 **Personnel:** 256

COLDWATER—Comanche County

★ **COMANCHE COUNTY HOSPITAL (171312)**, 202 South Frisco Street, Zip 67029–9101, Mailing Address: HC 65, Box 8A, Zip 67029–9500; tel. 620/582–2144 **A**9 10 18 **F**3 11 30 31 40 43 53 59 61 68 75 78 93 102 128 133 **P**6 **S** Great Plains Health Alliance, Inc., Wichita, KS
Primary Contact: Nancy Zimmerman, R.N., Administrator
CFO: Lisa Brooks, Chief Financial Officer
CMO: Daniel Schowengerdt, M.D., Chief of Staff
CIO: LaNell Wagnon, Director Medical Records
CHR: Lisa Brooks, Chief Financial Officer
CNO: Sandra Dobrinski, Director of Nursing
Web address: www.gpha.com
Control: County–Government, nonfederal **Service:** General Medical and Surgical

Staffed Beds: 12 **Admissions:** 79 **Census:** 2 **Outpatient Visits:** 12410 **Births:** 0 **Total Expense ($000):** 4415 **Payroll Expense ($000):** 1969 **Personnel:** 48

COLUMBUS—Cherokee County

★ **MERCY MAUDE NORTON HOSPITAL (171308)**, 220 North Pennsylvania Avenue, Zip 66725–1110; tel. 620/429–2545 **A**9 10 18 **F**11 15 39 40 45 57 59 77 81 93 119 133 **S** Mercy Health, Chesterfield, MO
Primary Contact: Cindy Neely, Administrator
Web address: www.mercy.net/newsroom–mercy–maude–norton–hospital–quick–facts
Control: Church–operated, Nongovernment, not–for profit **Service:** General Medical and Surgical

Staffed Beds: 18 **Admissions:** 130 **Census:** 2 **Outpatient Visits:** 10570 **Births:** 0 **Total Expense ($000):** 4883 **Payroll Expense ($000):** 2402 **Personnel:** 47

CONCORDIA—Cloud County

★ **CLOUD COUNTY HEALTH CENTER (171349)**, 1100 Highland Drive, Zip 66901–3923; tel. 785/243–1234 **A**9 10 18 **F**3 11 13 15 20 28 31 34 35 40 41 45 56 57 59 64 65 70 74 75 76 77 79 81 82 85 86 87 89 93 96 97 102 107 108 114 118 119 127 130 132 133 135 146 148 **P**6
Primary Contact: Don Bates, President and Chief Executive Officer
CFO: Pamela Blochlinger, Acting Vice President Finance
CMO: Justin Poore, D.O., Chief Medical Staff
CIO: Jenny Bergstrom, Project Manager Information Technology
CHR: Dawn Thoman, Vice President Human Resources
CNO: Michelle Metro, Vice President Nursing
Web address: www.cchc.com
Control: Other not–for–profit (including NFP Corporation) **Service:** General Medical and Surgical

Staffed Beds: 25 **Admissions:** 594 **Census:** 9 **Outpatient Visits:** 23259 **Births:** 31 **Total Expense ($000):** 14388 **Payroll Expense ($000):** 7133 **Personnel:** 150

KS

Many Facility Codes have changed. Please refer to the AHA Guide Code Chart. © 2014 AHA Guide

COUNCIL GROVE—Morris County

★ **MORRIS COUNTY HOSPITAL (171379)**, 600 North Washington Street,
Zip 66846–1422; tel. 620/767–6811 **A**9 10 18 **F**7 11 13 15 18 28 31 35 40
45 59 64 65 70 76 77 81 87 93 94 96 107 110 130 132 133 146 148 **P**5
Primary Contact: James H. Reagan, Jr., Ph.D., Chief Executive Officer
CFO: Ron Christenson, Chief Financial Officer
CMO: Joel Hornuug, M.D., Chief Medical Officer
CIO: Bill Lauer, Chief Information Officer
CHR: Don Zimmerman, Director Human Resources
CNO: Stephanne Wolf, Chief Nursing Officer
Web address: www.mrcohosp.com
Control: County–Government, nonfederal **Service:** General Medical and Surgical

Staffed Beds: 25 **Admissions:** 394 **Census:** 5 **Outpatient Visits:** 10999
Births: 37 **Total Expense ($000):** 9044 **Payroll Expense ($000):** 3055
Personnel: 86

DIGHTON—Lane County

★ **LANE COUNTY HOSPITAL (171303)**, 235 West Vine, Zip 67839–0969, Mailing
Address: P.O. Box 969, Zip 67839–0969; tel. 620/397–5321, (Total facility
includes 14 beds in nursing home–type unit) **A**9 10 18 **F**30 40 56 67 77 85 93
97 127 128 131 133 **P**6 **S** Great Plains Health Alliance, Inc., Wichita, KS
Primary Contact: Donna McGowan, Administrator
CFO: Marcia Gabel, Chief Financial Officer
CMO: Paul Chinburg, M.D., Medical Director
CHR: Dina Casey, Human Resources Officer
CNO: Jennifer Whipple, Director Nursing
Web address: www.lchospital.com
Control: County–Government, nonfederal **Service:** General Medical and Surgical

Staffed Beds: 31 **Admissions:** 78 **Census:** 16 **Outpatient Visits:** 13194
Births: 0 **Total Expense ($000):** 4565 **Payroll Expense ($000):** 2157
Personnel: 43

DODGE CITY—Ford County

☒ **WESTERN PLAINS MEDICAL COMPLEX (170175)**, 3001 Avenue A,
Zip 67801–6508, Mailing Address: P.O. Box 1478, Zip 67801–1478;
tel. 620/225–8400 **A**1 3 5 9 10 20 **F**3 8 11 13 15 17 18 20 22 28 29 30 34
35 40 50 51 60 64 70 72 73 74 75 76 77 79 81 85 88 89 90 93 107 108
110 111 115 119 129 130 133 146 **S** LifePoint Hospitals, Inc., Brentwood, TN
Primary Contact: Michael R. Burroughs, FACHE, Chief Executive Officer
CFO: Michael Gordian, Chief Financial Officer
CMO: Merrill Conant, M.D., Chief of Staff
CIO: Shawna Culver, Director Information Systems
CHR: Corry Israel, Director Human Resources
CNO: Edna Dunn, Chief Nursing Officer
Web address: www.westernplainsmc.com
Control: Corporation, Investor–owned, for–profit **Service:** General Medical and
Surgical

Staffed Beds: 89 **Admissions:** 2392 **Census:** 23 **Outpatient Visits:** 34091
Births: 739 **Personnel:** 245

EL DORADO—Butler County

☒ **SUSAN B. ALLEN MEMORIAL HOSPITAL (170017)**, 720 West Central Avenue,
Zip 67042–2112; tel. 316/321–3300 **A**1 5 9 10 **F**3 11 13 15 28 30 40 45 59
60 62 68 69 70 76 78 81 85 92 93 96 97 98 103 107 108 110 111 115 119
121 123 130 133 146 148
Primary Contact: Gayle Arnett, President and Chief Executive Officer
COO: David Shaw, Vice President and Chief Operating Officer
CFO: Robin Crawford, Vice President and Chief Financial Officer
CIO: Mark Rooker, Director Information Systems
CHR: D. Gay Kimble, Director Human Resources
CNO: Cecilia B. Goebel, R.N., Vice President and Chief Nursing Officer
Web address: www.sbamh.com
Control: Other not–for–profit (including NFP Corporation) **Service:** General
Medical and Surgical

Staffed Beds: 52 **Admissions:** 1488 **Census:** 14 **Outpatient Visits:** 77257
Births: 288 **Total Expense ($000):** 48868 **Payroll Expense ($000):** 20481
Personnel: 377

ELKHART—Morton County

★ **MORTON COUNTY HEALTH SYSTEM (170166)**, 445 Hilltop Street,
Zip 67950–0937, Mailing Address: P.O. Box 937, Zip 67950–0937;
tel. 620/697–2141, (Total facility includes 80 beds in nursing home–type unit) **A**9
10 20 **F**10 11 15 28 29 34 40 45 54 56 57 59 64 67 68 70 75 77 79 81 86
87 93 94 96 97 98 99 100 101 102 103 104 107 111 114 119 130 131 132
133 135 143 146 148 **P**5 6
Primary Contact: Joe Duerr, Chief Executive Officer
CHR: Sonja May, Director Human Resources
Web address: www.mchswecare.com
Control: County–Government, nonfederal **Service:** General Medical and Surgical

Staffed Beds: 120 **Admissions:** 519 **Census:** 79 **Outpatient Visits:** 23714
Births: 0 **Total Expense ($000):** 17061 **Payroll Expense ($000):** 8978
Personnel: 168

ELLINWOOD—Barton County

★ **ELLINWOOD DISTRICT HOSPITAL (171301)**, 605 North Main Street,
Zip 67526–1440; tel. 620/564–2548 **A**9 10 18 **F**11 40 64 65 93 107 127 128
133 **P**6 **S** Great Plains Health Alliance, Inc., Wichita, KS
Primary Contact: John Hughes, Administrator
CFO: Penny Stephenson, Chief Financial Officer
CMO: Christopher Brown, M.D., Chief of Staff
CIO: Becky L. Burns, Manager Health Information Management
CHR: Lindsay Owsley, Manager Human Resources
CNO: Aletha Budig, R.N., Director Nursing
Web address: www.ellinwooddistricthospital.org
Control: Other not–for–profit (including NFP Corporation) **Service:** General
Medical and Surgical

Staffed Beds: 25 **Admissions:** 223 **Census:** 9 **Outpatient Visits:** 13533
Births: 0 **Total Expense ($000):** 5696 **Payroll Expense ($000):** 2843
Personnel: 62

ELLSWORTH—Ellsworth County

★ **ELLSWORTH COUNTY MEDICAL CENTER (171327)**, 1604 Aylward Street,
Zip 67439–2541, Mailing Address: P.O. Box 87, Zip 67439–0087;
tel. 785/472–3111 **A**5 9 10 18 **F**3 11 28 29 34 35 40 45 47 53 57 59 62 64
67 77 85 86 87 93 97 107 114 119 127 128 130 133 146 **P**6
Primary Contact: Roger A. Masse, FACHE, Chief Executive Officer
CFO: Preston Sauers, Chief Financial Officer
CIO: Lynette Dick, Director of Support Services
CHR: Sandy Wedel, Director Human Resources
CNO: Amanda Thrasher, Director Nursing
Web address: www.ewmed.com
Control: County–Government, nonfederal **Service:** General Medical and Surgical

Staffed Beds: 20 **Admissions:** 635 **Census:** 8 **Outpatient Visits:** 32095
Births: 0 **Total Expense ($000):** 14399 **Payroll Expense ($000):** 6935
Personnel: 138

EMPORIA—Lyon County

★ **NEWMAN REGIONAL HEALTH (170001)**, 1201 West 12th Avenue,
Zip 66801–2597; tel. 620/343–6800 **A**5 9 10 20 **F**3 11 13 15 17 18 20 22
26 28 29 31 39 40 41 45 51 53 59 61 63 64 65 68 70 76 77 78 79 81 82
84 85 86 87 89 90 93 96 100 102 107 108 111 114 118 119 129 130 131
132 133 135 144 146 147 148 **P**6
Primary Contact: Robert N. Wright, Chief Executive Officer
CFO: Holly French, Chief Financial Officer
CMO: James Geitz, M.D., Chief of Staff
CIO: Kevin Ludwigsen, Director Information Systems
CHR: Kathy Orear, Director Human Resources
CNO: Julia Pyle, R.N., Chief Nursing Officer
Web address: www.newmanrh.org
Control: County–Government, nonfederal **Service:** General Medical and Surgical

Staffed Beds: 32 **Admissions:** 2297 **Census:** 24 **Outpatient Visits:** 96903
Births: 395 **Total Expense ($000):** 53071 **Payroll Expense ($000):** 23173
Personnel: 462

Hospital, Medicare Provider Number, Address, Telephone, Approval, Facility, and Physician Codes, Health Care System

★ American Hospital Association (AHA) membership
☐ The Joint Commission accreditation   ◇ DNV Healthcare Inc. accreditation
○ Healthcare Facilities Accreditation Program
△ Commission on Accreditation of Rehabilitation Facilities (CARF) accreditation

KS

EUREKA—Greenwood County

GREENWOOD COUNTY HOSPITAL (171339), 100 West 16th Street, Zip 67045–1064; tel. 620/583–7451 **A**5 9 10 18 **F**3 40 43 53 57 62 81 93 96 107 119 127 128 133 135 146 **P**6
Primary Contact: Thomas Henton, Chief Executive Officer and Administrator
CFO: Richard Goertz, Chief Financial Officer
CIO: Jason Clark, Director Quality Improvement, Risk Management and Information System
CHR: Janel M. Palmer, Director Human Resources
Web address: www.gwch.org
Control: County–Government, nonfederal **Service:** General Medical and Surgical

Staffed Beds: 25 Admissions: 458 Census: 4 Outpatient Visits: 16875
Births: 0 Total Expense ($000): 11680 Payroll Expense ($000): 5750
Personnel: 126

FORT SCOTT—-Bourbon County

✉ **MERCY HOSPITAL FORT SCOTT (170058)**, 401 Woodland Hills Boulevard, Zip 66701–8797; tel. 620/223–2200 **A**1 5 9 10 **F**3 7 11 13 15 28 29 30 34 35 40 53 57 59 62 63 65 70 72 75 76 77 79 81 82 84 85 90 93 97 107 108 110 111 114 118 119 127 129 130 131 132 133 143 144 145 146 148 **P**6 **S** Mercy Health, Chesterfield, MO
Primary Contact: Reta K. Baker, President
CFO: Shelly Hunter, Chief Financial Officer
CMO: Robert R. Nichols, M.D., Vice President Medical Affairs
CIO: Lori Sturgill, Vice President Business Partnership
CHR: Timothy Murphy, Vice President Human Resources
CNO: Patrick Callanan, Vice President Patient Care Services
Web address: www.mercykansas.com
Control: Church–operated, Nongovernment, not–for profit **Service:** General Medical and Surgical

Staffed Beds: 61 Admissions: 1813 Census: 18 Outpatient Visits: 74483
Births: 251 Total Expense ($000): 33796 Payroll Expense ($000): 15018
Personnel: 262

FREDONIA—Wilson County

★ **FREDONIA REGIONAL HOSPITAL (171374)**, 1527 Madison Street, Zip 66736–1751; Mailing Address: P.O. Box 579, Zip 66736–0579; tel. 620/378–2121 **A**9 10 18 **F**3 7 11 15 30 40 81 82 85 93 98 103 107 110 114 119 128 133 **S** Great Plains Health Alliance, Inc., Wichita, KS
Primary Contact: John Hart, Chief Executive Officer
CFO: Wendy Barton, Manager Business Office
CMO: Jennifer McKenney, M.D., Chief Medical Officer
CIO: Tyler Row, Director Information Technology
CHR: Debbie Marr, Administrative Assistant and Director Human Resources
CNO: Ryan Duft, R.N., Chief Nursing Officer
Web address: www.fredoniaregionalhospital.org
Control: City–Government, nonfederal **Service:** General Medical and Surgical

Staffed Beds: 34 Admissions: 709 Census: 13 Outpatient Visits: 19774
Births: 0 Total Expense ($000): 12514 Payroll Expense ($000): 4188
Personnel: 119

GARDEN CITY—Finney County

✉ **ST. CATHERINE HOSPITAL (170023)**, 401 East Spruce Street, Zip 67846–5679; tel. 620/272–2561 **A**1 5 9 10 20 **F**3 8 13 15 18 20 22 24 29 30 31 34 35 40 45 51 57 59 60 63 64 65 69 70 73 75 76 77 78 79 81 85 87 89 93 97 98 100 102 107 108 109 110 111 115 116 118 119 120 121 122 123 124 129 130 132 135 146 147 148 **P**5 6 **S** Catholic Health Initiatives, Englewood, CO
Primary Contact: Scott J. Taylor, President and Chief Executive Officer
CFO: Amanda Vaughan, Chief Financial Officer
CMO: Matthew C. Byrnes, M.D., Chief Medical Officer
CIO: Lance Kellenbarger, Site Director Information Systems
CHR: Kathy E. Morrison, Executive Director Human Resources
CNO: Margaret Elizabeth Prewitt, Vice President Patient Services and Chief Nursing Officer
Web address: www.StCatherineHosp.org
Control: Church–operated, Nongovernment, not–for profit **Service:** General Medical and Surgical

Staffed Beds: 110 Admissions: 3764 Census: 43 Outpatient Visits: 148924
Births: 770 Total Expense ($000): 88016 Payroll Expense ($000): 35625
Personnel: 541

GARDNER—Johnson County

★ △ **MEADOWBROOK REHABILITATION HOSPITAL (170180)**, 427 West Main Street, Zip 66030–1183; tel. 913/856–8747, (Total facility includes 42 beds in nursing home–type unit) **A**7 9 10 **F**34 80 87 90 91 92 128 130 143 148
Primary Contact: Jon W. Scott, Chief Executive Officer
CFO: Kelly Taul, Business Manager
CMO: David Edalati, M.D., Medical Director
CHR: Carrie Moore, Director Human Resources
CNO: Lisa Perez, R.N., Director Nursing
Web address: www.meadowbrookrehab.com
Control: Corporation, Investor–owned, for–profit **Service:** Rehabilitation

Staffed Beds: 96 Admissions: 506 Census: 58 Outpatient Visits: 0 Births: 0 Total Expense ($000): 11514 Payroll Expense ($000): 4945 Personnel: 141

GARNETT—Anderson County

★ **ANDERSON COUNTY HOSPITAL (171316)**, 421 South Maple, Zip 66032–1334, Mailing Address: P.O. Box 309, Zip 66032–0309; tel. 785/448–3131, (Total facility includes 30 beds in nursing home–type unit) **A**9 10 18 **F**3 7 11 15 29 30 34 35 40 41 45 57 59 64 65 67 75 79 81 87 93 97 107 108 110 114 127 130 133 135 **P**6 **S** Saint Luke's Health System, Kansas City, MO
Primary Contact: Dennis A. Hachenberg, FACHE, Chief Executive Officer
CFO: Vicki L. Mills, Chief Financial Officer
CMO: Mackenzie Peterson, M.D., Chief of Staff
CHR: Karen Gillespie, Director Human Resources
CNO: Margo L. Williams, R.N., Chief Nursing Officer
Web address: www.saint–lukes.org
Control: Other not–for–profit (including NFP Corporation) **Service:** General Medical and Surgical

Staffed Beds: 40 Admissions: 178 Census: 31 Outpatient Visits: 41331
Births: 0 Total Expense ($000): 18495 Payroll Expense ($000): 7358
Personnel: 142

GIRARD—Crawford County

★ **GIRARD MEDICAL CENTER (171376)**, 302 North Hospital Drive, Zip 66743–2000; tel. 620/724–8291 **A**9 10 18 **F**3 6 11 12 15 29 34 35 40 43 45 47 50 51 53 56 57 59 62 64 65 70 75 77 79 81 87 93 97 98 100 101 102 103 104 105 107 114 119 127 128 130 131 132 133 146 148 **P**6
Primary Contact: Michael E. Payne, Administrator
CFO: Holly Koch, Chief Financial Officer
CIO: Jeff Barnes, Director Information Technology
CHR: Gregory Sullivan, Manager Human Resources
CNO: Joyce Geier, Director Nursing
Web address: www.girardmedicalcenter.com
Control: Hospital district or authority, Government, nonfederal **Service:** General Medical and Surgical

Staffed Beds: 35 Admissions: 862 Census: 16 Outpatient Visits: 21023
Births: 0 Total Expense ($000): 18448 Payroll Expense ($000): 8792
Personnel: 192

GOODLAND—Sherman County

GOODLAND REGIONAL MEDICAL CENTER (171370), 220 West Second Street, Zip 67735–1602; tel. 785/890–3625 **A**9 10 18 **F**3 11 13 15 28 31 34 40 45 57 59 60 64 65 67 69 75 76 79 81 82 85 87 89 93 97 107 114 119 127 128 130 132 133 **P**6
Primary Contact: Marion A. Thompson, FACHE, Chief Executive Officer
CFO: James Precht, Chief Financial Officer
CIO: Christopher Biel, Chief Information Officer
CHR: Linda Taylor, Chief Human Resources Officer
CNO: Lori Gaydusek, Chief Nursing Officer
Web address: www.goodlandregional.com
Control: County–Government, nonfederal **Service:** General Medical and Surgical

Staffed Beds: 25 Admissions: 392 Census: 4 Outpatient Visits: 43398
Births: 44 Total Expense ($000): 16052 Payroll Expense ($000): 6427
Personnel: 139

GREAT BEND—Barton County

GREAT BEND REGIONAL HOSPITAL (170191), 514 Cleveland Street, Zip 67530–3562; tel. 620/792–8833 **A**5 9 10 20 **F**3 13 15 29 30 34 40 45 57 59 64 65 70 75 76 79 81 82 89 107 110 111 114 119 127 130 135 147 148
Primary Contact: Brent Hanson, Chief Executive Officer and HIPAA Security and Compliance Officer
CFO: Timothy Latimer, Chief Financial Officer
CMO: Randall Hildebrand, M.D., Chief Medical Officer
CHR: Gerrie Meyer, Director Human Resources
CNO: Adina Gregory, Chief Nursing Officer
Web address: www.greatbendsurgical.com
Control: Partnership, Investor–owned, for–profit **Service:** General Medical and Surgical

Staffed Beds: 33 Admissions: 1642 Census: 15 Outpatient Visits: 33316
Births: 328 Total Expense ($000): 36230 Payroll Expense ($000): 13919
Personnel: 289

GREENSBURG—Kiowa County

★ **KIOWA COUNTY MEMORIAL HOSPITAL (171332)**, 721 West Kansas Avenue, Zip 67054–1633; tel. 620/723–3341 **A**9 10 18 **F**3 7 11 40 50 53 59 64 68 107 115 127 128 133 **P**6 **S** Great Plains Health Alliance, Inc., Wichita, KS
Primary Contact: Mary Sweet, Administrator
CFO: Ron Tucker, Business Office Manager
CMO: Nizar Kibar, M.D., Chief Medical Staff
CIO: Jeremy Hoover, Chief Information Officer
CHR: Cathy McFall, Human Resources Manager
CNO: Vanessa Kirk, Director of Nursing
Web address: www.kcmh.net
Control: Other not–for–profit (including NFP Corporation) **Service:** General Medical and Surgical

Staffed Beds: 15 Admissions: 154 Census: 3 Outpatient Visits: 9940
Births: 0 Total Expense ($000): 7626 Payroll Expense ($000): 2954
Personnel: 73

Many Facility Codes have changed. Please refer to the AHA Guide Code Chart. © 2014 AHA Guide

HANOVER—Washington County

★ **HANOVER HOSPITAL (171365)**, 205 South Hanover, Zip 66945–8924, Mailing Address: P.O. Box 38, Zip 66945–0038; tel. 785/337–2214 **A**5 9 10 18 **F**2 7 40 53 67 69 81 133 **P**4
Primary Contact: Roger D. Warren, M.D., Administrator
CFO: Sheryl Adam, Chief Financial Officer
CMO: Roger D. Warren, M.D., Administrator
Control: Hospital district or authority, Government, nonfederal **Service:** General Medical and Surgical

> **Staffed Beds:** 25 **Admissions:** 127 **Census:** 20 **Outpatient Visits:** 1836 **Births:** 4 **Total Expense ($000):** 3586 **Payroll Expense ($000):** 1934 **Personnel:** 48

HARPER—Harper County

★ **HARPER HOSPITAL DISTRICT FIVE (171366)**, 700 West 13th Street, Zip 67058–1401; tel. 620/896–7324 **A**9 10 18 **F**3 10 29 34 35 40 43 45 46 50 53 54 57 59 64 65 67 68 69 75 77 79 81 84 87 93 97 107 111 114 119 125 127 128 129 130 131 133 135 146 147 148
Primary Contact: William Widener, Administrator and Chief Executive Officer
CFO: Sandra Owen, Director Fiscal and Accounting
CMO: Ralph Imlay, M.D., Chief of Staff
CIO: Cindi Beadman, Director Medical Records
CHR: Vicki Longbine, Director Human Resources
CNO: Karen Aldis, Director of Nursing
Web address: www.hhd5.com
Control: Hospital district or authority, Government, nonfederal **Service:** General Medical and Surgical

> **Staffed Beds:** 25 **Admissions:** 282 **Census:** 9 **Outpatient Visits:** 36130 **Births:** 0 **Total Expense ($000):** 7971 **Payroll Expense ($000):** 4155 **Personnel:** 91

HAYS—Ellis County

★ ◇ **HAYS MEDICAL CENTER (170013)**, 2220 Canterbury Drive, Zip 67601–2370, Mailing Address: P.O. Box 8100, Zip 67601–8100; tel. 785/623–5000 **A**3 5 9 10 19 20 21 **F**3 11 12 13 15 17 18 20 22 24 26 28 29 30 31 32 34 35 36 37 38 39 40 43 45 46 49 53 55 56 57 59 60 63 64 65 66 68 69 70 71 72 73 74 75 76 77 78 79 80 81 82 84 85 86 87 89 90 92 93 97 98 100 101 102 103 104 107 108 110 111 115 118 119 120 121 126 127 129 130 131 132 135 146 147 148 **P**6
Primary Contact: John H. Jeter, M.D., President and Chief Executive Officer
COO: Bryce A. Young, Chief Operating Officer
CFO: George Harms, Chief Financial Officer
CMO: Larry Watts, Chief Medical Officer
CIO: Scott Rohleder, Chief Information Officer
CHR: Bruce Whittington, Vice President Human Resources
CNO: Terry Siek, MSN, Chief Nursing Officer
Web address: www.haysmed.com
Control: Other not–for–profit (including NFP Corporation) **Service:** General Medical and Surgical

> **Staffed Beds:** 172 **Admissions:** 5837 **Census:** 76 **Outpatient Visits:** 323478 **Births:** 716 **Total Expense ($000):** 187219 **Payroll Expense ($000):** 79201 **Personnel:** 1149

HERINGTON—Dickinson County

HERINGTON MUNICIPAL HOSPITAL (171340), 100 East Helen Street, Zip 67449–1606; tel. 785/258–2207 **A**9 10 18 **F**1 4 15 16 17 28 29 40 45 57 64 67 70 72 73 77 80 81 88 89 90 93 97 98 107 119 127 128 133 148
Primary Contact: Michael J. Ryan, Chief Executive Officer
CFO: Patricia M. Moyer, Chief Financial Officer
CMO: John Mosier, D.O., Chief of Staff
CHR: Debbie Stewart, Human Resources Officer
CNO: Kathy Kershner, Director of Nursing
Web address: www.heringtonhospital.org
Control: City–Government, nonfederal **Service:** General Medical and Surgical

> **Staffed Beds:** 25 **Admissions:** 311 **Census:** 6 **Outpatient Visits:** 14770 **Births:** 0 **Total Expense ($000):** 6690 **Payroll Expense ($000):** 3210 **Personnel:** 70

HIAWATHA—Brown County

★ **HIAWATHA COMMUNITY HOSPITAL (171341)**, 300 Utah Street, Zip 66434–2314; tel. 785/742–2131 **A**5 9 10 18 **F**8 13 15 40 45 62 67 69 70 76 81 85 107 114 119 128 130 133 146 **P**6
Primary Contact: John Moore, Administrator
CFO: Jenny Knudson, Controller
CMO: Steffen Shamburg, M.D., Chief of Staff
CIO: Cheryl Wenger, Manager Health Information and Quality Assurance
CHR: Alison Keri, Director Human Resources
CNO: Lisa Thompson, MSN, Director of Nursing
Web address: www.hch–ks.org
Control: Other not–for–profit (including NFP Corporation) **Service:** General Medical and Surgical

> **Staffed Beds:** 25 **Admissions:** 730 **Census:** 7 **Outpatient Visits:** 27709 **Births:** 102 **Total Expense ($000):** 25042 **Payroll Expense ($000):** 10616 **Personnel:** 210

HILL CITY—Graham County

★ **GRAHAM COUNTY HOSPITAL (171325)**, 304 West Prout Street, Zip 67642–1435; tel. 785/421–2121 **A**5 9 10 18 **F**3 11 29 34 40 45 50 53 59 64 65 69 75 81 82 84 93 97 107 127 128 133 148
Primary Contact: Melissa Atkins, CPA, Chief Executive Officer
CHR: Donella Belleau, Director Human Resources
Web address: www.grahamcountyhospital.org
Control: County–Government, nonfederal **Service:** General Medical and Surgical

> **Staffed Beds:** 20 **Admissions:** 522 **Census:** 6 **Outpatient Visits:** 899 **Births:** 0 **Total Expense ($000):** 7814 **Payroll Expense ($000):** 3824 **Personnel:** 87

HILLSBORO—Marion County

★ **HILLSBORO COMMUNITY HOSPITAL (171357)**, 701 South Main Street, Zip 67063–1553; tel. 620/947–3114 **A**9 10 18 **F**3 11 29 30 34 35 40 45 47 50 57 59 64 65 75 77 81 85 86 87 93 107 114 127 130 131 133 146 **P**5 6 **S** Rural Community Hospitals of America, Kansas City, MO
Primary Contact: Marion Regier, Chief Executive Officer
COO: Johna Magnuson, Director Nursing
CIO: Marsha Setzkorn–Meyer, Director Public Relations and Marketing
CHR: Wendy McCarty. Director Human Resources
Web address: www.hchks.com
Control: Corporation, Investor–owned, for–profit **Service:** General Medical and Surgical

> **Staffed Beds:** 10 **Admissions:** 179 **Census:** 3 **Outpatient Visits:** 6472 **Births:** 0 **Total Expense ($000):** 4305 **Payroll Expense ($000):** 2031 **Personnel:** 39

HOISINGTON—Barton County

★ **CLARA BARTON HOSPITAL (171333)**, 250 West Ninth Street, Zip 67544–1706; tel. 620/653–2114 **A**9 10 18 **F**11 15 28 40 51 56 57 59 64 77 79 81 85 92 93 97 107 114 119 127 128 133 148 **P**6
Primary Contact: Curt Colson, President and Chief Executive Officer
CFO: James Blackwell, Vice President and Chief Financial Officer
CMO: Nathan Knackstedt, D.O., Chief of Staff
CHR: John Moshier, Director Human Resources
CNO: Jane Schepmann, Vice President and Chief Nursing Officer
Web address: www.clarabartonhospital.org
Control: Other not–for–profit (including NFP Corporation) **Service:** General Medical and Surgical

> **Staffed Beds:** 23 **Admissions:** 518 **Census:** 8 **Outpatient Visits:** 46745 **Births:** 0 **Total Expense ($000):** 17384 **Payroll Expense ($000):** 8194 **Personnel:** 173

HOLTON—Jackson County

★ **HOLTON COMMUNITY HOSPITAL (171319)**, 1110 Columbine Drive, Zip 66436–8824; tel. 785/364–2116 **A**5 9 10 18 **F**3 11 13 15 18 28 34 40 45 50 59 62 63 64 65 74 75 76 77 81 82 93 97 107 114 119 127 130 131 132 133 135 146 147 148
Primary Contact: Carrie L. Saia, R.N., Chief Executive Officer
CFO: Marlene Kranz, Controller
CMO: Lee Schnee, M.D., Chief Medical Staff
CIO: Keri Brucken, Director Health Information Management
CHR: Gretchen Snavely, Director Human Resources
CNO: April Zeller, Director Nursing
Web address: www.holtonhospital.com
Control: Other not–for–profit (including NFP Corporation) **Service:** General Medical and Surgical

> **Staffed Beds:** 12 **Admissions:** 295 **Census:** 4 **Outpatient Visits:** 55486 **Births:** 62 **Total Expense ($000):** 11072 **Payroll Expense ($000):** 5555 **Personnel:** 167

Hospital, Medicare Provider Number, Address, Telephone, Approval, Facility, and Physician Codes, Health Care System

★ American Hospital Association (AHA) membership
□ The Joint Commission accreditation ◇ DNV Healthcare Inc. accreditation
○ Healthcare Facilities Accreditation Program
△ Commission on Accreditation of Rehabilitation Facilities (CARF) accreditation

KS

HORTON—Brown County

HORTON COMMUNITY HOSPITAL (171320), 240 West 18th Street, Zip 66439–1245; tel. 785/486–2642 **A**9 10 18 **F**7 15 28 29 40 45 46 64 81 93 107 114 119 127 128 133 **P**6 **S** Rural Community Hospitals of America, Kansas City, MO
Primary Contact: James Noble, Chief Executive Officer
CFO: Sue Kidd, Chief Financial Officer
CMO: Galen Seymour, M.D., Chief of Staff
CHR: Barbara McClain, Human Resources
CNO: Cindy Rogers, Chief Nursing Officer
Web address: www.horton–hospital.com
Control: Corporation, Investor–owned, for–profit **Service:** General Medical and Surgical

Staffed Beds: 25 **Admissions:** 410 **Census:** 4 **Outpatient Visits:** 6641 **Births:** 0 **Total Expense ($000):** 6688 **Payroll Expense ($000):** 3287 **Personnel:** 66

HOXIE—Sheridan County

SHERIDAN COUNTY HEALTH COMPLEX (171347), 826 18th Street, Zip 67740–0167, Mailing Address: P.O. Box 167, Zip 67740–0167; tel. 785/675–3281, (Total facility includes 35 beds in nursing home–type unit) **A**9 10 18 **F**3 10 11 15 29 30 31 34 40 45 49 50 53 56 57 59 67 68 69 81 85 86 93 97 107 119 127 130 133 146 148
Primary Contact: James E. Wahlmeier, Chief Executive Officer
CFO: Christine Niblock, Chief Financial Officer
CMO: Thomas R. Plumeri, Chief of Staff
CNO: Maria Zimmerman, R.N., Chief Nursing Officer
Web address: www.sheridancountyhospital.com
Control: County–Government, nonfederal **Service:** General Medical and Surgical

Staffed Beds: 53 **Admissions:** 157 **Census:** 26 **Outpatient Visits:** 5900 **Births:** 0 **Total Expense ($000):** 7295 **Payroll Expense ($000):** 3753 **Personnel:** 112

HUGOTON—Stevens County

STEVENS COUNTY HOSPITAL (171335), 1006 South Jackson Street, Zip 67951–2858, Mailing Address: P.O. Box 10, Zip 67951–0010; tel. 620/544–8511, (Total facility includes 83 beds in nursing home–type unit) **A**9 10 18 **F**3 11 15 28 29 40 50 57 62 68 71 81 93 107 111 119 127 130 133 135 146 148
Primary Contact: Linda Stalcup, Chief Executive Officer
CMO: Samer Al–hashmi, M.D., Chief Medical Staff
Web address: www.healthcarefor the heartland.org
Control: County–Government, nonfederal **Service:** General Medical and Surgical

Staffed Beds: 100 **Admissions:** 214 **Census:** 70 **Outpatient Visits:** 90003 **Births:** 0 **Total Expense ($000):** 16566 **Payroll Expense ($000):** 8269 **Personnel:** 166

HUTCHINSON—Reno County

HUTCHINSON REGIONAL MEDICAL CENTER (170020), 1701 East 23rd Avenue, Zip 67502–1191; tel. 620/665–2000, (Total facility includes 60 beds in nursing home–type unit) **A**1 3 5 9 10 19 20 **F**3 7 10 11 13 18 20 22 24 28 29 30 31 40 43 47 48 49 50 51 60 62 63 64 67 68 70 74 75 76 77 78 79 81 82 83 84 85 89 90 93 98 102 103 106 107 108 111 114 115 119 120 121 123 125 126 128 129 130 146 148 **P**6
Primary Contact: Kevin J. Miller, FACHE, President and Chief Executive Officer
COO: Ken Johnson, Chief Operating Officer
CFO: Cassie Dolen, Vice President Finance and Chief Financial Officer
CMO: Thomas Smith, M.D., Vice President Medical Affairs
CIO: John Bissell, Chief Information Officer
CHR: Kevin Chiles, Vice President Human Resources
CNO: Julie R. Ward, MSN, Vice President Patient Care Services
Web address: www.hutchregional.com
Control: Other not–for–profit (including NFP Corporation) **Service:** General Medical and Surgical

Staffed Beds: 202 **Admissions:** 7228 **Census:** 153 **Outpatient Visits:** 130394 **Births:** 684 **Total Expense ($000):** 121634 **Payroll Expense ($000):** 46138 **Personnel:** 875

SUMMIT SURGICAL (170198), 1818 East 23rd Avenue, Zip 67502–1106; tel. 620/663–4800 **A**9 10 **F**3 29 45 50 64 79 81 82 85 **P**2
Primary Contact: Ann Hentzen Page, M.D., Chief Executive Officer
COO: Nancy Corwin, Chief Operating Officer
CMO: Ann Hentzen Page, M.D., Medical Director
CNO: Nancy Corwin, Chief Nursing Officer
Web address: www.summitks.com/index_surgical.htm
Control: Corporation, Investor–owned, for–profit **Service:** Surgical

Staffed Beds: 10 **Admissions:** 250 **Census:** 1 **Outpatient Visits:** 6663 **Births:** 0 **Total Expense ($000):** 5676 **Payroll Expense ($000):** 2142 **Personnel:** 43

INDEPENDENCE—Montgomery County

MERCY HOSPITAL INDEPENDENCE (170010), 800 West Myrtle Street, Zip 67301–3240, Mailing Address: P.O. Box 388, Zip 67301–0388; tel. 620/331–2200 **A**1 9 10 **F**1 3 4 11 12 13 15 16 17 18 28 30 32 34 35 40 45 50 53 57 59 62 63 65 67 68 70 72 73 76 77 79 80 81 84 88 89 90 91 93 97 98 107 108 110 111 114 118 119 127 128 129 130 131 133 135 143 144 146 **P**3 6 **S** Mercy Health, Chesterfield, MO
Primary Contact: David Steinmann, President
CFO: Shelly Hunter, Chief Financial Officer
CMO: Richenda Dawn Herren, M.D., Chief of Staff
CHR: Laura Sanders, Manager Human Resources
Web address: www.mercy.net/independenceks
Control: Church–operated, Nongovernment, not–for profit **Service:** General Medical and Surgical

Staffed Beds: 40 **Admissions:** 1068 **Census:** 10 **Outpatient Visits:** 50163 **Births:** 208 **Total Expense ($000):** 23246 **Payroll Expense ($000):** 9754 **Personnel:** 171

IOLA—Allen County

ALLEN COUNTY REGIONAL HOSPITAL (171373), 3066 N. Kentucky Street, Zip 66749–1951, Mailing Address: P.O. Box 540, Zip 66749–0540; tel. 620/365–1000 **A**1 9 10 18 **F**3 11 13 15 29 30 31 34 35 40 49 56 57 59 62 63 64 65 68 70 75 76 77 78 81 82 84 85 86 87 89 93 107 110 114 119 129 130 132 133 146 147 148 **S** HCA, Nashville, TN
Primary Contact: Ron Baker, Chief Executive Officer
CFO: Larry Peterson, Chief Financial Officer
CMO: Wesley Stone, D.O., Chief of Staff
CHR: Paula Sell, Director Human Resources
CNO: Patty McGuffin, R.N., Chief Nursing Officer
Web address: www.allencountyhospital.com
Control: County–Government, nonfederal **Service:** General Medical and Surgical

Staffed Beds: 25 **Admissions:** 787 **Census:** 10 **Outpatient Visits:** 20467 **Births:** 101 **Total Expense ($000):** 16869 **Payroll Expense ($000):** 6477 **Personnel:** 132

JETMORE—Hodgeman County

HODGEMAN COUNTY HEALTH CENTER (171369), 809 Bramley Street, Zip 67854–9320, Mailing Address: P.O. Box 310, Zip 67854–0310; tel. 620/357–8361, (Total facility includes 25 beds in nursing home–type unit) **A**10 18 **F**3 40 53 67 81 107 114 125 127 130 133 143 **P**4
Primary Contact: Teresa L. Deuel, Chief Executive Officer
Web address: www.hchconline.org
Control: County–Government, nonfederal **Service:** General Medical and Surgical

Staffed Beds: 38 **Admissions:** 238 **Census:** 23 **Outpatient Visits:** 32540 **Births:** 0 **Total Expense ($000):** 6285 **Payroll Expense ($000):** 2976 **Personnel:** 81

JOHNSON—Stanton County

STANTON COUNTY HOSPITAL (171343), 404 North Chestnut Street, Zip 67855–5001, Mailing Address: P.O. Box 779, Zip 67855–0779; tel. 620/492–6250, (Total facility includes 25 beds in nursing home–type unit) **A**9 10 18 **F**3 33 34 35 40 41 45 50 54 56 57 59 64 68 75 76 81 86 87 89 93 97 107 114 127 130 131 132 133 143 146 **P**6
Primary Contact: Jay Tusten, Chief Executive Officer
CFO: Barbara Anderson, Chief Financial Officer
CMO: William Troup, M.D., Chief of Staff
CIO: Marco Medina, Chief Information Officer
CHR: Camille Davidson, Director Human Resources
CNO: Marianne Mills, R.N., Chairperson
Web address: www.stantoncountyhospital.com
Control: County–Government, nonfederal **Service:** General Medical and Surgical

Staffed Beds: 34 **Admissions:** 147 **Census:** 25 **Outpatient Visits:** 14785 **Births:** 22 **Total Expense ($000):** 7507 **Payroll Expense ($000):** 3276 **Personnel:** 75

JUNCTION CITY—Geary County

GEARY COMMUNITY HOSPITAL (170074), 1102 St. Mary's Road, Zip 66441–4196, Mailing Address: P.O. Box 490, Zip 66441–0490; tel. 785/238–4131 **A**1 9 10 **F**3 7 8 11 19 28 29 30 32 34 35 40 45 48 50 55 56 57 59 61 62 63 64 65 68 70 75 76 77 79 81 85 86 87 97 98 103 107 108 109 110 111 113 114 115 118 119 127 129 130 131 132 133 135 144 145 146 147 148 **P**6
Primary Contact: Joseph Stratton, FACHE, Chief Executive Officer
COO: Alice J. Jensen, Chief Operating Officer
CFO: Darren K. Rumford, Chief Financial Officer
CMO: Anwar Khoury, M.D., Chief of Staff
CIO: Karl DeArmond, Director Information Systems
CHR: Teto E. Henderson, Director Human Resources
CNO: Dawn M. Engel, Chief Nursing Officer
Web address: www.gchks.org
Control: County–Government, nonfederal **Service:** General Medical and Surgical

Staffed Beds: 58 **Admissions:** 1422 **Census:** 15 **Outpatient Visits:** 54546 **Births:** 323 **Total Expense ($000):** 44118 **Payroll Expense ($000):** 19813 **Personnel:** 413

✉ **IRWIN ARMY COMMUNITY HOSPITAL**, 600 Caisson Hill Road, Zip 66442–7037; tel. 785/239–7000, (Nonreporting) **A**1 2 3 5 **S** Department of the Army, Office of the Surgeon General, Falls Church, VA
Primary Contact: Colonel Barry R. Pockrandt, Commander
COO: Lieutenant Colonel Daniel G. Bonnichsen, Deputy Commander for Administration
CFO: Lieutenant Colonel Daniel G. Bonnichsen, Deputy Commander for Administration
CMO: Lieutenant Colonel Mark S. Ochoa, M.D., Deputy Commander, Clinical Services
CIO: David Dougherty, Chief Information Management Officer
CHR: Hope Brunton, Chief Manpower Branch
CNO: Colonel Robert E. Dettmer, Deputy Commander for Health Services
Web address: www.iach.amedd.army.mil
Control: Army, Government, federal **Service:** General Medical and Surgical

Staffed Beds: 44

KANSAS CITY—Wyandotte County

☐ **KVC PRAIRIE RIDGE PSYCHIATRIC HOSPITAL**, 4300 Brenner Drive, Zip 66104–1163; tel. 913/334–0294 **A**1 3 5 **F**98 99 106
Primary Contact: B. Wayne Sims, President and Chief Executive Officer
COO: Ryan Speier, Vice President Administration
CMO: Vishal Adma, M.D., Medical Director
Web address: www.kvc.org
Control: Other not-for-profit (including NFP Corporation) **Service:** Children's hospital psychiatric

Staffed Beds: 120 **Admissions:** 2468 **Census:** 84 **Outpatient Visits:** 0 **Births:** 0 **Total Expense ($000):** 18648 **Payroll Expense ($000):** 7326 **Personnel:** 136

✉ **PROVIDENCE MEDICAL CENTER (170146)**, 8929 Parallel Parkway, Zip 66112–1689; tel. 913/596–4000, (Data for 275 days) **A**1 9 10 **F**3 13 15 17 18 20 22 24 28 29 30 31 34 35 40 41 44 45 49 56 57 59 64 70 74 75 76 77 78 79 81 82 84 85 87 89 93 97 102 103 107 108 110 111 114 119 120 121 123 124 129 130 131 132 135 143 146 147 148 **P**6 **S** Prime Healthcare Services, Ontario, CA
Primary Contact: Randall G. Nyp, FACHE, Chief Executive Officer
CFO: David Dulny, Chief Financial Officer
CMO: Sabato Sisillo, M.D., Chief Medical Officer
CIO: Charles Soeken, Director Information Technology
CHR: Brenda Farwell, Director Human Resources
CNO: Karen Orr, Chief Nursing Officer
Web address: www.providencekc.com
Control: Individual, Investor-owned, for-profit **Service:** General Medical and Surgical

Staffed Beds: 140 **Admissions:** 6260 **Census:** 85 **Outpatient Visits:** 94115 **Births:** 435 **Total Expense ($000):** 103127 **Payroll Expense ($000):** 38009 **Personnel:** 750

RAINBOW MENTAL HEALTH FACILITY (174010), 2205 West 36th Avenue, Zip 66103–2107; tel. 913/755–7000 **A**10 **F**11 30 50 86 87 98 101 103 130 135 146 **P**6
Primary Contact: Jerry A. Rea, Ph.D., Interim Superintendent
CFO: Donna Dean, Chief Financial Officer
CMO: Maria Gustilo, M.D., Medical Director
CHR: Marilyn Williamson, Chief Human Resources Officer
Web address: www.srskansas.org/osh/osh-rmhf_main.html
Control: State-Government, nonfederal **Service:** Psychiatric

Staffed Beds: 36 **Admissions:** 622 **Census:** 33 **Outpatient Visits:** 0 **Births:** 0 **Total Expense ($000):** 12635 **Payroll Expense ($000):** 3880 **Personnel:** 70

✉ **SELECT SPECIALTY HOSPITAL–KANSAS CITY (172005)**, 1731 North 90th Street, Zip 66112–1515; tel. 913/732–5900 **A**1 9 10 **F**1 3 18 29 82 85 91 130 148 **P**5 **S** Select Medical Corporation, Mechanicsburg, PA
Primary Contact: Matthew H. Blevins, Chief Executive Officer
Web address: www.selectspecialtyhospitals.com
Control: Corporation, Investor-owned, for-profit **Service:** Long-Term Acute Care hospital

Staffed Beds: 40 **Admissions:** 467 **Census:** 33 **Outpatient Visits:** 0 **Births:** 0 **Total Expense ($000):** 18227 **Payroll Expense ($000):** 6810 **Personnel:** 133

✉ **THE UNIVERSITY OF KANSAS HOSPITAL (170040)**, 3901 Rainbow Boulevard, Zip 66160–7200; tel. 913/588–5000, (Includes THE UNIVERSITY OF KANSAS HOSPITAL – INDIAN CREEK CAMPUS, 10720 Nall Avenue, Overland Park, Zip 66211–1206; tel. 913/754–5000) **A**1 2 3 5 8 9 10 **F**3 8 11 12 13 14 15 16 17 18 20 21 22 23 24 25 26 27 28 29 30 31 32 33 34 35 36 37 38 39 40 41 43 44 45 46 47 48 49 50 51 54 55 56 57 58 59 60 61 63 64 65 68 70 72 74 75 76 77 78 79 80 81 82 83 84 85 86 87 88 89 90 92 93 96 97 98 99 100 101 102 103 104 107 108 110 111 114 115 116 117 118 119 120 121 123 124 126 129 130 131 132 135 136 138 139 141 142 144 145 146 147 148 **P**6
Primary Contact: Bob Page, Chief Executive Officer
COO: Tammy Peterman, R.N., Executive Vice President, Chief Operating Officer and Chief Nursing Officer
CFO: Bill Marting, Senior Vice President and Chief Financial Officer
CMO: Lou Wetzel, M.D., Chief of Staff
CIO: Chris Hansen, Senior Vice President Ambulatory Services and Chief Information Officer
CHR: Alisa Ford, Vice President Human Resources
CNO: Tammy Peterman, R.N., Executive Vice President, Chief Operating Officer and Chief Nursing Officer
Web address: www.kumed.com
Control: Hospital district or authority, Government, nonfederal **Service:** General Medical and Surgical

Staffed Beds: 696 **Admissions:** 29585 **Census:** 484 **Outpatient Visits:** 562977 **Births:** 1756 **Total Expense ($000):** 1147611 **Payroll Expense ($000):** 379934 **Personnel:** 6188

KINGMAN—Kingman County

★ **KINGMAN COMMUNITY HOSPITAL (171378)**, 750 Avenue D. West, Zip 67068–0376; tel. 620/532–3147 **A**9 10 18 **F**3 11 15 17 18 28 29 31 34 35 40 54 56 57 59 62 64 67 69 70 75 77 78 81 86 87 89 90 93 97 107 114 119 128 130 132 133 145 146 148
Primary Contact: Edward E. Riley, Chief Executive Officer and Administrator
CFO: Kent Hudson, Chief Financial Officer
CIO: Jay Gehring, Director Information Systems
CHR: Nancy Stucky, Director Human Resources and Public Relations
CNO: Nita McFarland, Director of Nursing
Web address: www.kchks.com
Control: Other not-for-profit (including NFP Corporation) **Service:** General Medical and Surgical

Staffed Beds: 25 **Admissions:** 580 **Census:** 10 **Outpatient Visits:** 26388 **Births:** 0 **Total Expense ($000):** 10431 **Payroll Expense ($000):** 4974 **Personnel:** 122

KINSLEY—Edwards County

★ **EDWARDS COUNTY HOSPITAL AND HEALTHCARE CENTER (171317)**, 620 West Eighth Street, Zip 67547–2329, Mailing Address: P.O. Box 99, Zip 67547–0099; tel. 620/659–3621 **A**9 10 18 **F**3 7 11 15 18 19 28 29 30 34 35 39 40 53 56 57 59 64 65 67 68 77 79 81 93 97 98 103 107 110 111 127 128 130 133 146 148
Primary Contact: Robert Krickbaum, Chief Executive Officer
CHR: Tammy K. Lampe, Director Human Resources
Web address: www.edwardscohospital.com
Control: County-Government, nonfederal **Service:** General Medical and Surgical

Staffed Beds: 22 **Admissions:** 490 **Census:** 14 **Outpatient Visits:** 10038 **Births:** 0 **Total Expense ($000):** 8137 **Payroll Expense ($000):** 3213 **Personnel:** 66

KIOWA—Barber County

★ **KIOWA DISTRICT HOSPITAL AND MANOR (171331)**, 810 Drumm Street, Zip 67070–1626; tel. 620/825–4131, (Total facility includes 34 beds in nursing home–type unit) **A**9 10 18 **F**2 29 40 45 56 64 81 85 92 93 97 107 111 119 127 130 133 **P**6
Primary Contact: Janell Goodno, Interim Chief Executive Officer
CFO: Robin Lewis, Chief Financial Officer
CMO: Paul Wilhelm, M.D., Chief of Staff
CHR: Tara Girty, Director Human Resources
Control: Hospital district or authority, Government, nonfederal **Service:** General Medical and Surgical

Staffed Beds: 58 **Admissions:** 152 **Census:** 21 **Outpatient Visits:** 5423 **Births:** 0 **Total Expense ($000):** 4201 **Payroll Expense ($000):** 2058 **Personnel:** 57

LA CROSSE—Rush County

★ **RUSH COUNTY MEMORIAL HOSPITAL (171342)**, 801 Locust Street,
Zip 67548–9673, Mailing Address: P.O. Box 520, Zip 67548–0520;
tel. 785/222-2545, (Total facility includes 20 beds in nursing home–type unit) **A**9
10 18 **F**3 40 45 50 53 57 59 63 64 77 81 93 97 107 111 114 119 127
133 **P**6
Primary Contact: Brenda Legleiter, R.N., Chief Executive Officer
CFO: Lorin Haas, Chief Financial Officer
CMO: Oldrich Bubenik, M.D., Chief of Staff
CHR: David Caudill, Director Human Resources
Web address: www.rushcountymemorialhospital.com
Control: County–Government, nonfederal **Service:** General Medical and Surgical

Staffed Beds: 36 **Admissions:** 179 **Census:** 27 **Outpatient Visits:** 5182
Births: 0 **Total Expense ($000):** 5597 **Payroll Expense ($000):** 2401
Personnel: 76

LAKIN—Kearny County

KEARNY COUNTY HOSPITAL (171313), 500 Thorpe Street, Zip 67860–9625;
tel. 620/355–7111, (Total facility includes 75 beds in nursing home–type unit) **A**5
9 10 18 **F**2 3 6 10 13 15 28 34 35 40 45 50 56 59 62 64 67 68 69 75 76
81 85 86 89 93 97 107 119 125 128 131 132 133 143 **P**6
Primary Contact: Benjamin Anderson, Chief Executive Officer and Administrator
CFO: ReChelle Kennedy, Chief Financial Officer
CMO: Arlo Reimer, M.D., Chief of Staff
CIO: Scott Good, Manager Information Services
CHR: Donna Winright, Director Human Resources and Senior Services
Web address: www.kearnycountyhospital.com
Control: County–Government, nonfederal **Service:** General Medical and Surgical

Staffed Beds: 100 **Admissions:** 501 **Census:** 70 **Outpatient Visits:** 41276
Births: 187 **Total Expense ($000):** 17774 **Payroll Expense ($000):** 9359
Personnel: 211

LARNED—Pawnee County

☐ **LARNED STATE HOSPITAL (174006)**, 1301 Kansas Highway 264, Zip 67550;
tel. 620/285–2131 **A**1 10 **F**30 50 53 57 61 68 75 77 86 87 98 99 101 103
106 130 132 135 143 146
Primary Contact: Thomas Kinlen, Superintendent
COO: Steve Spain, Chief Operating Officer
CMO: Sayed Jehan, M.D., Interim Medical Director
CIO: Sid Smith, Director Information Resources
CHR: Kerri Barnard, Director Human Resources
CNO: Holly Hertel, Director Nursing
Web address: www.larnedstatehospital.org
Control: State–Government, nonfederal **Service:** Psychiatric

Staffed Beds: 520 **Admissions:** 1406 **Census:** 294 **Outpatient Visits:** 0
Births: 0 **Total Expense ($000):** 61829 **Payroll Expense ($000):** 31367
Personnel: 732

★ **PAWNEE VALLEY COMMUNITY HOSPITAL (171345)**, 923 Carroll Avenue,
Zip 67550–2429; tel. 620/285–3161 **A**9 10 18 **F**3 11 28 29 30 34 40 45 46
57 68 77 81 84 87 91 93 94 102 107 115 119 129 130 131 133 135 148
Primary Contact: Shae Veach, Interim Administrator
COO: Bryce A. Young, Chief Operating Officer
CFO: George Harms, Chief Financial Officer
CMO: David Sanger, M.D., Chief Medical Officer
CHR: Bruce Whittington, Vice President Human Resources
CNO: Paul Henry Carrington, Chief Nursing Officer
Web address: www.pawneevalleyhospital.com
Control: County–Government, nonfederal **Service:** General Medical and Surgical

Staffed Beds: 25 **Admissions:** 326 **Census:** 6 **Outpatient Visits:** 13610
Births: 0 **Total Expense ($000):** 9953 **Payroll Expense ($000):** 4696
Personnel: 89

LAWRENCE—Douglas County

☒ △ **LAWRENCE MEMORIAL HOSPITAL (170137)**, 325 Maine Street,
Zip 66044–1360; tel. 785/505–5000, (Total facility includes 12 beds in nursing
home–type unit) **A**1 3 5 7 9 10 20 **F**3 11 13 15 18 20 22 26 28 29 30 31 34
35 36 38 39 40 44 45 49 50 51 54 55 56 57 59 61 64 65 70 74 75 76 77
78 79 81 82 84 85 86 87 89 90 91 93 94 96 97 100 102 107 110 111 114
115 116 118 119 120 124 126 128 129 130 131 132 135 146 147 148
P6 8
Primary Contact: Eugene W. Meyer, President and Chief Executive Officer
COO: Karen J. Shumate, R.N., Chief Operating Officer
CFO: Joe Pedley, CPA, Vice President and Chief Financial Officer
CIO: Jane Maskus, Vice President and Chief Information Officer
Web address: www.lmh.org
Control: City–Government, nonfederal **Service:** General Medical and Surgical

Staffed Beds: 152 **Admissions:** 6669 **Census:** 64 **Outpatient Visits:** 160733
Births: 1132 **Total Expense ($000):** 174211 **Payroll Expense ($000):**
72127 **Personnel:** 1200

LEAVENWORTH—Leavenworth County

DWIGHT D. EISENHOWER VETERANS AFFAIRS MEDICAL CENTER See
Veterans Affairs Eastern Kansas Health Care System, Topeka

☒ **SAINT JOHN HOSPITAL (170009)**, 3500 South Fourth Street,
Zip 66048–5043; tel. 913/680–6000, (Data for 275 days) **A**1 9 10 **F**3 8 15 18
29 30 34 40 44 45 46 54 56 57 59 64 68 70 74 75 77 81 84 85 93 98 103
107 111 114 119 130 133 135 146 148 **P**6 **S** Prime Healthcare Services,
Ontario, CA
Primary Contact: Randall G. Nyp, FACHE, President and Chief Executive Officer
CFO: David Dulny, Chief Financial Officer
CMO: Sabato Sisillo, M.D., Chief Medical Officer
CIO: Charles Soeken, Director Information Technology
CHR: Brenda Farwell, Director Human Resources
CNO: Jodi Fincher, Vice President Patient Care Services
Web address: www.providence–health.org/sjh
Control: Individual, Investor–owned, for–profit **Service:** General Medical and
Surgical

Staffed Beds: 40 **Admissions:** 1008 **Census:** 21 **Outpatient Visits:** 45736
Births: 0 **Total Expense ($000):** 23999 **Payroll Expense ($000):** 8926
Personnel: 174

☒ **SAINT LUKE'S CUSHING HOSPITAL (170133)**, 711 Marshall Street,
Zip 66048–3235; tel. 913/684–1100 **A**1 5 9 10 **F**3 11 13 15 28 29 31 34 40
45 50 51 57 59 64 68 70 74 75 76 77 79 81 82 85 87 93 94 98 100 101
102 103 107 108 110 111 114 119 129 130 132 146 148 **S** Saint Luke's
Health System, Kansas City, MO
Primary Contact: Adele Ducharme, R.N., MSN, Chief Executive Officer
CFO: Julie Murphy, Chief Financial Officer
CMO: Donald Peghee, M.D., President
CHR: Donna Kunz, Director Human Resources
CNO: Karin Sundblom, Chief Nursing Officer
Web address: www.https://www.saintlukeshealthsystem.org/location/cushing–
memorial–hospital
Control: Other not–for–profit (including NFP Corporation) **Service:** General
Medical and Surgical

Staffed Beds: 53 **Admissions:** 1721 **Census:** 16 **Outpatient Visits:** 31470
Births: 265 **Total Expense ($000):** 33239 **Payroll Expense ($000):** 12949
Personnel: 247

LEAWOOD—Johnson County

☐ **DOCTOR'S HOSPITAL (170194)**, 4901 College Boulevard, Zip 66211–1602;
tel. 913/529–1801 **A**1 10 **F**1 4 16 17 39 67 70 72 73 79 80 81 82 88 89 90
98 111 128 **P**5
Primary Contact: Phil Harness, Chief Executive Officer
Web address: www.dshospital.net
Control: Partnership, Investor–owned, for–profit **Service:** General Medical and
Surgical

Staffed Beds: 9 **Admissions:** 145 **Census:** 1 **Outpatient Visits:** 9916 **Births:**
0 **Total Expense ($000):** 16602 **Payroll Expense ($000):** 1986 **Personnel:**
39

KANSAS CITY ORTHOPAEDIC INSTITUTE (170188), 3651 College Boulevard,
Zip 66211–1910; tel. 913/338–4100 **A**3 5 9 10 **F**29 77 79 81 82 93 111
Primary Contact: Charles E. Rhoades, M.D., Chief Executive Officer
CIO: Jim Leveling, Director Information Technology
CHR: Laura Sinclair, Director Human Resources
Web address: www.kcoi.com
Control: Partnership, Investor–owned, for–profit **Service:** Orthopedic

Staffed Beds: 9 **Admissions:** 795 **Census:** 5 **Outpatient Visits:** 28973
Births: 0 **Personnel:** 107

LENEXA—Johnson County

☐ **MINIMALLY INVASIVE SURGERY CENTER (170199)**, 11217 Lakeview
Avenue, Zip 66219–1399; tel. 913/322–7401 **A**1 10 **F**12 70 81 107 111
115 119
Primary Contact: Parajeet Sabharrwal, Administrator
Web address: www.laplose.com/
Control: State–Government, nonfederal **Service:** Surgical

Staffed Beds: 11 **Admissions:** 143 **Census:** 1 **Outpatient Visits:** 1312
Births: 0 **Total Expense ($000):** 4712 **Payroll Expense ($000):** 85
Personnel: 16

LEOTI—Wichita County

★ **WICHITA COUNTY HEALTH CENTER (171306)**, 211 East Earl Street,
Zip 67861–9620; tel. 620/375–2233, (Total facility includes 12 beds in nursing
home–type unit) **A**9 10 18 **F**2 3 11 29 34 35 40 41 45 50 56 57 59 64 67 69
75 77 86 87 89 93 97 107 119 127 128 130 133 135 146 **P**6
Primary Contact: Tyson Sterling, Chief Executive Officer
CFO: Janice Campas, Chief Financial Officer
CMO: Jeffrey Alpert, M.D., Medical Director
CHR: Patti Whalen, Manager Human Resources
CNO: Teresa Clark, Director of Nursing
Web address: www.wichitacountyhealthcenter.com
Control: County–Government, nonfederal **Service:** General Medical and Surgical

Staffed Beds: 37 **Admissions:** 129 **Census:** 18 **Outpatient Visits:** 5976
Births: 0 **Total Expense ($000):** 6729 **Payroll Expense ($000):** 3412
Personnel: 84

Many Facility Codes have changed. Please refer to the AHA Guide Code Chart. © 2014 AHA Guide

LIBERAL—Seward County

☐ **SOUTHWEST MEDICAL CENTER (170068)**, 315 West 15th Street,
Zip 67901–2455, Mailing Address: Box 1340, Zip 67905–1340;
tel. 620/624–1651, (Total facility includes 18 beds in nursing home–type unit) **A**1
9 10 19 20 **F**1 3 4 11 13 15 16 17 29 31 34 40 45 48 49 57 59 67 68 70
72 73 75 76 77 79 80 81 85 87 88 89 90 93 96 98 103 104 107 108 110
111 114 118 119 128 129 130 131 145
Primary Contact: William Ermann, President and Chief Executive Officer
COO: Michele Gillespie, Vice President of Operations
CFO: William Ermann, Vice President and Chief Financial Officer
CNO: Jo L. Harrison, Vice President of Patient Care Services
Web address: www.swmedcenter.com
Control: County–Government, nonfederal **Service:** General Medical and Surgical

Staffed Beds: 101 **Admissions:** 2080 **Census:** 18 **Outpatient Visits:** 44399
Births: 714 **Total Expense ($000):** 39961 **Payroll Expense ($000):** 16903
Personnel: 351

LINCOLN—Lincoln County

LINCOLN COUNTY HOSPITAL (171360), 624 North Second Street,
Zip 67455–1738, Mailing Address: P.O. Box 406, Zip 67455–0406;
tel. 785/524–4403 **A**9 10 18 **F**11 40 69 107 114 119 127 128 133 **P**6
Primary Contact: Steven L. Granzow, Chief Executive Officer
Control: County–Government, nonfederal **Service:** General Medical and Surgical

Staffed Beds: 14 **Admissions:** 183 **Census:** 2 **Outpatient Visits:** 4463
Births: 0 **Total Expense ($000):** 6712 **Payroll Expense ($000):** 2901
Personnel: 72

LINDSBORG—Mcpherson County

★ **LINDSBORG COMMUNITY HOSPITAL (171358)**, 605 West Lincoln Street,
Zip 67456–2328; tel. 785/227–3308 **A**9 10 18 **F**3 28 29 40 53 59 62 64 67
77 81 93 97 107 115 119 128 130 133 144 **P**6
Primary Contact: Larry VanDerWege, Administrator
CFO: Laraine Gengler, Chief Financial Officer
CIO: Jeremy Snapp, Director Information Systems
CHR: Brad Malm, Director Human Resources and Education
CNO: Beth Hedberg, R.N., Director Nursing
Web address: www.lindsborghospital.org
Control: Other not–for–profit (including NFP Corporation) **Service:** General
Medical and Surgical

Staffed Beds: 25 **Admissions:** 135 **Census:** 1 **Outpatient Visits:** 19356
Births: 0 **Total Expense ($000):** 7682 **Payroll Expense ($000):** 3645
Personnel: 81

LYONS—Rice County

★ **RICE COUNTY DISTRICT HOSPITAL (171330)**, 619 South Clark Street,
Zip 67554–3003, Mailing Address: P.O. Box 828, Zip 67554–0828;
tel. 620/257–5173 **A**9 10 18 **F**1 3 10 13 29 30 34 35 40 43 45 57 67 70 75
76 77 81 89 93 107 125 127 128 130 132 133 143
Primary Contact: George M. Stover, Chief Executive Officer
CFO: Terry Pound, Chief Financial Officer
CMO: Stacy Dashiell, M.D., Chief of Staff
CNO: Judy Hogdson, R.N., Chief Nursing Officer
Web address: www.ricecountyhospital.com
Control: Hospital district or authority, Government, nonfederal **Service:** General
Medical and Surgical

Staffed Beds: 25 **Admissions:** 356 **Census:** 16 **Outpatient Visits:** 18432
Births: 76 **Total Expense ($000):** 14595 **Payroll Expense ($000):** 7252
Personnel: 137

MANHATTAN—Riley County

MANHATTAN SURGICAL CENTER (170190), 1829 College Avenue,
Zip 66502–3381; tel. 785/776–5100 **A**9 10 **F**29 45 48 51 68 81 82 130
Primary Contact: Scott Chapman, Administrator
Web address: www.manhattansurgical.com
Control: Partnership, Investor–owned, for–profit **Service:** Surgical

Staffed Beds: 13 **Admissions:** 391 **Census:** 2 **Outpatient Visits:** 9211
Births: 0 **Personnel:** 82

★ ○ **MERCY REGIONAL HEALTH CENTER (170142)**, 1823 College Avenue,
Zip 66502–3346; tel. 785/776–3322, (Data for 273 days) **A**5 9 10 11 19 **F**3
11 12 13 15 18 20 22 28 29 30 31 34 35 37 40 44 45 46 49 60 64 70 73
74 75 76 77 78 79 81 82 84 85 86 87 89 90 93 96 102 103 104 107 108
110 111 115 119 129 130 132 133 146 147 148 **S** Ascension Health, Saint
Louis, MO
Primary Contact: John R. Broberg, FACHE, Senior Administrator
COO: Carla J. Yost, R.N., Administrator Operations
CFO: James Fraser, Administrator Finance
CIO: Andy Gagnon, Director Information Technology
CHR: Renee Reed, Director Human Resources
CNO: Carla J. Yost, R.N., Administrator Nursing
Web address: www.mercyregional.org
Control: Other not–for–profit (including NFP Corporation) **Service:** General
Medical and Surgical

Staffed Beds: 96 **Admissions:** 3733 **Census:** 46 **Outpatient Visits:** 71417
Births: 806 **Total Expense ($000):** 62597 **Payroll Expense ($000):** 24792
Personnel: 459

MANKATO—Jewell County

JEWELL COUNTY HOSPITAL (171309), 100 Crestvue Avenue,
Zip 66956–2407, Mailing Address: P.O. Box 327, Zip 66956–0327;
tel. 785/378–3137, (Total facility includes 19 beds in nursing home–type unit) **A**9
10 18 **F**2 3 29 32 40 50 58 64 75 77 87 93 107 127 133 147
Primary Contact: Doyle L. McKimmy, FACHE, Chief Executive Officer
COO: Eric Borden, Chief Operating Officer and Chief Financial Officer
CFO: Eric Borden, Chief Operating Officer and Chief Financial Officer
Web address: www.jewellcountyhospital.com
Control: County–Government, nonfederal **Service:** General Medical and Surgical

Staffed Beds: 41 **Admissions:** 73 **Census:** 13 **Outpatient Visits:** 4858
Births: 0 **Total Expense ($000):** 4299 **Payroll Expense ($000):** 2195
Personnel: 72

MARION—Marion County

★ **ST. LUKE HOSPITAL AND LIVING CENTER (171356)**, 535 South Freeborn,
Zip 66861–1256; tel. 620/382–2177, (Total facility includes 32 beds in nursing
home–type unit) **A**9 10 18 **F**3 11 15 28 29 34 40 45 62 64 81 94 97 107 108
114 119 127 128 133 **P**6 **S** QHR, Brentwood, TN
Primary Contact: Jeremy Ensey, Chief Executive Officer
CFO: Bev Reid, Chief Financial Officer
CMO: Don Hodson, M.D., Chief Medical Officer
CIO: Jeff Methvin, Manager Information Technology
CHR: Sharon Zogelman, Director Human Resources
Web address: www.slhmarion.org
Control: Hospital district or authority, Government, nonfederal **Service:** General
Medical and Surgical

Staffed Beds: 37 **Admissions:** 170 **Census:** 33 **Outpatient Visits:** 22401
Births: 0 **Total Expense ($000):** 8939 **Payroll Expense ($000):** 3698
Personnel: 97

MARYSVILLE—Marshall County

★ **COMMUNITY MEMORIAL HEALTHCARE (171363)**, 708 North 18th Street,
Zip 66508–1338; tel. 785/562–2311 **A**9 10 18 **F**3 13 15 28 29 30 31 34 35
40 43 45 50 57 59 62 64 68 69 75 76 77 78 79 81 87 93 94 97 107 108
114 127 128 129 130 131 132 133 135 146 147 148 **P**6
Primary Contact: Curtis R. Hawkinson, Chief Executive Officer
CMO: Randall Brown, M.D., Chief of Staff
CIO: Colleen Behrens, Director Information Technology
CHR: Jessie Schneider, Director Human Resources
CNO: Diane Luebcke, R.N., Director Nursing
Web address: www.cmhcare.org
Control: Other not–for–profit (including NFP Corporation) **Service:** General
Medical and Surgical

Staffed Beds: 25 **Admissions:** 749 **Census:** 10 **Outpatient Visits:** 25157
Births: 62 **Total Expense ($000):** 20753 **Payroll Expense ($000):** 9149
Personnel: 186

Hospital, Medicare Provider Number, Address, Telephone, Approval, Facility, and Physician Codes, Health Care System

★ American Hospital Association (AHA) membership
☐ The Joint Commission accreditation ◇ DNV Healthcare Inc. accreditation
○ Healthcare Facilities Accreditation Program
△ Commission on Accreditation of Rehabilitation Facilities (CARF) accreditation

KS

MCPHERSON—Mcpherson County

★ **MCPHERSON HOSPITAL (170105)**, 1000 Hospital Drive, Zip 67460–2326; tel. 620/241–2250 **A**5 9 10 **F**3 7 11 13 15 28 34 35 40 45 50 53 57 59 64 65 70 75 76 77 79 81 82 85 97 107 108 114 119 133 146 **P**6
Primary Contact: Robert Monical, President and Chief Executive Officer
COO: Terri Gehring, Vice President Operations
CFO: George Halama, Vice President Finance
CHR: Jill Wenger, Vice President Human Resources
CNO: Beth Worden, Director Nursing Services
Web address: www.mcphersonhospital.org
Control: Other not–for–profit (including NFP Corporation) **Service:** General Medical and Surgical

Staffed Beds: 41 **Admissions:** 1084 **Census:** 11 **Outpatient Visits:** 55904
Births: 156 **Total Expense ($000):** 23411 **Payroll Expense ($000):** 10635
Personnel: 265

MEMORIAL HOSPITAL See McPherson Hospital

MEADE—Meade County

★ **MEADE DISTRICT HOSPITAL (171321)**, 510 East Carthage Street, Zip 67864–6401, Mailing Address: P.O. Box 820, Zip 67864–0820; tel. 620/873–2141, (Total facility includes 59 beds in nursing home–type unit) **A**9 10 18 **F**3 15 28 29 34 35 40 45 53 56 57 59 62 64 79 81 82 85 87 93 107 108 114 119 127 128 130 131 133 143 148 **P**6
Primary Contact: Michael P. Thomas, Administrator
CIO: Matt Bobo, Chief Information Officer
Web address: www.meadehospital.com
Control: Hospital district or authority, Government, nonfederal **Service:** General Medical and Surgical

Staffed Beds: 79 **Admissions:** 282 **Census:** 47 **Outpatient Visits:** 17024
Births: 0 **Total Expense ($000):** 14420 **Payroll Expense ($000):** 7368
Personnel: 185

MEDICINE LODGE—Barber County

★ **MEDICINE LODGE MEMORIAL HOSPITAL (171334)**, 710 North Walnut Street, Zip 67104–1019; tel. 620/886–3771 **A**9 10 18 **F**7 11 40 44 45 56 64 81 93 107 119 127 128 133 148 **P**6 **S** Great Plains Health Alliance, Inc., Wichita, KS
Primary Contact: Kevin A. White, Administrator
CFO: Thomas G. Lee, Chief Financial Officer
CHR: Johnnie Davis, Director Human Resources
CNO: Kathryn I. Burns, R.N., Director of Nursing
Web address: www.mlmh.net/
Control: Hospital district or authority, Government, nonfederal **Service:** General Medical and Surgical

Staffed Beds: 25 **Admissions:** 256 **Census:** 13 **Outpatient Visits:** 22430
Births: 0 **Total Expense ($000):** 8169 **Payroll Expense ($000):** 4284
Personnel: 102

MINNEAPOLIS—Ottawa County

★ **OTTAWA COUNTY HEALTH CENTER (171328)**, 215 East Eighth, Zip 67467–1902, Mailing Address: P.O. Box 290, Zip 67467–0290; tel. 785/392–2122, (Total facility includes 17 beds in nursing home–type unit) **A**5 9 10 18 **F**10 28 35 40 53 56 62 64 67 85 86 93 128 130 133 143 **S** Great Plains Health Alliance, Inc., Wichita, KS
Primary Contact: Jody Parks, Administrator
CFO: Cheryl Lanoue, Chief Financial Officer
CIO: Linda Wright, Director Information
CNO: Marlene Gawith, Director of Nursing
Web address: www.ottawacountyhealthcenter.com
Control: Other not–for–profit (including NFP Corporation) **Service:** General Medical and Surgical

Staffed Beds: 42 **Admissions:** 247 **Census:** 31 **Outpatient Visits:** 11050
Births: 0 **Total Expense ($000):** 5474 **Payroll Expense ($000):** 2765
Personnel: 76

MINNEOLA—Ford County

★ **MINNEOLA DISTRICT HOSPITAL (171368)**, 212 Main Street, Zip 67865–8511, Mailing Address: P.O. Box 127, Zip 67865–0127; tel. 620/885–4264, (Total facility includes 36 beds in nursing home–type unit) **A**9 10 18 **F**13 29 40 45 46 56 57 64 65 67 81 83 93 102 107 127 128 130 133 148 **P**6 **S** Great Plains Health Alliance, Inc., Wichita, KS
Primary Contact: Deborah Bruner, Chief Executive Officer and Administrator
CFO: Marion Blanton, Chief Financial Officer
CMO: Tony Luna, M.D., Chief of Staff
CHR: Vena Harris, Director Human Resources
Web address: www.minneolahealthcare.com
Control: Hospital district or authority, Government, nonfederal **Service:** General Medical and Surgical

Staffed Beds: 54 **Admissions:** 455 **Census:** 38 **Outpatient Visits:** 22896
Births: 32 **Total Expense ($000):** 10234 **Payroll Expense ($000):** 5139
Personnel: 128

MOUNDRIDGE—Mcpherson County

★ **MERCY HOSPITAL (170075)**, 218 East Pack Street, Zip 67107–8815, Mailing Address: P.O. Box 180, Zip 67107–0180; tel. 620/345–6391 **A**5 9 10 **F**4 13 16 17 29 30 40 45 67 70 72 73 76 80 81 88 89 90 93 98 128 130 133
Primary Contact: Doyle K. Johnson, Administrator
CFO: Royce Holdeman, Chief Financial Officer
Web address: www.mercyh.org/
Control: Church–operated, Nongovernment, not–for profit **Service:** General Medical and Surgical

Staffed Beds: 21 **Admissions:** 294 **Census:** 5 **Outpatient Visits:** 7163
Births: 35 **Total Expense ($000):** 2996 **Payroll Expense ($000):** 1780
Personnel: 35

NEODESHA—Wilson County

★ **WILSON MEDICAL CENTER (171344)**, 2600 Ottawa Road, Zip 66757–1897, Mailing Address: P.O. Box 360, Zip 66757–0360; tel. 620/325–2611 **A**9 10 18 **F**3 11 29 34 35 40 44 45 53 57 59 64 81 82 85 89 107 108 110 119 127 128 133 148 **S** QHR, Brentwood, TN
Primary Contact: Dennis R. Shelby, Chief Executive Officer
CFO: John Gutschenritter, Chief Financial Officer
CIO: Julie Quanstrom, Director Information Systems
CHR: Laura Dean, Director Human Resources
CNO: Michelle Bohannon, Director of Nursing Operations and Risk, Compliance, Quality and Safety
Web address: www.wilsonmedical.org
Control: County–Government, nonfederal **Service:** General Medical and Surgical

Staffed Beds: 15 **Admissions:** 309 **Census:** 7 **Outpatient Visits:** 12902
Births: 0 **Total Expense ($000):** 12396 **Payroll Expense ($000):** 4947
Personnel: 121

NESS CITY—Ness County

★ **NESS COUNTY HOSPITAL (171336)**, 312 Custer Street, Zip 67560–1654; tel. 785/798–2291, (Total facility includes 43 beds in nursing home–type unit) **A**9 10 18 **F**3 7 15 32 40 45 59 62 65 67 93 111 114 119 125 127 128 133
Primary Contact: Curt Thomas, Administrator
CFO: Debra Frank. Chief Financial Officer
CMO: Mikhail Imseis, M.D., Chief of Staff
CIO: Vicki Howe, Health Information Management
CHR: Shelly McDonald, Chief Human Resources Officer
CNO: Brenda Dinges, Director of Nursing
Web address: www.nchospital.org
Control: Hospital district or authority, Government, nonfederal **Service:** General Medical and Surgical

Staffed Beds: 63 **Admissions:** 158 **Census:** 36 **Outpatient Visits:** 9711
Births: 0 **Total Expense ($000):** 8543 **Payroll Expense ($000):** 3703
Personnel: 98

NEWTON—Harvey County

★ ○ **NEWTON MEDICAL CENTER (170103)**, 600 Medical Center Drive, Zip 67114–8780, Mailing Address: P.O. Box 308, Zip 67114–0308; tel. 316/283–2700 **A**5 9 10 11 **F**3 8 13 15 20 22 28 29 30 40 45 49 51 59 64 68 70 73 75 76 79 81 85 86 90 103 107 108 110 111 114 118 119 126 130 131 133 146 147 148 **P**6
Primary Contact: Steven G. Kelly, President and Chief Executive Officer
COO: J. Michael Keller, Vice President Operations
CFO: Todd Kasitz, Vice President Finance
CIO: Mike Cottle, Chief Information Officer
CHR: Todd Tangeman, Vice President Human Resources
Web address: www.newtonmedicalcenter.com
Control: Other not–for–profit (including NFP Corporation) **Service:** General Medical and Surgical

Staffed Beds: 103 **Admissions:** 2769 **Census:** 39 **Outpatient Visits:** 63359
Births: 519 **Total Expense ($000):** 62624 **Payroll Expense ($000):** 29382
Personnel: 566

☐ **PRAIRIE VIEW (174016)**, 1901 East First Street, Zip 67114–5010, Mailing Address: P.O. Box 467, Zip 67114–0467; tel. 316/284–6400, (Nonreporting) **A**1 9 10
Primary Contact: Jessie Kaye, Chief Executive Officer
CFO: Lisa Ramsey, Chief Financial Officer
CIO: Merle Enns, Director Information Services
CHR: Joy Robb, Vice President Human Resources
Web address: www.prairieview.org
Control: Other not–for–profit (including NFP Corporation) **Service:** Psychiatric

Staffed Beds: 38

Many Facility Codes have changed. Please refer to the AHA Guide Code Chart. © 2014 AHA Guide

KS

NORTON—Norton County

★ **NORTON COUNTY HOSPITAL (171348)**, 102 East Holme, Zip 67654–1406, Mailing Address: P.O. Box 250, Zip 67654–0250; tel. 785/877–3351 **A**5 9 10 18 **F**3 13 15 28 29 30 31 34 35 40 45 50 56 59 64 65 67 69 76 78 79 81 82 86 93 107 110 119 127 128 130 131 133 146 148 **P**6
Primary Contact: Richard Miller, Administrator and Chief Executive Officer
CFO: Ryan Stover, Chief Financial Officer
CHR: Shannan Hempler, Director Human Resources
Web address: www.ntcohosp.com
Control: County–Government, nonfederal **Service:** General Medical and Surgical

> **Staffed Beds:** 25 **Admissions:** 571 **Census:** 6 **Outpatient Visits:** 62908
> **Births:** 75 **Total Expense ($000):** 11001 **Payroll Expense ($000):** 5622
> **Personnel:** 126

OAKLEY—Logan County

LOGAN COUNTY HOSPITAL (171326), 211 Cherry Street, Zip 67748–1201; tel. 785/672–3211, (Total facility includes 42 beds in nursing home–type unit) **A**9 10 18 **F**3 26 27 28 40 45 50 53 64 67 69 81 93 107 127 130 133 143 148 **P**6
Primary Contact: Darcy Howard, Interim Chief Executive Officer
COO: Aimee Zimmerman, R.N., Chief Operations Officer
CFO: Darcy Howard, Chief Financial Officer
CMO: Celeste Rains, D.O., Chief of Staff
CIO: Terry Grace, Director Information Technology
CHR: Steve Allison, Director Human Resources
CNO: Marcia Kruse, R.N., Director Nursing
Web address: www.logancountyhospital.org
Control: County–Government, nonfederal **Service:** General Medical and Surgical

> **Staffed Beds:** 59 **Admissions:** 270 **Census:** 43 **Outpatient Visits:** 12593
> **Births:** 0 **Total Expense ($000):** 12554 **Payroll Expense ($000):** 6698
> **Personnel:** 166

OBERLIN—Decatur County

★ **DECATUR HEALTH SYSTEMS (171352)**, 810 West Columbia Street, Zip 67749–2450, Mailing Address: P.O. Box 268, Zip 67749–0268; tel. 785/475–2208, (Total facility includes 37 beds in nursing home–type unit) **A**9 10 18 **F**3 15 28 29 31 34 35 40 45 53 56 57 62 64 69 75 78 81 84 85 86 93 107 114 127 130 133 135
Primary Contact: Johnathan Owens, Chief Executive Officer
CFO: Amanda Fortin, Manager Finance
CMO: Elizabeth Sliter, M.D., Chairman Medical Staff
CIO: Natasha Weishapl, Manager Business Office and Human Resources
CHR: Natasha Weishapl, Manager Business Office and Human Resources
Web address: www.decaturhealthsystems.org
Control: City–County, Government, nonfederal **Service:** General Medical and Surgical

> **Staffed Beds:** 61 **Admissions:** 253 **Census:** 27 **Outpatient Visits:** 8026
> **Births:** 0 **Total Expense ($000):** 7006 **Payroll Expense ($000):** 3811
> **Personnel:** 85

OLATHE—Johnson County

☐ **OLATHE MEDICAL CENTER (170049)**, 20333 West 151st Street, Zip 66061–5350; tel. 913/791–4200 **A**1 2 5 9 10 **F**3 8 11 12 13 15 18 20 22 24 26 28 29 30 31 34 35 39 40 41 46 49 56 57 58 59 61 62 63 64 65 68 70 74 75 76 77 78 79 81 82 84 85 86 87 89 92 93 107 108 110 111 115 116 117 118 119 129 130 131 132 135 144 145 146 147 148
Primary Contact: Frank H. Devocelle, President and Chief Executive Officer
COO: John Staton, Senior Vice President Operations
CFO: Tierney Lynn Grasser, Senior Vice President and Chief Financial Officer
CHR: David Klimek, Vice President Human Resources
CNO: Dorothy Carey, Senior Vice President and Chief Nursing Officer
Web address: www.ohsi.com
Control: Other not–for–profit (including NFP Corporation) **Service:** General Medical and Surgical

> **Staffed Beds:** 229 **Admissions:** 10141 **Census:** 108 **Outpatient Visits:** 301162 **Births:** 1168 **Personnel:** 1338

ONAGA—Pottawatomie County

★ **COMMUNITY HEALTHCARE SYSTEM (171354)**, 120 West Eighth Street, Zip 66521–9574; tel. 785/889–4272, (Total facility includes 78 beds in nursing home–type unit) **A**9 10 18 **F**2 3 5 6 10 11 12 13 15 29 31 32 34 35 36 40 43 45 50 53 56 57 59 62 64 65 67 70 74 75 76 77 78 79 81 82 84 85 86 87 89 93 97 99 100 101 102 103 104 105 106 107 114 119 125 127 128 130 131 132 133 134 135 143 144 145 146 147 148 **P**6
Primary Contact: Greg Unruh, Chief Executive Officer
COO: Marcia S. Walsh, M.P.H., Chief Operating Officer
CFO: Monica Holthaus, Chief Financial Officer
CMO: Marcus Weiser, D.O., Chief of Staff
CIO: Rod Evans, Chief Information Officer
CHR: Terry D. Bernatis, Director Human Resources
CNO: Rosalind Lewis, R.N., Chief Nursing Officer
Web address: www.chcsks.org
Control: Other not–for–profit (including NFP Corporation) **Service:** General Medical and Surgical

> **Staffed Beds:** 150 **Admissions:** 1006 **Census:** 79 **Outpatient Visits:** 97028
> **Births:** 86 **Total Expense ($000):** 27913 **Payroll Expense ($000):** 16324
> **Personnel:** 296

OSAWATOMIE—Miami County

☐ **OSAWATOMIE STATE HOSPITAL (174004)**, 500 State Hospital Drive, Zip 66064–1813, Mailing Address: P.O. Box 500, Zip 66064–0500; tel. 913/755–7000 **A**1 10 **F**11 30 50 75 86 87 98 101 103 130 132 135 146 **P**6
Primary Contact: Jerry A. Rea, Ph.D., Superintendent
CMO: Maria Gustilo, M.D., Medical Director
CHR: Dezerae Curran, Director Human Resources
Web address: www.srskansas.org/osh/osh–rmhf_info.html
Control: State–Government, nonfederal **Service:** Psychiatric

> **Staffed Beds:** 176 **Admissions:** 2363 **Census:** 175 **Outpatient Visits:** 0
> **Births:** 0 **Total Expense ($000):** 29007 **Payroll Expense ($000):** 16171
> **Personnel:** 399

OSBORNE—Osborne County

★ **OSBORNE COUNTY MEMORIAL HOSPITAL (171364)**, 424 West New Hampshire Street, Zip 67473–2314, Mailing Address: P.O. Box 70, Zip 67473–0070; tel. 785/346–2121 **A**9 10 18 **F**3 11 13 40 45 64 69 76 81 107 128 133 **P**6 **S** Great Plains Health Alliance, Inc., Wichita, KS
Primary Contact: Kiley Floyd, Administrator
CFO: Linda Murphy, Chief Financial Officer
CMO: Barbara Brown, D.O., Chief of Staff
CIO: Kiley Floyd, Administrator
Web address: www.ocmh.org
Control: County–Government, nonfederal **Service:** General Medical and Surgical

> **Staffed Beds:** 25 **Admissions:** 216 **Census:** 7 **Outpatient Visits:** 10912
> **Births:** 14 **Total Expense ($000):** 5900 **Payroll Expense ($000):** 2848
> **Personnel:** 65

OSWEGO—Labette County

★ **OSWEGO COMMUNITY HOSPITAL (171302)**, 800 Barker Drive, Zip 67356–9014; tel. 620/795–2921 **A**9 10 18 **F**3 9 12 32 34 35 40 57 59 64 65 75 77 90 93 107 127 130 132 133 135 147 148 **P**6 **S** Rural Community Hospitals of America, Kansas City, MO
Primary Contact: Daniel Hiben, Chief Executive Officer
CFO: Christina Schlatter, Chief Financial Officer
CMO: Gordon Kern, M.D., Medical Director
CHR: Christina Schlatter, Chief Financial Officer
Web address: www.oswegocommunityhospital.com
Control: Corporation, Investor–owned, for–profit **Service:** General Medical and Surgical

> **Staffed Beds:** 12 **Admissions:** 155 **Census:** 5 **Outpatient Visits:** 8415
> **Births:** 0 **Total Expense ($000):** 4329 **Payroll Expense ($000):** 2218
> **Personnel:** 44

OTTAWA—Franklin County

⊠ **RANSOM MEMORIAL HOSPITAL (170014)**, 1301 South Main Street, Zip 66067–3598; tel. 785/229–8200 **A**1 5 9 10 **F**3 11 13 15 28 30 34 35 36 40 45 46 49 53 56 57 59 64 70 75 76 77 79 81 82 85 86 92 93 96 97 107 108 110 111 115 118 119 129 130 131 132 133 134 135 144 146 147 148 **P**8
Primary Contact: Matthew M. Heyn, Chief Executive Officer
CFO: Dean Ohmart, Assistant Administrator and Chief Financial Officer
Web address: www.ransom.org
Control: County–Government, nonfederal **Service:** General Medical and Surgical

> **Staffed Beds:** 44 **Admissions:** 1447 **Census:** 12 **Outpatient Visits:** 103362
> **Births:** 159 **Total Expense ($000):** 33880 **Payroll Expense ($000):** 17599
> **Personnel:** 293

Hospital, Medicare Provider Number, Address, Telephone, Approval, Facility, and Physician Codes, Health Care System

★ American Hospital Association (AHA) membership
☐ The Joint Commission accreditation   ◇ DNV Healthcare Inc. accreditation
○ Healthcare Facilities Accreditation Program
△ Commission on Accreditation of Rehabilitation Facilities (CARF) accreditation

KS

OVERLAND PARK—Johnson County

☐ **CHILDREN'S MERCY SOUTH (173300)**, 5808 West 110th Street,
Zip 66211–2504; tel. 913/696–8000 **A**1 9 10 **F**3 9 29 30 32 35 36 40 41 44
48 50 59 62 64 68 75 77 79 81 82 85 87 93 94 100 101 104 107 111 114
119 129 130 131 132 134 144 146 148 **P**6 8
Primary Contact: Randall L. O'Donnell, Ph.D., President and Chief Executive Officer
CFO: Sandra A J Lawrence, Executive Vice President and Chief Financial Officer
CMO: Charles Roberts, M.D., Medical Director
CIO: Jean Ann Breedlove, Chief Information Officer
CHR: Dan Wright, Vice President Human Resources
Web address: www.childrens–mercy.org
Control: Other not–for–profit (including NFP Corporation) **Service:** Children's
general

Staffed Beds: 50 **Admissions:** 2162 **Census:** 15 **Outpatient Visits:** 118212
Births: 0 **Total Expense ($000):** 90545 **Payroll Expense ($000):** 51386
Personnel: 616

HEARTLAND SPINE & SPECIALTY HOSPITAL See The University of Kansas
Hospital – Indian Creek Campus

✠ **MENORAH MEDICAL CENTER (170182)**, 5721 West 119th Street,
Zip 66209–3722; tel. 913/498–6000 **A**1 2 9 10 **F**3 12 13 15 18 20 22 24 26
28 29 30 31 34 35 38 40 45 46 47 49 55 57 58 59 60 64 65 68 70 72 74
75 76 77 78 79 81 82 85 86 87 90 93 97 102 107 108 110 111 114 115
117 119 121 124 126 129 130 131 132 135 144 145 146 147 148 **S** HCA,
Nashville, TN
Primary Contact: Steven D. Wilkinson, President and Chief Executive Officer
COO: Lenetra S. King, Chief Operating Officer
CFO: Deborah Gafford, Chief Financial Officer
CMO: Denise K. Miller, M.D., Chief Medical Officer
CIO: Christina McGinnis, Director Information Technology
CHR: Amy Hunt, Director Human Resources
CNO: Kelly Reno, R.N., Chief Nursing Officer
Web address: www.menorahmedicalcenter.com
Control: Corporation, Investor–owned, for–profit **Service:** General Medical and
Surgical

Staffed Beds: 158 **Admissions:** 6773 **Census:** 81 **Outpatient Visits:** 67598
Births: 904 **Total Expense ($000):** 161189 **Payroll Expense ($000):** 47968
Personnel: 728

✠ **OVERLAND PARK REGIONAL MEDICAL CENTER (170176)**, 10500 Quivira
Road, Zip 66215–2306, Mailing Address: P.O. Box 15959, Zip 66215–5959;
tel. 913/541–5000 **A**1 5 9 10 **F**3 13 15 18 20 22 24 26 28 29 30 31 34 35
37 40 43 45 49 50 56 57 59 60 61 64 65 67 70 72 73 74 75 76 77 78 79
81 82 83 84 85 86 87 90 92 93 107 108 110 111 114 115 119 126 129
130 131 135 144 145 146 147 148 **S** HCA, Nashville, TN
Primary Contact: Kevin J. Hicks, President and CEO
COO: Dean Carucci, Chief Operating Officer
CFO: Shari Collier, Chief Financial Officer
CMO: John A. Romito, M.D., Chief Medical Officer
CHR: Connie Miller, Vice President Human Resources
Web address: www.oprmc.com
Control: Corporation, Investor–owned, for–profit **Service:** General Medical and
Surgical

Staffed Beds: 276 **Admissions:** 9955 **Census:** 142 **Outpatient Visits:** 62320
Births: 3001 **Total Expense ($000):** 137747 **Payroll Expense ($000):**
54115 **Personnel:** 775

☐ **PROMISE HOSPITAL OF OVERLAND PARK (172004)**, 6509 West 103rd
Street, Zip 66212–1728; tel. 913/649–3701, (Total facility includes 52 beds in
nursing home–type unit) **A**1 9 10 **F**1 29 60 128 143 **S** Promise Healthcare, Boca
Raton, FL
Primary Contact: Karen Leverich, Chief Executive Officer
CFO: William Scott, Chief Financial Officer
CHR: Darren Enochs, Director Human Resources
Web address: www.promise–overlandpark.com
Control: Corporation, Investor–owned, for–profit **Service:** Long–Term Acute Care
hospital

Staffed Beds: 104 **Admissions:** 644 **Census:** 58 **Outpatient Visits:** 0 **Births:**
0 **Total Expense ($000):** 7272 **Payroll Expense ($000):** 5371 **Personnel:**
119

☒ **SAINT LUKE'S SOUTH HOSPITAL (170185)**, 12300 Metcalf Avenue,
Zip 66213–1324; tel. 913/317–7000 **A**1 9 10 **F**3 8 12 13 15 18 20 22 26 28
29 30 31 34 39 40 45 47 49 54 55 57 58 59 60 64 70 71 72 74 75 76 77
78 79 80 81 82 84 85 86 87 90 92 93 94 96 102 107 108 110 111 114 115
117 118 119 129 130 131 132 141 146 148 **S** Saint Luke's Health System,
Kansas City, MO
Primary Contact: Jani L. Johnson, President and Chief Executive Officer
CFO: Shelby Frigon, Chief Financial Officer
CMO: Bakul Sangani, M.D., President Medical Staff
CIO: Deborah Gash, Chief Information Officer
CHR: Donna Kunz, Manager Human Resources
CNO: Julia Woods, R.N., Vice President and Chief Nursing Officer
Web address: www.saintlukeshealthsystem.org/south
Control: Church–operated, Nongovernment, not–for profit **Service:** General
Medical and Surgical

Staffed Beds: 110 **Admissions:** 5288 **Census:** 57 **Outpatient Visits:** 79521
Births: 857 **Total Expense ($000):** 106194 **Payroll Expense ($000):** 33491
Personnel: 464

PAOLA—Miami County

☐ **MIAMI COUNTY MEDICAL CENTER (170109)**, 2100 Baptiste Drive,
Zip 66071–1314, Mailing Address: P.O. Box 365, Zip 66071–0365;
tel. 913/294–2327 **A**1 5 9 10 **F**3 11 30 40 43 59 61 64 68 75 77 78 79 81
82 85 87 89 90 93 107 108 110 111 114 119 127 129 130 131 146 148
Primary Contact: Paul W. Luce, R.N., MSN, Vice President Operations
Web address: www.olathehealth.org
Control: Other not–for–profit (including NFP Corporation) **Service:** General
Medical and Surgical

Staffed Beds: 18 **Admissions:** 402 **Census:** 3 **Outpatient Visits:** 29676
Births: 0 **Personnel:** 121

PARSONS—Labette County

★ ○ **LABETTE HEALTH (170120)**, 1902 South U.S. Highway 59,
Zip 67357–7404; tel. 620/421–4880 **A**9 10 11 19 20 **F**3 11 13 15 29 30 34
40 43 50 53 57 59 62 70 75 76 77 79 81 82 85 86 90 93 97 107 111 114 119
127 129 130 131 132 143 144 146 147 148 **P**6
Primary Contact: Jodi A. Schmidt, President and Chief Executive Officer
CFO: Thomas Macaronas, Chief Financial Officer
CHR: Christina Sykes, Director Human Resources
Web address: www.labettehealth.com
Control: County–Government, nonfederal **Service:** General Medical and Surgical

Staffed Beds: 55 **Admissions:** 2411 **Census:** 23 **Outpatient Visits:** 71121
Births: 218 **Total Expense ($000):** 60596 **Payroll Expense ($000):** 24526
Personnel: 540

PARSONS STATE HOSPITAL AND TRAINING CENTER, 2601 Gabriel Avenue,
Zip 67357–2341, Mailing Address: P.O. Box 738, Zip 67357–0738;
tel. 620/421–6550 **F**35 39 67 130 146
Primary Contact: Jerry A. Rea, Ph.D., Superintendent
CFO: John Spare, Accountant
CMO: Rema Menon, M.D., Clinical Director
CIO: Ron Malmstrom, Information Research Specialist
CHR: Tim B. Posch, Business Manager and Director Personnel
Web address: www.pshtc.org
Control: State–Government, nonfederal **Service:** Institution for mental retardation

Staffed Beds: 188 **Admissions:** 20 **Census:** 176 **Outpatient Visits:** 0 **Births:**
0 **Total Expense ($000):** 26991 **Payroll Expense ($000):** 16344
Personnel: 430

PHILLIPSBURG—Phillips County

★ **PHILLIPS COUNTY HOSPITAL (171353)**, 1150 State Street, Zip 67661–1743,
Mailing Address: P.O. Box 607, Zip 67661–0607; tel. 785/543–5226 **A**9 10 18
F3 11 15 28 30 31 40 45 50 59 64 68 75 77 78 81 86 87 93 107 114 119
127 128 130 132 133 145 146 148 **P**6 **S** Great Plains Health Alliance, Inc.,
Wichita, KS
Primary Contact: David Engel, Chief Executive Officer
CFO: Christi Driggs, Chief Financial Officer
CMO: Ben Stephenson, M.D., Chief of Staff
CIO: Steven Seems, Director of Information Technology
CHR: Peggy Fabin, Director Human Resources
CNO: Gail Boaldin, R.N., Director Nursing
Web address: www.phillipshospital.org
Control: Other not–for–profit (including NFP Corporation) **Service:** General
Medical and Surgical

Staffed Beds: 25 **Admissions:** 227 **Census:** 5 **Outpatient Visits:** 25789
Births: 1 **Total Expense ($000):** 9481 **Payroll Expense ($000):** 4263
Personnel: 94

KS

Many Facility Codes have changed. Please refer to the AHA Guide Code Chart. © 2014 AHA Guide

PITTSBURG—Crawford County

⊠ **VIA CHRISTI HOSPITAL IN PITTSBURG (170006)**, 1 Mt. Carmel Way,
Zip 66762–7587; tel. 620/232–0109 **A**1 2 5 9 10 **F**3 5 8 11 12 13 15 18 20
22 26 28 29 30 31 34 35 40 42 43 45 46 47 48 50 51 53 54 56 57 58 59
62 64 68 69 70 71 73 75 76 77 78 79 80 81 82 84 85 86 89 90 93 99 100
101 103 104 107 108 109 110 111 112 114 115 116 117 118 119 120 121
122 123 126 129 130 131 132 133 135 143 144 145 146 147 148 **P**8
S Ascension Health, Saint Louis, MO
Primary Contact: Randall R. Cason, FACHE, President and Chief Executive Officer
COO: Drew Talbott, Vice President Operations
CFO: Mike Joy, Chief Financial Officer
CIO: Troy Mascher, Director Information Systems
CHR: Connie McCune, Vice President Human Resources
Web address: www.viachristi.org
Control: Church–operated, Nongovernment, not–for profit **Service:** General
Medical and Surgical

Staffed Beds: 111 **Admissions:** 3007 **Census:** 37 **Outpatient Visits:** 86975
Births: 383 **Total Expense ($000):** 63636 **Payroll Expense ($000):** 27550
Personnel: 663

PLAINVILLE—Rooks County

★ **ROOKS COUNTY HEALTH CENTER (171311)**, 1210 North Washington Street,
Zip 67663–1632, Mailing Address: P.O. Box 389, Zip 67663–0389;
tel. 785/434–4553 **A**5 9 10 18 **F**3 11 13 15 18 28 31 34 35 40 43 45 50 57
59 64 67 76 77 81 87 93 96 102 107 110 114 119 125 128 130 133 135
143 144 146 147 148
Primary Contact: Michael Sinclair, Chief Executive Officer
COO: William D. Stahl, Chief Operating Officer
CFO: Julie Price, Chief Financial Officer
CMO: Lynn Fisher, M.D., Chief of Staff
CIO: Kathy Ramsay, R.N., Director Communications and Development
CHR: Cindi Knipp, Director Human Resources
Web address: www.rookscountyhealthcenter.com
Control: Hospital district or authority, Government, nonfederal **Service:** General
Medical and Surgical

Staffed Beds: 20 **Admissions:** 423 **Census:** 7 **Outpatient Visits:** 21427
Births: 28 **Total Expense ($000):** 12724 **Payroll Expense ($000):** 4951
Personnel: 118

PRATT—Pratt County

★ **PRATT REGIONAL MEDICAL CENTER (170027)**, 200 Commodore Street,
Zip 67124–2903; tel. 620/672–7451, (Total facility includes 47 beds in nursing
home–type unit) **A**5 9 10 20 **F**3 15 30 31 34 40 45 49 56 57 59 61 62
64 68 69 70 75 76 77 79 81 82 85 86 87 89 90 93 107 108 114 118 119
124 127 128 130 131 133 145 146 147 148 **P**6
Primary Contact: Susan M. Page, President and Chief Executive Officer
CFO: Vincent Scot Wilczek, Vice President and Chief Financial Officer
CIO: Vikki Mader, Director Health Information Services
CHR: Ken Brown, Vice President and Chief Human Resource Officer
CNO: Sherry L. Besser, R.N., Vice President Quality, Risk Management and Chief
Nursing Officer
Web address: www.prmc.org
Control: Other not–for–profit (including NFP Corporation) **Service:** General
Medical and Surgical

Staffed Beds: 85 **Admissions:** 1477 **Census:** 53 **Outpatient Visits:** 82515
Births: 273 **Total Expense ($000):** 37853 **Payroll Expense ($000):** 18621
Personnel: 352

QUINTER—Gove County

GOVE COUNTY MEDICAL CENTER (171367), 520 West Fifth Street,
Zip 67752–9705, Mailing Address: P.O. Box 129, Zip 67752–0129;
tel. 785/754–3341, (Total facility includes 45 beds in nursing home–type unit) **A**5
9 10 18 **F**3 11 13 28 29 31 34 40 45 57 62 67 75 81 93 107 119 125 133
135 143 148
Primary Contact: Richard Q. Bergling, Chief Executive Officer
CFO: Alan Waites, Chief Financial Officer
CIO: Brad Mullins, Director Information Technology
CHR: Valerie Schneider, Director Human Resources
CNO: Annie Staats, R.N., Director Nursing
Web address: www.gcmc.ws
Control: County–Government, nonfederal **Service:** General Medical and Surgical

Staffed Beds: 66 **Admissions:** 705 **Census:** 45 **Outpatient Visits:** 9648
Births: 66 **Total Expense ($000):** 13213 **Payroll Expense ($000):** 5985
Personnel: 171

RANSOM—Ness County

★ **GRISELL MEMORIAL HOSPITAL DISTRICT ONE (171300)**, 210 South
Vermont Avenue, Zip 67572–9525; tel. 785/731–2231, (Total facility includes 34
beds in nursing home–type unit) **A**9 10 18 **F**3 40 56 67 69 85 93 97 127 128
133 **P**6 **S** Great Plains Health Alliance, Inc., Wichita, KS
Primary Contact: Kristine Ochs, R.N., Administrator
CFO: Misty Beach, Chief Financial Officer
CMO: Allen McLain, M.D., Chief of Staff
CNO: Joni Pfaff, Chief Nursing Officer
Web address: www.grisellmemorialhospital.org
Control: Hospital district or authority, Government, nonfederal **Service:** General
Medical and Surgical

Staffed Beds: 46 **Admissions:** 81 **Census:** 33 **Outpatient Visits:** 7223
Births: 0 **Total Expense ($000):** 5004 **Payroll Expense ($000):** 2475
Personnel: 72

RUSSELL—Russell County

★ **RUSSELL REGIONAL HOSPITAL (171350)**, 200 South Main Street,
Zip 67665–2920; tel. 785/483–3131, (Total facility includes 21 beds in nursing
home–type unit) **A**9 10 18 **F**11 15 29 30 32 34 35 40 50 53 57 59 64 65 66
67 69 75 85 87 93 107 108 110 115 119 127 130 131 133 135 145 146
147 148 **P**6
Primary Contact: Harold Courtois, Chief Executive Officer
CFO: Kevin Kreutzer, Chief Financial Officer
CMO: Earl Merkel, M.D., Chief of Staff
CIO: David Schraeder, Director Information Systems
CHR: Sharon Collins, Director Human Resources and Executive Administrative
Assistant
CNO: Karen Deatherage, Director of Nursing
Web address: www.russellhospital.org
Control: Other not–for–profit (including NFP Corporation) **Service:** General
Medical and Surgical

Staffed Beds: 46 **Admissions:** 394 **Census:** 25 **Outpatient Visits:** 22128
Births: 0 **Total Expense ($000):** 13238 **Payroll Expense ($000):** 6737
Personnel: 168

SABETHA—Nemaha County

★ **SABETHA COMMUNITY HOSPITAL (171338)**, 14th and Oregon Streets,
Zip 66534–0229, Mailing Address: P.O. Box 229, Zip 66534–0229;
tel. 785/284–2121 **A**9 10 18 **F**3 11 13 15 28 34 35 40 45 50 56 57 59 62
63 64 68 75 76 77 79 81 82 84 85 86 93 107 110 114 119 128 130 132
133 146 148 **P**6 **S** Great Plains Health Alliance, Inc., Wichita, KS
Primary Contact: Lora Key, Chief Executive Officer
CFO: Lori Lackey, Chief Financial Officer
CMO: Gregg Wenger, M.D., Chief of Staff
CIO: Holli Dieckmann, Director Health Information
CHR: Julie K. Holthaus, Director Human Resources
CNO: Stacy Scott, Director Nursing
Web address: www.sabethahospital.com
Control: Other not–for–profit (including NFP Corporation) **Service:** General
Medical and Surgical

Staffed Beds: 25 **Admissions:** 381 **Census:** 5 **Outpatient Visits:** 41328
Births: 69 **Total Expense ($000):** 10864 **Payroll Expense ($000):** 5226
Personnel: 113

SAINT FRANCIS—Cheyenne County

★ **CHEYENNE COUNTY HOSPITAL (171310)**, 210 West First Street,
Zip 67756–3540, Mailing Address: P.O. Box 547, Zip 67756–0547;
tel. 785/332–2104 **A**5 9 10 18 **F**3 8 11 13 28 29 31 40 57 59 64 65 66 68
76 77 78 81 85 89 93 97 107 119 127 128 133 148 **P**6 **S** Great Plains Health
Alliance, Inc., Wichita, KS
Primary Contact: Scott Jenkins, Administrator
CFO: Heidi Tice, Chief Financial Officer
CMO: Mary Beth Miller, M.D., Chief of Staff
CIO: Carol Sloper, Manager Information Technology
CHR: Sara Wilson, Director Human Resources
CNO: Judith Ann Hodgson, Chief Nursing Officer
Web address: www.cheyennecountyhospital.com
Control: Other not–for–profit (including NFP Corporation) **Service:** General
Medical and Surgical

Staffed Beds: 16 **Admissions:** 363 **Census:** 4 **Outpatient Visits:** 18466
Births: 12 **Total Expense ($000):** 8546 **Payroll Expense ($000):** 4144
Personnel: 77

Hospital, Medicare Provider Number, Address, Telephone, Approval, Facility, and Physician Codes, Health Care System

★ American Hospital Association (AHA) membership
□ The Joint Commission accreditation   ◇ DNV Healthcare Inc. accreditation
○ Healthcare Facilities Accreditation Program
△ Commission on Accreditation of Rehabilitation Facilities (CARF) accreditation

KS

SALINA—Saline County

★ ○ **SALINA REGIONAL HEALTH CENTER (170012)**, 400 South Santa Fe Avenue, Zip 67401-4198, Mailing Address: P.O. Box 5080, Zip 67402-5080; tel. 785/452-7000, (Includes SALINA REGIONAL HEALTH CENTER– PENN CAMPUS, 139 North Penn Street, Zip 67401, Mailing Address: P.O. Box 5080, Zip 67402-5080; tel. 913/452-7000; SALINA REGIONAL HEALTH CENTER–SANTA FE CAMPUS, 400 South Santa Fe Avenue, Zip 67401, Mailing Address: Box 5080, Zip 67402-5080; tel. 913/452-7000) **A**2 3 5 9 10 11 20 **F**3 13 15 20 22 24 28 29 30 31 35 40 43 45 46 47 48 49 51 53 54 57 59 63 64 65 68 70 71 72 73 74 76 77 78 79 81 85 86 87 89 90 98 99 100 101 102 103 104 105 107 108 110 111 114 115 116 117 118 119 120 121 122 123 126 129 130 143 144 145 146 147 148 **P**6
Primary Contact: Micheal Terry, President and Chief Executive Officer
COO: Joel Phelps, Chief Operating Officer
CFO: Joe Tallon, Vice President Finance
CIO: Larry Barnes, Vice President Information Technology
CHR: David Moody, Vice President Human Resources
Web address: www.srhc.com
Control: Other not-for-profit (including NFP Corporation) **Service:** General Medical and Surgical

Staffed Beds: 198 **Admissions:** 8654 **Census:** 107 **Outpatient Visits:** 181054 **Births:** 1157 **Total Expense ($000):** 160773 **Payroll Expense ($000):** 70242 **Personnel:** 1316

SALINA SURGICAL HOSPITAL (170187), 401 South Sante Fe, Zip 67401-4143; tel. 785/827-0610 **A**9 10 **F**29 45 48 49 51 74 79 81 85 89 131
Primary Contact: LuAnn Puvogel, R.N., Administrator
CFO: Elizabeth Bishop, Manager Business Office
CMO: Michael Johnson, M.D., Medical Director
CIO: Earl Akers, Supervisor Information Technology
CHR: Elizabeth Bishop, Manager Business Office
CNO: Jolene Glavin, R.N., Director Nursing
Web address: www.salinasurgical.com/
Control: Partnership, Investor-owned, for-profit **Service:** Surgical

Staffed Beds: 16 **Admissions:** 620 **Census:** 5 **Outpatient Visits:** 7736 **Births:** 0 **Total Expense ($000):** 16090 **Payroll Expense ($000):** 4764 **Personnel:** 88

SATANTA—Haskell County

★ **SATANTA DISTRICT HOSPITAL (171324)**, 401 South Cheyenne Street, Zip 67870-0159, Mailing Address: P.O. Box 159, Zip 67870-0159; tel. 620/649-2761, (Total facility includes 44 beds in nursing home–type unit) **A**9 10 18 **F**3 11 40 45 57 64 67 68 75 81 82 87 93 104 107 119 127 128 130 133 **P**4 **S** Great Plains Health Alliance, Inc., Wichita, KS
Primary Contact: Jeremy Clingenpeel, Administrator
CFO: Libby Anderson, Chief Financial Officer
CMO: Virgilio Taduran, M.D., Chief Medical Officer
CIO: Ben Leppke, Chief Information Officer
CHR: Samantha Hett, Manager Human Resources
CNO: Tina Pendergraft, Chief Nursing Officer
Web address: www.satantahospital.org
Control: Hospital district or authority, Government, nonfederal **Service:** General Medical and Surgical

Staffed Beds: 57 **Admissions:** 234 **Census:** 43 **Outpatient Visits:** 26115 **Births:** 0 **Total Expense ($000):** 12315 **Payroll Expense ($000):** 5550 **Personnel:** 132

SCOTT CITY—Scott County

★ **SCOTT COUNTY HOSPITAL (171372)**, 201 East Albert Avenue, Zip 67871-1203; tel. 620/872-5811 **A**9 10 18 **F**3 7 13 15 28 29 30 31 35 40 45 46 50 57 59 62 64 68 69 75 76 77 81 82 85 93 107 110 119 127 128 130 133 135 148 **P**6
Primary Contact: Mark Burnett, President and Chief Executive Officer
COO: Karma Huck, Chief Operating Officer
CFO: Joe S. Meyer, Chief Financial Officer
CMO: Elizabeth Hineman, M.D., Chief Medical Staff
CHR: Pamela R. Wheeler, Manager Human Resources
Web address: www.scotthospital.net
Control: Other not-for-profit (including NFP Corporation) **Service:** General Medical and Surgical

Staffed Beds: 22 **Admissions:** 660 **Census:** 10 **Outpatient Visits:** 17470 **Births:** 54 **Total Expense ($000):** 16608 **Payroll Expense ($000):** 8219 **Personnel:** 204

SEDAN—Chautauqua County

SEDAN CITY HOSPITAL (171318), 300 North Street, Zip 67361-1051, Mailing Address: P.O. Box C, Zip 67361-0427; tel. 620/725-3115 **A**9 10 18 **F**29 34 40 57 64 93 107 128 130 133 148
Primary Contact: Michelle Williams, Administrator
CFO: Jennifer Seever, Regional Chief Financial Officer
CMO: James McDermott, M.D., Chief of Staff
Control: City-Government, nonfederal **Service:** General Medical and Surgical

Staffed Beds: 25 **Admissions:** 198 **Census:** 2 **Outpatient Visits:** 7556 **Births:** 0 **Total Expense ($000):** 3750 **Payroll Expense ($000):** 1720 **Personnel:** 38

SENECA—Nemaha County

★ **NEMAHA VALLEY COMMUNITY HOSPITAL (171315)**, 1600 Community Drive, Zip 66538-9739; tel. 785/336-6181 **A**9 10 18 **F**11 12 13 15 28 31 40 56 57 59 64 75 77 78 79 81 84 85 89 93 107 114 119 127 129 130 131 132 133 **P**6
Primary Contact: Stan Regehr, President and Chief Executive Officer
CFO: Connie Ingwerson, Chief Financial Officer
CHR: Lynn Hartter, Director Human Resources
CNO: Lynda Cross, R.N., Director of Nurses
Web address: www.nemvch.org
Control: Other not-for-profit (including NFP Corporation) **Service:** General Medical and Surgical

Staffed Beds: 24 **Admissions:** 222 **Census:** 3 **Outpatient Visits:** 19100 **Births:** 56 **Total Expense ($000):** 10849 **Payroll Expense ($000):** 5319 **Personnel:** 119

SHAWNEE MISSION—Johnson County

✠ **MID–AMERICA REHABILITATION HOSPITAL (173026)**, 5701 West 110th Street, Zip 66211-2503; tel. 913/491-2400 **A**1 10 **F**29 35 56 64 86 87 90 91 93 95 96 130 132 143 148 **S** HEALTHSOUTH Corporation, Birmingham, AL
Primary Contact: Troy DeDecker, Chief Executive Officer
CFO: Richard Lane, Chief Financial Officer
CMO: Cielo Dehning, M.D., Medical Director
CHR: Cathy Loudon, Director Human Resources
CNO: Amy McKay, Chief Nursing Officer
Web address: www.midamericarehabhospital.com
Control: Corporation, Investor-owned, for-profit **Service:** Rehabilitation

Staffed Beds: 98 **Admissions:** 2070 **Census:** 72 **Outpatient Visits:** 9428 **Births:** 0 **Total Expense ($000):** 25535 **Payroll Expense ($000):** 12824 **Personnel:** 242

✠ **SHAWNEE MISSION MEDICAL CENTER (170104)**, 9100 West 74th Street, Zip 66204-4004, Mailing Address: Box 2923, Zip 66201-1323; tel. 913/676-2000 **A**1 2 3 5 9 10 **F**3 4 5 8 11 12 13 15 17 18 20 22 24 28 29 30 31 32 34 35 36 40 42 45 46 47 48 49 52 53 54 55 56 57 58 59 60 61 62 64 65 67 70 72 74 75 76 77 78 79 81 82 83 84 85 86 87 89 93 96 97 98 100 101 102 103 104 105 107 108 110 111 114 115 117 118 119 120 121 123 124 126 129 130 131 132 135 144 145 146 147 148 **P**6 **S** Adventist Health System Sunbelt Health Care Corporation, Altamonte Springs, FL
Primary Contact: Ken J. Bacon, President and Chief Executive Officer
COO: Trevor Wright, Senior Vice President and Chief Operating Officer
CFO: Karsten Randolph, Executive Vice President and Chief Financial Officer
CMO: Sherri Martin, M.D., President Medical Staff
CIO: Mike Allen, Director Information Services
CHR: Brad Hoffman, Administrative Director Human Resources
CNO: Sheri Hawkins, Chief Nursing Officer
Web address: www.shawneemission.org
Control: Church-operated, Nongovernment, not-for profit **Service:** General Medical and Surgical

Staffed Beds: 393 **Admissions:** 19896 **Census:** 216 **Outpatient Visits:** 534781 **Births:** 4464 **Total Expense ($000):** 337900 **Payroll Expense ($000):** 138169 **Personnel:** 2438

SMITH CENTER—Smith County

★ **SMITH COUNTY MEMORIAL HOSPITAL (171377)**, 614 South Main Street, Zip 66967-3001; tel. 785/282-6845, (Total facility includes 28 beds in nursing home–type unit) **A**5 9 10 18 **F**2 13 15 28 30 31 40 45 53 64 67 68 69 75 76 81 85 93 107 114 119 127 128 133 **P**6 **S** Great Plains Health Alliance, Inc., Wichita, KS
Primary Contact: Allen Van Driel, FACHE, Administrator
CFO: Julie Williams, Chief Financial Officer
CIO: Tammy Gaston, Chief Information Officer
CHR: Jody Maxwell, Manager Business Office
CNO: Sarah Ragsdale, R.N., Chief Nursing Officer
Web address: www.gpha.com
Control: Other not-for-profit (including NFP Corporation) **Service:** General Medical and Surgical

Staffed Beds: 53 **Admissions:** 413 **Census:** 30 **Outpatient Visits:** 24005 **Births:** 27 **Total Expense ($000):** 10370 **Payroll Expense ($000):** 4849 **Personnel:** 119

STAFFORD—Stafford County

★ **STAFFORD COUNTY HOSPITAL (171323)**, 502 South Buckeye Street, Zip 67578-2035, Mailing Address: P.O. Box 190, Zip 67578-0190; tel. 620/234-5221 **A**9 10 18 **F**3 15 29 35 40 57 59 62 64 67 77 93 107 128 130 133 **P**5
Primary Contact: Todd Taylor, Chief Executive Officer
CFO: MeKinzie Hudson, Chief Financial Officer
Web address: www.staffordcountyhospital.org
Control: Hospital district or authority, Government, nonfederal **Service:** General Medical and Surgical

Staffed Beds: 25 **Admissions:** 69 **Census:** 6 **Outpatient Visits:** 39868 **Births:** 0 **Total Expense ($000):** 3621 **Payroll Expense ($000):** 1595 **Personnel:** 43

Many Facility Codes have changed. Please refer to the AHA Guide Code Chart. © 2014 AHA Guide

SYRACUSE—Hamilton County

★ **HAMILTON COUNTY HOSPITAL (171322)**, 700 North Huser Street,
Zip 67878–0948, Mailing Address: P.O. Box 948, Zip 67878–0948;
tel. 620/384–7461, (Total facility includes 44 beds in nursing home–type unit) **A**9
10 18 **F**3 18 35 40 50 56 57 59 64 68 81 86 93 97 107 114 125 127 128
130 133 **P**6
Primary Contact: Bryan D. Coffey, Chief Executive Officer
CMO: John Carey, M.D., Chief Medical Director
CIO: Mark Kleymann, Manager Information Technology
CHR: Angela Talbot, Manager Human Resources
Web address: www.myhch.org
Control: County–Government, nonfederal **Service:** General Medical and Surgical

Staffed Beds: 69 **Admissions:** 274 **Census:** 29 **Outpatient Visits:** 5173
Births: 0 **Total Expense ($000):** 6353 **Payroll Expense ($000):** 3222
Personnel: 87

TOPEKA—Shawnee County

COLMERY–O'NEIL VETERANS AFFAIRS MEDICAL CENTER See Veterans
Affairs Eastern Kansas Health Care System

KANSAS NEUROLOGICAL INSTITUTE, 3107 West 21st Street,
Zip 66604–3298; tel. 785/296–5301 **F**29 30 35 39 67 91 97 130 143 146 **P**6
Primary Contact: Brent Widick, Interim Superintendent
CFO: Sara Mock, Director Administrative Services
CMO: Kimberley Scott, Director Health Care Services
CIO: Cheryl Fuller, Director Information Resources
CHR: Shawna Mercer, Director Human Resources
Web address: www.srsnet.srs.ks.gov/hospitals/kni/
Control: State–Government, nonfederal **Service:** Institution for mental retardation

Staffed Beds: 153 **Admissions:** 1 **Census:** 150 **Outpatient Visits:** 0 **Births:**
0 **Total Expense ($000):** 28812 **Payroll Expense ($000):** 15468
Personnel: 447

⊞ **KANSAS REHABILITATION HOSPITAL (173025)**, 1504 S.W. Eighth Avenue,
Zip 66606–1632; tel. 785/235–6600 **A**1 9 10 **F**29 53 62 64 75 86 90 91 93
95 96 130 132 148 **S** HEALTHSOUTH Corporation, Birmingham, AL
Primary Contact: William J. Overbey, Chief Executive Officer
CMO: Joseph Sankoorikal, M.D., Chief Medical Staff
CHR: Dina Cox, Director Human Resources
CNO: Carol Swanger, Chief Nursing Officer
Web address: www.kansasrehabhospital.com
Control: Corporation, Investor–owned, for–profit **Service:** Rehabilitation

Staffed Beds: 59 **Admissions:** 1203 **Census:** 40 **Outpatient Visits:** 15426
Births: 0 **Total Expense ($000):** 15927 **Payroll Expense ($000):** 8268
Personnel: 164

⊞ **SELECT SPECIALTY HOSPITAL–TOPEKA (172006)**, 1700 S.W. Seventh
Street, Suite 840, Zip 66606–1660; tel. 785/295–5551 **A**1 10 **F**1 3 29 75 77
85 87 130 148 **S** Select Medical Corporation, Mechanicsburg, PA
Primary Contact: Linda Sherman, Chief Executive Officer
CMO: Jed McKee, M.D., Medical Director
CNO: Sarah Herrmann, R.N., Chief Nursing Officer
Web address: www.selectspecialtyhospitals.com/company/locations/topeka.aspx
Control: Corporation, Investor–owned, for–profit **Service:** Long–Term Acute Care
hospital

Staffed Beds: 34 **Admissions:** 311 **Census:** 22 **Outpatient Visits:** 0 **Births:**
0 **Total Expense ($000):** 10599 **Payroll Expense ($000):** 4851 **Personnel:**
87

⊞ △ **ST. FRANCIS HEALTH CENTER (170016)**, 1700 S.W. 7th Street,
Zip 66606–1690; tel. 785/295–8000 **A**1 2 7 9 10 **F**3 12 13 15 18 20 22 24
26 28 29 30 31 34 35 36 37 38 40 45 47 48 49 50 51 53 54 56 57 58 59
60 61 62 64 65 70 71 73 74 75 76 77 78 79 80 81 82 85 86 87 89 90 92
93 95 96 107 108 110 111 114 115 116 117 118 119 120 121 123 126
130 131 132 135 144 146 147 **P**6 **S** SCL Health System, Denver, CO
Primary Contact: Robert J. Erickson, Chief Executive Officer
COO: David P. Setchel, Chief Operating Officer
CFO: Debra Cartwright, Chief Financial Officer
CMO: Thomas Hamilton, D.O., Chief Medical Officer
CIO: Kevin Mapes, Director Kansas Division System and Technology Service
Center
CHR: Steve Saffa, Director Human Resources
CNO: Scott E. Wells, MSN, Chief Nursing Officer
Web address: www.stfrancistopeka.org
Control: Church–operated, Nongovernment, not–for profit **Service:** General
Medical and Surgical

Staffed Beds: 274 **Admissions:** 8505 **Census:** 111 **Outpatient Visits:**
491192 **Births:** 921 **Total Expense ($000):** 244870 **Payroll Expense
($000):** 103809 **Personnel:** 1470

⊞ **STORMONT–VAIL HEALTHCARE (170086)**, 1500 S.W. Tenth Avenue,
Zip 66604–1353; tel. 785/354–6000 **A**1 2 5 9 10 **F**3 11 12 13 15 17 18 19
20 22 24 26 28 29 30 31 34 35 37 40 43 44 45 47 49 51 55 56 57 58 59
60 61 64 65 68 70 71 72 74 75 76 77 78 79 81 82 84 85 86 87 88 89 91
93 97 98 99 101 102 103 104 105 107 108 110 111 112 114 115 117 119
120 121 123 129 130 131 132 135 143 144 145 146 147 148 **P**6
Primary Contact: Randall Peterson, President and Chief Executive Officer
COO: Janet Stanek, Executive Vice President
CFO: Kevin Han, Vice President and Chief Financial Officer
CMO: Kent Palmberg, M.D., Senior Vice President and Chief Medical Officer
CIO: Judy Corzine, Administrative Director and Chief Information Officer
CHR: Bernard H. Becker, Vice President and Chief Human Resources Officer
CNO: Carol Perry, R.N., Vice President and Chief Nursing Officer
Web address: www.stormontvail.org
Control: Other not–for–profit (including NFP Corporation) **Service:** General
Medical and Surgical

Staffed Beds: 394 **Admissions:** 19744 **Census:** 243 **Outpatient Visits:**
126787 **Births:** 1889 **Total Expense ($000):** 495839 **Payroll Expense
($000):** 256236 **Personnel:** 3604

⊞ **VETERANS AFFAIRS EASTERN KANSAS HEALTH CARE SYSTEM**, 2200 Gage
Boulevard, Zip 66622–0002; tel. 785/350–3111, (Includes COLMERY–O'NEIL
VETERANS AFFAIRS MEDICAL CENTER, 2200 Gage Boulevard,
tel. 785/350–3111; DWIGHT D. EISENHOWER VETERANS AFFAIRS MEDICAL
CENTER, 4101 S. 4th Street Trafficway, Leavenworth, Zip 66048–5055;
tel. 913/682–2000), (Nonreporting) **A**1 3 5 **S** Department of Veterans Affairs,
Washington, DC
Primary Contact: Anthony Rudy Klopfer, FACHE, Director
COO: John Moon, Associate Director
CMO: Rajeev Trehan, M.D., Chief of Staff
CIO: Joni Davin, Director Information and Business Management Service Line
Web address: www.topeka.va.gov/
Control: Veterans Affairs, Government, federal **Service:** General Medical and
Surgical

Staffed Beds: 213

TRIBUNE—Greeley County

★ **GREELEY COUNTY HEALTH SERVICES (171359)**, 506 Third Street,
Zip 67879–9684, Mailing Address: P.O. Box 338, Zip 67879–0338;
tel. 620/376–4221, (Total facility includes 32 beds in nursing home–type unit) **A**5
9 10 18 **F**3 28 40 45 59 64 65 66 69 81 92 93 97 107 111 127 133 147
S QHR, Brentwood, TN
Primary Contact: Lee Rhodes, Interim Administrator and Chief Executive Officer
CFO: Jennifer Deal, Chief Financial Officer
CMO: Wendel Ellis, D.O., Chief Medical Staff
CIO: Shanon Schneider, Chief Information Officer
CHR: Katelyn Reynolds, Manager Human Resources
CNO: Amy Baehler, Director Nursing
Web address: www.mygchs.com
Control: Other not–for–profit (including NFP Corporation) **Service:** General
Medical and Surgical

Staffed Beds: 50 **Admissions:** 362 **Census:** 32 **Outpatient Visits:** 10119
Births: 0 **Total Expense ($000):** 9927 **Payroll Expense ($000):** 4767
Personnel: 111

ULYSSES—Grant County

★ **BOB WILSON MEMORIAL GRANT COUNTY HOSPITAL (170110)**, 415 North
Main Street, Zip 67880–2133; tel. 620/356–1266 **A**9 10 20 **F**3 11 13 15 29
30 34 35 40 45 50 57 59 62 64 68 75 79 81 82 85 86 87 91 93 96 97 107
119 127 130 133 146 148 **P**6
Primary Contact: Arthur H. Frable, Chief Executive Officer
CFO: Robert Jacobi, Chief Financial Officer
CIO: Chris Moffet, Director Information Services
CHR: Tammy Oxford, Director Human Resources
Web address: www.bwmgch.com
Control: County–Government, nonfederal **Service:** General Medical and Surgical

Staffed Beds: 26 **Admissions:** 366 **Census:** 4 **Outpatient Visits:** 10095
Births: 74 **Total Expense ($000):** 11651 **Payroll Expense ($000):** 5227
Personnel: 124

Hospital, Medicare Provider Number, Address, Telephone, Approval, Facility, and Physician Codes, Health Care System

★ American Hospital Association (AHA) membership
☐ The Joint Commission accreditation
◇ DNV Healthcare Inc. accreditation
○ Healthcare Facilities Accreditation Program
△ Commission on Accreditation of Rehabilitation Facilities (CARF) accreditation

KS

WAKEENEY—Trego County

★ **TREGO COUNTY–LEMKE MEMORIAL HOSPITAL (171355)**, 320 North 13th Street, Zip 67672–2099; tel. 785/743–2182, (Total facility includes 37 beds in nursing home–type unit) **A**9 10 18 **F**3 8 10 11 15 28 29 34 40 45 53 57 59 62 64 67 69 71 81 86 89 93 107 110 114 127 128 130 133 143 146 148 **P**6 **S** Great Plains Health Alliance, Inc., Wichita, KS
Primary Contact: David Augustine, Interim Chief Executive Officer
CFO: Gail Jensen, Chief Financial Officer
CMO: Gordon Lang, M.D., Chief of Staff
CIO: Jolene Schuster, Director Information Technology
CHR: Cindy Meiar, Human Resources and Payroll Coordinator
CNO: Sandy Purinton, Chief Nursing Officer
Web address: www.tclmh.org
Control: County–Government, nonfederal **Service:** General Medical and Surgical

Staffed Beds: 62 **Admissions:** 940 **Census:** 52 **Outpatient Visits:** 34709 **Births:** 0 **Total Expense ($000):** 16433 **Payroll Expense ($000):** 7455 **Personnel:** 168

WAMEGO—Pottawatomie County

★ **WAMEGO HEALTH CENTER (171337)**, 711 Genn Drive, Zip 66547–1179; tel. 785/456–2295 **A**9 10 18 **F**3 11 15 29 32 34 35 40 45 56 59 64 65 75 77 81 93 97 107 114 119 127 130 132 133 142 143 146 147 148 **P**6
Primary Contact: Shannan Flach, Chief Executive Officer
COO: Brian Smith, Director Risk Management, Quality and Safety
CFO: Keith Zachariasen, Chief Financial Officer
CMO: Roland Darey, M.D., Medical Director
CIO: Wes Janzen, Chief Information Officer
CHR: Renee Reed, Director Human Resources
CNO: Tresha Flanary, R.N., Chief Clinical Services Officer
Web address: www.wamegocityhospital.com
Control: Other not–for–profit (including NFP Corporation) **Service:** General Medical and Surgical

Staffed Beds: 18 **Admissions:** 158 **Census:** 3 **Outpatient Visits:** 14460 **Births:** 1 **Total Expense ($000):** 7116 **Payroll Expense ($000):** 3561 **Personnel:** 103

WASHINGTON—Washington County

WASHINGTON COUNTY HOSPITAL (171351), 304 East Third Street, Zip 66968–2033; tel. 785/325–2211 **A**5 9 10 18 **F**2 3 11 13 15 28 29 30 31 35 40 45 53 57 64 67 70 81 85 93 107 114 128 130 133 148
Primary Contact: Roxanne Schottel, Chief Executive Officer
CFO: Linda Rettig, Director Financial Services
Web address: www.washingtoncountyhospital.com
Control: County–Government, nonfederal **Service:** General Medical and Surgical

Staffed Beds: 25 **Admissions:** 118 **Census:** 6 **Outpatient Visits:** 4548 **Births:** 13 **Total Expense ($000):** 4168 **Payroll Expense ($000):** 1681 **Personnel:** 46

WELLINGTON—Sumner County

★ **SUMNER REGIONAL MEDICAL CENTER (170039)**, 1323 North A Street, Zip 67152–4350; tel. 620/326–7451, (Total facility includes 9 beds in nursing home–type unit) **A**5 9 10 **F**10 11 13 15 31 35 40 45 56 59 64 76 77 78 79 81 82 85 98 103 107 108 110 111 119 128 129 130
Primary Contact: Leonard Hernandez, President and Chief Executive Officer
CFO: Kim Weaver, CPA, Chief Financial Officer
CIO: Lori Young, Manager Health Information Management
CHR: Allen Keller, Director Human Resources
CNO: Darlene Cooney, Director Nursing
Web address: www.srmcks.org
Control: City–Government, nonfederal **Service:** General Medical and Surgical

Staffed Beds: 61 **Admissions:** 709 **Census:** 14 **Outpatient Visits:** 16157 **Births:** 130 **Total Expense ($000):** 14429 **Payroll Expense ($000):** 5728 **Personnel:** 115

WICHITA—Sedgwick County

☐ **AMG SPECIALTY HOSPITAL–WICHITA (172003)**, 8080 East Pawnee Street, Zip 67207–5475; tel. 316/682–0004 **A**1 10 **F**1 29 30 77 130 148 **P**5 **S** AMG Integrated Healthcare Management, Lafayette, LA
Primary Contact: Robert A. Loepp, Jr., FACHE, Chief Executive Officer
CFO: Myra Dick, Manager Business Office
CIO: Michelle Bradley, Director Health Information Management
CHR: Adrienne Burkholder, Director Human Resources
Web address: www.amgwichita.com/
Control: Corporation, Investor–owned, for–profit **Service:** Long–Term Acute Care hospital

Staffed Beds: 26 **Admissions:** 265 **Census:** 17 **Outpatient Visits:** 0 **Births:** 0 **Total Expense ($000):** 7281 **Payroll Expense ($000):** 3196 **Personnel:** 93

KANSAS HEART HOSPITAL (170186), 3601 North Webb Road, Zip 67226–8129; tel. 316/630–5000 **A**9 10 **F**3 17 18 20 22 24 29 30 64 81 85 86 107 115 119
Primary Contact: Thomas L. Ashcom, M.D., Ph.D., Chief Executive Officer
COO: Joyce Heismeyer, Chief Operating Officer
CFO: Steve Smith, Chief Financial Officer
CHR: Teresa E. Wolfe, Manager Human Resources
CNO: Susan Bradford, Director Nursing
Web address: www.kansasheart.com
Control: Corporation, Investor–owned, for–profit **Service:** Heart

Staffed Beds: 54 **Admissions:** 1725 **Census:** 20 **Outpatient Visits:** 9033 **Births:** 0 **Personnel:** 183

KANSAS SPINE AND SPECIALTY HOSPITAL (170196), 3333 North Webb Road, Zip 67226–8123; tel. 316/462–5000 **A**9 10 **F**3 29 77 79 81 82 85 87 107 111 114
Primary Contact: Thomas M. Schmitt, Chief Executive Officer
CFO: Kevin P. Vaughn, Chief Financial Officer
CIO: Michael Knocke, Chief Information Officer
CHR: Jean–Marie Jimeson, Manager Human Resources
Web address: www.ksspine.com
Control: Corporation, Investor–owned, for–profit **Service:** General Medical and Surgical

Staffed Beds: 36 **Admissions:** 1972 **Census:** 12 **Outpatient Visits:** 4938 **Births:** 0 **Personnel:** 91

KANSAS SURGERY AND RECOVERY CENTER (170183), 2770 North Webb Road, Zip 67226–8112; tel. 316/634–0090 **A**9 10 **F**51 64 68 81 85 87 107 111 114 119
Primary Contact: Ely Bartal, M.D., Chief Executive Officer
CFO: Ashley Simon, Chief Financial Officer
CMO: Ely Bartal, M.D., Chief Executive Officer and Medical Director
CIO: Jonathan Wells, Supervisor Information Technology
CNO: Becky Bailey, R.N., Director Nursing
Web address: www.ksrc.org
Control: Partnership, Investor–owned, for–profit **Service:** General Medical and Surgical

Staffed Beds: 32 **Admissions:** 1364 **Census:** 10 **Outpatient Visits:** 7076 **Births:** 0 **Total Expense ($000):** 23141 **Payroll Expense ($000):** 6123 **Personnel:** 125

✠ **ROBERT J. DOLE VETERANS AFFAIRS MEDICAL CENTER**, 5500 East Kellogg, Zip 67218–1607; tel. 316/685–2221, (Nonreporting) **A**1 3 5 **S** Department of Veterans Affairs, Washington, DC
Primary Contact: Francisco Vazquez, Director
CFO: Ronald Dreher, Finance Officer
CMO: Kent Murray, M.D., Chief of Staff
CIO: Sharon Williamson, Chief Information Technology
CHR: Nancy Gerstner, Manager Human Resources
Web address: www.wichita.va.gov
Control: Veterans Affairs, Government, federal **Service:** General Medical and Surgical

Staffed Beds: 41

✠ **SELECT SPECIALTY HOSPITAL–WICHITA (172007)**, 929 North St. Francis Street, Zip 67214–3821; tel. 316/261–8303 **A**1 10 **F**1 3 12 18 29 50 56 60 61 75 82 84 85 86 87 130 148 **S** Select Medical Corporation, Mechanicsburg, PA
Primary Contact: Peggy Cliffe, Chief Executive Officer
CHR: Renee Schaffer, Coordinator Human Resources
CNO: Lindsey Cahoj, Chief Nursing Officer
Web address: www.selectspecialtyhospitals.com/company/locations/wichita.aspx
Control: Corporation, Investor–owned, for–profit **Service:** Long–Term Acute Care hospital

Staffed Beds: 58 **Admissions:** 505 **Census:** 37 **Outpatient Visits:** 0 **Births:** 0 **Total Expense ($000):** 17721 **Payroll Expense ($000):** 6645 **Personnel:** 141

Many Facility Codes have changed. Please refer to the AHA Guide Code Chart.

© 2014 AHA Guide

KS

* **VIA CHRISTI HOSPITAL ON ST. FRANCIS (170122)**, 929 North St. Francis Street, Zip 67214–3882; tel. 316/268–5000, (Includes GOOD SHEPHERD CAMPUS, 8901 East Orme, Zip 67207; tel. 316/858–0333; ST. FRANCIS CAMPUS, 929 North St. Francis Street, tel. 316/268–5000; Sherry Hausmann, Senior Administrator; ST. JOSEPH CAMPUS, 3600 East Harry Street, Zip 67218–3713; tel. 316/685–1111; Claudio J. Ferraro, President) **A**1 2 3 5 9 10 13 **F**3 5 7 11 12 13 15 16 17 18 19 20 21 22 23 24 26 27 29 30 31 32 34 35 38 40 43 44 45 46 48 49 50 51 54 56 57 58 59 60 61 62 64 68 70 72 74 75 76 77 78 79 80 81 82 84 85 86 87 88 89 92 93 97 98 99 100 101 102 103 104 105 107 108 110 111 114 115 116 117 118 119 120 121 123 124 126 130 131 132 135 136 141 142 143 146 147 148 **P**6
S Ascension Health, Saint Louis, MO
Primary Contact: Sherry Hausmann, Senior Administrator
CFO: Jeff Seirer, Interim Chief Financial Officer
CMO: Darrell Youngman, D.O., Chief Medical Officer
CIO: Abdul Bengali, Chief Information Officer
CHR: Judy Espinoza, Chief Human Resources Officer
CNO: Linda Goodwin, R.N., Chief Nursing Officer
Web address: www.via–christi.org
Control: Church–operated, Nongovernment, not–for profit **Service:** General Medical and Surgical

Staffed Beds: 719 **Admissions:** 32162 **Census:** 432 **Outpatient Visits:** 323211 **Births:** 2553 **Total Expense ($000):** 512114 **Payroll Expense ($000):** 212514 **Personnel:** 3753

* **VIA CHRISTI HOSPITAL ON ST. TERESA (170200)**, 14800 West St. Teresa, Zip 67235–9602; tel. 316/796–7000 **A**1 9 10 **F**3 8 13 18 20 22 29 30 34 35 40 45 50 64 68 70 75 76 78 79 81 85 87 90 94 107 108 111 114 118 119 130 146 147 148 **S** Ascension Health, Saint Louis, MO
Primary Contact: Kevin Strecker, President
Web address: www.via–christi.org/st–teresa
Control: Church–operated, Nongovernment, not–for profit **Service:** General Medical and Surgical

Staffed Beds: 70 **Admissions:** 2034 **Census:** 22 **Outpatient Visits:** 20724 **Births:** 380 **Total Expense ($000):** 42925 **Payroll Expense ($000):** 14338 **Personnel:** 186

VIA CHRISTI REGIONAL MEDICAL CENTER See Via Christi Hospital on St. Francis

* **VIA CHRISTI REHABILITATION HOSPITAL (173028)**, 1151 North Rock Road, Zip 67206–1262; tel. 316/634–3400 **A**1 9 10 **F**11 29 30 34 35 44 50 54 57 59 64 77 86 87 90 92 93 94 96 119 129 130 131 132 143 146 148 **S** Ascension Health, Saint Louis, MO
Primary Contact: Cindy LaFleur, Senior Administrator
CMO: Kevin Rieg, M.D., President Medical Staff
Web address: www.via–christi.org
Control: Church–operated, Nongovernment, not–for profit **Service:** Rehabilitation

Staffed Beds: 58 **Admissions:** 756 **Census:** 26 **Outpatient Visits:** 100743 **Births:** 0 **Total Expense ($000):** 23351 **Payroll Expense ($000):** 11790 **Personnel:** 230

* **WESLEY MEDICAL CENTER (170123)**, 550 North Hillside, Zip 67214–4976; tel. 316/962–2000, (Includes GALICHIA HEART HOSPITAL, 2610 North Woodlawn, Zip 67220; tel. 316/858–2610; Stephen J. Harris, Chief Executive Officer; THE CHILDREN'S CENTER AT WESLEY, 550 North Hillside Street, Zip 67214–4910) **A**1 3 5 9 10 **F**3 7 11 12 13 15 17 18 19 20 22 24 26 28 29 31 33 34 35 39 40 41 42 43 44 45 46 48 49 50 51 54 55 56 57 58 59 60 64 65 68 70 72 73 74 76 78 79 81 85 86 87 88 89 92 93 94 97 100 102 107 108 111 114 115 119 121 123 124 126 129 130 131 132 134 135 146 147 148 **P**6 **S** HCA, Nashville, TN
Primary Contact: Hugh C. Tappan, President and Chief Executive Officer
COO: Bill Voloch, Chief Operating Officer
CFO: Matt Leary, Chief Financial Officer
CMO: Francie H. Ekengren, M.D., Chief Medical Officer
CIO: Jeffrey Schauf, Director Information Systems
CHR: Nikki Freeman, Vice President Human Resources
CNO: Catherine Blise, R.N., Chief Nursing Officer
Web address: www.wesleymc.com
Control: Corporation, Investor–owned, for–profit **Service:** General Medical and Surgical

Staffed Beds: 584 **Admissions:** 25652 **Census:** 329 **Outpatient Visits:** 221803 **Births:** 5868 **Total Expense ($000):** 384452 **Payroll Expense ($000):** 144799 **Personnel:** 2410

* **WESLEY REHABILITATION HOSPITAL (173027)**, 8338 West 13th Street North, Zip 67212–2984; tel. 316/729–9999 **A**1 9 10 **F**29 34 35 62 64 68 90 91 93 95 96 132 147 148 **S** HEALTHSOUTH Corporation, Birmingham, AL
Primary Contact: James F. Grocholski, FACHE, Chief Executive Officer
CFO: Bob Peck, Chief Financial Officer
CMO: Kevin F. Brown, D.O., Medical Director
CIO: Debbie Patterson, Director Health Information Management
CHR: Betty Shuman, Director Human Resources
CNO: Jessika M. Workman, Chief Nursing Officer
Web address: www.wesleyrehabhospital.com
Control: Corporation, Investor–owned, for–profit **Service:** Rehabilitation

Staffed Beds: 65 **Admissions:** 985 **Census:** 38 **Outpatient Visits:** 22028 **Births:** 0 **Total Expense ($000):** 17236 **Payroll Expense ($000):** 8500 **Personnel:** 171

WICHITA SPECIALTY HOSPITAL See AMG Specialty Hospital–Wichita

WINCHESTER—Jefferson County

★ **F. W. HUSTON MEDICAL CENTER (171314)**, 408 Delaware Street, Zip 66097–4003; tel. 913/774–4340, (Total facility includes 43 beds in nursing home–type unit) **A**9 10 18 **F**2 3 10 40 56 57 64 67 69 75 77 93 97 103 104 107 128 130 133 143 **P**6 8
Primary Contact: LaMont Cook, Administrator
CFO: Jason Johnson, Controller
CMO: William Greiner, M.D., Chief of Staff
CIO: Jason Johnson, Controller
CHR: Melody Keirns, Manager Human Resources
CNO: Heather R. Aranda, R.N., Chief Nursing Officer
Web address: www.jcmhospital.org
Control: Other not–for–profit (including NFP Corporation) **Service:** General Medical and Surgical

Staffed Beds: 74 **Admissions:** 86 **Census:** 34 **Outpatient Visits:** 5034 **Births:** 0 **Total Expense ($000):** 4842 **Payroll Expense ($000):** 3127 **Personnel:** 57

JEFFERSON COUNTY MEMORIAL HOSPITAL See F. W. Huston Medical Center

WINFIELD—Cowley County

★ **WILLIAM NEWTON HOSPITAL (171383)**, 1300 East Fifth Street, Zip 67156–2407; tel. 620/221–2300 **A**5 9 10 18 **F**3 9 11 13 15 28 29 34 35 39 40 43 45 57 59 62 64 65 70 74 75 76 77 78 79 81 82 85 86 87 93 102 107 108 110 111 114 118 119 121 123 127 129 130 131 132 133 135 146 147 148
Primary Contact: J. Ben Quinton, Administrator
COO: Shona Salzman, Chief Operating Officer
CFO: Debbie Hockenbury, Assistant Administrator and Chief Financial Officer
CMO: Bryan Dennett, M.D., Chief of Staff
CIO: Randy Mayo, Director Information Technology
CHR: Cathy McClurg, Director Human Resources
CNO: Tina Wheeler, R.N., Director Nursing
Web address: www.wnmh.org
Control: City–Government, nonfederal **Service:** General Medical and Surgical

Staffed Beds: 25 **Admissions:** 980 **Census:** 9 **Outpatient Visits:** 70049 **Births:** 225 **Total Expense ($000):** 27066 **Payroll Expense ($000):** 12716 **Personnel:** 256

KENTUCKY

ALBANY—Clinton County

CLINTON COUNTY HOSPITAL (180106), 723 Burkesville Road,
Zip 42602–1654; tel. 606/387–6421, (Nonreporting) **A**9 10
Primary Contact: John David Mullins, Jr., Administrator
CHR: Pat Beard, Director Human Resources
Web address: www.clintoncountyhospital.com
Control: Other not–for–profit (including NFP Corporation) **Service:** General
Medical and Surgical

Staffed Beds: 42

ASHLAND—Boyd County

☐ **KING'S DAUGHTERS MEDICAL CENTER (180009)**, 2201 Lexington Avenue,
Zip 41101–2874, Mailing Address: P.O. Box 151, Zip 41105–0151;
tel. 606/408–4000, (Total facility includes 143 beds in nursing home–type unit)
A1 2 9 10 **F**3 7 8 9 10 11 12 13 15 17 18 20 22 24 26 29 30 31 34 35 37
38 40 44 45 46 47 48 49 50 51 54 55 56 57 58 59 60 61 62 64 65 69 70
71 72 74 75 76 77 78 79 81 82 84 85 86 87 89 90 91 92 93 96 97 98 100
101 102 103 107 108 110 111 114 115 117 118 119 126 127 128 129 130
131 132 135 143 144 145 146 147 148 **P**8
Primary Contact: Kristine Whitlatch, President and Chief Executive Officer
COO: Bob Lucas, Vice President Operations
CFO: Paul L. McDowell, Vice President Finance and Chief Financial Officer
CMO: Phil Fioret, M.D., Vice President Medical Affairs
CIO: David Oliver, Director Information Systems
CHR: Larry Higgins, Vice President Human Resources
Web address: www.kdmc.com
Control: Other not–for–profit (including NFP Corporation) **Service:** General
Medical and Surgical

Staffed Beds: 465 Admissions: 22021 Census: 369 Outpatient Visits:
334738 Births: 1380 Total Expense ($000): 530522 Payroll Expense
($000): 234323 Personnel: 3084

✠ **OUR LADY OF BELLEFONTE HOSPITAL (180036)**, St. Christopher Drive,
Zip 41101, Mailing Address: P.O. Box 789, Zip 41105–0789; tel. 606/833–3333
A1 2 9 10 12 13 **F**3 4 5 8 11 12 15 18 19 20 28 29 30 31 34 35 37 39 40
44 45 49 50 53 54 55 56 57 58 59 62 64 65 66 69 70 71 74 75 77 78 79
81 82 84 85 86 87 89 93 96 97 98 100 101 102 103 106 107 108 110 111
114 115 118 119 129 130 131 132 135 143 144 145 146 147 148 **P**7 8
S Bon Secours Health System, Inc., Marriottsville, MD
Primary Contact: Kevin Halter, Chief Executive Officer
CFO: Joe Buchheit, Chief Financial Officer
CMO: Dan Goulson, M.D., Chief Medical Officer
CIO: Mike Gomez, Site Manager Medical Information Systems
CHR: Judy Daniels, Vice President Human Resources
Web address: www.olbh.com
Control: Church–operated, Nongovernment, not–for profit **Service:** General
Medical and Surgical

Staffed Beds: 151 Admissions: 6984 Census: 75 Outpatient Visits: 232238
Births: 0 Total Expense ($000): 142268 Payroll Expense ($000): 42571
Personnel: 1061

BARBOURVILLE—Knox County

☐ **KNOX COUNTY HOSPITAL (181328)**, 80 Hospital Drive, Zip 40906–7363,
Mailing Address: P.O. Box 10, Zip 40906–0010; tel. 606/546–4175 **A**1 9 10 18
F3 8 11 15 28 40 45 46 49 50 81 93 107 108 110 119 130 133
S Pacer Health Corporation, Miami Lakes, FL
Primary Contact: Ray B. Canady, Chief Executive Officer and Administrator
CFO: Amanda Ellis, Chief Financial Officer
CMO: Kamran Hasni, M.D., Chief of Medical Staff
CIO: Evan Davis, Director Technology and Environmental Services
CHR: Janet Wilder, Director Human Resources
CNO: Brenda Graham, Chief Nursing Officer
Web address: www.knoxcohospital.com
Control: Hospital district or authority, Government, nonfederal **Service:** General
Medical and Surgical

Staffed Beds: 25 Admissions: 1416 Census: 14 Outpatient Visits: 31500
Births: 0 Total Expense ($000): 16375 Payroll Expense ($000): 9117
Personnel: 182

BARDSTOWN—Nelson County

✠ **FLAGET MEMORIAL HOSPITAL (180025)**, 4305 New Shepherdsville Road,
Zip 40004–9019; tel. 502/350–5000 **A**1 9 10 **F**11 12 13 15 18 28 29 30 31
34 35 37 40 45 49 59 62 63 64 70 76 78 79 81 82 84 85 87 96 107 111
116 117 119 127 128 129 130 132 144 146 147 148 **P**3 **S** Catholic Health
Initiatives, Englewood, CO
Primary Contact: Beverly Sue Downs, R.N., MSN, FACHE, President
COO: Norma Goss, R.N., Chief Operating Officer and Chief Nursing Officer
CFO: John Bradford, Vice President Finance
CMO: Amy Farrell, M.D., Chief of Staff
CNO: Norma Goss, R.N., Chief Operating Officer and Chief Nursing Officer
Web address: www.flaget.com
Control: Other not–for–profit (including NFP Corporation) **Service:** General
Medical and Surgical

Staffed Beds: 40 Admissions: 2454 Census: 23 Outpatient Visits: 66091
Births: 260 Total Expense ($000): 68042 Payroll Expense ($000): 16647
Personnel: 283

BENTON—Marshall County

✠ **MARSHALL COUNTY HOSPITAL (181327)**, 615 Old Symsonia Road,
Zip 42025–5042; tel. 270/527–4800 **A**1 9 10 18 **F**3 7 11 15 18 19 28 29 30
34 35 40 51 53 57 59 62 77 79 81 85 89 90 93 107 108 119 128 132 133
135 **P**6
Primary Contact: David G. Fuqua, Chief Executive Officer
CFO: Janice Kelley, Chief Financial Officer
CMO: Robert Beale, M.D., Chief of Staff
CIO: Patrick Waters, Director Information Technology
CHR: Jeannie Lee, Director Human Resources
Web address: www.marshallcountyhospital.org
Control: Hospital district or authority, Government, nonfederal **Service:** General
Medical and Surgical

Staffed Beds: 25 Admissions: 1040 Census: 12 Outpatient Visits: 27442
Births: 0 Total Expense ($000): 18614 Payroll Expense ($000): 7519
Personnel: 213

BEREA—Madison County

✠ **SAINT JOSEPH BEREA (181329)**, 305 Estill Street, Zip 40403–1909;
tel. 859/986–3151 **A**1 5 9 10 18 **F**3 29 40 45 70 77 79 81 82 91 97 107
111 114 119 133 **P**4 **S** Catholic Health Initiatives, Englewood, CO
Primary Contact: Eric Gilliam, Chief Executive Officer
CFO: Christy Spitser, Vice President Finance
CMO: Patrick Kelleher, M.D., Chief Medical Staff
CHR: Sandra Turquesa, Human Resources Business Partner
CNO: Leslie Crawford, Chief Nursing Executive
Web address: www.kentuckyonehealth.org/berea
Control: Church–operated, Nongovernment, not–for profit **Service:** General
Medical and Surgical

Staffed Beds: 25 Admissions: 1035 Census: 11 Outpatient Visits: 53356
Births: 0 Total Expense ($000): 28481 Payroll Expense ($000): 10370
Personnel: 157

BOWLING GREEN—Warren County

COMMONWEALTH REGIONAL SPECIALTY HOSPITAL (182005), 250 Park
Drive, 6th Floor, Zip 42101–1760, Mailing Address: P.O. Box 90010,
Zip 42102–9010; tel. 270/796–6200 **A**10 **F**1 3 29 30 34 35 50 57 68 70 84
85 87 130 135 143 146 148 **S** Commonwealth Health Corporation, Bowling
Green, KY
Primary Contact: Emily Howard Martin, Administrator
CFO: Ronald G. Sowell, Executive Vice President
CMO: Doug Thomson, M.D., Chief Medical Officer
CIO: Jean Cherry, Executive Vice President
CHR: Lynn Williams, Vice President
Web address: www.commonwealthregionalspecialtyhospital.org
Control: Other not–for–profit (including NFP Corporation) **Service:** Long–Term
Acute Care hospital

Staffed Beds: 24 Admissions: 217 Census: 17 Outpatient Visits: 0 Births:
0 Personnel: 59

Many Facility Codes have changed. Please refer to the AHA Guide Code Chart.   © 2014 AHA Guide

☐ **MEDICAL CENTER AT BOWLING GREEN (180013)**, 250 Park Street, Zip 42101–1795, Mailing Address: P.O. Box 90010, Zip 42102–9010; tel. 270/745–1000 **A**1 2 9 10 19 **F**1 3 7 12 13 15 17 18 20 22 24 26 28 29 30 31 32 34 35 37 39 40 46 50 51 56 57 59 60 62 64 68 70 72 74 75 76 78 79 80 81 82 84 85 86 87 89 91 93 98 100 102 103 104 105 107 108 110 111 114 116 117 119 121 123 129 130 132 135 145 146 147 148 **S** Commonwealth Health Corporation, Bowling Green, KY
Primary Contact: Connie Smith, Chief Executive Officer
CFO: Ronald G. Sowell, Executive Vice President
CIO: Jean Cherry, Executive Vice President and Chief Information Officer
CHR: Lynn Williams, Vice President Human Resources
CNO: Betsy Kullman, R.N., Executive Vice President and Chief Nursing Officer
Web address: www.themedicalcenter.org
Control: Other not–for–profit (including NFP Corporation) **Service:** General Medical and Surgical

Staffed Beds: 337 **Admissions:** 17452 **Census:** 236 **Outpatient Visits:** 123388 **Births:** 2299 **Personnel:** 1724

☐ **RIVENDELL BEHAVIORAL HEALTH (184017)**, 1035 Porter Pike, Zip 42103–9581; tel. 270/843–1199, (Nonreporting) **A**1 9 10 **S** Universal Health Services, Inc., King of Prussia, PA
Primary Contact: Janice Richardson, Chief Executive Officer and Managing Director
CFO: Tim Gore, Chief Financial Officer
Web address: www.rivendellbehavioral.com
Control: Corporation, Investor–owned, for–profit **Service:** Psychiatric

Staffed Beds: 125

⊞ △ **SOUTHERN KENTUCKY REHABILITATION HOSPITAL (183029)**, 1300 Campbell Lane, Zip 42104–4162; tel. 270/782–6900, (Nonreporting) **A**1 7 9 10 **S** Vibra Healthcare, Mechanicsburg, PA
Primary Contact: Stuart Locke, Chief Executive Officer
COO: Dana Lewis, Director Clinical Services
CMO: Jim Farrage, M.D., Medical Director
CHR: Suzanne Cornett, Director Human Resources
Web address: www.skyrehab.com
Control: Corporation, Investor–owned, for–profit **Service:** Rehabilitation

Staffed Beds: 60

⊞ **TRISTAR GREENVIEW REGIONAL HOSPITAL (180124)**, 1801 Ashley Circle, Zip 42104–3362; tel. 270/793–1000 **A**1 2 9 10 19 **F**3 8 11 15 18 20 22 29 31 34 35 37 40 45 46 48 49 50 51 57 59 64 65 68 70 74 75 77 78 79 81 82 85 86 87 107 108 110 111 114 118 119 128 130 131 132 133 135 145 146 **S** HCA, Nashville, TN
Primary Contact: Michael Sherrod, Chief Executive Officer
COO: Andre Boyd, Sr., Chief Operating Officer
CFO: Richard Patterson, Chief Financial Officer
CMO: Nagy Morji, Chief of Staff
CIO: Cyndi Talley, Director Information Systems
CHR: Judy Fulkerson, Director Human Resources
CNO: Anne Leonard, R.N., Chief Nursing Officer
Web address: www.greenviewhospital.com
Control: Corporation, Investor–owned, for–profit **Service:** General Medical and Surgical

Staffed Beds: 167 **Admissions:** 4335 **Census:** 57 **Outpatient Visits:** 47585 **Births:** 0 **Total Expense ($000):** 69010 **Payroll Expense ($000):** 21340 **Personnel:** 426

CUMBERLAND COUNTY HOSPITAL (181317), 299 Glasgow Road, Zip 42717–9696, Mailing Address: P.O. Box 280, Zip 42717–0280; tel. 270/864–2511, (Nonreporting) **A**9 10 18
Primary Contact: Richard Neikirk, Chief Executive Officer
CFO: Rick Capps, Chief Financial Officer
CMO: Christian Konsavage, M.D., Chief of Staff
CHR: Martha Young, Director Human Resources
Web address: www.cchospital.org
Control: Other not–for–profit (including NFP Corporation) **Service:** General Medical and Surgical

Staffed Beds: 25

★ **TRIGG COUNTY HOSPITAL (181304)**, 254 Main Street, Zip 42211–9153, Mailing Address: P.O. Box 312, Zip 42211–0312; tel. 270/522–3215 **A**9 10 18 **F**3 7 8 11 15 29 30 34 40 45 50 54 57 59 75 77 81 87 93 97 100 101 103 104 107 111 119 130 133 135 143 **P**6
Primary Contact: Alisa Coleman, Chief Executive Officer
CFO: Liz Snodgrass, Chief Financial Officer
CMO: Stuart Harris, M.D., Chief of Staff
CHR: Janet James, Director Human Resources
Web address: www.trigghospital.org
Control: County–Government, nonfederal **Service:** General Medical and Surgical

Staffed Beds: 25 **Admissions:** 427 **Census:** 7 **Outpatient Visits:** 18969 **Births:** 0 **Total Expense ($000):** 13406 **Payroll Expense ($000):** 6120 **Personnel:** 153

⊞ **TAYLOR REGIONAL HOSPITAL (180087)**, 1700 Old Lebanon Road, Zip 42718–9600; tel. 270/465–3561 **A**1 2 9 10 **F**3 8 11 13 15 18 20 28 29 30 31 34 35 39 40 43 45 46 48 49 50 51 54 56 57 59 64 65 68 70 75 76 77 78 79 81 85 86 93 97 107 108 110 111 114 117 118 119 120 127 129 130 131 132 134 135 141 143 146 147 148 **S** Catholic Health Initiatives, Englewood, CO
Primary Contact: Jane Wheatley, Chief Executive Officer
CFO: David Massengale, Chief Financial Officer
CIO: Christopher Michael Gibbs, Director Information Management Systems
CHR: Andrea Settle, Director Human Resources
Web address: www.trhosp.org
Control: Hospital district or authority, Government, nonfederal **Service:** General Medical and Surgical

Staffed Beds: 90 **Admissions:** 2844 **Census:** 33 **Outpatient Visits:** 89305 **Births:** 335 **Total Expense ($000):** 64482 **Payroll Expense ($000):** 29054 **Personnel:** 580

☐ **NICHOLAS COUNTY HOSPITAL (181303)**, 2323 Concrete Road, Zip 40311–9721, Mailing Address: P.O. Box 232, Zip 40311–0232; tel. 859/289–7181, (Includes JOHNSON–MATHERS NURSING HOME), (Nonreporting) **A**1 9 10 18
Primary Contact: Benny Nolen, Interim Administrator
CFO: Wesley Berry, Chief Financial Officer
CMO: Osias Villaflor, M.D., Chief Medical Staff
CHR: Wendy Price, Manager Human Resources
Web address: www.johnsonmathers.org
Control: Other not–for–profit (including NFP Corporation) **Service:** General Medical and Surgical

Staffed Beds: 122

★ **CARROLL COUNTY MEMORIAL HOSPITAL (181310)**, 309 11th Street, Zip 41008–1400; tel. 502/732–4321 **A**9 10 18 **F**3 11 15 18 28 29 34 40 45 50 56 57 59 68 74 75 77 79 81 82 85 86 93 94 97 107 108 111 114 119 127 128 129 130 133 148 **P**6 **S** Alliant Management Services, Louisville, KY
Primary Contact: Michael A. Kozar, Chief Executive Officer
CMO: Kathy Short, D.O., Family Practice
CHR: Kimberly Adams, Manager Human Resources
CNO: Lisa Penick, R.N., Chief Nursing Officer
Web address: www.ccmhosp.com
Control: Hospital district or authority, Government, nonfederal **Service:** General Medical and Surgical

Staffed Beds: 25 **Admissions:** 716 **Census:** 8 **Outpatient Visits:** 10674 **Births:** 0

⊞ **WESTLAKE REGIONAL HOSPITAL (180149)**, 901 Westlake Drive, Zip 42728–1123, Mailing Address: P.O. Box 1269, Zip 42728–6269; tel. 270/384–4753 **A**1 9 10 **F**4 15 29 38 40 57 81 87 93 97 98 100 103 105 107 111 119 127 130 133 147
Primary Contact: Neal Gold, Chief Executive Officer
CFO: David R. Hayes, Chief Financial Officer
CMO: Charles Giles, M.D., President Medical Staff
CHR: Tonya Grant, Director Human Resources
CNO: Gidgett Warren, Director of Nursing
Web address: www.westlakeregionalhospital.com
Control: Hospital district or authority, Government, nonfederal **Service:** General Medical and Surgical

Staffed Beds: 32 **Admissions:** 727 **Census:** 10 **Outpatient Visits:** 50228 **Births:** 0 **Total Expense ($000):** 15508 **Payroll Expense ($000):** 7262 **Personnel:** 164

Hospital, Medicare Provider Number, Address, Telephone, Approval, Facility, and Physician Codes, Health Care System

★ American Hospital Association (AHA) membership
☐ The Joint Commission accreditation   ◇ DNV Healthcare Inc. accreditation

○ Healthcare Facilities Accreditation Program
△ Commission on Accreditation of Rehabilitation Facilities (CARF) accreditation

CORBIN—Whitley County

★ ◇ **BAPTIST HEALTH CORBIN (180080)**, 1 Trillium Way, Zip 40701–8420;
tel. 606/528–1212, (Nonreporting) **A**9 10 21 **S** Baptist Health, Louisville, KY
Primary Contact: Larry Gray, President
CMO: David Worthy, M.D., Vice President and Chief Medical Officer
CIO: Jeff Thurmond, Vice President Information Systems
CHR: Tim Perry, Executive Director Human Services
CNO: Anthony Powers, Vice President Patient Care Services
Web address: www.baptistregional.com
Control: Other not–for–profit (including NFP Corporation) **Service:** General Medical and Surgical

Staffed Beds: 268

◇ **OAK TREE HOSPITAL (182006)**, 1 Trillium Way, Lower Level,
Zip 40701–8727; tel. 606/523–5150 **A**10 21 **F**1 3 29 30 39 60 130 148
Primary Contact: R. Alan Coppock, FACHE, President
CFO: Jeff Hamlin, Director Finance
CMO: Bill Durham, M.D., Chief Medical Officer
CIO: Jackie Lucas, Vice President
CHR: Janice Caldwell, Director Human Resources
Web address: www.oaktreecorbin.com
Control: Other not–for–profit (including NFP Corporation) **Service:** Long–Term Acute Care hospital

Staffed Beds: 32 **Admissions:** 273 **Census:** 22 **Outpatient Visits:** 0 **Births:** 0

COVINGTON—Kenton County

NORTHKEY COMMUNITY CARE (184006), 502 Farrell Drive,
Zip 41011–3799, Mailing Address: P.O. Box 2680, Zip 41012–2680;
tel. 859/578–3200 **A**9 10 **F**50 98 99 101 102 104
Primary Contact: Owen Nichols, PsyD, President and Chief Executive Officer
CFO: John Metzger, Controller
Web address: www.northkey.org
Control: Other not–for–profit (including NFP Corporation) **Service:** Children's hospital psychiatric

Staffed Beds: 34 **Admissions:** 654 **Census:** 12 **Births:** 0 **Total Expense ($000):** 3874 **Payroll Expense ($000):** 1492

ST. ELIZABETH MEDICAL CENTER–NORTH See St. Elizabeth Covington

CYNTHIANA—Harrison County

✠ **HARRISON MEMORIAL HOSPITAL (180079)**, 1210 KY Highway 36E,
Zip 41031–7498; tel. 859/234–2300 **A**1 9 10 **F**3 11 13 15 18 20 28 29 30
31 34 35 36 39 40 44 45 47 49 50 53 57 59 61 64 68 69 70 74 75 76 77
78 79 81 82 85 86 87 89 93 97 107 108 111 115 118 119 129 130 131
132 133 135 146 147 148 **P**6 8
Primary Contact: Sheila Currans, Chief Executive Officer
CFO: David Mellett, Chief Financial Officer
CIO: Martha Sullivan, Chief Information Officer
CHR: Rebecca Jenkins, Director Human Resources Management
CNO: Wendy Reeder, R.N., Chief Nursing Officer
Web address: www.harrisonmemhosp.com
Control: Other not–for–profit (including NFP Corporation) **Service:** General Medical and Surgical

Staffed Beds: 49 **Admissions:** 1644 **Census:** 16 **Outpatient Visits:** 47932 **Births:** 263 **Total Expense ($000):** 33827 **Payroll Expense ($000):** 14577 **Personnel:** 279

DANVILLE—Boyle County

✠ **EPHRAIM MCDOWELL REGIONAL MEDICAL CENTER (180048)**, 217 South
Third Street, Zip 40422–1823; tel. 859/239–1000, (Total facility includes 24
beds in nursing home–type unit) **A**1 5 9 10 19 **F**1 3 4 8 10 11 15 16 17 18
20 22 28 29 30 31 32 34 35 40 43 45 46 49 51 53 56 57 59 60 64 65 66
67 70 72 73 75 76 77 78 79 80 81 82 84 85 87 88 89 90 93 96 97 98 100
101 102 103 107 108 110 111 114 117 118 119 125 127 128 129 130 132
144 146 147 148 **P**5
Primary Contact: Vicki A. Darnell, R.N., MSN, President and Chief Executive Officer
COO: Sally M. Davenport, MS, Chief Nursing Officer and Chief Operating Officer
CFO: William R. Snapp, III, Vice President Finance and Chief Financial Officer
CMO: Eric Guerrant, M.D., President Medical Staff
CIO: Angela Allen–Johnson, Director Information Services
CHR: Carl Metz, Vice President Human Resources
CNO: Sally M. Davenport, MS, Chief Nursing Officer and Chief Operating Officer
Web address: www.emrmc.org
Control: Other not–for–profit (including NFP Corporation) **Service:** General Medical and Surgical

Staffed Beds: 159 **Admissions:** 7264 **Census:** 102 **Outpatient Visits:** 133428 **Births:** 676 **Total Expense ($000):** 130629 **Payroll Expense ($000):** 47725 **Personnel:** 975

EDGEWOOD—Kenton County

✠ **HEALTHSOUTH NORTHERN KENTUCKY REHABILITATION HOSPITAL
(183027)**, 201 Medical Village Drive, Zip 41017–3407; tel. 859/341–2044 **A**1
9 10 **F**64 79 82 90 93 94 **P**6 **S** HEALTHSOUTH Corporation, Birmingham, AL
Primary Contact: Richard R. Evens, Chief Executive Officer
CFO: Lisa McGue, Controller
CMO: Neal Moser, M.D., Medical Director
CHR: Bridgette Keith, Director Human Resources
CNO: Terri Ballard, Chief Nursing Officer
Web address: www.healthsouthkentucky.com
Control: Corporation, Investor–owned, for–profit **Service:** Rehabilitation

Staffed Beds: 40 **Admissions:** 1130 **Census:** 36 **Outpatient Visits:** 3240 **Births:** 0 **Total Expense ($000):** 11882 **Payroll Expense ($000):** 6743 **Personnel:** 117

☐ **ST. ELIZABETH EDGEWOOD (180035)**, 1 Medical Village Drive,
Zip 41017–3403; tel. 859/301–2000, (Includes ST. ELIZABETH COVINGTON,
1500 James Simpson Jr. Way, Covington, Zip 41014–1585; tel. 859/655–8800)
A1 2 3 5 9 10 **F**3 5 8 13 14 15 17 18 20 22 24 26 28 29 30 31 34 35 36 38
40 44 45 46 47 48 49 50 55 57 58 59 60 63 64 68 70 71 72 73 74 75 76
77 78 79 80 81 82 83 84 85 86 87 92 93 97 98 100 103 104 105 107 108
109 110 111 114 115 116 117 118 119 120 121 123 126 129 130 131 132
135 145 146 147 148 **P**6 **S** St. Elizabeth Healthcare, Edgewood, KY
Primary Contact: John S. Dubis, FACHE, President and Chief Executive Officer
COO: John S. Dubis, FACHE, President and Chief Executive Officer
CFO: Garren Colvin, Senior Vice President and Chief Financial Officer
CMO: Karl Schmitt, M.D., Chief of Staff
CIO: Alex Rodriguez, Vice President and Chief Information Officer
CHR: Martin Oscadal, Vice President Human Resources
Web address: www.stelizabeth.com
Control: Church–operated, Nongovernment, not–for profit **Service:** General Medical and Surgical

Staffed Beds: 499 **Admissions:** 27105 **Census:** 351 **Outpatient Visits:** 788707 **Births:** 4291 **Total Expense ($000):** 605947 **Payroll Expense ($000):** 222557 **Personnel:** 3358

ST. ELIZABETH HEALTHCARE–EDGEWOOD See St. Elizabeth Edgewood

ELIZABETHTOWN—Hardin County

✠ **HARDIN MEMORIAL HOSPITAL (180012)**, 913 North Dixie Avenue,
Zip 42701–2503; tel. 270/737–1212, (Total facility includes 15 beds in nursing
home–type unit) **A**1 2 5 9 10 19 **F**3 8 11 12 13 15 17 18 20 22 28 29 30 31
32 34 35 37 39 40 44 45 48 49 50 51 52 54 57 58 59 64 68 70 71 73 74
75 76 77 78 79 80 81 82 84 85 86 87 89 93 94 96 98 102 107 108 110
111 114 115 117 118 119 120 121 124 126 128 129 130 131 132 134 135
144 146 147 148 **S** Baptist Health, Louisville, KY
Primary Contact: Dennis B. Johnson, President & CEO
COO: Diane Logsdon, Vice President Planning and Development
CFO: John Dempsey, Vice President and Chief Financial Officer
CMO: Stephen Toadvine, M.D., Chief Medical Officer
CIO: Trey Hyberger, Director Information Technology
CHR: Kathy Fetterley, Vice President and Chief Human Resources Officer
CNO: Sharon Wright, R.N., Vice President and Chief Nursing Officer
Web address: www.hmh.net
Control: County–Government, nonfederal **Service:** General Medical and Surgical

Staffed Beds: 268 **Admissions:** 12727 **Census:** 157 **Outpatient Visits:** 348548 **Births:** 1548 **Total Expense ($000):** 230012 **Payroll Expense ($000):** 101705 **Personnel:** 1774

✠ **HEALTHSOUTH LAKEVIEW REHABILITATION HOSPITAL (183028)**, 134
Heartland Drive, Zip 42701–2778; tel. 270/769–3100, (Nonreporting) **A**1 10
S HEALTHSOUTH Corporation, Birmingham, AL
Primary Contact: Lori Jarboe, Chief Executive Officer
CFO: Scott Hart, Controller
CMO: Toni Abang, M.D., Medical Director
CHR: Janet Morris, Director Human Resources
Web address: www.healthsouthlakeview.com
Control: Corporation, Investor–owned, for–profit **Service:** Rehabilitation

Staffed Beds: 40

FLEMINGSBURG—Fleming County

✠ **FLEMING COUNTY HOSPITAL (180053)**, 55 Foundation Drive,
Zip 41041–9815, Mailing Address: P.O. Box 388, Zip 41041–0388;
tel. 606/849–5000 **A**1 9 10 **F**15 28 29 31 34 35 40 45 50 57 59 78 79 81
87 93 107 108 110 111 114 118 119 129 130 133 135 146 **P**6 **S** QHR,
Brentwood, TN
Primary Contact: David M. Faulkner, Chief Executive Officer
CMO: Amanda Applegate, M.D., Chief of Staff
CIO: Don Daugherty, Director Information Systems
CHR: Marsha Mitchell, Director Human Resources
CNO: Lynda Skaggs, Chief Nursing Officer
Web address: www.flemingcountyhospital.org
Control: Other not–for–profit (including NFP Corporation) **Service:** General Medical and Surgical

Staffed Beds: 52 **Admissions:** 1418 **Census:** 15 **Outpatient Visits:** 28507 **Births:** 0 **Total Expense ($000):** 23812 **Payroll Expense ($000):** 8903 **Personnel:** 260

FLORENCE—Boone County

☐ **GATEWAY REHABILITATION HOSPITAL (183030)**, 5940 Merchant Street, Zip 41042–1158; tel. 859/426–2400 **A**1 9 10 **F**29 34 35 56 57 59 64 74 75 79 82 90 93 94 96 132 148
Primary Contact: Samantha Billig, Chief Executive Officer
CFO: Margaret Cesarez, Chief Financial Officer
CNO: Jenna Wellbrock, Chief Nursing Officer
Web address: www.gatewayflorence.com/
Control: Corporation, Investor–owned, for–profit **Service:** Rehabilitation

Staffed Beds: 40 **Admissions:** 913 **Census:** 26 **Births:** 0 **Personnel:** 108

☐ **ST. ELIZABETH FLORENCE (180045)**, 4900 Houston Road, Zip 41042–4824; tel. 859/212–5200, (Total facility includes 16 beds in nursing home–type unit) **A**1 9 10 **F**3 11 12 15 18 20 28 29 30 34 35 40 44 45 47 48 49 50 55 56 57 59 60 64 70 71 74 75 77 78 79 80 81 82 85 86 87 92 93 97 98 100 101 102 107 108 110 111 115 118 119 128 129 130 132 135 144 146 147 **P**6 **S** St. Elizabeth Healthcare, Edgewood, KY
Primary Contact: Chris Carle, Senior Vice President and Chief Operating Officer
COO: Chris Carle, Senior Vice President and Chief Operating Officer
CFO: Garren Colvin, Senior Vice President Finance and Chief Financial Officer
CMO: George Hall, M.D., Vice President Medical Affairs
CIO: Alex Rodriguez, Vice President and Chief Information Officer
CHR: Martin Oscadal, Senior Vice President Human Resources
Web address: www.stelizabeth.com
Control: Church–operated, Nongovernment, not–for profit **Service:** General Medical and Surgical

Staffed Beds: 169 **Admissions:** 9301 **Census:** 114 **Outpatient Visits:** 163117 **Births:** 0 **Total Expense ($000):** 99091 **Payroll Expense ($000):** 40230 **Personnel:** 616

ST. ELIZABETH HEALTHCARE FLORENCE See St. Elizabeth Florence

FORT CAMPBELL—Montgomery County

☒ **COLONEL FLORENCE A. BLANCHFIELD ARMY COMMUNITY HOSPITAL**, 650 Joel Drive, Zip 42223–5318; tel. 270/798–8040, (Nonreporting) **A**1 3 5 **S** Department of the Army, Office of the Surgeon General, Falls Church, VA
Primary Contact: Colonel Paul Cordts, Commander
CMO: Lieutenant Colonel Michael Place, M.D., Deputy Commander Clinical Services
CHR: Major Travis Burchett, Troop Commander Human Resources
Web address: www.campbell.amedd.army.mil/
Control: Army, Government, federal **Service:** General Medical and Surgical

Staffed Beds: 66

FORT KNOX—Hardin County

☒ **IRELAND ARMY COMMUNITY HOSPITAL**, 289 Ireland Avenue, Zip 40121–5111; tel. 502/624–9333, (Nonreporting) **A**1 5 **S** Department of the Army, Office of the Surgeon General, Falls Church, VA
Primary Contact: Colonel Matthew Rettke, Commander
Web address: www.iach.knox.amedd.army.mil/
Control: Army, Government, federal **Service:** General Medical and Surgical

Staffed Beds: 33

FORT THOMAS—Campbell County

CARDINAL HILL SPECIALTY HOSPITAL See Select Specialty Hospital–Northern Kentucky

☒ **SELECT SPECIALTY HOSPITAL–NORTHERN KENTUCKY (182004)**, 85 North Grand Avenue, Zip 41075–1793; tel. 859/572–3880, (Nonreporting) **A**1 10 **S** Select Medical Corporation, Mechanicsburg, PA
Primary Contact: Victor J. Galfano, FACHE, Chief Executive Officer
Web address: www.selectspecialtyhospitals.com/company/locations/northern–kentucky.aspx
Control: Corporation, Investor–owned, for–profit **Service:** Long–Term Acute Care hospital

Staffed Beds: 33

☐ **ST. ELIZABETH FORT THOMAS (180001)**, 85 North Grand Avenue, Zip 41075–1796; tel. 859/572–3100, (Total facility includes 26 beds in nursing home–type unit) **A**1 2 9 10 **F**3 4 5 11 15 17 18 20 28 29 30 31 34 35 40 44 45 47 48 49 50 55 56 57 59 60 61 63 64 70 71 74 75 77 78 79 80 81 82 85 86 87 92 93 97 100 101 102 107 108 110 111 114 115 118 119 120 121 123 126 128 129 130 132 135 146 147 **P**6 **S** St. Elizabeth Healthcare, Edgewood, KY
Primary Contact: Thomas Saalfeld, Senior Vice President and Chief Operating Officer
COO: Thomas Saalfeld, Senior Vice President and Chief Operating Officer
CFO: Garren Colvin, Senior Vice President and Chief Financial Officer
CMO: George Hall, M.D., Vice President Medical Affairs
CIO: Alex Rodriguez, Vice President and Chief Information Officer
CHR: Martin Oscadal, Senior Vice President Human Resources
Web address: www.stelizabeth.com
Control: Church–operated, Nongovernment, not–for profit **Service:** General Medical and Surgical

Staffed Beds: 171 **Admissions:** 7377 **Census:** 105 **Outpatient Visits:** 131182 **Births:** 0 **Total Expense ($000):** 85664 **Payroll Expense ($000):** 37465 **Personnel:** 588

ST. ELIZABETH HEALTHCARE FORT THOMAS See St. Elizabeth Fort Thomas

FRANKFORT—Franklin County

☒ **FRANKFORT REGIONAL MEDICAL CENTER (180127)**, 299 King's Daughters Drive, Zip 40601–4186; tel. 502/875–5240 **A**1 2 9 10 19 **F**3 13 15 17 18 20 22 28 29 30 31 34 40 43 45 49 50 51 57 60 64 68 70 72 74 75 76 77 78 79 81 82 85 87 89 93 107 111 119 124 129 130 133 145 146 147 148 **S** HCA, Nashville, TN
Primary Contact: Chip Peal, Chief Executive Officer
CMO: Willis P. McKee, Jr., M.D., Chief Medical Officer
CIO: Craig Willard, Director Information Technology and Systems
CHR: Bev Young, Director Human Resources
Web address: www.frankfortregional.com
Control: Corporation, Investor–owned, for–profit **Service:** Long–Term Acute Care hospital

Staffed Beds: 134 **Admissions:** 4832 **Census:** 51 **Outpatient Visits:** 82574 **Births:** 818 **Total Expense ($000):** 68184 **Payroll Expense ($000):** 26083 **Personnel:** 405

FRANKLIN—Simpson County

☒ **MEDICAL CENTER AT FRANKLIN (181318)**, 1100 Brookhaven Road, Zip 42134–2746; tel. 270/598–4800 **A**1 9 10 18 **F**1 3 4 15 16 17 28 29 30 32 34 35 40 46 57 59 64 67 68 70 72 73 75 77 80 81 86 87 88 89 90 93 98 107 111 114 119 127 128 130 133 135 146 148 **S** Commonwealth Health Corporation, Bowling Green, KY
Primary Contact: Eric Hagan, R.N., Vice President/Administrator
CFO: Ronald G. Sowell, Executive Vice President
CIO: Jean Cherry, Executive Vice President & Chief Information Officer
Web address: www.themedicalcenterfranklin.org
Control: Other not–for–profit (including NFP Corporation) **Service:** General Medical and Surgical

Staffed Beds: 25 **Admissions:** 1245 **Census:** 18 **Outpatient Visits:** 21324 **Births:** 0 **Personnel:** 126

FULTON—Fulton County

☒ **PARKWAY REGIONAL HOSPITAL (180117)**, 2000 Holiday Lane, Zip 42041–8468; tel. 270/472–2522, (Nonreporting) **A**1 9 10 **S** Community Health Systems, Inc., Franklin, TN
Primary Contact: John Ballard, Ph.D., Chief Executive Officer
CFO: Dana Lawrence, Chief Financial Officer
CMO: Chris Gooch, M.D., Chief of Staff
CHR: Janice Bone, Director Human Resources
CNO: Gina Leath, R.N., Chief Nursing Officer
Web address: www.parkwayregionalhospital.com
Control: Corporation, Investor–owned, for–profit **Service:** General Medical and Surgical

Staffed Beds: 70

Hospital, Medicare Provider Number, Address, Telephone, Approval, Facility, and Physician Codes, Health Care System

★ American Hospital Association (AHA) membership
☐ The Joint Commission accreditation
◇ DNV Healthcare Inc. accreditation
○ Healthcare Facilities Accreditation Program
△ Commission on Accreditation of Rehabilitation Facilities (CARF) accreditation

GEORGETOWN—Scott County

✠ **GEORGETOWN COMMUNITY HOSPITAL (180101)**, 1140 Lexington Road, Zip 40324–9362; tel. 502/868–1100 **A**1 5 9 10 **F**3 11 12 13 15 18 28 29 30 31 34 35 40 45 46 48 49 50 57 59 60 68 70 75 76 78 79 81 82 85 87 91 92 93 100 107 108 109 110 111 114 115 116 117 119 124 129 130 131 132 133 146 147 **S** LifePoint Hospitals, Inc., Brentwood, TN
Primary Contact: William Haugh, Administrator
CFO: Patrick C. Bolander, Chief Financial Officer
CMO: Brian Allen, M.D., President Medical Staff
CHR: Marrianne Slonina, Director Human Resources
Web address: www.georgetowncommunityhospital.com
Control: Corporation, Investor–owned, for–profit **Service:** General Medical and Surgical

Staffed Beds: 58 **Admissions:** 1869 **Census:** 18 **Outpatient Visits:** 55051
Births: 199 **Total Expense ($000):** 40415 **Payroll Expense ($000):** 14203
Personnel: 268

GLASGOW—Barren County

☐ **T. J. SAMSON COMMUNITY HOSPITAL (180017)**, 1301 North Race Street, Zip 42141–3483; tel. 270/651–4444, (Nonreporting) **A**1 3 5 9 10 19
Primary Contact: Bud Wethington, Chief Executive Officer
COO: Margie Gentry, Controller
CFO: Steve Fischer, Chief Financial Officer
CMO: Michael Shadowen, M.D., Chief of Staff
CIO: Scott Werkstell, Director Information System
CHR: LaDonna Rogers, Director Human Resources
CNO: Margaret Billingsley, R.N., Chief Nursing Officer
Web address: www.tjsamson.org
Control: Other not–for–profit (including NFP Corporation) **Service:** General Medical and Surgical

Staffed Beds: 196

GREENSBURG—Green County

JANE TODD CRAWFORD HOSPITAL (181325), 202–206 Milby Street, Zip 42743–1100, Mailing Address: P.O. Box 220, Zip 42743–0220; tel. 270/932–4211, (Nonreporting) **A**9 10 18
Primary Contact: Rex A. Tungate, Administrator
CMO: James G. Bland, M.D., Chief of Staff
Control: County–Government, nonfederal **Service:** General Medical and Surgical

Staffed Beds: 45

GREENVILLE—Muhlenberg County

✠ **MUHLENBERG COMMUNITY HOSPITAL (180004)**, 440 Hopkinsville Street, Zip 42345–1172, Mailing Address: P.O. Box 387, Zip 42345–0387; tel. 270/338–8000, (Nonreporting) **A**1 9 10 **S** Alliant Management Services, Louisville, KY
Primary Contact: Stephen L. Meredith, Interim Chief Executive Officer
CFO: Joseph Swab, Chief Financial Officer
CMO: Vincent P. Genovese, M.D., President Medical Staff
CIO: Alan Trail, Director Information Systems
CHR: Lisa R. Hope, Director Human Resources
CNO: Kathy Mitchell, Chief Nursing Officer
Web address: www.mchky.org
Control: Other not–for–profit (including NFP Corporation) **Service:** General Medical and Surgical

Staffed Beds: 90

HARDINSBURG—Breckinridge County

✠ **BRECKINRIDGE MEMORIAL HOSPITAL (181319)**, 1011 Old Highway 60, Zip 40143–2597; tel. 270/756–7000, (Total facility includes 18 beds in nursing home–type unit) **A**1 9 10 18 **F**3 28 29 30 34 35 40 42 48 49 50 53 56 57 59 62 68 75 77 79 81 82 85 86 87 93 100 107 110 111 119 127 129 130 132 133 135 143 148 **P**6 **S** Alliant Management Services, Louisville, KY
Primary Contact: Jeffrey L. Buckley, Interim Chief Executive Officer
CFO: Robert Haralson, Chief Financial Officer
CMO: Robert Chambliss, M.D., Chief Medical Officer
CIO: Virginia D. Bradley, Chief Information Officer
CHR: Clara Cordelia Hall, Chief Human Resources Officer
CNO: Angela Portman, Chief Nursing Officer and Co–Interim Administrator
Web address: www.breckinridgehealth.org/
Control: Other not–for–profit (including NFP Corporation) **Service:** General Medical and Surgical

Staffed Beds: 43 **Admissions:** 1048 **Census:** 30 **Outpatient Visits:** 33498
Births: 0 **Total Expense ($000):** 17161 **Payroll Expense ($000):** 6723
Personnel: 210

HARLAN—Harlan County

☐ **HARLAN ARH HOSPITAL (180050)**, 81 Ball Park Road, Zip 40831–1792; tel. 606/573–8100 **A**1 9 10 19 **F**3 11 13 15 29 30 32 34 35 40 43 50 54 57 59 62 64 70 75 76 77 78 79 81 82 85 86 87 89 93 97 98 102 103 107 108 111 115 118 119 127 129 130 132 146 147 148 **P**6 **S** Appalachian Regional Healthcare, Inc., Lexington, KY
Primary Contact: Paul V. Miles, Interim Community Chief Executive Officer
CFO: Brad Burkhart, Assistant Administrator
CHR: Sabra Howard, Manager Human Resources
Web address: www.arh.org
Control: Other not–for–profit (including NFP Corporation) **Service:** General Medical and Surgical

Staffed Beds: 137 **Admissions:** 4502 **Census:** 52 **Outpatient Visits:** 63667
Births: 285 **Total Expense ($000):** 58740 **Payroll Expense ($000):** 16521
Personnel: 428

HARRODSBURG—Mercer County

✠ **JAMES B. HAGGIN MEMORIAL HOSPITAL (181302)**, 464 Linden Avenue, Zip 40330–1862; tel. 859/734–5441, (Nonreporting) **A**1 5 9 10 18 **S** Alliant Management Services, Louisville, KY
Primary Contact: Victoria L. Reed, R.N., FACHE, Chief Executive Officer
CFO: Tony Patterson, Chief Financial Officer
Web address: www.hagginhosp.org
Control: Other not–for–profit (including NFP Corporation) **Service:** General Medical and Surgical

Staffed Beds: 25

HARTFORD—Ohio County

✠ **OHIO COUNTY HOSPITAL (181323)**, 1211 Main Street, Zip 42347–1619; tel. 270/298–7411 **A**1 9 10 18 **F**3 11 15 17 18 28 29 30 31 34 35 40 41 45 47 49 54 57 58 59 63 64 65 70 74 75 77 78 79 81 85 88 89 92 93 97 107 108 110 111 115 119 127 128 129 130 131 132 133 134 135 144 145 146 147 148 **P**6 **S** QHR, Brentwood, TN
Primary Contact: Blaine Pieper, Chief Executive Officer
CFO: John Tichenor, Chief Financial Officer
CMO: Janna Pathi, M.D., Chief Medical Officer
CHR: Sue Wydick, Director Human Resources
CNO: Athena Minor, Chief Nursing Officer
Web address: www.ohiocountyhospital.com
Control: Other not–for–profit (including NFP Corporation) **Service:** General Medical and Surgical

Staffed Beds: 25 **Admissions:** 1076 **Census:** 10 **Outpatient Visits:** 51855
Births: 0 **Total Expense ($000):** 30412 **Payroll Expense ($000):** 15197
Personnel: 381

HAZARD—Perry County

☐ **HAZARD ARH REGIONAL MEDICAL CENTER (180029)**, 100 Medical Center Drive, Zip 41701–9421; tel. 606/439–6600 **A**1 2 3 5 9 10 19 **F**3 11 12 13 15 17 18 20 22 24 26 28 29 30 31 32 34 35 40 43 46 47 48 49 50 54 57 59 61 62 64 70 71 73 74 75 76 77 78 79 81 82 85 86 87 89 90 93 97 98 101 102 103 107 108 110 111 115 116 118 119 120 121 124 127 129 130 132 146 147 148 **P**6 **S** Appalachian Regional Healthcare, Inc., Lexington, KY
Primary Contact: Donald R. Fields, Senior Community Chief Executive Officer
COO: Donald R. Fields, Senior Community Chief Executive Officer
CMO: J. D. Miller, M.D., Chief Medical Officer
CIO: Jeff Brady, Director Information Systems
CHR: Sheila Cornett, Manager Human Resources
Web address: www.arh.org
Control: Other not–for–profit (including NFP Corporation) **Service:** General Medical and Surgical

Staffed Beds: 308 **Admissions:** 12046 **Census:** 203 **Outpatient Visits:** 92472 **Births:** 381 **Total Expense ($000):** 148093 **Payroll Expense ($000):** 35510 **Personnel:** 1053

HENDERSON—Henderson County

☐ **METHODIST HOSPITAL (180056)**, 1305 North Elm Street, Zip 42420–2775, Mailing Address: P.O. Box 48, Zip 42419–0048; tel. 270/827–7700 **A**1 9 10 13 **F**1 3 4 11 13 15 16 17 18 20 29 30 31 34 35 36 40 45 46 47 49 50 51 53 57 58 59 64 66 67 68 70 71 72 73 74 75 76 77 78 79 80 81 82 85 86 87 88 89 90 92 93 98 102 107 108 110 111 114 116 119 126 127 128 129 130 131 132 135 146 147 148 **P**8
Primary Contact: Bruce D. Begley, Executive Director
COO: David B. Park, Chief Operating Officer and General Counsel
CMO: James Fellows, M.D., Chief of Staff
CIO: Jamie Reid, Information Systems Director
CHR: Ty Kahle, Director Human Resources
CNO: Lois Morgan, MSN, Vice President and Chief Nursing Officer
Web address: www.methodisthospital.net
Control: Church–operated, Nongovernment, not–for profit **Service:** General Medical and Surgical

Staffed Beds: 158 **Admissions:** 5082 **Census:** 67 **Outpatient Visits:** 288380
Births: 668 **Total Expense ($000):** 102913 **Payroll Expense ($000):** 39252
Personnel: 1079

Many Facility Codes have changed. Please refer to the AHA Guide Code Chart.   © 2014 AHA Guide

HOPKINSVILLE—Christian County

☐ **CUMBERLAND HALL HOSPITAL (184014)**, 270 Walton Way, Zip 42240–6808; tel. 270/886–1919 **A**1 9 10 **F**98 99 100 101 102 103 105 **S** Universal Health Services, Inc., King of Prussia, PA
Primary Contact: James Spruyt, Chief Executive Officer
CFO: Chris Jagoditz, Chief Financial Officer
CMO: Deepak Patel, M.D., Medical Director
CIO: Patricia Gray, Director Health Information Management
CHR: Kelly Hagy, Director Human Resources
CNO: Scott Thomason, Director of Nursing
Web address: www.cumberlandhallhospital.com
Control: Corporation, Investor–owned, for–profit **Service:** Psychiatric

> **Staffed Beds:** 97 **Admissions:** 1709 **Census:** 57 **Outpatient Visits:** 0 **Births:** 0 **Total Expense ($000):** 10000 **Payroll Expense ($000):** 4875 **Personnel:** 145

⊡ **JENNIE STUART MEDICAL CENTER (180051)**, 320 West 18th Street, Zip 42240–1965, Mailing Address: P.O. Box 2400, Zip 42241–2400; tel. 270/887–0100, (Nonreporting) **A**1 9 10 **S** QHR, Brentwood, TN
Primary Contact: Eric A. Lee, President and Chief Executive Officer
CMO: Casey Covington, M.D., President Elect, Medical Staff
CIO: Jerry Houston, Director Information Systems
CHR: Austin Moss, Vice President Human Resources
Web address: www.jsmc.org
Control: Other not–for–profit (including NFP Corporation) **Service:** General Medical and Surgical

> **Staffed Beds:** 139

☐ **WESTERN STATE HOSPITAL (184002)**, Russellville Road, Zip 42240–3017, Mailing Address: P.O. Box 2200, Zip 42241–2200; tel. 270/889–6025 **A**1 10 **F**98 102 103 130 **P**5
Primary Contact: Roger Westfall, Director
CFO: Jessica Cates, Fiscal Manager
CMO: Nayyar Iqbal, M.D., Director Medical Staff
CIO: Valerie Majors, Director Information Services
CHR: James L. Hayes, Director Human Resources
CNO: Jill Thomas, Director of Nursing
Web address: www.westernstatehospital.ky.gov
Control: State–Government, nonfederal **Service:** Psychiatric

> **Staffed Beds:** 205 **Admissions:** 2030 **Census:** 113 **Outpatient Visits:** 0 **Births:** 0 **Total Expense ($000):** 16441 **Payroll Expense ($000):** 10165 **Personnel:** 598

HORSE CAVE—Hart County

★ **CAVERNA MEMORIAL HOSPITAL (181314)**, 1501 South Dixie Street, Zip 42749–1477; tel. 270/786–2191 **A**9 10 18 **F**3 15 34 40 45 57 59 64 70 81 85 89 107 111 114 119 127 128 133 135 **P**6 **S** Alliant Management Services, Louisville, KY
Primary Contact: Alan B. Alexander, Chief Executive Officer
CFO: Richard Snapp, Chief Financial Officer
CMO: Evelyn Salisbury, M.D., Chief of Staff
CIO: Brad Lowe, Director Information Systems
CHR: Cathy Szabo, Director Human Resources
CNO: Vanessa Burd, R.N., Chief Nursing Officer
Web address: www.cavernahospital.com
Control: Other not–for–profit (including NFP Corporation) **Service:** General Medical and Surgical

> **Staffed Beds:** 25 **Admissions:** 314 **Census:** 3 **Outpatient Visits:** 17641 **Births:** 0 **Total Expense ($000):** 10817 **Payroll Expense ($000):** 4952 **Personnel:** 110

HYDEN—Leslie County

MARY BRECKINRIDGE ARH HOSPITAL (181316), 130 Kate Ireland Drive, Zip 41749–9071, Mailing Address: P.O. Box 447–A, Zip 41749–0717; tel. 606/672–2901 **A**9 10 18 **F**2 3 11 15 29 30 32 34 35 40 41 50 57 59 62 65 68 75 77 81 87 92 93 107 110 115 119 130 133 135 146 **P**6 **S** Appalachian Regional Healthcare, Inc., Lexington, KY
Primary Contact: Mallie S. Noble, Administrator
COO: Nathan W. Lee, Chief Executive Officer
CFO: Robert Besten, Chief Financial Officer
CMO: Roy Varghese, M.D., Chief of Staff
CIO: Frank Baker, Chief Information Officer
CHR: Beulah Couch, Director Human Resources
Web address: www.frontiernursing.org
Control: Other not–for–profit (including NFP Corporation) **Service:** General Medical and Surgical

> **Staffed Beds:** 25 **Admissions:** 1014 **Census:** 11 **Outpatient Visits:** 9000 **Births:** 0 **Personnel:** 118

IRVINE—Estill County

★ **MARCUM AND WALLACE MEMORIAL HOSPITAL (181301)**, 60 Mercy Court, Zip 40336–1331; tel. 606/723–2115 **A**9 10 18 **F**3 15 29 30 34 40 43 57 59 75 81 87 97 107 110 115 118 119 127 129 133 **S** Mercy Health, Cincinnati, OH
Primary Contact: Susan Starling, President and Chief Executive Officer
CFO: Lori Witt, Site Finance Director
CMO: Maher Kassis, M.D., Chief Medical Staff
CHR: Dana Stepp, Human Resources Officer
CNO: Trena Stocker, Chief Nursing Executive
Web address: www.marcumandwallace.org
Control: Church–operated, Nongovernment, not–for profit **Service:** General Medical and Surgical

> **Staffed Beds:** 25 **Admissions:** 1030 **Census:** 11 **Outpatient Visits:** 74450 **Births:** 0 **Total Expense ($000):** 17342 **Payroll Expense ($000):** 7751 **Personnel:** 140

JACKSON—Breathitt County

⊡ **KENTUCKY RIVER MEDICAL CENTER (180139)**, 540 Jett Drive, Zip 41339–9622; tel. 606/666–6000, (Nonreporting) **A**1 9 10 20 **S** Community Health Systems, Inc., Franklin, TN
CFO: Michael Ackley, Chief Financial Officer
CMO: Eunice Johnson, M.D., Chief Medical Staff
CIO: Diana Tyra, Director Health Information
CHR: Naomi Mitchell, Director Human Resources
Web address: www.kentuckyrivermc.com
Control: Corporation, Investor–owned, for–profit **Service:** General Medical and Surgical

> **Staffed Beds:** 54

LA GRANGE—Oldham County

★ ○ **BAPTIST HEALTH LA GRANGE (180138)**, 1025 New Moody Lane, Zip 40031–9154; tel. 502/222–5388, (Total facility includes 30 beds in nursing home–type unit) **A**3 5 9 10 11 **F**3 7 11 13 15 18 28 29 30 34 35 36 40 43 45 46 49 50 54 56 57 59 64 68 70 74 75 76 77 78 79 81 82 85 86 87 93 97 107 108 110 111 114 119 128 129 130 131 132 133 135 146 147 148 **P**6 **S** Baptist Health, Louisville, KY
Primary Contact: Chris Roty, President
CFO: Jim Morris, Vice President Finance
CMO: Matt McDanald, M.D., Chief Medical Officer
CIO: David Bensema, Chief Information Officer
CHR: Melissa Payton, Manager Human Resources
CNO: Karen Higdon, R.N., Vice President and Chief Nursing Officer
Web address: www.baptisthealthlagrange.com
Control: Other not–for–profit (including NFP Corporation) **Service:** General Medical and Surgical

> **Staffed Beds:** 108 **Admissions:** 3480 **Census:** 48 **Outpatient Visits:** 45366 **Births:** 551 **Total Expense ($000):** 47447 **Payroll Expense ($000):** 21461 **Personnel:** 334

LEBANON—Marion County

⊡ **SPRING VIEW HOSPITAL (180024)**, 320 Loretto Road, Zip 40033–1300; tel. 270/692–3161 **A**1 9 10 **F**3 11 13 15 28 29 34 35 40 45 48 49 50 51 57 59 64 70 75 76 79 81 85 86 87 90 92 93 107 108 110 111 114 118 119 127 130 133 135 146 147 148 **P**6 **S** LifePoint Hospitals, Inc., Brentwood, TN
Primary Contact: Timothy R. Trottier, Chief Executive Officer
CFO: Denise Thomas, Chief Financial Officer
CIO: Douglas Bland, Manager Information Services
CHR: Ann Dabney, Manager Human Resources
CNO: Linda Hunter, Chief Nursing Officer
Web address: www.springviewhospital.com
Control: Corporation, Investor–owned, for–profit **Service:** General Medical and Surgical

> **Staffed Beds:** 60 **Admissions:** 1552 **Census:** 15 **Outpatient Visits:** 40722 **Births:** 348 **Total Expense ($000):** 22930 **Payroll Expense ($000):** 9870 **Personnel:** 224

Hospital, Medicare Provider Number, Address, Telephone, Approval, Facility, and Physician Codes, Health Care System

★ American Hospital Association (AHA) membership
☐ The Joint Commission accreditation
◇ DNV Healthcare Inc. accreditation
○ Healthcare Facilities Accreditation Program
△ Commission on Accreditation of Rehabilitation Facilities (CARF) accreditation

LEITCHFIELD—Grayson County

☐ **TWIN LAKES REGIONAL MEDICAL CENTER (180070)**, 910 Wallace Avenue, Zip 42754–2414; tel. 270/259–9400 **A**1 9 10 **F**3 11 13 15 28 29 30 31 34 40 53 57 59 68 70 78 79 81 82 85 86 87 93 107 108 110 111 115 118 119 129 130 131 132 133 135 144 146 148 **P**6 **S** Alliant Management Services, Louisville, KY
Primary Contact: Wayne Meriwether, Chief Executive Officer
COO: Deneace Clemons, Chief Operating Officer
CFO: Scott Arndell, Chief Financial Officer
CMO: John Evans, M.D., Chief Medical Officer
CIO: Mandy Bryant, Chief Information Officer
CHR: Mandi Filburn, Director Human Resources
Web address: www.tlrmc.com
Control: Other not–for–profit (including NFP Corporation) **Service:** General Medical and Surgical

Staffed Beds: 75 **Admissions:** 2741 **Census:** 29 **Outpatient Visits:** 82697 **Births:** 367 **Total Expense ($000):** 36604 **Payroll Expense ($000):** 13442 **Personnel:** 309

LEXINGTON—Fayette County

✠ **BAPTIST HEALTH LEXINGTON (180103)**, 1740 Nicholasville Road, Zip 40503–1499; tel. 859/260–6100 **A**1 2 9 10 **F**3 11 12 13 15 17 18 20 22 24 26 28 29 30 31 34 35 36 40 44 48 49 53 54 55 56 57 58 59 60 62 64 68 70 72 74 75 76 77 78 79 81 84 85 86 87 89 92 93 97 107 108 110 111 114 115 117 118 119 120 121 124 126 129 130 131 132 135 144 146 147 148 **S** Baptist Health, Louisville, KY
Primary Contact: William G. Sisson, President
COO: Karen S. Hill, R.N., Chief Operating Officer and Chief Nursing Officer
CMO: Preston Nunelley, M.D., Chief Medical Officer
CIO: Lisa Fluty, Director Information Services
CHR: Lynette Walker, R.N., Vice President Human Resources
Web address: www.centralbap.com
Control: Other not–for–profit (including NFP Corporation) **Service:** General Medical and Surgical

Staffed Beds: 344 **Admissions:** 18318 **Census:** 225 **Outpatient Visits:** 241346 **Births:** 3567 **Total Expense ($000):** 389905 **Payroll Expense ($000):** 14096 **Personnel:** 2192

★ △ **CARDINAL HILL REHABILITATION HOSPITAL (183026)**, 2050 Versailles Road, Zip 40504–1405; tel. 859/254–5701, (Total facility includes 74 beds in nursing home–type unit) **A**3 5 7 9 10 **F**2 3 9 11 29 30 32 34 35 38 50 53 56 57 58 59 62 64 65 68 74 75 79 86 87 90 91 92 93 94 95 96 128 130 131 132 134 135 143 146
Primary Contact: Gary Payne, Chief Executive Officer
CFO: Marty Lautner, Vice President Finance and Chief Financial Officer
CMO: William Lester, M.D., Vice President Medical Affairs
CIO: LouAnn Hyder, Director Information Integrity Management
CHR: Barry K. Lindeman, Director Human Resources
CNO: Maureen Couture, Chief Nursing Officer and Vice President Nursing
Web address: www.cardinalhill.org
Control: Other not–for–profit (including NFP Corporation) **Service:** Rehabilitation

Staffed Beds: 232 **Admissions:** 2171 **Census:** 93 **Outpatient Visits:** 38300 **Births:** 0 **Total Expense ($000):** 61219 **Payroll Expense ($000):** 32095 **Personnel:** 594

★ **CONTINUING CARE HOSPITAL (182002)**, 150 North Eagle Creek Drive, 5th Floor, Zip 40509–1805; tel. 859/967–5744 **A**10 **F**82 84 128 **S** Catholic Health Initiatives, Englewood, CO
Primary Contact: Tonja Williams, MSN, R.N., President
CMO: Michael Miedler, M.D., Chief Medical Officer
CNO: Regina Masters, R.N., Director of Nursing
Control: Church–operated, Nongovernment, not–for profit **Service:** Long–Term Acute Care hospital

Staffed Beds: 45 **Admissions:** 517 **Census:** 37 **Outpatient Visits:** 0 **Births:** 0 **Total Expense ($000):** 18463 **Payroll Expense ($000):** 5520 **Personnel:** 97

☐ **EASTERN STATE HOSPITAL (184004)**, 627 West Fourth Street, Zip 40508–1294; tel. 859/246–7000, (Nonreporting) **A**1 3 5 9 10
Primary Contact: David Hanna, Ph.D., Interim Chief Executive Officer
COO: Susan M. Griffith, Chief Operations Officer
CFO: Tambara Nalle, Chief Financial Officer
CMO: Scott A. Haas, M.D., Chief Medical Officer
CIO: Bud Stone, Director Information Systems
CHR: Jerry Kersey, Director Employee Relations
CNO: Kristan Mowder, Director Administration and Patient Care Services
Web address: www.bluegrass.org
Control: State–Government, nonfederal **Service:** Psychiatric

Staffed Beds: 197

FEDERAL MEDICAL CENTER, 3301 Leestown Road, Zip 40511–8799; tel. 859/255–6812, (Nonreporting)
Primary Contact: Francisco Quintana, Warden
CFO: Mike Kinsel, Controller
CMO: Michael Growse, M.D., Clinical Director
Control: Department of Justice, Government, federal **Service:** Hospital unit of an institution (prison hospital, college infimary, etc.)

Staffed Beds: 22

☐ **RIDGE BEHAVIORAL HEALTH SYSTEM (184009)**, 3050 Rio Dosa Drive, Zip 40509–1540; tel. 859/269–2325, (Nonreporting) **A**1 3 5 9 10 **S** Universal Health Services, Inc., King of Prussia, PA
Primary Contact: Nina W. Eisner, Chief Executive Officer and Managing Director
COO: Samantha Castle, Chief Operating Officer
CFO: Richard McDowell, Chief Financial Officer
CMO: Michael Rieser, M.D., Medical Director
CHR: Samantha Castle, Chief Operating Officer
CNO: Georgia Swank, Chief Nursing Officer
Web address: www.ridgebhs.com
Control: Corporation, Investor–owned, for–profit **Service:** Psychiatric

Staffed Beds: 110

✠ **SAINT JOSEPH EAST (180143)**, 150 North Eagle Creek Drive, Zip 40509–1805; tel. 859/967–5000 **A**1 5 9 10 **F**3 8 12 13 15 17 18 20 22 24 26 28 29 30 31 40 47 49 50 60 68 70 72 73 74 75 76 77 78 79 81 82 85 86 89 90 93 107 108 111 115 118 119 120 121 122 123 126 128 129 142 146 147 148 **S** Catholic Health Initiatives, Englewood, CO
Primary Contact: Eric Gilliam, President
COO: Christine Mays, R.N., Chief Operating Officer and Chief Nurse Executive
CFO: Melinda S. Evans, Vice President Finance
CIO: Janie Fergus, Director and Chief Information Officer
Web address: www.sjhlex.org
Control: Church–operated, Nongovernment, not–for profit **Service:** General Medical and Surgical

Staffed Beds: 144 **Admissions:** 8247 **Census:** 87 **Outpatient Visits:** 108197 **Births:** 2522 **Total Expense ($000):** 145598 **Payroll Expense ($000):** 42180 **Personnel:** 720

✠ **SAINT JOSEPH HOSPITAL (180010)**, One St. Joseph Drive, Zip 40504–3754; tel. 859/278–3436 **A**1 3 5 9 10 **F**1 3 8 11 12 15 17 18 19 20 22 24 25 26 27 28 29 30 31 34 35 37 40 41 42 45 47 49 50 51 54 55 56 57 58 59 62 64 65 66 67 68 70 74 77 78 79 81 82 83 84 85 86 87 89 90 92 93 94 96 97 107 110 111 114 115 116 117 118 119 120 121 123 126 127 129 130 132 135 141 144 146 147 148 **S** Catholic Health Initiatives, Englewood, CO
Primary Contact: John E. Smithhisler, President
COO: Christine Mays, R.N., Chief Operating Officer and Chief Nurse Executive
CFO: Melinda S. Evans, Vice President Finance
CIO: Janie Fergus, Director and Chief Information Officer
Web address: www.sjhlex.org
Control: Church–operated, Nongovernment, not–for profit **Service:** General Medical and Surgical

Staffed Beds: 291 **Admissions:** 16176 **Census:** 229 **Outpatient Visits:** 98076 **Births:** 0 **Total Expense ($000):** 297331 **Payroll Expense ($000):** 81974 **Personnel:** 1300

✠ **SELECT SPECIALTY HOSPITAL–LEXINGTON (182003)**, 310 South Limestone Street, 3rd Floor, Zip 40508–3008; tel. 859/226–7096, (Nonreporting) **A**1 10 **S** Select Medical Corporation, Mechanicsburg, PA
Primary Contact: Mary Lou Guinle, FACHE, Chief Executive Officer
CMO: Fadi Bacha, M.D., Chief Medical Officer
CHR: Tina Kirkland–Rose, Coordinator Human Resources
CNO: Katie Meredith, Chief Nursing Officer
Web address: www.lexington.selectspecialtyhospitals.com/
Control: Corporation, Investor–owned, for–profit **Service:** Long–Term Acute Care hospital

Staffed Beds: 41

☐ **SHRINERS HOSPITALS FOR CHILDREN–LEXINGTON (183300)**, 1900 Richmond Road, Zip 40502–1298; tel. 859/266–2101, (Nonreporting) **A**1 3 5 9 10 **S** Shriners Hospitals for Children, Tampa, FL
Primary Contact: Tony Lewgood, Administrator
CFO: Robert Montgomery, Chief Financial Officer
CMO: Chester Tylkowski, M.D., Chief of Staff
CIO: David Brian, Director Information Services
Web address: www.shrinershospitalsforchildren.org/Hospitals/Locations/Lexington.aspx
Control: Other not–for–profit (including NFP Corporation) **Service:** Children's orthopedic

Staffed Beds: 50

Many Facility Codes have changed. Please refer to the AHA Guide Code Chart.
© 2014 AHA Guide

⊞ **UNIVERSITY OF KENTUCKY ALBERT B. CHANDLER HOSPITAL (180067)**, 800 Rose Street, Zip 40536–0293; tel. 859/323–5000, (Includes KENTUCKY CHILDREN'S HOSPITAL, N–100 – 800 Rose Street, tel. 859/257–1000; UK HEALTHCARE GOOD SAMARITAN HOSPITAL, 310 South Limestone Street, Zip 40508–3008; tel. 859/226–7000; Michael Karpf, M.D., Executive Vice President of Health Affairs) **A**1 2 3 5 8 9 10 **F**3 5 6 7 9 11 12 13 15 16 17 18 19 20 21 22 23 24 26 27 28 29 30 31 32 34 35 36 37 38 39 40 41 43 44 45 46 47 48 49 50 51 52 54 55 56 57 58 59 60 61 64 65 66 68 70 72 73 74 75 76 77 78 79 81 82 84 85 86 87 88 89 92 93 94 95 96 97 98 99 100 101 102 103 104 107 108 110 111 113 114 115 118 119 120 121 123 124 126 129 130 131 132 134 135 136 137 138 139 140 141 142 145 146 147 148 **P**6
Primary Contact: Michael Karpf, M.D., Executive Vice President of Health Affairs
CHR: Kimberly P. Wilson, Director Human Resources
Web address: www.ukhealthcare.uky.edu
Control: State–Government, nonfederal **Service:** General Medical and Surgical

Staffed Beds: 721 **Admissions:** 35565 **Census:** 577 **Outpatient Visits:** 1120845 **Births:** 1858 **Total Expense ($000):** 902797 **Payroll Expense ($000):** 278949 **Personnel:** 5836

UNIVERSITY OF KENTUCKY HOSPITAL See University of Kentucky Albert B. Chandler Hospital

⊞ **VETERANS AFFAIRS MEDICAL CENTER–LEXINGTON**, 1101 Veterans Drive, Zip 40502–2235; tel. 859/281–4901, (Total facility includes 61 beds in nursing home–type unit) **A**1 3 5 **F**3 4 5 8 12 18 20 22 26 29 30 31 33 34 35 36 38 39 40 44 45 46 47 48 49 52 54 56 57 58 59 60 61 63 64 65 66 68 70 74 75 77 78 79 81 82 83 84 85 86 87 91 92 93 95 96 97 98 100 102 103 104 105 106 107 111 114 116 117 118 119 128 129 130 131 132 135 143 144 146 147 148 **P**6 **S** Department of Veterans Affairs, Washington, DC
Primary Contact: Emma Metcalf, MSN, R.N., Director
CFO: Patricia Swisshelm, Acting Chief Fiscal Service
CMO: Patricia Breeden, M.D., Chief of Staff
CIO: Jeffrey Sutton, Chief Information Officer
CHR: Laura Faulkner, Chief Human Resource Management Service
CNO: Mary Kelly McCullough, Associate Director Patient Care Services
Web address: www.lexington.va.gov/
Control: Veterans Affairs, Government, federal **Service:** General Medical and Surgical

Staffed Beds: 199 **Admissions:** 7795 **Census:** 136 **Outpatient Visits:** 470742 **Births:** 0 **Personnel:** 1941

LIBERTY—Casey County

☐ **CASEY COUNTY HOSPITAL (181309)**, 187 Wolford Avenue, Zip 42539–3278; tel. 606/787–6275, (Nonreporting) **A**1 9 10 18
Primary Contact: Rex A. Tungate, Administrator
Control: County–Government, nonfederal **Service:** General Medical and Surgical

Staffed Beds: 24

LONDON—Laurel County

⊞ **SAINT JOSEPH – LONDON (180011)**, 1001 Saint Joseph Lane, Zip 40741–8345; tel. 606/330–6000 **A**1 9 10 19 **F**3 13 15 17 18 20 22 24 26 28 29 30 31 34 35 40 42 49 50 51 57 59 60 61 64 68 70 74 76 78 79 81 82 85 87 89 92 93 107 110 111 114 115 119 129 130 131 146 147 **S** Catholic Health Initiatives, Englewood, CO
Primary Contact: Greg D. Gerard, President
CFO: Christy Spitser, Vice President Finance and Business Development
CMO: Shelley Stanko, M.D., Chief Medical Officer
CHR: Sandra Turquesa, Senior Human Resources Business Partner
CNO: Chris Schweighardt, R.N., Chief Nursing Officer
Web address: www.saintjosephhealthsystem.org
Control: Church–operated, Nongovernment, not–for profit **Service:** General Medical and Surgical

Staffed Beds: 114 **Admissions:** 7366 **Census:** 75 **Outpatient Visits:** 111163 **Births:** 1130 **Total Expense ($000):** 153193 **Payroll Expense ($000):** 40514 **Personnel:** 646

LOUISA—Lawrence County

⊞ **THREE RIVERS MEDICAL CENTER (180128)**, 2485 Highway 644, Zip 41230–9242, Mailing Address: P.O. Box 769, Zip 41230–0769; tel. 606/638–9451, (Nonreporting) **A**1 9 10 20 **S** Community Health Systems, Inc., Franklin, TN
Primary Contact: Greg Kiser, Chief Executive Officer
CFO: Michael Ackley, Chief Financial Officer
CHR: Pat Hart, Director Human Resources
Web address: www.threeriversmedicalcenter.com
Control: Corporation, Investor–owned, for–profit **Service:** General Medical and Surgical

Staffed Beds: 80

LOUISVILLE—Jefferson County

⊞ △ **BAPTIST HEALTH LOUISVILLE (180130)**, 4000 Kresge Way, Zip 40207–4676; tel. 502/897–8100 **A**1 2 3 5 7 9 10 **F**3 5 8 11 12 13 15 17 18 20 22 24 26 28 29 30 31 33 34 36 37 38 40 44 45 46 47 48 49 50 51 53 54 56 57 58 59 60 61 62 64 68 70 72 74 75 76 78 79 81 82 83 84 85 86 87 89 90 93 97 98 100 101 102 103 104 105 107 108 110 111 114 115 116 117 118 119 120 121 123 124 126 129 130 131 132 134 135 145 146 147 148 **S** Baptist Health, Louisville, KY
Primary Contact: David L. Gray, FACHE, President
CFO: Jim Morris, Vice President Finance
CMO: Kenneth Anderson, M.D., Vice President and Chief Medical Officer
CIO: Shari Price, Director Information Services
CHR: Steven Rudolf, Vice President Human Resources
CNO: Karen Newman, Ed.D., Vice President and Chief Nursing Officer
Web address: www.baptisteast.com
Control: Other not–for–profit (including NFP Corporation) **Service:** General Medical and Surgical

Staffed Beds: 519 **Admissions:** 26051 **Census:** 354 **Outpatient Visits:** 271962 **Births:** 2923 **Total Expense ($000):** 453169 **Payroll Expense ($000):** 171690 **Personnel:** 2846

☐ **CENTRAL STATE HOSPITAL (184015)**, 10510 LaGrange Road, Zip 40223–1228; tel. 502/253–7000 **A**1 3 5 10 **F**29 30 59 75 98 101 102 **P**6
Primary Contact: Vital Shah, M.D., Director
CFO: Robert Underhill, Director of Business Services
CMO: Vital Shah, M.D., Director
CIO: Steven Puckett, Director Information Technology
CHR: Josie Goodman, Associate Director
CNO: Michelle Napier, Director of Nursing
Control: State–Government, nonfederal **Service:** Psychiatric

Staffed Beds: 112 **Admissions:** 1044 **Census:** 59 **Total Expense ($000):** 28916 **Payroll Expense ($000):** 16622 **Personnel:** 342

★ △ **FRAZIER REHAB INSTITUTE**, 220 Abraham Flexner Way, Zip 40202–1887; tel. 502/582–7400 **A**3 5 7 9 **F**28 29 30 34 35 42 43 44 50 54 56 57 58 59 60 68 74 75 77 78 79 82 84 85 86 87 90 91 93 95 96 100 130 131 132 146 148 **P**6 **S** Catholic Health Initiatives, Englewood, CO
Primary Contact: Randy L. Napier, President
CFO: Robert Steltenpohl, Vice President and Chief Financial Officer
CMO: Darryl Kaelin, M.D., Medical Director
CHR: Lisa Burris, Manager Human Resources
Web address: www.frazierrehab.org
Control: Other not–for–profit (including NFP Corporation) **Service:** Rehabilitation

Staffed Beds: 79 **Admissions:** 1658 **Census:** 67 **Outpatient Visits:** 96386 **Births:** 0 **Total Expense ($000):** 56245 **Payroll Expense ($000):** 20931 **Personnel:** 391

⊞ **JEWISH HOSPITAL (180040)**, 200 Abraham Flexner Way, Zip 40202–1886; tel. 502/587–4011 **A**1 2 3 5 9 10 **F**1 3 8 11 14 15 17 18 20 22 24 26 28 29 30 31 34 35 36 37 40 42 43 44 45 46 47 48 49 50 53 54 56 57 58 59 60 61 64 67 68 70 74 75 76 78 79 80 82 84 85 87 89 92 97 98 100 107 108 110 111 112 114 115 116 117 118 119 121 123 124 126 130 131 132 135 136 137 138 139 140 141 142 145 146 **P**6 **S** Catholic Health Initiatives, Englewood, CO
Primary Contact: Joseph Gilene, President
CFO: Ronald Farr, Chief Financial Officer
CMO: James P. Ketterhagen, M.D., Senior Vice President and Chief Medical Officer
CIO: Thomas Wittman, Chief Information Officer
CHR: Julie McGregor, Vice President and Chief People Officer
CNO: Cheryl Fugatte, MSN, Vice President and Chief Nursing Officer
Web address: www.jewishhospital.org
Control: Other not–for–profit (including NFP Corporation) **Service:** General Medical and Surgical

Staffed Beds: 342 **Admissions:** 17110 **Census:** 251 **Outpatient Visits:** 106941 **Births:** 0 **Total Expense ($000):** 253300 **Payroll Expense ($000):** 96777 **Personnel:** 1682

KINDRED HOSPITAL LOUISVILLE AT JEWISH HOSPITAL See Kindred Hospital–Louisville

⊞ **KINDRED HOSPITAL–LOUISVILLE (182001)**, 1313 Saint Anthony Place, Zip 40204–1740; tel. 502/587–7001, (Includes KINDRED HOSPITAL LOUISVILLE AT JEWISH HOSPITAL, 200 Abraham Flexner Way, 2nd Floor, Zip 40202; tel. 502/587–3999; David Johnson, Chief Executive Officer), (Nonreporting) **A**1 3 5 10 **S** Kindred Healthcare, Louisville, KY
Primary Contact: Wayne Blanchard, Market Chief Executive Officer
Web address: www.kindredlouisville.com/
Control: Corporation, Investor–owned, for–profit **Service:** Long–Term Acute Care hospital

Staffed Beds: 197

Hospital, Medicare Provider Number, Address, Telephone, Approval, Facility, and Physician Codes, Health Care System

★ American Hospital Association (AHA) membership
☐ The Joint Commission accreditation
◇ DNV Healthcare Inc. accreditation
○ Healthcare Facilities Accreditation Program
△ Commission on Accreditation of Rehabilitation Facilities (CARF) accreditation

KY

★ **KOSAIR CHILDREN'S HOSPITAL**, 231 East Chestnut Street, Zip 40202–1821; tel. 502/629–6000 **A**2 3 5 9 **F**3 8 11 19 21 23 25 27 29 30 31 32 34 35 38 39 40 41 42 43 44 45 50 54 57 58 59 64 65 68 72 74 75 78 79 81 82 84 85 86 87 88 89 92 93 96 98 99 100 101 102 107 108 111 114 115 119 130 131 132 134 136 137 138 146 **S** Norton Healthcare, Louisville, KY
Primary Contact: Thomas D. Kmetz, President
Web address: www.kosairchildrens.com/
Control: Other not–for–profit (including NFP Corporation) **Service:** Children's general

Staffed Beds: 260 **Admissions:** 10523 **Census:** 212 **Outpatient Visits:** 144205 **Births:** 0 **Total Expense ($000):** 299912 **Payroll Expense ($000):** 98015 **Personnel:** 1578

★ **NORTON AUDUBON HOSPITAL**, One Audubon Plaza Drive, Zip 40217–1300, Mailing Address: P.O. Box 17550, Zip 40217–0550; tel. 502/636–7111 **A**2 3 5 9 **F**3 5 11 15 17 18 20 22 24 26 28 29 30 31 34 35 37 40 45 46 47 48 49 50 56 57 59 64 68 70 74 75 78 79 81 82 85 86 87 107 108 110 111 112 114 115 118 119 129 130 131 132 146 147 **S** Norton Healthcare, Louisville, KY
Primary Contact: Jon Cooper, President
CFO: Jonathan Presser, Vice President Finance and Operations
Web address: www.nortonhealthcare.com/NortonAudubonHospital
Control: Other not–for–profit (including NFP Corporation) **Service:** General Medical and Surgical

Staffed Beds: 278 **Admissions:** 13993 **Census:** 187 **Outpatient Visits:** 132294 **Births:** 0 **Total Expense ($000):** 222157 **Payroll Expense ($000):** 77895 **Personnel:** 1327

★ **NORTON BROWNSBORO HOSPITAL**, 4960 Norton Healthcare Boulevard, Zip 40241–2831; tel. 502/446–8000 **A**9 **F**3 15 18 20 22 29 30 31 34 35 36 37 40 44 45 46 47 48 49 56 57 58 59 64 68 70 74 75 78 79 81 82 85 86 87 92 107 108 110 111 112 114 115 119 129 130 131 132 146 148 **S** Norton Healthcare, Louisville, KY
Primary Contact: John D. Harryman, Chief Administrative Officer
CFO: Andy Strausbaugh, Vice President Finance and Operations
CMO: Gregory Juhl, M.D., Medical Director
CNO: Regina J. Hymer, DNP, RN, CENP, MSN, Vice President Patient Care Services and Chief Nursing Officer
Web address: www.nortonhealthcare.com/nortonbrownsborohospital
Control: Other not–for–profit (including NFP Corporation) **Service:** General Medical and Surgical

Staffed Beds: 117 **Admissions:** 6562 **Census:** 66 **Outpatient Visits:** 74434 **Births:** 0 **Total Expense ($000):** 124002 **Payroll Expense ($000):** 37566 **Personnel:** 692

NORTON HEALTHCARE PAVILION See Norton Hospital

⊠ **NORTON HOSPITAL (180088)**, 200 East Chestnut Street, Zip 40202–1800, Mailing Address: P.O. Box 35070, Zip 40232–5070; tel. 502/629–8000, (Includes NORTON HEALTHCARE PAVILION, 315 East Broadway, Zip 40202–1703; tel. 502/629–2000) **A**1 2 3 5 9 10 **F**3 11 12 13 15 17 18 20 22 24 26 28 29 30 31 34 35 36 38 39 40 43 44 45 46 49 50 51 53 55 56 57 59 64 68 70 74 75 76 78 79 81 82 84 85 86 87 92 93 96 98 100 101 102 107 108 110 111 114 115 116 117 118 119 126 130 132 146 147 148 **S** Norton Healthcare, Louisville, KY
Primary Contact: Matthew Ayers, Chief Executive Officer
CFO: Carl Amorose, Vice President Finance
Web address: www.nortonhealthcare.com/nortonhospital
Control: Other not–for–profit (including NFP Corporation) **Service:** General Medical and Surgical

Staffed Beds: 348 **Admissions:** 16667 **Census:** 246 **Outpatient Visits:** 95103 **Births:** 3129 **Total Expense ($000):** 317913 **Payroll Expense ($000):** 100618 **Personnel:** 1556

★ **NORTON SUBURBAN HOSPITAL**, 4001 Dutchmans Lane, Zip 40207–4799; tel. 502/893–1000 **A**2 3 5 9 **F**3 8 11 12 13 15 18 19 20 29 30 34 35 36 40 44 45 47 49 50 56 57 59 64 68 70 72 73 74 75 76 78 79 81 82 85 86 87 107 108 110 111 114 115 118 119 120 121 123 124 126 130 132 134 135 146 147 **S** Norton Healthcare, Louisville, KY
Primary Contact: Charlotte Ipsan, President
CFO: Mark Kircher, Associate Vice President Finance
CMO: Steven Hester, M.D., Vice President Medical Affairs
CIO: Joseph DeVenuto, Vice President and Chief Information Officer
Web address: www.nortonhealthcare.com/nortonsuburbanhospital
Control: Other not–for–profit (including NFP Corporation) **Service:** General Medical and Surgical

Staffed Beds: 351 **Admissions:** 13536 **Census:** 164 **Outpatient Visits:** 87568 **Births:** 5195 **Total Expense ($000):** 196163 **Payroll Expense ($000):** 68623 **Personnel:** 1193

★ **OUR LADY OF PEACE**, 2020 Newburg Road, Zip 40205–1879; tel. 502/479–4500 **A**3 5 9 **F**5 29 30 34 35 43 53 59 68 98 99 100 101 104 105 106 130 132 143 146 **S** Catholic Health Initiatives, Englewood, CO
Primary Contact: Jennifer Nolan, President
COO: Martha S. Mather, Chief Operating Officer and Vice President
CFO: Beckie Kistler, Director of Finance
CHR: Jan Ostbloom, Human Resources Consultant
CNO: Brad Lincks, R.N., Chief Nursing Officer and Vice President
Web address: www.hopehasaplace.org
Control: Other not–for–profit (including NFP Corporation) **Service:** Psychiatric

Staffed Beds: 261 **Admissions:** 6163 **Census:** 184 **Outpatient Visits:** 22064 **Births:** 0 **Total Expense ($000):** 53588 **Payroll Expense ($000):** 25537 **Personnel:** 516

⊠ **ROBLEY REX VETERANS AFFAIRS MEDICAL CENTER**, 800 Zorn Avenue, Zip 40206–1499; tel. 502/287–4000, (Nonreporting) **A**1 2 3 5 **S** Department of Veterans Affairs, Washington, DC
Primary Contact: Marylee Rothschild, M.D., Interim Director
CFO: Barbara Roberts, Chief Financial Officer
CMO: Marylee Rothschild, M.D., Chief of Staff
CIO: Augustine Bittner, Chief Information Officer
CHR: Angela Dutton, Chief Human Resources Management Service
Web address: www.louisville.va.gov
Control: Veterans Affairs, Government, federal **Service:** General Medical and Surgical

Staffed Beds: 116

★ **STS. MARY & ELIZABETH HOSPITAL**, 1850 Bluegrass Avenue, Zip 40215–1199; tel. 502/361–6000 **A**3 5 9 **F**3 8 11 12 15 18 20 22 29 30 31 34 35 39 40 42 43 44 45 47 49 50 53 54 59 60 64 68 69 70 74 75 78 79 81 82 84 85 86 87 107 108 110 111 114 115 118 119 129 130 132 135 146 147 148 **P**6 **S** Catholic Health Initiatives, Englewood, CO
Primary Contact: Jennifer Nolan, President
COO: Kenneth Johnson, Vice President
CFO: Elaine Hayes, Controller
CMO: Val Slayton, M.D., Vice President Medical Affairs
CHR: Julie McGregor, Director Human Resources
Web address: www.jhsmh.org
Control: Other not–for–profit (including NFP Corporation) **Service:** General Medical and Surgical

Staffed Beds: 163 **Admissions:** 9646 **Census:** 112 **Outpatient Visits:** 108112 **Births:** 0 **Total Expense ($000):** 124579 **Payroll Expense ($000):** 41612 **Personnel:** 686

TEN BROECK DUPONT See The Brook at Dupont

☐ **THE BROOK AT DUPONT (184007)**, 1405 Browns Lane, Zip 40207–4608; tel. 502/896–0495 **A**1 9 10 **F**4 5 56 64 98 99 100 101 102 103 104 105 106 **S** Universal Health Services, Inc., King of Prussia, PA
Primary Contact: Paul Andrews, Chief Executive Officer
Web address: www.thebrookhospitals.com/
Control: Corporation, Investor–owned, for–profit **Service:** Psychiatric

Staffed Beds: 88 **Admissions:** 1957 **Census:** 58 **Outpatient Visits:** 11356 **Births:** 0

☐ **THE BROOK HOSPITAL – KMI (184008)**, 8521 Old LaGrange Road, Zip 40242–3800; tel. 502/426–6380, (Nonreporting) **A**1 5 9 10 **S** Universal Health Services, Inc., King of Prussia, PA
Primary Contact: Paul Andrews, Chief Executive Officer
COO: Kim Peabody, Chief Operating Officer
CFO: Dennis Collins, Chief Financial Officer
CMO: Timothy Burke, M.D., Medical Director
CIO: Joel Roy, Manager Information Systems
CHR: Christina Taylor, Director Human Resources
Web address: www.thebrookhospitals.com
Control: Corporation, Investor–owned, for–profit **Service:** Psychiatric

Staffed Beds: 94

⊠ **UNIVERSITY OF LOUISVILLE HOSPITAL (180141)**, 530 South Jackson Street, Zip 40202–3611; tel. 502/562–3000 **A**1 2 3 5 8 9 10 **F**3 13 15 16 17 18 20 22 24 26 29 30 31 34 35 39 40 43 45 46 47 49 50 51 54 56 57 58 59 60 61 64 65 68 70 71 72 73 74 75 76 78 79 80 81 82 84 85 86 87 92 93 94 98 100 102 104 107 108 110 111 114 115 117 118 119 120 121 123 124 126 130 132 135 136 144 146 148 **S** Catholic Health Initiatives, Englewood, CO
Primary Contact: Kenneth P. Marshall, President
CMO: Mark P. Pfeifer, M.D., Senior Vice President and Chief Medical Officer
CIO: Troy May, Chief Information Officer
CNO: Mary Jane Adams, R.N., Senior Vice President and Chief Nursing Officer
Web address: www.ulh.org
Control: Other not–for–profit (including NFP Corporation) **Service:** General Medical and Surgical

Staffed Beds: 301 **Admissions:** 16915 **Census:** 258 **Outpatient Visits:** 160755 **Births:** 1516 **Total Expense ($000):** 462339 **Payroll Expense ($000):** 146094 **Personnel:** 1852

VETERANS AFFAIRS MEDICAL CENTER–LOUISVILLE See Robley Rex Veterans Affairs Medical Center

Many Facility Codes have changed. Please refer to the AHA Guide Code Chart. © 2014 AHA Guide

MADISONVILLE—Hopkins County

✠ **BAPTIST HEALTH MADISONVILLE (180093)**, 900 Hospital Drive,
Zip 42431–1694; tel. 270/825–5100, (Nonreporting) **A**1 2 3 5 9 10 19 20
S Baptist Health, Louisville, KY
Primary Contact: Michael A. Baumgartner, President
CIO: Sheila Bruce, Director Information System
CHR: David Lang, Vice President Human Resources
Web address: www.baptisthealthmadisonville.com
Control: Other not–for–profit (including NFP Corporation) **Service:** General
Medical and Surgical

Staffed Beds: 197

MANCHESTER—Clay County

✠ ○ **MANCHESTER MEMORIAL HOSPITAL (180043)**, 210 Marie Langdon
Drive, Zip 40962–6388; tel. 606/598–5104 **A**1 9 10 11 19 20 **F**3 13 15 29 30
34 35 40 45 50 57 59 62 65 68 70 71 75 76 77 81 85 86 87 89 93 97 107
108 110 111 115 119 127 130 135 143 146 147 **S** Adventist Health System
Sunbelt Health Care Corporation, Altamonte Springs, FL
Primary Contact: Erika Skula, President and Chief Executive Officer
CFO: Daniel T. Walker, Vice President Finance and Chief Financial Officer
CMO: Neeraj Mahboob, M.D., Chief Medical Officer
CHR: Joe Skula, Director Human Resources
CNO: Stephen O'Neal, R.N., Chief Clinical Officer
Web address: www.manchestermemorial.org
Control: Church–operated, Nongovernment, not–for profit **Service:** General
Medical and Surgical

Staffed Beds: 63 Admissions: 2446 Census: 20 Outpatient Visits: 37408 Births: 186 Total Expense ($000): 51306 Payroll Expense ($000): 23520 Personnel: 318

MARION—Crittenden County

✠ **CRITTENDEN COUNTY HOSPITAL (180095)**, 520 West Gum Street,
Zip 42064–1516, Mailing Address: P.O. Box 386, Zip 42064–0386;
tel. 270/965–5281, (Nonreporting) **A**1 9 10 20
Primary Contact: Greg R. McNeil, Chief Executive Officer
COO: Robin Curnel, MSN, Chief Operating Officer and Chief Nursing Officer
CFO: Karen Paris, Controller
CMO: Steven Burkhart, M.D., Chief Medical Officer
CIO: Reese Baker, Director Information Systems
CHR: Jan Gregory, Chief of Human Resources
CNO: Robin Curnel, MSN, Chief Operating Officer and Chief Nursing Officer
Web address: www.crittenden–health.org
Control: Other not–for–profit (including NFP Corporation) **Service:** General
Medical and Surgical

Staffed Beds: 48

MARTIN—Floyd County

✠ **SAINT JOSEPH – MARTIN (181305)**, 11203 Main Street, Zip 41649;
tel. 606/285–6400 **A**1 9 10 18 **F**3 15 18 28 35 40 56 81 104 111 114 119
127 130 **S** Catholic Health Initiatives, Englewood, CO
Primary Contact: Kathy Stumbo, President
CFO: Robert Brock, Vice President Finance
CMO: John Triplett, D.O., President Medical Staff
CIO: Chris Dye, Director Information Systems
Web address: www.saintjosephmartin.org
Control: Church–operated, Nongovernment, not–for profit **Service:** General
Medical and Surgical

Staffed Beds: 25 Admissions: 819 Census: 10 Outpatient Visits: 29017 Births: 0 Total Expense ($000): 20352 Payroll Expense ($000): 6856 Personnel: 96

MAYFIELD—Graves County

✠ **JACKSON PURCHASE MEDICAL CENTER (180116)**, 1099 Medical Center
Circle, Zip 42066–1159; tel. 270/251–4100 **A**1 9 10 19 **F**3 11 12 13 15 18
22 28 29 30 31 34 35 37 40 43 46 47 48 49 51 57 59 64 68 74 75 76 77
79 80 81 85 87 89 93 97 107 110 111 115 117 119 129 131 132 133 135
143 146 147 148 **S** LifePoint Hospitals, Inc., Brentwood, TN
Primary Contact: David Anderson, Chief Executive Officer
CFO: Vicki Parks, Chief Financial Officer
CMO: David Zetter, M.D., Chief of Staff
CIO: Tracy Watt, Director Information Systems
CHR: Tressa B. Hargrove, Director Human Resources
CNO: Julia Grove, Chief Nursing Officer
Web address: www.jacksonpurchase.com
Control: Corporation, Investor–owned, for–profit **Service:** General Medical and
Surgical

Staffed Beds: 106 Admissions: 3819 Census: 50 Outpatient Visits: 81013 Births: 368 Total Expense ($000): 56676 Payroll Expense ($000): 24332 Personnel: 465

MAYSVILLE—Mason County

✠ **MEADOWVIEW REGIONAL MEDICAL CENTER (180019)**, 989 Medical Park
Drive, Zip 41056–8750; tel. 606/759–5311, (Nonreporting) **A**1 9 10 **S** LifePoint
Hospitals, Inc., Brentwood, TN
Primary Contact: Robert Parker, Chief Executive Officer
CFO: Clayton Kolodziejczyk, Chief Financial Officer
CMO: Eric Lohman, M.D., Chief of Staff
CHR: Diana Kennedy, Director Human Resources
Web address: www.meadowviewregional.com
Control: Corporation, Investor–owned, for–profit **Service:** General Medical and
Surgical

Staffed Beds: 101

MCDOWELL—Floyd County

☐ **MCDOWELL ARH HOSPITAL (181331)**, Route 122, Zip 41647, Mailing
Address: P.O. Box 247, Zip 41647–0247; tel. 606/377–3400 **A**1 9 10 18 **F**3
11 15 29 30 34 35 40 43 50 57 59 62 64 65 70 73 75 77 81 82 86 87 89
90 93 97 98 107 111 114 119 127 130 133 146 **P**6 **S** Appalachian Regional
Healthcare, Inc., Lexington, KY
Primary Contact: Russell Barker, Community Chief Executive Officer
COO: Russell Barker, Community Chief Executive Officer
CFO: Joseph Grossman, Chief Financial Officer
CMO: Mary A. Hall, Chief Medical Staff
CIO: Jeff Brady, Director Information Systems
CHR: Stephanie Owens, Manager Human Resources
Web address: www.arh.org
Control: Other not–for–profit (including NFP Corporation) **Service:** General
Medical and Surgical

Staffed Beds: 25 Admissions: 772 Census: 8 Outpatient Visits: 32463 Births: 0 Total Expense ($000): 14801 Payroll Expense ($000): 5347 Personnel: 118

MIDDLESBORO—Bell County

☐ **MIDDLESBORO ARH HOSPITAL (180020)**, 3600 West Cumberland Avenue,
Zip 40965–2614, Mailing Address: P.O. Box 340, Zip 40965–0340;
tel. 606/242–1100 **A**1 9 10 **F**3 11 13 15 17 29 30 34 35 39 40 50 57 59 62
64 70 75 76 77 79 81 85 86 87 89 90 93 97 107 108 111 114 118 119 127
130 133 146 147 148 **P**6 **S** Appalachian Regional Healthcare, Inc.,
Lexington, KY
Primary Contact: Michael Slusher, Community Chief Executive Officer
CFO: Jeremy Hall, Assistant Administrator and Chief Financial Officer
CMO: Maria Hortillosa, M.D., Chief of Staff
CIO: Lisa Dooley, Health Information Officer
CHR: Marina Cawood, Administrative Assistant
CNO: Stacy England, Community Chief Nursing Officer
Web address: www.arh.org/middlesboro
Control: Other not–for–profit (including NFP Corporation) **Service:** General
Medical and Surgical

Staffed Beds: 96 Admissions: 2518 Census: 27 Outpatient Visits: 56949 Births: 280 Total Expense ($000): 37434 Payroll Expense ($000): 10124 Personnel: 237

MONTICELLO—Wayne County

WAYNE COUNTY HOSPITAL (181321), 166 Hospital Street, Zip 42633–2416;
tel. 606/348–9343 **A**9 10 18 **F**3 15 29 30 40 47 75 81 107 108 114 119
127 133 135 146 **P**6
Primary Contact: Joseph Murrell, Chief Executive Officer
CFO: Anne Sawyer, Chief Financial Officer
CMO: Cory Ryan, M.D., Chief of Staff
CIO: Angela Griffin, Privacy Officer
CHR: Mollie Dick, Coordinator Human Resources
CNO: Lora Elam, R.N., Chief Nursing Officer
Web address: www.waynehospital.org
Control: Other not–for–profit (including NFP Corporation) **Service:** General
Medical and Surgical

Staffed Beds: 25 Admissions: 751 Census: 12 Outpatient Visits: 38352 Births: 0 Total Expense ($000): 13808 Payroll Expense ($000): 5532 Personnel: 158

Hospital, Medicare Provider Number, Address, Telephone, Approval, Facility, and Physician Codes, Health Care System

★ American Hospital Association (AHA) membership
☐ The Joint Commission accreditation ◇ DNV Healthcare Inc. accreditation
○ Healthcare Facilities Accreditation Program
△ Commission on Accreditation of Rehabilitation Facilities (CARF) accreditation

MOREHEAD—Rowan County

✠ **ST. CLAIRE REGIONAL MEDICAL CENTER (180018)**, 222 Medical Circle, Zip 40351–1179; tel. 606/783–6500, (Total facility includes 10 beds in nursing home–type unit) **A**1 2 3 5 9 10 19 20 **F**3 5 11 13 15 18 20 22 28 29 30 31 34 35 38 39 40 45 48 49 50 51 54 56 57 58 59 60 61 62 63 64 65 68 70 74 75 76 77 78 79 81 82 84 85 86 87 89 90 93 97 98 99 100 101 102 103 104 107 108 110 111 115 118 119 128 129 130 132 135 146 147 148 **P**6
Primary Contact: Mark J. Neff, FACHE, President and Chief Executive Officer
CFO: G.R. Sonny Jones, Vice President Finance and Chief Financial Officer
CMO: Will L. Melahn, M.D., Vice President Medical Affairs and Chief Medical Officer
CIO: Randy McCleese, Vice President Information Services and Chief Information Officer
CHR: Travis A. Bailey, Vice President Administration
CNO: Lerae Wilson, R.N., Vice President Patient Services and Chief Nursing Officer
Web address: www.st-claire.org
Control: Church–operated, Nongovernment, not–for profit **Service:** General Medical and Surgical

Staffed Beds: 133 **Admissions:** 5280 **Census:** 69 **Outpatient Visits:** 236482 **Births:** 452 **Total Expense ($000):** 125397 **Payroll Expense ($000):** 62834 **Personnel:** 1065

MORGANFIELD—Union County

✠ **METHODIST HOSPITAL UNION COUNTY (181306)**, 4604 Highway 60 West, Zip 42437–9570; tel. 270/389–5000 **A**1 9 10 18 **F**3 7 11 15 29 30 34 40 45 57 68 75 77 81 85 93 107 114 119 130 133 135 146
Primary Contact: Patrick Donahue, Vice President and Administrator
CFO: Gregory P. Hebbeler, Chief Financial Officer
CMO: Debra Wallace, M.D., Chief of Staff
CNO: Peggy F. Creighton, R.N., Director of Nursing Services
Web address: www.methodisthospitaluc.net
Control: Church–operated, Nongovernment, not–for profit **Service:** General Medical and Surgical

Staffed Beds: 25 **Admissions:** 753 **Census:** 14 **Outpatient Visits:** 23651 **Births:** 0 **Total Expense ($000):** 13676 **Payroll Expense ($000):** 5689 **Personnel:** 133

MOUNT STERLING—Montgomery County

✠ **SAINT JOSEPH MOUNT STERLING (180064)**, 225 Falcon Drive, Zip 40353–1158, Mailing Address: P.O. Box 7, Zip 40353–0007; tel. 859/497–5000 **A**1 5 9 10 **F**3 13 15 17 28 29 34 35 40 45 46 57 59 64 70 74 76 77 78 79 81 86 87 93 107 108 114 119 129 130 132 133 135 146 147 148 **S** Catholic Health Initiatives, Englewood, CO
Primary Contact: Benny Nolen, President
CFO: Amanda Kinman, Director of Finance
CMO: Jeff McGinnis, M.D., President Medical Staff
CIO: Jeff Ryder, Director Information Systems
CHR: Annette Saadat, Human Resources Business Partner
CNO: Cinda Fluke, R.N., Chief Nursing Officer
Web address: www.sjhlex.org
Control: Church–operated, Nongovernment, not–for profit **Service:** General Medical and Surgical

Staffed Beds: 40 **Admissions:** 2147 **Census:** 23 **Outpatient Visits:** 64522 **Births:** 298 **Total Expense ($000):** 44933 **Payroll Expense ($000):** 11941 **Personnel:** 227

MOUNT VERNON—Rockcastle County

✠ **ROCKCASTLE REGIONAL HOSPITAL AND RESPIRATORY CARE CENTER (180115)**, 145 Newcomb Avenue, Zip 40456–2728, Mailing Address: P.O. Box 1310, Zip 40456–1310; tel. 606/256–2195, (Total facility includes 79 beds in nursing home–type unit) **A**1 9 10 **F**3 15 29 30 31 32 34 35 40 53 57 59 64 65 68 75 77 81 90 93 107 111 115 119 127 128 130 132 133 135 148
Primary Contact: Stephen A. Estes, Chief Executive Officer
CFO: Charles Black, Jr., Chief Financial Officer
CMO: Jon A. Arvin, M.D., Chief Medical Officer
CIO: Maleigha Amyx, Chief Information Officer
CHR: Carmen Poynter, Director Human Resources
CNO: Cynthia Burton, R.N., Chief Nursing Officer
Web address: www.rockcastleregional.org
Control: Other not–for–profit (including NFP Corporation) **Service:** General Medical and Surgical

Staffed Beds: 105 **Admissions:** 1027 **Census:** 96 **Outpatient Visits:** 46325 **Births:** 0 **Total Expense ($000):** 46788 **Payroll Expense ($000):** 22162 **Personnel:** 519

MURRAY—Calloway County

✠ **MURRAY–CALLOWAY COUNTY HOSPITAL (180027)**, 803 Poplar Street, Zip 42071–2432; tel. 270/762–1100, (Total facility includes 170 beds in nursing home–type unit) **A**1 2 9 10 19 **F**2 3 7 11 12 13 14 15 18 20 28 29 30 31 34 35 40 45 47 49 50 51 53 57 59 62 63 66 68 70 74 75 76 77 78 79 81 82 84 85 87 90 92 93 94 104 107 108 111 114 115 119 121 127 128 129 130 131 132 135 146 147 148 **P**5
Primary Contact: Colonel Jerome Penner, Chief Executive Officer
CFO: Dirk Morgan, Vice President
CIO: Annette Ballard, Director Information Systems
CHR: John R. Wilson, Vice President, Human Resources
CNO: Lisa Ray, R.N., Vice President Patient Care Services
Web address: www.murrayhospital.org
Control: City–County, Government, nonfederal **Service:** General Medical and Surgical

Staffed Beds: 270 **Admissions:** 4373 **Census:** 206 **Outpatient Visits:** 93440 **Births:** 561 **Total Expense ($000):** 95501 **Payroll Expense ($000):** 36732 **Personnel:** 971

OWENSBORO—Daviess County

✠ △ **OWENSBORO HEALTH REGIONAL HOSPITAL (180038)**, 1201 Pleasant Valley Road, Zip 42303; tel. 270/417–2000, (Includes HEALTHPARK, 1006 Ford Avenue, Zip 42301, Mailing Address: P.O. Box 2839, Zip 42302; tel. 270/688–5433), (Total facility includes 30 beds in nursing home–type unit) **A**1 2 5 7 9 10 19 20 **F**3 5 11 12 13 15 17 18 20 22 24 26 28 29 30 31 32 34 35 40 45 46 49 53 54 56 57 58 59 61 62 64 65 66 70 72 74 75 76 77 78 79 81 82 85 86 87 89 90 91 92 93 97 98 100 101 102 103 104 105 107 108 110 111 114 115 116 117 118 119 120 121 123 124 126 127 128 129 130 131 132 135 144 145 146 147 148 **P**6 8
Primary Contact: Philip A. Patterson, President and Chief Executive Officer
COO: Greg Strahan, Chief Operating Officer
CFO: John Hackbarth, CPA, Senior Vice President Finance and Chief Financial Officer
CMO: Wathen Medley, M.D., Chief Medical Officer
CIO: Michael Elley, Chief Information Officer
CHR: Mia Suter, Chief Administration Officer
CNO: Vicki Stogsdill, R.N., Chief Nursing Officer
Web address: www.owensborohealth.org
Control: Other not–for–profit (including NFP Corporation) **Service:** General Medical and Surgical

Staffed Beds: 347 **Admissions:** 17419 **Census:** 222 **Outpatient Visits:** 555453 **Births:** 1801 **Total Expense ($000):** 378717 **Payroll Expense ($000):** 124395 **Personnel:** 3117

RIVERVALLEY BEHAVIORAL HEALTH HOSPITAL (184013), 1000 Industrial Drive, Zip 42301–8715; tel. 270/689–6500 **A**9 10 **F**29 40 59 98 99 100 101 102 104 105 130 **P**6
Primary Contact: Gayle DiCesare, President and Chief Executive Officer
COO: Michelle Parks, Administrator
CFO: J. Michael Mountain, Chief Financial Officer
CMO: David Harmon, D.O., Vice President Medical Services
CIO: Travis Taggart, Director Information Technology
CHR: Cathryn Gaddis, Director Human Resources
Web address: www.rvbh.com
Control: Other not–for–profit (including NFP Corporation) **Service:** Children's hospital psychiatric

Staffed Beds: 80 **Admissions:** 509 **Census:** 16 **Outpatient Visits:** 0 **Births:** 0 **Total Expense ($000):** 5180 **Payroll Expense ($000):** 2241 **Personnel:** 61

OWENTON—Owen County

★ **NEW HORIZONS HEALTH SYSTEMS (181312)**, 330 Roland Avenue, Zip 40359–1502; tel. 502/484–3663, (Nonreporting) **A**9 10 18
Primary Contact: Bernard T. Poe, Administrator and Chief Executive Officer
COO: Bernard T. Poe, Administrator and Chief Executive Officer
CMO: Larry C. Johnson, M.D., Medical Director Rural Health Clinic
CIO: Edward Seale, Chief Information Officer
CHR: Kelly Perkins, Director Human Resources
CNO: Eileen Fowler, Clinical Director and Chief Nursing Officer
Web address: www.newhorizonsmedicalcenter.com
Control: Other not–for–profit (including NFP Corporation) **Service:** General Medical and Surgical

Staffed Beds: 25

Many Facility Codes have changed. Please refer to the AHA Guide Code Chart.   © 2014 AHA Guide

PADUCAH—Mccracken County

⊞ **BAPTIST HEALTH PADUCAH (180104)**, 2501 Kentucky Avenue,
Zip 42003–3200; tel. 270/575–2100, (Nonreporting) **A**1 2 9 10 19 **S** Baptist
Health, Louisville, KY
Primary Contact: William A. Brown, FACHE, President and CEO
CFO: Michelle Hayden, Chief Financial Officer
CMO: Bradley W. Housman, M.D., Chief Medical Officer
CIO: Brad Nelson, Director Information Services
CHR: Kal Keitel, SPHR, Executive Director Human Resources
CNO: Polly Bechtold, MSN, Chief Nursing Officer
Web address: www.westernbaptist.com
Control: Other not–for–profit (including NFP Corporation) **Service:** General
Medical and Surgical

Staffed Beds: 271

⊞ △ **LOURDES HOSPITAL (180102)**, 1530 Lone Oak Road, Zip 42003–7900,
Mailing Address: P.O. Box 7100, Zip 42002–7100; tel. 270/444–2444 **A**1 7 9
10 19 **F**7 8 11 13 15 17 18 20 22 24 26 28 29 30 31 34 35 40 42 45 46 54
57 59 60 62 63 64 66 68 70 74 75 76 77 78 79 81 82 83 84 85 87 90 93
96 97 98 100 101 102 103 105 107 110 111 114 115 117 119 127 129
130 131 132 135 136 141 143 146 147 148 **P**3 6 **S** Mercy Health,
Cincinnati, OH
Primary Contact: Steven Grinnell, President and Chief Executive Officer
CFO: Mark Thompson, Vice President Finance and Chief Financial Officer
CHR: Kim Lindsey, Chief Human Resources Officer
Web address: www.lourdes–pad.org
Control: Church–operated, Nongovernment, not–for profit **Service:** General
Medical and Surgical

Staffed Beds: 262 **Admissions:** 10890 **Census:** 138 **Outpatient Visits:**
225739 **Births:** 307 **Total Expense ($000):** 200057 **Payroll Expense
($000):** 80683

PAINTSVILLE—Johnson County

⊞ **PAUL B. HALL REGIONAL MEDICAL CENTER (180078)**, 625 James S.
Trimble Boulevard, Zip 41240–0000; tel. 606/789–3511, (Nonreporting) **A**1 9 10
S Community Health Systems, Inc., Franklin, TN
Primary Contact: Deborah Trimble, R.N., Chief Executive Officer
CFO: Pattie Major, Chief Financial Officer
CMO: F. K. Belhasen, M.D., Medical Director
CHR: Carla J. Stapleton, Director Human Resources
Web address: www.pbhrmc.com
Control: Corporation, Investor–owned, for–profit **Service:** General Medical and
Surgical

Staffed Beds: 72

PARIS—Bourbon County

⊞ **BOURBON COMMUNITY HOSPITAL (180046)**, 9 Linville Drive,
Zip 40361–2196; tel. 859/987–3600 **A**1 9 10 **F**1 3 15 28 29 34 35 38 39 40
44 49 50 51 56 57 59 64 67 68 70 74 75 79 80 81 86 87 93 98 99 100
101 102 103 107 108 110 111 114 119 129 130 133 146 148 **P**7 **S** LifePoint
Hospitals, Inc., Brentwood, TN
Primary Contact: Joseph G. Koch, Chief Executive Officer
CFO: Michael Snedegar, Chief Financial Officer
CMO: C. Ray Young, M.D., Chief Medical Officer
CIO: Phil Osborne, Director Information Technology
CHR: Roger K. Davis, Director Human Resources
Web address: www.bourbonhospital.com
Control: Corporation, Investor–owned, for–profit **Service:** General Medical and
Surgical

Staffed Beds: 58 **Admissions:** 1738 **Census:** 23 **Outpatient Visits:** 27886
Births: 0 **Total Expense ($000):** 19075 **Payroll Expense ($000):** 10090
Personnel: 162

PIKEVILLE—Pike County

☐ **PIKEVILLE MEDICAL CENTER (180044)**, 911 Bypass Road, Zip 41501–1689;
tel. 606/218–3500 **A**1 2 9 10 13 19 20 **F**3 11 12 13 15 18 20 22 24 26 28
29 30 31 34 35 39 40 45 49 50 51 57 59 60 61 62 64 66 68 69 70 72 74
75 76 77 78 79 81 82 84 85 86 87 89 90 93 95 96 97 100 108 110 111
115 116 117 118 119 121 123 124 127 129 130 131 132 135 146 147
148 **P**6
Primary Contact: Walter E. May, President and Chief Executive Officer
COO: Juanita Deskins, Chief Operating Officer
CFO: Michael Hagy, Chief Financial Officer
CIO: Sonja Elder, Director Information Services
CNO: Debra Parsons, Chief Nursing Officer
Web address: www.pikevillehospital.org
Control: Other not–for–profit (including NFP Corporation) **Service:** General
Medical and Surgical

Staffed Beds: 243 **Admissions:** 11971 **Census:** 162 **Outpatient Visits:**
416140 **Births:** 1060 **Total Expense ($000):** 342848 **Payroll Expense
($000):** 141027 **Personnel:** 2200

PINEVILLE—Bell County

○ **PINEVILLE COMMUNITY HOSPITAL ASSOCIATION (180021)**, 850 Riverview
Avenue, Zip 40977–1452; tel. 606/337–3051, (Nonreporting) **A**9 10 11
Primary Contact: J. Milton Brooks, III, Administrator
CFO: Colan Kelly, Chief Financial Officer
CMO: Michael Peterson, M.D., Chief of Staff
CIO: David Hall, Chief Information Officer
CHR: Josh Collett, Director Human Resources
CNO: Dinah Jarvis, Director of Nursing
Web address: www.pinevillehospital.com
Control: Other not–for–profit (including NFP Corporation) **Service:** General
Medical and Surgical

Staffed Beds: 150

PRESTONSBURG—Floyd County

★ ◇ **HIGHLANDS REGIONAL MEDICAL CENTER (180005)**, 5000 Kentucky
Route 321, Zip 41653–1273, Mailing Address: P.O. Box 668, Zip 41653–0668;
tel. 606/886–8511, (Nonreporting) **A**2 5 9 10 19 21
Primary Contact: Harold C. Warman, Jr., FACHE, President and Chief Executive
Officer
COO: Chris Hoffman, Chief Operating Officer
CFO: Jack Blackwell, Chief Financial Officer
CIO: Michael Roberts, Chief Information Officer
CHR: Susan Renee' Ellis, R.N., Vice President of Human Resources
CNO: Terresa O. Booher, Vice President of Patient Care Services
Web address: www.hrmc.org
Control: Other not–for–profit (including NFP Corporation) **Service:** General
Medical and Surgical

Staffed Beds: 145

PRINCETON—Caldwell County

⊞ **CALDWELL MEDICAL CENTER (181322)**, 100 Medical Center Drive,
Zip 42445–2430, Mailing Address: P.O. Box 410, Zip 42445–0410;
tel. 270/365–0300 **A**1 9 10 18 **F**11 15 28 29 34 35 40 57 59 62 68 77 81
85 107 108 111 118 119 129 133 135 146 **S** QHR, Brentwood, TN
Primary Contact: Charles D. Lovell, Jr., FACHE, President and Chief Executive
Officer
CFO: Shane Whittington, Chief Financial Officer
CHR: Rhonda Burns, Director Human Resources
CNO: Douglas James, Chief Nursing Officer
Web address: www.caldwellhosp.org
Control: Other not–for–profit (including NFP Corporation) **Service:** General
Medical and Surgical

Staffed Beds: 25 **Admissions:** 551 **Census:** 8 **Outpatient Visits:** 28766
Births: 0 **Total Expense ($000):** 16765 **Payroll Expense ($000):** 5312
Personnel: 120

RADCLIFF—Hardin County

☐ **LINCOLN TRAIL BEHAVIORAL HEALTH SYSTEM (184012)**, 3909 South
Wilson Road, Zip 40160–8944, Mailing Address: P.O. Box 369, Zip 40159–0369;
tel. 270/351–9444, (Nonreporting) **A**1 9 10 **S** Universal Health Services, Inc.,
King of Prussia, PA
Primary Contact: Charles L. Webb, Jr., Chief Executive Officer
CFO: Debbie Ditto, CPA, Controller
CMO: Muhammad W. Sajid, M.D., Medical Director
CHR: Charlotte C. Davis, Director Human Resources
Web address: www.lincolnbehavioral.com
Control: Corporation, Investor–owned, for–profit **Service:** Psychiatric

Staffed Beds: 67

Hospital, Medicare Provider Number, Address, Telephone, Approval, Facility, and Physician Codes, Health Care System

★ American Hospital Association (AHA) membership
☐ The Joint Commission accreditation ◇ DNV Healthcare Inc. accreditation
○ Healthcare Facilities Accreditation Program
△ Commission on Accreditation of Rehabilitation Facilities (CARF) accreditation

RICHMOND—Madison County

★ ○ **BAPTIST HEALTH RICHMOND (180049)**, 801 Eastern Bypass,
Zip 40475–2405, Mailing Address: P.O. Box 1600, Zip 40476–2603;
tel. 859/623–3131 **A**9 10 11 19 **F**3 11 13 18 20 22 26 28 29 30 34 35 40
46 48 49 50 51 57 59 68 70 74 75 79 81 84 85 87 91 92 93 97 107 108
110 111 115 118 119 124 129 130 132 133 146 147 **S** Baptist Health,
Louisville, KY
Primary Contact: Todd Jones, President
CMO: Roshan Pais, M.D., Chief of Staff
CIO: Kelly Bonzo, Director
CHR: Joy M. Benedict, Director Human Resources
CNO: Tammy Sullivan, R.N., Chief Nursing Officer
Web address: www.baptisthealthrichmond.com
Control: Other not–for–profit (including NFP Corporation) **Service:** General
Medical and Surgical

Staffed Beds: 66 **Admissions:** 3179 **Census:** 33 **Outpatient Visits:** 95292
Births: 768 **Total Expense ($000):** 66804 **Payroll Expense ($000):** 28355
Personnel: 581

RUSSELL SPRINGS—Russell County

★ **RUSSELL COUNTY HOSPITAL (181330)**, 153 Dowell Road, Zip 42642–4579,
Mailing Address: P.O. Box 1610, Zip 42642–1610; tel. 270/866–4141,
(Nonreporting) **A**9 10 18 **S** Baptist Health, Louisville, KY
Primary Contact: Robert L. Ramey, Chief Executive Officer
CFO: Michael Logan, Chief Financial Officer
CMO: Sam Bradley, M.D., Chief of Staff
CIO: Monte Monsanto, Chief Information Systems
CHR: Jennifer Dykes, Director Human Resources
CNO: Judy Chenoweth, Chief Nursing Officer
Web address: www.russellcohospital.org
Control: County–Government, nonfederal **Service:** General Medical and Surgical

Staffed Beds: 25

RUSSELLVILLE—Logan County

⊞ **LOGAN MEMORIAL HOSPITAL (180066)**, 1625 South Nashville Road,
Zip 42276–8834, Mailing Address: P.O. Box 10, Zip 42276–0010;
tel. 270/726–4011 **A**1 9 10 **F**3 15 28 29 30 34 40 45 50 51 57 59 64 70 75
79 81 87 93 107 110 111 114 119 127 129 130 132 133 146 **S** LifePoint
Hospitals, Inc., Brentwood, TN
Primary Contact: James Bills, Chief Executive Officer
CFO: Theresa Fite, Chief Financial Officer
CIO: Mike Katz, Director Information Systems
CHR: Courtney Jackson, Director Human Resources
CNO: John Jones, Chief Nursing Officer
Web address: www.loganmemorial.com
Control: Corporation, Investor–owned, for–profit **Service:** General Medical and
Surgical

Staffed Beds: 53 **Admissions:** 1013 **Census:** 13 **Outpatient Visits:** 39228
Births: 0

SALEM—Livingston County

★ **LIVINGSTON HOSPITAL AND HEALTHCARE SERVICES (181320)**, 131
Hospital Drive, Zip 42078–8043; tel. 270/988–2299, (Nonreporting) **A**9 10 18
S Alliant Management Services, Louisville, KY
Primary Contact: Mark A. Edwards, Chief Executive Officer
CMO: William Guyette, M.D., President Medical Staff
CIO: Shannan Landreth, Information Systems
CHR: Carla Wiggins, Director Human Resources
CNO: Joanna Stone, Chief Nursing Officer
Web address: www.lhhs.org
Control: Other not–for–profit (including NFP Corporation) **Service:** General
Medical and Surgical

Staffed Beds: 25

SCOTTSVILLE—Allen County

MEDICAL CENTER AT SCOTTSVILLE (181324), 456 Burnley Road,
Zip 42164–6355; tel. 270/622–2800, (Total facility includes 110 beds in nursing
home–type unit) **A**9 10 18 **F**1 3 4 15 16 17 28 29 30 34 35 40 56 57 59 64
67 68 70 71 72 73 74 75 79 80 81 85 86 87 88 89 90 93 97 98 102 103
104 107 111 113 114 119 130 132 133 143 146 148
S Commonwealth Health Corporation, Bowling Green, KY
Primary Contact: Eric Hagan, R.N., Vice President/Administrator
CFO: Ronald G. Sowell, Chief Financial Officer
CIO: Jean Cherry, Chief Information Officer
CHR: Lynn Williarns, Vice President Human Resources
Web address: www.themedicalcenterscottsville.org/
Control: Other not–for–profit (including NFP Corporation) **Service:** General
Medical and Surgical

Staffed Beds: 135 **Admissions:** 777 **Census:** 157 **Outpatient Visits:** 20712
Births: 0 **Personnel:** 197

SHELBYVILLE—Shelby County

⊞ **JEWISH HOSPITAL–SHELBYVILLE (180016)**, 727 Hospital Drive,
Zip 40065–1699; tel. 502/647–4000 **A**1 9 10 **F**3 11 15 18 28 29 30 34 35
39 40 43 44 45 46 50 57 59 64 68 70 75 79 81 82 84 85 87 91 93 107
108 110 111 114 119 129 132 135 146 147 148 **P**6 **S** Catholic Health
Initiatives, Englewood, CO
Primary Contact: Rob Murphy, President
CFO: Erika McGimsey, Controller
CMO: Tony Perez, M.D., President Medical Staff
CHR: Cindy Stewart Rattray, Director Human Resources
Web address: www.jhsmh.org
Control: Other not–for–profit (including NFP Corporation) **Service:** General
Medical and Surgical

Staffed Beds: 32 **Admissions:** 1791 **Census:** 19 **Outpatient Visits:** 48642
Births: 0 **Total Expense ($000):** 33589 **Payroll Expense ($000):** 10275
Personnel: 165

SOMERSET—Pulaski County

⊞ **LAKE CUMBERLAND REGIONAL HOSPITAL (180132)**, 305 Langdon Street,
Zip 42503–2750, Mailing Address: P.O. Box 620, Zip 42502–0620;
tel. 606/679–7441, (Total facility includes 12 beds in nursing home–type unit) **A**1
2 9 10 19 20 **F**3 8 11 12 13 15 17 18 20 22 24 28 29 30 31 34 35 39 40
45 47 49 50 51 54 56 57 59 61 64 65 68 70 73 74 75 76 77 78 79 81 82
85 86 87 89 90 93 97 98 102 103 107 108 109 110 111 114 115 119 120
121 124 127 128 129 130 131 132 135 144 146 147 148 **S** LifePoint
Hospitals, Inc., Brentwood, TN
Primary Contact: Timothy A. Bess, Chief Executive Officer
COO: Rebecca Segal, Chief Operating Officer
CFO: Steve Sloan, Chief Financial Officer
CMO: Michael Citak, M.D., Chief Medical Officer
CIO: Thomas Gilbert, Director Information Technology Services
CHR: James Hughes, Director Human Resources
CNO: Sheryl Glasscock, Chief Nursing Officer
Web address: www.lakecumberlandhospital.com
Control: Corporation, Investor–owned, for–profit **Service:** General Medical and
Surgical

Staffed Beds: 295 **Admissions:** 11271 **Census:** 149 **Outpatient Visits:**
114333 **Births:** 1316 **Total Expense ($000):** 137172 **Payroll Expense**
($000): 51169 **Personnel:** 1204

SOUTH WILLIAMSON—Pike County

☐ **WILLIAMSON ARH HOSPITAL (180069)**, 260 Hospital Drive, Zip 41503–4072;
tel. 606/237–1710, (Total facility includes 35 beds in nursing home–type unit) **A**1
9 10 19 **F**3 11 13 15 29 30 34 35 40 43 50 54 57 59 62 64 67 70 74 75 76
77 79 81 82 85 86 87 89 90 93 97 107 108 111 115 118 119 127 128 129
130 132 146 147 **P**6 **S** Appalachian Regional Healthcare, Inc., Lexington, KY
Primary Contact: Timothy H. Hatfield, Community Chief Executive Officer
CMO: J. D. Miller, M.D., Vice President Medical Affairs
CIO: Jeff Brady, Chief Information Officer
Web address: www.arh.org
Control: Other not–for–profit (including NFP Corporation) **Service:** General
Medical and Surgical

Staffed Beds: 126 **Admissions:** 2749 **Census:** 52 **Outpatient Visits:** 41637
Births: 112 **Total Expense ($000):** 42819 **Payroll Expense ($000):** 11700
Personnel: 279

STANFORD—Lincoln County

⊞ **EPHRAIM MCDOWELL FORT LOGAN HOSPITAL (181315)**, 110 Metker Trail,
Zip 40484–1020; tel. 606/365–4600 **A**1 9 10 18 **F**3 11 13 15 29 30 34 35
40 43 57 59 64 76 81 87 89 107 110 111 119 130 133 135 146
Primary Contact: Mike Jackson, President and Chief Executive Officer
CFO: William R. Snapp, III, Vice President and Chief Financial Officer
CMO: Naren James, M.D., Chief of Staff
CIO: Sharon McWhorter, Director Information Systems
Web address: www.fortloganhospital.org
Control: Other not–for–profit (including NFP Corporation) **Service:** General
Medical and Surgical

Staffed Beds: 22 **Admissions:** 729 **Census:** 6 **Outpatient Visits:** 36659
Births: 329 **Total Expense ($000):** 14097 **Payroll Expense ($000):** 6872
Personnel: 135

TOMPKINSVILLE—Monroe County

⊞ **MONROE COUNTY MEDICAL CENTER (180105)**, 529 Capp Harlan Road,
Zip 42167–1840; tel. 270/487–9231, (Nonreporting) **A**1 9 10 **S** QHR,
Brentwood, TN
Primary Contact: Vicky McFall, Chief Executive Officer
CFO: Rickie F. Brown, Chief Financial Officer
CIO: Paul McKiddy, Director Information Technology
CHR: Sue Page, Director Human Resources
Web address: www.mcmccares.com
Control: Other not–for–profit (including NFP Corporation) **Service:** General
Medical and Surgical

Staffed Beds: 49

Many Facility Codes have changed. Please refer to the AHA Guide Code Chart.
© 2014 AHA Guide

VERSAILLES—Woodford County

★ **BLUEGRASS COMMUNITY HOSPITAL (181308)**, 360 Amsden Avenue,
Zip 40383–1286; tel. 859/873–3111 **A**9 10 18 **F**29 40 45 50 59 70 79 81 82
93 107 110 111 119 133 **S** LifePoint Hospitals, Inc., Brentwood, TN
Primary Contact: Tommy Haggard, Chief Executive Officer
CFO: Shellie Shouse, Chief Financial Officer
CMO: Michele Welling, M.D., Chief of Staff
CHR: Marcia Carter, Director Human Resources
CNO: Kathy Russell, R.N., Chief Nursing Officer
Web address: www.bluegrasscommunityhospital.com
Control: Corporation, Investor–owned, for–profit **Service:** General Medical and
Surgical

Staffed Beds: 16 **Admissions:** 375 **Census:** 3 **Births:** 0

WEST LIBERTY—Morgan County

☐ **MORGAN COUNTY ARH HOSPITAL (181307)**, 476 Liberty Road,
Zip 41472–2049, Mailing Address: P.O. Box 579, Zip 41472–0579;
tel. 606/743–3186 **A**1 9 10 18 **F**11 15 29 30 34 35 40 43 54 57 59 62 64
75 82 86 87 93 97 107 114 119 127 129 130 132 133 146 **P**6 **S** Appalachian
Regional Healthcare, Inc., Lexington, KY
Primary Contact: Stephen M. Gavalchik, FACHE, Community Chief Executive
Officer
COO: Paul V. Miles, Chief Operating Officer
CMO: J. D. Miller, M.D., Vice President Medical Affairs
CIO: Jeff Brady, Director Information Systems
CHR: Lisa Redding, Manager Human Resources
Web address: www.arh.org
Control: Other not–for–profit (including NFP Corporation) **Service:** General
Medical and Surgical

Staffed Beds: 25 **Admissions:** 407 **Census:** 4 **Outpatient Visits:** 23090
Births: 0 **Total Expense ($000):** 12467 **Payroll Expense ($000):** 4313
Personnel: 99

WHITESBURG—Letcher County

☐ **WHITESBURG ARH HOSPITAL (180002)**, 240 Hospital Road,
Zip 41858–7627; tel. 606/633–3600 **A**1 9 10 **F**3 11 13 15 29 30 34 35 40
43 50 54 57 59 62 64 70 75 76 77 81 82 85 86 87 89 93 97 107 108 111
114 118 119 127 129 130 133 146 147 **P**6 **S** Appalachian Regional
Healthcare, Inc., Lexington, KY
Primary Contact: Dena C. Sparkman, FACHE, Community Chief Executive Officer
COO: Paul V. Miles, Vice President Administration
CFO: Joseph Grossman, Vice President Fiscal Affairs
CMO: Ricky M. Collins, M.D., Chief of Staff
CIO: Brent Styer, Director Information Technology
CHR: Daniel Fitzpatrick, Director Human Resources
Web address: www.arh.org/whitesburg
Control: Other not–for–profit (including NFP Corporation) **Service:** General
Medical and Surgical

Staffed Beds: 87 **Admissions:** 3631 **Census:** 39 **Outpatient Visits:** 55640
Births: 408 **Total Expense ($000):** 42363 **Payroll Expense ($000):** 11951
Personnel: 273

WILLIAMSTOWN—Grant County

ST. ELIZABETH GRANT (181311), 238 Barnes Road, Zip 41097–9482;
tel. 859/824–8240 **A**9 10 18 **F**3 11 15 29 30 31 34 35 38 40 42 44 46 50
57 59 63 64 68 74 75 78 79 84 93 97 107 108 110 111 114 119 129 130
131 132 135 146 148 **P**6 **S** St. Elizabeth Healthcare, Edgewood, KY
Primary Contact: John Mitchell, Assistant Vice President Operations
Web address: www.stelizabeth.com
Control: Church–operated, Nongovernment, not–for profit **Service:** General
Medical and Surgical

Staffed Beds: 16 **Admissions:** 288 **Census:** 3 **Outpatient Visits:** 42225
Births: 0 **Total Expense ($000):** 14763 **Payroll Expense ($000):** 5895
Personnel: 87

ST. ELIZABETH MEDICAL CENTER–GRANT COUNTY See St. Elizabeth Grant

WINCHESTER—Clark County

⊠ **CLARK REGIONAL MEDICAL CENTER (180092)**, 175 Hospital Drive,
Zip 40391–9591; tel. 859/745–3500, (Nonreporting) **A**1 5 9 10 **S** LifePoint
Hospitals, Inc., Brentwood, TN
Primary Contact: Cherie Sibley, R.N., Chief Executive Officer
CFO: Amber Goodpaster, Chief Financial Officer
CMO: Nicholas Kouns, D.O., Chief of Staff
CHR: Deidre Bradley, Vice President Human Resources
CNO: Barbara Kinder, R.N., Chief Clinical Officer
Web address: www.clarkregional.org
Control: Corporation, Investor–owned, for–profit **Service:** General Medical and
Surgical

Staffed Beds: 100

LA

LOUISIANA

ABBEVILLE—Vermilion Parish

✠ **ABBEVILLE GENERAL HOSPITAL (190034)**, 118 North Hospital Drive, Zip 70510–4077, Mailing Address: P.O. Box 580, Zip 70511–0580; tel. 337/893–5466 **A**1 9 10 **F**11 13 15 29 30 31 34 40 45 50 54 59 60 64 66 70 75 76 79 81 82 85 86 87 89 97 98 103 105 108 114 119 127 128 130 133 146 **P**6
Primary Contact: Ray A. Landry, Chief Executive Officer
CFO: Troy Hair, Chief Financial Officer
CIO: Kelly Hair, Director Information Technology
CNO: Denise Noel, Chief Nursing Officer
Web address: www.abbgen.net
Control: Hospital district or authority, Government, nonfederal **Service:** General Medical and Surgical

Staffed Beds: 60 Admissions: 1804 Census: 30 Outpatient Visits: 78118 Births: 177 Total Expense ($000): 36473 Payroll Expense ($000): 18186 Personnel: 382

ALEXANDRIA—Rapides Parish

◇ **CENTRAL LOUISIANA SURGICAL HOSPITAL (190298)**, 651 North Bolton Avenue, Zip 71301–7449, Mailing Address: P.O. Box 8646, Zip 71306–1646; tel. 318/443–3511 **A**9 10 21 **F**12 39 68 74 79 81 82 85 86 89 90 107 111 119 130
Primary Contact: Louise Barker, R.N., Chief Executive Officer
CFO: Michael Fuselier, FACHE, Chief Financial Officer
CMO: Renick Webb, M.D., Chief Medical Director
CHR: Debbie Norman, Director Human Resources
CNO: Carol Wells, R.N., Chief Nursing Officer
Web address: www.clshospital.com
Control: Partnership, Investor–owned, for–profit **Service:** Surgical

Staffed Beds: 24 Admissions: 1168 Census: 8 Births: 0 Total Expense ($000): 36378 Payroll Expense ($000): 9793 Personnel: 211

✠ **CHRISTUS ST. FRANCES CABRINI HOSPITAL (190019)**, 3330 Masonic Drive, Zip 71301–3899; tel. 318/487–1122 **A**1 2 9 10 **F**11 12 13 15 18 20 22 24 26 28 29 30 31 34 35 40 45 46 49 54 57 58 59 63 64 70 72 74 76 77 78 79 81 82 84 85 87 89 90 93 96 97 98 103 107 108 109 110 111 114 115 116 117 118 119 120 121 126 129 130 131 132 145 146 147 148 **P**6 **S** CHRISTUS Health, Irving, TX
Primary Contact: Stephen F. Wright, President and Chief Executive Officer
COO: Lisa R. Lauve, R.N., Regional Chief Nursing Executive and Chief Operating Officer
CFO: Debbie White, Chief Financial Officer
CHR: Wendy White, Regional Vice President Human Resources
Web address: www.cabrini.org/
Control: Church–operated, Nongovernment, not–for profit **Service:** General Medical and Surgical

Staffed Beds: 281 Admissions: 11165 Census: 166 Outpatient Visits: 169924 Births: 1068 Total Expense ($000): 185487 Payroll Expense ($000): 64390 Personnel: 1491

COMPASS BEHAVIORAL CENTER OF ALEXANDRIA (194106), 6410 Masonic Drve, Zip 71301–2319; tel. 318/473–0035, (Nonreporting) **S** Compass Health, Crowley, LA
Primary Contact: Angie Hudson, Administrator
Web address: www.compasshealthcare.com/site191.php
Control: Other not–for–profit (including NFP Corporation) **Service:** Psychiatric

Staffed Beds: 16

✠ **DUBUIS HOSPITAL OF ALEXANDRIA (192012)**, 3330 Masonic Drive, 4th Floor, Zip 71301–3841; tel. 318/448–4938 **A**1 10 **F**1 3 29 77 84 85 148 **S** Dubuis Health System, Houston, TX
Primary Contact: Beth Parsons, R.N., Administrator
CNO: Kimberly Bennett, Director Patient Care
Web address: www.christusdubuis.org/CHRISTUSDubuisHospitalofAlexandriaLA
Control: Church–operated, Nongovernment, not–for profit **Service:** Long–Term Acute Care hospital

Staffed Beds: 25 Admissions: 283 Census: 19 Outpatient Visits: 0 Births: 0 Personnel: 68

✠ **HEALTHSOUTH REHABILITATION HOSPITAL OF ALEXANDRIA (193031)**, 104 North Third Street, Zip 71301–8581; tel. 318/449–1370, (Nonreporting) **A**1 10 **S** HEALTHSOUTH Corporation, Birmingham, AL
Primary Contact: James W. McClung, Chief Executive Officer
CFO: Linda Wright, Chief Financial Officer
CMO: Vasudeva Dhulipala, M.D., Medical Director
CHR: Suzie Wagner, Director Human Resources
CNO: Karin Jones, Chief Nursing Officer
Web address: www.healthsouthalexandria.com
Control: Partnership, Investor–owned, for–profit **Service:** Rehabilitation

Staffed Beds: 47

☐ **LONGLEAF HOSPITAL (194022)**, 110 John Eskew Drive, Zip 71303; tel. 318/445–5111, (Nonreporting) **A**1 9 10 **S** Acadia Healthcare Company, Inc., Franklin, TN
Primary Contact: Eric Kennedy, Chief Executive Officer
Web address: www.crossroadshospital.com
Control: Corporation, Investor–owned, for–profit **Service:** Psychiatric

Staffed Beds: 70

☐ **OCEANS BEHAVIORAL HOSPITAL OF ALEXANDRIA (194096)**, 2621 North Bolton Avenue, Zip 71303–4506; tel. 318/448–8473, (Nonreporting) **A**1 9 10 **S** Oceans Healthcare, Lake Charles, LA
Primary Contact: Gene Amons, Administrator
Web address: www.obha.info/
Control: Corporation, Investor–owned, for–profit **Service:** Psychiatric

Staffed Beds: 24

✠ **RAPIDES REGIONAL MEDICAL CENTER (190026)**, 211 Fourth Street, Zip 71301–8421; tel. 318/473–3000 **A**1 2 3 5 9 10 **F**3 11 13 15 17 18 19 20 22 24 26 28 29 30 31 32 34 35 36 38 40 41 43 44 45 46 47 48 49 50 51 52 54 55 57 59 60 61 64 65 66 68 70 72 74 75 76 77 78 79 81 82 84 85 86 87 88 89 97 107 108 110 111 114 115 118 119 120 121 123 124 129 130 131 132 135 146 147 148 **P**1 **S** HCA, Nashville, TN
Primary Contact: Jason E. Cobb, FACHE, Chief Executive Officer
COO: Becky Barnes, Chief Operating Officer
CFO: Randy Rogers, FACHE, Chief Financial Officer
CMO: David Rhodes, M.D., Senior Vice President Medical Affairs and Chief Medical Officer
CHR: Stephen W. Scull, Vice President Ethics and Compliance officer
CNO: Diane Fulton, R.N., Chief Nursing Officer
Web address: www.rapidesregional.com
Control: Partnership, Investor–owned, for–profit **Service:** General Medical and Surgical

Staffed Beds: 357 Admissions: 15855 Census: 240 Outpatient Visits: 138624 Births: 2020 Total Expense ($000): 203556 Payroll Expense ($000): 75835 Personnel: 1383

☐ **RIVERSIDE HOSPITAL OF LOUISIANA (192043)**, 211 Fourth Street, 5th Floor, Zip 71301–8421; tel. 318/767–2900, (Nonreporting) **A**1 10
Primary Contact: William Bush, Chief Executive Officer
Web address: www.riversidehospital.net
Control: Corporation, Investor–owned, for–profit **Service:** Long–Term Acute Care hospital

Staffed Beds: 27

AMITE—Tangipahoa Parish

★ **HOOD MEMORIAL HOSPITAL (191309)**, 301 West Walnut Street, Zip 70422–2098; tel. 985/748–9485 **A**9 10 18 **F**29 35 40 57 59 64 65 86 97 107 108 119 127 133
Primary Contact: Edward Dugar, Interim Chief Executive Officer
CFO: Mike Estay, Chief Financial Officer
CHR: Cynthia Rutherford, Manager Business Office
Control: Hospital district or authority, Government, nonfederal **Service:** General Medical and Surgical

Staffed Beds: 25 Admissions: 438 Census: 6 Outpatient Visits: 11457 Births: 0 Total Expense ($000): 9399 Payroll Expense ($000): 4214 Personnel: 124

ARCADIA—Bienville Parish

BIENVILLE MEDICAL CENTER (191320), 1175 Pine Street, Suite 200, Zip 71001–3122; tel. 318/263–4700, (Nonreporting) **A**9 10 18 **S** Allegiance Health Management, Shreveport, LA
Primary Contact: Kirk Lemoine, Chief Operating Officer
Control: Other not–for–profit (including NFP Corporation) **Service:** General Medical and Surgical

Staffed Beds: 21

BASTROP—Morehouse Parish

☐ **LIBERTY HEALTHCARE SYSTEMS (194083)**, 4673 Eugene Ware Boulevard, Zip 71220–1425; tel. 318/281–2448 **A**1 9 10 **F**98 99 130 **P**6
Primary Contact: Christine Murphy, MS, Administrator
CFO: Paul Coburn, Chief Financial Officer
CMO: Tommy Dansby, Chief Medical Officer
CHR: Gloria Board, Director Human Resources
Web address: www.libertybh.com/
Control: Partnership, Investor–owned, for–profit **Service:** Children's hospital psychiatric

Staffed Beds: 60 Admissions: 925 Census: 25 Outpatient Visits: 0 Births: 0

Many Facility Codes have changed. Please refer to the AHA Guide Code Chart. © 2014 AHA Guide

★ **MOREHOUSE GENERAL HOSPITAL (190116)**, 323 West Walnut Avenue,
Zip 71220–4521, Mailing Address: P.O. Box 1060, Zip 71221–1060;
tel. 318/283–3600, (Nonreporting) **A**9 10
Primary Contact: Stephen R. Pitts, Chief Executive Officer
CFO: James Allbritton, Chief Financial Officer
CMO: John Coats, M.D., Chief Medical Staff
CIO: B. J. Vail, Director Information Systems
CHR: Debbie Spann, Director Human Resources
CNO: Melinda Jones, R.N., Chief Nursing Officer
Web address: www.mghospital.com
Control: Hospital district or authority, Government, nonfederal **Service:** General
Medical and Surgical

Staffed Beds: 40

STERLINGTON REHABILITATION HOSPITAL (193058), 370 West Hickory
Avenue, Zip 71220–4521; tel. 318/556–1191 **A**10 **F**29 30 35 64 65 67 86 90
91 92 93 97 103 104 127 130 148
Primary Contact: William H. Means, Jr., Administrator
COO: Tena Hughes, R.N., Program Director and Director Nursing
CFO: William H. Means, Jr., Administrator
CMO: James M. Smith, M.D., Medical Director
CIO: Debbie Chunn, Director Medical Records
CHR: Renee Walker, Director Human Resources
Web address: www.sterlingtonrehab.com
Control: County–Government, nonfederal **Service:** General Medical and Surgical

Staffed Beds: 10 **Admissions:** 250 **Census:** 9 **Outpatient Visits:** 7159
Births: 0 **Total Expense ($000):** 5286 **Payroll Expense ($000):** 3405
Personnel: 85

STERLINGTON REHABILITATION HOSPITAL (193069), 370 West Hickory
Avenue, Zip 71220–4442, Mailing Address: P.O. Box 627, Sterlington,
Zip 71280–0627; tel. 318/665–9950, (Nonreporting) **A**10
Primary Contact: Cathy Waldrop, Administrator
Web address: www.www.sterlingtonrehab.com
Control: Corporation, Investor–owned, for–profit **Service:** Rehabilitation

Staffed Beds: 10

BATON ROUGE—East Baton Rouge Parish

☐ **BATON ROUGE BEHAVIORAL HOSPITAL (194066)**, 4040 North Boulevard,
Zip 70806; tel. 225/300–8470, (Nonreporting) **A**1 10
Primary Contact: Eric Gintoli, Hospital Administrator
Web address: www.batonrougebehavioral.com
Control: Corporation, Investor–owned, for–profit **Service:** Psychiatric

Staffed Beds: 15

☐ **BATON ROUGE GENERAL MEDICAL CENTER (190065)**, 3600 Florida Street,
Zip 70806–3889, Mailing Address: P.O. Box 2511, Zip 70821–2511;
tel. 225/387–7000, (Includes BATON ROUGE GENERAL MEDICAL
CENTER–BLUEBONNET, 8585 Picardy Avenue, Zip 70809–3679, Mailing
Address: P.O. Box 84330, Zip 70884–4330; tel. 225/763–4000) **A**1 2 3 5 6 8
9 10 **F**3 8 11 12 13 15 16 17 18 19 20 22 24 26 28 29 30 31 34 35 38 40
44 45 46 47 49 50 53 56 57 58 59 60 61 64 65 68 70 72 74 75 76 77 78
79 81 82 84 86 87 88 89 90 93 96 97 98 101 102 103 104 107 108 110
111 114 115 117 118 120 121 123 124 126 127 128 129 130 131 132
135 143 144 146 147 148 **P**4 6
Primary Contact: Mark F. Slyter, FACHE, Chief Executive Officer
CFO: Kendall Johnson, Chief Financial Officer
CMO: Floyd Roberts, M.D., Chief Medical Officer
CIO: David Hastings, Director Information Technology
CHR: Paul Douglas, Vice President Human Resources
Web address: www.brgeneral.org
Control: Other not–for–profit (including NFP Corporation) **Service:** General
Medical and Surgical

Staffed Beds: 466 **Admissions:** 20131 **Census:** 307 **Outpatient Visits:**
243484 **Births:** 762 **Total Expense ($000):** 340519 **Payroll Expense
($000):** 125285 **Personnel:** 2845

☐ **BATON ROUGE REHABILITATION HOSPITAL (193028)**, 8595 United Plaza
Boulevard, Zip 70809–2251; tel. 225/927–0567, (Nonreporting) **A**1 10
Primary Contact: Trisha Guidry, Administrator
CFO: Nicholas Hluchy, Business Analyst, Support Services Manager
CMO: Sundararama R. Vatsavai, M.D., Medical Director
CIO: Roxane Bingham, Director Marketing
CHR: Michelle Smith, Coordinator Human Resources
CNO: Derrick Landreneau, Director of Nursing
Web address: www.brrehab.com
Control: Corporation, Investor–owned, for–profit **Service:** Rehabilitation

Staffed Beds: 80

BETHESDA REHABILITATION HOSPITAL (193092), 7414 Sumrall Drive,
Zip 70812–1240, Mailing Address: 8225 Summa Avenue, Suite B.,
Zip 70809–3422; tel. 225/767–2034, (Nonreporting) **A**10
Primary Contact: Lionel Murphy, Chief Executive Officer and Administrator
Control: Corporation, Investor–owned, for–profit **Service:** Rehabilitation

Staffed Beds: 18

HEALTHSOUTH REHABILITATION HOSPITAL OF BATON ROUGE See Baton
Rouge Rehabilitation Hospital

OCEANS BEHAVIORAL HOSPITAL OF BATON ROUGE (194086), 11135
Florida Boulevard, Zip 70815–2013; tel. 225/356–7030 **A**9 10 **F**29 56 98 100
101 103 104 105 130 **P**5 **S** Oceans Healthcare, Lake Charles, LA
Primary Contact: Valerie Dalton, R.N., Administrator
Web address: www.obhbr.info/
Control: Corporation, Investor–owned, for–profit **Service:** Psychiatric

Staffed Beds: 20 **Admissions:** 439 **Census:** 16 **Outpatient Visits:** 400
Births: 0

✇ **OCHSNER MEDICAL CENTER–BATON ROUGE (190202)**, 17000 Medical
Center Drive, Zip 70816–3224; tel. 225/752–2470 **A**1 9 10 **F**3 8 11 12 13 14
15 18 20 22 24 26 29 30 31 34 35 40 45 46 48 49 51 57 58 59 60 64 70
72 74 75 76 77 78 79 81 82 85 86 87 93 97 102 104 107 108 110 111 116
117 119 126 129 130 131 132 135 144 146 147 148 **P**3 **S** Ochsner Health
System, New Orleans, LA
Primary Contact: Eric McMillen, Chief Executive Officer
CFO: Stephanie Bushart, Chief Financial Officer
CMO: F. Ralph Dauterive, M.D., Vice President Medical Affairs
CHR: Jan Rivers, Director Human Resources
Web address: www.ochsner.org/page.cfm?id=103
Control: Other not–for–profit (including NFP Corporation) **Service:** General
Medical and Surgical

Staffed Beds: 159 **Admissions:** 6370 **Census:** 66 **Outpatient Visits:** 78014
Births: 1267 **Total Expense ($000):** 119658 **Payroll Expense ($000):**
39231 **Personnel:** 585

✇ **OUR LADY OF THE LAKE REGIONAL MEDICAL CENTER (190064)**, 5000
Hennessy Boulevard, Zip 70808–4375; tel. 225/765–6565, (Includes OUR LADY
OF THE LAKE CHILDREN'S HOSPITAL, 5000 Hennessy Boulevard,
tel. 225/765–8886), (Total facility includes 390 beds in nursing home–type unit)
A1 2 3 5 8 9 10 **F**3 4 5 8 10 11 12 14 15 17 18 19 20 21 22 24 26 28 29
30 31 34 35 37 38 39 40 41 42 43 46 47 49 50 51 53 54 55 56 57 58 59
60 61 64 66 68 70 71 74 75 77 78 79 81 84 85 86 87 88 89 90 93 94 96
97 98 99 100 101 102 103 104 105 107 108 110 111 114 115 116 117
118 119 125 126 127 129 130 131 132 135 141 142 143 146 148 **P**6
S Franciscan Missionaries of Our Lady Health System, Inc., Baton Rouge, LA
Primary Contact: K. Scott Wester, FACHE, President and Chief Executive Officer
COO: Terrie Sterling, R.N., Chief Operating Officer
CFO: Jeff Limbocker, Chief Financial Officer
CMO: Richard Vath, M.D., Vice President Medical Affairs
CIO: Vindell Washington, M.D., Vice President Performance Excellence and
Technology
CHR: Cora Ford, Vice President Human Resources
CNO: Debbie Ford, R.N., Vice President Patient Care Services
Web address: www.ololrmc.com
Control: Church–operated, Nongovernment, not–for profit **Service:** General
Medical and Surgical

Staffed Beds: 1087 **Admissions:** 32156 **Census:** 741 **Outpatient Visits:**
452919 **Births:** 0 **Total Expense ($000):** 786342 **Payroll Expense ($000):**
290457 **Personnel:** 5690

☐ **PROMISE HOSPITAL BATON ROUGE – MAIN CAMPUS (192045)**, 5130
Mancuso Lane, Zip 70809–3583; tel. 225/490–9600, (Nonreporting) **A**1
S Promise Healthcare, Boca Raton, FL
Primary Contact: Patrick G. Ryan, Chief Executive Officer
COO: Michael R. Sanders, MS, Chief Operating Officer
CFO: Trina Arceneaux, Assistant Chief Financial Officer
CMO: Subhaker Gummadi, M.D., Chief Medical Staff
CIO: Charmaine T. Mosby, Area Director Health Information Management
CHR: Marilyn Hamilton, Director Human Resources
CNO: Larrie Arceneaux, Chief Clinical Officer
Web address: www.promise-batonrouge.com
Control: Corporation, Investor–owned, for–profit **Service:** Long–Term Acute Care
hospital

Staffed Beds: 54

Hospital, Medicare Provider Number, Address, Telephone, Approval, Facility, and Physician Codes, Health Care System

★ American Hospital Association (AHA) membership
☐ The Joint Commission accreditation
◇ DNV Healthcare Inc. accreditation
◯ Healthcare Facilities Accreditation Program
△ Commission on Accreditation of Rehabilitation Facilities (CARF) accreditation

LA

PROMISE HOSPITAL OF BATON ROUGE – MID–CITY CAMPUS (192004), 3600 Florida Boulevard, 4th Floor, Zip 70806–3842; tel. 225/387–7770, (Nonreporting) **A**10 **S** Promise Healthcare, Boca Raton, FL
Primary Contact: Michael R. Sanders, MS, Administrator and Chief Operating Officer
COO: Michael J. Nolan, Area Chief Operating Officer and Safety
CMO: Subhaker Gummadi, M.D., President Medical Staff
Web address: www.promise–batonrougemidcity.com
Control: Corporation, Investor–owned, for–profit **Service:** Long–Term Acute Care hospital

Staffed Beds: 28

☐ **PROMISE HOSPITAL OF BATON ROUGE – OCHSNER CAMPUS (192049)**, 17000 Medical Center Drive, 3rd Floor, Zip 70816–3246; tel. 225/236–5440, (Nonreporting) **A**1 10 **S** Promise Healthcare, Boca Raton, FL
Primary Contact: Michael R. Sanders, MS, Administrator and Chief Operating Officer
COO: Michael J. Nolan, Area Safety Director
CMO: Venkat Banda, M.D., President Medical Staff
CHR: Wendy Cobbs, Director of Human Resources
Web address: www.promise–batonrougeochsner.com
Control: Corporation, Investor–owned, for–profit **Service:** Long–Term Acute Care hospital

Staffed Beds: 29

SAGE REHABILITATION HOSPITAL (193078), 8000 Summa Avenue, Zip 70809–3423, Mailing Address: P.O. Box 82681, Zip 70884–2681; tel. 225/819–0703, (Total facility includes 15 beds in nursing home–type unit) **A**10 **F**29 54 74 75 77 90 91 93 128 130
Primary Contact: Gayla Bryant, R.N., Administrator
CMO: Christopher Belleau, M.D., Medical Director
CHR: Kathy Ringe, Director of Human Resources
CNO: Beth Sibley, Director of Nursing
Web address: www.sage–rehab.org
Control: Individual, Investor–owned, for–profit **Service:** Rehabilitation

Staffed Beds: 42 Admissions: 660 Census: 30 Outpatient Visits: 0 Births: 0 Personnel: 181

SPINE HOSPITAL OF LOUISIANA (190266), 10105 Park Rowe Avenue, Suite 250, Zip 70810–1684; tel. 225/763–9900, (Nonreporting) **A**9 10
Primary Contact: Robert D. Blair, Chief Executive Officer
CFO: Allison Doherty, Chief Financial Officer
CMO: Shawn Dunn, M.D., Medical Director
CHR: Shannon Juge, Human Resources Representative
Web address: www.theneuromedicalcenter.com
Control: Corporation, Investor–owned, for–profit **Service:** Surgical

Staffed Beds: 23

☐ **SURGICAL SPECIALTY CENTER OF BATON ROUGE (190251)**, 8080 Bluebonnet Boulevard, Zip 70810–7827; tel. 225/408–8080, (Nonreporting) **A**1 9 10
Primary Contact: Craig P. Hume, Chief Executive Officer
Web address: www.sscbr.com
Control: Corporation, Investor–owned, for–profit **Service:** Surgical

Staffed Beds: 14

THE NEUROMEDICAL CENTER REHABILITATION HOSPITAL (193090), 10101 Park Rowe Avenue, Suite 500, Zip 70810–1685; tel. 225/906–2999, (Nonreporting) **A**10 **S** AMG Integrated Healthcare Management, Lafayette, LA
Primary Contact: Jay Ivy, R.N., Chief Executive Officer
Web address: www.theneuromedicalcenter.com
Control: Corporation, Investor–owned, for–profit **Service:** Rehabilitation

Staffed Beds: 23

✦ **WOMAN'S HOSPITAL (190128)**, 100 Woman's Way, Zip 70817–5100, Mailing Address: P.O. Box 95009, Zip 70895–9009; tel. 225/927–1300 **A**1 2 9 10 **F**3 11 12 13 15 29 31 32 34 35 36 38 45 50 53 54 57 58 59 61 64 65 68 70 71 72 74 75 76 77 78 79 81 84 85 86 87 93 107 110 111 115 119 126 129 130 131 132 134 135 146 147 **P**6
Primary Contact: Teri G. Fontenot, FACHE, President and Chief Executive Officer
CFO: Stephanie Anderson, Executive Vice President and Chief Operating Officer
CMO: Susan Puyau, M.D., Medical Director
CIO: Paul Kirk, Vice President
CHR: Donna L. Bodin, Vice President
CNO: Patricia Johnson, R.N., Senior Vice President
Web address: www.womans.org
Control: Other not–for–profit (including NFP Corporation) **Service:** Obstetrics and gynecology

Staffed Beds: 216 Admissions: 12027 Census: 135 Outpatient Visits: 104117 Births: 8490 Total Expense ($000): 230677 Payroll Expense ($000): 108530 Personnel: 1573

BERNICE—Union Parish

REEVES MEMORIAL MEDICAL CENTER (191326), 409 First Street, Zip 71222–4001, Mailing Address: P.O. Box 697, Zip 71222–0697; tel. 318/285–9066, (Nonreporting) **A**9 10 18
Primary Contact: Landon Tooke, Chief Executive Officer
COO: Beth Jones, Chief Operating Officer
CFO: Charolette Thompson, Chief Financial Officer
CMO: R. Brian Harris, M.D., Chief of Staff
CHR: Robin Adams, Director Human Resources
Web address: www.reevesmemorial.com/
Control: Hospital district or authority, Government, nonfederal **Service:** General Medical and Surgical

Staffed Beds: 11

TRI–WARD GENERAL HOSPITAL See Reeves Memorial Medical Center

BOGALUSA—Washington Parish

☐ **OUR LADY OF THE ANGELS HOSPITAL (190095)**, 433 Plaza Street, Zip 70427–3793; tel. 985/730–6700, (Includes AMG SPECIALTY HOSPITAL – BOGALUSA, 621 Columbia Street, Zip 70427–0040; tel. 985/735–1322; BOGALUSA COMMUNITY MEDICAL CENTER, 433 Plaza Street, tel. 985/730–6700), (Nonreporting) **A**1 3 9 **S** Franciscan Missionaries of Our Lady Health System, Inc., Baton Rouge, LA
Primary Contact: Rene Ragas, Chief Operating Officer
COO: Rene Ragas, Chief Operating Officer
CFO: Brooke Cummings, Chief Financial Officer
CMO: Hamid Hussain, M.D., Medical Director
CIO: Mike Gilly, Chief Information Officer
CHR: Christi Brown, Director Human Resources
CNO: Mark Kellar, R.N., Interim Chief Nursing Officer
Web address: www.oloah.org
Control: Other not–for–profit (including NFP Corporation) **Service:** General Medical and Surgical

Staffed Beds: 74

BOSSIER CITY—Bossier Parish

☐ **CORNERSTONE HOSPITAL OF BOSSIER CITY (192006)**, 4900 Medical Drive, Zip 71112–4521; tel. 318/747–9500, (Nonreporting) **A**1 10 **S** Cornerstone Healthcare Group, Dallas, TX
Primary Contact: Sheri Burnette, R.N., Chief Executive Officer and Administrator
CFO: Chad Deardorff, Chief Financial Officer
CMO: James Jackson, M.D., Chief of Staff
Web address: www.chghospitals.com/
Control: Corporation, Investor–owned, for–profit **Service:** Long–Term Acute Care hospital

Staffed Beds: 54

◇ **PATHWAY REHABILITATION HOSPITAL (193094)**, 4900 Medical Drive, Zip 71112–4521; tel. 318/841–5555, (Nonreporting) **A**10 21
Primary Contact: James Manning, Administrator
Web address: www.pathrehab.com
Control: Corporation, Investor–owned, for–profit **Service:** Rehabilitation

Staffed Beds: 24

RED RIVER BEHAVIORAL CENTER (194079), 2800 Melrose Avenue, Zip 71111–5870; tel. 318/549–2033, (Nonreporting) **A**9 10
Primary Contact: Susan Kottenbrook, Chief Executive Officer
Web address: www.redriverbehavioral.com/
Control: Partnership, Investor–owned, for–profit **Service:** Psychiatric

Staffed Beds: 20

WILLIS–KNIGHTON BOSSIER HEALTH CENTER See WK Bossier Health Center

✦ △ **WK BOSSIER HEALTH CENTER (190236)**, 2400 Hospital Drive, Zip 71111–2385; tel. 318/212–7000 **A**1 7 9 10 **F**3 8 11 12 13 15 18 20 22 24 28 29 30 34 35 38 40 44 45 46 47 48 49 50 53 54 56 57 59 60 61 64 65 66 70 74 75 76 77 78 79 80 81 82 84 85 86 87 89 93 96 97 100 101 102 103 107 108 109 110 111 114 115 118 119 126 127 129 130 131 132 135 144 146 147 148 **P**7 **S** Willis–Knighton Health System, Shreveport, LA
Primary Contact: Clifford M. Broussard, FACHE, Administrator
COO: Charles D. Daigle, Chief Operating Officer
CFO: Ramona D. Fryer, Chief Financial Officer
CMO: Charles Powers, M.D., Administrative Medical Director
CIO: Charles Laster, Director Information Management
CHR: Debbie McCall, Director Human Resources
CNO: Sharon Hudnell, R.N., Chief Nursing Officer
Web address: www.wkhs.com/wkb/
Control: Other not–for–profit (including NFP Corporation) **Service:** General Medical and Surgical

Staffed Beds: 166 Admissions: 10799 Census: 88 Outpatient Visits: 117710 Births: 942 Personnel: 857

BREAUX BRIDGE—St. Martin Parish

GENESIS BEHAVIORAL HOSPITAL (194089), 606 Latiolais Drive,
Zip 70517–4231, Mailing Address: PO BOX 159, Zip 70517–0159;
tel. 337/442–6084 **A**9 10 **F**98 100 101 102 103 104 105 **P**1
Primary Contact: Will Arledge, Administrator
COO: Gretchen Kaltenbach, R.N., Chief Operating Officer
CFO: Will Arledge, Chief Financial Officer
Control: Corporation, Investor–owned, for–profit **Service:** Psychiatric

Staffed Beds: 18 Admissions: 526 Census: 16 Outpatient Visits: 16512
Births: 0 **Total Expense ($000):** 5537 **Payroll Expense ($000):** 2026
Personnel: 71

★ **ST. MARTIN HOSPITAL (191302)**, 210 Champagne Boulevard,
Zip 70517–3700, Mailing Address: P.O. Box 357, Zip 70517–0357;
tel. 337/332–2178 **A**9 10 18 **F**3 11 15 28 29 34 35 38 40 57 59 64 75 77
90 93 96 107 108 109 110 114 119 128 133 **P**8 **S** Lafayette General Health,
Lafayette, LA
Primary Contact: Katherine D. Hebert, Chief Executive Officer
CFO: Shadelle Huval, Director Finance
CHR: Rena B. Mouisset, Director Human Resources and Contract Compliance
Web address: www.stmartinhospital.org
Control: Other not–for–profit (including NFP Corporation) **Service:** General
Medical and Surgical

Staffed Beds: 25 Admissions: 413 Census: 9 Births: 0 **Total Expense
($000):** 13583 **Payroll Expense ($000):** 5675 **Personnel:** 136

BROUSSARD—Lafayette Parish

☐ **OCEANS BEHAVIORAL HOSPITAL OF BROUSSARD (194073)**, 418 Albertson
Parkway, Zip 70518–4971; tel. 337/237–6444, (Nonreporting) **A**1 9 10
S Oceans Healthcare, Lake Charles, LA
Primary Contact: Amy Dysart–Credeur, Administrator
Web address: www.obhb.info/
Control: Corporation, Investor–owned, for–profit **Service:** Psychiatric

Staffed Beds: 38

BUNKIE—Avoyelles Parish

BUNKIE GENERAL HOSPITAL (191311), 427 Evergreen Highway, Zip 71322,
Mailing Address: P.O. Box 380, Zip 71322–0380; tel. 318/346–6681,
(Nonreporting) **A**9 10 18
Primary Contact: Linda F. Deville, Chief Executive Officer
CFO: Frances Deglandon, Chief Financial Officer
CMO: Mohit Srivastava, M.D., Chief of Staff
CIO: Johnny Bergeron, Chief Information Officer
CHR: Tina Louise Juneau, Director Human Resources
CNO: Corey Jeansonne, Chief Nursing Officer
Web address: www.bunkiegeneral.com
Control: Hospital district or authority, Government, nonfederal **Service:** General
Medical and Surgical

Staffed Beds: 18

CAMERON—Cameron Parish

SOUTH CAMERON MEMORIAL HOSPITAL (190307), 5360 West Creole
Highway, Zip 70631–5127; tel. 337/542–4111, (Nonreporting) **A**10
Primary Contact: David Byrns, Chief Executive Officer
Control: Hospital district or authority, Government, nonfederal **Service:** General
Medical and Surgical

Staffed Beds: 49

CHALMETTE—Saint Bernard Parish

⊠ **ST. BERNARD PARISH HOSPITAL (190308)**, 8000 West Judge Perez Drive,
Zip 70043–1668; tel. 504/826–9500 **A**1 10 **F**3 8 15 18 20 22 24 29 34 40
45 46 49 53 57 59 70 77 79 81 91 107 108 110 111 114 119 129 148
Primary Contact: Wayne J. Landry, Chief Executive Officer
COO: Charles Lindell, Chief Operating Officer
CFO: Joseph Kemka, Chief Financial Officer
CMO: Paul Verrette, M.D., Chief Medical Officer
CIO: Zane Looney, Chief Information Officer
CHR: Melody M. O'Connell, Director Human Resources
CNO: Scott Dassau, Chief Nursing Officer
Web address: www.sbph.net
Control: Hospital district or authority, Government, nonfederal **Service:** General
Medical and Surgical

Staffed Beds: 40 Admissions: 1622 Census: 20 Outpatient Visits: 8500
Births: 0

CHURCH POINT—Acadia Parish

ACADIA–ST. LANDRY HOSPITAL (191319), 810 South Broadway Street,
Zip 70525–4497; tel. 337/684–5435, (Nonreporting) **A**9 10 18
Primary Contact: F. Peter Savoy, III, Chief Executive Officer
CFO: Judy Young, Chief Financial Officer
CMO: Ty Hargroder, M.D., Chief of Staff
CHR: Judy Young, Chief Financial Officer
Web address: www.aslh.org
Control: Other not–for–profit (including NFP Corporation) **Service:** General
Medical and Surgical

Staffed Beds: 25

CLINTON—East Feliciana Parish

AMG SPECIALTY HOSPITAL–FELICIANA (192041), 9725 Grace Lane,
Zip 70722–4925; tel. 225/683–1600, (Nonreporting) **A**10 **S** AMG Integrated
Healthcare Management, Lafayette, LA
Primary Contact: Keith Carruth, Chief Executive Officer
Web address: www.amgfeliciana.com/
Control: Corporation, Investor–owned, for–profit **Service:** Long–Term Acute Care
hospital

Staffed Beds: 16

COLUMBIA—Caldwell Parish

CALDWELL MEMORIAL HOSPITAL (190190), 411 Main Street,
Zip 71418–6704, Mailing Address: P.O. Box 899, Zip 71418–0899;
tel. 318/649–6111, (Nonreporting) **A**9 10
Primary Contact: Heather Clark, Chief Executive Officer
COO: Lisa Patrick, Chief Operating Officer
Control: Other not–for–profit (including NFP Corporation) **Service:** General
Medical and Surgical

Staffed Beds: 25

CITIZENS MEDICAL CENTER (190184), 7939 U.S. Highway 165,
Zip 71418–1079, Mailing Address: P.O. Box 1079, Zip 71418–1079;
tel. 318/649–6106, (Nonreporting) **A**9 10
Primary Contact: Steve Barbo, R.N., Administrator
Control: Hospital district or authority, Government, nonfederal **Service:** General
Medical and Surgical

Staffed Beds: 40

COUSHATTA—Red River Parish

⊠ **CHRISTUS COUSHATTA HEALTH CARE CENTER (191312)**, 1635 Marvel
Street, Zip 71019–9022, Mailing Address: P.O. Box 589, Zip 71019–0589;
tel. 318/932–2000 **A**1 9 10 18 **F**3 15 29 30 34 35 39 40 41 50 54 56 57 59
64 65 66 67 68 75 77 78 81 82 91 93 97 103 107 110 115 116 117 119
120 127 128 130 133 135 147 148 **S** CHRISTUS Health, Irving, TX
Primary Contact: Michael Harrington, Chief Executive Officer
CFO: Scott Merryman, Chief Financial Officer
CMO: Jonathan Weisul, M.D., Vice President Medical Affairs and Chief Medical
Officer
CIO: Bruce Honea, Director Information Services
CHR: Donnette Craig, Director Human Resources
Web address: www.christuscoushatta.org
Control: Church–operated, Nongovernment, not–for profit **Service:** Hospital unit
of an institution (prison hospital, college infimary, etc.)

Staffed Beds: 25 Admissions: 1095 Census: 12 Outpatient Visits: 38000
Births: 0 **Personnel:** 75

SPECIALTY REHABILITATION HOSPITAL OF COUSHATTA (193080), 1110
Ringgold Avenue Suite B., Zip 71019–9073; tel. 318/932–1770,
(Nonreporting) **A**10
Primary Contact: Craig Ball, Chief Executive Officer
COO: Charlie Ball, Chief Operating Officer
CFO: Connie Ball, Chief Financial Officer
CMO: Jalal Joudeh, M.D., Chief Medical Officer
CHR: Denise Logan, Director Human Resources
Web address: www.specialtyhealthcare.com
Control: Individual, Investor–owned, for–profit **Service:** Rehabilitation

Staffed Beds: 12

Hospital, Medicare Provider Number, Address, Telephone, Approval, Facility, and Physician Codes, Health Care System

★ American Hospital Association (AHA) membership
☐ The Joint Commission accreditation ◇ DNV Healthcare Inc. accreditation
○ Healthcare Facilities Accreditation Program
△ Commission on Accreditation of Rehabilitation Facilities (CARF) accreditation

---

LA

COVINGTON—St. Tammany Parish

◇ **FAIRWAY MEDICAL CENTER (190267)**, 67252 Industry Lane, Zip 70433–8704; tel. 985/809–9888, (Nonreporting) **A**9 10 21
Primary Contact: Benjamin Patterson, Chief Executive Officer
CFO: Denise Businelle, Chief Financial Officer
CMO: William Preau, M.D., Medical Director
CIO: Skip Federico, Director Information Systems
CHR: Pam Collins, Director Human Resources
Web address: www.fairwaymedical.com
Control: Corporation, Investor–owned, for–profit **Service:** General Medical and Surgical

Staffed Beds: 21

✠ **LAKEVIEW REGIONAL MEDICAL CENTER (190177)**, 95 Judge Tanner Boulevard, Zip 70433–7507; tel. 985/867–3800, (Nonreporting) **A**1 9 10 **S** HCA, Nashville, TN
Primary Contact: Bret G. Kolman, CPA, FACHE, Chief Executive Officer
CFO: Carolyn Ridge, Chief Financial Officer
CMO: George Barnes, M.D., Medical Director
CIO: Jinilinn Cass, Director Medical Records
CHR: Lyle Theriot, Director Human Resources
Web address: www.lakeviewregional.com
Control: Corporation, Investor–owned, for–profit **Service:** General Medical and Surgical

Staffed Beds: 172

MMO GREENBRIER HOSPITAL (194069), 201 Greenbrier Boulevard, Zip 70433–7236; tel. 985/893–2970 **A**9 10 **F**29 35 50 54 56 64 75 98 100 101 102 103 104 105 130
Primary Contact: William Fuqua, Administrator
CMO: Jason Coe, M.D., Medical Director
Web address: www.mmoinc.com
Control: Corporation, Investor–owned, for–profit **Service:** Psychiatric

Staffed Beds: 60 **Admissions:** 2129 **Census:** 45 **Outpatient Visits:** 6821 **Births:** 0 **Total Expense ($000):** 9866 **Payroll Expense ($000):** 6193

NORTHSHORE SPECIALTY HOSPITAL See Post Acute Northshore Specialty Hospital

✠ **POST ACUTE NORTHSHORE SPECIALTY HOSPITAL (192048)**, 20050 Crestwood Boulevard, Zip 70433–5207; tel. 985/875–7525 **A**1 10 **F**1 29 35 54 60 64 130 143 148 **S** Post Acute Medical, LLC, Enola, PA
Primary Contact: Stephanie Morvant, Chief Executive Officer
COO: John Bauer, Chief Operating Officer
CFO: Karick Stober, Chief Financial Officer
CMO: Adam Burick, M.D., Chief Medical Officer
CIO: Bryan Munchel, Senior Vice President and Chief Information Officer
CHR: Waynea Finley, Senior Vice President Human Resources
CNO: Marsha Medlin, Senior Vice President of Clinical and Operations
Web address: www.northshoreltach.com
Control: Partnership, Investor–owned, for–profit **Service:** Long–Term Acute Care hospital

Staffed Beds: 58 **Admissions:** 424 **Census:** 30 **Outpatient Visits:** 2983 **Births:** 0 **Total Expense ($000):** 15594 **Payroll Expense ($000):** 5085 **Personnel:** 116

✠ **REGENCY HOSPITAL OF COVINGTON (192051)**, 195 Highland Park Entrance, Zip 70433–7164; tel. 985/867–3977, (Nonreporting) **A**1 10 **S** Select Medical Corporation, Mechanicsburg, PA
Primary Contact: Kiley P. Cedotal, Chief Executive Officer
CMO: Merrill Laurent, M.D., Medical Director
CHR: Deanna Jorgensen, Coordinator Human Resources
CNO: Teri Kessel–Fox, Director Clinical Services
Web address: www.regencyhospital.com
Control: Corporation, Investor–owned, for–profit **Service:** Long–Term Acute Care hospital

Staffed Beds: 38

✠ **ST. TAMMANY PARISH HOSPITAL (190045)**, 1202 South Tyler Street, Zip 70433–2330; tel. 985/898–4000 **A**1 2 9 10 **F**3 8 11 12 13 15 17 18 20 22 24 26 28 29 30 31 34 35 37 40 43 45 48 49 50 54 57 59 62 63 64 65 69 70 72 74 75 76 77 78 79 81 82 84 85 86 87 89 90 92 93 96 97 107 108 109 110 111 114 115 119 124 126 129 130 132 135 146 147 148 **P**6
Primary Contact: Patti M. Ellish, FACHE, President and Chief Executive Officer
COO: Sharon A. Toups, Senior Vice President and Chief Operating Officer
CFO: Sandra P. Dipietro, Chief Financial Officer
CFO: Tim Lessing, Chief Financial Officer
CMO: Robert Capitelli, M.D., Senior Vice President and Chief Medical Officer
CIO: Craig Doyle, Director and Chief Information Officer
CHR: Jean M. Holtman, Vice President Human Resources
CNO: Kerry K. Milton, R.N., Chief Nursing Officer
Web address: www.stph.org
Control: Hospital district or authority, Government, nonfederal **Service:** General Medical and Surgical

Staffed Beds: 218 **Admissions:** 10362 **Census:** 131 **Outpatient Visits:** 273507 **Births:** 1644 **Total Expense ($000):** 218361 **Payroll Expense ($000):** 87911 **Personnel:** 1376

CROWLEY—Acadia Parish

★ **ACADIA GENERAL HOSPITAL (190044)**, 1305 Crowley Rayne Highway, Zip 70526–8202; tel. 337/783–3222, (Nonreporting) **A**9 10
Primary Contact: Heather L. Harper, Chief Executive Officer
CMO: Neal J. Duhon, M.D., Chief of Staff
Web address: www.alh.org
Control: Other not–for–profit (including NFP Corporation) **Service:** General Medical and Surgical

Staffed Beds: 178

★ **COMPASS BEHAVIORAL CENTER OF CROWLEY (194085)**, 1526 North Avenue I., Zip 70526–2434; tel. 337/788–3380 **A**9 10 **F**64 98 100 101 103 104 105 **P**8 **S** Compass Health, Crowley, LA
Primary Contact: Allison Kidder, Administrator
Web address: www.compasshealthcare.com
Control: Corporation, Investor–owned, for–profit **Service:** Psychiatric

Staffed Beds: 34 **Admissions:** 640 **Census:** 20 **Outpatient Visits:** 21279 **Births:** 0 **Total Expense ($000):** 7560 **Payroll Expense ($000):** 3807 **Personnel:** 44

KAILO LTAC HOSPITAL (192050), 713 North Avenue L., Zip 70526–3832; tel. 337/783–2859 **A**10 **F**1 2 29 34 35 38 50 54 56 57 59 75 101 103 104 105 130 132 148 **P**5
Primary Contact: E. Paul Broussard, Chief Executive Officer
CHR: Kevin V. Broussard, Chief Human Resources Officer
Control: State–Government, nonfederal **Service:** Long–Term Acute Care hospital

Staffed Beds: 15 **Admissions:** 98 **Census:** 7 **Outpatient Visits:** 0 **Births:** 0 **Total Expense ($000):** 4095 **Payroll Expense ($000):** 1431 **Personnel:** 42

CUT OFF—Lafourche Parish

★ ◇ **LADY OF THE SEA GENERAL HOSPITAL (191325)**, 200 West 134th Place, Zip 70345–4143; tel. 985/632–6401 **A**9 10 18 21 **F**15 29 34 35 40 45 50 57 59 60 62 70 81 85 86 87 93 108 110 111 114 119 127 130 133 146 148
Primary Contact: Karen S. Collins, R.N., Chief Executive Officer
COO: Lloyd Guidry, Chief Operating Officer
CFO: Jacquelyn Richoux, Chief Financial Officer
CMO: William Crenshaw, M.D., Chief of Staff
CIO: Bennie Smith, Chief Information Officer
CHR: Bennie Smith, Director Human Resources and Risk Management
CNO: Holly Griffin, R.N., Chief Nursing Officer
Web address: www.losgh.org
Control: Hospital district or authority, Government, nonfederal **Service:** General Medical and Surgical

Staffed Beds: 25 **Admissions:** 1011 **Census:** 12 **Outpatient Visits:** 47366 **Births:** 0 **Total Expense ($000):** 30373 **Payroll Expense ($000):** 12823 **Personnel:** 270

DE RIDDER—Beauregard Parish

✠ **BEAUREGARD MEMORIAL HOSPITAL (190050)**, 600 South Pine Street, Zip 70634–4942, Mailing Address: P.O. Box 730, Zip 70634–0730; tel. 337/462–7100 **A**1 9 10 **F**3 11 13 15 18 20 26 28 29 30 31 34 35 39 40 45 46 50 53 57 64 70 75 76 78 79 81 85 89 91 93 96 107 108 110 111 114 119 129 130 133 146 148 **P**6
Primary Contact: Robert M. Charron, Chief Executive Officer
CFO: Darrell L. Kingham, CPA, Vice President Finance
CMO: Steven Farquhar, M.D., President Medical Staff
CIO: Meg Jackson, Director Biomedical and Management Information Systems
CHR: Kelli C. Broocks, Director Human Resources, Public Relations and Physician Recruitment
CNO: Anita Thibodeaux, Chief Nursing Officer
Web address: www.beauregard.org
Control: Hospital district or authority, Government, nonfederal **Service:** General Medical and Surgical

Staffed Beds: 60 **Admissions:** 2554 **Census:** 27 **Outpatient Visits:** 53544 **Births:** 349 **Total Expense ($000):** 34794 **Payroll Expense ($000):** 15495 **Personnel:** 311

DELHI—Richland Parish

RICHLAND PARISH HOSPITAL (191323), 407 Cincinnati Street, Zip 71232–3007; tel. 318/878–5171, (Nonreporting) **A**9 10 18
Primary Contact: Michael W. Carroll, Administrator
CIO: Barbra Hutchison, Director Medical Records
CHR: Patsy Stout, Director Personnel
Web address: www.delhihospital.com
Control: Hospital district or authority, Government, nonfederal **Service:** General Medical and Surgical

Staffed Beds: 25

Many Facility Codes have changed. Please refer to the AHA Guide Code Chart. © 2014 AHA Guide

DENHAM SPRINGS—Livingston Parish

AMG SPECIALTY HOSPITAL–DENHAM SPRINGS (192008), 8375 Florida Boulevard, Zip 70726–7806; tel. 225/665–2664, (Nonreporting) **A**10 **S** AMG Integrated Healthcare Management, Lafayette, LA
Primary Contact: Karen Crayton, Administrator
CFO: Jessica McGee, Chief Financial Officer
CMO: Durwin Walker, M.D., Chief Medical Officer
CHR: Kim Hernandez, Chief Human Resources Officer
CNO: Sharon Faulkner, Chief Nursing Officer
Web address: www.amgdenham.com/
Control: Corporation, Investor–owned, for–profit **Service:** Long–Term Acute Care hospital

Staffed Beds: 117

DEQUINCY—Calcasieu Parish

☐ **DEQUINCY MEMORIAL HOSPITAL (191307)**, 110 West Fourth Street, Zip 70633–3508, Mailing Address: P.O. Box 1166, Zip 70633–1166; tel. 337/786–1200, (Nonreporting) **A**1 9 10 18
Primary Contact: Michael Ashford, Administrator
CFO: Vicky Kelley, Chief Financial Officer
CMO: Jalal Joudeh, M.D., Chief of Staff
Web address: www.dequincyhospital.com
Control: City–Government, nonfederal **Service:** General Medical and Surgical

Staffed Beds: 19

DERIDDER—Beauregard Parish

☐ **OCEANS BEHAVIORAL HOSPITAL OF DE RIDDER (194081)**, 1420 Blankenship Drive, Zip 70634–4604; tel. 337/460–9472, (Nonreporting) **A**1 9 10 **S** Oceans Healthcare, Lake Charles, LA
Primary Contact: Sheila Langston, Administrator
Web address: www.obhd.info/
Control: Corporation, Investor–owned, for–profit **Service:** Psychiatric

Staffed Beds: 20

DONALDSONVILLE—Ascension Parish

⊞ **PREVOST MEMORIAL HOSPITAL (191308)**, 301 Memorial Drive, Zip 70346–4376; tel. 225/473–7931 **A**1 9 10 18 **F**3 11 15 29 40 57 59 107 110 119 133 146
Primary Contact: Vincent A. Cataldo, Administrator
CFO: Jane Arboneaux, Chief Financial Officer
CMO: Michel Y. Hirsch, M.D., Chief Medical Staff
CHR: Linda Cataldo, Human Resources Secretary
Web address: www.prevosthospital.net
Control: Hospital district or authority, Government, nonfederal **Service:** General Medical and Surgical

Staffed Beds: 25 Admissions: 89 Census: 1 Outpatient Visits: 21747
Births: 0 Total Expense ($000): 6884 Payroll Expense ($000): 2948
Personnel: 51

FARMERVILLE—Union Parish

LIBERTY HEALTHCARE SYSTEMS See Serenity Springs Specialty Hospital

SERENITY SPRINGS SPECIALTY HOSPITAL (194074), 309 North Main Street, Zip 71241–2825; tel. 318/368–0110, (Nonreporting) **A**9 10
Primary Contact: Adrian Williams, Chief Executive Officer
Web address: www.serenityhospital.com
Control: Corporation, Investor–owned, for–profit **Service:** Psychiatric

Staffed Beds: 18

UNION GENERAL HOSPITAL (191301), 901 James Avenue, Zip 71241–2234, Mailing Address: P.O. Box 398, Zip 71241–0398; tel. 318/368–9751 **A**9 10 18 **F**15 32 35 40 45 56 81 93 104 107 110 114 119 127 128 133 143 **P**6
Primary Contact: Evalyn Ormond, Chief Executive Officer
CFO: William Adcock, Chief Financial Officer
CHR: Sheri Cooper, Director Human Resources
Web address: www.uniongen.com
Control: Other not–for–profit (including NFP Corporation) **Service:** General Medical and Surgical

Staffed Beds: 25 Admissions: 349 Census: 3 Outpatient Visits: 26827
Births: 0 Total Expense ($000): 11547 Payroll Expense ($000): 4599
Personnel: 105

FERRIDAY—Concordia Parish

RIVERLAND MEDICAL CENTER (191318), 1700 N.E. Wallace Boulevard, Zip 71334–0111, Mailing Address: P.O. Box 111, Zip 71334–0111; tel. 318/757–6551 **A**9 10 18 **F**3 15 29 30 34 35 40 45 57 59 70 75 77 81 85 86 104 107 108 110 115 119 130 133 135 146 148 **P**6
Primary Contact: William H. Rucker, Administrator
COO: Maryrose Welch, Chief Compliance Officer
CMO: Huey Moak, M.D., Chief of Staff
CIO: Nekisha Smith, Director Medical Records
CHR: Jeannie Couture, Manager Personnel
CNO: Vickie Zuccaro, R.N., Director of Nursing
Web address: www.riverlandmedcenter.com/
Control: Hospital district or authority, Government, nonfederal **Service:** General Medical and Surgical

Staffed Beds: 25 Admissions: 781 Census: 8 Outpatient Visits: 19600
Births: 0 Total Expense ($000): 14062 Payroll Expense ($000): 6242
Personnel: 156

FORT POLK—Vernon Parish

⊞ **BAYNE–JONES ARMY COMMUNITY HOSPITAL**, 1585 3rd Street, Zip 71459–5102; tel. 337/531–3928 **A**1 **F**3 7 8 13 15 29 30 32 33 34 35 38 39 40 44 45 46 50 54 57 59 64 65 68 75 76 77 79 81 82 85 87 97 99 100 101 104 107 110 111 115 119 130 131 132 135 143 144 146 147 148 **S** Department of the Army, Office of the Surgeon General, Falls Church, VA
Primary Contact: Colonel Mark C. Wilhite, Commander
COO: Larry R. Patterson, Deputy Commander Administration
CFO: Captain Dustin Mullins, Chief Resource Management
CMO: Colonel Thomas Starkey, M.D., Deputy Commander FDR Clinical Services
CIO: Major William Callahan, Chief Information Management Division
CHR: Captain Dustin Mullins, Chief Human Resources
CNO: Colonel Bridget Little, Deputy Commander Nursing
Web address: www.polk.amedd.army.mil
Control: Army, Government, federal **Service:** General Medical and Surgical

Staffed Beds: 22 Admissions: 1460 Census: 8 Outpatient Visits: 280138
Births: 654 Total Expense ($000): 78889 Payroll Expense ($000): 41230
Personnel: 1056

FRANKLIN—St. Mary Parish

★ **FRANKLIN FOUNDATION HOSPITAL (191310)**, 1097 Northwest Boulevard, Zip 70538–3407, Mailing Address: P.O. Box 577, Zip 70538–0577; tel. 337/828–0760 **A**9 10 18 **F**3 11 13 15 18 26 28 29 34 40 45 50 57 59 68 70 74 75 76 77 79 81 85 93 107 110 111 114 119 130 133 135 146 147 148 **P**6 **S** QHR, Brentwood, TN
Primary Contact: Claudia Ann Eisenmann, Chief Executive Officer
CFO: Ron Bailey, Chief Financial Officer
CMO: Jesus Chua, M.D., Chief of Staff
CIO: John Spradlin, Information Systems Director
CHR: Elmo Vinas, Director Human Resources
CNO: Jennifer Wise, Chief Nursing Officer
Web address: www.franklinfoundation.org
Control: Hospital district or authority, Government, nonfederal **Service:** General Medical and Surgical

Staffed Beds: 22 Admissions: 880 Census: 12 Outpatient Visits: 25670
Births: 127 Total Expense ($000): 22184 Payroll Expense ($000): 10802
Personnel: 180

FRANKLINTON—Washington Parish

☐ **RIVERSIDE MEDICAL CENTER (191313)**, 1900 Main Street, Zip 70438–3688; tel. 985/839–4431, (Nonreporting) **A**1 9 10 18
Primary Contact: Kyle Magee, M.D., Chief Executive Officer
COO: Ben Lott, Vice President of Clinical Services
CFO: Michael J. Magee, Chief Financial Officer
CMO: Chris Foret, M.D., Chief of Staff
CHR: John Seal, Director Human Resources
CNO: Ben Lott, Vice President of Clinical Services
Web address: www.rmchospital.com
Control: Hospital district or authority, Government, nonfederal **Service:** General Medical and Surgical

Staffed Beds: 25

GONZALES—Ascension Parish

⊞ **SEASIDE HEALTH SYSTEM (194103)**, 615 East Worthy Road, Zip 70737–4240, Mailing Address: TX, tel. 225/238–3043, (Nonreporting) **A**1 9 10
Primary Contact: Lawrence Conkerton, Administrator
Web address: www.seasidehc.com
Control: Partnership, Investor–owned, for–profit **Service:** Psychiatric

Staffed Beds: 24

Hospital, Medicare Provider Number, Address, Telephone, Approval, Facility, and Physician Codes, Health Care System

★ American Hospital Association (AHA) membership
☐ The Joint Commission accreditation   ◇ DNV Healthcare Inc. accreditation
○ Healthcare Facilities Accreditation Program
△ Commission on Accreditation of Rehabilitation Facilities (CARF) accreditation

---

LA

✠ **ST. ELIZABETH HOSPITAL (190242)**, 1125 West Highway 30, Zip 70737–5004; tel. 225/647–5000 **A**1 9 10 **F**3 8 11 12 15 29 30 34 35 40 43 45 46 47 48 49 51 57 59 66 70 74 75 79 80 81 82 85 107 108 110 111 114 115 119 130 133 146 **P**6 **S** Franciscan Missionaries of Our Lady Health System, Inc., Baton Rouge, LA
Primary Contact: Robert L. Burgess, President and Chief Executive Officer
COO: Sue Knight, CPA, Chief Operating Officer
CFO: Scott Richard, Vice President Finance and Chief Financial Officer
CMO: Chris Trevino, M.D., Chief Medical Officer
CIO: Shannon Simpson, Director Information Services
CHR: Melissa Miller, Director Human Resources
CNO: Yvonne Pellerin, Chief Nursing Officer
Web address: www.steh.com
Control: Church–operated, Nongovernment, not–for profit **Service:** General Medical and Surgical

Staffed Beds: 38 Admissions: 2476 Census: 28 Outpatient Visits: 270522 Births: 0 Total Expense ($000): 105637 Payroll Expense ($000): 39815 Personnel: 844

☐ **ST. JAMES BEHAVIORAL HEALTH HOSPITAL (194088)**, 3136 South Saint Landry Road, Zip 70737–5801; tel. 225/647–7524, (Nonreporting) **A**1 10
Primary Contact: Rick Bennett, Administrator
COO: Wendell Smith, Chief Operating Officer
CFO: Rama Kongara, Chief Financial Officer
CMO: Lance Bullock, M.D., Medical Director
CHR: Dessa Frederick, Manager Human Resources
Web address: www.sjbhh.net
Control: Corporation, Investor–owned, for–profit **Service:** Psychiatric

Staffed Beds: 10

GREENSBURG—St. Helena Parish

ST. HELENA PARISH HOSPITAL (191300), 16874 Highway 43, Zip 70441–4834; tel. 225/222–6111, (Nonreporting) **A**9 10 18
Primary Contact: Naveed Awan, FACHE, Chief Executive Officer
CFO: Theresa Brinkhaus, Chief Financial Officer
CMO: Anjanette Varnado, M.D., Chief Medical Officer
CHR: Lorraine L. Ballard, Director Human Resources
Web address: www.sthelenaparishhospital.com
Control: Other not–for–profit (including NFP Corporation) **Service:** General Medical and Surgical

Staffed Beds: 25

GRETNA—Jefferson Parish

UNITED MEDICAL HEALTHWEST–NEW ORLEANS (193074), 3201 Wall Boulevard, Suite B., Zip 70056–7755; tel. 504/433–5551, (Nonreporting) **A**9 10 **S** United Medical Rehabilitation Hospitals, Gretna, LA
Primary Contact: John E.H. Mills, President and Chief Executive Officer
Web address: www.umrhospital.com/
Control: Individual, Investor–owned, for–profit **Service:** Rehabilitation

Staffed Beds: 15

HAMMOND—Tangipahoa Parish

◇ **CYPRESS POINTE SURGICAL HOSPITAL (190303)**, 42570 South Airport Road, Zip 70403–0946; tel. 985/510–6200, (Nonreporting) **A**9 10 21
Primary Contact: Don D. Trexler, Chief Executive Officer
COO: Scot Treitler, Chief Financial Officer and Chief Operating Officer
CFO: Scot Treitler, Chief Financial Officer and Chief Operating Officer
CNO: Denise Fortenberry, Chief Nursing Officer and Chief Compliance Officer
Web address: www.cpsh.org
Control: Corporation, Investor–owned, for–profit **Service:** Surgical

Staffed Beds: 24

✠ △ **NORTH OAKS MEDICAL CENTER (190015)**, 15790 Paul Vega, MD, Drive, Zip 70403–1436, Mailing Address: P.O. Box 2668, Zip 70404–2668; tel. 985/345–2700 **A**1 7 9 10 19 **F**13 15 18 20 22 24 26 28 29 30 31 32 34 40 45 49 50 54 56 57 58 59 63 64 68 70 72 73 74 75 77 78 79 81 82 84 85 86 87 93 94 96 102 107 108 110 111 114 115 118 119 126 129 130 131 132 135 143 144 146 147 148 **P**6 **S** North Oaks Health System, Hammond, LA
Primary Contact: Michele K. Sutton, FACHE, Administrator
CFO: Shirley Hsing, Senior Vice President and Chief Financial Officer
CMO: Robert Peltier, M.D., Senior Vice President and Chief Medical Officer
CIO: Jacob Goodson, Director Information Technology
CHR: Jeff Jarreau, Senior Vice President Human Resources
CNO: Shelly Welch, R.N., Senior Vice President and Chief Nursing Officer
Web address: www.northoaks.org
Control: Hospital district or authority, Government, nonfederal **Service:** General Medical and Surgical

Staffed Beds: 344 Admissions: 11090 Census: 163 Outpatient Visits: 390611 Births: 1387 Total Expense ($000): 265645 Payroll Expense ($000): 144677 Personnel: 2071

☐ **NORTH OAKS REHABILITATION HOSPITAL (193044)**, 1900 South Morrison Boulevard, Zip 70403–5742; tel. 504/230–5700 **A**1 10 **F**29 56 75 86 87 90 130 132 143 **P**6 **S** North Oaks Health System, Hammond, LA
Primary Contact: Sybil K. Paulson, R.N., Administrator
Web address: www.northoaks.org
Control: Hospital district or authority, Government, nonfederal **Service:** Rehabilitation

Staffed Beds: 27 Admissions: 476 Census: 16 Outpatient Visits: 0 Births: 0 Total Expense ($000): 11949 Payroll Expense ($000): 2372 Personnel: 39

✠ **POST ACUTE SPECIALTY HOSPITAL OF HAMMOND (192036)**, 42074 Veterans Avenue, Zip 70403–1408; tel. 985/902–8148 **A**1 10 **F**1 29 75 77 148 **P**1 **S** Post Acute Medical, LLC, Enola, PA
Primary Contact: Jerry Elenbaas, Administrator
Web address: www.warmsprings.org/locations/hos/h2/
Control: Partnership, Investor–owned, for–profit **Service:** Long–Term Acute Care hospital

Staffed Beds: 40 Admissions: 381 Census: 26 Outpatient Visits: 0 Births: 0 Total Expense ($000): 13163 Payroll Expense ($000): 4743 Personnel: 147

UNITED MEDICAL REHABILITATION HOSPITAL (193079), 15717 Belle Drive, Zip 70403–1439; tel. 985/340–5998, (Includes UNITED MEDICAL REHABILITATION HOSPITAL – GONZALES, 333 East Worthy Road, Gonzales, Zip 70737–4234; tel. 225/450–2231; Bruce Walker, MSN, R.N., Chief Executive Officer), (Nonreporting) **A**10 **S** United Medical Rehabilitation Hospitals, Gretna, LA
Primary Contact: Cyrillia Bonds, Administrator
CFO: Warren Swenson, Chief Financial Officer
CMO: Luis Franco, M.D., Medical Director
CHR: Mark Gros, Director Human Resources
Web address: www.umrhospital.com
Control: Corporation, Investor–owned, for–profit **Service:** Rehabilitation

Staffed Beds: 20

HOMER—Claiborne Parish

HOMER MEMORIAL HOSPITAL (190114), 620 East College Street, Zip 71040–3202; tel. 318/927–2024 **A**9 10 **F**3 15 29 31 34 35 38 40 45 50 56 57 62 64 70 75 78 81 85 86 87 89 98 101 103 107 108 114 119 128 130 132 133 148 **S** QHR, Brentwood, TN
Primary Contact: Derrick A. Frazier, Chief Executive Officer
CFO: Robert A. Boullion, Chief Financial Officer
CFO: Ed Brown, Interim Chief Financial Officer
CMO: Mark Haynes, M.D., Chief of Staff
CIO: Landon Dick, Chief Information Officer
CHR: William Colvin, Human Resources Officer
CNO: Ginger S. Smith, Chief Nursing Officer
Web address: www.homerhospital.com
Control: City–Government, nonfederal **Service:** General Medical and Surgical

Staffed Beds: 60 Admissions: 1820 Census: 28 Outpatient Visits: 21508 Births: 0 Total Expense ($000): 18882 Payroll Expense ($000): 7933 Personnel: 169

HOUMA—Terrebonne Parish

AMG SPECIALTY HOSPITAL–HOUMA (192037), 629 Dunn Street, Zip 70360–4707; tel. 985/274–0001 **A**10 **F**1 29 130 **S** AMG Integrated Healthcare Management, Lafayette, LA
Primary Contact: Ricky Robeson, Chief Executive Officer
Control: Corporation, Investor–owned, for–profit **Service:** Long–Term Acute Care hospital

Staffed Beds: 40 Admissions: 466 Census: 32 Outpatient Visits: 0 Births: 0 Total Expense ($000): 11578 Payroll Expense ($000): 5392 Personnel: 108

☐ **COMPASS BEHAVIORAL CENTER OF HOUMA (194109)**, 4701 West Park Avenue, Zip 70364–4426; tel. 985/876–1715, (Nonreporting) **A**1 10 **S** Compass Health, Crowley, LA
Primary Contact: Daniel Shea, Administrator
Web address: www.compasshealthcare.com/site83.php
Control: Corporation, Investor–owned, for–profit **Service:** Psychiatric

Staffed Beds: 20

✠ **LEONARD J. CHABERT MEDICAL CENTER (190183)**, 1978 Industrial Boulevard, Zip 70363–7094; tel. 985/873–2200 **A**1 3 5 9 10 **F**3 15 18 20 29 31 32 34 35 38 39 40 44 45 46 47 48 49 50 51 55 58 59 61 64 65 66 68 70 74 75 77 78 79 81 82 84 85 86 87 89 91 92 93 94 97 98 100 101 102 107 108 110 111 114 115 119 130 132 143 146 147 148 **P**1 **S** Ochsner Health System, New Orleans, LA
Primary Contact: Ritchie Dupre, Chief Executive Officer
CMO: Michael Garcia, M.D., Medical Director
CIO: Susan Arceneaux, R.N., Coordinator Information Technology
CHR: Bain Manning, Director Human Resources
Web address: www.ochsner.org/locations/leonard_j_chabert_medical_center/
Control: State–Government, nonfederal **Service:** General Medical and Surgical

Staffed Beds: 74 **Admissions:** 3637 **Census:** 49 **Outpatient Visits:** 210091 **Births:** 0 **Total Expense ($000):** 100244 **Payroll Expense ($000):** 35578 **Personnel:** 678

PHYSICIANS ALLIANCE HOSPITAL OF HOUMA See AMG Specialty Hospital–Houma

PHYSICIANS MEDICAL CENTER (190241), 218 Corporate Drive, Zip 70360–2768; tel. 985/853–1390, (Nonreporting) **A**9 10
Primary Contact: Connie Martin, Chief Executive Officer and Administrator
Web address: www.physicianshouma.com/
Control: Partnership, Investor–owned, for–profit **Service:** Surgical

Staffed Beds: 10

✠ △ **TERREBONNE GENERAL MEDICAL CENTER (190008)**, 8166 Main Street, Zip 70360–3498; tel. 985/873–4141, (Total facility includes 8 beds in nursing home–type unit) **A**1 2 7 9 10 19 **F**8 11 13 14 15 17 18 20 22 24 26 29 30 31 34 35 40 44 49 50 51 53 57 59 64 65 68 70 72 74 75 76 77 78 79 81 84 85 86 87 89 90 91 92 93 107 108 109 110 111 114 117 118 119 121 123 124 128 130 132 134 135 146 147 148 **P**3 5 6
Primary Contact: Phyllis L. Peoples, MSN, R.N., President and Chief Executive Officer
COO: Diane Yeates, Chief Operating Officer
CFO: Dean Verret, Vice President Financial Services
CMO: Robert Gamble, M.D., Chief of Staff
CIO: Jeff Sardella, Director Information Technology
CHR: Mickie Rousseau, Director Human Resources
CNO: Teresita McNabb, R.N., Vice President Nursing Services
Web address: www.tgmc.com
Control: Hospital district or authority, Government, nonfederal **Service:** General Medical and Surgical

Staffed Beds: 230 **Admissions:** 10039 **Census:** 133 **Outpatient Visits:** 115774 **Births:** 1967 **Total Expense ($000):** 190557 **Payroll Expense ($000):** 66391 **Personnel:** 1281

INDEPENDENCE—Tangipahoa Parish

☐ **LALLIE KEMP MEDICAL CENTER (191321)**, 52579 Highway 51 South, Zip 70443–2231; tel. 985/878–9421, (Nonreporting) **A**1 5 9 10 18
Primary Contact: Sherre Pack–Hookfin, Administrator
COO: Lisa G. Bruhl, Chief Operating Officer
CFO: Chad Thompson, Chief Financial Officer
CMO: Kathy Willis, M.D., Medical Director
CIO: Charles Tate, Director Information Technology
CHR: Diane Farnham, Acting Director Human Resources
Web address: www.lsuhospitals.org/Hospitals/LK/LK.aspx
Control: State–Government, nonfederal **Service:** General Medical and Surgical

Staffed Beds: 25

JACKSON—East Feliciana Parish

☐ **EASTERN LOUISIANA MENTAL HEALTH SYSTEM (194008)**, 4502 Highway 951, Zip 70748–5842, Mailing Address: P.O. Box 498, Zip 70748–0498; tel. 225/634–0100 **A**1 10 **F**29 30 35 39 50 59 74 75 87 98 100 101 103 104 106 130 135 146 **P**6 **S** Louisiana State Hospitals, Baton Rouge, LA
Primary Contact: Hampton P. S. Lea, Acting Chief Executive Officer
CFO: Laura Lott, Administrative Director
CMO: John W. Thompson, M.D., Chief of Staff
CIO: Deborah Brandon, Director Total Quality Management
CHR: Vikki Riggle, Director Human Resources
CNO: Mary Fontenelle, Executive Nurse Director
Web address: www.wwwprd.doa.louisiana.gov/laservices/publicpages/ServiceDetail.cfm?service_id=2445
Control: State–Government, nonfederal **Service:** Psychiatric

Staffed Beds: 473 **Admissions:** 1086 **Census:** 460 **Outpatient Visits:** 19213 **Births:** 0 **Total Expense ($000):** 94226 **Personnel:** 1316

VILLA FELICIANA MEDICAL COMPLEX (190199), 5002 Highway 10, Zip 70748–3627, Mailing Address: P.O. Box 438, Zip 70748–0438; tel. 225/634–4017 **A**10 **F**1 3 29 65 67 85 86 91 94 106 128 130 132 135 143 148 **P**8
Primary Contact: Mark Anders, Administrator
CFO: Kim Jelks, Fiscal Officer
CMO: John F. Piker, M.D., Medical Director
CIO: Michael James, Information Technology Technical Support Specialist 1
CHR: Sandra Delatte, Director Human Resources
CNO: Linda Williams, Director of Nursing
Web address: www.dhh.state.la.us/
Control: State–Government, nonfederal **Service:** Long–Term Acute Care hospital

Staffed Beds: 307 **Admissions:** 14 **Census:** 11 **Outpatient Visits:** 0 **Births:** 0 **Total Expense ($000):** 17450 **Payroll Expense ($000):** 8729 **Personnel:** 202

JENA—La Salle Parish

★ **LASALLE GENERAL HOSPITAL (190145)**, 187 Ninth Street, Zip 71342–3901, Mailing Address: P.O. Box 2780, Zip 71342–2780; tel. 318/992–9200 **A**9 10 **F**7 11 15 18 20 29 40 45 53 57 59 62 64 71 81 89 93 107 108 110 111 114 118 119 127 130 133 **P**6
Primary Contact: Douglas A. Newman, Chief Executive Officer
CHR: Allyson Fannin, Director Human Resources
CNO: Carolyn Francis, R.N., Director of Nursing
Web address: www.lasallegeneralhospital.com
Control: Hospital district or authority, Government, nonfederal **Service:** General Medical and Surgical

Staffed Beds: 49 **Admissions:** 543 **Census:** 6 **Outpatient Visits:** 31139 **Births:** 0 **Total Expense ($000):** 19885 **Payroll Expense ($000):** 10133 **Personnel:** 215

JENNINGS—Jefferson Davis Parish

☐ **JENNINGS AMERICAN LEGION HOSPITAL (190053)**, 1634 Elton Road, Zip 70546–3614; tel. 337/616–7000, (Nonreporting) **A**1 9 10
Primary Contact: Dana D. Williams, Chief Executive Officer
COO: Keith J. Simpson, Chief Operating Officer
CFO: Chris Kohlenberg, Chief Financial Officer
CIO: Gary Courrege, Chief Information Officer
CHR: Ruth Carnes, Manager Human Resources
CNO: Theresa L. Woods, MSN, Chief Nursing Officer
Web address: www.jalh.com
Control: Other not–for–profit (including NFP Corporation) **Service:** General Medical and Surgical

Staffed Beds: 60

JENNINGS SENIOR CARE HOSPITAL (194082), 1 Hospital Drive, Suite 201, Zip 70546–3641; tel. 337/785–8003, (Nonreporting) **A**9 10
Primary Contact: Rusty Phillips, Administrator
Control: Corporation, Investor–owned, for–profit **Service:** Psychiatric

Staffed Beds: 18

☐ **MMO WESTEND HOSPITAL (194075)**, 1530 Highway 90 West, Zip 70546–4022; tel. 337/616–8122, (Nonreporting) **A**1 9 10
Primary Contact: Jessica Adkinson, Administrator
CFO: Ronnie Callais, Chief Financial Officer
CMO: Charles Bramliet, M.D., Medical Director
CHR: Gloria Conner, Director Human Resources
Web address: www.mmoinc.com
Control: Corporation, Investor–owned, for–profit **Service:** Psychiatric

Staffed Beds: 20

REHABILITATION HOSPITAL OF JENNINGS (193067), 1 Hospital Drive, Suite 101, Zip 70546–3641; tel. 337/821–5353 **A**10 **F**29 30 34 35 56 57 62 65 68 75 77 91 130 148
Primary Contact: Michael Holland, M.D., Chief Executive Officer
Web address: www.jenningsrehab.com
Control: Partnership, Investor–owned, for–profit **Service:** Rehabilitation

Staffed Beds: 16 **Admissions:** 219 **Census:** 9 **Outpatient Visits:** 0 **Births:** 0 **Total Expense ($000):** 1487 **Payroll Expense ($000):** 1383 **Personnel:** 41

LA

JONESBORO—Jackson Parish

★ **JACKSON PARISH HOSPITAL (191317)**, 165 Beech Springs Road,
Zip 71251–2059; tel. 318/259–4435, (Nonreporting) **A**9 10 18
Primary Contact: Lloyd Monger, Administrator
CFO: David Sanders, Chief Financial Officer
CHR: Elizabeth Cheatwood, Human Resource Director and Administrative Assistant
Web address: www.jacksonparishhospital.com
Control: Hospital district or authority, Government, nonfederal **Service:** General Medical and Surgical

Staffed Beds: 25

KAPLAN—Vermilion Parish

ABROM KAPLAN MEMORIAL HOSPITAL (191322), 1310 West Seventh
Street, Zip 70548–2910; tel. 337/643–8300 **A**9 10 18 **F**34 40 45 57 59 62 77
81 107 108 110 114 119 128 133 **S** Lafayette General Health, Lafayette, LA
Primary Contact: Bryce Quebodeaux, Chief Executive Officer
CFO: Mary Melancon, Chief Financial Officer
CMO: Scott Bergeaux, M.D., Chief Medical Staff
CIO: Bryce Quebodeaux, Chief Information Technology Officer
CHR: Mary Melancon, Chief Financial Officer
CNO: Darnell Kohlenberg, R.N., Director of Nursing
Web address: www.lafayettegeneral.com
Control: Hospital district or authority, Government, nonfederal **Service:** General Medical and Surgical

Staffed Beds: 35 Admissions: 867 Census: 13 Outpatient Visits: 18728
Births: 0 Total Expense ($000): 9930 Payroll Expense ($000): 3760
Personnel: 98

KENNER—Jefferson Parish

LOUISIANA EXTENDED CARE HOSPITAL OF KENNER See Ochsner Extended Care Hospital of Kenner

☐ **OCEANS BEHAVIORAL HOSPITAL OF GREATER NEW ORLEANS (194098)**,
716 Village Road, Zip 70065–2751; tel. 504/464–8895, (Nonreporting) **A**1 9 10
S Oceans Healthcare, Lake Charles, LA
Primary Contact: Deborah Spier, Administrator
Web address: www.obhgno.info/
Control: Corporation, Investor–owned, for–profit **Service:** Psychiatric

Staffed Beds: 18

☐ **OCHSNER EXTENDED CARE HOSPITAL OF KENNER (192015)**, 180 West
Esplanade Avenue, 5th Floor, Zip 70065–2467; tel. 504/464–8590,
(Nonreporting) **A**1 10 **S** LHC Group, Lafayette, LA
Primary Contact: Fritz Nelson, Administrator
Web address: www.lhcgroup.com/
Control: Corporation, Investor–owned, for–profit **Service:** Long–Term Acute Care hospital

Staffed Beds: 34

⊞ **OCHSNER MEDICAL CENTER – KENNER (190274)**, 180 West Esplanade
Avenue, Zip 70065–6001; tel. 504/468–8600 **A**1 3 5 8 9 10 **F**3 13 15 18 20
22 24 26 28 29 30 34 35 37 40 43 45 46 47 49 54 57 58 59 60 64 65 68
70 72 74 75 76 77 78 79 81 82 84 85 87 93 97 102 107 108 110 111 115
116 119 120 124 129 130 131 132 135 146 147 148 **S** Ochsner Health
System, New Orleans, LA
Primary Contact: Stephen Robinson, Chief Executive Officer
COO: Eddy Ramirez, Assistant Vice President Business Development
CFO: Mark Eckert, Vice President Finance
CMO: James Tebbe, M.D., Vice President Medical Affairs
CIO: Dere Krummel, Director Information Systems
CHR: Wendy L. Willis, Assistant Vice President Human Resources
Web address: www.ochsner.org/locations/ochsner_health_center_kenner_w_
esplanade_ave/
Control: Other not–for–profit (including NFP Corporation) **Service:** General Medical and Surgical

Staffed Beds: 119 Admissions: 5445 Census: 56 Outpatient Visits: 106254
Births: 1251 Total Expense ($000): 100206 Payroll Expense ($000):
38174 Personnel: 596

☐ **ST. THERESA SPECIALTY HOSPITAL (192030)**, 3601 Loyola Drive,
Zip 70065–1797; tel. 504/904–7600, (Nonreporting) **A**1 10
Primary Contact: Glynda Troyo, Chief Executive Officer
CFO: Ethan Thompson, Chief Financial Officer
CMO: Ricardo Febry, M.D., Medical Director
CHR: Nicole Wilson, Manager Human Resources
CNO: Collette Jackson, R.N., Director of Clinical Services
Web address: www.stmck.com
Control: Corporation, Investor–owned, for–profit **Service:** Long–Term Acute Care hospital

Staffed Beds: 31

KENTWOOD—Tangipahoa Parish

OCEANS BEHAVIORAL HOSPITAL OF KENTWOOD (194091), 921 Avenue G.,
Zip 70444–2636; tel. 985/229–0717, (Nonreporting) **A**9 10 **S** Oceans
Healthcare, Lake Charles, LA
Primary Contact: Gina Isbell, Administrator
Web address: www.obhk.info/
Control: Corporation, Investor–owned, for–profit **Service:** Psychiatric

Staffed Beds: 18

SOUTHEAST REGIONAL MEDICAL CENTER (192040), 719 Avenue G.,
Zip 70444–2601; tel. 985/229–9193, (Nonreporting) **A**10
Primary Contact: Lionel Murphy, Chief Executive Officer
Control: Corporation, Investor–owned, for–profit **Service:** Long–Term Acute Care hospital

Staffed Beds: 14

KINDER—Allen Parish

★ **ALLEN PARISH HOSPITAL (190133)**, 108 Sixth Avenue, Zip 70648–3187,
Mailing Address: P.O. Box 1670, Zip 70648–1670; tel. 337/738–2527,
(Nonreporting) **A**9 10
Primary Contact: Jackie Reviel, Interim Administrator
COO: Terry Willet, Chief Financial Officer
CMO: Ejiro Ughouwa, M.D., Chief of Staff
CIO: Bill Marcantel, Chief Information Systems
CHR: Amand Lambert, Director Human Resources
Web address: www.allenparishhospital.com
Control: Hospital district or authority, Government, nonfederal **Service:** General Medical and Surgical

Staffed Beds: 44

LA PLACE—St. John The Baptist Parish

⊞ **RIVER PARISHES HOSPITAL (190175)**, 500 Rue De Sante, Zip 70068–5418;
tel. 985/652–7000, (Nonreporting) **A**1 9 10 **S** LifePoint Hospitals, Inc.,
Brentwood, TN
Primary Contact: Robert L. Marshall, Jr., FACHE, Chief Executive Officer
CFO: Michael Mayeux, Chief Financial Officer
CMO: Andrew St. Martin, M.D., Chief of Staff
CIO: Cheryl Lipari, Director Information Technology
CHR: Katherine Trepagnier, Director Human Resources
CNO: Vanessa Peters, Chief Nursing Officer
Web address: www.riverparisheshospital.com
Control: Corporation, Investor–owned, for–profit **Service:** General Medical and Surgical

Staffed Beds: 106

LACOMBE—St. Tammany Parish

☐ **LOUISIANA HEART HOSPITAL (190250)**, 64030 Highway 434,
Zip 70445–3456; tel. 985/690–7500, (Nonreporting) **A**1 9 10
Primary Contact: Roy Wright, FACHE, President and Chief Executive Officer
CFO: Suzette Duhe, Chief Financial Officer
CMO: Anthony Morales, M.D., Medical Director
CHR: Wendy F. Alexander, Director Human Resources
CNO: Glenda Dobson, Vice President Clinical Services
Web address: www.louisianaheart.com
Control: Corporation, Investor–owned, for–profit **Service:** Heart

Staffed Beds: 58

MAGNOLIA BEHAVIORAL HEALTHCARE (194080), 64026 Highway 434, Suite
300, Zip 70445–5417; tel. 985/882–0226 **A**9 10 **F**56 98 103 104 130
Primary Contact: Gerry Morris, Administrator
Web address: www.magnoliabehavioralhealth.com
Control: Corporation, Investor–owned, for–profit **Service:** Psychiatric

Staffed Beds: 16 Admissions: 383 Census: 14 Outpatient Visits: 12074
Births: 0 Total Expense ($000): 5479 Payroll Expense ($000): 3060
Personnel: 55

LAFAYETTE—Lafayette Parish

ACADIA OPTIMA HOSPITAL (194078), 1131 Rue De Belier, Zip 70506–6532;
tel. 337/991–0571, (Nonreporting) **A**10 **S** Acadia Healthcare Company, Inc.,
Franklin, TN
Primary Contact: Michael E. Geissler, Chief Executive Officer
Web address: www.optimaspecialtyhospital.com/
Control: Corporation, Investor–owned, for–profit **Service:** General Medical and Surgical

Staffed Beds: 24

Many Facility Codes have changed. Please refer to the AHA Guide Code Chart.

ACADIA VERMILION HOSPITAL (194044), 2520 North University Avenue, Zip 70507–5306; tel. 337/234–5614, (Nonreporting) **A**9 10 **S** Acadia Healthcare Company, Inc., Franklin, TN
Primary Contact: Joseph R. Rodriguez, Chief Executive Officer
CFO: Doug Lahasky, Chief Financial Officer
CMO: Bob Winston, M.D., Medical Director
CHR: Claire Rowland, Director Human Resources
Web address: www.acadiavermilion.com
Control: Corporation, Investor–owned, for–profit **Service:** Psychiatric

Staffed Beds: 44

AMG SPECIALTY HOSPITAL–LAFAYETTE (192029), 310 Youngsville Highway, Zip 70508–4524; tel. 337/839–9880 **A**10 **F**1 3 29 30 34 35 50 56 60 75 77 79 82 84 85 91 119 130 135 143 148 **P**5 **S** AMG Integrated Healthcare Management. Lafayette, LA
Primary Contact: Jason Branson, Chief Executive Officer
CFO: Jessica McGee, Chief Financial Officer
CMO: Maximo LaMarche, M.D., Chief Medical Officer
CHR: Heather Lamarche, Manager Human Resources
CNO: Mary Bollich, Director of Nurses
Web address: www.amglafayette.com
Control: Corporation, Investor–owned, for–profit **Service:** Long–Term Acute Care hospital

Staffed Beds: 58 **Admissions:** 430 **Census:** 27 **Outpatient Visits:** 0 **Births:** 0 **Personnel:** 108

COMMUNITY SPECIALTY HOSPITAL (192020), 408 S.E. Evangeline Thruway, Zip 70501–7129; tel. 337/234–4031, (Nonreporting) **A**10
Primary Contact: Mark Goff, Owner and Administrator
COO: John E. Jumonville, III, Chief Operating Officer
CFO: Carolyn Guidry, Business Manager
CMO: John Charles Dugal, M.D., Medical Director
Control: Corporation, Investor–owned, for–profit **Service:** Long–Term Acute Care hospital

Staffed Beds: 22

⊞ **HEART HOSPITAL OF LAFAYETTE (190263)**, 1105 Kaliste Saloom Road, Zip 70508–5705; tel. 337/521–1000 **A**1 9 10 **F**3 17 18 20 22 24 26 28 29 30 34 35 40 46 50 57 59 64 68 74 75 81 85 87 107 108 115 135
Primary Contact: Michelle B. Crain, R.N., MSN, Administrator and Chief Operating Officer
CFO: Rachel Hebert, Chief Financial Officer
CHR: Thomas Duhon, Director Human Resources
Web address: www.hearthospitallaf.net
Control: Partnership, Investor–owned, for–profit **Service:** Heart

Staffed Beds: 32 **Admissions:** 1443 **Census:** 15 **Outpatient Visits:** 19770 **Births:** 0 **Total Expense ($000):** 34560 **Payroll Expense ($000):** 12986 **Personnel:** 191

KINDRED HOSPITAL LAFAYETTE See Post Acute Medical Specialty Hospital of Lafayette

LAFAYETTE BEHAVIORAL HEALTH, 302 Dulles Drive, Zip 70506–3008; tel. 337/262–4190, (Nonreporting)
Primary Contact: Kandy Collins, MSN, Director
Web address: www.lafayettegeneral.com
Control: State–Government, nonfederal **Service:** Psychiatric

Staffed Beds: 20

⊞ **LAFAYETTE GENERAL MEDICAL CENTER (190002)**, 1214 Coolidge Avenue, Zip 70503–2696, Mailing Address: P.O. Box 52009 OCS, Zip 70505–2009; tel. 337/289–7991 **A**1 2 9 10 **F**3 8 11 12 13 15 18 19 20 21 22 26 28 29 30 31 34 35 40 45 47 48 49 50 53 54 56 57 59 64 65 70 72 74 75 76 77 78 79 81 85 87 89 90 98 100 103 107 108 110 111 114 115 117 118 119 120 121 123 124 126 130 132 135 144 146 147 148 **P**8 **S** Lafayette General Health, Lafayette, LA
Primary Contact: Patrick W. Gandy, CPA, Executive Vice President and Chief Executive Officer
CFO: Roger Mattke, Chief Financial Officer
CMO: Angela Mayeux–Hebert, Vice President Medical Affairs
CIO: Edwina Mallery, Assistant Vice President Information Systems
CHR: Sheena Cumbest, Assistant Vice President Human Resources
CNO: Rebecca Benoit, R.N., Chief Nursing Officer
Web address: www.lafayettegeneral.org
Control: Other not–for–profit (including NFP Corporation) **Service:** General Medical and Surgical

Staffed Beds: 377 **Admissions:** 16673 **Census:** 232 **Outpatient Visits:** 187954 **Births:** 1825 **Total Expense ($000):** 267161 **Payroll Expense ($000):** 85956 **Personnel:** 1907

LAFAYETTE GENERAL SURGICAL HOSPITAL (190268), 1000 West Pinhook Road, Zip 70503–2460; tel. 337/289–8088 **A**9 10 **F**3 29 51 68 79 81 141 **P**2 **S** Lafayette General Health, Lafayette, LA
Primary Contact: Carrie E. Templeton, FACHE, Chief Executive Officer
CFO: Sandi Hernandez, Controller
CHR: Sheena Cumbest, Assistant Vice President Human Resources
CNO: Susan Woollen, R.N., Director of Nursing
Web address: www.lgsh.us
Control: Partnership, Investor–owned, for–profit **Service:** General Medical and Surgical

Staffed Beds: 10 **Admissions:** 49 **Census:** 1 **Outpatient Visits:** 9638 **Births:** 0 **Total Expense ($000):** 12006 **Payroll Expense ($000):** 3303 **Personnel:** 55

LAFAYETTE PHYSICAL REHABILITATION HOSPITAL (193093), 307 Polly Lane, Zip 70508–4960; tel. 337/314–1111, (Nonreporting) **A**10 **S** AMG Integrated Healthcare Management, Lafayette, LA
Primary Contact: Jonathan Landreth, Chief Executive Officer
Control: Corporation, Investor–owned, for–profit **Service:** Rehabilitation

Staffed Beds: 32

☐ **LAFAYETTE SURGICAL SPECIALTY HOSPITAL (190259)**, 1101 Kaliste Saloom Road, Zip 70508–5705; tel. 337/769–4100, (Nonreporting) **A**1 9 10 **S** National Surgical Hospitals, Chicago, IL
Primary Contact: Buffy Domingue, Chief Executive Officer
CFO: Stephanie Guidry, Chief Financial Officer
CNO: Selina Guidry, Chief Nursing Officer
Web address: www.lafayettesurgical.com
Control: Corporation, Investor–owned, for–profit **Service:** Surgical

Staffed Beds: 20

LONG TERM ACUTE CARE OF ACADIANA See AMG Specialty Hospital–Lafayette

LOUISIANA EXTENDED CARE HOSPITAL OF LAFAYETTE (192032), 1214 Coolidge Boulevard, 8th Floor, Zip 70503–2621; tel. 337/289–8180, (Includes EUNICE EXTENDED CARE HOSPITAL, 1879 Highway 190, Eunice, Zip 70535; tel. 337/546–0024; Cayle P. Guillory, Administrator; IBERIA EXTENDED CARE HOSPITAL, 2315 East Main Street, 3rd Floor, New Iberia, Zip 70560–4031; tel. 337/369–1100; Kevin Frank, Administrator), (Nonreporting) **A**10 **S** LHC Group, Lafayette, LA
Primary Contact: Kevin Frank, Administrator
Web address: www.lhcgroup.com
Control: Other not–for–profit (including NFP Corporation) **Service:** Long–Term Acute Care hospital

Staffed Beds: 42

OPTIMA SPECIALTY HOSPITAL See Acadia Optima Hospital

⊞ **OUR LADY OF LOURDES REGIONAL MEDICAL CENTER (190102)**, 4801 Ambassador Caffery Parkway, Zip 70508–6917; tel. 337/470–2000 **A**1 2 9 10 **F**3 9 11 12 15 16 18 20 22 24 26 28 29 30 31 32 34 35 38 40 42 43 48 49 50 51 53 54 56 57 58 59 60 64 65 66 68 70 71 74 75 77 78 79 81 82 84 85 86 87 90 93 96 107 108 110 111 114 115 117 118 119 126 127 129 130 132 134 135 143 144 146 147 148 **P**6 **S** Franciscan Missionaries of Our Lady Health System, Inc., Baton Rouge, LA
Primary Contact: William F. Barrow, II, President and Chief Executive Officer
COO: Donna F. Landry, Chief Operating Officer
CFO: Ronald E. Hogan, Chief Financial Officer
CMO: Andy Blalock, M.D., Physician Executive
CIO: Nona Mire, Director Information Systems
CHR: Jennifer Lynch Trahan, Assistant Vice President Human Resources
Web address: www.lourdesrmc.com
Control: Church–operated, Nongovernment, not–for profit **Service:** General Medical and Surgical

Staffed Beds: 186 **Admissions:** 10417 **Census:** 142 **Outpatient Visits:** 124392 **Births:** 0 **Total Expense ($000):** 235883 **Payroll Expense ($000):** 72395 **Personnel:** 1182

◇ **PARK PLACE SURGICAL HOSPITAL (190255)**, 4811 Ambassador Caffery Parkway, Zip 70508–6917; tel. 337/237–8119, (Nonreporting) **A**9 10 21
Primary Contact: Brandon Moore, Administrator and Chief Executive Officer
Web address: www.parkplacesurgery.com/
Control: Partnership, Investor–owned, for–profit **Service:** Surgical

Staffed Beds: 10

Hospital, Medicare Provider Number, Address, Telephone, Approval, Facility, and Physician Codes, Health Care System

★ American Hospital Association (AHA) membership
☐ The Joint Commission accreditation
◇ DNV Healthcare Inc. accreditation
○ Healthcare Facilities Accreditation Program
△ Commission on Accreditation of Rehabilitation Facilities (CARF) accreditation

LA

✠ **POST ACUTE MEDICAL SPECIALTY HOSPITAL OF LAFAYETTE (192033)**, 204 Energy Parkway, Zip 70508–3816; tel. 337/232–1905, (Data for 98 days) **A**1 10 **F**1 3 28 29 30 34 35 50 56 59 67 74 75 77 85 91 143 148 **P**5 **S** Post Acute Medical, LLC, Enola, PA
Primary Contact: Brian Holt, Chief Executive Officer
CFO: Karick Stober, Chief Financial Officer
CMO: Vitalis C. Okechukwu, M.D., President Medical Staff
CHR: Waynea Finley, Senior Vice President Human Resources
CNO: Eileen Turner, Director of Nursing
Web address: www.postacutemedical.com
Control: Partnership, Investor–owned, for–profit **Service:** Long–Term Acute Care hospital

Staffed Beds: 50 **Admissions:** 95 **Census:** 22 **Outpatient Visits:** 0 **Births:** 0 **Total Expense ($000):** 3730 **Payroll Expense ($000):** 1489 **Personnel:** 91

✠ **REGIONAL MEDICAL CENTER OF ACADIANA (190205)**, 2810 Ambassador Caffery Parkway, Zip 70506–5906; tel. 337/981–2949, (Includes WOMEN'S AND CHILDREN'S HOSPITAL, 4600 Ambassador Caffery Parkway, Zip 70508–6923, Mailing Address: P.O. Box 88030, Zip 70598–8030; tel. 337/521–9100) **A**1 9 10 **F**3 13 15 17 18 19 20 22 24 28 29 30 31 34 40 41 45 46 47 48 52 59 60 65 70 72 73 74 76 77 78 79 81 88 89 90 93 97 107 110 111 114 115 117 119 129 130 131 146 147 148 **S** HCA, Nashville, TN
Primary Contact: Kathy J. Bobbs, FACHE, President Chief Executive Officer
COO: Leona Boullion, Chief Operating Officer
CFO: James Miller, CPA, Chief Financial Officer
CMO: Charles Wyatt, M.D., Medical Director
CIO: Tony Istre, Director Information Technology Services
CHR: Raymond E. Langham, Vice President Human Resources
CNO: John Marker, Chief Nursing Officer
Web address: www.medicalcenterofacadiana.com
Control: Corporation, Investor–owned, for–profit **Service:** General Medical and Surgical

Staffed Beds: 292 **Admissions:** 10870 **Census:** 146 **Total Expense ($000):** 138168 **Payroll Expense ($000):** 51914

☐ **UNIVERSITY HOSPITAL AND CLINICS (190006)**, 2390 West Congress Street, Zip 70506–4298; tel. 337/261–6000, (Nonreporting) **A**1 2 3 5 9 10 **S** Lafayette General Health, Lafayette, LA
Primary Contact: Jared Stark, Chief Executive Officer
COO: Glenn L. Craig, Chief Operating Officer
CFO: Brian T. Kirk, Vice President Finance
CMO: James B. Falterman, Jr., M.D., Medical Director
CIO: J. Barry Daigle, Manager Information Systems
CNO: Laurence Marie Vincent, Chief Nursing Officer
Web address: www.lafayettegeneral.com
Control: Other not–for–profit (including NFP Corporation) **Service:** General Medical and Surgical

Staffed Beds: 105

LAKE CHARLES—Calcasieu Parish

CALCASIEU OAKS GERIATRIC PSYCHIATRIC HOSPITAL, 2837 Ernest Street, Zip 70601–8785; tel. 337/439–8111, (Nonreporting) **A**9 **S** Pacer Health Corporation, Miami Lakes, FL
Primary Contact: Charles Getwood, Assistant Chief Executive Officer
Control: Corporation, Investor–owned, for–profit **Service:** Psychiatric

Staffed Beds: 24

✠ △ **CHRISTUS ST. PATRICK HOSPITAL OF LAKE CHARLES (190027)**, 524 Dr. Michael Debakey Drive, Zip 70601–5799, Mailing Address: P.O. Box 3401, Zip 70602–3401; tel. 337/436–2511 **A**1 2 7 9 10 **F**3 11 15 17 18 20 22 24 26 28 29 30 31 32 34 35 38 40 44 45 46 47 48 49 50 56 57 59 61 64 65 70 74 75 78 79 81 84 85 86 87 89 90 93 96 97 98 100 101 102 103 104 105 107 108 110 118 119 120 121 122 124 126 130 131 132 134 135 146 147 148 **P**8 **S** CHRISTUS Health, Irving, TX
Primary Contact: Donald H. Lloyd, II, Administrator
COO: Dianne P. Teal, MSN, Vice President Clinical Operations
CMO: David Engleking, M.D., Vice President Medical Affairs
CHR: Wendy White, Assistant Administrator Human Resources
Web address: www.stpatrickhospital.org
Control: Church–operated, Nongovernment, not–for profit **Service:** General Medical and Surgical

Staffed Beds: 160 **Admissions:** 7270 **Census:** 119 **Outpatient Visits:** 72275 **Births:** 0 **Total Expense ($000):** 122388 **Payroll Expense ($000):** 37374 **Personnel:** 719

✠ **LAKE AREA MEDICAL CENTER (190201)**, 4200 Nelson Road, Zip 70605–4118; tel. 337/474–6370 **A**1 9 10 **F**12 13 15 20 22 29 40 45 46 47 48 49 50 57 70 72 75 76 77 79 81 85 89 91 93 107 110 114 119 130 132 146 147 **S** Community Health Systems, Inc., Franklin, TN
Primary Contact: Bryan S. Bateman, Chief Executive Officer
CFO: Dawn Johnson–Hatcher, Chief Financial Officer
CMO: Floyd Guidry, M.D., Medical Director
CIO: Aaron Cook, Director Information Services
CHR: Charles Buchert, Director Human Resources
CNO: Robbin Odom, R.N., Chief Nursing Officer
Web address: www.women–childrens.com
Control: Corporation, Investor–owned, for–profit **Service:** General Medical and Surgical

Staffed Beds: 88 **Admissions:** 2875 **Census:** 27 **Outpatient Visits:** 48065 **Births:** 1289 **Total Expense ($000):** 44420 **Payroll Expense ($000):** 18711 **Personnel:** 354

✠ **LAKE CHARLES MEMORIAL HOSPITAL (190060)**, 1701 Oak Park Boulevard, Zip 70601–8911; tel. 337/494–3000 **A**1 2 3 5 9 10 **F**3 8 11 13 14 15 17 18 20 22 24 25 26 28 29 30 31 34 37 40 43 45 49 50 51 53 56 57 58 60 62 64 66 68 70 71 72 73 74 75 76 77 78 79 81 85 86 87 88 89 90 93 98 99 102 103 107 108 110 111 114 115 119 120 121 123 124 127 129 130 131 132 135 143 144 146 147 148 **P**1 6 7
Primary Contact: Larry M. Graham, FACHE, President and Chief Executive Officer
COO: Timothy O. Coffey, Senior Vice President Operations
CFO: Charles P. Whitson, CPA, Senior Vice President Finance
CMO: Kevin Mocklin, M.D., Director Medical Staff
CIO: Belinda Sommers, Chief Information Officer
CHR: Ginger Consigney, Vice President Human Resources
Web address: www.lcmh.com
Control: Other not–for–profit (including NFP Corporation) **Service:** General Medical and Surgical

Staffed Beds: 306 **Admissions:** 11224 **Census:** 162 **Outpatient Visits:** 220453 **Births:** 1629 **Total Expense ($000):** 201889 **Payroll Expense ($000):** 66258 **Personnel:** 1883

LAKE CHARLES MEMORIAL HOSPITAL FOR WOMEN, 1900 West Gauthier Road, Zip 70605–7170; tel. 337/480–7000, (Nonreporting) **A**9
Primary Contact: Marilyn McSwain, R.N., MSN, Administrator
Web address: www.lcmh.com/womens–hospital
Control: Corporation, Investor–owned, for–profit **Service:** Obstetrics and gynecology

Staffed Beds: 38

LCMH SPECIALTY HOSPITAL (192019), 2837 Ernest Street, Building B., Zip 70601–8785; tel. 337/480–8990 **A**10 **F**1 3 130 148
Primary Contact: Ellen Smith, Administrator
Web address: www.lcmh.com/
Control: Other not–for–profit (including NFP Corporation) **Service:** Long–Term Acute Care hospital

Staffed Beds: 29 **Admissions:** 201 **Census:** 15 **Outpatient Visits:** 0 **Births:** 0 **Total Expense ($000):** 5351 **Payroll Expense ($000):** 2205 **Personnel:** 35

OCEANS BEHAVIORAL HOSPITAL OF LAKE CHARLES (194090), 302 West Mcneese Street, Zip 70605–5604; tel. 337/474–7581, (Nonreporting) **A**9 10 **S** Oceans Healthcare, Lake Charles, LA
Primary Contact: Christin Bennett, Administrator
Web address: www.obhlc.info/
Control: Corporation, Investor–owned, for–profit **Service:** Psychiatric

Staffed Beds: 20

LAKE PROVIDENCE—East Carroll Parish

EAST CARROLL PARISH HOSPITAL (190208), 336 North Hood Street, Zip 71254–2140; tel. 318/559–4023, (Nonreporting) **A**9 10
Primary Contact: LaDonna Englerth, Administrator
Control: Hospital district or authority, Government, nonfederal **Service:** General Medical and Surgical

Staffed Beds: 11

LEESVILLE—Vernon Parish

✠ **BYRD REGIONAL HOSPITAL (190164)**, 1020 West Fertitta Boulevard, Zip 71446–4645; tel. 337/239–9041 **A**1 9 10 **F**3 13 15 18 20 29 34 37 40 45 48 50 54 57 65 70 76 79 81 87 107 110 111 115 119 **P**7 **S** Community Health Systems, Inc., Franklin, TN
Primary Contact: Roger C. LeDoux, Chief Executive Officer
CFO: Wendell Wilkes, Chief Financial Officer
CMO: Francis Fraser, M.D., Chief of Staff
CHR: Karolyne Christian, Director Human Resources
CNO: Beth Westerchil, Chief Nursing Officer
Web address: www.byrdregional.com
Control: Corporation, Investor–owned, for–profit **Service:** General Medical and Surgical

Staffed Beds: 60 **Admissions:** 3310 **Census:** 32 **Outpatient Visits:** 31092 **Births:** 349 **Total Expense ($000):** 40763 **Payroll Expense ($000):** 13916 **Personnel:** 302

Many Facility Codes have changed. Please refer to the AHA Guide Code Chart. © 2014 AHA Guide

DOCTOR'S HOSPITAL OF DEER CREEK (190297), 815 South 10th Street, Zip 71446–4611, Mailing Address: P.O. Box 1391, Zip 71496–1391; tel. 337/392–5088, (Nonreporting) **A**9 10
Primary Contact: Jeffrey Morrow, Chief Executive Officer
CMO: Gregory D. Lord, M.D., Medical Director
CIO: Kim Smith, Director Business Office
CHR: Annette Hillman, Director Human Resources
CNO: Brenda Willis, Director of Nursing
Web address: www.dhdc.md
Control: Corporation, Investor–owned, for–profit **Service:** General Medical and Surgical

Staffed Beds: 10

☐ **LEESVILLE REHABILITATION HOSPITAL (193086)**, 900 South 6th Street, Zip 71446–4723; tel. 337/392–8118, (Nonreporting) **A**1 10
Primary Contact: Jack M. Causey, Administrator and Chief Executive Officer
CMO: Gregory D. Lord, M.D., Chief Medical Officer
CHR: Jackie Rubar, Administrative Assistant and Director Human Resources
Web address: www.leesvillerehab.com
Control: Corporation, Investor–owned, for–profit **Service:** Rehabilitation

Staffed Beds: 16

☐ **TRI PARISH REHABILITATION HOSPITAL (193050)**, 8088 Hawks Road, Zip 71446–6649; tel. 337/462–8880, (Nonreporting) **A**1 10
Primary Contact: Heath Hairgrove, Administrator
Web address: www.triparishrehab.com
Control: Corporation, Investor–owned, for–profit **Service:** Rehabilitation

Staffed Beds: 33

LULING—St. Charles Parish

PREMIER REHABILITATION (193064), 1125 Paul Maillard Road, Zip 70070–4351; tel. 985/785–5233, (Nonreporting) **A**10
Primary Contact: Chenell Barnes, Administrator
Web address: www.specialtyhealthcare.com
Control: Corporation, Investor–owned, for–profit **Service:** Rehabilitation

Staffed Beds: 21

☐ **ST. CHARLES PARISH HOSPITAL (190079)**, 1057 Paul Maillard Road, Zip 70070–4349, Mailing Address: P.O. Box 87, Zip 70070–0087; tel. 985/785–6242, (Nonreporting) **A**1 9 10
Primary Contact: Fred Martinez, Jr., Chief Executive Officer
CFO: Peter Torsch, Chief Financial Officer
CMO: Vadakkipalayam N. Devarajan, Chief Medical Staff
CIO: Angela Duet, Director Information Technology
CHR: James Moses, Director Human Resources
CNO: Jean Hill, Chief Nursing Officer and Chief Clinical Officer
Web address: www.stch.net
Control: Hospital district or authority, Government, nonfederal **Service:** General Medical and Surgical

Staffed Beds: 59

LUTCHER—St. James Parish

⊠ **ST. JAMES PARISH HOSPITAL (191305)**, 1645 Lutcher Avenue, Zip 70071–5150; tel. 225/869–5512 **A**1 9 10 18 **F**3 15 29 30 34 35 40 45 50 57 59 64 75 77 80 81 107 110 111 114 119 128 132 133 135
Primary Contact: Mary Ellen Pratt, FACHE, Chief Executive Officer
CFO: Tracy L. George, Chief Financial Officer
CIO: Susan Duhon, Director Medical Records
CHR: Lisa Faucheux, Director Human Resources
CNO: Rhonda Zeringue, Chief Nursing Officer
Web address: www.sjph.org
Control: Hospital district or authority, Government, nonfederal **Service:** General Medical and Surgical

Staffed Beds: 25 Admissions: 672 Census: 12 Outpatient Visits: 26919 Births: 0 Total Expense ($000): 20764 Payroll Expense ($000): 7890 Personnel: 230

MAMOU—Evangeline Parish

☐ **SAVOY MEDICAL CENTER (190025)**, 801 Poinciana Avenue, Zip 70554–2298; tel. 337/468–5261, (Nonreporting) **A**1 9 10
Primary Contact: George Patrick Derouen, Chief Executive Officer
COO: Gerald Fuselier, Chief Operating Officer
CMO: Greg Savoy, M.D., Chief Medical Officer
CIO: Daniel Lahaye, Manager
CHR: Annette Thibodeaux, Director Human Resources
Web address: www.savoymedicalcenter.com
Control: Corporation, Investor–owned, for–profit **Service:** General Medical and Surgical

Staffed Beds: 180

MANDEVILLE—St. Tammany Parish

☐ **NORTHLAKE BEHAVIORAL HOSPITAL (194007)**, 23515 Highway 190, Zip 70448–7334, Mailing Address: P.O. Box 3850, Zip 70470–3850; tel. 985/626–6300, (Nonreporting) **A**1 3 5 10
Primary Contact: Richard Kramer, Interim Chief Executive Officer
COO: Richard Kramer, Chief Operating Officer
CMO: Girishkumar Shah, M.D., Clinical Director
CIO: Mike Ziemba, Information Technology Project Lead
CHR: Daphne Stewart, Director Human Resources
Web address: www.selh.org
Control: State–Government, nonfederal **Service:** Psychiatric

Staffed Beds: 153

MANSFIELD—De Soto Parish

DE SOTO REGIONAL HEALTH SYSTEM (190118), 207 Jefferson Street, Zip 71052–2603, Mailing Address: P.O. Box 1636, Zip 71052–1636; tel. 318/871–3100 **A**9 10 20 **F**3 15 29 30 31 32 35 40 41 46 49 53 57 64 81 85 107 108 110 111 114 115 119 127 130 133 148 **P**6 **S** Willis–Knighton Health System, Shreveport, LA
Primary Contact: Todd Eppler, FACHE, Chief Executive Officer
CMO: Leigh Dillard, M.D., Chief of Staff
CHR: Rhonda Potter, Director Human Resources
CNO: Vernadine Mitchell, R.N., Chief Nursing Officer
Web address: www.desotoregional.com
Control: Other not–for–profit (including NFP Corporation) **Service:** General Medical and Surgical

Staffed Beds: 10 Admissions: 929 Census: 10 Outpatient Visits: 22361 Births: 0 Total Expense ($000): 16730 Payroll Expense ($000): 8172 Personnel: 199

MANY—Sabine Parish

SABINE MEDICAL CENTER (190218), 240 Highland Drive, Zip 71449–3718; tel. 318/256–5691, (Nonreporting) **A**9 10 20 **S** Allegiance Health Management, Shreveport, LA
Primary Contact: Jay Quebedeaux, Chief Executive Officer
COO: Doug Plummer, Chief Operating Officer
CFO: Frances F. Hopkins, Chief Financial Officer
CNO: Karen Ford, Chief Nursing Officer
Web address: www.sabinemedicalcenter.net
Control: Individual, Investor–owned, for–profit **Service:** General Medical and Surgical

Staffed Beds: 44

MARKSVILLE—Avoyelles Parish

☐ **AVOYELLES HOSPITAL (190099)**, 4231 Highway 1192, Zip 71351–4711, Mailing Address: P.O. Box 249, Zip 71351–0249; tel. 318/253–8611 **A**1 9 10 **F**3 15 29 30 34 40 56 57 64 65 70 75 81 85 86 107 110 114 119 128 133 135 146
Primary Contact: David M. Mitchel, Chief Executive Officer
CFO: Suzette Fatula, Chief Financial Officer
CMO: Fernando Garcia, M.D., Chief of Staff
CIO: Billy Tingle, Director Information Systems and Respiratory Therapy
CHR: Allison Ferguson, Director Human Resources
CNO: Cindy K. Juneau, Chief Nursing Officer
Web address: www.avoyelleshospital.com
Control: Corporation, Investor–owned, for–profit **Service:** General Medical and Surgical

Staffed Beds: 35 Admissions: 1116 Census: 14 Outpatient Visits: 39639 Births: 0 Total Expense ($000): 14402 Payroll Expense ($000): 6974 Personnel: 173

MARRERO—Jefferson Parish

LOUISIANA CONTINUING CARE HOSPITAL (192007), 1111 Medical Center Boulevard, Suite S–550, Zip 70072–3151; tel. 504/349–2470, (Nonreporting) **A**10
Primary Contact: James Fritschen, Chief Executive Officer
Control: Corporation, Investor–owned, for–profit **Service:** Long–Term Acute Care hospital

Staffed Beds: 56

Hospital, Medicare Provider Number, Address, Telephone, Approval, Facility, and Physician Codes, Health Care System

★ American Hospital Association (AHA) membership
☐ The Joint Commission accreditation
◇ DNV Healthcare Inc. accreditation
○ Healthcare Facilities Accreditation Program
△ Commission on Accreditation of Rehabilitation Facilities (CARF) accreditation

LA

⊞ △ **WEST JEFFERSON MEDICAL CENTER (190039)**, 1101 Medical Center Boulevard, Zip 70072–3191; tel. 504/347–5511 **A**1 2 3 5 7 9 10 **F**3 6 7 11 12 13 15 17 18 20 22 24 26 28 29 30 31 34 35 37 38 39 40 41 43 45 46 47 49 50 51 53 56 57 59 61 64 65 68 70 72 74 75 76 78 79 81 82 84 85 86 87 89 90 91 93 96 97 98 100 101 102 104 105 107 108 110 111 114 115 117 118 119 120 121 124 126 127 129 130 132 135 144 146 147 148 **P**6 7
Primary Contact: Nancy R. Cassagne, FACHE, Chief Executive Officer
COO: Angela Greener, Chief Administrative Officer
CMO: Mark Workman, M.D., Chief Medical Officer
CIO: Nicholas Thimis, Chief Information Officer
CHR: Frank Martinez, Vice President Human Resources
CNO: Anthony DiGerolamo, R.N., Chief Nursing Officer
Web address: www.wjmc.org
Control: Hospital district or authority, Government, nonfederal **Service:** General Medical and Surgical

Staffed Beds: 277 **Admissions:** 12493 **Census:** 181 **Outpatient Visits:** 279657 **Births:** 1201 **Total Expense ($000):** 265249 **Payroll Expense ($000):** 96845 **Personnel:** 1719

METAIRIE—Jefferson Parish

⊞ △ **EAST JEFFERSON GENERAL HOSPITAL (190146)**, 4200 Houma Boulevard, Zip 70006–2996; tel. 504/454–4000, (Includes DOCTORS HOSPITAL OF JEFFERSON, 4320 Houma Boulevard, Zip 70006–2973; tel. 504/849–4000) **A**1 2 3 5 7 9 10 **F**3 7 8 11 13 14 15 17 18 20 22 24 26 28 29 30 31 34 35 37 40 45 46 47 48 49 50 51 53 55 56 57 58 59 60 63 64 68 70 72 73 74 75 76 77 78 79 81 82 84 85 86 87 90 91 92 93 94 96 97 98 102 103 107 108 109 110 111 112 115 116 117 118 119 120 121 122 123 124 126 128 129 130 131 132 135 145 146 147 148
Primary Contact: Mark J. Peters, M.D., President and Chief Executive Officer
COO: Judy Brown, Executive Vice President and Chief Operating Officer
CFO: Bruce Naremore, Senior Vice President and Chief Financial Officer
CMO: Raymond P. DeCorte, M.D., Chief Medical Officer
CIO: Steve Baker, Chief Information Officer
CHR: Frank Martinez, Senior Vice President Human Resources
CNO: Ruby Brewer, RN, Senior Vice President and Chief Quality Officer
Web address: www.ejgh.org
Control: Hospital district or authority, Government, nonfederal **Service:** General Medical and Surgical

Staffed Beds: 437 **Admissions:** 17881 **Census:** 258 **Outpatient Visits:** 205504 **Births:** 1657 **Total Expense ($000):** 340998 **Payroll Expense ($000):** 114870 **Personnel:** 2237

◇ **OMEGA HOSPITAL (190302)**, 2525 Severn Avenue, Zip 70002–5932; tel. 504/832–4200, (Nonreporting) **A**10 21
Primary Contact: Debbie Schenck, Administrator
Web address: www.omega–institute.com
Control: Individual, Investor–owned, for–profit **Service:** Surgical

Staffed Beds: 10

MINDEN—Webster Parish

⊞ **MINDEN MEDICAL CENTER (190144)**, 1 Medical Plaza, Zip 71055–3330, Mailing Address: P.O. Box 5003, Zip 71058–5003; tel. 318/377–2321 **A**1 9 10 19 **F**11 13 15 18 20 22 29 30 34 40 45 46 56 57 59 62 64 70 75 76 77 79 81 82 87 89 90 93 98 103 107 111 115 119 129 130 132 146 147 148 **S** LifePoint Hospitals, Inc., Brentwood, TN
Primary Contact: George E. French, III, FACHE, Chief Executive Officer
CFO: Jim Williams, Chief Financial Officer
CMO: G. Max Stell, M.D., Medical Director
CIO: Mace Morgan, Director Information Systems
CHR: Mary Winget, Director Human Resources
CNO: Donna Carter, MSN, Chief Nursing Officer
Web address: www.mindenmedicalcenter.com
Control: Corporation, Investor–owned, for–profit **Service:** General Medical and Surgical

Staffed Beds: 161 **Admissions:** 4035 **Census:** 50 **Outpatient Visits:** 41146 **Births:** 679 **Total Expense ($000):** 53644 **Payroll Expense ($000):** 19867 **Personnel:** 445

MONROE—Ouachita Parish

E. A. CONWAY MEDICAL CENTER See University Health Conway

☐ **MONROE SURGICAL HOSPITAL (190245)**, 2408 Broadmoor Boulevard, Zip 71201–2963; tel. 318/410–0002, (Nonreporting) **A**1 9 10
Primary Contact: Robyn Hemphill, Interim Chief Executive Officer and Chief Nursing Officer
Web address: www.monroesurgical.com
Control: Corporation, Investor–owned, for–profit **Service:** Surgical

Staffed Beds: 10

★ ◇ **P & S SURGICAL HOSPITAL (190246)**, 312 Grammont Street Suite 101, Zip 71201–7403; tel. 318/388–4040 **A**9 10 21 **F**3 12 18 20 22 26 29 34 35 37 39 51 64 65 68 85 107 111 130 132 135 141 **P**2 7
Primary Contact: Linda S. Holyfield, R.N., MSN, President and Chief Executive Officer
COO: Terri Hicks, Chief Operating Officer and Chief Financial Officer
CFO: Terri Hicks, Chief Operating Officer and Chief Financial Officer
CMO: Lauren Jane Mickey, M.D., Chief of Staff
CIO: Christy Childers, Director Information Technology
CHR: Cheniere Craig, Director Human Resources
CNO: Debbie W. Austin, R.N., Vice President Patient Care Services
Web address: www.pssurgery.com
Control: Partnership, Investor–owned, for–profit **Service:** Surgical

Staffed Beds: 22 **Admissions:** 585 **Census:** 5 **Outpatient Visits:** 8262 **Births:** 0 **Personnel:** 155

SPECIALTY EXTENDED CARE HOSPITAL OF MONROE (192016), 309 Jackson Street, 7th Floor, Zip 71201–7407, Mailing Address: P.O. Box 1532, Zip 71210–1532; tel. 318/966–4126, (Nonreporting) **A**10
Primary Contact: Cleta Munholland, Administrator
Web address: www.ihcgroup.com
Control: Church–operated, Nongovernment, not–for profit **Service:** Long–Term Acute Care hospital

Staffed Beds: 32

⊞ **ST. FRANCIS MEDICAL CENTER (190125)**, 309 Jackson Street, Zip 71201–7407, Mailing Address: P.O. Box 1901, Zip 71210–1901; tel. 318/966–4000, (Includes ST. FRANCIS NORTH HOSPITAL, 3421 Medical Park Drive, Zip 71203–2399; tel. 318/388–1946; Cindy J. Rogers, FACHE, Administrator) **A**1 2 9 10 **F**2 3 12 13 15 17 18 19 20 21 22 23 24 26 27 28 29 30 31 32 34 35 37 39 40 44 45 46 49 50 54 55 56 57 59 64 65 68 69 70 72 74 75 76 77 78 79 81 85 87 88 89 90 92 93 96 97 98 102 103 104 105 107 108 110 111 114 115 116 117 118 119 124 128 129 130 131 132 134 135 144 146 147 148 **P**8 **S** Franciscan Missionaries of Our Lady Health System, Inc., Baton Rouge, LA
Primary Contact: Louis H. Bremer, Jr., President and Chief Executive Officer
COO: Kristin Wolkart, Chief Operating Officer
CFO: Ronald E. Hogan, Regional Chief Financial Officer
CMO: Robert Seegers, M.D., Vice President Medical Affairs
CHR: James Novak, Vice President, Human Resources
CNO: Kayla Johnson, R.N., Vice President Patient Care Services and Chief Nursing Officer
Web address: www.stfran.com
Control: Church–operated, Nongovernment, not–for profit **Service:** General Medical and Surgical

Staffed Beds: 343 **Admissions:** 17036 **Census:** 259 **Outpatient Visits:** 270001 **Births:** 1712 **Total Expense ($000):** 257879 **Payroll Expense ($000):** 99945 **Personnel:** 1840

ST. FRANCIS SPECIALTY HOSPITAL See Specialty Extended Care Hospital of Monroe

☐ **UNIVERSITY HEALTH CONWAY (190011)**, 4864 Jackson Street, Zip 71202–6497, Mailing Address: P.O. Box 1881, Zip 71210–8005; tel. 318/330–7000 **A**1 3 5 9 10 **F**8 11 13 15 30 31 40 43 49 50 54 59 61 64 65 66 70 72 75 76 77 78 81 87 89 97 98 100 102 107 108 110 111 114 118 119 130 135 146 **P**1
Primary Contact: Larry Donner, Administrator
CFO: Dorothy Whittington, Chief Financial Officer
CMO: Richard Cavell, M.D., Medical Director
CIO: Todd Walters, Director of UHC Information Technology Services
CHR: Rob Hartmann, Assistant Director Human Resources Management
CNO: Louise Kenney, Director of Nursing
Web address: www.uhsystem.com
Control: State–Government, nonfederal **Service:** General Medical and Surgical

Staffed Beds: 97 **Admissions:** 4935 **Census:** 67 **Outpatient Visits:** 135495 **Births:** 855 **Personnel:** 517

MORGAN CITY—St. Mary Parish

⊞ **TECHE REGIONAL MEDICAL CENTER (190014)**, 1125 Marguerite Street, Zip 70380–1855, Mailing Address: P.O. Box 2308, Zip 70381–2308; tel. 985/384–2200 **A**1 9 10 20 **F**3 13 15 18 20 22 29 30 31 34 40 45 50 57 60 70 76 79 81 85 89 90 93 98 102 104 105 107 108 110 111 115 119 130 141 146 147 **S** LifePoint Hospitals, Inc., Brentwood, TN
Primary Contact: James P. Frazier, III, Chief Executive Officer
COO: Don Knight, Assistant Administrator and Risk Manager
CFO: Michael Mayeux, Chief Financial Officer
CMO: Eric Melancon, Chief of Staff
CIO: Cheryl Lipari, Manager Information Systems
CHR: Timothy Hebert, Director Human Resources
Web address: www.techeregional.com
Control: Corporation, Investor–owned, for–profit **Service:** General Medical and Surgical

Staffed Beds: 165 **Admissions:** 3092 **Census:** 43 **Outpatient Visits:** 51725 **Births:** 425 **Total Expense ($000):** 41455 **Payroll Expense ($000):** 14180 **Personnel:** 256

NAPOLEONVILLE—Assumption Parish

★ **ASSUMPTION COMMUNITY HOSPITAL (191303)**, 135 Highway 402,
Zip 70390–2217; tel. 985/369–3600 **A**9 10 18 **F**32 34 35 40 57 58 59 64 65
90 127 135 **S** Franciscan Missionaries of Our Lady Health System, Inc., Baton
Rouge, LA
Primary Contact: Wayne M. Arboneaux, Chief Executive Officer
CHR: Letonia Pierre, Coordinator Human Resources
CNO: Donna Mullings, Director of Nursing
Web address: www.ololrmc.com
Control: Other not–for–profit (including NFP Corporation) **Service:** General
Medical and Surgical

Staffed Beds: 6 **Admissions:** 63 **Census:** 1 **Outpatient Visits:** 36763 **Births:**
0 **Total Expense ($000):** 6216 **Payroll Expense ($000):** 2263 **Personnel:**
41

NATCHITOCHES—Natchitoches Parish

LOUISIANA EXTENDED CARE HOSPITAL OF NATCHITOCHES (192035), 501
Keyser Avenue, Zip 71457–6018; tel. 318/354–2044 **A**10 **F**1 3 28 29 34 38 44
50 57 59 68 74 75 85 86 87 91 97 130 148 **S** LHC Group, Lafayette, LA
Primary Contact: John Rivoire, Administrator
Web address: www.lhcgroup.com
Control: Partnership, Investor–owned, for–profit **Service:** Long–Term Acute Care
hospital

Staffed Beds: 21 **Admissions:** 222 **Census:** 15 **Outpatient Visits:** 0 **Births:**
0

✠ **NATCHITOCHES REGIONAL MEDICAL CENTER (190007)**, 501 Keyser
Avenue, Zip 71457–6036, Mailing Address: P.O. Box 2009, Zip 71457–2009;
tel. 318/214–4200, (Total facility includes 112 beds in nursing home–type unit)
A1 9 10 20 **F**2 3 7 10 11 13 15 18 26 29 34 35 40 45 46 50 54 56 57 59
64 68 70 75 76 77 79 81 82 87 91 92 98 99 100 101 102 103 104 107 110
111 115 119 125 126 127 129 130 131 133 135 143 144 146 147 148 **P**5
S CHRISTUS Health, Irving, TX
Primary Contact: Brad McCormick, Chief Financial Officer
CMO: Phyllis Mason, M.D., Chief Medical Officer
CIO: Steve Gentry, Manager Information Technology
CHR: Ernie Scott, Director Human Resources
CNO: Dawna DeBlieux, Chief Nurse Executive
Web address: www.natchitocheshospital.org
Control: County–Government, nonfederal **Service:** General Medical and Surgical

Staffed Beds: 208 **Admissions:** 2696 **Census:** 27 **Outpatient Visits:** 50748
Births: 625 **Total Expense ($000):** 43774 **Payroll Expense ($000):** 18557
Personnel: 493

NEW IBERIA—Iberia Parish

✠ ○ **DAUTERIVE HOSPITAL (190003)**, 600 North Lewis Street,
Zip 70563–2043; tel. 337/365–7311 **A**1 9 10 11 19 **F**13 15 17 18 28 29 40
56 57 70 76 81 86 87 89 90 93 98 103 107 111 119 130 132 146 **S** HCA,
Nashville, TN
Primary Contact: Wayne D. Thompson, Interim Chief Executive Officer
CFO: Laura Allen, Chief Financial Officer
CMO: Mike Alvarez, M.D., Chief Medical Officer
CIO: Terry Stewart, Director Information Systems
CHR: Candice Ardoin, Director Human Resources
Web address: www.dauterivehospital.com
Control: Corporation, Investor–owned, for–profit **Service:** General Medical and
Surgical

Staffed Beds: 103 **Admissions:** 2527 **Census:** 30 **Outpatient Visits:** 25315
Births: 488 **Total Expense ($000):** 48658 **Payroll Expense ($000):** 18634
Personnel: 222

☐ **IBERIA MEDICAL CENTER (190054)**, 2315 East Main Street,
Zip 70560–4031, Mailing Address: P.O. Box 13338, Zip 70562–3338;
tel. 337/364–0441 **A**1 9 10 **F**3 11 13 15 18 20 22 28 29 30 31 34 39 40 45
46 47 48 49 50 57 68 70 72 74 75 76 77 78 79 81 85 93 97 100 108 110
115 119 127 130 146 **P**6 **S** HealthTech Management Services, Brentwood, TN
Primary Contact: Parker A. Templeton, FACHE, Chief Executive Officer
COO: Shane P. Myers, Chief Operating Officer
CFO: Stephanie Kirk, Chief Financial Officer
CMO: Shawn Baquet, Chief of Staff
CIO: Vance Robinson, Chief Information Officer
CHR: Lori Spann, Director Human Resources
CNO: Elizabeth Gondron, R.N., Vice President and Chief Nursing Officer
Web address: www.iberiamedicalcenter.com
Control: Hospital district or authority, Government, nonfederal **Service:** General
Medical and Surgical

Staffed Beds: 84 **Admissions:** 3896 **Census:** 36 **Outpatient Visits:** 94827
Births: 444 **Total Expense ($000):** 57359 **Payroll Expense ($000):** 22952
Personnel: 482

☐ **IBERIA REHABILITATION HOSPITAL (190304)**, 532 Jefferson Terrace,
Zip 70560–4948; tel. 337/364–6923 **A**1 9 10 **F**3 16 28 29 34 56 57 59 67
74 75 77 79 82 83 84 85 86 87 90 94 96 143 148
Primary Contact: Athan Oliver, Administrator and Chief Executive Officer
Web address: www.iberiarehab.net/
Control: Partnership, Investor–owned, for–profit **Service:** Rehabilitation

Staffed Beds: 24 **Admissions:** 330 **Census:** 12 **Outpatient Visits:** 0 **Births:**
0 **Personnel:** 55

NEW ORLEANS—Orleans Parish

☐ **BEACON BEHAVIORAL HOSPITAL – NEW ORLEANS (194102)**, 14500 Hayne
Boulevard, Suite 200, Zip 70128–1751; tel. 504/210–0460, (Nonreporting) **A**1
9 10
Primary Contact: Jessika Scallion, Administrator
Control: Corporation, Investor–owned, for–profit **Service:** Psychiatric

Staffed Beds: 24

☐ △ **CHILDREN'S HOSPITAL (193300)**, 200 Henry Clay Avenue,
Zip 70118–5720; tel. 504/899–9511 **A**1 2 3 5 7 9 10 **F**3 8 11 16 17 19 21
23 25 27 29 30 31 32 34 35 39 40 41 50 54 55 57 58 59 60 61 64 65 66
71 72 74 75 77 78 79 80 81 82 84 85 86 88 89 90 91 92 93 97 98 99 100
102 104 107 108 111 113 115 119 126 130 131 132 136 137 138 141 146
148 **P**4 8 **S** LCMC Health, New Orleans, LA
Primary Contact: Mary R. Perrin, President and Chief Executive Officer
CFO: Courtney Garrett, CPA, Chief Financial Officer
CMO: John Heaton, M.D., Senior Vice President and Medical Director
CIO: Tammy Reites, Vice President Patient Financial Services
CHR: Doug Mittelstaedt, Vice President Human Resources
CNO: Diane Michel, Vice President Nursing
Web address: www.chnola.org
Control: Other not–for–profit (including NFP Corporation) **Service:** Children's
general

Staffed Beds: 283 **Admissions:** 7031 **Census:** 136 **Outpatient Visits:**
428611 **Births:** 0 **Personnel:** 1664

☐ **COMMUNITY CARE HOSPITAL (194056)**, 1421 General Taylor Street,
Zip 70115–3717; tel. 504/899–2500, (Nonreporting) **A**1 10
Primary Contact: Paul B. Kavanaugh, President and Chief Executive Officer
Web address: www.communitycarehospital.com
Control: State–Government, nonfederal **Service:** Psychiatric

Staffed Beds: 36

☐ **INTERIM LSU PUBLIC HOSPITAL (190005)**, 2021 Perdido Street,
Zip 70112–1396; tel. 504/903–3000, (Data for 184 days) **A**1 2 5 8 9 10 **F**1 3
4 8 9 12 15 16 17 18 20 22 24 26 29 30 31 34 35 39 40 43 45 46 49 50
51 57 58 61 64 65 66 67 70 72 73 74 75 78 79 80 81 85 86 87 88 89 90
92 97 98 100 102 106 107 108 110 111 115 116 117 118 119 126 128
130 132 135 141 146 147 148 **S** LCMC Health, New Orleans, LA
Primary Contact: Cindy Nuesslein, Chief Executive Officer
COO: Adler Voltaire, Chief Administrative Officer
CFO: Ed Burke, Chief Financial Officer
CMO: Cathi E. Fontenot, M.D., Medical Director
CIO: Mitch Perlin, Chief Information Officer
CHR: Ronald Broadus, Assistant Administrator Human Resources
Web address: www.umcno.org
Control: Other not–for–profit (including NFP Corporation) **Service:** General
Medical and Surgical

Staffed Beds: 195 **Admissions:** 5124 **Census:** 162 **Outpatient Visits:**
176535 **Births:** 0 **Total Expense ($000):** 206891 **Payroll Expense ($000):**
56581 **Personnel:** 1719

✠ **KINDRED HOSPITAL–NEW ORLEANS (192009)**, 3601 Coliseum Street,
Zip 70115–3606; tel. 504/899–1555 **A**1 9 10 **F**1 28 29 30 46 75 77 86 87
91 96 98 103 130 143 148 **S** Kindred Healthcare, Louisville, KY
Primary Contact: Jan Turk, Chief Executive Officer
CFO: Laurie Champagne, Controller
Web address: www.kindredhospitalnola.com
Control: Corporation, Investor–owned, for–profit **Service:** Long–Term Acute Care
hospital

Staffed Beds: 75 **Admissions:** 575 **Census:** 43 **Outpatient Visits:** 0 **Births:**
0

MEDICAL CENTER OF LOUISIANA AT NEW ORLEANS See Interim LSU Public
Hospital

Hospital, Medicare Provider Number, Address, Telephone, Approval, Facility, and Physician Codes, Health Care System

★ American Hospital Association (AHA) membership
☐ The Joint Commission accreditation   ◇ DNV Healthcare Inc. accreditation
○ Healthcare Facilities Accreditation Program
△ Commission on Accreditation of Rehabilitation Facilities (CARF) accreditation

LA

✠ △ **OCHSNER MEDICAL CENTER (190036)**, 1514 Jefferson Highway, Zip 70121–2429; tel. 504/842–3000, (Includes OCHSNER BAPTIST MEDICAL CENTER, 2700 Napoleon Avenue, Zip 70115–6914; tel. 504/899–9311; Dawn Anuszkiewicz, Chief Executive Officer; OCHSNER MEDICAL CENTER – WEST BANK, 2500 Belle Chasse Highway, Gretna, Zip 70056–7127; tel. 504/392–3131; Travis Capers, Chief Executive Officer; OCHSNER MEDICAL CENTER FOR CHILDREN, 1514 Jefferson Highway, tel. 504/842–3000), (Total facility includes 32 beds in nursing home–type unit) **A**1 2 3 5 7 8 9 10 **F**2 3 5 8 9 11 12 13 14 15 17 18 19 20 21 22 23 24 25 26 27 28 29 30 31 32 34 35 37 38 40 41 43 44 45 46 47 48 49 50 51 54 55 56 57 58 59 60 61 64 65 68 70 72 74 75 76 77 78 79 81 82 84 85 86 87 88 89 90 93 94 96 97 98 99 100 101 102 103 104 105 107 108 110 111 113 114 115 117 118 119 120 121 123 124 126 128 129 130 131 132 134 135 136 137 138 139 140 141 142 145 146 147 148 **P**6 **S** Ochsner Health System, New Orleans, LA
Primary Contact: Robert K. Wolterman, Chief Executive Officer
CFO: Scott J. Posecai, Executive Vice President and Chief Financial Officer
CMO: Patrick J. Quinlan, M.D., Chief Executive Officer
CIO: Lynn Witherspoon, Vice President and Chief Information Officer
CHR: Joan Mollohan, Vice President Human Resources
Web address: www.ochsner.org
Control: Other not–for–profit (including NFP Corporation) **Service:** General Medical and Surgical

Staffed Beds: 877 **Admissions:** 36881 **Census:** 539 **Outpatient Visits:** 416064 **Births:** 3370 **Total Expense ($000):** 1094733 **Payroll Expense ($000):** 386784 **Personnel:** 7467

PSYCHIATRIC PAVILION NEW ORLEANS See Beacon Behavioral Hospital – New Orleans

☐ **RIVER OAKS HOSPITAL (194031)**, 1525 River Oaks Road West, Zip 70123–2162; tel. 504/734–1740, (Includes RIVER OAKS CHILD AND ADOLESCENT HOSPITAL, 1525 River Oaks Road West, tel. 504/734–1740) **A**1 9 10 **F**4 5 98 99 102 105 130 **S** Universal Health Services, Inc., King of Prussia, PA
Primary Contact: Evelyn Nolting, Chief Executive Officer and Managing Director
CFO: James Todd, Chief Financial Officer
CMO: Lincoln Paine, M.D., Medical Director
CIO: Vincent Chatelain, Director Business Development
CHR: Wanda Hoffmann, Director Human Resources
Web address: www.riveroakshospital.com
Control: Corporation, Investor–owned, for–profit **Service:** Psychiatric

Staffed Beds: 126 **Admissions:** 3636 **Census:** 82 **Outpatient Visits:** 0 **Births:** 0

SEASIDE BEHAVIORAL CENTER (194100), 4201 Woodland Drive, Zip 70131–7339; tel. 504/393–4223, (Nonreporting) **A**9 10
Primary Contact: Mary L. Matamoros, R.N., Chief Executive Officer
Control: Partnership, Investor–owned, for–profit **Service:** Psychiatric

Staffed Beds: 24

☐ **ST. CATHERINE MEMORIAL HOSPITAL (192023)**, 14500 Hayne Boulevard, Zip 70128–1751; tel. 504/210–3000, (Nonreporting) **A**1 10
Primary Contact: John Gray, Administrator
Web address: www.stcatherine–hospital.com
Control: Corporation, Investor–owned, for–profit **Service:** Long–Term Acute Care hospital

Staffed Beds: 21

★ ◇ **ST. CHARLES SURGICAL HOSPITAL (190300)**, 1717 Saint Charles Avenue, Zip 70130–5223; tel. 504/529–6600, (Nonreporting) **A**10 21
Primary Contact: Cheri Saltaformaggio, Chief Executive Officer
Web address: www.scsh.com
Control: Corporation, Investor–owned, for–profit **Service:** Surgical

Staffed Beds: 39

✠ △ **TOURO INFIRMARY (190046)**, 1401 Foucher Street, Zip 70115–3593; tel. 504/897–7011, (Includes TOURO REHABILITATION CENTER, 1401 Foucher Street, Zip 70115–3515; tel. 504/897–8560), (Total facility includes 120 beds in nursing home–type unit) **A**1 2 3 5 7 9 10 **F**3 8 10 11 13 15 18 20 22 24 28 29 30 31 34 35 36 37 39 40 43 44 45 50 53 54 55 57 59 60 61 63 64 68 70 72 74 75 76 77 78 79 81 83 84 85 86 87 90 93 96 97 107 108 109 110 111 114 115 116 117 118 119 120 121 123 124 125 126 128 130 131 132 135 143 146 147 148 **P**8 **S** LCMC Health, New Orleans, LA
Primary Contact: James T. Montgomery, FACHE, President
COO: Susan Pitoscia, MSN, Chief Operating Officer
CFO: Cynthia Polt, Chief Financial Officer
CIO: Jeff Lott, Director Information Services
CHR: Chad Courrege, Vice President Human Resources
CNO: Penny A. Menge, MSN, Chief Nursing Officer and Vice President Patient Care Services
Web address: www.touro.com
Control: Other not–for–profit (including NFP Corporation) **Service:** General Medical and Surgical

Staffed Beds: 534 **Admissions:** 14756 **Census:** 210 **Outpatient Visits:** 297175 **Births:** 3347 **Total Expense ($000):** 225614 **Payroll Expense ($000):** 88155 **Personnel:** 1530

✠ **TULANE MEDICAL CENTER (190176)**, 1415 Tulane Avenue, Zip 70112–2600; tel. 504/988–5263, (Includes TULANE–LAKESIDE HOSPITAL, 4700 South I. 10 Service Road West, Metairie, Zip 70001–1269; tel. 504/780–4200), (Nonreporting) **A**1 2 3 5 8 9 10 **S** HCA, Nashville, TN
Primary Contact: William Lunn, M.D., Chief Executive Officer
COO: Jennifer Eslinger, Chief Operating Officer
CFO: Todd LaCaze, Chief Financial Officer
CMO: John Pigott, M.D., Chief Medical Officer
CIO: Sue Rachuig, Director Information Services
CHR: Leah Grau, Director Human Resources
CNO: Danita S. Sullivan, R.N., Chief Nursing Officer
Web address: www.tuhc.com
Control: Corporation, Investor–owned, for–profit **Service:** General Medical and Surgical

Staffed Beds: 327

NEW ROADS—Pointe Coupee Parish

★ **POINTE COUPEE GENERAL HOSPITAL (191316)**, 2202 False River Drive, Zip 70760–2614; tel. 225/638–6331 **A**9 10 18 **F**29 40 45 77 81 87 93 107 111 125 133 **P**5
Primary Contact: Chad E. Olinde, CPA, Administrator and Chief Executive Officer
CFO: John Cazayoux, Chief Financial Officer
CMO: Carol Smothers, M.D., Chief of Staff
CIO: Anthony Sauro, Chief Information Officer
CHR: Lisa Patterson, Director Human Resources
CNO: Elaine Hurme, Chief Nursing Officer
Web address: www.pcgh.org
Control: Hospital district or authority, Government, nonfederal **Service:** General Medical and Surgical

Staffed Beds: 25 **Admissions:** 492 **Census:** 8 **Outpatient Visits:** 21729 **Births:** 0 **Total Expense ($000):** 16297 **Payroll Expense ($000):** 6869 **Personnel:** 160

OAK GROVE—West Carroll Parish

WEST CARROLL MEMORIAL HOSPITAL (190081), 706 Ross Street, Zip 71263–9798; tel. 318/428–3237, (Nonreporting) **A**9 10
Primary Contact: R. Randall Morris, Administrator
Control: Other not–for–profit (including NFP Corporation) **Service:** General Medical and Surgical

Staffed Beds: 21

OAKDALE—Allen Parish

☐ **OAKDALE COMMUNITY HOSPITAL (190106)**, 130 North Hospital Drive, Zip 71463–3035, Mailing Address: P.O. Box 629, Zip 71463–0629; tel. 318/335–3700, (Nonreporting) **A**1 9 10
Primary Contact: Calvin Green, Chief Executive Officer
CFO: Suzette Fatula, Chief Financial Officer and Compliance Officer
CMO: Tommy Davis, M.D., Chief of Staff
CIO: Melissa Welch, Director Health Information Management
CHR: Becky Johnson, Director Human Resources
CNO: Annette Wyble Hatsfelt, Chief Nursing Officer
Web address: www.oakdalecommunityhospital.com/
Control: Partnership, Investor–owned, for–profit **Service:** General Medical and Surgical

Staffed Beds: 27

OLLA—Caldwell Parish

HARDTNER MEDICAL CENTER (191315), 1102 North Pine Road, Zip 71465–4804; tel. 318/495–3131 **A**9 10 18 **F**7 29 32 34 35 39 40 45 46 50 56 57 59 64 79 81 92 93 98 103 104 107 111 119 127 129 130 133 148 **P**4
Primary Contact: Paul G. Mathews, CPA, Administrator
CIO: Sarah Thompson, Director Health Information Management
CNO: Cherry B. Salter, Director of Nursing
Web address: www.hardtnermedical.com
Control: Hospital district or authority, Government, nonfederal **Service:** General Medical and Surgical

Staffed Beds: 35 **Admissions:** 1815 **Census:** 16 **Outpatient Visits:** 10768 **Births:** 0 **Total Expense ($000):** 21783 **Payroll Expense ($000):** 9863

OPELOUSAS—St. Landry Parish

☐ **OCEANS BEHAVIORAL HOSPITAL OF OPELOUSAS (194095)**, 1310 Heather Drive, Zip 70570–7714; tel. 337/948–8820, (Nonreporting) **A**1 9 10 **S** Oceans Healthcare, Lake Charles, LA
Primary Contact: Remi Savoy, Administrator
Web address: www.obho.info/
Control: Corporation, Investor–owned, for–profit **Service:** Psychiatric

Staffed Beds: 20

Many Facility Codes have changed. Please refer to the AHA Guide Code Chart. © 2014 AHA Guide

OPELOUSAS GENERAL HEALTH SYSTEM (190017), 539 East Prudhomme Street, Zip 70570–6499, Mailing Address: P.O. Box 1389, Zip 70571–1389; tel. 337/948–3011, (Includes OPELOUSAS GENERAL HEALTH SYSTEM–SOUTH CAMPUS, 3983 I–49 South Service Road, Zip 70570–8975; tel. 337/948–2100) **A**1 2 9 10 19 **F**3 13 15 18 20 22 28 29 30 31 34 35 38 40 49 51 57 59 61 70 73 74 75 76 77 78 79 80 81 86 87 89 90 93 98 103 104 107 108 110 111 114 117 118 119 121 129 130 132 135 146 147
Primary Contact: Mark E. Marley, FACHE, President and Chief Executive Officer
COO: Bob Hardy, Chief Operating Officer
CFO: James B. Juneau, Chief Financial Officer
CMO: Richard Harmon, Chief of Staff
CIO: Jared Lormand, Vice President Information Technology
CHR: Suzanne F. Kidder, Director Human Resources
CNO: Karen Gremillion, R.N., Chief Nursing Officer
Web address: www.opelousasgeneral.com
Control: Hospital district or authority, Government, nonfederal **Service:** General Medical and Surgical

Staffed Beds: 224 **Admissions:** 7235 **Census:** 84 **Outpatient Visits:** 121430 **Births:** 1135 **Total Expense ($000):** 149542 **Payroll Expense ($000):** 47345 **Personnel:** 968

ST. LANDRY EXTENDED CARE HOSPITAL (192034), 3983 1–49 South Service Road, 2nd Floor, Zip 70570; tel. 337/948–5184, (Includes EVANGELINE EXTENDED CARE HOSPITAL–MAMOU, 801 Poinciana Avenue, Mamou, Zip 70554–2243; tel. 337/468–4203), (Nonreporting) **A**10
Primary Contact: Biff David, Administrator
Web address: www.lhcgroup.com
Control: Corporation, Investor–owned, for–profit **Service:** Long–Term Acute Care hospital

Staffed Beds: 23

ALEXANDRIA VETERANS AFFAIRS HEALTH CARE SYSTEM, 2495 Shreveport Highway, 71 N., Zip 71360–4044, Mailing Address: P.O. Box 69004, Alexandria, Zip 71306–9004; tel. 318/473–0010, (Nonreporting) **A**1 2 3 5 **S** Department of Veterans Affairs, Washington, DC
Primary Contact: Martin J. Traxler, Director
CFO: Bianca A. Obey, Chief Financial Officer
CMO: Robert Bernard, M.D., Chief of Staff
CIO: Robin McBryde, Chief Information Officer
CHR: Alex Love, Acting Manager Human Resources
CNO: Amy Lesniewski, Associate Director Patient Care Services
Web address: www.alexandria.va.gov/
Control: Veterans Affairs, Government, federal **Service:** General Medical and Surgical

Staffed Beds: 143

CENTRAL LOUISIANA STATE HOSPITAL (194025), 242 West Shamrock Avenue, Zip 71360–6439, Mailing Address: P.O. Box 5031, Zip 71361–5031; tel. 318/484–6200, (Nonreporting) **A**1 10 **S** Louisiana State Hospitals, Baton Rouge, LA
Primary Contact: Ronald G. Williams, Administrator
COO: Paul Benoit, Associate Administrator
CFO: Tina Darbonne, Chief Financial Officer
CMO: L. Lee Tynes, Jr., M.D., Medical Director
CIO: William Haynes, Director Information Technology
CHR: Tom Crout, MS, Director Human Resources
Web address: www.dhh.louisiana.gov/index.cfm/directory/detail/217
Control: State–Government, nonfederal **Service:** Psychiatric

Staffed Beds: 128

VETERANS AFFAIRS MEDICAL CENTER – ALEXANDRIA See Alexandria Veterans Affairs Health Care System

MMO REHABILITATION AND WELLNESS CENTER (193070), 59213 Riverwest Drive, Zip 70764–6552; tel. 225/687–8100, (Nonreporting) **A**10
Primary Contact: Bridget Suire, Acting Administrator
Web address: www.mmoinc.com
Control: Other not–for–profit (including NFP Corporation) **Service:** Rehabilitation

Staffed Beds: 8

OCHSNER ST. ANNE GENERAL HOSPITAL (191324), 4608 Highway 1, Zip 70394–2623; tel. 985/537–6841 **A**1 9 10 18 **F**3 8 13 15 17 18 29 30 34 35 40 45 57 59 65 70 72 73 74 75 76 79 81 85 89 98 100 103 107 111 114 119 130 133 135 147 **S** Ochsner Health System, New Orleans, LA
Primary Contact: Timothy J. Allen, FACHE, Chief Executive Officer
COO: Jonathan Carothers, Chief Operating Officer
CHR: Ann Ritchie, Director Human Resources
CNO: Allyson Dill Vedros, R.N., Chief Nursing Officer
Web address: www.ochsnerstanne.org
Control: Other not–for–profit (including NFP Corporation) **Service:** General Medical and Surgical

Staffed Beds: 35 **Admissions:** 1565 **Census:** 17 **Outpatient Visits:** 46177 **Births:** 232 **Total Expense ($000):** 24623 **Payroll Expense ($000):** 14629 **Personnel:** 287

PHOENIX BEHAVIORAL HOSPITAL (194097), 2021 Crowley Rayne Highway, Zip 70578–4027; tel. 337/788–0091, (Nonreporting) **A**1 9 10
Primary Contact: Joseph Tidwell, Administrator
Control: Corporation, Investor–owned, for–profit **Service:** Psychiatric

Staffed Beds: 18

RICHARDSON MEDICAL CENTER (190151), 254 Highway 3048 Christian Drive, Zip 71269–0388, Mailing Address: P.O. Box 388, Zip 71269–0388; tel. 318/728–4181, (Nonreporting) **A**9 10
Primary Contact: James W. Barrett, Jr., Chief Executive Officer
CFO: Shawnia Taylor, Chief Financial Officer
CMO: David Thompson, M.D., Chief of Staff
CHR: Rita Brown, Director Human Resources
Web address: www.richardsonmed.org
Control: Hospital district or authority, Government, nonfederal **Service:** General Medical and Surgical

Staffed Beds: 38

ALLEGIANCE HEALTH CENTER OF RUSTON (194087), 1401 Ezell Street, Zip 71270–7218; tel. 318/255–8085, (Nonreporting) **A**9 10 **S** Allegiance Health Management, Shreveport, LA
Primary Contact: Donna K. Thompson, Chief Executive Officer
Web address: www.ahmgt.com
Control: Corporation, Investor–owned, for–profit **Service:** Psychiatric

Staffed Beds: 14

GREEN CLINIC SURGICAL HOSPITAL (190257), 1118 Farmerville Street, Zip 71270–5914; tel. 318/232–7700, (Nonreporting) **A**9 10
Primary Contact: Chad Conner, Administrator
CIO: Deedra Pearce, Director Information Technology
CNO: Cheryl Holloway, Director of Nursing
Web address: www.gcsurgical.com
Control: Corporation, Investor–owned, for–profit **Service:** Other specialty

Staffed Beds: 13

LIFECARE SPECIALTY HOSPITAL OF NORTH LOUISIANA (192022), 1401 Ezell Street, Zip 71270–7218; tel. 318/251–3126 **A**1 10 **F**1 29 93 107 129 132 **P**5 **S** LifeCare Management Services, Plano, TX
Primary Contact: Brent Martin, Administrator
Web address: www.lifecare–hospitals.com/hospital.php?id=19
Control: Corporation, Investor–owned, for–profit **Service:** Long–Term Acute Care hospital

Staffed Beds: 55 **Admissions:** 271 **Census:** 43 **Births:** 0

NORTHERN LOUISIANA MEDICAL CENTER (190086), 401 East Vaughn Avenue, Zip 71270–5950; tel. 318/254–2100, (Nonreporting) **A**1 9 10 19 **S** Community Health Systems, Inc., Franklin, TN
Primary Contact: Brady Dubois, Chief Executive Officer
CFO: Frank Malek, Chief Financial Officer
CMO: Derek McCiusky, M.D., Chief of Staff
CIO: Heather Nolan, Director Information Services
CHR: Tonya Duggan, Director Human Resources
Web address: www.northernlouisianamedicalcenter.com
Control: Other not–for–profit (including NFP Corporation) **Service:** General Medical and Surgical

Staffed Beds: 91

LA

SAINT FRANCISVILLE—West Feliciana Parish

⊞ **WEST FELICIANA PARISH HOSPITAL (191306)**, 5266 Commerce Street,
Zip 70775, Mailing Address: P.O. Box 368, Zip 70775–0368; tel. 225/635–3811
A1 9 10 18 **F**34 35 40 57 58 107 119 128 130 133 135 143
Primary Contact: Lee Chastant, M.D., Chief Executive Officer
CFO: Linda Harvey, Chief Financial Officer
CHR: Neta F. Leake, Administrative Assistant Human Resources
Web address: www.wfph.org
Control: Hospital district or authority, Government, nonfederal **Service:** General
Medical and Surgical

Staffed Beds: 22 **Admissions:** 72 **Census:** 1 **Outpatient Visits:** 24034 **Births:** 0 **Total Expense ($000):** 15059 **Payroll Expense ($000):** 5868 **Personnel:** 122	

SHREVEPORT—Caddo Parish

☐ **BRENTWOOD HOSPITAL (194020)**, 1006 Highland Avenue, Zip 71101–4103;
tel. 318/678–7500 **A**1 9 10 **F**4 5 50 98 99 100 101 102 103 105 **P**6
S Universal Health Services, Inc., King of Prussia, PA
Primary Contact: William Weaver, Chief Executive Officer
CFO: Kae Bell, Chief Financial Officer
CMO: Daniel Feeney, M.D., Medical Director
CHR: Dianna F. Thomas, Director Human Resources
Web address: www.brentwoodbehavioral.com
Control: Corporation, Investor–owned, for–profit **Service:** Psychiatric

Staffed Beds: 172 **Admissions:** 5463 **Census:** 138 **Outpatient Visits:** 2389 **Births:** 0 **Total Expense ($000):** 21774 **Payroll Expense ($000):** 11582 **Personnel:** 328	

⊞ **CHRISTUS HIGHLAND MEDICAL CENTER (190041)**, One St. Mary Place,
Zip 71101–4399; tel. 318/681–4500, (Includes CHRISTUS HIGHLAND MEDICAL
CENTER, 1453 East Bert Kouns Industrial Loop, Zip 71105–6050;
tel. 318/681–5000; Stephen F. Wright, President and Chief Executive Officer) **A**1
2 3 5 9 10 **F**3 11 12 13 15 17 18 20 22 24 26 29 30 31 32 34 35 40 43 45
46 47 48 49 53 54 55 56 57 58 59 61 64 70 72 74 75 76 77 78 79 81 82
85 86 87 88 89 90 93 96 97 102 107 108 110 111 114 115 119 120 121
123 124 126 130 131 132 134 135 146 147 148 **S** CHRISTUS Health,
Irving, TX
Primary Contact: Stephen F. Wright, President and Chief Executive Officer
COO: William Lunn, M.D., Chief Operating Officer
CFO: Scott Merryman, Chief Financial Officer
CMO: Philip Cole, M.D., Vice President Medical Affairs and Chief Medical Officer
CIO: Mary Merryman, Regional Director Information Management
CHR: Wendy White, Vice President Human Resources
CNO: Charlotte Knoll, R.N., Chief Nursing Executive
Web address: www.christusschumpert.org
Control: Church–operated, Nongovernment, not–for profit **Service:** General
Medical and Surgical

Staffed Beds: 302 **Admissions:** 10965 **Census:** 153 **Outpatient Visits:** 179927 **Births:** 1037 **Total Expense ($000):** 201680 **Payroll Expense ($000):** 66481 **Personnel:** 927	

⊞ **LIFECARE HOSPITALS OF SHREVEPORT (192011)**, 9320 Linwood Avenue,
Zip 71106–7003; tel. 318/688–8504, (Includes LIFECARE HOSPITALS OF
SHREVEPORT–WILLIS KNIGHTON, 8001 Youree Drive, Zip 71115–2302; Keith
Cox, Chief Executive Officer and Administrator; LIFECARE HOSPITALS OF SOUTH
SHREVEPORT–WILLIS KNIGHTON NORTH, 2550 Kings Highway, Zip 71103–3922;
Keith Cox, Chief Executive Officer and Administrator), (Nonreporting) **A**1 9 10
S LifeCare Management Services, Plano, TX
Primary Contact: Keith Cox, Administrator
Web address: www.lifecare–hospitals.com
Control: Corporation, Investor–owned, for–profit **Service:** Long–Term Acute Care
hospital

Staffed Beds: 119	

⊞ **OVERTON BROOKS VETERANS AFFAIRS MEDICAL CENTER**, 510 East
Stoner Avenue, Zip 71101–4295; tel. 318/221–8411, (Nonreporting) **A**1 2 3 5
S Department of Veterans Affairs, Washington, DC
Primary Contact: Shirley Bealer, Medical Center Director
CFO: Kim Lane, Chief Fiscal Service
CIO: Janey Taylor, Chief Information and Technology
CHR: Michael L. Palmier, Chief Human Resources Management
Web address: www.shreveport.va.gov/
Control: Veterans Affairs, Government, federal **Service:** General Medical and
Surgical

Staffed Beds: 100	

PHYSICIANS BEHAVIORAL HOSPITAL (194094), 2025 Desoto Street,
Zip 71103–4717; tel. 318/550–0520, (Nonreporting) **A**9 10
Primary Contact: Tom McCardell, Administrator
Control: Corporation, Investor–owned, for–profit **Service:** Psychiatric

Staffed Beds: 12	

☐ **PROMISE HOSPITAL OF LOUISIANA – SHREVEPORT CAMPUS (192010)**,
1800 Irving Place, Zip 71101–4608; tel. 318/425–4096, (Includes PROMISE
HOSPITAL OF LOUISIANA – BOSSIER CITY CAMPUS, 2525 Viking Drive, Bossier
City, Zip 71111–2103; tel. 318/841–2525), (Nonreporting) **A**1 9 10 **S** Promise
Healthcare, Boca Raton, FL
Primary Contact: Rick Stockton, Chief Executive Officer
Web address: www.promise–shreveport.com
Control: Corporation, Investor–owned, for–profit **Service:** Long–Term Acute Care
hospital

Staffed Beds: 146	

PROMISE SPECIALTY HOSPITAL OF SHREVEPORT See Promise Hospital of
Louisiana – Shreveport Campus

☐ **SHRINERS HOSPITALS FOR CHILDREN–SHREVEPORT (193301)**, 3100
Samford Avenue, Zip 71103–4289; tel. 318/222–5704 **A**1 3 5 9 10 **F**34 50 59
64 68 79 81 85 89 93 94 119 130 131 146 **S** Shriners Hospitals for Children,
Tampa, FL
Primary Contact: Garry Kim Green, FACHE, Administrator
CFO: Randy Tabor, Director Fiscal Services
CMO: Philip E. Gates, M.D., Chief of Staff
CIO: Kim Crockett, Director Management Information Systems
CHR: Rena Arbuthnot, Director Human Resources
CNO: Gail Rains, R.N., Director Patient Care Services
Web address: www.shrinershospitalsforchildren.org/Hospitals/Locations/
Shreveport.aspx
Control: Other not–for–profit (including NFP Corporation) **Service:** Children's
orthopedic

Staffed Beds: 45 **Admissions:** 361 **Census:** 3 **Outpatient Visits:** 12626 **Births:** 0 **Personnel:** 162	

SPECIALISTS HOSPITAL – SHREVEPORT (190278), 1500 Line Avenue,
Zip 71101–4639; tel. 318/213–3800, (Nonreporting) **A**9 10
Primary Contact: Kandi Moore, Administrator
Web address: www.specialistshospitalshreveport.com/
Control: Corporation, Investor–owned, for–profit **Service:** General Medical and
Surgical

Staffed Beds: 15	

☐ **UNIVERSITY HEALTH SHREVEPORT (190098)**, 1501 Kings Highway,
Zip 71103–4228, Mailing Address: P.O. Box 33932, Zip 71130–3932;
tel. 318/675–5000, (Includes CHILDREN'S HOSPITAL OF SHREVEPORT, 1501
Kings Highway, Mailing Address: PO Box 33932, Zip 71130–3932;
tel. 318/675–5000), (Nonreporting) **A**1 2 3 5 9 10
Primary Contact: Roderick L. Williams, M.P.H., President
COO: Betty Johnson, Associate Administrator
CFO: Harold White, Vice Chancellor
CMO: Kevin Sittig, M.D., Senior Associate Dean and Chief Medical Officer
CIO: Marcus Hobgood, Director Information Services
CHR: David Fuqua, Director Human Resources Management
Web address: www.lsuhscshreveport.edu
Control: State–Government, nonfederal **Service:** General Medical and Surgical

Staffed Beds: 502	

⊞ △ **WILLIS–KNIGHTON MEDICAL CENTER (190111)**, 2600 Greenwood Road,
Zip 71103–3908, Mailing Address: P.O. Box 32600, Zip 71130–2600;
tel. 318/212–4600, (Includes WILLIS–KNIGHTON PIERREMONT HEALTH CENTER,
8001 Youree Drive, Zip 71115; tel. 318/212–3000; WILLIS–KNIGHTON SOUTH –
THE CENTER FOR WOMEN'S HEALTH, 2510 Bert Kouns Industrial Loop,
Zip 71118; tel. 318/212–5000; Keri Elrod, Administrator) **A**1 2 3 5 7 9 10 **F**3 5
17 70 72 76 81 88 89 90 98 128 **P**7 **S** Willis–Knighton Health System,
Shreveport, LA
Primary Contact: Jaf Fielder, Vice President and Administrator
COO: Charles D. Daigle, Senior Vice President and Chief Operating Officer
CMO: Dan Moller, M.D., Chief Medical Officer
CHR: Jaf Fielder, Vice President and Administrator
CNO: Debbie D. Olds, R.N., Director of Nursing
Web address: www.wkhs.com
Control: Other not–for–profit (including NFP Corporation) **Service:** General
Medical and Surgical

Staffed Beds: 898 **Admissions:** 37522 **Census:** 450 **Outpatient Visits:** 380499 **Births:** 2349 **Personnel:** 4185	

SLIDELL—St. Tammany Parish

AMG SPECIALTY HOSPITAL–SLIDELL (192046), 1400 Lindberg Drive,
Zip 70458–8056; tel. 985/326–0440, (Nonreporting) **A**10 **S** AMG Integrated
Healthcare Management, Lafayette, LA
Primary Contact: Richard Daughdrill, R.N., Chief Executive Officer
COO: Gene Smith, Senior Vice President Operations
CFO: Jessica McGee, Chief Financial Officer
CMO: Marie Mahoney, M.D., Chief Medical Officer
CHR: Kim Hernandez, Director Human Resources
Web address: www.amgslidell.com/
Control: Partnership, Investor–owned, for–profit **Service:** Long–Term Acute Care
hospital

Staffed Beds: 40	

NORTHSHORE REGIONAL MEDICAL CENTER See Ochsner Medical Center –
North Shore

Many Facility Codes have changed. Please refer to the AHA Guide Code Chart. © 2014 AHA Guide

LA

✠ **OCHSNER MEDICAL CENTER – NORTH SHORE (190204)**, 100 Medical Center Drive, Zip 70461–5520; tel. 985/646–5000 **A**1 9 10 **F**3 13 15 17 18 20 22 24 26 29 30 31 34 35 40 41 44 45 46 49 50 51 57 59 61 62 64 68 70 72 74 75 76 77 78 79 81 84 85 86 87 88 89 90 91 93 95 96 97 102 107 108 109 110 111 113 114 116 117 118 119 129 130 132 135 146 147 148 **S** Ochsner Health System, New Orleans, LA
Primary Contact: Polly J. Davenport, R.N., Chief Executive Officer
COO: Alan Hodges, Chief Operating Officer
CFO: Forrest Whichard, Chief Financial Officer
CMO: James Newcomb, M.D., Vice President Medical
CHR: Terri Joseph–Taylor, Chief Human Resource Manager
CNO: Cheryl Woods, Chief Nursing Officer
Web address: www.ochsner.org/locations/northshore
Control: Other not–for–profit (including NFP Corporation) **Service:** General Medical and Surgical

Staffed Beds: 110 **Admissions:** 4816 **Census:** 58 **Outpatient Visits:** 65773 **Births:** 206 **Total Expense ($000):** 81951 **Payroll Expense ($000):** 33514 **Personnel:** 608

✠ **SLIDELL MEMORIAL HOSPITAL (190040)**, 1001 Gause Boulevard, Zip 70458–2987; tel. 985/280–2200, (Nonreporting) **A**1 2 3 5 9 10
Primary Contact: John William Davis, Chief Executive Officer and Chief Financial Officer
COO: Bruce Clement, Chief Operating Officer
CFO: Sandy Badinger, Chief Financial Officer
CHR: Jeanne M. Stachovsky, Director Human Resources
CNO: Lynn Strain, R.N., Chief Nursing Officer
Web address: www.slidellmemorial.org
Control: Hospital district or authority, Government, nonfederal **Service:** General Medical and Surgical

Staffed Beds: 175

☐ **SOUTHERN SURGICAL HOSPITAL (190270)**, 1700 Lindberg Drive, Zip 70458–8062; tel. 985/641–0600 **A**1 9 10 **F**3 8 12 29 57 70 79 81 82 85 107 111 112 119 130 131 132 **P**5
Primary Contact: Michael J. Pisciotta, Chief Executive Officer
CFO: Michael J. Maurin, Chief Financial Officer
CMO: J. Gosey, M.D., Medical Director
CIO: Buddy Graves, Chief Information Officer
CHR: Lorrie Alfred, Director Human Resources
Web address: www.sshla.com/
Control: Partnership, Investor–owned, for–profit **Service:** Surgical

Staffed Beds: 37 **Admissions:** 1200 **Census:** 10 **Outpatient Visits:** 2100 **Births:** 0

STERLING SURGICAL HOSPITAL (190256), 989 Robert Boulevard, Zip 70458–2009; tel. 985/690–8200, (Nonreporting) **A**9 10
Primary Contact: Kevin Schneider, Chief Executive Officer
Control: Corporation, Investor–owned, for–profit **Service:** Other specialty

Staffed Beds: 10

SPRINGHILL—Webster Parish

☐ **SPRINGHILL MEDICAL CENTER (190088)**, 2001 Doctors Drive, Zip 71075–4526, Mailing Address: P.O. Box 920, Zip 71075–0920; tel. 318/539–1000 **A**1 9 10 **F**3 15 18 26 29 30 32 34 35 40 45 46 47 48 49 50 51 57 59 64 65 66 68 70 75 79 81 82 85 86 87 93 98 103 104 107 108 110 111 114 119 127 129 130 131 133 135 146 148 **P**6 **S** Willis–Knighton Health System, Shreveport, LA
Primary Contact: Vince Sedminik, Chief Executive Officer
CFO: Layla Chase, Chief Financial Officer
CMO: Jerry W. Sessions, M.D., Chief Medical Staff
CIO: Brian Griffin, Director Information Services
CHR: Ashley Ortego, Director Human Resources and Marketing
CNO: Dana Jones, R.N., Chief Nursing Officer
Web address: www.smccare.com
Control: Other not–for–profit (including NFP Corporation) **Service:** General Medical and Surgical

Staffed Beds: 58 **Admissions:** 1097 **Census:** 14 **Outpatient Visits:** 36048 **Births:** 0

SULPHUR—Calcasieu Parish

✠ **CORNERSTONE HOSPITAL OF SOUTHWEST LOUISIANA (192013)**, 703 Cypress Street, Zip 70663–5053; tel. 337/310–6000, (Nonreporting) **A**1 10 **S** Cornerstone Healthcare Group, Dallas, TX
Primary Contact: David Smith, Chief Executive Officer
CFO: Amy Bryant, Chief Financial Officer
Web address: www.chghospitals.com/sulphur/
Control: Partnership, Investor–owned, for–profit **Service:** Long–Term Acute Care hospital

Staffed Beds: 30

☐ **WEST CALCASIEU CAMERON HOSPITAL (190013)**, 701 Cypress Street, Zip 70663–5000, Mailing Address: P.O. Box 2509, Zip 70664–2509; tel. 337/527–7034 **A**1 9 10 **F**3 11 13 15 18 20 22 26 28 29 31 32 34 35 37 39 40 45 50 51 53 54 56 57 59 65 66 70 74 75 76 77 78 79 81 83 85 86 87 89 91 92 93 102 107 108 110 111 114 115 120 127 130 132 135 143 146 147 148 **P**3 4
Primary Contact: Janie Fruge, R.N., MSN, Chief Executive Officer
CFO: Jobie James, Chief Financial Officer
CIO: Trey Rion, Chief Information Officer
CHR: Christi Kingsley, Director Human Resources
CNO: Brenda Quesnel, R.N., Vice President of Patient Care and Chief Nursing Officer
Web address: www.wcch.com
Control: Hospital district or authority, Government, nonfederal **Service:** General Medical and Surgical

Staffed Beds: 79 **Admissions:** 3273 **Census:** 33 **Outpatient Visits:** 28776 **Births:** 296

TALLULAH—Madison Parish

MADISON PARISH HOSPITAL (191314), 900 Johnson Street, Zip 71282–4537; tel. 318/574–2374, (Nonreporting) **A**9 10 18
Primary Contact: Ted Topolewski, Chief Executive Officer
CIO: Charles Whitaker, Director Information Technology
CHR: Chasity Whitaker, Administrative Assistant
Web address: www.madisonparishhospital.com
Control: Other not–for–profit (including NFP Corporation) **Service:** General Medical and Surgical

Staffed Beds: 25

THIBODAUX—Lafourche Parish

✠ △ **THIBODAUX REGIONAL MEDICAL CENTER (190004)**, 602 North Acadia Road, Zip 70301–4847, Mailing Address: P.O. Box 1118, Zip 70302–1118; tel. 985/447–5500 **A**1 2 7 9 10 **F**3 8 11 12 13 15 18 19 20 22 24 28 29 30 31 32 34 40 46 49 57 59 62 64 70 73 74 75 76 77 78 79 81 82 85 86 87 90 92 93 96 97 98 103 104 105 107 108 110 111 115 116 117 119 120 121 123 124 126 127 129 130 131 132 146 147 148
Primary Contact: Greg K. Stock, Chief Executive Officer
COO: Scott Flowers, Vice President Professional Services
CFO: Steve C. Gaubert, Chief Financial Officer
CMO: Allen Vander, M.D., Chief Medical Staff
CIO: Bernie Clement, Chief Information Officer
CHR: Eric Degravelle, Director Human Resources
Web address: www.thibodaux.com
Control: Hospital district or authority, Government, nonfederal **Service:** General Medical and Surgical

Staffed Beds: 154 **Admissions:** 8666 **Census:** 97 **Outpatient Visits:** 146818 **Births:** 927 **Total Expense ($000):** 137060 **Payroll Expense ($000):** 55617 **Personnel:** 1019

VIDALIA—Concordia Parish

☐ **PROMISE HOSPITAL OF MISS LOU (192028)**, 209 Front Street, Zip 71373–2837; tel. 318/336–6500, (Nonreporting) **A**1 10 **S** Promise Healthcare, Boca Raton, FL
Primary Contact: Benny Costello, Chief Executive Officer
COO: Howard B. Koslow, President and Chief Executive Officer
CFO: James Hopwood, Chief Financial Officer
CMO: Randy Tillman, M.D., Chief Medical Staff
CIO: Robert Greene, Director Information Technology
CHR: Roxan Houghton, Director Human Resources
CNO: Regetta Woods, Chief Nursing Officer and Chief Clinical Officer
Web address: www.promise–misslou.com
Control: Corporation, Investor–owned, for–profit **Service:** Long–Term Acute Care hospital

Staffed Beds: 40

LA

VILLE PLATTE—Evangeline Parish

✠ **MERCY REGIONAL MEDICAL CENTER (190167)**, 800 East Main Street, Zip 70586–4618, Mailing Address: P.O. Box 349, Zip 70586–0349; tel. 337/363–5684, (Includes ACADIAN MEDICAL CENTER, 3501 Highway 190, Eunice, Zip 70535–5129; tel. 337/580–7500; Scott M. Smith, Chief Executive Officer), (Nonreporting) **A**1 9 10 **S** LifePoint Hospitals, Inc., Brentwood, TN
Primary Contact: Scott M. Smith, Chief Executive Officer
COO: Sandy Morein, Chief Operating Officer
CFO: Micheal Fontenot, Chief Financial Officer
CMO: Brandon Fontenot, M.D., Chief of Staff
CIO: Courtney Bieber, Director Information Systems
CHR: Cody Ardoin, Director Human Resources
CNO: Sandy Morein, Chief Operating Officer and Chief Nursing Officer
Web address: www.mercyregionalmedicalcenter.com
Control: Corporation, Investor–owned, for–profit **Service:** General Medical and Surgical

Staffed Beds: 60

VIVIAN—Caddo Parish

NORTH CADDO MEDICAL CENTER (191304), 1000 South Spruce Street, Zip 71082–3232, Mailing Address: P.O. Box 792, Zip 71082–0792; tel. 318/375–3235, (Nonreporting) **A**5 6 9 10 18
Primary Contact: David C. Jones, Administrator
CFO: Carol Reisz, Chief Financial Officer
CMO: John H. Haynes, Jr., M.D., Chief of Medical Staff
CIO: Allyson Allums, Director Medical Records
CHR: Lanell Audirsch, Administrative Assistant
Web address: www.northcaddomedicalcenter.com
Control: Hospital district or authority, Government, nonfederal **Service:** General Medical and Surgical

Staffed Beds: 25

WEST MONROE—Ouachita Parish

☐ **CORNERSTONE HOSPITAL–WEST MONROE (192031)**, 6198 Cypress Street, Zip 71291–9010; tel. 318/396–5600, (Nonreporting) **A**1 10 **S** Cornerstone Healthcare Group, Dallas, TX
Primary Contact: Chris Simpson, Chief Executive Officer
COO: Jay Quintana, Vice President Operations
CFO: Kurt Schultz, Chief Financial Officer
CMO: Khaled Shafici, M.D., President Medical Staff
CIO: Adam Davis, Chief Information Officer
CHR: Dan Perkins, Corporate Director Human Resources
Web address: www.chghospitals.com/chwm.html
Control: Corporation, Investor–owned, for–profit **Service:** Long–Term Acute Care hospital

Staffed Beds: 40

◇ **GLENWOOD REGIONAL MEDICAL CENTER (190160)**, 503 McMillan Road, Zip 71291–5327; tel. 318/329–4200 **A**2 9 10 21 **F**3 5 8 11 13 15 17 18 20 22 24 26 28 29 30 31 32 34 35 36 37 40 42 43 45 46 49 50 54 56 57 59 60 64 65 68 70 71 72 74 75 77 78 79 81 85 86 87 90 92 93 94 96 98 103 104 106 107 108 109 110 111 114 115 116 117 118 119 126 128 129 130 132 133 135 144 146 147 148 **P**8 **S** IASIS Healthcare, Franklin, TN
Primary Contact: Matthew S. Roberts, Chief Executive Officer
COO: Larry D. Walker, Chief Operating Officer
CFO: John DeSantis, Chief Financial Officer
CMO: Ron Hammett, M.D., Chief of Staff
CIO: Ronnie Maxwell, Director Information Systems
CHR: Jan Walker, Director Human Resources
CNO: Jeremy Tinnerello, R.N., Chief Nursing Officer
Web address: www.grmc.com
Control: Corporation, Investor–owned, for–profit **Service:** General Medical and Surgical

Staffed Beds: 268 **Admissions:** 12277 **Census:** 180 **Outpatient Visits:** 69664 **Births:** 885 **Total Expense ($000):** 118521 **Payroll Expense ($000):** 46928 **Personnel:** 909

LOUISIANA EXTENDED CARE HOSPITAL WEST MONROE (192055), 503 McMillan Road, 3rd Floor, Zip 71291–5327; tel. 318/329–4300, (Nonreporting) **A**10 **S** LHC Group, Lafayette, LA
Primary Contact: Cleta Munholland, Administrator
Control: Corporation, Investor–owned, for–profit **Service:** Long–Term Acute Care hospital

Staffed Beds: 18

◇ **OUACHITA COMMUNITY HOSPITAL (190261)**, 1275 Glenwood Drive, Zip 71291–5539; tel. 318/322–1339 **A**9 10 21 **F**3 12 34 35 37 45 56 57 65 75 79 81 82 85 132 135
Primary Contact: Robert L. Colvin, Administrator
CFO: John DeSantis, Chief Financial Officer
CMO: H. Jerrel Fontenot, M.D., Medical Director
CNO: Brenda Wallace, R.N., Chief Nursing Officer
Web address: www.ouachitacommunityhospital.com
Control: Partnership, Investor–owned, for–profit **Service:** Surgical

Staffed Beds: 10 **Admissions:** 78 **Census:** 1 **Births:** 0 **Personnel:** 30

WINNFIELD—Winn Parish

☐ **SPECIALTY HOSPITAL OF WINNFIELD (192052)**, 915 First Street, Zip 71483–2945; tel. 318/648–0212, (Nonreporting) **A**1 10
Primary Contact: William Bush, Chief Executive Officer
CFO: Charlie Jurek, Business Office Manager
CIO: Shamada Venzant, Manager Health Information
Control: Corporation, Investor–owned, for–profit **Service:** Long–Term Acute Care hospital

Staffed Beds: 20

WINN PARISH MEDICAL CENTER (190090), 301 West Boundary Street, Zip 71483–3427, Mailing Address: P.O. Box 152, Zip 71483–0152; tel. 318/648–3000, (Nonreporting) **A**9 10
Primary Contact: Patricia Flowers, Interim Chief Executive Officer
CFO: Dana McGee, Chief Financial Officer
CMO: James Lee, M.D., Chief of Staff
CHR: Ashley S. Files, Director Human Resources
CNO: Toby Wise, Chief Nursing Officer
Web address: www.winnparishmedical.com
Control: Partnership, Investor–owned, for–profit **Service:** General Medical and Surgical

Staffed Beds: 60

WINNSBORO—Franklin Parish

★ **FRANKLIN MEDICAL CENTER (190140)**, 2106 Loop Road, Zip 71295–3344, Mailing Address: P.O. Box 1300, Zip 71295–1300; tel. 318/435–9411, (Nonreporting) **A**9 10
Primary Contact: Blake Kramer, Chief Executive Officer
CMO: Jay Busby, M.D., President Medical Staff
CIO: Judy Ogden, Director Information Technology
Web address: www.fmc–cares.com
Control: Hospital district or authority, Government, nonfederal **Service:** General Medical and Surgical

Staffed Beds: 43

ZACHARY—East Baton Rouge Parish

✠ **LANE REGIONAL MEDICAL CENTER (190020)**, 6300 Main Street, Zip 70791–4037; tel. 225/658–4000, (Total facility includes 38 beds in nursing home–type unit) **A**1 9 10 **F**3 11 13 15 18 20 22 26 29 34 35 36 39 40 45 46 48 50 54 56 57 59 62 64 67 70 73 75 76 77 79 80 81 85 87 90 93 107 108 110 111 114 115 119 130 146 148 **P**6
Primary Contact: Randall M. Olson, Chief Executive Officer
CFO: Mark Anderson, Chief Financial Officer
CMO: Brad Smith, M.D., Chief Medical Staff
CIO: Scarlet Collier, Chief Information Officer
CHR: David Beck, Chief Operating Officer and Director Human Resources
CNO: Jennifer S. Johnson, R.N., Chief Nursing Officer
Web address: www.lanermc.org
Control: Hospital district or authority, Government, nonfederal **Service:** General Medical and Surgical

Staffed Beds: 180 **Admissions:** 4626 **Census:** 96 **Outpatient Visits:** 37817 **Births:** 529 **Total Expense ($000):** 75918 **Payroll Expense ($000):** 32865 **Personnel:** 643

Many Facility Codes have changed. Please refer to the AHA Guide Code Chart. © 2014 AHA Guide

MAINE

AUGUSTA—Kennebec County

✠ **MAINE VETERANS AFFAIRS MEDICAL CENTER**, 1 VA Center,
Zip 04330–6719; tel. 207/623–8411, (Total facility includes 87 beds in nursing
home–type unit) **A**1 **F**3 5 8 18 28 29 30 31 33 34 35 38 39 40 42 44 45 50
53 54 56 57 58 59 60 61 62 63 64 65 66 68 70 71 74 75 77 78 79 81 82
83 84 85 87 91 93 94 97 98 100 102 103 104 105 107 111 112 115 119
127 129 130 132 135 143 146 147 148 **P**6 **S** Department of Veterans Affairs,
Washington, DC
Primary Contact: Ryan S. Lilly, Acting Director
CFO: Daniel Howard, Chief Financial Officer
CMO: Timothy J. Richardson, M.D., Chief of Staff
CIO: Richard McNaughton, Chief Information Management Service
CHR: Christine Miller, Chief Human Resources Management Services
Web address: www.maine.va.gov/
Control: Veterans Affairs, Government, federal **Service:** General Medical and
Surgical

Staffed Beds: 157 **Admissions:** 2614 **Census:** 114 **Outpatient Visits:**
408138 **Births:** 0 **Total Expense ($000):** 280955 **Payroll Expense ($000):**
122757 **Personnel:** 1308

✠ **MAINEGENERAL MEDICAL CENTER (200039)**, 35 Medical Center Parkway,
Zip 04330; tel. 207/872–1000, (Includes MAINEGENERAL MEDICAL
CENTER–AUGUSTA CAMPUS, 6 East Chestnut Street, Zip 04330–9988;
tel. 207/626–1000; Chuck Hays, President) **A**1 2 10 19 **F**3 5 11 12 13 15 20
22 26 28 29 30 31 34 35 40 44 45 46 51 54 57 58 59 60 63 64 65 66 70
74 75 76 77 78 79 81 82 84 85 86 87 89 90 91 93 94 96 97 98 99 100
101 102 103 104 105 107 108 110 114 115 116 117 118 119 120 121 123
124 126 129 130 131 132 135 143 144 145 146 147 148 **P**6 8
Primary Contact: Chuck Hays, President
COO: Paul Stein, Chief Operating Officer
CFO: Michael J. Koziol, Chief Financial Officer
CMO: Steve Diaz, M.D., Chief Medical Officer
CIO: Daniel Burgess, Chief Information Officer
CHR: Rebecca Lamey, Vice President Human Resources
CNO: Sherri Woodward, R.N., Senior Vice President and Chief Nurse Executive
Web address: www.mainegeneral.org
Control: Other not–for–profit (including NFP Corporation) **Service:** General
Medical and Surgical

Staffed Beds: 258 **Admissions:** 10959 **Census:** 148 **Outpatient Visits:**
1463351 **Births:** 1034 **Total Expense ($000):** 370046 **Payroll Expense
($000):** 166176 **Personnel:** 2716

MAINEGENERAL MEDICAL CENTER–AUGUSTA CAMPUS See MaineGeneral
Medical Center

☐ **RIVERVIEW PSYCHIATRIC CENTER (204007)**, 250 Arsenal Street,
Zip 04330–5742; tel. 207/624–3900 **A**1 10 **F**29 30 39 64 75 86 87 97 98
100 101 103 104 130 132 135
Primary Contact: Mary Louise McEwen, Superintendent
CFO: Jenny Boyden, Chief Financial Officer
CMO: William Nelson, M.D., Medical Director
CHR: Kristine Albert, Personnel Officer
CNO: Tami Cooper, Acting Director of Nursing
Web address: www.state.me.us/dhhs/riverview
Control: State–Government, nonfederal **Service:** Psychiatric

Staffed Beds: 92 **Admissions:** 183 **Census:** 81 **Outpatient Visits:** 6295
Births: 0

VETERANS AFFAIRS MEDICAL CENTER See Maine Veterans Affairs Medical
Center

BANGOR—Penobscot County

☐ **DOROTHEA DIX PSYCHIATRIC CENTER (204004)**, 656 State Street,
Zip 04401–5609, Mailing Address: P.O. Box 926, Zip 04402–0926;
tel. 207/941–4000 **A**1 10 **F**98 101 104 130 **P**6
Primary Contact: Sharon Sprague, Superintendent
CFO: Steven Thebarge, Chief Operating Officer and Chief Financial Officer
CMO: Marjorie Snyder, M.D., Clinical Director
CIO: Larry Larson, Management Analyst
CHR: Ruth Mullaney, Personnel Officer
Web address: www.maine.gov/dhhs/ddpc/index.shtml
Control: State–Government, nonfederal **Service:** Psychiatric

Staffed Beds: 51 **Admissions:** 138 **Census:** 43 **Outpatient Visits:** 51 **Births:**
0 **Total Expense ($000):** 17345 **Payroll Expense ($000):** 9032 **Personnel:**
195

✠ **EASTERN MAINE MEDICAL CENTER (200033)**, 489 State Street,
Zip 04401–6674, Mailing Address: P.O. Box 404, Zip 04402–0404;
tel. 207/973–7000, (Includes ROSS SKILLED NURSING FACILITY) **A**1 2 3 5 9 10
13 **F**3 11 12 13 15 17 18 19 20 22 24 26 28 29 30 31 34 36 37 39 40 43
44 45 46 47 48 49 50 51 53 54 55 57 58 59 61 64 70 72 74 75 76 77 78
79 81 82 84 85 86 87 88 89 90 92 93 94 96 97 102 107 108 110 111 114
115 117 118 119 120 121 123 124 126 129 130 131 132 144 145 146 147
148 **P**6 **S** Eastern Maine Healthcare Systems, Brewer, ME
Primary Contact: Deborah Carey Johnson, R.N., President and Chief Executive
Officer
CFO: Elmer Doucette, Vice President and Chief Financial Officer
CMO: James Raczek, M.D., Sr. Vice President of Operations and Chief Medical
Officer
CIO: Catherine Bruno, FACHE, Chief Information Officer
CHR: Greg Howat, Vice President Human Resources
CNO: Jodi Galli, Chief Nursing Officer
Web address: www.emh.org
Control: Other not–for–profit (including NFP Corporation) **Service:** General
Medical and Surgical

Staffed Beds: 364 **Admissions:** 19908 **Census:** 286 **Outpatient Visits:**
427008 **Births:** 1648 **Total Expense ($000):** 618521 **Payroll Expense
($000):** 257862 **Personnel:** 3567

✠ **ST. JOSEPH HOSPITAL (200001)**, 360 Broadway, Zip 04401–3979, Mailing
Address: P.O. Box 403, Zip 04402–0403; tel. 207/262–1000 **A**1 9 10 **F**8 15
18 20 28 29 30 31 35 40 45 48 49 51 55 56 57 62 63 64 70 74 75 78 79
81 84 85 86 87 107 108 110 115 118 119 129 130 132 135 146 147 148
S Covenant Health Systems, Inc., Tewksbury, MA
Primary Contact: Mary Prybylo, President and Chief Executive Officer
CFO: Michael A. Hendrix, Jr., Chief Financial Officer
CMO: William Wood, M.D., Vice President Medical Affairs
CHR: Paige A. Hagerstrom, Director Human Resources
CNO: Dianne Swandal, R.N., Vice President Patient Care
Web address: www.sjhhealth.com
Control: Church–operated, Nongovernment, not–for profit **Service:** General
Medical and Surgical

Staffed Beds: 84 **Admissions:** 5799 **Census:** 50 **Outpatient Visits:** 66841
Births: 0 **Total Expense ($000):** 94483 **Payroll Expense ($000):** 38879
Personnel: 754

✠ **THE ACADIA HOSPITAL (204006)**, 268 Stillwater Avenue, Zip 04401–3945,
Mailing Address: P.O. Box 422, Zip 04402–0422; tel. 207/973–6100 **A**1 10 **F**5
29 30 50 57 66 68 75 77 87 98 99 100 101 103 104 105 130 132 **P**6
S Eastern Maine Healthcare Systems, Brewer, ME
Primary Contact: Daniel B. Coffey, President and Chief Executive Officer
CFO: Marie Suitter, Chief Financial Officer
CMO: Anthony Ng, M.D., Vice President and Chief Medical Officer
CIO: Jeanne Paradis, Director Information Services
CHR: Paul Bolin, Vice President Human Resources
CNO: Wayne Steller, Vice President Chief Nursing Officer
Web address: www.acadiahospital.org
Control: Other not–for–profit (including NFP Corporation) **Service:** Psychiatric

Staffed Beds: 68 **Admissions:** 1443 **Census:** 55 **Outpatient Visits:** 88930
Births: 0 **Total Expense ($000):** 45391 **Payroll Expense ($000):** 24932
Personnel: 400

BAR HARBOR—Hancock County

★ **MOUNT DESERT ISLAND HOSPITAL (201304)**, 10 Wayman Lane,
Zip 04609–1625, Mailing Address: P.O. Box 8, Zip 04609–0008;
tel. 207/288–5081 **A**9 10 18 **F**3 5 6 10 11 13 15 28 29 31 34 35 36 40 50
54 56 57 59 64 65 70 74 75 76 77 78 79 81 82 84 85 87 91 92 93 97 99
100 101 104 107 108 114 119 125 127 130 131 132 133 135 145 146 147
P6 7
Primary Contact: Arthur J. Blank, President and Chief Executive Officer
CFO: Christina Harding, Vice President Finance
CMO: David Painter, M.D., President Medical Staff
CIO: Bruce Donlin, Director Information Services
CHR: Joanne Harris, Director Human Resources
CNO: Tom Mockus, R.N., Interim Chief Nursing Officer
Web address: www.mdihospital.org
Control: Other not–for–profit (including NFP Corporation) **Service:** General
Medical and Surgical

Staffed Beds: 25 **Admissions:** 1194 **Census:** 9 **Outpatient Visits:** 113968
Births: 140 **Total Expense ($000):** 51355 **Payroll Expense ($000):** 23479
Personnel: 360

Hospital, Medicare Provider Number, Address, Telephone, Approval, Facility, and Physician Codes, Health Care System

★ American Hospital Association (AHA) membership
☐ The Joint Commission accreditation   ◇ DNV Healthcare Inc. accreditation

○ Healthcare Facilities Accreditation Program
△ Commission on Accreditation of Rehabilitation Facilities (CARF) accreditation

---

BELFAST—Waldo County

WALDO COUNTY GENERAL HOSPITAL (201312), 118 Northport Avenue, Zip 04915–6072, Mailing Address: P.O. Box 287, Zip 04915–0287; tel. 207/338–2500 **A**9 10 18 **F**3 11 13 15 18 19 28 29 30 31 35 39 40 45 46 51 57 59 62 63 64 65 70 74 75 76 78 79 81 83 85 93 97 107 108 110 111 114 117 118 119 127 129 130 132 133 135 145 146 147 148 **P**8 **S** MaineHealth, Portland, ME
Primary Contact: Mark A. Biscone, Executive Director
COO: Dan Bennett, Director Operations
CFO: Linda Drinkwater, Chief Financial Officer
CMO: Kent Clark, M.D., Chief Medical Affairs and Quality
CIO: David Felton, Manager Information Systems
CHR: Karen Littlefield, Manager Human Resources
CNO: Heather Iorio Quesnel, Director of Nursing
Web address: www.wcgh.org
Control: Other not–for–profit (including NFP Corporation) **Service:** General Medical and Surgical

Staffed Beds: 25 **Admissions:** 1440 **Census:** 15 **Outpatient Visits:** 134195 **Births:** 178 **Total Expense ($000):** 69877 **Payroll Expense ($000):** 34919 **Personnel:** 513

BIDDEFORD—York County

SOUTHERN MAINE HEALTH CARE – BIDDEFORD MEDICAL CENTER X (200019), One Medical Center Drive, Zip 04005–9496, Mailing Address: P.O. Box 626, Zip 04005–0626; tel. 207/283–7000, (Includes SOUTHERN MAINE HEALTH CARE – BIDDEFORD MEDICAL CENTER, One Medical Center Drive, tel. 207/283–7000; SOUTHERN MAINE HEALTH CARE – SANFORD MEDICAL CENTER, 25 June Street, Sanford, Zip 04073–2645; tel. 207/324–4310; Edward J. McGeachey, President and Chief Executive Officer), (Nonreporting) **A**1 2 10
Primary Contact: Edward J. McGeachey, President and Chief Executive Officer
COO: Patricia Aprile, Senior Vice President and Chief Operating Officer
CFO: Norman Belair, Senior Vice President and Chief Financial Officer
CMO: Michael Albaum, M.D., Senior Vice President and Chief Medical Officer
CIO: Mary Jane Kamps, Chief Information Officer
CHR: Yvonne C. McAllister, Senior Director Human Resources
CNO: Patricia M. Camire, MS, Senior Vice President Clinical Services and Chief Nursing Officer
Web address: www.smhc.org
Control: Other not–for–profit (including NFP Corporation) **Service:** General Medical and Surgical

Staffed Beds: 191

BLUE HILL—Hancock County

★ **BLUE HILL MEMORIAL HOSPITAL (201300)**, 57 Water Street, Zip 04614–5231; tel. 207/374–3400 **A**9 10 18 **F**8 15 18 28 29 31 32 34 35 40 41 43 44 45 50 51 57 59 64 65 66 75 78 79 80 81 85 86 87 91 93 96 97 107 110 111 119 130 133 146 147 148 **S** Eastern Maine Healthcare Systems, Brewer, ME
Primary Contact: John Ronan, President and Chief Executive Officer
CFO: Wendy Jones, Interim Chief Financial Officer
CHR: David Wheaton, Director Human Resources
CNO: Kathy Lirakis, R.N., Chief Nursing Officer
Web address: www.bhmh.org
Control: Other not–for–profit (including NFP Corporation) **Service:** General Medical and Surgical

Staffed Beds: 25 **Admissions:** 755 **Census:** 10 **Outpatient Visits:** 197880 **Births:** 1 **Total Expense ($000):** 35850 **Payroll Expense ($000):** 16988 **Personnel:** 312

BRIDGTON—Cumberland County

★ **BRIDGTON HOSPITAL (201310)**, 10 Hospital Drive, Zip 04009–1148; tel. 207/647–6000 **A**9 10 18 **F**3 8 11 13 15 29 30 31 34 35 38 40 45 50 53 54 57 59 64 65 70 75 76 78 79 81 85 87 93 94 97 107 108 110 111 114 118 119 128 130 131 132 133 144 146 148 **P**6 8
Primary Contact: R. David Frum, President
COO: John A. Ludwig, R.N., Vice President Operations
CFO: Philip Morissette, Chief Financial Officer
CMO: Alan Verrill, M.D., President Medical Staff
CHR: Kirk Miklavic, Director Human Resources
Web address: www.bridgtonhospital.org
Control: Other not–for–profit (including NFP Corporation) **Service:** General Medical and Surgical

Staffed Beds: 25 **Admissions:** 1100 **Census:** 13 **Outpatient Visits:** 106600 **Births:** 134 **Total Expense ($000):** 42187 **Payroll Expense ($000):** 16702 **Personnel:** 262

BRUNSWICK—Cumberland County

✠ **MiD COAST HOSPITAL (200021)**, 123 Medical Center Drive, Zip 04011–2652; tel. 207/373–6000 **A**1 2 10 **F**3 5 11 12 13 15 18 20 28 29 30 31 32 34 35 36 40 41 44 45 46 47 48 49 51 53 54 57 58 59 61 64 66 68 70 74 75 76 77 78 79 81 82 84 85 86 87 89 92 93 97 98 103 105 107 108 110 111 115 118 119 129 130 131 132 134 135 144 146 147 148 **P**6
Primary Contact: Lois N. Skillings, R.N., MSN, President and Chief Executive Officer
COO: Philip A. Ortolani, Vice President Operations
CFO: Robert N. McCue, Vice President Finance
CMO: Scott Mills, M.D., Vice President Medical Staff Administration and Chief Medical Officer
CIO: Gale Stoy, Manager Information Systems
CHR: Coleen M. Farrell, Vice President Human Resources
CNO: Deborah MacLeod, MS, Vice President Nursing and Patient Care Services
Web address: www.midcoasthealth.com
Control: Other not–for–profit (including NFP Corporation) **Service:** General Medical and Surgical

Staffed Beds: 92 **Admissions:** 4547 **Census:** 53 **Outpatient Visits:** 179876 **Births:** 577 **Total Expense ($000):** 124209 **Payroll Expense ($000):** 58412 **Personnel:** 860

★ **PARKVIEW ADVENTIST MEDICAL CENTER (200025)**, 329 Maine Street, Zip 04011–3398; tel. 207/373–2000 **A**9 10 **F**11 15 29 30 31 34 35 36 37 38 40 45 50 56 59 61 64 65 66 68 70 75 77 78 79 81 82 85 86 87 93 107 108 110 111 114 116 117 119 130 132 135 145 146 147 **P**8
Primary Contact: Randee Reynolds, President
CFO: William Gannon, Chief Financial Officer
CMO: Trudi Chase, M.D., President Medical Staff
CIO: Bill McQuaid, Assistant Vice President and Chief Information Officer
CHR: Samantha Blais, Manager Human Resource
CNO: Sharon Bagalio, R.N., Chief Nursing Officer
Web address: www.parkviewamc.org
Control: Church–operated, Nongovernment, not–for profit **Service:** General Medical and Surgical

Staffed Beds: 55 **Admissions:** 732 **Census:** 8 **Outpatient Visits:** 59260 **Births:** 0 **Total Expense ($000):** 30348 **Payroll Expense ($000):** 10261 **Personnel:** 149

CALAIS—Washington County

★ **CALAIS REGIONAL HOSPITAL (201305)**, 24 Hospital Lane, Zip 04619–1398; tel. 207/454–7521 **A**9 10 18 **F**3 11 13 15 28 29 31 32 34 35 36 40 42 45 46 50 57 59 62 64 65 68 70 75 76 77 79 81 85 89 90 93 97 107 108 110 111 114 119 127 128 129 130 132 133 146 147 148 **S** QHR, Brentwood, TN
Primary Contact: Michael K. Lally, Chief Executive Officer
CFO: Nancy Glidden, Chief Financial Officer
CMO: David Feiner, M.D., Chief Staff
CIO: Dee Dee Travis, Director Community Relations
CHR: Kristi K. Saunders, Director and Compliance Officer
CNO: Cheryl Zwingman–Bagley, R.N., Chief Nursing Officer
Web address: www.calaishospital.com
Control: Other not–for–profit (including NFP Corporation) **Service:** General Medical and Surgical

Staffed Beds: 25 **Admissions:** 719 **Census:** 7 **Outpatient Visits:** 31182 **Births:** 65 **Total Expense ($000):** 33508 **Payroll Expense ($000):** 14010 **Personnel:** 231

CARIBOU—Aroostook County

✠ **CARY MEDICAL CENTER (200031)**, 163 Van Buren Road, Suite 1, Zip 04736–3567; tel. 207/498–3111, (Total facility includes 9 beds in nursing home–type unit) **A**1 9 10 **F**3 8 11 13 15 28 29 31 32 34 35 36 38 40 43 44 51 53 54 56 57 59 61 64 67 68 70 75 76 77 78 79 81 82 84 85 86 87 89 90 93 97 107 108 111 115 118 119 121 130 131 132 135 144 146 147 148 **S** QHR, Brentwood, TN
Primary Contact: Kris A. Doody, R.N., Chief Executive Officer
COO: Shawn Anderson, Chief Operating Officer
CFO: Galen Dickinson, Chief Financial Officer
CMO: Regen Gallagher, M.D., Chief Medical Officer
CIO: Dave Silsbee, Chief Information Officer
CHR: Paula A. Parent, R.N., Director Human Resources and Nursing Administration
Web address: www.carymedicalcenter.org
Control: City–Government, nonfederal **Service:** General Medical and Surgical

Staffed Beds: 49 **Admissions:** 1846 **Census:** 29 **Outpatient Visits:** 72892 **Births:** 204 **Total Expense ($000):** 50720 **Payroll Expense ($000):** 19920 **Personnel:** 399

Many Facility Codes have changed. Please refer to the AHA Guide Code Chart. © 2014 AHA Guide

DAMARISCOTTA—Lincoln County

★ **LINCOLN HEALTH (201302)**, 35 Miles Street, Zip 04543–4047;
tel. 207/563–1234, (Includes MILES MEMORIAL HOSPITAL, 35 Miles Street,
tel. 207/563–1234; ST. ANDREWS HOSPITAL AND HEALTHCARE CENTER, 6 St.
Andrews Lane, Boothbay Harbor, Zip 04538–1732, Mailing Address: P.O. Box
417, Zip 04538–0417; tel. 207/633–2121; James W. Donovan, President and
Chief Executive Officer), (Total facility includes 54 beds in nursing home–type unit)
A9 10 18 20 **F**3 11 13 15 29 30 32 34 35 40 43 44 45 50 57 59 64 65 67
70 75 76 79 81 85 86 87 93 96 97 107 108 110 111 114 118 119 127 128
130 132 133 135 144 146 147 148 **P**6 **S** MaineHealth, Portland, ME
Primary Contact: James W. Donovan, President and Chief Executive Officer
COO: Cynthia Leavitt, R.N., Senior Vice President, Hospital Operations
CFO: Wayne Printy, Chief Financial Officer and Senior Vice President Finance
CMO: Russell Mack, M.D., Chief Medical Officer
CIO: Brooks Betts, Vice President and Chief Information Officer
CHR: Thomas R. Girard, Vice President Human Resources
Web address: www.lchcare.org
Control: Other not–for–profit (including NFP Corporation) **Service:** General
Medical and Surgical

Staffed Beds: 111 **Admissions:** 1927 **Census:** 78 **Outpatient Visits:** 102947
Births: 113 **Total Expense ($000):** 71485 **Payroll Expense ($000):** 20512
Personnel: 482

DOVER–FOXCROFT—Piscataquis County

★ **MAYO REGIONAL HOSPITAL (201309)**, 897 West Main Street,
Zip 04426–1099; tel. 207/564–8401 **A**9 10 18 **F**3 5 7 8 11 13 15 18 28 29
30 31 34 35 38 40 45 50 57 59 64 65 70 71 75 76 77 78 79 81 85 86 87
93 96 97 99 104 107 110 111 114 119 127 128 129 130 132 133 135 146
147 148
Primary Contact: Marie E. Vienneau, FACHE, President and Chief Executive Officer
CFO: Daniel Forgues, Chief Financial Officer and Vice President Finance
CMO: Warren MacDonald, M.D., President Medical Staff
CHR: Kenneth S. Proctor, MS, Director Human Resources
CNO: Lynne Gagnon, R.N., Chief Nursing Officer
Web address: www.mayohospital.com
Control: Hospital district or authority, Government, nonfederal **Service:** General
Medical and Surgical

Staffed Beds: 25 **Admissions:** 1207 **Census:** 13 **Outpatient Visits:** 114867
Births: 110 **Total Expense ($000):** 45770 **Payroll Expense ($000):** 24408
Personnel: 393

ELLSWORTH—Hancock County

☒ **MAINE COAST MEMORIAL HOSPITAL (200050)**, 50 Union Street,
Zip 04605–1599; tel. 207/664–5311 **A**1 9 10 **F**13 15 18 26 28 29 31 34 35
40 45 51 55 57 59 61 64 65 68 70 74 75 76 77 78 79 81 84 85 93 97 107
108 111 115 119 129 130 132 133 145 146 147 148 **P**6
Primary Contact: Charles D. Therrien, Chief Executive Officer
CFO: Chris Frauenhofer, Chief Financial Officer
CMO: Sheena Whittaker, M.D., President Medical Staff
CIO: Mary Jo MacLaughlin, Director Information Systems
CHR: Karen Dickson, Director, Human Resources
Web address: www.mainehospital.org
Control: Other not–for–profit (including NFP Corporation) **Service:** General
Medical and Surgical

Staffed Beds: 48 **Admissions:** 2617 **Census:** 24 **Outpatient Visits:** 79329
Births: 312 **Total Expense ($000):** 80548 **Payroll Expense ($000):** 40701
Personnel: 516

FARMINGTON—Franklin County

☒ **FRANKLIN MEMORIAL HOSPITAL (200037)**, 111 Franklin Health Commons,
Zip 04938–6144; tel. 207/778–6031, (Nonreporting) **A**1 9 10 20
Primary Contact: Rebecca L. Arsenault, R.N., MS, President and Chief Executive
Officer
COO: Gerald Cayer, Executive Vice President and Chief Operating Officer
CFO: Wayne Bennett, Chief Financial Officer
CMO: Michael Rowland, M.D., Vice President Medical Affairs
CIO: Ralph Johnson, Chief Information Officer
CHR: Joline Hart, Vice President Human Resources
Web address: www.fchn.org
Control: Other not–for–profit (including NFP Corporation) **Service:** General
Medical and Surgical

Staffed Beds: 48

FORT FAIRFIELD—Aroostook County

COMMUNITY GENERAL HEALTH CENTER See The Aroostook Medical Center,
Presque Isle

FORT KENT—Aroostook County

☒ **NORTHERN MAINE MEDICAL CENTER (200052)**, 194 East Main Street,
Zip 04743–1497; tel. 207/834–3155, (Total facility includes 45 beds in nursing
home–type unit) **A**1 10 20 **F**13 15 28 29 31 34 40 45 54 57 59 62 64 67 68
70 75 76 77 78 79 81 82 86 87 98 99 100 101 102 103 104 107 108 111
115 119 127 128 130 131 132 135 146 147 **P**6
Primary Contact: Peter Sirois, Chief Executive Officer
CFO: Cindy Daigle, Chief Financial Officer
CMO: Michael Sullivan, M.D., Chief Medical Officer
CIO: Adam Landry, Coordinator Computer Systems
CHR: Robin Damboise, Director Human Resources
CNO: Alain Bois, R.N., Director of Nursing
Web address: www.nmmc.org
Control: Other not–for–profit (including NFP Corporation) **Service:** General
Medical and Surgical

Staffed Beds: 81 **Admissions:** 1289 **Census:** 60 **Outpatient Visits:** 51131
Births: 63 **Total Expense ($000):** 44399 **Payroll Expense ($000):** 24287
Personnel: 415

GREENVILLE—Piscataquis County

★ **CHARLES A. DEAN MEMORIAL HOSPITAL (201301)**, 364 Pritham Avenue,
Zip 04441–1395, Mailing Address: P.O. Box 1129, Zip 04441–1129;
tel. 207/695–5200, (Nonreporting) **A**10 18 **S** Eastern Maine Healthcare Systems,
Brewer, ME
Primary Contact: Geno Murray, President and Chief Executive Officer
CFO: Edward Olivier, Chief Financial Officer
CMO: Darin Peck, M.D., Chief of Staff
Web address: www.cadean.org
Control: Other not–for–profit (including NFP Corporation) **Service:** General
Medical and Surgical

Staffed Beds: 36

HOULTON—Aroostook County

★ **HOULTON REGIONAL HOSPITAL (201308)**, 20 Hartford Street,
Zip 04730–1891; tel. 207/532–9471 **A**9 10 18 **F**1 3 4 11 13 15 16 17 28 29
30 34 40 43 59 65 67 70 72 73 75 76 79 80 81 83 84 85 86 87 88 89 90
93 97 98 107 108 110 111 114 119 127 128 130 132 133 135 146 148
Primary Contact: Thomas J. Moakler, Chief Executive Officer
CHR: Vicky Moody, Director Human Resources
Web address: www.houlton.net/hrh
Control: Other not–for–profit (including NFP Corporation) **Service:** General
Medical and Surgical

Staffed Beds: 25 **Admissions:** 1277 **Census:** 23 **Outpatient Visits:** 97910
Births: 172 **Total Expense ($000):** 45219 **Payroll Expense ($000):** 21178
Personnel: 355

LEWISTON—Androscoggin County

☒ △ **CENTRAL MAINE MEDICAL CENTER (200024)**, 300 Main Street,
Zip 04240–7027; tel. 207/795–0111 **A**1 2 3 5 7 9 10 13 **F**3 11 12 13 15 18
19 20 22 24 26 28 29 30 31 32 34 35 36 40 41 43 44 45 46 47 48 49 50
51 52 53 55 57 58 59 61 64 65 66 67 68 70 71 73 74 75 76 77 78 79 81
82 84 85 86 87 89 90 91 92 93 97 102 107 108 110 114 115 118 119 120
121 123 124 129 130 131 132 135 143 146 147 148 **P**8
Primary Contact: Tina Legere, President
CFO: Philip Morissette, Chief Financial Officer
CMO: David Lauver, M.D., Chief Division Hospital Based Care
CIO: Denis Tanguay, Chief Information Officer
CHR: Kirk Miklavic, Director, Human Resources
CNO: Sharron Sieleman, R.N., VP, Nursing
Web address: www.cmmc.org
Control: Other not–for–profit (including NFP Corporation) **Service:** General
Medical and Surgical

Staffed Beds: 190 **Admissions:** 10000 **Census:** 111 **Outpatient Visits:**
752109 **Births:** 730 **Total Expense ($000):** 308920 **Payroll Expense
($000):** 130088 **Personnel:** 1695

Hospital, Medicare Provider Number, Address, Telephone, Approval, Facility, and Physician Codes, Health Care System

★ American Hospital Association (AHA) membership
☐ The Joint Commission accreditation   ◇ DNV Healthcare Inc. accreditation
○ Healthcare Facilities Accreditation Program
△ Commission on Accreditation of Rehabilitation Facilities (CARF) accreditation

ME

✠ **ST. MARY'S REGIONAL MEDICAL CENTER (200034)**, 318 Sabattus Street, Zip 04240–5553, Mailing Address: P.O. Box 291, Zip 04243–0291; tel. 207/777–8100 **A**1 2 10 **F**3 4 5 7 11 13 15 17 18 20 28 29 30 31 34 35 40 44 45 46 49 50 51 53 54 57 58 59 60 61 64 65 68 70 74 75 76 77 78 79 80 81 82 84 85 86 87 89 91 93 96 97 98 99 100 101 102 103 104 105 107 108 110 111 114 116 117 118 119 129 130 131 132 134 135 144 146 147 148 **P**1 6 **S** Covenant Health Systems, Inc., Tewksbury, MA
Primary Contact: Lee T. Myles, President and Chief Executive Officer
COO: Susan Keiler, Chief Operating Officer
CFO: Carolyn Kasabian, Chief Financial Officer
CMO: Ira Shapiro, M.D., Chief Medical Officer
CIO: Rene Dumont, Vice President Strategic Growth
CHR: Nicole Morin–Scribner, Director Human Resources
CNO: Karen Clark, Vice President Patient Care Services
Web address: www.stmarysmaine.com
Control: Other not–for–profit (including NFP Corporation) **Service:** General Medical and Surgical

Staffed Beds: 171 **Admissions:** 6032 **Census:** 82 **Outpatient Visits:** 309928 **Births:** 597 **Total Expense ($000):** 147509 **Payroll Expense ($000):** 71264 **Personnel:** 1101

LINCOLN—Penobscot County

★ **PENOBSCOT VALLEY HOSPITAL (201303)**, 7 Transalpine Road, Zip 04457–4222, Mailing Address: P.O. Box 368, Zip 04457–0368; tel. 207/794–3321 **A**10 18 **F**3 8 11 26 29 30 34 40 41 45 50 53 57 59 64 65 68 70 77 79 81 82 84 85 93 107 108 115 119 127 128 130 132 133 135 147 148 **S** QHR, Brentwood, TN
Primary Contact: Lynn W. Beasley, FACHE, Interim Chief Executive Officer
CFO: Ann Marie Rush, Chief Financial Officer
CHR: Sarah Loman, Director Human Resources
Web address: www.pvhme.org
Control: Other not–for–profit (including NFP Corporation) **Service:** General Medical and Surgical

Staffed Beds: 25 **Admissions:** 1102 **Census:** 14

MACHIAS—Washington County

★ **DOWN EAST COMMUNITY HOSPITAL (201311)**, 11 Hospital Drive, Zip 04654–3325; tel. 207/255–3356, (Total facility includes 28 beds in nursing home–type unit) **A**9 10 18 **F**3 8 13 15 28 29 34 35 40 56 57 59 63 64 65 75 77 79 81 82 83 84 85 90 93 97 107 108 110 111 119 127 128 129 130 133 146 147 148 **P**6
Primary Contact: Ralph Gabarro, Interim Chief Executive Officer
CFO: Lynnette Parr, Chief Financial Officer
CMO: Rodney Sparks, M.D., Chief Staff
CIO: Lynnette Parr, Chief Financial Officer
CHR: Ernestine O. Reisman, Vice President Human Resources
CNO: Charleen Ryan, Vice President Nursing Services
Web address: www.dech.org
Control: Other not–for–profit (including NFP Corporation) **Service:** General Medical and Surgical

Staffed Beds: 53 **Admissions:** 874 **Census:** 34 **Outpatient Visits:** 28188 **Births:** 162 **Total Expense ($000):** 36968 **Payroll Expense ($000):** 17415 **Personnel:** 236

MARS HILL—Aroostook County

AROOSTOOK HEALTH CENTER See The Aroostook Medical Center, Presque Isle

MILLINOCKET—Penobscot County

★ **MILLINOCKET REGIONAL HOSPITAL (201307)**, 200 Somerset Street, Zip 04462–1298; tel. 207/723–5161, (Nonreporting) **A**9 10 18
Primary Contact: Robert Peterson, Chief Executive Officer
CFO: Christine McLaughlin, Vice President Finance
CMO: Daniel Herbert, M.D., Medical Administrative Officer
CHR: Lisa Arsenault, Vice President Human Resources and Compliance
CNO: Jason Fugleberg, R.N., Vice President Patient Services and Chief Nursing Officer
Web address: www.mrhme.org
Control: Other not–for–profit (including NFP Corporation) **Service:** General Medical and Surgical

Staffed Beds: 25

NORWAY—Oxford County

★ **STEPHENS MEMORIAL HOSPITAL (201315)**, 181 Main Street, Zip 04268–5664; tel. 207/743–5933 **A**9 10 18 **F**3 7 13 15 28 29 30 31 34 35 40 43 45 57 59 61 64 65 68 75 76 78 79 80 81 85 89 93 96 97 102 107 108 110 111 115 119 127 130 132 146 148 **S** MaineHealth, Portland, ME
Primary Contact: Timothy A. Churchill, President
CMO: James Eshleman, D.O., President Medical Staff
CHR: Roberta Metivier, Vice President Human Resources and Administrator, Western Main Nursing Home
Web address: www.wmhcc.com
Control: Other not–for–profit (including NFP Corporation) **Service:** General Medical and Surgical

Staffed Beds: 25 **Admissions:** 1432 **Census:** 13 **Outpatient Visits:** 104094 **Births:** 166 **Total Expense ($000):** 52078 **Payroll Expense ($000):** 24065 **Personnel:** 402

PITTSFIELD—Somerset County

✠ **SEBASTICOOK VALLEY HEALTH (201313)**, 447 North Main Street, Zip 04967–3707; tel. 207/487–4000 **A**1 9 10 18 **F**7 11 15 28 29 35 40 45 50 51 57 59 64 65 70 75 78 79 81 85 87 93 96 97 107 108 111 115 118 119 127 129 130 132 133 135 143 146 147 148 **P**6 **S** Eastern Maine Healthcare Systems, Brewer, ME
Primary Contact: Terri Vieira, President and Chief Executive Officer
COO: Michael Peterson, Chief Operating Officer
CFO: Randal Clark, Vice President Finance
CMO: Robert Schlager, M.D., Chief Medical Officer
CIO: Michael Peterson, Chief Operating Officer
CHR: Tammy Hatch, Manager
Web address: www.sebasticookvalleyhealth.org
Control: Other not–for–profit (including NFP Corporation) **Service:** General Medical and Surgical

Staffed Beds: 25 **Admissions:** 679 **Census:** 9 **Births:** 0

PORTLAND—Cumberland County

✠ **MAINE MEDICAL CENTER (200009)**, 22 Bramhall Street, Zip 04102–3175; tel. 207/662–0111, (Includes BARBARA BUSH CHILDREN'S HOSPITAL, 22 Bramhall Street, Zip 04102–3134; tel. 207/662–0111; MAINE MEDICAL CENTER, BRIGHTON CAMPUS, 335 Brighton Avenue, Zip 04102–9735, Mailing Address: P.O. Box 9735, Zip 04102–9735; tel. 207/879–8000) **A**1 2 3 5 8 10 **F**3 5 6 8 11 12 13 15 17 18 19 20 21 22 23 24 25 26 27 28 29 30 31 32 34 35 36 38 40 41 42 43 44 45 46 47 48 49 50 51 52 54 55 56 57 58 59 60 61 64 65 66 68 70 72 73 74 75 76 78 79 80 81 82 84 85 86 87 88 89 91 92 97 98 99 100 101 102 103 104 105 107 108 110 111 115 117 118 119 120 121 123 124 126 129 130 131 132 134 135 138 141 144 146 147 148 **P**4 6 8 **S** MaineHealth, Portland, ME
Primary Contact: Richard W. Petersen, President and Chief Executive Officer
COO: Jeff Sanders, Chief Operating Officer
CFO: Lou Inzana, Senior Vice President and Chief Financial Officer
CMO: Peter Bates, M.D., Vice President Medical Affairs and Chief Medical Officer
CIO: Barry Blumenfeld, M.D., Chief Information Officer
CHR: Judith M. West, Senior Vice President Human Resources and Chief Human Resources Officer
Web address: www.mmc.org
Control: Other not–for–profit (including NFP Corporation) **Service:** General Medical and Surgical

Staffed Beds: 637 **Admissions:** 27430 **Census:** 384 **Outpatient Visits:** 514391 **Births:** 1823 **Total Expense ($000):** 911047 **Payroll Expense ($000):** 376015 **Personnel:** 5634

✠ **MERCY HOSPITAL OF PORTLAND (200008)**, 144 State Street, Zip 04101–3795; tel. 207/879–3000, (Data for 273 days) **A**1 2 10 **F**3 4 5 11 13 15 18 20 26 29 30 31 34 35 36 40 44 45 48 49 50 51 54 55 56 57 58 59 61 64 68 70 72 74 75 76 77 78 79 81 82 84 86 87 93 96 97 100 102 107 108 110 111 114 115 117 119 130 132 135 143 144 146 147 148 **P**6 **S** Eastern Maine Healthcare Systems, Brewer, ME
Primary Contact: Eileen F. Skinner, FACHE, President and Chief Executive Officer
COO: Robert Nutter, Chief Operating Officer, Vice President of Human Resources and Support Services
CFO: Michael Hachey, Senior Vice President and Chief Financial Officer
CMO: Scott Rusk, M.D., Vice President Medical Administration
CIO: Craig Dreher, Chief Information Officer
CHR: Elizabeth B. Christensen, Director Human Resources
CNO: Bette Neville, R.N., Vice President and Chief Nursing Officer
Web address: www.mercyhospital.org
Control: Church–operated, Nongovernment, not–for profit **Service:** General Medical and Surgical

Staffed Beds: 148 **Admissions:** 5514 **Census:** 69 **Outpatient Visits:** 268557 **Births:** 631 **Total Expense ($000):** 165139 **Payroll Expense ($000):** 74407 **Personnel:** 1007

Many Facility Codes have changed. Please refer to the AHA Guide Code Chart. © 2014 AHA Guide

✖ **NEW ENGLAND REHABILITATION HOSPITAL OF PORTLAND (203025)**, 335 Brighton Avenue, Zip 04102–2363; tel. 207/775–4000 **A**1 10 **F**29 34 35 75 79 82 90 93 95 96 131 132 135 146 **S** HEALTHSOUTH Corporation, Birmingham, AL
Primary Contact: Jeanine Chesley, Chief Executive Officer
CMO: Elissa Charbonneau, D.O., Medical Director
CHR: Leigh Baade, Director Human Resources
Web address: www.nerhp.org
Control: Partnership, Investor–owned, for–profit **Service:** Rehabilitation

> **Staffed Beds:** 90 **Admissions:** 1906 **Census:** 74 **Outpatient Visits:** 13277 **Births:** 0 **Total Expense ($000):** 22936 **Payroll Expense ($000):** 13914 **Personnel:** 233

PRESQUE ISLE—Aroostook County

✖ **THE AROOSTOOK MEDICAL CENTER (200018)**, 140 Academy Street, Zip 04769–3171, Mailing Address: P.O. Box 151, Zip 04769–0151; tel. 207/768–4000, (Includes AROOSTOOK HEALTH CENTER, 15 Highland Avenue, Mars Hill, Zip 04758; tel. 207/768–4900; ARTHUR R. GOULD MEMORIAL HOSPITAL, 140 Academy Street, Zip 04769, Mailing Address: P.O. Box 151, Zip 04769; tel. 207/768–4000; COMMUNITY GENERAL HEALTH CENTER, 3 Green Street, Fort Fairfield, Zip 04742; tel. 207/768–4700), (Total facility includes 64 beds in nursing home–type unit) **A**1 10 **F**3 7 8 12 13 15 18 20 28 29 30 31 32 34 35 36 38 40 45 50 51 52 53 54 56 57 59 60 61 63 64 65 67 68 69 70 74 75 76 77 78 79 80 81 82 84 85 86 87 89 90 91 92 93 96 97 99 104 107 108 110 114 115 118 119 121 123 128 129 130 131 132 134 135 143 146 147 148 **P**6 **S** Eastern Maine Healthcare Systems, Brewer, ME
Primary Contact: Sylvia Getman, President and Chief Executive Officer
COO: Jay Reynolds, M.D., Chief Medical Officer and Chief Clinical Officer
CFO: C. Bruce Sandstrom, Vice President and Chief Financial Officer
CMO: Jay Reynolds, M.D., Chief Medical Officer and Chief Clinical Officer
CIO: Kyle Johnson, Chief Information Officer
CHR: Joseph Siddiqui, Vice President Human Resources
CNO: Roland Eugene Joy, Jr., Vice President and Chief Nursing Officer
Web address: www.tamc.org
Control: Other not–for–profit (including NFP Corporation) **Service:** General Medical and Surgical

> **Staffed Beds:** 122 **Admissions:** 2187 **Census:** 80 **Outpatient Visits:** 180884 **Births:** 202 **Total Expense ($000):** 104253 **Payroll Expense ($000):** 56455 **Personnel:** 773

ROCKPORT—Knox County

✖ **PEN BAY MEDICAL CENTER (200063)**, 6 Glen Cove Drive, Zip 04856–4240; tel. 207/596–8000, (Total facility includes 84 beds in nursing home–type unit) **A**1 2 10 20 **F**3 4 5 6 13 15 17 18 28 29 30 31 32 34 35 40 43 45 51 58 59 61 64 65 67 70 74 75 76 77 78 79 81 82 83 85 86 87 89 93 97 98 100 107 114 118 119 128 129 130 131 132 134 135 144 146 147 148 **P**1 **S** MaineHealth, Portland, ME
Primary Contact: Mark A. Biscone, Interim Chief Executive Officer
COO: Eric Waters, Vice President Operations
CFO: Maura Kelly, Vice President Fiscal Services
CMO: Dana L. Goldsmith, M.D., Vice President Medical Affairs
CIO: Brooks Betts, Director Information Systems and Chief Information Officer
CHR: Thomas R. Girard, Vice President Human Resources
Web address: www.penbayhealthcare.org
Control: Other not–for–profit (including NFP Corporation) **Service:** General Medical and Surgical

> **Staffed Beds:** 165 **Admissions:** 3967 **Census:** 129 **Outpatient Visits:** 155970 **Births:** 325 **Total Expense ($000):** 121933 **Payroll Expense ($000):** 56224 **Personnel:** 870

PENOBSCOT BAY MEDICAL CENTER See Pen Bay Medical Center

RUMFORD—Oxford County

★ **RUMFORD HOSPITAL (201306)**, 420 Franklin Street, Zip 04276–2145; tel. 207/369–1000 **A**9 10 18 **F**3 8 11 13 15 18 28 29 30 31 34 35 38 40 45 50 53 57 59 64 65 70 75 76 77 78 79 81 85 87 89 93 94 97 98 107 110 114 117 121 128 130 132 133 146 148 **P**6 8
Primary Contact: R. David Frum, President
CNO: Becky Hall, R.N., Director Nursing
Web address: www.rumfordhospital.org
Control: Other not–for–profit (including NFP Corporation) **Service:** General Medical and Surgical

> **Staffed Beds:** 21 **Admissions:** 1031 **Census:** 15 **Outpatient Visits:** 80555 **Births:** 99 **Total Expense ($000):** 33988 **Payroll Expense ($000):** 13738 **Personnel:** 241

SKOWHEGAN—Somerset County

★ **REDINGTON–FAIRVIEW GENERAL HOSPITAL (201314)**, Fairview Avenue, Zip 04976, Mailing Address: P.O. Box 468, Zip 04976–0468; tel. 207/474–5121 **A**9 10 18 **F**3 7 11 13 15 18 28 29 30 31 34 35 40 50 53 56 57 59 65 68 70 74 75 76 77 78 79 81 82 85 92 93 97 107 108 110 114 115 118 119 130 131 132 134 135 146 147 **P**6
Primary Contact: Richard Willett, Chief Executive Officer
CFO: Dana Kempton, Associate Director and Chief Financial Officer
CMO: Michael Lambke, M.D., Medical Director
CHR: Deborah Buckingham, R.N., Director Human Resources
CNO: Sherry L. Rogers, MS, Chief Nursing Officer
Web address: www.rfgh.net
Control: Other not–for–profit (including NFP Corporation) **Service:** General Medical and Surgical

> **Staffed Beds:** 25 **Admissions:** 1568 **Census:** 14 **Outpatient Visits:** 78214 **Births:** 156 **Total Expense ($000):** 73195 **Payroll Expense ($000):** 36718 **Personnel:** 516

WATERVILLE—Kennebec County

★ ○ **INLAND HOSPITAL (200041)**, 200 Kennedy Memorial Drive, Zip 04901–4595; tel. 207/861–3000 **A**9 10 11 **F**3 13 15 18 28 29 30 34 35 36 40 45 48 50 51 54 57 59 64 65 68 70 74 75 76 79 81 82 83 85 86 89 93 97 107 108 110 111 115 118 119 127 129 132 135 144 146 147 148 **S** Eastern Maine Healthcare Systems, Brewer, ME
Primary Contact: John Dalton, President and Chief Executive Officer
COO: Daniel Booth, Vice President Operations and Chief Human Resources Officer
CFO: Dean Bither, Chief Financial Officer
CMO: Michael Palumbo, D.O., Vice President Medical Affairs and Chief Education
CIO: Kevin Dieterich, Director Information Services
CHR: Daniel Booth, Vice President Operations
Web address: www.inlandhospital.org
Control: Other not–for–profit (including NFP Corporation) **Service:** General Medical and Surgical

> **Staffed Beds:** 26 **Admissions:** 1251 **Census:** 12 **Outpatient Visits:** 87080 **Births:** 350 **Total Expense ($000):** 66416 **Payroll Expense ($000):** 29260 **Personnel:** 497

WESTBROOK—Cumberland County

✖ **SPRING HARBOR HOSPITAL (204005)**, 123 Andover Road, Zip 04092–3850; tel. 207/761–2200 **A**1 10 **F**5 50 59 68 75 77 80 87 98 99 101 130 132 135 146 **S** MaineHealth, Portland, ME
Primary Contact: Dennis P. King, Chief Executive Officer
COO: Mary Jane Krebs, Senior Vice President Intensive Services and Chief Administrative Officer
CFO: Michael Abbatiello, Chief Financial Officer
CMO: Girard Robinson, M.D., Senior Vice President Medical and Clinical Affairs
CIO: Susan Moulton, Interim Director Health Information Management
CHR: Timothy McNulty, Director Human Resources
Web address: www.springharbor.org
Control: Other not–for–profit (including NFP Corporation) **Service:** Psychiatric

> **Staffed Beds:** 88 **Admissions:** 2367 **Census:** 74 **Outpatient Visits:** 1327 **Births:** 0 **Total Expense ($000):** 30927 **Payroll Expense ($000):** 16654 **Personnel:** 317

YORK—York County

★ **YORK HOSPITAL (200020)**, 15 Hospital Drive, Zip 03909–1099; tel. 207/363–4321 **A**2 9 10 **F**3 5 8 11 13 15 17 18 20 22 26 28 29 30 31 32 34 36 40 42 43 45 48 49 50 53 54 56 57 59 62 64 65 69 70 71 74 75 76 77 78 79 81 85 87 89 92 93 96 97 100 103 104 107 108 110 111 112 114 119 129 130 131 132 135 143 144 146 148 **P**6
Primary Contact: Jud Knox, President
COO: Stephen Pelletier, Leader Guest Services
CFO: Robin LaBonte, Leader Financial Care
CMO: Lawrence Petrovich, M.D., Chief Medical Officer
CIO: Robin LaBonte, Leader Financial Care
CHR: Olivia Chayer, Lead Human Resources
CNO: Kathy Lane, Leader–ICU, Home Care, MedSurg
Web address: www.yorkhospital.com
Control: Other not–for–profit (including NFP Corporation) **Service:** General Medical and Surgical

> **Staffed Beds:** 79 **Admissions:** 3448 **Census:** 38 **Outpatient Visits:** 321206 **Births:** 328 **Total Expense ($000):** 150104 **Payroll Expense ($000):** 71000 **Personnel:** 1062

Hospital, Medicare Provider Number, Address, Telephone, Approval, Facility, and Physician Codes, Health Care System

★ American Hospital Association (AHA) membership
□ The Joint Commission accreditation ◇ DNV Healthcare Inc. accreditation
○ Healthcare Facilities Accreditation Program
△ Commission on Accreditation of Rehabilitation Facilities (CARF) accreditation

MARYLAND

ANNAPOLIS—Anne Arundel County

✠ **ANNE ARUNDEL MEDICAL CENTER (210023)**, 2001 Medical Parkway, Zip 21401–3019; tel. 443/481–1000, (Total facility includes 40 beds in nursing home–type unit) **A**1 2 5 9 10 **F**3 4 5 6 9 11 12 13 14 15 18 20 22 26 28 29 30 31 32 34 35 36 37 38 39 40 41 44 45 46 49 50 51 53 54 55 56 57 58 59 60 61 63 64 65 66 68 70 71 72 74 75 76 77 78 79 81 82 83 84 85 86 87 89 91 92 93 94 96 97 100 101 102 103 105 107 108 110 111 114 115 116 117 118 119 120 121 123 124 126 129 130 131 132 134 135 145 146 147 148 **P**1 6 7
Primary Contact: Victoria Bayless, President and Chief Executive Officer
COO: Sherry Perkins, Ph.D., Chief Operating Officer and Chief Nursing Officer
CFO: Robert Reilly, Vice President and Chief Financial Officer
CMO: Mitchell Schwartz, M.D., Chief Medical Officer
CIO: Barbara Baldwin, Chief Information Officer
CHR: Julie McGovern, Vice President Human Resources
Web address: www.aahs.org
Control: Other not–for–profit (including NFP Corporation) **Service:** General Medical and Surgical

Staffed Beds: 450 **Admissions:** 28600 **Census:** 282 **Outpatient Visits:** 493550 **Births:** 5297 **Total Expense ($000):** 494091 **Payroll Expense ($000):** 186518 **Personnel:** 3352

BALTIMORE—Baltimore City County

✠ **BON SECOURS BALTIMORE HEALTH SYSTEM (210013)**, 2000 West Baltimore Street, Zip 21223–1558; tel. 410/362–3000 **A**1 9 10 **F**3 11 15 18 20 26 29 30 31 40 44 49 58 59 60 64 66 70 78 79 81 84 85 87 98 99 100 101 102 103 104 105 107 108 110 111 115 119 130 143 146 148 **P**6
S Bon Secours Health System, Inc., Marriottsville, MD
Primary Contact: Samuel Lee Ross, M.D., MS, Chief Executive Officer
CFO: Richard Jones, Chief Financial Officer
CMO: Sidney Mir, M.D., Vice President Medical Affairs and Chief Medical Officer
CIO: Sanjay Purushotham, Executive Director Information Systems
CNO: Lesia Douglas, R.N., Vice President Patient Care Services and Chief Nurse Executive
Web address: www.bonsecoursbaltimore.com
Control: Church–operated, Nongovernment, not–for profit **Service:** General Medical and Surgical

Staffed Beds: 93 **Admissions:** 5842 **Census:** 72 **Outpatient Visits:** 390661 **Births:** 0 **Total Expense ($000):** 127713 **Payroll Expense ($000):** 49126 **Personnel:** 670

FRANKLIN SQUARE HOSPITAL CENTER See MedStar Franklin Square Medical Center

GOOD SAMARITAN HOSPITAL OF MARYLAND See MedStar Good Samaritan Hospital

✠ **GREATER BALTIMORE MEDICAL CENTER (210044)**, 6701 North Charles Street, Zip 21204–6892; tel. 443/849–2000, (Total facility includes 24 beds in nursing home–type unit) **A**1 2 3 5 9 10 **F**3 8 11 12 13 18 20 22 26 29 30 31 34 35 40 41 44 45 46 47 48 49 50 51 55 56 57 58 59 60 61 63 66 68 70 72 73 74 75 76 77 78 79 81 82 83 84 85 86 87 89 92 96 97 102 107 108 114 115 119 120 121 123 124 126 128 129 130 132 135 136 142 145 146 147 148 **P**4
Primary Contact: John B. Chessare, M.D., M.P.H., FACHE, President and Chief Executive Officer
COO: Keith R. Poisson, Executive Vice President and Chief Operating Officer
CFO: Eric L. Melchior, Executive Vice President and Chief Financial Officer
CMO: John R. Saunders, M.D., Senior Vice President Medical Affairs and Chief Medical Officer
CIO: Tanya Townsend, Chief Information Officer
CHR: Deloris Simpson–Tuggle, Vice President Human Resources and Organizational Development and Chief Human Resources Officer
CNO: Jody Porter, R.N., Senior Vice President Patient Care Services and Chief Nursing Officer
Web address: www.gbmc.org
Control: Other not–for–profit (including NFP Corporation) **Service:** General Medical and Surgical

Staffed Beds: 270 **Admissions:** 16898 **Census:** 199 **Outpatient Visits:** 80184 **Births:** 3976 **Total Expense ($000):** 379063 **Payroll Expense ($000):** 179904 **Personnel:** 3042

HARBOR HOSPITAL See MedStar Harbor Hospital

✠ **JOHNS HOPKINS BAYVIEW MEDICAL CENTER (210029)**, 4940 Eastern Avenue, Zip 21224–2780; tel. 410/550–0100, (Total facility includes 124 beds in nursing home–type unit) **A**1 2 3 5 8 9 10 **F**2 3 4 5 6 8 9 11 12 13 15 16 17 18 20 22 26 28 29 30 31 32 34 35 36 38 40 41 43 44 45 46 47 48 49 50 51 54 56 57 58 59 60 61 64 65 66 68 70 71 72 74 75 76 77 78 79 80 81 84 85 86 87 89 90 92 93 94 97 98 99 100 101 102 103 104 105 107 110 111 114 115 116 118 119 120 126 128 129 130 131 132 134 135 141 143 146 147 148 **S** Johns Hopkins Health System, Baltimore, MD
Primary Contact: Richard G. Bennett, M.D., President
COO: Charlie Reuland, Sc.D., Executive Vice President and Chief Operating Officer
CFO: Carl H. Francioli, Vice President Finance
CIO: Sandy Reckert, Director Communications and Public Affairs
CHR: Craig R. Brodian, Vice President Human Resources
Web address: www.hopkinsbayview.org
Control: Other not–for–profit (including NFP Corporation) **Service:** General Medical and Surgical

Staffed Beds: 504 **Admissions:** 22013 **Census:** 375 **Outpatient Visits:** 434765 **Births:** 1506 **Total Expense ($000):** 433014 **Payroll Expense ($000):** 147516 **Personnel:** 3217

✠ △ **JOHNS HOPKINS HOSPITAL (210009)**, 600 North Wolfe Street, Zip 21287–2182; tel. 410/955–5000, (Includes JOHNS HOPKINS CHILDREN'S CENTER, 600 North Wolfe Street, Zip 21287–0005; tel. 410/955–5000) **A**1 2 3 5 7 8 9 10 **F**3 5 6 7 8 9 11 13 14 15 16 17 18 19 20 21 22 23 24 25 26 27 28 29 30 31 32 34 35 36 38 39 40 41 43 44 45 46 47 48 49 50 51 52 54 55 56 57 58 59 60 61 63 64 65 66 68 70 72 74 75 76 77 78 79 80 81 82 83 84 85 86 87 88 89 90 92 93 94 96 97 98 99 100 101 102 103 104 105 107 108 110 111 112 114 115 116 117 118 119 120 121 123 124 126 129 130 131 132 134 135 136 137 138 139 140 141 142 143 145 146 147 148 **S** Johns Hopkins Health System, Baltimore, MD
Primary Contact: Ronald R. Peterson, President
COO: Judy A. Reitz, Sc.D., Executive Vice President and Chief Operating Officer
CFO: Ronald J. Werthman, Senior Vice President Finance, Chief Financial Officer and Treasurer
CMO: Redonda G. Miller, M.D., Vice President Medical Affairs
CIO: Stephanie L. Reel, Senior Vice President Information Services
CHR: Bonnie Windsor, Senior Vice President Human Resources
CNO: Karen B. Haller, Ph.D., Vice President Nursing and Patient Care Services
Web address: www.hopkinsmedicine.org
Control: Other not–for–profit (including NFP Corporation) **Service:** General Medical and Surgical

Staffed Beds: 986 **Admissions:** 47864 **Census:** 825 **Outpatient Visits:** 577906 **Births:** 1986 **Total Expense ($000):** 1897158 **Payroll Expense ($000):** 555013 **Personnel:** 9619

☐ △ **KENNEDY KRIEGER INSTITUTE (213301)**, 707 North Broadway, Zip 21205–1890; tel. 443/923–9200, (Nonreporting) **A**1 3 5 7 9 10
Primary Contact: Gary W. Goldstein, M.D., President and Chief Executive Officer
COO: James M. Anders, Jr., Administrator and Chief Operating Officer
CFO: Michael J. Neuman, Vice President Finance
CMO: Michael V. Johnston, M.D., Chief Medical Officer and Senior Vice President Medical Programs
CIO: Kenneth Davis, Assistant Vice President Information Systems
CHR: Michael Loughran, Vice President Human Resources
Web address: www.kennedykrieger.org
Control: Other not–for–profit (including NFP Corporation) **Service:** Children's other specialty

Staffed Beds: 70

☐ △ **LEVINDALE HEBREW GERIATRIC CENTER AND HOSPITAL (210064)**, 2434 West Belvedere Avenue, Zip 21215–5267; tel. 410/601–2400, (Total facility includes 361 beds in nursing home–type unit) **A**1 7 9 10 **F**1 2 11 29 30 50 56 60 67 68 69 82 84 87 90 93 103 104 105 128 130 132 146 148 **P**6 **S** LifeBridge Health, Baltimore, MD
Primary Contact: Barry Eisenberg, FACHE, Chief Operating Officer and Executive Director
CMO: Susan M. Levy, M.D., Vice President Medical Affairs
CIO: Tressa Springmann, Vice President and Chief Information Officer
CHR: Cheryl T. Boyer, Vice President Human Resources
CNO: Candy Hamner, Vice President and Chief Nursing Officer
Web address: www.sinai–balt.com
Control: Other not–for–profit (including NFP Corporation) **Service:** Long–Term Acute Care hospital

Staffed Beds: 490 **Admissions:** 2158 **Census:** 430 **Outpatient Visits:** 23759 **Births:** 0 **Total Expense ($000):** 92705 **Payroll Expense ($000):** 40711 **Personnel:** 862

Many Facility Codes have changed. Please refer to the AHA Guide Code Chart.   © 2014 AHA Guide

✠ **MEDSTAR FRANKLIN SQUARE MEDICAL CENTER (210015)**, 9000 Franklin Square Drive, Zip 21237–3901; tel. 443/777-7000 **A**1 2 3 5 8 9 10 **F**3 5 11 12 13 14 15 18 20 22 26 28 29 30 31 32 33 34 35 36 37 38 39 40 41 44 45 46 47 48 49 50 51 55 56 57 58 59 60 61 64 65 66 68 70 71 72 74 75 76 77 78 79 81 82 85 86 87 89 92 93 94 97 98 99 100 101 102 103 104 107 108 109 110 111 115 118 119 126 129 130 131 132 134 135 145 146 147 148 **P**6 **S** MedStar Health, Columbia, MD
Primary Contact: Samuel E. Moskowitz, President
CFO: Robert P. Lally, Jr., Vice President Finance
CMO: Tony Sclama, M.D., Vice President Medical Affairs
CIO: Stephen Mannion, Assistant Vice President Information Systems Customer Service
CHR: Karen Robertson–Keck, Vice President Human Resources
CNO: Lawrence F. Strassner III, Ph.D., Senior Vice President Operations and Chief Nursing Officer
Web address: www.medstarfranklin.org
Control: Other not–for–profit (including NFP Corporation) **Service:** General Medical and Surgical

Staffed Beds: 385 **Admissions:** 21907 **Census:** 261 **Outpatient Visits:** 478614 **Births:** 2493 **Total Expense ($000):** 455380 **Payroll Expense ($000):** 197647 **Personnel:** 2965

✠ △ **MEDSTAR GOOD SAMARITAN HOSPITAL (210056)**, 5601 Loch Raven Boulevard, Zip 21239–2995; tel. 443/444–8000, (Total facility includes 30 beds in nursing home–type unit) **A**1 2 3 5 7 9 10 **F**3 9 11 14 15 17 18 20 26 28 29 30 31 34 35 36 37 38 40 44 45 50 51 53 55 56 57 58 59 60 61 64 65 66 68 70 74 75 77 78 79 80 81 82 84 85 86 87 90 91 93 96 97 99 100 101 102 103 104 107 108 110 111 114 118 119 121 124 128 129 130 131 132 135 146 148 **P**6 **S** MedStar Health, Columbia, MD
Primary Contact: Jeffrey A. Matton, President
CFO: Deana Stout, Vice President Financial Services
Web address: www.goodsam–md.org
Control: Other not–for–profit (including NFP Corporation) **Service:** General Medical and Surgical

Staffed Beds: 308 **Admissions:** 14103 **Census:** 209 **Outpatient Visits:** 156973 **Births:** 0 **Total Expense ($000):** 314560 **Payroll Expense ($000):** 130256 **Personnel:** 1895

✠ **MEDSTAR HARBOR HOSPITAL (210034)**, 3001 South Hanover Street, Zip 21225–1290; tel. 410/350–3200 **A**1 2 3 5 9 10 **F**3 9 11 13 14 15 18 20 26 29 30 31 34 35 36 40 44 45 46 48 49 50 51 53 55 56 57 58 59 60 61 64 65 66 68 70 72 74 75 76 77 78 79 81 82 84 85 86 87 89 92 93 94 97 102 103 107 108 110 111 114 119 120 121 129 130 131 132 135 146 147 **P**6 **S** MedStar Health, Columbia, MD
Primary Contact: Dennis W. Pullin, FACHE, President
COO: Jill Donaldson, Vice President Operations
CFO: David R. Pitman, Vice President Finance
CMO: Allan Birenberg, Vice President Medical Affairs
CIO: Cynthia Tanebaum, Director Information Services
CHR: Karen Evelius, Director Human Resources
CNO: Lenora Addison, Vice President Patient Care and Nursing
Web address: www.harborhospital.org
Control: Other not–for–profit (including NFP Corporation) **Service:** General Medical and Surgical

Staffed Beds: 213 **Admissions:** 8874 **Census:** 100 **Outpatient Visits:** 189890 **Births:** 1436 **Total Expense ($000):** 198343 **Payroll Expense ($000):** 81189 **Personnel:** 1114

✠ △ **MEDSTAR UNION MEMORIAL HOSPITAL (210024)**, 201 East University Parkway, Zip 21218–2895; tel. 410/554–2000 **A**1 2 3 5 7 9 10 **F**3 5 8 9 11 14 15 17 18 20 22 24 26 28 29 30 31 34 35 37 38 39 40 41 43 44 45 46 47 48 49 50 51 52 53 54 55 56 57 58 59 60 61 63 64 65 66 68 70 74 75 77 78 79 80 81 82 84 85 86 87 89 90 91 92 93 94 96 97 98 100 101 102 103 104 105 107 108 110 111 114 115 118 119 120 121 123 129 130 131 132 135 142 146 148 **P**6 **S** MedStar Health, Columbia, MD
Primary Contact: Bradley Chambers, President
COO: Neil MacDonald, Vice President Operations
CFO: Joseph B. Smith, Vice President Finance
CMO: Stuart Bell, M.D., Vice President Medical Affairs
CIO: Janet Decker, Assistant Vice President
CHR: Linda Layman, Director Human Resources
CNO: Sharon A. Bottcher, R.N., Vice President Patient Care Services
Web address: www.medstarunionmemorial.org
Control: Other not–for–profit (including NFP Corporation) **Service:** General Medical and Surgical

Staffed Beds: 246 **Admissions:** 14044 **Census:** 162 **Outpatient Visits:** 165656 **Births:** 0 **Total Expense ($000):** 410098 **Payroll Expense ($000):** 166182 **Personnel:** 2062

✠ **MERCY MEDICAL CENTER (210008)**, 301 St. Paul Place, Zip 21202–2165; tel. 410/332–9000 **A**1 2 3 5 8 9 10 **F**3 4 8 11 13 14 15 17 18 20 29 30 31 34 35 36 37 39 40 41 44 45 46 47 48 49 50 51 55 57 58 59 64 65 66 68 70 72 74 75 76 77 78 79 81 82 85 86 87 89 92 93 94 100 102 107 108 110 111 114 115 116 117 118 119 120 121 123 124 126 128 129 130 132 135 141 142 143 144 145 146 147 148 **P**6
Primary Contact: Thomas R. Mullen, President and Chief Executive Officer
COO: Susan D. Finlayson, R.N., Senior Vice President of Operations
CFO: Justin Deibel, Senior Vice President and Chief Financial Officer
CMO: Scott A. Spier, M.D., Senior Vice President Medical Affairs
CIO: Kathleen Perry, Senior Vice President and Chief Information Officer
CHR: Tammy Janus, Senior Vice President Human Resources
CNO: Kim Bushnell, R.N., Chief Nursing Officer
Web address: www.mdmercy.com
Control: Church–operated, Nongovernment, not–for profit **Service:** General Medical and Surgical

Staffed Beds: 288 **Admissions:** 17219 **Census:** 199 **Outpatient Visits:** 316728 **Births:** 2966 **Total Expense ($000):** 430501 **Payroll Expense ($000):** 152423 **Personnel:** 3490

✠ △ **MT. WASHINGTON PEDIATRIC HOSPITAL (213300)**, 1708 West Rogers Avenue, Zip 21209–4545; tel. 410/578–8600, (Nonreporting) **A**1 3 5 7 9 10 **S** University of Maryland Medical System, Baltimore, MD
Primary Contact: Sheldon J. Stein, President and Chief Executive Officer
CFO: Mary Miller, Vice President Finance and Business Development
CMO: Richard Katz, M.D., Vice President Medical Affairs
CIO: Tim Brady, Director Information Systems
CHR: Thomas J. Ellis, Vice President Human Resources
Web address: www.mwph.org
Control: Other not–for–profit (including NFP Corporation) **Service:** Children's other specialty

Staffed Beds: 70

✠ **SAINT AGNES HOSPITAL (210011)**, 900 Caton Avenue, Zip 21229–5201; tel. 410/368–6000 **A**1 2 3 5 9 10 **F**3 8 11 12 13 14 15 17 18 20 22 26 28 29 30 31 32 34 35 40 41 44 46 49 50 53 54 55 56 57 58 59 60 61 64 65 68 70 72 74 75 76 77 78 79 81 82 84 85 86 87 88 89 92 93 96 97 102 103 107 108 110 111 114 115 117 118 119 120 121 123 124 129 130 131 132 134 135 144 146 147 148 **P**6 **S** Ascension Health, Saint Louis, MO
Primary Contact: Bonnie Phipps, President and Chief Executive Officer
CFO: Scott Furniss, Senior Vice President and Chief Financial Officer
CMO: Adrian Long, M.D., Executive Vice President and Chief Medical Officer
CIO: William Greskovich, Chief Information Officer
CHR: James Bobbitt, Vice President Human Resources
CNO: Yolanda Copeland, R.N., Senior Vice President and Chief Nursing Officer
Web address: www.stagnes.org
Control: Church–operated, Nongovernment, not–for profit **Service:** General Medical and Surgical

Staffed Beds: 339 **Admissions:** 17932 **Census:** 205 **Outpatient Visits:** 512375 **Births:** 1864 **Total Expense ($000):** 386454 **Payroll Expense ($000):** 198232 **Personnel:** 2502

☐ **SHEPPARD PRATT HEALTH SYSTEM (214000)**, 6501 North Charles Street, Zip 21204–6819, Mailing Address: P.O. Box 6815, Zip 21285–6815; tel. 410/938–3000 **A**1 3 5 9 10 **F**10 30 35 38 56 58 64 75 87 98 99 101 103 104 105 106 130 132 143 144 146
Primary Contact: Steven S. Sharfstein, M.D., President and Chief Executive Officer
CFO: Gerald Noll, Vice President and Chief Financial Officer
CMO: Robert Roca, M.D., Vice President Medical Affairs
CIO: Greg Merkle, Director Information Systems
CHR: Cathy Doughty, Vice President Human Resources
CNO: Ernestine Y. Cosby, Vice President Clinical Services and Chief Nursing Officer
Web address: www.sheppardpratt.org
Control: Other not–for–profit (including NFP Corporation) **Service:** Psychiatric

Staffed Beds: 333 **Admissions:** 9683 **Census:** 281 **Outpatient Visits:** 41350 **Births:** 0 **Total Expense ($000):** 186820 **Payroll Expense ($000):** 96351 **Personnel:** 2060

Hospital, Medicare Provider Number, Address, Telephone, Approval, Facility, and Physician Codes, Health Care System

★ American Hospital Association (AHA) membership
☐ The Joint Commission accreditation
◇ DNV Healthcare Inc. accreditation
○ Healthcare Facilities Accreditation Program
△ Commission on Accreditation of Rehabilitation Facilities (CARF) accreditation

✠ △ **SINAI HOSPITAL OF BALTIMORE (210012)**, 2401 West Belvedere Avenue, Zip 21215–5271; tel. 410/601–9000 **A**1 3 5 7 9 10 **F**3 5 6 8 9 11 12 13 15 17 18 19 20 22 24 26 28 29 30 31 32 34 35 36 38 39 40 41 43 44 45 46 47 48 49 50 55 56 57 58 59 60 61 64 65 66 68 70 72 73 74 75 76 77 78 79 81 82 85 86 87 88 89 90 92 93 94 95 96 97 98 100 101 102 103 104 105 107 108 110 111 114 115 117 118 119 120 121 123 124 126 129 130 132 134 135 143 146 147 **P**6 **S** LifeBridge Health, Baltimore, MD
Primary Contact: Amy Perry, President
CFO: David Krajewski, Senior Vice President and Chief Financial Officer
CMO: Daniel C. Silverman, M.D., Vice President and Chief Medical Officer
CIO: Karen Barker, Vice President and Chief Information Officer
CHR: Cheryl T. Boyer, Vice President Human Resources
CNO: Diane Johnson, R.N., Vice President Patient Care Services and Chief Nursing Officer
Web address: www.lifebridgehealth.org
Control: Other not–for–profit (including NFP Corporation) **Service:** General Medical and Surgical

Staffed Beds: 434 **Admissions:** 25871 **Census:** 349 **Outpatient Visits:** 183029 **Births:** 2188 **Total Expense ($000):** 680646 **Payroll Expense ($000):** 301301 **Personnel:** 4069

☐ **SPRING GROVE HOSPITAL CENTER (214018)**, 55 Wade Avenue, Zip 21228–4663; tel. 410/402–6000, (Nonreporting) **A**1 3 5 9 10
Primary Contact: David S. Helsel, M.D., Chief Executive Officer
CFO: Edward Swartz, Chief Financial Officer
CMO: Kelly Phillips, M.D., Clinical Director and Chief Staff
Web address: www.springgrove.com
Control: State–Government, nonfederal **Service:** Psychiatric

Staffed Beds: 425

UNION MEMORIAL HOSPITAL See MedStar Union Memorial Hospital

✠ **UNIVERSITY OF MARYLAND MEDICAL CENTER (210002)**, 22 South Greene Street, Zip 21201–1595; tel. 410/328–8667, (Includes UNIVERSITY OF MARYLAND HOSPITAL FOR CHILDREN, 22 South Greene Street, Zip 21201–1544; tel. 800/492–5538) **A**1 2 3 5 8 9 10 **F**3 4 5 6 7 9 11 12 13 14 15 16 17 18 19 20 21 22 23 24 25 26 27 28 29 30 31 32 33 34 35 36 38 39 40 41 43 44 45 46 47 48 49 50 51 52 54 55 56 57 58 59 60 61 64 65 66 67 68 70 71 72 73 74 75 76 77 78 79 80 81 82 84 85 86 87 88 89 90 92 93 94 97 98 99 100 101 102 103 104 105 106 107 108 109 110 111 114 115 116 117 118 119 120 121 123 124 126 129 130 131 132 134 135 136 137 138 139 140 141 142 143 144 145 146 147 148 **P**6 **S** University of Maryland Medical System, Baltimore, MD
Primary Contact: Jeffrey A. Rivest, FACHE, President and Chief Executive Officer
CFO: Keith D. Persinger, Senior Vice President Finance and Chief Financial Officer
CMO: Jonathan Gottlieb, M.D., Senior Vice President and Chief Medical Officer
CIO: Jon P. Burns, Chief Information Officer
CHR: R. Keith Allen, Senior Vice President Human Resources
CNO: Lisa Rowen, R.N., Senior Vice President and Chief Nursing Officer
Web address: www.umm.edu
Control: Other not–for–profit (including NFP Corporation) **Service:** General Medical and Surgical

Staffed Beds: 718 **Admissions:** 34952 **Census:** 604 **Outpatient Visits:** 273080 **Births:** 1569 **Total Expense ($000):** 1199308 **Payroll Expense ($000):** 503979 **Personnel:** 9390

✠ **UNIVERSITY OF MARYLAND MEDICAL CENTER MIDTOWN CAMPUS (210038)**, 827 Linden Avenue, Zip 21201–4606; tel. 410/225–8000 **A**1 3 5 9 10 **F**1 5 11 15 18 20 29 30 31 34 35 40 44 45 49 50 56 57 59 60 61 64 65 66 68 70 74 75 77 78 79 81 82 85 87 93 94 96 97 98 100 101 102 103 104 106 107 108 111 114 115 118 119 129 143 147 148 **S** University of Maryland Medical System, Baltimore, MD
Primary Contact: Jeffrey A. Rivest, FACHE, President and Chief Executive Officer
COO: Donald Ray, Vice President of Operations
CFO: Keith D. Persinger, Chief Financial Officer
CMO: W. Eugene Egerton, M.D., Chief Medical Officer
CIO: Jon P. Burns, Senior Vice President and Chief Information Officer
CHR: Paula Henderson, Vice President Human Resources
CNO: Marie Vasbinder, Chief Nursing Officer
Web address: www.marylandgeneral.org
Control: Other not–for–profit (including NFP Corporation) **Service:** General Medical and Surgical

Staffed Beds: 225 **Admissions:** 7527 **Census:** 137 **Outpatient Visits:** 118473 **Births:** 586 **Total Expense ($000):** 188089 **Payroll Expense ($000):** 76729 **Personnel:** 1178

✠ △ **UNIVERSITY OF MARYLAND REHABILITATION AND ORTHOPAEDIC INSTITUTE (210058)**, 2200 Kernan Drive, Zip 21207–6697; tel. 410/448–2500 **A**1 3 5 7 9 10 **F**1 8 39 70 74 79 81 82 90 91 93 94 95 96 107 115 120 130 131 132 148 **S** University of Maryland Medical System, Baltimore, MD
Primary Contact: Michael Jablonover, M.D., President and Chief Executive Officer
COO: Juanita D. Robbins, Chief Operating and Development Officer
CFO: W. Walter Augustin, III, CPA, Vice President Financial Services and Chief Financial Officer
CMO: John P. Straumanis, M.D., Vice President Medical Affairs and Chief Medical Officer
CIO: Linda Hines, Vice President Information Technology and Information Systems
CHR: Paula Henderson, Vice President of Human Resources
CNO: Cheryl D. Lee, R.N., Vice President of Patient Care Services and Chief Nursing Officer
Web address: www.umrehabortho.org
Control: Other not–for–profit (including NFP Corporation) **Service:** Rehabilitation

Staffed Beds: 157 **Admissions:** 3662 **Census:** 112 **Outpatient Visits:** 69136 **Births:** 0 **Total Expense ($000):** 101870 **Payroll Expense ($000):** 44113 **Personnel:** 622

✠ △ **VETERANS AFFAIRS MARYLAND HEALTH CARE SYSTEM–BALTIMORE DIVISION**, 10 North Greene Street, Zip 21201–1524; tel. 410/605–7001, (Includes VETERANS AFFAIRS MARYLAND HEALTH CARE SYSTEM–PERRY POINT DIVISION, Circle Drive, Perry Point, Zip 21902; tel. 410/642–2411; Dennis H. Smith, Director), (Total facility includes 275 beds in nursing home–type unit) **A**1 2 3 5 7 8 9 **F**3 4 5 17 18 29 30 31 34 35 36 38 39 40 45 46 50 53 54 55 56 57 58 59 60 61 62 63 64 65 68 70 74 75 77 78 79 81 82 83 84 85 86 87 90 91 92 93 94 96 97 98 100 101 102 103 104 105 106 107 111 114 115 117 118 119 128 129 130 132 133 135 143 144 145 146 147 148 **S** Department of Veterans Affairs, Washington, DC
Primary Contact: Dennis H. Smith, Director
CFO: Major Tom Scheffler, Chief Fiscal Officer
CMO: Dorothy Snow, M.D., Chief of Staff
CIO: Sharon Zielinski, Chief Information Resource Officer
CHR: Jeff Craig, Chief Human Resource Management
Web address: www.maryland.va.gov/
Control: Veterans Affairs, Government, federal **Service:** General Medical and Surgical

Staffed Beds: 727 **Admissions:** 8720 **Census:** 510 **Outpatient Visits:** 648038 **Births:** 0 **Total Expense ($000):** 561488 **Payroll Expense ($000):** 314307 **Personnel:** 3362

BEL AIR—Harford County

✠ **UPPER CHESAPEAKE MEDICAL CENTER (210049)**, 500 Upper Chesapeake Drive, Zip 21014–4324; tel. 443/643–1000 **A**1 2 9 10 **F**3 11 13 15 18 20 22 26 28 29 30 31 34 35 36 38 40 41 42 45 46 49 50 51 54 57 59 60 64 65 68 70 71 74 75 76 77 78 79 81 82 84 85 86 87 89 92 93 96 107 108 110 111 114 115 118 119 121 124 130 131 132 143 146 147 **S** University of Maryland Medical System, Baltimore, MD
Primary Contact: Lyle Ernest Sheldon, FACHE, President and Chief Executive Officer
CFO: Joseph E. Hoffman, III, Executive Vice President and Chief Financial Officer
CMO: Peggy Vaughan, M.D., Senior Vice President Medical Affairs
CIO: Rick Casteel, Vice President Management Information Systems and Chief Information Officer
CHR: Toni M. Shivery, Vice President Human Resources
Web address: www.uchs.org
Control: Other not–for–profit (including NFP Corporation) **Service:** General Medical and Surgical

Staffed Beds: 181 **Admissions:** 12589 **Census:** 131 **Outpatient Visits:** 173763 **Births:** 1399 **Total Expense ($000):** 228971 **Payroll Expense ($000):** 87097 **Personnel:** 1446

BERLIN—Worcester County

✠ **ATLANTIC GENERAL HOSPITAL (210061)**, 9733 Healthway Drive, Zip 21811–1155; tel. 410/641–1100 **A**1 9 10 **F**3 8 11 12 15 17 18 29 30 31 34 35 38 40 45 50 54 57 58 59 64 65 66 70 74 75 77 78 79 81 84 85 87 92 97 99 104 107 108 110 111 114 119 129 132 135 144 146 147 148 **P**7
Primary Contact: Michael A. Franklin, FACHE, President and Chief Executive Officer
COO: Kim Justice, Vice President Planning and Operations
CFO: Cheryl Nottingham, Chief Financial Officer
CMO: Stephen F. Waters, M.D., Medical Director
CIO: Andrew Fowler, Vice President Information Services
CHR: Jim Brannon, Vice President Human Resources
CNO: Colleen Wareing, Vice President Patient Care Services
Web address: www.atlanticgeneral.org
Control: Other not–for–profit (including NFP Corporation) **Service:** General Medical and Surgical

Staffed Beds: 51 **Admissions:** 3086 **Census:** 32 **Outpatient Visits:** 104828 **Births:** 0 **Total Expense ($000):** 94140 **Payroll Expense ($000):** 41115 **Personnel:** 626

BETHESDA—Montgomery County

NATIONAL INSTITUTES OF HEALTH CLINICAL CENTER, (Biomedical Research), 9000 Rockville Pike, Building 10, Room 6–2551, Zip 20892–1504; tel. 301/496–4000, (Includes CHILDREN'S INN AT NIH, 7 West Drive, Zip 20814–1509; tel. 301/496–5672) **A**1 3 5 8 **F**3 4 5 14 20 22 26 30 31 36 39 45 52 55 58 59 60 61 64 65 68 70 74 75 77 78 79 81 82 84 85 86 87 89 91 92 93 94 95 96 98 99 100 101 104 105 107 108 111 112 114 115 116 117 118 119 120 121 124 126 129 130 132 135 136 141 142 145 146 148 **S** U. S. Indian Health Service, Rockville, MD
Primary Contact: John I. Gallin, M.D., Director
COO: Maureen E. Gormley, R.N., Chief Operating Officer
CFO: Maria Joyce, Chief Financial Officer
CMO: David K. Henderson, M.D., Deputy Director Clinical Care
CIO: Jon W. McKeeby, Chief Information Officer
CHR: Bonnie Tuma, Human Resources Team Lead
CNO: Clare Hastings, R.N., Chief Nurse Officer
Web address: www.clinicalcenter.nih.gov
Control: Public Health Service, Government, federal **Service:** Other specialty

Staffed Beds: 146 **Admissions:** 5887 **Census:** 141 **Outpatient Visits:** 102119 **Births:** 0 **Total Expense ($000):** 402227 **Payroll Expense ($000):** 167471 **Personnel:** 1985

NATIONAL NAVAL MEDICAL CENTER See Walter Reed National Military Medical Center

SUBURBAN HOSPITAL (210022), 8600 Old Georgetown Road, Zip 20814–1497; tel. 301/896–3100 **A**1 2 3 5 9 10 **F**3 5 8 11 15 17 18 20 22 24 26 28 29 30 31 34 35 36 37 38 39 40 41 43 44 45 46 49 50 51 56 57 58 59 60 64 70 71 74 75 77 78 79 81 82 84 85 87 89 92 93 98 99 100 101 102 103 104 105 107 108 110 111 115 118 119 120 121 123 126 129 130 132 135 146 148 **P**6 **S** Johns Hopkins Health System, Baltimore, MD
Primary Contact: Gene E. Green, M.D., President
COO: Jacky Schultz, R.N., Executive Vice President and Chief Operating Officer
CFO: Marty Basso, Senior Vice President Finance
CMO: Robert Rothstein, M.D., Vice President Medical Affairs
CIO: Christopher T. Timbers, Vice President and Chief Information Officer
CNO: Barbara Stewart Jacobs, MSN, Chief Nurse Officer
Web address: www.suburbanhospital.org
Control: Other not–for–profit (including NFP Corporation) **Service:** General Medical and Surgical

Staffed Beds: 233 **Admissions:** 13210 **Census:** 165 **Outpatient Visits:** 120554 **Births:** 0 **Total Expense ($000):** 251082 **Payroll Expense ($000):** 99223 **Personnel:** 1508

WALTER REED NATIONAL MILITARY MEDICAL CENTER, 8901 Wisconsin Avenue, Zip 20889–5600; tel. 301/295–4611, (Nonreporting) **A**1 2 3 5 **S** Bureau of Medicine and Surgery, Department of the Navy, Washington, DC
Primary Contact: Colonel John M. Gaal, Deputy Commander Administration
CFO: Commander Joseph Pickel, Director Resource Management
CIO: Commander Cayetano Thornton, Chief Information Officer
CHR: Captain Jaime Carroll, Department Head
Web address: www.wrnmmc.capmed.mil/SitePages/home.aspx
Control: Navy, Government, federal **Service:** General Medical and Surgical

Staffed Beds: 240

CAMBRIDGE—Dorchester County

EASTERN SHORE HOSPITAL CENTER (214002), 5262 Woods Road, Zip 21613–3796, Mailing Address: P.O. Box 800, Zip 21613–0800; tel. 410/221–2300, (Nonreporting) **A**1 9 10
Primary Contact: Randy L. Bradford, Chief Executive Officer
COO: William Webb, Assistant Superintendent
CFO: William Webb, Assistant Superintendent
CMO: Evangeline Garcia, M.D., Clinical Director
CHR: Cassandra Stanley, Director Personnel
CNO: Lisa Hines, Director Nursing
Web address: www.dhmh.state.md.us/eshc
Control: State–Government, nonfederal **Service:** Psychiatric

Staffed Beds: 76

UNIVERSITY OF MARYLAND SHORE MEDICAL CENTER AT DORCHESTER, 300 Byrn Street, Zip 21613–1908; tel. 410/228–5511 **A**1 9 **F**3 11 15 18 20 29 30 31 34 35 40 43 44 45 50 57 59 62 64 68 70 74 75 77 78 81 82 84 85 86 87 91 93 98 99 100 101 102 103 104 105 107 108 110 111 113 118 119 129 130 132 146 **S** University of Maryland Medical System, Baltimore, MD
Primary Contact: Kenneth D. Kozel, FACHE, President and Chief Executive Officer
COO: Jim Ross, Interim Senior Vice President and Chief Operating Officer
CFO: Joanne A. Hahey, Senior Vice President and Chief Financial Officer
CMO: William Huffner, M.D., Vice President Medical Affairs
CIO: Elizabeth Fish, Chief Information Officer
CHR: Susan Coe, Regional Vice President Human Resources
Web address: www.shorehealth.org
Control: Other not–for–profit (including NFP Corporation) **Service:** General Medical and Surgical

Staffed Beds: 46 **Admissions:** 2611 **Census:** 29 **Outpatient Visits:** 44577 **Births:** 0 **Total Expense ($000):** 42328 **Payroll Expense ($000):** 19538 **Personnel:** 256

CHESTERTOWN—Kent County

CHESTER RIVER HOSPITAL CENTER See University of Maryland Shore Medical Center at Chestertown

UNIVERSITY OF MARYLAND SHORE MEDICAL CENTER AT CHESTERTOWN (210030), 100 Brown Street, Zip 21620–1499; tel. 410/778–3300 **A**1 9 10 **F**3 11 15 18 28 29 30 31 34 35 39 40 41 42 45 46 47 50 53 55 56 57 59 60 62 63 64 65 68 70 75 78 79 80 81 82 84 85 87 97 102 107 110 111 115 119 128 129 130 132 143 146 147 **S** University of Maryland Medical System, Baltimore, MD
Primary Contact: Kenneth D. Kozel, FACHE, President and Chief Executive Officer
CFO: Joanne A. Hahey, Vice President Finance and Chief Financial Officer
CMO: William Huffner, M.D., Chief Medical Officer
CIO: Elizabeth Fish, Senior Director Site Executive and Information Technology
CHR: Susan Coe, Vice President Human Resources
CNO: Christopher J. Parker, R.N., Senior Vice President Patient Care Services and Chief Nursing Officer
Web address: www.umms.org/hospitals/shore–health–system.htm
Control: Other not–for–profit (including NFP Corporation) **Service:** General Medical and Surgical

Staffed Beds: 47 **Admissions:** 2214 **Census:** 28 **Outpatient Visits:** 36313 **Births:** 0 **Total Expense ($000):** 51866 **Payroll Expense ($000):** 19681 **Personnel:** 266

CHEVERLY—Prince George's County

GLADYS SPELLMAN SPECIALTY HOSPITAL AND NURSING CENTER, 2900 Mercy Lane, Zip 20785–1157; tel. 301/618–2010, (Nonreporting)
Primary Contact: Stewart R. Seitz, Chief Executive Officer
CFO: Ketty Taboado, Chief Financial Officer
CMO: Paul A. Devore, M.D., Medical Director
CIO: Dennis Lilik, Chief Information Officer
CHR: Michael Jacobs, Vice President Human Resources
Web address: www.dimensionshealth.org
Control: Corporation, Investor–owned, for–profit **Service:** Chronic disease

Staffed Beds: 30

PRINCE GEORGE'S HOSPITAL CENTER (210003), 3001 Hospital Drive, Zip 20785–1189; tel. 301/618–2000 **A**1 3 5 9 10 **F**3 11 13 15 17 18 20 22 24 26 28 29 31 34 35 38 40 42 43 45 46 47 48 49 50 54 55 56 57 59 60 61 63 64 65 66 68 69 70 72 74 75 76 77 78 79 81 82 84 85 86 87 89 92 93 97 98 100 101 102 103 104 105 107 108 110 111 114 115 118 119 130 131 132 134 135 142 144 146 148 **P**6 **S** Dimensions Healthcare System, Cheverly, MD
Primary Contact: John A. O'Brien, FACHE, President
CMO: David Goldman, M.D., Vice President Medical Affairs and Education
CIO: Dennis Lilik, Chief Information Officer
CHR: Michael Jacobs, Vice President Human Resources
Web address: www.princegeorgeshospital.org
Control: Other not–for–profit (including NFP Corporation) **Service:** General Medical and Surgical

Staffed Beds: 284 **Admissions:** 10560 **Census:** 159 **Outpatient Visits:** 93852 **Births:** 2143 **Total Expense ($000):** 247769 **Payroll Expense ($000):** 111500 **Personnel:** 1575

MD

CLINTON—Prince George's County

✠ **MEDSTAR SOUTHERN MARYLAND HOSPITAL CENTER (210062)**, 7503 Surratts Road, Zip 20735–3358; tel. 301/868–8000, (Total facility includes 24 beds in nursing home–type unit) (Data for 203 days) **A**1 2 9 10 **F**3 11 12 13 15 17 18 20 22 26 28 29 30 31 32 34 35 36 37 39 40 44 45 46 47 48 49 50 57 59 64 65 68 70 73 74 75 76 77 78 79 80 81 82 85 86 87 89 91 92 93 96 98 100 101 102 103 105 107 108 114 115 118 119 128 129 130 132 135 143 145 146 147 148 **P**6 **S** MedStar Health, Columbia, MD
Primary Contact: Christine R. Wray, President and Chief Executive Officer
CFO: Charles R. Stewart, Vice President Business, Finance and Corporate Compliance
CMO: J. Andrew Sumner, M.D., Vice President Medical Affairs
CIO: Lou Mavromatis, Vice President Data Processing
CHR: Paul Zeller, Vice President Human Resources
Web address: www.smhchealth.org
Control: Other not–for–profit (including NFP Corporation) **Service:** General Medical and Surgical

Staffed Beds: 287 **Admissions:** 7603 **Census:** 137 **Outpatient Visits:** 310956 **Births:** 836 **Total Expense ($000):** 105815 **Payroll Expense ($000):** 42698 **Personnel:** 1418

SOUTHERN MARYLAND HOSPITAL CENTER See MedStar Southern Maryland Hospital Center

COLUMBIA—Howard County

✠ **HOWARD COUNTY GENERAL HOSPITAL (210048)**, 5755 Cedar Lane, Zip 21044–2999; tel. 410/740–7890 **A**1 2 5 9 10 **F**3 8 11 13 15 18 20 22 26 28 29 30 31 32 34 35 36 39 40 41 44 45 46 47 49 50 51 55 56 57 58 59 60 61 64 68 70 72 74 75 76 77 78 79 81 82 84 85 86 87 89 91 92 93 96 98 100 101 102 103 107 108 110 111 115 119 120 121 129 130 131 132 134 135 146 147 148 **S** Johns Hopkins Health System, Baltimore, MD
Primary Contact: Steven C. Snelgrove, President
COO: Jay H. Blackman, Senior Vice President and Chief Operating Officer
CFO: James Young, Senior Vice President Finance and Chief Financial Officer
CIO: Rick Edwards, Director Information Systems
CHR: Dorothy Brillantes, Senior Vice President Human Resources
Web address: www.hcgh.org
Control: Other not–for–profit (including NFP Corporation) **Service:** General Medical and Surgical

Staffed Beds: 267 **Admissions:** 15994 **Census:** 181 **Outpatient Visits:** 149949 **Births:** 3460 **Total Expense ($000):** 222013 **Payroll Expense ($000):** 90624 **Personnel:** 1434

CRISFIELD—Somerset County

☐ **MCCREADY FOUNDATION (210045)**, 201 Hall Highway, Zip 21817–1299; tel. 410/968–1200, (Nonreporting) **A**1 9 10
Primary Contact: Joy A. Strand, Chief Executive Officer
CFO: Gary W. Broadwater, Chief Financial Officer
Web address: www.mccreadyfoundation.org
Control: Other not–for–profit (including NFP Corporation) **Service:** General Medical and Surgical

Staffed Beds: 89

CUMBERLAND—Allegany County

☐ **THOMAS B. FINAN CENTER (214012)**, 10102 Country Club Road S.E., Zip 21502–8339, Mailing Address: P.O. Box 1722, Zip 21501–1722; tel. 301/777–2240, (Nonreporting) **A**1 9 10
Primary Contact: Judith Hott, Chief Executive Officer
COO: John Cullen, Assistant Superintendent
CFO: Craig Alexander, Fiscal Specialist
CMO: David Millis, M.D., Clinical Director
CHR: Chris Loney, Director Personnel
CNO: Gayle Walter, Director of Nursing
Web address: www.dhmh.state.md.us
Control: State–Government, nonfederal **Service:** Psychiatric

Staffed Beds: 80

✠ △ **WESTERN MARYLAND REGIONAL MEDICAL CENTER (210027)**, 12500 Willowbrook Road, Zip 21502–6393, Mailing Address: P.O. Box 539, Zip 21501–0539; tel. 240/964–7000, (Total facility includes 88 beds in nursing home–type unit) **A**1 2 7 9 10 **F**3 5 11 13 14 15 17 18 20 22 24 26 28 29 30 31 32 34 35 40 43 44 45 50 51 53 54 56 57 58 59 60 62 63 64 66 68 70 73 74 75 76 77 78 79 80 81 82 85 86 87 89 90 93 94 96 97 98 100 102 103 104 107 108 110 111 114 115 116 117 118 119 120 121 123 124 128 129 130 132 134 135 144 146 148 **P**6
Primary Contact: Barry P. Ronan, President and Chief Executive Officer
COO: Nancy D. Adams, R.N., Senior Vice President and Chief Operating Officer and Chief Nurse Executive
CFO: Kimberly S. Repac, Senior Vice President and Chief Financial Officer
CMO: Gerald Goldstein, M.D., Senior Vice President and Chief Medical Officer
CIO: William Byers, Vice President and Chief Information Officer
CHR: Denise G. Kiraly, Director Human Resources
CNO: Nancy D. Adams, R.N., Senior Vice President and Chief Operating Officer and Chief Nurse Executive
Web address: www.wmhs.com
Control: Other not–for–profit (including NFP Corporation) **Service:** General Medical and Surgical

Staffed Beds: 355 **Admissions:** 13139 **Census:** 232 **Outpatient Visits:** 515201 **Births:** 1004 **Total Expense ($000):** 290612 **Payroll Expense ($000):** 104097 **Personnel:** 1783

EAST NEW MARKET—Dorchester County

WARWICK MANOR BEHAVIORAL HEALTH, 3680 Warwick Road, Zip 21631–1420; tel. 410/943–8108, (Nonreporting)
Primary Contact: Marie McBee, Chief Executive Officer
Web address: www.warwickmanor.org/
Control: Corporation, Investor–owned, for–profit **Service:** Alcoholism and other chemical dependency

Staffed Beds: 42

EASTON—Talbot County

✠ △ **UNIVERSITY OF MARYLAND SHORE MEDICAL CENTER AT EASTON (210037)**, 219 South Washington Street, Zip 21601–2996; tel. 410/822–1000 **A**1 2 7 9 10 **F**3 8 11 13 15 18 20 22 28 29 30 31 34 35 36 37 39 40 42 43 44 45 49 51 54 57 58 59 60 62 63 64 65 70 74 76 78 79 81 82 83 84 85 86 89 90 91 93 100 102 107 108 111 114 116 117 118 119 120 121 123 124 126 129 130 132 144 147 148 **P**3 **S** University of Maryland Medical System, Baltimore, MD
Primary Contact: Kenneth D. Kozel, FACHE, President and Chief Executive Officer
COO: Jim Ross, Interim Senior Vice President and Chief Operating Officer
CFO: Joanne A. Hahey, Senior Vice President and Chief Financial Officer
CMO: William Huffner, M.D., Chief Medical Officer
CIO: Elizabeth Fish, Chief Information Officer
CHR: Susan Coe, Regional Vice President Human Resources
CNO: Christopher J. Parker, R.N., Chief Nursing Officer
Web address: www.shorehealth.org
Control: Other not–for–profit (including NFP Corporation) **Service:** General Medical and Surgical

Staffed Beds: 132 **Admissions:** 9200 **Census:** 97 **Outpatient Visits:** 169230 **Births:** 1126 **Total Expense ($000):** 163581 **Payroll Expense ($000):** 67672 **Personnel:** 867

ELKTON—Cecil County

✠ **UNION HOSPITAL (210032)**, 106 Bow Street, Zip 21921–5596; tel. 410/398–4000 **A**1 2 3 5 9 10 **F**2 3 11 13 15 18 26 29 30 31 34 35 40 44 45 46 49 50 51 54 57 59 61 63 64 69 70 74 75 76 77 78 79 81 82 84 85 86 87 89 92 97 98 100 102 104 105 107 108 110 111 114 118 119 129 130 131 132 135 146 147 148 **P**6
Primary Contact: Kenneth S. Lewis, M.D., JD, President and Chief Executive Officer
COO: David N. Gipson, Senior Vice President and Chief Clinical Operations Officer
CFO: Laurie Beyer, Senior Vice President and Chief Financial Officer
CMO: Cydney Teal, M.D., Vice President Medical Affairs
CIO: Anne Lara, Chief Information Officer
CHR: Terrence Lovell, Vice President Human Resources
CNO: Katie Boston, Senior Vice President Patient Care Services
Web address: www.uhcc.com
Control: Other not–for–profit (including NFP Corporation) **Service:** General Medical and Surgical

Staffed Beds: 119 **Admissions:** 5748 **Census:** 59 **Outpatient Visits:** 156443 **Births:** 684 **Total Expense ($000):** 141135 **Payroll Expense ($000):** 63221 **Personnel:** 936

Many Facility Codes have changed. Please refer to the AHA Guide Code Chart. © 2014 AHA Guide

FORT WASHINGTON—Prince George's County

☒ **FORT WASHINGTON MEDICAL CENTER (210060)**, 11711 Livingston Road,
Zip 20744–5164; tel. 301/292–7000 **A**1 9 10 **F**3 29 34 35 40 45 46 47 49
50 57 59 64 70 71 74 75 79 81 85 87 92 107 108 110 119 130
Primary Contact: Verna Stroman Meacham, President and Chief Executive Officer
CFO: Joseph B. Tucker, Senior Vice President and Chief Financial Officer
CMO: Elias Debbas, M.D., President Medical Staff
CIO: Fred Ashby, Director Information Technology
CHR: Alexander Morris, Corporate Director Human Resources
CNO: Marjorie Quint–Bouzid, Chief Nursing Officer and Vice President Patient Care
Services
Web address: www.fortwashingtonmc.org
Control: Other not–for–profit (including NFP Corporation) **Service:** General
Medical and Surgical

Staffed Beds: 37 **Admissions:** 2393 **Census:** 24 **Outpatient Visits:** 50264 **Births:** 0 **Total Expense ($000):** 29170 **Payroll Expense ($000):** 18408 **Personnel:** 378	

FREDERICK—Frederick County

☒ **FREDERICK MEMORIAL HOSPITAL (210005)**, 400 West Seventh Street,
Zip 21701–4593; tel. 240/566–3300, (Nonreporting) **A**1 2 5 9 10
Primary Contact: Thomas A. Kleinhanzl, President and Chief Executive Officer
COO: John R. Verbus, Senior Vice President and Chief Operating Officer
CFO: Michelle K. Mahan, Senior Vice President and Chief Financial Officer
CMO: Manuel Casiano, M.D., Vice President Medical Affairs
CIO: David Quirke, Vice President Information Services
CHR: Terry O'Malley, Vice President Human Resources
CNO: Cheryl Cioffi, R.N., Vice President Patient Care Services and Chief Nursing
Officer
Web address: www.fmh.org
Control: Other not–for–profit (including NFP Corporation) **Service:** General
Medical and Surgical

Staffed Beds: 295

GLEN BURNIE—Anne Arundel County

☒ **UNIVERSITY OF MARYLAND BALTIMORE WASHINGTON MEDICAL CENTER
(210043)**, 301 Hospital Drive, Zip 21061–5899; tel. 410/787–4000 **A**1 2 9 10
F3 8 11 13 14 18 20 22 26 28 29 30 31 34 35 40 41 44 45 46 48 49 50 54
55 56 57 58 59 60 64 65 68 70 74 75 76 77 78 79 81 82 84 85 87 89 93
98 100 102 105 107 108 111 114 115 118 119 120 121 123 126 129 130
131 132 135 146 147 148 **P**6 **S** University of Maryland Medical System,
Baltimore, MD
Primary Contact: Karen E. Olscamp, President and Chief Executive Officer
COO: Kathleen McCollum, Chief Operating Officer and Senior Vice President
Clinical Integration
CFO: Al Pietsch, CPA, Senior Vice President and Chief Financial Officer
CMO: Lawrence Linder, M.D., Senior Vice President and Chief Medical Officer
CIO: Linda Hines, Vice President and Site Executive
CHR: Kathy Poehler, Vice President Human Resources
CNO: Catherine Whitaker, R.N., Vice President and Chief Nursing Officer
Web address: www.bwmc.umms.org
Control: Other not–for–profit (including NFP Corporation) **Service:** General
Medical and Surgical

Staffed Beds: 323 **Admissions:** 19786 **Census:** 234 **Outpatient Visits:** 139112 **Births:** 862 **Total Expense ($000):** 329749 **Payroll Expense ($000):** 139804 **Personnel:** 2195

HAGERSTOWN—Washington County

☐ **BROOK LANE HEALTH SERVICES (214003)**, 13218 Brook Lane Drive,
Zip 21742–1435, Mailing Address: P.O. Box 1945, Zip 21742–1945;
tel. 301/733–0330 **A**1 9 10 **F**5 26 27 30 56 68 98 99 100 101 103 104 105
130 143 146 **P**4 6
Primary Contact: R. Lynn Rushing, Chief Executive Officer
CFO: Floyd Klauka, Chief Financial Officer
CMO: David Gonzalez, M.D., Medical Director
CIO: Sharon Gladfelter, Health Information Officer
CHR: Patricia Bourdeau, Director Human Resources
CNO: Jason Allen, Director of Nursing
Web address: www.brooklane.org
Control: Other not–for–profit (including NFP Corporation) **Service:** Psychiatric

Staffed Beds: 43 **Admissions:** 1775 **Census:** 36 **Outpatient Visits:** 64545 **Births:** 0 **Total Expense ($000):** 22559 **Payroll Expense ($000):** 13708 **Personnel:** 317

☒ △ **MERITUS MEDICAL CENTER (210001)**, 11116 Medical Campus Road,
Zip 21742–6710; tel. 301/790–8000 **A**1 2 7 9 10 **F**3 5 11 12 13 15 17 18 20
22 26 28 29 30 31 34 35 38 40 43 44 49 51 52 54 56 57 58 59 60 61 62
64 65 70 74 75 76 77 78 79 81 82 83 84 85 86 87 89 90 93 94 96 97 98
99 100 101 102 103 104 105 107 108 111 114 115 118 119 120 121 123
130 131 132 135 143 144 145 146 147 148 **P**6 8
Primary Contact: Joseph P. Ross, President and Chief Executive Officer
CFO: Raymond A. Grahe, Senior Vice President Strategic Ventures and Chief
Financial Officer
CMO: Heather Lorenzo, M.D., Vice President and Chief Medical Officer
CIO: Jake Dorst, Vice President and Chief Information Officer
CHR: Christopher Bumbaugh, Executive Human Resources
CNO: Jesus Cepero, Ph.D., Vice President Chief Nursing Officer
Web address: www.meritushealth.com
Control: Other not–for–profit (including NFP Corporation) **Service:** General
Medical and Surgical

Staffed Beds: 257 **Admissions:** 15827 **Census:** 184 **Outpatient Visits:** 192147 **Births:** 1974 **Total Expense ($000):** 285886 **Payroll Expense ($000):** 108219 **Personnel:** 1849

WASHINGTON COUNTY HEALTH SYSTEM See Meritus Medical Center

☐ △ **WESTERN MARYLAND HOSPITAL CENTER (212002)**, 1500 Pennsylvania
Avenue, Zip 21742–3194; tel. 301/791–4200, (Nonreporting) **A**1 7 9 10
Primary Contact: Cynthia Miller Pellegrino, Chief Executive Officer
COO: David Davis, Chief Operating Officer
CFO: Kelly Edmonds, Chief Financial Officer
CMO: Monica Stallworth, M.D., Chief of Staff
CIO: Ron Keplinger, Chief Information Officer
CHR: David Davis, Chief Operating Officer
Web address: www.wmhc.us
Control: State–Government, nonfederal **Service:** Long–Term Acute Care hospital

Staffed Beds: 120

HAVRE DE GRACE—Harford County

☒ **HARFORD MEMORIAL HOSPITAL (210006)**, 501 South Union Avenue,
Zip 21078–3493; tel. 443/843–5000 **A**1 2 9 10 **F**3 11 12 15 29 30 31 34 35
36 38 40 42 46 49 50 51 57 59 60 64 65 66 68 70 71 74 75 77 78 79 81
82 84 85 86 87 92 93 96 98 102 103 104 107 108 110 111 114 115 118
119 129 130 131 132 135 146 148 **S** University of Maryland Medical System,
Baltimore, MD
Primary Contact: Lyle Ernest Sheldon, FACHE, President and Chief Executive
Officer
CFO: Joseph E. Hoffman, III, Executive Vice President and Chief Financial Officer
CMO: Peggy Vaughan, M.D., Senior Vice President Medical Affairs
CIO: Rick Casteel, Vice President Management Information Systems and Chief
Information Officer
CHR: Toni M. Shivery, Vice President Human Resources
Web address: www.uchs.org
Control: Other not–for–profit (including NFP Corporation) **Service:** General
Medical and Surgical

Staffed Beds: 89 **Admissions:** 4727 **Census:** 59 **Outpatient Visits:** 90179 **Births:** 0 **Total Expense ($000):** 79558 **Payroll Expense ($000):** 38069 **Personnel:** 676

JESSUP—Howard County

☐ **CLIFTON T. PERKINS HOSPITAL CENTER**, 8450 Dorsey Run Road,
Zip 20794–9486; tel. 410/724–3000 **A**1 3 5 **F**3 11 29 39 75 98 106 143 146
Primary Contact: Sheilah Davenport, JD, MS, R.N., Chief Executive Officer and
Superintendent
COO: Steve Mason, Assistant Superintendent and Chief Operating Officer
CFO: George Parnel, Chief Financial Officer
CMO: Muhammed Ajanah, M.D., Clinical Director
CIO: Chanda Hamilton, Chief Information Officer
CHR: Beverly Stacie, Director Human Resources
Web address: www.dhmh.state.md.us/perkins/
Control: State–Government, nonfederal **Service:** Psychiatric

Staffed Beds: 250 **Admissions:** 102 **Census:** 239 **Outpatient Visits:** 0 **Births:** 0 **Total Expense ($000):** 59599 **Payroll Expense ($000):** 35157 **Personnel:** 569

Hospital, Medicare Provider Number, Address, Telephone, Approval, Facility, and Physician Codes, Health Care System

★ American Hospital Association (AHA) membership
☐ The Joint Commission accreditation   ◇ DNV Healthcare Inc. accreditation

○ Healthcare Facilities Accreditation Program
△ Commission on Accreditation of Rehabilitation Facilities (CARF) accreditation

MD

LA PLATA—Charles County

⊞ **UNIVERSITY OF MARYLAND CHARLES REGIONAL MEDICAL CENTER (210035)**, 5 Garrett Avenue, Zip 20646–5960, Mailing Address: P.O. Box 1070, Zip 20646–1070; tel. 301/609–4000 **A**1 2 9 10 **F**3 11 13 15 18 28 29 30 31 34 35 36 38 40 44 45 50 51 56 57 59 60 61 64 70 74 76 77 78 79 81 82 85 86 87 89 92 93 96 97 107 108 110 111 114 115 118 119 129 130 132 135 145 146 147 148 **S** University of Maryland Medical System, Baltimore, MD
Primary Contact: Noel A. Cervino, President and Chief Executive Officer
CFO: Erik Boas, Vice President Finance
CMO: Sanjeeb Mishra, M.D., Chief of Staff
CHR: Stacey M. Cook, MS, Director Human Resources
Web address: www.charlesregional.org
Control: Other not–for–profit (including NFP Corporation) **Service:** General Medical and Surgical

Staffed Beds: 110 **Admissions:** 7728 **Census:** 87 **Outpatient Visits:** 64503 **Births:** 782 **Total Expense ($000):** 104846 **Payroll Expense ($000):** 46851 **Personnel:** 745

LANHAM—Prince George's County

⊞ **DOCTORS COMMUNITY HOSPITAL (210051)**, 8118 Good Luck Road, Zip 20706–3574; tel. 301/552–8118 **A**1 9 10 **F**3 8 12 15 18 28 29 30 31 34 35 40 49 57 59 60 64 70 75 77 78 79 81 82 84 85 86 87 90 93 107 108 111 114 115 119 126 130 146
Primary Contact: Philip B. Down, Chief Executive Officer
COO: Paul Grenaldo, Executive Vice President and Chief Operating Officer
CFO: Camille Bash, Chief Financial Officer
CMO: Gabriel Jaffe, M.D., Vice President Medical Affairs
CIO: Alan Johnson, Chief Information Officer
CHR: Paul Hagens, Vice President Human Resources
Web address: www.dchweb.org
Control: Other not–for–profit (including NFP Corporation) **Service:** General Medical and Surgical

Staffed Beds: 207 **Admissions:** 10857 **Census:** 140 **Outpatient Visits:** 77439 **Births:** 0 **Total Expense ($000):** 178023 **Payroll Expense ($000):** 80289 **Personnel:** 1257

LAUREL—Prince George's County

☐ △ **LAUREL REGIONAL HOSPITAL (210055)**, 7300 Van Dusen Road, Zip 20707–9463; tel. 301/725–4300 **A**1 7 9 10 **F**1 3 11 13 15 18 20 29 30 31 34 35 40 46 49 50 51 57 59 60 61 63 64 65 66 68 69 70 74 75 77 78 79 80 81 82 84 85 87 90 92 93 98 100 102 103 104 105 107 108 110 111 114 115 118 119 129 130 132 146 148 **P**6 **S** Dimensions Healthcare System, Cheverly, MD
Primary Contact: John Spearman, President and Chief Operating Officer
COO: John Spearman, Interim Chief Operating Officer
CFO: Lisa Goodlett, Senior Vice President and Chief Financial Officer
CMO: Trudy Hall, M.D., Vice President Medical Affairs
CIO: David Peterson, Chief Information Officer
CHR: John Peeples, Senior Vice President Human Resources
CNO: June Meyer, MSN, Vice President Chief Nursing Officer
Web address: www.laurelregionalhospital.org
Control: Other not–for–profit (including NFP Corporation) **Service:** General Medical and Surgical

Staffed Beds: 160 **Admissions:** 5985 **Census:** 84 **Outpatient Visits:** 39905 **Births:** 911 **Total Expense ($000):** 109322 **Payroll Expense ($000):** 51977 **Personnel:** 681

LEONARDTOWN—St. Mary's County

⊞ **MEDSTAR ST. MARY'S HOSPITAL (210028)**, 25500 Point Lookout Road, Zip 20650–2015, Mailing Address: P.O. Box 527, Zip 20650–0527; tel. 301/475–6001 **A**1 9 10 **F**3 11 13 15 18 28 29 30 31 32 34 35 36 39 40 44 45 48 50 51 53 54 56 57 59 60 63 64 65 66 68 70 71 74 75 76 77 78 79 81 82 84 85 86 87 89 93 98 100 101 102 103 104 105 107 108 110 111 114 115 118 119 129 130 132 134 135 144 146 147 148 **P**6 **S** MedStar Health, Columbia, MD
Primary Contact: Christine R. Wray, President
CFO: Richard Braam, Vice President Finance
CMO: Avani D. Shah, M.D., Chief of Medical Staff
CIO: Donald Sirk, Director Information Systems
CHR: Evelyn Campos–Diaz, Director Human Resources
CNO: Mary Lou Watson, MS, Vice President Nursing
Web address: www.medstarstmarys.org
Control: Other not–for–profit (including NFP Corporation) **Service:** General Medical and Surgical

Staffed Beds: 90 **Admissions:** 7477 **Census:** 63 **Outpatient Visits:** 230847 **Births:** 1118 **Total Expense ($000):** 123492 **Payroll Expense ($000):** 57343 **Personnel:** 972

OAKLAND—Garrett County

⊞ **GARRETT COUNTY MEMORIAL HOSPITAL (210017)**, 251 North Fourth Street, Zip 21550–1375; tel. 301/533–4000, (Total facility includes 10 beds in nursing home–type unit) **A**1 9 10 **F**3 11 13 28 30 32 34 35 38 40 45 50 53 56 57 59 64 65 70 75 76 79 81 85 87 89 102 107 108 114 118 119 128 130 135 141 146 148 **P**6
Primary Contact: Mark Boucot, President and Chief Executive Officer
CFO: Tracy Lipscomb, Vice President Financial Services and Chief Financial Officer
CIO: Stephen Peterson, Vice President Chief Information Officer
CHR: Annette Livengood, Vice President Human Resources
CNO: Kendra Thayer, Vice President Clinical and Support Services and Chief Nursing Officer
Web address: www.gcmh.com
Control: Other not–for–profit (including NFP Corporation) **Service:** General Medical and Surgical

Staffed Beds: 59 **Admissions:** 2271 **Census:** 24 **Outpatient Visits:** 70045 **Births:** 297 **Total Expense ($000):** 39163 **Payroll Expense ($000):** 16605 **Personnel:** 320

OLNEY—Montgomery County

⊞ **MEDSTAR MONTGOMERY MEDICAL CENTER (210018)**, 18101 Prince Philip Drive, Zip 20832–1512; tel. 301/774–8882 **A**1 2 9 10 **F**3 5 11 12 13 18 20 26 28 29 30 31 34 37 38 40 41 45 46 48 49 50 51 53 55 56 57 59 65 68 70 74 75 76 77 78 79 80 81 82 84 85 86 89 92 93 98 99 100 102 103 104 105 107 108 111 114 115 118 119 126 129 130 132 134 135 146 **S** MedStar Health, Columbia, MD
Primary Contact: Peter W. Monge, President
CFO: David A. Havrilla, Chief Financial Officer
CMO: Frederick Finelli, M.D., Vice President Medical Affairs
CIO: Chistiane Brown, Assistant Vice President
CHR: Kevin Mell, Vice President Operations
CNO: Connie Stone, R.N., Chief Nursing Officer
Web address: www.medstarmontgomery.org
Control: Other not–for–profit (including NFP Corporation) **Service:** General Medical and Surgical

Staffed Beds: 150 **Admissions:** 8615 **Census:** 92 **Outpatient Visits:** 70195 **Births:** 706 **Total Expense ($000):** 143429 **Payroll Expense ($000):** 58108 **Personnel:** 789

PERRY POINT—Cecil County

VETERANS AFFAIRS MARYLAND HEALTH CARE SYSTEM–PERRY POINT DIVISION See Veterans Affairs Maryland Health Care System–Baltimore Division, Baltimore

PRINCE FREDERICK—Calvert County

⊞ **CALVERT MEMORIAL HOSPITAL (210039)**, 100 Hospital Road, Zip 20678–4017; tel. 410/535–4000, (Total facility includes 18 beds in nursing home–type unit) **A**1 9 10 **F**3 11 13 14 20 26 28 29 30 31 32 34 35 36 38 40 41 46 49 54 56 57 59 61 64 65 68 70 74 75 76 77 78 79 81 82 84 85 86 87 89 93 94 96 98 99 100 101 102 104 105 107 108 111 112 114 115 119 127 129 130 132 134 135 144 146 147 148 **P**4
Primary Contact: James J. Xinis, President and Chief Executive Officer
COO: Dean Teague, Chief Operating Officer
CFO: Robert Kertis, Vice President Finance
CMO: Barbara Estes, M.D., Chief of Staff
CIO: Ed Grogan, Vice President Information Services and Chief Information Officer
CHR: Anthony M. Bladen, Vice President Human Resources
CNO: Diane Couchman, Vice President Patient Care Services and Chief Nursing Executive
Web address: www.calverthospital.com
Control: Other not–for–profit (including NFP Corporation) **Service:** General Medical and Surgical

Staffed Beds: 130 **Admissions:** 7175 **Census:** 78 **Outpatient Visits:** 135712 **Births:** 826 **Total Expense ($000):** 119395 **Payroll Expense ($000):** 50102 **Personnel:** 936

RANDALLSTOWN—Baltimore County

☐ **NORTHWEST HOSPITAL (210040)**, 5401 Old Court Road, Zip 21133–5185; tel. 410/521–2200, (Total facility includes 29 beds in nursing home–type unit) **A**1 9 10 **F**3 8 11 12 15 18 20 26 28 29 30 31 34 35 36 37 38 40 45 49 50 56 57 59 60 63 64 65 68 70 74 75 77 79 80 81 82 83 84 85 86 87 92 93 97 98 100 102 107 110 111 114 115 119 126 128 129 130 131 132 135 146 147 148 **S** LifeBridge Health, Baltimore, MD
Primary Contact: Brian M. White, President
CFO: Nancy Kane, Assistant Vice President Finance LifeBridge Health
CMO: Ronald L. Ginsberg, M.D., Vice President Medical Affairs
CIO: Tressa Springmann, Vice President and Chief Information Officer
CHR: Valerie Brandenburg, Director Human Resources
CNO: Susan L. Jalbert, R.N., Vice President Patient Care Services and Chief Nursing Officer
Web address: www.lifebridgehealth.org
Control: Other not–for–profit (including NFP Corporation) **Service:** General Medical and Surgical

Staffed Beds: 253 **Admissions:** 14799 **Census:** 201 **Outpatient Visits:** 120341 **Births:** 0 **Total Expense ($000):** 206698 **Payroll Expense ($000):** 84952 **Personnel:** 1374

Many Facility Codes have changed. Please refer to the AHA Guide Code Chart. © 2014 AHA Guide

MD

ROCKVILLE—Montgomery County

☐ **ADVENTIST BEHAVIORAL HEALTH ROCKVILLE (214013)**, 14901 Broschart Road, Zip 20850–3318; tel. 301/251–4500, (Nonreporting) **A**1 9 10 **S** Adventist HealthCare, Gaithersburg, MD
Primary Contact: Kevin Young, FACHE, President
CFO: Randy Reimer, Chief Financial Officer
CMO: Peter H. Levine, M.D., Executive Medical Director Behavioral Health Services
CIO: Kathleen Dyer, Vice President and Chief Information Officer
CHR: Mary Cloutier, Director Human Resources
Web address: www.adventistbehavioralhealth.com
Control: Other not–for–profit (including NFP Corporation) **Service:** Psychiatric

Staffed Beds: 283

☐ △ **ADVENTIST REHABILITATION HOSPITAL OF MARYLAND (213029)**, 9909 Medical Center Drive, Zip 20850–6361; tel. 240/864–6000, (Nonreporting) **A**1 7 9 10 **S** Adventist HealthCare, Gaithersburg, MD
Primary Contact: Brent Reitz, President
COO: Jason Makaroff, Chief Operating Officer and Associate Vice President
CFO: Jim Litsinger, Chief Financial Officer
CMO: Terrence P. Sheehan, M.D., Medical Director
CHR: Carrie Hibbard, Human Resource Business Partner
CNO: Valerie Summerlin, R.N., Chief Nursing Officer
Web address: www.adventistrehab.com
Control: Other not–for–profit (including NFP Corporation) **Service:** Rehabilitation

Staffed Beds: 77

POTOMAC RIDGE BEHAVIORAL HEALTH See Adventist Behavioral Health Rockville

☐ **SHADY GROVE ADVENTIST HOSPITAL (210057)**, 9901 Medical Center Drive, Zip 20850–3395; tel. 240/826–6000 **A**1 2 9 10 **F**3 12 13 15 18 20 22 26 28 29 30 31 39 40 41 42 45 48 50 51 53 55 57 60 61 64 66 68 70 72 74 75 76 77 78 79 81 82 84 85 87 89 102 107 108 110 111 114 115 116 117 119 120 121 126 129 130 146 148 **S** Adventist HealthCare, Gaithersburg, MD
Primary Contact: John Sackett, Chief Executive Officer
COO: Eunmee Shim, Vice President Operations
CFO: Daniel Cochran, Vice President and Chief Financial Officer
CMO: Kevin Smothess, M.D., Vice President Chief Medical Officer
CIO: christopher Ghion, Vice President and Chief Information Officer
CHR: Eric Brown, Senior Business Partner
CNO: Skip Margot, Vice President Patient Care Services and Chief Nurse Executive
Web address: www.adventisthealthcare.com
Control: Church–operated, Nongovernment, not–for profit **Service:** General Medical and Surgical

Staffed Beds: 331 Admissions: 20315 Census: 218 Outpatient Visits: 102000 Births: 4981 Total Expense ($000): 318000 Payroll Expense ($000): 119000 Personnel: 1800

SALISBURY—Wicomico County

☐ **DEER'S HEAD HOSPITAL CENTER (212003)**, 351 Deer's Head Hospital Road, Zip 21801–3201, Mailing Address: P.O. Box 2018, Zip 21802–2018; tel. 410/543–4000, (Total facility includes 57 beds in nursing home–type unit) **A**1 9 10 **F**1 3 11 28 29 30 44 50 56 57 59 60 61 65 68 75 77 82 84 85 86 87 90 91 93 94 96 128 130 132 135 146 148 **P**6
Primary Contact: Mary Beth Waide, R.N., MS, JD, Chief Executive Officer
COO: Michael Dollinger, Chief Operating Officer and Assistant Superintendent
CFO: Kenneth Waller, Fiscal Administrator
CMO: Michael P. Buchness, M.D., Director Medical
CIO: Mac Beattie, Computer Network Specialist
CHR: Luanne G. Dashield, Personnel Administrator
CNO: Tess Iten, Director of Nursing and Chief Nursing Officer
Web address: www.deershead.org
Control: State–Government, nonfederal **Service:** Chronic disease

Staffed Beds: 69 Admissions: 172 Census: 62 Outpatient Visits: 12944 Births: 0 Total Expense ($000): 22065 Payroll Expense ($000): 9629 Personnel: 214

✪ △ **HEALTHSOUTH CHESAPEAKE REHABILITATION HOSPITAL (213028)**, 220 Tilghman Road, Zip 21804–1921; tel. 410/546–4600, (Nonreporting) **A**1 7 9 10 **S** HEALTHSOUTH Corporation, Birmingham, AL
Primary Contact: Steven Walas, Chief Executive Officer
CFO: Karen Rounsley, Controller
CHR: Belinda Thompson, Coordinator Human Resources
CNO: Belle Goslee, Chief Nursing Officer
Web address: www.healthsouthchesapeake.com
Control: Corporation, Investor–owned, for–profit **Service:** Rehabilitation

Staffed Beds: 54

✉ **PENINSULA REGIONAL MEDICAL CENTER (210019)**, 100 East Carroll Street, Zip 21801–5422; tel. 410/546–6400, (Total facility includes 30 beds in nursing home–type unit) **A**1 2 9 10 **F**3 12 13 15 17 18 20 22 24 26 28 29 30 31 34 35 40 43 45 46 47 48 49 50 51 53 54 57 58 59 60 61 62 64 68 70 71 72 74 75 76 77 78 79 81 82 84 85 87 89 93 96 97 98 100 102 107 108 110 111 114 115 116 117 118 119 120 121 123 124 126 128 130 132 143 144 145 146 147 148 **P**5 8
Primary Contact: Margaret Naleppa, President and Chief Executive Officer
COO: Cindy Lunsford, Executive Vice President and Chief Operating Officer
CFO: Bruce Ritchie, Vice President of Finance and Chief Financial Officer
CMO: Charles B. Silvia, M.D., Chief Medical Officer and Vice President Medical Affairs
CIO: Raymond Adkins, Chief Information Officer
CHR: Scott Peterson, Vice President of People and Organizational Development
CNO: Karen C. Poisker, MSN, Vice President Patient Care Services and Chief Nursing Officer
Web address: www.peninsula.org
Control: Other not–for–profit (including NFP Corporation) **Service:** General Medical and Surgical

Staffed Beds: 357 Admissions: 18653 Census: 224 Outpatient Visits: 535184 Births: 1945 Total Expense ($000): 374588 Payroll Expense ($000): 149254 Personnel: 2263

SILVER SPRING—Montgomery County

✉ **HOLY CROSS HOSPITAL (210004)**, 1500 Forest Glen Road, Zip 20910–1487; tel. 301/754–7000 **A**1 2 3 5 8 9 10 **F**2 3 11 12 13 15 17 18 19 20 22 26 29 30 31 32 34 35 36 37 39 40 41 45 46 49 50 54 55 56 57 58 59 60 64 66 68 70 72 74 75 76 77 78 79 81 82 84 85 86 87 89 93 97 100 107 108 110 111 114 115 119 120 121 123 124 126 129 130 131 132 134 144 146 147 **S** Catholic Health East / Trinity Health, Livonia, MI
Primary Contact: Judith Rogers, R.N., Ph.D., President and Chief Executive Officer
CFO: Anne Gillis, Chief Financial Officer
CMO: Blair Eig, M.D., Senior Vice President Medical Affairs
CIO: Matthew Trimmer, Director Information Services
CHR: J. Manuel Ocasio, Vice President Human Resources
CNO: Celia Guarino, R.N., Vice President and Chief Nursing Officer
Web address: www.holycrosshealth.org
Control: Church–operated, Nongovernment, not–for profit **Service:** General Medical and Surgical

Staffed Beds: 425 Admissions: 31982 Census: 353 Outpatient Visits: 182593 Births: 8643 Total Expense ($000): 379895 Payroll Expense ($000): 169266 Personnel: 2263

SAINT LUKE INSTITUTE, 8901 New Hampshire Avenue, Zip 20903–3611; tel. 301/445–7970, (Nonreporting)
Primary Contact: Father Stephen J. Rossetti, Ph.D., President and Chief Executive Officer
COO: Sister Danile Lynch, Chief Operating Officer
Web address: www.sli.org
Control: Other not–for–profit (including NFP Corporation) **Service:** Psychiatric

Staffed Beds: 24

SYKESVILLE—Carroll County

☐ **SPRINGFIELD HOSPITAL CENTER (214004)**, 6655 Sykesville Road, Zip 21784–7966; tel. 410/970–7000 **A**1 9 10 **F**11 35 39 44 53 56 57 68 75 77 86 87 98 101 103 130 132 135 146 **P**6
Primary Contact: Paula A. Langmead, Chief Executive Officer
COO: Dan Triplett, Acting Chief Operating Officer
CFO: Keith Hardesty, Chief Financial Officer
CMO: Kim Bright, M.D., Clinical Director
CIO: Denise Maskell, Chief Information Officer
CNO: Gloria Merek, Director of Nursing
Web address: www.dhmh.state.md.us/springfield
Control: State–Government, nonfederal **Service:** Psychiatric

Staffed Beds: 220 Admissions: 310 Census: 231 Outpatient Visits: 0 Births: 0 Total Expense ($000): 69224 Payroll Expense ($000): 42215 Personnel: 809

TAKOMA PARK—Montgomery County

☐ △ **WASHINGTON ADVENTIST HOSPITAL (210016)**, 7600 Carroll Avenue, Zip 20912–6392; tel. 301/891–7600 **A**1 2 3 5 7 9 10 **F**13 15 17 18 20 22 24 26 28 29 30 31 34 35 40 45 49 50 56 57 58 59 60 61 64 65 66 68 69 70 71 74 75 76 77 78 79 81 82 84 85 86 90 92 93 97 98 100 102 104 105 107 110 111 114 115 116 117 119 120 121 123 124 126 129 130 132 146 147 148 **S** Adventist HealthCare, Gaithersburg, MD
Primary Contact: Erik Wangsness, President
Web address: www.adventisthealthcare.com
Control: Church–operated, Nongovernment, not–for profit **Service:** General Medical and Surgical

Staffed Beds: 252 Admissions: 11609 Census: 165 Births: 1567 Total Expense ($000): 213396 Payroll Expense ($000): 82831

Hospital, Medicare Provider Number, Address, Telephone, Approval, Facility, and Physician Codes, Health Care System

★ American Hospital Association (AHA) membership
☐ The Joint Commission accreditation
◇ DNV Healthcare Inc. accreditation
○ Healthcare Facilities Accreditation Program
△ Commission on Accreditation of Rehabilitation Facilities (CARF) accreditation

TOWSON—Baltimore County

☒ **UNIVERSITY OF MARYLAND ST. JOSEPH MEDICAL CENTER (210063)**, 7601 Osler Drive, Zip 21204–7582; tel. 410/337–1000 **A**1 2 9 **F**3 11 12 13 15 17 18 20 22 24 26 28 29 30 31 34 35 36 37 40 41 44 45 46 47 48 49 50 55 56 57 58 59 60 61 64 65 66 68 70 71 72 74 75 76 77 78 79 81 82 84 85 86 87 89 91 92 93 97 98 99 100 101 102 103 104 105 107 108 110 114 115 118 119 120 121 122 123 124 126 129 130 131 132 134 135 144 146 147 148 **P**6 **S** University of Maryland Medical System, Baltimore, MD
Primary Contact: Mohan Suntha, M.D., President and Chief Executive Officer
COO: Craig Carmichael, Vice President, Operations
CMO: Gail Cunningham, Interim Chief Medical Officer
CIO: Sean Shuffield, Regional Chief Information Officer
CNO: Pamela Jamieson, Vice President Patient Care Services and Chief Nursing Officer
Web address: www.sjmcmd.org
Control: Other not–for–profit (including NFP Corporation) **Service:** General Medical and Surgical

Staffed Beds: 320 **Admissions:** 15176 **Census:** 165 **Outpatient Visits:** 149796 **Births:** 1935 **Total Expense ($000):** 382468 **Payroll Expense ($000):** 144597 **Personnel:** 1662

WESTMINSTER—Carroll County

☒ **CARROLL HOSPITAL CENTER (210033)**, 200 Memorial Avenue, Zip 21157–5799; tel. 410/848–3000 **A**1 2 9 10 **F**3 5 11 13 15 18 19 20 22 26 28 29 30 31 32 34 35 36 37 38 39 40 44 45 49 50 51 54 55 56 57 58 59 62 63 64 65 68 70 74 75 76 77 78 79 81 82 83 84 85 86 87 89 93 94 98 99 100 101 102 103 104 105 107 108 109 111 114 115 118 119 120 121 126 129 130 131 132 134 135 145 146 147 148 **P**6 8
Primary Contact: Leslie Simmons, R.N., FACHE, President and Chief Executive Officer
CFO: Kevin Kelbly, Senior Vice President Finance and Corporate Fiscal Affairs
CMO: Mark Olszyk, M.D., Vice President Medical Affairs and Chief Medical Officer
CIO: Jennifer Moore, Interim Chief Information Officer
CHR: Tracey Ellison, Vice President Human Resources
CNO: Stephanie Reid, R.N., Vice President of Quality and Chief Nursing Officer
Web address: www.carrollhospitalcenter.org
Control: Other not–for–profit (including NFP Corporation) **Service:** General Medical and Surgical

Staffed Beds: 158 **Admissions:** 11585 **Census:** 107 **Outpatient Visits:** 171895 **Births:** 1084 **Total Expense ($000):** 274836 **Payroll Expense ($000):** 120810 **Personnel:** 1401

Many Facility Codes have changed. Please refer to the AHA Guide Code Chart.

MASSACHUSETTS

ATHOL—Worcester County

☐ **ATHOL MEMORIAL HOSPITAL (221303)**, 2033 Main Street, Zip 01331–3598; tel. 978/249–3511, (Nonreporting) **A**1 9 10 18
Primary Contact: Winfield S. Brown, FACHE, President and Chief Executive Officer
COO: Michael Grimmer, Chief Operating Officer
CFO: Robert Crosby, Chief Financial Officer
CMO: Mohsen Noreldin, M.D., President Medical Staff
CIO: Carol Roosa, Vice President Information Services and Chief Information Officer
CNO: Lucille Songer, Chief Nursing Officer
Web address: www.atholhospital.org
Control: Other not–for–profit (including NFP Corporation) **Service:** General Medical and Surgical

Staffed Beds: 12

ATTLEBORO—Bristol County

☐ **ARBOUR–FULLER HOSPITAL (224021)**, 200 May Street, Zip 02703–5520; tel. 508/761–8500, (Nonreporting) **A**1 9 10 **S** Universal Health Services, Inc., King of Prussia, PA
Primary Contact: Kevin Burchill, Chief Executive Officer
CFO: James Rollins, Chief Financial Officer
CMO: Aminadav Zakai, M.D., Medical Director
CHR: Brian Jenkins, Director Human Resources
Web address: www.arbourhealth.com
Control: Corporation, Investor–owned, for–profit **Service:** Psychiatric

Staffed Beds: 46

✠ **STURDY MEMORIAL HOSPITAL (220008)**, 211 Park Street, Zip 02703–3137, Mailing Address: PO Box 2963, Zip 02703–0963; tel. 508/222–5200 **A**1 2 9 10 **F**3 8 13 15 18 20 28 29 30 31 32 34 35 36 39 40 44 45 46 49 50 56 57 58 59 61 64 70 74 75 76 77 78 79 81 82 85 86 87 89 93 97 100 107 108 109 110 111 115 118 119 129 130 131 132 134 144 146 147 148 **P**6
Primary Contact: Bruce S. Auerbach, President and Chief Executive Officer
CFO: Joseph Casey, Chief Financial Officer
CMO: Daniel Pietro, M.D., Medical Director
CHR: Cheryl Barrows, Vice President Human Resources
CNO: Marita Prater, MS, Vice President Patient Care Services
Web address: www.sturdymemorial.org
Control: Other not–for–profit (including NFP Corporation) **Service:** General Medical and Surgical

Staffed Beds: 128 Admissions: 5946 Census: 71 Outpatient Visits: 219043 Births: 751 Total Expense ($000): 149234 Payroll Expense ($000): 75452 Personnel: 1008

AYER—Middlesex County

☐ **NASHOBA VALLEY MEDICAL CENTER (220098)**, 200 Groton Road, Zip 01432–3300; tel. 978/784–9000 **A**1 9 10 **F**3 11 18 26 28 29 30 31 35 40 50 56 59 70 74 75 77 78 79 81 82 85 87 89 93 98 103 107 110 111 114 119 129 130 131 132 135 146 147 148 **S** Steward Health Care System, LLC, Boston, MA
Primary Contact: Salvatore Perla, President
CFO: Ben Moll, Assistant Chief Financial Officer
CMO: Michael Older, M.D., President Medical Staff
Web address: www.nashobamed.com
Control: Corporation, Investor–owned, for–profit **Service:** General Medical and Surgical

Staffed Beds: 48 Admissions: 1734 Census: 15 Births: 0 Total Expense ($000): 39406 Payroll Expense ($000): 16604

BEDFORD—Middlesex County

✠ **BEDFORD VETERANS AFFAIRS MEDICAL CENTER, EDITH NOURSE ROGERS MEMORIAL VETERANS HOSPITAL**, 200 Springs Road, Zip 01730–1198; tel. 781/687–2000, (Total facility includes 255 beds in nursing home–type unit) **A**1 3 5 **F**1 2 3 5 6 12 18 29 30 34 35 38 39 53 54 56 57 58 59 61 62 63 64 65 66 75 77 82 83 84 86 87 92 93 94 97 98 100 101 102 103 104 105 106 130 132 135 143 144 146 147 148 **P**1 **S** Department of Veterans Affairs, Washington, DC
Primary Contact: Christine Croteau, Director
COO: Mark Fontaine–Westhart, Associate Director
CFO: Edward Koetting, Chief Financial Officer
CMO: Dan Berlowitz, M.D., Acting Chief of Staff
CHR: Robert Colpitts, Chief Human Resource Service
CNO: Mary Ann Petrillo, R.N., Acting Associate Director, Nursing
Web address: www.bedford.va.gov/guide/
Control: Veterans Affairs, Government, federal **Service:** Psychiatric

Staffed Beds: 316 Admissions: 1167 Census: 230 Outpatient Visits: 217684 Births: 0 Total Expense ($000): 188962 Payroll Expense ($000): 95744 Personnel: 1218

BELMONT—Middlesex County

✠ **MCLEAN HOSPITAL (224007)**, 115 Mill Street, Zip 02478–1064; tel. 617/855–2000 **A**1 3 5 9 10 **F**4 5 29 50 53 56 58 64 68 74 77 86 98 99 100 101 103 104 105 106 111 119 130 132 134 146 **P**6 **S** Partners HealthCare System, Inc., Boston, MA
Primary Contact: Scott L. Rauch, M.D., President
COO: Michele L. Gougeon, Executive Vice President and Chief Operating Officer
CFO: David A. Lagasse, Senior Vice President Fiscal Affairs
CMO: Joseph Gold, M.D., Chief Medical Officer
CIO: Andrew Laband, Chief Information Officer
CHR: Jean Mansfield, Director Human Resources
CNO: Linda Flaherty, R.N., Senior Vice President, Patient Care Services
Web address: www.mclean.harvard.edu
Control: Other not–for–profit (including NFP Corporation) **Service:** Psychiatric

Staffed Beds: 177 Admissions: 5962 Census: 156 Outpatient Visits: 109486 Births: 0 Total Expense ($000): 179681 Payroll Expense ($000): 75391 Personnel: 1559

BEVERLY—Essex County

✠ **BEVERLY HOSPITAL (220033)**, 85 Herrick Street, Zip 01915–1777; tel. 978/922–3000, (Includes ADDISON GILBERT HOSPITAL, 298 Washington Street, Gloucester, Zip 01930–4887; tel. 978/283–4000) **A**1 2 5 9 10 **F**3 5 8 11 12 13 15 18 20 22 26 28 29 30 31 32 34 35 40 42 43 44 45 46 47 48 49 50 51 53 54 55 56 57 59 60 61 63 64 65 68 70 73 74 75 76 77 78 79 81 82 83 84 85 86 87 89 91 92 93 96 97 98 100 102 103 104 105 107 108 110 111 114 115 119 130 131 132 134 135 141 142 145 146 147 148 **P**1 5 6 **S** Lahey Health, Burlington, MA
Primary Contact: Denis S. Conroy, President
COO: Pauline Pike, Chief Operating Officer
CFO: Gary P. Marlow, Chief Financial Officer
CMO: Peter H. Short, M.D., Senior Vice President Medical Affairs
CIO: Robert Laramie, Chief Information Officer
CHR: Althea C. Lyons, Vice President Human Resources and Development
Web address: www.beverlyhospital.org
Control: Other not–for–profit (including NFP Corporation) **Service:** General Medical and Surgical

Staffed Beds: 404 Admissions: 19042 Census: 246 Outpatient Visits: 166774 Births: 2196 Total Expense ($000): 311705 Payroll Expense ($000): 144988 Personnel: 2104

BOSTON—Suffolk County

☐ **ARBOUR HOSPITAL (224013)**, 49 Robinwood Avenue, Zip 02130–2156; tel. 617/522–4400, (Nonreporting) **A**1 9 10 **S** Universal Health Services, Inc., King of Prussia, PA
Primary Contact: Laura Ames, Chief Executive Officer
Web address: www.arbourhealth.com
Control: Other not–for–profit (including NFP Corporation) **Service:** Psychiatric

Staffed Beds: 118

Hospital, Medicare Provider Number, Address, Telephone, Approval, Facility, and Physician Codes, Health Care System

★ American Hospital Association (AHA) membership
☐ The Joint Commission accreditation   ◇ DNV Healthcare Inc. accreditation
○ Healthcare Facilities Accreditation Program
△ Commission on Accreditation of Rehabilitation Facilities (CARF) accreditation

✠ **BETH ISRAEL DEACONESS MEDICAL CENTER (220086)**, 330 Brookline Avenue, Zip 02215–5491; tel. 617/667–7000, (Includes BETH ISRAEL DEACONESS HOSPITAL–NEEDHAM CAMPUS, 148 Chestnut Street, Needham, Zip 02492; tel. 781/453–3000; John M. Fogarty, President and Chief Executive Officer) **A**1 2 3 5 8 9 10 **F**3 6 9 11 12 13 14 15 17 18 20 22 24 26 28 29 30 31 34 35 36 37 38 40 43 44 45 46 47 48 49 50 51 53 54 55 56 57 58 59 60 61 63 64 65 66 68 70 71 72 73 74 75 76 77 78 79 81 82 84 85 86 87 91 92 93 94 97 98 100 101 102 103 104 107 108 109 110 111 112 113 114 115 116 117 118 119 120 121 123 124 126 129 130 131 132 135 136 138 139 142 143 144 145 146 147 148 **P**5 7 8
Primary Contact: Kevin Tabb, M.D., President and Chief Executive Officer
COO: Nancy A. Formella, R.N., Chief Operating Officer
CFO: Steven P. Fischer, Chief Financial Officer
CIO: John Halamka, M.D., Chief Information Officer
CHR: Julie Bieber, Senior Vice President Human Resources
CNO: Marsha L. Maurer, R.N., Chief Nursing Officer Patient Care Services
Web address: www.bidmc.harvard.edu
Control: Other not–for–profit (including NFP Corporation) **Service:** General Medical and Surgical

Staffed Beds: 649 Admissions: 31340 Census: 478 Outpatient Visits: 610236 Births: 4867 Total Expense ($000): 1309379 Payroll Expense ($000): 535480 Personnel: 7435

✠ **BOSTON CHILDREN'S HOSPITAL (223302)**, 300 Longwood Avenue, Zip 02115–5737; tel. 617/355–6000 **A**1 3 5 8 9 10 **F**3 5 8 11 12 14 18 19 20 21 22 23 24 25 26 27 28 29 30 31 32 34 35 36 37 38 39 40 41 43 44 45 46 48 49 50 51 54 55 57 58 59 60 61 62 63 64 65 67 68 72 74 75 77 78 79 80 81 82 83 84 85 86 87 88 89 92 93 94 97 98 99 100 101 102 104 107 108 109 111 112 113 114 115 116 117 118 119 120 121 123 124 126 129 130 131 132 134 135 136 137 138 139 140 141 142 143 144 146 147 148 **P**3 5
Primary Contact: Sandra L. Fenwick, Chief Executive Officer and President
COO: Kevin B. Churchwell, M.D., Chief Operating Officer and Executive Vice President of Health Affairs
CFO: Douglas M. Vanderslice, Senior Vice President and Chief Financial Officer
CIO: Daniel Nigrin, M.D., Vice President Information Services and Chief Information Officer
CHR: Inez Stewart, Vice President
Web address: www.childrenshospital.org/
Control: Other not–for–profit (including NFP Corporation) **Service:** Children's general

Staffed Beds: 395 Admissions: 15218 Census: 282 Outpatient Visits: 659329 Births: 0 Total Expense ($000): 1260335 Payroll Expense ($000): 442786 Personnel: 8363

✠ **BOSTON MEDICAL CENTER (220031)**, 1 Boston Medical Center Place, Zip 02118–2908; tel. 617/638–8000 **A**1 2 3 5 8 9 10 **F**3 5 8 9 12 13 15 17 18 20 22 24 26 28 29 30 31 32 34 35 36 38 40 41 43 44 45 46 47 48 49 50 51 54 55 56 57 58 59 61 64 65 66 68 70 72 73 74 75 76 77 78 79 81 82 84 85 86 87 88 89 90 97 99 100 101 102 103 104 107 108 110 111 114 116 117 118 119 120 121 123 124 126 129 130 131 132 134 135 136 138 142 143 144 145 146 147 148 **P**7
Primary Contact: Kate Walsh, President and Chief Executive Officer
CFO: Ronald E. Bartlett, Chief Financial Officer
CMO: Ravin Davidoff, M.D., Chief Medical Officer
CHR: Stephanie Lovell, Vice President and General Counsel
Web address: www.bmc.org
Control: Other not–for–profit (including NFP Corporation) **Service:** General Medical and Surgical

Staffed Beds: 461 Admissions: 23752 Census: 316 Outpatient Visits: 1036040 Births: 2501 Total Expense ($000): 1005099 Payroll Expense ($000): 382296 Personnel: 5285

✠ **BRIGHAM AND WOMEN'S FAULKNER HOSPITAL (220119)**, 1153 Centre Street, Zip 02130–3446; tel. 617/983–7000 **A**1 3 5 8 9 10 **F**3 5 11 12 15 18 28 29 30 32 34 35 40 43 44 45 46 48 50 51 57 58 59 60 64 65 68 70 74 75 77 79 81 82 84 85 86 87 93 94 96 98 100 102 103 104 105 107 108 110 111 114 115 119 126 129 130 131 132 135 145 146 147 **S** Partners HealthCare System, Inc., Boston, MA
Primary Contact: Michael Gustafson, M.D., Chief Operating Officer
COO: Michael Gustafson, M.D., Chief Operating Officer
CFO: Vincent McDermott, Vice President, Finance and Real Estate
CMO: Margaret M. Duggan, M.D., Chief Medical Officer
CIO: Jim Anzeveno, Chief Information Officer
CHR: Laura Barnett, Executive Director, Human Resources
CNO: Judy M. Hayes, R.N., Vice President Nursing and Chief Nursing Officer
Web address: www.brighamandwomensfaulkner.org/index.asp
Control: Other not–for–profit (including NFP Corporation) **Service:** General Medical and Surgical

Staffed Beds: 90 Admissions: 7249 Census: 88 Outpatient Visits: 190911 Births: 0 Total Expense ($000): 190616 Payroll Expense ($000): 84749 Personnel: 942

✠ **BRIGHAM AND WOMEN'S HOSPITAL (220110)**, 75 Francis Street, Zip 02115–6110; tel. 617/732–5500 **A**1 3 5 8 9 10 **F**3 5 6 8 9 11 12 13 14 15 16 17 18 20 22 24 26 28 29 30 31 32 33 34 35 36 37 38 39 40 43 44 45 46 47 48 49 50 51 52 54 55 56 57 58 59 60 61 63 64 65 66 68 70 71 72 74 75 76 77 78 79 81 82 83 84 85 86 87 92 93 97 99 100 101 102 103 104 105 107 108 110 111 112 114 115 116 117 118 119 120 121 123 124 126 129 130 131 132 133 134 135 136 137 138 140 141 142 143 144 145 146 147 148 **P**6 **S** Partners HealthCare System, Inc., Boston, MA
Primary Contact: Elizabeth Nabel, M.D., President
COO: Mairead Hickey, Ph.D., Executive Vice President and Chief Operating Officer
CFO: Michael Reney, Chief Financial Officer
CMO: Stanley Ashley, M.D., Chief Medical Officer
CIO: William C. Johnston, Interim Vice President, Information System
CHR: Julie Celano, Vice President Human Resources
CNO: Jacqueline G. Somerville, R.N., Senior Vice President for Patient Care Services and Chief Nursing Officer
Web address: www.brighamandwomens.org
Control: Other not–for–profit (including NFP Corporation) **Service:** General Medical and Surgical

Staffed Beds: 793 Admissions: 43406 Census: 705 Outpatient Visits: 806582 Births: 7867 Total Expense ($000): 2356951 Payroll Expense ($000): 694024 Personnel: 13120

☐ **CARNEY HOSPITAL (220017)**, 2100 Dorchester Avenue, Zip 02124–5615; tel. 617/296–4000, (Nonreporting) **A**1 2 3 5 9 10 **S** Steward Health Care System, LLC, Boston, MA
Primary Contact: Andrew Davis, President
COO: Christian Stroucken, Chief Operating Officer
CFO: David McGrail, Vice President Finance
CMO: Alexander White, Vice President Medical Affairs
CHR: Mary Orlandi, Manager Human Resources
Web address: www.carneyhospital.org
Control: Corporation, Investor–owned, for–profit **Service:** General Medical and Surgical

Staffed Beds: 133

✠ **DANA–FARBER CANCER INSTITUTE (220162)**, 450 Brookline Avenue, Zip 02215–5418; tel. 617/632–3000 **A**1 3 5 9 10 **F**3 11 14 15 29 30 31 32 34 35 36 44 50 54 55 57 58 59 64 65 66 68 71 75 77 78 82 83 84 85 86 87 99 100 101 104 107 108 110 111 114 115 117 119 120 121 123 124 130 132 134 135 136 146 147 148 **P**6
Primary Contact: Edward J. Benz, Jr., M.D., President and Chief Executive Officer
COO: Dorothy E. Puhy, Executive VP and Chief Operating Officer
CMO: Lawrence N. Shulman, M.D., Senior Vice President Medical Affairs and Chief Medical Officer
CIO: Jeffrey R. Kessler, Vice President Information Services
CHR: Emily Barclay, Vice President Human Resources
Web address: www.dana–farber.org
Control: Other not–for–profit (including NFP Corporation) **Service:** General Medical and Surgical

Staffed Beds: 30 Admissions: 990 Census: 24 Outpatient Visits: 355443 Births: 0 Total Expense ($000): 1014752 Payroll Expense ($000): 307777 Personnel: 3964

☐ **DR. SOLOMON CARTER FULLER MENTAL HEALTH CENTER (224040)**, 85 East Newton Street, Zip 02118–2340; tel. 617/626–8700, (Nonreporting) **A**3 5 6 10
Primary Contact: Mary–Louise White, M.D., Chief Executive Officer
Control: Other not–for–profit (including NFP Corporation) **Service:** Psychiatric

Staffed Beds: 32

✠ **FRANCISCAN HOSPITAL FOR CHILDREN (223300)**, 30 Warren Street, Zip 02135–3680; tel. 617/254–3800 **A**1 3 5 9 10 **F**8 29 32 38 39 62 64 68 74 75 81 86 89 90 91 93 97 98 100 104 105 106 130 132 **P**5
Primary Contact: John D. Nash, FACHE, President and Chief Executive Officer
COO: Donna Polselli, Chief Operating Officer
CFO: Alex Denucci, Chief Financial Officer
CMO: Jane E. O'Brien, M.D., Medical Director
CIO: Sean McKeon, Director, Information Technology
CHR: Nancy Murphy, Vice President, Human Resources
CNO: Mary Lou Kelleher, R.N., Vice President, Nursing
Web address: www.franciscanhospital.org
Control: Other not–for–profit (including NFP Corporation) **Service:** Children's rehabilitation

Staffed Beds: 112 Admissions: 806 Census: 58 Outpatient Visits: 28530 Births: 0 Total Expense ($000): 55316 Payroll Expense ($000): 27698 Personnel: 502

MA

★ △ **HEBREW REHABILITATION CENTER (222007)**, 1200 Centre Street, Zip 02131–1097; tel. 617/363–8000, (Total facility includes 50 beds in nursing home–type unit) **A**7 10 **F**1 2 6 18 29 30 34 35 39 50 53 56 57 58 59 60 63 64 65 68 69 75 77 82 83 84 93 97 100 103 104 119 128 130 143 146 148 **P**6
Primary Contact: Mary K. Moscato, President
COO: Gregory P. Toot, Vice President, Post–Acute Care and Professional Services
CFO: Katherine Howard, Vice President Finance and Planning
CMO: Helen Chen, M.D., Chief Medical Officer
CIO: Fran Hinckley, Chief Information Officer
CHR: Deborah Lemmerman, Vice President, Human Resources
CNO: Tammy B. Retalic, R.N., Vice President Nursing and Patient and Family Centered Care
Web address: www.hebrewseniorlife.org
Control: Other not–for–profit (including NFP Corporation) **Service:** Long–Term Acute Care hospital

> **Staffed Beds:** 725 **Admissions:** 1409 **Census:** 668 **Outpatient Visits:** 35050 **Births:** 0 **Total Expense ($000):** 118710 **Payroll Expense ($000):** 72880 **Personnel:** 1065

☐ **MASSACHUSETTS EYE AND EAR INFIRMARY (220075)**, 243 Charles Street, Zip 02114–3002; tel. 617/523–7900 **A**1 3 5 9 10 **F**3 7 8 11 29 30 31 34 35 36 40 41 44 50 54 55 56 57 58 59 64 65 66 68 74 75 77 78 81 82 85 86 87 89 107 111 114 119 130 132 141 143 144 146 148 **P**6
Primary Contact: John R. Fernandez, President and Chief Executive Officer
CFO: CarolAnn Williams, Chief Financial Officer
CIO: Leo Hill, Chief Information Officer
CHR: Martha Pyle Farrell, Vice President Human Resources and General Counsel
Web address: www.masseyeandear.org
Control: Other not–for–profit (including NFP Corporation) **Service:** Eye, ear, nose, and throat

> **Staffed Beds:** 41 **Admissions:** 1512 **Census:** 16 **Outpatient Visits:** 339109 **Births:** 0 **Total Expense ($000):** 222149 **Payroll Expense ($000):** 67503 **Personnel:** 1737

✠ **MASSACHUSETTS GENERAL HOSPITAL (220071)**, 55 Fruit Street, Zip 02114–2696; tel. 617/726–2000, (Includes MASSGENERAL HOSPITAL FOR CHILDREN, 55 Fruit Street, Zip 02114–2621; tel. 888/644–3248) **A**1 3 5 8 9 10 **F**2 3 5 6 8 9 11 12 13 14 15 16 17 18 19 20 21 22 23 24 25 26 27 28 29 30 31 32 33 34 35 36 37 38 39 40 41 43 44 45 46 47 48 49 50 51 52 53 54 55 56 57 58 59 60 61 62 63 64 65 66 68 70 71 72 74 76 77 78 79 80 81 82 84 85 86 87 88 89 91 92 93 94 95 96 97 98 99 100 101 102 103 104 107 108 110 111 112 113 114 115 116 117 118 119 120 121 122 123 124 126 129 130 131 132 134 135 136 137 138 139 140 141 142 143 144 145 146 147 148 **P**6 7 **S** Partners HealthCare System, Inc., Boston, MA
Primary Contact: Peter L. Slavin, M.D., President
CFO: Sally Mason Boemer, Senior Vice President Finance
CMO: Britain Nicholson, M.D., Chief Medical Officer
CIO: Keith Jennings, Chief Information Officer
CHR: Jeff Davis, Senior Vice President Human Resources
CNO: Jeanette R. Ives Erickson, MS, Senior Vice President Patient Care and Chief Nurse
Web address: www.massgeneral.org
Control: Other not–for–profit (including NFP Corporation) **Service:** General Medical and Surgical

> **Staffed Beds:** 999 **Admissions:** 49079 **Census:** 810 **Outpatient Visits:** 962603 **Births:** 3695 **Total Expense ($000):** 3098945 **Payroll Expense ($000):** 986809 **Personnel:** 17036

✠ **NEW ENGLAND BAPTIST HOSPITAL (220088)**, 125 Parker Hill Avenue, Zip 02120–2847; tel. 617/754–5800 **A**1 3 5 9 10 **F**3 8 9 11 14 18 20 29 30 34 35 36 37 44 45 50 51 53 54 57 58 59 60 64 65 68 70 74 75 77 79 81 82 85 86 87 91 92 93 96 97 100 107 108 111 119 130 131 132 141 143 144 146 148
Primary Contact: Trish Hannon, FACHE, President and Chief Executive Officer
CFO: Thomas Gheringhelli, Chief Financial Officer
CIO: Maureen Mulkerrin, Vice President Technology Risk Management, Corporate Compliance and Chief Information Officer
CHR: Linda Thompson, Vice President Human Resources
CNO: Mary Sullivan Smith, R.N., Vice President Clinical Operations and Chief Nursing Officer
Web address: www.nebh.org
Control: Other not–for–profit (including NFP Corporation) **Service:** Orthopedic

> **Staffed Beds:** 118 **Admissions:** 7743 **Census:** 69 **Outpatient Visits:** 139107 **Births:** 0 **Total Expense ($000):** 213522 **Payroll Expense ($000):** 79118 **Personnel:** 1072

✠ **RADIUS SPECIALTY HOSPITAL BOSTON (222010)**, 59 Townsend Street, Zip 02119–1318; tel. 617/989–8400 **A**1 10 **F**1 28 29 61 119 148
Primary Contact: Daniel Mitchell, President and Chief Executive Officer
CFO: Scott T. Kosowicz, Chief Financial Officer
CMO: James Quirk, M.D., Chief Medical Officer
CHR: Christine Bresnahan, Manager Human Resources
Web address: www.radiushospital.com
Control: Corporation, Investor–owned, for–profit **Service:** Long–Term Acute Care hospital

> **Staffed Beds:** 122 **Admissions:** 1078 **Census:** 84 **Outpatient Visits:** 0 **Births:** 0 **Total Expense ($000):** 36328 **Payroll Expense ($000):** 18263 **Personnel:** 315

☐ **SHRINERS HOSPITALS FOR CHILDREN–BOSTON (223304)**, (Pediatric Burns, Orthopaedics, Cleft Lip & Palate), 51 Blossom Street, Zip 02114–2601; tel. 617/722–3000 **A**1 3 5 10 **F**3 16 29 30 34 35 57 64 68 75 77 79 81 85 86 87 93 99 104 130 132 141 143 146 148 **S** Shriners Hospitals for Children, Tampa, FL
Primary Contact: C. Thomas D'Esmond, FACHE, Administrator
CFO: Maria Chung, CPA, Director Fiscal Services
CMO: Matthias B. Donelan, M.D., Chief of Staff
CIO: Mary Dolan, Regional Director Information Services and HIPAA Security Official
CHR: John Donlin, Regional Director Human Resources – Boston, Erie, and Springfield
Web address: www.shrinershospitalsforchildren.org/Hospitals/Locations/Boston.aspx
Control: Other not–for–profit (including NFP Corporation) **Service:** Children's other specialty

> **Staffed Beds:** 30 **Admissions:** 1064 **Census:** 7 **Outpatient Visits:** 5664 **Births:** 0 **Total Expense ($000):** 30629 **Payroll Expense ($000):** 13905 **Personnel:** 181

✠ **TUFTS MEDICAL CENTER (220116)**, 800 Washington Street, Zip 02111–1552; tel. 617/636–5000 **A**1 2 3 5 8 9 10 **F**3 12 13 14 15 17 18 19 20 21 22 23 24 25 26 27 28 29 30 31 32 33 40 43 44 45 47 49 50 51 52 55 56 57 58 59 61 64 65 68 70 71 72 74 75 76 77 78 79 81 82 84 85 86 87 88 89 93 97 98 99 100 102 104 107 108 111 114 115 116 117 118 119 120 121 123 124 126 129 130 131 132 134 135 136 137 138 143 146 147 148 **P**5
Primary Contact: Michael Wagner, M.D., President and Chief Executive Officer
CFO: C. Okey Agba, Senior Vice President, Chief Financial Officer and Treasurer
CMO: David Fairchild, M.D., Chief Medical Officer
CIO: William Shickolovich, Chief Information Officer
CNO: Therese M. Hudson–Jinks, R.N., Chief Nursing Officer
Web address: www.tuftsmedicalcenter.org
Control: Other not–for–profit (including NFP Corporation) **Service:** General Medical and Surgical

> **Staffed Beds:** 293 **Admissions:** 19046 **Census:** 274 **Outpatient Visits:** 401046 **Births:** 1144 **Total Expense ($000):** 609285 **Payroll Expense ($000):** 256939 **Personnel:** 4616

★ △ **VETERANS AFFAIRS BOSTON HEALTHCARE SYSTEM**, 1400 VFW Parkway, Zip 02132–4927; tel. 617/323–7700, (Nonreporting) **A**3 5 7 8 **S** Department of Veterans Affairs, Washington, DC
Primary Contact: Vincent Ng, Director
CFO: Joe Costa, Chief Financial Officer
CMO: Brian Hoffman, M.D., Chief Medical Services
CIO: David M. Goodman, Ph.D., Chief Information Officer
CHR: William Warfield, Chief Human Resources Management
Web address: www.boston.va.gov/
Control: Veterans Affairs, Government, federal **Service:** General Medical and Surgical

> **Staffed Beds:** 361

VETERANS AFFAIRS MEDICAL CENTER See Brockton Veterans Affairs Medical Center, Brockton

BRADFORD—Essex County

✠ △ **WHITTIER REHABILITATION HOSPITAL (222047)**, 145 Ward Hill Avenue, Zip 01835–6928; tel. 978/372–8000, (Nonreporting) **A**1 7 10 **S** Whittier Health Network, Haverhill, MA
Primary Contact: Alfred J. Arcidi, M.D., Senior Vice President
Web address: www.whittierhealth.com
Control: Partnership, Investor–owned, for–profit **Service:** Long–Term Acute Care hospital

> **Staffed Beds:** 60

Hospital, Medicare Provider Number, Address, Telephone, Approval, Facility, and Physician Codes, Health Care System

★ American Hospital Association (AHA) membership
☐ The Joint Commission accreditation
◇ DNV Healthcare Inc. accreditation
○ Healthcare Facilities Accreditation Program
△ Commission on Accreditation of Rehabilitation Facilities (CARF) accreditation

MA

BRAINTREE—Norfolk County

☐ **BRAINTREE REHABILITATION HOSPITAL (223027)**, 250 Pond Street, Zip 02184–5351; tel. 781/348–2500 **A**1 5 10 **F**29 34 35 54 57 59 64 74 75 77 78 79 86 87 90 91 92 93 101 108 119 130 131 132 146 **P**5 **S** Five Star Quality Care, Newton, MA
Primary Contact: Randy Doherty, CPA, Chief Executive Officer
CFO: Thomas Whalen, Chief Financial Officer
CMO: Arthur Williams, M.D., Medical Director
CHR: Tara Spellacy, Director Human Resources
CNO: Jinia Drinkwater, R.N., Director Patient Care Services
Web address: www.braintreerehabhospital.com
Control: Corporation, Investor–owned, for–profit **Service:** Rehabilitation

> **Staffed Beds:** 187 **Admissions:** 2364 **Census:** 100 **Outpatient Visits:** 109670 **Births:** 0 **Total Expense ($000):** 58734 **Payroll Expense ($000):** 34775 **Personnel:** 487

BRIDGEWATER—Plymouth County

BRIDGEWATER STATE HOSPITAL, 20 Administration Road, Zip 02324–3201; tel. 508/279–4521, (Nonreporting) **A**3 5
Primary Contact: Kenneth W. Nelson, Superintendent
CFO: Diane Wholley, Director Fiscal Services
Control: State–Government, nonfederal **Service:** Psychiatric

> **Staffed Beds:** 350

BRIGHTON—Suffolk County

CARITAS ST. ELIZABETH'S MEDICAL CENTER See St. Elizabeth's Medical Center

✠ **KINDRED HOSPITAL–BOSTON (222045)**, 1515 Commonwealth Avenue, Zip 02135–3617; tel. 617/254–1100, (Nonreporting) **A**1 10 **S** Kindred Healthcare, Louisville, KY
Primary Contact: Susan Downey, R.N., MS, Chief Executive Officer
CFO: Lawrence J. Toye, Chief Financial Officer
CMO: Mark Rohrer, M.D., Chief Medical Officer
Web address: www.kindredbos.com/
Control: Corporation, Investor–owned, for–profit **Service:** Long–Term Acute Care hospital

> **Staffed Beds:** 59

☐ **ST. ELIZABETH'S MEDICAL CENTER (220036)**, 736 Cambridge Street, Zip 02135–2997; tel. 617/789–3000, (Nonreporting) **A**1 2 3 5 8 9 10 **S** Steward Health Care System, LLC, Boston, MA
Primary Contact: Kevin R. Hannifan, President
COO: Nathan Howell, Chief Operating Officer
CFO: Jeffrey P. Dion, Vice President Finance
CIO: Joseph Schmitt, Chief Information Officer
CHR: Claudia Henderson, Chief Human Resources
Web address: www.stewardhealth.org/St_Elizabeths
Control: Corporation, Investor–owned, for–profit **Service:** General Medical and Surgical

> **Staffed Beds:** 338

BROCKTON—Plymouth County

★ **BROCKTON VETERANS AFFAIRS MEDICAL CENTER**, 940 Belmont Street, Zip 02301–5596; tel. 508/583–4500, (Includes VETERANS AFFAIRS MEDICAL CENTER, 1400 VFW Parkway, West Roxbury, Boston, Zip 02132, Mailing Address: 1400 VVF Parkway, West Roxbury, Zip 02132; tel. 617/323–7700; William H. Kelleher, Director), (Nonreporting) **A**3 5 8 **S** Department of Veterans Affairs, Washington, DC
Primary Contact: Vincent Ng, Interim Director
CFO: Joe Costa, Acting Chief Fiscal Officer
Web address: www.boston.va.gov/
Control: Veterans Affairs, Government, federal **Service:** General Medical and Surgical

> **Staffed Beds:** 375

CARITAS GOOD SAMARITAN MEDICAL CENTER See Good Samaritan Medical Center

☐ **GOOD SAMARITAN MEDICAL CENTER (220111)**, 235 North Pearl Street, Zip 02301–1794; tel. 508/427–3000, (Includes GOOD SAMARITAN MEDICAL CENTER – CUSHING CAMPUS, 235 North Pearl Street, Zip 02401–1794; tel. 508/427–3000), (Nonreporting) **A**1 2 3 5 9 10 **S** Steward Health Care System, LLC, Boston, MA
Primary Contact: John A. Jurczyk, FACHE, Interim President
COO: Donna Rubinate, R.N., Chief Operating Officer
CFO: Thomas Whalen, Vice President Finance
CMO: Scott Stewart, M.D., Vice President Medical Management
CIO: Lori Caswell, Director Information Technology
CHR: David J. Cronin, Regional Vice President Human Resources
Web address: www.stewardhealth.org/Good–Samaritan
Control: Corporation, Investor–owned, for–profit **Service:** General Medical and Surgical

> **Staffed Beds:** 190

✠ **SIGNATURE HEALTHCARE BROCKTON HOSPITAL (220052)**, 680 Centre Street, Zip 02302–3395; tel. 508/941–7000, (Total facility includes 29 beds in nursing home–type unit) **A**1 2 6 9 10 **F**3 11 12 13 15 17 18 20 22 24 28 29 30 31 32 34 35 38 40 45 46 47 48 49 50 51 52 54 55 56 57 58 59 60 61 64 65 66 68 70 73 74 75 76 77 78 79 81 82 84 85 87 89 93 97 98 100 101 102 103 104 105 107 108 110 111 114 115 116 117 118 119 120 121 123 128 130 131 132 135 143 144 146 147 148 **P**6 8
Primary Contact: Kim Norton Hollon, FACHE, Chief Executive Officer
CFO: James Papadakos, Chief Financial Officer
CMO: Vera De Palo, M.D., Chief Medical Officer
CIO: Marc Delacroix, Chief Information Officer
CHR: David Fisher, Vice President Human Resources
CNO: Kim Walsh, Chief Nursing Officer
Web address: www.signature–healthcare.org
Control: Other not–for–profit (including NFP Corporation) **Service:** General Medical and Surgical

> **Staffed Beds:** 245 **Admissions:** 11925 **Census:** 145 **Outpatient Visits:** 362941 **Births:** 963 **Total Expense ($000):** 205609 **Payroll Expense ($000):** 93547 **Personnel:** 1272

BROOKLINE—Norfolk County

☐ **ARBOUR H. R. I. HOSPITAL (224018)**, 227 Babcock Street, Zip 02446–6799; tel. 617/731–3200, (Nonreporting) **A**1 9 10 **S** Universal Health Services, Inc., King of Prussia, PA
Primary Contact: Patrick Moallemian, Chief Executive Officer and Managing Director
CFO: James Rollins, Chief Financial Officer
CMO: Anthony Raynes, M.D., Psychiatrist in Chief
CHR: Kris Munson, Director Human Resources
Web address: www.arbourhealth.com
Control: Corporation, Investor–owned, for–profit **Service:** Psychiatric

> **Staffed Beds:** 68

☐ **BOURNEWOOD HEALTH SYSTEMS (224022)**, 300 South Street, Zip 02467–3658; tel. 617/469–0300 **A**1 3 5 9 10 **F**4 5 98 99 104 105 130 132 **P**1
Primary Contact: Philip A. Mason, Chief Executive Officer
CFO: Michael Gale, Chief Financial Officer
CMO: Carmel Heinsohn, M.D., Medical Director
CHR: Paula Berardi, Manager Human Resources
Web address: www.bournewood.com
Control: Corporation, Investor–owned, for–profit **Service:** Psychiatric

> **Staffed Beds:** 81 **Admissions:** 3470 **Census:** 76 **Outpatient Visits:** 11129 **Births:** 0 **Total Expense ($000):** 19653 **Payroll Expense ($000):** 12272 **Personnel:** 181

BURLINGTON—Middlesex County

✠ **LAHEY HOSPITAL & MEDICAL CENTER, BURLINGTON (220171)**, 41 Mall Road, Zip 01805–0001; tel. 781/744–5100, (Includes LAHEY MEDICAL CENTER, PEABODY, 1 Essex Center Drive, Peabody, Zip 01960–2901; tel. 978/538–4000) **A**1 2 3 5 8 9 10 **F**3 5 8 9 11 12 14 15 17 18 20 22 24 26 28 29 30 31 34 35 36 37 38 40 42 43 44 45 46 47 48 49 50 51 53 54 55 56 57 58 59 61 64 65 66 68 70 74 75 77 78 79 81 82 84 85 86 87 91 92 93 94 96 97 99 100 101 102 103 104 107 108 110 111 114 115 116 117 118 119 120 121 123 124 126 129 130 131 132 135 136 138 139 141 142 143 144 145 146 147 148 **P**6 **S** Lahey Health, Burlington, MA
Primary Contact: Joanne Conroy, M.D., Chief Executive Officer
COO: Richard R. Bias, Chief Operating Officer
CFO: Timothy P. O'Connor, Executive Vice President and Chief Financial Officer
CMO: Andrew Villanueva, M.D., Interim Chief Medical Officer
CIO: Bruce Metz, Ph.D., Senior Vice President and Chief Information Officer
CHR: Elizabeth P. Conrad, Senior Vice President and Chief Human Resource Officer
CNO: Lisa Colombo, R.N., Senior Vice President and Chief Nursing Officer
Web address: www.lahey.org
Control: Other not–for–profit (including NFP Corporation) **Service:** General Medical and Surgical

> **Staffed Beds:** 341 **Admissions:** 20955 **Census:** 280 **Outpatient Visits:** 925234 **Births:** 0 **Total Expense ($000):** 733829 **Payroll Expense ($000):** 261286 **Personnel:** 5200

MA

CAMBRIDGE—Middlesex County

⊞ **CAMBRIDGE HEALTH ALLIANCE (220011)**, 1493 Cambridge Street, Zip 02139–1099; tel. 617/665–1000, (Includes CAMBRIDGE HOSPITAL, 1493 Cambridge Street, tel. 617/498–1000; SOMERVILLE HOSPITAL, 230 Highland Avenue, Somerville, Zip 02143; tel. 617/666–4400; WHIDDEN MEMORIAL HOSPITAL, 103 Garland Street, Everett, Zip 02149–5095; tel. 617/389–6270) **A**1 2 3 5 8 9 10 **F**5 11 13 15 29 30 31 32 34 35 36 38 39 40 44 45 46 47 48 49 50 56 57 58 59 61 64 65 66 68 70 75 76 77 78 79 81 82 86 87 93 97 98 99 100 101 102 103 104 107 108 110 111 114 115 119 129 130 131 132 134 135 143 146 147 148 **P**6
Primary Contact: Patrick R. Wardell, Chief Executive Officer
CFO: Jill I. Batty, Chief Financial Officer
CMO: Assaad Sayah, M.D., Chief Medical Officer
CIO: Judith S. Klickstein, Chief Information Officer
CHR: Joy U. Curtis, Senior Vice President Human Resources
CNO: Elizabeth Cadigan, R.N., Senior Vice President Patient Care Services and Chief Nursing Officer
Web address: www.challiance.org
Control: Hospital district or authority, Government, nonfederal **Service:** General Medical and Surgical

Staffed Beds: 219 Admissions: 11745 Census: 162 Outpatient Visits: 661310 Births: 1217 Total Expense ($000): 554460 Payroll Expense ($000): 302023 Personnel: 3211

⊞ **MOUNT AUBURN HOSPITAL (220002)**, 330 Mount Auburn Street, Zip 02138–5597; tel. 617/492–3500 **A**1 2 3 5 8 9 10 **F**3 5 11 12 13 14 15 17 18 20 22 24 26 28 29 30 31 34 35 37 40 45 49 50 51 52 55 56 57 58 59 60 61 62 64 65 68 70 73 74 75 76 77 78 79 81 82 86 87 93 97 98 100 101 102 103 104 107 108 110 111 114 115 117 118 119 120 121 123 124 126 129 130 131 132 135 144 145 146 147 **P**5 6 7
Primary Contact: Jeanette G. Clough, President and Chief Executive Officer
COO: Nicholas T. Dileso, R.N., Chief Operating Officer
CFO: William Sullivan, Chief Financial Officer
CMO: A. Kim Saal, M.D., President Medical Staff
CIO: Bob Todd, Director Information Systems
CHR: Tom Fabiano, Director Human Resources
Web address: www.mountauburnhospital.org
Control: Other not–for–profit (including NFP Corporation) **Service:** General Medical and Surgical

Staffed Beds: 187 Admissions: 10814 Census: 133 Outpatient Visits: 174104 Births: 2566 Total Expense ($000): 293321 Payroll Expense ($000): 140311 Personnel: 2274

SPAULDING HOSPITAL CAMBRIDGE See Spaulding Hospital for Continuing Medical Care Cambridge

⊞ **SPAULDING HOSPITAL FOR CONTINUING MEDICAL CARE CAMBRIDGE (222000)**, 1575 Cambridge Street, Zip 02138–4308; tel. 617/876–4344, (Nonreporting) **A**1 10 **S** Partners HealthCare System, Inc., Boston, MA
Primary Contact: Maureen Banks, R.N., MS, President
COO: Timothy Lynch, Vice President Operations
CFO: Mary Shaughnessy, Vice President Finance
CMO: Jonathon Schwartz, M.D., Medical Director and Chief Medical Officer
CIO: John Wilder, Director Information Systems
CHR: Jack Carroll, Senior Director Human Resources
Web address: www.spauldingnetwork.org
Control: Other not–for–profit (including NFP Corporation) **Service:** Long–Term Acute Care hospital

Staffed Beds: 180

CANTON—Norfolk County

⊞ **MASSACHUSETTS HOSPITAL SCHOOL (222025)**, 3 Randolph Street, Zip 02021–2351; tel. 781/828–2440, (Nonreporting) **A**1 10 **S** Massachusetts Department of Public Health, Boston, MA
Primary Contact: Brian V. Devin, Chief Executive Officer
CFO: Sharon Porter, Chief Financial Officer
CMO: Aruna Sachdev, M.D., Medical Director
CIO: Robert Lima, Director Information Systems
CHR: Trish Scully, Manager Employment Services
Web address: www.mhsf.us/
Control: State–Government, nonfederal **Service:** Children's Long–Term Acute Care

Staffed Beds: 80

CHARLESTOWN—Suffolk County

⊞ △ **SPAULDING REHABILITATION HOSPITAL (223034)**, 300 First Avenue, Zip 02129–3109; tel. 617/573–7000 **A**1 3 5 7 10 **F**3 7 29 30 34 35 36 39 50 57 58 59 60 64 74 75 77 82 85 86 87 90 91 92 93 94 95 96 100 104 119 129 130 131 132 143 146 148 **S** Partners HealthCare System, Inc., Boston, MA
Primary Contact: David E. Storto, President
COO: Maureen Banks, R.N., Chief Operating Officer
CFO: Mary Shaughnessy, Vice President Finance
CMO: Ross Zafonte, D.O., Chief, Physical Medicine and Rehabilitation and Vice President Medical Affairs, Research and Education
CIO: John Campbell, Director Management Information Systems
CHR: Russell Averna, Director Human Resources
Web address: www.spauldingrehab.org
Control: Other not–for–profit (including NFP Corporation) **Service:** Rehabilitation

Staffed Beds: 164 Admissions: 2250 Census: 135 Outpatient Visits: 158985 Births: 0 Total Expense ($000): 120050 Payroll Expense ($000): 56674 Personnel: 1118

CLINTON—Worcester County

★ ◇ **CLINTON HOSPITAL (220058)**, 201 Highland Street, Zip 01510–1096; tel. 978/368–3000, (Nonreporting) **A**3 5 9 10 21 **S** UMass Memorial Health Care, Inc., Worcester, MA
Primary Contact: Sheila Daly, President and Chief Executive Officer
CFO: Steven McCue, Chief Financial Officer
CHR: Martha Chiarchiaro, Vice President Human Resources
CNO: Charlene Elie, Vice President Patient Care Services
Web address: www.clintonhospital.org
Control: Other not–for–profit (including NFP Corporation) **Service:** General Medical and Surgical

Staffed Beds: 41

CONCORD—Middlesex County

⊞ **EMERSON HOSPITAL (220084)**, 133 Old Road to Nine Acre Corner, Zip 01742–9120; tel. 978/369–1400 **A**1 5 9 10 **F**3 7 8 11 12 13 14 15 17 18 28 29 30 31 32 34 35 36 37 38 40 45 48 49 50 51 54 57 59 60 62 64 65 68 74 75 76 77 78 79 81 85 86 87 89 93 98 100 101 102 103 104 105 107 110 111 114 115 119 121 128 129 130 131 132 141 145 146 148 **P**5 8
Primary Contact: Christine C. Schuster, R.N., President and Chief Executive Officer
CFO: John O. Wilhelm, Jr., Senior Vice President and Chief Financial Officer
CMO: C. Gregory Martin, M.D., Chief Medical Officer
CIO: John O. Wilhelm, Jr., Senior Vice President and Chief Financial Officer
Web address: www.emersonhospital.org
Control: Other not–for–profit (including NFP Corporation) **Service:** General Medical and Surgical

Staffed Beds: 170 Admissions: 7855 Census: 109 Outpatient Visits: 252816 Births: 1150 Total Expense ($000): 186353 Payroll Expense ($000): 8588 Personnel: 968

EAST SANDWICH—Barnstable County

⊞ △ **SPAULDING REHABILITATION HOSPITAL CAPE COD (223032)**, 311 Service Road, Zip 02537–1370; tel. 508/833–4000, (Nonreporting) **A**1 7 10 **S** Partners HealthCare System, Inc., Boston, MA
Primary Contact: Maureen Banks, R.N., MS, President
COO: Stephanie Nadolny, Vice President Clinical Services
CFO: Mary Shaughnessy, Vice President Finance
CMO: David Lowell, M.D., Medical Director
CIO: John Campbell, Chief Information Officer
CHR: Del Pontremoli, Director Human Resources
Web address: www.rhci.org
Control: Other not–for–profit (including NFP Corporation) **Service:** Rehabilitation

Staffed Beds: 60

EVERETT—Middlesex County

WHIDDEN MEMORIAL HOSPITAL See Cambridge Health Alliance, Cambridge

FALL RIVER—Bristol County

CHARLTON MEMORIAL HOSPITAL See Southcoast Hospitals Group

☐ **DR. J. CORRIGAN MENTAL HEALTH CENTER (224028)**, 49 Hillside Street, Zip 02720–5266; tel. 508/235–7200, (Nonreporting) **A**1 10 **S** Massachusetts Department of Mental Health, Boston, MA
Primary Contact: Roberta H. Guez, Director
Control: State–Government, nonfederal **Service:** Psychiatric

Staffed Beds: 16

MA

Hospital, Medicare Provider Number, Address, Telephone, Approval, Facility, and Physician Codes, Health Care System

★ American Hospital Association (AHA) membership
☐ The Joint Commission accreditation ◇ DNV Healthcare Inc. accreditation

○ Healthcare Facilities Accreditation Program
△ Commission on Accreditation of Rehabilitation Facilities (CARF) accreditation

MA

☐ **SAINT ANNE'S HOSPITAL (220020)**, 795 Middle Street, Zip 02721–1798; tel. 508/674–5741, (Nonreporting) **A**1 2 9 10 **S** Steward Health Care System, LLC, Boston, MA
Primary Contact: Craig A. Jesiolowski, FACHE, President
CFO: Michael Bushell, Vice President Finance, Business Development and Support Services
CMO: Harvey Kowaloff, M.D., Vice President Medical Affairs
CHR: Lisa Berry, Director
CNO: Carole Billington, R.N., Vice President Patient Care Services
Web address: www.saintanneshospital.org
Control: Corporation, Investor–owned, for–profit **Service:** General Medical and Surgical

Staffed Beds: 92

⊞ **SOUTHCOAST HOSPITALS GROUP (220074)**, 363 Highland Avenue, Zip 02720–3703; tel. 508/679–3131, (Includes CHARLTON MEMORIAL HOSPITAL, 363 Highland Avenue, tel. 508/679–3131; ST. LUKE'S HOSPITAL, 101 Page Street, New Bedford, Zip 02740; tel. 508/997–1515; TOBEY HOSPITAL, 43 High Street, Wareham, Zip 02571; tel. 508/295–0880) **A**1 2 9 10 **F**3 8 11 12 13 14 15 17 18 20 22 24 26 28 29 30 31 32 34 35 36 37 40 41 44 45 46 47 48 49 50 51 54 55 56 57 58 59 60 61 64 68 70 71 73 74 75 76 77 78 79 81 82 83 84 85 86 87 89 90 91 92 93 98 101 102 103 107 108 110 111 114 115 117 118 119 120 121 122 123 124 126 130 131 132 134 144 145 146 147 148 **P**5 6
Primary Contact: Keith A. Hovan, R.N., President and Chief Executive Officer
COO: Linda Bodenmann, Chief Operating Officer
CFO: Gary F. Conner, Chief Financial Officer
CMO: Robert Caldas, D.O., Chief Medical Officer
CIO: Joan McFaul, Senior Vice President and Chief Information Officer
CHR: David DeJesus, Senior Vice President Human Resources
CNO: Carol Conley, R.N., Chief Nursing Officer
Web address: www.southcoast.org
Control: Other not–for–profit (including NFP Corporation) **Service:** General Medical and Surgical

Staffed Beds: 587 Admissions: 37124 Census: 502 Outpatient Visits: 898475 Births: 3403 Total Expense ($000): 559367 Payroll Expense ($000): 324345 Personnel: 4368

FALMOUTH—Barnstable County

⊞ **FALMOUTH HOSPITAL (220135)**, 100 Ter Heun Drive, Zip 02540–2599; tel. 508/548–5300 **A**1 2 9 10 **F**3 8 11 13 15 18 20 28 29 30 34 35 36 38 40 45 50 53 54 57 59 60 61 64 65 68 70 74 75 76 77 78 79 81 82 85 86 87 89 93 96 99 100 101 102 103 104 107 108 110 111 115 118 119 129 130 131 132 135 143 144 146 147 148 **P**6 8 **S** Cape Cod Healthcare, Inc., Hyannis, MA
Primary Contact: Susan M. Wing, R.N., Interim Chief Operating Officer
COO: Jeff Dykens, CPA, Chief Operating Officer
CFO: Michael Connors, Senior Vice President and Chief Financial Officer
CMO: James D. Butterick, M.D., Chief Medical Officer
CIO: Jeanne M. Fallon, Chief Information Officer
CHR: Emily Schorer, Vice President, Human Resources
Web address: www.capecodhealth.org
Control: Other not–for–profit (including NFP Corporation) **Service:** General Medical and Surgical

Staffed Beds: 95 Admissions: 12155 Census: 64 Outpatient Visits: 133863 Births: 449 Total Expense ($000): 135268 Payroll Expense ($000): 62078 Personnel: 471

FRAMINGHAM—Middlesex County

⊞ **METROWEST MEDICAL CENTER (220175)**, 115 Lincoln Street, Zip 01702–6342; tel. 508/383–1000, (Includes FRAMINGHAM UNION HOSPITAL, 115 Lincoln Street, Zip 01702; tel. 508/383–1000; LEONARD MORSE HOSPITAL, 67 Union Street, Natick, Zip 01760; tel. 508/650–7000) **A**1 2 3 5 9 10 **F**3 5 12 13 14 15 18 20 22 26 28 29 30 31 32 34 35 36 40 44 45 49 50 54 56 57 59 61 62 63 64 65 68 70 72 74 75 76 78 79 81 83 85 86 87 89 93 97 98 99 100 102 103 104 105 107 108 110 114 115 118 119 120 121 129 130 131 132 134 135 143 144 146 147 148 **S** TENET Healthcare Corporation, Dallas, TX
Primary Contact: Barbara J. Doyle, R.N., MS, Chief Executive Officer
CHR: Rebecca Heffernan, Director Human Resources
CNO: Donna T. Gemme, R.N., Chief Nursing Officer
Web address: www.mwmc.com
Control: Corporation, Investor–owned, for–profit **Service:** General Medical and Surgical

Staffed Beds: 143 Admissions: 11332 Census: 137 Outpatient Visits: 335935 Births: 846 Total Expense ($000): 246120 Payroll Expense ($000): 120022 Personnel: 1802

GARDNER—Worcester County

☐ **HEYWOOD HOSPITAL (220095)**, 242 Green Street, Zip 01440–1373; tel. 978/632–3420, (Nonreporting) **A**1 5 9 10
Primary Contact: Winfield S. Brown, FACHE, President and Chief Executive Officer
CFO: Robert Crosby, Senior Vice President and Chief Financial Officer
CHR: Thomas Cady, Vice President Human Resources
Web address: www.heywood.org
Control: Other not–for–profit (including NFP Corporation) **Service:** General Medical and Surgical

Staffed Beds: 128

GLOUCESTER—Essex County

ADDISON GILBERT HOSPITAL See Beverly Hospital, Beverly

GREAT BARRINGTON—Berkshire County

⊞ **FAIRVIEW HOSPITAL (221302)**, 29 Lewis Avenue, Zip 01230–1713; tel. 413/528–0790 **A**1 9 10 18 **F**3 11 13 15 18 29 30 34 35 40 45 46 49 50 54 57 59 64 65 68 70 75 76 79 81 85 86 87 89 93 94 107 108 110 114 119 130 131 132 133 135 146 147 148 **P**6 **S** Berkshire Health Systems, Inc., Pittsfield, MA
Primary Contact: Eugene A. Dellea, President
COO: Doreen M. Sylvia–Hutchinson, Vice President Operations and Chief Nurse Executive
CFO: Anthony Rinaldi, Executive Vice President
CMO: Brian Burke, M.D., President Medical Staff
CHR: Laura Farkas, Director Human Resources
Web address: www.bhs1.org/body_fh.cfm?id=39
Control: Other not–for–profit (including NFP Corporation) **Service:** General Medical and Surgical

Staffed Beds: 24 Admissions: 1025 Census: 10 Outpatient Visits: 75075 Births: 151 Total Expense ($000): 42707 Payroll Expense ($000): 20725 Personnel: 240

GREENFIELD—Franklin County

⊞ **BAYSTATE FRANKLIN MEDICAL CENTER (220016)**, 164 High Street, Zip 01301–2613; tel. 413/773–0211 **A**1 9 10 **F**3 11 12 13 14 15 18 24 28 29 30 31 34 35 36 40 45 46 47 48 50 51 55 57 59 60 64 68 70 74 75 76 77 78 79 81 82 85 86 87 89 93 98 100 101 105 107 108 110 111 115 118 119 129 130 131 132 146 147 148 **S** Baystate Health, Inc., Springfield, MA
Primary Contact: Steven F. Bradley, President, Baystate Northern Region
COO: Gina Campbell, Chief Operating Officer
CFO: Andrea Nathanson, Director Finance
CMO: Gerda Maissel, M.D., Chief Medical Officer
CHR: Kerry Damon, Director Human Resources
CNO: Leesa–Lee Keith, R.N., Chief Nursing Officer
Web address: www.baystatehealth.com/fmc
Control: Other not–for–profit (including NFP Corporation) **Service:** General Medical and Surgical

Staffed Beds: 90 Admissions: 3864 Census: 42 Outpatient Visits: 110016 Births: 463 Total Expense ($000): 78573 Payroll Expense ($000): 32615 Personnel: 407

HAVERHILL—Essex County

BALDPATE HOSPITAL (224033), 83 Baldpate Road, Zip 01833–2303; tel. 978/352–2131, (Nonreporting) **A**9 10
Primary Contact: Lucille M. Batal, Administrator
Web address: www.baldpateh.com
Control: Corporation, Investor–owned, for–profit **Service:** Psychiatric

Staffed Beds: 59

☐ **MERRIMACK VALLEY HOSPITAL (220174)**, 140 Lincoln Avenue, Zip 01830–6798; tel. 978/374–2000, (Nonreporting) **A**1 9 10 **S** Steward Health Care System, LLC, Boston, MA
Primary Contact: Michael F. Collins, Chief Executive Officer
COO: Diane Lovallo, R.N., Chief Nursing Officer
CMO: George Kwass, M.D., Chief of Staff
CIO: Mark Nightingale, Senior Administrator
CHR: Gina Lagana, Director Human Resources
Web address: www.steward.org/merrimack–valley
Control: Corporation, Investor–owned, for–profit **Service:** General Medical and Surgical

Staffed Beds: 90

WHITTIER PAVILION (224039), 76 Summer Street, Zip 01830–5814; tel. 978/373–8222, (Nonreporting) **A**9 10 **S** Whittier Health Network, Haverhill, MA
Primary Contact: Alfred L. Arcidi, M.D., Chief Executive Officer
Web address: www.whittierhealth.com
Control: Partnership, Investor–owned, for–profit **Service:** Psychiatric

Staffed Beds: 65

Many Facility Codes have changed. Please refer to the AHA Guide Code Chart. © 2014 AHA Guide

HOLYOKE—Hampden County

✠ **HOLYOKE MEDICAL CENTER (220024)**, 575 Beech Street, Zip 01040–2223; tel. 413/534–2500 **A**1 2 5 9 10 **F**3 5 9 11 13 14 15 17 18 28 29 31 34 35 38 40 44 45 46 49 50 57 59 64 65 68 70 74 75 76 77 78 79 81 82 85 86 87 89 91 92 93 96 98 100 101 102 104 105 107 108 110 111 114 118 119 124 129 130 132 135 143 145 146 147 148 **P**8
Primary Contact: Spiros Hatiras, FACHE, President and Chief Executive Officer
CFO: Antonio Correia, Chief Financial Officer
CMO: Karen Ferroni, M.D., Medical Director
CIO: Carl Cameron, Director Information Systems
CHR: Mary Kelleher, Vice President Human Resources
Web address: www.holyokehealth.com
Control: Other not–for–profit (including NFP Corporation) **Service:** General Medical and Surgical

Staffed Beds: 198 **Admissions:** 5469 **Census:** 66 **Outpatient Visits:** 276266 **Births:** 438 **Total Expense ($000):** 116542 **Payroll Expense ($000):** 66379	

HYANNIS—Barnstable County

✠ **CAPE COD HOSPITAL (220012)**, 27 Park Street, Zip 02601–5230; tel. 508/771–1800 **A**1 2 5 9 10 20 **F**3 11 13 14 15 17 18 20 22 24 26 29 30 31 34 35 37 38 40 45 49 50 51 54 57 61 64 65 68 70 74 75 76 77 78 79 81 82 85 86 87 89 93 97 98 99 100 101 102 103 104 105 107 108 110 111 114 115 119 120 121 123 124 126 130 131 132 143 144 146 147 **P**6 8 **S** Cape Cod Healthcare, Inc., Hyannis, MA
Primary Contact: Michael K. Lauf, President and Chief Executive Officer
COO: Arthur Mombourquette, Chief Operating Officer
CFO: Michael Connors, Senior Vice President and Chief Financial Officer
CMO: Donald Guadagnoli, M.D., Chief Medical Officer
CIO: Jeanne M. Fallon, Senior Vice President and Chief Information Officer
CHR: Emily Schorer, Senior Vice President Human Resources
CNO: Judith Quinn, Vice President Patient Care Services
Web address: www.capecodhealth.org
Control: Other not–for–profit (including NFP Corporation) **Service:** General Medical and Surgical

Staffed Beds: 259 **Admissions:** 15416 **Census:** 181 **Outpatient Visits:** 582656 **Births:** 772 **Total Expense ($000):** 394531 **Payroll Expense ($000):** 154488 **Personnel:** 1403	

JAMAICA PLAIN—Suffolk County

☐ **LEMUEL SHATTUCK HOSPITAL (222006)**, 170 Morton Street, Zip 02130–3735; tel. 617/522–8110 **A**1 3 10 **F**3 5 8 15 18 29 30 31 39 45 50 58 59 60 61 64 65 68 70 74 75 77 78 79 81 87 90 93 94 97 98 103 104 106 107 108 110 114 115 118 119 130 132 135 146 148 **P**6 **S** Massachusetts Department of Public Health, Boston, MA
Primary Contact: Paul Romary, Chief Executive Officer
CFO: Mike Donovan, Chief Financial Officer
CMO: Kenneth Freedman, M.D., Chief Medical Officer
CIO: Kathryn Noonan, Director Information Management
CHR: Jill Sampson, Director Human Resources
Web address: www.mass.gov/shattuckhospital
Control: State–Government, nonfederal **Service:** General Medical and Surgical

Staffed Beds: 260 **Admissions:** 1645 **Census:** 227 **Outpatient Visits:** 22487 **Births:** 0 **Total Expense ($000):** 87501 **Personnel:** 699	

LAWRENCE—Essex County

✠ **LAWRENCE GENERAL HOSPITAL (220010)**, 1 General Street, Zip 01841–2961, Mailing Address: P.O. Box 189, Zip 01842–0389; tel. 978/683–4000 **A**1 2 9 10 **F**7 11 12 13 15 16 17 20 22 28 29 30 34 35 40 43 45 46 49 50 51 57 59 60 65 68 70 73 74 75 76 77 78 79 81 85 87 88 89 100 107 108 110 114 115 119 129 130 132 135 144 146 147 148 **P**5 6 8
Primary Contact: Dianne J. Anderson, MS, R.N., President and Chief Executive Officer
COO: Denise S. Palumbo, MSN, Executive Vice President and Chief Operating Officer
CFO: Deborah J. Wilson, Senior Vice President and Chief Financial Officer
CMO: Neil S. Meehan, D.O., Chief Medical Officer and Chief Medical Information Officer
CIO: Jeffrey L. Brown, Director Information Systems
CHR: Cynthia Phelan, Vice President Human Resources
CNO: Elizabeth Hale, R.N., Vice President Patient Services and Chief Nursing Officer
Web address: www.lawrencegeneral.org
Control: Other not–for–profit (including NFP Corporation) **Service:** General Medical and Surgical

Staffed Beds: 189 **Admissions:** 11316 **Census:** 114 **Outpatient Visits:** 223718 **Births:** 1513 **Total Expense ($000):** 209925 **Payroll Expense ($000):** 103902 **Personnel:** 1011	

LEEDS—Hampshire County

✠ **VA CENTRAL WESTERN MASSACHUSETTS HEALTHCARE SYSTEM**, 421 North Main Street, Zip 01053–9764; tel. 413/582–3000, (Total facility includes 32 beds in nursing home–type unit) **A**1 **F**5 29 30 36 38 39 53 54 56 57 58 59 61 62 63 64 65 66 74 75 77 82 87 91 93 94 97 98 99 100 102 103 104 107 114 119 127 128 130 135 143 144 146 147 **P**6 **S** Department of Veterans Affairs, Washington, DC
Primary Contact: Roger L. Johnson, Director
COO: Joyce Fredrick, Associate Director
CFO: Andrew McMahon, Chief Fiscal Officer
CMO: Neil Nusbaum, M.D., Chief of Staff
CIO: Michael Marley, Chief Information Officer
CHR: Pablo Feliciano, Manager Human Resources
Web address: www.centralwesternmass.va.gov/
Control: Veterans Affairs, Government, federal **Service:** Psychiatric

Staffed Beds: 117 **Admissions:** 997 **Census:** 86 **Outpatient Visits:** 300000 **Births:** 0 **Total Expense ($000):** 140000 **Payroll Expense ($000):** 80000	

LEOMINSTER—Worcester County

✠ **HEALTHALLIANCE HOSPITALS (220001)**, 60 Hospital Road, Zip 01453–2205; tel. 978/466–2000 **A**1 2 5 9 10 13 **F**3 13 15 28 29 30 31 34 35 36 40 45 46 49 50 51 59 62 63 64 68 70 75 76 77 78 81 82 84 85 89 92 93 107 108 110 114 115 119 130 135 144 146 **P**6 **S** UMass Memorial Health Care, Inc., Worcester, MA
Primary Contact: Deborah K. Weymouth, President and Chief Executive Officer
CFO: John Bronhard, Interim Chief Financial Officer
CMO: Daniel H. O'Leary, M.D., Chief Medical Officer
CIO: Christopher Walden, Vice President and Chief Information Officer
CHR: Cynthia Ring, Vice President Human Resources and Patient Experience
CNO: Paul MacKinnon, MS, Senior Vice President Patient Care Services and Chief Nursing Officer
Web address: www.healthalliance.com
Control: Other not–for–profit (including NFP Corporation) **Service:** General Medical and Surgical

Staffed Beds: 89 **Admissions:** 6558 **Census:** 76 **Outpatient Visits:** 246760 **Births:** 983 **Total Expense ($000):** 154024 **Payroll Expense ($000):** 64133 **Personnel:** 845	

LOWELL—Middlesex County

✠ **LOWELL GENERAL HOSPITAL (220063)**, 295 Varnum Avenue, Zip 01854–2134; tel. 978/937–6000, (Includes LOWELL GENERAL HOSPITAL, SAINTS CAMPUS, 1 Hospital Drive, Zip 01852–1311; tel. 978/458–1411; Stephen J. Guimond, President and Chief Executive Officer) **A**1 2 3 5 9 10 **F**3 8 11 12 13 15 18 20 22 26 28 29 30 31 32 34 35 36 38 40 41 43 44 45 49 50 51 54 55 56 57 58 59 60 61 62 63 64 65 66 68 70 73 74 75 76 77 78 79 81 82 84 85 86 87 89 93 97 107 108 110 114 115 118 119 120 121 123 124 126 129 130 131 132 134 135 144 146 147 **P**5 6 8
Primary Contact: Normand E. Deschene, FACHE, Chief Executive Officer
COO: Amy J. Hoey, R.N., Executive Vice President and Chief Operating Officer
CFO: Susan Green, Senior Vice President Finance, Chief Financial Officer
CMO: David Pickul, M.D., Chief Medical Officer, Circle Health
CIO: Brian Sandager, Chief Information Officer
CHR: Sabrina M. Granville, Senior Vice President and Chief Human Resources Officer
CNO: Cecelia Lynch, R.N., Vice President Patient Care Services and Chief Nursing Officer
Web address: www.lowellgeneral.org
Control: Other not–for–profit (including NFP Corporation) **Service:** General Medical and Surgical

Staffed Beds: 338 **Admissions:** 20916 **Census:** 221 **Outpatient Visits:** 570050 **Births:** 2269 **Total Expense ($000):** 402297 **Payroll Expense ($000):** 160694 **Personnel:** 2420	

SAINTS MEDICAL CENTER See Lowell General Hospital, Saints Campus

LUDLOW—Hampden County

✠ **HEALTHSOUTH REHABILITATION HOSPITAL OF WESTERN MASSACHUSETTS (223030)**, 14 Chestnut Place, Zip 01056–3476; tel. 413/589–7581, (Nonreporting) **A**1 10 **S** HEALTHSOUTH Corporation, Birmingham, AL
Primary Contact: Victoria Healy, Chief Executive Officer
CMO: Adnan Dahdul, M.D., Medical Director
CHR: Mary Mazza, Director Human Resources
CNO: Deborah Cabanas, R.N., Chief Nursing Officer
Web address: www.healthsouthrehab.org
Control: Corporation, Investor–owned, for–profit **Service:** Rehabilitation

Staffed Beds: 53	

Hospital, Medicare Provider Number, Address, Telephone, Approval, Facility, and Physician Codes, Health Care System

★ American Hospital Association (AHA) membership
☐ The Joint Commission accreditation
◇ DNV Healthcare Inc. accreditation
○ Healthcare Facilities Accreditation Program
△ Commission on Accreditation of Rehabilitation Facilities (CARF) accreditation

LYNN—Essex County

UNION CAMPUS See North Shore Medical Center, Salem

UNION HOSPITAL See Union Campus

MARLBOROUGH—Bristol County

✠ **UMASS MEMORIAL–MARLBOROUGH HOSPITAL (220049)**, 157 Union Street, Zip 01752–1297; tel. 508/481–5000, (Nonreporting) **A**1 5 9 10 **S** UMass Memorial Health Care, Inc., Worcester, MA
Primary Contact: Steven P. Roach, FACHE, President and Chief Executive Officer
COO: John Kelly, Chief Nursing Officer and Chief Operating Officer
CFO: Steven McCue, Chief Financial Officer
CHR: Jane Fontaine, Vice President Human Resources
CNO: John Kelly, Chief Nursing Officer and Chief Operating Officer
Web address: www.marlboroughhospital.org
Control: Other not–for–profit (including NFP Corporation) **Service:** General Medical and Surgical

Staffed Beds: 67

MEDFORD—Middlesex County

LAWRENCE MEMORIAL HOSPITAL OF MEDFORD See Hallmark Health System, Melrose

MELROSE—Middlesex County

✠ **HALLMARK HEALTH SYSTEM (220070)**, 585 Lebanon Street, Zip 02176–3225; tel. 781/979–3000, (Includes LAWRENCE MEMORIAL HOSPITAL OF MEDFORD, 170 Governors Avenue, Medford, Zip 02155–1643; tel. 781/306–6000; MELROSE–WAKEFIELD HOSPITAL, 585 Lebanon Street, Zip 02176; tel. 781/979–3000; Michael V. Sack, FACHE, Chief Executive Officer) **A**1 2 5 10 **F**2 3 11 12 13 15 18 20 22 26 28 29 30 31 34 35 38 40 41 45 46 47 49 50 51 54 55 56 57 58 59 60 61 62 63 64 65 68 70 72 74 75 76 77 78 79 81 82 84 85 86 87 93 97 98 100 101 102 103 104 107 108 110 111 114 115 119 120 121 123 124 130 131 132 135 141 144 146 147 148 **P**5 6
Primary Contact: Michael V. Sack, FACHE, President and Chief Executive Officer
COO: William J. Doherty, M.D., Executive Vice President and Chief Operating Officer
CFO: James A. Nania, System Vice President and Chief Financial Officer
CMO: Steven Sbardella, M.D., Chief Medical Officer
CIO: Carol Ann Dresser, Vice President Information Services and Chief Information Officer
CHR: David P. Ryan, Vice President Human Resources
Web address: www.hallmarkhealth.org
Control: Other not–for–profit (including NFP Corporation) **Service:** General Medical and Surgical

Staffed Beds: 297 **Admissions:** 11529 **Census:** 170 **Outpatient Visits:** 533892 **Births:** 938 **Total Expense ($000):** 257108 **Payroll Expense ($000):** 130960 **Personnel:** 1323

METHUEN—Essex County

☐ **HOLY FAMILY HOSPITAL AND MEDICAL CENTER (220080)**, 70 East Street, Zip 01844–4597; tel. 978/687–0151, (Nonreporting) **A**1 2 5 9 10 **S** Steward Health Care System, LLC, Boston, MA
Primary Contact: Joseph Roach, Chief Executive Officer
COO: Martha M. McDrury, R.N., Chief Operating Officer and Chief Nursing Officer
CFO: Kevin Kilday, Vice President Finance
CHR: Patricia Gauron, Director Human Resources
CNO: Martha M. McDrury, R.N., Chief Operating Officer and Chief Nursing Officer
Web address: www.stewardhealth.org/Holy–Family–Hospital
Control: Corporation, Investor–owned, for–profit **Service:** General Medical and Surgical

Staffed Beds: 239

MILFORD—Worcester County

✠ **MILFORD REGIONAL MEDICAL CENTER (220090)**, 14 Prospect Street, Zip 01757–3003; tel. 508/473–1190, (Includes WHITINSVILLE MEDICAL CENTER, 18 Granite Street, Whitinsville, Zip 01588; tel. 508/234–6311) **A**1 2 5 9 10 **F**3 11 12 13 15 18 20 28 29 30 31 32 34 35 40 41 47 49 50 51 52 57 59 64 65 68 70 74 75 76 77 79 80 81 82 83 84 85 86 87 89 93 107 108 110 114 115 118 119 124 126 130 131 132 134 135 146 147 148 **P**6
Primary Contact: Francis M. Saba, Chief Executive Officer
COO: Peggy Novick, Vice President, Clinical Support and Outpatient Services
CFO: Jeanne Lynskey, Vice President and Chief Financial Officer
CMO: William Muller, M.D., Vice President Medical Affairs
CIO: Nicole Heim, Chief Information Officer
CHR: Linda Greason, Vice President Human Resources
CNO: Nancy Tomaso, Vice President, Patient Care Services
Web address: www.milfordregional.org
Control: Other not–for–profit (including NFP Corporation) **Service:** General Medical and Surgical

Staffed Beds: 121 **Admissions:** 7767 **Census:** 80 **Outpatient Visits:** 358044 **Births:** 879 **Total Expense ($000):** 175745 **Payroll Expense ($000):** 80393 **Personnel:** 1486

MILTON—Norfolk County

☐ **BETH ISRAEL DEACONESS HOSPITAL–MILTON (220108)**, 199 Reedsdale Road, Zip 02186–3926; tel. 617/696–4600, (Nonreporting) **A**1 9 10
Primary Contact: Peter J. Healy, Chief Executive Officer
CIO: Jean Fernandez, Chief Information Officer
CHR: Kathleen Harrington, Vice President Human Resources
Web address: www.miltonhospital.org
Control: Other not–for–profit (including NFP Corporation) **Service:** General Medical and Surgical

Staffed Beds: 82

NANTUCKET—Nantucket County

✠ **NANTUCKET COTTAGE HOSPITAL (220177)**, 57 Prospect Street, Zip 02554–2799; tel. 508/825–8100 **A**1 9 10 **F**13 15 28 29 31 35 40 45 50 57 59 60 64 68 70 75 76 77 78 79 81 82 84 85 86 87 89 93 100 102 107 110 111 115 119 130 132 133 147 148 **P**5 **S** Partners HealthCare System, Inc., Boston, MA
Primary Contact: Margot Hartmann, M.D., Ph.D., President and Chief Executive Officer
COO: Jim Kelly, Chief Operating Officer
CFO: David J. Burke, Director Finance and Chief Financial Officer
CMO: Jock Lawrason, M.D., Chief Medical Officer
CIO: Terry Hughes, Director Information Systems
CHR: Susan Partridge, Director Human Resources
CNO: Bonnie J. Kester, R.N., Vice President Patient Care Services and Chief Nursing Officer
Web address: www.nantuckethospital.org
Control: Other not–for–profit (including NFP Corporation) **Service:** General Medical and Surgical

Staffed Beds: 19 **Admissions:** 633 **Census:** 4 **Outpatient Visits:** 32039 **Births:** 127 **Total Expense ($000):** 36164 **Payroll Expense ($000):** 16352 **Personnel:** 222

NATICK—Middlesex County

LEONARD MORSE HOSPITAL See MetroWest Medical Center, Framingham

NEEDHAM—Norfolk County

BETH ISRAEL DEACONESS HOSPITAL–NEEDHAM CAMPUS See Beth Israel Deaconess Medical Center, Boston

NEW BEDFORD—Bristol County

✠ **NEW BEDFORD REHABILITATION HOSPITAL (222043)**, 4499 Acushnet Avenue, Zip 02745–4707; tel. 508/995–6900 **A**1 10 **F**1 12 18 28 29 50 56 57 64 74 75 77 79 87 93 94 96 101 103 104 130 135 146 148 **P**6 **S** Vibra Healthcare, Mechanicsburg, PA
Primary Contact: Edward B. Leary, Chief Executive Officer
CFO: Cheryl Perry, Chief Financial Officer
CMO: Albert Loerinc, M.D., Medical Director
CHR: Ilene Mirabella, Director Human Resources
CNO: Emmanuel Berthil, Chief Clinical Officer
Web address: www.newbedfordrehab.com
Control: Corporation, Investor–owned, for–profit **Service:** Long–Term Acute Care hospital

Staffed Beds: 90 **Admissions:** 631 **Census:** 76 **Outpatient Visits:** 4079 **Births:** 0 **Total Expense ($000):** 24676 **Payroll Expense ($000):** 13978 **Personnel:** 159

ST. LUKE'S HOSPITAL See Southcoast Hospitals Group, Fall River

NEWBURYPORT—Essex County

✠ **ANNA JAQUES HOSPITAL (220029)**, 25 Highland Avenue, Zip 01950–3894; tel. 978/463–1000 **A**1 9 10 **F**3 13 14 15 18 20 26 28 29 31 34 40 43 45 46 50 64 65 70 75 76 77 78 79 81 82 85 89 93 98 102 105 107 108 110 111 115 116 117 118 119 129 130 135 146 148 **P**8
Primary Contact: Delia O'Connor, FACHE, President and Chief Executive Officer
CFO: Mark L. Goldstein, Chief Financial Officer
CMO: Gail Fayre, M.D., Medical Director
CIO: Robert Buchanan, Chief Information Officer
CHR: Stephen Salvo, Vice President Human Resources
CNO: Richard Maki, R.N., Vice President Nursing and Chief Nursing Officer
Web address: www.ajh.org
Control: Other not–for–profit (including NFP Corporation) **Service:** General Medical and Surgical

Staffed Beds: 123 **Admissions:** 7007 **Census:** 84 **Outpatient Visits:** 242780 **Births:** 667 **Total Expense ($000):** 110003 **Payroll Expense ($000):** 52728 **Personnel:** 710

Many Facility Codes have changed. Please refer to the AHA Guide Code Chart.   © 2014 AHA Guide

MA

NEWTON LOWER FALLS—Middlesex County

☒ **NEWTON–WELLESLEY HOSPITAL (220101)**, 2014 Washington Street, Zip 02462–1699; tel. 617/243–6000, (Includes MASSGENERAL FOR CHILDREN AT NEWTON–WELLESLEY HOSPITAL, 2000 Washington Street, Newton, Zip 02462–1650; tel. 617/243–6585) **A**1 2 3 5 9 10 **F**3 8 11 12 13 15 18 28 29 30 31 34 35 36 38 40 41 44 45 46 47 48 49 50 51 52 53 54 55 56 57 58 59 60 64 65 68 70 74 75 76 77 78 79 81 82 84 85 86 87 89 93 94 97 98 100 101 102 107 108 110 111 113 114 115 116 117 118 119 129 130 131 132 135 143 144 146 147 148 **P**1 6 **S** Partners HealthCare System, Inc., Boston, MA
Primary Contact: Kerry Watson, President
COO: Patrick Jordan, III, Chief Operating Officer
CFO: Jerry Hadley, Interim Vice President Finance and Chief Financial Officer
CMO: Leslie Selbovitz, M.D., Senior Vice President Medical Affairs
CIO: Beth Downie, Chief Information Officer
CHR: Beth Taylor, Vice President, Human Resources
CNO: Elaine Bridge, R.N., Senior Vice President Patient Care Services and Chief Nursing Officer
Web address: www.nwh.org
Control: Other not–for–profit (including NFP Corporation) **Service:** General Medical and Surgical

Staffed Beds: 240 **Admissions:** 15411 **Census:** 166 **Outpatient Visits:** 564551 **Births:** 4056 **Personnel:** 2463

NORTHAMPTON—Hampshire County

☒ **COOLEY DICKINSON HOSPITAL (220015)**, 30 Locust Street, Zip 01060–2093, Mailing Address: P.O. Box 5001, Zip 01061–5001; tel. 413/582–2000 **A**1 2 9 10 **F**3 11 13 14 15 18 20 28 29 30 31 34 35 36 38 39 40 49 50 51 54 57 59 60 61 64 68 70 74 75 76 78 79 81 82 85 86 87 89 93 96 98 100 102 107 108 110 111 114 115 119 120 121 123 126 130 131 132 134 135 144 146 147 148 **P**8
Primary Contact: Joanne Marqusee, President and Chief Executive Officer
CFO: Laurie Lamoureux, Director of Finance
CMO: Mark Novotny, M.D., Chief Medical Officer
CIO: Lee Martinez, Chief Information Officer
CHR: Lori A. Kerwood, Director Human Resources
CNO: Gregory A. Bird, R.N., Interim Chief Nursing Officer
Web address: www.cooley–dickinson.org
Control: Other not–for–profit (including NFP Corporation) **Service:** General Medical and Surgical

Staffed Beds: 88 **Admissions:** 7461 **Census:** 79 **Outpatient Visits:** 228408 **Births:** 848 **Total Expense ($000):** 150102 **Payroll Expense ($000):** 66465 **Personnel:** 856

NORWOOD—Norfolk County

☐ **NORWOOD HOSPITAL (220126)**, 800 Washington Street, Zip 02062–3487; tel. 781/769–4000, (Nonreporting) **A**1 2 5 9 10 **S** Steward Health Care System, LLC, Boston, MA
Primary Contact: Emily L. Holliman, President
COO: William P. Fleming, Chief Operating Officer
CFO: Mark Johnson, Chief Financial Officer
CHR: Kimberly Brosnan, Director Human Resources
CNO: Mary Kinneman, R.N., Chief Nursing Officer, Vice President Patient Care Services
Web address: www.stewardhealth.org/Norwood–Hospital
Control: Corporation, Investor–owned, for–profit **Service:** General Medical and Surgical

Staffed Beds: 205

OAK BLUFFS—Dukes County

☒ **MARTHA'S VINEYARD HOSPITAL (221300)**, One Hospital Road, Zip 02557, Mailing Address: P.O. Box 1477, Zip 02557–1477; tel. 508/693–0410 **A**1 9 10 18 **F**3 8 13 15 18 28 29 30 31 39 40 45 50 57 68 70 75 76 78 79 81 85 86 89 93 97 107 110 111 115 119 130 133 146 147 **P**6 **S** Partners HealthCare System, Inc., Boston, MA
Primary Contact: Timothy J. Walsh, Chief Executive Officer
CFO: Edward Olivier, Chief Financial Officer
CMO: Pieter Pil, M.D., Chief Medical Staff
CHR: Ken Chisholm, Director Human Resources
CNO: Carol A. Bardwell, R.N., Chief Nurse Executive
Web address: www.marthasvineyardhospital.org
Control: Other not–for–profit (including NFP Corporation) **Service:** General Medical and Surgical

Staffed Beds: 25 **Admissions:** 1377 **Census:** 16 **Outpatient Visits:** 84319 **Births:** 122 **Personnel:** 258

PALMER—Hampden County

☒ **WING MEMORIAL HOSPITAL (220030)**, 40 Wright Street, Zip 01069–1138; tel. 413/283–7651 **A**1 5 9 10 **F**3 5 11 12 15 18 29 30 31 33 34 36 37 40 49 50 51 56 57 59 61 62 63 64 65 68 70 74 75 77 78 79 81 82 85 89 92 93 97 98 99 100 101 103 104 107 108 110 115 118 119 124 129 130 131 132 146 147 148 **P**6 **S** UMass Memorial Health Care, Inc., Worcester, MA
Primary Contact: Charles E. Cavagnaro, III, M.D., President and Chief Executive Officer
CFO: Keary T. Allicon, Vice President Finance and Chief Financial Officer
CMO: David L. Maguire, M.D., Vice President Medical Affairs
CIO: Kenneth Riley, Director Information Systems
CHR: Thomas Guilfoil, Director Human Resources
Web address: www.winghealth.org
Control: Other not–for–profit (including NFP Corporation) **Service:** General Medical and Surgical

Staffed Beds: 74 **Admissions:** 3136 **Census:** 47 **Outpatient Visits:** 233898 **Births:** 0 **Total Expense ($000):** 93363 **Payroll Expense ($000):** 42081 **Personnel:** 708

PEABODY—Essex County

☒ **KINDRED HOSPITAL BOSTON–NORTH SHORE (222044)**, 15 King Street, Zip 01960–4379; tel. 978/531–2900, (Nonreporting) **A**1 10 **S** Kindred Healthcare, Louisville, KY
Primary Contact: Yolande Wilson, Chief Executive Officer
COO: Beth Cullum, Chief Operating Officer
CFO: Amber Tatum, Controller
CMO: M. Akbarian, M.D., Medical Director
CHR: Jan Pray, Coordinator Payroll and Benefits
CNO: Michelle Mastin, Chief Clinical Officer
Web address: www.kindredbns.com
Control: Corporation, Investor–owned, for–profit **Service:** Long–Term Acute Care hospital

Staffed Beds: 50

PEMBROKE—Plymouth County

PEMBROKE HOSPITAL, 199 Oak Street, Zip 02359–1953; tel. 781/829–7000 **A**9 **F**29 34 40 64 75 98 99 101 102 103 105 132 **P**6 **S** Universal Health Services, Inc., King of Prussia, PA
Primary Contact: Thomas P. Hickey, Chief Executive Officer and Managing Director
CFO: Diane Airosus, Chief Financial Officer
CMO: Gary Jacobson, M.D., Chief Medical Officer
Web address: www.arbourhealth.com/organizations/pembroke–hospital/
Control: Corporation, Investor–owned, for–profit **Service:** Psychiatric

Staffed Beds: 115 **Admissions:** 3279 **Census:** 107 **Outpatient Visits:** 5660 **Births:** 0

PITTSFIELD—Berkshire County

☒ **BERKSHIRE MEDICAL CENTER (220046)**, 725 North Street, Zip 01201–4124; tel. 413/447–2000, (Includes HILLCREST HOSPITAL, 165 Tor Court, Zip 01201–3099, Mailing Address: Box 1155, Zip 01202–1155; tel. 413/443–4761) **A**1 2 3 5 8 9 10 12 13 **F**3 4 5 8 12 13 14 15 17 18 20 26 28 29 30 31 32 34 35 38 39 40 43 44 49 50 51 53 54 55 56 57 58 59 60 61 62 64 65 68 70 71 74 75 76 77 78 79 81 82 84 85 86 87 89 90 92 93 94 96 98 99 100 101 102 103 104 105 107 108 110 111 112 114 115 116 117 118 119 120 121 122 123 124 126 129 130 131 132 134 135 144 145 146 147 148 **P**6 **S** Berkshire Health Systems, Inc., Pittsfield, MA
Primary Contact: David E. Phelps, President and Chief Executive Officer
COO: Diane Kelly, R.N., Chief Operating Officer
CFO: Darlene Rodowicz, Chief Financial Officer
CMO: Robert Cella, M.D., Vice President Medical Affairs
CIO: William Young, Chief Information Officer
CHR: Arthur D. Milano, Vice President Human Resources
Web address: www.bhs1.org/body_bmc.cfm?id=43
Control: Other not–for–profit (including NFP Corporation) **Service:** General Medical and Surgical

Staffed Beds: 270 **Admissions:** 12782 **Census:** 158 **Outpatient Visits:** 466471 **Births:** 595 **Total Expense ($000):** 322967 **Payroll Expense ($000):** 156999 **Personnel:** 2121

MA

Hospital, Medicare Provider Number, Address, Telephone, Approval, Facility, and Physician Codes, Health Care System

★ American Hospital Association (AHA) membership
☐ The Joint Commission accreditation ◇ DNV Healthcare Inc. accreditation
○ Healthcare Facilities Accreditation Program
△ Commission on Accreditation of Rehabilitation Facilities (CARF) accreditation

MA

PLYMOUTH—Plymouth County

✠ **BETH ISRAEL DEACONESS HOSPITAL PLYMOUTH (220060)**, 275 Sandwich Street, Zip 02360–2196; tel. 508/746–2000 **A**1 2 9 10 **F**3 13 15 17 18 20 28 29 30 31 34 35 36 37 40 44 45 51 57 58 59 61 62 64 68 70 74 75 76 77 78 79 81 82 85 86 87 89 93 96 98 100 102 103 104 107 108 109 110 111 115 117 118 119 120 121 123 126 129 130 131 132 134 135 143 144 146 147 148 **P**6
Primary Contact: Peter J. Holden, President and Chief Executive Officer
COO: James E. Fanale, M.D., Senior Vice President System Development
CFO: Jason Radzevich, Vice President Finance
CIO: Ronald Rutherford, Chief Information Officer
CNO: Donna Doherty, R.N., Vice President of Nursing and Chief Nursing Officer
Web address: www.bidplymouth.org
Control: Other not–for–profit (including NFP Corporation) **Service:** General Medical and Surgical

Staffed Beds: 155 **Admissions:** 7898 **Census:** 102 **Outpatient Visits:** 265534 **Births:** 624 **Total Expense ($000):** 194262 **Payroll Expense ($000):** 78581 **Personnel:** 892	

POCASSET—Barnstable County

☐ **CAPE COD & ISLAND COMMUNITY MENTAL HEALTH CENTER (224031)**, 830 County Road, Zip 02559–2110; tel. 508/564–9600, (Nonreporting) **A**1 10
Primary Contact: Steven Jochim, Administrator
Control: Other not–for–profit (including NFP Corporation) **Service:** Psychiatric

Staffed Beds: 24	

QUINCY—Norfolk County

☐ **QUINCY MEDICAL CENTER (220067)**, 114 Whitwell Street, Zip 02169–1899; tel. 617/773–6100, (Nonreporting) **A**1 3 5 9 10 **S** Steward Health Care System, LLC, Boston, MA
Primary Contact: Donna Rubinate, R.N., Interim President
CMO: Kevin McCusker, M.D., Chief Medical Officer
CHR: Gail Flynn, Interim Director Human Resources
CNO: Lorena Silva, MSN, Vice President Patient Care Services, Chief Nursing Officer
Web address: www.quincymc.org
Control: Other not–for–profit (including NFP Corporation) **Service:** General Medical and Surgical

Staffed Beds: 116	

ROCHDALE—Worcester County

VIBRA HOSPITAL OF WESTERN MASSACHUSETTS–CENTRAL CAMPUS See Vibra Hospital of Western Massachusetts, Springfield

SALEM—Essex County

NORTH SHORE CHILDREN'S HOSPITAL See MassGeneral for Children at North Shore Medical Center

✠ **NORTH SHORE MEDICAL CENTER (220035)**, 81 Highland Avenue, Zip 01970–2714; tel. 978/741–1200, (Includes MASSGENERAL FOR CHILDREN AT NORTH SHORE MEDICAL CENTER, 57 Highland Avenue, Zip 01970–6508; tel. 978/745–2100; SALEM CAMPUS, 81 Highland Avenue, Zip 01970; tel. 978/741–1200; UNION CAMPUS, 500 Lynnfield Street, Lynn, Zip 01904–1487; tel. 781/581–9200) **A**1 3 5 9 10 **F**5 12 13 15 17 18 20 22 24 26 28 29 30 31 32 34 35 36 38 40 41 43 45 46 49 50 51 55 57 59 61 63 64 68 70 73 74 75 76 77 78 79 81 82 84 85 86 87 89 93 98 99 100 101 102 103 104 105 107 108 111 114 116 118 119 121 123 129 130 131 132 135 143 146 147 148 **P**6 8 **S** Partners HealthCare System, Inc., Boston, MA
Primary Contact: Robert G. Norton, President and Chief Executive Officer
CFO: Sally Mason Boemer, Chief Financial Officer
CMO: Mitchell S. Rein, M.D., Chief Medical Officer
CIO: Patricia George, Chief Information Officer
CHR: Arthur Bowes, Senior Vice President Human Resources
CNO: Beatrice Thibedeau, R.N., Senior Vice President Patient Care Services and Chief Nursing Officer
Web address: www.nsmc.partners.org
Control: Other not–for–profit (including NFP Corporation) **Service:** General Medical and Surgical

Staffed Beds: 411 **Admissions:** 18428 **Census:** 249 **Outpatient Visits:** 646398 **Births:** 1361 **Total Expense ($000):** 434120 **Payroll Expense ($000):** 197769 **Personnel:** 2403	

SALEM HOSPITAL See Salem Campus

✠ **SPAULDING HOSPITAL FOR CONTINUING MEDICAL CARE NORTH SHORE (222026)**, 1 Dove Avenue, Zip 01970–2999; tel. 978/825–8900, (Nonreporting) **A**1 10 **S** Partners HealthCare System, Inc., Boston, MA
Primary Contact: Maureen Banks, R.N., MS, President
COO: Joanne Fucile, MSN, Vice President Patient Care Services
CFO: Virginia Mirisola, Fiscal Director
CIO: Robert Sawyer, Senior Project Specialist
CHR: Colleen M. Moran, Director Human Resources
Web address: www.shaughnessy-kaplan.org
Control: Other not–for–profit (including NFP Corporation) **Service:** Long–Term Acute Care hospital

Staffed Beds: 160	

SOMERVILLE—Middlesex County

SOMERVILLE HOSPITAL See Cambridge Health Alliance, Cambridge

SOUTH WEYMOUTH—Norfolk County

✠ **SOUTH SHORE HOSPITAL (220100)**, 55 Fogg Road, Zip 02190–2432; tel. 781/624–8000 **A**1 2 3 5 9 10 **F**3 7 11 13 15 17 18 20 22 24 26 28 29 30 31 32 34 35 36 37 40 41 43 44 45 46 49 50 51 53 54 55 57 58 59 60 62 63 64 65 68 70 72 73 74 75 76 78 79 81 82 84 85 86 87 89 91 92 93 107 108 110 111 114 115 118 119 124 126 129 130 132 134 135 143 146 147 148 **P**1
Primary Contact: Richard H. Aubut, R.N., President and Chief Executive Officer
COO: Joseph Cahill, Executive Vice President and Chief Operating Officer
CFO: Michael Cullen, Senior Vice President and Chief Financial Officer
CMO: John Stevenson, M.D., Senior Vice President and Chief Medical Officer
CIO: Del Dixon, Chief Information Officer
CHR: Robert Wheeler, Vice President Human Resources
Web address: www.southshorehospital.org
Control: Other not–for–profit (including NFP Corporation) **Service:** General Medical and Surgical

Staffed Beds: 361 **Admissions:** 21603 **Census:** 242 **Outpatient Visits:** 546165 **Births:** 3358 **Total Expense ($000):** 457496 **Payroll Expense ($000):** 217311 **Personnel:** 3162	

SOUTHBRIDGE—Worcester County

✠ **HARRINGTON MEMORIAL HOSPITAL (220019)**, 100 South Street, Zip 01550–4051; tel. 508/765–9771 **A**1 5 8 11 13 15 17 18 19 28 29 30 31 32 34 35 38 39 40 42 45 48 49 50 51 54 57 59 61 64 65 68 70 71 74 75 76 77 78 79 81 82 85 86 87 89 92 93 94 96 98 99 100 101 102 103 104 105 107 108 110 111 114 115 117 118 119 129 130 131 132 134 135 146 147 148 **P**8
Primary Contact: Edward H. Moore, President and Chief Executive Officer
COO: Douglas Crapser, Executive Vice President
CFO: Thomas Sullivan, Vice President Fiscal Services
CMO: Arthur Russo, M.D., Director Medical Affairs
CIO: Harry Lemieux, Chief Information Officer
CHR: Christopher Canniff, Executive Director, Human Resources
CNO: Thomas W. Hijeck, R.N., Vice President Nursing Services and Chief Nursing Officer
Web address: www.harringtonhospital.org
Control: Other not–for–profit (including NFP Corporation) **Service:** General Medical and Surgical

Staffed Beds: 114 **Admissions:** 4091 **Census:** 52 **Outpatient Visits:** 317859 **Births:** 294 **Total Expense ($000):** 107380 **Payroll Expense ($000):** 52360 **Personnel:** 657	

SPRINGFIELD—Hampden County

✠ **BAYSTATE MEDICAL CENTER (220077)**, 759 Chestnut Street, Zip 01199–0001; tel. 413/794–0000, (Includes BAYSTATE CHILDREN'S HOSPITAL, 759 Chestnut Street, Zip 01199–1001; tel. 413/794–0000) **A**1 3 5 8 9 10 **F**1 3 4 8 12 13 14 15 16 17 18 19 20 22 24 26 28 29 30 31 32 34 35 38 40 41 43 44 45 46 47 48 49 50 51 52 53 54 55 59 60 61 64 65 66 67 68 70 72 73 74 75 76 77 78 79 80 81 82 84 85 86 87 88 89 90 91 92 93 97 98 99 100 101 102 103 104 105 107 108 110 111 113 114 115 118 119 120 121 123 124 126 128 129 130 131 132 135 138 141 143 145 146 147 148 **P**8 **S** Baystate Health, Inc., Springfield, MA
Primary Contact: Mark R. Tolosky, JD, FACHE, President and Chief Executive Officer
COO: Nancy Shendell–Falik, R.N., Senior Vice President, Chief Operating Officer and Chief Nursing Officer
CFO: Dennis Chalke, Chief Financial Officer and Treasurer
CMO: John Schreiber, M.D., President and Chief Physician Executive
CIO: Joel L. Vengco, MS, Vice President, Chief Information Officer
CHR: Paula C. Squires, Senior Vice President Human Resources
CNO: Nancy Shendell–Falik, R.N., Senior Vice President, Chief Operating Officer and Chief Nursing Officer
Web address: www.baystatehealth.org/bmc
Control: Other not–for–profit (including NFP Corporation) **Service:** General Medical and Surgical

Staffed Beds: 715 **Admissions:** 35431 **Census:** 493 **Outpatient Visits:** 824724 **Births:** 4038 **Total Expense ($000):** 922685 **Payroll Expense ($000):** 354504 **Personnel:** 6322	

KINDRED HOSPITAL PARK VIEW See Vibra Hospital of Western Massachusetts

Many Facility Codes have changed. Please refer to the AHA Guide Code Chart. © 2014 AHA Guide

✠ △ **MERCY MEDICAL CENTER (220066)**, 271 Carew Street, Zip 01104–2398, Mailing Address: P.O. Box 9012, Zip 01102–9012; tel. 413/748–9000 **A**1 2 7 9 10 **F**3 4 5 8 12 13 14 15 18 20 26 29 30 31 34 35 38 40 44 45 46 47 48 49 50 51 55 56 57 58 59 61 64 68 70 74 75 76 77 78 79 81 82 83 84 85 86 87 89 90 91 92 93 96 98 99 100 101 102 103 104 105 106 107 108 110 111 113 114 115 116 117 118 119 120 121 123 124 126 130 131 132 134 135 143 146 147 148 **P**6 **S** Catholic Health East / Trinity Health, Livonia, MI
Primary Contact: Daniel P. Moen, President and Chief Executive Officer
COO: Scott A. Wolf, D.O., Senior Vice President, Medical Affairs, Chief Medical Officer and Chief Operating Officer
CFO: Thomas W. Robert, Senior Vice President of Finance and Chief Financial Officer
CMO: Scott A. Wolf, D.O., Senior Vice President, Medical Affairs, Chief Medical Officer and Chief Operating Officer
CIO: Joan Methe, Chief Information Officer
CHR: Leonard F. Pansa, Senior Vice President Human Resources and Administrative Services
CNO: Sharon Adams, R.N., Senior Vice President Patient Care Services and Chief Quality Officer
Web address: www.mercycares.com
Control: Other not–for–profit (including NFP Corporation) **Service:** General Medical and Surgical

Staffed Beds: 301 **Admissions:** 14860 **Census:** 222 **Outpatient Visits:** 699908 **Births:** 1326 **Total Expense ($000):** 222739 **Payroll Expense ($000):** 94161 **Personnel:** 1498

☐ **SHRINERS HOSPITALS FOR CHILDREN–SPRINGFIELD (223303)**, 516 Carew Street, Zip 01104–2396; tel. 413/787–2000 **A**1 3 5 10 **F**11 29 34 35 37 39 44 50 58 59 62 64 68 75 77 79 81 85 86 87 89 91 92 93 94 96 108 119 130 146 148 **P**1 6 **S** Shriners Hospitals for Children, Tampa, FL
Primary Contact: Charles Walczak, FACHE, Regional Administrator
COO: Charles Walczak, FACHE, Regional Administrator
CFO: Richard Fulkerson, Director Fiscal Services
CMO: David M. Drvaric, M.D., Chief of Staff
CIO: Mary Dolan, Director Information Services
CHR: John Donlin, Director Human Resources
Web address: www.shrinershospitalsforchildren.org/Hospitals/Locations/Springfield.aspx
Control: Other not–for–profit (including NFP Corporation) **Service:** Children's orthopedic

Staffed Beds: 20 **Admissions:** 149 **Census:** 2 **Outpatient Visits:** 10889 **Births:** 0 **Total Expense ($000):** 20045 **Payroll Expense ($000):** 8737 **Personnel:** 139

✠ **VIBRA HOSPITAL OF WESTERN MASSACHUSETTS (222046)**, 1400 State Street, Zip 01109–2550; tel. 413/726–6700, (Includes VIBRA HOSPITAL OF WESTERN MASSACHUSETTS–CENTRAL CAMPUS, 111 Huntoon Memorial Highway, Rochdale, Zip 01542; tel. 508/892–6000; Scott MacLean, Administrator), (Nonreporting) **A**1 10 **S** Vibra Healthcare, Mechanicsburg, PA
Primary Contact: Jake Socha, Chief Executive Officer
CFO: Anna Dyrkacz, Chief Financial Officer
CHR: Donna Ciarefella, Director Human Resources
Web address: www.vhwmass.com
Control: Corporation, Investor–owned, for–profit **Service:** Long–Term Acute Care hospital

Staffed Beds: 202

STOCKBRIDGE—Berkshire County

✠ **AUSTEN RIGGS CENTER**, 25 Main Street, Zip 01262, Mailing Address: P.O. Box 962, Zip 01262–0962; tel. 413/298–5511 **A**1 3 5 **F**98 105 106 130
Primary Contact: James L. Sacksteder, M.D., Medical Director and Chief Executive Officer
CFO: Chauncey Collins, Director Operations and Finance
CIO: Ave Schwartz, Chief Information Officer
CHR: Bertha Mary Connelley, Director Human Resources
CNO: Jane Bloom, Ph.D., Chief Nursing Officer
Web address: www.austenriggs.org
Control: Other not–for–profit (including NFP Corporation) **Service:** Psychiatric

Staffed Beds: 74 **Admissions:** 85 **Census:** 60 **Outpatient Visits:** 0 **Births:** 0 **Total Expense ($000):** 16731 **Payroll Expense ($000):** 9019 **Personnel:** 141

STOUGHTON—Norfolk County

✠ **KINDRED HOSPITAL NORTHEAST–STOUGHTON (222002)**, 909 Sumner Street, 1st Floor, Zip 02072–3396; tel. 781/297–8200, (Nonreporting) **A**1 10 **S** Kindred Healthcare, Louisville, KY
Primary Contact: Robert A. Gundersen, Market Chief Executive Officer
Web address: www.khstoughton.com
Control: Corporation, Investor–owned, for–profit **Service:** Long–Term Acute Care hospital

Staffed Beds: 170

☐ △ **NEW ENGLAND SINAI HOSPITAL AND REHABILITATION CENTER (222027)**, 150 York Street, Zip 02072–1881; tel. 781/344–0600, (Nonreporting) **A**1 3 5 7 10 **S** Steward Health Care System, LLC, Boston, MA
Primary Contact: Judith C. Waterston, R.N., MS, President and Chief Executive Officer
CFO: Victoria Lobban, Vice President Finance
CMO: Lawrence S. Hotes, M.D., Chief Medical Officer
CIO: Michael West, Manager Systems Account
CHR: Julie Burke, Director Human Resources
CNO: Mary Beth Urquhart, Vice President Patient Care Services and Director of Quality
Web address: www.newenglandsinai.org
Control: Other not–for–profit (including NFP Corporation) **Service:** Long–Term Acute Care hospital

Staffed Beds: 212

TAUNTON—Bristol County

☐ **MORTON HOSPITAL AND MEDICAL CENTER (220073)**, 88 Washington Street, Zip 02780–2465; tel. 508/828–7000, (Nonreporting) **A**1 2 9 10 **S** Steward Health Care System, LLC, Boston, MA
Primary Contact: Kimberly S. Bassett, R.N., President
COO: Donna Maher, R.N., Chief Operating Officer
CFO: Carmen Acker, Chief Financial Officer
CMO: Kelly Hoye, M.D., Vice President Medical Affairs
CNO: Jane Metzger, Ph.D., Chief Nursing Officer
Web address: www.mortonhospital.org
Control: Other not–for–profit (including NFP Corporation) **Service:** General Medical and Surgical

Staffed Beds: 153

☐ **TAUNTON STATE HOSPITAL (224001)**, 60 Hodges Avenue Extension, Zip 02780–3034, Mailing Address: PO Box 4007, Zip 02780–0997; tel. 508/977–3000 **A**1 10 **F**30 50 53 68 98 **S** Massachusetts Department of Mental Health, Boston, MA
Primary Contact: Kathleen Duke, Chief Executive Officer
COO: Kathleen Duke, Interim Chief Operating Officer
CHR: Trish Scully, Director Human Resources
Control: State–Government, nonfederal **Service:** Psychiatric

Staffed Beds: 45 **Admissions:** 125 **Census:** 70 **Outpatient Visits:** 0 **Births:** 0 **Total Expense ($000):** 21938 **Payroll Expense ($000):** 16575 **Personnel:** 165

TEWKSBURY—Middlesex County

☐ **TEWKSBURY HOSPITAL (222003)**, 365 East Street, Zip 01876–1998; tel. 978/851–7321, (Nonreporting) **A**1 10 **S** Massachusetts Department of Public Health, Boston, MA
Primary Contact: Debra Tosti, Chief Executive Officer
COO: Betsy L. Schwechheimer, Chief Operating Officer
CFO: Maureen DiPalma, Chief Financial Officer
CMO: James DeVita, M.D., Chief Medical Officer
CNO: Janice E. Bishop, R.N., Chief Nursing Officer
Web address: www.mass.gov
Control: State–Government, nonfederal **Service:** Long–Term Acute Care hospital

Staffed Beds: 720

MA

Hospital, Medicare Provider Number, Address, Telephone, Approval, Facility, and Physician Codes, Health Care System

★ American Hospital Association (AHA) membership
☐ The Joint Commission accreditation
◇ DNV Healthcare Inc. accreditation
○ Healthcare Facilities Accreditation Program
△ Commission on Accreditation of Rehabilitation Facilities (CARF) accreditation

MA

WALTHAM—Middlesex County

☐ **WALDEN PSYCHIATRIC CARE (224038)**, 9 Hope Avenue, Zip 02453–2741;
tel. 781/647–6700 **A**1 9 10 **F**98 99 **P**6
Primary Contact: Stuart Koman, Ph.D., President and Chief Executive Officer
COO: Paula Vass, Vice President Clinical Operations
CFO: Lawrence Behan, Vice President Administration and Finance, Chief Financial
Officer
CMO: James Greenblatt, M.D., Chief Medical Officer, Vice President Medical
Clinical Services
CIO: Lawrence Behan, Vice President Administration and Finance, Chief Financial
Officer
CHR: Carol Pender, Assistant Vice President Human Resources
CNO: Stephen Reider, R.N., Director of Nursing, Assistant Vice President Patient
Care Services
Web address: www.waldenbehavioralcare.com/
Control: Partnership, Investor–owned, for–profit **Service:** Psychiatric

Staffed Beds: 45 **Admissions:** 1500 **Census:** 41 **Outpatient Visits:** 0 **Births:**
0 **Total Expense ($000):** 8423 **Payroll Expense ($000):** 5238 **Personnel:**
85

WARE—Hampshire County

✠ **BAYSTATE MARY LANE HOSPITAL (220050)**, 85 South Street,
Zip 01082–1697; tel. 413/967–6211 **A**1 9 10 **F**15 29 34 35 40 45 50 54 57
59 64 70 75 77 79 81 82 89 92 93 97 107 108 110 114 119 129 130 132
146 **S** Baystate Health, Inc., Springfield, MA
Primary Contact: Mohammed Shafeeq Ahmed, M.D., Interim President
COO: Mohammed Shafeeq Ahmed, M.D., Chief Operating Officer and Chief
Medical Officer
CFO: Curtis Davis, Director Finance
CMO: Mohammed Shafeeq Ahmed, M.D., Chief Operating Officer and Chief
Medical Officer
CIO: Joel L. Vengco, MS, Vice President and Chief Information Officer, Baystate
Health
CHR: Donna Arsenault, Director Human Resources
CNO: Lisa Beaudry, M.P.H., Director, Patient Care
Web address: www.baystatehealth.com
Control: Other not–for–profit (including NFP Corporation) **Service:** General
Medical and Surgical

Staffed Beds: 25 **Admissions:** 1098 **Census:** 9 **Outpatient Visits:** 71278
Births: 0 **Total Expense ($000):** 26169 **Payroll Expense ($000):** 11672
Personnel: 173

WAREHAM—Plymouth County

TOBEY HOSPITAL See Southcoast Hospitals Group, Fall River

WESTBOROUGH—Worcester County

☐ **WHITTIER REHABILITATION HOSPITAL (222048)**, 150 Flanders Road,
Zip 01581–1017; tel. 508/871–2000, (Nonreporting) **A**1 10 **S** Whittier Health
Network, Haverhill, MA
Primary Contact: Alfred J. Arcidi, M.D., Senior Vice President
Web address: www.whittierhealth.com
Control: Partnership, Investor–owned, for–profit **Service:** Long–Term Acute Care
hospital

Staffed Beds: 74

WESTFIELD—Hampden County

✠ **NOBLE HOSPITAL (220065)**, 115 West Silver Street, Zip 01085–3628;
tel. 413/568–2811, (Nonreporting) **A**1 2 5 9 10
Primary Contact: Ron Bryant, President and Chief Executive Officer
CFO: John Shaver, Chief Financial Officer
CMO: Stanley Strzempko, M.D., Vice President Medical Affairs and Chief Medical
Officer
CIO: Steven Cummings, Chief Operating Officer and Chief Information Officer
CHR: Joanne Ollson, Vice President Human Resources
CNO: Diane Brunelle, MSN, Vice President of Patient Care Services and Chief
Nursing Officer
Web address: www.noblehealth.org
Control: Other not–for–profit (including NFP Corporation) **Service:** General
Medical and Surgical

Staffed Beds: 97

☐ **WESTERN MASSACHUSETTS HOSPITAL (222023)**, 91 East Mountain Road,
Zip 01085–1801; tel. 413/562–4131, (Nonreporting) **A**1 10 **S** Massachusetts
Department of Public Health, Boston, MA
Primary Contact: Derrick Tallman, Chief Executive Officer
CMO: Chabilal Neergheen, M.D., Medical Director
CHR: James E. Duggan, Director Human Resources
Web address: www.mass.gov/eohhs/gov/departments/dph/programs/western–
massachusetts–hospital.html
Control: State–Government, nonfederal **Service:** Long–Term Acute Care hospital

Staffed Beds: 70

WESTWOOD—Norfolk County

☐ **WESTWOOD LODGE HOSPITAL (224023)**, 45 Clapboardtree Street,
Zip 02090–2903; tel. 781/762–7764, (Nonreporting) **A**1 9 10 **S** Universal Health
Services, Inc., King of Prussia, PA
Primary Contact: Gregory Brownstein, Chief Executive Officer
CFO: Charles Denno, Chief Financial Officer
Web address: www.arbourhealth.com
Control: Corporation, Investor–owned, for–profit **Service:** Psychiatric

Staffed Beds: 65

WHITINSVILLE—Worcester County

WHITINSVILLE MEDICAL CENTER See Milford Regional Medical Center, Milford

WINCHESTER—Middlesex County

✠ **WINCHESTER HOSPITAL (220105)**, 41 Highland Avenue, Zip 01890–1496;
tel. 781/729–9000 **A**1 2 3 5 9 10 **F**3 8 12 13 15 18 26 28 29 30 31 32 34
35 36 38 40 41 44 45 46 49 50 51 53 54 56 57 59 62 64 68 70 73 74 75
76 77 78 79 81 82 85 86 87 89 92 93 107 108 110 114 115 118 119 120
121 126 129 130 131 132 135 144 145 146 147 148
Primary Contact: Kevin F. Smith, President and Chief Executive Officer
CFO: Matthew Woods, Executive Vice President Finance and Chief Financial Officer
CMO: Richard Iseke, M.D., Vice President Medical Affairs
CHR: Anne Lang, Vice President Human Resources and Compliance and Privacy
Officer
CNO: Kathy Schuler, R.N., Vice President of Patient Care Services
Web address: www.winchesterhospital.org
Control: Other not–for–profit (including NFP Corporation) **Service:** General
Medical and Surgical

Staffed Beds: 200 **Admissions:** 11610 **Census:** 130 **Outpatient Visits:**
586109 **Births:** 1963 **Total Expense ($000):** 266414 **Payroll Expense
($000):** 124138 **Personnel:** 1835

WOBURN—Middlesex County

☐ **NEW ENGLAND REHABILITATION HOSPITAL (223026)**, Two Rehabilitation
Way, Zip 01801–6098; tel. 781/935–5050 **A**1 10 **F**29 90 91 93 95 96 130
132 143 146 148 **S** Five Star Quality Care, Newton, MA
Primary Contact: Joel Rudin, Chief Executive Officer
CFO: Lester Felege, Controller
CMO: A. Deniz Ozel, M.D., Medical Director
CHR: Annamarie Cronin, Director Human Resources
Web address: www.newenglandrehab.com
Control: Corporation, Investor–owned, for–profit **Service:** Rehabilitation

Staffed Beds: 210 **Admissions:** 2504 **Census:** 97 **Outpatient Visits:** 35053
Births: 0 **Total Expense ($000):** 50139 **Payroll Expense ($000):** 29239
Personnel: 413

WORCESTER—Worcester County

ADCARE HOSPITAL OF WORCESTER (220062), 107 Lincoln Street,
Zip 01605–2499; tel. 508/799–9000, (Nonreporting) **A**5 9 10
Primary Contact: David W. Hillis, Chairman and Chief Executive Officer
COO: Jeffrey W. Hillis, Chief Operating Officer
CFO: Christine Judycki–Crepeault, Chief Financial Officer
CMO: Ronald F. Pike, M.D., Medical Director
CHR: Joan L. Bertrand, Vice President Human Resources
CNO: Judith Richards, Director of Nursing
Web address: www.adcare.com
Control: Other not–for–profit (including NFP Corporation) **Service:** Alcoholism and
other chemical dependency

Staffed Beds: 114

✠ **FAIRLAWN REHABILITATION HOSPITAL (223029)**, 189 May Street,
Zip 01602–4339; tel. 508/791–6351 **A**1 3 5 10 **F**3 28 29 34 35 56 57 59 64
74 75 77 79 82 86 87 90 91 93 95 96 130 132 135 146 148 **P**8
S HEALTHSOUTH Corporation, Birmingham, AL
Primary Contact: R. David Richer, Chief Executive Officer
CFO: John Flaherty, Controller
CMO: Peter Bagley, M.D., Medical Director
CIO: Crystal Anson, Director Health Information
CHR: Rosalie Lawless, Director Human Resources
CNO: Judith Chuli, R.N., Chief Nursing Officer
Web address: www.fairlawnrehab.org
Control: Corporation, Investor–owned, for–profit **Service:** Rehabilitation

Staffed Beds: 110 **Admissions:** 2483 **Census:** 91 **Outpatient Visits:** 9490
Births: 0 **Total Expense ($000):** 30467 **Payroll Expense ($000):** 17243
Personnel: 351

Many Facility Codes have changed. Please refer to the AHA Guide Code Chart. © 2014 AHA Guide

✦ **SAINT VINCENT HOSPITAL (220176)**, 123 Summer Street, Zip 01608–1216; tel. 508/363–5000 **A**1 2 3 5 9 10 12 **F**12 13 15 17 18 20 22 24 26 28 29 30 31 35 38 40 45 46 47 49 50 57 59 60 64 68 70 74 75 76 77 78 79 81 82 84 85 86 87 89 92 93 97 98 100 101 102 107 108 110 111 114 115 116 117 118 119 120 121 123 124 126 129 130 131 132 135 146 147 148 **P**5 **S** TENET Healthcare Corporation, Dallas, TX
Primary Contact: Steven MacLauchlan, President and CEO
COO: Deborah Bitsoli, Chief Operating Officer
CFO: Peter D'Elia, Chief Financial Officer
CMO: Douglas Waite, M.D., Chief Medical Officer
CHR: Jan Peters, Vice President Human Resources
Web address: www.stvincenthospital.com
Control: Corporation, Investor–owned, for–profit **Service:** General Medical and Surgical

Staffed Beds: 283 **Admissions:** 17516 **Census:** 190 **Outpatient Visits:** 224277 **Births:** 1893 **Total Expense ($000):** 329020 **Payroll Expense ($000):** 145482 **Personnel:** 1391

✦ **UMASS MEMORIAL MEDICAL CENTER (220163)**, 119 Belmont Street, Zip 01605–2982; tel. 508/334–1000, (Includes HAHNEMANN CAMPUS, 281 Lincoln Street, Zip 01605; tel. 508/334–1000; MEMORIAL CAMPUS, 119 Belmont Street, Zip 01605; tel. 508/334–1000; UMASS MEMORIAL CHILDREN'S MEDICAL CENTER, 55 Lake Avenue North, Zip 01655–0002; tel. 508/334–1000; UNIVERSITY CAMPUS, 55 Lake Avenue North, Zip 01655–0002; tel. 508/334–1000) **A**1 2 3 5 8 9 10 **F**3 5 7 8 9 12 13 14 15 16 17 18 19 20 22 24 25 26 29 30 31 32 34 38 40 41 43 45 46 47 48 49 50 51 52 55 56 58 59 60 61 64 65 68 70 72 73 74 75 76 78 79 81 82 84 85 87 88 89 92 93 97 98 99 100 101 102 103 104 105 107 108 110 114 115 118 119 120 121 123 124 126 127 129 130 131 132 133 134 135 136 138 139 142 144 145 146 147 148 **P**5 6 8 **S** UMass Memorial Health Care, Inc., Worcester, MA
Primary Contact: Patrick L. Muldoon, FACHE, President and CEO
COO: Andrew Sussman, M.D., Chief Operating Officer
CFO: Therese Day, Chief Financial Officer
CMO: Stephen E. Tosi, M.D., Chief Medical Officer
CIO: George Brenkle, Chief Information Officer
Web address: www.umassmemorial.org
Control: Other not–for–profit (including NFP Corporation) **Service:** General Medical and Surgical

Staffed Beds: 804 **Admissions:** 38403 **Census:** 558 **Outpatient Visits:** 996278 **Births:** 3980 **Total Expense ($000):** 1433377 **Payroll Expense ($000):** 485746 **Personnel:** 7800

☐ **WORCESTER RECOVERY CENTER AND HOSPITAL (224032)**, 305 Belmont Street, Zip 01604–1695; tel. 508/368–3300, (Nonreporting) **A**1 3 5 10 **S** Massachusetts Department of Mental Health, Boston, MA
Primary Contact: Anthony Riccitelli, Chief Operating Officer
COO: Anthony Riccitelli, Chief Operating Officer
CIO: Ron Medciros, Director Applied Information Technology
Control: State–Government, nonfederal **Service:** Psychiatric

Staffed Beds: 126

Hospital, Medicare Provider Number, Address, Telephone, Approval, Facility, and Physician Codes, Health Care System

★ American Hospital Association (AHA) membership ◯ Healthcare Facilities Accreditation Program
☐ The Joint Commission accreditation ◇ DNV Healthcare Inc. accreditation △ Commission on Accreditation of Rehabilitation Facilities (CARF) accreditation

MICHIGAN

ADRIAN—Lenawee County

★ ○ **PROMEDICA BIXBY HOSPITAL (230005)**, 818 Riverside Avenue,
Zip 49221–1446; tel. 517/265–0900 **A**2 9 10 11 **F**3 11 13 15 18 20 28 30
34 40 43 45 46 50 51 57 59 64 68 70 74 75 76 77 78 79 81 82 85 91 92
93 100 102 104 107 108 110 111 114 117 118 119 120 121 126 130 131
132 135 141 143 145 146 148 **P**6 8 **S** ProMedica Health System, Toledo, OH
Primary Contact: Timothy Jakacki, President
CFO: Bernie Nawrocki, Administrative Director Finance
CIO: Stephanie Sonnenberg, Director Information Technology
CHR: Cathy J. Davis, Director Human Resources
CNO: Kathryn M. Greenlee, R.N., Vice President, Clinical Services/CNO
Web address: www.promedica.org
Control: Other not–for–profit (including NFP Corporation) **Service:** General
Medical and Surgical

Staffed Beds: 66 **Admissions:** 3953 **Census:** 38 **Outpatient Visits:** 132656
Births: 742 **Total Expense ($000):** 71546 **Payroll Expense ($000):** 26512
Personnel: 473

ALLEGAN—Allegan County

★ ◇ **ALLEGAN GENERAL HOSPITAL (231328)**, 555 Linn Street,
Zip 49010–1524; tel. 269/673–8424 **A**9 10 18 21 **F**12 15 28 29 31 32 34 35
40 45 47 48 50 57 59 62 64 65 68 70 75 77 78 79 81 85 86 87 93 96 99
100 101 104 107 108 110 114 119 127 129 130 131 132 135 145 146
S QHR, Brentwood, TN
Primary Contact: Gerald J. Barbini, President and Chief Executive Officer
CFO: Richard Harning, Vice President Finance and Chief Financial Officer
CMO: Nabil Nouna, M.D., Chief of Staff
CIO: David Federinko, Chief Information Officer
CHR: Denise A. Eberth, Director Human Resources
Web address: www.aghosp.org
Control: Other not–for–profit (including NFP Corporation) **Service:** General
Medical and Surgical

Staffed Beds: 25 **Admissions:** 812 **Census:** 8 **Outpatient Visits:** 85160
Births: 0 **Total Expense ($000):** 44735 **Payroll Expense ($000):** 18122
Personnel: 281

ALMA—Gratiot County

GRATIOT MEDICAL CENTER See MidMichigan Medical Center–Gratiot

⊞ △ **MIDMICHIGAN MEDICAL CENTER–GRATIOT (230030)**, 300 East
Warwick Drive, Zip 48801–1014; tel. 989/463–1101 **A**1 7 9 10 19 **F**3 11 12
13 15 18 20 28 29 31 32 34 35 40 50 51 55 56 57 59 60 61 64 65 68 70
74 75 76 77 78 79 81 82 85 89 90 92 93 96 98 100 101 102 103 105 107
108 110 111 114 115 116 117 118 119 124 126 127 129 130 132 135 144
145 146 148 **S** MidMichigan Health, Midland, MI
Primary Contact: Mark A. Santamaria, President
CFO: Jeff Provenzano, Vice President and Chief Financial Officer
Web address: www.midmichigan.org/gratiot
Control: Other not–for–profit (including NFP Corporation) **Service:** General
Medical and Surgical

Staffed Beds: 100 **Admissions:** 5108 **Census:** 63 **Outpatient Visits:** 139440
Births: 591 **Total Expense ($000):** 105313 **Payroll Expense ($000):** 35278
Personnel: 574

ALPENA—Alpena County

⊞ **ALPENA REGIONAL MEDICAL CENTER (230036)**, 1501 West Chisholm
Street, Zip 49707–1401; tel. 989/356–7390 **A**1 2 9 10 19 20 **F**3 11 13 14 15
20 22 28 29 31 34 35 40 43 44 45 46 47 48 49 50 59 62 64 65 70 71 73
74 75 77 78 79 81 82 85 86 87 90 93 96 97 98 99 100 101 102 103 104
106 107 108 110 111 114 115 118 119 129 130 131 132 135 146 147
148 **P**6
Primary Contact: Karmon T. Bjella, Chief Executive Officer
COO: Aldean J. Moe, Chief Operating Officer
CFO: George J. Smart, VP Finance & IT
CHR: Diane Shields, Chief Human Resources Officer
CNO: Gayle Bruski, R.N., Chief Nursing Officer
Web address: www.alpenaregionalmedicalcenter.org
Control: County–Government, nonfederal **Service:** General Medical and Surgical

Staffed Beds: 125 **Admissions:** 4835 **Census:** 60 **Outpatient Visits:** 216592
Births: 366 **Total Expense ($000):** 119824 **Payroll Expense ($000):** 50153
Personnel: 875

ANN ARBOR—Washtenaw County

⊞ **UNIVERSITY OF MICHIGAN HOSPITALS AND HEALTH CENTERS (230046)**,
1500 East Medical Center Drive, Zip 48109–5000; tel. 734/936–4000, (Includes
C. S. MOTT CHILDREN'S HOSPITAL, 1540 East Hospital Drive, Zip 48109–5475;
tel. 734/936–4000; Paul A. King, Executive Director) **A**1 2 3 5 8 9 10 **F**3 5 6 8
9 11 12 13 15 16 17 18 19 20 21 22 23 24 25 26 27 28 29 30 31 32 34 35
36 37 38 39 40 41 43 44 45 46 47 48 49 50 51 52 53 54 55 56 57 58 59
60 61 62 64 65 66 68 69 70 72 74 75 76 77 78 79 80 81 82 84 85 86 87
88 89 90 91 92 93 94 95 97 98 99 100 101 102 103 104 107 108 110 111
112 114 115 116 117 118 119 120 121 123 124 126 127 129 130 131 132
134 135 136 137 138 139 140 141 142 145 146 147 148 **P**6
Primary Contact: Tony Denton, JD, Interim Chief Executive Officer
COO: Tony Denton, JD, Chief Operating Officer
CFO: Paul Castillo, Chief Financial Officer
CMO: Darrell Campbell, M.D., Chief Clinical Affairs
CIO: Sue Schade, Chief Information Officer
CHR: Deborah Childs, Chief Human Resources Officer
Web address: www.med.umich.edu
Control: Other not–for–profit (including NFP Corporation) **Service:** General
Medical and Surgical

Staffed Beds: 939 **Admissions:** 46997 **Census:** 780 **Outpatient Visits:**
1972732 **Births:** 4144 **Total Expense ($000):** 2349447 **Payroll Expense
($000):** 903941 **Personnel:** 14119

⊞ **VETERANS AFFAIRS ANN ARBOR HEALTHCARE SYSTEM**, 2215 Fuller Road,
Zip 48105–2399; tel. 734/769–7100, (Total facility includes 40 beds in nursing
home–type unit) **A**1 2 3 5 8 9 **F**3 5 12 18 20 22 24 26 28 29 30 31 34 35 36
38 39 40 45 46 48 49 50 54 56 57 58 59 60 61 62 63 64 65 68 70 71 74
75 77 78 79 81 82 83 84 85 86 87 91 92 93 94 96 97 98 100 101 102 103
104 105 107 108 111 114 115 116 117 119 121 123 126 128 129 130 132
135 143 144 146 147 148 **P**6 **S** Department of Veterans Affairs,
Washington, DC
Primary Contact: Robert P. McDivitt, FACHE, Director
COO: Himanshu Singh, M.D., Associate Director
CFO: Joel Wallinga, Chief Financial Officer
CMO: Eric Young, M.D., Chief of Staff
CIO: Rob Whitehurst, Chief, Office of Information and Technology
CHR: Stephanie Hunter, Chief Human Resources
CNO: Stacey Breedveld, R.N., Associate Director for Patient Care
Web address: www.annarbor.va.gov
Control: Veterans Affairs, Government, federal **Service:** General Medical and
Surgical

Staffed Beds: 145 **Admissions:** 5332 **Census:** 86 **Outpatient Visits:** 844837
Births: 0 **Total Expense ($000):** 423194 **Payroll Expense ($000):** 168366
Personnel: 3387

AUBURN HILLS—Oakland County

□ **HAVENWYCK HOSPITAL (234023)**, 1525 University Drive, Zip 48326–2673;
tel. 248/373–9200 **A**1 9 10 **F**98 99 102 103 105 106 130 **P**8 **S** Universal
Health Services, Inc., King of Prussia, PA
Primary Contact: Diane Henneman, Chief Executive Officer
CFO: David Kunkle, Chief Financial Officer
CMO: Hani Mekhael, M.D., Chief Staff
CHR: Amy Giannosa, Director Human Resources
CNO: Mitzi Sawicki, Director of Nursing
Web address: www.havenwyckhospital.com
Control: Corporation, Investor–owned, for–profit **Service:** Psychiatric

Staffed Beds: 253 **Admissions:** 6708 **Census:** 219 **Outpatient Visits:** 4592
Births: 0 **Total Expense ($000):** 43888 **Payroll Expense ($000):** 16287
Personnel: 390

BAD AXE—Huron County

HURON MEDICAL CENTER (230118), 1100 South Van Dyke Road,
Zip 48413–9615; tel. 989/269–9521 **A**9 10 20 **F**3 11 13 14 15 18 20 28 29
31 32 34 35 40 45 53 56 57 59 64 70 74 75 76 77 78 79 81 82 85 90 93
97 107 108 114 119 126 127 130 132 134 135 144 146 **P**6
Primary Contact: Jeffery Longbrake, President and Chief Executive Officer
CFO: Kristen Hedley, Controller
CMO: Christopher Gong, M.D., Chief Staff
CHR: Nancy Bouck, Director Human Resources
CNO: Carrie Franzel, Chief Nursing Officer
Web address: www.huronmedicalcenter.org
Control: Other not–for–profit (including NFP Corporation) **Service:** General
Medical and Surgical

Staffed Beds: 35 **Admissions:** 1733 **Census:** 15 **Outpatient Visits:** 55925
Births: 438 **Total Expense ($000):** 44127 **Payroll Expense ($000):** 18207
Personnel: 357

BATTLE CREEK—Calhoun County

⊞ **BATTLE CREEK VETERANS AFFAIRS MEDICAL CENTER**, 5500 Armstrong Road, Zip 49037–7314; tel. 269/966–5600, (Total facility includes 90 beds in nursing home–type unit) **A**1 9 **F**3 4 5 7 12 29 30 34 35 36 38 39 50 53 54 56 57 58 59 61 62 63 64 65 68 74 75 77 82 83 84 86 87 91 92 93 94 96 97 98 100 101 102 103 104 106 107 108 111 119 127 128 130 132 135 141 143 144 146 147 148 **S** Department of Veterans Affairs, Washington, DC
Primary Contact: Mary Beth Skupien, Director
COO: Edward G. Dornoff, Associate Director
CFO: James M. Rupert, Chief Fiscal Services
CMO: Wilfredo Rodriguez, M.D., Chief of Staff
CIO: Scott Hershberger, Acting Chief Information Management Services
CHR: Palma Simkins, Chief Human Resources Management Services
CNO: Kay Bower, Associate Director for Patient Care Services
Web address: www.battlecreek.va.gov/
Control: Veterans Affairs, Government, federal **Service:** Psychiatric

Staffed Beds: 188 **Admissions:** 2816 **Census:** 235 **Outpatient Visits:** 462547 **Births:** 0 **Personnel:** 1456

⊞ **BRONSON BATTLE CREEK (230075)**, 300 North Avenue, Zip 49017–3307; tel. 269/245–8000, (Includes FIELDSTONE CENTER, 165 North Washington Avenue, Zip 49037; tel. 269/245–8570; MAIN CAMPUS, 300 North Avenue, Zip 49017; tel. 616/966–8000) **A**1 2 9 10 **F**3 5 6 9 11 13 15 18 20 26 28 29 30 31 34 35 38 40 43 44 45 46 49 50 51 54 55 56 57 58 59 60 62 64 65 66 68 70 71 74 75 76 77 78 79 81 82 84 85 86 87 92 93 97 98 100 101 102 103 104 107 108 110 111 114 115 117 118 119 120 121 123 126 129 130 131 132 135 143 144 146 147 148 **P**6 8 **S** Bronson Healthcare Group, Inc., Kalamazoo, MI
Primary Contact: Frank J. Sardone, President and Chief Executive Officer
COO: James E. Mckernan, Chief Operating Officer
CFO: Mary Meitz, Senior Vice President and Chief Financial Officer
CMO: Daniel Stewart, M.D., Vice President Medical Affairs
CIO: Paul Peabody, Vice President Information Technology and Chief Information Officer
CHR: John Hayden, Senior Vice President and Human Resources Officer
CNO: Susan Watson, MSN, Vice President
Web address: www.bronsonhealth.com
Control: Other not–for–profit (including NFP Corporation) **Service:** General Medical and Surgical

Staffed Beds: 198 **Admissions:** 9641 **Census:** 106 **Outpatient Visits:** 224910 **Births:** 871 **Total Expense ($000):** 202157 **Payroll Expense ($000):** 92505 **Personnel:** 1290

⊞ **SELECT SPECIALTY HOSPITAL–BATTLE CREEK (232035)**, 300 North Avenue, Zip 49017–3307; tel. 269/245–4675, (Nonreporting) **A**1 9 10 **S** Select Medical Corporation, Mechanicsburg, PA
Primary Contact: Salvatore Iweimrin, R.N., Chief Executive Officer
Web address: www.selectspecialtyhospitals.com/company/locations/battlecreek.aspx
Control: Corporation, Investor–owned, for–profit **Service:** Long–Term Acute Care hospital

Staffed Beds: 25

☐ **SOUTHWEST REGIONAL REHABILITATION CENTER (233025)**, 393 East Roosevelt Avenue, Zip 49017–3333; tel. 269/965–3206 **A**1 9 10 **F**3 29 64 90 93 96 130 132 146 148 **P**6
Primary Contact: Kevin Arnold, President and Chief Executive Officer
COO: Amy Davis, Chief Operating Officer
CFO: Bruce Hart, Chief Financial Officer
CMO: Mehmet Ismailoglu, M.D., Medical Director
CIO: Rick Albaugh, Manager Information Services
CHR: Josh Schultz, Manager Corporate Services
Web address: www.sw–rehab.org
Control: Other not–for–profit (including NFP Corporation) **Service:** Rehabilitation

Staffed Beds: 26 **Admissions:** 700 **Census:** 17 **Outpatient Visits:** 14158 **Births:** 0 **Total Expense ($000):** 12108 **Payroll Expense ($000):** 6000 **Personnel:** 112

VETERANS AFFAIRS MEDICAL CENTER See Battle Creek Veterans Affairs Medical Center

BAY CITY—Bay County

⊞ △ **MCLAREN BAY REGION (230041)**, 1900 Columbus Avenue, Zip 48708–6831; tel. 989/894–3000, (Includes BAY REGIONAL MEDICAL CENTER–WEST CAMPUS, 3250 East Midland Road, Zip 48706; tel. 989/667–6750) **A**1 2 7 9 10 12 13 **F**3 7 11 13 15 17 18 20 22 24 26 28 29 30 31 32 34 35 36 38 40 44 45 46 47 48 49 50 57 58 59 64 65 68 70 73 74 75 76 78 79 81 82 85 86 87 89 90 92 93 96 97 98 100 102 103 107 108 110 111 114 115 119 120 121 123 124 129 130 131 132 135 141 143 146 147 148 **P**6 **S** McLaren Health Care Corporation, Flint, MI
Primary Contact: Alice M. Gerard, President and Chief Executive Officer
CFO: Stephen J. Scannell, Chief Financial Officer
CMO: Jay Summer, M.D., Vice President Corporate Medical Affairs
CIO: Ronald Strachan, Chief Information Officer
CHR: Carolyn Potter, Vice President Human Resources
CNO: Ellen E. Talbott, R.N., Vice President Patient Care Services
Web address: www.bayregional.org
Control: Other not–for–profit (including NFP Corporation) **Service:** General Medical and Surgical

Staffed Beds: 338 **Admissions:** 15222 **Census:** 194 **Outpatient Visits:** 354101 **Births:** 866 **Total Expense ($000):** 260762 **Payroll Expense ($000):** 117422 **Personnel:** 1829

★ ○ **MCLAREN BAY SPECIAL CARE (232020)**, 3250 East Midland Road, Suite 1, Zip 48706–2835; tel. 989/667–6802 **A**9 10 11 **F**1 3 29 31 79 87 96 148 **S** McLaren Health Care Corporation, Flint, MI
Primary Contact: Cheryl A. Burzynski, President
CFO: Stephen J. Scannell, Chief Financial Officer
CMO: Janet Sutton, M.D., Medical Director
CIO: Greg Jacobs, Manager
CHR: Carolyn Potter, Vice President Human Resources
Web address: www.bayspecialcare.org
Control: Other not–for–profit (including NFP Corporation) **Service:** Long–Term Acute Care hospital

Staffed Beds: 26 **Admissions:** 346 **Census:** 26 **Outpatient Visits:** 0 **Births:** 0 **Total Expense ($000):** 8302 **Payroll Expense ($000):** 3978 **Personnel:** 78

BERRIEN CENTER—Berrien County

☐ **LAKELAND SPECIALTY HOSPITAL–BERRIEN CENTER (232025)**, 6418 Deans Hill Road, Zip 49102–9750; tel. 269/473–3003, (Nonreporting) **A**1 9 10 **S** Lakeland Healthcare, Saint Joseph, MI
Primary Contact: Loren Hamel, M.D., President and Chief Executive Officer
Web address: www.lakelandhealth.org
Control: Other not–for–profit (including NFP Corporation) **Service:** Long–Term Acute Care hospital

Staffed Beds: 26

BIG RAPIDS—Mecosta County

⊞ **SPECTRUM HEALTH BIG RAPIDS HOSPITAL (230093)**, 605 Oak Street, Zip 49307–2099; tel. 231/796–8691 **A**1 9 10 20 **F**3 11 13 15 17 28 29 31 34 35 40 43 45 53 59 62 63 64 65 75 76 77 78 79 81 85 86 87 89 90 93 107 108 110 111 115 119 124 127 129 130 132 135 146 148 **P**1 **S** Spectrum Health, Grand Rapids, MI
Primary Contact: Mary Kay VanDriel, President
COO: Catherine Rybicki, Vice President Physician Services and Chief Operating Officer
CFO: Thomas Khoerl, Vice President Finance
CIO: Patrick Whiteside, Manager Information Services
CHR: Ricky Green, Senior Human Resources Business Partner
CNO: Netty S. Cove, R.N., Vice President Patient Services and Chief Nursing Officer
Web address: www.mcmcbr.com
Control: County–Government, nonfederal **Service:** General Medical and Surgical

Staffed Beds: 49 **Admissions:** 2275 **Census:** 19 **Outpatient Visits:** 125920 **Births:** 650 **Total Expense ($000):** 58341 **Payroll Expense ($000):** 26233 **Personnel:** 461

MI

Hospital, Medicare Provider Number, Address, Telephone, Approval, Facility, and Physician Codes, Health Care System

★ American Hospital Association (AHA) membership
☐ The Joint Commission accreditation   ◇ DNV Healthcare Inc. accreditation

○ Healthcare Facilities Accreditation Program
△ Commission on Accreditation of Rehabilitation Facilities (CARF) accreditation

BRIGHTON—Livingston County

★ **BRIGHTON CENTER FOR RECOVERY (230279)**, 12851 Grand River Road, Zip 48116–8506; tel. 810/227–1211 **A**10 **F**4 5 35 68 75 104 132 **P**3 5 6 7 8 **S** Ascension Health, Saint Louis, MO
Primary Contact: Raymond Waller, Director
COO: Raymond Waller, Director
CFO: Michael J. Felczak, Jr., Finance Manager
CMO: Jeffrey Berger, M.D., Chief Medical Officer
CIO: Frank Sanzone, Manager Information Technology
CHR: Marney Daugherty, Worklife Services Consultant
CNO: Barbara Shaw, Chief Nursing Officer
Web address: www.brightonrecovery.org
Control: Other not–for–profit (including NFP Corporation) **Service:** Alcoholism and other chemical dependency

Staffed Beds: 99 **Admissions:** 4250 **Census:** 92 **Outpatient Visits:** 23630 **Births:** 0 **Total Expense ($000):** 13982 **Payroll Expense ($000):** 7873 **Personnel:** 141

CADILLAC—Wexford County

✉ **MERCY HOSPITAL CADILLAC (230081)**, 400 Hobart Street, Zip 49601–2389; tel. 231/876–7200 **A**1 9 10 20 **F**3 11 13 15 18 28 29 30 31 34 35 40 44 45 50 51 53 59 64 66 68 70 75 76 77 78 79 81 82 85 87 89 93 97 107 108 111 114 115 116 119 127 129 130 132 146 147 148 **P**6 8 **S** Catholic Health East / Trinity Health, Livonia, MI
Primary Contact: Mary L. Neff, R.N., President and Chief Nursing Officer
CFO: Kristin Ellis
CMO: James Whelan, Chief Medical Officer
CHR: Mary Rosser, Director Human Resources
Web address: www.munsonhealthcare.org
Control: Church–operated, Nongovernment, not–for profit **Service:** General Medical and Surgical

Staffed Beds: 65 **Admissions:** 3676 **Census:** 34 **Outpatient Visits:** 77872 **Births:** 325 **Total Expense ($000):** 63330 **Payroll Expense ($000):** 22848 **Personnel:** 470

CARO—Tuscola County

☐ **CARO CENTER (234025)**, 2000 Chambers Road, Zip 48723–9296; tel. 989/673–3191, (Nonreporting) **A**1 9 10
Primary Contact: Rose Laskowski, R.N., Director
COO: Rose Laskowski, R.N., Director
CFO: Mary Jo Drzewiecki–Burger, Administrative Manager
CMO: William Clark, M.D., Chief Clinical Affairs
CIO: Michele Wills, Registered Health Information Administrator
CHR: Barbara Frank, Human Resource Specialist
Control: State–Government, nonfederal **Service:** Psychiatric

Staffed Beds: 193

★ **CARO COMMUNITY HOSPITAL (231329)**, 401 North Hooper Street, Zip 48723–1476, Mailing Address: P.O. Box 435, Zip 48723–0435; tel. 989/673–3141 **A**9 10 18 **F**3 11 15 29 34 40 45 50 57 59 65 75 81 82 85 87 92 93 97 107 108 110 115 119 129 130 132 135 **P**6
Primary Contact: Marc Augsburger, President and Chief Executive Officer
CFO: Ron Srebinski, Chief Financial Officer
CHR: Allyson Joyce, Vice President Human Resources
CNO: Kelly Whittaker, Vice President Nursing
Web address: www.cch-mi.org
Control: Other not–for–profit (including NFP Corporation) **Service:** General Medical and Surgical

Staffed Beds: 25 **Admissions:** 158 **Census:** 1 **Outpatient Visits:** 29598 **Births:** 0 **Total Expense ($000):** 11290 **Payroll Expense ($000):** 4707 **Personnel:** 106

CARSON CITY—Montcalm County

★ ○ **CARSON CITY HOSPITAL (230208)**, 406 East Elm Street, Zip 48811–9693, Mailing Address: P.O. Box 879, Zip 48811–0879; tel. 989/584–3131 **A**9 10 11 19 **F**11 13 15 29 30 31 34 35 37 40 45 46 57 59 62 65 68 70 74 75 76 77 78 79 81 82 93 97 98 100 101 102 104 107 108 110 111 115 119 126 127 130 132 135 146 147 148 **P**8
Primary Contact: Matthew J. Thompson, Chief Executive Officer
CFO: Richard Reid, Vice President Chief Finance Officer
CMO: Robert Seals, D.O., Medical Director
CIO: Richard Terry, Vice President & Chief Information Officer
CHR: Georgette Russell, Vice President of Talent & Organizational Effectiveness
CNO: Nancy Weaver, Vice President of Nursing, Chief Nursing Officer
Web address: www.carsoncityhospital.com
Control: Other not–for–profit (including NFP Corporation) **Service:** General Medical and Surgical

Staffed Beds: 62 **Admissions:** 2093 **Census:** 16 **Outpatient Visits:** 65019 **Births:** 363 **Total Expense ($000):** 63931 **Payroll Expense ($000):** 29440 **Personnel:** 477

CASS CITY—Tuscola County

★ **HILLS & DALES GENERAL HOSPITAL (231316)**, 4675 Hill Street, Zip 48726–1099; tel. 989/872–2121 **A**9 10 18 **F**3 11 15 29 30 31 32 34 35 40 46 53 56 57 59 61 64 74 75 77 79 81 85 86 87 93 97 107 108 109 110 115 118 119 127 129 130 131 132 135 144 146 147 148 **P**6
Primary Contact: Jean Anthony, R.N., President and Chief Executive Officer
CFO: Kenneth Baranski, Chief Financial Officer
CMO: Donald Robbins, Jr., M.D., Chief Staff
CHR: Tom Bardwell, Vice President Human Resources
CNO: Jennifer TerBush, Director of Nursing
Web address: www.hdghmi.org
Control: Other not–for–profit (including NFP Corporation) **Service:** General Medical and Surgical

Staffed Beds: 25 **Admissions:** 545 **Census:** 4 **Outpatient Visits:** 58994 **Births:** 1 **Total Expense ($000):** 25520 **Payroll Expense ($000):** 11585 **Personnel:** 212

CHARLEVOIX—Charlevoix County

✉ **CHARLEVOIX AREA HOSPITAL (231322)**, 14700 Lake Shore Drive, Zip 49720–1999; tel. 231/547–4024 **A**1 9 10 18 **F**11 13 15 28 31 32 34 35 40 50 57 59 75 77 78 79 81 82 93 107 108 111 115 119 129 130 131 132 133 135 144 146 **P**6
Primary Contact: Lyn Jenks, Chief Executive Officer
COO: Christine Wilhelm, Vice President Operations
CFO: Robert Zimmerman, Vice President Financial Services
CMO: Craig Boss, M.D., Chief Medical Officer
CIO: David Priest, Director Information Systems
CHR: Patty Fitzgerald, Staff Services
CNO: Bernadette Green Cole, R.N., Chief Nursing Officer
Web address: www.cah.org
Control: Other not–for–profit (including NFP Corporation) **Service:** General Medical and Surgical

Staffed Beds: 25 **Admissions:** 1063 **Census:** 8 **Outpatient Visits:** 37380 **Births:** 201 **Total Expense ($000):** 38048 **Payroll Expense ($000):** 17338 **Personnel:** 338

CHARLOTTE—Eaton County

✉ **HAYES GREEN BEACH MEMORIAL HOSPITAL (231327)**, 321 East Harris Street, Zip 48813–1629; tel. 517/543–1050 **A**1 9 10 18 **F**3 7 11 15 18 26 28 29 34 35 36 40 45 46 50 53 57 59 62 64 65 68 69 75 77 79 81 82 85 87 89 92 93 97 107 108 110 111 114 118 119 129 130 131 132 135 143 144 146 148 **P**6 **S** QHR, Brentwood, TN
Primary Contact: Matthew Rush, President and Chief Executive Officer
CFO: Kim Capps, Chief Financial Officer
CMO: Hugh Lindsey, M.D., Chief Medical Officer
CIO: Kevin Neugent, Chief Information Officer
CHR: Jennifer C. Bucienski, Vice President Human Resources
CNO: Maureen Hillary, Chief Nursing Officer
Web address: www.hgbhealth.com
Control: Other not–for–profit (including NFP Corporation) **Service:** General Medical and Surgical

Staffed Beds: 25 **Admissions:** 721 **Census:** 6 **Outpatient Visits:** 148953 **Births:** 0 **Total Expense ($000):** 48347 **Payroll Expense ($000):** 20455 **Personnel:** 382

CHELSEA—Washtenaw County

✉ **CHELSEA COMMUNITY HOSPITAL (230259)**, 775 South Main Street, Zip 48118–1383; tel. 734/593–6000 **A**1 3 5 9 10 **F**1 3 5 8 9 11 15 28 29 30 31 34 35 36 40 45 51 53 56 59 62 64 65 68 70 75 77 78 79 81 82 84 85 86 87 90 91 93 97 98 99 100 101 102 104 107 110 111 114 115 119 128 129 130 131 132 134 135 146 147 148 **S** Catholic Health East / Trinity Health, Livonia, MI
Primary Contact: Nancy Kay Graebner, President and Chief Executive Officer
CFO: Barb Fielder, Vice President Finance
CMO: Randall T. Forsch, M.D., Chief Medical Officer
CHR: Jeremy Stephens, Vice President and Chief Human Resources Officer
CNO: Kathy M. Brubaker, R.N., Chief Nursing Officer
Web address: www.cch.org
Control: Other not–for–profit (including NFP Corporation) **Service:** General Medical and Surgical

Staffed Beds: 96 **Admissions:** 4085 **Census:** 50 **Outpatient Visits:** 207728 **Births:** 0 **Total Expense ($000):** 108390 **Payroll Expense ($000):** 48047 **Personnel:** 666

Many Facility Codes have changed. Please refer to the AHA Guide Code Chart. © 2014 AHA Guide

CLARE—Clare County

MIDMICHIGAN MEDICAL CENTER–CLARE (230180), 703 North McEwan Street, Zip 48617–1440; tel. 989/802–5000, (Nonreporting) **A**1 5 9 10 **S** MidMichigan Health, Midland, MI
Primary Contact: Raymond Stover, President and Chief Executive Officer
CFO: Josh Wiggins, Vice President Controller
CMO: David Bremer, D.O., Chief of Staff
CIO: Michael Larson, Vice President Chief Information Officer
CNO: Glenn King, R.N., Vice President, Chief Nursing Officer
Web address: www.midmichigan.org
Control: Other not–for–profit (including NFP Corporation) **Service:** General Medical and Surgical

Staffed Beds: 55

CLINTON TOWNSHIP—Macomb County

HENRY FORD MACOMB HOSPITALS (230047), 15855 19 Mile Road, Zip 48038–6324; tel. 586/263–2300, (Includes HENRY FORD MACOMB HOSPITAL – MOUNT CLEMENS CAMPUS, 215 North Avenue, Mount Clemens, Zip 48043; tel. 586/466–9300; ST. JOSEPH'S MERCY HOSPITAL–WEST, 15855 19 Mile Road, Zip 48038; tel. 586/263–2707; ST. JOSEPH'S MERCY–NORTH, 80650 North Van Dyke, Romeo, Zip 48065; tel. 810/798–3551) **A**1 2 9 10 12 13 **F**3 7 11 12 13 15 18 19 20 22 24 26 28 29 30 31 32 34 35 36 38 40 43 44 45 46 47 49 50 51 54 56 57 58 59 60 61 64 65 66 68 69 70 74 75 76 77 78 79 81 82 84 85 86 87 89 90 92 93 96 97 98 99 100 101 102 103 104 105 107 108 110 111 114 115 117 118 119 120 121 124 126 129 131 132 134 144 146 147 148 **P**6 8 **S** Henry Ford Health System, Detroit, MI
Primary Contact: Barbara Rossmann, R.N., President and Chief Executive Officer
COO: Gary Beaulac, Chief Operating Officer
CFO: Terry Goodbalian, Vice President Finance and Chief Financial Officer
CMO: Charles Kelly, D.O., Vice President Medical Affairs and Chief Medical Officer
CHR: Joel Gibson, Vice President Human Resources
Web address: www.henryfordmacomb.com
Control: Other not–for–profit (including NFP Corporation) **Service:** General Medical and Surgical

Staffed Beds: 433 Admissions: 21723 **Census:** 312 **Outpatient Visits:** 422157 **Births:** 1727 **Total Expense ($000):** 416808 **Payroll Expense ($000):** 166356 **Personnel:** 2719

COLDWATER—Branch County

COMMUNITY HEALTH CENTER OF BRANCH COUNTY (230022), 274 East Chicago Street, Zip 49036–2041; tel. 517/279–5400 **A**1 9 10 13 19 **F**3 8 11 12 13 15 28 29 30 31 34 37 40 43 45 57 59 61 62 63 64 65 70 74 75 76 78 79 81 84 85 87 89 91 92 93 96 97 98 100 101 102 103 104 107 108 110 111 115 116 117 118 119 127 129 130 132 146 148 **P**6 8
Primary Contact: Randy DeGroot, President and Chief Executive Officer
COO: Mary R. Rose, R.N., Chief Clinical Officer
CMO: Joudat Daoud, M.D., Chief of Staff
CIO: Joel Lederman, Director Information Systems
CHR: Amy Jensen, Director Human Resources
Web address: www.chcbc.com
Control: County–Government, nonfederal **Service:** General Medical and Surgical

Staffed Beds: 86 Admissions: 3628 **Census:** 38 **Outpatient Visits:** 144386 **Births:** 287 **Total Expense ($000):** 68556 **Payroll Expense ($000):** 30579 **Personnel:** 502

COMMERCE TOWNSHIP—Oakland County

DMC HURON VALLEY–SINAI HOSPITAL (230277), 1 William Carls Drive, Zip 48382–2201; tel. 248/937–3300, (Includes DMC SURGERY HOSPITAL, 30671 Stephenson Highway, Madison Heights, Zip 48071–1678; tel. 248/733–2200; Andrei Soran, MSN, President) **A**1 9 10 12 **F**3 4 11 12 13 15 16 17 18 20 22 26 28 29 30 31 34 35 37 39 40 44 45 46 47 48 49 50 51 53 57 58 59 60 61 64 65 68 70 72 73 74 75 76 77 78 79 80 81 82 84 85 86 87 88 89 90 92 98 101 107 108 110 111 114 115 117 119 120 121 123 124 126 129 130 131 132 135 141 146 147 148 **P**1 6 **S** TENET Healthcare Corporation, Dallas, TX
Primary Contact: Andrei Soran, MSN, President
COO: Karen Fordham, Vice President Chief Operating Officer
CFO: William Lantzy, Vice President Finance
CMO: Marc Bocknek, D.O., Vice President Medical Affairs
CHR: Ayanna Weber, Director Human Resources
CNO: Cathy Grant, R.N., Associate Vice President, Patient Services
Web address: www.hvsh.org
Control: Corporation, Investor–owned, for–profit **Service:** General Medical and Surgical

Staffed Beds: 220 Admissions: 10314 **Census:** 118 **Outpatient Visits:** 108145 **Births:** 1200 **Total Expense ($000):** 183568 **Payroll Expense ($000):** 60146 **Personnel:** 1105

DEARBORN—Wayne County

OAKWOOD HOSPITAL–DEARBORN (230020), 18101 Oakwood Boulevard, Zip 48124–4089, Mailing Address: P.O. Box 2500, Zip 48123–2500; tel. 313/593–7000 **A**1 2 3 5 8 9 10 **F**3 11 12 13 15 17 18 20 22 24 26 28 29 30 31 32 34 35 37 38 39 40 43 44 47 49 50 52 55 56 57 58 59 60 61 64 65 68 70 72 73 74 75 76 77 78 79 80 81 82 84 85 86 87 89 92 93 96 97 100 102 107 108 110 111 114 115 118 119 120 121 123 124 126 130 131 132 135 146 147 148 **P**8 **S** Oakwood Healthcare, Inc., Dearborn, MI
Primary Contact: Kelly C. Smith, Division President
CFO: Matt LeGault, Chief Financial Administrator
CMO: Malcolm S. Henoch, M.D., Chief Medical Officer
CIO: Paula Smith, Leader Information Services and Chief Information Officer
CHR: Sherry Huffman, Administrator Human Resources
CNO: Kimberlie McAllister, Administrator Nursing Operations
Web address: www.oakwood.org
Control: Other not–for–profit (including NFP Corporation) **Service:** General Medical and Surgical

Staffed Beds: 524 Admissions: 29783 **Census:** 417 **Outpatient Visits:** 182184 **Births:** 4157 **Total Expense ($000):** 572284 **Payroll Expense ($000):** 211574 **Personnel:** 3065

DECKERVILLE—Sanilac County

DECKERVILLE COMMUNITY HOSPITAL (231311), 3559 Pine Street, Zip 48427–7703, Mailing Address: P.O. Box 126, Zip 48427–0126; tel. 810/376–2835, (Nonreporting) **A**9 10 18
Primary Contact: David West, Administrator
COO: David West, Administrator
CFO: Valerie Bryant, Chief Financial Officer
CMO: Bassam Afaneh, M.D., Chief of Staff
Web address: www.deckervillehosp.org
Control: Other not–for–profit (including NFP Corporation) **Service:** General Medical and Surgical

Staffed Beds: 15

DETROIT—Wayne County

BCA STONECREST HOSPITAL See Stonecrest Center

CHILDREN'S HOSPITAL OF MICHIGAN (233300), 3901 Beaubien Street, Zip 48201–2119; tel. 313/745–5437 **A**1 3 5 7 9 10 **F**3 7 11 16 17 18 19 20 21 22 23 24 25 26 27 29 30 31 32 34 35 38 39 40 41 43 44 45 48 49 50 51 54 55 57 58 59 60 61 63 64 65 68 72 74 75 77 78 79 80 81 82 84 85 86 87 88 89 90 91 92 93 94 95 96 97 99 100 101 102 107 108 111 114 115 116 117 118 119 120 121 123 124 129 130 131 132 134 136 137 138 139 141 144 146 148 **P**1 6 **S** TENET Healthcare Corporation, Dallas, TX
Primary Contact: Larry M. Gold, Chief Executive Officer
COO: Chad M. Grant, Chief Operating Officer
CMO: Rudolph Valentini, M.D., Chief Medical Officer
CHR: Walter Tetteh, Director Human Resources
CNO: Claudine N. Hoppen, MSN, Interim Chief Nursing Officer
Web address: www.chmkids.org
Control: Corporation, Investor–owned, for–profit **Service:** Children's general

Staffed Beds: 222 Admissions: 11010 **Census:** 140 **Outpatient Visits:** 281425 **Births:** 0 **Total Expense ($000):** 350300 **Payroll Expense ($000):** 131974 **Personnel:** 1746

DETROIT RECEIVING HOSPITAL/UNIVERSITY HEALTH CENTER (230273), 4201 Saint Antoine Street, Zip 48201–2153; tel. 313/745–3000 **A**1 3 5 9 10 **F**3 16 17 18 29 30 34 35 38 40 42 43 44 49 50 56 57 58 59 61 64 65 66 68 70 74 75 77 79 81 82 84 85 87 98 99 100 102 103 104 107 114 115 119 129 130 131 132 135 141 143 144 146 148 **P**1 6 **S** TENET Healthcare Corporation, Dallas, TX
Primary Contact: Iris Taylor, Ph.D., R.N., President
COO: Jeff Dawkins, Chief Operating Officer
CFO: Gloria Larkins, Vice President Finance
CMO: Safwan Badr, M.D., Executive Vice President and Chief Medical Officer
CIO: Michael LeRoy, Senior Vice President and Chief Information Officer
CHR: Paulette Griffin, Vice President Human Resources
Web address: www.dmc.org
Control: Corporation, Investor–owned, for–profit **Service:** General Medical and Surgical

Staffed Beds: 268 Admissions: 13874 **Census:** 185 **Outpatient Visits:** 166607 **Births:** 0 **Total Expense ($000):** 270163 **Payroll Expense ($000):** 99212 **Personnel:** 1275

Hospital, Medicare Provider Number, Address, Telephone, Approval, Facility, and Physician Codes, Health Care System

★ American Hospital Association (AHA) membership
□ The Joint Commission accreditation ◇ DNV Healthcare Inc. accreditation
○ Healthcare Facilities Accreditation Program
△ Commission on Accreditation of Rehabilitation Facilities (CARF) accreditation

© 2014 AHA Guide *Many Facility Codes have changed. Please refer to the AHA Guide Code Chart.* Hospitals **A321**

MI

✠ **DMC HARPER UNIVERSITY HOSPITAL (230104)**, 3990 John R Street, Zip 48201–2018; tel. 313/745–8040 **A**1 3 5 9 10 **F**1 3 4 8 9 11 12 13 15 17 18 20 22 24 26 28 29 30 34 35 36 39 40 42 44 45 46 47 48 49 50 51 52 54 55 56 57 58 59 60 61 63 64 65 66 67 70 72 73 74 75 76 77 78 79 80 81 82 83 84 85 86 87 89 90 92 94 97 98 100 107 108 111 112 114 115 119 126 128 130 131 132 133 134 135 136 138 141 143 146 147 148 **P**1 6 **S** TENET Healthcare Corporation, Dallas, TX
Primary Contact: Reginald J. Eadie, M.D., Chief Executive Officer
COO: Valerie Gibson, Chief Operating Officer
CFO: Tina Wood, Chief Financial Officer
CMO: Patricia Wilkerson–Uddyback, M.D., Chief Medical Officer
CIO: Michael LeRoy, Senior Vice President and Chief Information Officer
CHR: Deloris Hunt, Corporate Vice President Human Resources
CNO: Christine Bowen, R.N., Chief Nursing Officer
Web address: www.harperhospital.org
Control: Corporation, Investor–owned, for–profit **Service:** General Medical and Surgical

Staffed Beds: 535 **Admissions:** 18462 **Census:** 276 **Outpatient Visits:** 206883 **Births:** 4753 **Total Expense ($000):** 349240 **Payroll Expense ($000):** 167422 **Personnel:** 2825

HARPER UNIVERSITY HOSPITAL See DMC Harper University Hospital

✠ **HENRY FORD HOSPITAL (230053)**, 2799 West Grand Boulevard, Zip 48202–2608; tel. 313/916–2600 **A**1 2 3 5 8 9 10 **F**3 4 5 6 8 9 11 12 15 17 18 19 20 22 24 26 27 28 29 30 31 32 33 34 35 36 38 39 40 42 43 44 45 46 47 48 49 50 51 52 53 54 55 56 57 58 59 60 61 63 64 65 66 68 70 71 72 73 74 75 76 77 78 79 80 81 82 83 84 85 86 87 91 92 93 96 97 98 99 100 101 102 103 104 105 107 108 110 111 112 113 114 115 116 117 118 119 120 121 123 124 129 130 131 132 134 135 136 137 138 139 140 141 142 144 145 146 147 148 **P**6 **S** Henry Ford Health System, Detroit, MI
Primary Contact: John Popovich, M.D., President and Chief Executive Officer
COO: Veronica Hall, R.N., Chief Operating Officer
CFO: Joseph Schmitt, III, Senior Vice President Finance and Chief Financial Officer
CIO: Mary Alice Annecharico, Chief Information Officer
CHR: Kathy Oswald, Senior Vice President and Chief Human Resources Officer
CNO: Gwen Gnam, R.N., Chief Nursing Officer
Web address: www.henryfordhealth.org
Control: Other not–for–profit (including NFP Corporation) **Service:** General Medical and Surgical

Staffed Beds: 673 **Admissions:** 37436 **Census:** 579 **Outpatient Visits:** 1939012 **Births:** 2681 **Total Expense ($000):** 1631344 **Payroll Expense ($000):** 817387 **Personnel:** 9166

✠ △ **JOHN D. DINGELL VETERANS AFFAIRS MEDICAL CENTER**, 4646 John R Street, Zip 48201–1932; tel. 313/576–1000, (Total facility includes 109 beds in nursing home–type unit) **A**1 2 3 5 7 8 9 **F**3 4 5 8 9 11 12 17 18 20 22 26 29 30 31 34 35 36 38 39 40 44 45 49 50 54 56 57 58 59 60 61 62 63 64 65 66 67 68 70 74 75 77 78 79 80 81 82 83 84 85 86 87 90 93 94 97 98 100 101 102 103 104 105 107 108 111 114 115 118 119 121 123 126 127 128 129 130 132 135 143 144 145 146 147 148 **P**6 **S** Department of Veterans Affairs, Washington, DC
Primary Contact: Pamela J. Reeves, M.D., Director
COO: Annette Walker, Associate Director
CFO: Sherry Kilgore, Chief Financial Management Service
CMO: Scott Gruber, M.D., Chief of Staff
CIO: Jonathan Small, Chief Operations Information and Technology
CHR: Kathleen Osinski, Chief Human Resources Service
CNO: Belina Brown–Tezera, MSN, Associate Director Patient Care Services
Web address: www.detroit.va.gov/
Control: Veterans Affairs, Government, federal **Service:** General Medical and Surgical

Staffed Beds: 188 **Admissions:** 4777 **Census:** 172 **Outpatient Visits:** 489802 **Births:** 0 **Total Expense ($000):** 305916 **Payroll Expense ($000):** 197127 **Personnel:** 1964

✠ **KARMANOS CANCER CENTER (230297)**, 4100 John R Street, Zip 48201–2013; tel. 313/576–8670 **A**1 2 3 5 9 10 **F**3 14 15 29 31 34 35 36 38 39 44 50 52 54 55 56 57 58 59 64 65 68 70 74 75 78 79 81 82 83 84 85 86 87 100 107 108 110 111 113 114 115 119 120 121 123 124 126 130 132 135 136 146 147 148 **P**6
Primary Contact: Gerold Bepler, M.D., Ph.D., President and Chief Executive Officer
COO: Gary Morrison, Chief Operating Officer
CFO: Michael Grisdela, Chief Financial Officer
CMO: George Yoo, M.D., Chief Medical Officer
CIO: Scott McCarter, Chief Information Officer
CHR: David Jansen, Vice President Human Resources
Web address: www.karmanos.org
Control: Other not–for–profit (including NFP Corporation) **Service:** Cancer

Staffed Beds: 90 **Admissions:** 4018 **Census:** 75 **Outpatient Visits:** 183068 **Births:** 0 **Total Expense ($000):** 224680 **Payroll Expense ($000):** 59408 **Personnel:** 1095

✠ **KINDRED HOSPITAL DETROIT (232027)**, 4777 East Outer Drive, Zip 48234–3241; tel. 313/369–5800 **A**1 9 10 **F**1 148 **S** Kindred Healthcare, Louisville, KY
Primary Contact: Reginald Lee, Chief Executive Officer
CFO: Clayton Kubacki, Interim Controller
CMO: Kevin Potts, M.D., Medical Director
CHR: Angela Moncrief–Wells, Coordinator Human Resources
Web address: www.kindreddetroit.com/
Control: Public Health Service, Government, federal **Service:** Long–Term Acute Care hospital

Staffed Beds: 77 **Admissions:** 708 **Census:** 51 **Outpatient Visits:** 0 **Births:** 0 **Total Expense ($000):** 23848 **Payroll Expense ($000):** 10096

✠ △ **REHABILITATION INSTITUTE OF MICHIGAN (233027)**, 261 Mack Avenue, Zip 48201–2495; tel. 313/745–1203 **A**1 3 5 7 9 10 **F**3 29 30 34 35 36 44 50 53 59 64 68 86 87 90 91 92 93 94 95 96 119 130 131 132 134 146 148 **P**1 6 **S** TENET Healthcare Corporation, Dallas, TX
Primary Contact: William H. Restum, Ph.D., President
COO: Patty Jobbitt, Vice President Operations
CFO: Kevin Smith, Vice President Finance and Support Services
CMO: Ali Bitar, M.D., Vice President Medical Affairs
CHR: Walter Tetteh, Director Human Resources
CNO: Julia Libcke, R.N., VP Patient Care Services
Web address: www.rimrehab.org
Control: Corporation, Investor–owned, for–profit **Service:** Rehabilitation

Staffed Beds: 74 **Admissions:** 1365 **Census:** 60 **Outpatient Visits:** 251743 **Births:** 0 **Total Expense ($000):** 82414 **Payroll Expense ($000):** 44434 **Personnel:** 592

✠ **SELECT SPECIALTY HOSPITAL–NORTHWEST DETROIT (232032)**, 6071 West Outer Drive, Zip 48235–2624; tel. 313/966–4747, (Nonreporting) **A**1 9 10 **S** Select Medical Corporation, Mechanicsburg, PA
Primary Contact: Marilouise Riska, Chief Executive Officer
Web address: www.selectspecialtyhospitals.com/company/locations/northwestdetroit.aspx
Control: Corporation, Investor–owned, for–profit **Service:** Long–Term Acute Care hospital

Staffed Beds: 36

✠ **SINAI–GRACE HOSPITAL (230024)**, 6071 West Outer Drive, Zip 48235–2679; tel. 313/966–3300 **A**1 3 5 8 9 10 13 **F**3 5 7 8 11 13 15 17 18 20 22 24 26 28 29 30 34 35 37 38 39 40 43 44 45 47 49 50 51 52 54 55 56 57 58 59 60 61 63 64 65 66 68 70 72 74 75 76 77 78 79 80 81 82 83 84 85 86 87 90 93 94 96 97 98 100 101 102 103 104 107 108 110 111 114 115 117 118 119 120 121 123 126 129 130 131 132 134 135 141 143 144 146 147 148 **P**1 6 **S** TENET Healthcare Corporation, Dallas, TX
Primary Contact: Reginald J. Eadie, M.D., Interim President
CFO: Michael Prusatis, Vice President Finance
CMO: Matthew Griffin, M.D., Vice President Medical Affairs
CHR: Paulette Griffin, Director Human Resources
Web address: www.sinaigrace.org
Control: Corporation, Investor–owned, for–profit **Service:** General Medical and Surgical

Staffed Beds: 310 **Admissions:** 20001 **Census:** 277 **Outpatient Visits:** 221684 **Births:** 1545 **Total Expense ($000):** 345765 **Payroll Expense ($000):** 135581 **Personnel:** 1916

✠ **ST. JOHN HOSPITAL AND MEDICAL CENTER (230165)**, 22101 Moross Road, Zip 48236–2148; tel. 313/343–4000 **A**1 2 3 5 8 9 10 **F**3 8 9 11 12 13 14 15 17 18 20 22 24 26 28 29 30 31 32 36 37 38 39 40 41 42 43 44 45 46 47 48 49 50 54 55 56 57 58 59 60 61 63 64 65 66 68 70 72 73 74 75 76 77 78 79 80 81 82 84 85 86 87 88 89 90 91 92 93 95 96 97 98 100 101 102 103 107 108 110 111 114 115 116 117 118 119 120 121 123 124 126 130 131 132 135 138 141 142 143 144 146 147 148 **P**3 6 7 8 **S** Ascension Health, Saint Louis, MO
Primary Contact: David Brooks, President
CFO: Tomasine Marx, Chief Financial Officer
CMO: Kevin Grady, M.D., Chief Medical Officer
CIO: Claudia Allen, Chief Information Officer
CHR: Joanne E. Tuscany, Director Human Resources
CNO: Maryann Barnes, MS, Vice President and Chief Nursing Officer East Region
Web address: www.stjohn.org
Control: Church–operated, Nongovernment, not–for profit **Service:** General Medical and Surgical

Staffed Beds: 673 **Admissions:** 31512 **Census:** 427 **Outpatient Visits:** 935015 **Births:** 3290 **Total Expense ($000):** 700308 **Payroll Expense ($000):** 257659 **Personnel:** 3686

☐ **STONECREST CENTER (234038)**, 15000 Gratiot Avenue, Zip 48205–1973; tel. 313/245–0600 **A**1 9 10 **F**3 29 50 68 87 98 99 102 103 130 132 135 **P**6 **S** Acadia Healthcare Company, Inc., Franklin, TN
Primary Contact: Steve Savage, Chief Executive Officer
Web address: www.bcastonecrestcenter.com
Control: Corporation, Investor–owned, for–profit **Service:** Psychiatric

Staffed Beds: 81 **Admissions:** 2202 **Census:** 71 **Outpatient Visits:** 0 **Births:** 0 **Total Expense ($000):** 18061 **Payroll Expense ($000):** 7521 **Personnel:** 171

TRIUMPH HOSPITAL DETROIT See Kindred Hospital Detroit

Many Facility Codes have changed. Please refer to the AHA Guide Code Chart. © 2014 AHA Guide

DOWAGIAC—Cass County

✠ **BORGESS–LEE MEMORIAL HOSPITAL (231315)**, 420 West High Street,
Zip 49047–1943; tel. 269/782–8681 **A**1 9 10 18 **F**3 11 15 18 29 30 31 34
35 40 41 50 54 57 59 64 65 68 70 75 77 78 79 81 85 86 87 93 97 100
104 107 108 114 119 127 128 130 132 133 135 146 148 **P**6 **S** Ascension
Health, Saint Louis, MO
Primary Contact: John E. Ryder, Chief Operating Officer
COO: John E. Ryder, Chief Operating Officer
CFO: Ken Holst, Chief Financial Officer
CMO: Robert Hill, M.D., Chief Medical Officer
CHR: Pete Krueger, Director Human Resources
CNO: James Nemeth, Chief Nursing Officer
Web address: www.borgess.com
Control: Church–operated, Nongovernment, not–for profit **Service:** General
Medical and Surgical

Staffed Beds: 25 **Admissions:** 692 **Census:** 5 **Outpatient Visits:** 95841
Births: 0 **Total Expense ($000):** 26183 **Payroll Expense ($000):** 13325
Personnel: 221

EAST CHINA—St. Clair County

✠ **ST. JOHN RIVER DISTRICT HOSPITAL (230241)**, 4100 River Road,
Zip 48054–2909; tel. 810/329–7111 **A**1 9 10 **F**3 7 11 13 15 18 20 29 31 34
35 36 40 43 44 45 49 50 56 59 60 63 64 65 68 70 74 75 76 77 78 79 81
82 84 85 87 89 92 93 97 102 107 108 110 111 115 116 117 119 129 130
132 146 147 148 **P**3 6 7 8 **S** Ascension Health, Saint Louis, MO
Primary Contact: Frank W. Poma, President
CFO: Tomasine Marx, Chief Financial Officer
CMO: H. Lee Bacheldor, D.O., Medical Director
CHR: Dawn Beindit, Director Work Life Services
CNO: Joyce Kasperski, Director Nursing
Web address: www.stjohn.org
Control: Church–operated, Nongovernment, not–for profit **Service:** General
Medical and Surgical

Staffed Beds: 68 **Admissions:** 1656 **Census:** 16 **Outpatient Visits:** 57127
Births: 274 **Total Expense ($000):** 39390 **Payroll Expense ($000):** 17042
Personnel: 291

EATON RAPIDS—Eaton County

★ ◇ **EATON RAPIDS MEDICAL CENTER (231324)**, 1500 South Main Street,
Zip 48827–1952, Mailing Address: P.O. Box 130, Zip 48827–0130;
tel. 517/663–2671 **A**9 10 18 21 **F**3 15 29 34 35 40 41 50 53 57 59 64 65
66 68 75 77 81 85 86 91 93 97 107 110 114 119 127 129 130 131 132
133 146 147 148
Primary Contact: Timothy Johnson, President and Chief Executive Officer
CFO: Shari Glynn, Vice President Finance and Chief Financial Officer
CMO: Ashok K. Gupta, M.D., Chief of Staff
CIO: Mark Rodge, Director Information Systems
CHR: Laurie Field, Director Human Resources
Web address: www.eatonrapidsmedicalcenter.org
Control: Other not–for–profit (including NFP Corporation) **Service:** General
Medical and Surgical

Staffed Beds: 20 **Admissions:** 305 **Census:** 2 **Outpatient Visits:** 55999
Births: 0 **Total Expense ($000):** 19756 **Payroll Expense ($000):** 9254
Personnel: 180

ESCANABA—Delta County

✠ **OSF ST. FRANCIS HOSPITAL AND MEDICAL GROUP (231337)**, 3401
Ludington Street, Zip 49829–1377; tel. 906/786–3311 **A**1 9 10 18 **F**3 11 13
15 18 28 29 30 34 35 40 45 46 56 57 59 62 63 64 65 66 68 70 74 75 76
77 78 79 81 83 84 85 86 92 93 96 97 107 108 110 111 115 119 127 129
130 131 132 133 144 145 146 147 148 **P**6 **S** OSF Healthcare System,
Peoria, IL
Primary Contact: David Lord, President and Chief Executive Officer
CFO: Fred Wagner, Chief Financial Officer
CMO: Mark Povich, D.O., Medical Director
CIO: Mark Irving, Manager Management Information Systems
CHR: Elizabeth Zorza, Assistant Administrator
CNO: Joy Hopkins, Vice President Patient Care Services
Web address: www.osfstfrancis.org
Control: Church–operated, Nongovernment, not–for profit **Service:** General
Medical and Surgical

Staffed Beds: 33 **Admissions:** 1620 **Census:** 13 **Outpatient Visits:** 121658
Births: 277 **Total Expense ($000):** 72218 **Payroll Expense ($000):** 28157
Personnel: 405

FARMINGTON HILLS—Oakland County

★ ○ **BOTSFORD HOSPITAL (230151)**, 28050 Grand River Avenue,
Zip 48336–5933; tel. 248/471–8000 **A**9 10 11 12 13 **F**3 8 9 11 12 13 15 17
18 20 22 26 28 29 30 31 32 34 35 36 39 40 41 43 44 45 46 47 48 49
50 51 54 56 57 58 59 60 61 63 64 65 68 70 74 75 76 77 78 79 80 81 82
83 84 85 86 87 89 90 92 93 94 96 97 98 100 101 102 103 107 108 110
111 114 115 118 119 120 121 123 124 126 129 130 131 132 134 135 144
146 147 148 **P**1 4 5 6 7
Primary Contact: Paul E. LaCasse, D.O., President and Chief Executive Officer
COO: David Marcellino, Corporate Executive Vice President and Chief
Administrative Officer
CFO: Regina Doxtader, Corporate Vice President and Chief Financial Officer
CMO: David Walters, D.O., Vice President and Chief Clinical Officer
CIO: Brian McPherson, Chief Information Officer
CHR: Barbara Palmer, Corporate Vice President Human Resources
CNO: Marge Hasler, R.N., Vice President Patient Care Services and Chief Nursing
Officer
Web address: www.botsford.org
Control: Other not–for–profit (including NFP Corporation) **Service:** General
Medical and Surgical

Staffed Beds: 306 **Admissions:** 15184 **Census:** 195 **Outpatient Visits:**
491165 **Births:** 843 **Total Expense ($000):** 276296 **Payroll Expense
($000):** 134238 **Personnel:** 1839

FERNDALE—Oakland County

✠ **HENRY FORD KINGSWOOD HOSPITAL (234011)**, 10300 West Eight Mile
Road, Zip 48220–2100; tel. 248/398–3200 **A**1 9 10 **F**4 29 30 32 34 35 44 50
56 57 59 68 75 77 80 82 86 87 98 99 101 103 130 134 135 **P**6 **S** Henry
Ford Health System, Detroit, MI
Primary Contact: C. Edward Coffey, M.D., Chief Executive Officer and Director
Behavioral Health Services
CFO: Tony Gaglio, Chief Financial Officer
CMO: Robert Lagrou, D.O., Medical Director
CNO: Cheryl Taylor, R.N., Director of Nursing
Web address: www.henryford.com
Control: Other not–for–profit (including NFP Corporation) **Service:** Psychiatric

Staffed Beds: 100 **Admissions:** 4178 **Census:** 70 **Outpatient Visits:** 0
Births: 0 **Total Expense ($000):** 19690 **Payroll Expense ($000):** 11641
Personnel: 198

FLINT—Genesee County

✠ **HURLEY MEDICAL CENTER (230132)**, One Hurley Plaza, Zip 48503–5993;
tel. 810/262–6887, (Includes HURLEY CHILDREN'S HOSPITAL, 1 Hurley Plaza,
Zip 48503–5902) **A**1 2 3 5 8 9 10 **F**3 5 11 12 13 15 16 17 18 19 20 22 26
28 29 30 31 32 33 35 39 40 41 43 45 46 49 50 51 53 54 55 56 57 58 59 60
64 66 70 72 74 75 76 77 78 79 80 81 82 84 85 86 87 88 89 90 93 96 97
98 100 101 102 103 104 107 108 110 111 114 115 118 119 120 121 123
124 126 129 130 131 132 135 141 143 146 147 148
Primary Contact: Melany Gavulic, President & Chief Executive Officer
COO: Melany Gavulic, Senior Vice President Operations & COO
CFO: Cass Wisniewski, Interim Chief Financial Officer
CMO: Michael Jaggi, D.O., Vice President and Chief Medical Officer
CIO: Gary Townsend, Chief Information Officer
CHR: Beth Brophy, Interim VP for Human Resources
CNO: Teresa Bourque, Sr. Administrator for Nursing/Chief Nurse
Web address: www.hurleymc.com
Control: City–Government, nonfederal **Service:** General Medical and Surgical

Staffed Beds: 418 **Admissions:** 16999 **Census:** 277 **Outpatient Visits:**
416069 **Births:** 2687 **Total Expense ($000):** 372062 **Payroll Expense
($000):** 156496 **Personnel:** 2365

✠ **MCLAREN FLINT (230141)**, 401 South Ballenger Highway, Zip 48532–3685;
tel. 810/342–2000 **A**1 2 3 5 8 9 10 **F**3 5 11 12 13 15 17 18 20 22 24 26 28
29 30 31 32 34 35 36 38 39 40 43 44 45 46 49 50 52 53 54 55 56 57 58
59 60 61 64 68 70 74 75 76 77 78 79 81 82 84 85 86 87 89 90 91 93 96
97 98 99 100 101 102 103 104 105 107 108 111 114 115 118 119 120
121 123 124 126 129 130 131 132 135 141 144 146 147 148 **P**6 7
S McLaren Health Care Corporation, Flint, MI
Primary Contact: Donald C. Kooy, President and Chief Executive Officer
COO: Brent Wheeler, Vice President Ancillary and Support Services
CFO: Rick Wyles, Chief Financial Officer
CMO: Jason White, M.D., Vice President of Medical Affairs
CIO: Ronald Strachan, Chief Information Officer
CHR: Rachelle Hulett, Vice President Human Resources
CNO: Diane Kallas, Vice President of Nursing Services
Web address: www.mclarenregional.org
Control: Other not–for–profit (including NFP Corporation) **Service:** General
Medical and Surgical

Staffed Beds: 336 **Admissions:** 21550 **Census:** 269 **Outpatient Visits:**
387452 **Births:** 500 **Total Expense ($000):** 409929 **Payroll Expense
($000):** 175559 **Personnel:** 2558

MI

Hospital, Medicare Provider Number, Address, Telephone, Approval, Facility, and Physician Codes, Health Care System

★ American Hospital Association (AHA) membership ○ Healthcare Facilities Accreditation Program
□ The Joint Commission accreditation ◇ DNV Healthcare Inc. accreditation △ Commission on Accreditation of Rehabilitation Facilities (CARF) accreditation

MI

⊞ **SELECT SPECIALTY HOSPITAL–FLINT (232012)**, 401 South Ballenger Highway, 5th Floor Central, Zip 48532–3638; tel. 810/342–4500, (Nonreporting) **A**1 9 10 **S** Select Medical Corporation, Mechanicsburg, PA
Primary Contact: Patricia Adams, Chief Executive Officer
CMO: Jitendra P. Katneni, M.D., Medical Director
CHR: Gayle Barthel, Coordinator Human Resources
CNO: Kathleen Gallardo, Chief Nursing Officer
Web address: www.selectspecialtyhospitals.com/company/locations/flint.aspx
Control: Corporation, Investor–owned, for–profit **Service:** Long–Term Acute Care hospital

Staffed Beds: 26

FRANKFORT—Benzie County

★ **PAUL OLIVER MEMORIAL HOSPITAL (231300)**, 224 Park Avenue, Zip 49635–9658; tel. 231/352–2200, (Total facility includes 39 beds in nursing home–type unit) **A**9 10 18 **F**11 15 28 30 34 35 40 45 46 50 53 57 59 60 64 75 77 81 86 87 93 107 110 111 115 119 129 130 132 133 143 146 148 **S** Munson Healthcare, Traverse City, MI
Primary Contact: Peter Marinoff, President
CMO: George Ryckman, D.O., Chief of Staff
CHR: Julie Banktson, Manager Human Resources
Web address: www.munsonhealthcare.org
Control: Other not–for–profit (including NFP Corporation) **Service:** General Medical and Surgical

Staffed Beds: 47 Admissions: 105 Census: 33 Outpatient Visits: 42920 Births: 0 Total Expense ($000): 15209 Payroll Expense ($000): 4904 Personnel: 116

FREMONT—Newaygo County

⊞ **SPECTRUM HEALTH GERBER MEMORIAL (230106)**, 212 South Sullivan Avenue, Zip 49412–1548; tel. 231/924–3300 **A**1 9 10 **F**3 11 13 15 28 29 31 32 34 35 36 40 43 45 48 50 53 59 62 64 68 70 75 76 77 78 79 81 86 87 93 96 107 108 110 111 115 118 119 127 129 130 131 132 135 146 147 **S** Spectrum Health, Grand Rapids, MI
Primary Contact: Randall Stasik, President and Chief Executive Officer
COO: Janice Stone, Vice President Clinical Integration
CFO: Deidre Weller, Vice President, Finance
CMO: Kevin Gerth, M.D., Chief of Staff
CIO: Shane Meeks, Manager Technology Information Systems
CHR: Christine Schurkamp, Senior Human Resources Business Partner
Web address: www.spectrumhealth.org
Control: Other not–for–profit (including NFP Corporation) **Service:** General Medical and Surgical

Staffed Beds: 40 Admissions: 2295 Census: 17 Outpatient Visits: 116732 Births: 444 Total Expense ($000): 63836 Payroll Expense ($000): 25326 Personnel: 489

GARDEN CITY—Wayne County

★ ○ **GARDEN CITY HOSPITAL (230244)**, 6245 North Inkster Road, Zip 48135–4001; tel. 734/421–3300 **A**9 10 11 12 13 **F**3 4 11 13 15 17 18 20 22 26 28 29 31 34 35 36 40 43 44 45 46 47 49 50 57 59 62 64 65 68 70 71 74 75 76 77 78 79 80 81 82 85 87 89 90 91 92 93 96 97 107 110 111 112 114 115 119 129 130 131 132 135 143 146 148 **P**5 6 **S** Prime Healthcare Services, Ontario, CA
Primary Contact: Saju George, Chief Administrative Officer
COO: Saju George, Chief Administrative Officer
CFO: Timothy Jodway, Chief Financial Officer
CMO: Kirsten Waarala, D.O., Vice President Medical Services
CIO: William Moncrief, Director Information Systems
CHR: Steven Solomon, Vice President Human Resources
CNO: Bette Fitz, Chief Nursing Officer
Web address: www.gchosp.org
Control: Other not–for–profit (including NFP Corporation) **Service:** General Medical and Surgical

Staffed Beds: 170 Admissions: 8780 Census: 111 Outpatient Visits: 135829 Births: 652 Total Expense ($000): 132453 Payroll Expense ($000): 57212 Personnel: 1042

GAYLORD—Otsego County

⊞ **OTSEGO MEMORIAL HOSPITAL (230133)**, 825 North Center Avenue, Zip 49735–1592; tel. 989/731–2100, (Includes MCREYNOLDS HALL), (Total facility includes 34 beds in nursing home–type unit) **A**1 9 10 20 **F**3 13 15 28 29 31 32 34 35 36 37 40 43 44 45 46 49 50 51 54 56 57 59 64 65 70 74 75 76 77 78 79 81 82 85 86 87 93 96 97 107 108 110 111 115 118 119 124 127 128 129 130 131 132 134 135 144 146 147 148 **P**6
Primary Contact: Thomas R. Lemon, Chief Executive Officer
CFO: Robert Courtois, Vice President Finance
CMO: Jon Foltz, M.D., Chief of Staff
CIO: Timothy Hella, Chief Information Officer
CHR: Terra Deming, Director Human Resources
CNO: Diane Fisher, R.N., VP, Patient Care Services
Web address: www.myomh.org
Control: Other not–for–profit (including NFP Corporation) **Service:** General Medical and Surgical

Staffed Beds: 80 Admissions: 1677 Census: 47 Outpatient Visits: 190615 Births: 267 Total Expense ($000): 74537 Payroll Expense ($000): 36371 Personnel: 605

GLADWIN—Gladwin County

⊞ **MIDMICHIGAN MEDICAL CENTER–GLADWIN (231325)**, 515 Quarter Street, Zip 48624–1959; tel. 989/426–9286, (Nonreporting) **A**1 5 9 10 18 **S** MidMichigan Health, Midland, MI
Primary Contact: Raymond Stover, President and Chief Executive Officer
CFO: Josh Wiggins, Vice President and Controller
CMO: Cheryl Loubert, M.D., Chief Medical Staff
CIO: Dan Waltz, Vice President and Chief Information Officer
CNO: Glenn King, R.N., Vice President and Chief Nursing Officer
Web address: www.midmichigan.org
Control: Other not–for–profit (including NFP Corporation) **Service:** General Medical and Surgical

Staffed Beds: 25

GRAND BLANC—Genesee County

⊞ △ **GENESYS REGIONAL MEDICAL CENTER (230197)**, One Genesys Parkway, Zip 48439–8066; tel. 810/606–5000 **A**1 3 5 7 9 10 12 13 **F**3 11 13 17 18 20 22 24 26 28 29 30 31 32 34 35 37 40 41 43 44 45 46 47 48 49 50 51 54 57 58 59 60 61 64 68 70 73 74 75 76 77 78 79 81 82 84 85 86 87 89 90 92 93 96 97 102 107 108 111 114 115 117 118 119 126 129 130 132 135 144 145 146 147 148 **P**1 6 **S** Ascension Health, Saint Louis, MO
Primary Contact: Elizabeth Aderholdt, President and Chief Executive Officer
COO: Christopher Palazzolo, Senior Vice President and Chief Operating Officer
CFO: Nancy Haywood, Chief Financial Officer
CMO: James C. Bonnette, M.D., Chief Clinical Officer
CIO: Daniel Stross, Chief Information Officer
CNO: Julie A. Gorczyca, R.N., Chief Nursing Officer
Web address: www.genesys.org
Control: Church–operated, Nongovernment, not–for profit **Service:** General Medical and Surgical

Staffed Beds: 410 Admissions: 20785 Census: 276 Outpatient Visits: 610711 Births: 2081 Total Expense ($000): 407194 Payroll Expense ($000): 179583 Personnel: 2653

GRAND HAVEN—Ottawa County

★ ◇ **NORTH OTTAWA COMMUNITY HOSPITAL (230174)**, 1309 Sheldon Road, Zip 49417–2488; tel. 616/842–3600 **A**9 10 21 **F**3 7 11 12 13 15 29 30 34 35 40 43 45 50 51 57 59 61 62 63 64 65 68 69 70 74 75 76 79 81 86 87 89 97 107 108 115 119 126 129 130 131 132 135 143 144 145 146 147 148 **P**6
Primary Contact: Shelleye Yaklin, President and Chief Executive Officer
CFO: Donald J. Longpre, Vice President Finance and Chief Financial Officer
CMO: Haney Assaad, Vice President Medical Affairs
CIO: Joe Abbott, Director Information Systems
CHR: Carla Wallis, Director Human Resources
CNO: Cindy Van Kampen, Chief Nursing Officer
Web address: www.noch.org
Control: Other not–for–profit (including NFP Corporation) **Service:** General Medical and Surgical

Staffed Beds: 57 Admissions: 1739 Census: 14 Outpatient Visits: 101320 Births: 374 Total Expense ($000): 62271 Payroll Expense ($000): 23228 Personnel: 551

Many Facility Codes have changed. Please refer to the AHA Guide Code Chart. © 2014 AHA Guide

GRAND RAPIDS—Kent County

☐ **FOREST VIEW PSYCHIATRIC HOSPITAL (234030)**, 1055 Medical Park Drive S.E., Zip 49546–3607; tel. 616/942–9610 **A**1 9 10 **F**75 87 98 99 100 101 102 104 105 130 132 **S** Universal Health Services, Inc., King of Prussia, PA
Primary Contact: Andrew Hotaling, Chief Executive Officer
CFO: Andre Pierre, Chief Financial Officer
CMO: James VanHaren, M.D., Medical Director
CHR: Mike Henderson, Director Human Resources
CNO: Marilynn Switzer, Director of Nursing
Web address: www.forestviewhospital.com
Control: Corporation, Investor–owned, for–profit **Service:** Psychiatric

Staffed Beds: 82 **Admissions:** 2489 **Census:** 71 **Outpatient Visits:** 10060 **Births:** 0 **Total Expense ($000):** 16779 **Payroll Expense ($000):** 7526 **Personnel:** 133

✠ **GREAT LAKES SPECIALTY HOSPITAL–GRAND RAPIDS CAMPUS (232026)**, 200 S.E. Jefferson Avenue, 5th Floor, Zip 49503–4502; tel. 616/965–8650, (Nonreporting) **A**1 9 10 **S** Select Medical Corporation, Mechanicsburg, PA
Primary Contact: Brian Pangle, Chief Executive Officer
CMO: Mark J. Ivey, M.D., Medical Director
CNO: Tracie Peterson, R.N., Chief Nursing Officer
Web address: www.selectmedicalcorp.com
Control: Corporation, Investor–owned, for–profit **Service:** Long–Term Acute Care hospital

Staffed Beds: 20

LIFECARE HOSPITALS OF WESTERN MICHIGAN See Great Lakes Specialty Hospital–Grand Rapids Campus

✠ △ **MARY FREE BED REHABILITATION HOSPITAL (233026)**, 235 Wealthy Street S.E., Zip 49503–5247; tel. 616/840–8000 **A**1 7 9 10 **F**30 34 54 56 58 64 68 75 77 78 79 82 86 90 91 92 93 94 95 96 100 104 119 130 131 132 143 146 **P**6
Primary Contact: Kent Riddle, Chief Executive Officer
COO: Jim Wilson, Chief Operating Officer
CFO: Randall DeNeff, Vice President Finance
CMO: John Butzer, M.D., Medical Director
CIO: Jeff Burns, Manager of Information Technology
CNO: Linda Page, Chief Nursing Officer
Web address: www.maryfreebed.com
Control: Other not–for–profit (including NFP Corporation) **Service:** Rehabilitation

Staffed Beds: 80 **Admissions:** 1198 **Census:** 61 **Outpatient Visits:** 66451 **Births:** 0 **Total Expense ($000):** 46627 **Payroll Expense ($000):** 35133 **Personnel:** 816

✠ **MERCY HEALTH SAINT MARY'S (230059)**, 200 Jefferson Avenue S.E., Zip 49503–4598; tel. 616/685–5000 **A**1 2 3 5 9 10 **F**3 6 13 15 18 20 22 26 28 29 30 34 35 36 37 40 42 43 44 45 46 48 49 50 53 54 55 56 57 58 59 60 61 64 65 66 68 70 72 74 75 76 77 78 79 80 81 82 83 84 85 86 87 97 98 100 102 105 107 108 110 111 114 115 116 117 118 119 120 121 123 124 126 129 130 132 135 138 144 146 148 **P**6 8 **S** Catholic Health East / Trinity Health, Livonia, MI
Primary Contact: Bill Manns, President
COO: Randall J. Wagner, Chief Operating Officer
CFO: Steve Eavenson, Vice President Finance
CMO: Rolland Mambourg, M.D., Vice President Medical Affairs
CIO: Jim Keller, Site Director Information Services
CHR: Thomas L. Karel, Vice President Organization and Talent Effectiveness
CNO: Elizabeth A. Murphy, R.N., Vice President for Patient Care Services
Web address: www.mercyhealthsaintmarys.org
Control: Church–operated, Nongovernment, not–for profit **Service:** General Medical and Surgical

Staffed Beds: 364 **Admissions:** 20648 **Census:** 275 **Outpatient Visits:** 1097868 **Births:** 2024 **Total Expense ($000):** 458749 **Payroll Expense ($000):** 133281 **Personnel:** 2863

✠ **PINE REST CHRISTIAN MENTAL HEALTH SERVICES (234006)**, 300 68th Street S.E., Zip 49548–6927, Mailing Address: P.O. Box 165, Zip 49501–0165; tel. 616/455–5000 **A**1 5 9 10 **F**4 5 6 29 30 32 34 35 38 55 56 58 59 66 68 75 77 82 86 87 98 99 100 101 102 103 104 105 106 130 132 134 135 146 **P**6
Primary Contact: Mark C. Eastburg, Ph.D., President and Chief Executive Officer
COO: Robert Nykamp, Vice President and Chief Operating Officer
CFO: Paul H. Karsten, Vice President Finance and Chief Financial Officer
CMO: Alan Armstrong, M.D., Chief Medical Officer
Web address: www.pinerest.org
Control: Other not–for–profit (including NFP Corporation) **Service:** Psychiatric

Staffed Beds: 200 **Admissions:** 5673 **Census:** 150 **Outpatient Visits:** 298552 **Births:** 0 **Total Expense ($000):** 107300 **Payroll Expense ($000):** 61000 **Personnel:** 1239

✠ **SPECTRUM HEALTH – BUTTERWORTH HOSPITAL (230038)**, 100 Michigan Street N.E., Zip 49503–2560; tel. 616/774–7444, (Includes HELEN DEVOS CHILDREN'S HOSPITAL, 100 Michigan Street N.E., tel. 616/391–9000; SPECTRUM HEALTH, 100 Michigan Street N.E., Zip 49503–2551; tel. 616/391–1774; SPECTRUM HEALTH – BLODGETT CAMPUS, 1840 Wealthy Street S.E., Zip 49506–2921; tel. 616/774–7444) **A**1 2 3 5 9 10 **F**3 7 8 9 11 12 13 15 16 17 18 19 20 21 22 23 24 25 26 27 28 29 30 31 32 34 35 36 37 38 40 41 43 44 45 46 47 48 49 50 51 52 54 55 56 57 58 59 60 61 64 65 66 68 70 71 72 73 74 75 76 77 78 79 80 81 82 84 85 86 87 88 89 90 93 96 99 100 107 108 110 111 112 113 114 115 116 117 118 119 120 121 123 124 126 130 131 132 134 135 136 137 138 140 144 145 146 147 148 **P**6 8 **S** Spectrum Health, Grand Rapids, MI
Primary Contact: Christina Freese–Decker, President, Spectrum Health Hospital Group
CFO: Doug Welday, Vice President Finance
CMO: Ralph Rogers, M.D., Vice President Medical Affairs and Chief Medical Officer
CIO: Michael Rosencrance, Vice President Information Services
CHR: David Beach, Vice President Human Resources
CNO: Shawn Ulreich, R.N., Vice President Clinical Operations and Chief Nursing Executive
Web address: www.spectrum–health.org
Control: Other not–for–profit (including NFP Corporation) **Service:** General Medical and Surgical

Staffed Beds: 1078 **Admissions:** 56350 **Census:** 723 **Outpatient Visits:** 1321749 **Births:** 7443 **Total Expense ($000):** 1560751 **Payroll Expense ($000):** 439405 **Personnel:** 6415

✠ △ **SPECTRUM HEALTH SPECIAL CARE HOSPITAL (232029)**, 750 Fuller Avenue N.E., Zip 49503–1995; tel. 616/486–3000, (Nonreporting) **A**1 7 9 10 **S** Spectrum Health, Grand Rapids, MI
Primary Contact: Chuck Tozer, Administrator
COO: Linda Joel, Vice President Operations
CFO: Larry Oberst, Vice President Finance
CMO: Peter Sholler, M.D., Medical Director
CIO: Mary Nader, Director Information Technology
CHR: Mark Pakkala, Director Human Resources
CNO: Jennifer Groeneweg, R.N., Director of Nursing
Web address: www.spectrum–health.org
Control: Other not–for–profit (including NFP Corporation) **Service:** Long–Term Acute Care hospital

Staffed Beds: 36

GRAYLING—Crawford County

✠ **MERCY HOSPITAL GRAYLING (230058)**, 1100 East Michigan Avenue, Zip 49738–1312; tel. 989/348–5461, (Total facility includes 39 beds in nursing home–type unit) **A**1 9 10 20 **F**3 11 13 15 28 29 30 32 34 35 36 38 40 44 45 50 51 54 56 57 58 59 64 65 66 70 75 76 77 79 81 85 86 87 93 97 107 108 111 115 119 127 129 130 131 135 146 147 148 **P**6 8 **S** Catholic Health East / Trinity Health, Livonia, MI
Primary Contact: Stephanie J. Riemer–Matuzak, Chief Executive Officer
COO: Kirsten Korth–White, Vice President Physician Network and Ambulatory Service
CFO: Lori Shively, Vice President of Finance
CMO: Vince Schultz, M.D., Chief Medical Officer
CHR: Kirsten Korth–White, Vice President Physician Network and Ambulatory Services
CNO: Chris Ward, Interim Chief Nursing Officer
Web address: www.mercygrayling.munsonhealthcare.org/
Control: Church–operated, Nongovernment, not–for profit **Service:** General Medical and Surgical

Staffed Beds: 94 **Admissions:** 3406 **Census:** 61 **Outpatient Visits:** 144146 **Births:** 323 **Total Expense ($000):** 69702 **Payroll Expense ($000):** 28453 **Personnel:** 439

MI

Hospital, Medicare Provider Number, Address, Telephone, Approval, Facility, and Physician Codes, Health Care System

★ American Hospital Association (AHA) membership
☐ The Joint Commission accreditation
◇ DNV Healthcare Inc. accreditation
○ Healthcare Facilities Accreditation Program
△ Commission on Accreditation of Rehabilitation Facilities (CARF) accreditation

MI

GREENVILLE—Montcalm County

☒ **SPECTRUM HEALTH UNITED HOSPITAL (230035)**, 615 South Bower Street, Zip 48838–2614; tel. 616/754–4691, (Includes SPECTRUM HEALTH KELSEY HOSPITAL, 418 Washington Avenue, Lakeview, Zip 48850; tel. 989/352–7211), (Total facility includes 70 beds in nursing home–type unit) **A**1 9 10 **F**3 8 11 13 15 18 29 31 32 34 35 40 41 43 44 45 50 57 64 65 70 75 76 77 78 79 81 85 86 87 89 93 97 107 108 110 111 114 115 119 124 127 128 130 131 132 133 135 146 147 148 **P**8 **S** Spectrum Health, Grand Rapids, MI
Primary Contact: Brian Brasser, President
COO: Priscilla Mahar, Chief Clinical Officer
CFO: Ryan K. Johnson, Vice President Finance
CMO: Kevin O'Connor, D.O., President Medical Staff
CIO: David Dutmers, Manager Technology Information System
CHR: Mary Fenske, Human Resource Business Partner
CNO: Andrea M. Leslie, MSN, Chief Nursing Officer
Web address: www.spectrumhealth.org/
Control: Other not–for–profit (including NFP Corporation) **Service:** General Medical and Surgical

Staffed Beds: 116 **Admissions:** 3105 **Census:** 88 **Outpatient Visits:** 164410 **Births:** 388 **Total Expense ($000):** 78088 **Payroll Expense ($000):** 30592 **Personnel:** 641

GROSSE POINTE—Wayne County

☒ **BEAUMONT HOSPITAL GROSSE POINTE (230089)**, 468 Cadieux Road, Zip 48230–1507; tel. 313/473–1000 **A**1 3 5 9 10 **F**3 11 12 13 15 18 20 22 26 28 29 30 31 34 35 36 39 40 43 44 45 46 47 48 49 50 51 53 54 57 58 59 60 61 62 63 64 65 66 68 69 70 71 74 75 76 77 78 80 81 82 84 85 86 87 89 92 93 94 96 97 100 107 108 110 111 114 115 116 117 118 119 124 126 129 130 131 132 135 145 146 147 148 **P**6 **S** Beaumont Health System, Royal Oak, MI
Primary Contact: Richard P. Swaine, President
COO: Chris Stesney–Ridenour, Vice President Operations
CFO: Nickolas A. Vitale, Senior Vice President and Chief Financial Officer
CMO: Donna Hoban, M.D., Senior Vice President and Physician–in–Chief
CIO: Subra Sripada, Senior Vice President and Chief Information Officer
CHR: Jay T. Holden, Vice President, Human Resources
CNO: Phyllis Reynolds, R.N., VP, Nursing
Web address: www.beaumont.edu/grosse–pointe–hospital–campus
Control: Other not–for–profit (including NFP Corporation) **Service:** General Medical and Surgical

Staffed Beds: 250 **Admissions:** 10900 **Census:** 123 **Outpatient Visits:** 277245 **Births:** 682 **Total Expense ($000):** 153720 **Payroll Expense ($000):** 50232 **Personnel:** 1142

☒ **SELECT SPECIALTY HOSPITAL–GROSSE POINTE (232038)**, 468 Cadieux Road, 3 North East, Zip 48230–1507; tel. 313/473–6131, (Nonreporting) **A**1 9 10 **S** Select Medical Corporation, Mechanicsburg, PA
Primary Contact: Miriam Deemer, Chief Executive Officer
Web address: www.grossepointe.selectspecialtyhospitals.com/
Control: Corporation, Investor–owned, for–profit **Service:** Long–Term Acute Care hospital

Staffed Beds: 30

HANCOCK—Houghton County

☒ **PORTAGE HEALTH (230108)**, 500 Campus Drive, Zip 49930–1569; tel. 906/483–1000, (Total facility includes 60 beds in nursing home–type unit) **A**1 9 10 20 **F**3 7 8 11 13 15 28 29 30 31 32 34 35 40 43 50 53 54 56 57 59 60 62 63 64 65 67 68 69 70 75 76 77 78 79 81 84 85 86 87 89 90 93 94 97 107 108 110 111 115 119 127 129 130 131 132 133 144 145 146 147 148 **P**6
Primary Contact: Diane Torres, Interim President and Chief Executive Officer
CFO: Brian Donahue, Chief Financial Officer
CMO: Mary Beth Hines, D.O., Chief Medical Officer
CIO: John Steenport, Director Information Technology
CHR: Robbyn Lucier, Director Human Resources
Web address: www.portagehealth.org
Control: Other not–for–profit (including NFP Corporation) **Service:** General Medical and Surgical

Staffed Beds: 96 **Admissions:** 1612 **Census:** 74 **Outpatient Visits:** 105826 **Births:** 328 **Total Expense ($000):** 79969 **Payroll Expense ($000):** 37773 **Personnel:** 595

HARBOR BEACH—Huron County

HARBOR BEACH COMMUNITY HOSPITAL (231313), 210 South First Street, Zip 48441–1236; tel. 989/479–3201, (Total facility includes 39 beds in nursing home–type unit) **A**9 10 18 **F**2 3 15 29 34 35 40 56 57 59 64 75 81 86 93 107 108 110 114 118 119 127 128 130 132 133 146 147 148 **P**6
Primary Contact: Edward L. Gamache, President and Chief Executive Officer
CFO: Jill Wehner, Vice President Financial Services
CMO: Richard Lloyd, D.O., Chief of Staff
CIO: Tami Nickrand, Director Information Technology
CHR: Tina Osantoski, Director Human Resources
CNO: Deb Geiger, Executive Director of Acute Care
Web address: www.hbch.org
Control: Other not–for–profit (including NFP Corporation) **Service:** General Medical and Surgical

Staffed Beds: 54 **Admissions:** 150 **Census:** 33 **Outpatient Visits:** 10407 **Births:** 0 **Total Expense ($000):** 11662 **Payroll Expense ($000):** 4926 **Personnel:** 126

HASTINGS—Barry County

☒ **PENNOCK HOSPITAL (230040)**, 1009 West Green Street, Zip 49058–1710; tel. 269/945–3451 **A**1 9 10 **F**3 11 13 15 29 30 32 34 35 36 39 40 44 45 50 53 54 56 57 59 62 63 64 65 68 70 74 75 76 77 79 81 82 84 85 86 87 89 91 93 96 97 107 108 110 111 115 119 125 126 129 130 131 132 135 144 146 147 148 **P**6 8
Primary Contact: Sheryl Lewis Blake, FACHE, Chief Executive Officer
COO: Carla Wilson–Neil, FACHE, Chief Operating Officer
CFO: Connie Downs, Chief Financial Officer
CMO: Douglas Smendik, M.D., Chief Medical Officer
CHR: Sherri Thrasher, JD, Director Human Resources
CNO: Steve Marzolf, R.N., Chief Nursing Officer
Web address: www.pennockhealth.com
Control: Other not–for–profit (including NFP Corporation) **Service:** General Medical and Surgical

Staffed Beds: 58 **Admissions:** 2462 **Census:** 24 **Outpatient Visits:** 422141 **Births:** 332 **Total Expense ($000):** 57088 **Payroll Expense ($000):** 25419 **Personnel:** 434

HILLSDALE—Hillsdale County

★ ○ **HILLSDALE COMMUNITY HEALTH CENTER (230037)**, 168 South Howell Street, Zip 49242–2081; tel. 517/437–4451, (Total facility includes 21 beds in nursing home–type unit) **A**9 10 11 12 13 19 **F**3 11 12 13 15 28 29 31 34 35 38 40 45 48 50 59 62 70 74 75 76 78 79 81 82 87 89 93 97 98 102 104 107 110 111 115 119 127 128 130 131 132 135 146 147 148 **P**6 8
Primary Contact: Duke Anderson, President and Chief Executive Officer
CFO: Valerie Fetters, Chief Financial Officer
CMO: Barry Collins, D.O., Chief of Staff
CIO: Sheila Puffenberger, Manager Information Technology
CHR: Stacy Mellon, Manager Human Resource
CNO: Julie Walters, Chief Nursing Officer
Web address: www.hchc.com
Control: Other not–for–profit (including NFP Corporation) **Service:** General Medical and Surgical

Staffed Beds: 84 **Admissions:** 3313 **Census:** 50 **Outpatient Visits:** 120776 **Births:** 350 **Total Expense ($000):** 57080 **Payroll Expense ($000):** 20994 **Personnel:** 409

HOLLAND—Ottawa County

★ ◇ **HOLLAND HOSPITAL (230072)**, 602 Michigan Avenue, Zip 49423–4999; tel. 616/392–5141, (Nonreporting) **A**9 10 21
Primary Contact: Dale Sowders, President and Chief Executive Officer
CFO: Terry L. Steele, Vice President Finance and Chief Financial Officer
CMO: William Vandervliet, M.D., Vice President Medical Affairs
CIO: Randy J. Paruch, Director, Information Systems
CHR: Michael Matthews, Vice President Human Resources
CNO: Patti J. VanDort, MSN, Vice President Nursing/Chief Nursing Officer
Web address: www.hollandhospital.org
Control: Other not–for–profit (including NFP Corporation) **Service:** General Medical and Surgical

Staffed Beds: 130

Many Facility Codes have changed. Please refer to the AHA Guide Code Chart. © 2014 AHA Guide

HOWELL—Livingston County

⊠ **ST. JOSEPH MERCY LIVINGSTON HOSPITAL (230069)**, 620 Byron Road, Zip 48843–1093; tel. 517/545–6000 **A**1 3 5 9 10 13 **F**3 5 8 11 15 18 28 29 30 31 34 35 40 41 42 45 51 54 56 57 59 62 63 64 65 66 68 70 74 75 77 78 79 81 82 83 84 85 86 87 93 97 100 104 107 108 110 111 114 115 119 120 130 131 132 134 135 141 145 146 147 148 **P**5 6 **S** Catholic Health East / Trinity Health, Livonia, MI
Primary Contact: Robert F. Casalou, President and Chief Executive Officer
COO: Robin Damschroder, Chief Operating Officer
CFO: Kathy O'Connor, Vice President Finance and Controller
CMO: Mark Baumeier, M.D., Chief of Staff
CIO: Frank Rademacher, Director, Information Systems
CHR: Tonia Schemer, Interim Chief Human Resources
CNO: Joyce Young, R.N., VP, Patient Services & Chief Nursing Officer
Web address: www.stjoeslivingston.org/livingston
Control: Church–operated, Nongovernment, not–for profit **Service:** General Medical and Surgical

Staffed Beds: 36 **Admissions:** 3413 **Census:** 29 **Outpatient Visits:** 283111 **Births:** 0 **Total Expense ($000):** 108963 **Payroll Expense ($000):** 37344 **Personnel:** 623

IONIA—Ionia County

⊠ **SPARROW IONIA HOSPITAL (231331)**, 520 East Washington Street, Zip 48846–1870, Mailing Address: Box 1001, Zip 48846–6001; tel. 616/523–1400 **A**1 9 10 18 **F**3 12 15 29 31 34 35 40 45 50 54 57 59 64 65 68 70 74 75 77 78 79 81 85 89 93 107 108 110 115 119 127 129 130 131 146 148 **P**6 **S** Sparrow Health System, Lansing, MI
Primary Contact: William Roeser, President and Chief Executive Officer
COO: Kevin A. Price, Vice President and Chief Operating Officer
CFO: Mark Brisboe, VP and Chief Financial Officer
CMO: Amy Jentz, M.D., Chief of Staff
CIO: Bob Neal, Information Technology
CHR: Debbie Olsen, Human Resource Partner
CNO: Rachelle S. Burk, R.N., Vice President Patient Care Services and Chief Nursing Officer
Web address: www.sparrow.org/sparrowionia
Control: Other not–for–profit (including NFP Corporation) **Service:** General Medical and Surgical

Staffed Beds: 25 **Admissions:** 536 **Census:** 4 **Outpatient Visits:** 53521 **Births:** 0 **Total Expense ($000):** 31123 **Payroll Expense ($000):** 12565 **Personnel:** 222

IRON MOUNTAIN—Dickinson County

⊠ **DICKINSON COUNTY HEALTHCARE SYSTEM (230055)**, 1721 South Stephenson Avenue, Zip 49801–3637; tel. 906/774–1313 **A**1 9 10 20 **F**3 11 13 15 18 28 29 31 34 35 40 45 46 50 51 53 57 59 61 62 64 70 74 75 76 77 79 80 81 85 86 87 89 91 92 93 96 107 108 110 111 114 115 119 120 121 123 127 129 130 131 132 133 135 145 146 148 **P**6
Primary Contact: John Schon, Administrator and Chief Executive Officer
COO: Jeff Gussert, Director Operations
CFO: Eileen Sparpana, Director Finance
CMO: Don Kube, M.D., Chief of Staff
CIO: Dean Decremer, Chief Information Officer
CHR: Paula Swartout, HR Manager
CNO: Susan Hadley, R.N., Director of Nursing
Web address: www.dchs.org
Control: County–Government, nonfederal **Service:** General Medical and Surgical

Staffed Beds: 96 **Admissions:** 3152 **Census:** 30 **Outpatient Visits:** 250485 **Births:** 457 **Total Expense ($000):** 91428 **Payroll Expense ($000):** 39644 **Personnel:** 600

⊠ **OSCAR G. JOHNSON VETERANS AFFAIRS MEDICAL CENTER**, 325 East H Street, Zip 49801–4792; tel. 906/774–3300, (Nonreporting) **A**1 9 **S** Department of Veterans Affairs, Washington, DC
Primary Contact: James W. Rice, Director
Web address: www.ironmountain.va.gov/
Control: Veterans Affairs, Government, federal **Service:** General Medical and Surgical

Staffed Beds: 17

VETERANS AFFAIRS MEDICAL CENTER See Oscar G. Johnson Veterans Affairs Medical Center

IRON RIVER—Iron County

⊠ **NORTHSTAR HEALTH SYSTEM (231318)**, 1400 West Ice Lake Road, Zip 49935–9526; tel. 906/265–6121 **A**1 9 10 18 **F**7 11 15 28 29 31 32 33 34 35 40 43 50 54 56 57 59 60 62 63 64 70 75 77 78 79 81 86 87 89 93 97 104 107 111 115 119 128 130 131 132 133 135 144 145 146 147 148
Primary Contact: Connie L. Koutouzos, R.N., MSN, Chief Executive Officer and President
CFO: Glenn E. Dobson, Chief Financial Officer
CMO: Nasseem Rizkalla, M.D., Chief Medical Officer
CIO: Matthew Welch, Chief Clinical Information Officer and Director of Pharmacy
CHR: Carol Bastianello, Director Employee Services
CNO: Nancy Lynn Ponozzo, Chief Nursing Officer
Web address: www.northstarhs.org
Control: Other not–for–profit (including NFP Corporation) **Service:** General Medical and Surgical

Staffed Beds: 14 **Admissions:** 745 **Census:** 8 **Outpatient Visits:** 57482 **Births:** 0 **Total Expense ($000):** 37867 **Payroll Expense ($000):** 15195 **Personnel:** 272

IRONWOOD—Gogebic County

⊠ **ASPIRUS GRAND VIEW HOSPITAL (231333)**, N10561 Grand View Lane, Zip 49938–9622; tel. 906/932–2525 **A**1 9 10 18 **F**3 11 13 15 18 28 29 31 34 35 40 44 45 50 56 57 59 62 64 65 66 68 70 75 76 77 78 79 81 85 86 87 89 97 100 101 102 103 104 105 107 108 110 115 119 129 130 131 132 133 146 147 148 **P**6 **S** Aspirus, Inc., Wausau, WI
Primary Contact: Paula L. Chermside, Chief Operating Officer
COO: Paula L. Chermside, Chief Operating Officer
CFO: Charmaine Chiantello, Chief Financial Officer
CMO: Chris Pogliano, M.D., Chief Medical Staff
CIO: Ron Eyer, Manager Information Services
CHR: Keri Van Epern, Manager Human Resources
CNO: Grace Tousignant, R.N., Chief Nursing Officer
Web address: www.aspirusgrandview.org
Control: Other not–for–profit (including NFP Corporation) **Service:** General Medical and Surgical

Staffed Beds: 25 **Admissions:** 1161 **Census:** 10 **Outpatient Visits:** 77457 **Births:** 134 **Total Expense ($000):** 31011 **Payroll Expense ($000):** 12124 **Personnel:** 327

ISHPEMING—Marquette County

★ **BELL HOSPITAL (231321)**, 901 Lakeshore Drive, Zip 49849–1367; tel. 906/486–4431 **A**9 10 18 **F**3 7 11 13 15 29 30 32 34 40 50 51 53 57 59 65 68 70 75 76 77 79 81 82 85 87 92 93 96 97 107 108 110 119 129 131 133 135 144 146 147 **P**6
Primary Contact: Mitchell D. Leckelt, Interim Chief Executive Officer
CFO: Teresa J. Morrison, Chief Financial Officer
CMO: Douglas LaBelle, M.D., Chief Medical Officer
CIO: Jeffrey Wagner, Supervisor Information Systems
CHR: Ruth Solinski, Vice President Organizational Development
CNO: Verno Davidson, R.N., Chief Nursing Officer
Web address: www.bellhospital.org
Control: Other not–for–profit (including NFP Corporation) **Service:** General Medical and Surgical

Staffed Beds: 25 **Admissions:** 1041 **Census:** 6 **Outpatient Visits:** 73193 **Births:** 254 **Total Expense ($000):** 39325 **Payroll Expense ($000):** 16497 **Personnel:** 250

JACKSON—Jackson County

⊠ **ALLEGIANCE HEALTH (230092)**, 205 North East Avenue, Zip 49201–1753; tel. 517/788–4800, (Total facility includes 20 beds in nursing home–type unit) **A**1 2 3 5 9 10 **F**3 4 5 8 9 11 13 15 17 18 20 22 24 26 28 29 30 31 34 35 38 40 44 45 46 47 48 49 50 51 53 54 56 57 59 61 62 63 64 65 68 69 70 73 74 75 76 77 78 79 81 82 84 85 87 89 92 93 96 98 99 100 101 102 103 104 105 106 107 108 110 111 114 115 119 121 123 126 128 129 130 131 132 135 146 147 148 **P**6
Primary Contact: Georgia R. Fojtasek, President and Chief Executive Officer
COO: Karen Chaprnka, Senior Vice President and Chief Operating Officer
CFO: Jeanne Wickens, Senior Vice President Finance and Chief Financial Officer
CMO: Ray King, M.D., Senior Vice President and Chief Medical Officer
CIO: Richard Warren, Vice President Health Information Systems
CHR: George A. Hunter, Vice President Human Resources
CNO: Ondrea Bates, Senior Vice President Patient Care Continuum and Chief Nursing Officer
Web address: www.allegiancehealth.org
Control: Other not–for–profit (including NFP Corporation) **Service:** General Medical and Surgical

Staffed Beds: 303 **Admissions:** 18000 **Census:** 208 **Outpatient Visits:** 477123 **Births:** 1701 **Total Expense ($000):** 433553 **Payroll Expense ($000):** 189302 **Personnel:** 3314

Hospital, Medicare Provider Number, Address, Telephone, Approval, Facility, and Physician Codes, Health Care System

★ American Hospital Association (AHA) membership
☐ The Joint Commission accreditation ◇ DNV Healthcare Inc. accreditation
○ Healthcare Facilities Accreditation Program
△ Commission on Accreditation of Rehabilitation Facilities (CARF) accreditation

⊞ **CARELINK OF JACKSON (232036)**, 110 North Elm Avenue, Zip 49202–3595; tel. 517/787–1440, (Nonreporting) **A**1 9 10
Primary Contact: J. Mark Fall, Chief Executive Officer
COO: Charlotte Hyatt, MSN, Chief Operating Officer and Chief Nursing Officer
CFO: Dale L. Friesen, Chief Financial Officer
CMO: Robert Albertson, M.D., Chief Medical Officer
CNO: Charlotte Hyatt, MSN, Chief Operating Officer and Chief Nursing Officer
Web address: www.carelinkofjackson.org
Control: Other not–for–profit (including NFP Corporation) **Service:** Long–Term Acute Care hospital

Staffed Beds: 44

DUANE L. WATERS HOSPITAL, 3857 Cooper Street, Zip 49201–7521; tel. 517/780–5600, (Nonreporting)
Primary Contact: Gerald De Voss, Acting Administrator
Control: State–Government, nonfederal **Service:** Hospital unit of an institution (prison hospital, college infimary, etc.)

Staffed Beds: 150

KALAMAZOO—Kalamazoo County

⊞ △ **BORGESS MEDICAL CENTER (230117)**, 1521 Gull Road, Zip 49048–1640; tel. 269/226–7000 **A**1 3 5 7 9 10 **F**1 3 7 8 9 11 12 13 15 17 18 20 22 24 26 28 29 30 31 32 33 34 35 36 37 38 39 40 43 44 45 46 49 50 53 54 56 57 58 59 60 61 64 68 70 74 75 76 77 78 79 81 82 84 85 86 87 90 91 92 93 94 96 97 98 99 100 101 102 103 104 105 107 108 110 114 115 118 119 126 129 130 131 132 135 144 146 147 148 **P**1 3 6 **S** Ascension Health, Saint Louis, MO
Primary Contact: Paul A. Spaude, FACHE, President and Chief Executive Officer
COO: Mark Anthony, Executive Vice President and Chief Operating Officer
CFO: Richard Felbinger, Senior Vice President and Chief Financial Officer
CMO: Robert Hill, M.D., Vice President Medical Staff Affairs
CIO: Donna Roach, Chief Information Officer
CHR: Laura Lentenbrink, Vice President, Human Resources
CNO: Lois J. Van Donselaar, R.N., Vice President & Chief Nursing Officer
Web address: www.borgess.com
Control: Church–operated, Nongovernment, not–for profit **Service:** General Medical and Surgical

Staffed Beds: 387 Admissions: 19735 Census: 261 Outpatient Visits: 549269 Births: 1364 Total Expense ($000): 393712 Payroll Expense ($000): 170540 Personnel: 2206

⊞ **BRONSON METHODIST HOSPITAL (230017)**, 601 John Street, Zip 49007–5346; tel. 269/341–6000, (Includes BRONSON VICKSBURG HOSPITAL, 13326 North Boulevard, Vicksburg, Zip 49097–1099; tel. 269/649–2321; Frank J. Sardone, President and Chief Executive Officer; CHILDREN'S HOSPITAL AT BRONSON, 601 John Street, Zip 49007–5341; tel. 269/341–7654) **A**1 3 5 9 10 **F**3 9 11 12 13 15 16 17 18 19 20 22 24 26 28 29 30 31 32 34 35 37 39 40 41 42 43 44 45 46 47 49 50 51 55 56 57 58 59 60 61 62 64 65 66 68 70 71 72 74 75 76 77 78 79 80 81 82 83 84 85 86 87 88 89 92 93 97 102 107 108 110 111 114 115 117 118 119 126 130 131 132 134 135 141 145 146 147 148 **P**6 **S** Bronson Healthcare Group, Inc., Kalamazoo, MI
Primary Contact: Frank J. Sardone, President and Chief Executive Officer
COO: Kenneth L. Taft, Executive Vice President and Chief Operating Officer
CFO: Mary Meitz, Vice President Finance
CMO: Scott Larson, M.D., Vice President Medical Affairs and Chief Medical Officer
CIO: Paul Peabody, Vice President Information Technology and Chief Information Officer
CHR: John Hayden, Vice President and Chief Human Resources Officer
CNO: Denise Neely, R.N., Vice President and Chief Nursing Officer
Web address: www.bronsonhealth.com
Control: Other not–for–profit (including NFP Corporation) **Service:** General Medical and Surgical

Staffed Beds: 405 Admissions: 21270 Census: 275 Outpatient Visits: 558081 Births: 3430 Total Expense ($000): 583657 Payroll Expense ($000): 268126 Personnel: 3301

☐ **KALAMAZOO PSYCHIATRIC HOSPITAL (234026)**, 1312 Oakland Drive, Zip 49008–1205; tel. 269/337–3000 **A**1 9 10 12 13 **F**3 39 50 53 56 65 74 75 77 86 87 97 98 101 103 130 132 135 143 146 **P**6
Primary Contact: James J. Coleman, Ed.D., Director
COO: James J. Coleman, Ed.D., Director
CFO: Sue Glenn, Director Administrative Services
CMO: N. Gajare, M.D., Chief Clinical Affairs
CIO: Gerry Wood, Information Technologist
CHR: Kerry Bloom, Director Human Resources
Control: State–Government, nonfederal **Service:** Psychiatric

Staffed Beds: 203 Admissions: 380 Census: 162 Outpatient Visits: 0 Births: 0 Total Expense ($000): 54420 Payroll Expense ($000): 27160 Personnel: 531

KALKASKA—Kalkaska County

★ **KALKASKA MEMORIAL HEALTH CENTER (231301)**, 419 South Coral Street, Zip 49646–2503; tel. 231/258–7500, (Total facility includes 88 beds in nursing home–type unit) **A**9 10 18 **F**2 10 15 28 34 35 40 44 45 50 53 56 57 59 60 64 65 66 81 84 87 93 97 107 110 111 114 119 127 128 129 130 132 134 143 144 146 147 148 **S** Munson Healthcare, Traverse City, MI
Primary Contact: Kevin L. Rogols, FACHE, Administrator
COO: Sheila Atwood, R.N., Chief Operating Officer
CMO: Jeremy Holmes, D.O., Chief of Staff
CHR: Kimberly Babcock, Administrator Human Resources
CNO: Christine Bissonette, R.N., Chief Nursing Officer
Web address: www.munsonhealthcare.org
Control: Hospital district or authority, Government, nonfederal **Service:** General Medical and Surgical

Staffed Beds: 96 Admissions: 153 Census: 84 Outpatient Visits: 63851 Births: 0 Total Expense ($000): 28104 Payroll Expense ($000): 10969 Personnel: 237

L'ANSE—L'Anse County

☐ **BARAGA COUNTY MEMORIAL HOSPITAL (231307)**, 18341 U.S. Highway 41, Zip 49946–8024; tel. 906/524–3300 **A**1 9 10 18 **F**3 5 11 15 28 31 34 40 45 53 57 59 62 63 64 74 77 78 79 81 82 84 85 89 93 107 108 110 114 118 119 127 130 132 133 146 **P**6
Primary Contact: Tim E. Zwickey, Chief Executive Officer
CFO: Gail Jestila–Peltola, Chief Financial Officer
CMO: Alin Sora, M.D., Chief of Staff
CIO: Taylor Makela, Director Information Technology
CHR: Tim E. Zwickey, Chief Executive Officer
CNO: Margie Hale, R.N., Director of Nursing
Web address: www.bcmh.org
Control: County–Government, nonfederal **Service:** General Medical and Surgical

Staffed Beds: 15 Admissions: 560 Census: 7 Outpatient Visits: 25773 Births: 1 Total Expense ($000): 22527 Payroll Expense ($000): 7490 Personnel: 105

LAKEVIEW—Montcalm County

SPECTRUM HEALTH KELSEY HOSPITAL See Spectrum Health United Hospital, Greenville

LANSING—Ingham County

★ ○ **MCLAREN GREATER LANSING (230167)**, 401 West Greenlawn Avenue, Zip 48910–2819; tel. 517/975–6000, (Includes INGHAM REGIONAL MEDICAL CENTER, GREENLAWN CAMPUS, 401 West Greenlawn Avenue, tel. 517/334–2121; MCLAREN ORTHOPEDIC HOSPITAL, 2727 South Pennsylvania Avenue, Zip 48910–3490; tel. 517/975–6000; Rick Wright, President and Chief Executive Officer) **A**2 3 5 9 10 11 12 13 **F**3 8 11 13 15 17 18 20 22 24 26 28 29 30 31 34 35 37 40 44 45 49 50 56 57 58 59 60 61 63 64 65 66 70 74 75 76 77 78 79 80 81 82 84 85 86 87 89 90 93 97 98 100 101 102 103 104 107 108 110 111 114 115 116 117 118 119 120 121 124 126 129 130 131 132 135 146 147 148 **P**8 **S** McLaren Health Care Corporation, Flint, MI
Primary Contact: Rick Wright, President and Chief Executive Officer
COO: Thomas Mee, R.N., Chief Operating Officer
CFO: Dale Thompson, Chief Financial Officer
CMO: Linda Peterson, M.D., Vice President Medical Affairs
CHR: Floyd Chasse, Vice President Human Resources
Web address: www.irmc.org
Control: Other not–for–profit (including NFP Corporation) **Service:** General Medical and Surgical

Staffed Beds: 322 Admissions: 13942 Census: 157 Outpatient Visits: 379172 Births: 1184 Total Expense ($000): 271110 Payroll Expense ($000): 109035 Personnel: 1865

⊞ ○ △ **SPARROW HOSPITAL (230230)**, 1215 East Michigan Avenue, Zip 48912–1811; tel. 517/364–1000, (Includes SPARROW REGIONAL CHILDREN'S CENTER, 1215 East Michigan Avenue, tel. 517/364–1000) **A**1 2 3 5 7 9 10 11 12 13 **F**1 2 3 4 5 7 9 10 11 20 22 24 26 28 29 30 33 34 35 36 38 40 41 43 44 45 46 49 50 51 54 55 56 57 58 59 60 63 64 65 66 68 70 72 74 75 76 77 78 79 81 82 84 85 86 87 88 89 90 92 93 96 97 98 99 100 101 102 103 104 105 107 108 109 110 114 115 116 117 118 119 120 121 123 124 126 129 131 132 135 143 144 146 147 148 **P**1 6 **S** Sparrow Health System, Lansing, MI
Primary Contact: Dennis A. Swan, JD, FACHE, President and Chief Executive Officer
COO: Joseph Ruth, Executive Vice President and Chief Operating Officer
CFO: Paula Reichle, Senior Vice President and Chief Operating Officer
CMO: Brian D. Schroeder, M.D., Senior Vice President and Chief Medical Officer
CIO: Thomas Bres, Vice President and Chief Administrative Officer
CHR: Paul Sturgis, Vice President and Chief Human Resources Officer
CNO: Mary Lou Wesley, R.N., Senior Vice President and Chief Nursing Officer
Web address: www.sparrow.org
Control: Other not–for–profit (including NFP Corporation) **Service:** General Medical and Surgical

Staffed Beds: 679 Admissions: 35038 Census: 455 Outpatient Visits: 471864 Births: 4254 Total Expense ($000): 782587 Payroll Expense ($000): 363123 Personnel: 4947

Many Facility Codes have changed. Please refer to the AHA Guide Code Chart. © 2014 AHA Guide

★ ○ **SPARROW SPECIALTY HOSPITAL (232037)**, 1210 West Saginaw Street, Zip 48915–1927, Mailing Address: P.O. Box 85201, Zip 48915–1927; tel. 517/364–6800 **A**9 10 11 **F**1 3 29 30 36 60 68 85 100 101 119 130 148 **S** Sparrow Health System, Lansing, MI
Primary Contact: Kira Carter–Robertson, President and Chief Executive Officer
CFO: David Przybylski, Interim Controller
CMO: Paul Entler, D.O., Medical Director
CHR: Teresa Verscheure, Executive Director Human Resources
CNO: Tina Gross, Director of Clinical Services
Web address: www.sparrowspecialty.org
Control: Other not–for–profit (including NFP Corporation) **Service:** Long–Term Acute Care hospital

Staffed Beds: 36 **Admissions:** 309 **Census:** 24 **Outpatient Visits:** 0 **Births:** 0 **Total Expense ($000):** 11414 **Payroll Expense ($000):** 5535 **Personnel:** 121

LAPEER—Lapeer County

★ ○ **MCLAREN LAPEER REGION (230193)**, 1375 North Main Street, Zip 48446–1350; tel. 810/667–5500, (Total facility includes 19 beds in nursing home–type unit) **A**2 9 10 11 **F**3 11 13 15 18 20 28 29 30 31 34 40 43 45 46 49 50 51 54 56 57 59 64 68 70 74 75 76 77 78 79 81 82 83 85 86 87 92 93 97 98 102 107 108 111 114 115 119 123 124 128 129 130 131 132 135 144 146 148 **S** McLaren Health Care Corporation, Flint, MI
Primary Contact: Barton Buxton, Ed.D., President and Chief Executive Officer
COO: Thomas Mee, R.N., Vice President Operations
CFO: Mary Beth Callahan, Chief Financial Officer
CMO: Gary Salem, M.D., Vice President Medical Affairs
CIO: Gayle Consiglio, Chief Information Officer
CHR: Amy Dorr, Vice President Human Resources
Web address: www.lapeerregional.org
Control: Other not–for–profit (including NFP Corporation) **Service:** General Medical and Surgical

Staffed Beds: 159 **Admissions:** 7498 **Census:** 89 **Outpatient Visits:** 131838 **Births:** 490 **Total Expense ($000):** 106566 **Payroll Expense ($000):** 46147 **Personnel:** 589

LAURIUM—Houghton County

⌧ **ASPIRUS KEWEENAW HOSPITAL (231319)**, 205 Osceola Street, Zip 49913–2134; tel. 906/337–6500 **A**1 9 10 18 **F**3 7 11 13 15 17 18 28 29 30 31 34 35 36 40 45 52 53 56 57 59 61 62 63 64 65 70 75 77 78 79 81 85 87 89 92 93 107 108 110 111 115 118 119 127 129 130 131 132 133 135 145 146 147 148 **P**6 **S** Aspirus, Inc., Wausau, WI
Primary Contact: Michael Hauswirth, Chief Operating Officer
COO: Michael Hauswirth, Chief Operating Officer
CFO: Walt Kiiskila, Interim Chief Executive Officer
CMO: Glenn Kauppila, D.O., Chief of Staff
CIO: Dave Olsson, Director of Marketing
CHR: Chad D. Rowe, Regional Director Human Resources
CNO: Grace Tousignant, R.N., Chief Nursing Officer
Web address: www.aspiruskeweenaw.org
Control: Other not–for–profit (including NFP Corporation) **Service:** General Medical and Surgical

Staffed Beds: 25 **Admissions:** 981 **Census:** 9 **Outpatient Visits:** 36792 **Births:** 89 **Total Expense ($000):** 35615 **Payroll Expense ($000):** 17927 **Personnel:** 321

LINCOLN PARK—Wayne County

⌧ **VIBRA HOSPITAL OF SOUTHEASTERN MICHIGAN (232019)**, 26400 West Outer Drive, Zip 48146–2088; tel. 313/386–2000, (Nonreporting) **A**1 9 10 **S** Vibra Healthcare, Mechanicsburg, PA
Primary Contact: Denise Wayne, Chief Executive Officer
COO: Cindy Brassinger, Chief Operating Officer
CFO: Douglas Morris, Chief Financial Officer
CHR: Karen D. Gray, Director Human Resources
Web address: www.vhsemichigan.com/
Control: Corporation, Investor–owned, for–profit **Service:** Long–Term Acute Care hospital

Staffed Beds: 140

LIVONIA—Wayne County

⌧ **ST. MARY MERCY HOSPITAL (230002)**, 36475 Five Mile Road, Zip 48154–1988; tel. 734/655–4800 **A**1 2 9 10 **F**3 4 5 12 13 15 18 20 22 26 28 29 30 31 34 35 36 38 40 45 46 47 49 50 51 56 57 58 59 63 64 68 70 74 75 76 78 79 81 83 84 85 87 90 93 97 98 100 101 102 103 104 107 108 110 111 114 115 116 117 118 119 120 121 126 129 130 131 132 135 143 145 146 147 148 **P**6 **S** Catholic Health East / Trinity Health, Livonia, MI
Primary Contact: David A. Spivey, President and Chief Executive Officer
COO: C. W. Lauderbach, Jr., Vice President Clinical Services
CFO: Mike Samyn, Vice President, Finance and Chief Financial Officer
CIO: Janet Yim, Director Information Services
CHR: Kenneth Antczak, Vice President Human Resources
Web address: www.stmarymercy.org
Control: Church–operated, Nongovernment, not–for profit **Service:** General Medical and Surgical

Staffed Beds: 285 **Admissions:** 16931 **Census:** 223 **Outpatient Visits:** 206033 **Births:** 685 **Total Expense ($000):** 235481 **Payroll Expense ($000):** 98967 **Personnel:** 1409

LUDINGTON—Mason County

★ ◇ **SPECTRUM HEALTH LUDINGTON HOSPITAL (230110)**, One Atkinson Drive, Zip 49431–1906; tel. 231/843–2591 **A**9 10 20 21 **F**3 8 11 13 15 17 28 29 31 34 35 40 45 49 51 54 57 59 62 68 75 77 78 79 81 82 85 89 92 93 98 100 102 103 107 108 110 111 114 115 118 119 129 130 131 132 135 146 147 148 **S** Spectrum Health, Grand Rapids, MI
Primary Contact: Mark Vipperman, President
COO: Drew H. Dostal, R.N., Vice President Operations
CFO: Kerri Nelson, Chief Financial Officer
CMO: Steve Strbich, D.O., Chief of Staff
CIO: Sue Luskin, Director Information Services
CHR: Jill Vasquez, Manager Human Resources
CNO: Helen Johnson, R.N., Vice President Patient Services
Web address: www.mmcwm.com
Control: Other not–for–profit (including NFP Corporation) **Service:** General Medical and Surgical

Staffed Beds: 80 **Admissions:** 2238 **Census:** 26 **Outpatient Visits:** 95139 **Births:** 296 **Total Expense ($000):** 62086 **Payroll Expense ($000):** 23107 **Personnel:** 466

MANISTEE—Manistee County

WEST SHORE MEDICAL CENTER (231335), 1465 East Parkdale Avenue, Zip 49660–9709; tel. 231/398–1000 **A**9 10 18 **F**3 7 11 13 15 17 28 29 32 34 35 39 40 46 51 53 54 57 59 74 75 76 77 79 81 85 86 93 107 108 110 111 115 118 119 129 132 135 146 147 148 **P**6
Primary Contact: James Barker, President
COO: Donn J. Lemmer, Vice President Finance
CFO: Donn J. Lemmer, Vice President Finance
CMO: Joel Anhalt, D.O., Chief of Staff
CHR: Kim Weckesser, Director Human Resources
CNO: Thomas Kane, Vice President Patient Care
Web address: www.westshoremedcenter.org
Control: County–Government, nonfederal **Service:** General Medical and Surgical

Staffed Beds: 25 **Admissions:** 1568 **Census:** 14 **Outpatient Visits:** 94118 **Births:** 169 **Total Expense ($000):** 56564 **Payroll Expense ($000):** 24225 **Personnel:** 315

MANISTIQUE—Schoolcraft County

★ **SCHOOLCRAFT MEMORIAL HOSPITAL (231303)**, 7870W U.S. Highway 2, Zip 49854–8992; tel. 906/341–3200 **A**9 10 18 **F**3 11 15 28 29 30 31 32 34 35 40 41 44 45 50 53 56 57 59 62 63 64 65 70 75 77 78 79 81 84 85 86 87 93 97 107 108 110 114 118 119 127 129 130 132 133 144 146 147 148 **P**6
Primary Contact: Tanya Hoar, Chief Executive Officer and Chief Financial Officer
CFO: Tanya Hoar, Chief Executive Officer and Chief Financial Officer
CMO: David Schoenow, M.D., Chief Medical Officer
CIO: Kent La Croix, Supervisor Information Technology
CHR: Gina Lindquist, Director Human Resources
CNO: Cindy Olli, R.N., Chief Nursing Officer
Web address: www.scmh.org
Control: County–Government, nonfederal **Service:** General Medical and Surgical

Staffed Beds: 12 **Admissions:** 466 **Census:** 5 **Outpatient Visits:** 35711 **Births:** 0 **Total Expense ($000):** 26156 **Payroll Expense ($000):** 12439 **Personnel:** 186

Hospital, Medicare Provider Number, Address, Telephone, Approval, Facility, and Physician Codes, Health Care System

★ American Hospital Association (AHA) membership
□ The Joint Commission accreditation
◇ DNV Healthcare Inc. accreditation
○ Healthcare Facilities Accreditation Program
△ Commission on Accreditation of Rehabilitation Facilities (CARF) accreditation

MARLETTE—Sanilac County

MARLETTE REGIONAL HOSPITAL (231330), 2770 Main Street, Zip 48453–1141, Mailing Address: P.O. Box 307, Zip 48453–0307; tel. 989/635–4000, (Nonreporting) **A**9 10 18
Primary Contact: Daniel Babcock, Chief Executive Officer
CFO: James L. Singles, Chief Financial Officer
CMO: Jabir Akhtar, M.D., Chief of Staff
CIO: Paul Gugel, Manager Information Technology
CHR: Connie Kennedy, Director Human Resources
CNO: Hilda Hebberd, R.N., Senior Director Clinical Services
Web address: www.marletteregionalhospital.org
Control: Other not–for–profit (including NFP Corporation) **Service:** General Medical and Surgical

Staffed Beds: 74

MARQUETTE—Marquette County

⊞ **MARQUETTE GENERAL HOSPITAL (230054)**, 580 West College Avenue, Zip 49855–2736; tel. 906/228–9440 **A**1 2 3 5 9 10 13 19 20 **F**3 4 5 7 8 11 12 13 14 15 17 18 20 22 24 26 28 29 30 31 32 34 35 37 38 40 43 45 46 48 49 50 51 53 55 56 57 58 59 60 62 63 64 65 68 70 72 74 75 76 77 78 79 81 82 85 86 87 89 90 93 94 98 99 100 101 102 103 104 107 108 110 111 114 115 116 117 118 119 120 121 122 123 124 127 129 130 131 132 135 143 145 146 147 148 **P**6 **S** Duke LifePoint Healthcare, Brentwood, TN
Primary Contact: Edward D. Banos, Chief Executive Officer
COO: Mitchell D. Leckelt, Assistant Administrator
CFO: Steve Embree, Chief Financial Officer
CMO: Tom Noren, M.D., Chief Medical Officer
CIO: Doug Stacy, Director Information Technology
CHR: Ruth Solinski, Senior Director Human Resources
CNO: Dagmar Raica, R.N., Chief Nursing Officer
Web address: www.mgh.org
Control: Corporation, Investor–owned, for–profit **Service:** General Medical and Surgical

Staffed Beds: 268 **Admissions:** 9213 **Census:** 132 **Outpatient Visits:** 229568 **Births:** 629 **Total Expense ($000):** 327208 **Payroll Expense ($000):** 129015 **Personnel:** 2184

MARSHALL—Calhoun County

★ ◇ **OAKLAWN HOSPITAL (230217)**, 200 North Madison Street, Zip 49068–1199; tel. 269/781–4271 **A**9 10 21 **F**3 11 13 15 18 19 26 28 29 30 31 32 34 35 36 37 38 40 44 45 46 48 50 53 54 57 58 59 60 62 63 64 65 68 69 70 74 75 76 77 78 79 81 82 85 86 87 89 93 94 97 98 99 100 101 102 103 104 105 106 107 108 110 111 114 115 117 118 119 126 129 130 131 132 135 146 147 148 **P**1 6
Primary Contact: Ginger Williams, M.D., President and Chief Executive Officer
COO: Sharon L. Thomas–Boyd, Chief Support and Ancillary Services Officer
CFO: Gregg M. Beeg, FACHE, Chief Financial Officer
CIO: Natalie Spivak, Director Information Services
CHR: Jan Sinclair, Chief Personnel Officer
CNO: Kristin Sims, MSN, Chief Nursing Officer
Web address: www.oaklawnhospital.org
Control: Other not–for–profit (including NFP Corporation) **Service:** General Medical and Surgical

Staffed Beds: 78 **Admissions:** 3793 **Census:** 35 **Outpatient Visits:** 164986 **Births:** 746 **Total Expense ($000):** 111852 **Payroll Expense ($000):** 52985 **Personnel:** 823

MIDLAND—Midland County

⊞ **MIDMICHIGAN MEDICAL CENTER–MIDLAND (230222)**, 4000 Wellness Drive, Zip 48670–2000; tel. 989/839–3000, (Nonreporting) **A**1 2 3 5 9 10 19 20 **S** MidMichigan Health, Midland, MI
Primary Contact: Gregory H. Rogers, President
CFO: Scott D. Currie, Vice President and Chief Financial Officer
CMO: Margueritte Kuhn, M.D., Vice President Medical Affairs
CIO: C. Harlan Goodrich, Vice President and Chief Information Officer
CNO: Jan Penney, R.N., Vice President and Chief Nursing Officer
Web address: www.midmichigan.org
Control: Other not–for–profit (including NFP Corporation) **Service:** General Medical and Surgical

Staffed Beds: 246

MONROE—Monroe County

⊞ **MERCY MEMORIAL HOSPITAL SYSTEM (230099)**, 718 North Macomb Street, Zip 48162–7815; tel. 734/240–8400, (Total facility includes 70 beds in nursing home–type unit) **A**1 2 9 10 **F**3 5 8 11 13 15 18 20 28 29 30 34 35 38 40 41 44 45 46 49 50 51 54 56 57 59 62 63 64 65 69 70 71 74 75 76 77 79 81 84 85 86 87 89 92 93 97 98 99 100 101 102 103 104 107 108 109 110 111 113 114 115 116 117 118 119 126 129 130 131 132 135 145 146 147 148 **P**6
Primary Contact: Annette S. Phillips, President and Chief Executive Officer
CFO: Thomas Schilling, Chief Financial Officer and Senior Vice President Finance
CMO: Gary L. Moorman, D.O., Chief Medical Officer and Senior Vice President Medical Affairs
CIO: Bruce Kelly, Chief Information Officer
CHR: Aline Lafferty, Vice President Human Resources
CNO: Pamela A. Urbanski, R.N., Chief Nursing Officer, Senior Vice President, Patient Care Services
Web address: www.mercymemorial.org
Control: Other not–for–profit (including NFP Corporation) **Service:** General Medical and Surgical

Staffed Beds: 179 **Admissions:** 9388 **Census:** 106 **Outpatient Visits:** 169410 **Births:** 801 **Total Expense ($000):** 163275 **Payroll Expense ($000):** 69541 **Personnel:** 1226

MOUNT CLEMENS—Macomb County

HENRY FORD MACOMB HOSPITAL – MOUNT CLEMENS CAMPUS See Henry Ford Macomb Hospitals, Clinton Township

★ ○ **MCLAREN MACOMB (230227)**, 1000 Harrington Boulevard, Zip 48043–2992; tel. 586/493–8000 **A**2 9 10 11 12 13 **F**3 7 8 12 13 15 18 20 22 24 26 28 29 30 31 34 35 36 37 39 40 42 43 45 47 48 49 50 51 52 54 57 58 59 60 61 62 63 64 65 66 68 70 71 74 75 76 77 78 79 81 82 85 86 87 89 92 93 97 100 102 107 108 109 110 111 112 114 115 116 117 118 119 120 121 124 126 129 130 131 132 135 145 146 147 148 **P**8 **S** McLaren Health Care Corporation, Flint, MI
Primary Contact: Mark S. O'Halla, President and Chief Executive Officer
COO: Sue Durst, R.N., Vice President Plant Operations
CMO: Michael K. Smith, D.O., Vice President Medical Affairs
Web address: www.mclaren.org/macomb/macomb.aspx
Control: Other not–for–profit (including NFP Corporation) **Service:** General Medical and Surgical

Staffed Beds: 288 **Admissions:** 14706 **Census:** 161 **Outpatient Visits:** 156800 **Births:** 935 **Total Expense ($000):** 272950 **Payroll Expense ($000):** 114620 **Personnel:** 1708

⊞ **SELECT SPECIALTY HOSPITAL–MACOMB COUNTY (232023)**, 215 North Avenue, Zip 48043–1700; tel. 586/307–9000, (Nonreporting) **A**1 9 10 **S** Select Medical Corporation, Mechanicsburg, PA
Primary Contact: Jon P. O'Malley, Chief Executive Officer
CFO: Sharon Ryan, Regional Controller
CMO: Arsenio V. Deleon, M.D., Chief Medical Officer
CHR: Katelyn Andre, Human Resource Coordinator
CNO: Lydia Alaszewski, Chief Nursing Officer
Web address: www.macomb.selectspecialtyhospitals.com/
Control: Corporation, Investor–owned, for–profit **Service:** Long–Term Acute Care hospital

Staffed Beds: 36

MOUNT PLEASANT—Isabella County

★ ○ **MCLAREN CENTRAL MICHIGAN (230080)**, 1221 South Drive, Zip 48858–3257; tel. 989/772–6700 **A**9 10 11 19 **F**3 12 13 15 18 20 22 26 28 29 30 31 34 35 40 44 45 48 49 50 51 54 57 59 62 64 65 68 70 74 75 76 77 78 79 81 82 85 86 87 89 96 97 107 108 110 111 114 117 118 119 120 121 123 124 129 130 131 132 144 145 146 147 148 **P**1 **S** McLaren Health Care Corporation, Flint, MI
Primary Contact: William P. Lawrence, President and Chief Executive Officer
CFO: Gregg Beeg, Chief Financial Officer
CMO: Ashok Vashishta, M.D., Vice President Medical Affairs
CIO: Nicolette Zalud, Customer Site Manager
CHR: Carolyn Potter, Vice President Human Resources
CNO: Sheri Myers, Vice President Patient Care Services
Web address: www.cmch.org
Control: Other not–for–profit (including NFP Corporation) **Service:** General Medical and Surgical

Staffed Beds: 78 **Admissions:** 3590 **Census:** 29 **Outpatient Visits:** 170490 **Births:** 544 **Total Expense ($000):** 83533 **Payroll Expense ($000):** 37333 **Personnel:** 584

MI

MUNISING—Alger County

MUNISING MEMORIAL HOSPITAL (231308), 1500 Sand Point Road,
Zip 49862–1406; tel. 906/387–4110, (Nonreporting) **A**9 10 18
Primary Contact: Kevin P. Calhoun, Chief Executive Officer
CFO: Barb Trombley, Director Financial Services
CMO: Christine Krueger, M.D., Chief of Staff
CHR: Melissa Hall, Human Resources
CNO: Andrea Wills, R.N., Chief Nursing Executive
Web address: www.munisingmemorial.org
Control: Other not–for–profit (including NFP Corporation) **Service:** General
Medical and Surgical

| Staffed Beds: 25 |

MUSKEGON—Muskegon County

☒ **GREAT LAKES SPECIALTY HOSPITAL–MUSKEGON (232021)**, 1700 Clinton
Street, 3 South, Zip 49442–5502; tel. 231/728–5811, (Nonreporting) **A**1 9 10
S Select Medical Corporation, Mechanicsburg, PA
Primary Contact: Mark Holcomb, Administrator
Web address: www.greatlakesspecialtyhospital.com
Control: Corporation, Investor–owned, for–profit **Service:** Long–Term Acute Care
hospital

| Staffed Beds: 31 |

☒ **MERCY HEALTH, HACKLEY CAMPUS (230066)**, 1700 Clinton Street,
Zip 49442–5502, Mailing Address: P.O. Box 3302, Zip 49443–3302;
tel. 231/726–3511 **A**1 2 9 10 **F**3 11 12 13 15 26 29 30 35 40 45 49 50 51
53 54 57 59 61 64 68 70 74 76 77 79 81 82 84 85 87 89 90 91 93 96 97
98 99 100 101 102 103 104 105 106 107 108 109 111 114 115 116 117
118 119 127 144 146 147 148 **P**6 7 8 **S** Catholic Health East / Trinity Health,
Livonia, MI
Primary Contact: Greg Loomis, President
CFO: Gary Allore, Chief Financial Officer
CMO: F. Remington Sprague, M.D., Chief Medical Officer
CIO: William Stefl, Director Information Systems
CNO: Kimberly Maguire, R.N., Chief Nursing Officer
Web address: www.mercyhealthmuskegon.com
Control: Other not–for–profit (including NFP Corporation) **Service:** General
Medical and Surgical

| Staffed Beds: 213 **Admissions:** 8619 **Census:** 100 **Outpatient Visits:** |
| 260965 **Births:** 2059 **Total Expense ($000):** 165805 **Payroll Expense** |
| **($000):** 60853 **Personnel:** 1018 |

☒ ○ **MERCY HEALTH, MERCY CAMPUS (230004)**, 1500 East Sherman
Boulevard, Zip 49444–1849; tel. 231/672–2000, (Includes MERCY HEALTH,
GENERAL CAMPUS, 1700 Oak Avenue, Zip 49442; tel. 231/672–3311; Greg
Loomis, Interim President and Chief Operating Officer) **A**1 2 9 10 11 12 13 **F**3 7
11 12 15 16 18 20 22 24 26 28 29 30 31 34 35 40 44 50 51 53 54 56 57 58
59 64 68 70 74 75 77 78 79 81 82 84 85 86 87 91 93 94 97 107 108 111
114 115 116 117 118 119 120 121 122 123 124 129 130 131 132 135 144
146 147 148 **P**6 7 8 **S** Catholic Health East / Trinity Health, Livonia, MI
Primary Contact: Greg Loomis, President
CFO: Gary Allore, Chief Financial Officer
CMO: F. Remington Sprague, M.D., Chief Medical Officer
CIO: William Stefl, Director Information Systems
CNO: Kimberly Maguire, R.N., Chief Nursing Officer
Web address: www.mercyhealth.com
Control: Other not–for–profit (including NFP Corporation) **Service:** General
Medical and Surgical

| Staffed Beds: 188 **Admissions:** 8927 **Census:** 101 **Outpatient Visits:** |
| 650389 **Births:** 0 **Total Expense ($000):** 289341 **Payroll Expense ($000):** |
| 128663 **Personnel:** 1904 |

SELECT SPECIALTY HOSPITAL–WESTERN MICHIGAN See Great Lakes
Specialty Hospital–Muskegon

NEW BALTIMORE—Macomb County

HARBOR OAKS HOSPITAL (234021), 35031 23 Mile Road, Zip 48047–3649;
tel. 586/725–5777, (Nonreporting) **A**9 10 **S** Acadia Healthcare Company, Inc.,
Franklin, TN
Primary Contact: Sari Abromovich, Chief Executive Officer
CFO: Michael Ferguson, Chief Financial Officer
CMO: James D. Adamo, M.D., Medical Director
CHR: Zena Ridley, Director Human Resources
CNO: Leeann Duncan, Director Patient Care Services
Web address: www.harboroaks.com
Control: Corporation, Investor–owned, for–profit **Service:** Psychiatric

| Staffed Beds: 45 |

NEWBERRY—Luce County

★ ◇ **HELEN NEWBERRY JOY HOSPITAL (231304)**, 502 West Harrie Street,
Zip 49868–1209; tel. 906/293–9200, (Includes HELEN NEWBERRY JOY
HOSPITAL ANNEX), (Total facility includes 48 beds in nursing home–type unit) **A**9
10 18 21 **F**15 18 28 29 30 31 32 34 35 36 38 40 44 45 53 57 59 63 64 65
75 78 81 85 86 87 93 97 107 108 111 114 118 119 127 128 129 130 131
132 133 134 135 143 144 146 148 **P**6
Primary Contact: Scott Pillion, Chief Executive Officer
CMO: Raghu Rao, M.D., Chief of Staff
CIO: Michelle Sears, Director Information Systems
CHR: Roger Bergh, Director Human Resources
Web address: www.hnjh.org
Control: County–Government, nonfederal **Service:** General Medical and Surgical

| Staffed Beds: 73 **Admissions:** 638 **Census:** 52 **Outpatient Visits:** 25854 |
| **Births:** 0 **Total Expense ($000):** 32816 **Payroll Expense ($000):** 15099 |
| **Personnel:** 308 |

NORTHVILLE—Wayne County

☐ **HAWTHORN CENTER**, 18471 Haggerty Road, Zip 48168–9575;
tel. 248/735–6771, (Nonreporting) **A**1 9
Primary Contact: Roy Kelly, Facility Director
CIO: Robert W. Bailey, Chief Information Officer
Control: State–Government, nonfederal **Service:** Children's hospital psychiatric

| Staffed Beds: 69 |

NOVI—Oakland County

PROVIDENCE PARK HOSPITAL See Providence Hospital, Southfield

ONTONAGON—Ontonagon County

☒ **ASPIRUS ONTONAGON HOSPITAL (231309)**, 601 South Seventh Street,
Zip 49953–1459; tel. 906/884–8000, (Nonreporting) **A**1 9 10 18 **S** Aspirus,
Inc., Wausau, WI
Primary Contact: Michael Hauswirth, Chief Operating Officer
COO: Michael Hauswirth, Chief Operating Officer
CMO: Richard Chaltry, M.D., Director Medical Staff
CHR: Gina Linna, Manager Human Resources
CNO: Deanna Wilson, VP Patient Care Services/Site Manager
Web address: www.aspirus–ontonagon.org
Control: City–Government, nonfederal **Service:** General Medical and Surgical

| Staffed Beds: 18 |

OWOSSO—Shiawassee County

☒ **MEMORIAL HEALTHCARE (230121)**, 826 West King Street, Zip 48867–2120;
tel. 989/723–5211, (Total facility includes 32 beds in nursing home–type unit) **A**1
2 5 9 10 **F**11 13 15 28 29 30 31 32 34 35 36 38 40 45 50 51 56 57 59 62
63 64 65 69 70 74 75 76 78 79 81 82 85 87 89 93 97 98 100 101 102 107
108 110 111 115 119 127 128 129 130 131 132 143 144 146 147 148
P6 7
Primary Contact: Brian Long, FACHE, President and Chief Executive Officer
CFO: Brian Long, FACHE, President and Chief Executive Officer
CMO: Wael Salman, M.D., Vice President Medical Affairs
CIO: Frank Fear, Vice President Ancillary Services and Chief Information Officer
CHR: Ruthann Liagre, Vice President Human Resources
CNO: Dawn Blackwell, R.N., VP, Patient Care Services
Web address: www.memorialhealthcare.org
Control: Other not–for–profit (including NFP Corporation) **Service:** General
Medical and Surgical

| Staffed Beds: 149 **Admissions:** 3520 **Census:** 63 **Outpatient Visits:** 356941 |
| **Births:** 452 **Total Expense ($000):** 106283 **Payroll Expense ($000):** 49078 |
| **Personnel:** 934 |

Hospital, Medicare Provider Number, Address, Telephone, Approval, Facility, and Physician Codes, Health Care System

★ American Hospital Association (AHA) membership
☐ The Joint Commission accreditation   ◇ DNV Healthcare Inc. accreditation

○ Healthcare Facilities Accreditation Program
△ Commission on Accreditation of Rehabilitation Facilities (CARF) accreditation

---

MI

PAW PAW—Van Buren County

✠ **BRONSON LAKEVIEW HOSPITAL (231332)**, 408 Hazen Street,
Zip 49079–1019, Mailing Address: P.O. Box 209, Zip 49079–0209;
tel. 269/657–3141 **A**1 10 18 **F**3 6 11 15 29 30 34 35 40 44 56 57 59 64 65
66 68 74 75 77 81 85 86 87 93 97 98 100 101 102 103 107 110 114 119
127 129 130 132 146 147 148 **P**6 **S** Bronson Healthcare Group, Inc.,
Kalamazoo, MI
Primary Contact: Kirk Richardson, Chief Operating Officer
COO: Kirk Richardson, Vice President Chief Operating Officer Chief Nursing Officer
CMO: Matthew Dommer, M.D., Chief Medical Officer
CIO: Paul Peabody, Vice President Information Technology Chief Information
Officer
CHR: John Hayden, Senior Vice President and Chief Human Resources Officer
CNO: Kirk Richardson, Vice President Chief Operating Officer Chief Nursing Officer
Web address: www.bronsonhealth.com/lakeview
Control: Other not–for–profit (including NFP Corporation) **Service:** General
Medical and Surgical

Staffed Beds: 35 **Admissions:** 950 **Census:** 13 **Outpatient Visits:** 89415
Births: 0 **Total Expense ($000):** 35755 **Payroll Expense ($000):** 13610
Personnel: 337

PETOSKEY—Emmet County

✠ △ **MCLAREN NORTHERN MICHIGAN (230105)**, 416 Connable Avenue,
Zip 49770–2297; tel. 231/487–4000 **A**1 2 7 9 10 19 20 **F**3 12 13 15 17 18
20 22 24 26 28 29 30 31 32 34 35 36 38 40 42 44 45 49 50 51 53 57 58
59 60 64 68 70 74 75 76 77 78 79 81 82 85 86 87 89 90 91 93 94 96 107
108 110 111 114 115 119 120 121 123 124 129 130 132 135 146 148
S McLaren Health Care Corporation, Flint, MI
Primary Contact: David M. Zechman, FACHE, President and Chief Executive Officer
COO: Mary–Anne D. Ponti, R.N., Chief Operating Officer
CFO: David Bellamy, Chief Financial Officer
CMO: Kirk Lufkin, M.D., VPMA
CIO: Matt Raab, Site Executive
CHR: Gene Kaminski, Vice President Human Resources
CNO: Jennifer Woods, R.N., Chief Nursing Officer
Web address: www.northernhealth.org
Control: Other not–for–profit (including NFP Corporation) **Service:** General
Medical and Surgical

Staffed Beds: 188 **Admissions:** 9191 **Census:** 99 **Outpatient Visits:** 223483
Births: 672 **Total Expense ($000):** 223637 **Payroll Expense ($000):** 73716
Personnel: 1238

PIGEON—Huron County

✠ **SCHEURER HOSPITAL (231310)**, 170 North Caseville Road, Zip 48755–9781;
tel. 989/453–3223, (Total facility includes 19 beds in nursing home–type unit) **A**1
9 10 18 **F**3 7 10 11 15 28 29 30 31 34 36 40 44 45 50 53 54 56 57 59 64
68 69 75 77 78 79 81 85 86 87 91 93 97 107 108 110 114 119 125 127
130 131 132 133 143 146 **P**6
Primary Contact: Dwight Gascho, President and Chief Executive Officer
CFO: Terry Lutz, Chief Financial Officer
CMO: Scott Reiter, D.O., Chief of Staff
CIO: Suzanne LeMaire, Manager Health Information Management Services and
Corporate Compliance Officer
CHR: Gregory S. Foy, Human Resources System Leader
CNO: Sue Lathrom, Director of Nursing/Patient Care System Leader
Web address: www.scheurer.org
Control: Other not–for–profit (including NFP Corporation) **Service:** General
Medical and Surgical

Staffed Beds: 44 **Admissions:** 602 **Census:** 23 **Outpatient Visits:** 42668
Births: 0 **Total Expense ($000):** 33829 **Payroll Expense ($000):** 16078
Personnel: 322

PLAINWELL—Allegan County

✠ **BORGESS–PIPP HOSPITAL (232034)**, 411 Naomi Street, Zip 49080–1222;
tel. 269/685–6811, (Nonreporting) **A**1 9 10 **S** Ascension Health, Saint Louis, MO
Primary Contact: John E. Ryder, Administrator and Chief Operating Officer
Web address: www.borgess.com
Control: Other not–for–profit (including NFP Corporation) **Service:** Long–Term
Acute Care hospital

Staffed Beds: 43

PONTIAC—Oakland County

☐ **DOCTORS' HOSPITAL OF MICHIGAN (230013)**, 461 West Huron Street,
Zip 48341–1601; tel. 248/857–7200, (Nonreporting) **A**1 9 10
Primary Contact: Robert Barrow, Chief Executive Officer
COO: Dennis Franks, Vice President Operations
CFO: Dennis Franks, Interim Chief Financial Officer
CMO: Ray Breitenbach, M.D., Chief of Staff
CIO: Albert Sinisi, Director Information Systems
Web address: www.dhofm.com
Control: Other not–for–profit (including NFP Corporation) **Service:** General
Medical and Surgical

Staffed Beds: 106

★ ○ **MCLAREN OAKLAND (230207)**, 50 North Perry Street, Zip 48342–2253;
tel. 248/338–5000, (Total facility includes 120 beds in nursing home–type unit)
A9 10 11 12 13 **F**3 4 7 8 11 12 14 15 18 20 24 26 28 29 30 31 32 33 34
35 36 40 42 43 44 45 50 53 54 57 59 62 63 64 65 66 68 70 74 75 77 78
79 81 82 90 92 93 94 98 103 107 108 111 114 118 119 124 128 130 131
132 135 136 137 138 139 140 141 142 143 144 146 148 **P**4 8 **S** McLaren
Health Care Corporation, Flint, MI
Primary Contact: Clarence Sevillian, President and Chief Executive Officer
CFO: Fred Korte, Chief Financial Officer
CMO: Steven Calkin, D.O., Vice President Medical Affairs
CIO: Darin Boka, Chief Information Officer
CHR: Dwan Cosby, Manager Human Resources
CNO: Michele Carey, Vice President Patient Care and Chief Nursing Officer
Web address: www.pohmedical.org
Control: Other not–for–profit (including NFP Corporation) **Service:** General
Medical and Surgical

Staffed Beds: 285 **Admissions:** 5784 **Census:** 195 **Outpatient Visits:**
153060 **Births:** 0 **Total Expense ($000):** 149818 **Payroll Expense ($000):**
61267 **Personnel:** 1067

✠ **SELECT SPECIALTY HOSPITAL–PONTIAC (232030)**, 44405 Woodward
Avenue, 8th Floor, Zip 48341–5023; tel. 248/452–5252, (Nonreporting) **A**1 9 10
S Select Medical Corporation, Mechanicsburg, PA
Primary Contact: Peggy Kingston, Chief Executive Officer
CMO: Fadi Salloum, M.D., Medical Director
CNO: Cathy Boyd, Chief Nursing Officer
Web address: www.selectspecialtyhospitals.com/company/locations/pontiac.aspx
Control: Corporation, Investor–owned, for–profit **Service:** Long–Term Acute Care
hospital

Staffed Beds: 30

✠ **ST. JOSEPH MERCY OAKLAND (230029)**, 44405 Woodward Avenue,
Zip 48341–5023; tel. 248/858–3000 **A**1 2 3 5 9 10 12 13 **F**3 8 12 13 15 17
18 20 22 24 26 28 29 30 31 34 35 36 39 40 43 44 45 46 48 49 50 53 54
55 56 57 58 59 61 64 65 66 68 70 72 74 75 76 77 78 79 81 82 84 85 86
87 89 90 92 93 97 98 100 101 102 103 105 107 108 110 111 114 115 118
119 126 129 130 131 132 135 144 146 147 148 **P**6 **S** Catholic Health East /
Trinity Health, Livonia, MI
Primary Contact: Jack Weiner, President and Chief Executive Officer
COO: Barbara Hertzler, Chief Operating Officer
CFO: Michael Gusho, Chief Financial Officer
CMO: Michael Smith, M.D., Vice President Medical Affairs
CIO: Robert Jones, Director Management Information Systems
CHR: Ane McNeil, Vice President Human Resources
CNO: Ann McDonald–Upton, Chief Nursing Officer
Web address: www.stjoesoakland.com
Control: Church–operated, Nongovernment, not–for profit **Service:** General
Medical and Surgical

Staffed Beds: 409 **Admissions:** 19180 **Census:** 257 **Outpatient Visits:**
361678 **Births:** 1859 **Total Expense ($000):** 381732 **Payroll Expense
($000):** 147757 **Personnel:** 2430

PORT HURON—St. Clair County

✠ ○ **PORT HURON HOSPITAL (230216)**, 1221 Pine Grove Avenue,
Zip 48060–3511; tel. 810/987–5000 **A**1 2 9 10 11 **F**3 5 11 12 13 15 17 18
20 22 24 26 29 30 31 32 34 35 36 39 40 44 45 46 48 49 50 51 54 56 57
58 59 61 64 65 66 68 70 72 74 75 76 78 79 81 82 84 85 86 87 89 92 93
96 97 98 99 100 101 102 103 104 107 108 110 111 114 115 116 117 118
119 129 130 131 132 134 135 144 145 146 147 148 **P**6 **S** Blue Water Health
Services Corporation, Port Huron, MI
Primary Contact: Thomas D. DeFauw, FACHE, President and Chief Executive
Officer
COO: David S. McEwen, Vice President Operations
CFO: John Liston, Chief Financial Officer
CMO: Michael W. Tawney, D.O., Vice President Medical Affairs
CIO: Mark Richard, Chief Information Officer
CHR: Doris A. Seidl, Vice President Human Resources
CNO: Jennifer Montgomery, FACHE, Vice President, Nursing
Web address: www.porthuronhospital.org
Control: Other not–for–profit (including NFP Corporation) **Service:** General
Medical and Surgical

Staffed Beds: 186 **Admissions:** 10631 **Census:** 130 **Outpatient Visits:**
155832 **Births:** 1202 **Total Expense ($000):** 159140 **Payroll Expense
($000):** 66703 **Personnel:** 1215

Many Facility Codes have changed. Please refer to the AHA Guide Code Chart. © 2014 AHA Guide

✠ **ST. JOSEPH MERCY PORT HURON (230031)**, 2601 Electric Avenue, Zip 48060–6518; tel. 810/985–1500 **A**1 2 9 10 **F**3 11 12 15 18 20 29 30 31 34 35 37 40 45 49 50 54 56 57 58 59 61 62 63 64 66 70 74 75 77 78 79 81 82 83 85 86 87 90 91 93 96 97 107 108 110 114 118 119 120 121 123 126 130 131 132 135 146 147 148 **P**6 8 **S** Catholic Health East / Trinity Health, Livonia, MI
Primary Contact: Rebekah Smith, R.N., President and Chief Executive Officer
COO: Janet Herbert, Vice President Operations and Chief Nursing Officer
CFO: Chris Fulks, Vice President Finance
CMO: Robert Camara, M.D., Chief Medical Officer
CIO: Peggy Assessor, Director Information Services
CNO: Janet Herbert, Vice President Operations and Chief Nursing Officer
Web address: www.mymercy.us
Control: Church–operated, Nongovernment, not–for profit **Service:** General Medical and Surgical

Staffed Beds: 119 **Admissions:** 4223 **Census:** 54 **Outpatient Visits:** 123883 **Births:** 0 **Total Expense ($000):** 82322 **Payroll Expense ($000):** 31147 **Personnel:** 612	

REED CITY—Osceola County

✠ **SPECTRUM HEALTH REED CITY HOSPITAL (231323)**, 300 North Patterson Road, Zip 49677–8041, Mailing Address: P.O. Box 75, Zip 49677–0075; tel. 231/832–3271, (Total facility includes 50 beds in nursing home–type unit) **A**1 9 10 18 **F**3 15 29 30 31 34 35 40 45 50 53 54 57 59 64 65 70 75 77 78 79 81 84 85 86 87 93 97 107 108 110 111 114 118 119 120 121 123 124 127 128 129 130 131 133 146 147 **P**6 8 **S** Spectrum Health, Grand Rapids, MI
Primary Contact: Mary Kay VanDriel, President
COO: Cathy Rybicki, Chief Operating Officer
CFO: Thomas Knoerl, Vice President Finance
CMO: Thomas Campana, M.D., Chief of Staff
CIO: Brandi Johnson, Site Manager Technology Information Systems
CHR: Kris Miller, Senior Human Resources Business Partner
CNO: Scott Lombard, Acting Chief Nursing Officer
Web address: www.reedcity.spectrum–health.org
Control: Other not–for–profit (including NFP Corporation) **Service:** General Medical and Surgical

Staffed Beds: 75 **Admissions:** 940 **Census:** 59 **Outpatient Visits:** 375718 **Births:** 0 **Total Expense ($000):** 49318 **Payroll Expense ($000):** 17907 **Personnel:** 353	

ROCHESTER—Oakland County

☐ △ **CRITTENTON HOSPITAL MEDICAL CENTER (230254)**, 1101 West University Drive, Zip 48307–1831; tel. 248/652–5000, (Nonreporting) **A**1 3 5 7 9 10
Primary Contact: Roy A. Powell, President and Chief Executive Officer
COO: Gregory A. Partamian, Chief Operating Officer
CFO: Donna Kopinski, Chief Financial Officer
CMO: Frank Sottile, M.D., Chief Medical Officer
CIO: Tom Ventameglia, Director Information Systems
Web address: www.crittenton.com
Control: Other not–for–profit (including NFP Corporation) **Service:** General Medical and Surgical

Staffed Beds: 244	

ROGERS CITY—Presque Isle County

ROGERS CITY REHABILITATION HOSPITAL (233029), 555 North Bradley Highway, Suite C., Zip 49779–1539; tel. 989/734–7545, (Nonreporting) **A**9 10
Primary Contact: Joyal Pavey, Executive Director
CFO: Dylan Moore, Controller
CMO: Diana Hernandez Drozdowicz, M.D., Medical Director
Web address: www.rogerscityrehab.com
Control: Corporation, Investor–owned, for–profit **Service:** Rehabilitation

Staffed Beds: 15	

ROMEO—Macomb County

ST. JOSEPH'S MERCY–NORTH See Henry Ford Macomb Hospitals, Clinton Township

ROYAL OAK—Oakland County

✠ **BEAUMONT HOSPITAL – ROYAL OAK (230130)**, 3601 West Thirteen Mile Road, Zip 48073–6712; tel. 248/898–5000, (Includes BEAUMONT CHILDREN'S HOSPITAL, 3601 West 13 Mile Road, tel. 248/898–5000) **A**1 2 3 5 8 9 10 13 **F**3 5 6 11 12 13 14 15 17 18 19 20 22 24 26 28 29 30 31 32 34 35 36 37 38 39 40 41 43 44 45 46 47 48 49 50 51 52 53 54 55 56 57 58 59 60 61 62 63 64 65 66 68 70 71 72 74 75 76 77 78 79 80 81 82 83 84 85 86 87 88 89 90 91 92 93 94 95 96 97 98 99 100 101 102 103 104 105 107 108 109 110 111 114 115 116 117 118 119 120 121 123 124 126 129 130 131 132 134 135 138 139 141 142 143 144 145 146 147 148 **P**6 **S** Beaumont Health System, Royal Oak, MI
Primary Contact: Shane Cerone, President
COO: Gene Michalski, Executive Vice President and Chief Operating Officer
CFO: Nickolas A. Vitale, Executive Vice President and Chief Financial Officer
CMO: David Wood, M.D., Executive Vice President and Chief Medical Officer
CIO: Subra Sripada, Senior Vice President and Chief Information Officer
CHR: Jay T. Holden, Senior Vice President Chief Human Resources Officer
CNO: Maureen Bowman, Vice President of Nursing and Chief Nursing Officer
Web address: www.beaumont.edu/royal–oak–hospital–campus
Control: Other not–for–profit (including NFP Corporation) **Service:** General Medical and Surgical

Staffed Beds: 1070 **Admissions:** 56745 **Census:** 815 **Outpatient Visits:** 1257517 **Births:** 5186 **Total Expense ($000):** 1089505 **Payroll Expense ($000):** 372971 **Personnel:** 8166	

SAGINAW—Saginaw County

✠ **ALEDA E. LUTZ VETERANS AFFAIRS MEDICAL CENTER**, 1500 Weiss Street, Zip 48602–5298; tel. 989/497–2500, (Total facility includes 81 beds in nursing home–type unit) **A**1 9 **F**3 5 8 11 15 18 29 30 31 34 35 36 38 39 44 45 50 53 54 56 57 58 59 61 63 64 68 74 75 77 78 81 82 83 84 85 86 87 93 94 97 100 101 102 103 104 107 108 119 127 128 130 131 132 133 135 136 137 138 139 140 141 142 143 144 146 147 148 **P**6 **S** Department of Veterans Affairs, Washington, DC
Primary Contact: Peggy W. Kearns, MS, FACHE, Medical Center Director
COO: Stephanie Young, Associate Director
CFO: Jeff Drew, Fiscal Officer
CMO: Gregory Movsesian, M.D., Acting Chief of Staff
CIO: Angie Schmus, Chief Information Technology
CHR: Thomas Stredney, Chief Human Resources Management Service
CNO: Penny Holland, Associate Director for Patient Care Services
Web address: www.saginaw.va.gov/
Control: Veterans Affairs, Government, federal **Service:** General Medical and Surgical

Staffed Beds: 100 **Admissions:** 1344 **Census:** 54 **Outpatient Visits:** 343180 **Births:** 0 **Total Expense ($000):** 162051 **Payroll Expense ($000):** 70273 **Personnel:** 984	

★ ○ △ **COVENANT MEDICAL CENTER (230070)**, 1447 North Harrison Street, Zip 48602–4727; tel. 989/583–0000, (Includes COVENANT MEDICAL CENTER–COOPER, 700 Cooper Avenue, Zip 48602–5399; tel. 517/583–0000; COVENANT MEDICAL CENTER–HARRISON, 1447 North Harrison Street, Zip 48602–4785; tel. 517/583–0000), (Total facility includes 20 beds in nursing home–type unit) **A**2 3 5 7 9 10 11 **F**3 8 11 12 13 15 17 18 19 20 22 24 25 26 27 28 29 30 31 35 36 40 41 42 43 45 46 47 48 49 50 54 57 58 59 60 61 62 63 64 65 70 72 74 75 76 77 78 79 81 82 83 84 86 87 88 89 90 91 92 93 94 97 107 108 110 111 113 114 115 118 119 120 121 123 124 126 128 129 130 131 132 135 143 144 146 147 148 **P**7 8
Primary Contact: Spencer Maidlow, President and Chief Executive Officer
COO: Edward Bruff, Executive Vice President and Chief Operating Officer
CFO: Mark E. Gronda, Vice President and Chief Financial Officer
CMO: John Kosanovich, M.D., Vice President Covenant Healthcare and Chief Executive Officer Covenant Medical Group
CIO: Keith Grantham, Director Information Technology
CHR: Kevin Birchmeier, Director Human Resources
CNO: Carol Stoll, Vice President Patient Services and Chief Nursing Officer
Web address: www.covenanthealthcare.com
Control: Other not–for–profit (including NFP Corporation) **Service:** General Medical and Surgical

Staffed Beds: 532 **Admissions:** 26715 **Census:** 353 **Outpatient Visits:** 505030 **Births:** 3049 **Total Expense ($000):** 481425 **Payroll Expense ($000):** 210559 **Personnel:** 3840	

MI

Hospital, Medicare Provider Number, Address, Telephone, Approval, Facility, and Physician Codes, Health Care System	
★ American Hospital Association (AHA) membership	○ Healthcare Facilities Accreditation Program
☐ The Joint Commission accreditation ◇ DNV Healthcare Inc. accreditation	△ Commission on Accreditation of Rehabilitation Facilities (CARF) accreditation

☐ **HEALTHSOURCE SAGINAW (230275)**, 3340 Hospital Road, Zip 48603–9622, Mailing Address: P.O. Box 6280, Zip 48608–6280; tel. 989/790–7700, (Nonreporting) **A**1 9 10
Primary Contact: Lisa Lapham, Interim Chief Executive Officer
CFO: Lisa Lapham, Chief Financial Officer
CMO: Daniel Duffy, D.O., Chief Medical Director
CIO: Randall Sanborn, Director Information Technology
CNO: Susan Graham, R.N., Nurse Executive
Web address: www.healthsourcesaginaw.org
Control: Other not–for–profit (including NFP Corporation) **Service:** Psychiatric

Staffed Beds: 106

☒ **SELECT SPECIALTY HOSPITAL–SAGINAW (232033)**, 1447 North Harrison Street, 8th Floor, Zip 48602–4785; tel. 989/583–4235, (Nonreporting) **A**1 9 10 **S** Select Medical Corporation, Mechanicsburg, PA
Primary Contact: Matthew Cannon, Chief Executive Officer
Web address: www.selectspecialtyhospitals.com/company/locations/saginaw.aspx
Control: Corporation, Investor–owned, for–profit **Service:** Long–Term Acute Care hospital

Staffed Beds: 32

☒ **ST. MARY'S OF MICHIGAN (230077)**, 800 South Washington Avenue, Zip 48601–2594; tel. 989/907–8000 **A**1 2 3 5 9 10 **F**2 3 11 12 15 17 18 20 22 24 26 28 29 30 31 34 35 40 42 43 44 45 49 50 54 57 58 59 64 66 68 70 74 77 78 79 80 81 82 85 86 87 92 93 96 97 100 102 107 108 110 111 114 115 118 119 120 121 123 124 126 129 130 132 146 **P**6 8 **S** Ascension Health, Saint Louis, MO
Primary Contact: John R. Graham, President and Chief Executive Officer
CFO: Gina Butcher, Chief Financial Officer
CMO: Raghu Sarvepalli, M.D., Vice President of Medical Affairs
CIO: Alex Veletsos, Chief Information Officer
CHR: Paula Coffee, Director Human Resources
CNO: Bernie Jore, Chief Nursing Officer
Web address: www.stmarysofmichigan.org
Control: Church–operated, Nongovernment, not–for profit **Service:** General Medical and Surgical

Staffed Beds: 236 Admissions: 10711 **Census:** 153 **Outpatient Visits:** 165749 **Births:** 0 **Total Expense ($000):** 256879 **Payroll Expense ($000):** 100614 **Personnel:** 1680

SAINT IGNACE—Mackinac County

★ **MACKINAC STRAITS HEALTH SYSTEM (231306)**, 1140 North State Street, Zip 49781–1048; tel. 906/643–8585, (Total facility includes 48 beds in nursing home–type unit) **A**9 10 18 **F**15 18 28 29 31 32 40 42 43 53 54 56 59 60 64 65 77 78 91 93 97 104 107 110 111 114 119 127 128 130 132 133 144 146 147 **P**6
Primary Contact: Rodney M. Nelson, Chief Executive Officer
CFO: Jason Anderson, Chief Financial Officer
CMO: Carl Hawkins, M.D., Chief of Staff
CHR: Karen Cheeseman, Executive Vice President
CNO: Wendy Frush, R.N., Nursing Executive
Web address: www.mshosp.org
Control: Other not–for–profit (including NFP Corporation) **Service:** General Medical and Surgical

Staffed Beds: 63 Admissions: 307 **Census:** 49 **Outpatient Visits:** 31040 **Births:** 0 **Total Expense ($000):** 30706 **Payroll Expense ($000):** 10758 **Personnel:** 181

SAINT JOHNS—Clinton County

☒ **SPARROW CLINTON HOSPITAL (231326)**, 805 South Oakland Street, Zip 48879–2253; tel. 989/227–3400 **A**1 9 10 18 **F**3 8 11 15 18 19 31 32 34 35 40 45 50 53 57 59 64 68 70 75 77 78 79 81 85 93 107 108 110 111 114 119 129 130 131 133 145 146 148 **P**6 **S** Sparrow Health System, Lansing, MI
Primary Contact: Edward Bruun, President and Chief Executive Officer
COO: Kevin A. Price, Vice President and Chief Operating Officer
CFO: Mark Brisboe, VP and Chief Financial Officer
CMO: Christopher Beal, M.D., Chief of Staff
Web address: www.sparrowclinton.org
Control: Other not–for–profit (including NFP Corporation) **Service:** General Medical and Surgical

Staffed Beds: 25 Admissions: 671 **Census:** 5 **Outpatient Visits:** 56383 **Births:** 0 **Total Expense ($000):** 37497 **Payroll Expense ($000):** 14531 **Personnel:** 192

SAINT JOSEPH—Berrien County

☐ **LAKELAND REGIONAL MEDICAL CENTER–ST. JOSEPH (230021)**, 1234 Napier Avenue, Zip 49085–2158; tel. 269/983–8300, (Nonreporting) **A**1 2 9 10 13 **S** Lakeland Healthcare, Saint Joseph, MI
Primary Contact: Loren Hamel, M.D., President and Chief Executive Officer
CFO: Timothy Calhoun, Vice President Finance and Chief Financial Officer
CMO: Stephen Hempel, M.D., President Medical Staff
CIO: Emily Gallay, Vice President and Chief Information Officer
CHR: Gerard Guinane, Vice President Human Resources and Diversity Management
Web address: www.lakelandhealth.org
Control: Other not–for–profit (including NFP Corporation) **Service:** General Medical and Surgical

Staffed Beds: 250

SALINE—Washtenaw County

☐ **CENTER FOR FORENSIC PSYCHIATRY (234041)**, 8303 Platt Road, Zip 48176–9773, Mailing Address: P.O. Box 2060, Ann Arbor, Zip 48106–2060; tel. 734/429–2531, (Nonreporting) **A**1 10
Primary Contact: Carol E. Holden, M.D., Director
Web address: www.michigan.gov
Control: County–Government, nonfederal **Service:** Psychiatric

Staffed Beds: 210

SANDUSKY—Sanilac County

MCKENZIE HEALTH SYSTEM (231314), 120 North Delaware Street, Zip 48471–1087; tel. 810/648–3770, (Nonreporting) **A**9 10 18
Primary Contact: Steve Barnett, MS, President and Chief Executive Officer
COO: Janet Herbert, R.N., Chief Operating Officer
CFO: Amy Ruedisueli, Chief Financial Officer
CMO: Mark E. English, M.D., Chief of Staff
CHR: Carrie Krampits, Director Human Resources
CNO: Tammy Cliff, R.N., Director Nursing Services
Web address: www.mckenziehealth.org
Control: Other not–for–profit (including NFP Corporation) **Service:** General Medical and Surgical

Staffed Beds: 25

SAULT SAINTE MARIE—Chippewa County

★ ◇ **WAR MEMORIAL HOSPITAL (230239)**, 500 Osborn Boulevard, Zip 49783–1884; tel. 906/635–4460, (Total facility includes 51 beds in nursing home–type unit) **A**9 10 20 21 **F**3 11 12 13 15 18 28 29 30 31 34 35 36 38 40 43 44 45 50 53 54 56 57 59 60 61 64 65 66 68 70 74 75 76 77 79 81 82 85 87 92 93 96 97 98 100 101 103 104 107 108 110 111 115 119 127 128 129 130 131 132 133 135 143 144 146 147 148
Primary Contact: David B. Jahn, President and Chief Executive Officer
COO: Marla Bunker, Vice President Nursing and Chief Operating Officer
CFO: Kevin Kalchik, Chief Financial Officer
CMO: Ted Ludwig, Chief Medical Officer
CIO: Steve Pietrangelo, Director Information Services
CHR: Susan Sliger, Director Human Resources
CNO: Sue Tetzlaff, Vice President of Nursing
Web address: www.warmemorialhospital.org
Control: Other not–for–profit (including NFP Corporation) **Service:** General Medical and Surgical

Staffed Beds: 133 Admissions: 3294 **Census:** 87 **Outpatient Visits:** 145045 **Births:** 339 **Total Expense ($000):** 91603 **Payroll Expense ($000):** 38222 **Personnel:** 781

SHELBY—Oceana County

☒ **MERCY HEALTH PARTNERS, LAKESHORE CAMPUS (231320)**, 72 South State Street, Zip 49455–1299; tel. 231/861–2156 **A**1 9 10 18 **F**3 11 15 29 30 34 35 40 57 59 68 81 85 87 89 97 107 111 115 119 127 129 132 146 **S** Catholic Health East / Trinity Health, Livonia, MI
Primary Contact: Jay Bryan, President and Chief Executive Officer
CFO: Mark Gross, Senior Business Director Finance
Web address: www.mercyhealthmuskegon.com
Control: Other not–for–profit (including NFP Corporation) **Service:** General Medical and Surgical

Staffed Beds: 24 Admissions: 340 **Census:** 3 **Outpatient Visits:** 21795 **Births:** 0 **Total Expense ($000):** 20833 **Payroll Expense ($000):** 10240 **Personnel:** 200

MI

SHERIDAN—Montcalm County

★ **SHERIDAN COMMUNITY HOSPITAL (231312)**, 301 North Main Street, Zip 48884-9235, Mailing Address: P.O. Box 279, Zip 48884-0279; tel. 989/291-3261 **A**9 10 18 **F**3 15 18 34 40 45 54 57 59 64 77 81 85 93 97 107 114 119 127 129 132 133 146
Primary Contact: Randolph K. Flechsig, Administrator
COO: Steve Scott, Chief Operating Officer
CFO: Randolph K. Flechsig, Administrator
CMO: Maria Charlotte Alvarez, M.D., Chief of Staff
CIO: David Bussler, Chief Information Officer
CHR: Sharon Bowers, R.N., Manager of Community, Public and Employee Relations
CNO: Elizabeth Edwards, R.N., Director, Nursing Services
Web address: www.sheridanhospital.com
Control: Other not-for-profit (including NFP Corporation) **Service:** General Medical and Surgical

Staffed Beds: 22 **Admissions:** 302 **Census:** 3 **Outpatient Visits:** 26773 **Births:** 0 **Total Expense ($000):** 14994 **Payroll Expense ($000):** 7630 **Personnel:** 217

SOUTH HAVEN—Van Buren County

SOUTH HAVEN COMMUNITY HOSPITAL See South Haven Health System

✠ **SOUTH HAVEN HEALTH SYSTEM (230085)**, 955 South Bailey Avenue, Zip 49090-6743; tel. 269/637-5271 **A**1 9 10 **F**3 11 13 15 28 29 30 31 34 35 36 40 41 46 50 53 54 57 59 62 64 65 68 75 76 77 78 79 81 82 85 87 89 91 93 96 97 107 108 110 114 115 119 127 129 130 131 132 135 146 147 **P**4
Primary Contact: Joanne Urbanski, President and Chief Executive Officer
CFO: Mark Gross, Executive Vice President and Chief Financial Officer
CMO: Allan Caudill, M.D., Chief of Staff
CIO: Dennis Sorenson, Supervisor Information Technology
CHR: Kim Wise, Director Human Resources
Web address: www.sh-hs.org
Control: Hospital district or authority, Government, nonfederal **Service:** General Medical and Surgical

Staffed Beds: 82 **Admissions:** 1217 **Census:** 9 **Outpatient Visits:** 123372 **Births:** 402 **Total Expense ($000):** 42001 **Payroll Expense ($000):** 19956 **Personnel:** 310

SOUTHFIELD—Oakland County

★ ◇ **OAKLAND REGIONAL HOSPITAL (230301)**, 22401 Foster Winter Drive, Zip 48075-3724; tel. 248/423-5100, (Total facility includes 26 beds in nursing home-type unit) **A**9 10 11 **F**45 79 81 82 85 90 93 111 115 119 128 130
Primary Contact: Daniel R. Babb, Chief Executive Officer
COO: Amelia Jones, Chief Operating Officer
CMO: Robert Barbosa, D.O., Chief Medical Officer
CIO: William Moncrief, ORH IT Client Executive
CHR: Gordon Meyer, Director Human Resources
Web address: www.oaklandregionalhospital.com
Control: Corporation, Investor-owned, for-profit **Service:** General Medical and Surgical

Staffed Beds: 71 **Admissions:** 1073 **Census:** 28 **Outpatient Visits:** 12304 **Births:** 0 **Total Expense ($000):** 28956 **Payroll Expense ($000):** 7340 **Personnel:** 130

✠ **PROVIDENCE HOSPITAL (230019)**, 16001 West Nine Mile Road, Zip 48075-4818, Mailing Address: P.O. Box 2043, Zip 48037-2043; tel. 248/424-3000, (Includes PROVIDENCE PARK HOSPITAL, 47601 Grand River Avebue, Novi, Zip 48374-1233; tel. 248/465-4100; Peter Karadjoff, President) **A**1 2 3 5 9 10 **F**3 5 8 9 11 12 13 15 17 18 20 22 24 26 28 29 30 31 34 35 36 38 39 40 44 45 46 47 48 49 50 51 54 55 56 57 58 59 60 61 63 64 65 66 68 70 72 74 75 76 77 78 79 80 81 82 84 85 86 87 89 90 92 93 97 98 99 100 101 102 103 104 105 107 108 110 111 114 115 116 117 118 119 120 121 123 124 126 129 130 131 132 135 141 143 146 147 148
S Ascension Health, Saint Louis, MO
Primary Contact: Michael Wiemann, M.D., President
CFO: Douglas Winner, Chief Financial Officer
CHR: Sue Gronbach, Director Human Resources
Web address: www.providence-stjohnhealth.org
Control: Church-operated, Nongovernment, not-for profit **Service:** General Medical and Surgical

Staffed Beds: 626 **Admissions:** 33999 **Census:** 414 **Outpatient Visits:** 314333 **Births:** 4067 **Total Expense ($000):** 610601 **Payroll Expense ($000):** 237019 **Personnel:** 3559

STRAITH HOSPITAL FOR SPECIAL SURGERY (230071)

✠ **STRAITH HOSPITAL FOR SPECIAL SURGERY (230071)**, 23901 Lahser Road, Zip 48033-6035; tel. 248/357-3360 **A**1 9 10 **F**29 64 65 81 91 130 141 148 **P**5
Primary Contact: H. Roger Jones, Chief Executive Officer
CFO: Bradley Bescoe, Chief Financial Officer
Web address: www.straith.org/
Control: Other not-for-profit (including NFP Corporation) **Service:** General Medical and Surgical

Staffed Beds: 24 **Admissions:** 670 **Census:** 15 **Outpatient Visits:** 1326 **Births:** 0 **Total Expense ($000):** 10654 **Payroll Expense ($000):** 4366 **Personnel:** 98

STANDISH—Arenac County

✠ **ST. MARY'S OF MICHIGAN STANDISH HOSPITAL (231305)**, 805 West Cedar Street, Zip 48658-9526; tel. 989/846-4521, (Nonreporting) **A**1 9 10 18 **S** Ascension Health, Saint Louis, MO
Primary Contact: John R. Graham, President and Chief Executive Officer
CFO: Tony Doud, Controller
CMO: Jaya Sankaran, M.D., Chief of Staff
CIO: Tammy Copes, Director Information Systems
CHR: Renee Reetz, Director Human Resources
Web address: www.stmarysofmichigan.org/standish
Control: Other not-for-profit (including NFP Corporation) **Service:** General Medical and Surgical

Staffed Beds: 68

STURGIS—St. Joseph County

★ ◇ **STURGIS HOSPITAL (230096)**, 916 Myrtle Street, Zip 49091-2326; tel. 269/651-7824 **A**9 10 21 **F**3 11 13 15 28 29 30 31 34 35 40 45 46 49 50 57 59 62 63 64 65 68 70 75 76 77 78 79 81 82 85 87 89 93 97 102 107 108 110 115 118 119 127 129 130 132 144 146 147 148 **P**6 **S** QHR, Brentwood, TN
Primary Contact: Robert J. LaBarge, Chief Executive Officer
CFO: David Miller, Chief Financial Officer
CMO: Ashish Verma, M.D., President Medical Staff
CIO: Rita Denison, Manager Information Systems
CHR: Mary Kay Schultz, Director Human Resources
CNO: Charlotte J. Pavilanis, R.N., Director of Patient Care Services
Web address: www.sturgishospital.com
Control: Other not-for-profit (including NFP Corporation) **Service:** General Medical and Surgical

Staffed Beds: 49 **Admissions:** 1638 **Census:** 13 **Outpatient Visits:** 90494 **Births:** 422 **Total Expense ($000):** 44164 **Payroll Expense ($000):** 20366 **Personnel:** 266

TAWAS CITY—Iosco County

✠ **ST. JOSEPH HEALTH SYSTEM (230100)**, 200 Hemlock Street, Zip 48763-9237, Mailing Address: P.O. Box 659, Zip 48764-0659; tel. 989/362-3411, (Nonreporting) **A**1 9 10 20 **S** Ascension Health, Saint Louis, MO
Primary Contact: Ann M. Balfour, R.N., President
CFO: Linda Stancill, Vice President and Chief Financial Officer
CHR: Nancy Bodenner, Director Human Resources
Web address: www.sjhsys.org
Control: Other not-for-profit (including NFP Corporation) **Service:** General Medical and Surgical

Staffed Beds: 20

TAYLOR—Wayne County

✠ **OAKWOOD HOSPITAL-TAYLOR (230270)**, 10000 Telegraph Road, Zip 48180-3330; tel. 313/295-5000 **A**1 3 5 9 10 **F**3 11 15 29 30 34 37 38 39 40 44 46 49 50 56 57 59 60 61 64 65 68 70 74 75 78 79 81 82 84 85 86 87 90 92 93 96 98 100 101 102 103 105 107 108 111 114 118 119 128 130 131 132 135 146 148 **P**8 **S** Oakwood Healthcare, Inc., Dearborn, MI
Primary Contact: Lee Ann Odom, Division President
CFO: Mark Deming, Controller
CMO: Vijay Khanna, M.D., Chief of Staff
CIO: Paula Smith, Chief Information Officer
CHR: Sherry Huffman, Administrator Human Resources
Web address: www.oakwood.org
Control: Other not-for-profit (including NFP Corporation) **Service:** General Medical and Surgical

Staffed Beds: 133 **Admissions:** 7675 **Census:** 130 **Outpatient Visits:** 65316 **Births:** 0 **Total Expense ($000):** 127348 **Payroll Expense ($000):** 51740 **Personnel:** 783

MI

TECUMSEH—Lenawee County

★ **PROMEDICA HERRICK HOSPITAL (231334)**, 500 East Pottawatamie Street, Zip 49286–2018; tel. 517/424–3000, (Total facility includes 25 beds in nursing home–type unit) **A**9 10 18 **F**3 11 15 18 30 34 38 40 43 45 46 47 53 57 59 64 68 70 74 75 77 79 81 85 91 92 93 98 100 101 102 104 107 108 110 114 119 124 128 129 130 132 135 145 146 147 **P**6 8 **S** ProMedica Health System, Toledo, OH
Primary Contact: Timothy Jakacki, President
CFO: Bernie Nawrocki, Administrative Director Finance
CMO: Julie Yaroch, D.O., Vice President Medical Affairs
CIO: Stephanie Sonnenberg, Director Information Technology
CHR: Cathy J. Davis, Director Human Resources
CNO: Kathryn M. Greenlee, R.N., Vice President, Clinical Services/CNO
Web address: www.promedica.org
Control: Other not–for–profit (including NFP Corporation) **Service:** General Medical and Surgical

Staffed Beds: 60 **Admissions:** 1572 **Census:** 37 **Outpatient Visits:** 44531 **Births:** 0 **Total Expense ($000):** 37604 **Payroll Expense ($000):** 12113 **Personnel:** 173

THREE RIVERS—St. Joseph County

★ ○ △ **THREE RIVERS HEALTH (230015)**, 701 South Health Parkway, Zip 49093–8352; tel. 269/278–1145, (Nonreporting) **A**7 9 10 11 **S** QHR, Brentwood, TN
Primary Contact: William B. Russell, Chief Executive Officer
COO: Laurie Herbert, Vice President Operations
CFO: Steve Andrews, Chief Financial Officer
CIO: Dave Parks, Chief Information Officer
Web address: www.threerivershealth.org
Control: Hospital district or authority, Government, nonfederal **Service:** General Medical and Surgical

Staffed Beds: 35

TRAVERSE CITY—Grand Traverse County

⊞ **MUNSON MEDICAL CENTER (230097)**, 1105 Sixth Street, Zip 49684–2386; tel. 231/935–5000 **A**1 2 3 5 9 10 12 13 19 20 **F**3 4 5 6 11 12 13 15 17 18 20 22 24 26 28 29 30 31 32 34 35 36 38 39 40 43 44 45 46 48 49 50 53 54 55 56 57 58 59 60 61 62 63 64 65 68 70 71 72 74 75 76 77 78 79 81 82 84 85 86 87 89 90 92 93 94 96 97 98 100 101 102 103 104 105 107 108 110 111 114 115 116 117 118 119 120 121 123 124 126 129 130 131 132 134 135 141 142 143 144 145 146 147 148 **P**6 **S** Munson Healthcare, Traverse City, MI
Primary Contact: Alfred E. Pilong, President
COO: Derk Pronger, Chief Operating Officer
CFO: Mark A. Helper, Vice President, Chief Financial Officer
CMO: David S. McGreaham, M.D., Vice President Medical Affairs
CIO: Christopher J. Podges, Vice President and Chief Information Officer
CHR: Sue Peters, Vice President Human Resources
CNO: James Fischer, R.N., Vice President Patient Care Services/Chief Nursing Officer
Web address: www.munsonhealthcare.org
Control: Other not–for–profit (including NFP Corporation) **Service:** General Medical and Surgical

Staffed Beds: 391 **Admissions:** 22386 **Census:** 295 **Outpatient Visits:** 493624 **Births:** 1812 **Total Expense ($000):** 482774 **Payroll Expense ($000):** 191007 **Personnel:** 2935

TRENTON—Wayne County

⊞ ○ **OAKWOOD HOSPITAL–SOUTHSHORE (230176)**, 5450 Fort Street, Zip 48183–4625; tel. 734/671–3800 **A**1 9 10 11 12 13 **F**3 8 11 13 15 17 18 20 22 26 28 29 30 31 34 35 38 39 40 43 44 46 47 49 50 56 57 59 60 61 64 65 68 70 74 75 76 78 79 80 81 82 85 86 87 92 93 96 100 102 107 108 110 111 115 118 119 130 131 132 135 146 147 148 **P**8 **S** Oakwood Healthcare, Inc., Dearborn, MI
Primary Contact: Edith M. Hughes, R.N., President
COO: David J. Campbell, Executive Vice President Operations Systems Strategy and Growth
CFO: Paul Lauzau, Controller
CMO: Iqbal Nasir, M.D., Chief of Staff
CIO: Paula Smith, Vice President Information Services and Chief Information Officer
CHR: Juliet Hafford, Director Human Resources
Web address: www.oakwood.org
Control: Other not–for–profit (including NFP Corporation) **Service:** General Medical and Surgical

Staffed Beds: 173 **Admissions:** 8660 **Census:** 92 **Outpatient Visits:** 63800 **Births:** 657 **Total Expense ($000):** 139498 **Payroll Expense ($000):** 49803 **Personnel:** 689

TROY—Oakland County

⊞ **BEAUMONT HOSPITAL – TROY (230269)**, 44201 Dequindre Road, Zip 48085–1117; tel. 248/964–5000 **A**1 3 5 9 10 **F**3 11 12 13 14 15 17 18 20 22 24 26 28 29 30 31 32 34 35 36 39 40 44 45 46 47 48 49 50 51 53 54 55 56 57 58 59 60 61 62 63 64 65 66 68 70 71 72 74 75 76 77 78 79 80 81 82 84 85 86 87 89 90 91 92 93 94 96 97 100 102 103 107 108 109 110 111 114 115 117 118 119 120 121 123 126 129 130 131 132 135 141 142 143 145 146 147 148 **P**6 **S** Beaumont Health System, Royal Oak, MI
Primary Contact: Nancy Susick, MSN, President
CFO: Mark Leonard, Vice President Finance
CMO: Roger Howard, M.D., Senior Vice President and Medical Director
CIO: Subra Sripada, Senior Vice President and Chief Information Officer
CHR: Lisa Ouelette, Director Human Resources
Web address: www.beaumont.edu/troy–hospital–campus
Control: Other not–for–profit (including NFP Corporation) **Service:** General Medical and Surgical

Staffed Beds: 458 **Admissions:** 30756 **Census:** 333 **Outpatient Visits:** 868377 **Births:** 3490 **Total Expense ($000):** 505224 **Payroll Expense ($000):** 214020 **Personnel:** 3121

VICKSBURG—Kalamazoo County

BRONSON VICKSBURG HOSPITAL See Bronson Methodist Hospital, Kalamazoo

WARREN—Macomb County

☐ **BEHAVIORAL CENTER OF MICHIGAN (234042)**, 4050 East 12 Mile Road, Zip 48092–2534; tel. 586/261–2266 **A**1 9 10 **F**4 5 29 38 62 64 65 66 75 82 87 98 102 103 104 105 130 132 **P**6 7
Primary Contact: Ryan Gunabalan, Chief Executive Officer
COO: Efren Lusterio, Director of Nursing
CFO: Mark Corey, Chief Financial Officer
CMO: Eleanor Medina, M.D., Chief Medical Officer
CIO: Kashmira Khade, Coordinator Non–Clinical Services
CHR: Erin R. Youngblood, Chief Human Resources Officer
Web address: www.behavioralcenter.com
Control: Corporation, Investor–owned, for–profit **Service:** Psychiatric

Staffed Beds: 42 **Admissions:** 1121 **Census:** 32 **Outpatient Visits:** 308 **Births:** 0

☐ **SOUTHEAST MICHIGAN SURGICAL HOSPITAL (230264)**, 21230 Dequindre, Zip 48091–2287; tel. 586/427–1000, (Nonreporting) **A**1 9 10 **S** National Surgical Hospitals, Chicago, IL
Primary Contact: Yvonne Kughn, Chief Executive Officer
CMO: Benjamin Paolucci, D.O., Chief of Staff
CHR: Dawn Meiers, Coordinator Medical Staff and Personnel Services
Web address: www.nshinc.com
Control: Corporation, Investor–owned, for–profit **Service:** Surgical

Staffed Beds: 13

⊞ **ST. JOHN MACOMB–OAKLAND HOSPITAL (230195)**, 11800 East 12 Mile Road, Zip 48093–3472; tel. 586/573–5000, (Includes ST. JOHN MACOMB–OAKLAND HOSPITAL, MACOMB CENTER, 11800 East Twelve Mile Road, tel. 586/573–5000; ST. JOHN MACOMB–OAKLAND HOSPITAL, OAKLAND CENTER, 27351 Dequindre, Madison Heights, Zip 48071–3487; tel. 248/967–7000) **A**1 9 10 12 13 **F**3 11 12 13 15 17 18 20 22 24 26 28 29 30 31 34 35 36 38 39 40 44 46 49 50 51 56 57 58 59 60 61 63 64 65 68 70 74 75 76 77 78 79 80 81 82 84 85 86 87 90 91 92 93 95 96 97 98 100 101 102 103 105 107 108 110 111 114 115 116 117 118 119 121 123 126 129 130 131 135 141 143 146 147 148 **P**3 6 7 8 **S** Ascension Health, Saint Louis, MO
Primary Contact: Terry Hamilton, President
CFO: Tomasine Marx, Chief Financial Officer
CMO: Gary L. Berg, D.O., Chief Medical Officer
CIO: Mary Kay LaChance, Director Information Systems
CHR: Joanne E. Tuscany, Director Worklife Services
CNO: Constance O'Malley, Chief Nursing Officer
Web address: www.stjohnprovidence.org/macomb
Control: Church–operated, Nongovernment, not–for profit **Service:** General Medical and Surgical

Staffed Beds: 524 **Admissions:** 27315 **Census:** 373 **Outpatient Visits:** 443582 **Births:** 1160 **Total Expense ($000):** 375870 **Payroll Expense ($000):** 155310 **Personnel:** 2545

WATERVLIET—Berrien County

COMMUNITY HOSPITAL See Lakeland Community Hospital Watervliet
☐ △ **LAKELAND COMMUNITY HOSPITAL WATERVLIET (230078)**, 400 Medical Park Drive, Zip 49098–9225; tel. 269/463–3111 **A**1 7 9 10 **F**3 11 15 29 30 34 35 38 40 45 50 54 57 59 64 68 75 77 79 81 85 86 87 90 93 97 107 119 127 130 131 132 135 144 146 **S** Lakeland Healthcare, Saint Joseph, MI
Primary Contact: Ray Cruse, Chief Executive Officer
CFO: Chris Kuhlmann, Chief Financial Officer
CHR: Heather West, Director Human Resources
Control: Other not–for–profit (including NFP Corporation) **Service:** General Medical and Surgical

Staffed Beds: 38 **Admissions:** 763 **Census:** 10 **Outpatient Visits:** 48296 **Births:** 0 **Total Expense ($000):** 26477 **Payroll Expense ($000):** 12114 **Personnel:** 235

MI

WAYNE—Wayne County

☒ **OAKWOOD HOSPITAL–WAYNE (230142)**, 33155 Annapolis Street, Zip 48184–2405; tel. 734/467–4000 **A**1 9 10 13 **F**3 11 13 15 18 20 22 26 28 29 30 31 34 35 38 40 43 44 47 49 50 57 59 60 61 64 65 68 70 74 75 76 78 79 80 81 82 84 85 86 87 92 93 96 100 102 107 108 111 114 115 118 119 130 131 132 135 146 147 148 **P**8 **S** Oakwood Healthcare, Inc., Dearborn, MI
Primary Contact: Eric W. Widner, Division President
CFO: Jay Bonnell, Controller
CMO: Ashok Jain, M.D., Chief of Staff
CIO: Paula Smith, Senior Vice President Chief Information Officer
CHR: Robert L. James, Director Human Resources
CNO: Diane L. Hartley, R.N., Director of Patient Care Services
Web address: www.oakwood.org
Control: Other not–for–profit (including NFP Corporation) **Service:** General Medical and Surgical

Staffed Beds: 204 **Admissions:** 8128 **Census:** 87 **Outpatient Visits:** 87968 **Births:** 982 **Total Expense ($000):** 132420 **Payroll Expense ($000):** 55582 **Personnel:** 815

WEST BLOOMFIELD—Oakland County

★ ◇ **HENRY FORD WEST BLOOMFIELD HOSPITAL (230302)**, 6777 West Maple Road, Zip 48322–3013; tel. 248/661–4100 **A**9 10 21 **F**3 11 12 13 15 18 20 26 28 29 30 31 32 33 34 35 36 38 40 44 45 46 47 49 50 51 53 55 56 57 58 59 60 61 64 65 67 68 70 74 75 76 77 78 79 81 82 84 85 86 87 89 93 97 100 102 103 107 108 110 111 114 115 116 117 118 119 120 123 124 126 130 131 132 135 143 146 147 148 **P**6 **S** Henry Ford Health System, Detroit, MI
Primary Contact: Lynn M. Torossian, President and Chief Executive Officer
COO: Christine Zambrini, Chief Operating Officer and Chief Nursing Officer
Web address: www.henryford.com
Control: Other not–for–profit (including NFP Corporation) **Service:** General Medical and Surgical

Staffed Beds: 191 **Admissions:** 12957 **Census:** 141 **Outpatient Visits:** 492925 **Births:** 1979 **Total Expense ($000):** 254479 **Payroll Expense ($000):** 95429 **Personnel:** 1465

WEST BRANCH—Ogemaw County

★ ◯ **WEST BRANCH REGIONAL MEDICAL CENTER (230095)**, 2463 South M–30, Zip 48661–1199; tel. 989/345–3660 **A**9 10 11 20 **F**3 11 15 17 20 28 29 30 34 35 40 50 57 59 63 64 75 77 79 81 84 93 107 111 114 115 117 119 130 146 148 **P**6
Primary Contact: Edward A. Napierala, FACHE, Chief Executive Officer
CFO: Robert McGrail, Chief Financial Officer
CMO: Patrick Morse, M.D., President Medical Staff
CHR: Kent Allen, Director Human Resources
CNO: Lanette Lumbardo, MS, Chief Nursing Officer
Web address: www.wbrmc.com
Control: City–Government, nonfederal **Service:** General Medical and Surgical

Staffed Beds: 88 **Admissions:** 2041 **Census:** 24 **Outpatient Visits:** 72373 **Births:** 0 **Total Expense ($000):** 39644 **Payroll Expense ($000):** 13343 **Personnel:** 304

WESTLAND—Wayne County

☐ **WALTER P. REUTHER PSYCHIATRIC HOSPITAL (234035)**, 30901 Palmer Road, Zip 48186–5389; tel. 734/367–8400, (Nonreporting) **A**1 9 10
Primary Contact: Richard T. Young, FACHE, Director
CMO: H. Bandla, M.D., Chief Clinical Affairs
CHR: Deborah Moore, Director Human Resources
CNO: E. McDade, R.N.
Web address: www.mhweb.org/wayne/reuther.htm
Control: State–Government, nonfederal **Service:** Psychiatric

Staffed Beds: 239

WYANDOTTE—Wayne County

★ △ ◇ **HENRY FORD WYANDOTTE HOSPITAL (230146)**, 2333 Biddle Avenue, Zip 48192–4668; tel. 734/246–6000 **A**7 9 10 12 13 21 **F**3 8 11 12 13 15 17 18 20 22 26 28 29 30 31 32 34 35 36 38 40 42 44 45 46 47 49 50 51 54 56 57 58 59 60 61 64 65 66 68 69 70 74 75 76 77 78 79 80 81 82 84 85 86 87 90 92 93 94 96 98 100 101 102 103 107 108 110 111 114 115 116 117 118 119 126 129 130 131 132 135 146 147 148 **P**6 **S** Henry Ford Health System, Detroit, MI
Primary Contact: Denise Brooks–Williams, President and Chief Executive Officer
COO: Rand O'Leary, Senior Vice President and Chief Operating Officer
CFO: Terry Goodbalian, Vice President, Finance and Chief Financial Officer
CMO: Dennis R. Lemanski, D.O., Senior Vice President Medical Affairs and Medical Education/CMO
CIO: Mary Alice Annecharico, Senior VP and CIO, Henry Ford Health System
CNO: Josephine Sclafani Wahl, R.N., VP, Patient Care Services & CNO
Web address: www.henryfordhealth.org
Control: Other not–for–profit (including NFP Corporation) **Service:** General Medical and Surgical

Staffed Beds: 355 **Admissions:** 19061 **Census:** 243 **Outpatient Visits:** 350472 **Births:** 1600 **Total Expense ($000):** 273171 **Payroll Expense ($000):** 115592 **Personnel:** 1872

☒ **SELECT SPECIALTY HOSPITAL–DOWNRIVER (232031)**, 2333 Biddle Avenue, 8th Floor, Zip 48192–4668; tel. 734/246–5500, (Nonreporting) **A**1 9 10 **S** Select Medical Corporation, Mechanicsburg, PA
Primary Contact: Miriam Deemer, Interim Chief Executive Officer
CMO: Roderick Boyer, M.D., Medical Director
CHR: Barb Wierzbicki, Manager Human Resources
Web address: www.downriver.selectspecialtyhospitals.com/
Control: Corporation, Investor–owned, for–profit **Service:** Long–Term Acute Care hospital

Staffed Beds: 40

WYOMING—Kent County

★ ◯ **METRO HEALTH HOSPITAL (230236)**, 5900 Byron Center Avenue S.W., Zip 49519–9606, Mailing Address: P.O. Box 916, Zip 49509–0916; tel. 616/252–7200 **A**9 10 11 12 13 **F**3 12 13 15 18 20 22 26 29 30 31 34 35 40 44 45 48 49 50 54 57 58 59 64 65 66 70 71 74 75 76 77 78 79 80 81 82 85 86 87 92 94 97 107 108 110 111 114 115 119 126 129 130 131 132 135 146 147 148 **P**8
Primary Contact: Michael D. Faas, President and Chief Executive Officer
COO: Svetlana Dembitskaya, Chief Operating Officer
CFO: Tim Susterich, Chief Financial Officer
CMO: David Duffey, D.O., Chief Medical Officer
CIO: William Lewkowski, Executive Vice President Information Services and Chief Information Officer
CHR: Erika Duncan, Vice President Human Resources
CNO: Ingrid Cheslek, R.N., Chief Nursing Officer
Web address: www.metrohealth.net
Control: Other not–for–profit (including NFP Corporation) **Service:** General Medical and Surgical

Staffed Beds: 208 **Admissions:** 9653 **Census:** 138 **Outpatient Visits:** 422068 **Births:** 1936 **Total Expense ($000):** 265034 **Payroll Expense ($000):** 93402 **Personnel:** 1652

YPSILANTI—Washtenaw County

☐ **FOREST HEALTH MEDICAL CENTER (230144)**, 135 South Prospect Street, Zip 48198–7914; tel. 734/547–4700 **A**1 9 10 **F**12 30 46 64 74 75 79 81 82 85 111 119 130 132
Primary Contact: Trevor J. Dyksterhouse, President
COO: Andrea Walrath, Chief Operating Officer
CFO: David Althoen, Director Financial Planning and Analysis
CMO: Steven Poplawski, M.D., Medical Director
CIO: Andrea Walrath, Chief Operating Officer
CHR: Amy Mohr, Coordinator Human Resources
Web address: www.barixclinics.com
Control: Corporation, Investor–owned, for–profit **Service:** General Medical and Surgical

Staffed Beds: 24 **Admissions:** 913 **Census:** 6 **Outpatient Visits:** 9674 **Births:** 0 **Personnel:** 51

MI

Hospital, Medicare Provider Number, Address, Telephone, Approval, Facility, and Physician Codes, Health Care System

★ American Hospital Association (AHA) membership
☐ The Joint Commission accreditation ◇ DNV Healthcare Inc. accreditation
◯ Healthcare Facilities Accreditation Program
△ Commission on Accreditation of Rehabilitation Facilities (CARF) accreditation

---

✠ **SELECT SPECIALTY HOSPITAL–ANN ARBOR (232024)**, 5301 East Huron River Drive, 7th Floor, Zip 48197–1051; tel. 734/712–0111, (Nonreporting) **A**1 9 10 **S** Select Medical Corporation, Mechanicsburg, PA
Primary Contact: John F. O'Malley, FACHE, Chief Executive Officer
CMO: Hamid Halimi, M.D., Medical Director
CHR: Leah Warshaw, Coordinator Human Resources
CNO: Tim Varney, R.N., Chief Nursing Officer
Web address: www.selectspecialtyhospitals.com/company/locations/annarbor.aspx
Control: Corporation, Investor–owned, for–profit **Service:** Long–Term Acute Care hospital

Staffed Beds: 36

✠ **ST. JOSEPH MERCY HOSPITAL ANN ARBOR (230156)**, 5301 Mcauley Drive, Zip 48197–1051, Mailing Address: P.O. Box 995, Ann Arbor, Zip 48106–0995; tel. 734/712–3456 **A**1 3 5 8 10 **F**3 4 5 6 8 9 11 12 13 15 17 18 19 20 22 24 26 28 29 30 31 32 34 35 36 37 38 40 41 42 43 44 45 46 50 51 53 54 56 57 58 59 61 62 63 64 65 66 67 68 70 71 72 73 74 75 76 77 78 79 80 81 82 83 84 85 86 87 89 90 91 92 93 94 97 98 99 100 101 102 103 104 105 107 108 109 110 111 114 115 117 118 119 120 121 123 124 125 126 128 129 130 131 132 134 135 141 143 144 145 146 147 **P**5 6 **S** Catholic Health East / Trinity Health, Livonia, MI
Primary Contact: Robert F. Casalou, President and Chief Executive Officer
COO: Robin Damschroder, Chief Operating Officer
CFO: Kathy O'Connor, Vice President Finance
CIO: Frank Rademacher, Senior Director Information Systems
CNO: Joyce Young, R.N., Chief Nursing Officer
Web address: www.sjmercyhealth.org
Control: Church–operated, Nongovernment, not–for profit **Service:** General Medical and Surgical

Staffed Beds: 537 **Admissions:** 31857 **Census:** 405 **Outpatient Visits:** 1111197 **Births:** 3486 **Total Expense ($000):** 737452 **Payroll Expense ($000):** 272856 **Personnel:** 5617

ZEELAND—Ottawa County

✠ **SPECTRUM HEALTH ZEELAND COMMUNITY HOSPITAL (230003)**, 8333 Felch Street, Zip 49464–2608; tel. 616/772–4644 **A**1 9 10 **F**3 12 13 15 18 29 32 34 35 39 40 45 50 56 57 59 64 65 68 69 70 74 75 76 78 79 81 85 87 89 92 97 107 108 110 111 119 129 130 132 135 144 146 **S** Spectrum Health, Grand Rapids, MI
Primary Contact: Henry A. Veenstra, President
CFO: Ryan J. Powers, Vice President Finance
CMO: Ruel R. Lirio, M.D., Clinical Physician Advisor
CIO: Imran Syed, Manager Technology Information Services
CHR: Jennifer F. Becksvoort, Senior Human Resource Business Partner
CNO: Jane Czerew, Vice President Clinical Services and Quality
Web address: www.spectrumhealth.org/zeeland
Control: Other not–for–profit (including NFP Corporation) **Service:** General Medical and Surgical

Staffed Beds: 50 **Admissions:** 2381 **Census:** 19 **Outpatient Visits:** 85178 **Births:** 566 **Total Expense ($000):** 45378 **Payroll Expense ($000):** 15360 **Personnel:** 299

ZEELAND COMMUNITY HOSPITAL See Spectrum Health Zeeland Community Hospital

Many Facility Codes have changed. Please refer to the AHA Guide Code Chart. © 2014 AHA Guide

MINNESOTA

ADA—Norman County

BRIDGES MEDICAL CENTER See Essentia Health Ada

★ **ESSENTIA HEALTH ADA (241313)**, 201 9th Street West, Zip 56510–1279; tel. 218/784–5000, (Nonreporting) **A**9 10 18 **S** Essentia Health, Duluth, MN
Primary Contact: Ryan Hill, Chief Executive Officer
CMO: Jeff Peterson, M.D., Chief of Staff
CHR: Shayla Hennenberg, Director Human Resources
Web address: www.essentiahealth.org
Control: Other not–for–profit (including NFP Corporation) **Service:** General Medical and Surgical

Staffed Beds: 14

AITKIN—Crow Wing County

☒ **RIVERWOOD HEALTHCARE CENTER (241305)**, 200 Bunker Hill Drive, Zip 56431–1865; tel. 218/927–2121 **A**1 2 9 10 18 **F**3 8 11 13 15 28 29 31 32 34 35 40 43 45 54 56 57 59 64 65 70 75 76 77 78 79 81 82 86 87 93 97 104 107 110 111 114 119 127 129 130 131 132 133 135 144 145 146 147 148 **P**6
Primary Contact: Chad D. Cooper, Chief Executive Officer
CMO: Mark Heggem, M.D., Chief Medical Officer
CIO: Daryl Kallevig, Chief Information Officer
CHR: Cindi Hills, Director Human Resources
CNO: Kristine Layne, R.N., Chief Nursing Officer
Web address: www.riverwoodhealthcare.org
Control: Other not–for–profit (including NFP Corporation) **Service:** General Medical and Surgical

Staffed Beds: 25 Admissions: 1130 Census: 10 Outpatient Visits: 68644 Births: 71 Total Expense ($000): 50783 Payroll Expense ($000): 20182 Personnel: 326

ALBANY—Stearns County

★ **ALBANY AREA HOSPITAL AND MEDICAL CENTER (241331)**, 300 Third Avenue, Zip 56307–9363; tel. 320/845–2121 **A**9 10 18 **F**13 15 29 30 34 35 40 45 50 59 64 65 76 77 79 81 93 107 114 119 127 129 130 132 133 135 146 **P**6 **S** Catholic Health Initiatives, Englewood, CO
Primary Contact: Tressa Schmidt, Administrator
CFO: Steve Smith, Chief Financial Officer
CMO: Aaron Gersch, M.D., Chief of Staff
CHR: Bernie Cekalla, Manager Human Resources
CNO: Diane Roerick, Interim Chief Nursing Executive
Web address: www.albanyareahospital.com
Control: Church–operated, Nongovernment, not–for profit **Service:** General Medical and Surgical

Staffed Beds: 17 Admissions: 299 Census: 3 Outpatient Visits: 7371 Births: 18 Total Expense ($000): 8377 Payroll Expense ($000): 2802 Personnel: 49

ALBERT LEA—Freeborn County

☐ **MAYO CLINIC HEALTH SYSTEM IN ALBERT LEA (240043)**, 404 West Fountain Street, Zip 56007–2473; tel. 507/373–2384, (Nonreporting) **A**1 5 9 10 **S** Mayo Clinic, Rochester, MN
Primary Contact: Mark Ciota, M.D., Chief Executive Officer
CFO: Sheri Dankert, Chief Financial Officer
CMO: John Grzybowski, M.D., Medical Director
CHR: Monica Fleegel, Director Human Resources
CNO: Lori Routh, R.N., Nurse Administrator
Web address: www.almedcenter.org
Control: Other not–for–profit (including NFP Corporation) **Service:** General Medical and Surgical

Staffed Beds: 129

ALEXANDRIA—Sherburne County

☐ **COMMUNITY BEHAVIORAL HEALTH HOSPITAL – ALEXANDRIA (244012)**, 1610 8th Avenue East, Zip 56308–2472; tel. 320/335–6201, (Nonreporting) **A**1 10 **S** Minnesota Department of Human Services, Saint Paul, MN
Primary Contact: Jennifer Westrum, Administrator
CFO: Shirley Jacobson, Chief Financial Officer
Web address: www.health.state.mn.us
Control: State–Government, nonfederal **Service:** Psychiatric

Staffed Beds: 16

★ ○ **DOUGLAS COUNTY HOSPITAL (240030)**, 111 17th Avenue East, Zip 56308–3798; tel. 320/762–1511 **A**2 9 10 11 19 20 **F**3 8 11 13 15 28 29 30 31 32 34 35 36 40 43 45 50 57 61 64 65 68 69 70 76 77 78 79 81 85 86 87 89 91 93 97 107 108 111 115 117 118 119 129 130 131 132 135 144 146 **P**6
Primary Contact: Carl P. Vaagenes, Chief Executive Officer
CFO: Nate Meyer, Director Finance
CHR: Shelly Gompf, Director Human Resources
Web address: www.dchospital.com
Control: County–Government, nonfederal **Service:** General Medical and Surgical

Staffed Beds: 99 Admissions: 3576 Census: 36 Outpatient Visits: 54645 Births: 651 Personnel: 707

ANNANDALE—Wright County

☐ **COMMUNITY BEHAVIORAL HEALTH HOSPITAL – ANNANDALE (244011)**, 400 Annandale Boulevard, Zip 55302–3141; tel. 651/259–3850, (Nonreporting) **A**1 10 **S** Minnesota Department of Human Services, Saint Paul, MN
Primary Contact: Tracanne L. Nelson, MS, Administrator
CMO: Shabeer A. Ahmed, M.D., Clinical Director
CNO: Lennetta M. Reynolds, Administrative Supervisor
Web address: www.health.state.mn.us
Control: State–Government, nonfederal **Service:** Psychiatric

Staffed Beds: 16

ANOKA—Anoka County

☐ **ANOKA–METROPOLITAN REGIONAL TREATMENT CENTER (244002)**, 3301 Seventh Avenue, Zip 55303–4516; tel. 651/431–5000, (Nonreporting) **A**1 10 **S** Minnesota Department of Human Services, Saint Paul, MN
Primary Contact: Tina Sneen, Interim Hospital Administrator
Web address: www.health.state.mn.us
Control: State–Government, nonfederal **Service:** Psychiatric

Staffed Beds: 200

APPLETON—Swift County

★ **APPLETON AREA HEALTH SERVICES (241341)**, 30 South Behl Street, Zip 56208–1699; tel. 320/289–2422, (Nonreporting) **A**9 10 18
Primary Contact: Jeffrey A. Cook, Chief Executive Officer
CFO: Anne Kells, Interim Chief Financial Officer
Web address: www.appletonareahealth.com
Control: City–Government, nonfederal **Service:** General Medical and Surgical

Staffed Beds: 68

ARLINGTON—Sibley County

★ **SIBLEY MEDICAL CENTER (241311)**, 601 West Chandler Street, Zip 55307–2127; tel. 507/964–2271, (Nonreporting) **A**9 10 18
Primary Contact: Todd Sandberg, Chief Executive Officer and Administrator
CFO: Darla Anderson, Chief Financial Officer
CMO: Ehtaisham Mohammed, M.D., Chief Medical Officer
CIO: Chris Bulau, Manager Information Technology
CHR: Sara Christiansen, Interim Director Human Resources
CNO: Sandy Domeier, Director Patient Care Services
Web address: www.sibleymedical.org
Control: City–Government, nonfederal **Service:** General Medical and Surgical

Staffed Beds: 17

MN

Hospital, Medicare Provider Number, Address, Telephone, Approval, Facility, and Physician Codes, Health Care System

★ American Hospital Association (AHA) membership
☐ The Joint Commission accreditation   ◇ DNV Healthcare Inc. accreditation

○ Healthcare Facilities Accreditation Program
△ Commission on Accreditation of Rehabilitation Facilities (CARF) accreditation

MN

AURORA—St. Louis County

★ **ESSENTIA HEALTH NORTHERN PINES (241340)**, 5211 Highway 110, Zip 55705–1599; tel. 218/229–2211, (Total facility includes 50 beds in nursing home–type unit) **A**9 10 18 **F**28 29 34 38 40 50 56 59 65 75 77 79 81 87 91 93 97 99 100 101 102 103 104 107 128 130 133 **P**6 **S** Essentia Health, Duluth, MN
Primary Contact: Laura Ackman, Chief Operating Officer and Administrator
CFO: Barbara Johnson, Chief Financial Officer
CMO: Michelle Oman, D.O., Chief Medical Officer
CHR: Kim Carlson, Director Human Resources
CNO: Cindy Loe, Director of Nursing
Web address: www.essentiahealth.org/NorthernPines/FindaClinic/Essentia–HealthNorthern–Pines–36.aspx
Control: Other not–for–profit (including NFP Corporation) **Service:** General Medical and Surgical

Staffed Beds: 58 **Admissions:** 211 **Census:** 52 **Outpatient Visits:** 13742 **Births:** 0 **Total Expense ($000):** 14802 **Payroll Expense ($000):** 7305 **Personnel:** 124	

WHITE COMMUNITY HOSPITAL See Essentia Health Northern Pines

AUSTIN—Mower County

MAYO CLINIC HEALTH SYSTEM IN AUSTIN (240117), 1000 First Drive N.W., Zip 55912–2904; tel. 507/433–7351, (Nonreporting) **A**5 9 **S** Mayo Clinic, Rochester, MN
Primary Contact: Mark Ciota, M.D., Chief Executive Officer
CFO: Sheri Dankert, Vice President Finance
CMO: Cynthia Dube, M.D., Medical Director
CIO: Tammy Kritzer, Vice President Clinic Operations
CHR: Rodney Nording, Vice President Organizational Support
CNO: Lori Routh, R.N., Nurse Administrator
Web address: www.austinmedicalcenter.org
Control: Other not–for–profit (including NFP Corporation) **Service:** General Medical and Surgical

Staffed Beds: 82	

BAGLEY—Clearwater County

★ **SANFORD BAGLEY MEDICAL CENTER (241328)**, 203 Fourth Street N.W., Zip 56621–8307; tel. 218/694–6501, (Nonreporting) **A**9 10 18 **S** Sanford Health, Sioux Falls, SD
Primary Contact: Kirby Johnson, Administrator
CMO: Esther Potti, M.D., Chief Medical Staff
Web address: www.clearwaterhealthservices.com
Control: County–Government, nonfederal **Service:** General Medical and Surgical

Staffed Beds: 95	

BAUDETTE—Lake Of The Woods County

★ **LAKEWOOD HEALTH CENTER (241301)**, 600 Main Avenue South, Zip 56623–2855; tel. 218/634–2120, (Nonreporting) **A**9 10 18 **S** Catholic Health Initiatives, Englewood, CO
Primary Contact: Jason Breuer, President
CFO: Lynn Ellis, Chief Financial Officer
CIO: Darlene Bushaw, Information Technology Systems Site Lead
CHR: Lois Slick, Director Human Resources
Web address: www.lakewoodhealthcenter.org
Control: Church–operated, Nongovernment, not–for profit **Service:** General Medical and Surgical

Staffed Beds: 59	

BAXTER—Crow Wing County

☐ **COMMUNITY BEHAVIORAL HEALTH HOSPITAL – BAXTER (244015)**, 14241 Grand Oaks Drive, Zip 56425–8749; tel. 218/316–3101 **A**1 10 **F**98 101 102 106 130 **P**6 **S** Minnesota Department of Human Services, Saint Paul, MN
Primary Contact: Richard G. Slieter, Jr., Administrator
Control: State–Government, nonfederal **Service:** Psychiatric

Staffed Beds: 16 **Admissions:** 183 **Census:** 14 **Outpatient Visits:** 0 **Births:** 0 **Total Expense ($000):** 4823 **Payroll Expense ($000):** 3397	

BEMIDJI—Beltrami County

☐ **COMMUNITY BEHAVIORAL HEALTH HOSPITAL – BEMIDJI (244014)**, 800 Bemidji Avenue North, Zip 56601–3054; tel. 218/308–2400, (Nonreporting) **A**1 10 **S** Minnesota Department of Human Services, Saint Paul, MN
Primary Contact: Larry A. Laudon, Administrator
Control: State–Government, nonfederal **Service:** Psychiatric

Staffed Beds: 16	

NORTH COUNTRY REGIONAL HOSPITAL See Sanford Bemidji Medical Center

★ **SANFORD BEMIDJI MEDICAL CENTER (240100)**, 1300 Anne Street N.W., Zip 56601–5103; tel. 218/751–5430, (Total facility includes 78 beds in nursing home–type unit) **A**2 9 10 19 20 **F**3 7 8 10 11 13 14 15 18 20 22 28 29 30 31 34 35 40 44 45 46 49 50 51 53 54 55 56 57 58 59 60 62 63 64 65 68 70 74 75 76 77 78 79 81 82 85 86 87 90 93 96 97 103 104 107 108 110 111 114 115 117 119 120 121 123 124 125 126 127 128 129 130 131 132 133 135 141 142 144 145 146 148 **P**6 **S** Sanford Health, Sioux Falls, SD
Primary Contact: Dan Olson, President
CFO: Craig Boyer, Vice President Finance
CMO: Daniel DeKrey, M.D., Chief of Staff
CIO: Dan Moffatt, Chief Information Officer
Web address: www.nchs.com
Control: Other not–for–profit (including NFP Corporation) **Service:** General Medical and Surgical

Staffed Beds: 196 **Admissions:** 6041 **Census:** 141 **Outpatient Visits:** 252179 **Births:** 1015 **Total Expense ($000):** 117264 **Payroll Expense ($000):** 48678 **Personnel:** 1232	

BENSON—Swift County

★ **SWIFT COUNTY–BENSON HOSPITAL (241365)**, 1815 Wisconsin Avenue, Zip 56215–1653; tel. 320/843–1311, (Nonreporting) **A**9 10 18
Primary Contact: Frank Lawatsch, Chief Executive Officer
CFO: Jayne Thielke, Chief Financial Officer
CMO: Richard Horecka, Chief Medical Officer
CIO: Jayne Thielke, Chief Financial Officer
CHR: Naomi Sands, Administrative Assistant and Manager Human Resources
Web address: www.scbh.org
Control: Hospital district or authority, Government, nonfederal **Service:** General Medical and Surgical

Staffed Beds: 18	

BIGFORK—Itasca County

★ **BIGFORK VALLEY HOSPITAL (241316)**, 258 Pine Tree Drive, Zip 56628, Mailing Address: P.O. Box 258, Zip 56628–0258; tel. 218/743–3177, (Nonreporting) **A**9 10 18
Primary Contact: Aaron Saude, Interim Chief Executive Officer
CFO: Christine Lokken, Manager of Finance
CMO: Edwin Anderson, M.D., Chief of Staff and Chief Medical Officer
CIO: Sally Sedgwick, Manager Public Relations and Marketing
CHR: Jennifer Drotts, Manager Human Resources
CNO: Nancy Probst, R.N., Chief Nursing Officer
Web address: www.bigforkvalley.org
Control: Hospital district or authority, Government, nonfederal **Service:** General Medical and Surgical

Staffed Beds: 60	

BLUE EARTH—Faribault County

✚ **UNITED HOSPITAL DISTRICT (241369)**, 515 South Moore Street, Zip 56013–2158, Mailing Address: P.O. Box 160, Zip 56013–0160; tel. 507/526–3273 **A**1 9 10 18 **F**3 4 5 7 8 11 12 13 15 17 28 29 30 31 34 35 40 43 54 57 59 62 63 64 65 69 70 71 75 76 77 81 82 85 86 89 93 94 104 107 114 119 128 129 130 132 133 134 135 144 146 148 **P**6
Primary Contact: Jeffrey M. Lang, Chief Executive Officer
CFO: Larry Lee, Chief Financial Officer
Web address: www.uhd.org
Control: Hospital district or authority, Government, nonfederal **Service:** General Medical and Surgical

Staffed Beds: 49 **Admissions:** 788 **Census:** 20 **Outpatient Visits:** 52360 **Births:** 54 **Total Expense ($000):** 27738 **Payroll Expense ($000):** 11889	

BRAINERD—Crow Wing County

✚ **ESSENTIA HEALTH ST. JOSEPH'S MEDICAL CENTER (240075)**, 523 North Third Street, Zip 56401–3098; tel. 218/829–2861, (Nonreporting) **A**1 2 9 10 19 20 **S** Essentia Health, Duluth, MN
Primary Contact: Adam Rees, President
COO: Mike Larson, Chief Operating Officer
CFO: Dave Pilot, Chief Financial Officer
CMO: Peter Henry, M.D., Chief Medical Officer
CIO: Pam Marlatt, Business Systems Director
CHR: Sarah Carlson, Director Human Resources
CNO: Patricia DeLong, Chief Nursing Officer
Web address: www.essentiahealth.org
Control: Church–operated, Nongovernment, not–for profit **Service:** General Medical and Surgical

Staffed Beds: 162	

ST. JOSEPH'S MEDICAL CENTER See Essentia Health St. Joseph's Medical Center

Many Facility Codes have changed. Please refer to the AHA Guide Code Chart. © 2014 AHA Guide

BRECKENRIDGE—Wilkin County

★ **CHI ST. FRANCIS HEALTH (241377)**, 2400 St. Francis Drive, Zip 56520–1025; tel. 218/643–3000, (Total facility includes 120 beds in nursing home–type unit) **A**5 9 10 18 **F**3 5 8 11 13 15 28 29 30 34 35 38 40 43 45 46 50 56 57 59 64 65 75 79 81 87 93 96 97 99 100 101 103 104 107 110 111 115 119 125 127 128 129 130 131 132 133 146 **P**6 **S** Catholic Health Initiatives, Englewood, CO
Primary Contact: David A. Nelson, President
CFO: Becky Thompson, Chief Financial Officer
CHR: Gail Grant, Director Human Resources
Web address: www.sfcare.org
Control: Church–operated, Nongovernment, not–for profit **Service:** General Medical and Surgical

Staffed Beds: 145 **Admissions:** 850 **Census:** 113 **Outpatient Visits:** 20595 **Births:** 155 **Total Expense ($000):** 30756 **Payroll Expense ($000):** 12727 **Personnel:** 274

BUFFALO—Wright County

✠ **BUFFALO HOSPITAL (240076)**, 303 Catlin Street, Zip 55313–1947; tel. 763/682–1212 **A**1 9 10 **F**3 11 13 15 18 28 29 31 32 34 35 36 40 43 44 45 50 57 59 64 75 76 77 78 79 80 81 85 86 87 89 93 107 110 111 114 118 119 129 130 131 132 135 146 148 **S** Allina Health, Minneapolis, MN
Primary Contact: Jennifer Myster, President
COO: Laura Jenkins, Director Operations Finance and Business Development
CFO: Sandra Matrella, Manager Finance
CMO: Corey Martin, M.D., Director Medical Affairs
CIO: Lois Nevinski, Manager Information Services
CHR: Nikki Mills, Director Human Resources and Operations
CNO: Gretchen A. Frederick, R.N., Director Patient Care Services
Web address: www.buffalohospital.org
Control: Other not–for–profit (including NFP Corporation) **Service:** General Medical and Surgical

Staffed Beds: 44 **Admissions:** 2530 **Census:** 16 **Outpatient Visits:** 72857 **Births:** 875 **Total Expense ($000):** 62038 **Payroll Expense ($000):** 24745 **Personnel:** 345

BURNSVILLE—Dakota County

✠ **FAIRVIEW RIDGES HOSPITAL (240207)**, 201 East Nicollet Boulevard, Zip 55337–5799; tel. 952/892–2000 **A**1 2 3 9 10 **F**3 11 13 15 18 19 20 22 28 29 30 31 34 35 40 41 43 44 45 46 49 50 52 55 57 59 60 64 65 68 70 72 74 75 76 77 78 79 81 82 84 85 87 89 93 100 107 108 110 111 114 115 118 119 126 130 132 146 148 **P**6 **S** Fairview Health Services, Minneapolis, MN
Primary Contact: Beth Krehbiel, R.N., FACHE, President and Chief Executive Officer
COO: Brian A. Knapp, Vice President Operations
CFO: Alan Lem, Vice President Finance
CMO: Lizbeth Thomas, M.D., Vice President Medical Affairs
CHR: Mary Kaphings, Director Human Resources
CNO: Carol Koeppel–Olsen, R.N., Vice President Patient Care Services
Web address: www.fairview.org
Control: Other not–for–profit (including NFP Corporation) **Service:** General Medical and Surgical

Staffed Beds: 171 **Admissions:** 11148 **Census:** 107 **Outpatient Visits:** 104447 **Births:** 2413 **Total Expense ($000):** 173058 **Payroll Expense ($000):** 82494 **Personnel:** 1000

CAMBRIDGE—Isanti County

✠ **CAMBRIDGE MEDICAL CENTER (240020)**, 701 South Dellwood Street, Zip 55008–1920; tel. 763/689–7700 **A**1 9 10 **F**3 4 5 11 13 14 15 18 28 29 30 31 32 34 35 38 40 43 45 50 55 56 57 59 61 64 65 69 70 74 75 76 77 78 79 81 82 85 86 87 89 93 97 98 99 100 101 102 103 104 107 108 111 114 119 125 129 130 131 132 134 135 144 145 146 147 148 **P**5 6 **S** Allina Health, Minneapolis, MN
Primary Contact: Gary Shaw, President
CFO: Nancy Treacy, Director Finance
CHR: Diane Rasmussen, Director Human Resources
CNO: Sherri Abrahamson–Baty, Director Patient Care Services
Web address: www.allina.com/ahs/cambridge.nsf
Control: Other not–for–profit (including NFP Corporation) **Service:** General Medical and Surgical

Staffed Beds: 78 **Admissions:** 3570 **Census:** 37 **Outpatient Visits:** 92627 **Births:** 465 **Total Expense ($000):** 75880 **Payroll Expense ($000):** 30774 **Personnel:** 648

CANBY—Yellow Medicine County

★ **SANFORD CANBY MEDICAL CENTER (241347)**, 112 St. Olaf Avenue South, Zip 56220–1433; tel. 507/223–7277, (Includes SENIOR HAVEN CONVALESCENT NURSING CENTER), (Total facility includes 68 beds in nursing home–type unit) **A**9 10 18 **F**3 7 10 11 13 15 28 29 31 34 35 39 40 45 46 53 56 59 60 62 64 65 70 71 75 76 79 81 85 89 93 107 110 119 127 128 130 132 133 143 144 **P**6 **S** Sanford Health, Sioux Falls, SD
Primary Contact: Lori Sisk, R.N., Chief Executive Officer
CFO: Allison Nelson, Chief Financial Officer
CMO: Maritza Lopez, M.D., Chief of Staff
CIO: Cheryl L. Ferguson, Associate Administrator
Web address: www.sanfordcanby.org
Control: Other not–for–profit (including NFP Corporation) **Service:** General Medical and Surgical

Staffed Beds: 93 **Admissions:** 424 **Census:** 69 **Outpatient Visits:** 27903 **Births:** 28 **Total Expense ($000):** 21000 **Payroll Expense ($000):** 10125 **Personnel:** 207

CANNON FALLS—Goodhue County

☐ **MAYO CLINIC HEALTH SYSTEM IN CANNON FALLS (241346)**, 1116 West Mill Street, Zip 55009–1898; tel. 507/263–4221, (Nonreporting) **A**1 9 10 18 **S** Mayo Clinic, Rochester, MN
Primary Contact: Thomas J. Witt, M.D., President and Chief Executive Officer
COO: Glenn Christian, Administrator
CFO: Edward A. Tusa, Chief Financial Officer
CMO: Tarlochan Turna, M.D., Medical Director
CHR: Mary Garlets, Director Human Resources
Web address: www.mayoclinichealthsystem.org/locations/cannon–falls
Control: Hospital district or authority, Government, nonfederal **Service:** General Medical and Surgical

Staffed Beds: 21

CASS LAKE—Cass County

★ **U. S. PUBLIC HEALTH SERVICE INDIAN HOSPITAL (241358)**, 7th Street & Grant Utley Avenue N.W., Zip 56633, Mailing Address: Rural Route 3, Box 211, Zip 56633; tel. 218/335–3200 **A**5 9 10 18 **F**39 40 63 64 80 119 133 135 144 **S** U. S. Indian Health Service, Rockville, MD
Primary Contact: Norine Smith, Chief Executive Officer
CMO: Antonio Guimaraes, M.D., Clinical Director
CHR: Terrance Lascano, Administrative Officer
CNO: Roberta A. Williams, Director of Nursing
Web address: www.ihs.gov
Control: PHS, Indian Service, Government, federal **Service:** General Medical and Surgical

Staffed Beds: 9 **Admissions:** 69 **Census:** 1 **Outpatient Visits:** 112857 **Births:** 0 **Total Expense ($000):** 18571 **Payroll Expense ($000):** 8774

CLOQUET—Carlton County

★ **COMMUNITY MEMORIAL HOSPITAL (241364)**, 512 Skyline Boulevard, Zip 55720–1199; tel. 218/879–4641, (Nonreporting) **A**9 10 18
Primary Contact: Rick Breuer, Chief Executive Officer and Administrator
CFO: Brad Anderson, Chief Financial Officer
CIO: Sam Jacobson, Director Management Information Systems
Web address: www.cloquethospital.com
Control: Other not–for–profit (including NFP Corporation) **Service:** General Medical and Surgical

Staffed Beds: 113

COOK—St. Louis County

★ **COOK HOSPITAL AND CONVALESCENT NURSING CARE UNIT (241312)**, 10 Fifth Street S.E., Zip 55723–9745; tel. 218/666–5945, (Total facility includes 28 beds in nursing home–type unit) **A**9 10 18 **F**2 3 11 15 28 29 35 40 43 50 53 56 57 64 77 81 93 96 107 110 111 119 128 130 133 148
Primary Contact: Allen J. Vogt, Chief Executive Officer
CFO: Kaylee S. Hoard, Chief Financial Officer
Web address: www.cookhospital.org
Control: Hospital district or authority, Government, nonfederal **Service:** General Medical and Surgical

Staffed Beds: 42 **Admissions:** 277 **Census:** 28 **Outpatient Visits:** 15098 **Births:** 0 **Total Expense ($000):** 12090 **Payroll Expense ($000):** 4817 **Personnel:** 102

MN

Hospital, Medicare Provider Number, Address, Telephone, Approval, Facility, and Physician Codes, Health Care System

★ American Hospital Association (AHA) membership
☐ The Joint Commission accreditation ◇ DNV Healthcare Inc. accreditation
○ Healthcare Facilities Accreditation Program
△ Commission on Accreditation of Rehabilitation Facilities (CARF) accreditation

COON RAPIDS—Anoka County

✠ **MERCY HOSPITAL (240115)**, 4050 Coon Rapids Boulevard, Zip 55433–2586; tel. 763/236–6000 **A**1 2 3 5 9 10 **F**3 8 11 13 17 18 20 22 24 26 28 29 30 31 34 35 36 37 38 40 43 45 49 53 55 59 63 64 65 68 69 70 74 75 77 78 79 81 82 85 87 89 93 97 98 99 100 101 102 103 104 105 107 108 111 115 119 126 130 132 135 146 147 148 **P**4 5 6 **S** Allina Health, Minneapolis, MN
Primary Contact: Sara J. Criger, President
COO: Brandi Lunneborg, Vice President Operations
CFO: Gerald Pietz, Vice President Finance
CMO: Ryan Else, M.D., Vice President Medical Affairs
CIO: Susan Heichert, Chief Information Officer
CHR: Nancy Watson, Director Human Resources
CNO: MariBeth Olson, R.N., Vice President Patient Care Services
Web address: www.allinamercy.org
Control: Other not–for–profit (including NFP Corporation) **Service:** General Medical and Surgical

Staffed Beds: 254 **Admissions:** 20126 **Census:** 197 **Outpatient Visits:** 137969 **Births:** 1969 **Total Expense ($000):** 366687 **Payroll Expense ($000):** 133094 **Personnel:** 1471

CROOKSTON—Polk County

✠ **RIVERVIEW HEALTH (241320)**, 323 South Minnesota Street, Zip 56716–1601; tel. 218/281–9200, (Total facility includes 24 beds in nursing home–type unit) **A**1 5 9 10 18 **F**2 3 5 6 11 13 15 28 34 40 43 45 47 50 57 59 62 70 76 77 79 81 93 97 107 110 111 115 119 127 128 129 130 131 132 133 135 145 146 148 **P**6
Primary Contact: Carrie Michalski, President and Chief Executive Officer
COO: Chris Bruggeman, Chief Operating Officer
CFO: Betty Arvidson, Chief Financial Officer
CMO: Idatonye I. Afonya, M.D., Chief of Staff
CIO: Jason King, Chief Information Officer
CHR: Jean Tate, Manager Human Resources
CNO: Sandra Boice, Chief Nursing Officer
Web address: www.riverviewhealth.org
Control: Other not–for–profit (including NFP Corporation) **Service:** General Medical and Surgical

Staffed Beds: 49 **Admissions:** 933 **Census:** 32 **Outpatient Visits:** 39104 **Births:** 92 **Total Expense ($000):** 52491 **Payroll Expense ($000):** 24304 **Personnel:** 470

CROSBY—Crow Wing County

✠ **CUYUNA REGIONAL MEDICAL CENTER (241353)**, 320 East Main Street, Zip 56441–1690; tel. 218/546–7000, (Total facility includes 117 beds in nursing home–type unit) **A**1 2 9 10 18 **F**3 7 12 13 15 18 28 29 31 34 35 40 43 45 46 47 48 49 50 51 56 57 59 62 63 64 65 68 70 75 76 77 78 79 81 82 84 85 86 87 91 92 93 94 97 99 100 101 103 104 107 110 111 115 116 117 118 119 124 127 128 130 131 132 133 143 144 146 147 148 **P**6
Primary Contact: John H. Solheim, Chief Executive Officer
COO: Amy Hart, Chief Operating Officer
CFO: Kyle Bauer, Chief Financial Officer
CMO: Robert Westin, M.D., Chief Medical Officer
CHR: Rebecca A. Thiesfeld, Executive Director Human Resources
CNO: Renee Steffin, Chief Nursing Officer
Web address: www.cuyunamed.org
Control: Hospital district or authority, Government, nonfederal **Service:** General Medical and Surgical

Staffed Beds: 142 **Admissions:** 2529 **Census:** 127 **Outpatient Visits:** 130556 **Births:** 290 **Total Expense ($000):** 91485 **Payroll Expense ($000):** 33935 **Personnel:** 630

DAWSON—Lac Qui Parle County

JOHNSON MEMORIAL HEALTH SERVICES (241314), 1282 Walnut Street, Zip 56232–2333; tel. 320/769–4323, (Total facility includes 56 beds in nursing home–type unit) **A**9 10 18 **F**3 7 8 10 11 15 28 34 40 43 56 57 62 64 65 68 69 71 76 77 81 84 93 107 110 111 119 127 128 130 131 135 145 146 **P**6
Primary Contact: Kathy Johnson, Chief Executive Officer and Administrator
CFO: Crystal Bothun, Chief Financial Officer
CMO: Ralph Gerbig, M.D., Chief of Staff
CIO: Derrick Ochsendorf, Manager Information Technology and Systems
CHR: Ellen Alberg, Director Human Resources
CNO: Lori Andreas, Director Patient Care Services
Web address: www.jmhsmn.org
Control: Hospital district or authority, Government, nonfederal **Service:** General Medical and Surgical

Staffed Beds: 78 **Admissions:** 241 **Census:** 56 **Outpatient Visits:** 1859 **Births:** 5 **Total Expense ($000):** 13503 **Payroll Expense ($000):** 7072 **Personnel:** 144

DEER RIVER—Itasca County

★ **ESSENTIA HEALTH–DEER RIVER (241360)**, 115 10th Avenue N.E., Zip 56636–8795; tel. 218/246–2900, (Total facility includes 32 beds in nursing home–type unit) **A**9 10 18 **F**2 3 7 12 13 15 28 29 31 32 34 35 40 45 56 57 59 62 64 65 70 74 75 76 77 79 81 82 85 91 92 93 95 97 107 108 110 111 115 118 119 135 143 144 146 147 148
Primary Contact: Jeffry Stampohar, Chief Executive Officer
CMO: David Goodall, M.D., Chief Medical Staff
CHR: Brittany Mohler, Director Human Resources
Web address: www.drhc.org
Control: Other not–for–profit (including NFP Corporation) **Service:** General Medical and Surgical

Staffed Beds: 52 **Admissions:** 569 **Census:** 12

DETROIT LAKES—Becker County

✠ **ESSENTIA HEALTH ST. MARY'S – DETROIT LAKES (240101)**, 1027 Washington Avenue, Zip 56501–3409; tel. 218/847–5611, (Total facility includes 96 beds in nursing home–type unit) **A**1 5 9 10 20 **F**7 10 11 13 15 18 28 29 30 31 40 41 43 56 57 59 62 64 65 70 75 76 77 79 81 89 93 97 104 107 110 111 119 125 128 130 131 132 135 144 146 147 148 **S** Essentia Health, Duluth, MN
Primary Contact: Peter Jacobson, President
CFO: Ryan Hill, Chief Financial Officer
CMO: Rich Vetter, M.D., Associate Chief
CIO: Ken Gilles, Associate Chief Information Officer
CHR: Diane Sundrud, Human Resource Service Partner
CNO: Kay Larson, R.N., Chief Nursing Officer
Web address: www.essentiahealth.org
Control: Other not–for–profit (including NFP Corporation) **Service:** General Medical and Surgical

Staffed Beds: 131 **Admissions:** 2716 **Census:** 107 **Outpatient Visits:** 13740 **Births:** 492 **Total Expense ($000):** 74336 **Payroll Expense ($000):** 36000 **Personnel:** 451

ST. MARY'S INNOVIS HEALTH See Essentia Health St. Mary's – Detroit Lakes

DULUTH—St. Louis County

✠ △ **ESSENTIA HEALTH DULUTH (240019)**, 502 East Second Street, Zip 55805–1982; tel. 218/727–8762 **A**1 3 5 7 9 10 **F**3 5 11 12 15 16 29 30 31 32 34 35 49 50 51 52 54 55 56 57 59 61 64 65 70 74 75 77 78 79 81 82 84 85 86 87 90 92 93 94 96 97 98 99 100 101 103 104 105 107 108 110 111 114 115 116 117 118 119 120 121 123 124 129 130 131 132 134 135 141 144 146 147 148 **P**6 **S** Essentia Health, Duluth, MN
Primary Contact: Barb Wessberg, Administrator
CFO: Kevin Boren, Chief Financial Officer
CMO: Hugh Renier, M.D., Vice President Medical Affairs
CIO: Dennis Dassenko, Chief Information Officer
CHR: Diane Davidson, Senior Vice President Human Resources
CNO: Sandee Carlson, Director of Nursing
Web address: www.smdcmedicalcenter.org
Control: Other not–for–profit (including NFP Corporation) **Service:** General Medical and Surgical

Staffed Beds: 154 **Admissions:** 3924 **Census:** 75 **Outpatient Visits:** 35886 **Births:** 17 **Total Expense ($000):** 357662 **Payroll Expense ($000):** 196456 **Personnel:** 2433

✠ **ESSENTIA HEALTH ST. MARY'S MEDICAL CENTER (240002)**, 407 East Third Street, Zip 55805–1984; tel. 218/786–4000, (Includes ST. MARY'S CHILDREN'S HOSPITAL, 407 East Third Street, Zip 55805–1950; tel. 218/786–5437) **A**1 2 3 5 9 10 **F**3 11 12 13 17 18 20 22 24 26 28 29 30 34 35 37 38 40 43 45 46 47 48 49 50 57 59 63 65 67 70 72 74 76 78 79 81 83 84 85 86 87 88 89 102 107 108 111 115 119 126 129 130 132 135 141 146 **P**6 **S** Essentia Health, Duluth, MN
Primary Contact: James Garvey, Executive Vice President, Operations and Administrator
CMO: Hugh Renier, M.D., Vice President Medical Affairs
CIO: Tess Jettergren, Director Clinical Informatics
CHR: Glen Porter, Vice President Human Resources
Web address: www.essentiahealth.org/StMarysMedicalCenter/FindaClinic/Essentia–HealthSt–Marys–Medical–Center–46.aspx
Control: Other not–for–profit (including NFP Corporation) **Service:** General Medical and Surgical

Staffed Beds: 310 **Admissions:** 18206 **Census:** 225 **Outpatient Visits:** 98674 **Births:** 1284 **Total Expense ($000):** 322542 **Payroll Expense ($000):** 144824 **Personnel:** 2021

SMDC MEDICAL CENTER See Essentia Health Duluth

Many Facility Codes have changed. Please refer to the AHA Guide Code Chart. © 2014 AHA Guide

MN

☒ △ **ST. LUKE'S HOSPITAL (240047)**, 915 East First Street, Zip 55805–2193; tel. 218/249–5555 **A**1 2 3 5 7 9 10 **F**3 8 9 11 12 13 15 17 18 20 22 24 26 28 29 30 31 34 35 39 40 43 46 47 48 49 51 53 54 57 58 59 60 61 62 63 64 65 70 74 75 76 77 78 79 81 82 83 84 85 86 87 90 92 93 97 98 100 102 104 107 108 110 114 115 117 118 119 120 121 123 124 126 129 130 131 132 144 145 146 148 **P**6
Primary Contact: John Strange, President and Chief Executive Officer
CFO: Eric Lohn, Vice President and Chief Financial Officer
CMO: Gary Peterson, M.D., Vice President Medical Affairs and Medical Director
CIO: Clark Averill, Director Information Technology
CHR: Marla Halvorson, Director Human Resources
CNO: Susan Hamel, Chief Nursing Officer
Web address: www.slhduluth.com
Control: Other not–for–profit (including NFP Corporation) **Service:** General Medical and Surgical

Staffed Beds: 267 **Admissions:** 10074 **Census:** 132 **Outpatient Visits:** 149258 **Births:** 910 **Total Expense ($000):** 320925 **Payroll Expense ($000):** 175431 **Personnel:** 1969

ST. MARY'S MEDICAL CENTER See Essentia Health St. Mary's Medical Center

EDINA—Hennepin County

☒ **FAIRVIEW SOUTHDALE HOSPITAL (240078)**, 6401 France Avenue South, Zip 55435–2199; tel. 952/924–5000 **A**1 2 3 5 9 10 **F**3 5 8 11 12 13 15 17 18 20 22 24 26 28 29 30 31 34 35 38 40 43 45 46 49 50 51 55 57 59 60 64 65 68 70 73 74 75 76 77 78 79 81 82 83 84 85 87 92 93 94 98 100 102 107 108 110 111 114 115 117 118 119 121 124 126 129 130 131 132 134 135 146 147 148 **P**6 **S** Fairview Health Services, Minneapolis, MN
Primary Contact: Bradley Beard, President
CFO: Alan Lem, Vice President Finance
CHR: Rich Lutz, Director Human Resources
Web address: www.fairview.org
Control: Other not–for–profit (including NFP Corporation) **Service:** General Medical and Surgical

Staffed Beds: 326 **Admissions:** 17679 **Census:** 203 **Outpatient Visits:** 125976 **Births:** 2904 **Total Expense ($000):** 376872 **Payroll Expense ($000):** 151315 **Personnel:** 1842

ELBOW LAKE—Grant County

ELEAH MEDICAL CENTER See Prairie Ridge Hospital and Health Services

★ **PRAIRIE RIDGE HOSPITAL AND HEALTH SERVICES (241379)**, 1411 Highway 79 E., Zip 56531–4611; tel. 218/685–4461 **A**9 10 18 **F**7 15 28 31 40 43 45 46 47 48 53 59 64 67 81 90 93 107 128 133 148 **P**5
Primary Contact: Thomas Kooiman, Chief Executive Officer
CFO: Loraine Martineau, Chief Financial Officer
CMO: David Bjork, M.D., Chief Medical Officer
CNO: Manda Westrom, Director of Nursing
Web address: www.eleahmed.org
Control: Other not–for–profit (including NFP Corporation) **Service:** General Medical and Surgical

Staffed Beds: 12 **Admissions:** 171 **Census:** 1 **Outpatient Visits:** 24838 **Births:** 0 **Total Expense ($000):** 14317 **Payroll Expense ($000):** 4032 **Personnel:** 106

ELY—St. Louis County

★ **ELY–BLOOMENSON COMMUNITY HOSPITAL (241318)**, 328 West Conan Street, Zip 55731–1198; tel. 218/365–3271 **A**9 10 18 **F**13 15 28 31 40 45 53 62 64 76 81 107 110 119 130 133 148 **P**6
Primary Contact: John Fossum, Chief Executive Officer and Administrator
CFO: Scott Kellerman, Chief Financial Officer
CHR: Rochelle Sjoberg, Director Human Resources
CNO: Becky Gaulke, Chief Nursing Officer
Web address: www.ebch.org
Control: Other not–for–profit (including NFP Corporation) **Service:** General Medical and Surgical

Staffed Beds: 25 **Admissions:** 339 **Census:** 4 **Outpatient Visits:** 8339 **Births:** 24 **Total Expense ($000):** 15467 **Payroll Expense ($000):** 5102 **Personnel:** 42

FAIRMONT—Martin County

☒ **MAYO CLINIC HEALTH SYSTEM IN FAIRMONT (240166)**, 800 Medical Center Drive, Zip 56031–4575; tel. 507/238–8100, (Includes LUTZ WING CONVALESCENT AND NURSING CARE UNIT), (Total facility includes 40 beds in nursing home–type unit) **A**1 9 10 20 **F**3 11 13 15 17 18 28 29 30 31 34 40 43 59 64 65 68 75 76 77 78 79 81 82 84 85 86 87 92 93 97 99 100 101 103 104 107 108 110 111 115 118 119 128 129 130 132 133 144 146 **P**6
S Mayo Clinic, Rochester, MN
Primary Contact: Robert Bartingale, Administrator
COO: Gayle B. Hansen, R.N., Chief Operating Officer
CFO: Brian Suter, Chief Financial Officer
CMO: Rufus Rodriguez, M.D., Medical Director
Web address: www.fairmontmedicalcenter.org
Control: Other not–for–profit (including NFP Corporation) **Service:** General Medical and Surgical

Staffed Beds: 96 **Admissions:** 2292 **Census:** 52 **Outpatient Visits:** 151957 **Births:** 244 **Total Expense ($000):** 82738 **Payroll Expense ($000):** 41143 **Personnel:** 511

FARIBAULT—Rice County

★ **DISTRICT ONE HOSPITAL (240071)**, 200 State Avenue, Zip 55021–6345; tel. 507/334–6451, (Nonreporting) **A**9 10
Primary Contact: Stephen J. Pribyl, FACHE, Chief Executive Officer
COO: Joan Boysen, Chief Operating Officer
CFO: Rick Miller, Chief Financial Officer
CMO: Brant Barr, M.D., Chief Medical Officer
CIO: Glenn Gregersen, Director Information Technology
CHR: Lucy G. Dupree, Director Human Resources
CNO: Lynette Dickson, Director Clinical Operations and Director of Nursing
Web address: www.districtonehospital.com
Control: Hospital district or authority, Government, nonfederal **Service:** General Medical and Surgical

Staffed Beds: 42

FERGUS FALLS—Otter Tail County

☐ **COMMUNITY BEHAVIORAL HEALTH HOSPITAL – FERGUS FALLS (244013)**, 1801 West Alcott Avenue, Zip 56537–2661, Mailing Address: P.O. Box 478, Zip 56538–0478; tel. 218/332–5001, (Nonreporting) **A**1 9 10 **S** Minnesota Department of Human Services, Saint Paul, MN
Primary Contact: Brenda Schleske, Interim Administrator
Control: State–Government, nonfederal **Service:** Psychiatric

Staffed Beds: 16

☒ △ **LAKE REGION HEALTHCARE (240052)**, 712 South Cascade Street, Zip 56537–2900, Mailing Address: P.O. Box 728, Zip 56538–0728; tel. 218/736–8000 **A**1 7 9 10 20 **F**3 10 11 13 15 17 28 29 30 31 32 33 34 35 36 40 41 43 44 45 50 51 53 54 56 57 58 59 61 64 65 68 70 74 75 76 77 78 79 81 84 85 86 87 89 90 92 93 94 96 97 98 100 101 102 103 104 107 108 110 111 115 118 119 120 121 123 130 131 132 135 144 146 147 148
Primary Contact: Larry A. Schulz, Chief Executive Officer
CFO: Brett Longtin, Chief Financial Officer
CMO: Wade Swenson, M.D., Chief of Staff
CIO: Wade A. Jurkas, Director Computer Information Systems
CHR: Cheryl Buck, Vice President Human Resources
CNO: Lucia E. Anderson, Senior Vice President Nursing and Chief Nurse Executive
Web address: www.lrhc.org
Control: Other not–for–profit (including NFP Corporation) **Service:** General Medical and Surgical

Staffed Beds: 108 **Admissions:** 2672 **Census:** 30 **Outpatient Visits:** 51704 **Births:** 324 **Total Expense ($000):** 103375 **Payroll Expense ($000):** 36846 **Personnel:** 714

FOSSTON—Polk County

★ **ESSENTIA HEALTH FOSSTON (241357)**, 900 Hilligoss Boulevard S.E., Zip 56542–1599; tel. 218/435–1133, (Total facility includes 50 beds in nursing home–type unit) **A**9 10 18 **F**2 3 7 10 11 13 28 29 31 34 35 40 43 44 45 50 56 57 59 62 63 64 65 68 69 70 75 76 77 78 79 80 81 82 84 85 87 93 97 107 114 127 128 129 130 131 132 133 135 145 146 148 **P**5 6 **S** Essentia Health, Duluth, MN
Primary Contact: Kevin Gish, Administrator and Vice President
CFO: Kim Bodensteiner, Chief Financial Officer
CHR: Diane Sundrud, Director Human Resources
Web address: www.essentiahealth.org
Control: Other not–for–profit (including NFP Corporation) **Service:** General Medical and Surgical

Staffed Beds: 75 **Admissions:** 558 **Census:** 49 **Outpatient Visits:** 45219 **Births:** 94 **Total Expense ($000):** 22353 **Payroll Expense ($000):** 12476 **Personnel:** 182

MN

Hospital, Medicare Provider Number, Address, Telephone, Approval, Facility, and Physician Codes, Health Care System

★ American Hospital Association (AHA) membership
☐ The Joint Commission accreditation ◇ DNV Healthcare Inc. accreditation
◯ Healthcare Facilities Accreditation Program
△ Commission on Accreditation of Rehabilitation Facilities (CARF) accreditation

FIRST CARE MEDICAL SERVICES See Essentia Health Fosston

FRIDLEY—Anoka County

✠ **UNITY HOSPITAL (240132)**, 550 Osborne Road N.E., Zip 55432–2799;
tel. 763/236–5000 **A**1 2 5 9 10 **F**3 4 5 11 12 13 18 20 22 24 26 28 29 30 31 34 35 36 40 43 45 49 50 53 55 56 57 59 64 65 69 70 73 75 76 77 78 79 81 82 85 86 87 89 93 98 99 100 101 102 103 104 107 108 111 114 115 119 130 132 135 145 146 147 148 **S** Allina Health, Minneapolis, MN
Primary Contact: Helen J. Strike, R.N., President
COO: Patrick Belland, Vice President Operations
CFO: Lisa K. Anderson, Vice President Finance
CMO: Paul Kettler, M.D., Vice President Medical Affairs
CIO: Susan Heichert, Chief Information Officer
CHR: Kenneth E. Auer, Director Human Resources
CNO: Mari J. Holt, R.N., Vice President Patient Care Services
Web address: www.allina.com
Control: Other not–for–profit (including NFP Corporation) **Service:** General Medical and Surgical

Staffed Beds: 220 **Admissions:** 12397 **Census:** 133 **Outpatient Visits:** 92022 **Births:** 1147 **Total Expense ($000):** 187598 **Payroll Expense ($000):** 76644 **Personnel:** 913

GLENCOE—Mcleod County

★ **GLENCOE REGIONAL HEALTH SERVICES (241355)**, 1805 Hennepin Avenue North, Zip 55336–1416; tel. 320/864–3121, (Total facility includes 110 beds in nursing home–type unit) **A**9 10 18 **F**3 7 11 13 15 17 28 29 31 34 40 43 48 56 64 68 70 75 76 77 78 81 86 87 89 93 97 107 110 114 119 125 128 130 132 133 135 146 **P**6 **S** HealthPartners, Bloomington, MN
Primary Contact: Jon D. Braband, FACHE, President and Chief Executive Officer
CFO: John C. Doidge, Vice President Finance
CMO: John H. Bergseng, D.O., Vice President Medical Affairs
CIO: Tony Alsleben, Director Information Technology
CHR: Jill Hatlestad, Vice President Human Resources and Organizational Support
CNO: Gayle Sturgis, Vice President Nursing
Web address: www.grhsonline.org
Control: Other not–for–profit (including NFP Corporation) **Service:** General Medical and Surgical

Staffed Beds: 135 **Admissions:** 847 **Census:** 108 **Outpatient Visits:** 25000 **Births:** 172 **Total Expense ($000):** 50543 **Payroll Expense ($000):** 23704 **Personnel:** 376

GLENWOOD—Pope County

★ **GLACIAL RIDGE HEALTH SYSTEM (241376)**, 10 Fourth Avenue S.E., Zip 56334–1898; tel. 320/634–4521 **A**9 10 18 **F**7 11 12 13 15 17 28 31 34 35 40 41 43 53 59 62 63 64 75 76 79 81 93 107 110 114 119 127 130 133 146 148 **P**6
Primary Contact: Kirk A. Stensrud, Chief Executive Officer
CFO: Kyle Chase, Chief Financial Officer
CMO: Robert Montenegro, M.D., Chief of Staff
CIO: Heidi Engle, Manager Information Technology
CHR: Gordon Paulson, Manager Personnel
CNO: Lynn Flesner, Director of Nursing
Web address: www.glacialridge.org
Control: Hospital district or authority, Government, nonfederal **Service:** General Medical and Surgical

Staffed Beds: 19 **Admissions:** 750 **Census:** 8 **Outpatient Visits:** 14398 **Births:** 54 **Total Expense ($000):** 22468 **Payroll Expense ($000):** 10954 **Personnel:** 179

GOLDEN VALLEY—Hennepin County

✠ **REGENCY HOSPITAL OF MINNEAPOLIS (242005)**, 1300 Hidden Lakes Parkway, Zip 55422–4286; tel. 763/588–2750 **A**1 10 **F**1 29 60 75 77 84 85 107 114 130 135 148 **P**8 **S** Select Medical Corporation, Mechanicsburg, PA
Primary Contact: John P. Allen, Chief Executive Officer
CMO: Alaka Nagaraj, M.D., Medical Director
CNO: Caren Gaytko, Chief Nursing Officer
Web address: www.regencyhospital.com
Control: Corporation, Investor–owned, for–profit **Service:** Long–Term Acute Care hospital

Staffed Beds: 64 **Admissions:** 624 **Census:** 53 **Outpatient Visits:** 0 **Births:** 0 **Personnel:** 269

GRACEVILLE—Big Stone County

★ **ESSENTIA HEALTH–HOLY TRINITY HOSPITAL (241321)**, 115 West Second Street, Zip 56240–4845, Mailing Address: P.O. Box 157, Zip 56240–0157; tel. 320/748–7223, (Nonreporting) **A**9 10 18 **S** Essentia Health, Duluth, MN
Primary Contact: John Campion, Administrator
CFO: John Campion, Interim Chief Financial Officer
CMO: Arthur Van Vranken, M.D., Chief Medical Officer
CIO: Brad Tostenson, Chief Information Officer
CHR: Jenny Lee, Human Resources Generalist
CNO: Jill Johnsrud, Director of Nursing
Web address: www.essentiahealth.org/HolyTrinityHospital/FindaClinic/Essentia–HealthHoly–Trinity–Hospital–96.aspx
Control: Other not–for–profit (including NFP Corporation) **Service:** General Medical and Surgical

Staffed Beds: 60

GRACEVILLE HEALTH CENTER See Essentia Health–Holy Trinity Hospital

GRAND MARAIS—Cook County

★ **COOK COUNTY NORTH SHORE HOSPITAL (241317)**, 515 5th Avenue West, Zip 55604–3017; tel. 218/387–3040, (Total facility includes 37 beds in nursing home–type unit) **A**9 10 18 **F**3 7 11 13 15 28 31 40 45 50 56 59 62 64 76 77 84 85 89 93 107 110 111 114 119 128 130 133 148
Primary Contact: Kimber L. Wraalstad, FACHE, Administrator
CFO: Vera Schumann, Director of Finance and Controller
CIO: Greg Johnson, IT Coordinator
CHR: Shelly Starkey, Human Resources Coordinator
CNO: Bridget Sobieck, Director of Nursing
Web address: www.nshorehospital.com
Control: Hospital district or authority, Government, nonfederal **Service:** General Medical and Surgical

Staffed Beds: 53 **Admissions:** 215 **Census:** 37 **Outpatient Visits:** 12313 **Births:** 5 **Total Expense ($000):** 13290 **Payroll Expense ($000):** 5853 **Personnel:** 118

GRAND RAPIDS—Itasca County

✠ **GRAND ITASCA CLINIC AND HOSPITAL (240064)**, 1601 Golf Course Road, Zip 55744–8648; tel. 218/326–5000 **A**1 9 10 20 **F**3 11 12 13 15 17 18 28 29 31 33 35 36 38 40 43 44 45 50 53 56 59 61 62 64 65 75 76 77 78 81 82 85 86 87 93 96 97 107 108 110 111 115 118 119 129 130 131 132 135 141 146 147 148 **P**6
Primary Contact: Michael Youso, Chief Executive Officer
CFO: Sarah S. Gustafson, Vice President of Finance
CHR: Julie Schmidt, Director Human Resources
CNO: Sue Skinner, Vice President of Patient Care Services
Web address: www.granditasca.org
Control: Other not–for–profit (including NFP Corporation) **Service:** General Medical and Surgical

Staffed Beds: 31 **Admissions:** 2035 **Census:** 17 **Outpatient Visits:** 201503 **Births:** 313 **Total Expense ($000):** 76292 **Payroll Expense ($000):** 38429 **Personnel:** 506

GRANITE FALLS—Yellow Medicine County

★ **GRANITE FALLS MUNICIPAL HOSPITAL AND MANOR (241343)**, 345 Tenth Avenue, Zip 56241–1499; tel. 320/564–3111, (Nonreporting) **A**9 10 18
Primary Contact: George Gerlach, Chief Executive Officer
CFO: Val Hoffman, Chief Financial Officer
CIO: Kris Wilke, Manager Health Information
CHR: Sue Tollefson, Coordinator Payroll Personnel
CNO: Patty Massman, Director of Nursing
Web address: www.granitefallshealthcare.com
Control: City–Government, nonfederal **Service:** General Medical and Surgical

Staffed Beds: 25

HALLOCK—Kittson County

★ **KITTSON MEMORIAL HEALTHCARE CENTER (241336)**, 1010 South Birch Street, Zip 56728–4215, Mailing Address: P.O. Box 700, Zip 56728–0700; tel. 218/843–3612, (Nonreporting) **A**9 10 18
Primary Contact: Cindy Urbaniak, Chief Executive Officer
CFO: Todd Christensen, Chief Financial Officer
CMO: Thomas Lohstreter, M.D., Chief of Staff
CIO: Holly Knutson, Manager Information Technology
CHR: Carlene Cole, Manager Human Resources
CNO: Tawnya Sorenson, Director of Nursing
Web address: www.kmhc.net
Control: Other not–for–profit (including NFP Corporation) **Service:** General Medical and Surgical

Staffed Beds: 85

MN

HASTINGS—Dakota County

✠ **REGINA HOSPITAL (240059)**, 1175 Nininger Road, Zip 55033–1098;
tel. 651/480–4100, (Nonreporting) **A**1 9 10 **S** Allina Health, Minneapolis, MN
Primary Contact: Ty W. Erickson, President
CFO: Andy Rolling, Director of Finance
CMO: James Noreen, M.D., Chief Medical Officer
CHR: Robert P. Verchota, Vice President Support Services
CNO: Karen S. Strauman, R.N., Vice President Patient Care Services
Web address: www.reginamedical.org
Control: Other not–for–profit (including NFP Corporation) **Service:** General
Medical and Surgical

Staffed Beds: 50

HENDRICKS—Lincoln County

★ **HENDRICKS COMMUNITY HOSPITAL (241339)**, 503 East Lincoln Street,
Zip 56136–9598, Mailing Address: P.O. Box 106, Zip 56136–0106;
tel. 507/275–3134, (Total facility includes 58 beds in nursing home–type unit) **A**9
10 18 **F**2 3 7 10 11 15 17 28 29 31 34 35 40 59 62 63 70 81 89 93 125
127 128 130 132 133 146
Primary Contact: Jeffrey Gollaher, Chief Executive Officer
CMO: Tabb McCluskey, M.D., Chief Medical Officer
CHR: Lynn R. Olson, Director Human Resources
Web address: www.hendrickshosp.org
Control: Other not–for–profit (including NFP Corporation) **Service:** General
Medical and Surgical

Staffed Beds: 70 Admissions: 179 Census: 54 Outpatient Visits: 12359
Births: 0 Total Expense ($000): 12194 Payroll Expense ($000): 5911
Personnel: 115

HIBBING—St. Louis County

✠ **RANGE REGIONAL HEALTH SERVICES (240040)**, 750 East 34th Street,
Zip 55746–4600; tel. 218/262–4881 **A**1 2 9 10 **F**3 11 13 15 28 29 30 34 35
40 43 45 48 59 64 70 75 76 77 81 85 86 89 93 98 102 107 108 110 111
115 116 119 120 121 129 130 132 143 144 146 147 148 **P**6 **S** Fairview
Health Services, Minneapolis, MN
Primary Contact: Debra K. Boardman, FACHE, President and Chief Executive
Officer
COO: Patrick Sharp, Senior Vice President and Chief Operating Officer
CFO: Tom Fink, Vice President Regional Finance Officer
CMO: Susan Rudberg, M.D., Chief Medical Officer
CIO: Jessica Valento, Director Information Systems
CHR: Mitch Vincent, Vice President Organizational Support
CNO: Connie Harle, Senior Vice President and Chief Nursing Officer
Web address: www.range.fairview.org
Control: Other not–for–profit (including NFP Corporation) **Service:** General
Medical and Surgical

Staffed Beds: 85 Admissions: 2861 Census: 35 Outpatient Visits: 149154
Births: 387 Total Expense ($000): 108078 Payroll Expense ($000): 52786
Personnel: 818

HUTCHINSON—Mcleod County

✠ **HUTCHINSON HEALTH (240187)**, 1095 Highway 15 South, Zip 55350–3182;
tel. 320/234–5000 **A**1 9 10 20 **F**3 5 11 13 15 18 26 28 29 31 34 35 36 38
40 43 45 56 57 59 64 65 69 70 75 76 77 78 79 81 82 85 87 93 97 98 99
100 101 102 103 104 107 110 111 115 119 127 129 130 131 132 144 146
147 148 **P**6 **S** Allina Health, Minneapolis, MN
Primary Contact: Steven Mulder, M.D., President and Chief Executive Officer
COO: Jim Lyons, Chief Operating Officer
CFO: Pamela Larson, Division Director Financial Services
CMO: Brian Pollman, Chief Medical Officer
CIO: Jim Lyons, Chief Operating Officer
CHR: Rebecca Streich, Manager Human Resources and Education Manager
CNO: Mary Kay Henze, Chief Nursing Officer
Web address: www.hutchhealth.com
Control: Other not–for–profit (including NFP Corporation) **Service:** General
Medical and Surgical

Staffed Beds: 57 Admissions: 2103 Census: 21 Outpatient Visits: 214383
Births: 264 Total Expense ($000): 78006 Payroll Expense ($000): 28846
Personnel: 465

INTERNATIONAL FALLS—Koochiching County

✠ **RAINY LAKE MEDICAL CENTER (241322)**, 1400 Highway 71,
Zip 56649–2189; tel. 218/283–4481, (Nonreporting) **A**1 9 10 18 **S** QHR,
Brentwood, TN
Primary Contact: Daniel Odegaard, FACHE, Chief Executive Officer
CFO: Melissa Marcotte, Chief Financial Officer
CIO: Michael Blesi, Director Information Technology
CNO: Donita Ettestad, R.N., Chief Nursing Officer
Web address: www.rainylakemedical.com
Control: Other not–for–profit (including NFP Corporation) **Service:** General
Medical and Surgical

Staffed Beds: 25

JACKSON—Jackson County

★ **SANFORD JACKSON MEDICAL CENTER (241315)**, 1430 North Highway,
Zip 56143–1093; tel. 507/847–2420, (Nonreporting) **A**9 10 18 **S** Sanford
Health, Sioux Falls, SD
Primary Contact: Mary J. Ruyter, Chief Executive Officer
CFO: Gail Eike, Chief Financial Officer
CMO: Sister Marie Paul Lockerd, M.D., Chief Medical Officer
CNO: Dawn Schnell, Chief Nursing Officer
Web address: www.sanfordjackson.org
Control: Other not–for–profit (including NFP Corporation) **Service:** General
Medical and Surgical

Staffed Beds: 20

LAKE CITY—Goodhue County

☐ **MAYO CLINIC HEALTH SYSTEM IN LAKE CITY (241338)**, 500 West Grant
Street, Zip 55041–1143; tel. 651/345–3321, (Nonreporting) **A**1 9 10 18 **S** Mayo
Clinic, Rochester, MN
Primary Contact: Susan M. Stiene, R.N., MS, Interim Chief Administrative Officer
CFO: David Biren, Chief Financial Officer
CMO: Dennis Spano, M.D., Medical Director
CHR: Jacqueline Ryan, Director Human Resources
Web address: www.lakecitymedicalcenter.org
Control: Other not–for–profit (including NFP Corporation) **Service:** General
Medical and Surgical

Staffed Beds: 108

LE SUEUR—Le Sueur County

★ **MINNESOTA VALLEY HEALTH CENTER (241375)**, 621 South Fourth Street,
Zip 56058–2298; tel. 507/665–3375, (Includes GARDENVIEW NURSING HOME),
(Nonreporting) **A**9 10 18 **S** Essentia Health, Duluth, MN
Primary Contact: Pam Williams, Chief Executive Officer
CFO: Patricia Schlegel, Executive Director Finance
CMO: Carolyn Stelter, M.D., Chief of Staff
CHR: Bonnie Barnhardt, Executive Director Human Resources
Web address: www.mvhc.org
Control: Other not–for–profit (including NFP Corporation) **Service:** General
Medical and Surgical

Staffed Beds: 64

LITCHFIELD—Meeker County

★ **MEEKER MEMORIAL HOSPITAL (241366)**, 612 South Sibley Avenue,
Zip 55355–3398; tel. 320/693–3242 **A**9 10 18 **F**11 13 15 28 29 31 34 40 43
45 57 59 70 75 76 77 78 81 89 90 93 103 107 110 111 114 119 130 132
133 146 148
Primary Contact: Kyle R. Rasmussen, Chief Executive Officer
CFO: Stephen Plaisance, Chief Financial Officer
CMO: Tim Peterson, M.D., Chief of Staff
CIO: Troy Bruning, Director Information Technology
CHR: Cindi Twardy, Manager Human Resources
CNO: Ann Lien, R.N., Chief Nursing Officer
Web address: www.meekermemorial.org
Control: County–Government, nonfederal **Service:** General Medical and Surgical

Staffed Beds: 39 Admissions: 1033 Census: 15 Outpatient Visits: 23990
Births: 144 Total Expense ($000): 27484 Payroll Expense ($000): 9931
Personnel: 151

MN

Hospital, Medicare Provider Number, Address, Telephone, Approval, Facility, and Physician Codes, Health Care System

★ American Hospital Association (AHA) membership
☐ The Joint Commission accreditation
◇ DNV Healthcare Inc. accreditation
○ Healthcare Facilities Accreditation Program
△ Commission on Accreditation of Rehabilitation Facilities (CARF) accreditation

LITTLE FALLS—Morrison County

✠ **ST. GABRIEL'S HOSPITAL (241370)**, 815 Second Street S.E.,
Zip 56345–3596; tel. 320/632–5441 **A**1 9 10 18 **F**3 11 13 15 26 28 29 30
31 34 40 43 45 57 59 62 63 64 65 68 70 75 76 77 79 81 84 85 86 87 93
107 108 110 111 115 119 127 128 130 131 132 133 146 **P**6 **S** Catholic
Health Initiatives, Englewood, CO
Primary Contact: Lee Boyles, President
CFO: Steve Smith, Assistant Vice President Finance
CMO: Susan Okoniewski, M.D., Chief of Staff
Web address: www.stgabriels.com
Control: Church–operated, Nongovernment, not–for profit **Service:** General
Medical and Surgical

Staffed Beds: 25 **Admissions:** 1433 **Census:** 12 **Outpatient Visits:** 41876
Births: 174 **Total Expense ($000):** 46098 **Payroll Expense ($000):** 14355

LONG PRAIRIE—Todd County

★ **CENTRACARE HEALTH–LONG PRAIRIE (241326)**, 20 Ninth Street S.E.,
Zip 56347–1404; tel. 320/732–2141, (Nonreporting) **A**9 10 18 **S** CentraCare
Health, Saint Cloud, MN
Primary Contact: Daniel J. Swenson, FACHE, Administrator and Chief Executive
Officer
CFO: Larry Knutson, Director Finance
CMO: Rene Elddy, M.D., Chief of Staff
Web address: www.centracare.com
Control: Other not–for–profit (including NFP Corporation) **Service:** General
Medical and Surgical

Staffed Beds: 20

LONG PRAIRIE MEMORIAL HOSPITAL AND HOME See CentraCare
Health–Long Prairie

MN

LUVERNE—Rock County

★ **SANFORD LUVERNE MEDICAL CENTER (241371)**, 1600 North Kniss Avenue,
Zip 56156–1067; tel. 507/283–2321 **A**9 10 18 **F**3 4 5 7 8 11 13 15 18 19 28
29 31 32 34 35 40 43 45 56 57 59 63 64 65 67 68 74 75 76 77 78 79 81
82 83 84 85 86 87 90 93 96 97 107 111 114 118 119 128 129 131 132
133 135 146 147 148 **P**6 **S** Sanford Health, Sioux Falls, SD
Primary Contact: Tammy Loosbrock, Chief Executive Officer
COO: Nancy E. Drenth, Director Ancillary Services
CFO: Stanley Knobloch, Chief Financial Officer
CMO: Stephen Chesley, Chief of Staff
CNO: Nyla H. Sandbulte, R.N., Chief Nursing Officer
Web address: www.sanfordluverne.org
Control: Other not–for–profit (including NFP Corporation) **Service:** General
Medical and Surgical

Staffed Beds: 25 **Admissions:** 582 **Census:** 6 **Outpatient Visits:** 30721
Births: 107 **Total Expense ($000):** 21759 **Payroll Expense ($000):** 8986
Personnel: 165

MADELIA—Watonwan County

✠ **MADELIA COMMUNITY HOSPITAL (241323)**, 121 Drew Avenue S.E.,
Zip 56062–1899; tel. 507/642–3255 **A**1 3 5 9 10 18 **F**11 13 15 34 35 40 57
59 62 64 68 69 75 76 77 81 84 85 86 93 102 107 110 114 128 130 132
133 144 145
Primary Contact: Candace Fenske, Chief Executive Officer
CFO: Donna M. Klinkner, Chief Financial Officer
CMO: Todd Gavin, Chief Medical Officer
CIO: Valerie Juhl, Director of Health
CHR: Donna M. Klinkner, Chief Financial Officer
CNO: Deidre Hruby, Director of Patient Care
Web address: www.mchospital.org
Control: Other not–for–profit (including NFP Corporation) **Service:** General
Medical and Surgical

Staffed Beds: 21 **Admissions:** 126 **Census:** 1 **Outpatient Visits:** 3895
Births: 2 **Total Expense ($000):** 10421 **Payroll Expense ($000):** 3914
Personnel: 58

MADISON—Lac Qui Parle County

★ **MADISON HOSPITAL (241372)**, 900 Second Avenue, Zip 56256–1006;
tel. 320/598–7556 **A**9 10 18 **F**10 11 15 28 29 30 34 40 43 57 59 62 64 65
76 77 78 79 81 84 89 93 97 107 110 111 119 127 130 132 133 145
147 **P**5
Primary Contact: Steven T. Moburg, Chief Executive Officer
CFO: Carol Borgerson, Business Office Manager and Chief Financial Officer
CIO: Jerry Harberts, Information Technologist
CHR: Bridget Sabin, Director Human Resources
Web address: www.madisonlutheranhome.com
Control: Other not–for–profit (including NFP Corporation) **Service:** General
Medical and Surgical

Staffed Beds: 12 **Admissions:** 212 **Census:** 2 **Outpatient Visits:** 12530
Births: 10 **Total Expense ($000):** 6337 **Payroll Expense ($000):** 2155
Personnel: 58

MAHNOMEN—Mahnomen County

★ **MAHNOMEN HEALTH CENTER (241300)**, 414 West Jefferson Avenue,
Zip 56557–4912, Mailing Address: P.O. Box 396, Zip 56557–0396;
tel. 218/935–2511, (Nonreporting) **A**9 10 18 **S** Sanford Health, Sioux Falls, SD
Primary Contact: Susan K. Klassen, Chief Executive Officer and Administrator
CFO: Mary Pazdernik, Chief Financial Officer
CMO: Anju Gurung, M.D., Chief Medical Officer
CHR: Kristi Stall, Chief Human Resources Officer
Web address: www.mahnomenhealthcenter.com
Control: City–County, Government, nonfederal **Service:** General Medical and
Surgical

Staffed Beds: 18

MANKATO—Blue Earth County

✠ **MAYO CLINIC HEALTH SYSTEM IN MANKATO (240093)**, 1025 Marsh Street,
Zip 56001–4752, Mailing Address: P.O. Box 8673, Zip 56002–8673;
tel. 507/625–4031 **A**1 3 5 9 10 19 20 **F**3 11 12 13 15 18 20 22 26 27 28 29
30 31 33 34 35 36 38 39 40 41 43 45 49 53 54 56 57 58 59 60 61 62 63
64 65 66 68 70 74 75 76 77 78 79 81 82 83 84 85 86 87 89 91 92 93 97
98 99 100 102 103 104 107 108 110 111 114 115 116 118 119 120 121
123 126 127 129 130 132 135 144 146 147 148 **P**6 **S** Mayo Clinic,
Rochester, MN
Primary Contact: Gregory Kutcher, M.D., President and Chief Executive Officer
CFO: Stanley Marczak, Chief Financial Officer
CMO: Brian Whited, M.D., Medical Director
CIO: Thomas Borowski, Chief Information Officer
CHR: Julie Oliver, Chief Human Resources Officer
Web address: www.isj–mhs.org
Control: Other not–for–profit (including NFP Corporation) **Service:** General
Medical and Surgical

Staffed Beds: 166 **Admissions:** 10536 **Census:** 107 **Outpatient Visits:**
373581 **Births:** 1469 **Total Expense ($000):** 287327 **Payroll Expense
($000):** 156850 **Personnel:** 1895

MAPLE GROVE—Hennepin County

✠ ◇ **MAPLE GROVE HOSPITAL (240214)**, 9875 Hospital Drive,
Zip 55369–4648; tel. 763/581–1000 **A**1 9 10 21 **F**3 13 15 18 29 30 40 45
60 68 70 73 76 77 79 81 84 85 89 100 102 107 108 111 115 118 119 130
146 148 **P**8 **S** North Memorial Health Care, Robbinsdale, MN
Primary Contact: Andrew S. Cochrane, Chief Executive Officer
COO: Colleen Nadeau, Vice President and Patient Care Operations
CFO: Robert Geiman, Senior Financial Analyst
CHR: Kate J. Law, Director Human Resources
CNO: Faith Zwirchitz, Director Nursing and Professional Practice
Web address: www.maplegrovehospital.org
Control: Other not–for–profit (including NFP Corporation) **Service:** General
Medical and Surgical

Staffed Beds: 108 **Admissions:** 7729 **Census:** 56 **Outpatient Visits:** 159504
Births: 4025 **Total Expense ($000):** 114040 **Payroll Expense ($000):**
39781 **Personnel:** 679

MARSHALL—Lyon County

★ **AVERA MARSHALL REGIONAL MEDICAL CENTER (241359)**, 300 South
Bruce Street, Zip 56258–3900; tel. 507/532–9661, (Nonreporting) **A**9 10 18
S Avera Health, Sioux Falls, SD
Primary Contact: Mary B. Maertens, FACHE, President and Chief Executive Officer
CFO: Sharon Williams, Vice President Finance and Information Technology
CMO: Edward Woiske, M.D., Chief Medical Officer
CIO: Sharon Williams, Vice President Finance and Information Technology
CHR: Sonya Kayser, Human Resources Officer
Web address: www.averamarshall.org
Control: City–Government, nonfederal **Service:** General Medical and Surgical

Staffed Beds: 25

MELROSE—Stearns County

★ **CENTRACARE HEALTH–MELROSE (241330)**, 525 Main Street West,
Zip 56352–1043; tel. 320/256–4231, (Total facility includes 75 beds in nursing
home–type unit) **A**9 10 18 **F**2 6 7 10 13 15 28 30 34 35 40 46 56 57 59 75
76 77 78 79 81 82 85 89 93 99 103 107 110 115 119 121 122 125 127
128 129 130 132 133 146 148 **S** CentraCare Health, Saint Cloud, MN
Primary Contact: Gerry Gilbertson, FACHE, Administrator
COO: Gerry Gilbertson, FACHE, Administrator
CFO: Adam Paulson, Director Finance
CMO: Dante Beretta, M.D., Chief of Staff
CIO: Janet Kruzel, Business Office Manager
CHR: Joyce Chan, Chief Human Resources Officer
CNO: Keri Wimmer, R.N., Patient Care Director
Web address: www.centracare.com
Control: Other not–for–profit (including NFP Corporation) **Service:** General
Medical and Surgical

Staffed Beds: 93 **Admissions:** 583 **Census:** 78 **Outpatient Visits:** 22074
Births: 76 **Total Expense ($000):** 24544 **Payroll Expense ($000):** 11150
Personnel: 209

MINNEAPOLIS—Hennepin County

ABBOTT NORTHWESTERN HOSPITAL (240057), 800 East 28th Street,
Zip 55407–3799; tel. 612/863–4000, (Includes SISTER KENNY REHABILITATION
INSTITUTE, 810 East 27th Street, Zip 55407; tel. 612/874–4000), (Total facility
includes 40 beds in nursing home–type unit) **A**1 2 3 5 8 9 10 **F**3 8 9 11 12 13 15
17 18 19 20 22 24 26 28 29 30 31 34 35 36 37 38 39 40 41 42 43 44 45
46 47 48 49 50 51 52 53 54 55 56 57 58 59 60 61 63 64 65 66 68 70 71
74 75 76 77 78 79 81 82 83 84 85 86 87 90 91 92 93 94 95 96 97 98 99
100 101 102 103 104 105 107 108 109 110 111 112 113 114 115 116 117
118 119 120 121 123 124 126 128 129 130 131 132 136 137 138 141
143 144 145 146 147 148 **P**6 **S** Allina Health, Minneapolis, MN
Primary Contact: Ben Bache–Wiig, M.D., President
CFO: Brian Weinreis, Vice President Operations and Finance
CMO: Penny Ann Wheeler, M.D., President and Chief Medical Officer
CIO: Susan Heichert, Senior Vice President and Chief Information Officer
CHR: Margaret Butler, Vice President Human Resources
CNO: Terry J. Graner, R.N., Vice President Patient Care
Web address: www.abbottnorthwestern.com
Control: Other not–for–profit (including NFP Corporation) **Service:** General
Medical and Surgical

Staffed Beds: 670 **Admissions:** 38168 **Census:** 457 **Outpatient Visits:**
401955 **Births:** 5157 **Total Expense ($000):** 980073 **Payroll Expense
($000):** 403666 **Personnel:** 3970

CHILDREN'S HOSPITALS AND CLINICS OF MINNESOTA (243302), 2525
Chicago Avenue South, Zip 55404–4518; tel. 612/813–6100, (Includes
CHILDREN'S HOSPITALS AND CLINICS OF MINNESOTA, 345 North Smith Avenue,
Saint Paul, Zip 55102–2346; tel. 651/220–6000) **A**1 3 5 9 10 **F**3 8 9 11 12 17
18 19 20 21 22 23 24 25 26 27 28 29 30 31 32 34 35 36 38 39 40 41 43
44 48 50 51 54 55 57 58 59 60 61 62 63 64 65 66 68 72 73 74 75 77 78
79 80 81 82 84 85 86 87 88 89 91 93 97 99 100 101 102 104 107 108 109
111 112 113 114 115 117 118 119 129 130 131 132 134 135 136 143 145
146 148 **P**6 8
Primary Contact: Alan L. Goldbloom, M.D., Chief Executive Officer
COO: David S. Overman, President and Chief Operating Officer
CFO: K. Alec Mahmood, Chief Financial Officer
CMO: Phillip M. Kibort, M.D., Vice President Medical Affairs and Chief Medical
Officer
CIO: Jeffrey D. Young, Chief Information Officer
CHR: Samantha Hanson, Chief Human Resources Officer
CNO: Roxanne Fernandes, R.N., Chief Nursing Officer
Web address: www.childrensmn.org
Control: Other not–for–profit (including NFP Corporation) **Service:** Children's
general

Staffed Beds: 383 **Admissions:** 13024 **Census:** 263 **Outpatient Visits:**
525541 **Births:** 0 **Total Expense ($000):** 647638 **Payroll Expense ($000):**
304549 **Personnel:** 3586

FAIRVIEW RIVERSIDE HOSPITAL See University of Minnesota Medical Center,
Fairview

HENNEPIN COUNTY MEDICAL CENTER (240004), 701 Park Avenue
South, Zip 55415–1829; tel. 612/873–3000, (Includes HCMC DEPARTMENT OF
PEDIATRICS, 701 Park Avenue, Zip 55415–1623; tel. 612/873–2064) **A**1 2 3 5
7 8 9 10 **F**3 5 7 12 13 15 16 18 20 22 24 26 28 29 30 31 32 33 34 35 36
38 39 40 41 43 44 45 46 48 49 50 51 53 54 55 56 57 58 59 60 61 64 65
66 68 70 72 74 75 76 77 78 79 81 82 84 85 86 87 88 89 90 92 93 94 96
97 98 99 100 101 102 103 104 105 107 108 110 111 112 114 115 117
118 119 120 121 129 130 131 132 134 135 138 141 144 145 146 147
148 **P**6
Primary Contact: Jon Pryor, M.D., Chief Executive Officer
CFO: Larry Kryzaniak, Chief Financial Officer
CMO: Michael Belzer, M.D., Medical Director
CIO: Nancy Garrett, Chief Analytics and Information Technology Officer
CHR: Walter Chesley, Vice President Human Resources
CNO: Kathy R. Wilde, R.N., Chief Nursing Officer
Web address: www.hcmc.org
Control: County–Government, nonfederal **Service:** General Medical and Surgical

Staffed Beds: 447 **Admissions:** 22090 **Census:** 331 **Outpatient Visits:**
537467 **Births:** 2259 **Total Expense ($000):** 773288 **Payroll Expense
($000):** 430085 **Personnel:** 5026

MINNEAPOLIS VETERANS AFFAIRS HEALTH CARE SYSTEM, One
Veterans Drive, Zip 55417–2399; tel. 612/725–2000, (Nonreporting) **A**1 2 3 5 7
8 **S** Department of Veterans Affairs, Washington, DC
Primary Contact: Patrick J. Kelly, FACHE, Director
COO: Kurt Thielen, Manager Business Office
CFO: LeAnn Stomberg, Chief Financial Officer
CMO: Kent Crossley, M.D., Acting Chief of Staff
CIO: Karl Reid, Chief Information Officer
CHR: Kevin Upham, Chief Human Resources Officer
CNO: Helen Pearlman, Nurse Executive
Web address: www.minneapolis.va.gov
Control: Veterans Affairs, Government, federal **Service:** General Medical and
Surgical

Staffed Beds: 279

PARK NICOLLET METHODIST HOSPITAL (240053), 6500 Excelsior
Boulevard, Zip 55426–4702; Mailing Address: Minneapolis, tel. 952/993–5000
A1 2 3 5 7 9 10 **F**3 8 12 13 15 18 20 22 24 26 28 29 30 31 33 34 35 36 40
43 45 46 47 49 51 52 53 55 56 58 59 60 61 62 63 64 65 67 68 70 73 74
75 76 77 78 79 81 82 84 85 86 87 89 90 92 93 94 96 97 99 100 102 104
106 107 108 109 110 111 115 116 117 118 119 120 121 123 124 126 129
130 131 132 144 146 147 148 **S** HealthPartners, Bloomington, MN
Primary Contact: David Abelson, M.D., President and Chief Executive Officer
COO: Michael Kaupa, Executive Vice President and Chief Operating Officer
CFO: Sheila McMillan, Chief Financial Officer
CMO: Steven Connelly, M.D., Chief Medical Officer
CIO: Julie Flaschenriem, Chief Information Officer
CHR: Paul Dominski, Vice President Human Resources
CNO: Roxanna L. Gapstur, Ph.D., Chief Nursing Officer
Web address: www.parknicollet.com
Control: Other not–for–profit (including NFP Corporation) **Service:** General
Medical and Surgical

Staffed Beds: 393 **Admissions:** 23843 **Census:** 215 **Outpatient Visits:**
56216 **Births:** 2911 **Total Expense ($000):** 1231365 **Payroll Expense
($000):** 635273 **Personnel:** 3506

PHILLIPS EYE INSTITUTE (240196), 2215 Park Avenue, Zip 55404–3756;
tel. 612/775–8800 **A**1 9 10 **F**81 **S** Allina Health, Minneapolis, MN
Primary Contact: Daniel S. Conrad, M.D., Chief Executive Officer
CFO: Chris Verdon, Director Finance
CMO: Emmett Carpel, M.D., Medical Director and Chief of Staff
CNO: Margaret Watry, Director of Patient Care Services and Nurse Executive
Web address: www.allinahealth.org/ahs/pei.nsf/
Control: Other not–for–profit (including NFP Corporation) **Service:** Eye, ear,
nose, and throat

Staffed Beds: 8 **Admissions:** 126 **Census:** 1 **Outpatient Visits:** 15246
Births: 0 **Total Expense ($000):** 30598 **Payroll Expense ($000):** 9349
Personnel: 118

SHRINERS HOSPITALS FOR CHILDREN–TWIN CITIES (243303), 2025 East
River Parkway, Zip 55414–3696; tel. 612/596–6100, (Nonreporting) **A**1 3 5 10
S Shriners Hospitals for Children, Tampa, FL
Primary Contact: Charles C. Lobeck, Administrator
CMO: Kenneth Guidera, M.D., Chief of Staff
CHR: Karen Frigen, Director Human Resources
Web address: www.shrinershospitalsforchildren.org/Hospitals/Locations/twincities.
aspx
Control: Other not–for–profit (including NFP Corporation) **Service:** Children's
orthopedic

Staffed Beds: 40

SISTER KENNY REHABILITATION INSTITUTE See Abbott Northwestern
Hospital

ST. MARY'S HOSPITAL AND REHABILITATION CENTER See University of
Minnesota Medical Center, Fairview

UNIVERSITY OF MINNESOTA HOSPITAL AND CLINIC See University of
Minnesota Medical Center, Fairview

⊞ **UNIVERSITY OF MINNESOTA MEDICAL CENTER, FAIRVIEW (240080)**, 2450 Riverside Avenue, Zip 55454–1400; tel. 612/672–6000, (Includes FAIRVIEW RIVERSIDE HOSPITAL, 2312 South Sixth Street, Zip 55454; tel. 612/371–6300; ST. MARY'S HOSPITAL AND REHABILITATION CENTER, 2414 South Seventh Street, Zip 55454; tel. 612/338–2229; UNIVERSITY OF MINNESOTA CHILDREN'S HOSPITAL, FAIRVIEW, 420 Delaware Street, S.E., Zip 55455–0341; tel. 888/543–7866; UNIVERSITY OF MINNESOTA HOSPITAL AND CLINIC, 420 S.E. Delaware Street, Zip 55455–0392; tel. 612/626–3000), (Total facility includes 36 beds in nursing home–type unit) **A**1 3 5 8 9 10 **F**2 3 4 5 6 8 9 11 12 13 14 15 17 18 19 20 21 22 23 24 25 26 27 28 29 30 31 32 33 34 35 36 37 38 39 40 41 43 44 45 46 47 48 49 50 51 52 54 55 56 57 58 59 60 61 64 65 66 68 70 71 72 73 74 75 76 77 78 79 80 81 82 84 85 86 87 88 89 90 91 92 93 96 97 98 99 100 101 102 103 104 105 106 107 108 109 110 111 112 113 114 115 116 117 118 119 120 121 123 124 126 128 129 130 131 132 133 134 135 136 137 138 139 140 141 142 143 145 146 147 148 **P**5 **S** Fairview Health Services, Minneapolis, MN
Primary Contact: Carolyn Wilson, R.N., President
CFO: John Doherty, Vice President Finance
CMO: Barbara Gold, M.D., Chief Medical Officer
CHR: Don Moschkau, Senior Director Human Resources
CNO: Laura Reed, Chief Nursing Officer
Web address: www.fairview.org
Control: Other not–for–profit (including NFP Corporation) **Service:** General Medical and Surgical

Staffed Beds: 844 **Admissions:** 35626 **Census:** 625 **Outpatient Visits:** 759896 **Births:** 2429 **Total Expense ($000):** 1265932 **Payroll Expense ($000):** 461530 **Personnel:** 6404

VETERANS AFFAIRS MEDICAL CENTER See Minneapolis Veterans Affairs Health Care System

MONTEVIDEO—Chippewa County

★ **CHIPPEWA COUNTY–MONTEVIDEO HOSPITAL (241325)**, 824 North 11th Street, Zip 56265–1683; tel. 320/269–8877 **A**9 10 18 **F**3 7 11 13 15 28 29 30 31 34 35 40 43 50 57 59 62 64 74 75 78 79 81 85 87 93 94 97 107 110 114 119 129 130 132 133 146 148 **P**2 4 6
Primary Contact: Mark E. Paulson, Chief Executive Officer
CFO: Darlene Boike, Chief Financial Officer
CIO: Jane Myhre, MS, Director Health Information
CNO: Linda M. Nelson, R.N., Director of Nursing Services
Web address: www.montevideomedical.com
Control: City–County, Government, nonfederal **Service:** General Medical and Surgical

Staffed Beds: 25 **Admissions:** 875 **Census:** 8 **Outpatient Visits:** 54609 **Births:** 117

MONTICELLO—Wright County

⊞ **CENTRACARE HEALTH–MONTICELLO (241362)**, 1013 Hart Boulevard, Zip 55362–8230; tel. 763/295–2945, (Total facility includes 89 beds in nursing home–type unit) (Data for 91 days) **A**1 3 5 9 10 18 **F**3 7 11 13 15 30 31 34 40 43 51 69 70 75 78 79 81 90 107 111 115 117 119 120 121 123 128 130 132 133 146 147 148 **S** CentraCare Health, Saint Cloud, MN
Primary Contact: Mary Ellen Wells, FACHE, Administrator
CFO: Nancy Friesen, Chief Financial Officer
CMO: Mark Dietz, Chief Medical Officer
CIO: Ruth Kremer, Director Information Services
CHR: Kathy Voss, Director Human Resources
CNO: Euretta Sorenson, R.N., Chief Nursing Officer
Web address: www.newrivermedical.com
Control: Other not–for–profit (including NFP Corporation) **Service:** General Medical and Surgical

Staffed Beds: 110 **Admissions:** 245 **Census:** 95 **Outpatient Visits:** 6135 **Births:** 0 **Total Expense ($000):** 14938 **Payroll Expense ($000):** 6055 **Personnel:** 324

MOOSE LAKE—Carlton County

★ **MERCY HOSPITAL (241350)**, 710 South Kenwood Avenue, Zip 55767–9405; tel. 218/485–4481 **A**9 10 18 **F**3 7 8 11 13 15 28 29 31 34 35 40 43 45 46 53 57 59 62 64 68 70 75 76 77 79 81 85 86 87 89 93 107 111 114 119 130 131 132 133 135 143 144 146 148 **P**5
Primary Contact: Michael Delff, Chief Executive Officer
CHR: Sonya Towle, Director Human Resources
CNO: Donita Korpela, R.N., Director of Patient Care Services
Web address: www.mercymooselake.org
Control: Hospital district or authority, Government, nonfederal **Service:** General Medical and Surgical

Staffed Beds: 25 **Admissions:** 755 **Census:** 7 **Outpatient Visits:** 26974 **Births:** 118 **Total Expense ($000):** 30113 **Payroll Expense ($000):** 13383 **Personnel:** 211

MORA—Kanabec County

⊞ **FIRSTLIGHT HEALTH SYSTEM (241367)**, 301 South Highway 65 South, Zip 55051–1899; tel. 320/679–1212 **A**1 9 10 18 **F**3 7 11 12 13 15 28 30 31 34 35 40 43 51 53 57 59 70 75 76 77 78 79 81 84 85 87 93 94 107 110 111 115 118 119 127 130 132 133 135 146
Primary Contact: Randy Ulseth, Chief Executive Officer
CFO: Gordy Forbort, Chief Financial Officer
CIO: Becky Gallik, Information Sytems Manager
CHR: Kim Carlson, Director Human Resources
CNO: Diane Bankers, Director of Nursing
Web address: www.firstlighthealthsystem.org
Control: County–Government, nonfederal **Service:** General Medical and Surgical

Staffed Beds: 25 **Admissions:** 1257 **Census:** 8 **Outpatient Visits:** 32277 **Births:** 151 **Total Expense ($000):** 50570 **Payroll Expense ($000):** 18398 **Personnel:** 326

MORRIS—Stevens County

★ **STEVENS COMMUNITY MEDICAL CENTER (241363)**, 400 East First Street, Zip 56267–1408, Mailing Address: P.O. Box 660, Zip 56267–0660; tel. 320/589–1313 **A**9 10 18 **F**3 11 12 13 15 28 29 31 34 35 40 44 45 50 57 59 64 70 76 77 79 81 85 86 87 89 97 107 111 114 119 130 131 132 133 135 145 146 148 **P**6
Primary Contact: John Rau, President and Chief Executive Officer
CFO: Kerrie McEvilly, Director Finance and Information Systems
CIO: Kerrie McEvilly, Director Finance and Information Systems
CHR: Karla Larson, Director Human Resources
Web address: www.scmcinc.org
Control: Other not–for–profit (including NFP Corporation) **Service:** General Medical and Surgical

Staffed Beds: 25 **Admissions:** 956 **Census:** 9 **Outpatient Visits:** 71374 **Births:** 97 **Total Expense ($000):** 35043 **Payroll Expense ($000):** 17612 **Personnel:** 249

NEW PRAGUE—Scott County

⊞ **MAYO CLINIC HEALTH SYSTEM IN NEW PRAGUE (241361)**, 301 Second Street N.E., Zip 56071–1799; tel. 952/758–4431 **A**1 9 10 18 **F**8 11 13 15 17 28 29 30 31 34 35 36 39 40 43 46 53 57 59 63 64 68 70 74 75 76 77 78 79 81 82 85 87 89 90 93 97 107 108 111 114 117 119 125 129 130 131 132 133 135 146 147 **P**6 **S** Mayo Clinic, Rochester, MN
Primary Contact: Mary J. Klimp, FACHE, Administrator
CMO: Marty Herrmann, M.D., Medical Director
Web address: www.mayoclinichealthsystem.org/locations/new-prague
Control: Other not–for–profit (including NFP Corporation) **Service:** General Medical and Surgical

Staffed Beds: 25 **Admissions:** 760 **Census:** 9 **Outpatient Visits:** 59521 **Births:** 147 **Total Expense ($000):** 35573 **Payroll Expense ($000):** 13048 **Personnel:** 162

NEW ULM—Brown County

⊞ **NEW ULM MEDICAL CENTER (241378)**, 1324 Fifth Street North, Zip 56073–1553; tel. 507/217–5000 **A**1 9 10 18 **F**3 4 5 11 13 15 28 29 31 32 34 35 36 40 43 45 55 56 57 59 64 65 68 70 75 76 77 78 79 81 82 85 87 93 94 97 98 99 100 101 102 103 104 107 108 111 114 119 129 130 131 132 135 144 146 148 **S** Allina Health, Minneapolis, MN
Primary Contact: Toby Freier, President
CFO: Steve Schneider, Director of Operations
CMO: Daniel Holmbert, Director of Medical Affairs
CHR: Anne Makepeace, Director Human Resources
Web address: www.newulmmedicalcenter.com
Control: Other not–for–profit (including NFP Corporation) **Service:** General Medical and Surgical

Staffed Beds: 45 **Admissions:** 2267 **Census:** 19 **Outpatient Visits:** 115999 **Births:** 315 **Total Expense ($000):** 72963 **Payroll Expense ($000):** 24336 **Personnel:** 478

NORTHFIELD—Dakota County

★ **NORTHFIELD HOSPITAL (240014)**, 2000 North Avenue, Zip 55057–1498; tel. 507/646–1000, (Includes LONG TERM CARE CENTER), (Total facility includes 40 beds in nursing home–type unit) **A**9 10 **F**3 7 11 15 29 30 31 34 35 40 43 45 46 47 48 49 57 59 62 63 64 68 69 70 75 76 77 78 79 81 85 86 87 93 94 97 107 110 111 113 115 117 119 120 128 129 130 131 132 133 146 147 **P**6
Primary Contact: Steve Underdahl, Chief Executive Officer
COO: Jerry Ehn, Chief Operating Officer
CFO: Timothy L. Gronseth, Vice President and Chief Financial Officer
CMO: Jeff Meland, M.D., Vice President, Chief Medical Officer
CHR: Vicki Stevens, Human Resources Executive
CNO: Tammy Hayes, Chief Nursing Officer and Long Term Care Administrator
Web address: www.northfieldhospital.org
Control: City–Government, nonfederal **Service:** General Medical and Surgical

Staffed Beds: 77 **Admissions:** 1772 **Census:** 50 **Outpatient Visits:** 121102 **Births:** 544 **Total Expense ($000):** 77046 **Payroll Expense ($000):** 31124 **Personnel:** 430

OLIVIA—Renville County

★ **RC HOSPITAL AND CLINICS (241306)**, 611 East Fairview Avenue,
Zip 56277–4213; tel. 320/523–1261 **A**9 10 18 **F**3 8 13 15 17 28 29 34 35
40 41 43 45 46 57 59 63 64 65 68 70 76 77 79 81 82 85 86 89 93 94 97
107 114 119 127 128 129 130 131 132 133 147 148 **P**6
Primary Contact: Nathan Blad, Chief Executive Officer
CFO: Nathan Blad, Chief Financial Officer
CIO: Cherry Weigel, Director Health Information Management
Web address: www.rchospital.com
Control: County–Government, nonfederal **Service:** General Medical and Surgical

Staffed Beds: 25 **Admissions:** 424 **Census:** 5 **Outpatient Visits:** 42044
Births: 16 **Total Expense ($000):** 16961 **Payroll Expense ($000):** 7824
Personnel: 108

ONAMIA—Mille Lacs County

★ **MILLE LACS HEALTH SYSTEM (241356)**, 200 North Elm Street,
Zip 56359–7901; tel. 320/532–3154, (Total facility includes 57 beds in nursing
home–type unit) **A**9 10 18 **F**7 11 15 28 29 31 33 34 40 43 45 50 59 62 63 64
75 77 81 85 93 98 103 107 110 114 127 129 130 132 133 135 144 **P**6
Primary Contact: Bill Nelson, Chief Executive Officer
COO: Kim Kucera, Chief Operating Officer
CFO: John Unzen, Chief Financial Officer
CMO: Thomas H. Bracken, M.D., Vice President Medical Affairs
Web address: www.mlhealth.org
Control: Other not–for–profit (including NFP Corporation) **Service:** General Medical and Surgical

Staffed Beds: 85 **Admissions:** 928 **Census:** 69 **Outpatient Visits:** 25186
Births: 1 **Total Expense ($000):** 35730 **Payroll Expense ($000):** 17374
Personnel: 340

ORTONVILLE—Big Stone County

★ **ORTONVILLE AREA HEALTH SERVICES (241342)**, 450 Eastvold Avenue,
Zip 56278–1133; tel. 320/839–2502, (Nonreporting) **A**5 9 10 18 **S** Sanford
Health, Sioux Falls, SD
Primary Contact: Richard M. Ash, Chief Executive Officer
CFO: Kevin Benson, Chief Financial Officer
CMO: Stacy Longnecker, Chief of Staff
CIO: Barbara Voecks, Chief Information Officer
CHR: Kim McCrea, Chief Human Resources Officer
CNO: Jennifer Wiik, Chief Nursing Officer
Web address: www.oahs.us
Control: City–Government, nonfederal **Service:** General Medical and Surgical

Staffed Beds: 81

OWATONNA—Steele County

⊞ **OWATONNA HOSPITAL (240069)**, 2250 N.W. 26th Street, Zip 55060–5503;
tel. 507/451–3850 **A**1 9 10 **F**11 13 28 29 34 35 40 57 76 77 79 80 81 89
93 98 100 101 102 103 107 108 119 129 130 131 145 **S** Allina Health,
Minneapolis, MN
Primary Contact: David L. Albrecht, President
CFO: Mark T. Gillen, Director Finance and Operations
CHR: Sarah Stumme, Director Human Resources
CNO: Anne Draeger, Chief Nursing Officer
Web address: www.owatonnahospital.com
Control: Other not–for–profit (including NFP Corporation) **Service:** General Medical and Surgical

Staffed Beds: 43 **Admissions:** 2713 **Census:** 26 **Outpatient Visits:** 34358
Births: 548 **Total Expense ($000):** 46825 **Payroll Expense ($000):** 17023
Personnel: 225

PARK RAPIDS—Hubbard County

⊞ **CHI ST. JOSEPH'S HEALTH (241380)**, 600 Pleasant Avenue,
Zip 56470–1431; tel. 218/732–3311 **A**1 5 9 10 18 **F**3 11 12 13 15 28 29 30
32 34 35 39 40 43 45 47 57 59 63 64 65 70 75 76 77 79 81 82 84 85 93
107 108 110 114 118 119 129 130 131 132 133 134 146 **S** Catholic Health
Initiatives, Englewood, CO
Primary Contact: Benjamin Koppelman, President
CFO: Jay Ross, Chief Financial Officer
CMO: Darryl Beehler, D.O., Chief of Staff
CHR: John Tormanen, Director Mission and Human Resources
CNO: Deb Haagenson, R.N., Vice President of Patient Care
Web address: www.sjahs.org
Control: Church–operated, Nongovernment, not–for profit **Service:** General Medical and Surgical

Staffed Beds: 25 **Admissions:** 1500 **Census:** 15 **Outpatient Visits:** 34498
Births: 110 **Total Expense ($000):** 42413 **Payroll Expense ($000):** 15869
Personnel: 228

PAYNESVILLE—Stearns County

★ **CENTRACARE HEALTH–PAYNESVILLE (241349)**, 200 West 1st Street,
Zip 56362–1496; tel. 320/243–3767, (Total facility includes 52 beds in nursing
home–type unit) **A**9 10 18 **F**7 10 11 13 15 17 28 31 40 43 56 64 75 81 85
107 110 115 119 125 127 128 130 133 143 145 146 148 **P**8 **S** CentraCare
Health, Saint Cloud, MN
Primary Contact: Dennis C. Miley, Administrator
CFO: Gregg Redfield, Director Finance
CMO: Timothy Malling, M.D., Chief of Staff
CHR: Paulette Hagen, Human Resources and Administrative Services Director
CNO: Rachel A. Walz, Director Patient Care
Web address: www.centracare.com
Control: Hospital district or authority, Government, nonfederal **Service:** General Medical and Surgical

Staffed Beds: 77 **Admissions:** 572 **Census:** 57 **Outpatient Visits:** 19274
Births: 88 **Total Expense ($000):** 33814 **Payroll Expense ($000):** 15859
Personnel: 197

PERHAM—Otter Tail County

⊞ **PERHAM HEALTH (241373)**, 1000 Coney Street West, Zip 56573–1108;
tel. 218/347–4500, (Total facility includes 96 beds in nursing home–type unit) **A**1
9 10 18 **F**3 10 13 15 28 29 30 33 34 35 36 40 43 45 56 57 59 62 64 69 75
76 77 81 85 86 89 93 97 107 110 111 115 119 125 128 130 131 132 133
144 146 147 148 **S** Sanford Health, Sioux Falls, SD
Primary Contact: Chuck Hofius, Chief Executive Officer
CFO: Brad D. Wurgler, Chief Financial Officer
CMO: Tim Studer, President Medical Staff
CIO: Jim Rieber, Director Information Systems
CHR: Nicole Schell, Director Human Resources
CNO: Bonnie Johnson, R.N., Vice President of Patient Services
Web address: www.perhamhealth.org
Control: Hospital district or authority, Government, nonfederal **Service:** General Medical and Surgical

Staffed Beds: 121 **Admissions:** 1002 **Census:** 98 **Outpatient Visits:** 72298
Births: 127 **Total Expense ($000):** 43748 **Payroll Expense ($000):** 18824
Personnel: 400

PIPESTONE—Pipestone County

★ **PIPESTONE COUNTY MEDICAL CENTER AVERA (241374)**, 916 4th Avenue
S.W., Zip 56164–1890; tel. 507/825–5811 **A**9 10 18 **F**8 13 15 28 29 31 34
40 45 46 47 48 50 53 56 57 59 62 63 64 65 68 75 76 77 79 81 82 85 93
107 110 111 114 119 130 131 132 133 135 146 148 **P**6 **S** Avera Health,
Sioux Falls, SD
Primary Contact: Bradley D. Burris, Chief Executive Officer
CFO: Dave Keeler, Chief Financial Officer
CHR: Judy Raschke, Director Human Resources
CNO: Jessica Smidt, R.N., Director of Nursing
Web address: www.pcmchealth.org
Control: County–Government, nonfederal **Service:** General Medical and Surgical

Staffed Beds: 25 **Admissions:** 383 **Census:** 4 **Outpatient Visits:** 29975
Births: 70 **Total Expense ($000):** 21771 **Payroll Expense ($000):** 9974
Personnel: 173

PRINCETON—Sherburne County

⊞ **FAIRVIEW NORTHLAND MEDICAL CENTER (240141)**, 911 Northland Drive,
Zip 55371–2173; tel. 763/389–1313 **A**1 5 9 10 **F**3 11 13 15 18 19 20 26 28
29 30 31 32 34 35 40 43 45 46 50 57 59 64 70 75 76 77 78 81 85 86 87
89 91 93 100 107 110 111 114 115 119 129 130 132 146 **P**6 **S** Fairview
Health Services, Minneapolis, MN
Primary Contact: John W. Herman, Chief Executive Officer
CFO: Kim Ericson, Vice President Finance
CMO: Greg Schoen, M.D., Regional Medical Director
CHR: Caity Eggen, Senior Director Human Resources and Ancillary Services
Web address: www.northland.fairview.org
Control: Other not–for–profit (including NFP Corporation) **Service:** General Medical and Surgical

Staffed Beds: 31 **Admissions:** 1673 **Census:** 13 **Outpatient Visits:** 52305
Births: 453 **Total Expense ($000):** 56524 **Payroll Expense ($000):** 24253
Personnel: 269

Hospital, Medicare Provider Number, Address, Telephone, Approval, Facility, and Physician Codes, Health Care System

★ American Hospital Association (AHA) membership
□ The Joint Commission accreditation ◇ DNV Healthcare Inc. accreditation
○ Healthcare Facilities Accreditation Program
△ Commission on Accreditation of Rehabilitation Facilities (CARF) accreditation

RED WING—Goodhue County

☒ **MAYO CLINIC HEALTH SYSTEM IN RED WING (240018)**, 701 Hewitt Boulevard, Zip 55066–2848, Mailing Address: P.O. Box 95, Zip 55066–0095; tel. 651/267–5000, (Nonreporting) **A**1 9 10 **S** Mayo Clinic, Rochester, MN
Primary Contact: Thomas J. Witt, M.D., President and Chief Executive Officer
CMO: Jack Alexander, M.D., Chief Medical Officer
CHR: Kim Trittin, Manager Human Resources
Web address: www.mayoclinichealthsystem.org/locations/red-wing
Control: Other not–for–profit (including NFP Corporation) **Service:** General Medical and Surgical

Staffed Beds: 134

REDLAKE—Beltrami County

☐ **U.S. PUBLIC HEALTH SERVICE INDIAN HOSPITAL (240206)**, Highway 1, Zip 56671, Mailing Address: P.O. Box 497, Zip 56671–0497; tel. 218/679–3912, (Nonreporting) **A**1 9 10 **S** U. S. Indian Health Service, Rockville, MD
Primary Contact: Mark Karzon, Chief Executive Officer
CMO: John Robinson, M.D., Clinical Director
Web address: www.ihs.gov
Control: PHS, Indian Service, Government, federal **Service:** General Medical and Surgical

Staffed Beds: 19

REDWOOD FALLS—Redwood County

★ **REDWOOD AREA HOSPITAL (241351)**, 100 Fallwood Road, Zip 56283–1828; tel. 507/637–4500 **A**9 10 18 **F**2 3 11 13 15 29 31 34 35 40 45 46 57 59 62 63 75 77 81 84 93 107 115 119 129 130 131 133 146 148
Primary Contact: Bryan Lydick, Chief Executive Officer
CFO: Thomas Richard, Director Budget and Revenue Cycle
CIO: Tom Balko, Manager Information Systems
CHR: Jody Rindfleisch, Manager Human Resources
CNO: Dawn Allen, R.N., Chief Clinical Officer
Web address: www.redwoodareahospital.org
Control: City–Government, nonfederal **Service:** General Medical and Surgical

Staffed Beds: 25 **Admissions:** 558 **Census:** 4 **Outpatient Visits:** 21019 **Births:** 98 **Total Expense ($000):** 20995 **Payroll Expense ($000):** 8062 **Personnel:** 132

ROBBINSDALE—Hennepin County

★ △ ◇ **NORTH MEMORIAL MEDICAL CENTER (240001)**, 3300 Oakdale Avenue North, Zip 55422–2926; tel. 763/520–5200 **A**2 3 5 7 9 10 21 **F**3 7 11 12 13 15 17 18 20 22 24 26 28 29 30 31 32 34 35 38 40 43 44 45 46 49 50 53 54 55 56 57 58 59 60 62 63 64 68 70 72 73 74 75 76 77 78 79 81 82 83 84 85 86 87 89 90 91 92 93 96 97 98 100 102 103 104 105 107 108 110 111 114 115 117 118 119 124 126 129 130 132 133 135 143 144 146 147 148 **P**6 8 **S** North Memorial Health Care, Robbinsdale, MN
Primary Contact: Gayle Mattson, R.N., President
CFO: Todd Ostendorf, Chief Financial Officer
CMO: J. Kevin Croston, M.D., Chief Medical Officer
CIO: Patrick Taffe, Vice President Information Services
CHR: David Abrams, Vice President Human Resources
Web address: www.northmemorial.com
Control: Other not–for–profit (including NFP Corporation) **Service:** General Medical and Surgical

Staffed Beds: 355 **Admissions:** 18940 **Census:** 221 **Outpatient Visits:** 526436 **Births:** 1037 **Total Expense ($000):** 629297 **Payroll Expense ($000):** 299748 **Personnel:** 3359

ROCHESTER—Olmsted County

☐ **COMMUNITY BEHAVIORAL HEALTH HOSPITAL – ROCHESTER (244017)**, 251 Wood Lake Drive S.E., Zip 55904–5530; tel. 507/206–2561, (Nonreporting) **A**1 9 10 **S** Minnesota Department of Human Services, Saint Paul, MN
Primary Contact: Douglas Panser, Interim Administrator
CFO: Shirley Jacobson, Chief Financial Officer
CMO: Peter S. Millen, Chief Medical Officer MHSATS
CIO: Thomas Baden, Jr., Chief Information Officer
CHR: Connie Jones, Director Human Resources
CNO: Pamela R. Bajari, R.N., Nurse Executive MHSATS
Web address: www.health.state.mn.us
Control: State–Government, nonfederal **Service:** Psychiatric

Staffed Beds: 16

☒ △ **MAYO CLINIC HOSPITAL – ROCHESTER (240010)**, 1216 Second Street S.W., Zip 55902–1906; tel. 507/255–5123, (Includes MAYO CLINIC – SAINT MARYS HOSPITAL, 1216 Second Street S.W., Zip 55902–1970; tel. 507/255–5123; ROCHESTER METHODIST HOSPITAL, 201 West Center Street, Zip 55902–3084; tel. 507/266–7890) **A**1 2 3 5 7 8 9 10 **F**3 4 5 6 8 9 11 12 13 14 15 17 18 19 20 21 22 23 24 25 26 27 28 29 30 31 34 35 36 37 38 39 40 41 43 44 45 46 47 48 49 50 51 52 53 54 55 56 57 58 59 60 61 63 64 65 66 68 70 72 73 74 75 76 77 78 79 80 81 82 83 84 85 86 87 88 89 90 91 92 93 94 95 96 97 98 99 100 101 102 103 104 105 106 107 108 110 111 112 114 115 116 117 118 119 124 126 130 132 134 135 136 137 138 139 140 141 142 143 144 146 148 **P**6 **S** Mayo Clinic, Rochester, MN
Primary Contact: Lynn Frederick, Administrator
COO: Shirley Weis, Chief Administrative Officer
CFO: Kedrick D. Adkins, Chief Financial Officer
CMO: Amy Williams, M.D., Chief Medical Officer
CIO: Chris Ross, Chief Information Technology Officer
CHR: Ken Schneider, Chair Human Resources
CNO: Pamela O. Johnson, MS, Chief Nursing Officer
Web address: www.mayoclinic.org
Control: Other not–for–profit (including NFP Corporation) **Service:** General Medical and Surgical

Staffed Beds: 1243 **Admissions:** 56437 **Census:** 785 **Outpatient Visits:** 270222 **Births:** 2333 **Personnel:** 28465

★ ◇ **OLMSTED MEDICAL CENTER (240006)**, 1650 Fourth Street S.E., Zip 55904–4717, Mailing Address: 210 Ninth Street S.E., Zip 55904–6756; tel. 507/288–3443 **A**9 10 21 **F**3 11 12 13 15 18 28 29 30 34 40 44 45 50 54 57 58 59 64 65 68 74 75 76 77 79 80 81 82 85 86 87 92 93 97 99 100 102 104 107 108 110 111 115 119 129 130 131 132 135 146 147 148 **P**6
Primary Contact: Kathryn Lombardo, M.D., President
CFO: Kevin A. Higgins, Chief Financial Officer
CMO: David E. Westgard, M.D., Chief Medical Officer
CIO: Susan M. Schuett, Chief Information Officer
CHR: David P. Johnson, Director Human Resources
Web address: www.olmmed.org
Control: Other not–for–profit (including NFP Corporation) **Service:** General Medical and Surgical

Staffed Beds: 38 **Admissions:** 1778 **Census:** 12 **Outpatient Visits:** 339448 **Births:** 867 **Total Expense ($000):** 166791 **Payroll Expense ($000):** 85924 **Personnel:** 823

ROSEAU—Roseau County

☒ **LIFECARE MEDICAL CENTER (241344)**, 715 Delmore Avenue, Zip 56751–1599; tel. 218/463–2500, (Total facility includes 100 beds in nursing home–type unit) **A**1 5 9 10 18 **F**3 7 10 11 13 15 28 29 30 31 32 34 35 36 40 43 45 53 56 57 59 62 63 64 65 68 75 76 77 81 82 84 85 86 93 104 107 110 111 115 118 119 128 129 130 132 133 135 144 146 147 148 **P**6
Primary Contact: Keith Okeson, President and Chief Executive Officer
COO: Susan C. Lisell, Vice President of Clinical Services
CFO: Cathy Huss, Chief Financial Officer
CIO: Kevin Schumacher, Director of Information Services
CHR: Carol Klotz, Director Human Resources
CNO: Roxanne Fabian, Director of Nursing–Acute Care
Web address: www.lifecaremedicalcenter.org
Control: Other not–for–profit (including NFP Corporation) **Service:** General Medical and Surgical

Staffed Beds: 125 **Admissions:** 900 **Census:** 102 **Outpatient Visits:** 37542 **Births:** 219 **Total Expense ($000):** 35305 **Payroll Expense ($000):** 15927 **Personnel:** 295

SAINT CLOUD—Stearns County

☒ △ **ST. CLOUD HOSPITAL (240036)**, 1406 Sixth Avenue North, Zip 56303–1901; tel. 320/251–2700 **A**1 2 3 5 7 9 10 13 20 **F**3 5 11 12 13 14 15 17 18 19 20 22 24 26 27 28 29 30 31 32 34 35 36 37 38 39 40 43 44 45 46 47 48 49 50 51 54 56 57 58 59 60 61 62 63 64 66 68 69 70 72 74 75 76 77 78 79 80 81 82 84 85 86 87 88 89 90 92 93 94 96 97 98 99 100 101 102 103 104 105 106 107 108 110 111 114 115 117 118 119 120 121 123 124 126 129 130 131 132 134 135 141 145 146 147 148 **P**6 **S** CentraCare Health, Saint Cloud, MN
Primary Contact: Craig J. Broman, FACHE, President
COO: Linda A. Chmielewski, R.N., Vice President Operations
CFO: Greg Klugherz, Vice President Corporate Services and Chief Financial Officer
CMO: Mark Matthias, M.D., Vice President of Medical Affairs
CIO: Amy Porwoll, Vice President of Information Systems
CHR: Duane Rasmusson, Vice President Human Resources
CNO: Linda A. Chmielewski, R.N., Vice President Operations
Web address: www.centracare.com
Control: Other not–for–profit (including NFP Corporation) **Service:** General Medical and Surgical

Staffed Beds: 474 **Admissions:** 26318 **Census:** 301 **Outpatient Visits:** 468069 **Births:** 2516 **Total Expense ($000):** 609159 **Payroll Expense ($000):** 260694 **Personnel:** 4416

Many Facility Codes have changed. Please refer to the AHA Guide Code Chart. © 2014 AHA Guide

☒ **ST. CLOUD VETERANS AFFAIRS HEALTH CARE SYSTEM**, 4801 Veterans Drive, Zip 56303–2099; tel. 320/252–1670, (Total facility includes 225 beds in nursing home–type unit) **A**1 **F**2 3 4 5 6 8 9 11 12 15 18 29 30 31 34 35 36 38 39 44 45 47 50 53 54 56 57 58 59 61 63 64 65 68 74 75 77 78 79 81 82 83 84 85 86 87 91 92 93 94 97 98 100 102 103 104 105 106 107 111 115 119 128 130 132 135 143 144 146 147 148 **S** Department of Veterans Affairs, Washington, DC
Primary Contact: Barry I. Bahl, Director
COO: Barry I. Bahl, Director
CFO: Joseph Schmitz, Chief Financial Officer
CMO: Susan Markstrom, M.D., Chief of Staff
CIO: Denise Hanson, Information Technology Specialist
CHR: Lisa Rosendahl, Director Human Resources
CNO: Meri Hauge, R.N., Associate Director of Patient Care Services and Nurse Executive
Web address: www.stcloud.va.gov
Control: Veterans Affairs, Government, federal **Service:** General Medical and Surgical

Staffed Beds: 388 **Admissions:** 2371 **Census:** 350 **Outpatient Visits:** 369873 **Births:** 0 **Total Expense ($000):** 214464 **Payroll Expense ($000):** 104208 **Personnel:** 1506

VETERANS AFFAIRS MEDICAL CENTER See St. Cloud Veterans Affairs Health Care System

SAINT JAMES—Watonwan County

☐ **MAYO CLINIC HEALTH SYSTEM IN SAINT JAMES (241333)**, 1101 Moulton and Parsons Drive, Zip 56081–5550; tel. 507/375–3261 **A**1 9 10 18 **F**3 15 18 28 34 35 40 43 53 57 59 64 75 81 86 87 97 107 110 114 119 128 129 130 132 133 144 146 148 **P**6 **S** Mayo Clinic, Rochester, MN
Primary Contact: Ryan J. Smith, Administrator
COO: Richard Grace, Chief Administrative Officer
CFO: James Tarasovich, Chief Financial Officer
CMO: Jennifer Langbehn, Medical Director
CIO: Thomas Borowski, Chief Information Officer
CHR: Gayle B. Hansen, R.N., Chief Integration Officer
CNO: Mark Fratzke, R.N., Chief Nursing Officer and Chief Operating Officer
Web address: www.mayoclinichealthsystem.org/locations/st-james
Control: Other not–for–profit (including NFP Corporation) **Service:** General Medical and Surgical

Staffed Beds: 13 **Admissions:** 229 **Census:** 4 **Outpatient Visits:** 38297 **Births:** 0 **Total Expense ($000):** 16772 **Payroll Expense ($000):** 5414 **Personnel:** 58

SAINT PAUL—Ramsey County

☒ **BETHESDA HOSPITAL (242004)**, 559 Capitol Boulevard, Zip 55103–2101; tel. 651/232–2000 **A**1 3 5 9 10 **F**1 3 6 11 29 30 38 44 45 50 53 56 60 61 64 68 74 75 77 79 85 86 87 91 93 100 101 103 104 105 107 111 114 119 130 132 146 **P**8 **S** HealthEast Care System, Saint Paul, MN
Primary Contact: Catherine Barr, Senior Vice President and President, Bethesda Hospital
CFO: Lea Jilek, Director Finance
CMO: Stephen J. Kolar, M.D., Vice President Medical Affairs
CIO: Mac McClurkan, Chief Information Officer
Web address: www.healtheast.org
Control: Other not–for–profit (including NFP Corporation) **Service:** Long–Term Acute Care hospital

Staffed Beds: 126 **Admissions:** 1173 **Census:** 97 **Outpatient Visits:** 9949 **Births:** 0 **Total Expense ($000):** 75928 **Payroll Expense ($000):** 34698 **Personnel:** 414

☐ △ **GILLETTE CHILDREN'S SPECIALTY HEALTHCARE (243300)**, (Pediatric Specialty Hospital), 200 East University Avenue, Zip 55101–2598; tel. 651/291–2848 **A**1 3 5 7 9 10 **F**3 29 30 35 36 39 50 54 64 68 71 74 79 81 82 84 85 88 89 90 91 92 93 94 107 111 115 119 129 130 146 **P**6
Primary Contact: Barbara Joers, President and Chief Executive Officer
CFO: James Haddican, Vice President Finance
CMO: Steven Koop, M.D., Medical Director
CIO: Timothy Getsay, Chief Information Officer
CHR: Betty Rivard, Vice President Human Resources
Web address: www.gillettechildrens.org
Control: Other not–for–profit (including NFP Corporation) **Service:** Children's other specialty

Staffed Beds: 60 **Admissions:** 2328 **Census:** 34 **Outpatient Visits:** 153566 **Births:** 0 **Total Expense ($000):** 199267 **Payroll Expense ($000):** 95378 **Personnel:** 1129

☐ △ **REGIONS HOSPITAL (240106)**, 640 Jackson Street, Zip 55101–2595; tel. 651/254–3456 **A**1 2 3 5 7 8 9 10 **F**3 4 5 7 8 13 15 16 17 18 20 22 24 26 28 29 30 31 34 35 36 38 40 42 43 45 46 47 48 49 50 51 53 54 55 56 57 58 59 60 64 65 68 70 71 72 74 75 76 77 78 79 81 82 84 85 86 87 88 90 92 93 96 98 100 101 102 103 104 105 106 107 108 109 110 111 112 114 115 116 117 119 124 126 128 129 130 131 132 135 143 146 147 148 **S** HealthPartners, Bloomington, MN
Primary Contact: Brock D. Nelson, President and Chief Executive Officer
CFO: Heidi Conrad, Vice President and Chief Financial Officer
CMO: Charles Fazio, Chief Health Officer and Medical Director Health Plan
CIO: Kim LaReau, Vice President and Chief Information Officer
CHR: Kim Egan, Executive Director Human Resources
CNO: Chris Boese, Vice President and Chief Nursing Officer
Web address: www.regionshospital.com
Control: Other not–for–profit (including NFP Corporation) **Service:** General Medical and Surgical

Staffed Beds: 446 **Admissions:** 24395 **Census:** 326 **Outpatient Visits:** 245910 **Births:** 2481 **Total Expense ($000):** 608837 **Payroll Expense ($000):** 289294 **Personnel:** 2863

☒ **ST. JOHN'S HOSPITAL (240210)**, 1575 Beam Avenue, Zip 55109–1126; tel. 651/232–7000 **A**1 2 10 **F**3 13 15 28 29 30 31 34 35 36 37 38 40 43 44 49 50 54 55 57 59 61 63 64 68 70 72 74 75 76 77 78 79 81 85 86 87 89 93 96 97 100 102 104 107 108 110 111 114 115 116 117 118 119 121 123 126 130 131 132 146 147 148 **P**8 **S** HealthEast Care System, Saint Paul, MN
Primary Contact: Scott L. North, FACHE, Senior Vice President and President, Acute Care Hospitals
COO: Paul Torgerson, Senior Vice President Chief Administrative Officer and General Counsel
CFO: Douglas Davenport, Senior Vice President and Chief Financial Officer
CMO: Stephen J. Kolar, M.D., Vice President Medical Affairs
CIO: Joanne Sundquist, Chief Information Officer
CHR: Dawn Kessler, Senior Vice President Human Resources
CNO: Debra J. Hurd, R.N., Vice President Nursing Acute Care
Web address: www.stjohnshospital-mn.org
Control: Other not–for–profit (including NFP Corporation) **Service:** General Medical and Surgical

Staffed Beds: 192 **Admissions:** 13795 **Census:** 117 **Outpatient Visits:** 213109 **Births:** 2525 **Total Expense ($000):** 230814 **Payroll Expense ($000):** 84691 **Personnel:** 959

☒ **ST. JOSEPH'S HOSPITAL (240063)**, 45 West 10th Street, Zip 55102–1053; tel. 651/232–3000 **A**1 2 3 5 9 10 **F**3 4 5 11 12 13 15 17 18 20 22 24 26 28 29 30 31 34 35 36 37 38 40 43 44 45 49 50 52 61 63 64 68 70 74 75 76 77 78 79 81 85 87 92 93 96 97 98 100 101 102 103 104 105 107 108 111 114 119 120 121 124 130 132 146 **S** HealthEast Care System, Saint Paul, MN
Primary Contact: Scott L. North, FACHE, Senior Vice President and President, Acute Care Hospitals
CMO: Stephen J. Kolar, M.D., Vice President Medical Affairs
Web address: www.healtheast.org
Control: Other not–for–profit (including NFP Corporation) **Service:** General Medical and Surgical

Staffed Beds: 234 **Admissions:** 11866 **Census:** 165 **Outpatient Visits:** 104808 **Births:** 1083 **Total Expense ($000):** 254765 **Payroll Expense ($000):** 95359 **Personnel:** 1191

☒ △ **UNITED HOSPITAL (240038)**, 333 North Smith Avenue, Zip 55102–2389; tel. 651/241–8000 **A**1 2 3 5 7 9 10 **F**3 8 12 13 15 18 20 22 24 26 28 29 30 31 34 35 36 37 40 43 46 49 50 58 60 61 64 65 70 74 75 76 77 78 79 81 82 85 87 90 91 92 93 97 98 100 101 102 103 104 105 107 108 110 111 112 113 114 115 118 119 120 121 123 124 126 129 130 132 146 148 **P**8 **S** Allina Health, Minneapolis, MN
Primary Contact: Thomas O'Connor, President
CFO: John Bien, Vice President Finance
CMO: Alison Peterson, Vice President Medical Affairs
CIO: Susan Heichert, Senior Vice President
CHR: James McGlade, Director Human Resources
CNO: Mandy Richards, R.N., Vice President Patient Care
Web address: www.allina.com
Control: Other not–for–profit (including NFP Corporation) **Service:** General Medical and Surgical

Staffed Beds: 392 **Admissions:** 22978 **Census:** 255 **Outpatient Visits:** 167500 **Births:** 3431 **Total Expense ($000):** 433764 **Payroll Expense ($000):** 164695 **Personnel:** 2372

MN

SAINT PETER—Nicollet County

☐ **COMMUNITY BEHAVIORAL HEALTH HOSPITAL – ST. PETER (244010)**, 2000 Klein Street, Zip 56082–5800; tel. 507/933–5001, (Nonreporting) **A**1 5 10 **S** Minnesota Department of Human Services, Saint Paul, MN
Primary Contact: Christopher Schiffer, Administrator
CFO: Shirley Jacobson, Chief Financial Officer
Web address: www.health.state.mn.us
Control: State–Government, nonfederal **Service:** Psychiatric

Staffed Beds: 16

★ ◇ **RIVER'S EDGE HOSPITAL AND CLINIC (241334)**, 1900 North Sunrise Drive, Zip 56082–5376; tel. 507/931–2200 **A**5 9 10 18 21 **F**3 7 28 29 34 40 41 43 44 50 53 57 59 63 64 65 68 75 77 81 86 87 89 90 92 93 97 107 110 115 119 128 130 132 133 135 143 144 148 **P**6
Primary Contact: George A. Rohrich, FACHE, Chief Executive Officer
CFO: Ann Lauer, Director Finance
CMO: Michael Sparacino, M.D., Chief Medical Staff
CIO: Kevin Schaefer, Manager Information Services
CNO: Paula Meskan, Director of Nursing
Web address: www.riversedgehealth.org
Control: City–Government, nonfederal **Service:** General Medical and Surgical

Staffed Beds: 17 **Admissions:** 422 **Census:** 5 **Outpatient Visits:** 24650 **Births:** 0 **Total Expense ($000):** 18472 **Payroll Expense ($000):** 7052 **Personnel:** 140

SANDSTONE—Pine County

★ **ESSENTIA HEALTH SANDSTONE (241309)**, 109 Court Avenue South, Zip 55072–5120; tel. 320/245–2212, (Total facility includes 45 beds in nursing home–type unit) **A**9 10 18 **F**7 11 12 15 28 29 30 34 35 40 45 59 64 65 75 77 80 81 85 91 92 93 107 110 114 128 130 132 133 148 **P**5 6 **S** Essentia Health, Duluth, MN
Primary Contact: Michael D. Hedrix, Interim Chief Executive Officer
CFO: Chris Johnson, Assistant Administrator and Chief Financial Officer
CMO: Sarah Aldredge, M.D., Chief Medical Officer
Web address: www.pinemedicalcenter.org
Control: Hospital district or authority, Government, nonfederal **Service:** General Medical and Surgical

Staffed Beds: 70 **Admissions:** 311 **Census:** 54 **Outpatient Visits:** 16934 **Births:** 0 **Total Expense ($000):** 16587 **Payroll Expense ($000):** 8006 **Personnel:** 165

SAUK CENTRE—Stearns County

★ **CENTRACARE HEALTH–SAUK CENTRE (241368)**, 425 North Elm Street, Zip 56378–1010; tel. 320/352–2221, (Nonreporting) **A**9 10 18 **S** CentraCare Health, Saint Cloud, MN
Primary Contact: Delano Christianson, Administrator
CFO: Delano Christianson, Administrator
Web address: www.centracare.com/hospitals/sauk_centre/index.html
Control: City–Government, nonfederal **Service:** General Medical and Surgical

Staffed Beds: 85

SHAKOPEE—Scott County

⊞ **ST. FRANCIS REGIONAL MEDICAL CENTER (240104)**, 1455 St. Francis Avenue, Zip 55379–3380; tel. 952/428–3000 **A**1 2 5 9 10 **F**3 12 13 15 28 29 30 31 34 35 36 38 40 41 43 45 46 50 51 53 57 58 59 64 68 75 76 77 78 79 80 81 82 84 86 87 89 93 107 108 110 111 115 117 118 119 120 124 129 130 131 132 144 146 147 148 **S** Allina Health, Minneapolis, MN
Primary Contact: Mike McMahan, Chief Executive Officer
CFO: Cynthia Vincent, Vice President Finance
CMO: Brian Prokosch, M.D., Vice President Medical Affairs
CIO: Joe Delveaux, Manager Information Services
CHR: Ann Glaves, Vice President Human Resources
CNO: Debora Ryan, R.N., Vice President Patient Care
Web address: www.stfrancis–shakopee.com
Control: Other not–for–profit (including NFP Corporation) **Service:** General Medical and Surgical

Staffed Beds: 86 **Admissions:** 5454 **Census:** 40 **Outpatient Visits:** 107777 **Births:** 1262 **Total Expense ($000):** 112245 **Payroll Expense ($000):** 40882 **Personnel:** 493

SLAYTON—Murray County

★ **MURRAY COUNTY MEDICAL CENTER (241319)**, 2042 Juniper Avenue, Zip 56172–1017; tel. 507/836–6111, (Nonreporting) **A**9 10 18 **S** Sanford Health, Sioux Falls, SD
Primary Contact: John M. Osse, Interim Chief Executive Officer
CFO: Renee Logan, Chief Financial Officer
CMO: Joyce Tarbet, M.D., Chief Medical Officer
CIO: Justin Keller, Chief Information Officer
CHR: Nancy Andert, Director Human Resources
CNO: Lorrie Mortensen, R.N., Chief Patient Services
Web address: www.murraycountymed.org
Control: County–Government, nonfederal **Service:** General Medical and Surgical

Staffed Beds: 18

SLEEPY EYE—Brown County

SLEEPY EYE MEDICAL CENTER (241327), 400 Fourth Avenue N.W., Zip 56085–1109, Mailing Address: P.O. Box 323, Zip 56085–0323; tel. 507/794–3571 **A**9 10 18 **F**13 15 28 34 40 43 45 59 68 76 77 81 91 93 107 114 119 127 129 130 133 **P**6
Primary Contact: Kevin Sellheim, Chief Executive Officer
CHR: Connie Dahlberg, Director Business and Employee
CNO: Karee Schmiesing, Director of Nursing
Web address: www.semedicalcenter.org
Control: City–Government, nonfederal **Service:** General Medical and Surgical

Staffed Beds: 16 **Admissions:** 360 **Census:** 3 **Outpatient Visits:** 10960 **Births:** 36 **Total Expense ($000):** 10549 **Payroll Expense ($000):** 4808 **Personnel:** 90

SPRINGFIELD—Brown County

☐ **MAYO CLINIC HEALTH SYSTEM IN SPRINGFIELD (241352)**, 625 North Jackson Avenue, Zip 56087–1714, Mailing Address: P.O. Box 146, Zip 56087–0146; tel. 507/723–6201 **A**1 9 10 18 **F**3 15 28 32 34 39 40 45 57 59 65 75 81 85 89 93 97 107 110 114 128 133 135 146 148 **P**6 **S** Mayo Clinic, Rochester, MN
Primary Contact: Scott D. Thoreson, FACHE, Administrator
COO: Scott D. Thoreson, FACHE, Administrator
CFO: James Tarasovich, Chief Financial Officer
CMO: Joseph Hamm, Chief Medical Director
Web address: www.smc–mhs.org
Control: Other not–for–profit (including NFP Corporation) **Service:** General Medical and Surgical

Staffed Beds: 24 **Admissions:** 175 **Census:** 3 **Outpatient Visits:** 22426 **Births:** 0 **Total Expense ($000):** 14176 **Payroll Expense ($000):** 5074 **Personnel:** 61

STAPLES—Todd County

LAKEWOOD HEALTH SYSTEM (241329), 49725 County 83, Zip 56479–5280; tel. 218/894–1515, (Total facility includes 100 beds in nursing home–type unit) **A**9 10 18 **F**3 6 7 8 10 11 12 13 15 28 29 30 31 34 35 36 39 40 43 50 52 53 56 57 59 62 63 64 65 68 75 77 78 79 81 82 84 85 86 87 93 98 99 100 101 102 103 104 105 107 110 114 119 125 127 128 129 130 131 132 133 135 143 146 147 148 **P**7
Primary Contact: Tim Rice, President and Chief Executive Officer
CFO: Jim Dregney, Chief Financial Officer
CMO: John Halfen, M.D., Medical Director
CHR: Janet Jacobson, Director Human Resources
CNO: Teresa Fisher, Chief Nursing Officer
Web address: www.lakewoodhealthsystem.com
Control: Other not–for–profit (including NFP Corporation) **Service:** General Medical and Surgical

Staffed Beds: 135 **Admissions:** 2162 **Census:** 110 **Outpatient Visits:** 229500 **Births:** 468 **Total Expense ($000):** 89129 **Payroll Expense ($000):** 36969 **Personnel:** 686

STILLWATER—Washington County

⊞ **LAKEVIEW HOSPITAL (240066)**, 927 Churchill Street West, Zip 55082–6605; tel. 651/439–5330 **A**1 5 9 10 **F**3 7 8 13 15 18 26 28 29 30 31 34 35 36 40 43 45 50 62 63 64 70 75 78 79 81 84 85 87 92 93 96 107 108 110 111 115 118 119 129 130 132 135 141 146 **S** HealthPartners, Bloomington, MN
Primary Contact: Theodore Wegleitner, President
CFO: Douglas E. Johnson, Chief Financial Officer
CMO: Thomas Anderson, Vice President Medical Affairs
CIO: Emad Awwad, Director Care Delivery Sites Information Systems and Technology
CHR: Angy Duchesneau, Senior Director Human Resources
CNO: Jo Sittlow, Vice President Patient Care and Chief Nursing Officer
Web address: www.lakeview.org
Control: Other not–for–profit (including NFP Corporation) **Service:** General Medical and Surgical

Staffed Beds: 54 **Admissions:** 3623 **Census:** 27 **Outpatient Visits:** 14985 **Births:** 494 **Total Expense ($000):** 85732 **Payroll Expense ($000):** 36060

MN

Many Facility Codes have changed. Please refer to the AHA Guide Code Chart.
© 2014 AHA Guide

THIEF RIVER FALLS—Pennington County

MERITCARE THIEF RIVER FALLS NORTHWEST MEDICAL CENTER See Sanford Thief River Falls Medical Center

★ **SANFORD THIEF RIVER FALLS MEDICAL CENTER (241381)**, 120 LaBree Avenue South, Zip 56701–2840; tel. 218/681–4240 **A**9 10 18 **F**3 7 8 11 13 15 28 29 31 33 34 35 39 40 43 45 50 53 60 64 68 70 75 76 77 78 79 81 82 85 87 93 97 98 99 100 101 102 104 106 107 110 111 115 119 129 131 132 135 146 147 148 **S** Sanford Health, Sioux Falls, SD
Primary Contact: Brian J. Carlson, FACHE, Chief Executive Officer
COO: Rob Lovejoy, Chief Operating Officer
CFO: Casey R. Johnson, Chief Financial Officer
CMO: Janell Hudson, Chief Clinical Officer
CHR: Rob Lovejoy, Chief Operating Officer
Web address: www.sanfordhealth.org
Control: Other not–for–profit (including NFP Corporation) **Service:** General Medical and Surgical

> **Staffed Beds:** 35 **Admissions:** 1757 **Census:** 18 **Outpatient Visits:** 41351
> **Births:** 269 **Total Expense ($000):** 63169 **Payroll Expense ($000):** 22830
> **Personnel:** 555

TRACY—Lyon County

★ **SANFORD TRACY MEDICAL CENTER (241303)**, 251 Fifth Street East, Zip 56175–1536; tel. 507/629–3200 **A**9 10 18 **F**3 28 29 31 32 34 40 41 42 43 45 50 56 57 59 62 64 65 68 77 81 85 87 89 91 93 97 107 108 111 114 125 127 129 130 131 132 133 135 143 **S** Sanford Health, Sioux Falls, SD
Primary Contact: Stacy Barstad, Chief Executive Officer
CMO: Muhammad Ali, M.D., Chief Medical Officer
CIO: Janet Theisen, Chief Information Officer
CHR: Becky Foster, Manager Human Resources
CNO: Jeri Schons, R.N., Chief Nursing Officer
Web address: www.sanfordtracy.org
Control: Other not–for–profit (including NFP Corporation) **Service:** General Medical and Surgical

> **Staffed Beds:** 25 **Admissions:** 215 **Census:** 2 **Outpatient Visits:** 17567
> **Births:** 0 **Total Expense ($000):** 10051 **Payroll Expense ($000):** 4762
> **Personnel:** 92

TWO HARBORS—Lake County

LAKE VIEW MEMORIAL HOSPITAL (241308), 325 11th Avenue, Zip 55616–1360; tel. 218/834–7300 **A**9 10 18 **F**10 15 17 28 35 40 43 53 59 63 64 75 77 81 82 84 93 111 114 119 130 133 144 148
Primary Contact: Greg Ruberg, Administrator
CFO: Eric Lohn, Chief Financial Officer
Web address: www.lvmhospital.com
Control: Other not–for–profit (including NFP Corporation) **Service:** General Medical and Surgical

> **Staffed Beds:** 17 **Admissions:** 237 **Census:** 6 **Outpatient Visits:** 31183
> **Births:** 0 **Total Expense ($000):** 13378 **Payroll Expense ($000):** 5320
> **Personnel:** 94

TYLER—Lincoln County

TYLER HEALTHCARE CENTER AVERA (241348), 240 Willow Street, Zip 56178–1166; tel. 507/247–5521, (Nonreporting) **A**9 10 18 **S** Avera Health, Sioux Falls, SD
Primary Contact: Dale K. Kruger, Chief Executive Officer and Chief Financial Officer
CFO: Dale K. Kruger, Chief Executive Officer and Chief Financial Officer
Web address: www.www1.avera.org/amck/regionalfacilities/tyler/index.aspx
Control: Other not–for–profit (including NFP Corporation) **Service:** General Medical and Surgical

> **Staffed Beds:** 25

VIRGINIA—St. Louis County

⊠ △ **ESSENTIA HEALTH–VIRGINIA (240084)**, 901 Ninth Street North, Zip 55792–2398; tel. 218/741–3340, (Total facility includes 90 beds in nursing home–type unit) **A**1 7 9 10 **F**3 8 11 13 15 17 28 29 30 34 35 40 41 43 45 46 51 56 57 59 63 64 65 70 75 76 80 81 85 87 89 90 107 108 110 111 114 115 119 127 128 129 130 132 146 147 148 **P**6
Primary Contact: Daniel Milbridge, Administrator and Chief Operating Officer
CFO: Steven Feltman, CPA, Chief Financial Officer
CMO: Michelle Oman, D.O., Chief Medical Officer
CNO: Michelle Fleming, Chief Nursing Officer
Web address: www.essentiahealth.org
Control: Other not–for–profit (including NFP Corporation) **Service:** General Medical and Surgical

> **Staffed Beds:** 154 **Admissions:** 2144 **Census:** 151 **Outpatient Visits:** 47692
> **Births:** 254 **Total Expense ($000):** 51470 **Payroll Expense ($000):** 22665
> **Personnel:** 356

WABASHA—Wabasha County

★ **SAINT ELIZABETH'S MEDICAL CENTER (241335)**, 1200 Grant Boulevard West, Zip 55981–1042; tel. 651/565–4531, (Total facility includes 146 beds in nursing home–type unit) **A**9 10 18 **F**2 6 10 11 12 13 15 28 29 30 34 35 40 43 45 46 49 50 53 56 59 62 65 70 75 76 77 81 85 93 94 107 110 114 119 125 128 130 133 143 145 146 148 **S** Ascension Health, Saint Louis, MO
Primary Contact: Thomas Crowley, President and Chief Executive Officer
CFO: John Wolfe, Chief Financial Officer
CMO: Brian E. Kelly, M.D., President Medical Staff
CHR: Jim Root, Vice President Human Resources
CNO: Kathy Lueders, R.N., Director of Nursing–Acute Care
Web address: www.stelizabethswabasha.org
Control: Church–operated, Nongovernment, not–for profit **Service:** General Medical and Surgical

> **Staffed Beds:** 166 **Admissions:** 541 **Census:** 142 **Outpatient Visits:** 22793
> **Births:** 74 **Total Expense ($000):** 23750 **Payroll Expense ($000):** 11623
> **Personnel:** 284

WACONIA—Carver County

★ ◇ **RIDGEVIEW MEDICAL CENTER (240056)**, 500 South Maple Street, Zip 55387–1791; tel. 952/442–2191, (Nonreporting) **A**2 9 10 21
Primary Contact: Robert Stevens, President and Chief Executive Officer
CFO: Gordon Gablenz, Vice President Finance
CIO: Tamara Korbel, Director Management Information Systems
CHR: Sarah M. Hastings, Vice President Human Resources
Web address: www.ridgeviewmedical.org
Control: Other not–for–profit (including NFP Corporation) **Service:** General Medical and Surgical

> **Staffed Beds:** 99

WADENA—Wadena County

⊠ **TRI-COUNTY HOSPITAL (241354)**, 415 Jefferson Street North, Zip 56482–1297; tel. 218/631–3510 **A**1 9 10 18 **F**3 7 11 13 15 17 28 31 34 35 40 50 54 57 59 64 65 70 75 76 77 81 85 86 87 89 93 99 104 107 110 111 114 115 118 119 127 129 130 131 132 133 135 146 147 148 **P**6
Primary Contact: Joel Beiswenger, Chief Executive Officer
CFO: Kim Aagard, Chief Financial Officer
CMO: John Pate, M.D., Chief Medical Officer
CIO: Bill Blaha, Manager Information Technology
CHR: Bryan Pederson, Human Resources Manager
CNO: Kathy Kleen, Chief Nursing Officer
Web address: www.tchc.org
Control: Other not–for–profit (including NFP Corporation) **Service:** General Medical and Surgical

> **Staffed Beds:** 25 **Admissions:** 1185 **Census:** 9 **Outpatient Visits:** 105175
> **Births:** 170 **Total Expense ($000):** 49727 **Payroll Expense ($000):** 20208
> **Personnel:** 350

WARREN—Marshall County

★ **NORTH VALLEY HEALTH CENTER (241337)**, 300 West Good Samaritan Drive, Zip 56762; tel. 218/745–4211, (Nonreporting) **A**9 10 18
Primary Contact: Ashley King, Chief Executive Officer
CFO: Mitchell Kotrba, Chief Financial Officer
Web address: www.nvhc.net
Control: Other not–for–profit (including NFP Corporation) **Service:** General Medical and Surgical

> **Staffed Beds:** 20

WASECA—Waseca County

⊠ **MAYO CLINIC HEALTH SYSTEM IN WASECA (241345)**, 501 North State Street, Zip 56093–2811; tel. 507/835–1210 **A**1 5 9 10 18 **F**3 8 11 15 18 28 29 31 32 34 35 40 45 50 53 56 57 59 63 64 65 74 75 77 79 81 82 87 90 93 97 103 104 107 110 111 114 119 128 130 131 132 133 143 144 146 147 148 **P**6 **S** Mayo Clinic, Rochester, MN
Primary Contact: Jeffrey Carlson, Administrator
CMO: Daniel Stahl, M.D., Medical Director
Web address: www.mayoclinichealthsystem.org
Control: Other not–for–profit (including NFP Corporation) **Service:** General Medical and Surgical

> **Staffed Beds:** 25 **Admissions:** 309 **Census:** 7 **Outpatient Visits:** 49936
> **Births:** 0 **Total Expense ($000):** 18428 **Payroll Expense ($000):** 7686
> **Personnel:** 96

Hospital, Medicare Provider Number, Address, Telephone, Approval, Facility, and Physician Codes, Health Care System

★ American Hospital Association (AHA) membership
□ The Joint Commission accreditation   ◇ DNV Healthcare Inc. accreditation
○ Healthcare Facilities Accreditation Program
△ Commission on Accreditation of Rehabilitation Facilities (CARF) accreditation

---

WESTBROOK—Cottonwood County

★ **SANFORD WESTBROOK MEDICAL CENTER (241302)**, 920 Bell Avenue, Zip 56183–9669, Mailing Address: P.O. Box 188, Zip 56183–0188; tel. 507/274–6121 **A**9 10 18 **F**3 29 31 34 35 40 42 43 56 57 59 62 64 65 68 71 75 77 81 85 86 87 89 91 93 97 99 100 101 102 103 104 107 108 114 125 127 130 131 132 133 135 143 **P**6 **S** Sanford Health, Sioux Falls, SD
Primary Contact: Stacy Barstad, Chief Executive Officer
COO: Gordon Kopperud, Director Operations
CIO: Janet Theisen, Chief Information Officer
CHR: Becky Foster, Manager Human Resources
Web address: www.sanfordwestbrook.org
Control: Other not–for–profit (including NFP Corporation) **Service:** General Medical and Surgical

Staffed Beds: 6 **Admissions:** 102 **Census:** 1 **Outpatient Visits:** 10541
Births: 0 **Total Expense ($000):** 6090 **Payroll Expense ($000):** 2365
Personnel: 40

WHEATON—Traverse County

★ **SANFORD WHEATON MEDICAL CENTER (241304)**, 401 12th Street North, Zip 56296–1099; tel. 320/563–8226 **A**9 10 18 **F**3 7 11 15 18 28 29 30 34 40 43 45 57 59 64 65 81 86 97 107 110 114 119 127 128 132 133 **S** Sanford Health, Sioux Falls, SD
Primary Contact: JoAnn M. Foltz, R.N., Chief Executive Officer
CFO: Shane Ayres, Chief Financial Officer
CHR: Brenda Petersen, Human Resources
CNO: Chelsie Falk, Chief Nursing Officer
Web address: www.sanfordhealth.org
Control: Other not–for–profit (including NFP Corporation) **Service:** General Medical and Surgical

Staffed Beds: 15 **Admissions:** 124 **Census:** 2 **Outpatient Visits:** 12279
Births: 0 **Total Expense ($000):** 7705 **Payroll Expense ($000):** 2732
Personnel: 51

WILLMAR—Kandiyohi County

☐ **CHILD AND ADOLESCENT BEHAVIORAL HEALTH SERVICES (244005)**, 1701 Technology Drive Northeast, Zip 56201–2275; tel. 320/231–5421, (Nonreporting) **A**1 10
Primary Contact: Mark Kragenbring, Administrator
Web address: www.dhs.state.mn.us
Control: County–Government, nonfederal **Service:** Psychiatric

Staffed Beds: 16

⊞ **RICE MEMORIAL HOSPITAL (240088)**, 301 Becker Avenue S.W., Zip 56201–3395; tel. 320/235–4543, (Total facility includes 78 beds in nursing home–type unit) **A**1 2 9 10 19 20 **F**7 11 12 13 15 18 28 29 30 31 34 35 36 39 40 43 45 47 48 49 50 57 59 60 63 64 68 70 73 75 76 77 78 79 81 82 84 86 87 89 90 93 98 100 101 102 103 104 105 107 108 111 115 118 119 121 128 129 130 131 132 135 143 146 147 148
Primary Contact: Michael Schramm, Chief Executive Officer
CFO: Bill Fenske, Chief Financial Officer
CMO: Kenneth Flowe, M.D., Chief Medical Officer
CIO: Teri Beyer, Chief Information Officer
CNO: Wendy Ulferts, R.N., Chief Nursing Officer
Web address: www.ricehospital.com
Control: City–Government, nonfederal **Service:** General Medical and Surgical

Staffed Beds: 188 **Admissions:** 3762 **Census:** 97 **Outpatient Visits:** 62975
Births: 835 **Total Expense ($000):** 98635 **Payroll Expense ($000):** 42963
Personnel: 541

WINDOM—Cottonwood County

★ **WINDOM AREA HOSPITAL (241332)**, 2150 Hospital Drive, Zip 56101–1287, Mailing Address: P.O. Box 339, Zip 56101–0339; tel. 507/831–2400 **A**9 10 18 **F**11 13 15 28 31 34 35 40 45 53 57 59 76 77 81 93 107 115 119 130 133 148 **S** Sanford Health, Sioux Falls, SD
Primary Contact: Geraldine F. Burmeister, FACHE, Chief Executive Officer
CFO: Kim Armstrong, Chief Financial Officer
CIO: Lori Ling, Information Technician
CHR: Emily Masters, Director Human Resources and Marketing
CNO: Kari Witte, Director Patient Care
Web address: www.windomareahospital.com
Control: City–Government, nonfederal **Service:** General Medical and Surgical

Staffed Beds: 25 **Admissions:** 442 **Census:** 5 **Outpatient Visits:** 28864
Births: 138 **Total Expense ($000):** 14338 **Payroll Expense ($000):** 5751
Personnel: 100

WINONA—Winona County

★ **WINONA HEALTH (240044)**, 855 Mankato Avenue, Zip 55987–4868, Mailing Address: P.O. Box 5600, Zip 55987–0600; tel. 507/454–3650 **A**2 9 10 20 **F**11 13 15 28 29 30 31 32 34 35 40 43 50 53 56 57 59 60 61 70 74 75 76 77 78 79 81 82 84 85 86 87 89 93 96 97 98 99 100 101 102 103 104 107 108 110 111 115 118 119 127 129 130 131 132 135 144 146 147 148 **P**6
Primary Contact: Rachelle H. Schultz, President and Chief Executive Officer
CFO: Jan Brosnahan, Chief Financial Officer
CMO: Dan Parker, M.D., Chief of Staff
CIO: Polly Peterson, Information Technology Director
CHR: Ashley Anderson, Manager Human Resources
Web address: www.winonahealth.org
Control: Other not–for–profit (including NFP Corporation) **Service:** General Medical and Surgical

Staffed Beds: 53 **Admissions:** 2678 **Census:** 27 **Outpatient Visits:** 220698
Births: 362 **Total Expense ($000):** 110788 **Payroll Expense ($000):** 47504
Personnel: 1046

WOODBURY—Washington County

⊞ **WOODWINDS HEALTH CAMPUS (240213)**, 1925 Woodwinds Drive, Zip 55125–4445; tel. 651/232–0228 **A**1 5 9 10 **F**3 13 15 28 29 30 31 34 35 36 37 38 40 43 44 45 49 50 57 59 61 63 64 68 70 74 75 76 77 78 79 81 85 86 87 93 96 97 107 108 111 114 119 130 132 146 **P**8 **S** HealthEast Care System, Saint Paul, MN
Primary Contact: Scott L. North, FACHE, Senior Vice President and President, Acute Care Hospitals
CFO: Douglas Davenport, Senior Vice President and Chief Financial Officer
CMO: John Kvasnicka, M.D., Medical Director Acute Care Services
CIO: Joanne Sunquist, Chief Information Officer
CHR: Stephanie R. Secrest, Group Director Human Resources and Acute Care Services
Web address: www.woodwinds.org
Control: Other not–for–profit (including NFP Corporation) **Service:** General Medical and Surgical

Staffed Beds: 86 **Admissions:** 7640 **Census:** 56 **Outpatient Visits:** 89231
Births: 1892 **Total Expense ($000):** 119796 **Payroll Expense ($000):** 44560 **Personnel:** 504

WORTHINGTON—Nobles County

SANFORD REGIONAL HOSPITAL WORTHINGTON See Sanford Worthington Medical Center

★ **SANFORD WORTHINGTON MEDICAL CENTER (240022)**, 1018 Sixth Avenue, Zip 56187–2202, Mailing Address: P.O. Box 997, Zip 56187–0997; tel. 507/372–2941 **A**9 10 20 **F**3 11 13 15 18 19 26 27 28 31 34 35 40 43 45 50 57 59 60 62 64 68 69 70 75 76 78 79 81 85 86 93 97 107 110 111 114 116 119 120 121 126 129 130 131 132 133 135 144 146 147 148 **S** Sanford Health, Sioux Falls, SD
Primary Contact: Michael Hammer, Chief Executive Officer
CFO: Linda Wagner, Chief Financial Officer
CMO: Charles Dike, M.D., Chief of Staff
CIO: Brad Klassen, Information Technology Coordinator
CNO: Jennifer Weg, R.N., Chief Nursing Officer
Web address: www.sanfordhealth.org
Control: Other not–for–profit (including NFP Corporation) **Service:** General Medical and Surgical

Staffed Beds: 48 **Admissions:** 1272 **Census:** 9 **Outpatient Visits:** 59496
Births: 410 **Total Expense ($000):** 30889 **Payroll Expense ($000):** 12964
Personnel: 208

WYOMING—Chisago County

⊞ **FAIRVIEW LAKES HEALTH SERVICES (240050)**, 5200 Fairview Boulevard, Zip 55092–8013; tel. 651/982–7000 **A**1 9 10 **F**3 11 13 15 18 26 28 29 30 32 34 35 40 43 45 51 57 59 62 63 64 65 68 70 75 76 77 78 79 81 84 85 87 93 96 107 110 111 114 115 119 129 130 131 132 134 144 146 147 148 **P**6 **S** Fairview Health Services, Minneapolis, MN
Primary Contact: John W. Herman, Chief Executive Officer
CFO: Kim Ericson, Vice President Finance
CMO: David Milbrandt, M.D., Vice President Medical Affairs
CNO: Margaret J. Swanson, Chief Nursing Officer
Web address: www.fairview.org/
Control: Other not–for–profit (including NFP Corporation) **Service:** General Medical and Surgical

Staffed Beds: 47 **Admissions:** 3304 **Census:** 25 **Outpatient Visits:** 89649
Births: 705 **Personnel:** 475

MN

Many Facility Codes have changed. Please refer to the AHA Guide Code Chart. © 2014 AHA Guide

MISSISSIPPI

ABERDEEN—Monroe County

★ ◇ **PIONEER COMMUNITY HOSPITAL OF ABERDEEN (251302)**, 400 South Chestnut Street, Zip 39730–3335, Mailing Address: P.O. Box 548, Zip 39730–0548; tel. 662/369–2455 **A**9 10 18 21 **F**29 35 40 43 53 70 75 81 86 87 89 90 93 97 98 103 107 119 128 130 131 133 **S** Pioneer Health Services, Magee, MS
Primary Contact: Harley Smith, Chief Executive Officer
CFO: Julie Gieger, Chief Financial Officer
CMO: Kevin Hayes, M.D., Chief of Staff
CHR: Lee Rob, Director Human Resources
Web address: www.pchaberdeen.com
Control: Corporation, Investor–owned, for–profit **Service:** General Medical and Surgical

Staffed Beds: 35 **Admissions:** 295 **Census:** 8 **Births:** 0 **Personnel:** 144

ACKERMAN—Choctaw County

★ ◇ **CHOCTAW COUNTY HOSPITAL (251334)**, 311 West Cherry Street, Zip 39735–8708; tel. 662/285–6235, (Total facility includes 60 beds in nursing home–type unit) **A**9 10 18 21 **F**29 40 43 70 77 87 89 90 93 107 119 128 130 133
Primary Contact: Jamie Rodgers, Interim Chief Executive Officer
Control: Corporation, Investor–owned, for–profit **Service:** General Medical and Surgical

Staffed Beds: 75 **Admissions:** 400 **Census:** 60 **Outpatient Visits:** 6066 **Births:** 0 **Personnel:** 150

AMORY—Monroe County

⊞ **GILMORE MEMORIAL REGIONAL MEDICAL CENTER (250025)**, 1105 Earl Frye Boulevard, Zip 38821–5500, Mailing Address: P.O. Box 459, Zip 38821–0459; tel. 662/256–7111 **A**1 9 10 **F**13 15 17 29 35 40 43 53 70 72 73 75 76 77 81 86 87 88 89 90 93 107 108 111 119 130 147 **P**6 **S** Community Health Systems, Inc., Franklin, TN
Primary Contact: J. Allen Tyra, Chief Executive
COO: Carol Upton, Regional Area Practice Manager
CFO: Bert Pickard, Chief Financial Officer
CMO: William Rogers, Chief Medical Officer
CIO: Jeff Wideman, Director Information Systems
CHR: Angie L. Weaver, Director Human Resources
CNO: Mary Franklin, R.N., Chief Nursing Officer
Web address: www.gilmorehealth.com
Control: Corporation, Investor–owned, for–profit **Service:** General Medical and Surgical

Staffed Beds: 95 **Admissions:** 2866 **Census:** 31 **Outpatient Visits:** 46037 **Births:** 572 **Personnel:** 239

BATESVILLE—Panola County

BATESVILLE SPECIALTY HOSPITAL, 303 Medical Center Drive, Zip 38606–8608; tel. 662/712–2484, (Nonreporting)
Primary Contact: Candace Eldib, Administrator
Control: Other not–for–profit (including NFP Corporation) **Service:** Long–Term Acute Care hospital

Staffed Beds: 12

★ **TRI–LAKES MEDICAL CENTER (250128)**, 303 Medical Center Drive, Zip 38606–8608; tel. 662/563–5611 **A**9 10 **F**3 4 5 11 12 13 15 18 19 28 29 30 32 34 35 38 40 43 45 48 50 56 57 59 64 65 68 70 76 77 81 85 87 89 97 98 100 101 102 103 104 107 108 114 119 127 129 130 132 135 143 147 **S** Community Health Systems, Inc., Franklin, TN
Primary Contact: Travis Sisson, Interim Chief Executive Officer
COO: Vince Brummett, Director Administrative Services
CMO: Michael R. Hovens, M.D., Chief Medical Officer
CIO: Will Morris, Director Information Technology
CHR: Arthur A. Wasek, Director Human Resources
Web address: www.trilakesmc.com
Control: Corporation, Investor–owned, for–profit **Service:** General Medical and Surgical

Staffed Beds: 112 **Admissions:** 3418 **Census:** 47 **Outpatient Visits:** 18110 **Births:** 201 **Personnel:** 314

BAY SAINT LOUIS—Hancock County

⊞ **HANCOCK MEDICAL CENTER (250162)**, 149 Drinkwater Boulevard, Zip 39520–1658, Mailing Address: P.O. Box 2790, Zip 39521–2790; tel. 228/467–8600 **A**1 10 **F**3 11 13 15 17 18 28 29 31 32 34 35 39 40 43 45 51 57 59 64 70 75 76 77 81 85 86 87 89 90 93 97 107 108 110 111 115 118 119 129 130 131 135 144 145 147 148 **S** Ochsner Health System, New Orleans, LA
Primary Contact: Thomas K. Steiner, Chief Executive Officer
CFO: Thomas Ramsey, Chief Financial Officer
CIO: Wes Griffith, IT Director
CHR: Cathy Benvenutti, Human Resource Director
CNO: Kim Pierson, R.N., Chief Nursing Officer
Web address: www.hmc.org
Control: County–Government, nonfederal **Service:** General Medical and Surgical

Staffed Beds: 86 **Admissions:** 1893 **Census:** 17 **Outpatient Visits:** 47463 **Births:** 204 **Total Expense ($000):** 39776 **Payroll Expense ($000):** 17422 **Personnel:** 284

BAY SPRINGS—Jasper County

★ **JASPER GENERAL HOSPITAL (250018)**, 15 A South Sixth Street, Zip 39422–9738, Mailing Address: P.O. Box 527, Zip 39422–0527; tel. 601/764–2101, (Includes JASPER COUNTY NURSING HOME), (Total facility includes 110 beds in nursing home–type unit) **A**9 10 **F**10 62 70 128 130 133
Primary Contact: M. Kenneth Posey, FACHE, Administrator
CFO: Steve Green, Comptroller
CMO: A. K. Lay, Jr., M.D., Chief Medical Officer
CHR: Beth Gable, Administrative Assistant
CNO: Becky Ulmer, R.N., Director of Nursing
Control: County–Government, nonfederal **Service:** General Medical and Surgical

Staffed Beds: 126 **Admissions:** 42 **Census:** 107 **Outpatient Visits:** 0 **Births:** 0 **Personnel:** 47

BELZONI—Humphreys County

PATIENT'S CHOICE MEDICAL CENTER OF HUMPHREYS COUNTY, 500 CCC Road, Zip 39038–3806, Mailing Address: P.O. Box 510, Zip 39038–0510; tel. 662/247–3831, (Nonreporting) **A**9 18
Primary Contact: Paula Lang, Chief Executive Officer
CHR: Ruth Hayes, Director Human Resources
Control: Corporation, Investor–owned, for–profit **Service:** General Medical and Surgical

Staffed Beds: 34

BILOXI—Harrison County

⊞ **BILOXI REGIONAL MEDICAL CENTER (250007)**, 150 Reynoir Street, Zip 39530–4199, Mailing Address: P.O. Box 128, Zip 39533–0128; tel. 228/432–1571 **A**1 9 10 **F**3 11 12 13 15 17 18 20 29 31 34 35 37 40 43 45 46 47 48 49 50 54 59 61 64 65 68 70 73 74 75 76 77 78 79 81 85 86 87 89 90 93 97 98 100 102 103 104 105 107 108 110 111 114 115 117 118 119 126 130 135 143 147 148 **S** Community Health Systems, Inc., Franklin, TN
Primary Contact: Monte J. Bostwick, Chief Executive Officer
COO: Joshua Self, Chief Operating Officer
CFO: Mark Wack, Chief Financial Officer
CMO: David Harris, M.D., President Medical Affairs
CIO: George Bickel, Director, Information Systems
CHR: Brion Stanford, Director Human Resources
CNO: Suzy Humphrey, Interim Chief Nursing Officer
Web address: www.biloxiregional.net
Control: Corporation, Investor–owned, for–profit **Service:** General Medical and Surgical

Staffed Beds: 198 **Admissions:** 7208 **Census:** 98 **Outpatient Visits:** 92023 **Births:** 808 **Personnel:** 660

MS

Hospital, Medicare Provider Number, Address, Telephone, Approval, Facility, and Physician Codes, Health Care System

★ American Hospital Association (AHA) membership
□ The Joint Commission accreditation ◇ DNV Healthcare Inc. accreditation
○ Healthcare Facilities Accreditation Program
△ Commission on Accreditation of Rehabilitation Facilities (CARF) accreditation

© 2014 AHA Guide *Many Facility Codes have changed. Please refer to the AHA Guide Code Chart.* Hospitals **A355**

⊞ **VETERANS AFFAIRS GULF COAST VETERANS HEALTH CARE SYSTEM**, 400 Veterans Avenue, Zip 39531–2410; tel. 228/523–5000, (Nonreporting) **A**1 3 5 **S** Department of Veterans Affairs, Washington, DC
Primary Contact: Anthony L. Dawson, FACHE, Director
COO: Alexander Murray, Interim Associate Director
CFO: John D. Williams, Jr., Chief Financial Officer
CMO: Kenneth B. Simon, M.D., Chief of Staff
CIO: David D. Wagner, Chief Information Management Service
CHR: Andrew Roberts, Interim Chief Human Resources Officer
CNO: Deatosha D. Haynes, Interim Associates Director for Patient
Web address: www.biloxi.va.gov/
Control: Veterans Affairs, Government, federal **Service:** General Medical and Surgical

Staffed Beds: 392

BOONEVILLE—Prentiss County

⊞ **BAPTIST MEMORIAL HOSPITAL–BOONEVILLE (250044)**, 100 Hospital Street, Zip 38829–3359; tel. 662/720–5000 **A**1 9 10 **F**3 12 15 17 28 29 30 40 42 43 70 75 81 87 89 90 93 98 103 107 108 111 118 119 130 132 133 **S** Baptist Memorial Health Care Corporation, Memphis, TN
Primary Contact: James Grantham, Administrator and Chief Executive Officer
CFO: Donavan Leonard, Chief Financial Officer
CMO: Nathan Baldwin, M.D., President Medical Staff
CIO: Linda Chaffin, Director Medical Review
CHR: Shannon Bolen, Director Human Resources
Web address: www.bmhcc.org/booneville
Control: Other not–for–profit (including NFP Corporation) **Service:** General Medical and Surgical

Staffed Beds: 66 Admissions: 1273 Census: 25 Outpatient Visits: 30584
Births: 0 Total Expense ($000): 22156 Payroll Expense ($000): 9119
Personnel: 203

BRANDON—Rankin County

⊞ **CROSSGATES RIVER OAKS HOSPITAL (250096)**, 350 Crossgates Boulevard, Zip 39042–2698; tel. 601/825–2811 **A**1 9 10 **F**3 17 18 29 30 34 40 41 43 45 46 57 70 74 78 79 81 86 87 89 90 91 92 93 98 103 107 108 110 111 115 119 129 130 **P**8 **S** Community Health Systems, Inc., Franklin, TN
Primary Contact: Glen Silverman, Chief Executive Officer
CFO: Christy Wilson, Chief Financial Officer
CMO: Edward Rigdon, M.D., Chief Medical Officer
CIO: Heather Holmes, Director Health Information Systems
CHR: Joy M. Hutson, Director Human Resources
CNO: Jacqueline C. Sullins, R.N., Chief Nursing Officer
Web address: www.crossgatesriveroaks.com
Control: Corporation, Investor–owned, for–profit **Service:** General Medical and Surgical

Staffed Beds: 149 Admissions: 3548 Census: 54 Outpatient Visits: 55367
Births: 0 Total Expense ($000): 48136 Payroll Expense ($000): 19739
Personnel: 306

BROOKHAVEN—Lincoln County

★ ◇ **KING'S DAUGHTERS MEDICAL CENTER (250057)**, 427 Highway 51 North, Zip 39601–2350, Mailing Address: P.O. Box 948, Zip 39602–0948; tel. 601/833–6011 **A**9 10 20 21 **F**3 7 11 13 15 17 28 29 30 34 35 40 41 43 45 51 53 54 57 59 60 64 65 68 70 73 75 76 77 79 80 81 85 88 89 93 94 96 97 107 108 111 114 115 118 119 126 129 130 131 132 135 143 147 148 **S** QHR, Brentwood, TN
Primary Contact: Alvin Hoover, FACHE, Chief Executive Officer
COO: Tom Hood, Chief Operating Officer
CFO: Randy B. Pirtle, Chief Financial Officer
CMO: Jeffrey Ross, M.D., Chief of Staff
CIO: Carl Smith, Director Information Systems
CHR: Celine Craig, Director Human Resources
CNO: Cheri Walker, R.N., Chief Nursing Officer
Web address: www.kdmc.org
Control: Other not–for–profit (including NFP Corporation) **Service:** General Medical and Surgical

Staffed Beds: 122 Admissions: 3182 Census: 37 Outpatient Visits: 66462
Births: 643 Total Expense ($000): 72887 Payroll Expense ($000): 29993
Personnel: 563

CALHOUN CITY—Calhoun County

★ **CALHOUN HEALTH SERVICES (251331)**, 140 Burke–Calhoun City Road, Zip 38916–9690; tel. 662/628–6611, (Total facility includes 120 beds in nursing home–type unit) **A**9 10 18 **F**7 40 43 68 70 87 89 93 98 103 107 119 128 130 133 **S** North Mississippi Health Services, Inc., Tupelo, MS
Primary Contact: James P. Franklin, Administrator
CFO: Kenneth Conley, Controller
CMO: Bruce Longest, M.D., President Medical Staff
Web address: www.nmhs.net/calhoun_city
Control: City–County, Government, nonfederal **Service:** General Medical and Surgical

Staffed Beds: 150 Admissions: 414 Census: 101 Births: 0 Total Expense ($000): 17566 Payroll Expense ($000): 7915 Personnel: 254

CANTON—Madison County

⊞ **MADISON RIVER OAKS MEDICAL CENTER (250038)**, Highway 16 East, Zip 39046–8823, Mailing Address: P.O. Box 1607, Zip 39046–1607; tel. 601/859–1331 **A**1 9 10 **F**3 8 13 15 29 35 40 43 45 57 70 76 79 81 85 87 89 107 108 110 114 119 126 130 **S** Community Health Systems, Inc., Franklin, TN
Primary Contact: Bryan Bogle, Chief Executive Officer
CMO: Robert Tatum, M.D., Chief of Staff
CIO: Michelle Hughes, Director Health Information Management
CHR: Jackie Williams, Director Human Resources
Web address: www.madisonriveroaks.com
Control: Partnership, Investor–owned, for–profit **Service:** General Medical and Surgical

Staffed Beds: 44 Admissions: 1923 Census: 17 Outpatient Visits: 36970
Births: 427 Personnel: 228

CARTHAGE—Leake County

★ **BAPTIST MEDICAL CENTER LEAKE (251315)**, 310 Ellis Street, Zip 39051–3809, Mailing Address: P.O. Box 909, Zip 39051–0909; tel. 601/267–1100, (Total facility includes 44 beds in nursing home–type unit) **A**9 10 18 **F**3 15 29 32 34 40 41 43 46 57 59 65 66 70 81 87 107 108 110 114 119 127 128 130 133 135 **P**6 **S** Mississippi Baptist Health System, Jackson, MS
Primary Contact: Daryl W. Weaver, Interim Chief Executive Officer
COO: C. Gerald Cotton, Interim Chief Operating Officer
CFO: David Jackson, Chief Financial Officer
CMO: Doug Perry, M.D., Chief of Staff
Web address: www.mbhs.com/locations/baptist–medical–center–leake/
Control: Other not–for–profit (including NFP Corporation) **Service:** General Medical and Surgical

Staffed Beds: 69 Admissions: 659 Census: 50 Outpatient Visits: 21653
Births: 2 Personnel: 212

CENTREVILLE—Wilkinson County

⊞ **FIELD MEMORIAL COMMUNITY HOSPITAL (251309)**, 270 West Main Street, Zip 39631, Mailing Address: P.O. Box 639, Zip 39631–0639; tel. 601/645–5221 **A**1 9 10 18 **F**15 18 29 30 34 39 40 43 45 57 59 61 64 70 75 77 79 81 89 90 93 107 114 118 127 130 133 135 **P**6
Primary Contact: Chad Netterville, Administrator
CFO: Bryan N. Stevens, Chief Financial Officer
CIO: Locke Wheeles, Information Technology Manager
CHR: Dana McNabb, Human Resources Manager
CNO: Robin Walker, Chief Nursing Officer
Web address: www.fmch.org
Control: County–Government, nonfederal **Service:** General Medical and Surgical

Staffed Beds: 25 Admissions: 510 Census: 5 Outpatient Visits: 14339
Births: 0 Total Expense ($000): 16301 Payroll Expense ($000): 7648
Personnel: 145

CHARLESTON—Tallahatchie County

TALLAHATCHIE GENERAL HOSPITAL (251304), 201 South Market, Zip 38921–2236, Mailing Address: P.O. Box 230, Zip 38921–0240; tel. 662/647–5535, (Total facility includes 98 beds in nursing home–type unit) **A**9 10 18 **F**29 40 53 70 86 87 93 107 128 130 133 143 **P**6
Primary Contact: Jim Blackwood, Chief Executive Officer
CFO: Sammie Bell, Jr., Chief Financial Officer
Control: County–Government, nonfederal **Service:** General Medical and Surgical

Staffed Beds: 116 Admissions: 239 Census: 95 Outpatient Visits: 0 Births: 0 Personnel: 263

CLARKSDALE—Coahoma County

⊞ **NORTHWEST MISSISSIPPI REGIONAL MEDICAL CENTER (250042)**, 1970 Hospital Drive, Zip 38614–7202, Mailing Address: P.O. Box 1218, Zip 38614–1218; tel. 662/627–3211 **A**1 9 10 19 **F**3 13 15 17 18 20 22 28 29 30 31 34 35 40 43 46 49 50 53 57 59 64 65 70 74 76 79 81 85 86 87 89 90 92 93 107 108 110 111 114 115 118 119 126 129 130 131 132 **S** Community Health Systems, Inc., Franklin, TN
Primary Contact: William G. Buck, Chief Executive Officer
CFO: Justin Stroud, Chief Financial Officer
CMO: Roger Weiner, Chief of Staff
CIO: Patricia Keenum, Health Information Management Systems Officer
CHR: Arthur A. Wasek, Director Human Resources
CNO: Loreather Stacker, R.N., Chief Nursing Executive
Web address: www.northwestregional.org
Control: Corporation, Investor–owned, for–profit **Service:** General Medical and Surgical

Staffed Beds: 181 Admissions: 4238 Census: 46 Outpatient Visits: 53513
Births: 831 Total Expense ($000): 51888 Payroll Expense ($000): 20783
Personnel: 406

Many Facility Codes have changed. Please refer to the AHA Guide Code Chart. © 2014 AHA Guide

CLEVELAND—Bolivar County

⊠ **BOLIVAR MEDICAL CENTER (250093)**, 901 East Sunflower Road,
Zip 38732–2833, Mailing Address: P.O. Box 1380, Zip 38732–1380;
tel. 662/846–0061, (Total facility includes 35 beds in nursing home–type unit) **A**1
9 10 20 **F**3 11 13 15 17 18 26 29 30 35 39 40 43 45 46 56 59 60 70 73 74
76 79 81 82 85 87 88 89 93 103 107 108 110 111 112 115 116 118 119
120 128 130 132 133 146 **S** LifePoint Hospitals, Inc., Brentwood, TN
Primary Contact: James Atkins, Interim Chief Executive Officer
CFO: Chad Miller, Chief Financial Officer
CMO: Michael Portner, M.D., Chief Medical Staff
CIO: Dusty Griffith, Director Information Systems
CHR: David Kent, Director Human Resources
Web address: www.bolivarmedical.com
Control: Corporation, Investor–owned, for–profit **Service:** General Medical and
Surgical

Staffed Beds: 127 **Admissions:** 3698 **Census:** 72 **Outpatient Visits:** 38968
Births: 469 **Personnel:** 378

COLLINS—Covington County

★ ◇ **COVINGTON COUNTY HOSPITAL (251325)**, Gerald McRaney Street,
Zip 39428–3899, Mailing Address: P.O. Box 1149, Zip 39428–1149;
tel. 601/765–6711, (Total facility includes 60 beds in nursing home–type unit) **A**9
10 18 21 **F**3 7 40 43 45 57 65 68 70 81 89 93 103 107 114 119 127 128
130 133 144
Primary Contact: Woody White, Chief Executive Officer
CFO: Kirstie Evans, Chief Financial Officer
CMO: Word Johnston, Medical Director
CIO: Ransom Jones, Information Technology Director
CHR: Beverly K. Ponder, Executive Assistant and Human Resources Coordinator
CNO: Martha Lynn Scott, Chief Patient Care Officer
Web address: www.covingtoncountyhospital.com
Control: County–Government, nonfederal **Service:** General Medical and Surgical

Staffed Beds: 94 **Admissions:** 635 **Census:** 64 **Outpatient Visits:** 31937
Births: 0 **Total Expense ($000):** 23355 **Payroll Expense ($000):** 10794
Personnel: 265

COLUMBIA—Marion County

MARION GENERAL HOSPITAL (250085), 1560 Sumrall Road,
Zip 39429–2654, Mailing Address: P.O. Box 630, Zip 39429–0630;
tel. 601/736–6303 **A**9 10 **F**11 29 35 39 40 43 61 70 75 81 87 89 90 93 97
107 108 111 119 130 133 144
Primary Contact: Bryan K. Maxie, Administrator
CMO: Mark Stevens, M.D., Chief Medical Staff
CIO: Donny Bracey, Director Information Services
CNO: Patricia Reid, Director of Nursing
Control: County–Government, nonfederal **Service:** General Medical and Surgical

Staffed Beds: 49 **Admissions:** 889 **Census:** 10 **Outpatient Visits:** 28994
Births: 0 **Total Expense ($000):** 15500 **Payroll Expense ($000):** 5907
Personnel: 136

COLUMBUS—Lowndes County

⊠ **BAPTIST MEMORIAL HOSPITAL–GOLDEN TRIANGLE (250100)**, 2520 Fifth
Street North, Zip 39705–2095, Mailing Address: P.O. Box 1307,
Zip 39703–1307; tel. 662/244–1000 **A**1 9 10 19 **F**3 4 5 7 11 13 15 17 18 20
22 24 26 28 29 30 31 34 39 40 41 43 45 47 49 50 51 57 59 61 64 65 70
73 75 76 77 78 79 80 81 83 84 85 87 88 89 93 96 98 100 102 104 105
106 107 108 109 110 111 114 115 116 117 118 119 120 121 123 124 126
129 130 132 134 135 147 148 **P**6 **S** Baptist Memorial Health Care Corporation,
Memphis, TN
Primary Contact: Paul Cade, Administrator and Chief Executive Officer
CFO: David Webb, Chief Financial Officer
CMO: John E. Reed, M.D., Medical Director
CIO: Sheila Bardwell, Director Information Systems
CHR: Bob McCallister, Director Human Resources
CNO: Mary Ellen Sumrall, Chief Nursing Officer
Web address: www.baptistonline.org/golden–triangle/
Control: Other not–for–profit (including NFP Corporation) **Service:** General
Medical and Surgical

Staffed Beds: 236 **Admissions:** 8597 **Census:** 104 **Outpatient Visits:**
108364 **Births:** 943 **Total Expense ($000):** 137098 **Payroll Expense**
($000): 44680 **Personnel:** 955

CORINTH—Alcorn County

☐ **MAGNOLIA REGIONAL HEALTH CENTER (250009)**, 611 Alcorn Drive,
Zip 38834–9321; tel. 662/293–1000 **A**1 9 10 13 19 **F**13 15 17 29 35 39 40
43 51 53 62 63 70 75 76 77 78 81 86 87 89 93 98 100 101 102 103 107
108 111 116 118 119 130 131 132 143 147 **P**7 8
Primary Contact: Ronny Humes, President and Chief Executive Officer
COO: Angela Nowlin, R.N., Senior VP, Operations
CFO: Jeff Taylor, Senior Vice President Finance
CMO: Felton Combest, M.D., Vice President Medical Affairs
CIO: David Parker, VP Information Technology
CHR: Regenia Brown, Vice President Human Resources
CNO: Pam B. Wallis, MSN, RN–B, MSN, Vice President Nursing Services
Web address: www.mrhc.org
Control: City–County, Government, nonfederal **Service:** General Medical and
Surgical

Staffed Beds: 200 **Admissions:** 7769 **Census:** 97 **Outpatient Visits:** 144961
Births: 625 **Personnel:** 1196

DE KALB—Kemper County

★ **JOHN C. STENNIS MEMORIAL HOSPITAL (251335)**, 14365 Highway 16
West, Zip 39328–7974; tel. 769/486–1000 **A**9 10 18 **F**29 40 43 70 75 107
119 133 **P**6 **S** Rush Health Systems, Meridian, MS
Primary Contact: Michael Nester, Administrator
Web address: www.johncstennismemorialhospital.com/jcsmh/
Control: Other not–for–profit (including NFP Corporation) **Service:** General
Medical and Surgical

Staffed Beds: 25 **Admissions:** 146 **Census:** 1 **Births:** 1 **Personnel:** 148

EUPORA—Webster County

⊠ **NORTH MISSISSIPPI MEDICAL CENTER–EUPORA (250020)**, 70 Medical
Plaza, Zip 39744–4018; tel. 662/258–6221, (Total facility includes 35 beds in
nursing home–type unit) **A**1 9 10 **F**3 7 8 11 12 18 20 22 24 26 28 30 32
34 35 37 38 40 42 43 53 57 59 64 65 68 70 71 74 79 83 84 86 87 89 98
107 111 115 117 119 126 127 128 129 130 133 135 148 **S** North Mississippi
Health Services, Inc., Tupelo, MS
Primary Contact: John R. Jones, Administrator
CFO: Adonna Mitchell, Director Fiscal Services
CMO: Christy Vowell, D.O., Chief of Staff
CIO: Helen Reed, Director Health Information
CHR: Dorothy Castle, Director Human Resources
Web address: www.nmhs.net/eupora
Control: Other not–for–profit (including NFP Corporation) **Service:** General
Medical and Surgical

Staffed Beds: 73 **Admissions:** 1203 **Census:** 51 **Outpatient Visits:** 18128
Births: 0 **Total Expense ($000):** 20041 **Payroll Expense ($000):** 8363
Personnel: 206

FAYETTE—Jefferson County

★ **JEFFERSON COUNTY HOSPITAL (250060)**, 870 South Main Street,
Zip 39069–5695, Mailing Address: P.O. Box 577, Zip 39069–0577;
tel. 601/786–3401 **A**9 10 **F**40 70 98 103
Primary Contact: Ada Wilson, R.N., Interim Administrator
CMO: Khar Omolara, M.D., Chief Medical Staff
CHR: Patricia Selmon, Director Public Relations and Chief Human Resources
Control: County–Government, nonfederal **Service:** General Medical and Surgical

Staffed Beds: 30 **Admissions:** 734 **Census:** 18 **Births:** 0 **Personnel:** 88

FLOWOOD—Rankin County

⊠ **RIVER OAKS HOSPITAL (250138)**, 1030 River Oaks Drive, Zip 39232–9553,
Mailing Address: P.O. Box 5100, Jackson, Zip 39296–5100; tel. 601/932–1030
A1 10 **F**3 11 12 13 15 18 20 29 30 31 35 39 40 45 49 51 60 61 63 70
72 73 74 75 76 77 78 79 81 85 87 89 90 93 110 111 115 126 130 147
S Community Health Systems, Inc., Franklin, TN
Primary Contact: L. Dwayne Blaylock, Chief Executive Officer
COO: Heather Sistrunk, R.N., Chief Operating Officer
CFO: Brad Sinclair, Chief Financial Officer
CIO: Pat Jones, Director Information Systems
CHR: Warren Weed, Director Human Resources
CNO: Sherry P. Cook, R.N., Chief Nursing Executive
Web address: www.riveroakshosp.com
Control: Corporation, Investor–owned, for–profit **Service:** General Medical and
Surgical

Staffed Beds: 158 **Admissions:** 5771 **Census:** 57 **Outpatient Visits:** 61866
Births: 1701 **Personnel:** 559

MS

Hospital, Medicare Provider Number, Address, Telephone, Approval, Facility, and Physician Codes, Health Care System

★ American Hospital Association (AHA) membership
☐ The Joint Commission accreditation   ◇ DNV Healthcare Inc. accreditation

○ Healthcare Facilities Accreditation Program
△ Commission on Accreditation of Rehabilitation Facilities (CARF) accreditation

✠ **WOMAN'S HOSPITAL (250136)**, 1026 North Flowood Drive, Zip 39232–9532, Mailing Address: P.O. Box 4546, Jackson, Zip 39296–4546; tel. 601/932–1000 **A**1 10 **F**8 13 15 30 34 35 39 59 64 70 72 73 76 81 85 105 108 119 130 147 **S** Community Health Systems, Inc., Franklin, TN
Primary Contact: Sherry J. Pitts, Chief Executive Officer
CFO: Jeff Bedford, Executive Vice President and Chief Financial Officer
CMO: Edra Kimmel, M.D., Chief of Staff
CHR: Warren Weed, Director Associate Relations
Web address: www.womanshospitalms.com
Control: Corporation, Investor–owned, for–profit **Service:** Obstetrics and gynecology

Staffed Beds: 60 **Admissions:** 1884 **Census:** 17 **Outpatient Visits:** 12593 **Births:** 1331 **Personnel:** 190

FOREST—Scott County

★ ◇ **LACKEY MEMORIAL HOSPITAL (251300)**, 330 Broad Street, Zip 39074–3508, Mailing Address: P.O. Box 428, Zip 39074–0428; tel. 601/469–4151, (Total facility includes 20 beds in nursing home–type unit) **A**9 10 18 21 **F**3 15 18 29 34 35 39 40 42 43 45 56 65 70 79 81 86 89 98 103 107 108 111 119 126 127 128 130 133 **P**5 6 **S** Pioneer Health Services, Magee, MS
Primary Contact: Donna Riser, Administrator
CFO: Julie Gieger, Chief Financial Officer
CMO: John Paul Lee, M.D., Chief of Staff
CIO: Eddie Pope, Chief Information Officer
CHR: Donn Paul, Chief Human Resources
Web address: www.lackeymemorialhospital.com
Control: Other not–for–profit (including NFP Corporation) **Service:** General Medical and Surgical

Staffed Beds: 55 **Admissions:** 1769 **Census:** 42 **Outpatient Visits:** 21684 **Births:** 0 **Personnel:** 214

GREENVILLE—Washington County

◇ **ALLEGIANCE SPECIALTY HOSPITAL OF GREENVILLE (252013)**, 300 South Washington Avenue, 3rd Floor, Zip 38701–4719; tel. 662/332–7344 **A**10 21 **F**1 3 29 34 57 70 85 87 130 148 **S** Allegiance Health Management, Shreveport, LA
Primary Contact: Vernail Herzog, Chief Executive Officer
CMO: Parvez Karim, M.D., Chief Medical Officer
CIO: Sharon Scott, Health Information Director
CHR: Sharon Taylor, Human Resources Director
CNO: John Read, Chief Nursing Officer
Web address: www.ahmgt.com
Control: Corporation, Investor–owned, for–profit **Service:** Long–Term Acute Care hospital

Staffed Beds: 39 **Admissions:** 264 **Census:** 21 **Outpatient Visits:** 0 **Births:** 0 **Total Expense ($000):** 9541 **Payroll Expense ($000):** 4149 **Personnel:** 55

★ **DELTA REGIONAL MEDICAL CENTER (250082)**, 1400 East Union Street, Zip 38703–3246; tel. 662/378–3783, (Includes THE KING'S DAUGHTERS HOSPITAL, 300 Washington Avenue, Zip 38701–3614, Mailing Address: P.O. Box 1857, Zip 38702–1857; tel. 662/378–2020) **A**9 10 19 **F**3 4 11 13 15 17 18 20 22 24 28 29 30 31 34 35 39 40 43 45 50 51 57 59 62 63 64 68 70 72 73 75 76 77 78 79 81 84 85 89 90 93 96 97 98 103 104 107 108 110 111 115 116 118 119 127 129 130 131 132 135 144 147 148 **P**6 8
Primary Contact: Scott Christensen, Chief Executive Officer
CFO: C. Thomas Moore, Chief Financial Officer
CIO: Jennifer Parker, Interim Director Information Systems
CHR: Chrissy Nicholson, Director Human Resources
CNO: Amy Walker, Chief Nursing Officer
Web address: www.deltaregional.com
Control: County–Government, nonfederal **Service:** General Medical and Surgical

Staffed Beds: 217 **Admissions:** 8340 **Census:** 114 **Outpatient Visits:** 97238 **Births:** 808 **Total Expense ($000):** 113458 **Payroll Expense ($000):** 50791 **Personnel:** 904

GREENWOOD—Leflore County

AMG SPECIALTY HOSPITAL–GREENWOOD (252010), 1401 River Road Floor 2, Zip 38930–4030; tel. 662/459–2681 **A**9 10 **F**1 130 **S** AMG Integrated Healthcare Management, Lafayette, LA
Primary Contact: Jennifer Wallace, Chief Executive Officer
CMO: Gutti Rao, M.D., Medical Director
CNO: Brenda Small, Chief Clinical Officer
Web address: www.amggreenwood.com/
Control: Partnership, Investor–owned, for–profit **Service:** Long–Term Acute Care hospital

Staffed Beds: 40 **Admissions:** 356 **Census:** 25 **Outpatient Visits:** 0 **Births:** 0 **Personnel:** 75

□ △ **GREENWOOD LEFLORE HOSPITAL (250099)**, 1401 River Road, Zip 38930–4030, Mailing Address: Drawer 1410, Zip 38935–1410; tel. 662/459–7000 **A**1 7 9 10 19 **F**3 8 13 15 17 18 20 29 31 32 33 35 39 40 43 45 53 56 57 59 61 68 70 74 75 76 79 81 85 86 87 89 90 93 94 96 98 103 108 110 111 114 117 118 119 127 129 130 132 145 147 148 **P**6 8
Primary Contact: James H. Jackson, Jr., Executive Director
COO: Dodie McElmurray, Chief Operating Officer
CFO: Dawne Holmes, Chief Financial Officer
CMO: John F. Lucas, III, M.D., Chief of Staff
CIO: Mark S. Hutson, Chief Information Officer
CHR: Key Britt, Associate Director
CNO: Rebecca Edwards, Chief Nursing Officer
Web address: www.glh.org
Control: City–County, Government, nonfederal **Service:** General Medical and Surgical

Staffed Beds: 180 **Admissions:** 6066 **Census:** 79 **Outpatient Visits:** 144232 **Births:** 585 **Total Expense ($000):** 115309 **Payroll Expense ($000):** 59135 **Personnel:** 890

GRENADA—Grenada County

★ ◇ **UNIVERSITY OF MISSISSIPPI MEDICAL CENTER GRENADA (250015)**, 960 Avent Drive, Zip 38901–5230; tel. 662/227–7000 **A**9 10 20 21 **F**3 7 8 11 13 15 17 29 30 32 34 35 39 40 43 53 57 59 60 62 64 65 70 73 76 77 80 81 85 87 89 90 93 94 96 97 107 108 110 111 115 118 119 127 128 129 130 143 147 148 **P**6 **S** University Hospitals and Health System, Jackson, MS
Primary Contact: David G. Putt, FACHE, Chief Executive Officer
CFO: John Herrington, Chief Financial Officer
CIO: Sarah Longest, Chief Information Officer
CHR: Claudette Hathcock, Administrative Director Human Resources
CNO: Kathy Beck, R.N., Chief Nursing Officer
Web address: www.glmc.net
Control: County–Government, nonfederal **Service:** General Medical and Surgical

Staffed Beds: 132 **Admissions:** 2712 **Census:** 33 **Outpatient Visits:** 38031 **Births:** 403 **Total Expense ($000):** 45941 **Payroll Expense ($000):** 18882 **Personnel:** 415

GULFPORT—Harrison County

✠ **GARDEN PARK MEDICAL CENTER (250123)**, 15200 Community Road, Zip 39503–3085, Mailing Address: P.O. Box 1240, Zip 39502–1240; tel. 228/575–7000 **A**1 9 10 **F**3 12 13 15 18 19 29 34 35 40 41 45 49 57 59 70 74 76 79 81 85 86 87 89 90 97 98 103 107 108 110 111 115 116 119 126 129 130 147 148 **S** HCA, Nashville, TN
Primary Contact: Brenda M. Waltz, FACHE, Chief Executive Officer
COO: Daphne David, Chief Operating Officer
CFO: Regina Ramazani, Chief Financial Officer
CIO: Jackson Balch, IT Director
CHR: Krystyna Varnado, Director Human Resources
CNO: Cheryl Thompson, Chief Nursing Officer
Web address: www.gpmedical.com
Control: Corporation, Investor–owned, for–profit **Service:** General Medical and Surgical

Staffed Beds: 130 **Admissions:** 4094 **Census:** 45 **Outpatient Visits:** 66218 **Births:** 503 **Total Expense ($000):** 66133 **Payroll Expense ($000):** 23644 **Personnel:** 437

✠ △ **MEMORIAL HOSPITAL AT GULFPORT (250019)**, 4500 13th Street, Zip 39501–2569, Mailing Address: P.O. Box 1810, Zip 39502–1810; tel. 228/867–4000, (Includes MEMORIAL BEHAVIORAL HEALTH, 11150 Highway 49 North, Zip 39503–4110; tel. 228/831–1700; Michael A. Zieman, Administrator) **A**1 2 7 9 10 **F**3 5 8 11 13 15 17 18 20 22 24 26 28 29 30 31 34 35 38 40 43 44 45 46 48 49 50 51 53 54 57 59 64 65 66 68 70 71 72 73 74 76 77 78 79 80 81 84 85 87 89 90 92 93 95 96 98 99 100 101 102 104 105 107 108 110 111 115 116 117 118 119 120 121 124 126 130 132 135 145 148 **P**3 8
Primary Contact: Gary G. Marchand, President and Chief Executive Officer
COO: Kent Nicaud, Chief Operating Officer
CFO: Jeffrey T. Steiner, Vice President Finance
CMO: Nancy Downs, M.D., Vice President Medical Affairs
CIO: Gene Thomas, Vice President, Information Systems, Chief Information Officer
CHR: Cathy Wood, Vice President, Human Resources
CNO: Jennifer Dumal, R.N., Chief Operating Officer of Clinical and Chief Nursing Officer
Web address: www.gulfportmemorial.com
Control: City–County, Government, nonfederal **Service:** General Medical and Surgical

Staffed Beds: 445 **Admissions:** 15791 **Census:** 198 **Outpatient Visits:** 451562 **Births:** 1293 **Total Expense ($000):** 387612 **Payroll Expense ($000):** 173878 **Personnel:** 2674

Many Facility Codes have changed. Please refer to the AHA Guide Code Chart.

MS

⊠ **SELECT SPECIALTY HOSPITAL–GULF COAST (252005)**, 1520 Broad Avenue, Suite 300, Zip 39501–3601; tel. 228/575–7500 **A**1 10 **F**1 70 87 90 130 **P**3 **S** Select Medical Corporation, Mechanicsburg, PA
Primary Contact: John O'Keefe, Chief Executive Officer
Web address: www.selectspecialtyhospitals.com/company/locations/gulfcoast. aspx
Control: Corporation, Investor–owned, for–profit **Service:** Long–Term Acute Care hospital

Staffed Beds: 61 **Admissions:** 372 **Census:** 27 **Outpatient Visits:** 0 **Births:** 0 **Personnel:** 124

HATTIESBURG—Forrest County

★ △ ◇ **FORREST GENERAL HOSPITAL (250078)**, 6051 U.S. Highway 49, Zip 39401–7200, Mailing Address: P.O. Box 16389, Zip 39404–6389; tel. 601/288–7000 **A**2 3 5 7 9 10 19 21 **F**3 4 5 8 12 13 15 17 18 20 22 24 26 28 29 30 31 34 35 37 40 43 46 47 49 53 57 58 59 60 62 63 64 68 70 72 73 75 76 77 78 79 81 85 86 87 89 90 91 92 93 95 96 98 99 100 102 103 104 106 107 108 111 114 115 118 119 120 121 123 124 126 127 128 130 131 132 135 147
Primary Contact: Evan S. Dillard, M.P.H., FACHE, President and Chief Executive Officer
COO: Douglas A. Jones, Chief Operating Officer
CFO: Andy Woodard, Chief Financial Officer
CMO: Steven E. Farrell, M.D., Chief Medical Officer
CNO: Micah Rehm, Chief Nursing Officer
Web address: www.forrestgeneral.com
Control: County–Government, nonfederal **Service:** General Medical and Surgical

Staffed Beds: 512 **Admissions:** 25831 **Census:** 333 **Outpatient Visits:** 131207 **Births:** 2163 **Total Expense ($000):** 364409 **Payroll Expense ($000):** 138311 **Personnel:** 2688

⊠ **REGENCY HOSPITAL OF HATTIESBURG (252009)**, 6051 U.S. Highway 495, 5th Floor, Zip 39401–6031; tel. 601/288–8510 **A**1 10 **F**40 70 **S** Select Medical Corporation, Mechanicsburg, PA
Primary Contact: Kathy A. Viator, R.N., Chief Executive Officer
CMO: Ralph Kahler, M.D., Medical Director
CHR: Jared Burns, Coordinator Human Resources
Web address: www.regencyhospital.com/hattiesburg
Control: Corporation, Investor–owned, for–profit **Service:** Long–Term Acute Care hospital

Staffed Beds: 33 **Admissions:** 426 **Census:** 25 **Outpatient Visits:** 0 **Births:** 0 **Personnel:** 112

⊠ **WESLEY MEDICAL CENTER (250094)**, 5001 Hardy Street, Zip 39402–1308, Mailing Address: P.O. Box 16509, Zip 39404–6509; tel. 601/268–8000 **A**1 9 10 19 **F**3 8 11 12 13 15 17 18 20 22 24 28 29 30 31 32 35 36 37 38 39 40 41 44 45 46 47 48 49 50 53 58 59 60 61 64 65 70 72 73 74 75 76 77 78 79 81 82 85 87 89 90 92 93 96 97 107 108 109 110 111 114 115 117 118 119 126 129 130 132 135 146 148 **P**6 7 **S** Community Health Systems, Inc., Franklin, TN
Primary Contact: Michael Neuendorf, Chief Executive Officer
CFO: Randy Humphrey, Chief Financial Officer
CMO: William Reno, III, M.D., President Medical Staff
CHR: Terry Trigg, Director Human Resources
Web address: www.wesley.com
Control: Corporation, Investor–owned, for–profit **Service:** General Medical and Surgical

Staffed Beds: 211 **Admissions:** 8109 **Census:** 110 **Outpatient Visits:** 93133 **Births:** 1417 **Personnel:** 1017

HAZLEHURST—Copiah County

★ **HARDY WILSON MEMORIAL HOSPITAL (251327)**, 233 Magnolia Street, Zip 39083–2228, Mailing Address: P.O. Box 889, Zip 39083–0889; tel. 601/894–4541 **A**9 10 18 **F**15 34 35 39 40 42 43 45 56 57 59 65 68 70 71 75 81 90 93 98 103 107 111 119 130 133 148
Primary Contact: William Giles, Interim Chief Executive Officer
Web address: www.hardywilsonhospital.com
Control: County–Government, nonfederal **Service:** General Medical and Surgical

Staffed Beds: 25 **Admissions:** 787 **Census:** 15 **Outpatient Visits:** 11529 **Births:** 0 **Personnel:** 186

HOLLY SPRINGS—Marshall County

ALLIANCE HEALTHCARE SYSTEM (250012), 1430 Highway 4 East, Zip 38635–2140, Mailing Address: P.O. Box 6000, Zip 38634–6000; tel. 662/252–1212 **A**9 10 20 **F**15 29 35 40 43 57 70 75 81 84 87 89 98 103 104 107 119 130 132 133 143
Primary Contact: Perry E. Williams, Sr., Administrator and Chief Executive Officer
COO: Cecelia Bost, Chief Operating Officer
CFO: William F. Magee, Chief Financial Officer
CMO: Subbu Rayudu, M.D., Chief of Staff
CIO: Saul Mbenga, Manager Information Technology
CHR: Judy Eggers, Manager Human Resources
Web address: www.alliancehealth.us
Control: Corporation, Investor–owned, for–profit **Service:** General Medical and Surgical

Staffed Beds: 40 **Admissions:** 536 **Census:** 8 **Outpatient Visits:** 7734 **Births:** 0 **Personnel:** 84

HOUSTON—Chickasaw County

☐ **TRACE REGIONAL HOSPITAL (250017)**, Highway 8 East, Zip 38851–9396, Mailing Address: P.O. Box 626, Zip 38851–0626; tel. 662/456–3700 **A**1 9 10 **F**3 11 15 30 34 35 40 42 45 57 59 61 64 66 70 75 81 89 90 91 93 98 103 107 111 114 119 127 128 130 133 135 146 148 **P**6 **S** Sunlink Health Systems, Atlanta, GA
Primary Contact: Gary L. Staten, Chief Executive Officer
CFO: Pamela W. Cook, Chief Financial Officer
CMO: Bill Brohawn, Chief of Staff
CHR: Sherry Craig, Director Human Resources
CNO: Marianne Johnson, Chief Nursing Officer
Web address: www.traceregional.com
Control: Corporation, Investor–owned, for–profit **Service:** General Medical and Surgical

Staffed Beds: 84 **Admissions:** 574 **Census:** 10 **Outpatient Visits:** 20435 **Births:** 0 **Personnel:** 208

INDIANOLA—Sunflower County

★ **SOUTH SUNFLOWER COUNTY HOSPITAL (250095)**, 121 East Baker Street, Zip 38751–2498; tel. 662/887–5235 **A**9 10 20 **F**13 15 17 40 43 45 70 76 81 107 110 111 114 119 127 130 **P**8
Primary Contact: Courtney Phillips, Chief Executive Officer
COO: Barbara Prichard, Assistant Administrator
CFO: Meredith Taylor, Comptroller
CMO: Wade Dowell, M.D., Chief of Staff
CIO: Julie Sterling, Manager Information System
Control: County–Government, nonfederal **Service:** General Medical and Surgical

Staffed Beds: 49 **Admissions:** 1254 **Census:** 9 **Outpatient Visits:** 11663 **Births:** 297 **Total Expense ($000):** 14288 **Payroll Expense ($000):** 5239 **Personnel:** 128

IUKA—Tishomingo County

⊠ **NORTH MISSISSIPPI MEDICAL CENTER–IUKA (250002)**, 1777 Curtis Drive, Zip 38852–1001, Mailing Address: P.O. Box 860, Zip 38852–0860; tel. 662/423–6051 **A**1 9 10 **F**7 17 29 34 35 40 43 53 57 64 65 68 70 75 86 87 89 90 91 93 107 108 111 114 119 129 130 132 133 134 135 **S** North Mississippi Health Services, Inc., Tupelo, MS
Primary Contact: Fred A. Truesdale, Jr., Administrator
CFO: Betty Moore, Business Manager
CMO: Margaret Glynn, M.D., Chief Medical Officer
CIO: Fred A. Truesdale, Jr., Administrator
CHR: Jane Chamblee, Manager Human Resources
Web address: www.nmhs.net
Control: Other not–for–profit (including NFP Corporation) **Service:** General Medical and Surgical

Staffed Beds: 48 **Admissions:** 676 **Census:** 6 **Outpatient Visits:** 18455 **Births:** 0 **Personnel:** 152

JACKSON—Hinds County

☐ **BRENTWOOD BEHAVIORAL HEALTHCARE OF MISSISSIPPI (254007)**, 3531 East Lakeland Drive, Zip 39232–8839; tel. 601/936–2024 **A**1 10 **F**35 98 99 101 102 104 105 130 132 **S** Universal Health Services, Inc., King of Prussia, PA
Primary Contact: Michael J. Carney, Chief Executive Officer
Web address: www.brentwoodjackson.com
Control: Corporation, Investor–owned, for–profit **Service:** Psychiatric

Staffed Beds: 105 **Admissions:** 2670 **Census:** 74 **Outpatient Visits:** 0 **Births:** 0 **Personnel:** 220

MS

Hospital, Medicare Provider Number, Address, Telephone, Approval, Facility, and Physician Codes, Health Care System

★ American Hospital Association (AHA) membership
☐ The Joint Commission accreditation   ◇ DNV Healthcare Inc. accreditation
○ Healthcare Facilities Accreditation Program
△ Commission on Accreditation of Rehabilitation Facilities (CARF) accreditation

✠ **CENTRAL MISSISSIPPI MEDICAL CENTER (250072)**, 1850 Chadwick Drive, Zip 39204–3479, Mailing Address: P.O. Box 59001, Zip 39284–9001; tel. 601/376–1000 **A**1 2 9 10 **F**13 15 16 17 29 35 40 43 51 60 61 70 72 73 75 76 77 78 80 81 86 87 89 90 93 97 98 100 102 103 104 107 108 111 116 118 119 130 132 147 **P**4 **S** Community Health Systems, Inc., Franklin, TN
Primary Contact: Charlotte W. Dupre', Chief Executive Officer
COO: Jon–Paul Croom, Chief Operating Officer
CFO: Scott Whittemore, Chief Financial Officer
CIO: John Simpson, Director Information Systems
CHR: Mark B. Cook, Director Human Resources
CNO: Lorie N. Ramsey, MSN, Chief Nursing Executive
Web address: www.centralmississippimedicalcenter.com
Control: Corporation, Investor–owned, for–profit **Service:** General Medical and Surgical

Staffed Beds: 217 **Admissions:** 7909 **Census:** 102 **Outpatient Visits:** 91117 **Births:** 650 **Personnel:** 617

✠ **G.V. (SONNY) MONTGOMERY VETERANS AFFAIRS MEDICAL CENTER**, 1500 East Woodrow Wilson Drive, Zip 39216–5199; tel. 601/362–4471, (Nonreporting) **A**1 2 3 5 **S** Department of Veterans Affairs, Washington, DC
Primary Contact: Joe Battle, Director
COO: Jed Fillingim, Acting Chief Operating Officer and Associate Director
CFO: Joy Willis, Acting Chief Fiscal Service
CMO: Kent Kirchner, M.D., Chief of Staff
CIO: Robert Wolak, Chief Information Resource Management Service
CHR: Sam Evans, Chief Human Resources Management
Web address: www.jackson.va.gov/
Control: Veterans Affairs, Government, federal **Service:** General Medical and Surgical

Staffed Beds: 323

✠ △ **METHODIST REHABILITATION CENTER (250152)**, 1350 Woodrow Wilson Drive, Zip 39216–5198; tel. 601/981–2611, (Total facility includes 60 beds in nursing home–type unit) **A**1 3 5 7 9 10 **F**29 35 70 77 81 86 87 90 93 119 130 132 143
Primary Contact: Mark A. Adams, President and Chief Executive Officer
COO: Joseph M. Morette, Executive Vice President
CFO: Gary Armstrong, Executive Vice President
CIO: Gary Armstrong, Executive Vice President
CHR: Steve Hope, Vice President Corporate Services
Web address: www.methodistrehab.org
Control: Other not–for–profit (including NFP Corporation) **Service:** Rehabilitation

Staffed Beds: 184 **Admissions:** 1057 **Census:** 107 **Outpatient Visits:** 42292 **Births:** 0 **Personnel:** 544

✠ **MISSISSIPPI BAPTIST MEDICAL CENTER (250102)**, 1225 North State Street, Zip 39202–2064; tel. 601/968–1000 **A**1 2 3 5 9 10 **F**3 4 5 8 11 12 13 15 17 18 19 20 22 24 26 27 28 29 30 31 34 35 36 39 40 41 44 45 46 47 48 49 50 51 52 53 54 55 57 59 61 64 65 68 70 71 72 73 74 75 76 78 79 80 81 85 86 89 90 91 92 93 94 98 100 103 104 105 107 108 109 110 111 114 115 116 117 118 119 120 121 122 123 124 126 127 129 130 132 144 145 146 147 148 **S** Mississippi Baptist Health System, Jackson, MS
Primary Contact: Kerry R. Tirman, JD, FACHE, President
CFO: Russell W. York, Chief Financial Officer
CMO: Eric A. McVey, M.D., Vice President and Chief Medical Officer
CIO: Steve M. Stanic, Vice President and Chief Information Officer
CHR: Lee Ann Foreman, Vice President Human Resources
CNO: Bobbie K. Ware, R.N., Vice President/Patient Care/Chief Nursing Officer
Web address: www.mbhs.org
Control: Other not–for–profit (including NFP Corporation) **Service:** General Medical and Surgical

Staffed Beds: 638 **Admissions:** 19417 **Census:** 293 **Outpatient Visits:** 155148 **Births:** 1147 **Personnel:** 2893

✠ **MISSISSIPPI HOSPITAL FOR RESTORATIVE CARE (252003)**, 1225 North State Street, Zip 39202–2097, Mailing Address: P.O. Box 23695, Zip 39225–3695; tel. 601/968–1000 **A**i 10 **F**3 29 39 56 61 70 80 85 130 **P**7 **S** Mississippi Baptist Health System, Jackson, MS
Primary Contact: Bobbie K. Ware, R.N., FACHE, Chief Executive Officer and Chief Nursing Officer
CFO: Russell W. York, Vice President and Chief Financial Officer
CMO: Holland M. Addison, M.D., Medical Director
CIO: Steve M. Stanic, Vice President and Chief Information Officer
CHR: Lee Ann Foreman, Vice President Human Resources
Web address: www.mbhs.org
Control: Other not–for–profit (including NFP Corporation) **Service:** Long–Term Acute Care hospital

Staffed Beds: 25 **Admissions:** 218 **Census:** 21 **Outpatient Visits:** 0 **Births:** 0 **Total Expense ($000):** 11119 **Payroll Expense ($000):** 4518 **Personnel:** 65

✠ **REGENCY HOSPITAL OF JACKSON (252012)**, 969 Lakeland Drive, 6th Floor, Zip 39216–4643; tel. 601/364–6200 **A**1 10 **F**1 3 18 29 70 74 79 130 148 **S** Select Medical Corporation, Mechanicsburg, PA
Primary Contact: Lorie Powell, Interim Chief Executive Officer
Web address: www.regencyhospital.com
Control: Corporation, Investor–owned, for–profit **Service:** Long–Term Acute Care hospital

Staffed Beds: 36 **Admissions:** 368 **Census:** 27 **Outpatient Visits:** 0 **Births:** 0 **Personnel:** 72

✠ **SELECT SPECIALTY HOSPITAL–JACKSON (252007)**, 5903 Ridgewood Road, Suite 100, Zip 39211–3700; tel. 601/899–3800 **A**1 10 **F**1 70 93 107 119 130 **P**6 **S** Select Medical Corporation, Mechanicsburg, PA
Primary Contact: Chandler Ewing, Chief Executive Officer
CFO: Melissa Smith, Controller
CIO: Jacqueline Barnes, Manager Health Information
CHR: Vicki Watson, Manager Human Resources
Web address: www.selectspecialtyhospitals.com/company/locations/jackson.aspx
Control: Corporation, Investor–owned, for–profit **Service:** Long–Term Acute Care hospital

Staffed Beds: 53 **Admissions:** 622 **Census:** 45 **Outpatient Visits:** 0 **Births:** 0 **Personnel:** 203

✠ **ST. DOMINIC–JACKSON MEMORIAL HOSPITAL (250048)**, 969 Lakeland Drive, Zip 39216–4606; tel. 601/200–2000 **A**1 2 3 5 9 10 **F**3 4 11 12 13 15 17 18 20 22 24 26 28 29 30 31 34 35 36 37 38 39 40 43 47 49 50 51 53 57 58 60 61 64 65 68 70 72 73 74 75 76 77 78 79 80 81 84 85 86 89 90 92 93 97 98 100 101 102 103 106 107 108 109 110 111 114 115 116 117 118 119 120 121 122 124 126 130 131 147 148 **P**8
Primary Contact: Lester K. Diamond, President
CFO: Matt Fisher, Vice President Finance
CMO: Lawrence Riddles, M.D., Executive Vice President Medical Affairs and Quality
CIO: Keith Van Camp, Vice President Information Services
CHR: Lorraine Washington, Vice President Human Resources
CNO: Theresa Horne, MS, Vice President Patient Care Services
Web address: www.stdom.com
Control: Other not–for–profit (including NFP Corporation) **Service:** General Medical and Surgical

Staffed Beds: 476 **Admissions:** 35204 **Census:** 352 **Outpatient Visits:** 162703 **Births:** 1486 **Total Expense ($000):** 383449 **Payroll Expense ($000):** 158727 **Personnel:** 2718

✠ △ **UNIVERSITY HOSPITAL (250001)**, 2500 North State Street, Zip 39216–4505; tel. 601/984–1000, (Includes BLAIR E. BATSON HOSPITAL FOR CHILDREN, 2500 North State State Room W019, Zip 39216–4500; tel. 601/984–1000; CHILDREN'S HEALTHCARE OF MISSISSIPPI, 2500 North State Street, Zip 39216–4500) **A**1 2 3 5 7 8 9 10 **F**3 7 8 11 12 13 15 17 18 19 20 21 22 23 24 25 26 27 28 29 30 31 32 34 35 37 38 39 40 41 43 44 45 46 47 48 49 50 52 53 54 56 57 58 59 60 61 64 65 66 68 70 72 73 74 75 76 77 78 79 80 81 84 85 86 87 88 89 90 92 93 94 96 97 98 99 100 101 102 103 104 107 108 110 111 112 114 115 116 117 118 119 120 121 124 126 127 129 130 131 132 134 135 136 137 138 139 141 142 143 144 147 148 **P**6 **S** University Hospitals and Health System, Jackson, MS
Primary Contact: Kevin S. Cook, Chief Executive Officer
CFO: Dan Janicak, Chief Financial Officer
CMO: William H. Cleland, M.D., Chief Medical Officer
CHR: Michael Estes, Director Human Resources
CNO: Janet Y. Harris, R.N., Chief Nursing Officer
Web address: www.umc.edu
Control: State–Government, nonfederal **Service:** General Medical and Surgical

Staffed Beds: 673 **Admissions:** 27748 **Census:** 494 **Outpatient Visits:** 197904 **Births:** 2267 **Total Expense ($000):** 751537 **Payroll Expense ($000):** 273693 **Personnel:** 4700

KEESLER AFB—Harrison County

✠ **U. S. AIR FORCE MEDICAL CENTER KEESLER**, 301 Fisher Street, Room 1A132, Zip 39534–2519; tel. 228/376–2550, (Nonreporting) **A**1 2 3 5 **S** Department of the Air Force, Washington, DC
Primary Contact: Colonel Thomas Harrell, M.D., Commander
COO: Brigadier General James Dougherty, Commander
CFO: Major Brenda Yi, Director Medical Resource Management and Chief Financial Officer
CMO: Colonel James Gasque, M.D., Chief Hospital Services
CIO: Major Samuel Silverthorne, Chief Information Officer
CHR: Major Brenda Yi, Director Medical Resource Management and Chief Financial Officer
Web address: www.keesler.af.mil
Control: Air Force, Government, federal **Service:** General Medical and Surgical

Staffed Beds: 56

Many Facility Codes have changed. Please refer to the AHA Guide Code Chart.
© 2014 AHA Guide

KILMICHAEL—Montgomery County

★ **KILMICHAEL HOSPITAL (250051)**, 301 Lamar Avenue, Zip 39747–9002, Mailing Address: P.O. Box 188, Zip 39747–0188; tel. 662/262–4311 **A**9 10 **F**70 89 133 **P**1
Primary Contact: Calvin D. Johnson, Administrator
Control: County–Government, nonfederal **Service:** General Medical and Surgical

Staffed Beds: 19 **Admissions:** 127 **Census:** 1 **Outpatient Visits:** 3488
Births: 0 **Personnel:** 30

KOSCIUSKO—Attala County

★ ◇ **MONTFORT JONES MEMORIAL HOSPITAL (250059)**, 220 Highway 12 West, Zip 39090–3208, Mailing Address: P.O. Box 887, Zip 39090–0887; tel. 662/289–4311 **A**9 10 21 **F**3 15 17 34 35 40 43 56 57 59 64 65 70 81 85 89 90 92 93 103 107 108 110 115 116 118 119 130 133 148
Primary Contact: John Dawson, Chief Executive Officer
CFO: Josh Harmond, Chief Financial Officer
CHR: Linnie Pearson, Coordinator Human Resources and Benefits
CNO: Allison Schuler, R.N., Chief Nursing Officer
Web address: www.montfortjones.com
Control: County–Government, nonfederal **Service:** General Medical and Surgical

Staffed Beds: 71 **Admissions:** 1286 **Census:** 16 **Outpatient Visits:** 26866
Births: 0 **Total Expense ($000):** 16729 **Payroll Expense ($000):** 6123
Personnel: 140

LAUREL—Jones County

★ ◇ **SOUTH CENTRAL REGIONAL MEDICAL CENTER (250058)**, 1220 Jefferson Street, Zip 39440–4374, Mailing Address: P.O. Box 607, Zip 39441–0607; tel. 601/426–4000, (Total facility includes 248 beds in nursing home–type unit) **A**9 10 19 20 21 **F**3 4 7 10 12 13 15 17 18 20 28 29 30 31 34 35 37 40 43 48 49 51 53 56 57 59 62 63 64 68 69 70 73 74 76 77 78 79 81 84 85 86 87 89 90 92 93 100 102 103 104 105 108 110 111 114 115 117 118 119 127 128 130 131 132 134 143 144 147 148 **P**6
Primary Contact: G. Douglas Higginbotham, President and Chief Executive Officer
CFO: Tom Canizaro, Vice President and Chief Financial Officer
CMO: James Holston, M.D., Vice President and Chief Quality Officer
CIO: Linda Gavin, Associate Executive Director Marketing and Physician Recruitment
CHR: Janet Staples, Vice President Human Resources
CNO: Beth W. Endom, R.N., Vice President and Chief Nursing Officer
Web address: www.scrmc.com
Control: County–Government, nonfederal **Service:** General Medical and Surgical

Staffed Beds: 442 **Admissions:** 7939 **Census:** 324 **Outpatient Visits:** 75313
Births: 876 **Total Expense ($000):** 141967 **Payroll Expense ($000):** 68964
Personnel: 1577

LEAKESVILLE—Greene County

GREENE COUNTY HOSPITAL (251329), 1017 Jackson Avenue, Zip 39451–9105; tel. 601/394–4139 **A**9 10 18 **F**40 43 70 107 133
Primary Contact: Deborah Berry, Director of Operations
CFO: Debbie Brannan, Chief Financial Officer
CMO: Larry Henderson, M.D., Medical Director
CHR: Carla Shows, Payroll Clerk
Web address: www.georgeregional.com
Control: County–Government, nonfederal **Service:** General Medical and Surgical

Staffed Beds: 3 **Admissions:** 20 **Census:** 1 **Births:** 0 **Personnel:** 57

LEXINGTON—Holmes County

⊠ **HOLMES COUNTY HOSPITAL AND CLINICS (251319)**, 239 Bowling Green Road, Zip 39095–5167; tel. 662/834–1321 **A**1 9 10 18 **F**3 15 29 34 40 43 56 57 59 64 70 86 87 89 93 107 108 115 118 119 127 130 133 **P**6 **S** University Hospitals and Health System, Jackson, MS
Primary Contact: David G. Putt, FACHE, Chief Executive Officer
CFO: John Herrington, Chief Financial Officer
CMO: Keith Stokes, Chief Medical Officer
CIO: Kelvin Jackson, LAN Administrator
CHR: Claudette Hathcock, Human Resources Director
Web address: www.ummchealth.com/holmes/
Control: State–Government, nonfederal **Service:** General Medical and Surgical

Staffed Beds: 25 **Admissions:** 233 **Census:** 2 **Outpatient Visits:** 12589
Births: 0 **Total Expense ($000):** 12194 **Payroll Expense ($000):** 6385
Personnel: 110

LOUISVILLE—Winston County

WINSTON MEDICAL CENTER (250027), 562 East Main Street, Zip 39339–2742, Mailing Address: P.O. Box 967, Zip 39339–0967; tel. 662/773–6211, (Total facility includes 120 beds in nursing home–type unit) **A**9 10 20 **F**3 15 29 32 34 35 40 43 45 57 59 66 70 81 89 93 103 107 108 110 114 119 128 130 133
Primary Contact: Lee McCall, Administrator
Web address: www.winstonmedical.org
Control: Other not–for–profit (including NFP Corporation) **Service:** General Medical and Surgical

Staffed Beds: 161 **Admissions:** 500 **Census:** 124 **Outpatient Visits:** 18944
Births: 0 **Personnel:** 216

LUCEDALE—Jackson County

GEORGE REGIONAL HOSPITAL (250036), 859 Winter Street, Zip 39452–6603, Mailing Address: P.O. Box 607, Zip 39452–0607; tel. 601/947–3161 **A**9 10 20 **F**3 11 13 15 17 18 30 34 35 40 43 45 47 48 49 53 54 57 59 65 68 70 76 81 86 87 93 107 108 111 119 130 133 135 146 148 **P**8
Primary Contact: Paul A. Gardner, CPA, Administrator
CFO: Debbie Brannan, Chief Financial Officer
CMO: Seth Scott, M.D., Chief of Staff
CHR: Carla Shows, Payroll Clerk
Web address: www.georgeregional.com
Control: County–Government, nonfederal **Service:** General Medical and Surgical

Staffed Beds: 48 **Admissions:** 1409 **Census:** 14 **Outpatient Visits:** 40840
Births: 185 **Personnel:** 300

MACON—Noxubee County

NOXUBEE GENERAL HOSPITAL (251307), 606 North Jefferson Street, Zip 39341–2242, Mailing Address: P.O. Box 480, Zip 39341–0480; tel. 662/726–4231, (Total facility includes 60 beds in nursing home–type unit) **A**9 10 18 **F**40 43 70 89 107 128 130 133
Primary Contact: Danny H. McKay, Administrator
Web address: www.noxubeecountyms.com/quality–of–life–noxubee–mississipp/health–care–noxubee–mississippi/
Control: County–Government, nonfederal **Service:** General Medical and Surgical

Staffed Beds: 85 **Admissions:** 844 **Census:** 65 **Outpatient Visits:** 4483
Births: 0 **Personnel:** 176

MAGEE—Simpson County

★ **MAGEE GENERAL HOSPITAL (250124)**, 300 Third Avenue S.E., Zip 39111–3698; tel. 601/849–5070 **A**9 10 **F**13 15 29 35 70 73 81 107 108 111 119 130 133
Primary Contact: Althea H. Crumpton, Administrator
CMO: Kelli Smith, M.D., Chief of Staff
CIO: Kirby Craft, Chief Information Officer
CHR: Steve Beckham, Director Human Resources
CNO: Cindy McIntyre, R.N., Administrative Director Clinical Services
Web address: www.mghosp.org
Control: Other not–for–profit (including NFP Corporation) **Service:** General Medical and Surgical

Staffed Beds: 64 **Admissions:** 1442 **Census:** 17 **Outpatient Visits:** 47274
Births: 294 **Personnel:** 235

MAGNOLIA—Pike County

BEACHAM MEMORIAL HOSPITAL (250049), 205 North Cherry Street, Zip 39652–2819, Mailing Address: P.O. Box 351, Zip 39652–0351; tel. 601/783–2351 **A**9 10 **F**3 34 35 36 57 59 65 68 70 107 114 127 130 133 146 148
Primary Contact: Guy Geller, Administrator and Chief Executive Officer
CMO: Lucius Lampton, M.D., Medical Director
CHR: Jackie McKenzie, Director Administrative Services
Web address: www.beachammemhos.com
Control: Other not–for–profit (including NFP Corporation) **Service:** General Medical and Surgical

Staffed Beds: 37 **Admissions:** 675 **Census:** 12 **Outpatient Visits:** 0 **Births:** 0 **Total Expense ($000):** 6228 **Payroll Expense ($000):** 3019 **Personnel:** 89

MS

Hospital, Medicare Provider Number, Address, Telephone, Approval, Facility, and Physician Codes, Health Care System

★ American Hospital Association (AHA) membership
□ The Joint Commission accreditation   ◇ DNV Healthcare Inc. accreditation

○ Healthcare Facilities Accreditation Program
△ Commission on Accreditation of Rehabilitation Facilities (CARF) accreditation

MARKS—Quitman County

QUITMAN COUNTY HOSPITAL (251314), 340 Getwell Drive, Zip 38646–9785; tel. 662/326–8031 **A**9 10 18 **F**3 40 43 56 64 70 89 90 103 106 107 114 119 133
Primary Contact: Wes Sigler, Administrator
CFO: Jane Moore, Director, Fiscal Services
CMO: James E. Warrington, Sr., M.D., Chief of Staff
CHR: Sandra Biffle, Personnel Clerk
CNO: Dana Hall, Director of Nursing
Control: Corporation, Investor–owned, for–profit **Service:** General Medical and Surgical

Staffed Beds: 33 **Admissions:** 461 **Census:** 9 **Outpatient Visits:** 9101 **Births:** 0 **Total Expense ($000):** 7726 **Payroll Expense ($000):** 3776 **Personnel:** 111

MCCOMB—Pike County

★ ◇ **SOUTHWEST MISSISSIPPI REGIONAL MEDICAL CENTER (250097)**, 215 Marion Avenue, Zip 39648–2705, Mailing Address: P.O. Box 1307, Zip 39649–1307; tel. 601/249–5500 **A**9 10 19 21 **F**3 8 11 12 13 15 17 18 20 22 24 28 29 30 31 32 34 39 40 41 43 45 47 49 50 53 57 59 64 66 68 70 72 73 74 75 76 77 78 79 81 84 85 86 87 89 92 93 94 107 108 110 111 112 114 115 118 119 120 121 126 127 129 130 131 132 135 145 148 **P**6 **S** Southwest Health Systems, Mccomb, MS
Primary Contact: Norman M. Price, FACHE, Chief Executive Officer
COO: Richard Williams, Chief Operating Officer
CFO: Charla Rowley, Chief Financial Officer
CMO: Kevin Richardson, M.D., Chief of Staff
CIO: Mike Moak, Chief Information Officer
CHR: Don Haskins, Administrative Director Human Resources
CNO: Katie McKinley, Assistant Administrator/Nursing
Web address: www.smrmc.com
Control: Hospital district or authority, Government, nonfederal **Service:** General Medical and Surgical

Staffed Beds: 143 **Admissions:** 7164 **Census:** 88 **Outpatient Visits:** 89646 **Births:** 746 **Personnel:** 949

MEADVILLE—Franklin County

FRANKLIN COUNTY MEMORIAL HOSPITAL (251330), 40 Union Church Road, Zip 39653–8336, Mailing Address: P.O. Box 636, Zip 39653–0636; tel. 601/384–5801 **A**9 10 18 **F**29 35 40 43 56 70 86 89 93 103 107 119 130 133 143 **P**6
Primary Contact: Mike Boleware, Administrator
Web address: www.fcmh.net
Control: County–Government, nonfederal **Service:** General Medical and Surgical

Staffed Beds: 35 **Admissions:** 349 **Census:** 7 **Outpatient Visits:** 3124 **Births:** 0 **Personnel:** 187

MENDENHALL—Simpson County

SIMPSON GENERAL HOSPITAL (251317), 1842 Simpson Highway 149, Zip 39114–3438; tel. 601/847–2221 **A**9 10 18 **F**3 11 30 34 35 40 44 54 56 57 59 61 64 65 66 68 70 81 85 86 87 90 98 103 107 114 119 127 130 132 133 134 **P**1 5
Primary Contact: Randall Neely, Chief Executive Officer
COO: Al Gary, COO
CFO: Al Gary, COO
CMO: Chip Holbrook, M.D., Chief of Staff
CIO: David Welch, Director Information Technology
CHR: Randall Neely, CEO
CNO: Sharon Burnham, Director of Nursing
Web address: www.simpsongeneralhospital.com
Control: Other not–for–profit (including NFP Corporation) **Service:** General Medical and Surgical

Staffed Beds: 35 **Admissions:** 658 **Census:** 11 **Outpatient Visits:** 10311 **Births:** 0 **Personnel:** 145

MERIDIAN—Lauderdale County

☐ **ALLIANCE HEALTH CENTER (250151)**, 5000 Highway 39 North, Zip 39301–1021; tel. 601/483–6211 **A**1 9 10 **F**4 35 70 86 87 98 99 101 102 103 **P**6 **S** Universal Health Services, Inc., King of Prussia, PA
Primary Contact: James Miller, Interim Chief Executive Officer
CFO: Robert Jackson, Chief Financial Officer
CMO: Terry Jordan, M.D., Chief of Staff
CIO: Brenda Smith, Director Financial Services
CHR: Shrea Johnson, Director Human Resources
Web address: www.alliancehealthcenter.com
Control: Corporation, Investor–owned, for–profit **Service:** Psychiatric

Staffed Beds: 134 **Admissions:** 3036 **Census:** 76 **Outpatient Visits:** 0 **Births:** 0 **Personnel:** 219

✖ **ANDERSON REGIONAL MEDICAL CENTER (250104)**, 2124 14th Street, Zip 39301–4040; tel. 601/553–6000 **A**1 2 9 10 19 **F**3 13 15 17 18 20 22 24 28 30 31 34 35 39 40 43 45 48 49 50 53 57 59 65 68 70 72 73 74 75 76 77 78 79 80 81 84 85 86 87 88 89 90 93 94 98 107 108 110 111 114 115 116 117 118 119 120 121 123 126 129 130 131 132 135 **P**7 8
Primary Contact: L. Ray Humphreys, Chief Executive Officer
CFO: Keith Heartsill, Vice President of Finance
CMO: Scot Bell, Chief Medical Officer
CHR: Sharon Futch, Interim Vice President Human Resources
CNO: Matt Edwards, Vice President Nursing Services and Chief Nursing Officer
Web address: www.andersonregional.org
Control: Other not–for–profit (including NFP Corporation) **Service:** General Medical and Surgical

Staffed Beds: 260 **Admissions:** 10303 **Census:** 142 **Outpatient Visits:** 111818 **Births:** 1246 **Total Expense ($000):** 152373 **Payroll Expense ($000):** 56642 **Personnel:** 1048

☐ △ **ANDERSON REGIONAL MEDICAL CENTER–SOUTH CAMPUS (250081)**, 1102 Constitution Avenue, Zip 39301–4001; tel. 601/703–5000 **A**1 7 9 10 **F**3 4 29 30 34 35 50 57 59 60 61 64 65 68 70 74 75 81 84 85 86 87 90 97 98 103 106 107 114 115 117 119 120 121 123 127 130 132 133 135 144 148 **P**7 8
Primary Contact: John G. Anderson, Vice President, Administrator
CFO: Keith Heartsill, Vice President Finance
CMO: Bradley Boone, M.D., Chief Medical Staff
CIO: Steve Taylor, Chief Information Officer
CHR: Sharon Futch, Interim Vice President Human Resources
CNO: Betty Cryer, Chief Nursing Officer
Web address: www.andersonregional.org
Control: Other not–for–profit (including NFP Corporation) **Service:** General Medical and Surgical

Staffed Beds: 69 **Admissions:** 585 **Census:** 19 **Outpatient Visits:** 26096 **Births:** 0 **Total Expense ($000):** 26852 **Payroll Expense ($000):** 8115 **Personnel:** 168

☐ **EAST MISSISSIPPI STATE HOSPITAL**, 1818 College Drive, Zip 39307, Mailing Address: Box 4128, West Station, Zip 39304–4128; tel. 601/482–6186 **A**1 **F**4 29 39 56 86 87 98 99 101 102 103 130 131 134 **S** Mississippi State Department of Mental Health, Jackson, MS
Primary Contact: Charles Carlisle, Director
CFO: Geri Doggett, Director Business
CMO: Gloria Gomez, M.D., Medical Director
CIO: Scotty Taylor, Information Technology Director
CHR: Shearmaine Calaway, Director Human Resources
CNO: Diane Nobles, Nurse Executive
Web address: www.emsh.state.ms.us
Control: State–Government, nonfederal **Service:** Psychiatric

Staffed Beds: 201 **Admissions:** 1031 **Census:** 180 **Outpatient Visits:** 0 **Births:** 0 **Personnel:** 669

✖ **REGENCY HOSPITAL OF MERIDIAN (252006)**, 1102 Constitution Avenue, 2nd Floor, Zip 39301–4001; tel. 601/484–7900 **A**1 10 **F**40 70 **S** Select Medical Corporation, Mechanicsburg, PA
Primary Contact: Clifton Quinn, Chief Executive Officer
Web address: www.regencyhospital.com
Control: Corporation, Investor–owned, for–profit **Service:** Long–Term Acute Care hospital

Staffed Beds: 40 **Admissions:** 394 **Census:** 30 **Outpatient Visits:** 0 **Births:** 0 **Personnel:** 108

RILEY HOSPITAL See Anderson Regional Medical Center–South Campus

★ ◇ **RUSH FOUNDATION HOSPITAL (250069)**, 1314 19th Avenue, Zip 39301–4195; tel. 601/483–0011 **A**9 10 19 21 **F**13 15 17 29 35 39 40 43 70 72 73 76 77 81 86 89 90 93 97 107 108 118 119 130 131 147 **P**3 8 **S** Rush Health Systems, Meridian, MS
Primary Contact: Morris A. Reece, President and Chief Executive Officer
COO: Morris A. Reece, President and Chief Operating Officer
CMO: W. Scot Bell, M.D., Chief Medical Officer
CIO: Angela Sherrill, Corporate Director Information System
CHR: Donnie Smith, Director Human Resources
Web address: www.rushhealthsystems.org/rfh/
Control: Other not–for–profit (including NFP Corporation) **Service:** General Medical and Surgical

Staffed Beds: 182 **Admissions:** 6759 **Census:** 87 **Outpatient Visits:** 24690 **Births:** 1034 **Personnel:** 896

MS

Many Facility Codes have changed. Please refer to the AHA Guide Code Chart.
© 2014 AHA Guide

★ **SPECIALTY HOSPITAL OF MERIDIAN (252004)**, 1314 19th Avenue, Zip 39301–4116; tel. 601/703–4211 **A**9 10 **F**3 30 31 34 57 59 65 68 70 78 85 87 94 96 127 133 135 144 148 **S** Rush Health Systems, Meridian, MS
Primary Contact: Elizabeth C. Mitchell, Vice President and Administrator
CFO: Lexie Fuller, Controller
CMO: Richmond Alexander, M.D., President Medical Staff
CIO: Angela Sherrill, Corporate Director Information System
CHR: Donnie Smith, Director of Human Resources
CNO: Kawanda Johnson, Director of Nursing
Web address: www.specialtyhospitalofmeridian.com/shm/
Control: Other not–for–profit (including NFP Corporation) **Service:** Long–Term Acute Care hospital

Staffed Beds: 49 **Admissions:** 595 **Census:** 47 **Outpatient Visits:** 0 **Births:** 0 **Personnel:** 121

MONTICELLO—Lawrence County

LAWRENCE COUNTY HOSPITAL (251305), Highway 84 East, Zip 39654–0788, Mailing Address: P.O. Box 788, Zip 39654–0788; tel. 601/587–4051 **A**9 10 18 **F**3 34 39 40 43 57 59 64 70 86 87 107 114 119 127 130 133 135 **S** Southwest Health Systems, Mccomb, MS
Primary Contact: Semmes Ross, Jr., Administrator
CFO: Jennifer Moak, Business Office Manager
Web address: www.smrmc.com
Control: County–Government, nonfederal **Service:** General Medical and Surgical

Staffed Beds: 25 **Admissions:** 404 **Census:** 4 **Outpatient Visits:** 8317 **Births:** 0 **Personnel:** 108

MORTON—Scott County

★ **SCOTT REGIONAL HOSPITAL (251323)**, 317 Highway 13 South, Zip 39117–3353, Mailing Address: P.O. Box 259, Zip 39117–0259; tel. 601/732–6301 **A**9 10 18 **F**3 30 34 35 40 42 43 45 57 68 70 77 81 89 93 107 111 119 129 130 133 135 **S** Rush Health Systems, Meridian, MS
Primary Contact: Michael R. Edwards, Administrator
CFO: Paul S. Black, Chief Financial Officer
CHR: Amy Sugg, Director Human Resources
Web address: www.scottregional.org/srh/
Control: Other not–for–profit (including NFP Corporation) **Service:** General Medical and Surgical

Staffed Beds: 25 **Admissions:** 575 **Census:** 5 **Outpatient Visits:** 12675 **Births:** 0 **Personnel:** 143

NATCHEZ—Adams County

⊞ **NATCHEZ COMMUNITY HOSPITAL (250122)**, 129 Jefferson Davis Boulevard, Zip 39120–5100, Mailing Address: P.O. Box 1203, Zip 39121–1203; tel. 601/445–6200 **A**1 9 10 **F**13 17 29 35 40 43 51 60 61 70 73 76 78 81 87 89 93 107 108 119 130 **P**6 **S** Community Health Systems, Inc., Franklin, TN
Primary Contact: Eric Robinson, Chief Executive Officer
Web address: www.natchezcommunityhospital.com/default.aspx
Control: Partnership, Investor–owned, for–profit **Service:** General Medical and Surgical

Staffed Beds: 101 **Admissions:** 3687 **Census:** 44 **Outpatient Visits:** 38915 **Births:** 459 **Personnel:** 252

☐ △ **NATCHEZ REGIONAL MEDICAL CENTER (250084)**, 54 Seargent S Prentiss Drive, Zip 39120–4726; tel. 601/443–2100 **A**1 7 9 10 **F**13 15 17 29 35 40 43 60 70 73 75 76 77 78 81 86 87 88 89 90 93 103 107 108 111 116 119 130 131 132 134 147 **P**3
Primary Contact: Donald Rentfro, Chief Executive Officer
CFO: Charles Mack, Vice President Finance and Chief Financial Officer
CMO: Leslie England, Chief of Staff
CIO: Leslie Makoro, Director Information management Systems
CHR: Jean E. Juchnowicz, Director Human Resources
Web address: www.natchezregional.com
Control: County–Government, nonfederal **Service:** General Medical and Surgical

Staffed Beds: 155 **Admissions:** 2961 **Census:** 37 **Outpatient Visits:** 35500 **Births:** 422 **Personnel:** 252

NEW ALBANY—Union County

⊞ **BAPTIST MEMORIAL HOSPITAL–UNION COUNTY (250006)**, 200 Highway 30 West, Zip 38652–3112; tel. 662/538–7631 **A**1 9 10 **F**3 7 11 13 15 17 29 30 34 35 39 40 41 51 57 59 70 75 76 77 79 81 84 85 86 87 89 90 93 107 108 110 111 115 118 119 130 132 133 135 147 148 **S** Baptist Memorial Health Care Corporation, Memphis, TN
Primary Contact: Walter Grace, Chief Executive Officer and Administrator
CFO: Kim High, Chief Financial Officer
CMO: Justin Lohmeier, M.D., Chief of Staff
CIO: Missy Coltharp, Director
CHR: Lori Goode, Director Human Resources
CNO: Randy White, Chief Nursing Officer
Web address: www.baptistonline.org/union-county/
Control: Other not–for–profit (including NFP Corporation) **Service:** General Medical and Surgical

Staffed Beds: 153 **Admissions:** 3643 **Census:** 31 **Outpatient Visits:** 46651 **Births:** 1164 **Total Expense ($000):** 47612 **Payroll Expense ($000):** 18100 **Personnel:** 414

NEWTON—Newton County

NEWTON REGIONAL HOSPITAL See Pioneer Community Hospital of Newton

★ ◇ **PIONEER COMMUNITY HOSPITAL OF NEWTON (251332)**, 9421 Eastside Drive, Zip 39345–8063; tel. 601/683–2031 **A**9 10 18 21 **F**3 11 29 34 35 39 40 43 45 46 53 57 64 65 68 70 77 79 81 89 90 93 98 103 107 111 114 119 127 130 133 148 **P**6 **S** Pioneer Health Services, Magee, MS
Primary Contact: Mark Norman, Administrator
CFO: Julie Gieger, Chief Financial Officer
CMO: Sohaib Arair, M.D., Chairman of Medical Staff
CIO: Jack York, Chief Information Officer
CHR: Dominica Johnson, Executive Administrative Assistant and Executive Assistant Human Resources and Payroll
CNO: Christie Malbrough, Director of Nursing
Web address: www.pchnewton.com
Control: Corporation, Investor–owned, for–profit **Service:** General Medical and Surgical

Staffed Beds: 30 **Admissions:** 753 **Census:** 10 **Outpatient Visits:** 12958 **Births:** 0 **Personnel:** 146

OCEAN SPRINGS—Jackson County

OCEAN SPRINGS HOSPITAL See Singing River Health System, Pascagoula

OLIVE BRANCH—Desoto County

METHODIST OLIVE BRANCH HOSPITAL (250167), 4250 Bethel Road, Zip 38654–8737; tel. 662/932–9000, (Data for 36 days) **A**10 **F**4 13 15 17 29 35 40 60 62 63 70 72 73 76 77 78 81 86 87 88 89 90 93 107 108 111 118 119 130 132 138 144 147 **P**8 **S** Methodist Le Bonheur Healthcare, Memphis, TN
Primary Contact: David G. Baytos, Chief Executive Officer
CFO: Larry Fogarty, Chief Financial Officer
CNO: Annelise Jensen, Chief Nursing Officer
Web address: www.methodisthealth.org/olivebranch
Control: Other not–for–profit (including NFP Corporation) **Service:** General Medical and Surgical

Staffed Beds: 44 **Admissions:** 67 **Census:** 7 **Outpatient Visits:** 2370 **Births:** 0 **Personnel:** 239

☐ **PARKWOOD BEHAVIORAL HEALTH SYSTEM (254005)**, 8135 Goodman Road, Zip 38654–2103; tel. 662/895–4900, (Total facility includes 40 beds in nursing home–type unit) **A**1 9 10 **F**4 5 29 34 35 54 64 75 86 87 98 99 100 101 102 103 104 105 106 130 **P**5 **S** Universal Health Services, Inc., King of Prussia, PA
Primary Contact: Coleby Wright, Chief Executive Officer
CFO: David Denegri, Chief Financial Officer
CMO: Paul King, M.D., Medical Director
CNO: Alicia Plunkett, Director of Nursing
Web address: www.parkwoodbhs.com
Control: Corporation, Investor–owned, for–profit **Service:** Psychiatric

Staffed Beds: 128 **Admissions:** 2483 **Census:** 102 **Outpatient Visits:** 0 **Births:** 0 **Personnel:** 186

MS

Hospital, Medicare Provider Number, Address, Telephone, Approval, Facility, and Physician Codes, Health Care System

★ American Hospital Association (AHA) membership
☐ The Joint Commission accreditation   ◇ DNV Healthcare Inc. accreditation
○ Healthcare Facilities Accreditation Program
△ Commission on Accreditation of Rehabilitation Facilities (CARF) accreditation

OXFORD—Lafayette County

☒ △ **BAPTIST MEMORIAL HOSPITAL–NORTH MISSISSIPPI (250034)**, 2301 South Lamar Boulevard, Zip 38655–5373, Mailing Address: P.O. Box 946, Zip 38655–6002; tel. 662/232–8100 **A**1 2 7 9 10 19 **F**3 7 8 11 12 13 15 17 18 20 22 24 25 26 28 29 30 31 34 35 40 42 43 45 47 48 49 50 53 54 57 59 64 68 70 73 74 76 78 79 81 83 84 85 86 87 89 90 96 107 108 110 111 114 115 116 117 118 119 120 121 123 126 129 130 131 132 135 141 145 147 148 **S** Baptist Memorial Health Care Corporation, Memphis, TN
Primary Contact: William C. Henning, Administrator and Chief Executive Officer
CFO: Dana Williams, Chief Financial Officer
CMO: Dennis P. Morgan, Chief of Staff
CIO: Linda Britt, Director Information Systems
CHR: Debbie Swan, Director Human Resources
CNO: Mark Ottens, Chief Nursing Officer
Web address: www.baptistonline.org/north–mississippi/
Control: Other not–for–profit (including NFP Corporation) **Service:** General Medical and Surgical

Staffed Beds: 217 **Admissions:** 7860 **Census:** 105 **Outpatient Visits:** 73488 **Births:** 907 **Total Expense ($000):** 148929 **Payroll Expense ($000):** 45928 **Personnel:** 742

PASCAGOULA—Jackson County

☒ △ **SINGING RIVER HEALTH SYSTEM (250040)**, 2809 Denny Avenue, Zip 39581–5301; tel. 228/809–5000, (Includes OCEAN SPRINGS HOSPITAL, 3109 Bienville Boulevard, Ocean Springs, Zip 39564–4361; tel. 228/818–1111; Heath Thompson, R.N., Administrator; SINGING RIVER HOSPITAL, 2809 Denny Avenue, tel. 228/809–5000; Davis Walton, Administrator) **A**1 2 7 9 10 **F**3 11 13 15 17 18 19 20 21 22 24 28 39 40 41 43 44 45 47 48 49 53 54 57 58 59 61 64 70 73 74 76 78 79 80 81 83 84 85 86 87 88 89 90 92 94 95 96 98 99 100 101 102 103 104 106 107 108 110 111 114 115 118 119 120 121 123 124 126 127 129 130 135 144 145 148
Primary Contact: Kevin Holland, Chief Executive Officer
COO: Larry D. Shoemaker, M.D., Chief Operating Officer
CFO: Lee Bond, Chief Financial Officer
CMO: Randy Roth, Interim Chief Medical Officer
CHR: Craig Summerlin, Chief Human Resources Officer
CNO: Judy Powers, Chief Nursing Officer
Web address: www.mysrhs.com
Control: County–Government, nonfederal **Service:** General Medical and Surgical

Staffed Beds: 381 **Admissions:** 18156 **Census:** 227 **Outpatient Visits:** 443178 **Births:** 1446 **Total Expense ($000):** 369296 **Payroll Expense ($000):** 148568 **Personnel:** 2372

PHILADELPHIA—Neshoba County

☐ **CHOCTAW HEALTH CENTER (250127)**, 210 Hospital Circle, Zip 39350–6781; tel. 601/656–2211, (Nonreporting) **A**1 9 10
Primary Contact: Tina Scott, Acting Health Director
CFO: Myrna Hancock, Director Financial Services
CMO: Juantina Johnson, Chief of Staff
CIO: Raymond Willis, IT Manager
CHR: Anna Denson, Human Resources Specialist
CNO: Regina Isaac, Director of Nursing
Web address: www.choctaw.org
Control: PHS, Indian Service, Government, federal **Service:** General Medical and Surgical

Staffed Beds: 35

NESHOBA COUNTY GENERAL HOSPITAL (250043), 1001 Holland Avenue, Zip 39350–2161, Mailing Address: P.O. Box 648, Zip 39350–0648; tel. 601/663–1200, (Total facility includes 160 beds in nursing home–type unit) **A**9 10 20 **F**3 6 11 15 29 30 35 40 43 45 46 54 57 59 64 65 70 77 81 85 87 89 90 93 107 110 114 117 119 127 128 130 132 133 143 144
Primary Contact: Lawrence Graeber, Chief Executive Officer
CFO: Calvin J. Brummund, Interim Chief Financial Officer
CMO: John Bowles, Medical Director
CHR: Hedda Stewart, Director Human Resources
Web address: www.neshobageneral.com
Control: County–Government, nonfederal **Service:** General Medical and Surgical

Staffed Beds: 208 **Admissions:** 1755 **Census:** 175 **Births:** 0 **Total Expense ($000):** 36324 **Payroll Expense ($000):** 18520 **Personnel:** 445

PICAYUNE—Pearl River County

HIGHLAND COMMUNITY HOSPITAL (250117), 130 Highland Parkway, Zip 39466–5574, Mailing Address: P.O. Box 909, Zip 39466–0909; tel. 601/358–9400 **A**9 10 **F**3 13 15 18 29 34 40 43 45 57 59 64 65 70 75 76 81 85 86 87 89 92 93 106 107 108 110 111 114 119 130 131 135 147
Primary Contact: Mark Stockstill, R.N., Administrator
CMO: Robert Lopez, Chief Medical Officer
CHR: Cynthia Render–Leach, Director Human Resources
CNO: Melissa Wise, Chief Nursing Officer
Web address: www.highlandch.com
Control: County–Government, nonfederal **Service:** General Medical and Surgical

Staffed Beds: 56 **Admissions:** 2116 **Census:** 18 **Outpatient Visits:** 47702 **Births:** 313 **Total Expense ($000):** 35603 **Payroll Expense ($000):** 15170 **Personnel:** 295

PONTOTOC—Pontotoc County

☒ **NORTH MISSISSIPPI MEDICAL CENTER–PONTOTOC (251308)**, 176 South Main Street, Zip 38863–3311, Mailing Address: P.O. Box 790, Zip 38863–0790; tel. 662/488–7640, (Total facility includes 44 beds in nursing home–type unit) **A**1 9 10 18 **F**3 11 34 35 40 43 57 65 68 70 83 84 86 87 90 107 114 119 128 130 133 **S** North Mississippi Health Services, Inc., Tupelo, MS
Primary Contact: Fred B. Hood, FACHE, Administrator
CFO: M. Denise Heard, Director Business Services
CHR: P. Marie Barnes, Director, Human Resources
CNO: Cathy Waldrop, Director, Hospital Nursing Services
Web address: www.nmhs.net
Control: Other not–for–profit (including NFP Corporation) **Service:** General Medical and Surgical

Staffed Beds: 69 **Admissions:** 330 **Census:** 46 **Outpatient Visits:** 15286 **Births:** 0 **Personnel:** 162

POPLARVILLE—Pearl River County

PEARL RIVER COUNTY HOSPITAL (251333), 305 West Moody Street, Zip 39470–7338, Mailing Address: P.O. Box 392, Zip 39470–0392; tel. 601/795–4543, (Total facility includes 126 beds in nursing home–type unit) **A**9 10 18 **F**3 35 40 42 43 64 65 70 93 107 117 119 127 128 130 133 143
Primary Contact: Steve Vaughan, Chief Executive Officer
CNO: Lisa Brown, Director of Nursing
Control: County–Government, nonfederal **Service:** General Medical and Surgical

Staffed Beds: 150 **Admissions:** 221 **Census:** 97 **Outpatient Visits:** 8114 **Births:** 0 **Total Expense ($000):** 21629 **Payroll Expense ($000):** 12207 **Personnel:** 337

PORT GIBSON—Claiborne County

CLAIBORNE COUNTY MEDICAL CENTER (251320), 123 McComb Avenue, Zip 39150–2915, Mailing Address: P.O. Box 1004, Zip 39150–1004; tel. 601/437–5141 **A**9 10 18 **F**3 34 40 42 43 64 70 89 98 103 119 127 130 133
Primary Contact: Linda Dunigan, Chief Executive Officer
CFO: Linda Caho–Mooney, Chief Financial Officer
CIO: Ada Ratliff, Chief Information Officer
Control: County–Government, nonfederal **Service:** General Medical and Surgical

Staffed Beds: 32 **Admissions:** 677 **Census:** 10 **Outpatient Visits:** 4652 **Births:** 0 **Personnel:** 70

PRENTISS—Jefferson Davis County

JEFFERSON DAVIS COMMUNITY HOSPITAL (251326), 1102 Rose Street, Zip 39474–5200, Mailing Address: P.O. Box 1288, Zip 39474–1288; tel. 601/792–4276, (Total facility includes 60 beds in nursing home–type unit) **A**9 10 18 **F**35 40 43 53 56 70 86 87 89 90 93 98 103 107 111 119 128 130 132 133
Primary Contact: Jimmy Graves, Interim Chief Executive Officer
CHR: Diane Daughdrill, Director Human Resources
Web address: www.jdchospital.com
Control: County–Government, nonfederal **Service:** General Medical and Surgical

Staffed Beds: 95 **Admissions:** 409 **Census:** 55 **Outpatient Visits:** 12141 **Births:** 0 **Personnel:** 132

PURVIS—Lamar County

☐ **SOUTH MISSISSIPPI STATE HOSPITAL (254008)**, 823 Highway 589, Zip 39475–4194; tel. 601/794–0100 **A**1 10 **F**3 50 98 130 **S** Mississippi State Department of Mental Health, Jackson, MS
Primary Contact: Clint Ashley, Director
CFO: Andy Tucker, Chief Financial Officer
CMO: Allen Harris, M.D., Clinical Director
CIO: Sabrina Young, Administrative Support Director
CHR: Kelly Reid, Human Resources Director
CNO: Pam Brinson, Nurse Executive
Web address: www.smsh.state.ms.us
Control: State–Government, nonfederal **Service:** Psychiatric

Staffed Beds: 50 **Admissions:** 603 **Census:** 45 **Outpatient Visits:** 0 **Births:** 0 **Personnel:** 105

QUITMAN—Clarke County

★ **H. C. WATKINS MEMORIAL HOSPITAL (251316)**, 605 South Archusa Avenue, Zip 39355–2331; tel. 601/776–6925 **A**9 10 18 **F**29 40 43 70 81 89 107 130 133 **S** Rush Health Systems, Meridian, MS
Primary Contact: Clinton Eaves, Administrator
CFO: Paul S. Black, Controller
CMO: O. Wayne Byrd, M.D., Chief of Staff
CIO: Melinda Smith, Chief Information Systems
CHR: Leigh Moore, Administrative Assistant Human Resources
Web address: www.watkinsmemorialhospital.com/hcwmh/
Control: Other not–for–profit (including NFP Corporation) **Service:** General Medical and Surgical

Staffed Beds: 25 **Admissions:** 263 **Census:** 3 **Outpatient Visits:** 6007 **Births:** 0 **Personnel:** 177

MS

Many Facility Codes have changed. Please refer to the AHA Guide Code Chart. © 2014 AHA Guide

RALEIGH—Smith County

PATIENTS CHOICE MEDICAL CENTER OF SMITH COUNTY (250163), 347 Magnolia Drive, Zip 39153–6011; tel. 601/782–9997 **A**10 **F**64 70 98 103 130 **P**6
Primary Contact: Tim Cockrell, Chief Executive Officer
Control: Corporation, Investor–owned, for–profit **Service:** General Medical and Surgical

Staffed Beds: 10 **Admissions:** 149 **Census:** 6 **Outpatient Visits:** 1037 **Births:** 0 **Personnel:** 24

RICHTON—Perry County

PERRY COUNTY GENERAL HOSPITAL (251306), 206 Bay Avenue, Zip 39476–2941; tel. 601/788–6316 **A**9 10 18 **F**3 34 40 43 57 70 107 119 127 130 133
Primary Contact: David Paris, Chief Executive Officer
Web address: www.pcghospital.com/
Control: Partnership, Investor–owned, for–profit **Service:** General Medical and Surgical

Staffed Beds: 22 **Admissions:** 242 **Census:** 2 **Births:** 0 **Total Expense ($000):** 6754 **Payroll Expense ($000):** 3475 **Personnel:** 57

RIPLEY—Tippah County

★ **TIPPAH COUNTY HOSPITAL (250010)**, 1005 City Avenue North, Zip 38663–1414, Mailing Address: P.O. Box 499, Zip 38663–0499; tel. 662/837–9221, (Total facility includes 40 beds in nursing home–type unit) **A**9 10 20 **F**15 29 40 43 53 70 81 89 107 119 128 130 133
Primary Contact: Mark Richey, Interim Administrator
CFO: Mark Richey, Chief Financial Officer
CMO: Charles M. Elliott, M.D., Chief of Staff
CHR: Tony Bell, Manager Personnel
Web address: www.tippahcounty.ripley.ms/hospital.html
Control: County–Government, nonfederal **Service:** General Medical and Surgical

Staffed Beds: 69 **Admissions:** 532 **Census:** 43 **Outpatient Visits:** 14599 **Births:** 0 **Personnel:** 172

ROLLING FORK—Sharkey County

SHARKEY–ISSAQUENA COMMUNITY HOSPITAL (250079), 108 South Fourth Street, Zip 39159–5146, Mailing Address: P.O. Box 339, Zip 39159–0339; tel. 662/873–4395 **A**9 10 **F**40 53 56 70 89 103 107 111 119 133
Primary Contact: Jerry Keever, Administrator
Control: County–Government, nonfederal **Service:** General Medical and Surgical

Staffed Beds: 29 **Admissions:** 548 **Census:** 8 **Births:** 0 **Personnel:** 73

RULEVILLE—Sunflower County

★ **NORTH SUNFLOWER MEDICAL CENTER (251318)**, 840 North Oak Avenue, Zip 38771–3227, Mailing Address: P.O. Box 369, Zip 38771–0369; tel. 662/756–2711, (Total facility includes 60 beds in nursing home–type unit) **A**9 10 18 **F**3 8 15 29 30 32 34 35 39 40 42 43 44 45 50 53 56 57 59 62 64 68 70 75 77 81 82 87 90 93 96 97 103 107 108 110 114 118 119 127 128 129 130 132 133 134 135 143 148 **P**6
Primary Contact: Wayne Walters, Chief Executive Officer
COO: Sam Miller, Chief Operating Officer
CFO: Nickie Moore, Chief Financial Officer
CMO: Bennie B. Wright, M.D., Chief of Staff
CIO: Roger Goss, Director, Information Services
CHR: Robbie Taylor, Director Human Resources
CNO: Lisa Miller, R.N., Director of Nursing
Web address: www.northsunflower.com
Control: County–Government, nonfederal **Service:** General Medical and Surgical

Staffed Beds: 95 **Admissions:** 832 **Census:** 73 **Outpatient Visits:** 16361 **Births:** 0 **Personnel:** 526

SENATOBIA—Tate County

☐ **NORTH OAK REGIONAL MEDICAL CENTER (250126)**, 401 Getwell Drive, Zip 38668–2213, Mailing Address: P.O. Box 648, Zip 38668–0648; tel. 662/562–3100 **A**1 9 10 **F**3 29 34 35 40 43 45 56 57 64 70 81 86 89 98 103 107 114 119 130
Primary Contact: Sonja Graham, Chief Executive Officer
CHR: Vickie Barksdale, Manager Human Resources
Web address: www.normc.org
Control: Corporation, Investor–owned, for–profit **Service:** General Medical and Surgical

Staffed Beds: 53 **Admissions:** 977 **Census:** 13 **Outpatient Visits:** 12150 **Births:** 0 **Personnel:** 133

SOUTHAVEN—Desoto County

⊠ △ **BAPTIST MEMORIAL HOSPITAL–DESOTO (250141)**, 7601 Southcrest Parkway, Zip 38671–4742; tel. 662/772–4000 **A**1 7 9 10 **F**3 8 11 13 15 17 18 20 22 24 26 28 29 30 31 35 40 43 44 45 46 47 48 49 50 51 57 59 60 64 68 70 71 73 74 75 76 77 78 79 80 81 84 85 86 87 90 93 96 107 108 110 111 114 115 116 117 118 119 120 121 123 124 126 129 130 131 132 135 143 144 147 148 **S** Baptist Memorial Health Care Corporation, Memphis, TN
Primary Contact: James Huffman, Chief Executive Officer and Administrator
CFO: Joe McWherter, Chief Financial Officer
CMO: Joann Wood, M.D., Chief Medical Officer
CHR: Walter Banks, Director Human Resources
Web address: www.baptistonline.org/desoto/
Control: Other not–for–profit (including NFP Corporation) **Service:** General Medical and Surgical

Staffed Beds: 250 **Admissions:** 15883 **Census:** 208 **Outpatient Visits:** 102676 **Births:** 1880 **Total Expense ($000):** 253192 **Payroll Expense ($000):** 85580 **Personnel:** 1612

STARKVILLE—Oktibbeha County

★ ◇ **OCH REGIONAL MEDICAL CENTER (250050)**, 400 Hospital Road, Zip 39759–2163, Mailing Address: P.O. Box 1506, Zip 39760–1506; tel. 662/323–4320 **A**9 10 21 **F**3 7 11 13 15 17 28 29 32 34 35 39 40 41 43 45 47 48 51 53 57 59 61 64 65 66 70 73 74 75 76 77 79 81 85 87 88 89 90 93 97 98 107 108 110 111 114 115 118 119 126 127 129 130 131 132 133 135 147 **P**6
Primary Contact: Richard G. Hilton, Administrator and Chief Executive Officer
COO: Mike Andrews, Administrator and Chief Operating Officer
CFO: Susan Russell, Chief Financial Officer
CIO: Chamath Wijewardane, Director Information Technology
CHR: Mike Andrews, Administrator and Chief Operating Officer
CNO: Martha Fulcher, MSN, Chief Nursing Officer
Web address: www.och.org
Control: County–Government, nonfederal **Service:** General Medical and Surgical

Staffed Beds: 96 **Admissions:** 2533 **Census:** 28 **Outpatient Visits:** 230105 **Births:** 929 **Total Expense ($000):** 67469 **Payroll Expense ($000):** 33502 **Personnel:** 583

TUPELO—Lee County

⊠ △ **NORTH MISSISSIPPI MEDICAL CENTER – TUPELO (250004)**, 830 South Gloster Street, Zip 38801–4934; tel. 662/377–3000, (Total facility includes 107 beds in nursing home–type unit) **A**1 2 3 5 7 9 10 19 **F**3 4 5 7 11 12 13 15 17 18 20 22 24 26 28 29 30 31 34 35 37 38 40 41 43 44 46 47 48 49 50 51 53 54 56 57 58 59 61 62 63 64 65 68 70 71 72 73 74 75 76 79 80 81 83 84 85 86 87 88 89 90 91 92 93 96 97 98 100 101 103 104 106 107 108 109 110 111 112 113 114 115 116 117 118 119 126 128 129 130 131 132 134 135 146 147 148 **S** North Mississippi Health Services, Inc., Tupelo, MS
Primary Contact: M. Shane Spees, President and Chief Executive Officer
CFO: Joseph A. Reppert, Executive Vice President and Chief Financial Officer
CHR: Rodger Brown, Vice President Human Resources
Web address: www.nmhs.net
Control: Other not–for–profit (including NFP Corporation) **Service:** General Medical and Surgical

Staffed Beds: 757 **Admissions:** 23936 **Census:** 475 **Outpatient Visits:** 237657 **Births:** 2001 **Personnel:** 3667

☐ **NORTH MISSISSIPPI STATE HOSPITAL (254009)**, 1937 Briar Ridge Road, Zip 38804–5963; tel. 662/690–4200 **A**1 10 **F**3 29 30 34 87 89 98 101 106 130 132 143 146 **S** Mississippi State Department of Mental Health, Jackson, MS
Primary Contact: Paul A. Callens, Ph.D., Director
CFO: Joe Rials, Director Fiscal Services
CMO: Ken Lippincott, M.D., Chief of Staff
CIO: James Wilhite, Director Systems Information
Web address: www.nmsh.state.ms.us
Control: State–Government, nonfederal **Service:** Psychiatric

Staffed Beds: 50 **Admissions:** 495 **Census:** 45 **Outpatient Visits:** 0 **Births:** 0 **Personnel:** 111

TYLERTOWN—Walthall County

★ **WALTHALL COUNTY GENERAL HOSPITAL (251324)**, 100 Hospital Drive, Zip 39667–2099; tel. 601/876–2122 **A**9 10 18 **F**40 43 70 81 89 93 107 119 130 133
Primary Contact: Bryan K. Maxie, Administrator
Web address: www.walthallhospitalms.org
Control: County–Government, nonfederal **Service:** General Medical and Surgical

Staffed Beds: 25 **Admissions:** 345 **Census:** 3 **Outpatient Visits:** 13450 **Births:** 0 **Personnel:** 96

MS

Hospital, Medicare Provider Number, Address, Telephone, Approval, Facility, and Physician Codes, Health Care System

★ American Hospital Association (AHA) membership
☐ The Joint Commission accreditation   ◇ DNV Healthcare Inc. accreditation
○ Healthcare Facilities Accreditation Program
△ Commission on Accreditation of Rehabilitation Facilities (CARF) accreditation

UNION—Newton County

★ **LAIRD HOSPITAL (251322)**, 25117 Highway 15, Zip 39365–9099;
tel. 601/774–8214 **A**9 10 18 **F**15 29 35 40 43 70 81 87 89 93 107 119 130
132 133 **S** Rush Health Systems, Meridian, MS
Primary Contact: Thomas G. Bartlett, III, Administrator
COO: Morris A. Reece, EVP/COO
CFO: Jennifer Flint, Chief Financial Officer
CMO: John Mutziger, M.D., Chief Medical Officer
CIO: Angela Sherrill, Chief Information Officer
CHR: Donnie Smith, Chief Human Resources Officer
CNO: Pam Rigdon, Director Nursing
Web address: www.lairdhospital.com/lh/
Control: Other not–for–profit (including NFP Corporation) **Service:** General
Medical and Surgical

Staffed Beds: 25 **Admissions:** 353 **Census:** 3 **Outpatient Visits:** 15851
Births: 0 **Personnel:** 231

VICKSBURG—Warren County

PROMISE HOSPITAL OF VICKSBURG (252008), 1111 North Frontage Road,
2nd Floor, Zip 39180–5102; tel. 601/619–3526 **A**10 **F**3 11 70 90 148
S Promise Healthcare, Boca Raton, FL
Primary Contact: Mike Harrell, Chief Executive Officer
COO: Dawn Posey, Chief Operating Officer
CFO: Christopher A. Stegall, Regional Chief Financial Officer and Chief Operating
Officer
CMO: Daniel Edney, M.D., Chief of Staff
CIO: Barbara Whiting, Director Health Information Management
CHR: Debbie Carson, Director Human Resources
Web address: www.promise-vicksburg.com
Control: Corporation, Investor–owned, for–profit **Service:** Long–Term Acute Care
hospital

Staffed Beds: 33 **Admissions:** 384 **Census:** 26 **Outpatient Visits:** 0 **Births:**
0 **Personnel:** 117

☒ **RIVER REGION MEDICAL CENTER (250031)**, 2100 Highway 61 North,
Zip 39183–8211, Mailing Address: P.O. Box 590, Zip 39181–0590;
tel. 601/883–5000, (Includes RIVER REGION WEST CAMPUS, 1111 North
Frontage Road, Zip 39180–5102; tel. 601/883–5000) **A**1 9 10 19 20 **F**4 13 15
17 29 35 39 40 43 51 56 60 70 73 75 76 77 78 81 87 89 90 93 97 98 100
101 102 103 108 111 118 119 130 131 132 147 **S** Community Health
Systems, Inc., Franklin, TN
Primary Contact: Gregory Pearson, Chief Executive Officer
CFO: John Milazzo, Chief Financial Officer
CMO: W. Briggs Hopson, M.D., Clinical Medical Director
CIO: J. B. White, Director Information Systems
CHR: Hal Harrington, Vice President Human Resources
Web address: www.riverregion.com
Control: Corporation, Investor–owned, for–profit **Service:** General Medical and
Surgical

Staffed Beds: 297 **Admissions:** 8917 **Census:** 135 **Outpatient Visits:**
135450 **Births:** 691 **Personnel:** 963

WATER VALLEY—Yalobusha County

★ **YALOBUSHA GENERAL HOSPITAL (250061)**, 630 South Main,
Zip 38965–3468, Mailing Address: P.O. Box 728, Zip 38965–0728;
tel. 662/473–1411, (Total facility includes 122 beds in nursing home–type unit)
A9 10 **F**3 7 29 30 33 59 65 70 107 114 119 127 128 130 133 143 **P**6
Primary Contact: Terry Varner, Administrator
COO: Ashlee Langdon, Controller
CHR: Katie Rotenberry–Baggett, Administrative Assistant and Human Resources
Web address: www.yalobushageneral.com/
Control: County–Government, nonfederal **Service:** General Medical and Surgical

Staffed Beds: 148 **Admissions:** 366 **Census:** 122 **Outpatient Visits:** 4900
Births: 0 **Total Expense ($000):** 18224 **Personnel:** 228

WAYNESBORO—Wayne County

☐ **WAYNE GENERAL HOSPITAL (250077)**, 950 Matthew Drive, Zip 39367–2590,
Mailing Address: P.O. Box 1249, Zip 39367–1249; tel. 601/735–5151 **A**1 9 10
20 **F**13 15 35 39 40 43 53 61 62 63 70 75 76 81 86 88 89 90 93 107 108
111 116 119 130 132 133
Primary Contact: Donald Hemeter, Administrator
Web address: www.waynegeneralhospital.org
Control: County–Government, nonfederal **Service:** General Medical and Surgical

Staffed Beds: 80 **Admissions:** 2035 **Census:** 26 **Outpatient Visits:** 32748
Births: 193 **Personnel:** 342

WEST POINT—Clay County

☒ **NORTH MISSISSIPPI MEDICAL CENTER–WEST POINT (250067)**, 835
Medical Center Drive, Zip 39773–9320; tel. 662/495–2300 **A**1 9 10 **F**3 7 8 11
13 15 17 28 29 30 31 32 34 35 39 40 42 43 45 48 53 57 59 64 65 70 73
75 76 78 79 80 81 85 86 87 89 90 97 107 108 109 110 114 119 120 129
130 132 133 135 143 145 147 **S** North Mississippi Health Services, Inc.,
Tupelo, MS
Primary Contact: James W. Hahn, Administrator
CFO: Kay Lawler, Business Office Manager
CMO: B. Keith Watson, M.D., Chief Medical Staff
CIO: Stacie Griggs, MIS Analyst
CHR: Brenda Johnson, Director Human Resources
CNO: Jane Windle, R.N., Director of Nurses
Web address: www.nmhs.net/westpoint
Control: Other not–for–profit (including NFP Corporation) **Service:** General
Medical and Surgical

Staffed Beds: 60 **Admissions:** 1944 **Census:** 21 **Outpatient Visits:** 44925
Births: 345 **Total Expense ($000):** 29711 **Payroll Expense ($000):** 14235
Personnel: 261

WHITFIELD—Rankin County

☒ **MISSISSIPPI STATE HOSPITAL (254010)**, 3550 Highway 468 West,
Zip 39193–5529, Mailing Address: P.O. Box 157–A, Zip 39193–0157;
tel. 601/351–8000, (Includes WHITFIELD MEDICAL SURGICAL HOSPITAL, Oak
Circle, Zip 39193; tel. 601/351–8023), (Total facility includes 423 beds in
nursing home–type unit) **A**1 9 10 **F**3 4 29 39 70 75 87 98 99 100 101 102
103 104 106 128 130 **P**1 **S** Mississippi State Department of Mental Health,
Jackson, MS
Primary Contact: James G. Chastain, FACHE, Director
COO: Kelly R. Breland, CPA, Director Support Services
CFO: Alicia Harris, Director Fiscal Services
CMO: Duncan Stone, D.D.S., Chief Medical Staff
CIO: Bart Uharriet, Director Information Services
CHR: Katie Storr, Director of Human Resources
CNO: Jackie Yates, R.N., Nurse Executive
Web address: www.msh.state.ms.us
Control: State–Government, nonfederal **Service:** Psychiatric

Staffed Beds: 899 **Admissions:** 2606 **Census:** 702 **Outpatient Visits:** 3686
Births: 0 **Total Expense ($000):** 126900 **Payroll Expense ($000):** 61767
Personnel: 1318

WIGGINS—Stone County

STONE COUNTY HOSPITAL (251303), 1434 East Central Avenue,
Zip 39577–9602; tel. 601/928–6600 **A**9 10 18 **F**3 7 19 27 29 34 40 43 45
47 50 55 57 59 65 68 70 77 79 81 85 86 87 89 90 92 96 97 107 111 115
119 127 129 130 133 145 148 **P**6
Primary Contact: Julie Cain, Administrator
Web address: www.schospital.net/
Control: Corporation, Investor–owned, for–profit **Service:** General Medical and
Surgical

Staffed Beds: 25 **Admissions:** 436 **Census:** 3 **Births:** 0 **Personnel:** 179

WINONA—Montgomery County

TYLER HOLMES MEMORIAL HOSPITAL (251312), 409 Tyler Holmes Drive,
Zip 38967–1599; tel. 662/283–4114 **A**9 10 18 **F**3 11 28 34 35 40 43 57 59
64 66 70 87 107 108 114 119 130 133 135 148 **P**8
Primary Contact: Rosamond M. Tyler, Administrator
CFO: Cori Bailey, Accountant
CHR: Becky Corley, Director Human Resources
Control: County–Government, nonfederal **Service:** General Medical and Surgical

Staffed Beds: 25 **Admissions:** 579 **Census:** 5 **Outpatient Visits:** 13421
Births: 0 **Total Expense ($000):** 14356 **Payroll Expense ($000):** 7015
Personnel: 140

YAZOO CITY—Yazoo County

★ **KING'S DAUGHTERS HOSPITAL (251313)**, 823 Grand Avenue,
Zip 39194–3233; tel. 662/746–2261 **A**9 10 18 **F**11 15 29 34 40 41 43 45 46
53 56 57 59 64 68 70 79 81 89 93 97 107 108 110 111 115 117 119 127
133 145 148
Primary Contact: Sean Johnson, Chief Executive Officer
COO: Marsha Jones, R.N., Director Nursing
CFO: James L. Miller, Chief Financial Officer
CMO: Marion Sigrest, M.D., Chief of Staff
CIO: Benton D. Estes, Materials Management
CHR: Stephanie Washington, Director Community Relations and Human Resources
CNO: Marsha Jones, R.N., Director of Nursing
Web address: www.kdhyazoo.com
Control: Other not–for–profit (including NFP Corporation) **Service:** General
Medical and Surgical

Staffed Beds: 25 **Admissions:** 803 **Census:** 9 **Outpatient Visits:** 18806
Births: 3 **Total Expense ($000):** 19111 **Payroll Expense ($000):** 8043
Personnel: 171

MS

Many Facility Codes have changed. Please refer to the AHA Guide Code Chart. © 2014 AHA Guide

MISSOURI

ALBANY—Gentry County

★ **NORTHWEST MEDICAL CENTER (261328)**, 705 North College Street,
Zip 64402–1433; tel. 660/726–3941 **A**9 10 18 **F**3 11 15 18 28 29 34 35 40
44 45 50 56 57 59 62 64 65 68 75 77 79 81 85 86 87 90 93 97 104 107
108 110 111 114 118 119 127 128 130 131 133 135 148 **P**6
Primary Contact: Jon D. Doolittle, President and Chief Executive Officer
COO: Nate Blackford, Chief Operating Officer
CFO: Tina Gillespie, Vice President and Chief Financial Officer
CMO: Angelia Martin, M.D., Chief of Staff
CIO: James Crouch, Vice President Technical Services
CHR: Vickie Cline, Director Human Resources
CNO: Miranda Floyd, R.N., Chief Nursing Officer
Web address: www.northwestmedicalcenter.org
Control: Other not–for–profit (including NFP Corporation) **Service:** General
Medical and Surgical

Staffed Beds: 25 **Admissions:** 645 **Census:** 8 **Outpatient Visits:** 45786
Births: 0 **Total Expense ($000):** 15636 **Payroll Expense ($000):** 7289
Personnel: 168

APPLETON CITY—St. Clair County

★ **ELLETT MEMORIAL HOSPITAL (261301)**, 610 North Ohio Avenue,
Zip 64724–1609, Mailing Address: P.O. Box 6, Zip 64724–0006;
tel. 660/476–2111 **A**9 10 18 **F**3 7 11 18 34 40 45 50 57 59 77 79 90 107
111 127 128 129 130 133 143 **P**6
Primary Contact: Raymond M. Magers, Chief Executive Officer
CFO: Tom Hollis, Chief Financial Officer
CMO: Richard R. Dailey, D.O., President Medical Staff
CIO: John Stamp, Director Information Services
CNO: Cathy Menninga, R.N., Chief Nursing Officer
Web address: www.ellettmemorial.com
Control: Hospital district or authority, Government, nonfederal **Service:** General
Medical and Surgical

Staffed Beds: 12 **Admissions:** 199 **Census:** 3 **Outpatient Visits:** 10862
Births: 0 **Total Expense ($000):** 7680 **Payroll Expense ($000):** 3361
Personnel: 70

AURORA—Lawrence County

⊞ **MERCY HOSPITAL AURORA (261316)**, 500 Porter Street, Zip 65605–2365;
tel. 417/678–2122 **A**1 9 10 18 **F**3 11 13 15 28 29 30 34 35 40 41 45 50 57
59 64 65 75 76 77 81 85 86 87 89 92 93 94 96 107 108 110 111 114 119
129 132 133 135 148 **P**6 **S** Mercy Health, Chesterfield, MO
Primary Contact: Douglas M. Stroemel, President
CFO: Sherry Clouse Day, CPA, Vice President Finance and Regional Chief Financial
Officer
CMO: Christie Hurt, M.D., Chief of Staff and Medical Director
CHR: George Roden, Vice President Human Resources
CNO: Nicki Gamet, R.N., Vice President and Chief Nursing Officer
Web address: www.stjohns.com/aboutus/aurora.aspx
Control: Church–operated, Nongovernment, not–for profit **Service:** General
Medical and Surgical

Staffed Beds: 25 **Admissions:** 675 **Census:** 6 **Outpatient Visits:** 30734
Births: 233 **Total Expense ($000):** 17589 **Payroll Expense ($000):** 8254
Personnel: 153

BELTON—Cass County

⊞ **BELTON REGIONAL MEDICAL CENTER (260214)**, 17065 South 71 Highway,
Zip 64012–4631; tel. 816/348–1200 **A**1 2 9 10 **F**3 15 18 20 29 30 31 34 35
37 40 43 45 57 59 65 68 70 74 75 77 78 79 81 82 85 87 90 93 107 108
110 111 118 119 129 130 131 132 146 **P**5 **S** HCA, Nashville, TN
Primary Contact: Todd Krass, Chief Executive Officer
CFO: Susan Shreeve, Chief Financial Officer
CMO: Douglas Bradley, M.D., Chief Medical Officer
CIO: Sarah Richardson, Director Information Systems
CHR: Yvonne Brewington, Director Human Resources
CNO: Karen Lee, MSN, Chief Nursing Officer
Web address: www.beltonregionalmedicalcenter.com
Control: Corporation, Investor–owned, for–profit **Service:** General Medical and
Surgical

Staffed Beds: 46 **Admissions:** 2062 **Census:** 20 **Outpatient Visits:** 104841
Births: 0 **Total Expense ($000):** 45359 **Payroll Expense ($000):** 14104
Personnel: 177

RESEARCH BELTON HOSPITAL See Belton Regional Medical Center

BETHANY—Harrison County

★ **HARRISON COUNTY COMMUNITY HOSPITAL (261312)**, 2600 Miller Street,
Zip 64424–2701, Mailing Address: P.O. Box 428, Zip 64424–0428;
tel. 660/425–2211 **A**9 10 18 **F**3 11 15 18 28 29 34 39 40 44 51 54 57 59
62 64 65 66 67 68 75 77 79 81 82 87 89 90 93 96 98 107 108 109 110
111 114 118 119 127 128 129 130 133 143 144 145 146 147 148 **P**5
Primary Contact: Richard C. Hamilton, Interim Chief Executive Officer
CFO: Jim Van Hoet, Chief Financial Officer
CIO: Will Holt, Director Information Technology
CHR: Cathie Chalfant, Director Human Resources
CNO: Crystal Hicks, R.N., Chief Nursing Officer
Web address: www.hcchospital.org
Control: Hospital district or authority, Government, nonfederal **Service:** General
Medical and Surgical

Staffed Beds: 19 **Admissions:** 355 **Census:** 5 **Outpatient Visits:** 38256
Births: 0 **Total Expense ($000):** 15822 **Payroll Expense ($000):** 6685
Personnel: 189

BLUE SPRINGS—Jackson County

⊞ **ST. MARY'S MEDICAL CENTER (260193)**, 201 West R. D. Mize Road,
Zip 64014–2518; tel. 816/228–5900 **A**1 9 10 13 **F**3 8 11 15 18 20 22 28 29
30 31 34 35 40 49 50 53 56 57 58 59 60 64 68 70 72 74 75 77 78 79 81
82 84 85 86 87 90 93 96 107 108 110 111 115 118 119 121 123 129 130
132 135 143 146 147 148 **S** Ascension Health, Saint Louis, MO
Primary Contact: Michael A. Dorsey, FACHE, Chief Executive Officer
CFO: Steven R. Cleary, Vice President Finance
CMO: Stephens Stoops, M.D., Chief Medical Officer
CNO: Debra Ohnoutka, Chief Nursing Officer
Web address: www.carondelethealth.org
Control: Church–operated, Nongovernment, not–for profit **Service:** General
Medical and Surgical

Staffed Beds: 146 **Admissions:** 4828 **Census:** 54 **Outpatient Visits:** 81735
Births: 500 **Total Expense ($000):** 77358 **Payroll Expense ($000):** 26717
Personnel: 432

BOLIVAR—Polk County

⊞ **CITIZENS MEMORIAL HOSPITAL (260195)**, 1500 North Oakland Avenue,
Zip 65613–3011; tel. 417/326–6000 **A**1 9 10 20 **F**3 7 11 13 15 18 20 22 26
28 29 31 34 35 36 39 40 43 44 46 50 51 54 56 57 59 62 63 64 66 70 74
75 76 77 78 79 80 81 82 83 84 85 86 87 89 90 93 94 96 97 98 100 102
103 104 107 108 110 111 115 117 119 124 127 128 129 130 131 132 133
135 143 146 147 148 **P**6
Primary Contact: Donald J. Babb, Chief Executive Officer
COO: Jeff Miller, Chief Operating Officer
CFO: Gary D. Fullbright, Comptroller
CMO: Michael Misko, M.D., Chief Medical Officer
CIO: Denni McColm, Chief Information Officer
CHR: Jeremy MacLaughlin, Director Human Resources
CNO: Lesa Stock, R.N., Chief Clinical Officer
Web address: www.citizensmemorial.com
Control: Hospital district or authority, Government, nonfederal **Service:** General
Medical and Surgical

Staffed Beds: 72 **Admissions:** 3113 **Census:** 31 **Outpatient Visits:** 294819
Births: 476 **Total Expense ($000):** 105477 **Payroll Expense ($000):** 48875
Personnel: 905

BONNE TERRE—St. Francois County

★ **PARKLAND HEALTH CENTER–BONNE TERRE (261315)**, 7245 Raider Road,
Zip 63628–3767; tel. 573/358–1400 **A**9 10 18 **F**3 11 29 30 31 34 35 40 50
53 57 59 64 65 75 77 78 86 90 93 107 129 130 135 146 **S** BJC HealthCare,
Saint Louis, MO
Primary Contact: Steven R. Marler, Administrator
CFO: Cheri L. Goldsmith, Director Financial Services
CMO: Blake Anderson, M.D., Chief of Staff
CHR: Sheri Graham, Director Human Resources and Administrative Services
CNO: Jeanne Boyer, R.N., Director of Nurses
Web address: www.parklandhealthcenter.org
Control: Other not–for–profit (including NFP Corporation) **Service:** General
Medical and Surgical

Staffed Beds: 3 **Admissions:** 29 **Census:** 1 **Outpatient Visits:** 21509 **Births:**
0 **Personnel:** 56

MO

BOONVILLE—Cooper County

★ **COOPER COUNTY MEMORIAL HOSPITAL (260004)**, 17651 B Highway, Zip 65233–2839, Mailing Address: P.O. Box 88, Zip 65233–0088; tel. 660/882–7461, (Total facility includes 14 beds in nursing home–type unit) **A**9 10 20 **F**3 7 11 28 29 34 35 40 45 53 57 59 62 64 67 68 75 79 81 85 89 93 94 107 111 114 119 127 128 130 131 132 133 135 146 148 **S** Rural Community Hospitals of America, Kansas City, MO
Primary Contact: Danielle Gearhart, Chief Executive Officer
CFO: Patricia Nowlin, Director Accounting
CMO: Mona Brownfield, M.D., Chief Medical Staff
CIO: Bill Fletcher, Director Information Technology
CHR: Patricia Nowlin, Director Human Resources
CNO: Nancy Fredrich, R.N., Chief Clinical Officer
Web address: www.coopercmh.com
Control: County–Government, nonfederal **Service:** General Medical and Surgical

Staffed Beds: 32 **Admissions:** 330 **Census:** 11 **Outpatient Visits:** 37343 **Births:** 0 **Total Expense ($000):** 13880 **Payroll Expense ($000):** 5586 **Personnel:** 137

BRANSON—Taney County

⌗ △ **COX MEDICAL CENTER BRANSON (260094)**, 251 Skaggs Road, Zip 65616–2031, Mailing Address: P.O. Box 650, Zip 65615–0650; tel. 417/335–7000 **A**1 5 7 9 10 19 20 **F**3 8 13 15 17 18 20 22 26 28 29 31 32 34 35 40 41 44 45 46 47 50 51 53 56 57 59 60 61 62 63 64 65 66 68 70 74 75 76 77 78 79 80 81 82 84 85 86 87 89 90 93 97 98 100 103 106 107 108 110 111 114 117 118 119 121 123 127 129 130 131 132 135 143 144 146 147 148 **P**3 6 8 **S** CoxHealth, Springfield, MO
Primary Contact: William K. Mahoney, President and Chief Executive Officer
CFO: David Strong, Chief Financial Officer/Vice President Finance
CHR: Carol Murrow, Vice President Business Development
Web address: www.skaggs.net
Control: Other not–for–profit (including NFP Corporation) **Service:** General Medical and Surgical

Staffed Beds: 124 **Admissions:** 5701 **Census:** 69 **Outpatient Visits:** 246004 **Births:** 566 **Total Expense ($000):** 152982 **Payroll Expense ($000):** 54955 **Personnel:** 1102

BRIDGETON—St. Louis County

⌗ **SSM DEPAUL HEALTH CENTER (260104)**, 12303 De Paul Drive, Zip 63044–2512; tel. 314/344–6000, (Total facility includes 52 beds in nursing home–type unit) **A**1 2 9 10 **F**3 5 11 12 13 15 17 18 20 22 24 28 29 30 31 34 35 36 38 40 43 44 49 50 51 53 59 60 61 64 68 69 70 73 74 75 76 78 79 81 82 84 85 86 87 89 98 99 100 101 102 103 104 105 107 108 111 114 115 117 119 120 121 124 126 128 130 132 135 143 144 146 147 148 **P**6 8 **S** SSM Health, Saint Louis, MO
Primary Contact: Sean Hogan, President
COO: Tina Garrison, Vice President Operations
CFO: Hal Holder, Director Finance
CMO: John Moore, M.D., Vice President Medical Affairs
CIO: Scott Feldmann, Director Information Technology
CHR: Gloria Reed, Leader Human Resources
CNO: Kathleen Bonser, R.N., Vice President Nursing and Chief Nursing Officer
Web address: www.ssmdepaul.com
Control: Church–operated, Nongovernment, not–for profit **Service:** General Medical and Surgical

Staffed Beds: 463 **Admissions:** 21587 **Census:** 329 **Outpatient Visits:** 219750 **Births:** 1223 **Total Expense ($000):** 327428 **Payroll Expense ($000):** 106218 **Personnel:** 1733

BROOKFIELD—Linn County

GENERAL JOHN J. PERSHING MEMORIAL HOSPITAL (261307), 130 East Lockling Avenue, Zip 64628–2337, Mailing Address: P.O. Box 408, Zip 64628–0408; tel. 660/258–2222 **A**9 10 18 **F**11 15 28 29 36 40 44 54 57 59 64 75 81 87 93 97 107 111 114 119 127 130 133 146 **P**6
Primary Contact: Phil Hamilton, R.N., Chief Executive Officer
CFO: Gary R. Tandy, Chief Financial Officer
CMO: B. K. Knowles, D.O., Chief of Staff
CIO: Elaine Sutton, Chief Information Officer
CHR: Amy Sayre, Director Human Resources
Web address: www.pershinghealthsystem.com
Control: Other not–for–profit (including NFP Corporation) **Service:** General Medical and Surgical

Staffed Beds: 25 **Admissions:** 878 **Census:** 9 **Outpatient Visits:** 61342 **Births:** 0 **Total Expense ($000):** 17435 **Payroll Expense ($000):** 6773 **Personnel:** 149

BUTLER—Bates County

BATES COUNTY MEMORIAL HOSPITAL (260034), 615 West Nursery Street, Zip 64730–1840, Mailing Address: P.O. Box 370, Zip 64730–0370; tel. 660/200–7000 **A**9 10 20 **F**3 7 11 15 28 29 30 31 34 40 50 57 59 64 68 70 77 78 79 81 87 90 93 107 108 109 110 111 115 118 119 127 129 130 132 133 143 **P**6
Primary Contact: Edward J. Hannon, Chief Executive Officer
CMO: James L. Miller, D.O., Chief of Staff
CIO: Marcia Cook, Director Information Technology
CHR: Melinda Jackson, Director Human Resources
Web address: www.bcmhospital.com
Control: County–Government, nonfederal **Service:** General Medical and Surgical

Staffed Beds: 49 **Admissions:** 865 **Census:** 11 **Outpatient Visits:** 67811 **Births:** 0 **Total Expense ($000):** 35103 **Payroll Expense ($000):** 12884 **Personnel:** 238

CAMERON—Clinton County

CAMERON REGIONAL MEDICAL CENTER (260057), 1600 East Evergreen, Zip 64429–2400, Mailing Address: P.O. Box 557, Zip 64429–0557; tel. 816/632–2101 **A**9 10 **F**3 11 12 13 15 28 29 30 31 34 35 39 40 46 47 49 56 57 59 61 62 63 64 67 70 74 75 76 77 78 79 81 82 84 85 86 87 89 90 98 100 104 107 110 111 115 119 128 129 130 131 133 143 146 147 148 **P**6
Primary Contact: Joseph F. Abrutz, Jr., Administrator
CFO: Rosa Patti, Chief Financial Officer
CIO: Bill Walser, Coordinator Technology
CHR: Pat Bestgen, Manager Human Resources
Web address: www.cameronregional.org
Control: Other not–for–profit (including NFP Corporation) **Service:** General Medical and Surgical

Staffed Beds: 58 **Admissions:** 3219 **Census:** 31 **Outpatient Visits:** 300977 **Births:** 130 **Total Expense ($000):** 45705 **Payroll Expense ($000):** 20257 **Personnel:** 348

CAPE GIRARDEAU—Cape Girardeau County

☐ **LANDMARK HOSPITAL (262015)**, 3255 Independence Street, Zip 63701–4914; tel. 573/335–1091, (Nonreporting) **A**1 9 10 **S** Landmark Hospitals, Cape Girardeau, MO
Primary Contact: Rodney Brown, Chief Executive Officer
COO: Michael L. Norman, Executive Vice President and Chief Operating Officer
CFO: Richard H. Hogan, CPA, Chief Financial Officer
CMO: William Fritsch, M.D., Medical Director
CIO: Renee Hesselrode, Director Health Information Management
CHR: Angela Kisner, Director Human Resources and Coordinator Medical Staff
Web address: www.landmarkhospitals.com
Control: Partnership, Investor–owned, for–profit **Service:** Long–Term Acute Care hospital

Staffed Beds: 30

⌗ **SAINT FRANCIS MEDICAL CENTER (260183)**, 211 St. Francis Drive, Zip 63703–5049; tel. 573/331–3000 **A**1 2 9 10 19 **F**3 9 11 12 13 15 17 18 20 22 24 26 28 29 30 31 32 34 35 39 40 44 45 46 47 48 49 50 53 54 55 56 57 58 59 60 61 62 64 65 70 72 73 74 75 76 77 78 79 80 81 82 83 84 85 86 87 89 90 91 92 93 96 97 107 108 110 111 114 115 117 118 119 120 121 123 124 126 129 130 131 132 135 141 142 143 144 145 146 147 148 **P**6
Primary Contact: Steven C. Bjelich, President and Chief Executive Officer
COO: Marilyn K. Curtis, Vice President Professional Services
CFO: Tony Balsano, Vice President Finance
CMO: James Schell, M.D., Vice President Medical Affairs
CIO: Edward E. Duryee, Director Information Systems
CHR: Teri Kreitzer, Director Human Resources
CNO: Jeannie Fadler, R.N., Vice President Patient Care Services
Web address: www.sfmc.net
Control: Church–operated, Nongovernment, not–for profit **Service:** General Medical and Surgical

Staffed Beds: 282 **Admissions:** 11747 **Census:** 172 **Outpatient Visits:** 355575 **Births:** 1037 **Total Expense ($000):** 387688 **Payroll Expense ($000):** 153428 **Personnel:** 2255

MO

Many Facility Codes have changed. Please refer to the AHA Guide Code Chart. © 2014 AHA Guide

☒ SOUTHEAST HOSPITAL (260110), 1701 Lacey Street, Zip 63701–5230; tel. 573/334–4822 **A**1 9 10 **F**3 11 13 15 17 18 20 22 24 26 28 29 30 31 32 34 35 40 45 50 51 53 54 57 58 59 60 61 62 63 64 65 68 70 72 73 74 75 76 77 78 79 80 81 82 85 86 87 88 89 90 92 93 96 97 98 100 102 107 108 111 115 119 120 121 123 124 126 127 129 130 131 132 144 146 147 148 **P**6 **S** SoutheastHEALTH, Cape Girardeau, MO
Primary Contact: Wayne Smith, President and Chief Executive Officer
COO: Sylvia Moore, Vice President and Chief Operating Officer
CFO: Bruce Fairbanks, Vice President and Chief Financial Officer
CMO: Matt Shoemaker, D.O., Vice President and Chief Medical Officer
CIO: Mike Dozier, Chief Information Officer
CHR: Lincoln Scott, Vice President Human Resources
CNO: Judy Aslin, MSN, Vice President and Chief Nursing Officer
Web address: www.sehealth.org/
Control: Other not–for–profit (including NFP Corporation) **Service:** General Medical and Surgical

> **Staffed Beds:** 221 **Admissions:** 9647 **Census:** 118 **Outpatient Visits:** 348492 **Births:** 894 **Total Expense ($000):** 308056 **Payroll Expense ($000):** 116227 **Personnel:** 2032

CARROLLTON—Carroll County

★ CARROLL COUNTY MEMORIAL HOSPITAL (261332), 1502 North Jefferson Street, Zip 64633–1948; tel. 660/542–1695 **A**9 10 18 **F**3 11 15 28 29 30 34 35 38 40 45 53 56 57 59 62 63 64 65 75 77 79 86 87 90 91 93 96 98 103 104 107 108 110 111 114 117 119 125 127 129 130 131 132 133 143 146 148 **P**6
Primary Contact: Jeff A. Tindle, Chief Executive Officer
COO: Marty Rucker, Chief Operating Officer
CFO: Amy Ireland, Chief Financial Officer
CMO: Timothy Reid, M.D., Chief Medical Staff
CIO: Brandyn Gladbach, Chief Information Technology Officer
CHR: Heather Calvert, Director Human Resources
CNO: Jeanne Rector, Chief Nursing Officer
Web address: www.carrollcountyhospital.org
Control: Other not–for–profit (including NFP Corporation) **Service:** General Medical and Surgical

> **Staffed Beds:** 25 **Admissions:** 332 **Census:** 4 **Outpatient Visits:** 44185 **Births:** 1 **Total Expense ($000):** 14052 **Payroll Expense ($000):** 5518 **Personnel:** 127

CARTHAGE—Jasper County

★ MERCY HOSPITAL CARTHAGE (260228), 3125 Drive Russell Smith Way, Zip 64836–7402; tel. 417/358–8121 **A**9 10 **F**3 7 11 13 15 28 29 30 34 35 40 45 50 53 57 59 62 64 67 68 69 70 75 76 79 81 89 90 98 104 107 111 114 119 127 129 130 131 132 133 135 146 147 **P**6 **S** Mercy Health, Chesterfield, MO
Primary Contact: Robert Y. Copeland, Jr., FACHE, Chief Executive Officer
CFO: Douglas Culver, Chief Financial Officer
CIO: Cheryl Lease–Homeyer, Lead Information Technology Business Partner
CHR: Colette St. Peter, Senior Manager Human Resources
Web address: www.mercy.net
Control: Church–operated, Nongovernment, not–for profit **Service:** General Medical and Surgical

> **Staffed Beds:** 49 **Admissions:** 2221 **Census:** 16 **Outpatient Visits:** 83689 **Births:** 271 **Total Expense ($000):** 63809 **Payroll Expense ($000):** 18556 **Personnel:** 353

CASSVILLE—Barry County

☒ MERCY HOSPITAL CASSVILLE (261317), 94 Main Street, Zip 65625–1610; tel. 417/847–6000 **A**1 9 10 18 **F**3 11 15 28 29 30 34 40 41 45 50 53 57 59 64 65 75 77 81 85 86 87 89 92 93 94 96 107 110 111 114 119 132 133 135 148 **P**6 **S** Mercy Health, Chesterfield, MO
Primary Contact: Douglas M. Stroemel, President
CFO: Sherry Clouse Day, CPA, Chief Financial Officer
CMO: Jamie Zengotita, M.D., Chief Medical Staff
CHR: George Roden, Vice President Human Resources
CNO: Nicki Gamet, R.N., Chief Nursing Officer
Web address: www.mercy.net/northwestarar/practice/mercy–hospital–cassville
Control: Church–operated, Nongovernment, not–for profit **Service:** General Medical and Surgical

> **Staffed Beds:** 18 **Admissions:** 321 **Census:** 3 **Outpatient Visits:** 27813 **Births:** 0 **Total Expense ($000):** 14250 **Payroll Expense ($000):** 6281 **Personnel:** 106

CHESTERFIELD—St. Louis County

☒ △ MERCY REHABILITATION HOSPITAL (263029), 14561 North Outer Forty Road, Zip 63017; tel. 314/881–4000 **A**1 7 9 10 **F**16 29 30 75 90 91 130 132 143 148 **S** Centerre Healthcare, Brentwood, TN
Primary Contact: Donna M. Flannery, Chief Executive Officer
CFO: Jerry Wise, Controller
CMO: Siresha Samudrala, M.D., Medical Director
Web address: www.stjohnsmercyrehab.com
Control: Partnership, Investor–owned, for–profit **Service:** Rehabilitation

> **Staffed Beds:** 90 **Admissions:** 1392 **Census:** 55 **Outpatient Visits:** 0 **Births:** 0 **Total Expense ($000):** 23921 **Payroll Expense ($000):** 10397 **Personnel:** 215

☒ ST. LUKE'S HOSPITAL (260179), 232 South Woods Mill Road, Zip 63017–3417; tel. 314/434–1500, (Total facility includes 140 beds in nursing home–type unit) **A**1 2 3 5 9 10 **F**3 10 11 13 15 17 18 20 22 24 26 28 29 30 31 32 34 35 36 39 40 41 42 44 45 46 48 49 50 52 53 54 55 56 57 58 59 60 61 62 63 64 65 66 68 69 70 71 73 74 75 76 77 78 79 81 82 83 84 85 86 87 89 90 93 97 107 108 110 111 114 118 119 120 121 123 124 126 128 129 130 131 132 135 144 145 146 147 148 **P**6 8
Primary Contact: Gary R. Olson, President and Chief Executive Officer
CFO: Scott Johnson, Vice President Finance
CIO: William Meyers, Chief Information Officer
CHR: Janette Taaffe, Administrator Human Resources
Web address: www.stlukes–stl.com
Control: Church–operated, Nongovernment, not–for profit **Service:** General Medical and Surgical

> **Staffed Beds:** 533 **Admissions:** 16194 **Census:** 296 **Outpatient Visits:** 898307 **Births:** 1869 **Total Expense ($000):** 444846 **Payroll Expense ($000):** 193830 **Personnel:** 3200

☒ ST. LUKE'S REHABILITATION HOSPITAL (263030), 14709 Olive Boulevard, Zip 63017–2221; tel. 314/317–5700 **A**1 9 10 **F**12 28 29 34 54 75 79 90 93 94 96 100 119 130 132 **P**8 **S** Kindred Healthcare, Louisville, KY
Primary Contact: Elizabeth A. Cooley, R.N., Chief Executive Officer
Web address: www.khrehabstluke.com
Control: Partnership, investor–owned, for–profit **Service:** Rehabilitation

> **Staffed Beds:** 35 **Admissions:** 624 **Census:** 22 **Outpatient Visits:** 0 **Births:** 0 **Total Expense ($000):** 8656 **Payroll Expense ($000):** 4656 **Personnel:** 80

CHILLICOTHE—Livingston County

☒ HEDRICK MEDICAL CENTER (261321), 2799 North Washington Street, Zip 64601–2902; tel. 660/646–1480 **A**1 9 10 18 **F**3 11 13 15 18 28 29 30 31 34 35 39 40 41 43 44 45 50 54 57 59 64 68 69 70 74 75 76 77 78 79 81 82 85 86 87 89 90 92 93 96 97 99 100 102 104 107 108 110 111 115 118 119 127 128 129 130 131 133 146 147 148 **P**6 **S** Saint Luke's Health System, Kansas City, MO
Primary Contact: Matthew J. Wenzel, Chief Executive Officer
CHR: Lisa Hecker, Director Human Resources
CNO: Catherine Hamilton, Chief Nursing Officer
Web address: www.saintlukeshealthsystem.org
Control: Other not–for–profit (including NFP Corporation) **Service:** General Medical and Surgical

> **Staffed Beds:** 25 **Admissions:** 991 **Census:** 13 **Outpatient Visits:** 89853 **Births:** 193 **Total Expense ($000):** 35667 **Payroll Expense ($000):** 14640 **Personnel:** 280

CLINTON—Henry County

☒ GOLDEN VALLEY MEMORIAL HEALTHCARE (260175), 1600 North Second Street, Zip 64735–1192; tel. 660/885–5511 **A**1 9 10 19 20 **F**3 7 11 12 13 15 17 18 28 29 30 31 34 35 40 45 47 48 49 53 57 59 61 62 64 68 70 74 75 76 77 78 79 81 85 86 87 90 93 96 107 108 111 115 118 119 127 128 129 130 131 132 133 143 146 147 148
Primary Contact: Randy S. Wertz, Chief Executive Officer
CFO: Gordon Glass, Chief Financial Officer
CIO: James Begin, Director Information Technology
CHR: Roger Cook, Director Human Resources
CNO: Mark David Mattes, R.N., Assistant Administrator/Patient Care Services
Web address: www.gvmh.org
Control: Hospital district or authority, Government, nonfederal **Service:** General Medical and Surgical

> **Staffed Beds:** 56 **Admissions:** 2732 **Census:** 25 **Outpatient Visits:** 238049 **Births:** 323 **Total Expense ($000):** 66984 **Payroll Expense ($000):** 32797 **Personnel:** 602

MO

Hospital, Medicare Provider Number, Address, Telephone, Approval, Facility, and Physician Codes, Health Care System

★ American Hospital Association (AHA) membership
☐ The Joint Commission accreditation ◇ DNV Healthcare Inc. accreditation
○ Healthcare Facilities Accreditation Program
△ Commission on Accreditation of Rehabilitation Facilities (CARF) accreditation

COLUMBIA—Boone County

ELLIS FISCHEL CANCER CENTER See University of Missouri Hospitals and Clinics

✠ **HARRY S. TRUMAN MEMORIAL VETERANS HOSPITAL**, 800 Hospital Drive, Zip 65201–5275; tel. 573/814–6000, (Total facility includes 41 beds in nursing home–type unit) **A**1 3 5 **F**3 4 5 17 18 20 22 24 28 29 30 31 34 35 39 40 44 49 54 56 58 59 61 62 63 64 67 70 74 75 78 79 81 82 84 85 86 87 90 92 93 94 97 98 100 101 102 103 104 105 106 107 108 111 115 118 119 127 128 129 130 132 135 146 147 **P**6 **S** Department of Veterans Affairs, Washington, DC
Primary Contact: Wade Vlosich, Director
COO: Robert G. Ritter, Associate Director
CFO: Deborah Henderson, Acting Chief Financial Officer
CMO: Lana Zerrer, M.D., Chief of Staff
CIO: Donna Krause, Chief Information Officer
CHR: Jimmy Powell, Manager Human Resources
Web address: www.columbiamo.va.gov
Control: Veterans Affairs, Government, federal **Service:** General Medical and Surgical

Staffed Beds: 126 **Admissions:** 3295 **Census:** 86 **Outpatient Visits:** 649727 **Births:** 0 **Total Expense ($000):** 293382 **Payroll Expense ($000):** 99114 **Personnel:** 1335

✠ **HOWARD A. RUSK REHABILITATION CENTER (263027)**, 315 Business Loop 70 West, Zip 65203–3248; tel. 573/817–2703 **A**1 3 5 9 10 **F**29 34 58 68 75 90 91 94 95 96 132 143 148 **S** HEALTHSOUTH Corporation, Birmingham, AL
Primary Contact: Larry Meeker, Chief Executive Officer
CFO: Ted Weatherford, Chief Financial Officer
CMO: Gregory Worsowicz, M.D., Medical Director
CHR: Robin Prater, Director Human Resources
CNO: Mary Schnell, R.N., Chief Nursing Officer
Web address: www.ruskrehab.com
Control: Partnership, Investor–owned, for–profit **Service:** Rehabilitation

Staffed Beds: 60 **Admissions:** 1095 **Census:** 47 **Outpatient Visits:** 5363 **Births:** 0 **Total Expense ($000):** 19190 **Payroll Expense ($000):** 8321 **Personnel:** 172

☐ **LANDMARK HOSPITAL OF COLUMBIA (262020)**, 604 Old 63 North, Zip 65201–6308; tel. 573/499–6600, (Nonreporting) **A**1 3 5 9 10 **S** Landmark Hospitals, Cape Girardeau, MO
Primary Contact: Mindy S. Moore, Chief Executive Officer
Web address: www.landmarkhospitals.com
Control: Partnership, Investor–owned, for–profit **Service:** Long–Term Acute Care hospital

Staffed Beds: 10

✠ **UNIVERSITY OF MISSOURI HOSPITALS AND CLINICS (260141)**, One Hospital Drive, Zip 65212–0001; tel. 573/882–4141, (Includes ELLIS FISCHEL CANCER CENTER, 115 Business Loop 70 West, Zip 65203; tel. 573/882–5460; WOMEN'S AND CHILDREN'S HOSPITAL, 404 Keene Street, Zip 65201–6626; tel. 573/875–9000; Keri Simon, Executive Director) **A**1 2 3 5 8 9 10 **F**3 4 7 9 11 12 13 15 16 17 18 19 20 22 24 26 28 29 30 31 32 34 35 37 38 39 40 41 42 43 44 45 46 47 48 49 50 51 52 53 54 55 56 57 58 59 60 61 64 65 66 68 70 71 72 73 74 75 76 77 78 79 81 82 83 84 85 86 87 88 89 92 93 97 98 99 100 101 102 103 104 107 108 110 111 114 115 117 118 119 120 121 123 124 126 129 130 131 132 134 135 138 141 142 143 144 146 147 148 **P**1 6 **S** University of Missouri Health Care, Columbia, MO
Primary Contact: Mitchell L. Wasden, Ed.D., Chief Executive Officer and Chief Operating Officer
CFO: Kevin Necas, Chief Financial Officer
CMO: Stevan Whitt, M.D., Chief Medical Officer
CHR: Sue Kopfle, Chief Human Resources Officer
CNO: Deborah Pasch, Chief Nurse Executive
Web address: www.muhealth.org
Control: State–Government, nonfederal **Service:** General Medical and Surgical

Staffed Beds: 472 **Admissions:** 23626 **Census:** 316 **Outpatient Visits:** 800520 **Births:** 1820 **Total Expense ($000):** 659472 **Payroll Expense ($000):** 219106 **Personnel:** 4398

CRYSTAL CITY—Jefferson County

★ ○ △ **MERCY HOSPITAL JEFFERSON (260023)**, Highway 61 South, Zip 63019, Mailing Address: P.O. Box 350, Zip 63019–0350; tel. 636/933–1000 **A**7 9 10 11 **F**3 4 5 7 8 11 12 13 15 18 20 22 24 26 29 30 34 35 37 40 44 45 49 50 51 53 54 57 59 62 63 64 70 74 75 76 77 79 81 82 84 85 86 87 89 90 92 93 94 96 97 98 100 101 102 103 104 107 110 111 114 115 116 117 118 119 129 130 131 132 135 143 144 146 147 148 **P**6 **S** Mercy Health, Chesterfield, MO
Primary Contact: Eric Ammons, President
CMO: Mark Briete, M.D., Vice President Medical Affairs
CIO: Jan Poneta, Director Information Services
CHR: Saundra G. Turner, Director Human Resources
Web address: www.mercy.net/crystalcitymo
Control: Other not–for–profit (including NFP Corporation) **Service:** General Medical and Surgical

Staffed Beds: 215 **Admissions:** 10976 **Census:** 125 **Outpatient Visits:** 107208 **Births:** 451 **Total Expense ($000):** 124566 **Payroll Expense ($000):** 49551 **Personnel:** 1163

DEXTER—Stoddard County

SOUTHEAST HEALTH CENTER OF STODDARD COUNTY (260160), 1200 North One Mile Road, Zip 63841–1000; tel. 573/624–5566 **A**9 10 **F**3 11 15 28 29 34 39 40 45 59 62 65 70 75 77 81 85 89 90 93 97 107 108 111 115 118 119 127 130 133 146 **P**6 **S** SoutheastHEALTH, Cape Girardeau, MO
Primary Contact: Adam Bracks, Chief Executive Officer
CHR: Judy Bowling, Director Human Resources
Web address: www.sehealth.org
Control: Other not–for–profit (including NFP Corporation) **Service:** General Medical and Surgical

Staffed Beds: 16 **Admissions:** 893 **Census:** 8 **Outpatient Visits:** 103084 **Births:** 0 **Total Expense ($000):** 16596 **Payroll Expense ($000):** 7819 **Personnel:** 193

DONIPHAN—Ripley County

★ **SOUTHEAST HEALTH CENTER OF RIPLEY COUNTY (260080)**, 109 Plum Street, Zip 63935–1299; tel. 573/996–2141 **A**9 10 **F**3 29 40 59 62 64 65 87 93 107 111 115 119 127 130 **P**6 **S** SoutheastHEALTH, Cape Girardeau, MO
Primary Contact: Christy Hardin, Chief Executive Officer
CFO: Rickie Maples, Interim Chief Financial Officer
CMO: Ureej Mansoor, M.D., Chief of Staff
CIO: Riley March, Manager Information Technology
CHR: Peggy Teasdale, Director Human Resources
Web address: www.sehealth.org/southeast–health–center–of–ripley–county/SoutheastHEALTH.aspx?nd=41
Control: Other not–for–profit (including NFP Corporation) **Service:** General Medical and Surgical

Staffed Beds: 8 **Admissions:** 245 **Census:** 2 **Outpatient Visits:** 46125 **Births:** 0 **Total Expense ($000):** 8028 **Payroll Expense ($000):** 3224 **Personnel:** 120

EL DORADO SPRINGS—Cedar County

CEDAR COUNTY MEMORIAL HOSPITAL (261323), 1401 South Park Street, Zip 64744–2037; tel. 417/876–2511 **A**9 10 18 **F**11 13 15 18 28 29 30 34 35 40 45 53 56 57 59 62 64 65 68 74 75 76 77 81 85 87 89 90 93 102 107 110 111 114 119 127 129 130 133 146 147 148 **P**6
Primary Contact: Jana Witt, Chief Executive Officer
CFO: Carla Gilbert, Director Finance
CMO: Rick Casey, M.D., Chief Medical Staff
CIO: Lois Willmore, Supervisor Health Information Management
CHR: Diana Pyle, Director Human Resources
CNO: Dixie Flynn, Chief Nursing Officer
Web address: www.cedarcountyhospital.org
Control: County–Government, nonfederal **Service:** General Medical and Surgical

Staffed Beds: 25 **Admissions:** 433 **Census:** 10 **Outpatient Visits:** 33547 **Births:** 24 **Total Expense ($000):** 12046 **Payroll Expense ($000):** 4779 **Personnel:** 106

ELLINGTON— County

○ **SOUTHEAST HEALTH CENTER OF REYNOLDS COUNTY (250229)**, 100 Highway 21 South, Zip 63638, Mailing Address: Rural Route 4, Box 4269, Zip 63638–9409; tel. 573/663–2511 **A**9 10 11 **F**3 29 40 54 59 64 65 107 111 114 130 **P**6 **S** SoutheastHEALTH, Cape Girardeau, MO
Primary Contact: Christy Hardin, Chief Executive Officer
COO: Steve Myers, Assistant Administrator
CFO: Katie Caudel, Controller
CIO: Thomas Barker, Director Information
Control: Other not–for–profit (including NFP Corporation) **Service:** General Medical and Surgical

Staffed Beds: 8 **Admissions:** 155 **Census:** 1 **Outpatient Visits:** 15105 **Births:** 0 **Total Expense ($000):** 5698 **Payroll Expense ($000):** 2623 **Personnel:** 59

EXCELSIOR SPRINGS—Clay County

★ **EXCELSIOR SPRINGS HOSPITAL (261322)**, (Long Term Care Facility), 1700 Rainbow Boulevard, Zip 64024–1190; tel. 816/630–6081, (Total facility includes 80 beds in nursing home–type unit) **A**9 10 18 **F**3 10 11 15 18 29 30 31 32 34 35 39 40 45 49 50 57 59 62 63 64 67 68 70 75 77 78 79 81 82 84 85 86 89 90 93 102 107 108 110 111 114 116 117 118 119 125 128 129 130 132 133 135 143 146 147
Primary Contact: Sally S. Nance, Chief Executive Officer
CFO: Dennis Hartman, Chief Financial Officer
CMO: Manoch Kuangparichat, M.D., President Medical Staff
CIO: Alicia Harrison, Data Management Officer
CHR: Joni Schwan, Director Human Resources
Web address: www.esmc.org
Control: City–Government, nonfederal **Service:** General Medical and Surgical

Staffed Beds: 105 **Admissions:** 466 **Census:** 76 **Outpatient Visits:** 24096 **Births:** 0 **Total Expense ($000):** 24580 **Payroll Expense ($000):** 10651 **Personnel:** 198

Many Facility Codes have changed. Please refer to the AHA Guide Code Chart.
© 2014 AHA Guide

MO

FAIRFAX—Atchison County

COMMUNITY HOSPITAL ASSOCIATION See Community Hospital–Fairfax

★ **COMMUNITY HOSPITAL–FAIRFAX (261303)**, 26136 U.S. Highway 59,
Zip 64446–9105, Mailing Address: P.O. Box 107, Zip 64446–0107;
tel. 660/686–2211 **A**9 10 18 **F**3 11 13 15 28 29 30 34 40 45 57 59 62 64
67 76 79 81 85 87 89 90 93 97 107 110 114 117 119 128 130 132 133
Primary Contact: Roger W. Steinkruger, Interim Chief Executive Officer
CFO: Suzanne Southard, Director Finance
CIO: Chris Hedlund, Director Information Systems
CHR: Amber Durr, Director Human Resources
Web address: www.fairfaxmed.com
Control: Other not–for–profit (including NFP Corporation) **Service:** General
Medical and Surgical

Staffed Beds: 18 **Admissions:** 507 **Census:** 5 **Outpatient Visits:** 15149
Births: 51 **Total Expense ($000):** 11846 **Payroll Expense ($000):** 4209
Personnel: 98

FARMINGTON—St. Francois County

○ **MINERAL AREA REGIONAL MEDICAL CENTER (260116)**, 1212 Weber Road,
Zip 63640–3325; tel. 573/756–4581 **A**9 10 11 19 **F**3 4 12 13 15 18 28 29
30 34 40 45 50 57 59 60 62 64 68 70 76 77 79 81 85 89 90 93 98 100
102 103 107 111 114 119 127 129 130 132 133 146 147 **S** Capella
Healthcare, Franklin, TN
Primary Contact: Lynn M. Mergen, Chief Executive Officer
CFO: Donald E. McDaniel, III, Chief Financial Officer
CMO: Erick Calmet, M.D., Chief of Staff
CIO: Kent Kamp, Director Information Systems
CHR: Regina K. Sons, Administrative Director Human Resources and Volunteer
Services Associate Ethics and Compliance Officer
CNO: Christinia Jepsen, R.N., Chief Nursing Officer
Web address: www.mineralarearegional.com
Control: Corporation, Investor–owned, for–profit **Service:** General Medical and
Surgical

Staffed Beds: 127 **Admissions:** 3123 **Census:** 36 **Outpatient Visits:** 82329
Births: 466 **Total Expense ($000):** 49827 **Payroll Expense ($000):** 19903
Personnel: 385

✠ **PARKLAND HEALTH CENTER (260163)**, 1101 West Liberty Street,
Zip 63640–1921; tel. 573/756–6451 **A**1 9 10 **F**3 11 13 15 28 29 30 34 35
40 45 46 49 50 53 57 59 64 65 69 70 74 75 76 77 79 81 85 86 89 93 98
103 107 108 111 115 118 119 130 132 135 143 146 147 148 **S** BJC
HealthCare, Saint Louis, MO
Primary Contact: Thomas P. Karl, President
COO: Steven R. Marler, Assistant Administrator
CFO: Cheri L. Goldsmith, Director Financial Services
CMO: Gary J. Grix, M.D., Chief of Staff
CHR: Sheri Graham, Director Human Resources and Administrative Services
CNO: Barbara Berrong, R.N., Chief Nursing Officer
Web address: www.parklandhealthcenter.org
Control: Other not–for–profit (including NFP Corporation) **Service:** General
Medical and Surgical

Staffed Beds: 98 **Admissions:** 3155 **Census:** 30 **Outpatient Visits:** 81768
Births: 379 **Total Expense ($000):** 74013 **Payroll Expense ($000):** 26507
Personnel: 424

☐ **SOUTHEAST MISSOURI MENTAL HEALTH CENTER (264005)**, 1010 West
Columbia Street, Zip 63640–2997; tel. 573/218–6792 **A**1 10 **F**4 11 30 39 53
65 75 77 86 87 97 98 101 103 106 130 132 135 143 146
Primary Contact: Julie Inman, Regional Executive Officer
CMO: Jay Englehart, M.D., Medical Director
CHR: Mark Remspecher, Director Human Resources
Web address: www.dmh.missouri.gov/southeast/
Control: State–Government, nonfederal **Service:** Psychiatric

Staffed Beds: 298 **Admissions:** 55 **Census:** 284 **Outpatient Visits:** 0 **Births:**
0 **Total Expense ($000):** 51246 **Payroll Expense ($000):** 29311
Personnel: 844

FENTON—St. Louis County

✠ **SSM ST. CLARE HEALTH CENTER (260081)**, 1015 Bowles Avenue,
Zip 63026–2394; tel. 636/496–2000 **A**1 9 10 **F**3 11 13 15 17 18 20 22 24
28 29 30 31 32 34 35 40 44 45 49 50 51 53 56 57 59 61 64 70 73 74 75
76 78 79 81 82 84 85 86 87 89 100 102 103 107 108 110 111 114 115
117 118 119 130 132 135 143 146 147 148 **P**6 8 **S** SSM Health, Saint
Louis, MO
Primary Contact: Ellis Hawkins, President
COO: Lee Bernstein, Regional Executive Vice President and Chief Operating
Officer
CFO: Karen Rewerts, Vice President Finance and Chief Financial Officer
CMO: Timothy J. Pratt, M.D., Vice President Medical Affairs and Chief Medical
Officer
CIO: Leighton Wassilak, Manager Information Systems and Telecommunications
CHR: Lindsay Wilson, Leader Human Resources
CNO: Wayne Laramie, Vice President Nursing
Web address: www.ssmstclare.com
Control: Church–operated, Nongovernment, not–for profit **Service:** General
Medical and Surgical

Staffed Beds: 184 **Admissions:** 10142 **Census:** 109 **Outpatient Visits:**
112209 **Births:** 1328 **Total Expense ($000):** 173431 **Payroll Expense**
($000): 54425 **Personnel:** 838

FORT LEONARD WOOD—Pulaski County

✠ **GENERAL LEONARD WOOD ARMY COMMUNITY HOSPITAL**, 126 Missouri
Avenue, Zip 65473–8952; tel. 573/596–0414, (Nonreporting) **A**1 **S** Department
of the Army, Office of the Surgeon General, Falls Church, VA
Primary Contact: Colonel Peter Nielsen, M.D., Commander
CFO: Major Michael Hogan, Chief Resource Management
CMO: Lieutenant Colonel John Lowery, M.D., Deputy Commander Clinical Services
CHR: Major Sandra Roper, Chief Human Resources
Web address: www.glwach.amedd.army.mil/
Control: Army, Government, federal **Service:** General Medical and Surgical

Staffed Beds: 42

FREDERICKTOWN—Madison County

MADISON MEDICAL CENTER (261302), 611 West Main Street,
Zip 63645–1111; tel. 573/783–3341, (Total facility includes 80 beds in nursing
home–type unit) **A**9 10 18 **F**6 11 15 18 28 31 35 40 45 59 62 64 67 70 74 77
78 79 81 85 87 92 93 97 103 107 111 119 127 128 130 133 146
Primary Contact: Lisa Twidwell, Administrator
CMO: P. A. George, M.D., Chief of Staff
CHR: Jennifer Penuel, Director Human Resources
Web address: www.madisonmedicalcenter.net
Control: County–Government, nonfederal **Service:** General Medical and Surgical

Staffed Beds: 97 **Admissions:** 676 **Census:** 86 **Outpatient Visits:** 59226
Births: 0 **Total Expense ($000):** 17569 **Payroll Expense ($000):** 9162
Personnel: 257

FULTON—Callaway County

☐ **CALLAWAY COMMUNITY HOSPITAL (260209)**, (Geriatric Psychiatry), 10
South Hospital Drive, Zip 65251–2510; tel. 573/642–3376 **A**1 3 5 9 10 **F**3 11
15 29 30 34 35 40 45 50 57 59 67 68 81 85 89 90 93 97 98 103 107 108
111 114 119 127 128 130 131 133 135 **P**6 **S** Sunlink Health Systems,
Atlanta, GA
Primary Contact: Allen D. AufderHeide, Chief Executive Officer
COO: Chuck Baker, R.N., Chief Operating Officer and Chief Nursing Officer
CFO: Allen D. AufderHeide, Chief Executive Officer and Chief Financial Officer
CHR: Martie Jeney, Director Human Resources
CNO: Chuck Baker, R.N., Chief Operating Officer and Chief Nursing Officer
Web address: www.mycallaway.org
Control: Corporation, Investor–owned, for–profit **Service:** General Medical and
Surgical

Staffed Beds: 37 **Admissions:** 629 **Census:** 11 **Outpatient Visits:** 36652
Births: 0 **Total Expense ($000):** 13036 **Payroll Expense ($000):** 6537
Personnel: 125

MO

Hospital, Medicare Provider Number, Address, Telephone, Approval, Facility, and Physician Codes, Health Care System

★ American Hospital Association (AHA) membership
☐ The Joint Commission accreditation ◇ DNV Healthcare Inc. accreditation
○ Healthcare Facilities Accreditation Program
△ Commission on Accreditation of Rehabilitation Facilities (CARF) accreditation

☐ **FULTON STATE HOSPITAL (264004)**, 600 East Fifth Street, Zip 65251–1753; tel. 573/592–4100 **A**1 3 5 10 **F**3 4 11 29 30 39 44 50 53 56 57 58 59 65 75 77 82 86 87 98 100 101 102 103 130 132 135 143 146 **P**6
Primary Contact: Marty Ann Martin–Forman, Chief Operating Officer
COO: Marty Ann Martin–Forman, Chief Operating Officer
CFO: Forrest Bud H. Smith, Jr., Chief Financial Officer
CMO: Sanjiv Sethi, M.D., Medical Director
CIO: Thomas Gillespie, Chief Information Officer
CHR: Lori Hollinger, Manager Human Resources
CNO: Sherry Lee, Chief Nurse Executive
Web address: www.dmh.missouri.gov/fulton
Control: State–Government, nonfederal **Service:** Psychiatric

Staffed Beds: 376 **Admissions:** 134 **Census:** 331 **Outpatient Visits:** 0 **Births:** 0 **Total Expense ($000):** 84175 **Payroll Expense ($000):** 43126 **Personnel:** 1200

HANNIBAL—Marion County

✠ **HANNIBAL REGIONAL HOSPITAL (260025)**, 6000 Hospital Drive, Zip 63401–6887, Mailing Address: P.O. Box 551, Zip 63401–0551; tel. 573/248–1300 **A**1 2 9 10 19 20 **F**3 13 15 18 20 22 26 28 31 34 40 45 47 49 51 57 59 60 62 64 68 70 74 75 76 77 78 79 81 82 85 86 87 89 92 93 96 107 108 110 111 115 117 118 119 120 121 123 129 130 132 135 145 148 **P**1
Primary Contact: Lynn W. Olson, President and Chief Executive Officer
CFO: Roger J. Dix, Vice President Finance
CMO: Bryson McHardy, M.D., President Medical Staff
CIO: Jeff W. Evans, Vice President Information and Technology
CHR: Susan R. Wathen, Vice President Human Resources
Web address: www.hrhonline.org
Control: Other not-for-profit (including NFP Corporation) **Service:** General Medical and Surgical

Staffed Beds: 91 **Admissions:** 4500 **Census:** 45 **Outpatient Visits:** 146119 **Births:** 600 **Total Expense ($000):** 110194 **Payroll Expense ($000):** 49902 **Personnel:** 797

HARRISONVILLE—Cass County

✠ **CASS REGIONAL MEDICAL CENTER (261324)**, 2800 East Rock Haven Road, Zip 64701–4411; tel. 816/380–3474 **A**1 9 10 18 **F**3 8 11 12 15 18 28 29 30 31 32 34 35 37 39 40 45 46 48 50 54 56 57 59 64 65 66 68 70 74 75 77 78 79 80 81 82 84 85 86 87 89 92 93 96 97 98 107 110 111 114 115 119 127 129 130 131 132 133 135 146 147 148 **P**3 6
Primary Contact: John Christopher Lang, Chief Executive Officer
CFO: Brent Probasco, Chief Financial Officer
CIO: Lester Vohs, Manager Information Systems
CHR: Carla Wallen, Manager Human Resources
Web address: www.cassregional.org
Control: County–Government, nonfederal **Service:** General Medical and Surgical

Staffed Beds: 35 **Admissions:** 1780 **Census:** 21 **Outpatient Visits:** 102306 **Births:** 0 **Total Expense ($000):** 57434 **Payroll Expense ($000):** 20935 **Personnel:** 377

HAYTI—Pemiscot County

PEMISCOT MEMORIAL HEALTH SYSTEM (260070), 946 East Road, Zip 63851–1245, Mailing Address: P.O. Box 489, Zip 63851–0489; tel. 573/359–1372, (Total facility includes 66 beds in nursing home–type unit) **A**9 10 **F**3 7 11 13 15 17 28 29 30 34 39 40 50 57 59 64 67 68 70 75 76 77 79 81 82 85 87 89 90 93 97 98 99 103 104 107 111 119 127 128 130 133 143 144 146 147 148 **P**6
Primary Contact: Kerry L. Noble, Chief Executive Officer
CHR: Jackie Powell, Director Human Resources
Web address: www.pemiscot.org/
Control: County–Government, nonfederal **Service:** General Medical and Surgical

Staffed Beds: 167 **Admissions:** 1552 **Census:** 72 **Outpatient Visits:** 95349 **Births:** 82 **Total Expense ($000):** 37357 **Payroll Expense ($000):** 16739 **Personnel:** 464

HERMANN—Gasconade County

★ **HERMANN AREA DISTRICT HOSPITAL (261314)**, 509 West 18th Street, Zip 65041–1547, Mailing Address: P.O. Box 470, Zip 65041–0470; tel. 573/486–2191 **A**9 10 18 **F**3 11 15 18 28 29 34 35 40 41 44 45 53 56 57 59 62 64 67 68 69 71 75 77 78 81 85 86 87 89 90 93 96 97 104 107 111 114 119 127 128 129 130 132 133 143 146 **P**6
Primary Contact: Dan McKinney, Administrator
COO: Matt Siebert, Assistant Administrator Ancillary Services
CFO: Michele Fehlings, Controller
CMO: Michael Rothermich, M.D., Chief of Staff
CIO: Chris Gooch, Information Technology Director
CHR: Gabrielle Gleeson, Human Resources
CNO: Sue Daller, R.N., Assistant Administrator Nursing
Web address: www.hadh.org
Control: Hospital district or authority, Government, nonfederal **Service:** General Medical and Surgical

Staffed Beds: 24 **Admissions:** 442 **Census:** 9 **Outpatient Visits:** 56795 **Births:** 0 **Total Expense ($000):** 17583 **Payroll Expense ($000):** 7685 **Personnel:** 170

HOUSTON—Texas County

TEXAS COUNTY MEMORIAL HOSPITAL (260024), 1333 South Sam Houston Boulevard, Zip 65483–2046; tel. 417/967–3311 **A**9 10 20 **F**3 7 13 15 28 29 34 40 45 57 59 62 63 64 70 76 81 85 86 87 89 93 97 107 110 111 115 119 127 128 129 130 133 143 148 **P**6
Primary Contact: Wesley E. Murray, Chief Executive Officer
CFO: Linda Pamperien, Chief Financial Officer
CMO: Charles Mueller, M.D., Chief of Staff
CHR: Anita Kuhn, Controller
Web address: www.tcmh.org
Control: County–Government, nonfederal **Service:** General Medical and Surgical

Staffed Beds: 47 **Admissions:** 1708 **Census:** 18 **Outpatient Visits:** 106859 **Births:** 262 **Total Expense ($000):** 29925 **Payroll Expense ($000):** 15435 **Personnel:** 336

INDEPENDENCE—Jackson County

✠ **CENTERPOINT MEDICAL CENTER (260095)**, 19600 East 39th Street, Zip 64057–2301; tel. 816/698–7000 **A**1 2 9 10 **F**3 8 13 15 17 18 20 22 24 26 28 29 30 31 34 35 38 40 43 49 50 54 55 56 57 59 60 64 70 71 72 73 74 75 76 77 78 79 80 81 82 84 85 86 87 92 93 107 108 110 111 114 115 116 117 119 126 129 130 131 132 135 144 145 146 147 148 **S** HCA, Nashville, TN
Primary Contact: David R. Williams, Chief Executive Officer
COO: Phil Buttell, Chief Operating Officer
CFO: James H. Brown, Chief Financial Officer
CMO: Christopher Sullivan, M.D., Chief Medical Officer
CIO: Carl Sifers, Director Information Technology and System Services
CHR: Kyla Stoltz, Vice President Human Resources
CNO: Lynn Barrett, Chief Nursing Officer
Web address: www.centerpointmedical.com
Control: Corporation, Investor–owned, for–profit **Service:** General Medical and Surgical

Staffed Beds: 221 **Admissions:** 14717 **Census:** 163 **Outpatient Visits:** 142350 **Births:** 1442 **Total Expense ($000):** 217806 **Payroll Expense ($000):** 66996 **Personnel:** 1140

JEFFERSON CITY—Cole County

✠ **CAPITAL REGION MEDICAL CENTER (260047)**, 1125 Madison Street, Zip 65101–5200, Mailing Address: P.O. Box 1128, Zip 65102–1128; tel. 573/632–5000 **A**1 3 5 9 10 12 13 19 **F**3 5 11 13 15 18 20 22 24 26 28 29 30 31 32 34 35 36 38 40 45 46 47 48 49 51 53 54 56 57 58 59 61 62 64 65 66 70 73 74 75 76 77 78 79 80 81 85 87 89 90 92 93 94 97 99 100 102 104 107 108 110 111 115 118 119 120 121 129 130 131 132 135 144 146 147 **P**2 6 **S** University of Missouri Health Care, Columbia, MO
Primary Contact: Gaspare Calvaruso, President
COO: Janet Weckenborg, FACHE, Vice President Operations
CFO: Tom Luebbering, Vice President Finance
CMO: Thomas Hetherington, M.D., Chief of Staff
CIO: Jason Cecil, Chief Information Officer
CHR: Robert Mazur, Vice President Human Resources
CNO: Tawny Sandifer, R.N., Vice President Patient Care
Web address: www.crmc.org
Control: Other not-for-profit (including NFP Corporation) **Service:** General Medical and Surgical

Staffed Beds: 114 **Admissions:** 6109 **Census:** 61 **Outpatient Visits:** 400772 **Births:** 883 **Total Expense ($000):** 152446 **Payroll Expense ($000):** 67231 **Personnel:** 1196

✠ **ST. MARYS HEALTH CENTER (260011)**, 100 St. Marys Medical Plaza, Zip 65101–1602; tel. 573/761–7000 **A**1 9 10 19 **F**3 11 13 15 17 18 20 22 24 28 29 30 31 32 34 35 40 45 49 50 57 59 64 70 73 74 75 76 77 78 79 80 81 82 84 85 86 87 89 93 96 98 100 101 102 103 104 107 108 110 111 114 115 118 119 129 130 131 132 135 141 144 146 147 148 **P**6 **S** SSM Health, Saint Louis, MO
Primary Contact: R. Brent VanConia, President
COO: Anthony Houston, Executive Vice President
CFO: James Stratton, Vice President Finance
CMO: Stephen Stewart, M.D., Vice President Medical Affairs
CHR: Susan Mankoski, Vice President Human Resources
CNO: Alice M. Chatley, R.N., Vice President Acute Care Services
Web address: www.lethealingbegin.com
Control: Church–operated, Nongovernment, not–for profit **Service:** General Medical and Surgical

Staffed Beds: 139 **Admissions:** 7232 **Census:** 81 **Outpatient Visits:** 207172 **Births:** 624 **Total Expense ($000):** 137335 **Payroll Expense ($000):** 47014 **Personnel:** 826

Many Facility Codes have changed. Please refer to the AHA Guide Code Chart. © 2014 AHA Guide

MO

JOPLIN—Newton County

★ ○ **FREEMAN HOSPITAL WEST (260137)**, 1102 West 32nd Street, Zip 64804–3503; tel. 417/347–1111, (Includes FREEMAN HOSPITAL EAST, 932 East 34th Street, Zip 64804–3999; tel. 417/623–4640), (Total facility includes 32 beds in nursing home–type unit) **A**9 10 11 13 **F**3 8 11 13 15 17 18 20 22 24 26 28 29 30 31 34 35 39 40 42 43 44 45 46 47 48 49 50 54 56 57 58 59 60 61 62 64 65 68 70 72 73 74 75 76 77 78 79 81 82 84 85 86 87 89 90 93 96 97 98 100 102 103 107 108 110 111 114 115 117 119 124 128 129 130 131 132 135 144 145 146 147 148 **P**1 6 **S** Freeman Health System, Joplin, MO
Primary Contact: Paula F. Baker, President and Chief Executive Officer
COO: Richard D. Schooler, M.D., Executive Vice President and Chief Operating Officer
CFO: Steve W. Graddy, Chief Financial Officer
CMO: Richard D. Schooler, M.D., Chief Medical Officer
CIO: Sue Annesser, Chief Information Officer
CHR: Mary Frerer, Chief Human Resources Officer
CNO: Jeffrey Carrier, R.N., Chief Clinical Officer
Web address: www.freemanhealth.com
Control: Other not–for–profit (including NFP Corporation) **Service:** General Medical and Surgical

Staffed Beds: 408 **Admissions:** 19204 **Census:** 290 **Outpatient Visits:** 766825 **Births:** 2424 **Total Expense ($000):** 444833 **Payroll Expense ($000):** 205303 **Personnel:** 3134

◇ **LANDMARK HOSPITAL OF JOPLIN (262016)**, 2040 West 32nd Street, Zip 64804–3512; tel. 417/627–1300, (Nonreporting) **A**9 10 21 **S** Landmark Hospitals, Cape Girardeau, MO
Primary Contact: Kenneth D'Amico, Chief Executive Officer
CMO: Jack Rhoads, M.D., Medical Director
CHR: Janice Nordstrom, Director Human Resources
CNO: Stephanie Slater-Nesuold, Director of Nursing
Web address: www.landmarkhospitals.com
Control: Partnership, Investor–owned, for–profit **Service:** Long–Term Acute Care hospital

Staffed Beds: 30

⊞ **MERCY HOSPITAL JOPLIN (260001)**, 2817 South St. John's Boulevard, Zip 64804–1626; tel. 417/781–2727, (Includes ST. JOHN'S REHABILITATION CENTER, 2727 McClelland Boulevard, Zip 64804; tel. 417/659–6716) **A**1 2 10 **F**3 4 5 7 11 13 15 17 18 20 22 24 26 28 29 30 31 34 35 37 38 39 40 44 45 46 49 50 54 57 58 59 60 61 62 63 64 65 66 68 70 74 75 76 77 78 79 81 82 85 86 87 90 93 94 97 98 99 100 101 102 103 104 105 106 107 108 110 111 114 115 117 118 119 126 127 129 130 131 132 134 135 144 146 147 148 **P**6 **S** Mercy Health, Chesterfield, MO
Primary Contact: Gary W. Pulsipher, President and Chief Executive Officer
COO: Michele Stewart, R.N., Chief Operating Officer
CFO: Shelly Hunter, Chief Financial Officer
CHR: Timothy Murphy, Vice President Human Resources
CNO: Marla G. Brady, R.N., Chief Nursing Officer
Web address: www.mercy.net/joplinmo
Control: Church–operated, Nongovernment, not–for profit **Service:** General Medical and Surgical

Staffed Beds: 179 **Admissions:** 8034 **Census:** 103 **Outpatient Visits:** 128020 **Births:** 422 **Total Expense ($000):** 189791 **Payroll Expense ($000):** 53633 **Personnel:** 975

KANSAS CITY—Jackson County

☐ **CENTER FOR BEHAVIORAL MEDICINE (264008)**, 1000 East 24th Street, Zip 64108–2776; tel. 816/512–7000, (Nonreporting) **A**1 3 5 10
Primary Contact: Denise Norbury, Chief Executive Officer
COO: Jeanette Simmons, Chief Operating Officer
CFO: Randy Riley, Chief Financial Officer
CMO: Nashaat Boutros, M.D., Clinical Director
CIO: Robert Curren, Director Information Technology
CHR: Silva Ward, Director Human Resources
CNO: John Tucker, Chief Nursing Executive
Web address: www.dmhonline.dmh.state.mo.us
Control: State–Government, nonfederal **Service:** Psychiatric

Staffed Beds: 118

⊞ **CHILDREN'S MERCY HOSPITALS AND CLINICS (263302)**, 2401 Gillham Road, Zip 64108–4619; tel. 816/234–3000 **A**1 2 3 5 8 9 10 **F**3 7 8 9 11 12 16 19 20 21 22 23 24 25 26 27 29 30 31 32 34 35 36 39 40 41 43 44 48 49 50 54 55 57 58 59 60 61 62 64 65 68 72 73 74 75 77 78 79 81 82 84 85 86 87 88 89 90 91 92 93 94 96 97 100 101 104 107 108 111 114 117 118 119 130 131 132 134 136 138 139 141 142 144 146 148 **P**6 8
Primary Contact: Randall L. O'Donnell, Ph.D., President and Chief Executive Officer
COO: Jo W. Stueve, Executive Vice President and Co–Chief Operating Officer
CFO: Sandra A J Lawrence, Executive Vice President and Chief Financial Officer
CMO: Charles Roberts, M.D., Executive Vice President and Executive Medical Director
CIO: Jean Ann Breedlove, Chief Information Officer
CNO: Cheri Hunt, R.N., Vice President Patient Care Services and Chief Nursing Officer
Web address: www.childrensmercy.org
Control: Other not–for–profit (including NFP Corporation) **Service:** Children's general

Staffed Beds: 301 **Admissions:** 11533 **Census:** 206 **Outpatient Visits:** 359508 **Births:** 96 **Total Expense ($000):** 791184 **Payroll Expense ($000):** 385833 **Personnel:** 5247

⊞ **CRITTENTON CHILDREN'S CENTER (264018)**, 10918 Elm Avenue, Zip 64134–4108; tel. 816/765–6600 **A**1 10 **F**5 29 30 32 34 35 50 68 75 77 86 87 98 99 100 101 102 104 106 130 132 146 **P**6 **S** Saint Luke's Health System, Kansas City, MO
Primary Contact: Janine Hron, Chief Executive Officer
CFO: Willard Staron, Chief Financial Officer
CMO: Eileen Duggan, M.D., Medical Director
CIO: Deborah Gash, Vice President and Chief Information Officer
CHR: Terri Neal, Director Human Resources
CNO: Belva Giesing, Chief Nursing Officer
Web address: www.crittentonkc.org
Control: Other not–for–profit (including NFP Corporation) **Service:** Children's hospital psychiatric

Staffed Beds: 46 **Admissions:** 2152 **Census:** 39 **Outpatient Visits:** 13766 **Births:** 0 **Total Expense ($000):** 25302 **Payroll Expense ($000):** 14406 **Personnel:** 296

⊞ **KANSAS CITY VETERANS AFFAIRS MEDICAL CENTER**, 4801 East Linwood Boulevard, Zip 64128–2226; tel. 816/861–4700, (Nonreporting) **A**1 2 3 5 **S** Department of Veterans Affairs, Washington, DC
Primary Contact: Kent D. Hill, Director
CFO: Bryan Bieri, Manager Finance
CIO: Eddie Johnson, Chief Information Technology Officer
CHR: Deborah Serratore, Chief Human Resources Officer
Web address: www.kansascity.va.gov/
Control: Veterans Affairs, Government, federal **Service:** General Medical and Surgical

Staffed Beds: 157

⊞ **KINDRED HOSPITAL KANSAS CITY (262011)**, 8701 Troost Avenue, Zip 64131–2767; tel. 816/995–2000 **A**1 9 10 **F**1 3 18 29 30 60 70 75 80 85 100 107 130 148 **S** Kindred Healthcare, Louisville, KY
Primary Contact: Alexander Gill, Chief Executive Officer
CFO: Brett Stevenson, Controller
CNO: Patricia J. Dixon, R.N., Chief Clinical Officer
Web address: www.kindredhospitalkc.com
Control: Corporation, Investor–owned, for–profit **Service:** Long–Term Acute Care hospital

Staffed Beds: 130 **Admissions:** 570 **Census:** 47 **Outpatient Visits:** 0 **Births:** 0 **Total Expense ($000):** 29199 **Payroll Expense ($000):** 8334 **Personnel:** 157

⊞ **KINDRED HOSPITAL NORTHLAND (262018)**, 500 Northwest 68th Street, Zip 64118–2455; tel. 816/420–6300 **A**1 9 10 **F**1 3 16 18 28 29 30 60 68 77 80 82 84 85 90 100 119 130 135 142 148 **S** Kindred Healthcare, Louisville, KY
Primary Contact: H. Frank Schneider, Chief Executive Officer
CFO: Austin Walker, Accounting Manager
CMO: Sean R. Muldoon, M.D., Senior Vice President and Chief Medical Officer–Kindred Healthcare, Hospital Division
CNO: Julie Duben, Chief Clinical Officer
Web address: www.khnorthland.com
Control: Corporation, Investor–owned, for–profit **Service:** Long–Term Acute Care hospital

Staffed Beds: 35 **Admissions:** 364 **Census:** 27 **Outpatient Visits:** 0 **Births:** 0 **Total Expense ($000):** 15741 **Payroll Expense ($000):** 5591 **Personnel:** 109

NORTHLAND LTAC HOSPITAL See Kindred Hospital Northland

MO

Hospital, Medicare Provider Number, Address, Telephone, Approval, Facility, and Physician Codes, Health Care System

★ American Hospital Association (AHA) membership
☐ The Joint Commission accreditation ◇ DNV Healthcare Inc. accreditation
○ Healthcare Facilities Accreditation Program
△ Commission on Accreditation of Rehabilitation Facilities (CARF) accreditation

✠ **RESEARCH MEDICAL CENTER (260027)**, 2316 East Meyer Boulevard, Zip 64132–1136; tel. 816/276–4000 **A**1 2 3 5 9 10 **F**3 4 8 11 13 15 16 17 18 20 22 24 26 28 29 30 31 34 35 38 39 40 42 43 45 46 47 49 50 51 52 53 55 57 58 59 60 61 64 68 70 72 73 74 75 76 77 78 79 80 81 82 84 85 86 87 90 91 93 94 96 97 98 107 108 110 111 112 114 115 116 118 119 120 121 122 124 129 130 131 132 134 135 138 143 146 147 148 **S** HCA, Nashville, TN
Primary Contact: Jacqueline DeSouza, Chief Executive Officer
COO: Eric Becker, Chief Operating Officer
CFO: Susan Shreeve, Chief Financial Officer
CMO: James Bower, M.D., Chief Medical Officer
CIO: Shawn Kegley, Director Information Services
CHR: Charlotte O'Neal, Vice President Human Resources
Web address: www.researchmedicalcenter.com
Control: Corporation, Investor–owned, for–profit **Service:** General Medical and Surgical

Staffed Beds: 361 **Admissions:** 14874 **Census:** 206 **Outpatient Visits:** 156588 **Births:** 1302 **Total Expense ($000):** 325652 **Payroll Expense ($000):** 92854 **Personnel:** 1438

★ **RESEARCH PSYCHIATRIC CENTER (264016)**, 2323 East 63rd Street, Zip 64130–3462; tel. 816/444–8161 **A**10 **F**4 5 29 35 87 98 99 100 101 102 103 104 105 130 **S** HCA, Nashville, TN
Primary Contact: Lisa St. Aubyn, Chief Executive Officer
COO: Kevin Walker, Vice President Operations
CFO: Susan Shreeve, Chief Financial Officer
CMO: Steven Segraves, M.D., Medical Director
CIO: Matt Untch, Controller
CHR: Peggy Tyson, Director Human Resources
Web address: www.researchpsychiatriccenter.com
Control: Corporation, Investor–owned, for–profit **Service:** Psychiatric

Staffed Beds: 100 **Admissions:** 3717 **Census:** 66 **Outpatient Visits:** 5065 **Births:** 0 **Total Expense ($000):** 24788 **Payroll Expense ($000):** 12006 **Personnel:** 193

✠ **SAINT LUKE'S HOSPITAL OF KANSAS CITY (260138)**, 4401 Wornall Road, Zip 64111–3220; tel. 816/932–9886, (Includes SAINT LUKE'S CANCER INSTITUTE, 4321 Washington, Medical Plaza III, Suite 5100, Zip 64111–3214; tel. 816/932–2823) **A**1 3 5 8 9 10 **F**3 9 11 12 13 15 17 18 20 22 24 25 26 28 29 30 31 32 34 35 36 37 38 39 40 43 44 45 46 47 48 49 50 53 54 55 56 57 58 59 60 61 62 64 65 66 68 70 71 72 73 74 75 76 77 78 79 81 82 84 85 86 87 89 90 91 92 93 94 95 96 97 100 101 102 103 104 107 108 110 111 114 115 116 117 118 119 120 121 123 124 126 129 130 131 132 135 137 138 139 141 146 147 148 **P**6 **S** Saint Luke's Health System, Kansas City, MO
Primary Contact: Julie L. Quirin, FACHE, Chief Executive Officer
COO: Brad Simmons, Chief Operating Officer
CFO: Amy Nachtigal, Chief Financial Officer
CMO: Peter Holt, M.D., Director Medical Affairs
CIO: Deborah Gash, Chief Information Officer
CHR: Doris Rogers, Vice President Human Resources
CNO: Debra White, Chief Nursing Officer
Web address: www.saint–lukes.org
Control: Church–operated, Nongovernment, not–for profit **Service:** General Medical and Surgical

Staffed Beds: 447 **Admissions:** 18628 **Census:** 295 **Outpatient Visits:** 369389 **Births:** 2358 **Total Expense ($000):** 555351 **Payroll Expense ($000):** 163499 **Personnel:** 2764

✠ **SAINT LUKE'S NORTH HOSPITAL – BARRY ROAD (260062)**, 5830 N.W. Barry Road, Zip 64154–2778; tel. 816/891–6000, (Includes SAINT LUKE'S NORTH HOSPITAL–SMITHVILLE CAMPUS, 601 South 169 Highway, Smithville, Zip 64089–9317; tel. 816/532–3700) **A**1 9 10 **F**3 11 13 15 17 18 20 22 26 28 29 30 31 32 34 35 36 38 40 44 45 49 50 53 54 57 58 59 64 65 69 70 71 73 74 75 76 77 78 79 80 81 82 84 85 86 87 89 90 92 93 96 97 98 99 100 101 102 103 104 105 107 108 110 111 114 115 116 117 118 119 129 130 131 132 134 135 141 143 146 147 148 **S** Saint Luke's Health System, Kansas City, MO
Primary Contact: Kevin T. Trimble, FACHE, President and Chief Executive Officer
CFO: Julie Murphy, Chief Financial Officer
CMO: Leonardo J. Lozada, M.D., Chief Physician Executive
CIO: LaDonna Seger, Director Information Services
CHR: Alan L. Abramovitz, Director Human Resources
CNO: Jeffrey Eye, R.N., Chief Nursing Officer
Web address: www.saint–lukes.org
Control: Church–operated, Nongovernment, not–for profit **Service:** General Medical and Surgical

Staffed Beds: 142 **Admissions:** 6896 **Census:** 80 **Outpatient Visits:** 89872 **Births:** 819 **Total Expense ($000):** 107410 **Payroll Expense ($000):** 38772 **Personnel:** 679

✠ **SELECT SPECIALTY HOSPITAL–WESTERN MISSOURI (262014)**, 2316 East Meyer Boulevard, 3 West, Zip 64132–1136; tel. 816/276–3300 **A**1 9 10 **F**1 3 29 **S** Select Medical Corporation, Mechanicsburg, PA
Primary Contact: Jeffrey Alexander, Chief Executive Officer
Web address: www.selectspecialtyhospitals.com/company/locations/westernmissouri.aspx
Control: Corporation, Investor–owned, for–profit **Service:** Long–Term Acute Care hospital

Staffed Beds: 34 **Admissions:** 366 **Census:** 24 **Outpatient Visits:** 0 **Births:** 0 **Total Expense ($000):** 13415 **Payroll Expense ($000):** 5402 **Personnel:** 95

SIGNATURE PSYCHIATRIC HOSPITAL (264030), 2900 Clay Edwards Drive, Zip 64116–3235; tel. 816/691–5101, (Nonreporting)
Primary Contact: Azfar Malik, M.D., Chief Executive Officer
COO: Susan Mathis, R.N., Chief Operating Officer and Chief Nurse Executive
CFO: Tariq F. Malik, CPA, Chief Financial Officer
CMO: Todd Hill, D.O., Medical Director
CIO: Mike Solom, Director Information Technology
CHR: Sheila Shipley, Human Resources Educator
CNO: Teresa Mathis, Administrator and Director of Nursing
Control: Corporation, Investor–owned, for–profit **Service:** Psychiatric

Staffed Beds: 24

✠ **ST. JOSEPH MEDICAL CENTER (260085)**, 1000 Carondelet Drive, Zip 64114–4673; tel. 816/942–4400 **A**1 2 9 10 **F**3 11 13 15 17 18 20 22 24 26 28 29 30 31 34 35 36 40 45 47 49 50 51 56 57 59 60 64 68 70 71 72 74 75 76 77 78 79 80 81 82 84 85 86 87 90 96 107 108 110 111 114 115 116 118 119 129 130 132 135 146 147 148 **S** Ascension Health, Saint Louis, MO
Primary Contact: Michael A. Dorsey, FACHE, Chief Executive Officer
CFO: Steven R. Cleary, Vice President Finance
CMO: Stephens Stoops, M.D., Chief Medical Officer
CHR: Donna Sumner, Vice President Human Resources and Organizational Development
CNO: Debra Ohnoutka, Chief Nursing Officer
Web address: www.carondelethealth.org
Control: Other not–for–profit (including NFP Corporation) **Service:** General Medical and Surgical

Staffed Beds: 190 **Admissions:** 9118 **Census:** 120 **Outpatient Visits:** 110496 **Births:** 938 **Total Expense ($000):** 163066 **Payroll Expense ($000):** 50856 **Personnel:** 915

✠ **TRUMAN MEDICAL CENTER–HOSPITAL HILL (260048)**, 2301 Holmes Street, Zip 64108–2640; tel. 816/404–1000 **A**1 2 3 5 8 9 10 **F**3 4 5 11 12 13 15 17 18 20 22 26 28 29 30 31 34 35 36 39 40 41 43 44 45 48 49 50 52 53 55 57 58 59 61 64 65 66 68 70 71 72 74 75 76 77 78 79 81 82 84 85 86 87 90 93 94 97 98 99 100 101 102 103 104 107 108 110 111 114 115 119 129 130 131 132 134 135 143 146 147 148 **P**5 6 **S** Truman Medical Centers, Kansas City, MO
Primary Contact: Charlie Shields, President and Chief Executive Officer
CFO: Allen Johnson, Chief Financial Officer
CMO: Mark Steele, M.D., Chief Medical Officer
CIO: Mitzi Cardenas, Chief Information Officer
CHR: Marcos DeLeon, Vice President Community Engagement
CNO: Lynette Wheeler, MSN, Chief Nursing Officer
Web address: www.trumed.org
Control: Other not–for–profit (including NFP Corporation) **Service:** General Medical and Surgical

Staffed Beds: 256 **Admissions:** 13031 **Census:** 179 **Outpatient Visits:** 583962 **Births:** 2086 **Total Expense ($000):** 342312 **Payroll Expense ($000):** 145043 **Personnel:** 2795

✠ **TRUMAN MEDICAL CENTER–LAKEWOOD (260102)**, 7900 Lee's Summit Road, Zip 64139–1236; tel. 816/404–7000, (Total facility includes 188 beds in nursing home–type unit) **A**1 3 5 9 10 **F**3 4 5 6 11 13 15 29 30 32 34 35 36 38 39 40 41 44 45 50 53 54 56 57 58 59 64 65 66 67 68 70 71 72 74 75 76 77 78 79 81 85 86 87 89 90 92 93 94 96 97 98 99 100 101 102 103 104 107 111 112 114 119 129 130 131 132 134 135 143 146 147 **P**5 6 **S** Truman Medical Centers, Kansas City, MO
Primary Contact: Charlie Shields, President and Chief Executive Officer
COO: Amy Peters, R.N., Interim Chief Operating Officer
CFO: Allen Johnson, Chief Financial Officer
CMO: Mark Steele, M.D., Chief Medical Officer
CIO: Mitzi Cardenas, Chief Information Officer
CHR: Marcos DeLeon, Vice President Community Engagement
CNO: Lynette Wheeler, MSN, Chief Nursing Officer
Web address: www.trumed.org
Control: Other not–for–profit (including NFP Corporation) **Service:** General Medical and Surgical

Staffed Beds: 296 **Admissions:** 5781 **Census:** 235 **Outpatient Visits:** 422031 **Births:** 1443 **Total Expense ($000):** 133380 **Payroll Expense ($000):** 61355 **Personnel:** 924

MO

✠ **TWO RIVERS BEHAVIORAL HEALTH SYSTEM (264017)**, 5121 Raytown Road, Zip 64133–2141; tel. 816/382–6300 **A**1 10 **F**4 5 29 30 34 35 38 75 86 87 98 99 101 102 103 104 105 130 132 134 143 **P**6 **S** Universal Health Services, Inc., King of Prussia, PA
Primary Contact: Cara Macaleer, Chief Executive Officer/Managing Director
CFO: Michael Delaney, Chief Financial Officer
CMO: Shahbaz Khan, M.D., Medical Director
CHR: Diane Peoples, Director Human Resources
CNO: Rebecca Dvorak, Chief Nursing Officer
Web address: www.tworivershospital.com
Control: Corporation, Investor–owned, for–profit **Service:** Psychiatric

> **Staffed Beds:** 105 **Admissions:** 2816 **Census:** 44 **Outpatient Visits:** 4648 **Births:** 0 **Total Expense ($000):** 14738 **Payroll Expense ($000):** 7039 **Personnel:** 121

VETERANS AFFAIRS MEDICAL CENTER See Kansas City Veterans Affairs Medical Center

KENNETT—Dunklin County

✠ **TWIN RIVERS REGIONAL MEDICAL CENTER (260015)**, 1301 First Street, Zip 63857–2508, Mailing Address: P.O. Box 728, Zip 63857–0728; tel. 573/888–4522 **A**1 9 10 **F**3 11 13 15 18 29 30 31 35 40 50 56 57 59 60 64 68 70 75 76 78 79 81 85 89 90 98 99 100 101 102 103 104 107 108 110 111 114 115 117 119 127 129 130 135 147 148 **S** Community Health Systems, Inc., Franklin, TN
Primary Contact: Matthew M. Lyden, Chief Executive Officer
CFO: Michelle Beachman, Chief Financial Officer
CHR: Mark Niemeier, Director Human Resources
Web address: www.twinriversregional.com
Control: Corporation, Investor–owned, for–profit **Service:** General Medical and Surgical

> **Staffed Beds:** 116 **Admissions:** 3477 **Census:** 34 **Outpatient Visits:** 76160 **Births:** 430 **Total Expense ($000):** 43950 **Payroll Expense ($000):** 14716 **Personnel:** 310

KIRKSVILLE—Adair County

★ ○ **NORTHEAST REGIONAL MEDICAL CENTER (260022)**, 315 South Osteopathy, Zip 63501–6401, Mailing Address: P.O. Box C8502, Zip 63501–8599; tel. 660/785–1000 **A**9 10 11 12 13 19 20 **F**3 12 13 15 18 20 24 28 29 30 34 35 39 40 43 45 46 49 50 51 53 57 59 60 62 64 68 70 74 75 76 77 79 81 82 85 86 87 89 90 93 107 108 110 111 114 115 119 127 129 130 131 132 133 135 146 147 148 **S** Community Health Systems, Inc., Franklin, TN
Primary Contact: Ranee C. Brayton, R.N., MSN, Chief Executive Officer
CFO: Tammy Cobb, Chief Financial Officer
CMO: John DeLeeuw, M.D., Chief of Staff
CIO: Chad Tatro, Supervisor Information Systems
CHR: Jim Bergman, Director Human Resources
CNO: Cindy Carter, Chief Nursing Officer
Web address: www.nermc.com
Control: Corporation, Investor–owned, for–profit **Service:** General Medical and Surgical

> **Staffed Beds:** 115 **Admissions:** 2925 **Census:** 33 **Outpatient Visits:** 69360 **Births:** 504 **Total Expense ($000):** 55647 **Payroll Expense ($000):** 19142 **Personnel:** 476

LAKE SAINT LOUIS—St. Charles County

✠ **SSM ST. JOSEPH HOSPITAL WEST (260200)**, 100 Medical Plaza, Zip 63367–1366; tel. 636/625–5200 **A**1 9 10 **F**3 11 13 15 17 20 22 28 29 30 31 34 35 36 38 40 41 43 44 49 50 51 53 55 56 57 59 60 61 64 68 70 73 74 75 76 78 79 81 82 84 85 86 87 89 100 102 107 108 110 111 114 118 119 129 130 132 135 146 147 148 **P**6 8 **S** SSM Health, Saint Louis, MO
Primary Contact: Lisle Wescott, President
CFO: Hal Holder, Director Finance
CMO: Michael Handler, M.D., Vice President Medical Administration
CIO: Sharon Gardner, Manager Information Systems
CHR: Sheila Shortt, R.N., Human Resources Consultant
CNO: Janet K. Pestle, R.N., Vice President Nursing and Chief Nursing Officer
Web address: www.ssmstjoseph.com
Control: Church–operated, Nongovernment, not–for profit **Service:** General Medical and Surgical

> **Staffed Beds:** 126 **Admissions:** 9167 **Census:** 84 **Outpatient Visits:** 132308 **Births:** 1147 **Total Expense ($000):** 127258 **Payroll Expense ($000):** 47468 **Personnel:** 723

LAMAR—Barton County

BARTON COUNTY MEMORIAL HOSPITAL (261325), 29 N.W. First Lane, Zip 64759–8105; tel. 417/681–5100 **A**9 10 18 **F**3 11 15 18 28 30 34 35 36 39 40 44 45 50 57 59 64 65 68 75 77 79 81 84 85 86 87 89 90 93 97 107 108 110 111 114 119 127 128 129 130 132 133 135 143 146 148
Primary Contact: Wendy Duvall, Chief Executive Officer
CIO: Brad Butler, Network Administrator
CHR: Sheila Boice, Director Human Resources
CNO: Marlys Buckner, Chief Nursing Officer
Web address: www.bcmh.net
Control: County–Government, nonfederal **Service:** General Medical and Surgical

> **Staffed Beds:** 25 **Admissions:** 1185 **Census:** 14 **Outpatient Visits:** 47537 **Births:** 0 **Total Expense ($000):** 21955 **Payroll Expense ($000):** 8081 **Personnel:** 200

LEBANON—Laclede County

✠ **MERCY HOSPITAL LEBANON (260059)**, 100 Hospital Drive, Zip 65536–9210; tel. 417/533–6100 **A**1 9 10 **F**3 11 13 15 28 29 30 31 32 35 36 37 40 50 53 57 59 64 65 68 70 71 75 76 77 78 79 81 82 83 85 86 87 89 90 93 102 107 108 110 111 114 119 129 130 131 132 133 135 144 146 147 148 **P**6 **S** Mercy Health, Chesterfield, MO
Primary Contact: Michele Schaefer, Interim President
CFO: Douglas M. Hoban, Vice President and Chief Financial Officer
Web address: www.stjohnslebanon.com
Control: Church–operated, Nongovernment, not–for profit **Service:** General Medical and Surgical

> **Staffed Beds:** 58 **Admissions:** 2449 **Census:** 20 **Outpatient Visits:** 140640 **Births:** 346 **Total Expense ($000):** 70851 **Payroll Expense ($000):** 25811 **Personnel:** 495

LEE'S SUMMIT—Jackson County

✠ **LEE'S SUMMIT MEDICAL CENTER (260190)**, 2100 S.E. Blue Parkway, Zip 64063–1007; tel. 816/282–5000 **A**1 9 10 **F**3 15 18 20 22 28 29 30 31 34 40 43 49 57 59 60 64 65 68 69 70 74 75 77 78 79 81 82 84 85 87 93 107 108 110 111 114 119 129 130 131 132 145 146 148 **S** HCA, Nashville, TN
Primary Contact: Matt Sogard, Chief Executive Officer
CFO: John Heurtin, Chief Financial Officer
CIO: Andrew Beechy, Manager Information Technology Systems
CHR: Linda Duncan, Director Human Resources
Web address: www.leessummitmedicalcenter.com
Control: Corporation, Investor–owned, for–profit **Service:** General Medical and Surgical

> **Staffed Beds:** 64 **Admissions:** 3519 **Census:** 35 **Outpatient Visits:** 96140 **Births:** 0 **Total Expense ($000):** 70535 **Payroll Expense ($000):** 30666 **Personnel:** 300

✠ **SAINT LUKE'S EAST HOSPITAL (260216)**, 100 N.E. Saint Luke's Boulevard, Zip 64086–6000; tel. 816/347–5000 **A**1 9 10 **F**3 13 15 18 20 22 26 28 29 30 31 34 35 38 40 43 44 45 46 49 50 56 57 58 59 60 62 65 70 71 72 73 74 75 76 77 78 79 80 81 82 84 85 86 87 92 93 94 96 100 107 108 110 111 114 115 117 118 119 120 121 126 129 130 131 132 135 145 146 147 148 **S** Saint Luke's Health System, Kansas City, MO
Primary Contact: Ronald L. Baker, Chief Executive Officer
COO: Gloria Solis, R.N., Chief Operating Officer and Chief Nursing Officer
CFO: Joseph P. Stasi, Chief Financial Officer
CHR: John Clabaugh, Director Human Resources
CNO: Gloria Solis, R.N., Chief Operating Officer and Chief Nursing Officer
Web address: www.saint–lukes.org
Control: Church–operated, Nongovernment, not–for profit **Service:** General Medical and Surgical

> **Staffed Beds:** 141 **Admissions:** 8835 **Census:** 87 **Outpatient Visits:** 106979 **Births:** 1759 **Total Expense ($000):** 146394 **Payroll Expense ($000):** 46540 **Personnel:** 781

MO

Hospital, Medicare Provider Number, Address, Telephone, Approval, Facility, and Physician Codes, Health Care System

★ American Hospital Association (AHA) membership
☐ The Joint Commission accreditation
◇ DNV Healthcare Inc. accreditation
○ Healthcare Facilities Accreditation Program
△ Commission on Accreditation of Rehabilitation Facilities (CARF) accreditation

MO

LEXINGTON—Lafayette County

⊞ **LAFAYETTE REGIONAL HEALTH CENTER (261320)**, 1500 State Street, Zip 64067–1107; tel. 660/259–2203 **A**1 9 10 18 **F**11 15 29 31 40 64 68 70 75 78 79 81 85 93 107 110 111 114 116 119 127 129 130 133 147 148 **P**6 **S** HCA, Nashville, TN
Primary Contact: Darrel Box, Chief Executive Officer
COO: Daniel Astleford, Vice President Operations
CFO: Teri James, Chief Financial Officer
CIO: Keith Richcreek, Manager Technical Services
CHR: Stephen Davidson, Director Human Resources
CNO: Kim Leakey, R.N., Chief Nursing Officer
Web address: www.lafayetteregionalhealthcenter.com
Control: Corporation, Investor–owned, for–profit **Service:** General Medical and Surgical

Staffed Beds: 25 **Admissions:** 1077 **Census:** 11 **Outpatient Visits:** 76520 **Births:** 0 **Total Expense ($000):** 26723 **Payroll Expense ($000):** 10176 **Personnel:** 200

LIBERTY—Clay County

⊞ **LIBERTY HOSPITAL (260177)**, 2525 Glenn Hendren Drive, Zip 64068–9600, Mailing Address: P.O. Box 1002, Zip 64069–1002; tel. 816/781–7200 **A**1 2 9 10 **F**3 9 11 13 15 18 20 22 24 28 29 30 31 34 35 40 43 44 45 47 49 59 62 63 64 68 69 70 73 74 75 76 77 78 79 80 81 82 84 85 86 87 89 92 93 97 102 107 108 110 111 114 115 118 119 126 129 130 132 143 146 148
Primary Contact: David Feess, President and Chief Executive Officer
CFO: Dan Williams, Vice President Finance and Support
CIO: Paul Klehn, Chief Information Technology Officer
CHR: Nancy E. Cattell, Vice President Human Resources
CNO: Shirley Heintz, R.N., Vice President Patient Care
Web address: www.Libertyhospital.org
Control: Hospital district or authority, Government, nonfederal **Service:** General Medical and Surgical

Staffed Beds: 250 **Admissions:** 10829 **Census:** 112 **Outpatient Visits:** 260360 **Births:** 1073 **Total Expense ($000):** 196640 **Payroll Expense ($000):** 83000 **Personnel:** 1167

LOUISIANA—Pike County

⊞ **PIKE COUNTY MEMORIAL HOSPITAL (261333)**, 2305 Georgia Street, Zip 63353–2559; tel. 573/754–5531 **A**1 9 10 18 **F**3 7 11 15 18 28 29 30 34 35 40 50 53 54 56 57 59 64 65 68 74 75 77 79 81 85 86 87 89 90 93 97 107 114 127 130 131 132 133 147 148
Primary Contact: Lorraine L. Harness, Administrator
COO: Justin Selle, Chief Operating Officer
CFO: Ann Tran, Chief Financial Officer
CIO: Jeremy Gruen, Director Information Systems
CHR: Connie Bair, Human Resources Assistant
Web address: www.pcmh–mo.org
Control: County–Government, nonfederal **Service:** General Medical and Surgical

Staffed Beds: 25 **Admissions:** 536 **Census:** 6 **Outpatient Visits:** 33622 **Births:** 0 **Total Expense ($000):** 15207 **Payroll Expense ($000):** 6848 **Personnel:** 157

MACON—Macon County

★ **SAMARITAN MEMORIAL HOSPITAL (261313)**, 1205 North Missouri Street, Zip 63552–2095; tel. 660/385–8700 **A**9 10 18 **F**3 7 8 11 15 18 28 29 31 34 35 40 45 53 56 57 59 60 63 64 68 71 75 78 79 81 82 84 85 86 87 89 90 93 94 107 111 115 119 127 128 129 130 131 132 134 143 146 148 **P**5
Primary Contact: Bernard A. Orman, Jr., Administrator
CFO: Susan Spencer, Chief Financial Officer
CHR: Suzanne Britt, Director Human Resources
Web address: www.samaritanhospital.net
Control: County–Government, nonfederal **Service:** General Medical and Surgical

Staffed Beds: 25 **Admissions:** 756 **Census:** 12 **Outpatient Visits:** 59491 **Births:** 0 **Total Expense ($000):** 23388 **Payroll Expense ($000):** 8768 **Personnel:** 185

MARSHALL—Saline County

★ **FITZGIBBON HOSPITAL (260142)**, 2305 South 65 Highway, Zip 65340–0250, Mailing Address: P.O. Box 250, Zip 65340–0250; tel. 660/886–7431 **A**5 9 10 20 **F**3 11 13 15 30 31 34 35 40 45 53 57 59 62 63 64 68 70 74 75 76 77 78 79 81 82 85 87 90 93 98 103 104 107 110 111 115 118 119 120 121 127 128 129 130 131 132 133 135 143 146 147 148
Primary Contact: Ronald A. Ott, Chief Executive Officer
COO: Angy Littrell, Chief Operating Officer
CFO: Angy Littrell, Chief Financial Officer
CMO: Darin Haug, D.O., Chief Medical Officer
CIO: Tom Jones, Manager Information Technology
CHR: Myron Lite, Director Human Resources
CNO: Kathryn Lynne Ott, MSN, Vice President Patient Care Services and Chief Nursing Officer
Web address: www.fitzgibbon.org
Control: Other not–for–profit (including NFP Corporation) **Service:** General Medical and Surgical

Staffed Beds: 52 **Admissions:** 2256 **Census:** 21 **Outpatient Visits:** 102374 **Births:** 267 **Total Expense ($000):** 45622 **Payroll Expense ($000):** 20761 **Personnel:** 530

MARYLAND HEIGHTS—St. Louis County

★ **RANKEN JORDAN PEDIATRIC BRIDGE HOSPITAL (263303)**, (Pediatric Bridge Hospital), 11365 Dorsett Road, Zip 63043–3411; tel. 314/872–6400 **A**9 10 **F**1 3 12 29 30 32 34 35 36 38 44 50 68 86 87 89 90 91 92 93 94 96 98 99 104 130 132 143 146 148 **P**6
Primary Contact: Laureen K. Tanner, R.N., MSN, FACHE, President and Chief Executive Officer
COO: Brett Moorehouse, FACHE, Vice President and Chief Operating Officer
CFO: Jean Bardwell, Vice President and Chief Financial Officer
CMO: Nicholas Holekamp, M.D., Chief Medical Officer
CIO: Jean Bardwell, Vice President and Chief Financial Officer
CHR: Thomas M. Irvin, Administrator Human Resources
CNO: Laureen K. Tanner, R.N., President and Chief Executive Officer
Web address: www.rankenjordan.org
Control: Other not–for–profit (including NFP Corporation) **Service:** Children's rehabilitation

Staffed Beds: 34 **Admissions:** 279 **Census:** 28 **Outpatient Visits:** 9405 **Births:** 0 **Total Expense ($000):** 28401 **Payroll Expense ($000):** 14544 **Personnel:** 289

MARYVILLE—Nodaway County

⊞ **ST. FRANCIS HOSPITAL AND HEALTH SERVICES (260050)**, 2016 South Main Street, Zip 64468–2655; tel. 660/562–2600 **A**1 9 10 20 **F**3 8 11 13 15 18 28 29 30 34 35 38 40 45 57 59 64 65 68 70 75 76 77 79 81 82 84 85 86 89 90 93 96 97 98 99 100 101 102 103 104 105 107 111 114 119 127 128 130 131 132 133 135 141 142 **P**6 **S** SSM Health, Saint Louis, MO
Primary Contact: Gray Cox, President
COO: Ty Griffith, Vice President Operations and Planning
CFO: Jocelyn Skidmore, Director Finance
CMO: Lisa DiStefano, M.D., President Medical Staff
CIO: Dave Lewis, Director Information Services
CHR: Melissa McClurg, Chief Human Resources Officer
CNO: Debbie Hoffman, Vice President Patient Services
Web address: www.stfrancismaryville.com
Control: Church–operated, Nongovernment, not–for profit **Service:** General Medical and Surgical

Staffed Beds: 57 **Admissions:** 1461 **Census:** 17 **Outpatient Visits:** 134245 **Births:** 317 **Total Expense ($000):** 60050 **Payroll Expense ($000):** 25984 **Personnel:** 396

MEMPHIS—Scotland County

★ **SCOTLAND COUNTY HOSPITAL (261310)**, 450 Sigler Avenue, Zip 63555–1726, Mailing Address: 450 East Sigler Avenue, Zip 63555–1726; tel. 660/465–8511, (Nonreporting) **A**9 10 18
Primary Contact: Randy Tobler, M.D., Interim Chief Executive Officer
CFO: Sheryl Templeton, Chief Financial Officer
CMO: Randy Tobler, M.D., Chief Medical Officer
CIO: Ken McMinn, Director Information Technology
CHR: Missy Smith, Coordinator Human Resources
CNO: Carla Cook, Director of Nursing
Web address: www.scotlandcountyhospital.com
Control: Hospital district or authority, Government, nonfederal **Service:** General Medical and Surgical

Staffed Beds: 25

SCOTLAND COUNTY MEMORIAL HOSPITAL See Scotland County Hospital

MEXICO—Audrain County

⊞ **AUDRAIN MEDICAL CENTER (260064)**, 620 East Monroe Street, Zip 65265–2919; tel. 573/582–5000 **A**1 2 9 10 19 20 **F**3 11 13 15 18 20 22 26 28 29 30 31 34 40 45 53 54 57 59 64 65 70 73 74 75 76 77 78 79 81 82 85 86 87 89 90 93 107 108 110 111 114 118 119 121 127 129 130 131 132 146 147 **P**6 **S** SSM Health, Saint Louis, MO
Primary Contact: David A. Neuendorf, FACHE, President and Chief Executive Officer
COO: Kari Wilson, R.N., Vice President Clinical Services, Chief Operating Officer and Chief Nursing Officer
CFO: James Stratton, Regional Vice President Finance
CMO: Joseph Corrado, M.D., Chief of Staff
CIO: Dawn Evans, Manager Information Technology
CHR: Christy Smiley, Director Human Resources
CNO: Kari Wilson, R.N., Vice President Clinical Services, Chief Operating Officer and Chief Nursing Officer
Web address: www.audrainmedicalcenter.com
Control: Church–operated, Nongovernment, not–for profit **Service:** General Medical and Surgical

Staffed Beds: 49 **Admissions:** 1948 **Census:** 18 **Outpatient Visits:** 142515 **Births:** 134 **Total Expense ($000):** 63019 **Payroll Expense ($000):** 22404 **Personnel:** 391

Many Facility Codes have changed. Please refer to the AHA Guide Code Chart. © 2014 AHA Guide

MILAN—Sullivan County

★ **SULLIVAN COUNTY MEMORIAL HOSPITAL (261306)**, 630 West Third Street, Zip 63556–1076; tel. 660/265–4212, (Total facility includes 14 beds in nursing home–type unit) **A**9 10 18 **F**28 29 34 40 53 57 59 64 67 68 75 77 79 87 97 107 111 114 119 127 128 130 133 147 148 **P**5 6
Primary Contact: Jerry Dover, Chief Executive Officer
COO: Amy J. Michael, Chief Operating Officer
CMO: Thomas Williams, D.O., Chief of Staff
CIO: Vern Johnson, Director Information Technology
CHR: Billie Ryals, Director Human Resources
CNO: Carol Fordyce, Director Patient Care Services
Web address: www.scmhospital.org
Control: County–Government, nonfederal **Service:** General Medical and Surgical

Staffed Beds: 39 **Admissions:** 260 **Census:** 24 **Outpatient Visits:** 17661 **Births:** 0 **Total Expense ($000):** 7290 **Payroll Expense ($000):** 3407 **Personnel:** 76

MOBERLY—Randolph County

✚ **MOBERLY REGIONAL MEDICAL CENTER (260074)**, 1515 Union Avenue, Zip 65270–9449; tel. 660/263–8400 **A**1 9 10 20 **F**3 13 15 18 20 22 26 28 29 34 35 38 39 40 44 45 46 49 50 51 53 56 57 59 64 65 70 74 75 76 77 79 80 81 85 86 87 89 93 97 98 100 103 107 108 111 114 117 118 119 127 129 130 131 132 133 135 146 147 148 **S** Community Health Systems, Inc., Franklin, TN
Primary Contact: Christian Jones, Chief Executive Officer
CFO: Tracey Matheis, Chief Financial Officer
CMO: Philip Stitzer, D.O., Chief Medical Officer
CIO: Doris Whelan, Chief Information Officer
CHR: Tim Clark, Director Human Resources
Web address: www.moberlyhospital.com
Control: Corporation, Investor–owned, for–profit **Service:** General Medical and Surgical

Staffed Beds: 94 **Admissions:** 2323 **Census:** 32 **Outpatient Visits:** 49314 **Births:** 181 **Total Expense ($000):** 52203 **Payroll Expense ($000):** 16001 **Personnel:** 293

MONETT—Barry County

☐ **COX MONETT (261329)**, 801 North Lincoln Avenue, Zip 65708–1641; tel. 417/235–3144 **A**1 9 10 18 **F**3 11 13 15 28 29 31 32 34 35 40 45 50 56 57 59 64 68 76 77 81 85 89 90 93 107 111 114 119 127 128 129 130 131 133 135 146 147 **P**6 **S** CoxHealth, Springfield, MO
Primary Contact: Genice Maroc, FACHE, President
CFO: Josh Powell, Facility Controller
CMO: Frank Romero, M.D., Vice President Medical Affairs and Chief Medical Officer
CHR: Debra Isenmann, Human Resources Generalist
CNO: Bev Eli, Chief Nursing Officer
Web address: www.coxhealth.com
Control: Other not–for–profit (including NFP Corporation) **Service:** General Medical and Surgical

Staffed Beds: 25 **Admissions:** 753 **Census:** 6 **Outpatient Visits:** 62493 **Births:** 290 **Total Expense ($000):** 29297 **Payroll Expense ($000):** 13689 **Personnel:** 241

MOUNT VERNON—Lawrence County

✚ **MISSOURI REHABILITATION CENTER (262001)**, 600 North Main Street, Zip 65712–1004; tel. 417/466–3711 **A**1 10 **F**1 3 11 28 29 30 44 50 53 57 59 64 68 70 75 77 90 91 93 96 119 129 130 135 143 146 148 **P**6 **S** University of Missouri Health Care, Columbia, MO
Primary Contact: Mike Powell, Executive Director
CFO: Amy Baker, Associate Director Finance Services
CMO: Jennie Gorham, D.O., Co–Medical Director
CIO: Tom Collier, Manager Information Systems
CHR: David Thiessen, Associate Director Support Services
CNO: Gail Getzendaner, Director of Nursing
Web address: www.muhealth.org/mrcrehab
Control: State–Government, nonfederal **Service:** Long–Term Acute Care hospital

Staffed Beds: 63 **Admissions:** 330 **Census:** 29 **Outpatient Visits:** 45958 **Births:** 0 **Total Expense ($000):** 31099 **Payroll Expense ($000):** 15909 **Personnel:** 307

MOUNTAIN VIEW—Howell County

✚ **MERCY ST. FRANCIS HOSPITAL (261335)**, 100 West Highway 60, Zip 65548–7125, tel. 417/934–7000 **A**1 9 10 18 **F**3 11 15 28 29 30 34 40 45 50 57 59 64 75 81 85 89 90 93 107 110 111 114 129 131 132 133 148 **P**6 **S** Mercy Health, Chesterfield, MO
Primary Contact: Robert Rogers, Interim President
CFO: Sherry Clouse Day, CPA, Chief Financial Officer
CMO: Barry Spoon, M.D., Chief of Staff
CHR: Tracy Smith, Director Human Resources
Web address: www.stjohns.com/aboutus/stfrancis.aspx
Control: Church–operated, Nongovernment, not–for profit **Service:** General Medical and Surgical

Staffed Beds: 20 **Admissions:** 438 **Census:** 5 **Outpatient Visits:** 22937 **Births:** 0 **Total Expense ($000):** 14956 **Payroll Expense ($000):** 6710 **Personnel:** 117

NEOSHO—Newton County

★ **FREEMAN NEOSHO HOSPITAL (261331)**, 113 West Hickory Street, Zip 64850–1705; tel. 417/455–4352 **A**9 10 18 **F**3 11 15 28 29 30 34 35 40 44 45 47 56 57 59 64 68 70 75 77 79 81 85 86 87 90 93 97 107 110 111 114 119 128 130 131 132 133 146 147 148 **P**3 **S** Freeman Health System, Joplin, MO
Primary Contact: Paula F. Baker, President and Chief Executive Officer
CFO: Steve W. Graddy, Chief Financial Officer
CMO: Rodney McFarland, M.D., Medical Director
CIO: Sue Annesser, Director Information Systems
CHR: Mary Frerer, Chief Human Resources Officer
Web address: www.freemanhealth.com
Control: Other not–for–profit (including NFP Corporation) **Service:** General Medical and Surgical

Staffed Beds: 25 **Admissions:** 1348 **Census:** 17 **Outpatient Visits:** 47641 **Births:** 0 **Total Expense ($000):** 21605 **Payroll Expense ($000):** 9328 **Personnel:** 170

NEVADA—Vernon County

HEARTLAND BEHAVIORAL HEALTH SERVICES, 1500 West Ashland Street, Zip 64772–1710; tel. 417/667–2666 **F**98 99 101 102 106 **P**6 **S** Universal Health Services, Inc., King of Prussia, PA
Primary Contact: Alyson Wysong–Harder, Chief Executive Officer
CFO: Bryan Bishop, Chief Financial Officer
CMO: Ahmad Tarar, M.D., Medical Director
CHR: Carri Compton–Ogle, Administrative Officer
CNO: Nathan Taylor, Director of Nursing
Web address: www.heartlandbehavioral.com
Control: Corporation, Investor–owned, for–profit **Service:** Psychiatric

Staffed Beds: 69 **Admissions:** 1546 **Census:** 43 **Outpatient Visits:** 0 **Births:** 0 **Total Expense ($000):** 14718 **Payroll Expense ($000):** 7257 **Personnel:** 108

✚ **NEVADA REGIONAL MEDICAL CENTER (260061)**, 800 South Ash Street, Zip 64772–3223; tel. 417/667–3355 **A**1 9 10 **F**3 11 13 15 18 26 27 28 29 30 31 32 34 35 39 40 41 45 50 54 57 59 62 63 64 65 70 74 75 76 77 78 79 81 82 84 85 86 87 89 90 91 93 94 96 98 101 102 103 104 107 110 111 114 119 127 129 130 131 132 133 135 143 144 146 148 **S** QHR, Brentwood, TN
Primary Contact: Kevin Leeper, Chief Executive Officer
CFO: Greg Shaw, Chief Financial Officer
CMO: Sean Gravely, D.O., Chief of Staff
CIO: Chris Crist, Director Information Technology
CHR: Heather Brockmeyer, Human Resource Administrative Officer
CNO: Cory Vokoun, Chief Nursing Officer
Web address: www.nrmchealth.com
Control: City–Government, nonfederal **Service:** General Medical and Surgical

Staffed Beds: 71 **Admissions:** 2421 **Census:** 29 **Outpatient Visits:** 84667 **Births:** 360 **Total Expense ($000):** 37180 **Payroll Expense ($000):** 14361 **Personnel:** 286

MO

Hospital, Medicare Provider Number, Address, Telephone, Approval, Facility, and Physician Codes, Health Care System

★ American Hospital Association (AHA) membership
☐ The Joint Commission accreditation ◇ DNV Healthcare Inc. accreditation
◯ Healthcare Facilities Accreditation Program
△ Commission on Accreditation of Rehabilitation Facilities (CARF) accreditation

NORTH KANSAS CITY—Clay County

✠ **NORTH KANSAS CITY HOSPITAL (260096)**, 2800 Clay Edwards Drive, Zip 64116–3220; tel. 816/691–2000 **A**1 2 5 9 10 **F**3 11 12 13 15 17 18 20 22 24 26 28 29 30 31 34 35 37 38 39 40 43 44 45 46 47 48 49 50 53 54 57 58 59 62 63 64 70 72 74 75 76 77 78 79 80 81 82 83 84 85 86 87 89 90 93 96 107 108 110 111 114 115 118 119 120 121 123 126 129 130 132 135 147
Primary Contact: Peggy Schmitt, President and Chief Executive Officer
COO: Jody Abbott, Senior Vice President and Chief Operating Officer
CFO: Jim McNey, Senior Vice President Finance and Chief Financial Officer
CMO: Gary L. Carter, M.D., Vice President and Chief Medical Officer
CIO: Paul Foelsch, Vice President and Chief Information Technology Officer
CHR: Beverly Johnson, Vice President Human Resources
CNO: Sarah G. Fields, R.N., Vice President Nursing
Web address: www.nkch.org
Control: City–Government, nonfederal **Service:** General Medical and Surgical

Staffed Beds: 415 **Admissions:** 19441 **Census:** 237 **Outpatient Visits:** 266074 **Births:** 1311 **Total Expense ($000):** 402093 **Payroll Expense ($000):** 141504 **Personnel:** 2536

O'FALLON—St. Charles County

✠ **PROGRESS WEST HOSPITAL (260219)**, Two Progress Point, Zip 63368–2208; tel. 636/344–1000 **A**1 9 10 **F**3 13 15 18 20 22 29 30 34 40 41 45 49 51 57 59 60 70 76 79 81 85 87 89 107 110 111 115 118 119 130 135 146 **S** BJC HealthCare, Saint Louis, MO
Primary Contact: Larry A. Tracy, Jr., FACHE, President
CFO: Glen Schweagel, Chief Financial Officer
CMO: Sean McIntosh, M.D., Chief of Staff
CHR: Michael J. Miller, Director Human Resources
CNO: Jill Skyles, R.N., Vice President and Chief Nurse Executive
Web address: www.progresswesthealthcare.org
Control: Other not–for–profit (including NFP Corporation) **Service:** General Medical and Surgical

Staffed Beds: 42 **Admissions:** 2952 **Census:** 25 **Outpatient Visits:** 45275 **Births:** 505 **Total Expense ($000):** 64785 **Payroll Expense ($000):** 21485 **Personnel:** 275

OSAGE BEACH—Camden County

✠ **LAKE REGIONAL HEALTH SYSTEM (260186)**, 54 Hospital Drive, Zip 65065–3050; tel. 573/348–8000, (Total facility includes 16 beds in nursing home–type unit) **A**1 2 9 10 **F**3 11 12 13 15 18 20 22 24 28 29 30 31 32 34 35 38 39 40 43 44 45 48 49 50 51 53 57 59 60 62 64 65 68 70 74 75 76 77 78 79 81 82 84 85 86 87 93 96 107 108 110 111 114 115 118 119 121 127 128 129 130 131 132 135 144 145 146 148 **P**6
Primary Contact: Michael E. Henze, Chief Executive Officer
COO: Kevin McRoberts, Senior Vice President of Operations
CFO: David Halsell, Senior Vice President and Chief Financial Officer
CMO: Robert Hyatt, M.D., Senior Vice President Medical Affairs
CIO: Scott Poest, Chief Information Officer
CHR: Tom Williams, Vice President Human Resources
CNO: Janice L. Dungan, Senior Vice President Clinical Services
Web address: www.lakeregional.com
Control: Other not–for–profit (including NFP Corporation) **Service:** General Medical and Surgical

Staffed Beds: 116 **Admissions:** 5588 **Census:** 66 **Outpatient Visits:** 296851 **Births:** 724 **Total Expense ($000):** 167765 **Payroll Expense ($000):** 67237 **Personnel:** 1081

PERRYVILLE—Perry County

✠ **PERRY COUNTY MEMORIAL HOSPITAL (261311)**, 434 North West Street, Zip 63775–1398; tel. 573/547–2536 **A**1 9 10 18 **F**3 7 8 11 13 15 28 29 30 31 34 35 40 44 48 51 53 54 56 57 59 62 64 66 68 75 76 77 78 79 81 85 87 89 90 92 93 97 99 100 101 102 103 104 107 111 114 117 119 129 130 131 132 133 135 143 144 145 147 148
Primary Contact: Patrick E. Carron, FACHE, President and Chief Executive Officer
COO: Lee Clinton, FACHE, Vice President Operations
CFO: Randall Wolf, Vice President Finance
CMO: Michael Steele, M.D., Chief of Staff
CIO: Ron Heuring, Director Information Systems
CHR: Christopher Wibbenmeyer, Director Human Resources
Web address: www.pchmo.org
Control: Other not–for–profit (including NFP Corporation) **Service:** General Medical and Surgical

Staffed Beds: 25 **Admissions:** 876 **Census:** 12 **Outpatient Visits:** 50094 **Births:** 142 **Total Expense ($000):** 31691 **Payroll Expense ($000):** 11507 **Personnel:** 354

PILOT KNOB—Iron County

IRON COUNTY MEDICAL CENTER (261336), 301 North Highway 21, Zip 63663–0548, Mailing Address: P.O. Box 548, Zip 63663–0548; tel. 573/546–1260 **A**9 10 18 **F**3 11 15 18 34 35 40 57 59 79 82 93 96 107 111 114 119 127 129 130 133 **P**6
Primary Contact: Terry Nichols, Chief Executive Officer
COO: Cyndi Basler, Chief Operating Officer
CFO: Justin Lattimore, Chief Financial Officer
CNO: Cindy Finley, Chief Nursing Officer
Web address: www.ironhospital.com
Control: Hospital district or authority, Government, nonfederal **Service:** General Medical and Surgical

Staffed Beds: 15 **Admissions:** 183 **Census:** 4 **Outpatient Visits:** 17875 **Births:** 0 **Total Expense ($000):** 10131 **Payroll Expense ($000):** 3048 **Personnel:** 53

POPLAR BLUFF—Butler County

✠ **BLACK RIVER MEDICAL CENTER (560227)**, (Acute Care Medical no surgery), 217 Physicians Park Drive, Zip 63901–3956, Mailing Address: 219 Physicians Park Drive, Zip 63901–3956; tel. 573/727–9080 **A**1 9 **F**3 15 29 34 40 57 59 65 80 86 107 108 110 111 115 118 119 135
Primary Contact: Christy Shawan, Chief Executive Officer
CFO: Phillip Crocker, Accounting Specialist
CMO: Christopher Pinderski, M.D., Medical Director of Emergency Room
CIO: James Hall, Information Technology Support
CHR: Angie Bolin, Executive Administrative Assistant and Human Resources Manager
CNO: E. Kay Fox, Director of Nursing
Web address: www.blackrivermed.com
Control: Other not–for–profit (including NFP Corporation) **Service:** Other specialty

Staffed Beds: 3 **Admissions:** 251 **Census:** 2 **Outpatient Visits:** 7845 **Births:** 0 **Total Expense ($000):** 11070 **Payroll Expense ($000):** 3915 **Personnel:** 75

✠ **JOHN J. PERSHING VETERANS AFFAIRS MEDICAL CENTER**, 1500 North Westwood Boulevard, Zip 63901–3318; tel. 573/686–4151, (Total facility includes 40 beds in nursing home–type unit) **A**1 **F**3 5 11 15 29 30 33 34 36 38 39 40 45 53 54 56 59 62 63 64 65 75 77 79 81 83 84 86 87 90 93 94 97 100 104 107 111 114 119 127 128 129 130 135 143 144 146 147 **S** Department of Veterans Affairs, Washington, DC
Primary Contact: Marjorie Hedstrom, Director
COO: Seth Barlage, Associate Medical Center Director
CFO: Kristy Siebert, Manager Finance
CMO: Vijayachandran Nair, M.D., Chief of Staff
CIO: Janice Vernon, Supervisory Information Technology Specialist
CHR: Genise Denton, Manager Human Resources
CNO: Elizabeth A. Smith, Director of Nursing
Web address: www.poplarbluff.va.gov
Control: Veterans Affairs, Government, federal **Service:** General Medical and Surgical

Staffed Beds: 58 **Admissions:** 1370 **Census:** 39 **Outpatient Visits:** 109481 **Births:** 0 **Total Expense ($000):** 115160 **Payroll Expense ($000):** 35443 **Personnel:** 623

✠ **POPLAR BLUFF REGIONAL MEDICAL CENTER (260119)**, (Behavior Health), 3100 Oak Grove Road, Zip 63901, Mailing Address: P.O. Box 88, Zip 63902–0088; tel. 573/776–2000, (Includes POPLAR BLUFF REGIONAL MEDICAL CENTER–SOUTH CAMPUS, 621 Pine Boulevard, tel. 573/785–7721) **A**1 2 9 10 19 20 **F**3 11 13 15 17 18 20 22 24 28 29 30 31 35 40 43 45 46 49 50 51 53 54 57 59 60 64 65 68 70 74 75 76 77 78 79 80 81 82 85 87 89 90 93 98 102 107 108 111 114 117 118 119 121 126 127 130 131 132 146 148 **S** Community Health Systems, Inc., Franklin, TN
Primary Contact: Kenneth James, Chief Executive Officer
COO: Gerald Faircloth, Chief Operating Officer
CFO: Steve Dorris, Chief Financial Officer
CMO: Steve Pu, D.O., Chief Medical Officer
CIO: Gary Dollins, Director Management Information Systems
CHR: Denise Rushin, Director Human Resources
CNO: Melissa A. Samuelson, R.N., Chief Nurse Executive
Web address: www.poplarbluffregional.com
Control: Individual, Investor–owned, for–profit **Service:** General Medical and Surgical

Staffed Beds: 241 **Admissions:** 11354 **Census:** 122 **Outpatient Visits:** 176136 **Births:** 1405 **Total Expense ($000):** 134514 **Payroll Expense ($000):** 39449 **Personnel:** 961

MO

POTOSI—Washington County

★ **WASHINGTON COUNTY MEMORIAL HOSPITAL (261308)**, 300 Health Way, Zip 63664–1420; tel. 573/438–5451 **A**9 10 18 **F**3 11 15 28 29 33 34 35 40 45 57 59 64 65 74 75 77 79 81 87 90 93 97 98 104 106 107 108 110 111 114 119 127 129 130 133 144 145 146 147 148 **P**6
Primary Contact: Leah Osbahr, Administrator
COO: Leah Osbahr, Chief Executive Officer
CFO: Debbie Pratt, Chief Financial Officer
CMO: James Weber, D.O., Chief of Staff
CIO: Jim Smith, Director Information Systems
CHR: Christy Aubuchon, Director Personnel
CNO: Beverly Williams, R.N., Chief Nursing Officer
Web address: www.wcmhosp.org
Control: County–Government, nonfederal **Service:** General Medical and Surgical

Staffed Beds: 25 **Admissions:** 875 **Census:** 12 **Outpatient Visits:** 96260 **Births:** 0 **Total Expense ($000):** 28312 **Payroll Expense ($000):** 12726 **Personnel:** 289

RICHMOND—Ray County

RAY COUNTY MEMORIAL HOSPITAL (261327), 904 Wollard Boulevard, Zip 64085–2229; tel. 816/470–5432 **A**9 10 18 **F**3 11 15 29 40 45 62 64 68 74 75 78 79 81 82 85 87 93 107 108 110 111 115 117 119 130 133 146
Primary Contact: Earl N. Sheehy, Administrator
CFO: Donald Harr, Controller
CHR: Donna Strain, Director Human Resources
Web address: www.raycountyhospital.com
Control: County–Government, nonfederal **Service:** General Medical and Surgical

Staffed Beds: 25 **Admissions:** 870 **Census:** 10 **Outpatient Visits:** 16093 **Births:** 0 **Total Expense ($000):** 19858 **Payroll Expense ($000):** 8669 **Personnel:** 211

RICHMOND HEIGHTS—St. Louis County

⊞ △ **SSM SELECT REHABILITATION HOSPITAL (263031)**, (Rehabilitation), 1027 Bellevue Avenue, 3rd Floor, Zip 63117–1851, Mailing Address: 1027 Bellevue Avenue, Zip 63117–1851; tel. 314/768–5300, (Includes SSM SELECT REHABILITATION HOSPITAL, 12380 De Paul Drive, Bridgeton, Zip 63044–2511; tel. 314/447–9700; Timothy Wadman, Chief Executive Officer) **A**1 7 10 **F**3 29 35 44 64 74 77 79 85 87 90 91 92 93 94 96 130 131 132 148 **P**6 **S** Select Medical Corporation, Mechanicsburg, PA
Primary Contact: Timothy Wadman, Chief Executive Officer
Web address: www.ssm–select.com
Control: Partnership, Investor–owned, for–profit **Service:** Rehabilitation

Staffed Beds: 95 **Admissions:** 1823 **Census:** 74 **Outpatient Visits:** 263969 **Births:** 0 **Total Expense ($000):** 71273 **Payroll Expense ($000):** 39392 **Personnel:** 607

ROLLA—Phelps County

⊞ △ **PHELPS COUNTY REGIONAL MEDICAL CENTER (260017)**, 1000 West Tenth Street, Zip 65401–2905; tel. 573/458–8899, (Total facility includes 20 beds in nursing home–type unit) **A**1 2 7 9 10 19 20 **F**3 7 8 11 13 15 17 18 20 22 26 27 28 29 30 31 34 35 39 40 45 47 48 49 51 56 57 59 60 62 63 68 70 73 74 75 76 77 78 79 81 82 84 85 86 87 89 90 93 96 98 100 101 102 103 104 107 110 111 114 115 116 117 118 119 121 127 128 129 131 132 135 143 144 146 148
Primary Contact: John R. Denbo, Chief Executive Officer
CFO: Edward Clayton, Chief Financial Officer
CMO: Donald James, D.O., Chief Medical Officer
CIO: Jeff McKune, Director Information Technology
CHR: Frank A. Lazzaro, III, Chief Human Resources Officer
CNO: Keri S. Brookshire–Heavin, Chief Nurse Executive
Web address: www.pcrmc.com
Control: County–Government, nonfederal **Service:** General Medical and Surgical

Staffed Beds: 204 **Admissions:** 6673 **Census:** 93 **Outpatient Visits:** 257172 **Births:** 891 **Total Expense ($000):** 152138 **Payroll Expense ($000):** 53186 **Personnel:** 1674

SAINT CHARLES—St. Charles County

⊞ **CENTERPOINTE HOSPITAL (264012)**, 4801 Weldon Spring Parkway, Zip 63304–9101; tel. 636/441–7300 **A**1 9 10 **F**4 5 34 35 38 44 54 87 98 99 100 101 102 103 104 105 106 130 132 143
Primary Contact: Azfar Malik, M.D., Chief Executive Officer and Chief Medical Officer
COO: Susan Mathis, R.N., Chief Operating Officer and Chief Nurse Executive
CFO: Tariq F. Malik, CPA, Acting Chief Financial Officer
CMO: Azfar Malik, M.D., Chief Executive Officer and Chief Medical Officer
CIO: Jennifer Bourn, Director Health Information Services, Performance Improvement and Medical Staff Services
CHR: Kelli White, Manager Human Resources
CNO: Susan Mathis, R.N., Chief Operating Officer and Chief Nurse Executive
Web address: www.centerpointehospital.com
Control: Corporation, Investor–owned, for–profit **Service:** Psychiatric

Staffed Beds: 151 **Admissions:** 4510 **Census:** 95 **Outpatient Visits:** 61047 **Births:** 0 **Total Expense ($000):** 37697 **Payroll Expense ($000):** 17961 **Personnel:** 366

⊞ **SELECT SPECIALTY HOSPITAL–ST. LOUIS (262013)**, 300 First Capitol Drive, Unit 1, Zip 63301–2844; tel. 636/947–5010 **A**1 9 10 **F**1 29 74 75 148 **S** Select Medical Corporation, Mechanicsburg, PA
Primary Contact: Patrice L. Komoroski, Ph.D., R.N., Chief Executive Officer
Web address: www.selectspecialtyhospitals.com/company/locations/stlouis.aspx
Control: Corporation, Investor–owned, for–profit **Service:** Long–Term Acute Care hospital

Staffed Beds: 33 **Admissions:** 409 **Census:** 30 **Outpatient Visits:** 0 **Births:** 0 **Total Expense ($000):** 17682 **Payroll Expense ($000):** 6854 **Personnel:** 111

⊞ **SSM ST. JOSEPH HEALTH CENTER (260005)**, 300 First Capitol Drive, Zip 63301–2844; tel. 636/947–5000, (Includes SSM ST. JOSEPH HEALTH CENTER – WENTZVILLE, 500 Medical Drive, Wentzville, Zip 63385–3421; tel. 636/327–1000) **A**1 2 9 10 **F**3 4 5 11 13 15 17 18 20 22 24 26 28 29 30 31 34 35 38 40 41 42 43 44 45 46 49 50 53 54 55 56 57 58 59 60 61 64 68 70 73 74 75 76 78 79 81 82 85 86 87 90 96 97 98 99 100 101 102 103 104 105 107 108 110 111 114 118 119 120 121 129 130 132 134 135 144 146 147 148 **P**6 8 **S** SSM Health, Saint Louis, MO
Primary Contact: Michael E. Bowers, President
COO: Lee Bernstein, Regional Executive Vice President and Chief Operating Officer
CFO: Karen Rewerts, System Vice President Finance
CIO: Margaret Feilner, Director Information Services
CHR: Debbie G. Walkenhorst, System Vice President Talent Management
Web address: www.ssmstjoseph.com
Control: Church–operated, Nongovernment, not–for profit **Service:** General Medical and Surgical

Staffed Beds: 331 **Admissions:** 13601 **Census:** 195 **Outpatient Visits:** 157689 **Births:** 723 **Total Expense ($000):** 205837 **Payroll Expense ($000):** 75136 **Personnel:** 1155

SAINT JOSEPH—Buchanan County

★ **HEARTLAND LONG TERM ACUTE CARE HOSPITAL (262019)**, 5325 Faraon Street, Zip 64506–3488; tel. 816/271–6000 **A**9 10 **F**1 3 29 85 130 148
Primary Contact: James Mikes, Administrator
Web address: www.heartland–health.com
Control: Other not–for–profit (including NFP Corporation) **Service:** Long–Term Acute Care hospital

Staffed Beds: 41 **Admissions:** 293 **Census:** 25 **Outpatient Visits:** 0 **Births:** 0 **Total Expense ($000):** 13335 **Payroll Expense ($000):** 3835 **Personnel:** 70

⊞ **HEARTLAND REGIONAL MEDICAL CENTER (260006)**, 5325 Faraon Street, Zip 64506–3488; tel. 816/271–6000 **A**1 2 9 10 20 **F**3 8 9 11 12 13 15 17 18 20 22 24 26 28 29 30 31 32 33 34 35 36 37 39 40 43 45 47 48 49 50 53 54 57 58 59 62 63 64 65 66 70 71 74 75 76 77 78 79 80 81 82 84 85 86 87 89 92 93 94 96 97 98 100 102 103 104 107 108 110 111 114 115 118 119 120 121 123 124 126 129 130 131 134 135 143 144 146 147 148 **P**6
Primary Contact: Samuel Mark Laney, M.D., President and Chief Executive Officer
COO: Curt Kretzinger, Chief Operating Officer
CFO: John P. Wilson, Chief Financial Officer
CIO: Joe Boyce, M.D., Chief Information Officer
CHR: Michael Pulido, Chief Administrative Officer
CNO: Carolyn Paden, Associate Administrator Surgical Services
Web address: www.heartland–health.com
Control: Other not–for–profit (including NFP Corporation) **Service:** General Medical and Surgical

Staffed Beds: 352 **Admissions:** 16792 **Census:** 197 **Outpatient Visits:** 974217 **Births:** 1604 **Total Expense ($000):** 523153 **Payroll Expense ($000):** 231915 **Personnel:** 3025

MO

Hospital, Medicare Provider Number, Address, Telephone, Approval, Facility, and Physician Codes, Health Care System

★ American Hospital Association (AHA) membership
□ The Joint Commission accreditation   ◇ DNV Healthcare Inc. accreditation
○ Healthcare Facilities Accreditation Program
△ Commission on Accreditation of Rehabilitation Facilities (CARF) accreditation

---

☐ **NORTHWEST MISSOURI PSYCHIATRIC REHABILITATION CENTER (264007)**, 3505 Frederick Avenue, Zip 64506–2914; tel. 816/387–2300 **A**1 10 **F**4 29 30 34 50 58 59 65 68 75 77 86 87 97 98 101 102 103 130 132 135 143 146 **P**6
Primary Contact: Denise Norbury, Regional Executive Officer
COO: Mary Attebury, Chief Operating Officer
CFO: Randy Riley, Fiscal and Administrative Manager
CMO: James B. Reynolds, M.D., Medical Director
CIO: Robert Curren, Western Region Chief Information Technology Officer
CHR: Mary Blakey Gorman, Director Human Resources
CNO: Pam Nold, Chief Nurse Executive
Web address: www.dmh.mo.gov/nmprc/index.htm
Control: State–Government, nonfederal **Service:** Psychiatric

Staffed Beds: 108 **Admissions:** 50 **Census:** 108 **Outpatient Visits:** 0 **Births:** 0 **Total Expense ($000):** 20741 **Payroll Expense ($000):** 10608 **Personnel:** 336

SAINT LOUIS—St. Louis City County

✠ **BARNES–JEWISH HOSPITAL (260032)**, 1 Barnes–Jewish Hospital Plaza, Zip 63110–1003; tel. 314/747–3000, (Total facility includes 120 beds in nursing home–type unit) **A**1 2 3 5 8 9 10 **F**3 4 6 8 9 11 12 13 14 15 16 17 18 20 22 24 26 28 29 30 31 34 35 36 37 38 39 40 43 44 45 46 47 48 49 50 51 52 53 54 55 56 57 58 59 60 61 63 64 65 66 67 68 69 70 71 74 75 76 77 78 79 80 81 82 84 85 86 87 89 90 91 92 93 94 95 96 97 98 100 101 102 103 104 105 107 108 109 110 111 112 114 115 116 117 118 119 120 121 122 123 124 126 128 129 130 131 132 134 135 136 137 138 139 140 141 142 143 144 145 146 147 148 **P**6 **S** BJC HealthCare, Saint Louis, MO
Primary Contact: Richard J. Liekweg, President
CFO: Mark Krieger, Vice President and Chief Financial Officer
CMO: John Lynch, M.D., Vice President and Chief Medical Officer
CIO: Jerry Vuchak, Vice President Information Systems
CHR: John Beatty, Vice President Human Resources
CNO: Coreen Vlodarchyk, R.N., Vice President, Patient Care Services and Chief Nursing Officer
Web address: www.barnesjewish.org
Control: Other not–for–profit (including NFP Corporation) **Service:** General Medical and Surgical

Staffed Beds: 1322 **Admissions:** 55752 **Census:** 920 **Outpatient Visits:** 740556 **Births:** 3053 **Total Expense ($000):** 1665690 **Payroll Expense ($000):** 535276 **Personnel:** 9299

✠ **BARNES–JEWISH WEST COUNTY HOSPITAL (260162)**, 12634 Olive Boulevard, Zip 63141–6337; tel. 314/996–8000 **A**1 3 5 9 10 **F**3 12 15 18 29 34 35 40 45 46 47 49 50 51 57 59 64 65 68 70 74 75 77 78 79 81 82 85 90 93 100 107 110 111 114 115 117 119 120 121 126 129 130 131 142 145 146 148 **S** BJC HealthCare, Saint Louis, MO
Primary Contact: Doug Black, President
CFO: Diane M. Glen, Assistant Administrator
CMO: Sam B. Bhayani, M.D., Chief Medical Officer
CIO: Jerry Vuchak, Vice President Information Systems
CNO: Yoany Finetti, R.N., Chief Nursing Officer
Web address: www.barnesjewishwestcounty.org
Control: Other not–for–profit (including NFP Corporation) **Service:** General Medical and Surgical

Staffed Beds: 77 **Admissions:** 2623 **Census:** 20 **Outpatient Visits:** 102691 **Births:** 0 **Total Expense ($000):** 99302 **Payroll Expense ($000):** 29386

✠ **CHRISTIAN HOSPITAL (260180)**, 11133 Dunn Road, Zip 63136–6119; tel. 314/653–5000 **A**1 2 9 10 **F**3 4 5 7 8 11 15 17 18 20 22 24 26 28 29 30 31 34 35 40 42 45 46 47 49 50 51 53 56 57 58 59 60 63 64 65 68 70 74 75 77 78 79 80 81 82 84 85 86 87 90 92 93 94 96 98 100 101 102 103 104 105 107 108 109 110 111 112 113 114 115 116 117 118 119 120 121 123 126 129 130 132 135 146 147 148 **P**6 **S** BJC HealthCare, Saint Louis, MO
Primary Contact: Ronald B. McMullen, President
CMO: Sebastian Rueckert, M.D., Chief Medical Officer
CIO: Michael Kelly, Vice President
CHR: Bryan Hartwick, Vice President Human Resources
CNO: Jennifer Cordia, Vice President and Chief Nursing Executive
Web address: www.christianhospital.org
Control: Other not–for–profit (including NFP Corporation) **Service:** General Medical and Surgical

Staffed Beds: 258 **Admissions:** 14648 **Census:** 207 **Outpatient Visits:** 288338 **Births:** 0 **Total Expense ($000):** 296780 **Payroll Expense ($000):** 104339 **Personnel:** 1794

✠ ○ **DES PERES HOSPITAL (260176)**, 2345 Dougherty Ferry Road, Zip 63122–3313; tel. 314/966–9100 **A**1 3 5 9 10 11 12 13 **F**3 12 15 17 18 20 22 24 26 29 30 31 34 35 36 40 44 48 49 50 54 56 57 58 59 60 64 68 69 70 74 75 77 79 81 82 85 86 87 93 107 110 111 114 119 126 130 132 135 143 146 148 **S** TENET Healthcare Corporation, Dallas, TX
Primary Contact: John A. Grah, JD, FACHE, Chief Executive Officer
COO: Benson Chacko, Chief Operating Officer
CFO: Rhonda Rogers, Chief Financial Officer
CMO: Karen Webb, M.D., Chief Medical Officer
CIO: Kay Hannon, Director Information Systems
CHR: Kathaleen Clutts, Chief Human Resources Officer
CNO: Mary Ann Hampton, R.N., Chief Nursing Officer
Web address: www.despereshospital.com
Control: Corporation, Investor–owned, for–profit **Service:** General Medical and Surgical

Staffed Beds: 143 **Admissions:** 5472 **Census:** 58 **Outpatient Visits:** 34290 **Births:** 0 **Total Expense ($000):** 116590 **Payroll Expense ($000):** 34524 **Personnel:** 570

☐ **HAWTHORN CHILDREN PSYCHIATRIC HOSPITAL (264028)**, 1901 Pennsylvania, Zip 63133–1325; tel. 314/512–7800 **A**1 10 **F**98 99 106 **P**6
Primary Contact: Laurent D. Javois, Regional Executive Officer
COO: Marcia F. Perry, Chief Operating Officer
CFO: James D. Martin, Chief Financial Officer
CMO: Joshua Calhoun, M.D., Medical Director
CHR: Donna Harris–Brekel, Director Human Resources
CNO: Melody Patterson, Chief Nurse Executive
Web address: www.dmh.missouri.gov/hcph/
Control: State–Government, nonfederal **Service:** Children's hospital psychiatric

Staffed Beds: 52 **Admissions:** 141 **Census:** 38 **Outpatient Visits:** 0 **Births:** 0 **Total Expense ($000):** 13731 **Payroll Expense ($000):** 7906 **Personnel:** 191

✠ **KINDRED HOSPITAL–ST. LOUIS (262010)**, 4930 Lindell Boulevard, Zip 63108–1510; tel. 314/361–8700, (Includes KINDRED HOSPITAL ST. LOUIS–ST. ANTHONY'S, 10018 Kennerly Road, 3rd Floor, Zip 63128; tel. 314/525–8100; Robert S. Adcock, Chief Executive Officer) **A**1 9 10 **F**1 77 85 130 148 **S** Kindred Healthcare, Louisville, KY
Primary Contact: Stephanie Bridges, Chief Executive Officer
COO: Dakota Redd, R.N., Chief Clinical Officer
CFO: Maureen Roach, Senior Chief Financial Officer
CMO: Michael Holtzman, M.D., Medical Director
CIO: Thomas C. Christman, Director Plant Operations
CHR: Cindy Sander, Coordinator Human Resources
Web address: www.kindredstlouis.com/
Control: Corporation, Investor–owned, for–profit **Service:** Long–Term Acute Care hospital

Staffed Beds: 98 **Admissions:** 338 **Census:** 50 **Outpatient Visits:** 0 **Births:** 0 **Total Expense ($000):** 29493 **Payroll Expense ($000):** 10273

✠ **KINDRED HOSPITAL–ST. LOUIS AT MERCY (264028)**, 615 South New Ballas Road, 7th Floor, Zip 63141–8221; tel. 314/567–4326 **A**1 9 10 **F**3 29 77 80 85 130 148 **S** Kindred Healthcare, Louisville, KY
Primary Contact: George Einhorn, Interim Chief Executive Officer
CFO: Paul Veillon, CPA, Chief Financial Officer
CMO: Rekha Lakshmanan, M.D., Medical Director
Web address: www.kindredstlouismercy.com
Control: Corporation, Investor–owned, for–profit **Service:** Long–Term Acute Care hospital

Staffed Beds: 54 **Admissions:** 82 **Census:** 5 **Outpatient Visits:** 0 **Births:** 0 **Total Expense ($000):** 5593 **Payroll Expense ($000):** 1934 **Personnel:** 73

MERCY CONTINUING CARE HOSPITAL See Kindred Hospital–St. Louis at Mercy

✠ **MERCY HOSPITAL ST. LOUIS (260020)**, 615 South New Ballas Road, Zip 63141–8277; tel. 314/569–6000, (Includes MERCY CHILDREN'S HOSPITAL ST. LOUIS, 615 South New Ballas Road, Zip 63141–8221; tel. 314/251–6000), (Total facility includes 120 beds in nursing home–type unit) **A**1 2 3 5 8 9 10 **F**1 3 4 5 8 11 12 13 14 15 16 17 18 19 20 22 24 25 26 28 29 30 31 32 33 34 35 36 38 39 40 41 43 45 46 47 48 49 50 51 52 53 54 55 56 57 58 59 60 61 64 66 67 68 69 70 71 72 73 74 75 76 77 78 79 80 81 82 84 85 86 87 88 89 90 92 93 94 96 97 98 99 100 101 102 103 104 105 106 107 108 110 111 114 115 116 117 118 119 120 121 123 124 126 128 129 130 131 132 134 135 143 144 146 147 148 **P**6 8 **S** Mercy Health, Chesterfield, MO
Primary Contact: Jeffrey A. Johnston, President
COO: Eric J. Eoloff, Chief Operating Officer
CFO: Cheryl Matejka, Chief Financial Officer
CMO: Paul Hintze, M.D., Vice President Medical Affairs
CIO: Eugene Roth, Vice President Information Services
CHR: Rocky Ruello, Vice President Human Resources
Web address: www.mercy.net/stlouismo
Control: Other not–for–profit (including NFP Corporation) **Service:** General Medical and Surgical

Staffed Beds: 979 **Admissions:** 39927 **Census:** 606 **Outpatient Visits:** 886963 **Births:** 7908 **Total Expense ($000):** 758460 **Payroll Expense ($000):** 288344 **Personnel:** 4653

Many Facility Codes have changed. Please refer to the AHA Guide Code Chart. © 2014 AHA Guide

☐ **METROPOLITAN ST. LOUIS PSYCHIATRIC CENTER (264025)**, 5351 Delmar, Zip 63112–3198; tel. 314/877–0500 **A**1 3 5 10 **F**11 30 98 146
Primary Contact: Laurent D. Javois, Regional Executive Officer
COO: Michael Anderson, Ph.D., Chief Operating Officer
CFO: James D. Martin, Chief Financial Officer
CMO: Roy Wilson, M.D., Medical Director
CHR: Donna Harris–Brekel, Director Human Resources
CNO: Ebony Fisher, Chief Nurse Executive
Web address: www.dmh.missouri.gov/mpc
Control: State–Government, nonfederal **Service:** Psychiatric

Staffed Beds: 50 **Admissions:** 75 **Census:** 46 **Outpatient Visits:** 0 **Births:** 0 **Total Expense ($000):** 12967 **Payroll Expense ($000):** 6585 **Personnel:** 182

⊠ **MISSOURI BAPTIST MEDICAL CENTER (260108)**, 3015 North Ballas Road, Zip 63131–2329; tel. 314/996–5000 **A**1 2 3 5 9 10 **F**3 11 13 14 15 17 18 19 20 22 24 26 29 30 31 34 35 40 41 45 46 48 49 50 51 53 54 56 57 58 59 60 61 62 63 64 65 68 70 71 72 73 74 75 76 77 78 79 81 82 83 84 85 86 87 89 90 92 93 96 100 102 107 108 110 111 114 115 117 119 120 121 123 124 126 130 131 132 145 146 147 148 **P**6 **S** BJC HealthCare, Saint Louis, MO
Primary Contact: John Antes, President
CFO: Augusto A. Noronha, Vice President Finance and Chief Financial Officer
CMO: Mitchell Botney, M.D., Vice President Medical Affairs and Chief Medical Officer
CIO: Derrick Marcum, Director Information Systems
CHR: Sandra G. Young, Vice President Human Resources
CNO: Tim Mislan, MS, Vice President and Chief Nurse Executive
Web address: www.missouribaptist.org
Control: Other not–for–profit (including NFP Corporation) **Service:** General Medical and Surgical

Staffed Beds: 463 **Admissions:** 22606 **Census:** 246 **Outpatient Visits:** 334334 **Births:** 3914 **Total Expense ($000):** 462196 **Payroll Expense ($000):** 154780 **Personnel:** 2321

⊠ **SAINT LOUIS UNIVERSITY HOSPITAL (260105)**, 3635 Vista at Grand Boulevard, Zip 63110–0250, Mailing Address: P.O. Box 15250, Zip 63110–0250; tel. 314/577–8000 **A**1 2 3 5 8 9 10 **F**3 6 7 8 9 11 14 15 17 18 20 22 24 26 28 29 30 31 34 35 36 37 38 39 40 43 44 45 46 47 48 49 50 51 55 56 57 58 59 60 61 63 64 65 66 68 70 74 75 77 78 79 81 82 84 85 86 87 90 91 92 93 94 96 97 98 100 101 102 103 104 107 108 110 111 112 113 114 115 116 117 118 119 120 121 123 124 126 129 130 131 132 135 136 138 139 141 142 146 147 148 **P**1 **S** TENET Healthcare Corporation, Dallas, TX
Primary Contact: Phillip E. Sowa, Chief Executive Officer
COO: Robert William Hoefer, FACHE, Chief Operating Officer
CFO: Raymond Alvey, Chief Financial Officer
CMO: Nirav Patel, M.D., Interim Chief Medical Officer
CIO: Patrick Brennan, Director Information System Technology
CHR: Vera W. Daniel, Chief Human Resources Officer
CNO: Russell Schroeder, Chief Nursing Officer
Web address: www.sluhospital.com
Control: Corporation, Investor–owned, for–profit **Service:** General Medical and Surgical

Staffed Beds: 356 **Admissions:** 15353 **Census:** 241 **Outpatient Visits:** 126413 **Births:** 0 **Total Expense ($000):** 408204 **Payroll Expense ($000):** 87012 **Personnel:** 1349

☐ **SHRINERS HOSPITALS FOR CHILDREN–ST. LOUIS (263304)**, 2001 South Lindbergh Boulevard, Zip 63131–3597; tel. 314/432–3600 **A**1 3 5 9 10 **F**3 29 34 57 59 64 65 74 75 79 81 85 86 87 89 93 94 97 130 131 132 146 148 **S** Shriners Hospitals for Children, Tampa, FL
Primary Contact: John Gloss, FACHE, Administrator
CFO: Sandra K. Lawson, Interim Director Fiscal Services
CMO: Perry L. Schoenecker, M.D., Chief of Staff
CIO: Jeanne Hall, Director Information Systems
CHR: Mark Venable, Interim Director Human Resources
Web address: www.shrinershospitalsforchildren.org/Hospitals/Locations/Stlouis.aspx
Control: Other not–for–profit (including NFP Corporation) **Service:** Children's orthopedic

Staffed Beds: 42 **Admissions:** 400 **Census:** 6 **Outpatient Visits:** 9690 **Births:** 0 **Total Expense ($000):** 29521 **Payroll Expense ($000):** 10436 **Personnel:** 192

★ **SSM CARDINAL GLENNON CHILDREN'S MEDICAL CENTER (269807)**, 1465 South Grand Boulevard, Zip 63104–1095; tel. 314/577–5600 **A**3 5 9 10 **F**3 8 11 19 21 23 25 27 29 30 31 32 34 35 38 39 40 41 43 44 45 46 47 48 49 50 51 54 55 57 59 60 61 64 66 68 72 73 74 75 77 78 79 80 81 82 84 85 86 87 88 89 90 93 94 97 99 100 101 102 104 107 111 114 115 119 127 129 130 131 132 134 136 137 138 139 141 142 146 148 **P**6 8 **S** SSM Health, Saint Louis, MO
Primary Contact: Kathleen R. Becker, M.P.H., JD, Interim Chief Executive Officer
CFO: Karen Rewerts, Regional Vice President Finance and Chief Financial Officer
CMO: John Peter, M.D., Vice President Medical Affairs
CIO: Michael Paasch, Regional Vice President and Chief Information Officer
CHR: Debbie G. Walkenhorst, Network Vice President
Web address: www.cardinalglennon.com
Control: Church–operated, Nongovernment, not–for profit **Service:** Children's general

Staffed Beds: 176 **Admissions:** 6764 **Census:** 126 **Outpatient Visits:** 195719 **Births:** 0 **Total Expense ($000):** 284320 **Payroll Expense ($000):** 91309 **Personnel:** 1497

⊠ **SSM ST. MARY'S HEALTH CENTER (260091)**, 6420 Clayton Road, Zip 63117–1811; tel. 314/768–8000 **A**1 2 5 9 10 **F**3 4 13 15 17 18 20 22 24 26 28 29 30 31 34 35 37 38 40 44 45 46 49 50 51 52 55 56 57 58 59 60 61 64 66 70 72 73 74 75 76 78 79 81 82 84 85 86 87 97 98 100 101 102 103 104 105 107 108 110 111 114 115 119 120 121 129 130 132 135 143 144 146 147 148 **P**6 8 **S** SSM Health, Saint Louis, MO
Primary Contact: Kathleen R. Becker, M.P.H., JD, President
CFO: Jo Bertram, Vice President Finance
CMO: Darren E. Wethers, M.D., President Medical Staff
CIO: Robert Curran, Director Health Information Management
Web address: www.stmarys–stlouis.com
Control: Church–operated, Nongovernment, not–for profit **Service:** General Medical and Surgical

Staffed Beds: 381 **Admissions:** 19194 **Census:** 266 **Outpatient Visits:** 195451 **Births:** 3380 **Total Expense ($000):** 300849 **Payroll Expense ($000):** 107466 **Personnel:** 1709

☐ **ST. ALEXIUS HOSPITAL – BROADWAY CAMPUS (260210)**, 3933 South Broadway, Zip 63118–4601; tel. 314/865–7000, (Includes SOUTHPOINTE HOSPITAL, 2639 Miami Street, Zip 63118–3929; tel. 314/772–1456; ST. ALEXIUS HOSPITAL – FOREST PARK CAMPUS, 6150 Oakland Avenue, Zip 63139–3215; tel. 314/768–3000; Michael J. Motte, Chief Executive Officer) **A**1 6 9 10 **F**3 12 15 20 29 30 35 38 39 40 56 57 59 60 68 70 74 77 78 79 81 86 87 98 101 102 103 104 107 108 111 118 119 130 143 146 148 **P**6 **S** Success Healthcare, Boca Raton, FL
Primary Contact: Michael J. Motte, Chief Executive Officer
CFO: Matthew Brandt, Chief Financial Officer
Web address: www.stalexiushospital.com
Control: Corporation, Investor–owned, for–profit **Service:** General Medical and Surgical

Staffed Beds: 189 **Admissions:** 4575 **Census:** 99 **Outpatient Visits:** 30784 **Births:** 0 **Total Expense ($000):** 63902 **Payroll Expense ($000):** 32483 **Personnel:** 678

⊠ △ **ST. ANTHONY'S MEDICAL CENTER (260077)**, 10010 Kennerly Road, Zip 63128–2106; tel. 314/525–1000 **A**1 2 7 9 10 **F**3 4 5 8 11 13 15 17 18 20 22 24 26 28 29 30 31 34 35 36 38 40 41 42 43 47 48 49 50 51 53 54 56 57 59 60 61 62 63 64 65 68 69 70 73 74 75 76 77 78 79 80 81 82 84 85 86 87 89 90 91 92 93 94 95 96 97 98 99 100 101 102 103 104 105 107 108 110 111 114 115 118 119 120 121 122 123 124 126 129 130 131 132 143 144 146 147 148 **P**6
Primary Contact: David Sindelar, Chairman of the Board
COO: Christopher Bowe, M.D., Chief Operating Officer
CFO: Kenneth Venuto, Chief Financial Officer
CMO: David Morton, M.D., Chief Medical Officer
CIO: Jim Weldon, Chief Information Officer
CHR: Edward Carthew, Chief Human Resources Officer
CNO: Beverly Bokovitz, R.N., Chief Nursing Officer
Web address: www.stanthonysmedcenter.com
Control: Other not–for–profit (including NFP Corporation) **Service:** General Medical and Surgical

Staffed Beds: 569 **Admissions:** 28152 **Census:** 335 **Outpatient Visits:** 677406 **Births:** 1332 **Total Expense ($000):** 445213 **Payroll Expense ($000):** 203715 **Personnel:** 3137

ST. JOHN'S MERCY CHILDREN'S HOSPITAL See Mercy Children's Hospital St. Louis

ST. JOHN'S MERCY MEDICAL CENTER See Mercy Hospital St. Louis

MO

Hospital, Medicare Provider Number, Address, Telephone, Approval, Facility, and Physician Codes, Health Care System

★ American Hospital Association (AHA) membership
☐ The Joint Commission accreditation   ◇ DNV Healthcare Inc. accreditation
○ Healthcare Facilities Accreditation Program
△ Commission on Accreditation of Rehabilitation Facilities (CARF) accreditation

⊞ △ ST. LOUIS CHILDREN'S HOSPITAL (263301), One Children's Place, Zip 63110–1002; tel. 314/454–6000 **A**1 3 5 7 8 9 10 **F**5 7 11 16 17 19 20 21 22 23 25 26 27 29 30 31 32 34 35 38 39 40 41 42 43 44 45 46 47 48 49 50 54 57 58 59 60 61 62 63 64 65 68 71 72 74 75 77 78 79 81 82 83 84 85 86 87 88 89 90 92 93 96 99 100 101 102 104 107 108 109 111 112 114 115 119 129 130 131 132 134 135 136 137 138 139 140 141 142 143 144 145 146 148 **S** BJC HealthCare, Saint Louis, MO
Primary Contact: Joan Magruder, President
CFO: Michele McKee, Vice President and Chief Financial Officer
CMO: F. Sessions Cole, M.D., Chief Medical Officer
Web address: www.stlouischildrens.org
Control: Other not–for–profit (including NFP Corporation) **Service:** Children's general

Staffed Beds: 264 **Admissions:** 10542 **Census:** 209 **Outpatient Visits:** 158908 **Births:** 0 **Total Expense ($000):** 543182 **Payroll Expense ($000):** 162776 **Personnel:** 2542

□ ST. LOUIS PSYCHIATRIC REHABILITATION CENTER (264010), 5300 Arsenal Street, Zip 63139–1463; tel. 314/877–6500 **A**1 10 **F**11 30 39 65 68 75 86 87 98 100 101 106 130 143 146
Primary Contact: Laurent D. Javois, Regional Executive Officer
COO: Felix T. Vincenz, Ph.D., Chief Operating Officer
CFO: James D. Martin, Chief Financial Officer
CMO: Roy Wilson, M.D., Medical Director
CHR: Donna Harris–Brekel, Director Human Resources
CNO: Terra Buzzanga, Chief Nurse Executive
Web address: www.dmh.missouri.gov
Control: State–Government, nonfederal **Service:** Psychiatric

Staffed Beds: 180 **Admissions:** 27 **Census:** 179 **Outpatient Visits:** 0 **Births:** 0 **Total Expense ($000):** 36580 **Payroll Expense ($000):** 17551 **Personnel:** 529

□ ST. LOUIS REGIONAL PSYCHIATRIC STABILIZATION CENTER (264029), 5355 Delmar Boulevard, Zip 63112–3146; tel. 314/932–7110 **A**1 10 **F**29 30 98 119 130 **P**5
Primary Contact: John M. Eiler, President
Web address: www.stlpsc.org
Control: Other not–for–profit (including NFP Corporation) **Service:** Psychiatric

Staffed Beds: 25 **Admissions:** 1545 **Census:** 20 **Outpatient Visits:** 0 **Births:** 0 **Total Expense ($000):** 6964 **Payroll Expense ($000):** 4131 **Personnel:** 73

⊞ △ THE REHABILITATION INSTITUTE OF ST. LOUIS (263028), 4455 Duncan Avenue, Zip 63110–1111; tel. 314/658–3800 **A**1 7 9 10 **F**29 44 56 58 64 68 74 75 79 82 87 90 91 93 94 100 130 132 143 146 148 **S** HEALTHSOUTH Corporation, Birmingham, AL
Primary Contact: Tara Diebling, Chief Executive Officer
CFO: Tara Diebling, Chief Executive Officer
CMO: David Carr, M.D., Physician Medical Director
CHR: Heather Savage, Director Human Resources
CNO: Angelina Sherman, R.N., Chief Nursing Officer
Web address: www.rehabinstitutestl.com
Control: Partnership, Investor–owned, for–profit **Service:** Rehabilitation

Staffed Beds: 96 **Admissions:** 2009 **Census:** 81 **Outpatient Visits:** 40126 **Births:** 0 **Total Expense ($000):** 35419 **Payroll Expense ($000):** 17513 **Personnel:** 287

⊞ △ VETERANS AFFAIRS ST. LOUIS HEALTH CARE SYSTEM, 915 North Grand, Zip 63106–1621; tel. 314/652–4100, (Nonreporting) **A**1 3 5 7 **S** Department of Veterans Affairs, Washington, DC
Primary Contact: Marc Magill, Acting Director
COO: Keith D. Repko, Associate Medical Center Director
CFO: Karen Westerheide, Chief Financial Officer
CIO: Steve Warmbold, Director Information Management Service Line
CHR: Marie Lewis, Human Resources Liaison
CNO: Richard Holt, R.N., Associate Director Patient Care Services
Web address: www.stlouis.va.gov/
Control: Veterans Affairs, Government, federal **Service:** General Medical and Surgical

Staffed Beds: 344

⊞ BARNES–JEWISH ST. PETERS HOSPITAL (260191), 10 Hospital Drive, Zip 63376–1659; tel. 636/916–9000 **A**1 5 9 10 **F**3 8 11 13 15 18 20 22 28 29 30 31 34 35 40 41 49 57 59 64 70 75 76 77 78 79 81 85 86 87 90 93 107 108 110 111 114 115 118 119 120 121 123 124 129 130 132 135 146 147 148 **S** BJC HealthCare, Saint Louis, MO
Primary Contact: Larry A. Tracy, Jr., FACHE, President
COO: Ann Abad, Vice President Operations
CFO: Glen Schweagel, Vice President Finance
CMO: Daniel Bergmann, M.D., Chief Medical Officer
CIO: Cindy Gross, Assistant Administrator
CHR: Mike Miller, Director Human Resources
CNO: Jill Skyles, R.N., Vice President and Chief Nursing Officer
Web address: www.bjsph.org/
Control: Other not–for–profit (including NFP Corporation) **Service:** General Medical and Surgical

Staffed Beds: 113 **Admissions:** 5541 **Census:** 61 **Outpatient Visits:** 90967 **Births:** 436 **Total Expense ($000):** 119376 **Payroll Expense ($000):** 38940 **Personnel:** 559

★ SALEM MEMORIAL DISTRICT HOSPITAL (261318), Highway 72 North, Zip 65560–0774, Mailing Address: P.O. Box 774, Zip 65560–0774; tel. 573/729–6626, (Total facility includes 18 beds in nursing home–type unit) **A**9 10 18 **F**3 7 11 29 30 34 40 59 60 62 67 75 81 85 87 89 107 115 119 127 128 130 133 135 146
Primary Contact: Dennis P. Pryor, Administrator
CFO: Becky Cunningham, Controller
CMO: John Demorlis, M.D., Chief Medical Staff
CHR: Jodie Gorman, Director Human Resources
Web address: www.smdh.net
Control: Hospital district or authority, Government, nonfederal **Service:** General Medical and Surgical

Staffed Beds: 43 **Admissions:** 665 **Census:** 26 **Outpatient Visits:** 31221 **Births:** 0 **Total Expense ($000):** 19079 **Payroll Expense ($000):** 7621 **Personnel:** 177

⊞ BOTHWELL REGIONAL HEALTH CENTER (260009), 601 East 14th Street, Zip 65301–5972, Mailing Address: P.O. Box 1706, Zip 65302–1706; tel. 660/826–8833, (Total facility includes 10 beds in nursing home–type unit) **A**1 9 10 19 20 **F**3 9 11 12 13 14 15 18 20 22 28 29 30 31 34 35 39 40 51 54 56 57 59 60 62 63 64 65 68 70 73 74 75 76 77 78 79 80 81 82 84 85 86 87 89 92 93 107 108 110 111 114 115 116 117 118 119 120 121 123 124 127 128 129 130 131 132 135 146 147 148
Primary Contact: John M. Dawes, FACHE, Chief Executive Officer
COO: Mark I. Hirshberg, Chief Operating Officer
CFO: James A. Robertson, Jr., Chief Financial Officer
CIO: Tom Fairfax, Director Information Systems
CHR: Deb Clemmer, Vice President Human Resources
CNO: Regina W. Crow, R.N., Chief Nursing Officer
Web address: www.brhc.org
Control: City–Government, nonfederal **Service:** General Medical and Surgical

Staffed Beds: 132 **Admissions:** 5295 **Census:** 57 **Outpatient Visits:** 127547 **Births:** 569 **Total Expense ($000):** 99448 **Payroll Expense ($000):** 38108 **Personnel:** 723

□ MISSOURI DELTA MEDICAL CENTER (260113), 1008 North Main Street, Zip 63801–5044; tel. 573/471–1600 **A**1 9 10 19 20 **F**3 11 13 15 18 28 29 30 31 32 34 35 39 40 44 50 51 53 54 56 57 59 62 64 68 70 74 75 76 77 78 79 81 82 84 85 86 87 89 90 93 97 98 103 107 108 109 110 111 115 116 117 118 119 127 129 130 131 132 144 146 147 148 **P**6
Primary Contact: Jason Schrumpf, President
CFO: Jon Branstetter, Vice President Finance
Web address: www.missouridelta.com
Control: Other not–for–profit (including NFP Corporation) **Service:** General Medical and Surgical

Staffed Beds: 110 **Admissions:** 4179 **Census:** 55 **Outpatient Visits:** 216212 **Births:** 469 **Total Expense ($000):** 91003 **Payroll Expense ($000):** 42146 **Personnel:** 783

MO

Many Facility Codes have changed. Please refer to the AHA Guide Code Chart. © 2014 AHA Guide

SPRINGFIELD—Greene County

☒ △ **COX MEDICAL CENTERS (260040)**, 1423 North Jefferson Street, Zip 65802–1988; tel. 417/269–3000, (Includes COX MEDICAL CENTER NORTH, 1423 North Jefferson Avenue, Zip 65802; tel. 417/269–3000; COX MEDICAL CENTER SOUTH, 3801 South National Avenue, Zip 65807; tel. 417/269–6000) **A**1 2 3 5 7 9 10 **F**3 4 5 7 11 12 13 15 17 18 19 20 22 24 26 28 29 30 31 32 34 35 38 39 40 42 43 44 45 46 47 49 50 51 52 53 54 55 56 57 58 59 60 61 62 64 65 68 69 70 71 72 74 75 76 77 78 79 80 81 82 84 85 86 87 88 89 90 92 93 95 96 97 98 99 100 101 102 103 104 107 108 110 111 114 115 117 118 119 120 121 124 126 127 128 129 130 131 132 134 135 143 144 146 147 148 **P**3 6 **S** CoxHealth, Springfield, MO
Primary Contact: Steven D. Edwards, President and Chief Executive Officer
CFO: Jacob McWay, Senior Vice President and Chief Financial Officer
CMO: Frank Romero, M.D., Chief Medical Officer
CIO: Bruce Robison, Vice President and Chief Information Officer
CHR: John Hursh, Vice President Human Resources
CNO: Karen Kramer, R.N., Vice President and System Chief Nursing Officer
Web address: www.coxhealth.com
Control: Other not–for–profit (including NFP Corporation) **Service:** General Medical and Surgical

Staffed Beds: 659 **Admissions:** 32321 **Census:** 435 **Outpatient Visits:** 1358563 **Births:** 3220 **Total Expense ($000):** 890807 **Payroll Expense ($000):** 325128 **Personnel:** 6232

☐ **LAKELAND BEHAVIORAL HEALTH SYSTEM (264024)**, 440 South Market Street, Zip 65806–2026; tel. 417/865–5581 **A**1 10 **F**98 99 103 106 130 **S** Acadia Healthcare Company, Inc., Franklin, TN
Primary Contact: Nathan Duncan, Chief Executive Officer
COO: Randy Fox, Director Performance Improvement and Risk Management
CFO: Rick Crump, Chief Financial Officer
CMO: Richard Aiken, M.D., Medical Director
CIO: Brad Strothkamp, Chief Information Systems
CHR: Dave England, Director Human Resources
Web address: www.lakeland–hospital.com
Control: Corporation, Investor–owned, for–profit **Service:** Psychiatric

Staffed Beds: 122 **Admissions:** 1002 **Census:** 90 **Outpatient Visits:** 0 **Births:** 0 **Total Expense ($000):** 19814 **Payroll Expense ($000):** 11216 **Personnel:** 314

☒ △ **MERCY HOSPITAL SPRINGFIELD (260065)**, 1235 East Cherokee Street, Zip 65804–2263; tel. 417/820–2000, (Includes MERCY CHILDREN'S HOSPITAL SPRINGFIELD, 1235 East Cherokee Street, Zip 65804–2203; tel. 417/820–2000; MERCY ORTHOPEDIC HOSPITAL SPRINGFIELD, 3050 East Riverbluff Boulevard, Ozark, Zip 65721; tel. 417/820–5611; Robert Steele, M.D., President), (Total facility includes 25 beds in nursing home–type unit) **A**1 2 3 5 7 9 10 **F**3 5 6 7 8 9 11 12 13 14 15 16 17 18 19 20 21 22 24 25 26 28 29 30 31 32 34 35 36 37 38 39 40 43 44 45 46 47 48 49 50 51 53 54 55 56 57 58 59 60 61 62 63 64 65 66 67 68 70 71 72 73 74 75 76 77 78 79 81 82 84 85 86 87 88 89 90 91 92 93 94 96 97 98 99 100 101 102 103 104 107 108 110 111 114 115 116 117 118 119 120 121 123 124 126 127 128 129 130 131 132 134 135 143 144 145 146 147 148 **P**6 8 **S** Mercy Health, Chesterfield, MO
Primary Contact: Jon D. Swope, Interim President
COO: Jay Guffey, Senior Vice President and Chief Operating Officer
CFO: Scott Reynolds, Vice President Finance
CMO: Allan Allphin, M.D., Chief of Staff
CIO: Lori Sturgill, Vice President Business Partnership
CHR: Tanya Maricn, Interim Vice President Human Resources
CNO: Lisa Person, MSN, Vice President and Chief Nursing Officer
Web address: www.mercy.net/springfieldmo
Control: Church–operated, Nongovernment, not–for profit **Service:** General Medical and Surgical

Staffed Beds: 660 **Admissions:** 36408 **Census:** 479 **Outpatient Visits:** 598448 **Births:** 3075 **Total Expense ($000):** 842115 **Payroll Expense ($000):** 252671 **Personnel:** 8125

MERCY REHABILITION HOSPITAL SPRINGFIELD (263032), 5904 South Southwood Road, Zip 65804–5234; tel. 417/227–9000, (Nonreporting) **S** Centerre Healthcare, Brentwood, TN
Primary Contact: Duke Saldivar, FACHE, Chief Executive Officer
CFO: Melissa Campbell, Controller
CMO: Hollis Bell, M.D., Medical Director
CHR: Sarah Eiffert, Director Human Resources
CNO: Jennifer Friedline, R.N., Director of Nursing
Web address: www.mercy.net
Control: Partnership, Investor–owned, for–profit **Service:** Rehabilitation

Staffed Beds: 60

○ **OZARKS COMMUNITY HOSPITAL (260207)**, 2828 North National, Zip 65803–4306; tel. 417/837–4000 **A**9 10 11 **F**3 29 40 45 50 54 59 65 68 74 75 77 78 79 81 82 85 86 87 89 90 93 97 98 100 104 107 108 111 114 119 127 129 130 143 147 148 **P**6
Primary Contact: Paul Taylor, Chief Executive Officer
CFO: Misty Hampshire, Chief Financial Officer
Web address: www.ochonline.com
Control: Corporation, Investor–owned, for–profit **Service:** General Medical and Surgical

Staffed Beds: 21 **Admissions:** 882 **Census:** 14 **Outpatient Visits:** 236111 **Births:** 0 **Total Expense ($000):** 50262 **Payroll Expense ($000):** 14497 **Personnel:** 565

☒ **SELECT SPECIALTY HOSPITAL–SPRINGFIELD (262017)**, 1630 East Primrose Street, Zip 65804–7929; tel. 417/885–4700 **A**1 10 **F**1 3 29 45 85 107 114 148 **S** Select Medical Corporation, Mechanicsburg, PA
Primary Contact: Julie De Jean, Chief Executive Officer
CHR: Tonya Eddington, Coordinator Human Resources
Web address: www.selectspecialtyhospitals.com/company/locations/springfield.aspx
Control: Corporation, Investor–owned, for–profit **Service:** Long–Term Acute Care hospital

Staffed Beds: 44 **Admissions:** 562 **Census:** 39 **Outpatient Visits:** 0 **Births:** 0 **Total Expense ($000):** 20936 **Payroll Expense ($000):** 7513 **Personnel:** 164

STE. GENEVIEVE—Ste. Genevieve County

★ **STE. GENEVIEVE COUNTY MEMORIAL HOSPITAL (261330)**, 800 Suite Genevieve Drive, Zip 63670–1434; tel. 573/883–2751 **A**10 18 **F**3 11 13 15 18 28 29 31 34 35 39 40 50 53 56 57 59 62 64 65 68 75 76 77 78 79 81 82 85 86 87 89 92 93 107 110 111 115 119 124 127 129 130 131 132 133 135 146 147 148 **P**6
Primary Contact: Thomas Keim, Chief Executive Officer
CFO: Susan Eckenfels, Chief Financial Officer
CMO: Joseph Sharlow, M.D.. Chief of Staff
CHR: Sarah Jo Kelley, Director Human Resources
CNO: Rita Brumfield, R.N., Chief Nursing Officer
Web address: www.stegenevievehospital.org
Control: County–Government, nonfederal **Service:** General Medical and Surgical

Staffed Beds: 25 **Admissions:** 1016 **Census:** 10 **Outpatient Visits:** 99828 **Births:** 116 **Total Expense ($000):** 35491 **Payroll Expense ($000):** 14840 **Personnel:** 300

SULLIVAN—Crawford County

★ **MISSOURI BAPTIST SULLIVAN HOSPITAL (261337)**, 751 Sappington Bridge Road, Zip 63080–2354; tel. 573/468–4186 **A**9 10 18 **F**3 4 7 11 13 15 28 29 30 31 34 35 40 53 56 57 59 63 64 65 70 75 76 77 78 79 81 82 83 84 85 86 87 89 90 93 97 98 102 103 104 107 111 115 119 127 129 130 131 132 133 146 **S** BJC HealthCare, Saint Louis, MO
Primary Contact: Tony Schwarm, President
CFO: Kim Lubbring, Director Financial Services
CMO: Thomas Jackson, M.D., Chief of Staff
CHR: Kathleen Reed, Manager Human Resources
CNO: Carmen J. Bartolotta, Chief Nursing Officer
Web address: www.missouribaptistsullivan.org
Control: Other not–for–profit (including NFP Corporation) **Service:** General Medical and Surgical

Staffed Beds: 35 **Admissions:** 1764 **Census:** 20 **Outpatient Visits:** 97037 **Births:** 294 **Total Expense ($000):** 46415 **Payroll Expense ($000):** 17075 **Personnel:** 348

SWEET SPRINGS—Saline County

I–70 COMMUNITY HOSPITAL (261334), 105 Hospital Drive, Zip 65351–2229; tel. 660/335–4700 **A**9 10 18 **F**3 11 29 34 35 40 45 59 64 65 68 75 83 85 87 89 90 93 102 107 111 114 119 127 128 133 143 148 **S** Rural Community Hospitals of America, Kansas City, MO
Primary Contact: Julie Davenport, Chief Executive Officer
CFO: John Ross, Chief Financial Officer
CMO: Deborah Herrmann, M.D., Chief of Staff
CIO: Diane Swift, Director Medical Records
CHR: Diane Steinkuhler, Administrative Assistant Human Resources
CNO: Geri Fuhrman, Chief Nursing Officer
Web address: www.i70medcenter.com
Control: Corporation, Investor–owned, for–profit **Service:** General Medical and Surgical

Staffed Beds: 15 **Admissions:** 220 **Census:** 3 **Outpatient Visits:** 14234 **Births:** 0 **Total Expense ($000):** 10596 **Payroll Expense ($000):** 3210 **Personnel:** 59

MO

Hospital, Medicare Provider Number, Address, Telephone, Approval, Facility, and Physician Codes, Health Care System

★ American Hospital Association (AHA) membership
☐ The Joint Commission accreditation   ◇ DNV Healthcare Inc. accreditation
○ Healthcare Facilities Accreditation Program
△ Commission on Accreditation of Rehabilitation Facilities (CARF) accreditation

TRENTON—Grundy County

★ **WRIGHT MEMORIAL HOSPITAL (261309)**, 191 Iowa Boulevard,
Zip 64683–8343; tel. 660/358–5700 **A**9 10 18 **F**3 11 13 15 28 29 30 31 34
35 40 45 50 57 59 64 68 75 76 77 78 79 81 82 84 85 87 89 90 93 102
104 107 108 111 115 119 127 129 130 133 146 148 **P**1 **S** Saint Luke's
Health System, Kansas City, MO
Primary Contact: Gary W. Jordan, FACHE, Chief Executive Officer
CFO: Leslie Reed, Chief Financial Officer
CMO: Gerald C. Zabielski, M.D., Chief Medical Staff
CHR: Jenny Donovan, Director Human Resources
Web address: www.saintlukeshealthsystem.org
Control: Other not–for–profit (including NFP Corporation) **Service:** General
Medical and Surgical

Staffed Beds: 25 **Admissions:** 774 **Census:** 9 **Outpatient Visits:** 64524
Births: 219 **Total Expense ($000):** 25322 **Payroll Expense ($000):** 9139
Personnel: 171

TROY—Lincoln County

☐ **LINCOLN COUNTY MEDICAL CENTER (261319)**, 1000 East Cherry Street,
Zip 63379–1513; tel. 636/528–8551 **A**1 9 10 18 **F**3 11 15 17 18 28 29 30
34 35 40 44 45 50 51 57 59 62 64 65 68 70 75 77 79 81 85 86 87 89 90
93 104 107 110 111 113 114 119 127 129 130 131 132 133 135 144 146
148 **P**6
Primary Contact: Patrick G. Bira, FACHE, JD, Chief Executive Officer
CFO: Mark Thorn, FACHE, Chief Financial Officer
CIO: Travis Boyd, Director Information Technology
CHR: Mary Kay Kunza, Manager Human Resources
CNO: Becky O'Neal, R.N., Interim Chief Nursing Officer
Web address: www.lcmctroy.com
Control: County–Government, nonfederal **Service:** General Medical and Surgical

Staffed Beds: 25 **Admissions:** 944 **Census:** 11 **Outpatient Visits:** 74935
Births: 0 **Total Expense ($000):** 37346 **Payroll Expense ($000):** 16376
Personnel: 292

UNIONVILLE—Putnam County

PUTNAM COUNTY MEMORIAL HOSPITAL (261305), 1926 Oak Street,
Zip 63565–1180, Mailing Address: P.O. Box 389, Zip 63565–0389;
tel. 660/947–2411 **A**9 10 18 **F**3 15 28 29 34 35 40 45 50 57 59 64 65 75
77 81 85 87 89 90 93 97 104 107 111 114 119 127 128 129 130 133 **P**5
Primary Contact: Cindy Cummings, Chief Executive Officer
COO: Jerry Cummings, Chief Operating Officer
CFO: Doug Wismer, Chief Financial Officer
CMO: Dawn Ann Fairley, M.D., Chief of Staff
CHR: Debbie Douglas, Director Human Resources
CNO: Gayle Pickens, Chief Nursing Officer
Web address: www.pcmhosp.com
Control: County–Government, nonfederal **Service:** General Medical and Surgical

Staffed Beds: 15 **Admissions:** 179 **Census:** 3 **Outpatient Visits:** 16277
Births: 0 **Total Expense ($000):** 9175 **Payroll Expense ($000):** 2972
Personnel: 118

WARRENSBURG—Johnson County

✠ **WESTERN MISSOURI MEDICAL CENTER (260097)**, 403 Burkarth Road,
Zip 64093–3101; tel. 660/747–2500 **A**1 9 10 20 **F**3 8 11 12 13 15 17 18 28
29 30 31 32 34 35 40 45 47 57 59 61 64 65 68 70 75 76 77 78 79 81 82
85 89 90 93 102 107 108 110 111 115 118 119 127 129 130 131 132 133
135 146 147 148 **P**6
Primary Contact: Susan M. Stiles, President and Chief Executive Officer
COO: Michael L. Gasparini, Vice President Clinical Services and Chief Operating
Officer
CFO: Terri Bradley, CPA, Vice President Financial Services and Chief Financial
Officer
CIO: Bill Ladd, Director Information Services
CHR: Dennis Long, Director Human Resources
CNO: Darinda Reberry, Chief Nursing Officer
Web address: www.wmmc.com
Control: County–Government, nonfederal **Service:** General Medical and Surgical

Staffed Beds: 72 **Admissions:** 3027 **Census:** 28 **Outpatient Visits:** 131291
Births: 720 **Total Expense ($000):** 75629 **Payroll Expense ($000):** 27280
Personnel: 478

WASHINGTON—Franklin County

✠ **MERCY HOSPITAL WASHINGTON (260052)**, 901 East Fifth Street,
Zip 63090–3127; tel. 636/239–8000 **A**1 9 10 **F**3 4 8 11 12 13 14 15 17 18
20 22 28 29 30 31 32 34 35 39 40 43 46 48 49 50 51 52 53 57 59 61 64
66 68 69 70 73 75 76 77 78 79 80 81 82 84 85 87 89 90 93 94 96 97 99
100 101 104 107 108 110 111 114 116 117 118 119 120 121 127 129 130
131 132 134 135 144 146 147 148 **P**6 8 **S** Mercy Health, Chesterfield, MO
Primary Contact: Terri L. McLain, FACHE, President
COO: Joan Frost, R.N., Chief Operating Officer
CFO: Cheryl Matejka, Chief Financial Officer
CMO: Thomas Riechers, M.D., Chief Medical Staff
CIO: Michael McCreary, Chief of Services
CHR: Barbara Grayson, Vice President Human Resources
CNO: Stacy Blankenship, Chief Nursing Officer
Web address: www.mercy.net
Control: Other not–for–profit (including NFP Corporation) **Service:** General
Medical and Surgical

Staffed Beds: 187 **Admissions:** 6484 **Census:** 57 **Outpatient Visits:** 277104
Births: 855 **Total Expense ($000):** 132900 **Payroll Expense ($000):** 52071
Personnel: 750

WENTZVILLE—St. Charles County

SSM ST. JOSEPH HEALTH CENTER – WENTZVILLE See SSM St. Joseph
Health Center, Saint Charles

WEST PLAINS—Howell County

✠ **OZARKS MEDICAL CENTER (260078)**, 1100 Kentucky Avenue,
Zip 65775–2029, Mailing Address: P.O. Box 1100, Zip 65775–1100;
tel. 417/256–9111 **A**1 9 10 19 20 **F**2 3 5 11 13 15 17 18 20 22 24 28 29 30
31 34 38 40 44 45 49 50 57 59 61 62 63 64 68 70 74 75 76 77 78 79 81
82 84 85 86 87 89 90 91 93 94 98 99 100 101 102 103 104 107 108 110
111 115 118 119 120 121 127 129 130 131 132 135 144 145 146 147
148 **P**8
Primary Contact: Thomas Keller, President and Chief Executive Officer
COO: Jeanne M. Looper, Chief Operating Officer
CFO: Kim Thompson, Vice President and Chief Financial Officer
CMO: Edward R. Henegar, D.O., Vice President Medical Affairs
CIO: Edward Boys, Chief Information Officer
CHR: Greg Shannon, Director Human Resources
CNO: Marcia Robson, R.N., Chief Nursing Officer
Web address: www.ozarksmedicalcenter.com
Control: Other not–for–profit (including NFP Corporation) **Service:** General
Medical and Surgical

Staffed Beds: 114 **Admissions:** 5326 **Census:** 51 **Outpatient Visits:** 576295
Births: 630 **Total Expense ($000):** 123271 **Payroll Expense ($000):** 59709
Personnel: 1035

WINDSOR—Henry County

☐ **ROYAL OAKS HOSPITAL (264020)**, 307 North Main, Zip 65360–1449;
tel. 660/647–2182 **A**1 3 5 10 **F**30 98 99 100 101 102 103 104 105
Primary Contact: Alan W. Greiman, Administrator
CFO: Dave Turner, Chief Financial Officer
CMO: Syed Arshad Husain, M.D., Executive Vice President and Chief Medical
Officer
CIO: Richard Colvert, Chief Information Officer
CHR: Diane Coletta, Director Human Resources
CNO: Erin Allee, R.N., Director Nursing Services
Web address: www.royal–oaks–hospital.org
Control: Other not–for–profit (including NFP Corporation) **Service:** Psychiatric

Staffed Beds: 41 **Admissions:** 1296 **Census:** 27 **Outpatient Visits:** 0 **Births:**
0 **Total Expense ($000):** 12853 **Payroll Expense ($000):** 6099 **Personnel:**
150

MO

MONTANA

ANACONDA—Deer Lodge County

★ **COMMUNITY HOSPITAL OF ANACONDA (271335)**, 401 West Pennsylvania Street, Zip 59711; tel. 406/563–8500, (Total facility includes 62 beds in nursing home–type unit) **A**9 10 18 **F**1 3 6 8 11 13 15 29 30 31 34 40 43 45 50 57 59 62 63 64 75 77 79 81 82 87 93 107 111 114 119 128 130 133 135 143 144 146 148 **P**6 **S** Providence Health & Services, Renton, WA
Primary Contact: Steve McNeece, Chief Executive Officer
COO: Laura Austin, Chief Financial Officer and Chief Operating Officer
CFO: Laura Austin, Chief Financial Officer and Chief Operating Officer
CMO: Shawna Baker, M.D., Chief of Staff
CIO: Laura Austin, Chief Financial Officer and Chief Operating Officer
CHR: Meg Hickey–Boynton, Director Human Resources and Marketing
CNO: Jamie Johnson, R.N., VP of Nursing
Web address: www.communityhospitalofanaconda.org
Control: Other not–for–profit (including NFP Corporation) **Service:** General Medical and Surgical

Staffed Beds: 87 **Admissions:** 1006 **Census:** 67 **Outpatient Visits:** 50082 **Births:** 40 **Total Expense ($000):** 34717 **Payroll Expense ($000):** 15992 **Personnel:** 266

BAKER—Fallon County

FALLON MEDICAL COMPLEX (271301), 202 South 4th Street West, Zip 59313–9156, Mailing Address: P.O. Box 820, Zip 59313–0820; tel. 406/778–3331, (Total facility includes 15 beds in nursing home–type unit) **A**9 10 18 **F**11 15 28 32 34 36 40 56 57 59 62 64 65 68 69 75 81 93 97 107 110 114 119 127 128 130 133 146 148 **P**6
Primary Contact: David Espeland, Chief Executive Officer
CFO: Selena Nelson, Chief Financial Officer
CMO: Darryl Espeland, D.O., Chief Medical Staff
CIO: Susan Stevens, Information Technology Specialist
CHR: Theresa Weimer, Director Personnel
CNO: Susan Lunde, R.N., Director of Nursing
Web address: www.fallonmedical.org
Control: Other not–for–profit (including NFP Corporation) **Service:** General Medical and Surgical

Staffed Beds: 40 **Admissions:** 224 **Census:** 32 **Outpatient Visits:** 19587 **Births:** 0 **Total Expense ($000):** 8807 **Payroll Expense ($000):** 4373 **Personnel:** 93

BIG SANDY—Chouteau County

★ **BIG SANDY MEDICAL CENTER (271311)**, 166 Montana Avenue East, Zip 59520–8474, Mailing Address: P.O. Box 530, Zip 59520–0530; tel. 406/378–2188, (Total facility includes 22 beds in nursing home–type unit) **A**9 10 18 **F**40 64 93 127 128 133
Primary Contact: Harry Bold, Administrator
CFO: Nora Grubb, Chief Financial Officer
Web address: www.bsmc.org
Control: Other not–for–profit (including NFP Corporation) **Service:** General Medical and Surgical

Staffed Beds: 30 **Admissions:** 87 **Census:** 19 **Outpatient Visits:** 3242 **Births:** 0 **Total Expense ($000):** 3227 **Payroll Expense ($000):** 1910 **Personnel:** 37

BIG TIMBER—Sweet Grass County

★ **PIONEER MEDICAL CENTER (271313)**, 301 West Seventh Avenue, Zip 59011–7893, Mailing Address: P.O. Box 1228, Zip 59011–1228; tel. 406/932–4603, (Total facility includes 25 beds in nursing home–type unit) **A**9 10 18 **F**2 7 10 29 34 35 40 41 45 57 59 63 64 65 69 75 77 93 97 107 114 127 128 130 131 132 133 **P**3 6
Primary Contact: Erik Wood, Chief Executive Officer
CFO: Kyle Gee, Chief Financial Officer
CMO: Benjamin P. Bullington, M.D., Chief of Staff
CHR: Miki Gregorich, Director Human Resources
CNO: Randi Pike, Director of Nursing
Web address: www.pmcmt.org/
Control: County–Government, nonfederal **Service:** General Medical and Surgical

Staffed Beds: 50 **Admissions:** 135 **Census:** 34 **Outpatient Visits:** 10042 **Births:** 0 **Personnel:** 93

BILLINGS—Yellowstone County

☐ **ADVANCED CARE HOSPITAL OF MONTANA (272001)**, 3528 Gabel Road, Zip 59102–7307; tel. 406/373–8000, (Nonreporting) **A**1 9 10 **S** Ernest Health, Inc., Albuquerque, NM
Primary Contact: Diana Parker, Chief Executive Officer
Web address: www.achm.ernesthealth.com
Control: Corporation, Investor–owned, for–profit **Service:** Long–Term Acute Care hospital

Staffed Beds: 40

⊞ **BILLINGS CLINIC (270004)**, 2800 10th Avenue North, Zip 59101–0703, Mailing Address: P.O. Box 37000, Zip 59107–7000; tel. 406/657–4000, (Total facility includes 125 beds in nursing home–type unit) **A**1 2 9 10 19 **F**3 7 8 9 10 11 12 13 15 17 18 20 22 24 26 27 28 29 30 31 32 34 35 36 38 40 43 44 45 46 48 49 50 51 52 54 55 56 57 58 59 60 61 63 64 65 66 68 70 71 72 74 75 76 77 78 79 81 82 84 85 86 87 91 92 93 97 98 99 100 101 102 103 104 105 107 108 110 111 114 115 116 117 118 119 120 121 124 126 128 129 130 131 132 134 135 143 144 146 147 148 **P**6
Primary Contact: Nicholas Wolter, M.D., Chief Executive Officer
CFO: Connie F. Prewitt, Chief Financial Officer
CMO: Randall K. Gibb, M.D., Chief Medical Officer
CIO: Chris E. Stevens, Chief Information Officer
CHR: Karla Stauffer, Executive Director People Resources
CNO: Lu Byrd, R.N., Vice President Hospital Operations and Chief Nursing Officer
Web address: www.billingsclinic.com
Control: Other not–for–profit (including NFP Corporation) **Service:** General Medical and Surgical

Staffed Beds: 387 **Admissions:** 15007 **Census:** 293 **Outpatient Visits:** 966526 **Births:** 1347 **Total Expense ($000):** 500582 **Payroll Expense ($000):** 247983 **Personnel:** 3284

⊞ △ **ST. VINCENT HEALTHCARE (270049)**, 1233 North 30th Street, Zip 59101–0165, Mailing Address: P.O. Box 35200, Zip 59107–5200; tel. 406/237–7000 **A**1 2 7 9 10 **F**3 8 11 12 13 15 17 18 19 20 22 24 28 29 30 31 32 34 35 36 37 38 39 40 43 44 45 47 49 50 51 56 57 59 60 61 64 68 70 71 72 74 75 76 77 78 79 81 82 84 85 86 87 88 89 90 92 93 97 99 100 101 103 104 107 108 111 114 115 116 117 118 119 120 121 123 124 125 126 129 130 131 132 134 135 143 144 145 146 147 148 **P**6 **S** SCL Health System, Denver, CO
Primary Contact: Steve Loveless, Acting President and Chief Executive Officer
CMO: Michael Schweitzer, M.D., Chief Medical Officer
CIO: Al Rooney, Director Information Systems
Web address: www.svh–mt.org
Control: Church–operated, Nongovernment, not–for profit **Service:** General Medical and Surgical

Staffed Beds: 249 **Admissions:** 11753 **Census:** 147 **Outpatient Visits:** 488567 **Births:** 1357 **Total Expense ($000):** 362248 **Payroll Expense ($000):** 135376 **Personnel:** 1841

BOZEMAN—Gallatin County

⊞ **BOZEMAN DEACONESS HOSPITAL (270057)**, 915 Highland Boulevard, Zip 59715–6902; tel. 406/585–5000, (Nonreporting) **A**1 2 9 10 20
Primary Contact: Kevin M. Pitzer, President and Chief Executive Officer
Web address: www.bozemandeaconess.org
Control: Other not–for–profit (including NFP Corporation) **Service:** General Medical and Surgical

Staffed Beds: 70

MT

Hospital, Medicare Provider Number, Address, Telephone, Approval, Facility, and Physician Codes, Health Care System

★ American Hospital Association (AHA) membership
☐ The Joint Commission accreditation ◇ DNV Healthcare Inc. accreditation
○ Healthcare Facilities Accreditation Program
△ Commission on Accreditation of Rehabilitation Facilities (CARF) accreditation

BUTTE—Silver Bow County

⊠ **ST. JAMES HEALTHCARE (270017)**, 400 South Clark Street,
Zip 59701–2328; tel. 406/723–2500 **A**1 9 10 19 20 **F**3 11 13 15 18 20 22
26 28 29 30 31 34 35 40 43 45 46 47 48 49 50 51 54 56 57 59 64 65 68
70 72 75 76 77 78 79 81 82 85 86 87 89 93 97 107 108 111 114 115 116
117 118 119 120 121 122 123 126 127 130 131 132 135 145 146 147 148
S SCL Health System, Denver, CO
Primary Contact: Charles T. Wright, President and Chief Executive Officer
CFO: Jay Doyle, Chief Financial Officer
CMO: Dennis Salisbury, M.D., Vice President for Medical Affairs
CHR: Trisha Palmer, Director
CNO: Shannon S. Holland, R.N., Vice President of Patient Care Service
Web address: www.stjameshealthcare.org
Control: Other not–for–profit (including NFP Corporation) **Service:** General
Medical and Surgical

Staffed Beds: 56 **Admissions:** 3714 **Census:** 39 **Outpatient Visits:** 73873
Births: 449 **Total Expense ($000):** 99183 **Payroll Expense ($000):** 37119
Personnel: 529

CHESTER—Liberty County

LIBERTY MEDICAL CENTER (271334), 315 West Madison Avenue, Zip 59522,
Mailing Address: P.O. Box 705, Zip 59522–0705; tel. 406/759–5181 **A**9 10 18
F2 3 10 11 34 35 40 43 45 56 57 59 64 81 86 87 93 97 107 114 119 127
130 133 **P**6
Primary Contact: Dustin Ahrens, Chief Executive Officer
CFO: Shari Meissner, Chief Financial Officer
CMO: Anna Earl, M.D., Chief of Staff
CIO: Marilyn Snyder, Chief Information Officer
CHR: Jane Allen, Director Human Resources and Payroll
Web address: www.lchnh.org
Control: Other not–for–profit (including NFP Corporation) **Service:** General
Medical and Surgical

Staffed Beds: 25 **Admissions:** 35 **Census:** 1 **Outpatient Visits:** 9634 **Births:**
0 **Total Expense ($000):** 6016 **Payroll Expense ($000):** 3268 **Personnel:**
79

CHOTEAU—Teton County

★ **TETON MEDICAL CENTER (271307)**, 915 4th Street North West,
Zip 59422–9123; tel. 406/466–5763, (Total facility includes 30 beds in nursing
home–type unit) **A**9 10 18 **F**2 3 15 34 35 40 41 53 54 56 57 59 63 64 68 77
87 93 107 127 128 130 131 133 143 146 **P**6
Primary Contact: Louie King, Chief Executive Officer
Web address: www.tetonmedicalcenter.net
Control: Hospital district or authority, Government, nonfederal **Service:** General
Medical and Surgical

Staffed Beds: 40 **Admissions:** 212 **Census:** 28 **Outpatient Visits:** 8212
Births: 0 **Total Expense ($000):** 6656 **Payroll Expense ($000):** 3699
Personnel: 103

CIRCLE—McCone County

★ **MCCONE COUNTY HEALTH CENTER (271305)**, 605 Sullivan Avenue,
Zip 59215, Mailing Address: P.O. Box 48, Zip 59215–0048; tel. 406/485–3381
A9 10 18 **F**2 3 11 40 41 65 69 93 133 135 143 146
Primary Contact: Nancy Rosaaen, Chief Executive Officer
CFO: Nancy Rosaaen, Chief Executive Officer
CHR: Jacque Gardner, Administrative Assistant, Clinic Manager, Co–Chief Financial
Officer and Chief Human Resources
Web address: www.mcconehealth.org/
Control: County–Government, nonfederal **Service:** General Medical and Surgical

Staffed Beds: 25 **Admissions:** 65 **Census:** 24 **Outpatient Visits:** 3587
Births: 0 **Total Expense ($000):** 3250 **Payroll Expense ($000):** 1568
Personnel: 40

COLUMBUS—Stillwater County

★ **STILLWATER COMMUNITY HOSPITAL (271330)**, 44 West Fourth Avenue
North, Zip 59019–0959, Mailing Address: P.O. Box 959, Zip 59019–0959;
tel. 406/322–5316, (Data for 273 days) **A**9 10 18 **F**15 28 29 32 34 35 40 45
46 57 59 62 65 68 75 93 107 130 133 145 **P**1
Primary Contact: Tim Russell, Administrator
Web address: www.billingsclinic.com
Control: Other not–for–profit (including NFP Corporation) **Service:** General
Medical and Surgical

Staffed Beds: 10 **Admissions:** 98 **Census:** 1 **Outpatient Visits:** 6974 **Births:**
0 **Total Expense ($000):** 7820 **Payroll Expense ($000):** 1771 **Personnel:**
37

CONRAD—Pondera County

PONDERA MEDICAL CENTER (271324), 805 Sunset Boulevard,
Zip 59425–1717, Mailing Address: P.O. Box 758, Zip 59425–0758;
tel. 406/271–3211, (Total facility includes 59 beds in nursing home–type unit) **A**9
10 18 **F**3 6 7 11 13 15 28 29 34 35 40 43 53 57 59 62 63 65 66 77 81 87
91 93 97 102 107 119 128 130 133 144 146 148 **P**6
Primary Contact: Bill O'Leary, Chief Executive Officer
CFO: Randy Nightengale, Chief Financial Officer
CMO: Jay Taylor, M.D., Chief of Staff
CIO: Sean Kavanagh, Supervisor Information Technology and Information Systems
CHR: Melissa Proff, Director Human Resources
Web address: www.ponderamedical.com
Control: Other not–for–profit (including NFP Corporation) **Service:** General
Medical and Surgical

Staffed Beds: 79 **Admissions:** 171 **Census:** 54 **Outpatient Visits:** 7539
Births: 30 **Total Expense ($000):** 12393 **Payroll Expense ($000):** 6899
Personnel: 192

CROW AGENCY—Big Horn County

CROW/NORTHERN CHEYENNE HOSPITAL (271339), 10110 South 7650
East, Zip 59022–0009, Mailing Address: P.O. Box 9, Zip 59022–0009;
tel. 406/638–2626, (Nonreporting) **A**10 18 **S** U. S. Indian Health Service,
Rockville, MD
Primary Contact: Clayton Old Elk, Service Unit Director
CMO: Jim Upchurch, M.D., Chief Medical Officer
CIO: Melanie Falls Down, Site Manager
Web address: www.ihs.gov/facilitiesservices/areaoffices/billings/crow/index.asp
Control: Public Health Service, Government, federal **Service:** General Medical
and Surgical

Staffed Beds: 24

CULBERTSON—Roosevelt County

★ **ROOSEVELT MEDICAL CENTER (271308)**, 818 Second Avenue East,
Zip 59218, Mailing Address: P.O. Box 419, Zip 59218–0419; tel. 406/787–6401
A9 10 18 **F**2 3 7 11 15 34 35 40 43 50 56 57 59 65 69 93 97 99 103 119
127 128 130 133 143 146 **P**6
Primary Contact: Audrey Stromberg, Administrator
CFO: Jennifer Kessner, Financial Director
CMO: Don Helland, M.D., Chief Medical Officer
CIO: Brian Fordyce, Director Information Technology
CHR: Elizabeth Raaum, Manger Business Office
Web address: www.roosmem.org
Control: Other not–for–profit (including NFP Corporation) **Service:** General
Medical and Surgical

Staffed Beds: 25 **Admissions:** 71 **Census:** 21 **Outpatient Visits:** 8301
Births: 0 **Total Expense ($000):** 4700 **Payroll Expense ($000):** 2603
Personnel: 56

CUT BANK—Glacier County

NORTHERN ROCKIES MEDICAL CENTER (271337), 802 Second Street S.E.,
Zip 59427–3329; tel. 406/873–2251 **A**9 10 18 **F**8 11 29 34 40 50 57 59 64
65 66 81 89 91 93 97 107 108 119 127 129 130 133 **P**4 6
Primary Contact: Cherie Taylor, Chief Executive Officer
CFO: Treasure Berkram, Chief Financial Officer
CMO: Adron Medley, M.D., Chief Medical Staff
CHR: Kandie Lemieux, Administrative Assistant and Director Human Resources
Web address: www.nmrcinc.org
Control: Other not–for–profit (including NFP Corporation) **Service:** General
Medical and Surgical

Staffed Beds: 13 **Admissions:** 176 **Census:** 2 **Outpatient Visits:** 13028
Births: 0 **Total Expense ($000):** 6958 **Payroll Expense ($000):** 3772
Personnel: 97

DEER LODGE—Powell County

DEER LODGE MEDICAL CENTER (271314), 1100 Hollenbeck Lane,
Zip 59722–2317; tel. 406/846–2212 **A**9 10 18 **F**3 11 34 40 43 45 48 57 59
64 79 81 82 91 93 107 114 119 127 133 136 137 138 139 140 141 142
143 144 145 146 147 148 **P**6
Primary Contact: Tony Pfaff, Chief Executive Officer
CFO: Jaena Richards, Chief Financial Officer
CMO: Michelle Corbin, M.D., Chief of Staff
CIO: Chris Foster, Director Health Information Management
Web address: www.dlmed.org/
Control: Other not–for–profit (including NFP Corporation) **Service:** General
Medical and Surgical

Staffed Beds: 16 **Admissions:** 279 **Census:** 4 **Outpatient Visits:** 8244
Births: 0 **Total Expense ($000):** 7770 **Payroll Expense ($000):** 3019
Personnel: 57

DILLON—Beaverhead County

★ **BARRETT HOSPITAL & HEALTHCARE (271318)**, 600 Highway 91 South, Zip 59725–7379; tel. 406/683–3000 **A**9 10 18 **F**3 13 15 28 29 32 34 35 37 38 40 43 44 45 50 57 59 62 63 64 65 68 75 76 77 79 81 82 83 84 85 86 87 89 93 94 97 107 108 110 111 115 118 119 120 130 131 132 133 146 148 **P**5 6 **S** HealthTech Management Services, Brentwood, TN
Primary Contact: Ken Westman, Chief Executive Officer
CFO: Dick Achter, Chief Financial Officer
CMO: Carol Kennedy, Chief Clinical Officer
CIO: Dick Achter, Chief Financial Officer
CHR: Geoff Roach, Director Human Resources
Web address: www.barretthospital.org
Control: Hospital district or authority, Government, nonfederal **Service:** General Medical and Surgical

Staffed Beds: 25 Admissions: 607 Census: 5 Outpatient Visits: 30340
Births: 77 Total Expense ($000): 31643 Payroll Expense ($000): 13651
Personnel: 219

EKALAKA—Carter County

DAHL MEMORIAL HEALTHCARE ASSOCIATION (271302), 215 Sandy Street, Zip 59324, Mailing Address: P.O. Box 46, Zip 59324–0046; tel. 406/775–8730, (Total facility includes 23 beds in nursing home–type unit) **A**9 10 18 **F**2 7 40 41 57 59 65 69 127 128 130 131 133 135 143 146 148 **P**6
Primary Contact: Nadine Elmore, Chief Executive Officer
CFO: Nadine Elmore, Chief Executive Officer
CMO: Darryl Espeland, D.O., Chief Nursing Officer
CIO: Davie Ann Barrere, Coordinator Information Technology
CHR: Vicki Fix, Director Human Resources
CNO: Patricia Rogers, Director of Nursing
Web address: www.dahlmemorial.com
Control: Other not–for–profit (including NFP Corporation) **Service:** General Medical and Surgical

Staffed Beds: 31 Admissions: 22 Census: 17 Outpatient Visits: 2690
Births: 0 Total Expense ($000): 2342 Payroll Expense ($000): 1234
Personnel: 36

ENNIS—Madison County

MADISON VALLEY MEDICAL CENTER (271329), 305 North Main Street, Zip 59729–8001, Mailing Address: P.O. Box 397, Zip 59729–0397; tel. 406/682–4222, (Nonreporting) **A**9 10 18
Primary Contact: John Bishop, Chief Executive Officer and Chief Financial Officer
CFO: John Bishop, Chief Executive Officer and Chief Financial Officer
CMO: Cindy Sharp, M.D., Chief Medical Officer
CIO: Bo Nix, Chief Information Officer
Web address: www.mvmedcenter.org
Control: Other not–for–profit (including NFP Corporation) **Service:** General Medical and Surgical

Staffed Beds: 9

FORSYTH—Rosebud County

★ **ROSEBUD HEALTH CARE CENTER (271327)**, 383 North 17th Avenue, Zip 59327–0268, Mailing Address: P.O. Box 268, Zip 59327–0268; tel. 406/346–2161, (Total facility includes 31 beds in nursing home–type unit) **A**9 10 18 **F**2 30 32 34 40 41 43 45 50 57 59 75 93 97 107 127 128 131 132 133 143 144 145 146 148 **P**3 4 5
Primary Contact: Ryan Tooke, Chief Executive Officer
CMO: William Anderson, M.D., Medical Director
CHR: Karla Allies, Director Human Resources
Web address: www.rosebudhealthcare.com/
Control: Other not–for–profit (including NFP Corporation) **Service:** General Medical and Surgical

Staffed Beds: 55 Admissions: 255 Census: 31 Outpatient Visits: 10322
Births: 0 Total Expense ($000): 7233 Payroll Expense ($000): 3877
Personnel: 100

FORT BENTON—Chouteau County

MISSOURI RIVER MEDICAL CENTER (271304), 1501 St. Charles Street, Zip 59442–0249, Mailing Address: P.O. Box 249, Zip 59442–0249; tel. 406/622–3331, (Total facility includes 41 beds in nursing home–type unit) **A**9 10 18 **F**2 3 10 40 57 59 63 64 84 89 93 107 114 119 127 128 130 131 133 135 143 146 **P**5 **S** Benefis Health System, Great Falls, MT
Primary Contact: Jay Pottenger, Administrator
CFO: Jay Pottenger, Chief Executive Officer and Chief Financial Officer
CIO: Bryan Cartwright, Chief Information Technology Officer
CHR: Carolyn Johnsrud, Manager Human Resources
CNO: Janice Woodhouse, Director of Nursing
Web address: www.mrmcfb.org
Control: Hospital district or authority, Government, nonfederal **Service:** Long–Term Acute Care hospital

Staffed Beds: 52 Admissions: 174 Census: 31 Outpatient Visits: 6850
Births: 0 Total Expense ($000): 5485 Payroll Expense ($000): 2809
Personnel: 58

FORT HARRISON—Lewis And Clark County

✠ **VETERANS AFFAIRS MONTANA HEALTH CARE SYSTEM**, 3687 Veterans Drive, Zip 59636–9703, Mailing Address: P.O. Box 1500, Zip 59636–1500; tel. 406/442–6410, (Total facility includes 30 beds in nursing home–type unit) **A**1 **F**3 4 5 4 8 28 29 30 31 33 35 36 38 39 40 44 50 51 53 54 55 56 59 61 63 64 65 66 70 71 74 75 77 78 79 81 82 83 84 85 87 91 92 93 94 97 98 100 101 102 103 104 105 106 107 108 111 115 116 117 118 119 127 129 130 132 135 143 144 146 147 148 **P**6 **S** Department of Veterans Affairs, Washington, DC
Primary Contact: Christine Gregory, R.N., Director
CFO: Brian Gustafson, Chief Financial Officer
CMO: Kurt Werner, M.D., Chief of Staff
CIO: Paul Gauthier, Chief Information Resources Management
CHR: Aggie Hamilton, Chief Human Resources
Web address: www.montana.va.gov/
Control: Veterans Affairs, Government, federal **Service:** General Medical and Surgical

Staffed Beds: 100 Admissions: 1829 Census: 23 Outpatient Visits: 405125
Births: 0 Total Expense ($000): 240354 Payroll Expense ($000): 70619
Personnel: 1091

GLASGOW—Valley County

✠ **FRANCES MAHON DEACONESS HOSPITAL (271316)**, 621 Third Street South, Zip 59230–2699; tel. 406/228–3500 **A**1 9 10 18 **F**3 7 11 13 15 28 29 30 31 34 35 40 42 43 53 56 57 59 61 64 70 75 76 78 79 81 82 86 87 89 93 100 102 105 107 108 110 111 114 118 119 127 128 130 131 133 135 145 146 **P**6 7
Primary Contact: Randall G. Holom, Chief Executive Officer
COO: Ellen Guttenberg, Chief Operating Officer
CFO: Del Gienger, Director Financial Services
CMO: Gordon Bell, M.D., Chief of Staff
CIO: David L. Nixdorf, Director Support Services
CHR: Shelly Van Buren, Director Human Resources
CNO: Brenda Koessl, R.N., Director of Nursing Services
Web address: www.fmdh.org
Control: Other not–for–profit (including NFP Corporation) **Service:** General Medical and Surgical

Staffed Beds: 25 Admissions: 639 Census: 6 Outpatient Visits: 34174
Births: 159 Total Expense ($000): 19450 Payroll Expense ($000): 9422
Personnel: 166

GLENDIVE—Dawson County

★ **GLENDIVE MEDICAL CENTER (271332)**, 202 Prospect Drive, Zip 59330–1999; tel. 406/345–3306, (Total facility includes 71 beds in nursing home–type unit) **A**9 10 18 **F**3 10 11 13 15 28 29 30 31 35 38 40 41 43 50 56 57 59 61 62 63 64 67 69 70 75 76 77 78 79 81 82 87 89 93 94 98 102 103 104 107 108 111 115 119 127 128 130 131 132 133 143 144 146 147 148 **P**6 7 8
Primary Contact: Parker Powell, Chief Executive Officer
CFO: Barbara Markham, Chief Financial Officer
CMO: Joseph M. Leal, Jr., M.D., Chief of Staff
CIO: Barbara Markham, Chief Financial Officer
CHR: Joetta J. Pearcy, Director, Human Resources
Web address: www.gmc.org
Control: Other not–for–profit (including NFP Corporation) **Service:** General Medical and Surgical

Staffed Beds: 96 Admissions: 862 Census: 57 Outpatient Visits: 27870
Births: 75 Total Expense ($000): 27539 Payroll Expense ($000): 12744
Personnel: 237

MT

Hospital, Medicare Provider Number, Address, Telephone, Approval, Facility, and Physician Codes, Health Care System

★ American Hospital Association (AHA) membership
□ The Joint Commission accreditation
◇ DNV Healthcare Inc. accreditation
○ Healthcare Facilities Accreditation Program
△ Commission on Accreditation of Rehabilitation Facilities (CARF) accreditation

GREAT FALLS—Cascade County

△ **BENEFIS HOSPITALS (270012)**, 1101 26th Street South, Zip 59405–5104; tel. 406/455–5000, (Includes BENEFIS HEALTH CARE–EAST CAMPUS, 1101 26th Street, Zip 59405; tel. 406/761–1200; BENEFIS HEALTH CARE–WEST CAMPUS, 500 15th Avenue South, Mailing Address: P.O. Box 5013, Zip 59403–5013; tel. 406/727–3333), (Total facility includes 146 beds in nursing home–type unit) **A**2 7 9 10 20 **F**3 4 5 6 8 10 11 12 13 15 17 18 20 22 24 26 28 29 30 31 34 35 37 38 40 43 45 48 49 50 53 54 55 56 57 58 59 61 62 63 64 65 70 71 72 73 74 75 76 77 78 79 80 81 82 83 84 85 86 87 88 89 90 92 93 96 97 98 100 101 102 103 104 105 107 108 110 111 113 114 115 119 120 121 123 124 126 127 128 129 130 131 132 133 134 135 136 141 143 144 145 146 147 148 **P**4 5 7 8 **S** Benefis Health System, Great Falls, MT
Primary Contact: John H. Goodnow, Chief Executive Officer
COO: Julie Hickethier, R.N., Senior Vice President
CMO: Paul Dolan, M.D., Chief Medical Affairs Officer
CIO: Lee Roath, System Chief Information Officer
CHR: Terry Olinger, System Chief Human Resources Officer
Web address: www.benefis.org
Control: Other not–for–profit (including NFP Corporation) **Service:** General Medical and Surgical

> **Staffed Beds:** 434 **Admissions:** 13139 **Census:** 295 **Outpatient Visits:** 355950 **Births:** 1540 **Total Expense ($000):** 340741 **Payroll Expense ($000):** 139657 **Personnel:** 2212

GREAT FALLS CLINIC MEDICAL CENTER (270086), 1411 9th Street South, Zip 59405–4507; tel. 406/216–8000, (Nonreporting) **A**9 10
Primary Contact: David B. Rowe, Chief Executive Officer
COO: Vicki Newmiller, Chief Operating Officer
CFO: Cheryl Cornwell, Chief Financial Officer
CMO: Nicholas Bonfilio, M.D., Chief of Staff
Web address: www.greatfallsclinicmedicalcenter.com
Control: Corporation, Investor–owned, for–profit **Service:** Surgical

> **Staffed Beds:** 20

HAMILTON—Ravalli County

★ **MARCUS DALY MEMORIAL HOSPITAL (271340)**, 1200 Westwood Drive, Zip 59840–2345; tel. 406/363–2211 **A**9 10 18 **F**1 3 7 8 11 13 15 17 28 29 30 34 35 40 45 50 57 59 62 63 64 65 70 74 75 76 77 79 81 83 84 89 93 97 102 105 107 110 111 115 119 127 128 129 130 131 132 133 144 145 146 148
Primary Contact: John M. Bartos, Chief Executive Officer
CFO: Donja Erdman, Chief Financial Officer
CMO: John Moreland, M.D., Chief Medical Officer
CIO: Cheryl Dohlzel, Director Information Technology
CHR: Debbie M. Morris, Director Human Resources
CNO: Susan Hill, R.N., Director of Nursing
Web address: www.mdmh.org
Control: Other not–for–profit (including NFP Corporation) **Service:** General Medical and Surgical

> **Staffed Beds:** 37 **Admissions:** 1520 **Census:** 14 **Outpatient Visits:** 46998 **Births:** 138 **Total Expense ($000):** 47983 **Payroll Expense ($000):** 25190 **Personnel:** 380

HARDIN--Big Horn County

★ **BIG HORN COUNTY MEMORIAL HOSPITAL (271338)**, 17 North Miles Avenue, Zip 59034–2323; tel. 406/665–2310, (Total facility includes 36 beds in nursing home–type unit) **A**9 10 18 **F**10 11 13 15 40 43 50 57 59 64 65 68 75 76 77 81 85 86 87 93 107 110 111 114 119 125 128 130 132 133 143 146
Primary Contact: George Minder, Chief Executive Officer
CFO: Roxie Cain, Chief Financial Officer
Web address: www.bighornhospital.org
Control: Other not–for–profit (including NFP Corporation) **Service:** General Medical and Surgical

> **Staffed Beds:** 61 **Admissions:** 422 **Census:** 44 **Outpatient Visits:** 8298 **Births:** 38 **Total Expense ($000):** 13256 **Payroll Expense ($000):** 7244 **Personnel:** 166

HARLEM—Blaine County

FORT BELKNAP U. S. PUBLIC HEALTH SERVICE INDIAN HOSPITAL (271315), 669 Agency Main Street, Zip 59526–9455; tel. 406/353–3100, (Nonreporting) **A**10 18 **S** U. S. Indian Health Service, Rockville, MD
Primary Contact: Steve Fox, Chief Executive Officer
CMO: Ethel L. Moore, M.D., Director of Medical Affairs
CIO: Mikki Grant, Chief Information Officer
CHR: Charlotte Lamebull, Administrative Officer
CNO: Diana Hunter, Director of Nursing
Web address: www.ihs.gov
Control: PHS, Indian Service, Government, federal **Service:** General Medical and Surgical

> **Staffed Beds:** 6

HARLOWTON—Wheatland County

★ **WHEATLAND MEMORIAL HEALTHCARE (271321)**, 530 Third Street North West, Zip 59036, Mailing Address: P.O. Box 287, Zip 59036–0287; tel. 406/632–4351 **A**9 10 18 **F**3 15 16 17 30 32 34 35 40 43 50 56 57 59 61 64 65 70 72 75 77 85 87 88 89 93 97 107 110 118 119 127 128 130 132 133 135 143 146 147 **P**6
Primary Contact: Mike Zwicker, Chief Executive Officer
CFO: Doug Lewis, Chief Financial Officer
CMO: Kathy Jutila, M.D., Chief of Staff
CIO: Ray Hetherington, Network Administrator
CHR: Peggy Hiner, Director Human Resources
CNO: Lauri Ann Cooney, Director Nursing
Web address: www.wheatlandmemorial.org
Control: Other not–for–profit (including NFP Corporation) **Service:** General Medical and Surgical

> **Staffed Beds:** 25 **Admissions:** 87 **Census:** 20 **Outpatient Visits:** 15314 **Births:** 0 **Total Expense ($000):** 4973 **Payroll Expense ($000):** 2881 **Personnel:** 56

HAVRE—Hill County

★ **NORTHERN MONTANA HOSPITAL (270032)**, 30 13th Street, Zip 59501–5222, Mailing Address: P.O. Box 1231, Zip 59501–1231; tel. 406/265–2211, (Total facility includes 115 beds in nursing home–type unit) **A**9 10 20 **F**10 11 13 15 28 29 34 35 36 38 40 50 53 56 57 59 60 63 64 68 70 75 76 77 79 81 82 84 85 89 93 97 99 101 102 103 104 105 107 108 110 111 115 118 119 127 128 129 130 132 133 135 146 148 **P**6
Primary Contact: David Henry, President and Chief Executive Officer
COO: Julia Mariani, Vice President Business Operations
CFO: Kim Lucke, Vice President Finance
CHR: Bonnie O'Neill, Vice President Employee Services
CNO: Brenda L. Sturm, MSN, Vice President, Patient Care Services
Web address: www.nmhcare.org
Control: Other not–for–profit (including NFP Corporation) **Service:** General Medical and Surgical

> **Staffed Beds:** 142 **Admissions:** 1636 **Census:** 110 **Outpatient Visits:** 87636 **Births:** 378 **Total Expense ($000):** 48082 **Payroll Expense ($000):** 27115 **Personnel:** 506

HELENA—Lewis And Clark County

⊞ **SHODAIR CHILDREN'S HOSPITAL (274004)**, 2755 Colonial Drive, Zip 59601–4926, Mailing Address: P.O. Box 5539, Zip 59604–5539; tel. 406/444–7500 **A**1 9 10 **F**55 98 99 101 104 106 130 **P**6
Primary Contact: John P. Casey, Administrator
COO: John P. Casey, Administrator
CFO: Ron Wiens, Chief Financial Officer
CMO: Heather Zaluski, M.D., President Medical Staff
CIO: Judy Jackson, Director Health Information Management and Privacy Officer
Web address: www.shodairhospital.org
Control: Other not–for–profit (including NFP Corporation) **Service:** Children's hospital psychiatric

> **Staffed Beds:** 88 **Admissions:** 845 **Census:** 67 **Outpatient Visits:** 3338 **Births:** 0 **Total Expense ($000):** 20906 **Payroll Expense ($000):** 12293 **Personnel:** 264

⊞ **ST. PETER'S HOSPITAL (270003)**, 2475 Broadway, Zip 59601–4928; tel. 406/442–2480 **A**1 2 9 10 20 **F**3 7 11 13 15 18 20 22 28 29 30 31 34 35 40 45 46 49 50 51 54 56 57 59 60 62 63 64 65 70 74 75 76 78 79 81 82 84 89 92 93 98 102 103 107 108 110 111 114 115 116 117 119 120 121 122 129 130 132 133 135 144 146 147 148 **P**6
Primary Contact: Nate Olson, Chief Executive Officer
CFO: John Green, Vice President Finance
CIO: Tammy K. Buyok, Vice President Support Services
CHR: Thomas Gregg, Vice President Human Resources
Web address: www.stpetes.org
Control: Other not–for–profit (including NFP Corporation) **Service:** General Medical and Surgical

> **Staffed Beds:** 123 **Admissions:** 6037 **Census:** 73 **Outpatient Visits:** 167349 **Births:** 798 **Total Expense ($000):** 162334 **Payroll Expense ($000):** 67490 **Personnel:** 984

JORDAN—Garfield County

GARFIELD COUNTY HEALTH CENTER (271310), 332 Leavitt Avenue, Zip 59337, Mailing Address: P.O. Box 389, Zip 59337–0389; tel. 406/557–2500, (Total facility includes 20 beds in nursing home–type unit) **A**9 10 18 **F**40 56 57 128
Primary Contact: Hanz Arnston, R.N., Chief Executive Officer
CFO: Charlotte Herbold, Manager Business Officer
CMO: David M. Kidder, D.O., Chief Medical Officer
CIO: Charlotte Herbold, Manager Business Officer
CHR: Hanz Arnston, R.N., Chief Executive Officer
CNO: Sarah Nordlund, Director of Nursing
Control: County–Government, nonfederal **Service:** General Medical and Surgical

> **Staffed Beds:** 24 **Admissions:** 17 **Census:** 17 **Births:** 0

Many Facility Codes have changed. Please refer to the AHA Guide Code Chart.
© 2014 AHA Guide

MT

KALISPELL—Flathead County

HEALTHCENTER NORTHWEST See The HealthCenter

★ △ **KALISPELL REGIONAL MEDICAL CENTER (270051)**, 310 Sunnyview Lane, Zip 59901–3129; tel. 406/752–5111, (Includes PATHWAYS TREATMENT CENTER, 200 Heritage Way, Zip 59901; tel. 406/756–3950) **A**2 7 9 10 19 20 **F**3 4 5 8 13 15 18 20 22 24 26 28 29 30 31 35 36 40 43 45 46 49 50 56 57 58 59 62 63 64 68 70 72 74 75 76 77 78 79 81 84 85 86 87 90 98 99 100 101 102 103 104 105 107 108 114 115 118 119 120 121 123 126 129 130 131 132 143 144 145 146 147 148 **P**6
Primary Contact: Velinda Stevens, President
COO: Ted W. Hirsch, Senior Executive Director
CFO: Charles T. Pearce, Chief Financial and Information Officer
CHR: Deb Wilson, Director Human Resources
Web address: www.krmc.org
Control: Other not-for-profit (including NFP Corporation) **Service:** General Medical and Surgical

Staffed Beds: 163 Admissions: 7735 Census: 90 Outpatient Visits: 182284 Births: 638 Total Expense ($000): 223409 Payroll Expense ($000): 104231 Personnel: 1904

★ **THE HEALTHCENTER (270087)**, 320 Sunnyview Lane, Zip 59901–3129; tel. 406/751–7550 **A**9 10 **F**3 8 15 31 36 39 64 68 74 78 79 81 82 85 87 100 107 110 111 114 115 117 119 126 147 **P**2
Primary Contact: Tate J. Kreitinger, Chief Executive Officer
CFO: Charles T. Pearce, Chief Financial and Information Officer
CIO: Charles T. Pearce, Chief Financial and Information Officer
CHR: Susan Stevens, Director Human Resources
CNO: Victoria Johnson, R.N., Nursing Director of Surgical and Medical Services
Web address: www.krmc.org
Control: Corporation, Investor-owned, for-profit **Service:** General Medical and Surgical

Staffed Beds: 30 Admissions: 709 Census: 4 Outpatient Visits: 38949 Births: 0 Total Expense ($000): 27528 Payroll Expense ($000): 7012 Personnel: 142

LEWISTOWN—Fergus County

★ **CENTRAL MONTANA MEDICAL CENTER (271345)**, 408 Wendell Avenue, Zip 59457–2261; tel. 406/535–7711, (Total facility includes 65 beds in nursing home–type unit) **A**9 10 18 **F**3 7 11 13 15 28 29 31 34 35 40 43 45 50 53 57 59 62 63 64 65 74 75 76 77 79 81 84 85 86 87 89 91 92 93 94 97 107 108 110 111 115 119 128 129 130 131 132 133 146 148 **P**6 **S** QHR, Brentwood, TN
Primary Contact: Christopher Noland, Interim Chief Executive Officer
CFO: Alan Aldrich, Chief Financial Officer
CHR: Torie A. Lynch, Manager Human Resources
CNO: Delilah Duffy, Interim Chief Nurse Officer
Web address: www.cmmccares.com
Control: Other not-for-profit (including NFP Corporation) **Service:** General Medical and Surgical

Staffed Beds: 90 Admissions: 926 Census: 55 Outpatient Visits: 52285 Births: 101 Total Expense ($000): 27300 Payroll Expense ($000): 14401 Personnel: 300

LIBBY—Lincoln County

★ **CABINET PEAKS MEDICAL CENTER (271320)**, 209 Health Park Drive, Zip 59923–2130; tel. 406/283–7000 **A**5 9 10 18 **F**3 11 13 15 17 28 29 30 31 34 35 40 45 56 57 59 64 68 70 75 76 77 79 81 82 84 85 86 87 89 91 93 97 102 107 110 111 114 119 129 130 131 132 133 135 144 146 147 148 **P**6
Primary Contact: Bruce Whitfield, CPA, Chief Executive Officer and Chief Financial Officer
CFO: Bruce Whitfield, CPA, Chief Executive Officer and Chief Financial Officer
CMO: Jay Maloney, M.D., Chief of Staff
Web address: www.sjlh.com
Control: Other not-for-profit (including NFP Corporation) **Service:** General Medical and Surgical

Staffed Beds: 25 Admissions: 780 Census: 6

LIVINGSTON—Park County

★ **LIVINGSTON MEMORIAL HOSPITAL (271317)**, 504 South 13th Street, Zip 59047–3727; tel. 406/222–3541 **A**9 10 18 **F**13 15 17 28 29 34 35 36 40 43 45 50 57 59 62 63 64 65 66 67 68 70 75 76 77 78 79 81 82 85 86 87 89 93 102 107 108 110 111 114 119 124 128 129 130 131 133 135 **P**3
Primary Contact: Bren Lowe, Chief Executive Officer
CFO: Ryan Speas, Director Finance
CMO: D. Scott Coleman, Medical Director
CHR: Connie Dunn, Director Human Resources
Web address: www.livingstonhealthcare.org
Control: Other not-for-profit (including NFP Corporation) **Service:** General Medical and Surgical

Staffed Beds: 25 Admissions: 931 Census: 9 Outpatient Visits: 32171 Births: 86 Total Expense ($000): 28370 Payroll Expense ($000): 14762 Personnel: 277

MALTA—Phillips County

★ **PHILLIPS COUNTY HOSPITAL (271312)**, 417 South Fourth East, Zip 59538–8825, Mailing Address: P.O. Box 640, Zip 59538–0640; tel. 406/654–1100 **A**9 10 18 **F**3 29 31 34 40 41 43 50 56 57 59 62 66 84 90 93 107 114 127 132 133 **P**4
Primary Contact: Ward C. VanWichen, Chief Executive Officer
CFO: Stephanie Denham, Chief Financial Officer and Human Resources Officer
CMO: Ed Medina, M.D., Medical Director
CHR: Stephanie Denham, Chief Financial Officer and Human Resources Officer
CNO: Lonna Crowder, Director of Nursing
Web address: www.pchospital.us/
Control: Other not-for-profit (including NFP Corporation) **Service:** General Medical and Surgical

Staffed Beds: 6 Admissions: 226 Census: 2 Outpatient Visits: 7178 Births: 0 Total Expense ($000): 5486 Payroll Expense ($000): 2562 Personnel: 71

MILES CITY—Custer County

⊞ **HOLY ROSARY HEALTHCARE (271347)**, 2600 Wilson Street, Zip 59301–5094; tel. 406/233–2600, (Total facility includes 65 beds in nursing home–type unit) **A**1 9 10 18 **F**3 13 15 28 29 30 31 32 34 35 40 48 56 57 59 63 64 65 68 70 75 76 77 78 79 81 84 85 89 93 94 97 99 100 101 103 104 107 108 110 111 115 119 124 127 129 130 131 133 143 144 146 147 148 **P**6 **S** SCL Health System, Denver, CO
Primary Contact: Paul Lewis, Chief Executive Officer
CFO: Calvin Carey, VP Finance and Support Services
CMO: Michael Bush, M.D., Chief Medical Officer
CHR: Cathy Rodenbaugh, Director Human Resources
CNO: Lisa Sanford, VP Patient Care/CNO
Web address: www.holyrosaryhealthcare.org
Control: Church-operated, Nongovernment, not-for profit **Service:** General Medical and Surgical

Staffed Beds: 90 Admissions: 1489 Census: 64 Outpatient Visits: 47397 Births: 294 Total Expense ($000): 38766 Payroll Expense ($000): 15848 Personnel: 272

MISSOULA—Missoula County

⊞ △ **COMMUNITY MEDICAL CENTER (270023)**, 2827 Fort Missoula Road, Zip 59804–7408; tel. 406/728–4100 **A**1 7 9 10 19 **F**2 3 11 13 17 18 20 22 26 28 29 30 31 34 35 37 40 43 45 46 47 48 49 51 54 57 59 64 65 68 70 72 73 74 75 76 78 79 81 82 83 84 85 87 88 89 90 91 92 93 94 96 97 107 108 110 115 116 117 118 119 126 130 132 134 135 143 144 145 146 147 148 **P**6 7
Primary Contact: Stephen G. Carlson, President and Chief Executive Officer
COO: Devin Huntley, Vice President Operations
CFO: David Richhart, Vice President Fiscal Services
CMO: David Lechner, M.D., Chief Medical Officer and Vice President Innovation
CIO: Stan Moser, Vice President Information Systems
CHR: Joe Schmier, Director Human Resources, Payroll & Employee Health
CNO: Jan Perry, R.N., Vice President Patient Care Services
Web address: www.communitymed.org
Control: Other not-for-profit (including NFP Corporation) **Service:** General Medical and Surgical

Staffed Beds: 133 Admissions: 5175 Census: 63 Outpatient Visits: 133150 Births: 1500 Total Expense ($000): 151994 Payroll Expense ($000): 63261 Personnel: 1134

MT

Hospital, Medicare Provider Number, Address, Telephone, Approval, Facility, and Physician Codes, Health Care System

★ American Hospital Association (AHA) membership
□ The Joint Commission accreditation ◇ DNV Healthcare Inc. accreditation
○ Healthcare Facilities Accreditation Program
△ Commission on Accreditation of Rehabilitation Facilities (CARF) accreditation

MT

✠ △ **ST. PATRICK HOSPITAL (270014)**, 500 West Broadway,
Zip 59802–4096, Mailing Address: P.O. Box 4587, Zip 59806–4587;
tel. 406/543–7271 **A**1 2 5 7 9 10 19 **F**3 5 8 11 12 15 18 19 20 21 22 23 24
25 26 27 28 29 30 31 34 35 36 38 40 43 45 49 50 53 57 58 59 61 64 65
68 70 74 75 77 78 79 81 82 84 85 86 88 89 90 92 93 96 97 98 99 100
101 102 103 104 105 107 108 110 111 113 114 115 116 117 118 119 121
123 124 126 127 129 130 131 132 135 141 146 147 148 **P**4 6 7
S Providence Health & Services, Renton, WA
Primary Contact: Jeff Fee, Chief Executive Officer
CFO: Kirk Bodlovic, Regional Chief Financial Officer
CHR: Karyn Trainor, Director Human Resources
CNO: Joyce Dombrouski, R.N., Regional Chief Nursing Officer
Web address: www.saintpatrick.org
Control: Church–operated, Nongovernment, not–for profit **Service:** General
Medical and Surgical

Staffed Beds: 193 **Admissions:** 8879 **Census:** 119 **Outpatient Visits:**
229732 **Births:** 0 **Total Expense ($000):** 225011 **Payroll Expense ($000):**
65821 **Personnel:** 1336

PHILIPSBURG—Granite County

GRANITE COUNTY MEDICAL CENTER (271303), 310 Sansome Street,
Zip 59858–0729, Mailing Address: P.O. Box 729, Zip 59858–0729;
tel. 406/859–3271, (Data for 274 days) **A**9 10 18 **F**32 35 39 40 57 67 93 97
108 127 133
Primary Contact: Daniel W. Boatman, Chief Executive Officer
CFO: Susan Ossello, Chief Financial Officer
CMO: John Moore, M.D., Medical Director
Web address: www.gcmedcenter.org/
Control: Hospital district or authority, Government, nonfederal **Service:** General
Medical and Surgical

Staffed Beds: 25 **Admissions:** 50 **Census:** 1 **Outpatient Visits:** 2124 **Births:**
0 **Total Expense ($000):** 2993 **Payroll Expense ($000):** 1478 **Personnel:**
57

PLAINS—Sanders County

★ **CLARK FORK VALLEY HOSPITAL (271323)**, 10 Kruger Road, Zip 59859,
Mailing Address: P.O. Box 768, Zip 59859–0768; tel. 406/826–4800, (Total
facility includes 28 beds in nursing home–type unit) **A**9 10 18 **F**3 11 13 15 28
29 30 32 34 35 36 40 43 44 45 50 57 58 59 62 63 64 65 68 70 74 75 76
77 81 82 83 84 85 89 93 97 107 110 114 118 119 127 128 130 132 133
135 143 146 147 148 **P**3 6
Primary Contact: Gregory S. Hanson, M.D., Chief Executive Officer
CFO: Carla Neiman, Chief Financial Officer
CMO: Ronald Black, M.D., Chief of Staff
CIO: Carla Neiman, Chief Financial Officer
CHR: Barry Fowler, Director Human and System Resources
Web address: www.cfvh.org
Control: Other not–for–profit (including NFP Corporation) **Service:** General
Medical and Surgical

Staffed Beds: 44 **Admissions:** 383 **Census:** 27 **Outpatient Visits:** 25626
Births: 45 **Total Expense ($000):** 16437 **Payroll Expense ($000):** 7713
Personnel: 118

PLENTYWOOD—Sheridan County

SHERIDAN MEMORIAL HOSPITAL (271322), 440 West Laurel Avenue,
Zip 59254–1596; tel. 406/765–1420, (Total facility includes 78 beds in nursing
home–type unit) **A**9 10 18 **F**3 7 11 13 15 17 35 40 50 57 59 62 63 67 75 77
81 87 93 107 110 114 119 127 128 130 132 133 145 146 147
Primary Contact: Sandra Christensen, Chief Executive Officer
CIO: Troy McClymont, Chief Information Technology Officer
CNO: Kathy Tangedal, Chief Nursing Officer
Web address: www.sheridanhospital.org
Control: Other not–for–profit (including NFP Corporation) **Service:** General
Medical and Surgical

Staffed Beds: 97 **Admissions:** 335 **Census:** 58 **Outpatient Visits:** 11839
Births: 0 **Total Expense ($000):** 11274 **Payroll Expense ($000):** 5747
Personnel: 153

POLSON—Lake County

✠ **PROVIDENCE ST. JOSEPH MEDICAL CENTER (271343)**, 6 Thirteenth Avenue
East, Zip 59860–5315, Mailing Address: P.O. Box 1010, Zip 59860–1010;
tel. 406/883–5377 **A**1 9 10 18 **F**3 10 13 15 28 29 30 34 35 40 43 46 50 57
59 64 68 75 76 77 79 81 82 84 85 87 89 93 97 100 102 107 110 111 114
119 125 127 129 130 131 133 146 147 148 **P**6 **S** Providence Health &
Services, Renton, WA
Primary Contact: James R. Kiser, II, Chief Executive Officer
COO: Colleen Nielsen, Director Operations
CFO: Kirk Bodlovic, Vice President and Chief Financial Officer
CMO: Kelly Bagnell, M.D., Chief of Staff
Web address: www.saintjoes.org
Control: Church–operated, Nongovernment, not–for profit **Service:** General
Medical and Surgical

Staffed Beds: 22 **Admissions:** 758 **Census:** 7 **Outpatient Visits:** 67693
Births: 135 **Total Expense ($000):** 29458 **Payroll Expense ($000):** 13387
Personnel: 165

POPLAR—Roosevelt County

★ **POPLAR COMMUNITY HOSPITAL (271300)**, H and Court Avenue, Zip 59255,
Mailing Address: P.O. Box 38, Zip 59255–0038; tel. 406/768–3452 **A**9 10 18
F3 7 40 43 50 57 59 78 87 99 100 101 102 103 104 107 110 119 130 133
143 147 **P**3 6
Primary Contact: Margaret B. Norgaard, Chief Executive Officer
CHR: Annie Block, Director Human Resources
Web address: www.nemhs.net
Control: Other not–for–profit (including NFP Corporation) **Service:** General
Medical and Surgical

Staffed Beds: 20 **Admissions:** 121 **Census:** 8 **Outpatient Visits:** 9440
Births: 0 **Total Expense ($000):** 6862 **Payroll Expense ($000):** 3136
Personnel: 71

RED LODGE—Carbon County

★ **BEARTOOTH BILLINGS CLINIC (271326)**, 2525 North Broadway,
Zip 59068–9222, Mailing Address: P.O. Box 590, Zip 59068–0590;
tel. 406/446–2345 **A**9 10 18 **F**3 11 15 18 28 29 34 35 40 43 44 45 50 56
57 59 62 63 64 65 68 75 77 81 85 86 87 93 94 96 97 107 110 114 119
130 131 133 135 146 148 **P**6
Primary Contact: Kelley Evans, Chief Executive Officer
CFO: Kyle Gee, Chief Financial Officer
CMO: William George, M.D., Chief of Staff
CHR: Katie Nordstrom, Director Human Resources
CNO: Bridgett Chartier, Director of Nursing
Web address: www.beartoothbillingsclinic.org
Control: Other not–for–profit (including NFP Corporation) **Service:** General
Medical and Surgical

Staffed Beds: 10 **Admissions:** 255 **Census:** 3 **Outpatient Visits:** 57778
Births: 0 **Total Expense ($000):** 12474 **Payroll Expense ($000):** 3697
Personnel: 101

RONAN—Lake County

★ **ST. LUKE COMMUNITY HEALTHCARE (271325)**, 107 Sixth Avenue S.W.,
Zip 59864–2634; tel. 406/676–4441, (Total facility includes 75 beds in nursing
home–type unit) **A**9 10 18 **F**2 13 15 28 29 34 40 43 45 53 54 57 59 61 64 65
75 76 79 81 85 93 97 107 108 110 111 115 119 127 128 129 131 133 135
144 145 **P**6
Primary Contact: Steve J. Todd, Chief Executive Officer
CFO: Paul Soukup, Chief Financial Officer
CMO: Paul D. Gochis, M.D., Chief of Staff
CHR: Theresa Jones, Manager Human Resources
Web address: www.stlukehealthnet.org
Control: Other not–for–profit (including NFP Corporation) **Service:** General
Medical and Surgical

Staffed Beds: 105 **Admissions:** 1087 **Census:** 61 **Outpatient Visits:** 75797
Births: 167 **Total Expense ($000):** 34237 **Payroll Expense ($000):** 17449
Personnel: 304

ROUNDUP—Musselshell County

★ **ROUNDUP MEMORIAL HEALTHCARE (271346)**, 1202 Third Street West,
Zip 59072–1816, Mailing Address: P.O. Box 40, Zip 59072–0040;
tel. 406/323–2301, (Nonreporting) **A**9 10 18
Primary Contact: Bradley Howell, Chief Executive Officer
CFO: Kyle Gee, Regional Vice President Financial Operations
CMO: Mark Ward, M.D., Chief of Staff
CHR: Michelle Clement, Executive Assistant/Human Resources Director
CNO: Emily Shoup, Director Nursing Services
Web address: www.rmhmt.org/
Control: Other not–for–profit (including NFP Corporation) **Service:** General
Medical and Surgical

Staffed Beds: 46

SAINT MARY—Glacier County

**U. S. PUBLIC HEALTH SERVICE BLACKFEET COMMUNITY HOSPITAL
(270074)**, 760 New Hospital Circle, Zip 59417–0760, Mailing Address: P.O. Box
760, Browning, Zip 59417–0760; tel. 406/338–6100, (Nonreporting) **A**5 10 **S** U.
S. Indian Health Service, Rockville, MD
Primary Contact: Merlin Gilham, Chief Executive Officer
Web address: www.ihs.gov
Control: PHS, Indian Service, Government, federal **Service:** General Medical and
Surgical

Staffed Beds: 25

Many Facility Codes have changed. Please refer to the AHA Guide Code Chart. © 2014 AHA Guide

SCOBEY—Daniels County

DANIELS MEMORIAL HEALTHCARE CENTER (271342), 105 Fifth Avenue East, Zip 59263, Mailing Address: P.O. Box 400, Zip 59263–0400; tel. 406/487–2296, (Total facility includes 30 beds in nursing home–type unit) **A**9 10 18 **F**2 11 29 31 34 35 40 43 50 56 57 59 64 65 67 69 75 77 85 86 87 91 93 97 102 103 107 114 127 130 131 132 133 143 146 148 **P**6
Primary Contact: David Hubbard, Chief Executive Officer
CMO: Don Sawdey, M.D., Medical Director
CHR: Edith Huda, Director Human Resources
CNO: Kathy Ware, Director of Nursing
Web address: www.danielsmemorialhealthcare.org
Control: Hospital district or authority, Government, nonfederal **Service:** General Medical and Surgical

Staffed Beds: 54 **Admissions:** 212 **Census:** 30 **Outpatient Visits:** 4923 **Births:** 0 **Total Expense ($000):** 6687 **Payroll Expense ($000):** 3451 **Personnel:** 98

SHELBY—Toole County

★ **MARIAS MEDICAL CENTER (271328)**, 640 Park Drive, Zip 59474–1663, Mailing Address: P.O. Box 915, Zip 59474–0915; tel. 406/434–3200, (Total facility includes 63 beds in nursing home–type unit) **A**9 10 18 **F**7 10 11 13 15 17 40 43 45 56 57 59 64 70 75 77 78 79 81 82 93 107 110 111 115 119 125 128 129 130 133
Primary Contact: Mark A. Cross, Chief Executive Officer
CFO: Melissa Ostberg, Chief Financial Officer
CMO: Melanie Hardy, D.O., Chief of Staff
CIO: Jayce Yarn, Director Information Technology
CHR: Cindy Lamb, Director Human Resources
CNO: Tamra Fender, Chief Nursing Officer
Web address: www.mmcmt.org
Control: County–Government, nonfederal **Service:** General Medical and Surgical

Staffed Beds: 88 **Admissions:** 418 **Census:** 42 **Outpatient Visits:** 13304 **Births:** 24 **Total Expense ($000):** 14813 **Payroll Expense ($000):** 7313 **Personnel:** 97

SHERIDAN—Madison County

★ **RUBY VALLEY HOSPITAL (271319)**, 220 East Crofoot Street, Zip 59749–7714, Mailing Address: P.O. Box 336, Zip 59749–0336; tel. 406/842–5453 **A**9 10 18 **F**2 11 28 29 34 35 38 40 56 57 59 64 65 66 75 82 86 90 91 93 97 100 107 114 119 127 128 130 133 135 147 148 **P**6
Primary Contact: John H. Semingson, Chief Executive Officer
CFO: Dennis Holschbach, Chief Financial Officer and Director Human Resources
CMO: Roman Hendrickson, M.D., Medical Director
CHR: Dennis Holschbach, Chief Financial Officer and Director Human Resources
CNO: Ted Woirhaye, R.N., Director of Nursing
Web address: www.rubyvalleyhospital.com/
Control: Hospital district or authority, Government, nonfederal **Service:** General Medical and Surgical

Staffed Beds: 8 **Admissions:** 130 **Census:** 2 **Outpatient Visits:** 4699 **Births:** 0 **Total Expense ($000):** 4666 **Payroll Expense ($000):** 2876 **Personnel:** 55

SIDNEY—Richland County

★ **SIDNEY HEALTH CENTER (271344)**, 216 14th Avenue S.W., Zip 59270–3586; tel. 406/488–2100, (Total facility includes 56 beds in nursing home–type unit) **A**9 10 18 **F**2 3 13 15 17 28 30 31 34 35 40 41 45 50 56 57 59 62 63 64 68 70 75 76 78 79 81 82 84 85 86 87 89 93 96 107 108 110 111 115 119 120 121 122 123 128 129 130 133 135 144 145 146 147 148 **P**6 7
Primary Contact: Richard Haraldson, Chief Executive Officer
CFO: Tina Montgomery, Chief Financial Officer
CMO: Rajohn Karanjai, M.D., Chief Medical Officer
CIO: Brian Fay, Director Information Systems
CHR: Lisa Aisenbrey, Administrator Human Resources and Support Services
Web address: www.sidneyhealth.org
Control: Other not–for–profit (including NFP Corporation) **Service:** General Medical and Surgical

Staffed Beds: 81 **Admissions:** 962 **Census:** 68 **Outpatient Visits:** 39896 **Births:** 133 **Total Expense ($000):** 47866 **Payroll Expense ($000):** 18101 **Personnel:** 346

SUPERIOR—Mineral County

★ **MINERAL COMMUNITY HOSPITAL (271331)**, 1208 6th Avenue East, Zip 59872–9618, Mailing Address: P.O. Box 66, Zip 59872–0066; tel. 406/822–4841 **A**9 10 18 **F**10 29 31 40 43 45 57 69 75 81 89 93 107 110 119 133 143
Primary Contact: Larry E. Putnam, Interim Chief Executive Officer
CFO: Cliff Case, Chief Financial Officer
CMO: Roger Pafford, M.D., Medical Director
CHR: Stacy Conrow–Ververis, Director Human Resources
CNO: Kirsten Locke, Director of Nursing Services
Web address: www.mineralcommunityhospital.com/
Control: Other not–for–profit (including NFP Corporation) **Service:** General Medical and Surgical

Staffed Beds: 25 **Admissions:** 149 **Census:** 15 **Outpatient Visits:** 6032 **Births:** 0 **Total Expense ($000):** 6896 **Payroll Expense ($000):** 3413 **Personnel:** 69

TERRY—Prairie County

PRAIRIE COMMUNITY HEALTH CENTER See Prairie Community Hospital

★ **PRAIRIE COMMUNITY HOSPITAL (271309)**, 312 South Adams Avenue, Zip 59349–0156, Mailing Address: P.O. Box 156, Zip 59349–0156; tel. 406/635–5511 **A**9 10 18 **F**1 3 32 34 40 43 57 59 64 65 67 69 75 87 90 127 128 133 135 146 147 148 **P**6
Primary Contact: Candyce Payne, Administrator
CFO: Laurie Chandler, Financial Officer
CIO: Laurie Chandler, Chairman
CNO: Kay Schaaf, Chief Nursing Officer
Web address: www.prairiecommunityhospital.org/
Control: Hospital district or authority, Government, nonfederal **Service:** General Medical and Surgical

Staffed Beds: 22 **Admissions:** 49 **Census:** 19 **Outpatient Visits:** 2011 **Births:** 0 **Total Expense ($000):** 2061 **Payroll Expense ($000):** 903 **Personnel:** 30

TOWNSEND—Broadwater County

BROADWATER HEALTH CENTER (271333), 110 North Oak Street, Zip 59644–2306; tel. 406/266–3186, (Nonreporting) **A**9 10 18
Primary Contact: Kyle Hopstad, Chief Executive Officer
CFO: Jennifer Clowes, Chief Financial Officer
CMO: Kathleen Trapp, M.D., Medical Director
CHR: April Campbell, Director Human Resources
CNO: Gary Buchanan, Director of Nursing
Web address: www.broadwaterhealthcenter.com
Control: County–Government, nonfederal **Service:** General Medical and Surgical

Staffed Beds: 9

WARM SPRINGS—Deer Lodge County

MONTANA STATE HOSPITAL (274086), 300 Garnet Way, Zip 59756–0300, Mailing Address: P.O. Box 300, Zip 59756–0300; tel. 406/693–7000 **A**10 **F**29 38 39 50 59 66 68 74 75 77 86 97 98 100 103 106 119 130 132 135 **P**6
Primary Contact: John W. Glueckert, Administrator
CFO: Tracey Thun, Director Business and Support Services
CMO: Thomas Gray, M.D., Medical Director
CIO: Melinda Bridgewater, Director, Information Services
CHR: Todd Thun, Director Human Resources
CNO: Dave Olson, Director of Nursing
Web address: www.msh.mt.gov
Control: State–Government, nonfederal **Service:** Psychiatric

Staffed Beds: 201 **Admissions:** 604 **Census:** 168 **Outpatient Visits:** 0 **Births:** 0 **Total Expense ($000):** 33490 **Payroll Expense ($000):** 17909 **Personnel:** 404

WHITE SULPHUR SPRINGS—Meagher County

MOUNTAINVIEW MEDICAL CENTER (271306), 16 West Main Street, Zip 59645–9036, Mailing Address: P.O. Box Q, Zip 59645–0817; tel. 406/547–3321, (Nonreporting) **A**9 10 18
Primary Contact: Aaron Rogers, Chief Executive Officer
Web address: www.mvmc.org
Control: Other not–for–profit (including NFP Corporation) **Service:** General Medical and Surgical

Staffed Beds: 25

MT

WHITEFISH—Flathead County

★ **NORTH VALLEY HOSPITAL (271336)**, 1600 Hospital Way, Zip 59937–7849;
tel. 406/863–3500 **A**9 10 18 **F**3 11 13 15 28 29 30 31 34 35 37 40 43 45
50 51 54 56 57 59 64 68 70 75 76 79 81 82 85 86 87 89 97 100 102 103
104 107 110 111 115 119 126 127 128 129 130 131 132 133 135 144 146
148 **P**6 **S** QHR, Brentwood, TN
Primary Contact: Jason A. Spring, FACHE, Chief Executive Officer
COO: Christina Bogers, Chief Clinical Officer
CFO: Wesley D. White, Chief Financial Officer
CMO: Ronald Miller, M.D., Chief Medical Officer
CIO: Michael Barnes, Chief Information Officer
CHR: Susan G. Werth, Director Human Resources
Web address: www.nvhosp.org
Control: Other not–for–profit (including NFP Corporation) **Service:** General
Medical and Surgical

Staffed Beds: 25 **Admissions:** 1498 **Census:** 13 **Outpatient Visits:** 48109
Births: 468 **Total Expense ($000):** 41074 **Payroll Expense ($000):** 14278
Personnel: 323

WOLF POINT—Roosevelt County

★ **TRINITY HOSPITAL (271341)**, 315 Knapp Street, Zip 59201–1826;
tel. 406/653–6500, (Total facility includes 60 beds in nursing home–type unit) **A**9
10 18 **F**3 6 7 8 13 15 29 31 32 34 40 43 45 50 56 57 59 64 69 70 75 76
78 81 92 110 119 120 125 127 128 130 133 143 145 **P**5
Primary Contact: Margaret B. Norgaard, Chief Executive Officer
Web address: www.nemhs.net
Control: Other not–for–profit (including NFP Corporation) **Service:** General
Medical and Surgical

Staffed Beds: 82 **Admissions:** 468 **Census:** 62 **Outpatient Visits:** 15372
Births: 158 **Total Expense ($000):** 16110 **Payroll Expense ($000):** 6606
Personnel: 183

MT

Many Facility Codes have changed. Please refer to the AHA Guide Code Chart. © 2014 AHA Guide

NEBRASKA

AINSWORTH—Brown County

BROWN COUNTY HOSPITAL (281325), 945 East Zero Street,
Zip 69210–1547; tel. 402/387–2800 **A**9 10 18 **F**15 28 31 40 43 57 59 62 77
79 81 93 94 107 110 111 114 119 127 128 130 133
Primary Contact: Shannon Sorensen, Chief Executive Officer
CFO: Ken Smith, Chief Financial Officer
CMO: Melvin Campbell, M.D., Medical Staff Chairman
CIO: Mike Depko, Director Information Technology
CHR: Lisa Fischer, Director Human Resources
CNO: Tammy Brown, R.N., Director of Nursing
Web address: www.browncountyhospital.org
Control: County–Government, nonfederal **Service:** General Medical and Surgical

Staffed Beds: 18 **Admissions:** 204 **Census:** 3 **Outpatient Visits:** 11297
Births: 0 **Total Expense ($000):** 8345 **Payroll Expense ($000):** 3513
Personnel: 80

ALBION—Boone County

★ **BOONE COUNTY HEALTH CENTER (281334)**, 723 West Fairview Street,
Zip 68620–1725, Mailing Address: P.O. Box 151, Zip 68620–0151;
tel. 402/395–2191 **A**9 10 18 **F**3 11 13 15 28 29 31 32 34 35 38 40 45 50
52 53 57 59 62 64 65 74 75 76 77 78 79 81 82 85 86 87 93 104 107 108
110 111 115 116 119 127 128 129 130 131 132 133 134 135 145 146 147
148 **P**5 6
Primary Contact: Victor N. Lee, FACHE, President and Chief Executive Officer
CFO: Mandy Kumm, Vice President Fiscal Services
CIO: Larry Zoucha, Chief Information Officer
CHR: Jennifer Beierman, Director Human Resources
Web address: www.boonecohealth.org
Control: County–Government, nonfederal **Service:** General Medical and Surgical

Staffed Beds: 25 **Admissions:** 733 **Census:** 9 **Outpatient Visits:** 85333
Births: 97 **Total Expense ($000):** 26681 **Payroll Expense ($000):** 12510
Personnel: 210

ALLIANCE—Box Butte County

⊞ **BOX BUTTE GENERAL HOSPITAL (281360)**, 2101 Box Butte Avenue,
Zip 69301–4445, Mailing Address: P.O. Box 810, Zip 69301–0810;
tel. 308/762–6660 **A**1 9 10 18 **F**3 5 11 13 15 28 29 32 34 35 36 38 40 43
47 45 50 53 57 59 60 64 68 69 75 77 78 79 81 82 85 86 87 92 93 97 100
101 104 107 108 111 114 116 118 119 127 129 130 131 132 133 134 135
146 148
Primary Contact: Dan Griess, FACHE, Chief Executive Officer
COO: Lori Mazanec, Chief Operating Officer
CFO: Tracy E. Jatczak, CPA, Chief Financial Officer
Web address: www.bbgh.org
Control: County–Government, nonfederal **Service:** General Medical and Surgical

Staffed Beds: 25 **Admissions:** 977 **Census:** 10 **Outpatient Visits:** 33220
Births: 90 **Total Expense ($000):** 30940 **Payroll Expense ($000):** 13788
Personnel: 236

ALMA—Harlan County

★ **HARLAN COUNTY HEALTH SYSTEM (281300)**, 717 North Brown Street,
Zip 68920–2132, Mailing Address: P.O. Box 836, Zip 68920–0836;
tel. 308/928–2151 **A**9 10 18 **F**1 3 4 11 15 16 17 29 30 31 40 45 46 50 64
67 70 72 73 80 81 85 86 88 89 90 93 98 107 110 114 119 127 128 130
132 133 135 146 147 **P**6 **S** Great Plains Health Alliance, Inc., Wichita, KS
Primary Contact: Manuela Wolf, R.N., Chief Executive Officer
CFO: Sue Lans, Comptroller
CMO: Cameron Knachstedt, D.O., Chief of Medical Staff
CIO: Michael Andrews, Coordinator Information Systems
CHR: Ana York, Coordinator Human Resources and Benefits
CNO: Katherine Fleischmann, Director of Nursing
Web address: www.harlancountyhealth.com
Control: County–Government, nonfederal **Service:** General Medical and Surgical

Staffed Beds: 19 **Admissions:** 133 **Census:** 3 **Outpatient Visits:** 16298
Births: 0 **Total Expense ($000):** 7680 **Payroll Expense ($000):** 3024
Personnel: 62

ATKINSON—Holt County

WEST HOLT MEMORIAL HOSPITAL (281343), 406 West Neely Street,
Zip 68713–4801; tel. 402/925–2811 **A**9 10 18 **F**15 28 40 43 57 93 107 119
127 129 130 131 133 146 **S** Faith Regional Health Services, Norfolk, NE
Primary Contact: Michael F. Coyle, Chief Executive Officer
CFO: Karen Nollette, Chief Financial Officer
CMO: John Tubbs, M.D., Chief of Staff
CIO: Mark Johnson, Chief Information Officer
CHR: Margaret Linse, Administrative Secretary and Director Human Resources
CNO: Tom Hoover, Director of Nursing
Web address: www.westholtmed.org
Control: Other not–for–profit (including NFP Corporation) **Service:** General
Medical and Surgical

Staffed Beds: 17 **Admissions:** 182 **Census:** 2 **Outpatient Visits:** 11124
Births: 0 **Total Expense ($000):** 6427 **Payroll Expense ($000):** 3824
Personnel: 86

AUBURN—Nemaha County

★ ◇ **NEMAHA COUNTY HOSPITAL (281324)**, 2022 13th Street,
Zip 68305–1799; tel. 402/274–4366 **A**9 10 18 21 **F**1 3 4 7 11 12 15 16 17
28 29 30 31 35 40 43 62 64 67 68 70 72 73 74 75 77 78 79 80 81 82 85
87 88 89 90 93 94 98 107 110 111 114 117 119 128 129 133 135 141
147 148
Primary Contact: Marty Fattig, Chief Executive Officer
COO: Kermit Moore, R.N., Chief Operating Officer and Chief Nursing Officer
CFO: Stacy Taylor, Chief Financial Officer
CHR: Susan Shupp, Director Human Resources
Web address: www.nchnet.org
Control: County–Government, nonfederal **Service:** General Medical and Surgical

Staffed Beds: 20 **Admissions:** 230 **Census:** 3 **Outpatient Visits:** 19176
Births: 0 **Total Expense ($000):** 11318 **Payroll Expense ($000):** 4434
Personnel: 76

AURORA—Hamilton County

★ **MEMORIAL COMMUNITY HEALTH (281320)**, 1423 Seventh Street,
Zip 68818–1197; tel. 402/694–3171, (Total facility includes 49 beds in nursing
home–type unit) **A**9 10 18 **F**10 11 13 15 28 31 34 35 40 43 45 47 48 49 56
57 59 64 65 67 68 71 75 76 77 78 79 81 82 85 90 93 94 96 97 107 110
119 125 128 129 130 131 133 146
Primary Contact: Diane R. Keller, Chief Executive Officer
CFO: Phil Fendt, Chief Financial Officer
CMO: Jeff Muilenburg, Chief of Staff
CIO: Deb Auah, Supervisor Information Technology
CHR: Laurie Andrews, Chief Human Resources Officer
CNO: Cheryl A. Erickson, R.N., Director of Nursing
Web address: www.memorialcommunityhealth.org
Control: Other not–for–profit (including NFP Corporation) **Service:** General
Medical and Surgical

Staffed Beds: 63 **Admissions:** 279 **Census:** 2 **Outpatient Visits:** 22133
Births: 43 **Total Expense ($000):** 20603 **Payroll Expense ($000):** 12050
Personnel: 220

MEMORIAL HOSPITAL See Memorial Community Health

BASSETT—Rock County

ROCK COUNTY HOSPITAL (281333), 102 East South Street,
Zip 68714–5508; tel. 402/684–3366, (Total facility includes 30 beds in nursing
home–type unit) **A**9 10 18 **F**7 11 15 28 40 53 57 81 84 107 110 127 128 133
Primary Contact: Stacey A. Knox, Administrator
CMO: John Tubbs, M.D., Chief of Staff
CHR: Jackie Carpenter, Office Manager
CNO: Connie Olson, R.N., Director of Nursing
Web address: www.rockcountyhospital.com
Control: County–Government, nonfederal **Service:** General Medical and Surgical

Staffed Beds: 54 **Admissions:** 244 **Census:** 26 **Outpatient Visits:** 5503
Births: 0 **Total Expense ($000):** 5336 **Payroll Expense ($000):** 2865
Personnel: 79

NE

Hospital, Medicare Provider Number, Address, Telephone, Approval, Facility, and Physician Codes, Health Care System

★ American Hospital Association (AHA) membership
□ The Joint Commission accreditation   ◇ DNV Healthcare Inc. accreditation

○ Healthcare Facilities Accreditation Program
△ Commission on Accreditation of Rehabilitation Facilities (CARF) accreditation

BEATRICE—Gage County

☒ **BEATRICE COMMUNITY HOSPITAL AND HEALTH CENTER (281364)**, 4800 Hospital Parkway, Zip 68310–6906, Mailing Address: P.O. Box 278, Zip 68310–0278; tel. 402/228–3344 **A**1 9 10 18 **F**3 13 15 28 31 34 35 40 45 57 62 63 64 65 68 69 70 75 76 78 79 81 82 85 87 93 107 108 110 111 114 118 119 127 129 130 131 132 133 135 146 147
Primary Contact: Thomas W. Sommers, FACHE, President and Chief Executive Officer
CFO: Alan W. Streeter, Chief Financial Officer
CMO: Eric Thomsen, M.D., Chief of Staff
CHR: Kathryn G. Humble, Chief Human Resources Officer
CNO: Julie L. Jones, R.N., Chief Nursing Officer
Web address: www.beatricecommunityhospital.com
Control: Other not-for-profit (including NFP Corporation) **Service:** General Medical and Surgical

Staffed Beds: 25 **Admissions:** 1019 **Census:** 11 **Outpatient Visits:** 143124 **Births:** 207 **Total Expense ($000):** 53780 **Payroll Expense ($000):** 22947 **Personnel:** 411

BELLEVUE—Sarpy County

☐ **BELLEVUE MEDICAL CENTER (280132)**, 2500 Bellevue Medical Center Drive, Zip 68123–1591; tel. 402/763–3000, (Nonreporting) **A**1 3 5 9 10
Primary Contact: William S. Dinsmoor, Chief Executive Officer
COO: Paulette Davidson, FACHE, Chief Operating Officer
CFO: Stephanie Daubert, Chief Financial Officer
CMO: Marlin G. Stahl, M.D., Chief Medical Officer
CIO: Mark Weiss, Executive Director Enterprise Technology Services
CHR: Deb Dinsmoor, Director Human Resource Operations
CNO: Lisa Walters, R.N., Director of Nursing
Web address: www.bellevuemed.com
Control: Partnership, Investor–owned, for–profit **Service:** General Medical and Surgical

Staffed Beds: 55

BENKELMAN—Dundy County

★ **DUNDY COUNTY HOSPITAL (281340)**, 1313 North Cheyenne Street, Zip 69021–3074, Mailing Address: P.O. Box 626, Zip 69021–0626; tel. 308/423–2204, (Nonreporting) **A**9 10 18
Primary Contact: Rita A. Jones, Chief Executive Officer
COO: Wendy Elkins, Director Operations
CFO: Charles Milner, Chief Financial Officer
CMO: Jose Garcia, M.D., Chief Medical Staff
CIO: David Craw, Head Information Technology
CHR: Sandy Noffsinger, Executive Assistant, Risk Manager and Director Marketing
CNO: Jan Cole–Hudson, R.N., Director Nursing Services
Web address: www.bwtelcom.net/dch
Control: County–Government, nonfederal **Service:** General Medical and Surgical

Staffed Beds: 14

BLAIR—Washington County

★ **MEMORIAL COMMUNITY HOSPITAL AND HEALTH SYSTEM (281359)**, 810 North 22nd Street, Zip 68008–1199, Mailing Address: P.O. Box 250, Zip 68008–0250; tel. 402/426–2182, (Nonreporting) **A**9 10 18
Primary Contact: Robert C. Copple, FACHE, President and CEO
CMO: Bradley Sawtelle, M.D., President Medical Staff
CHR: Kristine Nielsen, Manager Human Resources
CNO: Laura Stawniak, R.N., Chief Nursing Executive
Web address: www.mchhs.org
Control: Other not-for-profit (including NFP Corporation) **Service:** General Medical and Surgical

Staffed Beds: 25

BRIDGEPORT—Morrill County

MORRILL COUNTY COMMUNITY HOSPITAL (281318), 1313 S Street, Zip 69336–0579, Mailing Address: P.O. Box 579, Zip 69336–0579; tel. 308/262–1616 **A**9 10 18 **F**18 28 34 35 36 40 41 43 45 46 47 56 57 59 62 65 66 69 75 77 79 81 90 93 107 111 114 119 127 128 130 133 **P**6
Primary Contact: Robin Stuart, Chief Executive Officer
COO: Robin Stuart, Chief Operating Officer
CFO: Connie Christensen, Chief Financial Officer
CMO: John Post, M.D., Medical Director
CIO: Lori Shengle, Director Information Technology
CHR: Rhea Basa, Director Human Resources
CNO: Sylvia Marie Lichius, R.N., Chief Nursing Officer
Web address: www.morrillcountyhospital.org
Control: County–Government, nonfederal **Service:** General Medical and Surgical

Staffed Beds: 11 **Admissions:** 87 **Census:** 1 **Outpatient Visits:** 25290 **Births:** 0 **Total Expense ($000):** 8170 **Payroll Expense ($000):** 3818

BROKEN BOW—Custer County

JENNIE M. MELHAM MEMORIAL MEDICAL CENTER (281365), 145 Memorial Drive, Zip 68822–1378, Mailing Address: P.O. Box 250, Zip 68822–0250; tel. 308/872–4100, (Nonreporting) **A**9 10 18
Primary Contact: Michael J. Steckler, President and Chief Executive Officer
CFO: Tim Schuckman, Chief Financial Officer
CIO: Tim Schuckman, Chief Financial Officer
CNO: Shelly Amsberry, Director of Nursing
Web address: www.brokenbow–ne.com/community/healthcare/melham.htm
Control: Other not-for-profit (including NFP Corporation) **Service:** General Medical and Surgical

Staffed Beds: 25

CALLAWAY—Custer County

★ **CALLAWAY DISTRICT HOSPITAL (281335)**, 211 East Kimball, Zip 68825–2589, Mailing Address: P.O. Box 100, Zip 68825–0100; tel. 308/836–2228, (Nonreporting) **A**9 10 18
Primary Contact: Marvin Neth, Chief Executive Officer
CHR: Carol Koch, Manager Human Resources
Web address: www.callawayhospital.org
Control: Hospital district or authority, Government, nonfederal **Service:** General Medical and Surgical

Staffed Beds: 12

CAMBRIDGE—Furnas County

★ **TRI VALLEY HEALTH SYSTEM (281348)**, 1305 West Highway 6 and 34, Zip 69022–0488, Mailing Address: P.O. Box 488, Zip 69022–0488; tel. 308/697–3329, (Nonreporting) **A**9 10 18 **S** HealthTech Management Services, Brentwood, TN
Primary Contact: Gregg Magers, Interim Chief Executive Officer
CFO: Diana Rippe, Chief Financial Officer
CMO: Shelly Kasper-Cope, M.D., Chief of Staff
CIO: Doug Hall, Director Information Systems
CHR: Tammy Claussen, Human Resources Executive
Web address: www.trivalleyhealth.com
Control: Other not-for-profit (including NFP Corporation) **Service:** General Medical and Surgical

Staffed Beds: 51

CENTRAL CITY—Merrick County

★ **LITZENBERG MEMORIAL COUNTY HOSPITAL (281328)**, 1715 26th Street, Zip 68826–9620; tel. 308/946–3015, (Nonreporting) **A**9 10 18
Primary Contact: Julie Murray, Chief Executive Officer
CFO: Tanya Sharp, Chief Financial Officer
CHR: Shauna Graham, Director of Professional Services Human Resources, Marketing Foundation
Web address: www.lmchealth.com
Control: County–Government, nonfederal **Service:** General Medical and Surgical

Staffed Beds: 20

CHADRON—Dawes County

★ **CHADRON COMMUNITY HOSPITAL AND HEALTH SERVICES (281341)**, 825 Centennial Drive, Zip 69337–9400; tel. 308/432–5586, (Nonreporting) **A**5 9 10 18
Primary Contact: Harold L. Krueger, Jr., Chief Executive Officer
CFO: Russ Bohnenkamp, Director Finance
CMO: Jerry McLain, M.D., Chief of Staff
CIO: Anna Turman, Chief Information Officer
CHR: Ellen Krueger, Director Human Resources
CNO: Cheryl Cassiday, R.N., Director of Nursing
Web address: www.chadronhospital.com
Control: Other not-for-profit (including NFP Corporation) **Service:** General Medical and Surgical

Staffed Beds: 25

Many Facility Codes have changed. Please refer to the AHA Guide Code Chart. © 2014 AHA Guide

NE

COLUMBUS—Platte County

☒ **COLUMBUS COMMUNITY HOSPITAL (280111)**, 4600 38th Street,
Zip 68601–1664, Mailing Address: P.O. Box 1800, Zip 68602–1800;
tel. 402/564–7118, (Total facility includes 4 beds in nursing home–type unit) **A**1
9 10 20 **F**3 8 11 13 15 17 28 29 34 35 37 38 39 40 43 45 57 59 62 63 64
65 68 69 70 75 76 77 79 81 82 84 85 86 87 93 107 108 110 111 115 116
117 118 119 127 128 129 130 131 132 133 135 146 148 **P**8
Primary Contact: Michael T. Hansen, FACHE, President and Chief Executive Officer
COO: James P. Goulet, Vice President Operations
CFO: J. Joseph Barbaglia, Vice President Financial Services
CMO: Mark Howerter, M.D., President Medical Staff
CIO: Cheryl Tira, Director Information Systems
CHR: Scott E. Messersmith, Director Human Resources
CNO: Linda K. Walline, R.N., Vice President Nursing
Web address: www.columbushosp.org
Control: Other not–for–profit (including NFP Corporation) **Service:** General
Medical and Surgical

Staffed Beds: 51 **Admissions:** 2377 **Census:** 19 **Outpatient Visits:** 56710
Births: 530 **Total Expense ($000):** 59653 **Payroll Expense ($000):** 28673
Personnel: 433

COZAD—Dawson County

★ **COZAD COMMUNITY HOSPITAL (281327)**, 300 East 12th Street,
Zip 69130–1505, Mailing Address: P.O. Box 108, Zip 69130–0108;
tel. 308/784–2261, (Nonreporting) **A**9 10 18
Primary Contact: Lyle E. Davis, Administrator
Web address: www.cozadhealthcare.com
Control: Hospital district or authority, Government, nonfederal **Service:** General
Medical and Surgical

Staffed Beds: 21

CREIGHTON—Knox County

★ **AVERA CREIGHTON HOSPITAL (281331)**, 1503 Main Street,
Zip 68729–3007, Mailing Address: P.O. Box 186, Zip 68729–0186;
tel. 402/358–5700, (Nonreporting) **A**9 10 18 **S** Avera Health, Sioux Falls, SD
Primary Contact: Jennifer Poppen, Chief Executive Officer
CFO: Gregory Beckmann, Finance Controller
CHR: Candace Timmerman, Director Human Resources
CNO: Jean M. Henes, R.N., Director of Nursing
Web address: www.avera.org/creighton/
Control: Other not–for–profit (including NFP Corporation) **Service:** General
Medical and Surgical

Staffed Beds: 70

CRETE—Saline County

★ **CRETE AREA MEDICAL CENTER (281354)**, 2910 Betten Drive,
Zip 68333–3084, Mailing Address: P.O. Box 220, Zip 68333–0220;
tel. 402/826–2102 **A**9 10 18 **F**13 15 28 29 31 34 40 43 57 59 64 65 68 78
79 81 93 97 107 111 114 117 119 127 129 130 131 133 143 146 147 **P**6
S Bryan Health, Lincoln, NE
Primary Contact: Tad M. Hunt, MS, President and Chief Executive Officer
CFO: Bryce Betke, Chief Financial Officer
CMO: Jason Hesser, M.D., Chief of Staff
CIO: Sheri Thompson, Director Information Technology
CHR: Bobbie Wilson, Director Human Resources
CNO: Ruth M. Stephens, MSN, Chief Nursing Officer
Web address: www.creteareamedicalcenter.com
Control: Other not–for–profit (including NFP Corporation) **Service:** General
Medical and Surgical

Staffed Beds: 24 **Admissions:** 396 **Census:** 4 **Outpatient Visits:** 56376
Births: 101 **Total Expense ($000):** 16950 **Payroll Expense ($000):** 7679
Personnel: 133

DAVID CITY—Butler County

★ **BUTLER COUNTY HEALTH CARE CENTER (281332)**, 372 South Ninth Street,
Zip 68632–2116; tel. 402/367–1200, (Nonreporting) **A**9 10 18
Primary Contact: Donald T. Naiberk, Administrator
CFO: Ron Jones, Chief Financial Officer
CMO: Victor Thoendel, M.D., Chief Medical Officer
CIO: Cindy Neesen, Director of Information Technology
CHR: Andra Vandenberg, Director Human Resources
CNO: Sue M. Birkel, R.N., Director of Nursing
Web address: www.bchccnet.org
Control: County–Government, nonfederal **Service:** General Medical and Surgical

Staffed Beds: 25

ELKHORN—Douglas County

METHODIST WOMEN'S HOSPITAL See Nebraska Methodist Hospital, Omaha

FAIRBURY—Jefferson County

★ **JEFFERSON COMMUNITY HEALTH CENTER (281319)**, 2200 H Street,
Zip 68352–1119, Mailing Address: P.O. Box 277, Zip 68352–0277;
tel. 402/729–3351, (Total facility includes 39 beds in nursing home–type unit) **A**9
10 18 **F**2 3 13 15 28 29 30 31 34 35 40 45 50 53 57 59 62 75 77 78 79 81
85 86 87 93 107 110 114 119 128 130 131 132 133 135 146
Primary Contact: Chad Jurgens, Chief Executive Officer
CFO: Chance Klasek, CPA, Chief Financial Officer
CIO: Dennis Ahl, Director Information Technology
CHR: Sandra A. Bauer, Director Human Resources
Web address: www.jchc.us
Control: Other not–for–profit (including NFP Corporation) **Service:** General
Medical and Surgical

Staffed Beds: 64 **Admissions:** 426 **Census:** 41 **Outpatient Visits:** 17427
Births: 32 **Total Expense ($000):** 15040 **Payroll Expense ($000):** 6521
Personnel: 160

FALLS CITY—Richardson County

★ **COMMUNITY MEDICAL CENTER (281352)**, 3307 Barada Street,
Zip 68355–2470, Mailing Address: P.O. Box 399, Zip 68355–0399;
tel. 402/245–2428 **A**9 10 18 **F**3 13 15 28 31 34 35 40 43 45 59 75 78 81
85 93 97 107 111 119 127 130 133 135 **P**6
Primary Contact: Ryan C. Larsen, FACHE, Chief Executive Officer
CFO: Scott Sawyer, Chief Financial Officer
CIO: Karen Brown, Director Health Information Management
CHR: Shannon Weinmann, Director Human Resources
CNO: Ivy Campbell, Director of Nursing
Web address: www.cmcfc.org
Control: Other not–for–profit (including NFP Corporation) **Service:** General
Medical and Surgical

Staffed Beds: 24 **Admissions:** 809 **Census:** 9 **Outpatient Visits:** 47626
Births: 72 **Total Expense ($000):** 20640 **Payroll Expense ($000):** 7223
Personnel: 166

FRANKLIN—Franklin County

★ **FRANKLIN COUNTY MEMORIAL HOSPITAL (281311)**, 1406 Q Street,
Zip 68939–0315, Mailing Address: P.O. Box 315, Zip 68939–0315;
tel. 308/425–6221, (Nonreporting) **A**9 10 18
Primary Contact: Linda Bush, Chief Executive Officer
CFO: Amy Richards, Accounting
CMO: Linda Mazour, M.D., President
CIO: Cathy Webber, Chief Information Officer
Web address: www.fcmh.com
Control: County–Government, nonfederal **Service:** General Medical and Surgical

Staffed Beds: 14

FREMONT—Dodge County

☐ **FREMONT HEALTH (280077)**, 450 East 23rd Street, Zip 68025–2387;
tel. 402/721–1610, (Total facility includes 112 beds in nursing home–type unit)
A1 2 9 10 **F**3 11 13 15 17 18 20 22 26 28 29 30 31 34 35 37 40 45 56 57
59 62 63 64 68 70 73 74 75 76 77 78 79 81 85 86 87 89 93 99 100 103
104 107 108 110 111 114 119 120 121 123 124 126 128 129 130 131 132
143 146
Primary Contact: Patrick M. Booth, Chief Executive Officer
CFO: Michael Sindelar, Vice President and Chief Financial Officer
CIO: Richard Beran, Director Information Technology and Chief Information Officer
CHR: Bethany Childers, Director Human Resources
CNO: Peggy S. Kennedy, R.N., Vice President and Chief Nurse Executive
Web address: www.fremonthealth.org
Control: County–Government, nonfederal **Service:** General Medical and Surgical

Staffed Beds: 202 **Admissions:** 4012 **Census:** 126 **Outpatient Visits:** 61942
Births: 323 **Total Expense ($000):** 89983 **Payroll Expense ($000):** 35293
Personnel: 722

FRIEND—Saline County

WARREN MEMORIAL HOSPITAL (281330), 905 Second Street,
Zip 68359–1133; tel. 402/947–2541, (Nonreporting) **A**9 10 18
Primary Contact: Christopher R. Bjornberg, Chief Executive Officer
CFO: James Houlihan, Chief Financial Officer
CMO: Roger Meyer, M.D., Chief of Staff
CIO: Matt Scott, Chief Information Officer
CHR: Stacy Kirchhoff, Coordinator Human Resources
CNO: Melinda Johanna Kentfield, Chief Nursing Officer
Web address: www.wmhospital.com
Control: City–Government, nonfederal **Service:** General Medical and Surgical

Staffed Beds: 63

NE

Hospital, Medicare Provider Number, Address, Telephone, Approval, Facility, and Physician Codes, Health Care System

★ American Hospital Association (AHA) membership   ○ Healthcare Facilities Accreditation Program
☐ The Joint Commission accreditation   ◇ DNV Healthcare Inc. accreditation   △ Commission on Accreditation of Rehabilitation Facilities (CARF) accreditation

GENEVA—Fillmore County

FILLMORE COUNTY HOSPITAL (281301), 1900 F Street, Zip 68361–1325, Mailing Address: P.O. Box 193, Zip 68361–0193; tel. 402/759–3167, (Nonreporting) **A**9 10 18
Primary Contact: Paul Utemark, Chief Executive Officer
CFO: Jeanne Ackland, Director of Finance
CMO: John Jacobsen, M.D., Chief of Staff
CIO: Tyler Gewecke, Information Technology Technician
CHR: Abby Tuberville, Human Resource Generalist
Web address: www.fhsofgeneva.org
Control: County–Government, nonfederal **Service:** General Medical and Surgical

Staffed Beds: 25

GENOA—Nance County

GENOA COMMUNITY HOSPITAL (281312), 706 Ewing Avenue, Zip 68640–3035, Mailing Address: P.O. Box 310, Zip 68640–0310; tel. 402/993–2283, (Nonreporting) **A**9 10 18
Primary Contact: Austin M. Gillard, Chief Executive Officer
CFO: Jennifer Wieck, Director Financial Services
CMO: Brian Buhlke, M.D., Medical Director
CHR: Michelle Mueller, Manager Human Resources
CNO: Amanda Roebuck, Director Patient Care Services
Web address: www.genoamedical.org/
Control: City–County, Government, nonfederal **Service:** General Medical and Surgical

Staffed Beds: 65

GORDON—Sheridan County

★ **GORDON MEMORIAL HOSPITAL (281358)**, 300 East Eighth Street, Zip 69343–1123; tel. 308/282–0401, (Nonreporting) **A**9 10 18
Primary Contact: Jimmie W. Hansel, Ph.D., Interim Chief Executive Officer
CFO: Heidi Cushing, Director Finance
CMO: Christopher P. Costa, M.D., Chief of Staff
CIO: Ray Waldron, Director Information Technology
CHR: Shelley Beguin, Director Human Resources
CNO: Glenda Capler, Interim Director of Nursing
Web address: www.gordonmemorial.org
Control: Hospital district or authority, Government, nonfederal **Service:** General Medical and Surgical

Staffed Beds: 25

GOTHENBURG—Dawson County

★ **GOTHENBURG MEMORIAL HOSPITAL (281313)**, 910 20th Street, Zip 69138–1237, Mailing Address: P.O. Box 469, Zip 69138–0469; tel. 308/537–3661, (Nonreporting) **A**9 10 18
Primary Contact: Mick Brant, FACHE, Chief Executive Officer
CFO: Taci Bartlett, Chief Financial Officer
CMO: Gerald Matzke, M.D., Medical Director
CIO: Tinna Therrien, Chief Information Officer and Director Clinical Infomatics
CHR: Marsha Engel, Director Human Resources
CNO: Carolyn Evenson, R.N., Chief Nursing Officer
Web address: www.ghospital.org
Control: Hospital district or authority, Government, nonfederal **Service:** General Medical and Surgical

Staffed Beds: 12

GRAND ISLAND—Hall County

⊞ **CHI HEALTH SAINT FRANCIS (280023)**, 2620 West Faidley Avenue, Zip 68803–4297, Mailing Address: P.O. Box 9804, Zip 68802–9804; tel. 308/384–4600, (Includes SAINT FRANCIS MEMORIAL HEALTH CENTER, 2116 West Faidley Avenue, Zip 68803, Mailing Address: P.O. Box 9804, Zip 68802; tel. 308/384–4600), (Total facility includes 34 beds in nursing home–type unit) **A**1 2 3 5 9 10 19 **F**3 4 5 11 12 13 15 17 18 19 20 22 28 30 31 34 35 40 43 45 47 50 51 53 59 60 62 63 64 65 68 70 72 74 75 76 77 78 79 81 82 84 85 89 90 91 97 104 105 110 120 121 123 128 129 130 132 135 145 146 148 **S** Catholic Health Initiatives, Englewood, CO
Primary Contact: Daniel P. McElligott, FACHE, President
CFO: Lisa Webb, Vice President Finance
CMO: Michael Hein, M.D., Vice President Medical Affairs
CHR: Diana Shaffer, Director Human Resources
CNO: Beth Bartlett, Vice President Nursing
Web address: www.saintfrancisgi.org
Control: Church–operated, Nongovernment, not–for profit **Service:** General Medical and Surgical

Staffed Beds: 215 Admissions: 6687 Census: 92 Outpatient Visits: 192108 Births: 978 Total Expense ($000): 137450 Payroll Expense ($000): 40340 Personnel: 902

GRANT—Perkins County

★ **PERKINS COUNTY HEALTH SERVICES (281356)**, 900 Lincoln Avenue, Zip 69140–3095; tel. 308/352–7200, (Includes GOLDEN OURS CONVALESCENT HOME), (Nonreporting) **A**9 10 18
Primary Contact: James LeBrun, Chief Executive Officer
CFO: Tiffany Weber, Chief Financial Officer
CMO: Ruth Demmel, M.D., Chief Medical Officer
CIO: Jennifer Baumgartner, Chief Information Officer
CHR: Julie Bedell, Manager Human Resources
CNO: Dana McArtor, R.N., Director of Nursing
Web address: www.pchsgrant.com
Control: Hospital district or authority, Government, nonfederal **Service:** General Medical and Surgical

Staffed Beds: 20

HASTINGS—Adams County

⊠ **MARY LANNING HEALTHCARE (280032)**, 715 North St. Joseph Avenue, Zip 68901–4497; tel. 402/463–4521, (Nonreporting) **A**1 2 9 10 19
Primary Contact: Eric A. Barber, President and Chief Executive Officer
COO: Mark Callahan, Chief Operating Officer
CFO: Shawn A. Nordby, Chief Financial Officer
CMO: Michael Skoch, M.D., Chief Medical Officer
CIO: Aaron Young, Director Information Technology Services
CHR: Bruce E. Cutright, MS, Vice President Human Resources
CNO: Ronda S. Ehly, R.N., Chief Nursing Officer
Web address: www.marylanning.org
Control: Other not–for–profit (including NFP Corporation) **Service:** General Medical and Surgical

Staffed Beds: 161

HEBRON—Thayer County

★ **THAYER COUNTY HEALTH SERVICES (281304)**, 120 Park Avenue, Zip 68370–2019, Mailing Address: P.O. Box 49, Zip 68370–0049; tel. 402/768–6041, (Nonreporting) **A**9 10 18
Primary Contact: Michael G. Burcham, Sr., Chief Executive Officer
CFO: Cameron Meyer, Chief Financial Officer
CMO: Bryan Hubl, M.D., Chief of Staff
CIO: Dan Engle, Chief Information Officer
CHR: Heidi Winters, Director of Human Resources
CNO: Susan L. Moore, R.N., Director of Nursing
Web address: www.thayercountyhealth.com
Control: County–Government, nonfederal **Service:** General Medical and Surgical

Staffed Beds: 19

HENDERSON—York County

HENDERSON HEALTH CARE SERVICES (281308), 1621 Front Street, Zip 68371–8902; tel. 402/723–4512, (Nonreporting) **A**9 10 18
Primary Contact: Cheryl Brown, Administrator
CMO: James M. Ohrt, M.D., Director Medical Staff
CHR: Lynette Friesen, Manager Human Resources
Web address: www.hendersonhealthcare.org/getpage.php?name=message
Control: Other not–for–profit (including NFP Corporation) **Service:** General Medical and Surgical

Staffed Beds: 56

HOLDREGE—Phelps County

★ ◇ **PHELPS MEMORIAL HEALTH CENTER (281362)**, 1215 Tibbals Street, Zip 68949–1255; tel. 308/995–2211, (Nonreporting) **A**9 10 18 21 **S** QHR, Brentwood, TN
Primary Contact: Mark Harrel, Chief Executive Officer
CFO: Loren D. Schroder, Chief Financial Officer
CMO: Stuart Embury, M.D., Chief Medical Officer
CIO: Leora Smith, Information System and Health Information Management Team Leader
CHR: Cindy Jackson, Director Human Resources
Web address: www.phelpsmemorial.com
Control: Other not–for–profit (including NFP Corporation) **Service:** General Medical and Surgical

Staffed Beds: 25

NE

IMPERIAL—Chase County

CHASE COUNTY COMMUNITY HOSPITAL (281351), 600 West 12th Street, Zip 69033–3130, Mailing Address: P.O. Box 819, Zip 69033–0819; tel. 308/882–7111 **A**9 10 18 **F**11 15 28 29 30 31 34 35 40 41 42 43 45 57 59 64 75 81 91 93 107 110 114 127 133 **P**6
Primary Contact: Steven Lewis, Chief Executive Officer
CFO: Renee Fink, CPA, Chief Financial Officer
CMO: Jonathan Richman, M.D., Chief of Staff
CIO: Jen Harris, Director Health Information Management
CHR: Julie Sharp, Supervisor Human Resources
CNO: Kathy Geier, Director of Nursing
Web address: www.chasecountyhospital.com
Control: County–Government, nonfederal **Service:** General Medical and Surgical

Staffed Beds: 22 **Admissions:** 22 **Census:** 2 **Outpatient Visits:** 14185 **Total Expense ($000):** 10842 **Payroll Expense ($000):** 4642 **Personnel:** 86

KEARNEY—Buffalo County

✠ **CHI HEALTH GOOD SAMARITAN (280009)**, 10 East 31st Street, Zip 68847–2926, Mailing Address: P.O. Box 1990, Zip 68848–1990; tel. 308/865–7100, (Includes RICHARD H. YOUNG BEHAVIORAL HEALTH CENTER, 1755 Prairie View Place, Zip 68848, Mailing Address: P.O. Box 1750, Zip 68848–1705; tel. 308/865–2000; Michelle Hansen, Interim Director), (Total facility includes 16 beds in nursing home–type unit) **A**1 2 3 5 9 10 19 20 **F**7 9 12 13 15 18 20 22 24 28 29 30 31 34 35 37 40 43 44 45 46 48 49 50 51 53 57 58 59 60 64 68 69 70 71 72 74 75 76 77 78 79 81 82 83 84 85 86 87 89 90 92 93 98 99 101 102 103 104 107 108 110 111 114 115 116 117 118 119 120 121 123 124 126 128 129 130 132 134 135 146 148 **S** Catholic Health Initiatives, Englewood, CO
Primary Contact: Michael H. Schnieders, FACHE, President
CFO: Lisa Webb, Vice President for Operational Finance
CMO: Dennis Edwards, M.D., Vice President Medical Affairs
CIO: Katie Gartner, Director Health Information Management
CHR: Carol Lindstrom, Director Human Resources
CNO: Carol R. Wahl, R.N., Vice President Patient Care Services
Web address: www.gshs.org
Control: Church–operated, Nongovernment, not–for profit **Service:** General Medical and Surgical

Staffed Beds: 233 **Admissions:** 10095 **Census:** 140 **Outpatient Visits:** 67742 **Births:** 964 **Total Expense ($000):** 188158 **Payroll Expense ($000):** 57159 **Personnel:** 1049

GOOD SAMARITAN HEALTH SYSTEMS See CHI Health Good Samaritan

KEARNEY REGIONAL MEDICAL CENTER (280134), 804 22nd Avenue, Zip 68845–2206; tel. 855/404–5762, (Nonreporting)
Primary Contact: Larry Speicher, Chief Executive Officer
CIO: Travis Gregg, Director Support Services
CHR: Steve Beck, MS, Manager Human Resources
CNO: Adrienne Carney, R.N., Director Nursing and Surgical Services
Web address: www.kearneyregional.com
Control: Service: General Medical and Surgical

Staffed Beds: 21

KIMBALL—Kimball County

★ **KIMBALL HEALTH SERVICES (281305)**, 505 South Burg Street, Zip 69145–1398; tel. 308/235–1952, (Nonreporting) **A**9 10 18
Primary Contact: Ken Hunter, R.N., Chief Executive Officer
CFO: David Usher, Chief Financial Officer
CMO: James Plate, M.D., Chief of Staff
CIO: Charles Walker, Director Information Technology
CHR: James R. Imler, Director Human Resources
CNO: Richard Harriger, Director of Emergency Services
Web address: www.kimballhealth.org
Control: County–Government, nonfederal **Service:** General Medical and Surgical

Staffed Beds: 10

LEXINGTON—Dawson County

★ **LEXINGTON REGIONAL HEALTH CENTER (281361)**, 1201 North Erie Street, Zip 68850–1560, Mailing Address: P.O. Box 980, Zip 68850–0980; tel. 308/324–5651, (Nonreporting) **A**9 10 18
Primary Contact: Leslie Marsh, Chief Executive Officer
COO: Jim Hain, Chief Operating Officer
CFO: Wade Eschenbrenner, Chief Financial Officer
CMO: Francisca Acosta–Carlson, M.D., Chief of Staff
CIO: Robb Hanna, Executive Director Information Technology
CHR: Jill Denker, Executive Director Human Resources
CNO: Dana Steiner, R.N., Executive Director of Nursing Services
Web address: www.lexingtonregional.org
Control: Hospital district or authority, Government, nonfederal **Service:** General Medical and Surgical

Staffed Beds: 25

LINCOLN—Lancaster County

✠ △ **BRYAN MEDICAL CENTER (280003)**, 1600 South 48th Street, Zip 68506–1299; tel. 402/489–0200, (Includes BRYAN MEDICAL CENTER–EAST, 1600 South 48th Street, tel. 402/489–0200; BRYAN MEDICAL CENTER–WEST, 2300 South 16th Street, Zip 68502–3781; tel. 402/475–1011) **A**1 2 7 9 10 **F**3 4 5 8 12 13 15 17 18 19 20 22 24 26 28 29 30 31 34 35 37 38 39 40 43 45 46 47 48 49 50 54 56 57 58 59 61 64 68 70 71 72 74 75 76 78 79 81 82 84 85 86 87 89 90 92 93 96 98 99 101 102 103 104 105 107 108 110 111 112 114 115 117 118 119 120 123 124 126 129 130 131 132 145 146 147 148 **S** Bryan Health, Lincoln, NE
Primary Contact: John T. Woodrich, President and Chief Operating Officer
CFO: Russell Gronewold, Chief Financial Officer
CMO: Carolyn Cody, M.D., Vice President Medical Affairs
CIO: George Carr, Chief Information Officer
CHR: Jan Garvin, Vice President Human Resources
CNO: Lisa M. Vail, R.N., Chief Nursing Officer and Vice President of Patient Care Services
Web address: www.bryanhealth.com
Control: Other not–for–profit (including NFP Corporation) **Service:** General Medical and Surgical

Staffed Beds: 351 **Admissions:** 21901 **Census:** 258 **Outpatient Visits:** 218718 **Births:** 2821 **Total Expense ($000):** 413928 **Payroll Expense ($000):** 146881 **Personnel:** 2626

★ **CHI HEALTH NEBRASKA HEART (280128)**, 7500 South 91st Street, Zip 68526–9437; tel. 402/327–2700, (Nonreporting) **A**9 10 **S** Catholic Health Initiatives, Englewood, CO
Primary Contact: Deepak Gangahar, President
CFO: Dan Schonlau, Chief Financial Officer and Vice President of Finance
CMO: Peter Dionisopoulof, Chief Medical Officer
Web address: www.neheart.com
Control: Other not–for–profit (including NFP Corporation) **Service:** Heart

Staffed Beds: 52

✠ **CHI HEALTH ST ELIZABETH (280020)**, 555 South 70th Street, Zip 68510–2494; tel. 402/219–8000 **A**1 2 3 5 9 10 **F**3 8 11 12 13 15 16 29 30 31 34 35 37 39 40 44 45 46 47 48 49 50 51 53 55 58 59 60 61 64 65 68 70 72 74 75 76 78 79 80 81 84 85 86 87 89 92 107 108 110 111 114 115 116 117 118 119 120 121 123 124 126 129 130 131 132 144 145 146 147 148 **S** Catholic Health Initiatives, Englewood, CO
Primary Contact: Kim S. Moore, President
CFO: Dan Schonlau, Chief Financial Officer and Vice President of Finance
CMO: Michael Ferris, M.D., Chief Medical Officer
CIO: Richard Bohaty, Director Information Technology
CHR: Cody Koch, Director Human Resources
Web address: www.saintelizabethonline.com
Control: Other not–for–profit (including NFP Corporation) **Service:** General Medical and Surgical

Staffed Beds: 260 **Admissions:** 11785 **Census:** 139 **Outpatient Visits:** 105712 **Births:** 2086 **Total Expense ($000):** 213235 **Payroll Expense ($000):** 64486 **Personnel:** 1035

LINCOLN DIVISION See Veterans Affairs Nebraska–Western Iowa Health Care System

☐ **LINCOLN REGIONAL CENTER (284003)**, West Prospector Place and South Folsom, Zip 68522–2299, Mailing Address: P.O. Box 94949, Zip 68509–4949; tel. 402/479–5207, (Nonreporting) **A**1 9 10
Primary Contact: William R. Gibson, Chief Executive Officer
COO: Stacey Werth–Sweeney, Facility Operating Officer
CFO: Randy Willey, Business Manager
CMO: Vijay Dewan, M.D., Clinical Director
CHR: Scott Rasmussen, Director Human Resources
Web address: www.hhs.state.ne.us/beh/rc
Control: State–Government, nonfederal **Service:** Psychiatric

Staffed Beds: 253

NE

Hospital, Medicare Provider Number, Address, Telephone, Approval, Facility, and Physician Codes, Health Care System

★ American Hospital Association (AHA) membership
☐ The Joint Commission accreditation   ◇ DNV Healthcare Inc. accreditation
○ Healthcare Facilities Accreditation Program
△ Commission on Accreditation of Rehabilitation Facilities (CARF) accreditation

LINCOLN SURGICAL HOSPITAL (280127), 1710 South 70th Street, Suite 200, Zip 68506–1677; tel. 402/484–9090, (Nonreporting) **A**9 10
Primary Contact: Robb Linafelter, Chief Executive Officer
Web address: www.lincolnsurgery.com
Control: Corporation, Investor–owned, for–profit **Service:** Other specialty

Staffed Beds: 7

△ **MADONNA REHABILITATION HOSPITAL (282000)**, 5401 South Street, Zip 68506–2134; tel. 402/489–7102, (Total facility includes 125 beds in nursing home–type unit) **A**7 9 10 **F**1 10 28 29 30 32 34 35 36 50 53 54 56 57 58 59 64 65 67 74 75 77 79 82 84 86 87 90 91 92 93 94 95 96 128 130 131 132 135 143 146 148 **P**4 6
Primary Contact: Marsha Lommel, FACHE, President and Chief Executive Officer
COO: Paul Dongilli, Jr., Ph.D., Executive Vice President and Chief Operating Officer
CFO: Victor J. Witkowicz, Senior Vice President and Chief Financial Officer
CMO: Thomas Stadler, M.D., Vice President Medical Affairs and Chief Medical Officer
CIO: David Rolfe, Chief Information Officer
CHR: Lou Ann Manske, Director Human Resources
Web address: www.madonna.org
Control: Other not–for–profit (including NFP Corporation) **Service:** Rehabilitation

Staffed Beds: 308 Admissions: 1730 Census: 219 Outpatient Visits: 56932
Births: 0 Total Expense ($000): 79709 Payroll Expense ($000): 57275
Personnel: 1145

NEBRASKA PENAL AND CORRECTIONAL HOSPITAL, 14th And Pioneer Streets, Zip 68501; tel. 402/471–3161, (Nonreporting)
Primary Contact: George E. Lewis, M.D., Medical Officer
Web address: www.corrections.nebraska.gov
Control: State–Government, nonfederal **Service:** Hospital unit of an institution (prison hospital, college infimary, etc.)

Staffed Beds: 12

★ **VETERANS AFFAIRS NEBRASKA–WESTERN IOWA HEALTH CARE SYSTEM**, 600 South 70th Street, Zip 68510–2493; tel. 402/489–3802, (Includes LINCOLN DIVISION, 600 South 70th Street, tel. 402/489–3802), (Total facility includes 46 beds in nursing home–type unit) **A**9 **F**3 5 8 11 12 18 20 22 29 30 31 34 35 36 37 38 39 40 45 46 47 48 49 50 51 53 54 56 57 58 59 60 61 63 64 65 70 71 74 75 77 78 79 81 82 83 84 85 86 87 91 92 93 94 97 98 100 101 102 103 104 105 106 107 108 109 111 114 115 116 117 119 127 128 129 130 132 135 143 144 145 146 147 148 **S** Department of Veterans Affairs, Washington, DC
Primary Contact: Marci Mylan, Director
CIO: David Daiker, Chief Information Resource Management
CHR: Dave Peters, Chief Human Resources Officer
Web address: www.nebraska.va.gov/
Control: Veterans Affairs, Government, federal **Service:** General Medical and Surgical

Staffed Beds: 132 Admissions: 4547 Census: 85 Outpatient Visits: 551362
Births: 0 Personnel: 3318

NIOBRARA VALLEY HOSPITAL (281303), 401 South Fifth Street, Zip 68746–0118, Mailing Address: P.O. Box 118, Zip 68746–0118; tel. 402/569–2451, (Nonreporting) **A**9 10 18 **S** Faith Regional Health Services, Norfolk, NE
Primary Contact: Kelly Kalkowski, Chief Executive Officer
CFO: Martha Nelson, Chief Financial Officer
Web address: www.nvhcares.org
Control: Other not–for–profit (including NFP Corporation) **Service:** General Medical and Surgical

Staffed Beds: 20

⊞ **COMMUNITY HOSPITAL (281363)**, 1301 East H Street, Zip 69001–1328, Mailing Address: P.O. Box 1328, Zip 69001–1328; tel. 308/344–2650 **A**1 9 10 18 **F**3 11 13 15 28 29 31 34 35 40 43 45 48 51 57 59 62 63 64 74 75 76 77 78 79 81 82 85 86 87 90 91 93 94 96 107 110 111 114 116 118 119 124 127 129 130 132 133 135 145 146 147 148 **P**3 6
Primary Contact: James P. Ulrich, Jr., President and Chief Executive Officer
CFO: Troy Bruntz, Vice President Finance and Chief Financial Officer
CMO: Walter Eskildsen, M.D., Chief of Staff
CIO: Lori Beeby, Director Information Systems
CHR: Leanne R. Miller, Director Human Resources
CNO: Janelle Kircher, R.N., Vice President, Patient Care Services
Web address: www.chmccook.org
Control: Other not–for–profit (including NFP Corporation) **Service:** General Medical and Surgical

Staffed Beds: 25 Admissions: 946 Census: 10 Outpatient Visits: 30247
Births: 125 Total Expense ($000): 36455 Payroll Expense ($000): 12922
Personnel: 213

★ **KEARNEY COUNTY HEALTH SERVICES (281306)**, 727 East First Street, Zip 68959–1705; tel. 308/832–3400, (Total facility includes 34 beds in nursing home–type unit) **A**9 10 18 **F**10 15 28 34 40 41 43 45 59 64 65 67 81 89 97 99 103 104 107 110 114 119 127 128 130 133 145 146 147 148
Primary Contact: Fred J. Meis, Chief Executive Officer
CFO: Rebekah Mussman, Chief Financial Officer
CMO: Eddie Pierce, M.D., Chief Medical Staff
CHR: Rebecca L. Cooke, Director Human Resources
CNO: Mary Bunger, R.N., Director Nursing Services
Web address: www.kchs.org
Control: County–Government, nonfederal **Service:** General Medical and Surgical

Staffed Beds: 44 Admissions: 174 Census: 28 Outpatient Visits: 7892
Births: 0 Total Expense ($000): 9093 Payroll Expense ($000): 4543
Personnel: 104

★ **CHI HEALTH ST. MARY'S (281342)**, 1314 Third Avenue, Zip 68410–1930; tel. 402/873–3321 **A**9 10 18 **F**3 13 15 17 28 31 35 40 45 64 67 68 69 70 75 76 78 79 81 82 85 87 89 107 110 111 114 118 119 128 129 132 133 135 148 **S** Catholic Health Initiatives, Englewood, CO
Primary Contact: Daniel J. Kelly, President
CFO: Tim H. Schnack, Vice President Operations Finance
CMO: Jonathan Stelling, M.D., Vice President Medical Affairs
CNO: Brenda Jean Sebek, R.N., Vice President Patient Care Services
Web address: www.stmaryshospitalnecity.org
Control: Church–operated, Nongovernment, not–for profit **Service:** General Medical and Surgical

Staffed Beds: 18 Admissions: 447 Census: 4 Outpatient Visits: 30728
Births: 117 Total Expense ($000): 16580 Payroll Expense ($000): 5694
Personnel: 128

★ **ANTELOPE MEMORIAL HOSPITAL (281326)**, 102 West Ninth Street, Zip 68756–1114, Mailing Address: P.O. Box 229, Zip 68756–0229; tel. 402/887–4151, (Nonreporting) **A**9 10 18
Primary Contact: Jack W. Green, Administrator
CFO: Martha Nelson, Chief Financial Officer
CMO: Troy Dawson, M.D., President Medical Staff
CIO: Kevin Trease, Chief Information Officer
CHR: Mary A. Schwager, Director Human Resources
CNO: Merry Sprout, R.N., Chief Nursing Officer
Web address: www.amhne.org/
Control: Other not–for–profit (including NFP Corporation) **Service:** General Medical and Surgical

Staffed Beds: 25

⊞ **FAITH REGIONAL HEALTH SERVICES (280125)**, 2700 West Norfolk Avenue, Zip 68701–4438, Mailing Address: P.O. Box 869, Zip 68702–0869; tel. 402/644–7201, (Includes EAST CAMPUS, 1500 Koenigstein Avenue, Zip 68701; tel. 402/371–3402; WEST CAMPUS, 2700 Norfolk Avenue, Zip 68701, Mailing Address: P.O. Box 869, Zip 68702–0869; tel. 402/371–4880), (Nonreporting) **A**1 2 3 5 9 10 20 **S** Faith Regional Health Services, Norfolk, NE
Primary Contact: Mark D. Klosterman, FACHE, President and Chief Executive Officer
CFO: Johnathan Wilker, Vice President Finance and Chief Financial Officer
CMO: Dean O. French, M.D., Chief of Staff
CHR: Janet Pinkelman, Director Human Resources
Web address: www.frhs.org
Control: Other not–for–profit (including NFP Corporation) **Service:** General Medical and Surgical

Staffed Beds: 245

⊞ **GREAT PLAINS HEALTH (280065)**, 601 West Leota Street, Zip 69101–6598, Mailing Address: P.O. Box 1167, Zip 69103–1167; tel. 308/696–8000 **A**1 2 3 5 9 10 19 20 **F**3 8 12 13 15 18 20 22 28 29 30 31 34 35 40 43 45 48 50 51 57 59 60 62 63 68 70 73 74 75 76 78 79 81 82 84 89 93 98 99 102 103 104 105 107 108 110 111 115 116 117 119 120 121 122 124 129 130 131 132 135 146 147 148 **P**8
Primary Contact: Melvin McNea, Interim Chief Executive Officer
COO: Melvin McNea, Chief Operating Officer
CFO: Krystal Claymore, Chief Financial Officer
CIO: Jim Saul, Chief Information Officer
CHR: Jayne Johnson, Director of Human Resources
CNO: Tadd Greenfield, Chief Nursing Officer
Web address: www.gprmc.com
Control: Other not–for–profit (including NFP Corporation) **Service:** General Medical and Surgical

Staffed Beds: 101 Admissions: 5191 Census: 51 Outpatient Visits: 246865
Births: 548 Total Expense ($000): 122602 Payroll Expense ($000): 49340
Personnel: 860

NE

Many Facility Codes have changed. Please refer to the AHA Guide Code Chart. © 2014 AHA Guide

O'NEILL—Holt County

★ **AVERA ST. ANTHONY'S HOSPITAL (281329)**, 300 North Second Street, Zip 68763–1514, Mailing Address: P.O. Box 270, Oneill, Zip 68763–0270; tel. 402/336–2611 **A**9 10 18 **F**3 8 13 15 28 29 30 31 32 34 35 38 40 45 46 48 52 56 57 59 60 61 62 64 65 68 74 75 76 77 78 79 81 82 86 87 90 91 93 94 96 107 108 111 112 114 119 120 124 127 129 130 131 133 135 143 146 148 **P**1 6 **S** Avera Health, Sioux Falls, SD
Primary Contact: Ronald J. Cork, President and Chief Executive Officer
CFO: Michael Garman, Chief Financial Officer
CIO: Michael Garman, Chief Financial Officer
CHR: Kathryn Hillje, Human Resource and Marketing Partner
Web address: www.avera.org/st-anthonys
Control: Church–operated, Nongovernment, not–for profit **Service:** General Medical and Surgical

Staffed Beds: 25 **Admissions:** 879 **Census:** 10 **Outpatient Visits:** 36912 **Births:** 149 **Total Expense ($000):** 34209 **Payroll Expense ($000):** 13166 **Personnel:** 212

OAKLAND—Burt County

★ **OAKLAND MERCY HOSPITAL (281321)**, 601 East Second Street, Zip 68045–1499; tel. 402/685–5601 **A**9 10 18 **F**11 15 18 20 22 24 26 28 29 30 31 34 35 40 44 50 57 59 75 81 93 97 107 108 110 114 119 127 128 132 133 148 **P**6 **S** Catholic Health East / Trinity Health, Livonia, MI
Primary Contact: John W. Werner, Chief Executive Officer
COO: John W. Werner, Chief Executive Officer
CFO: Terri Mentink, Chief Financial Officer
CMO: Tracie Martin, M.D., Chief Medical Officer
Web address: www.oaklandhospital.org
Control: Church–operated, Nongovernment, not–for profit **Service:** General Medical and Surgical

Staffed Beds: 18 **Admissions:** 157 **Census:** 2 **Outpatient Visits:** 6084 **Births:** 0 **Total Expense ($000):** 6026 **Payroll Expense ($000):** 3070 **Personnel:** 53

OGALLALA—Keith County

★ **OGALLALA COMMUNITY HOSPITAL (281355)**, 2601 North Spruce Street, Zip 69153–2465; tel. 308/284–4011 **A**9 10 18 **F**3 13 15 29 31 34 35 40 43 56 59 64 65 75 78 79 81 85 93 107 119 129 130 132 133 148 **S** Banner Health, Phoenix, AZ
Primary Contact: Sharon Lind, MSN, Chief Executive Officer
CFO: Dena Klockman, Chief Financial Officer
CMO: Kurt Johnson, M.D., Chief of Staff
CHR: Laurie K. Sinner, Chief Human Resource Officer
CNO: Aileen Chandler, Director of Nursing
Web address: www.bannerhealth.com/Locations/Nebraska/Ogallala+Community+Hospital
Control: Other not–for–profit (including NFP Corporation) **Service:** General Medical and Surgical

Staffed Beds: 18 **Admissions:** 515 **Census:** 4 **Outpatient Visits:** 34572 **Births:** 95 **Total Expense ($000):** 13511 **Payroll Expense ($000):** 5109 **Personnel:** 105

OMAHA—Douglas County

☐ **BOYS TOWN NATIONAL RESEARCH HOSPITAL (283300)**, 555 North 30th Street, Zip 68131–2198; tel. 402/498–6511 **A**1 3 5 9 10 **F**3 34 35 58 65 68 79 81 86 87 89 97 99 104 106 107 108 111 119 129 130 131 **P**6
Primary Contact: John K. Arch, FACHE, Director
CFO: Leigh Jean Koinzan, Director Finance
CMO: Edward Kolb, M.D., Medical Director
CIO: Ann Ducey, Chief Information Officer
CHR: Michael Gell, Director Human Resources
Web address: www.boystownhospital.org
Control: Other not–for–profit (including NFP Corporation) **Service:** Children's general

Staffed Beds: 127 **Admissions:** 276 **Census:** 2 **Outpatient Visits:** 208740 **Births:** 0 **Total Expense ($000):** 91378 **Payroll Expense ($000):** 40550 **Personnel:** 833

⊞ **CHI HEALTH BERGAN MERCY (280060)**, 7500 Mercy Road, Zip 68124–2319; tel. 402/398–6060, (Includes LASTING HOPE RECOVERY CENTER, 415 South 25th Avenue, Zip 68131; tel. 402/717–5300; Robin Conyers, Administrator) **A**1 2 3 5 9 10 **F**3 8 11 13 15 17 18 20 22 24 26 28 29 30 31 32 34 35 37 38 40 43 44 45 46 47 48 49 50 51 53 54 55 56 57 58 59 60 61 62 63 64 65 68 70 72 74 75 76 77 78 79 80 81 82 83 84 85 86 87 89 92 93 97 98 100 105 107 108 109 110 111 114 115 116 117 118 119 120 121 123 124 126 127 130 131 132 134 143 144 145 146 147 148 **P**6 8 **S** Catholic Health Initiatives, Englewood, CO
Primary Contact: Marie E. Knedler, R.N., FACHE, President
COO: Chris Evans, Vice President Operations
CFO: Tim H. Schnack, Vice President Financial Services
CMO: Kevin Reagan, M.D., Chief Medical Officer
CIO: Steven P. Houston, Vice President Strategy and Technology
CHR: Nancy Wallace, Vice President Human Resources
CNO: Jane Carmody, R.N., Vice President and System Chief Nursing Officer
Web address: www.alegent.com/bergan
Control: Church–operated, Nongovernment, not–for profit **Service:** General Medical and Surgical

Staffed Beds: 336 **Admissions:** 15681 **Census:** 212 **Outpatient Visits:** 123590 **Births:** 3337 **Total Expense ($000):** 211155 **Payroll Expense ($000):** 90776 **Personnel:** 1610

⊞ **CHI HEALTH CREIGHTON UNIVERSITY MEDICAL CENTER (280030)**, 601 North 30th Street, Zip 68131–2197; tel. 402/449–4000 **A**1 3 5 8 9 10 **F**3 11 12 13 15 17 18 20 22 24 26 28 29 30 31 32 34 35 38 40 41 43 45 46 47 48 49 50 51 52 53 54 56 57 58 59 60 61 64 65 68 70 72 73 74 75 76 77 78 79 81 82 85 88 89 93 96 97 107 108 109 110 111 114 115 119 120 121 124 126 129 130 131 132 141 143 146 147 148 **P**6 8 **S** Catholic Health Initiatives, Englewood, CO
Primary Contact: Kevin J. Nokels, FACHE, President
COO: Todd Defreece, Vice President Operations
CFO: Tim H. Schnack, Chief Financial Officer
CMO: Devin Fox, M.D., Chief Medical Officer
CIO: Ellen Deao, Director Information Services
CHR: Rebecca Ruetsch, Human Resource Partner
CNO: Francine M. Sparby, MS, Chief Nursing Officer
Web address: www.alegentcreighton.com
Control: Church–operated, Nongovernment, not–for profit **Service:** General Medical and Surgical

Staffed Beds: 214 **Admissions:** 7855 **Census:** 106 **Outpatient Visits:** 81201 **Births:** 1024 **Personnel:** 1198

⊞ △ **CHI HEALTH IMMANUEL (280081)**, 6901 North 72nd Street, Zip 68122–1799; tel. 402/572–2121, (Total facility includes 165 beds in nursing home–type unit) **A**1 2 3 5 7 9 10 **F**3 4 5 6 11 12 13 15 17 18 20 22 26 28 29 30 31 32 34 35 36 37 38 40 42 43 44 45 49 50 51 53 55 56 57 58 59 62 63 64 68 70 72 73 74 75 76 77 78 79 80 81 82 83 84 85 86 87 88 89 90 91 92 93 96 97 98 99 100 101 102 103 104 105 106 107 108 109 110 111 114 115 117 118 119 120 121 123 124 126 128 129 130 131 132 134 136 142 146 147 148 **P**6 8 **S** Catholic Health Initiatives, Englewood, CO
Primary Contact: Ann Schumacher, R.N., MSN, President
CFO: Tim H. Schnack, Chief Financial Officer
CHR: Nancy Wallace, Vice President Human Resources
CNO: Jane Carmody, R.N., Chief Nursing Officer
Web address: www.alegent.com/immanuel
Control: Church–operated, Nongovernment, not–for profit **Service:** General Medical and Surgical

Staffed Beds: 285 **Admissions:** 9277 **Census:** 161 **Outpatient Visits:** 216344 **Births:** 558 **Total Expense ($000):** 172531 **Payroll Expense ($000):** 62501 **Personnel:** 1211

⊞ **CHI HEALTH LAKESIDE (280130)**, 16901 Lakeside Hills Court, Zip 68130–2318; tel. 402/717–8000 **A**1 2 9 10 **F**3 8 12 13 15 17 18 20 22 26 28 29 30 31 32 34 35 36 38 39 40 44 45 46 49 53 54 55 56 59 60 63 64 68 70 72 73 74 75 76 77 78 79 81 82 83 84 85 86 93 94 97 99 100 102 103 104 107 108 110 111 114 115 118 119 120 121 122 123 124 126 129 130 131 132 134 143 146 147 148 **P**6 8 **S** Catholic Health Initiatives, Englewood, CO
Primary Contact: Cindy Alloway, President
COO: Joan E. Neuhaus, Senior Vice President Chief Operating Officer
CFO: Tim H. Schnack, Chief Financial Officer
CMO: Patricia Murdock–Langan, Chief Medical Officer
CIO: Karun Kapur, Regional Chief Information Officer
CHR: Nancy Wallace, Vice President Human Resources
CNO: Jane Carmody, R.N., Chief Nursing Officer
Web address: www.alegent.org
Control: Church–operated, Nongovernment, not–for profit **Service:** General Medical and Surgical

Staffed Beds: 137 **Admissions:** 7418 **Census:** 72 **Outpatient Visits:** 103031 **Births:** 1128 **Total Expense ($000):** 91098 **Payroll Expense ($000):** 35063 **Personnel:** 750

NE

Hospital, Medicare Provider Number, Address, Telephone, Approval, Facility, and Physician Codes, Health Care System

★ American Hospital Association (AHA) membership
☐ The Joint Commission accreditation ◇ DNV Healthcare Inc. accreditation
◯ Healthcare Facilities Accreditation Program
△ Commission on Accreditation of Rehabilitation Facilities (CARF) accreditation

✥ **CHILDREN'S HOSPITAL AND MEDICAL CENTER (283301)**, 8200 Dodge Street, Zip 68114–4113; tel. 402/955–5400 **A**1 3 5 9 10 **F**3 7 11 12 13 19 21 23 25 27 29 30 31 32 34 35 40 41 43 45 46 48 49 50 54 55 59 62 64 68 72 74 75 76 77 78 79 81 82 84 85 88 89 92 93 99 104 107 108 111 115 119 126 129 130 131 132 137 143 144 145 146 148 **P**6
Primary Contact: Gary A. Perkins, FACHE, President and Chief Executive Officer
CFO: Amy Hatcher, Chief Financial Officer
CMO: Carl H. Gumbiner, M.D., Senior Vice President Medical Affairs and Chief Medical Officer
CIO: George Reynolds, M.D., Vice President, Chief Information Officer and Chief Medical Information Officer
CHR: Corliss Lovstad, Vice President Human Resources
CNO: Debra Arnow, R.N., VP Patient Care & Chief Nursing Officer
Web address: www.childrensomaha.org
Control: Other not–for–profit (including NFP Corporation) **Service:** Children's general

Staffed Beds: 126 **Admissions:** 4830 **Census:** 89 **Outpatient Visits:** 306693 **Births:** 5 **Total Expense ($000):** 267412 **Payroll Expense ($000):** 113116 **Personnel:** 1448

★ ○ **DOUGLAS COUNTY COMMUNITY MENTAL HEALTH CENTER (284009)**, 4102 Woolworth Avenue, Zip 68105–1899; tel. 402/444–7000, (Nonreporting) **A**3 5 9 10 11
Primary Contact: Sherry L. Glasnapp, Director
CFO: DeDe Will, Director Finance
CMO: Sidney A. Kauzlarich, M.D., Medical Director
CIO: Dianne Wallace, County Information Manager
CHR: Lee A. Lazure, Director Civil Service Commission
CNO: Marti Christensen, Director of Psychiatric Nursing
Web address: www.co.douglas.ne.us
Control: County–Government, nonfederal **Service:** Psychiatric

Staffed Beds: 30

MIDWEST SURGICAL HOSPITAL (280131), 7915 Farnam Drive, Zip 68114–4504; tel. 402/399–1900, (Nonreporting) **A**9 10
Primary Contact: Charles Livingston, Chief Executive Officer
Web address: www.mwsurgicalhospital.com
Control: Corporation, Investor–owned, for–profit **Service:** Surgical

Staffed Beds: 19

✥ **NEBRASKA MEDICAL CENTER (280013)**, 987400 Nebraska Medical Center, Zip 68198–7400; tel. 402/552–2000 **A**1 2 3 5 8 9 10 **F**3 6 11 12 13 15 16 17 18 20 22 24 26 29 30 31 34 37 38 40 41 43 44 45 46 47 48 49 50 53 54 57 58 59 61 64 65 68 70 72 74 76 77 78 79 80 81 82 84 85 86 87 88 89 91 92 93 94 96 97 98 101 107 108 110 111 113 114 115 116 117 118 119 120 121 123 124 126 129 130 131 132 135 136 137 138 139 141 142 145 146 147 148 **P**5 8
Primary Contact: William S. Dinsmoor, Chief Executive Officer
COO: Rosanna D. Morris, R.N., Chief Operating Officer
CFO: Stephanie Daubert, Chief Financial Officer
CMO: Harris Frankel, M.D., Senior Vice President Medical Affairs
CIO: Mark Weiss, Executive Director, Enterprise Technical Services
CHR: Tadd M. Pullin, Interim Vice President, Human Resources
CNO: Rosanna D. Morris, R.N., CNO & Senior VP Patient Care Services
Web address: www.nebraskamed.com
Control: Other not–for–profit (including NFP Corporation) **Service:** General Medical and Surgical

Staffed Beds: 525 **Admissions:** 23050 **Census:** 352 **Outpatient Visits:** 417804 **Births:** 1819 **Total Expense ($000):** 704720 **Payroll Expense ($000):** 254044 **Personnel:** 4690

✥ △ **NEBRASKA METHODIST HOSPITAL (280040)**, 8303 Dodge Street, Zip 68114–4199; tel. 402/354–4000, (Includes METHODIST WOMEN'S HOSPITAL, 707 North 190th Plaza, Elkhorn, Zip 68022–3974; tel. 402/815–4000; Susan Korth, M.P.H., Ph.D., Vice President and Chief Operating Officer) **A**1 2 3 5 7 9 10 **F**3 8 11 12 13 15 17 18 20 22 24 26 28 29 30 31 34 35 40 45 46 47 48 49 50 51 52 53 54 55 56 57 58 59 62 63 64 65 66 68 70 72 74 75 76 77 78 79 81 82 83 84 85 86 87 90 91 92 93 96 100 101 104 107 108 110 111 114 115 117 118 119 120 121 123 124 126 129 130 132 135 136 141 143 146 147 148 **S** Nebraska Methodist Health System, Inc., Omaha, NE
Primary Contact: Stephen L. Goeser, FACHE, President and Chief Executive Officer
CFO: Linda K. Burt, Corporate Vice President Finance
CMO: William Shiffermiller, M.D., Vice President Medical Affairs
CIO: Roger Hertz, Vice President Information Technology
CHR: Holly Huerter, Vice President Human Resources
CNO: Teri Tipton, MSN, Chief Nursing Officer and Vice President Patient Care Services
Web address: www.bestcare.org
Control: Other not–for–profit (including NFP Corporation) **Service:** General Medical and Surgical

Staffed Beds: 394 **Admissions:** 16564 **Census:** 239 **Outpatient Visits:** 124389 **Births:** 3914 **Total Expense ($000):** 405104 **Payroll Expense ($000):** 149767 **Personnel:** 2136

☐ **NEBRASKA ORTHOPAEDIC HOSPITAL (280129)**, 2808 South 143rd Plaza, Zip 68144–5611; tel. 402/609–1600 **A**1 3 5 9 10 **F**3 9 29 34 35 37 39 40 44 50 57 58 59 64 77 79 81 82 85 86 87 93 94 96 111 131 141 142 **P**6
Primary Contact: Tom Macy, FACHE, Chief Executive Officer
COO: Mark E. Longacre, FACHE, Chief Operating Officer
CFO: Anna McCaslin, Chief Financial Officer
CMO: Ian Crabb, M.D., Chief Medical Officer
CIO: Tim Pugsley, Chief Information Officer
CHR: Lori L. Thompson, Manager Human Resources
CNO: Nancy Laughlin, R.N., Chief Nursing Officer
Web address: www.neorthohospital.com
Control: Partnership, Investor–owned, for–profit **Service:** Orthopedic

Staffed Beds: 24 **Admissions:** 1425 **Census:** 10 **Outpatient Visits:** 58364 **Births:** 0 **Total Expense ($000):** 58739 **Payroll Expense ($000):** 17552 **Personnel:** 307

✥ **NEBRASKA SPINE HOSPITAL (280133)**, 6901 North 72nd Street, Suite 20300, Zip 68122–1755, Mailing Address: 6901 North 72nd Street, Zip 68122–1709; tel. 402/572–3000, (Nonreporting) **A**1 9 10 **S** Catholic Health Initiatives, Englewood, CO
Primary Contact: Troy P. Stockman, Chief Executive Officer
Web address: www.nebraskaspinehospital.com
Control: Partnership, Investor–owned, for–profit **Service:** Orthopedic

Staffed Beds: 34

✥ **SELECT SPECIALTY HOSPITAL–OMAHA (282001)**, 1870 South 75th Street, Zip 68124–1700; tel. 402/361–5700, (Nonreporting) **A**1 9 10 **S** Select Medical Corporation, Mechanicsburg, PA
Primary Contact: Thomas N. Theroult, Chief Executive Officer
CMO: Guillermo Huerta, M.D., Chief Medical Officer
CIO: Cynde McCall, R.N., Chief Nursing Officer
CHR: Nicole Nelson, Human Resources Coordinator
CNO: Cynde McCall, R.N., Chief Nursing Officer
Web address: www.selectspecialtyhospitals.com/company/locations/omahacentral.aspx
Control: Corporation, Investor–owned, for–profit **Service:** Long–Term Acute Care hospital

Staffed Beds: 52

✥ **VETERANS AFFAIRS – WESTERN IOWA HEALTHCARE SYSTEM**, 4101 Woolworth Avenue, Zip 68105–1873; tel. 402/346–8800, (Nonreporting) **A**1 2 3 5 8 9 **S** Department of Veterans Affairs, Washington, DC
Primary Contact: Marci Mylan, Director
COO: Denise Harrison, Associate Director
CFO: Kirk Kay, Chief Financial Officer
CMO: Grace Stringfellow, M.D., Chief of Staff
CIO: Jennifer Rosenbalm, Manager Business Office
CHR: Cheryl M. DeWispelare, Chief Human Resources Officer
CNO: Eileen M. Kingston, R.N., Nurse Executive, Associate Director Patient Care
Web address: www.nebraska.va.gov/
Control: Veterans Affairs, Government, federal **Service:** General Medical and Surgical

Staffed Beds: 126

ORD—Valley County

★ **VALLEY COUNTY HEALTH SYSTEM (281353)**, 2707 L. Street, Zip 68862–1275; tel. 308/728–4200, (Nonreporting) **A**9 10 18
Primary Contact: William T. Sugg, President and Chief Executive Officer
CFO: Ashley Woodward, Director Financial Services
CMO: Jennifer Bengston, M.D., Chief Medical Officer
CIO: Shane Molacek, Chief Information Officer
CHR: Danielle Proskocil, Director Human Resources
Web address: www.valleycountyhospital.org
Control: County–Government, nonfederal **Service:** General Medical and Surgical

Staffed Beds: 85

OSCEOLA—Polk County

ANNIE JEFFREY MEMORIAL COUNTY HEALTH CENTER (281314), 531 Beebe Street, Zip 68651–5537, Mailing Address: P.O. Box 428, Zip 68651–0428; tel. 402/747–2031 **A**9 10 18 **F**3 11 13 15 28 29 34 35 40 43 45 53 57 59 63 64 68 75 76 77 79 81 85 87 91 93 107 110 111 114 117 119 129 130 131 132 133
Primary Contact: Joseph W. Lohrman, Chief Executive Officer
CFO: Joseph W. Lohrman, Chief Executive Officer
CMO: David Jameson, M.D., Chief of Staff
CIO: Frank Vrba, Chief Information Officer
CHR: Sue Leif, R.N., Director Human Resources
Web address: www.ajhc.org
Control: County–Government, nonfederal **Service:** General Medical and Surgical

Staffed Beds: 12 **Admissions:** 184 **Census:** 2 **Outpatient Visits:** 4405 **Births:** 21 **Total Expense ($000):** 6613 **Payroll Expense ($000):** 2311 **Personnel:** 55

NE

Many Facility Codes have changed. Please refer to the AHA Guide Code Chart. © 2014 AHA Guide

OSHKOSH—Garden County

GARDEN COUNTY HEALTH SERVICES (281310), 1100 West Second Street, Zip 69154–6152; tel. 308/772–3283, (Nonreporting) **A**9 10 18
Primary Contact: Jimmie W. Hansel, Ph.D., Chief Executive Officer
CFO: Jennifer Moffat, Staff Accountant
CMO: Harold Keenan, M.D., Chief Medical Officer
CIO: DeeDee Dunlap, Information Officer
CHR: Ricca Sanford, Director Human Resources
CNO: Darlene Schaeffer, Chief Nursing Officer
Web address: www.gchealth.org
Control: County–Government, nonfederal **Service:** General Medical and Surgical

Staffed Beds: 50

OSMOND—Pierce County

★ **OSMOND GENERAL HOSPITAL (281347)**, 402 North Maple Street, Zip 68765–5726, Mailing Address: P.O. Box 429, Zip 68765–0429; tel. 402/748–3393, (Nonreporting) **A**9 10 18
Primary Contact: Celine M. Mlady, Chief Executive Officer
CFO: Jodi Aschoff, Chief Financial Officer
CMO: David Mwebe, M.D., Chief of Staff
Web address: www.osmondhospital.com
Control: Other not–for–profit (including NFP Corporation) **Service:** General Medical and Surgical

Staffed Beds: 25

PAPILLION—Sarpy County

⌧ **CHI HEALTH MIDLANDS (280105)**, 11111 South 84th Street, Zip 68046–4122; tel. 402/593–3000 **A**1 2 9 10 **F**3 11 13 15 17 18 20 22 26 28 29 30 34 35 36 38 40 43 44 45 46 49 50 51 53 56 57 59 60 61 62 63 64 65 68 70 76 77 79 81 84 85 86 87 93 97 107 110 111 114 115 117 118 119 129 130 131 132 135 143 146 147 **P**6 8 **S** Catholic Health Initiatives, Englewood, CO
Primary Contact: Cindy Alloway, President
CFO: Ryan Reinke, Chief Financial Officer
CMO: Jeffrey Strohmyer, M.D., Chief Medical Officer
CIO: Kenneth Lawonn, Senior Vice President and Chief Information Officer
CHR: Nancy Wallace, Interim Senior Vice President Human Resources
Web address: www.alegent.org/midlands
Control: Church–operated, Nongovernment, not–for profit **Service:** General Medical and Surgical

Staffed Beds: 61 Admissions: 2036 Census: 19 Outpatient Visits: 43441 Births: 253 Total Expense ($000): 39976 Payroll Expense ($000): 16303 Personnel: 271

PAWNEE CITY—Pawnee County

★ **PAWNEE COUNTY MEMORIAL HOSPITAL AND RURAL HEALTH CLINIC (281302)**, 600 I Street, Zip 68420–3001, Mailing Address: P.O. Box 433, Zip 68420–0433; tel. 402/852–2231 **A**9 10 18 **F**7 8 15 28 29 31 34 40 43 45 56 59 65 75 77 78 79 81 82 86 93 97 107 111 119 127 129 133
Primary Contact: James A. Kubik, Administrator
CHR: Jennifer Bartels, Director Human Resources
CNO: Kris Meyer, R.N., Director of Nursing
Web address: www.pawneehospital.com
Control: County–Government, nonfederal **Service:** General Medical and Surgical

Staffed Beds: 11 Admissions: 52 Census: 1 Outpatient Visits: 3831 Births: 0 Total Expense ($000): 6087 Payroll Expense ($000): 2805 Personnel: 60

PENDER—Thurston County

★ **PENDER COMMUNITY HOSPITAL (281349)**, 100 Hospital Drive, Zip 68047–0100, Mailing Address: P.O. Box 100, Zip 68047–0100; tel. 402/385–3083, (Nonreporting) **A**9 10 18 **S** Catholic Health East / Trinity Health, Livonia, MI
Primary Contact: Melissa Kelly, Administrator
COO: Melissa Kelly, Chief Operating Officer
CFO: Melissa Kelly, Chief Financial Officer
CMO: Matt Timm, M.D., Medical Director
CIO: Teresa Heise, Coordinator Management Information Systems
CHR: Nancy Suhr, Manager Human Resources
CNO: Katie Peterson, R.N., Director of Nursing
Web address: www.pendercommunityhospital.com
Control: Hospital district or authority, Government, nonfederal **Service:** General Medical and Surgical

Staffed Beds: 67

PLAINVIEW—Pierce County

★ **CHI HEALTH PLAINVIEW (281346)**, 704 North Third Street, Zip 68769–2047, Mailing Address: P.O. Box 489, Zip 68769–0489; tel. 402/582–4245 **A**9 10 18 **F**18 28 35 40 59 62 81 93 107 127 133 **S** Catholic Health Initiatives, Englewood, CO
Primary Contact: Richard B. Gamel, Operations Leader
CFO: Rebecca Lambrecht, Manager Finance
CMO: W. Brad Lockee, M.D., Chief of Staff
CHR: Diane Blair, Human Resources and Admissions
Web address: www.alegentcreighton.com/plainview–hospital
Control: Church–operated, Nongovernment, not–for profit **Service:** General Medical and Surgical

Staffed Beds: 8 Admissions: 182 Census: 2 Outpatient Visits: 4825 Births: 0 Total Expense ($000): 7655 Payroll Expense ($000): 3279 Personnel: 58

RED CLOUD—Webster County

WEBSTER COUNTY COMMUNITY HOSPITAL (281316), Sixth Avenue and Franklin Street, Zip 68970–0465, Mailing Address: P.O. Box 465, Zip 68970–0465; tel. 402/746–5600 **A**9 10 18 **F**3 15 18 28 29 30 32 34 35 40 41 45 50 56 57 59 64 65 68 70 75 77 78 79 81 82 83 84 89 90 91 93 94 96 97 107 110 111 112 118 119 127 128 129 130 133 145 146
Primary Contact: Luke Poore, Administrator
CFO: Marcia Olson, Business Office Manager
CMO: Amy Springer, Medical Director
CIO: Eilleen Berry, Manager Information Technology
CHR: Marcia Olson, Business Office Manager
Web address: www.websterhospital.org
Control: County–Government, nonfederal **Service:** General Medical and Surgical

Staffed Beds: 13 Admissions: 80 Census: 2 Births: 0 Personnel: 47

SAINT PAUL—Howard County

HOWARD COUNTY COMMUNITY HOSPITAL See Howard County Medical Center

★ **HOWARD COUNTY MEDICAL CENTER (281338)**, 1113 Sherman Street, Zip 68873–1546, Mailing Address: P.O. Box 406, Zip 68873–0406; tel. 308/754–4421, (Nonreporting) **A**9 10 18
Primary Contact: Arlan D. Johnson, Chief Executive Officer
COO: Jillyn Klein, Chief Operating Officer
CFO: Chalee Fernau, Controller
CMO: Angela Brennan, M.D., Chief of Staff
CIO: Kari Pierson, Manager
CHR: Leslie Smith, Director Human Resources
CNO: Gabe Bodeman, Director of Nursing
Web address: www.hcmc.us.com
Control: County–Government, nonfederal **Service:** General Medical and Surgical

Staffed Beds: 25

SCHUYLER—Colfax County

★ **CHI HEALTH SCHUYLER (281323)**, 104 West 17th Street, Zip 68661–1304; tel. 402/352–2441, (Nonreporting) **A**9 10 18 **S** Catholic Health Initiatives, Englewood, CO
Primary Contact: Connie Peters, R.N., President
CFO: Tim H. Schnack, Chief Financial Officer
CIO: Kenneth Lawonn, Senior Vice President and Chief Information Officer
CHR: Nancy Wallace, Vice President Human Resources
CNO: Jane Carmody, R.N., Vice President and System Chief Nursing Officer
Web address: www.alegent.com
Control: Church–operated, Nongovernment, not–for profit **Service:** General Medical and Surgical

Staffed Beds: 25

NE

SCOTTSBLUFF—Scotts Bluff County

✠ △ **REGIONAL WEST MEDICAL CENTER (280061)**, 4021 Avenue B,
Zip 69361–4695; tel. 308/635–3711 **A**1 2 3 5 7 9 10 19 20 **F**8 11 12 14 15
17 20 28 29 30 40 43 45 47 58 59 62 63 64 65 68 69 70 72 74 76 77 78
79 81 85 89 90 92 93 98 99 107 108 110 111 114 115 119 120 121 123
129 130 131 146 147 148 **P**6
Primary Contact: John Mentgen, President and Chief Executive Officer
CFO: David Griffiths, Vice President and Chief Financial Officer
CMO: Jon Morgan, M.D., Chief Medical Officer
CIO: Steve Mathews, Vice President and Chief Information Officer
CHR: Bradford L. Evans, Director Human Resources
CNO: Shirley Knodel, R.N., Chief Nursing Officer
Web address: www.rwhs.org
Control: Other not–for–profit (including NFP Corporation) **Service:** General
Medical and Surgical

Staffed Beds: 107 **Admissions:** 7425 **Census:** 76 **Outpatient Visits:** 327988
Births: 875 **Total Expense ($000):** 171878 **Payroll Expense ($000):** 61414
Personnel: 1032

SEWARD—Seward County

★ **MEMORIAL HEALTH CARE SYSTEMS (281339)**, 300 North Columbia Avenue,
Zip 68434–2228; tel. 402/643–2971, (Nonreporting) **A**9 10 18
Primary Contact: Roger J. Reamer, Chief Executive Officer
CFO: Greg Jerger, Chief Financial Officer
CMO: Tricia Sams, M.D., Medical Director
CIO: Carol Carlson, Director Community Relations
Web address: www.mhcs.us
Control: Other not–for–profit (including NFP Corporation) **Service:** General
Medical and Surgical

Staffed Beds: 25

SIDNEY—Cheyenne County

★ **SIDNEY REGIONAL MEDICAL CENTER (281357)**, 645 Osage Street,
Zip 69162–1799; tel. 308/254–5825, (Total facility includes 63 beds in nursing
home–type unit) **A**5 9 10 18 **F**1 8 10 11 13 15 17 18 19 28 29 30 31 34 35
40 41 45 49 50 51 56 57 59 62 63 64 65 67 68 70 75 76 77 78 79 81 84
85 87 89 92 93 94 97 107 108 109 110 111 114 119 127 128 129 130 131
132 133 135 146 148
Primary Contact: Jason Petik, Chief Executive Officer
CMO: Mandy Shaw, M.D., Chief of Staff
CIO: Jennifer Brockhaus, Chief Information Officer
CHR: Catherine T. Arterburn, R.N., Vice President Human Resources
CNO: Julie A. Slagle, R.N., Vice President Patient Care Services
Web address: www.sidneyrmc.com
Control: Other not–for–profit (including NFP Corporation) **Service:** General
Medical and Surgical

Staffed Beds: 88 **Admissions:** 786 **Census:** 57 **Outpatient Visits:** 91522
Births: 62 **Total Expense ($000):** 35552 **Payroll Expense ($000):** 15774
Personnel: 290

SUPERIOR—Nuckolls County

★ **BRODSTONE MEMORIAL HOSPITAL (281315)**, 520 East Tenth Street,
Zip 68978–1225, Mailing Address: P.O. Box 187, Zip 68978–0187;
tel. 402/879–3281, (Nonreporting) **A**9 10 18
Primary Contact: John E. Keelan, Administrator and Chief Executive Officer
COO: Dena C. Alvarez, R.N., COO & Chief Compliance Officer
CFO: Sandy Borden, Chief Financial Officer
CMO: Timothy Blecha, M.D., Medical Director
CIO: Tim Hiatt, Chief Information Officer
CHR: Jeremy Littrell, Director Human Resources
CNO: Kori Field, Director of Nursing
Web address: www.brodstonehospital.org
Control: Other not–for–profit (including NFP Corporation) **Service:** General
Medical and Surgical

Staffed Beds: 25

SYRACUSE—Otoe County

★ **COMMUNITY MEMORIAL HOSPITAL (281309)**, 1579 Midland Street,
Zip 68446–9732, Mailing Address: P.O. Box N., Zip 68446–0518;
tel. 402/269–2011 **A**9 10 18 **F**1 3 11 15 28 29 40 43 45 53 59 62 64 67 79
81 89 90 93 107 110 127 128 133
Primary Contact: Michael Harvey, President and Chief Executive Officer
COO: Julie Werner, Chief Operating Officer
CFO: Michael Harvey, President and Chief Executive Officer
CMO: Zak Tempelmeyer, M.D., Chief Medical Staff
CIO: Matthew Steinblock, Systems Administrator
CHR: Karrie Beach, Director Human Resources
CNO: Pat Howell, Chief Nursing Officer
Web address: www.syracusecmh.org
Control: Hospital district or authority, Government, nonfederal **Service:** General
Medical and Surgical

Staffed Beds: 10 **Admissions:** 328 **Census:** 2 **Outpatient Visits:** 32761
Births: 0 **Total Expense ($000):** 12170 **Payroll Expense ($000):** 5622
Personnel: 102

TECUMSEH—Johnson County

★ **JOHNSON COUNTY HOSPITAL (281350)**, 202 High Street, Zip 68450–2443,
Mailing Address: P.O. Box 599, Zip 68450–0599; tel. 402/335–3361,
(Nonreporting) **A**9 10 18
Primary Contact: Diane Newman, Administrator
COO: Diane Newman, Administrator
CFO: Janice Oehm, Manager Business Office
CMO: Keith Shuey, M.D., Chief Medical Staff
CIO: Fred Pooch, Supervisor Information Technology
CHR: Susan Hessheimer, Director Human Resources
Web address: www.jchosp.com
Control: County–Government, nonfederal **Service:** General Medical and Surgical

Staffed Beds: 25

VALENTINE—Cherry County

★ **CHERRY COUNTY HOSPITAL (281344)**, 510 North Green Street,
Zip 69201–1932, Mailing Address: P.O. Box 410, Zip 69201–0410;
tel. 402/376–2525, (Nonreporting) **A**5 9 10 18
Primary Contact: Brent A. Peterson, Administrator
CFO: Peggy Snell, Chief Finance Officer
Control: County–Government, nonfederal **Service:** General Medical and Surgical

Staffed Beds: 25

WAHOO—Saunders County

★ **SAUNDERS MEDICAL CENTER (281307)**, 1760 County Road J.,
Zip 68066–4152; tel. 402/443–4191, (Nonreporting) **A**9 10 18
Primary Contact: Tyler Toline, Interim Chief Executive Officer
COO: Julie A. Rezac, R.N., Chief Operating Officer
CFO: Tricia Fox, Director Finance
CMO: Leo L. Meduna, M.D., Chief Medical Officer
CIO: Carrie Stephens, Director of Information Technology and Support Services
CHR: Karen Leise, Coordinator Human Resources
CNO: James Nelson, MSN, Director of Nursing
Web address: www.saundersmedicalcenter.com
Control: County–Government, nonfederal **Service:** General Medical and Surgical

Staffed Beds: 87

WAYNE—Wayne County

★ **PROVIDENCE MEDICAL CENTER (281345)**, 1200 Providence Road,
Zip 68787–1299; tel. 402/375–3800 **A**9 10 18 **F**3 7 13 15 28 29 30 31 34
35 36 40 50 53 57 59 62 63 64 68 75 76 81 84 85 93 107 110 111 114
119 128 130 132 133 135
Primary Contact: Thomas J. Lee, FACHE, Administrator/CEO
CFO: Kim Hixson, Chief Financial Officer
CHR: Jackie Backer, Director Human Resources
CNO: Laura Gamble, Director Clinical Services
Web address: www.providencemedical.com
Control: Other not–for–profit (including NFP Corporation) **Service:** General
Medical and Surgical

Staffed Beds: 25 **Admissions:** 484 **Census:** 6 **Outpatient Visits:** 17433
Births: 51 **Total Expense ($000):** 16501 **Payroll Expense ($000):** 7566
Personnel: 156

WEST POINT—Cuming County

★ **ST. FRANCIS MEMORIAL HOSPITAL (281322)**, 430 North Monitor Street,
Zip 68788–1555; tel. 402/372–2404, (Total facility includes 63 beds in nursing
home–type unit) **A**9 10 18 **F**3 6 11 13 15 28 29 30 31 34 35 40 43 45 50 53
57 59 62 63 64 68 75 76 77 78 79 81 82 85 86 90 92 93 94 98 99 100
103 107 111 114 119 127 128 129 130 131 132 133 135 146 147 148 **P**6
S Franciscan Sisters of Christian Charity Sponsored Ministries, Inc.,
Manitowoc, WI
Primary Contact: Ronald O. Briggs, FACHE, President and Chief Executive Officer
COO: Jerry Wordekemper, Chief Operating Officer
CFO: Dennis Dinslage, Vice President Finance and Chief Financial Officer
CMO: Scott Green, M.D., Chief of Staff
CIO: Jean Meiergerd, Chief Information Officer
CHR: Terri Ridder, Director Human Resources
CNO: Carol Kampschnieder, Vice President Clinical and Regulatory Services
Web address: www.fcswp.org
Control: Church–operated, Nongovernment, not–for profit **Service:** General
Medical and Surgical

Staffed Beds: 92 **Admissions:** 558 **Census:** 65 **Outpatient Visits:** 66637
Births: 57 **Total Expense ($000):** 29069 **Payroll Expense ($000):** 13609
Personnel: 217

NE

Many Facility Codes have changed. Please refer to the AHA Guide Code Chart.
© 2014 AHA Guide

WINNEBAGO—Thurston County

☐ **U. S. PUBLIC HEALTH SERVICE INDIAN HOSPITAL (280119)**, Highway 7577,
Zip 68071; tel. 402/878–2231, (Nonreporting) **A**1 9 10 **S** U. S. Indian Health
Service, Rockville, MD
Primary Contact: Patricia Medina, Service Unit Director
CFO: Audrey Parker, Budget Analyst
Web address: www.ihs.gov
Control: PHS, Indian Service, Government, federal **Service:** General Medical and
Surgical

Staffed Beds: 30

YORK—York County

★ **YORK GENERAL HOSPITAL (281336)**, 2222 North Lincoln Avenue,
Zip 68467–1095; tel. 402/362–6671, (Total facility includes 129 beds in nursing
home–type unit) **A**9 10 18 **F**3 10 11 12 13 15 28 29 31 34 35 40 45 53 56 57
59 60 62 64 68 70 75 76 77 78 79 81 82 85 86 87 89 93 96 107 108 110
111 115 117 118 119 125 128 129 130 131 132 133 145 146 148
Primary Contact: Charles K. Schulz, Chief Executive Officer
CFO: Bob McQuistan, Vice President Finance
CMO: Todd Fago, M.D., Chief of Staff
CIO: Chris Kraft, Director Information Systems
CHR: Cathy Norquest, Director Human Resources
CNO: Jenny Obermier, VP, Director of Nursing
Web address: www.yorkgeneral.org
Control: Other not–for–profit (including NFP Corporation) **Service:** General
Medical and Surgical

Staffed Beds: 154 **Admissions:** 1111 **Census:** 127 **Outpatient Visits:** 38139
Births: 103 **Total Expense ($000):** 37593 **Payroll Expense ($000):** 17529
Personnel: 400

NE

Hospital, Medicare Provider Number, Address, Telephone, Approval, Facility, and Physician Codes, Health Care System

★ American Hospital Association (AHA) membership
☐ The Joint Commission accreditation ◇ DNV Healthcare Inc. accreditation

◯ Healthcare Facilities Accreditation Program
△ Commission on Accreditation of Rehabilitation Facilities (CARF) accreditation

NEVADA

BATTLE MOUNTAIN—Lander County

BATTLE MOUNTAIN GENERAL HOSPITAL (291303), 535 South Humboldt Street, Zip 89820–1988; tel. 775/635–2550 **A**9 10 18 **F**3 7 18 34 40 43 50 57 59 65 68 75 77 86 93 97 107 119 127 130 131 132 133 143
Primary Contact: Philip S. Hanna, Administrator and Chief Executive Officer
CFO: Cindy Fagg, Fiscal Officer
CMO: Mark S. Meyers, M.D., Chief of Staff
CIO: Terry Dunn, Director Information Technology
CHR: Lori Sherbondy, Director Human Resources
CNO: Kelley Price, R.N., Chief Nursing Officer
Web address: www.bmgh.org
Control: Hospital district or authority, Government, nonfederal **Service:** General Medical and Surgical

Staffed Beds: 7 **Admissions:** 131 **Census:** 1 **Outpatient Visits:** 66253 **Births:** 3 **Total Expense ($000):** 12000 **Payroll Expense ($000):** 7800 **Personnel:** 117

BOULDER CITY—Clark County

BOULDER CITY HOSPITAL (291309), 901 Adams Boulevard, Zip 89005–2213; tel. 702/293–4111, (Nonreporting) **A**9 10 18
Primary Contact: Thomas Maher, Chief Executive Officer and Administrator
COO: Rae Cummings, Chief Operating Officer
CMO: Derek Meeks, D.O., Chief of Staff
CIO: Scott Brooks, Manager Information Technology
CHR: Belinda McGraw, Director Human Resources
CNO: Andre Pastian, R.N., Chief Nursing Officer
Web address: www.bouldercityhospital.org
Control: Other not-for-profit (including NFP Corporation) **Service:** General Medical and Surgical

Staffed Beds: 25

CALIENTE—Lincoln County

GROVER C. DILS MEDICAL CENTER (291312), 700 North Spring Street, Zip 89008, Mailing Address: P.O. Box 1010, Zip 89008–1010; tel. 775/726–3171, (Nonreporting) **A**9 10 18
Primary Contact: Jason Bleak, Administrator and Chief Executive Officer
COO: Jason Bleak, Administrator and Chief Executive Officer
CFO: Sherlyn Fackrell, Finance Controller
CMO: R. William Katschke, Jr., M.D., Medical Director
CHR: Rozanne Mangum, Administrative Assistant and Director Human Resources
Web address: www.dilsmedicalcenter.org
Control: Other not-for-profit (including NFP Corporation) **Service:** Other specialty

Staffed Beds: 20

CARSON CITY—Carson City County

CARSON TAHOE CONTINUING CARE HOSPITAL (292008), 775 Fleischmann Way, 2nd Floor, Zip 89703–2995; tel. 775/445–7795, (Nonreporting) **A**9 10
Primary Contact: Kelly Wilcher, Chief Executive Officer
CFO: Ann Beck, Vice President and Chief Financial Officer
CMO: Jose Aguirre, M.D., Medical Director
CIO: Scott Waters, Director Information Technology
CHR: Angie Rodriguez, Human Resources Business Partner
CNO: Stu Talley, Chief Nursing Officer
Web address: www.carsontahoe.com
Control: Other not-for-profit (including NFP Corporation) **Service:** Long–Term Acute Care hospital

Staffed Beds: 29

✖ **CARSON TAHOE REGIONAL MEDICAL CENTER (290019)**, 1600 Medical Parkway, Zip 89703–4625, Mailing Address: P.O. Box 2168, Zip 89702–2168; tel. 775/445–8672 **A**1 2 9 10 19 20 **F**3 4 5 8 11 12 13 15 17 18 20 22 24 28 29 30 31 34 35 38 40 42 48 49 57 59 64 65 68 70 74 75 76 77 78 79 81 85 86 87 89 90 91 93 98 99 100 101 102 103 104 105 107 108 111 114 119 120 121 123 124 130 132 135 144 146 147 148
Primary Contact: Edward L. Epperson, Chief Executive Officer
CFO: Ann Beck, Vice President Finance
CMO: Jeffrey Sanders, M.D., Chief of Staff
CIO: Cheri Glockner, Director Development
CHR: Jim Lewandowski, Interim Director of Human Resources
CNO: Anna Anders, Interim Vice President Patient Care
Web address: www.carsontahoe.com
Control: Other not-for-profit (including NFP Corporation) **Service:** General Medical and Surgical

Staffed Beds: 190 **Admissions:** 10362 **Census:** 125 **Outpatient Visits:** 211746 **Total Expense ($000):** 195786 **Payroll Expense ($000):** 67420 **Personnel:** 988

☐ **SIERRA SURGERY HOSPITAL (290051)**, 1400 Medical Parkway, Zip 89703–4624; tel. 775/883–1700 **A**1 9 10 **F**3 8 15 29 51 64 65 68 75 79 81 82 85 87 107 108 110 111 114 131
Primary Contact: Ken Doran, Interim Chief Executive Officer
CFO: Sheryl Hayden, Chief Financial Officer
Web address: www.sierrasurgery.com
Control: Partnership, Investor–owned, for–profit **Service:** Surgical

Staffed Beds: 15 **Admissions:** 760 **Census:** 5 **Births:** 0 **Total Expense ($000):** 30138 **Payroll Expense ($000):** 7883 **Personnel:** 104

ELKO—Elko County

✖ **NORTHEASTERN NEVADA REGIONAL HOSPITAL (290008)**, 2001 Errecart Boulevard, Zip 89801–8333; tel. 775/738–5151 **A**1 9 10 20 **F**3 11 13 15 18 20 28 29 30 31 34 40 45 46 49 50 51 57 59 60 68 70 75 76 79 81 82 89 98 101 102 103 107 108 111 114 115 119 129 146 **S** LifePoint Hospitals, Inc., Brentwood, TN
Primary Contact: Gene Miller, Chief Executive Officer
CFO: Grant Trollope, Chief Financial Officer
CIO: Jeff Morgan, Director Information Systems
CHR: Laura Elliott, Director Human Resources
CNO: Dona E. Townsend, Chief Nursing Officer
Web address: www.nnrhospital.com
Control: Corporation, Investor–owned, for–profit **Service:** General Medical and Surgical

Staffed Beds: 75 **Admissions:** 2797 **Census:** 22 **Outpatient Visits:** 63786 **Births:** 671 **Total Expense ($000):** 44618 **Payroll Expense ($000):** 17916

ELY—White Pine County

✖ **WILLIAM BEE RIRIE HOSPITAL (291302)**, 1500 Avenue H, Zip 89301–2699; tel. 775/289–3001 **A**1 9 10 18 **F**8 13 15 29 31 32 35 40 44 45 50 57 59 64 65 66 68 75 76 77 79 81 82 85 86 87 89 93 102 104 107 108 110 111 114 119 127 129 130 135 **P**6
Primary Contact: Jan Jensen, R.N., Chief Executive Officer and Administrator
CMO: G. N. Christensen, M.D., Chief Medical Officer
CIO: Destin Brandis, Chief Information Officer
CHR: Vicki Pereace, Manager Human Resources
Web address: www.elynevadahospital.org
Control: Hospital district or authority, Government, nonfederal **Service:** General Medical and Surgical

Staffed Beds: 15 **Admissions:** 370 **Census:** 3 **Outpatient Visits:** 27200 **Births:** 74 **Total Expense ($000):** 27622 **Payroll Expense ($000):** 13273 **Personnel:** 99

FALLON—Churchill County

✖ **BANNER CHURCHILL COMMUNITY HOSPITAL (290006)**, 801 East Williams Avenue, Zip 89406–3052; tel. 775/867–7000 **A**1 9 10 20 **F**3 7 11 13 15 29 30 31 34 35 40 45 47 50 57 59 65 68 70 75 76 78 79 81 85 86 87 93 97 107 108 110 111 114 118 119 130 146 148 **S** Banner Health, Phoenix, AZ
Primary Contact: Hoyt Skabelund, Chief Executive Officer
CFO: Steven Fraker, Chief Financial Officer
CMO: Tedd McDonald, M.D., Chief Medical Officer
CHR: Darlene Alvis, Chief Human Resources Officer
CNO: Robert H. Carnahan, II, Chief Nursing Officer
Web address: www.bannerhealth.com/Locations/Nevada/Banner+Churchill+Community+Hospital
Control: Other not-for-profit (including NFP Corporation) **Service:** General Medical and Surgical

Staffed Beds: 40 **Admissions:** 1849 **Census:** 17 **Births:** 369 **Total Expense ($000):** 37183 **Payroll Expense ($000):** 14379 **Personnel:** 259

GARDNERVILLE—Douglas County

★ **CARSON VALLEY MEDICAL CENTER (291306)**, 1107 Highway 395, Zip 89410; tel. 775/782–1500 **A**9 10 18 **F**11 15 29 31 34 35 40 45 47 48 50 53 54 56 57 59 60 64 68 70 75 77 79 81 93 103 107 108 110 111 115 118 119 127 129 130 132 133 135 144 146 148
Primary Contact: Susan Davila, Chief Executive Officer and Administrator
COO: Linda Lilleboe, R.N., Director Operations
CFO: Julie Howes, Director Finance
CMO: Evan Easley, M.D., Chief Medical Officer
CIO: Brian Gould, Director Information System
CHR: Lisa Tremaine, Manager Human Resources
CNO: Christy Raynes, R.N., Director Clinical Services
Web address: www.carsonvalleymedicalcenter.com
Control: Other not-for-profit (including NFP Corporation) **Service:** General Medical and Surgical

Staffed Beds: 23 **Admissions:** 804 **Census:** 6 **Births:** 0 **Total Expense ($000):** 40193 **Payroll Expense ($000):** 15388 **Personnel:** 305

Many Facility Codes have changed. Please refer to the AHA Guide Code Chart.

NV

HAWTHORNE—Mineral County

MOUNT GRANT GENERAL HOSPITAL (291300), First and A Street, Zip 89415, Mailing Address: P.O. Box 1510, Zip 89415–1510; tel. 775/945–2461, (Nonreporting) **A**9 10 18
Primary Contact: Richard Munger, Administrator
Web address: www.mtgrantgenhospital.org/
Control: Other not–for–profit (including NFP Corporation) **Service:** General Medical and Surgical

Staffed Beds: 11

HENDERSON—Clark County

✠ **HEALTHSOUTH REHABILITATION HOSPITAL – HENDERSON (293032)**, 10301 Jeffreys Street, Zip 89052–3922; tel. 702/939–9400, (Nonreporting) **A**1 10 **S** HEALTHSOUTH Corporation, Birmingham, AL
Primary Contact: Nina Beck, Interim Chief Executive Officer
CFO: Robert Bollard, Chief Financial Officer
Web address: www.hendersonrehabhospital.com
Control: Corporation, Investor–owned, for–profit **Service:** Rehabilitation

Staffed Beds: 70

SEVEN HILLS BEHAVIORAL INSTITUTE (294012), 3021 West Horizon Ridge Parkway, Zip 89052–3990; tel. 702/646–5000 **A**9 10 **F**4 5 29 34 38 56 64 98 99 101 103 104 105 130 132 143 148 **P**8 **S** Acadia Healthcare Company, Inc., Franklin, TN
Primary Contact: Robert L. Turner, Ph.D., Chief Executive Officer
CMO: Keith Breiland, M.D., Medical Director
Web address: www.sevenhillsbi.com
Control: Corporation, Investor–owned, for–profit **Service:** Psychiatric

Staffed Beds: 58 **Admissions:** 2722 **Census:** 53 **Outpatient Visits:** 2634 **Births:** 0 **Total Expense ($000):** 11532 **Payroll Expense ($000):** 5850 **Personnel:** 138

✠ **ST. ROSE DOMINICAN HOSPITALS – ROSE DE LIMA CAMPUS (290012)**, 102 East Lake Mead Parkway, Zip 89015–5524; tel. 702/616–5000 **A**1 9 10 **F**3 8 12 15 18 20 29 30 31 32 34 35 38 40 43 44 45 49 50 57 59 62 63 64 65 68 70 74 75 77 78 79 81 82 84 85 86 87 90 93 96 102 107 108 111 114 119 130 131 132 135 143 146 147 148 **S** Dignity Health, San Francisco, CA
Primary Contact: Teressa Conley, Interim President and Chief Executive Officer
COO: Teressa Conley, Vice President and Chief Operating Officer
CFO: Kevin Walters, Chief Financial Officer
CMO: Stephen K. Jones, M.D., Vice President Medical Staff Affairs
Web address: www.strosehospitals.org
Control: Church–operated, Nongovernment, not–for profit **Service:** General Medical and Surgical

Staffed Beds: 109 **Admissions:** 6163 **Census:** 86 **Outpatient Visits:** 43694 **Births:** 0 **Total Expense ($000):** 136282 **Payroll Expense ($000):** 62630 **Personnel:** 663

✠ **ST. ROSE DOMINICAN HOSPITALS – SIENA CAMPUS (290045)**, 3001 St. Rose Parkway, Zip 89052; tel. 702/616–5000 **A**1 3 5 9 10 **F**3 7 13 15 18 20 21 22 23 24 26 28 29 30 31 32 34 35 38 40 41 43 44 45 46 50 57 59 64 68 70 72 74 75 76 77 78 79 81 82 83 84 85 86 87 88 89 93 102 107 108 110 111 114 115 119 126 130 131 132 135 146 147 148 **S** Dignity Health, San Francisco, CA
Primary Contact: Brian G. Brannman, President and Chief Executive Officer
COO: Teressa Conley, Chief Operating Officer
CFO: Kevin Walters, Chief Financial Officer
CMO: Robert Pretzlaff, M.D., Chief Medical Officer
CIO: Russ Patterson, Director Information Technology
CHR: Linda Gerstenberger, Vice President Human Resources
Web address: www.strosehospitals.com
Control: Church–operated, Nongovernment, not–for profit **Service:** General Medical and Surgical

Staffed Beds: 219 **Admissions:** 16601 **Census:** 185 **Outpatient Visits:** 76028 **Births:** 3347 **Total Expense ($000):** 304024 **Payroll Expense ($000):** 133440 **Personnel:** 1629

INCLINE VILLAGE—Washoe County

★ **INCLINE VILLAGE COMMUNITY HOSPITAL (291301)**, 880 Alder Avenue, Zip 89451–8335; tel. 775/833–4100, (Nonreporting) **A**3 5 9 10 18 **S** Tahoe Forest Health System, Truckee, CA
Primary Contact: Judy Newland, R.N., Chief Nursing Officer
COO: Virginia Razo, Chief Operating Officer
CFO: Crystal Betts, Chief Financial Officer
CIO: Mark Griffiths, Director Management Information Systems
CHR: Jayne O'Flanagan, Director Human Resources
Web address: www.tfhd.com
Control: Hospital district or authority, Government, nonfederal **Service:** General Medical and Surgical

Staffed Beds: 6

LAS VEGAS—Clark County

☐ **CENTENNIAL HILLS HOSPITAL MEDICAL CENTER (290054)**, 6900 North Durango Drive, Zip 89149–4409; tel. 702/835–9700, (Nonreporting) **A**1 9 10 **S** Universal Health Services, Inc., King of Prussia, PA
Primary Contact: Sajit Pullarkat, Chief Executive Officer and Managing Director
Web address: www.centennialhillshospital.com
Control: Corporation, Investor–owned, for–profit **Service:** General Medical and Surgical

Staffed Beds: 165

✠ **COMPLEX CARE HOSPITAL AT TENAYA (292006)**, 2500 North Tenaya, Zip 89128–0482; tel. 702/562–2021, (Nonreporting) **A**1 9 10 **S** LifeCare Management Services, Plano, TX
Primary Contact: Colin O'Sullivan, Acting Chief Executive Officer
COO: Paul D'Ambrosio, Chief Operating Officer
CFO: Anna Rich, Chief Financial Officer
CMO: C. Dean Milne, D.O., Medical Director
CIO: Lynn Tunson, Manager Medical Records
CHR: Belinda McGraw, Director Human Resources
CNO: Robin Wolf, Chief Nursing Officer
Web address: www.lifecare–hospitals.com
Control: Corporation, Investor–owned, for–profit **Service:** Long–Term Acute Care hospital

Staffed Beds: 70

☐ **DESERT SPRINGS HOSPITAL MEDICAL CENTER (290022)**, 2075 East Flamingo Road, Zip 89119–5121; tel. 702/733–8800, (Nonreporting) **A**1 9 10 **S** Universal Health Services, Inc., King of Prussia, PA
Primary Contact: Samuel Kaufman, Chief Executive Officer and Managing Director
CMO: Adel R. Shehata, M.D., Medical Director
CIO: Tom Schoenig, System Director Information Services
CHR: Shirley A. Shadwick, Administrator Human Resources
Web address: www.desertspringshospital.com
Control: Corporation, Investor–owned, for–profit **Service:** General Medical and Surgical

Staffed Beds: 346

DESERT WILLOW TREATMENT CENTER, 6171 West Charleston Boulevard, Zip 89146–1126; tel. 702/486–8900, (Nonreporting) **A**3 5
Primary Contact: Linda Santangelo, Ph.D., Director
Control: State–Government, nonfederal **Service:** Psychiatric

Staffed Beds: 58

HARMON MEDICAL AND REHABILITATION HOSPITAL (290042), 2170 East Harmon Avenue, Zip 89119–7840; tel. 702/794–0100, (Nonreporting) **A**10 **S** Fundamental Long Term Care Holdings, LLC, Sparks Glencoe, MD
Primary Contact: Bonnie Essex Hillegass, Chief Executive Officer
Control: Corporation, Investor–owned, for–profit **Service:** Rehabilitation

Staffed Beds: 118

✠ **HEALTHSOUTH DESERT CANYON REHABILITATION HOSPITAL (293033)**, 9175 West Oquendo Road, Zip 89148–1234; tel. 702/252–7342 **A**1 10 **F**3 29 77 78 79 90 91 93 132 **S** HEALTHSOUTH Corporation, Birmingham, AL
Primary Contact: Andrea Davis, Chief Executive Officer
CMO: Bevins Chue, M.D., Medical Director
CNO: Timothy Murphy, R.N., Chief Nursing Officer
Web address: www.healthsouthdesertcanyon.com
Control: Corporation, Investor–owned, for–profit **Service:** Rehabilitation

Staffed Beds: 50 **Admissions:** 1268 **Census:** 43 **Outpatient Visits:** 3846 **Births:** 0

✠ **HEALTHSOUTH REHABILITATION HOSPITAL–LAS VEGAS (293026)**, 1250 South Valley View Boulevard, Zip 89102–1861; tel. 702/877–8898 **A**1 10 **F**3 28 29 57 60 65 68 74 75 77 79 90 95 96 130 132 143 148 **S** HEALTHSOUTH Corporation, Birmingham, AL
Primary Contact: Michael Ward, Chief Executive Officer
CFO: Patrick Landry, Controller
CHR: Debra Tafoya, Director Human Resources
CNO: Elizabeth Solomon, R.N., Regional Quality/Risk Director and Interim Chief Nursing Officer
Web address: www.healthsouthlasvegas.com
Control: Corporation, Investor–owned, for–profit **Service:** Rehabilitation

Staffed Beds: 79 **Admissions:** 1638 **Census:** 55 **Outpatient Visits:** 0 **Births:** 0 **Total Expense ($000):** 17877 **Payroll Expense ($000):** 12509 **Personnel:** 178

NV

Hospital, Medicare Provider Number, Address, Telephone, Approval, Facility, and Physician Codes, Health Care System

★ American Hospital Association (AHA) membership
☐ The Joint Commission accreditation
◇ DNV Healthcare Inc. accreditation
○ Healthcare Facilities Accreditation Program
△ Commission on Accreditation of Rehabilitation Facilities (CARF) accreditation

☐ **HORIZON SPECIALTY HOSPITAL (292003)**, 640 Desert Lane, Zip 89106–4207; tel. 702/382–3155, (Nonreporting) A1 9 10 S Fundamental Long Term Care Holdings, LLC, Sparks Glencoe, MD
Primary Contact: William Fox, Chief Executive Officer and Administrator
CFO: Darnell Bennett, Director Finance
CMO: Syed Rahman, M.D., Chief of Staff
CIO: Azena Ansi, Manager Health Information Management
CHR: Melvin Layugan, Director Human Resources
Web address: www.horizonspecialtyhosp.com/
Control: Corporation, Investor–owned, for–profit **Service:** Long–Term Acute Care hospital

Staffed Beds: 25

KINDRED HOSPITAL LAS VEGAS, DESERT SPRINGS CAMPUS See Kindred Hospital Las Vegas–Sahara

☒ **KINDRED HOSPITAL LAS VEGAS–SAHARA (292002)**, 5110 West Sahara Avenue, Zip 89146–3406; tel. 702/871–1418, (Includes KINDRED HOSPITAL LAS VEGAS, DESERT SPRINGS CAMPUS, 2075 East Flamingo Road, Suite 114, Zip 89119; tel. 702/894–5728; KINDRED HOSPITAL–FLAMINGO, 2250 East Flamingo Road, Zip 89119; tel. 702/871–1418), (Nonreporting) A1 9 10 S Kindred Healthcare, Louisville, KY
Primary Contact: Elaine Glaser, Chief Executive Officer
CFO: William Lysaght, Chief Financial Officer
CMO: Paul Stewart, M.D., Medical Director
CHR: Jim Sturgeon, Area Director Human Resources
Web address: www.kindredhospitalvs.com/
Control: Corporation, Investor–owned, for–profit **Service:** Long–Term Acute Care hospital

Staffed Beds: 238

☐ **MONTEVISTA HOSPITAL (294009)**, 5900 West Rochelle Avenue, Zip 89103–3327; tel. 702/364–1111, (Nonreporting) A1 9 10 S Strategic Behavioral Health, LLC, Memphis, TN
Primary Contact: Richard Failla, Chief Executive Officer
CMO: William Bauer, M.D., Medical Director
CHR: Carol Nelson, Director Human Resources
Web address: www.montevistahospital.com
Control: Corporation, Investor–owned, for–profit **Service:** Psychiatric

Staffed Beds: 80

☒ **MOUNTAINVIEW HOSPITAL (290039)**, 3100 North Tenaya Way, Zip 89128–0436; tel. 702/255–5000 A1 3 5 9 10 F3 11 12 13 15 18 20 22 24 26 28 29 31 34 35 40 45 46 47 48 49 50 70 74 75 77 78 79 81 90 91 93 107 108 111 112 114 115 116 117 119 126 130 146 147 148 P1 S HCA, Nashville, TN
Primary Contact: Chris Mowan, Chief Executive Officer
CFO: Lana Arad, Chief Financial Officer
CMO: Jack Collier, M.D., Chief of Staff
CHR: Robert Nettles, Director Human Resources
CNO: Natalie Ransom, Chief Nursing Officer
Web address: www.mountainview–hospital.com
Control: Corporation, Investor–owned, for–profit **Service:** General Medical and Surgical

Staffed Beds: 340 Admissions: 17232 Census: 246 Outpatient Visits: 67067 Births: 1717 Total Expense ($000): 283054 Payroll Expense ($000): 110363 Personnel: 1106

PROGRESSIVE HOSPITAL (292007), 4015 South McLeod Drive, Zip 89121–4305; tel. 702/433–2200 A9 10 F1 29 30 85 130 148 P5
Primary Contact: Rosemary Thiele, Chief Executive Officer
CFO: Ruth Knutson, Chief Financial Officer
CMO: Anthony Pollard, D.O., Chief Medical Officer
CNO: Arlene Harper, R.N., Chief Nursing Officer
Web address: www.progressivehospital.com/
Control: Partnership, Investor–owned, for–profit **Service:** Long–Term Acute Care hospital

Staffed Beds: 24 Admissions: 183 Census: 14 Outpatient Visits: 0 Births: 0 Total Expense ($000): 6638 Payroll Expense ($000): 3020 Personnel: 63

☐ **RED ROCK BEHAVIORAL HOSPITAL (294008)**, 5975 West Twain Avenue, Zip 89103–1237; tel. 702/214–8099, (Nonreporting) A1 9 10 S Strategic Behavioral Health, LLC, Memphis, TN
Primary Contact: Toby Davis, Chief Executive Officer
Web address: www.redrockhospital.com
Control: Other not–for–profit (including NFP Corporation) **Service:** Psychiatric

Staffed Beds: 22

☒ **SOUTHERN HILLS HOSPITAL AND MEDICAL CENTER (290047)**, 9300 West Sunset Road, Zip 89148–4844; tel. 702/880–2100 A1 9 10 F3 11 13 15 17 20 22 26 29 34 37 40 44 45 49 50 56 57 59 64 65 68 70 72 74 75 76 77 78 79 81 85 87 98 102 103 104 107 108 110 111 113 114 115 119 126 130 135 145 146 147 S HCA, Nashville, TN
Primary Contact: Kimball Anderson, FACHE, Chief Executive Officer
CFO: Jennifer Le, Chief Financial Officer
CMO: Eric Ramos, M.D., Division Chief Medical Officer
CIO: Joe Grandiosi, Director Information Technology
CHR: Brian Wood, Director Human Resources
CNO: Maura Wright, Chief Nursing Officer
Web address: www.southernhillshospital.com
Control: Corporation, Investor–owned, for–profit **Service:** General Medical and Surgical

Staffed Beds: 134 Admissions: 6979 Census: 81 Outpatient Visits: 35440 Births: 1279

☐ **SOUTHERN NEVADA ADULT MENTAL HEALTH SERVICES (294002)**, 6161 West Charleston Boulevard, Zip 89146–1126; tel. 702/486–6000, (Nonreporting) A1 3 5 10
Primary Contact: James Northrop, Director
Web address: www.mhds.state.nv.us
Control: State–Government, nonfederal **Service:** Psychiatric

Staffed Beds: 293

☐ **SPRING MOUNTAIN SAHARA (294010)**, 5460 West Sahara, Zip 89146–3307; tel. 702/216–8900 A1 9 10 F29 56 64 98 103 104 130 S Universal Health Services, Inc., King of Prussia, PA
Primary Contact: Darryl S. Dubroca, Chief Executive Officer and Managing Director
Web address: www.springmountainsahara.com
Control: Corporation, Investor–owned, for–profit **Service:** Psychiatric

Staffed Beds: 30 Admissions: 768 Census: 24 Outpatient Visits: 896 Births: 0 Total Expense ($000): 5912 Payroll Expense ($000): 2737 Personnel: 48

☒ **SPRING MOUNTAIN TREATMENT CENTER (294011)**, 7000 West Spring Mountain Road, Zip 89117–3816; tel. 702/873–2400 A1 5 9 10 F29 98 99 105 130 S Universal Health Services, Inc., King of Prussia, PA
Primary Contact: Darryl S. Dubroca, Chief Executive Officer and Managing Director
Web address: www.springmountaintreatmentcenter.com/
Control: Corporation, Investor–owned, for–profit **Service:** Psychiatric

Staffed Beds: 82 Admissions: 3143 Census: 64 Outpatient Visits: 1755 Births: 0 Total Expense ($000): 16046 Payroll Expense ($000): 6870 Personnel: 161

☐ **SPRING VALLEY HOSPITAL MEDICAL CENTER (290046)**, 5400 South Rainbow Boulevard, Zip 89118–1859; tel. 702/853–3000, (Nonreporting) A1 9 10 S Universal Health Services, Inc., King of Prussia, PA
Primary Contact: Leonard Freehof, Chief Executive Officer and Managing Director
COO: Matthew Wheelus, Chief Operating Officer
CFO: Carl Caley, Chief Financial Officer
CMO: S. Daniel, M.D., Chief Medical Officer
CHR: Angelique Ford, Administrator Human Resources
CNO: Margaret Covelli, R.N., Chief Nursing Officer
Web address: www.springvalleyhospital.com
Control: Corporation, Investor–owned, for–profit **Service:** General Medical and Surgical

Staffed Beds: 169

☒ **ST. ROSE DOMINICAN HOSPITALS – SAN MARTIN CAMPUS (290053)**, 8280 West Warm Springs Road, Zip 89113–3612; tel. 702/492–8000 A1 9 10 F3 8 13 15 18 20 22 24 26 28 29 30 31 32 34 35 38 40 44 45 47 49 50 57 59 64 68 70 73 74 75 76 77 78 79 80 81 82 84 85 86 87 93 102 107 108 110 111 115 119 126 130 131 132 135 146 147 148 S Dignity Health, San Francisco, CA
Primary Contact: Victoria J. VanMeetren, President
CFO: Melissa Walker, Chief Financial Officer
CMO: Robert Pretzlaff, M.D., Chief Medical Officer
CIO: Roy Hagerman, Site Manager Information Technology
CHR: Linda Gerstenberger, Vice President Human Resources
Web address: www.strosehospitals.org
Control: Church–operated, Nongovernment, not–for profit **Service:** General Medical and Surgical

Staffed Beds: 147 Admissions: 7408 Census: 86 Outpatient Visits: 35073 Births: 876 Total Expense ($000): 161271 Payroll Expense ($000): 64130 Personnel: 669

☐ **SUMMERLIN HOSPITAL MEDICAL CENTER (290041)**, 657 Town Center Drive, Zip 89144–6367; tel. 702/233–7000, (Nonreporting) A1 9 10 S Universal Health Services, Inc., King of Prussia, PA
Primary Contact: Robert S. Freymuller, Chief Executive Officer
Web address: www.summerlinhospital.com
Control: Corporation, Investor–owned, for–profit **Service:** General Medical and Surgical

Staffed Beds: 148

NV

Many Facility Codes have changed. Please refer to the AHA Guide Code Chart. © 2014 AHA Guide

✠ △ **SUNRISE HOSPITAL AND MEDICAL CENTER (290003)**, 3186 Maryland Parkway, Zip 89109–2306, Mailing Address: P.O. Box 98530, Zip 89193; tel. 702/731–8000, (Includes SUNRISE CHILDREN'S HOSPITAL) **A**1 2 3 5 7 9 10 **F**3 11 12 13 15 17 18 19 20 21 22 23 24 25 26 27 28 29 30 31 32 34 35 39 40 41 43 45 46 49 50 51 57 58 59 60 61 64 65 68 70 72 74 75 76 77 78 79 81 82 84 85 87 88 89 90 92 96 107 108 110 111 114 115 116 117 118 119 124 126 130 132 135 146 147 148 **S** HCA, Nashville, TN
Primary Contact: Todd Sklamberg, President
CFO: Daniel Perritt, Chief Financial Officer
CMO: Katherine Keeley, M.D., Chief of Staff
CIO: Alan Burt, Director Information Services
CNO: Lori J. Brown, MSN, Chief Nursing Officer
Web address: www.sunrisehospital.com
Control: Corporation, Investor–owned, for–profit **Service:** General Medical and Surgical

Staffed Beds: 664 **Admissions:** 28016 **Census:** 436 **Outpatient Visits:** 160640 **Births:** 4500 **Total Expense ($000):** 455749 **Payroll Expense ($000):** 192930 **Personnel:** 2434

✠ **UNIVERSITY MEDICAL CENTER (290007)**, 1800 West Charleston Boulevard, Zip 89102–2386; tel. 702/383–2000, (Includes CHILDREN'S HOSPITAL OF NEVADA AT UMC, 1800 West Charleston Boulevard, Zip 89102–2329; tel. 702/383–2000) **A**1 2 3 5 8 9 10 **F**3 12 13 16 17 18 19 20 21 22 23 24 25 26 27 28 29 30 31 32 38 43 45 46 47 49 55 61 54 57 61 64 66 67 68 70 72 73 74 75 76 77 78 79 81 84 85 87 88 89 93 97 107 111 114 115 118 119 127 130 132 135 138 141 144 146 147 148 **P**1 8
Primary Contact: Lawrence Barnard, Chief Executive Officer
COO: Mason VanHouweling, Chief Operating Officer
CFO: Stephanie Merrill, Chief Financial Officer
CMO: Joan Brookhyser, Medical Center Director and Chief Executive Officer
CIO: Ernie McKinley, Chief Information Officer
CHR: John Espinoza, Chief Human Resources Officer
CNO: Gregg Fusto, Chief Nursing Officer
Web address: www.umcsn.com
Control: County–Government, nonfederal **Service:** General Medical and Surgical

Staffed Beds: 541 **Admissions:** 28246 **Census:** 382 **Outpatient Visits:** 534987 **Births:** 3559 **Total Expense ($000):** 588626 **Payroll Expense ($000):** 230768 **Personnel:** 3551

☐ **VALLEY HOSPITAL MEDICAL CENTER (290021)**, 620 Shadow Lane, Zip 89106–4119; tel. 702/388–4000, (Nonreporting) **A**1 9 10 12 13 **S** Universal Health Services, Inc., King of Prussia, PA
Primary Contact: Samuel Kaufman, Chief Executive Officer, Managing Director
CFO: Betsy A. Sponsler, Chief Financial Officer
CMO: Dost Wattoo, M.D., Chief of Staff
CIO: Tom Schoenig, Regional Director Information Services
CHR: Dana Thorne, Administrator Human Resources
Web address: www.valleyhospital.net
Control: Corporation, Investor–owned, for–profit **Service:** General Medical and Surgical

Staffed Beds: 365

LOVELOCK—Pershing County

PERSHING GENERAL HOSPITAL (291304), 855 Sixth Street, Zip 89419, Mailing Address: P.O. Box 661, Zip 89419–0661; tel. 775/273–2621, (Nonreporting) **A**9 10 18
Primary Contact: Patty Bianchi, Interim Chief Executive Officer and Administrator
CFO: Marjorie Skinner, Director Finance
CMO: Yousri Gadallah, M.D., Chief Medical Officer
CIO: Jim Weeldreyer, Manager Information Technology
CHR: Cynthia Hixenbaugh, Director Human Resources
Web address: www.pershinghospital.org
Control: Hospital district or authority, Government, nonfederal **Service:** General Medical and Surgical

Staffed Beds: 47

MESQUITE—Clark County

✠ **MESA VIEW REGIONAL HOSPITAL (291307)**, 1299 Bertha Howe Avenue, Zip 89027–7500; tel. 702/346–8040 **A**1 9 10 18 **F**3 11 13 15 29 30 34 35 40 45 46 51 56 57 59 64 75 76 77 79 81 85 87 107 108 110 111 114 119 130 132 133 135 146 147 148 **P**7 **S** Community Health Systems, Inc., Franklin, TN
Primary Contact: Patricia Holden, Chief Executive Officer
CFO: Eric S. Hardy, Chief Financial Officer
Web address: www.mesaviewhospital.com
Control: Corporation, Investor–owned, for–profit **Service:** General Medical and Surgical

Staffed Beds: 25 **Admissions:** 720 **Census:** 5 **Outpatient Visits:** 14684 **Births:** 99 **Total Expense ($000):** 23127 **Payroll Expense ($000):** 9332 **Personnel:** 178

NELLIS AFB—Clark County

✠ **MIKE O'CALLAGHAN FEDERAL HOSPITAL**, 4700 Las Vegas Boulevard North, Suite 2419, Zip 89191–6600; tel. 702/653–2000, (Nonreporting) **A**1 3 5 **S** Department of the Air Force, Washington, DC
Primary Contact: Colonel Christian Benjamin, USAF, MC, Commander
COO: Colonel Linnes L. Chester, USAF, Administrator
CFO: Major Kari Turkal–Barrett, Flight Commander Resource Management Officer
CMO: Lieutenant Colonel Markham Brown, M.D., Chief Medical Staff
CIO: Major Kevin Seeley, Chief Information Officer
Web address: www.lasvegas.va.gov/
Control: Air Force, Government, federal **Service:** General Medical and Surgical

Staffed Beds: 46

NORTH LAS VEGAS—Clark County

◇ **NORTH VISTA HOSPITAL (290005)**, 1409 East Lake Mead Boulevard, Zip 89030–7197; tel. 702/649–7711, (Nonreporting) **A**9 10 21 **S** IASIS Healthcare, Franklin, TN
Primary Contact: Cathy N. Story, Chief Executive Officer
CFO: George Wiley, Chief Financial Officer
CNO: Mary Jo Russo, R.N., Chief Nursing Officer
Web address: www.northvistahospital.com
Control: Corporation, Investor–owned, for–profit **Service:** General Medical and Surgical

Staffed Beds: 198

✠ **VETERANS AFFAIRS SOUTHERN NEVADA HEALTHCARE SYSTEM**, 6900 North Pecos Road, tel. 702/791–9000, (Nonreporting) **A**1 5 **S** Department of Veterans Affairs, Washington, DC
Primary Contact: Isabel Duff, MS, Director
CFO: Richard O. Hays, Chief Fiscal Service
CMO: Ramanujam Komanduri, M.D., Chief of Staff
Web address: www.lasvegas.va.gov/
Control: Veterans Affairs, Government, federal **Service:** General Medical and Surgical

Staffed Beds: 57

PAHRUMP—Nye County

★ **DESERT VIEW HOSPITAL (291311)**, 360 South Lola Lane, Zip 89048–0884; tel. 775/751–7500 **A**9 10 18 **F**3 15 18 29 34 40 45 57 59 65 77 79 81 86 107 111 119 133 148 **P**6 **S** Rural Health Group, Nephi, UT
Primary Contact: Kelly H. Adams, Chief Executive Officer
CFO: Ryan Eggleston, Chief Financial Officer
CMO: Fredric Siegel, M.D., Chief of Staff
CHR: Lisa Doty, Manager Human Resources
CNO: Markeeta Araujo, Chief Nursing Officer
Web address: www.desertviewhospital.com
Control: Corporation, Investor–owned, for–profit **Service:** General Medical and Surgical

Staffed Beds: 25 **Admissions:** 1412 **Census:** 11 **Births:** 0

DESERT VIEW REGIONAL MEDICAL CENTER See Desert View Hospital

RENO—Washoe County

✠ **RENOWN REGIONAL MEDICAL CENTER (290001)**, 1155 Mill Street, Zip 89502–1576; tel. 775/982–4100, (Includes RENOWN CHILDREN'S HOSPITAL, 1155 Mill Street, tel. 775/982–5437) **A**1 2 3 5 9 10 **F**3 5 11 13 15 17 18 19 20 21 22 23 24 25 26 27 28 29 30 31 32 34 35 37 40 41 43 45 49 54 56 57 58 59 60 61 62 64 65 66 68 70 72 73 74 75 76 77 78 79 81 82 84 85 86 87 88 89 92 93 99 100 101 102 103 104 105 107 108 109 110 111 114 115 118 119 120 121 123 124 126 130 131 132 135 143 144 145 146 147 148 **S** Renown Health, Reno, NV
Primary Contact: Gregory E. Boyer, Chief Executive Officer
COO: Kris Gaw, Chief Operating Officer
CFO: Sam King, Chief Financial Officer
CMO: Charles Johnson, M.D., Chief of Staff
CIO: Charles Scully, Chief Information Officer
CHR: Michelle Sanchez–Bickley, Vice President Human Resources
Web address: www.renown.org
Control: Other not–for–profit (including NFP Corporation) **Service:** General Medical and Surgical

Staffed Beds: 642 **Admissions:** 27679 **Census:** 390 **Outpatient Visits:** 323048 **Births:** 4073 **Total Expense ($000):** 467185 **Payroll Expense ($000):** 153040 **Personnel:** 3457

NV

★ △ **RENOWN REHABILITATION HOSPITAL**, 1495 Mill Street, Zip 89502–1479; tel. 775/982–3500 **A**3 5 7 **F**29 54 77 82 90 93 96 143 148 **P**6 **S** Renown Health, Reno, NV
Primary Contact: Randall W. Ross, Chief Executive Officer
CFO: Dawn Ahner, Chief Financial Officer
CIO: Charles Scully, Chief Information Officer
CHR: Michelle Sanchez–Bickley, Vice President Human Resources
CNO: Melodie Osborn, Chief Nursing Officer
Web address: www.renown.org
Control: Other not–for–profit (including NFP Corporation) **Service:** Rehabilitation

Staffed Beds: 62 **Admissions:** 1045 **Census:** 40 **Outpatient Visits:** 20278
Births: 0 **Total Expense ($000):** 21380 **Payroll Expense ($000):** 10773
Personnel: 165

✠ **RENOWN SOUTH MEADOWS MEDICAL CENTER (290049)**, 10101 Double R Boulevard, Zip 89521–5931; tel. 775/982–7000 **A**1 3 5 9 10 **F**8 10 12 29 30 35 39 40 46 49 68 70 74 75 79 81 84 85 87 93 97 107 108 111 119 125 130 131 146 **S** Renown Health, Reno, NV
Primary Contact: Randall W. Ross, Chief Executive Officer
CFO: Gina Nelson, Chief Financial Officer
CMO: Max Jackson, M.D., Chief Medical Officer
CIO: Charles Scully, Chief Information Officer
CHR: Michelle Sanchez–Bickley, Vice President Human Resources
CNO: Melodie Osborn, Chief Nursing Officer
Web address: www.renown.org
Control: Other not–for–profit (including NFP Corporation) **Service:** General Medical and Surgical

Staffed Beds: 76 **Admissions:** 2908 **Census:** 25 **Outpatient Visits:** 56915
Births: 0 **Total Expense ($000):** 60739 **Payroll Expense ($000):** 22093
Personnel: 331

☐ **SAINT MARY'S REGIONAL MEDICAL CENTER (290009)**, 235 West Sixth Street, Zip 89503–4548; tel. 775/770–3000 **A**1 2 3 5 9 10 **F**3 12 13 15 17 18 20 22 24 26 28 29 30 31 35 39 40 45 46 47 48 49 53 54 56 58 62 63 64 70 72 74 75 76 77 78 79 81 82 84 85 87 89 93 95 102 107 108 110 111 114 115 118 119 120 121 124 126 130 132 146 147 148 **S** Prime Healthcare Services, Ontario, CA
Primary Contact: Helen Lidholm, Chief Executive Officer
CFO: John R. Deakyne, Chief Financial Officer
CIO: Cindy Mullins, Director Information Technology
CHR: David Milovich, Vice President Human Resources
Web address: www.saintmarysreno.org
Control: Corporation, Investor–owned, for–profit **Service:** General Medical and Surgical

Staffed Beds: 281 **Admissions:** 15242 **Census:** 156 **Outpatient Visits:** 142496 **Births:** 1872 **Total Expense ($000):** 261217 **Payroll Expense ($000):** 100399 **Personnel:** 1295

✠ **TAHOE PACIFIC HOSPITALS (292004)**, 201 West Liberty Street, Suite 310, Zip 89501–2017; tel. 775/355–5970, (Includes TAHOE PACIFIC HOSPITALS – WEST, 235 West Sixth Street, 5th Floor, Zip 89503–4548) **A**1 9 10 **F**1 3 29 35 **P**8 **S** LifeCare Management Services, Plano, TX
Primary Contact: Colin O'Sullivan, Administrator
COO: Theresa Fegan, R.N., Chief Clinical Officer
CFO: Nena Swenson, Financial Manager
CMO: T. Brian Callister, M.D., Chief Medical Officer
CIO: Kaylene Reeves, Director
CHR: Nelson Coy, Director Human Resources
Web address: www.lifecare–hospitals.com
Control: Corporation, Investor–owned, for–profit **Service:** Long–Term Acute Care hospital

Staffed Beds: 60 **Admissions:** 490 **Census:** 38 **Outpatient Visits:** 0 **Births:** 0 **Total Expense ($000):** 21758 **Payroll Expense ($000):** 9895 **Personnel:** 153

✠ **VETERANS AFFAIRS SIERRA NEVADA HEALTH CARE SYSTEM**, 975 Kirman Avenue, Zip 89502–0993; tel. 775/786–7200, (Total facility includes 60 beds in nursing home–type unit) **A**3 5 **F**1 3 4 5 18 20 22 29 30 31 34 35 36 38 39 40 44 45 46 47 49 50 54 56 57 58 59 60 61 62 63 64 65 66 68 70 74 75 77 78 79 81 82 83 84 85 86 87 90 91 92 93 94 96 97 98 100 101 102 103 104 107 111 114 115 119 127 129 130 132 135 143 144 146 147 148 **S** Department of Veterans Affairs, Washington, DC
Primary Contact: Lisa M. Howard, Acting Director
COO: Lisa M. Howard, Associate Director
CFO: Kelly Manson, Chief Financial Officer
CMO: Steven Brilliant, M.D., Chief of Staff
CIO: Jack Smith, Acting Chief Information Resources Management Service
CHR: Debbie Jenkins, Chief Human Resources Management Service
CNO: Rachel Crossley, R.N., Chief Patient Care Services
Web address: www.reno.va.gov/
Control: Veterans Affairs, Government, federal **Service:** General Medical and Surgical

Staffed Beds: 124 **Admissions:** 3046 **Census:** 69 **Outpatient Visits:** 307388
Births: 0 **Total Expense ($000):** 240000 **Payroll Expense ($000):** 122807
Personnel: 1210

☐ **WEST HILLS HOSPITAL (294003)**, 1240 East Ninth Street, Zip 89512–2964; tel. 775/323–0478 **A**1 9 10 **F**5 98 99 100 101 102 104 105 **S** Universal Health Services, Inc., King of Prussia, PA
Primary Contact: Allison Zednicek, Chief Executive Officer
CFO: Erich Koch, Chief Financial Officer
CMO: Philip Rich, M.D., Chief Medical Officer
CHR: Don Gay, Director Human Resources
Web address: www.westhillshospital.net
Control: Corporation, Investor–owned, for–profit **Service:** Psychiatric

Staffed Beds: 190 **Admissions:** 2361 **Census:** 45 **Outpatient Visits:** 2733
Births: 0 **Total Expense ($000):** 11330 **Payroll Expense ($000):** 6163
Personnel: 112

WILLOW SPRINGS CENTER, 690 Edison Way, Zip 89502–4135; tel. 775/858–3303 **A**3 5 **F**98 99 104 106
Primary Contact: Jim Serratt, Chief Executive Officer
CFO: Joe Bradick, Chief Financial Officer
CMO: Dana Arlien, M.D., Chief Medical Officer
CNO: Sam McCord, Chief Nursing Officer
Web address: www.willowspringscenter.com
Control: Corporation, Investor–owned, for–profit **Service:** Children's hospital psychiatric

Staffed Beds: 116 **Admissions:** 408 **Census:** 97 **Outpatient Visits:** 7020
Births: 0 **Total Expense ($000):** 14415 **Payroll Expense ($000):** 7987
Personnel: 144

SPARKS—Washoe County

☐ **NORTHERN NEVADA ADULT MENTAL HEALTH SERVICES (294000)**, 480 Galletti Way, Zip 89431–5564; tel. 775/688–2001, (Nonreporting) **A**1 3 5 9 10
Primary Contact: Cody Phinney, Administrator
CFO: Elizabeth O'Brien, Chief Financial Officer
CIO: Lois Repass, Quality Assurance Specialist and Coordinator Performance Improvement
Web address: www.mhds.state.nv.us/
Control: State–Government, nonfederal **Service:** Psychiatric

Staffed Beds: 70

☐ **NORTHERN NEVADA MEDICAL CENTER (290032)**, 2375 East Prater Way, Zip 89434–9641; tel. 775/331–7000, (Nonreporting) **A**1 9 10 **S** Universal Health Services, Inc., King of Prussia, PA
Primary Contact: Alan C. Olive, Chief Executive Officer
COO: Tiffany Meert, Chief Operating Officer
CFO: Ryan Heit, Chief Financial Officer
CHR: Patricia Downs, Director Human Resources
Web address: www.nnmc.com
Control: Corporation, Investor–owned, for–profit **Service:** General Medical and Surgical

Staffed Beds: 80

TONOPAH—Nye County

NYE REGIONAL MEDICAL CENTER (290020), 825 South Main Street, Zip 89049, Mailing Address: P.O. Box 391, Zip 89049–0391; tel. 775/482–6233, (Nonreporting) **A**9 10 20
Primary Contact: Mercy Peterson, Interim Chief Executive Officer
CMO: Vincent Scoccia, D.O., Chief Medical Staff
CIO: Mercy Peterson, Assistant Administrator
CHR: Leilani Gordon, Director Human Resources and Payroll
Web address: www.nyeregional.org
Control: Corporation, Investor–owned, for–profit **Service:** General Medical and Surgical

Staffed Beds: 44

WINNEMUCCA—Humboldt County

★ **HUMBOLDT GENERAL HOSPITAL (291308)**, 118 East Haskell Street, Zip 89445–3299; tel. 775/623–5222, (Nonreporting) **A**9 10 18
Primary Contact: James G. Parrish, FACHE, Chief Executive Officer
COO: Craig Prest, Director Operation Services
CFO: Sandi Lehman, Chief Financial Officer
CMO: B. Leonard Perkinson, M.D., Chief of Staff
CHR: Rose Marie Green, Director Human Resources
CNO: Darlene Bryan, R.N., Chief Nursing Officer
Web address: www.hghospital.ws
Control: Hospital district or authority, Government, nonfederal **Service:** General Medical and Surgical

Staffed Beds: 52

YERINGTON—Lyon County

SOUTH LYON MEDICAL CENTER (290002), 213 South Whitacre, Zip 89447–2561, Mailing Address: P.O. Box 940, Zip 89447–0940; tel. 775/463–2301, (Nonreporting) **A**9 10 20
Primary Contact: Toni A. Inserra, Interim Administrator
Web address: www.southlyonmedicalcenter.org
Control: Other not–for–profit (including NFP Corporation) **Service:** General Medical and Surgical

Staffed Beds: 63

NV

NEW HAMPSHIRE

BERLIN—Coos County

ANDROSCOGGIN VALLEY HOSPITAL (301310), 59 Page Hill Road, Zip 03570–3531; tel. 603/752–2200 **A**10 18 **F**3 8 11 12 13 15 17 28 29 30 34 40 41 43 45 47 57 59 61 64 67 70 74 75 76 77 79 81 82 85 89 92 93 102 107 108 114 119 128 129 130 131 132 133 146 147 **P**6
Primary Contact: Russell G. Keene, Chief Executive Officer
CFO: Jeremy Roberge, Director Reimbursement
CMO: Keith M. Shute, M.D., Senior Vice President Medical Affairs and Clinical Services
CIO: Linda M. Laperle, Vice President Administrative Services
CHR: James A. Wheeler, Vice President Human Relations and Community Development
Web address: www.avhnh.org
Control: Other not–for–profit (including NFP Corporation) **Service:** General Medical and Surgical

Staffed Beds: 25 **Admissions:** 1202 **Census:** 15 **Outpatient Visits:** 64365 **Births:** 122 **Total Expense ($000):** 53607 **Payroll Expense ($000):** 23936 **Personnel:** 302

CLAREMONT—Sullivan County

✠ **VALLEY REGIONAL HOSPITAL (301308)**, 243 Elm Street, Zip 03743–4921; tel. 603/542–7771 **A**1 9 10 18 **F**2 3 11 14 15 28 29 34 35 38 40 43 45 49 50 51 54 57 59 62 63 64 68 70 74 75 77 79 81 84 85 87 93 97 104 107 108 110 114 118 119 130 132 133 135 146 147 **P**6
Primary Contact: Peter J. Wright, Chief Executive Officer
CFO: Steven Monette, Chief Financial Officer
CMO: Oliver Herfort, M.D., Chief Medical Officer
CIO: Patricia Witthaus, Director Information Services
CHR: Shelly Bragg, Director Human Resources
CNO: Margaret Burns, R.N., Vice President Patient Services and Chief Nursing Officer
Web address: www.vrh.org
Control: Other not–for–profit (including NFP Corporation) **Service:** General Medical and Surgical

Staffed Beds: 25 **Admissions:** 780 **Census:** 11 **Outpatient Visits:** 71802 **Births:** 0 **Total Expense ($000):** 39410 **Payroll Expense ($000):** 17030 **Personnel:** 271

COLEBROOK—Coos County

UPPER CONNECTICUT VALLEY HOSPITAL (301300), 181 Corliss Lane, Zip 03576–3207; tel. 603/237–4971 **A**9 10 18 **F**3 15 29 30 31 34 35 40 43 45 50 56 57 59 64 67 68 75 78 81 85 93 102 107 110 114 119 128 130 133 134 135 146 147 148 **P**6
Primary Contact: Peter L. Gosline, Chief Administrative Officer
CFO: Celeste Pitts, Chief Financial Officer
CMO: Nicole Paier–Mullan, M.D., Medical Director
CIO: Heather Leighton, Director, Revenue Cycle and Privacy Officer
CHR: Heidi L. Saari, Director, Human Resources
CNO: Laurie Cotnoir, Director Nursing and Quality
Web address: www.ucvh.org
Control: Other not–for–profit (including NFP Corporation) **Service:** General Medical and Surgical

Staffed Beds: 16 **Admissions:** 386 **Census:** 6 **Outpatient Visits:** 18549 **Births:** 0 **Total Expense ($000):** 14872 **Payroll Expense ($000):** 6003 **Personnel:** 95

CONCORD—Merrimack County

★ ◇ **CONCORD HOSPITAL (300001)**, 250 Pleasant Street, Zip 03301–2598; tel. 603/225–2711 **A**2 3 5 9 10 21 **F**3 8 12 13 14 15 17 18 20 22 24 26 28 29 30 31 33 34 35 36 37 38 39 40 42 43 44 46 49 50 51 53 54 55 56 57 58 59 61 64 65 66 68 69 71 74 75 76 77 78 79 80 81 82 83 84 85 86 87 89 93 97 98 99 100 101 102 103 104 105 107 108 110 111 114 115 118 119 120 121 123 126 129 130 131 132 134 135 144 145 146 147 148 **P**6
Primary Contact: Robert P. Steigmeyer, President and Chief Executive Officer
COO: Joseph M. Conley, Chief Operating Officer
CFO: Bruce R. Burns, Chief Financial Officer
CMO: David F. Green, M.D., Chief Medical Officer
CIO: Deane Morrison, Chief Information Officer
CHR: Robin A. Moore, Vice President Human Resources
CNO: Diane Wood–Allen, MS, Chief Nursing Officer
Web address: www.concordhospital.org
Control: Other not–for–profit (including NFP Corporation) **Service:** General Medical and Surgical

Staffed Beds: 237 **Admissions:** 12372 **Census:** 152 **Outpatient Visits:** 710716 **Births:** 1341 **Total Expense ($000):** 376707 **Payroll Expense ($000):** 179508 **Personnel:** 3015

✠ **HEALTHSOUTH REHABILITATION HOSPITAL (303027)**, 254 Pleasant Street, Zip 03301–2508; tel. 603/226–9800 **A**1 10 **F**29 34 35 64 74 79 90 91 93 95 96 130 132 **S** HEALTHSOUTH Corporation, Birmingham, AL
Primary Contact: Catherine Devaney, Chief Executive Officer
CFO: Jeanine Chesley, Controller
CMO: Safwan Kazmouz, M.D., Chief Medical Director
CHR: Myra Nixon, Director Human Resources
CNO: Joseph Adamski, Chief Nursing Officer
Web address: www.healthsouthrehabconcordnh.com
Control: Corporation, Investor–owned, for–profit **Service:** Rehabilitation

Staffed Beds: 50 **Admissions:** 894 **Census:** 32 **Outpatient Visits:** 5107 **Births:** 0 **Total Expense ($000):** 15972 **Payroll Expense ($000):** 6794 **Personnel:** 112

☐ **NEW HAMPSHIRE HOSPITAL (304000)**, 36 Clinton Street, Zip 03301–2359; tel. 603/271–5300 **A**1 10 **F**3 29 30 39 56 57 61 68 74 75 77 86 87 98 99 101 103 130 135 146 **P**4 6
Primary Contact: Robert J. MacLeod, Chief Executive Officer
CFO: Jamie Dall, Chief Financial Officer
CMO: David G. Folks, M.D., Chief Medical Officer
CIO: David Levesque, Director, Information Systems
CHR: Mark Bussiere, Administrator Human Resources
CNO: Roberta A. Vitale–Nolen, Administrator, Patient Care Services
Web address: www.dhhs.state.nh.us/dhhs/default.htm
Control: State–Government, nonfederal **Service:** Psychiatric

Staffed Beds: 158 **Admissions:** 1967 **Census:** 141 **Outpatient Visits:** 0 **Births:** 0 **Total Expense ($000):** 46822 **Payroll Expense ($000):** 27301 **Personnel:** 554

DERRY—Rockingham County

✠ **PARKLAND MEDICAL CENTER (300017)**, One Parkland Drive, Zip 03038–2750; tel. 603/432–1500, (Nonreporting) **A**1 2 9 10 **S** HCA, Nashville, TN
Primary Contact: Chris Accashian, Chief Executive Officer
COO: Jeff Scionti, Chief Operating Officer
CFO: Jacob Wisemann, Chief Financial Officer
CMO: Edward Yourtee, M.D., Chief Medical Officer
CIO: Brad George, Director Information Systems
CHR: Molly Lahti, Director Human Resources
CNO: Eileen Keefe, Chief Nursing Officer
Web address: www.parklandmedicalcenter.com
Control: Corporation, Investor–owned, for–profit **Service:** General Medical and Surgical

Staffed Beds: 82

NH

Hospital, Medicare Provider Number, Address, Telephone, Approval, Facility, and Physician Codes, Health Care System

★ American Hospital Association (AHA) membership
☐ The Joint Commission accreditation
◇ DNV Healthcare Inc. accreditation
○ Healthcare Facilities Accreditation Program
△ Commission on Accreditation of Rehabilitation Facilities (CARF) accreditation

---

DOVER—Strafford County

✠ **WENTWORTH–DOUGLASS HOSPITAL (300018)**, 789 Central Avenue, Zip 03820–2589; tel. 603/742–5252 **A**1 2 9 10 **F**3 11 13 17 18 19 20 22 26 28 29 30 31 32 34 35 36 39 40 41 42 43 44 45 46 47 49 50 51 54 55 57 58 59 61 62 63 64 65 68 70 73 74 75 76 77 78 79 81 82 84 85 86 87 89 92 93 94 97 100 101 107 108 110 111 114 115 118 119 120 121 123 124 126 129 130 132 134 135 143 144 145 146 147 148 **P**6 8
Primary Contact: Gregory J. Walker, Chief Executive Officer
COO: Daniel N. Dunn, Vice President Operations
CFO: Peter Walcek, Vice President Finance
CMO: Paul Cass, D.O., Chief Medical & Clinical Integration Officer
CIO: Jeffrey Pollock, Chief Information Officer
CHR: Erin Flanigan, Vice President Human Resources
CNO: Sheila Woolley, R.N., Vice President, Patient Care Services
Web address: www.wdhospital.com
Control: Other not–for–profit (including NFP Corporation) **Service:** General Medical and Surgical

Staffed Beds: 126 **Admissions:** 6144 **Census:** 70 **Outpatient Visits:** 256432 **Births:** 1019 **Total Expense ($000):** 216408 **Payroll Expense ($000):** 89468 **Personnel:** 1406

EXETER—Rockingham County

★ ◇ **EXETER HOSPITAL (300023)**, 5 Alumni Drive, Zip 03833–2128; tel. 603/778–7311 **A**2 9 10 21 **F**3 8 13 14 15 18 20 22 26 28 29 30 31 32 34 35 36 37 38 40 44 45 46 47 48 49 50 51 52 53 54 55 57 58 59 64 70 74 75 76 77 78 79 80 81 84 85 86 87 89 93 107 108 110 111 114 118 119 120 121 123 124 129 130 131 132 135 143 144 146 147 148
Primary Contact: Kevin J. Callahan, President and Chief Executive Officer
CFO: Kevin J. O'Leary, Senior Vice President and Chief Financial Officer
CMO: Richard Hollister, President of Medical Staff
CIO: David Briden, Chief Information Officer
CHR: Christopher M. Callahan, Vice President Human Resources
CNO: Susan Burns–Tisdale, Senior Vice President Clinical Operations, Interim CNO
Web address: www.ehr.org
Control: Other not–for–profit (including NFP Corporation) **Service:** General Medical and Surgical

Staffed Beds: 99 **Admissions:** 5529 **Census:** 59 **Outpatient Visits:** 165495 **Births:** 621 **Total Expense ($000):** 176396 **Payroll Expense ($000):** 68008 **Personnel:** 1125

FRANKLIN—Merrimack County

★ **FRANKLIN REGIONAL HOSPITAL (301306)**, 15 Aiken Avenue, Zip 03235–1299; tel. 603/934–2060 **A**10 18 **F**3 11 15 18 29 30 34 35 36 39 40 44 45 46 47 48 49 50 57 58 59 61 64 65 66 68 70 74 75 77 78 79 81 82 83 84 85 86 87 93 97 99 100 101 102 103 107 119 127 128 130 131 132 133 135 146 147 148 **P**4 6 **S** LRGHealthcare, Laconia, NH
Primary Contact: Charles K. Van Sluyter, Interim Chief Executive Officer
CMO: Peter Doane, M.D., Chief Medical Officer
CIO: Kevin Irish, Chief Information Officer
CHR: Cass Walker, Senior Vice President Administrative Services
CNO: Ellen Wolff, R.N., Chief Nursing Officer and Senior Vice President Patient Care Services
Web address: www.lrgh.org
Control: Other not–for–profit (including NFP Corporation) **Service:** General Medical and Surgical

Staffed Beds: 25 **Admissions:** 803 **Census:** 15 **Outpatient Visits:** 53547 **Births:** 0 **Total Expense ($000):** 39926 **Payroll Expense ($000):** 18221 **Personnel:** 195

GREENFIELD—Hillsborough County

CROTCHED MOUNTAIN REHABILITATION CENTER, 1 Verney Drive, Zip 03047–5000; tel. 603/547–3311, (Nonreporting)
Primary Contact: Donald L. Shumway, Chief Executive Officer
COO: Michael Redmond, Senior Vice President and Chief Operating Officer
CFO: Thomas Zubricki, Vice President Finance, Chief Financial Officer
CMO: W. Carl Cooley, M.D., Chief Medical Officer
CIO: Jerry Hunter, Vice President, Information Technology
CHR: Lorrie Rudis, Vice President, Human Resources
Web address: www.cmf.org
Control: Other not–for–profit (including NFP Corporation) **Service:** Rehabilitation

Staffed Beds: 181

HAMPSTEAD—Rockingham County

☐ **HAMPSTEAD HOSPITAL (304001)**, 218 East Road, Zip 03841–2305; tel. 603/329–5311, (Nonreporting) **A**1 10
Primary Contact: Phillip J. Kubiak, President
COO: Cynthia A. Gove, Chief Operating Officer
CFO: Cherie Clough–Berry, Vice President, Finance
CMO: Michael Knight, M.D., Medical Director
CIO: Sandra J. Lucia, Director Health Information and Corporate Compliance Officer
CHR: Lisa M. Ryan, Coordinator Human Resources
CNO: Julie D'Apollo, R.N., Director of Nursing
Web address: www.hampsteadhospital.com
Control: Corporation, Investor–owned, for–profit **Service:** Psychiatric

Staffed Beds: 60

KEENE—Cheshire County

✠ **CHESHIRE MEDICAL CENTER (300019)**, 580 Court Street, Zip 03431–1718; tel. 603/354–5400 **A**1 2 9 10 **F**3 12 13 15 17 18 28 29 30 31 34 35 38 40 43 44 45 46 49 51 53 56 59 61 64 65 68 70 74 75 76 77 78 79 81 82 84 85 86 87 89 90 91 92 93 94 96 97 98 99 100 101 102 103 104 105 107 108 110 111 114 115 118 119 121 129 130 131 132 133 135 146 147 148
Primary Contact: Arthur W. Nichols, President and Chief Executive Officer
CFO: Robert K. Cochrane, Interim Vice President, Finance
CMO: Don Caruso, M.D., Chief Medical Officer
CIO: Peter Malloy, Chief Information Officer
CHR: Julie Green, Vice President Human Resources
CNO: Cynthia Coughlin, MS, Chief Nursing Officer
Web address: www.cheshire–med.com
Control: Other not–for–profit (including NFP Corporation) **Service:** General Medical and Surgical

Staffed Beds: 140 **Admissions:** 4420 **Census:** 53 **Outpatient Visits:** 154913 **Births:** 473 **Total Expense ($000):** 141378 **Payroll Expense ($000):** 53811 **Personnel:** 1062

LACONIA—Belknap County

★ **LAKES REGION GENERAL HOSPITAL (300005)**, 80 Highland Street, Zip 03246–3298; tel. 603/524–3211 **A**10 19 20 **F**3 5 7 8 11 12 13 15 18 28 29 30 31 32 34 35 36 37 39 40 43 44 45 46 47 48 49 50 53 56 57 58 59 60 61 64 65 66 68 70 74 75 76 77 78 79 81 82 83 84 85 86 87 93 97 98 99 100 101 102 103 107 108 114 118 119 129 130 131 132 133 135 144 146 147 148 **P**4 6 **S** LRGHealthcare, Laconia, NH
Primary Contact: Charles K. Van Sluyter, Interim Chief Executive Officer
CFO: Henry D. Lipman, Senior Vice President, Financial Strategy and External Relations
CMO: Peter Doane, M.D., Chief Medical Officer
CIO: Kevin Irish, Chief Information Officer
CHR: Cass Walker, Senior Vice President, Administrative Services
CNO: Ellen Wolff, R.N., Chief Nursing Officer/Senior VP/Patient Care Services
Web address: www.lrgh.org
Control: Other not–for–profit (including NFP Corporation) **Service:** General Medical and Surgical

Staffed Beds: 88 **Admissions:** 4439 **Census:** 63 **Outpatient Visits:** 215171 **Births:** 345 **Total Expense ($000):** 177883 **Payroll Expense ($000):** 79265 **Personnel:** 1024

LANCASTER—Coos County

★ **WEEKS MEDICAL CENTER (301303)**, 173 Middle Street, Zip 03584–3508; tel. 603/788–4911 **A**9 10 18 **F**3 11 15 18 28 29 30 31 32 34 35 36 40 45 50 51 56 57 59 61 62 63 64 65 66 68 70 71 75 77 78 79 81 85 87 91 92 93 94 97 100 104 107 108 110 111 114 116 117 118 119 127 130 131 132 133 134 135 146 147 148 **P**6
Primary Contact: Scott W. Howe, Chief Executive Officer
CMO: Lars Nielson, M.D., Chief Medical Officer
CIO: Darrell Bodnar, Director Information
CHR: Linda Rexford, Director Human Resources
CNO: Donna Walker, Chief Nurse Executive
Web address: www.weeksmedical.org
Control: Other not–for–profit (including NFP Corporation) **Service:** General Medical and Surgical

Staffed Beds: 25 **Admissions:** 919 **Census:** 11 **Outpatient Visits:** 80898 **Births:** 0 **Total Expense ($000):** 43871 **Payroll Expense ($000):** 24828 **Personnel:** 341

LEBANON—Grafton County

★ **ALICE PECK DAY MEMORIAL HOSPITAL (301305)**, 10 Alice Peck Day Drive, Zip 03766–2650; tel. 603/448–3121 **A**9 10 18 **F**3 11 13 15 29 34 35 36 37 39 40 41 42 45 47 50 51 54 56 57 59 63 64 65 66 67 75 76 77 79 81 82 83 84 85 93 97 100 107 110 113 114 115 119 128 129 130 131 133 135 145 146 147 148 **P**5 6
Primary Contact: Susan E. Mooney, M.D., MS, President and Chief Executive Officer
COO: J. Todd Miller, Vice President and Chief Operating Officer
CFO: Evalie M. Crosby, CPA, Vice President Finance and Chief Financial Officer
CMO: Randy Lea, M.D., Vice President and Chief Medical Officer
CIO: Kristin Kneisel, Interim Director, Information Services
CHR: Brenda Blair, Vice President Human Resources
CNO: Beverley A. Rankin, R.N., Vice President & Chief Nursing Officer
Web address: www.alicepeckday.org
Control: Other not–for–profit (including NFP Corporation) **Service:** General Medical and Surgical

Staffed Beds: 25 **Admissions:** 1018 **Census:** 14 **Outpatient Visits:** 97679 **Births:** 324 **Total Expense ($000):** 52041 **Payroll Expense ($000):** 29338 **Personnel:** 375

Many Facility Codes have changed. Please refer to the AHA Guide Code Chart. © 2014 AHA Guide

⊠ **DARTMOUTH–HITCHCOCK MEDICAL CENTER (300003)**, One Medical Center Drive, Zip 03756–0001; tel. 603/650–5000, (Includes CHILDREN'S HOSPITAL AT DARTMOUTH, One Medical Center Drive, Zip 03756; tel. 603/650–5000) **A**1 3 5 8 9 10 19 20 **F**3 5 6 7 8 9 11 12 13 14 15 17 18 19 20 21 22 23 24 25 26 27 28 29 30 31 32 34 35 36 37 38 39 40 41 43 44 45 46 47 48 49 50 51 52 53 54 55 56 57 58 59 60 61 63 64 65 66 68 70 71 72 74 75 76 77 78 79 80 81 82 84 85 86 87 88 89 91 92 93 94 96 97 98 99 100 101 102 103 104 105 107 108 110 111 112 114 115 116 117 118 119 120 121 123 124 126 129 130 131 132 134 135 136 138 141 142 143 145 146 147 148 **P**6
Primary Contact: James Weinstein, D.O., MS, President and Chief Executive Officer
CFO: Robin F. Kilfeather–Mackey, Chief Financial Officer
CMO: Edward J. Merrens, M.D., Medical Director
CIO: Terrence Carroll, Ph.D., Vice President, Information Services
CHR: John S. Malanowski, Chief Human Resources Officer
CNO: Gay L. Landstrom, MS, Chief Nursing Officer
Web address: www.hitchcock.org
Control: Other not–for–profit (including NFP Corporation) **Service:** General Medical and Surgical

Staffed Beds: 388 Admissions: 19685 Census: 304 Outpatient Visits: 856700 **Births:** 1051 **Total Expense ($000):** 1025317 **Payroll Expense ($000):** 485699 **Personnel:** 5773

LITTLETON—Grafton County

★ **LITTLETON REGIONAL HOSPITAL (301302)**, 600 Saint Johnsbury Road, Zip 03561–3442; tel. 603/444–9000 **A**9 10 18 **F**3 11 13 15 18 26 28 29 31 32 34 35 36 38 40 43 44 45 50 51 56 57 59 64 65 67 70 74 75 76 77 78 79 81 84 85 86 87 89 90 92 93 96 97 100 104 107 108 110 111 115 118 119 127 128 129 130 131 133 143 146 147 148 **P**6
Primary Contact: Warren K. West, FACHE, Chief Executive Officer
CFO: Robert L. Fotter, Chief Financial Officer
CIO: Scott Vachon, Director Information Technology
CHR: Georgene Novak, Director Human Resources
CNO: Linda Gilmore, Chief Nursing Officer/Chief Administrative Officer
Web address: www.littletonhospital.org
Control: Other not–for–profit (including NFP Corporation) **Service:** General Medical and Surgical

Staffed Beds: 25 Admissions: 1396 Census: 15 Outpatient Visits: 53107 **Births:** 277 **Total Expense ($000):** 77588 **Payroll Expense ($000):** 31553

MANCHESTER—Hillsborough County

⊠ **CATHOLIC MEDICAL CENTER (300034)**, 100 McGregor Street, Zip 03102–3770; tel. 603/668–3545 **A**1 2 10 **F**3 9 11 12 13 15 18 20 22 24 26 28 29 30 31 32 34 35 36 37 38 39 40 41 43 44 46 47 48 49 50 53 57 58 59 60 61 63 64 65 66 70 71 73 74 75 76 77 78 79 80 81 82 84 85 86 87 90 93 96 100 102 104 105 107 108 110 111 114 115 118 119 124 126 129 130 131 132 134 135 143 144 146 147 148 **P**6
Primary Contact: Joseph Pepe, M.D., President and Chief Executive Officer
COO: Alexander J. Walker, Senior Vice President Operations and Strategic Development
CFO: Edward L. Dudley, III, Executive Vice President and Chief Financial Officer
CMO: Raef Fahmy, DPM, Chief Medical Officer and Medical Information Officer
CIO: Brian Tew, Vice President and Chief Information Officer
CHR: Merryll Rosenfeld, Vice President, Human Resources
CNO: Robert A. Duhaime, R.N., Senior Vice President Clinical Operations and Chief Nursing Officer
Web address: www.catholicmedicalcenter.org
Control: Other not–for–profit (including NFP Corporation) **Service:** General Medical and Surgical

Staffed Beds: 235 Admissions: 9807 Census: 131 Outpatient Visits: 170363 **Births:** 1066 **Total Expense ($000):** 265585 **Payroll Expense ($000):** 112824 **Personnel:** 1386

⊠ **ELLIOT HOSPITAL (300012)**, One Elliot Way, Zip 03103–3502; tel. 603/669–5300, (Nonreporting) **A**1 2 9 10
Primary Contact: James L. Woodward, President and Chief Executive Officer
COO: Rick Phelps, M.D., President and Chief Operating Officer
CFO: Richard Elwell, Senior Vice President and Chief Financial Officer
CMO: Greg Baxter, M.D., Senior Vice President Medical Affairs and Chief Medical Officer
CIO: Denise Purington, Vice President and Chief Information Officer
CHR: Catherine Bardier, Vice President, Human Resources
CNO: Joni Spring, R.N., Vice President Patient Care Services and Chief Nursing Officer
Web address: www.elliothospital.org
Control: Other not–for–profit (including NFP Corporation) **Service:** General Medical and Surgical

Staffed Beds: 264

★ **MANCHESTER VETERANS AFFAIRS MEDICAL CENTER**, 718 Smyth Road, Zip 03104–4098; tel. 603/624–4366, (Nonreporting) **A**5 **S** Department of Veterans Affairs, Washington, DC
Primary Contact: Tammy A. Krueger, Acting Director
COO: Richard T. Rose, Associate Director
CFO: Frank Ryan, Chief Financial Officer
CMO: Andrew Breuder, M.D., Chief of Staff
CIO: John Foote, Chief Information Officer
CHR: Mary Ellen Kenney, Chief Human Services
Web address: www.manchester.va.gov/
Control: Veterans Affairs, Government, federal **Service:** Rehabilitation

Staffed Beds: 90

VETERANS AFFAIRS MEDICAL CENTER See Manchester Veterans Affairs Medical Center

NASHUA—Hillsborough County

⊠ **SOUTHERN NEW HAMPSHIRE MEDICAL CENTER (300020)**, 8 Prospect Street, Zip 03060–3925, Mailing Address: P.O. Box 2014, Zip 03061–2014; tel. 603/577–2000 **A**1 2 3 5 9 10 **F**3 11 13 15 18 20 22 26 28 29 30 31 34 35 40 42 43 49 50 51 52 57 59 61 65 68 70 72 74 75 76 77 78 79 81 84 85 86 87 89 93 96 98 100 102 104 105 107 110 111 115 118 119 126 129 130 131 132 135 143 146 147 148 **P**6
Primary Contact: Thomas E. Wilhelmsen, Jr., President and Chief Executive Officer
CFO: Michael S. Rose, Senior Vice President Finance and Chief Financial Officer
CMO: Stephanie Wolf–Rosenblum, M.D., Chief Medical Officer
CIO: Andrew Watt, M.D., Vice President, Chief Information Officer and Chief Medical Information Officer
CHR: Gerry J. Graham, Director Human Resource Operations
Web address: www.snhmc.org
Control: Other not–for–profit (including NFP Corporation) **Service:** General Medical and Surgical

Staffed Beds: 158 Admissions: 7595 Census: 88 Outpatient Visits: 225127 **Births:** 1346 **Total Expense ($000):** 170795 **Payroll Expense ($000):** 80919 **Personnel:** 1398

⊠ △ **ST. JOSEPH HOSPITAL (300011)**, 172 Kinsley Street, Zip 03060–3648; tel. 603/882–3000 **A**1 2 7 10 **F**3 4 11 12 13 15 18 20 22 28 29 30 31 32 34 35 36 37 40 43 44 49 50 51 54 55 56 57 59 61 62 63 64 65 68 70 74 75 76 77 78 79 81 82 83 84 85 86 87 89 90 93 94 97 98 104 107 108 110 111 115 116 117 119 126 129 130 131 132 135 144 146 147 148 **P**6 8 **S** Covenant Health Systems, Inc., Tewksbury, MA
Primary Contact: Richard Boehler, M.D., President and Chief Executive Officer
COO: Pam Duchene, R.N., Vice President Patient Care Services
CFO: Richard Plamondon, Vice President Finance and Chief Financial Officer
CIO: Keith A. Choinka, Vice President Information Systems and Chief Information Officer
CHR: Jacqueline Woolley, Vice President Human Resources
Web address: www.stjosephhospital.com
Control: Church–operated, Nongovernment, not–for profit **Service:** General Medical and Surgical

Staffed Beds: 126 Admissions: 5820 Census: 75 Outpatient Visits: 189334 **Births:** 462 **Total Expense ($000):** 157262 **Payroll Expense ($000):** 68267 **Personnel:** 1006

NEW LONDON—Merrimack County

★ **NEW LONDON HOSPITAL (301304)**, 273 County Road, Zip 03257–5736; tel. 603/526–2911, (Total facility includes 58 beds in nursing home–type unit) **A**9 10 18 **F**3 7 11 15 18 29 30 31 32 34 40 41 45 50 51 54 56 57 59 64 67 70 74 75 77 78 79 81 82 84 85 87 89 92 94 97 99 100 102 104 107 110 111 114 119 127 128 129 130 131 133 134 146 147 148 **P**6
Primary Contact: Bruce King, President and Chief Executive Officer
CFO: Donald Griffin, CPA, Chief Financial Officer
CMO: James M. Murphy, M.D., Chief Medical Officer Regional Development and Outpatient Services
CIO: David Foss, Chief Information Officer
CHR: Shari Bostwick, Director Human Resources
CNO: Sally Patten, MS, Chief Nursing Officer
Web address: www.newlondonhospital.org
Control: Other not–for–profit (including NFP Corporation) **Service:** General Medical and Surgical

Staffed Beds: 83 Admissions: 1304 Census: 68 Outpatient Visits: 152290 **Births:** 0 **Total Expense ($000):** 56677 **Payroll Expense ($000):** 27607 **Personnel:** 377

NH

Hospital, Medicare Provider Number, Address, Telephone, Approval, Facility, and Physician Codes, Health Care System

★ American Hospital Association (AHA) membership
□ The Joint Commission accreditation
◇ DNV Healthcare Inc. accreditation
○ Healthcare Facilities Accreditation Program
△ Commission on Accreditation of Rehabilitation Facilities (CARF) accreditation

NORTH CONWAY—Carroll County

MEMORIAL HOSPITAL (301307), 3073 White Mountain Highway, Zip 03860–7101; tel. 603/356–5461, (Total facility includes 45 beds in nursing home–type unit) **A**9 10 18 **F**3 11 13 15 28 29 30 31 34 35 36 40 43 45 50 51 57 59 64 67 68 70 75 76 77 78 79 81 82 85 86 87 90 94 96 97 105 107 110 115 119 128 129 130 131 132 133 144 146 147 **P**6 **S** MaineHealth, Portland, ME
Primary Contact: Scott McKinnon, President and Chief Executive Officer
CFO: Diane Maheux, Vice President Finance
CMO: Ray Rabideau, M.D., Senior Vice President and Chief Medical Officer
CIO: Curtis Kerbs, Vice President Information Services
CHR: Margaret Phillips, Director Human Resources
CNO: Ethnee Garner, Vice President Nursing Services
Web address: www.memorialhospitalnh.org
Control: Other not–for–profit (including NFP Corporation) **Service:** General Medical and Surgical

Staffed Beds: 70 **Admissions:** 1618 **Census:** 57 **Outpatient Visits:** 58342 **Births:** 251 **Total Expense ($000):** 61826 **Payroll Expense ($000):** 17440 **Personnel:** 400

PETERBOROUGH—Hillsborough County

★ **MONADNOCK COMMUNITY HOSPITAL (301309)**, 452 Old Street Road, Zip 03458–1295; tel. 603/924–7191 **A**5 9 10 18 **F**3 13 15 28 29 30 31 34 35 36 38 39 40 41 44 45 50 53 56 57 59 64 65 70 74 75 76 77 78 79 81 82 85 86 87 89 93 97 99 100 101 102 103 104 107 108 110 118 119 130 131 132 133 134 135 141 142 146 147 148 **P**6
Primary Contact: Cynthia McGuire, Chief Executive Officer
CFO: Richard Scheinblum, Chief Financial Officer
CMO: John Schlegelmilch, M.D., Chief Medical Officer
CIO: Nancy Barisano, Chief Information Officer
CHR: John Sansone, Director Human Resources
CNO: Vicki Loughery, R.N., Chief Nursing Officer
Web address: www.monadnockhospital.org
Control: Other not–for–profit (including NFP Corporation) **Service:** General Medical and Surgical

Staffed Beds: 25 **Admissions:** 1351 **Census:** 13 **Outpatient Visits:** 73515 **Births:** 325 **Total Expense ($000):** 72272 **Payroll Expense ($000):** 31810 **Personnel:** 541

PLYMOUTH—Grafton County

★ **SPEARE MEMORIAL HOSPITAL (301311)**, 16 Hospital Road, Zip 03264–1199; tel. 603/536–1120 **A**9 10 18 **F**3 13 15 28 29 30 31 32 34 35 39 40 45 53 54 57 59 64 70 75 76 77 78 79 81 84 85 93 94 97 107 110 111 113 114 119 127 129 130 131 132 133 144 146 147 **P**8
Primary Contact: Michelle McEwen, President and Chief Executive Officer
CFO: Thomas Lenkowski, Chief Financial Officer
CMO: Joseph Ebner, M.D., Chief Medical Officer
CHR: Laurie Bolognani, Human Resources Officer
CNO: Kristine Hering, R.N., Chief Nursing Officer
Web address: www.spearehospital.com
Control: Other not–for–profit (including NFP Corporation) **Service:** General Medical and Surgical

Staffed Beds: 25 **Admissions:** 1453 **Census:** 13

PORTSMOUTH—Rockingham County

⊞ **PORTSMOUTH REGIONAL HOSPITAL (300029)**, 333 Borthwick Avenue, Zip 03801–7128; tel. 603/436–5110, (Nonreporting) **A**1 2 9 10 **S** HCA, Nashville, TN
Primary Contact: Anne Jamieson, FACHE, Chief Executive Officer
COO: Stuart Hemming, Chief Operating Officer
CFO: Richard Senger, Chief Financial Officer
CMO: Tim Pike, M.D., Chief Medical Officer
CIO: Ed Sovetskhy, Director Information Services
CHR: Jackie Brayton, Vice President Human Resources
Web address: www.portsmouthhospital.com
Control: Corporation, Investor–owned, for–profit **Service:** General Medical and Surgical

Staffed Beds: 165

ROCHESTER—Strafford County

★ **FRISBIE MEMORIAL HOSPITAL (300014)**, 11 Whitehall Road, Zip 03867–3297; tel. 603/332–5211 **A**9 10 **F**3 7 11 13 17 18 20 21 28 29 31 32 34 35 40 42 45 46 49 50 56 57 59 64 68 70 75 76 77 78 79 81 82 83 86 87 89 93 97 98 103 104 105 107 111 115 117 118 119 129 130 132 135 146 147 **P**5 8
Primary Contact: Alvin D. Felgar, President and Chief Executive Officer
CFO: John A. Marzinzik, Vice President Finance
CMO: Susan Gaire, M.D., President Medical Staff
CHR: Carol Themelis, Vice President Human Resources
Web address: www.frisbiehospital.com
Control: Other not–for–profit (including NFP Corporation) **Service:** General Medical and Surgical

Staffed Beds: 82 **Admissions:** 3330 **Census:** 39 **Outpatient Visits:** 133577 **Births:** 391 **Total Expense ($000):** 123535 **Payroll Expense ($000):** 52657 **Personnel:** 802

SALEM—Rockingham County

☐ △ **NORTHEAST REHABILITATION HOSPITAL (303026)**, 70 Butler Street, Zip 03079–3925; tel. 603/893–2900 **A**1 7 10 **F**29 30 34 35 54 57 62 64 68 74 75 77 79 82 85 86 87 90 93 95 96 130 131 132 135 146
Primary Contact: John F. Prochilo, Chief Executive Officer and Administrator
COO: Robert Kotsonis, Chief Operating Officer
CFO: Charles Champagne, Chief Financial Officer
CMO: James A. Whitlock, Jr., M.D., Medical Director
CIO: Kevin Glynn, Chief Information Officer
CHR: Thomas A. Prince, Vice President Human Resources
CNO: Helene Thibodeau, R.N., Vice President Patient Care Services
Web address: www.northeastrehab.com
Control: Corporation, Investor–owned, for–profit **Service:** Rehabilitation

Staffed Beds: 135 **Admissions:** 2942 **Census:** 99 **Outpatient Visits:** 176922 **Births:** 0 **Total Expense ($000):** 66284 **Payroll Expense ($000):** 36039 **Personnel:** 729

WOLFEBORO—Carroll County

★ **HUGGINS HOSPITAL (301312)**, 240 South Main Street, Zip 03894–4455, Mailing Address: P.O. Box 912, Zip 03894–0912; tel. 603/569–7500 **A**9 10 18 **F**2 3 10 11 15 28 34 40 45 50 56 57 59 64 65 70 74 75 79 81 85 86 87 93 97 107 110 111 114 119 125 130 131 132 133 135 146 147 **P**6
Primary Contact: Michael Connelly, President
CFO: Jeremy Roberge, Chief Financial Officer
CMO: John Boornazian, M.D., Chief Medical Officer
CIO: Pam McGovern, Director Technology
CHR: Laura Stauss, Director of Human Resources
Web address: www.hugginshospital.org
Control: Other not–for–profit (including NFP Corporation) **Service:** General Medical and Surgical

Staffed Beds: 25 **Admissions:** 1119 **Census:** 14 **Outpatient Visits:** 153168 **Births:** 0 **Total Expense ($000):** 53223 **Payroll Expense ($000):** 21297

WOODSVILLE—Grafton County

★ **COTTAGE HOSPITAL (301301)**, 90 Swiftwater Road, Zip 03785–1421, Mailing Address: P.O. Box 2001, Zip 03785–2001; tel. 603/747–9000 **A**9 10 18 **F**3 11 13 15 18 28 29 30 31 34 35 40 43 46 49 50 59 64 65 67 68 70 74 75 76 77 78 79 81 82 84 85 87 89 93 97 107 111 114 119 127 128 130 132 133 135 146 147 148
Primary Contact: Maria Ryan, Ph.D., Chief Executive Officer
COO: Lori Hughes, R.N., Chief Nursing Officer, Vice President Operations and Patient Care Services
CFO: Steven L. Plant, Chief Financial Officer
CIO: Rick Fredrick, Director Information Technology
CNO: Lori Hughes, R.N., Chief Nursing Officer, Vice President Operations & Patient Care Services
Web address: www.cottagehospital.org
Control: Other not–for–profit (including NFP Corporation) **Service:** General Medical and Surgical

Staffed Beds: 25 **Admissions:** 711 **Census:** 7 **Outpatient Visits:** 40091 **Births:** 84 **Total Expense ($000):** 28978 **Payroll Expense ($000):** 12358 **Personnel:** 221

NH

Many Facility Codes have changed. Please refer to the AHA Guide Code Chart. © 2014 AHA Guide

NEW JERSEY

ATLANTIC CITY—Atlantic County

★ ◇ **ACUITY SPECIALTY HOSPITAL OF NEW JERSEY (312023)**, 1925 Pacific Avenue, 7th Floor, Zip 08401–6713; tel. 609/441–2122, (Nonreporting) **A**10 21 **S** AcuityHealthcare, LP, Charlotte, NC
Primary Contact: Monica Titus, President and Chief Executive Officer
Web address: www.acuityhealthcare.net
Control: Corporation, Investor–owned, for–profit **Service:** Long–Term Acute Care hospital

Staffed Beds: 30

⊞ **ATLANTICARE REGIONAL MEDICAL CENTER (310064)**, 1925 Pacific Avenue, Zip 08401–6713; tel. 609/441–8994, (Includes ATLANTICARE REGIONAL MEDICAL CENTER–MAINLAND DIVISION, Jimmie Leeds Road, Pomona, Zip 08240; tel. 609/652–1000) **A**1 2 9 10 **F**1 3 4 7 11 12 13 15 16 17 18 20 22 24 26 29 30 31 34 35 36 37 38 40 41 42 43 45 46 47 48 49 50 54 57 58 59 60 61 64 66 67 68 70 71 72 73 74 75 76 78 79 80 81 82 84 85 86 87 88 89 90 93 97 98 99 100 102 103 104 105 106 107 108 110 111 114 115 116 117 118 119 120 121 123 124 126 128 130 132 135 143 146 147 148 **P**6 **S** AtlantiCare, Egg Harbor Township, NJ
Primary Contact: Lori Herndon, R.N., President and Chief Executive Officer
COO: Lori Herndon, R.N., President and Chief Executive Officer
CFO: Walter Greiner, Chief Financial Officer
CMO: Marilouise Vendetti, M.D., Chief Medical Officer
CIO: Christopher A. Scanzera, Vice President and Chief Information Officer
CHR: Richard Lovering, Corporate Vice President Human Resources and Organizational Development
CNO: Robyn Begley, R.N., Chief Nursing Officer
Web address: www.atlanticare.org
Control: Other not–for–profit (including NFP Corporation) **Service:** General Medical and Surgical

Staffed Beds: 534 **Admissions:** 30043 **Census:** 375 **Outpatient Visits:** 315700 **Births:** 2364 **Total Expense ($000):** 601962 **Payroll Expense ($000):** 260698 **Personnel:** 3395

BAYONNE—Hudson County

☐ **BAYONNE MEDICAL CENTER (310025)**, 29th Street & Avenue E., Zip 07002–4699; tel. 201/858–5000, (Nonreporting) **A**1 2 6 9 10 **S** CarePoint Health, Jersey City, NJ
Primary Contact: Mark Spektor, M.D., President and Chief Executive Officer
CIO: Don Lutz, Chief Information Officer
CHR: Jennifer Dobin, Vice President Human Resources
Web address: www.bayonnemedicalcenter.org
Control: Corporation, Investor–owned, for–profit **Service:** General Medical and Surgical

Staffed Beds: 170

BELLE MEAD—Somerset County

⊞ **CARRIER CLINIC (314012)**, 252 County Route 601, Zip 08502–0147, Mailing Address: P.O. Box 147, Zip 08502–0147; tel. 908/281–1000 **A**1 3 5 9 10 **F**4 5 98 99 100 101 102 103 **P**6
Primary Contact: Donald J. Parker, President and Chief Executive Officer
CFO: Randolph Jacobson, Chief Financial Officer
CMO: David Buch, M.D., Chief Medical Officer
CIO: Peter Schwartz, Manager Information Services
CHR: Trish Toole, Vice President Administrative Services
CNO: Carol Kosztyo, R.N., Vice President, Patient Care Services
Web address: www.carrierclinic.org
Control: Other not–for–profit (including NFP Corporation) **Service:** Psychiatric

Staffed Beds: 278 **Admissions:** 5913 **Census:** 217 **Outpatient Visits:** 1308 **Births:** 0 **Total Expense ($000):** 60592 **Payroll Expense ($000):** 37773 **Personnel:** 622

EAST MOUNTAIN HOSPITAL (314026), 252 County Route 601, Zip 08502; tel. 908/281–1500, (Nonreporting) **A**10
Primary Contact: Michael Voorhees, MS, Executive Director
CFO: Randolph Jacobson, Chief Financial Officer
CMO: Bohdan Cehelyk, M.D., Chief Medical Officer
CIO: Peter Schwartz, Director Information Systems
CHR: Patricia Toole, Vice President Human Resources
CNO: Deborah Charette, Director of Nursing
Web address: www.eastmountainhospital.com
Control: Corporation, Investor–owned, for–profit **Service:** Psychiatric

Staffed Beds: 16

BELLEVILLE—Essex County

⊞ **CLARA MAASS MEDICAL CENTER (310009)**, One Clara Maass Drive, Zip 07109–3557; tel. 973/450–2000 **A**1 2 3 5 9 10 **F**3 8 11 12 13 15 18 19 20 22 28 29 30 31 34 35 38 40 41 44 45 47 49 50 51 54 55 56 57 58 59 60 61 62 63 64 65 66 68 70 73 74 75 77 78 79 81 82 83 84 85 86 91 92 93 94 98 101 102 103 104 107 108 110 111 114 115 116 117 118 119 120 121 123 124 126 129 130 132 143 144 146 147 148 **S** Barnabas Health, West Orange, NJ
Primary Contact: Mary Ellen Clyne, Ph.D., President and Chief Executive Officer
CFO: Yasmir Bisal, Vice President Finance
CMO: Frank Mazzarella, M.D., Chief Medical Officer
CIO: Michael McTigue, Chief Information Officer
CHR: Jim Rolek, Vice President Human Resources
CNO: Lea Rodriguez, Chief Nursing Officer
Web address: www.barnabashealth.org/hospitals/clara_maass/index.html
Control: Other not–for–profit (including NFP Corporation) **Service:** General Medical and Surgical

Staffed Beds: 429 **Admissions:** 16910 **Census:** 228 **Outpatient Visits:** 123785 **Births:** 1533 **Total Expense ($000):** 245865 **Payroll Expense ($000):** 105308 **Personnel:** 1388

BERKELEY HEIGHTS—Union County

★ **RUNNELLS SPECIALIZED HOSPITAL OF UNION COUNTY (314027)**, 40 Watchung Way, Zip 07922–2618; tel. 908/771–5700, (Nonreporting) **A**9 10
Primary Contact: Sandra Adour, Acting Administrator
CFO: Michael Drummond, Chief Financial Officer
CMO: Raymond Lanza, D.O., Medical Director
CHR: Greg Hardoby, Director Personnel
CNO: Patricia Spina, R.N., Director of Nursing
Web address: www.ucnj.org/runnells
Control: County–Government, nonfederal **Service:** Other specialty

Staffed Beds: 344

BERLIN—Camden County

★ **VIRTUA BERLIN (310022)**, 100 Townsend Avenue, Zip 08009–9035; tel. 856/322–3000 **A**9 10 **F**3 11 29 30 34 35 38 40 45 46 47 48 49 50 55 56 57 63 64 65 68 70 74 75 81 82 84 85 87 90 92 93 100 107 108 111 115 119 130 146 148 **S** Virtua Health, Marlton, NJ
Primary Contact: Gary L. Long, Senior Vice President Population Management
COO: Christopher A. Chekouras, Vice President and Chief Operating Officer
CFO: Robert Segin, Chief Financial Officer
CMO: John Matsinger, D.O., Medical Director
CIO: Alfred Campanella, Vice President and Chief Information Officer
CHR: Michael Pepe, Ph.D., Chief Human Resources Officer
Web address: www.virtua.org
Control: Other not–for–profit (including NFP Corporation) **Service:** General Medical and Surgical

Staffed Beds: 83 **Admissions:** 3393 **Census:** 46 **Outpatient Visits:** 31352 **Births:** 0 **Total Expense ($000):** 75449 **Payroll Expense ($000):** 25577 **Personnel:** 279

BOONTON TOWNSHIP—Morris County

SAINT CLARE'S HOSPITAL/BOONTON TOWNSHIP See Saint Clare's Health System, Denville

BRICK—Ocean County

☐ **SHORE REHABILITATION INSTITUTE (313033)**, 425 Jack Martin Boulevard, Zip 08724–7732; tel. 732/836–4500, (Nonreporting) **A**1 10
Primary Contact: Amit Mohan, Executive Director
CFO: Richard C. Smith, Senior Vice President Finance
CMO: Lisa M. Luciano, D.O., Medical Director
CNO: Maria Clohsey, Director of Nursing
Web address: www.shorerehabilitationinstitute.com
Control: Other not–for–profit (including NFP Corporation) **Service:** Rehabilitation

Staffed Beds: 40

NJ

BRICK TOWNSHIP—Ocean County

⌧ **OCEAN MEDICAL CENTER (310052)**, 425 Jack Martin Boulevard, Zip 08724–7732; tel. 732/840–2200 **A**1 2 9 10 **F**3 11 12 13 15 17 18 20 22 28 29 30 31 32 34 35 36 38 39 40 41 42 43 44 45 46 47 48 49 50 53 54 55 56 57 59 60 63 64 65 66 68 70 71 73 74 75 76 77 78 79 80 81 82 84 85 86 87 89 91 92 93 94 96 97 100 101 102 103 107 108 110 111 114 115 116 117 118 119 120 121 123 126 129 130 131 132 134 135 144 146 147 148 **S** Meridian Health, Neptune, NJ
Primary Contact: Dean Q. Lin, FACHE, President
COO: Regina Foley, R.N., Vice President Nursing and Operations
CFO: Robert Palermo, Vice President Finance
CMO: James Clarke, M.D., Vice President Medical Affairs and Clinical Effectiveness
CIO: Rebecca Weber, Senior Vice President and Chief Information Officer
CHR: Sherrie String, Senior Vice President Human Resources
Web address: www.meridianhealth.com
Control: Other not–for–profit (including NFP Corporation) **Service:** General Medical and Surgical

Staffed Beds: 265 **Admissions:** 12640 **Census:** 172 **Outpatient Visits:** 155210 **Births:** 903 **Total Expense ($000):** 220073 **Payroll Expense ($000):** 95273 **Personnel:** 1262

BRIDGETON—Cumberland County

BRIDGETON HEALTH CENTER See Inspira Medical Center–Vineland, Vineland

BROWNS MILLS—Burlington County

☐ **DEBORAH HEART AND LUNG CENTER (310031)**, 200 Trenton Road, Zip 08015–1705; tel. 609/893–6611, (Nonreporting) **A**1 3 5 9 10 13
Primary Contact: Joseph P. Chirichella, President and Chief Executive Officer
CFO: R. Grant Leidy, Vice President Finance
CMO: Lynn McGrath, M.D., Vice President Medical Affairs
CHR: James Carlino, Vice President Human Resources
Web address: www.deborah.org
Control: Other not–for–profit (including NFP Corporation) **Service:** Other specialty

Staffed Beds: 89

CAMDEN—Camden County

⌧ **COOPER UNIVERSITY HEALTH CARE (310014)**, One Cooper Plaza, Zip 08103–1489; tel. 856/342–2000, (Includes CHILDEN'S REGIONAL HOSPITAL AT COOPER, One Cooper Plaza, Zip 08103; tel. 800/826–6737) **A**1 2 3 5 8 9 10 13 **F**3 8 11 12 13 15 17 18 19 20 22 24 26 29 30 31 32 34 35 36 37 39 40 41 43 44 45 46 47 48 49 50 51 52 54 55 56 57 58 59 60 61 64 65 66 68 70 72 73 74 75 76 78 79 80 81 82 84 85 86 87 88 89 92 93 96 97 98 99 100 101 102 103 104 107 108 109 110 111 114 115 117 118 119 120 121 123 124 126 129 130 131 132 135 144 146 147 148 **P**6
Primary Contact: Adrienne Kirby, Ph.D., President and CEO
CFO: Gary J. Lesneski, Senior Executive VP and General Counsel
CMO: Anthony J. Mazzarelli, M.D., Senior VP and Chief Medical Officer
CHR: Douglas H. Allen, Senior Vice President Human Resources
Web address: www.cooperhealth.org
Control: Other not–for–profit (including NFP Corporation) **Service:** General Medical and Surgical

Staffed Beds: 489 **Admissions:** 25042 **Census:** 373 **Outpatient Visits:** 266670 **Births:** 2035 **Total Expense ($000):** 650574 **Payroll Expense ($000):** 241085 **Personnel:** 4721

⌧ △ **OUR LADY OF LOURDES MEDICAL CENTER (310029)**, 1600 Haddon Avenue, Zip 08103–3117; tel. 856/757–3500 **A**1 2 6 7 9 10 **F**3 7 11 12 13 15 17 18 20 22 24 26 28 29 30 31 32 34 35 36 37 38 40 44 46 47 49 50 55 56 57 58 59 60 61 64 65 66 68 70 72 73 74 75 76 78 79 81 82 84 85 86 87 89 90 95 96 100 107 108 110 111 114 115 118 119 126 130 132 134 135 138 139 142 146 147 148 **S** Catholic Health East / Trinity Health, Livonia, MI
Primary Contact: Alexander J. Hatala, FACHE, President and Chief Executive Officer
COO: Mark Nessel, Chief Operating Officer
CFO: Michael Hammond, Chief Financial Officer
CMO: Alan R. Pope, M.D., Chief Medical Officer
CIO: Maureen Hetu, Chief Information Officer
CHR: Jennifer L. Moughan, Chief Human Resources Officer
CNO: Audrey Jadczak, R.N., Vice President Chief Nursing Officer
Web address: www.lourdesnet.org
Control: Other not–for–profit (including NFP Corporation) **Service:** General Medical and Surgical

Staffed Beds: 350 **Admissions:** 13540 **Census:** 192 **Outpatient Visits:** 128243 **Births:** 1084 **Total Expense ($000):** 272344 **Payroll Expense ($000):** 100305 **Personnel:** 1701

CAPE MAY COURT HOUSE—Cape May County

⌧ **CAPE REGIONAL MEDICAL CENTER (310011)**, Two Stone Harbor Boulevard, Zip 08210–9990; tel. 609/463–2000 **A**1 2 9 10 **F**3 8 11 13 15 18 20 28 29 30 31 34 35 40 44 45 46 49 50 53 57 59 64 70 74 75 76 77 78 79 81 82 84 85 86 87 89 91 93 97 107 111 114 118 119 120 121 123 130 132 135 143 146 148
Primary Contact: Joanne Carrocino, FACHE, President and Chief Executive Officer
CFO: Mark Gill, Vice President Finance and Chief Financial Officer
CMO: David Tarantino, M.D., Vice President Medical Affairs
CIO: Richard Wheatley, Chief Information Officer
CHR: Byron Hunter, Vice President Human Resources
CNO: Deborah Baehser, Vice President Patient Care Services
Web address: www.caperegional.com
Control: Other not–for–profit (including NFP Corporation) **Service:** General Medical and Surgical

Staffed Beds: 180 **Admissions:** 7541 **Census:** 80 **Outpatient Visits:** 175876 **Births:** 449 **Total Expense ($000):** 110086 **Payroll Expense ($000):** 47308 **Personnel:** 816

CEDAR GROVE—Essex County

☐ **ESSEX COUNTY HOSPITAL CENTER (314020)**, 204 Grove Avenue, Zip 07009–1436; tel. 973/571–2800, (Nonreporting) **A**1 10
Primary Contact: Frank J. Del Gaudio, Administrator
CFO: Ian Finnell, Business Manager
CMO: Robert Stern, M.D., Medical Director
CIO: Anthony C. Greco, Compliance Officer
CHR: Mary Ann Root, Supervisor Personnel
Web address: www.essexcountynj.org
Control: County–Government, nonfederal **Service:** Psychiatric

Staffed Beds: 180

CHERRY HILL—Camden County

★ ○ **KENNEDY HEALTH SYSTEM (310086)**, 2201 Chapel Avenue West, Zip 08002–2048; tel. 856/488–6500, (Includes KENNEDY UNIVERSITY HOSPITAL – STRATFORD, 18 East Laurel Road, Stratford, Zip 08084; tel. 609/346–6000; KENNEDY UNIVERSITY HOSPITAL – WASHINGTON TOWNSHIP, 435 Hurffville–Cross Keys Road, Turnersville, Zip 08012; tel. 609/582–2500) **A**2 10 11 12 **F**3 4 5 7 8 11 12 13 15 18 20 22 29 30 31 32 34 35 38 39 40 44 46 49 50 54 55 56 57 59 60 61 62 64 65 66 68 70 72 73 74 75 76 78 79 81 82 84 85 86 87 89 93 97 98 99 100 101 102 103 104 105 107 108 110 111 114 115 117 118 119 121 123 126 129 130 131 132 134 143 146 147 148
Primary Contact: Joseph W. Devine, President and Chief Executive Officer
CFO: Gary G. Terrinoni, Chief Financial Officer and Executive Vice President Administration
CMO: David Condoluci, M.D., Senior Vice President and Chief Medical Officer
CIO: Thomas Balcavage, Vice President Information Systems and Chief Information Officer Technology
CHR: Anneliese McMenamin, Vice President Human Resources
CNO: Helene M. Burns, MSN, Chief Nursing Executive
Web address: www.kennedyhealth.org
Control: Other not–for–profit (including NFP Corporation) **Service:** General Medical and Surgical

Staffed Beds: 540 **Admissions:** 26429 **Census:** 327 **Outpatient Visits:** 371192 **Births:** 933 **Total Expense ($000):** 443989 **Payroll Expense ($000):** 181928

KENNEDY MEMORIAL HOSPITALS–UNIVERSITY MEDICAL CENTER See Kennedy Health System

CHESTER—Morris County

KESSLER INSTITUTE FOR REHABILITATION See Kessler Institute for Rehabilitation, West Orange

NJ

Many Facility Codes have changed. Please refer to the AHA Guide Code Chart. © 2014 AHA Guide

DENVILLE—Morris County

✶ **SAINT CLARE'S HEALTH SYSTEM (310050)**, 25 Pocono Road, Zip 07834–2954; tel. 973/625–6000, (Includes SAINT CLARE'S HEALTH CENTER AT SUSSEX, 20 Walnut Street, Sussex, Zip 07461; tel. 973/702–2200; SAINT CLARE'S HOSPITAL/BOONTON TOWNSHIP, 130 Powerville Road, Boonton Township, Zip 07005; tel. 973/316–1800; SAINT CLARE'S HOSPITAL/DENVILLE, 25 Pocono Road, Zip 07834; tel. 973/625–6000; SAINT CLARE'S HOSPITAL/DOVER, 400 West Blackwell Street, Dover, Zip 07801–3311; tel. 973/989–3000) **A**1 2 9 10 **F**1 3 4 5 7 10 11 12 13 14 15 18 20 22 26 28 29 30 31 34 35 36 38 40 41 42 44 45 46 47 48 49 50 51 54 56 57 58 59 62 64 65 66 68 70 71 73 74 75 76 77 78 79 81 82 83 84 85 86 87 89 92 93 97 98 99 100 101 102 103 104 105 106 107 108 109 110 111 112 114 116 117 118 119 120 121 123 125 126 127 129 130 131 132 134 135 143 145 146 147 **P**5 **S** Catholic Health Initiatives, Englewood, CO
Primary Contact: Leslie D. Hirsch, FACHE, President and Chief Executive Officer
COO: Joe Nolan, Chief Operating Officer
CFO: Dianne Halford, Chief Financial Officer
CMO: Alma Ratcliffe, M.D., Executive Vice President Medical Staff and Business Development
CIO: Tero Caamano, Director Information Technology
CHR: Kay Bryant, Executive Director Human Resources
CNO: Debbie Regen, MS, Vice President and Chief Nursing Officer
Web address: www.saintclares.org
Control: Church–operated, Nongovernment, not–for profit **Service:** General Medical and Surgical

Staffed Beds: 412 **Admissions:** 16348 **Census:** 200 **Outpatient Visits:** 195323 **Births:** 1197 **Total Expense ($000):** 301056 **Payroll Expense ($000):** 126466 **Personnel:** 1845

SAINT CLARE'S HOSPITAL/DENVILLE See Saint Clare's Health System

DOVER—Morris County

✶ **KINDRED HOSPITAL–NEW JERSEY MORRIS COUNTY (312020)**, 400 West Blackwell Street, Zip 07801–2525; tel. 973/537–3818, (Includes KINDRED HOSPITAL NEW JERSEY – RAHWAY, 865 Stone Street, Rahway, Zip 07065; tel. 732/453–2950; KINDRED HOSPITAL NEW JERSEY – WAYNE, 224 Hamburg Turnpike, Wayne, Zip 07470; tel. 973/636–7200; Alice M. O'Connor, R.N., Administrator), (Nonreporting) **A**1 10 **S** Kindred Healthcare, Louisville, KY
Primary Contact: Barbara Callaghan, Chief Executive Officer
CFO: Rishab Punjabi, Chief Financial Officer
CHR: Neil Rosner, Area Director Human Resources
Web address: www.khmorriscounty.com/
Control: Corporation, Investor–owned, for–profit **Service:** Long–Term Acute Care hospital

Staffed Beds: 117

EAST ORANGE—Essex County

✶ **EAST ORANGE GENERAL HOSPITAL (310083)**, 300 Central Avenue, Zip 07018–2897; tel. 973/672–8400 **A**1 9 10 **F**11 15 18 29 30 34 35 38 40 45 46 53 57 59 60 61 68 70 71 74 77 79 81 84 93 97 98 99 102 104 105 106 107 108 110 111 114 119 130 148 **P**6
Primary Contact: Kevin J. Slavin, FACHE, President and Chief Executive Officer
CFO: Al Aboud, Chief Financial Officer
CMO: Valentine Burroughs, M.D., Chief Medical Officer
CIO: Thomas Ciccarelli, Chief Information Officer
CHR: Chester Banks, Director Human Resources
CNO: Mary Anne Marra, R.N., Vice President/Chief Nursing Officer
Web address: www.evh.org
Control: Other not–for–profit (including NFP Corporation) **Service:** General Medical and Surgical

Staffed Beds: 190 **Admissions:** 6933 **Census:** 125 **Outpatient Visits:** 99071 **Births:** 0 **Total Expense ($000):** 110498 **Payroll Expense ($000):** 51791

✶ **VETERANS AFFAIRS NEW JERSEY HEALTH CARE SYSTEM**, 385 Tremont Avenue, Zip 07018–1095; tel. 973/676–1000, (Includes EAST ORANGE DIVISION, 385 Tremont Avenue, tel. 973/676–1000; LYONS DIVISION, 151 Knollcroft Road, Lyons, Zip 07939–9998; tel. 908/647–0180) **A**1 2 3 5 **F**3 4 5 11 15 18 20 24 29 30 31 33 34 35 38 39 40 45 46 50 53 54 56 57 58 59 60 61 62 64 68 70 71 74 75 77 78 79 81 82 83 84 85 86 87 91 92 93 94 96 97 98 100 101 102 103 104 105 106 107 111 114 119 121 123 128 129 130 132 133 135 143 146 147 148 **P**6 **S** Department of Veterans Affairs, Washington, DC
Primary Contact: Kenneth H. Mizrach, Director
COO: Kenneth H. Mizrach, Director
CFO: Tyrone Taylor, Chief Financial Officer
CMO: Steven L. Lieberman, M.D., Chief of Staff
CIO: Kamesha Scarlett, Chief Information Resource Management
CHR: Nancy Hamilton, Chief Human and Learning Resources
CNO: Patrick J. Troy, R.N., Associate Director Patient Care Services
Web address: www.newjersey.va.gov/
Control: Veterans Affairs, Government, federal **Service:** General Medical and Surgical

Staffed Beds: 439 **Admissions:** 4763 **Census:** 107 **Outpatient Visits:** 20351 **Births:** 0 **Total Expense ($000):** 485201 **Payroll Expense ($000):** 294487 **Personnel:** 1830

EDISON—Middlesex County

★ △ **JFK JOHNSON REHABILITATION INSTITUTE**, 65 James Street, Zip 08820–3947; tel. 732/321–7050 **A**7 **F**3 9 28 29 30 35 36 50 53 54 64 82 90 91 92 93 94 96 130 131 132 143 **P**6 **S** JFK Health System, Edison, NJ
Primary Contact: Anthony Cuzzola, Vice President Rehabilitation Services
Web address: www.njrehab.org
Control: Other not–for–profit (including NFP Corporation) **Service:** Rehabilitation

Staffed Beds: 90 **Admissions:** 1963 **Census:** 73 **Outpatient Visits:** 42391 **Births:** 0 **Total Expense ($000):** 63838 **Payroll Expense ($000):** 41698 **Personnel:** 582

✶ **JFK MEDICAL CENTER (310108)**, 65 James Street, Zip 08820–3947; tel. 732/321–7000, (Nonreporting) **A**1 2 3 5 9 10 **S** JFK Health System, Edison, NJ
Primary Contact: Raymond F. Fredericks, President and CEO
COO: Scott Gebhard, Executive VP and Chief Operating Officer
CFO: Richard C. Smith, Senior Vice President and Chief Financial Officer
CMO: William F. Oser, M.D., Senior Vice President and Chief Medical Officer
CHR: Shirley Higgins–Bowers, Vice President Human Resources
CNO: Patricia G. Rackovan, Senior Vice President & Chief Nurse Executive
Web address: www.jfkmc.org
Control: Other not–for–profit (including NFP Corporation) **Service:** General Medical and Surgical

Staffed Beds: 441

ELIZABETH—Union County

✶ **TRINITAS REGIONAL MEDICAL CENTER (310027)**, 225 Williamson Street, Zip 07202–3625; tel. 908/994–5000, (Includes TRINITAS HOSPITAL, 925 East Jersey Street, Zip 07201; tel. 908/994–5000; TRINITAS REGIONAL MEDICAL CENTER – NEW POINT CAMPUS, 655 East Jersey Street, Zip 07206; tel. 908/994–5000), (Total facility includes 124 beds in nursing home–type unit) **A**1 2 6 9 10 13 **F**3 5 7 8 11 12 13 15 17 18 20 22 28 29 30 31 32 34 35 36 38 40 44 45 46 48 49 53 56 57 58 59 60 61 64 65 66 68 70 73 74 75 76 77 78 79 81 82 84 85 86 87 93 97 98 99 100 101 102 103 104 105 106 107 108 110 111 114 118 119 120 121 123 124 126 128 129 130 132 134 135 141 143 146 147 **P**6
Primary Contact: Gary S. Horan, FACHE, President and Chief Executive Officer
CFO: Karen Lumpp, Senior Vice President and Chief Financial Officer
CMO: William McHugh, M.D., Medical Director and Chief Medical Officer
CIO: Judy Comitto, Vice President Information Services and Chief Information Officer
CHR: Glenn Nacion, Vice President Human Resources
CNO: Mary McTigue, Vice President Patient Care Services and Chief Nursing Officer
Web address: www.trinitasrmc.com
Control: Other not–for–profit (including NFP Corporation) **Service:** General Medical and Surgical

Staffed Beds: 458 **Admissions:** 15456 **Census:** 386 **Outpatient Visits:** 449549 **Births:** 2219 **Total Expense ($000):** 291308 **Payroll Expense ($000):** 133642 **Personnel:** 2310

NJ

Hospital, Medicare Provider Number, Address, Telephone, Approval, Facility, and Physician Codes, Health Care System

★ American Hospital Association (AHA) membership
□ The Joint Commission accreditation   ◇ DNV Healthcare Inc. accreditation
○ Healthcare Facilities Accreditation Program
△ Commission on Accreditation of Rehabilitation Facilities (CARF) accreditation

---

ELMER—Salem County

★ ◇ **INSPIRA MEDICAL CENTER–ELMER (310069)**, 501 West Front Street, Zip 08318–2101; tel. 856/363–1000 **A**9 10 21 **F**3 8 11 12 13 15 18 20 28 29 30 34 38 40 44 50 57 59 64 68 70 74 75 76 77 78 79 81 82 85 86 87 89 93 107 108 110 111 119 130 131 132 134 146 147 148 **S** Inspira Health Network, Mullica Hill, NJ
Primary Contact: John A. DiAngelo, President and Chief Executive Officer
COO: David Yhlen, Chief Operating Officer
CFO: Thomas Baldosaro, Chief Financial Officer
CMO: Steven C. Linn, M.D., Chief Medical Officer
CIO: Thomas Pacek, Vice President Information Systems and Chief Information Officer
CHR: Erich Florentine, Chief People Officer
CNO: Elizabeth Sheridan, Chief Operating Officer and Chief Nursing Executive
Web address: www.inspirahealthnetwork.org/?id=5281&sid=1
Control: Other not–for–profit (including NFP Corporation) **Service:** General Medical and Surgical

Staffed Beds: 88 **Admissions:** 3799 **Census:** 39 **Outpatient Visits:** 70023 **Births:** 331 **Total Expense ($000):** 58909 **Payroll Expense ($000):** 27519 **Personnel:** 290

ENGLEWOOD—Bergen County

✠ **ENGLEWOOD HOSPITAL AND MEDICAL CENTER (310045)**, 350 Engle Street, Zip 07631–1898; tel. 201/894–3000 **A**1 2 3 5 9 10 **F**7 8 12 13 15 17 18 19 20 22 24 26 28 29 30 31 34 35 36 38 40 45 46 49 50 51 54 55 56 57 58 59 60 64 70 72 74 75 77 78 79 81 82 83 84 85 86 87 91 92 93 94 98 99 100 101 102 103 104 105 106 107 108 109 110 111 112 114 115 116 117 118 119 120 121 124 126 129 130 143 145 146 148 **P**6
Primary Contact: Warren Geller, President and Chief Executive Officer
CFO: Anthony T. Orlando, Senior Vice President Finance
CMO: Michael Harris, M.D., Chief Medical Officer
CIO: Ronald Fuschillo, Chief Information Officer
CNO: Madelyn Pearson, R.N., Sr. Vice President Patient Care Services
Web address: www.englewoodhospital.com
Control: Other not–for–profit (including NFP Corporation) **Service:** General Medical and Surgical

Staffed Beds: 265 **Admissions:** 15419 **Census:** 199 **Outpatient Visits:** 658574 **Births:** 2007 **Total Expense ($000):** 398528 **Payroll Expense ($000):** 129605 **Personnel:** 2145

FLEMINGTON—Hunterdon County

✠ **HUNTERDON MEDICAL CENTER (310005)**, 2100 Wescott Drive, Zip 08822–4604; tel. 908/788–6100 **A**1 2 3 5 9 10 **F**3 4 5 8 11 12 13 14 15 18 20 22 27 28 29 30 31 32 33 35 38 40 45 46 47 48 49 53 54 58 59 60 61 62 64 65 68 70 71 74 75 76 77 78 79 81 82 83 84 85 86 87 89 91 92 93 94 97 98 99 100 101 102 103 104 105 106 107 108 110 114 118 119 121 123 127 129 130 131 132 134 135 146 147 148
Primary Contact: Robert P. Wise, FACHE, President and Chief Executive Officer
COO: Lawrence N. Grand, Executive Vice President and Chief Operating Officer
CFO: Gail Kosyla, Chief Financial Officer
CMO: George Roksvaag, M.D., Chief Medical Officer
CIO: Glenn Mamary, Chief Information Officer
CHR: Violet Kocsis, Chief Human Resources Officer
CNO: Patricia Steingall, R.N., Vice President, Patient Care Services
Web address: www.hunterdonhealthcare.org
Control: Other not–for–profit (including NFP Corporation) **Service:** General Medical and Surgical

Staffed Beds: 178 **Admissions:** 8166 **Census:** 99 **Outpatient Visits:** 623919 **Births:** 916 **Total Expense ($000):** 264336 **Payroll Expense ($000):** 126472 **Personnel:** 1980

FREEHOLD—Monmouth County

✠ **CENTRASTATE HEALTHCARE SYSTEM (310111)**, 901 West Main Street, Zip 07728–2549; tel. 732/431–2000 **A**1 2 3 5 9 10 **F**3 11 12 13 15 18 19 20 28 29 30 31 32 34 35 38 40 41 45 46 49 56 57 58 59 61 64 65 66 70 73 74 75 76 77 78 79 81 82 84 86 87 89 92 93 97 98 100 101 102 107 108 110 114 118 119 120 121 123 124 126 129 130 131 132 134 135 144 146 147 148
Primary Contact: John Gribbin, FACHE, President and Chief Executive Officer
CFO: John Dellocono, Senior Vice President and Chief Financial Officer
CMO: Jack H. Dworkin, M.D., Vice President Medical Affairs and Chief Medical Officer
CHR: Fran Keane, Vice President Human Resources
CNO: Linda W. Geisler, R.N., Vice President Patient Services
Web address: www.centrastate.com
Control: Other not–for–profit (including NFP Corporation) **Service:** General Medical and Surgical

Staffed Beds: 283 **Admissions:** 14209 **Census:** 165 **Outpatient Visits:** 253292 **Births:** 1395 **Total Expense ($000):** 232672 **Payroll Expense ($000):** 102693 **Personnel:** 1452

HACKENSACK—Bergen County

✠ **HACKENSACK UNIVERSITY MEDICAL CENTER (310001)**, 30 Prospect Avenue, Zip 07601–1914; tel. 201/996–2000, (Includes THE JOSEPH M. SANZARI CHILDREN'S HOSPITAL, 30 Prospect Avenue, tel. 201/996–2000) **A**1 2 3 5 8 9 10 **F**2 3 4 5 6 7 8 9 10 11 12 13 14 15 16 17 18 19 20 22 24 26 27 28 29 30 31 32 33 34 35 36 37 38 39 40 41 42 43 44 45 46 47 48 49 50 51 52 53 54 55 56 57 58 59 60 61 64 65 68 69 70 71 72 73 74 75 76 77 78 79 80 81 82 84 85 86 87 88 89 90 91 92 93 94 96 97 98 99 100 101 102 103 104 107 108 109 110 111 113 114 115 116 117 118 119 120 121 123 124 126 129 130 131 132 134 135 136 138 141 142 143 144 145 146 147 148 **P**1 5 6 **S** Hackensack University Health Network, Hackensack, NJ
Primary Contact: Robert C. Garrett, FACHE, President and Chief Executive Officer
COO: Ketul J. Patel, Executive Vice President and Chief Operations and Strategy Officer
CFO: Robert Glenning, Executive Vice President Finance and Chief Financial Officer
CMO: Peter A. Gross, M.D., Senior Vice President and Chief Medical Officer
CHR: Nancy R. Corcoran, Senior Vice President Human Resources and Quality Service
Web address: www.hackensackumc.org
Control: Other not–for–profit (including NFP Corporation) **Service:** General Medical and Surgical

Staffed Beds: 710 **Admissions:** 70093 **Census:** 592 **Outpatient Visits:** 2665470 **Births:** 6177 **Total Expense ($000):** 1338706 **Payroll Expense ($000):** 609490 **Personnel:** 7286

HACKETTSTOWN—Warren County

HACKETTSTOWN REGIONAL MEDICAL CENTER (310115), 651 Willow Grove Street, Zip 07840–1799; tel. 908/852–5100, (Nonreporting) **A**9 10 **S** Adventist HealthCare, Gaithersburg, MD
Primary Contact: Jason C. Coe, President and Chief Executive Officer
COO: Stella Visaggio, Chief Operating Officer
CFO: Robert Peterson, Chief Financial Officer
CMO: Kenneth Janowski, M.D., Chief Medical Officer
CIO: Dorothy Cox, Manager Information Systems
CHR: Jeanne Jepson, Director Human Resources
CNO: Linda Ambacher, Interim Chief Nursing Officer
Web address: www.hrmcnj.org
Control: Church–operated, Nongovernment, not–for profit **Service:** General Medical and Surgical

Staffed Beds: 111

HAMILTON—Mercer County

✠ **ROBERT WOOD JOHNSON UNIVERSITY HOSPITAL AT HAMILTON (310110)**, One Hamilton Health Place, Zip 08690–3599; tel. 609/586–7900 **A**1 2 5 9 10 **F**3 8 9 11 12 13 15 17 18 22 26 28 29 30 31 32 34 35 36 37 39 40 41 44 46 47 48 49 50 51 53 54 55 56 57 58 59 60 61 63 64 65 66 68 69 70 71 73 74 75 76 77 78 79 81 82 84 85 86 87 92 93 96 97 100 102 103 107 108 110 111 114 115 116 117 118 119 120 121 123 124 126 129 130 131 132 134 135 143 144 145 146 147 148 **P**6 **S** Robert Wood Johnson Health System & Network, New Brunswick, NJ
Primary Contact: Richard Freeman, President and Chief Executive Officer
COO: Barbara H. Smith, Senior Vice President & Chief Operating Officer
CFO: James M. Maher, Senior Vice President and Chief Financial Officer
CMO: Ronald Ryder, D.O., President of the Medical Staff
CNO: Lisa Breza, R.N., Vice President and Chief Nursing Officer
Web address: www.rwjhamilton.org
Control: Other not–for–profit (including NFP Corporation) **Service:** General Medical and Surgical

Staffed Beds: 242 **Admissions:** 11716 **Census:** 145 **Outpatient Visits:** 430896 **Births:** 1051 **Total Expense ($000):** 187713 **Payroll Expense ($000):** 79673 **Personnel:** 1088

HAMMONTON—Camden County

☐ **ANCORA PSYCHIATRIC HOSPITAL (314005)**, 301 Spring Garden Road, Zip 08037–9699; tel. 609/561–1700 **A**1 10 **F**30 39 56 68 75 87 97 98 130 135 143 146 **P**6 **S** Division of Mental Health and Addiction Services, Department of Human Services, State of New Jersey, Trenton, NJ
Primary Contact: John Lubitsky, Chief Executive Officer
CFO: John Holmes, Business Manager
CMO: David Roat, D.O., Medical Director
CIO: Charlene Ruberti, Director Information Technology Development
CHR: Alfred Filipini, Manager Human Resources
CNO: Catherine Jones, Chief Nursing Officer
Web address: www.state.nj.us/humanservices/dmhs/oshm/aph/
Control: State–Government, nonfederal **Service:** Psychiatric

Staffed Beds: 500 **Admissions:** 750 **Census:** 490 **Outpatient Visits:** 0 **Births:** 0 **Total Expense ($000):** 166431 **Payroll Expense ($000):** 85341 **Personnel:** 1658

NJ

Many Facility Codes have changed. Please refer to the AHA Guide Code Chart. © 2014 AHA Guide

HOBOKEN—Hudson County

☐ **HOBOKEN UNIVERSITY MEDICAL CENTER (310040)**, 308 Willow Avenue, Zip 07030–3889; tel. 201/418–1000, (Nonreporting) **A**1 3 5 9 10 **S** CarePoint Health, Jersey City, NJ
Primary Contact: Ann Logan, Chief Operating Officer and Chief Nursing Officer
CFO: Vincent Riccitelli, Vice President and Chief Financial Officer
CMO: Meika Roberson, M.D., Chief Medical Officer
CIO: Steve Goriah, Chief Information Officer
CHR: Roberto Gonzalez, Executive Director Human Resources
CNO: Ann Logan, Chief Operating Officer and Chief Nursing Officer
Web address: www.hobokenumc.com
Control: Corporation, Investor–owned, for–profit **Service:** General Medical and Surgical

Staffed Beds: 364

HOLMDEL—Monmouth County

☒ **BAYSHORE COMMUNITY HOSPITAL (310112)**, 727 North Beers Street, Zip 07733–1598; tel. 732/739–5900 **A**1 2 9 10 **F**3 11 12 15 18 20 22 28 29 30 31 32 34 35 36 38 39 40 41 43 44 45 46 49 50 51 54 55 56 57 59 60 63 64 65 66 68 69 70 71 74 75 77 78 79 80 81 82 84 85 86 87 91 92 93 94 96 97 100 101 102 103 107 108 110 111 114 116 117 118 119 129 130 131 132 134 135 146 147 148 **S** Meridian Health, Neptune, NJ
Primary Contact: Timothy J. Hogan, FACHE, Regional President
COO: Anthony V. Cava, Chief Operating Officer
CFO: Joseph M. Lemaire, Executive Vice President Finance and Partner Company Operations
CMO: Ian Leber, M.D., Chief Medical Officer
CIO: Rebecca Weber, Senior Vice President and Chief Information Officer
CHR: Sherrie String, Senior Vice President Human Resources
CNO: Linda Walsh, R.N., Vice President Chief Nursing Executive
Web address: www.bchs.com
Control: Other not–for–profit (including NFP Corporation) **Service:** General Medical and Surgical

Staffed Beds: 153 **Admissions:** 6960 **Census:** 101 **Outpatient Visits:** 80677 **Births:** 0 **Total Expense ($000):** 109814 **Payroll Expense ($000):** 50281 **Personnel:** 770

JERSEY CITY—Hudson County

☐ **CHRIST HOSPITAL (310016)**, 176 Palisade Avenue, Zip 07306–1196, Mailing Address: 176 Palisades Avenue, Zip 07306–1196; tel. 201/795–8200, (Nonreporting) **A**1 6 9 10 12 13 **S** CarePoint Health, Jersey City, NJ
Primary Contact: Nizar Kifaieh, M.D., President and Chief Medical Officer
CFO: Patrick Ryan, Chief Financial Officer
CMO: Nizar Kifaieh, M.D., President and Chief Medical Officer
CHR: Josiane Deroncerey, Director Human Resources
CNO: William Atkinson, Vice President Patient Care Services and Chief Nursing Officer
Web address: www.christhospital.org
Control: Other not–for–profit (including NFP Corporation) **Service:** General Medical and Surgical

Staffed Beds: 381

◇ **JERSEY CITY MEDICAL CENTER (310074)**, 355 Grand Street, Zip 07302–4321; tel. 201/915–2000 **A**3 5 9 10 21 **F**3 4 5 7 11 12 13 15 17 18 20 22 24 26 29 30 31 34 35 38 39 40 41 43 45 46 47 48 49 50 54 55 56 57 59 60 61 64 65 66 68 70 71 72 73 74 75 76 77 78 79 81 82 84 85 87 89 92 93 96 97 98 99 100 101 102 104 105 106 107 108 110 111 112 114 115 119 130 134 135 143 144 146 148 **P**6 **S** Barnabas Health, West Orange, NJ
Primary Contact: Joseph F. Scott, FACHE, President and Chief Executive Officer
CFO: Paul R. Goldberg, Chief Financial Officer
CMO: Kenneth Garay, M.D., Chief Medical Officer
CIO: Stephen Li, Vice President Management Information Systems
CHR: Mary Cataudella, Corporate Director Human Resources
Web address: www.barnabashealth.org/Jersey–City–Medical–Center.aspx
Control: Other not–for–profit (including NFP Corporation) **Service:** General Medical and Surgical

Staffed Beds: 316 **Admissions:** 15250 **Census:** 213 **Outpatient Visits:** 254274 **Births:** 1981 **Total Expense ($000):** 317983 **Payroll Expense ($000):** 137870 **Personnel:** 2051

LAKEWOOD—Ocean County

☒ **MONMOUTH MEDICAL CENTER, SOUTHERN CAMPUS (310084)**, 600 River Avenue, Zip 08701–5237; tel. 732/363–1900 **A**1 2 9 10 **F**3 11 13 15 18 20 28 29 30 31 32 34 35 36 38 40 41 43 44 50 54 56 57 58 59 60 61 64 68 70 73 74 75 76 77 78 79 81 82 84 86 87 89 93 96 97 98 100 101 102 103 104 105 107 108 111 114 117 119 130 131 132 133 134 135 146 147 148 **S** Barnabas Health, West Orange, NJ
Primary Contact: Michael Mimoso, FACHE, President and Chief Executive Officer
COO: Judy Colorado, R.N., Chief Nursing Officer and Chief Nursing Officer
CFO: Gerald Tofani, Chief Financial Officer
CMO: Todd Phillips, M.D., Interim Vice President, Medical Affairs
CIO: Chris Butler, Deputy CIO/System Vice President
CHR: Michele Schweers, Vice President Human Resources
CNO: Judy Colorado, R.N., Chief Nursing Officer and Chief Operating Officer
Web address: www.barnabashealth.org/hospitals/monmouth–medical–center–southern–campus.aspx
Control: Other not–for–profit (including NFP Corporation) **Service:** General Medical and Surgical

Staffed Beds: 240 **Admissions:** 9375 **Census:** 140 **Outpatient Visits:** 95040 **Births:** 922 **Total Expense ($000):** 130854 **Payroll Expense ($000):** 63504 **Personnel:** 784

SPECIALTY HOSPITAL OF CENTRAL JERSEY (312013), 600 River Avenue, 4 West, Zip 08701–5237; tel. 732/942–3588, (Nonreporting) **A**10
Primary Contact: Violeta Peters, R.N., Chief Executive Officer
CFO: Kristin Prentiss, Chief Financial Officer
CMO: Howard Lebowitz, M.D., Chief Medical Officer
CHR: Mary Pat Napolitano, Director Human Resources
CNO: Judy Boccellato, R.N., Chief Nursing Officer
Web address: www.acutecarehs.com
Control: Corporation, Investor–owned, for–profit **Service:** Long–Term Acute Care hospital

Staffed Beds: 50

LAWRENCEVILLE—Mercer County

☒ **ST. LAWRENCE REHABILITATION CENTER (313027)**, 2381 Lawrenceville Road, Zip 08648–2025; tel. 609/896–9500, (Total facility includes 60 beds in nursing home–type unit) **A**1 10 **F**29 30 34 35 57 64 68 90 93 96 108 119 128 130 132 143 146 148
Primary Contact: Darlene S. Hanley, R.N., President and Chief Executive Officer
COO: Shirley Pukala, R.N., Assistant Administrator of Operations
CFO: Thomas W. Boyle, Chief Financial Officer
CMO: Kevin McGuigan, M.D., Medical Director
CIO: Joseph Castronuevo, Director Information Management
CHR: John Levi, Director of Human Resources
CNO: Magdalena Sokolowski, R.N., Director of Nursing
Web address: www.slrc.org
Control: Church–operated, Nongovernment, not–for profit **Service:** Rehabilitation

Staffed Beds: 120 **Admissions:** 2386 **Census:** 96 **Outpatient Visits:** 19565 **Births:** 0 **Total Expense ($000):** 32834 **Payroll Expense ($000):** 18753 **Personnel:** 324

LIVINGSTON—Essex County

☒ **SAINT BARNABAS MEDICAL CENTER (310076)**, 94 Old Short Hills Road, Zip 07039–5672; tel. 973/322–5000 **A**1 2 3 5 8 9 10 12 13 **F**3 8 11 12 13 16 17 18 19 20 22 24 26 28 29 30 31 32 34 35 36 38 39 40 41 44 45 46 47 48 49 50 54 55 56 57 58 59 60 61 62 63 64 65 66 68 69 70 71 72 73 74 75 76 77 78 79 81 82 84 85 86 87 88 89 92 93 94 96 97 100 102 103 107 108 111 114 115 118 119 120 121 123 124 126 129 130 132 134 135 138 141 142 146 147 148 **P**7 **S** Barnabas Health, West Orange, NJ
Primary Contact: John F. Bonamo, M.D., MS, President and Chief Executive Officer
COO: Patrick Ahearn, Chief Operating Officer and Senior Vice President
CFO: Richard Davis, Chief Financial Officer
CMO: Gregory Rokosz, D.O., Senior Vice President Medical and Academic Affairs
CIO: Michael McTigue, Chief Information Officer
CHR: Arnold D. Manzo, Vice President Human Resources
CNO: Jennifer A. O'Neill, R.N., Vice President Patient Care Services
Web address: www.barnabashealth.org/hospitals/saint_barnabas/index.html
Control: Other not–for–profit (including NFP Corporation) **Service:** General Medical and Surgical

Staffed Beds: 545 **Admissions:** 32892 **Census:** 400 **Outpatient Visits:** 209939 **Births:** 5691 **Total Expense ($000):** 605891 **Payroll Expense ($000):** 220520 **Personnel:** 3079

NJ

LONG BRANCH—Monmouth County

⊞ **MONMOUTH MEDICAL CENTER, LONG BRANCH CAMPUS (310075)**, 300 Second Avenue, Zip 07740–6303; tel. 732/222–5200, (Includes CHILDREN'S HOSPITAL AT MONMOUTH MEDICAL CENTER, 300 Second Avenue, tel. 732/222–5200) **A**1 2 3 5 8 9 10 **F**3 5 8 9 11 12 13 14 15 17 18 19 20 22 28 29 30 31 32 34 35 36 38 40 41 45 46 47 48 49 50 51 52 53 54 55 56 57 58 59 60 61 63 64 65 66 68 70 72 73 74 75 76 77 78 79 81 82 83 84 85 86 87 88 89 97 98 99 100 101 102 103 104 105 106 107 108 109 110 111 112 114 115 119 120 121 123 124 126 129 130 131 132 133 134 135 143 144 145 146 147 148 **P**5 6 **S** Barnabas Health, West Orange, NJ
Primary Contact: Frank J. Vozos, M.D., FACS, President and Chief Executive Officer
COO: Bill Arnold, Chief Operating Officer
CFO: David McClung, Chief Financial Officer
CMO: Eric Burkett, M.D., Vice President Medical Affairs
CIO: Chris Butler, Chief Information Officer
CHR: Richard Kiernan, Vice President Human Resources
CNO: Diann Johnston, Vice President of Patient Care Services
Web address: www.barnabashealth.org/hospitals/monmouth_medical/index.html
Control: Other not–for–profit (including NFP Corporation) **Service:** General Medical and Surgical

Staffed Beds: 294 **Admissions:** 17715 **Census:** 227 **Outpatient Visits:** 244403 **Births:** 4729 **Total Expense ($000):** 323303 **Payroll Expense ($000):** 129565 **Personnel:** 1879

LYONS—Somerset County

LYONS DIVISION See Veterans Affairs New Jersey Health Care System, East Orange

MANAHAWKIN—Ocean County

⊞ **SOUTHERN OCEAN MEDICAL CENTER (310113)**, 1140 Route 72 West, Zip 08050–2499; tel. 609/597–6011, (Total facility includes 20 beds in nursing home–type unit) **A**1 2 9 10 **F**3 11 12 13 15 18 20 28 29 30 31 32 34 35 36 39 40 41 43 44 45 46 48 49 50 51 54 55 56 57 59 60 63 64 65 66 68 70 71 74 75 76 77 78 79 80 81 82 84 85 86 87 91 93 94 96 97 100 101 102 103 107 108 110 111 114 115 116 117 118 119 128 129 130 131 132 134 135 146 147 148 **S** Meridian Health, Neptune, NJ
Primary Contact: Joseph P. Coyle, President
COO: Kim Frazee, R.N., Vice President Physician and Business Development
CFO: Joseph M. Lemaire, Executive Vice President
CMO: Theodore Zaleski, M.D., Vice President Clinical Effectiveness
CIO: Rebecca Weber, Senior Vice President and Chief Information Officer
CHR: Susan Tillman–Taylor, Manager Human Resources
CNO: Donna Ciufo, R.N., Vice President and Chief Nurse Executive
Web address: www.soch.com
Control: Other not–for–profit (including NFP Corporation) **Service:** General Medical and Surgical

Staffed Beds: 135 **Admissions:** 6439 **Census:** 89 **Outpatient Visits:** 100024 **Births:** 354 **Total Expense ($000):** 122920 **Payroll Expense ($000):** 49704 **Personnel:** 696

MARLTON—Burlington County

⊞ △ **MARLTON REHABILITATION HOSPITAL (313032)**, 92 Brick Road, Zip 08053–2177; tel. 856/988–8778 **A**1 7 10 **F**34 50 57 59 60 64 68 75 77 85 86 87 90 91 92 93 94 95 96 107 111 114 116 119 130 132 148 **P**8 **S** Vibra Healthcare, Mechanicsburg, PA
Primary Contact: Michael Long, MS, Chief Executive Officer
CFO: Stuart Moss, Chief Financial Officer
CMO: Kenneth Wu, M.D., Medical Director
CHR: Joanne Cernava, Director Human Resources
CNO: Chris Kreeley, Director Nursing
Web address: www.marltonrehab.com
Control: Corporation, Investor–owned, for–profit **Service:** Rehabilitation

Staffed Beds: 61 **Admissions:** 1672 **Census:** 52 **Outpatient Visits:** 17560 **Births:** 0 **Total Expense ($000):** 22135 **Payroll Expense ($000):** 10845 **Personnel:** 163

⊞ **VIRTUA MARLTON**, 90 Brick Road, Zip 08053–2177; tel. 856/355–6000 **A**1 2 9 **F**3 20 22 26 29 31 40 45 46 47 49 56 60 64 68 70 75 78 79 81 82 84 85 87 93 107 111 119 129 130 141 146 **S** Virtua Health, Marlton, NJ
Primary Contact: Gary L. Long, Senior Vice President Population Management
CFO: Robert Segin, Executive Vice President & Chief Financial Officer
CMO: John Matsinger, D.O., Chief Medical Officer
CIO: Thomas Gordon, Chief Information Officer
CHR: Rhonda R. Jordan, Chief Human Resources Officer
CNO: Tracy Carlino, R.N., Chief Nursing Officer
Web address: www.virtua.org
Control: Other not–for–profit (including NFP Corporation) **Service:** General Medical and Surgical

Staffed Beds: 192 **Admissions:** 9184 **Census:** 127 **Outpatient Visits:** 45770 **Births:** 0 **Total Expense ($000):** 206373 **Payroll Expense ($000):** 58307 **Personnel:** 687

□ **WEISMAN CHILDREN'S REHABILITATION HOSPITAL (313302)**, 92 Brick Road 3rd Floor, Zip 08053–2177; tel. 856/489–4520, (Nonreporting) **A**1 10
Primary Contact: Thomas J. Lonergan, Chief Executive Officer
COO: Michael Rosiak, Chief Operating Officer
CMO: Connie Domingo, M.D., Medical Director
CIO: Darren Pedersen, Coordinator Information Technology
CHR: Jill Koerner, Manager Employee Relations
CNO: Daniel William Pfeffer, Nurse Executive
Web address: www.weismanchildrens.com
Control: Corporation, Investor–owned, for–profit **Service:** Children's rehabilitation

Staffed Beds: 24

MONTCLAIR—Essex County

⊞ **HACKENSACK UNIVERSITY MEDICAL CENTER MOUNTAINSIDE (310054)**, 1 Bay Avenue, Zip 07042–4898; tel. 973/429–6000 **A**1 2 3 5 6 9 10 **F**3 8 12 13 14 15 18 20 22 26 28 29 30 31 34 35 38 39 40 42 43 44 45 46 48 49 50 51 52 53 54 55 56 57 59 60 66 67 68 70 73 74 75 76 77 78 79 81 82 84 85 86 87 91 93 94 97 98 102 103 104 105 107 108 109 110 111 114 115 116 117 118 119 120 121 123 124 126 128 129 130 131 132 134 135 144 145 146 147 148 **P**5 **S** LHP Hospital Group, Plano, TX
Primary Contact: John A. Fromhold, Chief Executive Officer
CFO: Anthony M. Esposito, Jr., CPA, Vice President Chief Financial Officer
CMO: Theresa Soroko, M.D., Chief Medical Officer
CIO: Robert Gates, Director Information Technology
CHR: Fran Corridon, Vice President Human Resources and Shared Services
CNO: Bonnie Michaels, R.N., Vice President and Chief Nursing Officer
Web address: www.mountainsidenow.com
Control: Partnership, Investor–owned, for–profit **Service:** General Medical and Surgical

Staffed Beds: 228 **Admissions:** 10484 **Census:** 142 **Outpatient Visits:** 103870 **Births:** 1332 **Total Expense ($000):** 195842 **Payroll Expense ($000):** 86956 **Personnel:** 1345

MORRIS PLAINS—Morris County

□ **GREYSTONE PARK PSYCHIATRIC HOSPITAL (314016)**, 59 Koch Avenue, Zip 07950–4400; tel. 973/538–1800, (Nonreporting) **A**1 10 **S** Division of Mental Health and Addiction Services, Department of Human Services, State of New Jersey, Trenton, NJ
Primary Contact: Janet J. Monroe, R.N., Chief Executive Officer
COO: Ross Friedman, Chief Operating Officer
CFO: Jack Frey, Acting Business Manager
CMO: Cherry Monroy–Miller, M.D., Acting Medical Director
CIO: David Saleem, Director Information Technology
CHR: James Frey, Jr., Acting Manager Human Resources
CNO: Doreen Sperber–Weiss, Ph.D., Chief Nursing Officer
Web address: www.state.nj.us/humanservices/dmhs/oshm/gpph/
Control: State–Government, nonfederal **Service:** Psychiatric

Staffed Beds: 557

MORRISTOWN—Morris County

⊞ **MORRISTOWN MEDICAL CENTER (310015)**, 100 Madison Avenue, Zip 07960–6136; tel. 973/971–5000, (Includes REHABILITATION INSTITUTE AT THE MOUNT KEMBLE DIVISION ; GORYEB CHILDREN'S HOSPITAL, 100 Madison Avenue, tel. 800/247–9580), (Total facility includes 40 beds in nursing home–type unit) **A**1 2 3 5 8 9 10 **F**3 5 6 7 8 9 11 12 13 14 15 17 18 19 20 22 24 26 28 29 30 31 32 33 34 35 36 37 38 39 40 41 43 44 45 46 47 48 49 50 51 52 53 54 55 56 57 58 59 60 61 62 63 64 65 66 68 69 70 71 72 73 74 75 76 77 78 79 81 82 83 84 85 86 87 88 89 90 91 92 93 94 95 96 97 98 99 100 101 102 103 104 105 107 108 110 111 114 115 116 117 118 119 120 121 123 126 128 129 130 131 132 134 135 141 143 144 145 146 147 148 **P**2 3 5 6 **S** Atlantic Health System, Morristown, NJ
Primary Contact: David J. Shulkin, M.D., President
COO: Deborah Visconi, Director, Hospital Operations
CFO: Kevin Lenahan, Vice President Finance and Chief Financial Officer
CMO: Jan Schwarz–Miller, M.D., Vice President Quality and Chief Medical Officer
CIO: Linda Reed, Vice President and Chief Information Officer
CHR: Andrew L. Kovach, Vice President Human Resources and Chief Administrative Officer
CNO: Trish O'Keefe, R.N., Chief Nursing Officer and Chief Experience Officer
Web address: www.atlantichealth.org/Morristown/
Control: Other not–for–profit (including NFP Corporation) **Service:** General Medical and Surgical

Staffed Beds: 662 **Admissions:** 35884 **Census:** 530 **Outpatient Visits:** 379326 **Births:** 4254 **Total Expense ($000):** 901065 **Payroll Expense ($000):** 391327 **Personnel:** 5239

NJ

MOUNT HOLLY—Burlington County

✠ **VIRTUA MEMORIAL (310057)**, 175 Madison Avenue, Zip 08060–2099; tel. 609/267–0700 **A**1 3 5 9 10 **F**3 11 12 13 15 18 20 22 28 29 30 31 40 41 45 46 48 49 56 60 70 73 74 75 76 77 78 79 81 85 86 87 89 92 93 98 102 105 107 108 110 111 114 115 118 119 120 121 123 126 129 130 143 146 147 **S** Virtua Health, Marlton, NJ
Primary Contact: Matthew Zuino, Vice President
CFO: Robert Segin, Chief Financial Officer
CMO: James P. Dwyer, D.O., Executive Vice President and Chief Medical Officer
CHR: E. D. Dunn, Vice President Human Resources
Web address: www.virtua.org
Control: Other not–for–profit (including NFP Corporation) **Service:** General Medical and Surgical

Staffed Beds: 333 **Admissions:** 17791 **Census:** 231 **Outpatient Visits:** 182998 **Births:** 2415 **Total Expense ($000):** 280950 **Payroll Expense ($000):** 90539 **Personnel:** 1262

VIRTUA MEMORIAL HOSPITAL BURLINGTON COUNTY See Virtua Memorial

NEPTUNE—Monmouth County

✠ **JERSEY SHORE UNIVERSITY MEDICAL CENTER (310073)**, 1945 Route 33, Zip 07754–0397; tel. 732/775–5500, (Includes K. HOVNANIAN CHILDREN'S HOSPITAL, 1945 State Route 33, Zip 07753–4859; tel. 800/560–9990) **A**1 2 3 5 8 9 10 13 **F**3 5 11 12 13 17 18 19 20 22 24 26 28 29 30 31 32 34 35 36 38 39 40 41 43 44 45 46 47 48 49 50 52 54 55 56 57 58 59 60 61 63 64 66 68 70 71 72 73 74 75 76 77 78 79 80 81 82 84 85 86 87 88 89 91 92 93 94 96 97 98 99 100 101 102 103 104 105 107 108 111 114 115 116 117 118 119 120 121 123 126 129 130 131 132 134 135 145 146 147 148 **S** Meridian Health, Neptune, NJ
Primary Contact: Steven G. Littleson, FACHE, President
COO: Robert H. Adams, Vice President Operations
CFO: John Gantner, Executive Vice President Finance and Partner Company Operations
CMO: David Kountz, M.D., Senior Vice President Medical Affairs
CIO: Rebecca Weber, Senior Vice President and Chief Information Officer
Web address: www.meridianhealth.com
Control: Other not–for–profit (including NFP Corporation) **Service:** General Medical and Surgical

Staffed Beds: 519 **Admissions:** 25856 **Census:** 379 **Outpatient Visits:** 213646 **Births:** 1985 **Total Expense ($000):** 555867 **Payroll Expense ($000):** 218447 **Personnel:** 2832

NEW BRUNSWICK—Middlesex County

☐ **CHILDREN'S SPECIALIZED HOSPITAL–PSE&G (313300)**, 200 Somerset Street, Zip 08901–1942; tel. 732/258–7000, (Includes CHILDREN'S SPECIALIZED HOSPITAL, 150 New Providence Road, Mountainside, Zip 07092–2590; tel. 908/233–3720), (Total facility includes 68 beds in nursing home–type unit) **A**1 3 5 10 **F**29 32 35 54 64 65 74 75 77 79 90 91 93 94 97 99 104 130 146 **S** Robert Wood Johnson Health System & Network, New Brunswick, NJ
Primary Contact: Amy B. Mansue, President and Chief Executive Officer
COO: Warren E. Moore, Executive Vice President and Chief Operating Officer
CFO: Joseph J. Dobosh, Jr., Vice President and Chief Financial Officer
CMO: Frank V. Castello, M.D., Medical Director
CIO: Pat DeMartino, Chief Information Officer
CHR: William Dwyer, Vice President Human Resources
Web address: www.childrens–specialized.org
Control: Other not–for–profit (including NFP Corporation) **Service:** Children's rehabilitation

Staffed Beds: 128 **Admissions:** 517 **Census:** 122 **Outpatient Visits:** 534655 **Births:** 0 **Total Expense ($000):** 114009 **Payroll Expense ($000):** 65375 **Personnel:** 901

✠ **ROBERT WOOD JOHNSON UNIVERSITY HOSPITAL (310038)**, 1 Robert Wood Johnson Place, Zip 08901–1928; tel. 732/828–3000, (Includes BRISTOL–MYERS SQUIBB CHILDREN'S HOSPITAL, One Robert Wood Johnson Place, Zip 08901, Mailing Address: P.O. Box 2601, Zip 08903–2601; tel. 732/828–3000) **A**1 2 3 5 8 9 10 **F**3 6 7 8 9 11 12 13 14 15 17 18 19 20 22 24 26 28 29 30 31 32 34 35 36 37 38 39 40 41 43 44 45 46 47 48 49 50 51 52 53 54 55 56 57 58 59 60 61 62 63 64 65 66 68 70 71 72 73 74 75 76 77 78 79 81 82 83 84 85 86 87 88 89 91 92 93 94 96 97 99 100 102 104 107 108 109 110 111 112 113 114 115 116 117 118 119 120 121 123 124 126 129 130 131 132 134 135 136 137 138 141 142 143 146 147 148 **P**3 6 7 **S** Robert Wood Johnson Health System & Network, New Brunswick, NJ
Primary Contact: Stephen K. Jones, President and Chief Executive Officer
COO: Michael A. Antoniades, Executive Vice President and Chief Operating Officer
CFO: Brian M. Reilly, Chief Financial Officer
CMO: Joshua M. Bershad, M.D., Senior Vice President Medical Affairs and Chief Medical Officer
CIO: Robert G. Irwin, Vice President Information Systems
CHR: Martin S. Everhart, Senior Vice President Human Resources
CNO: Lori Colineri, MSN, Senior Vice President Nursing and Chief Nursing Officer
Web address: www.rwjuh.edu
Control: Other not–for–profit (including NFP Corporation) **Service:** General Medical and Surgical

Staffed Beds: 610 **Admissions:** 32204 **Census:** 514 **Outpatient Visits:** 274306 **Births:** 2254 **Total Expense ($000):** 812364 **Payroll Expense ($000):** 307648 **Personnel:** 4030

✠ **SAINT PETER'S UNIVERSITY HOSPITAL (310070)**, 254 Easton Avenue, Zip 08901–1780; tel. 732/745–8600, (Includes THE CHILDREN'S HOSPITAL AT SAINT PETER'S UNIVERSITY, 254 Easton Avenue, Zip 08901–1766; tel. 732/565–5437) **A**1 2 3 5 8 9 10 **F**2 3 11 12 13 15 17 18 19 20 21 22 26 27 28 29 30 31 32 34 35 37 38 39 40 41 44 45 46 49 50 51 54 55 56 57 58 59 60 61 64 65 66 68 70 71 72 73 74 75 76 77 78 79 81 82 83 84 85 86 87 88 89 91 92 93 94 95 96 97 100 102 105 107 108 110 111 113 114 115 118 119 120 121 123 126 129 130 131 132 135 143 144 145 146 147 148 **P**3 6
Primary Contact: Ronald C. Rak, JD, Chief Executive Officer
COO: Kenneth N. Sable, M.D., Executive Vice President and Chief Operating Officer
CFO: Garrick J. Stoldt, Vice President and Chief Financial Officer
CMO: Anthony Passannante, Jr., M.D., Vice President, Chief Medical Officer and Co–Chief Quality Officer
CIO: Frank DiSanzo, Vice President and Chief Information Officer and Chief Strategy Officer
CHR: Susan Ballestero, Vice President and Chief Human Resources Officer
CNO: Elizabeth Wise, R.N., Chief Nursing Officer and Vice President, Patient Care Services
Web address: www.saintpetersuh.com
Control: Church–operated, Nongovernment, not–for profit **Service:** General Medical and Surgical

Staffed Beds: 374 **Admissions:** 19277 **Census:** 240 **Outpatient Visits:** 370055 **Births:** 5618 **Total Expense ($000):** 405817 **Payroll Expense ($000):** 194185 **Personnel:** 2650

NEWARK—Essex County

◇ **COLUMBUS HOSPITAL LTACH (312024)**, 495 North Thirteenth Street, Zip 07107–1317; tel. 973/587–7777, (Nonreporting) **A**10 21
Primary Contact: Matthew Hamilton, President and Chief Executive Officer
Web address: www.columbusltach.org
Control: Corporation, Investor–owned, for–profit **Service:** Long–Term Acute Care hospital

Staffed Beds: 66

✠ **NEWARK BETH ISRAEL MEDICAL CENTER (310002)**, 201 Lyons Avenue, Zip 07112–2027; tel. 973/926–7000, (Includes CHILDREN'S HOSPITAL OF NEW JERSEY, 201 Lyons Avenue, tel. 973/926–7000) **A**1 2 3 5 8 9 10 12 13 **F**2 3 12 15 17 18 19 20 21 22 23 24 25 26 27 28 29 30 31 32 34 35 38 39 40 41 44 46 47 48 49 50 55 56 57 58 59 60 61 64 68 70 71 72 73 74 75 76 77 78 79 81 82 84 85 86 87 88 89 92 93 97 98 99 100 101 102 104 105 107 108 110 111 114 115 117 119 120 121 126 129 130 131 132 135 137 138 140 141 142 143 146 147 148 **P**8 **S** Barnabas Health, West Orange, NJ
Primary Contact: John A. Brennan, M.D., M.P.H., President and Chief Executive Officer
COO: Darrell K. Terry, Sr., Senior Vice President Operations
CFO: Douglas A. Zehner, Chief Financial Officer
CHR: Zach Lipner, Vice President Human Resources
Web address: www.barnabashealth.org/hospitals/newark_beth_israel/index.html
Control: Other not–for–profit (including NFP Corporation) **Service:** General Medical and Surgical

Staffed Beds: 362 **Admissions:** 20591 **Census:** 365 **Outpatient Visits:** 295542 **Births:** 3298 **Total Expense ($000):** 513513 **Payroll Expense ($000):** 252949 **Personnel:** 3117

NJ

Hospital, Medicare Provider Number, Address, Telephone, Approval, Facility, and Physician Codes, Health Care System

★ American Hospital Association (AHA) membership
☐ The Joint Commission accreditation
◇ DNV Healthcare Inc. accreditation
○ Healthcare Facilities Accreditation Program
△ Commission on Accreditation of Rehabilitation Facilities (CARF) accreditation

⊠ **SAINT MICHAEL'S MEDICAL CENTER (310096)**, 111 Central Avenue, Zip 07102–1909; tel. 973/877–5350 **A**1 2 3 5 9 10 **F**3 5 12 15 17 18 20 22 24 26 29 30 31 34 35 37 38 40 45 47 48 49 50 57 58 59 61 64 66 68 70 71 74 75 77 78 79 81 82 85 87 91 92 97 98 100 107 108 110 111 114 115 119 121 126 130 132 143 146 147 148 **S** Catholic Health East / Trinity Health, Livonia, MI
Primary Contact: David A. Ricci, President and Chief Executive Officer
COO: Dennis Pettigrew, Chief Operating Officer
CFO: Dennis Pettigrew, Chief Financial Officer
CMO: Joseph DePasquale, M.D., Interim Chief Medical Officer
CIO: Tom Addington, Chief Information Officer
CHR: Dennis Sparks, Vice President Human Resources
CNO: Johanna Magner, Interim Chief Nursing Officer
Web address: www.smmcnj.org
Control: Church–operated, Nongovernment, not–for profit **Service:** General Medical and Surgical

Staffed Beds: 147 **Admissions:** 8433 **Census:** 114 **Outpatient Visits:** 101403 **Births:** 0 **Total Expense ($000):** 208238 **Payroll Expense ($000):** 76353 **Personnel:** 1107

⊠ **UNIVERSITY HOSPITAL (310119)**, 150 Bergen Street, Zip 07103–2496; tel. 973/972–4300 **A**1 2 3 5 8 9 10 **F**1 3 4 7 8 11 15 16 17 18 20 22 24 26 28 29 31 32 34 35 37 38 39 40 41 43 44 45 46 47 48 49 50 54 55 57 58 59 60 61 64 65 66 67 68 70 71 72 73 74 75 76 77 78 79 80 81 82 84 85 86 87 88 89 90 92 93 96 97 98 100 102 107 108 110 111 114 118 119 120 121 123 124 126 128 130 131 132 134 135 139 141 142 145 146 147 148
Primary Contact: James R. Gonzalez, President and Chief Executive Officer
CFO: Thomas M. Daly, Chief Financial Officer
CMO: Suzanne Atkin, M.D., Chief of Staff and Associate Dean Clinical Affairs
CIO: Richard Tunnell, Director Information Systems Technology and Health Management Information Systems
CHR: Gerard Garcia, Acting Vice President Human Resources
Web address: www.uhnj.org
Control: State–Government, nonfederal **Service:** General Medical and Surgical

Staffed Beds: 300 **Admissions:** 14898 **Census:** 234 **Outpatient Visits:** 264148 **Births:** 1466 **Total Expense ($000):** 598689 **Payroll Expense ($000):** 269689 **Personnel:** 3277

NEWTON—Sussex County

⊠ **NEWTON MEDICAL CENTER (310028)**, 175 High Street, Zip 07860–1004; tel. 973/383–2121 **A**1 2 9 10 **F**3 5 6 8 9 11 12 13 14 15 18 19 20 26 28 29 30 31 32 33 34 35 37 38 39 40 41 44 45 46 47 48 49 50 53 54 55 56 57 58 59 60 61 62 64 65 66 68 69 70 71 73 74 75 76 77 78 79 81 82 83 84 85 86 87 89 91 92 93 94 95 96 97 98 99 100 101 102 103 104 105 106 107 108 110 111 114 118 119 126 129 130 131 132 134 135 143 144 145 146 147 148 **P**6 **S** Atlantic Health System, Morristown, NJ
Primary Contact: Joseph DiPaolo, President
CFO: Kevin Lenahan, Director Corporate Accounting, Budgets, Grants and Reimbursements
CMO: David Lazarus, M.D., Medical Director Clinical Affairs
CIO: Linda Reed, Vice President Information Systems and Chief Information Officer
CHR: Andrew L. Kovach, Vice President Human Resources and Chief Administrative Officer
Web address: www.atlantichealth.org/newton/
Control: Other not–for–profit (including NFP Corporation) **Service:** General Medical and Surgical

Staffed Beds: 148 **Admissions:** 7711 **Census:** 101 **Outpatient Visits:** 99094 **Births:** 466 **Total Expense ($000):** 137228 **Payroll Expense ($000):** 67917 **Personnel:** 1005

NORTH BERGEN—Hudson County

⊠ **PALISADES MEDICAL CENTER (310003)**, 7600 River Road, Zip 07047–6217; tel. 201/854–5000 **A**1 3 5 10 **F**3 7 8 11 12 13 15 30 34 35 38 40 43 45 49 56 57 59 68 70 73 74 75 76 77 78 79 81 82 84 85 86 87 89 93 102 104 107 110 111 114 115 119 129 130 132 143 146 147 148
Primary Contact: Bruce J. Markowitz, President and Chief Executive Officer
COO: David J. Berkowitz, Vice President and Chief Operating Officer
CFO: John Calandriello, Vice President and Chief Financial Officer
CMO: Suresh Raina, M.D., Vice President Medical Staff and Chief Medical Officer
CIO: Albert Porco, Director Management Information Systems
CHR: Donna Cahill, Vice President Human Resources
CNO: Ruben D. Fernandez, R.N., Vice President and Chief Nursing Officer
Web address: www.palisadesmedical.org
Control: Other not–for–profit (including NFP Corporation) **Service:** General Medical and Surgical

Staffed Beds: 206 **Admissions:** 9985 **Census:** 123 **Outpatient Visits:** 88152 **Births:** 1555 **Total Expense ($000):** 146866 **Payroll Expense ($000):** 65751 **Personnel:** 845

OLD BRIDGE—Middlesex County

OLD BRIDGE DIVISION See Raritan Bay Medical Center, Perth Amboy

PARAMUS—Bergen County

☐ **BERGEN REGIONAL MEDICAL CENTER (310058)**, 230 East Ridgewood Avenue, Zip 07652–4142; tel. 201/967–4000, (Nonreporting) **A**1 10
Primary Contact: Joseph S. Orlando, President
COO: Susan Mendelowitz, Executive Vice President and Chief Operating Officer
CFO: Connie Magdangal, Executive Vice President and Chief Financial Officer
CMO: Robert M. Harris, M.D., President Medical and Dental Staff
CIO: Ronald Li, Vice President Management Information Systems
CHR: Guy Mennonna, Senior Vice President Human Resources
Web address: www.bergenregional.com
Control: County–Government, nonfederal **Service:** Psychiatric

Staffed Beds: 432

PASSAIC—Passaic County

⊠ **ST. MARY'S HOSPITAL (310006)**, 350 Boulevard, Zip 07055–2840; tel. 973/365–4300, (Nonreporting) **A**1 9 10
Primary Contact: Edward Condit, President and Chief Executive Officer
CFO: Nicholas Lanza, Controller
CMO: Ronald Poblete, M.D., President Medical and Dental Staff
CHR: Cathy Lynch–Kilic, Vice President Human Resources
Web address: www.smh–passaic.org
Control: Other not–for–profit (including NFP Corporation) **Service:** General Medical and Surgical

Staffed Beds: 221

PATERSON—Passaic County

★ ◇ **ST. JOSEPH'S REGIONAL MEDICAL CENTER (310019)**, 703 Main Street, Zip 07503–2691; tel. 973/754–2000, (Includes ST. JOSEPH'S CHILDREN'S HOSPITAL, 703 Main Street, Zip 07503–2621; tel. 973/754–2500; ST. JOSEPH'S WAYNE HOSPITAL, 224 Hamburg Turnpike, Wayne, Zip 07470–2100; tel. 973/942–6900; Daniel B. Kline, Administrator), (Total facility includes 151 beds in nursing home–type unit) **A**2 3 5 9 10 12 13 21 **F**3 5 7 8 11 12 13 14 15 17 18 19 20 21 22 24 26 27 28 29 30 31 32 34 35 37 38 39 40 41 43 44 45 46 47 48 49 50 54 55 56 57 58 59 60 61 62 63 64 65 66 68 70 71 72 73 74 75 76 77 78 79 81 82 83 84 85 86 87 88 89 90 92 93 94 96 97 98 99 100 101 102 103 104 105 107 108 109 110 111 112 114 115 116 117 118 119 120 121 123 126 129 130 131 132 133 134 135 143 144 145 146 147 148 **P**3 5 6
Primary Contact: William A. McDonald, President and Chief Executive Officer
COO: Jeff Joyner, Vice President of Operations
CFO: Jack Robinson, Chief Financial Officer
CMO: James Labagnara, M.D., Vice President Medical Affairs
CIO: Jane Wu, Chief Information Officer
CHR: John Bruno, Vice President Human Resources
CNO: Maria Brennan, R.N., Vice President and Chief Nursing Officer
Web address: www.stjosephshealth.org
Control: Church–operated, Nongovernment, not–for profit **Service:** General Medical and Surgical

Staffed Beds: 700 **Admissions:** 33028 **Census:** 500 **Outpatient Visits:** 409013 **Births:** 3347 **Total Expense ($000):** 699973 **Payroll Expense ($000):** 324136 **Personnel:** 3981

PEAPACK—Somerset County

☐ **MATHENY MEDICAL AND EDUCATIONAL CENTER (312014)**, (special hospital/med. complex/dd), 65 Highland Avenue, Zip 07977, Mailing Address: P.O. Box 339, Zip 07977–0339; tel. 908/234–0011 **A**1 5 10 **F**2 29 35 39 64 82 86 87 93 100 130 146 147 148 **P**6
Primary Contact: Steven M. Proctor, President
COO: Christopher King, Director Operations and Administrative Services
CFO: Wayne Guberman, Director Finance
CMO: Gary E. Eddey, M.D., Medical Director
CIO: Ron Daniel, Manager Information Systems
CHR: Nancy Petrillo, Director Human Resources
Web address: www.matheny.org
Control: Other not–for–profit (including NFP Corporation) **Service:** Other specialty

Staffed Beds: 102 **Admissions:** 6 **Census:** 100 **Outpatient Visits:** 2028 **Births:** 0 **Total Expense ($000):** 50470 **Payroll Expense ($000):** 29300 **Personnel:** 453

NJ

Many Facility Codes have changed. Please refer to the AHA Guide Code Chart. © 2014 AHA Guide

PENNINGTON—Mercer County

⌧ **CAPITAL HEALTH MEDICAL CENTER–HOPEWELL (310044)**, 1 Capital Way, Zip 08534–2520; tel. 609/303–4000 **A**1 2 5 6 9 10 **F**3 7 8 11 12 13 15 18 19 20 22 29 30 31 32 34 35 36 39 40 41 44 45 46 47 48 49 50 51 52 54 55 57 58 59 60 64 65 66 68 69 70 73 74 75 76 78 79 81 82 84 85 86 87 89 90 94 96 97 107 108 109 110 111 114 115 117 118 119 120 121 123 124 126 129 130 132 135 143 144 145 146 147 148 **S** Capital Health, Trenton, NJ
Primary Contact: Al Maghazehe, Ph.D., FACHE, Chief Executive Officer
COO: Larry DiSanto, Executive Vice President and Chief Operating Officer
CFO: Shane Fleming, Chief Financial Officer
CMO: Robert Remstein, D.O., Vice President Medical Affairs
CIO: Eugene Grochala, Vice President Information Systems
CHR: J. Scott Clemmensen, Vice President Human Resources and Leadership Enhancement
CNO: Eileen M. Horton, Vice President Patient Services and Chief Nursing Officer
Web address: www.capitalhealth.org
Control: Other not–for–profit (including NFP Corporation) **Service:** General Medical and Surgical

Staffed Beds: 223 **Admissions:** 14694 **Census:** 145 **Outpatient Visits:** 119070 **Births:** 2570 **Personnel:** 1358

PERTH AMBOY—Middlesex County

☐ **CARE ONE AT RARITAN BAY MEDICAL CENTER (312018)**, 530 New Brunswick Avenue, Zip 08861–3654; tel. 732/324–6090, (Nonreporting) **A**1 10
Primary Contact: Sharon Bready, R.N., Chief Executive Officer
CFO: Richard Burguillos, Chief Financial Officer
Web address: www.care–one.com
Control: Corporation, Investor–owned, for–profit **Service:** Long–Term Acute Care hospital

Staffed Beds: 30

⌧ **RARITAN BAY MEDICAL CENTER (310039)**, 530 New Brunswick Avenue, Zip 08861–3654; tel. 732/442–3700, (Includes OLD BRIDGE DIVISION, One Hospital Plaza, Old Bridge, Zip 08857; tel. 732/360–1000; PERTH AMBOY DIVISION, 530 New Brunswick Avenue, Zip 08861–3685; tel. 732/442–3700) **A**1 3 5 9 10 **F**5 7 9 11 12 13 15 18 20 22 26 29 30 31 34 35 36 38 39 40 45 46 49 50 51 54 56 57 59 60 61 64 65 66 68 70 74 75 76 77 78 79 81 82 87 89 92 93 94 97 98 100 101 102 103 104 107 108 110 111 114 115 117 119 129 130 132 143 146 147 148 **P**6
Primary Contact: Michael R. D'Agnes, FACHE, President and Chief Executive Officer
COO: Vincent Costantino, Vice President Operations and Human Resources
CFO: Thomas Shanahan, Chief Financial Officer and Senior Vice President
CMO: Michael Ciencewicki, M.D., Vice President Medical Affairs
CHR: Vincent Costantino, Vice President Operations and Human Resources
Web address: www.rbmc.org
Control: Other not–for–profit (including NFP Corporation) **Service:** General Medical and Surgical

Staffed Beds: 277 **Admissions:** 12923 **Census:** 176 **Outpatient Visits:** 142975 **Births:** 1207 **Total Expense ($000):** 228037 **Payroll Expense ($000):** 103091 **Personnel:** 1705

PHILLIPSBURG—Warren County

☐ **ST. LUKE'S HOSPITAL – WARREN CAMPUS (310060)**, 185 Roseberry Street, Zip 08865–1690; tel. 908/859–6700 **A**1 2 3 5 9 10 13 **F**2 3 8 11 15 18 20 28 29 30 31 34 35 39 40 45 48 49 53 56 59 61 64 65 66 68 70 74 75 77 78 79 81 82 85 86 87 91 92 93 97 98 100 102 103 104 106 107 108 110 111 114 118 119 124 129 130 131 132 134 146 147 148 **S** St. Luke's University Health Network, Bethlehem, PA
Primary Contact: Scott R. Wolfe, CPA, President
COO: Alice Wilson, FACHE, Vice President Administration
CMO: Edward Gilkey, M.D., Vice President Medical Affairs
CHR: Morgan G. Mahl, Director Human Resources
CNO: Gail Newton, R.N., Vice President Patient Care Services
Web address: www.slhn.org
Control: Other not–for–profit (including NFP Corporation) **Service:** General Medical and Surgical

Staffed Beds: 140 **Admissions:** 4545 **Census:** 63 **Outpatient Visits:** 118113 **Births:** 0 **Total Expense ($000):** 109015 **Payroll Expense ($000):** 45211 **Personnel:** 679

PISCATAWAY—Middlesex County

UNIVERSITY HOSPITAL (314011), 671 Hoes Lane, Zip 08854–8021; tel. 732/235–5900 **A**3 5 9 10 **F**87 98 99 101 102 103 104 105 106 **P**6
Primary Contact: Christopher O. Kosseff, President and Chief Executive Officer
COO: Rosemarie Rosati, Chief Operating Officer
CFO: Alan Weinkrantz, Chief Financial Officer, Finance
CMO: Theresa Miskimen, M.D., Vice President Medical Services
CIO: Adam Levinson, Associate Director, Information Services
CNO: Michele A. Miller, R.N., Vice President, Acute and Nursing Services
Web address: www.ubhc.rutgers.edu
Control: State–Government, nonfederal **Service:** Psychiatric

Staffed Beds: 48 **Admissions:** 1039 **Census:** 36 **Outpatient Visits:** 72994 **Births:** 0 **Total Expense ($000):** 202883 **Payroll Expense ($000):** 109213 **Personnel:** 114

PLAINSBORO—Middlesex County

UNIVERSITY MEDICAL CENTER AT PRINCETON See University Medical Center of Princeton at Plainsboro

⌧ **UNIVERSITY MEDICAL CENTER OF PRINCETON AT PLAINSBORO (310010)**, One Plainsboro Road, Zip 08536–1913; tel. 609/853–7100, (Includes ACUTE GENERAL HOSPITAL, MERWICK UNIT–EXTENDED CARE AND REHABILITATION, PRINCETON HOUSE UNIT–COMMUNITY MENTAL HEALTH AND SUBSTANCE ABUSE) **A**1 2 3 5 9 10 **F**3 4 5 8 11 12 13 14 15 18 19 20 22 26 28 29 30 31 32 34 35 36 38 39 40 41 45 46 47 48 49 50 51 53 54 55 56 57 58 59 60 62 63 64 65 66 68 70 73 74 75 76 77 78 79 81 82 84 85 86 87 89 90 91 92 93 96 97 98 99 100 101 102 103 104 105 107 108 110 111 114 115 116 117 118 119 120 121 123 124 126 129 130 131 132 134 135 143 145 146 147 148 **P**6
Primary Contact: Barry S. Rabner, President and Chief Executive Officer
CFO: Bruce Traub, Chief Financial Officer
CIO: Anne Searle, Chief Information Officer
CHR: Marcia M. Telthorster, Vice President Human Resources
Web address: www.princetonhcs.org
Control: Other not–for–profit (including NFP Corporation) **Service:** General Medical and Surgical

Staffed Beds: 369 **Admissions:** 17019 **Census:** 241 **Outpatient Visits:** 714057 **Births:** 2009 **Total Expense ($000):** 371953 **Payroll Expense ($000):** 135166 **Personnel:** 2601

POMONA—Atlantic County

ATLANTICARE REGIONAL MEDICAL CENTER–MAINLAND DIVISION See AtlantiCare Regional Medical Center, Atlantic City

⌧ △ **BACHARACH INSTITUTE FOR REHABILITATION (313030)**, 61 West Jimmie Leeds Road, Zip 08240–9102, Mailing Address: P.O. Box 723, Zip 08240–0723; tel. 609/652–7000, (Nonreporting) **A**1 7 10
Primary Contact: Richard J. Kathrins, Ph.D, President and Chief Executive Officer
CFO: Jeanne Vuksta, Chief Financial Officer
CMO: Craig Anmuth, M.D., Medical Director
CIO: Jeff Rees, Director Information Systems
CHR: Diane Croshaw, Vice President Human Resources
Web address: www.bacharach.org
Control: Other not–for–profit (including NFP Corporation) **Service:** Rehabilitation

Staffed Beds: 80

POMPTON PLAINS—Morris County

⌧ **CHILTON MEDICAL CENTER (310017)**, 97 West Parkway, Zip 07444–1696; tel. 973/831–5000 **A**1 2 9 10 **F**3 7 11 12 13 15 17 18 19 20 22 28 29 30 31 32 34 35 38 40 41 44 45 47 49 50 54 57 59 64 65 66 70 73 74 75 76 77 78 79 81 82 85 86 87 89 93 97 102 107 108 109 110 111 114 115 118 119 121 123 126 129 130 131 132 135 146 147 148 **P**6 **S** Atlantic Health System, Morristown, NJ
Primary Contact: Deborah Zastocki, R.N., FACHE, FACHE, President and Chief Executive Officer
COO: Thomas Scott, Chief Operating Officer
CFO: Michael Richetti, Chief Financial Officer
CMO: Charles Ross, M.D., Vice President Medical Affairs
CIO: Karen S. Smith, Director Information Services
CHR: Julia McGovern, Vice President Human Resources
Web address: www.chiltonmemorial.org
Control: Other not–for–profit (including NFP Corporation) **Service:** General Medical and Surgical

Staffed Beds: 260 **Admissions:** 9706 **Census:** 130 **Outpatient Visits:** 157529 **Births:** 861 **Total Expense ($000):** 170362 **Payroll Expense ($000):** 76213 **Personnel:** 994

NJ

Hospital, Medicare Provider Number, Address, Telephone, Approval, Facility, and Physician Codes, Health Care System

★ American Hospital Association (AHA) membership
☐ The Joint Commission accreditation
◇ DNV Healthcare Inc. accreditation
○ Healthcare Facilities Accreditation Program
△ Commission on Accreditation of Rehabilitation Facilities (CARF) accreditation

RAHWAY—Union County

KINDRED HOSPITAL NEW JERSEY – RAHWAY See Kindred Hospital–New Jersey Morris County, Dover

✠ **ROBERT WOOD JOHNSON UNIVERSITY HOSPITAL RAHWAY (310024)**, 865 Stone Street, Zip 07065–2797; tel. 732/381–4200, (Total facility includes 24 beds in nursing home–type unit) **A**1 10 **F**3 11 15 17 20 29 30 31 34 35 38 40 46 47 49 50 53 56 57 59 64 65 68 70 74 75 77 78 79 81 82 86 87 93 97 100 101 102 107 108 111 117 118 119 128 129 130 132 134 143 144 146 147 148 **S** Robert Wood Johnson Health System & Network, New Brunswick, NJ
Primary Contact: Kirk C. Tice, President and Chief Executive Officer
CFO: Peter Bihuniak, Vice President Finance
CMO: Radha Vinnakota, M.D., President Medical Staff
CIO: Denine Izzi, Site Manager Information Systems
CHR: Kathryn Tarantino, Vice President Administration
CNO: Lynn Kearney, VP Patient Services & Chief Nursing Officer
Web address: www.rwjuhr.com
Control: Other not–for–profit (including NFP Corporation) **Service:** General Medical and Surgical

Staffed Beds: 147 **Admissions:** 6158 **Census:** 94 **Outpatient Visits:** 53337 **Births:** 0 **Total Expense ($000):** 97071 **Payroll Expense ($000):** 41771 **Personnel:** 716

RED BANK—Monmouth County

✠ △ **RIVERVIEW MEDICAL CENTER (310034)**, 1 Riverview Plaza, Zip 07701–1864; tel. 732/741–2700 **A**1 2 7 9 10 **F**3 5 11 13 15 18 20 22 28 29 30 31 32 34 35 36 37 38 39 40 41 43 44 45 46 49 50 51 54 55 56 57 59 60 61 63 64 65 66 68 70 71 73 74 75 76 77 78 79 80 81 82 84 85 86 87 90 91 92 93 94 96 97 98 99 100 101 102 103 104 105 107 108 110 111 114 115 116 117 118 119 120 121 123 124 126 129 130 131 132 134 135 146 147 148 **S** Meridian Health, Neptune, NJ
Primary Contact: Timothy J. Hogan, FACHE, Regional President
COO: Kelly O'Brien, Chief Operating Officer
CFO: Joseph Lemaire, Executive Vice President Finance
CMO: Joseph Reichman, M.D., Vice President Medical Affairs and Clinical Effectiveness
CIO: Rebecca Weber, Senior Vice President Information Technology
CHR: Sherrie String, Senior Vice President Human Resources
CNO: Kathy McKean, M.P.H., Vice President, Chief Nursing Executive
Web address: www.riverviewmedicalcenter.com
Control: Other not–for–profit (including NFP Corporation) **Service:** General Medical and Surgical

Staffed Beds: 275 **Admissions:** 12441 **Census:** 183 **Outpatient Visits:** 142230 **Births:** 1392 **Total Expense ($000):** 224456 **Payroll Expense ($000):** 95976 **Personnel:** 1262

RIDGEWOOD—Bergen County

✠ **VALLEY HOSPITAL (310012)**, 223 North Van Dien Avenue, Zip 07450–2726; tel. 201/447–8000 **A**1 2 5 9 10 **F**3 11 15 17 18 19 20 22 24 26 28 29 30 31 32 34 35 36 37 38 40 41 45 46 47 48 49 50 51 52 53 54 55 56 57 58 59 60 61 64 65 66 68 69 70 72 73 74 75 76 77 78 79 80 81 82 84 85 86 87 88 89 91 92 93 94 96 97 100 101 102 103 107 108 109 110 111 112 114 115 116 118 119 120 121 123 124 126 129 130 131 132 134 135 143 145 146 147 148 **P**6
Primary Contact: Audrey Meyers, FACHE, President and Chief Executive Officer
COO: Peter Diestel, Senior Vice President and Chief Operating Officer
CFO: Richard Keenan, Senior Vice President Finance and Chief Financial Officer
CMO: Mitchell Rubinstein, M.D., Vice President Medical Affairs
CIO: Eric R. Carey, Vice President Information Systems and Chief Information Officer
CNO: Ann Marie Leichman, R.N., Vice President Patient Care Services and Chief Nursing Officer
Web address: www.valleyhealth.com
Control: Other not–for–profit (including NFP Corporation) **Service:** General Medical and Surgical

Staffed Beds: 446 **Admissions:** 29515 **Census:** 340 **Outpatient Visits:** 287236 **Births:** 3199 **Total Expense ($000):** 539414 **Payroll Expense ($000):** 239404 **Personnel:** 3257

ROCHELLE PARK—Bergen County

✠ **SELECT SPECIALTY HOSPITAL–NORTHEAST NEW JERSEY (312019)**, 96 Parkway, Zip 07662–4200; tel. 201/221–2358, (Nonreporting) **A**1 10 **S** Select Medical Corporation, Mechanicsburg, PA
Primary Contact: Barbara E. Hannan, MS, R.N., Chief Executive Officer
Web address: www.selectspecialtyhospitals.com/company/locations/northeastnewjersey.aspx
Control: Corporation, Investor–owned, for–profit **Service:** Long–Term Acute Care hospital

Staffed Beds: 59

SADDLE BROOK—Bergen County

KESSLER INSTITUTE FOR REHABILITATION See Kessler Institute for Rehabilitation, West Orange

SALEM—Salem County

✠ **MEMORIAL HOSPITAL OF SALEM COUNTY (310091)**, 310 Woodstown Road, Zip 08079–2080; tel. 856/935–1000 **A**1 9 10 **F**3 12 15 18 28 29 30 40 45 46 47 49 51 54 56 60 64 70 74 75 77 79 81 82 85 89 93 97 100 107 108 110 111 114 116 119 129 130 146 148 **S** Community Health Systems, Inc., Franklin, TN
Primary Contact: Ryan Jensen, Chief Executive Officer
CFO: Donald Bevers, Chief Financial Officer
CIO: Brian McCarthy, Director Information Systems
Web address: www.salemhospitalnj.org
Control: Corporation, Investor–owned, for–profit **Service:** General Medical and Surgical

Staffed Beds: 110 **Admissions:** 3701 **Census:** 38 **Outpatient Visits:** 45112 **Births:** 195 **Total Expense ($000):** 52026 **Payroll Expense ($000):** 20233 **Personnel:** 318

SECAUCUS—Hudson County

LIBERTYHEALTH–MEADOWLANDS HOSPITAL MEDICAL CENTER See Meadowlands Hospital Medical Center

◇ **MEADOWLANDS HOSPITAL MEDICAL CENTER (310118)**, 55 Meadowlands Parkway, Zip 07094–2977; tel. 201/392–3100, (Nonreporting) **A**9 10 21
Primary Contact: Thomas Considine, Chief Executive Officer
COO: Lynn McVey, Chief Operating Officer
CMO: Michael Sciarra, M.D., Chief Medical Officer
CHR: Elizabeth Garrity, Director Human Resources
CNO: Felicia Karsos, Chief Nursing Officer
Web address: www.meadowlandshospital.org
Control: Partnership, Investor–owned, for–profit **Service:** General Medical and Surgical

Staffed Beds: 163

SOMERS POINT—Atlantic County

✠ **SHORE MEDICAL CENTER (310047)**, 1 East New York Avenue, Zip 08244–2340; tel. 609/653–3500 **A**1 2 9 10 **F**3 11 13 15 17 18 20 22 28 29 30 31 34 35 36 37 40 44 45 49 50 54 57 59 60 61 64 66 68 70 73 74 75 76 77 78 79 81 82 84 85 86 87 89 92 93 107 108 110 111 114 118 119 120 121 123 129 130 132 135 143 146 147 148
Primary Contact: Ronald W. Johnson, FACHE, President and Chief Executive Officer
COO: Linda S. Kenwood, R.N., Chief Nursing Officer and Chief Operating Officer
CFO: James T. Foley, CPA, Vice President and Chief Financial Officer
CMO: Jeanne M. Rowe, M.D., Chief Medical Officer
CIO: Fred Banner, Chief Information Officer
CHR: Alan Beatty, Vice President Human Resources
CNO: Linda S. Kenwood, R.N., Chief Nursing Officer and Chief Operating Officer
Web address: www.shoremedicalcenter.org
Control: Other not–for–profit (including NFP Corporation) **Service:** General Medical and Surgical

Staffed Beds: 198 **Admissions:** 10212 **Census:** 113 **Outpatient Visits:** 100596 **Births:** 1055 **Total Expense ($000):** 207267 **Payroll Expense ($000):** 73737 **Personnel:** 1037

SOMERVILLE—Somerset County

✠ **ROBERT WOOD JOHNSON UNIVERSITY HOSPITAL SOMERSET (310048)**, 110 Rehill Avenue, Zip 08876–2598; tel. 908/685–2200, (Nonreporting) **A**1 2 3 5 9 10 **S** Robert Wood Johnson Health System & Network, New Brunswick, NJ
Primary Contact: Vincent D. Joseph, Interim Administrator
COO: Maureen Schneider, MSN, Senior Vice President Clinical Program Development and Chief Operating Officer
CFO: James De Rosa, Vice President Finance
CMO: Richard Paris, M.D., Chief Medical Officer
CIO: Dave Dyer, Vice President and Chief Information Officer
CHR: Mary Ann Bross, Vice President Human Resources
Web address: www.smchealthwise.com
Control: State–Government, nonfederal **Service:** General Medical and Surgical

Staffed Beds: 333

STRATFORD—Camden County

KENNEDY UNIVERSITY HOSPITAL – STRATFORD See Kennedy Health System, Cherry Hill

Many Facility Codes have changed. Please refer to the AHA Guide Code Chart.

© 2014 AHA Guide

NJ

SUMMIT—Union County

⊞ **OVERLOOK MEDICAL CENTER (310051)**, 99 Beauvoir Avenue, Zip 07901–3533; tel. 908/522–2000 **A**1 2 3 5 8 9 10 13 **F**3 5 6 7 8 9 11 12 13 14 15 17 18 19 20 22 28 29 30 31 32 34 35 36 37 38 39 40 41 42 44 45 46 47 48 49 50 51 52 53 54 55 56 57 58 59 60 61 62 63 64 65 66 68 69 70 71 72 73 74 75 76 77 78 79 81 82 83 84 85 86 87 89 91 92 93 94 95 96 97 98 99 100 101 102 103 104 105 107 108 110 111 113 114 115 116 117 118 119 120 121 123 124 126 129 130 131 132 134 135 143 144 145 146 147 148 **P**3 5 6 **S** Atlantic Health System, Morristown, NJ
Primary Contact: Alan R. Lieber, President
CFO: Kevin Lenahan, Vice President Finance and Chief Financial Officer
CMO: John R. Audett, M.D., Medical Director Clinical Affairs
CIO: Linda Reed, Vice President and Chief Information Officer
CHR: Andrew L. Kovach, Vice President Human Resources and Chief Administrative Officer
CNO: Mary Patricia Sullivan, R.N., Chief Nursing Officer
Web address: www.atlantichealth.org/Overlook
Control: Other not–for–profit (including NFP Corporation) **Service:** General Medical and Surgical

Staffed Beds: 461 **Admissions:** 22391 **Census:** 293 **Outpatient Visits:** 246913 **Births:** 2471 **Total Expense ($000):** 541535 **Payroll Expense ($000):** 252932 **Personnel:** 3384

☐ **SUMMIT OAKS HOSPITAL (314001)**, 19 Prospect Street, Zip 07901–2530; tel. 908/522–7000, (Nonreporting) **A**1 9 10 **S** Universal Health Services, Inc., King of Prussia, PA
Primary Contact: James P. Gallagher, Chief Executive Officer
Web address: www.summitoakshospital.com/
Control: Corporation, Investor–owned, for–profit **Service:** Psychiatric

Staffed Beds: 90

SUSSEX—Sussex County

SAINT CLARE'S HEALTH CENTER AT SUSSEX See Saint Clare's Health System, Denville

TEANECK—Bergen County

HOLY NAME HOSPITAL See Holy Name Medical Center

⊞ **HOLY NAME MEDICAL CENTER (310008)**, 718 Teaneck Road, Zip 07666–4281; tel. 201/833–3000 **A**1 2 5 6 9 10 **F**2 3 7 11 12 13 15 18 19 20 22 28 29 30 31 32 34 35 36 37 39 40 44 45 46 47 49 50 51 53 54 55 56 57 58 59 60 62 63 64 65 66 68 70 73 74 75 76 77 78 79 81 82 83 84 85 86 87 89 91 93 94 97 98 100 102 103 107 108 110 111 114 115 116 117 118 119 120 121 123 124 126 129 130 131 132 133 135 143 144 146 147 148 **P**4 5
Primary Contact: Michael Maron, President and Chief Executive Officer
CFO: Ryan Kennedy, Chief Financial Officer
CMO: Adam D. Jarrett, M.D., Executive Vice President and Chief Medical Officer
CIO: Michael Skvarenina, Assistant Vice President Information Systems
CHR: April Rodgers, Vice President, Human Resources
CNO: Sheryl A. Slonim, Executive Vice President and Chief Nursing Officer
Web address: www.holyname.org
Control: Other not–for–profit (including NFP Corporation) **Service:** General Medical and Surgical

Staffed Beds: 318 **Admissions:** 18728 **Census:** 212 **Outpatient Visits:** 331114 **Births:** 1423 **Total Expense ($000):** 297182 **Payroll Expense ($000):** 128204 **Personnel:** 2092

TINTON FALLS—Monmouth County

⊞ **REHABILITATION HOSPITAL OF TINTON FALLS (313035)**, 2 Centre Plaza, Zip 07724–9744; tel. 732/460–5320 **A**1 10 **F**29 64 68 74 75 82 90 93 94 95 96 100 119 148 **S** HEALTHSOUTH Corporation, Birmingham, AL
Primary Contact: Linda A. Savino, MS, Chief Executive Officer
CFO: Lynne Traister, Controller
CMO: Todd Cooperman, M.D., Medical Director
CHR: Anita Saum, Director Human Resources
Web address: www.rehabnj.com
Control: Corporation, Investor–owned, for–profit **Service:** Rehabilitation

Staffed Beds: 60 **Admissions:** 1451 **Census:** 50 **Outpatient Visits:** 8483 **Births:** 0 **Total Expense ($000):** 17648 **Payroll Expense ($000):** 10726 **Personnel:** 219

TOMS RIVER—Ocean County

⊞ **BARNABAS HEALTH BEHAVIORAL HEALTH CENTER (314022)**, 1691 Highway 9, Zip 08755–1245; tel. 732/914–1688, (Nonreporting) **A**1 9 10 **S** Barnabas Health, West Orange, NJ
Primary Contact: Joe Hicks, President and Chief Executive Officer
Web address: www.barnabashealth.org/hospitals/psychiatric/index.html
Control: Other not–for–profit (including NFP Corporation) **Service:** Psychiatric

Staffed Beds: 40

⊞ **COMMUNITY MEDICAL CENTER (310041)**, 99 Route 37 West, Zip 08755–6423; tel. 732/557–8051 **A**1 2 9 10 **F**3 11 13 15 17 18 20 22 28 29 30 31 32 34 35 36 38 40 41 43 44 47 48 49 50 53 54 55 56 57 58 59 60 61 62 63 64 68 69 70 73 74 75 76 77 78 79 81 83 84 85 86 87 89 92 93 96 100 102 107 108 109 110 111 114 115 118 119 120 121 123 124 126 128 129 130 131 132 133 134 143 146 147 148 **P**6 **S** Barnabas Health, West Orange, NJ
Primary Contact: Stephanie L. Bloom, FACHE, President and Chief Executive Officer
COO: Frank Gelormini, Chief Operating Officer
CFO: Mark Ostrander, Vice President Financial Services
CMO: John Crisanti, M.D., Vice President Medical Affairs
CIO: Shawn Fitzsimmons, Director Information Technology Services
CHR: Mary Deno, Vice President Human Resources
CNO: Fern Papalia, Vice President, Patient Care Services
Web address: www.barnabashealth.org/hospitals/community_medical/index.html
Control: Other not–for–profit (including NFP Corporation) **Service:** General Medical and Surgical

Staffed Beds: 523 **Admissions:** 23451 **Census:** 319 **Outpatient Visits:** 220737 **Births:** 1426 **Total Expense ($000):** 316999 **Payroll Expense ($000):** 123162 **Personnel:** 1932

⊞ **HEALTHSOUTH REHABILITATION HOSPITAL OF TOMS RIVER (313029)**, 14 Hospital Drive, Zip 08755–6470; tel. 732/244–3100, (Nonreporting) **A**1 10 **S** HEALTHSOUTH Corporation, Birmingham, AL
Primary Contact: Patricia Ostaszewski, MS, Chief Executive Officer
COO: Patricia Ostaszewski, MS, Chief Executive Officer
CFO: Janet Turso, Controller
CMO: Carol Sonatore, D.O., Medical Director
CIO: Coleen Rossi, Director Quality Services
CHR: Lori Munyan, Director, Human Resources
CNO: Susan Castor, Chief Nursing Officer
Web address: www.rehabnjtomsriver.com/
Control: Corporation, Investor–owned, for–profit **Service:** Rehabilitation

Staffed Beds: 129

SAINT BARNABAS BEHAVIORAL HEALTH CENTER See Barnabas Health Behavioral Health Center

TRENTON—Mercer County

⊞ **CAPITAL HEALTH REGIONAL MEDICAL CENTER (310092)**, 750 Brunswick Avenue, Zip 08638–4143; tel. 609/394–6000 **A**1 3 5 6 9 10 **F**3 7 11 13 15 18 19 29 30 34 40 42 43 44 45 46 47 48 50 54 57 58 59 60 64 65 66 68 70 72 73 74 75 76 77 78 79 81 82 84 85 87 89 93 94 96 97 98 99 100 101 102 105 107 108 109 111 114 115 118 119 129 130 132 135 143 144 145 146 147 148 **S** Capital Health, Trenton, NJ
Primary Contact: Al Maghazehe, Ph.D., FACHE, Chief Executive Officer
COO: Larry DiSanto, Executive Vice President and Chief Operating Officer
CFO: Shane Fleming, Chief Financial Officer
CMO: Steve Lowenthal, M.D., Vice President Medical Affairs
CIO: Eugene Grochala, Vice President Information Systems
CHR: J. Scott Clemmensen, Vice President Human Resources and Leadership Enhancement
CNO: Eileen M. Horton, Vice President, Patient Services/Chief Nursing Officer
Web address: www.capitalhealth.org
Control: Other not–for–profit (including NFP Corporation) **Service:** General Medical and Surgical

Staffed Beds: 271 **Admissions:** 10788 **Census:** 162 **Outpatient Visits:** 170868 **Births:** 311 **Personnel:** 1452

⊞ **ST. FRANCIS MEDICAL CENTER (310021)**, 601 Hamilton Avenue, Zip 08629–1986; tel. 609/599–5000 **A**1 2 6 9 10 **F**2 3 11 12 15 17 18 20 22 24 26 29 30 31 34 35 40 45 46 48 50 56 57 58 59 60 61 62 64 65 66 68 69 70 71 74 75 78 79 81 82 84 85 86 87 92 93 97 98 99 100 101 102 103 104 105 107 108 110 111 114 115 118 119 121 123 124 129 130 132 135 143 144 146 147 148 **P**5 6 **S** Catholic Health East / Trinity Health, Livonia, MI
Primary Contact: Christy Stephenson, Interim Chief Executive Officer
CFO: Mark Kelly, Vice President Finance
CMO: C. James Romano, M.D., President Medical Staff
CIO: Richard Dowgun, Chief Information Officer
CHR: Laura James, Director Human Resources
Web address: www.stfrancismedical.com
Control: Church–operated, Nongovernment, not–for profit **Service:** General Medical and Surgical

Staffed Beds: 163 **Admissions:** 5490 **Census:** 74 **Outpatient Visits:** 96963 **Births:** 0 **Total Expense ($000):** 125615 **Payroll Expense ($000):** 42658 **Personnel:** 942

NJ

Hospital, Medicare Provider Number, Address, Telephone, Approval, Facility, and Physician Codes, Health Care System

★ American Hospital Association (AHA) membership
☐ The Joint Commission accreditation
◇ DNV Healthcare Inc. accreditation

○ Healthcare Facilities Accreditation Program
△ Commission on Accreditation of Rehabilitation Facilities (CARF) accreditation

☐ **TRENTON PSYCHIATRIC HOSPITAL (314013)**, Route 29 and Sullivan Way, Zip 08628–3425, Mailing Address: P.O. Box 7500, West Trenton, Zip 08628–0500; tel. 609/633–1500 **A**1 10 **F**11 30 39 65 68 75 77 86 98 101 106 130 132 135 **S** Division of Mental Health and Addiction Services, Department of Human Services, State of New Jersey, Trenton, NJ
Primary Contact: Teresa A. McQuaide, Chief Executive Officer
COO: Christopher Morrison, Deputy Chief Executive Officer
CFO: Joseph Canale, Business Manager
CMO: Lawrence Rossi, M.D., Clinical Director
CIO: Scott Eustace, Director Health Information Technology
CHR: Marybeth Longo, Manager Human Resources
CNO: Colleen Birkhofer, Chief Nursing Officer
Web address: www.state.nj.us/humanservices/dmhs/oshm/tph/
Control: State–Government, nonfederal **Service:** Psychiatric

Staffed Beds: 431 **Admissions:** 645 **Census:** 431 **Outpatient Visits:** 0 **Births:** 0 **Total Expense ($000):** 82500 **Personnel:** 1239

TURNERSVILLE—Camden County

KENNEDY UNIVERSITY HOSPITAL – WASHINGTON TOWNSHIP See Kennedy Health System, Cherry Hill

VINELAND—Cumberland County

✠ **HEALTHSOUTH REHABILITATION HOSPITAL OF VINELAND (313036)**, 1237 West Sherman Avenue, Zip 08360–6920; tel. 856/696–7100 **A**1 10 **F**29 34 59 90 103 130 132 135 148 **S** HEALTHSOUTH Corporation, Birmingham, AL
Primary Contact: Tammy Feuer, Chief Executive Officer
CMO: Eugenio Rocksmith, M.D., Medical Director
CHR: Dawn Pearson, Director Human Resources
Web address: www.healthsouthvineland.com
Control: Corporation, Investor–owned, for–profit **Service:** Rehabilitation

Staffed Beds: 41 **Admissions:** 936 **Census:** 36 **Outpatient Visits:** 0 **Births:** 0 **Total Expense ($000):** 11986 **Payroll Expense ($000):** 6729 **Personnel:** 118

★ ◇ **INSPIRA MEDICAL CENTER–VINELAND (310032)**, 1505 West Sherman Avenue, Zip 08360–6912; tel. 856/641–8000, (Includes BRIDGETON HEALTH CENTER, 333 Irving Avenue, Bridgeton, Zip 08302–2100; tel. 856/575–4500) **A**2 9 10 21 **F**3 8 11 12 13 15 17 18 20 28 29 30 34 35 37 38 40 42 44 49 50 54 57 59 60 64 68 70 72 73 74 75 76 77 78 79 81 82 85 86 87 89 93 98 99 100 101 102 103 104 105 107 108 110 111 114 115 118 119 120 121 123 126 130 131 132 134 144 146 147 148 **P**6 **S** Inspira Health Network, Mullica Hill, NJ
Primary Contact: John A. DiAngelo, President and Chief Executive Officer
COO: Elizabeth Sheridan, Chief Operating Officer and Chief Nursing Executive
CFO: Thomas Baldosaro, Chief Financial Officer
CMO: Steven C. Linn, M.D., Chief Medical Officer
CIO: Thomas Pacek, Vice President Information Systems and Chief Information Officer
CHR: Erich Florentine, Chief People Officer
CNO: Elizabeth Sheridan, Chief Operating Officer and Chief Nursing Executive
Web address: www.inspirahealthnetwork.org/?id=5280&sid=1
Control: Other not–for–profit (including NFP Corporation) **Service:** General Medical and Surgical

Staffed Beds: 335 **Admissions:** 17962 **Census:** 232 **Outpatient Visits:** 288553 **Births:** 1894 **Total Expense ($000):** 313808 **Payroll Expense ($000):** 139194 **Personnel:** 1508

VOORHEES—Camden County

★ **VIRTUA VOORHEES (310022)**, 100 Bowman Drive, Zip 08043–9612; tel. 856/325–3000, (Includes VOORHEES PEDIATRIC FACILITY, 1304 Laurel Oak Road, Zip 08043–4310; tel. 888/873–5437) **A**3 5 10 **F**3 11 13 29 30 31 34 35 40 41 45 46 48 49 50 55 58 59 64 66 68 70 72 73 74 75 76 78 79 81 82 86 87 88 89 90 92 93 107 108 111 115 116 117 119 126 129 130 143 145 146 147 **S** Virtua Health, Marlton, NJ
Primary Contact: Gary L. Long, Senior Vice President Population Management
COO: Michael S. Kotzen, Vice President and Chief Operating Officer
CFO: Robert Rosvold, Director Finance
CMO: James P. Dwyer, D.O., Executive Vice President and Chief Medical Officer
CIO: Alfred Campanella, Chief Information Officer
Web address: www.virtua.org
Control: Other not–for–profit (including NFP Corporation) **Service:** General Medical and Surgical

Staffed Beds: 398 **Admissions:** 22458 **Census:** 261 **Outpatient Visits:** 247149 **Births:** 5100 **Total Expense ($000):** 397835 **Payroll Expense ($000):** 127876 **Personnel:** 1566

WAYNE—Passaic County

KINDRED HOSPITAL NEW JERSEY – WAYNE See Kindred Hospital–New Jersey Morris County, Dover

WEST ORANGE—Essex County

✠ △ **KESSLER INSTITUTE FOR REHABILITATION (313025)**, 1199 Pleasant Valley Way, Zip 07052–1424; tel. 973/731–3600, (Includes KESSLER INSTITUTE FOR REHABILITATION, 201 Pleasant Hill Road, Chester, Zip 07930–2141; tel. 973/252–6300; Sue Kida, Chief Executive Officer; KESSLER INSTITUTE FOR REHABILITATION, 300 Market Street, Saddle Brook, Zip 07663–5309; tel. 201/368–6000; Philip J. Driscoll, Jr., Chief Executive Officer; KESSLER INSTITUTE FOR REHABILITATION, 1199 Pleasant Valley Way, tel. 973/731–3600; Bonnie Evans, Chief Executive Officer) **A**1 3 5 7 10 **F**3 29 53 54 56 64 74 75 77 79 82 87 90 91 92 93 94 95 96 119 130 131 132 146 148 **P**6 **S** Select Medical Corporation, Mechanicsburg, PA
Primary Contact: Robert Brehm, Division President
CMO: Bruce M. Gans, M.D., Executive Vice President and Chief Medical Officer
CHR: Ken Caldera, Director Human Resources
Web address: www.kessler–rehab.com
Control: Corporation, Investor–owned, for–profit **Service:** Rehabilitation

Staffed Beds: 336 **Admissions:** 6939 **Census:** 296 **Outpatient Visits:** 118348 **Births:** 0

KESSLER INSTITUTE FOR REHABILITATION See Kessler Institute for Rehabilitation

WESTAMPTON—Burlington County

HAMPTON BEHAVIORAL HEALTH CENTER (314021), 650 Rancocas Road, Zip 08060–5613; tel. 609/267–7000 **A**9 10 **F**35 98 99 100 102 103 104 105 130 132 143 **P**6 **S** Universal Health Services, Inc., King of Prussia, PA
Primary Contact: Craig Hilton, Chief Executive Officer
COO: Joanne Wijaya, Chief Operating Officer
CFO: Guy DiStefano, Chief Financial Officer
CMO: Charles Trigiani, D.O., Medical Director
CHR: Lori DeCelis, Director Human Resources
CNO: Kathleena Cohen, Director of Nursing
Web address: www.hamptonhospital.com
Control: Corporation, Investor–owned, for–profit **Service:** Psychiatric

Staffed Beds: 110 **Admissions:** 2539 **Census:** 102 **Outpatient Visits:** 16110 **Births:** 0 **Total Expense ($000):** 20444 **Payroll Expense ($000):** 13700 **Personnel:** 249

WESTWOOD—Bergen County

✠ **HACKENSACK UNIVERSITY MEDICAL CENTER AT PASCACK VALLEY (310037)**, 250 Old Hook Road, Zip 07675–3123; tel. 201/880–2700, (Data for 214 days) **A**1 **F**3 13 15 18 20 29 30 34 35 40 44 45 46 47 49 50 70 72 74 76 77 78 79 81 82 85 87 93 100 108 110 111 115 119 129 130 135 146 147 **S** LHP Hospital Group, Plano, TX
Primary Contact: Chad Melton, Chief Executive Officer
COO: John Osgood, Interim Chief Operating Officer
CFO: Jason Pritchard, Chief Financial Officer
CMO: George Lin, M.D., Physician Advisor
CIO: Anthony Teri, Director Information Technology
CHR: Theodora Carter, Administrative Director Human Resources
CNO: Susan Giordano, R.N., Chief Nursing Officer
Web address: www.hackensackumcpv.com/
Control: Partnership, Investor–owned, for–profit **Service:** General Medical and Surgical

Staffed Beds: 128 **Admissions:** 1410 **Census:** 27 **Outpatient Visits:** 10239 **Births:** 84 **Total Expense ($000):** 47288 **Payroll Expense ($000):** 20451 **Personnel:** 448

WILLINGBORO—Burlington County

✠ **LOURDES MEDICAL CENTER OF BURLINGTON COUNTY (310061)**, 218–A Sunset Road, Zip 08046–1162; tel. 609/835–2900 **A**1 2 9 10 13 **F**3 7 11 12 15 17 18 29 30 31 34 35 36 38 40 42 44 45 46 47 49 50 55 56 57 59 60 61 64 66 68 70 74 75 78 79 81 82 85 86 87 93 98 100 107 108 109 110 111 114 118 119 129 130 132 135 146 147 148 **P**8 **S** Catholic Health East / Trinity Health, Livonia, MI
Primary Contact: Mark Nessel, Executive Vice President and Chief Operating Officer
COO: Robert Ruggero, Senior Vice President Operations
CFO: Michael Hammond, Chief Financial Officer
CMO: Alan R. Pope, M.D., Vice President, Medical Affairs
CIO: Mike Elfert, Director Information Services
CHR: Richard P. Kropp, Vice President Human Resources
CNO: Audrey Jadczak, R.N., Vice President/Chief Nursing Officer
Web address: www.lourdesnet.org
Control: Other not–for–profit (including NFP Corporation) **Service:** General Medical and Surgical

Staffed Beds: 125 **Admissions:** 6778 **Census:** 102 **Outpatient Visits:** 115861 **Births:** 0 **Total Expense ($000):** 113131 **Payroll Expense ($000):** 43925 **Personnel:** 689

NJ

✠ **LOURDES SPECIALTY HOSPITAL OF SOUTHERN NEW JERSEY (312022)**, 218 Sunset Road, Zip 08046–1110; tel. 609/835–3650 **A**1 10 **F**1 3 29 60 75 77 85 87 91 100 107 111 119 130 132 148 **S** AcuityHealthcare, LP, Charlotte, NC
Primary Contact: Cheri Cowperthwait, R.N., Chief Executive Officer
CFO: James Weinstein, Chief Financial Officer
CHR: Lisa M. Sinnott, Director Human Resources
CNO: Kim Fetterolf, R.N., Chief Clinical Officer
Web address: www.acuityhealthcarenj.com
Control: Hospital district or authority, Government, nonfederal **Service:** Long–Term Acute Care hospital

Staffed Beds: 69 **Admissions:** 473 **Census:** 36 **Outpatient Visits:** 0 **Births:** 0 **Total Expense ($000):** 26862 **Payroll Expense ($000):** 12464 **Personnel:** 182

WOODBRIDGE—Middlesex County

WOODBRIDGE DEVELOPMENT CENTER, Rahway Avenue, Zip 07095–3697, Mailing Address: P.O. Box 189, Zip 07095–0189; tel. 732/499–5951, (Nonreporting)
Primary Contact: Amy R. Bailon, M.D., Medical Director
Web address: www.state.nj.us/
Control: State–Government, nonfederal **Service:** Hospital unit within an institution for the mentally retarded

Staffed Beds: 125

WOODBURY—Gloucester County

✠ **INSPIRA MEDICAL CENTER–WOODBURY (310081)**, 509 North Broad Street, Zip 08096–1697; tel. 856/845–0100 **A**1 3 5 9 10 **F**3 11 13 15 17 18 20 22 28 29 30 34 35 38 39 40 41 49 50 56 57 58 59 60 61 62 64 66 67 70 73 74 75 76 77 79 80 81 85 86 89 91 93 96 97 98 99 100 102 104 105 107 110 114 115 118 119 129 130 132 135 143 146 147 148 **P**6 **S** Inspira Health Network, Mullica Hill, NJ
Primary Contact: Eileen K. Cardile, R.N., MS, Executive Vice President, Inspira Health Network and President, Inspira Medical Center–Woodbury
COO: John W. Graham, Executive Vice President and Chief Operating Officer
CIO: Robert Mizia, Director Information Systems and Chief Information Officer
CHR: Robert Manestrina, Vice President Human Resources
CNO: Gina Mumolie, Senior Vice President and Chief Nurse Executive
Web address: www.inspirahealthnetwork.org/?id=5282&sid=1
Control: Other not–for–profit (including NFP Corporation) **Service:** General Medical and Surgical

Staffed Beds: 240 **Admissions:** 12099 **Census:** 152 **Outpatient Visits:** 126949 **Births:** 851 **Total Expense ($000):** 176343 **Payroll Expense ($000):** 78167 **Personnel:** 1262

WYCKOFF—Bergen County

✠ **CHRISTIAN HEALTH CARE CENTER (314019)**, 301 Sicomac Avenue, Zip 07481–2194; tel. 201/848–5200, (Total facility includes 166 beds in nursing home–type unit) **A**1 9 10 **F**2 6 10 29 30 34 35 50 56 57 59 63 64 69 86 87 90 93 96 98 99 101 103 104 105 125 128 130 132 143 146 148 **P**6
Primary Contact: Douglas A. Struyk, CPA, President and Chief Executive Officer
COO: Denise Ratcliffe, Executive Vice President and Chief Operating Officer
CFO: Kevin Stagg, Executive Vice President Finance and Chief Financial Officer
CMO: Howard Gilman, M.D., Medical Executive
CIO: Jennifer D'Angelo, Assistant Vice President Information Services
CHR: Bob Zierold, Senior Vice President Human Resources
CNO: Marianne Guerriero, Nurse Executive
Web address: www.chccnj.org
Control: Other not–for–profit (including NFP Corporation) **Service:** Psychiatric

Staffed Beds: 520 **Admissions:** 2118 **Census:** 503 **Outpatient Visits:** 50636 **Births:** 0 **Total Expense ($000):** 71420 **Payroll Expense ($000):** 41309 **Personnel:** 1160

NJ

Hospital, Medicare Provider Number, Address, Telephone, Approval, Facility, and Physician Codes, Health Care System

★ American Hospital Association (AHA) membership
□ The Joint Commission accreditation   ◇ DNV Healthcare Inc. accreditation
○ Healthcare Facilities Accreditation Program
△ Commission on Accreditation of Rehabilitation Facilities (CARF) accreditation

NEW MEXICO

ACOMA— County

☐ **ACOMA–CANONCITO–LAGUNA HOSPITAL (320070)**, 80B Veterans Boulevard, Zip 87034, Mailing Address: P.O. Box 130, San Fidel, Zip 87049–0130; tel. 505/552–5300, (Nonreporting) **A**1 10 **S** U. S. Indian Health Service, Rockville, MD
Primary Contact: William Thorne, Jr., Chief Executive Officer
Web address: www.ihs.gov/albuquerque/index.cfm?module=dsp_abq_acoma_canoncito_laguna
Control: PHS, Indian Service, Government, federal **Service:** General Medical and Surgical

Staffed Beds: 25

ALAMOGORDO—Otero County

★ ◇ **GERALD CHAMPION REGIONAL MEDICAL CENTER (320004)**, 2669 North Scenic Drive, Zip 88310–8799; tel. 575/439–6100 **A**9 10 20 21 **F**3 8 11 13 18 29 30 31 34 35 40 43 45 50 51 56 57 58 59 60 64 70 74 75 76 77 78 79 81 85 86 87 90 92 96 97 98 101 103 104 105 107 108 111 114 116 117 119 129 130 132 133 142 146 147 148 **P**6
Primary Contact: Robert J. Heckert, Jr., Chief Executive Officer
CFO: Morgan Hay, Chief Financial Officer
CMO: Arthur Austin, M.D., Vice President Medical Affairs
CIO: Ana Castro, Director Information Services and Clinical Information Services
CHR: Karen O'Brien, Director Human Resources
CNO: Catherine A. Rhyne, M.P.H., Chief Nursing Officer
Web address: www.gcrmc.org
Control: Other not-for-profit (including NFP Corporation) **Service:** General Medical and Surgical

Staffed Beds: 102 **Admissions:** 3483 **Census:** 40 **Outpatient Visits:** 89742 **Births:** 483 **Total Expense ($000):** 105726 **Payroll Expense ($000):** 34701 **Personnel:** 524

ALBUQUERQUE—Bernalillo County

☐ **AMG SPECIALTY HOSPITAL–ALBUQUERQUE (322003)**, 235 Elm Street N.E., Zip 87102–3672; tel. 505/842–5550, (Nonreporting) **A**1 9 10 **S** AMG Integrated Healthcare Management, Lafayette, LA
Primary Contact: Elizabeth Rees, Chief Executive Officer
CFO: Julie Lenzo, Director Business Office
CMO: Jeffrey Ross, M.D., Medical Director
CHR: Robin Stendel–Freels, Coordinator Human Resources
Web address: www.amgalbuquerque.com/
Control: Partnership, Investor–owned, for-profit **Service:** Long–Term Acute Care hospital

Staffed Beds: 24

HAVEN BEHAVIORAL SENIOR CARE OF ALBUQUERQUE (324013), 5400 Gibson Boulevard S.E., 4th Floor, Zip 87108–4729; tel. 505/254–4500, (Nonreporting) **A**5
Primary Contact: John Baker, Interim Chief Executive Officer
Web address: www.havenbehavioral.com/albuquerque–nm
Control: Corporation, Investor–owned, for-profit **Service:** Psychiatric

Staffed Beds: 32

✠ **HEALTHSOUTH REHABILITATION HOSPITAL (323027)**, 7000 Jefferson Street N.E., Zip 87109–4313; tel. 505/344–9478 **A**1 9 10 **F**28 29 34 35 56 57 59 60 62 64 74 75 77 79 90 91 93 94 95 96 130 132 143 148 **S** HEALTHSOUTH Corporation, Birmingham, AL
Primary Contact: Sylvia K. Kelly, Chief Executive Officer
CFO: Byron Aten, Controller
CMO: Angela Walker, M.D., Medical Director
CHR: Victoria Otero, Director Human Resources
CNO: Veronica Gadomski, R.N., Chief Nursing Officer
Web address: www.healthsouthnewmexico.com
Control: Corporation, Investor–owned, for-profit **Service:** Rehabilitation

Staffed Beds: 87 **Admissions:** 1790 **Census:** 65 **Outpatient Visits:** 8684 **Births:** 0 **Total Expense ($000):** 19540 **Payroll Expense ($000):** 11672 **Personnel:** 214

✠ **KINDRED HOSPITAL–ALBUQUERQUE (322002)**, 700 High Street N.E., Zip 87102–2565; tel. 505/242–4444 **A**1 9 10 **F**1 3 16 29 30 67 70 75 80 90 91 98 107 130 135 148 **S** Kindred Healthcare, Louisville, KY
Primary Contact: Dianne Chartier, R.N., Interim Chief Executive Officer
CFO: Margaret Wantland, Chief Financial Officer
CMO: Jeffrey Dorf, M.D., Medical Director
CHR: Donald Whitney, Director Human Resources
CNO: Gary Gum, R.N., Chief Nursing Officer
Web address: www.kindredalbuquerque.com/
Control: Corporation, Investor–owned, for-profit **Service:** General Medical and Surgical

Staffed Beds: 61 **Admissions:** 492 **Census:** 39 **Births:** 0

★ ◇ **LOVELACE MEDICAL CENTER (320009)**, 601 Martin Luther King Avenue N.E., Zip 87102–3619; tel. 505/727–8000, (Includes HEART HOSPITAL OF NEW MEXICO, 504 Elm Street, Zip 87102; tel. 505/724–2000; Ronald C. Winger, President), (Nonreporting) **A**3 5 9 10 21 **S** Ardent Health Services, Nashville, TN
Primary Contact: Troy Greer, Chief Executive Officer
CMO: Jean D. Remillard, M.D., Chief Medical Officer/Chief Quality Officer
CHR: Helen V. Nielsen, Director Human Resources
CNO: Laurie S. Bigham, R.N., Chief Nursing Officer
Web address: www.lovelace.com/albuquerque–hospital/lovelace–medical–center#.UDZ1laDhf48
Control: Corporation, Investor–owned, for-profit **Service:** General Medical and Surgical

Staffed Beds: 263

★ △ **LOVELACE REHABILITATION HOSPITAL (323028)**, 505 Elm Street N.E., Zip 87102–2500; tel. 505/727–4700 **A**3 5 7 9 10 **F**3 29 30 90 143 148 **S** Ardent Health Services, Nashville, TN
Primary Contact: Derrick Jones, Chief Executive Officer
CFO: Andrea Solin, Chief Financial Officer
CHR: Helen V. Nielsen, Director Human Resources
CNO: Cynthia Rankin, Chief Nursing Officer
Web address: www.lovelace.com
Control: Corporation, Investor–owned, for-profit **Service:** Rehabilitation

Staffed Beds: 52 **Admissions:** 1152 **Census:** 43

★ ◇ **LOVELACE WESTSIDE HOSPITAL (320074)**, 10501 Golf Course Road N.W., Zip 87114–5000, Mailing Address: P.O. Box 25555, Zip 87125–0555; tel. 505/727–2000 **A**3 5 9 10 21 **F**3 12 13 15 29 30 34 39 40 41 49 51 57 59 68 70 72 73 76 79 81 85 93 107 110 111 115 119 130 133 135 146 148 **S** Ardent Health Services, Nashville, TN
Primary Contact: Farron Sneed, FACHE, Chief Executive Officer
COO: Karrie Brazaski, R.N., Chief Operating Officer and Chief Nursing Officer
Web address: www.lovelace.com/albuquerque–hospital/lovelace–westside–hospital#.UDZ1t6Dhf48
Control: Corporation, Investor–owned, for-profit **Service:** General Medical and Surgical

Staffed Beds: 80 **Admissions:** 2142 **Census:** 19 **Outpatient Visits:** 37831 **Births:** 177 **Total Expense ($000):** 47492 **Payroll Expense ($000):** 16693 **Personnel:** 257

★ ◇ **LOVELACE WOMEN'S HOSPITAL (320017)**, 4701 Montgomery Boulevard N.E., Zip 87109–1251, Mailing Address: P.O. Box 25555, Zip 87125–0555; tel. 505/727–7800 **A**3 5 9 10 21 **F**8 11 13 15 29 34 35 40 43 46 49 57 59 64 70 72 73 76 78 79 81 85 89 91 93 107 108 110 111 114 115 116 117 119 126 130 132 146 147 **S** Ardent Health Services, Nashville, TN
Primary Contact: Sheri Milone, Chief Executive Officer and Administrator
COO: Janelle Raborn, Chief Operating Officer
CFO: Joseph Sereno, Chief Financial Officer
CHR: Carol Shelton, Director Human Resources
CNO: Jane Ritter, R.N., Chief Nursing Officer
Web address: www.lovelace.com/albuquerque–hospital/lovelace–womens–hospital#.UDZ17KDhf48
Control: Corporation, Investor–owned, for-profit **Service:** General Medical and Surgical

Staffed Beds: 78 **Admissions:** 5712 **Census:** 46 **Outpatient Visits:** 144641

✠ **PRESBYTERIAN HOSPITAL (320021)**, 1100 Central Avenue S.E., Zip 87106–4934, Mailing Address: P.O. Box 26666, Zip 87125–6666; tel. 505/841–1234 **A**1 2 3 5 9 10 **F**3 7 8 10 11 14 17 18 19 20 21 22 23 24 25 26 27 29 30 31 35 38 40 44 45 46 47 48 49 51 53 57 59 60 68 70 72 74 75 76 77 78 79 81 84 85 86 87 88 89 92 93 96 100 101 107 108 111 113 114 115 118 119 124 126 130 131 132 138 142 144 145 146 147 148 **P**6 **S** Presbyterian Healthcare Services, Albuquerque, NM
Primary Contact: Sandra C. Podley, Administrator
COO: Paul Briggs, Executive Vice President and Chief Operating Officer
CFO: Dale Maxwell, Executive Vice President and Chief Financial Officer
CMO: Jayne McCormick, M.D., Chief Medical Officer CDS
CIO: Lee Marley, VP/Information Services Chief Application Officer
CHR: Lee Patchell, Lead Human Resources Business Partner
CNO: Ann L. Wright, R.N., Assistant Central Delivery System CNO
Web address: www.phs.org
Control: Other not-for-profit (including NFP Corporation) **Service:** General Medical and Surgical

Staffed Beds: 405 **Admissions:** 31232 **Census:** 347 **Outpatient Visits:** 1394398 **Births:** 3795 **Total Expense ($000):** 787655 **Payroll Expense ($000):** 343594 **Personnel:** 4093

NM

Many Facility Codes have changed. Please refer to the AHA Guide Code Chart. © 2014 AHA Guide

★ **PRESBYTERIAN KASEMAN HOSPITAL (320079)**, 8300 Constitution Avenue N.E., Zip 87110–7624, Mailing Address: P.O. Box 26666, Zip 87125–6666; tel. 505/291–2000 **A**9 **F**3 5 29 30 31 40 50 53 56 63 64 65 68 75 78 79 81 82 84 85 86 87 93 97 98 99 100 101 102 103 104 105 107 108 111 114 117 118 119 120 121 123 128 129 130 132 134 146 148 **P**6 **S** Presbyterian Healthcare Services, Albuquerque, NM
Primary Contact: Doyle Boykin, R.N., MSN, Administrator
COO: Paul Briggs, Executive VP/Chief Operating Officer
CFO: Dale Maxwell, Senior VP Chief Financial Officer
CMO: Jayne McCormick, M.D., Chief Medical Officer CDS
CIO: Lee Marley, VP/Information Services Chief Application Officer
CHR: Cindy McGill, Senior Vice President Human Resources
Web address: www.phs.org
Control: Other not–for–profit (including NFP Corporation) **Service:** Surgical

Staffed Beds: 105 **Admissions:** 2336 **Census:** 77 **Outpatient Visits:** 109300 **Births:** 0 **Total Expense ($000):** 81232 **Payroll Expense ($000):** 31545 **Personnel:** 512

TURQUOISE LODGE HOSPITAL, 5901 Zuni Road S.E., Zip 87108–3073; tel. 505/841–8978, (Nonreporting)
Primary Contact: Shauna Hartley, Hospital Administrator
CFO: Juliette Aragon, Finance Director
CIO: Eric Gurule, Chief Information Officer
CHR: Mario Lechuga, Director Human Resources
CNO: Debra Jane Green, R.N., Director of Nursing
Web address: www.health.state.nm.us
Control: State–Government, nonfederal **Service:** Alcoholism and other chemical dependency

Staffed Beds: 34

⊞ **UNIVERSITY OF NEW MEXICO HOSPITALS (320001)**, 2211 Lomas Boulevard N.E., Zip 87106–2745; tel. 505/272–2111, (Includes CARRIE TINGLEY HOSPITAL, 1127 University Boulevard N.E., Zip 87102–1715; tel. 505/272–5200; Crystal E. Frantz, MSN, R.N., Executive Director; MENTAL HEALTH CENTER, 2600 Marble N.E., Zip 87131–2600; tel. 505/272–2800; UNIVERSITY OF NEW MEXICO CHILDREN'S PSYCHIATRIC HOSPITAL, 1001 Yale Boulevard N.E., Zip 87131–3830; tel. 505/272–2890; UNM CHILDREN'S HOSPITAL, 2211 Lomas Boulevard, N.E., tel. 505/272–2111) **A**1 2 3 5 8 9 10 **F**3 8 9 11 13 15 16 17 18 19 20 21 22 23 24 25 26 27 28 29 30 31 32 34 35 38 40 41 43 44 45 46 47 48 49 50 51 54 56 57 59 60 61 63 64 65 68 70 72 73 74 75 76 77 78 79 81 82 83 84 85 86 87 88 89 90 92 93 94 95 96 97 107 108 109 110 111 114 115 116 117 118 119 121 123 126 129 130 131 132 135 136 138 144 146 147 148 **S** University of New Mexico Hospitals, Albuquerque, NM
Primary Contact: Stephen W. McKernan, Chief Executive Officer
COO: Paul F. Herzog, Chief Operating Officer
CFO: Ella Watt, Chief Financial Officer
CMO: Robert Katz, M.D., Vice President Clinical Affairs
CIO: Ron Margolis, Chief Information Officer
CHR: Jim Pendergast, Administrator Human Resources
Web address: www.unm.edu
Control: State–Government, nonfederal **Service:** General Medical and Surgical

Staffed Beds: 537 **Admissions:** 24164 **Census:** 414 **Outpatient Visits:** 628591 **Births:** 3204 **Total Expense ($000):** 759137 **Payroll Expense ($000):** 312495 **Personnel:** 5815

⊞ △ **VETERANS AFFAIRS MEDICAL CENTER**, 1501 San Pedro S.E., Zip 87108–5153; tel. 505/265–1711, (Nonreporting) **A**1 3 5 7 8 **S** Department of Veterans Affairs, Washington, DC
Primary Contact: George Marnell, Director
CFO: Michael McNeill, Chief Financial Management
CMO: Meghan Gerety, M.D., Chief of Staff
CIO: Ronald Ferrell, Chief Information Officer
CHR: Melvin Hooker, Chief Human Resources
Web address: www.southwest.va.gov/albuquerque/
Control: Veterans Affairs, Government, federal **Service:** General Medical and Surgical

Staffed Beds: 281

ARTESIA—Eddy County

★ **ARTESIA GENERAL HOSPITAL (320030)**, 702 North 13th Street, Zip 88210–1199; tel. 575/748–3333 **A**9 10 20 **F**3 11 15 18 29 30 34 40 43 45 46 47 48 50 51 56 57 59 64 65 68 75 79 81 85 92 93 98 101 103 107 110 111 115 119 124 127 130 131 133 **P**6 **S** Community Hospital Corporation, Plano, TX
Primary Contact: Kenneth W. Randall, Chief Executive Officer
CFO: Carl Hollingsworth, Chief Financial Officer
CMO: Joe Salgado, M.D., Chief of Staff
CHR: Bruce Hinshaw, Director Human Resources
CNO: Wendi Hulett, Chief Nursing Officer
Web address: www.artesiageneral.com
Control: Other not–for–profit (including NFP Corporation) **Service:** General Medical and Surgical

Staffed Beds: 30 **Admissions:** 1125 **Census:** 16 **Outpatient Visits:** 62070 **Births:** 0 **Total Expense ($000):** 39948 **Payroll Expense ($000):** 18498 **Personnel:** 256

CARLSBAD—Eddy County

⊞ **CARLSBAD MEDICAL CENTER (320063)**, 2430 West Pierce Street, Zip 88220–3597; tel. 575/887–4100, (Nonreporting) **A**1 9 10 19 20 **S** Community Health Systems, Inc., Franklin, TN
Primary Contact: Elmer Hyde, Chief Executive Officer
CFO: Craig Morse, Chief Financial Officer
CIO: Thomas Motejzik, Director Information Systems
CHR: Michael L. Turner, Director Human Resources
CNO: Connie Shofner, Chief Nursing Officer
Web address: www.carlsbadmedicalcenter.com
Control: Corporation, Investor–owned, for–profit **Service:** General Medical and Surgical

Staffed Beds: 127

CLAYTON—Union County

★ **UNION COUNTY GENERAL HOSPITAL (321304)**, 300 Wilson Street, Zip 88415–3304, Mailing Address: P.O. Box 489, Zip 88415–0489; tel. 575/374–2585 **A**9 10 18 **F**3 11 13 29 31 35 40 45 50 57 59 62 64 65 68 70 76 77 81 82 85 87 89 93 97 102 107 114 119 129 130 133 144 145 148 **S** HealthTech Management Services, Brentwood, TN
Primary Contact: Scott Manis, Chief Executive Officer
CFO: Alexander B. Altman, III, Chief Financial Officer
CMO: Daniel Radunsky, M.D., Medical Staff President
CIO: David Hall, Chief Information Officer
CHR: Jill Swagerty, Director Human Resources
CNO: Stacye Bradley, R.N., Chief Nursing Officer
Web address: www.unioncountygeneral.com/
Control: Other not–for–profit (including NFP Corporation) **Service:** General Medical and Surgical

Staffed Beds: 21 **Admissions:** 323 **Census:** 3 **Outpatient Visits:** 20724 **Births:** 14 **Total Expense ($000):** 12466 **Payroll Expense ($000):** 4430 **Personnel:** 95

CLOVIS—Curry County

⊞ **PLAINS REGIONAL MEDICAL CENTER (320022)**, 2100 Martin Luther King Boulevard, Zip 88101–9412, Mailing Address: P.O. Box 1688, Zip 88102–1688; tel. 575/769–2141 **A**1 9 10 **F**3 8 11 13 15 20 28 29 30 31 35 39 40 45 47 48 50 51 53 54 57 58 61 62 63 64 65 68 69 70 75 76 77 78 79 81 84 85 87 89 93 97 107 108 110 111 112 114 115 116 119 120 121 123 129 130 135 146 147 148 **P**6 **S** Presbyterian Healthcare Services, Albuquerque, NM
Primary Contact: Bo Beames, Interim Administrator
CMO: Brian Willmon, M.D., Medical Director
CHR: Cindy Duncan, Manager Human Resources
CNO: Terri A. Marney, R.N., Director of Nursing
Web address: www.phs.org
Control: Other not–for–profit (including NFP Corporation) **Service:** General Medical and Surgical

Staffed Beds: 50 **Admissions:** 4637 **Census:** 37 **Outpatient Visits:** 78071 **Births:** 1151 **Total Expense ($000):** 84874 **Payroll Expense ($000):** 30298 **Personnel:** 495

NM

Hospital, Medicare Provider Number, Address, Telephone, Approval, Facility, and Physician Codes, Health Care System

★ American Hospital Association (AHA) membership
□ The Joint Commission accreditation   ◇ DNV Healthcare Inc. accreditation

○ Healthcare Facilities Accreditation Program
△ Commission on Accreditation of Rehabilitation Facilities (CARF) accreditation

CROWNPOINT—McKinley County

★ **U. S. PUBLIC HEALTH SERVICE INDIAN HOSPITAL (320062)**, Route 9 and State Road 371, Zip 87313, Mailing Address: P.O. Box 358, Zip 87313–0358; tel. 505/786–5291, (Nonreporting) **A**10 **S** U. S. Indian Health Service, Rockville, MD
Primary Contact: Anslem Roanhorse, Chief Executive Officer
CFO: Darlene Kirk, Manager Finance
CMO: John Johnson, M.D., Clinical Director
CIO: Jimmy Burbank, Chief Information Officer
CHR: Christina Bitsilly, Human Resource Specialist
CNO: Alex Daniels, Chief Nurse Executive
Web address: www.ihs.gov
Control: PHS, Indian Service, Government, federal **Service:** General Medical and Surgical

Staffed Beds: 12

DEMING—Luna County

☒ **MIMBRES MEMORIAL HOSPITAL (321309)**, 900 West Ash Street, Zip 88030–4098, Mailing Address: P.O. Box 710, Zip 88031–0710; tel. 575/546–2761, (Nonreporting) **A**1 9 10 18 **S** Community Health Systems, Inc., Franklin, TN
Primary Contact: Steve Westenhofer, Chief Executive Officer
CFO: Trisha Smith, Interim Chief Financial Officer
CHR: Johanna Gramer, Director Human Resources
CNO: Joy Harrell, R.N., Interim Chief Nursing Officer
Web address: www.mimbresmemorial.com
Control: Corporation, Investor–owned, for–profit **Service:** General Medical and Surgical

Staffed Beds: 99

ESPANOLA—Rio Arriba County

☒ **ESPANOLA HOSPITAL (320011)**, 1010 Spruce Street, Zip 87532–2746; tel. 505/753–7111 **A**1 9 10 20 **F**3 7 8 13 15 29 32 34 35 40 45 50 53 57 59 62 70 75 76 79 81 85 93 107 108 110 114 115 118 119 129 146 **P**6 **S** Presbyterian Healthcare Services, Albuquerque, NM
Primary Contact: Brenda Romero, Administrator
CFO: Lupe Lucero, Chief Financial Officer
CMO: Fernando Bayardo, M.D., Chief Medical Officer
CHR: Julie Mackenzie, Manager Human Resources
CNO: Sharon Redman, Director Patient Care Services
Web address: www.phs.org
Control: Other not–for–profit (including NFP Corporation) **Service:** General Medical and Surgical

Staffed Beds: 46 **Admissions:** 2305 **Census:** 21 **Outpatient Visits:** 158377 **Births:** 329 **Total Expense ($000):** 53522 **Payroll Expense ($000):** 23969 **Personnel:** 292

FARMINGTON—San Juan County

☒ ◇ **SAN JUAN REGIONAL MEDICAL CENTER (320005)**, 801 West Maple Street, Zip 87401–5630; tel. 505/609–2000, (Includes SAN JUAN REGIONAL MEDICAL CENTER REHABILITATION HOSPITAL, 525 South Schwartz, Zip 87401; tel. 505/609–2625) **A**1 2 5 9 10 19 20 21 **F**3 7 8 11 13 15 18 20 22 26 28 29 30 31 32 34 35 39 40 43 47 48 49 50 53 54 57 59 60 64 65 68 70 74 75 76 78 79 81 82 85 86 87 89 90 93 96 97 98 99 100 102 107 108 111 112 114 115 118 119 121 130 132 135 143 144 146 148 **P**5 6
Primary Contact: Rick D. Wallace, FACHE, President and Chief Executive Officer
COO: John Buffington, Chief Operating Officer
CFO: J. Michael Philips, Chief Strategy Officer
CMO: Melanie Yeats, M.D., Vice President Medical Affairs
CIO: Sheri Rawlings, Chief Information Officer
CHR: Elizabeth Volkerding, Director Workforce Excellence
CNO: Suzanne E. Smith, R.N., Chief Nursing Officer
Web address: www.sanjuanregional.com
Control: Other not–for–profit (including NFP Corporation) **Service:** General Medical and Surgical

Staffed Beds: 200 **Admissions:** 10788 **Census:** 123 **Outpatient Visits:** 157366 **Births:** 1337 **Total Expense ($000):** 248130 **Payroll Expense ($000):** 115987 **Personnel:** 1629

GALLUP—McKinley County

☒ **GALLUP INDIAN MEDICAL CENTER (320061)**, 516 East Nizhoni Boulevard, Zip 87301–5748, Mailing Address: P.O. Box 1337, Zip 87305–1337; tel. 505/722–1000 **A**1 5 10 **F**5 8 13 15 18 29 34 39 40 43 50 59 61 64 65 66 70 74 76 79 81 83 84 85 89 99 100 107 115 119 130 144 147 148 **S** U. S. Indian Health Service, Rockville, MD
Primary Contact: Vida J. Khow, Chief Executive Officer
CFO: Agnes Kee, Financial Manager
CMO: Douglas G. Peter, M.D., Chief Medical Officer
CIO: Adrian C. Haven, Site Manager
CHR: Karen Lee, Director Human Resources
CNO: Selva Thompson, R.N., Chief Nurse Executive
Web address: www.ihs.gov/facilitiesservices/areaoffices/navajo/naihs–hcc–gallup.asp
Control: PHS, Indian Service, Government, federal **Service:** General Medical and Surgical

Staffed Beds: 84 **Admissions:** 1513 **Census:** 15 **Outpatient Visits:** 244000 **Births:** 538 **Total Expense ($000):** 130932 **Payroll Expense ($000):** 68817 **Personnel:** 933

☒ **REHOBOTH MCKINLEY CHRISTIAN HEALTH CARE SERVICES (320038)**, 1901 Red Rock Drive, Zip 87301–5683; tel. 505/863–7000 **A**1 5 9 10 20 **F**3 5 11 13 15 28 29 30 32 34 35 40 45 50 57 59 62 63 64 65 68 70 75 76 77 81 85 89 93 104 107 108 110 111 115 119 129 130 132 133 135 146 147 **P**6
Primary Contact: Barry L. Mousa, Chief Executive Officer
CFO: Bart Hansen, Chief Financial Officer
CMO: John Mezoff, M.D., Chief Medical Officer
CIO: Jose Rodriguez, Director Information Technology
CHR: Tracy Towns, Chief Human Resources Officer
CNO: Nancy Santiesteban, R.N., Chief Nursing Officer
Web address: www.rmch.org
Control: Other not–for–profit (including NFP Corporation) **Service:** General Medical and Surgical

Staffed Beds: 60 **Admissions:** 2725 **Census:** 29 **Outpatient Visits:** 112479 **Births:** 486 **Total Expense ($000):** 52153 **Payroll Expense ($000):** 25193 **Personnel:** 471

GRANTS—Cibola County

☒ **CIBOLA GENERAL HOSPITAL (321308)**, 1016 East Roosevelt Avenue, Zip 87020–2118; tel. 505/287–4446 **A**1 9 10 18 **F**3 13 15 29 30 34 40 45 46 50 56 57 59 64 65 66 68 70 75 76 77 81 85 93 97 107 110 115 119 127 130 133 135 147 148 **S** QHR, Brentwood, TN
Primary Contact: Donald Weidemann, Chief Executive Officer
CFO: Jeff Rimel, Chief Financial Officer
CMO: Janice Shipley, M.D., Chief Medical Officer
CIO: Rick Smith, Director Information Services
CHR: Sheila Cox, Director Human Resources
CNO: Glenna Losito, R.N., Chief Nursing Officer
Web address: www.cibolahospital.com
Control: Other not–for–profit (including NFP Corporation) **Service:** General Medical and Surgical

Staffed Beds: 25 **Admissions:** 941 **Census:** 8 **Outpatient Visits:** 21997 **Births:** 218 **Total Expense ($000):** 23890 **Payroll Expense ($000):** 10720 **Personnel:** 173

HOBBS—Lea County

☒ **LEA REGIONAL MEDICAL CENTER (320065)**, 5419 North Lovington Highway, Zip 88240–9125, Mailing Address: P.O. Box 3000, Zip 88241–9501; tel. 575/492–5000 **A**1 9 10 19 20 **F**3 11 13 14 15 18 20 29 30 34 40 45 49 50 51 56 57 59 64 68 69 70 71 74 75 76 77 79 81 85 87 89 93 98 100 102 103 106 107 110 111 114 119 128 129 144 146 147 **P**6 **S** Community Health Systems, Inc., Franklin, TN
Primary Contact: Timothy Thornell, FACHE, Chief Executive Officer
CFO: Steven Smith, Chief Financial Officer
CMO: Truett Maddox, M.D., Chief of Staff
CIO: Terry Purcell, Director Information Services
CHR: Lisa D. Thompson, Director Human Resources
CNO: Patrick A. Dunn, R.N., Chief Nursing Officer
Web address: www.learegionalmedical.com
Control: Corporation, Investor–owned, for–profit **Service:** General Medical and Surgical

Staffed Beds: 195 **Admissions:** 3845 **Census:** 35 **Outpatient Visits:** 52488 **Births:** 1064 **Total Expense ($000):** 53681 **Payroll Expense ($000):** 17857 **Personnel:** 377

LAS CRUCES—Dona Ana County

☐ **ADVANCED CARE HOSPITAL OF SOUTHERN NEW MEXICO (322004)**, 4451 East Lohman Avenue, Zip 88011–8267; tel. 575/521–6600, (Nonreporting) **A**1 9 10 **S** Ernest Health, Inc., Albuquerque, NM
Primary Contact: Suzanne Quillen, R.N., Chief Executive Officer
Web address: www.achsnm.ernesthealth.com
Control: Corporation, Investor–owned, for–profit **Service:** Long–Term Acute Care hospital

Staffed Beds: 40

Many Facility Codes have changed. Please refer to the AHA Guide Code Chart. © 2014 AHA Guide

✚ **MEMORIAL MEDICAL CENTER (320018)**, 2450 South Telshor Boulevard, Zip 88011–5076; tel. 575/522–8641 **A**1 2 9 10 **F**3 8 11 13 15 17 18 20 22 24 26 28 29 30 31 35 39 40 44 45 49 50 51 54 57 59 60 61 62 64 65 68 70 72 74 75 76 78 79 81 85 89 93 97 98 102 103 107 108 111 114 115 118 119 121 122 123 124 130 132 135 147 148 **S** LifePoint Hospitals, Inc., Brentwood, TN
Primary Contact: John Harris, Chief Executive Officer
COO: Steven T. Ruwoldt, Chief Operating Officer
CFO: James McGonnell, Chief Financial Officer
CMO: Bruce San Filippo, M.D., Chief Medical Officer
CHR: Laura Pierce, Chief Administrative Officer Human Resources
CNO: Ann Debooy, R.N., Chief Nursing Officer
Web address: www.mmclc.org
Control: Corporation, Investor–owned, for–profit **Service:** General Medical and Surgical

Staffed Beds: 224 **Admissions:** 10062 **Census:** 119 **Outpatient Visits:** 172611 **Births:** 1548 **Total Expense ($000):** 157930 **Payroll Expense ($000):** 57509 **Personnel:** 1037

✚ **MESILLA VALLEY HOSPITAL (324010)**, 3751 Del Rey Boulevard, Zip 88012–8526; tel. 575/382–3500 **A**1 9 10 **F**87 98 99 100 101 103 104 106 **S** Universal Health Services, Inc., King of Prussia, PA
Primary Contact: Robert Mansfield, Chief Executive Officer
CFO: Judith H. Culp, Chief Financial Officer
CMO: Ernest Flores, M.D., Chief of Staff and Medical Director
CHR: Linda Moya, Director Human Resources
Web address: www.mesillavalleyhospital.com
Control: Corporation, Investor–owned, for–profit **Service:** Psychiatric

Staffed Beds: 120 **Admissions:** 1842 **Census:** 81 **Outpatient Visits:** 9313 **Births:** 0 **Total Expense ($000):** 18611 **Payroll Expense ($000):** 7583 **Personnel:** 177

✚ **MOUNTAINVIEW REGIONAL MEDICAL CENTER (320085)**, 4311 East Lohman Avenue, Zip 88011–8255; tel. 575/556–7600, (Nonreporting) **A**1 9 10 **S** Community Health Systems, Inc., Franklin, TN
Primary Contact: Denten Park, Chief Executive Officer
CFO: Gene Alexander, Chief Financial Officer
CIO: Donald Harlow, Director of Information Services
CHR: Timothy C. Egan, Director, Human Resources
CNO: Willa Dixon, R.N., Chief Nursing Officer
Web address: www.mountainviewregional.com
Control: Corporation, Investor–owned, for–profit **Service:** General Medical and Surgical

Staffed Beds: 142

✚ **REHABILITATION HOSPITAL OF SOUTHERN NEW MEXICO (323032)**, 4441 East Lohman Avenue, Zip 88011–8267; tel. 575/521–6400, (Nonreporting) **A**1 9 10 **S** Ernest Health, Inc., Albuquerque, NM
Primary Contact: Sabrina Martin, Chief Operating Officer
COO: Sabrina Martin, Chief Operating Officer
CFO: Jared Udall, Chief Financial Officer
CMO: Kimberly Encapera, M.D., Medical Director
CHR: Yolanda Mendoza, Director Human Resources
CNO: Carole Carson, Director of Nursing Operations
Web address: www.rhsnm.ernesthealth.com
Control: Corporation, Investor–owned, for–profit **Service:** Rehabilitation

Staffed Beds: 40

LAS VEGAS—San Miguel County

✚ **ALTA VISTA REGIONAL HOSPITAL (320003)**, 104 Legion Drive, Zip 87701–4804; tel. 505/426–3500, (Nonreporting) **A**1 9 10 20 **S** Community Health Systems, Inc., Franklin, TN
Primary Contact: R. Chris Wolf, Chief Executive Officer
CMO: Nancy Wright, M.D., Chief Medical Staff
CIO: Laird Thornton, Director Information Systems
CHR: Michael Freeman, Director Human Resources
CNO: Rhonda Clark, Interim Chief Nursing Officer
Web address: www.altavistaregionalhospital.com
Control: Corporation, Investor–owned, for–profit **Service:** General Medical and Surgical

Staffed Beds: 52

☐ **NEW MEXICO BEHAVIORAL HEALTH INSTITUTE AT LAS VEGAS**, 3695 Hot Springs Boulevard, Zip 87701–9549; tel. 505/454–2100, (Nonreporting) **A**1 9
Primary Contact: Steve Martinez, Executive Director and Administrator
CFO: Albino Martinez, Director Finance and Budget
Web address: www.health.state.nm.us
Control: State–Government, nonfederal **Service:** Psychiatric

Staffed Beds: 257

LOS ALAMOS—Los Alamos County

✚ **LOS ALAMOS MEDICAL CENTER (320033)**, 3917 West Road, Zip 87544–2293; tel. 505/661–9500, (Nonreporting) **A**1 9 10 20 **S** LifePoint Hospitals, Inc., Brentwood, TN
Primary Contact: Feliciano Jiron, Chief Executive Officer
CFO: Emma Canlas, Chief Financial Officer
CMO: Barbara Van Eeckhout, M.D., Chief of Staff
CIO: Kevin Vigil, Director Information Systems
CHR: Jacqueline Carroll, Director Human Resources
CNO: Tracie Stratton, Chief Nursing Officer
Web address: www.losalamosmedicalcenter.com
Control: Corporation, Investor–owned, for–profit **Service:** General Medical and Surgical

Staffed Beds: 36

LOVINGTON—Lea County

★ ◇ **NOR–LEA GENERAL HOSPITAL (321305)**, 1600 North Main Avenue, Zip 88260–2871; tel. 575/396–6611 **A**9 10 18 21 **F**3 9 11 15 18 26 28 29 30 31 32 34 35 39 40 45 46 49 50 51 54 57 59 64 65 66 68 74 75 77 78 81 89 93 97 103 107 108 110 111 115 119 127 129 130 132 133 135 147 148 **P**6
Primary Contact: David B. Shaw, Chief Executive Officer and Administrator
COO: Dan Hamilton, Director Inpatient Services
CFO: Allyson Roberts, CPA, Chief Financial Officer
CMO: Ronald Hopkins, D.O., Chief of Staff
CIO: Brent Kelley, Director Information Technology
CHR: David Camp, Director Human Resources
CNO: Cyndie Cribbs, Director of Nursing
Web address: www.nlgh.org
Control: Hospital district or authority, Government, nonfederal **Service:** General Medical and Surgical

Staffed Beds: 25 **Admissions:** 732 **Census:** 5 **Outpatient Visits:** 162819 **Births:** 0 **Total Expense ($000):** 49065 **Payroll Expense ($000):** 17836 **Personnel:** 319

MESCALERO—Otero County

☐ **MESCALERO PUBLIC HEALTH SERVICE INDIAN HOSPITAL (320058)**, 318 Abalone Loop, Zip 88340, Mailing Address: Box 210, Zip 88340–0210; tel. 505/671–4441, (Nonreporting) **A**1 9 10 **S** U. S. Indian Health Service, Rockville, MD
Primary Contact: Dorlynn Simmons, Chief Executive Officer
CFO: Rainey Enjady, Administrative Officer
CIO: Kathy Murphy, Site Manager
Web address: www.ihs.gov
Control: Public Health Service, Government, federal **Service:** General Medical and Surgical

Staffed Beds: 13

PORTALES—Roosevelt County

◇ **ROOSEVELT GENERAL HOSPITAL (320084)**, 42121 U.S. Highway 70, Zip 88130, Mailing Address: P.O. Box 868, Zip 88130–0868; tel. 575/359–1800, (Nonreporting) **A**9 10 21
Primary Contact: Larry E. Leaming, Ph.D., FACHE, Chief Executive Officer
CFO: Eva Steven, Chief Financial Officer
CMO: Les Donaldson, M.D., Chief of Staff
CHR: Cindy Duncan, Director Human Resources
Web address: www.myrgh.org
Control: Hospital district or authority, Government, nonfederal **Service:** General Medical and Surgical

Staffed Beds: 22

RATON—Colfax County

★ **MINERS' COLFAX MEDICAL CENTER (321307)**, 200 Hospital Drive, Zip 87740–2099; tel. 575/445–7700, (Includes MINERS' HOSPITAL OF NEW MEXICO, Hospital Drive, Zip 87740, Mailing Address: Box 1067, Zip 87740; tel. 505/445–2741), (Nonreporting) **A**9 10 18
Primary Contact: Shawn Lerch, Chief Executive Officer
CFO: Albino Martinez, Director Budget and Finance
CIO: Richard Laner, Jr., Manager Information Systems
CHR: Jamie Johnson, Director Human Resources
Web address: www.minershosp.com
Control: County–Government, nonfederal **Service:** General Medical and Surgical

Staffed Beds: 33

NM

RIO RANCHO—Sandoval County

★ **PRESBYTERIAN RUST MEDICAL CENTER (320021)**, 2400 Unser Boulevard S.E., Zip 87124–4740; tel. 505/253–7878 **A**9 10 **F**3 11 13 18 19 20 22 29 30 40 45 50 51 53 60 64 68 70 72 75 76 79 81 82 85 87 91 93 107 108 111 114 115 118 119 130 146 **P**6 **S** Presbyterian Healthcare Services, Albuquerque, NM
Primary Contact: Jeff McBee, Administrator
Web address: www.phs.org/phs/riorancho/index.htm
Control: Other not–for–profit (including NFP Corporation) **Service:** General Medical and Surgical

Staffed Beds: 86 **Admissions:** 5568 **Census:** 58 **Outpatient Visits:** 46140 **Births:** 1229 **Total Expense ($000):** 104356 **Payroll Expense ($000):** 33966 **Personnel:** 506

◇ **UNM SANDOVAL REGIONAL MEDICAL CENTER (320089)**, 3001 Broadmoor Boulevard N.E., Zip 87144–2100; tel. 505/994–7000 **A**9 10 21 **F**3 7 15 29 30 35 40 43 45 46 47 48 70 79 81 93 98 103 107 108 109 110 111 114 115 119 124 146 147 **P**8 **S** University of New Mexico Hospitals, Albuquerque, NM
Primary Contact: Jamie A. Silva-Steele, R.N., Interim Chief Executive Officer
CFO: Darlene Fernandez, Chief Financial Officer
CMO: J. Anthony Ogburn, M.D., Chief Medical Officer
CNO: Pamela Demarest, R.N., Chief Nursing Officer
Web address: www.hospitals.unm.edu/
Control: Other not–for–profit (including NFP Corporation) **Service:** Psychiatric

Staffed Beds: 72 **Admissions:** 1691 **Census:** 19 **Outpatient Visits:** 27450 **Births:** 0 **Total Expense ($000):** 55260 **Payroll Expense ($000):** 19314 **Personnel:** 379

ROSWELL—Chaves County

⊠ **EASTERN NEW MEXICO MEDICAL CENTER (320006)**, 405 West Country Club Road, Zip 88201–5209; tel. 575/622–8170, (Nonreporting) **A**1 3 5 9 10 19 **S** Community Health Systems, Inc., Franklin, TN
Primary Contact: Maridel Acosta-Cruz, Chief Executive Officer
COO: Warren Yehl, Chief Operating Officer
CFO: Leanne Hacker, Chief Financial Officer
CMO: Richard Pinon, Chief Medical Officer
CIO: Deepak Surl, Chief Information Officer
CHR: Sheila Nunez, Director Human Resources
CNO: Kathy Williams, Chief Nursing Officer
Web address: www.enmmc.com
Control: Corporation, Investor–owned, for–profit **Service:** General Medical and Surgical

Staffed Beds: 149

★ **LOVELACE REGIONAL HOSPITAL – ROSWELL (320086)**, 117 East 19th Street, Zip 88201–5151; tel. 575/627–7000 **A**9 10 **F**3 11 13 18 20 22 24 26 29 30 34 35 36 38 40 44 45 46 47 48 49 50 51 54 57 59 68 70 75 76 77 79 81 82 83 84 86 87 93 107 111 114 119 130 131 132 135 141 146 147 **P**6 7 **S** Ardent Health Services, Nashville, TN
Primary Contact: Dawn M. Tschabrun, R.N., Chief Executive Officer
CNO: Kristin Trotter, Chief Nursing Officer
Web address: www.lovelace.com
Control: Corporation, Investor–owned, for–profit **Service:** General Medical and Surgical

Staffed Beds: 26 **Admissions:** 2117 **Census:** 15 **Outpatient Visits:** 41429 **Births:** 867 **Total Expense ($000):** 32426 **Payroll Expense ($000):** 12302 **Personnel:** 227

☐ **NEW MEXICO REHABILITATION CENTER (323026)**, 72 Gail Harris Street, Zip 88203–8116; tel. 575/347–3400, (Includes PECOS VALLEY LODGE, 31 Gail Harris Avenue, Zip 88201; tel. 505/347–5491), (Nonreporting) **A**1 10
Primary Contact: Martha C. Gorman, R.N., MSN, Administrator
COO: Martha C. Gorman, R.N., Administrator
CFO: Janie Davies, Chief Financial Officer
CMO: Stephen Dorman, M.D., Chief Medical Officer
CIO: Dennis Hoefs, Manager Information Technology
CHR: Teresa Casarez, Director Human Resources
CNO: Gayle Nash, R.N., Chief Nursing Officer
Control: State–Government, nonfederal **Service:** Rehabilitation

Staffed Beds: 41

RUIDOSO—Lincoln County

⊠ **LINCOLN COUNTY MEDICAL CENTER (321306)**, 211 Sudderth Drive, Zip 88345–6043, Mailing Address: P.O. Box 8000, Zip 88355–8000; tel. 575/257–8200 **A**1 9 10 18 **F**7 11 13 15 29 30 35 39 40 45 46 53 56 57 59 64 68 70 76 77 78 81 85 87 91 93 103 107 110 111 115 119 132 135 144 146 148 **P**6 **S** Presbyterian Healthcare Services, Albuquerque, NM
Primary Contact: Alfred Santos, Administrator
CFO: Dudley McCauley, Controller
CMO: Gary Jackson, D.O., Medical Director
CHR: Susanne Johnston, Manager Human Resources
Web address: www.phs.org
Control: Other not–for–profit (including NFP Corporation) **Service:** General Medical and Surgical

Staffed Beds: 25 **Admissions:** 1740 **Census:** 11 **Outpatient Visits:** 32343 **Births:** 363 **Total Expense ($000):** 34187 **Payroll Expense ($000):** 16423 **Personnel:** 219

SANTA FE—Santa Fe County

⊠ △ **CHRISTUS ST. VINCENT REGIONAL MEDICAL CENTER (320002)**, 455 St. Michael's Drive, Zip 87505–7663, Mailing Address: P.O. Box 2107, Zip 87504–2107; tel. 505/983–3361, (Includes CHRISTUS ST. VINCENT PHYSICIANS MEDICAL CENTER, 2990 Rodeo Park Drive East, Zip 87505; tel. 505/428–5400; J. Alex Valdez, JD, President and Chief Executive Officer) **A**1 2 3 5 7 9 10 20 **F**3 8 12 13 15 17 18 19 20 21 22 24 26 28 29 30 31 32 34 35 36 37 38 39 40 41 43 45 46 47 48 49 50 51 53 54 56 57 64 65 66 68 70 73 74 75 76 77 78 79 81 82 83 84 85 86 87 88 89 90 91 92 93 97 98 100 101 102 103 104 107 108 109 110 111 112 113 114 115 116 117 118 119 120 121 122 124 126 129 130 131 132 135 143 144 146 147 148 **S** CHRISTUS Health, Irving, TX
Primary Contact: Bruce J. Tassin, President and Chief Executive Officer
COO: Jason Adams, Chief Operating Officer
CFO: Bob Moon, Chief Financial Officer
CMO: John C. Beeson, M.D., Chief Medical Officer
CIO: Ron Dekeyzer, Regional Director Information Systems
CHR: Pearl Mohnkern, Vice President and Director Human Resources
CNO: Christine Kipp, R.N., Chief Nursing Officer
Web address: www.stvin.org
Control: Other not–for–profit (including NFP Corporation) **Service:** General Medical and Surgical

Staffed Beds: 268 **Admissions:** 11746 **Census:** 135 **Births:** 1089

☐ **PHS SANTA FE INDIAN HOSPITAL (320057)**, 1700 Cerrillos Road, Zip 87505–3554; tel. 505/988–9821 **A**1 5 9 10 **F**34 39 50 59 64 65 75 87 89 93 104 108 119 127 130 **S** U. S. Indian Health Service, Rockville, MD
Primary Contact: Robert J. Lyon, Chief Executive Officer
CMO: Bret Smoker, M.D., Clinical Director
CIO: Vernita Jones, Site Manager
Control: PHS, Indian Service, Government, federal **Service:** General Medical and Surgical

Staffed Beds: 4 **Admissions:** 149 **Census:** 2 **Outpatient Visits:** 12255 **Births:** 0

SANTA ROSA—Guadalupe County

★ **GUADALUPE COUNTY HOSPITAL (320067)**, 117 Camino de Vida, Zip 88435–2267; tel. 575/472–3417 **A**9 10 20 **F**3 29 34 35 40 57 59 64 65 68 82 87 107 114 119 130 132 **P**5
Primary Contact: Christina Campos, Administrator
COO: Christina Campos, Administrator
CFO: Bret Goebel, Finance Officer
CMO: Randal Brown, M.D., Chief of Staff
CIO: Kenneth Matthews, Manager Information Technology
CHR: Colleen Gallegos, Director Human Resources
Web address: www.gchnm.org
Control: County–Government, nonfederal **Service:** General Medical and Surgical

Staffed Beds: 10 **Admissions:** 218 **Census:** 2 **Outpatient Visits:** 5839 **Births:** 0 **Total Expense ($000):** 6211 **Payroll Expense ($000):** 1465

SANTA TERESA—Dona Ana County

☐ **PEAK BEHAVIORAL HEALTH SERVICES (324012)**, 5065 McNutt Road, Zip 88008–9442; tel. 575/589–3000, (Nonreporting) **A**1 9 10 **S** Strategic Behavioral Health, LLC, Memphis, TN
Primary Contact: Carol Eck, President
COO: Doug Ginn, Executive Vice President Operations
CFO: Espie Herrara, Chief Financial Officer
CHR: Norma Oaxaca, Director Human Resources
Web address: www.peakbehavioral.com/
Control: Corporation, Investor–owned, for–profit **Service:** Psychiatric

Staffed Beds: 36

NM

Many Facility Codes have changed. Please refer to the AHA Guide Code Chart. © 2014 AHA Guide

SHIPROCK—San Juan County

✠ **NORTHERN NAVAJO MEDICAL CENTER (320059)**, Highway 491 North, Zip 87420–0160, Mailing Address: P.O. Box 160, Zip 87420–0160; tel. 505/368–6001, (Nonreporting) **A**1 5 10 **S** U. S. Indian Health Service, Rockville, MD
Primary Contact: Fannessa Comer, Chief Executive Officer
CFO: Shawn Morgan, Acting Finance Officer
CMO: George C. Baacke, II, M.D., Acting Clinical Director
CIO: Roland Chapman, Chief Information Officer
CHR: Gloria Redhorse–Charley, Director Human Resources
CNO: Lavenia Diswood, R.N., Chief Nurse Executive
Web address: www.ihs.gov/
Control: Public Health Service, Government, federal **Service:** General Medical and Surgical

Staffed Beds: 62

SILVER CITY—Grant County

✠ **GILA REGIONAL MEDICAL CENTER (320016)**, 1313 East 32nd Street, Zip 88061–7251; tel. 575/538–4000 **A**1 9 10 20 **F**3 7 11 13 15 30 31 35 37 40 41 45 50 51 53 57 59 62 63 64 70 73 75 76 78 79 81 85 87 89 93 98 102 103 107 108 111 115 119 120 121 123 129 130 132 148 **P**5
Primary Contact: Brian Cunningham, Interim Chief Executive Officer
CFO: Craig Stewart, Chief Financial Officer
CIO: David Furnas, Chief Information Officer
CHR: Barbara Barela, Director Human Resources
CNO: Patricia Sheyka, Chief Nursing Officer
Web address: www.grmc.org
Control: County–Government, nonfederal **Service:** General Medical and Surgical

Staffed Beds: 68 **Admissions:** 3041 **Census:** 27 **Outpatient Visits:** 73006
Births: 404

SOCORRO—Socorro County

✠ **SOCORRO GENERAL HOSPITAL (321301)**, 1202 Highway 60 West, Zip 87801–3914, Mailing Address: P.O. Box 1009, Zip 87801–1009; tel. 505/835–1140 **A**1 9 10 18 **F**3 8 11 13 15 29 30 34 35 40 45 57 59 62 63 64 68 75 77 81 83 85 91 93 100 103 107 114 130 132 133 134 135 147 **P**6 **S** Presbyterian Healthcare Services, Albuquerque, NM
Primary Contact: Veronica Pound, R.N., Administrator
CFO: Scott Shannon, Director Finance
CMO: Darla Bejnar, M.D., Chief Medical Officer
CHR: Pam Miller–Balfour, Director Human Resources
CNO: Veronica Pound, R.N., Interim Administrator and Director of Patient Care
Web address: www.phs.org
Control: Other not–for–profit (including NFP Corporation) **Service:** General Medical and Surgical

Staffed Beds: 14 **Admissions:** 480 **Census:** 3 **Outpatient Visits:** 20364
Births: 149 **Total Expense ($000):** 24299 **Payroll Expense ($000):** 11929
Personnel: 165

TAOS—Taos County

★ ◇ **HOLY CROSS HOSPITAL (320013)**, 1397 Weimer Road, Zip 87571–6253; tel. 575/758–8883 **A**9 10 20 21 **F**11 13 15 18 29 30 34 35 36 40 43 45 46 50 59 64 68 70 75 76 77 79 81 82 86 87 89 107 110 114 115 118 119 127 130 132 145 146 147 148 **P**8 **S** QHR, Brentwood, TN
Primary Contact: Phillip W. Lowe, Interim Chief Executive Officer
COO: Spencer Hamons, Chief Information Officer and Chief Operating Officer
CFO: Steve Rozenboom, Chief Financial Officer
CMO: Loretta Ortiz y Pino, M.D., Chief Medical Officer
CIO: Spencer Hamons, Chief Information Officer and Chief Operating Officer
CHR: Lisa Clark, Human Resources Officer
CNO: Mary Anna Abeyta, R.N., Chief Nursing/Clinical Services Officer
Web address: www.taoshospital.org
Control: Other not–for–profit (including NFP Corporation) **Service:** General Medical and Surgical

Staffed Beds: 35 **Admissions:** 1923 **Census:** 18 **Outpatient Visits:** 69808
Births: 246 **Total Expense ($000):** 50781 **Payroll Expense ($000):** 21676
Personnel: 356

TRUTH OR CONSEQUENCES—Sierra County

★ **SIERRA VISTA HOSPITAL (321300)**, 800 East Ninth Avenue, Zip 87901–1961; tel. 575/894–2111 **A**9 10 18 **F**7 11 15 16 30 34 40 54 57 59 65 67 93 99 102 104 107 110 127 128 130 133 **P**6
Primary Contact: Michael P. Zimmerman, Chief Executive Officer
CFO: Bret Gobel, Chief Financial Officer
CMO: James F. Malcolmson, M.D., Chief of Staff
CIO: Dan Morrell, Manager Information Systems
CHR: Mindee Holguin, Manager Human Resources
CNO: Palmer Greene, R.N., Chief Nursing Officer
Web address: www.svhnm.org
Control: City–County, Government, nonfederal **Service:** General Medical and Surgical

Staffed Beds: 15 **Admissions:** 367 **Census:** 3 **Outpatient Visits:** 21126
Births: 0

TUCUMCARI—Quay County

★ **DR. DAN C. TRIGG MEMORIAL HOSPITAL (321302)**, 301 East Miel De Luna Avenue, Zip 88401–3810, Mailing Address: P.O. Box 608, Zip 88401–0608; tel. 575/461–7000 **A**9 10 18 **F**3 11 15 29 35 38 40 45 59 62 63 64 65 68 81 85 87 97 99 101 103 104 107 110 114 119 127 130 133 135 146 148 **P**6 **S** Presbyterian Healthcare Services, Albuquerque, NM
Primary Contact: Lance C. Labine, Administrator
CMO: Darrell Willis, M.D., Chief of Staff
CNO: Vickie Gutierrez, Director of Patient Care
Web address: www.phs.org
Control: Other not–for–profit (including NFP Corporation) **Service:** General Medical and Surgical

Staffed Beds: 10 **Admissions:** 274 **Census:** 3 **Outpatient Visits:** 13534
Births: 0 **Total Expense ($000):** 14427 **Payroll Expense ($000):** 5597
Personnel: 100

ZUNI—McKinley County

☐ **U. S. PUBLIC HEALTH SERVICE INDIAN HOSPITAL (320060)**, Route 301 North B. Street, Zip 87327, Mailing Address: P.O. Box 467, Zip 87327–0467; tel. 505/782–4431, (Nonreporting) **A**1 9 10 **S** U. S. Indian Health Service, Rockville, MD
Primary Contact: Jean Othole, Chief Executive Officer
CFO: Clyde Yatsattie, Administrative Officer
CMO: David Kessler, M.D., Clinical Director
CHR: Cynthia Tsalate, Human Resource Specialist
Web address: www.ihs.gov
Control: PHS, Indian Service, Government, federal **Service:** General Medical and Surgical

Staffed Beds: 32

NM

NEW YORK

ALBANY—Albany County

✠ **ALBANY MEDICAL CENTER (330013)**, 43 New Scotland Avenue, Zip 12208–3478; tel. 518/262–3125, (Includes ALBANY MEDICAL CENTER SOUTH–CLINICAL CAMPUS, 25 Hackett Boulevard, Zip 12208–3499; tel. 518/242–1200; Timothy W. Duffy, General Director) **A**1 2 3 5 8 9 10 19 **F**3 6 7 8 11 12 13 15 17 18 19 20 21 22 23 24 25 26 27 28 29 30 31 32 34 35 36 38 39 40 41 43 44 45 46 47 49 50 51 52 53 54 55 56 57 58 59 60 61 64 65 68 70 72 73 74 75 76 77 78 79 81 82 85 86 87 88 89 90 92 93 96 98 100 102 103 104 105 107 108 109 110 111 114 115 116 117 118 119 120 121 123 124 126 130 131 132 135 138 142 145 146 148
Primary Contact: James J. Barba, President and Chief Executive Officer
COO: Bernadette R. Pedlow, Senior Vice President Business and Chief Operating Officer
CFO: William C. Hasselbarth, Chief Financial Officer
CMO: Dennis McKenna, M.D., Interim Vice President Medical Affairs
CIO: George Hickman, Executive Vice President and Chief Information Officer
CHR: Catherine Halakan, Senior Vice President
Web address: www.amc.edu
Control: Other not–for–profit (including NFP Corporation) **Service:** General Medical and Surgical

Staffed Beds: 688 Admissions: 31699 Census: 543 Outpatient Visits: 347669 Births: 2034 Total Expense ($000): 733006 Payroll Expense ($000): 242983 Personnel: 5349

★ **ALBANY MEMORIAL HOSPITAL (330003)**, 600 Northern Boulevard, Zip 12204–1083; tel. 518/471–3221 **A**5 9 10 **F**8 40 57 59 70 77 107 **S** Catholic Health East / Trinity Health, Livonia, MI
Primary Contact: Ann Errichetti, M.D., Chief Executive Officer
CFO: Lori Santos, Vice President Finance
CMO: Robert Cella, M.D., Chief Medical Officer
CIO: Jonathan Goldberg, Chief Information Officer
CHR: Judy Gray, Vice President Human Resources
Web address: www.nehealth.com
Control: Other not–for–profit (including NFP Corporation) **Service:** General Medical and Surgical

Staffed Beds: 73 Admissions: 3354 Census: 53 Outpatient Visits: 157777 Births: 0 Total Expense ($000): 85023 Payroll Expense ($000): 36254

✠ **ALBANY STRATTON VETERANS AFFAIRS MEDICAL CENTER**, 113 Holland Avenue, Zip 12208–3473; tel. 518/626–5000, (Total facility includes 45 beds in nursing home–type unit) **A**1 2 3 5 8 9 **F**2 3 4 5 12 15 17 18 20 22 28 29 30 31 34 35 39 40 45 46 47 49 50 54 55 56 57 58 59 60 61 62 63 64 65 68 70 74 75 77 78 79 81 82 83 84 85 86 87 91 92 93 94 97 98 100 102 103 104 105 106 107 108 109 110 111 115 119 121 122 126 127 128 129 130 132 135 143 146 147 148 **S** Department of Veterans Affairs, Washington, DC
Primary Contact: Linda W. Weiss, MS, FACHE, Director
CFO: Gerard Scorzelli, Chief Financial Officer
CMO: Lourdes Irizarry, M.D., Chief of Staff
CIO: Ron Diaz, Manager Operations
CHR: Kenneth Kio, Manager Human Resources
CNO: Deborah Spath, R.N., Associate Director Patient and Nurses Services
Web address: www.albany.va.gov/
Control: Veterans Affairs, Government, federal **Service:** General Medical and Surgical

Staffed Beds: 150 Admissions: 2968 Census: 88 Outpatient Visits: 349410 Births: 0 Total Expense ($000): 224932 Payroll Expense ($000): 133338 Personnel: 1293

☐ **CAPITAL DISTRICT PSYCHIATRIC CENTER (334046)**, 75 New Scotland Avenue, Zip 12208–3474; tel. 518/447–9611, (Nonreporting) **A**1 3 5 10 **S** New York State Office of Mental Health, Albany, NY
Primary Contact: William Dickson, Acting Executive Director
CMO: Beatrice Kovasznay, M.D., Clinical Director
Web address: www.omh.ny.gov/omhweb/facilities/cdpc/facility.htm
Control: State–Government, nonfederal **Service:** Psychiatric

Staffed Beds: 200

✠ **ST. PETER'S HOSPITAL (330057)**, 315 South Manning Boulevard, Zip 12208–1789; tel. 518/525–1550 **A**1 2 3 5 9 10 19 **F**4 5 8 11 12 13 15 17 18 19 20 21 22 23 24 26 27 28 29 30 31 34 35 36 37 38 39 40 45 46 47 48 49 50 51 53 54 56 57 59 60 61 62 63 64 65 66 68 69 70 71 72 73 74 75 77 78 79 81 82 84 85 86 87 92 93 97 107 108 109 110 111 114 115 116 117 118 119 120 121 123 124 126 129 130 132 133 135 143 145 146 147 148 **P**6 **S** Catholic Health East / Trinity Health, Livonia, MI
Primary Contact: Ann Errichetti, M.D., Chief Executive Officer
CFO: Lori Santos, Chief Financial Officer
CMO: Robert Cella, M.D., Chief Medical Officer
CIO: Jonathan Goldberg, Chief Information Officer
CHR: Judy Gray, Vice President Human Resources
CNO: Jane O'Rourke, R.N., Chief Nursing Officer, Vice President Operations
Web address: www.sphcs.org
Control: Church–operated, Nongovernment, not–for profit **Service:** General Medical and Surgical

Staffed Beds: 442 Admissions: 23259 Census: 334 Outpatient Visits: 425935 Births: 2515 Total Expense ($000): 475045 Payroll Expense ($000): 181322 Personnel: 2583

ALEXANDRIA BAY—Jefferson County

★ **RIVER HOSPITAL (331309)**, 4 Fuller Street, Zip 13607–1316; tel. 315/482–2511 **A**9 10 18 **F**3 11 15 18 29 34 35 40 45 50 57 59 64 68 81 84 87 93 97 104 105 107 114 119 130 133 135 147
Primary Contact: Ben Moore, III, President and Chief Executive Officer
COO: William Connor, Assistant Administrator and Director Human Resources
CFO: Traci Mintonye, Chief Financial Officer
CMO: Prasad Yitta, M.D., Medical Director
CIO: John Smithers, Network Specialist
CHR: William Connor, Assistant Administrator and Director Human Resources
CNO: Ann Narrow, Director of Nursing
Web address: www.riverhospital.org
Control: Other not–for–profit (including NFP Corporation) **Service:** General Medical and Surgical

Staffed Beds: 11 Admissions: 152 Census: 4 Outpatient Visits: 48411 Births: 0 Total Expense ($000): 17108 Payroll Expense ($000): 9824 Personnel: 170

AMITYVILLE—Suffolk County

☐ **BRUNSWICK PSYCH CENTER (334026)**, 81 Louden Avenue, Zip 11701–2736; tel. 516/789–7000, (Nonreporting) **A**1 10
Primary Contact: Sandip Singh, Acting Chief Executive Officer
Control: Corporation, Investor–owned, for–profit **Service:** Psychiatric

Staffed Beds: 50

☐ **SOUTH OAKS HOSPITAL (334027)**, 400 Sunrise Highway, Zip 11701–2508; tel. 631/264–4000 **A**1 9 10 **F**4 5 53 98 99 103 104 105 **S** North Shore–Long Island Jewish Health System, Great Neck, NY
Primary Contact: Robert E. Detor, Chief Executive Officer
CFO: Patricia Porter, Chief Financial Officer
CMO: Tina Walch, M.D., Medical Director
CHR: Pam Duffy, Vice President Human Resources
Web address: www.longislandhome.org
Control: Other not–for–profit (including NFP Corporation) **Service:** Psychiatric

Staffed Beds: 260 Admissions: 4849 Census: 144 Outpatient Visits: 99253 Births: 0 Total Expense ($000): 53395 Payroll Expense ($000): 31306 Personnel: 528

AMSTERDAM—Montgomery County

ST. MARY'S AMSTERDAM CAMPUS See St. Mary's Healthcare

✠ **ST. MARY'S HEALTHCARE (330047)**, 427 Guy Park Avenue, Zip 12010–1054; tel. 518/842–1900, (Includes ST. MARY'S AMSTERDAM CAMPUS, 4988 State Highway 30, Zip 12010–1699; tel. 518/842–3100), (Nonreporting) **A**1 9 10 **S** Ascension Health, Saint Louis, MO
Primary Contact: Victor Giulianelli, FACHE, President and Chief Executive Officer
COO: Scott Bruce, Vice President Operations
CMO: Timothy Shoen, M.D., Vice President Medical Staff Services
CIO: James DeGroff, Director Technology and Network Services
CHR: Beth Case, Vice President Human Resources
Web address: www.smha.org
Control: Church–operated, Nongovernment, not–for profit **Service:** General Medical and Surgical

Staffed Beds: 153

Many Facility Codes have changed. Please refer to the AHA Guide Code Chart. © 2014 AHA Guide

NY

AUBURN—Cayuga County

☒ **AUBURN COMMUNITY HOSPITAL (330235)**, 17 Lansing Street,
Zip 13021–1943; tel. 315/255–7011, (Total facility includes 80 beds in nursing
home–type unit) **A**1 9 10 20 **F**1 3 12 13 15 26 28 29 30 31 34 35 40 45 49
50 51 53 54 55 57 59 64 70 76 78 79 81 82 85 89 98 103 107 108 110
111 114 119 124 129 130 132 135 144 146 147 148
Primary Contact: Scott A. Berlucchi, FACHE, President and Chief Executive Officer
COO: Thomas Filiak, Vice President Administration
CFO: Patrick M. Facteau, Chief Financial Officer
CMO: John A. Riccio, M.D., Chief Medical Officer
CIO: Chris Ryan, Chief Information Officer
CHR: Patrick M. Facteau, Chief Financial Officer
CNO: Tammy Sunderlin, Director of Nursing
Web address: www.auburnhospital.org
Control: Other not–for–profit (including NFP Corporation) **Service:** General
Medical and Surgical

> **Staffed Beds:** 179 **Admissions:** 4594 **Census:** 136 **Outpatient Visits:**
> 141095 **Births:** 386 **Total Expense ($000):** 89503 **Payroll Expense ($000):**
> 38250 **Personnel:** 664

BATAVIA—Genesee County

☒ **UNITED MEMORIAL MEDICAL CENTER (330073)**, 127 North Street,
Zip 14020–1631; tel. 585/343–6030, (Includes UNITED MEMORIAL MEDICAL
CENTER–BANK STREET, 127 North Street, Zip 14020–2260;
tel. 716/343–3131; UNITED MEMORIAL MEDICAL CENTER–NORTH STREET, 16
Banks Street, Zip 14020–1697; tel. 585/343–6030) **A**1 9 10 **F**3 4 8 13 15 17
18 19 28 29 30 31 34 35 40 42 43 49 54 57 59 64 65 70 75 76 77 78 79
81 82 84 85 86 87 89 97 107 111 114 115 119 127 129 130 131 135 144
146 147 148
Primary Contact: Mark C. Schoell, Chief Executive Officer
CFO: Robert Chiavetta, Vice President Finance
CMO: Michael Merrill, M.D., Interim Vice President Medical Affairs
CIO: Kurt Calman, Chief Information Officer
CHR: Sonja Gonyea, Director Human Resources
CNO: Mary Beth Bowen, R.N., Vice President Nursing and Chief Nursing Officer
Web address: www.ummc.org
Control: Other not–for–profit (including NFP Corporation) **Service:** General
Medical and Surgical

> **Staffed Beds:** 131 **Admissions:** 3726 **Census:** 55 **Outpatient Visits:** 218859
> **Births:** 626 **Total Expense ($000):** 77933 **Payroll Expense ($000):** 33514
> **Personnel:** 754

★ **VETERANS AFFAIRS WESTERN NEW YORK HEALTHCARE
SYSTEM–BATAVIA DIVISION**, 222 Richmond Avenue, Zip 14020–1288;
tel. 585/297–1000, (Nonreporting) **A**5 9 **S** Department of Veterans Affairs,
Washington, DC
Primary Contact: Brian G. Stiller, Director Medical Center
Web address: www.buffalo.va.gov/batavia.asp
Control: Veterans Affairs, Government, federal **Service:** General Medical and
Surgical

> **Staffed Beds:** 128

BATH—Steuben County

☒ **BATH VETERANS AFFAIRS MEDICAL CENTER**, 76 Veterans Avenue,
Zip 14810–0842; tel. 607/664–4000, (Nonreporting) **A**1 **S** Department of
Veterans Affairs, Washington, DC
Primary Contact: Michael J. Swartz, FACHE, Medical Center Director
COO: David Krueger, Associate Director
CFO: Jill Haynes, Financial Coach
CMO: Felipe Diaz, M.D., Chief of Staff
CIO: Karen Clancy, Manager Information Systems Operations
CHR: Susan DeSalvo, Manager Human Resources
Web address: www.bath.va.gov
Control: Veterans Affairs, Government, federal **Service:** General Medical and
Surgical

> **Staffed Beds:** 371

★ ◇ **IRA DAVENPORT MEMORIAL HOSPITAL (330144)**, 7571 State Route 54,
Zip 14810–9590; tel. 607/776–8500, (Nonreporting) **A**9 10 21 **S** Arnot Health,
Elmira, NY
Primary Contact: James B. Watson, President and Chief Operating Officer
COO: James B. Watson, President and Chief Operating Officer
CFO: Ronald J. Kintz, Chief Financial Officer
CMO: Dennis O'Connor, M.D., Medical Director
CIO: Gregg Martin, Chief Information Officer
CHR: Brian K. Forrest, Director Human Resources
CNO: Linda Donley, Vice President Operations
Web address: www.arnothealth.org
Control: Other not–for–profit (including NFP Corporation) **Service:** General
Medical and Surgical

> **Staffed Beds:** 184

BAY SHORE—Suffolk County

☒ △ **SOUTHSIDE HOSPITAL (330043)**, 301 East Main Street,
Zip 11706–8458; tel. 631/968–3000 **A**1 2 3 5 7 9 10 **F**3 11 13 15 17 18 20
22 24 26 28 29 30 31 32 34 35 36 38 40 41 43 44 45 46 49 50 54 55 56
57 58 59 60 61 62 63 64 65 66 69 70 73 74 75 76 77 78 79 81 82 84 85
86 87 89 90 93 96 97 98 100 101 102 103 107 108 110 111 114 115 118
119 120 121 123 126 129 130 131 132 135 146 147 148 **P**5 6 **S** North
Shore–Long Island Jewish Health System, Great Neck, NY
Primary Contact: Donna Moravick, R.N., MSN, Executive Director
CFO: Robert Power, Associate Executive Director Finance
CMO: Jay Enden, M.D., Medical Director
CIO: Lowney Mincy, Director Information Services
CHR: Anne J. Barrett, Associate Executive Director Human Resources
Web address: www.southsidehospital.org
Control: Other not–for–profit (including NFP Corporation) **Service:** General
Medical and Surgical

> **Staffed Beds:** 300 **Admissions:** 18726 **Census:** 265 **Outpatient Visits:**
> 153813 **Births:** 2615 **Total Expense ($000):** 418079 **Payroll Expense**
> **($000):** 204702 **Personnel:** 2238

BELLEROSE—Queens County, See New York City

BETHPAGE—Nassau County

☐ **ST. JOSEPH HOSPITAL (330332)**, 4295 Hempstead Turnpike,
Zip 11714–5769; tel. 516/579–6000 **A**1 9 10 **F**3 8 15 17 18 29 30 34 35 39
40 45 46 49 50 51 56 57 59 60 64 65 68 69 70 74 75 79 81 85 86 87 89
93 107 108 110 111 114 119 129 130 132 135 141 146 148 **S** Catholic
Health Services of Long Island, Rockville Centre, NY
Primary Contact: Drew Pallas, Executive Vice President and Chief Administrative
Officer
CFO: John Morahan, Vice President Finance
CMO: Howard Sussman, M.D., Chief Medical Officer
CHR: Peter Chiacchiaro, Vice President Human Resources
CNO: Barbara Gibbons, Vice President Patient Care Services
Web address: www.stjosephhospitalny.org
Control: Other not–for–profit (including NFP Corporation) **Service:** General
Medical and Surgical

> **Staffed Beds:** 140 **Admissions:** 6234 **Census:** 90 **Outpatient Visits:** 48399
> **Births:** 0 **Total Expense ($000):** 107040 **Payroll Expense ($000):** 44522
> **Personnel:** 648

BINGHAMTON—Broome County

BINGHAMTON GENERAL HOSPITAL See United Health Services
Hospitals–Binghamton

☐ **GREATER BINGHAMTON HEALTH CENTER (334012)**, 425 Robinson Street,
Zip 13904–1735; tel. 607/724–1391 **A**1 10 **F**29 30 54 56 65 71 75 77 86 98
99 100 101 103 104 105 106 130 132 135 143 146 **P**1 **S** New York State
Office of Mental Health, Albany, NY
Primary Contact: Mark Stephany, Executive Director
CFO: Cherry Randall, Business Officer
CHR: Renee O'Brien, Director Human Resources
Web address: www.omh.ny.gov/omhweb/facilities/bipc/facility.htm
Control: State–Government, nonfederal **Service:** Psychiatric

> **Staffed Beds:** 115 **Admissions:** 373 **Census:** 111 **Outpatient Visits:** 23176
> **Births:** 0 **Total Expense ($000):** 37413 **Personnel:** 391

☒ **OUR LADY OF LOURDES MEMORIAL HOSPITAL, INC. (330011)**, 169
Riverside Drive, Zip 13905–4246; tel. 607/798–5111 **A**1 2 9 10 **F**3 11 12 13
15 18 19 28 29 30 31 32 34 35 36 39 40 44 45 46 47 49 50 51 53 54 56
57 59 60 62 63 64 65 66 68 70 71 74 75 76 77 78 79 81 84 85 86 87 89
93 97 99 100 101 103 104 107 108 110 111 114 115 118 119 120 121
123 124 126 127 129 130 131 132 134 135 143 144 145 146 147 148 **P**6
S Ascension Health, Saint Louis, MO
Primary Contact: David Patak, President and Chief Executive Officer
COO: Linda Miller, DNP, R.N., Senior Vice President Operations and Chief Nursing
Officer
CFO: Gregg Hayton, Vice President Finance and Chief Financial Officer
CMO: Lisa Harris, M.D., Senior Vice President Medical Affairs
CIO: Thomas Ellerson, Chief Information Officer
CHR: Jim Silkworth, Chief Human Resources Officer
CNO: Linda Miller, DNP, R.N., Senior Vice President Operations and Chief Nursing
Officer
Web address: www.lourdes.com
Control: Church–operated, Nongovernment, not–for profit **Service:** General
Medical and Surgical

> **Staffed Beds:** 154 **Admissions:** 10100 **Census:** 115 **Outpatient Visits:**
> 1413373 **Births:** 1180 **Total Expense ($000):** 267888 **Payroll Expense**
> **($000):** 115326 **Personnel:** 1721

NY

Hospital, Medicare Provider Number, Address, Telephone, Approval, Facility, and Physician Codes, Health Care System

★ American Hospital Association (AHA) membership
☐ The Joint Commission accreditation   ◇ DNV Healthcare Inc. accreditation

○ Healthcare Facilities Accreditation Program
△ Commission on Accreditation of Rehabilitation Facilities (CARF) accreditation

---

UNITED HEALTH SERVICES HOSPITALS–BINGHAMTON (330394), 10–42 Mitchell Avenue, Zip 13903–1678; tel. 607/763–6000, (Includes BINGHAMTON GENERAL HOSPITAL, 10–42 Mitchell Avenue, Zip 13903; tel. 607/762–2200; WILSON MEMORIAL REGIONAL MEDICAL CENTER, 33–57 Harrison Street, Johnson City, Zip 13790; tel. 607/763–6000) **A**8 9 10 12 13 **F**1 3 4 5 8 11 12 13 15 17 18 20 22 24 26 28 29 30 31 32 33 34 35 37 38 39 40 43 45 46 49 50 51 52 54 57 58 59 60 61 64 65 68 70 72 74 75 76 77 78 79 81 84 85 86 87 89 90 92 93 96 97 98 100 101 102 103 104 107 108 110 114 115 118 119 124 126 127 130 131 132 135 146 147 148 **P**3 **S** United Health Services, Binghamton, NY
Primary Contact: Matthew J. Salanger, President and Chief Executive Officer
COO: John Carrigg, Executive Vice President and Chief Operating Officer
CFO: David MacDougall, Chief Financial Officer
CMO: Rajesh J. Dave', M.D., Executive Vice President and Chief Medical Officer
CHR: Michael McNally, Vice President Human Resources
CNO: E. Kay Boland, R.N., Vice President and Chief Nursing Officer
Web address: www.uhs.net
Control: Other not–for–profit (including NFP Corporation) **Service:** General Medical and Surgical

Staffed Beds: 456 **Admissions:** 17420 **Census:** 294 **Outpatient Visits:** 957965 **Births:** 1582 **Total Expense ($000):** 509384 **Payroll Expense ($000):** 194234 **Personnel:** 3721

BRENTWOOD—Suffolk County

☐ **PILGRIM PSYCHIATRIC CENTER (334013)**, 998 Crooked Hill Road, Zip 11717–1019; tel. 631/761–3500, (Nonreporting) **A**1 10 **S** New York State Office of Mental Health, Albany, NY
Primary Contact: Kathy O'Keefe, Executive Director
CFO: Florence Corwin, Director for Administration
CMO: Inderjit Singh, M.D., Clinical Director
CIO: Douglas Cargonara, Ph.D., Chief Information Officer
CHR: Florence Corwin, Director Administration
Web address: www.omh.ny.gov/omhweb/facilities/pgpc/facility.htm
Control: State–Government, nonfederal **Service:** Psychiatric

Staffed Beds: 569

BRONX—Bronx County, See New York City

BRONXVILLE—Westchester County

☒ **LAWRENCE HOSPITAL CENTER (330061)**, 55 Palmer Avenue, Zip 10708–3403; tel. 914/787–1000 **A**1 2 5 9 10 **F**3 7 11 12 13 15 18 28 29 30 31 34 35 36 40 41 45 46 47 48 50 51 55 57 59 60 62 63 64 65 68 69 70 72 73 74 75 77 78 79 81 82 84 85 87 91 92 93 94 107 108 110 111 114 115 118 119 129 130 131 132 135 141 146 147 148
Primary Contact: Edward M. Dinan, President and Chief Executive Officer
COO: James Y. Lee, Executive Vice President and Chief Operating Officer
CFO: Murray Askinazi, Senior Vice President and Chief Financial Officer
CMO: Werner Roeder, M.D., Vice President Medical Affairs
CHR: Tom Mastroianni, Vice President Human Resources
CNO: Rose Ann O'Hare, R.N., Senior Vice President Patient Services
Web address: www.lawrencehealth.org
Control: Other not–for–profit (including NFP Corporation) **Service:** General Medical and Surgical

Staffed Beds: 187 **Admissions:** 11328 **Census:** 159 **Outpatient Visits:** 159850 **Births:** 1839 **Total Expense ($000):** 204031 **Payroll Expense ($000):** 85281 **Personnel:** 1126

BROOKLYN—Kings County, See New York City

BUFFALO—Erie County

BRYLIN HOSPITALS (334022), 1263 Delaware Avenue, Zip 14209–2402; tel. 716/886–8200 **A**9 10 **F**5 54 98 99 103 104
Primary Contact: Eric D. Pleskow, President and Chief Executive Officer
CFO: E. Paul Hettich, Chief Financial Officer
CMO: Maria Cartagena, M.D., Chief Medical Officer
CIO: Pawel Wieczorek, Director Information Technology
CHR: Jacquelyn Bixler, Vice President Human Resources
Web address: www.brylin.com
Control: Corporation, Investor–owned, for–profit **Service:** Psychiatric

Staffed Beds: 88 **Admissions:** 1374 **Census:** 39 **Outpatient Visits:** 16105 **Births:** 0 **Total Expense ($000):** 14330 **Payroll Expense ($000):** 8449 **Personnel:** 222

☐ **BUFFALO PSYCHIATRIC CENTER (334052)**, 400 Forest Avenue, Zip 14213–1298; tel. 716/885–2261, (Nonreporting) **A**1 3 5 10 **S** New York State Office of Mental Health, Albany, NY
Primary Contact: Thomas Dodson, Executive Director
COO: Celia Spacone, M.D., Director Operations
CFO: Pamela Esposito, Director Administration
CMO: Jeffery Grace, M.D., Clinical Director
CIO: Anne Buchheit, Coordinator Mental Health Local Information Systems
CHR: Charles Siewert, Director Human Resources
CNO: Susan Fallis, Chief Nursing Officer
Web address: www.omh.ny.gov
Control: State–Government, nonfederal **Service:** Psychiatric

Staffed Beds: 240

☒ **ERIE COUNTY MEDICAL CENTER (330219)**, 462 Grider Street, Zip 14215–3098; tel. 716/898–3000, (Total facility includes 390 beds in nursing home–type unit) **A**1 3 5 9 10 **F**3 4 5 8 15 16 17 18 20 22 24 26 29 30 31 33 34 35 38 39 40 43 45 50 53 54 55 57 58 59 60 62 63 64 65 66 67 68 70 71 74 75 77 78 79 81 82 83 84 85 87 90 91 93 94 96 97 98 99 100 101 102 103 104 105 107 110 111 115 119 128 130 131 132 138 146 148 **P**4 5 6
Primary Contact: Richard C. Cleland, FACHE, President and Chief Operating Officer and Interim Chief Executive Officer
COO: Richard C. Cleland, FACHE, President and Chief Operating Officer
CFO: Michael Sammarco, M.D., Chief Financial Officer
CMO: Brian Murray, M.D., Medical Director
CIO: Leslie Feidt, Chief Information Officer
CHR: Kathleen O'Hara, Vice President Human Resources
CNO: Karen Ziemianski, R.N., Senior Vice President Nursing
Web address: www.ecmc.edu
Control: Hospital district or authority, Government, nonfederal **Service:** General Medical and Surgical

Staffed Beds: 876 **Admissions:** 16890 **Census:** 739 **Outpatient Visits:** 419755 **Births:** 0 **Total Expense ($000):** 467046 **Payroll Expense ($000):** 172109 **Personnel:** 2708

△ ◇ **KALEIDA HEALTH (330005)**, 100 High Street, Zip 14203–1154; tel. 716/859–5600, (Includes DE GRAFF MEMORIAL HOSPITAL, 445 Tremont Street, North Tonawanda, Zip 14120–0750, Mailing Address: P.O. Box 0750, Zip 14120–0750; tel. 716/694–4500; Tamara Owen, President; MILLARD FILLMORE SUBURBAN HOSPITAL, 1540 Maple Road, Williamsville, Zip 14221; tel. 716/688–3100; WOMEN AND CHILDREN'S HOSPITAL, 219 Bryant Street, Zip 14222–2099; tel. 716/878–7000; Cheryl Klass, President), (Total facility includes 380 beds in nursing home–type unit) **A**3 5 7 10 21 **F**1 2 3 9 11 12 13 15 17 18 19 20 21 22 24 26 27 28 29 30 31 32 34 35 36 37 38 39 40 41 43 44 45 46 47 48 49 50 51 54 55 58 59 60 61 62 63 64 65 66 68 70 71 72 73 74 75 76 77 78 79 80 81 82 83 84 85 86 87 88 89 90 91 92 93 94 96 97 99 100 101 102 104 105 107 108 109 110 111 114 115 119 126 128 129 130 131 132 134 143 146 147 148 **P**2 4 5 6
Primary Contact: Jody Lomeo, Interim CEO
CFO: Joseph Kessler, Executive Vice President and Chief Financial Officer
CMO: Margaret Paroski, M.D., Executive Vice President and Chief Medical Officer
CIO: Francis Meyer, Vice President Information Systems Technology
Web address: www.kaleidahealth.org
Control: Other not–for–profit (including NFP Corporation) **Service:** General Medical and Surgical

Staffed Beds: 1368 **Admissions:** 49875 **Census:** 1165 **Outpatient Visits:** 492041 **Births:** 5335 **Total Expense ($000):** 1230784 **Payroll Expense ($000):** 532876 **Personnel:** 7384

☒ **MERCY HOSPITAL (330279)**, 565 Abbott Road, Zip 14220–2095; tel. 716/826–7000, (Total facility includes 84 beds in nursing home–type unit) **A**1 3 5 9 10 **F**3 8 13 15 17 18 20 22 24 26 29 30 32 34 35 39 40 42 45 48 49 54 57 59 60 64 65 66 70 72 74 75 78 79 81 83 84 85 86 87 89 90 92 93 94 96 97 107 108 110 111 114 115 118 119 126 128 129 130 131 132 146 147 **P**5 6 **S** Catholic Health System, Buffalo, NY
Primary Contact: Charles J. Urlaub, President and Chief Executive Officer
COO: John J. Herman, Chief Operating Officer
CFO: James H. Dunlop, Jr., CPA, Senior Vice President Finance and Chief Financial Officer
CMO: Timothy Gabryel, M.D., Vice President Medical Affairs and Medical Director
CIO: Michael Galang, M.D., Chief Information Officer
CHR: Joseph A. Scrivo, Jr., Director Human Resources
CNO: Kathleen Guarino, R.N., Vice President Patient Care Services
Web address: www.chsbuffalo.org
Control: Church–operated, Nongovernment, not–for profit **Service:** General Medical and Surgical

Staffed Beds: 438 **Admissions:** 19506 **Census:** 346 **Outpatient Visits:** 351108 **Births:** 2358 **Total Expense ($000):** 354432 **Payroll Expense ($000):** 147687 **Personnel:** 2231

☐ **ROSWELL PARK CANCER INSTITUTE (330354)**, Elm and Carlton Streets, Zip 14263–0001; tel. 716/845–2300 **A**1 2 3 5 8 9 10 **F**3 8 14 15 18 29 30 31 32 34 35 38 39 44 45 46 47 49 50 55 56 57 58 59 63 64 65 66 67 68 70 74 75 77 78 79 81 82 84 85 86 87 89 90 93 94 96 97 98 100 104 107 108 110 111 112 114 115 116 117 118 119 120 121 123 124 126 130 132 135 136 141 145 146 147 148 **P**6
Primary Contact: Donald L. Trump, M.D., President and Chief Executive Officer
COO: Joyce M. Yasko, Ph.D., Chief Operating Officer
CFO: Gregory McDonald, Vice President Finance and Chief Financial Officer
CMO: Anthony Picone, M.D., Medical Director
CIO: Kerry Kerlin, Vice President Information Technology
CHR: Vicki Garcia, Vice President Human Resources
CNO: Maureen Kelly, R.N., Chief Nursing Officer
Web address: www.roswellpark.org
Control: Hospital district or authority, Government, nonfederal **Service:** Cancer

Staffed Beds: 132 **Admissions:** 5284 **Census:** 107 **Outpatient Visits:** 204450 **Births:** 0 **Total Expense ($000):** 628116 **Payroll Expense ($000):** 232922 **Personnel:** 3407

NY

Many Facility Codes have changed. Please refer to the AHA Guide Code Chart. © 2014 AHA Guide

☒ **SISTERS OF CHARITY HOSPITAL OF BUFFALO (330078)**, 2157 Main Street, Zip 14214–2692; tel. 716/862–1000, (Total facility includes 80 beds in nursing home–type unit) **A**1 2 3 5 9 10 12 13 **F**2 3 5 8 12 13 15 17 18 28 29 30 31 32 34 35 39 40 45 47 49 52 54 57 59 60 62 64 65 66 68 70 71 72 73 74 75 76 77 78 79 81 82 84 85 86 87 90 92 93 94 96 97 107 108 110 111 114 115 118 119 128 129 130 131 132 146 147 148 **P**5 6 **S** Catholic Health System, Buffalo, NY
Primary Contact: Peter U. Bergmann, President and Chief Executive Officer
COO: Matthew Hamp, Chief Operating Officer
CFO: James H. Dunlop, Jr., CPA, Chief Financial Officer
CMO: Nady Shehata, M.D., Vice President Medical Affairs
CIO: Michael Galang, M.D., Chief Information Officer
CHR: David DeLorenzo, Senior Director Human Resources
CNO: Mary E. Dillon, MS, Vice President Patient Care Services
Web address: www.chsbuffalo.org
Control: Church–operated, Nongovernment, not–for profit **Service:** General Medical and Surgical

Staffed Beds: 467 **Admissions:** 17420 **Census:** 310 **Outpatient Visits:** 726807 **Births:** 3353 **Total Expense ($000):** 317518 **Payroll Expense ($000):** 143090 **Personnel:** 2260

☒ **VETERANS AFFAIRS WESTERN NEW YORK HEALTHCARE SYSTEM–BUFFALO DIVISION**, 3495 Bailey Avenue, Zip 14215–1129; tel. 716/834–9200, (Nonreporting) **A**1 2 3 5 8 9 **S** Department of Veterans Affairs, Washington, DC
Primary Contact: Brian G. Stiller, Director Medical Center
CFO: Susan Gage, Financial Manager
CMO: Ali El–Solh, M.D., Interim Chief of Staff
CIO: Margaret Senker, Chief Information Officer
Web address: www.buffalo.va.gov/index.asp
Control: Veterans Affairs, Government, federal **Service:** General Medical and Surgical

Staffed Beds: 113

WOMEN AND CHILDREN'S HOSPITAL See KALEIDA Health

CALLICOON—Sullivan County

☐ **GROVER M. HERMAN HOSPITAL (331303)**, 8881 Route 97, Zip 12723; tel. 845/887–5530, (Nonreporting) **A**1 9 10 18 **S** Greater Hudson Valley Health System, Middletown, NY
Primary Contact: Chris L. White, Administrator
Web address: www.crmcny.org
Control: Other not–for–profit (including NFP Corporation) **Service:** General Medical and Surgical

Staffed Beds: 25

CANANDAIGUA—Ontario County

★ **CANANDAIGUA VETERANS AFFAIRS MEDICAL CENTER**, 400 Fort Hill Avenue, Zip 14424–1159; tel. 585/394–2000, (Nonreporting) **A**3 5 **S** Department of Veterans Affairs, Washington, DC
Primary Contact: Craig Howard, Director
CMO: Robert Babcock, M.D., Chief of Staff
CIO: Patricia Simon, Manager Information Systems
Web address: www.canandaigua.va.gov/
Control: Veterans Affairs, Government, federal **Service:** Psychiatric

Staffed Beds: 80

☒ **F. F. THOMPSON HOSPITAL (330074)**, 350 Parrish Street, Zip 14424–1731; tel. 585/396–6000, (Total facility includes 188 beds in nursing home–type unit) **A**1 9 10 **F**3 11 13 15 18 28 29 30 32 34 35 40 45 49 54 57 59 60 74 75 76 77 79 81 85 89 93 96 97 107 108 110 111 115 118 119 126 128 129 130 131 132 135 144 145 146 147 148 **S** University of Rochester Medical Center, Rochester, NY
Primary Contact: Michael Stapleton, President and Chief Executive Officer
COO: Kurt Koczent, Executive Vice President and Chief Operating Officer
CFO: Mark Prunoske, Chief Financial Officer and Senior Vice President Finance
CMO: David Baum, M.D., Senior Vice President Medical Services
CIO: Mark Halladay, Director Information Services
CHR: Jennifer DeVault, Vice President Associate Services
CNO: Hazel Robertshaw, R.N., Chief Nursing Officer, Vice President Patient Services
Web address: www.thompsonhealth.com
Control: Other not–for–profit (including NFP Corporation) **Service:** General Medical and Surgical

Staffed Beds: 251 **Admissions:** 5126 **Census:** 232 **Outpatient Visits:** 200015 **Births:** 652 **Total Expense ($000):** 115120 **Payroll Expense ($000):** 53364 **Personnel:** 906

THOMPSON HEALTH See F. F. Thompson Hospital

CARMEL—Putnam County

ARMS ACRES, 75 Seminary Hill Road, Zip 10512–1921; tel. 845/225–3400, (Nonreporting) **A**9
Primary Contact: Patrice Wallace–Moore, Chief Executive Officer and Executive Director
CFO: Jason Burczeuski, Controller
CMO: Fred Hesse, M.D., Medical Director
CIO: Dolores Watson, Director Health Information Management
CHR: Kim Halpin, Director Human Resources
CNO: Barbara Klein, R.N., Director of Nursing
Web address: www.armsacres.com
Control: Corporation, Investor–owned, for–profit **Service:** Alcoholism and other chemical dependency

Staffed Beds: 146

☒ **PUTNAM HOSPITAL CENTER (330273)**, 670 Stoneleigh Avenue, Zip 10512–3997; tel. 845/279–5711 **A**1 2 9 10 **F**3 8 11 12 13 15 17 18 28 29 30 31 34 35 36 38 40 41 45 46 49 55 56 57 59 61 64 65 68 74 75 76 77 78 79 81 82 83 84 85 87 89 92 93 94 97 98 100 102 103 104 105 107 108 110 111 114 118 119 120 121 126 129 130 131 132 143 146 148 **S** Health Quest Systems, Inc., LaGrangeville, NY
Primary Contact: James Caldas, President
COO: Maureen Zipparo, Chief Operating Officer
CFO: Anthony Mirdita, Chief Financial Officer
CMO: Ronald Tatelbaum, M.D., Interim Vice President Medical Affairs
CIO: Robert Diamond, Vice President and Chief Information Officer
CHR: Joan L. Calabrese, Director Human Resources
Web address: www.health–quest.org
Control: Other not–for–profit (including NFP Corporation) **Service:** General Medical and Surgical

Staffed Beds: 164 **Admissions:** 6410 **Census:** 86 **Outpatient Visits:** 200062 **Births:** 391 **Total Expense ($000):** 146152 **Payroll Expense ($000):** 48433 **Personnel:** 628

CARTHAGE—Jefferson County

☒ **CARTHAGE AREA HOSPITAL (330263)**, 1001 West Street, Zip 13619–9703; tel. 315/493–1000, (Nonreporting) **A**1 9 10 20
Primary Contact: Richard Duvall, Chief Operating Officer
COO: Richard Duvall, Chief Operating Officer
CFO: Donald Schnackel, Chief Financial Officer
CMO: Mirza Ashraf, M.D., Medical Director
CIO: Joe Virkler, Chief Information Officer
CHR: Cathy Siedlecki, Director Human Resources
CNO: Susan Kellogg, Administrator Patient Care Services
Web address: www.carthagehospital.com
Control: Other not–for–profit (including NFP Corporation) **Service:** General Medical and Surgical

Staffed Beds: 55

CASTLE POINT—Dutchess County

VETERAN AFFAIRS HUDSON VALLEY HEALTH CARE SYSTEM–CASTLE POINT DIVISION See Veterans Affairs Hudson Valley Health Care System–F.D. Roosevelt Hospital, Montrose

CATSKILL—Greene County

KAATERSKILL CARE See Columbia Memorial Hospital, Hudson

CLIFTON SPRINGS—Ontario County

★ ◇ **CLIFTON SPRINGS HOSPITAL AND CLINIC (330265)**, 2 Coulter Road, Zip 14432–1189; tel. 315/462–9561, (Nonreporting) **A**9 10 21
Primary Contact: Robert Cercek, Regional President of Operations
CFO: Sharon Kelley, Chief Financial Officer
CIO: Eric Jansen, Director Information Systems
CHR: Kathy Babb, Manager Human Resources
CNO: Donna P. Smith, R.N., Vice President Patient Care Services and Chief Nursing Officer
Web address: www.cliftonspringshospital.org
Control: Other not–for–profit (including NFP Corporation) **Service:** General Medical and Surgical

Staffed Beds: 212

NY

COBLESKILL—Schoharie County

⊞ **COBLESKILL REGIONAL HOSPITAL (330268)**, 178 Grandview Drive, Zip 12043–5144; tel. 518/254–3456, (Nonreporting) **A**1 9 10 **S** Bassett Healthcare Network, Cooperstown, NY
Primary Contact: Eric H. Stein, FACHE, President and Chief Executive Officer
CFO: Leanna Jensen, Vice President Finance and Chief Financial Officer
CMO: Roy Korn, M.D., Medical Director
CIO: Bridgette West, Director Patient Access Services
CHR: Christine Pirri, Senior Director Human Resources
CNO: Susan Oakes Ferrucci, Vice President Patient Services and Chief Nursing Officer
Web address: www.cobleskillhospital.org
Control: Other not–for–profit (including NFP Corporation) **Service:** General Medical and Surgical

Staffed Beds: 40

COOPERSTOWN—Otsego County

⊞ **BASSETT MEDICAL CENTER (330136)**, One Atwell Road, Zip 13326–1394; tel. 607/547–3100 **A**1 2 3 5 8 9 10 19 20 **F**3 8 11 12 13 15 18 20 22 24 26 28 29 30 31 32 34 35 38 39 40 43 44 45 48 49 50 51 54 56 57 58 59 60 61 64 65 68 70 71 74 75 76 77 78 79 81 82 84 85 86 87 89 92 93 94 97 98 99 100 101 102 103 104 107 108 109 110 111 114 115 116 117 118 119 120 121 123 124 126 129 130 131 132 134 135 141 142 143 144 146 147 148 **P**6 **S** Bassett Healthcare Network, Cooperstown, NY
Primary Contact: Vance Brown, M.D., President and Chief Executive Officer
COO: Bertine C. McKenna, Ph.D., Executive Vice President and Chief Operating Officer
CFO: Nicholas Nicoletta, Corporate Vice President and Chief Financial Officer
CMO: William W. LeCates, M.D., Medical Director
CIO: Scott C. Groom, Vice President Information Services and Chief Information Officer
CHR: Sara Z. Albright, Vice President Human Resources
CNO: Judi Brendle, Vice President Clinical Support and Chief Nursing Officer
Web address: www.bassett.org
Control: Other not–for–profit (including NFP Corporation) **Service:** General Medical and Surgical

Staffed Beds: 164 **Admissions:** 8898 **Census:** 131 **Outpatient Visits:** 667579 **Births:** 860 **Total Expense ($000):** 422456 **Payroll Expense ($000):** 223434 **Personnel:** 3165

CORNING—Steuben County

⊞ **CORNING HOSPITAL (330277)**, 176 Denison Parkway East, Zip 14830–2899; tel. 607/937–7200 **A**1 9 10 **F**3 8 11 13 15 28 29 31 32 34 35 37 38 40 44 45 49 50 53 57 59 64 70 75 76 77 78 79 81 82 87 89 92 93 100 107 108 110 111 115 119 120 121 124 129 130 131 132 135 145 146 147 148 **S** Guthrie Healthcare System, Sayre, PA
Primary Contact: Shirley P. Magana, R.N., MSN, President and Chief Operating Officer
COO: Shirley P. Magana, R.N., President and Chief Operating Officer
CFO: Francis M. Macafee, Vice President Finance and Chief Financial Officer
CMO: Chris Wentzel, M.D., Interim Medical Director
CIO: Carolyn Handrick, Manager Public Relations
CHR: Laura Manning, Administrative Director
CNO: Debra Raupers, MSN, Chief Nursing Officer
Web address: www.corninghospital.com
Control: Other not–for–profit (including NFP Corporation) **Service:** General Medical and Surgical

Staffed Beds: 82 **Admissions:** 3969 **Census:** 42 **Outpatient Visits:** 130490 **Births:** 409 **Total Expense ($000):** 71704 **Payroll Expense ($000):** 26115 **Personnel:** 531

CORNWALL—Orange County

ST. LUKE'S CORNWALL HOSPITAL – CORNWALL CAMPUS See St. Luke's Cornwall Hospital, Newburgh

CORTLAND—Cortland County

⊞ **CORTLAND REGIONAL MEDICAL CENTER (330175)**, 134 Homer Avenue, Zip 13045–1206; tel. 607/756–3500, (Total facility includes 82 beds in nursing home–type unit) **A**1 9 10 20 **F**2 3 8 11 13 15 28 29 34 35 40 45 49 50 54 56 57 59 62 64 68 70 75 76 77 79 81 82 85 86 87 89 91 93 96 98 100 102 107 108 110 111 114 115 118 129 128 130 131 132 133 135 144 146 147 148 **P**6
Primary Contact: Mark Webster, President and CEO
COO: Dennis Trepanier, Interim Chief Operating Officer
CFO: Denise Wrinn, Vice President Finance and Chief Financial Officer
CMO: Roger Scott, D.O., Vice President Medical Affairs and Chief Medical Officer
CIO: Robert J. Duthe, Director Information Systems and Chief Information Officer
CHR: Bonita N. Lindberg, Director Human Resources
CNO: Mary Wright, Vice President Nursing Services and Chief Nursing Officer
Web address: www.cortlandregional.org
Control: Other not–for–profit (including NFP Corporation) **Service:** General Medical and Surgical

Staffed Beds: 205 **Admissions:** 4229 **Census:** 145 **Outpatient Visits:** 129385 **Births:** 458 **Total Expense ($000):** 89048 **Payroll Expense ($000):** 37613 **Personnel:** 687

CORTLANDT MANOR—Westchester County

☐ **HUDSON VALLEY HOSPITAL CENTER (330267)**, 1980 Crompond Road, Zip 10567–4182; tel. 914/737–9000 **A**1 9 10 **F**3 8 9 11 12 13 15 18 28 29 30 31 34 35 37 40 45 46 47 53 57 59 67 70 72 74 75 76 77 78 79 81 82 85 86 87 89 93 107 108 110 111 115 119 121 130 131 132 135 145 146 147 148
Primary Contact: John C. Federspiel, President and Chief Executive Officer
COO: Deborah Neuendorf, Vice President Administration
CFO: Mark Webster, Vice President Finance
CMO: William Higgins, M.D., Vice President Medical Affairs
CIO: Bud Sorbello, Director Management Information Systems
CHR: Jeane L. Costella, Vice President
CNO: Kathleen Webster, R.N., Vice President Patient Services
Web address: www.hvhc.org
Control: Other not–for–profit (including NFP Corporation) **Service:** General Medical and Surgical

Staffed Beds: 128 **Admissions:** 7633 **Census:** 95

CUBA—Allegany County

CUBA MEMORIAL HOSPITAL (331301), 140 West Main Street, Zip 14727–1398; tel. 585/968–2000, (Nonreporting) **A**9 10 18
Primary Contact: Andrew Boser, Chief Executive Officer
CFO: Jack Ormond, Chief Financial Officer
Web address: www.cubamemorialhospital.com
Control: Other not–for–profit (including NFP Corporation) **Service:** General Medical and Surgical

Staffed Beds: 81

DANSVILLE—Livingston County

⊞ **NICHOLAS H. NOYES MEMORIAL HOSPITAL (330238)**, 111 Clara Barton Street, Zip 14437–9503; tel. 585/335–6001, (Nonreporting) **A**1 9 10
Primary Contact: Amy Pollard, R.N., President and Chief Executive Officer
CFO: Jay T. Maslyn, Chief Financial Officer
CMO: Douglas Mayhle, M.D., Medical Director
CIO: John Dorak, Chief Information Officer
CNO: Tamara West, R.N., Vice President Patient Care
Web address: www.noyes–health.org
Control: Other not–for–profit (including NFP Corporation) **Service:** General Medical and Surgical

Staffed Beds: 54

DELHI—Delaware County

⊞ **O'CONNOR HOSPITAL (331305)**, 460 Andes Road, State Route 28, Zip 13753–7407; tel. 607/746–0300 **A**1 9 10 18 **F**15 29 34 35 40 45 46 50 56 57 59 64 75 77 79 81 85 86 87 91 92 93 96 107 110 111 119 130 132 133 135 147 **S** Bassett Healthcare Network, Cooperstown, NY
Primary Contact: Daniel M. Ayres, Chief Executive Officer
CFO: Nicholas Nicoletta, Vice President and Chief Financial Officer
CMO: Alberto Gaitan, M.D., Medical Director
CHR: Barbara Green, Director Human Resources
CNO: Debra Neale, R.N., Chief Nursing Officer
Web address: www.bassett.org
Control: Other not–for–profit (including NFP Corporation) **Service:** General Medical and Surgical

Staffed Beds: 16 **Admissions:** 317 **Census:** 7 **Outpatient Visits:** 30674 **Births:** 0 **Total Expense ($000):** 20271 **Payroll Expense ($000):** 7042 **Personnel:** 155

DIX HILLS—Suffolk County

☐ **SAGAMORE CHILDREN'S PSYCHIATRIC CENTER**, 197 Half Hollow Road, Zip 11746–5861; tel. 631/370–1700, (Nonreporting) **A**1 **S** New York State Office of Mental Health, Albany, NY
Primary Contact: Kathy O'Keefe, Interim Executive Director
COO: Cathy Stein, Chief Inpatient Services
CFO: Jane Alexander, Director Facility Administrative Services
CIO: Bryan Doherty, Management Information Technology Services I
CHR: Nancy Angell, Associate Administrator Personnel
CNO: Sandra King, Chief Nursing Officer
Web address: www.omh.ny.gov
Control: State–Government, nonfederal **Service:** Children's hospital psychiatric

Staffed Beds: 69

DUNKIRK—Chautauqua County

★ ◇ **BROOKS MEMORIAL HOSPITAL (330229)**, 529 Central Avenue, Zip 14048–2599; tel. 716/366–1111, (Nonreporting) **A**9 10 21
Primary Contact: J. Gary Rhodes, FACHE, Interim President and Chief Executive Officer
CFO: Ralph Webdale, Vice President Finance
CIO: Kathy Kucharski, Director Management Information Systems
CHR: Joan VanDette, Vice President Human Resources
Web address: www.brookshospital.org
Control: Other not–for–profit (including NFP Corporation) **Service:** General Medical and Surgical

Staffed Beds: 65

Many Facility Codes have changed. Please refer to the AHA Guide Code Chart. © 2014 AHA Guide

NY

EAST MEADOW—Nassau County

☒ **NASSAU UNIVERSITY MEDICAL CENTER (330027)**, 2201 Hempstead Turnpike, Zip 11554–1859; tel. 516/572–0123, (Nonreporting) **A**1 3 5 9 10 12 13
Primary Contact: Victor Politi, M.D., President and Chief Executive Officer
COO: Harold E. McDonald, Deputy Executive Director and Senior Vice President Administration
CFO: John P. Maher, Executive Vice President and Chief Financial Officer
CMO: Victor Scarmato, M.D., Acting Medical Director
CIO: Farooq Ajmal, Vice President and Chief Information Officer
CHR: Maureen Roarty, Executive Vice President Human Resources
CNO: Kathy Skarka, MSN, Executive Vice President Patient Care Services
Web address: www.nuhealth.net
Control: Hospital district or authority, Government, nonfederal **Service:** General Medical and Surgical

Staffed Beds: 481

ELIZABETHTOWN—Essex County

☒ **ELIZABETHTOWN COMMUNITY HOSPITAL (331302)**, Park Street, Zip 12932–0277, Mailing Address: P.O. Box 277, Zip 12932–0277; tel. 518/873–6377 **A**1 9 10 18 **F**3 7 11 12 15 28 29 30 31 32 34 35 40 45 46 50 53 54 57 59 60 64 65 68 75 77 78 81 87 90 93 97 107 110 111 115 119 127 130 132 133 145 146 147 **P**6
Primary Contact: Rodney C. Boula, Administrator and Chief Executive Officer
COO: Matthew Nolan, Director Facilities and Operations
CFO: Alan Chardavoyne, Controller
CMO: Rob DeMuro, M.D., President Medical Staff
CHR: Michelle Meachem, Director Human Resources
Web address: www.ech.org
Control: Other not–for–profit (including NFP Corporation) **Service:** General Medical and Surgical

Staffed Beds: 25 Admissions: 509 Census: 10 Outpatient Visits: 35064 Births: 0 Total Expense ($000): 19955 Payroll Expense ($000): 10742 Personnel: 144

ELLENVILLE—Ulster County

★ **ELLENVILLE REGIONAL HOSPITAL (331310)**, 10 Healthy Way, Zip 12428–5612; tel. 845/647–6400, (Nonreporting) **A**9 10 18
Primary Contact: Steven L. Kelley, President and Chief Executive Officer
CFO: Patricia Gavis, Chief Financial Officer
CMO: Walter Sperling, M.D., Medical Director
CHR: Deborah Briggs, Vice President Human Resources, Marketing, Volunteer Services and Community Relations
CNO: Ann Marie Kelly, Chief Nursing Officer
Web address: www.ellenvilleregional.org
Control: Other not–for–profit (including NFP Corporation) **Service:** General Medical and Surgical

Staffed Beds: 25

ELMHURST—Queens County, See New York City

ELMIRA—Chemung County

★ ◇ **ARNOT OGDEN MEDICAL CENTER (330090)**, 600 Roe Avenue, Zip 14905–1629; tel. 607/737–4100, (Total facility includes 40 beds in nursing home–type unit) **A**2 6 9 10 21 **F**11 12 15 17 18 20 22 24 26 28 29 30 31 35 39 40 45 46 48 49 50 51 53 54 56 57 59 60 61 65 68 70 72 73 74 75 76 77 78 79 81 87 89 91 93 97 100 103 106 107 110 111 115 116 119 128 129 130 131 132 135 143 146 147 148 **S** Arnot Health, Elmira, NY
Primary Contact: H. Fred Farley, R.N., Ph.D., FACHE, President and Chief Operating Officer
CFO: Ronald J. Kintz, Vice President and Treasurer
CMO: William Huffner, M.D., Vice President Medical Affairs
CIO: Gregg Martin, Manager Management Information Systems
CHR: Brian K. Forrest, Director Human Resources
CNO: Mary M. Vosburgh, R.N., Vice President Nursing and Chief Nursing Officer
Web address: www.aomc.org
Control: Other not–for–profit (including NFP Corporation) **Service:** General Medical and Surgical

Staffed Beds: 216 Admissions: 12082 Census: 150 Outpatient Visits: 298042 Births: 1400 Total Expense ($000): 361500 Payroll Expense ($000): 178000 Personnel: 2038

☐ **ELMIRA PSYCHIATRIC CENTER (334045)**, 100 Washington Street, Zip 14901–2898; tel. 607/737–4739 **A**1 10 **F**29 35 39 54 64 98 99 101 103 104 106 132 **P**6 **S** New York State Office of Mental Health, Albany, NY
Primary Contact: Mark Stephany, Executive Director
COO: Karen Patterson, Deputy Director Operations
CFO: J. Paul Bedzyk, Deputy Director Administration
CMO: Kurt Hahn, M.D., Acting Clinical Director
CIO: Jeremy Newcomer, Director Information Services
CHR: Patricia Santulli, Director Human Resources
CNO: Pam Seeley, Chief Nursing Officer
Web address: www.omh.ny.gov/omhweb/facilities/elpc/facility.htm
Control: State–Government, nonfederal **Service:** Psychiatric

Staffed Beds: 100 Admissions: 290 Census: 82 Outpatient Visits: 51183 Births: 0 Total Expense ($000): 34843 Payroll Expense ($000): 20858 Personnel: 366

★ ◇ **ST. JOSEPH'S HOSPITAL (330108)**, 555 St. Joseph's Boulevard, Zip 14901–3223; tel. 607/733–6541, (Includes TWIN TIERS REHABILITATION CENTER), (Total facility includes 85 beds in nursing home–type unit) **A**9 10 21 **F**4 11 29 30 31 34 35 36 40 41 45 46 48 49 50 56 57 58 59 64 65 66 68 74 75 77 83 84 85 86 87 90 91 92 93 94 96 97 98 100 101 102 103 106 107 111 114 119 128 130 132 135 143 144 145 146 **S** Arnot Health, Elmira, NY
Primary Contact: H. Fred Farley, R.N., Ph.D., FACHE, President and Chief Operating Officer
COO: H. Fred Farley, R.N., President and Chief Operating Officer
CFO: Ronald J. Kintz, Senior Vice President Finance and Chief Financial Officer
CMO: William Huffner, M.D., Chief Medical Officer and Senior Vice President Medical Affairs
CIO: Gregg Martin, Chief Information Officer
CHR: Brian K. Forrest, Vice President Human Resources
CNO: Mary M. Vosburgh, R.N., Vice President Nursing and Chief Nursing Officer
Web address: www.stjosephs.org
Control: Other not–for–profit (including NFP Corporation) **Service:** General Medical and Surgical

Staffed Beds: 250 Admissions: 3983 Census: 142 Outpatient Visits: 77532 Births: 0 Total Expense ($000): 53100 Payroll Expense ($000): 19748

ENDICOTT—Broome County

UHS WALK–IN – ENDICOTT See United Health Services Hospitals–Binghamton, Binghamton

FAR ROCKAWAY—Queens County, See New York City

FLUSHING—Queens County, See New York City

FOREST HILLS—Queens County, See New York City

FRESH MEADOWS—Queens County

CORNERSTONE OF MEDICAL ARTS CENTER HOSPITAL, 159–05 Union Turnpike, Zip 11366–1950; tel. 212/755–0200, (Nonreporting) **A**9
Primary Contact: Norman J. Sokolow, Chairman and Chief Executive Officer
COO: Thomas C. Puzo, President and Chief Operating Officer
CFO: Jeff OniFather, Chief Financial Officer
CMO: Sami Kaddouri, M.D., Medical Director
CHR: Gloria Burtch, Director Human Resources
Web address: www.cornerstoneny.com
Control: Corporation, Investor–owned, for–profit **Service:** Alcoholism and other chemical dependency

Staffed Beds: 162

GENEVA—Ontario County

☒ **GENEVA GENERAL HOSPITAL (330058)**, 196 North Street, Zip 14456–1694; tel. 315/787–4000 **A**1 9 10 **F**3 8 11 13 15 17 18 28 29 30 31 32 34 35 40 45 50 54 57 59 60 61 64 66 69 70 74 75 76 77 78 79 81 85 86 87 90 92 93 96 97 107 108 110 111 115 118 119 129 130 131 132 135 146 147 **P**6 **S** Finger Lakes Health, Geneva, NY
Primary Contact: Jose Acevedo, M.D., President and Chief Executive Officer
COO: James Hiserodt, Senior Vice President Operations
CFO: Pamela Johnson, Treasurer and Chief Financial Officer
CMO: Jason Feinberg, M.D., Vice President Medical Affairs and Chief Medical Officer
CIO: John Oates, Director Information Systems
CHR: Patrick R. Boyle, Vice President Human Resources
CNO: Eileen Gage, R.N., Vice President Nursing
Web address: www.flhealth.org
Control: Other not–for–profit (including NFP Corporation) **Service:** General Medical and Surgical

Staffed Beds: 132 Admissions: 3926 Census: 48 Outpatient Visits: 437034 Births: 188 Total Expense ($000): 67314 Payroll Expense ($000): 45708 Personnel: 761

NY

Hospital, Medicare Provider Number, Address, Telephone, Approval, Facility, and Physician Codes, Health Care System

★ American Hospital Association (AHA) membership
☐ The Joint Commission accreditation
◇ DNV Healthcare Inc. accreditation
○ Healthcare Facilities Accreditation Program
△ Commission on Accreditation of Rehabilitation Facilities (CARF) accreditation

GLEN COVE—Nassau County

✠ **GLEN COVE HOSPITAL (330181)**, 101 St. Andrews Lane, Zip 11542–2254; tel. 516/674–7300 **A**1 2 3 5 9 10 **F**3 8 9 11 14 15 17 18 28 29 30 31 32 33 34 35 36 38 39 40 44 45 46 47 48 49 50 54 55 56 57 58 59 60 61 63 64 65 66 68 69 70 74 75 77 78 79 81 82 84 85 86 87 90 91 92 93 94 96 97 98 100 101 102 103 104 107 108 110 111 115 117 118 119 121 130 131 132 135 143 146 147 **P**5 6 **S** North Shore–Long Island Jewish Health System, Great Neck, NY
Primary Contact: Susan Kwiatek, R.N., Executive Director
COO: Michele Frankel, Associate Executive Director Finance
CFO: Michele Frankel, Associate Executive Director Finance
CMO: Barbara Barnett, M.D., Medical Director
CHR: Thomas Salvo, Associate Executive Director Human Resources
CNO: Cathy Sheerin, R.N., Director Patient Care Services
Web address: www.northshorelij.com
Control: Other not–for–profit (including NFP Corporation) **Service:** General Medical and Surgical

Staffed Beds: 235 **Admissions:** 8025 **Census:** 148 **Outpatient Visits:** 79674 **Births:** 0 **Total Expense ($000):** 183737 **Payroll Expense ($000):** 98572 **Personnel:** 987

GLEN OAKS—Queens County, See New York City

GLENS FALLS—Warren County

✠ **GLENS FALLS HOSPITAL (330191)**, 100 Park Street, Zip 12801–4413; tel. 518/926–1000 **A**1 2 5 9 10 **F**8 11 13 15 17 18 20 22 28 29 30 31 32 34 35 36 40 45 46 47 49 50 51 54 55 56 58 59 60 64 70 74 75 76 77 78 81 85 87 89 90 92 93 97 98 99 100 102 104 105 107 110 111 114 115 116 117 119 120 121 127 129 130 135 144 145 146 147 148 **P**6
Primary Contact: Dianne Shugrue, President and Chief Executive Officer
COO: Mark Holtz, Senior Vice President Operations and Chief Operating Officer
CFO: Mitchell Amado, Senior Vice President Finance and Chief Financial Officer
CMO: Robert W. Pringle, M.D., Vice President Medical Affairs and Chief Medical Officer
CIO: John Kelleher, Vice President Information Technology and Chief Information Officer
CHR: Kyle Brock, Vice President Human Resources
CNO: Donna Kirker NEA–BC, R.N., Vice President Patient Services and Chief Nursing Officer
Web address: www.glensfallshospital.org
Control: Other not–for–profit (including NFP Corporation) **Service:** General Medical and Surgical

Staffed Beds: 363 **Admissions:** 14913 **Census:** 197 **Outpatient Visits:** 823658 **Births:** 1330 **Total Expense ($000):** 306583 **Payroll Expense ($000):** 147072 **Personnel:** 2273

GLENVILLE—Schenectady County

CONIFER PARK, 79 Glenridge Road, Zip 12302–4523; tel. 518/399–6446, (Nonreporting) **A**9
Primary Contact: Jeanne Gluchowski, Executive Director
COO: Jeanne Gluchowski, Executive Director
CFO: Jason Burczeuski, Controller
CMO: John Melbourne, M.D., Medical Director
CIO: Amy Kentera, Chief Information Officer
CHR: Maureen Fowler, Director Human Resources
Web address: www.libertymgt.com
Control: Corporation, Investor–owned, for–profit **Service:** Alcoholism and other chemical dependency

Staffed Beds: 225

GLOVERSVILLE—Fulton County

★ ◇ **NATHAN LITTAUER HOSPITAL AND NURSING HOME (330276)**, 99 East State Street, Zip 12078–1203; tel. 518/725–8621, (Total facility includes 84 beds in nursing home–type unit) **A**5 9 10 21 **F**3 8 11 13 15 18 28 29 30 31 32 34 35 36 37 40 45 46 50 53 54 57 59 61 64 65 70 74 75 76 77 78 79 81 82 85 86 87 89 93 97 107 108 110 115 118 119 128 130 131 132 135 145 146 147 **P**6
Primary Contact: Laurence E. Kelly, President and Chief Executive Officer
CFO: Michael Ostrander, Chief Financial Officer
CMO: Frederick Goldberg, M.D., Vice President Medical Affairs and Chief Medical Officer
CIO: Martin Brown, Vice President Information Services and Chief Information Officer
CHR: Lana Wydra, Vice President Human Resources
CNO: Regina Mulligan, Vice President Nursing
Web address: www.nlh.org
Control: Other not–for–profit (including NFP Corporation) **Service:** General Medical and Surgical

Staffed Beds: 158 **Admissions:** 3244 **Census:** 111 **Outpatient Visits:** 242462 **Births:** 360 **Total Expense ($000):** 89706 **Payroll Expense ($000):** 45265 **Personnel:** 778

GOUVERNEUR—St. Lawrence County

✠ **GOUVERNEUR HOSPITAL (331315)**, 77 West Barney Street, Zip 13642–1040; tel. 315/287–1000, (Total facility includes 40 beds in nursing home–type unit) **A**1 9 10 18 **F**3 8 11 15 29 40 45 54 59 64 75 77 81 85 93 97 107 108 111 114 119 127 128 133 **P**6 **S** St. Lawrence Health System, Potsdam, NY
Primary Contact: Marlinda L. LaValley, Chief Executive Officer
CFO: Richard T. Lang, Chief Financial Officer
CMO: Donald Schuessler, M.D., Medical Director
CIO: Linda Fishel, Manager Information Services
CHR: Cathy Chirico, Director Human Resources
Web address: www.gvnrhospital.org
Control: Other not–for–profit (including NFP Corporation) **Service:** General Medical and Surgical

Staffed Beds: 65 **Admissions:** 414 **Census:** 43 **Outpatient Visits:** 48232 **Births:** 0 **Total Expense ($000):** 19562 **Payroll Expense ($000):** 7184 **Personnel:** 174

GREENPORT—Suffolk County

✠ **EASTERN LONG ISLAND HOSPITAL (330088)**, 201 Manor Place, Zip 11944–1298; tel. 631/477–1000 **A**1 9 10 **F**3 4 17 18 28 29 34 40 45 47 49 53 56 59 64 65 68 70 74 78 79 81 82 85 93 97 98 100 102 103 106 107 110 111 119 130 132 135 146
Primary Contact: Paul J. Connor, III, President and Chief Executive Officer
CFO: Robert A. Ragona, Vice President Finance
CMO: Lloyd Simon, M.D., Medical Director
CIO: Dan Scotto, Director Data Processing
CHR: August F. Menchini, Director Human Resources
CNO: D. Patricia Pispisa, Vice President Patient Care Services
Web address: www.elih.org
Control: Other not–for–profit (including NFP Corporation) **Service:** General Medical and Surgical

Staffed Beds: 90 **Admissions:** 2891 **Census:** 51 **Outpatient Visits:** 42800 **Births:** 0 **Total Expense ($000):** 47357 **Payroll Expense ($000):** 21043 **Personnel:** 304

HAMILTON—Madison County

✠ **COMMUNITY MEMORIAL HOSPITAL (330249)**, 150 Broad Street, Zip 13346–9518; tel. 315/824–1100, (Total facility includes 40 beds in nursing home–type unit) **A**1 9 10 **F**3 11 18 29 40 45 53 56 57 64 70 74 79 81 85 89 93 97 107 108 110 111 119 127 128 130 135 144 146
Primary Contact: Sean Fadale, President and Chief Executive Officer
CFO: Richard S. Kirby, Executive Vice President and Chief Financial Officer
CMO: Michael S. Jastremski, M.D., Vice President Medical Affairs and Director Emergency Services
Web address: www.communitymemorial.org
Control: Other not–for–profit (including NFP Corporation) **Service:** General Medical and Surgical

Staffed Beds: 76 **Admissions:** 1540 **Census:** 50 **Outpatient Visits:** 11908 **Births:** 0 **Total Expense ($000):** 36463 **Payroll Expense ($000):** 16161 **Personnel:** 329

HARRIS—Sullivan County

✠ **CATSKILL REGIONAL MEDICAL CENTER (330386)**, 68 Harris Bushville Road, Zip 12742–5030, Mailing Address: P.O. Box 800, Zip 12742–0800; tel. 845/794–3300, (Total facility includes 64 beds in nursing home–type unit) **A**1 9 10 19 20 **F**2 3 4 8 11 13 15 17 18 28 29 30 31 34 35 38 40 42 45 51 54 56 57 59 65 68 70 76 78 79 81 85 86 87 89 93 96 97 98 102 103 107 111 115 119 127 128 130 132 133 146 147 148 **S** Greater Hudson Valley Health System, Middletown, NY
Primary Contact: Gerard Galarneau, M.D., Chief Executive Officer and Chief Medical Officer
CFO: Frank Hemeon, Interim Chief Financial Officer
CMO: Gerard Galarneau, M.D., Chief Executive Officer and Chief Medical Officer
CIO: John Lynch, Vice President Chief Information Officer
CHR: Zigmund Nowicki, Director Human Resources
CNO: Rolland Bojo, R.N., Chief Nursing Officer, Administrator Patient Care and Services
Web address: www.crmcny.org
Control: Other not–for–profit (including NFP Corporation) **Service:** General Medical and Surgical

Staffed Beds: 196 **Admissions:** 4053 **Census:** 119 **Outpatient Visits:** 88857 **Births:** 608 **Total Expense ($000):** 88898 **Payroll Expense ($000):** 39550 **Personnel:** 596

HOLLISWOOD—Queens County, See New York City

HORNELL—Steuben County

☒ **ST. JAMES MERCY HEALTH SYSTEM (330151)**, 411 Canisteo Street,
Zip 14843–2197; tel. 607/324–8000, (Nonreporting) **A**1 9 10 20 **S** Catholic
Health East / Trinity Health, Livonia, MI
Primary Contact: Jennifer Sullivan, President and Chief Executive Officer
CFO: Stan Konopko, Chief Financial Officer
CMO: John Carroll, M.D., Chief Medical Officer
CIO: Jason Soles, Manager Information Systems
CHR: Jennifer Spike, Director Human Resources
CNO: Kathleen Brodbeck, MSN, RN–B, Chief Nursing Officer
Web address: www.stjamesmercy.org
Control: Other not–for–profit (including NFP Corporation) **Service:** General
Medical and Surgical

Staffed Beds: 102

HUDSON—Columbia County

★ **COLUMBIA MEMORIAL HOSPITAL (330094)**, 71 Prospect Avenue,
Zip 12534–2907; tel. 518/828–7601, (Includes KAATERSKILL CARE, 161
Jefferson Heights, Catskill, Zip 12414; tel. 518/943–6363), (Nonreporting) **A**9 10
Primary Contact: Jay P. Cahalan, Chief Executive Officer
COO: Karen Tassey, MS, Chief Operating Officer
CFO: Vincent Dingman, III, Chief Financial Officer
CMO: V. Richard Back, M.D., Chief Medical Officer
CIO: Cathleen Crowley, Chief Information Officer
CHR: Patricia Finnegan, Vice President
Web address: www.columbiamemorial.com
Control: Other not–for–profit (including NFP Corporation) **Service:** General
Medical and Surgical

Staffed Beds: 218

HUNTINGTON—Suffolk County

☒ **HUNTINGTON HOSPITAL (330045)**, 270 Park Avenue, Zip 11743–2799;
tel. 631/351–2200 **A**1 2 9 10 **F**3 11 12 13 15 17 18 20 22 26 29 30 31 34
35 36 38 40 43 44 45 49 50 53 54 55 56 57 58 59 60 63 64 65 66 68 69
70 73 74 75 76 78 79 81 82 84 85 86 87 89 91 93 97 98 100 101 102 103
107 108 110 111 114 115 118 119 130 132 135 146 147 148 **P**5 6 **S** North
Shore–Long Island Jewish Health System, Great Neck, NY
Primary Contact: Kevin F. Lawlor, President and Chief Executive Officer
CFO: Michael Fagan, Chief Financial Officer
CMO: Michael Grosso, M.D., Senior Vice President Medical Affairs
CIO: Linda Fischer, Director Information Services
CHR: Donna Cice, Vice President Human Resources
CNO: Susan Knoepffler, R.N., Vice President Nursing
Web address: www.hunthosp.org
Control: Other not–for–profit (including NFP Corporation) **Service:** General
Medical and Surgical

Staffed Beds: 290 Admissions: 15036 Census: 199 Outpatient Visits: 122371 Births: 1394 Total Expense ($000): 321440 Payroll Expense ($000): 158321 Personnel: 1661

IRVING—Chautauqua County

◇ **LAKE SHORE HEALTH CARE CENTER**, 845 Route 5 and 20, Zip 14081–9716;
tel. 716/951–7000, (Nonreporting) **A**9 21
Primary Contact: John P. Galati, Interim Chief Executive Officer
CMO: James Wild, M.D., Medical Director
CIO: Louis Di Rienzo, Chief Information Officer
CHR: Tracie Luther, Vice President Human Resources
Web address: www.tlchealth.org
Control: Other not–for–profit (including NFP Corporation) **Service:** General
Medical and Surgical

Staffed Beds: 200

ITHACA—Tompkins County

☒ **CAYUGA MEDICAL CENTER AT ITHACA (330307)**, 101 Dates Drive,
Zip 14850–1342; tel. 607/274–4011 **A**1 2 5 9 10 **F**3 8 12 13 15 18 20 22 28
29 30 31 34 38 40 41 45 49 51 54 57 59 61 64 70 72 74 75 76 77 78 79
81 82 84 85 86 87 90 93 98 99 100 101 102 103 107 108 110 111 114
115 116 118 119 121 129 130 131 132 133 135 144 145 146 147 148 **P**6
Primary Contact: John Rudd, President and Chief Executive Officer
CFO: John Collett, Vice President and Chief Financial Officer
CMO: David M. Evelyn, M.D., Vice President Medical Affairs
CIO: Brett Mello, Chief Information Officer
CHR: Alan Pedersen, Vice President Human Resources
CNO: Susan Nohelty, R.N., Vice President Patient Services
Web address: www.cayugamed.org
Control: Other not–for–profit (including NFP Corporation) **Service:** General
Medical and Surgical

Staffed Beds: 193 Admissions: 6418 Census: 76 Outpatient Visits: 205363 Births: 850 Total Expense ($000): 170506 Payroll Expense ($000): 63114 Personnel: 1146

JACKSON HEIGHTS—Queens County, See New York City

JAMAICA—Queens County, See New York City

JAMESTOWN—Chautauqua County

☒ **WOMAN'S CHRISTIAN ASSOCIATION HOSPITAL (330239)**, 207 Foote
Avenue, Zip 14701–7077, Mailing Address: P.O. Box 840, Zip 14702–0840;
tel. 716/487–0141 **A**1 2 9 10 **F**3 4 5 8 11 13 15 18 19 20 28 29 31 32 34
35 40 45 46 57 59 64 68 69 70 74 75 76 77 78 79 81 82 83 84 85 86 87
89 90 92 93 96 98 99 100 101 102 103 104 107 108 110 111 117 119 121
126 129 130 131 132 135 141 146 147 148
Primary Contact: Betsy T. Wright, President and Chief Executive Officer
CMO: Marlene Garone, M.D., Vice President Medical Affairs and Medical Director
CIO: Keith Robison, Chief Information Officer
CHR: Karen Bohall, Director Human Resources
Web address: www.wcahospital.org
Control: Other not–for–profit (including NFP Corporation) **Service:** General
Medical and Surgical

Staffed Beds: 197 Admissions: 6708 Census: 101 Outpatient Visits: 262904 Births: 634 Total Expense ($000): 106295 Payroll Expense ($000): 42699 Personnel: 908

JOHNSON CITY—Broome County

WILSON MEMORIAL REGIONAL MEDICAL CENTER See United Health Services
Hospitals–Binghamton, Binghamton

KATONAH—Westchester County

☐ **FOUR WINDS HOSPITAL (334002)**, 800 Cross River Road, Zip 10536–3549;
tel. 914/763–8151, (Nonreporting) **A**1 9 10
Primary Contact: Martin A. Buccolo, Ph.D., Chief Executive Officer
COO: Moira Morrissey, Chief Operating Officer and General Counsel
CFO: Barry S. Weinstein, Chief Financial Officer
CMO: Jonathan Bauman, M.D., Chief Medical Officer
CIO: Barry S. Weinstein, Chief Financial Officer
CHR: Susan Cusano, Director Human Resources
Web address: www.fourwindshospital.com
Control: Partnership, Investor–owned, for–profit **Service:** Psychiatric

Staffed Beds: 175

KENMORE—Erie County

☒ **KENMORE MERCY HOSPITAL (330102)**, 2950 Elmwood Avenue,
Zip 14217–1390; tel. 716/447–6100, (Total facility includes 160 beds in nursing
home–type unit) **A**1 9 10 **F**3 15 17 18 29 30 31 32 34 35 39 40 45 49 54 57
59 60 64 65 66 68 70 74 75 78 79 81 84 85 86 87 90 92 93 94 96 97 107
108 110 111 114 115 118 119 126 128 129 130 131 132 146 **P**5 6
S Catholic Health System, Buffalo, NY
Primary Contact: James M. Millard, President and Chief Executive Officer
COO: Walter Ludwig, Chief Operating Officer
CFO: James H. Dunlop, Jr., CPA, Senior Vice President and Chief Financial Officer
CMO: James Fitzpatrick, M.D., Vice President Medical Affairs
CHR: Laura Cianflone, Director Human Resources
CNO: Cheryl Hayes, Vice President Patient Care Services
Web address: www.chsbuffalo.org
Control: Church–operated, Nongovernment, not–for profit **Service:** General
Medical and Surgical

Staffed Beds: 315 Admissions: 8492 Census: 250 Outpatient Visits: 147319 Births: 0 Total Expense ($000): 149824 Payroll Expense ($000): 65965 Personnel: 1046

Hospital, Medicare Provider Number, Address, Telephone, Approval, Facility, and Physician Codes, Health Care System	
★ American Hospital Association (AHA) membership	○ Healthcare Facilities Accreditation Program
☐ The Joint Commission accreditation ◇ DNV Healthcare Inc. accreditation	△ Commission on Accreditation of Rehabilitation Facilities (CARF) accreditation

KINGSTON—Ulster County

BENEDICTINE HOSPITAL See Health Alliance Hospital – Mary's Avenue Campus

☒ **HEALTH ALLIANCE HOSPITAL – BROADWAY CAMPUS (330004)**, 396 Broadway, Zip 12401–4692; tel. 845/331-3131 **A**1 9 10 13 19 **F**3 8 11 13 15 18 20 28 29 30 34 35 36 40 45 49 50 54 56 57 59 60 63 64 68 70 74 75 76 77 79 81 82 83 84 85 86 87 92 93 102 107 108 111 114 115 119 130 131 132 135 146 147 148 **S** HealthAlliance of the Hudson Valley, Kingston, NY
Primary Contact: David Scarpino, President and Chief Executive Officer
COO: Robert Seidman, Chief Operating Officer
CFO: Steven J. Haas, Chief Financial Officer
CMO: Frank Ehrlich, M.D., Chief Medical Officer
CIO: John Finch, Vice President Information Services
CHR: Greg M. Howard, Director Human Resource
Web address: www.hahv.org
Control: Other not–for–profit (including NFP Corporation) **Service:** General Medical and Surgical

Staffed Beds: 150 **Admissions:** 8146 **Census:** 106 **Outpatient Visits:** 64573 **Births:** 417 **Total Expense ($000):** 109394 **Payroll Expense ($000):** 42590 **Personnel:** 832

☐ **HEALTH ALLIANCE HOSPITAL – MARY'S AVENUE CAMPUS (330224)**, 105 Marys Avenue, Zip 12401–5894; tel. 845/338-2500 **A**1 2 9 10 19 **F**3 4 8 11 15 18 20 29 30 31 34 35 36 45 49 50 54 56 57 59 63 64 66 68 70 74 75 78 79 81 82 83 84 85 86 87 90 98 105 107 108 110 114 119 120 121 123 129 130 131 132 146 147 148 **P**7 **S** HealthAlliance of the Hudson Valley, Kingston, NY
Primary Contact: David Scarpino, President and Chief Executive Officer
COO: Robert Seidman, Chief Operating Officer
CFO: Steven J. Haas, Chief Financial Officer
CMO: Frank Ehrlich, M.D., Chief Medical Officer
CIO: John Finch, Chief Information and Community Officer
CHR: Greg M. Howard, Vice President Human Resources
Web address: www.hahv.org
Control: Other not–for–profit (including NFP Corporation) **Service:** General Medical and Surgical

Staffed Beds: 120 **Admissions:** 3758 **Census:** 76 **Outpatient Visits:** 33204 **Births:** 0 **Total Expense ($000):** 60401 **Payroll Expense ($000):** 24615 **Personnel:** 537

KINGSTON HOSPITAL See Health Alliance Hospital – Broadway Campus

LEWISTON—Niagara County

☒ **MOUNT ST. MARY'S HOSPITAL AND HEALTH CENTER (330188)**, 5300 Military Road, Zip 14092–1903; tel. 716/297-4800, (Total facility includes 250 beds in nursing home–type unit) **A**1 9 10 **F**3 4 11 13 15 17 18 28 29 30 34 35 40 49 50 51 54 56 57 59 60 64 65 66 68 70 74 75 76 77 79 81 82 84 85 87 92 93 97 107 108 110 111 114 115 119 128 130 131 132 135 143 146 147 148 **P**5 **S** Ascension Health, Saint Louis, MO
Primary Contact: Judith A. Maness, FACHE, President and Chief Executive Officer
COO: Gary Tucker, Senior Vice President Operations and Chief Operating Officer
CFO: Stephen Franko, Vice President Finance and Chief Financial Officer
CMO: Domonic F. Falsetti, M.D., Chief of Staff and Medical Director
CHR: Deborah J. Serafin, Vice President Human Resources
CNO: Barbara A. Bucci, R.N., Vice President Patient Care and Chief Nursing Officer
Web address: www.msmh.org
Control: Church–operated, Nongovernment, not–for profit **Service:** General Medical and Surgical

Staffed Beds: 377 **Admissions:** 5938 **Census:** 320 **Outpatient Visits:** 153560 **Births:** 266 **Total Expense ($000):** 112365 **Payroll Expense ($000):** 54669 **Personnel:** 649

LITTLE FALLS—Herkimer County

★ **LITTLE FALLS HOSPITAL (331311)**, 140 Burwell Street, Zip 13365–1725; tel. 315/823-1000, (Nonreporting) **A**9 10 18 **S** Bassett Healthcare Network, Cooperstown, NY
Primary Contact: Michael L. Ogden, President and Chief Executive Officer
CFO: James Vielkind, Chief Financial Officer
CMO: Mark Winther, M.D., Medical Director
CIO: Duane Merry, Chief Information Officer
CHR: Marlene Little, Senior Director
CNO: Heidi Camardello, Vice President Patient Care Services and Chief Nursing Officer
Web address: www.lfhny.org
Control: Other not–for–profit (including NFP Corporation) **Service:** General Medical and Surgical

Staffed Beds: 59

LITTLE NECK—Queens County, See New York City

LOCKPORT—Niagara County

★ **EASTERN NIAGARA HOSPITAL (330163)**, 521 East Avenue, Zip 14094–3299; tel. 716/514-5700, (Includes EASTERN NIAGARA HOSPITAL LOCKPORT, 521 East Avenue, tel. 716/514-5700; EASTERN NIAGARA HOSPITAL NEWFANE, 2600 William Street, Newfane, Zip 14108–1093; tel. 716/778-5111) **A**9 10 **F**3 4 11 15 18 19 28 29 30 31 34 40 45 46 47 48 49 50 51 57 59 60 63 65 68 70 74 75 76 77 79 81 82 83 84 85 87 89 93 94 98 99 100 102 107 108 110 111 115 118 119 126 130 132 135 144 146 147 148
Primary Contact: Clare A. Haar, Chief Executive Officer
COO: David J. Di Bacco, Chief Operating Officer
CFO: Michael F. Ickowski, Chief Financial Officer
CMO: Bruce J. Cusenz, M.D., Medical Director
CHR: Joseph Farrauto, Director Human Resources
CNO: Mary Beth Campo, MS, Director of Nursing
Web address: www.enhs.org
Control: Other not–for–profit (including NFP Corporation) **Service:** General Medical and Surgical

Staffed Beds: 140 **Admissions:** 5513 **Census:** 75 **Outpatient Visits:** 816430 **Births:** 450 **Total Expense ($000):** 68238 **Payroll Expense ($000):** 32322

LONG ISLAND CITY—Queens County, See New York City

LOWVILLE—Lewis County

☒ **LEWIS COUNTY GENERAL HOSPITAL (330213)**, 7785 North State Street, Zip 13367–1297; tel. 315/376-5200, (Total facility includes 160 beds in nursing home–type unit) **A**1 9 10 20 **F**2 3 6 8 11 13 15 29 30 34 40 45 50 54 56 57 59 62 63 70 75 76 77 78 79 81 82 85 86 87 89 91 93 96 97 107 108 110 111 115 119 124 127 129 130 131 132 133 143 146 147 148 **P**6 8
Primary Contact: Eric Burch, Chief Executive Officer
CFO: Jeffrey Hellinger, Interim Chief Financial Officer
CMO: Catherine Williams, M.D., Medical Director
CIO: Rob Uttendorfsky, Director Information Management
CHR: James Swords, Director Human Resources
CNO: Jennifer Shaver, Director of Nursing
Web address: www.lcgh.net
Control: County–Government, nonfederal **Service:** General Medical and Surgical

Staffed Beds: 214 **Admissions:** 1546 **Census:** 170 **Outpatient Visits:** 116759 **Births:** 312 **Total Expense ($000):** 65845 **Payroll Expense ($000):** 25554 **Personnel:** 575

MALONE—Franklin County

☒ **ALICE HYDE MEDICAL CENTER (330084)**, 133 Park Street, Zip 12953–1243, Mailing Address: P.O. Box 729, Zip 12953–0729; tel. 518/483-3000, (Total facility includes 75 beds in nursing home–type unit) **A**1 9 10 20 **F**3 11 13 15 17 18 28 29 31 34 35 36 39 40 45 50 57 59 60 64 68 70 75 76 77 78 79 81 82 84 85 86 87 90 93 97 107 108 110 111 115 119 121 127 128 129 130 131 132 135 143 144 146 148
Primary Contact: Douglas F. DiVello, President and Chief Executive Officer
COO: Kevin Hart, Senior Director Support Services and Facilities
CFO: Sean Curtin, Chief Financial Officer
CMO: Leonardo Dishman, M.D., Chief Medical Officer
CIO: Jana Grose, Chief Information Officer
CHR: Emily Campbell, Director Human Resources
CNO: Julie Marshall, Chief Nursing Officer
Web address: www.alicehyde.com
Control: Other not–for–profit (including NFP Corporation) **Service:** General Medical and Surgical

Staffed Beds: 135 **Admissions:** 2220 **Census:** 97 **Outpatient Visits:** 146610 **Births:** 302 **Total Expense ($000):** 67158 **Payroll Expense ($000):** 33530 **Personnel:** 524

MANHASSET—Nassau County

MANHASSET AMBULATORY CARE PAVILION See Long Island Jewish Medical Center, New Hyde Park

☒ **NORTH SHORE UNIVERSITY HOSPITAL (330106)**, 300 Community Drive, Zip 11030–3816; tel. 516/562-0100 **A**1 2 3 5 8 9 10 **F**3 6 7 8 9 11 12 13 14 15 17 18 19 20 21 22 23 24 26 29 30 31 32 34 35 36 37 38 39 40 41 43 44 45 46 47 48 49 50 51 52 53 54 55 56 57 58 59 60 61 62 63 64 65 66 68 69 70 71 72 73 74 75 76 77 78 79 80 81 82 83 84 85 86 87 91 92 93 94 97 98 99 100 101 102 103 104 107 108 109 110 111 112 113 114 115 116 117 118 119 120 121 123 124 126 129 130 131 132 134 135 136 138 141 142 143 144 145 146 147 148 **P**5 6 **S** North Shore–Long Island Jewish Health System, Great Neck, NY
Primary Contact: Alessandro Bellucci, M.D., Executive Director
CFO: Frank Rizzo, Chief Financial Officer, Central Region
CMO: Michael Gitman, M.D., Medical Director
CIO: Nympha Meindel, R.N., Chief Information Officer
CHR: Debra Bierman, Associate Executive Director Human Resources
CNO: Kerri Scanlon, MSN, Chief Nursing Officer
Web address: www.northshorelij.com
Control: Other not–for–profit (including NFP Corporation) **Service:** General Medical and Surgical

Staffed Beds: 764 **Admissions:** 45638 **Census:** 691 **Outpatient Visits:** 975861 **Births:** 6593 **Total Expense ($000):** 1604349 **Payroll Expense ($000):** 839263 **Personnel:** 15098

Many Facility Codes have changed. Please refer to the AHA Guide Code Chart. © 2014 AHA Guide

MANHATTAN—New York County, See New York City

MARCY—Oneida County

☐ **CENTRAL NEW YORK PSYCHIATRIC CENTER**, 9005 Old River Road,
Zip 13403–3000, Mailing Address: P.O. Box 300, Zip 13403–0300;
tel. 315/765–3600, (Nonreporting) **A**1 **S** New York State Office of Mental Health,
Albany, NY
Primary Contact: Maureen Bosco, Executive Director
Web address: www.omh.ny.gov
Control: State–Government, nonfederal **Service:** Psychiatric

Staffed Beds: 226

MARGARETVILLE—Delaware County

☐ **MARGARETVILLE HOSPITAL (331304)**, 42084 State Highway 28,
Zip 12455–2820; tel. 845/586–2631, (Nonreporting) **A**1 9 10 18
S HealthAlliance of the Hudson Valley, Kingston, NY
Primary Contact: Sandra A. Horan, Executive Director
CHR: Linda Mead, Director Human Resources
Web address: www.margaretvillehospital.org
Control: Other not–for–profit (including NFP Corporation) **Service:** General
Medical and Surgical

Staffed Beds: 15

MASSENA—St. Lawrence County

✠ **MASSENA MEMORIAL HOSPITAL (330223)**, One Hospital Drive,
Zip 13662–1097; tel. 315/764–1711 **A**1 9 10 20 **F**3 8 11 13 15 16 17 18 20
29 31 34 35 40 50 51 55 56 57 59 60 64 70 72 73 76 78 80 81 82 85 86
87 88 89 93 97 107 108 109 110 111 114 116 117 118 119 130 132 135
146 147 148 **P**3 6
Primary Contact: Charles F. Fahd, II, Chief Executive Officer
CFO: James Smith, Chief Financial Officer
CMO: Nimesh Desai, M.D., Medical Director
CIO: Jana Grose, Chief Information Officer
CHR: Jonnie Dorothy, Senior Director Human Resources
CNO: Sue Beaulieu, Chief Nurse Executive
Web address: www.massenahospital.org
Control: City–Government, nonfederal **Service:** General Medical and Surgical

Staffed Beds: 50 **Admissions:** 2230 **Census:** 25 **Outpatient Visits:** 126244
Births: 283 **Total Expense ($000):** 50324 **Payroll Expense ($000):** 22836
Personnel: 351

MEDINA—Orleans County

★ △ **MEDINA MEMORIAL HOSPITAL (330053)**, 200 Ohio Street,
Zip 14103–1095; tel. 585/798–2000, (Nonreporting) **A**7 9 10 **S** HealthTech
Management Services, Brentwood, TN
Primary Contact: Dolores A. Horvath, Chief Executive Officer
COO: Wendy Jackson, Chief Operating Officer and Chief Nursing Officer
CFO: David Britton, Interim Chief Financial Officer
CMO: Joseph Misiti, M.D., President Medical Staff
CHR: Mary Williams, Director Human Resources
CNO: Wendy Jackson, Chief Operating Officer and Chief Nursing Officer
Web address: www.medinamemorial.org
Control: State–Government, nonfederal **Service:** General Medical and Surgical

Staffed Beds: 101

MIDDLETOWN—Orange County

✠ △ **ORANGE REGIONAL MEDICAL CENTER (330126)**, 707 East Main Street,
Zip 10940–2650; tel. 845/333–1000 **A**1 2 7 9 10 **F**3 5 8 11 12 13 15 17 18
19 20 22 26 28 29 30 31 34 35 40 49 51 54 55 57 59 60 64 68 70 72 74
75 76 77 78 79 81 82 83 84 85 86 87 89 90 93 96 98 99 100 101 102 103
104 105 107 108 110 111 114 115 117 118 119 120 121 123 124 126 129
130 132 135 144 146 147 148 **S** Greater Hudson Valley Health System,
Middletown, NY
Primary Contact: Scott Batulis, President and Chief Executive Officer
COO: Timothy P. Selz, Vice President
CFO: Mitch Amodo, Vice President and Chief Financial Officer
CMO: James Oxley, D.O., Vice President Medical Affairs
CIO: Shafiq Rab, Chief Information Officer
CHR: Deborah Carr, Vice President Human Resources
Web address: www.ormc.org
Control: Other not–for–profit (including NFP Corporation) **Service:** General
Medical and Surgical

Staffed Beds: 301 **Admissions:** 18456 **Census:** 251 **Outpatient Visits:**
155332 **Births:** 1654 **Total Expense ($000):** 366403 **Payroll Expense
($000):** 139719

MINEOLA—Nassau County

✠ **WINTHROP–UNIVERSITY HOSPITAL (330167)**, 259 First Street,
Zip 11501–3957; tel. 516/663–0333, (Includes CHILDREN'S MEDICAL CENTER,
259 First Street, tel. 516/663–0333) **A**1 2 3 5 8 9 10 **F**3 5 6 8 9 11 12 13 14
15 17 18 19 20 22 24 26 28 29 30 31 32 34 35 37 38 39 40 41 43 44 45
46 47 48 49 50 51 53 54 55 56 57 58 59 60 61 62 63 64 65 66 68 69 70
71 72 73 74 75 76 77 78 79 81 82 84 85 86 87 88 89 92 93 94 97 100
103 107 108 110 111 113 114 115 116 117 118 119 120 121 123 124 126
129 130 131 132 134 135 141 142 145 146 147 148 **P**5 6 7 8
Primary Contact: John F. Collins, President and Chief Executive Officer
COO: Garry Schwall, Chief Operating Officer
CFO: Palmira Cataliotti, Senior Vice President, Chief Financial Officer and
Treasurer
CMO: Michael Ammazzalorso, M.D., Chief Medical Officer
CIO: Nicholas Casabona, Chief Information Officer
CHR: Stacey Pfeffer, Senior Vice President Human Resources
CNO: Valerie Terzano, MS, Chief Nursing Officer, Senior Vice President Nursing
Web address: www.winthrop.org
Control: Other not–for–profit (including NFP Corporation) **Service:** General
Medical and Surgical

Staffed Beds: 505 **Admissions:** 31292 **Census:** 450 **Outpatient Visits:**
382919 **Births:** 4923 **Total Expense ($000):** 1103957 **Payroll Expense
($000):** 557342 **Personnel:** 6699

MONTOUR FALLS—Schuyler County

✠ **SCHUYLER HOSPITAL (331313)**, 220 Steuben Street, Zip 14865–9709;
tel. 607/535–7121, (Total facility includes 120 beds in nursing home–type unit)
A1 9 10 18 **F**3 11 12 14 15 18 29 30 34 35 40 45 57 59 64 70 75 77 81 82
85 87 91 92 93 94 97 107 110 111 114 119 128 129 130 131 133 135 146
147 148 **P**6
Primary Contact: Andrew R. Manzer, President and Chief Executive Officer
CMO: Michael Eisman, M.D., Medical Director
CHR: Troy Preston, Director Human Resources
Web address: www.schuylerhospital.org
Control: Other not–for–profit (including NFP Corporation) **Service:** General
Medical and Surgical

Staffed Beds: 139 **Admissions:** 1098 **Census:** 125 **Outpatient Visits:** 40658
Births: 0 **Total Expense ($000):** 29959 **Payroll Expense ($000):** 16382
Personnel: 329

MONTROSE—Westchester County

✠ **VETERANS AFFAIRS HUDSON VALLEY HEALTH CARE SYSTEM–F.D.
ROOSEVELT HOSPITAL**, 2094 Albany Post Road, Zip 10548–1454, Mailing
Address: P.O. Box 100, Zip 10548–0100; tel. 914/737–4400, (Includes
VETERAN AFFAIRS HUDSON VALLEY HEALTH CARE SYSTEM–CASTLE POINT
DIVISION, Castle Point, Zip 12511–9999; tel. 914/831–2000; VETERANS
AFFAIRS HUDSON VALLEY HEALTH CARE SYSTEM–MONTROSE DIVISION,
Zip 10548; tel. 914/737–4400) **A**1 3 5 9 **F**3 4 5 12 18 22 24 26 28 29 30 31
34 35 37 38 39 45 46 47 49 53 55 56 57 59 61 63 65 68 71 74 75 77 78
79 80 81 82 84 86 87 93 94 97 98 100 101 102 103 104 106 107 108 110
111 114 115 117 120 122 127 128 130 132 134 135 143 144 145 146
147 **S** Department of Veterans Affairs, Washington, DC
Primary Contact: Margaret B. Caplan, Director
COO: John M. Grady, Associate Director
CFO: John Walsh, Chief Fiscal Services
CMO: Joanne J. Malina, M.D., Chief of Staff
CIO: Thomas Rooney, Chief Information Resource Management
CHR: Dardanella Russell, Chief Human Resources Management Service
Web address: www.hudsonvalley.va.gov/
Control: Veterans Affairs, Government, federal **Service:** Psychiatric

Staffed Beds: 403 **Admissions:** 1668 **Census:** 273 **Outpatient Visits:**
337981 **Births:** 0 **Total Expense ($000):** 239226 **Payroll Expense ($000):**
124979 **Personnel:** 1349

NY

Hospital, Medicare Provider Number, Address, Telephone, Approval, Facility, and Physician Codes, Health Care System

★ American Hospital Association (AHA) membership ○ Healthcare Facilities Accreditation Program
☐ The Joint Commission accreditation ◇ DNV Healthcare Inc. accreditation △ Commission on Accreditation of Rehabilitation Facilities (CARF) accreditation

MOUNT KISCO—Westchester County

☒ **NORTHERN WESTCHESTER HOSPITAL (330162)**, 400 East Main Street,
Zip 10549–3477; tel. 914/666–1200 **A**1 2 5 9 10 **F**3 8 12 13 15 17 18 19 28
29 30 31 32 34 35 36 37 40 43 46 47 48 49 50 51 54 55 56 57 59 60 61
64 65 68 70 72 73 74 75 76 78 79 81 82 84 85 86 87 89 91 92 93 97 98
99 100 101 102 103 107 108 109 110 111 114 115 118 119 120 121 123
124 126 129 130 131 132 135 146 147 148
Primary Contact: Joel Seligman, President and Chief Executive Officer
CFO: John Partenza, Vice President and Treasurer
CMO: Marla Koroly, M.D., Chief Medical Officer and Senior Vice President Medical
Affairs
CIO: Sue Prince, Director Information Systems
CHR: Kerry Flynn Barrett, Vice President Human Resources
CNO: Lauraine Szekely, R.N., Senior Vice President, Patient Care
Web address: www.nwhc.net
Control: Other not–for–profit (including NFP Corporation) **Service:** General
Medical and Surgical

Staffed Beds: 181 **Admissions:** 8646 **Census:** 104 **Outpatient Visits:**
146552 **Births:** 1621 **Total Expense ($000):** 234745 **Payroll Expense
($000):** 93612 **Personnel:** 1350

MOUNT VERNON—Westchester County

☐ **MONTEFIORE MOUNT VERNON (330086)**, 12 North Seventh Avenue,
Zip 10550–2098; tel. 914/664–8000, (Data for 56 days) **A**1 3 5 9 10 **F**3 8 14
15 18 29 30 31 34 35 38 40 45 50 59 60 61 64 65 66 68 74 75 77 78 79
81 84 85 86 87 92 93 98 100 102 107 110 111 114 119 130 146 147
S Montefiore Health System, Bronx, NY
Primary Contact: Susan Green–Lorenzen, SVP, Operations
CFO: Albert M. Farina, Chief Financial Officer
CMO: Gary Ishkanian, M.D., Vice President Medical Affairs
CIO: Barbara Cooke, Director Health Information Systems
CHR: Dennis H. Ashley, Vice President Human Resources
Web address: www.sshsw.org
Control: Other not–for–profit (including NFP Corporation) **Service:** General
Medical and Surgical

Staffed Beds: 80 **Admissions:** 512 **Census:** 65 **Outpatient Visits:** 19872
Births: 0 **Total Expense ($000):** 12247 **Payroll Expense ($000):** 5329
Personnel: 455

NEW HAMPTON—Orange County

☐ **MID–HUDSON FORENSIC PSYCHIATRIC CENTER (334061)**, Route 17M,
Zip 10958, Mailing Address: P.O. Box 158, Zip 10958–0158;
tel. 845/374–8700, (Nonreporting) **A**1 10 **S** New York State Office of Mental
Health, Albany, NY
Primary Contact: Peggi Healy, Executive Director
Web address: www.omh.ny.gov
Control: State–Government, nonfederal **Service:** Psychiatric

Staffed Beds: 268

NEW HYDE PARK—Queens County, See New York City

NEW ROCHELLE—Westchester County

☒ **MONTEFIORE NEW ROCHELLE (330184)**, 16 Guion Place, Zip 10801–5502;
tel. 914/632–5000, (Total facility includes 150 beds in nursing home–type unit)
(Data for 56 days) **A**1 2 3 5 9 10 **F**2 3 8 11 12 13 15 18 28 29 30 31 32 35
37 40 43 45 50 55 61 64 65 66 68 70 73 74 76 77 78 79 81 82 84 85 87
89 90 92 93 97 100 107 108 110 114 119 128 129 130 132 146 **P**5
S Montefiore Health System, Bronx, NY
Primary Contact: Anthony J. Alfano, President and Chief Executive Officer
COO: John P. Mamangakis, Senior Vice President
CFO: Albert M. Farina, Senior Vice President and Chief Financial Officer
CMO: Richard Barone, M.D., Medical Director
CIO: Barbara Cooke, Director Health Information Systems
CHR: Dennis H. Ashley, Vice President Human Resources
CNO: Pamela M. Dupuis, R.N., Senior Vice President Patient Care Services
Web address: www.montefiorehealthsystem.org
Control: Other not–for–profit (including NFP Corporation) **Service:** General
Medical and Surgical

Staffed Beds: 267 **Admissions:** 1156 **Census:** 222 **Outpatient Visits:** 14764
Births: 150 **Total Expense ($000):** 29900 **Payroll Expense ($000):** 12661
Personnel: 1121

NEW YORK (Includes all hospitals located within the five boroughs)
BRONX - Bronx County (Mailing Address - Bronx)
BROOKLYN - Kings County (Mailing Address - Brooklyn)
MANHATTAN - New York County (Mailing Address - New York)
**QUEENS - Queens County (Mailing Addresses - Bellerose, Elmhurst, Far
Rockaway, Flushing, Forest Hills, Glen Oaks, Holliswood, Jackson Heights,
Jamaica, Little Neck, Long Island City, New Hyde Park, and Queens
Village)**
RICHMOND VALLEY - Richmond County (Mailing Address - Staten Island)

☒ **BELLEVUE HOSPITAL CENTER (330204)**, 462 First Avenue, Zip 10016–9198;
tel. 212/562–4141, (Data for 265 days) **A**1 3 5 9 10 **F**3 4 5 8 11 12 13 15 17
18 19 20 22 24 26 28 29 30 31 34 35 36 38 39 40 41 43 44 45 46 48 49
50 52 55 56 57 58 59 60 61 64 65 66 68 70 71 72 73 74 75 76 77 78 79
81 82 84 85 86 87 88 89 90 91 92 93 94 96 97 98 99 100 101 102 103
104 105 107 108 110 111 114 115 118 119 130 132 134 135 141 143 144
146 147 148 **S** New York City Health and Hospitals Corporation, New York, NY
Primary Contact: Steven Alexander, Executive Director
COO: William Hicks, Chief Operating Officer
CFO: Aaron Cohen, Chief Financial Officer
CMO: Nate Link, M.D., Medical Director
CIO: Eli Tarlow, Chief Information Officer
CHR: Howard Kritz, Director Human Resources
Web address: www.nyc.gov/bellevue
Control: City–Government, nonfederal **Service:** General Medical and Surgical

Staffed Beds: 812 **Admissions:** 21867 **Census:** 676 **Outpatient Visits:**
519947 **Births:** 1089 **Total Expense ($000):** 813842 **Payroll Expense
($000):** 290781 **Personnel:** 4596

BETH ISRAEL MEDICAL CENTER See Mount Sinai Beth Israel

BETH ISRAEL MEDICAL CENTER–KINGS HIGHWAY DIVISION See Mount Sinai
Beth Israel Brooklyn

☐ **BRONX PSYCHIATRIC CENTER (334053)**, 1500 Waters Place, Bronx,
Zip 10461–2796; tel. 718/931–0600, (Nonreporting) **A**1 3 5 10 **S** New York
State Office of Mental Health, Albany, NY
Primary Contact: Pamela Turner, Executive Director
CFO: Robert Erway, Director for Administration
Web address: www.omh.ny.gov
Control: State–Government, nonfederal **Service:** Psychiatric

Staffed Beds: 450

☒ **BRONX–LEBANON HOSPITAL CENTER HEALTH CARE SYSTEM (330009)**,
1276 Fulton Avenue, Bronx, Zip 10456–3499; tel. 718/590–1800, (Includes
BRONX–LEBANON SPECIAL CARE CENTER, 1265 Fulton Avenue, Zip 10465;
tel. 718/579–7000; CONCOURSE DIVISION, 1650 Grand Concourse, Zip 10457;
tel. 718/590–1800; FULTON DIVISION, 1276 Fulton Avenue, Zip 10456;
tel. 718/590–1800; HIGHBRIDGE WOODYCREST CENTER, 936 Woodycrest
Avenue, Zip 10452; tel. 718/293–3200), (Total facility includes 330 beds in
nursing home–type unit) **A**1 3 5 8 9 10 **F**2 3 4 5 8 9 11 12 13 15 17 18 19 20
22 26 28 29 30 31 32 34 35 37 38 39 40 41 44 45 46 47 48 49 50 51 52
54 55 56 57 58 59 60 61 64 65 66 68 70 71 72 73 74 75 76 77 78 79 80
81 82 83 84 85 86 87 88 89 91 92 93 94 96 97 98 99 100 101 102 103
104 105 106 107 108 109 110 111 113 114 115 118 119 123 128 129 130
131 132 133 134 135 145 146 147 148 **P**6
Primary Contact: Miguel A. Fuentes, Jr., President and Chief Executive Officer
COO: Steven Anderman, Chief Operating Officer
CFO: Victor DeMarco, Chief Financial Officer
CMO: Milton A. Gumbs, M.D., Vice President and Medical Director
CIO: Ivan Durbak, Chief Information Officer
CHR: Selena Griffin–Mahon, Assistant Vice President Human Resources
Web address: www.bronxcare.org
Control: Other not–for–profit (including NFP Corporation) **Service:** General
Medical and Surgical

Staffed Beds: 972 **Admissions:** 30419 **Census:** 752 **Outpatient Visits:**
1051504 **Births:** 2276 **Total Expense ($000):** 724558 **Payroll Expense
($000):** 350522 **Personnel:** 4106

NY

Many Facility Codes have changed. Please refer to the AHA Guide Code Chart. © 2014 AHA Guide

☐ **BROOKDALE HOSPITAL MEDICAL CENTER (330233)**, One Brookdale Plaza, Brooklyn, Zip 11212–3139; tel. 718/240–5000, (Total facility includes 448 beds in nursing home–type unit) **A**1 3 5 9 10 **F**2 3 8 10 11 12 13 15 17 18 19 20 22 26 28 29 30 31 32 34 35 38 39 40 41 42 43 44 45 46 49 50 51 54 55 56 57 58 59 60 61 64 65 66 68 70 71 72 73 74 75 76 77 78 79 80 81 82 83 84 85 86 87 88 89 92 93 97 98 99 100 101 102 103 104 107 108 110 111 114 119 122 126 128 129 130 131 132 133 134 135 144 145 146 147 **P**6
Primary Contact: Mark Toney, President and Chief Executive Officer
CFO: James Porter, Chief Financial Officer
CMO: Estevan Garcia, M.D., Chief Medical Officer
CIO: David Reitzel, Chief Information Officer
CHR: Margaret M. Brubaker, Senior Vice President Human Resources
CNO: Suzanne Pennacchio, Senior Vice President Patient Care Services
Web address: www.brookdalehospital.org
Control: Other not–for–profit (including NFP Corporation) **Service:** General Medical and Surgical

Staffed Beds: 789 **Admissions:** 17526 **Census:** 710 **Outpatient Visits:** 237002 **Births:** 1271 **Total Expense ($000):** 522385 **Payroll Expense ($000):** 227148 **Personnel:** 3627

☐ **BROOKLYN HOSPITAL CENTER (330056)**, 121 DeKalb Avenue, Brooklyn, Zip 11201–5425; tel. 718/250–8000 **A**1 3 5 8 9 10 **F**3 4 8 12 13 14 15 17 18 20 29 30 31 32 34 35 38 39 40 49 50 51 54 56 57 59 60 61 62 64 65 66 68 70 72 74 75 76 77 78 79 80 81 82 83 84 85 86 87 88 89 90 97 100 102 104 107 108 110 111 114 115 118 119 121 123 129 130 131 132 135 143 144 146 147 148 **P**6 **S** New York Presbyterian Healthcare System, New York, NY
Primary Contact: Richard B. Becker, M.D., President, Chief Executive Officer and Interim Chief Medical Officer
COO: Wayne Allen, Acting Chief Operating Officer
CFO: Joseph Guarracino, Senior Vice President and Chief Financial Officer
CIO: Irene Farrelly, Vice President and Chief Information Officer
CHR: Ira Warm, Senior Vice President Human Resources
Web address: www.tbh.org
Control: Church–operated, Nongovernment, not–for profit **Service:** General Medical and Surgical

Staffed Beds: 332 **Admissions:** 17039 **Census:** 255 **Outpatient Visits:** 308800 **Births:** 2226 **Total Expense ($000):** 372582 **Payroll Expense ($000):** 195041 **Personnel:** 4075

✠ **CALVARY HOSPITAL (332006)**, 1740 Eastchester Road, Bronx, Zip 10461–2392; tel. 718/863–6900 **A**1 9 10 **F**1 29 30 35 39 62 63 64 68 74 78 82 84 87 119 121 130 132 134 146 148 **P**6
Primary Contact: Frank A. Calamari, President and Chief Executive Officer
COO: Richard J. Kutilek, Chief Operating Officer
CFO: Andrew Greco, Chief Financial Officer
CMO: Michael J. Brescia, M.D., Executive Medical Director
CIO: Patrick Martin, Director Information Systems
CHR: Michael T. Troncone, Chief Human Resources Officer
CNO: Margaret Pelkowski, R.N., Vice President Patient Care Services
Web address: www.calvaryhospital.org
Control: Church–operated, Nongovernment, not–for profit **Service:** Long–Term Acute Care hospital

Staffed Beds: 225 **Admissions:** 2955 **Census:** 204 **Outpatient Visits:** 116307 **Births:** 0 **Total Expense ($000):** 110267 **Payroll Expense ($000):** 57467 **Personnel:** 791

COLER–GOLDWATER SPECIALTY HOSPITAL AND NURSING FACILITY See Henry J. Carter Specialty Hospital and Nursing Facility

CONCOURSE DIVISION See Bronx–Lebanon Hospital Center Health Care System, Bronx

✠ **CONEY ISLAND HOSPITAL (330196)**, 2601 Ocean Parkway, Brooklyn, Zip 11235–7795; tel. 718/616–3000 **A**1 3 5 9 10 12 13 **F**3 4 5 8 9 11 13 15 17 18 19 20 28 29 30 31 32 34 35 38 39 40 41 45 46 49 50 51 54 55 56 57 58 59 60 61 64 65 66 68 70 71 72 74 75 76 77 78 79 81 83 84 85 87 89 90 91 93 94 96 97 98 99 100 102 103 104 106 107 108 110 111 114 115 118 119 130 132 135 143 146 147 148 **S** New York City Health and Hospitals Corporation, New York, NY
Primary Contact: Arthur Wagner, Senior Vice President and Executive Director
COO: Vito Bucculato, Chief Operating Officer
CFO: Paul Pandolfini, Chief Financial Officer
CMO: John Maese, M.D., Chief Medical Officer
CIO: Robert Kee, Chief Information Officer
CHR: Rodney Parker, Senior Associate Executive Director
CNO: Terry Mancher, R.N., Chief Nurse Executive
Web address: www.nyc.gov/html/hhc/html/facilities/coneyisland.shtml
Control: City–Government, nonfederal **Service:** General Medical and Surgical

Staffed Beds: 231 **Admissions:** 10321 **Census:** 192 **Outpatient Visits:** 262666 **Births:** 474 **Total Expense ($000):** 434533 **Payroll Expense ($000):** 157028 **Personnel:** 2771

☐ **CREEDMOOR PSYCHIATRIC CENTER (334004)**, 79–25 Winchester Boulevard, Jamaica, Zip 11427–2128, (Nonreporting) **A**1 10 **S** New York State Office of Mental Health, Albany, NY
Primary Contact: Ann Marie Barbarotta, Executive Director
CFO: Viodelda Ho–Shing, Deputy Director Administration
CIO: Randy Karr, Chief Information Officer
CHR: Adrienne Jones, Director Human Resources
Web address: www.omh.ny.gov
Control: State–Government, nonfederal **Service:** Psychiatric

Staffed Beds: 420

✠ **ELMHURST HOSPITAL CENTER (330128)**, 79–01 Broadway, Elmhurst, Zip 11373–1329; tel. 718/334–4000 **A**1 2 3 5 9 10 **F**3 5 8 9 13 14 15 17 18 20 22 26 29 30 31 32 34 35 38 40 41 43 45 49 50 51 53 55 56 57 59 60 61 64 68 70 72 73 74 75 76 77 78 79 81 82 83 84 85 86 87 89 90 92 93 97 98 99 100 101 102 103 104 105 107 108 110 111 115 119 121 126 130 131 132 134 135 143 146 147 **P**6 **S** New York City Health and Hospitals Corporation, New York, NY
Primary Contact: Chris D. Constantino, Executive Director
COO: Wayne Zimmermann, Chief Operating Officer
CFO: Alina Moran, Chief Financial Officer
CMO: Jasmin Moshirpur, M.D., Dean and Medical Director
CIO: Vincent Smith, Chief Information Officer
CHR: Jeannith Michelen, Associate Executive Director
CNO: Joann Bernadette Gull, Chief Nursing Officer
Web address: www.nyc.gov/html/hhc/ehc/html/home/home.shtml
Control: City–Government, nonfederal **Service:** General Medical and Surgical

Staffed Beds: 551 **Admissions:** 23838 **Census:** 460 **Outpatient Visits:** 666122 **Births:** 3423 **Total Expense ($000):** 625051 **Payroll Expense ($000):** 219098 **Personnel:** 3157

☐ **FLUSHING HOSPITAL MEDICAL CENTER (330193)**, 4500 Parsons Boulevard, Flushing, Zip 11355–2205; tel. 718/670–5000 **A**1 3 5 9 10 **F**3 4 5 7 8 10 11 13 15 17 18 29 30 31 32 34 35 36 39 40 41 45 50 56 57 59 60 61 63 64 65 68 70 71 72 74 75 76 77 78 79 81 82 84 85 87 89 91 92 93 97 98 100 101 102 103 104 107 110 111 114 119 128 130 132 135 146 147 148 **P**5 7
Primary Contact: Bruce J. Flanz, President and Chief Executive Officer
COO: Robert V. Levine, Executive Vice President and Chief Operating Officer
CFO: Mounir F. Doss, Executive Vice President and Chief Financial Officer
CMO: Siamack Nemazie, M.D., Director, Patient Safety Officer
CIO: Tony Gatto, Director Management Information Systems
CHR: Sheila Garvey, Vice President Human Resources
Web address: www.flushinghospital.org
Control: Other not–for–profit (including NFP Corporation) **Service:** General Medical and Surgical

Staffed Beds: 299 **Admissions:** 15429 **Census:** 250 **Outpatient Visits:** 145735 **Births:** 2913 **Total Expense ($000):** 283920 **Payroll Expense ($000):** 114618 **Personnel:** 1602

✠ **FOREST HILLS HOSPITAL (330353)**, 102–01 66th Road, Forest Hills, Zip 11375–2029; tel. 718/830–4000 **A**1 2 9 10 **F**3 8 12 13 15 18 29 30 31 34 35 37 38 40 45 46 49 50 51 52 55 57 58 59 60 63 64 65 66 68 70 73 74 75 76 77 78 79 81 82 84 85 86 87 97 100 102 107 111 115 119 130 132 135 143 146 147 148 **P**5 6 **S** North Shore–Long Island Jewish Health System, Great Neck, NY
Primary Contact: Rita Mercieca, R.N., Executive Director
COO: Mark J. Solazzo, Senior Vice President and Chief Operating Officer
CFO: Robert S. Shapiro, Senior Vice President and Chief Financial Officer
CMO: Lawrence Smith, M.D., Senior Vice President and Chief Medical Officer
CIO: John Bosco, Vice President and Chief Information Officer
Web address: www.northshorelij.com
Control: Other not–for–profit (including NFP Corporation) **Service:** General Medical and Surgical

Staffed Beds: 235 **Admissions:** 15933 **Census:** 199 **Outpatient Visits:** 74075 **Births:** 2134 **Total Expense ($000):** 223358 **Payroll Expense ($000):** 110827 **Personnel:** 1297

FULTON DIVISION See Bronx–Lebanon Hospital Center Health Care System, Bronx

GOLDWATER MEMORIAL HOSPITAL See Henry J. Carter Specialty Hospital and Nursing Facility

☐ **GRACIE SQUARE HOSPITAL (334048)**, 420 East 76th Street, Zip 10021–3396; tel. 212/988–4400 **A**1 9 10 **F**35 87 98 103 117 130 **S** New York Presbyterian Healthcare System, New York, NY
Primary Contact: Frank Bruno, Chief Executive Officer
Web address: www.nygsh.org
Control: Other not–for–profit (including NFP Corporation) **Service:** Psychiatric

Staffed Beds: 157 **Admissions:** 3094 **Census:** 150 **Outpatient Visits:** 0 **Births:** 0 **Total Expense ($000):** 38674 **Payroll Expense ($000):** 19733 **Personnel:** 145

NY

Hospital, Medicare Provider Number, Address, Telephone, Approval, Facility, and Physician Codes, Health Care System

★ American Hospital Association (AHA) membership
☐ The Joint Commission accreditation   ◇ DNV Healthcare Inc. accreditation
○ Healthcare Facilities Accreditation Program
△ Commission on Accreditation of Rehabilitation Facilities (CARF) accreditation

☒ △ **HARLEM HOSPITAL CENTER (330240)**, 506 Lenox Avenue, Zip 10037–1802; tel. 212/939–1000, (Includes HARLEM GENERAL CARE UNIT AND HARLEM PSYCHIATRIC UNIT) **A**1 3 5 7 9 10 **F**3 4 5 8 11 12 13 15 16 17 18 19 20 29 30 34 35 38 39 40 41 43 44 45 49 50 52 53 55 57 58 59 60 61 64 65 68 70 71 72 73 74 75 76 77 79 81 82 84 85 86 87 89 90 93 94 97 98 99 100 101 102 103 104 107 108 110 111 114 115 118 119 130 134 135 146 147 148 **S** New York City Health and Hospitals Corporation, New York, NY
Primary Contact: Denise C. Soares, R.N., Executive Director
Web address: www.nyc.gov/html/hhc/harlem
Control: City–Government, nonfederal **Service:** General Medical and Surgical

Staffed Beds: 273 **Admissions:** 12352 **Census:** 204 **Outpatient Visits:** 323727 **Births:** 1005 **Total Expense ($000):** 406218 **Payroll Expense ($000):** 138048 **Personnel:** 2117

☒ **HENRY J. CARTER SPECIALTY HOSPITAL AND NURSING FACILITY (332008)**, 1752 Park Avenue, Zip 10035; tel. 646/686–0000, (Includes COLER MEMORIAL HOSPITAL, Roosevelt Island, Zip 10044; tel. 212/848–6000; GOLDWATER MEMORIAL HOSPITAL, Franklin D. Roosevelt Island, Zip 10044; tel. 212/318–8000), (Total facility includes 1389 beds in nursing home–type unit) **A**1 3 5 10 **F**1 3 11 28 29 30 39 58 61 68 74 75 77 84 85 87 90 100 103 107 114 119 128 130 132 135 146 148 **P**4 **S** New York City Health and Hospitals Corporation, New York, NY
Primary Contact: Robert K. Hughes, Executive Director
CFO: Gloria Ranghelli, Deputy Chief Financial Officer
CMO: Yolanda Bruno, M.D., Medical Director
CHR: Howard Kritz, Director
Web address: www.coler–goldwater.org
Control: City–Government, nonfederal **Service:** Long–Term Acute Care hospital

Staffed Beds: 2016 **Admissions:** 1571 **Census:** 1326 **Outpatient Visits:** 0 **Births:** 0 **Total Expense ($000):** 328824 **Payroll Expense ($000):** 140358 **Personnel:** 2400

☒ **HOSPITAL FOR SPECIAL SURGERY (330270)**, 535 East 70th Street, Zip 10021–4898; tel. 212/606–1000 **A**1 3 5 8 9 10 **F**3 8 9 29 30 32 33 34 35 36 37 38 43 44 50 53 54 56 57 58 59 64 66 68 70 74 75 77 79 80 81 82 84 85 86 87 89 92 93 94 97 100 107 109 111 114 115 116 117 118 119 121 123 126 130 131 132 133 134 141 142 146 147 148 **P**8 **S** New York Presbyterian Healthcare System, New York, NY
Primary Contact: Louis A. Shapiro, President and Chief Executive Officer
COO: Lisa Goldstein, Executive Vice President and Chief Operating Officer
CFO: Stacey Malakoff, Executive Vice President and Chief Financial Officer
CMO: Todd Albert, M.D., Surgeon–in–Chief and Medical Director
CIO: Jamie Nelson, Vice President and Chief Information Officer
CHR: Bruce Slawitsky, Vice President Human Resources
CNO: Stephanie J. Goldberg, MSN, Senior Vice President and Chief Nursing Officer
Web address: www.hss.edu
Control: Other not–for–profit (including NFP Corporation) **Service:** Orthopedic

Staffed Beds: 199 **Admissions:** 14224 **Census:** 147 **Outpatient Visits:** 373654 **Births:** 0 **Total Expense ($000):** 790835 **Payroll Expense ($000):** 339184 **Personnel:** 3780

☐ **INTERFAITH MEDICAL CENTER (330397)**, 1545 Atlantic Avenue, Brooklyn, Zip 11213–1122; tel. 718/613–4000, (Nonreporting) **A**1 3 5 9 10
Primary Contact: Patrick Sullivan, Interim President and Chief Executive Officer
CFO: Gregg Dixon, CPA, Chief Financial Officer
CMO: Jochanan Weisenfreund, M.D., Senior Vice President Academic and Medical Affairs
CIO: Mark Lederman, Chief Information Officer
CHR: Venra Mathurin, Vice President Human Resources
Web address: www.interfaithmedical.com
Control: Other not–for–profit (including NFP Corporation) **Service:** General Medical and Surgical

Staffed Beds: 277

JACK D WEILER HOSPITAL OF ALBERT EINSTEIN COLLEGE OF MEDICINE
See Montefiore Medical Center, Bronx

☒ **JACOBI MEDICAL CENTER (330127)**, 1400 Pelham Parkway South, Bronx, Zip 10461–1197; tel. 718/918–5000 **A**1 3 5 9 10 **F**3 4 5 8 11 12 13 15 16 17 18 20 29 30 31 32 34 35 38 39 40 41 43 44 45 49 50 51 55 56 57 58 59 60 61 62 64 65 66 70 72 73 74 75 76 77 78 79 80 81 82 84 85 87 88 89 90 92 93 94 96 97 98 99 100 101 102 103 104 107 108 110 111 117 119 130 131 132 134 135 144 146 147 148 **P**6 **S** New York City Health and Hospitals Corporation, New York, NY
Primary Contact: William P. Walsh, Senior Vice President and Executive Director
COO: Christopher Fugazy, Chief Operating Officer
CFO: Kathy Garramone, Chief Financial Officer
CMO: John McNelis, M.D., Acting Medical Director
CIO: Diane Carr, Chief Information Officer
CHR: Dolores Leite, Chief Human Resource Executive
CNO: Ellen O'Connor, Chief Nursing Officer
Web address: www.nyc.gov/html/hhc/jacobi/home.html
Control: City–Government, nonfederal **Service:** General Medical and Surgical

Staffed Beds: 457 **Admissions:** 18919 **Census:** 383 **Outpatient Visits:** 457314 **Births:** 1966 **Total Expense ($000):** 676152 **Payroll Expense ($000):** 246063 **Personnel:** 3668

☒ **JAMAICA HOSPITAL MEDICAL CENTER (330014)**, 8900 Van Wyck Expressway, Jamaica, Zip 11418–2832; tel. 718/206–6000, (Total facility includes 224 beds in nursing home–type unit) **A**1 3 5 9 10 **F**1 3 7 11 13 15 17 18 19 20 22 26 29 30 31 32 38 39 40 41 43 44 45 49 50 52 53 54 55 56 57 58 59 60 61 62 64 65 66 68 70 71 72 73 74 75 76 77 78 79 80 81 82 83 84 85 86 87 89 90 92 93 94 96 97 98 100 101 102 103 104 107 108 110 111 114 115 118 119 129 130 131 132 134 135 143 144 146 147 **P**5 7 8
Primary Contact: Bruce J. Flanz, President and Chief Executive Officer
COO: William Lynch, Executive Vice President and Chief Operating Officer
CFO: Mounir F. Doss, Executive Vice President and Chief Financial Officer
CMO: Antonietta Morisco, M.D., Medical Director, Chairman Anesthesiology
CIO: Sami Boshut, Director Management Information Systems
CHR: Sheila Garvey, Vice President Human Resources
CNO: Jacqueline A. Holley, R.N., Vice President Nursing
Web address: www.JamaicaHospital.org
Control: Other not–for–profit (including NFP Corporation) **Service:** General Medical and Surgical

Staffed Beds: 648 **Admissions:** 23142 **Census:** 547 **Outpatient Visits:** 356111 **Births:** 2298 **Total Expense ($000):** 574440 **Payroll Expense ($000):** 225218 **Personnel:** 3248

☒ △ **JAMES J. PETERS VETERANS AFFAIRS MEDICAL CENTER**, 130 West Kingsbridge Road, Bronx, Zip 10468–3904; tel. 718/584–9000, (Total facility includes 84 beds in nursing home–type unit) **A**1 2 3 5 7 8 **F**3 8 9 11 12 18 29 30 31 33 34 35 36 38 39 40 43 44 45 46 47 48 49 50 51 53 54 56 57 58 59 60 61 62 63 64 65 66 68 70 71 74 75 77 78 79 80 81 82 83 84 85 86 87 90 91 92 93 94 95 96 97 98 100 101 102 103 104 107 108 109 111 114 115 118 119 120 123 126 130 131 132 135 146 147 148 **S** Department of Veterans Affairs, Washington, DC
Primary Contact: Erik Langhoff, M.D., Ph.D., Director
CFO: Gregory Angelo, Chief Fiscal Program
CMO: Clive Rosendorff, M.D., Chief Medical Program
CIO: Linda Bund, Chief Information Officer and Director Education
CHR: Peter Tinker, Chief Human Resources Officer
CNO: Kathleen Capitulo, Ph.D., Chief Nurse Executive
Web address: www.bronx.va.gov/
Control: Veterans Affairs, Government, federal **Service:** General Medical and Surgical

Staffed Beds: 325 **Admissions:** 4215 **Census:** 108 **Outpatient Visits:** 365211 **Births:** 0 **Total Expense ($000):** 233344 **Payroll Expense ($000):** 150685 **Personnel:** 1884

☒ **KINGS COUNTY HOSPITAL CENTER (330202)**, 451 Clarkson Avenue, Brooklyn, Zip 11203–2097; tel. 718/245–3131 **A**1 2 3 5 9 10 **F**3 4 5 8 9 11 12 13 15 17 18 19 20 24 26 28 29 30 31 32 34 35 38 39 40 41 43 46 47 49 50 51 52 53 56 57 58 59 60 64 65 68 70 71 72 73 74 75 76 77 78 79 81 82 83 84 85 86 87 88 89 90 91 92 93 94 97 98 99 100 101 102 103 104 105 106 107 108 110 111 114 115 116 119 120 121 123 129 130 131 132 134 135 143 144 145 146 147 148 **P**6 **S** New York City Health and Hospitals Corporation, New York, NY
Primary Contact: Ernest Baptiste, Executive Director
COO: Robert R. Miller, II, Chief Operating Officer
CFO: Julian John, Chief Financial Officer
CMO: Ghassan Jamaleddine, M.D., Medical Director
CIO: Dino Civan, Chief Information Officer
CHR: Michelle Emmons, Associate Executive Director
CNO: Opal Sinclair–Chung, R.N., Chief Nursing Officer, Deputy Executive Director
Web address: www.nyc.gov/html/hhc/kchc/html/home/home.shtml
Control: City–Government, nonfederal **Service:** General Medical and Surgical

Staffed Beds: 599 **Admissions:** 25837 **Census:** 540 **Outpatient Visits:** 717480 **Births:** 2450 **Total Expense ($000):** 825425 **Payroll Expense ($000):** 361448 **Personnel:** 4974

☐ **KINGSBORO PSYCHIATRIC CENTER (334058)**, 681 Clarkson Avenue, Brooklyn, Zip 11203–2125; tel. 718/221–7395, (Nonreporting) **A**1 3 5 **S** New York State Office of Mental Health, Albany, NY
Primary Contact: Deborah Parchment, Executive Director
CFO: Yinusa Awolowo, Business Officer
CMO: Jeffery Lucey, M.D., Clinical Director
CIO: George Gavora, Director Program Evaluation
CHR: Vera Thompson, Director Human Resources
CNO: Deborah Denigris, Chief Nursing Officer
Web address: www.omh.ny.gov/omhweb/facilities/kbpc/facility/htm
Control: State–Government, nonfederal **Service:** Psychiatric

Staffed Beds: 290

Many Facility Codes have changed. Please refer to the AHA Guide Code Chart. © 2014 AHA Guide

☐ △ **KINGSBROOK JEWISH MEDICAL CENTER (330201)**, 585 Schenectady Avenue, Brooklyn, Zip 11203–1891; tel. 718/604–5000, (Total facility includes 466 beds in nursing home–type unit) **A**1 3 5 7 9 10 **F**3 8 15 17 18 28 29 30 31 34 35 39 40 45 46 48 49 50 54 56 57 59 60 61 64 65 68 70 74 75 77 78 79 80 81 82 84 85 87 90 91 92 93 94 96 97 98 100 101 103 104 107 108 110 111 114 115 119 128 130 131 135 143 146 147 148
Primary Contact: Linda Brady, M.D., President and Chief Executive Officer
COO: Robert Dubicki, Executive Vice President and Chief Operating Officer
CFO: John Schmitt, Senior Vice President and Chief Financial Officer
CMO: Sibte Burney, M.D., Senior Vice President Medical Affairs and Chief Medical Officer
CIO: Daniel Morreale, Vice President and Chief Information Officer
CHR: John McKeon, Vice President Human Resources
CNO: Jane Lederer, R.N., Vice President and Chief Nursing Officer
Web address: www.kingsbrook.org
Control: Other not–for–profit (including NFP Corporation) **Service:** General Medical and Surgical

Staffed Beds: 771 **Admissions:** 10320 **Census:** 644 **Outpatient Visits:** 133412 **Births:** 0 **Personnel:** 1766

☒ **LENOX HILL HOSPITAL (330119)**, 100 East 77th Street, Zip 10075–1850; tel. 212/434–2000, (Includes MANHATTAN EYE, EAR AND THROAT HOSPITAL, 210 East 64th Street, Zip 10021–9885; tel. 212/838–9200; Philip P. Rosenthal, Executive Director) **A**1 3 5 8 9 10 **F**7 8 9 11 12 13 14 15 17 18 20 22 24 26 29 30 31 32 34 35 36 37 38 39 40 43 44 45 46 47 48 49 50 51 54 55 56 57 58 59 60 61 62 63 64 65 66 68 70 72 74 75 76 77 78 79 81 82 84 85 86 87 89 91 92 93 97 98 99 100 101 102 103 104 107 108 110 111 115 117 118 119 126 130 131 132 135 141 143 146 147 148 **P**5 6 **S** North Shore–Long Island Jewish Health System, Great Neck, NY
Primary Contact: Dennis Connors, Executive Director
CMO: Marc L. Napp, M.D., Vice President Medical Affairs
CIO: Beth Dituro, Divisional Chief Information Officer
Web address: www.lenoxhillhospital.org
Control: Other not–for–profit (including NFP Corporation) **Service:** General Medical and Surgical

Staffed Beds: 508 **Admissions:** 29417 **Census:** 384 **Outpatient Visits:** 194181 **Births:** 4163 **Total Expense ($000):** 754576 **Payroll Expense ($000):** 360844 **Personnel:** 4056

☒ **LINCOLN MEDICAL AND MENTAL HEALTH CENTER (330080)**, 234 East 149th Street, Bronx, Zip 10451–5504; tel. 718/579–5700 **A**1 2 3 5 9 10 **F**3 5 8 11 13 15 18 19 29 30 31 32 34 35 38 39 40 41 43 45 50 55 56 57 58 59 60 61 64 65 66 68 70 71 72 73 74 75 76 77 78 79 81 82 84 85 86 87 88 89 93 97 98 99 100 101 102 103 104 107 108 110 114 115 119 121 123 130 132 134 135 143 144 146 147 148 **P**4 **S** New York City Health and Hospitals Corporation, New York, NY
Primary Contact: Milton Nunez, Executive Director
CFO: Caswell Samms, Network Chief Financial Officer
CMO: Melissa Schori, M.D., Medical Director
CIO: Maricar Barrameda, Chief Information Officer
CHR: Jeannith Michelen, Senior Associate Executive Director
Web address: www.nyc.gov/html/hhc/lincoln/
Control: City–Government, nonfederal **Service:** General Medical and Surgical

Staffed Beds: 338 **Admissions:** 19930 **Census:** 262 **Outpatient Visits:** 552929 **Births:** 2206 **Total Expense ($000):** 539183 **Payroll Expense ($000):** 195418 **Personnel:** 3214

☒ **LONG ISLAND JEWISH MEDICAL CENTER (330195)**, 270–05 76th Avenue, New Hyde Park, Zip 11040–1496; tel. 718/470–7000, (Includes MANHASSET AMBULATORY CARE PAVILION, 1554 Northern Boulevard, Manhasset, Zip 11030; tel. 516/365–2070; STEVEN AND ALEXANDRA COHEN CHILDREN'S MEDICAL CENTER OF NEW YORK, 270–05 76th Avenue, Zip 11040; tel. 718/470–3000; ZUCKER HILLSIDE HOSPITAL, 75–59 263rd Street, Glen Oaks, Zip 11004; tel. 718/470–8000) **A**1 2 3 5 8 9 10 13 **F**2 3 5 6 7 8 9 11 12 13 14 15 17 18 19 20 21 22 23 24 25 26 27 29 30 31 32 33 34 35 38 39 40 41 42 43 44 45 46 47 48 49 50 51 53 54 55 56 57 58 59 60 61 62 63 64 65 66 68 70 72 73 74 75 76 77 78 79 80 81 82 84 85 86 87 88 89 92 93 97 98 99 100 101 102 103 104 105 106 107 108 109 110 111 114 115 116 117 118 119 120 121 123 124 126 129 130 131 132 134 135 136 141 142 143 144 145 146 147 148 **P**5 6 **S** North Shore–Long Island Jewish Health System, Great Neck, NY
Primary Contact: Chantal Weinhold, Executive Director
CIO: Ty Knox, Chief Information Officer
CHR: Ronald W. Stone, Regional Chief Human Resource Officer
Web address: www.lij.edu
Control: Other not–for–profit (including NFP Corporation) **Service:** General Medical and Surgical

Staffed Beds: 885 **Admissions:** 49937 **Census:** 817 **Outpatient Visits:** 752437 **Births:** 6561 **Total Expense ($000):** 1611986 **Payroll Expense ($000):** 799526 **Personnel:** 14178

☒ **LUTHERAN MEDICAL CENTER (330306)**, 150 55th Street, Brooklyn, Zip 11220–2559; tel. 718/630–7000 **A**1 3 5 9 10 13 **F**3 7 8 11 12 13 14 15 17 18 19 20 22 29 30 31 32 34 35 36 38 39 40 41 43 44 45 49 50 51 52 54 55 56 57 58 59 60 61 64 65 66 68 70 72 73 74 75 76 77 78 79 81 82 84 85 86 87 89 90 91 92 93 94 96 97 98 100 101 102 103 104 107 108 110 111 114 115 119 121 123 124 130 131 132 134 135 143 146 147 148 **P**6
Primary Contact: Wendy Z. Goldstein, President and Chief Executive Officer
COO: Claudia Caine, President and Chief Operating Officer
CFO: Richard Langfelder, Executive Vice President and Chief Financial Officer
CIO: Steve Art, Senior Vice President and Chief Information Officer
CHR: Frank Scheets, Senior Vice President
Web address: www.lmcmc.com
Control: Other not–for–profit (including NFP Corporation) **Service:** General Medical and Surgical

Staffed Beds: 387 **Admissions:** 24475 **Census:** 341 **Outpatient Visits:** 722886 **Births:** 3911 **Total Expense ($000):** 596568 **Payroll Expense ($000):** 278216 **Personnel:** 4042

☒ **MAIMONIDES MEDICAL CENTER (330194)**, 4802 Tenth Avenue, Brooklyn, Zip 11219–2916; tel. 718/283–6000, (Includes MAIMONIDES INFANTS AND CHILDREN'S HOSPITAL OF BROOKLYN, 4802 Tenth Avenue, tel. 718/283–6000) **A**1 2 3 5 8 9 10 12 13 **F**2 3 7 8 9 11 12 13 14 15 17 18 19 20 22 24 26 28 29 30 31 32 34 35 38 39 40 41 44 45 46 47 48 49 50 51 52 54 55 56 57 58 59 60 61 64 65 66 68 70 72 73 74 75 76 77 78 79 81 82 84 85 86 87 88 89 91 92 93 96 97 98 99 100 101 102 103 104 107 108 110 111 114 115 117 118 119 120 121 123 124 126 129 130 131 132 135 144 145 146 147 148 **P**5 6
Primary Contact: Pamela S. Brier, President and Chief Executive Officer
COO: Mark McDougle, Executive Vice President and Chief Operating Officer
CFO: Robert Naldi, Chief Financial Officer
CMO: Samuel Kopel, M.D., Medical Director
CIO: Walter Fahey, Chief Information Officer
Web address: www.maimonidesmed.org/
Control: Other not–for–profit (including NFP Corporation) **Service:** General Medical and Surgical

Staffed Beds: 644 **Admissions:** 37388 **Census:** 622 **Outpatient Visits:** 502153 **Births:** 8537 **Total Expense ($000):** 1061424 **Payroll Expense ($000):** 532292 **Personnel:** 5629

☐ **MANHATTAN PSYCHIATRIC CENTER–WARD'S ISLAND (334054)**, 600 East 125th Street, Zip 10035–6000; tel. 646/672–6767, (Nonreporting) **A**1 3 5 10 **S** New York State Office of Mental Health, Albany, NY
Primary Contact: Vinny Miccoli, Executive Director
Web address: www.omh.ny.gov
Control: State–Government, nonfederal **Service:** Psychiatric

Staffed Beds: 745

☒ **MEMORIAL SLOAN–KETTERING CANCER CENTER (330154)**, 1275 York Avenue, Zip 10065–6007; tel. 212/639–2000 **A**1 2 3 5 8 9 10 **F**3 11 14 15 29 31 32 34 35 36 37 39 44 45 46 47 49 50 54 55 56 57 58 59 60 61 64 66 68 70 74 75 77 78 79 81 82 84 85 86 87 89 92 93 94 96 99 100 103 104 107 108 110 111 112 114 115 117 118 119 120 121 123 124 126 130 132 135 136 142 143 144 145 146 147 148 **P**6
Primary Contact: Craig B. Thompson, M.D., President and Chief Executive Officer
COO: John R. Gunn, Executive Vice President and Chief Operating Officer
CFO: Michael Gutnick, Senior Vice President Finance
CMO: Jose Baselga, M.D., Physician–in–Chief
CIO: Patricia Skarulis, Vice President Information Systems
CHR: Kerry Besset, Senior Vice President Human Resources
CNO: Elizabeth Nelkin McCormick, MSN, Chief Nursing Officer
Web address: www.mskcc.org
Control: Other not–for–profit (including NFP Corporation) **Service:** Cancer

Staffed Beds: 471 **Admissions:** 22326 **Census:** 395 **Outpatient Visits:** 1373083 **Births:** 0 **Total Expense ($000):** 2268828 **Payroll Expense ($000):** 927080 **Personnel:** 12730

NY

Hospital, Medicare Provider Number, Address, Telephone, Approval, Facility, and Physician Codes, Health Care System

★ American Hospital Association (AHA) membership
☐ The Joint Commission accreditation
◇ DNV Healthcare Inc. accreditation
○ Healthcare Facilities Accreditation Program
△ Commission on Accreditation of Rehabilitation Facilities (CARF) accreditation

✠ **METROPOLITAN HOSPITAL CENTER (330199)**, 1901 First Avenue, Zip 10029–7404; tel. 212/423–6262, (Includes METROPOLITAN GENERAL CARE UNIT, METROPOLITAN DRUG DETOXIFICATION AND METROPOLITAN PSYCHIATRIC UNIT) **A**1 3 5 9 10 **F**3 4 8 9 11 13 15 17 18 19 28 29 30 31 32 34 38 39 40 41 43 44 45 46 49 50 51 55 56 57 58 59 60 61 64 65 66 68 70 72 73 74 75 76 77 78 79 81 82 84 85 87 89 90 92 93 96 97 98 99 100 101 102 103 104 107 108 110 111 114 119 130 131 132 133 134 135 141 144 146 147 148 **S** New York City Health and Hospitals Corporation, New York, NY
Primary Contact: Meryl Weinberg, Executive Director
COO: Elizabeth Guzman, Chief Operating Officer
CFO: Tracy V. Green, Chief Financial Officer
CMO: Richard Stone, M.D., Medical Director
CIO: Eli Tarlow, Chief Information Officer
CHR: April Alexander, Director Human Resources
CNO: Lillian Diaz, R.N., Chief Nursing Officer
Web address: www.nyc.gov/html/hhc/mhc/html/home/home.shtml
Control: City–Government, nonfederal **Service:** General Medical and Surgical

Staffed Beds: 317 **Admissions:** 14404 **Census:** 249 **Outpatient Visits:** 423896 **Births:** 1212 **Total Expense ($000):** 337549 **Payroll Expense ($000):** 131252 **Personnel:** 1946

✠ **MONTEFIORE MEDICAL CENTER (330059)**, 111 East 210th Street, Bronx, Zip 10467–2401; tel. 718/920–4321, (Includes CHILDREN'S HOSPITAL OF MONTEFIORE, 3415 Bainbridge Avenue, Zip 10467–2403; tel. 718/741–2426; JACK D WEILER HOSPITAL OF ALBERT EINSTEIN COLLEGE OF MEDICINE, 1825 Eastchester Road, Zip 10461–2373; tel. 718/904–2000; MONTEFIORE MEDICAL CENTER – NORTH DIVISION, 600 East 233rd Street, Zip 10466–2697; tel. 718/920–9000) **A**1 2 3 5 8 9 10 **F**3 4 5 6 7 8 9 10 12 13 14 15 17 18 19 20 21 22 23 24 25 26 27 28 29 30 31 32 34 35 36 37 38 39 40 41 42 44 45 46 47 48 49 50 51 52 54 55 56 57 58 59 60 61 62 63 64 65 66 68 70 71 72 73 74 75 76 77 78 79 80 81 82 83 84 85 86 87 88 89 90 92 93 94 97 98 99 100 101 102 103 104 107 108 110 111 114 115 118 119 120 121 123 124 126 129 130 131 132 134 135 136 137 138 139 141 142 143 144 145 146 147 148 **P**5 6 **S** Montefiore Health System, Bronx, NY
Primary Contact: Steven M. Safyer, M.D., President and Chief Executive Officer
COO: Robert B. Conaty, Executive Vice President Operations
CFO: Joel A. Perlman, Executive Vice President Finance
CMO: Gary Kalkut, M.D., Senior Vice President and Chief Medical Officer
CIO: Jack Wolf, Vice President Information Systems
Web address: www.montefiore.org
Control: Other not–for–profit (including NFP Corporation) **Service:** General Medical and Surgical

Staffed Beds: 1516 **Admissions:** 83568 **Census:** 1411 **Outpatient Visits:** 1815138 **Births:** 5629 **Total Expense ($000):** 3218324 **Payroll Expense ($000):** 1508508 **Personnel:** 18347

MORGAN STANLEY CHILDREN'S HOSPITAL OF NEW YORK–PRESBYTERIAN See New York–Presbyterian Hospital

✠ **MOUNT SINAI BETH ISRAEL (330169)**, First Avenue and 16th Street, Zip 10003–3803; tel. 212/420–2000, (Includes MOUNT SINAI BETH ISRAEL BROOKLYN, 3201 Kings Highway, Brooklyn, Zip 11234; tel. 718/252–3000; Lin H. Mo, M.P.H., President), (Total facility includes 28 beds in nursing home–type unit) **A**1 2 3 5 8 9 10 **F**3 4 5 7 8 9 11 13 14 15 17 18 19 20 22 24 26 28 29 30 31 32 33 34 35 36 38 39 40 41 43 44 45 46 47 48 49 50 51 52 53 54 55 56 57 58 59 60 61 63 64 65 66 68 70 72 74 75 76 77 78 79 81 82 83 84 85 86 87 88 89 90 92 93 94 96 97 98 99 100 101 102 103 104 107 108 110 111 114 115 117 118 119 120 121 123 126 128 129 130 131 132 135 144 145 146 147 148 **P**5 6 **S** Mount Sinai Health System, New York, NY
Primary Contact: Susan Somerville, R.N., President
COO: Kevin Molloy, Senior Vice President and Chief Operating Officer
CFO: Donald Scanlon, Chief Corporate Services, Mount Sinai Health System
CMO: Jeremy Boal, M.D., Executive Vice President and Chief Medical Officer
CIO: Kumar Chatani, Senior Vice President and Chief Information Officer Mount Sinai Health System
CHR: Jane Maksoud, R.N., Senior Vice President Human Resources and Labor Relations, Mount Sinai Health System
CNO: Mary Walsh, R.N., Vice President Patient Care Services and Chief Nursing Officer
Web address: www.bethisraelny.org
Control: Other not–for–profit (including NFP Corporation) **Service:** General Medical and Surgical

Staffed Beds: 1037 **Admissions:** 52583 **Census:** 818 **Outpatient Visits:** 552807 **Births:** 3853 **Total Expense ($000):** 1452236 **Payroll Expense ($000):** 703291 **Personnel:** 8154

✠ △ **MOUNT SINAI HOSPITAL (330024)**, One Gustave L. Levy Place, Zip 10029–6574; tel. 212/241–6500, (Includes KRAVIS CHILDREN'S HOSPITAL, One Gustave L. Levy Pl, Zip 10029, Mailing Address: PO Box 1153, Zip 10002–0916; tel. 800/637–4624) **A**1 2 3 5 7 8 9 10 **F**3 4 6 7 8 9 11 12 13 14 15 17 18 19 20 21 22 23 24 25 26 27 28 29 30 31 32 34 35 36 37 38 39 40 41 42 43 44 45 46 47 48 49 50 51 52 54 55 56 57 58 59 60 61 63 64 65 66 68 70 71 72 73 74 75 76 77 78 79 80 81 82 83 84 85 86 87 88 89 90 91 92 93 94 95 96 97 98 99 100 101 102 103 104 105 107 108 110 111 114 115 116 117 118 119 120 121 123 124 126 129 130 131 132 134 135 136 137 138 139 141 142 143 144 145 146 147 148 **P**5 6 **S** Mount Sinai Health System, New York, NY
Primary Contact: David L. Reich, M.D., President
COO: David L. Reich, M.D., President and Chief Operating Officer
CFO: Donald Scanlon, Chief Financial Officer
CMO: Vicki LoPachin, Chief Medical Officer
CIO: Kumar Chatani, Senior Vice President and Chief Information Officer Mount Sinai Health System
CHR: Jane Maksoud, R.N., Senior Vice President Human Resources and Labor Relations
CNO: Carol A. Porter, R.N., Chief Nursing Officer, Senior Vice President
Web address: www.mountsinai.org
Control: Other not–for–profit (including NFP Corporation) **Service:** General Medical and Surgical

Staffed Beds: 1037 **Admissions:** 52040 **Census:** 850 **Outpatient Visits:** 699604 **Births:** 6552 **Total Expense ($000):** 1699715 **Payroll Expense ($000):** 645776 **Personnel:** 8170

MOUNT SINAI QUEENS (330258), 25–10 30th Avenue, Long Island City, Zip 11102–2448; tel. 718/932–1000 **A**10 **F**3 8 15 18 29 30 31 32 34 35 40 43 45 49 50 54 56 57 59 60 63 64 65 66 68 70 74 75 77 78 79 80 81 82 84 85 86 87 93 97 100 107 111 119 135 141 143 146 147 148 **P**6 **S** Mount Sinai Health System, New York, NY
Primary Contact: Caryn A. Schwab, Executive Director
COO: Judy Trilivas, Vice President and Chief Operating Officer
CFO: Salvatore Morello, Vice President Finance
CMO: Brian Radbill, M.D., Chief Medical Officer
CIO: Jack Abuin, Director Management Information Systems
CHR: Norma Calame, Director Human Resources
CNO: Kathleen Scher, R.N., Vice President Nursing
Web address: www.mshq.org
Control: Other not–for–profit (including NFP Corporation) **Service:** General Medical and Surgical

Staffed Beds: 182 **Admissions:** 9629 **Census:** 157 **Outpatient Visits:** 107364 **Births:** 2 **Total Expense ($000):** 153242 **Payroll Expense ($000):** 79958 **Personnel:** 1098

MOUNT SINAI ROOSEVELT HOSPITAL See Mount Sinai St. Luke's

✠ **MOUNT SINAI ST. LUKE'S (330046)**, 1111 Amsterdam Avenue, Zip 10025–1716; tel. 212/523–4000, (Includes MOUNT SINAI ROOSEVELT HOSPITAL, 1000 Tenth Avenue, Zip 10019; tel. 212/523–4000; Evan Flatow, M.D., President) **A**1 3 5 8 9 10 **F**3 4 5 7 8 11 12 13 14 15 17 18 20 22 24 26 29 30 31 32 34 35 38 39 40 41 43 44 46 49 50 52 54 55 56 57 58 59 60 61 63 64 65 66 68 70 72 74 75 76 77 78 79 81 82 84 85 86 87 89 90 92 93 94 96 97 98 99 100 101 102 103 104 105 107 108 110 111 114 115 119 120 121 123 124 126 130 131 132 134 135 144 145 146 147 148 **P**5 6 **S** Mount Sinai Health System, New York, NY
Primary Contact: Arthur A. Gianelli, M.P.H., President
COO: Kevin Molloy, Senior Vice President and Chief Operating Officer
CFO: Donald Scanlon, Chief Corporate Services, Mount Sinai Health System
CMO: Jeremy Boal, M.D., Executive Vice President and Chief Medical Officer
CIO: Kumar Chatani, Chief Information Officer, Mount Sinai Health System
CHR: Jane Maksoud, R.N., Senior Vice President Human Resources and Labor Relations, Mount Sinai Health System
CNO: Mary Walsh, R.N., Vice President Patient Care Services and Chief Nursing Officer
Web address: www.stlukeshospitalnyc.org
Control: Other not–for–profit (including NFP Corporation) **Service:** General Medical and Surgical

Staffed Beds: 683 **Admissions:** 39856 **Census:** 634 **Outpatient Visits:** 612619 **Births:** 6298 **Total Expense ($000):** 1210202 **Payroll Expense ($000):** 588366 **Personnel:** 5866

NEW YORK CITY CHILDREN'S CENTER, 74–03 Commonwealth Boulevard, Jamaica, Zip 11426–1890; tel. 718/264–4506, (Includes BRONX CHILDREN'S PSYCHIATRIC CENTER, 1000 Waters Place, Bronx, Zip 10461–2799; tel. 718/239–3600; BROOKLYN CHILDREN'S PSYCHIATRIC CENTER, 1819 Bergen Street, Brooklyn, Zip 11233–4513; tel. 718/221–4500), (Nonreporting) **S** New York State Office of Mental Health, Albany, NY
Primary Contact: Anita Daniels, Acting Executive Director
CMO: David M. Rube, M.D., Clinical Director
CIO: Ed Yunusov, Coordinator Facility Information Center
Web address: www.omh.ny.gov
Control: State–Government, nonfederal **Service:** Children's hospital psychiatric

Staffed Beds: 84

NY

☐ **NEW YORK COMMUNITY HOSPITAL (330019)**, 2525 Kings Highway, Brooklyn, Zip 11229–1705; tel. 718/692–5300 **A**1 9 10 **F**7 8 18 30 34 35 40 45 46 49 70 78 79 80 81 82 87 107 119 130 146 **S** New York Presbyterian Healthcare System, New York, NY
Primary Contact: Steve Meyers, Interim Chief Executive Officer
COO: Una E. Morrissey, R.N., Senior Vice President, Chief Nursing Officer and Chief Operating Officer
CFO: Leonardo Tamburello, Divisional Chief Financial Officer
CMO: Herbert Rader, M.D., Vice President and Medical Director
CIO: Edward B. Stolyar, D.O., Director Management Information Systems
CHR: Steve Meyers, Director Human Resources
Web address: www.nych.com
Control: Other not–for–profit (including NFP Corporation) **Service:** General Medical and Surgical

Staffed Beds: 127 **Admissions:** 7671 **Census:** 123 **Births:** 0 **Total Expense ($000):** 94345 **Payroll Expense ($000):** 42607 **Personnel:** 493

☒ **NEW YORK EYE AND EAR INFIRMARY OF MOUNT SINAI (330100)**, 310 East 14th Street, Zip 10003–4201; tel. 212/979–4000 **A**1 3 5 9 10 **F**3 11 29 30 34 35 43 44 50 54 57 58 59 64 66 68 74 81 82 85 86 87 91 92 93 94 107 114 119 129 130 132 142 146 **S** Mount Sinai Health System, New York, NY
Primary Contact: James Tsai, M.D., President
COO: Allan Fine, Chief Operating Officer
CFO: Donald Scanlon, Chief Corporate Services, Mount Sinai Health System
CMO: Jeremy Boal, M.D., Executive Vice President and Chief Medical Officer
CIO: Kumar Chatani, Chief Information Officer, Mount Sinai Health System
CHR: Jane Maksoud, R.N., Senior Vice President Human Resources and Labor Relations, Mount Sinai Health System
CNO: Sonja Tennaro, Ed.D., Senior Vice President Clinical Operations
Web address: www.nyee.edu
Control: Other not–for–profit (including NFP Corporation) **Service:** Eye, ear, nose, and throat

Staffed Beds: 32 **Admissions:** 557 **Census:** 3 **Outpatient Visits:** 217243 **Births:** 0 **Total Expense ($000):** 145269 **Payroll Expense ($000):** 62186 **Personnel:** 907

☐ **NEW YORK HOSPITAL QUEENS (330055)**, 56–45 Main Street, Flushing, Zip 11355–5045; tel. 718/670–1231 **A**1 2 3 5 9 10 **F**1 3 4 5 6 7 8 9 12 13 14 15 16 17 18 19 20 21 22 23 24 25 26 27 28 29 30 31 33 34 35 36 37 38 39 40 41 42 43 44 45 46 47 48 49 50 51 53 54 55 56 57 58 59 60 61 62 63 64 65 66 67 68 70 71 72 73 74 75 76 77 78 79 80 81 82 83 84 85 86 87 88 89 90 91 92 93 95 96 97 98 107 108 109 110 111 112 113 114 115 118 119 120 121 122 123 124 125 126 127 128 130 131 132 133 134 135 143 144 145 146 147 148 **P**4 **S** New York Presbyterian Healthcare System, New York, NY
Primary Contact: Stephen S. Mills, President and Chief Executive Officer
COO: John E. Sciortino, Senior Vice President and Chief Operating Officer
CFO: Kevin J. Ward, Vice President and Chief Financial Officer
CMO: Stephen Rimar, M.D., Senior Vice President Medical Affairs
CIO: Thomas Kemp, Chief Information Officer
CHR: Lorraine Orlando, Vice President Human Resources
Web address: www.nyhq.org
Control: Other not–for–profit (including NFP Corporation) **Service:** General Medical and Surgical

Staffed Beds: 559 **Admissions:** 32986 **Census:** 426 **Outpatient Visits:** 162081 **Births:** 4216 **Total Expense ($000):** 693997 **Payroll Expense ($000):** 335230 **Personnel:** 4020

☒ **NEW YORK METHODIST HOSPITAL (330236)**, 506 Sixth Street, Brooklyn, Zip 11215–3609; tel. 718/780–3000 **A**1 2 3 5 8 9 10 **F**3 6 8 9 11 12 13 15 17 18 19 20 22 24 26 29 30 31 32 33 34 35 36 39 40 41 43 44 45 46 47 48 49 50 51 52 54 55 56 57 58 59 60 61 63 64 65 66 68 70 72 74 75 76 77 78 79 81 82 83 84 85 87 88 89 90 92 93 95 96 97 98 99 102 103 104 107 108 109 110 111 114 118 119 120 121 123 124 126 129 130 131 132 135 144 145 146 147 148 **P**4 6 7 **S** New York Presbyterian Healthcare System, New York, NY
Primary Contact: Mark J. Mundy, President and Chief Executive Officer
CFO: Michael P. Breslin, Senior Vice President Finance
CMO: Stanley Sherbell, M.D., Executive Vice President Medical Affairs
CIO: Rick Plisko, Director information Systems
CHR: Dennis Buchanan, Vice President Human Resources
CNO: Rebecca L. Flood, R.N., Senior Vice President Nursing
Web address: www.nym.org
Control: Other not–for–profit (including NFP Corporation) **Service:** General Medical and Surgical

Staffed Beds: 591 **Admissions:** 35975 **Census:** 551 **Outpatient Visits:** 482951 **Births:** 5579 **Total Expense ($000):** 726027 **Payroll Expense ($000):** 283633 **Personnel:** 3938

☒ **NEW YORK PRESBYTERIAN LOWER MANHATTAN HOSPITAL (330064)**, 170 William Street, Zip 10038–2649; tel. 212/312–5000, (Nonreporting) **A**1 9 10 **S** New York Presbyterian Healthcare System, New York, NY
Primary Contact: Robert E. Kelly, M.D., President
COO: Michael Fosina, M.P.H., SVP and Chief Operating Officer
CMO: Steven G. Friedman, M.D., Interim Chief Medical Officer and Chair, Department of Surgery
CIO: Frank Negro, Interim Chief Information Officer
CNO: Kit Yuen, R.N., Interim Chief Nursing Officer
Web address: www.nyp.org/lowermanhattan
Control: Other not–for–profit (including NFP Corporation) **Service:** General Medical and Surgical

Staffed Beds: 128

☐ **NEW YORK STATE PSYCHIATRIC INSTITUTE (334009)**, 1051 Riverside Drive, Zip 10032–1007; tel. 212/543–5000, (Nonreporting) **A**1 3 5 10 **S** New York State Office of Mental Health, Albany, NY
Primary Contact: Jeffrey A. Lieberman, M.D., Executive Director
COO: Janelle Dierkens, Chief Administration Officer
CFO: Jonathan Segal, Chief Financial Officer
CMO: David Lowenthal, M.D., Clinical Director
CIO: Joseph Grun, Chief Information Officer
CHR: Rebecca Dechabert, Acting Director Personnel
Web address: www.nyspi.org
Control: State–Government, nonfederal **Service:** Psychiatric

Staffed Beds: 58

☒ △ **NEW YORK–PRESBYTERIAN HOSPITAL (330101)**, 525 East 68th Street, Zip 10065–4870; tel. 212/746–5454, (Includes MORGAN STANLEY CHILDREN'S HOSPITAL OF NEW YORK–PRESBYTERIAN, 3959 Broadway, Zip 10032–3784; tel. 212/305–2500; NEW YORK–PRESBYTERIAN HOSPITAL, WESTCHESTER DIVISION, 21 Bloomingdale Road, White Plains, Zip 10605; tel. 914/682–9100; NEW YORK–PRESBYTERIAN HOSPITAL/WEILL CORNELL MEDICAL CENTER, 525 East 68th Street, Zip 10021–4885; tel. 212/746–5454; NEW YORK–PRESBYTERIAN/COLUMBIA UNIVERSITY MEDICAL CENTER, 161 Fort Washington Avenue, Zip 10032; tel. 212/305–2500; PAYNE WHITNEY PSYCHIATRIC CLINIC, 525 East 68th Street, Zip 10021; tel. 212/746–3800; PHYLLIS AND DAVID KOMANSKY CENTER FOR CHILDREN'S HEALTH, 525 East 68th Street, tel. 212/746–5454; THE ALLEN PAVILION, 5141 Broadway, Zip 10032; tel. 212/932–5000) **A**1 2 3 5 7 8 9 10 **F**3 4 7 9 11 12 13 14 15 16 17 18 19 20 21 22 23 24 25 26 27 28 29 30 31 32 34 35 36 37 38 39 40 41 43 44 45 46 47 48 49 50 51 52 53 54 55 56 57 58 59 60 61 64 65 66 68 70 72 73 74 75 76 77 78 79 80 81 82 84 85 86 87 88 89 90 92 93 94 96 97 98 99 100 101 102 103 104 105 107 108 109 110 111 112 114 115 116 117 118 119 120 121 123 124 126 129 130 131 132 134 135 136 137 138 139 140 141 142 143 144 145 146 147 148 **S** New York Presbyterian Healthcare System, New York, NY
Primary Contact: Steven J. Corwin, M.D., Chief Executive Officer
CFO: Phyllis R. Lantos, Executive Vice President, Corporate Chief Financial Officer and Treasurer
CMO: Laura Forese, M.D., Senior Vice President and Chief Medical Officer
CIO: Aurelia Boyer, Senior Vice President and Chief Information Officer
CHR: G. Thomas Ferguson, Senior Vice President and Chief Human Resources Officer
Web address: www.nyp.org
Control: Other not–for–profit (including NFP Corporation) **Service:** General Medical and Surgical

Staffed Beds: 2364 **Admissions:** 112220 **Census:** 1954 **Outpatient Visits:** 1997596 **Births:** 14600 **Total Expense ($000):** 4062347 **Payroll Expense ($000):** 1945813 **Personnel:** 20490

☒ **NORTH CENTRAL BRONX HOSPITAL (330385)**, 3424 Kossuth Avenue, Bronx, Zip 10467–2489; tel. 718/519–3500 **A**1 3 5 9 10 **F**3 5 8 11 12 13 15 18 28 29 30 32 34 35 38 39 40 41 43 44 45 46 48 50 51 55 56 57 58 59 60 61 64 65 66 68 70 72 73 74 75 76 77 78 79 80 81 82 84 85 87 92 93 94 96 97 98 99 100 101 102 103 104 105 107 108 110 111 115 119 130 131 132 135 144 146 147 148 **P**6 **S** New York City Health and Hospitals Corporation, New York, NY
Primary Contact: William P. Walsh, Executive Director
COO: Sheldon McLeod, Chief Operating Officer
CFO: Kathy Garramone, Chief Financial Officer
CMO: Joseph Skarzynski, M.D., Medical Director
CIO: Diane Carr, Chief Information Officer
CHR: Dolores Leite, Chief Human Resource Executive
CNO: Elizabeth Gerdts, Chief Nursing Officer
Web address: www.nyc.gov/html/hhc/ncbh/html/home/home.shtml
Control: City–Government, nonfederal **Service:** General Medical and Surgical

Staffed Beds: 207 **Admissions:** 7238 **Census:** 124 **Outpatient Visits:** 224593 **Births:** 1468 **Total Expense ($000):** 201564 **Payroll Expense ($000):** 75134 **Personnel:** 1209

NYU HOSPITAL FOR JOINT DISEASES See NYU Langone Medical Center's Hospital for Joint Diseases

NY

Hospital, Medicare Provider Number, Address, Telephone, Approval, Facility, and Physician Codes, Health Care System

★ American Hospital Association (AHA) membership
☐ The Joint Commission accreditation ◇ DNV Healthcare Inc. accreditation
○ Healthcare Facilities Accreditation Program
△ Commission on Accreditation of Rehabilitation Facilities (CARF) accreditation

✠ △ **NYU LANGONE MEDICAL CENTER (330214)**, 550 First Avenue, Zip 10016–6402; tel. 212/263–7300, (Includes NYU CHILDREN'S HOSPITAL, 545 First Avenue, Zip 10016–6401; tel. 212/263–7300; NYU LANGONE MEDICAL CENTER'S HOSPITAL FOR JOINT DISEASES, 301 East 17th Street, Zip 10003–3890; tel. 212/598–6000; David A. Dibner, FACHE, Senior Vice President Hospital Operations and Musculoskeletal Strategic Area; RUSK INSTITUTE, 400 East 34th Street, Zip 10016), (Data for 305 days) **A**1 5 7 8 9 10 **F**3 5 6 8 9 11 12 13 14 15 17 18 19 20 21 22 23 24 25 26 27 28 29 30 31 32 34 35 36 37 38 39 40 41 43 44 45 46 47 48 49 50 52 53 54 55 56 57 58 59 60 61 63 64 65 66 68 70 72 73 74 75 76 77 78 79 80 81 82 84 85 86 87 88 89 90 91 92 93 95 96 97 98 99 100 101 102 103 104 107 108 110 111 114 115 116 117 118 119 120 121 123 124 126 129 130 131 132 134 135 136 138 139 141 144 145 146 147 148 **P**5 6
Primary Contact: Robert I. Grossman, M.D., Chief Executive Officer
COO: Bernard Birnbaum, M.D., Senior Vice President, Vice Dean and Chief Hospital Operations
CFO: Michael Burke, Senior Vice President and Corporate Chief Financial Officer
CMO: Robert Press, M.D., Chief Medical Officer
CIO: Nader Mherabi, Senior Vice President and Vice Dean, Chief Information Officer
CHR: Nancy Sanchez, Senior Vice President and Vice Dean Human Resources
CNO: Kimberly S. Glassman, Ph.D., Chief Nursing Officer
Web address: www.nyumedicalcenter.org
Control: Other not–for–profit (including NFP Corporation) **Service:** General Medical and Surgical

Staffed Beds: 669 Admissions: 26676 Census: 419 Outpatient Visits: 746935 Births: 3959 Total Expense ($000): 1919870 Payroll Expense ($000): 675690 Personnel: 8877

PAYNE WHITNEY PSYCHIATRIC CLINIC See New York–Presbyterian Hospital

QUEENS CHILDREN'S PSYCHIATRIC CENTER See New York City Children's Center

✠ **QUEENS HOSPITAL CENTER (330231)**, 82–68 164th Street, Jamaica, Zip 11432–1104; tel. 718/883–3000 **A**1 2 3 5 9 10 **F**3 5 8 11 13 14 15 18 29 30 31 32 34 35 38 39 40 45 50 53 54 56 57 59 61 64 70 72 73 76 77 78 79 81 83 84 85 87 90 93 97 98 99 100 102 103 104 105 107 111 115 116 119 121 129 130 134 135 146 147 **P**6 **S** New York City Health and Hospitals Corporation, New York, NY
Primary Contact: Julius Wool, Executive Director
COO: Robert Rossdale, Deputy Executive Director
CFO: Brian Stacey, Chief Financial Officer
CMO: Jasmin Moshirpur, M.D., Chief Medical Officer
CIO: Vincent Smith, Chief Information Officer
CHR: Jeannith Michelen, Senior Associate Executive Director
CNO: Joan Gabriele, Deputy Executive Director
Web address: www.nyc.gov/html/hhc/qhc/html/home/home.shtml
Control: City–Government, nonfederal **Service:** General Medical and Surgical

Staffed Beds: 281 Admissions: 13193 Census: 248 Outpatient Visits: 425964 Births: 1781 Total Expense ($000): 408548 Payroll Expense ($000): 135015 Personnel: 1804

✠ **RICHMOND UNIVERSITY MEDICAL CENTER (330028)**, 355 Bard Avenue, Staten Island, Zip 10310–1664; tel. 718/818–1234 **A**1 2 3 5 9 10 **F**3 4 5 7 8 11 13 14 15 17 18 19 20 26 29 30 31 32 34 35 38 40 41 43 45 47 49 50 51 55 56 57 58 59 61 64 65 66 68 70 71 72 73 74 75 76 77 78 79 80 81 82 84 85 86 87 88 89 91 92 93 94 97 98 99 100 101 102 103 104 107 108 109 110 111 114 115 119 126 130 131 132 135 143 144 146 147 148
Primary Contact: Daniel J. Messina, Ph.D., FACHE, President and Chief Executive Officer
CMO: Edward Arsura, M.D., Chief Medical Officer
CHR: Patricia Caldari, Vice President
Web address: www.rumcsi.org
Control: Other not–for–profit (including NFP Corporation) **Service:** General Medical and Surgical

Staffed Beds: 386 Admissions: 15414 Census: 250 Outpatient Visits: 139411 Births: 2847 Total Expense ($000): 287801 Payroll Expense ($000): 139437 Personnel: 1789

☐ **ROCKEFELLER UNIVERSITY HOSPITAL (330387)**, 1230 York Avenue, Zip 10065–6399; tel. 212/327–8000, (Nonreporting) **A**1 10
Primary Contact: James G. Krueger, M.D., Ph.D., Chief Executive Officer
CMO: Barbara O'Sullivan, M.D., Medical Director
Web address: www.rucares.org
Control: Other not–for–profit (including NFP Corporation) **Service:** Other specialty

Staffed Beds: 40

ROOSEVELT HOSPITAL See Mount Sinai Roosevelt Hospital

☐ **SOUTH BEACH PSYCHIATRIC CENTER (334043)**, 777 Seaview Avenue, Staten Island, Zip 10305–3409; tel. 718/667–2300, (Nonreporting) **A**1 3 5 10 **S** New York State Office of Mental Health, Albany, NY
Primary Contact: Rosanne Gaylor, M.D., Acting Executive Director
CHR: George Bouquio, Director Human Resources
Web address: www.omh.ny.gov/omhweb/facilities/sbpc/facility.htm
Control: State–Government, nonfederal **Service:** Psychiatric

Staffed Beds: 340

✠ **ST. BARNABAS HOSPITAL (330399)**, 183rd Street & Third Avenue, Bronx, Zip 10457–9998; tel. 718/960–9000, (Total facility includes 199 beds in nursing home–type unit) **A**1 3 5 6 9 10 12 13 **F**1 3 4 5 6 7 8 9 11 13 15 16 17 18 19 20 22 25 28 29 30 31 32 34 35 36 38 39 40 41 43 44 45 46 47 49 50 51 54 55 56 57 58 59 60 61 64 65 66 67 68 70 71 72 73 74 75 76 77 78 79 80 81 82 83 85 86 87 88 89 90 91 92 93 94 97 98 99 100 101 102 103 104 107 108 109 110 111 114 115 117 119 121 128 130 131 132 134 135 143 146 147 148 **P**6
Primary Contact: Scott Cooper, M.D., Chief Executive Officer
COO: Len Walsh, Executive Vice President and Chief Operating Officer
CFO: Todd Gorlewski, Senior Vice President and Chief Financial Officer
CMO: Jerry Balentine, D.O., Executive Vice President and Chief Medical Director
CIO: Jitendra Barmecha, M.D., Senior Vice President and Chief Information Officer
CHR: Marc Wolf, Assistant Vice President Human Resources
CNO: Denise Richardson, R.N., Senior Vice President and Chief Nursing Officer
Web address: www.sbhny.org
Control: Other not–for–profit (including NFP Corporation) **Service:** General Medical and Surgical

Staffed Beds: 660 Admissions: 17138 Census: 442 Outpatient Visits: 544404 Births: 1148 Total Expense ($000): 339833 Payroll Expense ($000): 143832 Personnel: 2191

☐ **ST. JOHN'S EPISCOPAL HOSPITAL–SOUTH SHORE (330395)**, 327 Beach 19th Street, Far Rockaway, Zip 11691–4423; tel. 718/869–7000, (Nonreporting) **A**1 3 5 9 10 12 13
Primary Contact: Richard L. Brown, Interim Chief Executive Officer
COO: Patrick L. Sullivan, Chief Operating Officer
CFO: Kathleen Garcia, Controller
CMO: Raymond Pastore, M.D., Chief Medical Officer
CIO: Michael J. Piro, Chief Information Officer
CHR: Roger Franco, Director Human Resources
Web address: www.ehs.org
Control: Church–operated, Nongovernment, not–for profit **Service:** General Medical and Surgical

Staffed Beds: 251

✠ △ **STATEN ISLAND UNIVERSITY HOSPITAL (330160)**, 475 Seaview Avenue, Staten Island, Zip 10305–3436; tel. 718/226–9000 **A**1 2 3 5 7 8 9 10 **F**3 4 5 7 8 11 12 13 14 15 16 17 18 19 20 22 24 26 29 30 31 32 34 35 36 38 39 40 41 43 44 45 48 49 50 51 52 54 55 56 57 58 59 60 61 63 64 65 66 68 70 72 73 74 75 76 77 78 79 81 82 83 84 85 86 87 88 89 90 91 92 93 94 95 96 97 98 100 101 102 103 104 105 107 108 110 111 114 115 116 117 118 119 120 121 123 124 126 129 130 132 134 135 145 146 147 148 **P**6 **S** North Shore–Long Island Jewish Health System, Great Neck, NY
Primary Contact: Anthony C. Ferreri, President and Chief Executive Officer
COO: Donna Proske, MS, Executive Director
CFO: Thomas Reca, Sr., Senior Vice President Finance and Chief Financial Officer
CMO: Mark Jarrett, M.D., Chief Medical Officer
CIO: Kathy Kania, Chief Information Officer
CHR: Margaret DiAlto, Vice President Human Resources
CNO: Dian I. Johnson, MSN, Chief Nurse Executive
Web address: www.siuh.edu
Control: Other not–for–profit (including NFP Corporation) **Service:** General Medical and Surgical

Staffed Beds: 663 Admissions: 41028 Census: 590 Outpatient Visits: 931260 Births: 2992 Total Expense ($000): 820534 Payroll Expense ($000): 424566 Personnel: 4914

STEVEN AND ALEXANDRA COHEN CHILDREN'S MEDICAL CENTER OF NEW YORK See Long Island Jewish Medical Center, New Hyde Park

✠ **SUNY DOWNSTATE MEDICAL CENTER UNIVERSITY HOSPITAL (330350)**, 445 Lenox Road, Brooklyn, Zip 11203–2017; tel. 718/270–1000, (Includes THE CHILDREN'S HOSPITAL AT SUNY DOWNSTATE, 450 Clarkson Avenue, Zip 11203–2012; tel. 718/270–1625; UNIVERSITY HOSPITAL OF BROOKLYN AT LONG ISLAND COLLEGE HOSPITAL, 339 Hicks Street, Zip 11201–5509; tel. 718/780–1000; George P. Caralis, Interim Chief Executive Officer) **A**1 2 3 5 8 9 10 **F**7 8 9 13 14 15 17 18 19 20 21 22 23 24 25 26 27 28 29 30 31 32 34 35 36 37 38 39 40 41 42 44 45 46 47 48 49 50 51 52 53 54 55 56 57 58 59 60 61 64 65 66 68 73 74 75 76 77 78 79 81 82 84 86 87 88 89 90 91 92 93 94 97 98 99 100 101 102 103 104 107 108 110 111 112 114 115 116 117 118 119 120 121 124 126 129 130 131 132 138 143 144 145 146 147 148
Primary Contact: John F. Williams, Jr., M.D., Ed.D., M.P.H., President
COO: David Conley, Chief Administrative Officer
CFO: Gerry Dantis, Assistant Vice President Finance
CMO: Michael Lucchesi, M.D., Interim Chief Medical Officer
CIO: Ernest P. Weber, Jr., Interim Chief Information Officer
CHR: Hendrina Goeloe-Alston, Assistant Vice President Personnel
Web address: www.downstate.edu
Control: State–Government, nonfederal **Service:** General Medical and Surgical

Staffed Beds: 686 Admissions: 22106 Census: 382 Outpatient Visits: 430702 Births: 1617 Total Expense ($000): 873703 Payroll Expense ($000): 392080 Personnel: 5219

Many Facility Codes have changed. Please refer to the AHA Guide Code Chart. © 2014 AHA Guide

TERENCE CARDINAL COOKE HEALTH CARE CENTER (332022), 1249 Fifth Avenue, Zip 10029–4413; tel. 212/360–1000, (Nonreporting) **A**10
Primary Contact: Mitch Marsh, Interim Executive Director
COO: Neil Pollack, Senior Administrator
CFO: Ann Marie Covone, Senior Vice President and Chief Financial Officer
CMO: Anthony Lechich, M.D., Chief Medical Officer
CIO: Mitze Amoroso, Chief Information Officer
CHR: Hugo A. Pizarro, Vice President Human Resources
CNO: Monica McGibbon, Chief Nursing Officer
Web address: www.tcchcc.org/
Control: Church–operated, Nongovernment, not–for profit **Service:** Long–Term Acute Care hospital

Staffed Beds: 28

THE ALLEN PAVILION See New York–Presbyterian Hospital

☒ **VETERANS ADMINISTRATION NEW YORK HARBOR HEALTHCARE SYSTEM**, 800 Poly Place, Brooklyn, Zip 11209–7104; tel. 718/630–3500, (Includes VETERANS AFFAIRS MEDICAL CENTER, 423 East 23rd Street, New York, Zip 10010–5050; tel. 212/686–7500), (Total facility includes 142 beds in nursing home–type unit) **A**1 2 3 5 8 **F**2 3 4 5 7 8 9 12 15 17 18 20 22 24 26 28 29 30 31 33 34 35 38 39 40 44 45 46 48 49 50 53 54 56 57 58 59 60 61 62 63 64 65 68 70 74 75 77 78 79 80 81 82 83 84 85 86 87 90 92 93 94 95 96 97 98 100 101 102 103 104 105 106 107 108 110 111 114 115 118 119 120 121 123 124 128 129 130 131 132 135 143 146 147 148 **P**6 **S** Department of Veterans Affairs, Washington, DC
Primary Contact: Martina A. Parauda, Director
CFO: Daniel Downey, Chief Fiscal Service
CIO: Maria Schay, Chief Information Officer
Web address: www.nyharbor.va.gov
Control: Veterans Affairs, Government, federal **Service:** General Medical and Surgical

Staffed Beds: 476 Admissions: 7690 Census: 324 Outpatient Visits: 686152 Births: 0 Total Expense ($000): 723288 Payroll Expense ($000): 309601 Personnel: 3530

VETERANS AFFAIRS MEDICAL CENTER See James J. Peters Veterans Affairs Medical Center

☒ **WOODHULL MEDICAL AND MENTAL HEALTH CENTER (330396)**, 760 Broadway, Brooklyn, Zip 11206–5383; tel. 718/963–8000 **A**1 3 5 9 10 **F**3 4 5 8 11 13 15 29 30 31 34 35 38 39 40 41 43 45 46 48 49 53 54 55 56 57 58 59 60 61 64 65 66 68 70 71 72 73 74 75 76 77 78 79 81 82 83 84 85 86 87 89 90 93 94 97 98 99 100 101 102 103 104 107 111 119 130 132 135 143 146 147 **P**6 **S** New York City Health and Hospitals Corporation, New York, NY
Primary Contact: George M. Proctor, Senior Vice President and Executive Director
COO: Eve Borzon, R.N., Chief Operating Officer
CFO: Rick Walker, Network, Chief Financial Officer
CMO: Edward Fishkin, M.D., Medical Director
CIO: Cynthia Bianchi, Chief Information Officer
CHR: Irma Suarez, Network Deputy Executive Director
CNO: Angela Imelda Edwards, R.N., Chief Nurse Executive
Web address: www.nyc.gov/html/hhc
Control: City–County, Government, nonfederal **Service:** General Medical and Surgical

Staffed Beds: 334 Admissions: 13859 Census: 275 Outpatient Visits: 511427 Births: 2184 Total Expense ($000): 450381 Payroll Expense ($000): 155415 Personnel: 2228

☐ **WYCKOFF HEIGHTS MEDICAL CENTER (330221)**, 374 Stockholm Street, Brooklyn, Zip 11237–4006; tel. 718/963–7272, (Nonreporting) **A**1 3 5 9 10 12 13
Primary Contact: Ramon J. Rodriguez, President and Chief Executive Officer
COO: David Rock, Executive Vice President and Chief Operating Officer
CFO: Frank A. Vutrano, Chief Financial Officer
CMO: Gustavo Del Toro, M.D., Chief Medical Officer
CIO: Jebashini Jesurasa, Vice President, Chief Information Technology Officer
CHR: Margaret E. Cornelius, Vice President Human Resources
CNO: Catherine A. Gallogly–Simon, R.N., Chief Nursing Officer
Web address: www.wyckoffhospital.org
Control: Other not–for–profit (including NFP Corporation) **Service:** General Medical and Surgical

Staffed Beds: 279

ZUCKER HILLSIDE HOSPITAL See Long Island Jewish Medical Center, New Hyde Park

☒ **NEWARK–WAYNE COMMUNITY HOSPITAL (330030)**, 1200 Driving Park Avenue, Zip 14513–1057, Mailing Address: P.O. Box 111, Zip 14513–0111; tel. 315/332–2022, (Total facility includes 180 beds in nursing home–type unit) **A**1 9 10 **F**2 3 6 8 11 13 15 28 29 30 34 35 38 40 44 50 54 55 56 57 59 61 64 68 70 74 75 76 77 79 80 81 85 86 87 90 93 97 98 100 102 103 107 110 111 114 118 119 126 128 130 131 132 135 143 146 147 148 **P**5 7 **S** Rochester Regional Health System, Rochester, NY
Primary Contact: Robert Cercek, Regional President Operations
CFO: Paula Tinch, Interim Chief Financial Officer
CMO: Rob Mayo, M.D., Chief Medical Officer
CIO: Chris Teumer, Vice President and Chief Information Officer
CHR: Janine Schue, Senior Vice President People Resources
CNO: Cheryl Sheridan, R.N., Senior Vice President and Chief Nursing Officer
Web address: www.rochestergeneral.org
Control: Other not–for–profit (including NFP Corporation) **Service:** General Medical and Surgical

Staffed Beds: 280 Admissions: 5188 Census: 227 Outpatient Visits: 156238 Births: 665 Total Expense ($000): 88419 Payroll Expense ($000): 41445 Personnel: 701

☒ **ST. LUKE'S CORNWALL HOSPITAL (330264)**, 70 Dubois Street, Zip 12550–4851; tel. 845/561–4400, (Includes ST. LUKE'S CORNWALL HOSPITAL – CORNWALL CAMPUS, 19 Laurel Avenue, Cornwall, Zip 12518–1499; tel. 845/534–7711; ST. LUKE'S CORNWALL HOSPITAL – NEWBURGH CAMPUS, 70 Dubois Street, Zip 12550–4898; tel. 845/561–4400) **A**1 2 9 10 **F**3 11 13 15 18 20 22 26 28 29 31 34 35 37 40 42 46 47 49 50 51 54 55 57 59 61 64 65 70 72 74 75 76 77 78 79 81 82 84 85 86 87 89 93 100 107 108 110 114 115 118 119 120 121 123 124 126 129 130 132 135 146 148
Primary Contact: Robert Ross, President and Chief Executive Officer
CFO: Thomas Gibney, Senior Vice President and Chief Financial Officer
CMO: Christine Jelalian, M.D., Medical Director
CIO: Cletis Earle, Vice President and Chief Information Officer
CHR: Glenn Courounis, Vice President People and Patient Experience
Web address: www.stlukescornwallhospital.org
Control: Other not–for–profit (including NFP Corporation) **Service:** General Medical and Surgical

Staffed Beds: 128 Admissions: 10399 Census: 123 Outpatient Visits: 165974 Births: 897 Total Expense ($000): 182174 Payroll Expense ($000): 70687 Personnel: 901

○ **NIAGARA FALLS MEMORIAL MEDICAL CENTER (330065)**, 621 Tenth Street, Zip 14301–1813, Mailing Address: P.O. Box 708, Zip 14302–0708; tel. 716/278–4000, (Nonreporting) **A**3 5 9 10 11 13
Primary Contact: Joseph A. Ruffolo, President and Chief Executive Officer
CMO: Fatma Patel, M.D., Vice President Medical Affairs
CIO: Diane Martin–Pratt, Director Information Systems
Web address: www.nfmmc.org
Control: Other not–for–profit (including NFP Corporation) **Service:** General Medical and Surgical

Staffed Beds: 288

DE GRAFF MEMORIAL HOSPITAL See KALEIDA Health, Buffalo

☒ △ **NORTHPORT VETERANS AFFAIRS MEDICAL CENTER**, 79 Middleville Road, Zip 11768–2200; tel. 631/261–4400, (Total facility includes 170 beds in nursing home–type unit) **A**1 2 3 5 7 8 **F**3 5 8 12 18 20 29 30 31 33 34 35 36 38 39 40 44 45 46 47 49 50 51 53 56 57 58 59 60 61 62 64 65 68 70 71 74 75 77 78 79 81 82 83 84 85 86 87 90 91 92 93 94 95 96 97 98 100 101 102 103 104 105 106 107 108 111 114 116 118 119 120 121 122 123 127 128 129 130 132 133 135 144 146 147 148 **S** Department of Veterans Affairs, Washington, DC
Primary Contact: Philip C. Moschitta, Director
COO: Maria Favale, FACHE, Associate Director
CFO: Mary Pat Hessman, Chief Fiscal
CMO: Edward Mack, M.D., Chief of Staff
CIO: Robert Ziskin, Chief Information Officer
CHR: Wilmino Sainbert, Chief Human Resources Management Service
CNO: Rosie Chatman, R.N., Associate Director Patient and Nursing Services
Web address: www.northport.va.gov/index.asp
Control: Veterans Affairs, Government, federal **Service:** General Medical and Surgical

Staffed Beds: 502 Admissions: 3855 Census: 247 Outpatient Visits: 577850 Births: 0 Personnel: 1795

NY

Hospital, Medicare Provider Number, Address, Telephone, Approval, Facility, and Physician Codes, Health Care System

★ American Hospital Association (AHA) membership
☐ The Joint Commission accreditation
◇ DNV Healthcare Inc. accreditation
○ Healthcare Facilities Accreditation Program
△ Commission on Accreditation of Rehabilitation Facilities (CARF) accreditation

NORWICH—Chenango County

★ ○ **CHENANGO MEMORIAL HOSPITAL (330033)**, 179 North Broad Street, Zip 13815–1097; tel. 607/337–4111, (Total facility includes 80 beds in nursing home–type unit) **A**9 10 11 **F**3 8 11 13 15 17 18 29 32 34 35 38 39 40 45 47 50 54 56 57 59 61 64 65 68 70 75 76 77 79 81 82 85 86 87 89 93 97 107 108 110 111 115 119 127 128 130 132 133 146 147 148 **P**6 **S** United Health Services, Binghamton, NY
Primary Contact: Drake M. Lamen, M.D., President and Chief Executive Officer
COO: Drake M. Lamen, M.D., President and Chief Executive Officer
CFO: Robert R. McCarthy, Vice President Finance and Chief Financial Officer
CMO: Drake M. Lamen, M.D., President and Chief Executive Officer, Chief Medical Officer
CIO: Tracy Lemczak, Manager Information Systems
CHR: Anne L. English, Director Human Resources
CNO: David Finney, R.N., Vice President Nursing
Web address: www.uhs.net/cmh
Control: Other not–for–profit (including NFP Corporation) **Service:** General Medical and Surgical

Staffed Beds: 138 **Admissions:** 1815 **Census:** 89 **Outpatient Visits:** 235958 **Births:** 282 **Total Expense ($000):** 64265 **Payroll Expense ($000):** 27469 **Personnel:** 521

NYACK—Rockland County

□ **NYACK HOSPITAL (330104)**, 160 North Midland Avenue, Zip 10960–1998; tel. 845/348–2000 **A**1 2 5 9 10 **F**4 5 8 11 13 14 15 17 29 30 31 40 43 45 49 62 70 72 75 77 78 79 81 82 83 84 85 86 87 91 93 107 108 111 118 119 129 130 135 146 148 **S** New York Presbyterian Healthcare System, New York, NY
Primary Contact: David H. Freed, President and Chief Executive Officer
CFO: John Burke, Chief Financial Officer
CMO: Michael E. Rader, M.D., Vice President and Medical Director
CIO: John Volanto, Vice President and Chief Information Officer
CHR: Mary K. Shinick, Vice President Human Resources
CNO: Celeste Ann Bethon, MS, Chief Nursing Officer
Web address: www.nyackhospital.org
Control: Other not–for–profit (including NFP Corporation) **Service:** General Medical and Surgical

Staffed Beds: 375 **Admissions:** 13002 **Census:** 166 **Outpatient Visits:** 177780 **Births:** 1661 **Total Expense ($000):** 214546 **Payroll Expense ($000):** 95678 **Personnel:** 1604

OCEANSIDE—Nassau County

⊞ **SOUTH NASSAU COMMUNITIES HOSPITAL (330198)**, One Healthy Way, Zip 11572–1551; tel. 516/632–3000 **A**1 2 3 5 9 10 13 **F**3 5 11 12 13 15 17 18 20 22 26 28 29 30 31 34 35 37 38 40 41 43 44 45 46 47 49 50 54 55 56 57 58 59 60 62 64 66 68 69 70 73 74 75 76 77 78 79 81 82 83 84 85 87 89 91 92 93 97 98 99 100 102 103 104 105 107 108 109 110 111 114 115 118 119 120 121 123 124 126 129 130 131 132 133 135 145 146 148 **P**8
Primary Contact: Richard J. Murphy, President and Chief Executive Officer
COO: Joseph Lamantia, Executive Vice President and Chief Operating Officer
CFO: Mark A. Bogen, Senior Vice President and Chief Financial Officer
CMO: Linda Efferen, M.D., Senior Vice President and Chief Medical Officer
CIO: John Mertz, Chief Information Officer
CHR: Paul Giordano, Vice President Human Resources
CNO: Sue Penque, R.N., Senior Vice President and Chief Nursing Officer
Web address: www.southnassau.org
Control: Other not–for–profit (including NFP Corporation) **Service:** General Medical and Surgical

Staffed Beds: 358 **Admissions:** 20345 **Census:** 314 **Outpatient Visits:** 373775 **Births:** 1555 **Total Expense ($000):** 406051 **Payroll Expense ($000):** 195259 **Personnel:** 2361

OGDENSBURG—St. Lawrence County

★ ◇ **CLAXTON–HEPBURN MEDICAL CENTER (330211)**, 214 King Street, Zip 13669–1142; tel. 315/393–3600 **A**2 9 10 20 21 **F**3 11 13 15 28 29 30 31 34 35 36 38 40 44 45 50 51 53 54 56 57 59 60 61 64 70 74 75 76 77 78 79 81 82 85 86 87 90 91 92 93 94 96 97 98 100 101 102 103 104 107 108 110 111 114 118 119 121 123 129 130 131 132 133 135 145 146 147 148 **P**6 7
Primary Contact: Gary Hart, M.D., Co–Interim CEO
COO: Vicki Perrine, FACHE, Chief Operating Officer
CFO: Kelley Tiernan, Chief Financial Officer
CMO: Gary Hart, M.D., Chief Medical Officer
CIO: James Flood, Director Information Systems
CHR: Lou–Ann McNally, Director Human Resources
CNO: David Ferris, Chief Nursing Officer and Vice President Patient Care Services
Web address: www.claxtonhepburn.org
Control: Other not–for–profit (including NFP Corporation) **Service:** General Medical and Surgical

Staffed Beds: 130 **Admissions:** 3337 **Census:** 56 **Outpatient Visits:** 172428 **Births:** 336 **Total Expense ($000):** 92551 **Payroll Expense ($000):** 42435 **Personnel:** 611

□ **ST. LAWRENCE PSYCHIATRIC CENTER (334003)**, 1 Chimney Point Drive, Zip 13669–2291; tel. 315/541–2001, (Nonreporting) **A**1 9 10 **S** New York State Office of Mental Health, Albany, NY
Primary Contact: Timothy Farrell, Executive Director
CMO: Harishankar Sanghi, M.D., Clinical Director
CHR: Rosie Turnbull, Director Human Resources
Web address: www.omh.ny.gov/omhweb/facilities/slpc/facility.htm
Control: State–Government, nonfederal **Service:** Psychiatric

Staffed Beds: 146

OLEAN—Cattaraugus County

⊞ **OLEAN GENERAL HOSPITAL (330103)**, 515 Main Street, Zip 14760–1513; tel. 716/373–2600 **A**1 3 5 9 10 19 **F**3 8 11 13 15 17 18 20 22 28 29 30 31 34 35 38 39 40 45 46 47 48 49 50 51 53 54 57 58 59 60 61 62 64 65 70 71 74 75 76 77 78 79 81 82 83 84 85 86 87 89 92 93 94 97 98 100 101 102 103 107 108 109 110 111 115 116 117 118 119 120 121 123 127 129 130 131 132 133 134 135 143 144 145 146 147 148 **P**6 **S** Upper Allegheny Health System, Olean, NY
Primary Contact: Timothy J. Finan, FACHE, President and Chief Executive Officer
COO: Garrett W. Hoover, FACHE, Chief Operating Officer
CFO: Richard G. Braun, Jr., CPA, Senior Vice President and Chief Financial Officer
CMO: William Mills, M.D., Senior Vice President Quality and Professional Affairs
CIO: Jason Yaworsky, Senior Vice President Information Systems and Chief Information Officer
CHR: Timothy M. McNamara, Senior Vice President Human Resources
CNO: Jeff S. Zewe, R.N., Vice President Patient Care Services and Chief Nursing Officer
Web address: www.ogh.org
Control: Other not–for–profit (including NFP Corporation) **Service:** General Medical and Surgical

Staffed Beds: 186 **Admissions:** 5981 **Census:** 82 **Outpatient Visits:** 202678 **Births:** 787 **Total Expense ($000):** 103131 **Payroll Expense ($000):** 40624 **Personnel:** 838

ONEIDA—Madison County

⊞ **ONEIDA HEALTHCARE (330115)**, 321 Genesee Street, Zip 13421–2611; tel. 315/363–6000, (Total facility includes 140 beds in nursing home–type unit) **A**1 9 10 **F**3 11 13 15 18 29 34 40 45 49 50 54 57 59 64 65 68 70 74 75 76 77 79 81 85 86 87 89 92 93 97 107 108 111 115 117 118 119 126 128 129 130 135 146 **P**6
Primary Contact: Gene Morreale, President and Chief Executive Officer
COO: Paul A. Scopac, Vice President of Operations and Chief Operating Officer
CMO: Dan J. Vick, M.D., Vice President of Medical Affairs and Chief Medical Officer
CIO: Mary McGuirl, Director Information Systems
CHR: John G. Margo, Vice President Human Resources
CNO: Janis Kohlbrenner, R.N., Vice President Clinical Services and Chief Nursing Officer
Web address: www.oneidahealthcare.org
Control: Other not–for–profit (including NFP Corporation) **Service:** General Medical and Surgical

Staffed Beds: 211 **Admissions:** 3096 **Census:** 167 **Outpatient Visits:** 163205 **Births:** 535 **Total Expense ($000):** 86659 **Payroll Expense ($000):** 38939 **Personnel:** 606

ONEONTA—Otsego County

★ ◇ **AURELIA OSBORN FOX MEMORIAL HOSPITAL (330085)**, 1 Norton Avenue, Zip 13820–2629; tel. 607/432–2000, (Total facility includes 131 beds in nursing home–type unit) **A**9 10 19 20 21 **F**2 3 11 13 15 26 28 29 30 34 35 39 40 45 46 47 48 50 51 53 54 56 57 59 64 65 68 74 75 76 77 81 85 86 87 93 96 97 104 107 108 110 111 115 118 119 120 121 123 128 129 130 144 146 147 **P**6 **S** Bassett Healthcare Network, Cooperstown, NY
Primary Contact: John R. Remillard, President
CFO: Mark J. Wright, Vice President Finance
CMO: Benjamin Friedell, Vice President Medical Affairs
CIO: Donna Schultes, Director Information Technology
CHR: Jennie Gliha, Vice President Human Resources
CNO: Robbin Scobie, Vice President Nursing
Web address: www.bassett.org/ao–fox–hospital/
Control: Other not–for–profit (including NFP Corporation) **Service:** General Medical and Surgical

Staffed Beds: 205 **Admissions:** 2768 **Census:** 162 **Outpatient Visits:** 210779 **Births:** 279 **Total Expense ($000):** 82851 **Payroll Expense ($000):** 37249 **Personnel:** 741

NY

ORANGEBURG—Rockland County

☐ **ROCKLAND CHILDREN'S PSYCHIATRIC CENTER**, 599 Convent Road,
Zip 10962–1162; tel. 845/359–7400, (Nonreporting) **A**1 3 5 **S** New York State
Office of Mental Health, Albany, NY
Primary Contact: Anita Daniels, Executive Director
COO: Kenneth Perrotte, Director Operations
CFO: Peter Gorey, Administrative Coordinator
CMO: Sadhana Sardana, M.D., Clinical Director
CIO: Mary Pivonka, Director Quality Management
Web address: www.omh.ny.gov/
Control: State–Government, nonfederal **Service:** Children's hospital psychiatric

Staffed Beds: 54

☐ **ROCKLAND PSYCHIATRIC CENTER (334015)**, 140 Old Orangeburg Road,
Zip 10962–1157; tel. 845/359–1000, (Nonreporting) **A**1 3 5 10 **S** New York
State Office of Mental Health, Albany, NY
Primary Contact: Christopher Tavella, Executive Director
Web address: www.omh.ny.gov/
Control: State–Government, nonfederal **Service:** Psychiatric

Staffed Beds: 525

OSSINING—Westchester County

OSSINING CORRECTIONAL FACILITIES HOSPITAL, 354 Hunter Street,
Zip 10562–5498; tel. 914/941–0108, (Nonreporting)
Primary Contact: John Perilli, M.D., Health Services Director
Control: State–Government, nonfederal **Service:** Hospital unit of an institution
(prison hospital, college infimary, etc.)

Staffed Beds: 25

OSWEGO—Oswego County

✠ **OSWEGO HOSPITAL (330218)**, 110 West Sixth Street, Zip 13126–2507;
tel. 315/349–5511 **A**1 9 10 20 **F**3 8 11 13 15 17 29 34 38 40 45 46 49 50
57 59 62 64 70 74 75 76 77 79 81 84 85 86 87 89 93 98 99 100 101 102
103 104 107 108 110 111 115 118 119 130 131 132 135 144 146 148 **P**6
Primary Contact: Ann C. Gilpin, President and Chief Executive Officer
COO: Allison Duggan, M.D., Vice President and Chief Operating Officer
CFO: Eric Campbell, Chief Financial Officer
CMO: Renato Mandanas, M.D., Chief Medical Officer
CIO: Barry W. Ryle, Chief Information Officer
CHR: Linda Daley, Vice President Human Resources
CNO: Valerie Favata, R.N., Chief Nursing Officer
Web address: www.oswegohealth.org
Control: Other not–for–profit (including NFP Corporation) **Service:** General
Medical and Surgical

Staffed Beds: 126 **Admissions:** 5142 **Census:** 71 **Outpatient Visits:** 352210
Births: 613 **Total Expense ($000):** 104156 **Payroll Expense ($000):** 49410
Personnel: 918

PATCHOGUE—Suffolk County

★ ◇ **BROOKHAVEN MEMORIAL HOSPITAL MEDICAL CENTER (330141)**,
101 Hospital Road, Zip 11772–4897; tel. 631/714–2941, (Nonreporting) **A**9 10
12 13 21
Primary Contact: Richard T. Margulis, President and Chief Executive Officer
COO: Ron Stephenson, Chief Operating Officer
CFO: Brenda Farrell, Vice President Finance
CMO: Robert Roche, M.D., Interim Chief Medical Officer
CIO: Kevin Conroy, Vice President and Chief Information Officer
CHR: Susan C. Hever, Director Human Resources
CNO: Kim K. Mendez, Ed.D., Vice President and Chief Nursing Officer
Web address: www.bmhmc.org
Control: Other not–for–profit (including NFP Corporation) **Service:** General
Medical and Surgical

Staffed Beds: 306

PENN YAN—Yates County

**SOLDIERS AND SAILORS MEMORIAL HOSPITAL OF YATES COUNTY
(331314)**, 418 North Main Street, Zip 14527–1085; tel. 315/531–2000 **A**9 10
18 **F**2 3 11 15 18 28 29 34 35 38 40 45 54 56 57 59 64 65 66 68 70 75 81
87 93 97 98 100 101 102 103 104 107 110 114 119 128 130 132 133 135
146 147 **P**6 **S** Finger Lakes Health, Geneva, NY
Primary Contact: Jose Acevedo, M.D., President and Chief Executive Officer
COO: Frank Korich, Vice President and Site Administrator
CFO: Pamela Johnson, Treasurer and Chief Financial Officer
CMO: Jason Feinberg, M.D., Vice President Medical Affairs and Chief Medical
Officer
CIO: John Oates, Director Information Systems
CHR: Patrick R. Boyle, Vice President Human Resources
CNO: Eileen Gage, R.N., Vice President Nursing
Web address: www.flhealth.org
Control: Other not–for–profit (including NFP Corporation) **Service:** General
Medical and Surgical

Staffed Beds: 186 **Admissions:** 924 **Census:** 152 **Outpatient Visits:** 157209
Births: 0 **Total Expense ($000):** 26338 **Payroll Expense ($000):** 15706
Personnel: 344

PLAINVIEW—Nassau County

✠ **PLAINVIEW HOSPITAL (330331)**, 888 Old Country Road, Zip 11803–4978;
tel. 516/719–3000 **A**1 2 9 10 12 13 **F**3 9 13 15 17 18 29 30 31 34 35 36 38
40 44 45 46 49 50 57 58 59 60 63 64 65 68 69 70 71 74 75 78 79 81 84
85 86 87 97 101 102 107 108 110 111 117 119 130 132 135 146 148 **P**5 6
S North Shore–Long Island Jewish Health System, Great Neck, NY
Primary Contact: Michael Fener, Executive Director
CMO: Alan Mensch, M.D., Senior Vice President Medical Affairs
CIO: Nicholas O'Connor, Vice President and Chief Information Officer
Web address: www.northshorelij.com
Control: Other not–for–profit (including NFP Corporation) **Service:** General
Medical and Surgical

Staffed Beds: 189 **Admissions:** 10351 **Census:** 139 **Outpatient Visits:**
57964 **Births:** 916 **Total Expense ($000):** 199771 **Payroll Expense ($000):**
98859 **Personnel:** 1074

PLATTSBURGH—Clinton County

✠ **CHAMPLAIN VALLEY PHYSICIANS HOSPITAL MEDICAL CENTER (330250)**,
75 Beekman Street, Zip 12901–1438; tel. 518/561–2000, (Total facility includes
96 beds in nursing home–type unit) **A**1 2 9 10 19 20 **F**3 7 8 11 13 14 15 18
20 22 26 28 29 30 31 34 35 36 38 39 40 41 43 45 46 49 50 53 56 58 59
64 68 70 76 77 78 79 81 83 84 85 87 89 93 94 96 98 99 102 107 108 110
111 114 115 116 117 118 119 120 121 123 126 128 130 132 143 144 145
146 147 148 **P**6
Primary Contact: Stephens M. Mundy, President and Chief Executive Officer
COO: Debra Donahue, Senior Vice President and Chief Operating Officer
CFO: Joyce Rafferty, Vice President Finance
CMO: Kent Hall, M.D., Vice President and Chief Medical Officer
CIO: Wouter Rietsema, M.D., Chief Quality and Information Officer
CHR: Michelle Lebeau, Vice President Human Resources
CNO: Debra Donahue, Senior Vice President and Chief Operating Officer
Web address: www.cvph.org
Control: Other not–for–profit (including NFP Corporation) **Service:** General
Medical and Surgical

Staffed Beds: 289 **Admissions:** 9289 **Census:** 246 **Outpatient Visits:**
336114 **Births:** 850 **Total Expense ($000):** 290102 **Payroll Expense
($000):** 138668 **Personnel:** 1849

POMONA—Rockland County

☐ **SUMMIT PARK HOSPITAL AND NURSING CARE CENTER (332014)**, 50
Sanatorium Road, Building A., Zip 10970–3555; tel. 845/364–2700,
(Nonreporting) **A**1 9 10
Primary Contact: Donna M. Pauldine, Deputy Commissioner
COO: Donna M. Pauldine, Deputy Commissioner
CFO: William Renc, Chief Fiscal Officer
CMO: Karen Castley, Medical Director
CHR: Theresa Sullivan, Director Human Resources
Web address: www.co.rockland.ny.us
Control: County–Government, nonfederal **Service:** Long–Term Acute Care
hospital

Staffed Beds: 408

NY

PORT JEFFERSON—Suffolk County

⊠ **JOHN T. MATHER MEMORIAL HOSPITAL (330185)**, 75 North Country Road, Zip 11777–2190; tel. 631/473–1320 **A**1 2 9 10 **F**5 8 12 14 15 17 29 34 35 36 37 38 40 44 49 51 55 56 57 59 60 64 65 69 70 75 77 78 79 81 82 85 87 93 98 99 100 102 103 104 105 107 108 110 111 114 115 118 119 120 126 129 130 132 146 147 148
Primary Contact: Kenneth D. Roberts, President
COO: Kevin J. Murray, Senior Vice President
CFO: Joseph Wisnoski, Vice President Finance and Chief Financial Officer
CMO: Joan Faro, M.D., Chief Medical Officer
CIO: Thomas Heiman, Vice President Information Services and Chief Information Officer
CHR: Diane Marotta, Vice President Human Resources
CNO: Marie Mulligan, R.N., Vice President Nursing
Web address: www.matherhospital.com
Control: Other not–for–profit (including NFP Corporation) **Service:** General Medical and Surgical

Staffed Beds: 248 Admissions: 11780 Census: 195 Outpatient Visits: 156825 Births: 0 Total Expense ($000): 265377 Payroll Expense ($000): 135203 Personnel: 1914

☐ △ **ST. CHARLES HOSPITAL (330246)**, 200 Belle Terre Road, Zip 11777–1928; tel. 631/474–6000, (Nonreporting) **A**1 2 7 9 10 **S** Catholic Health Services of Long Island, Rockville Centre, NY
Primary Contact: James O'Connor, Executive Vice President and Chief Administrative Officer
COO: Ronald Weingartner, Vice President Administration
CFO: Kathleen Vasil, Vice President Finance
CMO: Michael Sauter, M.D., Chief Medical Officer
CIO: Felix Pabon–Ramirez, Chief Information Officer
CNO: Nicolette Fiore–Lopez, R.N., Chief Nursing Officer
Web address: www.stcharleshospital.chsli.org
Control: Church–operated, Nongovernment, not–for profit **Service:** General Medical and Surgical

Staffed Beds: 289

PORT JERVIS—Orange County

⊠ **BON SECOURS COMMUNITY HOSPITAL (330135)**, 160 East Main Street, Zip 12771–2245, Mailing Address: P.O. Box 1014, Zip 12771–0268; tel. 845/858–7000, (Nonreporting) **A**1 9 10 **S** Bon Secours Health System, Inc., Marriottsville, MD
Primary Contact: Jeff Reilly, Senior Vice President Operations
COO: Gaynor Rosenstein, Vice President Operations
CMO: Jeffrey Auerbach, D.O., Medical Director
CHR: Kim Hirkaler, Director Human Resources
Web address: www.bonsecourscommunityhosp.org
Control: Church–operated, Nongovernment, not–for profit **Service:** General Medical and Surgical

Staffed Beds: 187

POTSDAM—St. Lawrence County

★ ◇ **CANTON–POTSDAM HOSPITAL (330197)**, 50 Leroy Street, Zip 13676–1799; tel. 315/265–3300 **A**9 10 20 21 **F**3 4 5 11 13 14 15 18 26 28 29 30 31 34 36 38 39 40 43 46 54 57 59 64 65 67 68 75 76 77 78 79 81 82 86 87 92 93 95 96 97 98 100 101 102 104 107 108 110 111 115 117 118 119 121 127 128 129 130 131 132 133 135 143 144 145 146 147 148 **P**6 **S** St. Lawrence Health System, Potsdam, NY
Primary Contact: David B. Acker, FACHE, President and CEO
COO: Linda Summers, Chief Operating Officer
CFO: Richard Jacobs, Vice President Finance and Chief Financial Officer
CMO: Robert T. Rogers, II, M.D., Medical Director
CIO: Jorge C. Grillo, Chief Information Officer
CHR: Darlene Lewis, Vice President Human Resources
CNO: Susan M. Hodgson, R.N., Vice President Patient Care Services and Chief Nursing Officer
Web address: www.cphospital.org
Control: Other not–for–profit (including NFP Corporation) **Service:** General Medical and Surgical

Staffed Beds: 94 Admissions: 4604 Census: 56 Outpatient Visits: 227711 Births: 389 Total Expense ($000): 107655 Payroll Expense ($000): 50327 Personnel: 806

POUGHKEEPSIE—Dutchess County

△ ◇ **MIDHUDSON REGIONAL HOSPITAL OF WESTCHESTER MEDICAL CENTER (330067)**, 241 North Road, Zip 12601–1154; tel. 845/483–5000 **A**2 7 9 10 21 **F**1 3 4 8 11 12 15 17 18 20 22 29 30 31 32 34 35 36 37 40 43 45 46 49 50 55 56 57 60 61 62 63 64 65 66 68 70 74 75 77 78 79 80 81 82 85 86 87 89 90 91 93 98 99 100 101 102 103 104 107 108 111 115 118 119 129 130 131 132 133 134 135 144 146 148
Primary Contact: Arthur Nizza, President
CFO: Will de la Pena, Chief Financial Officer
CMO: J. Keith Festa, M.D., Vice President Medical Affairs
CIO: Joseph McCann, Chief Information Officer
CHR: Helen Rinaudo, Vice President Human Resources
CNO: Patricia Nocket, Assistant Vice President Clinical Nursing Services
Web address: www.midhudsonregionalhospital.org
Control: Church–operated, Nongovernment, not–for profit **Service:** General Medical and Surgical

Staffed Beds: 322 Admissions: 7115 Census: 154 Births: 0

⊠ **VASSAR BROTHERS MEDICAL CENTER (330023)**, 45 Reade Place, Zip 12601–3947; tel. 845/454–8500 **A**1 2 9 10 **F**3 11 13 15 17 18 20 22 24 26 28 29 30 31 32 34 35 36 37 38 40 41 44 45 46 47 49 50 54 55 57 58 59 60 61 64 68 70 72 73 74 75 76 77 78 79 80 81 82 84 85 86 87 89 93 97 100 107 108 110 111 116 119 120 121 123 124 126 129 130 131 132 135 146 147 148 **P**3 6 **S** Health Quest Systems, Inc., LaGrangeville, NY
Primary Contact: Robert Friedberg, President
CFO: Katherine Bacher, Interim Senior Vice President and Chief Financial Officer
CMO: Ronald Tatelbaum, M.D., Chief Medical Officer – Health Quest
CIO: Robert Diamond, Chief Information Officer
CHR: Jeffrey McDonough, Vice President Human Resources
CNO: Lore Bogolin, Chief Nursing Officer and Vice President Care Services
Web address: www.health–quest.org
Control: Other not–for–profit (including NFP Corporation) **Service:** General Medical and Surgical

Staffed Beds: 365 Admissions: 16709 Census: 239 Births: 2181 Total Expense ($000): 391019 Payroll Expense ($000): 116791 Personnel: 1669

QUEENS—Queens County, See New York City

QUEENS VILLAGE—Queens County, See New York City

RHINEBECK—Dutchess County

⊠ △ **NORTHERN DUTCHESS HOSPITAL (330049)**, 6511 Springbrook Avenue, Zip 12572–3709, Mailing Address: P.O. Box 5002, Zip 12572–5002; tel. 845/876–3001, (Total facility includes 100 beds in nursing home–type unit) **A**1 7 9 10 **F**3 8 11 12 13 15 18 28 29 32 34 35 36 37 40 45 50 53 56 57 59 64 68 70 75 76 78 79 81 82 85 87 90 93 107 108 110 111 114 119 128 129 130 131 132 146 147 148 **S** Health Quest Systems, Inc., LaGrangeville, NY
Primary Contact: Denise George, R.N., President
CFO: Alan Mossoff, Chief Financial Officer
CMO: John Sabia, M.D., Vice President Medical Affairs
CIO: Robert Diamond, Senior Vice President and Chief Information Officer
CHR: Eileen Miller, Director Human Resources
Web address: www.health–quest.org/home_nd.cfm?id=9
Control: Other not–for–profit (including NFP Corporation) **Service:** General Medical and Surgical

Staffed Beds: 168 Admissions: 3913 Census: 139 Outpatient Visits: 79239 Births: 899 Total Expense ($000): 69447 Payroll Expense ($000): 30280 Personnel: 347

RICHMOND VALLEY—Richmond County, See New York City

RIVERHEAD—Suffolk County

☐ **PECONIC BAY MEDICAL CENTER (330107)**, 1300 Roanoke Avenue, Zip 11901–2031; tel. 631/548–6000, (Total facility includes 60 beds in nursing home–type unit) **A**1 9 10 12 13 **F**7 11 12 13 15 29 30 31 34 40 45 46 47 49 50 57 59 60 61 64 68 70 74 75 76 77 78 79 80 81 84 85 86 87 90 93 96 107 108 110 111 115 118 119 126 130 131 132 143 146 147 148 **P**7
Primary Contact: Andrew J. Mitchell, President and Chief Executive Officer
COO: Ronald McManus, Senior Vice President Clinical Services and Business Entities
CFO: Michael O'Donnell, Chief Financial Officer
CMO: Richard Kubiak, M.D., Vice President Medical Affairs
CIO: Arthur Crowe, Director Information Systems
CHR: Monica Chestnut–Rauls, Vice President Human Resources
CNO: Gerard Zunno, R.N., Vice President Patient Care Services
Web address: www.pbmchealth.org
Control: Other not–for–profit (including NFP Corporation) **Service:** General Medical and Surgical

Staffed Beds: 176 Admissions: 7453 Census: 133 Outpatient Visits: 104078 Births: 397 Total Expense ($000): 147146 Payroll Expense ($000): 60117 Personnel: 946

NY

Many Facility Codes have changed. Please refer to the AHA Guide Code Chart. © 2014 AHA Guide

ROCHESTER—Monroe County

⊞ **HIGHLAND HOSPITAL OF ROCHESTER (330164)**, 1000 South Avenue, Zip 14620–2733; tel. 585/473–2200 **A**1 3 5 9 10 19 **F**3 8 12 13 15 18 29 30 31 34 35 37 39 40 44 45 46 47 48 49 50 54 56 57 58 59 63 64 65 66 68 70 74 75 76 78 79 81 82 83 84 85 87 91 97 100 107 108 110 111 114 115 118 119 120 121 123 124 126 130 131 132 134 141 144 145 146 147 148 **P**6 **S** University of Rochester Medical Center, Rochester, NY
Primary Contact: Steven I. Goldstein, President and Chief Executive Officer
COO: Cindy Becker, Vice President and Chief Operating Officer
CFO: Adam Anolik, Chief Financial Officer
CMO: Raymond Mayewski, M.D., Chief Medical Officer
CIO: D. Jerome Powell, M.D., Chief Information Officer
CHR: Kathleen Gallucci, Chief Human Resources
CNO: Tommye Hinton, R.N., Chief Nursing Officer
Web address: www.stronghealth.com
Control: Hospital district or authority, Government, nonfederal **Service:** General Medical and Surgical

Staffed Beds: 261 **Admissions:** 16112 **Census:** 197 **Outpatient Visits:** 249970 **Births:** 3013 **Total Expense ($000):** 286029 **Payroll Expense ($000):** 136182 **Personnel:** 2114

⊞ **ROCHESTER GENERAL HOSPITAL (330125)**, 1425 Portland Avenue, Zip 14621–3099; tel. 585/922–4000 **A**1 2 3 5 9 10 **F**3 5 8 9 11 12 13 14 15 17 18 20 22 24 26 28 29 30 31 32 34 35 36 38 39 40 41 44 47 49 50 51 53 54 55 56 57 58 59 60 61 63 64 65 66 68 70 73 74 75 76 77 78 79 80 81 82 84 85 86 87 89 90 92 93 96 97 98 99 100 101 102 103 104 107 108 110 111 114 115 116 117 118 119 120 121 123 124 126 130 131 132 134 135 145 146 147 148 **P**5 7 **S** Rochester Regional Health System, Rochester, NY
Primary Contact: Robert Nesselbush, President
CMO: Rob Mayo, M.D., Chief Medical Officer
CHR: Janine Schue, Senior Vice President Human Resources
CNO: Cheryl Sheridan, R.N., Senior Vice President Patient Care Services
Web address: www.rochestergeneral.org
Control: Other not–for–profit (including NFP Corporation) **Service:** General Medical and Surgical

Staffed Beds: 520 **Admissions:** 30112 **Census:** 449 **Outpatient Visits:** 1512540 **Births:** 2362 **Total Expense ($000):** 777574 **Payroll Expense ($000):** 365323 **Personnel:** 5397

☐ **ROCHESTER PSYCHIATRIC CENTER (334020)**, 1111 Elmwood Avenue, Zip 14620–3005; tel. 585/241–1200, (Nonreporting) **A**1 3 5 10 **S** New York State Office of Mental Health, Albany, NY
Primary Contact: Elizabeth Suhre, Executive Director
COO: Joseph Coffey, Director Facility Administration
CFO: Rosanne Minnis, Business Officer
CMO: Laurence Guttmacher, M.D., Clinical Director
CIO: Lori Hintz, Coordinator Information Systems
CHR: Colomba Misseritti, Director Human Resources
CNO: Christopher Kirisits, Chief Nursing Officer
Web address: www.omh.ny.gov/omhweb/facilities/ropc/facility.htm
Control: State–Government, nonfederal **Service:** Psychiatric

Staffed Beds: 180

⊞ △ **STRONG MEMORIAL HOSPITAL OF THE UNIVERSITY OF ROCHESTER (330285)**, 601 Elmwood Avenue, Zip 14642–0002; tel. 585/275–2100, (Includes GOLISANO CHILDREN'S HOSPITAL, 601 Elmwood Avenue, Zip 14610; tel. 585/275–2182) **A**1 2 3 5 7 8 9 10 19 **F**3 5 6 8 9 11 12 13 14 15 16 17 18 19 20 21 22 23 24 25 26 27 28 29 30 31 32 33 34 35 38 39 40 41 43 44 45 46 47 48 49 50 51 52 53 54 55 56 57 58 59 61 63 64 65 68 70 71 72 73 74 75 76 77 78 79 81 82 83 84 85 86 87 88 89 90 91 92 93 94 96 97 98 99 100 101 102 103 104 105 107 108 110 111 114 115 116 117 118 119 120 121 123 124 126 129 130 131 132 134 135 136 137 138 139 141 142 143 144 146 147 148 **P**5 6 **S** University of Rochester Medical Center, Rochester, NY
Primary Contact: Steven I. Goldstein, President and Chief Executive Officer
COO: Kathleen M. Parrinello, Ph.D., Chief Operating Officer
CFO: Leonard J. Shute, Chief Financial Officer
CMO: Raymond Mayewski, M.D., Chief Medical Officer
CIO: D. Jerome Powell, M.D., Chief Information Officer
CHR: Charles J. Murphy, Associate Vice President Human Resources
Web address: www.urmc.rochester.edu
Control: Other not–for–profit (including NFP Corporation) **Service:** General Medical and Surgical

Staffed Beds: 777 **Admissions:** 37435 **Census:** 648 **Outpatient Visits:** 1355215 **Births:** 2936 **Total Expense ($000):** 1163325 **Payroll Expense ($000):** 477235 **Personnel:** 8962

⊞ **UNITY HOSPITAL (330226)**, 1555 Long Pond Road, Zip 14626–4182; tel. 585/723–7000, (Total facility includes 120 beds in nursing home–type unit) **A**1 2 3 5 9 10 **F**3 4 5 8 13 18 20 22 26 28 29 30 31 33 34 35 38 39 40 44 45 46 47 48 49 50 52 55 56 57 59 60 61 63 64 65 66 70 71 73 74 75 76 77 78 79 81 82 84 85 86 87 90 91 92 93 96 97 98 100 102 104 107 108 118 119 126 128 129 130 131 132 134 144 146 147 148 **P**6 **S** Rochester Regional Health System, Rochester, NY
Primary Contact: Warren Hern, President and Chief Executive Officer
COO: Stewart C. Putnam, Executive Vice President and Chief Operating Officer
CFO: Tom Crilly, Executive Vice President and Chief Financial Officer
CMO: James Haley, M.D., Senior Vice President and Chief Medical Officer
CIO: John Glynn, Senior Vice President and Chief Information Officer
CHR: Maryalice Keller, Vice President Brand and Talent Management
CNO: Jane McCormack, R.N., Vice President, Chief Nursing Officer and Nursing and Patient Care Services
Web address: www.unityhealth.org
Control: Other not–for–profit (including NFP Corporation) **Service:** General Medical and Surgical

Staffed Beds: 451 **Admissions:** 15541 **Census:** 241 **Outpatient Visits:** 1033792 **Births:** 1575 **Total Expense ($000):** 393287 **Payroll Expense ($000):** 194038 **Personnel:** 4243

ROCKVILLE CENTRE—Nassau County

☐ **MERCY MEDICAL CENTER (330259)**, 1000 North Village Avenue, Zip 11570–1000; tel. 516/705–2525 **A**1 2 9 10 **F**3 8 12 13 15 29 30 31 34 35 37 40 43 51 55 57 59 60 64 65 68 70 73 74 75 76 77 78 79 81 82 84 85 87 90 92 93 96 97 98 100 103 104 105 107 108 110 111 115 116 119 130 132 142 146 147 **S** Catholic Health Services of Long Island, Rockville Centre, NY
Primary Contact: Aaron Glatt, M.D., Executive Vice President and Chief Administrative Officer
COO: Ronald Steimel, Vice President Administration and Chief Operating Officer
CFO: William C. Armstrong, Senior Vice President and Chief Financial Officer
CMO: John Reilly, M.D., Vice President Medical Affairs and Chief Medical Officer
CIO: Marcy Dunn, Vice President Information Services and Chief Information Officer
CHR: Allison Cianciotto Croyle, Vice President of Human Resources
CNO: Beth Vlahavas, Vice President Patient Care Services and Chief Nursing Officer
Web address: www.mercymedicalcenter.chsli.org
Control: Church–operated, Nongovernment, not–for profit **Service:** General Medical and Surgical

Staffed Beds: 219 **Admissions:** 12702 **Census:** 183 **Outpatient Visits:** 110455 **Births:** 1104 **Personnel:** 1248

ROME—Oneida County

★ ○ **ROME MEMORIAL HOSPITAL (330215)**, 1500 North James Street, Zip 13440–2844; tel. 315/338–7000, (Total facility includes 80 beds in nursing home–type unit) **A**9 10 11 **F**3 5 8 13 15 18 26 27 29 30 31 34 35 37 40 46 49 56 57 59 61 64 65 66 70 74 75 76 77 78 79 80 81 84 85 86 87 89 93 97 98 101 102 103 106 107 108 110 111 115 118 119 120 121 123 128 129 130 131 132 135 146 147 148 **P**6
Primary Contact: Basil Ariglio, President and Chief Executive Officer
CFO: Dewey R. Rowlands, Vice President and Chief Financial Officer
CIO: Bruce Peterson, Chief Information Officer
CHR: Regina Chambers, Vice President Human Resource
CNO: Durinda Durr, Vice President and Chief Nursing Officer
Web address: www.romehospital.org
Control: Other not–for–profit (including NFP Corporation) **Service:** General Medical and Surgical

Staffed Beds: 203 **Admissions:** 4044 **Census:** 131 **Outpatient Visits:** 155090 **Births:** 573 **Total Expense ($000):** 82073 **Payroll Expense ($000):** 38427 **Personnel:** 693

NY

Hospital, Medicare Provider Number, Address, Telephone, Approval, Facility, and Physician Codes, Health Care System

★ American Hospital Association (AHA) membership
☐ The Joint Commission accreditation ◇ DNV Healthcare Inc. accreditation
○ Healthcare Facilities Accreditation Program
△ Commission on Accreditation of Rehabilitation Facilities (CARF) accreditation

© 2014 AHA Guide *Many Facility Codes have changed. Please refer to the AHA Guide Code Chart.* Hospitals **A453**

ROSLYN—Nassau County

⊞ **ST. FRANCIS HOSPITAL (330182)**, 100 Port Washington Boulevard, Zip 11576–1353; tel. 516/562–6000 **A**1 9 10 **F**3 7 11 12 15 17 18 19 20 21 22 23 24 26 27 28 29 30 31 34 35 36 37 38 39 40 43 44 45 46 47 49 50 53 54 55 56 57 58 59 60 61 62 63 64 65 66 68 70 71 74 75 77 78 79 81 82 83 84 85 86 87 93 94 97 100 102 107 108 109 110 111 114 115 116 117 118 119 124 126 130 131 132 135 141 145 146 147 148 **P**6 8 **S** Catholic Health Services of Long Island, Rockville Centre, NY
Primary Contact: Ruth Hennessey, Executive Vice President and Chief Administrative Officer
CFO: William C. Armstrong, Vice President and Chief Financial Officer
CMO: Jack Soterakis, M.D., Executive Vice President Medical Affairs
CIO: Marcy Dunn, Vice President Information Services and Chief Information Officer
CHR: Barbara Fierro, Director, Human Resources
CNO: Ann S. Cella, R.N., Senior Vice President, Patient Care Services
Web address: www.stfrancisheartcenter.com/index.html
Control: Church–operated, Nongovernment, not–for profit **Service:** General Medical and Surgical

Staffed Beds: 306 Admissions: 16418 Census: 269 Outpatient Visits: 194324 Births: 0 Total Expense ($000): 536935 Payroll Expense ($000): 247531 Personnel: 2791

SARANAC LAKE—Franklin County

★ ○ **ADIRONDACK MEDICAL CENTER (330079)**, 2233 State Route 86, Zip 12983–5644, Mailing Address: P.O. Box 471, Zip 12983–0471; tel. 518/891–4141, (Total facility includes 194 beds in nursing home–type unit) **A**9 10 11 19 20 **F**3 8 9 12 13 15 18 28 29 30 31 34 35 37 38 39 40 41 42 43 45 46 49 54 56 57 59 60 64 70 71 74 75 76 77 78 79 81 82 84 85 86 89 90 92 93 94 97 98 102 103 104 107 108 110 111 114 116 119 127 128 129 130 131 132 135 146 147 148 **P**1 5 **S** HealthTech Management Services, Brentwood, TN
Primary Contact: Chandler M. Ralph, President and Chief Executive Officer
COO: Patti Hammond, Chief Operating Officer
CFO: Tristan Glanville, Chief Financial Officer
CMO: John Broderick, M.D., Chief Medical Officer
CHR: Michael D. Lee, Chief Human Resources Officer
CNO: Linda McClarigan, R.N., Chief Nursing Officer
Web address: www.adirondackhealth.org
Control: Other not–for–profit (including NFP Corporation) **Service:** General Medical and Surgical

Staffed Beds: 271 Admissions: 2821 Census: 162 Outpatient Visits: 123478 Births: 167 Total Expense ($000): 97302 Payroll Expense ($000): 44681 Personnel: 778

SARATOGA SPRINGS—Saratoga County

☐ **FOUR WINDS HOSPITAL (334049)**, 30 Crescent Avenue, Zip 12866–5142; tel. 518/584–3600, (Nonreporting) **A**1 9 10
Primary Contact: Samuel A. Bastien, IV, Ph.D., Chief Executive Officer
CFO: Juanita Wheeler–Moore, Director Financial Services
CMO: Kevin P. Martin, M.D., Chief Medical Officer
CIO: Susan Snowdon, Director Information Technology
CHR: Susan M. Kirchner, Director Human Resources
CNO: James Colamaria, Director of Nursing
Web address: www.fourwindshospital.com
Control: Corporation, Investor–owned, for–profit **Service:** Children's hospital psychiatric

Staffed Beds: 83

⊞ **SARATOGA HOSPITAL (330222)**, 211 Church Street, Zip 12866–1003; tel. 518/587–3222, (Total facility includes 36 beds in nursing home–type unit) **A**1 2 5 9 10 **F**3 8 11 12 13 15 17 18 20 26 27 28 29 30 31 34 35 37 38 40 45 47 49 50 51 54 56 57 59 64 66 68 70 74 75 76 77 78 79 81 82 85 92 93 94 96 97 98 100 101 102 103 107 108 110 111 114 115 116 117 119 120 121 126 128 130 131 132 135 144 145 146 147 **P**6
Primary Contact: Angelo G. Calbone, President and Chief Executive Officer
CFO: Gary Foster, Vice President and Chief Financial Officer
CMO: Richard Falivena, D.O., Vice President and Chief Medical Officer
CIO: John Mangona, Vice President, Chief Information Officer and Compliance Officer
CHR: Jeffrey M. Methven, Vice President Ambulatory Services and Chief Human Resources Officer
CNO: Mary Jo LaPosta, Ph.D., Senior Vice President Patient Care and Organizational Execellence
Web address: www.saratogacare.org
Control: Other not–for–profit (including NFP Corporation) **Service:** General Medical and Surgical

Staffed Beds: 207 Admissions: 8480 Census: 159 Outpatient Visits: 220831 Births: 790 Total Expense ($000): 221567 Payroll Expense ($000): 100420 Personnel: 1770

SCHENECTADY—Schenectady County

⊞ **ELLIS HOSPITAL (330153)**, 1101 Nott Street, Zip 12308–2425; tel. 518/243–4000, (Includes BELLEVUE WOMAN'S CARE CENTER, 2210 Troy Road, Zip 12309–4797; tel. 518/346–9400; ELLIS HOSPITAL HEALTH CENTER, 600 McClellan Street, Zip 12304–1090; tel. 518/382–2000), (Total facility includes 82 beds in nursing home–type unit) **A**1 3 5 9 10 **F**8 12 13 15 18 20 22 24 26 28 29 30 31 35 38 39 40 54 59 60 62 64 65 68 70 72 74 75 76 77 78 79 81 82 84 89 93 98 99 100 101 102 103 104 107 108 110 111 114 115 117 119 120 121 126 128 129 130 146 147 148 **P**6
Primary Contact: James W. Connolly, President and Chief Executive Officer
COO: Paul A. Milton, Executive Vice President and Chief Operating Officer
CFO: Daniel Rinaldi, Chief Financial Officer
CMO: David Liebers, M.D., Chief Medical Officer and Vice President Medical Affairs
CIO: David Snyder, Chief Information Officer and Vice President Information Technology
CHR: Joseph Giansante, Vice President Human Resources
CNO: Kathleen A. Hale, MS, Vice President and Chief Nursing Officer
Web address: www.ellismedicine.org
Control: Other not–for–profit (including NFP Corporation) **Service:** General Medical and Surgical

Staffed Beds: 419 Admissions: 20996 Census: 330 Outpatient Visits: 680258 Births: 2569 Total Expense ($000): 378374 Payroll Expense ($000): 196559 Personnel: 2885

ELLIS HOSPITAL HEALTH CENTER See Ellis Hospital

ELLIS HOSPITAL MCCLELLAN CAMPUS See Ellis Hospital Health Center

⊞ △ **SUNNYVIEW REHABILITATION HOSPITAL (330406)**, 1270 Belmont Avenue, Zip 12308–2104; tel. 518/382–4500 **A**1 3 5 7 9 10 **F**3 28 29 53 56 57 59 64 74 79 90 93 94 119 130 132 135 **P**5 **S** Catholic Health East / Trinity Health, Livonia, MI
Primary Contact: Edward Eisenman, Chief Executive Officer
CFO: Kristin Signor, Director Finance
CMO: Lynne T. Nicolson, M.D., Medical Director
CIO: Patrick Clark, Manager Information Technology
CHR: Meghan Glowa, Director Human Resources
Web address: www.sunnyview.org
Control: Other not–for–profit (including NFP Corporation) **Service:** Rehabilitation

Staffed Beds: 115 Admissions: 2532 Census: 87 Outpatient Visits: 65852 Births: 0 Total Expense ($000): 46071 Payroll Expense ($000): 27241 Personnel: 560

SLEEPY HOLLOW—Westchester County

⊞ **PHELPS MEMORIAL HOSPITAL CENTER (330261)**, 701 North Broadway, Zip 10591–1020; tel. 914/366–3000 **A**1 2 3 5 9 10 **F**3 4 8 9 11 13 14 15 16 17 18 26 27 28 29 30 31 34 35 38 39 40 41 43 45 46 47 48 49 50 53 54 55 56 57 58 59 60 61 63 64 65 68 69 70 72 73 74 75 76 77 78 79 81 82 84 85 86 87 88 90 91 92 93 94 96 98 100 101 102 103 104 106 107 108 110 111 114 115 118 119 130 131 132 135 143 144 145 146 147 148
Primary Contact: Keith F. Safian, President and Chief Executive Officer
CFO: Vincent DeSantis, Vice President Finance
CHR: Jussi Maijala, Vice President, Human Resources
Web address: www.phelpshospital.org
Control: Other not–for–profit (including NFP Corporation) **Service:** General Medical and Surgical

Staffed Beds: 238 Admissions: 7134 Census: 135 Outpatient Visits: 326134 Births: 1041 Total Expense ($000): 220632 Payroll Expense ($000): 113275 Personnel: 1279

SMITHTOWN—Suffolk County

☐ **ST. CATHERINE OF SIENA MEDICAL CENTER (330401)**, 50 Route 25–A, Zip 11787–1348; tel. 631/862–3000, (Nonreporting) **A**1 9 10 **S** Catholic Health Services of Long Island, Rockville Centre, NY
Primary Contact: Dennis Verzi, Executive Vice President and Chief Administrative Officer
CFO: Dan Macksood, Regional Vice President and Chief Financial Officer
CHR: Danielle A. Robbins, Vice President Human Resources
Web address: www.stcatherinemedicalcenter.org
Control: Church–operated, Nongovernment, not–for profit **Service:** General Medical and Surgical

Staffed Beds: 503

Many Facility Codes have changed. Please refer to the AHA Guide Code Chart. © 2014 AHA Guide

SOUTHAMPTON—Suffolk County

✠ **SOUTHAMPTON HOSPITAL (330340)**, 240 Meeting House Lane,
Zip 11968–5090; tel. 631/726–8200 **A**1 9 10 12 13 **F**3 11 12 13 15 18 28
29 30 31 34 35 36 37 39 40 45 46 47 49 51 53 54 56 57 59 60 61 64 65
68 70 74 75 76 77 78 79 81 82 84 85 87 89 93 97 100 107 108 110 111
115 119 130 131 132 135 145 146 147 148 **P**4 6
Primary Contact: Robert S. Chaloner, President and Chief Executive Officer
COO: Frederic Weinbaum, M.D., Executive Vice President Operations and Chief
Medical Officer
CFO: Chris Schulteis, Vice President/Chief Financial Officer
CMO: Frederic Weinbaum, M.D., Executive Vice President Operations and Chief
Medical Officer
CIO: Jim Maul, Chief Information Officer and Director Information Services
CNO: Patricia Darcey, R.N., Vice President/Chief Nursing Officer
Web address: www.southamptonhospital.org
Control: Other not–for–profit (including NFP Corporation) **Service:** General
Medical and Surgical

Staffed Beds: 80 **Admissions:** 5438 **Census:** 55 **Outpatient Visits:** 814205 **Births:** 674 **Total Expense ($000):** 129504 **Payroll Expense ($000):** 58878 **Personnel:** 916

SPRINGVILLE—Erie County

BERTRAND CHAFFEE HOSPITAL (330111), 224 East Main Street,
Zip 14141–1497; tel. 716/592–2871, (Nonreporting) **A**9 10
Primary Contact: Nils Gunnersen, Administrator
CMO: J. Matthew Baker, M.D., President Medical Staff
CHR: Mary Beth Brown, Director Human Resources
Web address: www.chaffeehospitalandhome.com
Control: Other not–for–profit (including NFP Corporation) **Service:** General
Medical and Surgical

Staffed Beds: 24

STAR LAKE—St. Lawrence County

★ **CLIFTON–FINE HOSPITAL (331307)**, 1014 Oswegatchie Trail,
Zip 13690–3143; tel. 315/848–3351, (Nonreporting) **A**9 10 18
Primary Contact: Robert L. Seamon, Chief Executive Officer
CFO: Nancy Russell, Chief Financial Officer
CMO: David Welch, M.D., Medical Director
CIO: Devin Rice, Director Information Systems
CNO: Michelle Bristol, Director of Nursing
Web address: www.cliftonfinehospital.org
Control: Other not–for–profit (including NFP Corporation) **Service:** General
Medical and Surgical

Staffed Beds: 20

STATEN ISLAND—Richmond County, See New York City

STONY BROOK—Suffolk County

✠ **STONY BROOK UNIVERSITY MEDICAL CENTER (330393)**, State University of
New York, Zip 11794–8410; tel. 631/444–1077, (Includes STONY BROOK
CHILDREN'S HOSPITAL, 100 Nicolls Road, Zip 11794–0001; tel. 631/444–4000)
A1 2 3 5 8 9 10 **F**3 6 7 8 9 11 12 13 14 15 16 17 18 19 20 22 24 26 28 29
30 31 32 34 35 36 38 39 40 41 43 44 46 47 48 49 50 52 53 54 55
56 57 58 59 60 61 64 65 66 68 70 72 73 74 75 76 77 78 79 81 82 84 85
86 87 88 89 93 96 97 98 99 100 101 102 103 104 105 107 108 110 111
114 115 116 117 118 119 120 121 122 123 124 126 129 130 131 132 134
135 136 138 141 143 145 146 147 148 **P**1 6
Primary Contact: L. Reuven Pasternak, M.D., M.P.H., Vice President for Health
System and Chief Executive Officer
COO: Carol Gomes, FACHE, Chief Operating Officer
CFO: Gary E. Bie, CPA, Chief Financial Officer
CMO: Joseph H. Laver, M.D., Chief Medical Officer
CIO: Jim Murry, Chief Information Officer
CHR: Elizabeth McCoy, Chief Human Resources Management
CNO: Mary Ann T. Donohue, Ph.D., Chief Patient Care Services Officer
Web address: www.stonybrookmedicalcenter.org
Control: State–Government, nonfederal **Service:** General Medical and Surgical

Staffed Beds: 603 **Admissions:** 32080 **Census:** 520 **Outpatient Visits:** 347045 **Births:** 3055 **Total Expense ($000):** 982052 **Payroll Expense ($000):** 436013 **Personnel:** 4682

SUFFERN—Rockland County

✠ **GOOD SAMARITAN HOSPITAL (330158)**, 255 Lafayette Avenue,
Zip 10901–4869; tel. 845/368–5000, (Nonreporting) **A**1 2 9 10 **S** Bon Secours
Health System, Inc., Marriottsville, MD
Primary Contact: Mary Leahy, M.D., Chief Executive Officer
COO: Gerry Durney, Chief Operating Officer
CFO: Melinda Hancock, Interim Chief Financial Officer
CMO: Rodney W. Williams, M.D., Vice President Medical Affairs
CIO: Deborah K. Marshall, Vice President Public Relations
CHR: Pamela Tarulli, Senior Vice President Human Resources
Web address: www.goodsamhosp.org
Control: Church–operated, Nongovernment, not–for profit **Service:** General
Medical and Surgical

Staffed Beds: 308

SYOSSET—Nassau County

★ **SYOSSET HOSPITAL**, 221 Jericho Turnpike, Zip 11791–4515;
tel. 516/496–6500 **A**9 **F**3 12 15 18 29 30 31 34 35 36 38 40 44 45 50 57
58 59 60 62 63 64 65 68 70 74 78 79 81 82 84 85 87 97 98 100 101 102
107 108 119 126 130 132 135 146 148 **P**5 6 **S** North Shore–Long Island
Jewish Health System, Great Neck, NY
Primary Contact: Michael Fener, Executive Director
COO: Mark J. Solazzo, Regional Chief Operating Officer
CFO: Richard Reilly, Deputy Executive Director
CMO: Randolph DiLorenzo, M.D., Medical Director
CHR: Andrew S. Goldberg, Associate Executive Director
Web address: www.northshorelij.com
Control: Other not–for–profit (including NFP Corporation) **Service:** General
Medical and Surgical

Staffed Beds: 72 **Admissions:** 3397 **Census:** 50 **Outpatient Visits:** 47900 **Births:** 0 **Total Expense ($000):** 118787 **Payroll Expense ($000):** 60133 **Personnel:** 612

SYRACUSE—Onondaga County

COMMUNITY–GENERAL HOSPITAL OF GREATER SYRACUSE See Upstate
University Hospital at Community General

★ ◇ **CROUSE HOSPITAL (330203)**, 736 Irving Avenue, Zip 13210–1690;
tel. 315/470–7111 **A**3 5 9 10 21 **F**3 4 5 8 11 12 13 15 18 19 20 21 22 23
26 27 29 31 34 35 36 37 40 49 50 53 59 60 70 72 74 75 76 77 78 79 81
84 86 87 89 93 96 107 108 110 114 115 116 117 118 119 126 129 130
131 132 135 144 145 146 147 148
Primary Contact: Kimberly Boynton, President and Chief Executive Officer
COO: Jeffrey E. Tetrault, Director Facilities and Construction
CFO: Kelli Harris, Chief Financial Officer
CMO: Ronald Stahl, M.D., Chief Medical Officer
CIO: Kim Rose, Director Information Technology
CHR: John Bergemann, Director Human Resources
CNO: Ann Sedore, Ph.D., Chief Nursing Officer
Web address: www.crouse.org
Control: Other not–for–profit (including NFP Corporation) **Service:** General
Medical and Surgical

Staffed Beds: 501 **Admissions:** 20008 **Census:** 308 **Outpatient Visits:** 365833 **Births:** 3950 **Total Expense ($000):** 360903 **Payroll Expense ($000):** 153014 **Personnel:** 2270

□ **RICHARD H. HUTCHINGS PSYCHIATRIC CENTER (334001)**, 620 Madison
Street, Zip 13210–2319; tel. 315/426–3632, (Nonreporting) **A**1 3 5 10 **S** New
York State Office of Mental Health, Albany, NY
Primary Contact: Colleen A. Sawyer, R.N., MSN, Executive Director
COO: David Peppel, Director Operations
CFO: Robert Stapleton, Director Administration
CMO: Mark Cattalani, M.D., Clinical Director
CIO: Neil Nemi, Administrator Facility Information Center
CHR: Katherine Herron, Director Human Resources
Web address: www.omh.ny.gov
Control: State–Government, nonfederal **Service:** Psychiatric

Staffed Beds: 131

NY

★ ◇ **ST. JOSEPH'S HOSPITAL HEALTH CENTER (330140)**, 301 Prospect Avenue, Zip 13203–1807; tel. 315/448–5111 **A**3 5 9 10 21 **F**2 8 11 12 13 14 15 18 20 22 24 26 28 29 30 31 34 35 38 39 40 45 46 47 48 49 50 53 54 57 58 59 60 62 64 66 68 70 71 72 73 74 75 76 77 78 79 81 82 83 84 87 92 93 94 97 98 99 100 101 102 104 106 107 108 110 114 115 118 119 126 129 130 131 132 135 144 145 146 147 148 **S** Sisters of Saint Francis, Syracuse, NY
Primary Contact: Kathryn H. Ruscitto, President
COO: Mary W. Brown, Senior Vice President Operations
CFO: Meredith Price, Vice President Fiscal Services and Chief Financial Officer
CMO: Sandra Sulik, M.D., Vice President Medical Affairs
CIO: Charles Fennell, Vice President Information Management
CHR: Sallie Biittner, Vice President Human Resources
CNO: AnneMarie Czyz, R.N., Vice President for Clinical and Educational Services
Web address: www.sjhsyr.org
Control: Other not–for–profit (including NFP Corporation) **Service:** General Medical and Surgical

Staffed Beds: 431 **Admissions:** 26210 **Census:** 385 **Outpatient Visits:** 616538 **Births:** 2000 **Total Expense ($000):** 544251 **Payroll Expense ($000):** 232103 **Personnel:** 3700

✉ △ **SYRACUSE VETERANS AFFAIRS MEDICAL CENTER**, 800 Irving Avenue, Zip 13210–2716; tel. 315/425–4400, (Total facility includes 48 beds in nursing home–type unit) **A**1 3 5 7 8 **F**2 3 5 8 18 20 22 29 30 31 33 35 36 38 39 40 45 46 49 51 53 54 56 57 58 59 60 61 63 64 70 74 75 77 78 79 80 81 82 84 85 86 87 90 91 93 94 97 98 100 101 102 104 107 108 111 115 119 128 129 130 132 135 143 146 147 148 **P**6 **S** Department of Veterans Affairs, Washington, DC
Primary Contact: James Cody, Director
CFO: Elisabeth Kittell, Chief Financial Officer
CMO: William Marx, M.D., Chief of Staff
CIO: Dennis Wells, Chief Information Officer
CHR: Mark Antinelli, Manager Human Resources
CNO: Colene O'Neill, Associate Director Patient Nursing Services
Web address: www.syracuse.va.gov/
Control: Veterans Affairs, Government, federal **Service:** General Medical and Surgical

Staffed Beds: 161 **Admissions:** 4717 **Census:** 86 **Outpatient Visits:** 498867 **Births:** 0 **Total Expense ($000):** 296232 **Payroll Expense ($000):** 154423 **Personnel:** 1592

★ ◇ **UPSTATE UNIVERSITY HOSPITAL (330241)**, 750 East Adams Street, Zip 13210–2342; tel. 315/464–5540, (Includes GOLISANO CHILDREN'S HOSPITAL, 750 East Adams Street, tel. 315/464–4570; UPSTATE UNIVERSITY HOSPITAL AT COMMUNITY GENERAL, 4900 Broad Road, Zip 13215–2293; tel. 315/492–5011) **A**2 8 9 10 21 **F**3 6 9 12 13 15 16 17 18 20 21 22 23 24 25 26 27 28 29 30 31 34 35 36 37 38 39 40 41 43 44 45 46 47 48 49 50 51 52 53 54 55 56 57 58 59 61 64 65 66 70 74 76 78 79 81 82 84 85 86 87 88 89 90 92 93 95 96 97 98 99 100 101 102 104 107 108 109 110 111 114 115 118 119 120 121 123 124 126 129 130 131 132 135 136 138 141 142 145 146 147 148
Primary Contact: John B. McCabe, M.D., Chief Executive Officer
COO: Paul E. Seale, FACHE, Chief Operating Officer
CFO: Stuart M. Wright, CPA, Chief Financial Officer
CMO: Anthony Weiss, M.D., Medical Director
CIO: Terry Wagner, Chief Information Officer
CHR: Eric Frost, Associate Vice President Human Resources
CNO: Nancy E. Page, MS, Interim Chief Nursing Officer
Web address: www.upstate.edu/hospital
Control: State–Government, nonfederal **Service:** General Medical and Surgical

Staffed Beds: 594 **Admissions:** 27804 **Census:** 467 **Outpatient Visits:** 569347 **Births:** 1039 **Total Expense ($000):** 774265 **Payroll Expense ($000):** 293117 **Personnel:** 4662

VETERANS AFFAIRS MEDICAL CENTER See Syracuse Veterans Affairs Medical Center

★ **MOSES LUDINGTON HOSPITAL (331306)**, 1019 Wicker Street, Zip 12883–1097; tel. 518/585–2831 **A**9 10 18 **F**11 15 28 39 40 45 53 57 63 64 68 78 79 81 93 107 110 114 119 130 131 132 133 143
Primary Contact: Charlie Miceli, Interim Chief Executive Officer
CMO: Glen Chapman, M.D., Medical Director
CHR: Tamara Evens, Director Human Resources
Web address: www.interlakeshealth.com
Control: Other not–for–profit (including NFP Corporation) **Service:** General Medical and Surgical

Staffed Beds: 15 **Admissions:** 190 **Census:** 2 **Outpatient Visits:** 7156 **Births:** 1 **Personnel:** 127

★ **SAMARITAN HOSPITAL (330180)**, 2215 Burdett Avenue, Zip 12180–2475; tel. 518/271–3300, (Nonreporting) **A**5 9 10 **S** Catholic Health East / Trinity Health, Livonia, MI
Primary Contact: Norman E. Dascher, Jr., Chief Executive Officer
CFO: Daniel A. Kochie, CPA, Chief Financial Officer
CMO: Daniel C. Silverman, M.D., Chief Medical Officer, Acute Care Troy
CIO: Karen LeBlanc, Director, Applications
CNO: Jacqueline Priore, Chief Nursing Officer
Web address: www.nehealth.com
Control: Other not–for–profit (including NFP Corporation) **Service:** General Medical and Surgical

Staffed Beds: 238

★ **ST. MARY'S HOSPITAL (330232)**, 1300 Massachusetts Avenue, Zip 12180–1695; tel. 518/268–5000, (Includes SETON HEALTH SYSTEM–ST. MARY'S HOSPITAL, 1300 Massachusetts Avenue, Zip 12180; tel. 518/272–5000), (Nonreporting) **A**9 10 **S** Catholic Health East / Trinity Health, Livonia, MI
Primary Contact: Norman E. Dascher, Jr., Chief Executive Officer
CFO: Daniel A. Kochie, CPA, Chief Financial Officer
CMO: Daniel C. Silverman, M.D., Chief Medical Officer
CIO: Jonathan Goldberg, Vice President and Chief Information Officer
CHR: Barbara McCandless, Vice President Human Resources
CNO: Carol Crucetti, R.N., Chief Nursing Officer
Web address: www.setonhealth.org
Control: Church–operated, Nongovernment, not–for profit **Service:** General Medical and Surgical

Staffed Beds: 196

★ △ ◇ **FAXTON–ST. LUKE'S HEALTHCARE (330044)**, 1656 Champlin Avenue, Zip 13502–4830, Mailing Address: P.O. Box 479, Zip 13503–0479; tel. 315/624–6000, (Includes FAXTON CAMPUS, 1676 Sunset Avenue, Zip 13502–5475; tel. 315/624–6200; ST. LUKE'S CAMPUS, Zip 13413; tel. 315/624–6000) **A**2 7 9 10 21 **F**3 12 13 15 17 18 20 22 28 29 30 31 32 34 35 39 40 44 45 49 50 53 57 59 60 64 65 67 68 70 73 75 76 77 78 79 81 82 84 89 90 91 92 93 96 97 98 102 107 108 110 111 114 116 117 118 119 120 121 123 124 130 132 135 144 146 147 **P**6
Primary Contact: Scott H. Perra, President and Chief Executive Officer
CFO: Louis Aiello, Senior Vice President and Chief Financial Officer
CMO: Michael F. Trevisani, M.D., Senior Vice President and Chief Medical Officer
CHR: Anthony Scibelli, Senior Vice President Human Resources, Post Acute and Support Services
CNO: Patricia A. Roach, R.N., Senior Vice President and Chief Nursing Officer
Web address: www.mvnhealth.com
Control: Other not–for–profit (including NFP Corporation) **Service:** General Medical and Surgical

Staffed Beds: 319 **Admissions:** 14631 **Census:** 201 **Outpatient Visits:** 421625 **Births:** 2137 **Total Expense ($000):** 273485 **Payroll Expense ($000):** 124158 **Personnel:** 1772

□ **MOHAWK VALLEY PSYCHIATRIC CENTER (334021)**, 1400 Noyes Street, Zip 13502–3854; tel. 315/738–3800, (Nonreporting) **A**1 10 **S** New York State Office of Mental Health, Albany, NY
Primary Contact: Colleen A. Sawyer, R.N., MSN, Executive Director
Web address: www.omh.ny.gov/ornhweb/facilities/mvpc/facility.htm
Control: State–Government, nonfederal **Service:** Psychiatric

Staffed Beds: 614

★ ◇ **ST. ELIZABETH MEDICAL CENTER (330245)**, 2209 Genesee Street, Zip 13501–5999; tel. 315/798–8100 **A**9 10 12 13 21 **F**3 15 16 17 18 20 22 24 26 29 30 31 34 40 43 50 57 58 59 61 62 64 65 66 68 70 74 75 77 78 79 80 81 82 84 85 87 89 90 92 93 97 98 102 103 107 108 110 114 115 118 119 127 129 130 131 132 135 146 147 148 **P**6 **S** Sisters of Saint Francis, Syracuse, NY
Primary Contact: Scott H. Perra, Chief Executive Officer
COO: Robert Scholefield, Chief Operating Officer
CFO: Louis Aiello, Chief Financial Officer
CMO: Albert D'Accurzio, M.D., Medical Director
CIO: Robert Gillette, Chief Information Officer
CHR: Patrick Buckley, Vice President Human Resources
CNO: Varinya Sheppard, R.N., Chief Nursing Officer
Web address: www.stemc.org
Control: Church–operated, Nongovernment, not–for profit **Service:** General Medical and Surgical

Staffed Beds: 181 **Admissions:** 10504 **Census:** 147 **Outpatient Visits:** 485629 **Births:** 0 **Total Expense ($000):** 202517 **Payroll Expense ($000):** 96766 **Personnel:** 1724

ST. LUKE'S CAMPUS See Faxton–St. Luke's Healthcare

VALHALLA—Westchester County

☒ **BLYTHEDALE CHILDREN'S HOSPITAL (333301)**, 95 Bradhurst Avenue, Zip 10595–1697; tel. 914/592–7555, (Nonreporting) **A**1 9 10
Primary Contact: Larry L. Levine, President and Chief Executive Officer
COO: Maureen Desimone, Chief Operating Officer
CFO: John Canning, Chief Financial Officer
CMO: Joelle Mast, Ph.D., Chief Medical Officer
CHR: Ronald Gallo, Director Human Resources
Web address: www.blythedale.org
Control: Other not–for–profit (including NFP Corporation) **Service:** Children's rehabilitation

Staffed Beds: 92

☐ **WESTCHESTER MEDICAL CENTER (330234)**, 100 Woods Road, Zip 10595–1530; tel. 914/493–7000, (Includes MARIA FARERI CHILDREN'S HOSPITAL, 100 Woods Road, Zip 10595–1652; tel. 866/962–7337) **A**1 2 3 5 8 9 10 **F**3 8 12 13 14 15 16 17 18 19 20 21 22 23 24 25 26 27 28 29 30 31 32 34 35 36 37 38 39 40 41 43 44 45 46 47 48 49 50 52 54 55 56 57 58 59 60 61 64 65 66 68 70 71 72 73 74 75 76 77 78 79 81 82 84 85 86 87 88 89 90 91 92 94 97 98 99 100 101 102 103 104 107 108 110 111 114 115 116 117 118 119 120 121 123 124 126 129 130 131 132 134 135 136 137 138 139 141 142 145 146 147 148 **P**6
Primary Contact: Michael D. Israel, President and Chief Executive Officer
COO: Gary F. Brudnicki, Senior Executive Vice President, Chief Operating Officer and Chief Financial Officer
CFO: Gary F. Brudnicki, Senior Executive Vice President, Chief Operating Officer and Chief Financial Officer
CMO: Renee Garrick, M.D., Director, Executive Medical
CIO: John Moustakakis, Senior Vice President Information Systems and Chief Information Officer
CHR: Paul S. Hochenberg, Senior Vice President Human Resources
CNO: Patricia A. Wrobbel, Senior Vice President and Chief Nurse Executive
Web address: www.worldclassmedicine.com
Control: Hospital district or authority, Government, nonfederal **Service:** General Medical and Surgical

Staffed Beds: 652 **Admissions:** 21273 **Census:** 527 **Outpatient Visits:** 104394 **Births:** 825 **Total Expense ($000):** 849061 **Payroll Expense ($000):** 276243 **Personnel:** 2581

VALLEY STREAM—Nassau County

☒ **FRANKLIN HOSPITAL (330372)**, 900 Franklin Avenue, Zip 11580–2190; tel. 516/256–6000, (Total facility includes 120 beds in nursing home–type unit) **A**1 2 9 10 **F**2 3 11 12 17 18 26 29 30 31 34 35 40 43 45 49 50 56 57 58 59 60 62 63 64 65 68 70 74 75 77 78 79 81 82 83 84 85 86 87 92 94 97 98 100 102 103 107 108 111 114 118 119 128 130 132 135 143 146 148 **P**5 6 **S** North Shore–Long Island Jewish Health System, Great Neck, NY
Primary Contact: Catherine Hottendorf, R.N., MS, Executive Director
COO: Mark J. Solazzo, Executive Vice President and Chief Operating Officer
CFO: Elizabeth Zubko, Deputy Executive Director and Chief Financial Officer
CMO: Anthony J. Shallash, M.D., Interim Medical Director
CIO: John Bosco, Chief Information Officer
CHR: Karina Norr–McPhillips, Associate Executive Director Human Resources
CNO: Ralph Jay Civello, RN, MSN, Associate Executive Director Patient Care Services
Web address: www.northshorelij.com
Control: Other not–for–profit (including NFP Corporation) **Service:** General Medical and Surgical

Staffed Beds: 330 **Admissions:** 10904 **Census:** 253 **Outpatient Visits:** 70257 **Births:** 0 **Total Expense ($000):** 192076 **Payroll Expense ($000):** 95507 **Personnel:** 1175

WALTON—Delaware County

DELAWARE VALLEY HOSPITAL (331312), 1 Titus Place, Zip 13856–1498; tel. 607/865–2100 **A**9 10 18 **F**3 4 5 15 18 28 29 34 35 40 45 50 57 59 64 75 77 81 85 87 89 93 97 107 114 119 130 133 146 148 **S** United Health Services, Binghamton, NY
Primary Contact: Paul Summers, Interim President and Chief Executive Officer
CFO: Paul Summers, Chief Financial Officer
CMO: John Giannone, M.D., Chief Medical Officer
CIO: James Armstrong, Manager Information Technology
CHR: Paul Summers, Chief Human Resources Officer
CNO: Victoria Conkling, Vice President Patient Care Services and Chief Nursing Officer
Web address: www.uhs.net
Control: Other not–for–profit (including NFP Corporation) **Service:** General Medical and Surgical

Staffed Beds: 25 **Admissions:** 559 **Census:** 10 **Outpatient Visits:** 100067 **Births:** 0 **Total Expense ($000):** 15364 **Payroll Expense ($000):** 6890 **Personnel:** 156

WARSAW—Wyoming County

☐ **WYOMING COUNTY COMMUNITY HOSPITAL (330008)**, 400 North Main Street, Zip 14569–1025; tel. 585/786–8940, (Nonreporting) **A**1 9 10 20
Primary Contact: Donald T. Eichenauer, Chief Executive Officer
COO: Michael Corcimiglia, Chief Operating Officer
CMO: Scott Treutlein, M.D., Medical Director
CIO: Jane Beechler, Director Healthcare Information Systems
CHR: Denise M. Morley, Director Human Resources
CNO: Dawn James, Director of Nursing
Web address: www.wcchs.net
Control: County–Government, nonfederal **Service:** General Medical and Surgical

Staffed Beds: 75

WARWICK—Orange County

☒ **ST. ANTHONY COMMUNITY HOSPITAL (330205)**, 15 Maple Avenue, Zip 10990–1028; tel. 845/986–2276, (Nonreporting) **A**1 9 10 **S** Bon Secours Health System, Inc., Marriottsville, MD
Primary Contact: Jeff Reilly, Senior Vice President Operations
Web address: www.stanthonycommunityhosp.org
Control: Church–operated, Nongovernment, not–for profit **Service:** General Medical and Surgical

Staffed Beds: 73

WATERTOWN—Jefferson County

☒ **SAMARITAN MEDICAL CENTER (330157)**, 830 Washington Street, Zip 13601–4034; tel. 315/785–4000 **A**1 9 10 12 13 20 **F**3 5 8 13 15 18 20 29 30 31 35 40 49 51 57 60 64 68 70 73 74 75 76 77 78 79 81 82 87 89 90 93 97 98 99 100 102 103 104 107 108 111 114 116 119 120 121 126 127 129 130 135 146 147 148 **P**6
Primary Contact: Thomas H. Carman, President and Chief Executive Officer
CFO: Sean Mills, Chief Financial Officer
CMO: Mario Victoria, M.D., Vice President, Medical Affairs
CIO: M. Andrew Short, Vice President Information Services
CHR: Thomas Shatraw, Director Human Resources
CNO: Brian O'Hearn, Vice President Patient Care Services and Chief Nursing Officer
Web address: www.samaritanhealth.com
Control: Other not–for–profit (including NFP Corporation) **Service:** General Medical and Surgical

Staffed Beds: 208 **Admissions:** 9187 **Census:** 135 **Outpatient Visits:** 256096 **Births:** 1743 **Total Expense ($000):** 188366 **Payroll Expense ($000):** 84880 **Personnel:** 1374

WELLSVILLE—Allegany County

☒ **JONES MEMORIAL HOSPITAL (330096)**, 191 North Main Street, Zip 14895–1150, Mailing Address: P.O. Box 72, Zip 14895–0072; tel. 585/593–1100 **A**1 9 10 20 **F**3 8 11 13 15 17 28 29 30 31 34 35 36 40 43 57 59 61 64 68 70 75 76 77 78 79 81 82 85 89 93 97 107 110 114 119 129 131 132 133 146 147
Primary Contact: Eva Benedict, R.N., President and Chief Executive Officer
CFO: Tracy Gates, Chief Financial Officer
CMO: Frank Edwards, M.D., Medical Director
CIO: Tracy Gates, Chief Financial Officer
CHR: Brenda Sobeck, Director of Human Resources
CNO: Donna Bliven, Vice President Patient Care Services and Chief Nursing Officer
Web address: www.jmhny.org
Control: Other not–for–profit (including NFP Corporation) **Service:** General Medical and Surgical

Staffed Beds: 33 **Admissions:** 1727 **Census:** 19 **Outpatient Visits:** 145350 **Births:** 271 **Total Expense ($000):** 34326 **Payroll Expense ($000):** 16323 **Personnel:** 337

WEST HAVERSTRAW—Rockland County

☐ △ **HELEN HAYES HOSPITAL (330405)**, Route 9W, Zip 10993–1127; tel. 845/786–4000, (Nonreporting) **A**1 5 7 10
Primary Contact: Kathleen Martucci, Chief Operating Officer
COO: Kathleen Martucci, Chief Operating Officer
CFO: Lori A. Meszler, Chief Financial Officer
CMO: John T. Pellicone, M.D., Medical Director
CIO: Virgil Ennis, Chief Information Officer
CHR: Patrick J. Ryan, Chief Human Resources Officer
Web address: www.helenhayeshospital.org
Control: State–Government, nonfederal **Service:** Rehabilitation

Staffed Beds: 155

NY

WEST ISLIP—Suffolk County

☒ **GOOD SAMARITAN HOSPITAL MEDICAL CENTER (330286)**, 1000 Montauk Highway, Zip 11795–4927; tel. 631/376–3000, (Total facility includes 100 beds in nursing home–type unit) **A**1 2 9 10 12 13 **F**3 8 11 12 13 15 17 18 19 20 22 26 28 29 30 31 32 34 35 40 41 43 44 49 50 54 55 56 57 58 59 60 61 62 64 66 68 70 72 73 74 75 76 77 78 79 81 82 83 84 85 87 88 89 91 93 94 97 100 107 108 110 111 114 115 116 117 119 120 121 123 124 126 128 129 130 132 135 141 146 147 **P**6 8 **S** Catholic Health Services of Long Island, Rockville Centre, NY
Primary Contact: Nancy B. Simmons, Executive Vice President and Chief Administrative Officer
CFO: Dan Macksood, Regional Senior Vice President and Chief Financial Officer
CMO: Jerome Weiner, M.D., Senior Vice President Medical Affairs
CIO: Marcy Dunn, Vice President Information Services and Chief Information Officer
CHR: Lori Spina, Vice President Human Resources
CNO: Jeanne Dzurenko, M.P.H., Chief Nursing Officer and Senior Vice President Patient Care
Web address: www.good–samaritan–hospital.org
Control: Church–operated, Nongovernment, not–for profit **Service:** General Medical and Surgical

Staffed Beds: 531 **Admissions:** 24118 **Census:** 321 **Outpatient Visits:** 257398 **Births:** 2604 **Total Expense ($000):** 567052 **Payroll Expense ($000):** 254855 **Personnel:** 2724

WEST POINT—Orange County

☒ **KELLER ARMY COMMUNITY HOSPITAL**, 900 Washington Road, Zip 10996–1197, Mailing Address: U.S. Military Academy, Building 900, Zip 10996–1197; tel. 845/938–5169 **A**1 3 5 **F**3 13 15 29 30 32 34 35 36 38 40 44 45 50 54 57 59 64 65 68 75 76 77 79 81 85 86 87 97 99 100 101 102 104 107 110 111 115 131 132 135 141 146 **P**6 **S** Department of the Army, Office of the Surgeon General, Falls Church, VA
Primary Contact: Colonel Felicia Pehrson, M.D., Commanding Officer
COO: Lieutenant Colonel Thomas Bell, Deputy Commander Administration
CFO: Russell DeVries, Chief Business Operations
CMO: Lieutenant Colonel Michael Doyle, M.D., Deputy Commander Clinical Services
CIO: Patrick McGuinness, Chief Information Management
CHR: Margaret Greco, Chief Human Resources
Web address: www.kach.amedd.army.mil/
Control: Army, Government, federal **Service:** General Medical and Surgical

Staffed Beds: 18 **Admissions:** 874 **Census:** 5 **Outpatient Visits:** 119726 **Births:** 138 **Personnel:** 547

WEST SENECA—Erie County

☐ **WESTERN NEW YORK CHILDREN'S PSYCHIATRIC CENTER**, 1010 East and West Road, Zip 14224–3602; tel. 716/677–7000, (Nonreporting) **A**1 3 5 **S** New York State Office of Mental Health, Albany, NY
Primary Contact: Kathe Hayes, Executive Director
COO: David Privett, Deputy Director
CMO: Patrick Stein, M.D., Clinical Director
CIO: Dan Hrubiak, Associate Computer Program Analyst
CHR: Charles Siewert, Director Human Resources
Web address: www.omh.ny.gov
Control: State–Government, nonfederal **Service:** Children's hospital psychiatric

Staffed Beds: 46

WESTFIELD—Chautauqua County

★ **WESTFIELD MEMORIAL HOSPITAL (330166)**, 189 East Main Street, Zip 14787–1195; tel. 716/326–4921 **A**9 10 **F**3 8 11 14 15 18 34 40 45 57 59 68 75 79 81 86 87 93 107 108 110 119 129 135 147 148 **P**3 **S** Allegheny Health Network, Pittsburgh, PA
Primary Contact: Scott Whalen, Ph.D., FACHE, President and Chief Executive Officer
COO: Patricia Ballman, Director
CFO: Tina Gowen, System Controller
CMO: Russell Elwell, M.D., Medical Director
CIO: Cindy Harper, Manager Patient Data
Web address: www.wmhinc.org
Control: Other not–for–profit (including NFP Corporation) **Service:** General Medical and Surgical

Staffed Beds: 4 **Admissions:** 104 **Census:** 1 **Outpatient Visits:** 21976 **Births:** 0 **Personnel:** 77

WHITE PLAINS—Westchester County

☒ △ **BURKE REHABILITATION HOSPITAL (330404)**, 785 Mamaroneck Avenue, Zip 10605–2523; tel. 914/597–2500, (Nonreporting) **A**1 3 5 7 10
Primary Contact: Mary Beth Walsh, M.D., Chief Executive Officer
COO: Brian M. Swift, Senior Administrator Plant Operations
CFO: John Stewart, Director Finance
CMO: Mary Beth Walsh, M.D., Chief Executive Officer
CIO: Cathy Dwyer, Senior Administrator Information Systems
CHR: Annette Bucci, Senior Administrator Human Resources
CNO: Marie Spencer, Chief Nursing Officer and Senior Administrator
Web address: www.burke.org
Control: Other not–for–profit (including NFP Corporation) **Service:** Rehabilitation

Staffed Beds: 150

NEW YORK–PRESBYTERIAN HOSPITAL, WESTCHESTER DIVISION See New York–Presbyterian Hospital, New York

☒ **WHITE PLAINS HOSPITAL CENTER (330304)**, 41 East Post Road, Zip 10601–4699; tel. 914/681–0600 **A**1 2 5 9 10 **F**3 7 8 11 12 13 14 15 17 18 20 22 26 29 30 31 32 34 35 36 39 40 41 44 45 46 47 49 50 51 54 55 56 57 58 59 60 61 62 63 64 65 66 68 70 72 73 74 75 76 77 78 79 81 82 84 85 86 87 89 92 93 97 99 101 104 107 108 110 111 115 116 117 118 119 120 121 122 123 126 129 130 131 132 135 145 146 147 148
Primary Contact: Jon B. Schandler, Chief Executive Officer
COO: Edward F. Leonard, Executive Vice President and Chief Operating Officer
CFO: David Ho, Senior Vice President and Chief Financial Officer
CMO: Michael Palumbo, M.D., Executive Vice President and Medical Director
CIO: Elizabeth King, Director
CHR: John Sanchez, Vice President Human Resources
CNO: Leigh McMahon, MS, Senior Vice President Patient Care Services and Chief Nursing Officer
Web address: www.wphospital.org
Control: Other not–for–profit (including NFP Corporation) **Service:** General Medical and Surgical

Staffed Beds: 292 **Admissions:** 14703 **Census:** 184 **Outpatient Visits:** 154105 **Births:** 1838 **Total Expense ($000):** 368891 **Payroll Expense ($000):** 175146 **Personnel:** 2047

WILLIAMSVILLE—Erie County

MILLARD FILLMORE SUBURBAN HOSPITAL See KALEIDA Health, Buffalo

YONKERS—Westchester County

ANDRUS PAVILION See St. John's Riverside Hospital

☐ **ST. JOHN'S RIVERSIDE HOSPITAL (330208)**, 967 North Broadway, Zip 10701–1399; tel. 914/964–4444, (Includes ANDRUS PAVILION, 967 North Broadway, tel. 914/964–4444; PARKCARE PAVILION, Two Park Avenue, Zip 10703–3497; tel. 914/964–7300; ST. JOHN'S RIVERSIDE HOSPITAL – DOBBS FERRY PAVILION, 128 Ashford Avenue, Dobbs Ferry, Zip 10522–1896; tel. 914/693–0700), (Total facility includes 120 beds in nursing home–type unit) **A**1 2 9 10 **F**3 4 5 8 11 12 13 15 17 18 29 30 31 34 35 36 37 40 45 49 50 57 59 60 61 73 75 76 77 78 79 81 82 84 92 93 107 108 110 111 113 114 115 118 119 123 126 128 129 130 132 143 146 147 148 **P**6
Primary Contact: Ronald Corti, President and Chief Executive Officer
COO: Lynn M. Nelson, R.N., Chief Operating Officer and Chief Nursing Officer
CFO: Dennis M. Keane, Vice President Finance and Chief Financial Officer
CMO: Paul Antonecchia, M.D., Vice President Medical Affairs
CIO: Daniel Morreale, Chief Information Officer
CHR: Marc Leff, Vice President Human Resources
CNO: Lynn M. Nelson, R.N., Chief Operating Officer and Chief Nursing Officer
Web address: www.riversidehealth.org
Control: Other not–for–profit (including NFP Corporation) **Service:** General Medical and Surgical

Staffed Beds: 360 **Admissions:** 19989 **Census:** 284 **Outpatient Visits:** 222790 **Births:** 1536 **Total Expense ($000):** 245634 **Payroll Expense ($000):** 111056 **Personnel:** 2038

☒ **ST. JOSEPH'S MEDICAL CENTER (330006)**, 127 South Broadway, Zip 10701–4006; tel. 914/378–7000, (Total facility includes 200 beds in nursing home–type unit) **A**1 3 5 9 10 **F**2 3 4 5 8 11 15 18 29 30 31 34 35 38 39 40 45 47 48 49 54 56 57 58 59 60 61 62 64 68 70 74 75 77 78 79 81 82 85 87 89 93 94 97 98 99 100 101 102 103 104 105 106 107 108 110 111 115 118 119 128 130 132 134 135 143 144 145 146 **P**5 8
Primary Contact: Michael J. Spicer, President and Chief Executive Officer
COO: Frances Casola, Senior Vice President Operations
CFO: James J. Curcuruto, Senior Vice President Finance
CMO: Barry Perlman, M.D., Medical Director and Director Psychiatry
CIO: Deborah Di Bernardo, Chief Information Officer
CHR: Dean Civitello, Vice President Human Resources, Public Relations and Development
CNO: Jeffry E. Foltz, R.N., Vice President for Nursing
Web address: www.saintjosephs.org
Control: Other not–for–profit (including NFP Corporation) **Service:** General Medical and Surgical

Staffed Beds: 477 **Admissions:** 9283 **Census:** 438 **Outpatient Visits:** 1598321 **Births:** 0 **Total Expense ($000):** 245944 **Payroll Expense ($000):** 112631 **Personnel:** 1560

Many Facility Codes have changed. Please refer to the AHA Guide Code Chart. © 2014 AHA Guide

NORTH CAROLINA

AHOSKIE—Hertford County

✠ **VIDANT ROANOKE–CHOWAN HOSPITAL (340099)**, 500 South Academy Street, Zip 27910–3261, Mailing Address: P.O. Box 1385, Zip 27910–1385; tel. 252/209–3000 **A**1 9 10 **F**3 11 13 15 28 29 30 31 34 35 40 43 44 45 53 56 57 59 64 68 70 75 76 77 78 79 81 82 85 86 87 89 92 98 100 101 102 103 107 108 110 111 114 119 121 123 129 130 132 146 148 **S** Vidant Health, Greenville, NC
Primary Contact: Susan S. Lassiter, FACHE, President and Chief Executive Officer
CFO: Jon Graham, Chief Financial Officer
CMO: Jeff Severa, D.O., Chief of Staff
CHR: Debbie Sisler, Director Human Resources
CNO: Susan Mitchell, Vice President Patient Care Services
Web address: www.vidanthealth.com
Control: Other not–for–profit (including NFP Corporation) **Service:** General Medical and Surgical

Staffed Beds: 70 **Admissions:** 4603 **Census:** 56 **Outpatient Visits:** 70983 **Births:** 393 **Total Expense ($000):** 69203 **Payroll Expense ($000):** 27338 **Personnel:** 618

ALBEMARLE—Stanly County

✠ **STANLY REGIONAL MEDICAL CENTER (340119)**, 301 Yadkin Street, Zip 28001–3441, Mailing Address: P.O. Box 1489, Zip 28002–1489; tel. 704/984–4000 **A**1 9 10 **F**3 11 12 13 15 17 20 28 29 30 31 34 35 39 40 45 49 57 59 60 61 62 63 64 68 70 74 75 76 77 78 79 81 82 85 86 89 90 91 93 98 100 101 102 103 107 108 110 111 114 115 119 123 129 130 131 132 146 148 **S** Carolinas HealthCare System, Charlotte, NC
Primary Contact: Alfred P. Taylor, President and Chief Executive Officer
COO: Brian Freeman, Vice President of Operations
CFO: Nick Samilo, Vice President Fiscal Services and Chief Financial Officer
CMO: Paul D'Amico, M.D., Chief of Staff
CIO: Brian Freeman, Vice President of Operations
CHR: Paul Morlock, Vice President Human Resources
CNO: Judy Doran, R.N., Vice President of Hospital Services and Chief Nurse Executive
Web address: www.stanly.org
Control: Other not–for–profit (including NFP Corporation) **Service:** General Medical and Surgical

Staffed Beds: 104 **Admissions:** 4676 **Census:** 49 **Outpatient Visits:** 83139 **Births:** 622 **Total Expense ($000):** 97423 **Payroll Expense ($000):** 34938 **Personnel:** 627

ASHEBORO—Randolph County

✠ **RANDOLPH HOSPITAL (340123)**, 364 White Oak Street, Zip 27203–5400, Mailing Address: P.O. Box 1048, Zip 27204–1048; tel. 336/625–5151 **A**1 2 9 10 **F**3 8 13 15 18 28 29 30 31 34 35 37 40 45 48 49 50 53 56 57 58 59 61 62 64 68 70 74 75 76 77 78 79 80 81 82 83 84 85 86 87 89 91 92 93 94 96 97 107 109 110 111 114 115 119 120 121 123 130 131 132 143 146 **P**6
Primary Contact: Steven E. Eblin, Chief Executive Officer / President
CMO: Robert Dough, M.D., Chief of Staff
CIO: Angela Burgess, Chief Information Officer
Web address: www.randolphhospital.org
Control: Other not–for–profit (including NFP Corporation) **Service:** General Medical and Surgical

Staffed Beds: 101 **Admissions:** 5645 **Census:** 60 **Outpatient Visits:** 96487 **Births:** 798 **Total Expense ($000):** 95757 **Payroll Expense ($000):** 43703 **Personnel:** 950

ASHEVILLE—Buncombe County

★ **ASHEVILLE SPECIALTY HOSPITAL (342017)**, 428 Biltmore Avenue, 4th Floor, Zip 28801–4502; tel. 828/213–5400 **A**10 **F**1 3 29 30 36 77 85 91 148 **S** Mission Health System, Asheville, NC
Primary Contact: Robert C. Desotelle, President and Chief Executive Officer
COO: Michelle Stillman, Director of Care Management
CFO: Gregg Dixon, CPA, Chief Financial Officer
CMO: Joseph Aiello, M.D., Chief of Staff
CIO: Dorothy L. Porter, Director of Compliance/Risk/Quality
CHR: Jennifer Calloway, Human Resources Coordinator
CNO: Wanda Miller, R.N., Director of Clinical Services
Web address: www.missionhospitals.org/acute–care
Control: Partnership, Investor–owned, for–profit **Service:** Long–Term Acute Care hospital

Staffed Beds: 32 **Admissions:** 388 **Census:** 26 **Outpatient Visits:** 0 **Births:** 0 **Total Expense ($000):** 13328 **Payroll Expense ($000):** 5878 **Personnel:** 118

★ △ ◇ **CAREPARTNERS HEALTH SERVICES (343025)**, 68 Sweeten Creek Road, Zip 28803–2318, Mailing Address: P.C. Box 15025, Zip 28813–0025; tel. 828/277–4800 **A**7 9 10 21 **F**2 29 30 34 36 44 50 56 57 59 62 63 64 68 77 79 82 84 87 90 93 94 120 130 131 132 143 146 148
Primary Contact: Tracy Buchanan, Chief Executive Officer / President
COO: Gary Bowers, Chief Operating Officer
CFO: Gregg Diton, Chief Financial Officer
CIO: Drake Thomas, Chief Information Officer
CHR: Karen Vernon–Young, Vice President Human Resources and Communications
Web address: www.carepartners.org
Control: Other not–for–profit (including NFP Corporation) **Service:** Rehabilitation

Staffed Beds: 80 **Admissions:** 1341 **Census:** 49 **Outpatient Visits:** 78132 **Births:** 0 **Total Expense ($000):** 20038 **Payroll Expense ($000):** 12792 **Personnel:** 167

✠ **CHARLES GEORGE VETERANS AFFAIRS MEDICAL CENTER**, 1100 Tunnel Road, Zip 28805–2087; tel. 828/298–7911, (Total facility includes 85 beds in nursing home–type unit) **A**1 3 5 **F**3 4 5 12 18 20 22 24 26 28 29 30 31 34 35 36 38 39 40 42 45 49 50 56 57 58 59 61 62 63 64 65 68 70 71 74 75 77 78 79 81 82 83 84 85 86 87 91 92 93 94 97 98 100 101 102 103 104 107 108 111 114 115 119 127 128 130 132 135 145 146 147 148 **P**1 **S** Department of Veterans Affairs, Washington, DC
Primary Contact: Cynthia Breyfogle, FACHE, Director
CFO: Roger Eichmann, Chief Fiscal Officer
CMO: Webster Carl Bazemore, M.D., Interim Chief of Staff
CIO: Carla McLendon, Director Information Resource Management Services
CHR: James Sitlinger, Chief Human Resources Management
CNO: David Przestrzelski, Associate Director, Patient Care Services and Chief Nursing Executive
Web address: www.asheville.va.gov/
Control: Veterans Affairs, Government, federal **Service:** General Medical and Surgical

Staffed Beds: 257 **Admissions:** 5355 **Census:** 161 **Outpatient Visits:** 399355 **Births:** 0 **Total Expense ($000):** 213749 **Payroll Expense ($000):** 116508 **Personnel:** 1728

Hospital, Medicare Provider Number, Address, Telephone, Approval, Facility, and Physician Codes, Health Care System

★ American Hospital Association (AHA) membership
☐ The Joint Commission accreditation
◇ DNV Healthcare Inc. accreditation
○ Healthcare Facilities Accreditation Program
△ Commission on Accreditation of Rehabilitation Facilities (CARF) accreditation

NC

✠ **MISSION HOSPITAL (340002)**, 509 Biltmore Avenue, Zip 28801–4690; tel. 828/213–1111, (Includes MEMORIAL MISSION HOSPITAL, 509 Biltmore Avenue, tel. 828/255–4000; MISSION CHILDREN'S HOSPITAL, 509 Biltmore Avenue, Zip 28801–4601; tel. 828/213–1740; ST. JOSEPH'S HOSPITAL, 428 Biltmore Avenue, Zip 28801–9839; tel. 828/255–3100) **A**1 2 3 5 9 10 **F**3 7 8 11 12 13 15 17 18 19 20 22 24 26 28 29 30 31 32 34 35 36 37 39 40 43 44 45 46 47 48 49 50 51 53 54 55 56 57 58 59 60 61 64 65 68 70 71 72 73 74 75 76 77 78 79 80 81 82 84 85 86 87 88 89 91 92 93 95 96 97 98 99 100 101 102 103 104 105 107 108 110 111 114 115 116 117 118 119 120 121 123 124 126 129 130 131 132 134 135 142 143 146 147 148 **S** Mission Health System, Asheville, NC
Primary Contact: Ronald A. Paulus, M.D., President and Chief Executive Officer
COO: Brian W. Aston, Chief Operating Officer
CFO: Charles F. Ayscue, Senior Vice President Finance and Chief Financial Officer
CMO: William Hathaway, M.D., Chief Medical Officer
CIO: D. Arlo Jennings, Ph.D., Chief Information Officer
CHR: Maria Roloff, Vice President Human Resources
Web address: www.missionhospitals.org
Control: Other not–for–profit (including NFP Corporation) **Service:** General Medical and Surgical

> **Staffed Beds:** 763 **Admissions:** 40780 **Census:** 559 **Outpatient Visits:** 475199 **Births:** 3903 **Total Expense ($000):** 910685 **Payroll Expense ($000):** 281952 **Personnel:** 5852

BELHAVEN—Beaufort County

★ **VIDANT PUNGO HOSPITAL (341310)**, 202 East Water Street, Zip 27810–1450; tel. 252/943–2111, (Nonreporting) **A**9 10 18 **S** Vidant Health, Greenville, NC
Primary Contact: Harvey Case, President
CFO: Gerald Hardison, Director Finance
CMO: Gregory Jones, M.D., Chief of Staff
CIO: Jenny Brown, Director Human Resources and Public Relations
CHR: Jenny Brown, Director Human Resources and Public Relations
Web address: www.vidanthealth.com/vidant/dynamic–detail.aspx?id=11781
Control: Other not–for–profit (including NFP Corporation) **Service:** General Medical and Surgical

> **Staffed Beds:** 25

BLACK MOUNTAIN—Buncombe County

JULIAN F. KEITH ALCOHOL AND DRUG ABUSE TREATMENT CENTER (344023), 201 Tabernacle Road, Zip 28711–2599; tel. 828/669–3400, (Nonreporting) **A**10
Primary Contact: W. Douglas Baker, Director
CFO: Jackie Maurer, Fiscal Officer
CMO: Anthony Burnett, M.D., Medical Director
CHR: Faye Hamlin, Manager Human Resources
Web address: www.jfkadatc.net
Control: State–Government, nonfederal **Service:** Alcoholism and other chemical dependency

> **Staffed Beds:** 110

BOLIVIA—Brunswick County

✠ **NOVANT HEALTH BRUNSWICK MEDICAL CENTER (340158)**, 240 Hospital Drive N.E., Zip 28422–8346; tel. 910/721–1000 **A**1 9 10 **F**3 11 13 15 18 26 28 29 30 34 35 40 45 46 57 59 64 70 75 76 79 80 81 87 93 96 102 107 108 110 111 114 118 119 126 130 135 146 147 148 **S** Novant Health, Winston Salem, NC
Primary Contact: Shelbourn Stevens, President
CFO: Joan Thomas, Chief Financial Officer
CMO: Robert Hassler, M.D., Director Medical Affairs
CIO: Pamela Parrish, Director Information Systems
Web address: www.brunswicknovant.org
Control: Other not–for–profit (including NFP Corporation) **Service:** General Medical and Surgical

> **Staffed Beds:** 66 **Admissions:** 4262 **Census:** 41 **Outpatient Visits:** 120361 **Births:** 421 **Total Expense ($000):** 73597 **Payroll Expense ($000):** 20672 **Personnel:** 433

BOONE—Watauga County

✠ **WATAUGA MEDICAL CENTER (340051)**, 336 Deerfield Road, Zip 28607–5008, Mailing Address: P.O. Box 2600, Zip 28607–2600; tel. 828/262–4100 **A**1 2 9 10 19 20 **F**3 5 13 15 17 18 20 22 26 28 29 30 31 32 34 35 38 40 44 45 46 47 48 49 50 53 54 57 59 64 70 73 75 76 77 78 81 82 84 85 86 87 89 91 92 93 96 107 108 110 111 114 115 118 119 120 121 122 123 124 129 130 131 132 135 144 145 146 147 148 **P**6 8
S Appalachian Regional Healthcare System, Boone, NC
Primary Contact: Richard G. Sparks, Chief Executive Officer
CFO: Kevin B. May, Chief Financial Officer
CMO: Herman A. Godwin, Jr., M.D., Senior Vice President and Medical Director
CIO: Mike Quinto, Chief Information Officer
CHR: Amy Crabbe, Senior Vice President Human Resources
Web address: www.https://apprhs.org/contact–us
Control: Other not–for–profit (including NFP Corporation) **Service:** General Medical and Surgical

> **Staffed Beds:** 99 **Admissions:** 3913 **Census:** 39 **Outpatient Visits:** 132879 **Births:** 491 **Total Expense ($000):** 113721 **Payroll Expense ($000):** 39812 **Personnel:** 584

BREVARD—Transylvania County

✠ **TRANSYLVANIA REGIONAL HOSPITAL (341319)**, 260 Hospital Drive, Zip 28712–3378; tel. 828/884–9111, (Total facility includes 10 beds in nursing home–type unit) **A**1 9 10 18 **F**2 3 11 13 15 28 29 30 31 34 35 36 40 45 49 53 56 57 59 62 63 64 65 70 76 77 78 79 80 81 85 97 107 110 111 114 119 128 130 131 132 133 146 **P**6 **S** Mission Health System, Asheville, NC
Primary Contact: Catherine Landis, R.N., MS, President and Chief Nursing Officer
COO: Rebecca W. Carter, MSN, Vice President Patient Care and Chief Operating Officer
CFO: Marc Nakagawa, Vice President and Chief Financial Officer
CMO: Joe Cohen, M.D., Chief of Staff
CIO: Ed Coye, Director Information Technology
CHR: Mark L. Emory, System Director Human Resources
CNO: Rebecca W. Carter, MSN, Vice President Patient Care and Chief Operating Officer
Web address: www.trhospital.org
Control: Other not–for–profit (including NFP Corporation) **Service:** General Medical and Surgical

> **Staffed Beds:** 52 **Admissions:** 1618 **Census:** 16 **Outpatient Visits:** 61740 **Births:** 120 **Total Expense ($000):** 63649 **Payroll Expense ($000):** 23878 **Personnel:** 489

BRYSON CITY—Swain County

★ **SWAIN COUNTY HOSPITAL (341305)**, 45 Plateau Street, Zip 28713–4200; tel. 828/488–2155 **A**9 10 18 **F**8 11 15 29 30 35 40 44 57 59 62 63 68 75 77 81 82 84 85 91 93 103 107 119 130 133 146 148 **S** Duke LifePoint Healthcare, Brentwood, TN
Primary Contact: Steve Heatherly, Chief Executive Officer
CMO: David Zimmerman, M.D., Chief of Staff
Web address: www.westcare.org
Control: Other not–for–profit (including NFP Corporation) **Service:** General Medical and Surgical

> **Staffed Beds:** 25 **Admissions:** 468 **Census:** 4 **Outpatient Visits:** 29085 **Births:** 0 **Total Expense ($000):** 11448 **Payroll Expense ($000):** 4514 **Personnel:** 84

BURGAW—Pender County

✠ **PENDER MEMORIAL HOSPITAL (341307)**, 507 East Freemont Street, Zip 28425–5131; tel. 910/259–5451, (Total facility includes 43 beds in nursing home–type unit) **A**1 9 10 18 **F**3 11 15 29 34 40 45 54 57 59 62 64 68 81 85 86 87 93 96 107 110 114 119 128 129 130 133 135 143 146 148 **S** New Hanover Regional Medical Center, Wilmington, NC
Primary Contact: Ruth Glaser, President
CFO: Morrison Hall, Chief Financial Officer
CMO: Naseem Nasrallah, M.D., Chief of Staff
CIO: Ashley Hernandez, Chief Information Technology Officer
CHR: Lori McKoy, Business Partner
CNO: Denice Shackelford, R.N., Interim Chief Nurse Executive
Web address: www.pendermemorial.org
Control: County–Government, nonfederal **Service:** General Medical and Surgical

> **Staffed Beds:** 68 **Admissions:** 598 **Census:** 45 **Outpatient Visits:** 23985 **Births:** 0 **Total Expense ($000):** 20205 **Payroll Expense ($000):** 7421 **Personnel:** 193

BURLINGTON—Alamance County

✠ **ALAMANCE REGIONAL MEDICAL CENTER (340070)**, 1240 Huffman Mill Road, Zip 27215–8700, Mailing Address: P.O. Box 202, Zip 27216–0202; tel. 336/538–7000 **A**1 2 9 10 **F**3 8 9 12 13 15 18 20 22 24 28 29 30 31 32 34 35 36 38 39 40 44 45 46 47 49 50 53 54 55 56 57 58 59 60 64 68 70 73 74 76 77 78 79 81 82 84 85 86 87 89 91 93 94 96 97 98 100 101 102 103 107 108 110 111 114 117 118 119 120 121 123 126 130 131 132 135 144 145 146 147 148 **P**6 **S** Cone Health, Greensboro, NC
Primary Contact: Preston W. Hammock, President and Chief Executive Officer
COO: Preston W. Hammock, President and Chief Operating Officer
CFO: Rex Street, Senior Vice President and Chief Financial Officer
CMO: Andrew Lamb, M.D., Chief of Staff
CIO: Terri Andrews, Director Information Technology
CNO: Theresa M. Brodrick, R.N., Chief Nursing Officer
Web address: www.armc.com
Control: Other not–for–profit (including NFP Corporation) **Service:** General Medical and Surgical

Staffed Beds: 218 **Admissions:** 11285 **Census:** 132 **Outpatient Visits:** 178815 **Births:** 1304 **Total Expense ($000):** 241079 **Payroll Expense ($000):** 84224 **Personnel:** 1929

BUTNER—Granville County

☐ **CENTRAL REGIONAL HOSPITAL (344004)**, 300 Veazey Road, Zip 27509–1668; tel. 919/764–2000 **A**1 3 5 10 **F**3 30 39 74 75 98 99 103 106 119 130 143 146 **P**6
Primary Contact: Michael Hennike, Chief Executive Officer
COO: Cliff Hood, Chief Operating Officer
CFO: Steve Bruno, Manager Business
CMO: Stephen Oxley, M.D., Chief Medical Officer
CIO: Joe Thurber, Director Information Technology
CHR: Debbie Thomas, Director Human Resources
CNO: Amanda Dorgan, Chief Nursing Officer
Control: State–Government, nonfederal **Service:** Psychiatric

Staffed Beds: 382 **Admissions:** 1570 **Census:** 358 **Outpatient Visits:** 0 **Births:** 0 **Total Expense ($000):** 160208 **Payroll Expense ($000):** 94810 **Personnel:** 2052

☐ **JOHN UMSTEAD HOSPITAL (344004)**, 1003 12th Street, Zip 27509–1626; tel. 919/575–7211, (Includes ALCOHOL AND DRUG ABUSE TREATMENT CENTER, 205 West E Street, Zip 27509; tel. 919/575–7928; Cliff Hood, Director), (Nonreporting) **A**1 3 5 10
Primary Contact: Patricia L. Christian, Ph.D., R.N., Chief Executive Officer
Web address: www.juh.dhhs.state.nc.us
Control: State–Government, nonfederal **Service:** Psychiatric

Staffed Beds: 514

CAMP LEJEUNE—Onslow County

✠ **NAVAL HOSPITAL CAMP LEJEUNE**, 100 Brewster Boulevard, Zip 28547–2538, Mailing Address: P.O. Box 10100, Zip 28547–0100; tel. 910/450–4300, (Nonreporting) **A**1 **S** Bureau of Medicine and Surgery, Department of the Navy, Washington, DC
Primary Contact: Commander Matthew Case, Director Administration
Web address: www.med.navy.mil/sites/nhcl/Pages/default.aspx
Control: Navy, Government, federal **Service:** General Medical and Surgical

Staffed Beds: 117

CARY—Wake County

✠ **WAKEMED CARY HOSPITAL (340173)**, 1900 Kildaire Farm Road, Zip 27518–6616; tel. 919/350–2300, (Total facility includes 36 beds in nursing home–type unit) **A**1 9 10 **F**3 7 11 12 13 15 18 20 22 24 28 29 30 31 35 40 42 44 45 48 49 50 54 61 64 68 70 73 74 76 77 78 79 81 82 89 92 93 107 108 111 114 115 118 119 126 128 130 132 146 147 **P**6 **S** WakeMed Health & Hospitals, Raleigh, NC
Primary Contact: David C. Coulter, Senior Vice President and Administrator
COO: Thomas Gettinger, Chief Operating Officer and Executive Vice President
CFO: Michael D. DeVaughn, Executive Vice President and Chief Financial Officer
CMO: West Lawson, M.D., Chief Medical Officer
CIO: Denton Arledge, Vice President and Chief Information Officer
CHR: Jeanene R. Martin, M.P.H., Senior Vice President Human Resources
CNO: Cindy Boily, MSN, Senior Vice President and Chief Nursing Officer
Web address: www.wakemed.org
Control: Other not–for–profit (including NFP Corporation) **Service:** General Medical and Surgical

Staffed Beds: 192 **Admissions:** 9943 **Census:** 145 **Outpatient Visits:** 258721 **Births:** 2237 **Total Expense ($000):** 168661 **Payroll Expense ($000):** 63176 **Personnel:** 1038

CHAPEL HILL—Orange County

✠ △ **UNIVERSITY OF NORTH CAROLINA HOSPITALS (340061)**, 101 Manning Drive, Zip 27514–4220; tel. 919/966–4131, (Includes NORTH CAROLINA CHILDREN'S AND WOMEN'S HOSPITAL ; NORTH CAROLINA CHILDREN'S HOSPITAL, 101 Manning Drive, tel. 919/966–4131; NORTH CAROLINA NEUROSCIENCES HOSPITAL, University Campus, Zip 27514; tel. 919/966–1141) **A**1 2 3 5 7 8 9 10 **F**3 4 5 7 8 9 11 12 13 14 15 16 17 18 19 20 21 22 23 24 25 26 27 28 29 30 31 32 34 35 36 38 39 40 41 43 44 45 46 47 48 49 50 52 53 54 55 56 57 58 59 60 61 62 63 64 65 66 68 70 72 73 74 75 76 77 78 79 80 81 82 84 85 86 87 88 89 90 91 92 93 96 97 98 99 100 101 102 103 104 105 106 107 108 110 111 114 115 116 117 118 119 120 121 123 124 126 129 130 131 132 134 135 136 137 138 139 140 141 142 143 144 145 146 147 148 **S** UNC Health Care, Chapel Hill, NC
Primary Contact: Gary L. Park, President
COO: Brian Goldstein, M.D., Executive Vice President and Chief Operating Officer
CFO: Christopher Ellington, Executive Vice President and Chief Financial Officer
CMO: Tony Lindsey, M.D., Chief of Staff
CIO: Tracy Parham, MSN
CHR: William Rotella, Vice President Human Resources
CNO: Mary Crabtree Tonges, Ph.D., Senior Vice President and Chief Nursing Officer
Web address: www.unchealthcare.org
Control: State–Government, nonfederal **Service:** General Medical and Surgical

Staffed Beds: 818 **Admissions:** 37539 **Census:** 670 **Outpatient Visits:** 985577 **Births:** 3521 **Total Expense ($000):** 1107834 **Payroll Expense ($000):** 494149 **Personnel:** 8745

CHARLOTTE—Mecklenburg County

✠ △ **CAROLINAS MEDICAL CENTER (340113)**, 1000 Blythe Boulevard, Zip 28203–5871, Mailing Address: P.O. Box 32861, Zip 28232–2861; tel. 704/355–2000, (Includes CAROLINAS MEDICAL CENTER–MERCY, 2001 Vail Avenue, Zip 28207–1289; tel. 704/304–5000; Scott Jones, Vice President and Facility Executive; LEVINE CHILDREN'S HOSPITAL, 1000 Blythe Boulevard, Zip 28203; tel. 704/381–2000) **A**1 2 3 5 6 7 8 9 10 **F**3 4 5 7 8 12 13 15 17 18 19 20 21 22 23 24 25 26 27 28 29 30 31 32 34 35 36 37 38 39 40 41 42 43 44 45 46 47 48 49 50 52 54 55 56 57 58 59 60 61 62 64 65 66 68 70 71 72 73 74 75 76 77 78 79 80 81 82 83 84 85 86 87 88 89 90 93 96 97 98 99 100 101 102 103 104 105 106 107 108 109 111 114 115 116 117 118 119 120 121 123 124 126 129 130 131 132 134 135 136 137 138 139 141 142 143 145 146 147 148 **P**6 **S** Carolinas HealthCare System, Charlotte, NC
Primary Contact: Spencer Lilly, President
CFO: Greg A. Gombar, Chief Financial Officer
CMO: Roger A. Ray, M.D., Executive Vice President and Chief Medical Officer
CIO: Craig D. Richardville, Senior Vice President and Chief Information Officer
CHR: Debra Plousha–Moore, Senior Vice President Human Resources
Web address: www.carolinasmedicalcenter.org
Control: Hospital district or authority, Government, nonfederal **Service:** General Medical and Surgical

Staffed Beds: 1066 **Admissions:** 56978 **Census:** 838 **Outpatient Visits:** 870602 **Births:** 6117 **Total Expense ($000):** 1697056 **Payroll Expense ($000):** 505757 **Personnel:** 9844

✠ **CAROLINAS MEDICAL CENTER–PINEVILLE (340098)**, 10628 Park Road, Zip 28210; tel. 704/543–2000 **A**1 9 **F**3 13 17 18 20 22 24 26 28 29 30 40 42 45 49 50 64 70 72 73 74 75 76 77 79 81 82 84 86 87 90 91 92 93 100 107 111 112 114 115 119 126 129 130 132 146 147 148 **S** Carolinas HealthCare System, Charlotte, NC
Primary Contact: Christopher R. Hummer, President
Web address: www.carolinashealthcare.org/cmc–pineville
Control: Hospital district or authority, Government, nonfederal **Service:** General Medical and Surgical

Staffed Beds: 215 **Admissions:** 12418 **Census:** 147 **Outpatient Visits:** 147592 **Births:** 2619 **Total Expense ($000):** 227763 **Payroll Expense ($000):** 82093 **Personnel:** 1355

✠ **CAROLINAS MEDICAL CENTER–UNIVERSITY (340166)**, 8800 North Tryon Street, Zip 28262–3300, Mailing Address: P.O. Box 560727, Zip 28256–0727; tel. 704/863–6000 **A**1 9 10 **F**3 8 13 15 18 20 26 29 30 31 34 40 42 43 44 45 49 50 51 57 59 60 64 65 68 70 72 74 75 76 78 79 81 82 84 85 86 87 93 107 111 114 115 118 119 126 129 130 145 146 148 **S** Carolinas HealthCare System, Charlotte, NC
Primary Contact: William H. Leonard, President
CFO: Greg A. Gombar, Chief Financial Officer
CIO: John Knox, Senior Vice President and Chief Information Officer
Web address: www.carolinashealthcare.org/cmc–university
Control: Hospital district or authority, Government, nonfederal **Service:** General Medical and Surgical

Staffed Beds: 94 **Admissions:** 5755 **Census:** 58 **Outpatient Visits:** 143409 **Births:** 1494 **Total Expense ($000):** 136546 **Payroll Expense ($000):** 49433 **Personnel:** 753

Hospital, Medicare Provider Number, Address, Telephone, Approval, Facility, and Physician Codes, Health Care System

★ American Hospital Association (AHA) membership
☐ The Joint Commission accreditation
◇ DNV Healthcare Inc. accreditation
◯ Healthcare Facilities Accreditation Program
△ Commission on Accreditation of Rehabilitation Facilities (CARF) accreditation

NC

⊠ △ **CAROLINAS REHABILITATION (343026)**, 1100 Blythe Boulevard, Zip 28203–5864; tel. 704/355–4300 **A**1 7 9 10 **F**3 11 29 30 31 64 74 77 79 82 90 91 93 95 129 130 131 132 146 **P**1 **S** Carolinas HealthCare System, Charlotte, NC
Primary Contact: Robert G. Larrison, Jr., President
CFO: William Hopkins, Director Finance
CMO: William Bockenek, M.D., Chief Medical Officer
CIO: Craig D. Richardville, Chief Information Officer
CNO: Susan Chase, Vice President
Web address: www.carolinashealthcare.org/carolinas–rehab
Control: Other not–for–profit (including NFP Corporation) **Service:** Rehabilitation

Staffed Beds: 147 **Admissions:** 2868 **Census:** 123 **Outpatient Visits:** 77935 **Births:** 0 **Total Expense ($000):** 83432 **Payroll Expense ($000):** 37463 **Personnel:** 714

⊠ **CAROLINAS SPECIALTY HOSPITAL (342015)**, 10648 Park Road, Zip 28210; tel. 704/667–8060, (Nonreporting) **A**1 10 **S** AcuityHealthcare, LP, Charlotte, NC
Primary Contact: Daniel C. Dunmyer, Chief Executive Officer
CFO: Joanne Tyo, Chief Financial Officer
CMO: Joseph Lang, M.D., Chief of Staff
CHR: Doug Gallagher, Director Human Resources
CNO: Teshia Davis, Chief Clinical Officer
Web address: www.cshnc.com
Control: Corporation, Investor–owned, for–profit **Service:** Long–Term Acute Care hospital

Staffed Beds: 38

★ **NOVANT HEALTH CHARLOTTE ORTHOPAEDIC HOSPITAL (340153)**, 1901 Randolph Road, Zip 28207–1195; tel. 704/316–2000, (Total facility includes 16 beds in nursing home–type unit) **A**9 10 **F**3 11 29 30 37 44 50 51 64 68 75 79 81 82 86 87 107 111 118 119 128 130 131 132 146 **S** Novant Health, Winston Salem, NC
Primary Contact: Mike Riley, Senior Vice President and Chief Operating Officer
CFO: Tammy Geist, Chief Financial Officer
CIO: Shelia Cook, Director Information Systems
Web address: www.novanthealth.org
Control: Other not–for–profit (including NFP Corporation) **Service:** Orthopedic

Staffed Beds: 80 **Admissions:** 3703 **Census:** 39 **Outpatient Visits:** 24496 **Births:** 0 **Total Expense ($000):** 86341 **Payroll Expense ($000):** 22071 **Personnel:** 359

⊠ **NOVANT HEALTH PRESBYTERIAN MEDICAL CENTER (340053)**, 200 Hawthorne Lane, Zip 28204–2528, Mailing Address: P.O. Box 33549, Zip 28233–3549; tel. 704/384–4000, (Includes PRESBYTERIAN HEMBY CHILDREN'S HOSPITAL, 200 Hawthorne Lane, Zip 28204–2515; tel. 704/384–5134) **A**1 2 9 10 **F**3 5 7 8 11 12 13 15 17 18 19 20 22 24 26 28 29 30 31 32 34 35 36 38 40 41 45 46 47 48 49 53 54 55 56 57 58 59 60 61 63 64 65 68 70 71 72 73 74 75 76 77 78 79 81 82 85 86 87 88 89 91 92 93 98 99 100 101 102 103 104 105 107 108 111 112 113 114 115 116 117 118 119 120 121 124 126 129 130 132 135 142 143 145 146 147 148 **P**6 **S** Novant Health, Winston Salem, NC
Primary Contact: Harry L. Smith, Jr., President
COO: Amy Vance, Executive Vice President and Chief Operating Officer
CFO: Mark Moyer, Vice President and Chief Financial Officer
CMO: Stephen Wallenhaupt, M.D., Executive Vice President Medical Affairs
CIO: David B. Garrett, Senior Vice President Information Technology
CHR: Janet Smith–Hill, Senior Vice President Human Resources
Web address: www.presbyterian.org
Control: Other not–for–profit (including NFP Corporation) **Service:** General Medical and Surgical

Staffed Beds: 588 **Admissions:** 29736 **Census:** 423 **Outpatient Visits:** 383124 **Births:** 5154 **Total Expense ($000):** 551198 **Payroll Expense ($000):** 181696 **Personnel:** 3124

PRESBYTERIAN HOSPITAL See Novant Health Presbyterian Medical Center

PRESBYTERIAN–ORTHOPAEDIC HOSPITAL See Novant Health Charlotte Orthopaedic Hospital

CHEROKEE—Swain County

⊠ **CHEROKEE INDIAN HOSPITAL (340156)**, 1 Hospital Road, Zip 28719; tel. 828/497–9163 **A**1 10 **F**39 40 50 54 59 63 64 65 66 68 75 77 79 82 86 93 97 99 104 107 110 111 114 119 127 130 131 132 135 **P**6
Primary Contact: Casey Cooper, Chief Executive Officer
COO: Beth Greene, Chief Operating Officer
CFO: Chrissy Arch, Chief Financial Officer
CMO: Michael E. Toedt, M.D., Director Clinical Services
CIO: Anthony Taylor, Manager Information Technology
Control: PHS, Indian Service, Government, federal **Service:** General Medical and Surgical

Staffed Beds: 15 **Admissions:** 682 **Census:** 9 **Births:** 0

CLINTON—Sampson County

⊠ **SAMPSON REGIONAL MEDICAL CENTER (340024)**, 607 Beaman Street, Zip 28328–2697, Mailing Address: P.O. Box 260, Zip 28329–0260; tel. 910/592–8511 **A**1 9 10 **F**3 13 14 15 28 29 34 35 40 41 45 46 48 50 53 54 57 59 62 64 65 68 70 75 77 79 81 82 85 86 87 89 91 93 96 97 107 108 110 111 114 115 118 119 129 130 132 133 135 144 146 148 **P**6
Primary Contact: Shawn Howerton, M.D., Chief Executive Officer and President, Medical Staff
COO: Geraldine H. Shipp, Director of Risk Management
CFO: Jerry Heinzman, Senior Vice President and Chief Financial Officer
CMO: Shawn Howerton, M.D., Chief Executive Officer and President, Medical Staff
CIO: Kelly Lucas, Chief Information Officer
CHR: Michael W. Gilpin, Vice President Human Resources
CNO: Gayle Reiber, Interim Chief Nursing Officer
Web address: www.sampsonrmc.org
Control: County–Government, nonfederal **Service:** General Medical and Surgical

Staffed Beds: 105 **Admissions:** 3526 **Census:** 50 **Outpatient Visits:** 72732 **Births:** 447

CLYDE—Haywood County

⊠ **HAYWOOD REGIONAL MEDICAL CENTER (340184)**, 262 Leroy George Drive, Zip 28721–7430; tel. 828/456–7311 **A**1 9 10 **F**3 11 13 15 18 20 28 29 30 31 34 35 38 40 44 45 46 50 51 53 54 57 59 62 63 64 65 68 70 71 74 75 76 77 78 79 81 82 84 85 86 87 93 98 100 101 102 107 108 111 114 118 119 129 130 131 132 144 146 147 148 **P**8 **S** Duke LifePoint Healthcare, Brentwood, TN
Primary Contact: Janie Sinacore–Jaberg, R.N., MS, FACHE, Chief Executive Officer
COO: Teresa Reynolds, Chief Operating Officer
CFO: Rose Coyne, Interim CFO
CMO: Tyson Smith, M.D., Chief Medical Officer
CIO: Greg Copen, Chief Information Officer
CHR: Janet Millsaps, Vice President Human Resources
Web address: www.haymed.org
Control: Hospital district or authority, Government, nonfederal **Service:** General Medical and Surgical

Staffed Beds: 146 **Admissions:** 5481 **Census:** 57 **Outpatient Visits:** 250109 **Births:** 332 **Total Expense ($000):** 107352 **Payroll Expense ($000):** 46774 **Personnel:** 747

COLUMBUS—Polk County

⊠ **ST. LUKE'S HOSPITAL (341322)**, 101 Hospital Drive, Zip 28722–6418; tel. 828/894–3311 **A**1 9 10 18 **F**3 11 15 29 30 34 35 40 45 56 57 59 64 70 75 77 79 81 85 87 93 98 103 104 107 108 114 119 130 133 135 146 **P**6 **S** Carolinas HealthCare System, Charlotte, NC
Primary Contact: Kenneth A. Shull, FACHE, Chief Executive Officer
CFO: Christine M. Martin, Chief Financial Officer
CMO: James Holleman, M.D., Chief of Staff
CIO: David Pearson, Chief Information Officer
CHR: Amy Arledge, Vice President Support Services
Web address: www.saintlukeshospital.com
Control: Other not–for–profit (including NFP Corporation) **Service:** General Medical and Surgical

Staffed Beds: 35 **Admissions:** 1584 **Census:** 24 **Outpatient Visits:** 22003 **Births:** 1 **Total Expense ($000):** 26234 **Payroll Expense ($000):** 10732 **Personnel:** 276

CONCORD—Cabarrus County

⊠ **CAROLINAS MEDICAL CENTER–NORTHEAST (340001)**, 920 Church Street North, Zip 28025–2983; tel. 704/403–3000 **A**1 2 9 10 **F**3 5 8 9 11 12 13 15 17 18 20 22 24 26 28 29 30 31 34 37 38 40 42 43 44 45 46 49 50 51 53 55 56 57 58 59 60 61 64 65 68 70 71 72 73 74 75 76 77 78 79 81 82 84 85 86 87 88 89 93 97 98 99 100 102 103 104 105 107 108 111 114 115 116 117 118 119 121 123 124 126 129 130 131 132 135 145 146 147 148 **P**6 **S** Carolinas HealthCare System, Charlotte, NC
Primary Contact: Phyllis A. Wingate, FACHE, President
COO: Bill Hubbard, Vice President, Operations
CFO: Carol Hale, Vice President Finance
CMO: Dan Hagler, M.D., Vice President and Chief Medical Officer
CIO: Keith McNeice, Vice President and Chief Information Officer
CHR: Lesley Chambless, Assistant Vice President Workforce Relations
CNO: Kate Grew, MSN, Vice President/Chief Nurse Executive
Web address: www.carolinashealthcare.org
Control: Hospital district or authority, Government, nonfederal **Service:** General Medical and Surgical

Staffed Beds: 455 **Admissions:** 21189 **Census:** 255 **Outpatient Visits:** 504210 **Births:** 2630 **Total Expense ($000):** 447853 **Payroll Expense ($000):** 159967 **Personnel:** 2651

Many Facility Codes have changed. Please refer to the AHA Guide Code Chart. © 2014 AHA Guide

NC

DANBURY—Stokes County

★ ◇ **PIONEER COMMUNITY HOSPITAL OF STOKES (341317)**, 1570 Highway 8 and 89 North, Zip 27016, Mailing Address: P.O. Box 10, Zip 27016–0010; tel. 336/593–2831, (Total facility includes 40 beds in nursing home–type unit) **A**9 10 18 21 **F**3 15 34 40 42 54 56 57 59 64 79 81 90 93 97 103 104 107 114 119 127 128 130 133 135 146 148 **P**6 **S** Pioneer Health Services, Magee, MS
Primary Contact: Pamela P. Tillman, R.N., Chief Executive Officer
COO: Tim Fontaine, Chief Operating Officer
CFO: Julie Gieger, Chief Financial Officer
CMO: Samuel C. Newsome, M.D., Chief of Staff
CIO: Jack York, Chief Information Officer
CHR: Lashaunda Lash, Manager Human Resources
CNO: Jane Pantano, R.N., Chief Nursing Officer
Web address: www.pchstokes.com
Control: Individual, Investor–owned, for–profit **Service:** General Medical and Surgical

Staffed Beds: 65 **Admissions:** 151 **Census:** 47 **Outpatient Visits:** 24101 **Births:** 0

DUNN—Harnett County

✠ **HARNETT HEALTH SYSTEM (340071)**, 800 Tilghman Drive, Zip 28334–5599, Mailing Address: P.O. Box 1706, Zip 28335–1706; tel. 910/892–1000, (Includes CENTRAL HARTNETT HOSPITAL, 215 Brightwater Drive, Lillington, Zip 27546; tel. 910/892–1000) **A**1 9 10 **F**3 11 13 15 18 28 29 30 34 35 39 40 45 50 56 57 59 68 70 73 75 76 77 79 81 82 85 86 87 89 92 93 96 102 107 108 110 111 114 118 119 129 130 135 146 148 **S** WakeMed Health & Hospitals, Raleigh, NC
Primary Contact: Kenneth E. Bryan, FACHE, President and Chief Executive Officer
COO: Kenneth E. Bryan, FACHE, President and Chief Executive Officer
CFO: Lynn Lambert, Chief Financial Officer
CIO: Tim Krieger, Director Information Systems
CHR: Sondra Davis, Vice President Human Resources & System Development
CNO: Vicki Allen, R.N., Vice President Patient Care Services and Chief Nursing Officer
Web address: www.myharnetthealth.org/
Control: Other not–for–profit (including NFP Corporation) **Service:** General Medical and Surgical

Staffed Beds: 76 **Admissions:** 6336 **Census:** 70 **Outpatient Visits:** 93112 **Births:** 653 **Total Expense ($000):** 109214 **Payroll Expense ($000):** 49502 **Personnel:** 1113

DURHAM—Durham County

✠ **DUKE REGIONAL HOSPITAL (340155)**, 3643 North Roxboro Road, Zip 27704–2763; tel. 919/470–4000 **A**1 3 5 6 9 10 **F**3 8 11 12 13 15 17 18 20 22 24 26 28 29 30 31 34 35 40 44 45 48 50 51 57 58 59 60 64 66 68 70 73 74 75 76 77 78 79 80 81 82 84 85 86 87 90 96 98 100 102 107 108 110 111 115 118 119 120 121 123 124 126 130 131 132 146 147 148 **P**6 **S** Duke University Health System, Durham, NC
Primary Contact: Kathleen B. Galbraith, President
CFO: Jonathan B. Hoy, Chief Financial Officer
CMO: Barbara Griffith, M.D., Chief Medical Officer
CIO: Terry Mears, Director Information Systems
CHR: Richard J. Walsh, Ph.D., Chief Human Resources Officer
CNO: Victoria K. Orto, R.N., Chief Nursing and Patient Care Services Officer
Web address: www.durhamregional.org
Control: Other not–for–profit (including NFP Corporation) **Service:** General Medical and Surgical

Staffed Beds: 204 **Admissions:** 14732 **Census:** 204 **Outpatient Visits:** 111646 **Births:** 2128 **Total Expense ($000):** 272697 **Payroll Expense ($000):** 109556 **Personnel:** 1967

✠ **DUKE UNIVERSITY HOSPITAL (340030)**, 2301 Erwin Road, Zip 27705–4699, Mailing Address: P.O. Box 3708, Zip 27710–3708; tel. 919/684–8111, (Includes DUKE CHILDREN'S HOSPITAL & HEALTH CENTER, 2301 Erwin Road, Zip 27710–0001, Mailing Address: PO Box 3708, Zip 27702; tel. 919/684–8111) **A**1 2 3 5 8 9 10 **F**3 5 6 7 8 9 11 12 13 15 16 17 18 19 20 21 22 23 24 25 26 27 28 29 30 31 32 34 35 36 37 39 40 41 43 44 45 46 47 48 49 50 52 53 55 56 57 58 59 60 61 62 63 64 65 66 68 70 72 73 74 75 76 77 78 79 80 81 82 84 85 86 87 88 89 91 92 93 94 95 96 97 98 99 100 101 102 103 104 107 108 110 111 112 114 115 116 117 118 119 120 121 123 124 126 127 129 130 131 132 134 135 136 137 138 139 140 141 142 144 145 146 147 148 **P**1 **S** Duke University Health System, Durham, NC
Primary Contact: Kevin W. Sowers, R.N., MSN, President
CFO: Sabrina Olsen, Chief Financial Officer
CMO: Lisa C. Pickett, M.D., Chief Medical Officer
CIO: Jeffrey Ferranti, M.D., Chief Information Officer
CHR: Deborah Page, Chief Human Resources Officer
CNO: Mary Ann Fuchs, R.N., Chief Nursing Officer
Web address: www.dukehealth.org
Control: Other not–for–profit (including NFP Corporation) **Service:** General Medical and Surgical

Staffed Beds: 820 **Admissions:** 37365 **Census:** 676 **Outpatient Visits:** 995984 **Births:** 3016 **Total Expense ($000):** 1615816 **Payroll Expense ($000):** 486133 **Personnel:** 9805

DURHAM REGIONAL HOSPITAL See Duke Regional Hospital

✠ **DURHAM VETERANS AFFAIRS MEDICAL CENTER**, 508 Fulton Street, Zip 27705–3897; tel. 919/286–0411, (Nonreporting) **A**1 3 5 8 **S** Department of Veterans Affairs, Washington, DC
Primary Contact: DeAnne Seekins, Director
COO: Sara Haigh, Associate Director
CFO: David Kuboushek, Chief, Fiscal Service
CMO: John D. Shelburne, M.D., Chief of Staff
CIO: Toby Dickerson, Chief Information Resources Management Services
CHR: Jerry Freeman, Chief, Human Resources Management Services
CNO: Gregory S. Eagerton, Ph.D., Nurse Executive
Web address: www.durham.va.gov/
Control: Veterans Affairs, Government, federal **Service:** General Medical and Surgical

Staffed Beds: 154

☐ **NORTH CAROLINA SPECIALTY HOSPITAL (340049)**, 3916 Ben Franklin Boulevard, Zip 27704–2383; tel. 919/956–9300 **A**1 9 10 **F**3 64 79 81 82 85 86 87 119 126 130 131 135 148 **S** National Surgical Hospitals, Chicago, IL
Primary Contact: Randi L. Shults, Chief Executive Officer
CFO: Bill Wilson, Chief Financial Officer
CMO: Thomas Dimmig, M.D., Medical Director
CHR: Deborah Wheeler, Director Human Resources
CNO: John Medlin, Chief Nursing Officer
Web address: www.ncspecialty.com
Control: Partnership, Investor–owned, for–profit **Service:** General Medical and Surgical

Staffed Beds: 18 **Admissions:** 1647 **Census:** 11 **Outpatient Visits:** 9880 **Births:** 0 **Total Expense ($000):** 33741 **Payroll Expense ($000):** 10538 **Personnel:** 194

✠ **SELECT SPECIALTY HOSPITAL–DURHAM (342018)**, 3643 North Roxboro Road, 6th Floor, Zip 27704–2702; tel. 919/470–9137, (Nonreporting) **A**1 10 **S** Select Medical Corporation, Mechanicsburg, PA
Primary Contact: Robert F. Jernigan, Jr., Chief Executive Officer
Web address: www.selectspecialtyhospitals.com/company/locations/durham.aspx
Control: Corporation, Investor–owned, for–profit **Service:** Long–Term Acute Care hospital

Staffed Beds: 30

EDEN—Rockingham County

★ ◇ **MOREHEAD MEMORIAL HOSPITAL (340060)**, 117 East King's Highway, Zip 27288–5201; tel. 336/623–9711, (Total facility includes 121 beds in nursing home–type unit) **A**2 9 10 21 **F**3 11 13 15 18 26 28 29 30 34 35 40 45 47 48 49 50 57 59 64 68 70 74 75 76 77 79 81 82 85 87 89 90 93 97 107 108 110 111 114 118 119 122 123 128 129 130 132 135 143 146 147 148
Primary Contact: Howard N. Ainsley, Chief Executive Officer
CFO: Robert G. Hetrick, Vice President Finance and Chief Financial Officer
CHR: Tom Stevens, Director Personnel
Web address: www.morehead.org
Control: Other not–for–profit (including NFP Corporation) **Service:** General Medical and Surgical

Staffed Beds: 216 **Admissions:** 4831 **Census:** 155 **Outpatient Visits:** 172884 **Births:** 527 **Total Expense ($000):** 94404 **Payroll Expense ($000):** 44204 **Personnel:** 806

Hospital, Medicare Provider Number, Address, Telephone, Approval, Facility, and Physician Codes, Health Care System

★ American Hospital Association (AHA) membership
☐ The Joint Commission accreditation
◇ DNV Healthcare Inc. accreditation
○ Healthcare Facilities Accreditation Program
△ Commission on Accreditation of Rehabilitation Facilities (CARF) accreditation

NC

EDENTON—Chowan County

☒ **VIDANT CHOWAN HOSPITAL (341318)**, 211 Virginia Road, Zip 27932–9668,
Mailing Address: P.O. Box 629, Zip 27932–0629; tel. 252/482–8451 **A**1 9 10
18 **F**3 11 13 15 18 19 28 29 30 31 34 35 40 45 46 56 57 59 64 70 74 75
76 77 78 79 81 82 85 89 93 107 108 110 111 114 119 130 132 146 147
S Vidant Health, Greenville, NC
Primary Contact: Jeffrey N. Sackrison, FACHE, President
COO: Jeffery Dial, Vice President Operations
CFO: Brian Harvill, Vice President Financial Services
CMO: William Hope, IV, M.D., Chief of Medical Staff
CIO: Doug McMullen, Senior Technical Analyst
CHR: Debbie Swicegood, Director Human Resources
CNO: Cindy Coker, M.P.H., Vice President, Patient Care Services
Web address: www.vidanthealth.com
Control: Other not–for–profit (including NFP Corporation) **Service:** General
Medical and Surgical

Staffed Beds: 19 **Admissions:** 1726 **Census:** 17 **Outpatient Visits:** 36367
Births: 309 **Total Expense ($000):** 42691 **Payroll Expense ($000):** 17628
Personnel: 342

ELIZABETH CITY—Pasquotank County

☒ **SENTARA ALBEMARLE MEDICAL CENTER (340109)**, 1144 North Road
Street, Zip 27909–3473, Mailing Address: P.O. Box 1587, Zip 27906–1587;
tel. 252/335–0531 **A**1 9 10 **F**3 13 15 17 18 20 28 29 30 31 34 35 39 40 45
53 57 59 64 68 70 74 75 76 77 78 79 81 84 86 87 92 93 94 107 108 111
115 118 119 121 129 130 132 146 147 148 **S** Sentara Healthcare, Norfolk, VA
Primary Contact: Kenneth W. Wood, Interim President
COO: Jan King Robinson, Vice President, Operations
CFO: Craig Lewis, Interim Chief Financial Officer
CMO: Daniel S. Terryberry, M.D., Vice President of Medical Affairs
CIO: Steve Clark, Chief Information Officer
CHR: Brenda Rosecrans, Executive Director Human Resources
CNO: Kathy Lawrence, Interim Vice President of Patient Care Services
Web address: www.albemarlehealth.org
Control: Other not–for–profit (including NFP Corporation) **Service:** General
Medical and Surgical

Staffed Beds: 89 **Admissions:** 5204 **Census:** 59 **Outpatient Visits:** 150927
Births: 654 **Total Expense ($000):** 105688 **Payroll Expense ($000):** 38142
Personnel: 812

ELIZABETHTOWN—Bladen County

BLADEN COUNTY HOSPITAL See Cape Fear Valley – Bladen County Hospital

☒ **CAPE FEAR VALLEY – BLADEN COUNTY HOSPITAL (341315)**, 501 South
Poplar Street, Zip 28337–9375, Mailing Address: P.O. Box 398,
Zip 28337–0398; tel. 910/862–5100 **A**1 9 10 18 **F**3 11 13 14 15 28 29 30
34 35 40 45 59 68 70 76 77 81 89 90 97 107 114 119 133 135 146 147
S Cape Fear Valley Health System, Fayetteville, NC
Primary Contact: Dan Weatherly, On Site Administrator
CFO: Sandra Williams, Chief Financial Officer
CMO: Pearly Graham Hoskins, M.D., President Medical Staff
CIO: Craig Kellum, Director Management Information Systems
CHR: Ginger Parks, Director Human Resources
Web address: www.bchn.org
Control: Other not–for–profit (including NFP Corporation) **Service:** General
Medical and Surgical

Staffed Beds: 25 **Admissions:** 1067 **Census:** 10

ELKIN—Surry County

☒ **HUGH CHATHAM MEMORIAL HOSPITAL (340097)**, 180 Parkwood Drive,
Zip 28621–2430, Mailing Address: P.O. Box 560, Zip 28621–0560;
tel. 336/527–7000, (Total facility includes 127 beds in nursing home–type unit)
A1 9 10 **F**3 6 10 11 13 15 28 29 30 34 40 45 49 57 59 62 63 64 68 70 76
79 81 85 87 91 93 96 97 107 108 110 111 114 118 119 120 121 125 127
128 130 131 132 133 135 146 147 148 **P**6 **S** Alliant Management Services,
Louisville, KY
Primary Contact: Paul Hammes, Chief Executive Officer
COO: Mary Blackburn, Vice President Operations and Chief Practice Officer
CFO: Donald E. Trippel, Chief Financial Officer
CMO: Dominick Carbone, M.D., Chief of Staff
CIO: Lee Powe, Director Management Information Systems
CHR: Kathy Poteate, Interim Director Human Resources
CNO: Paula Moore, Chief Clinical Officer
Web address: www.hughchatham.org
Control: Other not–for–profit (including NFP Corporation) **Service:** General
Medical and Surgical

Staffed Beds: 208 **Admissions:** 4743 **Census:** 145 **Outpatient Visits:** 69422
Births: 517 **Total Expense ($000):** 69545 **Payroll Expense ($000):** 24885
Personnel: 712

FAYETTEVILLE—Cumberland County

☒ △ **CAPE FEAR VALLEY MEDICAL CENTER (340028)**, 1638 Owen Drive,
Zip 28304–3431, Mailing Address: P.O. Box 2000, Zip 28302–2000;
tel. 910/615–4000, (Includes SOUTHEASTERN REGIONAL REHABILITATION
CENTER ; BEHAVIORAL HEALTH CARE OF CAPE FEAR VALLEY HEALTH SYSTEM,
3425 Melrose Road, Zip 28304–1695; tel. 910/609–3000; SOUTHEASTERN
REGIONAL REHABILITATION CENTER, 1638 Owen Drive, Zip 28304;
tel. 910/609–4000) **A**1 2 3 5 7 9 10 13 **F**1 3 4 5 7 12 13 14 15 17 18 20 22
24 26 28 29 30 31 34 35 38 39 40 41 44 46 49 53 54 56 57 59 61 64 65
68 70 72 73 74 75 76 77 78 79 80 81 82 84 86 87 88 89 90 91 92 93 96
97 98 99 100 101 102 103 104 107 108 109 110 111 114 115 116 117
118 119 120 121 122 123 124 126 127 129 130 132 135 143 144 146 147
148 **P**6 **S** Cape Fear Valley Health System, Fayetteville, NC
Primary Contact: Michael Nagowski, Chief Executive Officer
CFO: Sandra Williams, Chief Financial Officer
CMO: Richard S. Taylor, M.D., Chief Medical Officer
CIO: Phillip E. Wood, Jr., Chief Information Officer
CHR: William B. Pryor, Senior Vice President, Human Resources
Web address: www.capefearvalley.com
Control: Other not–for–profit (including NFP Corporation) **Service:** General
Medical and Surgical

Staffed Beds: 660 **Admissions:** 33681 **Census:** 590 **Outpatient Visits:**
551723 **Births:** 4552 **Total Expense ($000):** 645112 **Payroll Expense
($000):** 308514 **Personnel:** 4801

☒ **FAYETTEVILLE VETERANS AFFAIRS MEDICAL CENTER**, 2300 Ramsey Street,
Zip 28301–3899; tel. 910/488–2120, (Nonreporting) **A**1 3 5 **S** Department of
Veterans Affairs, Washington, DC
Primary Contact: Elizabeth Goolsby, Director
COO: James Galkowski, Associate Director for Operations
CFO: Patrick Bullard, Chief Financial Officer
CMO: Greg Antoine, M.D., Chief of Staff
CIO: Kenneth Williams, Chief Information Officer
CHR: Joseph Whaley, Chief, Human Resources Management Service
CNO: Joyce Alexander–Hines, R.N., Associate Director, Patient Care Services
Web address: www.fayettevillenc.va.gov
Control: Veterans Affairs, Government, federal **Service:** General Medical and
Surgical

Staffed Beds: 58

☐ **HIGHSMITH–RAINEY SPECIALTY HOSPITAL (342014)**, 150 Robeson Street,
Zip 28301–5570; tel. 910/615–1000 **A**1 9 10 **F**1 11 29 30 34 35 50 51 56
58 68 70 82 86 87 107 119 130 132 146 148 **S** Cape Fear Valley Health
System, Fayetteville, NC
Primary Contact: Kevin Jackson, On Site Administrator
Web address: www.capefearvalley.com
Control: Other not–for–profit (including NFP Corporation) **Service:** Long–Term
Acute Care hospital

Staffed Beds: 66 **Admissions:** 328 **Census:** 6 **Births:** 0

VETERANS AFFAIRS MEDICAL CENTER See Fayetteville Veterans Affairs
Medical Center

FORT BRAGG—Cumberland County

☒ **WOMACK ARMY MEDICAL CENTER**, Normandy Drive, Zip 28307–5000;
tel. 910/907–6000, (Nonreporting) **A**1 3 5 **S** Department of the Army, Office of
the Surgeon General, Falls Church, VA
Primary Contact: Colonel Ronald Stephens, Commander
Web address: www.wamc.amedd.army.mil/
Control: Army, Government, federal **Service:** General Medical and Surgical

Staffed Beds: 156

FRANKLIN—Macon County

☒ **ANGEL MEDICAL CENTER (341326)**, 120 Riverview Street, Zip 28734–2612,
Mailing Address: P.O. Box 1209, Zip 28744–0569; tel. 828/524–8411,
(Nonreporting) **A**1 9 10 18 **S** Mission Health System, Asheville, NC
Primary Contact: James B. Bross, President and Chief Executive Officer
COO: Martin Wadewitz, Chief Operations Officer/ Vice President, Operations
CFO: George Kimbro, Vice President Finance
CIO: Ed Coye, Director Information Technology Mission Health System Hospitals
CHR: Teresa Mallonee, Director Human Resources
CNO: Sheila C. Price, R.N., Chief Nursing Officer/Vice President of Nursing
Web address: www.angelmed.org
Control: Hospital district or authority, Government, nonfederal **Service:** General
Medical and Surgical

Staffed Beds: 25

NC

Many Facility Codes have changed. Please refer to the AHA Guide Code Chart. © 2014 AHA Guide

GASTONIA—Gaston County

CAROMONT REGIONAL MEDICAL CENTER (340032), 2525 Court Drive, Zip 28054–2140, Mailing Address: P.O. Box 1747, Zip 28053–1747; tel. 704/834–2000 **A**1 2 9 10 **F**3 13 15 17 18 20 22 24 26 28 29 30 31 34 40 43 44 45 49 50 53 54 57 58 59 60 64 68 70 71 72 73 74 75 76 78 79 81 82 84 87 89 91 92 93 94 96 98 99 100 101 102 107 110 111 114 115 116 117 118 119 120 121 123 124 126 129 130 132 135 146 147 148
Primary Contact: Douglas R. Luckett, President and Chief Executive Officer
COO: Kathleen Besson, Executive Vice President and Chief Operating Officer
CFO: David O'Connor, Executive Vice President and Chief Financial Officer
CMO: Todd Davis, M.D., Vice President Medical Affairs, Patient Safety Officer
CIO: Mike Johnson, Vice President, Chief Information Officer
CHR: Elizabeth McCraw, Vice President, Human Resources
CNO: Bonnie H. Faust, R.N., Vice President Chief Nursing Officer
Web address: www.caromont.org
Control: Other not–for–profit (including NFP Corporation) **Service:** General Medical and Surgical

Staffed Beds: 423 **Admissions:** 20539 **Census:** 245 **Outpatient Visits:** 326055 **Births:** 2199 **Total Expense ($000):** 342737 **Payroll Expense ($000):** 140433 **Personnel:** 2542

GASTON MEMORIAL HOSPITAL See Caromont Regional Medical Center

GOLDSBORO—Wayne County

CHERRY HOSPITAL (344026), 201 Stevens Mill Road, Zip 27530–1057; tel. 919/731–3200 **A**1 10 **F**30 39 98 99 103 108 146
Primary Contact: J. Luckey Welsh, Jr., Chief Executive Officer
CFO: Susie Sherrod Sanders, Budget Officer
CMO: Jim Mayo, M.D., Clinical Director
CIO: Mike Letchworth, Manager Information Systems
CHR: Carol Thornton, Director Human Resources
CNO: Cherie Custer, Chief Nursing Officer
Web address: www.cherryhospital.org
Control: State–Government, nonfederal **Service:** Psychiatric

Staffed Beds: 197 **Admissions:** 1016 **Census:** 168 **Outpatient Visits:** 929 **Births:** 0 **Total Expense ($000):** 52060 **Personnel:** 923

WAYNE MEMORIAL HOSPITAL (340010), 2700 Wayne Memorial Drive, Zip 27534–9494, Mailing Address: P.O. Box 8001, Zip 27533–8001; tel. 919/736–1110 **A**1 9 10 19 20 **F**3 8 13 15 18 20 22 28 29 30 31 34 35 39 40 47 49 50 57 58 59 60 64 65 68 70 71 73 74 76 77 78 79 80 81 85 86 89 92 93 96 98 100 101 102 103 107 108 110 111 114 118 119 126 129 130 132 134 135 142 143 145 146 147 148 **P**6
Primary Contact: J. William Paugh, FACHE, President and Chief Executive Officer
COO: Thomas A. Bradshaw, Vice President Operations
CFO: Rebecca W. Craig, Vice President and Chief Financial Officer
CIO: Lori Cole, Director Information Management
CHR: Richard K. Rogers, FACHE, Vice President Human Resources
CNO: Shirley S. Harkey, R.N., Vice President, Patient Services
Web address: www.waynehealth.org
Control: Other not–for–profit (including NFP Corporation) **Service:** General Medical and Surgical

Staffed Beds: 274 **Admissions:** 10742 **Census:** 137 **Outpatient Visits:** 181034 **Births:** 1425 **Total Expense ($000):** 198089 **Payroll Expense ($000):** 80062 **Personnel:** 1602

GREENSBORO—Guilford County

KINDRED HOSPITAL–GREENSBORO (342012), 2401 Southside Boulevard, Zip 27406–3311; tel. 336/271–2800, (Nonreporting) **A**1 9 10 **S** Kindred Healthcare, Louisville, KY
Primary Contact: Christopher Haynes, Chief Executive Officer
CMO: Percy E. Jones, M.D., Chief of Staff
CIO: Little Shuford, Manager Medical Information
CHR: Michele Roberts, Hospital Recruiter
Web address: www.khgreensboro.com
Control: Corporation, Investor–owned, for–profit **Service:** Long–Term Acute Care hospital

Staffed Beds: 124

MOSES H. CONE MEMORIAL HOSPITAL (340091), 1200 North Elm Street, Zip 27401–1020; tel. 336/832–7000, (Includes ANNIE PENN HOSPITAL, 618 South Main Street, Reidsville, Zip 27320–5094; tel. 336/951–4000; Mickey Foster, President; BEHAVIORAL HEALTH CENTER, 700 Walter Reed Drive, Zip 27403–1129; tel. 336/832–9600; Debbie Green, R.N., MSN, President; MOSES H. CONE MEMORIAL HOSPITAL, 1200 North Elm Street, Zip 27401; tel. 336/832–7000; Judith A. Schanel, R.N., MSN, FACHE, President; WESLEY LONG COMMUNITY HOSPITAL, 501 North Elam Avenue, Zip 27403; tel. 336/832–1000; Paul A. Jeffrey, President; WOMEN'S HOSPITAL OF GREENSBORO, 801 Green Valley Road, Zip 27408; tel. 336/832–6500), (Total facility includes 92 beds in nursing home–type unit) **A**1 2 3 5 7 9 10 **F**3 5 7 8 11 12 13 15 17 18 20 22 24 26 28 29 30 31 32 34 35 36 37 39 40 41 42 43 44 45 46 47 49 50 54 55 56 57 58 59 60 61 63 64 66 68 70 72 74 75 76 77 78 79 80 81 82 83 84 85 86 87 88 89 90 92 93 95 96 97 98 99 100 101 102 103 104 107 108 110 111 114 115 117 118 119 120 121 123 124 126 128 129 130 131 132 134 135 144 145 146 147 148 **P**8 **S** Carolinas HealthCare System, Charlotte, NC
Primary Contact: Mickey Foster, President
COO: Terry Akin, President and Chief Operating Officer
CFO: Jeffrey Jones, Chief Financial Officer
CMO: William Bowman, M.D., Vice President Medical Affairs
CIO: Steve Horsley, Vice President and Chief Information Officer
CHR: Noel F. Burt, Ph.D., Chief Human Resources Officer
CNO: Theresa M. Brodrick, R.N., Executive Vice President and Chief Nursing Officer
Web address: www.conehealth.com/locations/moses–cone–hospital/
Control: Other not–for–profit (including NFP Corporation) **Service:** General Medical and Surgical

Staffed Beds: 1004 **Admissions:** 47397 **Census:** 703 **Outpatient Visits:** 726606 **Births:** 6205 **Total Expense ($000):** 1108297 **Payroll Expense ($000):** 371542 **Personnel:** 7534

SELECT SPECIALTY HOSPITAL–GREENSBORO (342020), 1200 North Elm Street, 5th Floor, Zip 27401–1004; tel. 336/832–8571, (Nonreporting) **A**1 10 **S** Select Medical Corporation, Mechanicsburg, PA
Primary Contact: Deana Knight, Chief Executive Officer
CHR: Karen Tracey, Chief Human Resources
CNO: Robin Clark, Chief Nursing Officer
Web address: www.selectspecialtyhospitals.com/company/locations/greensboro.aspx
Control: Corporation, Investor–owned, for–profit **Service:** Long–Term Acute Care hospital

Staffed Beds: 30

GREENVILLE—Pitt County

PITT COUNTY MEMORIAL HOSPITAL See Vidant Medical Center

VIDANT MEDICAL CENTER (340040), 2100 Stantonsburg Road, Zip 27834–2818, Mailing Address: P.O. Box 6028, Zip 27835–6028; tel. 252/847–4100, (Includes JAMES AND CONNIE MAYNARD CHILDREN'S HOSPITAL, 2101 Stantonsburg Road, Zip 27834–2817; tel. 252/847–5712; UNIVERSITY HEALTH SYSTEMS CHILDREN'S HOSPITAL, 2100 Stantonsburg Road, Mailing Address: PO Box 6028, Zip 27835–6028; tel. 252/847–4100) **A**1 2 3 5 7 8 9 10 **F**3 7 12 13 14 17 18 19 20 21 22 23 24 25 26 27 28 29 30 31 34 35 38 40 41 42 43 44 45 46 47 48 49 50 51 52 55 56 57 58 59 60 61 64 65 68 70 72 73 74 75 76 77 78 79 80 81 82 83 84 85 86 87 88 89 90 92 93 94 95 96 97 98 100 101 102 103 104 107 108 111 114 115 116 117 118 119 124 126 129 130 131 132 134 135 138 139 143 145 146 147 148 **P**6 **S** Vidant Health, Greenville, NC
Primary Contact: Stephen Lawler, President
CFO: David S. Hughes, Chief Financial Officer
CMO: Paul Shackelford, M.D., Chief Medical Officer
CIO: Donnette Herring, Chief Information Officer
CHR: Tyree Walker, Chief Human Resources Officer
CNO: Linda Hofler, Ph.D., Senior Vice President, Nurse Executive
Web address: www.https://www.vidanthealth.com/
Control: Other not–for–profit (including NFP Corporation) **Service:** General Medical and Surgical

Staffed Beds: 909 **Admissions:** 41167 **Census:** 713 **Outpatient Visits:** 397312 **Births:** 3569 **Total Expense ($000):** 998376 **Payroll Expense ($000):** 365045 **Personnel:** 6458

WALTER B. JONES ALCOHOL AND DRUG ABUSE TREATMENT CENTER (344024), 2577 West Fifth Street, Zip 27834–7813; tel. 252/830–3426, (Nonreporting) **A**10
Primary Contact: Ben Gregory, Director
CFO: Jo Ann Whitfield, Business Officer
CMO: Sonya Longest, M.D., Clinical Director
CNO: Cecelia Karas, Director of Nursing
Web address: www.ncdhhs.gov
Control: State–Government, nonfederal **Service:** Alcoholism and other chemical dependency

Staffed Beds: 80

Hospital, Medicare Provider Number, Address, Telephone, Approval, Facility, and Physician Codes, Health Care System

★ American Hospital Association (AHA) membership
□ The Joint Commission accreditation ◇ DNV Healthcare Inc. accreditation
○ Healthcare Facilities Accreditation Program
△ Commission on Accreditation of Rehabilitation Facilities (CARF) accreditation

NC

HAMLET—Richmond County

✠ **SANDHILLS REGIONAL MEDICAL CENTER (340106)**, 1000 West Hamlet Avenue, Zip 28345–4522, Mailing Address: P.O. Box 1109, Zip 28345–1109; tel. 910/205–8000 **A**1 9 10 **F**7 8 18 29 34 35 40 45 49 57 59 64 70 75 79 81 82 87 98 102 103 104 105 106 107 108 111 114 118 119 130 135 146 **P**6 **S** Community Health Systems, Inc., Franklin, TN
Primary Contact: Michael H. McNair, Chief Executive Officer
CFO: Patrick Sloan, Chief Financial Officer
CMO: Charlita Mangrum, M.D., Chief of Staff
CIO: Regina Yingling, Supervisor
CHR: Della Connor, Director Human Resource
CNO: Brenda Ewing, Chief Nursing Officer
Web address: www.sandhillsregional.com
Control: Corporation, Investor–owned, for–profit **Service:** General Medical and Surgical

Staffed Beds: 64 **Admissions:** 2750 **Census:** 26 **Outpatient Visits:** 13553 **Births:** 0 **Total Expense ($000):** 29198 **Payroll Expense ($000):** 8269 **Personnel:** 157

HENDERSON—Vance County

✠ △ **MARIA PARHAM MEDICAL CENTER (340132)**, 566 Ruin Creek Road, Zip 27536–2927; tel. 252/438–4143 **A**1 2 7 9 10 **F**3 11 13 15 18 20 28 29 30 31 34 35 39 40 44 45 46 48 49 50 52 60 62 64 68 70 74 75 76 77 78 79 80 81 82 85 86 87 90 91 92 93 94 96 97 107 108 110 111 114 118 119 120 121 123 129 130 131 132 135 146 147 148 **P**6 **S** Duke LifePoint Healthcare, Brentwood, TN
Primary Contact: Robert G. Singletary, Chief Executive Officer
COO: Tim Harclerode, Chief Operating Officer
CFO: Jim Chatman, Chief Financial Officer
CIO: Randy Williams, Director Management Information Systems
CHR: Tonya A. Jones, Vice President Human Resources
CNO: Cindy Faulkner, Chief Nursing Officer
Web address: www.mariaparham.com
Control: Partnership, Investor–owned, for–profit **Service:** General Medical and Surgical

Staffed Beds: 102 **Admissions:** 5135 **Census:** 64 **Outpatient Visits:** 123798 **Births:** 727 **Total Expense ($000):** 85693 **Payroll Expense ($000):** 29868 **Personnel:** 629

HENDERSONVILLE—Henderson County

★ ◇ **MARGARET R. PARDEE MEMORIAL HOSPITAL (340017)**, 800 North Justice Street, Zip 28791–3410; tel. 828/696–1000 **A**2 9 10 21 **F**3 4 5 11 13 15 18 22 28 29 30 31 34 35 36 38 39 40 44 45 48 49 50 56 57 58 59 62 63 65 68 69 70 74 75 76 77 78 79 81 82 85 86 87 89 93 94 97 98 100 101 102 103 104 107 108 110 111 114 115 118 119 121 123 129 130 131 132 135 143 144 146 147 148 **P**6 **S** UNC Health Care, Chapel Hill, NC
Primary Contact: James M. Kirby, II, President and Chief Executive Officer
CFO: Alan House, Chief Financial Officer
CMO: Robert Kiskaddon, M.D., Chief Medical Officer
CHR: Hope Reynolds, Executive Director Human Resources and Support Services
CNO: Patricia Ashe, R.N., Chief Nursing Officer
Web address: www.pardeehospital.org
Control: County–Government, nonfederal **Service:** General Medical and Surgical

Staffed Beds: 138 **Admissions:** 7478 **Census:** 77 **Outpatient Visits:** 252999 **Births:** 333 **Total Expense ($000):** 145515 **Payroll Expense ($000):** 57452 **Personnel:** 964

✠ ◯ **PARK RIDGE HEALTH (340023)**, 100 Hospital Drive, Zip 28792–5272; tel. 828/684–8501 **A**1 2 9 10 11 19 20 **F**3 11 13 15 18 28 29 30 31 32 34 35 40 43 45 46 47 48 49 50 56 57 59 62 65 68 70 71 74 75 76 77 78 79 80 81 82 83 85 87 93 94 98 101 102 103 104 105 107 108 110 111 113 114 115 118 119 129 130 131 132 135 142 146 147 148 **P**6 **S** Adventist Health System Sunbelt Health Care Corporation, Altamonte Springs, FL
Primary Contact: Jimm Bunch, President and Chief Executive Officer
CFO: Wendi Barber, Vice President Finance and Chief Financial Officer
CMO: Carlo Mainardi, M.D., Vice President Medical Affairs and Chief Medical Officer
CIO: Lee Strickland, Regional Director Information Technology
CNO: Craig Lindsey, R.N., Vice President Clinical Services/Chief Nursing Officer
Web address: www.parkridgehealth.org
Control: Other not–for–profit (including NFP Corporation) **Service:** General Medical and Surgical

Staffed Beds: 98 **Admissions:** 4187 **Census:** 57 **Outpatient Visits:** 354618 **Births:** 605 **Total Expense ($000):** 138634 **Payroll Expense ($000):** 59084 **Personnel:** 1007

HICKORY—Catawba County

✠ △ **CATAWBA VALLEY MEDICAL CENTER (340143)**, 810 Fairgrove Church Road S.E., Zip 28602–9643; tel. 828/326–3000 **A**1 2 5 7 9 10 **F**3 5 11 12 13 15 18 20 22 26 28 29 30 31 33 34 35 39 40 44 45 49 50 51 53 54 56 57 58 59 61 64 65 68 70 71 73 74 75 76 77 78 79 81 84 85 86 87 89 90 91 92 93 96 97 98 100 101 102 103 104 107 108 109 110 111 114 115 117 118 119 120 121 122 123 124 126 129 130 131 132 135 143 144 145 146 147 148
Primary Contact: J. Anthony Rose, President and Chief Executive Officer
COO: Edward L. Beard, R.N., Chief Operating Officer and Chief Nursing Officer
CFO: David J. Boone, Senior Vice President, Finance
CIO: Jerry Reardon, Director Information Systems
CHR: Phyllis Johnston, Vice President
CNO: Edward L. Beard, R.N., Chief Operating Officer and Chief Nursing Officer
Web address: www.catawbavalleymc.org
Control: County–Government, nonfederal **Service:** General Medical and Surgical

Staffed Beds: 220 **Admissions:** 10013 **Census:** 132 **Outpatient Visits:** 200241 **Births:** 1783 **Total Expense ($000):** 202102 **Payroll Expense ($000):** 89088 **Personnel:** 1330

✠ **FRYE REGIONAL MEDICAL CENTER (340116)**, 420 North Center Street, Zip 28601–5049; tel. 828/322–6070, (Includes FRYE REGIONAL MEDICAL CENTER–SOUTH CAMPUS, One Third Avenue N.W., Zip 28601, Mailing Address: P.O. Box 369, Zip 28603; tel. 704/315–5777) **A**1 2 9 10 **F**3 11 12 13 15 17 18 20 22 24 26 28 29 30 31 34 35 37 40 45 46 49 54 57 59 64 68 70 72 74 75 76 77 78 79 81 82 85 86 87 89 90 93 96 98 101 103 107 108 110 111 114 115 118 119 126 128 129 130 131 132 144 146 147 148 **P**6 **S** TENET Healthcare Corporation, Dallas, TX
Primary Contact: Steven D. Patonai, Chief Executive Officer
COO: Rich Ellis, Chief Operating Officer
CMO: Frank C. Smeeks, M.D., Chief Medical Officer
CHR: Liz Elich, Vice President Human Resources
Web address: www.fryemedctr.com
Control: Corporation, Investor–owned, for–profit **Service:** General Medical and Surgical

Staffed Beds: 306 **Admissions:** 11273 **Census:** 167 **Outpatient Visits:** 133156 **Births:** 432 **Personnel:** 1266

HIGH POINT—Guilford County

✠ △ **HIGH POINT REGIONAL HEALTH SYSTEM (340004)**, 601 North Elm Street, Zip 27262–4398, Mailing Address: P.O. Box HP–5, Zip 27261–1899; tel. 336/878–6000 **A**1 2 7 9 10 **F**3 4 5 11 12 13 15 17 18 20 22 24 26 28 29 30 31 34 35 38 39 40 43 44 45 49 50 51 52 53 54 55 57 58 59 60 61 62 64 66 68 70 71 73 74 75 76 77 78 79 80 81 82 84 85 86 87 90 93 98 100 101 102 103 104 107 108 109 110 111 114 115 116 117 118 119 120 121 123 126 130 131 132 135 144 145 146 147 148 **P**6 **S** UNC Health Care, Chapel Hill, NC
Primary Contact: Ernest L. Bovio, Jr., Chief Executive Officer
COO: Gregory W. Taylor, M.D., Vice President and Chief Operating Officer
CFO: Kimberly Crews, Vice President Finance and Chief Financial Officer
CMO: L. Dale Williams, M.D., Vice President and Chief Medical Director
CIO: Nancy Waters, Interim Chief Information Officer
CHR: Katherine Burns, Vice President Human Resources
CNO: Tammi Erving–Mengel, Vice President, Chief Nursing Officer
Web address: www.highpointregional.com
Control: Other not–for–profit (including NFP Corporation) **Service:** General Medical and Surgical

Staffed Beds: 335 **Admissions:** 16379 **Census:** 195 **Outpatient Visits:** 265526 **Births:** 1549 **Total Expense ($000):** 231053 **Payroll Expense ($000):** 88012 **Personnel:** 1712

HIGHLANDS—Macon County

✠ **HIGHLANDS–CASHIERS HOSPITAL (341316)**, 190 Hospital Drive, Zip 28741–7600, Mailing Address: P.O. Drawer 190, Zip 28741–0190; tel. 828/526–1200, (Total facility includes 80 beds in nursing home–type unit) **A**1 9 10 18 **F**3 11 15 28 29 30 34 35 40 45 46 47 48 53 57 59 64 65 74 75 77 79 81 82 91 97 107 108 110 111 113 119 128 129 130 133 146 147 148
Primary Contact: Craig B. James, FACHE, Chief Executive Officer
COO: Frank Leslie, Vice President Operations
CFO: Michael E. Daiken, Chief Financial Officer
CHR: Teresa Malloonee, Director Human Resources
CNO: Kathy Crist, Director of Patient Care Services
Web address: www.highlands–cashiershospital.org
Control: Other not–for–profit (including NFP Corporation) **Service:** General Medical and Surgical

Staffed Beds: 104 **Admissions:** 487 **Census:** 64 **Outpatient Visits:** 30746 **Births:** 0 **Total Expense ($000):** 22439 **Payroll Expense ($000):** 10084 **Personnel:** 231

Many Facility Codes have changed. Please refer to the AHA Guide Code Chart. © 2014 AHA Guide

HUNTERSVILLE—Mecklenburg County

☒ **NOVANT HEALTH HUNTERSVILLE MEDICAL CENTER (340183)**, 10030 Gilead Road, Zip 28078–7545, Mailing Address: P.O. Box 3508, Zip 28070–3508; tel. 704/316–4000 **A**1 9 10 **F**8 11 12 13 18 20 26 29 30 31 34 35 40 45 50 57 59 64 68 70 73 75 76 77 78 79 81 82 85 86 87 89 93 96 100 102 107 108 110 111 114 115 118 119 126 129 130 132 135 146 147 **S** Novant Health, Winston Salem, NC
Primary Contact: Tanya S. Blackmon, President
CFO: Jason Yanni, Senior Financial Analyst
CMO: David Cook, M.D., Chief Medical Officer
CIO: Richard B. McKnight, Senior Vice President and Chief Information Officer
CHR: Tracy Craig, Director Human Resources
Web address: www.novanthealth.org
Control: Other not–for–profit (including NFP Corporation) **Service:** General Medical and Surgical

Staffed Beds: 75 **Admissions:** 6150 **Census:** 61 **Outpatient Visits:** 137822 **Births:** 1040 **Total Expense ($000):** 108250 **Payroll Expense ($000):** 34339 **Personnel:** 550

JACKSONVILLE—Onslow County

☐ **BRYNN MARR HOSPITAL (344016)**, 192 Village Drive, Zip 28546–7299; tel. 910/577–1400, (Nonreporting) **A**1 10 **S** Universal Health Services, Inc., King of Prussia, PA
Primary Contact: Jay Kortemeyer, Chief Executive Officer
COO: Cynthia Waun, Chief Operating Officer and Risk Manager
CFO: David Warmerdam, Chief Financial Officer
CMO: Ashraf Mikhail, M.D., Medical Director
CIO: Cynthia Waun, Chief Operating Officer and Risk Manager
CHR: Jennifer Gier, Director Human Resources
CNO: Norman Taylor, Director of Nursing
Web address: www.brynnmarr.com
Control: Corporation, Investor–owned, for–profit **Service:** Psychiatric

Staffed Beds: 87

☒ **ONSLOW MEMORIAL HOSPITAL (340042)**, 317 Western Boulevard, Zip 28546–6379, Mailing Address: P.O. Box 1358, Zip 28541–1358; tel. 910/577–2345 **A**1 9 10 20 **F**3 8 11 13 15 19 20 28 29 34 35 40 45 46 47 48 49 54 57 59 60 64 68 70 72 73 75 76 77 79 81 82 84 85 86 87 89 93 96 107 108 110 111 117 118 119 126 129 131 132 135 146 147 148 **P**8
Primary Contact: Ed Piper, Ph.D., President and Chief Executive Officer
CFO: Roy Smith, Chief Financial Officer
CMO: Elizabeth D'Angelo, M.D., Chief of Staff
CIO: Christina Feak, Chief Information Officer
CHR: Sue Kegley, Director Human Resources
CNO: Crystal Hayden, MSN, Chief Nursing Officer
Web address: www.onslow.org
Control: Hospital district or authority, Government, nonfederal **Service:** General Medical and Surgical

Staffed Beds: 152 **Admissions:** 8362 **Census:** 89 **Outpatient Visits:** 136414 **Births:** 2170 **Total Expense ($000):** 135423 **Payroll Expense ($000):** 52349 **Personnel:** 1077

JEFFERSON—Ashe County

☒ **ASHE MEMORIAL HOSPITAL (341325)**, 200 Hospital Avenue, Zip 28640–9244; tel. 336/846–7101 **A**1 9 10 18 **F**3 8 11 13 15 28 30 34 35 40 45 46 48 53 57 59 64 75 76 79 80 81 85 86 89 93 107 108 110 111 114 118 119 127 130 132 133 135 141 142 146 147 **S** Novant Health, Winston Salem, NC
Primary Contact: Laura Lambeth, Chief Executive Officer
COO: Joe Thore, Chief Operating Officer
CFO: Joy McClure, Chief Financial Officer
CMO: Christopher Campbell, M.D., Chief of Staff
CIO: William Baldwin, Chief Information Officer
CHR: Sherry Cox, Chief Human Resources Officer
CNO: Sara Houser, Chief Nursing Officer
Web address: www.ashememorial.org
Control: Other not–for–profit (including NFP Corporation) **Service:** General Medical and Surgical

Staffed Beds: 25 **Admissions:** 1301 **Census:** 13 **Outpatient Visits:** 45859 **Births:** 130 **Total Expense ($000):** 26586 **Payroll Expense ($000):** 12289 **Personnel:** 269

KENANSVILLE—Duplin County

☒ **VIDANT DUPLIN HOSPITAL (340120)**, 401 North Main Street, Zip 28349–8801, Mailing Address: P.O. Box 278, Zip 28349–0278; tel. 910/296–0941 **A**1 9 10 **F**3 11 13 15 18 19 29 30 34 35 39 40 45 56 57 59 68 70 75 76 77 79 81 91 93 97 98 101 102 103 107 108 110 111 115 119 129 130 131 135 146 147 **S** Vidant Health, Greenville, NC
Primary Contact: Jay Briley, President
CFO: Lucinda Crawford, Vice President Financial Services
CMO: Danny Pate, M.D., Chief Medical Staff
CIO: Lucinda Crawford, Vice President Financial Services
CHR: Pansy Chase, Director Human Resources
CNO: Sue O. Taylor, Vice President Nursing
Web address: www.vidanthealth.com
Control: Other not–for–profit (including NFP Corporation) **Service:** General Medical and Surgical

Staffed Beds: 48 **Admissions:** 3411 **Census:** 44 **Outpatient Visits:** 51014 **Births:** 492 **Total Expense ($000):** 40953 **Payroll Expense ($000):** 17441 **Personnel:** 411

KINGS MOUNTAIN—Cleveland County

☒ **KINGS MOUNTAIN HOSPITAL (340037)**, 706 West King Street, Zip 28086–2708; tel. 980/487–5000 **A**1 9 10 **F**3 4 15 29 30 34 40 45 46 49 59 70 79 81 82 85 93 98 107 110 111 114 119 130 133 146 148 **S** Carolinas HealthCare System, Charlotte, NC
Primary Contact: Brian Gwyn, President and Chief Executive Officer
COO: Sheri Deshazo, Chief Operating Officer
CFO: Terry Edwards, Controller
CHR: Debra Kale, Director Human Resources
Web address: www.clevelandregional.org/kings–mountain–hospital.html
Control: Hospital district or authority, Government, nonfederal **Service:** General Medical and Surgical

Staffed Beds: 67 **Admissions:** 2519 **Census:** 34 **Outpatient Visits:** 49975 **Births:** 0 **Total Expense ($000):** 33835 **Payroll Expense ($000):** 14562 **Personnel:** 266

KINSTON—Lenoir County

CASWELL CENTER, 2415 West Vernon Avenue, Zip 28504–3321; tel. 252/208–4000, (Nonreporting)
Primary Contact: Leon Owens, Director
CFO: Jim Hall, Budget Officer
CMO: Tony Bright, M.D., Administrator Medical Services
CHR: Ken Lafone, Director Human Resources
Web address: www.caswellcenter.org
Control: State–Government, nonfederal **Service:** Institution for mental retardation

Staffed Beds: 829

☐ **LENOIR MEMORIAL HOSPITAL (340027)**, 100 Airport Road, Zip 28501–1634, Mailing Address: P.O. Box 1678, Zip 28503–1678; tel. 252/522–7000, (Total facility includes 26 beds in nursing home–type unit) **A**1 9 10 19 20 **F**3 8 11 13 18 20 22 28 29 30 31 34 35 38 40 43 45 47 48 49 50 53 56 57 59 60 61 64 65 68 70 75 76 77 78 79 80 81 82 85 86 87 89 90 93 102 107 108 111 114 115 118 119 120 121 128 129 130 132 134 135 143 145 146 147 148
Primary Contact: Gary E. Black, President and Chief Executive Officer
CFO: Sarah Mayo, Vice President Financial and Information Services
CMO: Wayne Jarman, M.D., President Medical Staff
CIO: Karl Vanderstouw, Director Management Information Systems
CHR: Jim Dobbins, Vice President Human Resources
CNO: Rosalind S. McDonald, MSN, Vice President Nursing Services
Web address: www.lenoirmemorial.org
Control: Other not–for–profit (including NFP Corporation) **Service:** General Medical and Surgical

Staffed Beds: 218 **Admissions:** 6521 **Census:** 102 **Outpatient Visits:** 82537 **Births:** 430 **Total Expense ($000):** 104553 **Payroll Expense ($000):** 45540 **Personnel:** 926

LAURINBURG—Scotland County

⊞ **SCOTLAND HEALTH CARE SYSTEM (340008)**, 500 Lauchwood Drive, Zip 28352–5599; tel. 910/291–7000 **A**1 2 9 10 **F**3 11 13 15 18 28 29 31 34 37 40 45 54 57 59 64 66 70 71 73 74 75 76 77 78 79 81 85 86 87 89 90 92 93 96 97 107 110 111 114 115 119 120 121 123 127 130 132 135 143 144 145 146 147 148 **P**8 **S** Carolinas HealthCare System, Charlotte, NC
Primary Contact: Gregory C. Wood, President and Chief Executive Officer
CFO: Matthew Pracht, Vice President Finance
CMO: Cheryl Davis, M.D., Chief Medical Officer
CIO: Gary Liuzzo, Director Information Systems
CHR: Ann Locklear, Vice President, Human Resources
CNO: Camille Utter, R.N., Chief Nursing Officer
Web address: www.scotlandhealth.org
Control: Other not-for-profit (including NFP Corporation) **Service:** General Medical and Surgical

Staffed Beds: 102 **Admissions:** 5769 **Census:** 59 **Outpatient Visits:** 204150 **Births:** 660 **Total Expense ($000):** 105889 **Payroll Expense ($000):** 37908 **Personnel:** 864

LENOIR—Caldwell County

⊞ **CALDWELL MEMORIAL HOSPITAL (340041)**, 321 Mulberry Street S.W., Zip 28645–5720, Mailing Address: P.O. Box 1890, Zip 28645–1890; tel. 828/757–5100 **A**1 2 9 10 **F**3 8 11 13 15 18 20 22 29 31 34 35 37 40 45 46 48 49 50 53 54 55 57 59 64 65 70 75 76 77 78 79 81 82 85 86 87 93 97 107 108 109 110 111 114 119 120 121 122 123 129 132 135 144 145 146 147 148 **P**6 **S** UNC Health Care, Chapel Hill, NC
Primary Contact: Laura S. Easton, R.N., President and Chief Executive Officer
COO: Rebecca Smith, Chief Operating Officer and Vice President
CFO: Donald F. Gardner, Vice President Finance/Chief Financial Officer
CMO: Edward Pearce, M.D., Chief of Staff
CIO: Rodney Christensen, Director Information Systems
CHR: Rebecca Smith, Vice President and Chief Operating Officer
CNO: Sharon M. Kimball, R.N., Vice President and Chief Nursing Officer
Web address: www.caldwell–mem.org
Control: Other not-for-profit (including NFP Corporation) **Service:** General Medical and Surgical

Staffed Beds: 76 **Admissions:** 3571 **Census:** 49 **Outpatient Visits:** 81288 **Births:** 460 **Total Expense ($000):** 104627 **Payroll Expense ($000):** 42683 **Personnel:** 826

LEXINGTON—Davidson County

LEXINGTON MEMORIAL HOSPITAL See Wake Forest Baptist Health–Lexington Medical Center

⊞ **WAKE FOREST BAPTIST HEALTH–LEXINGTON MEDICAL CENTER (340096)**, 250 Hospital Drive, Zip 27292–6728, Mailing Address: P.O. Box 1817, Zip 27293–1817; tel. 336/248–5161 **A**1 9 10 **F**3 11 13 15 17 18 26 28 29 30 31 32 34 35 40 45 50 57 59 64 65 68 70 75 78 79 80 81 82 85 86 87 91 93 107 110 111 114 115 119 121 123 129 130 131 135 145 146 147 148 **P**6 **S** Wake Forest Baptist Health, Winston–Salem, NC
Primary Contact: William B. James, FACHE, Chief Executive Officer
CFO: Danny Squires, Vice President and Chief Financial Officer
CMO: Gordon Kammire, M.D., Chief of Staff
CIO: Kevin Buchanan, Chief Information Officer
Web address: www.lexingtonmemorial.com
Control: Other not-for-profit (including NFP Corporation) **Service:** General Medical and Surgical

Staffed Beds: 77 **Admissions:** 3336 **Census:** 26 **Outpatient Visits:** 108132 **Births:** 656 **Total Expense ($000):** 66265 **Payroll Expense ($000):** 26588 **Personnel:** 608

LINCOLNTON—Lincoln County

⊞ **CAROLINAS MEDICAL CENTER–LINCOLN (340145)**, 433 McAlister Road, Zip 28092–4147; tel. 980/212–2000 **A**1 9 10 **F**3 8 11 13 15 18 28 29 30 31 34 40 44 45 50 51 57 59 64 68 70 73 74 75 76 77 78 79 81 82 84 85 87 91 93 94 96 107 108 111 114 115 118 119 129 130 131 132 135 146 148 **P**6 **S** Carolinas HealthCare System, Charlotte, NC
Primary Contact: Peter W. Acker, President
COO: Teresa C. Watson, Vice President Administration
CFO: Jarrett Morris, Vice President Finance
CIO: Jarrett Morris, Vice President Finance
CHR: Lesley Chambless, Vice President Human Resources
Web address: www.carolinashealthcare.org/body.cfm?id=7626
Control: Hospital district or authority, Government, nonfederal **Service:** General Medical and Surgical

Staffed Beds: 101 **Admissions:** 3853 **Census:** 42 **Outpatient Visits:** 95024 **Births:** 374 **Total Expense ($000):** 91261 **Payroll Expense ($000):** 34759 **Personnel:** 585

LINVILLE—Avery County

⊞ **CHARLES A. CANNON MEMORIAL HOSPITAL (341323)**, 434 Hospital Drive, Zip 28646, Mailing Address: P.O. Box 767, Zip 28646–0767; tel. 828/737–7000 **A**1 9 10 18 **F**3 13 15 18 20 22 28 29 30 31 38 40 45 50 64 68 70 76 77 78 81 85 91 93 98 101 102 104 107 110 115 119 129 130 133 146
S Appalachian Regional Healthcare System, Boone, NC
Primary Contact: Carmen Lacey, MSN, R.N., President
CFO: Kevin B. May, System Director Finance
CMO: Thomas M. Haizlip, Jr., M.D., Chief of Staff
CIO: Mark Heckle, Chief Information Officer
CHR: Amy Crabbe, Vice President People Services
CNO: Carmen Lacey, MSN, President and Director of Patient Care Services
Web address: www.https://apprhs.org/locations/cannon–memorial–hospital
Control: Other not-for-profit (including NFP Corporation) **Service:** General Medical and Surgical

Staffed Beds: 35 **Admissions:** 1792 **Census:** 26 **Outpatient Visits:** 41353 **Births:** 102 **Total Expense ($000):** 21776 **Payroll Expense ($000):** 9883 **Personnel:** 170

LOUISBURG—Franklin County

⊞ **NOVANT HEALTH FRANKLIN MEDICAL CENTER (340036)**, 100 Hospital Drive, Zip 27549–2256, Mailing Address: P.O. Box 609, Zip 27549–0609; tel. 919/497–8401 **A**1 9 10 **F**3 11 12 15 18 30 34 40 44 45 49 50 56 57 59 67 70 74 75 79 80 81 82 85 86 90 98 103 107 108 110 111 114 118 119 128 129 130 146 **S** Novant Health, Winston Salem, NC
Primary Contact: Jody Morris, President and Chief Operating Officer
CIO: Mark Elliott, Manager Information Systems
CHR: Joanna Holder, Director Human Resources
CNO: Lilly Wing, Chief Nursing Officer
Web address: www.https://www.novanthealth.org/franklin–medical–center.aspx
Control: Other not-for-profit (including NFP Corporation) **Service:** General Medical and Surgical

Staffed Beds: 43 **Admissions:** 1369 **Census:** 17 **Outpatient Visits:** 37787 **Births:** 0 **Total Expense ($000):** 31010 **Payroll Expense ($000):** 12113 **Personnel:** 228

LUMBERTON—Robeson County

⊞ **SOUTHEASTERN HEALTH (340050)**, 300 West 27th Street, Zip 28358–3075, Mailing Address: P.O. Box 1408, Zip 28359–1408; tel. 910/671–5000, (Total facility includes 115 beds in nursing home–type unit) **A**1 2 9 10 19 20 **F**3 5 7 9 12 13 15 17 18 20 22 24 28 29 30 31 34 35 37 40 45 48 49 50 53 54 57 59 60 61 62 63 64 67 68 70 71 72 73 74 75 76 77 78 79 80 81 82 83 84 85 87 89 92 93 98 102 103 107 108 111 112 113 114 115 116 118 119 120 121 126 127 128 129 130 131 132 135 143 144 146 147 148 **P**4 6
Primary Contact: Joann Anderson, President and Chief Executive Officer
CFO: C. Thomas Johnson, III, Vice President Finance and Chief Financial Officer
CMO: Barry Williamson, President Medical Staff
CIO: Eric Harper, Chief Information Officer
CHR: Susan Hayes, Director Human Resources
CNO: Renae Taylor, Chief Nursing Officer
Web address: www.srmc.org
Control: Other not-for-profit (including NFP Corporation) **Service:** General Medical and Surgical

Staffed Beds: 368 **Admissions:** 14956 **Census:** 423 **Outpatient Visits:** 423987 **Births:** 1527 **Total Expense ($000):** 229235 **Payroll Expense ($000):** 98288 **Personnel:** 2482

MARION—Mcdowell County

⊞ **MCDOWELL HOSPITAL (340087)**, 430 Rankin Drive, Zip 28752–6568, Mailing Address: P.O. Box 730, Zip 28752–0730; tel. 828/659–5000 **A**1 9 10 **F**3 11 13 15 28 29 30 31 34 35 39 40 45 54 57 59 64 65 70 76 77 78 79 81 82 85 90 91 93 97 107 108 110 111 114 119 127 130 131 132 133 135 146 147 148 **S** Mission Health System, Asheville, NC
Primary Contact: Lynn Ingram Boggs, President
CFO: Clint Stewart, Vice President Finance/Business Operations
CMO: Rex Henderson, M.D., Chief of Staff
CIO: Pam Belvins, Director Information Technology Member Hospitals Mission
CHR: Susan Parielle, Director Human Resources Affiliate Mission Health System
CNO: Kathy Hefner, Vice President Clinical Operations
Web address: www.mcdhospital.org
Control: Other not-for-profit (including NFP Corporation) **Service:** General Medical and Surgical

Staffed Beds: 49 **Admissions:** 2947 **Census:** 19 **Outpatient Visits:** 78734 **Births:** 161 **Total Expense ($000):** 51876 **Payroll Expense ($000):** 24775 **Personnel:** 327

NC

Many Facility Codes have changed. Please refer to the AHA Guide Code Chart. © 2014 AHA Guide

MATTHEWS—Mecklenburg County

✦ **NOVANT HEALTH MATTHEWS MEDICAL CENTER (340171)**, 1500 Matthews Township Parkway, Zip 28105–4656, Mailing Address: P.O. Box 3310, Zip 28106–3310; tel. 704/384–6500 **A**1 9 10 **F**3 11 12 13 15 18 20 22 26 29 30 31 34 35 36 40 45 49 56 57 59 64 68 70 73 75 76 77 78 79 81 82 84 85 86 87 89 92 93 107 108 110 113 118 119 126 129 130 132 145 146 147 148 **S** Novant Health, Winston Salem, NC
Primary Contact: Roland R. Bibeau, FACHE, President
COO: Amy Vance, Executive Vice President and Chief Operating Officer
CFO: Greg Klein, Senior Director Finance
CMO: Thomas Zweng, M.D., Senior Vice President Medical Affairs
CIO: David B. Garrett, Chief Information Officer
CHR: Susan Kennedy, Manager Human Resources
Web address: www.presbyterian.org
Control: Other not–for–profit (including NFP Corporation) **Service:** General Medical and Surgical

Staffed Beds: 137 **Admissions:** 7975 **Census:** 84 **Outpatient Visits:** 200298 **Births:** 1461 **Total Expense ($000):** 127633 **Payroll Expense ($000):** 41826 **Personnel:** 755

MOCKSVILLE—Davie County

✦ **WAKE FOREST BAPTIST HEALTH–DAVIE HOSPITAL (341313)**, 223 Hospital Street, Zip 27028–2038, Mailing Address: P.O. Box 1209, Zip 27028–1209; tel. 336/702–5500 **A**1 9 10 18 **F**3 15 30 34 35 40 59 64 81 85 107 114 119 130 133 **S** Wake Forest Baptist Health, Winston–Salem, NC
Primary Contact: Chad J. Brown, M.P.H., President
CFO: Danny Squires, Chief Financial Officer
CMO: Bret Nicks, M.D., Chief Medical Officer and Chief of Staff
CHR: Danielle Wright, Director Human Resources
CNO: Clyde A. Bristow, III, MSN, Chief Nursing Officer
Web address: www.daviehospital.org
Control: Other not–for–profit (including NFP Corporation) **Service:** General Medical and Surgical

Staffed Beds: 25 **Admissions:** 207 **Census:** 7 **Outpatient Visits:** 14334 **Births:** 0 **Total Expense ($000):** 10266 **Payroll Expense ($000):** 3676 **Personnel:** 91

MONROE—Union County

✦ **CAROLINAS MEDICAL CENTER–UNION (340130)**, 600 Hospital Drive, Zip 28112–6000, Mailing Address: P.O. Box 5003, Zip 28111–5003; tel. 704/993–3100, (Total facility includes 70 beds in nursing home–type unit) **A**1 2 9 10 **F**3 4 5 8 11 13 18 20 26 28 29 30 31 34 35 39 40 42 45 49 53 56 57 59 64 66 67 70 73 74 75 76 77 78 79 81 82 85 86 87 89 93 107 108 111 114 115 118 119 120 121 123 128 129 130 132 135 146 147 148 **S** Carolinas HealthCare System, Charlotte, NC
Primary Contact: Michael Lutes, President
COO: Dave Anderson, FACHE, Vice President Administration
CFO: John G. Moore, Vice President and Chief Financial Officer
CMO: Craig M. Slater, M.D., Chief Medical Officer
CIO: Lisa Sykes, Director Information Services
CHR: Rhonda McFarland, Director Human Resources
CNO: Denise White, MSN, Chief Nurse Executive
Web address: www.carolinashealthcare.org/cmc–union
Control: Hospital district or authority, Government, nonfederal **Service:** General Medical and Surgical

Staffed Beds: 227 **Admissions:** 8116 **Census:** 147 **Outpatient Visits:** 161606 **Births:** 1095 **Total Expense ($000):** 171413 **Payroll Expense ($000):** 60762 **Personnel:** 1123

MOORESVILLE—Iredell County

✦ **LAKE NORMAN REGIONAL MEDICAL CENTER (340129)**, 171 Fairview Road, Zip 28117–9500, Mailing Address: P.O. Box 3250, Zip 28117–3250; tel. 704/660–4010 **A**1 2 9 10 19 **F**3 8 11 12 13 15 18 20 29 30 31 34 35 37 40 41 45 46 47 48 49 50 51 56 57 59 60 61 62 64 65 68 70 72 73 74 75 76 77 78 79 81 82 84 85 86 87 93 96 97 100 107 108 110 111 114 115 116 117 118 119 126 129 130 131 132 135 145 146 147 148 **P**8 **S** Community Health Systems, Inc., Franklin, TN
Primary Contact: Stephen L. Midkiff, Chief Executive Officer
COO: Greg Page, Chief Operating Officer
CFO: James Stoner, Chief Financial Officer
CHR: Stephanie Williams, Market Director Human Resources
CNO: Marie Marks, Chief Nursing Officer
Web address: www.lnrmc.com
Control: Corporation, Investor–owned, for–profit **Service:** General Medical and Surgical

Staffed Beds: 123 **Admissions:** 4558 **Census:** 46 **Outpatient Visits:** 50422 **Births:** 892 **Personnel:** 613

MOREHEAD CiTY—Carteret County

✦ **CARTERET GENERAL HOSPITAL (340142)**, 3500 Arendell Street, Zip 28557–2901, Mailing Address: P.O. Box 1619, Zip 28557–1619; tel. 252/808–6000, (Nonreporting) **A**1 2 9 10 19 20
Primary Contact: Richard A. Brvenik, FACHE, President
CFO: Joanie King, Chief Financial Officer
CMO: Joseph Nutz, M.D., Vice President Medical Staff Services
CIO: Kyle Marek, Manager Information Services
CHR: Elizabeth Beswick, Vice President Human Resources and Public Relations
Web address: www.ccgh.org
Control: County–Government, nonfederal **Service:** General Medical and Surgical

Staffed Beds: 135

MORGANTON—Burke County

✦ **BLUE RIDGE HEALTHCARE HOSPITALS (340075)**, 2201 South Sterling Street, Zip 28655–4058; tel. 828/580–5000, (Includes GRACE HOSPITAL, 2201 South Sterling Street, tel. 828/580–5000; VALDESE GENERAL HOSPITAL, 720 Malcolm Boulevard, Valdese, Zip 28690–2872, Mailing Address: P.O. Box 700, Zip 28690–0700; tel. 828/874–2251) **A**1 2 9 10 **F**3 13 15 18 20 22 28 29 30 31 34 35 40 45 50 53 57 59 60 64 68 69 70 71 72 76 77 78 81 82 86 93 96 97 98 105 107 108 110 111 114 115 119 131 146 147 148 **S** Carolinas HealthCare System, Charlotte, NC
Primary Contact: Kathy C. Bailey, Ph.D., FACHE, President and Chief Executive Officer
CFO: Robert G. Fritts, Chief Financial Officer and Senior Vice President
CMO: Joe Mazzola, D.O., Senior Vice President Medical Affairs and Chief Medical Officer
CHR: Thomas Eure, Vice President Administration
CNO: Susan E. Brown, R.N., Sr. Vice President, Chief Nursing Officer
Control: Other not–for–profit (including NFP Corporation) **Service:** General Medical and Surgical

Staffed Beds: 175 **Admissions:** 8261 **Census:** 91 **Outpatient Visits:** 162480 **Births:** 892 **Total Expense ($000):** 174246 **Payroll Expense ($000):** 58526 **Personnel:** 1206

☐ **BROUGHTON HOSPITAL (344025)**, 1000 South Sterling Street, Zip 28655–3999; tel. 828/433–2111 **A**1 5 10 **F**3 30 39 53 56 59 65 75 77 86 87 91 92 98 99 100 101 102 103 106 108 130 132 135 146
Primary Contact: Vivian Streater, Co–Acting Chief Executive Officer
CFO: Bea Tullis, Chief Financial Officer and Budget Officer
CMO: George Krebs, M.D., Chief Medical Officer
CIO: Darin Kiracofe, Director Information Resource Management
CHR: Jean Buchanan, Director Human Resources
CNO: Vivian Streater, Chief Nursing Officer and Co–Acting Chief Executive Officer
Web address: www.ncdhhs.gov/dsohf/broughton
Control: State–Government, nonfederal **Service:** Psychiatric

Staffed Beds: 297 **Admissions:** 717 **Census:** 241 **Outpatient Visits:** 0 **Births:** 0 **Total Expense ($000):** 128451 **Payroll Expense ($000):** 51651 **Personnel:** 1177

MOUNT AIRY—Surry County

✦ **NORTHERN HOSPITAL OF SURRY COUNTY (340003)**, 830 Rockford Street, Zip 27030–5365, Mailing Address: P.O. Box 1101, Zip 27030–1101; tel. 336/719–7000, (Total facility includes 33 beds in nursing home–type unit) **A**1 9 10 **F**3 13 15 18 29 30 31 34 35 39 40 45 50 51 56 57 59 64 65 70 74 75 76 77 79 80 81 82 85 86 87 93 102 107 108 110 111 114 115 116 117 118 119 128 129 130 131 132 133 145 146 147 148 **P**6 **S** QHR, Brentwood, TN
Primary Contact: Bert Whitaker, Interim Chief Executive Officer
COO: Mike Leonard, Vice President Operations and Imaging Director
CFO: Andrea Hickling, Vice President Finance and Chief Finance Officer
CMO: Tamas Balogh, M.D., Chief of Staff
CIO: Robert Hall, Chief Information Officer
CNO: Robin Hodgin, R.N., Vice President of Patient Services and Chief Nursing Officer
Web address: www.northernhospital.com
Control: Hospital district or authority, Government, nonfederal **Service:** General Medical and Surgical

Staffed Beds: 108 **Admissions:** 4004 **Census:** 69 **Outpatient Visits:** 218256 **Births:** 387 **Total Expense ($000):** 75948 **Payroll Expense ($000):** 31893 **Personnel:** 638

MURPHY—Cherokee County

☒ **MURPHY MEDICAL CENTER (340160)**, 3990 U.S. Highway 64 East Alt,
Zip 28906–7917; tel. 828/837–8161, (Nonreporting) **A**1 9 10 **S** Carolinas
HealthCare System, Charlotte, NC
Primary Contact: Michael Stevenson, Chief Executive Officer
COO: Toni Lovingood, Chief Operating Officer
CFO: Steve Gilgen, Chief Financial Officer
CMO: Jeffrey H. Martin, M.D., Chief of Staff
CIO: Connie Stalcup, Manager Information Systems
CHR: Russ Paine, Human Resources Officer
CNO: Teresa Bowleg, R.N., Chief Nursing Officer
Web address: www.murphymedical.org
Control: Other not–for–profit (including NFP Corporation) **Service:** General
Medical and Surgical

Staffed Beds: 191

NAGS HEAD—Dare County

☒ **THE OUTER BANKS HOSPITAL (341324)**, 4800 South Croatan Highway,
Zip 27959–9704; tel. 252/449–4511 **A**1 9 10 18 **F**3 13 15 29 30 31 34 35
40 45 50 51 54 56 57 59 64 71 74 75 76 77 78 79 81 82 85 87 93 97 100
107 108 109 110 111 115 117 118 119 120 121 130 133 135 141 144 146
S Vidant Health, Greenville, NC
Primary Contact: Ronald A. Sloan, FACHE, President
CFO: Todd Warlitner, Vice President Business Operations
CMO: Roger Lever, M.D., President Medical Staff
CHR: Mary Kelley, Director Human Resources
CNO: Judy Bruno, R.N., Vice President, Clinical Operations
Web address: www.theouterbankshospital.com
Control: Other not–for–profit (including NFP Corporation) **Service:** General
Medical and Surgical

Staffed Beds: 21 Admissions: 1539 Census: 7 Outpatient Visits: 44147 Births: 377 Total Expense ($000): 46354 Payroll Expense ($000): 17049 Personnel: 300

NEW BERN—Craven County

☒ △ **CAROLINAEAST HEALTH SYSTEM (340131)**, 2000 Neuse Boulevard,
Zip 28560–3499, Mailing Address: P.O. Box 12157, Zip 28561–2157;
tel. 252/633–8111 **A**1 2 7 9 10 19 20 **F**3 7 11 13 15 17 18 20 22 24 26 28
29 30 31 34 35 40 45 47 48 49 53 54 57 59 60 61 62 64 67 68 70 74 75
76 77 78 79 81 85 87 89 90 92 93 94 96 98 100 101 102 103 104 105 107
108 110 111 113 114 115 116 117 118 119 120 121 123 126 129 130 132
135 143 146 147 148 **P**6
Primary Contact: G. Raymond Leggett, III, President and Chief Executive Officer
CFO: Tammy M. Sherron, Vice President Finance
CMO: Ronald B. May, M.D., Vice President Medical Affairs
CIO: Ronald B. May, M.D., Vice President Medical Affairs
CHR: Bruce A. Martin, Vice President Human Resources
CNO: Rosanne Leahy, Vice President Nursing Services
Web address: www.carolinaeasthealth.com
Control: Hospital district or authority, Government, nonfederal **Service:** General
Medical and Surgical

Staffed Beds: 350 Admissions: 12634 Census: 158 Outpatient Visits: 165458 Births: 1221 Total Expense ($000): 231590 Payroll Expense ($000): 87902 Personnel: 1647

NORTH WILKESBORO—Wilkes County

☒ **WILKES REGIONAL MEDICAL CENTER (340064)**, 1370 West D Street,
Zip 28659–3506, Mailing Address: P.O. Box 609, Zip 28659–0609;
tel. 336/651–8100, (Total facility includes 10 beds in nursing home–type unit) **A**1
9 10 **F**3 8 11 13 15 18 29 30 34 35 40 45 57 59 60 62 64 67 68 70 74 76
77 79 81 82 85 87 92 93 107 108 110 111 114 115 119 124 128 130 146
S Carolinas HealthCare System, Charlotte, NC
Primary Contact: J. Gene Faile, Chief Executive Officer and President
CFO: Barry Wald, Chief Financial Officer
CMO: Richard Barber, M.D., Chief Medical Officer
CIO: William Hofman, Manager Information Technology
CHR: Vanya Baker, Director
CNO: Sandy Sheppard, Vice President Patient Services
Web address: www.wilkesregional.com/
Control: City–Government, nonfederal **Service:** General Medical and Surgical

Staffed Beds: 107 Admissions: 4435 Census: 51 Outpatient Visits: 112202 Births: 482 Total Expense ($000): 67319 Payroll Expense ($000): 26043 Personnel: 564

OXFORD—Granville County

☒ **GRANVILLE HEALTH SYSTEM (340127)**, 1010 College Street,
Zip 27565–2507, Mailing Address: P.O. Box 947, Zip 27565–0947;
tel. 919/690–3000, (Total facility includes 80 beds in nursing home–type unit) **A**1
9 10 **F**2 3 7 11 13 15 18 19 29 30 31 34 35 38 39 40 45 50 54 55 56 57
59 64 66 70 75 76 77 78 79 81 82 85 86 93 99 100 101 103 104 107 108
110 111 118 119 124 127 128 129 130 132 133 143 144 146 147 148 **P**3
6 8
Primary Contact: L. Lee Isley, Ph.D., FACHE, Chief Executive Officer
COO: Cristina Rigsbee Carroll, Chief Operating Officer
CFO: Jeffrey Armstrong, CPA, Chief Financial Officer
CMO: Michael Mahan, M.D., Chief Medical Staff
CIO: Geoff Tanthorey, Director Information Systems
CHR: Scott Thomas, Administrative Director Human Resources/Communication
Web address: www.ghshospital.org
Control: County–Government, nonfederal **Service:** General Medical and Surgical

Staffed Beds: 142 Admissions: 2372 Census: 81 Outpatient Visits: 59685 Births: 295 Total Expense ($000): 56497 Payroll Expense ($000): 26213 Personnel: 509

PINEHURST—Moore County

☒ △ **FIRSTHEALTH MOORE REGIONAL HOSPITAL (340115)**, 155 Memorial
Drive, Zip 28374–8710, Mailing Address: P.O. Box 3000, Zip 28374–3000;
tel. 910/715–1000 **A**1 2 7 9 10 19 **F**3 4 5 11 12 13 15 17 18 20 22 24 26
28 29 30 31 34 35 40 44 45 46 47 48 49 50 51 53 54 55 56 57 58 59 60
64 65 68 70 72 74 75 76 77 78 79 81 82 86 87 89 90 93 96 98 99 100
101 102 103 104 105 107 108 111 114 115 118 119 120 121 124 126 129
130 132 134 135 143 146 147 148 **S** FirstHealth of the Carolinas,
Pinehurst, NC
Primary Contact: David J. Kilarski, Chief Executive Officer
COO: Brian Canfield, Chief Operating Officer
CFO: Lynn S. DeJaco, Chief Financial Officer
CMO: John F. Krahnert, M.D., Chief Medical Officer
CIO: David B. Dillehunt, Chief Information Officer
CHR: Daniel F. Biediger, Vice President Human Resources
CNO: Karen Robeano, R.N., Chief Nursing Officer and Vice President Patient Care
Services
Web address: www.firsthealth.org
Control: Other not–for–profit (including NFP Corporation) **Service:** General
Medical and Surgical

Staffed Beds: 371 Admissions: 20409 Census: 275 Outpatient Visits: 201319 Births: 1561 Total Expense ($000): 369184 Payroll Expense ($000): 138495 Personnel: 3062

PLYMOUTH—Washington County

★ ◇ **WASHINGTON COUNTY HOSPITAL (341314)**, 958 U.S. Highway 64 East,
Zip 27962–9591; tel. 252/793–4135, (Nonreporting) **A**9 10 18 21 **S** Rural
Community Hospitals of America, Kansas City, MO
Primary Contact: Cameron Highsmith, Chief Executive Officer
CFO: Al Arrowood, Chief Financial Officer
CMO: Robert Venable, M.D., Chief Medical Staff
CIO: Christina Craft, Director Information Systems
CNO: Kimberly Manning, Chief Nursing Officer
Control: County–Government, nonfederal **Service:** General Medical and Surgical

Staffed Beds: 25

RALEIGH—Wake County

CENTRAL PRISON HOSPITAL, 1300 Western Boulevard, Zip 27606–2148;
tel. 919/733–0800, (Nonreporting)
Primary Contact: Thomas J. Hawkins, Administrator
CFO: Annette Goforth, Manager Administrative Services
CMO: Olushola Metiko, M.D., Medical Director
Web address: www.doc.state.nc.us/dop/prisons/central.htm
Control: State–Government, nonfederal **Service:** Hospital unit of an institution
(prison hospital, college infimary, etc.)

Staffed Beds: 230

☒ **DUKE RALEIGH HOSPITAL (340073)**, 3400 Wake Forest Road,
Zip 27609–7373, Mailing Address: P.O. Box 28280, Zip 27611–8280;
tel. 919/954–3000 **A**1 2 9 10 **F**3 11 12 15 18 20 22 26 28 29 30 31 34 35
36 39 40 44 45 46 47 48 49 50 51 53 54 55 57 58 59 60 64 68 70 74 75
77 78 79 80 81 82 84 85 87 92 93 96 100 101 102 103 104 107 108 110
111 115 117 118 119 120 121 123 126 129 130 131 132 135 146 148 **P**6
S Duke University Health System, Durham, NC
Primary Contact: David Zaas, Chief Executive Officer
CMO: Ted Kunstling, M.D., Chief Medical Officer
CIO: Janis Curtis, Interim Director Information Technology
CHR: Donald K. Barnes, Chief Human Resources Officer
Web address: www.dukehealthraleigh.org
Control: Other not–for–profit (including NFP Corporation) **Service:** General
Medical and Surgical

Staffed Beds: 148 Admissions: 7796 Census: 92 Outpatient Visits: 146143 Births: 0 Total Expense ($000): 261995 Payroll Expense ($000): 82099 Personnel: 1351

NC

☐ **HOLLY HILL HOSPITAL (344014)**, 3019 Falstaff Road, Zip 27610–1812; tel. 919/250–7000 **A**1 10 **F**4 29 38 56 68 98 99 103 105 **S** Universal Health Services, Inc., King of Prussia, PA
Primary Contact: Michael McDonald, Chief Executive Officer
CFO: Ron Howard, Chief Financial Officer
CMO: Thomas Cornwall, M.D., Medical Director
CHR: Maria Teresa Sulit, Director Human Resources
Web address: www.hollyhillhospital.com
Control: Corporation, Investor–owned, for–profit **Service:** Psychiatric

> **Staffed Beds:** 168 **Admissions:** 6124 **Census:** 154 **Outpatient Visits:** 4095 **Births:** 0 **Total Expense ($000):** 25275 **Payroll Expense ($000):** 15345 **Personnel:** 337

LARRY B. ZIEVERINK, SR. ALCOHOLISM TREATMENT CENTER, 3000 Falstaff Road, Zip 27610–1897; tel. 919/250–1500, (Nonreporting)
Primary Contact: Martin D. Woodward, Director Acute Care Services
COO: Martin D. Woodward, Director Acute Care Services
CFO: Paul Gross, Human Services and Finance Officer
CMO: Enrique Lopez, M.D., Medical Director
CIO: Wil A. Glenn, Director Communications
Web address: www.wakegov.com/county/family/atc
Control: County–Government, nonfederal **Service:** Alcoholism and other chemical dependency

> **Staffed Beds:** 34

☒ **REX HEALTHCARE (340114)**, 4420 Lake Boone Trail, Zip 27607–6599; tel. 919/784–3100, (Total facility includes 227 beds in nursing home–type unit) **A**1 2 3 5 9 10 **F**3 7 8 11 12 13 14 15 17 18 20 22 24 26 28 29 30 31 34 35 36 40 44 45 46 47 48 49 50 53 54 56 57 58 59 60 62 64 65 66 68 70 71 73 74 75 76 77 78 79 81 82 84 85 86 87 89 92 93 96 97 100 102 107 108 110 111 114 115 116 117 118 119 120 121 123 126 128 129 130 131 132 135 142 143 144 145 146 147 148 **P**6 **S** UNC Health Care, Chapel Hill, NC
Primary Contact: David W. Strong, President
COO: Steve W. Burriss, Chief Operating Officer
CFO: Bernadette Spong, Chief Financial Officer
CMO: Linda H. Butler, M.D., Chief Medical Officer
CIO: Michelle Gray, Vice President and Regional Chief Information Officer
CHR: Sylvia D. Hackett, Vice President Human Resources
CNO: Colonel Joel Ray, MSN, Vice President and Chief Nursing Officer
Web address: www.rexhealth.com
Control: Other not–for–profit (including NFP Corporation) **Service:** General Medical and Surgical

> **Staffed Beds:** 660 **Admissions:** 27120 **Census:** 496 **Outpatient Visits:** 776555 **Births:** 5292 **Total Expense ($000):** 686150 **Payroll Expense ($000):** 310735 **Personnel:** 4677

☒ △ **WAKEMED RALEIGH CAMPUS (340069)**, 3000 New Bern Avenue, Zip 27610–1295; tel. 919/350–8000, (Total facility includes 19 beds in nursing home–type unit) **A**1 3 5 7 9 10 **F**3 7 8 11 12 13 15 17 18 20 22 24 26 28 29 30 31 32 34 35 37 38 40 41 42 43 44 45 48 49 50 53 54 56 57 58 59 60 61 62 63 64 65 66 68 70 71 72 73 74 75 76 77 78 79 80 81 85 86 87 88 89 90 92 93 95 96 97 107 108 110 111 114 115 118 119 126 128 130 131 132 135 143 144 146 147 148 **P**6 **S** WakeMed Health & Hospitals, Raleigh, NC
Primary Contact: Donald R. Gintzig, President and Chief Executive Officer
COO: Thomas Gettinger, Executive Vice President and Chief Operating Officer
CFO: Michael D. DeVaughn, Senior Vice President Finance and Chief Financial Officer
CMO: West Lawson, M.D., Chief Medical Officer
CIO: Denton Arledge, Vice President and Chief Information Officer
CHR: Jeanene R. Martin, M.P.H., Senior Vice President Human Resources
Web address: www.wakemed.org
Control: Other not–for–profit (including NFP Corporation) **Service:** General Medical and Surgical

> **Staffed Beds:** 683 **Admissions:** 33458 **Census:** 537 **Outpatient Visits:** 1221828 **Births:** 5149 **Total Expense ($000):** 868437 **Payroll Expense ($000):** 453501 **Personnel:** 6309

REIDSVILLE—Rockingham County

ANNIE PENN HOSPITAL See Moses H. Cone Memorial Hospital, Greensboro

ROANOKE RAPIDS—Halifax County

☒ **HALIFAX REGIONAL MEDICAL CENTER (340151)**, 250 Smith Church Road, Zip 27870–4914, Mailing Address: P.O. Box 1089, Zip 27870–1089; tel. 252/535–8011 **A**1 9 10 20 **F**3 11 13 15 18 24 29 31 34 35 38 39 40 45 47 50 57 58 59 60 64 65 68 69 70 75 76 77 78 79 81 85 86 87 91 93 97 98 100 101 102 103 106 107 108 109 110 111 114 119 124 127 129 130 132 135 146 148 **S** Novant Health, Winston Salem, NC
Primary Contact: William Mahone, President and Chief Executive Officer
CFO: Sherry Jensen, Chief Financial Officer
CIO: Robert Gordon, Manager Information Systems
CHR: William Mahone, Chief Human Resources Officer
CNO: Karen Daniels, MSN, Chief Nursing Officer
Web address: www.halifaxmedicalcenter.org
Control: Other not–for–profit (including NFP Corporation) **Service:** General Medical and Surgical

> **Staffed Beds:** 142 **Admissions:** 5669 **Census:** 78 **Outpatient Visits:** 75319 **Births:** 587 **Total Expense ($000):** 82890 **Payroll Expense ($000):** 34804 **Personnel:** 772

ROCKINGHAM—Richmond County

★ **FIRSTHEALTH RICHMOND MEMORIAL HOSPITAL (340035)**, 925 Long Drive, Zip 28379–4835; tel. 910/417–3000 **A**9 **F**3 13 15 18 20 28 29 30 34 35 40 45 46 47 48 49 50 53 57 59 64 70 75 76 77 81 82 85 87 89 92 93 96 107 108 110 111 114 119 120 129 131 132 134 135 145 146 147 148 **S** FirstHealth of the Carolinas, Pinehurst, NC
Primary Contact: John J. Jackson, President
COO: Allison G. Duckworth, R.N., Chief Operating Officer and Chief Nursing Officer
CFO: John D. Price, Chief Financial Officer
CMO: Matthew Vreeland, M.D., Chief Medical Officer
Web address: www.firsthealth.org
Control: Other not–for–profit (including NFP Corporation) **Service:** General Medical and Surgical

> **Staffed Beds:** 91 **Admissions:** 2747 **Census:** 23 **Outpatient Visits:** 64533 **Births:** 333 **Total Expense ($000):** 38813 **Payroll Expense ($000):** 18918 **Personnel:** 326

ROCKY MOUNT—Nash County

☒ **LIFECARE HOSPITALS OF NORTH CAROLINA (342013)**, 1051 Noell Lane, Zip 27804–1761; tel. 252/451–2300 **A**1 10 **F**1 3 29 30 50 74 75 77 82 85 130 148 **S** LifeCare Management Services, Plano, TX
Primary Contact: Robyn Perkerson, R.N., Administrator
COO: Robyn Perkerson, R.N., Administrator
CMO: Daniel Crocker, M.D., Chief Medical Officer
CHR: Vicky Goode, Director Human Resources
CNO: Brandee Chappell, Director of Nursing
Web address: www.lifecare–hospitals.com
Control: Corporation, Investor–owned, for–profit **Service:** Long–Term Acute Care hospital

> **Staffed Beds:** 41 **Admissions:** 505 **Census:** 39 **Outpatient Visits:** 0 **Births:** 0 **Total Expense ($000):** 18437 **Payroll Expense ($000):** 8194 **Personnel:** 153

☒ **NASH HEALTH CARE SYSTEMS (340147)**, 2460 Curtis Ellis Drive, Zip 27804–2237; tel. 252/443–8000 **A**1 2 9 10 **F**3 4 11 12 13 15 18 20 22 28 29 30 31 34 35 38 40 44 45 47 48 49 50 53 54 55 57 59 60 63 64 70 73 74 75 76 77 78 79 80 81 82 84 85 86 87 89 90 93 94 96 98 100 101 102 103 104 107 108 110 111 114 117 118 119 120 121 123 126 129 130 131 132 135 146 147 148 **P**6
Primary Contact: Larry H. Chewning, III, President and Chief Executive Officer
COO: Brad Weisner, Executive Vice President and Chief Operating Officer
CFO: Al Hooks, Senior Vice President and Chief Financial Officer
CMO: David R. Gorby, M.D., Vice President Quality and Patient Safety
CIO: David Hinkle, Senior Vice President and Chief Information Officer
CHR: Cam Blalock, Senior Vice President Corporate Services
CNO: Leslie Hall, R.N., Senior Vice President–Chief Nursing Officer
Web address: www.nhcs.org
Control: Hospital district or authority, Government, nonfederal **Service:** General Medical and Surgical

> **Staffed Beds:** 303 **Admissions:** 12540 **Census:** 186 **Outpatient Visits:** 178154 **Births:** 1151 **Total Expense ($000):** 225516 **Payroll Expense ($000):** 94182 **Personnel:** 1584

ROXBORO—Person County

✠ **PERSON MEMORIAL HOSPITAL (340159)**, 615 Ridge Road, Zip 27573–4629; tel. 336/599–2121, (Total facility includes 60 beds in nursing home–type unit) **A**1 9 10 **F**3 11 15 18 28 29 34 40 45 57 59 64 70 75 77 78 79 81 85 87 93 96 97 103 104 107 108 110 114 119 128 129 130 132 146 **P**6 **S** Duke LifePoint Healthcare, Brentwood, TN
Primary Contact: Beemal A. Shah, Chief Executive Officer
CFO: Jessi Ayers, Chief Financial Officer
CIO: Rhonda M. Elliott, Director Information Technology and Meaningful Use
CHR: Mary Barksdale, Director Human Resources
CNO: Lynn Peoples, Interim Chief Nursing Officer
Web address: www.personhospital.com
Control: Partnership, Investor–owned, for–profit **Service:** General Medical and Surgical

Staffed Beds: 106 **Admissions:** 1815 **Census:** 70 **Outpatient Visits:** 41368 **Births:** 0 **Total Expense ($000):** 30614 **Payroll Expense ($000):** 11063 **Personnel:** 244

RUTHERFORDTON—Rutherford County

✠ **RUTHERFORD REGIONAL HEALTH SYSTEM (340013)**, 288 South Ridgecrest Avenue, Zip 28139–2838; tel. 828/286–5000 **A**1 2 9 10 19 **F**3 11 13 15 18 19 20 22 28 29 30 31 34 35 40 45 48 49 50 53 57 59 62 64 70 74 75 76 77 78 79 81 82 85 86 87 89 93 97 98 100 101 102 104 106 107 108 110 111 114 115 118 119 130 131 132 135 146 147 **S** Duke LifePoint Healthcare, Brentwood, TN
Primary Contact: Cindy D. Buck, Chief Executive Officer
COO: John Domansky, Vice President Operations
CFO: Jeff Rush, Chief Financial Officer
CIO: Tommy Finley, Chief Information Officer
CHR: Robin B. Callas, R.N., Vice President Human Resources
Web address: www.rutherfordhosp.org
Control: Other not–for–profit (including NFP Corporation) **Service:** General Medical and Surgical

Staffed Beds: 121 **Admissions:** 6043 **Census:** 63 **Outpatient Visits:** 193371 **Births:** 553 **Total Expense ($000):** 90255 **Payroll Expense ($000):** 40262 **Personnel:** 736

SALISBURY—Rowan County

✠ **NOVANT HEALTH ROWAN MEDICAL CENTER (340015)**, 612 Mocksville Avenue, Zip 28144–2799; tel. 704/210–5000 **A**1 9 10 19 **F**3 6 8 11 13 15 17 18 20 22 26 28 29 30 31 32 34 35 37 39 40 44 45 46 48 49 50 51 53 54 56 57 59 60 61 63 64 68 70 71 73 74 75 76 77 78 79 81 84 85 86 87 90 91 92 93 94 96 98 100 102 103 107 108 110 111 115 116 117 118 119 120 121 123 126 130 131 132 135 146 147 148 **P**2 **S** Novant Health, Winston Salem, NC
Primary Contact: Dari Caldwell, R.N., Ph.D., FACHE, President
COO: Gary Blabon, Director Operations
CMO: Thomas F. Trahey, M.D., Vice President Medical Affairs
CHR: Tracey Aaron, Director Human Resources
CNO: Cora Greene, Chief Nursing Officer
Web address: www.rowan.org
Control: Other not–for–profit (including NFP Corporation) **Service:** General Medical and Surgical

Staffed Beds: 145 **Admissions:** 9625 **Census:** 130 **Outpatient Visits:** 117415 **Births:** 743 **Total Expense ($000):** 159713 **Payroll Expense ($000):** 54823 **Personnel:** 970

VETERANS AFFAIRS MEDICAL CENTER See W. G. (Bill) Heffner Veterans Affairs Medical Center

✠ **W. G. (BILL) HEFFNER VETERANS AFFAIRS MEDICAL CENTER**, 1601 Brenner Avenue, Zip 28144–2559; tel. 704/638–9000, (Nonreporting) **A**1 3 5 **S** Department of Veterans Affairs, Washington, DC
Primary Contact: Kaye Green, FACHE, Director
CFO: Steve Patil, Chief Financial Officer
CIO: Deborah Gunn, Chief Information Officer
CHR: Sandra Fischer, Director Human Resources
Web address: www.salisbury.va.gov
Control: Veterans Affairs, Government, federal **Service:** Psychiatric

Staffed Beds: 171

SANFORD—Lee County

✠ **CENTRAL CAROLINA HOSPITAL (340020)**, 1135 Carthage Street, Zip 27330–4162; tel. 919/774–2100, (Nonreporting) **A**1 9 10 **S** TENET Healthcare Corporation, Dallas, TX
Primary Contact: David E. Loving, Chief Executive Officer
CFO: Ronald Groteluschen, Chief Financial Officer
CIO: Jimmy Whitaker, Director Information Systems
CHR: Joseph F. Eastman, Director Human Resources
CNO: Tracy Temple, Chief Nursing Officer
Web address: www.centralcarolinahosp.com
Control: Corporation, Investor–owned, for–profit **Service:** General Medical and Surgical

Staffed Beds: 116

SCOTLAND NECK—Halifax County

★ **OUR COMMUNITY HOSPITAL (341302)**, 921 Junior High Road, Zip 27874–0405, Mailing Address: Box 405, Zip 27874–0405; tel. 252/826–4144, (Nonreporting) **A**9 10 18
Primary Contact: Thomas K. Majure, Administrator
CFO: Angela Hicks, Controller
CMO: Cornelius Artis, M.D., Chief Medical Officer
CIO: Dana Mobley, Chief Information Officer
CNO: Claudia Giddings, R.N., Chief Nursing Officer
Web address: www.och–bltc.org
Control: Other not–for–profit (including NFP Corporation) **Service:** General Medical and Surgical

Staffed Beds: 100

SHELBY—Cleveland County

✠ **CLEVELAND REGIONAL MEDICAL CENTER (340021)**, 201 East Grover Street, Zip 28150–3917; tel. 980/487–3000, (Total facility includes 120 beds in nursing home–type unit) **A**1 2 9 10 19 **F**1 3 8 11 13 15 18 20 28 29 30 31 32 34 35 38 39 40 43 44 47 48 49 50 51 56 57 59 61 64 65 67 70 74 75 76 77 78 79 80 81 82 85 86 87 89 93 102 106 107 108 110 111 114 115 118 119 121 123 128 130 131 132 135 143 145 146 147 148 **S** Carolinas HealthCare System, Charlotte, NC
Primary Contact: Brian Gwyn, President and Chief Executive Officer
COO: Brian Gwyn, President Chief Operating Officer
CFO: Christine M. Martin, Vice President and Chief Financial Officer
CMO: Charles M. Tomlinson, M.D., Chief Medical Officer
CIO: Craig D. Richardville, Chief Information Officer
CHR: Debra Kale, Vice President Human Resources
CNO: Veronica Poole–Adams, R.N., Vice President, Chief Operating Officer and Chief Nursing Executive
Web address: www.clevelandregional.org
Control: Hospital district or authority, Government, nonfederal **Service:** General Medical and Surgical

Staffed Beds: 364 **Admissions:** 8519 **Census:** 199 **Outpatient Visits:** 138000 **Births:** 1015 **Total Expense ($000):** 150867 **Payroll Expense ($000):** 59478 **Personnel:** 1199

★ **CRAWLEY MEMORIAL HOSPITAL (342019)**, 706 West King Street, Zip 28086, Mailing Address: P.O. Box 159, Boiling Springs, Zip 28086; tel. 980/487–1300, (Nonreporting) **A**10 **S** Carolinas HealthCare System, Charlotte, NC
Primary Contact: Denise R. Murray, Chief Executive Officer
CFO: Kliff Rodgers, Chief Financial Officer
CMO: Blake Spain, M.D., Chief Medical Officer
CIO: Brian Doerr, Chief Information Officer
CHR: Laurie Breedlove, Vice President Human Resources
CNO: Rachel Wood, Chief Nursing Officer
Web address: www.clevelandcountyhealthcaresystem.com/crawley–memorial.html
Control: Other not–for–profit (including NFP Corporation) **Service:** Long–Term Acute Care hospital

Staffed Beds: 41

SILER CITY—Chatham County

✠ **CHATHAM HOSPITAL (341311)**, 475 Progress Boulevard, Zip 27344–6787, Mailing Address: P.O. Box 649, Zip 27344–0649; tel. 919/799–4000 **A**1 9 10 18 **F**3 15 18 28 29 30 34 35 40 45 57 59 68 70 75 77 81 85 92 93 107 110 111 114 119 130 133 135 **S** UNC Health Care, Chapel Hill, NC
Primary Contact: Robert A. Enders, Jr., President
CFO: Brock Simonds, Interim Chief Financial Officer
CMO: James Davis, M.D., Chief Medical Staff
CIO: Louis Manz, Director Information and Communication Services
CHR: Jodie Sartor Solow, Director Human Resources
CNO: Linda B. Ellington, R.N., Interim Vice President and Chief Nursing Officer
Web address: www.chathamhospital.org
Control: Other not–for–profit (including NFP Corporation) **Service:** General Medical and Surgical

Staffed Beds: 25 **Admissions:** 662 **Census:** 8 **Outpatient Visits:** 38369 **Births:** 0 **Total Expense ($000):** 26133 **Payroll Expense ($000):** 8915 **Personnel:** 191

NC

Many Facility Codes have changed. Please refer to the AHA Guide Code Chart. © 2014 AHA Guide

SMITHFIELD—Johnston County

✠ **JOHNSTON UNC HEALTH CARE (340090)**, 509 North Bright Leaf Boulevard, Zip 27577–4407, Mailing Address: P.O. Box 1376, Zip 27577–1376; tel. 919/934–8171 **A**1 9 10 **F**3 8 11 13 15 18 20 26 28 29 30 31 34 35 40 42 45 49 50 53 54 56 57 59 61 62 63 64 66 68 70 73 74 75 76 79 81 82 85 86 87 89 92 93 97 98 100 107 108 110 111 114 115 119 120 121 122 126 130 132 144 146 147 148 **P**6 **S** UNC Health Care, Chapel Hill, NC
Primary Contact: Charles W. Elliott, Jr., Chief Executive Officer
COO: Ruth Marler, Chief Operating Officer Johnston Health Smithfield
CFO: Edward A. Klein, Chief Financial Officer
CMO: Donald Pocock, M.D., Vice President Medical Affairs
CIO: Teresa Chappell, Chief Information Officer
CHR: Timothy A. Hays, Vice President Human Resources
CNO: Linda Allen, MSN, Chief Nursing Officer
Web address: www.johnstonhealth.org
Control: Hospital district or authority, Government, nonfederal **Service:** General Medical and Surgical

Staffed Beds: 142 **Admissions:** 8928 **Census:** 92 **Outpatient Visits:** 157763 **Births:** 1299 **Total Expense ($000):** 156187 **Payroll Expense ($000):** 61354 **Personnel:** 1124

SOUTHPORT—Brunswick County

✠ **J. ARTHUR DOSHER MEMORIAL HOSPITAL (341327)**, 924 North Howe Street, Zip 28461–3099; tel. 910/457–3800, (Total facility includes 57 beds in nursing home–type unit) **A**1 9 10 18 **F**3 15 28 30 34 35 40 45 46 47 53 54 57 59 65 68 75 77 79 81 85 92 93 94 107 110 114 119 128 129 130 132 133 143 146
Primary Contact: Thomas R. Siemers, Chief Executive Officer
CFO: Don Porter, Senior Vice President and Chief Financial Officer
CMO: Brad L. Hilaman, M.D., Chief of Staff
CIO: Susan Shomaker, Director Information Management Systems
CHR: Pat Aderhold, Director Human Resources
CNO: Carol Northup, R.N., Chief Nursing Officer
Web address: www.dosher.org
Control: Other not–for–profit (including NFP Corporation) **Service:** General Medical and Surgical

Staffed Beds: 82 **Admissions:** 1221 **Census:** 62 **Outpatient Visits:** 58583 **Births:** 0 **Total Expense ($000):** 34549 **Payroll Expense ($000):** 14314 **Personnel:** 301

SPARTA—Alleghany County

✠ **ALLEGHANY MEMORIAL HOSPITAL (341320)**, 233 Doctors Street, Zip 28675–9247; tel. 336/372–5511 **A**1 9 10 18 **F**3 15 18 28 29 30 34 35 40 43 45 57 59 64 67 77 78 79 81 82 87 90 93 97 107 111 114 119 129 130 131 133 135 146 **S** Alliant Management Services, Louisville, KY
Primary Contact: Brent R. Lammers, Chief Executive Officer
CFO: Brett Liverman, Chief Financial Officer
CMO: Tammy Thone, M.D., Chief Medical Staff
CIO: Darlene Keith, Chief Information Systems
CNO: Wendy Onton, Chief Nursing Officer
Web address: www.amhsparta.org
Control: Other not–for–profit (including NFP Corporation) **Service:** General Medical and Surgical

Staffed Beds: 25 **Admissions:** 587 **Census:** 6 **Outpatient Visits:** 27489 **Births:** 0 **Total Expense ($000):** 12346 **Payroll Expense ($000):** 5232 **Personnel:** 137

SPRUCE PINE—Mitchell County

✠ **BLUE RIDGE REGIONAL HOSPITAL (340011)**, 125 Hospital Drive, Zip 28777–3035, Mailing Address: P.O. Drawer 9, Zip 28777–0009; tel. 828/765–4201, (Includes BLUE RIDGE MEDICAL CENTER – YANCEY CAMPUS, 800 Medical Campus Drive, Burnsville, Zip 28714–9010; tel. 828/682–0200; Will Wantland, Director) **A**1 9 10 **F**3 13 15 17 28 29 30 31 32 34 35 39 40 43 45 46 50 53 54 57 59 64 66 70 75 76 77 78 79 81 82 85 87 90 93 96 97 107 108 111 114 118 119 127 128 129 130 131 132 133 135 144 145 146 147 148 **P**6 **S** Mission Health System, Asheville, NC
Primary Contact: Lynn Ingram Boggs, President and Chief Executive Officer
COO: Rebecca W. Carter, MSN, Chief Nursing Officer and Chief Operating Officer
CFO: Clint Stewart, Chief Financial Officer
CMO: Jennifer Larson, M.D., Chief of Staff
CIO: Pam Blevins, R.N., Director, Clinical Informatics
CHR: Susan Parielle, Director Human Resources
CNO: Rebecca W. Carter, MSN, Chief Nursing Officer and Chief Operating Officer
Web address: www.spchospital.org
Control: Other not–for–profit (including NFP Corporation) **Service:** General Medical and Surgical

Staffed Beds: 42 **Admissions:** 1926 **Census:** 17 **Outpatient Visits:** 110283 **Births:** 143 **Total Expense ($000):** 39910 **Payroll Expense ($000):** 19820 **Personnel:** 365

STATESVILLE—Iredell County

✠ **DAVIS REGIONAL MEDICAL CENTER (340144)**, 218 Old Mocksville Road, Zip 28625–1930, Mailing Address: P.O. Box 1823, Zip 28687–1823; tel. 704/873–0281 **A**1 9 10 19 **F**13 15 17 18 20 22 26 28 29 34 40 43 49 50 51 53 56 57 59 60 70 73 76 77 78 79 81 82 84 85 86 87 89 90 92 93 94 98 102 103 107 108 110 111 115 119 126 129 130 131 132 146 147 148 **S** Community Health Systems, Inc., Franklin, TN
Primary Contact: William Chad French, Chief Executive Officer
CFO: Marcus Conley, Chief Financial Officer
CMO: Andrew Schneider, M.D., Chief of Staff
CIO: Janie Stikeleather, Director Marketing and Community Relations
CHR: Christine McKenzie, Director Human Resources
CNO: Janice S. Martin, R.N., Chief Nursing Officer
Web address: www.davisregional.com
Control: Corporation, Investor–owned, for–profit **Service:** General Medical and Surgical

Staffed Beds: 130 **Admissions:** 3999 **Census:** 54

✠ **IREDELL MEMORIAL HOSPITAL (340039)**, 557 Brookdale Drive, Zip 28677–4107, Mailing Address: P.O. Box 1828, Zip 28687–1828; tel. 704/873–5661, (Total facility includes 48 beds in nursing home–type unit) **A**1 2 9 10 **F**3 11 13 15 17 18 20 22 28 29 30 31 32 34 35 40 41 45 47 49 50 56 57 58 59 60 62 64 68 70 74 75 76 77 78 79 81 82 85 86 87 89 93 97 107 108 111 114 115 117 118 119 120 121 123 128 129 130 132 135 146 147 148 **P**6
Primary Contact: Ed Rush, President and Chief Executive Officer
COO: John Snow, Vice President Ancillary and Support Services
CFO: Skip Smith, Vice President Finance
CMO: Carla Pence, M.D., President Medical Staff
CIO: Kyle Smith, Director Information Systems
CHR: John Green, Vice President Professional Services and Facility Planning
CNO: Carol Biggs, Interim Vice President Nursing and Patient Care Services
Web address: www.iredellmemorial.org
Control: Other not–for–profit (including NFP Corporation) **Service:** General Medical and Surgical

Staffed Beds: 203 **Admissions:** 8458 **Census:** 125 **Outpatient Visits:** 121884 **Births:** 769 **Total Expense ($000):** 129637 **Payroll Expense ($000):** 58959 **Personnel:** 985

SYLVA—Jackson County

✠ **HARRIS REGIONAL HOSPITAL (340016)**, 68 Hospital Road, Zip 28779–2722; tel. 828/586–7000 **A**1 9 10 **F**3 7 8 11 13 15 28 29 30 31 34 35 40 46 50 54 62 63 64 68 70 72 75 76 77 78 79 81 82 84 85 86 87 89 93 107 108 110 111 114 119 120 121 129 130 131 135 143 144 146 147 148 **S** Duke LifePoint Healthcare, Brentwood, TN
Primary Contact: Steve Heatherly, Chief Executive Officer
CHR: Janet Millsaps, Chief Human Resources Officer
Web address: www.westcare.org
Control: Other not–for–profit (including NFP Corporation) **Service:** General Medical and Surgical

Staffed Beds: 86 **Admissions:** 3470 **Census:** 35 **Outpatient Visits:** 127267 **Births:** 537 **Total Expense ($000):** 93281 **Payroll Expense ($000):** 41875 **Personnel:** 640

TARBORO—Edgecombe County

✠ △ **VIDANT EDGECOMBE HOSPITAL (340107)**, 111 Hospital Drive, Zip 27886–2011; tel. 252/641–7700 **A**1 2 7 9 10 **F**3 11 12 13 15 18 28 29 30 31 40 45 50 57 59 70 73 75 76 78 79 81 82 85 87 89 90 92 93 96 107 110 111 119 127 130 131 132 135 145 146 **S** Vidant Health, Greenville, NC
Primary Contact: Wendell H. Baker, Jr., President
CFO: Charles Alford, Vice President Financial Services
CMO: Barry Bunn, M.D., Chief of Staff
CHR: Kadie Moore, Director Human Resources
CNO: Patrick Heins, Vice President Patient Care Services
Web address: www.https://www.vidanthealth.com/edgecombe/default.aspx
Control: Other not–for–profit (including NFP Corporation) **Service:** General Medical and Surgical

Staffed Beds: 59 **Admissions:** 4240 **Census:** 44 **Outpatient Visits:** 69386 **Births:** 455 **Total Expense ($000):** 71241 **Payroll Expense ($000):** 24712 **Personnel:** 460

Hospital, Medicare Provider Number, Address, Telephone, Approval, Facility, and Physician Codes, Health Care System

★ American Hospital Association (AHA) membership
☐ The Joint Commission accreditation ◇ DNV Healthcare Inc. accreditation
○ Healthcare Facilities Accreditation Program
△ Commission on Accreditation of Rehabilitation Facilities (CARF) accreditation

NC

THOMASVILLE—Davidson County

✠ ◇ **NOVANT HEALTH THOMASVILLE MEDICAL CENTER (340085)**, 207 Old Lexington Road, Zip 27360–3428, Mailing Address: P.O. Box 789, Zip 27361–0789; tel. 336/472–2000 **A**1 9 10 21 **F**13 15 18 20 28 29 30 34 35 40 45 47 48 56 57 59 64 70 74 75 76 77 78 79 81 83 84 85 86 87 89 91 93 98 103 104 107 108 111 114 117 118 119 124 129 130 131 132 135 146 147 148 **P**6 **S** Novant Health, Winston Salem, NC
Primary Contact: Kathie A. Johnson, R.N., MS, Ph.D., Chief Executive Officer
CNO: Christina Grabus, R.N., Chief Nursing Officer
Web address: www.thomasvillemedicalcenter.org
Control: Other not–for–profit (including NFP Corporation) **Service:** General Medical and Surgical

Staffed Beds: 66 **Admissions:** 4136 **Census:** 66 **Outpatient Visits:** 136549 **Births:** 556 **Total Expense ($000):** 71033 **Payroll Expense ($000):** 26103 **Personnel:** 538	

TROY—Montgomery County

✠ **FIRSTHEALTH MONTGOMERY MEMORIAL HOSPITAL (341303)**, 520 Allen Street, Zip 27371–2802, Mailing Address: P.O. Box 486, Zip 27371–0486; tel. 910/571–5000 **A**1 9 10 18 **F**3 11 15 29 30 40 45 59 64 81 85 87 93 97 107 110 114 119 127 129 133 146 **S** FirstHealth of the Carolinas, Pinehurst, NC
Primary Contact: Beth Walker, R.N., President
CFO: Bryan Hawkins, Controller
CHR: Tina H. Thompson, Coordinator Human Resources
Web address: www.firsthealth.org
Control: Other not–for–profit (including NFP Corporation) **Service:** General Medical and Surgical

Staffed Beds: 25 **Admissions:** 298 **Census:** 2 **Outpatient Visits:** 21873 **Births:** 0 **Total Expense ($000):** 11643 **Payroll Expense ($000):** 5839 **Personnel:** 104	

WADESBORO—Anson County

✠ **ANSON COMMUNITY HOSPITAL (340084)**, 500 Morven Road, Zip 28170–2745; tel. 704/694–5131, (Total facility includes 95 beds in nursing home–type unit) **A**1 9 10 **F**11 15 28 29 30 34 35 40 57 59 62 64 65 71 77 81 86 87 93 97 107 110 114 119 128 130 132 133 135 145 146 **S** Carolinas HealthCare System, Charlotte, NC
Primary Contact: Frederick G. Thompson, Ph.D., President
CFO: John G. Moore, Chief Financial Officer
CMO: A. Niazi, M.D., Chief of Staff
CIO: Lisa Sykes, IS/Communications Director
CHR: Rhonda McFarland, Director Human Resources
CNO: Paula Stegall, R.N., Chief Nurse Executive
Web address: www.carolinashealthcare.org/anson–community–hospital
Control: Hospital district or authority, Government, nonfederal **Service:** General Medical and Surgical

Staffed Beds: 125 **Admissions:** 507 **Census:** 80 **Outpatient Visits:** 23847 **Births:** 0 **Total Expense ($000):** 21375 **Payroll Expense ($000):** 9932 **Personnel:** 207	

WASHINGTON—Beaufort County

BEAUFORT COUNTY HOSPITAL See Vidant Beaufort Hospital

✠ **VIDANT BEAUFORT HOSPITAL (340186)**, 628 East 12th Street, Zip 27889–3409; tel. 252/975–4100 **A**1 9 10 **F**3 5 7 9 13 15 26 27 28 29 30 31 34 35 36 38 40 49 53 57 59 64 65 69 70 75 76 78 79 81 82 85 86 87 93 97 98 99 100 101 102 104 107 108 109 111 115 118 119 129 130 132 135 143 144 145 146 **S** Vidant Health, Greenville, NC
Primary Contact: Harvey Case, President
CFO: Charles Alford, Vice President Finance
CMO: Fred Teixeira, M.D., Chief of Staff
CIO: Amy Boyd, Information Systems Manager
CHR: Penny Coltrain, Director Human Resources
CNO: Lou Montana–Rhodes, Vice President of Patient Care Services
Web address: www.vidanthealth.com
Control: Hospital district or authority, Government, nonfederal **Service:** General Medical and Surgical

Staffed Beds: 43 **Admissions:** 3342 **Census:** 40 **Outpatient Visits:** 55812 **Births:** 330 **Total Expense ($000):** 62216 **Payroll Expense ($000):** 22003 **Personnel:** 470	

WHITEVILLE—Columbus County

✠ **COLUMBUS REGIONAL HEALTHCARE SYSTEM (340068)**, 500 Jefferson Street, Zip 28472–3634; tel. 910/642–8011 **A**1 9 10 19 **F**3 11 13 15 18 26 28 29 31 34 40 45 50 54 57 59 64 70 71 74 75 76 78 79 81 85 86 87 89 92 93 107 108 110 111 119 126 129 130 132 146 148 **P**6 7 **S** Carolinas HealthCare System, Charlotte, NC
Primary Contact: Duane L. Erwin, Interim Chief Executive Officer
CFO: Carl Biber, Chief Financial Officer
CMO: Craig M. Slater, M.D., Chief Medical Officer
CIO: Lisa Ward, Director Management Information Systems
CNO: Terry Beasley, R.N., Chief Nursing Officer
Web address: www.crhealthcare.org
Control: Hospital district or authority, Government, nonfederal **Service:** General Medical and Surgical

Staffed Beds: 103 **Admissions:** 4890 **Census:** 56 **Outpatient Visits:** 124638 **Births:** 446 **Total Expense ($000):** 71949 **Payroll Expense ($000):** 28892 **Personnel:** 504	

WILLIAMSTON—Martin County

✠ **MARTIN GENERAL HOSPITAL (340133)**, 310 South McCaskey Road, Zip 27892–2150, Mailing Address: P.O. Box 1128, Zip 27892–1128; tel. 252/809–6179, (Nonreporting) **A**1 9 10 **S** Community Health Systems, Inc., Franklin, TN
Primary Contact: Craig R. Fichter, Interim Chief Executive Officer
CFO: Craig R. Fichter, Chief Financial Officer
CIO: James Griffin, Manager Information Systems
CHR: Rebecca Edwards, Director Human Resources
CNO: Mary O'Prey, Chief Nursing Officer
Web address: www.martingeneral.com
Control: Corporation, Investor–owned, for–profit **Service:** General Medical and Surgical

Staffed Beds: 49	

WILMINGTON—New Hanover County

✠ △ **NEW HANOVER REGIONAL MEDICAL CENTER (340141)**, 2131 South 17th Street, Zip 28401–7483, Mailing Address: P.O. Box 9000, Zip 28402–9000; tel. 910/343–7000, (Includes CAPE FEAR HOSPITAL, 5301 Wrightsville Avenue, Zip 28403–6599; tel. 910/452–8100) **A**1 2 3 5 7 9 10 12 13 20 **F**3 7 8 11 12 13 15 17 18 22 24 26 28 29 30 31 34 35 36 37 39 40 43 44 45 46 48 49 50 53 54 56 57 58 59 60 61 64 65 66 68 70 72 73 74 75 76 77 78 79 80 81 82 84 85 86 87 88 89 90 92 93 94 96 97 98 100 101 102 103 107 108 110 111 114 115 117 118 119 121 123 126 130 131 132 135 144 146 147 148 **S** New Hanover Regional Medical Center, Wilmington, NC
Primary Contact: John K. Barto, Jr., President and Chief Executive Officer
COO: John H. Gizdic, Chief Operating Officer
CFO: Edwin J. Ollie, Executive Vice President and Chief Financial Officer
CMO: Sam Spicer, M.D., Vice President Medical Affairs
CIO: Avery Cloud, Vice President and Chief Information Officer
CHR: Keith A. Strawn, Vice President Human Resources
CNO: Mary Ellen Bonczek, R.N., Chief Nursing Executive
Web address: www.nhrmc.org
Control: County–Government, nonfederal **Service:** General Medical and Surgical

Staffed Beds: 668 **Admissions:** 38598 **Census:** 517 **Outpatient Visits:** 356800 **Births:** 3934 **Total Expense ($000):** 671121 **Payroll Expense ($000):** 260604 **Personnel:** 4435	

WILMINGTON TREATMENT CENTER (340168), 2520 Troy Drive, Zip 28401–7643; tel. 910/762–2727 **A**10 **F**4 5 29 54 64 82 132 **P**6 **S** CRC Health Group, Inc., Cupertino, CA
Primary Contact: Robert Pitts, Executive Director
COO: Paige Bottom, Director Operations
CFO: Virginia Powell, Director Finance
CMO: Patrick Martin, M.D., Medical Director
Web address: www.wilmtreatment.com
Control: Corporation, Investor–owned, for–profit **Service:** Alcoholism and other chemical dependency

Staffed Beds: 44 **Admissions:** 968 **Census:** 17 **Outpatient Visits:** 35000 **Births:** 0 **Total Expense ($000):** 12000 **Payroll Expense ($000):** 4100 **Personnel:** 112	

WILSON—Wilson County

TRIANGLE EAST NURSING CARE CENTER See WilMed Nursing Care Center

Many Facility Codes have changed. Please refer to the AHA Guide Code Chart.   © 2014 AHA Guide

☒ **WILSON MEDICAL CENTER (340126)**, 1705 Tarboro Street, S.W., Zip 27893–3428; tel. 252/399–8040 **A**1 2 9 10 19 **F**3 11 13 15 18 19 20 22 26 28 29 30 31 34 39 40 43 45 47 48 49 57 60 64 70 73 74 75 76 77 78 79 81 82 83 84 85 86 87 89 90 92 93 94 97 98 101 102 103 107 108 110 111 114 115 118 119 120 121 123 127 129 130 132 135 146 148 **P**6 **S** Duke LifePoint Healthcare, Brentwood, TN
Primary Contact: William E. Caldwell, Jr., Chief Executive Officer
COO: Bert Beard, Chief Operating Officer
CMO: Rick Guarino, M.D., Vice President Medical Affairs
CIO: Brian Dietrick, Director Information Systems
CHR: Denise O'Hara, Vice President Human Resources
Web address: www.wilmed.org
Control: Corporation, Investor–owned, for–profit **Service:** General Medical and Surgical

Staffed Beds: 206 Admissions: 6882 Census: 89 Outpatient Visits: 146419 Births: 993 Personnel: 1010

WINDSOR—Bertie County

☒ **VIDANT BERTIE HOSPITAL (341304)**, 1403 South King Street, Zip 27983–9666, Mailing Address: P.O. Box 40, Zip 27983–0040; tel. 252/794–6600 **A**1 9 10 18 **F**3 15 29 30 34 35 40 45 57 59 64 77 78 79 81 82 93 94 97 107 110 114 119 127 132 135 146 **S** Vidant Health, Greenville, NC
Primary Contact: Jeffrey N. Sackrison, FACHE, President
COO: Jeffery Dial, Chief Operating Officer
CFO: Brian Harvill, Vice President Financial Services
CMO: William Ballance, M.D., Chief of Medical Staff
CIO: Megan Booth–Mills, Director Planning and Marketing
CHR: Mary Beth Hill, Coordinator Human Resources
CNO: Silvia B. Rose, R.N., Director of Patient Care Services
Web address: www.vidanthealth.com
Control: Other not–for–profit (including NFP Corporation) **Service:** General Medical and Surgical

Staffed Beds: 6 Admissions: 494 Census: 5 Outpatient Visits: 23633 Births: 0 Total Expense ($000): 17019 Payroll Expense ($000): 7364 Personnel: 124

WINSTON SALEM—Forsyth County

BRENNER CHILDREN'S HOSPITAL & HEALTH SERVICES See Wake Forest Baptist Medical Center, Winston–Salem

WINSTON-SALEM—Forsyth County

MEDICAL PARK HOSPITAL See Novant Health Medical Park Hospital

☒ △ **NOVANT HEALTH FORSYTH MEDICAL CENTER (340014)**, 3333 Silas Creek Parkway, Zip 27103–3090; tel. 336/718–5000, (Includes KERNERSVILLE MEDICAL CENTER, 2911750 Kernersville Medical Parkway, Kernersville, Zip 27284–2932, Mailing Address: 1750 Kernersville Medical Parkway, Zip 27284–2932; tel. 336/564–4000; Joanne Allen, R.N., President) **A**1 2 3 5 7 9 10 **F**3 4 5 7 8 9 10 12 13 14 17 18 20 22 24 26 28 29 30 31 32 34 35 37 38 40 42 44 45 46 49 50 52 53 54 55 56 57 58 59 60 61 64 65 66 67 68 70 71 72 74 75 76 77 78 79 80 81 82 83 84 85 86 87 89 90 93 98 100 101 102 103 104 105 107 108 109 111 112 114 115 116 117 118 119 120 121 123 124 126 128 129 130 131 132 135 143 146 147 148 **P**6 **S** Novant Health, Winston Salem, NC
Primary Contact: Denise B. Mihal, R.N., Chief Executive Officer
CMO: Elms Allen, M.D., Senior Vice President Medical Affairs
CIO: David B. Garrett, Chief Information Officer
CHR: Janet Smith–Hill, Senior Vice President Human Resources
Web address: www.forsythmedicalcenter.org
Control: Other not–for–profit (including NFP Corporation) **Service:** General Medical and Surgical

Staffed Beds: 660 Admissions: 42795 Census: 644 Outpatient Visits: 397609 Births: 6130 Total Expense ($000): 706717 Payroll Expense ($000): 240839 Personnel: 4416

☒ **NOVANT HEALTH MEDICAL PARK HOSPITAL (340148)**, 1950 South Hawthorne Road, Zip 27103–3993; tel. 336/718–0600 **A**1 9 10 **F**3 29 35 39 64 68 74 78 79 81 82 85 89 126 130 131 146 **S** Novant Health, Winston Salem, NC
Primary Contact: Teresa Carter, Vice President and Chief Operating Officer
COO: Jeffery T. Lindsay, Executive Vice President and Chief Operating Officer
CMO: Elms Allen, M.D., Senior Vice President Medical Affairs
CHR: Vasilia Perimenis, Vice President Human Resources
Web address: www.novanthealth.org
Control: Other not–for–profit (including NFP Corporation) **Service:** General Medical and Surgical

Staffed Beds: 22 Admissions: 787 Census: 8 Outpatient Visits: 40465 Births: 0 Total Expense ($000): 46907 Payroll Expense ($000): 12327 Personnel: 249

☐ **OLD VINEYARD BEHAVIORAL HEALTH SERVICES (344007)**, 3637 Old Vineyard Road, Zip 27104–4842; tel. 336/794–3550 **A**1 10 **F**29 50 75 87 98 99 101 102 103 104 105 130 **S** Universal Health Services, Inc., King of Prussia, PA
Primary Contact: Kevin Patton, Chief Executive Officer
CFO: Ernest C. Priddy, III, Chief Financial Officer
CMO: Raj Thotakura, M.D., Medical Director
CHR: Jackie Pennino, Director Human Resources
CNO: Carol Fisher, Director of Nursing
Web address: www.oldvineyardbhs.com
Control: Corporation, Investor–owned, for–profit **Service:** Psychiatric

Staffed Beds: 102 Admissions: 4050 Census: 96 Outpatient Visits: 3287 Births: 0 Total Expense ($000): 19131 Payroll Expense ($000): 9350 Personnel: 166

☒ **SELECT SPECIALTY HOSPITAL–WINSTON–SALEM (342016)**, 3333 Silas Creek Parkway, 6th Floor, Zip 27103–3013; tel. 336/718–6300, (Nonreporting) **A**1 10 **S** Select Medical Corporation, Mechanicsburg, PA
Primary Contact: Leslie Deane, Chief Executive Officer
CHR: Sherry Meacham, Coordinator Human Resources
Web address: www.selectspecialtyhospitals.com/company/locations/winston–salem.aspx
Control: Corporation, Investor–owned, for–profit **Service:** Long–Term Acute Care hospital

Staffed Beds: 42

☒ △ **WAKE FOREST BAPTIST MEDICAL CENTER (340047)**, Medical Center Boulevard, Zip 27157–0001; tel. 336/716–2011, (Includes BRENNER CHILDREN'S HOSPITAL & HEALTH SERVICES, Medical Center Boulevard, Winston Salem, Zip 27157, Mailing Address: One Medical Center Boulevard, Zip 27157; tel. 336/716–2255) **A**1 3 5 7 8 9 10 **F**3 5 6 7 8 9 11 12 15 16 17 18 19 20 21 22 23 24 25 26 27 28 29 30 31 32 34 35 36 37 38 39 40 41 43 44 45 46 47 48 49 50 52 53 54 55 56 57 58 59 60 61 62 64 65 66 67 68 70 71 72 73 74 75 77 78 79 80 81 82 83 84 85 86 87 88 89 90 92 93 96 97 98 99 100 101 102 103 104 107 108 110 111 113 114 115 116 117 118 119 120 121 122 123 124 126 129 130 131 134 135 136 137 138 141 142 143 144 145 146 147 148 **P**6 7 **S** Wake Forest Baptist Health, Winston–Salem, NC
Primary Contact: John D. McConnell, M.D., Chief Executive Officer
COO: K. Carbone, M.D., President
CFO: C. Michael Rutherford, Vice President Financial Services and Chief Financial Officer
CMO: Russell M. Howerton, M.D., Chief Medical Officer
CIO: Chad Eckes, Vice President Information Services and Chief Information Officer
CHR: Cheryl Locke, Vice President and Chief Human Resource Officer
CNO: Maureen Sintich, R.N., Vice President and Chief Nursing Officer
Web address: www.wakehealth.edu
Control: Other not–for–profit (including NFP Corporation) **Service:** General Medical and Surgical

Staffed Beds: 854 Admissions: 39073 Census: 780 Outpatient Visits: 820478 Births: 10 Total Expense ($000): 1185475 Payroll Expense ($000): 435102 Personnel: 8319

WAKE FOREST UNIVERSITY HEALTH SERVICE (349803), Medical Center Boulevard, Zip 27109, Mailing Address: P.O. Box 7386, Zip 27109–7386; tel. 336/758–5937, (Nonreporting) **A**2 10
Primary Contact: Cecil Price, M.D., Director
Web address: www.wfu.edu
Control: Other not–for–profit (including NFP Corporation) **Service:** Hospital unit of an institution (prison hospital, college infimary, etc.)

Staffed Beds: 6

YADKINVILLE—Yadkin County

HOOTS MEMORIAL HOSPITAL See Yadkin Valley Community Hospital

★ ◇ **YADKIN VALLEY COMMUNITY HOSPITAL (341308)**, 624 West Main Street, Zip 27055–7804, Mailing Address: P.O. Box 68, Zip 27055–0068; tel. 336/679–2041, (Nonreporting) **A**9 10 18 21 **S** Rural Community Hospitals of America, Kansas City, MO
Primary Contact: Shawn Bright, Chief Executive Officer
CMO: James McGrath, M.D., Chief Medical Officer
CNO: Tina Elan, R.N., Chief Nursing Officer
Web address: www.yadkinhospital.com/
Control: Other not–for–profit (including NFP Corporation) **Service:** General Medical and Surgical

Staffed Beds: 22

Hospital, Medicare Provider Number, Address, Telephone, Approval, Facility, and Physician Codes, Health Care System

★ American Hospital Association (AHA) membership
☐ The Joint Commission accreditation   ◇ DNV Healthcare Inc. accreditation
◯ Healthcare Facilities Accreditation Program
△ Commission on Accreditation of Rehabilitation Facilities (CARF) accreditation

NC

NORTH DAKOTA

ASHLEY—Mcintosh County

★ **ASHLEY MEDICAL CENTER (351322)**, 612 North Center Avenue,
Zip 58413–7013, Mailing Address: P.O. Box 450, Zip 58413–0450;
tel. 701/288–3433, (Total facility includes 44 beds in nursing home–type unit) **A**9
10 18 **F**3 8 15 28 29 40 41 45 49 56 57 59 60 64 65 70 75 81 83 87 93 97
107 110 114 125 127 128 130 131 132 133 144 146 147 148
Primary Contact: Jerry Lepp, Chief Executive Officer
CMO: Udom Tinsa, M.D., Medical Director
Web address: www.amctoday.org
Control: Other not–for–profit (including NFP Corporation) **Service:** General
Medical and Surgical

> **Staffed Beds:** 64 **Admissions:** 183 **Census:** 44 **Outpatient Visits:** 4342
> **Births:** 0 **Total Expense ($000):** 6484 **Payroll Expense ($000):** 4295
> **Personnel:** 93

BELCOURT—Rolette County

☐ **PUBLIC HEALTH SERVICE INDIAN HOSPITAL – QUENTIN N. BURDICK
MEMORIAL HEALTH FACILITY (350063)**, 1300 Hospital Loop, Zip 58316,
Mailing Address: P.O. Box 160, Zip 58316–0160; tel. 701/477–6111 **A**1 3 5 10
F3 7 15 29 34 38 39 40 41 45 48 50 54 56 57 59 61 62 64 65 67 75 76 77
81 82 83 85 86 87 89 90 93 96 97 98 99 100 101 102 103 104 105 106
107 108 110 114 119 129 130 132 135 144 145 146 147 148 **S** U. S.
Indian Health Service, Rockville, MD
Primary Contact: Shelly Harris, Chief Executive Officer
CFO: Deland Davis, Chief Financial Officer
CMO: Vernon Azure, Clinical Director
CIO: Chance Wilkie, Information Technology Specialist
CHR: Donna Belgarde, Human Resources Specialist
CNO: Lynelle Hung, Director of Nursing
Web address: www.ihs.gov
Control: PHS, Indian Service, Government, federal **Service:** General Medical and
Surgical

> **Staffed Beds:** 27 **Admissions:** 322 **Census:** 6 **Outpatient Visits:** 197236
> **Births:** 285 **Total Expense ($000):** 36675 **Payroll Expense ($000):** 22461
> **Personnel:** 276

BISMARCK—Burleigh County

⊠ △ **SANFORD BISMARCK (350015)**, 300 North Seventh Street,
Zip 58501–4439, Mailing Address: P.O. Box 5525, Zip 58506–5525;
tel. 701/323–6000 **A**1 2 3 5 7 9 10 **F**3 7 9 11 12 13 15 17 18 20 22 24 26
28 29 30 31 32 33 34 35 36 37 38 40 43 44 45 48 49 50 51 52 53 54 56
57 58 59 60 61 62 63 64 65 68 69 70 72 73 74 75 76 77 78 79 81 82 85
86 87 88 89 90 91 92 93 96 97 98 99 100 101 102 103 104 105 107 108
110 111 114 115 116 117 118 119 126 128 129 130 131 132 135 138 144
146 147 148 **P**6 **S** Sanford Health, Sioux Falls, SD
Primary Contact: Craig Lambrecht, M.D., President
COO: Al Hurley, Clinic Chief Operating Officer
CFO: Kirk Cristy, Chief Financial Officer
CMO: Chris Meeker, M.D., Chief Medical Officer
CHR: Scott D. Boehm, Executive Vice President Human Resources and Facilities
CNO: Jan Kamphuis, Ph.D., Executive Vice President and Chief Nurse Executive
Web address: www.bismarck.sanfordhealth.org/
Control: Other not–for–profit (including NFP Corporation) **Service:** General
Medical and Surgical

> **Staffed Beds:** 208 **Admissions:** 10724 **Census:** 128 **Outpatient Visits:**
> 129537 **Births:** 845 **Total Expense ($000):** 357658 **Payroll Expense**
> **($000):** 183170 **Personnel:** 2693

SANFORD HEALTH See Sanford Bismarck

⊠ △ **ST. ALEXIUS MEDICAL CENTER (350002)**, 900 East Broadway,
Zip 58501–4586, Mailing Address: P.O. Box 5510, Zip 58506–5510;
tel. 701/530–7000, (Total facility includes 19 beds in nursing home–type unit) **A**1
2 3 5 7 9 10 **F**3 8 9 11 12 13 15 17 18 19 20 21 22 23 24 25 26 28 29 30
32 34 35 38 40 43 49 53 56 57 58 59 60 62 63 64 68 70 72 74 75 76 77
78 79 81 82 85 86 87 88 89 90 91 92 93 94 95 97 98 99 100 101 102 103
104 105 106 107 110 111 114 117 119 128 129 130 131 132 135 146 147
148 **P**8 **S** Benedictine Sisters of the Annunciation, Bismarck, ND
Primary Contact: Gary P. Miller, President and Chief Executive Officer
CFO: Susan Sisk, Chief Financial Officer
CMO: Shiraz Hyder, M.D., Director Medical Affairs
CIO: Todd Bortke, Director Information Systems
CHR: Tom Gregg, Vice President Human Resources
CNO: Rosanne Schmidt, R.N., Chief Nursing Officer
Web address: www.st.alexius.org
Control: Church–operated, Nongovernment, not–for profit **Service:** General
Medical and Surgical

> **Staffed Beds:** 271 **Admissions:** 11608 **Census:** 148 **Outpatient Visits:**
> 246278 **Births:** 1491 **Total Expense ($000):** 266630 **Payroll Expense**
> **($000):** 125226 **Personnel:** 2220

BOTTINEAU—Bottineau County

ST. ANDREW'S HEALTH CENTER (351307), 316 Ohmer Street,
Zip 58318–1045; tel. 701/228–9300 **A**5 9 10 18 **F**29 30 34 35 40 43 57 59
79 93 107 108 110 125 127 130 132 133 143 144 146 **S** Sisters of Mary of
the Presentation Health System, Fargo, ND
Primary Contact: Jodi Atkinson, President and Chief Executive Officer
CFO: Sean Rinkenberger, Chief Financial Officer
CMO: Jessica Skjolden, M.D., Chief of Staff
CIO: Jeff Ofstedal, Director Information Technology
CHR: Brenda Arneson, Administrative Assistant
CNO: Karla Spence, Director of Nursing
Web address: www.standrewshealth.com
Control: Church–operated, Nongovernment, not–for profit **Service:** General
Medical and Surgical

> **Staffed Beds:** 25 **Admissions:** 212 **Census:** 22 **Outpatient Visits:** 7700
> **Births:** 0 **Total Expense ($000):** 7002 **Payroll Expense ($000):** 2878
> **Personnel:** 90

BOWMAN—Bowman County

SOUTHWEST HEALTHCARE SERVICES (351313), 802 2nd Street Northwest,
Zip 58623–4483, Mailing Address: P.O. Drawer C, Zip 58623;
tel. 701/523–5265, (Nonreporting) **A**9 10 18
Primary Contact: Becky Hansen, Chief Executive Officer
CFO: Becky Hansen, Chief Financial Officer
Web address: www.swhealthcare.net
Control: Other not–for–profit (including NFP Corporation) **Service:** General
Medical and Surgical

> **Staffed Beds:** 89

CANDO—Towner County

★ **TOWNER COUNTY MEDICAL CENTER (351331)**, State Highway 281 North,
Zip 58324, Mailing Address: P.O. Box 688, Zip 58324–0688;
tel. 701/968–4411, (Nonreporting) **A**5 9 10 18
Primary Contact: Ivan Mitchell, Chief Executive Officer
CFO: Tammy Larson, Chief Financial Officer
CMO: Russ Petty, M.D., Chief of Staff
CIO: David Fite, Director Information Technology
CHR: Pat Klingenberg, Director Human Resources
Web address: www.tcmedcenter.org
Control: Other not–for–profit (including NFP Corporation) **Service:** General
Medical and Surgical

> **Staffed Beds:** 20

CARRINGTON—Foster County

★ **CARRINGTON HEALTH CENTER (351318)**, 800 North Fourth Street,
Zip 58421–1217, Mailing Address: P.O. Box 461, Zip 58421–0461;
tel. 701/652–3141, (Nonreporting) **A**5 9 10 18 **S** Catholic Health Initiatives,
Englewood, CO
Primary Contact: Mariann Doeling, R.N., President
COO: Brenda Rask, Vice President Operations
CFO: Cyndee Thormodson, Chief Financial Officer
CMO: Todd Schaffer, M.D., Chief Medical Officer
CIO: Keith Stauffer, Regional Chief Information Officer
CHR: Lesley Erlandson, Human Resources
Web address: www.carringtonhealthcenter.org
Control: Church–operated, Nongovernment, not–for profit **Service:** General
Medical and Surgical

> **Staffed Beds:** 49

CAVALIER—Pembina County

★ **PEMBINA COUNTY MEMORIAL HOSPITAL AND WEDGEWOOD MANOR
(351319)**, 301 Mountain Street East, Zip 58220–4015, Mailing Address: P.O.
Box 380, Zip 58220–0380; tel. 701/265–8461, (Total facility includes 50 beds
in nursing home–type unit) **A**5 9 10 18 **F**1 2 3 4 16 17 28 29 31 40 42 43 45
56 59 65 67 68 70 72 73 76 78 80 81 82 84 85 86 87 88 89 90 93 97 98
107 114 119 127 128 130 131 132 133 135 146 **P**5
Primary Contact: Everett A. Butler, Interim Chief Executive Officer
CMO: K. S. Sumra, M.D., Chief of Staff
CIO: Robert Heidt, Director Information Systems
Web address: www.cavalierhospital.com
Control: Other not–for–profit (including NFP Corporation) **Service:** General
Medical and Surgical

> **Staffed Beds:** 74 **Admissions:** 249 **Census:** 51 **Outpatient Visits:** 15201
> **Births:** 0 **Total Expense ($000):** 6457 **Payroll Expense ($000):** 4020
> **Personnel:** 130

Many Facility Codes have changed. Please refer to the AHA Guide Code Chart.

COOPERSTOWN—Griggs County

COOPERSTOWN MEDICAL CENTER (351306), 1200 Roberts Avenue, Zip 58425–7101; tel. 701/797–2221, (Nonreporting) **A**9 10 18
Primary Contact: Nikki Johnson, Interim Chief Executive Officer
CMO: Jeffrey Peterson, M.D., Medical Director
CHR: Pamela VenHuizen, Chief Human Resources Officer
Web address: www.coopermc.com
Control: Other not–for–profit (including NFP Corporation) **Service:** General Medical and Surgical

Staffed Beds: 10

CROSBY—Divide County

ST. LUKE'S HOSPITAL (351325), 702 First Street Southwest, Zip 58730–3329, Mailing Address: P.O. Box 10, Zip 58730–0010; tel. 701/965–6384, (Nonreporting) **A**5 9 10 18
Primary Contact: Leslie O. Urvand, Administrator
Web address: www.dcstlukes.org/
Control: Other not–for–profit (including NFP Corporation) **Service:** General Medical and Surgical

Staffed Beds: 12

DEVILS LAKE—Ramsey County

⊞ **MERCY HOSPITAL (351333)**, 1031 Seventh Street N.E., Zip 58301–2798; tel. 701/662–2131 **A**1 5 9 10 18 **F**3 11 13 17 27 28 29 34 35 40 43 45 50 53 57 70 75 76 81 87 89 93 **S** Catholic Health Initiatives, Englewood, CO
CFO: Cyndee Thormodson, Assistant Vice President Finance
CHR: Bonnie Mattern, Director Human Resources
CNO: Sarah Aliff, Vice President Patient Care Service and Chief Nursing Officer
Web address: www.mercyhospitaldl.com
Control: Other not–for–profit (including NFP Corporation) **Service:** General Medical and Surgical

Staffed Beds: 25 Admissions: 906 Census: 86 Outpatient Visits: 31321 Births: 295 Total Expense ($000): 19476 Payroll Expense ($000): 8523 Personnel: 140

DICKINSON—Stark County

⊞ **ST. JOSEPH'S HOSPITAL AND HEALTH CENTER (351336)**, 30 Seventh Street West, Zip 58601–4399; tel. 701/456–4000 **A**1 5 9 10 18 **F**3 8 11 13 15 28 29 30 34 35 40 53 57 59 64 70 75 76 79 81 84 85 86 87 89 97 107 108 111 114 119 127 129 130 132 133 146 **S** Catholic Health Initiatives, Englewood, CO
Primary Contact: Reed Reyman, President
CFO: Stephanie Franken, Vice President Operational Finance
CHR: Denise Lutz, Chief Human Resources Officer
CNO: DeeAnna Opstedahl, Vice President Patient Care Services
Web address: www.stjoeshospital.org
Control: Church–operated, Nongovernment, not–for profit **Service:** General Medical and Surgical

Staffed Beds: 25 Admissions: 1645 Census: 12 Outpatient Visits: 49635 Births: 503 Total Expense ($000): 53102 Payroll Expense ($000): 22004 Personnel: 315

ELGIN—Grant County

JACOBSON MEMORIAL HOSPITAL CARE CENTER (351314), 601 East Street North, Zip 58533–7105, Mailing Address: P.O. Box 367, Zip 58533–0367; tel. 701/584–2792 **A**9 10 18 **F**15 28 32 34 40 41 43 59 64 65 77 107 111 114 119 127 130 133 148
Primary Contact: Theo Stoller, Chief Executive Officer
CFO: Scott Ostenson, Chief Financial Officer
CMO: Deepak Goyal, M.D., Chief of Staff
CHR: Rynae Golke, Director Human Resources
Web address: www.jacobsonhospital.org
Control: Other not–for–profit (including NFP Corporation) **Service:** General Medical and Surgical

Staffed Beds: 25 Admissions: 120 Census: 17 Outpatient Visits: 8711 Births: 0 Total Expense ($000): 5487 Payroll Expense ($000): 2158 Personnel: 60

FARGO—Cass County

⊞ **ESSENTIA HEALTH FARGO (350070)**, 3000 32nd Avenue South, Zip 58103–6132; tel. 701/364–8000, (Nonreporting) **A**1 2 5 9 10 **S** Essentia Health, Duluth, MN
Primary Contact: Timothy Sayler, Chief Operating Officer
COO: Timothy Sayler, Chief Operating Officer
CFO: Dennis Fuhrman, Vice President Finance
CMO: Michael Briggs, M.D., Chief Medical Officer
CIO: Ken Gilles, Chief Information Officer
CHR: Keith Wahlund, Vice President Human Resources
Web address: www.essentiahealth.com
Control: Other not–for–profit (including NFP Corporation) **Service:** General Medical and Surgical

Staffed Beds: 94

⊞ **FARGO VETERANS AFFAIRS HEALTH CARE SYSTEM**, 2101 Elm Street North, Zip 58102–2498; tel. 701/232–3241, (Nonreporting) **A**1 2 3 5 **S** Department of Veterans Affairs, Washington, DC
Primary Contact: Lavonne Liversage, Director
COO: Dale DeKrey, MS, Associate Director Operations and Resources
CFO: Roger Sayler, Finance Officer
CMO: J. Brian Hancock, M.D., Chief of Staff
CIO: Raymond Nelson, Acting Chief Information Resource Management
CHR: Jason Wells, Chief Human Resources Management Service
CNO: Julie Bruhn, R.N., Associate Director Patient Care and Nurse Executive
Web address: www.fargo.va.gov/
Control: Veterans Affairs, Government, federal **Service:** General Medical and Surgical

Staffed Beds: 42

INNOVIS HEALTH See Essentia Health Fargo

KINDRED HOSPITAL FARGO See Vibra Hospital of Fargo

MERITCARE MEDICAL CENTER See Sanford Medical Center Fargo

⊞ **PRAIRIE ST. JOHN'S (354004)**, 510 4th Street South, Zip 58103–1914; tel. 701/476–7200 **A**1 9 10 **F**4 5 29 34 35 40 41 50 57 87 98 99 100 101 102 103 104 105 106 **P**6 **S** Universal Health Services, Inc., King of Prussia, PA
Primary Contact: Gregory LaFrancois, Chief Executive Officer
COO: Jennifer Faul, Chief Operating Officer
CFO: Tom Eide, Chief Financial Officer
CMO: Eduardo Meza, M.D., Medical Director
CHR: Michelle A. Parkinson, Director Human Resources
CNO: Jacki Toppen, Director of Nursing
Web address: www.prairie–stjohns.com
Control: Corporation, Investor–owned, for–profit **Service:** Psychiatric

Staffed Beds: 94 Admissions: 3100 Census: 70 Births: 0 Total Expense ($000): 25550 Payroll Expense ($000): 16136 Personnel: 310

⊞ △ **SANFORD MEDICAL CENTER FARGO (350011)**, 801 Broadway North, Zip 58122–3641; tel. 701/234–2000, (Includes SANFORD SOUTH UNIVERSITY, 1720 South University Drive, Zip 58103–4994; tel. 701/234–2000) **A**1 2 3 5 7 8 9 10 19 **F**3 7 8 9 11 12 13 15 17 18 19 20 21 22 23 24 25 26 27 28 29 30 31 32 33 34 35 36 37 38 39 40 43 44 45 46 47 48 49 50 51 52 53 54 55 56 57 58 59 60 61 62 63 64 65 68 70 71 72 73 74 75 76 78 79 80 81 82 83 84 85 86 87 88 89 90 91 92 93 96 97 98 99 100 101 102 103 104 105 107 111 112 114 115 116 117 118 119 120 121 123 124 126 129 130 131 132 135 138 141 142 143 144 145 146 147 148 **P**6 **S** Sanford Health, Sioux Falls, SD
Primary Contact: Paul Richard, President and Chief Executive Officer
COO: Karen A. Tobin, R.N., Chief Operating Officer
CFO: Tiffany Lawrence, Chief Financial Officer
CIO: Caryn Hewitt, Executive Partner Information Technology and Chief Information Officer
CHR: Ann Christenson, Executive Vice President Human Resources and Support Services
CNO: Carla L. Hansen, R.N., Chief Nurse Executive
Web address: www.sanfordhealth.org
Control: Other not–for–profit (including NFP Corporation) **Service:** General Medical and Surgical

Staffed Beds: 492 Admissions: 26744 Census: 342 Outpatient Visits: 414481 Births: 2435 Total Expense ($000): 792959 Payroll Expense ($000): 192470 Personnel: 3807

VETERANS AFFAIRS HEALTH CARE SYSTEM See Fargo Veterans Affairs Health Care System

---

Hospital, Medicare Provider Number, Address, Telephone, Approval, Facility, and Physician Codes, Health Care System

★ American Hospital Association (AHA) membership
□ The Joint Commission accreditation
◇ DNV Healthcare Inc. accreditation
○ Healthcare Facilities Accreditation Program
△ Commission on Accreditation of Rehabilitation Facilities (CARF) accreditation

✠ **VIBRA HOSPITAL OF FARGO (352004)**, 1720 University Drive South, Zip 58103–4940; tel. 701/241–9099, (Nonreporting) **A**1 9 10 **S** Vibra Healthcare, Mechanicsburg, PA
Primary Contact: Custer Huseby, Chief Executive Officer
Web address: www.vhfargo.com
Control: Corporation, Investor–owned, for–profit **Service:** Long–Term Acute Care hospital

Staffed Beds: 31

FORT YATES—Sioux County

U. S. PUBLIC HEALTH SERVICE INDIAN HOSPITAL (350064), N 10 North River Road, Zip 58538, Mailing Address: P.O. Box J, Zip 58538; tel. 701/854–3831, (Nonreporting) **A**5 9 10 **S** U. S. Indian Health Service, Rockville, MD
Primary Contact: Lisa Guardipee, Director
CFO: William Condon, Deputy Administrative Officer
Web address: www.ihs.gov
Control: PHS, Indian Service, Government, federal **Service:** General Medical and Surgical

Staffed Beds: 14

GARRISON—Mclean County

★ **GARRISON MEMORIAL HOSPITAL (351303)**, 407 Third Avenue S.E., Zip 58540–7235; tel. 701/463–2275, (Total facility includes 28 beds in nursing home–type unit) **A**5 9 10 18 **F**2 3 34 35 40 56 57 59 65 66 68 93 97 107 127 128 130 131 133 148 **P**6 **S** Benedictine Sisters of the Annunciation, Bismarck, ND
Primary Contact: Tod Graeber, Administrator
CMO: Vern Harchenko, M.D., Chief of Staff
CNO: Beth Hetletved, Director of Nurses
Web address: www.garrisonmh.com
Control: Church–operated, Nongovernment, not–for profit **Service:** General Medical and Surgical

Staffed Beds: 50 Admissions: 177 Census: 27 Outpatient Visits: 14500 Births: 0 Total Expense ($000): 6525 Payroll Expense ($000): 3698 Personnel: 105

GRAFTON—Walsh County

★ **UNITY MEDICAL CENTER (351320)**, 164 West 13th Street, Zip 58237–1896; tel. 701/352–1620, (Nonreporting) **A**5 9 10 18
Primary Contact: Alan O'Neil, Chief Executive Officer
CFO: Rachel Ray, Chief Financial Officer
Web address: www.unitymedcenter.com
Control: Other not–for–profit (including NFP Corporation) **Service:** General Medical and Surgical

Staffed Beds: 17

GRAND FORKS—Grand Forks County

✠ △ **ALTRU HEALTH SYSTEM (350019)**, 1200 South Columbia Road, Zip 58201–4036, Mailing Address: P.O. Box 6002, Zip 58206–6002; tel. 701/780–5000, (Includes ALTRU HOSPITAL, 1200 South Columbia Road, Zip 58201; tel. 701/780–5000; ALTRU REHABILITATION CENTER, 1300 South Columbia Road, Zip 58201; tel. 701/780–2311) **A**1 2 3 5 7 9 10 20 **F**3 5 7 8 10 11 12 13 14 15 18 20 22 24 28 29 30 31 32 33 34 35 36 37 38 40 43 44 45 48 49 50 52 53 55 56 57 58 59 60 61 62 63 64 65 69 70 71 72 74 75 77 78 79 81 82 83 84 85 86 87 90 91 92 93 94 96 97 98 99 100 101 102 103 104 105 107 108 110 111 114 117 119 121 123 124 125 129 130 131 132 135 143 144 145 146 147 148 **P**6
Primary Contact: David R. Molmen, Chief Executive Officer
COO: Brad Wehe, Chief Operating Officer
CFO: Dwight Thompson, Chief Financial Officer
CMO: Eric Lunn, M.D., Chief Medical Executive
CIO: Mark Waind, Administrative Director Information Services
CHR: Kellee J. Fisk, Chief People Resources Executive
CNO: Margaret M. Reed, R.N., Chief Nursing Executive
Web address: www.altru.org
Control: Other not–for–profit (including NFP Corporation) **Service:** General Medical and Surgical

Staffed Beds: 273 Admissions: 12812 Census: 176 Outpatient Visits: 750386 Births: 1648 Total Expense ($000): 458953 Payroll Expense ($000): 239607 Personnel: 3320

◇ **RICHARD P. STADTER PSYCHIATRIC CENTER (354005)**, 1451 44th Avenue South Unit A., Zip 58201–3434; tel. 701/772–2500, (Nonreporting) **A**9 10 21
Primary Contact: Bonnie Peterson, Chief Executive Officer
CFO: Michelle Currie, Chief Financial Officer
CMO: Thomas Peterson, M.D., President
CHR: Amanda Altendorf, Chief Human Resources and Quality Management
Web address: www.stadtercenter.com
Control: Corporation, Investor–owned, for–profit **Service:** Psychiatric

Staffed Beds: 34

HARVEY—Wells County

★ **ST. ALOISIUS MEDICAL CENTER (351327)**, 325 East Brewster Street, Zip 58341–1653; tel. 701/324–4651, (Total facility includes 95 beds in nursing home–type unit) **A**5 9 10 18 **F**15 28 30 40 45 53 56 57 59 77 81 85 93 107 110 114 125 128 130 131 132 133 146 147 **S** Sisters of Mary of the Presentation Health System, Fargo, ND
Primary Contact: Rockford Zastoupil, President and Chief Executive Officer
CFO: Sandra Teubner, Chief Financial Officer
Web address: www.staloisius.com
Control: Church–operated, Nongovernment, not–for profit **Service:** General Medical and Surgical

Staffed Beds: 110 Admissions: 469 Census: 83 Outpatient Visits: 6830 Births: 20 Total Expense ($000): 12643 Payroll Expense ($000): 6295 Personnel: 183

HAZEN—Mercer County

★ **SAKAKAWEA MEDICAL CENTER (351310)**, 510 Eighth Avenue N.E., Zip 58545–4637; tel. 701/748–2225, (Nonreporting) **A**5 9 10 18
Primary Contact: Darrold Bertsch, Chief Executive Officer
CFO: Renae Snyder, Chief Financial Officer
CHR: Laurie Hulm, Administrative Assistant
CNO: Marcie Schulz, Director Patient Care
Web address: www.sakmedcenter.com
Control: Other not–for–profit (including NFP Corporation) **Service:** General Medical and Surgical

Staffed Beds: 18

HETTINGER—Adams County

WEST RIVER REGIONAL MEDICAL CENTER (351330), 1000 Highway 12, Zip 58639–7530; tel. 701/567–4561 **A**5 9 10 18 **F**7 8 11 13 15 17 28 29 31 34 35 40 41 43 45 53 54 56 57 59 64 65 75 76 77 81 84 85 86 87 89 92 93 94 97 107 108 110 114 118 119 127 132 133 135 143 144 146 **P**5
Primary Contact: James K. Long, CPA, Administrator and Chief Executive Officer
CFO: Nathan Stadheim, Chief Financial Officer
CMO: Josh Ronum, Chief of Staff
CIO: Julia Gochenour, Manager Information Systems
CHR: Tera Fried, Manager Human Resources
CNO: Barbara Stadheim, Chief Nursing Officer
Web address: www.wrhs.org
Control: Other not–for–profit (including NFP Corporation) **Service:** General Medical and Surgical

Staffed Beds: 25 Admissions: 1049 Census: 12 Outpatient Visits: 14267 Births: 110 Total Expense ($000): 15651 Payroll Expense ($000): 6671 Personnel: 211

HILLSBORO—Traill County

★ **SANFORD HILLSBORO MEDICAL CENTER (351329)**, 12 Third Street S.E., Zip 58045–4840, Mailing Address: P.O. Box 609, Zip 58045–0609; tel. 701/636–3200, (Total facility includes 36 beds in nursing home–type unit) **A**5 9 10 18 **F**7 10 11 34 35 40 64 65 68 75 93 97 103 125 128 130 131 133 143 146 148 **S** Sanford Health, Sioux Falls, SD
Primary Contact: Jac McTaggart, Chief Executive Officer
CFO: Scott Awalt, Chief Financial Officer
CMO: Charles J. Breen, M.D., Medical Director
CHR: Jenny Jacobson, Manager Human Resources
Web address: www.hillsboromedicalcenter.com
Control: Other not–for–profit (including NFP Corporation) **Service:** General Medical and Surgical

Staffed Beds: 52 Admissions: 220 Census: 41 Outpatient Visits: 8824 Births: 0 Total Expense ($000): 8539 Payroll Expense ($000): 3523 Personnel: 89

JAMESTOWN—Stutsman County

✠ **JAMESTOWN REGIONAL MEDICAL CENTER (351335)**, 2422 20th Street S.W., Zip 58401–6201; tel. 701/252–1050 **A**1 5 10 18 **F**3 11 13 15 31 34 35 40 43 45 50 53 57 59 62 63 64 70 75 77 79 81 82 84 85 86 87 93 107 108 110 111 115 118 119 130 131 132 133 135 146
Primary Contact: K. C. DeBoer, President and Chief Executive Officer
COO: Ricki Ramlo, Chief Operating Officer and Vice President Operations
CFO: Brandon Vaughan, Chief Financial Officer and Vice President Finance
CMO: Derek Brickner, President Medical Staff
CIO: Jeff Gunkel, Chief Information Officer
CHR: Ricki Ramlo, Vice President Human Resources
CNO: Trisha Jungels, Chief Nursing Officer and Vice President Clinical Services
Web address: www.jamestownhospital.com
Control: Other not–for–profit (including NFP Corporation) **Service:** General Medical and Surgical

Staffed Beds: 25 Admissions: 1290 Census: 11 Outpatient Visits: 28613 Births: 359 Total Expense ($000): 36880 Payroll Expense ($000): 15225 Personnel: 289

NORTH DAKOTA STATE HOSPITAL (354003), 2605 Circle Drive S.E., Zip 58401–6905; tel. 701/253–3964, (Nonreporting) **A**1 5 9 10
Primary Contact: Alex Schweitzer, Superintendent and Chief Executive Officer
COO: Ken Schulz, Chief Operating Officer
CMO: Eduardo Yabut, M.D., Medical Director
CIO: Amy Shape, Information Technology
CHR: Lyle Grove, Human Resources Director
CNO: Leah Schulz, Director of Nursing
Web address: www.nd.gov/
Control: State–Government, nonfederal **Service:** Psychiatric

Staffed Beds: 140

KENMARE—Ward County

★ **KENMARE COMMUNITY HOSPITAL (351305)**, 317 First Avenue N.W., Zip 58746–7104, Mailing Address: P.O. Box 697, Zip 58746–0697; tel. 701/385–4296 **A**9 10 18 **F**40 53 56 57 59 64 93 127 128 130 133
Primary Contact: Margaret Shawn Smothers, Administrator
COO: Bev Heninger, Director of Nursing
CFO: Dennis Empey, Chief Financial Officer
CMO: Buki Oni, M.D., Chief Medical Officer
CIO: David Wanner, Director Information Technology
CHR: Ranae Ehlke, Administrative Secretary and Coordinator Risk Management and Human Resources
CNO: Bev Heninger, Director of Nursing
Web address: www.kenmarend.net/hospital.htm
Control: Other not–for–profit (including NFP Corporation) **Service:** General Medical and Surgical

Staffed Beds: 25 Admissions: 37 Census: 19 Outpatient Visits: 531 Births: 0 Total Expense ($000): 3444 Payroll Expense ($000): 2902 Personnel: 59

LANGDON—Cavalier County

★ **CAVALIER COUNTY MEMORIAL HOSPITAL (351323)**, 909 Second Street, Zip 58249–2407; tel. 701/256–6100 **A**5 9 10 18 **F**3 7 8 9 12 15 18 19 28 29 30 34 35 40 45 50 56 57 59 64 65 66 68 75 77 78 79 81 82 86 87 93 96 97 99 100 101 102 103 104 107 110 111 119 127 129 130 131 132 133 143 144 147 148 **P**6
Primary Contact: Lawrence Blue, Administrator and Chief Executive Officer
COO: Lawrence Blue, Administrator and Chief Executive Officer
CFO: Julie Feil, Accountant
CMO: Suresh Patel, M.D., Chief Medical Officer
CIO: Mary Jane Domres, Director Materials Management and Administrator Information Technology
CHR: Andrea Jacobson, Human Resource Officer
Web address: www.cavaliercountyhospital.com
Control: Other not–for–profit (including NFP Corporation) **Service:** General Medical and Surgical

Staffed Beds: 20 Admissions: 350 Census: 2 Outpatient Visits: 9521 Births: 0 Total Expense ($000): 7845 Payroll Expense ($000): 3007 Personnel: 50

LINTON—Emmons County

LINTON HOSPITAL (351328), 518 North Broadway, Zip 58552–7308, Mailing Address: P.O. Box 850, Zip 58552–0850; tel. 701/254–4511, (Nonreporting) **A**5 9 10 18
Primary Contact: Robert O. Black, Chief Executive Officer
CFO: Beverly Vilhauer, Chief Operating Officer and Chief Financial Officer
CMO: John Knecht, Chief Medical Staff
CHR: Sue Meidinger, Manager Business Office
CNO: Lukas Fischer, Chief Nursing Officer
Web address: www.lintonhospital.com
Control: Other not–for–profit (including NFP Corporation) **Service:** General Medical and Surgical

Staffed Beds: 14

LISBON—Ransom County

★ **LISBON AREA HEALTH SERVICES (351311)**, 905 Main Street, Zip 58054–4334, Mailing Address: P.O. Box 353, Zip 58054–0353; tel. 701/683–5241, (Nonreporting) **A**5 9 10 18 **S** Catholic Health Initiatives, Englewood, CO
Primary Contact: Peggy Larson, R.N., Administrator
COO: Sheri Heinisch, Compliance Officer
CFO: Amber Stowman, Controller
CHR: Janet Froemke, Human Resources Officer
Web address: www.lisbonhospital.com
Control: Church–operated, Nongovernment, not–for profit **Service:** General Medical and Surgical

Staffed Beds: 25

MANDAN—Morton County

TRIUMPH HOSPITAL – CENTRAL DAKOTAS See Vibra Hospital of Central Dakotas

⊞ **VIBRA HOSPITAL OF CENTRAL DAKOTAS (352005)**, 1000 18th Street N.W., Zip 58554–1612; tel. 701/667–2000, (Nonreporting) **A**1 9 10 **S** Vibra Healthcare, Mechanicsburg, PA
Primary Contact: Custer Huseby, Interim Chief Executive Officer
Web address: www.vhcentraldakotas.com
Control: Corporation, Investor–owned, for–profit **Service:** Long–Term Acute Care hospital

Staffed Beds: 41

MAYVILLE—Traill County

MERITCARE MAYVILLE UNION HOSPITAL See Sanford Mayville Medical Center

★ **SANFORD MAYVILLE MEDICAL CENTER (351309)**, 42 Sixth Avenue S.E., Zip 58257–1598; tel. 701/786–3800 **A**5 9 10 18 **F**7 40 43 45 50 65 77 81 93 97 107 128 129 130 133 **S** Sanford Health, Sioux Falls, SD
Primary Contact: Roger Baier, Chief Executive Officer
CFO: Shauna Slabik, Chief Financial Officer
CMO: Jane Ostlig, Chief Medical Officer
Web address: www.unionhospital.com
Control: Other not–for–profit (including NFP Corporation) **Service:** General Medical and Surgical

Staffed Beds: 18 Admissions: 270 Census: 5 Outpatient Visits: 18791 Births: 0 Total Expense ($000): 8724 Payroll Expense ($000): 2860 Personnel: 62

MCVILLE—Nelson County

NELSON COUNTY HEALTH SYSTEM (351308), 200 Main Street, Zip 58254, Mailing Address: P.O. Box 367, Zip 58254–0367; tel. 701/322–4328, (Nonreporting) **A**9 10 18
Primary Contact: Bruce D. Bowersox, Chief Executive Officer
CFO: Steve Forde, Chief Financial Officer
CMO: Erling Martinson, M.D., Medical Director
Web address: www.nelsoncountyhealthsystem.org
Control: Other not–for–profit (including NFP Corporation) **Service:** General Medical and Surgical

Staffed Beds: 58

MINOT—Ward County

⊞ △ **TRINITY HEALTH (350006)**, One Burdick Expressway West, Zip 58701–4406, Mailing Address: P.O. Box 5020, Zip 58702–5020; tel. 701/857–5000, (Includes TRINITY HOSPITAL–ST. JOSEPH'S, 407 3rd Street S.E., Zip 58702–5001; tel. 701/857–2000), (Total facility includes 230 beds in nursing home–type unit) **A**1 2 3 5 7 9 10 19 20 **F**3 4 5 8 10 11 13 14 15 17 18 20 22 24 28 29 30 31 34 35 36 40 43 44 45 46 49 50 54 55 56 57 58 59 60 62 63 64 65 68 70 72 74 75 76 77 78 79 81 82 85 86 87 89 90 91 92 93 94 96 97 98 99 100 101 102 103 104 105 107 108 110 111 114 115 116 117 118 119 120 121 123 124 125 126 127 128 129 130 131 132 143 144 146 147 148
Primary Contact: John M. Kutch, President
CFO: Dennis Empey, Chief Financial Officer
CIO: David Wanner, Chief Information Officer
CHR: Paul Simonson, Vice President
Web address: www.trinityhealth.org
Control: Other not–for–profit (including NFP Corporation) **Service:** General Medical and Surgical

Staffed Beds: 411 Admissions: 10503 Census: 319 Outpatient Visits: 210296 Births: 1567 Total Expense ($000): 364634 Payroll Expense ($000): 181389 Personnel: 2422

NORTHWOOD—Grand Forks County

★ **NORTHWOOD DEACONESS HEALTH CENTER (351312)**, 4 North Park Street, Zip 58267–4102, Mailing Address: P.O. Box 190, Zip 58267–0190; tel. 701/587–6060, (Nonreporting) **A**5 9 10 18 **S** Sanford Health, Sioux Falls, SD
Primary Contact: Pete Antonson, Chief Executive Officer
CMO: Jon Berg, M.D., Chief of Staff
CIO: Chad Peterson, Chief Information Officer
Web address: www.ndhc.net
Control: Church–operated, Nongovernment, not–for profit **Service:** General Medical and Surgical

Staffed Beds: 73

Hospital, Medicare Provider Number, Address, Telephone, Approval, Facility, and Physician Codes, Health Care System

★ American Hospital Association (AHA) membership
☐ The Joint Commission accreditation ◇ DNV Healthcare Inc. accreditation
○ Healthcare Facilities Accreditation Program
△ Commission on Accreditation of Rehabilitation Facilities (CARF) accreditation

OAKES—Dickey County

★ **OAKES COMMUNITY HOSPITAL (351315)**, 1200 North Seventh Street,
Zip 58474–2502; tel. 701/742–3291 **A**5 9 10 18 **F**28 29 31 34 40 59 81 82
85 107 111 119 127 133 **S** Catholic Health Initiatives, Englewood, CO
Primary Contact: Becki Thompson, President
CMO: Vani Nagala, M.D., Chief Medical Officer
CIO: Terry Engel, Manager Information Technology
CHR: Julie Entzminger, Manager Human Resources
Web address: www.oakeshospital.com
Control: Other not–for–profit (including NFP Corporation) **Service:** General
Medical and Surgical

Staffed Beds: 20 **Admissions:** 364 **Census:** 5 **Outpatient Visits:** 11146
Births: 0 **Total Expense ($000):** 11251 **Payroll Expense ($000):** 4772
Personnel: 66

PARK RIVER—Walsh County

★ **FIRST CARE HEALTH CENTER (351326)**, 115 Vivian Street, Zip 58270–4540,
Mailing Address: PO Box I., Zip 58270–0708; tel. 701/284–7500 **A**5 9 10 18
F11 15 28 29 30 31 34 35 40 45 50 59 64 65 68 77 81 93 104 107 110
111 114 119 127 130 133 135 **P**6
Primary Contact: Louise Dryburgh, Chief Executive Officer
CFO: Layne Ensrude, Chief Financial Officer
CMO: Joel Johnson, M.D., Chief Medical Staff
CNO: Lori Seim, R.N., Director Nursing Services
Web address: www.firstcarehc.com
Control: Other not–for–profit (including NFP Corporation) **Service:** General
Medical and Surgical

Staffed Beds: 14 **Admissions:** 327 **Census:** 6 **Outpatient Visits:** 28731
Births: 0 **Total Expense ($000):** 8849 **Payroll Expense ($000):** 3200
Personnel: 76

ROLLA—Rolette County

PRESENTATION MEDICAL CENTER (351316), 213 Second Avenue N.E.,
Zip 58367–7153, Mailing Address: P.O. Box 759, Zip 58367–0759;
tel. 701/477–3161 **A**5 9 10 18 **F**1 11 15 18 29 30 31 34 39 40 41 45 57 59
63 81 89 90 93 107 119 127 129 133 135 146 **S** Sisters of Mary of the
Presentation Health System, Fargo, ND
Primary Contact: Mark Kerr, Chief Executive Officer
CFO: Paula Wilkie, Chief Financial Officer
CMO: Roy Cordy, M.D., President Medical Staff
CHR: Tara Okerson, Director Human Resources
Web address: www.pmc-rolla.com
Control: Church–operated, Nongovernment, not–for profit **Service:** General
Medical and Surgical

Staffed Beds: 25 **Admissions:** 128 **Census:** 8 **Outpatient Visits:** 7682
Births: 0 **Total Expense ($000):** 8712 **Payroll Expense ($000):** 3348
Personnel: 88

RUGBY—Pierce County

★ **HEART OF AMERICA MEDICAL CENTER (351332)**, 800 Main Avenue South,
Zip 58368–2198; tel. 701/776–5261, (Nonreporting) **A**5 9 10 18
Primary Contact: Jeff Lingerfelt, Chief Executive Officer
CFO: Bonnie Kuehnemund, Comptroller
CIO: Jeremy Schonebery, Director Information Technology
Web address: www.hamc.com
Control: Other not–for–profit (including NFP Corporation) **Service:** General
Medical and Surgical

Staffed Beds: 20

STANLEY—Mountrail County

★ **MOUNTRAIL COUNTY MEDICAL CENTER (351301)**, 615 6th Street S.E.,
Zip 58784–4444, Mailing Address: P.O. Box 399, Zip 58784–0399;
tel. 701/628–2424 **A**9 10 18 **F**15 28 40 41 43 45 57 59 71 77 81 93 97 107
111 119 127 130 133 **P**6
Primary Contact: Michael Hall, Interim Chief Executive Officer
CFO: Susan Weston, CPA, Chief Financial Officer
CMO: Marla Longmuir, M.D., Chief Medical Officer
CIO: Kathy Janssen, Director Medical Records
CHR: Alisha McMahon, Director Human Resources
CNO: Belinda Moen, Interim Director of Nursing
Web address: www.stanleyhealth.org
Control: Other not–for–profit (including NFP Corporation) **Service:** General
Medical and Surgical

Staffed Beds: 11 **Admissions:** 71 **Census:** 1 **Outpatient Visits:** 14011
Births: 1 **Total Expense ($000):** 4629 **Payroll Expense ($000):** 1075
Personnel: 16

TIOGA—Williams County

★ **TIOGA MEDICAL CENTER (351300)**, 810 North Welo Street, Zip 58852–7157,
Mailing Address: P.O. Box 159, Zip 58852–0159; tel. 701/664–3305,
(Nonreporting) **A**3 5 9 10 18
Primary Contact: Randall K. Pederson, Chief Executive Officer
CMO: Swami P. Gade, M.D., Medical Director
CHR: Mary Ann Holm, Office Clerk
Web address: www.tiogahealth.org
Control: Other not–for–profit (including NFP Corporation) **Service:** General
Medical and Surgical

Staffed Beds: 55

TURTLE LAKE—McLean County

COMMUNITY MEMORIAL HOSPITAL (351304), 220 Fifth Avenue,
Zip 58575–4005, Mailing Address: P.O. Box 280, Zip 58575–0280;
tel. 701/448–2331 **A**9 10 18 **F**2 3 29 34 40 43 53 59 64 67 75 86 89 93
107 119 127 133 143 146
Primary Contact: Tod Graeber, Administrator
CFO: Janet Kurle, Chief Financial Officer
CNO: Jason Landenberger, Director of Nursing
Web address: www.wrtc.com/cullum/hospital
Control: Church–operated, Nongovernment, not–for profit **Service:** Long–Term
Acute Care hospital

Staffed Beds: 25 **Admissions:** 103 **Census:** 20 **Outpatient Visits:** 20900
Births: 0 **Total Expense ($000):** 4100 **Payroll Expense ($000):** 1900
Personnel: 55

VALLEY CITY—Barnes County

★ **MERCY HOSPITAL (351324)**, 570 Chautauqua Boulevard, Zip 58072–3199;
tel. 701/845–6400 **A**5 9 10 18 **F**3 11 28 29 30 32 34 40 42 43 45 50 64 75
77 81 84 85 86 87 92 93 107 110 114 130 131 132 133 146 **S** Catholic
Health Initiatives, Englewood, CO
Primary Contact: Keith E. Heuser, President
COO: Camille Settelmeyer, Assistant Administrator Clinical Services
CFO: Beth Smith, Controller
CHR: Lesley Erlandson, Human Resources Generalist
Web address: www.mercyhospitalvalleycity.org
Control: Church–operated, Nongovernment, not–for profit **Service:** General
Medical and Surgical

Staffed Beds: 19 **Admissions:** 513 **Census:** 10 **Outpatient Visits:** 15069
Births: 0 **Total Expense ($000):** 11943 **Payroll Expense ($000):** 4698
Personnel: 84

WATFORD CITY—Mckenzie County

★ **MCKENZIE COUNTY HEALTHCARE SYSTEM (351302)**, 516 North Main
Street, Zip 58854–7310; tel. 701/842–3000 **A**9 10 18 **F**3 11 28 29 34 40 43
50 57 59 64 81 85 93 94 97 107 119 127 129 131 133 146
Primary Contact: Daniel R. Kelly, Chief Executive Officer
COO: Michael Curtis, Chief Operating Officer
CFO: Geoffrey W. Hamilton, Interim Chief Financial Officer
CMO: Gary Ramage, M.D., Chief Medical Officer
CIO: Karn Pederson, Manager Health Information Management
CHR: Debbra Thompson, Manager Human Resources
CNO: Cheryl Faulkner, Chief Nursing Officer
Web address: www.mckenziehealth.com
Control: Other not–for–profit (including NFP Corporation) **Service:** General
Medical and Surgical

Staffed Beds: 24 **Admissions:** 150 **Census:** 1 **Outpatient Visits:** 13898
Births: 0 **Total Expense ($000):** 13207 **Payroll Expense ($000):** 5312
Personnel: 132

WILLISTON—Williams County

⊞ **MERCY MEDICAL CENTER (351334)**, 1301 15th Avenue West,
Zip 58801–3896; tel. 701/774–7400 **A**1 5 9 10 18 **F**3 13 15 28 29 30 31 34
35 40 45 47 50 51 56 59 64 65 70 75 76 77 78 79 81 82 85 87 93 97 102
107 108 110 111 114 118 119 120 121 123 124 129 130 132 133 135 141
142 143 146 147 148 **S** Catholic Health Initiatives, Englewood, CO
Primary Contact: Matthew Grimshaw, President
CMO: Brett Vibeto, M.D., Chief of Staff
CIO: Jeff Rust, Information Technology Systems Site Manager
CHR: Dan Bjerknes, Director Human Resources
CNO: Lori Hahn, Vice President Nursing Services
Web address: www.mercy–williston.org
Control: Church–operated, Nongovernment, not–for profit **Service:** General
Medical and Surgical

Staffed Beds: 25 **Admissions:** 1454 **Census:** 11 **Outpatient Visits:** 66790
Births: 668 **Total Expense ($000):** 59394 **Payroll Expense ($000):** 31050
Personnel: 474

★ **WISHEK COMMUNITY HOSPITAL AND CLINICS (351321)**, 1007 Fourth
Avenue South, Zip 58495–7527, Mailing Address: P.O. Box 647,
Zip 58495–0647; tel. 701/452–2326 **A**5 9 10 18 **F**3 7 11 15 17 18 28 29 30
32 34 35 36 40 42 44 50 53 56 57 59 60 62 63 64 65 67 68 75 81 83 87
90 91 92 93 97 107 114 127 128 130 131 133 143 146 147 **P**3 6
Primary Contact: Mark Rinehardt, Chief Executive Officer
CFO: Sahlenia Braun, Chief Financial Officer
CMO: Edgar Oliveira, M.D., Chief of Staff
CIO: Kari Buchholz, Director Health Information Management
CHR: Shar Bauer, Executive Secretary
Web address: www.wishekhospital.com
Control: Other not–for–profit (including NFP Corporation) **Service:** General
Medical and Surgical

Staffed Beds: 17 **Admissions:** 253 **Census:** 3 **Outpatient Visits:** 24281
Births: 0 **Total Expense ($000):** 6663 **Payroll Expense ($000):** 2650
Personnel: 77

Hospital, Medicare Provider Number, Address, Telephone, Approval, Facility, and Physician Codes, Health Care System

★ American Hospital Association (AHA) membership
□ The Joint Commission accreditation   ◇ DNV Healthcare Inc. accreditation
○ Healthcare Facilities Accreditation Program
△ Commission on Accreditation of Rehabilitation Facilities (CARF) accreditation

OH

OHIO

AKRON—Summit County

✠ **AKRON CHILDREN'S HOSPITAL (363303)**, One Perkins Square, Zip 44308–1062; tel. 330/543–1000 **A**1 2 3 5 8 9 10 13 **F**3 7 11 16 18 19 21 23 25 27 29 30 31 32 33 34 35 36 38 39 40 41 42 43 44 50 54 55 57 58 59 60 61 62 63 64 65 66 68 72 73 74 75 77 78 79 80 81 82 84 85 86 87 88 89 91 92 93 94 96 97 98 99 100 101 102 104 105 107 108 111 112 114 116 117 118 119 129 130 131 132 134 135 136 141 143 144 146 148 **P**6
Primary Contact: William H. Considine, President
COO: Grace Wakulchik, R.N., Chief Operating Officer
CFO: Michael Trainer, Chief Financial Officer
CMO: Robert McGregor, M.D., Chief Medical Officer
CIO: Tom Ogg, Vice President Information Services and Chief Information Officer
CHR: Walter Schwoeble, Vice President Human Resources
CNO: Lisa Aurilio, R.N., Vice President Patient Services and Chief Nursing Officer
Web address: www.akronchildrens.org
Control: Other not–for–profit (including NFP Corporation) **Service:** Children's general

Staffed Beds: 414 Admissions: 9508 Census: 193 Outpatient Visits: 790676 Births: 1 Total Expense ($000): 578931 Payroll Expense ($000): 289738 Personnel: 4039

✠ **AKRON GENERAL MEDICAL CENTER (360027)**, 1 Akron General Avenue, Zip 44307–2433; tel. 330/344–6000 **A**1 2 3 5 8 9 10 **F**3 5 8 11 12 13 14 15 17 18 20 22 24 26 28 29 30 31 34 35 36 38 39 40 42 43 44 45 46 47 48 49 50 51 52 53 54 55 56 57 58 59 60 61 64 65 66 68 70 71 72 74 75 77 78 79 81 82 84 85 86 87 91 92 93 94 96 97 98 100 101 102 103 104 105 107 108 109 110 111 112 114 115 116 117 118 119 120 121 123 124 126 129 130 131 132 134 135 143 144 145 146 147 148 **P**6 8 **S** Akron General Health System, Akron, OH
Primary Contact: Alan Papa, President
CFO: Sue McCarthy, Senior Vice President and Chief Financial Officer
CMO: David Peter, M.D., Senior Vice President Medical Affairs and Chief Medical Director
CIO: David Fiser, Vice President and Chief Information Officer
CHR: Don Corpora, Executive Vice President and Chief Human Resources Officer
Web address: www.akrongeneral.org
Control: Other not–for–profit (including NFP Corporation) **Service:** General Medical and Surgical

Staffed Beds: 442 Admissions: 22120 Census: 260 Outpatient Visits: 574150 Births: 3038 Total Expense ($000): 444210 Payroll Expense ($000): 186140 Personnel: 2509

✠ **SELECT SPECIALTY HOSPITAL–AKRON (362027)**, 200 East Market Street, Zip 44308–2015; tel. 330/761–7500, (Nonreporting) **A**1 10 **S** Select Medical Corporation, Mechanicsburg, PA
Primary Contact: Sonda Burns, Chief Executive Officer
Web address: www.selectspecialtyhospitals.com/company/locations/akron.aspx
Control: Corporation, Investor–owned, for–profit **Service:** Long–Term Acute Care hospital

Staffed Beds: 60

✠ **SUMMA AKRON CITY HOSPITAL (360020)**, 525 East Market Street, Zip 44304–1619; tel. 330/375–3000, (Includes SUMMA AKRON CITY HOSPITAL, 525 East Market Street, Zip 44309–2090, Mailing Address: P.O. Box 2090, Zip 44309–2090; tel. 330/375–3000; SUMMA SAINT THOMAS HOSPITAL, 444 North Main Street, Zip 44310; tel. 330/375–3000) **A**1 2 3 5 8 9 10 **F**1 2 3 4 5 6 8 9 11 12 13 15 17 18 20 22 24 26 28 29 30 31 33 34 35 36 37 38 39 40 41 42 43 44 45 46 47 48 49 50 51 52 53 54 55 56 57 60 61 62 63 64 65 66 70 71 73 74 75 76 77 78 79 80 81 82 83 84 85 86 87 92 93 96 97 98 99 100 101 102 103 104 105 107 108 109 110 111 114 115 116 117 118 119 120 121 123 124 126 129 130 131 132 133 135 144 146 147 148 **P**6 8 **S** Summa Health System, Akron, OH
Primary Contact: Thomas J. Strauss, President and Chief Executive Officer
COO: Robert Harrigan, President, Summa Hospitals
CMO: Erik N. Steele, D.O., Senior Vice President and Chief Medical Officer
CIO: Greg Kall, Vice President Human Resources
CHR: Kyle Klawitter, Vice President Human Resources
Web address: www.summahealth.org
Control: Other not–for–profit (including NFP Corporation) **Service:** General Medical and Surgical

Staffed Beds: 426 Admissions: 30569 Census: 378 Outpatient Visits: 456573 Births: 3122 Total Expense ($000): 689730 Payroll Expense ($000): 220754 Personnel: 4581

SUMMA AKRON CITY HOSPITAL See Summa Akron City Hospital

SUMMA HEALTH SYSTEM See Sumna Akron City Hospital

SUMMA REHAB HOSPITAL (363035), 29 North Adams Street, Zip 44304–1641; tel. 330/572–7300, (Nonreporting) **A**10 **S** Summa Health System, Akron, OH
Primary Contact: Cheryl Henthorn, Chief Executive Officer
Web address: www.summarehabhospital.com/
Control: Corporation, Investor–owned, for–profit **Service:** Rehabilitation

Staffed Beds: 60

SUMMA SAINT THOMAS HOSPITAL See Summa Akron City Hospital

ALLIANCE—Stark County

○ **ALLIANCE COMMUNITY HOSPITAL (360131)**, 200 East State Street, Zip 44601–4936; tel. 330/596–6000, (Total facility includes 68 beds in nursing home–type unit) **A**2 5 9 10 11 **F**3 8 11 13 15 28 29 30 31 34 35 36 40 45 49 50 51 56 57 59 60 62 63 64 68 69 70 74 75 76 77 79 81 82 85 86 87 90 93 96 98 103 107 108 110 111 115 118 119 128 129 130 132 135 143 146 147 148 **P**5 7 8
Primary Contact: Stanley W. Jonas, Chief Executive Officer
COO: Dale Wells, Chief Financial and Operating Officer
CFO: Dale Wells, Chief Financial and Operating Officer
CMO: Ashraf Ahmed, M.D., Senior Vice President Physician and Hospital Services
CIO: David W. Shroades, Vice President Technology Services
CHR: Nicole L. Russ, Vice President Colleague Relations
CNO: Amy Antonacci, MSN, Vice President Nursing Services
Web address: www.achosp.org
Control: Other not–for–profit (including NFP Corporation) **Service:** General Medical and Surgical

Staffed Beds: 196 Admissions: 3774 Census: 102 Outpatient Visits: 164651 Births: 418 Total Expense ($000): 89949 Payroll Expense ($000): 39082 Personnel: 800

AMHERST—Lorain County

☐ **SPECIALTY HOSPITAL OF LORAIN (362025)**, 254 Cleveland Avenue, Zip 44001–1620; tel. 440/988–6260, (Nonreporting) **A**1 10
Primary Contact: Julia M. Meeks, Chief Operating Officer
Control: Other not–for–profit (including NFP Corporation) **Service:** Long–Term Acute Care hospital

Staffed Beds: 30

ARCHBOLD—Fulton County

ARCHBOLD HOSPITAL See Community Hospitals and Wellness Centers, Bryan

ASHLAND—Ashland County

✠ **SAMARITAN REGIONAL HEALTH SYSTEM (360002)**, 1025 Center Street, Zip 44805–4011; tel. 419/289–0491 **A**1 5 9 10 **F**11 13 15 29 30 31 34 35 40 50 51 59 62 64 68 70 75 76 77 78 79 81 82 86 87 93 96 107 110 111 114 119 129 130 131 132 135 146 147 148
Primary Contact: Danny L. Boggs, President and Chief Executive Officer
CFO: Mary Griest, Vice President Finance and Chief Financial Officer
CMO: Philip Myers, M.D., Vice President Medical Affairs
CIO: Kathleen Metcalf, Chief Information Officer
CHR: Alyce Legg, Vice President Human Resources
CNO: Karin Schwan, Chief Nursing Officer, Vice President Patient Care Services
Web address: www.samaritanhospital.org
Control: Other not–for–profit (including NFP Corporation) **Service:** General Medical and Surgical

Staffed Beds: 49 Admissions: 2400 Census: 18 Outpatient Visits: 135487 Births: 445 Total Expense ($000): 71293 Payroll Expense ($000): 24034 Personnel: 483

ASHTABULA—Ashtabula County

☐ **ASHTABULA COUNTY MEDICAL CENTER (360125)**, 2420 Lake Avenue, Zip 44004–4954; tel. 440/997–2262, (Total facility includes 15 beds in nursing home–type unit) **A**1 5 9 10 20 **F**3 4 11 13 15 18 20 28 29 30 31 34 35 38 40 45 49 50 51 53 57 59 61 62 63 64 68 70 74 75 76 77 78 79 80 81 82 83 84 85 86 87 89 93 97 98 100 102 103 104 105 107 108 110 111 114 116 117 118 119 128 129 130 131 132 135 146 147 148 **P**4 6 8
Primary Contact: Michael J. Habowski, President and Chief Executive Officer
CFO: Donald L. Kepner, Chief Financial Officer
CMO: Robert Dlwgosh, M.D., Chief of Staff
CIO: Jared Swiger, Director Information Systems
CHR: Robert Sincich, Vice President Human Resources
Web address: www.acmchealth.org
Control: Other not–for–profit (including NFP Corporation) **Service:** General Medical and Surgical

Staffed Beds: 160 Admissions: 5431 Census: 70 Outpatient Visits: 219411 Births: 425 Total Expense ($000): 100092 Payroll Expense ($000): 44860 Personnel: 742

Many Facility Codes have changed. Please refer to the AHA Guide Code Chart. © 2014 AHA Guide

ATHENS—Athens County

☐ **APPALACHIAN BEHAVIORAL HEALTHCARE (364015)**, 100 Hospital Drive, Zip 45701–2301; tel. 740/594–5000, (Nonreporting) **A**1 10 **S** Ohio Department of Mental Health, Columbus, OH
Primary Contact: Jane E. Krason, R.N., Chief Executive Officer
CMO: Mark F. McGee, M.D., Chief Clinical Officer
CHR: Amy Grover, Director
Web address: www.mh.state.oh.us
Control: State–Government, nonfederal **Service:** Psychiatric

Staffed Beds: 224

☒ **O'BLENESS MEMORIAL HOSPITAL (360014)**, 55 Hospital Drive, Zip 45701–2302; tel. 740/593–5551 **A**1 9 10 12 13 19 20 **F**3 13 15 18 20 28 31 34 40 51 57 59 64 65 70 75 76 78 79 80 81 82 85 87 93 94 97 107 108 110 111 115 118 119 130 131 135 146 147 148 **P**6 **S** OhioHealth, Columbus, OH
Primary Contact: Greg Long, Chief Executive Officer
CFO: Robert Melaragno, Vice President Finance
CIO: Kristine Barr, Vice President Communication Services
CHR: Sandie Leasure, Senior Vice President Human Resources
Web address: www.obleness.org
Control: Other not–for–profit (including NFP Corporation) **Service:** General Medical and Surgical

Staffed Beds: 64 **Admissions:** 2802 **Census:** 21 **Outpatient Visits:** 82899
Births: 683 **Total Expense ($000):** 68571 **Payroll Expense ($000):** 21071
Personnel: 443

BARBERTON—Summit County

☒ **SUMMA BARBERTON CITIZENS HOSPITAL (360019)**, 155 Fifth Street N.E., Zip 44203–3332; tel. 330/615–3000 **A**1 2 3 5 9 10 **F**3 8 13 14 15 17 18 20 22 24 26 28 29 30 31 34 35 40 46 47 48 49 50 51 56 57 58 59 60 61 63 68 70 74 76 77 78 79 81 82 83 84 85 86 87 93 97 98 100 102 103 104 105 107 108 110 111 113 114 116 117 118 119 129 130 131 132 135 146 147 148 **P**6 8 **S** Summa Health System, Akron, OH
Primary Contact: Jason Niehaus, Senior Vice President Operations and Administrator
CFO: Charles Alderson, Chief Financial Officer
CMO: Jeffrey Morris, M.D., Medical Director
CIO: David Lynch, Regional Director Information Systems
CHR: Don Argiro, Regional Director Human Resources
CNO: Kathy Jobe, R.N., Chief Nursing Officer and Vice President Patient Care Services
Web address: www.summahealth.org/locations/hospitals/barberton
Control: Other not–for–profit (including NFP Corporation) **Service:** General Medical and Surgical

Staffed Beds: 190 **Admissions:** 9438 **Census:** 127 **Outpatient Visits:** 70724
Births: 649 **Total Expense ($000):** 157323 **Payroll Expense ($000):** 54631
Personnel: 1084

BARNESVILLE—Belmont County

☒ **BARNESVILLE HOSPITAL (361321)**, 639 West Main Street, Zip 43713–1039, Mailing Address: P.O. Box 309, Zip 43713–0309; tel. 740/425–3941 **A**1 9 10 18 **F**3 11 15 17 28 29 30 31 32 34 35 39 40 41 45 50 57 59 64 65 69 70 74 75 77 78 79 81 85 86 87 89 90 91 93 107 108 114 119 128 129 130 133 135 145 146 **P**6
Primary Contact: David D. Phillips, Chief Executive Officer and Administrator
CFO: Willie Cooper–Lohr, Chief Financial Officer
CMO: David J. Hilliard, D.O., Chief of Staff
CIO: Tiffany Gramby, Senior Director Information Management and Privacy Officer
CHR: Beth K. Brill, Senior Director Human Resources
CNO: Cynthia Touvelle, R.N., Senior Director Care Management and Chief Nursing Officer
Web address: www.barnesvillehospital.com
Control: Other not–for–profit (including NFP Corporation) **Service:** General Medical and Surgical

Staffed Beds: 25 **Admissions:** 977 **Census:** 11 **Outpatient Visits:** 33031
Births: 0 **Total Expense ($000):** 20110 **Payroll Expense ($000):** 8354
Personnel: 182

BATAVIA—Clermont County

☒ **MERCY HEALTH – CLERMONT HOSPITAL (360236)**, 3000 Hospital Drive, Zip 45103–1921; tel. 513/732–8200, (Nonreporting) **A**1 2 9 10 **S** Mercy Health, Cincinnati, OH
Primary Contact: Jeff Graham, Market Leader and President
CFO: Philip Wheeler, Director Finance
CMO: Parma Hariharan, M.D., Chief of Staff
CHR: Angie Ferrell, Director Human Resources
CNO: Gayle Heintzelman, R.N., Site Administrator and Chief Nursing Officer
Web address: www.e–mercy.com
Control: Church–operated, Nongovernment, not–for profit **Service:** General Medical and Surgical

Staffed Beds: 119

BEACHWOOD—Cuyahoga County

☒ **UNIVERSITY HOSPITALS AHUJA MEDICAL CENTER (360359)**, 3999 Richmond Road, Zip 44122–6046; tel. 216/593–5500 **A**1 9 10 **F**3 5 15 18 20 22 24 26 28 29 30 34 35 36 40 41 42 45 46 47 48 49 50 51 56 57 59 60 61 65 68 70 74 75 77 79 80 81 82 85 87 91 107 108 109 110 111 115 119 126 130 144 145 146 148 **S** University Hospitals, Cleveland, OH
Primary Contact: Susan V. Juris, President
Web address: www.uhhospitals.org/ahuja/tabid/7051/uhahujamedicalcenter.aspx
Control: Other not–for–profit (including NFP Corporation) **Service:** General Medical and Surgical

Staffed Beds: 144 **Admissions:** 6859 **Census:** 74 **Outpatient Visits:** 102500
Births: 0 **Total Expense ($000):** 124297 **Payroll Expense ($000):** 38306
Personnel: 757

BEAVERCREEK—Rock County County

★ ○ **SOIN MEDICAL CENTER (360360)**, 3535 Pentagon Boulevard, Zip 45431–1705; tel. 937/702–4000 **A**9 10 11 **F**3 11 13 18 20 29 30 34 35 38 40 43 44 45 46 48 49 50 53 56 57 59 60 61 64 68 70 73 74 75 76 77 78 79 81 82 85 86 87 102 107 108 111 114 115 116 117 118 119 126 130 132 135 146 147 148 **S** Kettering Health Network, Dayton, OH
Primary Contact: Terry M. Burns, President
COO: Ron D. Connovich, Chief Financial Officer and Chief Operating Officer
CFO: Ron D. Connovich, Chief Financial Officer and Chief Operating Officer
CMO: David Small, M.D., Chief Medical Officer
CIO: Andy Lehman, Vice President Information Systems
CHR: Amanda Koch, Director Human Resources
CNO: Belinda Mallett, R.N., Vice President, Patient Care and Clinical Services
Web address: www.khnetwork.org/soin
Control: Church–operated, Nongovernment, not–for profit **Service:** General Medical and Surgical

Staffed Beds: 85 **Admissions:** 4152 **Census:** 40 **Outpatient Visits:** 46072
Births: 383 **Total Expense ($000):** 101533 **Payroll Expense ($000):** 34640
Personnel: 546

BELLAIRE—Belmont County

☐ **BELMONT COMMUNITY HOSPITAL (360153)**, 4697 Harrison Street, Zip 43906–1338, Mailing Address: P.O. Box 653, Zip 43906–0653; tel. 740/671–1200, (Nonreporting) **A**1 9 10
Primary Contact: John DeBlasis, Vice President
CFO: James B. Murdy, Chief Financial Officer
CMO: C. N. Patel, M.D., Chief of Staff
CHR: Serge Gentile, Director Human Resources
Web address: www.wheelinghospital.org/facilities/bch/
Control: Other not–for–profit (including NFP Corporation) **Service:** General Medical and Surgical

Staffed Beds: 66

BELLEFONTAINE—Logan County

★ ◇ **MARY RUTAN HOSPITAL (360197)**, 205 Palmer Avenue, Zip 43311–2281; tel. 937/592–4015 **A**3 5 9 10 20 21 **F**3 11 13 14 15 18 20 28 29 30 31 32 34 40 50 54 57 59 64 66 68 70 75 76 77 78 79 81 82 85 86 87 89 107 108 110 111 115 118 119 129 130 132 133 135 146 147
Primary Contact: Mandy C. Goble, President and Chief Executive Officer
CFO: Ron Carmin, Vice President Fiscal Affairs
CMO: Grant Varian, M.D., Medical Director
CIO: Robert Reynolds, Director Information Systems
CHR: Vickie L. Crumley, Vice President Human Resources
CNO: Marcia Davis, Vice President Patient Services
Web address: www.maryrutan.org
Control: Other not–for–profit (including NFP Corporation) **Service:** General Medical and Surgical

Staffed Beds: 100 **Admissions:** 1636 **Census:** 14 **Outpatient Visits:** 92146
Births: 354 **Total Expense ($000):** 80178 **Payroll Expense ($000):** 30425
Personnel: 584

OH

BELLEVUE—Sandusky County

✠ **BELLEVUE HOSPITAL (360107)**, 1400 West Main Street, Zip 44811–9088, Mailing Address: P.O. Box 8004, Zip 44811–8004; tel. 419/483–4040 **A**1 5 9 10 **F**3 13 15 28 29 30 31 34 35 40 41 46 50 53 56 57 59 61 62 68 70 74 75 77 79 81 82 85 93 107 108 110 111 114 118 119 127 129 130 131 132 133 135 143 146 **P**8
Primary Contact: Michael Winthrop, President
CFO: Timothy Burt, Executive Vice President and Chief Financial Officer
CMO: Gregory Karasik, M.D., President Medical Staff
CIO: Kim Stults, Director, Information Systems
CHR: Lisa M. Sartain, Vice President, Human Resources
CNO: Sara Brokaw, Vice President Patient Care Services
Web address: www.bellevuehospital.com
Control: Other not-for-profit (including NFP Corporation) **Service:** General Medical and Surgical

Staffed Beds: 50 Admissions: 1320 Census: 12 Outpatient Visits: 77119 Births: 379 Total Expense ($000): 42378 Payroll Expense ($000): 16595 Personnel: 332

BLUFFTON—Allen County

✠ **BLUFFTON HOSPITAL (361322)**, 139 Garau Street, Zip 45817–1027; tel. 419/358–9010 **A**1 9 10 18 **F**11 13 15 18 40 45 54 57 59 64 70 76 81 82 93 110 114 119 130 135 146 148 **S** Blanchard Valley Health System, Findlay, OH
Primary Contact: Christine Keller, Chief Administrative Officer
CFO: David Cytlak, Vice President Finance
CMO: William H. Kose, M.D., Vice President Quality and Medical Affairs
CIO: David Cytlak, Vice President Finance
CHR: Ryan Fisher, Director Human Resources
CNO: Barbara J. Pasztor, R.N., Vice President Nursing and Patient Care Services
Web address: www.bvhealthsystem.org/?id=203&sid=1
Control: Other not-for-profit (including NFP Corporation) **Service:** General Medical and Surgical

Staffed Beds: 25 Admissions: 344 Census: 2 Outpatient Visits: 36267 Births: 245 Total Expense ($000): 13415 Payroll Expense ($000): 8532 Personnel: 113

BOARDMAN—Mahoning County

☐ **GREENBRIAR REHABILITATION HOSPITAL (363032)**, 8064 South Avenue, Suite One, Zip 44512–6153; tel. 330/726–3700, (Nonreporting) **A**1 9 10
Primary Contact: Daphne Bonner, Administrator
Control: Corporation, Investor–owned, for–profit **Service:** Rehabilitation

Staffed Beds: 29

MAHONING VALLEY HOSPITAL See Vibra Hospital of Mahoning Valley

✠ **ST. ELIZABETH BOARDMAN HEALTH CENTER (360276)**, 8401 Market Street, Zip 44512–6777; tel. 330/729–2929 **A**1 9 10 **F**3 8 11 14 15 18 29 30 31 34 35 40 45 46 47 49 50 59 60 68 70 74 75 77 78 79 81 84 87 93 94 107 108 110 111 114 115 118 119 120 121 123 129 130 146 148 **P**3 **S** Mercy Health, Cincinnati, OH
Primary Contact: Eugenia Aubel, President
CFO: Matt Love, Senior Vice President Finance
CMO: Nicholas Kreatsoulas, M.D., Vice President Medical Affairs and Chief Quality Officer
CIO: Maureen Kordupel, Director Relationship Manager
CHR: Scott Dimmick, Senior Vice President Human Resources
CNO: Lori DeNiro, Senior Director Nursing
Web address: www.ehealthconnection.com/regions/youngstown/content/show_facility.asp?facility_id=190
Control: Church–operated, Nongovernment, not–for profit **Service:** General Medical and Surgical

Staffed Beds: 128 Admissions: 8416 Census: 95 Outpatient Visits: 87342 Births: 0 Total Expense ($000): 91372 Payroll Expense ($000): 30217 Personnel: 521

✠ **VIBRA HOSPITAL OF MAHONING VALLEY (362023)**, 8049 South Avenue, Zip 44512–6154; tel. 330/726–5000, (Includes VIBRA HOSPITAL OF MAHONING VALLEY–TRUMBULL CAMPUS, 1350 East Market Street, 9th Floor, Warren, Zip 44483–6608; tel. 330/675–5591; Mary Lou Sankovich, R.N., MSN, Chief Executive Officer) **A**1 10 **F**1 3 29 130 148 **S** Vibra Healthcare, Mechanicsburg, PA
Primary Contact: Mary Lou Sankovich, R.N., MSN, Chief Executive Officer
CMO: Lawrence Goldstein, M.D., Chief Medical Officer
CNO: Mary Jane Larmon, Chief Clinical Officer
Web address: www.vhmvalley.com
Control: Corporation, Investor–owned, for–profit **Service:** Long–Term Acute Care hospital

Staffed Beds: 42 Admissions: 727 Census: 34 Outpatient Visits: 0 Births: 0 Total Expense ($000): 15165 Payroll Expense ($000): 5907 Personnel: 107

BORDMAN—Mahoning County

SELECT SPECIALTY HOSPITAL–YOUNGSTOWN, BOARDMAN CAMPUS See Select Specialty Hospital–Youngstown, Youngstown

BOWLING GREEN—Wood County

✠ **WOOD COUNTY HOSPITAL (360029)**, 950 West Wooster Street, Zip 43402–2603; tel. 419/354–8900 **A**1 3 5 9 10 **F**3 11 12 13 15 17 18 28 29 30 32 34 35 40 44 45 46 50 57 59 64 65 68 69 70 74 75 76 77 78 79 81 82 85 87 89 93 107 108 110 111 114 115 118 119 129 130 131 132 135 144 146 147 148 **P**8
Primary Contact: Stanley R. Korducki, President
CFO: Karol Bortel, Vice President Financial Services
CIO: Joanne White, Chief Information Officer
CHR: Frank Day, Vice President Patient Services
CNO: Sandra Beidelschies, MSN, Vice President Patient Services
Web address: www.woodcountyhospital.org
Control: Other not-for-profit (including NFP Corporation) **Service:** General Medical and Surgical

Staffed Beds: 102 Admissions: 3520 Census: 28 Outpatient Visits: 99561 Births: 325 Total Expense ($000): 80224 Payroll Expense ($000): 29597 Personnel: 628

BRYAN—Williams County

☐ **COMMUNITY HOSPITALS AND WELLNESS CENTERS (360121)**, 433 West High Street, Zip 43506–1679; tel. 419/636–1131, (Includes ARCHBOLD HOSPITAL, 121 Westfield Drive, Archbold, Zip 43502; tel. 419/445–4415; BRYAN HOSPITAL, 433 West High Street, Zip 43506; tel. 419/636–1131; MONTPELIER HOSPITAL, 909 East Snyder Avenue, Montpelier, Zip 43543; tel. 419/485–3154), (Nonreporting) **A**1 2 5 9 10 19
Primary Contact: Philip L. Ennen, Vice President and Chief Executive Officer
CFO: Leroy P. Feather, Vice President Finance
CIO: Greg Slattery, Vice President Information
CHR: Mary Ann Potts, Director Personnel
Web address: www.chwchospital.com
Control: Other not-for-profit (including NFP Corporation) **Service:** General Medical and Surgical

Staffed Beds: 113

BUCYRUS—Crawford County

★ ◇ **BUCYRUS COMMUNITY HOSPITAL (361316)**, 629 North Sandusky Avenue, Zip 44820–1821; tel. 419/562–4677 **A**5 9 10 18 21 **F**3 11 15 18 28 29 30 31 34 35 45 50 57 59 60 70 74 75 77 78 79 81 82 87 107 108 110 115 119 124 127 130 131 132 133 146 147 148 **S** Avita Health System, Galion, OH
Primary Contact: Jerome Morasko, Chief Executive Officer
COO: Andy Daniels, Chief Operating Officer
CMO: Michael A. Johnson, M.D., Chief of Staff
CIO: Joann Riedlinger, Vice President Nursing and Manager Information Systems
CHR: Jeanne Perkins, Vice President Nursing and Interim Manager Human Resources
Web address: www.bchonline.org
Control: Other not-for-profit (including NFP Corporation) **Service:** General Medical and Surgical

Staffed Beds: 25 Admissions: 999 Census: 10 Outpatient Visits: 15239 Births: 0 Total Expense ($000): 28282 Payroll Expense ($000): 11388 Personnel: 249

CADIZ—Harrison County

✠ **HARRISON COMMUNITY HOSPITAL (361311)**, 951 East Market Street, Zip 43907–9799; tel. 740/942–4631 **A**1 9 10 18 **F**7 11 15 18 28 29 30 31 34 35 40 45 47 50 51 53 57 58 59 62 64 65 68 74 75 77 78 79 81 82 85 86 87 93 97 107 108 110 111 114 119 129 130 132 133 135 143 146 147 148
Primary Contact: Clifford K. Harmon, Chief Executive Officer
CFO: Dean Sloane, Vice President Finance
CMO: Isam Tabbah, M.D., Chief of Staff
CIO: Will Combs, Director Information Technology
CHR: Pam Smith, Senior Director Human Resources
CNO: Janis Olinski, R.N., Vice President Clinical Services
Web address: www.harrisoncommunity.com
Control: Other not-for-profit (including NFP Corporation) **Service:** General Medical and Surgical

Staffed Beds: 25 Admissions: 419 Census: 6 Outpatient Visits: 41164 Births: 0 Total Expense ($000): 16835 Payroll Expense ($000): 6516 Personnel: 169

Many Facility Codes have changed. Please refer to the AHA Guide Code Chart. © 2014 AHA Guide

CAMBRIDGE—Guernsey County

☒ **SOUTHEASTERN OHIO REGIONAL MEDICAL CENTER (360203)**, 1341 North Clark Street, Zip 43725–9614, Mailing Address: P.O. Box 610, Zip 43725–0610; tel. 740/439–8000 **A**1 2 9 10 20 **F**1 3 4 7 11 13 15 16 17 18 20 28 29 30 31 32 34 35 40 43 46 48 49 51 57 59 60 62 63 64 65 66 67 70 72 73 75 76 77 78 79 80 81 82 83 84 85 86 87 88 89 90 91 93 96 97 98 107 108 110 111 114 116 118 119 128 129 130 131 132 135 144 146 147 148 **P**6 8
Primary Contact: Raymond M. Chorey, President and Chief Executive Officer
CFO: Donald P. Huelskamp, Vice President Finance and Chief Financial Officer
CMO: E. Edwin Conaway, M.D., Vice President Medical Affairs and Chief Medical Officer
CIO: James Hampton, Chief Information Officer
CHR: Steven Michael Brooks, Vice President Human Resources
CNO: Angela S. Long, Vice President Clinical Services and Chief Nursing Officer
Web address: www.seormc.org
Control: Other not-for-profit (including NFP Corporation) **Service:** General Medical and Surgical

Staffed Beds: 95 **Admissions:** 3812 **Census:** 33 **Outpatient Visits:** 135897 **Births:** 451

CANAL WINCHESTER—Fairfield County

☐ **DILEY RIDGE MEDICAL CENTER (360358)**, 7911 Diley Road, Zip 43110–9653; tel. 614/838–7911 **A**1 9 10 **F**3 15 29 30 35 40 50 54 64 68 85 87 107 110 111 114 119 130 147
Primary Contact: Jodi Wilson, President and Chief Operating Officer
COO: Jodi Wilson, President and Chief Operating Officer
Web address: www.dileyridgemedicalcenter.com
Control: Other not-for-profit (including NFP Corporation) **Service:** General Medical and Surgical

Staffed Beds: 10 **Admissions:** 9 **Census:** 1 **Outpatient Visits:** 48805 **Births:** 0 **Total Expense ($000):** 11686 **Payroll Expense ($000):** 4008 **Personnel:** 79

CANTON—Stark County

☐ **ACUTE CARE SPECIALTY HOSPITAL OF AULTMAN (362032)**, 2600 Sixth Street, S.W., Zip 44710–1702; tel. 330/363–4000, (Nonreporting) **A**1 10
Primary Contact: Jackie Toth, Administrator
Web address: www.aultman.org
Control: Other not-for-profit (including NFP Corporation) **Service:** Long–Term Acute Care hospital

Staffed Beds: 30

☒ △ **AULTMAN HOSPITAL (360084)**, 2600 Sixth Street S.W., Zip 44710–1702; tel. 330/452–9911, (Includes AULTMAN HOSPITAL PEDIATRIC SERVICES, 2600 Sixth Street, S.W., tel. 330/363–5455), (Total facility includes 60 beds in nursing home–type unit) **A**1 2 3 5 7 10 13 **F**3 7 8 11 12 13 14 15 17 18 20 22 24 26 28 29 30 31 34 35 39 40 43 44 45 48 49 50 51 53 54 55 56 57 58 59 60 61 62 63 64 68 70 71 72 74 75 76 77 78 79 81 82 83 84 85 86 87 89 90 93 96 97 98 102 103 104 105 106 107 108 109 110 111 114 117 118 119 123 127 128 129 130 131 132 133 134 135 143 144 145 146 147 148 **P**6 7 **S** Aultman Health Foundation, Canton, OH
Primary Contact: Edward J. Roth, III, President and Chief Executive Officer
CFO: Mark Wright, Vice President
CMO: Allison Oprandi, M.D., Chief Medical Officer
CIO: Liz Getz, Chief Information Officer
CHR: Sue Olivera, Vice President
CNO: Anne Gunther, R.N., Chief Nursing Officer
Web address: www.aultman.com
Control: Other not-for-profit (including NFP Corporation) **Service:** General Medical and Surgical

Staffed Beds: 545 **Admissions:** 24280 **Census:** 370 **Outpatient Visits:** 424181 **Births:** 2494 **Total Expense ($000):** 429896 **Payroll Expense ($000):** 177300 **Personnel:** 3508

☒ △ **MERCY MEDICAL CENTER (360070)**, 1320 Mercy Drive N.W., Zip 44708–2641; tel. 330/489–1000 **A**1 2 3 5 7 9 10 **F**3 11 13 15 17 18 20 22 24 26 28 29 30 31 34 35 39 40 43 44 46 48 49 50 51 53 54 57 58 59 60 61 62 63 64 66 68 70 72 74 75 76 77 78 79 80 81 82 84 85 86 87 89 90 91 92 93 96 97 107 108 110 111 114 115 116 117 118 119 120 121 123 126 129 130 131 132 135 143 144 146 147 148 **P**6 7 **S** Sisters of Charity Health System, Cleveland, OH
Primary Contact: Thomas E. Cecconi, President and Chief Executive Officer
COO: David D. Cemate, FACHE, Senior Vice President and Chief Operating Officer
CFO: David K. Stewart, Chief Financial Officer
CMO: David Gormsen, D.O., Chief Medical Officer
CIO: Trevor Clere, Director Information Technology
CHR: Patti Bresnahan, Director Human Resources
CNO: Barbara Yingling, R.N., Vice President Patient Care Services and Chief Nursing Officer
Web address: www.cantonmercy.org
Control: Other not-for-profit (including NFP Corporation) **Service:** General Medical and Surgical

Staffed Beds: 304 **Admissions:** 14013 **Census:** 183 **Outpatient Visits:** 624858 **Births:** 1616 **Total Expense ($000):** 285136 **Payroll Expense ($000):** 116326 **Personnel:** 2140

☒ **SELECT SPECIALTY HOSPITAL–CANTON (362016)**, 1320 Mercy Drive N.W., 6th Floor, Zip 44708–2614; tel. 330/489–8189, (Nonreporting) **A**1 10 **S** Select Medical Corporation, Mechanicsburg, PA
Primary Contact: Dawne Wheeler, Chief Executive Officer
Web address: www.selectspecialtyhospitals.com/company/locations/canton.aspx
Control: Corporation, Investor–owned, for–profit **Service:** Long–Term Acute Care hospital

Staffed Beds: 30

CHARDON—Geauga County

☐ **HEATHERHILL CARE COMMUNITIES (362014)**, 12340 Bass Lake Road, Zip 44024–8327; tel. 440/285–4040, (Nonreporting) **A**1 10
Primary Contact: Jim Homa, Chief Executive Officer
COO: Lisa Deering, Administrator
CFO: Valerie Love, Manager Business Office
CMO: Beejadi Makunda, M.D., Chief Medical Officer
CHR: Pam McCall, Director Human Resources
CNO: Alice Harvey, Director of Nursing
Web address: www.heatherhill.com
Control: Other not-for-profit (including NFP Corporation) **Service:** Long–Term Acute Care hospital

Staffed Beds: 214

☒ **UNIVERSITY HOSPITALS GEAUGA MEDICAL CENTER (360192)**, 13207 Ravenna Road, Zip 44024–7032; tel. 440/269–6000 **A**1 2 9 10 **F**3 8 11 12 13 14 15 18 20 22 26 28 29 30 31 32 34 35 36 37 38 39 40 41 43 44 47 49 50 51 54 56 57 58 59 60 62 64 65 68 70 74 75 76 77 78 79 81 82 85 86 87 91 92 93 96 97 98 100 101 102 103 107 108 110 111 114 115 116 117 118 119 120 121 123 124 129 130 131 132 134 135 143 146 147 148 **S** University Hospitals, Cleveland, OH
Primary Contact: M. Steven Jones, President
COO: M. Steven Jones, President
CFO: Paul Amantea, Director Finance
CMO: David Kosnosky, M.D., Chief Medical Officer
CIO: Lou Ciraldo, Information Services Representative
CHR: Danialle Lynce, Manager Human Resources
CNO: Peggy A. Kuhar, R.N., Chief Nursing Officer
Web address: www.uhhospitals.org/geauga/
Control: Other not-for-profit (including NFP Corporation) **Service:** General Medical and Surgical

Staffed Beds: 126 **Admissions:** 8399 **Census:** 81 **Outpatient Visits:** 152056 **Births:** 1098 **Total Expense ($000):** 106264 **Payroll Expense ($000):** 36118 **Personnel:** 642

Hospital, Medicare Provider Number, Address, Telephone, Approval, Facility, and Physician Codes, Health Care System

★ American Hospital Association (AHA) membership
☐ The Joint Commission accreditation
◇ DNV Healthcare Inc. accreditation
○ Healthcare Facilities Accreditation Program
△ Commission on Accreditation of Rehabilitation Facilities (CARF) accreditation

---

OH

CHILLICOTHE—Ross County

★ ◇ **ADENA MEDICAL CENTER (360159)**, 272 Hospital Road,
Zip 45601–9031; tel. 740/779–7500 **A**2 5 9 10 19 21 **F**3 5 8 13 15 17 18 20
22 24 26 28 29 30 31 32 34 35 38 40 41 42 45 46 49 51 54 56 57 59 60
62 63 64 68 70 71 73 74 75 76 77 78 79 80 81 82 84 85 87 89 92 93 96
97 98 99 100 101 102 104 107 108 110 111 114 115 117 118 119 120
121 123 126 128 129 130 131 132 133 135 144 145 146 147 148 **P**6
S Adena Health System, Chillicothe, OH
Primary Contact: Mark H. Shuter, President and Chief Executive Officer
CMO: John Fortney, M.D., Chief Medical Officer
CIO: Mark Moffitt, Chief Information Officer
CHR: Eric Perdue, Chief Human Resource Officer
CNO: Judith Henson, Chief Nursing Officer
Web address: www.adena.org
Control: Other not–for–profit (including NFP Corporation) **Service:** General
Medical and Surgical

Staffed Beds: 279 Admissions: 11184 Census: 109 Outpatient Visits:
485718 Births: 911 Total Expense ($000): 403548 Payroll Expense
($000): 185253 Personnel: 2391

⊞ **CHILLICOTHE VETERANS AFFAIRS MEDICAL CENTER**, 17273 State Route
104, Zip 45601–9718; tel. 740/773–1141, (Nonreporting) **A**1 5 **S** Department of
Veterans Affairs, Washington, DC
Primary Contact: Wendy J. Hepker, FACHE, Director
COO: Keith Sullivan, Associate Director
CFO: Rick Deckard, Chief Fiscal Service
CMO: Deborah Meesig, M.D., Chief of Staff
CIO: William Gawler, Chief Information Officer
CHR: Angela Young, Human Resources Officer
Web address: www.chillicothe.va.gov/
Control: Veterans Affairs, Government, federal **Service:** Psychiatric

Staffed Beds: 297

VETERANS AFFAIRS MEDICAL CENTER See Chillicothe Veterans Affairs
Medical Center

CINCINNATI—Hamilton County

⊞ **BETHESDA NORTH HOSPITAL (360179)**, 10500 Montgomery Road,
Zip 45242–4402; tel. 513/865–1111, (Includes BETHESDA BUTLER COUNTY
HOSPITAL, 3125 Hamilton Mason Road, Hamilton, Zip 45011–5307;
tel. 513/894–8888; John S. Prout, President and Chief Executive Officer) **A**1 3 5
9 10 **F**3 5 9 11 12 13 15 17 18 20 22 24 26 28 29 30 31 34 35 36 37 38
39 40 41 42 43 44 45 46 47 48 49 50 53 54 55 56 57 58 59 61 63 64 65
66 68 70 71 73 74 75 76 77 78 79 81 82 84 85 86 87 90 91 92 93 94 96
97 100 101 102 104 107 110 111 114 115 116 117 118 119 120 121 123
124 126 129 130 131 132 134 135 141 143 144 145 146 147 148
Primary Contact: Barb Boyne, Executive Director, Operations
COO: Jenny Oliphant, Executive Vice President and Chief Operating Officer
CFO: Michael Crofton, Senior Vice President and Chief Financial Officer
CMO: Georges Feghali, M.D., Senior Vice President Quality and Chief Medical
Officer
CIO: Rick Moore, Chief Information Officer
CHR: Walter L. McLarty, Chief Human Resources Officer
CNO: Mary Irvin, R.N., Senior Vice President and Chief Nursing Officer
Web address: www.trihealth.com
Control: Other not–for–profit (including NFP Corporation) **Service:** General
Medical and Surgical

Staffed Beds: 342 Admissions: 22620 Census: 256 Outpatient Visits:
300468 Births: 4256 Total Expense ($000): 446244 Payroll Expense
($000): 150424 Personnel: 3512

○ **BRIDGEWELL HOSPITAL OF CINCINNATI (364046)**, 5500 Verulam Avenue,
Zip 45213–2418; tel. 513/531–6444, (Nonreporting) **A**10 11
Primary Contact: Glenna Coffey, R.N., Chief Operating Officer
CNO: Doug Eppley, Director of Nursing
Web address: www.bridgewellhospitals.com
Control: Corporation, Investor–owned, for–profit **Service:** Psychiatric

Staffed Beds: 48

⊞ △ **CHRIST HOSPITAL (360163)**, 2139 Auburn Avenue, Zip 45219–2906;
tel. 513/585–2000 **A**1 2 3 5 7 9 10 **F**3 6 8 9 11 12 13 15 17 18 20 22 24 26
28 29 30 31 34 35 36 37 38 39 40 44 45 46 47 48 49 50 51 53 54 55 56
57 58 59 60 61 64 65 66 68 70 73 74 75 76 77 78 79 80 81 82 83 84 85
86 87 90 92 93 94 96 97 98 99 100 101 102 103 104 107 108 109 110
111 114 115 116 117 118 119 120 121 123 124 126 129 130 131 132 135
136 138 141 143 144 145 146 147 148 **P**6
Primary Contact: Michael Keating, President and Chief Executive Officer
COO: Victor DiPilla, Vice President and Chief Business Development Officer
CFO: Chris Bergman, Chief Financial Officer
CMO: Bernard B. Gawne, M.D., Vice President and Chief Medical Officer
CIO: Alex Vaillancourt, Chief Information Officer
CHR: Rick Tolson, Chief Administrative Officer and Chief Human Resources Officer
CNO: Deborah Marie Hayes, R.N., Chief Hospital Officer and Chief Nursing Officer
Web address: www.thechristhospital.com
Control: Other not–for–profit (including NFP Corporation) **Service:** General
Medical and Surgical

Staffed Beds: 520 Admissions: 24525 Census: 296 Outpatient Visits:
421236 Births: 3016 Total Expense ($000): 580027 Payroll Expense
($000): 196121 Personnel: 2981

⊞ △ **CINCINNATI CHILDREN'S HOSPITAL MEDICAL CENTER (363300)**,
3333 Burnet Avenue, Zip 45229–3039; tel. 513/636–4200, (Includes DIVISION
OF ADOLESCENT MEDICINE, CINCINNATI CENTER FOR DEVELOPMENTAL
DISORDERS, AND CONVALESCENT HOSPITAL FOR CHILDREN ; CHILDREN'S
HOSPITAL, Elland and Bethesda Avenues, Zip 45229) **A**1 2 3 5 7 8 9 10 **F**3 7 9
11 12 17 18 19 20 21 22 23 24 25 26 27 28 29 30 31 32 34 35 36 37 38
39 40 41 42 43 44 46 48 49 50 51 54 55 57 58 59 60 61 62 63 64 65 66
68 72 74 75 77 78 79 81 82 84 85 86 87 88 89 90 91 92 93 94 95 96 97
98 99 100 101 102 104 105 106 107 108 111 112 113 114 115 116 117
118 119 126 129 130 131 132 134 135 136 137 138 139 141 142 144 146
148 **P**1
Primary Contact: Michael Fisher, President and Chief Executive Officer
CFO: Scott J. Hamlin, Chief Financial Officer
CIO: Marianne Speight, Vice President Information System and Chief Information
Officer
Web address: www.cincinnatichildrens.org
Control: Other not–for–profit (including NFP Corporation) **Service:** Children's
general

Staffed Beds: 540 Admissions: 18244 Census: 368 Outpatient Visits:
1151937 Births: 12 Total Expense ($000): 1778685 Payroll Expense
($000): 891286 Personnel: 14172

⊞ **CINCINNATI VETERANS AFFAIRS MEDICAL CENTER**, 3200 Vine Street,
Zip 45220–2288; tel. 513/475–6300, (Total facility includes 57 beds in nursing
home–type unit) **A**1 2 3 5 8 **F**1 3 4 5 8 12 15 18 20 22 26 28 29 30 31 33 34
35 36 37 38 39 40 44 45 46 47 48 50 51 53 54 55 56 57 58 59 60 61 62
63 64 65 68 70 71 74 75 77 78 79 81 82 83 84 85 86 87 91 92 93 94 97
98 100 101 102 103 104 105 106 107 108 111 114 115 116 117 119 126
127 129 130 132 135 143 144 145 146 147 148 **S** Department of Veterans
Affairs, Washington, DC
Primary Contact: Linda D. Smith, FACHE, Director
COO: David Ninneman, Associate Director
CFO: Sandra Selvidge, Chief Fiscal Service
CMO: Robert E. Falcone, M.D., Chief of Staff
CIO: Vique Caro, Chief Information Officer
CHR: Sandra Stenger, Acting Chief Human Resources
CNO: Katheryn Cook, R.N., Nurse Executive
Web address: www.cincinnati.va.gov/
Control: Veterans Affairs, Government, federal **Service:** General Medical and
Surgical

Staffed Beds: 268 Admissions: 7365 Census: 224 Outpatient Visits:
593066 Births: 0 Total Expense ($000): 358264 Payroll Expense ($000):
168013 Personnel: 2181

⊞ **DANIEL DRAKE CENTER FOR POST ACUTE CARE (362004)**, 151 West
Galbraith Road, Zip 45216–1015; tel. 513/418–2500, (Nonreporting) **A**1 3 5 10
S UC Health, Cincinnati, OH
Primary Contact: Debra C. Hampton, Ph.D., Vice President, Administration and
Chief Nursing Officer
CFO: Duane Pifko, Interim Director Financial Services
Web address: www.drakecenter.uchealth.com
Control: Other not–for–profit (including NFP Corporation) **Service:** Long–Term
Acute Care hospital

Staffed Beds: 217

☒ △ **GOOD SAMARITAN HOSPITAL (360134)**, 375 Dixmyth Avenue, Zip 45220–2489; tel. 513/862–1400 **A**1 3 5 7 8 9 10 **F**3 5 6 9 11 12 13 15 17 18 20 22 24 26 28 29 30 31 34 35 36 37 38 39 40 41 42 44 45 46 47 48 49 50 53 54 55 56 57 58 59 61 63 64 65 66 68 70 71 72 74 75 76 77 78 79 81 82 84 85 86 87 90 91 92 93 94 96 97 98 99 100 101 102 103 104 105 107 108 110 111 114 115 116 117 118 119 120 121 123 126 129 130 131 132 134 135 141 143 144 145 146 147 148 **S** Catholic Health Initiatives, Englewood, CO
Primary Contact: Jamie Easterling, Executive Director, Operations
COO: Gerald P. Oliphant, Executive Vice President and Chief Operating Officer
CFO: Michael Crofton, Chief Financial Officer
CMO: Georges Feghali, M.D., Senior Vice President Quality and Chief Medical Officer
CIO: Rick Moore, Chief Information Officer
CHR: Walter L. McLarty, Chief Human Resources Officer
Web address: www.trihealth.com
Control: Church–operated, Nongovernment, not–for profit **Service:** General Medical and Surgical

Staffed Beds: 484 **Admissions:** 24247 **Census:** 336 **Outpatient Visits:** 242743 **Births:** 6227 **Total Expense ($000):** 476807 **Payroll Expense ($000):** 162544 **Personnel:** 3097

☒ **HEALTHSOUTH REHABILITATION HOSPITAL AT DRAKE (363034)**, 151 West Galbraith Road, Zip 45216–1015; tel. 513/418–5600 **A**1 9 10 **F**29 31 34 35 56 74 90 91 92 130 148 **S** HEALTHSOUTH Corporation, Birmingham, AL
Primary Contact: Brad Kennedy, Chief Executive Officer
CFO: Scott Corder, Controller
CMO: Mark Goddard, M.D., Medical Director
CHR: Jason Sparks, Director, Human Resources
CNO: Kathy McNally, Chief Nursing Officer
Web address: www.healthsouthatdrake.com
Control: Corporation, Investor–owned, for–profit **Service:** Rehabilitation

Staffed Beds: 60 **Admissions:** 905 **Census:** 36 **Outpatient Visits:** 0 **Births:** 0 **Total Expense ($000):** 11183 **Payroll Expense ($000):** 6132 **Personnel:** 71

☒ **MERCY HEALTH – ANDERSON HOSPITAL (360001)**, 7500 State Road, Zip 45255–2492; tel. 513/624–4500, (Nonreporting) **A**1 2 9 10 **S** Mercy Health, Cincinnati, OH
Primary Contact: Jeff Graham, Market Leader and President
COO: Katherine Edrington, R.N., Administrator
CFO: Patrick A. Kowalski, Chief Financial Officer
CMO: Leonard M. Randolph, Jr., M.D., Senior Vice President and Chief Medical Officer
CIO: Matt Eversole, Regional Vice President Information Services
CHR: Angie Ferrell, Director Human Resources
Web address: www.e–mercy.com
Control: Church–operated, Nongovernment, not–for profit **Service:** General Medical and Surgical

Staffed Beds: 188

☒ **MERCY HEALTH – WEST HOSPITAL (360234)**, 3300 Mercy Health Boulevard, Zip 45211; tel. 513/215–5000, (Nonreporting) **A**1 2 9 10 **S** Mercy Health, Cincinnati, OH
Primary Contact: Michael R. Stephens, Market Leader and President
COO: Michael Kramer, Chief Operating Officer
CHR: Liz Freedman, Director Human Resources
CNO: Stephanie Meade, MSN, Chief Nursing Officer
Web address: www.e–mercy.com/west–hospital
Control: Church–operated, Nongovernment, not–for profit **Service:** General Medical and Surgical

Staffed Beds: 250

☒ **SELECT SPECIALTY HOSPITAL – CINCINNATI NORTH (362034)**, 10500 Montgomery Road, Zip 45242–4402; tel. 513/865–5300 **A**1 10 **F**1 3 29 60 68 75 91 148 **S** Select Medical Corporation, Mechanicsburg, PA
Primary Contact: Mark S. Brodeur, FACHE, Chief Executive Officer
CMO: Sunil Dama, M.D., Medical Director
CHR: Elizabeth M. Wilson, Coordinator Human Resources
Web address: www.cincinnatinorth.selectspecialtyhospitals.com/
Control: Corporation, Investor–owned, for–profit **Service:** Long–Term Acute Care hospital

Staffed Beds: 25 **Admissions:** 195 **Census:** 15 **Outpatient Visits:** 0 **Births:** 0 **Total Expense ($000):** 9379 **Payroll Expense ($000):** 3892

☒ **SELECT SPECIALTY HOSPITAL–CINCINNATI (362019)**, 375 Dixmyth Avenue, 15th Floor, Zip 45220–2475; tel. 513/872–4444, (Nonreporting) **A**1 9 10 **S** Select Medical Corporation, Mechanicsburg, PA
Primary Contact: Curtis Ohashi, Chief Executive Officer
CMO: Brian Boster, M.D., Medical Director
CNO: Bobbi Schmidt, Chief Nursing Officer
Web address: www.selectspecialtyhospitals.com/company/locations/cincinnati.aspx
Control: Corporation, Investor–owned, for–profit **Service:** Long–Term Acute Care hospital

Staffed Beds: 35

☐ **SHRINERS HOSPITALS FOR CHILDREN–CINCINNATI BURNS HOSPITAL (363308)**, 3229 Burnet Avenue, Zip 45229–3095; tel. 513/872–6000, (Nonreporting) **A**1 10 **S** Shriners Hospitals for Children, Tampa, FL
Primary Contact: Tony Lewgood, Interim Administrator
CFO: James Lester, Director Fiscal Services
CMO: Richard J. Kagan, M.D., Chief of Staff
CIO: Mark Washam, Chief Information Officer
CHR: Sally Skillman, Director Human Resources
Web address: www.shrinershospitalsforchildren.org/Hospitals/Locations/Cincinnati.aspx
Control: Other not–for–profit (including NFP Corporation) **Service:** Children's other specialty

Staffed Beds: 30

☒ **SUMMIT BEHAVIORAL HEALTHCARE (364035)**, 1101 Summit Road, Zip 45237–2652; tel. 513/948–3600 **A**1 10 **F**4 30 39 75 77 87 98 101 103 130 135 146 **S** Ohio Department of Mental Health, Columbus, OH
Primary Contact: Elizabeth Banks, Chief Executive Officer
COO: Steven Burns, Director Fiscal Services
CFO: Steven Burns, Director Fiscal Services
CMO: Patrick McCullough, M.D., Chief Medical Services
CIO: Eric Bradley, Director Computer Information Services
CHR: Bobbie Carrelli, Director Human Resources
CNO: Kathy A. Smith, MSN, Nurse Executive
Web address: www.mh.state.oh.us/
Control: State–Government, nonfederal **Service:** Psychiatric

Staffed Beds: 291 **Admissions:** 715 **Census:** 252 **Outpatient Visits:** 0 **Births:** 0 **Total Expense ($000):** 46424 **Payroll Expense ($000):** 32695 **Personnel:** 411

☒ **THE JEWISH HOSPITAL – MERCY HEALTH (360016)**, 4777 East Galbraith Road, Zip 45236–2725; tel. 513/686–3000, (Nonreporting) **A**1 2 3 5 9 10 **S** Mercy Health, Cincinnati, OH
Primary Contact: Patricia Davis–Hagens, R.N., Chief Executive Officer
COO: Jack Hill, Chief Operating Officer and Administrator
Web address: www.jewishhospitalcincinnati.com/
Control: Other not–for–profit (including NFP Corporation) **Service:** General Medical and Surgical

Staffed Beds: 209

☐ **TRIHEALTH EVENDALE HOSPITAL (360362)**, 3155 Glendale Milford Road, Zip 45241–3134; tel. 513/454–2222, (Nonreporting) **A**1 2 9 10
Primary Contact: Kelvin Hanger, Chief Executive Officer
CFO: Michael Crofton, Chief Financial Officer
Web address: www.evendalemedical.com
Control: Other not–for–profit (including NFP Corporation) **Service:** Other specialty

Staffed Beds: 29

☒ **UNIVERSITY OF CINCINNATI MEDICAL CENTER (360003)**, 234 Goodman Street, Zip 45219–2316; tel. 513/584–1000 **A**1 2 3 5 8 10 **F**3 6 7 9 11 12 13 15 16 17 18 20 22 24 26 28 29 30 31 34 35 36 37 38 39 40 43 44 45 46 47 48 49 50 51 52 53 54 55 56 57 58 59 60 61 63 64 66 68 70 71 72 73 74 75 76 77 78 79 80 81 82 84 85 86 87 92 93 97 98 100 101 102 103 104 107 108 110 111 112 114 115 116 117 118 119 120 121 123 124 126 129 130 131 132 134 135 136 138 139 141 142 143 145 146 147 148 **P**6 **S** UC Health, Cincinnati, OH
Primary Contact: Lee Ann Liska, President and Chief Executive Officer
COO: Nancy Barone, Vice President and Executive Director Operations and Strategic Planning
CFO: Matthew Nealon, Vice President Financial Services
CMO: John Deledda, M.D., Vice President Medical Affairs
CIO: Jay Brown, Vice President and Chief Information Officer
CHR: Clarence Pauley, Vice President Human Resources
CNO: Jennifer Jackson, R.N., Vice President and Chief Nursing Officer
Web address: www.universityhospital.uchealth.com/
Control: Other not–for–profit (including NFP Corporation) **Service:** General Medical and Surgical

Staffed Beds: 536 **Admissions:** 31987 **Census:** 433 **Outpatient Visits:** 370370 **Births:** 2520 **Total Expense ($000):** 743083 **Payroll Expense ($000):** 249959 **Personnel:** 4472

Hospital, Medicare Provider Number, Address, Telephone, Approval, Facility, and Physician Codes, Health Care System

★ American Hospital Association (AHA) membership
☐ The Joint Commission accreditation
◇ DNV Healthcare Inc. accreditation
◯ Healthcare Facilities Accreditation Program
△ Commission on Accreditation of Rehabilitation Facilities (CARF) accreditation

---

OH

VETERANS AFFAIRS MEDICAL CENTER See Cincinnati Veterans Affairs Medical Center

CIRCLEVILLE—Pickaway County

⊞ **BERGER HEALTH SYSTEM (360170)**, 600 North Pickaway Street, Zip 43113–1447; tel. 740/474–2126 **A**1 5 9 10 **F**3 13 15 18 20 28 29 30 31 34 35 40 45 46 50 54 56 57 59 63 64 65 66 70 75 76 79 81 85 87 90 93 96 107 108 110 111 115 119 124 129 130 131 132 135 146 147 148
Primary Contact: Tim Colburn, President and Chief Executive Officer
CFO: Richard Filler, Chief Financial Officer
CMO: Brett Call, D.O., Chief of Staff
CIO: Andy Chileski, Chief Information Officer and Vice President Facilities
CHR: Suzanne Welker, Chief Human Resources Officer and Vice President Marketing Strategy
CNO: Brenda M. Strittmatter, Patient Services Officer
Web address: www.bergerhealth.com
Control: City-County, Government, nonfederal **Service:** General Medical and Surgical

> **Staffed Beds:** 69 **Admissions:** 2182 **Census:** 22 **Outpatient Visits:** 106042 **Births:** 375 **Total Expense ($000):** 65819 **Payroll Expense ($000):** 23004 **Personnel:** 415

CLEVELAND—Cuyahoga County

CLEVELAND CAMPUS See Northcoast Behavioral Healthcare System, Northfield

⊞ **CLEVELAND CLINIC (360180)**, 9500 Euclid Avenue, Zip 44195–5108; tel. 216/444–2200, (Includes CLEVELAND CLINIC CHILDREN'S HOSPITAL, 9500 Euclid Avenue, Zip 44103; tel. 800/223–2273) **A**1 3 5 8 9 10 **F**3 6 7 8 9 12 13 14 15 17 18 19 20 21 22 23 24 25 26 27 28 29 30 31 32 33 34 35 36 37 38 39 40 42 44 45 46 47 48 49 50 51 52 53 54 55 56 57 58 59 60 61 62 63 64 65 66 68 70 71 72 73 74 75 76 77 78 79 80 81 82 83 84 85 86 87 88 89 90 91 92 93 94 96 97 100 101 103 104 107 108 109 110 111 112 113 114 115 116 117 118 119 120 121 123 124 126 129 131 132 134 135 136 137 138 139 140 141 142 143 144 145 146 147 148 **P**6
S Cleveland Clinic Health System, Cleveland, OH
Primary Contact: Delos Cosgrove, M.D., President and Chief Executive Officer
CFO: Steven Glass, Chief Financial Officer
CMO: Joseph Hahn, M.D., Chief of Staff
CIO: C. Martin Harris, M.D., Chief Information Officer
CHR: Joseph Cabral, Chief Human Resources Officer
CNO: Katherine Hancock, R.N., Executive Chief Nursing Officer
Web address: www.clevelandclinic.org
Control: Other not-for-profit (including NFP Corporation) **Service:** General Medical and Surgical

> **Staffed Beds:** 1279 **Admissions:** 55036 **Census:** 982 **Outpatient Visits:** 5153358 **Births:** 103 **Total Expense ($000):** 4435292 **Payroll Expense ($000):** 2294248 **Personnel:** 28750

⊞ △ **CLEVELAND CLINIC CHILDREN'S HOSPITAL FOR REHABILITATION (363304)**, 2801 Martin Luther King Jr. Drive, Zip 44104–3865; tel. 216/448–6400 **A**1 7 9 10 **F**28 29 30 32 33 34 35 36 50 57 60 68 74 75 79 80 82 86 89 90 91 93 94 96 99 100 130 131 132 143 146 148
S Cleveland Clinic Health System, Cleveland, OH
Primary Contact: Michael J. McHugh, M.D., Medical Director
COO: Alec G. Kulik, Administrator
CFO: Debra Nyikes, Director Finance and Chief Financial Officer
CMO: Roberta Bauer, M.D., Acting Chair Medical Staff
CIO: C. Martin Harris, M.D., Chief Information Officer
CHR: Jan Hlahol, Manager Human Resources
Web address: www.my.clevelandclinic.org/childrens–hospital/default.aspx
Control: Other not-for-profit (including NFP Corporation) **Service:** Children's rehabilitation

> **Staffed Beds:** 25 **Admissions:** 224 **Census:** 14 **Outpatient Visits:** 65757 **Births:** 0 **Total Expense ($000):** 36209 **Payroll Expense ($000):** 20661 **Personnel:** 331

⊞ **FAIRVIEW HOSPITAL (360077)**, 18101 Lorain Avenue, Zip 44111–5656; tel. 216/476–7000 **A**1 2 3 5 9 10 13 **F**3 8 11 13 15 17 18 19 20 22 24 26 28 29 30 31 32 34 35 40 41 43 45 46 49 50 51 53 57 58 59 60 64 65 66 68 69 70 71 72 74 76 78 79 81 82 85 86 87 89 92 93 97 98 99 100 107 108 110 111 114 115 117 118 119 120 121 123 124 126 130 131 132 135 143 145 146 147 148 **S** Cleveland Clinic Health System, Cleveland, OH
Primary Contact: Neil Smith, D.O., President
COO: John C. Mills, Senior Vice President Operations
CFO: Ankit Chhabra, Director Finance
CMO: Brent Burkey, M.D., Chief Medical Officer
CIO: C. Martin Harris, M.D., Chief Information Officer
CHR: Ann Beatty, Director Human Resources
CNO: Deborah C. Small, R.N., Vice President Patient Care Services and Chief Nursing Officer
Web address: www.fairviewhospital.org
Control: Other not-for-profit (including NFP Corporation) **Service:** General Medical and Surgical

> **Staffed Beds:** 413 **Admissions:** 20443 **Census:** 250 **Outpatient Visits:** 268363 **Births:** 4554 **Total Expense ($000):** 340325 **Payroll Expense ($000):** 128754 **Personnel:** 2094

☐ **GRACE HOSPITAL (362015)**, 2307 West 14th Street, Zip 44113–3698; tel. 216/687–1500, (Nonreporting) **A**1 10
Primary Contact: Rajive Khanna, Chief Executive Officer
COO: Rajive Khanna, Chief Executive Officer
CFO: Michelle Hennis, Administrative Director Financial Services
CMO: John Nickels, M.D., President Medical Staff
Web address: www.gracehospital.org
Control: Other not-for-profit (including NFP Corporation) **Service:** Long–Term Acute Care hospital

> **Staffed Beds:** 87

HANNA HOUSE SKILLED NURSING FACILITY See University Hospitals Case Medical Center

⊞ **HILLCREST HOSPITAL (360230)**, 6780 Mayfield Road, Zip 44124–2203; tel. 440/312–4500 **A**1 2 9 10 **F**3 11 13 15 17 18 20 22 24 26 28 29 30 31 34 35 36 37 38 40 41 43 46 49 50 51 55 57 59 60 64 65 68 69 70 72 74 75 76 77 78 79 81 82 84 85 86 89 93 97 100 107 108 110 111 114 115 116 117 119 120 121 126 129 130 131 132 135 143 145 146 147 148 **S** Cleveland Clinic Health System, Cleveland, OH
Primary Contact: Brian J. Harte, M.D., President
Web address: www.hillcresthospital.org
Control: Other not-for-profit (including NFP Corporation) **Service:** General Medical and Surgical

> **Staffed Beds:** 413 **Admissions:** 21835 **Census:** 284 **Outpatient Visits:** 234772 **Births:** 4594 **Total Expense ($000):** 347149 **Payroll Expense ($000):** 127979 **Personnel:** 2088

⊞ **KINDRED HOSPITAL CLEVELAND–GATEWAY (362026)**, 2351 East 22nd Street, 7th Floor, Zip 44115–3111; tel. 216/363–2671, (Includes KINDRED HOSPITAL OF CLEVELAND, 11900 Fairhill Road, Zip 44120–1062; tel. 216/983–8030; Steve Jakubcanin, Executive Director) **A**1 10 **F**1 3 12 29 56 96 119 130 148 **P**5 **S** Kindred Healthcare, Louisville, KY
Primary Contact: Prentice Lipsey, Chief Executive Officer
Web address: www.kindredgateway.com
Control: Individual, Investor–owned, for–profit **Service:** Long–Term Acute Care hospital

> **Staffed Beds:** 51 **Admissions:** 219 **Census:** 23 **Outpatient Visits:** 0 **Births:** 0 **Total Expense ($000):** 12919 **Payroll Expense ($000):** 4468 **Personnel:** 71

KINDRED HOSPITAL OF CLEVELAND See Kindred Hospital Cleveland–Gateway

⊞ △ **LOUIS STOKES CLEVELAND VETERANS AFFAIRS MEDICAL CENTER**, 10701 East Boulevard, Zip 44106–1702; tel. 216/791–3800, (Total facility includes 150 beds in nursing home–type unit) **A**1 2 3 5 7 8 **F**3 4 5 6 9 11 12 17 18 20 22 24 26 28 29 30 31 34 35 37 38 39 40 44 45 46 47 49 50 51 54 56 57 58 59 60 61 62 63 64 65 66 68 70 71 74 75 77 78 79 80 81 82 83 84 85 86 87 90 91 92 93 94 95 96 97 98 100 101 102 103 104 105 106 107 108 109 111 114 115 116 117 118 119 120 121 123 124 125 126 127 128 129 130 132 135 143 144 146 147 148 **S** Department of Veterans Affairs, Washington, DC
Primary Contact: Susan Fuehrer, Director
COO: John Merkle, Deputy Director
CFO: Michael Pappas, Chief Fiscal Service Officer
CMO: Murray Altose, M.D., Chief of Staff
CIO: Steve Gaj, Facility Chief Information Officer
CHR: Charles Franks, Chief Human Resources
CNO: Innette Mary Sarduy, M.P.H., Associate Director Patient Care Services and Nurse Executive
Web address: www.cleveland.va.gov/
Control: Veterans Affairs, Government, federal **Service:** General Medical and Surgical

> **Staffed Beds:** 585 **Admissions:** 10985 **Census:** 362 **Outpatient Visits:** 1611771 **Births:** 0 **Total Expense ($000):** 811341 **Payroll Expense ($000):** 334318 **Personnel:** 4426

⊞ **LUTHERAN HOSPITAL (360087)**, 1730 West 25th Street, Zip 44113–3170; tel. 216/696–4300 **A**1 9 10 **F**3 4 5 15 29 30 34 35 37 40 50 56 57 58 59 60 65 70 74 75 77 79 81 82 85 86 87 93 98 103 104 105 107 111 114 119 129 130 131 132 135 143 146 148 **S** Cleveland Clinic Health System, Cleveland, OH
Primary Contact: Donald Malone, M.D., President
COO: Kris Bennett, Chief Operating Officer
CFO: Don Urbancsik, Director Finance
CMO: Ronald Golovan, M.D., Vice President Medical Operations
CIO: C. Martin Harris, M.D., Chief Information Officer
CHR: Sheree Laborie, Director Human Resources
CNO: Denise Minor, R.N., Chief Nursing Officer
Web address: www.lutheranhospital.org
Control: Other not-for-profit (including NFP Corporation) **Service:** General Medical and Surgical

> **Staffed Beds:** 198 **Admissions:** 7729 **Census:** 99 **Outpatient Visits:** 59384 **Births:** 0 **Total Expense ($000):** 95532 **Payroll Expense ($000):** 39400 **Personnel:** 621

Many Facility Codes have changed. Please refer to the AHA Guide Code Chart. © 2014 AHA Guide

⊠ △ **METROHEALTH MEDICAL CENTER (360059)**, 2500 MetroHealth Drive, Zip 44109–1998; tel. 216/778–7800, (Total facility includes 142 beds in nursing home–type unit) **A**1 2 3 5 7 8 9 10 13 **F**3 5 6 7 8 9 11 12 13 15 16 17 18 19 20 22 24 26 27 28 29 30 31 32 34 35 36 38 39 40 43 44 45 46 47 48 49 50 51 52 53 54 55 56 57 58 59 60 61 63 64 65 66 68 70 71 72 74 75 76 77 78 79 80 81 82 83 84 85 86 87 88 89 90 91 92 93 94 95 96 97 98 99 100 101 102 103 104 105 107 108 110 111 114 115 116 117 118 119 121 123 124 126 128 129 130 131 132 134 135 143 144 146 147 148 **P**6
Primary Contact: Akram Boutros, M.D., FACHE, President and Chief Executive Officer
COO: Edward Hills, D.D.S., Interim Chief Operating Officer
CFO: Craig Richmond, Senior Vice President and Chief Financial Officer
CMO: Alfred Connors, Senior Vice President Medical Affairs and Chief Medical Officer
CIO: James Schlesinger, Interim Chief Information Officer
CHR: Debbie Warman, Vice President Human Resources
CNO: Mavis Bechtle, MSN, Senior Vice President and Chief Nursing Officer
Web address: www.metrohealth.org
Control: County–Government, nonfederal **Service:** General Medical and Surgical

> **Staffed Beds:** 707 **Admissions:** 25678 **Census:** 498 **Outpatient Visits:** 1080905 **Births:** 2922 **Total Expense ($000):** 835788 **Payroll Expense ($000):** 448584 **Personnel:** 5690

RAINBOW BABIES AND CHILDREN'S HOSPITAL See University Hospitals Case Medical Center

SAINT LUKE'S MEDICAL CENTER See St. Vincent Charity Medical Center

☐ **ST. VINCENT CHARITY MEDICAL CENTER (360037)**, 2351 East 22nd Street, Zip 44115–3111; tel. 216/861–6200, (Includes SAINT LUKE'S MEDICAL CENTER, 11311 Shaker Boulevard, Zip 44104–3805; tel. 216/368–7000) **A**1 2 3 5 9 10 **F**3 4 5 12 15 17 18 20 22 24 28 29 30 31 33 34 35 37 39 40 45 50 54 56 57 59 60 61 62 64 65 66 68 70 71 74 75 77 78 79 81 82 84 85 86 87 93 97 98 100 102 103 107 108 110 114 118 119 130 146 148 **P**4 **S** Sisters of Charity Health System, Cleveland, OH
Primary Contact: David Perse, M.D., President and Chief Executive Officer
CFO: John Rusnaczyk, Senior Vice President and Chief Financial Officer
CMO: Joseph Sopko, M.D., Chief Medical Officer
CIO: Robin Stursa, Chief Information Officer
CHR: Ted Monczewski, Vice President Human Resources
CNO: Beverly Lozar, Chief Nursing Executive
Web address: www.stvincentcharity.com/
Control: Other not–for–profit (including NFP Corporation) **Service:** General Medical and Surgical

> **Staffed Beds:** 214 **Admissions:** 7738 **Census:** 109 **Outpatient Visits:** 147231 **Births:** 0 **Total Expense ($000):** 148170 **Payroll Expense ($000):** 59138 **Personnel:** 1095

⊠ **UH REGIONAL HOSPITALS (360075)**, 27100 Chardon Road, Zip 44143–1116; tel. 440/585–6500, (Includes UNIVERSITY HOSPITALS BEDFORD MEDICAL CENTER, 44 Blaine Avenue, Zip 44146–2709; tel. 440/735–3900; UNIVERSITY HOSPITALS RICHMOND MEDICAL CENTER, 27100 Chardon Road, tel. 440/585–6500) **A**1 10 12 13 **F**1 8 14 15 20 29 34 35 40 43 44 49 50 57 59 60 65 66 68 69 70 75 77 79 81 82 86 87 89 93 96 97 107 108 109 110 111 114 116 117 118 119 128 129 130 132 133 135 143 146 147 148 **S** University Hospitals, Cleveland, OH
Primary Contact: Robert G. David, President
CFO: Scott Platz, Director Finance
CMO: Rosemary Leeming, M.D., Chief Medical Officer
CHR: Stephanie W. Neonakis, Manager Human Resources
CNO: Michelle Giltner, Interim Chief Nursing Officer
Web address: www.uhhospitals.org
Control: Other not–for–profit (including NFP Corporation) **Service:** General Medical and Surgical

> **Staffed Beds:** 101 **Admissions:** 5302 **Census:** 61 **Outpatient Visits:** 119208 **Births:** 0 **Total Expense ($000):** 99601 **Payroll Expense ($000):** 38246 **Personnel:** 738

⊠ **UNIVERSITY HOSPITALS CASE MEDICAL CENTER (360137)**, 11100 Euclid Avenue, Zip 44106–1716; tel. 216/844–1000, (Includes ALFRED AND NORMA LERNER TOWER, BOLWELL HEALTH CENTER, HANNA PAVILION, LAKESIDE HOSPITAL, SAMUEL MATHER PAVILION ; HANNA HOUSE SKILLED NURSING FACILITY, 11100 Euclid Avenue, Zip 44106; RAINBOW BABIES AND CHILDREN'S HOSPITAL, 2101 Adelbert Road, Zip 44106–2624; tel. 216/844–3911; Patricia DePompei, President; UNIVERSITY MACDONALD WOMEN'S HOSPITAL, 2101 Adelbert Road, Zip 44106–2624; tel. 216/844–3911; Patricia DePompei, President), (Total facility includes 38 beds in nursing home–type unit) **A**1 2 3 5 8 9 10 **F**3 5 6 8 9 11 12 13 14 15 17 18 19 20 21 22 23 24 25 26 27 28 29 30 31 32 34 35 36 37 38 39 40 41 42 43 44 45 46 47 48 49 50 51 52 53 54 55 56 57 58 59 60 61 62 63 64 65 66 68 70 71 72 73 74 75 76 77 78 79 80 81 82 83 84 85 86 87 88 89 90 91 92 93 94 96 97 98 99 100 101 102 103 104 105 107 108 109 110 111 112 114 115 116 117 118 119 120 121 123 124 126 128 129 130 131 132 133 134 135 136 137 138 139 140 141 142 143 144 145 146 147 148 **P**6 7 **S** University Hospitals, Cleveland, OH
Primary Contact: Fred C. Rothstein, M.D., President
COO: Ron Dziedzicki, R.N., Chief Operating Officer
CFO: Sonia Salvino, Vice President Finance
CMO: Michael Anderson, M.D., Chief Medical Officer
CIO: John V. Foley, Chief Information Officer
CHR: Julie Chester, Vice President Human Resources
CNO: Catherine S. Koppelman, MSN, Chief Nursing Officer
Web address: www.UHhospitals.org
Control: Other not–for–profit (including NFP Corporation) **Service:** General Medical and Surgical

> **Staffed Beds:** 763 **Admissions:** 41626 **Census:** 629 **Outpatient Visits:** 441755 **Births:** 3892 **Total Expense ($000):** 1145505 **Payroll Expense ($000):** 402949 **Personnel:** 7655

VETERANS AFFAIRS MEDICAL CENTER See Louis Stokes Cleveland Veterans Affairs Medical Center

COLDWATER—Mercer County

⊠ **MERCER HEALTH (360058)**, 800 West Main Street, Zip 45828–1698; tel. 419/678–2341 **A**1 9 10 **F**3 7 11 12 13 15 18 28 29 30 31 34 35 40 44 45 47 50 51 54 57 59 61 62 64 65 70 75 76 77 78 79 81 82 85 87 92 93 94 97 107 108 110 111 114 118 119 130 131 132 133 134 135 143 144 145 146 147 148 **P**3
Primary Contact: Lisa R. Klenke, R.N., Chief Executive Officer and Chief Nursing Officer
CFO: George Boyles, Vice President Finance and Chief Financial Officer
CMO: A. Jean Thresher, M.D., Chief Medical Officer
CIO: DeWayne Marsee, Director Information Systems and Chief Information Officer
CHR: Ed Sweetnich, Vice President Human Resources
Web address: www.mercer–health.com
Control: Hospital district or authority, Government, nonfederal **Service:** General Medical and Surgical

> **Staffed Beds:** 60 **Admissions:** 1925 **Census:** 13 **Outpatient Visits:** 47414 **Births:** 362 **Total Expense ($000):** 43769 **Payroll Expense ($000):** 16082 **Personnel:** 377

COLUMBUS—Franklin County

⊠ **JAMES CANCER HOSPITAL AND SOLOVE RESEARCH INSTITUTE (360242)**, 300 West Tenth Avenue, Zip 43210–1280; tel. 614/293–3300 **A**1 2 3 5 8 9 10 **F**3 15 29 30 31 32 34 35 36 37 38 39 44 46 47 48 49 50 52 54 55 57 58 59 61 62 64 66 68 70 71 74 75 77 78 79 81 82 84 85 86 87 93 97 100 107 108 110 111 112 114 115 116 117 118 119 120 121 123 124 126 130 132 134 135 136 141 143 144 145 146 147 148 **P**6 **S** Ohio State University Health System, Columbus, OH
Primary Contact: Michael Caligiuri, Chief Executive Officer
COO: Dennis J. Smith, Chief Operating Officer
CFO: Bell Julian, Associate Executive Director and Chief Financial Officer
CIO: Twyla Pohar, Manager Computer Systems
CHR: Jill Hannah, Director Human Resources
Web address: www.jamesline.com
Control: State–Government, nonfederal **Service:** Cancer

> **Staffed Beds:** 228 **Admissions:** 10558 **Census:** 191 **Outpatient Visits:** 302611 **Births:** 0 **Total Expense ($000):** 596012 **Payroll Expense ($000):** 142221 **Personnel:** 2751

Hospital, Medicare Provider Number, Address, Telephone, Approval, Facility, and Physician Codes, Health Care System

★ American Hospital Association (AHA) membership
☐ The Joint Commission accreditation
◇ DNV Healthcare Inc. accreditation
○ Healthcare Facilities Accreditation Program
△ Commission on Accreditation of Rehabilitation Facilities (CARF) accreditation

OH

⊠ △ **MOUNT CARMEL (360035)**, 793 West State Street, Zip 43222–1551; tel. 614/234–5000, (Includes MOUNT CARMEL EAST HOSPITAL, 6001 East Broad Street, Zip 43213; tel. 614/234–6000; Claus von Zychlin, President; MOUNT CARMEL WEST HOSPITAL, 793 West State Street, Zip 43222; tel. 614/234–5000) **A**1 2 3 5 7 9 10 **F**3 11 12 13 15 17 18 20 22 24 26 28 29 30 31 34 35 37 40 43 44 45 46 47 48 49 50 51 54 55 57 58 59 61 63 64 65 66 68 70 72 74 75 76 78 79 81 83 84 85 86 87 90 92 96 97 98 100 101 102 103 104 107 108 109 110 111 114 115 116 117 118 119 120 121 123 124 126 130 131 132 145 146 147 148 **P**6 8 **S** Catholic Health East / Trinity Health, Livonia, MI
Primary Contact: Sean McKibben, President and Chief Operating Officer
COO: Mary R. Trimmer, Interim Chief Operating Officer
CFO: Keith T. Coleman, Chief Financial Officer
Web address: www.mountcarmelhealth.com
Control: Church–operated, Nongovernment, not–for profit **Service:** General Medical and Surgical

Staffed Beds: 728 **Admissions:** 39070 **Census:** 472 **Outpatient Visits:** 372048 **Births:** 3771 **Total Expense ($000):** 630014 **Payroll Expense ($000):** 213781 **Personnel:** 4610

⊠ △ **NATIONWIDE CHILDREN'S HOSPITAL (363305)**, 700 Children's Drive, Zip 43205–2664; tel. 614/722–2000 **A**1 3 5 7 8 9 10 **F**3 7 8 12 16 17 18 19 20 21 22 23 24 25 26 27 28 29 30 31 32 34 35 38 39 40 41 43 44 45 47 48 50 51 53 54 55 57 58 59 60 61 62 63 64 65 66 68 71 72 74 75 77 78 79 81 82 83 84 85 86 87 88 89 90 92 93 94 96 97 99 100 101 102 104 105 107 108 111 112 114 115 116 117 118 119 126 127 129 130 131 132 133 134 135 136 137 138 140 141 143 144 145 146 148 **P**6 8
Primary Contact: Steve Allen, M.D., Chief Executive Officer
COO: Rick Miller, President and Chief Operating Officer
CFO: Tim Robinson, Executive Vice President, Chief Financial and Administrative Officer and Treasurer
CMO: Richard Brilli, M.D., Chief Medical Officer
CIO: Denise Zabawski, Vice President Information Services and Chief Information Officer
CHR: Jose Balderrama, Vice President Human Resources
Web address: www.nationwidechildrens.org
Control: Other not–for–profit (including NFP Corporation) **Service:** Children's general

Staffed Beds: 523 **Admissions:** 17594 **Census:** 341 **Outpatient Visits:** 1048951 **Births:** 0 **Total Expense ($000):** 871991 **Payroll Expense ($000):** 402887 **Personnel:** 6910

☐ **OHIO HOSPITAL FOR PSYCHIATRY (364041)**, 880 Greenlawn Avenue, Zip 43223–2616; tel. 614/449–9664 **A**1 9 10 **F**56 64 98 103 104 105 130 **S** Acadia Healthcare Company, Inc., Franklin, TN
Primary Contact: Roxanne Jividen, Chief Executive Officer
COO: Shannon Robbins, Chief Operating Officer
CFO: Steve Snyder, Chief Financial Officer
CMO: Richard Nockowitz, M.D., Medical Director
CNO: Jayne Zink, Director of Nursing
Web address: www.ohiohospitalforpsychiatry.com/
Control: Corporation, Investor–owned, for–profit **Service:** Psychiatric

Staffed Beds: 90 **Admissions:** 2158 **Census:** 76 **Outpatient Visits:** 31049 **Births:** 0 **Total Expense ($000):** 14129 **Payroll Expense ($000):** 7340 **Personnel:** 169

⊠ △ **OHIO STATE UNIVERSITY WEXNER MEDICAL CENTER (360085)**, 370 West 9th Avenue, Zip 43210–1238; tel. 614/293–8000, (Includes OHIO STATE UNIVERSITY HOSPITALS EAST, 1492 East Broad Street, Zip 43205–1546; tel. 614/257–3000) **A**1 3 5 7 8 10 **F**3 4 5 6 8 9 11 12 13 15 16 17 18 20 22 24 26 28 29 30 31 33 34 35 36 37 38 39 40 43 44 45 46 47 48 49 50 51 52 53 54 55 56 57 58 59 60 61 62 64 65 66 68 70 72 73 74 75 77 78 79 80 81 82 84 85 86 87 90 91 92 93 94 95 96 97 98 99 100 101 102 103 104 105 107 108 110 111 112 113 114 115 118 119 126 129 130 131 132 134 135 137 138 139 140 141 142 143 144 145 146 147 148 **P**6 **S** Ohio State University Health System, Columbus, OH
Primary Contact: Steven Gabbe, M.D., Chief Executive Officer
COO: Peter E. Geier, Chief Operating Officer
CMO: Andrew Thomas, M.D., Chief Medical Officer
CIO: Phyllis Teater, Chief Information Officer
CHR: Kim Shumate, Human Resources Officer
CNO: Mary G. Nash, Ph.D., Chief Nursing Officer
Web address: www.medicalcenter.osu.edu
Control: State–Government, nonfederal **Service:** General Medical and Surgical

Staffed Beds: 965 **Admissions:** 46034 **Census:** 749 **Outpatient Visits:** 1182536 **Births:** 4482 **Total Expense ($000):** 1328212 **Payroll Expense ($000):** 405898 **Personnel:** 9934

⊠ ○ **OHIOHEALTH DOCTORS HOSPITAL (360152)**, 5100 West Broad Street, Zip 43228–1607; tel. 614/544–1000 **A**1 2 5 9 10 11 12 13 **F**3 13 15 17 18 20 22 24 26 28 29 30 34 35 36 40 45 46 47 48 49 50 57 58 59 64 65 66 68 70 72 74 75 76 79 81 85 87 92 93 97 100 107 109 110 111 114 115 116 117 119 120 121 123 126 130 131 134 135 145 146 147 148 **P**1 3 5 **S** OhioHealth, Columbus, OH
Primary Contact: Michael L. Reichfield, President
CFO: Troy Hammett, Vice President and Chief Financial Officer
CMO: Dean Colwell, D.O., Vice President Medical Affairs
CIO: Michael Krouse, Chief Information Officer
CHR: David Sullivan, Director Human Resources
Web address: www.ohiohealth.com
Control: Church–operated, Nongovernment, not–for profit **Service:** General Medical and Surgical

Staffed Beds: 243 **Admissions:** 8846 **Census:** 92 **Outpatient Visits:** 232026 **Births:** 886 **Total Expense ($000):** 225062 **Payroll Expense ($000):** 109401 **Personnel:** 1043

⊠ **OHIOHEALTH GRANT MEDICAL CENTER (360017)**, 111 South Grant Avenue, Zip 43215–1898; tel. 614/566–9000 **A**1 2 5 8 9 10 **F**3 7 8 9 11 13 15 17 18 20 22 24 26 28 29 30 31 34 35 36 37 40 42 43 45 46 47 48 49 50 53 54 56 57 58 59 60 61 64 66 67 68 70 72 74 75 76 78 79 80 81 82 83 84 85 86 87 97 100 102 107 108 109 110 111 114 115 116 117 119 120 121 123 124 126 129 130 131 132 135 143 144 146 147 148 **P**1 3 5 **S** OhioHealth, Columbus, OH
Primary Contact: Michael Lawson, President and Chief Operating Officer
COO: Michael Lawson, President and Chief Operating Officer
CMO: Greg Morrison, M.D., Vice President Medical Affairs
CIO: Michael Krouse, Chief Information Officer
CHR: Linda Simpson, Vice President Human Resources
CNO: Donna Hanly, R.N., Senior Vice President and Chief Nursing Officer
Web address: www.ohiohealth.com
Control: Church–operated, Nongovernment, not–for profit **Service:** General Medical and Surgical

Staffed Beds: 427 **Admissions:** 21216 **Census:** 253 **Outpatient Visits:** 581974 **Births:** 2560 **Total Expense ($000):** 551119 **Payroll Expense ($000):** 244505 **Personnel:** 2292

★ **OHIOHEALTH REHABILITATION HOSPITAL (363037)**, 1087 Dennison Avenue, 4th Floor, Zip 43201–3201; tel. 614/484–9700, (Nonreporting) **A**10 **S** Select Medical Corporation, Mechanicsburg, PA
Primary Contact: Eric Yap, Chief Executive Officer
Web address: www.ohiohealth–rehab.com
Control: Partnership, Investor–owned, for–profit **Service:** Rehabilitation

Staffed Beds: 144

⊠ **OHIOHEALTH RIVERSIDE METHODIST HOSPITAL (360006)**, 3535 Olentangy River Road, Zip 43214–3998; tel. 614/566–5000 **A**1 2 3 5 8 9 10 **F**3 7 8 11 12 13 14 15 17 18 20 22 24 26 28 29 30 31 33 34 35 36 37 38 39 40 43 44 45 46 47 48 49 50 51 53 54 55 56 57 58 59 60 61 62 63 64 65 66 68 69 70 71 72 74 75 76 77 78 79 80 81 82 83 84 85 86 87 90 91 92 93 94 96 97 98 100 102 103 104 105 107 108 110 111 114 115 116 117 118 119 120 121 123 124 126 129 130 132 135 143 144 145 146 147 148 **P**1 3 5 **S** OhioHealth, Columbus, OH
Primary Contact: Stephen Markovich, M.D., President
COO: Brian Jepson, Chief Operating Officer
CFO: Peter Bury, Vice President Finance
CMO: Thomas Harmon, M.D., Vice President Medical Affairs
CIO: Michael Krouse, Chief Information Officer
CHR: Shereen Solaiman, Vice President Human Resources
CNO: Lisa Gossett, MSN, Chief Nursing Officer
Web address: www.ohiohealth.com
Control: Church–operated, Nongovernment, not–for profit **Service:** General Medical and Surgical

Staffed Beds: 752 **Admissions:** 45696 **Census:** 525 **Outpatient Visits:** 784447 **Births:** 6359 **Total Expense ($000):** 842828 **Payroll Expense ($000):** 348929 **Personnel:** 4473

⊠ **REGENCY HOSPITAL OF COLUMBUS (362037)**, 1430 South High Street, Zip 43207–1045; tel. 614/456–0300, (Nonreporting) **A**1 10 **S** Select Medical Corporation, Mechanicsburg, PA
Primary Contact: Lisa J. Pettrey, MSN, R.N., Chief Executive Officer
Web address: www.regencyhospital.com/
Control: Corporation, Investor–owned, for–profit **Service:** Long–Term Acute Care hospital

Staffed Beds: 43

Many Facility Codes have changed. Please refer to the AHA Guide Code Chart. © 2014 AHA Guide

⊠ **SELECT SPECIALTY HOSPITAL–COLUMBUS (362022)**, 1087 Dennison Avenue, Zip 43201–3201; tel. 614/458–9000, (Includes SELECT SPECIALTY HOSPITAL–COLUMBUS, MOUNT CARMEL CAMPUS, 793 West State Street, Zip 43222–1551; tel. 614/234–0950), (Nonreporting) **A**1 10 **S** Select Medical Corporation, Mechanicsburg, PA
Primary Contact: John C. Yanes, Chief Executive Officer
CMO: Victoria Ruff, M.D., Medical Director
CHR: Charles Pankowski, Manager Human Resources
Web address: www.selectspecialtyhospitals.com/company/locations/columbus.aspx
Control: Corporation, Investor–owned, for–profit **Service:** Long–Term Acute Care hospital

Staffed Beds: 176

SELECT SPECIALTY HOSPITAL–COLUMBUS, MOUNT CARMEL CAMPUS See Select Specialty Hospital–Columbus

⊠ **TWIN VALLEY BEHAVIORAL HEALTHCARE (364007)**, 2200 West Broad Street, Zip 43223–1297; tel. 614/752–0333 **A**1 10 **F**29 30 39 65 68 87 98 100 101 105 130 132 135 146 **S** Ohio Department of Mental Health, Columbus, OH
Primary Contact: Veronica Lofton, Acting Chief Executive Officer
COO: David Blahnik, Chief Operating Officer
CFO: Tracy Gladen, Chief Financial Officer
CMO: R. Alan Freeland, M.D., Chief Clinical Officer
CIO: Missy McGarvey, Chief Information Officer
CHR: Marcia McKeen, Director Human Resources
CNO: Michael Breakwell, R.N., Nurse Executive
Web address: www.mh.state.oh.us/ibhs/bhos/tvbh.html
Control: State–Government, nonfederal **Service:** Psychiatric

Staffed Beds: 228 Admissions: 1971 Census: 211 Outpatient Visits: 0 Births: 0 Total Expense ($000): 48909 Payroll Expense ($000): 28261 Personnel: 481

CONCORD TOWNSHIP—Lake County

⊠ **LAKE HEALTH (360098)**, 7590 Auburn Road, Zip 44077–9176; tel. 440/375–8100, (Includes TRIPOINT MEDICAL CENTER, 7950 Auburn Road, Painesville, Zip 44077; Cynthia Moore–Hardy, FACHE, President and Chief Executive Officer) **A**1 9 10 **F**3 7 11 12 13 15 18 20 22 24 26 28 29 30 34 35 36 40 42 44 45 49 50 51 53 54 56 57 58 59 60 62 63 64 65 68 69 70 73 74 75 77 79 81 82 85 86 87 90 93 97 98 100 101 102 103 107 108 110 111 114 116 117 118 119 129 130 131 132 133 135 143 144 146 147 148 **P**1
Primary Contact: Cynthia Moore–Hardy, FACHE, President and Chief Executive Officer
CFO: Michael Kittoe, Chief Financial Officer
CMO: Michael Golen, M.D., Chief Medical Officer
CIO: Gerald Peters, Vice President Information Technologies and Chief Information Officer
CHR: Craig J. Ghidotti, Vice President Human Resources
CNO: Mary L. Ogrinc, R.N., Chief Nursing Officer, Senior Vice President Patient Care Services
Web address: www.lhs.net
Control: Other not–for–profit (including NFP Corporation) **Service:** General Medical and Surgical

Staffed Beds: 357 Admissions: 17064 Census: 203 Outpatient Visits: 460506 Births: 1872 Total Expense ($000): 308542 Payroll Expense ($000): 144849 Personnel: 2301

CONNEAUT—Ashtabula County

⊠ **UNIVERSITY HOSPITALS CONNEAUT MEDICAL CENTER (361308)**, 158 West Main Road, Zip 44030–2039; tel. 440/593–1131 **A**1 9 10 18 **F**3 7 11 15 18 28 29 34 35 37 40 51 59 64 70 75 77 78 79 81 82 86 87 93 107 110 111 114 119 130 132 133 135 143 146 147 148 **S** University Hospitals, Cleveland, OH
Primary Contact: M. Steven Jones, President
COO: Richard Trice, Director Operations
CFO: Michael McGrath, Manager Finance
CMO: Gary Huston, D.O., Chief Medical Officer
CIO: Cheryl Vibbard, Manager Health Information Services
CHR: Barbara Gurto, Manager Human Resources
CNO: Karen McNeil, Chief Nursing Officer
Web address: www.uhhospitals.org
Control: Other not–for–profit (including NFP Corporation) **Service:** General Medical and Surgical

Staffed Beds: 25 Admissions: 520 Census: 5 Outpatient Visits: 39360 Births: 0 Total Expense ($000): 24911 Payroll Expense ($000): 9157 Personnel: 178

COSHOCTON—Coshocton County

☐ **COSHOCTON COUNTY MEMORIAL HOSPITAL (360109)**, 1460 Orange Street, Zip 43812–2229, Mailing Address: P.O. Box 1330, Zip 43812–6330; tel. 740/622–6411, (Nonreporting) **A**1 5 9 10 20
Primary Contact: Robert Miller, Chief Executive Officer
CFO: Robin Nichols, Chief Financial Officer
CMO: Tammry S. Alverson, M.D., Chief of Staff
CIO: Seth Peterson, Director Information Services
CHR: Rick Davis, Chief Operating Officer and Support Services
Web address: www.ccmh.com
Control: Other not–for–profit (including NFP Corporation) **Service:** General Medical and Surgical

Staffed Beds: 109

CUYAHOGA FALLS—Summit County

CUYAHOGA FALLS GENERAL HOSPITAL See Summa Western Reserve Hospital

⊠ △ **EDWIN SHAW REHAB (360241)**, 330 Broadway Street East, Zip 44221–3312; tel. 330/436–0910, (Nonreporting) **A**1 7 9 10 **S** Akron General Health System, Akron, OH
Primary Contact: Thomas Whelan, President
CFO: Debbie Gorbach, Vice President and Treasurer
CMO: Anthony Hayek, D.O., Medical Director
CHR: Heather Sans, Human Resource Generalist
Web address: www.edwinshaw.com
Control: County–Government, nonfederal **Service:** Rehabilitation

Staffed Beds: 38

○ **SUMMA WESTERN RESERVE HOSPITAL (360150)**, 1900 23rd Street, Zip 44223–1499; tel. 330/971–7000 **A**9 10 11 12 13 **F**3 8 11 18 20 26 29 30 31 34 35 36 38 40 44 45 47 49 50 51 54 57 58 59 60 63 64 65 66 68 70 74 75 77 78 79 81 82 84 85 87 93 94 96 97 100 107 108 111 114 119 129 130 132 135 144 146 148 **P**6 8 **S** Summa Health System, Akron, OH
Primary Contact: Robert Kent, D.O., President and Chief Executive Officer
CFO: Jill Hiner, Vice President and Chief Financial Officer
CMO: Charles Feunning, M.D., President Medical Staff
CHR: Heather Milicevic, Director Human Resources
Web address: www.westernreservehospital.org
Control: Partnership, Investor–owned, for–profit **Service:** General Medical and Surgical

Staffed Beds: 57 Admissions: 3421 Census: 40 Outpatient Visits: 120490 Births: 0 Total Expense ($000): 103501 Payroll Expense ($000): 39105 Personnel: 715

DAYTON—Montgomery County

☐ **ACCESS HOSPITAL DAYTON (364050)**, 2611 Wayne Avenue, Zip 45420–1833; tel. 937/256–7802, (Nonreporting) **A**1 10
Primary Contact: Belinda Stevens, Chief Executive Officer
Web address: www.accesshospital.com/
Control: Corporation, Investor–owned, for–profit **Service:** Psychiatric

Staffed Beds: 28

☐ **CHILDREN'S MEDICAL CENTER (363306)**, One Children's Plaza, Zip 45404–1815; tel. 937/641–3000, (Nonreporting) **A**1 2 3 5 8 9 10
Primary Contact: Deborah A. Feldman, President and Chief Executive Officer
COO: Matthew P. Graybill, Chief Operating Officer
CFO: David T. Miller, Vice President and Chief Financial Officer
CMO: Adam Mezoff, M.D., Vice President and Chief Medical Officer
CIO: Beth Fredette, Chief Information Officer
Web address: www.childrensdayton.org
Control: Other not–for–profit (including NFP Corporation) **Service:** Children's general

Staffed Beds: 123

☐ **DAYTON REHABILITATION INSTITUTE (363033)**, One Elizabeth Place, Zip 45417–3445; tel. 937/424–8200 **A**1 10 **F**3 29 90 96 130 148 **S** Reliant Healthcare Partners, Richardson, TX
Primary Contact: Randy J. Kitchen, Chief Executive Officer
Web address: www.reliantdayton.com
Control: Partnership, Investor–owned, for–profit **Service:** Rehabilitation

Staffed Beds: 50 Admissions: 504 Census: 16 Outpatient Visits: 0 Births: 0 Total Expense ($000): 7486 Payroll Expense ($000): 3121 Personnel: 109

Hospital, Medicare Provider Number, Address, Telephone, Approval, Facility, and Physician Codes, Health Care System

★ American Hospital Association (AHA) membership
☐ The Joint Commission accreditation
◇ DNV Healthcare Inc. accreditation
○ Healthcare Facilities Accreditation Program
△ Commission on Accreditation of Rehabilitation Facilities (CARF) accreditation

OH

✠ △ **DAYTON VETERANS AFFAIRS MEDICAL CENTER**, 4100 West Third Street, Zip 45428–9000; tel. 937/268–6511, (Total facility includes 225 beds in nursing home–type unit) **A**1 2 3 5 7 8 **F**2 3 5 18 20 22 28 29 30 31 33 34 35 36 38 39 40 45 46 47 48 49 53 56 57 58 59 60 61 62 63 64 65 68 70 71 74 75 77 78 79 81 82 83 84 85 86 87 91 92 93 94 95 96 97 98 100 101 102 103 104 106 107 108 109 111 112 114 115 116 117 118 119 120 121 122 123 124 127 128 129 130 132 135 144 146 147 148 **P**5 6 **S** Department of Veterans Affairs, Washington, DC
Primary Contact: Glenn A. Costie, FACHE, Director
COO: Mark Murdock, Associate Director
CFO: Shannon Rappach, Chief Fiscal Services
CMO: James Hardy, D.O., Chief of Staff
CIO: Susan Sherer, Chief Information Resource Management
CHR: Rolanda Watkins, Chief Human Resources Management Service
CNO: Anna Jones Monnett, MS, Associate Director Patient Care Services
Web address: www.dayton.va.gov/
Control: Veterans Affairs, Government, federal **Service:** General Medical and Surgical

Staffed Beds: 471 **Admissions:** 5724 **Census:** 195 **Outpatient Visits:** 474454 **Births:** 0 **Total Expense ($000):** 203355 **Payroll Expense ($000):** 143512

✠ **GOOD SAMARITAN HOSPITAL (360052)**, 2222 Philadelphia Drive, Zip 45406–1813; tel. 937/734–2612 **A**1 2 3 5 9 10 **F**3 11 13 15 17 18 20 22 24 26 28 29 30 31 36 37 40 42 44 45 46 49 50 53 54 55 56 58 60 61 64 66 70 73 74 75 76 77 78 79 80 81 82 83 85 86 87 92 93 97 100 101 102 107 108 109 110 111 114 115 118 119 126 129 130 131 132 145 146 148 **P**6 **S** Catholic Health Initiatives, Englewood, CO
Primary Contact: Eloise Broner, President and Chief Executive Officer
COO: Mary E. Garman, R.N., Chief Operating Officer and Chief Nursing Officer
CMO: Daniel L. Schoulties, M.D., Vice President Medical Affairs
CHR: Barbara A. Johnson, Vice President Human Resources
CNO: Mary E. Garman, R.N., Chief Nursing Officer and Chief Operating Officer
Web address: www.goodsamdayton.com
Control: Church–operated, Nongovernment, not–for profit **Service:** General Medical and Surgical

Staffed Beds: 467 **Admissions:** 16270 **Census:** 194 **Outpatient Visits:** 247526 **Births:** 999 **Total Expense ($000):** 334099 **Payroll Expense ($000):** 128772 **Personnel:** 2062

★ ○ △ **GRANDVIEW MEDICAL CENTER (360133)**, 405 Grand Avenue, Zip 45405–4796; tel. 937/226–3200, (Includes SOUTHVIEW HOSPITAL AND FAMILY HEALTH CENTER, 1997 Miamisburg–Centerville Road, Zip 45459–3800; tel. 937/439–6000) **A**7 9 10 11 12 13 **F**3 11 12 13 15 18 20 22 24 28 29 30 31 34 35 36 38 39 40 42 44 45 47 48 49 50 51 53 54 56 57 58 59 60 61 64 65 66 68 70 73 74 75 76 77 78 79 81 82 85 86 87 93 96 97 98 100 101 102 103 104 105 107 108 110 111 114 115 116 117 118 119 120 121 123 124 129 130 131 132 135 141 144 145 146 147 148 **S** Kettering Health Network, Dayton, OH
Primary Contact: Russell Wetherell, President
CFO: Todd Anderson, Chief Financial Officer
CHR: Karen Borgert, Vice President Human Resources
Web address: www.ketteringhealth.org/grandview/
Control: Church–operated, Nongovernment, not–for profit **Service:** General Medical and Surgical

Staffed Beds: 280 **Admissions:** 11412 **Census:** 149 **Outpatient Visits:** 324989 **Births:** 1716 **Total Expense ($000):** 382860 **Payroll Expense ($000):** 136521 **Personnel:** 1479

HAVEN BEHAVIORAL SENIOR CARE OF DAYTON (364048), One Elizabeth Place, 4th Floor Southwest Tower, Zip 45417–3445; tel. 937/234–0100 **A**10 **F**98 103 **P**5 **S** Haven Behavioral Healthcare, Nashville, TN
Primary Contact: Keith Kuhn, Chief Executive Officer
CMO: Amita Patel, M.D., Medical Director
CNO: Cheryl Meyer, MSN, Director of Nursing
Web address: www.havenbehavioraldayton.com/
Control: Corporation, Investor–owned, for–profit **Service:** Psychiatric

Staffed Beds: 32 **Admissions:** 435 **Census:** 18

✠ **KINDRED HOSPITAL–DAYTON (362033)**, 1 Elizabeth Place, 5th Floor, Zip 45417–3445; tel. 937/222–5963, (Nonreporting) **A**1 10 **S** Kindred Healthcare, Louisville, KY
Primary Contact: Lynn Schoen, Chief Executive Officer
CMO: Felipe Rubio, M.D., Medical Director
CNO: Katherine Cass, R.N., Nurse Manager
Web address: www.khdayton.com
Control: Corporation, Investor–owned, for–profit **Service:** Long–Term Acute Care hospital

Staffed Beds: 67

✠ △ **MIAMI VALLEY HOSPITAL (360051)**, One Wyoming Street, Zip 45409–2793; tel. 937/208–8000 **A**1 2 3 5 7 8 9 10 **F**3 5 12 13 15 16 17 18 20 22 24 26 28 29 30 31 34 35 37 39 40 42 43 44 45 46 47 48 49 50 53 54 55 56 57 58 59 60 61 64 68 70 72 73 74 75 76 77 78 79 81 82 84 85 86 87 90 91 92 93 96 98 100 101 102 103 104 107 108 110 111 114 115 117 118 119 120 121 123 126 129 130 131 132 134 135 136 138 141 143 145 146 147 148 **P**6
Primary Contact: Mark S. Shaker, President and Chief Executive Officer
COO: Mikki Clancy, Chief Operating Officer
CFO: Thomas M. Duncan, Executive Vice President and Chief Financial Officer
CMO: Mark Williams, M.D., Vice President and Chief Medical Officer
CIO: Gary Ginter, Senior Vice President and Chief Information Officer
CHR: Barbara A. Johnson, Vice President Human Resources
CNO: Jolyn M. Angus, R.N., Chief Nursing Officer
Web address: www.miamivalleyhospital.org
Control: Other not–for–profit (including NFP Corporation) **Service:** General Medical and Surgical

Staffed Beds: 966 **Admissions:** 38534 **Census:** 459 **Outpatient Visits:** 301466 **Births:** 5000 **Total Expense ($000):** 764605 **Payroll Expense ($000):** 286014 **Personnel:** 5326

SOUTHVIEW HOSPITAL AND FAMILY HEALTH CENTER See Grandview Medical Center

☐ **THE MEDICAL CENTER AT ELIZABETH PLACE (360274)**, One Elizabeth Place, Zip 45417–3445; tel. 937/660–3100, (Nonreporting) **A**1 9 10
Primary Contact: Alexander M. Rintoul, Chief Executive Officer
Web address: www.regentsurgicalhealth.com/Partner+Centers/Medical+Center+at+Elizabeth+Place
Control: Partnership, Investor–owned, for–profit **Service:** General Medical and Surgical

Staffed Beds: 26

VETERANS AFFAIRS MEDICAL CENTER See Dayton Veterans Affairs Medical Center

DEFIANCE—Defiance County

✠ **MERCY HOSPITAL OF DEFIANCE (360270)**, 1404 East Second Street, Zip 43512–2440; tel. 419/782–8444 **A**1 10 **F**3 8 18 29 30 34 35 40 45 57 59 70 75 81 82 85 87 90 129 135 145 **P**8 **S** Mercy Health, Cincinnati, OH
Primary Contact: Sonya Selhorst, R.N., Administrator
COO: Kerry Knuth, Chief Operating Officer
CFO: James Puffenberger, Vice President and Chief Financial Officer
CMO: Jeffrey Pruitt, M.D., Chief of Staff
CHR: Susan Pscodna, Director Human Resources
CNO: Sonya Selhorst, R.N., Administrator and Chief Nursing Officer
Web address: www.ehealthconnection.com/regions/toledo/
Control: Other not–for–profit (including NFP Corporation) **Service:** General Medical and Surgical

Staffed Beds: 23 **Admissions:** 1169 **Census:** 10 **Outpatient Visits:** 11434 **Births:** 0

✠ **PROMEDICA DEFIANCE REGIONAL HOSPITAL (361328)**, 1200 Ralston Avenue, Zip 43512–1396; tel. 419/783–6955 **A**1 5 9 10 18 **F**3 11 13 15 18 20 28 31 32 34 40 43 57 59 64 66 68 70 75 76 77 78 79 81 85 86 87 93 98 100 101 102 103 104 105 107 108 110 111 114 118 119 129 130 132 135 144 146 147 148 **S** ProMedica Health System, Toledo, OH
Primary Contact: Julie Yaroch, D.O., President and Chief Executive Officer
CFO: Ken Swint, Director Finance
CMO: Stanislaw Dajczak, M.D., Chief of Staff
CIO: Patricia Swint, Director Information Management Systems
CHR: Carrie Miller, Director Human Resources
Web address: www.promedica.org
Control: Other not–for–profit (including NFP Corporation) **Service:** General Medical and Surgical

Staffed Beds: 35 **Admissions:** 2118 **Census:** 15 **Outpatient Visits:** 72317 **Births:** 643 **Total Expense ($000):** 46786 **Payroll Expense ($000):** 13447 **Personnel:** 124

DELAWARE—Delaware County

✠ △ **OHIOHEALTH GRADY MEMORIAL HOSPITAL (360210)**, 561 West Central Avenue, Zip 43015–1410; tel. 740/615–1000 **A**1 2 7 9 10 **F**3 13 15 18 20 26 28 29 30 31 34 35 40 45 46 48 50 54 57 58 59 60 63 64 66 68 70 75 76 77 78 79 81 82 85 86 87 92 93 96 97 102 107 108 109 110 111 114 119 124 129 130 131 132 134 135 146 147 148 **P**1 3 5 **S** OhioHealth, Columbus, OH
Primary Contact: Bruce P. Hagen, Regional Executive and President
COO: Steve Bunyard, Chief Operating Officer
CFO: David Hensel, Director Financial Operations
CMO: Barbara Evert, M.D., Vice President Medical Affairs
CIO: Michael Krouse, Chief Information Officer Information Services
CHR: Victoria L. Matlack, Manager and Human Resources Business Partner
CNO: Elizabeth Anne Biegler, R.N., Chief Nursing Officer
Web address: www.ohiohealth.com
Control: Church–operated, Nongovernment, not–for profit **Service:** General Medical and Surgical

Staffed Beds: 61 **Admissions:** 2914 **Census:** 28 **Outpatient Visits:** 110278 **Births:** 297 **Total Expense ($000):** 76476 **Payroll Expense ($000):** 33271 **Personnel:** 391

Many Facility Codes have changed. Please refer to the AHA Guide Code Chart. © 2014 AHA Guide

DENNISON—Tuscarawas County

☐ **TEN LAKES CENTER (364042)**, 819 North First Street, 3rd Floor, Zip 44621–1003; tel. 740/922–7499 **A**1 9 10 **F**98 103 105 130 **P**6 **S** Acadia Healthcare Company, Inc., Franklin, TN
Primary Contact: Debra C. Gardner, R.N., MSN, Administrator
Web address: www.tenlakescenter.com/
Control: Corporation, Investor–owned, for–profit **Service:** Psychiatric

Staffed Beds: 16 **Admissions:** 398 **Census:** 13 **Outpatient Visits:** 16 **Births:** 0 **Total Expense ($000):** 3523 **Payroll Expense ($000):** 1465 **Personnel:** 34

✠ **TRINITY HOSPITAL TWIN CITY (361302)**, 819 North First Street, Zip 44621–1098; tel. 740/922–2800 **A**1 9 10 18 **F**11 15 18 28 30 34 35 40 45 50 57 59 64 70 75 77 81 85 86 87 89 93 97 107 114 119 128 129 130 133 146 147 **P**4 **S** Sylvania Franciscan Health, Toledo, OH
Primary Contact: Joseph J. Mitchell, President
CFO: Woody Hathaway, Chief Financial Officer
CMO: Galen Durose, M.D., Chief of Staff
CHR: Bianca Love, Assistant Administrator Human Resources
CNO: Teresa Gagliardi, R.N., Chief Nursing Officer
Web address: www.trinitytwincity.org
Control: Church–operated, Nongovernment, not–for profit **Service:** General Medical and Surgical

Staffed Beds: 25 **Admissions:** 351 **Census:** 5 **Outpatient Visits:** 147818 **Births:** 0 **Total Expense ($000):** 19644 **Payroll Expense ($000):** 9978 **Personnel:** 199

DOVER—Tuscarawas County

★ ◇ **UNION HOSPITAL (360010)**, 659 Boulevard, Zip 44622–2077; tel. 330/343–3311 **A**5 9 10 19 21 **F**3 8 11 13 14 15 28 29 34 35 40 42 50 53 54 57 59 62 64 70 75 77 78 79 80 81 82 85 86 90 93 107 108 110 111 118 119 120 129 130 131 132 144 146 148 **P**6 8
Primary Contact: Bruce James, Chief Executive Officer
CFO: Eugene A. Thorn, III, Vice President Finance and Chief Financial Officer
CMO: Todd Meyerhoefer, M.D., Vice President Medical Affairs
CIO: David Baumgardner, Director Information Management
CHR: Darwin K. Smith, Vice President Human Resources
CNO: Diana Boyd, Vice President Nursing
Web address: www.unionhospital.org
Control: Other not–for–profit (including NFP Corporation) **Service:** General Medical and Surgical

Staffed Beds: 154 **Admissions:** 5175 **Census:** 56 **Outpatient Visits:** 298187 **Births:** 679 **Total Expense ($000):** 106564 **Payroll Expense ($000):** 44758 **Personnel:** 977

DUBLIN—Franklin County

☐ **DUBLIN SPRINGS (364049)**, 7625 Hospital Drive, Zip 43016–9649; tel. 614/717–1800 **A**1 10 **F**4 5 64 98 101 102 103 104 105 130 132 **P**5
Primary Contact: Garry W. Hoyes, Chief Executive Officer
CFO: Alexis Barbour, Director Finance
CMO: Mark Blair, M.D., Medical Director
CHR: Tam Wisler, Director Human Resources
CNO: Rolaine Weeks, R.N., Director of Nursing
Web address: www.dublinsprings.com/
Control: Corporation, Investor–owned, for–profit **Service:** Psychiatric

Staffed Beds: 72 **Admissions:** 1846 **Census:** 36 **Outpatient Visits:** 7189 **Births:** 0 **Total Expense ($000):** 10551 **Payroll Expense ($000):** 6040 **Personnel:** 160

✠ **OHIOHEALTH DUBLIN METHODIST HOSPITAL (360348)**, 7500 Hospital Drive, Zip 43016–8518; tel. 614/544–8000 **A**1 9 10 **F**3 13 15 18 20 22 29 30 34 40 45 46 57 59 62 68 70 76 77 79 81 82 85 87 97 107 110 111 115 119 126 129 130 131 132 135 144 146 147 148 **P**1 3 5 **S** OhioHealth, Columbus, OH
Primary Contact: Bruce P. Hagen, President
COO: Steve Bunyard, Chief Operating Officer
CMO: Barbara Evert, M.D., Vice President Medical Affairs
CIO: Michael Krouse, Senior Vice President Chief Information Officer
CHR: Victoria L. Matlack, Manager and Human Resources Business Partner
CNO: Elizabeth Anne Biegler, R.N., Chief Nursing Officer
Web address: www.ohiohealth.com
Control: Church–operated, Nongovernment, not–for profit **Service:** General Medical and Surgical

Staffed Beds: 100 **Admissions:** 5343 **Census:** 41 **Outpatient Visits:** 107254 **Births:** 1852 **Total Expense ($000):** 118684 **Payroll Expense ($000):** 45667 **Personnel:** 519

EAST LIVERPOOL—Columbiana County

✠ **EAST LIVERPOOL CITY HOSPITAL (360096)**, 425 West Fifth Street, Zip 43920–2498; tel. 330/385–7200 **A**1 9 10 **F**3 11 13 15 18 28 29 30 31 34 35 39 40 41 44 50 51 53 54 56 57 59 60 64 65 66 67 70 75 76 77 78 79 81 85 86 87 89 93 97 98 100 101 102 103 107 110 111 115 118 119 130 131 132 135 146 147 148 **P**6
Primary Contact: Kenneth Cochran, R.N., FACHE, President and Chief Executive Officer
CFO: Kyle Johnson, Vice President Finance
CMO: Steve LaTulippe, President Medical Staff
CIO: Frank Mader, Director Information Services
CHR: Teri Pasco, Director Human Resources
CNO: Stacie Call, R.N., Vice President Patient Care and Chief Nursing Officer
Web address: www.elch.org
Control: Other not–for–profit (including NFP Corporation) **Service:** General Medical and Surgical

Staffed Beds: 120 **Admissions:** 3718 **Census:** 39 **Outpatient Visits:** 111879 **Births:** 243 **Total Expense ($000):** 60518 **Payroll Expense ($000):** 23231 **Personnel:** 486

ELYRIA—Lorain County

✠ **UNIVERSITY HOSPITALS ELYRIA MEDICAL CENTER (360145)**, 630 East River Street, Zip 44035–5902; tel. 440/329–7500 **A**1 2 9 10 **F**3 8 11 12 13 15 17 18 20 22 24 26 28 29 30 31 34 35 37 40 42 50 53 54 57 59 62 64 68 70 73 74 75 76 77 78 79 81 82 85 86 87 89 92 93 94 98 107 108 110 111 114 115 118 119 126 129 130 131 135 146 148 **P**6 7 8 **S** University Hospitals, Cleveland, OH
Primary Contact: Donald S. Sheldon, M.D., President and Chief Executive Officer
CFO: David A. Cook, Vice President and Chief Financial Officer
CMO: Douglas McDonald, M.D., Vice President Medical Affairs
CIO: Char Wray, Vice President Chief Clinical Operations and Chief Information Officer
CHR: Daniel Miller, Vice President Human Resources
CNO: Jill Cooksey, Vice President Chief Nursing Officer
Web address: www.emh–healthcare.org
Control: Other not–for–profit (including NFP Corporation) **Service:** General Medical and Surgical

Staffed Beds: 257 **Admissions:** 12213 **Census:** 139 **Outpatient Visits:** 268612 **Births:** 903 **Total Expense ($000):** 194618 **Payroll Expense ($000):** 72749 **Personnel:** 1507

EUCLID—Cuyahoga County

✠ △ **EUCLID HOSPITAL (360082)**, 18901 Lake Shore Boulevard, Zip 44119–1090; tel. 216/531–9000, (Total facility includes 40 beds in nursing home–type unit) **A**1 7 10 **F**3 15 17 18 26 28 29 30 34 35 39 40 45 50 56 57 59 60 64 70 74 75 77 79 81 82 85 87 90 91 93 94 96 98 100 102 103 107 108 111 114 118 119 128 130 131 146 148 **S** Cleveland Clinic Health System, Cleveland, OH
Primary Contact: Mark Froimson, M.D., President
COO: Rich Lea, Vice President Operations
CFO: Don Urbancsik, Director Finance
CMO: Andrew Brobbey, M.D., Chief of Staff
CHR: Gloria Donnelly, Director Human Resources
CNO: Dawn A. Bailey, R.N., Vice President Nursing and Chief Nursing Officer
Web address: www.euclidhospital.org
Control: Other not–for–profit (including NFP Corporation) **Service:** General Medical and Surgical

Staffed Beds: 231 **Admissions:** 7698 **Census:** 137 **Outpatient Visits:** 92841 **Births:** 0 **Total Expense ($000):** 116407 **Payroll Expense ($000):** 49148 **Personnel:** 689

FAIRFIELD—Butler County

✠ △ **MERCY HEALTH – FAIRFIELD HOSPITAL (360056)**, 3000 Mack Road, Zip 45014–5335; tel. 513/870–7000 **A**1 2 7 9 10 **F**3 8 11 13 15 18 20 22 24 26 28 29 30 31 34 35 40 44 45 46 47 48 49 50 54 57 59 64 65 68 74 75 77 78 79 81 82 84 85 87 92 93 100 107 108 109 110 111 114 115 118 119 126 130 132 135 146 147 148 **S** Mercy Health, Cincinnati, OH
Primary Contact: Thomas S. Urban, Market Leader and President
CFO: Robin Yon, Site Finance Director
CMO: John Kennedy, M.D., Vice President Medical Affairs
CIO: Yousuf Ahmad, Divisional Senior Vice President and Chief Network Transformation Officer
CHR: Maggie Lund, Divisional Senior Vice President Human Resources
Web address: www.e–mercy.com
Control: Church–operated, Nongovernment, not–for profit **Service:** General Medical and Surgical

Staffed Beds: 236 **Admissions:** 18650 **Census:** 161 **Births:** 2030

Hospital, Medicare Provider Number, Address, Telephone, Approval, Facility, and Physician Codes, Health Care System

★ American Hospital Association (AHA) membership
☐ The Joint Commission accreditation
◇ DNV Healthcare Inc. accreditation
○ Healthcare Facilities Accreditation Program
△ Commission on Accreditation of Rehabilitation Facilities (CARF) accreditation

OH

FINDLAY—Hancock County

✠ **BLANCHARD VALLEY HOSPITAL (360095)**, 1900 South Main Street, Zip 45840–1214; tel. 419/423–4500, (Includes BLANCHARD VALLEY HOSPITAL, 1900 South Main Street, Zip 45840; tel. 419/423–4500) **A**1 2 3 5 9 10 19 **F**3 7 8 11 13 15 17 18 20 22 24 26 28 29 30 31 34 35 40 41 42 43 45 48 49 50 58 59 60 64 65 70 73 74 76 77 78 79 81 82 83 84 85 86 87 91 93 96 97 98 103 107 108 110 111 114 115 118 119 120 121 124 126 129 130 131 132 134 135 146 147 148 **P**5 **S** Blanchard Valley Health System, Findlay, OH
Primary Contact: Scott C. Malaney, President and Chief Executive Officer
CFO: David Cytlak, Chief Financial Officer
CMO: William H. Kose, M.D., Senior Vice President Medical Affairs
CIO: Jamie Sorg, Director Information Services and Information Security Officer
CHR: Ryan Fisher, Director Human Resources
CNO: Barbara J. Pasztor, R.N., Vice President Patient Care Services and Chief Nursing Officer
Web address: www.bvhealthsystem.org/?id=204&sid=1
Control: Other not–for–profit (including NFP Corporation) **Service:** General Medical and Surgical

Staffed Beds: 159 **Admissions:** 6988 **Census:** 70 **Outpatient Visits:** 212691 **Births:** 1416 **Total Expense ($000):** 139499 **Payroll Expense ($000):** 73129 **Personnel:** 1261

FOSTORIA—Hancock County

✠ **PROMEDICA FOSTORIA COMMUNITY HOSPITAL (361318)**, 501 Van Buren Street, Zip 44830–1534, Mailing Address: P.O. Box 907, Zip 44830–0907; tel. 419/435–7734 **A**1 5 9 10 18 **F**3 11 15 28 31 32 34 35 40 45 46 57 59 60 62 64 66 68 70 75 78 79 81 85 86 89 93 94 96 97 107 108 110 111 115 117 118 119 128 129 130 131 132 133 135 144 146 **P**7 **S** ProMedica Health System, Toledo, OH
Primary Contact: Holly L. Bristoll, President
COO: Tom Borer, Vice President Operations
CFO: Ken Swint, Vice President Finance and Chief Financial Officer
CMO: Terrence Fondessy, M.D., Vice President Medical Affairs
CIO: Rose Ann Laureto, Chief Information Officer
CNO: Paula Grieb, R.N., Chief Nursing Officer
Web address: www.promedica.org
Control: Other not–for–profit (including NFP Corporation) **Service:** General Medical and Surgical

Staffed Beds: 25 **Admissions:** 826 **Census:** 8 **Outpatient Visits:** 76970 **Births:** 0 **Total Expense ($000):** 35896 **Payroll Expense ($000):** 9712 **Personnel:** 165

FREMONT—Sandusky County

✠ **MEMORIAL HOSPITAL (360156)**, 715 South Taft Avenue, Zip 43420–3237; tel. 419/332–7321 **A**1 5 9 10 **F**3 11 13 15 28 29 30 34 35 38 40 44 45 46 47 48 50 53 56 57 59 60 61 62 63 64 65 68 69 70 74 75 76 77 79 80 81 82 84 85 86 87 89 91 92 93 96 97 99 100 101 103 104 107 108 110 111 114 115 116 117 119 129 130 131 132 141 142 146 147 148 **P**1 6
Primary Contact: Pamela Jensen, FACHE, President
CFO: David Brewer, Chief Financial Officer
CIO: Dustin Hufford, Chief Information Officer
CHR: Warrenette Parthemore, Director Human Resources
CNO: Jill A. Trosin, R.N., Chief Nursing Officer
Web address: www.promedica.org
Control: Other not–for–profit (including NFP Corporation) **Service:** General Medical and Surgical

Staffed Beds: 71 **Admissions:** 2122 **Census:** 18 **Outpatient Visits:** 87590 **Births:** 284 **Total Expense ($000):** 75866 **Payroll Expense ($000):** 27736 **Personnel:** 448

PHYSICIAN'S CHOICE HOSPITAL – FREMONT (360356), 2390 Enterprise Drive, Zip 43420–8507; tel. 419/461–1057, (Nonreporting)
Primary Contact: Jerome McTague, M.D., JD, Administrator and Chief Executive Officer
Web address: www.physicianschoicehospital.com
Control: Partnership, Investor–owned, for–profit **Service:** Other specialty

Staffed Beds: 8

GAHANNA—Franklin County

THE WOODS AT PARKSIDE (360247), 349 Olde Ridenour Road, Zip 43230–2528; tel. 614/471–2552, (Nonreporting) **A**10
Primary Contact: Harry Nguyen, Medical Director
Web address: www.thewoodsatparkside.com
Control: Partnership, Investor–owned, for–profit **Service:** Alcoholism and other chemical dependency

Staffed Beds: 50

GALION—Crawford County

★ ◇ **GALION COMMUNITY HOSPITAL (361325)**, 269 Portland Way South, Zip 44833–2399; tel. 419/468–4841 **A**9 10 18 21 **F**3 11 13 15 18 28 29 30 31 34 35 45 47 50 57 59 60 70 74 75 76 77 78 79 81 82 87 90 107 108 110 111 115 119 127 129 130 131 132 133 146 147 148 **S** Avita Health System, Galion, OH
Primary Contact: Jerome Morasko, President and Chief Executive Officer
CIO: Andy Daniels, Vice President Non–Clinical Operations and Information Systems
CHR: Traci L. Oswald, Vice President Human Resources
Web address: www.galionhospital.org
Control: Other not–for–profit (including NFP Corporation) **Service:** General Medical and Surgical

Staffed Beds: 35 **Admissions:** 1643 **Census:** 17 **Outpatient Visits:** 20932 **Births:** 393 **Total Expense ($000):** 77424 **Payroll Expense ($000):** 35640 **Personnel:** 568

GALLIPOLIS—Gallia County

☐ △ **HOLZER MEDICAL CENTER (360054)**, 100 Jackson Pike, Zip 45631–1563; tel. 740/446–5000, (Nonreporting) **A**1 2 5 7 9 10 19
Primary Contact: James R. Phillipe, President
CFO: Kenneth G. Payne, Chief Financial Officer
CMO: John Viall, M.D., Vice President Medical Affairs
CIO: John Allen, Chief Information Officer
CHR: Lisa B. Halley, Vice President Human Resources
Web address: www.holzer.org
Control: Other not–for–profit (including NFP Corporation) **Service:** General Medical and Surgical

Staffed Beds: 181

GARFIELD HEIGHTS—Cuyahoga County

✠ **MARYMOUNT HOSPITAL (360143)**, 12300 McCracken Road, Zip 44125–2975; tel. 216/581–0500 **A**1 2 10 **F**3 7 8 11 15 18 28 29 30 31 34 35 38 39 40 42 44 49 50 51 53 54 56 57 59 60 62 63 64 68 70 74 75 77 78 79 81 82 85 86 87 92 93 96 97 98 100 102 103 104 107 108 110 111 114 116 118 119 124 129 132 134 135 143 146 147 148 **S** Cleveland Clinic Health System, Cleveland, OH
Primary Contact: Joanne Zeroske, President
COO: Mark Nussbaum, Vice President Operations
CFO: Mike Stilgenbauer, Director Finance
CMO: Douglas Kohler, M.D., Vice President Medical Operations
CIO: Ralph A. Cagna, Director Information Technology Operations, Cleveland Clinic Health System South Market
CHR: Judith Santora, Human Resources Business Partner
CNO: Barbara Zinner, Chief Nursing Officer
Web address: www.marymount.org
Control: Other not–for–profit (including NFP Corporation) **Service:** General Medical and Surgical

Staffed Beds: 284 **Admissions:** 11887 **Census:** 170 **Outpatient Visits:** 118284 **Births:** 0 **Total Expense ($000):** 167581 **Payroll Expense ($000):** 61528 **Personnel:** 1013

GENEVA—Ashtabula County

✠ **UNIVERSITY HOSPITALS GENEVA MEDICAL CENTER (361307)**, 870 West Main Street, Zip 44041–1295; tel. 440/466–1141 **A**1 9 10 18 **F**3 7 11 15 18 29 34 35 40 46 51 59 64 68 70 75 77 78 79 81 82 86 87 93 107 110 111 114 119 129 130 132 133 135 143 146 147 **S** University Hospitals, Cleveland, OH
Primary Contact: M. Steven Jones, President
COO: Richard Trice, Director Operations
CFO: Michael McGrath, Manager Finance
CMO: Amitabh Goel, M.D., Chief Medical Officer
CIO: Cheryl Vibbard, Manager Health Information Systems
CHR: Barbara Gurto, Manager Human Resources
CNO: Karen McNeil, Chief Nursing Officer
Web address: www.uhhs.com
Control: Other not–for–profit (including NFP Corporation) **Service:** General Medical and Surgical

Staffed Beds: 25 **Admissions:** 1109 **Census:** 11 **Outpatient Visits:** 69807 **Births:** 0 **Total Expense ($000):** 30836 **Payroll Expense ($000):** 11413 **Personnel:** 232

GEORGETOWN—Brown County

☐ **SOUTHWEST REGIONAL MEDICAL CENTER (360116)**, 425 Home Street, Zip 45121–1407; tel. 937/378–7500 **A**1 9 10 **F**3 11 15 18 29 34 40 50 57 59 62 64 70 75 77 79 81 83 85 87 93 97 107 108 110 111 114 118 119 127 129 130 146 147 148 **P**6 **S** Southwest Healthcare System, Scottsdale, AZ
Primary Contact: Michael C. Patterson, Chief Executive Officer
Web address: www.swrmed.com
Control: Corporation, Investor–owned, for–profit **Service:** General Medical and Surgical

Staffed Beds: 40 **Admissions:** 749 **Census:** 6 **Outpatient Visits:** 34528 **Births:** 0 **Total Expense ($000):** 25942 **Payroll Expense ($000):** 10527 **Personnel:** 300

Many Facility Codes have changed. Please refer to the AHA Guide Code Chart.

GREEN SPRINGS—Sandusky County

☐ **ST. FRANCIS HEALTH CARE CENTRE (362007)**, 401 North Broadway, Zip 44836–9653; tel. 419/639–2626, (Nonreporting) **A**1 10
Primary Contact: Kim D. Eicher, Chief Executive Officer
CFO: Douglas Morris, Chief Financial Officer
CMO: John Yuhas, D.O., Medical Director
CHR: Joan E. Schmidt, Director Human Resources
Web address: www.sfhcc.org
Control: Church–operated, Nongovernment, not–for profit **Service:** Long–Term Acute Care hospital

Staffed Beds: 186

GREENFIELD—Highland County

△ ◇ **ADENA GREENFIELD MEDICAL CENTER (361304)**, 550 Mirabeau Street, Zip 45123–1617; tel. 937/981–9400, (Nonreporting) **A**7 9 10 18 21 **S** Adena Health System, Chillicothe, OH
Primary Contact: Kathy Dye, Interim Administrator
CFO: Ralph W. Sorrell, Sr., Chief Financial Officer
CIO: Marcus Bost, Director Information Services and Chief Information Officer
CHR: Brandt Lippert, Vice President Human Resources
Web address: www.adena.org
Control: Other not–for–profit (including NFP Corporation) **Service:** General Medical and Surgical

Staffed Beds: 25

GREENVILLE—Darke County

★ ○ **WAYNE HOSPITAL (360044)**, 835 Sweitzer Street, Zip 45331–1077; tel. 937/548–1141 **A**2 9 10 11 **F**3 8 11 13 15 29 30 31 34 35 39 40 41 45 57 59 64 65 70 75 76 78 79 81 84 85 86 89 93 107 108 110 111 114 118 119 129 130 131 132 135 141 146 147 148 **P**1
Primary Contact: Wayne G. Deschambeau, President and Chief Executive Officer
COO: Jeffrey R. Subler, Vice President Support Services
CFO: Dennis Lockard, Vice President Fiscal Services and Chief Financial Officer
CMO: Tom Brown, M.D., President Medical Staff
CIO: Shelton Monger, Director Information Technology
CHR: Peggy Schwartz, Vice President Human Resources
CNO: Kimberlee Freeman, R.N., Vice President Patient Care Services and Chief Nursing Officer
Web address: www.waynehealthcare.org
Control: Other not–for–profit (including NFP Corporation) **Service:** General Medical and Surgical

Staffed Beds: 63 **Admissions:** 2092 **Census:** 17 **Outpatient Visits:** 78886
Births: 300 **Total Expense ($000):** 50092 **Payroll Expense ($000):** 18634
Personnel: 328

HAMILTON—Butler County

☐ **BETHESDA BUTLER HOSPITAL (360269)**, 3125 Hamilton Mason Road, Zip 45011–5307; tel. 513/894–8888, (Nonreporting) **A**1 9
Primary Contact: Chuck Brown, Administrator
COO: Mary Ann Gellenbeck, Chief Operating Officer
CFO: Michael L. Griffin, Chief Financial Officer
CHR: Amy Turner, Director Human Resources
Web address: www.bcsurg.com
Control: Corporation, Investor–owned, for–profit **Service:** Surgical

Staffed Beds: 8

★ ○ **FORT HAMILTON HOSPITAL (360132)**, 630 Eaton Avenue, Zip 45013–2770; tel. 513/867–2000 **A**2 9 10 11 **F**3 11 13 15 18 20 22 24 28 29 30 31 34 35 40 45 46 50 53 54 59 64 68 70 73 74 75 76 78 79 81 82 85 86 87 93 98 100 105 107 108 110 111 114 115 116 117 119 120 121 124 129 130 131 135 144 146 147 **S** Kettering Health Network, Dayton, OH
Primary Contact: Mark T. Smith, JD, CPA, President
CHR: Joseph Geigle, Director Human Resources
Web address: www.khnetwork.org/fort_hamilton
Control: Church–operated, Nongovernment, not–for profit **Service:** General Medical and Surgical

Staffed Beds: 166 **Admissions:** 7996 **Census:** 91 **Outpatient Visits:** 104991
Births: 596 **Total Expense ($000):** 125255 **Payroll Expense ($000):** 53440
Personnel: 794

HICKSVILLE—Defiance County

☐ **COMMUNITY MEMORIAL HOSPITAL (361301)**, 208 North Columbus Street, Zip 43526–1299; tel. 419/542–6692, (Nonreporting) **A**1 9 10 18
Primary Contact: Michelle Waggoner, Chief Executive Officer
CNO: Jane Zachrich, Chief Nursing Officer
Web address: www.cmhosp.com
Control: Hospital district or authority, Government, nonfederal **Service:** General Medical and Surgical

Staffed Beds: 25

HILLSBORO—Highland County

☒ **HIGHLAND DISTRICT HOSPITAL (361332)**, 1275 North High Street, Zip 45133–8273; tel. 937/393–6100 **A**1 9 10 18 **F**3 11 13 15 29 30 31 34 35 40 45 47 49 57 59 62 64 74 76 77 78 79 81 85 86 87 92 93 94 96 98 103 107 111 118 119 127 130 131 132 133 135 146 148 **P**3
Primary Contact: James E. Baer, FACHE, President and Chief Executive Officer
CFO: Randal Lennartz, Vice President Finance
CMO: Ron Zile, M.D., Chief of Staff
CIO: Tim Bogard, Manager Information Technology
CHR: Melanie Wymer, Director Human Resources
CNO: Timothy Parry, R.N., Vice President Nursing
Web address: www.hdh.org
Control: Hospital district or authority, Government, nonfederal **Service:** General Medical and Surgical

Staffed Beds: 25 **Admissions:** 2107 **Census:** 19 **Outpatient Visits:** 79607
Births: 372 **Total Expense ($000):** 34229 **Payroll Expense ($000):** 13805
Personnel: 313

JACKSON—Jackson County

☐ **HOLZER MEDICAL CENTER – JACKSON (361320)**, 500 Burlington Road, Zip 45640–9360; tel. 740/288–4625, (Nonreporting) **A**1 9 10 18
Primary Contact: James R. Phillippe, II, President
CFO: Kevin Yeager, Vice President Fiscal Services
CMO: Nimal Dutla, M.D., Chief Medical Staff
CHR: Sandy Carlisle, Manager Human Resources
Web address: www.holzer.org
Control: Other not–for–profit (including NFP Corporation) **Service:** General Medical and Surgical

Staffed Beds: 24

KENTON—Hardin County

☒ **OHIOHEALTH HARDIN MEMORIAL HOSPITAL (361315)**, 921 East Franklin Street, Zip 43326–2099; tel. 419/673–0761 **A**1 9 10 18 **F**11 15 29 30 34 40 45 57 59 61 75 77 78 79 81 86 87 93 97 102 107 108 110 111 114 116 119 129 130 131 132 133 146 147 **S** OhioHealth, Columbus, OH
Primary Contact: Mark R. Seckinger, Administrator and Chief Executive Officer
CFO: Ron Snyder, Chief Financial Officer
Web address: www.hardinmemorial.org
Control: Other not–for–profit (including NFP Corporation) **Service:** General Medical and Surgical

Staffed Beds: 25 **Admissions:** 744 **Census:** 9 **Outpatient Visits:** 59022
Births: 0 **Total Expense ($000):** 19617 **Payroll Expense ($000):** 8520
Personnel: 181

KETTERING—Montgomery County

★ ○ △ **KETTERING MEDICAL CENTER (360079)**, 3535 Southern Boulevard, Zip 45429–1221; tel. 937/298–4331 **A**2 3 5 7 8 10 11 **F**3 11 12 13 15 17 18 20 22 24 26 28 29 30 31 34 35 38 39 40 43 44 45 46 47 48 49 50 51 52 53 54 56 57 58 59 60 61 64 65 66 68 70 71 72 74 75 76 77 78 79 81 82 84 85 86 87 90 92 93 96 97 102 107 108 110 111 114 115 116 117 118 119 120 121 123 124 126 129 130 131 132 135 141 145 146 147 148 **S** Kettering Health Network, Dayton, OH
Primary Contact: Roy G. Chew, Ph.D., President
COO: Chelcia Lambert, Chief Operating Officer and Chief Financial Officer
CFO: Chelcia Lambert, Chief Operating Officer and Chief Financial Officer
CMO: Gregory Wise, M.D., Vice President Medical Affairs
CIO: Jon Russell, Vice President Information Systems
CHR: Beverly Morris, Vice President Human Resources
CNO: Brenda Kuhn, Ph.D., Vice President Patient Care Services
Web address: www.kmcnetwork.org
Control: Church–operated, Nongovernment, not–for profit **Service:** General Medical and Surgical

Staffed Beds: 390 **Admissions:** 19859 **Census:** 253 **Outpatient Visits:** 268420 **Births:** 2325 **Total Expense ($000):** 576129 **Payroll Expense ($000):** 224302 **Personnel:** 2575

Hospital, Medicare Provider Number, Address, Telephone, Approval, Facility, and Physician Codes, Health Care System

★ American Hospital Association (AHA) membership
☐ The Joint Commission accreditation
◇ DNV Healthcare Inc. accreditation
○ Healthcare Facilities Accreditation Program
△ Commission on Accreditation of Rehabilitation Facilities (CARF) accreditation

OH

LAKEWOOD—Cuyahoga County

✠ **LAKEWOOD HOSPITAL (360212)**, 14519 Detroit Avenue, Zip 44107–4383; tel. 216/521–4200, (Total facility includes 25 beds in nursing home–type unit) **A**1 9 10 **F**3 6 13 15 20 22 26 28 29 30 34 35 40 45 46 49 50 56 57 59 60 64 65 68 70 74 75 76 77 79 81 82 85 86 87 90 93 98 100 101 102 103 107 108 111 119 128 130 132 134 143 146 147 148 **S** Cleveland Clinic Health System, Cleveland, OH
Primary Contact: Shannan Ritchie, Interim President
COO: Shannan Ritchie, Chief Operating Officer
CFO: Ankit Chhabra, Director Finance
CMO: William Riebel, M.D., Vice President Medical Operations
CIO: C. Martin Harris, M.D., Chief Information Officer
CHR: Sheree Laborie, Director Human Resources
CNO: Mary R. Sauer, R.N., Chief Nursing Officer
Web address: www.lakewoodhospital.org
Control: Other not–for–profit (including NFP Corporation) **Service:** General Medical and Surgical

Staffed Beds: 250 **Admissions:** 8515 **Census:** 132 **Outpatient Visits:** 146442 **Births:** 647 **Total Expense ($000):** 129902 **Payroll Expense ($000):** 52544 **Personnel:** 790

LANCASTER—Fairfield County

✠ △ **FAIRFIELD MEDICAL CENTER (360072)**, 401 North Ewing Street, Zip 43130–3371; tel. 740/687–8000 **A**1 2 5 7 9 10 13 **F**3 8 11 12 13 15 18 20 22 24 26 28 29 30 31 34 35 38 40 42 44 45 48 49 50 53 54 57 59 64 70 74 75 76 77 78 79 81 82 83 84 85 87 89 93 96 97 98 102 104 107 108 110 111 114 115 118 119 129 130 131 132 135 145 146 147 148
Primary Contact: Sky Gettys, Interim President and Chief Executive Officer
COO: Howard Sniderman, Chief Operating Officer
CFO: Sky Gettys, Chief Financial Officer
CMO: Steve Cox, M.D., Chief Medical Officer
CIO: Jean Robertson, M.D., Chief Information Officer
CNO: Cynthia Pearsall, Chief Nursing Officer
Web address: www.fmchealth.org
Control: Other not–for–profit (including NFP Corporation) **Service:** General Medical and Surgical

Staffed Beds: 222 **Admissions:** 9654 **Census:** 99 **Outpatient Visits:** 258144 **Births:** 1040 **Total Expense ($000):** 213144 **Payroll Expense ($000):** 84027 **Personnel:** 1789

LIMA—Allen County

✠ **INSTITUTE FOR ORTHOPAEDIC SURGERY (360263)**, 801 Medical Drive, Suite B., Zip 45804–4030; tel. 419/224–7586, (Nonreporting) **A**1 9 10 **S** Mercy Health, Cincinnati, OH
Primary Contact: Mark McDonald, M.D., President and Chief Executive Officer
CMO: Mark McDonald, M.D., President and Chief Executive Officer
CHR: Pat Farmer, Coordinator Human Resources and Safety Officer
Web address: www.ioshospital.com
Control: Partnership, Investor–owned, for–profit **Service:** Orthopedic

Staffed Beds: 3

✠ **KINDRED HOSPITAL LIMA (362020)**, 730 West Market Street, 6th Floor, Zip 45801–4602; tel. 419/224–1888, (Nonreporting) **A**1 10 **S** Kindred Healthcare, Louisville, KY
Primary Contact: Susan Krinke, Chief Executive Officer
Web address: www.khlima.com
Control: Corporation, Investor–owned, for–profit **Service:** Long–Term Acute Care hospital

Staffed Beds: 26

✠ △ **LIMA MEMORIAL HEALTH SYSTEM (360009)**, 1001 Bellefontaine Avenue, Zip 45804–2899; tel. 419/228–3335, (Total facility includes 17 beds in nursing home–type unit) **A**1 2 7 9 10 **F**3 11 13 15 17 18 20 22 24 28 29 30 31 34 35 36 40 41 43 44 49 50 51 54 57 58 59 60 62 63 64 65 68 70 73 74 75 76 77 78 79 81 82 84 85 86 89 90 93 96 107 108 110 111 114 115 118 119 121 123 124 126 130 131 132 135 146 147 148 **P**8
Primary Contact: Michael D. Swick, President and Chief Executive Officer
COO: Robert Armstrong, Senior Vice President and Chief Operating Officer
CFO: Eric Pohjala, Vice President and Chief Financial Officer
CMO: Kha H. Tran, M.D., Vice President Medical Affairs
CIO: Cheryl Homan, Administrative Director
CHR: Adam Cozad, Director Human Resources
CNO: Ann–Marie J. Pohl, R.N., Vice President and Chief Nursing Officer
Web address: www.limamemorial.org
Control: Other not–for–profit (including NFP Corporation) **Service:** General Medical and Surgical

Staffed Beds: 206 **Admissions:** 6458 **Census:** 81 **Outpatient Visits:** 272402 **Births:** 687 **Total Expense ($000):** 143570 **Payroll Expense ($000):** 55933 **Personnel:** 937

OAKWOOD CORRECTIONAL FACILITY, 3200 North West Street, Zip 45801–2000; tel. 419/225–8052, (Nonreporting)
Primary Contact: Christopher Yanai, Warden and Chief Executive Officer
CFO: Thomas Ferry, Business Administrator
CHR: Glenda Turner, Director Personnel
Web address: www.drc.state.oh.us/public/ocf.htm
Control: State–Government, nonfederal **Service:** Psychiatric

Staffed Beds: 61

✠ △ **ST. RITA'S MEDICAL CENTER (360066)**, 730 West Market Street, Zip 45801–4602; tel. 419/227–3361 **A**1 2 7 9 10 **F**3 4 5 8 9 11 13 15 17 18 20 22 24 26 28 29 30 31 32 34 35 36 39 40 42 43 45 46 47 49 50 53 54 56 57 58 59 60 61 62 63 64 66 68 70 72 73 74 75 76 77 78 79 81 82 84 85 86 87 89 90 92 93 96 98 102 103 104 105 107 108 110 111 112 114 115 116 117 118 119 120 121 123 126 128 129 130 131 132 135 144 146 147 148 **P**6 8 **S** Mercy Health, Cincinnati, OH
Primary Contact: Robert O. Baxter, President and Chief Executive Officer
COO: Brian Smith, Executive Vice President and Chief Operating Officer
CMO: Herbert Schumm, M.D., Vice President Medical Affairs
CHR: Will Cason, Vice President Human Resources
Web address: www.stritas.org
Control: Church–operated, Nongovernment, not–for profit **Service:** General Medical and Surgical

Staffed Beds: 415 **Admissions:** 18506 **Census:** 216 **Outpatient Visits:** 433723 **Births:** 1569 **Total Expense ($000):** 337966 **Payroll Expense ($000):** 110420 **Personnel:** 2045

TRIUMPH HOSPITAL LIMA See Kindred Hospital Lima

LODI—Medina County

✠ **LODI COMMUNITY HOSPITAL (361303)**, 225 Elyria Street, Zip 44254–1096; tel. 330/948–1222 **A**1 9 10 18 **F**3 11 15 18 26 28 29 30 34 35 40 45 59 64 65 75 77 81 82 91 93 96 97 107 114 119 129 130 132 133 146 **P**6 **S** Akron General Health System, Akron, OH
Primary Contact: Thomas Whelan, President
COO: Dana Kocsis, R.N., Vice President Nursing and Operations
CFO: Alan A. Ganci, Director Finance and Controller
CMO: David Peter, M.D., Senior Vice President Medical Affairs and Chief Medical Officer
CIO: Robb Baldauf, Coordinator Information Systems
CHR: Lynn Moraca, Director Human Resources
Web address: www.lodihospital.org
Control: Other not–for–profit (including NFP Corporation) **Service:** General Medical and Surgical

Staffed Beds: 25 **Admissions:** 352 **Census:** 6 **Outpatient Visits:** 25038 **Births:** 0 **Total Expense ($000):** 13365 **Payroll Expense ($000):** 6117 **Personnel:** 107

LOGAN—Hocking County

✠ **HOCKING VALLEY COMMUNITY HOSPITAL (361330)**, 601 State Route 664 North, Zip 43138–8541, Mailing Address: P.O. Box 966, Zip 43138–0966; tel. 740/380–8000, (Nonreporting) **A**1 9 10 18
Primary Contact: Julie Stuck, R.N., Interim Chief Executive Officer
CFO: Julie E. Grow, Chief Financial Officer
CMO: Duane Mast, M.D., Medical Director
CIO: John Burgess, Director Information Services
CHR: Robert F. Schmidt, Director Human Resources
CNO: Janelle Hicks, R.N., Vice President Patient Services
Web address: www.hvch.org
Control: County–Government, nonfederal **Service:** General Medical and Surgical

Staffed Beds: 65

LONDON—Madison County

✠ **MADISON COUNTY HOSPITAL (360189)**, 210 North Main Street, Zip 43140–1115; tel. 740/845–7000 **A**1 9 10 **F**3 11 13 15 18 29 30 31 34 40 45 53 57 59 68 70 75 76 77 78 79 81 82 85 87 89 93 107 108 110 111 114 118 119 129 130 131 132 135 146 147
Primary Contact: Dana E. Engle, Chief Executive Officer
CFO: Michael Browning, Chief Financial Officer
CMO: Mark Coate, M.D., Chief of Staff
CIO: Dennis Vogt, Director Information Technology
CHR: Becky Rozell, Chief Human Resources Officer
CNO: Jennifer Piccione, Chief Nursing and Clinical Services Officer
Web address: www.madisoncountyhospital.org
Control: Other not–for–profit (including NFP Corporation) **Service:** General Medical and Surgical

Staffed Beds: 55 **Admissions:** 1110 **Census:** 11 **Outpatient Visits:** 34476 **Births:** 235 **Total Expense ($000):** 32106 **Payroll Expense ($000):** 11491 **Personnel:** 237

Many Facility Codes have changed. Please refer to the AHA Guide Code Chart. © 2014 AHA Guide

LORAIN—Lorain County

⊞ △ **MERCY REGIONAL MEDICAL CENTER (360172)**, 3700 Kolbe Road, Zip 44053–1697; tel. 440/960–4000 **A**1 2 7 9 10 **F**8 11 13 15 18 20 22 24 26 28 29 30 31 34 35 36 38 39 40 41 46 50 53 54 56 57 59 61 62 63 64 65 66 68 70 74 75 76 77 78 79 81 82 84 85 87 89 90 93 96 97 98 102 103 104 105 107 111 114 115 116 119 120 121 129 130 131 132 135 143 146 147 148 **P**8 **S** Mercy Health, Cincinnati, OH
Primary Contact: Edwin M. Oley, President and Chief Executive Officer
COO: Robert Tonkinson, Chief Operating Officer and Chief Financial Officer
CFO: Robert Tonkinson, Chief Operating Officer and Chief Financial Officer
CMO: Sam El–Dalati, M.D., Chief Medical Officer
CHR: JC Fischer, Director Human Resources
CNO: Catherine Walsh, Interim Nursing Executive
Web address: www.community–health–partners.com
Control: Church–operated, Nongovernment, not–for profit **Service:** General Medical and Surgical

Staffed Beds: 259 **Admissions:** 12616 **Census:** 158 **Outpatient Visits:** 269784 **Births:** 766 **Total Expense ($000):** 197955 **Payroll Expense ($000):** 73166 **Personnel:** 1356

MANSFIELD—Richland County

⊞ **KINDRED HOSPITAL OF CENTRAL OHIO (362021)**, 335 Glessner Avenue, 5th Floor, Zip 44903–2269; tel. 419/526–0777, (Nonreporting) **A**1 10 **S** Kindred Healthcare, Louisville, KY
Primary Contact: Pamela A. Edson, Chief Executive Officer
Web address: www.khcentralohio.com/
Control: Corporation, Investor–owned, for–profit **Service:** Long–Term Acute Care hospital

Staffed Beds: 33

MEDCENTRAL – MANSFIELD HOSPITAL See OhioHealth MedCentral Mansfield Hospital

⊞ **OHIOHEALTH MEDCENTRAL MANSFIELD HOSPITAL (360118)**, 335 Glessner Avenue, Zip 44903–2265; tel. 419/526–8000, (Includes MANSFIELD HOSPITAL, 335 Glessner Avenue, tel. 419/526–8000) **A**1 2 5 9 10 **F**3 5 8 11 13 15 17 18 20 22 24 26 28 29 30 31 32 34 35 38 39 40 43 44 45 46 47 48 49 50 51 53 54 55 56 57 58 59 61 62 63 64 65 68 70 73 74 75 76 77 78 79 81 82 83 84 85 86 87 89 90 92 93 96 98 99 100 101 102 103 104 105 107 108 110 111 114 116 117 118 119 120 121 122 123 124 129 130 131 132 133 135 144 146 147 148 **P**3 **S** OhioHealth, Columbus, OH
Primary Contact: Jean Halpin, President
CFO: Michael Bichimer, Acting Vice President of Finance
CMO: Terry Weston, M.D., Vice President Physician Services
CIO: Cindy Sheets, Vice President Information Systems and Chief Information Officer
CHR: Beth Hildreth, Vice President Human Resources
CNO: Pam Crawford, R.N., Vice President of Nursing and Chief Nursing Officer
Web address: www.medcentral.org
Control: Other not–for–profit (including NFP Corporation) **Service:** General Medical and Surgical

Staffed Beds: 238 **Admissions:** 11378 **Census:** 134 **Outpatient Visits:** 268662 **Births:** 979 **Personnel:** 1650

MARIETTA—Washington County

★ ○ △ **MARIETTA MEMORIAL HOSPITAL (360147)**, 401 Matthew Street, Zip 45750–1699; tel. 740/374–1400, (Nonreporting) **A**2 5 7 9 10 11
Primary Contact: J. Scott Cantley, President and Chief Executive Officer
CFO: Eric L. Young, Vice President Finance and Chief Financial Officer
CMO: Matthew Macatol, M.D., President Medical Staff
CIO: Andy Altenburger, Chief Information Officer
CHR: Dee Ann Gehlauf, Senior Vice President Business and Organization Development
Web address: www.mhsystem.org
Control: Other not–for–profit (including NFP Corporation) **Service:** General Medical and Surgical

Staffed Beds: 152

★ **SELBY GENERAL HOSPITAL (361319)**, 1106 Colegate Drive, Zip 45750–1323; tel. 740/568–2000, (Nonreporting) **A**9 10 18
Primary Contact: Stephen Smith, President
CFO: Eric L. Young, Chief Financial Officer
CMO: David Spears, D.O., Chief of Staff
CHR: Tricia A. Engfehr, Chief Human Resources
CNO: Misti Spencer, Director Inpatient Services
Web address: www.selbygeneral.org
Control: Other not–for–profit (including NFP Corporation) **Service:** General Medical and Surgical

Staffed Beds: 25

MARION—Marion County

⊞ **OHIOHEALTH MARION GENERAL HOSPITAL (360011)**, 1000 McKinley Park Drive, Zip 43302–6397; tel. 740/383–8400 **A**1 2 9 10 19 **F**3 13 15 18 20 22 24 26 28 29 30 31 35 40 53 57 59 60 62 63 68 70 72 73 74 75 76 77 78 79 81 82 83 84 86 87 89 91 93 94 98 104 105 107 111 116 117 119 126 129 130 132 135 146 147 148 **S** OhioHealth, Columbus, OH
Primary Contact: John W. Sanders, President
COO: Joseph Hooper, Chief Operating Officer
CFO: Steven Brown, Chief Financial Officer
CMO: Julie Tome, M.D., Vice President North Central Region Medical Affairs
CIO: Chris King, Director Information Services
CHR: Gianna Ferrarotti, Director Human Resources North Region
CNO: Eric Wallis, R.N., Vice President Patient Care and Chief Nursing Officer
Web address: www.ohiohealth.com/mariongeneral
Control: Other not–for–profit (including NFP Corporation) **Service:** General Medical and Surgical

Staffed Beds: 170 **Admissions:** 7575 **Census:** 81 **Outpatient Visits:** 195028 **Births:** 975 **Total Expense ($000):** 151301 **Payroll Expense ($000):** 60695 **Personnel:** 1155

MARTINS FERRY—Belmont County

☐ **EAST OHIO REGIONAL HOSPITAL (360080)**, 90 North Fourth Street, Zip 43935–1648; tel. 740/633–1100, (Total facility includes 50 beds in nursing home–type unit) **A**1 9 10 **F**3 11 13 15 20 28 29 30 31 34 35 37 40 43 44 45 53 57 59 64 68 70 74 75 76 77 79 81 82 85 87 89 107 108 110 111 114 115 118 119 128 129 130 131 132 133 135 146 148 **P**6 **S** Ohio Valley Health Services and Education Corporation, Wheeling, WV
Primary Contact: Michael J. Caruso, President and Chief Executive Officer
COO: Bernie Albertini, Chief Administrative Officer
CFO: Lisa M. Simon, Senior Vice President Chief Financial Officer
CIO: Lisa M. Simon, Senior Vice President Chief Financial Officer
CHR: Robert Wright, Senior Human Resource Advisor
CNO: Christine Kerwood, Chief Nursing Officer
Web address: www.ovmc–eorh.com
Control: Other not–for–profit (including NFP Corporation) **Service:** General Medical and Surgical

Staffed Beds: 139 **Admissions:** 3586 **Census:** 72 **Outpatient Visits:** 135918 **Births:** 281 **Total Expense ($000):** 66454 **Payroll Expense ($000):** 24608 **Personnel:** 499

MARYSVILLE—Union County

★ ◇ **MEMORIAL HOSPITAL OF UNION COUNTY (360092)**, 500 London Avenue, Zip 43040–1594; tel. 937/644–6115 **A**5 9 10 21 **F**3 11 15 18 20 28 29 30 31 32 34 35 40 45 48 49 50 51 53 57 59 62 63 66 68 69 74 75 76 77 78 79 81 82 84 85 87 92 93 94 107 108 110 111 114 115 117 118 119 129 130 131 132 135 144 145 146 **P**6
Primary Contact: Olas A. Hubbs, III, FACHE, President and Chief Executive Officer
COO: Laurie A. Whittington, Chief Operating Officer
CFO: Jeffrey Ehlers, Chief Financial Officer
CMO: Matthew Hazelbaker, M.D., President Medical Staff
CIO: Carl Zani, Chief Technology Director
CHR: Larry C. Schleeter, Chief Human Resources Officer
CNO: Robin Slattman, Chief Nursing Officer
Web address: www.memorialhosp.org
Control: County–Government, nonfederal **Service:** General Medical and Surgical

Staffed Beds: 60 **Admissions:** 1990 **Census:** 14 **Outpatient Visits:** 110771 **Births:** 572 **Total Expense ($000):** 74269 **Payroll Expense ($000):** 30282 **Personnel:** 496

MASON—Warren County

⊞ **LINDNER CENTER OF HOPE (364044)**, 4075 Old Western Row Road, Zip 45040–3104; tel. 513/536–0311 **A**1 9 10 **F**4 5 29 30 35 98 99 101 103 104 105 106 111 130 **P**6
Primary Contact: Paul Keck, M.D., President and Chief Executive Officer
COO: Brian Owens, Chief Operating Officer
CFO: David McAdams, Chief Financial Officer
CIO: Cliff McClintick, Chief Information Officer
CHR: Debbie A. Strawser, Director Human Resources
Web address: www.lindnercenterofhope.org
Control: Other not–for–profit (including NFP Corporation) **Service:** Psychiatric

Staffed Beds: 48 **Admissions:** 1495 **Census:** 35 **Outpatient Visits:** 10729 **Births:** 0 **Total Expense ($000):** 28296 **Payroll Expense ($000):** 10247 **Personnel:** 246

Hospital, Medicare Provider Number, Address, Telephone, Approval, Facility, and Physician Codes, Health Care System

★ American Hospital Association (AHA) membership
☐ The Joint Commission accreditation
◇ DNV Healthcare Inc. accreditation
○ Healthcare Facilities Accreditation Program
△ Commission on Accreditation of Rehabilitation Facilities (CARF) accreditation

OH

MASSILLON—Stark County

★ ○ △ **AFFINITY MEDICAL CENTER (360151)**, 875 Eighth Street N.E.,
Zip 44646–8503, Mailing Address: P.O. Box 805, Zip 44648–0805;
tel. 330/832–8761, (Nonreporting) **A**7 9 10 11 12 13 **S** Community Health
Systems, Inc., Franklin, TN
Primary Contact: Ronald L. Bierman, Chief Executive Officer
CFO: James Hutchinson, CPA, Chief Financial Officer
Web address: www.affinitymedicalcenter.com
Control: Corporation, Investor–owned, for–profit **Service:** General Medical and
Surgical

Staffed Beds: 112

□ **HEARTLAND BEHAVIORAL HEALTHCARE (364031)**, 3000 Erie Stree South,
Zip 44646–7993, Mailing Address: 3000 Erie Street South, Zip 44646–7976;
tel. 330/833–3135, (Nonreporting) **A**1 5 10 **S** Ohio Department of Mental Health,
Columbus, OH
Primary Contact: Jeffrey Sims, Chief Executive Officer
CFO: Patricia Eddleman, Fiscal Officer
CMO: Steven Thomson, M.D., Medical Director
CIO: Robert Hobart, Director Management Information Systems
CHR: Jerald Wilhite, Administrator Human Resources
Web address: www.mh.state.oh.us/ibhs/bhos/hoh.html
Control: State–Government, nonfederal **Service:** Psychiatric

Staffed Beds: 130

MAUMEE—Lucas County

□ **ARROWHEAD BEHAVIORAL HEALTH HOSPITAL (364036)**, 1725 Timber Line
Road, Zip 43537–4015; tel. 419/891–9333, (Nonreporting) **A**1 9 10 **S** Universal
Health Services, Inc., King of Prussia, PA
Primary Contact: Edward Speedling, Chief Executive Officer and Managing
Director
CFO: Allison Duncan, Chief Financial Officer
CMO: Kenneth Adler, M.D., Medical Director
CIO: Peggy Montgomery, Director Medical Records
CHR: Dawn Bosworth, Director Human Resources
CNO: Anita Zych, Director of Nursing
Web address: www.arrowheadbehavioral.com
Control: Corporation, Investor–owned, for–profit **Service:** Other specialty

Staffed Beds: 42

★ ◇ **PROMEDICA ST. LUKE'S HOSPITAL (360090)**, 5901 Monclova Road,
Zip 43537–1899; tel. 419/893–5911 **A**2 3 5 9 10 21 **F**3 8 11 13 15 17 18 20
22 24 26 28 29 30 31 34 35 40 45 46 48 49 56 57 59 64 65 68 70 74 76
77 78 79 80 81 82 85 86 87 89 92 93 100 107 108 111 114 115 118 119
126 129 130 131 132 143 145 146 147 148 **P**8 **S** ProMedica Health System,
Toledo, OH
Primary Contact: Daniel L. Wakeman, President
COO: Daniel Schwanke, Chief Operating Officer
CMO: Stephen Bazeley, M.D., Vice President Medical Affairs
CIO: Patricia Swint, Director Information Technology
CHR: Connie Sessler, Director Human Resources
CNO: Maurine Weis, Chief Nursing Officer
Web address: www.stlukeshospital.com
Control: Other not–for–profit (including NFP Corporation) **Service:** General
Medical and Surgical

Staffed Beds: 182 **Admissions:** 10786 **Census:** 109 **Outpatient Visits:**
271319 **Births:** 857 **Total Expense ($000):** 169554 **Payroll Expense**
($000): 64198

MEDINA—Medina County

⊞ **MEDINA HOSPITAL (360091)**, 1000 East Washington Street, Zip 44256–2170;
tel. 330/725–1000 **A**1 2 5 9 10 **F**3 7 13 15 18 20 28 29 30 31 34 35 40 47
49 50 57 59 60 64 70 74 75 76 77 78 79 81 82 85 86 93 96 107 111 114
117 119 129 130 131 132 133 135 144 146 147 **S** Cleveland Clinic Health
System, Cleveland, OH
Primary Contact: Thomas Tulisiak, M.D., President
COO: Vicky Snyder, Chief Operating Officer and Chief Financial Officer
CFO: Vicky Snyder, Chief Operating Officer and Chief Financial Officer
CMO: Rick Shewbridge, M.D., Vice President Medical Operations
CIO: David Ingram, Director Management Information Systems
CHR: Tracie Curtis, Vice President Human Resources
CNO: Mary Kennedy, R.N., Chief Nursing Officer
Web address: www.medinahospital.org
Control: Other not–for–profit (including NFP Corporation) **Service:** General
Medical and Surgical

Staffed Beds: 136 **Admissions:** 6300 **Census:** 69 **Outpatient Visits:** 135103
Births: 899 **Total Expense ($000):** 105154 **Payroll Expense ($000):** 39494
Personnel: 648

MIAMISBURG—Montgomery County

⊞ **LIFECARE HOSPITAL OF DAYTON (362028)**, 4000 Miamisburg–Centerville
Road, Zip 45342–7615; tel. 937/384–8300, (Nonreporting) **A**1 9 10 **S** LifeCare
Management Services, Plano, TX
Primary Contact: Russell Dean, Administrator
CMO: Richard Gregg, M.D., Medical Director
CHR: Pam Fannin, Coordinator Human Resources
Web address: www.lifecare–hospitals.com
Control: Corporation, Investor–owned, for–profit **Service:** Long–Term Acute Care
hospital

Staffed Beds: 44

★ ○ **SYCAMORE MEDICAL CENTER (360239)**, 4000 Miamisburg–Centerville
Road, Zip 45342–7615; tel. 937/866–0551 **A**9 10 11 **F**3 11 12 15 18 20 28
29 30 31 34 35 38 39 40 44 45 47 48 49 50 53 54 56 57 58 59 60 61 64
65 66 68 70 74 75 77 78 79 81 82 84 85 86 87 93 97 98 99 100 101 102
103 104 105 107 108 110 111 114 115 118 119 129 130 131 132 134 135
141 145 146 148 **S** Kettering Health Network, Dayton, OH
Primary Contact: Walter Sackett, President
CMO: Gregory Wise, M.D., Vice President Medical Affairs
CIO: Jon Russell, Chief Information Officer
CHR: Beverly Morris, Vice President Human Resources
Web address: www.khnetwork.org
Control: Church–operated, Nongovernment, not–for profit **Service:** General
Medical and Surgical

Staffed Beds: 171 **Admissions:** 7827 **Census:** 89 **Outpatient Visits:** 122297
Births: 0 **Total Expense ($000):** 134117 **Payroll Expense ($000):** 54677
Personnel: 628

MIDDLE POINT—Van Wert County

□ **RIDGEVIEW BEHAVIORAL HOSPITAL (364047)**, 17872 Lincoln Highway,
Zip 45863–9700; tel. 419/968–2950, (Nonreporting) **A**1 10
Primary Contact: Pat Tracy, Administrator
Web address: www.ridgeviewhospital.net/
Control: Corporation, Investor–owned, for–profit **Service:** Psychiatric

Staffed Beds: 40

MIDDLEBURG HEIGHTS—Cuyahoga County

□ **SOUTHWEST GENERAL HEALTH CENTER (360155)**, 18697 Bagley Road,
Zip 44130–3497; tel. 440/816–8000 **A**1 2 5 10 **F**3 5 7 11 13 15 17 18 20 22
24 26 28 29 30 31 32 34 35 36 37 38 39 40 42 43 44 45 49 50 51 53 54
56 57 59 60 62 63 64 65 66 68 70 74 75 76 77 78 79 81 82 84 85 86 87
90 92 93 94 98 99 100 101 102 103 104 105 107 108 110 111 114 115
118 119 120 121 123 126 128 129 130 131 132 134 135 143 144 146 147
148 **P**6
Primary Contact: Thomas A. Selden, FACHE, President and Chief Executive Officer
CFO: Mary Ann Freas, Senior Vice President and Chief Financial Officer
CMO: Marilyn McNamara, M.D., Vice President Medical Affairs
CIO: Teresa Rini Barber, Vice President Support Services
CHR: Judy Murphy, Vice President Human Resources
CNO: Martha F. Bauschka, R.N., Vice President and Chief Nursing Officer
Web address: www.swgeneral.com
Control: Other not–for–profit (including NFP Corporation) **Service:** General
Medical and Surgical

Staffed Beds: 310 **Admissions:** 15987 **Census:** 208 **Outpatient Visits:**
403505 **Births:** 981 **Total Expense ($000):** 272539 **Payroll Expense**
($000): 108715 **Personnel:** 2049

MIDDLETOWN—Warren County

□ △ **ATRIUM MEDICAL CENTER (360076)**, One Medical Center Drive,
Zip 45005–1066; tel. 513/424–2111 **A**1 2 7 9 10 **F**3 13 15 17 18 20 22 24
26 28 29 30 31 34 35 39 40 43 44 45 46 47 48 49 50 54 56 57 59 60 61
64 68 70 73 74 75 76 77 78 79 80 81 82 84 85 86 87 90 91 92 93 94 96
98 100 101 102 103 107 108 110 111 114 115 116 117 118 119 126 130
131 135 141 145 146 147 148
Primary Contact: Carol Turner, President and Chief Executive Officer
CFO: Scott Shelton, Chief Financial Officer
CMO: Jeff Hoffman, M.D., Chief Medical Officer
CHR: Ted Ripperger, Administrative Director Human Resources
CNO: Marquita Turner, Chief Nursing Officer
Web address: www.atriummedcenter.org
Control: Other not–for–profit (including NFP Corporation) **Service:** General
Medical and Surgical

Staffed Beds: 160 **Admissions:** 7598 **Census:** 105 **Outpatient Visits:** 60053
Births: 876 **Total Expense ($000):** 218583 **Payroll Expense ($000):** 83914
Personnel: 1367

Many Facility Codes have changed. Please refer to the AHA Guide Code Chart. © 2014 AHA Guide

MILLERSBURG—Holmes County

☐ **POMERENE HOSPITAL (360148)**, 981 Wooster Road, Zip 44654–1094;
tel. 330/763–2001 **A**1 9 10 **F**3 11 13 15 18 29 30 34 35 40 50 53 55 57 59
68 70 74 75 79 81 85 86 87 93 107 108 110 114 119 127 130 131 132
135 144 146 148 **P**7
Primary Contact: Tony Snyder, Administrator and Chief Executive Officer
CFO: Jason Justus, Vice President Finance and Chief Financial Officer
CMO: Yasser Omran, M.D., President Medical Staff
CIO: Mark Jacobs, Director Information Services
CHR: Kim Croft, R.N., Executive Director Human Resources
CNO: Nicole Kolacz, Vice President Patient Services
Web address: www.pomerenehospital.org
Control: County–Government, nonfederal **Service:** General Medical and Surgical

Staffed Beds: 41 **Admissions:** 1435 **Census:** 13 **Outpatient Visits:** 38434
Births: 519 **Total Expense ($000):** 27046 **Payroll Expense ($000):** 11563
Personnel: 234

MONTPELIER—Williams County

**COMMUNITY HOSPITALS AND WELLNESS CENTERS–MONTPELIER
(361327)**, 909 East Snyder Avenue, Zip 43543–1251; tel. 419/385–3154,
(Nonreporting) **A**9 10 18
Primary Contact: Philip L. Ennen, President and Chief Executive Officer
Web address: www.chwchospital.com
Control: Corporation, Investor–owned, for–profit **Service:** General Medical and
Surgical

Staffed Beds: 35

MONTPELIER HOSPITAL See Community Hospitals and Wellness Centers, Bryan

MOUNT GILEAD—Morrow County

⊠ **MORROW COUNTY HOSPITAL (361313)**, 651 West Marion Road,
Zip 43338–1027; tel. 419/946–5015 **A**1 5 9 10 18 **F**3 11 15 18 28 29 30 34
35 40 45 50 54 59 62 64 70 74 75 77 78 79 80 81 85 90 93 97 107 108
110 118 119 127 129 130 131 133 135 144 146 **P**3 6 **S** OhioHealth,
Columbus, OH
Primary Contact: Christopher Truax, Chief Executive Officer
CFO: Joe Schueler, Chief Financial Officer
Web address: www.morrowcountyhospital.com
Control: County–Government, nonfederal **Service:** General Medical and Surgical

Staffed Beds: 23 **Admissions:** 513 **Census:** 5 **Outpatient Visits:** 162980
Births: 0 **Total Expense ($000):** 26387 **Payroll Expense ($000):** 9088

MOUNT VERNON—Knox County

⊠ **KNOX COMMUNITY HOSPITAL (360040)**, 1330 Coshocton Road,
Zip 43050–1495; tel. 740/393–9000 **A**1 2 9 10 20 **F**3 5 11 13 15 18 20 22
26 28 29 30 31 32 34 35 36 40 44 45 50 51 53 57 59 64 69 70 75 76 77
78 79 81 82 83 84 85 86 87 89 93 96 97 107 108 110 111 114 115 116
117 118 119 120 121 129 130 131 132 144 146 147 **P**6 **S** QHR,
Brentwood, TN
Primary Contact: Bruce D. White, Chief Executive Officer
COO: Bruce M. Behner, Chief Operating Officer
CFO: Michael Ambrosiani, Chief Financial Officer
CMO: Judy Schwartz, M.D., Chief Medical Officer
CIO: Kwi Holland, Vice President Information Services
CHR: Lisa Bragg, Vice President Human Resources
CNO: Sandra Beidelschies, MSN, Chief Nursing Officer
Web address: www.knoxcommhosp.org
Control: Other not–for–profit (including NFP Corporation) **Service:** General
Medical and Surgical

Staffed Beds: 49 **Admissions:** 2786 **Census:** 22 **Outpatient Visits:** 138258
Births: 384 **Total Expense ($000):** 112102 **Payroll Expense ($000):** 49081
Personnel: 763

NAPOLEON—Henry County

★ ◇ **HENRY COUNTY HOSPITAL (361309)**, 1600 East Riverview Avenue,
Zip 43545–9399; tel. 419/592–4015 **A**5 9 10 18 21 **F**3 5 11 15 18 29 30
31 34 35 36 40 45 50 53 57 59 64 65 68 70 75 76 78 79 81 82 85 86 87
93 99 100 101 104 107 108 110 114 119 130 132 133 135 146
Primary Contact: Kimberly Hupp Bordenkircher, Chief Executive Officer
CFO: Mary Clapp, Controller
CIO: Jeff Pompos, Manager Information Technology
CHR: Jennifer A. Fisher, Manager Human Resources
CNO: Patricia Frank, Chief Nursing Officer
Web address: www.henrycountyhospital.org
Control: Other not–for–profit (including NFP Corporation) **Service:** General
Medical and Surgical

Staffed Beds: 25 **Admissions:** 868 **Census:** 10 **Outpatient Visits:** 61795
Births: 108 **Total Expense ($000):** 25904 **Payroll Expense ($000):** 10261
Personnel: 203

NELSONVILLE—Athens County

★ **OHIOHEALTH DOCTORS HOSPITAL NELSONVILLE (361305)**, 1950 Mount
Saint Mary Drive, Zip 45764–1280; tel. 740/753–1931 **A**9 10 18 **F**3 15 29 34
40 45 57 59 64 65 75 77 81 84 97 107 110 114 119 130 133 **P**6
S OhioHealth, Columbus, OH
Primary Contact: LaMar L. Wyse, Chief Operating Officer
COO: LaMar L. Wyse, Chief Operating Officer
CFO: Shannon M. Atha, Director Finance
CMO: Marjorie Devol, M.D., Chief of Staff
CIO: Danny Canter, Manager Information Systems
CNO: Sandy Wood, Chief Clinical Officer
Web address: www.ohiohealth.com
Control: Other not–for–profit (including NFP Corporation) **Service:** General
Medical and Surgical

Staffed Beds: 25 **Admissions:** 382 **Census:** 5 **Outpatient Visits:** 27951
Births: 0 **Total Expense ($000):** 14474 **Payroll Expense ($000):** 6384
Personnel: 130

NEW ALBANY—Franklin County

⊠ **MOUNT CARMEL NEW ALBANY SURGICAL HOSPITAL (360266)**, 7333
Smith's Mill Road, Zip 43054–9291; tel. 614/775–6600 **A**1 9 10 **F**3 29 34 35
44 57 58 59 64 65 68 74 75 79 81 85 86 87 94 107 111 114 146 **P**6 8
S Catholic Health East / Trinity Health, Livonia, MI
Primary Contact: Richard D'Enbeau, Chief Operating Officer
Web address: www.mountcarmelhealth.com
Control: Church–operated, Nongovernment, not–for profit **Service:** Surgical

Staffed Beds: 60 **Admissions:** 4648 **Census:** 24 **Outpatient Visits:** 13350
Births: 0 **Total Expense ($000):** 82617 **Payroll Expense ($000):** 12470
Personnel: 191

NEWARK—Licking County

☐ **LICKING MEMORIAL HOSPITAL (360218)**, 1320 West Main Street,
Zip 43055–3699; tel. 740/348–4000 **A**1 2 5 9 10 **F**3 4 5 13 15 18 20 22 26
28 29 30 31 32 34 35 40 41 45 48 49 50 53 57 59 62 64 65 68 70 74 75
76 77 78 79 81 82 84 85 86 87 89 90 92 93 97 98 100 101 102 104 105
106 107 108 110 111 114 115 118 119 130 132 135 144 146 147 148 **P**6
Primary Contact: Robert A. Montagnese, President and Chief Executive Officer
CFO: Cindy Webster, Vice President Financial Services
CMO: Craig Cairns, M.D., Vice President Medical Affairs
CIO: Sallie Arnett, Vice President Information Systems
CHR: Anne Peterson, Vice President Human Resources and Support Services
Web address: www.lmhealth,org
Control: Other not–for–profit (including NFP Corporation) **Service:** General
Medical and Surgical

Staffed Beds: 199 **Admissions:** 7764 **Census:** 70 **Outpatient Visits:** 310048
Births: 1029 **Total Expense ($000):** 143535 **Payroll Expense ($000):**
58291 **Personnel:** 1271

NORTHFIELD—Summit County

☐ **NORTHCOAST BEHAVIORAL HEALTHCARE SYSTEM (364011)**, 1756
Sagamore Road, Zip 44067–1086; tel. 330/467–7131, (Includes CLEVELAND
CAMPUS, 1708 Southpoint Drive, Cleveland, Zip 44109–1999;
tel. 216/787–0500; NORTHFIELD CAMPUS, 1756 Sagamore Road, Zip 44067,
Mailing Address: P.O. Box 305, Zip 44067–0305; tel. 330/467–7131; TOLEDO
CAMPUS, 930 South Detroit Avenue, Toledo, Zip 43614–2701;
tel. 419/381–1881) **A**1 3 10 **F**30 53 65 75 77 82 98 106 130 135 146 **S** Ohio
Department of Mental Health, Columbus, OH
Primary Contact: Douglas W. Kern, Chief Executive Officer
CFO: Jeff Comfort, Vice President Administration
CIO: Karl Donenwirth, Vice President Information Services
Web address: www.mha.ohio.gov
Control: State–Government, nonfederal **Service:** Psychiatric

Staffed Beds: 260 **Admissions:** 1807 **Census:** 229 **Outpatient Visits:** 0
Births: 0 **Total Expense ($000):** 45907 **Payroll Expense ($000):** 25597
Personnel: 417

Hospital, Medicare Provider Number, Address, Telephone, Approval, Facility, and Physician Codes, Health Care System

★ American Hospital Association (AHA) membership
☐ The Joint Commission accreditation
◇ DNV Healthcare Inc. accreditation
○ Healthcare Facilities Accreditation Program
△ Commission on Accreditation of Rehabilitation Facilities (CARF) accreditation

NORWALK—Huron County

★ ○ **FISHER–TITUS MEDICAL CENTER (360065)**, 272 Benedict Avenue, Zip 44857–2374; tel. 419/668–8101, (Total facility includes 69 beds in nursing home–type unit) **A**2 5 9 10 11 19 **F**3 10 11 13 15 18 20 28 29 31 34 35 36 39 40 43 45 49 50 51 56 57 58 59 62 64 68 70 74 75 76 77 78 79 81 82 85 86 87 92 93 94 96 97 107 108 110 111 115 118 119 126 128 129 130 131 132 135 146 147 148 **P**2 6 7
Primary Contact: Lorna Strayer, Interim President and Chief Executive Officer
COO: Lorna Strayer, Executive Vice President
CFO: Duane L. Woods, Jr., Chief Financial Officer
CMO: Shankar Kurra, M.D., Senior Vice President Medical Affairs
CIO: John Britton, Vice President Information Services
CHR: Phillip Annarino, Vice President Human Resources
CNO: Suzanne Inglis, MSN, Senior Vice President Nursing Services
Web address: www.fisher–titus.org
Control: Other not–for–profit (including NFP Corporation) **Service:** General Medical and Surgical

Staffed Beds: 147 **Admissions:** 4255 **Census:** 99 **Outpatient Visits:** 160588 **Births:** 654 **Total Expense ($000):** 108563 **Payroll Expense ($000):** 42350 **Personnel:** 781

OBERLIN—Lorain County

✠ **MERCY ALLEN HOSPITAL (361306)**, 200 West Lorain Street, Zip 44074–1077; tel. 440/775–1211, (Total facility includes 8 beds in nursing home–type unit) **A**1 9 10 18 **F**3 7 8 11 15 29 30 34 35 40 50 65 69 70 74 75 79 81 85 87 93 97 107 108 110 119 127 128 129 130 131 132 133 146 **S** Mercy Health, Cincinnati, OH
Primary Contact: Susan Bowers, R.N., President
COO: Robert Tonkinson, Chief Operating Officer and Chief Financial Officer
CFO: Robert Tonkinson, Chief Operating Officer and Chief Financial Officer
CMO: Vamsee Amirneni, M.D., Chief of Staff
CNO: Catherine Walsh, Interim Chief Nursing Officer
Web address: www.mercyonline.org/mercy_allen_hospital.aspx
Control: Church–operated, Nongovernment, not–for profit **Service:** General Medical and Surgical

Staffed Beds: 25 **Admissions:** 959 **Census:** 15 **Outpatient Visits:** 45790 **Births:** 0 **Total Expense ($000):** 21833 **Payroll Expense ($000):** 8890 **Personnel:** 152

OREGON—Lucas County

✠ △ **MERCY ST. CHARLES HOSPITAL (360081)**, 2600 Navarre Avenue, Zip 43616–3297; tel. 419/696–7200 **A**1 7 9 10 **F**3 11 13 15 18 28 29 30 31 34 35 40 43 44 46 48 49 51 56 57 59 60 64 66 68 70 71 74 75 76 77 78 79 81 82 85 86 87 90 92 93 97 98 100 102 103 107 108 110 111 114 115 116 117 119 123 129 130 132 135 146 147 148 **P**8 **S** Mercy Health, Cincinnati, OH
Primary Contact: Jeffrey Dempsey, President and Chief Executive Officer
COO: Jeffrey Dempsey, President and Chief Executive Officer
CFO: Jim Puffenberger, Senior Vice President Northern Region and Chief Financial Officer
CMO: Norbert Stockort, M.D., Chief of Staff
CIO: Brian Sterns, Director Information Systems Services
CHR: Gary George, Regional Vice President Human Resources
CNO: Craig Slbers, Vice President Patient Care and Chief Nursing Officer
Web address: www.mercyweb.org
Control: Church–operated, Nongovernment, not–for profit **Service:** General Medical and Surgical

Staffed Beds: 264 **Admissions:** 9135 **Census:** 134 **Outpatient Visits:** 137143 **Births:** 437 **Personnel:** 842

✠ **PROMEDICA BAY PARK HOSPITAL (360259)**, 2801 Bay Park Drive, Zip 43616–4920; tel. 419/690–7900 **A**1 9 10 **F**3 11 13 15 18 29 30 31 34 35 40 49 50 51 57 58 59 64 68 70 74 75 76 77 78 79 81 82 85 86 87 92 93 107 108 110 111 114 118 119 124 126 129 130 131 132 135 146 147 148 **S** ProMedica Health System, Toledo, OH
Primary Contact: Holly L. Bristoll, President
COO: Darrell Wachowiak, Associate Vice President Operations
CFO: Scott Fought, Vice President Finance
CMO: David Lindstrom, M.D., Vice President Medical Affairs
CIO: Rose Ann Laureto, Corporate Vice President Information Resources
CHR: Kara Zimmerly, Manager Human Resources
CNO: Paula Grieb, R.N., Vice President Patient Care Service and Chief Nursing Officer
Web address: www.promedica.org
Control: Other not–for–profit (including NFP Corporation) **Service:** General Medical and Surgical

Staffed Beds: 72 **Admissions:** 3206 **Census:** 33 **Outpatient Visits:** 92041 **Births:** 580 **Total Expense ($000):** 71657 **Payroll Expense ($000):** 23229 **Personnel:** 404

ST. CHARLES MERCY HOSPITAL See Mercy St. Charles Hospital

ORRVILLE—Wayne County

✠ **AULTMAN ORRVILLE HOSPITAL (361323)**, 832 South Main Street, Zip 44667–2208; tel. 330/682–3010 **A**1 9 10 18 **F**3 8 11 13 14 15 29 30 34 35 40 45 50 51 53 55 57 59 68 70 75 77 81 82 85 86 87 93 108 110 111 115 118 119 129 130 131 132 133 135 143 146 147 **S** Aultman Health Foundation, Canton, OH
Primary Contact: Marchelle Suppan, DPM, President and Chief Executive Officer
COO: Judy Erb, Vice President Patient Care Services and Chief Nursing Officer
CFO: Matthew A. Stewart, Vice President Finance and Chief Financial Officer
CIO: Terry Andrews, Manager Information Technology
CHR: Jennifer Kessel, Director Human Resources
CNO: Judy Erb, Vice President Patient Services and Chief Nursing Officer
Web address: www.aultmanorrville.org
Control: Other not–for–profit (including NFP Corporation) **Service:** General Medical and Surgical

Staffed Beds: 25 **Admissions:** 742 **Census:** 5 **Outpatient Visits:** 50152 **Births:** 402 **Total Expense ($000):** 22536 **Payroll Expense ($000):** 9266 **Personnel:** 170

OXFORD—Butler County

★ ○ **MCCULLOUGH–HYDE MEMORIAL HOSPITAL (360046)**, 110 North Poplar Street, Zip 45056–1292; tel. 513/523–2111 **A**9 10 11 **F**3 11 13 15 28 29 30 31 32 34 35 36 40 45 47 49 54 57 59 64 65 69 70 74 75 76 77 78 79 81 82 85 89 93 94 107 108 110 111 114 118 119 129 130 131 132 135 143 144 146 147 148
Primary Contact: Bryan D. Hehemann, President and Chief Executive Officer
CFO: John R. Clements, Vice President and Chief Financial Officer
CIO: Kathy Dickman, Director Information Technology
CHR: Sharon Hancock, Director Human Resources
CNO: Pamela Collins, Vice President Chief Patient Services Officer
Web address: www.mhmh.org
Control: Other not–for–profit (including NFP Corporation) **Service:** General Medical and Surgical

Staffed Beds: 45 **Admissions:** 2238 **Census:** 21 **Outpatient Visits:** 133677 **Births:** 423 **Total Expense ($000):** 55739 **Payroll Expense ($000):** 22152 **Personnel:** 374

PARMA—Cuyahoga County

✠ △ **UNIVERSITY HOSPITALS PARMA MEDICAL CENTER (360041)**, 7007 Powers Boulevard, Zip 44129–5495; tel. 440/743–3000, (Total facility includes 11 beds in nursing home–type unit) **A**1 2 7 10 **F**2 3 10 11 12 13 15 17 18 20 22 24 26 28 29 30 31 34 35 36 40 44 45 49 50 51 53 55 56 57 58 59 62 63 64 65 68 69 70 71 74 75 77 78 79 81 82 85 86 87 90 93 96 98 100 101 103 107 108 111 114 115 116 117 118 119 120 121 126 128 130 131 132 135 143 146 147 148 **P**6 **S** University Hospitals, Cleveland, OH
Primary Contact: Nancy Tinsley, President and Chief Executive Officer
COO: David Cook, Chief Operating Officer
CHR: Daniel Miller, Vice President Human Resources
CNO: Sharon Thomas, Vice President and Chief Nursing Officer
Web address: www.parmahospital.org
Control: Other not–for–profit (including NFP Corporation) **Service:** General Medical and Surgical

Staffed Beds: 271 **Admissions:** 12656 **Census:** 157 **Outpatient Visits:** 245267 **Births:** 471 **Total Expense ($000):** 180305 **Payroll Expense ($000):** 70382 **Personnel:** 1400

PAULDING—Paulding County

☐ **PAULDING COUNTY HOSPITAL (361300)**, 1035 West Wayne Street, Zip 45879–1544; tel. 419/399–4080, (Nonreporting) **A**1 9 10 18
Primary Contact: Randy Ruge, Chief Executive Officer
COO: Randy Ruge, Chief Operating Officer
CFO: Rob Goshia, Chief Financial Officer
CMO: Wendell J. Spangler, M.D., Chief of Staff
CIO: Dan Kaufman, Director Information Services
CHR: Melanie Rittenour, Director Human Resources
Web address: www.pauldingcountyhospital.com
Control: County–Government, nonfederal **Service:** General Medical and Surgical

Staffed Beds: 25

PORT CLINTON—Ottawa County

✠ **MAGRUDER MEMORIAL HOSPITAL (361314)**, 615 Fulton Street, Zip 43452–2001; tel. 419/734–3131 **A**1 5 9 10 18 **F**3 11 15 18 28 29 31 34 35 40 44 45 46 48 50 53 57 59 64 65 70 74 75 78 79 81 82 85 86 87 89 93 107 108 110 115 118 119 129 130 131 132 133 135 146 147 148 **P**6 8
Primary Contact: J. Todd Almendinger, President and Chief Executive Officer
CFO: Ronald Weiner, Vice President Finance and Chief Financial Officer
CMO: Barry Cover, M.D., Medical Director
CIO: Charles Dellick, Director Information Technology
CHR: Jason Kraus, Director Human Resources
CNO: Kathy Durflinger, Vice President Nursing
Web address: www.magruderhospital.com
Control: Other not–for–profit (including NFP Corporation) **Service:** General Medical and Surgical

Staffed Beds: 25 **Admissions:** 805 **Census:** 6 **Outpatient Visits:** 90243 **Births:** 0 **Total Expense ($000):** 47357 **Payroll Expense ($000):** 19313 **Personnel:** 363

Many Facility Codes have changed. Please refer to the AHA Guide Code Chart. © 2014 AHA Guide

PORTSMOUTH—Scioto County

⊠ △ **SOUTHERN OHIO MEDICAL CENTER (360008)**, 1805 27th Street, Zip 45662–2640; tel. 740/356–5000 **A**1 2 5 7 9 10 13 19 20 **F**3 11 13 15 17 18 20 22 24 26 28 29 30 31 34 35 37 38 40 41 44 45 46 49 50 53 54 57 59 62 63 64 65 68 70 74 75 76 77 78 79 81 83 84 85 86 87 89 90 92 97 98 100 102 103 104 107 108 109 110 111 114 115 116 117 118 119 120 121 122 123 124 129 130 131 132 135 144 145 146 **P**3
Primary Contact: Randal M. Arnett, President and Chief Executive Officer
COO: Claudia L. Burchett, R.N., Vice President Patient Services
CFO: Dean Wray, Vice President Finance
CMO: Kendall Stewart, M.D., Medical Director
CIO: Brent Richard, Administrative Director Information Systems
CHR: Vicki Noel, Vice President Human Resources
CNO: Claudia L. Burchett, R.N., Vice President of Patient Services
Web address: www.somc.org
Control: Other not–for–profit (including NFP Corporation) **Service:** General Medical and Surgical

Staffed Beds: 245 **Admissions:** 12041 **Census:** 161 **Outpatient Visits:** 289945 **Births:** 1202 **Total Expense ($000):** 250368 **Payroll Expense ($000):** 93444 **Personnel:** 2058

PROCTORVILLE—Lawrence County

☐ **THREE GABLES SURGERY CENTER (360261)**, 5897 County Road 107, Zip 45669–8852, Mailing Address: P.O. Box 490, Zip 45669–0490; tel. 740/886–9911, (Nonreporting) **A**1 9 10
Primary Contact: Tony Aluise, Chief Executive Officer
Web address: www.threegablessurgery.com
Control: Partnership, Investor–owned, for–profit **Service:** Surgical

Staffed Beds: 8

RAVENNA—Portage County

☐ **ROBINSON MEMORIAL HOSPITAL (360078)**, 6847 North Chestnut Street, Zip 44266–3929, Mailing Address: P.O. Box 1204, Zip 44266–1204; tel. 330/297–0811, (Nonreporting) **A**1 2 3 5 9 10 **S** Summa Health System, Akron, OH
Primary Contact: Stephen Colecchi, President and Chief Executive Officer
CFO: Carl Ebner, Vice President Finance
CMO: Stephen Francis, M.D., Vice President Medical Affairs
CIO: David Baldwin, Chief Information Officer
CHR: Neil Everett, Vice President Human Resources
CNO: Linda Breedlove, Vice President of Patient Care Services and Chief Nursing Officer
Web address: www.robinsonmemorial.org
Control: Other not–for–profit (including NFP Corporation) **Service:** General Medical and Surgical

Staffed Beds: 141

ROCK CREEK—Ashtabula County

GLENBEIGH HOSPITAL AND OUTPATIENT CENTERS (360245), 2863 Route 45, Zip 44084, Mailing Address: P.O. Box 298, Zip 44084–0298; tel. 440/563–3400 **A**9 10 **F**4 5 29 30 34 36 53 54 57 75 86 87 100 130 132 135 **P**5
Primary Contact: Patricia Weston–Hall, Chief Executive Officer
CFO: Phil Pawlowski, Chief Financial Officer
CIO: Linda Advey, Manager Information Systems
CHR: Shirley Deary, Director Human Resources
Web address: www.glenbeigh.com
Control: Other not–for–profit (including NFP Corporation) **Service:** Alcoholism and other chemical dependency

Staffed Beds: 114 **Admissions:** 2893 **Census:** 70 **Outpatient Visits:** 90837 **Births:** 0 **Total Expense ($000):** 18761 **Payroll Expense ($000):** 9137 **Personnel:** 244

SAINT MARYS—Auglaize County

◇ **JOINT TOWNSHIP DISTRICT MEMORIAL HOSPITAL (360032)**, 200 St. Clair Street, Zip 45885–2400; tel. 419/394–3335, (Total facility includes 13 beds in nursing home–type unit) **A**9 10 21 **F**3 7 8 11 12 13 15 28 29 30 32 34 35 36 40 41 42 43 45 47 51 53 57 59 62 63 64 70 75 76 77 79 81 82 83 84 85 87 90 93 107 108 110 115 119 128 129 130 131 132 143 144 146 147 148
Primary Contact: Kevin W. Harlan, President
CFO: Jeffrey W. Vossler, Chief Financial Officer
CIO: Joshua Miller, Director Information Systems
CHR: Art Swain, Vice President Support Services
CNO: Debra McKee, R.N., Chief Nursing Officer
Web address: www.grandlakehealth.org
Control: Other not–for–profit (including NFP Corporation) **Service:** General Medical and Surgical

Staffed Beds: 53 **Admissions:** 2228 **Census:** 14 **Outpatient Visits:** 87128 **Births:** 241 **Total Expense ($000):** 63703 **Payroll Expense ($000):** 20416 **Personnel:** 416

SALEM—Columbiana County

⊠ **SALEM REGIONAL MEDICAL CENTER (360185)**, 1995 East State Street, Zip 44460–2423; tel. 330/332–1551, (Nonreporting) **A**1 5 9 10
Primary Contact: Anita Hackstedde, M.D., President and Chief Executive Officer
COO: Keith Meredith, Chief Operating Officer
CFO: Mike Giangardella, Vice President Finance and Administration
CMO: Anita Hackstedde, M.D., Vice President Medical Affairs
CIO: Mark L'Italien, Director Information Services
CHR: Barb Hirst, Vice President Human Resources and Chief Nursing Officer
CNO: Barb Hirst, Vice President Human Resources and Chief Nursing Officer
Web address: www.salemregional.com
Control: Other not–for–profit (including NFP Corporation) **Service:** General Medical and Surgical

Staffed Beds: 140

SANDUSKY—Erie County

◯ **FIRELANDS REGIONAL HEALTH SYSTEM (360025)**, 1111 Hayes Avenue, Zip 44870–3323; tel. 419/557–7400, (Includes FIRELANDS REGIONAL MEDICAL CENTER – MAIN CAMPUS, 1111 Hayes Avenue, Zip 44870; tel. 419/557–7400; FIRELANDS REGIONAL MEDICAL CENTER SOUTH CAMPUS, 1912 Hayes Avenue, Zip 44870–4736; tel. 419/557–7000) **A**2 6 9 10 11 12 13 19 **F**3 5 8 11 13 15 18 20 22 24 28 29 31 33 34 35 36 38 40 43 45 47 48 49 50 51 57 58 59 60 62 64 65 68 70 74 75 76 77 78 79 81 82 85 87 89 90 92 93 98 99 100 102 104 105 107 108 110 111 114 115 118 119 120 121 123 124 129 130 131 132 135 143 145 146 147 148 **P**7 8
Primary Contact: Martin Tursky, President and Chief Executive Officer
CFO: Daniel J. Moncher, Vice President and Chief Financial Officer
CMO: Brenda Violette, M.D., Director Medical Staff
CIO: Robert Ayres, Director Information Systems
CHR: James Sennish, Vice President Human Resources
Web address: www.firelands.com
Control: Other not–for–profit (including NFP Corporation) **Service:** General Medical and Surgical

Staffed Beds: 236 **Admissions:** 8666 **Census:** 118 **Outpatient Visits:** 286886 **Births:** 713 **Total Expense ($000):** 200174 **Payroll Expense ($000):** 80172 **Personnel:** 1711

SEAMAN—Adams County

⊠ **ADAMS COUNTY REGIONAL MEDICAL CENTER (361326)**, 230 Medical Center Drive, Zip 45679–8002; tel. 937/386–3400 **A**1 9 10 **F**3 15 28 29 30 31 34 40 45 47 53 54 57 59 62 64 65 75 77 78 79 81 85 86 93 107 110 111 115 116 119 129 130 131 132 133 148
Primary Contact: Saundra J. Stevens, Chief Executive Officer
CFO: Pete Dagenbach, Chief Financial Officer
CHR: Heather Hoop, Human Resources Generalist
CNO: Sharon Ashley, MSN, Chief Nursing Officer
Web address: www.acrmc.com
Control: County–Government, nonfederal **Service:** General Medical and Surgical

Staffed Beds: 25 **Admissions:** 839 **Census:** 8 **Outpatient Visits:** 55415 **Births:** 0 **Total Expense ($000):** 26588 **Payroll Expense ($000):** 9644 **Personnel:** 236

Hospital, Medicare Provider Number, Address, Telephone, Approval, Facility, and Physician Codes, Health Care System

★ American Hospital Association (AHA) membership
☐ The Joint Commission accreditation
◇ DNV Healthcare Inc. accreditation
◯ Healthcare Facilities Accreditation Program
△ Commission on Accreditation of Rehabilitation Facilities (CARF) accreditation

OH

SHELBY—Richland County

★ **OHIOHEALTH MEDCENTRAL SHELBY HOSPITAL (361324)**, 199 West Main Street, Zip 44875–1490; tel. 419/342–5015 **A**9 10 18 **F**3 11 13 15 18 29 30 31 34 35 40 57 59 64 68 69 70 75 76 78 79 81 93 107 110 114 119 130 133 146 **S** OhioHealth, Columbus, OH
Primary Contact: Jean Halpin, President
CNO: Trish DelGreco, Director of Nursing
Web address: www.medcentral.org/body.cfm?id=153
Control: Other not–for–profit (including NFP Corporation) **Service:** General Medical and Surgical

> **Staffed Beds:** 25 **Admissions:** 1386 **Census:** 12 **Outpatient Visits:** 35839 **Births:** 163 **Personnel:** 157

SIDNEY—Shelby County

★ ○ **WILSON MEMORIAL HOSPITAL (360013)**, 915 West Michigan Street, Zip 45365–2491; tel. 937/498–2311 **A**9 10 11 **F**3 11 13 15 20 28 29 30 31 40 45 46 49 56 57 59 62 63 64 68 70 75 76 77 78 79 81 85 86 87 89 93 98 103 107 108 111 118 119 124 129 130 131 132 135 144 146 147 **P**6
Primary Contact: Mark J. Dooley, Chief Executive Officer
COO: Craig Lannoye, Vice President Operations
CFO: Julie Covault, Vice President Finance
CMO: Robert J. McDevitt, M.D., Chief of Staff
CIO: Larry Meyers, Chief Information Officer
CHR: John R. Eve, Vice President Human Resources
CNO: Linda Maurer, Vice President Patient Care Services
Web address: www.wilsonhospital.com
Control: Other not–for–profit (including NFP Corporation) **Service:** General Medical and Surgical

> **Staffed Beds:** 71 **Admissions:** 2364 **Census:** 26 **Outpatient Visits:** 180607 **Births:** 783 **Total Expense ($000):** 66029 **Payroll Expense ($000):** 25148 **Personnel:** 615

SPRINGFIELD—Clark County

☐ **MENTAL HEALTH SERVICES FOR CLARK AND MADISON COUNTIES (364040)**, 474 North Yellow Springs Street, Zip 45504–2463; tel. 937/399–9500 **A**1 9 10 **F**98 100 101 102 103 104 105 143
Primary Contact: James Perry, Chief Executive Officer
Web address: www.mhscc.org
Control: Other not–for–profit (including NFP Corporation) **Service:** Psychiatric

> **Staffed Beds:** 16 **Admissions:** 770 **Census:** 13 **Outpatient Visits:** 88700 **Births:** 0 **Total Expense ($000):** 12727 **Payroll Expense ($000):** 7944 **Personnel:** 157

☐ **OHIO VALLEY SURGICAL HOSPITAL (360355)**, 100 West Main Street, Zip 45502–1312; tel. 937/521–3900, (Nonreporting) **A**1 9 10
Primary Contact: Steve Eisentrager, President
CFO: Amanda martin, Manager Human Resources
CMO: Thales Pavlatos, Medical Director
CIO: Jonathan Bisdorf, Director Information Technology
CNO: Beth Lizza, Chief Nursing Officer
Web address: www.ovsurgical.com/
Control: Partnership, Investor–owned, for–profit **Service:** Surgical

> **Staffed Beds:** 24

⊞ **SPRINGFIELD REGIONAL MEDICAL CENTER (360086)**, 100 Medical Center Drive, Zip 45504–2687; tel. 937/523–1000, (Includes SPRINGFIELD IMAGING CENTER, 1343 North Fountain Boulevard, Zip 45501–1380; tel. 937/390–5000) **A**1 2 6 9 10 **F**3 5 8 11 13 15 17 18 20 22 24 26 28 29 30 31 34 35 37 40 45 49 51 59 61 63 64 68 70 74 75 76 77 78 79 81 82 83 84 85 86 87 89 90 93 107 108 110 111 114 115 118 119 120 121 126 129 130 131 132 135 146 147 148 **P**6 **S** Mercy Health, Cincinnati, OH
Primary Contact: Paul C. Hiltz, FACHE, Market President and Chief Executive Officer
COO: Gary Hagens, Chief Operating Officer and Chief Medical Officer
CFO: William J. Kusnierz, Vice President and Chief Financial Officer
CMO: Gary Hagens, Chief Operating Officer and Chief Medical Officer
CIO: Denise Craven, Director Information Systems Relationship Management
CHR: Steven E. Kile, Director Human Resources
CNO: Sherry Nelson, JD, Chief Nursing Officer
Web address: www.community–mercy.org
Control: Church–operated, Nongovernment, not–for profit **Service:** General Medical and Surgical

> **Staffed Beds:** 254 **Admissions:** 16148 **Census:** 190 **Outpatient Visits:** 301603 **Births:** 1246 **Total Expense ($000):** 221350 **Payroll Expense ($000):** 70559 **Personnel:** 1126

STEUBENVILLE—Jefferson County

⊞ **ACUITY SPECIALTY HOSPITALS OHIO VALLEY (362035)**, 380 Summit Avenue, 3rd Floor, Zip 43952–2667; tel. 740/283–7600, (Includes ACUITY SPECIALTY HOSPITALS OHIO VALLEY AT BELMONT, 4697 Harrison Street, Bellaire, Zip 43906–1338; tel. 740/671–2086) **A**1 9 10 **F**1 18 29 30 45 46 56 60 74 75 86 97 103 107 111 114 119 130 143 148 **S** AcuityHealthcare, LP, Charlotte, NC
Primary Contact: Judy K. Weaver, MS, Chief Executive Officer
Web address: www.acuityhealthcare.net
Control: Individual, Investor–owned, for–profit **Service:** Long–Term Acute Care hospital

> **Staffed Beds:** 61 **Admissions:** 812 **Census:** 56 **Outpatient Visits:** 0 **Births:** 0 **Total Expense ($000):** 25952 **Payroll Expense ($000):** 13852 **Personnel:** 210

LIFE LINE HOSPITAL (362039), 200 School Street, Zip 43953–9610; tel. 740/346–2600, (Nonreporting) **A**10
Primary Contact: Susan T. Colpo, Chief Executive Officer
Web address: www.llhospital.com
Control: Partnership, Investor–owned, for–profit **Service:** Long–Term Acute Care hospital

> **Staffed Beds:** 30

⊞ **TRINITY HEALTH SYSTEM (360211)**, 380 Summit Avenue, Zip 43952–2699; tel. 740/283–7000, (Includes TRINITY MEDICAL CENTER EAST, 380 Summit Avenue, tel. 740/283–7000; TRINITY MEDICAL CENTER WEST, 4000 Johnson Road, Zip 43952–2393; tel. 740/264–8000) **A**1 2 6 9 10 **F**3 4 5 11 12 13 15 17 18 20 22 24 26 28 29 30 31 32 34 35 38 40 45 46 47 49 51 54 56 57 59 62 64 65 70 74 75 76 77 78 79 81 85 86 87 89 90 92 93 94 96 97 98 99 100 101 102 103 104 105 107 108 110 111 114 115 117 118 119 120 121 123 126 128 129 130 131 132 135 144 146 147 148 **P**6 **S** Sylvania Franciscan Health, Toledo, OH
Primary Contact: Fred B. Brower, President and Chief Executive Officer
COO: JoAnn M. Mulrooney, R.N., Chief Operating Officer
CFO: Dave Werkin, Vice President Finance and Chief Financial Officer
CMO: Gray Goncz, Vice President of Medical Affairs
CIO: Tom Kiger, Director Information Systems
CHR: Lewis C. Musso, Vice President Human Resources
Web address: www.trinityhealth.com
Control: Other not–for–profit (including NFP Corporation) **Service:** General Medical and Surgical

> **Staffed Beds:** 312 **Admissions:** 11033 **Census:** 178 **Outpatient Visits:** 272669 **Births:** 545 **Total Expense ($000):** 205184 **Payroll Expense ($000):** 75613 **Personnel:** 1567

SYLVANIA—Lucas County

⊞ △ **PROMEDICA FLOWER HOSPITAL (360074)**, 5200 Harroun Road, Zip 43560–2196; tel. 419/824–1444 **A**1 2 3 5 7 9 10 **F**3 9 11 12 13 15 18 24 28 29 30 31 34 35 36 38 40 47 48 49 50 57 58 59 60 64 68 70 75 76 77 78 79 81 82 84 85 86 87 90 91 92 93 94 96 97 98 100 101 102 103 107 108 109 110 111 114 116 117 118 119 120 121 123 124 126 129 130 131 132 146 147 **S** ProMedica Health System, Toledo, OH
Primary Contact: Neeraj Kanwal, M.D., President
CFO: Kathleen S. Hanley, Chief Financial Officer
CMO: John Evanoff, M.D., Vice President Medical Affairs
CIO: Ken Armstrong, Senior Vice President Information
CHR: Arturo Polizzi, Chief Human Resources Officer
CNO: Maurine Weis, Vice President Nursing and Chief Nursing Officer
Web address: www.promedica.org
Control: Other not–for–profit (including NFP Corporation) **Service:** General Medical and Surgical

> **Staffed Beds:** 269 **Admissions:** 10264 **Census:** 149 **Outpatient Visits:** 195857 **Births:** 971 **Total Expense ($000):** 199287 **Payroll Expense ($000):** 70899 **Personnel:** 1156

⊞ **REGENCY HOSPITAL OF TOLEDO (362036)**, 5220 Alexis Road, Zip 43560–2504; tel. 419/318–5700, (Nonreporting) **A**1 3 5 10 **S** Select Medical Corporation, Mechanicsburg, PA
Primary Contact: Diana D. Fisher, Chief Executive Officer
Web address: www.regencyhospital.com
Control: Corporation, Investor–owned, for–profit **Service:** Long–Term Acute Care hospital

> **Staffed Beds:** 35

Many Facility Codes have changed. Please refer to the AHA Guide Code Chart. © 2014 AHA Guide

TIFFIN—Seneca County

⊞ **MERCY TIFFIN HOSPITAL (360089)**, 45 St. Lawrence Drive, Zip 44883–8310; tel. 419/455–7000 **A**1 2 5 9 10 **F**3 11 12 13 15 18 19 20 28 29 30 31 34 35 36 40 46 49 50 51 56 57 59 62 64 66 68 70 74 75 76 77 78 79 81 82 83 84 85 86 87 89 97 107 108 110 111 115 118 119 121 123 124 129 130 132 133 134 135 145 146 147 148 **S** Mercy Health, Cincinnati, OH
Primary Contact: B. Lynn Detterman, President and Chief Executive Officer
CMO: Christopher Sears, M.D., President Medical Staff
Web address: www.mercyweb.org
Control: Church–operated, Nongovernment, not–for profit **Service:** General Medical and Surgical

Staffed Beds: 51 **Admissions:** 1816 **Census:** 18 **Outpatient Visits:** 74380 **Births:** 298 **Total Expense ($000):** 51678 **Payroll Expense ($000):** 15055 **Personnel:** 351

TOLEDO—Lucas County

☐ **ADVANCED SPECIALTY HOSPITAL OF TOLEDO (362038)**, 1015 Garden Lake Parkway, Zip 43614–2779; tel. 419/381–0037, (Nonreporting) **A**1 10
Primary Contact: Kim Burkholder–McNutt, Chief Executive Officer
CFO: Troy Holmes, Director Finance
CMO: B. Sarroui, M.D., Chief of Staff
CHR: Tina Hacker, Director Human Resources
CNO: Jennifer Olivier, Chief Clinical Officer
Web address: www.advancedspecialtyhospitals.com
Control: Corporation, Investor–owned, for–profit **Service:** Long–Term Acute Care hospital

Staffed Beds: 40

⊞ **MERCY ST. ANNE HOSPITAL (360262)**, 3404 West Sylvania Avenue, Zip 43623–4467; tel. 419/407–2663 **A**1 2 9 10 **F**3 11 15 18 29 30 31 34 35 36 38 40 45 46 56 57 59 64 65 68 70 74 75 78 79 81 82 84 85 86 87 92 107 108 110 111 114 116 117 118 119 122 123 129 130 132 135 146 147 **P**8 **S** Mercy Health, Cincinnati, OH
Primary Contact: Bradley J. Bertke, President and Chief Executive Officer
CFO: Robert Moon, Chief Financial Officer
CMO: Herbert Stockard, M.D., Chief Medical Officer
CIO: Rebecca S. Sykes, Chief Information Officer
CHR: Gary George, Regional Vice President Human Resources
CNO: Pamela Kadlick, Vice President Nursing
Web address: www.mercyweb.org
Control: Church–operated, Nongovernment, not–for profit **Service:** General Medical and Surgical

Staffed Beds: 96 **Admissions:** 4356 **Census:** 46 **Outpatient Visits:** 152229 **Births:** 0 **Personnel:** 513

⊞ **MERCY ST. VINCENT MEDICAL CENTER (360112)**, 2213 Cherry Street, Zip 43608–2691; tel. 419/251–3232, (Includes MERCY CHILDREN'S HOSPITAL, 2213 Cherry Street, tel. 419/251–8000) **A**1 2 3 5 9 10 12 13 **F**3 7 8 11 12 13 15 16 17 18 19 20 21 22 23 24 25 26 28 29 30 32 34 35 37 38 40 41 42 43 44 45 46 48 49 50 51 54 55 56 60 61 64 65 66 68 70 72 73 74 75 76 77 78 79 81 82 84 85 86 87 88 89 92 93 97 98 103 107 108 110 111 113 114 115 116 118 119 126 129 130 131 132 134 135 141 146 147 148 **P**8 **S** Mercy Health, Cincinnati, OH
Primary Contact: Kerry Tirman, President and Chief Operating Officer
COO: Kerry Tirman, President and Chief Operating Officer
CMO: Thomas Welch, M.D., Chief Medical Officer
CHR: Gary George, Senior Vice President Human Resources
CNO: Barbara Martin, Chief Nursing Officer
Web address: www.mercyweb.org
Control: Church–operated, Nongovernment, not–for profit **Service:** General Medical and Surgical

Staffed Beds: 431 **Admissions:** 17267 **Census:** 224 **Outpatient Visits:** 188800 **Births:** 1221 **Personnel:** 2591

☐ **NORTHWEST OHIO PSYCHIATRIC HOSPITAL (364014)**, 930 Detroit Avenue, Zip 43614–2701; tel. 419/381–1881 **A**1 10 **F**30 53 75 97 98 106 130 146 **S** Ohio Department of Mental Health, Columbus, OH
Primary Contact: Mychail Scheramic, M.D., Chief Executive Officer
CMO: Thomas Osinowo, M.D., Chief Medical Officer
CIO: Michael Carter, Administrator Information Technology
CHR: Lois Mason–Williams, Director of Human Resources
CNO: Deb Duris, Director of Nursing
Web address: www.mh.state.oh.us/
Control: State–Government, nonfederal **Service:** Psychiatric

Staffed Beds: 114 **Admissions:** 571 **Census:** 102 **Outpatient Visits:** 0 **Births:** 0 **Personnel:** 181

⊞ **PROMEDICA TOLEDO HOSPITAL (360068)**, 2142 North Cove Boulevard, Zip 43606–3896; tel. 419/291–4000, (Includes PROMEDICA WILDWOOD ORTHOPAEDIC AND SPINE HOSPITAL, 2901 North Reynolds Road, Zip 43615; tel. 419/578–7700; Holly L. Bristoll, President; TOLEDO CHILDREN'S HOSPITAL, 2142 North Cove Boulevard, Zip 43606), (Total facility includes 25 beds in nursing home–type unit) **A**1 3 5 9 10 13 **F**3 7 8 11 12 13 15 17 18 19 20 21 22 24 26 29 30 31 32 34 35 36 38 39 40 41 43 48 49 50 51 52 53 54 55 57 58 59 60 64 65 67 68 70 72 74 75 76 77 78 79 81 82 84 85 86 87 88 89 90 91 92 93 94 96 97 98 99 100 101 102 104 105 107 108 109 110 111 114 115 118 119 123 126 128 130 131 132 134 135 143 144 146 147 148 **S** ProMedica Health System, Toledo, OH
Primary Contact: Arturo Polizzi, President
CMO: Khurram Kamran, M.D., Vice President Medical Affairs
CIO: Rose Ann Laureto, Chief Information Officer
CHR: Arturo Polizzi, Chief Human Resources Officer
Web address: www.promedica.org
Control: Other not–for–profit (including NFP Corporation) **Service:** General Medical and Surgical

Staffed Beds: 656 **Admissions:** 30659 **Census:** 427 **Outpatient Visits:** 749946 **Births:** 3750 **Total Expense ($000):** 720995 **Payroll Expense ($000):** 241890 **Personnel:** 4124

⊞ △ **THE UNIVERSITY OF TOLEDO MEDICAL CENTER (360048)**, 3000 Arlington Avenue, Zip 43614–2595; tel. 419/383–4000 **A**1 2 3 5 7 8 9 10 **F**3 8 11 15 17 18 20 22 24 26 28 29 30 31 32 34 35 36 37 38 39 40 43 44 45 46 47 48 49 50 51 53 54 55 56 57 58 59 60 61 64 65 68 70 74 75 77 78 79 81 82 84 85 86 87 89 90 91 92 93 94 96 97 98 99 100 101 102 104 105 107 108 110 111 114 115 116 117 118 119 120 121 123 124 126 129 130 131 132 134 135 138 146 147 148
Primary Contact: David Morlock, Chief Executive Officer
COO: Carl Sirio, M.D., Professor, Vice President Medical Affairs, Associate Dean for Clinical Affairs, Chief Medical Information Officer
CFO: David Morlock, Chief Executive Officer, Executive Vice President Finance and Administration
CMO: Carl Sirio, M.D., Professor, Vice President Medical Affairs, Associate Deaf for Clinical Affairs, Chief Medical Information Officer
CIO: Godfrey Ovwigho, Vice President Information Technology and Chief Information Officer
CHR: Jovita Thomas–Williams, Associate Vice President Human Resources
CNO: Daniel Barbee, Vice President Clinical Affairs
Web address: www.utoledo.edu
Control: State–Government, nonfederal **Service:** General Medical and Surgical

Staffed Beds: 249 **Admissions:** 11803 **Census:** 174 **Outpatient Visits:** 266117 **Births:** 0 **Total Expense ($000):** 260092 **Payroll Expense ($000):** 104496 **Personnel:** 1881

TOLEDO CAMPUS See Northcoast Behavioral Healthcare System, Northfield

TROY—Miami County

☐ △ **UPPER VALLEY MEDICAL CENTER (360174)**, 3130 North County Road 25A, Zip 45373–1309; tel. 937/440–4000, (Includes DETTMER HOSPITAL, 3130 North Dixie Highway, Zip 45373–1039; tel. 937/440–7500), (Nonreporting) **A**1 2 5 7 9 10
Primary Contact: Thomas Parker, Chief Executive Officer
CFO: Tim Snider, Senior Vice President and Chief Financial Officer
CMO: Dan Bailey, M.D., Vice President Medical Affairs and Chief Medical Officer
CIO: William Watercutter, Director Management Information System
CHR: Tracy Moser, Director Human Resources
Web address: www.uvmc.com
Control: Other not–for–profit (including NFP Corporation) **Service:** General Medical and Surgical

Staffed Beds: 168

UPPER SANDUSKY—Wyandot County

★ **WYANDOT MEMORIAL HOSPITAL (361329)**, 885 North Sandusky Avenue, Zip 43351–1098; tel. 419/294–4991 **A**9 10 18 **F**3 11 13 15 17 18 28 29 31 34 35 40 45 53 57 59 64 65 74 75 76 77 78 79 81 82 85 86 87 89 92 93 97 107 108 110 111 115 117 118 119 124 129 130 132 133 135 146 148 **P**6
Primary Contact: Joseph A. D'Ettorre, Chief Executive Officer
COO: Ty Shaull, Chief Operating Officer
CFO: Alan H. Yeates, Vice President Fiscal Services
CHR: Vickie Underwood, Director Human Resources
CNO: Marty Gray, R.N., Director of Nursing
Web address: www.wyandotmemorial.org
Control: Hospital district or authority, Government, nonfederal **Service:** General Medical and Surgical

Staffed Beds: 25 **Admissions:** 925 **Census:** 12 **Outpatient Visits:** 58381 **Births:** 143 **Total Expense ($000):** 32844 **Payroll Expense ($000):** 10919 **Personnel:** 198

Hospital, Medicare Provider Number, Address, Telephone, Approval, Facility, and Physician Codes, Health Care System

★ American Hospital Association (AHA) membership
☐ The Joint Commission accreditation
◇ DNV Healthcare Inc. accreditation
○ Healthcare Facilities Accreditation Program
△ Commission on Accreditation of Rehabilitation Facilities (CARF) accreditation

---

OH

URBANA—Champaign County

★ **MERCY MEMORIAL HOSPITAL (361312)**, 904 Scioto Street, Zip 43078–2200; tel. 937/653–5231 **A**9 10 18 **F**3 5 8 11 15 28 29 30 34 35 40 45 50 59 63 70 75 77 79 81 84 85 91 93 107 108 110 111 114 119 130 133 135 146 148 **P**6 **S** Mercy Health, Cincinnati, OH
Primary Contact: Karen S. Gorby, R.N., MSN, FACHE, Administrator and Chief Nursing Officer
Web address: www.health–partners.org
Control: Church–operated, Nongovernment, not–for profit **Service:** General Medical and Surgical

Staffed Beds: 25 **Admissions:** 1116 **Census:** 10 **Outpatient Visits:** 78763 **Births:** 0 **Total Expense ($000):** 21631 **Payroll Expense ($000):** 7856 **Personnel:** 113

VAN WERT—Van Wert County

✠ **VAN WERT COUNTY HOSPITAL (360071)**, 1250 South Washington Street, Zip 45891–2599; tel. 419/238–2390 **A**1 5 9 10 **F**8 13 15 28 31 34 35 39 40 48 50 53 54 57 59 62 64 70 72 76 77 79 81 85 87 89 93 107 108 113 119 127 129 130 135 146 **P**7 8
Primary Contact: Mark J. Minick, President and Chief Executive Officer
CFO: Michael T. Holliday, Vice President Fiscal and Administrative Services
CMO: Jennifer Hohman, M.D., President Medical Staff
CIO: Brett Taylor, M.D., Manager Information
CHR: Joyce Pothast, Vice President Human and Environmental Services
CNO: Shelia Kay Brokenshire, Vice President of Nursing
Web address: www.vanwerthospital.org
Control: Other not–for–profit (including NFP Corporation) **Service:** General Medical and Surgical

Staffed Beds: 79 **Admissions:** 1185 **Census:** 11 **Outpatient Visits:** 116957 **Births:** 166 **Total Expense ($000):** 36357 **Payroll Expense ($000):** 11101 **Personnel:** 273

WADSWORTH—Medina County

☐ **SUMMA WADSWORTH–RITTMAN HOSPITAL (360195)**, 195 Wadsworth Road, Zip 44281–9505; tel. 330/331–1000 **A**1 5 9 10 **F**3 8 11 15 18 29 30 31 34 35 38 40 44 45 46 47 48 49 50 57 59 60 62 64 68 70 74 75 77 78 79 81 82 85 86 87 97 107 108 109 111 113 114 119 129 130 131 132 135 143 146 148 **P**6 8 **S** Summa Health System, Akron, OH
Primary Contact: Thomas DeBord, President
CFO: Charles Alderson, Chief Financial Officer
CMO: Jeffrey Morris, M.D., Vice President Medical Affairs
CIO: David Lynch, Regional Director Information Services
CHR: Don Argiro, Regional Director Human Resources
Web address: www.wrhhs.org
Control: Other not–for–profit (including NFP Corporation) **Service:** General Medical and Surgical

Staffed Beds: 50 **Admissions:** 2180 **Census:** 25 **Outpatient Visits:** 63226 **Births:** 0 **Total Expense ($000):** 44942 **Payroll Expense ($000):** 16389 **Personnel:** 314

WADSWORTH–RITTMAN HOSPITAL See Summa Wadsworth–Rittman Hospital

WARREN—Trumbull County

✠ △ **HILLSIDE REHABILITATION HOSPITAL (363026)**, 8747 Squires Lane N.E., Zip 44484–1649; tel. 330/841–3700, (Nonreporting) **A**1 5 7 9 10 **S** Community Health Systems, Inc., Franklin, TN
Primary Contact: Ian Cooper, Chief Executive Officer
CMO: Cynthia DiMauro, M.D., Medical Director
CIO: Timothy Roe, Chief Information Officer
CHR: Lisa Johnson, Vice President Human Resources
Web address: www.valleycarehealth.net
Control: Corporation, Investor–owned, for–profit **Service:** Rehabilitation

Staffed Beds: 65

✠ **ST. JOSEPH HEALTH CENTER (360161)**, 667 Eastland Avenue S.E., Zip 44484–4531; tel. 330/841–4000 **A**1 9 10 12 13 **F**3 5 8 11 12 13 15 28 29 30 31 34 35 40 42 43 44 45 46 49 50 51 53 54 56 57 59 60 61 64 66 68 69 70 74 75 76 77 78 79 81 82 83 84 85 86 87 89 93 97 107 108 111 114 117 118 119 120 121 123 126 129 130 132 135 143 144 146 147 148 **P**3 **S** Mercy Health, Cincinnati, OH
Primary Contact: Kathy Cook, R.N., MSN, President
COO: Robert W. Shroder, President and Chief Executive Officer
CFO: Donald E. Kline, Senior Vice President Finance
CMO: Nicholas Kreatsoulas, M.D., Vice President Medical Affairs
CHR: Molly Seals, Senior Vice President Human Resources and Learning
Web address: www.hmpartners.org
Control: Church–operated, Nongovernment, not–for profit **Service:** General Medical and Surgical

Staffed Beds: 141 **Admissions:** 7959 **Census:** 91 **Outpatient Visits:** 169849 **Births:** 794 **Total Expense ($000):** 132088 **Payroll Expense ($000):** 40017 **Personnel:** 674

TRUMBULL MEMORIAL HOSPITAL

✠ **TRUMBULL MEMORIAL HOSPITAL (360055)**, 1350 East Market Street, Zip 44483–6628; tel. 330/841–9011, (Nonreporting) **A**1 2 5 9 10 **S** Community Health Systems, Inc., Franklin, TN
Primary Contact: John Walsh, Chief Executive Officer
COO: Jay De Los Reyes, Chief Operating Officer
CFO: Anthony Seminaro, Chief Financial Officer
CMO: Thomas L. James, M.D., Chief Medical Officer
CIO: Barry Fitts, Chief Information Officer
CHR: Robert Sincich, Vice President Human Resources
CNO: Melissa Bennett, Chief Nursing Officer
Web address: www.vchs.net
Control: Corporation, Investor–owned, for–profit **Service:** General Medical and Surgical

Staffed Beds: 292

WARRENSVILLE HEIGHTS—Cuyahoga County

✠ **REGENCY HOSPITAL CLEVELAND EAST (362029)**, 4200 Interchange Corporate Center Road, Zip 44128–5631; tel. 216/910–3800, (Includes REGENCY HOSPITAL OF AKRON, 155 Fifth Street N.E., Barberton, Zip 44203; tel. 330/615–3792; Thomas Knoske, Chief Executive Officer; REGENCY HOSPITAL OF CLEVELAND – WEST, 6990 Engle Road, Middleburg Heights, Zip 44130–3420; tel. 440/202–4200; Timothy Rolsen, Chief Executive Officer), (Nonreporting) **A**1 10 **S** Select Medical Corporation, Mechanicsburg, PA
Primary Contact: Scott Williams, Chief Executive Officer
Web address: www.regencyhospital.com/
Control: Corporation, Investor–owned, for–profit **Service:** Long–Term Acute Care hospital

Staffed Beds: 44

✠ ○ **SOUTH POINTE HOSPITAL (360144)**, 20000 Harvard Road, Zip 44122–6805; tel. 216/491–6000 **A**1 2 9 10 11 12 13 **F**11 15 18 20 26 28 29 30 31 34 35 36 38 39 40 42 44 50 51 54 57 58 59 60 61 64 65 66 68 70 75 77 78 79 81 82 84 85 86 87 92 93 97 100 102 107 108 110 111 115 117 119 130 131 132 135 143 144 146 148 **S** Cleveland Clinic Health System, Cleveland, OH
Primary Contact: Robert S. Juhasz, D.O., President
COO: Andrea Jacobs, Chief Operating Officer
CFO: Lindsay Bird, Director Finance
CMO: Arun Gupta, M.D., Vice President Medical Affairs
CIO: Ralph A. Cagna, Director Information Technology
CHR: Doris A. Zajec, Director Human Resources
Web address: www.southpointehospital.org
Control: Other not–for–profit (including NFP Corporation) **Service:** General Medical and Surgical

Staffed Beds: 155 **Admissions:** 7302 **Census:** 95 **Outpatient Visits:** 123206 **Births:** 0 **Total Expense ($000):** 130093 **Payroll Expense ($000):** 50451 **Personnel:** 858

WASHINGTON COURT HOUSE—Fayette County

✠ **FAYETTE COUNTY MEMORIAL HOSPITAL (361331)**, 1430 Columbus Avenue, Zip 43160–1791; tel. 740/335–1210 **A**1 9 10 18 **F**3 7 8 11 15 18 29 30 34 35 40 45 50 57 59 64 68 70 79 81 82 85 86 87 89 90 93 97 107 108 110 114 119 127 128 129 130 131 132 133 135 144 146 148 **P**4 **S** Catholic Health East / Trinity Health, Livonia, MI
Primary Contact: Lyndon J. Christman, President and Chief Executive Officer
COO: Lenora Fitton, D.O., Chief of Staff
CFO: Thomas McDermott, Vice President Finance
CMO: John DesMarais, M.D., Chief Medical Officer
CIO: Bruce Denen, Manager Data Processing
CHR: Earlene Christensen, Director Human Resources
CNO: Beverly Hughes, R.N., Vice President Nursing
Web address: www.fcmh.org
Control: County–Government, nonfederal **Service:** General Medical and Surgical

Staffed Beds: 25 **Admissions:** 980 **Census:** 13 **Outpatient Visits:** 81009 **Births:** 0 **Total Expense ($000):** 47475 **Payroll Expense ($000):** 23315 **Personnel:** 419

WAUSEON—Fulton County

✠ **FULTON COUNTY HEALTH CENTER (361333)**, 725 South Shoop Avenue, Zip 43567–1701; tel. 419/335–2015, (Total facility includes 71 beds in nursing home–type unit) **A**1 2 5 9 10 18 **F**3 8 11 13 15 18 20 26 28 29 31 34 40 53 57 59 67 69 70 75 76 77 78 79 81 87 89 93 98 101 102 103 104 105 107 108 111 115 118 119 125 128 129 130 131 132 135 146 148
Primary Contact: Patti Finn, Chief Executive Officer
COO: Patti Finn, Chief Executive Officer
CFO: Darrell Topmiller, Director Finance
CIO: Larry Hefflinger, Director Information Systems
CHR: Kristy Snyder, Director Human Resources
CNO: Jo Short, Director of Nursing
Web address: www.fultoncountyhealthcenter.org
Control: Other not–for–profit (including NFP Corporation) **Service:** General Medical and Surgical

Staffed Beds: 106 **Admissions:** 1802 **Census:** 81 **Outpatient Visits:** 169046 **Births:** 276 **Total Expense ($000):** 58656 **Payroll Expense ($000):** 23727 **Personnel:** 666

Many Facility Codes have changed. Please refer to the AHA Guide Code Chart.

WAVERLY—Pike County

ADENA PIKE MEDICAL CENTER (361334), 100 Dawn Lane, Zip 45690–9138; tel. 740/947–2186, (Nonreporting) **A**9 10 18 **S** Adena Health System, Chillicothe, OH
Primary Contact: David M. Zanni, Associate Administrator
COO: Tina Perko, Vice President Operations
CFO: Sharon Novak, CPA, Vice President Finance
CHR: Berna Brock, Vice President Human Resources
Web address: www.pikecommunityhospital.org
Control: Other not–for–profit (including NFP Corporation) **Service:** General Medical and Surgical

Staffed Beds: 25

WEST CHESTER—Butler County

☐ **BECKETT SPRINGS (364051)**, 8614 Shepherd Farm Drive, Zip 45069; tel. 513/942–9500, (Nonreporting) **A**1 10
Primary Contact: David M. Polunas, Chief Executive Officer
Web address: www.springstone.com/hospitals.stmhl
Control: Corporation, Investor–owned, for–profit **Service:** Psychiatric

Staffed Beds: 48

✠ **WEST CHESTER HOSPITAL (360354)**, 7700 University Drive, Zip 45069–2505; tel. 513/298–3000, (Includes UNIVERSITY POINTE SURGICAL HOSPITAL, 7750 University Court, Zip 45069; tel. 513/475–8300) **A**1 10 **F**3 9 12 15 18 20 22 26 28 29 30 31 34 35 37 38 40 44 45 46 47 48 49 50 51 58 59 60 61 63 64 68 70 74 75 77 78 79 81 82 84 85 86 87 92 107 108 110 111 114 115 119 126 129 130 131 132 135 141 145 146 147 148 **P**6 **S** UC Health, Cincinnati, OH
Primary Contact: Kevin Joseph, M.D., Chief Executive Officer
COO: Tom G. Daskalakis, Chief Operating Officer
Web address: www.westchesterhospital.uchealth.com
Control: Other not–for–profit (including NFP Corporation) **Service:** General Medical and Surgical

Staffed Beds: 170 **Admissions:** 9319 **Census:** 96 **Outpatient Visits:** 113316 **Births:** 1 **Total Expense ($000):** 145050 **Payroll Expense ($000):** 47850 **Personnel:** 769

WESTERVILLE—Franklin County

✠ **MOUNT CARMEL ST. ANN'S (360012)**, 500 South Cleveland Avenue, Zip 43081–8998; tel. 614/898–4000 **A**1 3 5 9 10 **F**3 11 13 15 18 20 22 26 28 29 30 31 34 35 37 40 44 45 47 48 49 50 51 54 55 57 58 59 61 63 64 65 66 68 70 74 75 76 78 79 81 83 84 85 86 87 93 94 97 100 101 102 107 108 109 110 111 114 115 118 119 120 121 123 124 126 130 131 132 145 146 147 148 **P**6 8 **S** Catholic Health East / Trinity Health, Livonia, MI
Primary Contact: Janet Meeks, Chief Operating Officer
Web address: www.mountcarmelhealth.com
Control: Church–operated, Nongovernment, not–for profit **Service:** General Medical and Surgical

Staffed Beds: 242 **Admissions:** 20985 **Census:** 158 **Outpatient Visits:** 179314 **Births:** 4586 **Total Expense ($000):** 239213 **Payroll Expense ($000):** 83402 **Personnel:** 1421

WESTLAKE—Cuyahoga County

☐ **ST. JOHN MEDICAL CENTER (360123)**, 29000 Center Ridge Road, Zip 44145–5293; tel. 440/835–8000 **A**1 2 9 10 12 13 **F**3 8 13 15 17 18 20 22 24 26 28 29 30 31 34 35 39 40 43 44 45 46 47 49 50 51 54 56 57 59 64 65 68 70 71 74 75 76 78 79 80 81 82 84 85 86 87 89 92 93 100 107 108 110 111 114 115 119 130 132 143 144 146 147 148 **P**4 **S** Sisters of Charity Health System, Cleveland, OH
Primary Contact: William A. Young, Jr., President and Chief Executive Officer
CFO: Allen R. Tracy, Senior Vice President and Chief Financial Officer
CMO: Michael Dobrovich, M.D., Chief Medical Officer
CIO: James H. Carroll, Chief Information Officer
CHR: Gary Lazroff, Vice President Human Resources
Web address: www.sjws.net
Control: Other not–for–profit (including NFP Corporation) **Service:** General Medical and Surgical

Staffed Beds: 184 **Admissions:** 10555 **Census:** 101 **Outpatient Visits:** 137472 **Births:** 793 **Total Expense ($000):** 136376 **Payroll Expense ($000):** 55231 **Personnel:** 1020

ST. JOHN WEST SHORE HOSPITAL See St. John Medical Center

WILLARD—Huron County

✠ **MERCY WILLARD HOSPITAL (361310)**, 1100 Neal Zick Road, Zip 44890–9287; tel. 419/964–5000 **A**1 5 9 10 18 **F**3 5 15 18 28 29 30 34 35 40 46 57 59 68 70 74 75 77 79 81 84 85 87 89 93 107 111 114 117 119 129 130 131 132 133 135 143 145 146 147 **S** Mercy Health, Cincinnati, OH
Primary Contact: B. Lynn Detterman, President and Chief Executive Officer
CFO: Cindy Dennison, Senior Director Rural Division
CMO: Bill Back, M.D., Chief of Staff
CHR: Diana Olson, Chief Human Resources Officer
CNO: Pamela Napier, R.N., Chief Nursing Officer
Web address: www.mercyweb.org
Control: Church–operated, Nongovernment, not–for profit **Service:** General Medical and Surgical

Staffed Beds: 20 **Admissions:** 707 **Census:** 9 **Outpatient Visits:** 38481 **Births:** 0 **Total Expense ($000):** 25110 **Payroll Expense ($000):** 8227 **Personnel:** 160

WILLOUGHBY—Lake County

☐ **WINDSOR–LAURELWOOD CENTER FOR BEHAVIORAL MEDICINE (364029)**, 35900 Euclid Avenue, Zip 44094–4648; tel. 440/953–3000 **A**1 9 10 **F**4 5 54 64 98 99 100 101 102 103 104 105 130 132 143 **S** Universal Health Services, Inc., King of Prussia, PA
Primary Contact: Ric McAllister, Chief Executive Officer
CFO: Robin Stough, Chief Financial Officer
CMO: Leonard Barley, M.D., Chief Medical Officer
CIO: Cory Wheatcraft, Information Technology and Purchasing Officer
CHR: Pam Connell, Manager Human Resources
Web address: www.windsorlaurelwood.com
Control: Corporation, Investor–owned, for–profit **Service:** Psychiatric

Staffed Beds: 159 **Admissions:** 4907 **Census:** 129 **Outpatient Visits:** 10854 **Births:** 0 **Total Expense ($000):** 30742 **Payroll Expense ($000):** 11804 **Personnel:** 257

WILMINGTON—Clinton County

☐ **CLINTON MEMORIAL HOSPITAL (360175)**, 610 West Main Street, Zip 45177–2125; tel. 937/382–6611, (Nonreporting) **A**1 2 3 5 9 10 **S** RegionalCare Hospital Partners, Brentwood, TN
Primary Contact: Jeff R. Egbert, Interim Chief Executive Officer
COO: Bradley Mabry, Chief Operating Officer
CHR: Janet M. Blair, Director Human Resources
CNO: Paul C. Poparad, R.N., Chief Nursing Officer
Web address: www.cmhregional.com
Control: Corporation, Investor–owned, for–profit **Service:** General Medical and Surgical

Staffed Beds: 85

WOOSTER—Wayne County

☐ △ **WOOSTER COMMUNITY HOSPITAL (360036)**, 1761 Beall Avenue, Zip 44691–2342; tel. 330/263–8100, (Nonreporting) **A**1 2 5 7 9 10 19 **S** QHR, Brentwood, TN
Primary Contact: William E. Sheron, Chief Executive Officer
Web address: www.woosterhospital.org
Control: City–Government, nonfederal **Service:** General Medical and Surgical

Staffed Beds: 152

WRIGHT–PATTERSON AFB—Greene County

✠ **WRIGHT PATTERSON MEDICAL CENTER**, 4881 Sugar Maple Drive, Zip 45433–5529; tel. 937/257–9144 **A**1 2 3 5 **F**3 4 5 7 8 11 12 13 14 15 18 19 20 21 29 30 31 32 33 34 35 36 38 39 40 41 43 45 48 49 50 52 53 55 56 57 58 59 60 61 64 65 68 70 74 75 76 77 78 79 81 86 87 90 93 97 98 99 100 101 102 103 104 107 108 109 110 111 115 116 117 119 120 121 123 124 129 130 132 134 135 144 146 147 **S** Department of the Air Force, Washington, DC
Primary Contact: Brent Erickson, Administrator
COO: Brent Erickson, Administrator
CFO: Major Kelly Lesnick, Resource Manager Flight Commander
CMO: Gregory Sweitzer, Chief Medical Officer
CIO: John Beighle, Flight Medical Information Systems
CHR: Hubert Chatman, Chief Civilian Personnel
CNO: Colonel Daniel Gerke, Chief Nursing Officer
Web address: www.wpafb.af.mil/units/wpmc/
Control: Air Force, Government, federal **Service:** General Medical and Surgical

Staffed Beds: 62 **Admissions:** 3421 **Census:** 19 **Outpatient Visits:** 247171 **Births:** 379 **Total Expense ($000):** 128250 **Payroll Expense ($000):** 31459 **Personnel:** 1740

Hospital, Medicare Provider Number, Address, Telephone, Approval, Facility, and Physician Codes, Health Care System

★ American Hospital Association (AHA) membership
☐ The Joint Commission accreditation
◇ DNV Healthcare Inc. accreditation
○ Healthcare Facilities Accreditation Program
△ Commission on Accreditation of Rehabilitation Facilities (CARF) accreditation

OH

XENIA—Greene County

★ ○ **GREENE MEMORIAL HOSPITAL (360026)**, 1141 North Monroe Drive, Zip 45385–1600; tel. 937/352-2000 **A**3 5 9 10 11 **F**3 11 15 18 28 29 30 31 34 35 38 40 43 44 45 46 48 50 53 54 56 57 59 60 64 68 69 70 74 75 77 78 79 81 82 85 86 87 93 96 102 107 108 110 111 114 119 129 130 135 144 146 148 **S** Kettering Health Network, Dayton, OH
Primary Contact: Terry M. Burns, President
COO: Ron D. Connovich, Vice President
CFO: Ron D. Connovich, Chief Financial Officer
CMO: David Small, M.D., Chief Medical Officer
CIO: Andy Lehman, Chief Information Officer
CHR: Amanda Koch, Director Human Resources
CNO: Belinda Mallett, R.N., Vice President Patient Care and Clinical Services
Web address: www.greenehealth.org
Control: Church-operated, Nongovernment, not-for profit **Service:** General Medical and Surgical

Staffed Beds: 52 **Admissions:** 2591 **Census:** 27 **Outpatient Visits:** 97679 **Births:** 0 **Total Expense ($000):** 64097 **Payroll Expense ($000):** 24912 **Personnel:** 359

YOUNGSTOWN—Trumbull County

☐ **BELMONT PINES HOSPITAL (364038)**, 615 Churchill–Hubbard Road, Zip 44505–1379; tel. 330/759-2700, (Nonreporting) **A**1 9 10 **S** Universal Health Services, Inc., King of Prussia, PA
Primary Contact: George H. Perry, Ph.D., Chief Executive Officer
CFO: Robin Stough, Chief Financial Officer
CMO: Phillip Maiden, M.D., Medical Director
Web address: www.belmontpines.com
Control: Corporation, Investor-owned, for-profit **Service:** Psychiatric

Staffed Beds: 46

⊞ **NORTHSIDE MEDICAL CENTER (360141)**, 500 Gypsy Lane, Zip 44504–1315; tel. 330/884-1000, (Includes NORTHSIDE MEDICAL CENTER, 500 Gypsy Lane, Zip 44501–0240; tel. 330/747-1444), (Nonreporting) **A**1 3 5 9 10 **S** Community Health Systems, Inc., Franklin, TN
Primary Contact: W. Trent Crable, Chief Executive Officer
COO: Michael Seelman, Chief Operating Officer
CMO: Jay Osborne, M.D., Senior Vice President Medical Affairs
CHR: Lavern H. Carrera, Senior Vice President Human Resources
Web address: www.northsidemedicalcenter.net
Control: Corporation, Investor-owned, for-profit **Service:** General Medical and Surgical

Staffed Beds: 373

NORTHSIDE MEDICAL CENTER See Northside Medical Center

⊞ **SELECT SPECIALTY HOSPITAL–YOUNGSTOWN (362024)**, 1044 Belmont Avenue, Zip 44504–1006; tel. 330/480-2349, (Includes SELECT SPECIALTY HOSPITAL–YOUNGSTOWN, BOARDMAN CAMPUS, 8401 Market Street, 7th Floor, Bordman, Zip 44512–6725; Mailing Address: Youngstown, tel. 330/729-1700), (Nonreporting) **A**1 10 **S** Select Medical Corporation, Mechanicsburg, PA
Primary Contact: Sharon Noro, Chief Executive Officer
Web address: www.selectspecialtyhospitals.com/company/locations/youngstown.aspx
Control: Corporation, Investor-owned, for-profit **Service:** Long-Term Acute Care hospital

Staffed Beds: 51

⊞ △ **ST. ELIZABETH HEALTH CENTER (360064)**, 1044 Belmont Avenue, Zip 44504–1096, Mailing Address: P.O. Box 1790, Zip 44501–1790; tel. 330/746-7211 **A**1 3 5 7 9 10 **F**1 3 7 8 11 12 13 14 15 17 18 20 22 24 26 28 29 30 31 34 35 39 40 42 43 44 45 46 47 49 50 51 53 54 56 57 58 59 60 61 64 66 68 70 71 74 75 76 77 78 79 81 82 84 85 86 87 88 89 90 93 96 97 98 100 101 102 103 107 108 110 111 114 117 118 119 120 121 123 124 126 129 130 131 132 135 143 146 147 148 **P**3 **S** Mercy Health, Cincinnati, OH
Primary Contact: Robert W. Shroder, President and Chief Executive Officer
COO: Donald E. Koenig, Jr., Executive Vice President and Chief Operating Officer
CFO: Matt Love, Senior Vice President Finance
CMO: Nicholas Kreatsoulas, M.D., Senior Vice President and Chief Medical Officer and Chief Quality Officer
CIO: Maureen Kordupel, Director Relationship Manager
CHR: Scott Dimmick, Senior Vice President Human Resources
CNO: Catherine L. Tolbert, R.N., Senior Vice President Nursing and Clinical Services and Chief Nurse Executive
Web address: www.hmpartners.org
Control: Church-operated, Nongovernment, not-for profit **Service:** General Medical and Surgical

Staffed Beds: 405 **Admissions:** 18404 **Census:** 248 **Outpatient Visits:** 284508 **Births:** 1925 **Total Expense ($000):** 297129 **Payroll Expense ($000):** 94244 **Personnel:** 1761

☐ **SURGICAL HOSPITAL AT SOUTHWOODS (360352)**, 7630 Southern Boulevard, Zip 44512–5633; tel. 330/729-8000, (Nonreporting) **A**1 9 10
Primary Contact: Ed Muransky, Owner
Web address: www.surgeryatsouthwoods.com/
Control: Individual, Investor-owned, for-profit **Service:** Surgical

Staffed Beds: 12

ZANESVILLE—Muskingum County

★ ○ △ **GENESIS HEALTHCARE SYSTEM (360039)**, 2951 Maple Avenue, Zip 43701–1406; tel. 740/454-5000, (Includes BETHESDA HOSPITAL, 2951 Maple Avenue, Zip 43701–1465; tel. 614/454-4000; GOOD SAMARITAN MEDICAL AND REHABILITATION CENTER, 800 Forest Avenue, Zip 43701–2881; tel. 614/454-5000) **A**2 5 7 9 10 11 19 20 **F**3 5 8 11 13 15 17 18 20 22 24 26 28 29 30 31 32 34 35 36 40 43 44 45 46 47 48 50 51 54 58 59 60 63 64 65 68 70 73 74 75 76 77 78 79 80 81 82 83 84 85 86 87 89 90 91 92 93 94 96 98 99 100 101 102 103 104 105 107 108 109 110 111 114 115 116 117 118 119 120 121 123 124 126 129 130 131 132 135 144 146 147 148 **P**6 8 **S** Franciscan Sisters of Christian Charity Sponsored Ministries, Inc., Manitowoc, WI
Primary Contact: Matthew J. Perry, President and Chief Executive Officer
COO: Richard S. Helsper, Chief Operating Officer
CFO: Paul Masterson, Chief Financial Officer
CMO: Dan Scheerer, M.D., Chief Medical Officer
CIO: Edmund J. Romito, Chief Information Officer
CHR: Dianna LeVeck, Chief Human Resources Officer
CNO: Abby Nguyen, R.N., Chief Nursing Officer
Web address: www.genesishcs.org
Control: Other not-for-profit (including NFP Corporation) **Service:** General Medical and Surgical

Staffed Beds: 312 **Admissions:** 15312 **Census:** 169 **Outpatient Visits:** 382180 **Births:** 1405 **Total Expense ($000):** 311337 **Payroll Expense ($000):** 116810 **Personnel:** 2741

⊞ **SELECT SPECIALTY HOSPITAL–ZANESVILLE (362031)**, 800 Forest Avenue, 6th Floor, Zip 43701–2882; tel. 740/588-7888, (Nonreporting) **A**1 10 **S** Select Medical Corporation, Mechanicsburg, PA
Primary Contact: Linda Supplee, Chief Executive Officer
CMO: Armand Bermudez, M.D., Medical Director
CHR: Jacqueline Nezbeth, Human Resources Officer
CNO: Taryn Vierling, Chief Nursing Officer
Web address: www.selectspecialtyhospitals.com/company/locations/zanesville.aspx
Control: Corporation, Investor-owned, for-profit **Service:** Long-Term Acute Care hospital

Staffed Beds: 35

OKLAHOMA

ADA—Pontotoc County

⊞ **CHICKASAW NATION MEDICAL CENTER (370180)**, 1921 Stonecipher Drive, Zip 74820–3439; tel. 580/436–3980 **A**1 10 **F**3 5 7 8 13 15 18 29 30 34 38 39 40 43 45 50 53 54 57 58 59 60 61 64 65 66 68 69 70 75 76 79 81 82 85 86 87 89 91 92 93 97 99 100 104 107 110 111 114 119 127 130 132 135 143 144 146 147 148
Primary Contact: Judy Goforth Parker, Ph.D., Secretary of Health
CFO: Marty Wafford, Executive Officer of Support and Programs
CMO: Richard McClain, M.D., Chief Medical Officer
CIO: Desiree Traylor, Chief Information Officer
CHR: Jalinda Kelley, Secretary of Interior Services
CNO: Jerod Waters, Chief Nursing Officer
Web address: www.chickasaw.net
Control: PHS, Indian Service, Government, federal **Service:** General Medical and Surgical

Staffed Beds: 72 **Admissions:** 3082 **Census:** 26 **Outpatient Visits:** 521151 **Births:** 747 **Total Expense ($000):** 148554 **Payroll Expense ($000):** 61815 **Personnel:** 495

⊞ **MERCY HOSPITAL ADA (370020)**, 430 North Monte Vista, Zip 74820–4610; tel. 580/332–2323, (Data for 276 days) **A**1 2 9 10 19 20 **F**3 7 11 13 15 18 29 30 31 32 34 35 40 41 43 49 59 69 70 72 75 76 77 78 79 81 85 87 89 90 93 98 100 101 102 103 104 107 110 111 114 116 119 120 121 124 127 129 130 131 133 145 146 147 148 **P**6 **S** Mercy Health, Chesterfield, MO
Primary Contact: Diana Smalley, Acting Interim Chief Executive Officer
COO: Daniel J. Coats, Vice President Operations
CFO: Mary Garber, Vice President Finance
CMO: Imtiaz Ahmed, Chief of Staff
CHR: Katrina Godfrey, Director Human Resources
CNO: Karen Sweeney, MSN, Vice President, Chief Nursing Officer
Web address: www.mercy.net/ada
Control: Church–operated, Nongovernment, not–for profit **Service:** General Medical and Surgical

Staffed Beds: 156 **Admissions:** 4072 **Census:** 56 **Outpatient Visits:** 55105 **Births:** 340 **Total Expense ($000):** 51796 **Payroll Expense ($000):** 21599 **Personnel:** 557

☐ **ROLLING HILLS HOSPITAL (374016)**, 1000 Rolling Hills Lane, Zip 74820–9415; tel. 580/436–3600, (Nonreporting) **A**1 9 10 **S** Acadia Healthcare Company, Inc., Franklin, TN
Primary Contact: Selena Stockley, Chief Executive Officer
CMO: Robert Morton, M.D., Medical Director
CIO: Sherry Barnes, Director Health Information and Quality Management
CHR: Timothy Blackwell, Manager Human Resources
Web address: www.rollinghillshospital.com
Control: Corporation, Investor–owned, for–profit **Service:** Psychiatric

Staffed Beds: 44

ALTUS—Jackson County

⊞ **JACKSON COUNTY MEMORIAL HOSPITAL (370022)**, 1200 East Pecan Street, Zip 73521–6192, Mailing Address: P.O. Box 8190, Zip 73522–8190; tel. 580/379–5000 **A**1 3 5 9 10 19 20 **F**3 10 11 13 15 29 30 34 35 40 43 45 49 56 57 59 62 63 64 65 68 70 75 76 77 79 81 85 86 87 93 100 101 103 104 107 110 111 114 119 129 130 132 133 135 145 146 147 148 **P**6
Primary Contact: Steve L. Hartgraves, President and Chief Executive Officer
COO: Jim King, Executive Vice President and Chief Operating Officer
CFO: Nancy Davidson, Senior Vice President and Chief Financial Officer
CMO: M. George Zakhary, M.D., Chief of Staff
CIO: Dena Daniel, Director Information Systems
CHR: Richard Pope, Vice President Human Resources
CNO: Kay Bolding, R.N., Vice President Patient Care Services and Chief Nursing Officer
Web address: www.jcmh.com
Control: Hospital district or authority, Government, nonfederal **Service:** General Medical and Surgical

Staffed Beds: 69 **Admissions:** 3467 **Census:** 34 **Outpatient Visits:** 137117 **Births:** 481 **Total Expense ($000):** 68957 **Payroll Expense ($000):** 34090 **Personnel:** 705

ALVA—Woods County

SHARE MEDICAL CENTER (370080), 800 Share Drive, Zip 73717–3618, Mailing Address: P.O. Box 727, Zip 73717–0727; tel. 580/327–2800, (Total facility includes 65 beds in nursing home–type unit) **A**9 10 20 **F**3 15 29 30 34 40 45 57 59 63 64 67 69 81 85 87 93 97 100 102 104 107 110 119 129 130 133 146 148
Primary Contact: Kandice K. Allen, R.N., Chief Executive Officer
CFO: Kevin O'Brien, Chief Financial Officer
CMO: Elizabeth Kinzic, M.D., Chief of Staff
CIO: Alan Vaughan, IT Director
CHR: Mary Herold, Director Human Resources
CNO: Regina Wilson, R.N., Director of Nursing
Web address: www.smcok.com
Control: Hospital district or authority, Government, nonfederal **Service:** General Medical and Surgical

Staffed Beds: 90 **Admissions:** 202 **Census:** 59 **Outpatient Visits:** 20877 **Births:** 0 **Total Expense ($000):** 10214 **Payroll Expense ($000):** 4077 **Personnel:** 160

ANADARKO—Caddo County

PHYSICIANS' HOSPITAL IN ANADARKO (371314), 1002 Central Boulevard East, Zip 73005–4496; tel. 405/247–2551 **A**9 10 18 **F**3 8 11 29 35 40 45 47 85 93 107 114 130 133 146 **S** Southern Plains Medical Group, Oklahoma City, OK
Primary Contact: Jamey Lykins, Interim Chief Executive Officer
Web address: www.anadarkohospital.com
Control: Corporation, Investor–owned, for–profit **Service:** General Medical and Surgical

Staffed Beds: 25 **Admissions:** 318 **Census:** 3 **Outpatient Visits:** 6114 **Births:** 1

ANTLERS—Pushmataha County

PUSHMATAHA HOSPITAL & HOME HEALTH (370083), 510 East Main Street, Zip 74523–3262, Mailing Address: P.O. Box 518, Zip 74523–0518; tel. 580/298–3341, (Nonreporting) **A**9 10
Primary Contact: Paul Reano, Chief Executive Officer
COO: Nick Rowland, Chief Operating Officer
CFO: Rory Ward, Chief Financial Officer
CMO: G. Wayne Flatt, D.O., Chief Medical Director
CHR: Paula Schalski, Director Human Resources
CNO: Marla Barnes, Director of Nursing
Web address: www.pushhospital.com
Control: State–Government, nonfederal **Service:** General Medical and Surgical

Staffed Beds: 33

ARDMORE—Carter County

⊞ **MERCY HOSPITAL ARDMORE (370047)**, 1011 14th Avenue N.W., Zip 73401–1828; tel. 580/223–5400 **A**1 9 10 19 20 **F**3 8 11 13 15 18 20 22 28 29 30 31 34 40 41 43 45 57 59 62 70 74 76 78 79 81 82 83 84 85 87 89 90 93 107 108 110 111 114 117 118 119 120 121 123 129 130 146 148 **P**6 **S** Mercy Health, Chesterfield, MO
Primary Contact: Daryle Voss, FACHE, President
CFO: Karen Hendren, Vice President of Finance and Operations
CMO: Pam Kimbrough, M.D., Vice President Medical Affairs
CHR: Melinda Sharum, Director of Human Resources
CNO: Debra Pender, R.N., Vice President of Nursing
Web address: www.mercyok.net
Control: Church–operated, Nongovernment, not–for profit **Service:** General Medical and Surgical

Staffed Beds: 190 **Admissions:** 8642 **Census:** 97 **Outpatient Visits:** 120686 **Births:** 906 **Total Expense ($000):** 121101 **Payroll Expense ($000):** 38100 **Personnel:** 738

Hospital, Medicare Provider Number, Address, Telephone, Approval, Facility, and Physician Codes, Health Care System

★ American Hospital Association (AHA) membership
☐ The Joint Commission accreditation
◇ DNV Healthcare Inc. accreditation
○ Healthcare Facilities Accreditation Program
△ Commission on Accreditation of Rehabilitation Facilities (CARF) accreditation

OK

ATOKA—Atoka County

★ **ATOKA COUNTY MEDICAL CENTER (371300)**, 1501 South Virginia Avenue, Zip 74525–3233; tel. 580/889–3333 **A**9 10 18 **F**3 34 40 45 46 53 56 57 59 64 81 85 103 104 107 114 119 133 146
Primary Contact: Paul Reano, Chief Executive Officer
CFO: Jamie McGaugh, Controller
CMO: Lance Yarbrough, M.D., Chief of Medical Staff
CIO: Chad Henderson, Director Information Systems
CHR: Paula Schalski, Director Human Resources
CNO: Lezley Davidson, Chief Nursing Officer
Web address: www.atokamedicalcenter.org
Control: Hospital district or authority, Government, nonfederal **Service:** General Medical and Surgical

Staffed Beds: 25 **Admissions:** 734 **Census:** 6 **Outpatient Visits:** 11922 **Births:** 2 **Total Expense ($000):** 11732 **Payroll Expense ($000):** 3139 **Personnel:** 72

BARTLESVILLE—Washington County

★ ◇ **JANE PHILLIPS MEDICAL CENTER (370018)**, 3500 East Frank Phillips Boulevard, Zip 74006–2411; tel. 918/333–7200 **A**3 5 9 10 19 20 21 **F**3 8 11 13 15 17 18 20 22 24 28 29 30 31 34 35 40 43 46 49 50 51 53 57 58 59 60 61 62 64 68 74 75 76 77 78 79 81 82 84 85 86 87 90 92 93 96 98 102 103 107 111 114 115 116 117 118 119 121 123 127 129 130 131 135 143 145 146 147 148 **P**4 **S** Ascension Health, Saint Louis, MO
Primary Contact: David R. Stire, President and Chief Executive Officer
CFO: Mike Moore, Chief Financial Officer
CIO: Rob Poole, Director
CHR: Jennifer Workman, Director Human Resources
Web address: www.jpmc.org
Control: Church–operated, Nongovernment, not–for profit **Service:** General Medical and Surgical

Staffed Beds: 119 **Admissions:** 4684 **Census:** 52 **Outpatient Visits:** 87891 **Births:** 724 **Total Expense ($000):** 99913 **Payroll Expense ($000):** 38936 **Personnel:** 679

BEAVER—Beaver County

BEAVER COUNTY MEMORIAL HOSPITAL (371322), 212 East Eighth Street, Zip 73932, Mailing Address: P.O. Box 640, Zip 73932–0640; tel. 580/625–4551, (Nonreporting) **A**9 10 18
Primary Contact: Alissa Schlessman, Administrator
CMO: Gary Mathews, M.D., Medical Doctor
CHR: Karla Leisher, Business Office Manager
CNO: Stacey Perry, Director of Nursing
Web address: www.beavercountyhospitalauthority.org
Control: Hospital district or authority, Government, nonfederal **Service:** General Medical and Surgical

Staffed Beds: 24

BETHANY—Oklahoma County

△ **THE CHILDREN'S CENTER (373302)**, 6800 N.W. 39th Expressway, Zip 73008–2513; tel. 405/789–6711 **A**7 9 10 **F**1 29 35 39 53 59 75 79 90 91 93 107 130 146 148 **P**6
Primary Contact: Albert Gray, Chief Executive Officer
Web address: www.thechildrens–center.org
Control: Other not–for–profit (including NFP Corporation) **Service:** Children's general

Staffed Beds: 120 **Admissions:** 187 **Census:** 101 **Outpatient Visits:** 10375 **Births:** 0 **Total Expense ($000):** 27198 **Payroll Expense ($000):** 17562 **Personnel:** 443

BLACKWELL—Kay County

⊞ **INTEGRIS BLACKWELL REGIONAL HOSPITAL (370030)**, 710 South 13th Street, Zip 74631–3700; tel. 580/363–2311 **A**1 9 10 **F**3 15 29 30 34 40 57 59 62 64 65 79 81 107 108 111 119 128 129 130 133 146 **P**5 6 **S** Community Health Systems, Inc., Franklin, TN
Primary Contact: Andrew Wachtel, Chief Executive Officer
CFO: Sheryl Schmidtberger, Chief Financial Officer
CMO: Samuel Hague, M.D., Chief of Staff
CHR: Karen Ware, Director Human Resources
Web address: www.integris–health.com
Control: Corporation, Investor–owned, for–profit **Service:** General Medical and Surgical

Staffed Beds: 49 **Admissions:** 759 **Census:** 7 **Outpatient Visits:** 14407 **Total Expense ($000):** 11113 **Payroll Expense ($000):** 3534 **Personnel:** 88

BOISE CITY—Cimarron County

CIMARRON MEMORIAL HOSPITAL (371307), 100 South Ellis Street, Zip 73933; tel. 580/544–2501 **A**9 10 18 **F**15 29 32 34 40 50 57 59 65 66 68 75 85 89 90 93 97 107 113 127 129 130 133 148
Primary Contact: Tim Beard, Interim Chief Executive Officer
CFO: Darin A. Janssen, Chief Financial Officer
CIO: Tim Beard, Director, Information Technology
Web address: www.cimarronmemorialhospital.org
Control: County–Government, nonfederal **Service:** General Medical and Surgical

Staffed Beds: 25 **Admissions:** 157 **Census:** 2

BRISTOW—Creek County

BRISTOW MEDICAL CENTER (370041), 700 West 7th Avenue, Suite 6, Zip 74010–2302; tel. 918/367–2215, (Nonreporting) **A**9 10
Primary Contact: Jan Winter, Chief Executive Officer
CFO: Robin Van Vickle, Chief Financial Officer
Web address: www.bristowmedcenter.com
Control: Corporation, Investor–owned, for–profit **Service:** General Medical and Surgical

Staffed Beds: 17

BROKEN ARROW—Tulsa County

★ ◇ **ST. JOHN BROKEN ARROW (370235)**, 1000 West Boise Circle, Zip 74012–4900; tel. 918/994–8100 **A**9 10 21 **F**3 8 11 14 15 18 29 30 34 35 37 40 45 50 57 59 64 68 74 79 81 84 85 87 89 93 94 107 108 110 111 114 115 119 130 132 135 146 **P**1 5 **S** Ascension Health, Saint Louis, MO
Primary Contact: David L. Phillips, Chief Executive Officer
CFO: Michael R. Nevins, Chief Financial Officer
CMO: Todd Hoffman, M.D., Medical Director
CNO: Dwan Borens, Director of Nursing
Web address: www.stjohnbrokenarrow.com
Control: Church–operated, Nongovernment, not–for profit **Service:** General Medical and Surgical

Staffed Beds: 44 **Admissions:** 2549 **Census:** 15 **Outpatient Visits:** 62805 **Births:** 0 **Total Expense ($000):** 51651 **Payroll Expense ($000):** 11849 **Personnel:** 262

BUFFALO—Harper County

★ **HARPER COUNTY COMMUNITY HOSPITAL (371324)**, Highway 64 North, Zip 73834, Mailing Address: P.O. Box 60, Zip 73834–0060; tel. 580/735–2555 **A**9 10 18 **F**40 68 69 75 89 93 97 107 128 133 135 **P**6
Primary Contact: Georganna Buss, Chief Executive Officer
COO: Pam Dodd, Chief Operating Officer
CFO: Lisa Oakley, Chief Financial Officer
CNO: Melissa Madrid, R.N., Chief Nursing Officer
Web address: www.hcchospital.com/
Control: County–Government, nonfederal **Service:** General Medical and Surgical

Staffed Beds: 16 **Admissions:** 171 **Census:** 2 **Births:** 0

CARNEGIE—Caddo County

CARNEGIE TRI–COUNTY MUNICIPAL HOSPITAL (371334), 102 North Broadway, Zip 73015, Mailing Address: P.O. Box 97, Zip 73015–0097; tel. 580/654–1050, (Nonreporting) **A**9 10 18
Primary Contact: Shane Dunning, Administrator
Control: City–Government, nonfederal **Service:** General Medical and Surgical

Staffed Beds: 19

CHEYENNE—Roger Mills County

★ **ROGER MILLS MEMORIAL HOSPITAL (371303)**, Fifth and L. L Males Avenue, Zip 73628; tel. 580/497–3336 **A**9 10 18 **F**3 7 34 40 57 59 65 75 107 114 127 130 133
Primary Contact: Marilyn Bryan, Chief Executive Officer
CFO: Lois Wilson, Controller
Web address: www.rogermillsmemorialhospital.com/
Control: Hospital district or authority, Government, nonfederal **Service:** General Medical and Surgical

Staffed Beds: 15 **Admissions:** 38 **Census:** 1 **Outpatient Visits:** 3106 **Births:** 0 **Total Expense ($000):** 4171 **Payroll Expense ($000):** 2225 **Personnel:** 51

Many Facility Codes have changed. Please refer to the AHA Guide Code Chart.   © 2014 AHA Guide

CHICKASHA—Grady County

★ **GRADY MEMORIAL HOSPITAL (370054)**, 2220 West Iowa Avenue,
Zip 73018–2738; tel. 405/224–2300 **A**5 9 10 19 20 **F**3 8 11 13 15 17 29 30
34 35 40 43 45 57 59 65 68 69 70 73 76 79 81 82 85 89 91 93 107 110
111 114 115 119 127 128 129 130 132 133 144 146 147 **P**6
Primary Contact: Warren K. Spellman, Chief Executive Officer
CFO: Linda Hart, Vice President Finance
CMO: Thomas Essex, M.D., Chief of Staff
CIO: Sylvia Ho, Director Information Services
Web address: www.gradymem.org
Control: Hospital district or authority, Government, nonfederal **Service:** General
Medical and Surgical

Staffed Beds: 52 **Admissions:** 1556 **Census:** 14 **Outpatient Visits:** 84188
Births: 270 **Total Expense ($000):** 42903 **Payroll Expense ($000):** 21004
Personnel: 328

CLAREMORE—Rogers County

☐ **CLAREMORE INDIAN HOSPITAL (370173)**, 101 South Moore Avenue,
Zip 74017–5091; tel. 918/342–6200, (Nonreporting) **A**1 5 10 **S** U. S. Indian
Health Service, Rockville, MD
Primary Contact: George Valliere, Chief Executive Officer
CFO: LaLana Spears, Supervisor Accounting
CIO: David Ponder, Information Technology Officer
CHR: Quinn Proctor, Director Human Resources
CNO: Tamara Wampler, Chief Nursing Executive
Web address: www.ihs.gov
Control: PHS, Indian Service, Government, federal **Service:** General Medical and
Surgical

Staffed Beds: 46

★ **HILLCREST HOSPITAL CLAREMORE (370039)**, 1202 North Muskogee Place,
Zip 74017–3036; tel. 918/341–2556 **A**9 10 **F**3 11 13 15 18 20 22 26 28 29
30 34 35 37 40 45 49 51 59 64 70 74 76 77 79 81 82 85 86 87 93 98 103
107 108 110 111 119 126 128 129 130 131 133 135 145 146 147 148 **P**6
S Ardent Health Services, Nashville, TN
Primary Contact: David Chaussard, Chief Executive Officer
CFO: Brandon Bullard, Chief Financial Officer
CIO: Celeste Rodden, Chief Information Officer
CHR: Pat Goad, Director Human Resources
CNO: Randy Walker, Chief Nursing Officer
Web address: www.hillcrestclaremore.com
Control: Corporation, Investor–owned, for–profit **Service:** General Medical and
Surgical

Staffed Beds: 55 **Admissions:** 3272 **Census:** 33 **Outpatient Visits:** 37239
Births: 687 **Total Expense ($000):** 37269 **Payroll Expense ($000):** 14679
Personnel: 303

CLEVELAND—Pawnee County

★ **CLEVELAND AREA HOSPITAL (371320)**, 1401 West Pawnee Street,
Zip 74020–3019; tel. 918/358–2501 **A**9 10 18 **F**11 12 15 29 34 35 40 53 57
59 64 77 81 87 89 93 107 110 114 119 130 133 148
Primary Contact: Yonna Creason, R.N., Chief Executive Officer
COO: Yonna Creason, R.N., Chief Executive Officer
CMO: Jason Sims, M.D., Chief Medical Officer
CHR: Sherry Brown, Director Human Resources
Web address: www.clevelandareahospital.com
Control: Hospital district or authority, Government, nonfederal **Service:** General
Medical and Surgical

Staffed Beds: 14 **Admissions:** 196 **Census:** 4

CLINTON—Custer County

✠ **INTEGRIS CLINTON REGIONAL HOSPITAL (370029)**, 100 North 30th Street,
Zip 73601–3117, Mailing Address: P.O. Box 1569, Zip 73601–1569;
tel. 580/323–2363 **A**1 9 10 **F**3 11 13 29 30 31 34 35 40 45 59 62 63 68 70
75 76 77 78 81 90 93 107 108 111 119 121 123 129 130 131 133 146 147
148 **P**6 **S** Community Health Systems, Inc., Franklin, TN
Primary Contact: Robin E. Lake, Chief Executive Officer
CFO: Richard Foster, Chief Financial Officer
Web address: www.integris–health.com
Control: Corporation, Investor–owned, for–profit **Service:** General Medical and
Surgical

Staffed Beds: 49 **Admissions:** 1478 **Census:** 13 **Outpatient Visits:** 23821
Births: 307

COALGATE—Coal County

★ **COAL COUNTY GENERAL HOSPITAL (371319)**, 6 North Covington Street,
Zip 74538–2002, Mailing Address: P.O. Box 326, Zip 74538–0326;
tel. 580/927–2327, (Nonreporting) **A**10 18
Primary Contact: Billy Johnson, Chief Executive Officer
CFO: Diane Downard, Chief Financial Officer
CMO: R.J Helton, D.O., Chief of Staff
CIO: Matt Balliett, Chief Information Officer
CHR: Cyndie Martin, Director
CNO: Farra Ybarra, R.N., Chief Nursing Officer
Web address: www.hillcrest.com
Control: Other not–for–profit (including NFP Corporation) **Service:** General
Medical and Surgical

Staffed Beds: 92

CORDELL—Washita County

★ **CORDELL MEMORIAL HOSPITAL (371325)**, 1220 North Glenn English Street,
Zip 73632–2010; tel. 580/832–3339 **A**9 10 18 **F**7 40 57 59 65 89 107
128 133
Primary Contact: Landon Hise, Chief Executive Officer
CFO: Sue Kelley, Chief Financial Officer
Control: City–Government, nonfederal **Service:** General Medical and Surgical

Staffed Beds: 25 **Admissions:** 295 **Census:** 3 **Outpatient Visits:** 4705
Births: 0 **Total Expense ($000):** 4027 **Payroll Expense ($000):** 1774
Personnel: 42

CUSHING—Payne County

★ **HILLCREST HOSPITAL CUSHING (370099)**, 1027 East Cherry Street,
Zip 74023–4101, Mailing Address: P.O. Box 1409, Zip 74023–1409;
tel. 918/225–2915 **A**9 10 **F**3 13 15 18 28 29 30 34 35 40 45 50 51 54 56
57 59 62 64 68 70 75 76 77 79 81 85 87 93 98 103 107 108 110 111 114
119 127 129 130 132 133 143 146 147 148 **S** Ardent Health Services,
Nashville, TN
Primary Contact: Kevin Hawk, Chief Executive Officer
CFO: Joseph Mendoza, Chief Financial Officer
CHR: Jennifer Strope, Manager Human Resources
Web address: www.hillcrestcushing.com/
Control: Corporation, Investor–owned, for–profit **Service:** General Medical and
Surgical

Staffed Beds: 95 **Admissions:** 1862 **Census:** 21 **Outpatient Visits:** 22159
Births: 184 **Total Expense ($000):** 26565 **Payroll Expense ($000):** 9707
Personnel: 177

DRUMRIGHT—Creek County

DRUMRIGHT REGIONAL HOSPITAL (371331), 610 West Bypass,
Zip 74030–5957; tel. 918/382–2300 **A**9 10 18 **F**3 18 29 34 35 40 45 57 59
64 77 79 81 93 107 108 111 114 116 117 119 127 129 130 133 148 **P**3 6
S Rural Community Hospitals of America, Kansas City, MO
Primary Contact: Darrel Morris, Chief Executive Officer
CFO: Mark Conrath, Chief Financial Officer
Web address: www.drumrighthospital.com
Control: Corporation, Investor–owned, for–profit **Service:** General Medical and
Surgical

Staffed Beds: 15 **Admissions:** 601 **Census:** 6 **Outpatient Visits:** 8236
Births: 0 **Total Expense ($000):** 9142 **Payroll Expense ($000):** 3942
Personnel: 70

DUNCAN—Stephens County

✠ △ **DUNCAN REGIONAL HOSPITAL (370023)**, 1407 North Whisenant Drive,
Zip 73533–1650, Mailing Address: P.O. Box 2000, Zip 73534–2000;
tel. 580/252–5300, (Total facility includes 16 beds in nursing home–type unit) **A**1
5 7 9 10 20 **F**3 11 13 15 18 28 29 30 34 35 40 43 45 50 57 59 62 63 64
70 75 76 77 79 81 85 86 87 90 93 96 98 103 104 107 108 110 111 114
115 119 128 129 130 131 132 141 142 143 145 146 147 148 **P**6
Primary Contact: Jay R. Johnson, FACHE, President and Chief Executive Officer
CFO: Douglas R. Volinski, Vice President and Chief Financial Officer
CIO: Roger Neal, Vice President and Chief Information Officer
CHR: Mark Rhoades, Vice President and Chief Human Resources Officer
CNO: Cindy Rauh, R.N., Vice President and Chief Nursing Officer
Web address: www.duncanregional.com
Control: Other not–for–profit (including NFP Corporation) **Service:** General
Medical and Surgical

Staffed Beds: 117 **Admissions:** 4555 **Census:** 58 **Outpatient Visits:** 106221
Births: 545 **Total Expense ($000):** 79637 **Payroll Expense ($000):** 31238
Personnel: 854

Hospital, Medicare Provider Number, Address, Telephone, Approval, Facility, and Physician Codes, Health Care System

★ American Hospital Association (AHA) membership
☐ The Joint Commission accreditation
◇ DNV Healthcare Inc. accreditation
○ Healthcare Facilities Accreditation Program
△ Commission on Accreditation of Rehabilitation Facilities (CARF) accreditation

OK

OK

DURANT—Bryan County

✠ **MEDICAL CENTER OF SOUTHEASTERN OKLAHOMA (370014)**, 1800 University Boulevard, Zip 74701–3006, Mailing Address: P.O. Box 1207, Zip 74702–1207; tel. 580/924–3080 **A**1 9 10 13 19 **F**3 11 12 13 15 17 18 20 28 29 39 40 45 51 59 62 70 74 75 76 79 80 81 85 86 89 107 108 110 111 115 118 119 126 129 130 135 145 146 147 148 **P**8 **S** Community Health Systems, Inc., Franklin, TN
Primary Contact: Patricia Dorris, Executive Director
CFO: Cindy Rios, Chief Financial Officer
CMO: Kevin Gordon, M.D., Chief of Staff
CIO: Katy Stinson, Director Information Services
Web address: www.mymcso.com
Control: Corporation, Investor–owned, for–profit **Service:** General Medical and Surgical

Staffed Beds: 148 **Admissions:** 5864 **Census:** 59 **Outpatient Visits:** 53147 **Births:** 1031 **Personnel:** 451

EDMOND—Oklahoma County

☐ **AMG SPECIALTY HOSPITAL–EDMOND (372005)**, 1100 East Ninth Street, Zip 73034–5755; tel. 405/341–8150, (Nonreporting) **A**1 9 10 **S** AMG Integrated Healthcare Management, Lafayette, LA
Primary Contact: Ginger Creech, Chief Executive Officer
CFO: Rowena Davidson, Manager Business Office
CMO: Brian Levy, M.D., Medical Director
CHR: Pam Grimes, Director Human Resources
Web address: www.amgedmond.com/
Control: Corporation, Investor–owned, for–profit **Service:** Long–Term Acute Care hospital

Staffed Beds: 37

EDMOND MEDICAL CENTER See OU Medical Center Edmond

✠ **INTEGRIS HEALTH EDMOND (370236)**, 4801 Integris Parkway, Zip 73034–8864; tel. 405/657–3000 **A**1 9 10 **F**3 11 13 15 18 20 22 26 29 30 34 35 38 40 43 44 45 46 49 50 53 56 57 59 60 64 68 70 74 75 76 78 79 81 82 85 87 92 93 97 100 102 107 110 111 115 119 130 132 135 146 147 148 **P**6 7 **S** INTEGRIS Health, Oklahoma City, OK
Primary Contact: Avilla Williams, MS, President
CNO: Angela K. Kamermayer, MS, Chief Nursing Officer
Web address: www.integrisok.com/edmond
Control: Other not–for–profit (including NFP Corporation) **Service:** General Medical and Surgical

Staffed Beds: 40 **Admissions:** 1353 **Census:** 12 **Outpatient Visits:** 23580 **Births:** 350 **Total Expense ($000):** 30730 **Payroll Expense ($000):** 10496 **Personnel:** 180

OU MEDICAL CENTER EDMOND See OU Medical Center, Oklahoma City

★ **SUMMIT MEDICAL CENTER (370225)**, 1800 South Renaissance Boulevard, Zip 73013–3023; tel. 405/359–2400, (Nonreporting) **A**9 10
Primary Contact: Curtis Summers, Chief Executive Officer
Web address: www.summitmedcenter.com/
Control: Corporation, Investor–owned, for–profit **Service:** Other specialty

Staffed Beds: 15

EL RENO—Canadian County

★ **MERCY HOSPITAL EL RENO (370011)**, 2115 Parkview Drive, Zip 73036–2199, Mailing Address: P.O. Box 129, Zip 73036–0129; tel. 405/262–2640 **A**9 10 **F**3 7 8 29 30 35 40 45 50 62 64 65 77 79 81 82 85 93 107 111 114 119 132 135 146 **S** Mercy Health, Chesterfield, MO
Primary Contact: Doug Danker, Administrator
CMO: Michael Dean Sullivan, M.D., Chief of Staff
CIO: Karen Heldreth, Director Data Processing
CHR: Wendy Ward, Director Human Resources
Web address: www.mercyok.net
Control: Church–operated, Nongovernment, not–for profit **Service:** General Medical and Surgical

Staffed Beds: 48 **Admissions:** 504 **Census:** 4 **Outpatient Visits:** 24412 **Births:** 0 **Total Expense ($000):** 12277 **Payroll Expense ($000):** 5938 **Personnel:** 119

PARKVIEW HOSPITAL See Mercy Hospital El Reno

ELK CITY—Beckham County

✠ **GREAT PLAINS REGIONAL MEDICAL CENTER (370019)**, 1801 West Third Street, Zip 73644–5145, Mailing Address: P.O. Box 2339, Zip 73648–2339; tel. 580/225–2511 **A**1 9 10 **F**3 11 13 15 18 20 22 26 29 30 31 34 35 40 43 47 50 51 56 57 59 62 64 68 70 75 76 77 78 79 81 82 85 86 87 89 91 93 96 98 100 101 102 103 107 108 110 111 115 118 119 120 121 123 129 130 131 132 133 135 143 146 147 148
Primary Contact: Corey Lively, Chief Executive Officer
COO: Misty Carter, Director Human Resources and Chief Operating Officer
CFO: Monica Scott, Chief Financial Officer
CIO: Terry Davis, Chief Information Officer
CHR: Misty Carter, Director Human Resources
CNO: Laura Kurzendoerfer, R.N., Chief Nursing Officer
Web address: www.gprmc-ok.com
Control: Other not–for–profit (including NFP Corporation) **Service:** General Medical and Surgical

Staffed Beds: 46 **Admissions:** 1924 **Census:** 21 **Outpatient Visits:** 55314 **Births:** 442 **Total Expense ($000):** 43943 **Payroll Expense ($000):** 16538 **Personnel:** 349

ENID—Garfield County

INTEGRIS BASS BEHAVIORAL HEALTH SYSTEM See Integris Bass Meadowlake

✠ **INTEGRIS BASS BAPTIST HEALTH CENTER (370016)**, 600 South Monroe Street, Zip 73701–7211, Mailing Address: P.O. Box 3168, Zip 73702–3168; tel. 580/233–2300 **A**1 5 9 10 13 19 **F**3 11 13 15 17 18 20 22 24 28 29 30 31 35 40 43 45 49 57 62 68 70 74 75 76 77 78 79 81 85 98 99 103 107 108 111 114 117 118 119 120 121 127 128 129 132 144 146 147 148 **S** INTEGRIS Health, Oklahoma City, OK
Primary Contact: Edward Herrman, FACHE, R.N., President
CFO: Duane Miller, Chief Financial Officer
CNO: Cynthia Leathers, R.N., Chief Nursing Officer
Web address: www.integris-health.com
Control: Other not–for–profit (including NFP Corporation) **Service:** General Medical and Surgical

Staffed Beds: 167 **Admissions:** 4956 **Census:** 94 **Personnel:** 734

☐ **INTEGRIS BASS PAVILION (372016)**, 401 South Third Street, Zip 73701–5737; tel. 580/249–4260 **A**1 9 10 **F**1 11 29 30 40 43 68 75 77 82 85 93 131 132 146 148
Primary Contact: Edward Herrman, FACHE, R.N., President
CFO: Duane Miller, Chief Financial Officer
CHR: Stacy Froese, Regional Director Human Resources
CNO: Cynthia Leathers, R.N., Chief Nursing Officer
Web address: www.integris-health.com/integris/en-us/locations/bass-enid
Control: Other not–for–profit (including NFP Corporation) **Service:** General Medical and Surgical

Staffed Beds: 24 **Admissions:** 217 **Census:** 16 **Births:** 0 **Personnel:** 61

☐ △ **ST. MARY'S REGIONAL MEDICAL CENTER (370026)**, 305 South Fifth Street, Zip 73701–5899, Mailing Address: P.O. Box 232, Zip 73702–0232; tel. 580/233–6100 **A**1 5 7 9 10 **F**3 11 13 15 17 18 20 22 26 28 29 30 31 34 35 39 40 43 45 51 53 54 57 59 60 64 68 69 70 73 74 75 76 77 78 79 81 82 85 86 87 89 90 92 93 96 100 107 108 110 111 114 115 118 119 129 130 131 132 135 146 147 **S** Universal Health Services, Inc., King of Prussia, PA
Primary Contact: Stanley D. Tatum, FACHE, Chief Executive Officer
COO: Krista Roberts, Chief Operating Officer
CFO: David Jamin, Chief Financial Officer
CMO: Tim Teske, D.O., Chief of Staff
CIO: Tracy Anderson, Chief Information Officer
CHR: Linda Hoag, Director Human Resources
CNO: Douglas W. Coffey, R.N., Chief Nursing Officer
Web address: www.stmarysregional.com
Control: Corporation, Investor–owned, for–profit **Service:** General Medical and Surgical

Staffed Beds: 150 **Admissions:** 5074 **Census:** 72 **Outpatient Visits:** 74683 **Births:** 376 **Total Expense ($000):** 76463 **Payroll Expense ($000):** 30925 **Personnel:** 469

EUFAULA—Mcintosh County

EPIC MEDICAL CENTER (370169), 1 Hospital Drive, Zip 74432–4010, Mailing Address: P.O. Box 629, Zip 74432–0629; tel. 918/689–2535 **A**9 10 **F**40 45
Primary Contact: Vicki Schaff, Chief Operating Officer
COO: Vicki Schaff, Chief Operating Officer
CHR: Sondra Edwards, Human Resources Supervisor
CNO: Sharon Scanlon, Chief Nursing Officer
Web address: www.epichealthcare.net
Control: Corporation, Investor–owned, for–profit **Service:** General Medical and Surgical

Staffed Beds: 33 **Admissions:** 121 **Census:** 1 **Outpatient Visits:** 11467 **Births:** 0 **Total Expense ($000):** 3483 **Payroll Expense ($000):** 1994 **Personnel:** 44

FAIRFAX—Osage County

★ **FAIRFAX COMMUNITY HOSPITAL (371318)**, Taft Avenue and Highway 18, Zip 74637–4028, Mailing Address: P.O. Box 219, Zip 74637–0219; tel. 918/642–3291 **A**9 10 18 **F**3 29 40 45 57 77 81 90 93 107 117 128 129 133 **S** Rural Community Hospitals of America, Kansas City, MO
Primary Contact: Tina Steele, Chief Executive Officer and Chief Financial Officer
COO: Linda Thompson, Chief Operating Officer
CFO: Tina Steele, Chief Executive Officer and Chief Financial Officer
CMO: Arman Janloo, M.D., Chief Medical Staff
CIO: Lisa Drymon, Manager
CHR: Sharon Binkley, Director Human Resources
Control: Corporation, Investor–owned, for–profit **Service:** General Medical and Surgical

Staffed Beds: 15 **Admissions:** 153 **Census:** 1 **Outpatient Visits:** 3721 **Births:** 1 **Total Expense ($000):** 5329 **Payroll Expense ($000):** 2589 **Personnel:** 43

FAIRFAX MEMORIAL HOSPITAL See Fairfax Community Hospital

FAIRVIEW—Major County

FAIRVIEW REGIONAL MEDICAL CENTER (371329), 523 East State Road, Zip 73737–1453, Mailing Address: P.O. Box 548, Zip 73737–0548; tel. 580/227–3721 **A**9 10 18 **F**3 28 34 40 43 45 57 59 64 65 69 75 77 81 82 84 85 91 93 107 114 127 128 131 133 135 146 **P**6
Primary Contact: Roger Knak, Administrator
CFO: Christie Schakelaar, Chief Financial Officer
CMO: Solomon Ali, M.D., Chief of Staff
CIO: Bob Maynard, Chief Information Officer
CNO: Tamara Eitzen, Chief Nursing Officer
Web address: www.fairviewregionalmedicalcenter.com
Control: Hospital district or authority, Government, nonfederal **Service:** General Medical and Surgical

Staffed Beds: 25 **Admissions:** 224 **Census:** 3 **Outpatient Visits:** 10013 **Births:** 0 **Total Expense ($000):** 5518 **Payroll Expense ($000):** 3110 **Personnel:** 73

FORT SILL—Comanche County

☒ **REYNOLDS ARMY COMMUNITY HOSPITAL**, 4301 Wilson Street, Zip 73503–4472; tel. 580/558–3000 **A**1 3 5 **F**3 5 7 8 12 13 15 29 30 32 33 34 35 37 38 39 40 43 44 45 50 56 57 59 64 65 68 71 74 75 76 77 79 81 82 85 87 93 96 97 100 101 102 104 107 108 110 111 115 118 119 129 130 131 132 135 143 144 146 147 **S** Department of the Army, Office of the Surgeon General, Falls Church, VA
Primary Contact: Colonel Noel J. Cardenas, FACHE, Commander and Chief Executive Officer
COO: Lieutenant Jennifer R. House, Chief Operations and Readiness
CFO: Lieutenant Colonel David Rollins, Chief Resource Management Division
CMO: Lieutenant Colonel Timothy Switaj, Deputy Commander for Clinical Services
CIO: Russell Seymour, Chief Information Management Division
CHR: Jacqueline V. Jones, Chief Civilian Personnel Branch
CNO: Lieutenant Colonel Richard A. Behr, Deputy Commander for Health Services
Web address: www.rach.sill.amedd.army.mil
Control: Army, Government, federal **Service:** General Medical and Surgical

Staffed Beds: 24 **Admissions:** 2323 **Census:** 14 **Total Expense ($000):** 130199

FORT SUPPLY— County

NORTHWEST CENTER FOR BEHAVIORAL HEALTH (374001), 1 Mi East Highway 270, Zip 73841; tel. 580/766–2311 **A**10 **F**5 98 102 104 106 **P**6 **S** Oklahoma Department of Mental Health and Substance Abuse Services, Oklahoma City, OK
Primary Contact: Trudy Hoffman, Executive Director
Web address: www.ncbhok.org/
Control: State–Government, nonfederal **Service:** Psychiatric

Staffed Beds: 28 **Admissions:** 737 **Census:** 25 **Outpatient Visits:** 41364 **Births:** 0 **Total Expense ($000):** 13330 **Payroll Expense ($000):** 6506 **Personnel:** 179

FREDERICK—Tillman County

★ **MEMORIAL HOSPITAL AND PHYSICIAN GROUP (370051)**, 319 East Josephine Avenue, Zip 73542–2220; tel. 580/335–7565, (Total facility includes 30 beds in nursing home–type unit) **A**9 10 20 **F**11 29 40 59 62 64 67 81 89 93 107 119 133 **P**5 6
Primary Contact: Cindy Duncan, Administrator and Chief Executive Officer
Web address: www.frederickhospital.com
Control: Hospital district or authority, Government, nonfederal **Service:** General Medical and Surgical

Staffed Beds: 55 **Admissions:** 480 **Census:** 33 **Outpatient Visits:** 24825 **Births:** 0

GROVE—Delaware County

☒ **INTEGRIS GROVE HOSPITAL (370113)**, 1001 East 18th Street, Zip 74344–2907; tel. 918/786–2243 **A**1 9 10 20 **F**3 7 11 13 29 30 40 54 57 62 64 70 77 79 81 85 107 110 111 114 119 125 129 146 147 **S** INTEGRIS Health, Oklahoma City, OK
Primary Contact: Chris Hammes, FACHE, Interim President
CFO: Valerie Reeves, Chief Financial Officer
CMO: James Rutter, M.D., Chief of Staff
CHR: Stacy Froese, Regional Director Human Resources
CNO: Angela Bidleman, R.N., Chief Nursing Officer
Web address: www.integris-health.com
Control: Other not–for–profit (including NFP Corporation) **Service:** General Medical and Surgical

Staffed Beds: 58 **Admissions:** 2543 **Census:** 21 **Outpatient Visits:** 48158 **Births:** 279 **Total Expense ($000):** 54575 **Payroll Expense ($000):** 18918 **Personnel:** 226

GUTHRIE—Logan County

★ **MERCY HOSPITAL LOGAN COUNTY (371317)**, 200 South Academy Road, Zip 73044–8727, Mailing Address: P.O. Box 1017, Zip 73044–1017; tel. 405/282–6700 **A**9 10 18 **F**3 8 11 15 29 30 34 40 41 43 49 50 59 62 63 64 65 75 77 79 81 85 93 97 107 110 111 114 119 127 129 130 131 133 144 146 148 **P**6 **S** Mercy Health, Chesterfield, MO
Primary Contact: Joshua Tucker, Administrator
CMO: Jignesh Veragiwala, Chief of Staff
CHR: Mary Jo Messelt, Senior Human Resources Manager
CNO: Kim Williams, R.N., Director of Nursing
Web address: www.mercy.net
Control: Church–operated, Nongovernment, not–for profit **Service:** General Medical and Surgical

Staffed Beds: 25 **Admissions:** 835 **Census:** 13 **Outpatient Visits:** 67481 **Births:** 0 **Total Expense ($000):** 19669 **Payroll Expense ($000):** 9981 **Personnel:** 160

GUYMON—Texas County

★ **MEMORIAL HOSPITAL OF TEXAS COUNTY (370138)**, 520 Medical Drive, Zip 73942–4438; tel. 580/338–6515 **A**9 10 20 **F**3 11 13 15 29 34 40 43 45 57 59 64 65 68 70 75 76 79 81 82 85 89 107 108 110 111 114 119 146 147 **P**6
Primary Contact: Julie West, Interim Chief Executive Officer
CFO: Michele Reust, Controller
CIO: Sheldon Spence, Director of Revenue Cycle, IT
CHR: Sarah Wagner, Human Resources Officer
CNO: Dondie Rodgers, Interim Chief Nursing Officer
Web address: www.mhtcguymon.org
Control: County–Government, nonfederal **Service:** General Medical and Surgical

Staffed Beds: 14 **Admissions:** 957 **Census:** 7 **Total Expense ($000):** 19118

HEALDTON—Carter County

★ **MERCY HOSPITAL HEALDTON (371310)**, 918 South 8th Street, Zip 73438–0928, Mailing Address: P.O. Box 928, Zip 73438–0928; tel. 580/229–0701 **A**9 10 18 **F**3 28 34 40 64 107 114 133 **P**6 **S** Mercy Health, Chesterfield, MO
Primary Contact: Jeremy A. Jones, Administrator
CMO: Mark Newey, D.O., Chief of Staff
CHR: Melinda Sharum, Director Human Resources
Web address: www.mercyok.com
Control: Church–operated, Nongovernment, not–for profit **Service:** General Medical and Surgical

Staffed Beds: 22 **Admissions:** 240 **Census:** 6 **Outpatient Visits:** 8960 **Births:** 0 **Total Expense ($000):** 5143 **Payroll Expense ($000):** 2596 **Personnel:** 43

HENRYETTA—Okmulgee County

★ **HILLCREST HOSPITAL HENRYETTA (370183)**, Dewey Bartlett & Main Streets, Zip 74437–6820, Mailing Address: P.O. Box 1269, Zip 74437–1269; tel. 918/650–1100 **A**9 10 **F**3 4 15 29 40 45 54 56 62 64 65 68 79 81 85 87 93 98 102 103 107 110 111 114 119 129 130 133 143 148 **P**6 **S** Ardent Health Services, Nashville, TN
Primary Contact: Dee Renshaw, Chief Executive Officer
CFO: Joseph Mendoza, Chief Financial Officer
Web address: www.hillcresthenryetta.com/
Control: Corporation, Investor–owned, for–profit **Service:** General Medical and Surgical

Staffed Beds: 41 **Admissions:** 1041 **Census:** 18 **Outpatient Visits:** 14065 **Births:** 8 **Total Expense ($000):** 14673 **Payroll Expense ($000):** 5961 **Personnel:** 102

OK

HOBART—Kiowa County

★ **ELKVIEW GENERAL HOSPITAL (370153)**, 429 West Elm Street,
Zip 73651–1615; tel. 580/726–3324 **A**9 10 20 **F**3 15 28 29 31 34 35 40 45
56 59 62 79 81 85 89 93 107 108 110 111 115 118 119 129 133 146
148 **P**6
Primary Contact: Lisa Hart, Chief Executive Officer
COO: Harold Moad, Chief Operating Officer
CFO: Lisa Hart, Chief Financial Officer
CMO: Samatha Jackson, M.D., Chief of Staff
CIO: Chris Clark, Chief Technology Officer
CHR: Sharon Moad, Director Personnel
Web address: www.elkviewhospital.com
Control: Hospital district or authority, Government, nonfederal **Service:** General
Medical and Surgical

Staffed Beds: 38 **Admissions:** 1219 **Census:** 12 **Total Expense ($000):** 13736	

HOLDENVILLE—Hughes County

★ **HOLDENVILLE GENERAL HOSPITAL (371321)**, 100 McDougal Drive,
Zip 74848–2822; tel. 405/379–4200 **A**9 10 18 **F**3 11 29 30 40 45 57 59 64
65 81 82 93 97 107 111 115 127 133 135 146 148 **P**6
Primary Contact: Roberta Jeffrey, Chief Executive Officer
CFO: Drew Johnson, Chief Financial Officer
CMO: Tom Osborn, D.O., Chief Medical Staff
CIO: Mike Combs, Manager Information Technology
CHR: Heather Heard, Director Human Resources
CNO: Jackie Smith, R.N., Chief Nursing Officer
Web address: www.holdenvillegeneral.org
Control: City–Government, nonfederal **Service:** General Medical and Surgical

Staffed Beds: 25 **Admissions:** 420 **Census:** 7 **Outpatient Visits:** 31158
Births: 0 **Total Expense ($000):** 9824 **Payroll Expense ($000):** 4634
Personnel: 114

HOLLIS—Harmon County

★ **HARMON MEMORIAL HOSPITAL (370036)**, 400 East Chestnut Street,
Zip 73550–2030, Mailing Address: P.O. Box 791, Zip 73550–0791;
tel. 580/688–3363, (Nonreporting) **A**9 10 20
Primary Contact: Sheila Lewis, Administrator
CFO: Willie Mae Copeland, Chief Financial Officer
CMO: Akram Abraham, M.D., Chief of Staff
CHR: Abbey Welch, Director Human Resources
Control: Hospital district or authority, Government, nonfederal **Service:** General
Medical and Surgical

Staffed Beds: 72

HUGO—Choctaw County

CHOCTAW MEMORIAL HOSPITAL (370100), 1405 East Kirk Street,
Zip 74743–3603; tel. 580/317–9500 **A**9 10 **F**3 15 29 34 35 40 45 49 75 81
87 93 107 110 111 114 119 130 146
Primary Contact: Marcia O'Conner, Chief Executive Officer
CIO: Andy Richmond, Director Information Technology
CHR: Darlene Galyon, Director Human Resources
Web address: www.choctawmemorial.com
Control: Hospital district or authority, Government, nonfederal **Service:** General
Medical and Surgical

Staffed Beds: 32 **Admissions:** 1536 **Census:** 16 **Births:** 5

LANE FROST HEALTH AND REHABILITATION CENTER (372017), 2815 East
Jackson Street, Zip 74743–4250; tel. 580/326–9200, (Nonreporting) **A**10
Primary Contact: Robert F. Berry, Chief Executive Officer
Web address: www.lanefrosthealth.com/
Control: Other not–for–profit (including NFP Corporation) **Service:** Long–Term
Acute Care hospital

Staffed Beds: 25

IDABEL—Mccurtain County

★ **MCCURTAIN MEMORIAL HOSPITAL (370048)**, 1301 Lincoln Road,
Zip 74745–7341; tel. 580/286–7623 **A**9 10 20 **F**3 11 13 15 28 29 34 40 45
49 53 62 64 70 75 76 81 87 93 98 103 107 110 111 114 119 128 130 132
133 148 **P**6 8
Primary Contact: Jahni Tapley, JD, Interim Chief Executive Officer
CFO: Ray B. Whitmore, Chief Financial Officer
CMO: Michael C. West, M.D., Chief of Staff
CIO: Dana A. Stowell, Chief Information Officer
CNO: Pam Johnson, R.N., Chief Nursing Officer
Web address: www.mmhok.com
Control: Other not–for–profit (including NFP Corporation) **Service:** General
Medical and Surgical

Staffed Beds: 77 **Admissions:** 1576 **Census:** 18 **Outpatient Visits:** 33079
Births: 252 **Total Expense ($000):** 20519 **Payroll Expense ($000):** 11073
Personnel: 265

KINGFISHER—Kingfisher County

★ **MERCY HOSPITAL KINGFISHER (371313)**, 1000 Kingfisher Regional Hospital
Drive, Zip 73750–3528, Mailing Address: P.O. Box 59, Zip 73750–0059;
tel. 405/375–3141 **A**9 10 18 **F**3 15 29 40 59 81 91 93 107 111 119 133
146 **S** Mercy Health, Chesterfield, MO
Primary Contact: Brian Denton, Administrator
CMO: Brett Krablin, M.D., Chief of Staff
CIO: Chad Kliewer, Information Technology Specialist
CHR: Carolyn Bjerke, Director Human Resources
CNO: Hannah Powell, Chief Nursing Officer
Web address: www.kingfisherhospital.com
Control: Church–operated, Nongovernment, not–for profit **Service:** General
Medical and Surgical

Staffed Beds: 25 **Admissions:** 571 **Census:** 8 **Outpatient Visits:** 9210
Births: 0 **Total Expense ($000):** 15488 **Payroll Expense ($000):** 4784
Personnel: 84

LAWTON—Comanche County

⊠ △ **COMANCHE COUNTY MEMORIAL HOSPITAL (370056)**, 3401 West Gore
Boulevard, Zip 73505–6332, Mailing Address: P.O. Box 129, Zip 73502–0129;
tel. 580/355–8620, (Total facility includes 132 beds in nursing home–type unit)
A1 2 3 5 7 9 10 **F**3 7 8 11 12 13 15 17 18 20 22 24 26 28 29 30 31 32 34
35 40 43 45 47 48 49 50 51 54 56 57 58 59 62 64 65 66 68 70 72 74 75
76 77 78 79 80 81 82 84 85 86 90 91 92 93 96 97 98 103 104 107 108
110 111 114 115 117 118 119 120 121 123 124 127 128 129 130 131 132
134 135 143 144 146 147 148 **P**6
Primary Contact: Randall K. Segler, FACHE, Chief Executive Officer
COO: Sharon Dudley, Chief Operating Officer
CFO: Brent Smith, Chief Financial Officer
CMO: John A. Cox, Jr., M.D., President Medical Staff
CIO: James Wellman, Senior Director Information Services
CHR: Donna Wade, Senior Director Human Resources
CNO: Kim Holland, Senior Director Nursing Services
Web address: www.ccmhonline.com
Control: Hospital district or authority, Government, nonfederal **Service:** General
Medical and Surgical

Staffed Beds: 374 **Admissions:** 10251 **Census:** 245 **Outpatient Visits:**
162702 **Births:** 1129 **Total Expense ($000):** 225174 **Payroll Expense
($000):** 91850 **Personnel:** 1539

JIM TALIAFERRO COMMUNITY MENTAL HEALTH (374008), 602 S.W. 37th
Street, Zip 73505; tel. 580/248–5780, (Nonreporting) **A**9 10
Primary Contact: Debbie Moran, Executive Director
Web address: www.odmhsas.org
Control: State–Government, nonfederal **Service:** Psychiatric

Staffed Beds: 26

☐ **LAWTON INDIAN HOSPITAL (370170)**, 1515 Lawrie Tatum Road,
Zip 73507–3099; tel. 580/353–0350, (Nonreporting) **A**1 10 **S** U. S. Indian Health
Service, Rockville, MD
Primary Contact: Greg Ketcher, Administrator
COO: John Bear, Hospital Administrator Officer and Supervisor Human Resources
CFO: Sarabeth Sahmaunt, Supervisory Accountant
CMO: Richard Chadek, M.D., Clinical Director
CIO: William R. Harris, Chief Information Officer
CHR: John Bear, Hospital Administrator Officer and Supervisor Human Resources
CNO: Lenora Littledeer, R.N., Director of Nursing
Web address: www.ihs.gov
Control: PHS, Indian Service, Government, federal **Service:** General Medical and
Surgical

Staffed Beds: 26

☐ △ **SOUTHWESTERN MEDICAL CENTER (370097)**, 5602 S.W. Lee
Boulevard, Zip 73505–9635; tel. 580/531–4700 **A**1 3 5 7 9 10 **F**3 8 13 29 30
34 38 40 41 43 45 47 49 50 51 57 59 60 65 67 68 70 74 76 77 78 79 81
85 87 89 90 91 92 93 98 99 100 101 102 104 106 107 108 111 114 118
119 120 121 122 123 124 127 129 130 131 133 135 146 147 148 **P**6
S Capella Healthcare, Franklin, TN
Primary Contact: Stephen O. Hyde, FACHE, Chief Executive Officer
CFO: Wayne Colson, Chief Financial Officer
CMO: David Pagnanelli, M.D., Chief of Staff
CIO: Kent Lewis, Director Information Services
CHR: Danny Hale, Director Human Resources
CNO: Steven Vance Owens, RN, Chief Nursing Officer
Web address: www.swmconline.com
Control: Corporation, Investor–owned, for–profit **Service:** General Medical and
Surgical

Staffed Beds: 178 **Admissions:** 4423 **Census:** 89 **Outpatient Visits:** 58970
Births: 524 **Total Expense ($000):** 63610 **Payroll Expense ($000):** 21980
Personnel: 421

Many Facility Codes have changed. Please refer to the AHA Guide Code Chart. © 2014 AHA Guide

LINDSAY—Garvin County

LINDSAY MUNICIPAL HOSPITAL (370214), Highway 19 West, Zip 73052,
Mailing Address: P.O. Box 888, Zip 73052–0888; tel. 405/756–1404,
(Nonreporting) **A**9 10
Primary Contact: Norma N. Howard, Chief Executive Officer
Control: City–Government, nonfederal **Service:** General Medical and Surgical

Staffed Beds: 26

MADILL—Marshall County

✠ **INTEGRIS MARSHALL COUNTY MEDICAL CENTER (371326)**, 1 Hospital
Drive, Zip 73446, Mailing Address: P.O. Box 827, Zip 73446–0827;
tel. 580/795–3384 **A**1 9 10 18 **F**3 11 29 30 34 35 40 43 45 49 59 64 81 87
93 107 114 119 127 130 133 135 146 **P**5 **S** Community Health Systems, Inc.,
Franklin, TN
Primary Contact: Gregory Holder, Administrator and Chief Nursing Executive
CFO: Thomas Briggs, Chief Financial Officer
CMO: Joe Potter, M.D., Chief of Staff
CHR: Lori Friend, Director Human Resources
CNO: Holly Bain, Chief Nursing Officer
Web address: www.integrismarshallcounty.com
Control: Corporation, Investor–owned, for–profit **Service:** General Medical and
Surgical

Staffed Beds: 21 Admissions: 547 Census: 5 Outpatient Visits: 13081 Births: 0 Total Expense ($000): 10790 Payroll Expense ($000): 3523 Personnel: 78

MANGUM—Greer County

QUARTZ MOUNTAIN MEDICAL CENTER (371330), One Wickersham Drive,
Zip 73554–9116, Mailing Address: P.O. Box 280, Zip 73554–0280;
tel. 580/782–3353 **A**9 10 18 **F**29 40 41 45 57 68 81 82 93 107 111 119
127 128 129 133 148 **P**6
Primary Contact: Lindsay Crabb, Chief Executive Officer
COO: Danny Avery, Chief Financial Officer and Chief Operating Officer
CIO: Gregg Burnam, Chief Information Officer and Manager Business Office
Web address: www.mangumhealth.com
Control: Individual, Investor–owned, for–profit **Service:** General Medical and
Surgical

Staffed Beds: 25 Admissions: 200 Census: 2 Outpatient Visits: 9114 Births: 0

MARIETTA—Love County

★ **MERCY HEALTH LOVE COUNTY (371306)**, 300 Wanda Street,
Zip 73448–1200; tel. 580/276–3347 **A**9 10 18 **F**3 29 34 40 43 50 57 59 84
107 114 119 127 133 135 143 146 148 **S** Mercy Health, Chesterfield, MO
Primary Contact: Richard Barker, Administrator
CMO: J. T. O'Connor, M.D., Medical Director
CIO: Connie Graham, Public Information Officer
Web address: www.mercyhealthlovecounty.com
Control: Church–operated, Nongovernment, not–for profit **Service:** General
Medical and Surgical

Staffed Beds: 25 Admissions: 342 Census: 7 Outpatient Visits: 35093 Births: 0 Total Expense ($000): 12468 Payroll Expense ($000): 7114 Personnel: 136

MCALESTER—Pittsburg County

CARL ALBERT COMMUNITY MENTAL HEALTH CENTER (374006), 1101
East Monroe Avenue, Zip 74501–4826; tel. 918/426–7800, (Nonreporting) **A**10
Primary Contact: Debbie Moran, Executive Director
CFO: Konnie Taylor, Chief Financial Officer
CMO: William Mings, M.D., Medical Director
CHR: Judy Allen, Human Resource Specialist
Web address: www.odmhsas.org
Control: State–Government, nonfederal **Service:** Psychiatric

Staffed Beds: 15

★ △ ◇ **MCALESTER REGIONAL HEALTH CENTER (370034)**, One Clark
Bass Boulevard, Zip 74501–4267, Mailing Address: P.O. Box 1228,
Zip 74502–1228; tel. 918/426–1800 **A**7 9 10 19 20 21 **F**3 11 13 15 18 20
22 26 29 30 34 35 40 43 45 49 50 51 53 54 56 57 59 61 62 64 68 69 70
75 76 77 79 81 82 85 86 87 90 92 93 107 109 110 111 114 115 116 117
118 119 125 127 128 129 130 132 135 144 146 147 148 **P**2 6
Primary Contact: David N. Keith, FACHE, President and Chief Executive Officer
CFO: Melissa Walker, Senior Vice President and Chief Financial Officer
CIO: Frank Hilbert, Senior Vice President and Chief Information Officer
CHR: Steven Brooks, Vice President Human Resources
CNO: Danny Hardman, Senior Vice President and Chief Nursing Officer
Web address: www.mrhcok.com
Control: City–Government, nonfederal **Service:** General Medical and Surgical

Staffed Beds: 252 Admissions: 5365 Census: 63 Outpatient Visits: 92440 Births: 535 Total Expense ($000): 83718 Payroll Expense ($000): 33871 Personnel: 640

MIAMI—Ottawa County

✠ **INTEGRIS BAPTIST REGIONAL HEALTH CENTER (370004)**, 200 Second
Street S.W., Zip 74354–6830, Mailing Address: P.O. Box 1207,
Zip 74355–1207; tel. 918/542–6611 **A**1 9 10 20 **F**7 8 11 13 15 18 20 22 26
28 29 30 34 35 40 45 51 57 59 62 63 70 75 76 77 79 81 85 89 93 98 100
103 107 108 110 111 114 115 119 125 129 130 131 132 135 144 146 147
148 **S** INTEGRIS Health, Oklahoma City, OK
Primary Contact: Jordan Cash, President
CFO: Valerie Reeves, Chief Financial Officer
CMO: Elaine Mader, M.D., Chief of Staff
CHR: Jamil Haynes, Regional Director Human Resources
CNO: Lisa Halstead, Chief Nursing Officer
Web address: www.integris–health.com
Control: Other not–for–profit (including NFP Corporation) **Service:** General
Medical and Surgical

Staffed Beds: 84 Admissions: 2623 Census: 29 Outpatient Visits: 80229 Births: 360 Total Expense ($000): 53813 Payroll Expense ($000): 23335 Personnel: 295

★ **WILLOW CREST HOSPITAL (374017)**, 130 A Street S.W., Zip 74354–6800;
tel. 918/542–1836 **A**9 10 **F**29 75 98 99 101 102 106 130 **P**6
Primary Contact: Anne G. Anthony, FACHE, President and Chief Executive Officer
COO: Steven Goodman, Chief Operating Officer
CFO: Cindy Bell, Director Finance
CMO: Mark Elkington, M.D., Chief Medical Officer
CIO: Steven Goodman, Chief Operating Officer
CHR: Kathy Henderson, Director Human Resources
CNO: Kassi Davis, Director Patient Care Services
Web address: www.willowcresthospital.com
Control: Corporation, Investor–owned, for–profit **Service:** Children's hospital
psychiatric

Staffed Beds: 75 Admissions: 546 Census: 48 Outpatient Visits: 0 Births: 0 Total Expense ($000): 7726 Payroll Expense ($000): 4903 Personnel: 127

MIDWEST CITY—Oklahoma County

✠ **MIDWEST REGIONAL MEDICAL CENTER (370094)**, 2825 Parklawn Drive,
Zip 73110–4258; tel. 405/610–4411 **A**1 3 5 9 10 **F**3 7 8 11 13 14 15 17 18
20 22 26 29 30 31 34 40 43 46 49 50 57 59 70 74 77 78 79 81 85 86 87
91 93 98 100 101 102 103 107 108 110 111 114 115 118 119 126 130
132 143 146 147 **S** Community Health Systems, Inc., Franklin, TN
Primary Contact: Damon Brown, Chief Executive Officer
CFO: Shea Sutherland, Chief Financial Officer
CMO: Dan Donnell, M.D., Chief of Staff
CHR: Angela C. Giese, Director Human Resources
Web address: www.midwestregional.com
Control: Corporation, Investor–owned, for–profit **Service:** General Medical and
Surgical

Staffed Beds: 255 Admissions: 10954 Census: 128 Outpatient Visits: 110523 Births: 713 Total Expense ($000): 141043 Payroll Expense ($000): 49479 Personnel: 859

☐ **SPECIALTY HOSPITAL OF MIDWEST CITY (372012)**, 8210 National Avenue,
Zip 73110–8518; tel. 405/739–0800 **A**1 9 10 **F**1 3 18 29 34 40 65 75 77 79
85 86 87 135 143 148 **P**5 **S** Encore Healthcare, Columbia, MD
Primary Contact: Bobby Snyder, Chief Executive Officer
CFO: Veronica Scott, Business Office Manager
CHR: Anna Emamghoraishi, Human Resources
CNO: Jason Farris, Chief Nursing Officer
Control: Partnership, Investor–owned, for–profit **Service:** Long–Term Acute Care
hospital

Staffed Beds: 31 Admissions: 271 Census: 22 Outpatient Visits: 0 Births: 0 Total Expense ($000): 10036 Payroll Expense ($000): 3475 Personnel: 76

Hospital, Medicare Provider Number, Address, Telephone, Approval, Facility, and Physician Codes, Health Care System

★ American Hospital Association (AHA) membership
☐ The Joint Commission accreditation
◇ DNV Healthcare Inc. accreditation
◯ Healthcare Facilities Accreditation Program
△ Commission on Accreditation of Rehabilitation Facilities (CARF) accreditation

OK

MOORE—Cleveland County

MOORE MEDICAL CENTER See Norman Regional Health System, Norman

MUSKOGEE—Muskogee County

☒ **EASTAR HEALTH SYSTEM (370025)**, 300 Rockefeller Drive, Zip 74401–5081; tel. 918/682–5501, (Includes EASTAR HEALTH SYSTEM, EAST CAMPUS, 2900 North Main Street, Zip 74401–4078; tel. 918/687–7777) **A**1 2 9 10 19 **F**3 8 11 12 13 15 18 20 22 29 30 31 34 35 40 43 45 46 47 48 49 50 51 53 56 57 59 60 62 64 65 68 70 73 74 75 76 77 78 79 85 86 87 89 90 93 96 98 100 102 103 107 108 110 111 114 115 119 120 121 123 129 146 147 148 **P**6 **S** Capella Healthcare, Franklin, TN
Primary Contact: Anthony R. Young, Chief Executive Officer
COO: James F. Davidson, Chief Operating Officer
CFO: Scott Bailey, Chief Financial Officer
CMO: Jay Gregory, M.D., Chief Medical Officer
CIO: James Tolbert, Director Information Systems
CHR: Bill Peterson, Director Human Resources
CNO: Debbie Kifer, Chief Nursing Officer
Web address: www.eastarhealth.com
Control: Corporation, Investor–owned, for–profit **Service:** General Medical and Surgical

Staffed Beds: 206 **Admissions:** 7968 **Census:** 101 **Outpatient Visits:** 85028 **Births:** 686 **Total Expense ($000):** 110981 **Payroll Expense ($000):** 35028 **Personnel:** 801

EASTAR HEALTH SYSTEM, EAST CAMPUS See EASTAR Health System

☒ △ **JACK C. MONTGOMERY VETERANS AFFAIRS MEDICAL CENTER**, 1011 Honor Heights Drive, Zip 74401–1318; tel. 918/577–3000 **A**1 2 5 7 9 **F**3 5 8 12 18 29 30 31 34 35 36 38 39 40 44 45 50 53 54 55 56 57 58 59 63 64 65 67 70 74 75 77 78 79 81 82 83 84 85 86 87 90 92 93 94 96 97 98 100 101 102 103 104 105 107 108 111 114 119 127 130 132 133 135 143 146 147 148 **S** Department of Veterans Affairs, Washington, DC
Primary Contact: James R. Floyd, Director
CFO: Dwight Beal, Chief Fiscal Services
CMO: Thomas D. Schneider, D.O., Chief of Staff
CIO: Mark Carr, Chief Information Resource Management
CNO: Bonnie Pierce, MSN, Associate Director for Patient Care Services
Web address: www.muskogee.va.gov
Control: Veterans Affairs, Government, federal **Service:** General Medical and Surgical

Staffed Beds: 99 **Admissions:** 4874 **Census:** 62 **Outpatient Visits:** 457852 **Births:** 0 **Personnel:** 1219

MUSKOGEE REGIONAL MEDICAL CENTER See EASTAR Health System

SOLARA HOSPITAL OF MUSKOGEE (372022), 351 South 40th Street, Zip 74401–4916; tel. 918/682–6161 **A**9 10 **F**1 3 29 40 77 85 96 130 148 **S** Cornerstone Healthcare Group, Dallas, TX
Primary Contact: Craig Koele, Chief Executive Officer
CMO: Jeremiah Rutherford, Chief Medical Officer
Web address: www.chghospitals.com/muskogee/
Control: Corporation, Investor–owned, for–profit **Service:** Long–Term Acute Care hospital

Staffed Beds: 41 **Admissions:** 548 **Census:** 39 **Outpatient Visits:** 7 **Births:** 0 **Total Expense ($000):** 17525 **Payroll Expense ($000):** 6663 **Personnel:** 129

NORMAN—Cleveland County

☐ **GRIFFIN MEMORIAL HOSPITAL (374000)**, 900 East Main Street, Zip 73071–5305, Mailing Address: P.O. Box 151, Zip 73070–0151; tel. 405/321–4880 **A**1 9 10 **F**40 98 102 103 130 **P**6 **S** Oklahoma Department of Mental Health and Substance Abuse Services, Oklahoma City, OK
Primary Contact: Lawrence Gross, Executive Director
CFO: Bob Mathew, Director Finance
CMO: Stan Ardoin, M.D., Medical Director
Web address: www.odmhsas.org
Control: State–Government, nonfederal **Service:** Psychiatric

Staffed Beds: 120 **Admissions:** 1642 **Census:** 115 **Outpatient Visits:** 442 **Births:** 0 **Total Expense ($000):** 24909 **Payroll Expense ($000):** 11811 **Personnel:** 315

J. D. MCCARTY CENTER FOR CHILDREN WITH DEVELOPMENTAL DISABILITIES (373300), 2002 East Robinson, Zip 73071–7420; tel. 405/307–2800 **A**10 **F**3 29 35 64 65 75 77 87 90 91 93 130 135 146
Primary Contact: Vicki Kuestersteffen, Chief Executive Officer
CFO: Erik Paulson, Director of Finance
CMO: Thomas Thurston, M.D., Medical Director
CIO: Jeffery Setzer, Administrator Information Systems
CHR: Tina Martinez, Director Human Resources
Web address: www.jdmc.org
Control: State–Government, nonfederal **Service:** Children's rehabilitation

Staffed Beds: 36 **Admissions:** 222 **Census:** 33 **Outpatient Visits:** 8852 **Births:** 0 **Total Expense ($000):** 20296 **Payroll Expense ($000):** 10860 **Personnel:** 229

☒ △ **NORMAN REGIONAL HEALTH SYSTEM (370008)**, 901 North Porter Street, Zip 73071–6482, Mailing Address: P.O. Box 1308, Zip 73070–1308; tel. 405/307–1000, (Includes MOORE MEDICAL CENTER, 700 South Telephone Road, Moore, Zip 73160; tel. 405/793–9355; Ryan Gehris, Chief Administrative Officer; NORMAN REGIONAL HOSPITAL, 901 North Porter Street, Mailing Address: P.O. Box 1308, Zip 73070–1308; tel. 405/307–1000) **A**1 2 7 9 10 **F**3 7 11 12 13 15 17 18 20 22 24 28 29 30 31 32 34 35 36 37 39 40 42 43 44 45 47 48 49 50 53 54 55 56 57 58 59 63 64 65 69 70 72 74 75 76 77 78 79 80 81 82 83 84 85 86 87 89 90 93 94 96 97 98 100 101 102 103 104 107 110 111 114 115 117 118 119 120 123 126 127 129 130 131 132 135 143 145 146 147 148 **P**5 6 8
Primary Contact: David D. Whitaker, FACHE, President and Chief Executive Officer
COO: Greg Terrell, Senior Vice President and Chief Operating Officer
CFO: Ken Hopkins, Vice President Finance and Chief Financial Officer
CIO: John Meharg, Director Health Information Technology
CHR: Jim Beyer, Director Human Resources
CNO: Nancy Brown, R.N., Vice President Patient Care Services and Chief Nursing Officer
Web address: www.normanregional.com
Control: Hospital district or authority, Government, nonfederal **Service:** General Medical and Surgical

Staffed Beds: 364 **Admissions:** 17433 **Census:** 210 **Outpatient Visits:** 379176 **Births:** 3166 **Total Expense ($000):** 332554 **Payroll Expense ($000):** 141831 **Personnel:** 2498

☒ **NORMAN SPECIALTY HOSPITAL (372021)**, 1210 West Robinson Street, Zip 73069–7401; tel. 405/321–8824 **A**1 9 10 **F**1 3 29 30 35 40 60 68 74 75 77 87 91 100 119 130 146 148 **P**8
Primary Contact: Talitha Glosemeyer, M.P.H., FACHE, Administrator
CFO: Debra Anderson, Manager Patient Financial Services
CMO: Mehan Shahsavari, M.D., Chief of Staff
CHR: Beth Blankenship, Coordinator Human Resources
CNO: Linda Massey, R.N., Nurse Manager
Web address: www.normanspecialtyhospital.com
Control: Individual, Investor–owned, for–profit **Service:** Long–Term Acute Care hospital

Staffed Beds: 50 **Admissions:** 566 **Census:** 39 **Outpatient Visits:** 1 **Births:** 0 **Personnel:** 172

NOWATA—Nowata County

★ **JANE PHILLIPS NOWATA HEALTH CENTER (371305)**, 237 South Locust Street, Zip 74048–3660, Mailing Address: P.O. Box 426, Zip 74048–0426; tel. 918/273–3102 **A**9 10 18 **F**3 29 34 35 40 50 57 64 68 119 128 133 146 **P**5 **S** Ascension Health, Saint Louis, MO
Primary Contact: Scott Upton, Administrator
CMO: David Caughell, M.D., Chief of Staff
Web address: www.jpmc.org
Control: Church–operated, Nongovernment, not–for profit **Service:** General Medical and Surgical

Staffed Beds: 13 **Admissions:** 192 **Census:** 4 **Outpatient Visits:** 2775 **Births:** 0 **Total Expense ($000):** 3587 **Payroll Expense ($000):** 1970 **Personnel:** 42

OKEENE—Blaine County

★ **OKEENE MUNICIPAL HOSPITAL (371327)**, 207 East F Street, Zip 73763–9441, Mailing Address: P.O. Box 489, Zip 73763–0489; tel. 580/822–4417 **A**9 10 18 **F**3 29 34 40 45 50 59 64 68 81 85 93 97 107 111 119 129 130 132 133 135 **P**6
Primary Contact: Shelly Dunham, R.N., Chief Executive Officer
COO: Pat Lorenz, Chief Operating Officer
CFO: Sandra Lamle, Chief Financial Officer
CHR: Barbara Creps, Director Human Resources and Accounting
CNO: Tamara Fischer, Chief Nursing Officer
Web address: www.okeenehospital.com
Control: Hospital district or authority, Government, nonfederal **Service:** General Medical and Surgical

Staffed Beds: 17 **Admissions:** 177 **Census:** 5 **Outpatient Visits:** 19971 **Births:** 0 **Total Expense ($000):** 5456 **Payroll Expense ($000):** 2460 **Personnel:** 53

OKEMAH—Okfuskee County

★ ◇ **CREEK NATION COMMUNITY HOSPITAL (371333)**, 309 North 14th Street, Zip 74859–2028; tel. 918/623–1424, (Nonreporting) **A**9 10 18 21
Primary Contact: Sheryl Sharber–Howell, Administrator
COO: Rhonda Beaver, Chief Operating Officer
CFO: Tyler McIntosh, Chief Financial Officer
CMO: Lawrence Vark, M.D., Chief Medical Officer
CIO: Robert Coffee, Chief Information Officer
CHR: Russell B. Torbett, Director Human Resources
CNO: Annette James, Chief Nursing Officer
Web address: www.creekhealth.org
Control: Other not–for–profit (including NFP Corporation) **Service:** General Medical and Surgical

Staffed Beds: 18

Many Facility Codes have changed. Please refer to the AHA Guide Code Chart. © 2014 AHA Guide

OKLAHOMA CITY—Oklahoma County

☐ **CEDAR RIDGE HOSPITAL (374023)**, 6501 N.E. 50th Street, Zip 73141–9118; tel. 405/605–6111, (Nonreporting) **A**1 9 10 **S** Universal Health Services, Inc., King of Prussia, PA
Primary Contact: Robert Jackson, Interim Chief Executive Officer
Web address: www.cedarridgebhs.com
Control: Corporation, Investor–owned, for–profit **Service:** Psychiatric

Staffed Beds: 36

CHILDREN'S HOSPITAL OF OKLAHOMA See OU Medical Center

◇ **COMMUNITY HOSPITAL (370203)**, 3100 S.W. 89th Street, Zip 73159–7900; tel. 405/378–3755, (Nonreporting) **A**9 10 21
Primary Contact: Brian L. Clemens, President and Chief Executive Officer
Web address: www.communityhospitalokc.com
Control: Corporation, Investor–owned, for–profit **Service:** General Medical and Surgical

Staffed Beds: 40

✠ △ **DEACONESS HOSPITAL (370032)**, 5501 North Portland Avenue, Zip 73112–2099; tel. 405/604–6000, (Total facility includes 19 beds in nursing home–type unit) **A**1 2 7 9 10 **F**3 8 11 12 13 15 17 18 20 22 24 28 29 30 31 34 35 40 41 43 45 46 47 49 50 52 56 57 59 60 70 72 73 74 75 76 78 79 80 81 83 84 85 86 87 90 93 97 98 101 102 103 107 108 109 110 111 114 119 120 126 128 129 130 132 135 146 147 148 **P**8 **S** Community Health Systems, Inc., Franklin, TN
Primary Contact: Cathryn A. Hibbs, FACHE, Chief Executive Officer
CIO: Don Bandy, Director Information Technology
CHR: Ellen Gifford, Director Human Resources
CNO: Jayne Thomas, Chief Nursing Officer
Web address: www.deaconessokc.com
Control: Partnership, Investor–owned, for–profit **Service:** General Medical and Surgical

Staffed Beds: 273 **Admissions:** 8178 **Census:** 119 **Outpatient Visits:** 73992 **Births:** 954 **Total Expense ($000):** 113064 **Payroll Expense ($000):** 44401 **Personnel:** 934

EVERETT TOWER See OU Medical Center

✠ △ **INTEGRIS BAPTIST MEDICAL CENTER (370028)**, 3300 N.W. Expressway, Zip 73112–4418; tel. 405/949–3011, (Includes INTEGRIS MENTAL HEALTH SYSTEM–SPENCER, 2601 North Spencer Road, Spencer, Zip 73084–3699, Mailing Address: P.O. Box 11137, Oklahoma City, Zip 73136–0137; tel. 405/717–9800) **A**1 2 3 5 7 9 10 **F**3 4 8 11 12 13 15 16 17 18 20 22 24 26 28 29 30 31 32 34 35 36 38 39 40 43 44 45 46 49 50 52 54 55 56 57 58 59 60 62 63 64 68 70 71 72 73 74 75 76 77 78 79 80 81 82 83 84 85 86 87 88 89 90 92 93 96 97 98 99 100 101 102 104 106 107 108 110 111 114 115 116 118 119 120 121 123 124 126 129 130 131 132 133 134 135 137 138 139 140 141 142 143 146 147 148 **P**6 7 **S** INTEGRIS Health, Oklahoma City, OK
Primary Contact: Timothy J. Johnsen, MS, President
CFO: David R. Hadley, Managing Director and Chief Financial Officer
CMO: James P. White, M.D., Chief Medical Officer
CIO: John Delano, Vice President Chief Information Officer
CHR: Jason L. Eliot, Vice President Human Resources
CNO: Joni R. Tiller, R.N., Chief Nursing Officer
Web address: www.integrisok.com
Control: Other not–for–profit (including NFP Corporation) **Service:** General Medical and Surgical

Staffed Beds: 525 **Admissions:** 21564 **Census:** 395 **Outpatient Visits:** 174427 **Births:** 2571 **Total Expense ($000):** 592609 **Payroll Expense ($000):** 197934 **Personnel:** 3877

✠ △ **INTEGRIS SOUTHWEST MEDICAL CENTER (370106)**, 4401 South Western, Zip 73109–3413; tel. 405/636–7000 **A**1 2 7 9 10 13 **F**3 11 13 15 18 20 22 24 28 29 30 31 32 34 35 38 40 43 44 47 49 50 53 57 58 59 60 64 68 69 70 74 75 76 77 78 79 80 81 82 85 86 87 90 91 92 93 95 96 97 107 108 110 111 114 118 119 120 121 123 129 130 131 132 133 135 143 146 147 148 **P**6 7 **S** INTEGRIS Health, Oklahoma City, OK
Primary Contact: James D. Moore, FACHE, President
CFO: Errol Mitchell, Vice President
CMO: Son Nguyen, M.D., President of Medical Staff
CIO: John Delano, Vice President and Chief Information Officer
CHR: Lynn Ketch, Director
CNO: Marva Harrison, R.N., Vice President and Chief Nursing Officer
Web address: www.integris–health.com
Control: Other not–for–profit (including NFP Corporation) **Service:** General Medical and Surgical

Staffed Beds: 327 **Admissions:** 12041 **Census:** 188 **Outpatient Visits:** 151897 **Births:** 1111 **Total Expense ($000):** 231185 **Payroll Expense ($000):** 85572 **Personnel:** 1292

✠ **KINDRED HOSPITAL– OKLAHOMA CITY (372004)**, 1407 North Robinson Avenue, Zip 73103–4823; tel. 405/232–8000, (Includes KINDRED HOSPITAL–OKLAHOMA CITY SOUTH, 2129 S.W. 59th Street, Zip 73119; tel. 405/713–5955) **A**1 3 5 9 10 **F**29 40 46 60 68 70 85 87 119 130 145 148 **S** Kindred Healthcare, Louisville, KY
Primary Contact: Robert C. Gladney, Interim Chief Executive Officer
Web address: www.kindredoklahoma.com
Control: Corporation, Investor–owned, for–profit **Service:** General Medical and Surgical

Staffed Beds: 93 **Admissions:** 756 **Census:** 51 **Outpatient Visits:** 0 **Births:** 0 **Total Expense ($000):** 23813 **Payroll Expense ($000):** 9597 **Personnel:** 241

✠ **LAKESIDE WOMEN'S HOSPITAL (370199)**, 11200 North Portland Avenue, Zip 73120–5045; tel. 405/936–1500, (Data for 182 days) **A**1 9 10 **F**3 12 13 15 30 35 40 45 59 64 73 76 81 85 87 110 119 126 129 132 147 **P**6 **S** INTEGRIS Health, Oklahoma City, OK
Primary Contact: Kelley Brewer, R.N., MSN, President
CFO: Darla McCallister, Chief Financial Officer
CMO: Margaret Hall, M.D., Chief Medical Officer
Web address: www.lakeside–wh.net
Control: Corporation, Investor–owned, for–profit **Service:** Obstetrics and gynecology

Staffed Beds: 23 **Admissions:** 642 **Census:** 9 **Outpatient Visits:** 1437 **Births:** 601 **Total Expense ($000):** 9656 **Payroll Expense ($000):** 2957 **Personnel:** 132

MCBRIDE CLINIC ORTHOPEDIC HOSPITAL (370222), 9600 Broadway Extension, Zip 73114–7408; tel. 405/486–2100 **A**9 10 **F**3 29 34 40 64 68 77 79 81 82 85 86 87 107 111 114 119 130 131 146 **P**2 6
Primary Contact: Mark Galliart, Chief Executive Officer
COO: Christine H. Weigel, R.N., Clinical Operating Officer
CFO: Annie Bassett, Director Finance
CMO: Thomas Janssen, M.D., Chief of Staff
CIO: Ronnie Green, Director Information Systems
CHR: Cathy Withiam, Director Human Resources
Web address: www.mcbrideclinicorthopedichospital.com
Control: Corporation, Investor–owned, for–profit **Service:** Orthopedic

Staffed Beds: 32 **Admissions:** 3480 **Census:** 28 **Outpatient Visits:** 156826 **Births:** 0 **Total Expense ($000):** 112647 **Payroll Expense ($000):** 47701 **Personnel:** 661

✠ **MERCY HOSPITAL OKLAHOMA CITY (370013)**, 4300 West Memorial Road, Zip 73120–8362; tel. 405/755–1515 **A**1 2 9 10 **F**3 11 13 15 28 29 30 31 32 34 35 39 40 41 43 45 49 50 53 55 57 58 59 60 61 62 63 64 65 68 69 70 72 74 75 76 77 78 79 81 82 83 84 85 86 87 89 90 91 92 93 94 96 100 101 107 108 110 111 115 117 118 119 120 121 124 126 129 130 131 132 134 135 143 146 147 148 **P**6 **S** Mercy Health, Chesterfield, MO
Primary Contact: Jim Gebhart, Jr., FACHE, President
COO: Aaron Steffens, Chief Operating Officer
CFO: Jon Vitiello, Chief Financial Officer
CMO: Mark Johnson, M.D., Chief Medical Officer
CIO: Ellen Stephens, Vice President Information Services
CHR: Becky J. Payton, Vice President Human Resources
CNO: Linda T. Fanning, R.N., Chief Nursing Officer
Web address: www.mercyok.net
Control: Church–operated, Nongovernment, not–for profit **Service:** General Medical and Surgical

Staffed Beds: 369 **Admissions:** 16173 **Census:** 227 **Outpatient Visits:** 418814 **Births:** 3005 **Total Expense ($000):** 321069 **Payroll Expense ($000):** 104342 **Personnel:** 2076

☐ **MERCY REHABILITATION HOSPITAL OKLAHOMA CITY (373033)**, 5401 West Memorial Road, Zip 73142–2026; tel. 405/752–3935 **A**1 10 **F**3 29 30 87 90 91 96 130 148 **S** Centerre Healthcare, Brentwood, TN
Primary Contact: Sharon Smeltzer, Chief Executive Officer
Control: Partnership, Investor–owned, for–profit **Service:** Rehabilitation

Staffed Beds: 50 **Admissions:** 929 **Census:** 31 **Outpatient Visits:** 0 **Births:** 0 **Total Expense ($000):** 12723 **Payroll Expense ($000):** 6136 **Personnel:** 107

◇ **NORTHWEST SURGICAL HOSPITAL (370192)**, 9204 North May Avenue, Zip 73120–4419; tel. 405/848–1918, (Nonreporting) **A**9 10 21
Primary Contact: Brian L. Clemens, Chief Executive Officer
CFO: Cindy Thompson, Chief Financial Officer
CMO: Jimmy Conway, M.D., President Medical Staff
Web address: www.nwsurgicalokc.com/
Control: Corporation, Investor–owned, for–profit **Service:** Orthopedic

Staffed Beds: 9

Hospital, Medicare Provider Number, Address, Telephone, Approval, Facility, and Physician Codes, Health Care System

★ American Hospital Association (AHA) membership
☐ The Joint Commission accreditation
◇ DNV Healthcare Inc. accreditation
○ Healthcare Facilities Accreditation Program
△ Commission on Accreditation of Rehabilitation Facilities (CARF) accreditation

OK

☐ **OKLAHOMA CENTER FOR ORTHOPEDIC AND MULTI–SPECIALTY SURGERY (370212)**, 8100 South Walker, Suite C., Zip 73139–9402, Mailing Address: P.O. Box 890609, Zip 73189–0609; tel. 405/602–6500 **A**1 9 10 **F**3 8 29 34 35 39 40 45 47 48 54 57 59 64 74 79 81 82 85 86 93 94 97 107 111 131 148 **P**6 **S** United Surgical Partners International, Addison, TX
Primary Contact: Mike Kimzey, Chief Executive Officer and Administrator
CFO: Amy Taylor, Chief Financial Officer
CHR: Sherry Wagner, Director Human Resources
Web address: www.ocomhospital.com
Control: Partnership, Investor–owned, for–profit **Service:** General Medical and Surgical

Staffed Beds: 10 **Admissions:** 662 **Census:** 4 **Outpatient Visits:** 36916 **Births:** 0 **Total Expense ($000):** 39845 **Payroll Expense ($000):** 11091 **Personnel:** 203

✸ △ **OKLAHOMA CITY VETERANS AFFAIRS MEDICAL CENTER**, 921 N.E. 13th Street, Zip 73104–5028; tel. 405/456–1000 **A**1 3 5 7 8 9 **F**2 3 5 6 8 9 10 12 17 18 20 22 24 26 28 29 30 31 34 35 38 39 40 44 45 47 48 49 50 53 54 56 57 58 59 60 61 62 63 64 65 67 68 70 71 74 75 77 78 79 81 82 83 84 85 86 87 90 91 92 93 94 96 97 98 100 101 102 103 104 105 106 107 111 114 115 116 117 119 130 132 135 143 144 146 147 148 **S** Department of Veterans Affairs, Washington, DC
Primary Contact: Daniel L. Marsh, Director
CFO: Michele Pipgrass, Chief Fiscal Service
CMO: Mark Huycke, M.D., Chief of Staff
CIO: David Buckley, Acting Chief Information Management Services
CHR: Kyle Inhofe, Chief Human Resources Officer
CNO: Donna Delise, Associate Director Patient Care Services
Web address: www.oklahoma.va.gov
Control: Veterans Affairs, Government, federal **Service:** General Medical and Surgical

Staffed Beds: 192 **Admissions:** 6645 **Census:** 158 **Outpatient Visits:** 519952 **Births:** 0 **Total Expense ($000):** 240184 **Payroll Expense ($000):** 196003 **Personnel:** 2015

◇ **OKLAHOMA HEART HOSPITAL (370215)**, 4050 West Memorial Road, Zip 73120–8382; tel. 405/608–3200 **A**9 10 21 **F**17 18 20 22 24 26 28 29 30 34 35 40 64 68 74 75 81 86 87 100 102 107 108 116 117 126 146 **P**2
Primary Contact: John Harvey, M.D., President and Chief Executive Officer
COO: Peggy Tipton, Chief Operating Officer and Chief Nursing Officer
CFO: Carol Walker, Chief Financial Officer
CMO: John Harvey, M.D., President and Chief Executive Officer
CIO: Steve Miller, Chief Information Officer
CHR: Katherine Wynn, Director Human Resource
Web address: www.okheart.com
Control: Corporation, Investor–owned, for–profit **Service:** Heart

Staffed Beds: 99 **Admissions:** 7894 **Census:** 79 **Outpatient Visits:** 340916 **Births:** 0 **Total Expense ($000):** 185381 **Payroll Expense ($000):** 72640 **Personnel:** 1394

◇ **OKLAHOMA HEART HOSPITAL SOUTH CAMPUS (370234)**, 5200 East I–240 Service Road, Zip 73135; tel. 405/628–6000 **A**9 10 21 **F**17 18 20 22 24 26 28 29 30 34 35 40 53 64 68 74 75 81 82 100 107 116 117 146 **P**6
Primary Contact: John Harvey, M.D., President and Chief Executive Officer
Web address: www.okheart.com
Control: Corporation, Investor–owned, for–profit **Service:** Heart

Staffed Beds: 46 **Admissions:** 5008 **Census:** 39 **Outpatient Visits:** 56139 **Births:** 0 **Total Expense ($000):** 89735 **Payroll Expense ($000):** 32659 **Personnel:** 380

☐ ◇ **OKLAHOMA SPINE HOSPITAL (370206)**, 14101 Parkway Commons Drive, Zip 73134–6012; tel. 405/749–2700, (Nonreporting) **A**1 9 10 21
Primary Contact: Kevin Blaylock, Chief Executive Officer
Web address: www.oklahomaspine.com
Control: Corporation, Investor–owned, for–profit **Service:** Other specialty

Staffed Beds: 12

ONECORE HEALTH (370220), 1044 S.W. 44th Street, Suite 516, Zip 73109–3609; tel. 405/631–3085 **A**10 **F**3 40 79 81 82 87 111 **P**8
Primary Contact: Steve Hockert, Chief Executive Officer
CFO: Shaun Beggs, Chief Financial Officer
CMO: Joel L. Frazier, M.D., Medical Director
CNO: Teresa Carter, Vice President Patient Care Services
Web address: www.onecorehealth.com
Control: Corporation, Investor–owned, for–profit **Service:** Orthopedic

Staffed Beds: 8 **Admissions:** 103 **Census:** 1 **Outpatient Visits:** 787 **Births:** 0

✸ **OU MEDICAL CENTER (370093)**, 1200 Everett Drive, Zip 73104–5047, Mailing Address: P.O. Box 26307, Zip 73126–0307; tel. 405/271–3636, (Includes CHILDREN'S HOSPITAL OF OKLAHOMA, 940 N.E. 13th Street, Zip 73104, Mailing Address: P.O. Box 26307, Zip 73126; tel. 405/271–6165; EVERETT TOWER, 1200 Everett Drive, Zip 73104; tel. 405/271–4700; OU MEDICAL CENTER EDMOND, 1 South Bryant Avenue, Edmond, Zip 73034–6309; tel. 405/341–6100; PRESBYTERIAN TOWER, 700 N.E. 13th Street, Zip 73104–5070; tel. 405/271–5100) **A**1 2 3 5 8 9 10 **F**3 8 11 12 13 15 17 18 19 20 21 22 23 24 25 26 27 28 29 30 31 32 34 35 37 38 39 40 41 43 45 46 47 48 49 50 51 52 55 56 57 58 59 60 61 63 64 65 66 68 70 72 74 75 76 77 78 79 81 82 84 85 86 87 88 89 91 92 93 94 96 97 98 100 102 103 105 107 108 110 111 114 115 116 117 118 119 120 121 123 124 126 129 130 131 132 135 136 138 139 142 144 145 146 147 148 **S** HCA, Nashville, TN
Primary Contact: Charles Spicer, President and Chief Executive Officer
COO: Kristina Wallace, R.N., Chief Operating Officer
CFO: Mike Reese, Chief Financial Officer
CMO: Curt Steinhart, M.D., Chief Medical Officer
CIO: Larry Forsyth, Director Information Services
CHR: Jed M. Liuzza, Chief Human Resources Officer
CNO: Debra L. Pasley, Chief Nursing Officer
Web address: www.oumedicine.com/oumedicalcenter
Control: Corporation, Investor–owned, for–profit **Service:** General Medical and Surgical

Staffed Beds: 677 **Admissions:** 30754 **Census:** 503 **Outpatient Visits:** 321149 **Births:** 4501 **Total Expense ($000):** 724007 **Payroll Expense ($000):** 200205 **Personnel:** 3213

PRESBYTERIAN TOWER See OU Medical Center

✸ **SELECT SPECIALTY HOSPITAL–OKLAHOMA CITY (372009)**, 3524 N.W. 56th Street, Zip 73112–4518; tel. 405/606–6700 **A**1 9 10 **F**1 3 12 29 40 74 75 79 87 107 119 130 148 **S** Select Medical Corporation, Mechanicsburg, PA
Primary Contact: Connie Strickland, Chief Executive Officer
Web address: www.selectspecialtyhospitals.com/company/locations/oklahomacity.aspx
Control: Corporation, Investor–owned, for–profit **Service:** Long–Term Acute Care hospital

Staffed Beds: 72 **Admissions:** 923 **Census:** 66 **Outpatient Visits:** 0 **Births:** 0 **Total Expense ($000):** 29085 **Payroll Expense ($000):** 12804 **Personnel:** 214

✸ △ **ST. ANTHONY HOSPITAL (370037)**, 1000 North Lee Street, Zip 73102–1080, Mailing Address: P.O. Box 205, Zip 73101–0205; tel. 405/272–7000, (Includes BONE AND JOINT HOSPITAL, 1111 North Dewey Avenue, Zip 73103–2609; tel. 405/272–9671; Tammy Powell, FACHE, M.P.H., President) **A**1 2 3 5 7 9 10 12 13 **F**3 4 5 7 8 11 12 13 15 17 18 20 22 24 28 29 30 31 34 35 36 37 40 42 43 45 46 47 48 49 50 54 56 57 59 64 67 70 71 74 76 77 78 79 81 82 84 85 86 87 89 90 91 92 93 96 97 98 99 100 102 103 104 105 106 107 108 109 110 111 112 113 114 115 116 117 119 120 121 123 124 126 127 129 130 131 132 136 138 144 146 147 148 **P**7 **S** SSM Health, Saint Louis, MO
Primary Contact: Tammy Powell, FACHE, M.P.H., President
COO: Marti Jourden, FACHE, Chief Quality Officer
CFO: Shasta Manuel, Executive Director Finance
CMO: Kersey Winfree, M.D., Chief Medical Officer
CIO: Kevin Olson, Director Information Systems
CHR: Cynthia Brundise, Vice President Human Resources
Web address: www.saintsok.com
Control: Church–operated, Nongovernment, not–for profit **Service:** General Medical and Surgical

Staffed Beds: 524 **Admissions:** 21563 **Census:** 434 **Outpatient Visits:** 284164 **Births:** 1407 **Total Expense ($000):** 462158 **Payroll Expense ($000):** 157806 **Personnel:** 2557

☐ **SURGICAL HOSPITAL OF OKLAHOMA (370201)**, 100 S.E. 59th Street, Zip 73129–3616; tel. 405/634–9300 **A**1 10 **F**3 40 81 129
Primary Contact: Phil Ross, Chief Executive Officer
Web address: www.sh–ok.com/
Control: Partnership, Investor–owned, for–profit **Service:** General Medical and Surgical

Staffed Beds: 12 **Admissions:** 242 **Census:** 1 **Outpatient Visits:** 5278 **Births:** 0 **Total Expense ($000):** 12892 **Payroll Expense ($000):** 4007 **Personnel:** 71

✸ **VALIR REHABILITATION HOSPITAL (373025)**, 700 N.W. Seventh Street, Zip 73102–1212; tel. 405/236–3131 **A**1 10 **F**3 28 29 30 35 40 54 68 75 86 87 90 91 93 96 100 119 143
Primary Contact: Stacy Smith, R.N., Interim Chief Executive Officer
COO: Ginger Castleberry, Corporate Risk Manager, Quality and Patient Safety
CFO: Scott Brown, Chief Financial Officer
CMO: Tonya Washburn, M.D., Medical Director
CIO: Mark Dickey, Director Business Development
CHR: Bill Turner, Vice President Human Resources
Web address: www.valir.com
Control: Corporation, Investor–owned, for–profit **Service:** Rehabilitation

Staffed Beds: 45 **Admissions:** 1009 **Census:** 32 **Outpatient Visits:** 3804 **Births:** 0

VETERANS AFFAIRS MEDICAL CENTER See Oklahoma City Veterans Affairs Medical Center

OKMULGEE—Okmulgee County

GEORGE NIGH REHABILITATION CENTER See Muscogee Creek Nation
Physical Rehabilitation Center

★ **MUSCOGEE CREEK NATION MEDICAL CENTER (370057)**, 1401 Morris
Drive, Zip 74447–6429, Mailing Address: P.O. Box 1038, Zip 74447–1038;
tel. 918/756–4233 **A**9 10 **F**3 11 15 29 34 40 43 45 50 56 57 59 62 68 81
83 85 87 89 92 93 98 103 106 107 108 115 119 128 130 133 146 **P**6
Primary Contact: Sheridan Pickering, Chief Executive Officer
CFO: John W. Crawford, Chief Financial Officer
CMO: Michael Sandlin, M.D., Chief of Staff
CHR: Stacey R. Burton, Director Human Resources
Web address: www.okmulgeehospital.com
Control: Other not–for–profit (including NFP Corporation) **Service:** General
Medical and Surgical

Staffed Beds: 46 **Admissions:** 1053 **Census:** 17 **Outpatient Visits:** 27733 **Births:** 4 **Total Expense ($000):** 15422 **Payroll Expense ($000):** 8096 **Personnel:** 175	

MUSCOGEE CREEK NATION PHYSICAL REHABILITATION CENTER
(372023), 900 East Airport Road, Zip 74447–9082, Mailing Address: P.O. Box
1118, Zip 74447–1118; tel. 918/756–9211, (Total facility includes 8 beds in
nursing home–type unit) **A**10 **F**1 28 29 34 56 57 82 90 93 94 96 128 130 135
143 146 148 **P**5
Primary Contact: Gala McBee, Administrator
CFO: Djogan Djogan, Chief Financial Officer
CHR: Denaye Atwell, Manager Human Resources
Web address: www.gnrc.ouhsc.edu/
Control: State–Government, nonfederal **Service:** Rehabilitation

Staffed Beds: 38 **Admissions:** 346 **Census:** 15 **Outpatient Visits:** 5958 **Births:** 0 **Total Expense ($000):** 6063 **Payroll Expense ($000):** 3196 **Personnel:** 94	

OKMULGEE MEMORIAL HOSPITAL (370057), 1401 Morris Drive, Zip 74447,
Mailing Address: Box 1038, Zip 74447; tel. 918/756–4233, (Nonreporting)
A9 10
Primary Contact: Sheridan Pickering, Administrator
COO: Angela Daugherty, Chief Operating Officer
CFO: Djogan Huang, Assistant Chief Financial Officer
CMO: Lawrence Vark, M.D., Acting Chief Medical Officer
CIO: Sharon Riker, Administrator Hospital Applications
CHR: Jeremy Smith, Manager Human Resources
CNO: Rebecca Casselman, Director of Nursing
Web address: www.okmulgeehospital.com
Control: Other not–for–profit (including NFP Corporation) **Service:** General
Medical and Surgical

Staffed Beds: 70	

OWASSO—Tulsa County

★ **BAILEY MEDICAL CENTER (370228)**, 10502 North 110th East Avenue,
Zip 74055–6655; tel. 918/376–8000 **A**9 10 **F**3 12 13 15 18 29 34 40 45 51
57 70 76 79 81 94 107 108 110 111 115 119 129 132 146 147 **S** Ardent
Health Services, Nashville, TN
Primary Contact: Keith Mason, Chief Executive Officer
CFO: Brandon Bullard, Chief Financial Officer
CHR: Tandy Groves, Coordinator Human Resources
Web address: www.baileymedicalcenter.com
Control: Corporation, Investor–owned, for–profit **Service:** General Medical and
Surgical

Staffed Beds: 37 **Admissions:** 1341 **Census:** 8 **Outpatient Visits:** 28506 **Births:** 328 **Total Expense ($000):** 29955 **Payroll Expense ($000):** 9902 **Personnel:** 169	

★ **ST. JOHN OWASSO (370227)**, 12451 East 100th Street North,
Zip 74055–4600; tel. 918/274–5000 **A**9 10 **F**3 11 13 15 18 29 30 34 35 40
43 45 57 59 64 68 76 79 81 85 87 93 107 108 110 111 114 115 119 130
131 132 146 **P**5 6 **S** Ascension Health, Saint Louis, MO
Primary Contact: David L. Phillips, President and Chief Executive Officer
CFO: Michael R. Nevins, Chief Financial Officer
CMO: Tim Hepner, M.D., Medical Director
CIO: Mike Reeves, Chief Information Officer
CNO: Dan Hall, R.N., Director of Nursing
Web address: www.stjohnowasso.com
Control: Church–operated, Nongovernment, not–for profit **Service:** General
Medical and Surgical

Staffed Beds: 45 **Admissions:** 1757 **Census:** 11 **Outpatient Visits:** 59300 **Births:** 373 **Total Expense ($000):** 29272 **Payroll Expense ($000):** 10085 **Personnel:** 224	

PAULS VALLEY—Garvin County

★ **PAULS VALLEY GENERAL HOSPITAL (370156)**, 100 Valley Drive,
Zip 73075–6613, Mailing Address: P.O. Box 368, Zip 73075–0368;
tel. 405/238–5501 **A**9 10 20 **F**3 7 8 10 11 13 15 29 30 40 45 46 57 59 62
63 64 65 76 77 81 82 84 87 89 93 107 111 119 129 130 132 133 146 147
148 **P**3
Primary Contact: John Dolan, Chief Executive Officer
CFO: John Dolan, Chief Financial Officer
CIO: Craig Bowie, Information Technology Manager
CHR: Kari Kuykendall, Human Resources Specialist
CNO: Karla Brown, Interim Chief Nursing Officer
Web address: www.pvgh.net
Control: City–Government, nonfederal **Service:** General Medical and Surgical

Staffed Beds: 54 **Admissions:** 742 **Census:** 9	

PAWHUSKA—Osage County

PAWHUSKA HOSPITAL (371309), 1101 East 15th Street, Zip 74056–1920;
tel. 918/287–3232 **A**9 10 18 **F**3 11 29 34 35 40 50 57 64 68 75 77 90 93
107 128 133 135 **P**1
Primary Contact: Jesi Tatum, Administrator
CMO: Mike Priest, M.D., Chief of Staff
Web address: www.pawhuskahospital.org
Control: Church–operated, Nongovernment, not–for profit **Service:** General
Medical and Surgical

Staffed Beds: 27 **Admissions:** 64 **Census:** 1 **Outpatient Visits:** 8563 **Births:** 0 **Total Expense ($000):** 4894 **Payroll Expense ($000):** 2069 **Personnel:** 49	

PERRY—Noble County

★ **PERRY MEMORIAL HOSPITAL (370139)**, 501 North 14th Street,
Zip 73077–5099; tel. 580/336–3541 **A**9 10 20 **F**3 15 29 34 40 45 57 59 62
64 65 79 81 85 93 107 111 114 119 133 146 148 **S** QHR, Brentwood, TN
Primary Contact: Howard D. Turner, Chief Executive Officer
CFO: Courtney Kozikuski, Chief Financial Officer
CMO: Bruce Thompson, M.D., Chief of Staff
CIO: Randy Taylor, Chief Information Technology Officer
CHR: Deb Ellis, Director Human Resources
CNO: Jeannie Carey, R.N., Director Patient Care
Web address: www.pmh–ok.org
Control: Hospital district or authority, Government, nonfederal **Service:** General
Medical and Surgical

Staffed Beds: 26 **Admissions:** 460 **Census:** 9 **Outpatient Visits:** 23681 **Births:** 0 **Total Expense ($000):** 8375 **Payroll Expense ($000):** 3797 **Personnel:** 73	

PONCA CITY—Kay County

⊞ **PONCA CITY MEDICAL CENTER (370006)**, 1900 North 14th Street,
Zip 74601–2099; tel. 580/765–3321 **A**1 9 10 19 **F**3 13 15 20 28 29 30 31
34 35 40 43 46 49 51 53 56 57 59 64 65 66 68 69 70 74 75 76 77 78 79
81 82 85 89 90 93 97 107 110 111 114 117 118 119 129 130 131 132 133
135 145 146 147 148 **S** Community Health Systems, Inc., Franklin, TN
Primary Contact: R. Andrew Wachtel, FACHE, Chief Executive Officer
COO: Nikia Beene, Assistant Chief Executive Officer
CFO: Geoff Blomeley, Interim Chief Financial Officer
CIO: Rob Dreussi, Interim Director Information Systems
CHR: Lisa Zaloudek, Chief Human Resources Officer
CNO: Jeanne Stara, R.N., Chief Nursing Officer
Web address: www.poncamedcenter.com
Control: Corporation, Investor–owned, for–profit **Service:** General Medical and
Surgical

Staffed Beds: 72 **Admissions:** 3070 **Census:** 26 **Outpatient Visits:** 62167 **Births:** 624 **Total Expense ($000):** 47431 **Payroll Expense ($000):** 15182 **Personnel:** 349	

POTEAU—Le Flore County

★ **EASTERN OKLAHOMA MEDICAL CENTER (370040)**, 105 Wall Street,
Zip 74953–4433, Mailing Address: P.O. Box 1148, Zip 74953–1148;
tel. 918/647–8161 **A**9 10 **F**3 11 13 15 29 40 43 45 50 57 62 68 70 76 81
85 86 89 107 110 111 114 115 116 119 146 **P**4
Primary Contact: Michael J. Carter, Chief Executive Officer
CFO: Nancy Frier, Chief Financial Officer
CMO: Dennis Carter, M.D., Chief of Staff
CIO: Michael C. Huggins, Administrator Network System
CHR: Michele D. Oglesby, Manager Human Resources
Web address: www.eomchospital.com
Control: County–Government, nonfederal **Service:** General Medical and Surgical

Staffed Beds: 84 **Admissions:** 1930 **Census:** 25 **Outpatient Visits:** 27879 **Births:** 351 **Total Expense ($000):** 18365 **Payroll Expense ($000):** 8533 **Personnel:** 256	

Hospital, Medicare Provider Number, Address, Telephone, Approval, Facility, and Physician Codes, Health Care System

★ American Hospital Association (AHA) membership
□ The Joint Commission accreditation
◇ DNV Healthcare Inc. accreditation
○ Healthcare Facilities Accreditation Program
△ Commission on Accreditation of Rehabilitation Facilities (CARF) accreditation

PRAGUE—Lincoln County

★ **PRAGUE COMMUNITY HOSPITAL (371301)**, 1322 Klabzuba Avenue,
Zip 74864–9005, Mailing Address: P.O. Box S., Zip 74864–1090;
tel. 405/567–4922 **A**9 10 18 **F**18 29 34 40 43 45 57 59 64 65 68 81 93 107
111 119 127 128 129 130 133 148 **P**6 **S** Rural Community Hospitals of
America, Kansas City, MO
Primary Contact: William Holland, Chief Executive Officer
CFO: Doug Erickson, Chief Financial Officer
CMO: Darryl Jackson, D.O., Chief of Staff
CIO: Rhonda Whitnum, Director Health Improvement Management
CHR: Angie Brezny, Director Human Resources
Web address: www.praguehospital.com
Control: Corporation, Investor–owned, for–profit **Service:** General Medical and
Surgical

Staffed Beds: 15 **Admissions:** 176 **Census:** 2 **Outpatient Visits:** 20379
Births: 0 **Total Expense ($000):** 5989 **Payroll Expense ($000):** 3077
Personnel: 58

PRYOR—Mayes County

⊞ **INTEGRIS MAYES COUNTY MEDICAL CENTER (370015)**, 111 North Bailey
Street, Zip 74361–4201, Mailing Address: P.O. Box 278, Zip 74362–0278;
tel. 918/825–1600 **A**1 9 10 **F**3 11 15 18 29 30 34 35 40 46 47 48 49 57 59
62 63 64 65 68 75 77 79 81 87 91 92 93 94 97 107 108 111 114 119 130
132 133 135 146 147 148 **S** Community Health Systems, Inc., Franklin, TN
Primary Contact: Douglas K. Weaver, FACHE, President
CMO: Jason Joice, M.D., Chief Medical Staff
CHR: Pamela A. Guthrie, Chief Human Resources Officer
CNO: Mary Ozment, Chief Nursing Officer
Web address: www.integrismayescounty.com
Control: Corporation, Investor–owned, for–profit **Service:** General Medical and
Surgical

Staffed Beds: 24 **Admissions:** 675 **Census:** 5 **Outpatient Visits:** 27557
Births: 0 **Total Expense ($000):** 24061 **Payroll Expense ($000):** 8899
Personnel: 226

PURCELL—Mcclain County

PURCELL MUNICIPAL HOSPITAL (370158), 1500 North Green Avenue,
Zip 73080–1699, Mailing Address: P.O. Box 511, Zip 73080–0511;
tel. 405/527–6524 **A**9 10 **F**3 11 13 15 18 29 30 35 40 45 48 57 59 64 65
76 77 79 81 82 86 87 89 93 110 114 119 127 130 132 133 **P**8
Primary Contact: Kem Scully, Chief Executive Officer
COO: Lisa Roberts, Chief Operating Officer
CFO: Jennifer Warren, Chief Financial Officer
CMO: Heather Lynch, M.D., Chief of Staff
CIO: Jennifer Coates, Coordinator Information Technology
CHR: Tara Selfridge, Manager Human Resources
Web address: www.purcellhospital.com
Control: City–Government, nonfederal **Service:** General Medical and Surgical

Staffed Beds: 30 **Admissions:** 972 **Census:** 10 **Outpatient Visits:** 52202
Births: 28 **Total Expense ($000):** 14839 **Payroll Expense ($000):** 6283
Personnel: 156

SALLISAW—Sequoyah County

SEQUOYAH MEMORIAL HOSPITAL (370112), 213 East Redwood Street,
Zip 74955–2811, Mailing Address: P.O. Box 505, Zip 74955–0505;
tel. 918/774–1100 **A**9 10 **F**3 11 14 15 18 30 32 34 35 40 43 45 46 50 57
59 60 62 63 64 65 77 81 84 86 87 91 93 107 109 110 111 119 128 129
130 132 133 146 **P**4
Primary Contact: Debra R. Knoke, Chief Executive Officer
COO: Debra R. Knoke, Chief Executive Officer
CFO: Glenn Click, Chief Financial Officer
CMO: William E. Wood, M.D., Chief of Staff
CIO: Gary McClanahan, Chief Information Officer
Web address: www.sequoyahmemorial.com/home.php
Control: Hospital district or authority, Government, nonfederal **Service:** General
Medical and Surgical

Staffed Beds: 26 **Admissions:** 518 **Census:** 5

SAPULPA—Creek County

★ **ST. JOHN SAPULPA (371312)**, 519 South Division Street, Zip 74066–4501,
Mailing Address: P.O. Box 1368, Zip 74067–1368; tel. 918/224–4280 **A**9 10 18
F3 11 14 29 30 34 35 40 45 57 59 62 64 65 81 85 86 87 107 111 119 130
132 133 135 143 146 147 **P**5 6 **S** Ascension Health, Saint Louis, MO
Primary Contact: David L. Phillips, Chief Executive Officer
CFO: John W. Crawford, Chief Financial Officer
CMO: Jason Lepak, M.D., Medical Director
CNO: Kelly Johnson, R.N., Chief Nursing Officer
Web address: www.sjmc.org
Control: Church–operated, Nongovernment, not–for profit **Service:** General
Medical and Surgical

Staffed Beds: 25 **Admissions:** 1016 **Census:** 11 **Outpatient Visits:** 31201
Births: 0 **Total Expense ($000):** 22888 **Payroll Expense ($000):** 7797
Personnel: 171

SAYRE—Beckham County

★ **SAYRE MEMORIAL HOSPITAL (370103)**, 911 Hospital Drive,
Zip 73662–1206; tel. 580/928–5541, (Nonreporting) **A**9 10
Primary Contact: Donna Gail Robison, Interim Chief Executive Officer
CFO: Brenda K. Doyel, Chief Financial Officer
Web address: www.sayrehospital.org
Control: Other not–for–profit (including NFP Corporation) **Service:** General
Medical and Surgical

Staffed Beds: 46

SEILING—Dewey County

★ **SEILING COMMUNITY HOSPITAL (371332)**, Highway 60 N.E., Zip 73663,
Mailing Address: P.O. Box 720, Zip 73663–0720; tel. 580/922–7361 **A**9 10 18
F40 41 65 107 111 119 127 133 **P**5 **S** Rural Community Hospitals of America,
Kansas City, MO
Primary Contact: Donald E. Buchanan, Interim Chief Executive Officer
CFO: Nancy Freed, Chief Financial Officer
CMO: Kenneth Duffy, M.D., Medical Director
CHR: Sandy Landreth, Director Human Resources
Web address: www.seilinghospital.com
Control: Corporation, Investor–owned, for–profit **Service:** General Medical and
Surgical

Staffed Beds: 18 **Admissions:** 250 **Census:** 3 **Outpatient Visits:** 5006
Births: 0 **Total Expense ($000):** 4108 **Payroll Expense ($000):** 1664
Personnel: 47

SEMINOLE—Seminole County

⊞ **INTEGRIS SEMINOLE MEDICAL CENTER (370229)**, 2401 Wrangler
Boulevard, Zip 74868–1917; tel. 405/303–4000 **A**1 9 10 **F**3 11 15 18 29 30
34 35 40 41 51 57 59 65 68 79 81 82 93 102 107 108 110 111 114 119
130 135 146 148 **P**6 **S** Community Health Systems, Inc., Franklin, TN
Primary Contact: Jimmy D. Stuart, Chief Executive Officer
CMO: Nikki Chawla, M.D., Medical Director
CHR: Lori Friend, Human Resources Director
CNO: Barbara Lewis, Chief Nursing Officer
Web address: www.hma.com
Control: Corporation, Investor–owned, for–profit **Service:** General Medical and
Surgical

Staffed Beds: 32 **Admissions:** 807 **Census:** 6 **Outpatient Visits:** 22146
Births: 0 **Total Expense ($000):** 12355 **Payroll Expense ($000):** 4157
Personnel: 91

SHATTUCK—Ellis County

★ **NEWMAN MEMORIAL HOSPITAL (370007)**, 905 South Main Street,
Zip 73858–9205; tel. 580/938–2551 **A**9 10 20 **F**3 11 13 15 29 30 34 35 39
40 53 59 62 64 65 69 76 83 87 93 104 107 111 115 119 130 133 146 **P**6
Primary Contact: Jeffrey D. Shelton, Chief Executive Officer
CFO: Kellcie Skinner, Controller
CMO: Danna Stuart, M.D., Chief Medical Officer
CIO: Robert Neal, Manager Information Technology Services
CNO: Rylee Casper, R.N., Chief Nursing Officer
Web address: www.newmanmemorialhospital.org
Control: Other not–for–profit (including NFP Corporation) **Service:** General
Medical and Surgical

Staffed Beds: 27 **Admissions:** 339 **Census:** 3 **Total Expense ($000):** 19888

SHAWNEE—Pottawatomie County

SOLARA HOSPITAL OF SHAWNEE (372019), 1900 Gordon Cooper Drive, 2nd
Floor, Zip 74801–8603, Mailing Address: PO BOX 1245, Zip 74802–1245;
tel. 405/395–5800, (Nonreporting) **A**9 10 **S** Cornerstone Healthcare Group,
Dallas, TX
Primary Contact: Elizabeth Waytula, Chief Executive Officer
COO: Elizabeth Waytula, Chief Executive Officer
CMO: Keith Conaway, M.D., Chief Medical Officer
Web address: www.chghospitals.com/shawnee/
Control: Corporation, Investor–owned, for–profit **Service:** Long–Term Acute Care
hospital

Staffed Beds: 34

Many Facility Codes have changed. Please refer to the AHA Guide Code Chart. © 2014 AHA Guide

⊠ **ST. ANTHONY SHAWNEE HOSPITAL (370149)**, 1102 West MacArthur Street, Zip 74804–1744; tel. 405/273–2270 **A**1 2 9 10 19 **F**3 11 13 15 18 20 29 30 34 35 40 43 45 50 57 59 60 64 65 68 69 70 75 76 77 79 81 82 87 90 93 94 107 110 111 114 119 121 123 129 130 131 132 135 144 146 147 148 **P**6 **S** SSM Health, Saint Louis, MO
Primary Contact: Charles E. Skillings, President and Chief Executive Officer
COO: Angela Mohr, R.N., Vice President Nursing and Chief Operating Officer
CFO: Jennifer Pierce, Administrative Director of Finance
CMO: Gaynell Anderson, M.D., Medical Director
CHR: Michael Spears, Human Resource Leader
CNO: Angela Mohr, R.N., Vice President Nursing and Chief Operating Officer
Web address: www.stanthonyshawnee.com
Control: Other not–for–profit (including NFP Corporation) **Service:** General Medical and Surgical

> **Staffed Beds:** 131 **Admissions:** 4494 **Census:** 41 **Outpatient Visits:** 106713 **Births:** 870 **Total Expense ($000):** 70663 **Payroll Expense ($000):** 27070 **Personnel:** 456

UNITY HEALTH CENTER See St. Anthony Shawnee Hospital

SPENCER—Oklahoma County

INTEGRIS MENTAL HEALTH SYSTEM–SPENCER See Integris Baptist Medical Center, Oklahoma City

STIGLER—Haskell County

HASKELL COUNTY COMMUNITY HOSPITAL (371335), 401 Northwest H Street, Zip 74462–1625; tel. 918/967–4682, (Nonreporting) **A**9 10 18 **S** Rural Community Hospitals of America, Kansas City, MO
Primary Contact: Donald E. Buchanan, Interim Chief Executive Officer
CMO: Mark McCurry, M.D., Chief of Staff
CIO: Steve Hurst, Information Technology Specialist
Web address: www.haskellhospital.com
Control: Corporation, Investor–owned, for–profit **Service:** General Medical and Surgical

> **Staffed Beds:** 32

HASKELL COUNTY HEALTHCARE SYSTEM See Haskell County Community Hospital

STILLWATER—Payne County

★ △ ◇ **STILLWATER MEDICAL CENTER (370049)**, 1323 West Sixth Avenue, Zip 74074–4399, Mailing Address: P.O. Box 2408, Zip 74076–2408; tel. 405/372–1480 **A**7 9 10 19 20 21 **F**3 8 11 13 15 18 20 22 28 29 31 34 35 40 43 45 46 47 48 49 50 51 53 59 62 64 65 68 69 70 74 75 76 78 79 81 82 85 87 90 91 93 94 97 107 108 110 111 115 117 119 126 129 130 132 146 147 148 **P**6 7
Primary Contact: Jerry G. Moeller, FACHE, President and Chief Executive Officer
CFO: Alan Lovelace, Vice President and Chief Financial Officer
CMO: Steve Cummings, M.D., Chief of Medical Staff
CIO: Chris Roark, Chief Information Officer
CHR: Keith Hufnagel, Director Human Resources
CNO: Elizabeth Michael, R.N., Vice President Patient Care Services and Chief Nursing Officer
Web address: www.stillwater–medical.org
Control: Hospital district or authority, Government, nonfederal **Service:** General Medical and Surgical

> **Staffed Beds:** 87 **Admissions:** 5506 **Census:** 48 **Outpatient Visits:** 122106 **Births:** 983 **Total Expense ($000):** 117856 **Payroll Expense ($000):** 52242 **Personnel:** 1127

STILWELL—Adair County

MEMORIAL HOSPITAL (370178), 1401 West Locust, Zip 74960–3275, Mailing Address: P.O. Box 272, Zip 74960–0272; tel. 918/696–3101, (Nonreporting) **A**9 10
Primary Contact: Alan L. Adams, President
Web address: www.stilwellmemorialhospital.com
Control: Corporation, Investor–owned, for–profit **Service:** General Medical and Surgical

> **Staffed Beds:** 30

STROUD—Lincoln County

STROUD REGIONAL MEDICAL CENTER (371316), Highway 66 West, Zip 74079, Mailing Address: P.O. Box 530, Zip 74079–0530; tel. 918/968–3571 **A**9 10 18 **F**3 8 11 29 30 34 35 40 41 43 45 57 59 64 68 81 89 107 114 128 130 133 135 148 **P**5 **S** Southern Plains Medical Group, Oklahoma City, OK
Primary Contact: Tommy Smith, Chief Executive Officer
CFO: Richard E. Rentsch, President
CMO: Ken Darvin, M.D., Chief of Staff
CIO: Donna Buchanan, Director Nursing
CHR: Leannette Raffety, Administrative Generalist
Web address: www.stroudhospital.com/
Control: Other not–for–profit (including NFP Corporation) **Service:** General Medical and Surgical

> **Staffed Beds:** 25 **Admissions:** 247 **Census:** 3 **Births:** 0 **Total Expense ($000):** 17542 **Personnel:** 55

SULPHUR—Murray County

★ **ARBUCKLE MEMORIAL HOSPITAL (371328)**, 2011 West Broadway Street, Zip 73086–4221; tel. 580/622–2161 **A**9 10 18 **F**3 11 29 32 40 45 56 57 81 87 93 107 119 133 135 148 **P**6 **S** Mercy Health, Chesterfield, MO
Primary Contact: Darin Farrell, Chief Executive Officer
CFO: Denise Hancock, Chief Financial Officer
CMO: Teresa Lynn, D.O., Chief of Staff
CIO: Tiffany Sands, Manager Health Information
CHR: Sallie Tomlinson, Manager Human Resources
Web address: www.arbucklehospital.com/
Control: County–Government, nonfederal **Service:** General Medical and Surgical

> **Staffed Beds:** 13 **Admissions:** 526 **Census:** 10 **Outpatient Visits:** 25704 **Births:** 0 **Total Expense ($000):** 13436 **Payroll Expense ($000):** 6816 **Personnel:** 125

TAHLEQUAH—Cherokee County

★ ◇ **CHEROKEE NATION W.W. HASTINGS INDIAN HOSPITAL (370171)**, 100 South Bliss Avenue, Zip 74464–2512; tel. 918/458–3100, (Nonreporting) **A**10 21 **S** U. S. Indian Health Service, Rockville, MD
Primary Contact: Brian Hail, Chief Executive Officer
COO: Mitchell Thornbrugh, Administrative Officer
CMO: Douglas Nolan, M.D., Medical Director
CIO: Mitchell Thornbrugh, Acting Chief Information Officer
CNO: Valerie J. Rogers, Director of Nursing
Web address: www.cherokee.org
Control: PHS, Indian Service, Government, federal **Service:** General Medical and Surgical

> **Staffed Beds:** 58

★ **NORTHEASTERN HEALTH SYSTEM (370089)**, 1400 East Downing Street, Zip 74464–3324, Mailing Address: P.O. Box 1008, Zip 74465–1008; tel. 918/456–0641 **A**9 10 13 20 **F**3 7 11 13 15 17 18 20 22 24 28 29 30 34 35 39 40 43 45 46 47 49 51 57 59 60 64 68 70 74 75 76 77 78 79 80 81 82 85 87 89 90 93 97 98 103 107 108 110 111 114 115 116 117 119 120 121 123 129 130 135 148 **P**6
Primary Contact: Brian K. Woodliff, President and Chief Executive Officer Northeastern Health System
COO: Mark McCroskey, Vice President Operations
CFO: Julie Ward, Vice President Finance
CIO: Julie Ward, Vice President Finance
CHR: Phyllis Smith, Vice President Human Resources
CNO: Donna Dallis, R.N., Vice President Patient Care
Web address: www.tch–ok.org
Control: City–Government, nonfederal **Service:** General Medical and Surgical

> **Staffed Beds:** 90 **Admissions:** 3686 **Census:** 45 **Outpatient Visits:** 133117 **Births:** 380 **Total Expense ($000):** 73618 **Payroll Expense ($000):** 25451 **Personnel:** 683

TALIHINA—Latimer County

⊠ **CHOCTAW NATION HEALTH CARE CENTER (370172)**, One Choctaw Way, Zip 74571–2022; tel. 918/567–7000 **A**1 10 **F**3 11 13 15 18 30 32 34 35 38 39 40 43 45 50 53 54 56 57 58 59 61 64 65 68 71 74 75 76 79 81 85 86 87 89 91 92 93 94 96 97 99 100 101 103 104 107 111 114 115 119 127 129 130 132 134 135 144 146 147 148 **P**6
Primary Contact: Janet Sharp, Interim Chief Executive Officer
COO: Todd Hallmark, Chief Operating Officer
CMO: Jason Hill, M.D., Chief Medical Officer
CIO: Skip Leader, Chief Information Officer
CHR: Evelyn Jones, Director Human Resources
Web address: www.cnhsa.com
Control: PHS, Indian Service, Government, federal **Service:** General Medical and Surgical

> **Staffed Beds:** 44 **Admissions:** 1736 **Census:** 13 **Outpatient Visits:** 225000 **Births:** 600

Hospital, Medicare Provider Number, Address, Telephone, Approval, Facility, and Physician Codes, Health Care System

★ American Hospital Association (AHA) membership
☐ The Joint Commission accreditation
◇ DNV Healthcare Inc. accreditation
○ Healthcare Facilities Accreditation Program
△ Commission on Accreditation of Rehabilitation Facilities (CARF) accreditation

---

OK

TISHOMINGO—Johnston County

JOHNSTON MEMORIAL HOSPITAL See Mercy Hospital Tishomingo

★ **MERCY HOSPITAL TISHOMINGO (371304)**, 1000 South Byrd Street, Zip 73460–3299; tel. 580/371–2327 **A**9 10 18 **F**3 29 40 133 **S** Mercy Health, Chesterfield, MO
Primary Contact: Gary Sharum, Administrator
CFO: Lisa Dowling, Manager Finance
CHR: Arlita Hummelke, Manager Human Resources
Web address: www.mercy.net/
Control: Church–operated, Nongovernment, not–for profit **Service:** General Medical and Surgical

Staffed Beds: 25 Admissions: 393 Census: 5 Outpatient Visits: 4695
Births: 0 Total Expense ($000): 5288 Payroll Expense ($000): 2424
Personnel: 39

TULSA—Tulsa County

AMG SPECIALTY HOSPITAL–TULSA (372011), 1923 South Utica Avenue, 4 South, Zip 74104–6510; tel. 918/744–3047, (Includes CONTINUOUS CARE CENTERS OF OKLAHOMA, 744 West Ninth Street, 9th Floor, Zip 74127; tel. 918/599–4604), (Nonreporting) **A**9 10 **S** AMG Integrated Healthcare Management, Lafayette, LA
Primary Contact: Stacy Wilde, Chief Executive Officer
COO: Mike Harris, Chief Operating Officer
CFO: Basil Wyatt, Chief Financial Officer
CMO: Mark Myers, M.D., Chief Medical Officer
CIO: Dana Jetton, Chief Information Officer
CHR: Donna Nagel, Director Human Resources
Web address: www.amgihm.com
Control: Other not–for–profit (including NFP Corporation) **Service:** Long–Term Acute Care hospital

Staffed Beds: 46

BROOKHAVEN HOSPITAL (374012), 201 South Garnett Road, Zip 74128–1805; tel. 918/438–4257 **A**9 10 **F**4 5 29 30 38 74 75 77 98 104 106 130 132
Primary Contact: Rolf B. Gainer, Chief Executive Officer and Administrator
CFO: Kenneth Pierce, Chief Financial Officer
CMO: Mark Gage, D.O., Medical Director
CHR: Heather Dudley, Director Administrative Services
CNO: Matt Maxey, R.N., Director of Nursing
Web address: www.brookhavenhospital.com
Control: Corporation, Investor–owned, for–profit **Service:** Psychiatric

Staffed Beds: 64 Admissions: 1217 Census: 51 Outpatient Visits: 3035
Births: 0 Total Expense ($000): 10865 Payroll Expense ($000): 6313
Personnel: 176

CONTINUOUS CARE CENTERS OF TULSA See AMG Specialty Hospital–Tulsa

✠ **HILLCREST HOSPITAL – SOUTH (370202)**, 8801 South 101st East Avenue, Zip 74133–5716; tel. 918/294–4000 **A**1 9 10 **F**3 13 15 18 20 22 24 28 29 30 34 40 43 45 46 49 51 54 57 59 64 70 75 79 81 85 86 87 91 93 97 107 108 110 111 114 115 118 119 124 126 129 130 131 146 147 148 **S** Ardent Health Services, Nashville, TN
Primary Contact: Joseph H. Neely, FACHE, Chief Executive Officer
COO: Matthew Morgan, Associate Administrator
CFO: James Washecka, Chief Financial Officer
CMO: David L. Pohl, M.D., Chief of Staff
CIO: David Graser, Vice President and Chief Information Officer
CHR: Rachel Steward, Director Human Resources
CNO: Dava Baldridge, R.N., Chief Nursing Officer
Web address: www.southcresthospital.com
Control: Corporation, Investor–owned, for–profit **Service:** General Medical and Surgical

Staffed Beds: 160 Admissions: 6488 Census: 68 Outpatient Visits: 74313
Births: 1487 Total Expense ($000): 106627 Payroll Expense ($000): 33520 Personnel: 475

✠ ◇ **HILLCREST MEDICAL CENTER (370001)**, 1120 South Utica, Zip 74104–4090; tel. 918/579–1000 **A**1 3 5 9 10 21 **F**3 8 11 13 15 16 17 18 20 22 24 26 28 29 30 31 37 40 43 45 46 49 50 51 53 55 57 58 59 60 68 70 72 76 78 79 80 81 84 86 87 90 93 98 99 106 107 108 110 111 114 115 117 119 120 121 124 126 129 130 146 147 148 **S** Ardent Health Services, Nashville, TN
Primary Contact: Kevin J. Gross, Interim Chief Executive Officer
COO: Matthew Troup, Chief Operating Officer
CFO: Steve Winegeart, Chief Financial Officer
CMO: Steven Landgarten, M.D., Chief Medical Officer
CHR: Julie Eccleston, Vice President Human Resources
CNO: Kathleen Willis, R.N., Chief Nursing Officer
Web address: www.hillcrest.com/home
Control: Corporation, Investor–owned, for–profit **Service:** General Medical and Surgical

Staffed Beds: 532 Admissions: 23153 Census: 344 Outpatient Visits: 181921 Births: 2781 Total Expense ($000): 390358 Payroll Expense ($000): 130144 Personnel: 1737

✠ **LAUREATE PSYCHIATRIC CLINIC AND HOSPITAL (374020)**, 6655 South Yale Avenue, Zip 74136–3329; tel. 918/481–4000 **A**1 3 5 9 10 **F**4 5 98 99 100 101 102 103 104 105 106 146 **P**6 **S** Saint Francis Health System, Tulsa, OK
Primary Contact: William Schloss, Senior Vice President and Administrator
COO: William Schloss, Senior Vice President and Administrator
CFO: Barry L. Steichen, Executive Vice President, Chief Administrative Officer and Chief Financial Officer
CMO: Mark I. Frost, M.D., Vice President Medical Staff Affairs
CIO: Mark Stastny, Vice President Information Technology
CHR: Amy B. Adams, Executive Director Human Resources
CNO: Lynn A. Sund, R.N., Senior Vice President, Administrator and Chief Nursing Executive
Web address: www.laureate.com
Control: Other not–for–profit (including NFP Corporation) **Service:** Psychiatric

Staffed Beds: 75 Admissions: 3249 Census: 68 Outpatient Visits: 69771
Births: 0 Total Expense ($000): 29666 Payroll Expense ($000): 18299
Personnel: 338

MEADOWBROOK SPECIALTY HOSPITAL OF TULSA See Post Acute Medical Specialty Hospital of Tulsa

○ **OKLAHOMA STATE UNIVERSITY MEDICAL CENTER (370078)**, 744 West Ninth Street, Zip 74127–9020; tel. 918/599–1000 **A**9 10 11 12 13 **F**3 8 13 15 18 20 22 24 26 28 29 30 31 34 35 40 43 45 47 49 50 56 57 59 64 65 70 71 72 74 75 76 77 78 79 81 84 85 87 89 92 93 96 97 107 108 110 111 115 119 130 135 146 148 **P**6
Primary Contact: David Tew, Interim Chief Executive Officer
COO: Lisa Ellis, Chief Operating Officer
CMO: Damon Baker, D.O., Chief Medical Officer
CIO: Heidi Holmes, Chief Information Officer
CHR: Sunny J. Benjamin, Chief Human Resources Officer
CNO: Joy Upshaw, Chief Nursing Officer
Web address: www.osumc.net
Control: City–Government, nonfederal **Service:** General Medical and Surgical

Staffed Beds: 191 Admissions: 6505 Census: 82

OKLAHOMA SURGICAL HOSPITAL (370210), 2408 East 81st Street, Suite 300, Zip 74137–4215; tel. 918/477–5000 **A**9 10 **F**3 12 29 30 34 35 40 41 44 45 49 50 51 64 65 68 74 75 77 79 81 82 85 86 87 93 94 107 108 111 114 119 126 130 131 **P**2
Primary Contact: Rick Ferguson, Chief Executive Officer
COO: Beverly Pickett, R.N., Chief Nursing Officer
CFO: Dub Cleland, Chief Financial Officer
Web address: www.oklahomasurgicalhospital.com
Control: Partnership, Investor–owned, for–profit **Service:** General Medical and Surgical

Staffed Beds: 49 Admissions: 3450 Census: 21 Outpatient Visits: 21477
Births: 0 Total Expense ($000): 75561 Payroll Expense ($000): 16993
Personnel: 341

PARKSIDE HOSPITAL (374021), 1620 East 12th Street, Zip 74120–5407; tel. 918/582–2131, (Nonreporting) **A**3 5 9 10
Primary Contact: Debra Moore, Chief Executive Officer
CFO: Saunya Moore, Chief Financial Officer
CMO: Marvin Jin, M.D., Medical Director
CIO: Joe Vitali, Director Information Technology
CHR: David Patterson, Director Human Resources
Web address: www.parksideinc.org
Control: Other not–for–profit (including NFP Corporation) **Service:** Psychiatric

Staffed Beds: 70

○ **PINNACLE SPECIALTY HOSPITAL (370233)**, 2408 East 81st Street, Suite 600, Zip 74137–4200; tel. 918/392–2780 **A**10 11 **F**12 29 33 75 84 129 148
Primary Contact: Mark Stearns, Administrator
Web address: www.pinnaclespecialtyhospital.com/
Control: State–Government, nonfederal **Service:** General Medical and Surgical

Staffed Beds: 4 Admissions: 55 Census: 1 Births: 0

✠ **POST ACUTE MEDICAL SPECIALTY HOSPITAL OF TULSA (372018)**, 3219 South 79th East Avenue, Zip 74145–1343; tel. 918/663–8183 **A**1 9 10 **F**1 3 29 40 42 60 68 75 87 94 100 107 108 114 130 143 148 **P**8 **S** Post Acute Medical, LLC, Enola, PA
Primary Contact: Lee A. Simpson, Jr., Chief Executive Officer
CFO: Lee A. Simpson, Jr., Chief Executive Officer
Web address: www.postacutetulsa.com
Control: Corporation, Investor–owned, for–profit **Service:** Long–Term Acute Care hospital

Staffed Beds: 60 Admissions: 517 Census: 38 Outpatient Visits: 30 Births: 0 Total Expense ($000): 18333 Payroll Expense ($000): 7507 Personnel: 126

SAINT FRANCIS HEART HOSPITAL See Saint Francis Hospital

Many Facility Codes have changed. Please refer to the AHA Guide Code Chart. © 2014 AHA Guide

OK

✠ **SAINT FRANCIS HOSPITAL (370091)**, 6161 South Yale Avenue, Zip 74136–1902; tel. 918/494–2200, (Includes CHILDREN'S HOSPITAL AT SAINT FRANCIS, 6161 South Yale Avenue, tel. 918/502–6714; SAINT FRANCIS HEART HOSPITAL, 6161 South Yale Avenue, tel. 918/502–2022) **A**1 2 3 5 9 10 **F**3 7 8 11 12 13 15 17 18 19 20 21 22 23 24 25 26 27 28 29 30 31 32 35 37 39 40 41 43 44 45 46 47 48 49 50 51 54 55 56 57 58 60 61 64 66 68 69 70 72 73 74 75 76 77 78 79 80 81 82 83 84 85 86 87 88 89 90 92 93 107 108 110 111 112 114 115 116 118 119 120 121 123 124 126 129 130 131 132 135 136 138 141 146 148 **P**6 **S** Saint Francis Health System, Tulsa, OK
Primary Contact: Lynn A. Sund, R.N., MS, Senior Vice President, Administrator and Chief Nurse Executive
COO: Lynn A. Sund, R.N., Senior Vice President, Administrator and Chief Nurse Executive
CFO: Barry L. Steichen, Executive Vice President and Chief Financial Officer
CMO: Peter P. Aran, M.D., Senior Vice President and Chief Medical Officer
CIO: Mark Stastny, Vice President Information Technology
CHR: Amy B. Adams, Executive Director Human Resources
Web address: www.saintfrancis.com
Control: Other not–for–profit (including NFP Corporation) **Service:** General Medical and Surgical

Staffed Beds: 808 Admissions: 44240 Census: 610 Outpatient Visits: 364338 Births: 4185 Total Expense ($000): 643520 Payroll Expense ($000): 248275 Personnel: 4735

✠ **SAINT FRANCIS HOSPITAL SOUTH (370218)**, 10501 East 91St. Streeet, Zip 74133–5790; tel. 918/455–3535 **A**1 9 10 **F**11 13 15 18 20 22 26 29 34 35 37 39 40 44 48 49 50 57 58 61 64 68 70 72 75 76 79 81 82 107 108 110 111 114 115 118 119 130 146 148 **P**6 **S** Saint Francis Health System, Tulsa, OK
Primary Contact: David S. Weil, Senior Vice President and Administrator
COO: Barry L. Steichen, Executive Vice President
CFO: Barry L. Steichen, Executive Vice President
CMO: Peter P. Aran, M.D., Senior Vice President and Chief Medical Officer
CIO: Mark Stastny, Vice President Information Technology
CHR: Amy B. Adams, Executive Director Human Resources
CNO: Jimmie Cash, R.N., Executive Director and Patient Care
Web address: www.saintfrancis.com/south/
Control: Other not–for–profit (including NFP Corporation) **Service:** General Medical and Surgical

Staffed Beds: 78 Admissions: 3908 Census: 38 Outpatient Visits: 74928 Births: 1221 Total Expense ($000): 59900 Payroll Expense ($000): 21648 Personnel: 380

✠ **SELECT SPECIALTY HOSPITAL–TULSA MIDTOWN (372007)**, 1125 South Trenton Avenue, 3rd Floor, Zip 74120–5418; tel. 918/579–7300 **A**1 9 10 **F**1 3 29 85 87 130 148 **S** Select Medical Corporation, Mechanicsburg, PA
Primary Contact: Linda Tiemens, Chief Executive Officer
CMO: E. Joe Schelbar, M.D., Medical Director
CNO: Connie Ryan, Chief Nursing Officer
Web address: www.selectmedical.com
Control: Corporation, Investor–owned, for–profit **Service:** Long–Term Acute Care hospital

Staffed Beds: 56 Admissions: 375 Census: 29 Outpatient Visits: 0 Births: 0 Total Expense ($000): 15225 Payroll Expense ($000): 6631 Personnel: 115

☐ **SHADOW MOUNTAIN BEHAVIORAL HEALTH SYSTEM**, 6262 South Sheridan Road, Zip 74133–4055; tel. 918/492–8200 **A**1 9 **F**40 41 54 59 98 99 101 102 104 106 **P**6 **S** Universal Health Services, Inc., King of Prussia, PA
Primary Contact: Mike Kistler, Chief Executive Officer
CFO: Kirt Penrod, Chief Financial Officer
CMO: K. Michael Saliba, M.D., Medical Director
CHR: Jordan Cooke, Director Human Resources
Web address: www.shadowmountainbhs.com
Control: Corporation, Investor–owned, for–profit **Service:** Children's hospital psychiatric

Staffed Beds: 202 Admissions: 2293 Census: 186 Outpatient Visits: 28684 Births: 0 Total Expense ($000): 30764 Payroll Expense ($000): 12449 Personnel: 337

☐ **SOUTHWESTERN REGIONAL MEDICAL CENTER (370190)**, 10109 East 79th Street, Zip 74133–4564; tel. 918/286–5000 **A**1 2 10 **F**3 15 29 30 31 33 34 35 36 40 45 46 47 49 50 53 55 57 58 59 64 70 74 75 77 78 80 81 82 84 85 86 87 91 93 100 107 108 110 111 114 116 117 118 119 120 121 123 124 129 130 132 135 143 145 146 148 **P**6 **S** Cancer Treatment Centers of America, Schaumburg, IL
Primary Contact: Richard Haldeman, President and Chief Executive Officer
COO: Jay Foley, Chief Operating Officer
CFO: David Hedges, Chief Financial Officer
CMO: Daniel Nader, D.O., Chief of Staff
CIO: Craig Olson, Director Information Technology
CHR: Ryan Crawford, Director Talent
CNO: Denise Geuder, Vice President Patient Care Service and Chief Nursing Officer
Web address: www.cancercenter.com
Control: Corporation, Investor–owned, for–profit **Service:** Cancer

Staffed Beds: 40 Admissions: 948 Census: 21 Outpatient Visits: 70453 Births: 0

✠ **ST. JOHN MEDICAL CENTER (370114)**, 1923 South Utica Avenue, Zip 74104–6502; tel. 918/744–2345 **A**1 2 3 5 9 10 **F**1 3 8 9 11 12 13 14 15 17 18 19 20 22 24 26 28 29 30 34 35 37 39 40 43 45 46 47 48 49 50 51 53 54 56 57 58 59 60 61 62 63 64 65 66 67 68 70 72 73 74 75 76 77 78 79 80 81 82 83 84 85 86 87 88 89 90 92 93 94 96 97 98 100 104 107 108 110 111 114 115 116 117 118 119 120 121 123 124 126 128 129 130 131 132 135 138 141 143 145 146 147 148 **P**1 6 7 **S** Ascension Health, Saint Louis, MO
Primary Contact: Jeffrey D. Nowlin, President and Chief Operating Officer
COO: Jeffrey D. Nowlin, President and Chief Operating Officer
CFO: Wayne Walthall, Vice President and Chief Financial Officer
CMO: William Allred, M.D., Vice President Medical Affairs
CIO: Mike Reeves, Vice President
CHR: John Page Bachman, Corporate Vice President
CNO: Pamela Kiser, R.N., Chief Nursing Executive and Vice President of Nursing
Web address: www.sjmc.org
Control: Church–operated, Nongovernment, not–for profit **Service:** General Medical and Surgical

Staffed Beds: 547 Admissions: 28908 Census: 383 Outpatient Visits: 491943 Births: 2071 Total Expense ($000): 471236 Payroll Expense ($000): 153924 Personnel: 3079

✠ **TULSA SPINE AND SPECIALTY HOSPITAL (370216)**, 6901 South Olympia Avenue, Zip 74132–1843; tel. 918/388–5701, (Nonreporting) **A**1 9 10
Primary Contact: Terry L. Woodbeck, Administrator
CFO: Thom Biby, Chief Financial Officer
CMO: David Fell, M.D., Chief Medical Officer
Web address: www.tulsaspinehospital.com
Control: Corporation, Investor–owned, for–profit **Service:** General Medical and Surgical

Staffed Beds: 21

VINITA—Craig County

★ **CRAIG GENERAL HOSPITAL (370065)**, 735 North Foreman Street, Zip 74301–1418, Mailing Address: P.O. Box 326, Zip 74301–0326; tel. 918/256–7551 **A**9 10 20 **F**3 11 13 15 29 30 34 35 40 53 57 59 64 65 75 76 81 85 89 93 97 98 103 104 105 106 107 110 111 115 119 127 128 130 132 133 135 146 147 148
Primary Contact: Steven Chase, Chief Executive Officer
CMO: Ed Allensworth, M.D., Medical Director
CHR: Darlene R. Nolte, Chief Human Resource Officer
CNO: Robin Kemp, R.N., Chief Nursing Officer
Web address: www.craiggeneralhospital.com
Control: Hospital district or authority, Government, nonfederal **Service:** General Medical and Surgical

Staffed Beds: 53 Admissions: 1605 Census: 23 Outpatient Visits: 36381 Births: 67 Total Expense ($000): 28478 Payroll Expense ($000): 11428 Personnel: 275

OKLAHOMA FORENSIC CENTER, 24800 South 4420 Road, Zip 74301–5544, Mailing Address: P.O. Box 69, Zip 74301–0069; tel. 918/256–7841, (Nonreporting) **S** Oklahoma Department of Mental Health and Substance Abuse Services, Oklahoma City, OK
Primary Contact: Lori Jordan, Chief Executive Officer
CFO: Miriam Harris, Director Finance
CMO: Satwant Tandon, M.D., Director of Clinical Services
CIO: Kevin Marble, Director Information Technology
CHR: Julie Jacobs, Director Human Resources
CNO: Glenda Satterwhite, Director of Nursing
Web address: www.odmhsas.org
Control: State–Government, nonfederal **Service:** Psychiatric

Staffed Beds: 200

Hospital, Medicare Provider Number, Address, Telephone, Approval, Facility, and Physician Codes, Health Care System

★ American Hospital Association (AHA) membership
☐ The Joint Commission accreditation
◇ DNV Healthcare Inc. accreditation
◯ Healthcare Facilities Accreditation Program
△ Commission on Accreditation of Rehabilitation Facilities (CARF) accreditation

OK

WAGONER—Wagoner County

WAGONER COMMUNITY HOSPITAL (370166), 1200 West Cherokee Street, Zip 74467–4624, Mailing Address: P.O. Box 407, Zip 74477–0407; tel. 918/485–5514 **A**9 10 **F**3 11 12 15 28 29 30 34 39 40 41 45 50 51 56 57 59 64 65 68 70 74 75 79 81 82 85 87 89 98 102 103 104 107 108 110 114 116 119 130 131 132 135 146 148
Primary Contact: Jimmy Leopard, FACHE, Chief Executive Officer
COO: Louise Easter, R.N., Chief Operating Officer and Chief Nursing Officer
CFO: Rebecca Sharp, Chief Financial Officer
CMO: John Perry, M.D., Chief of Staff
CIO: Jim Riley, Director Information Technology
CHR: Barnetta Pofahl, Director Human Resources
CNO: Louise Easter, R.N., Chief Nursing Officer
Web address: www.wagonerhospital.com
Control: Hospital district or authority, Government, nonfederal **Service:** General Medical and Surgical

Staffed Beds: 100 **Admissions:** 2944 **Census:** 35 **Outpatient Visits:** 25774
Births: 0 **Total Expense ($000):** 17964 **Payroll Expense ($000):** 8228
Personnel: 168

WATONGA—Blaine County

★ **MERCY HOSPITAL WATONGA (371302)**, 500 North Clarence Nash Boulevard, Zip 73772–2845, Mailing Address: P.O. Box 370, Zip 73772–0370; tel. 580/623–7211 **A**9 10 18 **F**3 11 29 30 34 40 43 56 57 87 91 107 119 133 **P**6 **S** Mercy Health, Chesterfield, MO
Primary Contact: Bobby Stitt, R.N., Administrator
CFO: Patricia Dianne Robertson, Chief Financial Officer
CHR: Mary Jo Messelt, Manager Human Resources
Web address: www.mercy.net/watongaok/practice/mercy–hospital–watonga
Control: Church–operated, Nongovernment, not–for profit **Service:** General Medical and Surgical

Staffed Beds: 17 **Admissions:** 330 **Census:** 3 **Outpatient Visits:** 7061
Births: 0 **Total Expense ($000):** 4546 **Payroll Expense ($000):** 2121
Personnel: 39

WAURIKA—Jefferson County

★ **JEFFERSON COUNTY HOSPITAL (371311)**, Highway 70 and 81, Zip 73573–3075, Mailing Address: P.O. Box 90, Zip 73573–0090; tel. 580/228–2344 **A**9 10 18 **F**11 35 40 107 119 127 133 **P**6
Primary Contact: Jane McDowell, FACHE, Administrator
CFO: Richard Tallon, Chief Financial Officer
CMO: Rob Linzman, D.O., Chief of Staff
CIO: Nikki McGahey, Information Officer
Web address: www.jeffersoncountyhospital.net
Control: Hospital district or authority, Government, nonfederal **Service:** General Medical and Surgical

Staffed Beds: 25 **Admissions:** 273 **Census:** 3 **Outpatient Visits:** 11402
Births: 1 **Total Expense ($000):** 3345 **Payroll Expense ($000):** 1756
Personnel: 40

WEATHERFORD—Custer County

★ **WEATHERFORD REGIONAL HOSPITAL (371323)**, 3701 East Main Street, Zip 73096–3309; tel. 580/772–5551 **A**9 10 18 **F**3 11 13 15 29 34 40 43 45 64 68 75 76 77 81 86 87 93 107 110 111 115 119 130 133 135 144 146 147 148 **P**6
Primary Contact: Debbie Howe, Chief Executive Officer
CFO: Stephanie Helton, Chief Financial Officer
CMO: Jonathan Ray Long, M.D., Chief of Staff
CIO: Amy Outhier, Director Health Information Management
CHR: Tawnya Paden, Director Human Resources
CNO: Delvin Mast, R.N., Director of Nursing
Web address: www.weatherfordhospital.com
Control: Hospital district or authority, Government, nonfederal **Service:** General Medical and Surgical

Staffed Beds: 25 **Admissions:** 956 **Census:** 7 **Outpatient Visits:** 42674
Births: 213 **Total Expense ($000):** 19343 **Payroll Expense ($000):** 7687
Personnel: 175

WILBURTON—Latimer County

LATIMER COUNTY GENERAL HOSPITAL (370072), 806 Highway 2 North, Zip 74578–3698; tel. 918/465–2391, (Nonreporting) **A**9 10
Primary Contact: Dana Hugle, Administrator
CMO: Richard Valbuena, M.D., Medical Director
CHR: Rachel Chinnock, Chief Human Resources Officer
Control: County–Government, nonfederal **Service:** General Medical and Surgical

Staffed Beds: 24

WOODWARD—Woodward County

✠ **WOODWARD REGIONAL HOSPITAL (370002)**, 900 17th Street, Zip 73801–2448; tel. 580/256–5511 **A**1 9 10 20 **F**13 15 29 30 31 32 34 35 40 43 45 50 57 59 64 68 69 70 75 76 77 79 81 85 93 107 108 110 111 115 119 124 127 129 130 131 133 135 146 **P**6 **S** Community Health Systems, Inc., Franklin, TN
Primary Contact: David Wallace, Chief Executive Officer
CFO: Tom Earley, Chief Financial Officer
CIO: Larry Churchill, Director Information Services
CHR: Melinda Brock, Director Human Resources
CNO: Kimberly N. Arnold, R.N., Chief Nursing Officer and Interim Chief Quality Officer
Web address: www.woodwardhospital.com
Control: Corporation, Investor–owned, for–profit **Service:** General Medical and Surgical

Staffed Beds: 40 **Admissions:** 1641 **Census:** 14 **Outpatient Visits:** 45769
Births: 320 **Total Expense ($000):** 29276 **Payroll Expense ($000):** 11656
Personnel: 242

YUKON—Canadian County

✠ **INTEGRIS CANADIAN VALLEY HOSPITAL (370211)**, 1201 Health Center Parkway, Zip 73099–6381; tel. 405/717–6800 **A**1 9 10 **F**3 11 13 15 29 30 34 40 45 46 49 57 59 60 64 68 70 79 81 87 93 97 107 108 110 111 115 118 119 130 135 144 145 146 148 **S** INTEGRIS Health, Oklahoma City, OK
Primary Contact: Rex Van Meter, President
COO: Cindy White, CPA, Vice President of Operations
CFO: Errol Mitchell, Chief Financial Officer
CHR: Lynn Ketch, Human Resources Recruiter Generalist
CNO: Teresa Gray, Chief Nursing Officer and Assistant Vice President
Web address: www.integris–health.com
Control: Other not–for–profit (including NFP Corporation) **Service:** General Medical and Surgical

Staffed Beds: 75 **Admissions:** 2931 **Census:** 26 **Outpatient Visits:** 51242
Births: 1020 **Total Expense ($000):** 58495 **Payroll Expense ($000):** 24403
Personnel: 283

Many Facility Codes have changed. Please refer to the AHA Guide Code Chart. © 2014 AHA Guide

OREGON

ALBANY—Linn County

★ ◇ **SAMARITAN ALBANY GENERAL HOSPITAL (380022)**, 1046 Sixth Avenue, S.W., Zip 97321–1999; tel. 541/812–4000 **A**9 10 21 **F**3 5 11 12 13 15 18 28 29 30 31 34 35 36 37 40 43 45 47 49 50 53 54 57 59 61 63 64 67 68 70 72 74 75 76 77 78 79 81 83 84 85 86 87 89 92 93 97 107 108 110 111 114 116 117 119 129 130 131 132 135 144 145 146 147 148 **P**6 **S** Samaritan Health Services, Corvallis, OR
Primary Contact: David G. Triebes, Chief Executive Officer
CFO: Daniel B. Smith, Vice President Finance
Web address: www.samhealth.org
Control: Other not–for–profit (including NFP Corporation) **Service:** General Medical and Surgical

Staffed Beds: 70 **Admissions:** 2879 **Census:** 29 **Outpatient Visits:** 286221 **Births:** 578 **Total Expense ($000):** 156911 **Payroll Expense ($000):** 63542 **Personnel:** 757

ASHLAND—Jackson County

★ ◇ **ASANTE ASHLAND COMMUNITY HOSPITAL (380005)**, 280 Maple Street, Zip 97520–1593; tel. 541/201–4000 **A**9 10 21 **F**3 11 13 15 29 30 34 35 36 40 43 48 49 50 54 62 63 64 65 68 70 75 76 79 81 82 84 85 86 87 93 97 107 110 114 119 130 132 145 146 147 148 **P**6 **S** Asante Health System, Medford, OR
Primary Contact: Sheila Clough, Chief Executive Officer
CFO: Patrick Hocking, Chief Financial Officer
CMO: Bill Steinsick, M.D., Chief Medical Staff
CIO: Mark Hetz, Chief Information Officer
CHR: Gregg Edwards, Vice President Human Resources
CNO: Susan Montgomery, Chief Nursing Officer
Web address: www.ashlandhospital.org
Control: Other not–for–profit (including NFP Corporation) **Service:** General Medical and Surgical

Staffed Beds: 36 **Admissions:** 1369 **Census:** 12 **Outpatient Visits:** 55803 **Births:** 298 **Total Expense ($000):** 48024 **Payroll Expense ($000):** 20744 **Personnel:** 226

ASTORIA—Clatsop County

★ **COLUMBIA MEMORIAL HOSPITAL (381320)**, 2111 Exchange Street, Zip 97103–3329; tel. 503/325–4321 **A**9 10 18 **F**3 8 11 13 15 18 19 28 29 30 31 34 35 36 40 41 42 43 44 46 50 51 53 57 58 59 62 63 64 68 70 75 76 77 78 79 81 85 86 87 89 93 97 107 108 110 111 114 119 130 131 132 134 135 143 144 146 147 148 **P**6
Primary Contact: Erik Thorsen, Chief Executive Officer
CFO: Guy Rivers, Chief Financial Officer
CMO: Hugh Sabahi, M.D., President Professional Staff
CIO: Guy Rivers, Chief Financial Officer
CHR: Cheryl Martin, Manager Human Resources
CNO: Joe DaFoe, R.N., Chief Clinical Officer
Web address: www.columbiamemorial.org
Control: Other not–for–profit (including NFP Corporation) **Service:** General Medical and Surgical

Staffed Beds: 25 **Admissions:** 1530 **Census:** 11 **Outpatient Visits:** 143141 **Births:** 325 **Total Expense ($000):** 61914 **Payroll Expense ($000):** 30040 **Personnel:** 467

BAKER CITY—Baker County

☒ **SAINT ALPHONSUS MEDICAL CENTER – BAKER CITY (381315)**, 3325 Pocahontas Road, Zip 97814–1464; tel. 541/523–6461, (Total facility includes 30 beds in nursing home–type unit) **A**1 9 10 18 **F**3 11 13 15 29 31 34 35 36 37 40 43 44 45 50 57 59 64 67 70 75 76 77 79 81 82 83 85 91 93 97 107 110 111 116 117 119 121 133 143 146 147 148 **P**6 **S** Catholic Health East / Trinity Health, Livonia, MI
Primary Contact: H. Ray Gibbons, FACHE, Chief Executive Officer
CFO: Robert D. Wehling, Interim Chief Financial Officer
CHR: Jerry Nickell, Vice President Human Resource and Mission
Web address: www.saintalphonsus.org/bakercity
Control: Other not–for–profit (including NFP Corporation) **Service:** General Medical and Surgical

Staffed Beds: 55 **Admissions:** 1007 **Census:** 33 **Outpatient Visits:** 27313 **Births:** 102 **Total Expense ($000):** 31554 **Payroll Expense ($000):** 14849 **Personnel:** 259

ST. ELIZABETH HEALTH SERVICES See Saint Alphonsus Medical Center – Baker City

BANDON—Coos County

★ **SOUTHERN COOS HOSPITAL AND HEALTH CENTER (381304)**, 900 11th Street S.E., Zip 97411–9114; tel. 541/347–2426 **A**9 10 18 **F**3 15 35 40 45 50 57 65 68 75 81 82 85 87 107 110 114 119 130 132 133 135 148
Primary Contact: Charles W. Johnston, Chief Executive Officer
CFO: Robin Triplett, Chief Financial Officer
CIO: Mandy Calvert, Director Information Systems
CHR: Cyndy Vollmer, Director Human Resources
Web address: www.southerncoos.org
Control: Hospital district or authority, Government, nonfederal **Service:** General Medical and Surgical

Staffed Beds: 19 **Admissions:** 296 **Census:** 3 **Outpatient Visits:** 13539 **Births:** 0 **Total Expense ($000):** 14141 **Payroll Expense ($000):** 5502 **Personnel:** 109

BEND—Deschutes County

☒ **ST. CHARLES MEDICAL CENTER – BEND (380047)**, 2500 N.E. Neff Road, Zip 97701–6015; tel. 541/382–4321 **A**1 2 3 5 9 10 19 **F**3 8 11 12 13 14 15 18 19 20 21 22 24 26 28 29 30 31 34 35 36 37 38 40 42 43 45 46 47 49 50 51 54 57 59 60 62 63 64 65 67 68 70 72 74 75 76 77 78 79 81 82 84 85 86 87 89 90 91 92 93 98 99 100 101 102 104 107 108 110 111 114 115 116 117 118 119 120 121 123 124 126 129 130 132 135 142 144 146 148 **P**1 6 **S** St. Charles Health System, Inc., Bend, OR
Primary Contact: Robert Gomes, FACHE, Chief Executive Officer
CFO: Karen Shepard, Executive Vice President Finance and Chief Financial Officer
CMO: Michel Boileau, M.D., Chief Clinical Officer
CIO: William Winnenberg, Chief Information Officer
CHR: Rebecca Berry, Senior Director Human Resources
CNO: Karen Reed, R.N., Chief Nursing Officer
Web address: www.scmc.org
Control: Other not–for–profit (including NFP Corporation) **Service:** General Medical and Surgical

Staffed Beds: 260 **Admissions:** 15052 **Census:** 168 **Outpatient Visits:** 170408 **Births:** 1646 **Total Expense ($000):** 439767 **Payroll Expense ($000):** 178683 **Personnel:** 2247

BURNS—Harney County

HARNEY DISTRICT HOSPITAL (381307), 557 West Washington Street, Zip 97720–1497; tel. 541/573–7281 **A**9 10 18 **F**3 7 13 15 29 31 34 35 40 43 45 47 53 54 57 59 64 65 70 71 75 76 78 81 82 85 86 93 102 107 111 114 119 129 132 133 135 146 **P**6
Primary Contact: Jim Bishop, Chief Executive Officer
CFO: Catherine White, Chief Financial Officer
CMO: Kevin Johnston, M.D., Chief Medical Staff
CIO: Tanya Strong, Manager Information Technology
CHR: Sammie Masterson, Chief Human Resources Officer
CNO: Barbara Chambers, Chief Nursing Officer
Web address: www.harneydh.com
Control: Hospital district or authority, Government, nonfederal **Service:** General Medical and Surgical

Staffed Beds: 20 **Admissions:** 450 **Census:** 5 **Outpatient Visits:** 33496 **Births:** 53 **Total Expense ($000):** 18389 **Payroll Expense ($000):** 7892 **Personnel:** 145

CLACKAMAS—Clackamas County

☒ **KAISER PERMANENTE SUNNYSIDE MEDICAL CENTER (380091)**, 10180 S.E. Sunnyside Road, Zip 97015–8970; tel. 503/652–2880 **A**1 2 10 **F**3 11 12 13 15 17 18 20 22 24 26 30 31 34 37 40 45 46 47 49 51 60 61 64 68 70 74 75 76 77 78 79 81 84 85 86 87 93 94 97 102 107 108 111 114 115 119 130 141 146 147 148 **P**6 **S** Kaiser Foundation Hospitals, Oakland, CA
Primary Contact: Gary Petersen, Administrator
CFO: Rolf Norman, Chief Financial Officer
CMO: Rick Olson, M.D., Chief of Staff
CIO: Mark A. Burmester, Vice President Strategy and Communications
CHR: Rich Smith, Vice President Human Resources
Web address: www.kaiserpermanente.org
Control: Other not–for–profit (including NFP Corporation) **Service:** General Medical and Surgical

Staffed Beds: 283 **Admissions:** 22609 **Census:** 187 **Outpatient Visits:** 68375 **Births:** 2167 **Total Expense ($000):** 346684 **Payroll Expense ($000):** 142474 **Personnel:** 1852

OR

COOS BAY—Coos County

☒ **BAY AREA HOSPITAL (380090)**, 1775 Thompson Road, Zip 97420–2198; tel. 541/269–8111 **A**1 2 9 10 19 20 **F**3 11 12 13 15 18 28 29 31 34 35 37 40 43 45 46 48 50 51 57 59 62 68 70 73 74 75 76 77 78 79 81 82 83 84 85 89 91 92 93 98 99 100 101 102 104 107 108 110 111 114 118 119 120 121 123 129 130 132 135 142 146 148
Primary Contact: Paul Janke, FACHE, President and Chief Executive Officer
COO: Ben Pfau, Chief Facility and Information Officer
CFO: Sam Patterson, Chief Financial Officer
CMO: Terrance Bach, M.D., Director Medical Affairs
CIO: Bob Adams, Director Information Services
CHR: Suzie Q. McDaniel, Chief Human Resource Officer
CNO: Lori L. Krenos, R.N., Chief Nursing Officer
Web address: www.bayareahospital.org
Control: Hospital district or authority, Government, nonfederal **Service:** General Medical and Surgical

Staffed Beds: 126 **Admissions:** 5766 **Census:** 57 **Outpatient Visits:** 68290 **Births:** 663 **Total Expense ($000):** 123812 **Payroll Expense ($000):** 57643 **Personnel:** 827

COQUILLE—Coos County

★ **COQUILLE VALLEY HOSPITAL (381312)**, 940 East Fifth Street, Zip 97423–1699; tel. 541/396–3101 **A**9 10 18 **F**3 11 13 15 29 34 35 40 43 45 50 57 59 62 64 70 75 76 79 81 82 85 86 87 107 110 111 114 118 119 132 133 135 148 **P**6
Primary Contact: Dennis G. Zielinski, Chief Executive Officer and Administrator
CFO: Gail Ludington, Chief Financial Officer
CMO: James Sinnott, M.D., Chief Medical Staff
CIO: Curt Carpenter, Manager Information Technology
CHR: Monte Johnston, Manager Human Resources
Web address: www.cvhospital.org
Control: Hospital district or authority, Government, nonfederal **Service:** General Medical and Surgical

Staffed Beds: 25 **Admissions:** 643 **Census:** 6 **Outpatient Visits:** 23995 **Births:** 4 **Total Expense ($000):** 20738 **Payroll Expense ($000):** 6891 **Personnel:** 158

CORVALLIS—Benton County

★ ◇ **GOOD SAMARITAN REGIONAL MEDICAL CENTER (380014)**, 3600 N.W. Samaritan Drive, Zip 97330–3737, Mailing Address: P.O. Box 1068, Zip 97339–1068; tel. 541/768–5111 **A**2 9 10 12 13 19 21 **F**3 5 8 11 12 13 15 18 20 22 24 26 28 29 30 31 34 35 36 37 40 43 46 47 49 50 53 54 57 58 59 61 62 64 68 70 73 74 76 77 78 79 81 82 84 85 86 87 89 93 97 98 99 100 101 102 104 107 108 110 111 114 115 116 117 118 119 120 121 123 124 126 129 130 131 132 135 144 145 146 147 148 **P**6 **S** Samaritan Health Services, Corvallis, OR
Primary Contact: Larry A. Mullins, FACHE, Chief Executive Officer
COO: Becky A. Pape, R.N., Chief Operating Officer
CFO: Daniel B. Smith, Vice President Finance
CIO: Bob Power, Vice President Information Services
CHR: Doug Boysen, Chief Legal Counsel and Vice President Human Resources
CNO: William Howden, Vice President Nursing
Web address: www.samhealth.org
Control: Other not-for-profit (including NFP Corporation) **Service:** General Medical and Surgical

Staffed Beds: 165 **Admissions:** 9257 **Census:** 111 **Outpatient Visits:** 366420 **Births:** 974 **Total Expense ($000):** 328151 **Payroll Expense ($000):** 132560 **Personnel:** 1508

COTTAGE GROVE—Lane County

★ **PEACEHEALTH COTTAGE GROVE COMMUNITY MEDICAL CENTER (381301)**, 1515 Village Drive, Zip 97424–9700; tel. 541/942–0511 **A**9 10 18 **F**3 11 15 29 30 32 34 35 40 44 50 56 57 58 59 64 65 66 68 75 85 86 87 93 97 107 110 115 119 127 130 132 133 146 147 148 **P**6 **S** PeaceHealth, Vancouver, WA
Primary Contact: Chelsea Holland–Bak, Interim Administrator
Web address: www.peacehealth.org
Control: Church–operated, Nongovernment, not–for profit **Service:** General Medical and Surgical

Staffed Beds: 14 **Admissions:** 315 **Census:** 3 **Outpatient Visits:** 35917 **Births:** 0 **Total Expense ($000):** 28844 **Payroll Expense ($000):** 9666 **Personnel:** 122

DALLAS—Polk County

WEST VALLEY HOSPITAL (381308), 525 S.E. Washington Street, Zip 97338–2834, Mailing Address: P.O. Box 378, Zip 97338–0378; tel. 503/623–8301 **A**9 10 18 **F**3 15 35 40 43 50 59 64 75 79 81 85 93 97 107 108 110 111 114 119 131 132 133 143 146 148 **P**6 **S** Salem Health, Salem, OR
Primary Contact: Robert C. Brannigan, Administrator
COO: Robert C. Brannigan, Administrator
CFO: Aaron Crane, Chief Financial Officer
CMO: David Holloway, M.D., Chief Medical Officer
CIO: Cort Garrison, M.D., Chief Information Officer
CHR: Laurie C. Barr, Vice President Human Resources
CNO: Pamela Cortez, Director Clinical Operations
Web address: www.westvalleyhospital.org
Control: Other not-for-profit (including NFP Corporation) **Service:** General Medical and Surgical

Staffed Beds: 6 **Admissions:** 172 **Census:** 2 **Outpatient Visits:** 70998 **Births:** 0 **Total Expense ($000):** 19915 **Payroll Expense ($000):** 10075 **Personnel:** 110

ENTERPRISE—Wallowa County

★ **WALLOWA MEMORIAL HOSPITAL (381306)**, 601 Medical Parkway, Zip 97828–5124; tel. 541/426–3111, (Total facility includes 32 beds in nursing home–type unit) **A**3 5 9 10 18 **F**3 7 11 13 15 29 30 31 34 35 40 43 45 46 56 57 59 62 64 67 68 75 76 78 79 81 82 85 93 102 107 110 114 119 128 129 131 132 133 135 143 148 **P**6
Primary Contact: Larry Davy, Chief Executive Officer
CFO: Joe Wanner, Chief Financial Officer
CMO: Kenneth Rose, M.D., Chief Medical Staff
CIO: John Straughan, Director Information Technology
CHR: Linda Childers, Director Human Resources
CNO: Jenni Word, R.N., Chief Nursing Officer
Web address: www.wchcd.org
Control: Hospital district or authority, Government, nonfederal **Service:** General Medical and Surgical

Staffed Beds: 57 **Admissions:** 639 **Census:** 28 **Outpatient Visits:** 19346 **Births:** 52 **Total Expense ($000):** 18153 **Payroll Expense ($000):** 7515 **Personnel:** 128

EUGENE—Lane County

★ △ ◇ **PEACEHEALTH SACRED HEART MEDICAL CENTER, UNIVERSITY DISTRICT (380033)**, 1255 Hilyard Street, Zip 97401–3700, Mailing Address: P.O. Box 10905, Zip 97440–2905; tel. 541/686–7300 **A**7 9 10 21 **F**29 30 40 43 56 68 90 98 102 146 148 **P**6 **S** PeaceHealth, Vancouver, WA
Primary Contact: John G. Hill, Chief Executive Officer
CFO: Wendy Apland, Interim Chief Financial Officer
CMO: Bill Moshofsky, M.D., Chief of Staff
CIO: Don McMillan, Chief Information Officer
CHR: Craig Mills, Vice President Human Resources
Web address: www.peacehealth.org
Control: Church–operated, Nongovernment, not–for profit **Service:** General Medical and Surgical

Staffed Beds: 104 **Admissions:** 2490 **Census:** 52 **Outpatient Visits:** 106451 **Births:** 0 **Total Expense ($000):** 90472 **Payroll Expense ($000):** 36991 **Personnel:** 326

FLORENCE—Lane County

★ **PEACEHEALTH PEACE HARBOR MEDICAL CENTER (381316)**, 400 Ninth Street, Zip 97439–7398; tel. 541/997–8412 **A**9 10 18 **F**11 13 15 28 29 30 34 35 40 43 45 50 57 59 62 63 64 68 70 76 77 79 81 85 93 97 107 108 110 111 114 118 119 132 133 135 146 147 148 **P**6 **S** PeaceHealth, Vancouver, WA
Primary Contact: Rick Yecny, Chief Executive Officer and Chief Mission Officer
CMO: Ron Shearer, M.D., Regional Medical Director
CIO: Ginni Boughal, Director Health Information and Information Technology
CHR: Don Bourland, Vice President Human Resources
Web address: www.peacehealth.org
Control: Church–operated, Nongovernment, not–for profit **Service:** General Medical and Surgical

Staffed Beds: 21 **Admissions:** 989 **Census:** 9 **Outpatient Visits:** 92215 **Births:** 72 **Total Expense ($000):** 60045 **Payroll Expense ($000):** 30406 **Personnel:** 340

FOREST GROVE—Washington County

TUALITY FOREST GROVE HOSPITAL See Tuality Healthcare, Hillsboro

GOLD BEACH—Curry County

★ **CURRY GENERAL HOSPITAL (381322)**, 94220 Fourth Street,
Zip 97444–7756; tel. 541/247–3000 **A**9 10 18 **F**3 10 11 13 15 28 29 34 35
40 43 56 57 59 64 65 67 70 75 76 79 81 82 98 105 107 114 119 127 133
135 144 146 147 148
Primary Contact: Andrew P. Bair, Chief Executive Officer
COO: Kenneth G. Landau, Chief Operating Officer
CFO: Kenneth G. Landau, Chief Financial Officer
CIO: Chris Creighton, Manager Information Technology
CHR: Terri Tomberlin, Director Human Resources
CNO: Lora Maxwell, Chief Nursing Officer
Web address: www.curryhealthnetwork.com
Control: Hospital district or authority, Government, nonfederal **Service:** General
Medical and Surgical

Staffed Beds: 24 **Admissions:** 474 **Census:** 4 **Outpatient Visits:** 53337
Births: 59 **Total Expense ($000):** 24587 **Payroll Expense ($000):** 12376
Personnel: 187

GRANTS PASS—Josephine County

★ ◇ **ASANTE THREE RIVERS MEDICAL CENTER (380002)**, 500 S.W. Ramsey
Avenue, Zip 97527–5554; tel. 541/472–7000 **A**9 10 21 **F**11 13 15 29 30 31
34 35 40 43 45 46 50 57 59 64 65 70 75 76 78 81 87 93 102 107 108 110
111 118 119 122 130 132 143 146 147 148 **P**6 **S** Asante Health System,
Medford, OR
Primary Contact: Win Howard, Chief Executive Officer
COO: David Kinyon, Vice President of Operations and Outpatient Services
CFO: Patrick Hocking, Chief Financial Officer
CMO: Kenneth Lindsey, M.D., Vice President of Medical Affairs
CIO: Mark Hetz, Chief Information Officer
CHR: Gregg Edwards, Chief People Officer
CNO: Nancy Greer, R.N., Vice President Nursing
Web address: www.asante.org/trmc/
Control: Other not–for–profit (including NFP Corporation) **Service:** General
Medical and Surgical

Staffed Beds: 111 **Admissions:** 7027 **Census:** 61 **Outpatient Visits:** 250501
Births: 756 **Total Expense ($000):** 123558 **Payroll Expense ($000):** 42466
Personnel: 675

GRESHAM—Multnomah County

⊞ **LEGACY MOUNT HOOD MEDICAL CENTER (380025)**, 24800 S.E. Stark,
Zip 97030–3378; tel. 503/667–1122 **A**1 2 9 10 **F**3 11 13 15 18 20 26 28 29
30 31 32 34 35 38 40 44 45 46 48 49 50 51 57 59 60 64 68 70 74 75 76
77 78 79 81 85 86 87 93 100 101 102 107 108 110 111 114 115 118 119
120 121 123 126 129 130 132 146 147 148 **P**6 **S** Legacy Health,
Portland, OR
Primary Contact: Gretchen Nichols, R.N., Chief Administrative Officer
COO: Michael Newcomb, D.O., Senior Vice President and Chief Operating Officer
CFO: Linda Hoff, Senior Vice President and Chief Financial Officer
CMO: Lewis Low, M.D., Chief Medical Officer
CIO: John Jay Kenagy, Ph.D., Senior Vice President and Chief Information Officer
CHR: Sonja Steves, Senior Vice President Human Resources
CNO: Marcia Soderling, R.N., Hospital Nurse Executive
Web address: www.legacyhealth.org
Control: Other not–for–profit (including NFP Corporation) **Service:** General
Medical and Surgical

Staffed Beds: 91 **Admissions:** 5512 **Census:** 51 **Outpatient Visits:** 85759
Births: 957 **Total Expense ($000):** 102412 **Payroll Expense ($000):** 37936
Personnel: 507

HEPPNER—Morrow County

PIONEER MEMORIAL HOSPITAL (381310), 564 East Pioneer Drive,
Zip 97836–7318, Mailing Address: P.O. Box 9, Zip 97836–0009;
tel. 541/676–9133 **A**9 10 18 **F**3 7 17 34 35 40 45 50 57 59 62 63 64 66 68
69 75 97 107 119 127 133 143 148 **P**6
Primary Contact: Dan Grigg, Chief Executive Officer
CFO: Nicole Mahoney, Chief Financial Officer
CIO: Shawn Cutsforth, Information Systems Officer
CHR: Patti Allstott, Administrative Coordinator Human Resources and Grant Writer
Web address: www.morrowcountyhealthdistrict.org
Control: Hospital district or authority, Government, nonfederal **Service:** General
Medical and Surgical

Staffed Beds: 21 **Admissions:** 95 **Census:** 8 **Outpatient Visits:** 5667 **Births:**
0 **Total Expense ($000):** 8210 **Payroll Expense ($000):** 4303 **Personnel:**
59

HERMISTON—Umatilla County

★ ◇ **GOOD SHEPHERD HEALTH CARE SYSTEM (381325)**, 610 N.W. 11th
Street, Zip 97838–6601; tel. 541/667–3400 **A**9 10 18 21 **F**3 8 11 13 15 28
29 30 34 35 37 40 43 45 46 50 53 57 59 62 63 64 65 68 70 75 76 77 78
79 81 82 84 85 86 93 97 107 108 110 111 114 115 119 126 127 130 131
132 133 135 141 143 146 147 148 **P**3 4 7
Primary Contact: Dennis E. Burke, President and Chief Executive Officer
COO: David T. Hughes, FACHE, Senior Vice President Operations and Chief
Operating Officer
CFO: Jan D. Peter, Vice President Fiscal Services and Chief Financial Officer
CMO: Paul Campagna, M.D., President Medical Staff
CIO: Rob Rizk, Director Information Technology
CHR: Kelly B. Sanders, Vice President Human Resources
CNO: Theresa Brock, Vice President Nursing
Web address: www.gshealth.org
Control: Other not–for–profit (including NFP Corporation) **Service:** General
Medical and Surgical

Staffed Beds: 25 **Admissions:** 1870 **Census:** 14 **Outpatient Visits:** 62886
Births: 519 **Total Expense ($000):** 59476 **Payroll Expense ($000):** 26605
Personnel: 398

HILLSBORO—Washington County

⊞ **KAISER FOUNDATION HOSPITAL WESTSIDE MEDICAL CENTER (380103)**,
2875 N.W. Stucki Avenue, Zip 97124–5806; tel. 971/310–1000, (Data for 148
days) **A**1 **F**3 11 12 13 15 20 22 30 31 34 37 40 45 47 49 51 60 61 64 68
70 74 75 76 77 78 79 81 84 85 86 87 93 94 97 102 107 108 111 114 115
119 126 130 141 146 147 148 **S** Kaiser Foundation Hospitals, Oakland, CA
Primary Contact: Susan Mullaney, Chief Executive Officer
COO: Janet O'Hollaren, Chief Operating Officer
Control: Other not–for–profit (including NFP Corporation) **Service:** General
Medical and Surgical

Staffed Beds: 122 **Admissions:** 3357 **Census:** 56 **Outpatient Visits:** 11933
Births: 505 **Total Expense ($000):** 101100 **Payroll Expense ($000):** 40360
Personnel: 929

⊞ **TUALITY HEALTHCARE (380021)**, 335 S.E. Eighth Avenue, Zip 97123–4246;
tel. 503/681–1111, (Includes TUALITY COMMUNITY HOSPITAL, 335 S.E. Eighth
Avenue, Zip 97123, Mailing Address: P.O. Box 309, Zip 97123;
tel. 503/681–1111; TUALITY FOREST GROVE HOSPITAL, 1809 Maple Street,
Forest Grove, Zip 97116–1995; tel. 503/357–2173) **A**1 5 9 10 **F**3 11 13 15 17
18 20 22 24 26 28 29 30 31 32 34 35 36 37 40 44 45 47 49 50 53 54 56
57 59 62 64 68 70 71 74 75 76 77 78 79 80 81 82 85 86 87 92 93 97 98
100 103 104 107 108 110 111 114 115 118 119 129 130 131 132 135 143
144 145 146 147 148 **P**1 6
Primary Contact: Manuel S. Berman, President and Chief Executive Officer
COO: Steven P. Krautscheid, Ancillary Services Administrator
CFO: Tim Fleischmann, Chief Financial Officer
CIO: Sonney Sapra, Director Information Systems and Chief Information Officer
CHR: Kathy Ratliffe, Chief Human Resources Officer
CNO: Eunice A. Rech, MSN, Chief Clinical Officer and Administrator of Quality
Services
Web address: www.tuality.com
Control: Other not–for–profit (including NFP Corporation) **Service:** General
Medical and Surgical

Staffed Beds: 148 **Admissions:** 4515 **Census:** 57 **Outpatient Visits:** 241150
Births: 852 **Total Expense ($000):** 164440 **Payroll Expense ($000):** 77339
Personnel: 1092

HOOD RIVER—Hood River County

⊞ **PROVIDENCE HOOD RIVER MEMORIAL HOSPITAL (381318)**, 810 12th
Street, Zip 97031–1587, Mailing Address: P.O. Box 149, Zip 97031–0055;
tel. 541/386–3911 **A**1 10 18 **F**2 3 5 8 9 10 11 12 13 15 28 29 30 31 34 35
36 40 43 45 47 48 53 54 56 57 59 60 64 65 68 70 71 75 76 77 79 81 85
86 89 92 97 99 100 101 102 104 107 108 110 111 114 118 119 125 129
132 133 134 135 143 146 147 148 **P**6 **S** Providence Health & Services,
Renton, WA
Primary Contact: Edward E. Freysinger, Chief Executive Officer
CHR: Catherine Bourgault, Director Human Resources
Web address: www.providence.org/hoodriver
Control: Church–operated, Nongovernment, not–for profit **Service:** General
Medical and Surgical

Staffed Beds: 25 **Admissions:** 1556 **Census:** 11 **Outpatient Visits:** 159253
Births: 462 **Total Expense ($000):** 68360 **Payroll Expense ($000):** 24347
Personnel: 374

OR

Hospital, Medicare Provider Number, Address, Telephone, Approval, Facility, and Physician Codes, Health Care System

★ American Hospital Association (AHA) membership
□ The Joint Commission accreditation ◇ DNV Healthcare Inc. accreditation
○ Healthcare Facilities Accreditation Program
△ Commission on Accreditation of Rehabilitation Facilities (CARF) accreditation

JOHN DAY—Grant County

★ **BLUE MOUNTAIN HOSPITAL (381305)**, 170 Ford Road, Zip 97845–2009; tel. 541/575–1311, (Total facility includes 48 beds in nursing home–type unit) **A**3 5 9 10 18 **F**2 3 7 8 11 13 15 17 29 30 31 34 35 36 40 41 43 45 56 57 59 62 63 64 67 68 70 75 76 81 82 86 87 89 93 107 110 111 114 119 127 128 130 131 132 133 135 143 144 145 148 **P**6 **S** HealthTech Management Services, Brentwood, TN
Primary Contact: Robert Houser, FACHE, Chief Executive Officer
CFO: Carl J. Flanagan, CPA, Chief Financial Officer
CMO: Keith Thomas, M.D., Chief of Staff
CIO: Sean Tsao, Director Information Technology
CHR: Verlene Davis, Director Human Resources
CNO: Les McLeod, Director of Nursing Services
Web address: www.bluemountainhospital.org
Control: Hospital district or authority, Government, nonfederal **Service:** General Medical and Surgical

Staffed Beds: 64 **Admissions:** 388 **Census:** 31 **Outpatient Visits:** 23205 **Births:** 44 **Total Expense ($000):** 18867 **Payroll Expense ($000):** 10198 **Personnel:** 131

KLAMATH FALLS—Klamath County

★ ◇ **SKY LAKES MEDICAL CENTER (380050)**, 2865 Daggett Avenue, Zip 97601–1106; tel. 541/882–6311 **A**2 3 5 9 10 19 20 21 **F**3 5 8 11 13 15 18 20 22 29 30 31 34 35 37 40 43 44 45 46 47 48 50 51 53 54 56 57 59 61 62 64 68 70 71 75 76 77 78 79 81 83 84 85 86 87 89 92 93 94 96 97 100 102 107 108 110 111 114 115 116 117 118 119 120 121 123 130 131 132 134 135 141 142 145 146 148 **P**6
Primary Contact: Paul R. Stewart, President and Chief Executive Officer
CFO: Richard Rico, Vice President and Chief Financial Officer
CMO: Grant Niskanen, M.D., Vice President Medical Affairs
CHR: Don York, Vice President Human Resources
CNO: Annette E. Cole, R.N., Vice President and Chief Nursing Officer
Web address: www.skylakes.org
Control: Other not–for–profit (including NFP Corporation) **Service:** General Medical and Surgical

Staffed Beds: 100 **Admissions:** 5024 **Census:** 56 **Outpatient Visits:** 326469 **Births:** 770 **Total Expense ($000):** 166694 **Payroll Expense ($000):** 64350 **Personnel:** 1005

LA GRANDE—Union County

⊠ **GRANDE RONDE HOSPITAL (381321)**, 900 Sunset Drive, Zip 97850–1387, Mailing Address: P.O. Box 3290, Zip 97850–7290; tel. 541/963–8421 **A**1 9 10 18 **F**3 8 11 13 15 17 29 30 31 34 35 37 39 40 41 43 44 45 50 53 54 57 59 62 63 64 66 70 74 75 76 77 78 79 81 82 84 85 86 87 89 92 93 97 107 108 110 111 114 119 128 129 130 131 132 133 135 144 146 147 148 **P**6
Primary Contact: James A. Mattes, President and Chief Executive Officer
CFO: Wade Weis, Senior Director Finance
CIO: Parhez Sattar, Senior Director Information Technology
CHR: Kristi Puckett, Director Human Resources
Web address: www.grh.org
Control: Other not–for–profit (including NFP Corporation) **Service:** General Medical and Surgical

Staffed Beds: 25 **Admissions:** 1415 **Census:** 13 **Outpatient Visits:** 94637 **Births:** 266 **Total Expense ($000):** 65131 **Payroll Expense ($000):** 35328 **Personnel:** 442

LAKEVIEW—Lake County

★ **LAKE DISTRICT HOSPITAL (381309)**, 700 South J Street, Zip 97630–1679; tel. 541/947–2114, (Total facility includes 36 beds in nursing home–type unit) **A**5 9 10 18 **F**13 15 29 30 31 34 35 40 45 46 67 76 78 81 82 85 93 107 111 114 119 128 129 130 132 133 135 146 148 **P**4 6
Primary Contact: Charles B. Tveit, Chief Executive Officer
CFO: Cheryl J. Cornwell, Chief Financial Officer
CMO: Timothy Gallagher, M.D., Chief of Staff
CIO: Yoemy Waller, Director Information Technology Systems
CHR: Linda Michaelson, Director Human Resources
CNO: Teresa Squires, R.N., Chief Nursing Officer
Web address: www.lakehealthdistrict.org
Control: Hospital district or authority, Government, nonfederal **Service:** General Medical and Surgical

Staffed Beds: 60 **Admissions:** 503 **Census:** 26 **Outpatient Visits:** 26474 **Births:** 73 **Total Expense ($000):** 19763 **Payroll Expense ($000):** 8141 **Personnel:** 144

LEBANON—Linn County

★ ◇ **SAMARITAN LEBANON COMMUNITY HOSPITAL (381323)**, 525 North Santiam Highway, Zip 97355–4363, Mailing Address: P.O. Box 739, Zip 97355–0739; tel. 541/258–2101 **A**9 10 18 21 **F**3 11 13 15 28 29 30 31 34 35 40 43 44 45 46 47 50 53 59 60 64 68 70 75 76 78 79 81 82 85 86 87 89 92 93 97 107 108 110 111 114 116 117 118 119 130 131 132 135 144 146 147 148 **P**6 **S** Samaritan Health Services, Corvallis, OR
Primary Contact: Becky A. Pape, R.N., Chief Executive Officer
CFO: Daniel B. Smith, Vice President Finance
CMO: Alan Blake, M.D., President Medical Staff
CIO: Robert Power, Vice President Information Services
CHR: Connie Erwin, Manager
CNO: Wendie Wunderwald, Vice President Patient Care Services
Web address: www.samhealth.org
Control: Other not–for–profit (including NFP Corporation) **Service:** General Medical and Surgical

Staffed Beds: 25 **Admissions:** 1615 **Census:** 14 **Outpatient Visits:** 199835 **Births:** 291 **Total Expense ($000):** 83062 **Payroll Expense ($000):** 37881 **Personnel:** 457

LINCOLN CITY—Lincoln County

★ ◇ **SAMARITAN NORTH LINCOLN HOSPITAL (381302)**, 3043 N.E. 28th Street, Zip 97367–4518, Mailing Address: P.O. Box 767, Zip 97367–0767; tel. 541/994–3661 **A**9 10 18 21 **F**3 8 11 13 15 29 30 34 35 40 45 50 51 57 58 59 62 63 64 65 68 70 75 76 78 79 81 85 86 87 93 97 107 108 110 111 114 116 117 118 119 127 130 132 133 135 144 146 147 148 **P**6 **S** Samaritan Health Services, Corvallis, OR
Primary Contact: Marty Cahill, Chief Executive Officer
COO: Lesley Ogden, M.D., Chief Operating Officer
CFO: Kathryn Doksum, Director Finance
CMO: Raj Baman, D.O., President Medical Staff
CHR: Gina Tapp, Director Human Resources
CNO: Virginia Riffle, Vice President Patient Care Services
Web address: www.samhealth.org
Control: Other not–for–profit (including NFP Corporation) **Service:** General Medical and Surgical

Staffed Beds: 25 **Admissions:** 1073 **Census:** 9 **Outpatient Visits:** 78578 **Births:** 139 **Total Expense ($000):** 45667 **Payroll Expense ($000):** 22330 **Personnel:** 258

MADRAS—Jefferson County

★ **ST. CHARLES MADRAS (381324)**, 470 N.E. A Street, Zip 97741–1844; tel. 541/475–3882 **A**9 10 18 21 **F**3 13 15 29 30 34 35 40 43 45 50 57 59 62 63 64 67 68 70 75 76 79 81 85 87 89 90 98 107 110 115 119 128 132 133 135 146 **P**1 6 **S** St. Charles Health System, Inc., Bend, OR
Primary Contact: Jeanine Gentry, Chief Executive Officer
CHR: JoDee Tittle, Director Community and Human Resources
Web address: www.mvhd.org
Control: Hospital district or authority, Government, nonfederal **Service:** General Medical and Surgical

Staffed Beds: 25 **Admissions:** 881 **Census:** 8 **Outpatient Visits:** 21384 **Births:** 183 **Total Expense ($000):** 21973 **Payroll Expense ($000):** 12376 **Personnel:** 143

MCMINNVILLE—Yamhill County

☐ **WILLAMETTE VALLEY MEDICAL CENTER (380071)**, 2700 S.E. Stratus Avenue, Zip 97128–6255; tel. 503/472–6131 **A**1 2 9 10 **F**3 11 12 13 15 18 20 24 26 27 28 29 30 31 34 35 40 43 46 50 56 57 58 59 60 64 65 70 74 75 76 77 78 79 81 82 84 85 87 92 93 98 103 107 108 110 111 114 115 118 119 120 123 124 129 130 131 132 135 146 147 148 **P**6 **S** Capella Healthcare, Franklin, TN
Primary Contact: Peter A. Hofstetter, Chief Executive Officer
COO: Frank Almendarez, Chief Operating Officer
CFO: Meredith Nelson, Chief Financial Officer
CIO: Diane Farrow, Manager Information Technology and Systems
CHR: Drew Burke, Director Human Resources
Web address: www.wvmcweb.com
Control: Corporation, Investor–owned, for–profit **Service:** General Medical and Surgical

Staffed Beds: 88 **Admissions:** 3655 **Census:** 39 **Outpatient Visits:** 114117 **Births:** 505 **Total Expense ($000):** 73583 **Payroll Expense ($000):** 26057 **Personnel:** 446

Many Facility Codes have changed. Please refer to the AHA Guide Code Chart. © 2014 AHA Guide

OR

MEDFORD—Jackson County

★ ◇ **ASANTE ROGUE REGIONAL MEDICAL CENTER (380018)**, 2825 East Barnett Road, Zip 97504–8332; tel. 541/789–7000 **A**2 9 10 21 **F**11 12 13 15 17 18 19 20 21 22 23 24 25 26 27 28 29 30 31 32 34 35 37 40 43 45 46 50 51 57 58 59 60 63 64 65 70 72 74 75 76 78 79 81 82 85 86 87 89 90 93 94 98 100 102 107 108 110 111 112 115 119 120 121 122 126 130 132 143 146 147 148 **P**6 **S** Asante Health System, Medford, OR
Primary Contact: Scott A. Kelly, Chief Executive Officer
COO: Jose Romo, Vice President Operations
CFO: Patrick Hocking, Chief Financial Officer
CMO: Jamie Grebosky, M.D., Vice President of Medical Affairs
CIO: Mark Hetz, Chief Information Officer
CHR: Gregg Edwards, Chief People Officer
CNO: Jo Lynn Wallace, Vice President Nursing
Web address: www.asante.org
Control: Other not–for–profit (including NFP Corporation) **Service:** General Medical and Surgical

Staffed Beds: 320 **Admissions:** 15098 **Census:** 192 **Outpatient Visits:** 369796 **Births:** 1529 **Total Expense ($000):** 368935 **Payroll Expense ($000):** 110242 **Personnel:** 1683

✚ **PROVIDENCE MEDFORD MEDICAL CENTER (380075)**, 1111 Crater Lake Avenue, Zip 97504–6241; tel. 541/732–5000 **A**1 2 9 10 **F**3 11 13 15 17 18 20 22 29 30 31 32 34 35 40 43 45 49 50 51 55 56 57 59 61 62 63 64 68 70 74 75 76 77 78 79 81 82 84 85 86 87 90 92 93 96 97 102 107 110 114 115 118 119 120 121 123 124 126 130 132 143 146 147 148 **P**6 **S** Providence Health & Services, Renton, WA
Primary Contact: Cindy Mayo, R.N., FACHE, Chief Executive Officer
COO: Chris Pizzi, Chief Operating Officer and Chief Financial Officer
CFO: Chris Pizzi, Chief Operating Officer and Chief Financial Officer
CHR: Julie Levison, Director Human Resources
CNO: Sherri Steele, Chief Nursing Officer
Web address: www.providence.org
Control: Church–operated, Nongovernment, not–for profit **Service:** General Medical and Surgical

Staffed Beds: 114 **Admissions:** 6372 **Census:** 71 **Outpatient Visits:** 304104 **Births:** 522 **Total Expense ($000):** 156714 **Payroll Expense ($000):** 58697 **Personnel:** 832

MILWAUKIE—Clackamas County

✚ **PROVIDENCE MILWAUKIE HOSPITAL (380082)**, 10150 S.E. 32nd Avenue, Zip 97222–6516; tel. 503/513–8300 **A**1 3 5 9 10 **F**3 15 18 29 30 34 35 36 39 40 44 45 46 50 53 54 57 59 63 64 68 70 71 74 75 77 79 81 82 84 85 87 89 91 92 93 97 100 102 105 107 108 110 111 114 115 119 129 130 131 132 133 135 146 147 148 **P**6 **S** Providence Health & Services, Renton, WA
Primary Contact: Keith Hyde, Chief Executive Officer
COO: Lisa Halvorsen, Chief Nurse Executive
CFO: Elizabeth Sublette, Chief Financial Officer
CHR: Joann M. Pfister, Director Human Resources
CNO: Lisa Halvorsen, Chief Nurse Executive
Web address: www.providence.org
Control: Church–operated, Nongovernment, not–for profit **Service:** General Medical and Surgical

Staffed Beds: 51 **Admissions:** 2777 **Census:** 24 **Outpatient Visits:** 206351 **Births:** 136 **Total Expense ($000):** 81386 **Payroll Expense ($000):** 28224 **Personnel:** 356

NEWBERG—Yamhill County

✚ **PROVIDENCE NEWBERG MEDICAL CENTER (380037)**, 1001 Providence Drive, Zip 97132–7485; tel. 503/537–1555 **A**1 9 10 **F**3 11 13 15 18 20 29 30 34 35 40 45 49 50 57 59 60 64 68 70 75 76 77 79 81 85 87 93 100 107 108 110 111 114 118 119 129 130 132 135 146 147 148 **P**6 **S** Providence Health & Services, Renton, WA
Primary Contact: Lorinda Van Zanten, MSN, Chief Executive Officer
CFO: Jack R. Sumner, Assistant Administrator Finance
CMO: George Weghorst, M.D., Chief Medical Officer
CIO: Laureen O'Brien, Chief Information Officer
CHR: Cheryl Gebhart, Director Human Resources Providence Health Plan and Providence Medical Group
Web address: www.phsor.org
Control: Church–operated, Nongovernment, not–for profit **Service:** General Medical and Surgical

Staffed Beds: 40 **Admissions:** 2364 **Census:** 19 **Outpatient Visits:** 194229 **Births:** 525 **Total Expense ($000):** 74183 **Payroll Expense ($000):** 25432 **Personnel:** 377

NEWPORT—Lincoln County

★ ◇ **SAMARITAN PACIFIC COMMUNITIES HOSPITAL (381314)**, 930 S.W. Abbey Street, Zip 97365–4820, Mailing Address: P.O. Box 945, Zip 97365–0072; tel. 541/265–2244 **A**9 10 18 21 **F**3 8 11 13 15 17 28 29 30 31 34 35 40 45 47 50 54 57 59 62 63 64 65 68 70 75 76 77 78 79 81 85 87 89 92 93 97 107 110 111 114 118 119 129 130 132 133 135 144 146 147 148 **P**6 **S** Samaritan Health Services, Corvallis, OR
Primary Contact: David C. Bigelow, PharmD, Chief Executive Officer
CFO: Daniel B. Smith, Chief Financial Officer
CIO: Robert Power, Chief Information Officer
CHR: Gina Tapp, Director Human Resources
CNO: Lorie Williams, R.N., Vice President Nursing
Web address: www.samhealth.org
Control: Other not–for–profit (including NFP Corporation) **Service:** General Medical and Surgical

Staffed Beds: 25 **Admissions:** 1392 **Census:** 12 **Outpatient Visits:** 118351 **Births:** 186 **Total Expense ($000):** 67336 **Payroll Expense ($000):** 31026 **Personnel:** 360

ONTARIO—Malheur County

HOLY ROSARY MEDICAL CENTER See Saint Alphonsus Medical Center – Ontario

✚ **SAINT ALPHONSUS MEDICAL CENTER – ONTARIO (380052)**, 351 S.W. Ninth Street, Zip 97914–2693; tel. 541/881–7000 **A**1 3 5 9 10 **F**3 11 13 15 29 30 31 32 34 35 40 43 44 45 46 49 50 51 54 55 56 57 59 62 64 65 66 68 70 75 76 77 78 79 81 82 85 87 93 97 107 108 110 114 118 119 129 130 131 132 135 144 146 147 148 **P**6 **S** Catholic Health East / Trinity Health, Livonia, MI
Primary Contact: Karl Keeler, Chief Executive Officer
COO: Ken Hart, Vice President Operations
CFO: Lannie Checketts, Vice President Finance and Operations
CMO: Paul Gering, M.D., Vice President Medical Affairs
CHR: Stefanie Thiel, Senior Human Resources Business Partner
CNO: Dina Ellwanger, R.N., Chief Nursing Officer
Web address: www.saintalphonsus.org/ontario
Control: Church–operated, Nongovernment, not–for profit **Service:** General Medical and Surgical

Staffed Beds: 49 **Admissions:** 2587 **Census:** 20 **Outpatient Visits:** 78218 **Births:** 597 **Total Expense ($000):** 62082 **Payroll Expense ($000):** 27313 **Personnel:** 424

OREGON CITY—Clackamas County

✚ **PROVIDENCE WILLAMETTE FALLS MEDICAL CENTER (380038)**, 1500 Division Street, Zip 97045–1597; tel. 503/656–1631 **A**1 9 10 **F**13 15 29 30 34 35 36 40 44 45 46 50 53 54 57 59 63 64 68 70 74 75 76 77 78 79 81 82 84 85 87 91 92 93 97 98 100 107 108 111 114 119 130 131 132 133 135 146 147 **P**6 **S** Providence Health & Services, Renton, WA
Primary Contact: Russ Reinhard, Chief Executive
COO: Patricia A. Markesino, FACHE, Chief Nurse Executive and Chief Operating Officer
CFO: Elizabeth Sublette, Director Finance
CMO: James Watkins, M.D., President Medical Staff
CHR: Joann M. Pfister, Director Human Resources
CNO: Jessica Bailey-Oetker, Director Quality and Medical Staff
Web address: www.providence.org/pwfmc
Control: Church–operated, Nongovernment, not–for profit **Service:** General Medical and Surgical

Staffed Beds: 111 **Admissions:** 4542 **Census:** 36 **Outpatient Visits:** 134875 **Births:** 1155 **Total Expense ($000):** 88943 **Payroll Expense ($000):** 32075 **Personnel:** 442

PENDLETON—Umatilla County

✚ **ST. ANTHONY HOSPITAL (381319)**, 1601 S.E. Court Avenue, Zip 97801–3217; tel. 541/276–5121 **A**1 5 9 10 18 **F**3 11 13 15 18 29 30 31 35 40 43 45 50 51 53 54 57 59 62 63 64 65 68 75 76 77 78 79 81 85 86 87 93 97 107 108 110 111 114 117 118 119 127 129 130 131 132 133 134 135 144 146 147 **P**6 **S** Catholic Health Initiatives, Englewood, CO
Primary Contact: Harold S. Geller, Chief Executive Officer
CFO: Jim Schlenker, Vice President and Chief Financial Officer
CMO: Malcolm Townsley, M.D., Chief of Staff
CHR: Janeen K. Reding, Director Human Resources
Web address: www.sahpendleton.org
Control: Church–operated, Nongovernment, not–for profit **Service:** General Medical and Surgical

Staffed Beds: 25 **Admissions:** 1497 **Census:** 12 **Outpatient Visits:** 48097 **Births:** 401 **Total Expense ($000):** 46793 **Payroll Expense ($000):** 21257 **Personnel:** 375

Hospital, Medicare Provider Number, Address, Telephone, Approval, Facility, and Physician Codes, Health Care System

★ American Hospital Association (AHA) membership
□ The Joint Commission accreditation
◇ DNV Healthcare Inc. accreditation
○ Healthcare Facilities Accreditation Program
△ Commission on Accreditation of Rehabilitation Facilities (CARF) accreditation

PORTLAND—Multnomah County

✠ **ADVENTIST MEDICAL CENTER–PORTLAND (380060)**, 10123 S.E. Market Street, Zip 97216–2599; tel. 503/257–2500 **A**1 2 9 10 **F**3 9 11 13 15 18 20 22 24 26 28 29 30 31 34 35 36 37 40 44 45 46 49 53 54 57 58 59 62 63 64 70 71 74 75 76 77 78 79 81 82 83 84 85 86 87 89 93 97 98 100 102 107 108 110 111 114 115 118 119 120 121 123 126 129 130 131 132 135 144 146 147 148 **P**6 7 **S** Adventist Health, Roseville, CA
Primary Contact: Thomas Russell, President and Chief Executive Officer
COO: Ronald K. Benfield, Chief Operating Officer
CFO: V. Mark Perry, Chief Financial Officer
CMO: Wesley E. Rippey, M.D., Chief Medical Officer
CHR: Shane Voshell, Director Human Resources
CNO: Ellen Tryon, R.N., Chief Nursing Officer
Web address: www.adventisthealthnw.com
Control: Church–operated, Nongovernment, not–for profit **Service:** General Medical and Surgical

Staffed Beds: 248 Admissions: 12009 Census: 121 Outpatient Visits: 529815 Births: 1089 Total Expense ($000): 319344 Payroll Expense ($000): 129028 Personnel: 1543

☐ **CEDAR HILLS HOSPITAL (384012)**, 10300 S.W. Eastridge Street, Zip 97225–5004; tel. 503/944–5000, (Nonreporting) **A**1 9 10 **S** Universal Health Services, Inc., King of Prussia, PA
Primary Contact: Michael Sherbun, Ph.D., Chief Executive Officer
Web address: www.cedarhillshospital.com
Control: Corporation, Investor–owned, for–profit **Service:** Psychiatric

Staffed Beds: 78

DOERNBECHER CHILDREN'S HOSPITAL See OHSU Hospital

GOOD SAMARITAN HOSPITAL AND MEDICAL CENTER See Legacy Good Samaritan Hospital and Medical Center

✠ △ **LEGACY EMANUEL HOSPITAL AND HEALTH CENTER (380007)**, 2801 North Gantenbein Avenue, Zip 97227–1674; tel. 503/413–2100, (Includes RANDALL CHILDREN'S HOSPITAL, 2801 North Gantenbein Avenue, Zip 97227–1623; tel. 503/413–2200) **A**1 2 3 5 7 9 10 **F**3 7 11 13 15 16 17 18 19 20 21 22 23 24 25 26 27 29 30 31 32 34 35 38 39 40 41 43 44 45 46 47 49 50 51 54 55 56 57 59 60 61 64 65 66 68 70 72 74 75 76 77 78 79 80 81 83 84 85 86 87 88 89 93 97 98 99 100 101 102 107 108 110 111 112 114 115 118 119 126 127 129 130 131 132 135 144 146 147 148 **P**6 **S** Legacy Health, Portland, OR
Primary Contact: Lori Morgan, M.D., Chief Administrative Officer
CIO: Richard Gibson, Senior Vice President and Chief Information Officer
CHR: Sonja Steves, Senior Vice President Human Resources and Marketing
Web address: www.legacyhealth.org
Control: Other not–for–profit (including NFP Corporation) **Service:** General Medical and Surgical

Staffed Beds: 427 Admissions: 18880 Census: 282 Outpatient Visits: 482883 Births: 1940 Total Expense ($000): 596318 Payroll Expense ($000): 261595 Personnel: 3195

✠ **LEGACY GOOD SAMARITAN HOSPITAL AND MEDICAL CENTER (380017)**, 1015 N.W. 22nd Avenue, Zip 97210–3099; tel. 503/413–7711, (Includes GOOD SAMARITAN HOSPITAL AND MEDICAL CENTER, 1015 N.W. 22nd Avenue, Zip 97210; tel. 503/229–7711; REHABILITATION INSTITUTE OF OREGON, 2010 N.W. Kearney Street, Zip 97209; tel. 503/226–3774) **A**1 2 3 5 9 10 **F**3 8 11 12 13 15 18 20 22 24 26 29 30 31 34 35 38 40 44 45 46 47 49 50 51 55 56 57 58 59 60 61 64 65 68 70 74 75 76 77 78 79 80 81 82 83 84 85 86 87 90 91 93 94 96 97 98 100 101 102 103 107 108 110 111 114 115 116 117 118 119 120 121 123 124 126 129 130 132 135 138 142 143 145 146 147 148 **P**6 **S** Legacy Health, Portland, OR
Primary Contact: Jonathan Avery, Chief Administrative Officer
CIO: C. Matthew Calais, Senior Vice President and Chief Information Officer
CHR: Sonja Steves, Vice President Marketing
CNO: Cindy Evans, R.N., Chief Nursing Officer
Web address: www.legacyhealth.org
Control: Other not–for–profit (including NFP Corporation) **Service:** General Medical and Surgical

Staffed Beds: 247 Admissions: 11030 Census: 141 Outpatient Visits: 151507 Births: 996 Total Expense ($000): 264981 Payroll Expense ($000): 97439 Personnel: 1320

✠ **OHSU HOSPITAL (380009)**, 3181 S.W. Sam Jackson Park Road, Zip 97239–3098; tel. 503/494–8311, (Includes DOERNBECHER CHILDREN'S HOSPITAL, 3181 S.W. Sam Jackson Park Road, Zip 97201) **A**1 2 3 5 8 9 10 **F**3 5 6 8 9 12 13 15 17 18 19 20 21 22 23 24 25 26 27 28 29 30 31 32 34 35 36 37 38 39 40 41 43 44 45 46 47 48 49 50 51 52 53 54 55 56 57 58 59 60 61 64 66 68 70 71 72 74 75 76 77 78 79 81 82 84 85 86 87 88 89 92 93 95 96 97 98 100 103 104 107 108 110 111 114 115 117 118 119 120 121 123 124 126 127 129 130 131 132 134 135 136 137 138 139 141 145 146 147 148 **P**1
Primary Contact: Peter F. Rapp, Vice President and Executive Director
COO: Cynthia M. Grueber, Chief Operating Officer
CFO: Diana Gernhart, Chief Financial Officer
CMO: Charles M. Kilo, M.D., Chief Medical Officer
CIO: Bridget Haggerty, Chief Information Officer
CHR: Derek Carissimi, Vice President Human Resources
CNO: Dana Bjarnason, R.N., Vice President and Chief Nursing Officer
Web address: www.ohsu.edu
Control: Hospital district or authority, Government, nonfederal **Service:** General Medical and Surgical

Staffed Beds: 543 Admissions: 29748 Census: 460 Outpatient Visits: 766912 Births: 2449 Total Expense ($000): 1154841 Payroll Expense ($000): 414114 Personnel: 6664

✠ **PORTLAND VETERANS AFFAIRS MEDICAL CENTER**, 3710 S.W. U.S. Veterans Hospital Road, Zip 97239–2964, Mailing Address: P.O. Box 1034, Zip 97207–1034; tel. 503/220–8262, (Nonreporting) **A**1 2 3 5 8 **S** Department of Veterans Affairs, Washington, DC
Primary Contact: Joanne Krumberger, R.N., FACHE, Director
CFO: Annette Barkema, Chief Financial Officer
CMO: Thomas Anderson, M.D., Chief of Staff
CIO: James Horner, Chief Information Officer
CHR: Melody Mikutowski, Chief Human Resources Management
Web address: www.portland.va.gov/
Control: Veterans Affairs, Government, federal **Service:** General Medical and Surgical

Staffed Beds: 303

✠ **PROVIDENCE PORTLAND MEDICAL CENTER (380061)**, 4805 N.E. Glisan Street, Zip 97213–2933; tel. 503/215–5526 **A**1 2 3 5 9 10 **F**3 4 9 13 15 17 18 20 22 24 26 29 30 31 34 35 40 44 45 46 49 50 51 53 54 56 57 58 59 60 61 62 63 64 65 66 68 70 73 74 75 76 77 78 79 81 82 84 85 86 87 90 92 93 97 98 99 100 102 103 104 105 107 108 109 110 111 114 116 117 118 119 121 123 124 126 129 130 131 132 133 135 136 137 145 146 147 148 **P**6 **S** Providence Health & Services, Renton, WA
Primary Contact: Paul Gaden, Chief Executive Officer
COO: Krista Farnham, Chief Operating Officer
CFO: Eric Olson, Chief Financial Officer
CMO: Robert Wells, M.D., Chief Medical Officer
CIO: Mark Premo, Senior Director HC Intelligence
CHR: Jeannie Mikulic, Director Human Resources
CNO: Mary T. McFadden, MSN, Chief Nurse Executive
Web address: www.providence.org
Control: Church–operated, Nongovernment, not–for profit **Service:** General Medical and Surgical

Staffed Beds: 403 Admissions: 21249 Census: 276 Outpatient Visits: 1163928 Births: 2476 Total Expense ($000): 607764 Payroll Expense ($000): 200721 Personnel: 2571

✠ **PROVIDENCE ST. VINCENT MEDICAL CENTER (380004)**, 9205 S.W. Barnes Road, Zip 97225–6661; tel. 503/216–1234, (Includes CHILDREN AT PROVIDENCE ST. VINCENT, 9205 S.W. Barnes Road, Zip 97225–6603; tel. 503/216–4400) **A**1 2 3 5 9 10 **F**3 5 13 15 17 18 20 22 24 26 28 29 30 31 34 35 36 37 38 40 41 44 45 46 47 48 49 50 51 53 54 56 57 58 59 60 61 64 65 70 72 74 75 76 77 78 79 81 82 83 84 85 86 87 88 89 91 92 93 97 98 100 102 103 104 105 107 108 109 110 111 112 114 115 116 117 118 119 120 121 123 126 129 130 131 132 133 135 146 147 148 **P**6 **S** Providence Health & Services, Renton, WA
Primary Contact: Janice Burger, Chief Executive
CFO: William Olson, Director Finance
CIO: Kate Chester, Senior Coordinator Public Relations
Web address: www.providence.org/portland/hospitals
Control: Church–operated, Nongovernment, not–for profit **Service:** General Medical and Surgical

Staffed Beds: 552 Admissions: 27988 Census: 339 Outpatient Visits: 833359 Births: 4490 Total Expense ($000): 686399 Payroll Expense ($000): 208092 Personnel: 2727

REHABILITATION INSTITUTE OF OREGON See Legacy Good Samaritan Hospital and Medical Center

Many Facility Codes have changed. Please refer to the AHA Guide Code Chart. © 2014 AHA Guide

OR

☐ **SHRINERS HOSPITALS FOR CHILDREN–PORTLAND (383300)**, 3101 S.W. Sam Jackson Park Road, Zip 97239–3009; tel. 503/241–5090 **A**1 3 5 10 **F**3 29 34 35 37 50 53 58 64 68 75 77 79 81 85 86 87 89 91 93 94 130 131 132 134 146 148 **P**6 **S** Shriners Hospitals for Children, Tampa, FL
Primary Contact: J. Craig Patchin, Administrator
CFO: Mark Knudsen, Director Fiscal Services
CMO: Michael Aiona, M.D., Chief of Staff
CIO: Carl Montante, Director Information Systems and Information Technology
CHR: Rhonda Smith, Director Human Resources
CNO: Suzanne Diers, R.N., Director Patient Care Services
Web address: www.shrinershospitalsforchildren.org/Hospitals/Locations/Portland.aspx
Control: Other not–for–profit (including NFP Corporation) **Service:** Children's general

Staffed Beds: 8 **Admissions:** 529 **Census:** 7 **Outpatient Visits:** 10972 **Births:** 0 **Total Expense ($000):** 39183 **Payroll Expense ($000):** 18328 **Personnel:** 254

VETERANS AFFAIRS MEDICAL CENTER See Portland Veterans Affairs Medical Center

⊞ **VIBRA SPECIALTY HOSPITAL OF PORTLAND (382004)**, 10300 N.E. Hancock Street, Zip 97220–3831; tel. 503/257–5500 **A**1 9 10 **F**1 3 12 28 29 30 34 35 50 56 57 59 60 61 68 74 75 77 79 82 84 85 86 87 91 94 96 119 130 135 143 **P**6 **S** Vibra Healthcare, Mechanicsburg, PA
Primary Contact: Dave Tupper, Chief Executive Officer
CFO: Stephanie Lawrence, Chief Financial Officer
CMO: Cynthia Wallace, M.D., Medical Director
CIO: Marie Roof, Executive Vice President Information Systems
CHR: Kellie Bernert–Yap, Director Human Resources
CNO: Susan E. Brooker, R.N., Chief Clinical Officer
Web address: www.vshportland.com
Control: Individual, Investor–owned, for–profit **Service:** Long–Term Acute Care hospital

Staffed Beds: 68 **Admissions:** 471 **Census:** 34 **Outpatient Visits:** 0 **Births:** 0 **Total Expense ($000):** 28505 **Payroll Expense ($000):** 13973

PRINEVILLE—Crook County

★ **PIONEER MEMORIAL HOSPITAL (381313)**, 1201 N.E. Elm Street, Zip 97754–1206; tel. 541/447–6254 **A**9 10 18 **F**3 11 15 29 30 34 35 40 43 45 50 59 63 64 65 68 70 75 79 81 82 84 85 86 87 93 97 100 107 110 115 119 127 128 130 132 133 135 146 **P**1 6 **S** St. Charles Health System, Inc., Bend, OR
Primary Contact: Jeanine Gentry, Chief Executive Officer
CFO: Karen Shepard, Senior Vice President and Chief Financial Officer
CMO: Michel Boileau, M.D., Chief Clinical Officer
CHR: Rebecca Berry, Senior Director Human Resources
Web address: www.stcharleshealthcare.org
Control: Other not–for–profit (including NFP Corporation) **Service:** General Medical and Surgical

Staffed Beds: 25 **Admissions:** 682 **Census:** 7 **Outpatient Visits:** 38789 **Births:** 0 **Total Expense ($000):** 24318 **Payroll Expense ($000):** 12056 **Personnel:** 159

REDMOND—Deschutes County

⊞ **ST. CHARLES MEDICAL CENTER – REDMOND (380040)**, 1253 N.W. Canal Boulevard, Zip 97756–1395; tel. 541/548–8131 **A**1 9 10 20 **F**3 11 13 29 30 34 40 43 45 47 51 57 59 62 64 68 70 75 76 81 82 84 85 92 93 102 107 108 114 119 130 135 146 148 **P**1 6 **S** St. Charles Health System, Inc., Bend, OR
Primary Contact: Robert Gomes, FACHE, Chief Executive Officer
COO: Jim Kirkbride, Assistant Vice President Ancillary and Support Services
CFO: Karen Shepard, Senior Vice President Finance and Chief Financial Officer
CMO: Michel Boileau, M.D., Chief Clinical Officer
CIO: William Winnenberg, Chief Information Officer
CHR: Rebecca Berry, Senior Director Human Resources
CNO: Karen Reed, R.N., Chief Nursing Officer
Web address: www.stcharleshealthcare.org
Control: Other not–for–profit (including NFP Corporation) **Service:** General Medical and Surgical

Staffed Beds: 48 **Admissions:** 2258 **Census:** 17 **Outpatient Visits:** 63164 **Births:** 375 **Total Expense ($000):** 59589 **Payroll Expense ($000):** 30224 **Personnel:** 347

REEDSPORT—Douglas County

LOWER UMPQUA HOSPITAL DISTRICT (381311), 600 Ranch Road, Zip 97467–1795; tel. 541/271–2171 **A**9 10 18 **F**3 7 11 15 29 34 35 40 43 45 46 50 57 64 70 75 77 79 81 85 87 93 107 108 114 119 127 130 132 133 144 **P**6
Primary Contact: Sandra Reese, Administrator
CMO: Ronald Vail, M.D., Chief of Staff
CIO: Timothy Picou, Manager Information Technology
Web address: www.lowerumpquahospital.com
Control: Hospital district or authority, Government, nonfederal **Service:** General Medical and Surgical

Staffed Beds: 16 **Admissions:** 309 **Census:** 3 **Outpatient Visits:** 19997 **Births:** 0 **Total Expense ($000):** 19191 **Payroll Expense ($000):** 7273 **Personnel:** 134

ROSEBURG—Douglas County

⊞ **MERCY MEDICAL CENTER (380027)**, 2700 Stewart Parkway, Zip 97471–1281; tel. 541/673–0611 **A**1 9 10 19 20 **F**3 8 11 13 15 17 18 19 20 21 22 23 24 25 26 27 28 29 30 31 32 34 35 37 38 40 43 44 45 46 47 48 49 50 51 54 56 57 59 60 61 62 63 64 65 68 70 74 75 76 77 78 79 81 82 84 85 86 87 89 93 96 102 107 108 110 111 114 115 118 119 129 130 132 135 143 146 147 148 **P**6 **S** Catholic Health Initiatives, Englewood, CO
Primary Contact: Kelly C. Morgan, President and Chief Executive Officer
COO: Debbie Boswell, Chief Operating Officer and Chief Nursing Officer
CFO: John Kasberger, Vice President and Chief Financial Officer
CMO: Jason Gray, M.D., Chief Medical Officer
CIO: Kathleen Nickel, Director Communications
CHR: Deb Lightcap, Director Human Resources
CNO: Debbie Boswell, Chief Operating Officer and Chief Nursing Officer
Web address: www.mercyrose.org
Control: Church–operated, Nongovernment, not–for profit **Service:** General Medical and Surgical

Staffed Beds: 141 **Admissions:** 7141 **Census:** 72 **Outpatient Visits:** 337835 **Births:** 926 **Total Expense ($000):** 140778 **Payroll Expense ($000):** 51816 **Personnel:** 733

⊞ **VETERANS AFFAIRS ROSEBURG HEALTHCARE SYSTEM**, 913 N.W. Garden Valley Boulevard, Zip 97471–6513; tel. 541/440–1000, (Nonreporting) **A**1 **S** Department of Veterans Affairs, Washington, DC
Primary Contact: Carol Bogedain, FACHE, Director
COO: Steven Broskey, Associate Director
CHR: Larry Mentzer, Chief Human Resources Officer
CNO: Tracy Weistreich, Ph.D., Associate Director Patient Care Services/Nurse Executive
Web address: www.roseburg.va.gov/
Control: Veterans Affairs, Government, federal **Service:** General Medical and Surgical

Staffed Beds: 88

SALEM—Marion County

☐ **OREGON STATE HOSPITAL (384008)**, 2600 Center Street N.E., Zip 97301–2682; tel. 503/945–2870, (Nonreporting) **A**1 3 5 10
Primary Contact: Greg Roberts, Superintendent
Web address: www.oregon.gov/dhs/mentalhealth/osh/main.shtml
Control: State–Government, nonfederal **Service:** Psychiatric

Staffed Beds: 638

Hospital, Medicare Provider Number, Address, Telephone, Approval, Facility, and Physician Codes, Health Care System

★ American Hospital Association (AHA) membership
☐ The Joint Commission accreditation
◇ DNV Healthcare Inc. accreditation
○ Healthcare Facilities Accreditation Program
△ Commission on Accreditation of Rehabilitation Facilities (CARF) accreditation

✠ **SALEM HOSPITAL (380051)**, 890 Oak Street S.E., Zip 97301–3959, Mailing Address: P.O. Box 14001, Zip 97309–5014; tel. 503/561–5200, (Includes PSYCHIATRIC MEDICINE CENTER, 1127 Oak Street S.E., Zip 97301, Mailing Address: P.O. Box 14001, Zip 97309–5014; REGIONAL REHABILITATION CENTER, 2561 Center Street N.E., Zip 97301, Mailing Address: P.O. Box 14001, Zip 97309–5014; tel. 503/370–5986) **A**1 2 9 10 **F**3 11 12 13 15 17 18 19 20 22 24 26 28 29 30 31 34 35 36 37 38 40 43 45 46 47 48 49 50 53 54 55 56 57 58 59 64 67 68 70 72 74 75 76 77 78 79 81 82 84 85 86 87 89 90 91 92 93 94 95 96 97 98 99 100 102 103 104 105 106 107 108 109 110 111 112 113 114 115 116 117 118 119 120 121 122 123 124 126 129 130 131 132 135 145 146 147 148 **P**6 **S** Salem Health, Salem, OR
Primary Contact: Norman F. Gruber, President and Chief Executive Officer
COO: Cheryl R. Nester Wolfe, R.N., Senior Vice President Operations
CFO: Aaron Crane, Chief Financial Officer
CMO: W. David Holloway, M.D., Chief Medical Officer
CIO: Cort Garrison, M.D., Chief Information Officer
CHR: Laurie C. Barr, Vice President Human Resources
CNO: Martha G. Enriquez, R.N., Vice President Patient Care Services and Chief Nursing Officer
Web address: www.salemhospital.org
Control: Other not–for–profit (including NFP Corporation) **Service:** General Medical and Surgical

Staffed Beds: 417 **Admissions:** 21540 **Census:** 262 **Outpatient Visits:** 347270 **Births:** 3005 **Total Expense ($000):** 532175 **Payroll Expense ($000):** 228242 **Personnel:** 3152

SEASIDE—Clatsop County

✠ **PROVIDENCE SEASIDE HOSPITAL (381303)**, 725 South Wahanna Road, Zip 97138–7735; tel. 503/717–7000, (Total facility includes 22 beds in nursing home–type unit) **A**1 9 10 18 **F**3 12 13 15 18 29 30 31 32 34 35 40 45 46 56 57 59 61 64 65 66 67 70 75 76 77 78 79 81 82 83 84 85 86 87 91 92 93 97 107 108 110 111 114 119 127 128 130 132 133 135 143 146 147 148 **P**6 **S** Providence Health & Services, Renton, WA
Primary Contact: Michael Blauer, Chief Executive Officer
COO: Bonnie Thompson, Chief Operating Officer and Chief Nursing Officer
CFO: Pamela Hayes, Director Finance
CMO: Susan Heineck, M.D., President Professional Staff
CHR: Marti Hanen, Director Human Resources
CNO: Bonnie Thompson, Chief Operating Officer and Chief Nursing Officer
Web address: www.providence.org
Control: Church–operated, Nongovernment, not–for profit **Service:** General Medical and Surgical

Staffed Beds: 47 **Admissions:** 966 **Census:** 30 **Outpatient Visits:** 118657 **Births:** 94 **Total Expense ($000):** 50283 **Payroll Expense ($000):** 22751 **Personnel:** 301

SILVERTON—Marion County

✠ **SILVERTON HOSPITAL (380029)**, 342 Fairview Street, Zip 97381–1993; tel. 503/873–1500 **A**1 9 10 **F**3 11 13 15 20 26 28 29 30 34 35 40 43 47 50 54 57 59 64 65 66 68 70 75 76 77 79 81 85 86 87 89 107 108 110 111 114 115 119 124 127 130 131 132 133 135 143 144 146 147 148 **P**4 8
Primary Contact: Richard M. Cagen, President and Chief Executive Officer
COO: Christine Denning, Chief Operating Officer and Chief Nursing Officer
CFO: Daniel L. Jessup, Chief Financial Officer
CMO: Joseph Huang, M.D., Chief Medical and Quality Officer
CIO: Karen Brady, Chief Information Officer
CHR: Natalie J. Britton, Director Human Resources
CNO: Christine Denning, Chief Operating Officer and Chief Nursing Officer
Web address: www.silvertonhealth.org
Control: Other not–for–profit (including NFP Corporation) **Service:** General Medical and Surgical

Staffed Beds: 48 **Admissions:** 3231 **Census:** 24 **Outpatient Visits:** 166617 **Births:** 1638 **Total Expense ($000):** 96718 **Payroll Expense ($000):** 50805 **Personnel:** 695

SPRINGFIELD—Lane County

✠ **MCKENZIE–WILLAMETTE MEDICAL CENTER (380020)**, 1460 G Street, Zip 97477–4197; tel. 541/726–4400 **A**1 9 10 **F**3 11 13 17 18 20 22 24 28 29 30 31 34 35 39 40 41 43 45 46 47 49 50 57 59 70 73 76 78 79 81 82 85 87 89 93 107 108 111 115 118 119 126 129 130 132 146 147 148 **P**6 **S** Community Health Systems, Inc., Franklin, TN
Primary Contact: Chad Campbell, Chief Executive Officer
CFO: Rosanne Devault, Chief Financial Officer
CIO: David Blomquist, Director Information Technology
CHR: Megan A. O'Leary, Vice President Human Resources and Rehabilitation Services
Web address: www.mckweb.com
Control: Corporation, Investor–owned, for–profit **Service:** General Medical and Surgical

Staffed Beds: 113 **Admissions:** 6401 **Census:** 57 **Outpatient Visits:** 62492 **Births:** 641 **Total Expense ($000):** 120336 **Payroll Expense ($000):** 44918 **Personnel:** 579

★ ◇ **PEACEHEALTH SACRED HEART MEDICAL CENTER AT RIVERBEND (380102)**, 3333 Riverbend Drive, Zip 97477–8800; tel. 541/222–7300 **A**9 10 21 **F**3 11 12 13 19 20 21 22 24 26 28 29 30 31 37 38 40 43 45 46 47 49 51 57 60 64 68 70 72 74 75 76 78 79 81 84 85 89 93 102 107 108 111 115 118 119 126 129 130 146 148 **P**6 **S** PeaceHealth, Vancouver, WA
Primary Contact: John G. Hill, Chief Executive Officer
CFO: Wendy Apland, Regional Vice President of Finance/Chief Financial Officer
CIO: Tom Fricks, Interim Senior Vice President of Information Technology
CHR: Craig Mills, Regional Vice President Culture and People
Web address: www.peacehealth.org
Control: Church–operated, Nongovernment, not–for profit **Service:** General Medical and Surgical

Staffed Beds: 379 **Admissions:** 23221 **Census:** 269 **Outpatient Visits:** 96880 **Births:** 2910 **Total Expense ($000):** 509143 **Payroll Expense ($000):** 148634 **Personnel:** 2101

STAYTON—Marion County

✠ **SANTIAM MEMORIAL HOSPITAL (380056)**, 1401 North 10th Avenue, Zip 97383–1399; tel. 503/769–2175 **A**1 9 10 **F**3 7 11 13 15 29 30 40 41 43 50 65 70 76 81 85 87 89 90 107 111 115 119 128 130 133 135 143 **P**8
Primary Contact: Terry L. Fletchall, Administrator
COO: Maggie Hudson, Chief Financial and Operations Officer
CFO: Rachael Seeder, Controller
CMO: Guesly Dessieux, D.O., Chief Medical Officer
CIO: Trace Jacobs, Director Information Technology
CNO: Genny Baldwin, R.N., Chief Nursing Officer
Web address: www.santiamhospital.org
Control: Other not–for–profit (including NFP Corporation) **Service:** General Medical and Surgical

Staffed Beds: 40 **Admissions:** 1006 **Census:** 10 **Outpatient Visits:** 36255 **Births:** 114 **Total Expense ($000):** 38760 **Payroll Expense ($000):** 16726 **Personnel:** 240

THE DALLES—Wasco County

✠ △ **MID–COLUMBIA MEDICAL CENTER (380001)**, 1700 East 19th Street, Zip 97058–3317; tel. 541/296–1111 **A**1 2 7 9 10 19 20 **F**3 11 12 13 15 18 28 29 30 31 32 34 35 36 40 41 43 45 46 50 53 57 59 62 65 66 68 70 75 76 77 78 79 81 82 83 84 86 87 89 90 91 92 93 99 100 101 104 107 108 110 111 114 118 119 120 121 123 127 129 130 131 132 133 135 146 147 148 **P**4 6
Primary Contact: Duane Francis, President and Chief Executive Officer
CFO: Don Arbon, Vice President Finance
CMO: Judy Richardson, M.D., President Medical Staff
CIO: Erick Larson, Vice President and Chief Information Officer
CHR: Christine Espy, Director Human Resources
CNO: Regina P. Rose, R.N., Vice President Nursing Services
Web address: www.mcmc.net
Control: Other not–for–profit (including NFP Corporation) **Service:** General Medical and Surgical

Staffed Beds: 43 **Admissions:** 2167 **Census:** 19 **Outpatient Visits:** 115596 **Births:** 277 **Total Expense ($000):** 84005 **Payroll Expense ($000):** 39551 **Personnel:** 579

TILLAMOOK—Tillamook County

✠ **TILLAMOOK REGIONAL MEDICAL CENTER (381317)**, 1000 Third Street, Zip 97141–3430; tel. 503/842–4444 **A**1 9 10 18 **F**2 3 7 13 15 17 18 29 30 31 33 34 35 40 43 45 50 57 59 64 65 68 75 76 77 78 79 81 85 87 93 94 97 102 107 108 110 111 115 119 127 130 132 133 135 144 145 146 147 148 **P**6 **S** Adventist Health, Roseville, CA
Primary Contact: David Butler, President and Chief Executive Officer
CFO: Walt Larson, Vice President Finance
CMO: Mark Bowman, M.D., President Medical Staff
CNO: Kathy Saxon, R.N., Vice President Patient Care Services
Web address: www.tillamookregionalmc.com
Control: Church–operated, Nongovernment, not–for profit **Service:** General Medical and Surgical

Staffed Beds: 25 **Admissions:** 1109 **Census:** 8 **Outpatient Visits:** 93691 **Births:** 166 **Total Expense ($000):** 55377 **Payroll Expense ($000):** 24504 **Personnel:** 353

Many Facility Codes have changed. Please refer to the AHA Guide Code Chart. © 2014 AHA Guide

TUALATIN—Clackamas County

✠ **LEGACY MERIDIAN PARK MEDICAL CENTER (380089)**, 19300 S.W. 65th Avenue, Zip 97062–9741; tel. 503/692–1212 **A**1 2 9 10 **F**3 11 13 15 18 20 22 28 29 30 31 32 34 35 38 40 44 45 46 49 50 51 56 57 59 60 64 68 70 74 75 76 77 78 79 80 81 85 86 87 93 107 108 110 111 114 115 116 117 118 119 120 121 126 129 130 132 145 146 147 148 **P**6 **S** Legacy Health, Portland, OR
Primary Contact: Allyson Anderson, Chief Administrative Officer
COO: Michael Newcomb, D.O., Senior Vice President and Chief Operating Officer
CMO: Lewis Low, M.D., Senior Vice President and Chief Medical Officer
CIO: John Jay Kenagy, Ph.D., Senior Vice President and Chief Information Officer
CHR: Sonja Steves, Vice President Human Resources and Marketing
CNO: Carol Bradley, MSN, Senior Vice President and Chief Nursing Officer
Web address: www.legacyhealth.org
Control: Other not–for–profit (including NFP Corporation) **Service:** General Medical and Surgical

---

Staffed Beds: 130 **Admissions:** 8069 **Census:** 75 **Outpatient Visits:** 169935
Births: 946 **Total Expense ($000):** 159427 **Payroll Expense ($000):** 57563
Personnel: 768

OR

PENNSYLVANIA

PA

ABINGTON—Montgomery County

✠ **ABINGTON MEMORIAL HOSPITAL (390231)**, 1200 Old York Road, Zip 19001–3720; tel. 215/481–2000 **A**1 2 3 5 6 10 12 13 **F**3 6 8 9 11 12 13 15 17 18 19 20 22 24 26 28 29 30 31 32 34 35 36 37 38 39 40 43 44 45 46 49 50 52 53 54 55 56 59 60 61 62 63 64 65 66 68 70 72 74 75 76 77 78 79 81 82 83 84 85 86 87 89 90 91 92 93 94 96 97 98 99 100 101 102 103 104 107 108 110 111 114 115 118 119 120 121 123 124 126 129 130 131 132 135 146 147 148 **P**6 **S** Abington Health, Abington, PA
Primary Contact: Laurence M. Merlis, President and Chief Executive Officer
COO: Margaret M. McGoldrick, Executive Vice President and Chief Operating Officer
CFO: Michael Walsh, Senior Vice President Finance and Chief Financial Officer
CMO: John J. Kelly, M.D., Chief of Staff
CIO: Alison Ferren, Vice President Information Technology and Chief Information Officer
CHR: Meghan Patton, Vice President Human Resources
CNO: Theresa Reilly, MSN, Senior Vice President Patient Services and Chief Nursing Officer
Web address: www.abingtonhealth.org
Control: Other not–for–profit (including NFP Corporation) **Service:** General Medical and Surgical

Staffed Beds: 621 **Admissions:** 32052 **Census:** 385 **Outpatient Visits:** 614564 **Births:** 4843 **Total Expense ($000):** 687579 **Payroll Expense ($000):** 324531 **Personnel:** 4056

ALLENTOWN—Lehigh County

☐ △ **GOOD SHEPHERD REHABILITATION HOSPITAL (393035)**, 850 South 5th Street, Zip 18103–3308; tel. 610/776–3299 **A**1 3 5 7 9 10 **F**28 29 30 32 34 35 36 53 54 56 57 58 59 64 65 66 68 74 75 77 82 86 87 90 91 92 93 94 95 96 107 111 119 130 131 132 143 146 148 **P**1 **S** Good Shepherd Rehabilitation Network, Allentown, PA
Primary Contact: John Kristel, President and Chief Executive Officer
CFO: Ron Petula, Chief Financial Officer
Web address: www.goodshepherdrehab.org
Control: Other not–for–profit (including NFP Corporation) **Service:** Rehabilitation

Staffed Beds: 106 **Admissions:** 1940 **Census:** 79 **Outpatient Visits:** 209132 **Births:** 0 **Total Expense ($000):** 79598 **Payroll Expense ($000):** 31679 **Personnel:** 886

✠ **LEHIGH VALLEY HOSPITAL (390133)**, 1200 South Cedar Crest Boulevard, Zip 18103–6248, Mailing Address: P.O. Box 689, Zip 18105–1556; tel. 610/402–8000, (Includes LEHIGH VALLEY HEALTH NETWORK PEDIATRICS, 17th and Chew Streets, Zip 18102, Mailing Address: PO Box 7017, Zip 18105–7017; tel. 610/402–2273) **A**1 2 3 5 8 9 10 **F**3 6 8 9 11 12 13 15 16 17 18 19 20 22 24 26 28 29 30 31 32 33 34 35 36 37 38 39 40 41 43 44 45 46 47 48 49 50 51 53 54 55 56 57 58 59 60 61 62 63 64 66 68 70 71 72 74 76 77 78 79 80 81 82 84 85 86 87 88 89 90 92 93 96 97 98 99 100 101 102 104 105 106 107 108 110 111 115 118 119 120 121 123 124 126 128 129 130 131 132 134 135 138 141 142 143 144 146 147 148 **P**5 6 8 **S** Lehigh Valley Health Network, Allentown, PA
Primary Contact: Brian Nester, D.O., Interim President and Chief Executive Officer
COO: Terry Ann Capuano, R.N., Chief Operating Officer
CFO: Edward O'Dea, Vice President and Chief Financial Officer
CMO: Thomas Whalen, M.D., Chief Medical Officer
CIO: Harry Lukens, Senior Vice President and Chief Information Officer
CHR: Deborah A. Patrick, Senior Vice President Human Resources
CNO: Anne Panik, MS, Senior Vice President Patient Care Services and Chief Nursing Officer
Web address: www.lvhhn.org
Control: Other not–for–profit (including NFP Corporation) **Service:** General Medical and Surgical

Staffed Beds: 812 **Admissions:** 44674 **Census:** 661 **Outpatient Visits:** 341945 **Births:** 4304 **Total Expense ($000):** 1084845 **Payroll Expense ($000):** 369318 **Personnel:** 6654

☐ △ **SACRED HEART HOSPITAL (390197)**, 421 West Chew Street, Zip 18102–3490; tel. 610/776–4500, (Total facility includes 22 beds in nursing home–type unit) **A**1 3 5 7 9 10 13 **F**3 11 12 13 15 18 20 22 24 28 29 30 31 32 34 35 38 39 40 43 45 46 47 49 50 56 57 59 61 62 63 64 66 68 74 75 76 77 78 79 80 81 82 84 85 87 91 92 97 98 100 101 102 103 107 108 110 111 114 119 121 128 129 130 132 135 143 146 147 148 **P**8
Primary Contact: John L. Nespoli, Chief Executive Officer
CMO: Farrokh Sadr, M.D., Chief Medical Officer
CIO: Tracy Burkhart, Vice President Information Services
CHR: Joseph Mikitka, Vice President Human Resources
Web address: www.shh.org
Control: Other not–for–profit (including NFP Corporation) **Service:** General Medical and Surgical

Staffed Beds: 141 **Admissions:** 6021 **Census:** 116 **Outpatient Visits:** 160852 **Births:** 338 **Total Expense ($000):** 97955 **Payroll Expense ($000):** 40000 **Personnel:** 877

ST LUKE'S HOSPITAL – ALLENTOWN CAMPUS See St. Luke's University Hospital – Bethlehem Campus, Bethlehem

☐ **SURGICAL SPECIALTY CENTER AT COORDINATED HEALTH (390321)**, 1503 North Cedar Crest Boulevard, Zip 18104–2302; tel. 610/861–8080 **A**1 9 10 **F**3 8 15 29 33 34 54 57 59 64 65 68 77 79 81 82 85 93 96 97 107 108 110 111 114 115 117 119 130 131 141 147 148
Primary Contact: Emil DiIorio, M.D., Chief Executive Officer
Web address: www.coordinatedhealth.com
Control: Corporation, Investor–owned, for–profit **Service:** Surgical

Staffed Beds: 20 **Admissions:** 830 **Census:** 5 **Births:** 0 **Personnel:** 551

☐ **WESTFIELD HOSPITAL**, 4815 West Tilghman Street, Zip 18104–9374; tel. 610/973–8400 **A**1 9 **F**3 12 18 29 34 35 39 40 45 50 56 57 63 65 68 70 74 75 77 79 81 82 85 86 87 102 107 108 111 114 119 129 130 135 143 146
Primary Contact: Yasin N. Khan, M.D., Chief Executive Officer
Web address: www.westfieldhospital.com
Control: Partnership, Investor–owned, for–profit **Service:** General Medical and Surgical

Staffed Beds: 22 **Admissions:** 405 **Census:** 3 **Births:** 0 **Personnel:** 105

ALTOONA—Blair County

ALTOONA REGIONAL HEALTH SYSTEM See UPMC Altoona

✠ **HEALTHSOUTH REHABILITATION HOSPITAL OF ALTOONA (393040)**, 2005 Valley View Boulevard, Zip 16602–4598; tel. 814/944–3535 **A**1 10 **F**28 29 34 64 74 75 82 90 91 93 94 96 130 131 **P**5 **S** HEALTHSOUTH Corporation, Birmingham, AL
Primary Contact: Scott Filler, Chief Executive Officer
CFO: George Berger, Controller
CMO: Rakesh Patel, D.O., Medical Director
CIO: Kathleen Edwards, Manager Information Systems Operation
CHR: Christine Filer, Director Human Resources
CNO: Mary Gen Boyles, Chief Nursing Officer
Web address: www.healthsouthaltoona.com
Control: Corporation, Investor–owned, for–profit **Service:** Rehabilitation

Staffed Beds: 80 **Admissions:** 1947 **Census:** 71 **Outpatient Visits:** 44057 **Births:** 0 **Total Expense ($000):** 27877 **Payroll Expense ($000):** 14421 **Personnel:** 246

✠ **JAMES E. VAN ZANDT VETERANS AFFAIRS MEDICAL CENTER**, 2907 Pleasant Valley Boulevard, Zip 16602–4305; tel. 877/626–2500, (Nonreporting) **A**1 **S** Department of Veterans Affairs, Washington, DC
Primary Contact: William H. Mills, Director
CFO: Carl Parrish, Chief Fiscal Service
CMO: Santha Kurian, M.D., Chief of Staff
CIO: Michael Hynoski, Chief Information Resource Management
CHR: Gina Dunio, Chief Human Resources
Web address: www.altoona.va.gov/
Control: Veterans Affairs, Government, federal **Service:** General Medical and Surgical

Staffed Beds: 68

✠ **UPMC ALTOONA (390073)**, 620 Howard Avenue, Zip 16601–4804; tel. 814/889–2011 **A**1 2 3 5 9 10 12 13 **F**3 5 8 11 12 13 15 18 20 22 24 26 28 29 30 31 34 35 37 38 40 43 44 45 47 48 49 50 51 54 56 57 59 60 61 64 65 66 68 70 73 74 75 76 77 78 79 81 83 84 85 86 87 89 91 92 93 97 98 100 101 102 103 107 108 110 111 114 115 117 118 119 120 121 123 129 130 131 132 135 146 147 148 **S** UPMC, Pittsburgh, PA
Primary Contact: Gerald Murray, President
COO: Ron McConnell, Chief Operating Officer
CFO: Betsy Kreuz, Chief Financial Officer
CMO: Linnane Batzel, M.D., Senior Vice President Quality and Medical Affairs and Chief Medical Officer
CIO: Dale Fuller, Vice President and Chief Information Officer
CHR: Michelle A. Speck, Vice President Human Resources
CNO: Chris Rickens, R.N., Senior Vice President and Chief Nursing Officer
Web address: www.altoonaregional.org
Control: Other not–for–profit (including NFP Corporation) **Service:** General Medical and Surgical

Staffed Beds: 380 **Admissions:** 17641 **Census:** 225 **Outpatient Visits:** 337393 **Births:** 943 **Total Expense ($000):** 336144 **Payroll Expense ($000):** 134052 **Personnel:** 2022

Many Facility Codes have changed. Please refer to the AHA Guide Code Chart.   © 2014 AHA Guide

AMBLER—Montgomery County

☐ **HORSHAM CLINIC (394034)**, 722 East Butler Pike, Zip 19002–2310;
tel. 215/643–7800, (Nonreporting) **A**1 3 5 9 10 **S** Universal Health Services,
Inc., King of Prussia, PA
Primary Contact: Phyllis Weisfield, Chief Executive Officer and Managing Director
CFO: Jim Horan, Chief Financial Officer
CMO: James B. Congdon, M.D., Medical Director
CIO: Suzanne Scholz, Director Medical Records
CHR: Kathleen Nichelson, Director Human Resources
CNO: Calvin Litka, R.N., Director of Nursing
Web address: www.horshamclinic.com
Control: Individual, Investor–owned, for–profit **Service:** Psychiatric

Staffed Beds: 138

BEAVER—Beaver County

☐ **HERITAGE VALLEY HEALTH SYSTEM (390036)**, 1000 Dutch Ridge Road,
Zip 15009–9727; tel. 724/728–7000 **A**1 9 10 12 13 **F**3 11 13 14 15 18 20
22 24 26 28 29 30 32 34 35 38 40 46 49 50 53 54 55 57 59 60 64 66 70
73 74 75 76 77 78 79 81 82 84 85 86 89 90 92 93 96 97 98 100 101 102
103 104 107 108 110 111 115 116 118 119 120 121 129 130 131 132 135
145 147 148 **P**6 **S** Heritage Valley Health System, Beaver, PA
Primary Contact: Norman F. Mitry, President and Chief Executive Officer
CFO: Bryan J. Randall, Vice President Finance and Chief Financial Officer
CMO: John Cinicola, M.D., Chief Medical Officer
CIO: David Carleton, Chief Information Officer
CHR: Bruce Edwards, Vice President Human Resources
CNO: Marcia L. Ferrero, MS, Chief Nursing Officer
Web address: www.heritagevalley.org
Control: Other not–for–profit (including NFP Corporation) **Service:** General
Medical and Surgical

Staffed Beds: 273 **Admissions:** 14037 **Census:** 187 **Outpatient Visits:**
73329 **Births:** 947 **Total Expense ($000):** 207897 **Payroll Expense ($000):**
88472

☒ **KINDRED HOSPITAL–HERITAGE VALLEY (392043)**, 1000 Dutch Ridge Road,
Zip 15009–9727; tel. 724/773–8480, (Nonreporting) **A**1 9 10 **S** Kindred
Healthcare, Louisville, KY
Primary Contact: Janie Rosenberger–Slampack, Market Chief Executive Officer
CFO: Kevin Varley, Chief Financial Officer
CMO: Jeffrey Erukhimou, M.D., Medical Director
Web address: www.kindredhospitalhv.com/
Control: Corporation, Investor–owned, for–profit **Service:** Long–Term Acute Care
hospital

Staffed Beds: 35

BENSALEM—Bucks County

LIVENGRIN FOUNDATION, 4833 Hulmeville Road, Zip 19020–3099;
tel. 215/638–5200, (Nonreporting) **A**9
Primary Contact: Richard M. Pine, President and Chief Executive Officer
CFO: James D. Flis, Chief Financial Officer
CMO: William J. Lorman, Ph.D., Clinical Director
CIO: William Miller, Coordinator Management Information Systems
Web address: www.livengrin.org
Control: Other not–for–profit (including NFP Corporation) **Service:** Alcoholism and
other chemical dependency

Staffed Beds: 76

☒ **ROTHMAN SPECIALTY HOSPITAL (390322)**, 3300 Tillman Drive,
Zip 19020–2071; tel. 215/244–7400 **A**1 10 **F**29 65 79 81 85 89 107 141 146
Primary Contact: Kelly Doyle, Chief Executive Officer
Web address: www.rothmanspecialtyhospital.com/
Control: Partnership, Investor–owned, for–profit **Service:** Surgical

Staffed Beds: 24 **Admissions:** 959 **Census:** 4 **Births:** 0 **Personnel:** 122

BERWICK—Columbia County

☒ **BERWICK HOSPITAL CENTER (390072)**, 701 East 16th Street,
Zip 18603–2397; tel. 570/759–5000, (Total facility includes 240 beds in nursing
home–type unit) **A**1 9 10 **F**3 13 15 18 20 28 29 30 31 34 39 40 46 56 57 59
62 63 64 70 75 76 77 78 79 81 82 85 89 93 98 102 103 107 110 111 114
117 119 128 129 130 132 133 146 147 148 **P**6 **S** Community Health Systems,
Inc., Franklin, TN
Primary Contact: David P. Steitz, Chief Executive Officer
COO: Chad Kramer, Chief Operating Officer
CFO: Whitney Holloway, Chief Financial Officer
CMO: M. Joseph John, M.D., Chief of Staff
CIO: Jeff Leslie, Director Information Technology
CHR: Jackie Ridall, Director Human Resources
CNO: Kathleen Springman, Chief Nursing Officer
Web address: www.berwick–hospital.com
Control: Corporation, Investor–owned, for–profit **Service:** General Medical and
Surgical

Staffed Beds: 341 **Admissions:** 2600 **Census:** 202 **Outpatient Visits:** 93891
Births: 133 **Personnel:** 444

BETHLEHEM—Northampton County

☐ **COORDINATED HEALTH–BETHLEHEM (390314)**, 2310 Highland Avenue,
Zip 18020–8920, Mailing Address: 2300 Highland Avenue, Zip 18020;
tel. 610/861–8080 **A**1 10 **F**3 29 34 65 68 79 81 82 85 119 130 131 141
147 148
Primary Contact: Mark Holtz, Chief Operating Officer
Web address: www.coordinatedhealth.com
Control: Corporation, Investor–owned, for–profit **Service:** Orthopedic

Staffed Beds: 20 **Admissions:** 1003 **Census:** 8 **Births:** 0 **Personnel:** 133

☒ △ **GOOD SHEPHERD SPECIALTY HOSPITAL (392033)**, 2545 Schoenersville
Road, 3rd Floor, Zip 18017–7300; tel. 484/884–5051 **A**1 7 9 10 **F**1 3 29 30
36 77 85 87 91 93 95 130 148 **P**5 **S** Good Shepherd Rehabilitation Network,
Allentown, PA
Primary Contact: Greg Wuchter, Administrator
Web address: www.goodshepherdrehab.org
Control: Other not–for–profit (including NFP Corporation) **Service:** Long–Term
Acute Care hospital

Staffed Beds: 32 **Admissions:** 387 **Census:** 25 **Outpatient Visits:** 0 **Births:**
0 **Total Expense ($000):** 14477 **Payroll Expense ($000):** 4943 **Personnel:**
86

☒ **LEHIGH VALLEY HOSPITAL–MUHLENBERG (390263)**, 2545 Schoenersville
Road, Zip 18017–7300; tel. 484/884–2201 **A**1 2 9 10 12 13 **F**3 11 12 15 17
18 20 22 24 26 28 29 30 31 34 35 36 37 38 39 40 44 45 49 50 51 53 54
57 58 59 60 62 63 64 65 68 70 74 77 78 79 80 81 82 84 85 86 87 90 92
93 97 100 102 105 107 108 110 111 114 115 118 119 120 121 123 124
126 129 130 131 132 134 135 143 146 148 **P**5 6 8 **S** Lehigh Valley Health
Network, Allentown, PA
Primary Contact: Brian Nester, D.O., Interim President and Chief Executive Officer
COO: Terry Ann Capuano, R.N., Chief Operating Officer
CFO: Edward O'Dea, Chief Financial Officer
CMO: Thomas Whalen, M.D., Chief Medical Officer
CIO: Harry Lukens, Senior Vice President and Chief Information Officer
CHR: Deborah A. Patrick, Vice President Human Resources
CNO: Anne Panik, MS, Senior Vice President Patient Care Services and Chief
Nursing Officer
Web address: www.lvhhn.org
Control: Other not–for–profit (including NFP Corporation) **Service:** General
Medical and Surgical

Staffed Beds: 186 **Admissions:** 10872 **Census:** 144 **Outpatient Visits:**
173278 **Births:** 0 **Total Expense ($000):** 207144 **Payroll Expense ($000):**
74800 **Personnel:** 1315

Hospital, Medicare Provider Number, Address, Telephone, Approval, Facility, and Physician Codes, Health Care System

★ American Hospital Association (AHA) membership
☐ The Joint Commission accreditation   ◇ DNV Healthcare Inc. accreditation
○ Healthcare Facilities Accreditation Program
△ Commission on Accreditation of Rehabilitation Facilities (CARF) accreditation

PA

☐ △ **ST. LUKE'S UNIVERSITY HOSPITAL – BETHLEHEM CAMPUS (390049)**, 801 Ostrum Street, Zip 18015–1065; tel. 484/526–4000, (Includes ST LUKE'S HOSPITAL – ALLENTOWN CAMPUS, 1736 Hamilton Street, Allentown, Zip 18104–5656; tel. 610/628–8300) **A**1 2 3 5 6 7 8 9 10 12 13 **F**3 9 11 12 13 15 17 18 19 20 22 24 26 27 28 29 30 31 32 34 35 36 37 38 39 40 42 43 44 45 46 47 48 49 50 51 52 53 54 55 56 57 58 59 60 61 63 64 65 66 68 70 71 72 73 74 75 76 77 78 79 81 82 84 85 86 87 89 90 92 93 96 97 98 99 100 101 102 103 104 105 107 108 109 110 111 115 117 118 119 120 121 123 124 126 129 130 131 132 134 135 144 145 146 147 148 **P**6 8 **S** St. Luke's University Health Network, Bethlehem, PA
Primary Contact: Richard A. Anderson, President and Chief Executive Officer
COO: Carol Kuplen, R.N., Chief Operating Officer and Chief Nursing Officer
CFO: Tom Lichtenwalner, Vice President Finance
CMO: Jeffrey Jahre, M.D., Vice President Medical and Academic Affairs
CIO: Chad Brisendine, Chief Information Officer
CHR: Robert Zimmel, Senior Vice President Human Resources
Web address: www.slhn-lehighvalley.org
Control: Other not-for-profit (including NFP Corporation) **Service:** General Medical and Surgical

Staffed Beds: 593 **Admissions:** 27544 **Census:** 344 **Outpatient Visits:** 990127 **Births:** 3854 **Total Expense ($000):** 542435 **Payroll Expense ($000):** 224164 **Personnel:** 4102

BLOOMSBURG—Columbia County

★ **GEISINGER–BLOOMSBURG HOSPITAL (390003)**, 549 Fair Street, Zip 17815–1419; tel. 570/387–2100, (Nonreporting) **A**9 10 **S** Geisinger Health System, Danville, PA
Primary Contact: Lissa Bryan–Smith, Chief Administrative Officer
COO: Joseph M. DeVito, Vice President Finance and Chief Operating Officer
CFO: Joseph M. DeVito, Vice President Finance and Chief Operating Officer
CMO: James Joseph, M.D., President Medical Staff
CIO: Thomas Wray, Director Information
CHR: Mary Lenzini Howe, Vice President Human Resources
Web address: www.bloomhealth.net
Control: Other not-for-profit (including NFP Corporation) **Service:** General Medical and Surgical

Staffed Beds: 72

BRADFORD—Mckean County

☐ **BRADFORD REGIONAL MEDICAL CENTER (390118)**, 116 Interstate Parkway, Zip 16701–1036; tel. 814/368–4143, (Total facility includes 95 beds in nursing home–type unit) **A**1 9 10 **F**3 5 8 11 13 15 18 20 28 29 30 31 34 35 39 40 45 47 49 50 53 56 57 59 62 63 64 65 70 75 76 77 78 79 81 82 83 84 85 86 87 93 94 96 97 98 100 101 102 103 104 105 107 108 110 111 114 117 118 119 127 128 129 130 131 132 135 143 144 146 147 148 **P**6 **S** Upper Allegheny Health System, Olean, NY
Primary Contact: Timothy J. Finan, FACHE, President and Chief Executive Officer
COO: David A. Kobis, Senior Vice President and Chief Operating Officer
CFO: Richard G. Braun, Jr., CPA, Senior Vice President and Chief Financial Officer
CMO: William Mills, M.D., Senior Vice President Quality and Professional Affairs
CIO: Jason Yaworsky, Chief Information Officer
CHR: Timothy M. McNamara, Senior Vice President Human Resources
CNO: Jeff S. Zewe, R.N., Senior Vice President Patient Care and Chief Nursing Officer
Web address: www.brmc.com
Control: Other not-for-profit (including NFP Corporation) **Service:** General Medical and Surgical

Staffed Beds: 182 **Admissions:** 3120 **Census:** 122 **Outpatient Visits:** 135335 **Births:** 304 **Total Expense ($000):** 68038 **Payroll Expense ($000):** 29768 **Personnel:** 483

BRISTOL—Bucks County

☐ **LOWER BUCKS HOSPITAL (390070)**, 501 Bath Road, Zip 19007–3190; tel. 215/785–9200, (Nonreporting) **A**1 9 10 **S** Prime Healthcare Services, Ontario, CA
Primary Contact: Peter J. Adamo, Chief Executive Officer
COO: Matt Shelak, Chief Operating Officer
CFO: Courtney Coffman, Chief Financial Officer
CMO: Sanjay Bhatia, Chief Medical Officer
CIO: Steve Kane, Director Information Technology
CHR: Kellie T. Pearson, Director Human Resources
CNO: Pat Bain, Chief Nursing Officer
Web address: www.lowerbuckshosp.com
Control: Other not-for-profit (including NFP Corporation) **Service:** General Medical and Surgical

Staffed Beds: 150

BROOKVILLE—Jefferson County

PENN HIGHLANDS BROOKVILLE (391312), 100 Hospital Road, Zip 15825–1367; tel. 814/849–2312 **A**9 10 18 **F**3 11 15 18 28 29 30 34 35 39 40 45 46 57 59 62 64 65 75 77 81 82 85 86 93 98 102 103 104 107 108 110 114 118 119 127 129 130 131 132 133 145 146
Primary Contact: Julie Peer, President
CFO: Jessica Park, Director Accounting
CMO: Timothy Pendleton, M.D., President Medical Staff
CIO: Thomas Johnson, Director Information Systems
CHR: Rebecca Edwards, Chief Human Resources Officer
CNO: Debra A. Thomas, Director Patient Care Services and Chief Nursing Officer
Web address: www.phhealthcare.org/
Control: Other not-for-profit (including NFP Corporation) **Service:** General Medical and Surgical

Staffed Beds: 35 **Admissions:** 1154 **Census:** 17 **Outpatient Visits:** 78290 **Births:** 0 **Total Expense ($000):** 27565 **Payroll Expense ($000):** 10290 **Personnel:** 234

BRYN MAWR—Montgomery County

⊞ **BRYN MAWR HOSPITAL (390139)**, 130 South Bryn Mawr Avenue, Zip 19010–3160; tel. 484/337–3000 **A**1 2 3 5 9 10 13 **F**3 5 8 11 12 13 15 17 18 20 22 24 26 28 29 30 31 34 35 36 37 38 39 40 41 43 44 45 46 48 49 50 54 55 56 57 58 59 64 65 70 72 74 75 76 78 79 80 81 82 84 85 86 87 89 92 98 99 100 101 102 103 104 105 107 108 110 111 114 115 118 119 120 121 123 124 126 129 130 131 132 134 135 141 145 146 147 148 **S** Jefferson Health System, Radnor, PA
Primary Contact: Andrea F. Gilbert, FACHE, President
COO: Andrea F. Gilbert, FACHE, President
CFO: Michael J. Buongiorno, Executive Vice President Finance and Chief Financial Officer
CMO: Andrew J. Norton, M.D., Chief Medical Officer
CIO: Karen A. Thomas, Vice President and Chief Information Officer
CHR: Terry Dougherty, Director Human Resources
CNO: Barbara A. Wadsworth, MSN, Chief Nursing Officer
Web address: www.brynmawrhospital.org
Control: Other not-for-profit (including NFP Corporation) **Service:** General Medical and Surgical

Staffed Beds: 319 **Admissions:** 16080 **Census:** 188 **Outpatient Visits:** 213725 **Births:** 1598 **Total Expense ($000):** 284795 **Payroll Expense ($000):** 100625 **Personnel:** 1499

BUTLER—Butler County

★ **BUTLER HEALTH SYSTEM (390168)**, 1 Hospital Way, Zip 16001–4697; tel. 724/283–6666, (Total facility includes 25 beds in nursing home–type unit) **A**2 9 10 **F**3 4 5 12 13 15 18 20 22 24 26 28 29 31 32 35 40 45 57 59 70 74 76 79 81 82 85 87 93 98 100 103 107 108 111 114 118 119 128 129 130 132 135 146 147 148 **P**6
Primary Contact: Ken DeFurio, President and Chief Executive Officer
COO: Stephanie Roskovski, Chief Operating Officer
CFO: Anne Krebs, Chief Financial Officer
CMO: John C. Reefer, M.D., Director
CIO: Chuck Oleson, Chief Information Officer
CHR: Thomas A. Genevro, Vice President Human Resources
CNO: Karen A. Allen, R.N., Chief Nursing Officer
Web address: www.butlerhealthsystem.org
Control: Other not-for-profit (including NFP Corporation) **Service:** General Medical and Surgical

Staffed Beds: 288 **Admissions:** 12081 **Census:** 170 **Outpatient Visits:** 483708 **Births:** 696 **Total Expense ($000):** 203426 **Payroll Expense ($000):** 77611 **Personnel:** 1418

★ △ **VETERANS AFFAIRS BUTLER HEALTHCARE**, 325 New Castle Road, Zip 16001–2480; tel. 724/287–4781, (Nonreporting) **A**7 **S** Department of Veterans Affairs, Washington, DC
Primary Contact: John Gennaro, FACHE, Director
COO: Rebecca Hubscher, Associate Director Operations
CFO: Doug George, Chief Financial Officer
CMO: Timothy R. Burke, M.D., Chief of Staff
CIO: Kirk Hastings, Chief Information Technology
CHR: Christine Bruns, Chief Human Resources Officer
Web address: www.butler.va.gov
Control: Veterans Affairs, Government, federal **Service:** Other specialty

Staffed Beds: 126

VETERANS AFFAIRS MEDICAL CENTER See Veterans Affairs Butler Healthcare

PA

⊠ **HOLY SPIRIT HOSPITAL (390004)**, 503 North 21st Street, Zip 17011–2204; tel. 717/763–2100 **A**1 5 9 10 **F**3 8 11 12 13 14 15 17 18 20 22 24 26 28 29 30 31 34 35 37 38 40 44 46 49 50 54 57 58 59 61 62 63 64 65 70 72 73 74 75 76 77 78 79 80 81 82 84 85 86 87 98 99 100 101 102 103 104 105 107 108 110 111 114 115 118 119 124 126 129 130 132 134 135 145 146 147 148
Primary Contact: Sister Romaine Niemeyer, President and Chief Executive Officer
COO: Richard Schaffner, Senior Vice President and Chief Operating Officer
CFO: Manuel J. Evans, Senior Vice President Finance and Chief Financial Officer
CMO: Joseph Torchia, M.D., Senior Vice President Medical Affairs and Chief Medical Officer
CIO: Edith Dees, Vice President Information Services and Chief Information Officer
CHR: William Shartle, Senior Vice President Human Resources
CNO: Lisa F. Lewis, MSN, Vice President and Chief Nursing Officer
Web address: www.hsh.org
Control: Other not–for–profit (including NFP Corporation) **Service:** General Medical and Surgical

Staffed Beds: 294 **Admissions:** 15928 **Census:** 200 **Outpatient Visits:** 250376 **Births:** 1220 **Total Expense ($000):** 306235 **Payroll Expense ($000):** 114919 **Personnel:** 1833

⊠ **SELECT SPECIALTY HOSPITAL–CENTRAL PENNSYLVANIA (392039)**, 503 North 21st Street, 5th Floor, Zip 17011–2204; tel. 717/972–4575, (Includes SELECT SPECIALTY HOSPITAL–HARRISBURG, 2501 NorthThird Street, Landis Building, Harrisburg, Zip 17110–1904, Mailing Address: 2501 North Third Street, Landis Building, Zip 17110–1904; tel. 717/724–6605; SELECT SPECIALTY HOSPITAL–YORK, 1001 South George Street, York, Zip 17403–3676; tel. 717/851–2661; Marcia Medlin, Chief Executive Officer) **A**1 9 10 **F**1 3 5 12 28 29 30 31 34 38 39 45 46 47 48 49 50 57 63 74 75 78 79 82 84 87 100 107 108 109 110 111 112 113 114 115 116 117 118 119 130 133 **S** Select Medical Corporation, Mechanicsburg, PA
Primary Contact: Tom Mullin, Chief Executive Officer
Web address: www.selectspecialtyhospitals.com/company/locations/camphill.aspx
Control: Corporation, Investor–owned, for–profit **Service:** Long–Term Acute Care hospital

Staffed Beds: 54 **Admissions:** 623 **Census:** 43 **Births:** 0 **Personnel:** 201

STATE CORRECTIONAL INSTITUTION AT CAMP HILL, 2500 Lisburn Road, Zip 17011–8005, Mailing Address: P.O. Box 200, Zip 17001–0200; tel. 717/737–4531, (Nonreporting)
Primary Contact: Kathy Montag, Administrator Health Care
Web address: www.cor.state.pa.us/
Control: State–Government, nonfederal **Service:** Other specialty

Staffed Beds: 34

⊠ **CANONSBURG GENERAL HOSPITAL (390160)**, 100 Medical Boulevard, Zip 15317–9762; tel. 724/745–6100 **A**1 9 10 **F**3 7 8 11 15 18 29 30 31 32 34 35 40 44 45 46 47 48 49 50 51 54 55 57 59 64 65 66 67 68 70 74 75 78 79 81 82 85 86 87 90 91 92 93 94 97 107 108 110 111 114 118 119 129 130 131 132 134 146 147 **S** Allegheny Health Network, Pittsburgh, PA
Primary Contact: Jane B. Sarra, President and Chief Executive Officer
CFO: Gene Trout, Chief Financial Officer
CMO: Thomas B. Corkery, D.O., Chief Medical Officer
CIO: David Vincent, Director Information Systems
CHR: Martha L. Clister, Director Human Resources
Web address: www.wpahs.org
Control: Other not–for–profit (including NFP Corporation) **Service:** General Medical and Surgical

Staffed Beds: 104 **Admissions:** 3236 **Census:** 41 **Births:** 0 **Total Expense ($000):** 55115 **Personnel:** 393

⊠ **CARLISLE REGIONAL MEDICAL CENTER (390058)**, 361 Alexander Spring Road, Zip 17015–6940; tel. 717/249–1212, (Nonreporting) **A**1 9 10 **S** Community Health Systems, Inc., Franklin, TN
Primary Contact: Rich Newell, Chief Executive Officer
COO: P. Mark Harmon, Chief Operating Officer
CFO: Joanna Zimmerman, Chief Financial Officer
CMO: Michael Hilden, M.D., President Medical Staff
CIO: Sherry Aby, Director Information Management
CHR: Leslie Shatto, Director Human Resources
CNO: Ann M. Spade, Chief Nursing Executive
Web address: www.carlislermc.com/default.aspx
Control: Corporation, Investor–owned, for–profit **Service:** General Medical and Surgical

Staffed Beds: 165

⊠ **MEADOWS PSYCHIATRIC CENTER (394040)**, 132 The Meadows Drive, Zip 16828–9231; tel. 814/364–2161 **A**1 9 10 **F**29 38 54 98 99 102 103 104 105 **P**6 **S** Universal Health Services, Inc., King of Prussia, PA
Primary Contact: Jeffrey Herman, Chief Executive Officer
CFO: Rich Armentrout, Chief Financial Officer
CMO: Craig Richman, M.D., Medical Director
CHR: Mary Jane Schreffler, Director Human Resources
CNO: Ann Wayne, Director of Nursing
Web address: www.themeadows.net
Control: Corporation, Investor–owned, for–profit **Service:** Psychiatric

Staffed Beds: 107 **Admissions:** 2454 **Census:** 88 **Outpatient Visits:** 0 **Births:** 0 **Personnel:** 191

⊠ **CHAMBERSBURG HOSPITAL (390151)**, 112 North Seventh Street, Zip 17201–1720; tel. 717/267–3000 **A**1 2 3 5 9 10 **F**3 11 12 13 15 17 18 20 22 28 29 30 31 32 34 35 36 38 39 40 44 45 49 50 56 57 59 61 64 65 68 70 74 75 76 78 79 81 83 84 85 86 87 89 90 91 93 94 95 98 99 100 101 102 103 104 107 108 110 111 114 115 116 117 118 119 120 126 129 130 131 132 135 146 147 148 **P**8 **S** Summit Health, Chambersburg, PA
Primary Contact: Patrick W. O'Donnell, CPA, President and Chief Executive Officer
COO: John P. Massimilla, FACHE, Vice President Administration and Chief Operating Officer
CFO: Kimberly Rzomp, Vice President and Chief Financial Officer
CMO: Thomas Anderson, M.D., Vice President Medical Affairs
CIO: Michele Zeigler, Vice President and Chief Information Officer
CHR: Cathy A. Puhl, Vice President Human Resources
CNO: Sherri Stahl, R.N., Senior Vice President for Hospital Services
Web address: www.summithealth.org
Control: Other not–for–profit (including NFP Corporation) **Service:** General Medical and Surgical

Staffed Beds: 248 **Admissions:** 12137 **Census:** 139 **Outpatient Visits:** 324423 **Births:** 1331 **Total Expense ($000):** 237510 **Payroll Expense ($000):** 100143 **Personnel:** 1532

★ ○ **CLARION HOSPITAL (390093)**, One Hospital Drive, Zip 16214–8501; tel. 814/226–9500 **A**9 10 11 12 13 19 20 **F**3 7 11 13 15 29 30 31 35 40 48 49 51 57 59 64 70 74 76 77 78 79 81 82 84 85 90 107 108 111 115 119 129 130 132 133 135 145 146 148 **S** QHR, Brentwood, TN
Primary Contact: Byron Quinton, Chief Executive Officer
CFO: Vincent M. Lamorella, Chief Financial Officer
CIO: James Confer, Manager Information Systems
CHR: Brooke Divins, Manager Human Resources
CNO: Leslie Walters, R.N., Chief Nursing Officer
Web address: www.clarionhospital.org
Control: Other not–for–profit (including NFP Corporation) **Service:** General Medical and Surgical

Staffed Beds: 77 **Admissions:** 1944 **Census:** 20 **Outpatient Visits:** 165268 **Births:** 166 **Total Expense ($000):** 48671 **Payroll Expense ($000):** 17558 **Personnel:** 520

⊠ **CLARION PSYCHIATRIC CENTER (394043)**, 2 Hospital Drive, Zip 16214–8502; tel. 814/226–9545 **A**1 9 10 **F**98 99 101 102 105 **P**6 **S** Universal Health Services, Inc., King of Prussia, PA
Primary Contact: Robert Scheffler, Chief Executive Officer
CFO: Shelly Rhoades, Chief Financial Officer
CMO: Jeffrey Moll, M.D., Medical Director
CHR: Dianne C. Bilunka, Director Human Resources
CNO: Rhonda Massa, Director of Nursing
Web address: www.clarioncenter.com
Control: Individual, Investor–owned, for–profit **Service:** Psychiatric

Staffed Beds: 74 **Admissions:** 1995 **Census:** 58 **Outpatient Visits:** 0 **Births:** 0 **Personnel:** 137

CLARKS SUMMIT STATE HOSPITAL (394012), 1451 Hillside Drive, Zip 18411–9504; tel. 570/586–2011 **A**10 **F**29 30 34 35 38 39 50 53 56 57 59 65 68 75 77 86 87 91 97 98 100 101 103 106 130 132 135 143 146 **P**6
Primary Contact: Monica Bradbury, Chief Executive Officer
COO: Gordon Weber, Chief Operating Officer
CMO: David Waibel, M.D., Medical Director
CHR: William Abda, Chief Human Resources Officer
Web address: www.dpw.state.pa.us/
Control: State–Government, nonfederal **Service:** Psychiatric

Staffed Beds: 222 **Admissions:** 74 **Census:** 219 **Outpatient Visits:** 0 **Births:** 0 **Total Expense ($000):** 43088 **Payroll Expense ($000):** 22978 **Personnel:** 443

Hospital, Medicare Provider Number, Address, Telephone, Approval, Facility, and Physician Codes, Health Care System

★ American Hospital Association (AHA) membership
□ The Joint Commission accreditation ◇ DNV Healthcare Inc. accreditation
○ Healthcare Facilities Accreditation Program
△ Commission on Accreditation of Rehabilitation Facilities (CARF) accreditation

PA

CLEARFIELD—Clearfield County

CLEARFIELD HOSPITAL (390052), 809 Turnpike Avenue, Zip 16830–1232, Mailing Address: P.O. Box 992, Zip 16830–0992; tel. 814/765–5341 **A**9 10 **F**3 8 11 13 15 18 28 29 30 32 34 40 44 45 46 50 57 59 62 63 68 70 75 76 77 79 81 84 85 86 87 93 97 98 103 104 107 108 110 111 115 117 118 119 129 130 132 133 135 146 148 **P**6
Primary Contact: Gary Macioce, President and Chief Executive Officer
CFO: William Cain, Controller
CIO: Terry Trinidad, Director Management Information Systems
CHR: James G. Glade, Director Human Resources
CNO: Kathy Bedger, Chief Nursing Officer
Web address: www.clearfieldhosp.org
Control: Other not–for–profit (including NFP Corporation) **Service:** General Medical and Surgical

Staffed Beds: 96 **Admissions:** 2896 **Census:** 37 **Outpatient Visits:** 129606 **Births:** 197 **Total Expense ($000):** 68107 **Payroll Expense ($000):** 29707 **Personnel:** 500

COALDALE—Schuylkill County

☐ **ST. LUKE'S HOSPITAL – MINERS CAMPUS (390183)**, 360 West Ruddle Street, Zip 18218–1027; tel. 570/645–2131, (Total facility includes 48 beds in nursing home–type unit) **A**1 9 10 **F**3 15 18 28 29 31 34 35 40 43 45 46 49 50 51 53 54 56 57 59 60 62 64 65 68 70 75 77 78 79 81 85 86 93 107 108 110 111 115 118 119 127 128 129 130 131 132 145 146 148 **P**6 8 **S** St. Luke's University Health Network, Bethlehem, PA
Primary Contact: William E. Moyer, President
COO: Joel Fagerstrom, Executive Vice President and Chief Operating Officer
CFO: Michele Levitz, Director Finance
CMO: Glenn Freed, D.O., Medical Director
CIO: Chad Brisendine, Vice President and Chief Information Officer
CHR: Susan Van Why, Director Human Resources
CNO: Kimberly Sargent, Vice President Patient Services
Web address: www.slhn.org
Control: Other not–for–profit (including NFP Corporation) **Service:** General Medical and Surgical

Staffed Beds: 92 **Admissions:** 1922 **Census:** 64 **Outpatient Visits:** 108996 **Births:** 0 **Total Expense ($000):** 41389 **Payroll Expense ($000):** 19416 **Personnel:** 287

COATESVILLE—Chester County

☒ **BRANDYWINE HOSPITAL (390076)**, 201 Reeceville Road, Zip 19320–1536; tel. 610/383–8000 **A**1 2 6 9 10 **F**12 15 18 20 22 24 26 28 29 31 40 45 46 49 54 56 59 60 62 64 66 68 74 75 77 78 81 82 85 91 92 93 98 100 102 103 104 107 108 111 114 116 119 124 126 129 130 144 148 **S** Community Health Systems, Inc., Franklin, TN
Primary Contact: Bryan Burklow, Chief Executive Officer
COO: Jill Tillman, Assistant Chief Executive Officer
CFO: Jay Graham, Interim Chief Financial Officer
Web address: www.brandywinehospital.com
Control: Corporation, Investor–owned, for–profit **Service:** General Medical and Surgical

Staffed Beds: 140 **Admissions:** 7432 **Census:** 103 **Births:** 0 **Personnel:** 556

☒ **COATESVILLE VETERANS AFFAIRS MEDICAL CENTER**, 1400 Black Horse Hill Road, Zip 19320–2040; tel. 610/384–7711 **A**1 3 5 **F**2 3 4 5 6 10 29 30 34 38 39 54 56 57 58 59 61 62 63 64 65 74 75 77 82 84 87 93 97 98 102 103 104 106 107 111 112 115 130 132 135 144 146 147 148 **S** Department of Veterans Affairs, Washington, DC
Primary Contact: Gary W. Devansky, Director
CFO: Tony Wolfgang, Chief Financial Officer
CMO: Sheila Chellappa, M.D., Chief of Staff
CIO: Ryan McGettigan, Chief Information Officer
CHR: Andrew Sutton, Chief Human Resources Officer
CNO: Nancy A. Schmid, R.N., Associate Director Patient Care Services
Web address: www.coatesville.va.gov/
Control: Veterans Affairs, Government, federal **Service:** Psychiatric

Staffed Beds: 118 **Admissions:** 1607 **Census:** 70 **Births:** 0 **Personnel:** 1287

VETERANS AFFAIRS MEDICAL CENTER See Coatesville Veterans Affairs Medical Center

CONNELLSVILLE—Fayette County

HIGHLANDS HOSPITAL (390184), 401 East Murphy Avenue, Zip 15425–2700; tel. 724/628–1500 **A**9 10 **F**3 11 15 26 27 29 30 34 35 36 39 40 44 45 46 49 50 51 53 54 56 57 59 61 64 65 70 75 77 79 81 82 85 86 87 89 93 98 99 100 101 102 103 107 108 111 114 119 129 130 132 133 135 143 146
Primary Contact: Michelle P. Cunningham, Chief Executive Officer
CFO: John Andursky, Chief Financial Officer
CMO: Richard Grimaldi, President Medical Staff
CIO: John Andursky, Chief Financial Officer
CHR: Mary June Krosoff, Chief Human Resources Officer
CNO: Tammy Donaldson, Director of Nursing
Web address: www.highlandshospital.org
Control: Other not–for–profit (including NFP Corporation) **Service:** General Medical and Surgical

Staffed Beds: 71 **Admissions:** 2279 **Census:** 27 **Outpatient Visits:** 58822 **Births:** 0 **Total Expense ($000):** 22931 **Payroll Expense ($000):** 10007 **Personnel:** 265

CORRY—Erie County

CORRY MEMORIAL HOSPITAL (391308), 965 Shamrock Lane, Zip 16407; tel. 814/664–4641, (Nonreporting) **A**9 10 18
Primary Contact: Barbara Nichols, R.N., President and Chief Executive Officer
CFO: Michael Heller, Chief Financial Officer
CIO: Ken O'Day, Supervisor Information Systems
CHR: Sharon Kimmy, Coordinator Human Resources
CNO: Terry Delellis, R.N., Director of Nursing
Web address: www.corryhospital.com
Control: Other not–for–profit (including NFP Corporation) **Service:** General Medical and Surgical

Staffed Beds: 25

COUDERSPORT—Potter County

☒ **COLE MEMORIAL (391313)**, 1001 East Second Street, Zip 16915–8161; tel. 814/274–9300, (Total facility includes 49 beds in nursing home–type unit) **A**1 9 10 18 **F**3 10 11 13 15 28 29 30 31 35 36 40 45 49 53 57 59 62 63 64 70 76 77 78 79 81 82 87 92 93 98 103 107 108 111 114 119 121 127 128 129 130 131 132 133 145 146 147 148 **P**6
Primary Contact: Edward C. Pitchford, President and Chief Executive Officer
CFO: Ron Rapp, Controller
CMO: Brenda Wahlers, M.D., Chief of Staff
CIO: Geoff Mazur, Director Information Technology
CHR: James Evens, Executive Director Human Resources
Web address: www.charlescolehospital.org
Control: Other not–for–profit (including NFP Corporation) **Service:** General Medical and Surgical

Staffed Beds: 84 **Admissions:** 2012 **Census:** 70 **Outpatient Visits:** 221460 **Births:** 223 **Total Expense ($000):** 75152 **Payroll Expense ($000):** 26655 **Personnel:** 473

CRANBERRY—Butler County

UPMC PASSAVANT CRANBERRY See UPMC Passavant, Pittsburgh

DANVILLE—Montour County

DANVILLE STATE HOSPITAL (394004), 200 State Hospital Drive, Zip 17821–9198; tel. 570/271–4500 **A**10 **F**30 39 65 75 77 98 106 130 135 146 **P**6
Primary Contact: Theresa Long, Chief Executive Officer
COO: Thomas J. Burk, Chief Operating Officer
CFO: Patricia Riegert, Director Fiscal Services
CMO: Vikrant Mittal, M.D., Chief Medical Officer
CHR: Thomas J. Burk, Chief Operating Officer
CNO: Brenda Lahout, Chief Nurse Executive
Web address: www.dpw.state.pa.us/foradults/statehospitals/danvillestatehospital/index.htm
Control: State–Government, nonfederal **Service:** Psychiatric

Staffed Beds: 178 **Admissions:** 93 **Census:** 163 **Outpatient Visits:** 0 **Births:** 0 **Total Expense ($000):** 36977 **Payroll Expense ($000):** 19274 **Personnel:** 375

☒ **GEISINGER HEALTHSOUTH REHABILITATION HOSPITAL (393047)**, 2 Rehab Lane, Zip 17821–8498; tel. 570/271–6733, (Nonreporting) **A**1 9 10 **S** HEALTHSOUTH Corporation, Birmingham, AL
Primary Contact: Lorie Dillon, Chief Executive Officer
CFO: Sally Shipierski, Controller
CMO: Greg Burke, M.D., Medical Director
CHR: Christian Shirley, Director Human Resources
CNO: Kim Rankin, Chief Nursing Officer
Web address: www.geisingerhealthsouth.com
Control: Corporation, Investor–owned, for–profit **Service:** Rehabilitation

Staffed Beds: 42

Many Facility Codes have changed. Please refer to the AHA Guide Code Chart. © 2014 AHA Guide

⊞ **GEISINGER MEDICAL CENTER (390006)**, 100 North Academy Avenue, Zip 17822–2201; tel. 570/271–6211, (Includes GEISINGER–SHAMOKIN AREA COMMUNITY HOSPITAL, 4200 Hospital Road, Coal Township, Zip 17866–9697; tel. 570/644–4200; Thomas R. Harlow, FACHE, President and Chief Executive Officer), (Nonreporting) **A**1 2 3 5 8 9 10 13 19 **S** Geisinger Health System, Danville, PA
Primary Contact: Thomas P. Sokola, Chief Administrative Officer
COO: Frank J. Trembulak, Executive Vice President and Chief Operating Officer
CFO: Kevin F. Brennan, CPA, Executive Vice President and Chief Financial Officer
CMO: Albert Bothe, Jr., M.D., Chief Medical Officer
CIO: Frank Richards, Chief Information Officer
CHR: Amy Brayford, Chief Human Resources Officer
CNO: Susan M. Hallick, R.N., Executive Vice President and Chief Nursing Officer
Web address: www.geisinger.org
Control: Other not-for-profit (including NFP Corporation) **Service:** General Medical and Surgical

Staffed Beds: 402

⊞ **SELECT SPECIALTY HOSPITAL–DANVILLE (392047)**, 100 North Academy Avenue, 3rd Floor, Zip 17822–3050; tel. 570/214–9653, (Nonreporting) **A**1 9 10 **S** Select Medical Corporation, Mechanicsburg, PA
Primary Contact: Brian Mann, Chief Executive Officer
Web address: www.selectspecialtyhospitals.com/company/locations/danville.aspx
Control: Corporation, Investor–owned, for–profit **Service:** Long–Term Acute Care hospital

Staffed Beds: 30

DARBY—Delaware County

⊞ △ **MERCY FITZGERALD HOSPITAL (390156)**, 1500 Lansdowe Avenue, Zip 19023–1200; tel. 610/237–4000, (Includes MERCY FITZGERALD HOSPITAL, 1500 South Lansdowne Avenue, Zip 19023; tel. 610/237–4000; MERCY PHILADELPHIA HOSPITAL, 501 South 54th Street, Philadelphia, Zip 19143; tel. 215/748–9000) **A**1 2 3 7 9 10 12 13 **F**3 4 5 11 12 15 18 20 22 24 26 28 29 30 31 34 35 38 40 45 46 49 50 51 53 54 55 57 58 59 61 64 65 66 69 70 75 77 78 79 81 82 85 86 87 90 91 92 93 96 97 98 100 101 102 103 104 107 108 110 111 114 115 118 119 120 121 123 124 130 132 135 145 146 147 148 **S** Catholic Health East / Trinity Health, Livonia, MI
Primary Contact: Kathryn Conallen, Chief Executive Officer
COO: Ruth Thomas, Chief Operating Officer
CFO: Don Snenk, Chief Financial Officer
CMO: Jeff Komins, M.D., Chief Medical Officer
CIO: Jeff Byda, Vice President Information Technology
Web address: www.mercyhealth.org
Control: Church–operated, Nongovernment, not–for profit **Service:** General Medical and Surgical

Staffed Beds: 382 **Admissions:** 18226 **Census:** 228 **Outpatient Visits:** 214117 **Births:** 0 **Total Expense ($000):** 303911 **Payroll Expense ($000):** 118502 **Personnel:** 2003

DOWNINGTOWN—Chester County

ST. JOHN VIANNEY HOSPITAL, 151 Woodbine Road, Zip 19335–3057; tel. 610/269–2600, (Nonreporting)
Primary Contact: Edward Maguire, Administrator
Web address: www.sjvcenter.org
Control: Church–operated, Nongovernment, not–for profit **Service:** Psychiatric

Staffed Beds: 42

DOYLESTOWN—Bucks County

⊞ △ **DOYLESTOWN HOSPITAL (390203)**, 595 West State Street, Zip 18901–2597; tel. 215/345–2200, (Total facility includes 74 beds in nursing home–type unit) **A**1 2 5 7 9 10 **F**3 8 10 13 15 17 18 20 22 24 26 28 29 30 31 34 35 40 45 49 50 51 54 56 57 58 59 62 63 64 70 73 74 75 76 77 78 79 81 82 85 86 92 93 94 96 107 108 110 111 114 115 118 119 124 125 126 128 130 131 132 141 146 147 **P**5 6 8
Primary Contact: James L. Brexler, President and Chief Executive Officer
COO: Eleanor Wilson, R.N., Vice President and Chief Operating Officer
CFO: Daniel Upton, Vice President and Chief Financial Officer
CMO: Scott S. Levy, M.D., Vice President and Chief Medical Officer
CIO: Richard Lang, Ed.D., Vice President and Chief Information Officer
CHR: Barbara Hebel, Vice President Human Resources
CNO: Patricia A. Stover, Administrator Nursing
Web address: www.dh.org
Control: Other not–for–profit (including NFP Corporation) **Service:** General Medical and Surgical

Staffed Beds: 311 **Admissions:** 12603 **Census:** 203 **Outpatient Visits:** 296485 **Births:** 1161 **Total Expense ($000):** 248386 **Payroll Expense ($000):** 98953 **Personnel:** 1818

□ **FOUNDATIONS BEHAVIORAL HEALTH (394038)**, 833 East Butler Avenue, Zip 18901–2280; tel. 215/345–0444 **A**1 9 10 **F**98 99 100 101 102 105 106 **S** Universal Health Services, Inc., King of Prussia, PA
Primary Contact: Robert Weinhold, Chief Executive Officer
Web address: www.fbh.com
Control: Corporation, Investor–owned, for–profit **Service:** Children's hospital psychiatric

Staffed Beds: 96 **Admissions:** 942 **Census:** 45 **Outpatient Visits:** 0 **Births:** 0 **Personnel:** 213

DREXEL HILL—Delaware County

⊞ **DELAWARE COUNTY MEMORIAL HOSPITAL (390081)**, 501 North Lansdowne Avenue, Zip 19026–1114; tel. 610/284–8100 **A**1 2 3 5 9 10 12 **F**3 7 9 11 13 15 17 18 29 30 31 34 35 36 40 43 44 45 46 49 50 51 55 56 57 58 59 60 61 62 63 64 68 72 74 75 76 77 78 79 81 82 84 85 86 87 90 92 93 94 96 97 100 107 108 109 110 111 114 115 116 117 118 119 120 121 123 129 130 131 132 134 135 143 146 147 148 **P**6 **S** Crozer–Keystone Health System, Springfield, PA
Primary Contact: Robert Haffey, R.N., President
CFO: Richard I. Bennett, Senior Vice President and Chief Financial Officer
CMO: Seth Malin, M.D., President Medical and Dental Staff
CIO: Robert E. Wilson, Vice President and Chief Information Officer
Web address: www.crozer.org
Control: Other not–for–profit (including NFP Corporation) **Service:** General Medical and Surgical

Staffed Beds: 195 **Admissions:** 8806 **Census:** 110 **Outpatient Visits:** 163881 **Births:** 1715 **Total Expense ($000):** 179179 **Payroll Expense ($000):** 69460 **Personnel:** 880

DU BOIS—Clearfield County

□ **DUBOIS REGIONAL MEDICAL CENTER (390086)**, 100 Hospital Avenue, Zip 15801–1440, Mailing Address: P.O. Box 447, Zip 15801–0447; tel. 814/371–2200 **A**1 2 9 10 19 **F**5 11 13 15 17 18 19 20 22 24 26 27 28 29 30 31 34 35 40 49 51 54 55 57 58 59 62 63 64 70 72 74 76 77 78 79 81 82 85 89 90 93 97 98 99 104 107 108 111 115 116 117 119 120 121 122 129 130 131 132 133 135 146 147 148
Primary Contact: John Sutika, President
CFO: Brian S. Kline, Vice President and Chief Financial Officer
CMO: Gary Dugan, M.D., Vice President Medical Affairs
CHR: Robert J. McKee, Vice President Human Resources
Web address: www.drmc.org
Control: Other not–for–profit (including NFP Corporation) **Service:** General Medical and Surgical

Staffed Beds: 214 **Admissions:** 8057 **Census:** 100 **Births:** 999 **Total Expense ($000):** 225440 **Personnel:** 1764

EAGLEVILLE—Montgomery County

★ **EAGLEVILLE HOSPITAL (390278)**, 100 Eagleville Road, Zip 19403–1829, Mailing Address: P.O. Box 45, Zip 19408–0045; tel. 610/539–6000 **A**5 9 10 **F**4 29 34 35 50 61 68 75 86 98 100 101 103 130 132 134 143 146 147 **P**6
Primary Contact: Maureen King Pollock, Chief Executive Officer
COO: Lois Chepak, R.N., Chief Clinical Officer
CFO: Alfred P. Salvitti, Chief Financial Officer
CMO: Robert Wilson, D.O., Director Medical Services
CIO: Richard R. Mitchell, Director Information Technology
CHR: Zoe Yousaitis, Director Human Resources
Web address: www.eaglevillehospital.org
Control: Other not–for–profit (including NFP Corporation) **Service:** Alcoholism and other chemical dependency

Staffed Beds: 82 **Admissions:** 1926 **Census:** 44 **Outpatient Visits:** 0 **Births:** 0 **Total Expense ($000):** 32508 **Payroll Expense ($000):** 19027 **Personnel:** 363

Hospital, Medicare Provider Number, Address, Telephone, Approval, Facility, and Physician Codes, Health Care System

★ American Hospital Association (AHA) membership
□ The Joint Commission accreditation
◇ DNV Healthcare Inc. accreditation
○ Healthcare Facilities Accreditation Program
△ Commission on Accreditation of Rehabilitation Facilities (CARF) accreditation

EAST NORRITON—Montgomery County

☐ **EINSTEIN MEDICAL CENTER MONTGOMERY (390329)**, 559 West Germantown Pike, Zip 19403–4250; tel. 484/622–1000, (Data for 275 days) **A**1 9 10 **F**3 11 12 13 15 18 20 22 24 26 29 30 31 34 35 40 46 51 57 59 62 63 64 68 70 72 74 75 76 78 79 80 81 82 84 85 87 92 100 107 108 110 111 115 117 119 120 121 123 126 129 130 131 132 135 146 147 148 **S** Einstein Healthcare Network, Philadelphia, PA
Primary Contact: Beth Duffy, Chief Operating Officer
COO: Beth Duffy, Chief Operating Officer
CFO: David Ertel, Chief Financial Officer
CMO: Robert Czincila, D.O., Medical Staff President
CIO: Kenneth Levitan, Vice President and Chief Information Officer
CHR: Lynne R. Kornblatt, Chief Human Resources Officer
CNO: AnnMarie Papa, R.N., Vice President and Chief Nursing Officer
Control: Other not–for–profit (including NFP Corporation) **Service:** General Medical and Surgical

Staffed Beds: 146 **Admissions:** 6870 **Census:** 102 **Outpatient Visits:** 132329 **Births:** 1219 **Total Expense ($000):** 134735 **Payroll Expense ($000):** 43949 **Personnel:** 1040

EAST STROUDSBURG—Monroe County

✠ △ **POCONO MEDICAL CENTER (390201)**, 206 East Brown Street, Zip 18301–3006; tel. 570/421–4000 **A**1 2 7 9 10 19 20 **F**3 11 12 13 14 15 17 18 20 22 24 26 28 29 30 31 32 34 35 36 38 39 40 43 45 47 48 49 50 54 55 56 57 59 61 64 65 66 70 72 74 75 76 77 78 79 81 82 84 85 86 87 89 92 97 98 100 101 102 103 107 108 110 111 114 115 116 117 118 119 120 121 123 124 126 130 132 134 135 144 146 147 148 **P**6 7
Primary Contact: Jeffrey Snyder, Chief Executive Officer
CFO: Michael Wilk, Senior President Financial Services and Chief Financial Officer
CMO: William K. Cors, M.D., Vice President and Chief Medical Quality Officer
CIO: Ferd Feola, Chief Information Officer
CHR: Lynn M. Lansdowne, Vice President Human Resources
CNO: Paulette Nish, MSN, Vice President and Chief Nursing Officer
Web address: www.pmchealthsystem.org
Control: Other not–for–profit (including NFP Corporation) **Service:** General Medical and Surgical

Staffed Beds: 235 **Admissions:** 11842 **Census:** 148 **Outpatient Visits:** 266355 **Births:** 869 **Total Expense ($000):** 231935 **Payroll Expense ($000):** 95168 **Personnel:** 1648

EASTON—Northampton County

✠ **EASTON HOSPITAL (390162)**, 250 South 21st Street, Zip 18042–3892; tel. 610/250–4000 **A**1 2 3 5 9 10 **F**3 12 13 15 18 19 20 22 24 26 28 29 30 31 34 35 40 44 45 46 47 48 49 51 54 56 57 58 59 60 61 64 65 66 70 72 74 75 78 79 80 81 82 85 86 87 89 90 92 97 100 107 108 109 110 111 114 115 116 117 119 120 121 123 124 126 129 130 132 135 144 146 147 148 **S** Community Health Systems, Inc., Franklin, TN
Primary Contact: John A. Zidansek, President and Chief Executive Officer
CMO: David Lyon, M.D., Chief Medical Officer
CIO: Kenneth Castle, Chief Information Officer
CHR: Lori Ofner, Vice President Human Resources
Web address: www.easton–hospital.com
Control: Corporation, Investor–owned, for–profit **Service:** General Medical and Surgical

Staffed Beds: 224 **Admissions:** 8650 **Census:** 106 **Births:** 451 **Personnel:** 1141

☐ **ST. LUKE'S HOSPITAL – ANDERSON CAMPUS (390326)**, 1872 Riverside Circle, Zip 18045–5669; tel. 484/503–3000 **A**1 9 10 **F**3 11 15 18 20 22 24 26 29 30 31 34 35 38 40 44 45 46 49 50 51 53 54 55 57 59 60 63 64 68 70 74 75 77 78 79 81 82 84 85 86 87 93 96 102 107 108 110 111 115 118 119 120 121 123 124 130 132 144 145 146 **P**6 8 **S** St. Luke's University Health Network, Bethlehem, PA
Primary Contact: Edward Nawrocki, President
CMO: Justin P. Psaila, M.D., Vice President Medical Affairs
CNO: Darla Frack, RN, R.N., Vice President, Patient Services
Web address: www.mystlukesonline.org
Control: Other not–for–profit (including NFP Corporation) **Service:** General Medical and Surgical

Staffed Beds: 78 **Admissions:** 5055 **Census:** 50 **Outpatient Visits:** 118923 **Births:** 0 **Total Expense ($000):** 89883 **Payroll Expense ($000):** 28189 **Personnel:** 413

ELLWOOD CITY—Lawrence County

☐ **ELLWOOD CITY HOSPITAL (390008)**, 724 Pershing Street, Zip 16117–1474; tel. 724/752–0081, (Nonreporting) **A**9 10
Primary Contact: Carolyn Izzo, President and Chief Executive Officer
CFO: Christopher M. Little, Vice President and Chief Financial Officer
CIO: Dennis Crumb, Chief Information Officer
CHR: Paul Landman, Director Human Resources
CNO: Della Stabryla, Director of Nursing
Web address: www.TheEllwoodCityHospital.org
Control: Other not–for–profit (including NFP Corporation) **Service:** General Medical and Surgical

Staffed Beds: 95

EPHRATA—Lancaster County

☐ **EPHRATA COMMUNITY HOSPITAL (390225)**, 169 Martin Avenue, Zip 17522–1724, Mailing Address: P.O. Box 1002, Zip 17522–1002; tel. 717/733–0311 **A**1 2 9 10 **F**3 12 13 15 18 20 28 29 30 31 34 35 36 40 45 49 50 51 54 57 59 60 61 62 64 69 70 72 74 75 76 77 78 79 80 81 82 84 85 86 87 89 90 97 98 99 100 101 102 103 107 108 110 111 114 115 116 117 118 119 120 121 129 130 131 132 135 144 146 147 148 **P**6 8 **S** WellSpan Health, York, PA
Primary Contact: John M. Porter, Jr., President and Chief Executive Officer
COO: Robert Graupensperger, Executive Vice President
CFO: John A. Holmes, Chief Financial Officer
CMO: Vincent D. Glielmi, D.O., Senior Vice President Medical Affairs
CIO: John Jabour, Chief Information Officer
CHR: Barbara Mumma, Vice President Human Resources
CNO: Marcia A. Hansen, R.N., Vice President Patient Services and Chief Nursing Officer
Web address: www.ephratahospital.org
Control: Other not–for–profit (including NFP Corporation) **Service:** General Medical and Surgical

Staffed Beds: 130 **Admissions:** 6002 **Census:** 66 **Outpatient Visits:** 385601 **Births:** 747 **Total Expense ($000):** 207326 **Payroll Expense ($000):** 94937 **Personnel:** 1656

ERIE—Erie County

✠ **ERIE VETERANS AFFAIRS MEDICAL CENTER**, 135 East 38th Street, Zip 16504–1559; tel. 814/860–2576, (Nonreporting) **A**1 **S** Department of Veterans Affairs, Washington, DC
Primary Contact: Michael Adelman, M.D., Director
CFO: Joann Pritchard, Chief Financial Officer
CMO: Anthony Behm, D.O., Chief of Staff
CIO: Jonathan Seale, Chief Information Officer
CHR: Lynn Nies, Human Resources Officer
CNO: Dorene M. Sommers, Associate Director Patient Care Services
Web address: www.erie.va.gov/
Control: Veterans Affairs, Government, federal **Service:** General Medical and Surgical

Staffed Beds: 26

HAMOT MEDICAL CENTER See UPMC Hamot

✠ **HEALTHSOUTH REHABILITATION HOSPITAL OF ERIE (393046)**, 143 East Second Street, Zip 16507–1501; tel. 814/878–1200 **A**1 9 10 **F**29 34 90 91 95 96 132 **S** HEALTHSOUTH Corporation, Birmingham, AL
Primary Contact: Lucretia Atti, Chief Executive Officer
CFO: Lori Gibbens, Controller
CMO: Douglas Grisier, D.O., Medical Director
CIO: Sharon Zielinski, Manager Health Information
CHR: William Robinson, Director Human Resources
CNO: Evelyn Armstrong, Chief Nursing Officer
Web address: www.healthsoutherie.com
Control: Corporation, Investor–owned, for–profit **Service:** Rehabilitation

Staffed Beds: 100 **Admissions:** 1705 **Census:** 61 **Outpatient Visits:** 0 **Births:** 0 **Personnel:** 206

○ **MILLCREEK COMMUNITY HOSPITAL (390198)**, 5515 Peach Street, Zip 16509–2695; tel. 814/864–4031, (Total facility includes 24 beds in nursing home–type unit) **A**9 10 11 12 13 **F**3 4 8 13 15 20 22 24 26 28 29 30 65 66 68 70 74 75 76 79 80 81 82 85 92 93 95 97 98 99 100 102 103 105 107 108 110 111 114 118 119 128 129 130 135 143 146
Primary Contact: Mary L. Eckert, President and Chief Executive Officer
CFO: Richard P. Olinger, Chief Financial Officer
CMO: James Y. Lin, D.O., Chief of Staff
CIO: Cheryl Girardier, Director Information Technology
CHR: Polly Momeyer, Manager Human Resources
CNO: Katie Agresti, R.N., Director Patient Care Services
Web address: www.millcreekcommunityhospital.com
Control: Other not–for–profit (including NFP Corporation) **Service:** General Medical and Surgical

Staffed Beds: 168 **Admissions:** 4970 **Census:** 82 **Outpatient Visits:** 48007 **Births:** 132 **Total Expense ($000):** 41986 **Payroll Expense ($000):** 22262 **Personnel:** 457

Many Facility Codes have changed. Please refer to the AHA Guide Code Chart. © 2014 AHA Guide

✠ **SAINT VINCENT HEALTH CENTER (390009)**, 232 West 25th Street,
Zip 16544–0002; tel. 814/452–5000 **A**1 2 3 5 9 10 12 13 **F**3 5 8 9 11 12 13
15 17 18 20 22 24 26 28 29 30 31 32 33 34 35 36 38 39 40 42 44 45 49
50 51 53 54 56 57 58 59 60 61 62 63 64 65 66 68 70 71 72 74 75 76 77
78 79 80 81 82 84 85 86 87 89 90 92 93 97 98 100 101 102 103 104 107
108 110 111 114 115 117 118 119 120 121 123 124 126 129 130 131 132
133 135 144 146 147 148 **P**3 6 7 8 **S** Allegheny Health Network, Pittsburgh, PA
Primary Contact: Scott Whalen, Ph.D., FACHE, President and Chief Executive
Officer
COO: Thomas Fucci, Chief Operating Officer
CFO: Al Mansfield, Chief Financial Officer
CMO: Chris Clark, M.D., Senior Vice President Medical Affairs and Chief Medical
Officer
CIO: Richard B. Ong, Chief Information Officer
CHR: Johnie M. Atkinson, Chief Human Resources Officer
CNO: Maureen C. Chadwick, R.N., Chief Nursing Officer
Web address: www.svhs.org
Control: Other not–for–profit (including NFP Corporation) **Service:** General
Medical and Surgical

Staffed Beds: 407 **Admissions:** 13873 **Census:** 192 **Outpatient Visits:**
178457 **Births:** 1012 **Total Expense ($000):** 253698 **Payroll Expense**
($000): 79731 **Personnel:** 1893

✠ **SELECT SPECIALTY HOSPITAL–ERIE (392037)**, 252 West 11th Street,
Zip 16501–1702; tel. 814/874–5300, (Nonreporting) **A**1 9 10 **S** Select Medical
Corporation, Mechanicsburg, PA
Primary Contact: Randy Neiswonger, Chief Executive Officer
CNO: Keith Christiansen, Chief Nursing Officer
Web address: www.erie.selectspecialtyhospitals.com/
Control: Corporation, Investor–owned, for–profit **Service:** Long–Term Acute Care
hospital

Staffed Beds: 50

☐ **UPMC HAMOT (390063)**, 201 State Street, Zip 16550–0002;
tel. 814/877–6000 **A**1 2 3 5 9 10 13 **F**3 9 11 12 13 15 17 18 20 22 24 26
28 29 30 31 34 35 36 37 38 39 40 43 44 45 46 47 48 49 50 51 56 57 58
59 60 61 62 63 64 65 66 68 70 72 74 75 76 77 78 79 80 81 82 84 85 86
87 89 92 93 96 97 100 107 108 110 111 114 115 118 119 124 126 129
130 131 132 135 141 146 147 148 **P**6 8 **S** UPMC, Pittsburgh, PA
Primary Contact: V. James Fiorenzo, President
COO: David Gibbons, Executive Vice President and Chief Operating Officer
CFO: Stephen M. Danch, Chief Financial Officer
CMO: Richard Long, M.D., Chief Medical Officer
CIO: Lisa D. McChesney, R.N., Senior Director Information Systems
CHR: Brian Durniok, Vice President Human Resources
CNO: James E. Donnelly, Chief Nursing Officer and Vice President Patient Care
Services
Web address: www.hamot.org
Control: Other not–for–profit (including NFP Corporation) **Service:** General
Medical and Surgical

Staffed Beds: 331 **Admissions:** 18203 **Census:** 230 **Outpatient Visits:**
241057 **Births:** 2088 **Total Expense ($000):** 317238 **Payroll Expense**
($000): 106215 **Personnel:** 2112

VETERANS AFFAIRS MEDICAL CENTER See Erie Veterans Affairs Medical
Center

VETERANS AFFAIRS MEDICAL CENTER See Erie Veterans Affairs Medical Center

SHENANGO VALLEY CAMPUS See UPMC Horizon, Greenville

EVERETT—Bedford County

☐ **UPMC BEDFORD MEMORIAL (390117)**, 10455 Lincoln Highway,
Zip 15537–7046; tel. 814/623–6161 **A**1 9 10 20 **F**3 8 11 13 15 18 28 29 30
31 34 35 36 39 40 41 45 50 51 56 57 59 61 64 65 68 70 71 74 75 76 77
78 79 81 85 86 87 89 93 97 100 102 104 107 108 110 111 114 119 129 130
131 132 133 135 146 147 **S** UPMC, Pittsburgh, PA
Primary Contact: Roger P. Winn, President
CFO: Mario Wilfong, Vice President Finance and Administration
CIO: Mark Wiley, Manager Information Systems Development
CHR: Michelle A. Speck, Vice President Human Resources
CNO: Paula Thomas, R.N., Vice President Patient Services
Web address: www.upmcbedfordmemorial.com
Control: Other not–for–profit (including NFP Corporation) **Service:** General
Medical and Surgical

Staffed Beds: 27 **Admissions:** 1949 **Census:** 16 **Outpatient Visits:** 98746
Births: 299 **Total Expense ($000):** 42675 **Payroll Expense ($000):** 14916
Personnel: 304

FARRELL—Mercer County

SHENANGO VALLEY CAMPUS See UPMC Horizon, Greenville

FORT WASHINGTON—Montgomery County

☐ **BROOKE GLEN BEHAVIORAL HOSPITAL (394049)**, 7170 Lafayette Avenue,
Zip 19034–2301; tel. 215/641–5300, (Nonreporting) **A**1 3 5 9 10 **S** Universal
Health Services, Inc., King of Prussia, PA
Primary Contact: Neil Callahan, Chief Executive Officer
COO: William R. Mason, Chief Operating Officer
CFO: Robert Zagerman, Chief Financial Officer
CMO: Chand Nair, M.D., Medical Director
CHR: Dawn Kownacki, Director Human Resources
Web address: www.brookeglenhospital.com
Control: Corporation, Investor–owned, for–profit **Service:** Psychiatric

Staffed Beds: 146

GETTYSBURG—Adams County

✠ **GETTYSBURG HOSPITAL (390065)**, 147 Gettys Street, Zip 17325–2534;
tel. 717/334–2121 **A**1 9 10 **F**3 8 11 13 15 18 20 28 29 30 31 35 40 42 45
46 50 54 55 59 60 64 65 68 70 74 75 76 79 81 82 84 85 87 89 93 102
107 108 110 111 112 114 115 118 119 120 121 129 130 131 132 134 135
146 147 148 **P**8 **S** WellSpan Health, York, PA
Primary Contact: Jane E. Hyde, President
COO: Joseph H. Edgar, Senior Vice President Operations
CMO: Charles Marley, D.O., Vice President Medical Affairs
CIO: Robin Kimple, Director Information Services
CHR: Kim Brister, Director Human Resources
CNO: Kristen O'Shea, R.N., Vice President Patient Care Services
Web address: www.wellspan.org
Control: Other not–for–profit (including NFP Corporation) **Service:** General
Medical and Surgical

Staffed Beds: 76 **Admissions:** 4283 **Census:** 47 **Outpatient Visits:** 184523
Births: 527 **Total Expense ($000):** 124865 **Payroll Expense ($000):** 44635
Personnel: 687

GREENSBURG—Westmoreland County

☐ **EXCELA HEALTH WESTMORELAND HOSPITAL (390145)**, 532 West
Pittsburgh Street, Zip 15601–2282; tel. 724/832–4000 **A**1 9 10 **F**3 5 8 9 11
12 13 15 17 18 20 22 24 26 28 29 30 32 34 35 36 38 40 44 45 48 49 50
51 56 57 59 61 64 65 68 70 73 74 75 76 77 78 79 81 82 84 85 86 87 89
90 92 93 96 97 98 100 101 102 103 104 105 107 108 110 111 114 115
118 119 129 130 131 132 134 135 143 146 147 148 **S** Excela Health,
Greensburg, PA
Primary Contact: Ronald H. Ott, President
COO: Michael D. Busch, Executive Vice President and Chief Operating Officer
CFO: Jeffrey T. Curry, Executive Vice President and Chief Financial Officer
CMO: Jerome Granato, M.D., Senior Vice President and Chief Medical Officer
CIO: David Gawaluck, Vice President and Chief Information Officer
CHR: John Caverno, Chief Human Resources Officer
CNO: Helen K. Burns, Ph.D., Senior Vice President and Chief Nursing Officer
Web address: www.excelahealth.org
Control: Other not–for–profit (including NFP Corporation) **Service:** General
Medical and Surgical

Staffed Beds: 359 **Admissions:** 16985 **Census:** 225 **Outpatient Visits:**
324068 **Births:** 1727 **Total Expense ($000):** 222531 **Payroll Expense**
($000): 94219 **Personnel:** 1865

GREENVILLE—Mercer County

☐ ○ **UPMC HORIZON (390178)**, 110 North Main Street, Zip 16125–1726;
tel. 724/588–2100, (Includes GREENVILLE CAMPUS, 110 North Main Street,
Zip 16125–1795; tel. 724/588–2100; SHENANGO VALLEY CAMPUS, 2200
Memorial Drive, Farrell, Zip 16121–1398; tel. 724/981–3500), (Total facility
includes 25 beds in nursing home–type unit) **A**1 2 9 10 11 13 **F**3 11 12 13 15
18 20 26 28 29 30 31 32 34 35 39 40 43 44 45 47 49 50 53 54 56 57 59
61 64 65 68 70 74 75 76 77 78 79 81 82 85 86 87 90 92 97 107 108 110
111 114 115 116 117 118 119 121 123 128 129 130 131 132 133 135 146
147 148 **S** UPMC, Pittsburgh, PA
Primary Contact: Donald R. Owrey, President
CFO: David Shulik, Vice President and Chief Financial Officer
CMO: Samuel Daisley, D.O., Vice President Medical Affairs
CHR: Connie Mayle, Vice President Administrative Services
Web address: www.horizon.upmc.com
Control: Other not–for–profit (including NFP Corporation) **Service:** General
Medical and Surgical

Staffed Beds: 184 **Admissions:** 7217 **Census:** 94 **Outpatient Visits:** 214625
Births: 779 **Total Expense ($000):** 139940 **Payroll Expense ($000):** 40826
Personnel: 754

PA

PA

GROVE CITY—Mercer County

GROVE CITY MEDICAL CENTER (390266), 631 North Broad Street Extension, Zip 16127–4603; tel. 724/450–7000, (Total facility includes 20 beds in nursing home–type unit) **A**9 10 **F**3 13 15 18 20 28 29 31 34 35 40 45 46 49 50 51 54 57 59 60 64 70 75 76 78 79 81 82 87 93 107 108 110 111 115 117 118 119 124 127 128 129 130 132 135 146 147 148 **P**6
Primary Contact: Robert Jackson, Jr., Chief Executive Officer
CFO: David Poland, Vice President Finance
CMO: Armando Sciullo, D.O., Chief of Staff
CIO: Philip Swartwood, Director Information Systems
CHR: Donald Henley, Vice President Human Resources and Social Services
Web address: www.gcmcpa.org
Control: Other not–for–profit (including NFP Corporation) **Service:** General Medical and Surgical

Staffed Beds: 109 **Admissions:** 2043 **Census:** 31 **Outpatient Visits:** 105559 **Births:** 177 **Total Expense ($000):** 43104 **Payroll Expense ($000):** 16881 **Personnel:** 391

HANOVER—York County

⊞ **HANOVER HOSPITAL (390233)**, 300 Highland Avenue, Zip 17331–2297; tel. 717/316–3711 **A**1 9 10 **F**3 7 11 13 15 18 20 28 29 30 31 32 34 35 36 40 44 45 47 49 50 51 53 54 56 57 59 61 64 65 68 74 75 76 77 78 81 84 85 86 87 89 90 93 94 96 107 108 110 111 115 119 129 130 131 132 134 135 143 144 146 147 148
Primary Contact: James Wissler, President and Chief Executive Officer
COO: Michael A. Hockenberry, Vice President Operations
CFO: Michael W. Gaskins, Executive Vice President and Chief Financial Officer
CMO: Michael H. Ader, M.D., Vice President Medical Affairs
CIO: Pamela Owens, Director Health Information Management
CHR: Christine Miller, Vice President Human Resources
CNO: M. Patricia Saunders, R.N., Vice President Nursing
Web address: www.hanoverhospital.org
Control: Other not–for–profit (including NFP Corporation) **Service:** General Medical and Surgical

Staffed Beds: 106 **Admissions:** 5454 **Census:** 67 **Outpatient Visits:** 218579 **Births:** 625 **Total Expense ($000):** 132832 **Payroll Expense ($000):** 52584 **Personnel:** 1026

HARRISBURG—Dauphin County

COMMUNITY HOSPITAL See Pinnacle Health System

⊞ **PENNSYLVANIA PSYCHIATRIC INSTITUTE (394051)**, 2501 North Third Street, Zip 17110–1904; tel. 717/782–6420, (Nonreporting) **A**1 3 5 10
Primary Contact: William Daly, Chief Executive Officer
CFO: Michael Felice, Chief Financial Officer
Web address: www.ppimhs.org/
Control: Other not–for–profit (including NFP Corporation) **Service:** Psychiatric

Staffed Beds: 80

☐ **PINNACLE HEALTH SYSTEM (390067)**, 111 South Front Street, Zip 17101–2010, Mailing Address: P.O. Box 8700, Zip 17105–8700; tel. 717/782–3131, (Includes COMMUNITY HOSPITAL, 4300 Londonderry Road, Zip 17109–5397, Mailing Address: P.O. Box 3000, Zip 17105–3000; tel. 717/652–3000; HARRISBURG HOSPITAL, 111 South Front Street, Zip 17101–2099; tel. 717/782–3131; POLYCLINIC HOSPITAL, 2501 North Third Street, Zip 17110–1904; tel. 717/782–4141; Roger Longenderfer, M.D., President and Chief Executive Officer) **A**1 2 3 5 8 9 10 12 13 **F**3 7 11 12 13 14 15 17 18 19 20 22 24 26 27 29 30 31 34 35 36 37 40 45 46 47 48 49 50 52 53 54 55 56 57 58 59 60 63 64 65 66 68 70 72 74 75 76 77 78 79 81 82 84 85 86 87 89 90 91 93 95 96 97 102 107 108 109 110 111 114 115 116 117 118 119 120 121 123 124 126 130 131 132 134 138 142 143 146 147 148 **P**6
Primary Contact: Michael A. Young, FACHE, President and Chief Executive Officer
COO: Philip Guarneschelli, Senior Vice President and Chief Operating Officer
CFO: William H. Pugh, Senior Vice President Corporate Finance and Chief Financial Officer
CMO: Nirmal Joshi, M.D., Senior Vice President Medical Affairs and Chief Medical Officer
CIO: Steven Roth, Vice President Informatics and Chief Information Officer
CHR: Ann H. Gormley, Vice President Human Resources
Web address: www.pinnaclehealth.org
Control: Other not–for–profit (including NFP Corporation) **Service:** General Medical and Surgical

Staffed Beds: 607 **Admissions:** 31581 **Census:** 422 **Outpatient Visits:** 720974 **Births:** 3985 **Total Expense ($000):** 638441 **Payroll Expense ($000):** 226566 **Personnel:** 4795

POLYCLINIC HOSPITAL See Pinnacle Health System

SELECT SPECIALTY HOSPITAL–HARRISBURG See Select Specialty Hospital–Central Pennsylvania, Camp Hill

HASTINGS—Cambria County

★ **CONEMAUGH MINERS MEDICAL CENTER (390130)**, 290 Haida Avenue, Zip 16646–5610, Mailing Address: P.O. Box 689, Zip 16646–0689; tel. 814/247–3100 **A**9 10 20 **F**3 15 18 29 30 31 35 36 40 45 48 56 57 59 64 70 75 78 79 81 86 92 93 96 97 102 107 108 110 119 129 130 131 133 144 146 148 **P**8 **S** Duke LifePoint Healthcare, Brentwood, TN
Primary Contact: William R. Crowe, President
CFO: Kimberly Semelsberger, Vice President Financial Operations
CIO: James Homerski, Director Information Services
CHR: John Fresh, Vice President Human Resources
Web address: www.minersmedicalcenter.org
Control: Other not–for–profit (including NFP Corporation) **Service:** General Medical and Surgical

Staffed Beds: 30 **Admissions:** 533 **Census:** 7 **Outpatient Visits:** 52986 **Births:** 0 **Total Expense ($000):** 16615 **Payroll Expense ($000):** 5306 **Personnel:** 126

HAZLETON—Luzerne County

★ ○ **LEHIGH VALLEY HOSPITAL – HAZLETON (390185)**, 700 East Broad Street, Zip 18201–6897; tel. 570/501–4000 **A**9 10 11 **F**3 8 11 12 13 15 28 29 30 31 34 35 40 50 53 54 57 59 60 62 64 68 69 70 75 76 77 78 79 81 82 85 86 87 89 90 93 107 108 110 111 114 118 119 124 129 130 131 132 135 143 146 147 148 **P**2 **S** Lehigh Valley Health Network, Allentown, PA
Primary Contact: John R. Fletcher, President
CFO: William Bauer, Vice President Finance and Chief Financial Officer
CMO: Anthony Valente, M.D., Vice President Medical Affairs
CIO: Carl Shoener, Chief Information Officer
Web address: www.lvhn.org/hazleton/
Control: Other not–for–profit (including NFP Corporation) **Service:** General Medical and Surgical

Staffed Beds: 116 **Admissions:** 6740 **Census:** 86 **Outpatient Visits:** 157248 **Births:** 632 **Total Expense ($000):** 94259 **Payroll Expense ($000):** 42448 **Personnel:** 731

HERSHEY—Dauphin County

⊞ **PENN STATE MILTON S. HERSHEY MEDICAL CENTER (390256)**, 500 University Drive, Zip 17033–2360, Mailing Address: P.O. Box 850, Zip 17033–0850; tel. 717/531–8521, (Includes PENN STATE CHILDREN'S HOSPITAL, 500 University Drive, tel. 717/531–8521) **A**1 2 3 5 8 9 10 **F**3 5 6 7 8 9 11 12 13 14 15 17 18 19 20 21 22 23 24 25 26 27 28 29 30 31 32 34 35 36 37 38 40 41 43 44 45 46 47 48 49 50 51 52 53 54 55 56 57 58 59 60 61 64 65 66 68 70 72 73 74 75 76 77 78 79 80 81 82 84 85 86 87 88 89 91 92 93 96 97 99 100 101 102 103 104 105 106 107 108 109 110 111 114 115 116 117 118 119 120 121 123 124 126 129 130 131 132 134 135 136 137 138 139 141 142 143 144 145 146 147 148 **P**6
Primary Contact: A. Craig Hillemeier, M.D., Chief Executive Officer
COO: Alan L. Brechbill, Director and Chief Operating Officer
CFO: Kevin Haley, Chief Financial Officer
CMO: Carol V. Freer, M.D., Chief Medical Officer
CIO: Rod Dykehouse, Chief Information Officer
CHR: Lisa Abbott, Chief Human Resources Officer
CNO: Sherry M. Kwater, R.N., Chief Nursing Officer
Web address: www.pennstatehershey.org/web/guest/home
Control: Other not–for–profit (including NFP Corporation) **Service:** General Medical and Surgical

Staffed Beds: 508 **Admissions:** 26147 **Census:** 404 **Outpatient Visits:** 882793 **Births:** 1833 **Total Expense ($000):** 999676 **Payroll Expense ($000):** 367490 **Personnel:** 7917

HONESDALE—Wayne County

★ **WAYNE MEMORIAL HOSPITAL (390125)**, 601 Park Street, Zip 18431–1498; tel. 570/253–8100 **A**9 10 **F**3 11 13 15 18 28 30 31 34 35 36 37 39 40 45 46 49 50 51 53 54 56 57 59 61 62 63 64 65 75 76 77 78 79 81 86 90 92 93 99 100 101 102 103 104 107 108 110 111 115 116 117 119 124 129 130 131 132 133 134 135 146 147 148
Primary Contact: David L. Hoff, Chief Executive Officer
COO: John D. Conte, Director Facility Services
CFO: Michael J. Clifford, Director Finance
CMO: William Dewar, M.D., Chief of Staff
CIO: Tom Hoffman, Manager Information Systems
CHR: Elizabeth McDonald, Director Human Resources
CNO: Major Jim Pettinato, Director Patient Care Services
Web address: www.wmh.org
Control: Other not–for–profit (including NFP Corporation) **Service:** General Medical and Surgical

Staffed Beds: 104 **Admissions:** 3587 **Census:** 48 **Outpatient Visits:** 134135 **Births:** 386 **Total Expense ($000):** 72034 **Payroll Expense ($000):** 29727 **Personnel:** 572

Many Facility Codes have changed. Please refer to the AHA Guide Code Chart. © 2014 AHA Guide

HUMMELSTOWN—Dauphin County

☒ △ **PENN STATE HERSHEY REHABILITATION HOSPITAL (393053)**, 1135 Old West Chocolate Avenue, Zip 17036; tel. 717/832–2600, (Nonreporting) **A**1 7 9 10 **S** Select Medical Corporation, Mechanicsburg, PA
Primary Contact: Scott Guevin, Chief Executive Officer
CMO: Brenda Mallory, M.D., Medical Director
Web address: www.psh–rehab.com
Control: Corporation, Investor–owned, for–profit **Service:** Rehabilitation

Staffed Beds: 32

HUNTINGDON—Huntingdon County

☐ **J. C. BLAIR MEMORIAL HOSPITAL (390056)**, 1225 Warm Springs Avenue, Zip 16652–2398; tel. 814/643–2290 **A**1 9 10 20 **F**3 11 13 15 18 28 29 34 35 40 45 50 53 55 57 59 64 68 70 75 76 77 79 81 85 86 87 89 96 98 99 100 102 103 105 107 108 110 111 114 116 117 118 119 129 130 132 133 135 146 147 148
Primary Contact: Lisa Mallon, Chief Executive Officer
CFO: Edward M. Quinn, Interim Chief Financial Officer
CMO: James Hayden, M.D., Chief Medical Officer
CIO: Rusty Davis, Director Information Technology
CHR: Michael F. Hubert, Vice President Human Resources
CNO: Pam Matthias, Vice President of Patient Care Services
Web address: www.jcblair.org
Control: Other not–for–profit (including NFP Corporation) **Service:** General Medical and Surgical

Staffed Beds: 70 **Admissions:** 2134 **Census:** 20 **Outpatient Visits:** 114640 **Births:** 215 **Total Expense ($000):** 38474 **Payroll Expense ($000):** 18329 **Personnel:** 353

INDIANA—Indiana County

★ **INDIANA REGIONAL MEDICAL CENTER (390173)**, 835 Hospital Road, Zip 15701–3629, Mailing Address: P.O. Box 788, Zip 15701–0788; tel. 724/357–7000 **A**2 9 10 20 **F**3 11 15 18 28 29 31 32 34 35 40 44 45 46 47 49 53 56 57 59 64 65 70 71 74 75 76 77 78 79 81 82 83 84 85 87 89 90 98 102 103 107 108 111 114 115 118 119 120 121 123 124 129 130 132 144 146 147 148 **P**4 6
Primary Contact: Stephen A. Wolfe, President and Chief Executive Officer
COO: Dominic Paccapaniccia, Chief Operating Officer
CFO: Robert Gongaware, Senior Vice President Finance
CMO: Bruce A. Bush, M.D., Senior Vice President Medical Affairs
CIO: Wade Patrick, Senior Vice President Information Services
CHR: James W. Kinneer, Vice President Organizational Development
CNO: Cindy L. Virgil, MSN, Senior Vice President Patient Care Services
Web address: www.indianarmc.org
Control: Other not–for–profit (including NFP Corporation) **Service:** General Medical and Surgical

Staffed Beds: 164 **Admissions:** 7147 **Census:** 86 **Outpatient Visits:** 273907 **Births:** 601 **Total Expense ($000):** 131482 **Payroll Expense ($000):** 60149 **Personnel:** 954

JEFFERSON HILLS—Allegheny County

☒ **JEFFERSON HOSPITAL (390265)**, 565 Coal Valley Road, Zip 15025–3703, Mailing Address: Box 18119, Pittsburgh, Zip 15236–0119; tel. 412/469–5000, (Nonreporting) **A**1 9 10 **S** Allegheny Health Network, Pittsburgh, PA
Primary Contact: Louise Urban, R.N., President and Chief Executive Officer
CMO: Richard F. Collins, M.D., Executive Vice President and Chief Medical Officer
CIO: James Witenske, Chief Information Officer
Web address: www.jeffersonregional.com
Control: Other not–for–profit (including NFP Corporation) **Service:** General Medical and Surgical

Staffed Beds: 373

JERSEY SHORE—Lycoming County

☒ **JERSEY SHORE HOSPITAL (391300)**, 1020 Thompson Street, Zip 17740–1794; tel. 570/398–0100 **A**1 9 10 18 **F**3 15 18 28 29 30 34 35 40 45 46 47 48 50 57 59 75 77 79 81 82 85 93 107 108 109 110 111 115 119 129 130 131 133 135 144 145 147 148 **P**7 **S** QHR, Brentwood, TN
Primary Contact: David A. Shannon, President and Chief Executive Officer
CFO: Mark Rice, CPA, Controller
CMO: Thomas Connolly, M.D., Chief Medical Officer
CIO: Christine Haas, Chief Information Officer
CHR: Megan Switzer, Director Human Resources
Web address: www.jsh.org
Control: Other not–for–profit (including NFP Corporation) **Service:** General Medical and Surgical

Staffed Beds: 25 **Admissions:** 869 **Census:** 9 **Outpatient Visits:** 85625 **Births:** 0 **Total Expense ($000):** 30195 **Payroll Expense ($000):** 11835 **Personnel:** 296

JOHNSTOWN—Cambria County

☒ △ **CONEMAUGH MEMORIAL MEDICAL CENTER (390110)**, 1086 Franklin Street, Zip 15905–4398; tel. 814/534–9000, (Includes GOOD SAMARITAN MEDICAL CENTER, 1020 Franklin Street, Zip 15905–4186; tel. 814/533–1000; MEMORIAL MEDICAL CENTER – LEE CAMPUS, 320 Main Street, Zip 15901–1601; tel. 814/533–0123) **A**1 3 5 6 7 9 10 12 13 **F**3 5 8 11 12 13 14 15 17 18 20 22 24 26 28 29 30 31 32 34 35 40 42 43 44 45 46 49 50 51 53 54 55 56 57 59 61 62 63 64 68 70 72 74 75 76 77 78 79 81 82 83 84 85 86 87 89 90 92 93 97 98 99 100 101 103 104 107 108 110 111 114 115 118 119 126 129 130 131 132 134 135 144 145 146 147 148 **S** Duke LifePoint Healthcare, Brentwood, TN
Primary Contact: Steven E. Tucker, President
COO: Steven E. Tucker, President
CFO: Edward De Pasquale, Chief Financial Officer
CMO: William Carney, M.D., Interim Chief Medical Officer
CIO: Joseph Dado, Chief Information Officer
CHR: Brent J. Mallek, Chief Human Resources Officer
CNO: Claudia Rager, R.N., Vice President Patient Care Services
Web address: www.conemaugh.org
Control: Other not–for–profit (including NFP Corporation) **Service:** General Medical and Surgical

Staffed Beds: 555 **Admissions:** 23192 **Census:** 358 **Outpatient Visits:** 494162 **Births:** 1546 **Total Expense ($000):** 378559 **Payroll Expense ($000):** 154497 **Personnel:** 3169

MEMORIAL MEDICAL CENTER – LEE CAMPUS See Conemaugh Memorial Medical Center

☒ **SELECT SPECIALTY HOSPITAL–JOHNSTOWN (392031)**, 320 Main Street, 3rd Floor, Zip 15901–1601; tel. 814/534–7300, (Nonreporting) **A**1 9 10 **S** Select Medical Corporation, Mechanicsburg, PA
Primary Contact: Kelly Blake, Chief Executive Officer
CMO: Gary Davidson, M.D., Medical Director
Web address: www.selectspecialtyhospitals.com/company/locations/johnstown.aspx
Control: Corporation, Investor–owned, for–profit **Service:** Long–Term Acute Care hospital

Staffed Beds: 39

KANE—Mckean County

KANE COMMUNITY HOSPITAL (390104), 4372 Route 6, Zip 16735–3060; tel. 814/837–8585 **A**9 10 20 **F**3 11 12 15 17 18 28 29 30 31 34 35 40 41 45 46 50 53 57 59 62 64 65 70 75 77 79 81 82 85 89 91 93 107 108 110 111 114 118 119 128 129 130 131 132 133 135 145 146 147 **P**4 6
Primary Contact: J. Gary Rhodes, FACHE, Chief Executive Officer
CFO: Angela Hadzega, Chief Financial Officer
CMO: Linda Rettger, M.D., President Medical Staff
CIO: Margaret Twidale, Manager Information Systems
CHR: Marsha Keller, Director Human Resources
CNO: Pam Bray, Director of Nursing and Director Inpatient Services
Web address: www.kanehosp.com
Control: Other not–for–profit (including NFP Corporation) **Service:** General Medical and Surgical

Staffed Beds: 31 **Admissions:** 815 **Census:** 10 **Outpatient Visits:** 36214 **Births:** 0 **Total Expense ($000):** 18820 **Payroll Expense ($000):** 9439 **Personnel:** 178

KINGSTON—Luzerne County

☒ **FIRST HOSPITAL WYOMING VALLEY (394039)**, 562 Wyoming Avenue, Zip 18704–3721; tel. 570/552–3900 **A**1 9 10 **F**42 98 99 103 105 130 **P**6 **S** Community Health Systems, Inc., Franklin, TN
Primary Contact: Mark Schor, Chief Executive Officer
CFO: Kelly Knorr, Chief Financial Officer
CMO: David Liskov, M.D., Medical Director
CNO: Rhonda Sod, Chief Nursing Officer
Web address: www.firsthospital.net/Pages/home.aspx
Control: Corporation, Investor–owned, for–profit **Service:** Psychiatric

Staffed Beds: 127 **Admissions:** 3813 **Census:** 92 **Outpatient Visits:** 0 **Births:** 0 **Personnel:** 111

Hospital, Medicare Provider Number, Address, Telephone, Approval, Facility, and Physician Codes, Health Care System

★ American Hospital Association (AHA) membership
☐ The Joint Commission accreditation
◇ DNV Healthcare Inc. accreditation
○ Healthcare Facilities Accreditation Program
△ Commission on Accreditation of Rehabilitation Facilities (CARF) accreditation

PA

KITTANNING—Armstrong County

◇ **ACMH HOSPITAL (390163)**, One Nolte Drive, Zip 16201–7111; tel. 724/543–8500, (Nonreporting) **A**2 9 10 19 21
Primary Contact: John I. Lewis, President and Chief Executive Officer
CFO: Patrick Burns, Vice President Finance
CMO: Harold Altman, M.D., Chief Medical Officer
CIO: Dianne Emminger, Vice President Information Services
CHR: Anne Remaley, Vice President Human Resources
Web address: www.acmh.org
Control: Other not-for-profit (including NFP Corporation) **Service:** General Medical and Surgical

Staffed Beds: 170

LANCASTER—Lancaster County

✠ **LANCASTER GENERAL HEALTH (390100)**, 555 North Duke Street, Zip 17602–2250, Mailing Address: P.O. Box 3555, Zip 17604–3555; tel. 717/544–5511 **A**1 2 3 5 9 10 **F**3 11 12 13 14 15 17 18 19 20 22 24 26 28 29 30 31 32 34 35 36 37 39 40 43 44 45 46 47 49 50 51 54 55 56 57 58 59 60 61 64 65 66 68 70 72 73 74 75 76 77 78 79 80 81 82 85 86 87 89 91 92 93 96 97 98 100 102 107 108 110 112 114 115 117 118 119 120 121 123 124 126 129 130 132 135 141 142 145 146 147 148 **P**6
Primary Contact: Thomas E. Beeman, Ph.D., FACHE, President and Chief Executive Officer
COO: Marion A. McGowan, Executive Vice President and Chief Population Health Officer
CFO: Dennis Roemer, Executive Vice President and Chief Financial Officer
CMO: Lee M. Duke, II, M.D., Senior Vice President and Chief Physician Executive
CIO: Gary Davidson, Senior Vice President and Chief Information Officer
CHR: Regina Mingle, Senior Vice President and Chief Leadership Officer
CNO: Karen Oxler, Vice President Nursing
Web address: www.lancastergeneral.org
Control: Other not-for-profit (including NFP Corporation) **Service:** General Medical and Surgical

Staffed Beds: 631 **Admissions:** 32519 **Census:** 409 **Outpatient Visits:** 1394079 **Births:** 4267 **Total Expense ($000):** 734549 **Payroll Expense ($000):** 308124 **Personnel:** 4709

✠ **LANCASTER REGIONAL MEDICAL CENTER (390061)**, 250 College Avenue, Zip 17603–3363, Mailing Address: P.O. Box 3434, Zip 17604–3434; tel. 717/291–8211 **A**1 9 10 **F**3 15 18 20 22 24 26 28 29 30 31 34 35 37 40 45 47 48 49 50 51 56 57 59 64 68 70 74 75 77 78 79 81 82 84 85 87 90 91 92 93 96 98 100 101 102 103 107 108 110 111 114 119 121 126 129 130 131 135 146 **S** Community Health Systems, Inc., Franklin, TN
Primary Contact: Bob Moore, FACHE, Chief Executive Officer
COO: Russell Baxley, Chief Operating Officer
CFO: Mike Johnson, Chief Financial Officer
CMO: N. A. Mastropietro, M.D., Medical Director
CHR: Brian Hoffman, Director Human Resources
CNO: Michelle Reaser, R.N., Chief Nursing Executive
Web address: www.lancasterregional.com
Control: Corporation, Investor-owned, for-profit **Service:** General Medical and Surgical

Staffed Beds: 150 **Admissions:** 4692 **Census:** 73 **Outpatient Visits:** 102946 **Births:** 0 **Total Expense ($000):** 93773 **Payroll Expense ($000):** 29496 **Personnel:** 552

☐ **LANCASTER REHABILITATION HOSPITAL (393054)**, 675 Good Drive, Zip 17601–2426; tel. 717/406–3000, (Nonreporting) **A**1 10 **S** Centerre Healthcare, Brentwood, TN
Primary Contact: Tammy L. Ober, Chief Executive Officer
CFO: David Stark, Chief Financial Officer
CHR: Lisa Andrews, Director Human Resources
Web address: www.lancastergeneral.org
Control: Corporation, Investor-owned, for-profit **Service:** Rehabilitation

Staffed Beds: 10

LANGHORNE—Bucks County

☐ **BARIX CLINICS OF PENNSYLVANIA (390302)**, 280 Middletown Boulevard, Zip 19047–1816; tel. 267/572–3100, (Nonreporting) **A**1 10
Primary Contact: Vivian Costa, Director
Web address: www.barixclinics.com
Control: Partnership, Investor-owned, for-profit **Service:** Surgical

Staffed Beds: 40

BUCKS COUNTY CAMPUS See Aria Health, Philadelphia

✠ **ST. MARY MEDICAL CENTER (390258)**, 1201 Langhorne–Newtown Road, Zip 19047–1201; tel. 215/710–2000 **A**1 2 9 10 **F**2 12 15 17 18 20 22 24 26 28 29 30 31 32 34 35 40 41 43 53 55 56 57 58 59 64 70 72 74 75 76 77 78 79 81 82 84 86 87 89 90 91 92 93 94 107 108 110 111 114 115 116 117 118 119 120 121 123 124 129 130 132 135 146 147 148 **S** Catholic Health East / Trinity Health, Livonia, MI
Primary Contact: Gregory T. Wozniak, President and Chief Executive Officer
COO: Jeffrey N. Yarmel, Chief Operating Officer
CFO: Daniel Confalone, Chief Financial Officer and Vice President Finance
CMO: Deirdre Donaghy, M.D., Vice President Medical Affairs
CIO: Bonnie Buehler, Chief Information Officer
CHR: Mary Sweeney, Vice President Colleague Services and Development
CNO: Sharon Brown, R.N., Vice President Patient Care and Chief Nursing Officer
Web address: www.stmaryhealthcare.org
Control: Church-operated, Nongovernment, not-for profit **Service:** General Medical and Surgical

Staffed Beds: 323 **Admissions:** 23821 **Census:** 282 **Outpatient Visits:** 294638 **Births:** 2176 **Total Expense ($000):** 376582 **Payroll Expense ($000):** 148694 **Personnel:** 2357

LANSDALE—Montgomery County

✠ **ABINGTON HEALTH LANSDALE HOSPITAL (390012)**, 100 Medical Campus Drive, Zip 19446–1200; tel. 215/368–2100 **A**1 9 10 **F**3 8 11 15 18 28 29 30 31 34 35 39 40 45 49 50 57 59 64 65 69 70 74 77 78 79 81 82 85 90 93 107 111 114 115 119 129 130 132 146 147 148 **P**6 **S** Abington Health, Abington, PA
Primary Contact: Gary R. Candia, Ph.D., FACHE, Chief Executive Officer
COO: Katie Farrell, Chief Operating Officer
CFO: Raymond Leichner, Director Finance
CMO: Joseph Kraynak, M.D., Chief Medical Officer
CIO: Joan Lauman, Manager Clinical Systems
CHR: John Clarkin, Director Human Resource
Web address: www.amh.org/lansdale/index.aspx
Control: Other not-for-profit (including NFP Corporation) **Service:** General Medical and Surgical

Staffed Beds: 127 **Admissions:** 5323 **Census:** 57 **Outpatient Visits:** 97073 **Births:** 0 **Total Expense ($000):** 75686 **Payroll Expense ($000):** 31420 **Personnel:** 442

LATROBE—Westmoreland County

☐ **EXCELA LATROBE AREA HOSPITAL (390219)**, One Mellon Way, Zip 15650–1096; tel. 724/537–1000 **A**1 2 3 5 9 10 13 **F**3 7 8 11 12 15 29 30 34 35 38 40 44 45 48 49 50 51 53 56 57 59 60 64 65 68 70 74 75 77 78 79 81 82 85 86 87 92 93 97 98 99 100 101 104 107 108 110 111 114 115 118 119 126 129 130 132 134 135 143 146 147 148 **P**6 **S** Excela Health, Greensburg, PA
Primary Contact: Michael D. Busch, Executive Vice President and Chief Operating Officer
COO: Michael D. Busch, Executive Vice President and Chief Operating Officer
CMO: Carol J. Fox, M.D., Senior Vice President and Chief Medical Officer
CIO: David Gawaluck, Vice President and Chief Information Officer
CHR: Laurie English, Senior Vice President and Chief Human Resource Officer
CNO: Helen K. Burns, Ph.D., Senior Vice President and Chief Nursing Officer
Web address: www.excelahealth.org
Control: Other not-for-profit (including NFP Corporation) **Service:** General Medical and Surgical

Staffed Beds: 121 **Admissions:** 7048 **Census:** 74 **Outpatient Visits:** 249403 **Births:** 0 **Total Expense ($000):** 123314 **Payroll Expense ($000):** 40061 **Personnel:** 885

✠ **SELECT SPECIALTY HOSPITAL–LAUREL HIGHLANDS (392036)**, One Mellon Way, 3rd Floor, Zip 15650–1197; tel. 724/539–3230, (Nonreporting) **A**1 9 10 **S** Select Medical Corporation, Mechanicsburg, PA
Primary Contact: Laurie Kozorosky, Chief Executive Officer
Web address: www.selectspecialtyhospitals.com/company/locations/laurelhighlands.aspx
Control: Corporation, Investor-owned, for-profit **Service:** Long-Term Acute Care hospital

Staffed Beds: 40

LEBANON—Lebanon County

✠ **LEBANON VETERANS AFFAIRS MEDICAL CENTER**, 1700 South Lincoln Avenue, Zip 17042–7529; tel. 717/272–6621, (Nonreporting) **A**1 2 3 5 **S** Department of Veterans Affairs, Washington, DC
Primary Contact: Robert W. Callahan, Jr., Director
CFO: Geoffrey Smith, Chief Financial Officer
CMO: Kanan Chatterjee, M.D., Chief of Staff
CIO: Andru Ditzler, Chief Information Officer
CHR: Cindy Shiner, Manager Human Resources
Web address: www.lebanon.va.gov
Control: Veterans Affairs, Government, federal **Service:** General Medical and Surgical

Staffed Beds: 213

Many Facility Codes have changed. Please refer to the AHA Guide Code Chart. © 2014 AHA Guide

✠ **THE GOOD SAMARITAN HOSPITAL (390066)**, Fourth and Walnut Streets, Zip 17042–1281, Mailing Address: P.O. Box 1281, Zip 17042–1281; tel. 717/270–7500, (Total facility includes 19 beds in nursing home–type unit) **A**1 3 5 9 10 **F**3 8 11 13 14 15 17 18 20 22 24 26 28 29 30 31 34 35 40 45 49 50 51 53 57 59 60 62 63 64 68 70 75 76 77 78 79 80 81 82 84 85 87 89 90 92 93 94 96 97 107 108 110 111 114 118 119 128 129 130 132 135 146 148 **P**8
Primary Contact: Robert J. Longo, FACHE, President and Chief Executive Officer
COO: Kimberly Feeman, Senior Vice President and Chief Operating Officer
CFO: Robert J. Richards, Vice President Finance and Chief Financial Officer
CMO: Robert D. Shaver, M.D., Vice President Medical Affairs
CIO: Richard Follett, Chief Information Officer
CHR: Denise M. Garman, Director Human Resources
CNO: Jacquelyn M. Gould, MS, Vice President Patient Care Services and Chief Nursing Officer
Web address: www.gshleb.org
Control: Other not–for–profit (including NFP Corporation) **Service:** General Medical and Surgical

Staffed Beds: 164 **Admissions:** 7708 **Census:** 108 **Outpatient Visits:** 272348 **Births:** 848 **Total Expense ($000):** 170707 **Payroll Expense ($000):** 58577 **Personnel:** 1191

VETERANS AFFAIRS MEDICAL CENTER See Lebanon Veterans Affairs Medical Center

LEHIGHTON—Carbon County

✠ △ **GNADEN HUETTEN MEMORIAL HOSPITAL (390194)**, 211 North 12th Street, Zip 18235–1138; tel. 610/377–1300, (Total facility includes 91 beds in nursing home–type unit) **A**1 7 9 10 **F**3 11 15 28 29 30 34 35 40 50 57 59 62 64 65 68 70 74 75 77 79 81 82 85 87 90 93 94 97 98 102 107 111 114 116 117 119 124 128 130 132 133 135 146 147 148 **S** Blue Mountain Health System, Lehighton, PA
Primary Contact: Andrew E. Harris, Chief Executive Officer
CFO: Andrea Andrae, Chief Financial Officer
CMO: Dennis Kondash, D.O., Vice President Medical Affairs
CIO: Steve Kinkaid, Director Information Systems
CHR: Terrance J. Purcell, Vice President Support Services and Ambulatory Care
Web address: www.blmtn.org/?id=112&sid=1
Control: Other not–for–profit (including NFP Corporation) **Service:** General Medical and Surgical

Staffed Beds: 181 **Admissions:** 3515 **Census:** 151 **Outpatient Visits:** 64805 **Births:** 0 **Total Expense ($000):** 65947 **Payroll Expense ($000):** 30721 **Personnel:** 565

LEWISBURG—Union County

◇ **EVANGELICAL COMMUNITY HOSPITAL (390013)**, One Hospital Drive, Zip 17837–9350; tel. 570/522–2000 **A**9 10 19 21 **F**3 8 11 12 13 15 18 20 22 28 29 30 31 34 35 40 45 49 50 51 53 54 57 59 63 64 65 68 74 75 76 77 78 79 81 82 85 86 87 89 90 93 94 96 107 108 110 111 114 115 119 129 130 131 132 135 144 146 148 **P**7
Primary Contact: Michael N. O'Keefe, President and Chief Executive Officer
COO: Kendra A. Aucker, Vice President Operations
CFO: Jim Stopper, CPA, Interim Chief Financial Officer
CMO: J. Lawrence Ginsburg, M.D., Vice President Medical Affairs
CIO: Dale Moyer, Vice President Information Systems
CHR: Angela Hummel, Vice President Human Resources
CNO: Paul E. Tarves, R.N., Vice President Nursing Services
Web address: www.evanhospital.com
Control: Other not–for–profit (including NFP Corporation) **Service:** General Medical and Surgical

Staffed Beds: 130 **Admissions:** 6089 **Census:** 52 **Outpatient Visits:** 252583 **Births:** 1027 **Total Expense ($000):** 129427 **Payroll Expense ($000):** 53931 **Personnel:** 1337

U. S. PENITENTIARY INFIRMARY, Route 7, Zip 17837–9303; tel. 570/523–1251, (Nonreporting)
Primary Contact: Arnold Reyes, Administrator
Control: Department of Justice, Government, federal **Service:** Hospital unit of an institution (prison hospital, college infirmary, etc.)

Staffed Beds: 17

LEWISTOWN—Mifflin County

✠ **GEISINGER–LEWISTOWN HOSPITAL (390048)**, 400 Highland Avenue, Zip 17044–1198; tel. 717/248–5411 **A**1 2 5 6 9 10 19 20 **F**3 11 12 13 15 17 18 19 28 29 30 31 34 35 40 50 51 57 59 64 68 70 71 74 75 76 78 79 81 82 85 86 89 97 98 100 101 102 103 107 108 110 111 114 116 117 118 119 121 124 129 130 132 135 146 147 148 **P**6
Primary Contact: Kay A. Hamilton, R.N., MS, President and Chief Executive Officer
COO: Kirk E. Thomas, Vice President Operations
CFO: Randy E. Tewksbury, Vice President Finance
CMO: Daniel Reifsnyder, M.D., President Medical and Dental Staff
CIO: Ronald M. Cowan, Vice President Information Systems
CHR: N. Sue Reinke, Vice President Human Resources
Web address: www.lewistownhospital.org
Control: Other not–for–profit (including NFP Corporation) **Service:** General Medical and Surgical

Staffed Beds: 123 **Admissions:** 5220 **Census:** 57 **Births:** 534 **Total Expense ($000):** 92756 **Personnel:** 748

LITITZ—Lancaster County

✠ **HEART OF LANCASTER REGIONAL MEDICAL CENTER (390068)**, 1500 Highlands Drive, Zip 17543–7694; tel. 717/625–5000 **A**1 9 10 12 13 **F**3 12 13 15 18 20 29 30 31 34 35 44 45 47 49 50 57 59 60 64 68 70 72 74 75 76 77 79 81 82 85 87 89 107 108 110 111 114 119 126 130 146 147 148 **S** Community Health Systems, Inc., Franklin, TN
Primary Contact: Deborah J. Willwerth, R.N., MSN, Administrator
CIO: David Fisher, Director Information Systems
Web address: www.heartoflancaster.com
Control: Corporation, Investor–owned, for–profit **Service:** General Medical and Surgical

Staffed Beds: 148 **Admissions:** 2984 **Census:** 32 **Outpatient Visits:** 64379 **Births:** 935 **Total Expense ($000):** 52767 **Payroll Expense ($000):** 17795 **Personnel:** 344

LOCK HAVEN—Clinton County

✠ **LOCK HAVEN HOSPITAL (390071)**, 24 Cree Drive, Zip 17745–2699; tel. 570/893–5000, (Total facility includes 90 beds in nursing home–type unit) **A**1 9 10 **F**1 3 16 18 19 29 30 34 35 40 44 45 47 50 54 56 57 59 64 65 67 68 70 75 76 77 79 80 81 82 85 89 93 96 97 107 108 110 111 114 118 119 127 128 129 130 133 146 147 **S** Community Health Systems, Inc., Franklin, TN
Primary Contact: Steven T. Davis, Chief Executive Officer
CFO: Jennifer Lesher, Chief Financial Officer
CMO: Rajesh Patel, M.D., Chief of Staff
CIO: Judy Chapman, Interim Director Information Systems
CHR: Courtney Kunes, Director Human Resources
Web address: www.lockhavenhospital.com
Control: Corporation, Investor–owned, for–profit **Service:** General Medical and Surgical

Staffed Beds: 110 **Admissions:** 1365 **Census:** 79 **Outpatient Visits:** 48322 **Births:** 143 **Total Expense ($000):** 29933 **Payroll Expense ($000):** 15573 **Personnel:** 226

MALVERN—Chester County

✠ △ **BRYN MAWR REHABILITATION HOSPITAL (393025)**, 414 Paoli Pike, Zip 19355–3300, Mailing Address: P.O. Box 3007, Zip 19355–0707; tel. 484/596–5400 **A**1 7 9 10 **F**3 11 28 29 30 34 35 36 44 50 57 59 65 71 75 82 86 87 90 91 92 93 95 96 119 130 131 132 143 146 **P**5 **S** Jefferson Health System, Radnor, PA
Primary Contact: Donna Phillips, President
CFO: Dave Schmotzer, Chief Financial Officer
CMO: John Kraus, M.D., Chief Medical Officer
CIO: Karen A. Thomas, Chief Information Officer
Web address: www.brynmawrrehab.org
Control: Other not–for–profit (including NFP Corporation) **Service:** Rehabilitation

Staffed Beds: 148 **Admissions:** 2433 **Census:** 103 **Outpatient Visits:** 57657 **Births:** 0 **Total Expense ($000):** 59625 **Payroll Expense ($000):** 31505 **Personnel:** 513

PA

DEVEREUX CHILDREN'S BEHAVIORAL HEALTH CENTER, 655 Sugartown Road, Zip 19355–3303, Mailing Address: 655 Sugartown Road, Zip 19355–3303; tel. 800/345–1292 **F**29 98 99 106 **P**6 **S** Devereux, Villanova, PA
Primary Contact: David E. Woodward, Executive Director
CFO: Tim Evans, Assistant Financial Director
CMO: Jacquelyn Zavodnick, M.D., Medical Director
CIO: MaryLou Hettinger, Director Quality Management
CHR: Sean Maher, Director Human Resources
CNO: Deanna Reiss, Hospital Director of Nursing
Web address: www.devereux.org
Control: Other not–for–profit (including NFP Corporation) **Service:** Children's hospital psychiatric

Staffed Beds: 49 **Admissions:** 540 **Census:** 29 **Outpatient Visits:** 0 **Births:** 0 **Total Expense ($000):** 6646 **Payroll Expense ($000):** 3865 **Personnel:** 78

☐ **MALVERN INSTITUTE**, 940 King Road, Zip 19355–3166; tel. 610/647–0330, (Nonreporting) **A**1 9
Primary Contact: Richard Mangano, Administrator and Chief Executive Officer
CFO: Janet Corley, Accountant
Web address: www.malverninstitute.com
Control: Corporation, Investor–owned, for–profit **Service:** Alcoholism and other chemical dependency

Staffed Beds: 40

MC CONNELLSBURG—Fulton County

★ **FULTON COUNTY MEDICAL CENTER (391303)**, 214 Peach Orchard Road, Zip 17233–8559; tel. 717/485–3155, (Total facility includes 67 beds in nursing home–type unit) **A**9 10 18 **F**3 11 12 15 18 28 29 30 34 40 46 50 57 59 62 64 68 70 75 77 81 87 93 107 111 115 118 119 128 129 130 132 133 135 146 148
Primary Contact: Jason F. Hawkins, President and Chief Executive Officer
COO: William Buterbaugh, Director Support Services
CFO: Deborah A. Shughart, Vice President and Chief Financial Officer
CMO: Sharon E. Martin, M.D., President Medical Staff
CIO: Harold M. Gress, Jr., Manager Management Information Systems
CHR: Cheryl Rose, Human Resources Director
Web address: www.fcmcpa.org
Control: Other not–for–profit (including NFP Corporation) **Service:** General Medical and Surgical

Staffed Beds: 88 **Admissions:** 979 **Census:** 77 **Outpatient Visits:** 57861 **Births:** 0 **Total Expense ($000):** 34962 **Payroll Expense ($000):** 16795 **Personnel:** 295

MCKEES ROCKS—Allegheny County

⊞ **OHIO VALLEY GENERAL HOSPITAL (390157)**, 25 Heckel Road, Zip 15136–1694; tel. 412/777–6161 **A**1 6 9 10 **F**3 10 15 18 20 29 30 40 45 46 49 51 59 65 70 74 75 77 79 81 82 85 87 90 92 93 98 103 107 108 111 118 119 126 129 130 143 146 148 **P**6
Primary Contact: David W. Scott, President and Chief Executive Officer
CFO: Tad Tefera, Vice President Finance
CIO: Elaine Polinak, Director Information Management
CHR: Vicki Mell, Vice President Human Resources and Support Services
CNO: Roni Sue Bell, Director Nursing Services
Web address: www.ohiovalleyhospital.org
Control: Other not–for–profit (including NFP Corporation) **Service:** General Medical and Surgical

Staffed Beds: 138 **Admissions:** 3455 **Census:** 59 **Outpatient Visits:** 115059 **Births:** 0 **Total Expense ($000):** 68316 **Payroll Expense ($000):** 26013 **Personnel:** 450

MCKEESPORT—Allegheny County

⊞ **SELECT SPECIALTY HOSPITAL–MCKEESPORT (392045)**, 1500 Fifth Avenue, 6th Floor, Zip 15132–2422; tel. 412/664–2900 **A**1 9 10 **F**1 3 91 92 97 130 148 **S** Select Medical Corporation, Mechanicsburg, PA
Primary Contact: Jeffrey Gorddard, Chief Executive Officer
Web address: www.selectspecialtyhospitals.com/company/locations/mckeesport.aspx
Control: Corporation, Investor–owned, for–profit **Service:** Long–Term Acute Care hospital

Staffed Beds: 30 **Admissions:** 308 **Census:** 23 **Outpatient Visits:** 0 **Births:** 0 **Personnel:** 89

☐ **UPMC MCKEESPORT (390002)**, 1500 Fifth Avenue, Zip 15132–2422; tel. 412/664–2000, (Total facility includes 24 beds in nursing home–type unit) **A**1 3 5 9 10 12 13 **F**3 8 11 15 17 18 20 28 29 30 31 32 34 35 37 40 49 50 54 56 57 59 60 61 62 64 65 66 68 70 74 75 77 78 79 81 84 85 86 87 90 93 96 97 98 100 101 102 103 107 111 114 115 118 119 121 128 129 130 131 132 134 135 143 146 147 148 **S** UPMC, Pittsburgh, PA
Primary Contact: Mark Sevco, President
COO: Amy Bush, Vice President Operations
CFO: Christopher Stockhausen, Chief Financial Officer
CMO: R. Curtis Waligura, D.O., Vice President Medical Affairs, Chief Medical Officer
CIO: Terri Keeling, Vice President Information Systems
CHR: Kelli Reale, Vice President Human Resources
CNO: Leeanna McKibben, R.N., Vice President Patient Services and Chief Nursing Officer
Web address: www.mckeesport.upmc.com
Control: Other not–for–profit (including NFP Corporation) **Service:** General Medical and Surgical

Staffed Beds: 213 **Admissions:** 9535 **Census:** 153 **Outpatient Visits:** 132889 **Births:** 0 **Total Expense ($000):** 137136 **Payroll Expense ($000):** 47806 **Personnel:** 838

MEADOWBROOK—Montgomery County

◇ **HOLY REDEEMER HOSPITAL (390097)**, 1648 Huntingdon Pike, Zip 19046–8001; tel. 215/947–3000, (Total facility includes 21 beds in nursing home–type unit) **A**2 3 5 9 10 21 **F**3 10 13 15 17 18 20 22 29 30 31 34 35 36 39 40 41 44 45 46 49 50 53 54 55 56 57 58 59 61 62 63 64 69 70 72 74 75 76 77 78 79 81 82 84 85 86 87 92 93 97 98 100 103 104 107 108 109 110 114 115 117 118 119 120 121 123 128 129 130 131 132 134 135 141 143 146 147 148
Primary Contact: Michael B. Laign, President and Chief Executive Officer
CFO: Russell R. Wagner, Executive Vice President and Chief Financial Officer
CIO: Donald F. Friel, Executive Vice President
CHR: Joseph J. Cassidy, Vice President
CNO: Anne Catino, R.N., Vice President and Chief Nursing Officer
Web address: www.holyredeemer.com
Control: Other not–for–profit (including NFP Corporation) **Service:** General Medical and Surgical

Staffed Beds: 250 **Admissions:** 11829 **Census:** 156 **Outpatient Visits:** 306705 **Births:** 2675 **Total Expense ($000):** 180447 **Payroll Expense ($000):** 72920 **Personnel:** 1327

MEADVILLE—Crawford County

★ ◇ **MEADVILLE MEDICAL CENTER (390113)**, 751 Liberty Street, Zip 16335–2559; tel. 814/333–5000, (Total facility includes 32 beds in nursing home–type unit) **A**2 9 10 12 13 19 20 21 **F**3 4 5 11 13 15 18 20 22 28 29 30 31 35 36 38 40 45 46 49 53 57 59 63 64 70 75 76 77 78 79 81 82 85 86 87 89 90 91 93 98 99 103 107 110 111 114 115 118 119 120 128 129 130 131 132 146 147 148 **P**6 7
Primary Contact: Philip Pandolph, Chief Executive Officer
CMO: Denise Johnson, M.D., Medical Director
CIO: Mark Mahoney, Manager Information Systems
CHR: Greg Maras, Vice President Human Resources
Web address: www.mmchs.org
Control: Other not–for–profit (including NFP Corporation) **Service:** General Medical and Surgical

Staffed Beds: 210 **Admissions:** 7103 **Census:** 110 **Outpatient Visits:** 245852 **Births:** 567 **Total Expense ($000):** 152529 **Payroll Expense ($000):** 58036 **Personnel:** 1059

MECHANICSBURG—Cumberland County

HEALTHSOUTH REGIONAL SPECIALTY HOSPITAL See LifeCare Hospitals of Mechanicsburg

⊞ **HEALTHSOUTH REHABILITATION HOSPITAL OF MECHANICSBURG (393031)**, 175 Lancaster Boulevard, Zip 17055–3562; tel. 717/691–3700 **A**1 9 10 **F**28 29 34 54 57 59 64 68 75 77 79 82 90 91 92 93 94 95 96 130 132 146 148 **S** HEALTHSOUTH Corporation, Birmingham, AL
Primary Contact: Mark Freeburn, Chief Executive Officer
CMO: Michael Lupinacci, M.D., Medical Director
CHR: David Staskin, Director Human Resources
Web address: www.healthsouthpa.com
Control: Corporation, Investor–owned, for–profit **Service:** Rehabilitation

Staffed Beds: 75 **Admissions:** 1506 **Census:** 52 **Births:** 0 **Personnel:** 220

✠ **LIFECARE HOSPITALS OF MECHANICSBURG (392038)**, 4950 Wilson Lane, Zip 17055–4442; tel. 717/697–7706 **A**1 9 10 **F**1 3 29 60 77 91 **P**5 **S** LifeCare Management Services, Plano, TX
Primary Contact: Garrett Arneson, Chief Executive Officer
COO: Mary Ellen Kable, Chief Operating Officer
CFO: Nicholas Mezza, Director of Finance
CMO: Michael Gluck, M.D., Medical Director
CHR: Kimberly Link, Manager Human Resources
CNO: Mary Ellen Kable, Chief Nursing Officer
Web address: www.lifecare–hospitals.com/hospital.php?id=20
Control: Corporation, Investor–owned, for–profit **Service:** Long–Term Acute Care hospital

> **Staffed Beds: 68 Admissions: 336 Census: 25 Outpatient Visits: 0 Births: 0 Total Expense ($000): 14560 Payroll Expense ($000): 5806 Personnel: 109**

MEDIA—Delaware County

✠ **RIDDLE HOSPITAL (390222)**, 1068 West Baltimore Pike, Zip 19063–5177; tel. 484/227–9400, (Total facility includes 23 beds in nursing home–type unit) **A**1 2 9 10 **F**3 7 11 13 15 18 20 22 28 29 31 34 35 40 44 45 49 50 53 54 55 56 57 59 64 65 70 72 74 75 76 78 79 80 81 82 84 85 86 87 92 100 102 103 107 108 110 111 114 115 118 119 120 128 129 130 131 132 135 141 143 145 146 147 **P**5 **S** Jefferson Health System, Radnor, PA
Primary Contact: Gary L. Perecko, President
COO: Jeshahnton Essex, Vice President of Administration
CFO: Ed McKillip, Director of Finance
CMO: Joseph D. Hope, D.O., President Medical Staff
CHR: Mary Louise Ciciretti, Director Human Resources
CNO: Ann Marie T. Brooks, R.N., Vice President, Nursing
Web address: www.riddlehospital.org
Control: Other not–for–profit (including NFP Corporation) **Service:** General Medical and Surgical

> **Staffed Beds: 204 Admissions: 10521 Census: 126 Outpatient Visits: 132962 Births: 979 Total Expense ($000): 169477 Payroll Expense ($000): 61971 Personnel: 932**

RIDDLE MEMORIAL HOSPITAL See Riddle Hospital

MEYERSDALE—Somerset County

★ **CONEMAUGH MEYERSDALE MEDICAL CENTER (391302)**, 200 Hospital Drive, Zip 15552–1249; tel. 814/634–5911 **A**9 10 18 **F**15 29 34 40 57 81 85 93 107 110 119 126 129 133 146 148 **S** Duke LifePoint Healthcare, Brentwood, TN
Primary Contact: Mary L. Libengood, President
CFO: Heather Smith, Director Finance
CMO: Nathan Thomas, M.D., President Medical Staff
Web address: www.conemaugh.org
Control: Other not–for–profit (including NFP Corporation) **Service:** General Medical and Surgical

> **Staffed Beds: 20 Admissions: 346 Census: 5 Births: 0 Personnel: 113**

MONONGAHELA—Washington County

✠ **MONONGAHELA VALLEY HOSPITAL (390147)**, 1163 Country Club Road, Route 88, Zip 15063–1095; tel. 724/258–1000 **A**1 2 9 10 **F**3 8 9 11 12 15 17 18 20 22 28 29 30 31 32 34 35 39 40 45 48 49 50 51 54 56 57 59 61 64 68 70 74 75 77 78 79 80 81 82 85 86 87 89 90 92 93 96 98 100 101 102 103 107 108 110 115 118 119 120 121 123 124 129 130 131 132 134 135 146 147 148 **P**8
Primary Contact: Louis J. Panza, Jr., President and Chief Executive Officer
COO: Patrick J. Alberts, Senior Vice President and Chief Operating Officer
CFO: Daniel F. Simmons, Senior Vice President and Treasurer
CMO: Walter R. Cox, M.D., President Medical Staff
CIO: Thomas Lamb, Director Information Systems
CHR: Louis Goodman, Senior Vice President Human Resources
CNO: Mary Lou Murt, R.N., Senior Vice President Nursing
Web address: www.monvalleyhospital.com
Control: Other not–for–profit (including NFP Corporation) **Service:** General Medical and Surgical

> **Staffed Beds: 210 Admissions: 7766 Census: 114 Outpatient Visits: 289456 Births: 0 Total Expense ($000): 126567 Payroll Expense ($000): 53229 Personnel: 1067**

MONROEVILLE—Allegheny County

✠ **FORBES REGIONAL HOSPITAL (390267)**, 2570 Haymaker Road, Zip 15146–3513; tel. 412/858–2000 **A**1 2 3 5 9 10 **F**3 7 8 11 13 15 17 18 20 22 24 26 29 30 31 34 35 36 37 40 43 45 46 49 50 51 55 59 63 64 65 68 69 70 73 74 75 76 78 79 81 82 84 85 86 87 89 90 91 98 100 101 102 103 107 108 110 111 115 116 117 119 123 124 126 130 132 146 148 **P**6 **S** Allegheny Health Network, Pittsburgh, PA
Primary Contact: Reese Jackson, President and Chief Executive Officer
CFO: Tom Hipkiss, Vice President Finance
CMO: Mark Rubino, M.D., Chief Medical Officer
CIO: Sharon Lewis, Director Information Systems
CHR: Georgia Redding, Director Human Resources
CNO: Amber Egyud, Vice President Chief Nursing Officer
Web address: www.ahn.org
Control: Other not–for–profit (including NFP Corporation) **Service:** General Medical and Surgical

> **Staffed Beds: 349 Admissions: 12993 Census: 200 Outpatient Visits: 116940 Births: 799 Total Expense ($000): 190140 Payroll Expense ($000): 65204 Personnel: 1240**

HEALTHSOUTH HOSPITAL OF PITTSBURGH See LifeCare Hospitals of Pittsburgh – Monroeville

✠ **LIFECARE HOSPITALS OF PITTSBURGH – MONROEVILLE (392041)**, 2380 McGinley Road, Zip 15146–4400; tel. 412/856–2400 **A**1 9 10 **F**1 29 93 **P**5 **S** LifeCare Management Services, Plano, TX
Primary Contact: Kim Sperring, Administrator
CMO: Robert Crossey, D.O., Chief Medical Officer
CHR: Chelsea Webber, Director Human Resources
Web address: www.lifecare–hospitals.com/hospital.php?id=8
Control: Corporation, Investor–owned, for–profit **Service:** Long–Term Acute Care hospital

> **Staffed Beds: 87 Admissions: 486 Census: 37 Outpatient Visits: 3890 Births: 0 Total Expense ($000): 16857 Payroll Expense ($000): 6681 Personnel: 127**

UPMC EAST (390328), 2775 Mosside Boulevard, Zip 15146–2760; tel. 412/357–3000 **A**10 **F**3 18 20 22 26 28 29 30 31 34 35 40 45 46 49 50 57 59 60 62 63 64 68 70 74 77 78 79 81 84 85 87 92 100 107 108 111 115 119 120 121 122 123 130 132 135 146 148 **S** UPMC, Pittsburgh, PA
Primary Contact: Mark Sevco, President
CNO: Tamra Minton, R.N., Vice President Patient Care Services and Chief Nursing Officer
Web address: www.upmc.com/locations/hospitals/east/Pages/default.aspx
Control: Other not–for–profit (including NFP Corporation) **Service:** General Medical and Surgical

> **Staffed Beds: 115 Admissions: 5665 Census: 78 Outpatient Visits: 57935 Births: 0 Total Expense ($000): 96639 Payroll Expense ($000): 33371 Personnel: 647**

WESTERN PENNSYLVANIA HOSPITAL – FORBES REGIONAL CAMPUS See Forbes Regional Hospital

MONTROSE—Susquehanna County

ENDLESS MOUNTAIN HEALTH SYSTEMS (391306), 25 Grow Avenue, Zip 18801–1106; tel. 570/278–3801 **A**9 10 18 **F**3 15 34 40 44 45 50 53 57 59 64 65 77 79 81 85 93 107 110 111 114 119 130 132 133 135 146 **P**4
Primary Contact: Rexford Catlin, Chief Executive Officer
CIO: Gary Passmore, Chief Information Officer
CHR: Paula Anderson, Administrative Director Human Resources
Web address: www.endlesscare.org
Control: Other not–for–profit (including NFP Corporation) **Service:** General Medical and Surgical

> **Staffed Beds: 25 Admissions: 968 Census: 12 Births: 0 Personnel: 160**

MOUNT GRETNA—Lebanon County

✠ **PHILHAVEN (394020)**, 283 South Butler Road, Zip 17064–6085, Mailing Address: P.O. Box 550, Zip 17064–0550; tel. 717/273–8871 **A**1 9 10 **F**30 98 99 100 101 102 103 104 105 106 130 146 **P**6
Primary Contact: Phil Hess, Chief Executive Officer
COO: Phil Hess, Chief Executive Officer
CFO: Matt Rogers, Chief Financial Officer
CMO: Francis D. Sparrow, M.D., Medical Director
CIO: Lori Nolt, Director Information Technology
CHR: Denis Orthaus, Director Human Resources
CNO: Heidi McMullan, R.N., Chief Nursing Officer
Web address: www.philhaven.org
Control: Church–operated, Nongovernment, not–for profit **Service:** Psychiatric

> **Staffed Beds: 103 Admissions: 2385 Census: 87 Outpatient Visits: 124973 Births: 0 Total Expense ($000): 59670 Payroll Expense ($000): 39343 Personnel: 909**

Hospital, Medicare Provider Number, Address, Telephone, Approval, Facility, and Physician Codes, Health Care System

★ American Hospital Association (AHA) membership
□ The Joint Commission accreditation ◇ DNV Healthcare Inc. accreditation
○ Healthcare Facilities Accreditation Program
△ Commission on Accreditation of Rehabilitation Facilities (CARF) accreditation

PA

PA

MOUNT PLEASANT—Westmoreland County

☐ **EXCELA FRICK HOSPITAL (390217)**, 508 South Church Street, Zip 15666–1790; tel. 724/547–1500 **A**1 9 10 **F**3 8 12 15 29 30 34 35 40 45 49 57 59 64 65 68 70 74 75 77 78 79 81 85 86 87 92 93 96 102 107 108 110 111 114 118 119 129 130 132 135 143 146 148 **S** Excela Health, Greensburg, PA
Primary Contact: Ronald H. Ott, President
COO: Michael D. Busch, Executive Vice President and Chief Operating Officer
CFO: Jeffrey T. Curry, Executive Vice President and Chief Financial Officer
CMO: Jerome Granato, M.D., Senior Vice President and Chief Medical Officer
CIO: David Gawaluck, Vice President and Chief Information Officer
CHR: John Caverno, Chief Human Resources Officer
CNO: Helen K. Burns, Ph.D., Senior Vice President and Chief Nursing Officer
Web address: www.excelahealth.org/PatientsandVisitors/HospitalsFacilities/Hospitals/Frick.aspx
Control: Other not–for–profit (including NFP Corporation) **Service:** General Medical and Surgical

Staffed Beds: 63 **Admissions:** 3104 **Census:** 31 **Outpatient Visits:** 101812 **Births:** 0 **Total Expense ($000):** 46404 **Payroll Expense ($000):** 17068 **Personnel:** 343

MUNCY—Lycoming County

★ **MUNCY VALLEY HOSPITAL (391301)**, 215 East Water Street, Zip 17756–8700; tel. 570/546–8282, (Total facility includes 136 beds in nursing home–type unit) **A**9 10 18 **F**6 11 34 40 44 50 56 57 59 64 68 81 86 87 93 107 108 119 128 130 133 144 146 **P**7 **S** Susquehanna Health System, Williamsport, PA
Primary Contact: Ronald J. Reynolds, President
CFO: Charles J. Santangelo, CPA, Executive Vice President and Chief Financial Officer
CMO: George A. Manchester, M.D., Executive Vice President and Chief Medical Officer
CIO: Karen M. Armstrong, FACHE, Senior Vice President and Chief Information Officer
CHR: Christine A. Ballard, Vice President Human Resources
CNO: C. Cynthia Whipple, Administrative Director and Director of Nursing
Web address: www.susquehannahealth.org
Control: Other not–for–profit (including NFP Corporation) **Service:** General Medical and Surgical

Staffed Beds: 156 **Admissions:** 857 **Census:** 143 **Outpatient Visits:** 29364 **Births:** 0 **Total Expense ($000):** 37643 **Payroll Expense ($000):** 12871 **Personnel:** 253

NANTICOKE—Luzerne County

★ **SPECIAL CARE HOSPITAL (392025)**, 128 West Washington Street, Zip 18634–3113; tel. 570/735–5000, (Nonreporting) **A**9 10 **S** Community Health Systems, Inc., Franklin, TN
Primary Contact: Robert D. Williams, Chief Executive Officer
CFO: Robert Stiekes, Chief Financial Officer
Web address: www.specialcarehospital.net
Control: Corporation, Investor–owned, for–profit **Service:** Long–Term Acute Care hospital

Staffed Beds: 64

NATRONA HEIGHTS—Allegheny County

⌧ **ALLEGHENY VALLEY HOSPITAL (390032)**, 1301 Carlisle Street, Zip 15065–1152; tel. 724/224–5100 **A**1 2 6 9 10 **F**3 11 15 17 18 24 29 30 31 34 35 38 39 40 44 45 47 49 50 51 54 56 57 58 59 64 65 68 70 74 75 77 78 79 80 81 84 85 86 87 92 93 96 98 100 101 102 103 107 108 111 114 117 118 119 120 121 123 129 130 132 133 135 143 144 146 147 148 **S** Allegheny Health Network, Pittsburgh, PA
Primary Contact: David Goldberg, President & Interim Chief Executive Officer
CFO: James A. Kanuch, Vice President Finance
CMO: Thomas McClure, M.D., Vice President Medical Affairs and Chief Medical Officer
CIO: Linda Fergus, Manager Information Technology
CHR: Cindy Moser, Director Human Resources
Web address: www.wpahs.org
Control: Other not–for–profit (including NFP Corporation) **Service:** General Medical and Surgical

Staffed Beds: 228 **Admissions:** 7390 **Census:** 109 **Outpatient Visits:** 216933 **Births:** 3 **Total Expense ($000):** 117478 **Payroll Expense ($000):** 42346 **Personnel:** 824

NEW CASTLE—Lawrence County

☐ **JAMESON HOSPITAL (390016)**, 1211 Wilmington Avenue, Zip 16105–2516; tel. 724/658–9001, (Total facility includes 20 beds in nursing home–type unit) **A**1 6 9 10 19 **F**3 8 11 13 15 18 20 22 28 29 30 32 34 35 40 44 45 47 49 50 51 57 59 63 64 65 68 70 75 76 77 79 81 82 85 86 87 90 93 96 98 100 102 103 105 107 108 110 111 114 115 118 119 128 129 130 132 146 147
Primary Contact: Douglas Danko, President and Chief Executive Officer
CFO: James Aubel, Chief Financial Officer
CMO: Robert McGann, M.D., President Medical Staff
CIO: Frank Divito, Manager Information Systems
CHR: Neil A. Chessin, Vice President
CNO: Barbara Bernardi, R.N., Nurse Executive
Web address: www.jamesonhealth.org
Control: Other not–for–profit (including NFP Corporation) **Service:** General Medical and Surgical

Staffed Beds: 238 **Admissions:** 9238 **Census:** 122 **Outpatient Visits:** 308636 **Births:** 495 **Total Expense ($000):** 112526 **Payroll Expense ($000):** 47436 **Personnel:** 1048

NORRISTOWN—Montgomery County

⌧ ○ **MERCY SUBURBAN HOSPITAL (390116)**, 2701 DeKalb Pike, Zip 19401–1820; tel. 610/278–2000 **A**1 2 9 10 11 12 13 **F**3 12 15 18 28 29 30 31 34 40 45 46 50 54 56 57 59 64 70 74 75 77 78 79 81 82 85 87 93 98 103 107 108 110 111 114 115 118 120 121 126 129 130 132 135 146 147 **S** Catholic Health East / Trinity Health, Livonia, MI
Primary Contact: Kathryn Conallen, Interim Chief Executive Officer
COO: Christina Fitz–Patrick, R.N., Executive Director
CFO: David Wajda, Chief Financial Officer
CMO: Michael Magro, M.D., Chief Medical Officer
CIO: Michael Yulich, Director Information Services
CHR: Gretchen Pendleton, Chief Human Resources Officer
CNO: Mary Ellen Rauner, R.N., Chief Nursing Officer
Web address: www.mercyhealth.org
Control: Church–operated, Nongovernment, not–for profit **Service:** General Medical and Surgical

Staffed Beds: 126 **Admissions:** 4946 **Census:** 66 **Outpatient Visits:** 69719 **Births:** 0 **Total Expense ($000):** 110217 **Payroll Expense ($000):** 39271 **Personnel:** 738

☐ **MONTGOMERY COUNTY EMERGENCY SERVICE (394033)**, 50 Beech Drive, Zip 19403–5421; tel. 610/279–6100 **A**1 9 10 **F**4 5 7 29 35 38 50 64 98 99 100 101 102 103 104 130 **P**6
Primary Contact: Rocio Nell, M.D., Chief Executive Officer
COO: William Myers, Chief Operating Officer
CFO: William Myers, Chief Operating Officer
CHR: Karen Mossop, Director Human Resources
CNO: Virginia Graves, R.N., Nurse Executive
Web address: www.mces.org
Control: Other not–for–profit (including NFP Corporation) **Service:** Psychiatric

Staffed Beds: 81 **Admissions:** 2391 **Census:** 63 **Outpatient Visits:** 3020 **Births:** 0 **Total Expense ($000):** 17692 **Payroll Expense ($000):** 10927 **Personnel:** 210

NORRISTOWN STATE HOSPITAL (394001), 1001 Sterigere Street, Zip 19401–5300; tel. 610/270–1000 **A**3 5 10 **F**30 35 39 53 59 98 101 103 146 **P**6
Primary Contact: Edna I. McCutcheon, Chief Executive Officer
COO: Gary Raisner, Chief Operating Officer
CMO: Mia Marcovici, M.D., Chief Medical Officer
CHR: Richard Szczurowski, Director Human Resources
CNO: Taryn Mason–Jones, Chief Nurse Executive
Control: State–Government, nonfederal **Service:** Psychiatric

Staffed Beds: 232 **Admissions:** 23 **Census:** 281 **Outpatient Visits:** 62 **Births:** 0 **Total Expense ($000):** 69652 **Payroll Expense ($000):** 38378 **Personnel:** 580

☐ **VALLEY FORGE MEDICAL CENTER AND HOSPITAL (390272)**, 1033 West Germantown Pike, Zip 19403–3905; tel. 610/539–8500 **A**1 10 **F**3 4 29 61 68 75 82 100 130 132 148 **P**6
Primary Contact: Marian W. Colcher, President and Chief Executive Officer
CFO: Gregg Y. Slocum, Chief Financial Officer
CMO: Robert E. Colcher, M.D., Medical Director
CHR: Frederick D. Jackes, Assistant Administrator and Director Human Resources
Web address: www.vfmc.net
Control: Corporation, Investor–owned, for–profit **Service:** Alcoholism and other chemical dependency

Staffed Beds: 50 **Admissions:** 1346 **Census:** 44 **Outpatient Visits:** 0 **Births:** 0 **Personnel:** 172

Many Facility Codes have changed. Please refer to the AHA Guide Code Chart.   © 2014 AHA Guide

PA

OAKDALE—Allegheny County

✠ **KINDRED HOSPITAL–PITTSBURGH (392028)**, 7777 Steubenville Pike,
Zip 15071–3409; tel. 412/494–5500, (Nonreporting) **A**1 9 10 **S** Kindred
Healthcare, Louisville, KY
Primary Contact: Janie Rosenberger–Slampack, Market Chief Executive Officer
CFO: Kevin Varley, Chief Financial Officer
CMO: Ravi Alagar, M.D., Medical Director
CIO: Kurt Segeleon, Director Health Information Management
CHR: Nancy Smocynski, Director Payroll, Personnel and Human Resources
Web address: www.kindredhospitalpittsburgh.com/
Control: Corporation, Investor–owned, for–profit **Service:** Long–Term Acute Care
hospital

Staffed Beds: 63

OREFIELD—Lehigh County

KIDSPEACE CHILDREN'S HOSPITAL (394047), 5300 Kids Peace Drive,
Zip 18069–2044; tel. 610/799–8800 **A**9 10 **F**29 39 57 59 98 99 100 101 105
106 **P**7
Primary Contact: William R. Isemann, President and Chief Executive Officer
CMO: Andrew Clark, M.D., Medical Director
CIO: Eileen Tkacik, Vice President Information Technology and Patient Accounts
CHR: Elizabeth Perrong, Vice President Human Resources
CNO: Mary Ann Moore, Director of Nursing
Web address: www.kidspeace.org
Control: Other not–for–profit (including NFP Corporation) **Service:** Children's
hospital psychiatric

Staffed Beds: 96 **Admissions:** 2009 **Census:** 72 **Outpatient Visits:** 0 **Births:**
0 **Total Expense ($000):** 11944 **Payroll Expense ($000):** 7228 **Personnel:**
191

PALMERTON—Carbon County

✠ **PALMERTON HOSPITAL (390019)**, 135 Lafayette Avenue, Zip 18071–1596;
tel. 610/826–3141 **A**1 9 10 **F**2 3 11 12 15 28 29 34 35 40 44 46 47 49 50
56 57 59 64 65 68 70 74 75 77 79 81 85 86 87 92 93 97 98 102 103 107
108 110 119 129 130 132 135 146 **S** Blue Mountain Health System,
Lehighton, PA
Primary Contact: Andrew E. Harris, Chief Executive Officer
CFO: Andrea Andrae, Chief Financial Officer
CMO: Dennis Kondash, D.O., Vice President Medical Affairs
CIO: Steve Kinkaid, Director Information Systems
CHR: Terrance J. Purcell, Vice President Ambulatory Care and Support Services
Web address: www.ghmh.org/content/palmertoncampus.htm
Control: Other not–for–profit (including NFP Corporation) **Service:** General
Medical and Surgical

Staffed Beds: 60 **Admissions:** 1898 **Census:** 34 **Outpatient Visits:** 42257
Births: 0 **Total Expense ($000):** 29495 **Payroll Expense ($000):** 13188
Personnel: 278

PAOLI—Chester County

✠ **PAOLI HOSPITAL (390153)**, 255 West Lancaster Avenue, Zip 19301–1763;
tel. 484/565–1000 **A**1 2 9 10 **F**3 8 11 13 15 18 20 22 24 26 28 29 30 31 32
34 35 38 39 40 43 44 45 46 47 48 49 50 54 55 56 57 59 64 65 70 72 74
75 76 77 78 79 80 81 82 84 85 86 87 99 100 101 102 103 104 105 107
108 110 111 114 118 119 120 121 122 123 126 129 130 131 132 134
135 141 143 144 146 147 148 **P**5 **S** Jefferson Health System, Radnor, PA
Primary Contact: James Paradis, President
CFO: John Doyle, Vice President Finance
CMO: Andrew J. Norton, M.D., Chief Medical Officer
CIO: Karen A. Thomas, Vice President and Chief Information Officer
CHR: Deborah Fedora, Director Human Resources
CNO: Jan Nash, Ph.D., Vice President Patient Services and Chief Nursing Officer
Web address: www.mainlinehealth.org
Control: Other not–for–profit (including NFP Corporation) **Service:** General
Medical and Surgical

Staffed Beds: 231 **Admissions:** 13716 **Census:** 151 **Outpatient Visits:**
296675 **Births:** 2318 **Total Expense ($000):** 226770 **Payroll Expense
($000):** 77545 **Personnel:** 1157

PHILADELPHIA—Philadelphia County

ALBERT EINSTEIN MEDICAL CENTER See Einstein Medical Center Philadelphia

✠ △ **ARIA HEALTH (390115)**, 10800 Knights Road, Zip 19114–4200;
tel. 215/612–4000, (Includes BUCKS COUNTY CAMPUS, 380 North Oxford Valley
Road, Langhorne, Zip 19047–8399; tel. 215/949–5000; FRANKFORD CAMPUS,
Frankford Avenue and Wakeling Street, Zip 19124; tel. 215/831–2000) **A**1 3 5 6
7 9 10 12 13 **F**3 5 11 12 14 15 17 18 20 22 24 26 28 29 30 31 32 34 35
36 39 40 43 44 45 46 48 49 53 54 57 59 61 62 64 65 66 68 69 70 74 75
77 78 79 80 81 82 85 86 87 92 93 94 96 97 98 100 101 102 103 104 107
108 110 114 115 116 117 118 119 120 121 123 124 126 127 129 130 131
132 135 143 144 145 146 147 148 **P**6
Primary Contact: Kathleen Kinslow, Ed.D., President and Chief Executive Officer
COO: Sandra Gomberg, Chief Operating Officer
CFO: Andrew Devoe, Vice President Finance
CMO: Stanton Segal, M.D., Chief Medical Officer
CIO: Dan Walsh, Interim Chief Information Officer
CHR: Dorinda Carolina, Chief Human Resources Officer
CNO: Michelle E. Conley, R.N., Chief Nursing Officer
Web address: www.ariahealth.org
Control: Other not–for–profit (including NFP Corporation) **Service:** General
Medical and Surgical

Staffed Beds: 476 **Admissions:** 22656 **Census:** 295 **Outpatient Visits:**
292633 **Births:** 0 **Total Expense ($000):** 408036 **Payroll Expense ($000):**
165885 **Personnel:** 2702

☐ **BELMONT CENTER FOR COMPREHENSIVE TREATMENT (394023)**, 4200
Monument Road, Zip 19131–1625; tel. 215/877–2000 **A**1 3 5 9 10 **F**5 29 34
35 58 86 87 98 99 103 104 105 130 146 **P**6 **S** Einstein Healthcare Network,
Philadelphia, PA
Primary Contact: Sharon A. Bergen, Chief Operating Officer
COO: Sharon A. Bergen, Chief Operating Officer
CFO: Guy Romaniello, Director Fiscal Services
CMO: Richard Jaffe, M.D., Medical Director
CHR: Jenna Pacini, Human Resources Specialist
CNO: Nona Fain, Ph.D., Director of Nursing
Web address: www.einstein.edu/locations/belmont–behavioral–health/
Control: Other not–for–profit (including NFP Corporation) **Service:** Psychiatric

Staffed Beds: 147 **Admissions:** 3537 **Census:** 131 **Outpatient Visits:** 69183
Births: 0 **Total Expense ($000):** 40958 **Payroll Expense ($000):** 24955
Personnel: 373

✠ **CHESTNUT HILL HOSPITAL (390026)**, 8835 Germantown Avenue,
Zip 19118–2718; tel. 215/248–8200, (Nonreporting) **A**1 2 3 5 9 10
S Community Health Systems, Inc., Franklin, TN
Primary Contact: John D. Cacciamani, M.D., Chief Executive Officer
CFO: Brian Balutanski, CPA, Chief Financial Officer
CMO: John Scanlon, DPM, Chief Medical Officer
CIO: Beth Crossley, Director Information Systems
CHR: Marilyn DiCicco, Director Human Resources
CNO: Teresa M. Kelly, MSN, Chief Nursing Officer
Web address: www.chhealthsystem.com
Control: Corporation, Investor–owned, for–profit **Service:** General Medical and
Surgical

Staffed Beds: 212

☐ **CHILDREN'S HOSPITAL OF PHILADELPHIA (393303)**, 3401 Civic Center
Boulevard, Zip 19104–4319; tel. 215/590–1000 **A**1 3 5 8 9 10 **F**3 7 8 11 13
17 18 19 20 21 22 23 24 25 26 27 28 29 30 31 32 34 35 37 38 39 40 41
43 44 45 46 48 50 53 54 55 57 58 59 60 61 62 64 65 66 68 71 72 74 75
76 77 78 79 81 82 83 84 85 86 87 88 89 90 91 92 93 95 96 97 99 100
101 102 104 107 108 111 112 113 114 115 116 117 118 119 126 129 130
131 132 134 136 137 138 139 140 141 142 144 146 148 **P**6
Primary Contact: Steven M. Altschuler, M.D., President and Chief Executive Officer
COO: Madeline Bell, President and Chief Operating Officer
CFO: Thomas Todorow, Chief Financial Officer and Executive Vice President
CMO: Jan Boswinkel, M.D., Vice President Medical Operations and Chief Safety
Officer
CIO: Bryan Wolf, M.D., Senior Vice President and Chief Information Officer
CHR: Robert Croner, Executive Vice President and Chief Human Resources Officer
CNO: Paula M. Agosto, R.N., Senior Vice President and Chief Nursing Officer
Web address: www.chop.edu
Control: Other not–for–profit (including NFP Corporation) **Service:** Children's
general

Staffed Beds: 493 **Admissions:** 28996 **Census:** 423 **Outpatient Visits:**
1193124 **Births:** 379 **Total Expense ($000):** 1577737 **Payroll Expense
($000):** 715716 **Personnel:** 9693

PA

☐ **EASTERN REGIONAL MEDICAL CENTER (390312)**, 1331 East Wyoming Avenue, Zip 19124–3808; tel. 800/615–3055, (Nonreporting) **A**1 2 10 **S** Cancer Treatment Centers of America, Schaumburg, IL
Primary Contact: John McNeil, President and Chief Executive Officer
CFO: Steve Rusinko, Chief Financial Officer
CMO: Steven B. Standiford, M.D., Chief of Staff
CIO: Kristin Darby, Chief Information Officer
CHR: Ronald Gilg, Assistant Vice President Talent
CNO: Nancy Hesse, R.N., Senior Vice President Patient Care Services
Web address: www.cancercenter.com
Control: Corporation, Investor–owned, for–profit **Service:** Cancer

Staffed Beds: 22

☐ **EINSTEIN MEDICAL CENTER PHILADELPHIA (390142)**, 5501 Old York Road, Zip 19141–3098; tel. 215/456–7890, (Includes EINSTEIN MEDICAL CENTER ELKINS PARK, 60 Township Line Road, Elkins Park, Zip 19027–2220; tel. 215/663–6000; Ruth Lefton, Chief Operating Officer), (Total facility includes 60 beds in nursing home–type unit) **A**1 2 3 5 9 10 12 13 **F**3 8 11 12 13 15 17 18 20 22 24 26 29 30 31 32 34 35 39 40 41 43 45 46 47 48 49 50 55 56 57 59 60 61 64 65 66 68 70 72 73 74 75 76 78 79 81 82 83 84 85 86 87 90 92 93 95 96 97 98 100 103 107 108 110 111 114 115 118 119 120 121 123 124 126 128 129 130 131 132 134 138 139 142 145 146 147 148 **P**6 **S** Einstein Healthcare Network, Philadelphia, PA
Primary Contact: Barry R. Freedman, President and Chief Executive Officer
COO: A. Susan Bernini, Chief Operating Officer
CFO: David Ertel, Chief Financial Officer
CMO: Steven Sivak, M.D., Chair, Department of Medicine
CIO: Kenneth Levitan, Vice President and Chief Information Officer
CHR: Lynne R. Kornblatt, Chief Human Resources Officer
CNO: Richard Cuming, R.N., Vice President and Chief Nurse Executive
Web address: www.einstein.edu
Control: Other not–for–profit (including NFP Corporation) **Service:** General Medical and Surgical

Staffed Beds: 505 **Admissions:** 27218 **Census:** 506 **Outpatient Visits:** 518225 **Births:** 2878 **Total Expense ($000):** 695289 **Payroll Expense ($000):** 308616 **Personnel:** 4905

☐ **FAIRMOUNT BEHAVIORAL HEALTH SYSTEM (394027)**, 561 Fairthorne Avenue, Zip 19128–2499; tel. 215/487–4000 **A**1 9 10 **F**4 98 99 102 105 130 **P**6 **S** Universal Health Services, Inc., King of Prussia, PA
Primary Contact: Charles McLister, Chief Executive Officer
COO: Jennifer Riedel, Chief Operating Officer
CFO: Anthony Tortella, Chief Financial Officer
CMO: Silvia Gratz, D.O., Chief Medical Officer
CIO: Anthony Tortella, Chief Financial Officer
CHR: Theresa Mahoney, Director Human Resources
Web address: www.fairmountbhs.com
Control: Corporation, Investor–owned, for–profit **Service:** Psychiatric

Staffed Beds: 239 **Admissions:** 6237 **Census:** 220 **Outpatient Visits:** 9477 **Births:** 0 **Total Expense ($000):** 41080 **Payroll Expense ($000):** 25051

☒ **FOX CHASE CANCER CENTER–AMERICAN ONCOLOGIC HOSPITAL (390196)**, 333 Cottman Avenue, Zip 19111–2434; tel. 215/728–6900 **A**1 2 3 5 8 9 10 **F**3 8 11 15 29 30 31 34 35 36 45 46 47 49 50 55 57 58 59 60 61 62 64 68 70 71 75 77 78 79 81 82 84 85 86 87 93 100 104 107 108 109 110 111 114 115 116 117 118 119 120 121 123 124 126 130 132 135 144 145 146 147 148 **P**6 **S** Temple University Health System, Philadelphia, PA
Primary Contact: Richard Fisher, President and Chief Executive Officer
COO: Judith Lynn Bachman, Chief Operating Officer
CFO: Joseph Hediger, Chief Financial Officer
CMO: J. Robert Beck, M.D., Chief Medical Officer
CIO: Michael Sweeney, Chief Information Officer
Web address: www.fccc.edu
Control: Other not–for–profit (including NFP Corporation) **Service:** General Medical and Surgical

Staffed Beds: 66 **Admissions:** 4893 **Census:** 61 **Outpatient Visits:** 92001 **Births:** 0 **Total Expense ($000):** 215855 **Payroll Expense ($000):** 73432 **Personnel:** 1337

☒ **FRIENDS HOSPITAL (394008)**, 4641 Roosevelt Boulevard, Zip 19124–2343; tel. 215/831–4600 **A**1 3 5 9 10 **F**30 68 87 98 99 101 102 103 130 132 **P**1 **S** Universal Health Services, Inc., King of Prussia, PA
Primary Contact: Geoff Botak, Chief Executive Officer
COO: Diane Carugati, Chief Operating Officer
CFO: Michael Terwilliger, Chief Financial Officer
CMO: Marc Rothman, M.D., Medical Director
CIO: John Healy, Manager Information Technology
CHR: Paul Cavanaugh, Director Human Resources
Web address: www.friendshospital.com
Control: Corporation, Investor–owned, for–profit **Service:** Psychiatric

Staffed Beds: 192 **Admissions:** 5051 **Census:** 181 **Births:** 0 **Personnel:** 412

GIRARD MEDICAL CENTER (392026), Girard Avenue at Eighth Street, Zip 19122; tel. 215/787–2000, (Nonreporting) **A**9
Primary Contact: George J. Walmsley, III, CPA, President and Chief Executive Officer
Web address: www.nphs.com
Control: Other not–for–profit (including NFP Corporation) **Service:** Long–Term Acute Care hospital

Staffed Beds: 163

☒ **GOOD SHEPHERD PENN PARTNERS SPECIALTY HOSPITAL AT RITTENHOUSE (392050)**, 1800 Lombard Street, Zip 19146–1414; tel. 877/969–7342 **A**1 9 10 **F**1 3 28 29 30 34 35 44 50 57 58 60 64 68 75 77 84 85 86 87 90 91 93 94 95 96 100 130 131 132 148 **P**6
Primary Contact: Lisa Marsilio, Executive Director
CFO: Ron Petula, Vice President Finance
CMO: Michael Grippi, M.D., Chief Medical Officer
CHR: Jana Romano, Manager Human Resources
CNO: Lawanda Goehring, MSN, Chief Nursing Officer
Web address: www.phillyrehab.com
Control: Other not–for–profit (including NFP Corporation) **Service:** Long–Term Acute Care hospital

Staffed Beds: 38 **Admissions:** 388 **Census:** 30 **Outpatient Visits:** 108981 **Births:** 0 **Total Expense ($000):** 38759 **Payroll Expense ($000):** 17083 **Personnel:** 131

☒ **HAHNEMANN UNIVERSITY HOSPITAL (390290)**, Broad and Vine Streets, Zip 19102–1192; tel. 215/762–7000 **A**1 2 3 5 8 9 10 **F**3 8 12 13 14 15 17 18 20 22 24 26 28 29 31 34 35 40 43 45 46 48 49 50 51 56 57 58 59 64 65 70 72 74 75 76 77 78 79 80 81 82 85 87 91 92 97 98 100 102 103 105 107 108 110 111 114 115 118 119 120 121 123 124 126 129 130 131 132 136 137 138 139 142 143 144 147 148 **P**6 **S** TENET Healthcare Corporation, Dallas, TX
Primary Contact: Michael P. Halter, Chief Executive Officer
COO: James B. Burke, Chief Operating Officer
CFO: Richard Imbimbo, Chief Financial Officer
CMO: George Amrom, M.D., Vice President Medical Affairs
CIO: Tom Nataloni, Senior Director Information Technology
CHR: Steven Simmons, Chief Human Resources Officer
CNO: Rosemary Dunn, R.N., Chief Nursing Officer
Web address: www.hahnemannhospital.com
Control: Corporation, Investor–owned, for–profit **Service:** General Medical and Surgical

Staffed Beds: 496 **Admissions:** 17818 **Census:** 273 **Outpatient Visits:** 114293 **Births:** 2176 **Personnel:** 2473

☒ △ **HOSPITAL OF THE UNIVERSITY OF PENNSYLVANIA (390111)**, 3400 Spruce Street, Zip 19104–4206; tel. 215/662–4000 **A**1 2 3 5 7 8 9 10 **F**3 6 7 9 11 12 13 14 15 17 18 20 21 21 22 23 26 27 29 30 31 34 35 37 38 39 40 43 44 45 46 47 48 49 50 51 52 54 55 56 57 58 59 60 61 62 63 64 65 66 68 70 71 72 73 74 75 76 77 78 79 80 81 82 84 85 86 87 90 91 92 94 95 96 97 100 101 102 104 107 108 109 110 111 114 115 116 117 118 119 120 121 122 123 124 126 129 130 131 132 134 135 136 137 138 139 140 141 142 145 146 147 148 **P**6 **S** University of Pennsylvania Health System, Philadelphia, PA
Primary Contact: Garry L. Scheib, Executive Director
COO: Albert P. Black, Jr., Chief Operating Officer
CFO: Keith Kasper, Chief Financial Officer
CMO: Patrick J. Brennan, M.D., Senior Vice President and Chief Medical Officer
CIO: Michael Restuccia, Chief Information Officer
CHR: Denise Mariotti, Chief Human Resource Officer
CNO: Regina Cunningham, Ph.D., Chief Nurse Executive
Web address: www.pennhealth.com
Control: Other not–for–profit (including NFP Corporation) **Service:** General Medical and Surgical

Staffed Beds: 789 **Admissions:** 37665 **Census:** 698 **Outpatient Visits:** 1270240 **Births:** 4143 **Total Expense ($000):** 2104429 **Payroll Expense ($000):** 803244 **Personnel:** 12400

☒ **JEANES HOSPITAL (390080)**, 7600 Central Avenue, Zip 19111–2499; tel. 215/728–2000 **A**1 5 9 10 **F**3 11 12 15 18 20 22 24 26 28 29 30 31 34 35 40 44 45 56 57 59 60 62 65 68 70 74 75 77 78 79 81 82 85 90 91 92 93 107 108 110 111 114 115 116 117 119 124 129 130 132 145 146 147 148 **P**6 **S** Temple University Health System, Philadelphia, PA
Primary Contact: Linda J. Grass, President and Chief Executive Officer
COO: Judith Lynn Bachman, Chief Operating Officer
CMO: Andrea C. McCoy, M.D., Chief Medical Officer
CIO: Arthur C. Papacostas, M.D., Vice President and Chief Information Officer
CHR: Elisabeth Donahue, Associate Director Human Resources
CNO: Denise Anne Lavery Frasca, MSN, Vice President Patient Care Services and Chief Nursing Officer
Web address: www.jeanes.com
Control: Other not–for–profit (including NFP Corporation) **Service:** General Medical and Surgical

Staffed Beds: 160 **Admissions:** 7691 **Census:** 95 **Outpatient Visits:** 111806 **Births:** 0 **Total Expense ($000):** 158723 **Payroll Expense ($000):** 60901

Many Facility Codes have changed. Please refer to the AHA Guide Code Chart. © 2014 AHA Guide

☐ **KENSINGTON HOSPITAL (390025)**, 136 West Diamond Street,
Zip 19122–1721; tel. 215/426–8100, (Nonreporting) **A**1 9 10
Primary Contact: Eileen Hause, Chief Executive Officer
CFO: Kenneth Biddle, Controller
CMO: Luis F. Vera, M.D., Medical Director
CHR: Maria Dimichele, Administrative Assistant
CNO: Aleyamma John, R.N., Director of Nursing
Control: State–Government, nonfederal **Service:** General Medical and Surgical

Staffed Beds: 33

☒ **KINDRED HOSPITAL SOUTH PHILADELPHIA (392046)**, 1930 South Broad
Street, Zip 19145–2328; tel. 267/570–5200, (Nonreporting) **A**1 9 10 **S** Kindred
Healthcare, Louisville, KY
Primary Contact: Deborah Karn, Chief Executive Officer
COO: Diane K. White, MSN, Chief Clinical Officer
CFO: Kevin Varley, Chief Financial Officer
CMO: James Dovnarsky, M.D., Director Pulmonary Medical
CHR: Amy Cain, District Director Human Resources
CNO: Diane K. White, MSN, Chief Clinical Officer
Web address: www.khsouthphilly.com
Control: Corporation, Investor–owned, for–profit **Service:** Long–Term Acute Care
hospital

Staffed Beds: 58

☒ **KINDRED HOSPITAL–PHILADELPHIA (392027)**, 6129 Palmetto Street,
Zip 19111–5729; tel. 215/722–8555 **A**1 9 10 **F**3 29 84 130 148 **S** Kindred
Healthcare, Louisville, KY
Primary Contact: Margaret M. Murphy, Interim Chief Executive Officer
COO: Sandra Collins, Chief Clinical Officer
CFO: Thomas A. McMullen, Chief Financial Officer
Web address: www.kindredphila.com/
Control: Corporation, Investor–owned, for–profit **Service:** Long–Term Acute Care
hospital

Staffed Beds: 52 Admissions: 384 Census: 31 Outpatient Visits: 0 Births:
0

KIRKBRIDE CENTER (394007), 111 North 49th Street, Zip 19139–2718;
tel. 215/471–2600, (Nonreporting) **A**10
Primary Contact: Scott Weisenberger, Administrator
Web address: www.kirkbridecenter.com
Control: Partnership, Investor–owned, for–profit **Service:** Psychiatric

Staffed Beds: 205

☒ △ **MAGEE REHABILITATION HOSPITAL (393038)**, 1513 Race Street,
Zip 19102–1177; tel. 215/587–3000 **A**1 3 5 7 9 10 **F**2 29 34 35 50 60 64 68
74 75 77 79 82 86 90 91 92 93 94 95 96 130 132 146 148 **P**6 **S** Jefferson
Health System, Radnor, PA
Primary Contact: Jack A. Carroll, Ph.D., President and Chief Executive Officer
CFO: Patricia A. Underwood, Chief Financial Officer
CMO: Guy Fried, M.D., Chief Medical Officer
CIO: Travis Gathright, Chief Information and Corporate Compliance Officer
CHR: Scott Agostini, Director
Web address: www.mageerehab.org
Control: Other not–for–profit (including NFP Corporation) **Service:** Rehabilitation

Staffed Beds: 96 Admissions: 1028 Census: 75 Outpatient Visits: 60997
Births: 0 Total Expense ($000): 59763 Payroll Expense ($000): 33124
Personnel: 513

MERCY PHILADELPHIA HOSPITAL See Mercy Fitzgerald Hospital, Darby

METHODIST HOSPITAL See Thomas Jefferson University Hospital

☒ △ **NAZARETH HOSPITAL (390204)**, 2601 Holme Avenue, Zip 19152–2096;
tel. 215/335–6000, (Total facility includes 28 beds in nursing home–type unit) **A**1
7 9 10 **F**3 12 15 18 20 22 29 30 31 34 35 37 39 40 45 46 49 50 55 56 57
58 59 64 65 70 74 75 77 78 79 80 81 82 84 85 86 87 90 93 97 100 107
108 110 111 114 115 117 118 119 120 121 128 130 131 132 135 146 147
148 **P**7 **S** Catholic Health East / Trinity Health, Livonia, MI
Primary Contact: Nancy Cherone, Executive Director and Administrator
CFO: David Wajda, Chief Financial Officer
CMO: Mathew Matthew, M.D., Chief Medical Officer
CIO: Terry O'Neil, Chief Information Technology
CHR: Kathleen M. Pries, Director Human Resources
CNO: Michael Beshel, R.N., Vice President Patient Care and Chief Nursing Officer
Web address: www.nazarethhospital.org
Control: Other not–for–profit (including NFP Corporation) **Service:** General
Medical and Surgical

Staffed Beds: 231 Admissions: 9630 Census: 132 Outpatient Visits:
161783 Births: 0 Total Expense ($000): 141179 Payroll Expense ($000):
59507 Personnel: 1047

○ **NORTH PHILADELPHIA HEALTH SYSTEM (390132)**, 1524 West Girard
Avenue, Zip 19130–1613; tel. 215/787–9000, (Includes ST. JOSEPH'S
HOSPITAL, Girard Avenue at Sixteenth Street, Zip 19130; tel. 215/787–9000;
Catherine Kutzler, R.N., Vice President and Administrator), (Nonreporting) **A**9
10 11
Primary Contact: George J. Walmsley, III, CPA, President and Chief Executive
Officer
CFO: Ronald Kaplan, Chief Financial Officer
CIO: Tony Iero, Director Management Information Systems
CHR: James Gloner, Senior Vice President
Web address: www.nphs.com
Control: Other not–for–profit (including NFP Corporation) **Service:** General
Medical and Surgical

Staffed Beds: 315

☒ **PENN PRESBYTERIAN MEDICAL CENTER (390223)**, 51 North 39th Street,
Zip 19104–2699; tel. 215/662–8000, (Total facility includes 26 beds in nursing
home–type unit) **A**1 2 3 5 9 10 **F**3 4 5 7 9 11 12 15 17 18 20 22 24 26 29 30
31 32 34 35 36 37 39 40 44 45 46 49 50 51 54 56 57 58 59 60 61 62 63
64 65 66 68 70 74 75 77 78 79 81 82 84 85 86 87 92 94 96 97 98 100
101 104 107 108 109 110 111 114 115 118 119 126 128 130 131 132 134
135 141 142 143 146 147 148 **P**6 **S** University of Pennsylvania Health System,
Philadelphia, PA
Primary Contact: Michele M. Volpe, Executive Director and Chief Executive Officer
COO: Robert J. Russell, Associate Executive Director Operations
CFO: Anthony Zumpano, Chief Financial Officer
CMO: Kevin Fosnocht, M.D., Chief Medical Officer and Associate Executive
Director
CIO: Theresa Hiltunen, Entity Information Officer
CHR: Margorie Michele, Chief Human Resources Officer
CNO: James R. Ballinghoff, MSN, Chief Nursing Officer and Associate Executive
Director
Web address: www.pennmedicine.org/pmc/
Control: Other not–for–profit (including NFP Corporation) **Service:** General
Medical and Surgical

Staffed Beds: 331 Admissions: 15278 Census: 215 Outpatient Visits:
185062 Births: 0 Total Expense ($000): 455436 Payroll Expense ($000):
160702 Personnel: 1764

☒ **PENNSYLVANIA HOSPITAL (390226)**, 800 Spruce Street, Zip 19107–6192;
tel. 215/829–3000, (Total facility includes 21 beds in nursing home–type unit) **A**1
2 3 5 9 10 13 **F**3 8 9 11 12 15 17 18 20 22 24 26 29 30 31 34 35 36 37 38
40 44 45 46 49 50 52 54 55 56 57 58 59 60 61 64 65 68 70 72 74 75 76
77 78 79 80 81 82 84 85 86 87 97 98 99 100 101 102 103 104 107 108
110 111 114 115 116 117 118 119 121 123 124 126 128 129 130 131 132
134 135 141 142 145 146 147 148 **P**6 **S** University of Pennsylvania Health
System, Philadelphia, PA
Primary Contact: R. Michael Buckley, M.D., Executive Director
COO: Deborah L. Staples, Chief Operating Officer
CFO: Frank Anastasi, Chief Financial Officer
CMO: Daniel Feinberg, M.D., Chief Medical Officer
CIO: Linda Sinisi, Entity Information Officer
CHR: Denise Mariotti, Chief Human Resources Officer
Web address: www.pahosp.com
Control: Other not–for–profit (including NFP Corporation) **Service:** General
Medical and Surgical

Staffed Beds: 423 Admissions: 20664 Census: 300 Outpatient Visits:
190225 Births: 4699 Total Expense ($000): 493697 Payroll Expense
($000): 168535 Personnel: 2316

☒ △ **PHILADELPHIA VETERANS AFFAIRS MEDICAL CENTER**, 3900 Woodland
Avenue, Zip 19104–4594; tel. 215/823–5800, (Nonreporting) **A**1 3 5 7 8
S Department of Veterans Affairs, Washington, DC
Primary Contact: Daniel Hendee, Director
COO: Jeffrey Beiler, Associate Director
CFO: Graciela McDaniel, Chief Financial Officer
CMO: Dave Oslin, M.D., Chief of Staff
CIO: Adrienne Ficchi, Vice President Information Management
CHR: Gerald Morelli, Director Human Resources
Web address: www.philadelphia.va.gov/
Control: Veterans Affairs, Government, federal **Service:** General Medical and
Surgical

Staffed Beds: 280

PA

☐ **ROXBOROUGH MEMORIAL HOSPITAL (390304)**, 5800 Ridge Avenue, Zip 19128–1737; tel. 215/483–9900 **A**1 6 9 10 **F**3 15 18 24 29 31 34 40 44 49 50 56 57 59 65 68 70 74 77 78 79 81 82 84 85 90 93 96 98 103 104 107 108 110 111 116 119 129 130 143 146 148 **S** Prime Healthcare Services, Ontario, CA
Primary Contact: Peter J. Adamo, Chief Executive Officer
CFO: Thomas Reinboth, Chief Financial Officer
CHR: Michael Henrici, Associate Administrator
Web address: www.roxboroughmemorial.com
Control: Corporation, Investor–owned, for–profit **Service:** General Medical and Surgical

Staffed Beds: 140 **Admissions:** 5379 **Census:** 68 **Births:** 0 **Personnel:** 508

☒ **SHRINERS HOSPITALS FOR CHILDREN–PHILADELPHIA (393309)**, 3551 North Broad Street, Zip 19140–4160; tel. 215/430–4000 **A**1 3 5 10 **F**29 35 57 58 64 65 68 74 75 77 79 81 82 85 88 89 91 92 93 94 95 96 119 130 132 133 143 146 **S** Shriners Hospitals for Children, Tampa, FL
Primary Contact: Ernest N. Perilli, Administrator
CFO: Mario Salvati, Director Fiscal Services
CMO: Scott Kozin, M.D., Chief of Staff
CHR: Megan Hauser, Director Human Resources
CNO: Donald T. Wenzler, R.N., Chief Nursing Officer
Web address: www.shrinershospitalsforchildren.org/Hospitals/Locations/Philadelphia.aspx
Control: Other not–for–profit (including NFP Corporation) **Service:** Children's orthopedic

Staffed Beds: 39 **Admissions:** 841 **Census:** 14 **Outpatient Visits:** 11150 **Births:** 0 **Personnel:** 289

☒ **ST. CHRISTOPHER'S HOSPITAL FOR CHILDREN (393307)**, 3601 A. Street, Zip 19134–1043; tel. 215/427–5000 **A**1 3 5 8 9 10 **F**3 7 16 17 19 21 23 25 27 29 30 31 32 34 35 39 40 41 42 43 44 48 49 50 55 58 59 60 61 64 68 72 73 74 75 77 78 79 80 81 82 84 88 89 93 97 99 102 107 111 119 129 130 131 132 134 136 138 143 144 146 **P**6 **S** TENET Healthcare Corporation, Dallas, TX
Primary Contact: Carolyn Jackson, Chief Executive Officer
COO: Maria Scenna, Chief Operating Officer
CFO: Gil Cottle, Chief Financial Officer
CMO: Barbara Hoffman, M.D., Chief Medical Officer
CIO: Robert Taylor, Director Information Services
CHR: Stephen W. Krouse, Chief Human Resource Officer
CNO: Heidi Baur, R.N., Chief Nursing Officer
Web address: www.stchristophershospital.com
Control: Corporation, Investor–owned, for–profit **Service:** Children's general

Staffed Beds: 189 **Admissions:** 11605 **Census:** 121 **Outpatient Visits:** 134702 **Births:** 0 **Personnel:** 1879

☒ **TEMPLE UNIVERSITY HOSPITAL (390027)**, 3401 North Broad Street, Zip 19140–5103; tel. 215/707–2000, (Includes TEMPLE UNIVERSITY HOSPITAL – EPISCOPAL DIVISION, 100 East Lehigh Avenue, Zip 19125–1098; tel. 215/427–7000) **A**1 2 3 5 6 8 9 10 **F**3 8 11 12 13 14 15 16 17 18 20 22 24 26 28 29 30 31 34 35 37 38 40 41 42 43 44 45 46 47 48 49 50 53 54 55 56 57 58 59 60 61 64 68 70 72 73 74 75 77 78 79 80 81 82 83 84 85 86 87 90 92 93 94 96 97 98 99 100 101 102 103 104 107 108 109 110 111 114 115 118 119 120 121 123 124 126 129 130 131 132 135 136 137 138 139 140 141 142 146 147 148 **S** Temple University Health System, Philadelphia, PA
Primary Contact: John N. Kastanis, FACHE, Chief Executive Officer
COO: Rosemary Nolan, R.N., Chief Operating Officer
CFO: Gerald P. Oetzel, Chief Financial Officer
CMO: Susan Freeman, M.D., Chief Medical Officer
CIO: David Kamowski, Vice President and Chief Information Officer
CHR: John Lasky, Vice President and Chief Human Resources Officer
CNO: Elizabeth J. Craig, MSN, Chief Nursing Officer and Vice President Patient Services
Web address: www.tuh.templehealth.org/content/default.htm
Control: Other not–for–profit (including NFP Corporation) **Service:** General Medical and Surgical

Staffed Beds: 665 **Admissions:** 36929 **Census:** 562 **Outpatient Visits:** 329596 **Births:** 2024 **Total Expense ($000):** 812674 **Payroll Expense ($000):** 302666 **Personnel:** 4280

☒ △ **THOMAS JEFFERSON UNIVERSITY HOSPITAL (390174)**, 111 South 11th Street, Zip 19107–5084; tel. 215/955–6000, (Includes METHODIST HOSPITAL, 2301 South Broad Street, Zip 19148; tel. 215/952–9000) **A**1 2 3 5 7 8 9 10 **F**3 5 6 7 8 9 11 12 13 14 15 17 18 20 22 24 26 28 29 30 31 34 35 36 37 38 39 40 43 44 45 46 47 48 49 50 51 52 53 54 55 56 57 58 59 61 64 65 66 68 70 72 73 74 75 76 77 78 79 80 81 82 84 85 86 87 89 90 92 93 94 96 97 98 100 101 102 103 104 107 108 109 110 111 114 115 118 119 120 121 123 124 126 129 130 131 132 134 135 136 137 138 139 141 142 143 145 146 147 148 **P**2 6 8
Primary Contact: David P. McQuaid, FACHE, President
CFO: Neil Lubarsky, Senior Vice President Finance
CMO: Geno Merli, M.D., Chief Medical Officer
CIO: Stephen Tranquillo, Chief Information Officer
CHR: Mary Ellen Keeney, Vice President Human Resources
Web address: www.jeffersonhospital.org
Control: Other not–for–profit (including NFP Corporation) **Service:** General Medical and Surgical

Staffed Beds: 945 **Admissions:** 46386 **Census:** 679 **Outpatient Visits:** 475031 **Births:** 1994 **Total Expense ($000):** 1414184 **Payroll Expense ($000):** 470057 **Personnel:** 6996

TRIUMPH HOSPITAL PHILADELPHIA See Kindred Hospital South Philadelphia

VETERANS AFFAIRS MEDICAL CENTER See Philadelphia Veterans Affairs Medical Center

PHOENIXVILLE—Chester County

☒ **PHOENIXVILLE HOSPITAL (390127)**, 140 Nutt Road, Zip 19460–3900, Mailing Address: P.O. Box 3001, Zip 19460–0916; tel. 610/983–1000 **A**1 2 9 10 **F**1 3 4 8 11 12 13 16 17 18 20 22 24 26 28 29 31 32 35 36 38 39 40 45 49 50 51 56 57 59 61 64 67 69 70 72 73 74 75 76 77 78 79 80 81 82 85 86 87 89 90 93 98 100 102 107 108 111 118 119 126 128 130 132 134 135 146 147 **S** Community Health Systems, Inc., Franklin, TN
Primary Contact: Stephen M. Tullman, Chief Executive Officer
CFO: David Paulosky, Chief Financial Officer
CMO: David Stepansky, M.D., Chief Medical Officer
CIO: Terry Murphy, Director Information Services
CHR: Denise Chiolo, Chief Human Resources Officer
CNO: Sarah Strzelecki, Ed.D., Chief Nursing Officer
Web address: www.phoenixvillehospital.com
Control: Corporation, Investor–owned, for–profit **Service:** General Medical and Surgical

Staffed Beds: 113 **Admissions:** 6781 **Census:** 78 **Outpatient Visits:** 110735 **Births:** 774 **Total Expense ($000):** 152035 **Payroll Expense ($000):** 45784 **Personnel:** 762

PITTSBURGH—Allegheny County

☒ **ALLEGHENY GENERAL HOSPITAL (390050)**, 320 East North Avenue, Zip 15212–4756; tel. 412/359–3131 **A**1 2 3 5 8 9 10 **F**3 7 8 9 11 12 15 17 18 19 20 22 24 26 28 29 30 31 32 34 35 36 38 39 40 41 43 44 45 46 47 48 49 50 51 53 54 55 57 58 59 61 62 63 64 65 66 68 70 74 75 77 78 79 80 81 82 84 85 86 87 89 92 93 94 95 96 99 100 101 102 103 104 105 107 108 109 110 111 114 115 116 117 118 119 120 121 123 124 126 129 130 131 132 134 135 137 138 139 140 142 143 145 146 147 148 **P**6 **S** Allegheny Health Network, Pittsburgh, PA
Primary Contact: Michael Harlovic, R.N., President and Chief Executive Officer
COO: Ronald J. Andro, Chief Operating Officer
CMO: Tony Farah, M.D., President Medical Staff
CIO: John Foley, Chief Information Officer
Web address: www.wpahs.org/locations/allegheny–general–hospital
Control: Other not–for–profit (including NFP Corporation) **Service:** General Medical and Surgical

Staffed Beds: 385 **Admissions:** 22369 **Census:** 357 **Outpatient Visits:** 398369 **Births:** 0 **Total Expense ($000):** 737831 **Payroll Expense ($000):** 191625 **Personnel:** 3533

☐ **CHILDREN'S HOSPITAL OF PITTSBURGH OF UPMC (393302)**, 4401 Penn Avenue, Zip 15224–1334; tel. 412/692–5325 **A**1 3 5 9 10 **F**3 8 12 17 19 21 22 23 24 25 27 28 29 30 34 35 39 40 41 43 45 46 48 49 50 53 54 55 57 59 60 64 66 68 71 72 74 75 77 78 79 81 82 84 86 87 88 89 93 97 100 107 108 109 111 115 116 117 118 119 120 121 123 124 126 129 130 131 132 134 135 136 137 138 139 140 141 142 143 144 146 **S** UPMC, Pittsburgh, PA
Primary Contact: Christopher Gessner, President
COO: Christopher Gessner, President
CNO: Diane Hupp, R.N., Vice President Patient Care Services and Chief Nursing Officer
Web address: www.chp.edu
Control: Other not–for–profit (including NFP Corporation) **Service:** Children's general

Staffed Beds: 296 **Admissions:** 14250 **Census:** 217 **Outpatient Visits:** 312746 **Births:** 0 **Total Expense ($000):** 495150 **Payroll Expense ($000):** 145198 **Personnel:** 2649

EYE AND EAR HOSPITAL OF PITTSBURGH See UPMC Presbyterian Shadyside

✠ **HEALTHSOUTH HARMARVILLE REHABILITATION HOSPITAL (393027)**, Guys Run Road, Zip 15238–0460, Mailing Address: P.O. Box 11460, Zip 15238–0460; tel. 412/828–1300, (Total facility includes 40 beds in nursing home–type unit) **A**1 10 **F**29 62 75 77 79 86 90 93 95 96 128 132 146 148 **S** HEALTHSOUTH Corporation, Birmingham, AL
Primary Contact: Kenneth J. Anthony, Chief Executive Officer
CFO: Daniel A. Vrana, Controller
CMO: Thomas Franz, M.D., Medical Director
CHR: Eric Larson, Director Human Resources
Web address: www.healthsouthharmarville.com
Control: Corporation, Investor–owned, for–profit **Service:** Rehabilitation

> **Staffed Beds:** 202 **Admissions:** 2572 **Census:** 116 **Outpatient Visits:** 19685 **Births:** 0 **Total Expense ($000):** 34020 **Payroll Expense ($000):** 18497 **Personnel:** 293

✠ **KINDRED HOSPITAL PITTSBURGH–NORTH SHORE (392049)**, 1004 Arch Street, Zip 15212–5235; tel. 412/323–5800, (Nonreporting) **A**1 9 10 **S** Kindred Healthcare, Louisville, KY
Primary Contact: Janie Rosenberger–Slampack, Market Chief Executive Officer
Web address: www.kindrednorthshore.com/
Control: Corporation, Investor–owned, for–profit **Service:** Long–Term Acute Care hospital

> **Staffed Beds:** 111

✠ **LIFECARE HOSPITALS OF PITTSBURGH (392024)**, 225 Penn Avenue, Zip 15221–2148; tel. 412/247–2424, (Includes LIFECARE HOSPITALS OF PITTSBURGH – SUBURBAN CAMPUS, 100 South Jackson Avenue, 4th Floor, Zip 15202–3428; Kim Sperring, Administrator), (Total facility includes 40 beds in nursing home–type unit) **A**1 9 10 **F**1 3 29 30 85 87 103 107 114 128 130 146 148 **P**5 **S** LifeCare Management Services, Plano, TX
Primary Contact: Kim Sperring, Administrator
CFO: Nikki Aykul, Manager Business Office
CMO: Steven Sotos, M.D., President Medical Staff
CIO: George Fitzgerald, Regional Director Information Systems
CHR: Robin Arslanpay, Director Human Resources
Web address: www.lifecare–hospitals.com
Control: Corporation, Investor–owned, for–profit **Service:** Long–Term Acute Care hospital

> **Staffed Beds:** 236 **Admissions:** 1947 **Census:** 133 **Outpatient Visits:** 0 **Births:** 0 **Total Expense ($000):** 51250 **Payroll Expense ($000):** 23883 **Personnel:** 467

✠ **MAGEE–WOMENS HOSPITAL OF UPMC (390114)**, 300 Halket Street, Zip 15213–3108; tel. 412/641–1000, (Total facility includes 20 beds in nursing home–type unit) **A**1 2 3 5 8 9 10 **F**3 11 12 13 15 29 30 31 34 35 40 43 44 45 46 49 52 54 55 56 57 58 59 64 65 66 68 70 72 74 75 76 78 79 80 81 82 84 85 86 87 97 107 108 110 111 115 119 120 121 123 126 130 131 132 134 135 146 147 148 **S** UPMC, Pittsburgh, PA
Primary Contact: Leslie C. Davis, President
COO: Lou Baverso, Vice President Operations
CFO: Eileen Simmons, Chief Financial Officer
CMO: Dennis English, M.D., Vice President Medical Affairs
CIO: Harun Rashid, Chief Information Officer
CHR: Rhonda Larimore, Vice President Human Resources
CNO: Maribeth McLaughlin, R.N., Vice President Patient Care Services
Web address: www.magee.edu
Control: Other not–for–profit (including NFP Corporation) **Service:** Obstetrics and gynecology

> **Staffed Beds:** 363 **Admissions:** 20855 **Census:** 241 **Outpatient Visits:** 381033 **Births:** 9096 **Total Expense ($000):** 418060 **Payroll Expense ($000):** 111734 **Personnel:** 2016

✠ **SELECT SPECIALTY HOSPITAL–PITTSBURGH/UPMC (392044)**, 200 Lothrop Street, E824, Zip 15213–2536; tel. 412/586–9800 **A**1 9 10 **F**1 3 29 36 65 85 86 87 91 148 **S** Select Medical Corporation, Mechanicsburg, PA
Primary Contact: John St. Leger, Chief Executive Officer
CMO: Michael Donahue, M.D., Medical Director
CHR: Prudence Sloan, Coordinator Human Resources
CNO: Eli Babich, Chief Nursing Officer
Web address: www.selectspecialtyhospitals.com/company/locations/pittsburghupmc.aspx
Control: Corporation, Investor–owned, for–profit **Service:** Long–Term Acute Care hospital

> **Staffed Beds:** 32 **Admissions:** 289 **Census:** 24 **Outpatient Visits:** 0 **Births:** 0 **Personnel:** 85

□ **SOUTHWOOD PSYCHIATRIC HOSPITAL**, 2575 Boyce Plaza Road, Zip 15241–3925; tel. 412/257–2290, (Nonreporting) **A**1 9 **S** Acadia Healthcare Company, Inc., Franklin, TN
Primary Contact: Stephen J. Quigley, Chief Executive Officer
CFO: Frank Urban, Chief Financial Officer
CMO: Allan W. Clark, M.D., Medical Director
CHR: Erin J. Frohnhofer, Director Human Resources
Web address: www.southwoodhospital.com
Control: Corporation, Investor–owned, for–profit **Service:** Children's hospital psychiatric

> **Staffed Beds:** 156

✠ **ST. CLAIR HOSPITAL (390228)**, 1000 Bower Hill Road, Zip 15243–1873; tel. 412/942–4000 **A**1 2 9 10 **F**3 8 13 15 17 18 20 22 24 26 28 29 30 31 34 35 37 40 45 49 51 53 54 56 57 59 60 64 67 70 73 74 75 76 77 78 79 81 82 84 85 86 87 89 90 91 92 93 96 98 100 102 105 107 108 110 111 114 115 118 119 126 129 130 131 132 134 135 143 146 147 148 **P**7
Primary Contact: James M. Collins, President and Chief Executive Officer
COO: Michael J. Flanagan, Senior Vice President and Chief Operating Officer
CFO: Richard C. Chesnos, Senior Vice President Finance and Chief Financial Officer
CMO: G. Alan Yeasted, M.D., Senior Vice President and Chief Medical Officer
CIO: Richard Schaeffer, Vice President Information Systems and Chief Information Officer
CHR: Andrea Kalina, Vice President External Affairs and Chief Human Resources Officer
CNO: Joan Massella, Administrative Vice President and Chief Nursing Officer
Web address: www.stclair.org
Control: Other not–for–profit (including NFP Corporation) **Service:** General Medical and Surgical

> **Staffed Beds:** 303 **Admissions:** 16026 **Census:** 197 **Outpatient Visits:** 290214 **Births:** 1269 **Total Expense ($000):** 225841 **Payroll Expense ($000):** 88883 **Personnel:** 1879

★ **THE CHILDREN'S HOME OF PITTSBURGH (393304)**, 5324 Penn Avenue, Zip 15224–1733; tel. 412/441–4884, (Nonreporting) **A**9 10
Primary Contact: Pamela R. Schanwald, Chief Executive Officer
COO: Kimberly Reblock, M.D., Chief Operating Officer
CFO: Kimberly A. Phillips, Chief Financial Officer
CMO: Frederick C. Sherman, M.D., Chief Medical Officer
Web address: www.childrenshomepgh.org
Control: Other not–for–profit (including NFP Corporation) **Service:** Children's general

> **Staffed Beds:** 15

★ △ **THE CHILDREN'S INSTITUTE OF PITTSBURGH (393308)**, 1405 Shady Avenue, Zip 15217–1350; tel. 412/420–2400 **A**7 10 **F**3 29 30 34 54 58 59 64 74 75 79 82 85 86 87 90 91 93 96 97 98 99 100 104 107 130 131 132 146 148 **P**6
Primary Contact: David K. Miles, President and Chief Executive Officer
COO: Stacey Vaccaro, Chief Operating Officer
CFO: Jody Mulvihill, Vice President Finance
CMO: Maryanne Henderson, D.O., Chief Medical Officer
CIO: Sharon Dorogy, Director Health Information Management
CHR: Linda M. Allen, Vice President Human Resources
Web address: www.amazingkids.org
Control: Other not–for–profit (including NFP Corporation) **Service:** Children's rehabilitation

> **Staffed Beds:** 62 **Admissions:** 328 **Census:** 29 **Outpatient Visits:** 54504 **Births:** 0 **Total Expense ($000):** 31723 **Payroll Expense ($000):** 15742 **Personnel:** 319

□ △ **UPMC MERCY (390028)**, 1400 Locust Street, Zip 15219–5166; tel. 412/232–8111 **A**1 3 5 6 7 9 10 12 13 **F**3 4 8 13 15 16 17 18 19 20 22 24 26 28 30 31 32 34 35 36 39 40 43 45 49 50 51 54 57 58 59 60 61 62 64 65 66 68 70 72 74 75 76 77 78 79 81 82 84 85 86 87 90 91 92 93 94 95 96 97 98 101 102 107 108 111 114 115 116 118 119 126 129 130 141 142 146 147 148 **P**6 **S** UPMC, Pittsburgh, PA
Primary Contact: Will L. Cook, President
CFO: Jack Gaenzle, Senior Vice President Finance and Administration
CIO: Stephen D. Adams, Executive Vice President and Chief Information Officer
CHR: Kristen Bell, Director Human Resources
Web address: www.upmc.com/HospitalsFacilities/HFHome/Hospitals/Mercy/
Control: Other not–for–profit (including NFP Corporation) **Service:** General Medical and Surgical

> **Staffed Beds:** 488 **Admissions:** 21121 **Census:** 359 **Outpatient Visits:** 202152 **Births:** 1461 **Total Expense ($000):** 408283 **Payroll Expense ($000):** 129268 **Personnel:** 2162

UPMC MONTEFIORE See UPMC Presbyterian Shadyside

Hospital, Medicare Provider Number, Address, Telephone, Approval, Facility, and Physician Codes, Health Care System

★ American Hospital Association (AHA) membership
□ The Joint Commission accreditation   ◇ DNV Healthcare Inc. accreditation
○ Healthcare Facilities Accreditation Program
△ Commission on Accreditation of Rehabilitation Facilities (CARF) accreditation

☐ **UPMC PASSAVANT (390107)**, 9100 Babcock Boulevard, Zip 15237–5815; tel. 412/748–6700, (Includes UPMC PASSAVANT CRANBERRY, One St. Francis Way, Cranberry, Zip 16066; tel. 724/772–5300; Teresa G. Petrick, President), (Total facility includes 12 beds in nursing home–type unit) **A**1 2 9 10 F3 8 11 15 17 18 20 22 24 26 28 29 30 31 34 35 40 43 46 47 48 49 51 56 57 59 64 65 68 70 74 75 77 78 79 80 81 82 84 85 86 87 90 92 107 108 110 111 114 115 116 117 118 119 120 121 126 128 129 130 132 135 143 145 146 147 148 **S** UPMC, Pittsburgh, PA
Primary Contact: David T. Martin, President
CFO: Thomas M. Newman, Chief Financial Officer
CMO: James W. Boyle, M.D., Chief Medical Officer
CHR: Leeann Cerimele, Vice President Human Resources
CNO: Susan E. Hoolahan, R.N., Vice President Patient Care Services and Chief Nursing Officer
Web address: www.upmc.edu/passavant
Control: Other not–for–profit (including NFP Corporation) **Service:** General Medical and Surgical

Staffed Beds: 424 **Admissions:** 17392 **Census:** 264 **Outpatient Visits:** 299842 **Births:** 0 **Total Expense ($000):** 356063 **Payroll Expense ($000):** 100109 **Personnel:** 1669

☐ **UPMC PRESBYTERIAN SHADYSIDE (390164)**, 200 Lothrop Street, Zip 15213–2536; tel. 412/647–2345, (Includes EYE AND EAR HOSPITAL OF PITTSBURGH, 200 Lothrop Street, Zip 15213–2592; tel. 412/647–2345; UPMC MONTEFIORE, 3459 Fifth Avenue, Zip 15213; tel. 412/647–2345; John Innocenti, Sr., President and Chief Executive Officer; UPMC PRESBYTERIAN HOSPITAL, 200 Lothrop Street, Zip 15213; tel. 412/647–2345; UPMC SHADYSIDE, 5230 Centre Avenue, Zip 15232–1381; tel. 412/623–2121; WESTERN PSYCHIATRIC INSTITUTE AND CLINIC, 3811 O'Hara Street, Zip 15213–2593; tel. 412/624–2100), (Total facility includes 20 beds in nursing home–type unit) **A**1 2 5 6 8 9 10 12 13 F2 3 5 6 7 8 9 10 11 12 14 15 17 18 19 20 22 24 25 26 28 29 30 31 32 33 34 35 36 37 38 39 40 43 44 45 46 47 48 49 50 51 52 53 54 55 56 57 58 59 60 61 62 63 64 65 66 68 69 70 71 74 75 77 78 79 81 82 83 84 85 86 87 90 91 92 93 94 97 98 99 100 101 102 103 104 105 106 107 108 109 110 111 112 113 114 115 116 117 118 119 120 121 123 126 128 129 130 131 132 134 135 136 137 138 139 140 141 142 143 144 145 146 147 148 P6 **S** UPMC, Pittsburgh, PA
Primary Contact: John Innocenti, Sr., President and Chief Executive Officer
CFO: Eileen Simmons, Chief Financial Officer
CMO: Margaret Reidy, M.D., Vice President Medical Affairs
CIO: James Venturella, Chief Information Officer
CHR: Kathryn Devine, Vice President Human Resources
CNO: Holly Lorenz, R.N., Chief Nurse Executive
Web address: www.upmc.edu
Control: Other not–for–profit (including NFP Corporation) **Service:** General Medical and Surgical

Staffed Beds: 1582 **Admissions:** 64836 **Census:** 1280 **Outpatient Visits:** 1264948 **Births:** 0 **Total Expense ($000):** 2181991 **Payroll Expense ($000):** 535163 **Personnel:** 12038

☐ **UPMC ST. MARGARET (390102)**, 815 Freeport Road, Zip 15215–3301; tel. 412/784–4000 **A**1 2 3 5 6 9 10 13 F3 6 8 9 11 12 15 18 20 30 31 34 35 37 40 44 46 49 50 51 54 56 57 58 59 60 61 63 64 65 68 70 74 75 77 78 79 81 82 84 85 86 87 90 94 97 102 103 104 107 108 111 114 115 118 119 121 129 130 131 132 134 135 146 **S** UPMC, Pittsburgh, PA
Primary Contact: David J. Patton, President
COO: Merle Taylor, Vice President Operations
CFO: Thomas M. Newman, Vice President Finance
CMO: John Lagnese, M.D., Vice President Medical Affairs
CIO: Charles M. Rudek, Chief Information Officer
CHR: Tracey Stange Kolo, Vice President Human Resources
CNO: Mary C. Barkhymer, R.N., Vice President Patient Care Services and Chief Nursing Officer
Web address: www.upmc.com/locations/hospitals/st-margaret/Pages/default.aspx
Control: Other not–for–profit (including NFP Corporation) **Service:** General Medical and Surgical

Staffed Beds: 249 **Admissions:** 13440 **Census:** 185 **Outpatient Visits:** 189168 **Births:** 0 **Total Expense ($000):** 240112 **Payroll Expense ($000):** 74727 **Personnel:** 1285

☒ △ **VETERANS AFFAIRS PITTSBURGH HEALTHCARE SYSTEM**, University Drive, Zip 15240–1001; tel. 412/688–6000, (Includes VETERANS AFFAIRS MEDICAL CENTER, 7180 Highland Drive, Zip 15206–1297; tel. 412/365–4900; VETERANS AFFAIRS MEDICAL CENTER, University Drive C, tel. 412/688–6000), (Total facility includes 262 beds in nursing home–type unit) **A**1 2 7 8 9 F2 3 4 5 9 12 15 17 18 20 22 24 26 28 29 30 31 33 34 35 36 38 39 40 45 46 47 49 51 54 56 57 58 59 60 61 62 63 64 65 68 70 74 75 77 78 79 81 82 83 84 85 86 87 91 92 93 94 96 97 98 100 101 102 103 104 105 106 107 108 109 110 111 112 113 114 115 116 119 120 130 132 135 138 139 143 146 147 148 P6 **S** Department of Veterans Affairs, Washington, DC
Primary Contact: David S. Macpherson, M.D., M.P.H., Acting Director
CFO: Charles Thilges, Chief Financial Officer
CMO: Ali Sonel, M.D., Chief of Staff
CIO: John Kovac, Facility Chief Information Officer
CHR: Amber Mesoras, Chief Human Resources Officer
CNO: Ira Richmond, Associate Director Patient Care Services
Web address: www.pittsburgh.va.gov/
Control: Veterans Affairs, Government, federal **Service:** General Medical and Surgical

Staffed Beds: 582 **Admissions:** 10465 **Census:** 417 **Outpatient Visits:** 674776 **Births:** 0 **Total Expense ($000):** 564971 **Payroll Expense ($000):** 296753 **Personnel:** 3368

☒ **WEST PENN HOSPITAL (390090)**, 4800 Friendship Avenue, Zip 15224–1722; tel. 412/578–5000 **A**1 2 3 5 6 8 9 10 12 13 F3 8 11 12 13 15 16 17 18 20 22 24 26 29 30 31 34 35 37 39 40 45 46 47 48 49 50 51 52 54 55 56 57 58 59 63 64 65 68 70 72 74 75 76 77 78 79 80 81 82 84 85 86 87 89 90 91 92 93 96 97 100 102 107 108 109 110 111 114 115 116 117 118 119 120 121 123 124 126 129 130 131 132 135 136 141 145 146 147 148 P6 **S** Allegheny Health Network, Pittsburgh, PA
Primary Contact: Duke Rupert, President and Chief Executive Officer
CFO: James A. Kanuch, Vice President Finance
CMO: I. William Goldfarb, Chief Medical Officer
CIO: Jacqueline Dailey, Chief Information Officer
CHR: Sally Carozza, Director Human Resources
CNO: Paula A. Lacher, MSN, Chief Nursing Officer
Web address: www.wpahs.org
Control: Other not–for–profit (including NFP Corporation) **Service:** General Medical and Surgical

Staffed Beds: 308 **Admissions:** 8554 **Census:** 142 **Outpatient Visits:** 90580 **Births:** 2983 **Total Expense ($000):** 268832 **Payroll Expense ($000):** 72153 **Personnel:** 1321

WESTERN PSYCHIATRIC INSTITUTE AND CLINIC See UPMC Presbyterian Shadyside

PLEASANT GAP—Centre County

☒ **HEALTHSOUTH NITTANY VALLEY REHABILITATION HOSPITAL (393039)**, 550 West College Avenue, Zip 16823–7401; tel. 814/359–3421 **A**1 9 10 F29 30 34 35 44 59 60 64 74 75 77 86 87 90 91 93 94 95 96 130 132 135 143 **S** HEALTHSOUTH Corporation, Birmingham, AL
Primary Contact: Susan Hartman, Chief Executive Officer
CFO: Alan M. Phillips, Controller
CMO: Richard Allatt, M.D., Medical Director
CHR: Michelle Katz, Director Human Resources
CNO: Susan Evans, Chief Nursing Officer
Web address: www.nittanyvalleyrehab.com
Control: Corporation, Investor–owned, for–profit **Service:** Rehabilitation

Staffed Beds: 73 **Admissions:** 1109 **Census:** 40 **Births:** 0 **Personnel:** 161

POTTSTOWN—Montgomery County

☒ **POTTSTOWN MEMORIAL MEDICAL CENTER (390123)**, 1600 East High Street, Zip 19464–5093; tel. 610/327–7000 **A**1 2 9 10 F3 7 8 10 15 18 29 30 31 34 35 38 40 44 45 49 50 51 54 55 57 59 60 64 68 70 74 75 76 77 78 79 81 82 85 89 91 92 93 97 98 100 107 111 116 117 119 124 125 131 132 135 146 147 148 P6 **S** Community Health Systems, Inc., Franklin, TN
Primary Contact: J. Mark McLoone, FACHE, Chief Executive Officer
CFO: Debbie Konarski, Interim Chief Financial Officer
CMO: Richard F. Saylor, M.D., Chief Medical Officer
CIO: Ron Peterson, Chief Information Officer
CHR: Ruta Ore, Director Human Resources
Web address: www.pottstownmemorial.com
Control: Corporation, Investor–owned, for–profit **Service:** General Medical and Surgical

Staffed Beds: 224 **Admissions:** 9074 **Census:** 119 **Outpatient Visits:** 125632 **Births:** 515 **Total Expense ($000):** 137039 **Payroll Expense ($000):** 49218 **Personnel:** 797

Many Facility Codes have changed. Please refer to the AHA Guide Code Chart.   © 2014 AHA Guide

PA

POTTSVILLE—Schuylkill County

☒ △ **SCHUYLKILL MEDICAL CENTER – EAST NORWEGIAN STREET (390031)**, 700 East Norwegian Street, Zip 17901–2710; tel. 570/621–4000 **A**1 7 9 10 **F**3 5 11 15 18 29 30 31 34 39 40 45 49 56 57 59 64 70 74 75 77 78 79 81 85 86 90 93 98 100 103 107 108 109 110 115 117 118 119 130 132 135 146 147 148 **P**6 **S** Schuylkill Health System, Pottsville, PA
Primary Contact: Darnell F. Furer, MS, R.N., Acting Administrator
CFO: Diane Boris, Vice President and Chief Financial Officer
CMO: Thomas A. Curry, M.D., Vice President Medical Affairs for Clinical Effectiveness and Documentation
CIO: Tina Zanis, Director Information Technology
CHR: Martin Treasure, Director Human Resources
CNO: Darnell F. Furer, MS, Vice President of Patient Care Services
Web address: www.schuylkillhealth.com
Control: Other not–for–profit (including NFP Corporation) **Service:** General Medical and Surgical

Staffed Beds: 126 **Admissions:** 4403 **Census:** 71 **Outpatient Visits:** 103080 **Births:** 0 **Total Expense ($000):** 57978 **Payroll Expense ($000):** 26824 **Personnel:** 483

☒ **SCHUYLKILL MEDICAL CENTER – SOUTH JACKSON STREET (390030)**, 420 South Jackson Street, Zip 17901–3625; tel. 570/621–5000, (Total facility includes 11 beds in nursing home–type unit) **A**1 6 9 10 19 **F**3 11 13 15 18 19 28 29 30 32 34 35 38 40 45 49 51 54 56 57 59 62 64 70 74 75 76 77 78 79 81 82 85 86 89 92 93 96 98 99 100 101 102 104 105 107 108 110 111 115 118 119 124 126 128 129 130 131 132 146 147 **P**6 **S** Schuylkill Health System, Pottsville, PA
Primary Contact: Darnell F. Furer, MS, R.N., Acting Administrator
CFO: Diane Boris, Chief Financial Officer
CMO: Thomas A. Curry, M.D., Vice President Medical Affairs for Clinical Effectiveness and Documentation
CIO: Tina Zanis, Director Information Systems
CHR: Martin Treasure, Director Human Resources
CNO: Darnell F. Furer, MS, Vice President Patient Care Services and Chief Nursing Officer
Web address: www.schuylkillhealth.com
Control: Other not–for–profit (including NFP Corporation) **Service:** General Medical and Surgical

Staffed Beds: 190 **Admissions:** 6195 **Census:** 91 **Outpatient Visits:** 110623 **Births:** 896 **Total Expense ($000):** 85731 **Payroll Expense ($000):** 40532 **Personnel:** 775

PUNXSUTAWNEY—Jefferson County

PUNXSUTAWNEY AREA HOSPITAL (390199), 81 Hillcrest Drive, Zip 15767–2616; tel. 814/938–1800 **A**9 10 **F**3 13 15 18 29 30 34 35 40 45 50 51 57 59 60 61 62 68 70 74 75 76 77 79 81 82 85 86 93 104 107 108 110 111 114 116 117 118 119 130 132 133 135 146 147 148 **P**6
Primary Contact: Daniel D. Blough, Jr., Chief Executive Officer
CFO: Jack Sisk, Chief Financial Officer
CMO: Dajani Zuhd, M.D., President Medical Staff
CIO: Chuck States, Director Information Systems
CHR: Barbara Kostok, Manager Human Resources
CNO: Paula Spack, R.N., Vice President Nursing
Web address: www.pah.org
Control: Other not–for–profit (including NFP Corporation) **Service:** General Medical and Surgical

Staffed Beds: 44 **Admissions:** 1671 **Census:** 17 **Outpatient Visits:** 100721 **Births:** 121 **Total Expense ($000):** 31376 **Payroll Expense ($000):** 16636 **Personnel:** 331

QUAKERTOWN—Bucks County

☐ **ST. LUKE'S HOSPITAL – QUAKERTOWN CAMPUS (390035)**, 1021 Park Avenue, Zip 18951–1573; tel. 215/538–4500 **A**1 2 9 10 **F**3 11 15 18 28 29 30 31 34 35 38 40 44 45 49 50 51 53 54 56 57 59 60 64 65 66 68 69 70 74 75 77 78 79 81 82 85 86 87 92 93 98 100 102 103 107 108 109 110 111 115 118 119 129 130 132 135 145 146 147 148 **P**6 8 **S** St. Luke's University Health Network, Bethlehem, PA
Primary Contact: John B. Sylvia, President
CFO: Theresa Corrado, Director Finance
CMO: Thomas Filipowicz, M.D., Medical Director
CIO: Chad Brisendine, Chief Information Officer
CHR: Shelley Maley, Director Human Resources
Web address: www.slhhn.org
Control: Other not–for–profit (including NFP Corporation) **Service:** General Medical and Surgical

Staffed Beds: 57 **Admissions:** 3092 **Census:** 41 **Outpatient Visits:** 105203 **Births:** 0 **Total Expense ($000):** 56213 **Payroll Expense ($000):** 23510 **Personnel:** 299

READING—Berks County

☐ **HAVEN BEHAVIORAL HEALTH OF EASTERN PENNSYLVANIA (394052)**, 145 North 6th Street, 3rd Floor, Zip 19601–3096; tel. 610/406–4340, (Nonreporting) **A**1 9 10 **S** Haven Behavioral Healthcare, Nashville, TN
Primary Contact: John Baker, Interim Chief Executive Officer
CMO: Mark Putnam, M.D., Medical Director
CHR: Kathy Copenhaver, Director Human Resources
Web address: www.havenbehavioralhospital.com
Control: Corporation, Investor–owned, for–profit **Service:** Psychiatric

Staffed Beds: 48

☒ **HEALTHSOUTH READING REHABILITATION HOSPITAL (393026)**, 1623 Morgantown Road, Zip 19607–9455; tel. 610/796–6000, (Nonreporting) **A**1 9 10 **S** HEALTHSOUTH Corporation, Birmingham, AL
Primary Contact: Richard Kruczek, Chief Executive Officer
CFO: Jason Pulaski, Controller
CMO: Patti Brown, M.D., Medical Director
CHR: Edward Werner, Director Human Resources
CNO: Margaret Montgomery, Chief Nursing Officer
Web address: www.healthsouthreading.com
Control: Corporation, Investor–owned, for–profit **Service:** Rehabilitation

Staffed Beds: 60

☒ **ST. JOSEPH MEDICAL CENTER (390096)**, 2500 Bernville Road, Zip 19605–9453, Mailing Address: P.O. Box 316, Zip 19603–0316; tel. 610/378–2000, (Includes ST. JOSEPH MEDICAL CENTER–DOWNTOWN READING, 145 North Sixth Street, Zip 19601, Mailing Address: P.O. Box 316, Zip 19603–0316; tel. 610/376–2100) **A**1 2 9 10 12 13 **F**3 13 15 18 20 22 24 26 28 29 30 31 32 34 35 39 40 44 45 49 50 51 53 54 57 58 59 64 66 68 70 72 74 75 76 77 78 79 81 82 85 87 89 93 97 107 108 111 113 114 115 116 117 118 119 120 121 130 131 132 135 144 146 147 148 **P**6 **S** Catholic Health Initiatives, Englewood, CO
Primary Contact: John R. Morahan, FACHE, President and Chief Executive Officer
CFO: Lim David, Vice President Finance and Chief Financial Officer
CMO: Howard Davis, M.D., Vice President Medical Affairs
CHR: Scott Mengle, Vice President Human Resources
CNO: Sharon Strohecker, R.N., Vice President Clinical Operations and Chief Nursing Officer
Web address: www.thefutureofhealthcare.org
Control: Church–operated, Nongovernment, not–for profit **Service:** General Medical and Surgical

Staffed Beds: 180 **Admissions:** 8165 **Census:** 98 **Outpatient Visits:** 307970 **Births:** 730 **Total Expense ($000):** 189246 **Payroll Expense ($000):** 64568 **Personnel:** 1344

RENOVO—Clinton County

★ **BUCKTAIL MEDICAL CENTER (391304)**, 1001 Pine Street, Zip 17764–1620; tel. 570/923–1000, (Total facility includes 43 beds in nursing home–type unit) **A**9 10 18 **F**3 7 11 34 40 42 54 56 59 65 66 69 97 127 128 130 133 143 146
Primary Contact: Terry Hollinger, Chief Executive Officer
CFO: Wendy Janerella, Controller
CMO: Alvin Berlot, M.D., Medical Director
Web address: www.bucktailmed.org
Control: Other not–for–profit (including NFP Corporation) **Service:** General Medical and Surgical

Staffed Beds: 64 **Admissions:** 189 **Census:** 40 **Outpatient Visits:** 10900 **Births:** 0 **Total Expense ($000):** 6609 **Payroll Expense ($000):** 2553 **Personnel:** 74

RIDLEY PARK—Delaware County

TAYLOR HOSPITAL See Crozer–Chester Medical Center, Upland

ROARING SPRING—Blair County

☒ **NASON HOSPITAL (390062)**, 105 Nason Drive, Zip 16673–1202; tel. 814/224–2141 **A**1 9 10 **F**3 11 13 15 29 30 34 35 40 45 57 59 62 63 64 68 70 74 75 76 77 79 81 82 85 92 107 108 111 114 119 130 132 135 146 147 148 **P**3
Primary Contact: Raymond C. Askey, CPA, Acting Chief Executive Officer
CFO: Raymond C. Askey, CPA, Vice President Fiscal Services
CIO: Brian Lilly, Director Information Systems
CHR: Lorie Smith, Director Human Resources
Web address: www.nasonhospital.org
Control: Other not–for–profit (including NFP Corporation) **Service:** General Medical and Surgical

Staffed Beds: 45 **Admissions:** 2068 **Census:** 19 **Outpatient Visits:** 105693 **Births:** 573 **Total Expense ($000):** 30948 **Payroll Expense ($000):** 13354 **Personnel:** 268

ROYERSFORD—Montgomery County

◇ **PHYSICIANS CARE SURGICAL HOSPITAL (390324)**, 454 Enterprise Drive, Zip 19468–1200; tel. 610/495–3330 **A**9 10 21 **F**8 29 79 81 107 119
Primary Contact: David Orskey, Administrator
Web address: www.phycarehospital.com
Control: Partnership, Investor–owned, for–profit **Service:** Surgical

> **Staffed Beds:** 12 **Admissions:** 462 **Census:** 2 **Births:** 0 **Personnel:** 53

SAINT MARYS—Elk County

ELK REGIONAL HEALTH CENTER (390154), 763 Johnsonburg Road, Zip 15857–3498; tel. 814/788–8000, (Total facility includes 138 beds in nursing home–type unit) **A**9 10 20 **F**3 6 11 13 15 28 29 30 34 35 40 44 45 56 57 59 70 75 76 77 79 81 82 85 86 87 89 93 98 100 103 107 110 111 114 118 119 128 129 130 131 133 135 144 146 147 148
Primary Contact: Rose Campbell, R.N., President
CFO: Laurie MacDonald, Vice President Finance
CMO: David Johe, M.D., President Medical Staff
CIO: Mary Ann Schwabenbauer, Director Information Technology
CHR: Seanna D'Amore, Director Human Resources
Web address: www.elkregional.org
Control: Other not–for–profit (including NFP Corporation) **Service:** General Medical and Surgical

> **Staffed Beds:** 218 **Admissions:** 3171 **Census:** 165 **Outpatient Visits:** 165575 **Births:** 233 **Total Expense ($000):** 71734 **Payroll Expense ($000):** 35406 **Personnel:** 750

SAYRE—Bradford County

✠ **ROBERT PACKER HOSPITAL (390079)**, 1 Guthrie Square, Zip 18840–1698; tel. 570/888–6666 **A**1 2 3 5 9 10 12 13 19 **F**3 11 12 13 15 17 18 20 22 24 26 28 29 30 31 34 37 38 40 43 45 47 49 50 51 57 58 59 60 61 64 70 73 74 75 76 78 79 81 82 85 86 87 89 92 93 98 99 100 101 102 103 105 107 108 110 111 114 115 116 117 118 119 120 121 123 126 129 130 132 141 142 145 146 148 **S** Guthrie Healthcare System, Sayre, PA
Primary Contact: Marie T. Droege, President
CFO: Minh Dang, Vice President Finance
CMO: Brian Fillipo, M.D., Chief Medical Officer
CIO: Dale Swingle, Vice President Information Services
CHR: Frank Pinkosky, Senior Vice President
CNO: Bonnie J. Onofre, MS, Vice President and Chief Nursing Officer
Web address: www.guthrie.org
Control: Other not–for–profit (including NFP Corporation) **Service:** General Medical and Surgical

> **Staffed Beds:** 253 **Admissions:** 14093 **Census:** 185 **Outpatient Visits:** 154432 **Births:** 739 **Total Expense ($000):** 239391 **Payroll Expense ($000):** 75325 **Personnel:** 1380

SCRANTON—Lackawanna County

✠ △ **ALLIED SERVICES REHABILITATION HOSPITAL (393030)**, 475 Morgan Highway, Zip 18508–2605, Mailing Address: P.O. Box 1103, Zip 18501–1103; tel. 570/348–1300 **A**1 7 10 **F**11 29 34 53 56 59 64 74 75 77 78 79 86 87 90 91 93 94 96 130 143 146
Primary Contact: Karen Kearney, Vice President Inpatient Rehabilitation Services
CFO: Michael Avvisato, Senior Vice President and Chief Financial Officer
CMO: Gregory Basting, M.D., Vice President Medical Affairs
CIO: John Regula, Chief Information Officer
CHR: Judy P. Oprisko, Vice President
CNO: Jeana Sluck, R.N., Executive Director Nursing Clinical Inpatient Departments
Web address: www.allied–services.org
Control: Other not–for–profit (including NFP Corporation) **Service:** Rehabilitation

> **Staffed Beds:** 117 **Admissions:** 2126 **Census:** 59 **Outpatient Visits:** 67670 **Births:** 0 **Total Expense ($000):** 35646 **Payroll Expense ($000):** 17355 **Personnel:** 355

COMMUNITY MEDICAL CENTER HEALTHCARE SYSTEM See Geisinger–Community Medical Center

✠ **GEISINGER–COMMUNITY MEDICAL CENTER (390001)**, 1800 Mulberry Street, Zip 18510–2369; tel. 570/703–8000, (Nonreporting) **A**1 3 5 9 10 **S** Geisinger Health System, Danville, PA
Primary Contact: Anthony Aquilina, D.O., Interim Chief Executive Officer
CFO: Edward Chabalowski, Chief Financial Officer
CMO: Anthony Aquilina, D.O., Chief Medical Officer
CHR: Lois Wolfe, Director Human Resources
Web address: www.cmccare.org/
Control: Other not–for–profit (including NFP Corporation) **Service:** General Medical and Surgical

> **Staffed Beds:** 248

MERCY HOSPITAL OF SCRANTON See Regional Hospital of Scranton

✠ △ **MOSES TAYLOR HOSPITAL (390119)**, 700 Quincy Avenue, Zip 18510–1724; tel. 570/770–5000 **A**1 3 5 7 9 10 19 **F**3 7 13 15 18 29 30 31 34 40 49 51 56 57 59 60 61 62 64 65 66 68 70 72 74 75 76 77 78 79 81 85 86 87 89 93 98 103 107 108 110 111 114 129 130 132 135 146 147 **P**6 **S** Community Health Systems, Inc., Franklin, TN
Primary Contact: Justin Davis, Chief Executive Officer
CFO: Thomas Bisignani, Chief Financial Officer
CMO: Mary Sewatsky, M.D., Chief Medical Officer
CHR: Elizabeth Leo, Chief Human Resources Officer
CNO: Patricia Seliga, R.N., Chief Nursing Officer
Web address: www.mth.org
Control: Corporation, Investor–owned, for–profit **Service:** General Medical and Surgical

> **Staffed Beds:** 217 **Admissions:** 9314 **Census:** 119 **Outpatient Visits:** 159273 **Births:** 2544 **Total Expense ($000):** 126506 **Payroll Expense ($000):** 41816 **Personnel:** 869

✠ △ **REGIONAL HOSPITAL OF SCRANTON (390237)**, 746 Jefferson Avenue, Zip 18510–1624; tel. 570/348–7100 **A**1 2 3 5 7 9 10 12 **F**7 8 11 12 15 17 18 20 22 24 26 28 29 30 31 34 35 39 40 44 45 46 47 48 49 50 51 53 54 57 58 59 60 61 63 64 65 66 68 70 74 75 77 78 79 81 85 86 87 91 92 93 97 107 108 109 110 111 112 113 114 115 116 117 118 119 120 121 122 123 124 126 130 132 143 144 145 146 147 148 **P**6 **S** Community Health Systems, Inc., Franklin, TN
Primary Contact: Brooks Turkel, Chief Executive Officer
CFO: Stephen Franko, Vice President Finance and Chief Financial Officer
CMO: Anthony Yanni, M.D., Vice President Medical Affairs
CIO: Jorge Coronel, Chief Information Officer
Web address: www.regionalhospitalofscranton.net
Control: Corporation, Investor–owned, for–profit **Service:** General Medical and Surgical

> **Staffed Beds:** 192 **Admissions:** 9322 **Census:** 132 **Outpatient Visits:** 101119 **Births:** 0 **Total Expense ($000):** 152544 **Payroll Expense ($000):** 48097 **Personnel:** 803

SELLERSVILLE—Bucks County

✠ **GRAND VIEW HOSPITAL (390057)**, 700 Lawn Avenue, Zip 18960–1548, Mailing Address: P.O. Box 902, Zip 18960–0902; tel. 215/453–4000 **A**1 2 9 10 **F**3 7 11 13 15 18 19 28 29 31 32 34 35 37 40 44 45 49 50 54 56 57 58 59 61 62 63 64 65 68 70 71 72 74 76 77 78 79 81 84 85 86 87 89 90 93 96 97 107 108 110 111 114 115 117 118 119 121 123 130 131 132 134 135 145 146 147 148 **P**6
Primary Contact: Jean Keeler, President and Chief Executive Officer
COO: J. Mark Horne, Senior Vice President and Chief Operating Officer
CFO: Michael Keen, Senior Vice President and Chief Financial Officer
CMO: Jane Ferry, M.D., Vice President Medical Affairs
CIO: Jane Doll Loveless, Vice President Information Services
CNO: Kathleen Burkey, R.N., Vice President of Nursing
Web address: www.gvh.org
Control: Other not–for–profit (including NFP Corporation) **Service:** General Medical and Surgical

> **Staffed Beds:** 202 **Admissions:** 8767 **Census:** 105 **Outpatient Visits:** 306934 **Births:** 1434 **Total Expense ($000):** 167801 **Payroll Expense ($000):** 85277 **Personnel:** 1405

SENECA—Venango County

☐ **UPMC NORTHWEST (390091)**, 100 Fairfield Drive, Zip 16346–2130; tel. 814/676–7600, (Total facility includes 16 beds in nursing home–type unit) **A**1 2 9 10 19 **F**3 6 8 10 11 13 15 18 28 29 30 31 34 35 40 45 47 50 56 57 59 60 62 63 64 68 70 74 75 76 78 79 81 82 83 84 85 86 87 89 90 93 96 97 98 100 101 102 103 107 108 110 111 115 118 119 121 128 130 131 132 135 144 145 146 147 148 **S** UPMC, Pittsburgh, PA
Primary Contact: David Gibbons, President
COO: David J. Patton, Vice President Operations
CFO: W. Roger McCauley, Senior Vice President Administration and Chief Financial Officer
CMO: John Shonnard, M.D., Medical Director
CHR: Courtney Cox, Vice President Human Resources
Web address: www.upmc.com/locations/hospitals/northwest/Pages/default.aspx
Control: Other not–for–profit (including NFP Corporation) **Service:** General Medical and Surgical

> **Staffed Beds:** 180 **Admissions:** 7113 **Census:** 99 **Outpatient Visits:** 135514 **Births:** 547 **Total Expense ($000):** 90268 **Payroll Expense ($000):** 29383 **Personnel:** 622

Many Facility Codes have changed. Please refer to the AHA Guide Code Chart. © 2014 AHA Guide

SEWICKLEY—Allegheny County

⊞ **HEALTHSOUTH REHABILITATION HOSPITAL (393045)**, 303 Camp Meeting Road, Zip 15143–8322; tel. 412/741–9500 **A**1 10 **F**29 34 56 57 59 60 64 65 74 75 87 90 91 92 93 95 96 100 132 146 148 **S** HEALTHSOUTH Corporation, Birmingham, AL
Primary Contact: Leah Laffey, R.N., Chief Executive Officer
CFO: Daniel A. Vrana, Area Controller
CMO: Shelana Gibbs–McElvy, M.D., Medical Director
CIO: Jamie Smith, Supervisor Health Information Management Systems
CHR: Melissa Coleman, Director Human Resources
CNO: Christie Ryan, Chief Nursing Officer
Web address: www.healthsouthsewickley.com
Control: Corporation, Investor–owned, for–profit **Service:** Rehabilitation

Staffed Beds: 44 **Admissions:** 849 **Census:** 35 **Outpatient Visits:** 4006 **Births:** 0 **Total Expense ($000):** 10981 **Payroll Expense ($000):** 5682 **Personnel:** 92

☐ **SEWICKLEY VALLEY HOSPITAL, (A DIVISION OF VALLEY MEDICAL FACILITIES) (390037)**, 720 Blackburn Road, Zip 15143–1459; tel. 412/741–6600 **A**1 6 9 10 **F**3 8 11 12 13 14 15 18 20 28 29 30 32 34 35 38 40 46 49 50 53 54 55 57 59 60 64 70 74 75 76 77 78 79 81 82 84 85 86 90 92 93 96 97 98 100 101 102 103 104 107 108 109 110 111 115 118 119 120 121 126 129 130 132 135 145 **P**6 **S** Heritage Valley Health System, Beaver, PA
Primary Contact: Norman F. Mitry, President and Chief Executive Officer
CFO: Bryan J. Randall, Vice President Finance and Chief Financial Officer
CMO: John Cinicola, M.D., Chief Medical Officer
CIO: David Carleton, Chief Information Officer
CHR: Bruce Edwards, Vice President Human Resources
CNO: Linda Homyk, Chief Nursing Officer
Web address: www.heritagevalley.org
Control: Other not–for–profit (including NFP Corporation) **Service:** General Medical and Surgical

Staffed Beds: 179 **Admissions:** 8710 **Census:** 104 **Outpatient Visits:** 48369 **Births:** 851 **Total Expense ($000):** 132100 **Payroll Expense ($000):** 52059

SHARON—Mercer County

⊞ **SHARON REGIONAL HEALTH SYSTEM (390211)**, 740 East State Street, Zip 16146–3395; tel. 724/983–3911, (Total facility includes 38 beds in nursing home–type unit) **A**1 6 9 10 **F**3 5 11 12 13 15 17 18 19 20 22 24 26 28 29 30 31 34 35 38 39 40 44 45 47 48 49 50 51 54 56 57 58 59 60 62 63 64 65 70 73 74 75 76 77 78 79 80 81 82 84 85 86 87 89 90 92 93 96 98 99 100 101 102 103 104 105 107 108 110 111 114 115 118 119 120 121 123 127 128 129 130 131 132 134 135 146 147 148 **P**6 8 **S** Community Health Systems, Inc., Franklin, TN
Primary Contact: John R. Janoso, President and Chief Executive Officer
CFO: Jeffrey Chrobak, Vice President Finance and Chief Financial Officer
CHR: John Davidson, Vice President Human Resources
Web address: www.sharonregional.com
Control: Other not–for–profit (including NFP Corporation) **Service:** General Medical and Surgical

Staffed Beds: 256 **Admissions:** 9280 **Census:** 142 **Outpatient Visits:** 386434 **Births:** 262 **Total Expense ($000):** 166374

SHICKSHINNY—Luzerne County

CLEAR BROOK LODGE, 890 Bethel Road, Zip 18655; tel. 570/864–3116, (Nonreporting)
Primary Contact: Nicholas Colangelo, Chief Executive Officer
Web address: www.clearbrookinc.com
Control: Other not–for–profit (including NFP Corporation) **Service:** Alcoholism and other chemical dependency

Staffed Beds: 65

SHIPPENSBURG—Franklin County

☐ **ROXBURY TREATMENT CENTER (394050)**, 601 Roxbury Road, Zip 17257–9302; tel. 800/648–4673, (Nonreporting) **A**1 9 10 **S** Universal Health Services, Inc., King of Prussia, PA
Primary Contact: Shauna Radzieski, Chief Executive Officer
Web address: www.roxburyhospital.com
Control: Corporation, Investor–owned, for–profit **Service:** Psychiatric

Staffed Beds: 94

SOMERSET—Somerset County

★ **SOMERSET HOSPITAL (390039)**, 225 South Center Avenue, Zip 15501–2088; tel. 814/443–5000 **A**9 10 20 **F**3 8 11 13 15 17 18 20 22 26 28 29 30 32 34 35 40 45 49 50 53 57 59 62 63 64 68 74 76 77 79 80 81 82 85 86 87 89 93 97 98 99 100 103 104 107 108 111 115 119 129 130 131 132 133 135 141 146 147 148
Primary Contact: Craig M. Saylor, Interim CEO
COO: Andy Rush, Senior Vice President and Chief Operating Officer
CFO: Matthew Kociola, Senior Vice President and Chief Financial Officer
CIO: Jonathan Bauer, Director Information Systems
CHR: Mark P. Frick, Senior Vice President Human Resources
CNO: Suellen Lichtenfels, Vice President and Chief Nursing Officer
Web address: www.somersethospital.com
Control: Other not–for–profit (including NFP Corporation) **Service:** General Medical and Surgical

Staffed Beds: 111 **Admissions:** 3615 **Census:** 44 **Outpatient Visits:** 145104 **Births:** 355 **Total Expense ($000):** 62173 **Payroll Expense ($000):** 25686 **Personnel:** 636

SPRINGFIELD—Delaware County

SPRINGFIELD HOSPITAL See Crozer–Chester Medical Center, Upland

STATE COLLEGE—Centre County

⊞ **MOUNT NITTANY MEDICAL CENTER (390268)**, 1800 Park Avenue, Zip 16803–6797; tel. 814/231–7000 **A**1 2 3 5 9 10 **F**3 7 13 15 17 20 22 28 29 30 31 35 40 51 57 59 64 68 70 73 74 75 76 77 78 79 80 81 82 85 87 89 93 98 100 101 102 107 108 111 114 115 118 119 121 126 129 130 132 135 143 144 146 148
Primary Contact: Steven E. Brown, FACHE, President and Chief Executive Officer
CFO: Richard Wisniewski, Senior Vice President Finance and Chief Financial Officer
CMO: Jeffrey Ratner, M.D., Senior Vice President Medical Affairs
CIO: Wayne Thompson, Senior Vice President and Chief Information Officer
CHR: Jerry Dittmann, Vice President Human Resources
CNO: Janet Schachtner, R.N., Senior Vice President, Patient Care Services
Web address: www.mountnittany.org
Control: Other not–for–profit (including NFP Corporation) **Service:** General Medical and Surgical

Staffed Beds: 260 **Admissions:** 11569 **Census:** 130 **Outpatient Visits:** 269853 **Births:** 1363 **Total Expense ($000):** 309764 **Payroll Expense ($000):** 126796 **Personnel:** 1324

SUNBURY—Northumberland County

⊞ **SUNBURY COMMUNITY HOSPITAL AND OUTPATIENT CENTER (390084)**, 350 North Eleventh Street, Zip 17801–1611; tel. 570/286–3333, (Nonreporting) **A**1 9 10 **S** Community Health Systems, Inc., Franklin, TN
Primary Contact: Jeff Hunt, Chief Executive Officer
CFO: James J. Pachucki, Jr., Chief Financial Officer
CMO: Hasan Askari, M.D., Chief of Staff
CIO: Fax Rector, III, Director Information Technology
CHR: Talia Beatty, Director Human Resources
CNO: Catharine L. Keister, Chief Nursing Officer
Web address: www.sunburyhospital.com
Control: Other not–for–profit (including NFP Corporation) **Service:** General Medical and Surgical

Staffed Beds: 76

SUSQUEHANNA—Susquehanna County

BARNES–KASSON COUNTY HOSPITAL (391309), 2872 Turnpike Street, Zip 18847–2771; tel. 570/853–3135, (Total facility includes 58 beds in nursing home–type unit) **A**9 10 18 **F**3 7 8 11 15 17 18 28 29 30 34 35 39 40 50 59 62 64 65 66 68 70 77 79 81 86 93 94 97 100 107 111 114 119 127 128 130 133 134 147
Primary Contact: Sara F. Adornato, Executive Director
CFO: Sara F. Adornato, Executive Director
CMO: Pravinchandra Patel, M.D., Chief Medical Officer
CIO: Eric Detwiler, Director Information Technology
CHR: William D. Iveson, Jr., Clinical Operations Officer and Director Human Resources
Web address: www.barnes–kasson.org
Control: Other not–for–profit (including NFP Corporation) **Service:** General Medical and Surgical

Staffed Beds: 83 **Admissions:** 1008 **Census:** 62 **Outpatient Visits:** 76382 **Births:** 0 **Total Expense ($000):** 20549 **Personnel:** 253

PA

Hospital, Medicare Provider Number, Address, Telephone, Approval, Facility, and Physician Codes, Health Care System

★ American Hospital Association (AHA) membership
☐ The Joint Commission accreditation   ◇ DNV Healthcare Inc. accreditation
○ Healthcare Facilities Accreditation Program
△ Commission on Accreditation of Rehabilitation Facilities (CARF) accreditation

PA

TITUSVILLE—Crawford County

TITUSVILLE AREA HOSPITAL (390122), 406 West Oak Street,
Zip 16354–1404; tel. 814/827–1851, (Nonreporting) **A**9 10 20
Primary Contact: Anthony J. Nasralla, FACHE, President and Chief Executive
Officer
CFO: Paul Mattis, Vice President Finance
CMO: William Sonnenberg, M.D., President Medical Staff
CIO: Deanna Callahan, Director Information Systems
CHR: Jeffrey Saintz, Vice President Human Resources
Web address: www.titusvillehospital.org
Control: Other not–for–profit (including NFP Corporation) **Service:** General
Medical and Surgical

> **Staffed Beds:** 50

TORRANCE—Westmoreland County

TORRANCE STATE HOSPITAL (394026), Torrance Road, Zip 15779–0111,
Mailing Address: P.O. Box 111, Zip 15779–0111; tel. 724/459–8000 **A**10 **F**39
75 98 130 135 143 146 147 148
Primary Contact: Edna I. McCutcheon, Chief Executive Officer
COO: R. Brad Snyder, Chief Operating Officer
CFO: Michael Yahner, Chief Financial Officer
CMO: Herbert G. Chissell, M.D., Chief Medical Officer
Web address: www.dpw.state.pa.us
Control: State–Government, nonfederal **Service:** Psychiatric

> **Staffed Beds:** 351 **Admissions:** 408 **Census:** 330 **Outpatient Visits:** 0
> **Births:** 0 **Personnel:** 637

TOWANDA—Bradford County

MEMORIAL HOSPITAL (390236), 91 Hospital Drive, Zip 18848–9702;
tel. 570/265–2191, (Total facility includes 162 beds in nursing home–type unit)
A9 10 **F**3 7 11 13 15 17 28 29 34 35 40 45 50 57 59 62 63 68 70 75 76 79
81 82 85 93 107 110 111 114 119 128 129 130 133 143 **S** QHR,
Brentwood, TN
Primary Contact: Gary A. Baker, President
COO: William K. Rohrbach, Chief Operating Officer
CFO: William K. Rohrbach, Vice President Fiscal Affairs
CMO: Joseph Cama, M.D., President Medical Staff
CIO: Karen Brown, Manager Information Technology
CHR: Linda Berry, Vice President Human Resources
CNO: Lynn Dibble, Vice President Patient Care Services
Web address: www.memorialhospital.org
Control: Other not–for–profit (including NFP Corporation) **Service:** General
Medical and Surgical

> **Staffed Beds:** 203 **Admissions:** 1532 **Census:** 148 **Outpatient Visits:** 68102
> **Births:** 186 **Total Expense ($000):** 34255

TRANSFER—Mercer County

EDGEWOOD SURGICAL HOSPITAL (390307), 239 Edgewood Drive Extension,
Zip 16154–1817; tel. 724/646–0400, (Nonreporting) **A**9 10
Primary Contact: Michael Torn, Chief Executive Officer
Web address: www.edgewoodsurgical.com
Control: Corporation, Investor–owned, for–profit **Service:** Surgical

> **Staffed Beds:** 10

TROY—Bradford County

★ **TROY COMMUNITY HOSPITAL (391305)**, 275 Guthrie Drive, Zip 16947;
tel. 570/297–2121 **A**9 10 18 **F**3 11 15 28 30 34 40 45 50 57 64 75 81 82
85 87 93 96 107 110 111 119 129 130 133 135 146 148 **S** Guthrie
Healthcare System, Sayre, PA
Primary Contact: Staci Covey, R.N., MS, President
CFO: Bernie Smith, Chief Financial Officer
CMO: Vance A. Good, M.D., Chief Medical Staff
CIO: Dale Swingle, Vice President Information Services
CHR: Frank Pinkosky, Executive Vice President
CNO: Lori Barnett, R.N., Chief Nursing Officer
Web address: www.guthrie.org
Control: Other not–for–profit (including NFP Corporation) **Service:** General
Medical and Surgical

> **Staffed Beds:** 25 **Admissions:** 816 **Census:** 20 **Outpatient Visits:** 27732
> **Births:** 0 **Total Expense ($000):** 14445 **Payroll Expense ($000):** 5008
> **Personnel:** 105

TUNKHANNOCK— County

☒ **TYLER MEMORIAL HOSPITAL (390192)**, 5950 State Route 6,
Zip 18657–7905; tel. 570/836–2161 **A**1 9 10 **F**15 18 20 22 24 26 28 29 30
31 34 35 40 50 54 56 58 60 62 64 70 75 77 78 79 81 82 86 87 89 92 93
107 108 110 111 119 120 121 129 130 133 146 147 148 **S** Community
Health Systems, Inc., Franklin, TN
Primary Contact: Diane Ljungquist, R.N., MS, Chief Executive Officer
CFO: Robert Stiekes, Chief Financial Officer
CMO: Terrance Chilson, Chief of Staff
CNO: Patricia Casals, MSN, Chief Nursing Officer
Web address: www.tylermemorialhospital.net
Control: Corporation, Investor–owned, for–profit **Service:** General Medical and
Surgical

> **Staffed Beds:** 48 **Admissions:** 1081 **Census:** 12 **Births:** 0 **Personnel:** 180

TYRONE—Blair County

TYRONE HOSPITAL (391307), 187 Hospital Drive, Zip 16686–1808;
tel. 814/684–1255 **A**9 10 18 **F**3 15 40 75 77 79 81 82 93 107 119 130
133 146
Primary Contact: Stephen Gildea, Chief Executive Officer
CFO: Todd Dieffenbach, Chief Financial Officer
CMO: Kelly Biggs, M.D., Chief Medical Officer
CHR: Rosemary Jorden Best, Director Human Resources
CNO: Sharon Fisher, R.N., Chief Nursing Officer
Web address: www.tyronehospital.org
Control: Other not–for–profit (including NFP Corporation) **Service:** General
Medical and Surgical

> **Staffed Beds:** 25 **Admissions:** 591 **Census:** 6 **Outpatient Visits:** 36213
> **Births:** 0 **Total Expense ($000):** 20767 **Payroll Expense ($000):** 10428
> **Personnel:** 180

UNIONTOWN—Fayette County

☒ **UNIONTOWN HOSPITAL (390041)**, 500 West Berkeley Street,
Zip 15401–5596; tel. 724/430–5000, (Total facility includes 24 beds in nursing
home–type unit) **A**1 9 10 **F**11 12 13 15 18 20 22 26 28 29 34 35 40 45 49 51
54 57 59 64 70 73 74 75 76 77 78 79 81 84 89 90 92 93 95 96 102 107
108 110 111 114 115 118 119 128 130 132 135 146 148
Primary Contact: Steven P. Handy, CPA, Interim Chief Executive Officer
CFO: Steven P. Handy, CPA, Senior Vice President, Chief Financial Officer and
Chief Information Officer
CIO: Steven P. Handy, CPA, Senior Vice President, Chief Financial Officer and
Chief Information Officer
CHR: James Proud, Vice President Human Resources and Marketing
CNO: Betty Ann Rock, Vice President Nursing and Chief Nursing Officer
Web address: www.uniontownhospital.com
Control: Other not–for–profit (including NFP Corporation) **Service:** General
Medical and Surgical

> **Staffed Beds:** 180 **Admissions:** 10210 **Census:** 135 **Outpatient Visits:**
> 236783 **Births:** 1025 **Total Expense ($000):** 124562 **Payroll Expense**
> **($000):** 46619 **Personnel:** 1038

UPLAND—Delaware County

☒ **CROZER–CHESTER MEDICAL CENTER (390180)**, One Medical Center
Boulevard, Zip 19013–3995; tel. 610/447–2000, (Includes SPRINGFIELD
HOSPITAL, 190 West Sproul Road, Springfield, Zip 19064–2097;
tel. 610/328–8700; TAYLOR HOSPITAL, 175 East Chester Pike, Ridley Park,
Zip 19078–2212; tel. 610/595–6000) **A**1 2 3 5 8 10 12 13 **F**2 3 5 6 7 8 11
12 13 14 15 16 17 18 20 22 24 26 28 29 30 31 32 34 35 37 38 40 41 43
44 45 46 49 50 51 52 54 55 56 57 58 59 61 62 63 64 65 66 68 70 72 74
75 76 77 78 79 81 82 83 84 85 86 87 89 90 92 93 94 96 97 98 99 100
101 102 103 104 105 107 108 109 110 111 114 115 116 117 118 119 120
121 123 124 126 129 130 131 132 134 135 138 143 146 147 148 **P**6
S Crozer–Keystone Health System, Springfield, PA
Primary Contact: Patrick J. Gavin, President
CMO: Sat Arora, M.D., President Medical and Dental Staff
CIO: Robert E. Wilson, Vice President and Chief Information Officer
Web address: www.crozer.org
Control: Other not–for–profit (including NFP Corporation) **Service:** General
Medical and Surgical

> **Staffed Beds:** 428 **Admissions:** 23057 **Census:** 302 **Outpatient Visits:**
> 473763 **Births:** 1632 **Total Expense ($000):** 536204 **Payroll Expense**
> **($000):** 203541 **Personnel:** 2667

WARREN—Warren County

WARREN GENERAL HOSPITAL (390146), Two Crescent Park West, Zip 16365–0068, Mailing Address: P.O. Box 68, Zip 16365–0068; tel. 814/723–4973 **A**9 10 **F**4 11 13 15 28 29 30 31 34 35 39 40 44 45 50 51 57 59 62 63 64 70 76 77 78 79 81 84 85 86 87 89 92 93 97 98 103 107 108 110 111 113 114 117 119 120 121 130 131 133 146 **P**6
Primary Contact: Randy California, Interim Chief Executive Officer
COO: Randy California, Chief Operating Officer
CFO: Julie Jacobs, Chief Financial Officer
CMO: John Maljovec, M.D., Medical Director
CIO: Douglas Megill, Manager Information Systems
CHR: Stacy Ryan, Corporate Director Human Resources
CNO: Trudy Bloomquist, Director of Nursing
Web address: www.wgh.org
Control: Other not–for–profit (including NFP Corporation) **Service:** General Medical and Surgical

Staffed Beds: 89 **Admissions:** 3358 **Census:** 42 **Outpatient Visits:** 221811 **Births:** 373 **Total Expense ($000):** 73766 **Payroll Expense ($000):** 33126 **Personnel:** 518

WARREN STATE HOSPITAL (394016), 33 Main Drive, Zip 16365–5001; tel. 814/723–5500 **A**10 **F**4 39 50 56 75 77 82 98 100 101 103 128 130 132 135 143 146 **P**6
Primary Contact: Charlotte M. Uber, Chief Executive Officer
COO: Ronnie Cropper, Chief Operating Officer
CFO: Terry Crambes, Manager Finance
CMO: Asha Prabhu, M.D., Chief Medical Officer
CIO: Karen Byler, Information Technology Generalist
CHR: Nancy Saullo, Director Human Resources
CNO: Sara Flasher, Chief Nurse Executive
Web address: www.dpw.pa.gov
Control: State–Government, nonfederal **Service:** Psychiatric

Staffed Beds: 190 **Admissions:** 103 **Census:** 180 **Outpatient Visits:** 0 **Births:** 0 **Total Expense ($000):** 41105 **Payroll Expense ($000):** 20214 **Personnel:** 429

WASHINGTON—Washington County

☐ **ADVANCED SURGICAL HOSPITAL (390323)**, 100 Trich Drive Suite 1, Zip 15301–5990; tel. 724/884–0710, (Nonreporting) **A**1 10
Primary Contact: Anne S. Hast, R.N., Chief Executive Officer
CFO: Diane Hritz, Chief Financial Officer
Web address: www.ashospital.net
Control: Partnership, Investor–owned, for–profit **Service:** Orthopedic

Staffed Beds: 14

✠ **WASHINGTON HOSPITAL (390042)**, 155 Wilson Avenue, Zip 15301–3398; tel. 724/225–7000 **A**1 3 5 6 9 10 13 **F**3 5 11 12 13 15 18 20 22 24 26 28 29 30 31 32 34 35 36 38 39 40 45 46 49 50 53 54 56 57 59 60 61 63 64 65 70 74 75 76 77 78 79 81 82 83 84 85 86 89 90 91 92 93 94 96 97 98 99 100 101 102 103 107 108 110 111 114 115 119 126 130 131 132 134 135 146 147 148 **P**1 7
Primary Contact: Gary B. Weinstein, President and Chief Executive Officer
COO: Brook Ward, Executive Vice President
CFO: Alisa Rucker, Vice President Finance and Chief Financial Officer
CMO: Paul T. Cullen, M.D., Vice President Medical Affairs
CIO: Rodney Louk, Vice President Information Systems
CHR: Barbara A. McCullough, Vice President Human Resources
CNO: Karen A. Bray, R.N., Vice President Patient Care Services
Web address: www.washingtonhospital.org
Control: Other not–for–profit (including NFP Corporation) **Service:** General Medical and Surgical

Staffed Beds: 260 **Admissions:** 12628 **Census:** 143 **Outpatient Visits:** 671716 **Births:** 1022 **Total Expense ($000):** 222472 **Payroll Expense ($000):** 97491 **Personnel:** 1502

WAYNESBORO—Franklin County

✠ **WAYNESBORO HOSPITAL (390138)**, 501 East Main Street, Zip 17268–2394; tel. 717/765–4000 **A**1 9 10 19 **F**3 11 13 15 29 30 34 40 45 49 50 57 59 64 65 68 74 75 76 77 79 81 85 86 87 91 92 93 94 107 108 110 111 115 118 119 130 131 132 133 135 146 147 148 **P**8 **S** Summit Health, Chambersburg, PA
Primary Contact: Melissa Dubrow, Chief Operating Officer
COO: Melissa Dubrow, Vice President and Chief Operating Officer
CFO: Kimberly Rzomp, Vice President Finance
CMO: Thomas Anderson, M.D., Vice President Medical Affairs
CIO: Michele Zeigler, Vice President Information Services
CHR: Jennifer Knight, Manager Human Resources
CNO: Jill Keller, R.N., Vice President for Nursing Services, Quality and Risk Management
Web address: www.summithealth.org
Control: Other not–for–profit (including NFP Corporation) **Service:** General Medical and Surgical

Staffed Beds: 64 **Admissions:** 2712 **Census:** 26 **Outpatient Visits:** 97893 **Births:** 365 **Total Expense ($000):** 51352 **Payroll Expense ($000):** 26931 **Personnel:** 423

WAYNESBURG—Greene County

☐ **SOUTHWEST REGIONAL MEDICAL CENTER (390150)**, 350 Bonar Avenue, Zip 15370–1608; tel. 724/627–3101 **A**1 9 10 **F**3 10 15 18 29 30 40 51 53 54 60 62 64 70 74 77 78 80 81 82 85 87 93 98 102 103 104 105 107 108 111 116 117 118 119 129 130 133 144 146 147 148 **S** RegionalCare Hospital Partners, Brentwood, TN
Primary Contact: Cynthia Cowie, Chief Executive Officer
COO: Janel Mudry, Chief Operating Officer
CFO: James C. Rutkowski, Chief Financial Officer
CMO: Jamie Boris, M.D., President Medical Staff
CIO: Leslie Hayhurst, Director Information Systems
CHR: Patricia Marshall, Assistant Administrator Human Resources
CNO: Cynthia Cowie, Chief Nursing Officer
Web address: www.sw–rmc.com
Control: Corporation, Investor–owned, for–profit **Service:** General Medical and Surgical

Staffed Beds: 77 **Admissions:** 2666 **Census:** 35 **Births:** 0 **Total Expense ($000):** 36859 **Personnel:** 360

WELLSBORO—Tioga County

✠ **SOLDIERS AND SAILORS MEMORIAL HOSPITAL (390043)**, 32–36 Central Avenue, Zip 16901–1899; tel. 570/724–1631 **A**1 9 10 20 **F**3 11 13 15 17 28 34 40 48 49 64 65 70 75 76 79 81 85 93 98 102 103 104 107 108 110 111 115 118 119 129 130 146 **P**7 **S** Susquehanna Health System, Williamsport, PA
Primary Contact: Janie Hilfiger, President
CFO: Ronald Gilbert, Jr., Chief Financial Officer
CMO: Walter Laibinis, M.D., Chief Medical Officer
CIO: Timothy E. Schoener, Senior Vice President and Chief Information Officer
CHR: Christine A. Ballard, Vice President Human Resources
CNO: Matt Romania, Director of Nursing
Web address: www.susquehannahealth.org
Control: Other not–for–profit (including NFP Corporation) **Service:** General Medical and Surgical

Staffed Beds: 83 **Admissions:** 2753 **Census:** 30 **Outpatient Visits:** 102414 **Births:** 329 **Total Expense ($000):** 48380 **Payroll Expense ($000):** 20937 **Personnel:** 486

WERNERSVILLE—Berks County

WERNERSVILLE STATE HOSPITAL (394014), Route 422, Zip 19565–0300, Mailing Address: P.O. Box 300, Zip 19565–0300; tel. 610/678–3411 **A**10 **F**30 39 75 77 98 103 130 135 146
Primary Contact: Andrea Kepler, Chief Executive Officer
COO: Cheryl Benson, Chief Operating Officer
CMO: Dale K. Adair, M.D., Chief Medical Officer
CIO: William Edwards, Information Technology Generalist
CHR: Melvin McMinn, Director Human Resources
Web address: www.dpw.state.pa.us/
Control: State–Government, nonfederal **Service:** Psychiatric

Staffed Beds: 265 **Admissions:** 61 **Census:** 255 **Outpatient Visits:** 0 **Births:** 0 **Total Expense ($000):** 57306 **Payroll Expense ($000):** 27371 **Personnel:** 573

PA

Hospital, Medicare Provider Number, Address, Telephone, Approval, Facility, and Physician Codes, Health Care System

★ American Hospital Association (AHA) membership
☐ The Joint Commission accreditation
◇ DNV Healthcare Inc. accreditation
○ Healthcare Facilities Accreditation Program
△ Commission on Accreditation of Rehabilitation Facilities (CARF) accreditation

PA

WEST CHESTER—Chester County

✠ **CHESTER COUNTY HOSPITAL (390179)**, 701 East Marshall Street, Zip 19380–4412; tel. 610/431–5000 **A**1 2 3 5 9 10 **F**3 11 13 15 17 18 20 22 24 26 28 29 31 34 35 36 40 45 46 49 50 54 55 56 57 59 64 68 70 72 74 75 76 77 78 79 81 84 85 86 87 89 92 93 94 97 107 108 110 111 114 115 116 117 118 119 121 123 126 130 131 132 135 146 147 148 **P**6 **S** University of Pennsylvania Health System, Philadelphia, PA
Primary Contact: Michael J. Duncan, System Chief Executive Officer
COO: Michael Barber, System Chief Operating Officer
CFO: Kenneth E. Flickinger, System Chief Financial Officer
CMO: Richard D. Donze, D.O., Senior Vice President Medical Affairs
CIO: Karen Pinsky, M.D., Chief Medical Information Officer
CHR: Jacqueline Felicetti, Director Human Resources
CNO: Angela Coladonato, MSN, Chief Nursing Officer
Web address: www.chestercountyhospital.org
Control: Other not-for-profit (including NFP Corporation) **Service:** General Medical and Surgical

Staffed Beds: 221 **Admissions:** 13128 **Census:** 151 **Outpatient Visits:** 246802 **Births:** 2273 **Total Expense ($000):** 239658 **Payroll Expense ($000):** 101957 **Personnel:** 1601

✠ **LIFECARE HOSPITALS OF CHESTER COUNTY (392048)**, 400 East Marshall Street, Zip 19380–5412; tel. 484/826–0400 **A**1 9 10 **F**1 **P**5 **S** LifeCare Management Services, Plano, TX
Primary Contact: Garrett Arneson, Chief Executive Officer
Web address: www.lifecare-hospitals.com
Control: Corporation, Investor-owned, for-profit **Service:** Long-Term Acute Care hospital

Staffed Beds: 39 **Admissions:** 323 **Census:** 22 **Outpatient Visits:** 0 **Births:** 0 **Total Expense ($000):** 13992 **Payroll Expense ($000):** 5870 **Personnel:** 98

WEST GROVE—Chester County

✠ **JENNERSVILLE REGIONAL HOSPITAL (390220)**, 1015 West Baltimore Pike, Zip 19390–9459; tel. 610/869–1000 **A**1 2 9 10 **F**3 13 15 18 29 35 40 45 49 50 51 57 59 70 74 75 76 79 81 82 85 87 92 93 107 108 110 111 115 119 129 130 131 132 133 146 147 **P**6 **S** Community Health Systems, Inc., Franklin, TN
Primary Contact: Mathew Gooch, Chief Executive Officer
CFO: John McMahon, Chief Financial Officer
CMO: Tracy Carmellini, M.D., Chief of Staff
CHR: Debra Basquill, Director Human Resources
CNO: David Schmidt, R.N., Chief Nursing Officer
Web address: www.jennersville.com
Control: Corporation, Investor-owned, for-profit **Service:** General Medical and Surgical

Staffed Beds: 63 **Admissions:** 3178 **Census:** 32 **Outpatient Visits:** 17549 **Births:** 362 **Total Expense ($000):** 50444 **Payroll Expense ($000):** 18554 **Personnel:** 259

WEST READING—Berks County

✠ △ **READING HOSPITAL AND MEDICAL CENTER (390044)**, Sixth Avenue and Spruce Street, Zip 19611–1428, Mailing Address: P.O. Box 16052, Zip 19612–6052; tel. 610/988–8000 **A**1 2 3 5 6 7 8 9 10 12 13 **F**3 5 8 11 12 13 15 18 20 22 24 26 28 29 30 31 32 40 41 42 43 44 45 46 48 49 50 54 56 57 58 59 60 61 62 64 66 68 70 72 73 74 75 76 77 78 79 81 82 84 85 86 87 89 90 92 93 94 96 97 98 99 100 101 102 103 104 105 106 107 108 110 111 114 115 116 117 118 119 120 121 123 124 125 126 128 129 130 131 132 135 144 146 147 148 **P**6 8
Primary Contact: Clinton Matthews, President and Chief Executive Officer
CFO: Richard W. Jones, Chief Financial Officer
CMO: M. Joseph Grennan, Jr., M.D., Senior Vice President and Chief Medical Officer
CIO: Jayashree Raman, Vice President and Chief Information Officer
CNO: Mary Christine Agnew, R.N., Vice President and Chief Nursing Officer
Web address: www.readinghospital.org
Control: Other not-for-profit (including NFP Corporation) **Service:** General Medical and Surgical

Staffed Beds: 719 **Admissions:** 30137 **Census:** 468 **Outpatient Visits:** 801321 **Births:** 3331 **Total Expense ($000):** 724627 **Payroll Expense ($000):** 300599 **Personnel:** 4856

WILKES BARRE—Luzerne County

✠ **GEISINGER WYOMING VALLEY MEDICAL CENTER (390270)**, 1000 East Mountain Boulevard, Zip 18711–0027; tel. 570/808–7300, (Nonreporting) **A**1 2 3 5 9 10 13 **S** Geisinger Health System, Danville, PA
Primary Contact: Ronald R. Beer, FACHE, Vice President, Clinical Operations
CFO: Thomas A. Bielecki, Chief Financial Officer
CMO: Steven Pierdon, M.D., Executive Vice President and Chief Medical Officer
CIO: Frank Richards, Chief Information Officer
CHR: Margaret Heffers, Assistant Vice President Human Resources
Web address: www.geisinger.org
Control: Other not-for-profit (including NFP Corporation) **Service:** General Medical and Surgical

Staffed Beds: 178

WILKES–BARRE—Luzerne County

CLEAR BROOK MANOR, 1100 East Northampton Street, Zip 18702–9803; tel. 570/823–1171, (Nonreporting)
Primary Contact: Robert Piccone, President
Web address: www.clearbrookinc.com
Control: Other not-for-profit (including NFP Corporation) **Service:** Alcoholism and other chemical dependency

Staffed Beds: 50

✠ △ **JOHN HEINZ INSTITUTE OF REHABILITATION MEDICINE (393036)**, 150 Mundy Street, Zip 18702–6830; tel. 570/826–3800, (Total facility includes 21 beds in nursing home–type unit) **A**1 7 10 **F**3 11 29 30 32 35 54 57 59 62 64 68 75 77 82 86 90 91 92 93 130 131 132 143 146 148
Primary Contact: Karen Kearney, Vice President Inpatient Rehabilitation Services
CFO: Mike Avvisato, Vice President and Chief Financial Officer
CMO: Gregory Basting, M.D., Vice President Medical Affairs
CIO: John Regula, Chief Information Officer
CHR: Judy P. Oprisko, Vice President Human Resources
CNO: Maria Berlyn, Assistant Vice President Nursing Services
Web address: www.allied–services.org
Control: Other not-for-profit (including NFP Corporation) **Service:** Rehabilitation

Staffed Beds: 71 **Admissions:** 1549 **Census:** 55 **Outpatient Visits:** 84952 **Births:** 0 **Total Expense ($000):** 36300 **Payroll Expense ($000):** 19127 **Personnel:** 377

VETERANS AFFAIRS MEDICAL CENTER See Wilkes–Barre Veterans Affairs Medical Center

★ △ **WILKES–BARRE GENERAL HOSPITAL (390137)**, 575 North River Street, Zip 18764–0001; tel. 570/829–8111, (Includes WILKES–BARRE GENERAL HOSPITAL, 575 North River Street, Zip 18764; tel. 570/829–8111) **A**2 3 5 7 9 10 13 **F**3 4 8 12 13 15 17 18 20 22 24 28 29 30 31 34 37 40 44 45 48 49 50 51 53 54 56 57 59 61 64 66 70 73 74 75 76 78 79 81 85 86 87 89 90 93 96 107 108 111 112 114 115 116 117 118 119 121 123 126 129 130 132 145 146 147 148 **S** Community Health Systems, Inc., Franklin, TN
Primary Contact: Cornelio R. Catena, President and Chief Executive Officer
COO: Robert P. Hoffman, Vice President and Director Patient Care Services
CFO: Maggie Koehler, Senior Vice President and Chief Financial Officer
CMO: Ragupathy Veluswamy, M.D., Vice President Medical Affairs
CIO: Chris Galanda, Chief Information Officer
CHR: James Carmody, Vice President Human Resources
Web address: www.wvhc.org
Control: Corporation, Investor-owned, for-profit **Service:** General Medical and Surgical

Staffed Beds: 374 **Admissions:** 16041 **Census:** 226 **Outpatient Visits:** 517098 **Births:** 1115 **Total Expense ($000):** 265417 **Payroll Expense ($000):** 86326 **Personnel:** 1683

✠ △ **WILKES–BARRE VETERANS AFFAIRS MEDICAL CENTER**, 1111 East End Boulevard, Zip 18711–0030; tel. 570/824–3521, (Total facility includes 105 beds in nursing home–type unit) **A**1 2 3 5 7 9 **F**3 5 6 8 11 15 18 20 26 28 29 30 31 36 38 39 40 45 46 47 50 56 58 59 60 61 63 64 65 68 70 74 75 77 78 79 81 82 83 84 85 86 87 91 92 93 94 96 97 98 99 100 101 102 103 104 107 108 111 114 116 117 119 127 128 129 130 132 135 146 147 148 **S** Department of Veterans Affairs, Washington, DC
Primary Contact: Jeffrey Beiler, Interim Director
COO: Joesph P. Sharon, Associate Director
CFO: Donald E. Foote, Fiscal Officer
CMO: Mirza Z. Ali, M.D., Chief of Staff
CIO: David Longmore, Chief Information Officer
CHR: Dawn P. DeMorrow, Chief Human Resources Service
Web address: www.va.gov/vamcwb
Control: Veterans Affairs, Government, federal **Service:** General Medical and Surgical

Staffed Beds: 158 **Admissions:** 3225 **Census:** 146 **Outpatient Visits:** 396746 **Births:** 0 **Total Expense ($000):** 221235 **Payroll Expense ($000):** 85146 **Personnel:** 888

WYOMING VALLEY HEALTH CARE SYSTEM See Wilkes–Barre General Hospital

WILLIAMSPORT—Lycoming County

★ **DIVINE PROVIDENCE HOSPITAL (394048)**, 1100 Grampian Boulevard, Zip 17701–1995; tel. 570/326–8000 **A**9 10 **F**10 11 15 31 35 38 44 50 51 53 54 55 56 59 62 63 64 68 75 77 78 79 81 82 83 84 86 87 93 98 99 100 103 107 108 110 111 115 119 120 121 129 130 131 132 134 146 147 148 **P**7 **S** Susquehanna Health System, Williamsport, PA
Primary Contact: Robert E. Kane, President
COO: Neil G. Armstrong, FACHE, Vice President and Chief Operating Officer
Web address: www.susquehannahealth.org
Control: Other not-for-profit (including NFP Corporation) **Service:** Psychiatric

Staffed Beds: 31 **Admissions:** 683 **Census:** 19 **Outpatient Visits:** 272658 **Births:** 0 **Total Expense ($000):** 74498 **Payroll Expense ($000):** 19569 **Personnel:** 227

WILLIAMSPORT HOSPITAL AND MEDICAL CENTER See Williamsport Regional Medical Center

Many Facility Codes have changed. Please refer to the AHA Guide Code Chart. © 2014 AHA Guide

⊠ **WILLIAMSPORT REGIONAL MEDICAL CENTER (390045)**, 700 High Street, Zip 17701–3100; tel. 570/321–1000 **A**1 2 5 9 10 13 19 **F**7 9 11 12 13 15 17 18 20 22 24 26 28 29 30 32 34 35 37 38 40 44 45 46 47 48 49 50 52 53 54 56 57 58 59 60 61 65 68 70 73 74 75 76 77 79 81 85 86 87 89 90 91 92 93 94 96 97 107 108 110 114 115 116 117 118 119 120 121 123 124 126 130 132 134 135 143 144 146 147 **P**7 **S** Susquehanna Health System, Williamsport, PA
Primary Contact: Jan E. Fisher, President
COO: Jan E. Fisher, Executive Vice President and Chief Operating Officer and Williamsport Regional Medical Center President
CFO: Charles J. Santangelo, CPA, Executive Vice President and Chief Financial Officer
CIO: Timothy E. Schoener, Senior Vice President and Chief Information Officer
CHR: Christine A. Ballard, Senior Vice President Human Resources
CNO: Susan Duchman, R.N., Vice President and Chief Nursing Officer
Control: Other not–for–profit (including NFP Corporation) **Service:** General Medical and Surgical

Staffed Beds: 205 **Admissions:** 12111 **Census:** 143 **Outpatient Visits:** 148899 **Births:** 1241 **Total Expense ($000):** 244234 **Payroll Expense ($000):** 86854 **Personnel:** 1217

WINDBER—Somerset County

★ **WINDBER MEDICAL CENTER (390112)**, 600 Somerset Avenue, Zip 15963–1331; tel. 814/467–3000 **A**9 10 **F**3 12 15 18 28 30 34 35 36 40 45 53 55 56 57 58 59 62 63 70 75 79 81 83 84 85 93 107 110 111 114 117 118 119 127 129 130 131 132 135 146 147
Primary Contact: Thomas M. Kurtz, President and Chief Executive Officer
CFO: Richard Sukenik, CPA, Vice President Finance and Chief Financial Officer
CIO: Renee Adams, Director Information Technology
CHR: Jamie Brock, Director Human Resources
CNO: Mary Lee Dadey, R.N., Vice President of Nursing
Web address: www.windbercare.org
Control: Other not–for–profit (including NFP Corporation) **Service:** General Medical and Surgical

Staffed Beds: 45 **Admissions:** 1540 **Census:** 14 **Outpatient Visits:** 104369 **Births:** 179 **Total Expense ($000):** 48315 **Payroll Expense ($000):** 21780 **Personnel:** 429

WYNNEWOOD—Montgomery County

LANKENAU HOSPITAL See Lankenau Medical Center

⊠ **LANKENAU MEDICAL CENTER (390195)**, 100 Lancaster Avenue West, Zip 19096–3411; tel. 484/476–2000, (Total facility includes 22 beds in nursing home–type unit) **A**1 2 3 5 8 10 12 13 **F**3 11 13 15 17 18 20 22 24 26 28 29 30 31 32 34 35 38 39 40 43 44 45 46 47 48 49 50 54 55 56 57 58 59 64 65 66 70 71 72 74 75 76 77 78 79 81 82 84 85 86 87 92 97 100 102 103 107 108 110 111 114 115 118 119 120 121 124 126 128 129 130 131 132 135 138 141 143 145 146 148 **S** Jefferson Health System, Radnor, PA
Primary Contact: Phillip D. Robinson, President
CFO: Michael J. Buongiorno, Vice President Finance
CMO: Thomas G. McCarter, Jr., M.D., Chief Medical Officer
CIO: Karen A. Thomas, Acting Vice President and Chief Information Officer
CHR: Eileen McAnally, Senior Vice President Human Resources
Web address: www.mainlinehealth.org
Control: Other not–for–profit (including NFP Corporation) **Service:** General Medical and Surgical

Staffed Beds: 339 **Admissions:** 16972 **Census:** 223 **Outpatient Visits:** 309368 **Births:** 2744 **Total Expense ($000):** 352872 **Payroll Expense ($000):** 115906 **Personnel:** 2046

WYOMISSING—Berks County

⊠ **SURGICAL INSTITUTE OF READING (390316)**, 2752 Century Boulevard, Zip 19610–3345; tel. 610/378–8800 **A**1 9 10 **F**3 8 29 45 79 81 82 85 86 107 114
Primary Contact: Debbie Beissel, Chief Executive Officer
CFO: Cheryl Peterson, Business Office Manager
CHR: Megan Schaffer, Administrative Assistant
Web address: www.sireading.com
Control: Partnership, Investor–owned, for–profit **Service:** Surgical

Staffed Beds: 15 **Admissions:** 545 **Census:** 3 **Outpatient Visits:** 8449 **Births:** 0 **Total Expense ($000):** 15496 **Payroll Expense ($000):** 4186 **Personnel:** 84

YORK—York County

⊠ **HEALTHSOUTH REHABILITATION HOSPITAL OF YORK (393037)**, 1850 Normandie Drive, Zip 17408–1534; tel. 717/767–6941, (Nonreporting) **A**1 9 10 **S** HEALTHSOUTH Corporation, Birmingham, AL
Primary Contact: Steven Alwine, Chief Executive Officer
CFO: Joyce Henry, Controller
CMO: Bruce Sicilia, M.D., Medical Director
CIO: Laura Emig, Director Marketing Operations
CHR: Bradley Teahl, Director Human Resources
CNO: Julie Scott, Chief Nursing Officer
Web address: www.healthsouthyork.com
Control: Corporation, Investor–owned, for–profit **Service:** Rehabilitation

Staffed Beds: 90

★ ○ **MEMORIAL HOSPITAL (390101)**, 325 South Belmont Street, Zip 17403–2609, Mailing Address: P.O. Box 15118, Zip 17405–7118; tel. 717/843–8623 **A**9 10 11 12 13 **F**3 7 8 13 15 18 20 22 26 29 30 31 34 35 40 45 47 48 49 50 51 54 56 57 58 59 60 64 65 66 68 70 75 76 77 78 79 81 84 85 93 97 107 108 111 116 117 118 119 126 129 130 132 135 146 147 **P**6 **S** Community Health Systems, Inc., Franklin, TN
Primary Contact: Sally J. Dixon, Chief Executive Officer
CIO: James Mahoney, Chief Information Officer
CHR: Corey Hudak, Director Human Resources
CNO: Susan Gordon, R.N., Chief Nursing Officer
Web address: www.mhyork.org
Control: Other not–for–profit (including NFP Corporation) **Service:** General Medical and Surgical

Staffed Beds: 100 **Admissions:** 4775 **Census:** 51 **Births:** 589 **Personnel:** 784

☐ **OSS ORTHOPAEDIC SPECIALTY HOSPITAL (390325)**, 1861 Powder Mill Road, Zip 17402–4723; tel. 717/718–2000 **A**1 9 10 **F**3 29 62 64 79 81 82 85 86 87 94 107 111 119 130 131 135 144 **P**1 2 6
Primary Contact: Todd M. Lord, Chief Executive Officer
COO: Margaret Mooers, R.N., Chief Operating Officer and Chief Nursing Officer
CFO: Teresa Strausbaugh, Controller
CMO: Joseph Alhadeff, M.D., President
CIO: Tricia Wolf, Director Information Technology
CHR: Beth Patton, Director Human Resources
CNO: Margaret Mooers, R.N., Chief Operating Officer and Chief Nursing Officer
Web address: www.osshospital.com
Control: Partnership, Investor–owned, for–profit **Service:** Orthopedic

Staffed Beds: 30 **Admissions:** 1449 **Census:** 9 **Outpatient Visits:** 226318 **Births:** 0 **Total Expense ($000):** 77810 **Payroll Expense ($000):** 32167 **Personnel:** 477

SELECT SPECIALTY HOSPITAL–YORK See Select Specialty Hospital–Central Pennsylvania, Camp Hill

⊠ △ **YORK HOSPITAL (390046)**, 1001 South George Street, Zip 17403–3645; tel. 717/851–2345, (Includes WELLSPAN SURGERY AND REHABILLITATION HOSPITAL, 55 Monument Road, Zip 17403–5023; tel. 717/812–6100; Richard L. Seim, President) **A**1 2 3 5 7 8 9 10 12 13 **F**3 7 11 12 13 14 15 17 18 20 22 24 26 28 29 30 31 34 35 39 40 43 44 45 46 48 49 50 54 55 56 57 58 59 60 61 64 65 66 68 70 72 74 75 76 77 78 79 81 82 84 85 86 87 89 92 93 96 97 98 99 100 101 102 103 104 107 108 110 111 114 115 117 118 119 120 121 123 124 126 129 130 131 132 135 146 147 148 **S** WellSpan Health, York, PA
Primary Contact: Keith D. Noll, President
COO: Raymond Rosen, FACHE, Vice President Operations
CFO: Michael F. O'Connor, Senior Vice President Finance
CMO: Peter M. Hartmann, M.D., Vice President Medical Affairs
CIO: R. Hal Baker, M.D., Vice President and Chief Information Officer
CHR: Robert J. Batory, Vice President Human Resources
CNO: Astrid Davis, R.N., Chief Nursing Officer
Web address: www.wellspan.org
Control: Other not–for–profit (including NFP Corporation) **Service:** General Medical and Surgical

Staffed Beds: 552 **Admissions:** 29393 **Census:** 411 **Outpatient Visits:** 900000 **Births:** 3078 **Total Expense ($000):** 764302 **Payroll Expense ($000):** 254370 **Personnel:** 3960

PA

RHODE ISLAND

CRANSTON—Providence County

☐ **ELEANOR SLATER HOSPITAL (412001)**, 111 Howard Avenue, Zip 02920–0269, Mailing Address: P.O. Box 8269, Zip 02920–0269; tel. 401/462–3085, (Nonreporting) **A**1 10
Primary Contact: Paul J. Despres, Chief Executive Officer
CMO: Charlene Tate, M.D., Chief Medical Staff and Clinical Services
Web address: www.bhddh.ri.gov/esh/
Control: State–Government, nonfederal **Service:** Long–Term Acute Care hospital

Staffed Beds: 495

EAST PROVIDENCE—Providence County

☐ **EMMA PENDLETON BRADLEY HOSPITAL (414003)**, 1011 Veterans Memorial Parkway, Zip 02915–5099; tel. 401/432–1000 **A**1 3 5 9 10 **F**3 29 34 35 38 44 57 58 62 64 68 77 86 87 98 99 100 101 104 105 106 130 132 134 135 **S** Lifespan Corporation, Providence, RI
Primary Contact: Daniel J. Wall, President and Chief Executive Officer
CFO: Mamie Wakefield, Vice President Finance and Chief Financial Officer
CMO: Henry T. Sachs, III, M.D., Medical Director
CIO: Carole Cotter, Senior Vice President and Chief Information Officer
CHR: Rob Duval, Chief Human Resources Officer
CNO: Vareen O'Keefe Domaleski, MS, Vice Patient Care Services and Chief Nursing Officer
Web address: www.lifespan.org
Control: Other not–for–profit (including NFP Corporation) **Service:** Children's hospital psychiatric

Staffed Beds: 60 Admissions: 1683 Census: 56 Outpatient Visits: 19806
Births: 0 Total Expense ($000): 79225 Payroll Expense ($000): 48085
Personnel: 763

NEWPORT—Newport County

☐ △ **NEWPORT HOSPITAL (410006)**, 11 Friendship Street, Zip 02840–2299; tel. 401/846–6400 **A**1 2 7 9 10 **F**3 8 11 13 15 18 28 29 30 31 34 35 40 45 49 50 51 53 54 56 57 59 60 64 68 70 74 75 76 77 78 79 81 82 85 86 87 89 90 91 92 93 96 97 98 99 100 102 103 104 105 107 108 110 111 114 118 119 129 130 132 135 141 143 146 147 148 **S** Lifespan Corporation, Providence, RI
Primary Contact: Arthur J. Sampson, FACHE, Interim President
CFO: Frank J. Byrne, Vice President Finance
CMO: Thomas E. McGue, M.D., Vice President Medical Affairs and Chief Medical Officer
CHR: Barbara J. Arcangeli, Vice President Human Resources
CNO: Denise Sullivan, MSN, Vice President Nursing and Chief Nursing Officer
Web address: www.newporthospital.org
Control: Other not–for–profit (including NFP Corporation) **Service:** General Medical and Surgical

Staffed Beds: 119 Admissions: 4392 Census: 62 Outpatient Visits: 88416
Births: 502 Total Expense ($000): 106945 Payroll Expense ($000): 48532
Personnel: 600

NORTH PROVIDENCE—Providence County

☐ △ **ST. JOSEPH HEALTH SERVICES OF RHODE ISLAND (410005)**, 200 High Service Avenue, Zip 02904–5199; tel. 401/456–3000, (Includes OUR LADY OF FATIMA HOSPITAL, 200 High Service Avenue, Zip 02904; tel. 401/456–3000; Thomas Hughes, President; ST. JOSEPH HOSPITAL FOR SPECIALTY CARE, 21 Peace Street, Providence, Zip 02907; tel. 401/456–3000) **A**1 2 6 7 9 10 **F**3 8 15 18 24 29 30 31 32 34 35 37 39 40 46 48 49 50 51 56 57 59 65 66 68 70 74 75 77 78 79 81 82 84 87 90 93 94 97 98 102 103 104 107 108 111 114 116 119 130 131 132 133 135 146 147 148 **S** CharterCare Health Partners, Providence, RI
Primary Contact: Thomas Hughes, President
CFO: Michael E. Conklin, Jr., Chief Financial Officer
CIO: Susan Cerrone, Chief Information Officer
CHR: Darlene Souza, Vice President
CNO: Patricia A. Nadle, R.N., Chief Nursing Officer
Web address: www.saintjosephri.com
Control: Other not–for–profit (including NFP Corporation) **Service:** General Medical and Surgical

Staffed Beds: 125 Admissions: 6221 Census: 117 Outpatient Visits: 30707
Births: 0 Total Expense ($000): 143968 Payroll Expense ($000): 69013
Personnel: 749

NORTH SMITHFIELD—Providence County

LANDMARK MEDICAL CENTER–FOGARTY UNIT See Landmark Medical Center, Woonsocket

REHABILITATION HOSPITAL OF RHODE ISLAND (413025), 116 Eddie

☐ **REHABILITATION HOSPITAL OF RHODE ISLAND (413025)**, 116 Eddie Dowling Highway, Zip 02896–7327; tel. 401/766–0800 **A**1 9 10 **F**28 29 35 64 77 82 90 91 92 93 96 130 132 148 **S** Prime Healthcare Services, Ontario, CA
Primary Contact: Richard Charest, Chief Executive Officer
COO: Demetra Ouellette, Chief Operating Officer
CFO: Matthew Cotti, Chief Financial Officer
CMO: Jorge Mayoral, M.D., Medical Director
CIO: Colleen Ryan, Chief Information Officer and Vice President Professional Services
CHR: Mona M. Willis, Director Human Resources
Web address: www.rhri.net
Control: Partnership, Investor–owned, for–profit **Service:** Rehabilitation

Staffed Beds: 40 Admissions: 383 Census: 13 Births: 0

PAWTUCKET—Providence County

✦ △ **MEMORIAL HOSPITAL OF RHODE ISLAND (410001)**, 111 Brewster Street, Zip 02860–4499; tel. 401/729–2000 **A**1 2 3 5 7 8 9 10 **F**3 8 11 13 15 17 18 20 28 29 31 32 34 35 38 40 46 49 50 51 54 56 57 58 59 61 64 65 66 68 70 74 75 76 77 78 79 81 82 84 85 86 89 90 91 93 97 102 107 108 109 110 111 114 115 116 117 118 119 126 129 130 131 132 135 144 146 147 148 **P**6 8 **S** Care New England Health System, Providence, RI
Primary Contact: Edward M. Schottland, Acting President
CFO: Paul Beaudoin, Chief Financial Officer
CMO: Joseph Diaz, M.D., Chief Medical Officer
CHR: Lisa Pratt, Vice President Human Resources
CNO: Shelley A. MacDonald Gallagher, R.N., Senior Vice President for Patient Care Services
Web address: www.mhri.org
Control: Other not–for–profit (including NFP Corporation) **Service:** General Medical and Surgical

Staffed Beds: 150 Admissions: 5029 Census: 63 Outpatient Visits: 267024
Births: 460 Total Expense ($000): 171053 Payroll Expense ($000): 84690
Personnel: 992

PROVIDENCE—Providence County

✦ **BUTLER HOSPITAL (414000)**, 345 Blackstone Boulevard, Zip 02906–4829; tel. 401/455–6200 **A**1 3 5 9 10 **F**4 5 6 29 30 34 35 38 40 44 50 56 57 58 59 64 68 74 75 77 81 86 87 98 99 100 101 102 103 104 105 130 132 135 146 147 **P**6 **S** Care New England Health System, Providence, RI
Primary Contact: Lawrence Price, M.D., President and Chief Operating Officer
COO: Walter Dias, Vice President and Chief Operating Officer
CFO: Bonnie Baker, Vice President Finance and Chief Financial Officer
CMO: Steven Rasmussen, M.D., Medical Director
CIO: Cedric T. Priebe, M.D., Vice President and Chief Information Officer
CHR: Timothy Bigelow, Director Human Resources
Web address: www.butler.org
Control: Other not–for–profit (including NFP Corporation) **Service:** Psychiatric

Staffed Beds: 143 Admissions: 5743 Census: 126 Births: 0

☐ **MIRIAM HOSPITAL (410012)**, 164 Summit Avenue, Zip 02906–2853; tel. 401/793–2500 **A**1 2 3 5 8 9 10 **F**3 8 11 12 15 17 18 20 22 26 28 29 30 31 34 35 40 44 45 46 49 50 53 54 56 57 58 59 60 61 64 65 66 67 68 70 74 75 77 78 79 81 82 84 85 87 92 93 97 100 103 104 107 108 110 111 114 115 118 119 126 130 132 135 146 147 148 **P**3 5 6 **S** Lifespan Corporation, Providence, RI
Primary Contact: Arthur J. Sampson, FACHE, President
COO: Maria Ducharme, R.N., Interim Chief Nursing Officer
CFO: Mamie Wakefield, Chief Financial Officer
CMO: R. William Corwin, M.D., Vice President and Chief Medical Officer
CIO: Carole Cotter, Vice President and Chief Information Officer
CHR: Nancy McMahon, Vice President Human Resources
Web address: www.lifespan.org
Control: Other not–for–profit (including NFP Corporation) **Service:** General Medical and Surgical

Staffed Beds: 247 Admissions: 15002 Census: 169 Outpatient Visits: 201990 Births: 0 Total Expense ($000): 416682 Payroll Expense ($000): 177801 Personnel: 2220

RI

PROVIDENCE VETERANS AFFAIRS MEDICAL CENTER, 830 Chalkstone Avenue, Zip 02908–4799; tel. 401/273–7100 **A**1 2 3 5 **F**3 5 8 12 18 29 30 31 35 37 38 39 40 44 45 46 47 49 50 51 53 54 55 56 57 58 59 60 61 62 63 64 65 68 70 74 75 77 78 79 81 82 84 85 86 87 91 92 93 94 97 98 100 101 102 103 104 107 108 111 114 115 118 119 126 128 130 132 135 143 144 145 146 147 148 **S** Department of Veterans Affairs, Washington, DC
Primary Contact: Susan McKenzie, Director
COO: Erin Clare Sears, Associate Director of Operations
CMO: Satish C. Sharma, M.D., Chief of Staff
Web address: www.providence.va.gov/
Control: Veterans Affairs, Government, federal **Service:** General Medical and Surgical

Staffed Beds: 73 Admissions: 3546 Census: 52 Outpatient Visits: 403858 Births: 0 Total Expense ($000): 243279 Personnel: 1328

RHODE ISLAND HOSPITAL (410007), 593 Eddy Street, Zip 02903–4900; tel. 401/444–4000, (Includes HASBRO CHILDREN'S HOSPITAL, 593 Eddy Street, Zip 02903–4923; tel. 401/444–4000) **A**1 2 3 5 8 9 10 **F**3 6 7 8 11 15 16 17 18 19 20 21 22 23 24 26 29 30 31 32 34 35 38 39 40 41 43 44 45 46 47 48 49 50 51 53 54 55 56 57 58 59 60 61 64 65 66 68 70 74 75 77 78 79 81 82 84 85 86 87 88 89 92 93 94 97 98 99 100 101 102 103 104 105 107 108 110 111 114 115 116 117 118 119 120 121 123 124 129 130 131 132 134 135 138 142 145 146 148 **P**3 5 6 **S** Lifespan Corporation, Providence, RI
Primary Contact: Timothy J. Babineau, M.D., President and Chief Executive Officer
COO: Fredrick Macri, Executive Vice President
CFO: Mamie Wakefield, Senior Vice President and Chief Financial Officer
CMO: John B. Murphy, M.D., Vice President Medical Affairs and Chief Medical Officer
CIO: Carole Cotter, Senior Vice President and Chief Information Officer
CHR: Louis J. Sperling, Vice President Human Resources
Web address: www.rhodeislandhospital.org/
Control: Other not–for–profit (including NFP Corporation) **Service:** General Medical and Surgical

Staffed Beds: 645 Admissions: 33996 Census: 499 Outpatient Visits: 354255 Births: 0 Total Expense ($000): 1068518 Payroll Expense ($000): 487503 Personnel: 5737

ROGER WILLIAMS MEDICAL CENTER (410004), 825 Chalkstone Avenue, Zip 02908–4735; tel. 401/456–2000 **A**1 2 3 5 8 9 10 **F**3 5 8 12 15 18 26 29 30 31 34 35 37 40 45 46 47 48 49 50 51 56 57 58 59 60 61 62 64 65 68 74 75 78 79 81 84 85 86 87 92 97 98 100 101 102 103 104 105 106 107 108 110 111 112 114 115 118 119 129 130 131 132 135 136 146 147 148 **S** CharterCare Health Partners, Providence, RI
Primary Contact: Kimberly O'Connell, President
CFO: Addy Kane, Chief Financial Officer
CMO: Elaine Jones, M.D., President Medical Staff
CIO: Susan Cerrone Abely, Vice President and Chief Information Officer
Web address: www.rwmc.com
Control: Other not–for–profit (including NFP Corporation) **Service:** General Medical and Surgical

Staffed Beds: 86 Admissions: 6988 Census: 120 Outpatient Visits: 184130 Births: 0 Total Expense ($000): 144944 Payroll Expense ($000): 67896 Personnel: 903

ST. JOSEPH HOSPITAL FOR SPECIALTY CARE See St. Joseph Health Services of Rhode Island, North Providence

VETERANS AFFAIRS MEDICAL CENTER See Providence Veterans Affairs Medical Center

WOMEN & INFANTS HOSPITAL OF RHODE ISLAND (410010), 101 Dudley Street, Zip 02905–2499; tel. 401/274–1100 **A**1 2 3 5 8 9 10 **F**3 5 11 12 15 29 30 31 33 34 35 36 40 44 45 46 50 52 54 55 57 58 59 63 64 65 66 68 71 72 74 75 76 77 78 81 82 84 85 86 87 93 97 100 101 102 104 105 107 110 111 114 119 126 130 132 134 135 143 146 147 **P**5 6 8 **S** Care New England Health System, Providence, RI
Primary Contact: Mark R. Marcantano, President and Chief Operating Officer
COO: Mark R. Marcantano, President and Chief Operating Officer
CFO: Robert W. Pacheco, Vice President Finance
CMO: Raymond Powrie, M.D., Senior Vice President Quality and Clinical Effectiveness
CHR: Paul F. Heffernan, Vice President Human Resources
CNO: Angelleen Peters–Lewis, R.N., Chief Nurse and Senior Vice President Patient Care
Web address: www.womenandinfants.org
Control: Other not–for–profit (including NFP Corporation) **Service:** Obstetrics and gynecology

Staffed Beds: 247 Admissions: 11656 Census: 156 Outpatient Visits: 225940 Births: 8532 Total Expense ($000): 448916 Payroll Expense ($000): 194277 Personnel: 2038

SOUTH COUNTY HOSPITAL (410008), 100 Kenyon Avenue, Zip 02879–4299; tel. 401/782–8000 **A**2 9 10 **F**3 11 13 15 18 20 26 28 29 30 31 34 35 36 37 38 40 42 44 45 46 47 48 49 50 51 53 54 57 59 60 64 65 70 74 75 76 77 78 79 81 82 85 86 87 89 93 102 103 104 107 108 110 111 114 119 126 129 130 131 132 135 143 144 146 147 148 **P**4 6
Primary Contact: Louis R. Giancola, President and Chief Executive Officer
CFO: Thomas Breen, Vice President and Chief Financial Officer
CMO: Joseph J. O'Neill, M.D., Vice President Medical Affairs
CIO: Gary Croteau, Assistant Vice President and Chief Information Officer
CHR: Maggie Thomas, Vice President Human Resources and Practice Management
Web address: www.schospital.com
Control: Other not–for–profit (including NFP Corporation) **Service:** General Medical and Surgical

Staffed Beds: 85 Admissions: 4460 Census: 45 Outpatient Visits: 191030 Births: 521 Total Expense ($000): 121793 Payroll Expense ($000): 50688 Personnel: 794

KENT COUNTY MEMORIAL HOSPITAL (410009), 455 Tollgate Road, Zip 02886–2770; tel. 401/737–7000 **A**1 2 7 9 10 13 **F**3 8 11 13 15 17 18 20 22 26 29 30 31 34 35 36 40 44 45 46 47 48 49 50 51 56 57 58 59 60 61 63 64 65 68 70 73 74 75 76 77 78 79 81 82 84 85 86 87 89 90 93 97 98 100 102 103 105 107 108 110 111 114 118 119 126 129 130 131 132 143 146 147 148 **P**6 8 **S** Care New England Health System, Providence, RI
Primary Contact: Michael J. Dacey, M.D., MS, President and Chief Operating Officer
COO: Fran Falsey, Senior Vice President Site Operations
CFO: Paul Beaudoin, Senior Vice President Finance and Chief Financial Officer
CMO: Joseph W. Spinale, D.O., Senior Vice President and Chief Medical Officer
CHR: Marilyn J. Walsh, Vice President Human Resources
CNO: Rebecca Burke, R.N., Senior Vice President and Chief Nursing Officer
Web address: www.kentri.org
Control: Other not–for–profit (including NFP Corporation) **Service:** General Medical and Surgical

Staffed Beds: 306 Admissions: 13816 Census: 202 Outpatient Visits: 216204 Births: 1012 Total Expense ($000): 315507 Payroll Expense ($000): 130985 Personnel: 1452

WESTERLY HOSPITAL (410013), 25 Wells Street, Zip 02891–2934; tel. 401/596–6000, (Nonreporting) **A**2 9 10 21 **S** L+M Healthcare, New London, CT
Primary Contact: Bruce D. Cummings, President and Chief Executive Officer
CFO: James O'Keefe, Chief Financial Officer
CIO: Christopher Lehrach, M.D., Chief Transformation Officer for Interim Operations
CHR: Jodie Tate, Director Human Resources
Web address: www.westerlyhospital.org
Control: Other not–for–profit (including NFP Corporation) **Service:** General Medical and Surgical

Staffed Beds: 100

LANDMARK MEDICAL CENTER (410011), 115 Cass Avenue, Zip 02895–4731; tel. 401/769–4100, (Includes LANDMARK MEDICAL CENTER–FOGARTY UNIT, Eddie Dowling Highway, North Smithfield, Zip 02896; Mailing Address: Woonsocket, tel. 401/766–0800; LANDMARK MEDICAL CENTER–WOONSOCKET UNIT, 115 Cass Avenue, Zip 02895; tel. 401/769–4100), (Nonreporting) **A**1 2 9 10 **S** Prime Healthcare Services, Ontario, CA
Primary Contact: Richard Charest, President
CFO: Dana Diggins, Chief Financial Officer
CMO: Stanley Balon, M.D., President Medical Staff
CIO: Colleen Ryan, Director Management Information Systems
CHR: Mona M. Willis, Director Human Resources
Web address: www.landmarkmedical.org
Control: Corporation, Investor–owned, for–profit **Service:** General Medical and Surgical

Staffed Beds: 133

RI

Hospital, Medicare Provider Number, Address, Telephone, Approval, Facility, and Physician Codes, Health Care System

★ American Hospital Association (AHA) membership
□ The Joint Commission accreditation   ◇ DNV Healthcare Inc. accreditation
○ Healthcare Facilities Accreditation Program
△ Commission on Accreditation of Rehabilitation Facilities (CARF) accreditation

SOUTH CAROLINA

ABBEVILLE—Abbeville County

★ ◇ **ABBEVILLE AREA MEDICAL CENTER (421301)**, 420 Thomson Circle, Zip 29620–5656, Mailing Address: P.O. Box 887, Zip 29620–0887; tel. 864/366–5011 **A**9 10 18 21 **F**3 15 17 29 30 35 40 51 53 54 56 57 59 62 64 67 70 74 75 77 79 81 85 87 89 90 93 103 107 108 110 114 119 127 128 129 130 132 133 135 146 147 148 **P**5 **S** QHR, Brentwood, TN
Primary Contact: Richard D. Osmus, Chief Executive Officer
CFO: Timothy Wren, Chief Financial Officer
CMO: Michael Turner, M.D., Chief of Staff
CIO: Tim Stewart, Chief Information Officer
CHR: Alice Rigney, Chief Human Resources Officer
CNO: Lucile Culbreth, Chief Nursing Officer
Web address: www.abbevilleareamc.com
Control: County–Government, nonfederal **Service:** General Medical and Surgical

Staffed Beds: 25 **Admissions:** 592 **Census:** 6 **Outpatient Visits:** 13344 **Births:** 0 **Total Expense ($000):** 33107 **Payroll Expense ($000):** 14215 **Personnel:** 337

AIKEN—Aiken County

☐ **AIKEN REGIONAL MEDICAL CENTERS (420082)**, 302 University Parkway, Zip 29801–6302; tel. 803/641–5000, (Includes AURORA PAVILION, 655 Medical Park Drive, Zip 29801; tel. 803/641–5900) **A**1 5 9 10 **F**3 4 5 11 12 15 18 20 22 24 29 30 31 34 35 40 46 49 56 57 58 59 64 70 73 74 76 77 78 79 80 81 85 86 87 89 98 99 100 101 102 103 104 105 107 108 110 111 114 115 119 121 123 129 130 131 132 135 146 147 148 **S** Universal Health Services, Inc., King of Prussia, PA
Primary Contact: Carlos Milanes, Chief Executive Officer and Managing Director
COO: Justin Krueger, Chief Operating Officer
Web address: www.aikenregional.com
Control: Corporation, Investor–owned, for–profit **Service:** General Medical and Surgical

Staffed Beds: 271 **Admissions:** 11875 **Census:** 169 **Outpatient Visits:** 134762 **Births:** 1098 **Total Expense ($000):** 141287 **Payroll Expense ($000):** 52096 **Personnel:** 836

ANDERSON—Anderson County

✠ **ANMED HEALTH MEDICAL CENTER (420027)**, 800 North Fant Street, Zip 29621–5793; tel. 864/512–1000, (Includes ANMED HEALTH WOMEN'S AND CHILDREN'S HOSPITAL, 2000 East Greenville Street, Zip 29621; tel. 864/512–1000) **A**1 2 3 5 9 10 **F**3 4 5 11 12 13 14 15 17 18 20 22 24 26 28 29 30 31 34 35 37 39 40 43 45 46 48 49 50 51 53 54 56 57 58 59 60 61 62 64 65 68 70 71 73 74 75 76 77 78 79 80 81 84 85 86 87 89 90 91 97 98 100 101 102 103 104 105 107 108 110 111 114 115 117 118 119 121 123 126 127 129 130 131 132 135 144 146 147 148 **S** AnMed Health, Anderson, SC
Primary Contact: John A. Miller, Jr., FACHE, Chief Executive Officer
COO: William T. Manson, III, President
CFO: Jerry A. Parrish, Vice President
CMO: Mike Tillirson, D.O., Executive Vice President and Chief Medical Officer
CIO: Marty Stewart, Director Information Services
CHR: Doug Douglas, Vice President Human Resources
CNO: Tina M. Jury, MSN, Executive Vice President Patient Care Services and Chief Nursing Officer
Web address: www.anmedhealth.org
Control: Other not–for–profit (including NFP Corporation) **Service:** General Medical and Surgical

Staffed Beds: 414 **Admissions:** 19630 **Census:** 273 **Births:** 1900 **Total Expense ($000):** 457115 **Payroll Expense ($000):** 173702 **Personnel:** 3537

✠ **ANMED HEALTH REHABILITATION HOSPITAL (423029)**, 1 Spring Back Way, Zip 29621–2676; tel. 864/716–2600 **A**1 10 **F**3 29 30 56 74 75 79 90 91 93 94 95 96 **S** HEALTHSOUTH Corporation, Birmingham, AL
Primary Contact: Michele M. Skripps, R.N., Chief Executive Officer
CFO: Julie Saylors, Controller
CMO: William Vogentiz, M.D., Medical Director
CHR: Tara Myers, Director Human Resources
CNO: Carmella Burton, Chief Nursing Officer
Web address: www.anmedrehab.com
Control: Corporation, Investor–owned, for–profit **Service:** Rehabilitation

Staffed Beds: 55 **Admissions:** 1398 **Census:** 48 **Births:** 0 **Total Expense ($000):** 13196 **Payroll Expense ($000):** 7363 **Personnel:** 181

☐ **PATRICK B. HARRIS PSYCHIATRIC HOSPITAL (424011)**, 130 Highway 252, Zip 29621–5054; tel. 864/231–2600, (Nonreporting) **A**1 9 10
Primary Contact: John Fletcher, Chief Executive Officer
Web address: www.patrickbharrispsychiatrichospital.com/index.htm
Control: State–Government, nonfederal **Service:** Psychiatric

Staffed Beds: 121

BARNWELL—Barnwell County

☐ **SOUTHERN PALMETTO HOSPITAL (420016)**, 811 Reynolds Road, Zip 29812–1555; tel. 803/259–1000, (Nonreporting) **A**1 9 10 20
Primary Contact: Mary T. Valliant, R.N., MS, Chief Executive Officer
CFO: Troy Pickens, Chief Financial Officer
CMO: Dean Koukos, M.D., Chief Medical Staff
CIO: Randal Padgett, Manager Information Systems
CHR: Sherry Donaldson, Director Human Resources
CNO: Marsha Gantt, Interim Chief Nursing Officer
Web address: www.bchospital.org
Control: County–Government, nonfederal **Service:** General Medical and Surgical

Staffed Beds: 33

BEAUFORT—Beaufort County

✠ **BEAUFORT MEMORIAL HOSPITAL (420067)**, 955 Ribaut Road, Zip 29902–5441; tel. 843/522–5200 **A**1 2 9 10 19 20 **F**3 11 12 13 15 18 20 28 29 30 31 32 34 35 40 43 45 49 50 51 53 54 57 59 60 64 65 69 70 71 73 74 75 76 77 78 79 80 81 85 86 87 89 90 93 94 97 98 100 101 102 103 104 107 108 111 114 115 117 119 120 121 126 130 132 134 135 145 146 147 148
Primary Contact: Richard Kirk Toomey, FACHE, President and Chief Executive Officer
CFO: Jeffrey L. White, Senior Vice President and Chief Financial Officer
CMO: Kurt Gambla, D.O., Chief Medical Officer
CIO: Edward Ricks, Vice President and Chief Information Officer
CHR: David Homyk, Vice President Human Resources
CNO: Karen Carroll, MSN, Vice President and Chief Nursing Officer
Web address: www.bmhsc.org
Control: County–Government, nonfederal **Service:** General Medical and Surgical

Staffed Beds: 181 **Admissions:** 8664 **Census:** 111 **Births:** 1591 **Total Expense ($000):** 150176 **Payroll Expense ($000):** 66635

✠ **NAVAL HOSPITAL BEAUFORT**, 1 Pinckney Boulevard, Zip 29902–6122; tel. 843/228–5301, (Nonreporting) **A**1 5 **S** Bureau of Medicine and Surgery, Department of the Navy, Washington, DC
Primary Contact: Lieutenant Commander Willie Brown, Director Administration
Web address: www.med.navy.mil/sites/nhbeaufort/Pages/Welcome_Page.aspx
Control: Navy, Government, federal **Service:** General Medical and Surgical

Staffed Beds: 20

BENNETTSVILLE—Marlboro County

✠ **MARLBORO PARK HOSPITAL (420054)**, 1138 Cheraw Highway, Zip 29512–2466; tel. 843/479–2881 **A**1 9 10 **F**3 13 15 17 18 29 34 35 40 45 57 59 64 65 70 75 76 77 79 81 85 86 87 89 93 97 98 103 107 108 119 127 130 132 133 135 146 147 **S** Community Health Systems, Inc., Franklin, TN
Primary Contact: Jeff Reece, R.N., MSN, Chief Executive Officer
CFO: Phillip Fouts, Chief Financial Officer
CMO: William Chinery, M.D., Chief of Staff
CIO: Rod McLaurin, Director Information Systems
CHR: Jennifer Welch, Director Human Resources
CNO: Paula Jean Buning, Chief Nursing Officer
Web address: www.marlboroparkhospital.com
Control: Corporation, Investor–owned, for–profit **Service:** General Medical and Surgical

Staffed Beds: 102 **Admissions:** 1403 **Census:** 14 **Births:** 84 **Total Expense ($000):** 28047 **Payroll Expense ($000):** 9706 **Personnel:** 196

CAMDEN—Kershaw County

✠ **KERSHAWHEALTH (420048)**, 1315 Roberts Street, Zip 29020–3737, Mailing Address: P.O. Box 7003, Zip 29021–7003; tel. 803/432–4311, (Nonreporting) **A**1 9 10
Primary Contact: Terry Gunn, Interim Chief Executive Officer
COO: Mike Bunch, Executive Vice President, Chief Operating Officer and Chief Financial Officer
CHR: Angela F. Nettles, Director Human Resources
Web address: www.kershawhealth.com
Control: County–Government, nonfederal **Service:** General Medical and Surgical

Staffed Beds: 215

CHARLESTON—Charleston County

✠ **BON SECOURS ST. FRANCIS XAVIER HOSPITAL (420065)**, 2095 Henry Tecklenburg Drive, Zip 29414–5733; tel. 843/402–1000 **A**1 9 10 **F**1 3 7 12 13 14 15 20 28 29 30 31 34 35 40 43 45 46 47 48 49 50 51 56 57 59 60 64 68 70 73 74 75 76 77 78 79 80 81 82 84 85 86 87 89 93 94 100 107 108 110 111 114 118 128 130 131 132 145 146 147 148 **S** Carolinas HealthCare System, Charlotte, NC
Primary Contact: Allen P. Carroll, Senior Vice President and Chief Executive Officer
CFO: Bret Johnson, Chief Financial Officer
CMO: Steven D. Shapiro, M.D., Chief Medical Officer
CIO: Michael Taylor, Chief Information Officer
CNO: Pennie Peralta, R.N., VP, Nursing & Chief Nursing Officer
Web address: www.ropersaintfrancis.com
Control: Other not–for–profit (including NFP Corporation) **Service:** General Medical and Surgical

Staffed Beds: 170 **Admissions:** 9210 **Census:** 91 **Outpatient Visits:** 161368 **Births:** 2541 **Total Expense ($000):** 154767 **Payroll Expense ($000):** 50006 **Personnel:** 1009

✠ **HEALTHSOUTH REHABILITATION HOSPITAL OF CHARLESTON (423027)**, 9181 Medcom Street, Zip 29406–9168; tel. 843/820–7777 **A**1 10 **F**9 29 35 54 56 57 64 65 77 82 86 90 93 94 95 96 132 143 148 **S** HEALTHSOUTH Corporation, Birmingham, AL
Primary Contact: Troy Powell, Chief Executive Officer
CFO: Beckye Lariviere, Controller
CMO: William Livesay, Jr., D.O., Medical Director
CHR: Donna White, Director Human Resources
Web address: www.healthsouthcharleston.com
Control: Corporation, Investor–owned, for–profit **Service:** Rehabilitation

Staffed Beds: 49 **Admissions:** 997 **Census:** 37 **Outpatient Visits:** 0 **Births:** 0 **Total Expense ($000):** 14249 **Payroll Expense ($000):** 6561 **Personnel:** 108

✠ **MUSC MEDICAL CENTER OF MEDICAL UNIVERSITY OF SOUTH CAROLINA (420004)**, 169 Ashley Avenue, Zip 29425–8905; tel. 843/792–2300, (Includes CHILDREN'S HOSPITAL OF SOUTH CAROLINA AT MUSC, 171 Ashley Avenue, Zip 29425–8908; tel. 843/792–1414; Patrick J. Cawley, M.D., Vice President of Clinical Operations and Chief Executive Officer) **A**1 2 3 5 8 9 10 **F**3 4 5 6 7 9 11 12 13 14 15 16 17 18 19 20 21 22 23 24 25 26 27 28 29 30 31 32 34 35 37 38 39 40 41 43 44 45 46 47 48 49 50 51 52 53 54 55 56 57 59 60 61 64 66 67 68 70 71 72 73 74 75 76 77 78 79 80 81 82 84 85 86 87 88 89 92 93 94 97 98 99 100 101 102 103 104 105 107 108 109 110 111 114 115 116 117 118 119 120 121 123 124 126 129 130 131 132 134 135 136 137 138 139 140 141 142 144 145 146 147 148
Primary Contact: Patrick J. Cawley, M.D., Vice President of Clinical Operations and Chief Executive Officer
COO: Matthew Wain, Chief Operating Officer
CFO: Stephen Hargett, Administrator Finance and Support Services
CMO: Daniel Handel, M.D., Chief Medical Officer
CIO: Frank Clark, Chief Information Officer
CHR: Betts Ellis, Administrator Institutional Relations
CNO: Marilyn J. Schaffner, Ph.D., Administrator Clinical Services and Chief Nursing Officer
Web address: www.muschealth.com
Control: State–Government, nonfederal **Service:** General Medical and Surgical

Staffed Beds: 718 **Admissions:** 34441 **Census:** 603 **Outpatient Visits:** 978216 **Births:** 2149 **Total Expense ($000):** 1095700 **Payroll Expense ($000):** 387528 **Personnel:** 6601

☐ **PALMETTO LOWCOUNTRY BEHAVIORAL HEALTH (424006)**, 2777 Speissegger Drive, Zip 29405–8229; tel. 843/747–5830, (Total facility includes 32 beds in nursing home–type unit) **A**1 10 **F**4 64 98 99 102 103 104 105 106 **S** Universal Health Services, Inc., King of Prussia, PA
Primary Contact: Shari Baker, Chief Executive Officer
CFO: Stan Markowski, Chief Financial Officer
CMO: Steven Lopez, M.D., Chief Medical Officer
CHR: Sheila Simpson, Vice President Human Resources
CNO: Jo Good, Director of Nursing
Web address: www.palmettobehavioralhealth.com
Control: Corporation, Investor–owned, for–profit **Service:** Psychiatric

Staffed Beds: 112 **Admissions:** 2498 **Census:** 64 **Births:** 0 **Total Expense ($000):** 14910 **Payroll Expense ($000):** 7158 **Personnel:** 155

✠ **RALPH H. JOHNSON VETERANS AFFAIRS MEDICAL CENTER**, 109 Bee Street, Zip 29401–5799; tel. 843/577–5011, (Nonreporting) **A**1 2 3 5 8 **S** Department of Veterans Affairs, Washington, DC
Primary Contact: Scott R. Isaacks, Interim Director
COO: Scott R. Isaacks, Associate Director
CFO: Cassandra Helfer, Chief Financial Officer
CMO: Florence N. Hutchison, M.D., Chief of Staff
CIO: Timothy Babcock, Chief Information Officer
CHR: Amanda Dean, Human Resources Officer
CNO: Mary C. Fraggos, R.N., Associate Director of Nursing and Patient Care Services
Web address: www.charleston.va.gov/
Control: Veterans Affairs, Government, federal **Service:** General Medical and Surgical

Staffed Beds: 98

✠ △ **ROPER HOSPITAL (420087)**, 316 Calhoun Street, Zip 29401–1125; tel. 843/724–2000 **A**1 2 7 9 10 **F**1 3 7 8 9 14 15 17 18 20 22 24 26 28 29 30 31 34 35 37 40 42 43 45 49 50 51 54 55 56 57 58 59 60 61 62 63 64 65 67 68 69 70 74 75 77 78 79 80 81 82 84 85 86 87 90 92 93 94 95 96 100 107 108 110 111 114 115 117 118 119 120 121 123 124 126 128 129 130 131 132 135 136 143 144 146 147 148 **S** Carolinas HealthCare System, Charlotte, NC
Primary Contact: Matthew J. Severance, FACHE, Chief Executive Officer
CFO: Bret Johnson, Chief Financial Officer
CMO: Steven D. Shapiro, M.D., Vice President Medical Affairs
CIO: Melinda H. Cardell, Interim Vice President and Chief Information Officer
CHR: Melanie Stith, Vice President Human Resources
CNO: Carolyn Viall Donohue, MSN, Vice President Nursing
Web address: www.ropersaintfrancis.com
Control: Other not–for–profit (including NFP Corporation) **Service:** General Medical and Surgical

Staffed Beds: 308 **Admissions:** 13229 **Census:** 196 **Outpatient Visits:** 240010 **Births:** 0 **Total Expense ($000):** 314845 **Payroll Expense ($000):** 100398 **Personnel:** 2037

✠ **TRIDENT MEDICAL CENTER (420079)**, 9330 Medical Plaza Drive, Zip 29406–9195; tel. 843/797–7000, (Includes MONCKS CORNER MEDICAL CENTER, 401 North Live Oak Drive, Highway 17A, Moncks Corner, Zip 29461–5603; tel. 843/761–8721; SUMMERVILLE MEDICAL CENTER, 295 Midland Parkway, Summerville, Zip 29485–8104; tel. 843/832–5000) **A**1 2 3 5 9 10 **F**3 8 12 13 15 16 18 20 22 24 26 28 29 30 31 34 35 40 41 42 43 45 46 47 48 49 50 54 55 56 57 59 60 61 64 70 72 73 74 75 76 77 78 79 80 81 85 86 87 89 90 93 94 107 108 110 111 114 115 116 117 118 119 120 121 123 124 126 129 130 131 132 135 145 146 147 148 **S** HCA, Nashville, TN
Primary Contact: Todd Gallati, FACHE, President and Chief Executive Officer
CFO: Teresa Finch, Chief Financial Officer
CIO: Susan Murray, Director Information Services
CHR: Joe B. Hill, Jr., Vice President Human Resources
Web address: www.tridenthealthsystem.com
Control: Corporation, Investor–owned, for–profit **Service:** General Medical and Surgical

Staffed Beds: 404 **Admissions:** 21415 **Census:** 244 **Births:** 2821 **Personnel:** 1689

CHERAW—Chesterfield County

✠ **CHESTERFIELD GENERAL HOSPITAL (420062)**, 711 Chesterfield Highway, Zip 29520–7002; tel. 843/537–7881 **A**1 9 10 **F**3 8 13 15 18 28 29 30 34 35 40 45 56 57 59 68 70 76 77 79 81 85 86 87 89 90 102 107 108 114 118 119 128 130 132 133 135 **S** Community Health Systems, Inc., Franklin, TN
Primary Contact: Jeff Reece, R.N., MSN, Chief Executive Officer
CFO: Phillip Fouts, Chief Financial Officer
CMO: David Bersinger, M.D., Chief of Staff
CIO: Jim Spencer, Director Information System
CNO: Debbie Spells, Chief Nursing Officer
Web address: www.chesterfieldgeneral.com
Control: Corporation, Investor–owned, for–profit **Service:** General Medical and Surgical

Staffed Beds: 59 **Admissions:** 1814 **Census:** 18 **Outpatient Visits:** 27756 **Births:** 184 **Total Expense ($000):** 27818 **Payroll Expense ($000):** 10225 **Personnel:** 252

SC

Hospital, Medicare Provider Number, Address, Telephone, Approval, Facility, and Physician Codes, Health Care System

★ American Hospital Association (AHA) membership
☐ The Joint Commission accreditation   ◇ DNV Healthcare Inc. accreditation
○ Healthcare Facilities Accreditation Program
△ Commission on Accreditation of Rehabilitation Facilities (CARF) accreditation

---

SC

CHESTER—Chester County

✠ **CHESTER REGIONAL MEDICAL CENTER (420019)**, 1 Medical Park Drive, Zip 29706–9769; tel. 803/581–3151, (Nonreporting) **A**1 9 10 **S** Community Health Systems, Inc., Franklin, TN
Primary Contact: Page H. Vaughan, Chief Executive Officer
CFO: Tracey Claxton, Chief Financial Officer
CMO: Terry Dodge, M.D., Chief of Staff
CIO: Shaw Laird, Chief Information Officer
CHR: Karen Chapman, Director Human Resources
CNO: Betty Griffin, Interim Chief Nursing Officer
Web address: www.chesterregional.com
Control: Corporation, Investor–owned, for–profit **Service:** General Medical and Surgical

Staffed Beds: 36

CLINTON—Laurens County

✠ **GREENVILLE HEALTH SYSTEM – LAURENS COUNTY MEMORIAL HOSPITAL (420038)**, Highway 76 East, Zip 29325–2331, Mailing Address: P.O. Drawer 976, Zip 29325–0976; tel. 864/833–9100, (Includes LAURENS COUNTY HOSPITAL, Zip 29325; tel. 803/833–9100), (Total facility includes 14 beds in nursing home–type unit) **A**1 9 10 20 **F**1 3 11 13 15 18 28 29 30 34 35 40 45 46 59 70 76 79 80 81 87 88 89 90 107 108 110 119 128 129 130 132 146 147 **S** Greenville Health System, Greenville, SC
Primary Contact: Richard E. D'Alberto, FACHE, Campus President
CFO: Melanie McMaster, Director Operations
CMO: Michelle Hagenbuch, M.D., Chief of Staff
CIO: Gina Driggers, Manager Information Technology
CHR: Kelly C. Plaia, Manager Human Resources
Web address: www.ghs.org/laurens
Control: Hospital district or authority, Government, nonfederal **Service:** General Medical and Surgical

Staffed Beds: 70 **Admissions:** 2843 **Census:** 38 **Births:** 297 **Total Expense ($000):** 59924 **Payroll Expense ($000):** 22036 **Personnel:** 422

WHITTEN CENTER, Highway 76 East, Zip 29325, Mailing Address: P.O. Box 239, Zip 29325–0239; tel. 864/833–2733, (Nonreporting)
Primary Contact: Wes Leonard, Chief Executive Officer
Control: State–Government, nonfederal **Service:** Institution for mental retardation

Staffed Beds: 22

COLUMBIA—Richland County

EARLE E. MORRIS ALCOHOL AND DRUG TREATMENT CENTER, 610 Faison Drive, Zip 29203–3218; tel. 803/935–7100, (Nonreporting)
Primary Contact: George McConnell, Director
Web address: www.state.sc.us/dmh/morris_village/
Control: State–Government, nonfederal **Service:** Alcoholism and other chemical dependency

Staffed Beds: 120

☐ **G. WERBER BRYAN PSYCHIATRIC HOSPITAL (424005)**, 220 Faison Drive, Zip 29203–3210; tel. 803/935–7146, (Nonreporting) **A**1 10
Primary Contact: Harvey Miller, Director
COO: Jaclyn Upfield, Chief Operating Officer
CIO: Sam Livingston, Information Resource Consultant
CHR: Kim Church, Manager Human Resources
Web address: www.scdmh.org
Control: State–Government, nonfederal **Service:** Psychiatric

Staffed Beds: 198

✠ **HEALTHSOUTH REHABILITATION HOSPITAL OF COLUMBIA (423025)**, 2935 Colonial Drive, Zip 29203–6811; tel. 803/254–7777 **A**1 10 **F**29 50 53 60 64 77 90 91 92 93 94 95 96 97 119 **S** HEALTHSOUTH Corporation, Birmingham, AL
Primary Contact: W. Anthony Jackson, Chief Executive Officer
CFO: Jessica Burriss, Chief Financial Officer
CMO: Devin Troyer, M.D., Medical Director
CHR: Luanne Burton, Director Human Resources
CNO: April Brooks, Chief Nursing Officer
Web address: www.healthsouthcolumbia.com
Control: Corporation, Investor–owned, for–profit **Service:** Rehabilitation

Staffed Beds: 96 **Admissions:** 1660 **Census:** 62 **Births:** 0 **Total Expense ($000):** 17012 **Payroll Expense ($000):** 9739 **Personnel:** 160

✠ **INTERMEDICAL HOSPITAL OF SOUTH CAROLINA (422006)**, Taylor at Marion Street, Zip 29220, Mailing Address: PO BOX 11069, Zip 29211–1069; tel. 803/296–3757 **A**9 10 **F**1 3 29 34 57 85 130 148
Primary Contact: Armando Colombo, Chief Executive Officer
Web address: www.intermedicalhospital.com
Control: Other not–for–profit (including NFP Corporation) **Service:** Long–Term Acute Care hospital

Staffed Beds: 35 **Admissions:** 242 **Census:** 19 **Outpatient Visits:** 0 **Births:** 0 **Total Expense ($000):** 9581 **Payroll Expense ($000):** 2913 **Personnel:** 70

✠ **PALMETTO HEALTH BAPTIST (420085)**, Taylor at Marion Street, Zip 29220–0001; tel. 803/296–5010, (Total facility includes 22 beds in nursing home–type unit) **A**1 2 3 5 9 10 **F**1 3 5 11 12 13 15 18 20 29 30 31 34 40 45 47 48 49 51 54 57 59 61 62 63 64 68 70 71 72 73 74 75 76 77 78 79 80 81 82 84 85 86 87 89 90 93 94 98 99 100 101 102 103 104 105 107 108 110 111 112 114 115 116 117 118 119 124 128 130 132 145 146 147 148 **S** Palmetto Health, Columbia, SC
Primary Contact: Gregory B. Gattman, Acute Care Executive
COO: James M. Bridges, Executive Vice President and Chief Operating Officer
CFO: Paul K. Duane, Chief Financial Officer and Office of Health Reform
CMO: Mark J. Mayson, M.D., Medical Director
CIO: Michelle Edwards, Executive Vice President Information Technology
CHR: Trip Gregory, Senior Vice President Human Resources
Web address: www.palmettohealth.org
Control: Other not–for–profit (including NFP Corporation) **Service:** General Medical and Surgical

Staffed Beds: 400 **Admissions:** 20169 **Census:** 254 **Births:** 3439 **Total Expense ($000):** 298568 **Payroll Expense ($000):** 120929 **Personnel:** 1910

✠ **PALMETTO HEALTH BAPTIST PARKRIDGE (420106)**, 400 Palmetto Health Parkway, Zip 29212–1760, Mailing Address: P.O. BOX 2266, Zip 29202–2266; tel. 803/907–7000, (Nonreporting) **A**1 10 **S** Palmetto Health, Columbia, SC
Primary Contact: Sarah Kirby, Acute Care Executive
Web address: www.palmettohealth.org
Control: Other not–for–profit (including NFP Corporation) **Service:** General Medical and Surgical

Staffed Beds: 50

✠ **PALMETTO HEALTH RICHLAND (420018)**, Five Richland Medical Park Drive, Zip 29203–6897; tel. 803/434–7000, (Includes PALMETTO HEALTH CHILDREN'S HOSPITAL, Five Richland Medical Park Drive, Zip 29203–6863; tel. 803/434–6882) **A**1 2 3 5 8 9 10 **F**2 3 4 5 6 11 13 15 17 18 20 22 24 28 29 30 31 32 34 35 39 40 41 43 45 46 50 54 55 56 57 59 60 61 64 68 70 72 73 74 75 76 77 78 79 81 86 87 88 89 90 93 94 98 99 100 101 102 103 104 105 107 108 110 111 114 115 116 121 126 129 130 131 132 134 135 143 146 147 148 **S** Palmetto Health, Columbia, SC
Primary Contact: Jay Hamm, R.N., Chief Acute Care Executive
CFO: Paul K. Duane, Chief Financial Officer and Office of Health Reform
CMO: Eric Brown, M.D., Physician Executive
CHR: Robert Brinkerhoff, System Vice President
CNO: Carole A. Siegfried, MSN, Campus Nurse Executive
Web address: www.palmettohealth.org
Control: Other not–for–profit (including NFP Corporation) **Service:** General Medical and Surgical

Staffed Beds: 704 **Admissions:** 29932 **Census:** 554 **Outpatient Visits:** 492339 **Births:** 2272 **Total Expense ($000):** 660349 **Payroll Expense ($000):** 253651 **Personnel:** 4440

★ ◇ **PROVIDENCE HOSPITAL (420026)**, 2435 Forest Drive, Zip 29204–2098; tel. 803/865–4500, (Includes PROVIDENCE HOSPITAL NORTHEAST, 120 Gateway Corporate Boulevard, Zip 29203–9611; tel. 803/865–4500; Ryan Hall, Vice President) **A**9 10 21 **F**3 8 11 13 15 17 20 22 24 26 28 29 30 34 35 38 40 44 45 49 50 54 56 57 58 59 61 64 68 70 74 75 77 79 80 81 85 86 87 89 90 92 93 94 100 107 108 111 114 118 119 129 130 131 132 141 146 147 148 P5 **S** Sisters of Charity Health System, Cleveland, OH
Primary Contact: Michael French, Interim Chief Executive Officer
COO: W. Carl Martin, Chief Operating Officer
CFO: Pamela Gallagher, Chief Financial Officer
CMO: Wayne Sribnick, M.D., Senior Vice President and Chief Medical Officer
CIO: Lib Cumbee, Director Information Systems
CHR: Justin A. Lofurno, Director Human Resources
Web address: www.sistersofcharityhealth.org/health–care/providence–hospitals/
Control: Church–operated, Nongovernment, not–for profit **Service:** General Medical and Surgical

Staffed Beds: 314 **Admissions:** 10435 **Census:** 142 **Births:** 0 **Total Expense ($000):** 232205 **Payroll Expense ($000):** 77310 **Personnel:** 1145

PROVIDENCE HOSPITAL NORTHEAST See Providence Hospital

SOUTH CAROLINA DEPARTMENT OF CORRECTIONS HOSPITAL, 4344 Broad River Road, Zip 29210–4098; tel. 803/896–8567, (Nonreporting)
Primary Contact: John Solomon, M.D., Director
Web address: www.doc.sc.gov/
Control: State–Government, nonfederal **Service:** Hospital unit of an institution (prison hospital, college infirmary, etc.)

Staffed Beds: 70

☐ **WILLIAM S. HALL PSYCHIATRIC INSTITUTE (424003)**, 1800 Colonial Drive, Zip 29203–6827; tel. 803/898–1693, (Nonreporting) **A**1 3 5 10
Primary Contact: Angela Forand, Director
COO: Doug Glover, Controller
CFO: Doug Glover, Controller
CMO: Phyllis Bryant–Mobley, M.D., Director Medical Services
CIO: Mesa Foard, Director Information technology
CHR: Kim Church, Manager Human Resources
Web address: www.scdmh.org
Control: State–Government, nonfederal **Service:** Psychiatric

Staffed Beds: 58

Many Facility Codes have changed. Please refer to the AHA Guide Code Chart. © 2014 AHA Guide

✠ △ **WM. JENNINGS BRYAN DORN VETERANS AFFAIRS MEDICAL CENTER**, 6439 Garners Ferry Road, Zip 29209–1639; tel. 803/776–4000, (Nonreporting) **A**1 2 3 5 7 **S** Department of Veterans Affairs, Washington, DC
Primary Contact: Timothy McMurry, Director
COO: David Omura, Associate Director
CMO: Bernard L. DeKoning, M.D., Chief of Staff
CIO: Steve Chalphant, Director Information Management Service Line
CHR: Phyllis Jones, Chief Human Resources
CNO: Ruth W. Mustard, R.N., Associate Director Nursing and Patient Services
Web address: www.columbiasc.va.gov/
Control: Veterans Affairs, Government, federal **Service:** General Medical and Surgical

Staffed Beds: 216

CONWAY—Horry County

★ ◇ **CONWAY MEDICAL CENTER (420049)**, 300 Singleton Ridge Road, Zip 29526–9142, Mailing Address: P.O. Box 829, Zip 29528–0829; tel. 843/347–7111, (Total facility includes 113 beds in nursing home–type unit) **A**9 10 21 **F**1 3 8 11 12 13 15 18 20 26 28 29 30 34 35 40 45 46 49 50 51 53 57 59 60 61 68 70 71 73 75 76 77 79 81 84 85 86 87 89 90 93 94 107 108 110 111 114 115 118 119 128 129 130 132 135 145 146 147 148
Primary Contact: Philip A. Clayton, President and Chief Executive Officer
CFO: Bret Barr, Vice President Fiscal Services
CMO: Preston Strosnider, M.D., Vice President Medical Affairs
CIO: Mickey Waters, Director Information Technology
CHR: Matthew J. Securro, Vice President Human Resources
Web address: www.conwaymedicalcenter.com
Control: Other not–for–profit (including NFP Corporation) **Service:** General Medical and Surgical

Staffed Beds: 287 **Admissions:** 7880 **Census:** 188 **Births:** 1411 **Total Expense ($000):** 131638 **Payroll Expense ($000):** 48133 **Personnel:** 1023

☐ **LIGHTHOUSE CARE CENTER OF CONWAY (424002)**, 152 Waccamaw Medical Park Drive, Zip 29526–8901; tel. 843/347–8871, (Total facility includes 18 beds in nursing home–type unit) **A**1 9 10 **F**4 98 101 102 103 106 130 **S** Universal Health Services, Inc., King of Prussia, PA
Primary Contact: Thomas L. Ryba, Chief Executive Officer
CFO: Gabrielle Gale, Chief Financial Officer
CMO: Adedapo Oduwole, M.D., Medical Director
CIO: Gabrielle Gale, Chief Financial Officer
CHR: Lois Woodall, Director Human Resources
Web address: www.lighthousecarecenterofconway.com/
Control: Corporation, Investor–owned, for–profit **Service:** Psychiatric

Staffed Beds: 90 **Admissions:** 2166 **Census:** 73 **Outpatient Visits:** 0 **Births:** 0 **Personnel:** 183

DARLINGTON—Darlington County

MCLEOD MEDICAL CENTER–DARLINGTON (420057), 701 Cashua Ferry Road, Zip 29532–8488, Mailing Address: P.O. Box 1859, Zip 29540; tel. 843/395–1100 **F**1 3 4 15 34 35 38 56 57 59 61 64 68 77 81 85 90 93 94 97 98 100 101 103 104 107 110 114 119 127 128 130 132 133 135 147 148 **S** McLeod Health, Florence, SC
Primary Contact: Pat Godbold, Administrator
Web address: www.mcleodhealth.org
Control: Other not–for–profit (including NFP Corporation) **Service:** General Medical and Surgical

Staffed Beds: 50 **Admissions:** 272 **Census:** 22 **Births:** 0 **Total Expense ($000):** 13094 **Payroll Expense ($000):** 7288 **Personnel:** 122

DILLON—Dillon County

☐ **MCLEOD MEDICAL CENTER DILLON (420005)**, 301 East Jackson Street, Zip 29536–2509, Mailing Address: P.O. Box 1327, Zip 29536–1327; tel. 843/774–4111 **A**1 9 10 **F**3 11 13 15 28 29 30 32 34 35 40 50 57 59 64 66 68 70 75 76 79 81 82 85 87 89 90 94 107 111 114 119 130 132 134 135 146 147 148 **P**6 **S** McLeod Health, Florence, SC
Primary Contact: Deborah Locklair, FACHE, Administrator
CFO: Fulton Ervin, Senior Vice President and Chief Financial Officer
CMO: Walter B. Blum, M.D., Chief of Staff
CIO: Jenean Blackmon, Assistant Vice President and Chief Information Officer
CHR: Cynthia Causey, Associate Administrator Human and Mission Services
Web address: www.mcleodhealth.org
Control: Other not–for–profit (including NFP Corporation) **Service:** General Medical and Surgical

Staffed Beds: 63 **Admissions:** 2818 **Census:** 25 **Total Expense ($000):** 37727 **Payroll Expense ($000):** 15057 **Personnel:** 296

EASLEY—Pickens County

✠ **BAPTIST EASLEY HOSPITAL (420015)**, 200 Fleetwood Drive, Zip 29640–2022, Mailing Address: P.O. Box 2129, Zip 29641–2129; tel. 864/442–7200 **A**1 9 10 **F**3 11 13 15 20 28 29 30 34 35 39 40 56 57 59 64 70 76 79 81 85 86 87 89 107 108 111 114 119 124 130 132 146 147 **S** Palmetto Health, Columbia, SC
Primary Contact: Michael Batchelor, Chief Executive Officer
CFO: J. Larry Pope, Vice President Finance
CIO: Cynthia Ellenburg, Director Health Information Services
CHR: Richard B. Posey, Director Human Resources
CNO: Mary Ann Hunter, Director Nursing Services
Web address: www.baptisteasley.org
Control: Other not–for–profit (including NFP Corporation) **Service:** General Medical and Surgical

Staffed Beds: 89 **Admissions:** 4087 **Census:** 54 **Births:** 429 **Total Expense ($000):** 79444 **Payroll Expense ($000):** 29373 **Personnel:** 742

EDGEFIELD—Edgefield County

★ **EDGEFIELD COUNTY HOSPITAL (421304)**, 300 Ridge Medical Plaza, Zip 29824–4525; tel. 803/637–3174 **A**9 10 18 **F**3 28 29 34 35 40 45 59 65 66 68 77 79 81 84 90 93 94 107 115 119 127 128 130 133 146 **P**1
Primary Contact: Brandon Clary, Chief Executive Officer
CFO: William Garry, Chief Financial Officer
CMO: W. Hugh Morgan, M.D., Chief Medical Staff
CIO: Faye Burton, Director Health Information Management
CHR: Leslie G. Seigler, Executive Assistant and Coordinator Human Resources
Web address: www.myech.org
Control: County–Government, nonfederal **Service:** General Medical and Surgical

Staffed Beds: 25 **Admissions:** 402 **Census:** 6 **Births:** 0 **Total Expense ($000):** 12299 **Payroll Expense ($000):** 6211 **Personnel:** 188

FAIRFAX—Allendale County

★ **ALLENDALE COUNTY HOSPITAL (421300)**, 1787 Allendale Fairfax Highway, Zip 29827–9133, Mailing Address: P.O. Box 218, Zip 29827–0218; tel. 803/632–3311, (Total facility includes 44 beds in nursing home–type unit) **A**9 10 18 **F**1 3 15 34 35 40 56 57 59 61 64 67 68 77 87 90 97 107 110 114 119 127 128 130 133 147
Primary Contact: M. K. Hiatt, Administrator
Web address: www.achospital.org
Control: County–Government, nonfederal **Service:** General Medical and Surgical

Staffed Beds: 69 **Admissions:** 378 **Census:** 39 **Outpatient Visits:** 30623 **Births:** 0 **Personnel:** 124

FLORENCE—Florence County

✠ △ **CAROLINAS HOSPITAL SYSTEM (420091)**, 805 Pamplico Highway, Zip 29505–6050, Mailing Address: P.O. Box 100550, Zip 29502–0550; tel. 843/674–5000, (Total facility includes 24 beds in nursing home–type unit) **A**1 7 9 10 **F**4 5 6 8 13 15 17 18 20 22 24 26 28 29 30 31 34 35 40 41 43 45 53 55 56 57 58 59 60 61 62 63 64 67 68 70 72 73 74 75 76 77 78 79 81 82 86 87 88 89 90 93 94 97 107 110 111 114 115 116 117 119 121 128 129 130 132 135 143 145 146 147 148 **S** Community Health Systems, Inc., Franklin, TN
Primary Contact: Darcy Craven, Chief Executive Officer
CFO: Loren Rials, Chief Financial Officer
CMO: Kevin Shea, M.D., Chief of Staff
CIO: Lynn Northcutt, Chief Information Officer
CHR: Donna Damico, Director Human Resources
Web address: www.carolinashospital.com
Control: Corporation, Investor–owned, for–profit **Service:** General Medical and Surgical

Staffed Beds: 429 **Admissions:** 12444 **Census:** 201 **Births:** 875 **Total Expense ($000):** 186157 **Payroll Expense ($000):** 66466 **Personnel:** 1348

✠ **HEALTHSOUTH REHABILITATION HOSPITAL OF FLORENCE (423026)**, 900 East Cheves Street, Zip 29506–2704; tel. 843/679–9000 **A**1 10 **F**29 90 95 96 132 148 **S** HEALTHSOUTH Corporation, Birmingham, AL
Primary Contact: Jill Strawn, Chief Executive Officer
CFO: Robert Wheeler, Controller
CMO: Adora Matthews, M.D., Medical Director
CHR: Susan Trantham, Director Human Resources
Web address: www.healthsouthflorence.com
Control: Corporation, Investor–owned, for–profit **Service:** Rehabilitation

Staffed Beds: 88 **Admissions:** 1170 **Census:** 45 **Outpatient Visits:** 0 **Births:** 0 **Personnel:** 160

SC

Hospital, Medicare Provider Number, Address, Telephone, Approval, Facility, and Physician Codes, Health Care System

★ American Hospital Association (AHA) membership
☐ The Joint Commission accreditation
◇ DNV Healthcare Inc. accreditation
○ Healthcare Facilities Accreditation Program
△ Commission on Accreditation of Rehabilitation Facilities (CARF) accreditation

✠ **MCLEOD REGIONAL MEDICAL CENTER (420051)**, 555 East Cheves Street, Zip 29506–2617, Mailing Address: P.O. Box 100551, Zip 29502–0551; tel. 843/777–2000 **A1** 2 3 5 7 9 10 **F1** 3 7 8 11 13 15 17 18 20 22 24 26 28 29 30 31 32 34 35 38 39 40 43 45 46 47 48 49 50 51 53 54 56 57 58 59 60 61 62 63 64 66 67 68 70 71 72 73 74 75 76 77 78 79 80 81 82 84 85 86 87 88 89 90 92 93 94 96 97 98 100 101 102 103 104 107 108 110 111 114 115 116 119 123 127 128 129 130 131 132 133 135 143 144 145 146 147 148 **P6 S** McLeod Health, Florence, SC
Primary Contact: Robert L. Colones, President and Chief Executive Officer
COO: Ronald L. Boring, Senior Vice President and Chief Operating Officer
CFO: Fulton Ervin, Chief Financial Officer
CMO: Alva W. Whitehead, M.D., Vice President Medical Services
CIO: Jenean Blackmon, Associate Vice President and Chief Information Officer
CHR: Jeannette Glenn, Vice President Human Resources, Education and Training
Web address: www.mcleodhealth.org
Control: Other not–for–profit (including NFP Corporation) **Service:** General Medical and Surgical

Staffed Beds: 488 **Admissions:** 22302 **Census:** 322 **Total Expense ($000):** 471679 **Payroll Expense ($000):** 164614 **Personnel:** 2975	

✠ **REGENCY HOSPITAL OF FLORENCE (422007)**, 121 East Cedar Street, 4th Floor, Zip 29506–2576; tel. 843/661–3471 **A1** 10 **F1** 3 29 34 35 57 58 70 77 80 85 90 100 130 148 **S** Select Medical Corporation, Mechanicsburg, PA
Primary Contact: Amy Metz, Chief Executive Officer
CMO: Stephen Dersch, M.D., President Medical Staff
CHR: Tina Stokes, Manager Human Resources
Web address: www.regencyhospital.com
Control: Corporation, Investor–owned, for–profit **Service:** Long–Term Acute Care hospital

Staffed Beds: 40 **Admissions:** 421 **Census:** 33 **Outpatient Visits:** 0 **Births:** 0 **Total Expense ($000):** 16224 **Payroll Expense ($000):** 7393 **Personnel:** 118	

FORT JACKSON—Richland County

✠ **MONCRIEF ARMY COMMUNITY HOSPITAL**, 4500 Stuart Street, Zip 29207–5700; tel. 803/751–2160, (Nonreporting) **A1** 3 5 **S** Department of the Army, Office of the Surgeon General, Falls Church, VA
Primary Contact: Colonel Mark L. Higdon, Commander
CMO: Lieutenant Colonel Larry Andrew, M.D., Deputy Commander Clinical Services
Web address: www.moncrief.amedd.army.mil
Control: Army, Government, federal **Service:** General Medical and Surgical

Staffed Beds: 60	

GAFFNEY—Cherokee County

✠ **NOVANT HEALTH GAFFNEY MEDICAL CENTER (420043)**, 1530 North Limestone Street, Zip 29340–4738; tel. 864/487–4271 **A1** 9 10 **F3** 11 13 15 18 19 29 34 35 40 45 46 51 57 59 64 65 67 70 75 76 79 81 82 85 86 87 89 107 108 110 111 113 119 129 130 135 146 147 148 **S** Novant Health, Winston Salem, NC
Primary Contact: Brian Yates, Administrator
COO: Leslie Glover, Director Operations
CMO: Frank Phillips, M.D., Chief of Staff
CIO: Richard Bledsoe, Director Information Systems
CHR: Connie Gibson, R.N., Director Human Resources
CNO: Brian Nunn, R.N., Chief Nursing Officer
Web address: www.upstatecarolina.org
Control: Other not–for–profit (including NFP Corporation) **Service:** General Medical and Surgical

Staffed Beds: 125 **Admissions:** 2568 **Census:** 26 **Births:** 257 **Total Expense ($000):** 42389 **Payroll Expense ($000):** 13694 **Personnel:** 418	

GEORGETOWN—Georgetown County

✠ **GEORGETOWN MEMORIAL HOSPITAL (420020)**, 606 Black River Road, Zip 29440–3368, Mailing Address: Drawer 421718, Zip 29442–4203; tel. 843/527–7000 **A1** 3 5 9 10 19 **F3** 11 12 13 15 17 18 20 22 26 28 29 30 31 32 34 35 39 40 44 50 51 53 54 56 57 64 65 66 70 73 74 75 76 77 78 79 81 82 84 85 86 87 89 90 93 94 97 100 102 107 108 110 111 115 118 119 130 131 132 135 146 147 148 **S** Georgetown Hospital System, Georgetown, SC
Primary Contact: Gayle L. Resetar, Chief Operating Officer
COO: Gayle L. Resetar, Vice President and Chief Operating Officer
CFO: Terry L. Kiser, Vice President and Chief Financial Officer
CIO: Frank Scafidi, Vice President and Chief Information Officer
CHR: James F. Harper, Vice President and Chief Human Resources Officer
Web address: www.georgetownhospitalsystem.org
Control: Other not–for–profit (including NFP Corporation) **Service:** General Medical and Surgical

Staffed Beds: 136 **Admissions:** 4405 **Census:** 49 **Outpatient Visits:** 163591 **Births:** 296 **Total Expense ($000):** 110374 **Payroll Expense ($000):** 43244 **Personnel:** 746	

GREENVILLE—Greenville County

✠ △ **BON SECOURS ST. FRANCIS HEALTH SYSTEM (420023)**, One St. Francis Drive, Zip 29601–3207; tel. 864/255–1000, (Includes ST. FRANCIS EASTSIDE, 125 Commonwealth Drive, Zip 29615–4812; tel. 864/675–4000) **A1** 2 7 9 10 **F1** 3 8 11 12 13 15 17 18 20 22 24 26 28 29 30 31 32 34 35 36 39 40 44 45 46 47 48 49 50 51 53 54 55 57 58 59 60 61 62 63 64 66 68 69 70 71 73 74 75 76 77 78 79 80 81 82 83 84 85 86 87 89 90 94 96 97 107 108 110 111 114 115 118 119 124 126 128 129 130 132 135 136 141 146 147 **P6 S** Bon Secours Health System, Inc., Marriottsville, MD
Primary Contact: Mark S. Nantz, FACHE, Chief Executive Officer
COO: Daniel Duggan, Chief Operating Officer
CFO: Ronnie Hyatt, Senior Vice President Finance and Chief Financial Officer
CMO: Saria Saccoio, M.D., Chief Medical Officer
CIO: Rita Hooker, Administrative Director Information Services
CHR: Fernando Fleites, Senior Vice President Human Resources
CNO: Teri Ficicchy, R.N., Chief Nursing Officer
Web address: www.stfrancishealth.org
Control: Other not–for–profit (including NFP Corporation) **Service:** General Medical and Surgical

Staffed Beds: 331 **Admissions:** 17890 **Census:** 214 **Births:** 1997 **Total Expense ($000):** 388572 **Payroll Expense ($000):** 128197 **Personnel:** 2045	

✠ △ **GREENVILLE MEMORIAL HOSPITAL (420078)**, 701 Grove Road, Zip 29605–4295; tel. 864/455–7000, (Includes CHILDREN'S HOSPITAL, 701 Grove Road, Zip 29605–5611; tel. 864/455–7000; MARSHALL I. PICKENS HOSPITAL, 701 Grove Road, Zip 29605–5601; tel. 864/455–8988; ROGER C. PEACE REHABILITATION HOSPITAL, 701 Grove Road, tel. 864/455–7000), (Total facility includes 44 beds in nursing home–type unit) **A1** 2 3 5 7 8 9 10 **F1** 3 4 5 11 13 15 17 18 20 22 24 26 27 28 29 30 31 34 35 36 38 39 40 41 43 44 45 46 47 48 49 50 52 53 54 56 57 58 59 61 64 65 66 68 70 72 73 74 75 76 77 78 79 81 82 84 85 86 87 88 89 90 92 93 94 96 97 98 99 100 101 102 103 104 105 106 107 110 111 114 115 117 118 119 120 121 124 126 128 129 130 132 134 135 136 141 142 145 146 147 148 **S** Greenville Health System, Greenville, SC
Primary Contact: Paul F. Johnson, President
CNO: Michelle T. Smith, R.N., Chief Nursing Officer
Web address: www.ghs.org
Control: Other not–for–profit (including NFP Corporation) **Service:** General Medical and Surgical

Staffed Beds: 792 **Admissions:** 35963 **Census:** 595 **Outpatient Visits:** 494220 **Births:** 5142 **Total Expense ($000):** 735173 **Payroll Expense ($000):** 210312 **Personnel:** 5339	

✠ **PATEWOOD MEMORIAL HOSPITAL (420102)**, 175 Patewood Drive, Zip 29615–3570; tel. 864/797–1000 **A1** 9 10 **F1** 3 11 29 30 37 45 50 64 74 77 79 81 85 130 135 146 **S** Greenville Health System, Greenville, SC
Primary Contact: Beverly J. Haines, R.N., President
Web address: www.ghs.org/patewood
Control: Other not–for–profit (including NFP Corporation) **Service:** Surgical

Staffed Beds: 36 **Admissions:** 1198 **Census:** 7 **Outpatient Visits:** 5254 **Births:** 0 **Total Expense ($000):** 38602 **Payroll Expense ($000):** 9912 **Personnel:** 167	

✠ **REGENCY HOSPITAL OF GREENVILLE (422009)**, One St. Francis Drive, 4th Floor, Zip 29601–1438 **A1** 10 **F1** 3 29 60 75 77 85 97 128 **S** Select Medical Corporation, Mechanicsburg, PA
Primary Contact: Stephanie James, Chief Executive Officer
Web address: www.regencyhospital.com
Control: Corporation, Investor–owned, for–profit **Service:** Long–Term Acute Care hospital

Staffed Beds: 32 **Admissions:** 398 **Census:** 29 **Outpatient Visits:** 0 **Births:** 0 **Total Expense ($000):** 14559 **Payroll Expense ($000):** 6244 **Personnel:** 94	

☐ **SHRINERS HOSPITALS FOR CHILDREN–GREENVILLE (423300)**, 950 West Faris Road, Zip 29605–4277; tel. 864/271–3444 **A1** 3 5 9 10 **F2**9 59 64 68 75 77 79 81 85 87 89 90 93 94 128 130 131 146 148 **P6 S** Shriners Hospitals for Children, Tampa, FL
Primary Contact: Randall R. Romberger, Administrator
CFO: John Conti, Director Finance
CHR: Willis E. Tisdale, Director Human Resources
CNO: Ranae M. Thompson, R.N., Director Patient Care Services
Web address: www.shrinershospitalsforchildren.org/Hospitals/Locations/Greenville.aspx
Control: Other not–for–profit (including NFP Corporation) **Service:** Children's orthopedic

Staffed Beds: 15 **Admissions:** 341 **Census:** 2 **Births:** 0 **Total Expense ($000):** 21998 **Payroll Expense ($000):** 9494	

Many Facility Codes have changed. Please refer to the AHA Guide Code Chart. © 2014 AHA Guide

SC

GREENWOOD—Greenwood County

☐ **GREENWOOD REGIONAL REHABILITATION HOSPITAL (423030)**, 1530 Parkway, Zip 29646–4027; tel. 864/330–9070, (Total facility includes 12 beds in nursing home–type unit) **A**1 10 **F**3 29 75 90 128 130 132 143 148 **S** Ernest Health, Inc., Albuquerque, NM
Primary Contact: Kerry A. Trapnell, Chief Executive Officer
CFO: Charity Walker, Controller and Regional Business Officer Manager
CMO: Cam Monda, D.O., Medical Director
CNO: Teresa Nabors, Director of Nursing
Web address: www.grrh.ernesthealth.com
Control: Corporation, Investor–owned, for–profit **Service:** Rehabilitation

Staffed Beds: 54 **Admissions:** 1111 **Census:** 40 **Outpatient Visits:** 0 **Births:** 0 **Personnel:** 122

✠ ◇ **SELF REGIONAL HEALTHCARE (420071)**, 1325 Spring Street, Zip 29646–3860; tel. 864/725–4111 **A**1 2 3 5 9 10 19 20 21 **F**3 8 11 13 15 17 18 20 22 24 26 28 29 30 31 32 34 35 39 40 43 49 50 51 53 57 59 60 62 64 68 70 72 73 74 75 76 77 78 79 80 81 82 84 86 87 89 90 93 94 97 98 102 104 107 108 110 111 114 115 117 119 120 121 123 124 129 130 131 132 134 135 144 146 147 148
Primary Contact: James A. Pfeiffer, FACHE, President and Chief Executive Officer
CFO: Timothy Evans, Vice President and Chief Financial Officer
CMO: F Gregory Mappin, M.D., Vice President Medical Affairs and Chief Medical Officer
CIO: Andy Hartung, Director Information Systems
CHR: Michael Dixon, Director Human Resources
CNO: Linda Russell, Vice President and Chief Nursing Officer
Web address: www.selfregional.org
Control: County–Government, nonfederal **Service:** General Medical and Surgical

Staffed Beds: 311 **Admissions:** 11408 **Census:** 148 **Births:** 1515 **Total Expense ($000):** 287081 **Payroll Expense ($000):** 101932 **Personnel:** 1837

GREER—Greenville County

☐ **CAROLINA CENTER FOR BEHAVIORAL HEALTH (424010)**, 2700 East Phillips Road, Zip 29650–4816; tel. 864/235–2335 **A**1 9 10 **F**4 98 99 100 101 102 103 104 105 **S** Universal Health Services, Inc., King of Prussia, PA
Primary Contact: John Willingham, Chief Executive Officer and Managing Director
CFO: James P. Boynton, Jr., Chief Financial Officer
CMO: Gergana Dimitrova, M.D., Medical Director
CHR: George Hammett, Director Human Resources
Web address: www.thecarolinacenter.com
Control: Corporation, Investor–owned, for–profit **Service:** Psychiatric

Staffed Beds: 112 **Admissions:** 3546 **Census:** 98 **Births:** 0 **Total Expense ($000):** 21300 **Payroll Expense ($000):** 11045 **Personnel:** 259

✠ **GREER MEMORIAL HOSPITAL (420033)**, 830 South Bumcombe Road, Zip 29650–2400; tel. 864/797–8000, (Includes ROGER HUNTINGTON NURSING CENTER) **A**1 9 10 **F**1 3 11 13 15 18 28 29 30 34 35 40 44 47 49 50 57 59 61 64 65 68 70 76 77 79 81 82 85 86 87 89 94 107 110 111 114 119 129 130 146 147 **S** Greenville Health System, Greenville, SC
Primary Contact: John F. Mansure, FACHE, President
Web address: www.ghs.org
Control: Other not–for–profit (including NFP Corporation) **Service:** General Medical and Surgical

Staffed Beds: 70 **Admissions:** 3594 **Census:** 32 **Outpatient Visits:** 98874 **Births:** 676 **Total Expense ($000):** 72113 **Payroll Expense ($000):** 23439 **Personnel:** 393

★ **VILLAGE HOSPITAL (420103)**, 250 Westmoreland Road, Zip 29651–9013; tel. 864/530–6000 **A**9 10 **F**1 3 11 15 18 29 30 34 35 37 40 45 49 50 54 57 59 64 68 70 74 75 77 79 81 82 84 85 86 87 90 94 107 108 110 111 114 115 118 119 128 130 146 **S** Spartanburg Regional Healthcare System, Spartanburg, SC
Primary Contact: Anthony Kouskolekas, FACHE, President
Web address: www.villageatpelham.com
Control: Hospital district or authority, Government, nonfederal **Service:** General Medical and Surgical

Staffed Beds: 34 **Admissions:** 1698 **Census:** 16 **Outpatient Visits:** 41650 **Births:** 0 **Total Expense ($000):** 43469 **Payroll Expense ($000):** 14178 **Personnel:** 497

HARDEEVILLE—Jasper County

✠ **COASTAL CAROLINA HOSPITAL (420101)**, 1000 Medical Center Drive, Zip 29927–3446; tel. 843/784–8000 **A**1 9 10 **F**3 11 15 28 29 30 34 35 40 45 46 47 48 49 51 57 59 60 64 70 74 75 77 79 81 85 89 90 93 94 107 108 110 111 115 119 127 130 132 135 146 147 148 **S** TENET Healthcare Corporation, Dallas, TX
Primary Contact: Bradley S. Talbert, FACHE, Chief Executive Officer
CFO: Amanda Dyle, Chief Financial Officer
CIO: Carnel Aiken, Director Information Systems
CHR: Darlene Nester, Market Chief Human Resources Officer
CNO: Ashley Marie VonNida, Chief Nursing Officer
Web address: www.coastalhospital.com
Control: Corporation, Investor–owned, for–profit **Service:** General Medical and Surgical

Staffed Beds: 41 **Admissions:** 1819 **Census:** 19 **Births:** 0 **Total Expense ($000):** 34477 **Payroll Expense ($000):** 11740 **Personnel:** 214

HARTSVILLE—Darlington County

✠ **CAROLINA PINES REGIONAL MEDICAL CENTER (420010)**, 1304 West Bobo Newsom Highway, Zip 29550–4710; tel. 843/339–2100 **A**1 9 10 **F**3 11 13 15 20 28 29 30 34 35 40 43 46 49 57 64 70 73 75 76 79 81 82 85 86 87 89 90 93 107 108 110 111 115 118 119 129 130 131 132 135 146 147 148 **S** Community Health Systems, Inc., Franklin, TN
Primary Contact: J. Timothy Browne, FACHE, Chief Executive Officer
CFO: Wesley Knight, Chief Financial Officer
CIO: Denise Barefoot, Director Health Information Systems
CHR: Charlotte Adams, Director Associate Resources
CNO: Debbie Brand, Chief Nurse Executive
Web address: www.cprmc.com
Control: Corporation, Investor–owned, for–profit **Service:** General Medical and Surgical

Staffed Beds: 120 **Admissions:** 5085 **Census:** 49 **Births:** 598 **Total Expense ($000):** 65258 **Payroll Expense ($000):** 21683 **Personnel:** 352

HILTON HEAD ISLAND—Beaufort County

✠ **HILTON HEAD HOSPITAL (420080)**, 25 Hospital Center Boulevard, Zip 29926–2738; tel. 843/681–6122 **A**1 9 10 20 **F**3 11 13 15 17 18 20 22 24 26 28 29 30 32 34 35 40 46 47 48 49 50 51 53 54 57 59 60 61 64 65 68 70 74 76 77 78 79 81 85 86 89 94 96 107 110 111 114 115 118 119 130 131 132 135 146 147 148 **S** TENET Healthcare Corporation, Dallas, TX
Primary Contact: Mark T. O'Neil, Jr., President and Chief Executive Officer
CFO: Cassie Ball, Chief Financial Officer
CMO: Glenn Neil Love, M.D., Medical Director
CIO: Stephen Brendler, Director Information Systems
CHR: Darlene Nester, Chief Human Resources Officer
Web address: www.hiltonheadregional.com
Control: Partnership, Investor–owned, for–profit **Service:** General Medical and Surgical

Staffed Beds: 93 **Admissions:** 4970 **Census:** 54 **Births:** 630 **Total Expense ($000):** 84692 **Payroll Expense ($000):** 23858 **Personnel:** 522

KINGSTREE—Williamsburg County

✠ **WILLIAMSBURG REGIONAL HOSPITAL (421303)**, 500 Nelson Boulevard, Zip 29556–4027; tel. 843/355–8888 **A**1 9 10 18 **F**3 11 15 18 24 29 30 34 35 40 50 57 59 64 70 77 81 85 86 87 89 90 94 97 107 108 114 119 127 128 130 133 135 146 148
Primary Contact: Sharon Poston, President and Chief Executive Officer
COO: Dan Harrington, Chief Operating Officer and Director Human Resources
CFO: Kevin Gilder, Chief Financial Officer
CMO: Troy B. Gamble, Jr., M.D., Chief Medical Staff
CIO: David Slenszak, Director, Information Services
CHR: Dan Harrington, Chief Operating Officer and Director Human Resources
CNO: Bambi Floyd, Chief Nursing Officer
Web address: www.wmbgrh.com/
Control: Other not–for–profit (including NFP Corporation) **Service:** General Medical and Surgical

Staffed Beds: 25 **Admissions:** 961 **Census:** 12 **Outpatient Visits:** 32056 **Births:** 0

SC

Hospital, Medicare Provider Number, Address, Telephone, Approval, Facility, and Physician Codes, Health Care System

★ American Hospital Association (AHA) membership
☐ The Joint Commission accreditation
◇ DNV Healthcare Inc. accreditation
○ Healthcare Facilities Accreditation Program
△ Commission on Accreditation of Rehabilitation Facilities (CARF) accreditation

LAKE CITY—Florence County

★ **LAKE CITY COMMUNITY HOSPITAL (420066)**, 258 North Ron McNair Boulevard, Zip 29560–2462, Mailing Address: P.O. Box 1479, Zip 29560–1479; tel. 843/374–2036 **A**9 10 **F**3 11 15 28 29 34 35 40 50 56 57 59 61 64 65 69 75 77 79 81 85 86 87 93 94 107 108 111 113 114 119 127 130 132 144 146
Primary Contact: Henry McCutcheon, Jr., Chief Executive Officer
CFO: Henry McCutcheon, Jr., Chief Financial Officer
CMO: Stephen Askins, M.D., Chief of Staff
CIO: David Moon, Jr., Director Information Systems
CHR: Anne Poston, Director of Human Resources/Compliance
CNO: Renate Browder, R.N., Director of Nursing
Web address: www.lcchospital.org
Control: Hospital district or authority, Government, nonfederal **Service:** General Medical and Surgical

Staffed Beds: 30 **Admissions:** 948 **Census:** 8 **Births:** 0 **Total Expense ($000):** 16229 **Payroll Expense ($000):** 6771 **Personnel:** 176

LANCASTER—Lancaster County

✠ **SPRINGS MEMORIAL HOSPITAL (420036)**, 800 West Meeting Street, Zip 29720–2298; tel. 803/286–1214, (Total facility includes 14 beds in nursing home–type unit) **A**1 5 9 10 19 20 **F**1 3 8 11 13 15 17 18 20 29 30 31 34 35 40 47 48 49 51 57 59 62 63 64 68 70 72 73 74 75 76 78 79 80 81 85 89 90 93 94 102 107 108 110 111 114 115 118 119 128 129 130 132 135 146 147 148 **S** Community Health Systems, Inc., Franklin, TN
Primary Contact: Janice Dabney, Chief Executive Officer
CFO: Nathan Crabtree, Chief Financial Officer
CMO: Keith Shealy, M.D., Chief of Staff
CIO: Chrys Steele, Director Information Systems
CHR: Trent Elmore, Director Human Resources
Web address: www.springsmemorial.com
Control: Corporation, Investor–owned, for–profit **Service:** General Medical and Surgical

Staffed Beds: 186 **Admissions:** 6863 **Census:** 100 **Births:** 723 **Total Expense ($000):** 92138 **Payroll Expense ($000):** 29377

LORIS—Horry County

✠ **MCLEOD LORIS SEACOAST HOSPITAL (420105)**, 3655 Mitchell Street, Zip 29569–2827; tel. 843/716–7000, (Includes MCLEOD SEACOAST, 4000 Highway 9 East, Little River, Zip 29566–7833; tel. 843/390–8100), (Total facility includes 88 beds in nursing home–type unit) **A**1 9 10 **F**1 3 11 13 15 17 18 20 28 29 30 32 34 35 40 50 53 57 59 60 64 65 68 70 74 75 76 77 79 80 81 82 84 85 86 87 89 90 93 94 96 107 108 110 111 114 115 118 119 128 129 130 131 132 134 135 146 148 **P**6 **S** McLeod Health, Florence, SC
Primary Contact: Edward D. Tinsley, III, Chief Executive Officer
COO: Arnold Green, Senior Vice President and Chief Operating Officer
CFO: Fred O. Todd, Senior Vice President Finance
CMO: James N. Craigie, M.D., Vice President Medical Affairs
CHR: Teresa Pougnaud, Vice President Human Resources
Web address: www.mcleodhealth.org
Control: Other not–for–profit (including NFP Corporation) **Service:** General Medical and Surgical

Staffed Beds: 243 **Admissions:** 4620 **Census:** 116 **Total Expense ($000):** 92561 **Payroll Expense ($000):** 34077 **Personnel:** 364

MANNING—Clarendon County

★ ◇ **CLARENDON MEMORIAL HOSPITAL (420069)**, 10 Hospital Street, Zip 29102–3153, Mailing Address: P.O. Box 550, Zip 29102–0550; tel. 803/433–3000 **A**9 10 21 **F**1 3 7 11 13 15 18 28 29 34 35 39 40 45 50 51 53 54 56 57 59 62 64 65 67 70 75 79 81 85 89 90 91 93 94 96 107 108 110 111 114 118 119 127 128 129 130 132 135 143 146 147 148
Primary Contact: Richard Stokes, CPA, Chief Executive Officer
COO: Paul Schumacher, Chief Operating Officer
CFO: John Shaughnessy, Chief Financial Officer
CMO: Catherine Rabon, M.D., Chief Medical Officer
CIO: Pat Kolb, Manager Information Technology
CHR: Gail A. Richbourg, Director Human Resources
CNO: Natalie Davis, R.N., Interim Chief Nursing Officer
Web address: www.clarendonhealth.com
Control: Hospital district or authority, Government, nonfederal **Service:** General Medical and Surgical

Staffed Beds: 48 **Admissions:** 2197 **Census:** 27 **Outpatient Visits:** 121954 **Births:** 539 **Total Expense ($000):** 58668 **Payroll Expense ($000):** 25906 **Personnel:** 442

MOUNT PLEASANT—Charleston County

✠ **EAST COOPER MEDICAL CENTER (420089)**, 2000 Hospital Drive, Zip 29464–3764; tel. 843/881–0100 **A**1 3 5 9 10 **F**3 13 15 18 29 31 34 35 40 43 46 51 57 59 60 64 68 70 73 74 75 76 77 78 79 80 81 82 84 85 86 90 92 93 94 100 102 107 108 110 111 114 115 119 126 129 130 131 132 135 146 147 148 **S** TENET Healthcare Corporation, Dallas, TX
Primary Contact: Jason P. Alexander, FACHE, Chief Executive Officer
COO: Ramona Pickens, Chief Operating Officer
CFO: Brandon Willams, Chief Financial Officer
CMO: William Stroud, M.D., Chief Medical Officer
CIO: Michael Foster, Director Information Systems
CHR: Tracy Hunter, Chief Human Resources Officer
CNO: Terri Harris, R.N., Chief Nursing Officer
Web address: www.eastcoopermedctr.com
Control: Corporation, Investor–owned, for–profit **Service:** General Medical and Surgical

Staffed Beds: 140 **Admissions:** 5046 **Census:** 42 **Outpatient Visits:** 52120 **Births:** 1421 **Total Expense ($000):** 103092 **Payroll Expense ($000):** 27454 **Personnel:** 449

EAST COOPER REGIONAL MEDICAL CENTER See East Cooper Medical Center

✠ **MOUNT PLEASANT HOSPITAL (420104)**, 3500 Highway 17 North, Zip 29466–9123, Mailing Address: 3500 North Highway 17, Zip 29466–9123; tel. 843/606–7000 **A**1 9 10 **F**1 3 13 15 29 30 34 40 45 57 68 70 75 76 79 81 84 85 86 87 89 94 107 108 110 111 115 118 119 129 143 147 148 **S** Carolinas HealthCare System, Charlotte, NC
Primary Contact: John Sullivan, Chief Executive Officer
CFO: Bret Johnson, Chief Financial Officer
CMO: Steven D. Shapiro, M.D., Chief Medical Officer
CIO: Melinda H. Cardell, Interim Chief Information Officer
CHR: Meianie Stith, Vice President Human Resources
CNO: Tavia Buck, Interim Chief Nursing Officer
Web address: www.mymountpleasanthospital.com
Control: Other not–for–profit (including NFP Corporation) **Service:** General Medical and Surgical

Staffed Beds: 50 **Admissions:** 1522 **Census:** 11 **Outpatient Visits:** 40047 **Births:** 489 **Total Expense ($000):** 45671 **Payroll Expense ($000):** 12352 **Personnel:** 284

MT. PLEASANT—Mt. Pleasant County

KINDRED HOSPITAL–CHARLESTON See Vibra Hospital of Charleston

✠ **VIBRA HOSPITAL OF CHARLESTON (422005)**, 1200 Hospital Drive, Zip 29464; tel. 843/375–4000, (Total facility includes 35 beds in nursing home–type unit) (Data for 122 days) **A**1 10 **F**1 3 29 35 89 90 107 114 119 148 **S** Vibra Healthcare, Mechanicsburg, PA
Primary Contact: Darrell Jones, Chief Executive Officer
CFO: Julia Smith, Chief Financial Officer
CMO: Athena Beldecos, M.D., Medical Director
CHR: Julia Taylor, Area Director Human Resources
Web address: www.vhcharleston.com
Control: Corporation, Investor–owned, for–profit **Service:** Long–Term Acute Care hospital

Staffed Beds: 94 **Admissions:** 207 **Census:** 54 **Outpatient Visits:** 0 **Births:** 0 **Total Expense ($000):** 9012 **Payroll Expense ($000):** 3591 **Personnel:** 197

MULLINS—Marion County

★ **CAROLINAS HOSPITAL SYSTEM MARION (420055)**, 2829 East Highway 76, Zip 29574–6035, Mailing Address: P.O. Drawer 1150, Marion, Zip 29571–1150; tel. 843/431–2000, (Total facility includes 92 beds in nursing home–type unit) **A**9 10 **F**1 3 13 15 28 29 34 40 45 46 53 57 59 67 70 75 76 77 79 81 82 85 86 89 90 94 107 111 119 128 129 130 131 133 146 148 **S** Community Health Systems, Inc., Franklin, TN
Primary Contact: Ronnie Daves, Chief Executive Officer
CFO: Alta DuBose, Chief Financial Officer
CMO: Alvin Abinsay, M.D., Chief Medical Staff
CIO: Charlie Grantham, Manager Information Systems
CHR: Kay White, Director Human Resources and Diversity
Web address: www.carolinashospitalmarion.com/Pages/Home.aspx
Control: Corporation, Investor–owned, for–profit **Service:** General Medical and Surgical

Staffed Beds: 216 **Admissions:** 2709 **Census:** 109 **Births:** 268 **Total Expense ($000):** 61311 **Payroll Expense ($000):** 16774 **Personnel:** 376

MARION COUNTY MEDICAL CENTER See Carolinas Hospital System Marion

Many Facility Codes have changed. Please refer to the AHA Guide Code Chart. © 2014 AHA Guide

SC

MURRELLS INLET—Georgetown County

⊠ △ **WACCAMAW COMMUNITY HOSPITAL (420098)**, 4070 Highway 17
Bypass, Zip 29576–5033, Mailing Address: P.O. Drawer 3350, Zip 29576–2673;
tel. 843/652–1000 **A**1 7 9 10 **F**3 8 11 13 15 17 18 28 29 30 31 32 35 37 39
40 45 50 51 56 60 61 64 65 68 70 73 74 75 76 77 78 79 81 82 84 85 86
87 89 90 93 94 96 97 100 102 107 108 110 111 114 115 118 119 130 146
147 148 **S** Georgetown Hospital System, Georgetown, SC
Primary Contact: Gayle L. Resetar, Chief Operating Officer
CFO: Terry L. Kiser, Chief Financial Officer
CIO: Frank Scafidi, Chief Information Officer
Web address: www.gmhsc.com
Control: Other not-for-profit (including NFP Corporation) **Service:** General
Medical and Surgical

Staffed Beds: 169 **Admissions:** 7815 **Census:** 107 **Outpatient Visits:**
103422 **Births:** 586 **Total Expense ($000):** 127367 **Payroll Expense**
($000): 34571 **Personnel:** 631

MYRTLE BEACH—Horry County

⊠ **GRAND STRAND REGIONAL MEDICAL CENTER (420085)**, 809 82nd
Parkway, Zip 29572–4607; tel. 843/692–1000 **A**1 2 9 10 19 **F**3 11 13 15 17
18 20 22 24 26 28 29 30 31 34 35 37 39 40 42 43 46 47 49 50 54 56 57
59 60 64 70 73 74 75 76 77 78 79 81 82 85 86 87 88 89 90 107 108 110
111 114 115 118 119 126 128 130 132 135 146 147 **S** HCA, Nashville, TN
Primary Contact: Mark E. Sims, Chief Executive Officer
CFO: Turner Wortham, Chief Financial Officer
Web address: www.grandstrandmed.com
Control: Corporation, Investor-owned, for-profit **Service:** General Medical and
Surgical

Staffed Beds: 271 **Admissions:** 16177 **Census:** 194 **Births:** 981 **Personnel:**
1050

NEWBERRY—Newberry County

⊠ **NEWBERRY COUNTY MEMORIAL HOSPITAL (420053)**, 2669 Kinard Street,
Zip 29108–2911, Mailing Address: P.O. Box 497, Zip 29108–0497;
tel. 803/276–7570 **A**1 9 10 20 **F**1 3 7 11 13 15 17 28 29 30 31 32 34 35 40
45 47 53 56 57 59 64 68 70 75 76 77 78 79 81 82 85 86 87 89 90 93 94
103 104 107 108 109 110 111 114 119 128 129 130 133 135 143 146 147
148 **P**6 **S** QHR, Brentwood, TN
Primary Contact: Craig R. Cudworth, Interim Chief Executive Officer
CFO: Mike Reynolds, Chief Financial Officer
CMO: Mark Davis, M.D., Chief of Staff
CIO: David Wolff, Director Information Technology
CHR: Dyan Bowman, Director Human Resources
Web address: www.newberryhospital.org
Control: County-Government, nonfederal **Service:** General Medical and Surgical

Staffed Beds: 52 **Admissions:** 2055 **Census:** 22 **Outpatient Visits:** 63744
Births: 343 **Total Expense ($000):** 45931 **Payroll Expense ($000):** 18314
Personnel: 379

ORANGEBURG—Orangeburg County

⊠ **REGIONAL MEDICAL CENTER (420068)**, 3000 St. Matthews Road,
Zip 29118–1442; tel. 803/395–2200 **A**1 2 9 10 19 20 **F**3 11 13 14 15 17 18
20 28 29 30 31 32 35 39 40 44 45 46 47 48 50 53 57 58 59 60 61 62 65
68 70 71 73 74 75 76 77 78 79 81 82 84 85 86 87 89 90 93 94 97 98 100
101 102 103 107 108 110 111 114 119 121 127 129 130 131 132 134
135 144 146 147 148 **S** QHR, Brentwood, TN
Primary Contact: Thomas C. Dandridge, FACHE, President and Chief Executive
Officer
CFO: Cheryl S. Mason, Chief Financial Officer
CIO: Marilyn Tremblay, Chief Information Officer and Vice President
CHR: Howard Harris, Vice President Human Resources
CNO: Julia K. Yawn, MSN, Chief Nursing Officer and Vice President for Patient
Care Services
Web address: www.trmchealth.org
Control: County-Government, nonfederal **Service:** General Medical and Surgical

Staffed Beds: 313 **Admissions:** 10735 **Census:** 150 **Births:** 1086 **Total**
Expense ($000): 196647 **Payroll Expense ($000):** 92184 **Personnel:** 1457

☐ **WILLIAM J. MCCORD ADOLESCENT AND TREATMENT CENTER (424013)**,
910 Cook Road, Zip 29118–2124, Mailing Address: P.O. Box 1166,
Zip 29116–1166; tel. 803/534–2328, (Nonreporting) **A**1 10
Primary Contact: Michael Dennis, Director
Web address: www.mccordcenter.com
Control: Other not-for-profit (including NFP Corporation) **Service:** Alcoholism and
other chemical dependency

Staffed Beds: 15

PICKENS—Pickens County

★ ◇ **CANNON MEMORIAL HOSPITAL (420011)**, 123 West G. Acker Drive,
Zip 29671–2739, Mailing Address: P.O. Box 188, Zip 29671–0188;
tel. 864/878–4791 **A**9 10 21 **F**1 3 11 15 29 34 40 50 51 53 56 57 59 61 64
65 70 75 79 81 85 94 97 107 108 110 111 114 119 127 128 130 146 **P**8
S Carolinas HealthCare System, Charlotte, NC
Primary Contact: Norman G. Rentz, President and Chief Executive Officer
CFO: Will Grant, Chief Financial Officer
CMO: Daniel J. Dahlhausen, M.D., President of Medical Staff/Chief Medical Officer
CIO: Robert Furr, Director Information Services
CHR: Lisa G. Bryant, Director Human Resources
CNO: Donna K. Anderson, R.N., Chief Nursing Officer
Web address: www.cannonhospital.org
Control: Other not-for-profit (including NFP Corporation) **Service:** General
Medical and Surgical

Staffed Beds: 38 **Admissions:** 764 **Census:** 8 **Outpatient Visits:** 43204
Births: 0 **Total Expense ($000):** 23043 **Payroll Expense ($000):** 10303
Personnel: 227

ROCK HILL—York County

⊠ **HEALTHSOUTH REHABILITATION HOSPITAL OF ROCK HILL (423028)**, 1795
Dr. Frank Gaston Boulevard, Zip 29732–1190; tel. 803/326–3500 **A**1 10 **F**29
56 58 64 75 90 94 95 130 **S** HEALTHSOUTH Corporation, Birmingham, AL
Primary Contact: Britton Phelps, Chief Executive Officer
Web address: www.healthsouthrockhill.com
Control: Corporation, Investor-owned, for-profit **Service:** Rehabilitation

Staffed Beds: 50 **Admissions:** 1314 **Census:** 42 **Outpatient Visits:** 0 **Births:**
0 **Total Expense ($000):** 12771 **Payroll Expense ($000):** 6677

⊠ **PIEDMONT MEDICAL CENTER (420002)**, 222 Herlong Avenue, Zip 29732;
tel. 803/329–1234 **A**1 2 9 10 **F**3 7 11 12 13 15 17 18 20 22 24 26 28 29 30
31 34 35 40 43 45 49 50 57 59 60 64 70 73 74 75 76 77 78 79 81 82 85
86 89 90 91 93 98 100 102 107 108 110 111 114 115 118 119 130 132
135 146 147 148 **S** TENET Healthcare Corporation, Dallas, TX
Primary Contact: William Masterton, Chief Executive Officer
COO: David Clay, Chief Operating Officer
CFO: Jay M. Pennisson, Chief Financial Officer
CIO: Joel Dean, Director Information Services
CHR: Donald L. Currier, Vice President Human Resources
CNO: Ursula Lawrence, MSN, Chief Nursing Officer
Web address: www.piedmontmedicalcenter.com
Control: Corporation, Investor-owned, for-profit **Service:** General Medical and
Surgical

Staffed Beds: 280 **Admissions:** 13775 **Census:** 171 **Births:** 1740 **Total**
Expense ($000): 199631 **Payroll Expense ($000):** 66010 **Personnel:** 1427

SENECA—Oconee County

⊠ **OCONEE MEDICAL CENTER (420009)**, 298 Memorial Drive, Zip 29672–9499;
tel. 864/882–3351, (Includes LILA DOYLE NURSING CARE FACILITY), (Total
facility includes 120 beds in nursing home–type unit) **A**1 9 10 20 **F**3 7 11 13 15
20 28 29 30 31 34 35 40 54 56 57 59 61 62 63 64 67 70 71 74 75 76 77
78 79 81 82 86 87 89 90 93 97 100 107 108 114 119 128 130 132 135
143 146 148 **P**8
Primary Contact: Jeanne L. Ward, Ed.D., R.N., President and Chief Executive
Officer
COO: Hunter Kome, Chief Operating Officer
CFO: Kevin Herbert, Chief Financial Officer
CMO: Conrad K. Shuler, M.D., Chief Medical Officer
CIO: Jay Hansen, Director Information Services
CHR: Thomas C. Conley, Vice President Human Resources
CNO: Pat J. Smith, Vice President Nursing
Web address: www.oconeemed.org
Control: Other not-for-profit (including NFP Corporation) **Service:** General
Medical and Surgical

Staffed Beds: 248 **Admissions:** 6366 **Census:** 178 **Births:** 532 **Total**
Expense ($000): 111345 **Payroll Expense ($000):** 43851 **Personnel:** 894

SIMPSONVILLE—Greenville County

⊠ **HILLCREST MEMORIAL HOSPITAL (420037)**, 729 S.E. Main Street,
Zip 29681–3280; tel. 864/454–6100 **A**1 10 **F**1 3 11 12 15 18 29 30 34 35
40 44 45 50 57 58 59 61 64 68 70 79 81 85 86 90 107 110 111 114 119
129 130 132 135 146 **S** Greenville Health System, Greenville, SC
Primary Contact: Eric Bour, M.D., President
CFO: Pam DeVore, Financial Manager
Web address: www.ghs.org
Control: Other not-for-profit (including NFP Corporation) **Service:** General
Medical and Surgical

Staffed Beds: 36 **Admissions:** 1978 **Census:** 18 **Outpatient Visits:** 66514
Births: 0 **Total Expense ($000):** 50378 **Payroll Expense ($000):** 14398
Personnel: 236

SC

Hospital, Medicare Provider Number, Address, Telephone, Approval, Facility, and Physician Codes, Health Care System

★ American Hospital Association (AHA) membership
☐ The Joint Commission accreditation
◇ DNV Healthcare Inc. accreditation
○ Healthcare Facilities Accreditation Program
△ Commission on Accreditation of Rehabilitation Facilities (CARF) accreditation

SPARTANBURG—Spartanburg County

⌧ △ **MARY BLACK MEMORIAL HOSPITAL (420083)**, 1700 Skylyn Drive, Zip 29307–1061, Mailing Address: P.O. Box 3217, Zip 29304–3217; tel. 864/573–3000 **A**1 3 5 7 9 10 **F**3 13 15 18 20 29 30 31 34 35 40 45 47 49 50 51 56 57 59 60 64 68 70 73 74 76 77 78 79 81 85 89 90 93 94 96 98 102 103 107 108 110 111 114 115 119 126 129 130 135 141 142 146 147 148 **S** Community Health Systems, Inc., Franklin, TN
Primary Contact: Sean T. Dardeau, Chief Executive Officer
COO: Brandon Downey, Chief Operating Officer
CFO: Richard A. Meyer, Chief Financial Officer
CMO: Howard Bean, M.D., Chief Medical Officer
CIO: Jeff Nash, Director Information Technology and Services
CHR: Mark E. Garber, Director Human Resources
CNO: Chanda Flynn, R.N., Chief Nursing Officer
Web address: www.maryblackhealthsystem.com
Control: Corporation, Investor–owned, for–profit **Service:** General Medical and Surgical

Staffed Beds: 181 **Admissions:** 6464 **Census:** 79 **Births:** 970

⌧ **SPARTANBURG HOSPITAL FOR RESTORATIVE CARE (422004)**, 389 Serpentine Drive, Zip 29303–3026; tel. 864/560–3280, (Total facility includes 25 beds in nursing home–type unit) **A**1 10 **F**1 29 30 31 35 57 59 60 68 70 75 77 79 82 84 85 87 90 119 128 130 148 **S** Spartanburg Regional Healthcare System, Spartanburg, SC
Primary Contact: Anita M. Butler, Chief Executive Officer
Web address: www.srhs.com
Control: Hospital district or authority, Government, nonfederal **Service:** Long–Term Acute Care hospital

Staffed Beds: 116 **Admissions:** 853 **Census:** 47 **Outpatient Visits:** 0 **Births:** 0 **Total Expense ($000):** 21741 **Payroll Expense ($000):** 11127 **Personnel:** 212

★ **SPARTANBURG REGIONAL MEDICAL CENTER (420007)**, 101 East Wood Street, Zip 29303–3040; tel. 864/560–6000 **A**2 3 5 9 10 13 **F**3 7 11 12 13 15 17 18 20 22 24 26 28 29 30 31 34 35 36 37 38 39 40 43 45 46 47 48 49 50 53 54 56 57 58 59 60 61 62 63 64 65 66 68 70 71 72 73 74 75 76 77 78 79 81 82 83 84 85 86 87 88 89 90 94 97 98 99 100 101 102 103 104 105 107 108 110 111 114 115 117 118 119 120 123 124 126 129 130 131 132 135 143 144 145 146 147 148 **S** Spartanburg Regional Healthcare System, Spartanburg, SC
Primary Contact: Bruce Holstien, President and Chief Executive Officer
COO: Mark Aycock, Chief Operating Officer
CFO: Kenneth Meinke, Senior Vice President Administrative Services, Finance and Chief Financial Officer
CMO: Charles Morrow, M.D., Chief Medical Officer
CIO: Harold Moore, Chief Information Technology Officer
CHR: Kathy Sinclair, Vice President Human Resources
CNO: Susan Duggar, R.N., Vice President Nursing
Web address: www.spartanburgregional.com
Control: Hospital district or authority, Government, nonfederal **Service:** General Medical and Surgical

Staffed Beds: 514 **Admissions:** 24908 **Census:** 384 **Outpatient Visits:** 380205 **Births:** 2579 **Total Expense ($000):** 580675 **Payroll Expense ($000):** 180321 **Personnel:** 3436

SUMTER—Sumter County

⌧ **TUOMEY HEALTHCARE SYSTEM (420070)**, 129 North Washington Street, Zip 29150–4983; tel. 803/774–9000, (Total facility includes 18 beds in nursing home–type unit) **A**1 9 10 19 **F**1 3 13 15 20 28 29 30 31 32 34 35 40 48 49 50 51 54 56 59 60 62 63 64 68 70 71 73 75 76 77 78 79 80 81 84 85 86 87 89 90 94 102 107 108 110 111 114 117 119 121 128 129 130 131 132 135 146 147 148 **P**6
Primary Contact: Michael J. Schwartz, Interim Chief Executive Officer and President
CFO: Mark Lovell, Vice President and Chief Financial Officer
CMO: Gene Dickerson, M.D., Vice President Medical Affairs
CIO: Cheryl Martin, Chief Information Officer
CHR: Letitia Pringle–Miller, Administrative Director
CNO: Terrie Carlton, R.N., Vice President & Chief Nursing Officer
Web address: www.tuomey.com
Control: Other not–for–profit (including NFP Corporation) **Service:** General Medical and Surgical

Staffed Beds: 270 **Admissions:** 6143 **Census:** 183 **Outpatient Visits:** 139185 **Births:** 1029 **Total Expense ($000):** 181572 **Payroll Expense ($000):** 72452 **Personnel:** 1539

TRAVELERS REST—Greenville County

⌧ **NORTH GREENVILLE HOSPITAL (422008)**, 807 North Main Street, Zip 29690–1551; tel. 864/455–9206 **A**1 10 **F**1 3 15 29 30 34 35 40 44 50 64 68 75 79 85 86 87 107 110 111 114 119 128 130 146 148
Primary Contact: Stan Healy, Administrator
CMO: Amy Treece, M.D., Medical Director
CHR: Carol Bish, Human Resources Coordinator
CNO: Marian McVey, Chief Nursing Officer
Web address: www.ghs.org
Control: Other not–for–profit (including NFP Corporation) **Service:** Long–Term Acute Care hospital

Staffed Beds: 18 **Admissions:** 288 **Census:** 21 **Outpatient Visits:** 23962 **Births:** 0 **Total Expense ($000):** 26823 **Payroll Expense ($000):** 8290 **Personnel:** 143

☐ **SPRINGBROOK BEHAVIORAL HEALTH SYSTEM (424007)**, One Havenwood Lane, Zip 29690–9447, Mailing Address: P.O. Box 1005, Zip 29690–1005; tel. 864/834–8013, (Total facility includes 68 beds in nursing home–type unit) **A**1 9 10 **F**98 99 104 106
Primary Contact: Mike Rowley, Chief Executive Officer
COO: Mary Ann Bennett, R.N., Chief Operating Officer and Chief Nursing Officer
CFO: Bart Bennett, Chief Financial Officer
CMO: Mathew Fisher, M.D., Medical Director
CIO: Bart Bennett, Chief Information Technology Officer
CHR: Teresa Lipscomb, Director Human Resources
CNO: Mary Ann Bennett, R.N., Chief Operating Officer and Chief Nursing Officer
Web address: www.springbrookbehavioral.com
Control: Corporation, Investor–owned, for–profit **Service:** Psychiatric

Staffed Beds: 112 **Admissions:** 837 **Census:** 82 **Births:** 0 **Total Expense ($000):** 12135 **Payroll Expense ($000):** 6617 **Personnel:** 195

UNION—Union County

☐ **WALLACE THOMSON HOSPITAL (420039)**, 322 West South Street, Zip 29379–2857, Mailing Address: P.O. Box 789, Zip 29379–0789; tel. 864/427–0351, (Total facility includes 113 beds in nursing home–type unit) **A**1 9 10 **F**1 3 7 13 15 29 34 35 40 57 59 64 69 70 75 76 79 81 82 86 87 89 107 111 119 129 130 135 146 147
Primary Contact: Paul R. Newhouse, Chief Executive Officer
CFO: Jeff W. Rush, Chief Financial Officer
CIO: Billy Helmandollar, Director Information Services
CHR: Michelle Helton, Director Human Resources
Web address: www.wallacethomson.com
Control: Other not–for–profit (including NFP Corporation) **Service:** General Medical and Surgical

Staffed Beds: 172 **Admissions:** 2323 **Census:** 132 **Outpatient Visits:** 32525 **Births:** 121 **Total Expense ($000):** 38309 **Payroll Expense ($000):** 14014 **Personnel:** 413

VARNVILLE—Hampton County

★ **HAMPTON REGIONAL MEDICAL CENTER (420072)**, 503 Carolina Avenue West, Zip 29944–4735, Mailing Address: P.O. Box 338, Zip 29944–0338; tel. 803/943–2771 **A**9 10 20 **F**15 17 18 24 28 29 34 35 40 57 59 67 70 75 79 81 90 93 94 107 108 110 111 114 119 127 128 129 133
Primary Contact: Dave H. Hamill, President and Chief Executive Officer
Web address: www.hamptonregional.com
Control: Other not–for–profit (including NFP Corporation) **Service:** General Medical and Surgical

Staffed Beds: 32 **Admissions:** 646 **Census:** 8 **Births:** 0 **Total Expense ($000):** 20047 **Payroll Expense ($000):** 8191 **Personnel:** 204

WALTERBORO—Colleton County

⌧ **COLLETON MEDICAL CENTER (420030)**, 501 Robertson Boulevard, Zip 29488–5714; tel. 843/782–2000 **A**1 9 10 20 **F**3 11 13 15 18 26 29 30 32 34 35 36 40 45 47 49 56 57 59 60 64 65 68 70 75 76 77 79 81 82 85 86 87 89 90 93 94 96 98 102 107 108 110 111 114 119 129 130 131 132 146 147 148 **P**5 **S** HCA, Nashville, TN
Primary Contact: Brad Griffin, Chief Executive Officer
CFO: Jimmy O. Hiott, III, Chief Financial Officer
CMO: Kim Rakes–Stephens, M.D., Chief Medical Staff
CIO: Damien Noble, Director Information Technology and System
CHR: Wendy Glass, Director Human Resources
CNO: Anna Jonason, Ph.D., Chief Nursing Officer
Web address: www.colletonmedical.com
Control: Corporation, Investor–owned, for–profit **Service:** General Medical and Surgical

Staffed Beds: 131 **Admissions:** 4809 **Census:** 63 **Births:** 326 **Total Expense ($000):** 56177 **Payroll Expense ($000):** 20705 **Personnel:** 369

SC

Many Facility Codes have changed. Please refer to the AHA Guide Code Chart. © 2014 AHA Guide

WEST COLUMBIA—Lexington County

★ ◇ **LEXINGTON MEDICAL CENTER (420073)**, 2720 Sunset Boulevard,
Zip 29169–4810; tel. 803/791–2000 **A**2 9 10 21 **F**3 8 11 12 13 15 18 20 22
24 26 28 29 30 31 32 34 35 38 39 40 43 44 45 48 49 50 53 54 57 58 59
60 61 64 68 70 72 73 74 75 76 77 78 79 80 81 82 85 86 87 89 90 92 93
94 107 108 110 111 114 115 118 119 120 121 123 127 129 130 131 132
135 141 142 144 145 146 147 148 **P**6
Primary Contact: Michael J. Biediger, FACHE, President and Chief Executive
Officer
COO: Tod Augsburger, Senior Vice President and Chief Operating Officer
CFO: Melinda Kruzner, Chief Financial Officer
CMO: Brent Powers, M.D., Vice President/Chief Medical Officer
CIO: Kathleen R. Herald, Vice President and Chief Information Officer
CHR: Kathy A. Howell, Vice President Human Resources
CNO: Cindy Rohman, R.N., Vice President/Chief Nursing Officer
Web address: www.lexmed.com
Control: Hospital district or authority, Government, nonfederal **Service:** General
Medical and Surgical

Staffed Beds: 416 **Admissions:** 24624 **Census:** 315 **Births:** 3679 **Total
Expense ($000):** 451106 **Payroll Expense ($000):** 184343 **Personnel:**
3280

☐ **THREE RIVERS BEHAVIORAL HEALTH (424008)**, 2900 Sunset Boulevard,
Zip 29169–3422; tel. 803/796–9911, (Total facility includes 20 beds in nursing
home–type unit) **A**1 9 10 **F**4 5 35 98 99 100 101 103 104 105 106 **S** Universal
Health Services, Inc., King of Prussia, PA
Primary Contact: Elyssia Lowe, Chief Executive Officer
CFO: Christopher Jensen, Chief Financial Officer
CMO: Cheryl Dodds, M.D., Medical Director
CHR: Nita Sundberg, Director Human Resources
CNO: Regena Sellers, Chief Nursing Officer
Web address: www.threeriversbehavioral.org
Control: Corporation, Investor–owned, for–profit **Service:** Psychiatric

Staffed Beds: 118 **Admissions:** 2853 **Census:** 99 **Outpatient Visits:** 0
Births: 0 **Total Expense ($000):** 18806 **Payroll Expense ($000):** 9047
Personnel: 181

WINNSBORO—Fairfield County

☐ **FAIRFIELD MEMORIAL HOSPITAL (421302)**, 102 U.S. Highway 321 By–Pass
N., Zip 29180–9251, Mailing Address: P.O. Box 620, Zip 29180–0620;
tel. 803/635–5548, (Nonreporting) **A**1 5 9 10 18
Primary Contact: Michael Williams, FACHE, Administrator
CFO: Anne Bass, Chief Financial Officer
CMO: Larry D. Cantey, M.D., Chief Medical Officer
CIO: Reynolds Searle, Director Information Systems
CHR: Shawna Martin Lyde, Director Human Resources
Web address: www.fairfieldmemorial.com
Control: County–Government, nonfederal **Service:** General Medical and Surgical

Staffed Beds: 25

SC

SOUTH DAKOTA

ABERDEEN—Brown County

★ △ **AVERA ST. LUKE'S HOSPITAL (430014)**, 305 South State Street, Zip 57401–4527; tel. 605/622–5000, (Total facility includes 137 beds in nursing home–type unit) **A**2 7 9 10 19 **F**2 3 5 7 10 11 13 15 17 18 20 22 28 29 30 31 32 34 35 36 39 40 43 45 46 48 56 57 59 60 61 62 63 64 70 71 74 75 76 77 78 79 81 82 84 85 86 87 89 90 92 93 96 97 98 99 100 101 102 103 104 107 108 110 111 114 115 118 119 120 121 123 125 127 128 129 130 131 132 133 135 146 147 148 **P**6 **S** Avera Health, Sioux Falls, SD
Primary Contact: Todd Forkel, President and Chief Executive Officer
CFO: Geoff Durst, Vice President Finance
CMO: Shahid Chaudhary, M.D., Chief Medical Officer
CIO: Julie Kusler, Manager Information Services
CHR: Tracy Olson, Human Resource Officer
CNO: Jan Patterson, Chief Nursing Officer
Web address: www.avera.org/st–lukes–hospital/
Control: Church–operated, Nongovernment, not–for profit **Service:** General Medical and Surgical

Staffed Beds: 270 Admissions: 4890 Census: 190 Outpatient Visits: 264750 Births: 685 Total Expense ($000): 165544 Payroll Expense ($000): 78490 Personnel: 1216

DAKOTA PLAINS SURGICAL CENTER (430092), 701 8th Avenue N.W., Suite C., Zip 57401–1865; tel. 605/225–3300, (Nonreporting) **A**9 10
Primary Contact: Charles Livingston, Administrator
Control: Corporation, Investor–owned, for–profit **Service:** Surgical

Staffed Beds: 15

★ **SANFORD ABERDEEN MEDICAL CENTER (430097)**, 2905 3rd Avenue S.E., Zip 57401–5420; tel. 605/626–4200, (Data for 350 days) **A**9 10 **F**3 8 12 13 15 18 19 20 22 28 29 31 34 35 39 40 45 51 57 59 64 65 75 76 77 78 79 81 85 89 91 93 94 97 107 108 111 115 118 119 126 129 130 131 132 144 146 147 148 **P**6 **S** Sanford Health, Sioux Falls, SD
Primary Contact: Gordon Larson, Chief Executive Officer
CFO: Jeffrey Poppen, Chief Financial Officer
CMO: Samuel Nyamu, M.D., Chief Medical Officer
CHR: Jill Mohr, Manager Human Resources
CNO: Jen Wagenaar, Chief Nursing Officer
Web address: www.sanfordaberdeen.org/
Control: Other not–for–profit (including NFP Corporation) **Service:** General Medical and Surgical

Staffed Beds: 16 Admissions: 1368 Census: 14 Outpatient Visits: 25322 Births: 127 Total Expense ($000): 37271 Payroll Expense ($000): 12537 Personnel: 300

ARMOUR—Douglas County

DOUGLAS COUNTY MEMORIAL HOSPITAL (431305), 708 Eighth Street, Zip 57313–2102; tel. 605/724–2159 **A**9 10 18 **F**3 7 10 13 15 28 31 34 35 40 45 53 57 59 62 64 65 69 76 77 81 93 107 119 127 133 **P**6
Primary Contact: Heath Brouwer, Administrator
CFO: Dorothy Spease, Manager Business Office
Web address: www.dcmhsd.org
Control: Other not–for–profit (including NFP Corporation) **Service:** General Medical and Surgical

Staffed Beds: 11 Admissions: 190 Census: 2 Outpatient Visits: 9007 Births: 40 Total Expense ($000): 7944 Payroll Expense ($000): 3453 Personnel: 71

BOWDLE— County

★ **BOWDLE HOSPITAL (431318)**, 8001 West Fifth Street, Zip 57428, Mailing Address: P.O. Box 556, Zip 57428–0556; tel. 605/285–6146, (Total facility includes 38 beds in nursing home–type unit) **A**9 10 18 **F**2 7 10 28 40 43 45 53 59 65 107 119 127 128 133
Primary Contact: Sandy Schlechter, Chief Executive Officer
CFO: Lucas Turner, Chief Financial Officer
CMO: John Ottenbacher, Chief of Staff
Web address: www.bowdlehc.com
Control: City–Government, nonfederal **Service:** General Medical and Surgical

Staffed Beds: 50 Admissions: 320 Census: 37 Outpatient Visits: 4074 Births: 0 Personnel: 78

BRITTON—Marshall County

★ **MARSHALL COUNTY HEALTHCARE CENTER AVERA (431312)**, 413 Ninth Street, Zip 57430–2274; tel. 605/448–2253 **A**9 10 18 **F**10 11 28 29 34 35 40 41 53 57 59 62 64 65 77 86 87 133 146 **P**5 **S** Avera Health, Sioux Falls, SD
Primary Contact: Nick Fosness, Chief Executive Officer
Web address: www.avera.org
Control: Other not–for–profit (including NFP Corporation) **Service:** General Medical and Surgical

Staffed Beds: 18 Admissions: 208 Census: 3 Outpatient Visits: 6321 Births: 0 Total Expense ($000): 5588 Payroll Expense ($000): 2612 Personnel: 66

BROOKINGS—Brookings County

★ **BROOKINGS HEALTH SYSTEM (430008)**, 300 22nd Avenue, Zip 57006–2496; tel. 605/696–9000, (Total facility includes 79 beds in nursing home–type unit) **A**9 10 20 **F**3 7 8 11 13 28 29 30 31 32 34 35 40 41 43 45 57 59 62 63 64 65 69 70 75 76 77 79 81 82 85 87 89 93 102 107 111 114 118 119 125 126 127 128 129 130 133 146 147 148
Primary Contact: Jason R. Merkley, Chief Executive Officer
CFO: Heather VanMeveren, Chief Financial Officer
CMO: Richard Gudvangen, M.D., Medical Director and Chief of Staff
CHR: September Bessler, Manager Human Resources
CNO: Tammy Hillestad, Chief Nursing Officer
Web address: www.brookingshealth.org
Control: City–Government, nonfederal **Service:** General Medical and Surgical

Staffed Beds: 128 Admissions: 1330 Census: 85 Outpatient Visits: 10091 Births: 284 Total Expense ($000): 35292 Payroll Expense ($000): 16432 Personnel: 284

BURKE—Gregory County

★ **COMMUNITY MEMORIAL HOSPITAL (431309)**, 809 Jackson Street, Zip 57523–2065, Mailing Address: P.O. Box 319, Zip 57523–0319; tel. 605/775–2621 **A**9 10 18 **F**1 3 11 28 31 34 40 57 59 64 65 67 87 97 107 114 127 128 133 **S** Sanford Health, Sioux Falls, SD
Primary Contact: Jim Frank, Chief Executive Officer
CMO: Teresa Marts, M.D., Chief Medical Staff
CHR: Tami Lyon, Director Human Resources
Web address: www.sanfordhealth.org
Control: Other not–for–profit (including NFP Corporation) **Service:** General Medical and Surgical

Staffed Beds: 16 Admissions: 212 Census: 5 Outpatient Visits: 2250 Births: 0 Total Expense ($000): 4164 Payroll Expense ($000): 1943 Personnel: 56

CANTON—Lincoln County

★ **SANFORD CANTON–INWOOD MEDICAL CENTER (431333)**, 440 North Hiawatha Drive, Zip 57013–5800; tel. 605/764–1400 **A**9 10 18 **F**7 10 15 28 40 45 59 71 77 81 93 107 130 133 **S** Sanford Health, Sioux Falls, SD
Primary Contact: Scott C. Larson, Chief Executive Officer
CFO: Paul Gerhart, Chief Financial Officer
Web address: www.sanfordcantoninwood.org
Control: Other not–for–profit (including NFP Corporation) **Service:** General Medical and Surgical

Staffed Beds: 16 Admissions: 152 Census: 2 Outpatient Visits: 17699 Births: 0 Total Expense ($000): 5758 Payroll Expense ($000): 2544 Personnel: 75

CHAMBERLAIN—Brule County

★ **SANFORD CHAMBERLAIN MEDICAL CENTER (431329)**, 300 South Byron Boulevard, Zip 57325–9741; tel. 605/234–5511, (Total facility includes 44 beds in nursing home–type unit) **A**9 10 18 **F**3 8 13 15 18 19 28 29 31 34 35 40 43 50 57 59 68 70 75 76 77 78 81 85 86 87 89 93 100 101 102 103 107 110 114 119 130 131 132 133 146 148 **P**6 **S** Sanford Health, Sioux Falls, SD
Primary Contact: Erica Peterson, Chief Executive Officer and Chief Financial Officer
COO: Paul Miller, Director of Operations
CFO: Erica Peterson, Chief Executive Officer and Chief Financial Officer
CMO: John Jones, M.D., Chief Medical Staff
CHR: Dorothy Hieb, Director Human Resources
CNO: Sarah Talbott, Chief Nursing Officer
Web address: www.sanfordmiddakota.org
Control: Other not–for–profit (including NFP Corporation) **Service:** General Medical and Surgical

Staffed Beds: 69 Admissions: 441 Census: 41 Outpatient Visits: 26711 Births: 80 Total Expense ($000): 18962 Payroll Expense ($000): 8710 Personnel: 162

SD

SANFORD MID DAKOTA MEDICAL CENTER See Sanford Chamberlain Medical Center

CLEAR LAKE—Deuel County

★ **SANFORD CLEAR LAKE MEDICAL CENTER (431307)**, 701 Third Avenue South, Zip 57226–2016; tel. 605/874–2141 **A**9 10 18 **F**3 28 29 34 35 40 45 50 53 57 59 62 64 65 68 81 86 87 92 97 107 119 127 128 133 135 144 147 148 **P**6 **S** Sanford Health, Sioux Falls, SD
Primary Contact: Lori Sisk, R.N., Chief Executive Officer
CFO: Allison Nelson, Chief Financial Officer
CMO: Terrance Smith, M.D., Chairman Medical Staff
CNO: Stephanie Dobbs, Chief Nursing Officer
Web address: www.sanforddeuelcounty.org
Control: Other not–for–profit (including NFP Corporation) **Service:** General Medical and Surgical

Staffed Beds: 10 **Admissions:** 171 **Census:** 2 **Outpatient Visits:** 16309 **Births:** 0 **Total Expense ($000):** 5706 **Payroll Expense ($000):** 2904 **Personnel:** 69

CUSTER—Custer County

★ **CUSTER REGIONAL HOSPITAL (431323)**, 1039 Montgomery Street, Zip 57730–1397; tel. 605/673–2229, (Nonreporting) **A**9 10 18 **S** Regional Health, Rapid City, SD
Primary Contact: Veronica Schmidt, Chief Executive Officer
Web address: www.regionalhealth.com
Control: Other not–for–profit (including NFP Corporation) **Service:** General Medical and Surgical

Staffed Beds: 87

DAKOTA DUNES—Union County

SIOUXLAND SURGERY CENTER (430089), 600 North Sioux Point Road, Zip 57049–5000; tel. 605/232–3332, (Nonreporting) **A**9 10
Primary Contact: Greg Miner, Administrator
Web address: www.siouxlandsurg.com/
Control: Corporation, Investor–owned, for–profit **Service:** Other specialty

Staffed Beds: 40

DE SMET—Kingsbury County

★ **AVERA DE SMET MEMORIAL HOSPITAL (431332)**, 306 Prairie Avenue S.W., Zip 57231–2285, Mailing Address: P.O. Box 160, Zip 57231–0160; tel. 605/854–3329 **A**9 10 18 **F**3 15 28 34 35 40 59 68 93 133 **P**6 **S** Avera Health, Sioux Falls, SD
Primary Contact: Janice Schardin, R.N., MS, Administrator and Chief Executive Officer
Web address: www.desmetmemorial.org
Control: Other not–for–profit (including NFP Corporation) **Service:** General Medical and Surgical

Staffed Beds: 14 **Admissions:** 71 **Census:** 1 **Outpatient Visits:** 11116 **Births:** 0 **Total Expense ($000):** 3568 **Payroll Expense ($000):** 1551 **Personnel:** 26

DEADWOOD—Lawrence County

★ **LEAD–DEADWOOD REGIONAL HOSPITAL (431320)**, 61 Charles Street, Zip 57732–1303; tel. 605/722–6000 **A**9 10 18 **F**3 7 15 28 29 30 31 34 40 43 59 63 64 65 68 69 70 77 78 81 85 87 93 107 114 115 117 119 120 121 132 133 148 **S** Regional Health, Rapid City, SD
Primary Contact: Sherry Bea Smith, R.N., Chief Executive Officer
CFO: Sherry Bea Smith, R.N., Chief Executive Officer and Chief Financial Officer
CMO: Elizabeth Sayler, M.D., Chief of Staff
CHR: Kathryn L. Shockey, Director Human Resources
Web address: www.regionalhealth.com
Control: State–Government, nonfederal **Service:** General Medical and Surgical

Staffed Beds: 18 **Admissions:** 278 **Census:** 6 **Outpatient Visits:** 11539 **Births:** 0 **Total Expense ($000):** 9044 **Payroll Expense ($000):** 4264 **Personnel:** 78

DELL RAPIDS—Minnehaha County

AVERA DELLS AREA HEALTH CENTER See Avera Dells Area Hospital

★ **AVERA DELLS AREA HOSPITAL (431331)**, 909 North Iowa Avenue, Zip 57022–1231; tel. 605/428–5431 **A**9 10 18 **F**3 11 15 18 28 34 35 40 45 53 57 59 64 65 75 81 86 92 93 94 97 107 110 128 132 133 146 147 148 **P**6 **S** Avera Health, Sioux Falls, SD
Primary Contact: Lindsay Flannery, R.N., Administrator and Chief Executive Officer
CFO: Kory Holt, Division Controller Network Operations
CMO: Matt Herber, M.D., Chief of Staff
CIO: Thelma Haak, Manager Health Information
CHR: Dawn Ingalls, Regional Manager Human Resources
CNO: Karla Carstensen, Director Patient Care
Web address: www.www1.avera.org/amck/regionalfacilities/dellsareahealth/index.aspx
Control: Other not–for–profit (including NFP Corporation) **Service:** General Medical and Surgical

Staffed Beds: 23 **Admissions:** 259 **Census:** 3 **Outpatient Visits:** 18324 **Births:** 0 **Total Expense ($000):** 5485 **Payroll Expense ($000):** 2142 **Personnel:** 50

EAGLE BUTTE—Dewey County

U. S. PUBLIC HEALTH SERVICE INDIAN HOSPITAL (430083), 317 Main Street, Zip 57625–1012, Mailing Address: P.O. Box 1012, Zip 57625–1012; tel. 605/964–7724, (Nonreporting) **A**10 **S** U. S. Indian Health Service, Rockville, MD
Primary Contact: Charlene Red Thunder, Chief Executive Officer
CFO: Lisa Deal, Budget Analyst
Web address: www.ihs.gov
Control: Public Health Service, Government, federal **Service:** General Medical and Surgical

Staffed Beds: 11

EUREKA—Mcpherson County

★ **EUREKA COMMUNITY HEALTH SERVICES AVERA (431308)**, 410 Ninth Street, Zip 57437–2182, Mailing Address: P.O. Box 517, Zip 57437–0517; tel. 605/284–2661 **A**9 10 18 **F**10 28 34 35 40 41 45 59 62 65 93 133 **S** Avera Health, Sioux Falls, SD
Primary Contact: Carmen Weber, Administrator
CFO: Joyce Schwingler, Chief Financial Officer
Web address: www.avera.org
Control: Other not–for–profit (including NFP Corporation) **Service:** General Medical and Surgical

Staffed Beds: 6 **Admissions:** 87 **Census:** 1 **Outpatient Visits:** 5389 **Births:** 0 **Total Expense ($000):** 2208 **Payroll Expense ($000):** 897 **Personnel:** 28

FAULKTON—Faulk County

FAULKTON AREA MEDICAL CENTER (431301), 1300 Oak Street, Zip 57438–2149, Mailing Address: P.O. Box 100, Zip 57438–0100; tel. 605/598–6263 **A**9 10 18 **F**3 17 28 29 40 45 57 59 77 93 97 107 127 133 **P**5
Primary Contact: Jay A. Jahnig, Chief Executive Officer
COO: Jay A. Jahnig, Chief Executive Officer
CFO: Susan Miller, Financial Administrator
CMO: K. A. Bartholomew, M.D., Medical Director
CIO: Cheryl Bue, Health Information Transcriptionist
CHR: Blythe Smith, Administrative Assistant
CNO: Shannon Stuwe, Director of Nursing
Web address: www.faulktonmedical.org
Control: Other not–for–profit (including NFP Corporation) **Service:** General Medical and Surgical

Staffed Beds: 12 **Admissions:** 301 **Census:** 4 **Outpatient Visits:** 12704 **Births:** 0 **Total Expense ($000):** 8108 **Payroll Expense ($000):** 3502 **Personnel:** 71

FLANDREAU—Moody County

★ **AVERA FLANDREAU HOSPITAL (431310)**, 214 North Prairie Street, Zip 57028–1243; tel. 605/997–2433 **A**9 10 18 **F**3 28 34 35 40 45 57 59 64 65 75 81 86 92 93 97 107 127 128 132 133 146 148 **P**6 **S** Avera Health, Sioux Falls, SD
Primary Contact: Lindsay Flannery, R.N., Administrator and Chief Executive Officer
CFO: Kory Holt, Assistant Vice President for Financial Integration
CMO: Scott Peterson, M.D., President Medical Staff
CIO: Rose Reynolds, Director Health Information
CHR: Amy Aukes, Human Resources Analyst
Web address: www.avera.org/flandreau–medical/
Control: Other not–for–profit (including NFP Corporation) **Service:** General Medical and Surgical

Staffed Beds: 18 **Admissions:** 163 **Census:** 1 **Outpatient Visits:** 14054 **Births:** 0 **Total Expense ($000):** 4749 **Payroll Expense ($000):** 1996 **Personnel:** 41

SD

Hospital, Medicare Provider Number, Address, Telephone, Approval, Facility, and Physician Codes, Health Care System

★ American Hospital Association (AHA) membership
☐ The Joint Commission accreditation ◇ DNV Healthcare Inc. accreditation
○ Healthcare Facilities Accreditation Program
△ Commission on Accreditation of Rehabilitation Facilities (CARF) accreditation

AVERA FLANDREAU MEDICAL CENTER See Avera Flandreau Hospital

FORT MEADE—Meade County

✠ **VETERANS AFFAIRS BLACK HILLS HEALTH CARE SYSTEM**, 113 Comanche Road, Zip 57741–1099; tel. 605/347–2511, (Includes VETERANS AFFAIRS MEDICAL CENTER HOT SPRINGS CAMPUS, 500 North Fifth Street, Hot Springs, Zip 57747; tel. 605/745–2052), (Nonreporting) **A**1 5 9 **S** Department of Veterans Affairs, Washington, DC
Primary Contact: Stephen R. DiStasio, Director
CFO: Joseph Ferris, Chief Financial Officer
CHR: Denis Sullivan, Chief Human Resources Management
Web address: www.blackhills.va.gov/
Control: Veterans Affairs, Government, federal **Service:** General Medical and Surgical

Staffed Beds: 308

FREEMAN—Hutchinson County

★ **FREEMAN REGIONAL HEALTH SERVICES (431313)**, 510 East Eighth Street, Zip 57029–2086, Mailing Address: P.O. Box 370, Zip 57029–0370; tel. 605/925–4000, (Total facility includes 56 beds in nursing home–type unit) **A**9 10 18 **F**2 3 6 11 15 28 30 31 34 35 40 43 45 49 54 56 57 59 64 65 68 69 70 75 77 79 81 82 86 90 93 97 107 114 119 125 127 128 130 132 133 146 **P**6
Primary Contact: Daniel Gran, Chief Executive Officer
CFO: Mark Miller, Chief Financial Officer
Web address: www.freemanregional.com
Control: Other not–for–profit (including NFP Corporation) **Service:** General Medical and Surgical

Staffed Beds: 81 Admissions: 237 Census: 55 Outpatient Visits: 10000 Births: 0 Total Expense ($000): 9320 Payroll Expense ($000): 4095 Personnel: 108

GETTYSBURG—Potter County

★ **AVERA GETTYSBURG HOSPITAL (431302)**, 606 East Garfield Avenue, Zip 57442–1398; tel. 605/765–2480, (Total facility includes 50 beds in nursing home–type unit) **A**9 10 18 **F**3 6 11 28 29 30 34 35 36 40 50 59 64 67 75 77 79 81 82 86 87 93 107 125 128 130 132 133 146 **S** Avera Health, Sioux Falls, SD
Primary Contact: Mark Schmidt, President and Chief Executive Officer
Web address: www.st-marys.com
Control: Church–operated, Nongovernment, not–for profit **Service:** General Medical and Surgical

Staffed Beds: 60 Admissions: 82 Census: 47 Outpatient Visits: 4848 Births: 0 Total Expense ($000): 5770 Payroll Expense ($000): 2579 Personnel: 66

GREGORY—Gregory County

★ **AVERA GREGORY HOSPITAL (431338)**, 400 Park Avenue, Zip 57533–1302, Mailing Address: P.O. Box 408, Zip 57533–0408; tel. 605/835–8394, (Total facility includes 42 beds in nursing home–type unit) **A**9 10 18 **F**7 8 15 29 31 34 40 43 45 57 59 60 64 65 75 77 78 93 107 111 119 128 131 133 135 **S** Avera Health, Sioux Falls, SD
Primary Contact: Anthony Timanus, Chief Executive Officer
CFO: Trish Keiser, Comptroller
CMO: Rich Kafka, M.D., Chief Medical Officer
CIO: Justin Keegan, Director Support Services
CHR: Carol Postulka, Administrative Coordinator
Web address: www.gregoryhealthcare.org
Control: Other not–for–profit (including NFP Corporation) **Service:** General Medical and Surgical

Staffed Beds: 67 Admissions: 505 Census: 43 Births: 1 Personnel: 103

HOT SPRINGS—Fall River County

★ **FALL RIVER HOSPITAL (431322)**, 1201 Highway 71 South, Zip 57747–8800; tel. 605/745–3159, (Includes CASTLE MANOR), (Nonreporting) **A**9 10 18
Primary Contact: Tricia Uhlir, Chief Executive Officer
CFO: Jesse Naze, Chief Financial Officer
CMO: Rodney Larson, M.D., Medical Director
CIO: Dustin Kleinsasser, Information Technology and BioMed
CHR: Cindy Trent, Manager Personnel
Web address: www.frhssd.org
Control: Other not–for–profit (including NFP Corporation) **Service:** General Medical and Surgical

Staffed Beds: 61

VETERANS AFFAIRS MEDICAL CENTER HOT SPRINGS CAMPUS See Veterans Affairs Black Hills Health Care System, Fort Meade

HURON—Beadle County

★ **HURON REGIONAL MEDICAL CENTER (431335)**, 172 Fourth Street S.E., Zip 57350–2590; tel. 605/353–6200 **A**9 10 18 **F**3 11 13 14 15 28 29 30 31 34 35 40 41 43 45 57 59 60 62 63 64 68 70 75 77 78 79 81 85 86 93 102 107 108 110 111 115 118 119 130 132 133 146 148 **P**6 **S** QHR, Brentwood, TN
Primary Contact: David Dick, Chief Executive Officer
CFO: Marcia Zwanziger, Vice President Finance
CMO: Jim Schwaiger, M.D., Chief of Staff
CHR: Rhonda Hanson, Director Human Resources
CNO: Gail Robeson, Vice President Patient Services
Web address: www.huronregional.org
Control: Other not–for–profit (including NFP Corporation) **Service:** General Medical and Surgical

Staffed Beds: 25 Admissions: 1333 Census: 13 Outpatient Visits: 59554 Births: 362 Total Expense ($000): 29678 Payroll Expense ($000): 13597 Personnel: 237

MADISON—Lake County

★ **MADISON COMMUNITY HOSPITAL (431300)**, 917 North Washington Avenue, Zip 57042–1696; tel. 605/256–6551 **A**9 10 18 **F**7 11 13 15 28 31 34 35 40 41 43 57 59 62 64 70 75 76 77 81 82 85 87 89 93 97 107 110 114 119 129 132 133 135 143 145 146 148 **P**5
Primary Contact: Tamara Miller, R.N., Administrator
CFO: Teresa Mallett, Chief Financial Officer
CNO: Charlotte Charles, Director Acute Patient Services
Web address: www.madisonhospital.com
Control: Other not–for–profit (including NFP Corporation) **Service:** General Medical and Surgical

Staffed Beds: 25 Admissions: 548 Census: 7 Outpatient Visits: 29296 Births: 33 Total Expense ($000): 12926 Payroll Expense ($000): 6643 Personnel: 133

MARTIN—Bennett County

BENNETT COUNTY HOSPITAL AND NURSING HOME (431314), 102 Major Allen Street, Zip 57551–6005, Mailing Address: P.O. Box 70, Zip 57551–0070; tel. 605/685–6622, (Total facility includes 42 beds in nursing home–type unit) **A**9 10 18 **F**7 10 28 34 40 50 53 57 59 62 65 66 67 68 77 84 92 93 107 130 133 143
Primary Contact: Ethel Frein, Chief Executive Officer
CFO: Jean Kirk, Chief Financial Officer
CMO: Peter Knowles–Smith, M.D., Medical Director
CIO: Jean Kirk, Chief Financial Officer
CHR: T. J. Porter, Director Human Resources
Web address: www.bennettcountyhospital.com/
Control: Other not–for–profit (including NFP Corporation) **Service:** General Medical and Surgical

Staffed Beds: 53 Admissions: 207 Census: 40 Outpatient Visits: 48188 Births: 0 Total Expense ($000): 5101 Payroll Expense ($000): 3248 Personnel: 96

MILBANK—Grant County

★ **MILBANK AREA HOSPITAL AVERA (431326)**, 901 East Virgil Avenue, Zip 57252–2124; tel. 605/432–4538, (Includes ST. WILLIAM HOME FOR THE AGED), (Nonreporting) **A**9 10 18 **S** Avera Health, Sioux Falls, SD
Primary Contact: Natalie Gauer, Administrator
CMO: Kevin Bjordahl, M.D., Chief Medical Officer
CHR: Mona Schafer, Regional Manager Human Resources
Web address: www.averamilbank.org
Control: Other not–for–profit (including NFP Corporation) **Service:** General Medical and Surgical

Staffed Beds: 25

MILLER—Hand County

★ **AVERA HAND COUNTY MEMORIAL HOSPITAL (431337)**, 300 West Fifth Street, Zip 57362–1238; tel. 605/853–2421 **A**9 10 18 **F**3 8 11 15 17 28 29 34 35 40 43 45 46 50 53 57 59 64 74 77 78 81 87 93 107 114 119 128 129 132 133 146 148 **S** Avera Health, Sioux Falls, SD
Primary Contact: Bryan Breitling, Administrator
CFO: Debbie Pullman, Director Finance
CMO: Steve Schroeder, M.D., Chief of Staff
CIO: Janice Purrington, Coordinator Medical Records
CNO: Teresa E. Fanning, Director of Patient Care
Web address: www.avera.org
Control: Other not–for–profit (including NFP Corporation) **Service:** General Medical and Surgical

Staffed Beds: 9 Admissions: 291 Census: 4 Outpatient Visits: 11548 Births: 0 Total Expense ($000): 6792 Payroll Expense ($000): 3098 Personnel: 54

MITCHELL—Davison County

✠ **AVERA QUEEN OF PEACE HOSPITAL (430013)**, 525 North Foster, Zip 57301–2999; tel. 605/995–2000, (Total facility includes 109 beds in nursing home–type unit) **A**1 2 9 10 **F**3 10 12 13 15 28 29 30 31 34 35 39 40 43 48 50 53 56 57 59 62 63 64 65 69 70 71 75 76 77 78 79 81 82 84 85 86 89 93 94 96 102 107 110 111 114 116 118 119 121 123 125 127 128 129 130 131 132 133 135 144 146 147 148 **P**6 **S** Avera Health, Sioux Falls, SD
Primary Contact: Thomas A. Clark, Regional President and Chief Executive Officer
CFO: Will Flett, Vice President Finance and Chief Financial Officer
CMO: David Balt, D.O., Chief Medical Officer
CIO: Patti Brooks, Director Information Systems
CHR: Rita Lemon, Director Human Resources
CNO: Rochelle Reider, Vice President Patient Care
Web address: www.averaqueenofpeace.org
Control: Church–operated, Nongovernment, not–for profit **Service:** General Medical and Surgical

Staffed Beds: 194 **Admissions:** 2651 **Census:** 131 **Outpatient Visits:** 127449 **Births:** 475 **Total Expense ($000):** 81260 **Payroll Expense ($000):** 39321 **Personnel:** 437

MOBRIDGE—Walworth County

★ **MOBRIDGE REGIONAL HOSPITAL (431325)**, 1401 Tenth Avenue West, Zip 57601–1106, Mailing Address: P.O. Box 580, Zip 57601–0580; tel. 605/845–3692, (Nonreporting) **A**9 10 18
Primary Contact: Angelia K. Svihovec, Chief Executive Officer
COO: Beth Jensen, Director Clinic Operations
CFO: Renae Tisdall, Chief Financial Officer
CMO: Travis Henderson, M.D., Chief of Staff
CIO: Lynn Schott, Director Information Technology
CHR: Keri Wientjes, Director Human Resources
CNO: Kristi Voller, Director of Nursing
Web address: www.mobridgehospital.org
Control: Other not–for–profit (including NFP Corporation) **Service:** General Medical and Surgical

Staffed Beds: 25

PARKSTON—Hutchinson County

★ **AVERA ST. BENEDICT HEALTH CENTER (431330)**, 401 West Glynn Drive, Zip 57366–9605; tel. 605/928–3311, (Total facility includes 75 beds in nursing home–type unit) **A**9 10 18 **F**2 3 8 10 13 15 28 29 30 31 32 34 35 38 40 45 53 56 57 59 64 65 69 75 76 81 82 83 85 86 87 89 107 110 111 114 116 119 128 129 130 131 132 133 135 146 148 **P**6 **S** Avera Health, Sioux Falls, SD
Primary Contact: Gale N. Walker, President and Chief Executive Officer
CFO: Rita Blasius, Assistant Administrator and Chief Financial Officer
CMO: Jason Wickersham, M.D., Chief of Staff
CIO: Adam Popp, Director Information Systems
CHR: Phyllis Ehler, Director Human Resources
CNO: Denise Muntefering, Vice President Patient Care Services
Web address: www.averastbenedict.org
Control: Church–operated, Nongovernment, not–for profit **Service:** General Medical and Surgical

Staffed Beds: 100 **Admissions:** 469 **Census:** 76 **Outpatient Visits:** 20546 **Births:** 33 **Total Expense ($000):** 16786 **Payroll Expense ($000):** 8911 **Personnel:** 168

PHILIP—Haakon County

HANS P. PETERSON MEMORIAL HOSPITAL See Philip Health Services

★ **PHILIP HEALTH SERVICES (431319)**, 503 West Pine Street, Zip 57567–3300, Mailing Address: P.O. Box 790, Zip 57567–0790; tel. 605/859–2511, (Total facility includes 30 beds in nursing home–type unit) **A**9 10 18 **F**10 11 40 57 59 62 85 93 107 114 119 125 127 128 130 131 133 148 **P**6 **S** Regional Health, Rapid City, SD
Primary Contact: Kent Olson, Administrator and Chief Executive Officer
Control: Other not–for–profit (including NFP Corporation) **Service:** General Medical and Surgical

Staffed Beds: 48 **Admissions:** 148 **Census:** 30 **Outpatient Visits:** 9177 **Births:** 0 **Total Expense ($000):** 7965 **Payroll Expense ($000):** 4510 **Personnel:** 130

PIERRE—Hughes County

✠ **AVERA ST. MARY'S HOSPITAL (430015)**, 801 East Sioux Avenue, Zip 57501–3323; tel. 605/224–3100, (Total facility includes 90 beds in nursing home–type unit) **A**1 9 10 20 **F**1 2 3 4 8 11 13 15 16 17 28 29 30 31 34 38 40 41 43 45 48 49 50 51 59 60 64 67 68 70 72 73 76 77 78 79 80 81 82 83 84 85 87 88 89 90 93 98 107 110 111 114 119 125 128 129 130 133 144 146 147 148 **P**5 **S** Avera Health, Sioux Falls, SD
Primary Contact: Bob Sutton, President and Chief Executive Officer
CFO: Tom Wagner, Interim Vice President Finance
CMO: Denise Hanisch, M.D., Chief of Staff
CIO: Jamie Raske, Information Technology Lead
CHR: Paul Marso, Vice President Human Resources
Web address: www.avera.org/st-marys-pierre/
Control: Other not–for–profit (including NFP Corporation) **Service:** General Medical and Surgical

Staffed Beds: 164 **Admissions:** 1614 **Census:** 52 **Outpatient Visits:** 48539 **Births:** 423 **Total Expense ($000):** 31396 **Payroll Expense ($000):** 14992 **Personnel:** 336

PINE RIDGE—Shannon County

U. S. PUBLIC HEALTH SERVICE INDIAN HOSPITAL (430081), East Highway 18, Zip 57770, Mailing Address: P.O. Box 1201, Zip 57770–1201; tel. 605/867–5131, (Nonreporting) **A**10 **S** U. S. Indian Health Service, Rockville, MD
Primary Contact: Ellen Davis, Service Unit Director
CFO: Sophia Conny, Deputy Administrative Officer
CMO: Jan Colton, M.D., Acting Clinical Director
CHR: Annabelle Blackbear, Human Resources Specialist
Web address: www.ihs.gov
Control: Public Health Service, Government, federal **Service:** General Medical and Surgical

Staffed Beds: 45

PLATTE—Charles Mix County

★ **PLATTE HEALTH CENTER AVERA (431306)**, 601 East Seventh, Zip 57369–2123, Mailing Address: P.O. Box 200, Zip 57369–0200; tel. 605/337–3364, (Nonreporting) **A**9 10 18 **S** Avera Health, Sioux Falls, SD
Primary Contact: Mark Burket, Chief Executive Officer
CFO: Jerry Hoffman, Chief Financial Officer
Web address: www.phcavera.org
Control: Other not–for–profit (including NFP Corporation) **Service:** General Medical and Surgical

Staffed Beds: 65

RAPID CITY—Pennington County

BLACK HILLS SURGERY CENTER (430091), 216 Anamaria Drive, Zip 57701–7366, Mailing Address: 1868 Lombardy Drive, Zip 57703–4130; tel. 605/721–4900, (Nonreporting) **A**9 10
Primary Contact: Franklin Shobe, Administrator and Chief Executive Officer
Web address: www.bhsc.com
Control: Partnership, Investor–owned, for–profit **Service:** General Medical and Surgical

Staffed Beds: 26

INDIAN HEALTH SERVICE HOSPITAL (430082), 3200 Canyon Lake Drive, Zip 57702–8197; tel. 605/355–2280, (Nonreporting) **A**10 **S** U. S. Indian Health Service, Rockville, MD
Primary Contact: Helen Thompson, Interim Director
CFO: Helen Thompson, Administrative Officer
Web address: www.ihs.gov
Control: PHS, Indian Service, Government, federal **Service:** General Medical and Surgical

Staffed Beds: 5

SD

Hospital, Medicare Provider Number, Address, Telephone, Approval, Facility, and Physician Codes, Health Care System

★ American Hospital Association (AHA) membership
□ The Joint Commission accreditation   ◇ DNV Healthcare Inc. accreditation
○ Healthcare Facilities Accreditation Program
△ Commission on Accreditation of Rehabilitation Facilities (CARF) accreditation

---

⊠ △ RAPID CITY REGIONAL HOSPITAL (430077), 353 Fairmont Boulevard, Zip 57701–7393, Mailing Address: P.O. Box 6000, Zip 57709–6000; tel. 605/755–1000 **A**1 3 5 7 9 10 19 20 **F**3 5 11 12 13 15 17 18 20 22 24 26 28 29 30 31 34 35 36 38 40 43 44 45 46 47 48 49 51 56 57 58 59 60 62 63 64 65 66 68 70 72 73 74 75 76 77 78 79 80 81 82 84 85 86 87 88 89 90 91 92 93 98 99 100 101 102 104 107 108 110 111 115 119 120 121 122 123 124 126 129 130 131 132 135 141 143 146 148 **P**1 5 6 **S** Regional Health, Rapid City, SD
Primary Contact: Timothy H. Sughrue, Chief Executive Officer
COO: Mick Gibbs, Chief Operating Officer
CFO: Mark Thompson, Vice President Financial Services
CMO: David Houser, M.D., Vice President Medical Affairs
CIO: Richard Latuchie, Vice President Business Development
CHR: Maureen Henson, Vice President Human Resources
CNO: Rita K. Haxton, R.N., Vice President Patient Care Nursing
Web address: www.regionalhealth.com
Control: Other not–for–profit (including NFP Corporation) **Service:** General Medical and Surgical

Staffed Beds: 408 **Admissions:** 18306 **Census:** 281 **Outpatient Visits:** 179446 **Births:** 2365 **Total Expense ($000):** 372466 **Payroll Expense ($000):** 164242 **Personnel:** 2667

SAME DAY SURGERY CENTER (430093), 651 Cathedral Drive, Zip 57701–7368; tel. 605/755–9000, (Nonreporting) **A**9 10
Primary Contact: Doris Fritts, R.N., Executive Director
Web address: www.regionalhealth.com
Control: Corporation, Investor–owned, for–profit **Service:** Surgical

Staffed Beds: 8

REDFIELD—Spink County

COMMUNITY MEMORIAL HOSPITAL (431316), 110 West Tenth Avenue, Zip 57469–1520, Mailing Address: P.O. Box 420, Zip 57469–0420; tel. 605/472–1110, (Nonreporting) **A**9 10 18
Primary Contact: Nicholas R. Brandner, Chief Executive Officer
CFO: William Boyer, Chief Financial Officer
CHR: Rhonda Stroh, Chief Human Resources Officer
CNO: Julene J. Cass, R.N., Director of Nursing
Web address: www.redfield–sd.com/hospital.html
Control: City–Government, nonfederal **Service:** General Medical and Surgical

Staffed Beds: 25

ROSEBUD—Todd County

U. S. PUBLIC HEALTH SERVICE INDIAN HOSPITAL (430084), Highway 18, Soldier Creek Road, Zip 57570; tel. 605/747–2231, (Nonreporting) **A**10 **S** U. S. Indian Health Service, Rockville, MD
Primary Contact: Sophie M. Two Hawk, Chief Executive Officer
COO: Romeo Vivit, Chief Surgeon
CMO: Valerie Parker, M.D., Clinical Director
CHR: Michelle Zephier, Human Resource Specialist
Web address: www.ihs.gov
Control: PHS, Indian Service, Government, federal **Service:** General Medical and Surgical

Staffed Beds: 35

SCOTLAND—Bon Homme County

★ LANDMANN–JUNGMAN MEMORIAL HOSPITAL AVERA (431317), 600 Billars Street, Zip 57059–2026; tel. 605/583–2226, (Nonreporting) **A**9 10 18 **S** Avera Health, Sioux Falls, SD
Primary Contact: Jonathan Moe, Chief Executive Officer
CFO: Darcy Permann, Manager Business Office
Web address: www.ljmh.org
Control: Other not–for–profit (including NFP Corporation) **Service:** General Medical and Surgical

Staffed Beds: 19

SIOUX FALLS—Lincoln County

☐ AVERA HEART HOSPITAL OF SOUTH DAKOTA (430095), 4500 West 69th Street, Zip 57108–8148; tel. 605/977–7000 **A**1 9 10 **F**3 11 17 18 20 22 24 26 28 29 30 34 35 40 45 57 59 60 68 71 74 79 81 82 84 85 87 107 108 111 115 118 119 121 124 130 132 135 **P**2 **S** Avera Health, Sioux Falls, SD
Primary Contact: Jon Soderholm, President
CFO: Jean White, Vice President Finance
Web address: www.avera.org/heart–hospital
Control: Corporation, Investor–owned, for–profit **Service:** Heart

Staffed Beds: 53 **Admissions:** 2487 **Census:** 26 **Outpatient Visits:** 6840 **Births:** 0 **Personnel:** 373

⊠ △ AVERA MCKENNAN HOSPITAL AND UNIVERSITY HEALTH CENTER (430016), 1325 South Cliff Avenue, Zip 57105–1007, Mailing Address: P.O. Box 5045, Zip 57117–5045; tel. 605/322–8000, (Includes AVERA CHILDREN'S HOSPITAL, 1325 South Cliff Avenue, Zip 57105–1016, Mailing Address: PO Box 5045, Zip 57117–5045; tel. 605/322–5437), (Total facility includes 90 beds in nursing home–type unit) **A**1 2 3 5 7 8 9 10 **F**3 5 7 10 11 12 13 15 18 19 20 21 22 23 24 29 30 31 32 34 35 36 38 39 40 41 43 44 46 49 50 53 54 55 56 57 58 59 60 61 63 64 65 66 67 68 70 71 72 74 75 76 77 78 79 81 82 84 85 86 87 88 89 90 92 93 94 96 97 98 99 100 101 102 103 104 105 107 108 110 111 114 115 116 117 118 119 120 121 123 124 125 126 128 129 130 131 132 134 135 136 138 141 142 143 144 145 146 147 148 **P**6 **S** Avera Health, Sioux Falls, SD
Primary Contact: David Kapaska, D.O., Regional President and Chief Executive Officer
COO: Judy Blauwet, M.P.H., Senior Vice President Operations and Chief Nursing Officer
CFO: Julie Norton, Chief Financial Officer
CMO: Michael Elliott, M.D., Chief Medical Officer and Senior Vice President of Medical Affairs
CIO: Kristin Gross, Director Information Technology Center
CHR: Lynne D. Hagen, Human Resources Officer
CNO: Judy Blauwet, M.P.H., Senior Vice President of Hospital Operations and Chief Nursing Officer
Web address: www.averamckennan.org
Control: Church–operated, Nongovernment, not–for profit **Service:** General Medical and Surgical

Staffed Beds: 400 **Admissions:** 20386 **Census:** 290 **Outpatient Visits:** 230224 **Births:** 2008 **Total Expense ($000):** 671636 **Payroll Expense ($000):** 314559 **Personnel:** 3859

CHILDRENS CARE HOSPITAL AND SCHOOL (433300), 2501 West 26th Street, Zip 57105–2498; tel. 605/782–2300, (Nonreporting) **A**9 10
Primary Contact: David A. Timpe, Interim President and Chief Executive Officer
CFO: John Clark, Chief Financial Officer
CMO: Christiane Maroun, M.D., Chief of Staff
CHR: Tiffany Reilly, Director Human Resources
Web address: www.cchs.org
Control: Other not–for–profit (including NFP Corporation) **Service:** Children's rehabilitation

Staffed Beds: 114

⊠ △ SANFORD USD MEDICAL CENTER (430027), 1305 West 18th Street, Zip 57105–0496, Mailing Address: P.O. Box 5039, Zip 57117–5039; tel. 605/333–1000, (Includes SANFORD CHILDREN'S HOSPITAL, 1600 West 22nd Street, Zip 57105, Mailing Address: PO Box 5039, Zip 57117–5039; tel. 605/333–1000) **A**1 2 3 5 7 8 9 10 **F**3 7 8 9 11 12 14 15 17 18 19 20 21 22 23 24 25 26 27 28 29 30 31 32 34 35 36 37 38 40 43 44 45 46 48 49 50 51 52 53 54 55 56 57 58 59 60 61 63 64 65 70 71 72 73 74 75 76 77 78 79 80 81 83 84 85 86 87 88 89 90 91 92 93 94 96 97 99 100 101 107 108 110 111 114 115 116 117 118 119 120 121 123 124 126 129 130 131 132 134 135 138 141 142 143 146 147 148 **P**6 **S** Sanford Health, Sioux Falls, SD
Primary Contact: Paul A. Hanson, FACHE, President
COO: Brad J. Schipper, Chief Operating Officer
CFO: Merrilee Schultz, Chief Finance
CIO: Arlyn Broekhuis, Vice President and Chief Information Officer
CHR: Evan Burkett, Chief Human Resource Officer
Web address: www.sanfordhealth.org
Control: Other not–for–profit (including NFP Corporation) **Service:** General Medical and Surgical

Staffed Beds: 511 **Admissions:** 23552 **Census:** 301 **Outpatient Visits:** 432083 **Births:** 3089 **Total Expense ($000):** 545337 **Payroll Expense ($000):** 219048 **Personnel:** 5429

⊠ SELECT SPECIALTY HOSPITAL–SIOUX FALLS (432002), 1305 West 18th Street, Zip 57105–0401; tel. 605/322–3500, (Nonreporting) **A**1 9 10 **S** Select Medical Corporation, Mechanicsburg, PA
Primary Contact: Carol Ulmer, Chief Executive Officer
Web address: www.selectspecialtyhospitals.com/company/locations/siouxfalls.aspx
Control: Corporation, Investor–owned, for–profit **Service:** Long–Term Acute Care hospital

Staffed Beds: 21

SIOUX FALLS SPECIALTY HOSPITAL (430090), 910 East 20th Street, Zip 57105–1012; tel. 605/334–6730, (Nonreporting) **A**9 10
Primary Contact: Donald A. Schellpfeffer, M.D., Chief Executive Officer
CFO: Kyle Goldammer, Chief Financial Officer
CMO: Donald A. Schellpfeffer, M.D., Medical Director
Web address: www.sfsurgical.com
Control: Partnership, Investor–owned, for–profit **Service:** General Medical and Surgical

Staffed Beds: 35

Many Facility Codes have changed. Please refer to the AHA Guide Code Chart. © 2014 AHA Guide

⊠ **SIOUX FALLS VETERANS AFFAIRS HEALTH CARE SYSTEM**, 2501 West 22nd Street, Zip 57105–1305, Mailing Address: P.O. Box 5046, Zip 57117–5046; tel. 605/336–3230, (Total facility includes 58 beds in nursing home–type unit) **A**1 3 5 9 **F**5 8 18 29 30 31 33 34 35 36 38 39 40 45 46 50 53 54 56 57 58 59 60 62 63 64 65 68 70 71 74 75 77 78 79 81 82 84 85 86 87 91 92 93 94 97 98 100 101 102 103 104 107 111 118 119 127 130 131 132 134 143 146 147 148 **S** Department of Veterans Affairs, Washington, DC
Primary Contact: Darwin Goodspeed, Director
COO: Sara Ackert, Associate Director
CFO: Daniel Hubbard, Chief Financial Officer
CMO: Victor Waters, M.D., Chief of Staff
CIO: Eric Heiser, Chief Information Resource Management
CHR: Betsy Geiver, Chief Human Resources Officer
CNO: Barbara Teal, R.N., Associate Director Patient Care Services and Nurse Executive
Web address: www.siouxfalls.va.gov
Control: Veterans Affairs, Government, federal **Service:** General Medical and Surgical

Staffed Beds: 98 **Admissions:** 2892 **Census:** 82 **Outpatient Visits:** 281138
Births: 0 **Personnel:** 926

SISSETON—Roberts County

★ **COTEAU DES PRAIRIES HOSPITAL (431339)**, 205 Orchard Drive, Zip 57262–2398; tel. 605/698–7647 **A**9 10 18 **F**13 15 28 31 34 35 40 53 57 59 62 64 70 75 76 77 81 90 93 107 110 119 127 133 **P**6
Primary Contact: Dan C. Ellis, Chief Executive Officer
CFO: Larry Moen, Chief Financial Officer
CMO: David Staub, M.D., Chief of Staff
CIO: Cheryl Kaufman, Information Technology Technician
CHR: Leslie Hendrickson, Director Human Resources
CNO: Brenda Bostrom, Director of Nursing
Web address: www.cdphospital.com
Control: Other not–for–profit (including NFP Corporation) **Service:** General Medical and Surgical

Staffed Beds: 25 **Admissions:** 524 **Census:** 4 **Outpatient Visits:** 41958
Births: 188 **Total Expense ($000):** 13043 **Payroll Expense ($000):** 6093
Personnel: 127

SPEARFISH—Lawrence County

★ **SPEARFISH REGIONAL HOSPITAL (430048)**, 1440 North Main Street, Zip 57783–1504; tel. 605/644–4000 **A**9 10 20 **F**3 11 13 15 28 29 31 34 40 43 45 57 59 62 63 70 75 76 79 81 84 85 89 93 97 107 108 110 111 114 119 128 129 130 132 133 135 146 147 148 **P**6 **S** Regional Health, Rapid City, SD
Primary Contact: Larry W. Veitz, Chief Executive Officer
CFO: Marcia Olson, Director Finance
CHR: Colleen De Rosier, Coordinator Human Resource
CNO: Cathy Dill, R.N., Director Patient Services
Web address: www.regionalhealth.com
Control: Other not–for–profit (including NFP Corporation) **Service:** General Medical and Surgical

Staffed Beds: 35 **Admissions:** 1506 **Census:** 10 **Outpatient Visits:** 40143
Births: 430 **Total Expense ($000):** 31086 **Payroll Expense ($000):** 12994
Personnel: 222

★ **SPEARFISH REGIONAL SURGERY CENTER (430094)**, 1316 North 10th Street, Zip 57783–1530; tel. 605/642–3113, (Nonreporting) **A**9 10
Primary Contact: Michael DeLano, Administrator
COO: Matthew Long, Chief Operating Officer
CFO: Jeff Roehrich, Chief Financial Officer
CMO: Richard Keim, M.D., Chief Medical Officer
CIO: Bill Stoeckman, Chief Information Officer
CHR: Pat Akin, Chief Human Resource Officer
CNO: Peggy O'Sullivan, Director Patient Services
Web address: www.rcrh.org
Control: Other not–for–profit (including NFP Corporation) **Service:** Surgical

Staffed Beds: 4

STURGIS—Meade County

★ **STURGIS REGIONAL HOSPITAL (431321)**, 949 Harmon Street, Zip 57785–2452; tel. 605/720–2400, (Total facility includes 84 beds in nursing home–type unit) **A**9 10 18 **F**11 15 28 29 40 46 77 81 82 93 107 110 111 114 119 128 132 133 148 **S** Regional Health, Rapid City, SD
Primary Contact: Mark Schulte, FACHE, Chief Executive Officer
CFO: Jodie Mitchell, Facility Financial Director
CMO: Tom Hermann, Chief of Staff
CHR: Ginger Chord, Coordinator Human Resources
CNO: Rikki Plaggemeyer, Director Acute Care Nursing
Web address: www.regionalhealth.com/Our–Locations/Regional–Hospitals/ Sturgis–Regional–Hospital.aspx
Control: Other not–for–profit (including NFP Corporation) **Service:** General Medical and Surgical

Staffed Beds: 109 **Admissions:** 643 **Census:** 91 **Outpatient Visits:** 9661
Births: 0 **Total Expense ($000):** 16106 **Payroll Expense ($000):** 8241
Personnel: 197

TYNDALL—Bon Homme County

★ **ST. MICHAEL'S HOSPITAL AVERA (431327)**, 410 West 16th Avenue, Zip 57066–2318; tel. 605/589–3341 **A**9 10 18 **F**3 15 28 31 34 40 43 45 53 57 59 64 65 67 70 75 77 81 86 89 92 93 94 107 110 114 119 127 128 129 131 133 148 **P**6 **S** Avera Health, Sioux Falls, SD
Primary Contact: Carol Deurmier, Chief Executive Officer
CFO: Lisa Ronke, Director Finance
CMO: Melvin Wallinga, M.D., Medical Director
Web address: www.stmichaels–bhfp.org
Control: Church–operated, Nongovernment, not–for profit **Service:** General Medical and Surgical

Staffed Beds: 25 **Admissions:** 227 **Census:** 7 **Outpatient Visits:** 10324
Births: 0 **Total Expense ($000):** 7945 **Payroll Expense ($000):** 3063
Personnel: 62

VERMILLION—Clay County

★ **SANFORD VERMILLION MEDICAL CENTER (431336)**, 20 South Plum Street, Zip 57069–3346; tel. 605/624–2611, (Total facility includes 66 beds in nursing home–type unit) **A**9 10 18 **F**15 29 35 40 43 59 67 81 91 92 93 97 107 116 119 125 129 130 131 132 133 135 **P**8 **S** Sanford Health, Sioux Falls, SD
Primary Contact: Timothy J. Tracy, Chief Executive Officer
CFO: Valerie Osterberg, Chief Financial Officer
CMO: Roy Mortinsen, M.D., Chief of Staff
CIO: Mary C. Merrigan, Manager Public Relations
CHR: Cindy Benzel, Manager Human Resources
CNO: Jeff Berens, MS, Chief Nursing Officer
Web address: www.sanfordvermillion.org
Control: Other not–for–profit (including NFP Corporation) **Service:** General Medical and Surgical

Staffed Beds: 114 **Admissions:** 532 **Census:** 71 **Outpatient Visits:** 37388
Births: 111 **Total Expense ($000):** 16407 **Payroll Expense ($000):** 7442
Personnel: 151

VIBORG—Turner County

★ **PIONEER MEMORIAL HOSPITAL AND HEALTH SERVICES (431328)**, 315 North Washington Street, Zip 57070–2002, Mailing Address: P.O. Box 368, Zip 57070–0368; tel. 605/326–5161, (Total facility includes 52 beds in nursing home–type unit) **A**9 10 18 **F**6 10 15 28 30 34 40 43 45 53 56 57 59 63 65 69 75 79 81 87 97 107 111 119 125 127 128 130 132 133 **P**6 **S** Sanford Health, Sioux Falls, SD
Primary Contact: Thomas V. Richter, Chief Executive Officer
CFO: Anne Christiansen, Chief Financial Officer
CMO: Curtis Mark, M.D., Chief Medical Officer
Web address: www.pioneermemorial.org
Control: Other not–for–profit (including NFP Corporation) **Service:** General Medical and Surgical

Staffed Beds: 64 **Admissions:** 194 **Census:** 50 **Outpatient Visits:** 30026
Births: 0 **Total Expense ($000):** 12148 **Payroll Expense ($000):** 6502
Personnel: 142

SD

Hospital, Medicare Provider Number, Address, Telephone, Approval, Facility, and Physician Codes, Health Care System

★ American Hospital Association (AHA) membership
☐ The Joint Commission accreditation   ◇ DNV Healthcare Inc. accreditation

◯ Healthcare Facilities Accreditation Program
△ Commission on Accreditation of Rehabilitation Facilities (CARF) accreditation

WAGNER—Charles Mix County

★ **WAGNER COMMUNITY MEMORIAL HOSPITAL AVERA (431315)**, 513 Third Street S.W., Zip 57380–9675, Mailing Address: P.O. Box 280, Zip 57380–0280; tel. 605/384–3611 **A**9 10 18 **F**3 11 15 17 18 28 31 34 40 43 45 57 59 64 67 70 75 77 81 93 97 107 110 114 119 125 128 130 133 148 **P**6 **S** Avera Health, Sioux Falls, SD
Primary Contact: Bryan Slaba, Chief Executive Officer
CFO: Lisa Weisser, Supervisor Finance
CIO: Cindy Minder, Coordinator Information Systems
CHR: Marcia Podzimek, Chief Human Resources Officer
Web address: www.avera.org/wagnerhospital
Control: Other not–for–profit (including NFP Corporation) **Service:** General Medical and Surgical

Staffed Beds: 20 Admissions: 276 Census: 2 Outpatient Visits: 9422 Births: 0 Total Expense ($000): 8266 Payroll Expense ($000): 3222 Personnel: 56

WATERTOWN—Codington County

★ **PRAIRIE LAKES HEALTHCARE SYSTEM (430005)**, 401 9th Avenue N.W., Zip 57201–1548, Mailing Address: P.O. Box 1210, Zip 57201–6210; tel. 605/882–7000, (Nonreporting) **A**9 10 20
Primary Contact: Jill Fuller, R.N., Ph.D., President and Chief Executive Officer
COO: Traci Rabine, Vice President Clinic Operations
CFO: Adam Paul, Chief Financial Officer
CMO: Daniel Flaherty, M.D., Chief Medical Staff
CHR: Nathan Lake, Vice President Human Resources
CNO: Shelly Turbak, R.N., Chief Nursing Officer
Web address: www.prairielakes.com
Control: Other not–for–profit (including NFP Corporation) **Service:** General Medical and Surgical

Staffed Beds: 70

WEBSTER—Day County

★ **SANFORD WEBSTER MEDICAL CENTER (431311)**, 1401 West 1st Street, Zip 57274–1054, Mailing Address: P.O. Box 489, Zip 57274–0489; tel. 605/345–3336 **A**9 10 18 **F**15 28 29 34 35 40 43 57 59 63 64 70 71 77 81 86 87 91 93 97 107 111 114 119 127 128 130 131 133 148 **S** Sanford Health, Sioux Falls, SD
Primary Contact: David Rogers, Chief Executive Officer
CFO: Sheryl L. Pappas, Chief Financial Officer
Web address: www.sanfordhealth.org
Control: Other not–for–profit (including NFP Corporation) **Service:** General Medical and Surgical

Staffed Beds: 20 Admissions: 170 Census: 1 Outpatient Visits: 13343 Births: 0 Total Expense ($000): 7200 Payroll Expense ($000): 3311 Personnel: 58

WESSINGTON SPRINGS—Jerauld County

★ **AVERA WESKOTA MEMORIAL HOSPITAL (431324)**, 604 First Street N.E., Zip 57382–2166; tel. 605/539–1201 **A**9 10 18 **F**3 15 28 31 35 40 53 57 59 64 75 77 81 85 93 107 114 119 128 130 131 132 133 **P**5 **S** Avera Health, Sioux Falls, SD
Primary Contact: Gaea Blue, R.N., Administrator and Chief Executive Officer
CFO: Linda Jager, Director Finance
CMO: Thomas Dean, M.D., Chief of Staff
CNO: JoAnn Hettinger, R.N., Director of Patient Care Services
Web address: www.averaweskota.org
Control: Other not–for–profit (including NFP Corporation) **Service:** General Medical and Surgical

Staffed Beds: 23 Admissions: 95 Census: 2 Outpatient Visits: 5181 Births: 0 Total Expense ($000): 4202 Payroll Expense ($000): 1683 Personnel: 31

WINNER—Tripp County

★ **WINNER REGIONAL HEALTHCARE CENTER (431334)**, 745 East Eighth Street, Zip 57580–2631; tel. 605/842–7100, (Total facility includes 79 beds in nursing home–type unit) **A**9 10 18 **F**1 13 15 17 28 31 34 35 40 43 47 56 57 59 62 64 65 67 68 70 75 76 79 81 85 89 107 108 110 119 127 128 129 131 132 133 148 **P**3 5 **S** Sanford Health, Sioux Falls, SD
Primary Contact: Kevin Coffey, Chief Executive Officer
COO: Debra K. Davis, Director of Operations
CFO: Phil Husher, Chief Financial Officer
CMO: Tony L. Berg, M.D., Chief of Staff
CIO: Gary Burrus, Director Information Technology
CHR: Susan Hughes, Interim Director Human Resources
CNO: Julie Hennebold, R.N., Interim Chief Nursing Officer
Web address: www.winnerregional.org
Control: Other not–for–profit (including NFP Corporation) **Service:** General Medical and Surgical

Staffed Beds: 104 Admissions: 818 Census: 77 Outpatient Visits: 11194 Total Expense ($000): 19749 Payroll Expense ($000): 7778 Personnel: 238

YANKTON—Yankton County

⊞ **AVERA SACRED HEART HOSPITAL (430012)**, 501 Summit Avenue, Zip 57078–3855; tel. 605/668–8000, (Total facility includes 187 beds in nursing home–type unit) **A**1 2 5 9 10 19 **F**2 3 6 8 10 13 15 18 20 28 29 30 34 35 40 45 46 47 48 51 53 57 59 60 62 63 64 68 70 73 76 77 78 79 81 82 84 85 86 89 93 96 104 107 108 110 111 115 118 119 120 121 123 128 129 130 132 133 146 147 148 **S** Avera Health, Sioux Falls, SD
Primary Contact: Douglas R. Ekeren, Interim Chief Executive Officer
COO: Douglas R. Ekeren, Vice President Planning and Development
CFO: Jamie Schaefer, Vice President Finance
CMO: Barry A. Graham, M.D., Vice President Medical Affairs
CIO: Kathy Quinlivan, Director Management Information Systems
CHR: Jane E. Miller, Human Resources Officer
CNO: Barbara R. Larson, R.N., Vice President Patient Care Services
Web address: www.averasacredheart.com
Control: Church–operated, Nongovernment, not–for profit **Service:** General Medical and Surgical

Staffed Beds: 293 Admissions: 3556 Census: 221 Outpatient Visits: 96343 Births: 575 Total Expense ($000): 82928 Payroll Expense ($000): 36850 Personnel: 627

LEWIS AND CLARK SPECIALTY HOSPITAL (430096), 2601 Fox Run Parkway, Zip 57078–5341; tel. 605/665–5100, (Nonreporting) **A**9 10
Primary Contact: Michelle J. Jordan, Administrator
CFO: Terry Steichen, Business Officer
CHR: Elizabeth Steichen, Human Resources
Web address: www.lewisandclarkspecialty.com
Control: Corporation, Investor–owned, for–profit **Service:** Other specialty

Staffed Beds: 6

Many Facility Codes have changed. Please refer to the AHA Guide Code Chart. © 2014 AHA Guide

SD

TENNESSEE

ASHLAND CITY—Cheatham County

★ **TRISTAR CENTENNIAL MEDICAL CENTER AT ASHLAND CITY (441311)**, 313 North Main Street, Zip 37015–1347; tel. 615/792–3030, (Nonreporting) **A**9 10 18 **S** HCA, Nashville, TN
Primary Contact: Heather J. Rohan, Chief Executive Officer
COO: Brian Marger, Chief Operating Officer
CFO: David A. Summers, Chief Financial Officer
CMO: Divya Shroff, Chief Medical Officer
CIO: David Archer, Director Information Systems
CNO: Darrell White, R.N., Administrator and Chief Nursing Officer
Web address: www.tristarashlandcity.com/
Control: Corporation, Investor–owned, for–profit **Service:** General Medical and Surgical

Staffed Beds: 8

ATHENS—Mcminn County

☒ **STARR REGIONAL MEDICAL CENTER (440068)**, 1114 West Madison Avenue, Zip 37303–4150, Mailing Address: P.O. Box 250, Zip 37371–0250; tel. 423/745–1411 **A**1 9 10 **F**3 9 11 13 15 28 29 30 31 34 35 37 40 41 43 44 45 46 48 50 51 54 57 59 61 64 65 68 70 73 74 75 76 77 78 79 81 84 85 86 87 89 90 93 102 107 108 110 111 114 115 116 117 118 119 126 129 130 132 135 146 147 148 **S** LifePoint Hospitals, Inc., Brentwood, TN
Primary Contact: Richard Grogan, Interim Chief Executive Officer
CFO: David Alley, Chief Financial Officer
CNO: Margie Brusseau, R.N., Chief Nursing Officer
Web address: www.starrregional.com
Control: Corporation, Investor–owned, for–profit **Service:** General Medical and Surgical

Staffed Beds: 63 **Admissions:** 2311 **Census:** 24 **Outpatient Visits:** 88905 **Births:** 423 **Total Expense ($000):** 42441 **Payroll Expense ($000):** 14341 **Personnel:** 269

BARTLETT—Shelby County

☒ **SAINT FRANCIS HOSPITAL–BARTLETT (440228)**, 2986 Kate Bond Road, Zip 38133–4003; tel. 901/820–7000, (Nonreporting) **A**1 9 10 **S** TENET Healthcare Corporation, Dallas, TX
Primary Contact: Jeremy Clark, Chief Executive Officer
COO: Gwen Bonner, Chief Operating Officer
CFO: Tina Kovacs, Chief Financial Officer
CMO: Mahmood Ali, President Medical Staff
CIO: Mark Lawrence, Director Information Systems
CHR: Bill Stone, Chief Human Resources Officer
CNO: Kris Cherry, Chief Nursing Officer
Web address: www.saintfrancisbartlett.com
Control: Corporation, Investor–owned, for–profit **Service:** General Medical and Surgical

Staffed Beds: 100

BOLIVAR—Hardeman County

☒ **BOLIVAR GENERAL HOSPITAL (440181)**, 650 Nuckolls Road, Zip 38008–1532, Mailing Address: P.O. Box 509, Zip 38008–0509; tel. 731/658–3100 **A**1 9 10 **F**3 9 11 13 15 28 29 30 44 45 57 59 64 75 81 87 93 107 119 130 132 133 146 **S** West Tennessee Healthcare, Jackson, TN
Primary Contact: Ruby Kirby, Administrator
CFO: Terry Swindell, Controller
CMO: Suara Rahaman, M.D., Chief Medical Staff
CNO: Angela Lacy, Director of Nursing
Web address: www.wth.net
Control: Hospital district or authority, Government, nonfederal **Service:** General Medical and Surgical

Staffed Beds: 21 **Admissions:** 234 **Census:** 2 **Outpatient Visits:** 14794 **Births:** 2 **Total Expense ($000):** 7088 **Payroll Expense ($000):** 2801 **Personnel:** 66

☐ **WESTERN MENTAL HEALTH INSTITUTE (444008)**, 11100 Old Highway 64, West, Zip 38008–1554; tel. 731/228–2000, (Nonreporting) **A**1 10
Primary Contact: Roger Pursley, Chief Executive Officer
CFO: Richard Taylor, Chief Financial Officer
CMO: Doug King, M.D., Director Clinical Services
CIO: Earl Bates, Director Information Technology
CHR: Barry Young, Director Human Resources
Control: State–Government, nonfederal **Service:** Psychiatric

Staffed Beds: 247

BRISTOL—Sullivan County

☒ **SELECT SPECIALTY HOSPITAL–TRI CITIES (442016)**, One Medical Park Boulevard, 5th Floor, Zip 37620–8964; tel. 423/844–5900, (Nonreporting) **A**1 9 10 **S** Select Medical Corporation, Mechanicsburg, PA
Primary Contact: Eric Carroll, Chief Executive Officer
CMO: John Byers, M.D., Medical Director
CHR: William G. Ison, Human Resources Manager
CNO: Jeffrey Radford, Chief Nursing Officer
Web address: www.selectspecialtyhospitals.com/company/locations/tricities.aspx
Control: Corporation, Investor–owned, for–profit **Service:** Long–Term Acute Care hospital

Staffed Beds: 33

☒ **WELLMONT BRISTOL REGIONAL MEDICAL CENTER (440012)**, 1 Medical Park Boulevard, Zip 37620–7430; tel. 423/844–1121 **A**1 2 3 5 9 10 **F**3 8 11 13 15 17 18 20 22 24 28 29 30 31 34 35 37 38 39 40 43 44 46 47 49 51 54 56 57 58 59 60 61 62 63 64 67 70 73 74 75 76 77 78 79 81 82 83 84 85 86 87 89 90 91 92 93 94 96 97 98 99 100 101 102 103 104 106 107 108 110 111 114 115 118 119 120 121 123 124 126 129 130 131 132 135 145 146 147 148 **P**5 **S** Wellmont Health System, Kingsport, TN
Primary Contact: Greg Neal, President
COO: Christopher Hobson, Chief Operating Officer
CFO: Dale Poe, Vice President Hospital Division
CIO: Will Showalter, Senior Vice President Information Technology
CHR: Hamlin J. Wilson, Senior Vice President Human Resources
CNO: Timothy Craig Anderson, Jr., Chief Nursing Officer
Web address: www.wellmont.org
Control: Other not–for–profit (including NFP Corporation) **Service:** General Medical and Surgical

Staffed Beds: 312 **Admissions:** 15484 **Census:** 199 **Outpatient Visits:** 131701 **Births:** 925 **Total Expense ($000):** 215451 **Payroll Expense ($000):** 70237 **Personnel:** 1628

CAMDEN—Benton County

☒ **CAMDEN GENERAL HOSPITAL (441316)**, 175 Hospital Drive, Zip 38320–1617; tel. 731/584–6135 **A**1 9 10 18 **F**3 15 29 30 35 40 44 57 59 64 75 79 81 85 87 93 107 111 119 130 132 133 146 **S** West Tennessee Healthcare, Jackson, TN
Primary Contact: Denny R. Smith, Administrator
COO: James E. Ross, Chief Operating Officer
CFO: Terry Swindell, Chief Financial Officer
CMO: Jon R. Winter, D.O., Chief of Staff
CIO: Jeff Frieling, Vice President Information Systems
CHR: Barry Phillips, Executive Director Human Resources
Web address: www.wth.net
Control: Hospital district or authority, Government, nonfederal **Service:** General Medical and Surgical

Staffed Beds: 12 **Admissions:** 318 **Census:** 5 **Outpatient Visits:** 14503 **Births:** 0 **Total Expense ($000):** 6938 **Payroll Expense ($000):** 2921 **Personnel:** 71

CARTHAGE—Smith County

☒ **RIVERVIEW REGIONAL MEDICAL CENTER (441307)**, 158 Hospital Drive, Zip 37030–1096; tel. 615/735–1560, (Nonreporting) **A**1 9 10 18 **S** LifePoint Hospitals, Inc., Brentwood, TN
Primary Contact: Rod Harkleroad, R.N., Administrator
CHR: Gina Anderson, Human Resources Officer
CNO: Kathy Lewis, Chief Nursing Officer and Vice President Clinical Services
Web address: www.myriverviewmedical.com/
Control: Corporation, Investor–owned, for–profit **Service:** General Medical and Surgical

Staffed Beds: 25

TN

CELINA—Clay County

☐ **CUMBERLAND RIVER HOSPITAL (440141)**, 100 Old Jefferson Street, Zip 38551–4040, Mailing Address: P. O. Box 427, Zip 38551–0427; tel. 931/243–3581, (Nonreporting) **A**1 9 10
Primary Contact: Andrea Rich–McLerran, Chief Administrative Officer
CFO: Tricia Strong, Chief Financial Officer
CMO: Harry Horne, D.O., Chief of Staff
CIO: Margie Boone, Registered Health Information Technician
CHR: Susan Renodin Deaton, Chief Human Resources Officer
CNO: Patsy Marinich, Chief Nursing Officer
Web address: www.cumberlandriverhospital.com
Control: Corporation, Investor–owned, for–profit **Service:** General Medical and Surgical

Staffed Beds: 34

CENTERVILLE—Hickman County

✠ **SAINT THOMAS HICKMAN HOSPITAL (441300)**, 135 East Swan Street, Zip 37033–1417; tel. 931/729–4271, (Total facility includes 40 beds in nursing home–type unit) **A**1 9 10 18 **F**29 30 34 35 40 41 45 56 57 59 62 64 65 67 77 81 86 89 90 93 104 107 119 127 128 130 133 135 148 **P**6 **S** Ascension Health, Saint Louis, MO
Primary Contact: Jack M. Keller, Chief Executive Officer
COO: Robin Crowell, Chief Nursing Officer and Chief Operating Officer
CFO: Bailey Pratt, Chief Financial Officer
CMO: Zachary Hutchens, M.D., Chief Medical Officer
CHR: Patty Matney, Human Resources Consultant
CNO: Robin Crowell, Chief Nursing Officer and Chief Operating Officer
Web address: www.hickmanhospital.com
Control: Other not–for–profit (including NFP Corporation) **Service:** General Medical and Surgical

Staffed Beds: 65 Admissions: 87 Census: 31 Outpatient Visits: 13176 Births: 0 Total Expense ($000): 9223 Payroll Expense ($000): 6520 Personnel: 110

CHATTANOOGA—Hamilton County

✠ **ERLANGER MEDICAL CENTER (440104)**, 975 East Third Street, Zip 37403–2147; tel. 423/778–7000, (Includes ERLANGER EAST HOSPITAL, 1755 Gunbarrel Road, Zip 37421; tel. 423/778–8700; Teresa Radeker, Administrator; ERLANGER NORTH HOSPITAL, 632 Morrison Springs Road, Zip 37415; tel. 615/778–3300; T. C. THOMPSON CHILDREN'S HOSPITAL, 910 Blackford Street, Zip 37403; tel. 615/778–6011; Cynthia Rhodes, Administrator; WILLIE D. MILLER EYE CENTER, 975 East Third Street, Zip 37403; tel. 615/778–6011) **A**1 2 3 5 9 10 **F**3 5 7 8 9 10 11 12 13 14 15 16 17 18 19 20 21 22 23 24 25 26 27 28 29 30 31 32 34 35 36 37 38 39 40 41 42 43 44 45 46 47 48 49 50 51 52 53 54 55 56 57 58 59 60 61 62 63 64 65 66 68 70 71 72 73 74 75 76 77 78 79 80 81 82 83 84 85 86 87 88 89 91 92 93 94 97 98 99 100 101 102 103 104 105 107 108 110 111 114 115 116 117 118 119 120 121 123 124 126 127 129 130 131 132 133 134 135 138 141 142 143 144 145 146 147 148 **P**2 4 6 **S** Erlanger Health System, Chattanooga, TN
Primary Contact: Kevin M. Spiegel, FACHE, Chief Executive Officer
COO: Robert E. Brooks, FACHE, Executive Vice President and Chief Operating Officer
CFO: J. Britton Tabor, Senior VP and Chief Financial Officer
CMO: James Creel, M.D., Chief Medical Officer
CIO: Laurene Vamprine, Senior Vice President Information Systems
CHR: Gregg Gentry, Senior Vice President Human Resources
CNO: Janice Colleen Keys, MSN, Chief Nurse Executive
Web address: www.erlanger.org
Control: Hospital district or authority, Government, nonfederal **Service:** General Medical and Surgical

Staffed Beds: 540 Admissions: 28126 Census: 371 Outpatient Visits: 374021 Births: 5223 Total Expense ($000): 545007 Payroll Expense ($000): 234541 Personnel: 4116

ERLANGER WOMEN'S EAST HOSPITAL See Erlanger East Hospital

✠ **HEALTHSOUTH CHATTANOOGA REHABILITATION HOSPITAL (443032)**, 2412 McCallie Avenue, Zip 37404–3398; tel. 423/698–0221 **A**1 10 **F**29 34 90 92 95 96 130 132 148 **S** HEALTHSOUTH Corporation, Birmingham, AL
Primary Contact: Scott Rowe, Chief Executive Officer
COO: Scott Rowe, Chief Executive Officer
CFO: Karen Klassen, Controller
CMO: Amjad Munir, M.D., Medical Director
CIO: Denise Smith, Director Health Information
CHR: Deborah Hersom, Director Human Resources
CNO: Michelle Cowart, R.N., Chief Nursing Officer
Web address: www.healthsouthchattanooga.com
Control: Corporation, Investor–owned, for–profit **Service:** Rehabilitation

Staffed Beds: 50 Admissions: 1019 Census: 36 Outpatient Visits: 0 Births: 0 Total Expense ($000): 13321 Payroll Expense ($000): 6385 Personnel: 104

✠ **KINDRED HOSPITAL–CHATTANOOGA (442007)**, 709 Walnut Street, Zip 37402–1916; tel. 423/266–7721, (Nonreporting) **A**1 9 10 **S** Kindred Healthcare, Louisville, KY
Primary Contact: William J. Bryant, Chief Executive Officer
COO: Rick Rheinheimer, Chief Clinical Officer
CFO: Julia Smith, Chief Financial Officer
CMO: Randy Heisser, M.D., Medical Director
CHR: Kellie McCampbell, Coordinator Human Resources
Web address: www.kindredchattanooga.com/
Control: Corporation, Investor–owned, for–profit **Service:** Long–Term Acute Care hospital

Staffed Beds: 44

✠ **MEMORIAL HEALTH CARE SYSTEM (440091)**, 2525 De Sales Avenue, Zip 37404–1161; tel. 423/495–2525, (Includes MEMORIAL HOSPITAL HIXSON, 2051 Hamill Road, Hixson, Zip 37343–4026; tel. 423/495–7100), (Nonreporting) **A**1 2 3 5 9 10 **S** Catholic Health Initiatives, Englewood, CO
Primary Contact: James M. Hobson, Chief Executive Officer
CFO: Cheryl A. Sadro, Vice President and Chief Financial Officer
CMO: Kevin Lewis, M.D., Chief Medical Officer
CHR: Brad W. Pope, Vice President Human Resources
CNO: Danine Watson, R.N., Interim Vice President Nursing and Chief Nursing Officer
Web address: www.memorial.org
Control: Church–operated, Nongovernment, not–for profit **Service:** General Medical and Surgical

Staffed Beds: 336

☐ **MOCCASIN BEND MENTAL HEALTH INSTITUTE (444002)**, 100 Moccasin Bend Road, Zip 37405–4415; tel. 423/265–2271 **A**1 10 **F**30 34 50 56 57 59 65 75 77 86 87 98 100 101 102 103 130 132 135 143 146
Primary Contact: William L. Ventress, Chief Executive Officer
COO: Rob Cotterman, Assistant Superintendent Program Services
CFO: Sylvia Harris, Fiscal Director
CMO: Terry R. Holmes, M.D., Clinical Director
CIO: Mickey Williams, Manager Information Technology
CHR: Cynthia Honeycutt, Director Human Resources
CNO: Charlynne Parson, Nurse Executive
Web address: www.state.tn.us/mental/mhs/mbhmhi/moc.htm
Control: State–Government, nonfederal **Service:** Psychiatric

Staffed Beds: 150 Admissions: 2768 Census: 131 Outpatient Visits: 0 Births: 0 Total Expense ($000): 28432 Payroll Expense ($000): 15486 Personnel: 420

✠ **PARKRIDGE MEDICAL CENTER (440156)**, 2333 McCallie Avenue, Zip 37404–3258; tel. 423/698–6061, (Includes EAST RIDGE HOSPITAL, 941 Spring Creek Road, East Ridge, Zip 37412, Mailing Address: P.O. Box 91229, Zip 37412–6229; tel. 423/855–3500; Jarrett B. Millsaps, Jr., FACHE, Chief Executive Officer; PARKRIDGE EAST HOSPITAL, 941 Spring Creek Road, Zip 37412–3909; tel. 423/894–7870; Jarrett B. Millsaps, Jr., FACHE, Chief Executive Officer; PARKRIDGE VALLEY CHILD AND ADOLESCENT CAMPUS, 2200 Morris Hill Road, Zip 37421; tel. 423/894–4220; Brennan Francois, Chief Executive Officer) **A**1 2 3 5 9 10 **F**3 5 13 15 18 20 22 24 26 28 29 30 31 39 40 45 46 49 50 51 55 56 57 58 59 60 70 72 75 76 77 78 79 81 85 90 93 98 99 103 104 105 106 107 108 110 111 114 115 119 120 121 124 126 129 130 131 132 146 148 **S** HCA, Nashville, TN
Primary Contact: Darrell W. Moore, Chief Executive Officer
COO: Jim L. Coleman, Jr., Chief Operating Officer
CFO: Tom Jackson, Chief Financial Officer
CMO: Gary Lanham, Chief Medical Officer
CIO: David Cornelius, Director Information Systems
CHR: Carole Hoffman, Vice President
CNO: Jerri C. Underwood, R.N., Chief Nursing Officer
Web address: www.parkridgemedicalcenter.com
Control: Corporation, Investor–owned, for–profit **Service:** General Medical and Surgical

Staffed Beds: 464 Admissions: 15514 Census: 270 Outpatient Visits: 129882 Births: 1564 Total Expense ($000): 223591 Payroll Expense ($000): 80318 Personnel: 1376

✠ △ **SISKIN HOSPITAL FOR PHYSICAL REHABILITATION (443025)**, One Siskin Plaza, Zip 37403–1306; tel. 423/634–1200, (Total facility includes 29 beds in nursing home–type unit) **A**1 7 10 **F**29 35 53 59 64 75 77 82 90 93 95 128 130 132 146 148 **P**4
Primary Contact: Carol Sim, President and Chief Executive Officer
COO: Linda Knudson Lind, Senior Vice President and Chief Operating Officer
CFO: Carol Arnhart, Controller and Chief Financial Officer
CMO: David N. Bowers, M.D., Medical Director
CIO: Baret H. Avery, Chief Information Officer
CHR: M. Debby Barker, Director Human Resources
CNO: Karla Woodby, R.N., Director of Nursing
Web address: www.siskinrehab.org
Control: Other not–for–profit (including NFP Corporation) **Service:** Rehabilitation

Staffed Beds: 109 Admissions: 2019 Census: 77 Outpatient Visits: 33440 Births: 0 Total Expense ($000): 28939 Payroll Expense ($000): 15918 Personnel: 261

T. C. THOMPSON CHILDREN'S HOSPITAL See Erlanger Medical Center

WILLIE D. MILLER EYE CENTER See Erlanger Medical Center

Many Facility Codes have changed. Please refer to the AHA Guide Code Chart. © 2014 AHA Guide

TN

COVINGTON—Tipton County

✠ **BAPTIST MEMORIAL HOSPITAL–TIPTON (440131)**, 1995 Highway 51 South, Zip 38019–3635; tel. 901/476–2621 **A**1 9 10 **F**3 11 15 29 30 31 34 35 40 45 55 57 58 59 65 70 74 75 76 77 78 79 81 85 87 89 93 100 107 108 110 111 114 115 117 119 120 121 129 130 132 135 146 148 **P**6 **S** Baptist Memorial Health Care Corporation, Memphis, TN
Primary Contact: Samuel Lynd, Administrator and Chief Executive Officer
CFO: Monique Hart, Chief Financial Officer
CMO: Kenneth Afenya, M.D., Chief of Staff
CHR: Myra Cousar, Director Human Resources
CNO: Cheryl Furdge Berry, Chief Nursing Officer
Web address: www.baptistonline.org/tipton/
Control: Other not–for–profit (including NFP Corporation) **Service:** General Medical and Surgical

Staffed Beds: 44 **Admissions:** 1333 **Census:** 11 **Outpatient Visits:** 47599 **Births:** 412 **Total Expense ($000):** 70849 **Payroll Expense ($000):** 17400 **Personnel:** 288

CROSSVILLE—Cumberland County

✠ **CUMBERLAND MEDICAL CENTER (440009)**, 421 South Main Street, Zip 38555–5031; tel. 931/484–9511 **A**1 2 9 10 20 **F**3 11 13 15 18 20 28 29 30 31 34 35 40 41 45 47 48 49 51 53 57 58 59 62 68 70 74 75 76 77 78 79 81 82 85 86 87 93 97 107 108 110 111 114 119 120 121 129 130 132 135 146 148 **S** Covenant Health, Knoxville, TN
Primary Contact: Jeremy Biggs, President and Chief Administrative Officer
COO: Larry E. Moore, Executive Vice President and Chief Operating Officer and Chief Financial Officer
CFO: Larry E. Moore, Executive Vice President and Chief Operating Officer and Chief Financial Officer
CMO: Amanda Mandy Grubb, M.D., Chief Medical Officer
CIO: Joe Lowe, Director Management Information Systems
CHR: Angela J. Chaffin, Director Human Resources
CNO: Rebecca Foster, Chief Nursing Officer
Web address: www.cmchealthcare.org
Control: Other not–for–profit (including NFP Corporation) **Service:** General Medical and Surgical

Staffed Beds: 122 **Admissions:** 5014 **Census:** 60 **Outpatient Visits:** 89893 **Births:** 642 **Total Expense ($000):** 96238 **Payroll Expense ($000):** 40877 **Personnel:** 895

DAYTON—Rhea County

✠ **RHEA MEDICAL CENTER (441310)**, 9400 Rhea County Highway, Zip 37321–7922; tel. 423/775–1121, (Nonreporting) **A**1 9 10 18 **S** QHR, Brentwood, TN
Primary Contact: Kennedy L. Croom, Jr., Administrator and Chief Executive Officer
CFO: Harv Sanders, Chief Financial Officer
CMO: Michael Prostko, M.D., Chief of Staff
CHR: Peri Meadows, Director Human Resources
Web address: www.rheamedical.org
Control: County–Government, nonfederal **Service:** General Medical and Surgical

Staffed Beds: 25

DICKSON—Dickson County

✠ **TRISTAR HORIZON MEDICAL CENTER (440046)**, 111 Highway 70 East, Zip 37055–2080; tel. 615/446–0446, (Nonreporting) **A**1 2 9 10 **S** HCA, Nashville, TN
Primary Contact: John A. Marshall, Chief Executive Officer
CFO: Clarence Gray, Chief Financial Officer
CIO: Rick Stoker, Director Management Information Systems
CHR: Sheila Kight, Director Human Resources
CNO: Gina Bullington, Chief Nursing Officer
Web address: www.horizonmedicalcenter.com
Control: Corporation, Investor–owned, for–profit **Service:** General Medical and Surgical

Staffed Beds: 130

DYERSBURG—Dyer County

✠ **DYERSBURG REGIONAL MEDICAL CENTER (440072)**, 400 East Tickle Street, Zip 38024–3120; tel. 731/285–2410, (Nonreporting) **A**1 9 10 20 **S** Community Health Systems, Inc., Franklin, TN
Primary Contact: Ben Youree, Chief Executive Officer
CFO: Meredith Malone, Chief Financial Officer
CMO: Darren Johnson, M.D., Chief of Staff
CIO: Russ Shephard, Senior Systems Analyst
CHR: Beverly Ray, Director Human Resources
Web address: www.dyersburgregionalmc.com
Control: Corporation, Investor–owned, for–profit **Service:** General Medical and Surgical

Staffed Beds: 105

EAST RIDGE—Hamilton County

EAST RIDGE HOSPITAL See Parkridge Medical Center, Chattanooga

ELIZABETHTON—Carter County

☐ **SYCAMORE SHOALS HOSPITAL (440018)**, 1501 West Elk Avenue, Zip 37643–2874; tel. 423/542–1300 **A**1 9 10 **F**3 11 15 18 29 30 34 35 40 44 45 48 49 50 53 54 56 57 61 62 63 64 68 70 75 77 78 79 81 85 87 93 98 103 107 110 111 115 119 132 135 146 147 148 **P**6 8 **S** Mountain States Health Alliance, Johnson City, TN
Primary Contact: Dwayne Taylor, Chief Executive Officer
COO: Melanie Stanton, R.N., Chief Nursing Officer
CFO: Bradley Logan, Chief Financial Officer
CMO: Morris H. Seligman, M.D., Chief Medical Officer and Chief Medical Information Officer
CIO: Paul Merrywell, Chief Information Officer
CHR: Sharon Sheppard, Manager Human Resources
Web address: www.msha.com
Control: Other not–for–profit (including NFP Corporation) **Service:** General Medical and Surgical

Staffed Beds: 74 **Admissions:** 3429 **Census:** 42 **Outpatient Visits:** 65623 **Births:** 130 **Total Expense ($000):** 39907 **Payroll Expense ($000):** 16594 **Personnel:** 279

ERIN—Houston County

✠ **HOUSTON COUNTY COMMUNITY HOSPITAL (440232)**, 5001 East Main Street, Zip 37061–4115, Mailing Address: P.O. Box 489, Zip 37061–0489; tel. 931/289–4211, (Data for 280 days) **A**1 9 10 18 **F**15 29 40 41 45 81 93 107 115 119 133
Primary Contact: Gladys Anderson, Chief Executive Officer
CFO: Shannon Allison, Chief Financial Officer
CMO: Erin Chambers, M.D., Chief Medical Officer
CHR: Reta Brady, Administrative Assistant and Manager Human Resources
Web address: www.pcmc–erintn.com/
Control: County–Government, nonfederal **Service:** General Medical and Surgical

Staffed Beds: 25 **Admissions:** 352 **Census:** 5 **Outpatient Visits:** 8660 **Births:** 0 **Total Expense ($000):** 4434 **Payroll Expense ($000):** 2070 **Personnel:** 85

ERWIN—Unicoi County

✠ **UNICOI COUNTY MEMORIAL HOSPITAL (440001)**, 100 Greenway Circle, Zip 37650–2196, Mailing Address: P.O. Box 802, Zip 37650–0802; tel. 423/743–3141, (Total facility includes 46 beds in nursing home–type unit) **A**1 9 10 **F**1 11 15 29 30 35 40 50 63 67 70 77 79 81 85 86 93 107 110 111 114 119 128 130 131 135 146 **P**6
Primary Contact: Tracy Byers, Chief Executive Officer
CFO: Toni Buchanan, Chief Financial Officer
CMO: Jose Picaza, M.D., Chief of Staff
CIO: G. Keith Tittle, Director Information Technology
CHR: Susan Broyles, Director Human Resources and Safety
CNO: Debra Troutman, Chief Nursing Officer
Web address: www.msha.com
Control: Other not–for–profit (including NFP Corporation) **Service:** General Medical and Surgical

Staffed Beds: 71 **Admissions:** 1020 **Census:** 55 **Outpatient Visits:** 29856 **Births:** 0 **Total Expense ($000):** 18674 **Payroll Expense ($000):** 7171 **Personnel:** 133

ETOWAH—Mcminn County

✠ **STARR REGIONAL MEDICAL CENTER–ETOWAH (440054)**, 886 Highway 411 North, Zip 37331–1912; tel. 423/263–3600, (Total facility includes 88 beds in nursing home–type unit) **A**1 9 10 **F**3 8 11 14 29 30 34 35 40 41 50 51 56 57 59 61 65 67 70 75 77 79 80 81 85 93 102 103 107 108 118 119 128 130 146 148 **S** LifePoint Hospitals, Inc., Brentwood, TN
Primary Contact: Richard Grogan, Interim Chief Executive Officer
COO: Christopher Zeringue, Chief Operating Officer
CFO: David Alley, Chief Financial Officer
CMO: David Robins, D.O., Chief of Staff
CIO: Susan Hicks, Information Technology Director
CHR: Cathy Himes, Director Human Resources
CNO: Margie Brusseau, R.N., Chief Nursing Officer
Web address: www.starrregional.com
Control: Corporation, Investor–owned, for–profit **Service:** General Medical and Surgical

Staffed Beds: 140 **Admissions:** 1222 **Census:** 101 **Outpatient Visits:** 28528 **Births:** 0 **Total Expense ($000):** 23478 **Payroll Expense ($000):** 10344 **Personnel:** 185

Many Facility Codes have changed. Please refer to the AHA Guide Code Chart. © 2014 AHA Guide

TN

FAYETTEVILLE—Lincoln County

⊞ **LINCOLN COUNTY HEALTH SYSTEM (440102)**, 106 Medical Center Boulevard, Zip 37334–2684; tel. 931/438–1100, (Total facility includes 264 beds in nursing home–type unit) **A**1 9 10 **F**3 7 10 11 13 15 18 29 30 34 35 40 45 50 53 56 57 59 62 63 64 67 68 70 74 75 76 77 79 81 85 93 98 103 104 107 108 110 111 114 118 119 128 129 132 135 143 146 148 **P**6 **S** QHR, Brentwood, TN
Primary Contact: Jamie W. Guin, Jr., Chief Executive Officer
CFO: Michael Harbor, Chief Financial Officer
CMO: Richard Cline, D.O., Chief of Staff
CHR: Wendy Nogler, Director Human Resources
CNO: Vicky Groce, Chief Nursing Officer
Web address: www.lchealthsystem.com
Control: County–Government, nonfederal **Service:** General Medical and Surgical

Staffed Beds: 323 Admissions: 2585 Census: 236 Outpatient Visits: 46546 Births: 244 Total Expense ($000): 42980 Payroll Expense ($000): 19303 Personnel: 509

FRANKLIN—Williamson County

☐ **ROLLING HILLS HOSPITAL (444007)**, 2014 Quail Hollow Circle, Zip 37067–5967; tel. 615/628–5700, (Nonreporting) **A**1 10 **S** Universal Health Services, Inc., King of Prussia, PA
Primary Contact: Richard Clark, Chief Executive Officer
Web address: www.rollinghillshospital.org/
Control: Corporation, Investor–owned, for–profit **Service:** Psychiatric

Staffed Beds: 80

☐ **WILLIAMSON MEDICAL CENTER (440029)**, 4321 Carothers Parkway, Zip 37067–8542; tel. 615/435–5000 **A**1 2 9 10 **F**3 7 11 13 15 17 18 20 22 28 29 30 31 34 35 40 43 45 49 54 57 59 64 67 70 72 74 75 76 78 79 80 81 85 86 87 93 97 102 107 108 110 111 114 115 118 119 124 126 129 130 132 135 146 148 **P**6 8
Primary Contact: Donald Webb, Chief Executive Officer
COO: Julie Miller, Chief Operating Officer
CMO: Starling C. Evins, M.D., Chief of Staff
CIO: Steve Dycus, Director Marketing and Public Relations
CHR: Phyllis Molyneux, Associate Administrator Human Resources and Education
Web address: www.williamsonmedicalcenter.org
Control: County–Government, nonfederal **Service:** General Medical and Surgical

Staffed Beds: 185 Admissions: 9563 Census: 97 Outpatient Visits: 106919 Births: 1521 Total Expense ($000): 152915 Payroll Expense ($000): 64836 Personnel: 1069

GALLATIN—Sumner County

⊞ **SUMNER REGIONAL MEDICAL CENTER (440003)**, 555 Hartsville Pike, Zip 37066–2400, Mailing Address: P.O. Box 1558, Zip 37066–1558; tel. 615/452–4210, (Nonreporting) **A**1 2 9 10 **S** LifePoint Hospitals, Inc., Brentwood, TN
Primary Contact: Susan M. Peach, R.N., Chief Executive Officer
COO: Michael Herman, Chief Operating Officer
CIO: Vickie Carter, Information Systems Director
CHR: Ryan Williams, Human Resources Director
CNO: Anne Melton, Chief Nursing Officer
Web address: www.mysumnermedical.com
Control: Corporation, Investor–owned, for–profit **Service:** General Medical and Surgical

Staffed Beds: 145

GERMANTOWN—Shelby County

⊞ △ **BAPTIST REHABILITATION–GERMANTOWN (440147)**, 2100 Exeter Road, Zip 38138–3978; tel. 901/757–1350, (Total facility includes 18 beds in nursing home–type unit) **A**1 7 9 10 **F**3 29 30 34 35 54 57 59 64 68 75 77 79 86 87 90 91 92 93 96 107 111 114 119 128 130 131 132 135 143 146 148 **S** Baptist Memorial Health Care Corporation, Memphis, TN
Primary Contact: Janice Hill, Chief Executive Officer and Administrator
CFO: Catherine Saltz, Chief Financial Officer
CMO: Sunita Jain, M.D., Chief Medical Officer
CHR: Pam Hill, Director Human Resources
CNO: Donna Hale, Chief Nursing Officer
Web address: www.baptistonline.org/germantown/
Control: Other not–for–profit (including NFP Corporation) **Service:** Rehabilitation

Staffed Beds: 68 Admissions: 1061 Census: 37 Outpatient Visits: 11184 Births: 0 Total Expense ($000): 24241 Payroll Expense ($000): 12134 Personnel: 215

METHODIST LE BONHEUR GERMANTOWN HOSPITAL See Methodist Healthcare Memphis Hospitals, Memphis

GREENEVILLE—Greene County

⊞ **LAUGHLIN MEMORIAL HOSPITAL (440025)**, 1420 Tusculum Boulevard, Zip 37745–5825; tel. 423/787–5000, (Total facility includes 90 beds in nursing home–type unit) **A**1 2 9 10 19 **F**3 11 12 13 15 18 20 28 29 31 34 35 37 40 45 46 47 48 49 50 56 57 59 62 64 68 70 73 74 75 76 77 78 79 81 85 86 87 89 93 97 107 108 110 111 114 115 118 119 120 121 123 128 129 130 131 132 134 135 146 147 148 **P**6
Primary Contact: Charles H. Whitfield, Jr., President and Chief Executive Officer
CFO: Mark Compton, Chief Financial Officer
CMO: Mark Patterson, M.D., Chief Medical Officer
CIO: Rex Arrington, Chief Information Officer
CHR: Robert Roark, Director Human Resources
CNO: Brenda Cannon, R.N., Director of Nursing
Web address: www.laughlinmemorial.org
Control: Other not–for–profit (including NFP Corporation) **Service:** General Medical and Surgical

Staffed Beds: 224 Admissions: 3743 Census: 122 Outpatient Visits: 102400 Births: 229 Total Expense ($000): 72438 Payroll Expense ($000): 31764 Personnel: 610

⊞ **TAKOMA REGIONAL HOSPITAL (440050)**, 401 Takoma Avenue, Zip 37743–4647; tel. 423/639–3151 **A**1 9 10 **F**3 11 13 15 29 30 34 40 45 50 57 59 70 75 76 77 79 81 87 89 90 93 97 98 101 102 103 104 107 108 110 111 119 129 130 131 144 146 148 **S** Adventist Health System Sunbelt Health Care Corporation, Altamonte Springs, FL
Primary Contact: Daniel Wolcott, President
CFO: Steven Miller, Chief Financial Officer
CMO: Frederick Myers, M.D., Chief Medical Officer
CHR: Jack Lister, Director Human Resources
CNO: Tammy Albright, Chief Nursing Officer
Web address: www.takoma.org
Control: Church–operated, Nongovernment, not–for profit **Service:** General Medical and Surgical

Staffed Beds: 100 Admissions: 2347 Census: 29 Outpatient Visits: 176783 Births: 302 Total Expense ($000): 51579 Payroll Expense ($000): 22559 Personnel: 433

HARRIMAN—Roane County

⊞ **ROANE MEDICAL CENTER (440031)**, 8045 Roane Medical Center Drive, Zip 37748–8333; tel. 865/316–1000 **A**1 9 10 **F**3 11 15 18 20 28 29 40 45 57 70 77 79 81 85 93 107 108 110 111 119 129 130 133 146 **S** Covenant Health, Knoxville, TN
Primary Contact: Gaye Jolly, FACHE, President/Chief Administrative Officer
COO: Jason B. Pilant, Chief Operating Officer
CFO: Julie Utterback, Chief Financial Officer
CMO: Mark Browne, M.D., Chief Medical Officer
CIO: Mike Ward, Senior Vice President Chief Information Officer
CHR: Randall Carr, Director Human Resources
CNO: Carolyn Shipley, Chief Nursing Officer
Web address: www.roanemedical.com
Control: Other not–for–profit (including NFP Corporation) **Service:** General Medical and Surgical

Staffed Beds: 54 Admissions: 1958 Census: 24 Outpatient Visits: 55946 Births: 0 Total Expense ($000): 34898 Payroll Expense ($000): 11882 Personnel: 226

HARTSVILLE—Trousdale County

⊞ **TROUSDALE MEDICAL CENTER (441301)**, 500 Church Street, Zip 37074–1744; tel. 615/374–2221, (Nonreporting) **A**1 9 10 18 **S** LifePoint Hospitals, Inc., Brentwood, TN
Primary Contact: Rod Harkleroad, R.N., Chief Executive Officer
COO: William D. Mize, Chief Operating Officer
CFO: David Wilhoite, CPA, Senior Vice President Finance and Chief Financial Officer
CIO: David Young, Senior Vice President Planning and Technology
CHR: Amy Overstreet, Director Human Resources
Web address: www.mytrousdalemedical.com
Control: Corporation, Investor–owned, for–profit **Service:** General Medical and Surgical

Staffed Beds: 25

TN

HENDERSONVILLE—Sumner County

⊠ **TRISTAR HENDERSONVILLE MEDICAL CENTER (440194)**, 355 New Shackle Island Road, Zip 37075–2479; tel. 615/338–1000 **A**1 9 10 **F**3 13 15 18 20 22 29 30 34 40 42 45 46 49 50 51 58 64 70 74 76 77 79 81 82 84 85 93 107 108 110 111 114 115 119 146 **P**3 6 **S** HCA, Nashville, TN
Primary Contact: Regina Bartlett, Chief Executive Officer
COO: Cory Darling, Chief Operating Officer
CFO: Michael Morrison, Chief Financial Officer
CMO: Brett Branson, M.D., Chief of Staff
CIO: Hal Schultheis, Director Information Systems
CNO: Lisa Gann, R.N., Chief Nursing Officer
Web address: www.hendersonvillemedicalcenter.com
Control: Corporation, Investor–owned, for–profit **Service:** General Medical and Surgical

Staffed Beds: 96 **Admissions:** 5753 **Census:** 56 **Outpatient Visits:** 49142 **Births:** 800

HERMITAGE—Davidson County

⊠ **TRISTAR SUMMIT MEDICAL CENTER (440150)**, 5655 Frist Boulevard, Zip 37076–2053; tel. 615/316–3000 **A**1 2 9 10 **F**3 11 13 15 18 20 22 26 28 29 30 31 34 35 37 38 39 40 43 45 46 47 48 49 50 53 56 57 59 61 64 70 72 74 75 76 77 78 79 80 81 82 85 87 89 93 96 97 98 100 102 107 108 110 111 114 115 118 119 121 123 124 126 129 130 131 135 145 146 147 148 **P**6 **S** HCA, Nashville, TN
Primary Contact: Jeffrey T. Whitehorn, Chief Executive Officer
COO: Greg Caples, Chief Operating Officer
CFO: Bryan Shephard, Chief Financial Officer
CIO: Joel Bain, Director Information Services
CHR: Emily Dye, Vice President Human Resources
CNO: Mary Ann Angle, R.N., Chief Nursing Officer
Web address: www.summitmedctr.com
Control: Corporation, Investor–owned, for–profit **Service:** General Medical and Surgical

Staffed Beds: 188 **Admissions:** 10598 **Census:** 118 **Outpatient Visits:** 116867 **Births:** 1194 **Total Expense ($000):** 124073 **Payroll Expense ($000):** 45542 **Personnel:** 802

HUNTINGDON—Carroll County

⊠ **BAPTIST MEMORIAL HOSPITAL–HUNTINGDON (440016)**, 631 R.B. Wilson Drive, Zip 38344–1727; tel. 731/986–4461 **A**1 9 10 **F**3 7 15 28 29 30 32 34 35 40 50 57 59 61 62 63 64 65 68 70 75 77 79 81 82 85 86 87 93 102 107 111 115 118 119 130 131 132 133 135 146 148 **S** Baptist Memorial Health Care Corporation, Memphis, TN
Primary Contact: Susan M. Breeden, Administrator and Chief Executive Officer
CFO: Sharron Holland, Chief Financial Officer
CHR: Kim King, Director Human Resources and Public Relations
CNO: Kimberly Sanders, Chief Nursing Officer
Web address: www.baptistonline.org/huntingdon/
Control: Other not–for–profit (including NFP Corporation) **Service:** General Medical and Surgical

Staffed Beds: 33 **Admissions:** 629 **Census:** 8 **Outpatient Visits:** 17019 **Births:** 0 **Total Expense ($000):** 15972 **Payroll Expense ($000):** 6276 **Personnel:** 146

JACKSON—Madison County

⊠ △ **JACKSON–MADISON COUNTY GENERAL HOSPITAL (440002)**, 620 Skyline Drive, Zip 38301–3923; tel. 731/541–5000 **A**1 2 3 5 7 9 10 19 **F**3 7 8 11 13 15 17 18 20 22 24 26 28 29 30 31 34 35 40 44 45 46 47 48 49 51 53 56 57 58 59 60 63 64 65 68 70 72 74 75 76 77 78 79 80 81 82 83 84 85 86 87 88 89 90 92 93 94 96 97 107 108 110 111 112 115 116 117 118 119 120 121 124 126 129 130 131 132 135 145 146 147 148 **P**5 8 **S** West Tennessee Healthcare, Jackson, TN
Primary Contact: Bobby Arnold, President and Chief Executive Officer
COO: James E. Ross, Vice President and Chief Operating Officer
CFO: Jeff Blankenship, CPA, Vice President and Chief Financial Officer
CMO: Robert Gilroy, M.D., Chief of Staff
CIO: Jeff Frieling, Vice President and Chief Information Officer
CHR: Wendie Carlson, Vice President, Human Resources
CNO: Tina Prescott, Vice President, Hospital Services
Web address: www.wth.org
Control: Hospital district or authority, Government, nonfederal **Service:** General Medical and Surgical

Staffed Beds: 633 **Admissions:** 27920 **Census:** 425 **Outpatient Visits:** 183330 **Births:** 2974 **Total Expense ($000):** 491181 **Payroll Expense ($000):** 191122 **Personnel:** 3941

★ **PATHWAYS OF TENNESSEE (444010)**, 238 Summar Drive, Zip 38301–3906; tel. 731/541–8200 **A**10 **F**4 5 29 35 38 44 57 59 98 99 100 101 102 103 104 132 134 **S** West Tennessee Healthcare, Jackson, TN
Primary Contact: Pam Henson, Executive Director
CMO: Doug King, M.D., Medical Director
CIO: Jeff Frieling, Chief Information Officer
CHR: Wendy Carlson, Director Human Resources
Web address: www.wth.net
Control: Hospital district or authority, Government, nonfederal **Service:** Psychiatric

Staffed Beds: 25 **Admissions:** 607 **Census:** 8 **Outpatient Visits:** 129167 **Births:** 0 **Total Expense ($000):** 17002 **Payroll Expense ($000):** 9560 **Personnel:** 235

⊠ **REGIONAL HOSPITAL OF JACKSON (440189)**, 367 Hospital Boulevard, Zip 38305–2080; tel. 731/661–2000 **A**1 9 10 **F**3 11 13 15 18 20 22 28 29 30 31 34 35 39 40 45 49 50 51 56 57 59 60 62 64 68 70 74 75 76 77 78 79 80 81 82 85 87 89 92 93 97 107 108 110 111 112 114 115 119 129 130 132 146 147 **S** Community Health Systems, Inc., Franklin, TN
Primary Contact: Charles F. Miller, Chief Executive Officer
CFO: Richard Read, Chief Financial Officer
CMO: Michael Saridakis, M.D., Physician Adviser
CIO: Jimmy Anderson, Director of Information Systems
CHR: Barbara Euler, Director Human Resources
CNO: Jan Zimmer, R.N., Chief Nursing Officer
Web address: www.regionalhospitaljackson.com/Pages/Home.aspx
Control: Corporation, Investor–owned, for–profit **Service:** General Medical and Surgical

Staffed Beds: 134 **Admissions:** 5522 **Census:** 60 **Outpatient Visits:** 35216 **Births:** 317 **Personnel:** 485

JAMESTOWN—Fentress County

⊠ **JAMESTOWN REGIONAL MEDICAL CENTER (440083)**, 436 Central Avenue West, Zip 38556–3031, Mailing Address: P.O. Box 1500, Zip 38556–1500; tel. 931/879–8171, (Nonreporting) **A**1 9 10 20 **S** Community Health Systems, Inc., Franklin, TN
Primary Contact: Larry R. Jeter, Chief Executive Officer
CMO: Mark Hendrixson, M.D., Chief Medical Officer
CIO: Rick Smith, Director Information Systems
CHR: Shelia Russell, Director Human Resources
Web address: www.jamestownregional.org
Control: Corporation, Investor–owned, for–profit **Service:** General Medical and Surgical

Staffed Beds: 85

JASPER—Marion County

☐ **PARKRIDGE WEST HOSPITAL (440064)**, 1000 Highway 28, Zip 37347–3638; tel. 423/837–9500, (Nonreporting) **A**1 9 10 **S** HCA, Nashville, TN
Primary Contact: Shirley K. Scarlatti, Associate Chief Nursing Officer
Web address: www.parkridgewesthospital.com/
Control: Corporation, Investor–owned, for–profit **Service:** General Medical and Surgical

Staffed Beds: 68

JEFFERSON CITY—Jefferson County

ST. MARY'S JEFFERSON MEMORIAL HOSPITAL See Tennova Healthcare–Jefferson Memorial Hospital

⊠ **TENNOVA HEALTHCARE–JEFFERSON MEMORIAL HOSPITAL (440056)**, 110 Hospital Drive, Zip 37760–5281; tel. 865/471–2500, (Nonreporting) **A**1 9 10 **S** Community Health Systems, Inc., Franklin, TN
Primary Contact: Colin McRae, Chief Executive Officer
CFO: Roseann M. Devault, Chief Financial Officer
CMO: Richard Carter, M.D., Chief of Staff
CNO: Carol C. Wolfenbarger, R.N., Chief Nursing Officer
Web address: www.tennova.com/
Control: Corporation, Investor–owned, for–profit **Service:** General Medical and Surgical

Staffed Beds: 54

Many Facility Codes have changed. Please refer to the AHA Guide Code Chart. © 2014 AHA Guide

JELLICO—Campbell County

✈ **JELLICO COMMUNITY HOSPITAL (440180)**, 188 Hospital Lane,
Zip 37762–4400; tel. 423/784–7252 **A**1 9 10 **F**3 7 11 13 15 29 30 34 35 40
43 44 48 50 53 54 57 59 62 64 65 68 70 75 76 77 81 85 86 87 93 97 107
108 110 111 114 119 130 131 132 133 135 143 146 148 **P**6 **S** Adventist
Health System Sunbelt Health Care Corporation, Altamonte Springs, FL
Primary Contact: Erik Wangsness, Chief Executive Officer
COO: Pamela Hodge, R.N., Chief Nursing Officer and Coordinator Performance
Improvement
CFO: Keith Richardson, Chief Financial Officer
CMO: Gregory Wilkens, M.D., Chief of Staff
CIO: Derek Brown, Chief Information Officer
CHR: Vince Vannett, Director Human Resources
CNO: Pamela Hodge, R.N., Registered Nurse and Chief Nursing Officer
Web address: www.jellicohospital.com
Control: Other not–for–profit (including NFP Corporation) **Service:** General
Medical and Surgical

Staffed Beds: 31 **Admissions:** 1441 **Census:** 11 **Outpatient Visits:** 41001
Births: 201 **Total Expense ($000):** 32923 **Payroll Expense ($000):** 9438
Personnel: 266

JOHNSON CITY—Washington County

✈ **FRANKLIN WOODS COMMUNITY HOSPITAL (440184)**, 300 MedTech
Parkway, Zip 37604–2277; tel. 423/302–1000 **A**1 9 10 **F**3 13 29 30 34 39 40
44 50 56 59 68 70 74 75 76 77 79 81 86 87 93 97 107 108 111 114 115
118 119 126 130 143 146 147 **P**6 8 **S** Mountain States Health Alliance,
Johnson City, TN
Primary Contact: Lindy P. White, Chief Executive Officer
CFO: Bradley Logan, Chief Financial Officer
CHR: Brooke Graham, Human Resources Manager
CNO: Rhonda Mann, Chief Nursing Officer
Web address: www.msha.com
Control: Other not–for–profit (including NFP Corporation) **Service:** General
Medical and Surgical

Staffed Beds: 80 **Admissions:** 4198 **Census:** 42 **Outpatient Visits:** 41076
Births: 1123 **Total Expense ($000):** 42606 **Payroll Expense ($000):** 19207
Personnel: 337

✈ **JOHNSON CITY MEDICAL CENTER (440063)**, 400 North State of Franklin
Road, Zip 37604–6094; tel. 423/431–6111, (Includes NISWONGER CHILDREN'S
HOSPITAL, 400 North State Of Franklin Road, Zip 37604–6035;
tel. 423/431–6111; QUILLEN REHABILITATION HOSPITAL, 2511 Wesley Street,
Zip 37601–1723; tel. 423/283–0700; Ann Fleming, Senior Vice President;
WOODRIDGE HOSPITAL, 403 State of Franklin Road, Zip 37604–6034;
tel. 423/431–7111; Grace Pereira, Interim Chief Executive Officer), (Total facility
includes 34 beds in nursing home–type unit) **A**1 2 3 5 8 9 10 **F**3 5 7 11 12 13
15 17 18 19 20 21 22 23 24 25 26 27 28 29 30 31 32 34 35 38 39 40 41
43 44 45 46 47 48 49 50 51 52 53 54 55 56 57 58 59 60 61 62 63 64 68
70 72 74 75 76 77 78 79 81 82 84 85 86 87 88 89 90 91 93 97 99 100
101 102 103 104 105 107 108 110 111 115 117 118 119 120 121 123 124
126 128 129 130 131 132 134 135 143 146 147 148 **P**6 8 **S** Mountain States
Health Alliance, Johnson City, TN
Primary Contact: Tony Benton, Interim Chief Executive Officer Washington County
Hospitals
CFO: Shane Hilton, Vice President and Chief Financial Officer
CMO: Clay Runnels, Vice President Chief Medical Officer Washington County
CHR: Jamie Parsons, Human Resources Director
CNO: Rhonda Mann, Vice President and Chief Nursing Officer
Web address: www.msha.com
Control: Other not–for–profit (including NFP Corporation) **Service:** General
Medical and Surgical

Staffed Beds: 611 **Admissions:** 28739 **Census:** 450 **Outpatient Visits:**
261636 **Births:** 1235 **Total Expense ($000):** 301300 **Payroll Expense
($000):** 140581 **Personnel:** 2422

NORTH SIDE HOSPITAL See Franklin Woods Community Hospital

KINGSPORT—Sullivan County

✈ **HEALTHSOUTH REHABILITATION HOSPITAL (443027)**, 113 Cassel Drive,
Zip 37660–3775; tel. 423/246–7240, (Nonreporting) **A**1 10 **S** HEALTHSOUTH
Corporation, Birmingham, AL
Primary Contact: Susan Glenn, Chief Executive Officer
CFO: Natalie Tilson, Controller
CMO: James P. Little, M.D., Medical Director
CIO: Natalie Tilson, Controller
CHR: Joyce Jones, Director Human Resources
Web address: www.healthsouthkingsport.com
Control: Corporation, Investor–owned, for–profit **Service:** Rehabilitation

Staffed Beds: 50

☐ **INDIAN PATH MEDICAL CENTER (440176)**, 2000 Brookside Drive,
Zip 37660–4627; tel. 423/857–7000, (Total facility includes 22 beds in nursing
home–type unit) **A**1 9 10 **F**3 8 11 13 15 18 20 22 26 28 29 30 31 34 35 36
38 40 44 45 47 49 50 51 53 54 56 57 58 59 60 62 63 64 65 68 70 71 73
74 75 76 77 78 79 81 85 86 87 91 92 97 107 108 110 111 114 115 117
118 119 121 123 128 129 130 132 143 144 146 147 148 **P**6 8 **S** Mountain
States Health Alliance, Johnson City, TN
Primary Contact: Monty E. McLaurin, President and Chief Executive Officer
CFO: Pat Hale, Chief Financial Officer
CMO: Frank Lauro, M.D., Chief Medical Officer
CIO: Matthew Grissinger, Site Manager Information Systems
CHR: Kevin M. Smith, SPHR, Director Human Resources
CNO: Susan Fannon, Chief Nursing Officer
Web address: www.msha.com
Control: Other not–for–profit (including NFP Corporation) **Service:** General
Medical and Surgical

Staffed Beds: 261 **Admissions:** 6532 **Census:** 79 **Outpatient Visits:** 134006
Births: 801 **Total Expense ($000):** 93827 **Payroll Expense ($000):** 34141
Personnel: 541

✈ **WELLMONT HOLSTON VALLEY MEDICAL CENTER (440017)**, 130 West
Ravine Street, Zip 37660–3837, Mailing Address: P.O. Box 238,
Zip 37662–0238; tel. 423/224–4000, (Nonreporting) **A**1 2 3 5 9 10 **S** Wellmont
Health System, Kingsport, TN
Primary Contact: Tim Attebery, Chief Executive Officer
COO: Troy Clark, Chief Operating Officer
CFO: Dale Poe, Vice President Finance and Operations
CMO: Daniel Carlson, M.D., Chief Medical Officer
CIO: Will Showalter, Senior Vice President Information Technology
CHR: Hamlin J. Wilson, Senior Vice President Human Resources
CNO: Kathy Campbell, Interim Chief Nursing Officer
Web address: www.wellmont.org
Control: Other not–for–profit (including NFP Corporation) **Service:** General
Medical and Surgical

Staffed Beds: 318

KNOXVILLE—Knox County

☐ **EAST TENNESSEE CHILDREN'S HOSPITAL (443303)**, 2018 Clinch Avenue,
Zip 37916–2393, Mailing Address: P.O. Box 15010, Zip 37901–5010;
tel. 865/541–8000, (Nonreporting) **A**1 3 5 6 9 10
Primary Contact: Keith D. Goodwin, President and Chief Executive Officer
COO: Rudolph McKinley, Jr., Vice President Operations and Chief Operating Officer
CFO: Zane Goodrich, Vice President Finance
CMO: Joe Childs, M.D., Vice President Medical Services
CIO: John Hanks, Director Information Systems
CHR: Sue Wilburn, Vice President Human Resources and Organizational
Development
CNO: Laura P. Barnes, MSN, Vice President Patient Care Services and Chief
Nursing Officer
Web address: www.etch.com
Control: Other not–for–profit (including NFP Corporation) **Service:** Children's
general

Staffed Beds: 152

✈ △ **FORT SANDERS REGIONAL MEDICAL CENTER (440125)**, 1901 West
Clinch Avenue, Zip 37916–2307; tel. 865/541–1111, (Total facility includes 24
beds in nursing home–type unit) **A**1 2 7 9 10 **F**3 11 13 15 17 18 20 22 24 26
28 29 30 31 34 35 40 45 46 47 48 49 50 51 54 55 56 57 58 59 60 61 64
68 74 75 76 77 78 79 80 81 84 85 86 87 90 91 92 93 94 96 100 102 107
108 110 114 115 118 119 126 128 129 130 131 132 136 141 142 146
147 148 **S** Covenant Health, Knoxville, TN
Primary Contact: Keith Altshuler, President and Chief Administrative Officer
Web address: www.covenanthealth.com
Control: Other not–for–profit (including NFP Corporation) **Service:** General
Medical and Surgical

Staffed Beds: 386 **Admissions:** 15722 **Census:** 238 **Outpatient Visits:**
219628 **Births:** 2616 **Total Expense ($000):** 257039 **Payroll Expense
($000):** 81020 **Personnel:** 1478

MERCY MEDICAL CENTER WEST See Tennova Turkey Creek Medical Center

TN

Hospital, Medicare Provider Number, Address, Telephone, Approval, Facility, and Physician Codes, Health Care System

★ American Hospital Association (AHA) membership
☐ The Joint Commission accreditation ◇ DNV Healthcare Inc. accreditation
◯ Healthcare Facilities Accreditation Program
△ Commission on Accreditation of Rehabilitation Facilities (CARF) accreditation

⊞ **PARKWEST MEDICAL CENTER (440173)**, 9352 Park West Boulevard, Zip 37923–4325, Mailing Address: P.O. Box 22993, Zip 37933–0993; tel. 865/373–1000 **A**1 2 9 10 **F**3 13 15 17 18 20 22 24 26 28 29 30 31 34 35 37 40 45 46 47 48 49 50 51 56 58 60 64 68 70 74 75 76 77 78 79 80 81 82 84 85 87 98 103 107 108 110 111 115 118 119 126 129 130 131 132 135 141 142 146 147 148 **S** Covenant Health, Knoxville, TN
Primary Contact: Rick Lassiter, President and Chief Administrative Officer
COO: Emlyn Cobble, Vice President and Chief Support Officer
CFO: Scott Hamilton, Vice President and Chief Financial Officer
CHR: Randall Carr, Director Human Resources
CNO: Diane Oliver, R.N., Chief Nursing Officer
Web address: www.yesparkwest.com
Control: Other not–for–profit (including NFP Corporation) **Service:** General Medical and Surgical

Staffed Beds: 297 **Admissions:** 15707 **Census:** 201 **Outpatient Visits:** 149705 **Births:** 1651 **Total Expense ($000):** 236428 **Payroll Expense ($000):** 73324 **Personnel:** 1426

⊞ **SELECT SPECIALTY HOSPITAL–KNOXVILLE (442012)**, 1901 Clinch Avenue, 4th Floor North, Zip 37916–2307; tel. 865/541–2615, (Nonreporting) **A**1 9 10 **S** Select Medical Corporation, Mechanicsburg, PA
Primary Contact: Vanda Scott, M.D., Chief Executive Officer
CFO: David Elledge, Controller
CMO: Jano Janoyan, M.D., Medical Director
CIO: Vanda Scott, M.D., Chief Executive Officer
CHR: Christina Blanton, Administrative Assistant and Human Resources Coordinator
CNO: Danielle Connolly Robbins, Chief Nursing Officer
Web address: www.knoxville.selectspecialtyhospitals.com/
Control: Corporation, Investor–owned, for–profit **Service:** Long–Term Acute Care hospital

Staffed Beds: 35

⊞ **SELECT SPECIALTY HOSPITAL–NORTH KNOXVILLE (442015)**, 900 East Oak Hill Avenue, 4th Floor, Zip 37917–4505; tel. 865/545–7350, (Nonreporting) **A**1 9 10 **S** Select Medical Corporation, Mechanicsburg, PA
Primary Contact: Steve Plumlee, Chief Executive Officer
CFO: David Elledge, Controller
CMO: Jeff Summers, M.D., Medical Director
CIO: Steve Plumlee, Chief Executive Officer
CHR: Mallory Wilson, Administrative Assistant and Human Resources Coordinator
CNO: Nancy Johnson, Chief Nursing Officer
Web address: www.northknoxville.selectspecialtyhospitals.com/
Control: Corporation, Investor–owned, for–profit **Service:** Long–Term Acute Care hospital

Staffed Beds: 33

⊞ △ **TENNOVA PHYSICIANS REGIONAL MEDICAL CENTER (440120)**, 900 East Oak Hill Avenue, Zip 37917–4556; tel. 865/545–8000, (Includes TENNOVA NORTH KNOXVILLE MEDICAL CENTER, 7565 Dannaher Way, Powell, Zip 37849–4029; tel. 865/859–7000; Rob Followell, Chief Executive Officer; TENNOVA TURKEY CREEK MEDICAL CENTER, 10820 Parkside Drive, Zip 37934–1956; tel. 865/218–7092; Neil Heatherly, Chief Executive Officer) **A**1 2 7 9 10 **F**8 13 15 17 18 20 22 24 26 28 29 30 31 34 35 40 44 49 51 53 54 56 57 59 60 61 62 63 64 70 73 74 75 76 77 78 79 80 81 82 83 84 85 86 87 90 92 93 96 98 100 102 103 104 105 107 108 110 111 114 115 117 118 119 120 121 123 124 126 128 129 130 131 132 146 147 148 **S** Community Health Systems, Inc., Franklin, TN
Primary Contact: Karen Metz, Chief Executive Officer
CFO: Rhonda Maynard, Chief Financial Officer
CIO: Tom Lakins, Director Information Systems
CHR: Sarah M. Laboranti, Interim Director Human Resources
Web address: www.hma.com/content/physicians–regional–medical–center
Control: Corporation, Investor–owned, for–profit **Service:** General Medical and Surgical

Staffed Beds: 223 **Admissions:** 14876 **Census:** 214 **Outpatient Visits:** 219998 **Births:** 1427 **Total Expense ($000):** 203959 **Payroll Expense ($000):** 62426 **Personnel:** 1166

⊞ **UNIVERSITY OF TENNESSEE MEDICAL CENTER (440015)**, 1924 Alcoa Highway, Zip 37920–6900; tel. 865/305–9000 **A**1 2 3 5 8 9 10 13 **F**3 6 8 9 11 12 13 15 17 18 19 20 21 22 23 24 25 26 27 28 29 30 31 34 36 39 40 43 44 45 46 47 48 49 50 51 53 54 55 56 57 58 59 60 61 64 65 70 71 72 74 75 76 77 78 79 80 81 82 84 85 86 87 88 91 92 93 94 96 97 100 102 103 107 108 109 110 111 114 115 116 117 118 119 120 121 123 124 126 129 130 131 132 135 138 141 144 145 146 147 148 **P**5 6
Primary Contact: Joseph Landsman, President and Chief Executive Officer
COO: David Hall, Senior Vice President and Chief Operating Officer
CFO: Thomas Fisher, Senior Vice President and Chief Financial Officer
CMO: John W. Lacey, III, M.D., Senior Vice President and Chief Medical Officer
CIO: Eileen Clark, Director Computer Services
CHR: Betty Gissel, Vice President Human Resources
CNO: Janell Cecil, R.N., Senior Vice President and Chief Nursing Officer
Web address: www.utmedicalcenter.org
Control: Other not–for–profit (including NFP Corporation) **Service:** General Medical and Surgical

Staffed Beds: 546 **Admissions:** 24958 **Census:** 388 **Outpatient Visits:** 233812 **Births:** 3009 **Total Expense ($000):** 623745 **Payroll Expense ($000):** 219051 **Personnel:** 3170

LA FOLLETTE—Campbell County

⊞ **TENNOVA HEALTHCARE–LAFOLLETTE MEDICAL CENTER (440033)**, 923 East Central Avenue, Zip 37766–2768, Mailing Address: P.O. Box 1301, Zip 37766–1301; tel. 423/907–1200, (Total facility includes 98 beds in nursing home–type unit) **A**1 9 10 20 **F**3 15 18 29 30 31 40 50 68 70 77 78 81 84 85 93 98 103 107 108 110 111 119 127 128 129 131 146 148 **S** Community Health Systems, Inc., Franklin, TN
Primary Contact: Mark Cain, Chief Executive Officer
COO: Sara Heatherly–Lloyd, Chief Operating Officer
CFO: Wes Griffith, Chief Financial Officer
CMO: Jan Robbins, M.D., Chief of Staff
CIO: Doug Kibler, Management Information Systems Specialist
CHR: Bess Stout, Director Human Resources
CNO: Kathy R. Myers, MS, Chief Nursing Officer
Web address: www.tennova.com
Control: Corporation, Investor–owned, for–profit **Service:** General Medical and Surgical

Staffed Beds: 164 **Admissions:** 2869 **Census:** 123 **Outpatient Visits:** 60755 **Births:** 0 **Total Expense ($000):** 41424 **Payroll Expense ($000):** 18095 **Personnel:** 289

LAFAYETTE—Macon County

★ ◇ **MACON COUNTY GENERAL HOSPITAL (441305)**, 204 Medical Drive, Zip 37083–1799, Mailing Address: P.O. Box 378, Zip 37083–0378; tel. 615/666–2147 **A**9 10 18 21 **F**3 15 18 29 30 34 35 40 57 59 65 75 77 81 86 93 107 114 119 128 130 132 133 146 **S** QHR, Brentwood, TN
Primary Contact: Dennis A. Wolford, FACHE, Chief Executive Officer
CFO: Thomas J. Kidd, Assistant Administrator and Chief Financial Officer
Web address: www.mcgh.net
Control: Other not–for–profit (including NFP Corporation) **Service:** General Medical and Surgical

Staffed Beds: 25 **Admissions:** 857 **Census:** 9 **Outpatient Visits:** 27952 **Births:** 0 **Personnel:** 113

LAWRENCEBURG—Lawrence County

⊞ **SOUTHERN TENNESSEE REGIONAL HEALTH SYSTEM–LAWRENCEBURG (440175)**, 1607 South Locust Avenue, Zip 38464–4011, Mailing Address: P.O. Box 847, Zip 38464–0847; tel. 931/762–6571, (Nonreporting) **A**1 9 10 **S** LifePoint Hospitals, Inc., Brentwood, TN
Primary Contact: Jeff Noblin, FACHE, Chief Executive Officer
CFO: Kristie Taylor, Chief Financial Officer
CIO: Jason Weaver, Director Information Systems
CHR: Robert Augustin, Director Human Resources
CNO: Carol Laird, R.N., Chief Nursing Officer
Web address: www.crocketthospital.com
Control: Corporation, Investor–owned, for–profit **Service:** General Medical and Surgical

Staffed Beds: 90

LEBANON—Wilson County

⊞ **UNIVERSITY MEDICAL CENTER (440193)**, 1411 Baddour Parkway, Zip 37087–2513; tel. 615/444–8262, (Includes MCFARLAND SPECIALTY HOSPITAL, 500 Park Avenue, Zip 37087–3720; tel. 615/449–0500), (Nonreporting) **A**1 5 9 10 **S** Community Health Systems, Inc., Franklin, TN
Primary Contact: Matthew T. Caldwell, Chief Executive Officer
CMO: Andrew Jordan, M.D., Chief of Staff
CIO: Adrian Fung, Director Information Systems
Web address: www.universitymedicalcenter.com
Control: Corporation, Investor–owned, for–profit **Service:** General Medical and Surgical

Staffed Beds: 245

LENOIR CITY—Loudon County

⊞ **FORT LOUDOUN MEDICAL CENTER (440110)**, 550 Fort Loudoun Medical Center Drive, Zip 37772–5673; tel. 865/271–6000 **A**1 9 10 **F**3 11 15 18 28 29 30 34 35 40 45 50 57 59 68 70 77 79 81 85 93 102 107 108 110 111 114 118 119 130 135 146 148 **S** Covenant Health, Knoxville, TN
Primary Contact: Jeffrey Feike, President and Chief Administrative Officer
CNO: Teresa Fisher, R.N., Chief Nursing Officer
Web address: www.covenanthealth.com
Control: Other not–for–profit (including NFP Corporation) **Service:** General Medical and Surgical

Staffed Beds: 40 **Admissions:** 1742 **Census:** 18 **Outpatient Visits:** 66211 **Births:** 0 **Total Expense ($000):** 27169 **Payroll Expense ($000):** 10580 **Personnel:** 200

Many Facility Codes have changed. Please refer to the AHA Guide Code Chart. © 2014 AHA Guide

LEWISBURG—Marshall County

⊞ **MARSHALL MEDICAL CENTER (441309)**, 1080 North Ellington Parkway, Zip 37091–2227, Mailing Address: P.O. Box 1609, Zip 37091–1609; tel. 931/359–6241 **A**1 9 10 18 **F**3 11 15 29 30 34 40 45 50 56 57 59 68 75 77 81 92 93 108 110 111 114 119 129 131 132 133 135 146 **S** Maury Regional Health System, Columbia, TN
Primary Contact: Phyllis Brown, Chief Executive Officer
CFO: Kyle Jones, Controller
CMO: Tim Nash, M.D., Chief of Staff
CHR: Jeff M. Pierce, Manager Human Resources
CNO: Karen Martin, R.N., Chief Nursing Officer
Web address: www.mauryregional.com
Control: County-Government, nonfederal **Service:** General Medical and Surgical

Staffed Beds: 12 **Admissions:** 202 **Census:** 2 **Outpatient Visits:** 39608
Births: 0 **Total Expense ($000):** 13257 **Payroll Expense ($000):** 6276
Personnel: 128

LEXINGTON—Henderson County

⊞ **HENDERSON COUNTY COMMUNITY HOSPITAL (440008)**, 200 West Church Street, Zip 38351–2038; tel. 731/968–3646 **A**1 9 10 **F**7 15 18 29 30 34 35 39 40 50 57 59 68 75 79 81 82 86 87 93 97 107 108 110 111 114 119 120 127 132 145 146 **P**5 **S** Community Health Systems, Inc., Franklin, TN
Primary Contact: Dale Humphrey, Chief Executive Officer
CFO: John Bostwick, Interim Chief Financial Officer
CHR: Linda Durham, Director Human Resources
CNO: Charlene Morgan, Chief Nursing Officer
Web address: www.hendersoncchospital.com
Control: Corporation, Investor–owned, for–profit **Service:** General Medical and Surgical

Staffed Beds: 45 **Admissions:** 498 **Census:** 22 **Outpatient Visits:** 50187
Births: 0

LINDEN—Perry County

PERRY COMMUNITY HOSPITAL (440040), 2718 Squirrel Hollow Drive, Zip 37096–3526; tel. 931/589–2121, (Nonreporting) **A**9 10
Primary Contact: John B. Avery, III, Administrator
Control: Other not–for–profit (including NFP Corporation) **Service:** General Medical and Surgical

Staffed Beds: 53

LIVINGSTON—Overton County

⊞ **LIVINGSTON REGIONAL HOSPITAL (440187)**, 315 Oak Street, Zip 38570–1728, Mailing Address: P.O. Box 550, Zip 38570–0550; tel. 931/823–5611, (Nonreporting) **A**1 9 10 **S** LifePoint Hospitals, Inc., Brentwood, TN
Primary Contact: Joanne Fenton, MSN, FACHE, Chief Executive Officer
COO: Michelle Watson, Chief Operating Officer and Chief Nursing Officer
CFO: Joseph Ross, Chief Financial Officer
CMO: Trueman Smith, M.D., Chief Medical Officer
CIO: Joseph Ross, Chief Financial Officer
CHR: Valerie Guimaraes, Director Human Resources
Web address: www.livingstonregionalhospital.com
Control: Corporation, Investor–owned, for–profit **Service:** General Medical and Surgical

Staffed Beds: 82

LOUISVILLE—Blount County

PENINSULA HOSPITAL, 2347 Jones Bend Road, Zip 37777–5213, Mailing Address: P.O. Box 2000, Zip 37777–2000; tel. 865/970–9800 **F**4 5 29 30 34 35 38 50 64 68 98 99 101 104 130 **P**6
Primary Contact: Elizabeth P. Clary, R.N., Vice President Behavioral Health
COO: Todd Roberts, Manager Business Operations
CFO: Scott Hamilton, Chief Financial Officer
CMO: Reggie Raman, M.D., Medical Director
CIO: Shelby Bowers, Director Marketing and Public Relations
CHR: Anita Rivera, Director Human Resources
CNO: Heather Jett, Director Patient Care Services
Web address: www.peninsula–hospital.org
Control: Other not–for–profit (including NFP Corporation) **Service:** Psychiatric

Staffed Beds: 137 **Admissions:** 4918 **Census:** 82 **Outpatient Visits:** 85545
Births: 0 **Total Expense ($000):** 29835 **Payroll Expense ($000):** 15740
Personnel: 329

MADISON—Davidson County

★ **TRISTAR SKYLINE MADISON CAMPUS (440135)**, 500 Hospital Drive, Zip 37115–5032; tel. 615/769–5000, (Nonreporting) **A**9 **S** HCA, Nashville, TN
Primary Contact: Steve Otto, Chief Executive Officer
COO: Jill Howard, R.N., Chief Operating Officer
CFO: Bradley Schultz, Chief Financial Officer
CMO: Sunil Kaza, M.D., President Medical Staff
CIO: Troy Sypien, Director Information Technology and Systems
CHR: Robert A. Hooper, Director Human Resources
CNO: Laurie Turner, Chief Nursing Officer
Web address: www.skylinemadison.com
Control: Corporation, Investor–owned, for–profit **Service:** General Medical and Surgical

Staffed Beds: 284

MANCHESTER—Coffee County

MEDICAL CENTER OF MANCHESTER (441308), 481 Interstate Drive, Zip 37355–3108, Mailing Address: P.O. Box 1409, Zip 37349–4409; tel. 931/728–6354, (Nonreporting) **A**9 10 18
Primary Contact: Robert J. Couch, Chief Executive Officer
CMO: W. D. Daniel, D.O., Chief of Staff
CHR: Shelly Turner, Chief Clinical Services Officer
Control: Corporation, Investor–owned, for–profit **Service:** General Medical and Surgical

Staffed Beds: 25

UNITED REGIONAL MEDICAL CENTER (440007), 1001 McArthur Drive, Zip 37355–2455, Mailing Address: P.O. Box 1079, Zip 37349–1079; tel. 931/728–3586 **A**9 10 **F**3 15 29 30 34 40 44 50 57 59 65 75 77 81 82 85 86 87 89 91 93 94 107 111 114 116 117 119 128 129 130 133 146 148
Primary Contact: Martha McCormick, Chief Executive Officer
CFO: Pam Jernigan, Chief Financial Officer
CMO: James Van Winkle, M.D., Chief of Staff
CIO: Matt Burks, Director Information Technology
CHR: Sherry Holt, Director Human Resources
CNO: Stephanie Byars, Chief Nursing Officer
Web address: www.urmchealthcare.com
Control: Corporation, Investor–owned, for–profit **Service:** General Medical and Surgical

Staffed Beds: 36 **Admissions:** 1041 **Census:** 9 **Outpatient Visits:** 21825
Births: 0 **Total Expense ($000):** 11913 **Payroll Expense ($000):** 4948
Personnel: 105

MARTIN—Weakley County

★ **BEHAVIORAL HEALTHCARE CENTER AT MARTIN (444005)**, 458 Hannings Lane, Zip 38237–3308; tel. 731/588–2830, (Nonreporting) **A**10 **S** Tennessee Health Management, Parsons, TN
Primary Contact: Carrie Brawley, Administrator
Web address: www.tnhealthmanagement.com/BHC/martin/
Control: Partnership, Investor–owned, for–profit **Service:** Psychiatric

Staffed Beds: 16

⊞ **HEALTHSOUTH CANE CREEK REHABILITATION HOSPITAL (443030)**, 180 Mount Pelia Road, Zip 38237–3812; tel. 731/587–4231 **A**1 10 **F**30 56 82 90 94 95 96 130 132 143 **S** HEALTHSOUTH Corporation, Birmingham, AL
Primary Contact: Amy Vieth, Chief Executive Officer
CFO: Bethany Smith, Controller
CMO: Belinda Merritt, M.D., Medical Director
CIO: Jan Trowhill, Director Health Information Management Systems
CHR: Sharon Shihady, Director Human Resources
CNO: Lindsey Rotger, Chief Nursing Officer
Web address: www.healthsouthcanecreek.com
Control: Corporation, Investor–owned, for–profit **Service:** Rehabilitation

Staffed Beds: 40 **Admissions:** 782 **Census:** 27 **Outpatient Visits:** 0 **Births:** 0 **Total Expense ($000):** 7604 **Payroll Expense ($000):** 5723 **Personnel:** 91

⊞ **VOLUNTEER COMMUNITY HOSPITAL (440061)**, 161 Mount Pelia Road, Zip 38237–3811; tel. 731/587–4261, (Nonreporting) **A**1 9 10 **S** Community Health Systems, Inc., Franklin, TN
Primary Contact: Darrell Blaylock, Chief Executive Officer
CFO: Jason Draper, Chief Financial Officer
CMO: Elizabeth Lund, M.D., Chief of Staff
CHR: Tammie Bell, Director Human Resources
CNO: Donna Barfield, Chief Nursing Officer
Web address: www.volunteercommunityhospital.com
Control: Corporation, Investor–owned, for–profit **Service:** General Medical and Surgical

Staffed Beds: 65

TN

Hospital, Medicare Provider Number, Address, Telephone, Approval, Facility, and Physician Codes, Health Care System

★ American Hospital Association (AHA) membership
☐ The Joint Commission accreditation   ◇ DNV Healthcare Inc. accreditation
○ Healthcare Facilities Accreditation Program
△ Commission on Accreditation of Rehabilitation Facilities (CARF) accreditation

MARYVILLE—Blount County

⊞ **BLOUNT MEMORIAL HOSPITAL (440011)**, 907 East Lamar Alexander Parkway, Zip 37804–5016; tel. 865/983–7211, (Total facility includes 76 beds in nursing home–type unit) **A**1 2 9 10 **F**3 4 10 11 12 13 15 17 18 20 22 26 28 29 30 31 32 35 38 40 43 45 46 49 53 54 56 57 59 62 63 64 67 68 70 74 75 76 77 78 79 80 81 82 84 85 86 87 90 93 96 97 98 99 100 101 102 103 104 105 107 108 110 111 114 115 116 117 118 119 120 121 122 123 125 126 128 129 130 131 132 134 135 144 146 147 148 **P**6 7
Primary Contact: Don Heinemann, Administrator and Chief Executive Officer
CFO: Jonathan Smith, Assistant Administrator and Chief Financial Officer
CMO: G. Harold Naramore, M.D., Chief Medical Officer and In house Legal Counsel
CIO: Clay Puckett, Assistant Administrator and Chief Information Officer
CHR: Chris Wilkes, MS, Director Human Resources
CNO: Sonya Newman, R.N., Chief Nursing Officer
Web address: www.blountmemorial.org
Control: County–Government, nonfederal **Service:** General Medical and Surgical

Staffed Beds: 314 **Admissions:** 12244 **Census:** 211 **Outpatient Visits:** 250901 **Births:** 754 **Total Expense ($000):** 215869 **Payroll Expense ($000):** 99359 **Personnel:** 1987

MC MINNVILLE—Warren County

☐ **RIVER PARK HOSPITAL (440151)**, 1559 Sparta Street, Zip 37110–1316; tel. 931/815–4000 **A**1 9 10 **F**8 11 13 15 18 28 29 30 34 35 40 50 51 57 59 64 70 74 75 76 79 80 81 89 90 93 107 110 111 114 115 119 129 146 **P**6 **S** Capella Healthcare, Franklin, TN
Primary Contact: Timothy W. McGill, Chief Executive Officer
COO: Joseph Mazzo, Chief Operating Officer
CFO: Christina Patterson, Chief Financial Officer
CMO: Randal D. Rampp, M.D., Chief Medical Officer
CIO: Jeff Johnson, Director Information Systems
CHR: Deeann Johnson, Director Human Resources
Web address: www.riverparkhospital.com
Control: Corporation, Investor–owned, for–profit **Service:** General Medical and Surgical

Staffed Beds: 85 **Admissions:** 3207 **Census:** 31 **Outpatient Visits:** 35337 **Births:** 415 **Total Expense ($000):** 46697 **Payroll Expense ($000):** 15209 **Personnel:** 338

MCKENZIE—Carroll County

⊞ **MCKENZIE REGIONAL HOSPITAL (440182)**, 161 Hospital Drive, Zip 38201–1636; tel. 731/352–5344 **A**1 9 10 **F**3 29 40 53 76 81 85 89 93 107 119 131 133 146 **S** Community Health Systems, Inc., Franklin, TN
Primary Contact: Michael G. Morrical, Chief Executive Officer
CFO: Kevin Harvey, Chief Financial Officer
CHR: Tammie Bell, Director Human Resources
CNO: Penny V. Kirby, MSN, Chief Nursing Officer
Web address: www.mckenzieregionalhospital.com
Control: Corporation, Investor–owned, for–profit **Service:** General Medical and Surgical

Staffed Beds: 35 **Admissions:** 1286 **Census:** 9 **Outpatient Visits:** 12818 **Births:** 446 **Total Expense ($000):** 15661 **Payroll Expense ($000):** 5335 **Personnel:** 103

MEMPHIS—Shelby County

⊞ **BAPTIST MEMORIAL HOSPITAL – MEMPHIS (440048)**, 6019 Walnut Grove Road, Zip 38120–2173; tel. 901/226–5000, (Total facility includes 32 beds in nursing home–type unit) **A**1 2 3 5 9 10 **F**3 7 8 12 15 17 18 19 20 22 24 26 28 29 30 31 32 34 35 36 37 38 40 41 45 46 47 48 49 52 53 54 55 56 57 58 59 60 61 62 63 64 65 66 68 70 71 74 75 77 78 79 80 81 82 83 84 85 86 87 92 93 96 107 108 109 110 111 112 113 114 115 116 117 118 119 120 121 123 124 126 128 129 130 132 135 136 137 143 144 145 146 147 148 **S** Baptist Memorial Health Care Corporation, Memphis, TN
Primary Contact: Derick Ziegler, Administrator and Chief Executive Officer
CFO: Cyndi Pittman, Chief Financial Officer
CMO: Christian C. Patrick, M.D., Chief Medical Officer
CIO: Doug Reiselt, Vice President and Chief Information Officer
CHR: Jerry Barbaree, Director Human Resources
CNO: Becky Hunter, R.N., Chief Nursing Officer
Web address: www.baptistonline.org/memphis/
Control: Other not–for–profit (including NFP Corporation) **Service:** General Medical and Surgical

Staffed Beds: 605 **Admissions:** 24642 **Census:** 453 **Outpatient Visits:** 121958 **Births:** 0 **Total Expense ($000):** 496143 **Payroll Expense ($000):** 158801 **Personnel:** 2852

★ **BAPTIST MEMORIAL HOSPITAL FOR WOMEN (440222)**, 6225 Humphreys Boulevard, Zip 38120–2373; tel. 901/227–9000 **A**9 **F**3 7 8 12 13 15 18 19 20 21 22 23 24 25 26 27 28 29 30 31 32 34 35 36 37 38 41 45 46 47 48 49 52 53 54 55 56 57 58 59 60 61 64 65 66 68 70 71 72 73 74 75 76 77 78 79 81 82 83 84 85 86 87 89 92 93 96 107 108 109 110 111 112 113 114 115 116 117 118 119 120 121 123 124 126 129 130 132 135 136 137 143 144 145 146 147 148 **S** Baptist Memorial Health Care Corporation, Memphis, TN
Primary Contact: Anita Vaughn, Administrator and Chief Executive Officer
CFO: Margaret Williams, Chief Financial Officer
CMO: Judi Carney, M.D., President Medical Staff
CIO: Melissa Nelson, Assistant Administrator
CHR: Karen Ingram, Director Human Resources
CNO: Carol Thetford, Chief Nursing Officer
Web address: www.baptistonline.org/womens/
Control: Other not–for–profit (including NFP Corporation) **Service:** Obstetrics and gynecology

Staffed Beds: 140 **Admissions:** 6237 **Census:** 69 **Outpatient Visits:** 42956 **Births:** 4646 **Total Expense ($000):** 84767 **Payroll Expense ($000):** 31283 **Personnel:** 517

⊞ **BAPTIST MEMORIAL RESTORATIVE CARE HOSPITAL (442010)**, 6019 Walnut Grove Road, Zip 38120–2113; tel. 901/226–1400 **A**1 9 10 **F**1 3 29 68 75 130 148 **S** Baptist Memorial Health Care Corporation, Memphis, TN
Primary Contact: Janice Hill, R.N., Administrator
Web address: www.baptistonline.org/restorative–care/
Control: Other not–for–profit (including NFP Corporation) **Service:** Long–Term Acute Care hospital

Staffed Beds: 30 **Admissions:** 285 **Census:** 26 **Outpatient Visits:** 0 **Births:** 0 **Total Expense ($000):** 16965 **Payroll Expense ($000):** 5062 **Personnel:** 92

☐ **DELTA MEDICAL CENTER (440159)**, 3000 Getwell Road, Zip 38118–2299; tel. 901/369–8100 **A**1 9 10 **F**4 5 18 29 40 41 45 56 60 70 81 90 98 103 105 107 111 114 119 129 148 **S** Acadia Healthcare Company, Inc., Franklin, TN
Primary Contact: William Patterson, Chief Executive Officer
CFO: Joy Fergie, Chief Financial Officer
CMO: David Richardson, M.D., Chief of Staff
CIO: Patrick Duffee, Director Medical Information Systems
CHR: Karyn Erickson, Director Human Resources
Web address: www.deltamedcenter.com
Control: Corporation, Investor–owned, for–profit **Service:** Psychiatric

Staffed Beds: 173 **Admissions:** 3694 **Census:** 108 **Outpatient Visits:** 5817 **Births:** 0 **Total Expense ($000):** 43651 **Payroll Expense ($000):** 22887 **Personnel:** 447

⊞ **HEALTHSOUTH REHABILITATION HOSPITAL MEMPHIS–NORTH (443031)**, 4100 Austin Peay Highway, Zip 38128–2502; tel. 901/213–5400, (Nonreporting) **A**1 10 **S** HEALTHSOUTH Corporation, Birmingham, AL
Primary Contact: Marcia Taylor, Chief Executive Officer
CFO: Thaddeus Williams, Controller
CMO: Donald Sullivan, M.D., Medical Director
CHR: Adrienne Huntley, Director Human Resources
CNO: Charlotte Boyce, Chief Nursing Officer
Web address: www.healthsouthnorthmemphis.com
Control: Corporation, Investor–owned, for–profit **Service:** Rehabilitation

Staffed Beds: 40

⊞ **HEALTHSOUTH REHABILITATION HOSPITAL OF MEMPHIS (443029)**, 1282 Union Avenue, Zip 38104–3414; tel. 901/722–2000 **A**1 3 5 10 **F**3 28 29 30 34 60 68 75 87 90 91 93 96 130 148 **S** HEALTHSOUTH Corporation, Birmingham, AL
Primary Contact: Kevin Spears, Chief Executive Officer
CFO: Eric Gray, Chief Financial Officer
CMO: Jonathan D. Ellen, M.D., Medical Director
CHR: Sandra Milburn, Director Human Resources
CNO: Jennifer Ferrell, Chief Nursing Officer
Web address: www.healthsouthmemphis.com
Control: Partnership, Investor–owned, for–profit **Service:** Rehabilitation

Staffed Beds: 72 **Admissions:** 1536 **Census:** 53 **Outpatient Visits:** 7499 **Births:** 0 **Total Expense ($000):** 17133 **Payroll Expense ($000):** 8922 **Personnel:** 180

☐ **LAKESIDE BEHAVIORAL HEALTH SYSTEM (444004)**, 2911 Brunswick Road, Zip 38133–4199; tel. 901/377–4700 **A**1 10 **F**4 5 34 38 54 56 98 99 100 101 102 103 104 105 106 130 132 **S** Universal Health Services, Inc., King of Prussia, PA
Primary Contact: Joy Golden, Chief Executive Officer
CFO: Thomas Joyner, Chief Financial Officer
CMO: C. Hal Brunt, M.D., Medical Director
CIO: Jacob Arnett, Chief Information Technology Officer
CHR: Stacie Schroeppel, Director Human Resources
CNO: Lisa Weaver, Nurse Executive
Web address: www.lakesidebhs.com
Control: Corporation, Investor–owned, for–profit **Service:** Psychiatric

Staffed Beds: 311 **Admissions:** 7525 **Census:** 250 **Outpatient Visits:** 19552 **Births:** 0 **Total Expense ($000):** 33714 **Payroll Expense ($000):** 17349 **Personnel:** 430

LE BONHEUR CHILDREN'S HOSPITAL See Methodist Healthcare Memphis Hospitals

☐ **MEMPHIS MENTAL HEALTH INSTITUTE (444001)**, 951 Court Avenue, Zip 38103–2813, Mailing Address: P.O. Box 40966, Zip 38174–0966; tel. 901/577–1800 **A**1 3 5 10 **F**3 50 86 87 98 101 103 130 146 **P**6
Primary Contact: Lisa Daniel, Chief Executive Officer
CFO: Donny Hornsby, Director Fiscal Services
CHR: Claudette Seymour, Director Personnel
Web address: www.tn.gov/mental/mhs/mhs2.html
Control: State–Government, nonfederal **Service:** Psychiatric

Staffed Beds: 55 Admissions: 1213 Census: 50 Outpatient Visits: 0 Births: 0 Total Expense ($000): 19610 Payroll Expense ($000): 10414 Personnel: 197

☒ △ **MEMPHIS VETERANS AFFAIRS MEDICAL CENTER**, 1030 Jefferson Avenue, Zip 38104–2193; tel. 901/523–8990, (Nonreporting) **A**1 3 5 7 8 **S** Department of Veterans Affairs, Washington, DC
Primary Contact: C. Diane Knight, M.D., Director and Chief Executive Officer
CFO: Kristi Depperman, Chief Financial Officer
CMO: Christopher Marino, M.D., Chief of Staff
CIO: Robert Page, III, Chief Information and Technology Officer
CHR: Natalie Brown, Chief Human Resources Management Services
CNO: Karen Gillette, Associate Director Patient Care Services
Web address: www.memphis.va.gov/
Control: Veterans Affairs, Government, federal **Service:** General Medical and Surgical

Staffed Beds: 244

☐ **METHODIST EXTENDED CARE HOSPITAL (442013)**, 225 South Claybrook Street, Zip 38104–3537; tel. 901/516–2595 **A**1 10 **F**1 3 29 30 60 75 77 130 132 148 **S** Methodist Le Bonheur Healthcare, Memphis, TN
Primary Contact: Sandra Bailey–DeLeeuw, Chief Executive Officer
COO: Sandra Hugueley, Assistant Administrator and Chief Nursing Officer
CFO: Alison Moore, Chief Financial Officer
CMO: Hany Mounir Habashy, M.D., Chief Medical Director
CHR: Mayzelle Moore, Director Human Resources
CNO: Sandra Hugueley, Assistant Administrator and Chief Nursing Officer
Web address: www.methodisthealth.org
Control: Other not–for–profit (including NFP Corporation) **Service:** Long–Term Acute Care hospital

Staffed Beds: 36 Admissions: 456 Census: 31 Outpatient Visits: 0 Births: 0 Total Expense ($000): 15440 Payroll Expense ($000): 7393 Personnel: 126

☐ **METHODIST HEALTHCARE MEMPHIS HOSPITALS (440049)**, 1265 Union Avenue, Zip 38104–3415; tel. 901/516–7000, (Includes LE BONHEUR CHILDREN'S HOSPITAL, 50 North Dunlap Street, Zip 38103; tel. 901/287–5437; Meri Armour, Chief Executive Officer; METHODIST HEALTHCARE–NORTH HOSPITAL, 3960 New Covington Pike, Zip 38128; tel. 901/384–5389; Gyasi Chisley, Chief Executive Officer; METHODIST HEALTHCARE–SOUTH HOSPITAL, 1300 Wesley Drive, Zip 38116; tel. 901/516–3081; James L. Robinson, III, PsyD, Chief Executive Officer; METHODIST LE BONHEUR GERMANTOWN HOSPITAL, 7691 Poplar Avenue, Germantown, Zip 38138; tel. 901/516–6000; William A. Kenley, Chief Executive Officer) **A**1 2 3 5 8 9 10 **F**3 7 8 11 12 13 15 17 18 19 20 21 22 23 24 25 26 27 28 29 30 31 32 34 35 37 38 39 40 41 43 44 45 46 47 48 49 50 54 55 56 57 58 59 60 61 64 65 66 68 70 71 72 73 74 75 76 77 78 79 80 81 82 84 85 86 87 88 89 92 93 94 96 97 98 99 100 101 102 103 104 105 107 108 110 111 112 113 114 115 116 117 118 119 120 121 123 124 126 129 130 131 132 134 135 136 138 139 141 142 143 144 146 147 148 **P**5 6 8 **S** Methodist Le Bonheur Healthcare, Memphis, TN
Primary Contact: Michael O. Ugwueke, President and Chief Executive Officer
COO: James R. Carter, Jr., Chief Operating Officer
CFO: Chris J. McLean, Chief Financial Officer
CMO: Robin Womeodu, M.D., Chief Medical Officer
CIO: Andy Fowler, Senior Vice President Information Systems
CHR: Carol Ross–Spang, Senior Vice President
Web address: www.methodisthealth.org
Control: Other not–for–profit (including NFP Corporation) **Service:** General Medical and Surgical

Staffed Beds: 1437 Admissions: 62488 Census: 961 Outpatient Visits: 560882 Births: 5702 Total Expense ($000): 1329849 Payroll Expense ($000): 444106 Personnel: 8095

☒ **REGIONAL ONE HEALTH (440152)**, 877 Jefferson Avenue, Zip 38103–2897; tel. 901/545–7100 **A**1 3 5 8 9 10 **F**1 3 8 13 15 16 18 20 22 29 30 35 39 40 43 44 45 49 50 57 58 59 61 64 68 70 71 72 73 74 75 76 77 79 80 81 85 86 87 90 92 93 97 107 108 110 111 114 115 119 130 132 134 141 146 147 148
Primary Contact: Reginald W. Coopwood, M.D., President and Chief Executive Officer
COO: Rob Sumter, Executive Vice President and Chief Operating Officer
CFO: Rick Wagers, Senior Executive Vice President and Chief Financial Officer
CIO: Rob Sumter, Executive Vice President and Chief Operation Officer
CHR: Sarah Colley, Senior Vice President Human Resources
CNO: Pam Castleman, MSN, Chief Nursing Officer
Web address: www.regionalonehealth.org
Control: Other not–for–profit (including NFP Corporation) **Service:** General Medical and Surgical

Staffed Beds: 353 Admissions: 12709 Census: 251 Outpatient Visits: 193515 Births: 4086 Total Expense ($000): 331964 Payroll Expense ($000): 123925 Personnel: 2168

☒ **SAINT FRANCIS HOSPITAL (440183)**, 5959 Park Avenue, Zip 38119–5198, Mailing Address: P.O. Box 171808, Zip 38187–1808; tel. 901/765–1000 **A**1 2 3 5 9 10 **F**3 8 11 12 13 15 17 18 20 22 24 26 28 29 30 31 34 35 38 39 40 44 45 46 47 48 49 50 51 54 56 57 58 59 64 68 70 72 74 75 76 77 78 79 81 82 84 85 86 87 90 93 96 97 98 99 100 101 102 103 104 107 108 110 111 114 115 116 117 118 119 121 123 124 126 129 130 131 132 143 146 147 148 **S** TENET Healthcare Corporation, Dallas, TX
Primary Contact: David L. Archer, Chief Executive Officer
COO: Audrey Gregory, R.N., Chief Operating Officer
CFO: Bradley Robertson, Chief Financial Officer
CIO: Keith Scarbrough, Chief Information Officer
CHR: Keith Stanhill, Chief Human Resources Officer
CNO: Terri L. Stewart, R.N., Chief Nursing Officer
Web address: www.saintfrancishosp.com
Control: Corporation, Investor–owned, for–profit **Service:** General Medical and Surgical

Staffed Beds: 511 Admissions: 15487 Census: 239 Outpatient Visits: 117641 Births: 1543 Total Expense ($000): 248817 Payroll Expense ($000): 73037 Personnel: 1379

☒ **SELECT SPECIALTY HOSPITAL–MEMPHIS (442014)**, 5959 Park Avenue, 12th Floor, Zip 38119–5200; tel. 901/765–1245, (Nonreporting) **A**1 9 10 **S** Select Medical Corporation, Mechanicsburg, PA
Primary Contact: Mark E. Kimball, Chief Executive Officer
Web address: www.selectspecialtyhospitals.com/company/locations/memphis.aspx
Control: Corporation, Investor–owned, for–profit **Service:** Long–Term Acute Care hospital

Staffed Beds: 38

☒ **ST. JUDE CHILDREN'S RESEARCH HOSPITAL (443302)**, 262 Danny Thomas Place, Zip 38105–3678; tel. 901/595–3300, (Nonreporting) **A**1 3 5 9 10
Primary Contact: James Downing, Chief Executive Officer
CFO: Mike Canarios, Vice President and Chief Financial Officer
CIO: Clayton Naeve, Vice President and Chief Information Officer
CHR: Mary Anna Quinn, Vice President
Web address: www.stjude.org
Control: Other not–for–profit (including NFP Corporation) **Service:** Children's other specialty

Staffed Beds: 56

VETERANS AFFAIRS MEDICAL CENTER See Memphis Veterans Affairs Medical Center

MILAN—Gibson County

☒ **MILAN GENERAL HOSPITAL (440060)**, 4039 Highland Street, Zip 38358–3483; tel. 731/686–1591 **A**1 9 10 **F**3 15 29 30 35 40 44 45 57 59 64 68 70 81 85 87 107 119 130 132 133 146 **S** West Tennessee Healthcare, Jackson, TN
Primary Contact: Sherry Scruggs, Administrator
CMO: Joe Appleton, M.D., Chief of Surgery
CNO: Carolyn Drake, Director of Nursing
Web address: www.wth.org
Control: Hospital district or authority, Government, nonfederal **Service:** General Medical and Surgical

Staffed Beds: 28 Admissions: 289 Census: 4 Outpatient Visits: 12391 Births: 1 Total Expense ($000): 7776 Payroll Expense ($000): 3070 Personnel: 70

Hospital, Medicare Provider Number, Address, Telephone, Approval, Facility, and Physician Codes, Health Care System

★ American Hospital Association (AHA) membership
☐ The Joint Commission accreditation
◇ DNV Healthcare Inc. accreditation
○ Healthcare Facilities Accreditation Program
△ Commission on Accreditation of Rehabilitation Facilities (CARF) accreditation

TN

MORRISTOWN—Hamblen County

⊞ **LAKEWAY REGIONAL HOSPITAL (440067)**, 726 McFarland Street, Zip 37814–3990; tel. 423/586–2302, (Nonreporting) **A**1 9 10 19 **S** Community Health Systems, Inc., Franklin, TN
Primary Contact: Clyde Wood, Chief Executive Officer
CMO: Paul Cardali, M.D., Chief of Staff
CHR: Deirdre Helton, Director Human Resources
Web address: www.lakewayregionalhospital.com
Control: Corporation, Investor–owned, for–profit **Service:** General Medical and Surgical

Staffed Beds: 135

⊞ **MORRISTOWN–HAMBLEN HEALTHCARE SYSTEM (440030)**, 908 West Fourth North Street, Zip 37814–3894, Mailing Address: P.O. Box 1178, Zip 37816–1178; tel. 423/492–9000 **A**1 9 10 **F**3 11 13 15 18 19 20 22 26 28 29 30 31 34 35 40 45 46 49 50 56 57 59 60 64 74 76 78 79 80 81 85 93 98 102 103 107 108 110 111 114 117 118 119 121 129 141 142 146 147 148 **S** Covenant Health, Knoxville, TN
Primary Contact: Gordon Lintz, Chief Administrative Officer
CFO: Amy Herndon, Director Finance
CIO: Mike Ward, Chief Information Officer
CNO: Dedra Whitaker, R.N., Chief Nursing Officer
Web address: www.mhhs1.org
Control: Other not–for–profit (including NFP Corporation) **Service:** General Medical and Surgical

Staffed Beds: 159 Admissions: 6889 Census: 77 Outpatient Visits: 85686 Births: 761 Total Expense ($000): 81834 Payroll Expense ($000): 28641 Personnel: 562

MOUNTAIN CITY—Johnson County

★ **JOHNSON COUNTY COMMUNITY HOSPITAL (441304)**, 1901 South Shady Street, Zip 37683–2271; tel. 423/727–1100 **A**5 9 10 18 **F**3 15 18 28 30 34 35 40 44 57 62 64 68 87 93 97 103 104 107 108 110 111 114 119 127 **P**6 8 **S** Mountain States Health Alliance, Johnson City, TN
Primary Contact: Chastity Trivette, Interim Chief Executive Officer
CNO: Helen Pardue, Interim Chief Nursing Officer
Web address: www.msha.com
Control: Other not–for–profit (including NFP Corporation) **Service:** General Medical and Surgical

Staffed Beds: 2 Admissions: 23 Census: 1 Outpatient Visits: 38428 Births: 0 Total Expense ($000): 8018 Payroll Expense ($000): 3936 Personnel: 58

MOUNTAIN HOME— County

⊞ **JAMES H. QUILLEN VETERANS AFFAIRS MEDICAL CENTER**, Corner of Lamont & Veterans Way, Zip 37684, Mailing Address: P.O. Box 4000, Zip 37684–4000; tel. 423/926–1171, (Nonreporting) **A**1 2 3 5 **S** Department of Veterans Affairs, Washington, DC
Primary Contact: Charlene S. Ehret, FACHE, Director
CFO: Sandra Nash, Chief Fiscal Service
CMO: David Hecht, M.D., Chief of Staff
CIO: Karen Perry, Chief Information Resource Management Services
CHR: John Henderson, Chief Human Resources Management
CNO: Linda M. McConnell, R.N., Associate Medical Center Director Patient Care Services
Web address: www.mountainhome.va.gov/
Control: Veterans Affairs, Government, federal **Service:** General Medical and Surgical

Staffed Beds: 483

MURFREESBORO—Rutherford County

ALVIN C. YORK CAMPUS See Tennessee Valley Healthcare System, Nashville

⊞ **SAINT THOMAS RUTHERFORD HOSPITAL (440053)**, 1700 Medical Center Parkway, Zip 37129–2245; tel. 615/396–4100, (Nonreporting) **A**1 3 5 9 10 **S** Ascension Health, Saint Louis, MO
Primary Contact: Gordon B. Ferguson, President and Chief Executive Officer
COO: Elizabeth Lemons, Chief Operating Officer
CFO: Larry Spratlin, Chief Financial Officer
CMO: Scott Corlew, M.D., Chief Medical Officer
CHR: Carol Bragdon, Director Human Resources
CNO: Stacey Beaven, R.N., Chief Nursing Officer
Web address: www.mtmc.org
Control: Church–operated, Nongovernment, not–for profit **Service:** General Medical and Surgical

Staffed Beds: 286

TRUSTPOINT HOSPITAL (440231), 1009 North Thompson Lane, Zip 37129–4351; tel. 615/867–1111, (Nonreporting) **A**10 **S** Polaris Hospital Company, Brentwood, TN
Primary Contact: Jeffrey Woods, Chief Executive Officer
Web address: www.trustpointhospital.com
Control: Partnership, Investor–owned, for–profit **Service:** Rehabilitation

Staffed Beds: 60

NASHVILLE—Davidson County

CENTENNIAL MEDICAL CENTER See Tristar Centennial Medical Center

⊞ **KINDRED HOSPITAL–NASHVILLE (442006)**, 1412 County Hospital Road, Zip 37218–3007; tel. 615/687–2600, (Nonreporting) **A**1 10 **S** Kindred Healthcare, Louisville, KY
Primary Contact: William P. Macri, Chief Executive Officer
CFO: Philip L. Jones, Chief Financial Officer
CMO: Clyde Heflin, M.D., Chief Medical Officer
CHR: Robyn Dunman, Coordinator Human Resources
CNO: Tom Rone, Chief Clinical Officer
Web address: www.khnashville.com/
Control: Corporation, Investor–owned, for–profit **Service:** Long–Term Acute Care hospital

Staffed Beds: 58

☐ **MIDDLE TENNESSEE MENTAL HEALTH INSTITUTE (444014)**, 221 Stewarts Ferry Pike, Zip 37214–3325; tel. 615/902–7535 **A**1 3 5 10 **F**3 29 30 75 98 101 102 103 106 130
Primary Contact: Bob Micinski, Chief Executive Officer
CFO: Mark Stanley, Director Fiscal Services
CMO: Mohammad S. Jahan, M.D., Clinical Director
CHR: Margie Dunn, Director Human Resources
Web address: www.tn.gov/mental/mhs/mhs2.html
Control: State–Government, nonfederal **Service:** Psychiatric

Staffed Beds: 195 Admissions: 3158 Census: 167 Outpatient Visits: 0 Births: 0 Total Expense ($000): 40969 Payroll Expense ($000): 22647 Personnel: 544

MONROE CARELL JR. CHILDREN'S HOSPITAL AT VANDERBILT See Vanderbilt Hospital and Clinics

☐ **NASHVILLE GENERAL HOSPITAL (440111)**, 1818 Albion Street, Zip 37208–2918; tel. 615/341–4000, (Nonreporting) **A**1 2 3 5 9 10
Primary Contact: Denise R. Williams, Interim Chief Executive Officer
CFO: Robert Lonis, Interim Chief Financial Officer
CMO: Chike Nzerue, M.D., Chief Medical Officer
CIO: Chris Whorley, Chief Information Officer
CHR: Diana Wohlfardt, Director Human Resources
CNO: Leonora Collins, Chief Nursing Officer
Web address: www.nashvilleha.org
Control: City–County, Government, nonfederal **Service:** General Medical and Surgical

Staffed Beds: 98

⊞ **SAINT THOMAS HOSPITAL FOR SPINAL SURGERY (440218)**, 2011 Murphy Avenue, Suite 400, Zip 37203–2065; tel. 615/341–7500, (Nonreporting) **A**1 9 10 **S** Ascension Health, Saint Louis, MO
Primary Contact: Kathy Watson, R.N., Administrator and Chief Nursing Officer
CFO: Angie Crow, Director Finance
CMO: Carl Hampf, M.D., Chief Medical Officer
Web address: www.hospitalforspinalsurgery.com
Control: Partnership, Investor–owned, for–profit **Service:** General Medical and Surgical

Staffed Beds: 23

⊞ **SAINT THOMAS MIDTOWN HOSPITAL (440133)**, 2000 Church Street, Zip 37236–0002; tel. 615/284–5555, (Nonreporting) **A**1 3 5 9 10 **S** Ascension Health, Saint Louis, MO
Primary Contact: Bernard Sherry, President and CEO
COO: Renee A. Kessler, Chief Operating Officer
CFO: Carrie Teaford, Vice President Finance
CMO: William Thompson, M.D., Chief Medical Officer
CIO: Jim Drew, Chief Information Officer
CHR: Martha Underwood, Chief Human Resources Officer
Web address: www.sths.com
Control: Other not–for–profit (including NFP Corporation) **Service:** General Medical and Surgical

Staffed Beds: 425

⊞ **SAINT THOMAS WEST HOSPITAL (440082)**, 4220 Harding Road, Zip 37205–2095, Mailing Address: P.O. Box 380, Zip 37202–0380; tel. 615/222–2111, (Nonreporting) **A**1 2 3 5 9 10 **S** Ascension Health, Saint Louis, MO
Primary Contact: Bernard Sherry, President and CEO
COO: Don King, Chief Operating Officer
CFO: Lisa Davis, Vice President Finance
CMO: Dale Batchelor, M.D., Chief Medical Officer
CIO: Randy Cox, Vice President and Chief Information Officer
CHR: Bud Wood, Chief Human Resources Officer
CNO: Jennifer Elliott, Chief Nursing Officer
Web address: www.stthomas.org
Control: Church–operated, Nongovernment, not–for profit **Service:** General Medical and Surgical

Staffed Beds: 395

Many Facility Codes have changed. Please refer to the AHA Guide Code Chart. © 2014 AHA Guide

✠ **SELECT SPECIALTY HOSPITAL–NASHVILLE (442011)**, 2000 Hayes Street, Zip 37203–2318; tel. 615/284–4599, (Nonreporting) **A**1 9 10 **S** Select Medical Corporation, Mechanicsburg, PA
Primary Contact: Jennifer Causey, Chief Executive Officer
CNO: Karen Cagle, Chief Nursing Officer
Web address: www.selectspecialtyhospitals.com/company/locations/nashville.aspx
Control: Corporation, Investor–owned, for–profit **Service:** Long–Term Acute Care hospital

Staffed Beds: 47

✠ **TENNESSEE VALLEY HEALTHCARE SYSTEM**, 1310 24th Avenue South, Zip 37212–2637; tel. 615/327–4751, (Includes ALVIN C. YORK CAMPUS, 3400 Lebanon Pike, Murfreesboro, Zip 37129–1236; tel. 615/867–6000; NASHVILLE CAMPUS, 1310 24th Avenue South, tel. 615/327–4751), (Total facility includes 238 beds in nursing home–type unit) **A**1 3 5 8 **F**1 3 5 12 15 17 18 20 22 24 26 28 30 31 38 39 40 45 54 56 57 58 60 62 63 64 70 74 75 77 78 79 81 82 83 84 87 90 91 92 93 94 97 98 100 102 103 104 107 108 110 111 114 115 116 117 118 119 129 130 135 136 142 143 146 147 148 **S** Department of Veterans Affairs, Washington, DC
Primary Contact: Juan A. Morales, R.N., MSN, Health System Director
COO: Suzanne Jene, Chief Operating Officer
CFO: Lynn Menthcoast, Chief Fiscal Service
CMO: Roger Jones, M.D., Interim Chief of Staff
CIO: Paul Mardy, Chief Information Technology Officer
CHR: Shirley F. Pettite, Chief Human Resources Officer
CNO: Janice M. Cobb, R.N., Chief Nursing Officer
Web address: www.tennesseevalley.va.gov
Control: Veterans Affairs, Government, federal **Service:** General Medical and Surgical

Staffed Beds: 546 **Admissions:** 11263 **Census:** 326 **Outpatient Visits:** 1203794 **Births:** 0 **Total Expense ($000):** 629540 **Payroll Expense ($000):** 253468 **Personnel:** 3639

✠ **TRISTAR CENTENNIAL MEDICAL CENTER (440161)**, 2300 Patterson Street, Zip 37203–1528; tel. 615/342–1000, (Includes TRISTAR CENTENNIAL WOMEN'S & CHILDREN'S, 2221 Murphy Avenue, Zip 37203; tel. 615/342–1000), (Nonreporting) **A**1 2 3 5 9 10 **S** HCA, Nashville, TN
Primary Contact: Heather J. Rohan, Chief Executive Officer
COO: Micki J. Slingerland, Chief Operating Officer
CFO: David A. Summers, Chief Financial Officer
CHR: Jennifer Burden, Human Resources Director
Web address: www.tristarcentennial.com
Control: Corporation, Investor–owned, for–profit **Service:** General Medical and Surgical

Staffed Beds: 583

✠ △ **TRISTAR SKYLINE MEDICAL CENTER (440006)**, 3441 Dickerson Pike, Zip 37207–2539; tel. 615/769–2000, (Nonreporting) **A**1 2 7 9 10 **S** HCA, Nashville, TN
Primary Contact: Steve Otto, Chief Executive Officer
COO: Dustin Greene, Chief Operating Officer
CFO: Bradley Schultz, Chief Financial Officer
CMO: Sunil Kaza, M.D., President Medical Staff
CIO: Troy Sypien, Director Information Technology and Systems
CHR: Robert A. Hooper, Director Human Resources
CNO: Laurie Turner, Chief Nursing Officer
Web address: www.skylinemedicalcenter.com
Control: Corporation, Investor–owned, for–profit **Service:** General Medical and Surgical

Staffed Beds: 295

✠ **TRISTAR SOUTHERN HILLS MEDICAL CENTER (440197)**, 391 Wallace Road, Zip 37211–4859; tel. 615/781–4000, (Nonreporting) **A**1 2 9 10 **S** HCA, Nashville, TN
Primary Contact: Thomas H. Ozburn, Chief Executive Officer
COO: Richard Tumlin, Chief Operating Officer
CFO: John Porada, Chief Financial Officer
CMO: Robert McCain, M.D., Chief of Staff
CIO: Ronnie Gannon, Director Information Services
CHR: Gary Briggs, Director Human Resources
CNO: Brenda C. Logan, R.N., Chief Nursing Officer
Web address: www.southernhills.com
Control: Corporation, Investor–owned, for–profit **Service:** General Medical and Surgical

Staffed Beds: 87

✠ **VANDERBILT HOSPITAL AND CLINICS (440039)**, 1211 22nd Avenue North, Zip 37232–2102; tel. 615/322–5000, (Includes MONROE CARELL JR. CHILDREN'S HOSPITAL AT VANDERBILT, 2200 Children's Way, Zip 37232; tel. 615/936–1000; Luke Gregory, Chief Executive Officer; VANDERBILT PSYCHIATRIC HOSPITAL, 1601 23rd Avenue South, Zip 37212–3198; tel. 615/320–7770; William Parsons, D.O., Chief Administrative Officer) **A**1 2 3 5 8 9 10 **F**2 3 4 5 6 7 8 9 11 12 13 15 16 17 18 19 20 21 22 23 24 25 26 27 28 29 30 31 32 34 35 36 38 39 40 41 42 43 44 45 46 47 48 49 50 51 52 53 54 55 56 57 58 59 60 61 62 63 64 65 66 68 70 72 74 75 77 78 79 80 81 82 83 84 85 86 87 88 91 92 93 94 95 96 97 98 99 100 101 102 103 104 105 106 107 108 109 110 111 114 115 116 117 118 119 120 121 123 124 126 129 130 131 132 134 135 136 137 138 139 140 141 142 143 144 146 147 148 **P**6 **S** Vanderbilt Health, Nashville, TN
Primary Contact: David R. Posch, Chief Executive Officer
COO: Mitch Edgeworth, Adult Enterprise Chief Operating Officer
CFO: Cecelia B. Moore, CPA, Associate Vice Chancellor Finance
CMO: Paul Sternberg, M.D., Professor and Chairman
CIO: William Stead, Associate Vice Chancellor Health Affairs, Director Informatics Center and Chief Strategy and Information Officer
CHR: Traci Nordberg, Chief Human Resources Officer
CNO: Pam Jones, MSN, Associate Hospital Director and Chief Nursing Officer
Web address: www.mc.vanderbilt.edu
Control: Other not–for–profit (including NFP Corporation) **Service:** General Medical and Surgical

Staffed Beds: 998 **Admissions:** 57768 **Census:** 842 **Outpatient Visits:** 1833337 **Births:** 4540 **Total Expense ($000):** 1812645 **Payroll Expense ($000):** 671217 **Personnel:** 13472

VANDERBILT PSYCHIATRIC HOSPITAL See Vanderbilt Hospital and Clinics

✠ **VANDERBILT STALLWORTH REHABILITATION HOSPITAL (443028)**, 2201 Childrens Way, Zip 37212–3165; tel. 615/320–7600, (Nonreporting) **A**1 5 9 10 **S** HEALTHSOUTH Corporation, Birmingham, AL
Primary Contact: Susan Heath, Chief Executive Officer
CFO: Peggy Belyeu, Controller
CMO: Jeffery Johns, M.D., Medical Director
CHR: Ruth Beasley, Director Human Resources
CNO: Karen Lasher, Chief Nursing Officer
Web address: www.vanderbiltstallworthrehab.com
Control: Corporation, Investor–owned, for–profit **Service:** Rehabilitation

Staffed Beds: 80

VETERANS AFFAIRS TENNESSEE VALLEY HEALTHCARE SYSTEM See Tennessee Valley Healthcare System

NEWPORT—Cocke County

BAPTIST HOSPITAL OF COCKE COUNTY See Tennova Newport Medical Center

✠ **TENNOVA NEWPORT MEDICAL CENTER (440153)**, 435 Second Street, Zip 37821–3799; tel. 423/625–2200, (Nonreporting) **A**1 9 10 **S** Community Health Systems, Inc., Franklin, TN
Primary Contact: Spencer Thomas, Chief Executive Officer
CFO: Jon Richards, Chief Financial Officer
CMO: Larry Mathers, M.D., Chief of Staff
CNO: Tonia Hale, Chief Nursing Officer
Web address: www.tennova.com
Control: Corporation, Investor–owned, for–profit **Service:** General Medical and Surgical

Staffed Beds: 47

OAK RIDGE—Anderson County

✠ **METHODIST MEDICAL CENTER OF OAK RIDGE (440034)**, 990 Oak Ridge Turnpike, Zip 37830–6976, Mailing Address: P.O. Box 2529, Zip 37831–2529; tel. 865/835–1000 **A**1 2 9 10 **F**3 11 13 15 17 18 20 22 24 26 28 29 30 31 34 35 37 40 45 46 47 48 49 50 51 57 58 59 60 61 64 68 70 74 75 76 77 78 79 81 82 84 85 86 87 92 93 102 107 108 110 111 114 117 118 119 120 121 123 124 126 129 130 132 135 141 142 146 148 **S** Covenant Health, Knoxville, TN
Primary Contact: Michael Belbeck, President and Chief Administrative Officer
COO: Connie Martin, Vice President and Chief Support Officer
CFO: Julie Utterback, Vice President and Chief Financial Officer
CIO: Mike Ward, Senior Vice President and Chief Information Officer
CHR: Rick Akens, Director Human Resources
CNO: Sue Harris, Vice President and Chief Nursing Officer
Web address: www.mmcoakridge.com
Control: Other not–for–profit (including NFP Corporation) **Service:** General Medical and Surgical

Staffed Beds: 210 **Admissions:** 10404 **Census:** 129 **Outpatient Visits:** 162680 **Births:** 569 **Total Expense ($000):** 160278 **Payroll Expense ($000):** 52816 **Personnel:** 928

TN

Hospital, Medicare Provider Number, Address, Telephone, Approval, Facility, and Physician Codes, Health Care System

★ American Hospital Association (AHA) membership
☐ The Joint Commission accreditation   ◇ DNV Healthcare Inc. accreditation
○ Healthcare Facilities Accreditation Program
△ Commission on Accreditation of Rehabilitation Facilities (CARF) accreditation

RIDGEVIEW PSYCHIATRIC HOSPITAL AND CENTER (444003), 240 West Tyrone Road, Zip 37830–6571; tel. 865/482–1076, (Nonreporting) **A**10
Primary Contact: Brian Buuck, Chief Executive Officer
CFO: Mary Claire Duff, CPA, Chief Financial Officer
CMO: Renu Bhateja, M.D., President Medical Staff
CHR: Julie M. Wright, Director Human Resources
Web address: www.ridgeviewresources.com
Control: Other not–for–profit (including NFP Corporation) **Service:** Psychiatric

Staffed Beds: 20

PARIS—Henry County

☒ **HENRY COUNTY MEDICAL CENTER (440132)**, 301 Tyson Avenue, Zip 38242–4544, Mailing Address: P.O. Box 1030, Zip 38242–1030; tel. 731/642–1220, (Total facility includes 150 beds in nursing home–type unit) **A**1 9 10 **F**3 7 8 11 13 15 18 20 28 29 30 31 32 34 35 39 40 51 53 57 59 62 63 64 65 67 68 70 71 76 77 78 79 81 82 85 86 87 89 93 98 102 103 107 108 110 111 114 118 119 121 126 128 129 130 131 132 133 135 146 148 **P**6
Primary Contact: Thomas H. Gee, Administrator
CFO: Lisa Casteel, Assistant Administrator and Chief Financial Officer
CIO: Pam Ridley, Director Information Systems
CHR: Edwin L. Ledden, Assistant Administrator and Director Human Resources
CNO: James Caldwell, R.N., Chief Nursing Officer
Web address: www.hcmc–tn.org
Control: Hospital district or authority, Government, nonfederal **Service:** General Medical and Surgical

Staffed Beds: 251 **Admissions:** 3881 **Census:** 152 **Outpatient Visits:** 80946
Births: 364 **Total Expense ($000):** 72210 **Payroll Expense ($000):** 29887
Personnel: 673

PARSONS—Decatur County

☐ **DECATUR COUNTY GENERAL HOSPITAL (440070)**, 969 Tennessee Avenue South, Zip 38363–3700, Mailing Address: P.O. Box 250, Zip 38363–0250; tel. 731/847–3031, (Nonreporting) **A**1 9 10
Primary Contact: Scott Barber, Chief Executive Officer
CFO: Donna Hayes, Controller
CMO: Tom Hamilton, M.D., Chief of Staff
CHR: Shelley Bartholomew, Director Human Resources
Web address: www.dcgh.org
Control: County–Government, nonfederal **Service:** General Medical and Surgical

Staffed Beds: 40

PIKEVILLE—Bledsoe County

ERLANGER BLEDSOE HOSPITAL (441306), 71 Wheeler Avenue, Zip 37367, Mailing Address: P.O. Box 699, Zip 37367–0699; tel. 423/447–2112 **A**9 10 18 **F**3 11 15 18 28 29 30 34 35 38 40 41 44 50 54 56 57 59 61 63 64 65 66 68 75 82 84 86 87 92 93 97 102 103 107 110 119 127 130 131 133 135 144 146 147 148 **P**6 **S** Erlanger Health System, Chattanooga, TN
Primary Contact: Stephanie Boynton, Administrator
CMO: Arturo L. Quito, M.D., Chief of Staff
CIO: Debbie Rains, Coordinator Health Information Management
CHR: Patsy Brown, Site Coordinator Human Resources
Web address: www.erlanger.org
Control: Hospital district or authority, Government, nonfederal **Service:** General Medical and Surgical

Staffed Beds: 25 **Admissions:** 226 **Census:** 6 **Outpatient Visits:** 14075
Births: 0 **Total Expense ($000):** 9041 **Payroll Expense ($000):** 3379
Personnel: 71

POWELL—Knox County

MERCY MEDICAL CENTER NORTH See Tennova North Knoxville Medical Center

PULASKI—Giles County

☒ **SOUTHERN TENNESSEE REGIONAL HEALTH SYSTEM–PULASKI (440020)**, 1265 East College Street, Zip 38478–4541; tel. 931/363–7531, (Nonreporting) **A**1 9 10 **S** LifePoint Hospitals, Inc., Brentwood, TN
Primary Contact: Harold L. Siglar, Interim Chief Executive Officer
CFO: Donald Gavin, Chief Financial Officer
CMO: J. Michael Windland, M.D., Chief of Staff
CIO: Mitzi Foster, Director Information Services
CHR: Jane Petty, Director Human Resources
CNO: Sherry Sands, R.N., Chief Nursing Officer
Web address: www.hillsidehospital.com
Control: Corporation, Investor–owned, for–profit **Service:** General Medical and Surgical

Staffed Beds: 50

RIPLEY—Lauderdale County

★ ◇ **LAUDERDALE COMMUNITY HOSPITAL (441314)**, 326 Asbury Avenue, Zip 38063–5577; tel. 731/221–2200 **A**9 10 18 21 **F**11 15 28 29 30 34 35 40 45 57 59 64 74 75 77 79 81 85 87 93 107 114 119 130 132 133 134 135 146 148 **S** Rural Community Hospitals of America, Kansas City, MO
Primary Contact: Scott Tongate, Chief Executive Officer
CFO: Jim Sneed, Chief Financial Officer
CMO: Syed A. Zaidi, M.D., Chief of Staff
CIO: Jim Vaden, Director Information Systems
CHR: Gail Henderson, Manager Human Resources
Web address: www.lauderdalehospital.com/
Control: Corporation, Investor–owned, for–profit **Service:** General Medical and Surgical

Staffed Beds: 25 **Admissions:** 378 **Census:** 4 **Outpatient Visits:** 26470
Births: 0 **Total Expense ($000):** 14337 **Payroll Expense ($000):** 6035
Personnel: 129

ROGERSVILLE—Hawkins County

☒ **WELLMONT HAWKINS COUNTY MEMORIAL HOSPITAL (440032)**, 851 Locust Street, Zip 37857–2407, Mailing Address: P.O. Box 130, Zip 37857–0130; tel. 423/921–7000 **A**1 5 9 10 **F**3 11 15 29 30 31 34 35 40 45 50 57 59 64 68 75 77 78 79 81 82 85 87 93 97 107 108 118 119 129 130 146 **S** Wellmont Health System, Kingsport, TN
Primary Contact: Fred L. Pelle, FACHE, Interim Chief Executive Officer
CFO: Dale Poe, Chief Financial Officer
CHR: Robin Poteete, Manager Human Resources
Web address: www.wellmont.org
Control: Other not–for–profit (including NFP Corporation) **Service:** General Medical and Surgical

Staffed Beds: 16 **Admissions:** 1265 **Census:** 9 **Outpatient Visits:** 37772
Births: 0 **Total Expense ($000):** 43708 **Payroll Expense ($000):** 6525
Personnel: 161

SAVANNAH—Hardin County

★ ◇ **HARDIN MEDICAL CENTER (440109)**, 935 Wayne Road, Zip 38372–1904; tel. 731/926–8000, (Total facility includes 73 beds in nursing home–type unit) **A**9 10 21 **F**2 3 7 11 13 15 18 19 28 29 31 34 40 45 57 59 65 69 75 76 77 78 79 80 81 89 93 107 110 111 115 119 124 128 129 130 133 144 148
Primary Contact: Nicholas P. Lewis, Chief Executive Officer
CFO: Leigh Ann Hughes, Chief Financial Officer
CMO: Gilbert M. Thayer, M.D., Chief Medical Staff
CIO: Jacob Bomar, Director Information Technology
CHR: Jimmy Davis, Director Human Resources
CNO: Jesse Wint, Director of Nursing
Web address: www.hardinmedicalcenter.org
Control: County–Government, nonfederal **Service:** General Medical and Surgical

Staffed Beds: 122 **Admissions:** 1895 **Census:** 84 **Outpatient Visits:** 66745
Births: 320 **Total Expense ($000):** 37447 **Payroll Expense ($000):** 18165
Personnel: 409

SELMER—Mcnairy County

☒ **MCNAIRY REGIONAL HOSPITAL (440051)**, 705 East Poplar Avenue, Zip 38375–1828; tel. 731/645–3221, (Nonreporting) **A**1 9 10 **S** Community Health Systems, Inc., Franklin, TN
Primary Contact: Pamela W. Roberts, Chief Executive Officer
CFO: Meredith Jones, Chief Financial Officer
CMO: Ryan Bartz, D.O., Chief of Staff
CHR: Linda Durham, Director Human Resources
Web address: www.mcnairyregionalhospital.com
Control: Other not–for–profit (including NFP Corporation) **Service:** General Medical and Surgical

Staffed Beds: 45

SEVIERVILLE—Sevier County

☒ **LECONTE MEDICAL CENTER (440081)**, 742 Middle Creek Road, Zip 37862–5019, Mailing Address: P.O. Box 8005, Zip 37864–8005; tel. 865/446–7000, (Total facility includes 54 beds in nursing home–type unit) **A**1 5 9 10 **F**3 11 13 15 18 20 28 29 30 34 35 40 45 50 51 53 57 59 61 64 67 68 70 75 76 77 78 79 81 85 87 93 107 110 111 114 119 128 129 130 131 135 146 147 **S** Covenant Health, Knoxville, TN
Primary Contact: Jennifer Hanson, MS, R.N., President and Chief Administrative Officer
COO: Rick Carringer, Vice President Finance and Support Services
CFO: Rick Carringer, Vice President Finance and Support Services
CMO: Stephen Dill, M.D., Chief of Staff
CIO: Amanda Paletz, Director Marketing and Public Relations
CHR: Derek Winkle, Director Human Resources
Web address: www.lecontemedicalcenter.com
Control: Other not–for–profit (including NFP Corporation) **Service:** General Medical and Surgical

Staffed Beds: 123 **Admissions:** 4200 **Census:** 82 **Outpatient Visits:** 113838
Births: 944 **Total Expense ($000):** 64539 **Payroll Expense ($000):** 22995
Personnel: 439

Many Facility Codes have changed. Please refer to the AHA Guide Code Chart. © 2014 AHA Guide

TN

SEWANEE—Franklin County

SOUTHERN TENNESSEE REGIONAL HEALTH SYSTEM–SEWANEE See Southern Tennessee Regional Health System–Winchester, Winchester

SHELBYVILLE—Bedford County

⊠ **HERITAGE MEDICAL CENTER (440137)**, 2835 Highway 231 North, Zip 37160–7327; tel. 931/685–5433, (Nonreporting) **A**1 9 10 **S** Community Health Systems, Inc., Franklin, TN
Primary Contact: David V. Bunch, Chief Executive Officer
CFO: Mitchell Frank, Chief Financial Officer
CIO: Jonathon Willis, Director Information Services
CHR: Rob Thorne, Director Human Resources
CNO: Vickie Vaughn, Chief Nursing Officer
Web address: www.heritagemedicalcenter.com
Control: County–Government, nonfederal **Service:** General Medical and Surgical

Staffed Beds: 70

SMITHVILLE—Dekalb County

☐ **DEKALB COMMUNITY HOSPITAL (440148)**, 520 West Main Street, Zip 37166–1138, Mailing Address: P.O. Box 640, Zip 37166–0640; tel. 615/215–5000, (Nonreporting) **A**1 9 10 **S** Capella Healthcare, Franklin, TN
Primary Contact: Susan Conley, Chief Executive Officer
CMO: Hugh Don Cripps, M.D., Chief of Staff
CHR: Gingie Braswell, Director Human Resources
CNO: Kimberly Frazier, Chief Nursing Officer
Web address: www.dekalbcommunityhospital.com
Control: Corporation, Investor–owned, for–profit **Service:** General Medical and Surgical

Staffed Beds: 52

SMYRNA—Rutherford County

⊠ **TRISTAR STONECREST MEDICAL CENTER (440227)**, 200 StoneCrest Boulevard, Zip 37167–6810; tel. 615/768–2000, (Nonreporting) **A**1 2 9 10 **S** HCA, Nashville, TN
Primary Contact: Louis Caputo, Chief Executive Officer
COO: Andrew Tyrer, Chief Operating Officer
CFO: Joseph E. Bowman, Chief Financial Officer
CMO: William Mayfield, M.D., Chief of Staff
CHR: Cynthia Adams, Vice President Human Resources
CNO: Ruth Willard, Chief Nursing Officer
Web address: www.stonecrestmedical.com
Control: Corporation, Investor–owned, for–profit **Service:** General Medical and Surgical

Staffed Beds: 101

SNEEDVILLE—Hancock County

★ **WELLMONT HANCOCK COUNTY HOSPITAL (441313)**, 1519 Main Street, Zip 37869–3657; tel. 423/733–5000 **A**9 10 18 **F**3 29 30 34 35 40 50 57 59 68 87 107 108 118 119 133 **S** Wellmont Health System, Kingsport, TN
Primary Contact: Fred L. Pelle, FACHE, Interim Chief Executive Officer
COO: Tracey Moffatt, Chief Operating Officer
CFO: Regina Day, Chief Financial Officer
CMO: Troy Sybert, M.D., Chief Medical Officer
CIO: Will Showalter, Senior Vice President Information Technology
CHR: Robin Poteete, Manager Human Resources
CNO: Sheri Ives, R.N., Vice President Clinical Services
Web address: www.wellmont.org/Hospitals/Hancock–County–Hospital.aspx
Control: Other not–for–profit (including NFP Corporation) **Service:** General Medical and Surgical

Staffed Beds: 10 Admissions: 206 Census: 2 Outpatient Visits: 8180 Births: 0 Total Expense ($000): 5810 Payroll Expense ($000): 1731 Personnel: 39

SOMERVILLE—Fayette County

☐ **METHODIST HEALTHCARE–FAYETTE HOSPITAL (440168)**, 214 Lakeview Drive, Zip 38068–9737; tel. 901/516–4000 **A**1 9 10 **F**3 15 29 34 35 40 57 59 64 68 75 87 107 111 114 119 133 146 148 **S** Methodist Le Bonheur Healthcare, Memphis, TN
Primary Contact: William A. Kenley, Chief Executive Officer
CFO: Jane George, Controller
CMO: Barton Thrasher, M.D., Chief of Staff
CHR: Joanell West, Human Resources Generalist
CNO: Janet Hunt, R.N., Chief Nursing Officer
Web address: www.methodisthealth.org
Control: Other not–for–profit (including NFP Corporation) **Service:** General Medical and Surgical

Staffed Beds: 10 Admissions: 176 Census: 2 Outpatient Visits: 11962 Births: 0 Total Expense ($000): 6609 Payroll Expense ($000): 2822 Personnel: 50

SPARTA—White County

☐ **HIGHLANDS MEDICAL CENTER (440192)**, 401 Sewell Road, Zip 38583–1299; tel. 931/738–9211, (Nonreporting) **A**1 9 10 **S** Capella Healthcare, Franklin, TN
Primary Contact: William Little, Chief Executive Officer
CFO: Rodney VanDonkelaar, Chief Financial Officer
CMO: Robert Knowles, M.D., Chief of Staff
CIO: Glenn Wade, Director Information Systems
CHR: Kent Frisbee, Director Human Resources
CNO: Gearline Copeland, R.N., Chief Nursing Officer
Web address: www.whitecountyhospital.com
Control: Corporation, Investor–owned, for–profit **Service:** General Medical and Surgical

Staffed Beds: 44

SPRINGFIELD—Robertson County

⊠ **NORTHCREST MEDICAL CENTER (440065)**, 100 North Crest Drive, Zip 37172–3961; tel. 615/384–2411 **A**1 9 10 **F**3 11 13 15 18 20 22 28 29 30 34 40 41 45 46 50 57 59 64 68 70 76 77 81 84 85 87 89 107 108 109 110 111 114 115 119 120 121 122 123 124 129 130 132 135 146 148 **P**3
Primary Contact: Randy Davis, Chief Executive Officer
CFO: Kim Pridgen, Chief Financial Officer
CMO: Tommy Crunk, M.D., Chief of Staff
CHR: Amber King, Director Human Resources
CNO: Angie Beard, Chief Nursing Officer
Web address: www.northcrest.com
Control: Other not–for–profit (including NFP Corporation) **Service:** General Medical and Surgical

Staffed Beds: 80 Admissions: 3249 Census: 39 Outpatient Visits: 90820 Births: 520

SWEETWATER—Monroe County

⊠ **SWEETWATER HOSPITAL (440084)**, 304 Wright Street, Zip 37874–2823; tel. 865/213–8200, (Nonreporting) **A**1 9 10
Primary Contact: Scott Bowman, Administrator
CFO: Debbie Thompson, Chief Financial Officer
CMO: Tracey Beverley, M.D., Chief Medical Staff
CIO: Tony Sharp, Supervisor Information System
CHR: Lucretia Santelli, Director Human Resources
CNO: Andrea Henry, Director of Nursing
Web address: www.sweetwaterhospital.org
Control: Other not–for–profit (including NFP Corporation) **Service:** General Medical and Surgical

Staffed Beds: 59

TAZEWELL—Claiborne County

⊠ **CLAIBORNE MEDICAL CENTER (440057)**, 1850 Old Knoxville Road, Zip 37879–3625; tel. 423/626–4211, (Nonreporting) **A**1 9 10 20 **S** Covenant Health, Knoxville, TN
Primary Contact: Tim S. Brown, Chief Executive Officer
CFO: Tracee McFarland, Chief Financial Officer
CHR: Susan Stone, Director Human Resources
Web address: www.claibornehospital.org
Control: County–Government, nonfederal **Service:** General Medical and Surgical

Staffed Beds: 62

TULLAHOMA—Coffee County

⊠ **HARTON REGIONAL MEDICAL CENTER (440144)**, 1801 North Jackson Street, Zip 37388–8259; tel. 931/393–3000, (Nonreporting) **A**1 9 10 19 **S** Community Health Systems, Inc., Franklin, TN
Primary Contact: William R. Spray, Chief Executive Officer
COO: Trevor Castaneda, Chief Operating Officer
CFO: Shaun Adams, Chief Financial Officer
CMO: John D. Crabtree, M.D., Chief of Staff
CIO: Donald Cooper, Director Information Systems
CHR: Lenore Blackwell, Director Human Resources
CNO: Eddy L. Hannah, R.N., Chief Nursing Officer
Web address: www.hartonmedicalcenter.com
Control: Corporation, Investor–owned, for–profit **Service:** General Medical and Surgical

Staffed Beds: 104

Hospital, Medicare Provider Number, Address, Telephone, Approval, Facility, and Physician Codes, Health Care System

★ American Hospital Association (AHA) membership
☐ The Joint Commission accreditation
◇ DNV Healthcare Inc. accreditation
○ Healthcare Facilities Accreditation Program
△ Commission on Accreditation of Rehabilitation Facilities (CARF) accreditation

TN

TN

✠ **BAPTIST MEMORIAL HOSPITAL–UNION CITY (440130)**, 1201 Bishop Street,
Zip 38261–5403, Mailing Address: P.O. Box 310, Zip 38281–0310;
tel. 731/885–2410 **A**1 9 10 **F**4 5 7 11 13 15 18 20 26 29 30 34 35 40 45 48
50 51 53 57 58 59 63 64 70 75 76 79 80 81 82 84 85 86 87 89 91 93 98
99 100 101 102 104 105 107 108 109 110 111 115 118 119 124 130 132
135 146 **P**3 **S** Baptist Memorial Health Care Corporation, Memphis, TN
Primary Contact: Barry Bondurant, Administrator and Chief Executive Officer
CFO: Mike Perryman, Chief Financial Officer
CMO: Kofi Nuako, M.D., President Medical Staff
CIO: David Mercer, Coordinator Information Systems
CHR: Nicky Thomas, Director Human Resources
CNO: Lori Brown, Chief Nursing Officer
Web address: www.baptistonline.org/union–city/
Control: Other not–for–profit (including NFP Corporation) **Service:** General
Medical and Surgical

Staffed Beds: 85 **Admissions:** 2667 **Census:** 27 **Outpatient Visits:** 42319
Births: 265 **Total Expense ($000):** 42187 **Payroll Expense ($000):** 15944
Personnel: 331

THREE RIVERS HOSPITAL (441303), 451 Highway 13 South,
Zip 37185–2109, Mailing Address: P.O. Box 437, Zip 37185–0437;
tel. 931/296–4203, (Nonreporting) **A**9 10 18
Primary Contact: Freda Russell, R.N., Chief Executive Officer and Chief Nursing
Officer
CFO: Sandra Patrick, Chief Financial Officer
CMO: George Mathai, M.D., Chief of Staff
CIO: Joe Hildreth, Director Information Technology
CHR: Linda Rawlings, Director Human Resources and Personnel
CNO: Freda Russell, R.N., Chief Executive Officer and Chief Nursing Officer
Web address: www.threerivershospital.org
Control: Other not–for–profit (including NFP Corporation) **Service:** General
Medical and Surgical

Staffed Beds: 25

✠ **WAYNE MEDICAL CENTER (440010)**, 103 J. V. Mangubat Drive,
Zip 38485–2440, Mailing Address: P.O. Box 580, Zip 38485–0580;
tel. 931/722–5411, (Nonreporting) **A**1 9 10 20 **S** Maury Regional Health System,
Columbia, TN
Primary Contact: Paul Betz, FACHE, Interim Chief Executive Officer
CMO: Harish Veeramachaneni, M.D., Chief of Staff
CHR: Jeff M. Pierce, Manager Human Resources
Web address: www.mauryregional.com
Control: Other not–for–profit (including NFP Corporation) **Service:** General
Medical and Surgical

Staffed Beds: 78

✠ **SOUTHERN TENNESSEE REGIONAL HEALTH SYSTEM–WINCHESTER
(440058)**, 185 Hospital Road, Zip 37398–2404; tel. 931/967–8200, (Includes
SOUTHERN TENNESSEE REGIONAL HEALTH SYSTEM–SEWANEE, 1260 University
Avenue, Sewanee, Zip 37375–2303; tel. 931/598–5691; Ralph Underwood,
Administrator), (Total facility includes 46 beds in nursing home–type unit) **A**1 9 10
F3 13 15 17 18 20 28 29 34 38 40 42 45 46 48 56 57 59 70 74 75 76 77
79 81 85 86 87 90 93 98 103 107 108 110 111 114 119 128 129 130 131
135 146 147 148 **S** LifePoint Hospitals, Inc., Brentwood, TN
Primary Contact: J. Phillip Young, FACHE, Chief Executive Officer
CFO: Steve Moore, Chief Financial Officer
CIO: James Payne, Director Information Systems
CHR: Linda Tipps, Director Human Resources
Web address: www.southerntennessee.com
Control: Corporation, Investor–owned, for–profit **Service:** General Medical and
Surgical

Staffed Beds: 188 **Admissions:** 4950 **Census:** 77 **Outpatient Visits:** 76166
Births: 412 **Total Expense ($000):** 64418 **Payroll Expense ($000):** 30742
Personnel: 420

☐ **STONES RIVER HOSPITAL (440200)**, 324 Doolittle Road, Zip 37190–1139;
tel. 615/563–4001, (Nonreporting) **A**1 9 10 **S** Capella Healthcare, Franklin, TN
Primary Contact: Susan Conley, Chief Executive Officer
CMO: J. C. Wall, M.D., Chief of Staff
CHR: Brian Woods, Director Human Resources
CNO: Kimberly Frazier, Chief Nursing Officer
Web address: www.stonesriverhospital.com
Control: Corporation, Investor–owned, for–profit **Service:** General Medical and
Surgical

Staffed Beds: 60

TEXAS

ABILENE—Taylor County

✠ **ABILENE BEHAVIORAL HEALTH (454098)**, 4225 Woods Place,
Zip 79602–7991, Mailing Address: P.O. Box 5559, Zip 79608–5559;
tel. 325/698–6600 **A**1 9 10 **F**4 5 29 34 54 56 64 86 87 98 99 101 103 104
105 130 **S** Acadia Healthcare Company, Inc., Franklin, TN
Primary Contact: Sheila McDermott–Lord, Chief Executive Officer
Web address: www.abilenebehavioralhealth.com/
Control: Corporation, Investor–owned, for–profit **Service:** Psychiatric

Staffed Beds: 92 **Admissions:** 1901 **Census:** 62 **Outpatient Visits:** 8340
Births: 0 **Total Expense ($000):** 11214 **Payroll Expense ($000):** 5316
Personnel: 104

✠ **ABILENE REGIONAL MEDICAL CENTER (450558)**, 6250 U.S. Highway 83,
Zip 79606–5299; tel. 325/428–1000, (Total facility includes 25 beds in nursing
home–type unit) **A**1 9 10 **F**8 11 13 15 17 18 20 22 24 26 28 29 30 31 34 35
40 41 43 45 46 49 50 53 56 57 59 64 68 70 72 75 76 77 78 79 81 85 86
87 89 91 93 107 108 110 111 114 115 118 119 126 128 130 132 135 146
147 148 **P**3 **S** Community Health Systems, Inc., Franklin, TN
Primary Contact: Michael D. Murphy, Chief Executive Officer
CFO: Ron Bennett, Chief Financial Officer
CMO: Tim Bumann, D.O., Chief of Staff
CIO: Dennis Newquist, Director Information Systems
CHR: John J. Jeziorske, Director Human Resources
CNO: Jessica Kiehle, R.N., Chief Nursing Officer
Web address: www.abileneregional.com
Control: Partnership, Investor–owned, for–profit **Service:** General Medical and
Surgical

Staffed Beds: 205 **Admissions:** 6748 **Census:** 83 **Outpatient Visits:** 71951
Births: 1278 **Total Expense ($000):** 94672 **Payroll Expense ($000):** 34776
Personnel: 641

ACADIA ABILENE HOSPITAL See Abilene Behavioral Health

CONTINUE CARE HOSPITAL AT HENDRICK MEDICAL CENTER (452029),
1900 Pine Street, Zip 79601–2432; tel. 325/670–2384 **A**10 **F**1 29 31 68 85
130 132
Primary Contact: Tom Harlan, Chief Executive Officer
CFO: Gregory Taylor, Chief Financial Officer
CNO: Sherry Hendricksen, Chief Nursing Officer
Control: Church–operated, Nongovernment, not–for profit **Service:** Long–Term
Acute Care hospital

Staffed Beds: 19 **Admissions:** 199 **Census:** 15 **Outpatient Visits:** 0 **Births:**
0 **Total Expense ($000):** 5790 **Payroll Expense ($000):** 1646 **Personnel:**
17

✠ **HENDRICK HEALTH SYSTEM (450229)**, 1900 Pine Street, Zip 79601–2432;
tel. 325/670–2000, (Total facility includes 20 beds in nursing home–type unit) **A**1
9 10 **F**3 11 12 13 14 15 17 18 20 22 24 26 28 29 30 31 32 34 35 36 39 40
43 44 45 48 49 50 51 53 56 57 59 60 61 62 64 68 70 73 74 75 76 77 78
79 80 81 84 85 86 87 88 89 90 92 93 96 97 102 107 108 110 111 114 115
118 119 121 123 128 129 130 131 132 135 143 146 147 148 **P**8
Primary Contact: Tim Lancaster, FACHE, President and Chief Executive Officer
CFO: Jeremy Tyler Walker, Vice President and Chief Financial Officer
CMO: Steve Faehnle, M.D., Vice President Medical Affairs
CIO: Duane Donaway, Director Information Technology
CHR: Susan Wade, Assistant Vice President
CNO: Susie Cassle, R.N., Assistant Vice President Nursing Services
Web address: www.ehendrick.org
Control: Church–operated, Nongovernment, not–for profit **Service:** General
Medical and Surgical

Staffed Beds: 390 **Admissions:** 15976 **Census:** 234 **Outpatient Visits:**
285940 **Births:** 1512 **Total Expense ($000):** 282169 **Payroll Expense
($000):** 101206 **Personnel:** 1869

☐ **OCEANS BEHAVIORAL HOSPITAL ABILENE (454122)**, 6401 Directors
Parkway, Suite 200, Zip 79606–5869; tel. 325/691–0030, (Nonreporting) **A**1 10
Primary Contact: Daniel G. Carpenter, Administrator
Web address: www.oceansabilene.com
Control: Corporation, Investor–owned, for–profit **Service:** Psychiatric

Staffed Beds: 35

☐ **RELIANT REHABILITATION HOSPITAL ABILENE (673039)**, 6401 Directors
Parkway, Zip 79606–5869; tel. 325/691–1600 **A**1 9 10 **F**3 29 90 93 96 130
148 **S** Reliant Healthcare Partners, Richardson, TX
Primary Contact: Joe Roberson, Chief Executive Officer
Web address: www.reliantabilene.com
Control: Partnership, Investor–owned, for–profit **Service:** Rehabilitation

Staffed Beds: 30 **Admissions:** 451 **Census:** 11 **Outpatient Visits:** 87 **Births:**
0 **Total Expense ($000):** 6254 **Payroll Expense ($000):** 2286 **Personnel:**
46

ADDISON—Dallas County

◇ **METHODIST HOSPITAL FOR SURGERY (670073)**, 17101 North Dallas
Parkway, Zip 75001–7103; tel. 469/248–3900 **A**9 10 21 **F**3 29 30 35 40 64
70 81 93 107 111 112 119 130 146 **P**2
Primary Contact: Chris Shoup, President
CFO: Jade Andrews, Chief Financial Officer
CMO: Rajiv Pandit, M.D., Medical Director
CIO: Ronda Kirk Johnson, Manager Health Information Management
CNO: Patti Griffith, R.N., Chief Nursing Officer
Web address: www.methodisthospitalforsurgery.com/
Control: Corporation, Investor–owned, for–profit **Service:** Surgical

Staffed Beds: 32 **Admissions:** 2377 **Census:** 15 **Outpatient Visits:** 8310
Births: 0 **Total Expense ($000):** 85053 **Payroll Expense ($000):** 12902
Personnel: 205

ALICE—Jim Wells County

✠ **CHRISTUS SPOHN HOSPITAL ALICE (450828)**, 2500 East Main Street,
Zip 78332–4169; tel. 361/661–8000 **A**1 9 10 20 **F**3 11 13 15 18 20 22 28
29 30 35 39 40 42 43 45 46 49 50 57 59 68 70 75 76 77 79 81 85 86 87
89 93 97 98 100 101 102 103 107 108 111 114 119 127 130 146 148 **P**8
S CHRISTUS Health, Irving, TX
Primary Contact: Steven G. Daniel, Senior Vice President and Chief Operating
Officer
COO: Steven G. Daniel, Senior Vice President and Chief Operating Officer
CFO: Michael Guajardo, Director Finance
CMO: Jerry Liles, D.O.
CIO: William Morgan, Director Management Information Systems
CHR: Mindy Soliz, Director Human Resources
CNO: Margot Rios, R.N., Chief Nursing Officer
Web address: www.christusspohn.org/locations_alice.htm
Control: Church–operated, Nongovernment, not–for profit **Service:** General
Medical and Surgical

Staffed Beds: 91 **Admissions:** 3692 **Census:** 39 **Outpatient Visits:** 53524
Births: 545 **Total Expense ($000):** 51986 **Payroll Expense ($000):** 17673
Personnel: 233

ALLEN—Collin County

✠ **POST ACUTE/WARM SPRINGS REHABILITATION HOSPITAL OF ALLEN
(673025)**, 1001 Raintree Circle, Zip 75013–4912; tel. 972/908–2015, (Data for
267 days) **A**1 9 10 **F**3 28 29 30 34 40 56 59 60 74 75 79 90 91 94 96
100 130 132 146 148 **S** Post Acute Medical, LLC, Enola, PA
Primary Contact: Bill Kaupas, Chief Executive Officer
Web address: www.warmsprings.org
Control: Partnership, Investor–owned, for–profit **Service:** Rehabilitation

Staffed Beds: 39 **Admissions:** 596 **Census:** 26 **Outpatient Visits:** 0 **Births:**
0 **Total Expense ($000):** 8138 **Payroll Expense ($000):** 3087 **Personnel:**
96

TX

⊞ **TEXAS HEALTH PRESBYTERIAN HOSPITAL ALLEN (450840)**, 1105 Central Expressway North, Zip 75013–6103; tel. 972/747–1000 **A**1 9 10 **F**3 13 15 18 28 29 30 34 35 38 40 47 49 51 54 55 57 59 64 65 70 73 74 75 76 79 81 89 93 107 110 111 114 115 118 119 126 129 130 132 135 146 147 148
S Texas Health Resources, Arlington, TX
Primary Contact: Jeff Reecer, President
CFO: Dan Rich, Director Finance
CMO: Bob Schwab, M.D., Chief Medical Officer
CHR: Sharon Chisholm, Director Human Resources
CNO: Jane Cook, R.N., Chief Nursing Officer
Web address: www.texashealth.org
Control: Other not–for–profit (including NFP Corporation) **Service:** General Medical and Surgical

Staffed Beds: 73 **Admissions:** 3192 **Census:** 28 **Outpatient Visits:** 48567 **Births:** 587 **Total Expense ($000):** 69860 **Payroll Expense ($000):** 25143 **Personnel:** 292

ALPINE—Brewster County

⊞ **BIG BEND REGIONAL MEDICAL CENTER (451378)**, 2600 Highway 118 North, Zip 79830–2002; tel. 432/837–3447 **A**1 9 10 18 **F**3 29 30 34 35 40 43 45 49 57 59 64 68 70 75 76 81 85 89 93 107 119 132 133 146 147 148 **P**6
S Community Health Systems, Inc., Franklin, TN
Primary Contact: Michael J. Ellis, Chief Executive Officer
Web address: www.bigbendhealthcare.com
Control: Corporation, Investor–owned, for–profit **Service:** General Medical and Surgical

Staffed Beds: 25 **Admissions:** 794 **Census:** 6 **Outpatient Visits:** 11655 **Births:** 189 **Total Expense ($000):** 19129 **Payroll Expense ($000):** 6560 **Personnel:** 118

ALVIN—Brazoria County

ALVIN DIAGNOSTIC AND URGENT CARE CENTER See Clear Lake Regional Medical Center, Webster

AMARILLO—Potter County

⊞ **AMARILLO VETERANS AFFAIRS HEALTH CARE SYSTEM**, 6010 West Amarillo Boulevard, Zip 79106–1992; tel. 806/355–9703, (Nonreporting) **A**1 2 3 5 9
S Department of Veterans Affairs, Washington, DC
Primary Contact: Andrew Welch, Director
COO: Lance Robinson, Associate Director
CMO: James Gray, M.D., Chief Medical Service
CIO: Modesto Baca, Chief Information Officer
CHR: Ken Creamer, Chief Human Resource
Web address: www.amarillo.va.gov/
Control: Veterans Affairs, Government, federal **Service:** General Medical and Surgical

Staffed Beds: 55

⊞ ◇ **BAPTIST ST. ANTHONY HEALTH SYSTEM (450231)**, 1600 Wallace Boulevard, Zip 79106–1799; tel. 806/212–2000 **A**1 2 3 5 9 10 21 **F**3 7 8 11 12 13 15 17 18 19 20 22 24 26 28 29 30 31 34 35 40 45 46 48 49 51 53 54 57 59 62 63 64 70 72 74 75 76 77 78 79 81 82 85 86 87 88 89 90 91 93 96 107 108 110 111 114 115 117 119 126 129 130 131 145 146 147 148
Primary Contact: Bob Williams, President and Chief Executive Officer
COO: Michael Cruz, Vice President Operations
CFO: Brian Walton, Vice President and Chief Financial Officer
CMO: Mike Lamanteer, M.D., Vice President Medical Affairs
CIO: Lewis Brown, Director Information Technology
CHR: Cheryl L. Jones, Director Human Resources and Organizational Development
CNO: Belinda D. Gibson, R.N., Vice President Patient Services
Web address: www.bsahs.org
Control: Corporation, Investor–owned, for–profit **Service:** General Medical and Surgical

Staffed Beds: 312 **Admissions:** 19804 **Census:** 247 **Outpatient Visits:** 160902 **Births:** 2268 **Total Expense ($000):** 303470 **Payroll Expense ($000):** 111183 **Personnel:** 2411

KINDRED HOSPITAL–AMARILLO See Vibra Hospital of Amarillo

KINDRED REHABILITATION HOSPITAL AMARILLO See Vibra Rehabilitation Hospital of Amarillo

⊞ **NORTHWEST TEXAS HEALTHCARE SYSTEM (450209)**, 1501 South Coulter Avenue, Zip 79106–1770, Mailing Address: P.O. Box 1110, Zip 79105–1110; tel. 806/354–1000, (Includes CHILDREN'S HOSPITAL, 1501 South Coulter Street, tel. 806/354–1000; PSYCHIATRIC PAVILION, 7201 Evans, Zip 79106) **A**1 2 3 5 9 10 **F**3 4 5 11 12 13 15 17 18 20 22 24 26 28 29 30 31 32 34 35 37 38 39 40 43 44 45 46 48 49 50 54 56 57 59 60 61 64 66 68 70 72 74 75 76 77 78 79 81 84 86 87 88 89 90 92 93 94 96 97 98 99 100 101 102 103 104 105 107 108 110 111 115 118 119 126 130 132 135 146 147 148 **P**6
S Universal Health Services, Inc., King of Prussia, PA
Primary Contact: Mark W. Crawford, Chief Executive Officer
COO: Sharon Oxendale, Chief Operating Officer
CFO: Gene Winters, Chief Financial Officer
CMO: Nathan Goldstein, III, M.D., Chief Medical Officer
CIO: Bach Nguyen, Chief Information Officer
CHR: Dolores Deer, Director Human Resources
CNO: Valerie Kiper, MSN, Chief Nursing Officer
Web address: www.nwtexashealthcare.com
Control: Corporation, Investor–owned, for–profit **Service:** General Medical and Surgical

Staffed Beds: 414 **Admissions:** 17767 **Census:** 236 **Outpatient Visits:** 202170 **Births:** 2463 **Total Expense ($000):** 255937 **Payroll Expense ($000):** 83208 **Personnel:** 1549

NORTHWEST TEXAS SURGERY CENTER (450796), 3501 South Soncy Road Suite 118, Zip 79119–6405; tel. 806/359–7999 **A**10 **F**26 39 40 58 68 79 81 82 85 93 126 131
Primary Contact: Jeff Barnhart, Administrator
Control: Corporation, Investor–owned, for–profit **Service:** General Medical and Surgical

Staffed Beds: 4 **Admissions:** 154 **Census:** 1 **Outpatient Visits:** 4904 **Births:** 0 **Total Expense ($000):** 8848 **Payroll Expense ($000):** 2800 **Personnel:** 44

PHYSICIANS SURGICAL HOSPITAL – PANHANDLE CAMPUS, 7100 West 9th Avenue, Zip 79106–1704; tel. 806/212–0247, (Nonreporting)
Primary Contact: Brad McCall, President and Chief Executive Officer
CFO: Austin Jones, CPA, Chief Financial Officer
CMO: Robert Crabtree, M.D., Chief of Staff and Medical Director
CNO: Debbie Inman, Chief Nursing Officer
Web address: www.physurg.com/
Control: Partnership, Investor–owned, for–profit **Service:** General Medical and Surgical

Staffed Beds: 11

PHYSICIANS SURGICAL HOSPITAL – QUAIL CREEK (450875), 6819 Plum Creek, Zip 79124–1602; tel. 806/354–6100 **A**9 10 **F**3 29 30 40 44 50 68 75 79 81 82 85 89 130 135
Primary Contact: Brad McCall, President and Chief Executive Officer
CFO: Austin Jones, CPA, Chief Financial Officer
CMO: Robert Crabtree, M.D., Chief of Staff and Medical Director
CNO: Debbie Inman, Chief Nursing Officer
Web address: www.physurg.com
Control: Corporation, Investor–owned, for–profit **Service:** Surgical

Staffed Beds: 41 **Admissions:** 1664 **Census:** 10 **Outpatient Visits:** 13438 **Births:** 0 **Total Expense ($000):** 38978 **Payroll Expense ($000):** 9624 **Personnel:** 162

☐ **PLUM CREEK SPECIALTY HOSPITAL (452066)**, 5601 Plum Creek Drive, Zip 79124–1801; tel. 806/351–1000 **A**1 9 10 **F**1 3 29 75 85 148 **S** Encore Healthcare, Columbia, MD
Primary Contact: Billy Blasingame, Chief Executive Officer
Web address: www.specialtyhospital–plumcreek.net
Control: Corporation, Investor–owned, for–profit **Service:** Long–Term Acute Care hospital

Staffed Beds: 47 **Admissions:** 230 **Census:** 17 **Outpatient Visits:** 0 **Births:** 0 **Total Expense ($000):** 7877 **Payroll Expense ($000):** 2945 **Personnel:** 71

SPECIALTY HOSPITAL AT PLUM CREEK See Plum Creek Specialty Hospital

⊞ **VIBRA HOSPITAL OF AMARILLO (452060)**, 7501 Wallace Boulevard, Zip 79124–2150; tel. 806/467–7000 **A**1 9 10 **F**1 3 29 34 35 45 46 50 56 57 59 60 61 70 74 75 77 79 82 84 85 86 87 91 96 107 114 130 148 **P**8
S Vibra Healthcare, Mechanicsburg, PA
Primary Contact: Kay E. Peck, Ph.D., Chief Executive Officer
COO: Kay E. Peck, Ph.D., Chief Executive Officer
CFO: Carlene Wright, Chief Financial Officer
CMO: Pablo Rodrigues, M.D., Medical Director
CNO: Melany McCarty, R.N., Chief Clinical Officer
Web address: www.vhamarillo.com
Control: Corporation, Investor–owned, for–profit **Service:** Long–Term Acute Care hospital

Staffed Beds: 72 **Admissions:** 824 **Census:** 60 **Outpatient Visits:** 0 **Births:** 0 **Total Expense ($000):** 28438 **Payroll Expense ($000):** 10363 **Personnel:** 227

TX

⊠ **VIBRA REHABILITATION HOSPITAL OF AMARILLO (453096)**, 7200 West 9th Avenue, Zip 79106–1703; tel. 806/468–2900 **A**1 10 **F**3 29 56 60 75 77 82 87 90 91 96 130 143 148 **S** Vibra Healthcare, Mechanicsburg, PA
Primary Contact: Kay E. Peck, Ph.D., Chief Executive Officer
Web address: www.vrhamarillo.com
Control: Corporation, Investor–owned, for–profit **Service:** Rehabilitation

Staffed Beds: 44 **Admissions:** 785 **Census:** 23 **Outpatient Visits:** 0 **Births:** 0 **Total Expense ($000):** 8461 **Payroll Expense ($000):** 4404 **Personnel:** 132

ANAHUAC—Chambers County

★ **CHAMBERS COUNTY PUBLIC HOSPITAL DISTRICT 1 (451320)**, 200 Hospital Drive, Zip 77514, Mailing Address: P.O. Box 398, Zip 77514–0398; tel. 409/267–3143 **A**9 10 18 **F**3 8 11 29 34 35 40 43 45 47 50 53 54 56 57 59 64 70 80 81 86 88 89 93 107 111 114 119 128 130 133 **P**3
Primary Contact: Steven Gularte, Chief Executive Officer
CFO: Theresa Cheaney, Controller
CMO: Anthony Capili, M.D., Chief of Staff
CNO: Christi Morris, Director of Nursing
Web address: www.chambershealth.org
Control: Hospital district or authority, Government, nonfederal **Service:** General Medical and Surgical

Staffed Beds: 14 **Admissions:** 200 **Census:** 2 **Outpatient Visits:** 36227 **Births:** 0 **Total Expense ($000):** 11562 **Payroll Expense ($000):** 5194 **Personnel:** 105

ANDREWS—Andrews County

★ ◇ **PERMIAN REGIONAL MEDICAL CENTER (450144)**, Northeast By–Pass, Zip 79714, Mailing Address: P.O. Box 2108, Zip 79714–2108; tel. 432/523–2200 **A**9 10 20 21 **F**3 11 13 15 29 34 35 36 38 40 43 44 50 53 56 57 59 62 64 65 68 70 73 75 76 77 81 82 84 85 86 87 89 93 97 107 108 110 111 115 119 127 129 130 131 132 133 135 145 146 148 **P**5 6
Primary Contact: Russell Tippin, Chief Executive Officer and Administrator
CFO: Sandra Cox, Controller
CIO: Dan Smart, Chief Information Management Officer
CHR: Pam McCormick, Director Human Resources
Web address: www.permianregional.com
Control: Hospital district or authority, Government, nonfederal **Service:** General Medical and Surgical

Staffed Beds: 44 **Admissions:** 745 **Census:** 5 **Outpatient Visits:** 39258 **Births:** 298 **Total Expense ($000):** 32539 **Payroll Expense ($000):** 15435 **Personnel:** 255

ANGLETON—Brazoria County

⊠ **ANGLETON DANBURY MEDICAL CENTER (450591)**, 132 East Hospital Drive, Zip 77515–4197; tel. 979/849–7721 **A**1 9 10 **F**3 11 13 15 18 28 29 30 34 35 36 40 43 45 46 49 53 57 59 64 65 68 70 74 75 77 79 81 85 86 87 89 91 93 107 108 111 114 115 119 130 132 135 146 **P**1
Primary Contact: David A. Bleakney, Chief Executive Officer and Administrator
CFO: William D. Garwood, III, Associate Administrator and Chief Financial Officer
CMO: Craig L. McDonald, M.D., Chief Medical Officer
CHR: Paula Tobon–Stevens, Associate Administrator
CNO: Rose McCullough, R.N., Associate Administrator Patient Care and Chief Nursing Officer
Web address: www.admc.org
Control: Hospital district or authority, Government, nonfederal **Service:** General Medical and Surgical

Staffed Beds: 51 **Admissions:** 1765 **Census:** 17 **Outpatient Visits:** 46171 **Births:** 401 **Total Expense ($000):** 30555 **Payroll Expense ($000):** 11959 **Personnel:** 227

ANSON—Jones County

★ **ANSON GENERAL HOSPITAL (450078)**, 101 Avenue J, Zip 79501–2198; tel. 325/823–3231 **A**9 10 **F**7 11 29 40 45 62 75 77 81 107 127 133 **P**8
Primary Contact: Pamela Gonzales, Chief Operating Officer
CFO: Rick McDonald, Chief Financial Officer
CIO: Lynna B. Cox, Director Health Information Services
Control: City–Government, nonfederal **Service:** General Medical and Surgical

Staffed Beds: 30 **Admissions:** 309 **Census:** 6 **Outpatient Visits:** 10002 **Births:** 0 **Total Expense ($000):** 7469 **Payroll Expense ($000):** 3709 **Personnel:** 127

ARANSAS PASS—San Patricio County

CARE REGIONAL MEDICAL CENTER (450605), 1711 West Wheeler Avenue, Zip 78336–4536; tel. 361/758–8585 **A**9 10 **F**3 11 15 18 29 34 35 40 44 45 50 56 57 59 64 65 68 70 75 77 78 79 81 85 86 87 93 97 98 101 102 103 107 108 111 114 119 130 132 133 143 146 148 **P**7
Primary Contact: Sunil Reddy, Chief Executive Officer
CMO: Salim Surani, M.D., Chief of Staff
CIO: Greg Palmer, Administrator Information Technology Network
CHR: Kerry L. Upton, Administrative Director Human Resources
CNO: Christal Burns, R.N., Chief Nursing Officer
Web address: www.crmctx.com
Control: Corporation, Investor–owned, for–profit **Service:** General Medical and Surgical

Staffed Beds: 54 **Admissions:** 1026 **Census:** 14 **Outpatient Visits:** 24863 **Births:** 0 **Total Expense ($000):** 13872 **Payroll Expense ($000):** 6481 **Personnel:** 173

NORTH BAY HOSPITAL See Care Regional Medical Center

ARLINGTON—Tarrant County

ARLINGTON REHABILITATION HOSPITAL See Kindred Rehabilitation Hospital Arlington

☐ **BAYLOR ORTHOPEDIC AND SPINE HOSPITAL AT ARLINGTON (670067)**, 707 Highlander Boulevard, Zip 76015–4319; tel. 817/583–7100 **A**1 9 10 **F**3 29 40 75 79 81 82 85 86 107 111 114
Primary Contact: Allan Beck, Chief Executive Officer
Web address: www.baylorarlington.com/
Control: Partnership, Investor–owned, for–profit **Service:** General Medical and Surgical

Staffed Beds: 24 **Admissions:** 1121 **Census:** 8 **Outpatient Visits:** 8763 **Births:** 0 **Total Expense ($000):** 41211 **Payroll Expense ($000):** 7230 **Personnel:** 99

⊠ **HEALTHSOUTH REHABILITATION HOSPITAL OF ARLINGTON (453040)**, 3200 Matlock Road, Zip 76015–2911; tel. 817/468–4000 **A**1 9 10 **F**3 29 74 75 77 79 90 91 94 95 96 130 148 **S** HEALTHSOUTH Corporation, Birmingham, AL
Primary Contact: Mark S. Deno, Chief Executive Officer
CFO: Kathy Dickerson, Chief Financial Officer
CMO: Todd Daniels, M.D., Medical Director
CHR: Nancy Rosiles, Director Human Resources
CNO: David Jones, Chief Nursing Officer
Web address: www.healthsoutharlington.com
Control: Corporation, Investor–owned, for–profit **Service:** Rehabilitation

Staffed Beds: 85 **Admissions:** 1715 **Census:** 59 **Outpatient Visits:** 2097 **Births:** 0 **Total Expense ($000):** 23442 **Payroll Expense ($000):** 11384 **Personnel:** 216

⊠ **KINDRED HOSPITAL TARRANT COUNTY–ARLINGTON (452028)**, 1000 North Cooper Street, Zip 76011–5540; tel. 817/548–3400 **A**1 9 10 **F**1 3 29 30 40 56 57 77 80 82 93 130 148 **S** Kindred Healthcare, Louisville, KY
Primary Contact: Christina Richard, Administrator
CFO: Jennifer Penland, Controller
CMO: Bernard A. McGowen, M.D., Medical Director
Web address: www.kindredhospitalarl.com/
Control: Corporation, Investor–owned, for–profit **Service:** Long–Term Acute Care hospital

Staffed Beds: 55 **Admissions:** 543 **Census:** 41 **Outpatient Visits:** 450 **Births:** 0 **Total Expense ($000):** 18435 **Payroll Expense ($000):** 8391 **Personnel:** 152

⊠ **KINDRED REHABILITATION HOSPITAL ARLINGTON (453094)**, 2601 West Randol Mill Road, Zip 76012–4289; tel. 817/804–4400 **A**1 9 10 **F**3 29 34 57 59 74 75 86 87 90 94 96 130 132 146 148 **S** Kindred Healthcare, Louisville, KY
Primary Contact: Amy Hoffner, Administrator
CFO: Jennifer Penland, Controller
CNO: Katherine Kreis, Chief Clinical Officer
Web address: www.khrehabarlington.com
Control: Corporation, Investor–owned, for–profit **Service:** Rehabilitation

Staffed Beds: 24 **Admissions:** 573 **Census:** 19 **Outpatient Visits:** 0 **Births:** 0 **Total Expense ($000):** 6877 **Payroll Expense ($000):** 3837 **Personnel:** 70

TX

Hospital, Medicare Provider Number, Address, Telephone, Approval, Facility, and Physician Codes, Health Care System

★ American Hospital Association (AHA) membership
☐ The Joint Commission accreditation
◇ DNV Healthcare Inc. accreditation
○ Healthcare Facilities Accreditation Program
△ Commission on Accreditation of Rehabilitation Facilities (CARF) accreditation

✠ **MEDICAL CENTER OF ARLINGTON (450675)**, 3301 Matlock Road, Zip 76015–2998; tel. 817/465–3241 **A**1 2 9 10 **F**3 11 12 13 15 17 18 20 22 24 26 28 29 31 34 35 39 40 42 43 45 46 47 48 49 50 56 57 59 64 68 70 72 73 74 75 76 78 79 81 82 85 86 87 92 93 107 108 110 111 114 115 119 126 130 131 132 135 145 146 147 148 **S** HCA, Nashville, TN
Primary Contact: Winston Borland, FACHE, President and Chief Executive Officer
COO: LaSharndra Barbarin, Chief Operating Officer
CFO: Jeff Ardemagni, Chief Financial Officer
CMO: Edwin Duppstadt, M.D., Chief Medical Officer
CIO: Basil Holloway, Director Information Services
CHR: Jerry L. McMorrough, Vice President Human Resources
CNO: Omar Pineda, R.N., Chief Nursing Officer
Web address: www.medicalcenterarlington.com
Control: Corporation, Investor–owned, for–profit **Service:** General Medical and Surgical

Staffed Beds: 284 **Admissions:** 13970 **Census:** 191 **Outpatient Visits:** 92027 **Births:** 3979 **Total Expense ($000):** 178370 **Payroll Expense ($000):** 68702 **Personnel:** 1054

☐ **MILLWOOD HOSPITAL (454012)**, 1011 North Cooper Street, Zip 76011–5517; tel. 817/261–3121 **A**1 9 10 **F**4 5 29 30 35 54 56 71 87 98 99 100 101 102 103 104 105 130 132 **S** Universal Health Services, Inc., King of Prussia, PA
Primary Contact: Rick Paczkowski, Chief Executive Officer
CFO: Jeff Epperson, Chief Financial Officer
CMO: Ernest Brownlee, M.D., Medical Director
CIO: Linda Jones, Director Medical Records
CHR: Shirley Spurlock, Director Human Resources
Web address: www.millwoodhospital.com
Control: Partnership, Investor–owned, for–profit **Service:** Psychiatric

Staffed Beds: 122 **Admissions:** 4170 **Census:** 96 **Outpatient Visits:** 27850 **Births:** 0 **Total Expense ($000):** 24976 **Payroll Expense ($000):** 11027 **Personnel:** 270

☐ **SUNDANCE HOSPITAL (454113)**, 7000 U.S. Highway 287 South, Zip 76001; tel. 817/583–8080 **A**1 9 10 **F**4 98 99 101 102 103
Primary Contact: Rick Harding, Chief Executive Officer
Web address: www.sundancehealthcare.com
Control: Corporation, Investor–owned, for–profit **Service:** Psychiatric

Staffed Beds: 116 **Admissions:** 2475 **Census:** 53 **Outpatient Visits:** 0 **Births:** 0 **Total Expense ($000):** 9715 **Payroll Expense ($000):** 5751 **Personnel:** 158

✠ **TEXAS HEALTH ARLINGTON MEMORIAL HOSPITAL (450064)**, 800 West Randol Mill Road, Zip 76012–2503; tel. 817/548–6100 **A**1 2 9 10 **F**3 11 12 13 15 18 26 28 29 30 31 34 35 37 40 45 46 47 48 49 51 53 54 57 59 63 64 65 66 68 70 72 74 75 76 77 78 79 80 81 82 85 86 87 93 100 107 108 110 111 114 115 118 119 123 124 126 130 132 135 136 145 146 147 148 **S** Texas Health Resources, Arlington, TX
Primary Contact: Kirk King, FACHE, President
COO: Sandra L. Harris, R.N., Senior Vice President and Chief Operating Officer
CMO: Robert N. Cluck, M.D., Vice President and Medical Director
CHR: Yvonne Kyler, Director Human Resources
Web address: www.arlingtonmemorial.org
Control: Other not–for–profit (including NFP Corporation) **Service:** General Medical and Surgical

Staffed Beds: 299 **Admissions:** 11895 **Census:** 165 **Outpatient Visits:** 107679 **Births:** 1860 **Total Expense ($000):** 222143 **Payroll Expense ($000):** 93421 **Personnel:** 1320

☐ **TEXAS HEALTH HEART & VASCULAR HOSPITAL ARLINGTON (670071)**, 811 Wright Street, Zip 76012–4708; tel. 817/960–3500 **A**1 9 10 **F**3 17 18 20 22 24 26 29 30 60 64 65 68 81 85
Primary Contact: Baron L. Hamman, M.D., President
CFO: Kay Mason, Chief Financial Officer
CMO: William Nesbitt, M.D., President Medical Staff
CHR: Yvonne Kyler, Director Human Resources
Web address: www.texashealthheartandvascular.org/
Control: Partnership, Investor–owned, for–profit **Service:** Heart

Staffed Beds: 48 **Admissions:** 1249 **Census:** 14 **Outpatient Visits:** 2484 **Births:** 0 **Total Expense ($000):** 41321 **Payroll Expense ($000):** 8185 **Personnel:** 113

✠ **USMD HOSPITAL AT ARLINGTON (450872)**, 801 West Interstate 20, Zip 76017–5851; tel. 817/472–3400 **A**1 9 10 **F**3 12 29 34 35 39 40 45 49 50 51 57 58 59 64 70 74 75 78 79 81 82 85 87 92 107 108 111 114 119 124 126 132 **S** USMD Inc., Irving, TX
Primary Contact: Marcia Crim, R.N., MSN, Chief Executive Officer
CFO: Andrew Summers, Chief Financial Officer
CMO: M. Patrick Collini, M.D., President Medical Staff
CIO: Bob Rick, Vice President Information Technology
CHR: Bernardo Valle, Vice President Human Resources
CNO: Marcia Crim, R.N., Chief Nursing Officer and Chief Executive Officer
Web address: www.usmdarlington.com
Control: Partnership, Investor–owned, for–profit **Service:** General Medical and Surgical

Staffed Beds: 34 **Admissions:** 1552 **Census:** 13 **Outpatient Visits:** 34254 **Births:** 0 **Total Expense ($000):** 70174 **Payroll Expense ($000):** 15647 **Personnel:** 310

ASPERMONT—Stonewall County

STONEWALL MEMORIAL HOSPITAL (451318), 821 North Broadway, Zip 79502–2029, Mailing Address: P.O. Box C, Zip 79502–0902; tel. 940/989–3551 **A**9 10 18 **F**3 29 34 35 40 41 56 57 59 64 93 97 103 107 114 119 127 128 133 148 **P**5
Primary Contact: Andy Kolb, Chief Executive Officer
COO: Billie Carter, Chief Operating Officer and Assistant Administrator
CFO: Andy Kolb, Chief Executive Officer
CMO: Frederic K. Passmann, M.D., Chief of Staff
CIO: Billie Carter, Chief Operating Officer and Assistant Administrator
CHR: Andy Kolb, Chief Executive Officer
CNO: Jan Harris, R.N., Director of Nursing
Web address: www.smhdhealth.org/
Control: Hospital district or authority, Government, nonfederal **Service:** General Medical and Surgical

Staffed Beds: 12 **Admissions:** 119 **Census:** 2 **Outpatient Visits:** 13592 **Births:** 0 **Total Expense ($000):** 6917 **Payroll Expense ($000):** 3209 **Personnel:** 52

ATHENS—Henderson County

✠ **EAST TEXAS MEDICAL CENTER ATHENS (450389)**, 2000 South Palestine Street, Zip 75751–5610; tel. 903/676–1000 **A**1 9 10 **F**3 11 13 15 18 20 29 34 40 42 43 45 49 50 70 74 76 79 81 85 89 107 108 110 111 114 115 118 119 127 130 132 146 **S** East Texas Medical Center Regional Healthcare System, Tyler, TX
Primary Contact: Patrick L. Wallace, Administrator
CFO: David A. Travis, Chief Financial Officer
CHR: Jennifer Rummel, Director Human Resources
Web address: www.etmc.org
Control: Other not–for–profit (including NFP Corporation) **Service:** General Medical and Surgical

Staffed Beds: 127 **Admissions:** 6564 **Census:** 62 **Outpatient Visits:** 91410 **Births:** 832 **Total Expense ($000):** 73461 **Payroll Expense ($000):** 23690 **Personnel:** 469

AUBREY—Denton County

★ ◇ **BAYLOR EMERGENCY MEDICAL CENTER AT AUBREY (670062)**, 26791 Highway 380, Zip 76227; tel. 972/347–2525 **A**9 10 21 **F**3 29 40 75 87 107 119 **P**5 **S** Emerus, The Woodlands, TX
Primary Contact: John Wood, Chief Executive Officer
CFO: Michael Rzendzian, Chief Financial Officer
CMO: Amynah Kara, M.D., Chief Medical Officer
CIO: Trang Dawson, Chief Information Officer
CHR: Larry Guillory, Chief Human Resources Officer
CNO: Daniel Baas, R.N., Chief Nursing Officer
Web address: www.bemcataubrey.com
Control: Partnership, Investor–owned, for–profit **Service:** General Medical and Surgical

Staffed Beds: 16 **Admissions:** 41 **Census:** 1 **Outpatient Visits:** 9314 **Births:** 0 **Total Expense ($000):** 9304 **Payroll Expense ($000):** 2795 **Personnel:** 58

AUSTIN—Travis County

☐ **ARISE AUSTIN MEDICAL CENTER (450871)**, 3003 Bee Caves Road, Zip 78746–5542; tel. 512/314–3800, (Data for 183 days) **A**1 9 10 **F**3 29 37 40 51 59 64 65 68 70 77 79 81 82 85 107 111 119 126 148 **P**2
Primary Contact: Diana Zamora Magallanes, Chief Executive Officer
CFO: Lawrence Oldham, Chief Financial Officer
CMO: Robert Wills, M.D., Chief Medical Officer
CHR: Marilyn Jennings, Director Human Resources
Web address: www.austinsurgicalhospital.com
Control: Partnership, Investor–owned, for–profit **Service:** General Medical and Surgical

Staffed Beds: 23 **Admissions:** 814 **Census:** 14 **Outpatient Visits:** 2151 **Births:** 0 **Total Expense ($000):** 10312 **Payroll Expense ($000):** 3031 **Personnel:** 118

Many Facility Codes have changed. Please refer to the AHA Guide Code Chart. © 2014 AHA Guide

TX

AUSTIN LAKES HOSPITAL (454069), 1025 East 32nd Street,
Zip 78705–2714; tel. 512/544–5253 **A**1 5 9 10 **F**98 104 105 130 **S** Universal
Health Services, Inc., King of Prussia, PA
Primary Contact: Rick Buckelew, Chief Executive Officer
CFO: Greg Wysocki, Chief Financial Officer
CMO: Shiva Lam, M.D., Executive Medical Director
CHR: Dan Smith, Director Human Resources
CNO: Barbara Powers, R.N., Chief Nursing Officer
Web address: www.austinlakeshospital.com
Control: Corporation, Investor–owned, for–profit **Service:** Psychiatric

Staffed Beds: 58 **Admissions:** 2811 **Census:** 52 **Outpatient Visits:** 8870
Births: 0 **Total Expense ($000):** 11488 **Payroll Expense ($000):** 6183
Personnel: 118

AUSTIN OAKS HOSPITAL (454121), 1407 West Stassney Lane,
Zip 78745–2947; tel. 512/440–4800, (Data for 205 days) **A**10 **F**98 99 100 101
103 **S** Universal Health Services, Inc., King of Prussia, PA
Primary Contact: Ramona Key, Chief Executive Officer
Web address: www.austinoakshospital.com
Control: Partnership, Investor–owned, for–profit **Service:** Psychiatric

Staffed Beds: 80 **Admissions:** 567 **Census:** 19 **Outpatient Visits:** 0 **Births:**
0 **Total Expense ($000):** 4955 **Payroll Expense ($000):** 2474 **Personnel:**
82

AUSTIN STATE HOSPITAL (454084), 4110 Guadalupe Street,
Zip 78751–4296; tel. 512/452–0381 **A**1 3 5 10 **F**29 30 39 40 50 56 59 65
68 75 82 86 98 99 101 103 130 132 143 146 **P**1 **S** Texas Department of
State Health Services, Austin, TX
Primary Contact: Cathy Nottebart, Acting Superintendent
CMO: Ross Taylor, M.D., Clinical Director
CIO: Cindy Reed, Director Community Relations
Web address: www.dshs.state.tx.us/mhhospitals/austinsh/default.shtm
Control: State–Government, nonfederal **Service:** Psychiatric

Staffed Beds: 314 **Admissions:** 3595 **Census:** 271 **Outpatient Visits:** 0
Births: 0 **Total Expense ($000):** 70377 **Payroll Expense ($000):** 35323
Personnel: 834

⊞ **CENTRAL TEXAS REHABILITATION HOSPITAL (673027)**, 700 West 45th
Street, Zip 78751–2800; tel. 512/407–2111 **A**1 9 10 **F**3 29 59 74 79 82 90
91 96 130 132 148 **S** Kindred Healthcare, Louisville, KY
Primary Contact: Peggy Barrett, R.N., Chief Executive Officer
CFO: Tracey Allen, Controller
CMO: Mary Ann Gonzales, M.D., Medical Director
CIO: Peggy Barrett, R.N., Chief Executive Officer
CHR: Liza Cuero, Coordinator Human Resources
CNO: Kerry Radcliffe, JD, Chief Nursing Officer
Web address: www.khrehabcentraltexas.com/
Control: Partnership, Investor–owned, for–profit **Service:** Rehabilitation

Staffed Beds: 50 **Admissions:** 1032 **Census:** 36 **Outpatient Visits:** 0 **Births:**
0 **Total Expense ($000):** 16809 **Payroll Expense ($000):** 7326 **Personnel:**
100

CORNERSTONE HOSPITAL OF AUSTIN (452034), 4207 Burnet Road,
Zip 78756–3396; tel. 512/706–1900, (Includes CORNERSTONE HOSPITAL OF
AUSTIN, 1005 East 32nd Street, Zip 78705; tel. 512/867–5822; Edward J.
Sherwood, M.D., Chief Executive Officer) **A**1 9 10 **F**1 3 29 30 75 77 87 91 148
S Cornerstone Healthcare Group, Dallas, TX
Primary Contact: Scott Galliardt, Chief Executive Officer
CMO: David F. Pohl, M.D., Chief of Staff
Web address: www.chghospitals.com/austin/
Control: Corporation, Investor–owned, for–profit **Service:** Long–Term Acute Care
hospital

Staffed Beds: 157 **Admissions:** 622 **Census:** 44 **Outpatient Visits:** 0 **Births:**
0 **Total Expense ($000):** 19461 **Payroll Expense ($000):** 8841 **Personnel:**
177

⊞ **DELL CHILDREN'S MEDICAL CENTER OF CENTRAL TEXAS (453310)**, 4900
Mueller Boulevard, Zip 78723–3079; tel. 512/324–0000 **A**1 3 5 9 10 **F**3 11 19
21 23 25 27 29 30 31 32 34 35 39 40 41 43 44 46 49 50 53 54 58 59 61
64 65 68 71 72 74 75 77 78 79 80 81 82 83 84 85 86 87 88 89 93 100
104 107 111 112 114 115 118 119 126 129 130 131 132 135 137 143 146
148 **P**3 8 **S** Ascension Health, Saint Louis, MO
Primary Contact: Robert I. Bonar, Jr., Chief Executive Officer
Web address: www.dellchildrens.net
Control: Church–operated, Nongovernment, not–for profit **Service:** Children's
general

Staffed Beds: 248 **Admissions:** 7889 **Census:** 103 **Outpatient Visits:**
314534 **Births:** 0 **Total Expense ($000):** 318417 **Payroll Expense ($000):**
144523 **Personnel:** 2005

⊞ **HEALTHSOUTH REHABILITATION HOSPITAL OF AUSTIN (453044)**, 1215
Red River Street, Zip 78701–1921; tel. 512/474–5700 **A**1 9 10 **F**3 29 56 62
74 75 77 79 86 87 90 91 130 132 143 148 **P**5 **S** HEALTHSOUTH Corporation,
Birmingham, AL
Primary Contact: Sandra Hegland, Chief Executive Officer
CFO: Pamela McLaughlin, Chief Financial Officer
CMO: Johnny Shane Ross, Executive Medical Director
CHR: Debbie Belcher, Director Human Resources
CNO: Paul Bruce, Chief Nursing Officer
Web address: www.healthsouthaustin.com
Control: Corporation, Investor–owned, for–profit **Service:** Rehabilitation

Staffed Beds: 40 **Admissions:** 705 **Census:** 26 **Outpatient Visits:** 18245
Births: 0 **Total Expense ($000):** 14401 **Payroll Expense ($000):** 7249
Personnel: 112

NORTHWEST HILLS SURGICAL HOSPITAL (450808), 6818 Austin Center
Boulevard, Suite 100, Zip 78731–3199; tel. 512/346–1994 **A**1 9 10 **F**3 40 45
64 79 81
Primary Contact: Scott Cullen, Chief Executive Officer
CFO: Jenny Salome, Chief Financial Officer and Assistant Administrator
Web address: www.northwesthillssurgical.com
Control: Partnership, Investor–owned, for–profit **Service:** General Medical and
Surgical

Staffed Beds: 8 **Admissions:** 300 **Census:** 1 **Outpatient Visits:** 7019 **Births:**
0 **Total Expense ($000):** 21317 **Payroll Expense ($000):** 4296 **Personnel:**
85

RELIANT AUSTIN (673054), 330 West Ben White Boulevard, Zip 78704;
tel. 512/730–4800 **A**1 9 10 **F**3 29 90 96 130 148
Primary Contact: Jack Boggess, Chief Executive Officer
CNO: Vidette J. Forbes, R.N., Chief Nursing Officer and Chief Operating Officer
Web address: www.reliantaustin.com
Control: Partnership, Investor–owned, for–profit **Service:** Rehabilitation

Staffed Beds: 60 **Admissions:** 722 **Census:** 20 **Outpatient Visits:** 198
Births: 0 **Total Expense ($000):** 10615 **Payroll Expense ($000):** 4037
Personnel: 109

⊞ ◇ **SETON MEDICAL CENTER AUSTIN (450056)**, 1201 West 38th Street,
Zip 78705–1006; tel. 512/324–1000 **A**1 2 3 5 9 10 21 **F**3 11 12 13 15 18 20
22 24 26 28 29 30 31 34 35 40 43 44 45 46 49 50 51 57 58 59 60 61 64
68 70 72 74 75 76 77 78 79 81 82 84 85 86 87 93 107 108 111 114 115
119 126 130 131 132 135 137 145 146 148 **P**3 8 **S** Ascension Health, Saint
Louis, MO
Primary Contact: Katherine Henderson, Chief Executive Officer
COO: Charlotte Thrasher, Vice President and Chief Operating Officer
CFO: Douglas D. Waite, Chief Financial Officer
CMO: Carol Wratten, M.D., Vice President Medical Affairs
CIO: Gerry Lewis, Chief Information Officer
CHR: Fenorris Pearson, Chief Human Resources Officer
CNO: Angela Stalbaum, R.N., Chief Nursing Officer
Web address: www.seton.net
Control: Church–operated, Nongovernment, not–for profit **Service:** General
Medical and Surgical

Staffed Beds: 426 **Admissions:** 20585 **Census:** 267 **Outpatient Visits:**
80651 **Births:** 3168 **Total Expense ($000):** 372455 **Payroll Expense
($000):** 117342 **Personnel:** 2616

⊞ **SETON NORTHWEST HOSPITAL (450867)**, 11113 Research Boulevard,
Zip 78759–5236; tel. 512/324–6000 **A**1 2 3 5 9 10 **F**3 11 12 13 15 18 29 30
31 34 35 36 37 40 43 44 45 47 49 50 51 57 59 64 68 70 72 74 75 76 77
78 79 80 81 85 86 87 93 107 111 114 119 129 130 131 132 135 146 148
P3 8 **S** Ascension Health, Saint Louis, MO
Primary Contact: Michelle Robertson, R.N., President and Chief Executive Officer
CFO: Douglas D. Waite, Chief Financial Officer
CMO: Ed LeBlanc, M.D., Vice President Medical Affairs
CIO: Gerry Lewis, Chief Information Officer
CHR: Trennis Jones, Senior Vice President and Chief Administrative Officer
Web address: www.seton.net
Control: Church–operated, Nongovernment, not–for profit **Service:** General
Medical and Surgical

Staffed Beds: 64 **Admissions:** 4814 **Census:** 44 **Outpatient Visits:** 54507
Births: 902 **Total Expense ($000):** 75899 **Payroll Expense ($000):** 29912
Personnel: 542

TX

⊞ **SETON SHOAL CREEK HOSPITAL (454029)**, 3501 Mills Avenue, Zip 78731–6391; tel. 512/324–2000 **A**1 3 5 9 10 **F**4 5 29 30 34 68 86 87 98 99 100 101 103 104 130 132 135 146 **P**3 8 **S** Ascension Health, Saint Louis, MO
Primary Contact: Alan Isaacson, Vice President and Chief Operating Officer
COO: Alan Isaacson, Vice President and Chief Operating Officer
CFO: Douglas D. Waite, Chief Financial Officer
CMO: Kari Wolfe, M.D., Medical Director
CIO: Gerry Lewis, Chief Information Officer
CHR: Thomas Wilken, Vice President Human Resources
Web address: www.seton.net
Control: Church–operated, Nongovernment, not–for profit **Service:** Psychiatric

> **Staffed Beds:** 92 **Admissions:** 4845 **Census:** 67 **Outpatient Visits:** 33302
> **Births:** 0 **Total Expense ($000):** 26947 **Payroll Expense ($000):** 14602
> **Personnel:** 389

⊞ **SETON SOUTHWEST HOSPITAL (450865)**, 7900 F. M. 1826, Zip 78737–1407; tel. 512/324–9000 **A**1 9 10 **F**3 11 13 15 29 30 34 35 36 40 43 44 45 57 59 64 68 71 73 75 76 79 81 82 85 87 93 107 111 115 119 129 130 131 132 135 146 **P**3 8 **S** Ascension Health, Saint Louis, MO
Primary Contact: Mary Faria, FACHE, Administrator
Web address: www.seton.net
Control: Church–operated, Nongovernment, not–for profit **Service:** General Medical and Surgical

> **Staffed Beds:** 33 **Admissions:** 916 **Census:** 13 **Outpatient Visits:** 32242
> **Births:** 644 **Total Expense ($000):** 27568 **Payroll Expense ($000):** 10335
> **Personnel:** 181

⊞ ◇ **ST. DAVID'S MEDICAL CENTER (450431)**, 919 East 32nd Street, Zip 78705–2709, Mailing Address: P.O. Box 4039, Zip 78765–4039; tel. 512/476–7111, (Includes HEART HOSPITAL OF AUSTIN, 3801 North Lamar Boulevard, Zip 78756–4080; tel. 512/407–7000; David Laird, Chief Executive Officer; ST. DAVID'S GEORGETOWN HOSPITAL, 2000 Scenic Drive, Georgetown, Zip 78626–7726; tel. 512/943–3000; Hugh Brown, Chief Executive Officer) **A**1 2 3 5 9 10 21 **F**3 11 12 13 15 17 18 20 22 24 26 28 29 30 31 34 35 36 37 39 40 43 45 46 47 48 49 52 53 56 57 58 59 61 64 68 70 72 73 74 75 76 77 78 79 80 81 85 86 87 90 93 95 96 107 108 109 110 111 114 115 116 119 126 130 131 132 135 146 147 148 **P**3 6 8 **S** HCA, Nashville, TN
Primary Contact: Donald H. Wilkerson, Chief Executive Officer
COO: David Shimp, Chief Operating Officer
CFO: Julie Perez, Chief Financial Officer
CMO: John Marietta, M.D., Chief Medical Officer
CIO: Richard Lear, Director Information Systems
CHR: Julie Hajek, Director Human Resources
CNO: Susan E. Griffin, R.N., Chief Nursing Officer
Web address: www.stdavids.com
Control: Other not–for–profit (including NFP Corporation) **Service:** General Medical and Surgical

> **Staffed Beds:** 544 **Admissions:** 25895 **Census:** 375 **Outpatient Visits:** 193974 **Births:** 5319 **Total Expense ($000):** 451257 **Payroll Expense ($000):** 147893 **Personnel:** 2441

⊞ **ST. DAVID'S NORTH AUSTIN MEDICAL CENTER (450809)**, 12221 North MoPac Expressway, Zip 78758–2496; tel. 512/901–1000 **A**1 3 10 **F**3 12 13 15 18 20 22 24 26 28 29 30 34 35 37 40 42 43 45 47 49 53 54 56 57 59 64 67 68 70 72 73 74 75 76 77 78 79 81 82 85 86 87 90 93 107 108 111 115 118 119 126 129 130 131 132 144 145 146 147 148 **P**3 6 8 **S** HCA, Nashville, TN
Primary Contact: Allen Harrison, Chief Executive Officer
COO: Sheri Dube, Chief Operating Officer
CFO: Natalie Pack, Chief Financial Officer
CMO: Kenneth W. Mitchell, M.D., Medical Director
CIO: Marshall Pearson, Director Management Information Systems
CHR: Laura Light, Director Human Resources
Web address: www.northaustin.com
Control: Other not–for–profit (including NFP Corporation) **Service:** General Medical and Surgical

> **Staffed Beds:** 332 **Admissions:** 17835 **Census:** 255 **Outpatient Visits:** 136580 **Births:** 5909 **Total Expense ($000):** 238712 **Payroll Expense ($000):** 81262 **Personnel:** 1353

⊞ **ST. DAVID'S REHABILITATION CENTER**, 1005 East 32nd Street, Zip 78705–2713, Mailing Address: P.O. Box 4270, Zip 78765–4270; tel. 512/544–5100, (Nonreporting) **A**1 3 5 9 **S** HCA, Nashville, TN
Primary Contact: Diane Owens, Administrator
CFO: Cindy Brouillette, Chief Financial Officer
CMO: John Marietta, M.D., Chief Medical Officer
CIO: Debi Castleberry, Director Information System
CHR: De De Juel, Director Human Resources
Web address: www.stdavidsrehab.com/home.aspx
Control: Other not–for–profit (including NFP Corporation) **Service:** Rehabilitation

> **Staffed Beds:** 62

⊞ **ST. DAVID'S SOUTH AUSTIN MEDICAL CENTER (450713)**, 901 West Ben White Boulevard, Zip 78704–6903; tel. 512/447–2211 **A**1 2 3 5 9 10 **F**11 12 13 15 17 18 20 22 24 26 28 29 30 31 34 35 40 42 43 45 46 47 48 49 54 56 57 59 64 68 70 73 74 75 76 77 78 79 81 82 85 87 93 107 108 110 111 114 115 118 119 126 129 130 132 144 146 147 148 **P**3 6 8 **S** HCA, Nashville, TN
Primary Contact: Todd E. Steward, Chief Executive Officer
COO: Brett Matens, Chief Operating Officer
CFO: Wesley D. Fountain, Chief Financial Officer
CMO: Albert Gros, M.D., Chief Medical Officer
CIO: Richard Lear, Director Information Systems
CHR: Lisa Talbot, Director Human Resources
CNO: Sally A. Gillam, R.N., Chief Nursing Officer
Web address: www.southaustinmc.com
Control: Other not–for–profit (including NFP Corporation) **Service:** General Medical and Surgical

> **Staffed Beds:** 242 **Admissions:** 14854 **Census:** 183 **Outpatient Visits:** 139777 **Births:** 1535 **Total Expense ($000):** 188627 **Payroll Expense ($000):** 64165 **Personnel:** 1087

⊞ **TEXAS NEUROREHAB CENTER (452038)**, 1106 West Dittmar, Zip 78745–6328, Mailing Address: P.O. Box 150459, Zip 78715–0459; tel. 512/444–4835 **A**1 9 10 **F**1 10 29 43 54 74 75 79 93 108 130 148 **P**5 **S** Universal Health Services, Inc., King of Prussia, PA
Primary Contact: Janet Bitner, Interim Chief Executive Officer
COO: Omar Correa, Chief Operating Officer
CFO: Omar Correa, Chief Financial Officer
CMO: James Boysen, M.D., Executive Medical Director
CHR: Colleen Lewis, Director Human Resources
Web address: www.texasneurorehab.com
Control: Partnership, Investor–owned, for–profit **Service:** Long–Term Acute Care hospital

> **Staffed Beds:** 47 **Admissions:** 463 **Census:** 42 **Outpatient Visits:** 5482 **Births:** 0 **Total Expense ($000):** 12577 **Payroll Expense ($000):** 7466 **Personnel:** 322

TEXAS STAR RECOVERY (454111), 1106 West Dittmar Road, Zip 78745–6328; tel. 512/462–6729, (Nonreporting) **A**10
Primary Contact: Janet Bitner, Chief Operating Officer
Web address: www.texasstarrecovery.com
Control: Partnership, Investor–owned, for–profit **Service:** Psychiatric

> **Staffed Beds:** 28

THE HOSPITAL AT WESTLAKE MEDICAL CENTER (670006), 5656 Bee Caves Road, Zip 78746–5280; tel. 512/327–0000 **A**9 10 **F**3 18 20 22 24 26 28 29 37 40 45 51 53 58 59 64 68 70 75 77 79 81 82 85 93 96 107 108 111 114 115 119 129 130 131 135 148
Primary Contact: Rip Miller, Chief Executive Officer
CFO: Devon Culbert, Controller
CMO: Tom Burns, M.D., Chief of Staff
CHR: Kellie Bryson, Director Human Resources
Web address: www.westlakemedical.com
Control: Partnership, Investor–owned, for–profit **Service:** General Medical and Surgical

> **Staffed Beds:** 23 **Admissions:** 961 **Census:** 8 **Outpatient Visits:** 9866 **Births:** 0 **Total Expense ($000):** 35449 **Payroll Expense ($000):** 11159 **Personnel:** 193

⊞ ◇ **UNIVERSITY MEDICAL CENTER AT BRACKENRIDGE (450124)**, 601 East 15th Street, Zip 78701–1996; tel. 512/324–7000 **A**1 3 5 9 10 21 **F**3 11 13 15 18 20 22 24 26 29 30 31 34 35 37 39 40 43 44 45 47 49 55 57 58 59 60 64 65 66 68 70 71 72 74 75 76 77 78 79 81 82 84 85 87 93 97 104 107 108 110 111 114 115 118 119 124 130 132 135 143 146 148 **P**3 8 **S** Ascension Health, Saint Louis, MO
Primary Contact: Katherine Henderson, Chief Executive Officer
CFO: Douglas D. Waite, Chief Financial Officer
CMO: Jim Lindsey, M.D., Senior Vice President Medical Affairs
CIO: Gerry Lewis, Chief Information Officer
CHR: Fenorris Pearson, Chief Human Resources Officer
CNO: Michelle Ryerson, Chief Nursing Officer
Web address: www.seton.net
Control: Church–operated, Nongovernment, not–for profit **Service:** General Medical and Surgical

> **Staffed Beds:** 244 **Admissions:** 14688 **Census:** 181 **Outpatient Visits:** 648745 **Births:** 1831 **Total Expense ($000):** 582228 **Payroll Expense ($000):** 228658 **Personnel:** 2547

AZLE—Tarrant County

✠ **TEXAS HEALTH HARRIS METHODIST HOSPITAL AZLE (450419)**, 108 Denver Trail, Zip 76020–3614; tel. 817/444–8600 **A**1 9 10 **F**3 11 15 18 29 30 34 35 40 43 45 56 57 59 64 70 75 77 79 81 85 93 107 110 114 119 130 135 146 147 148 **S** Texas Health Resources, Arlington, TX
Primary Contact: Bob S. Ellzey, FACHE, President
CFO: Brian Blessing, Chief Financial Officer
CMO: Richard Niles, M.D., Chief of Staff
CIO: Edward Marx, Vice President and Chief Information Officer
CHR: Lance Waring, Director Human Resources
CNO: Valarie Gilbert, R.N., Chief Nursing Officer
Web address: www.texashealth.org/Azle
Control: Other not–for–profit (including NFP Corporation) **Service:** General Medical and Surgical

Staffed Beds: 31 **Admissions:** 1460 **Census:** 13 **Outpatient Visits:** 34537 **Births:** 0 **Total Expense ($000):** 29556 **Payroll Expense ($000):** 14218 **Personnel:** 197

BALLINGER—Runnels County

BALLINGER MEMORIAL HOSPITAL (451310), 608 Avenue B, Zip 76821–2499, Mailing Address: P.O. Box 617, Zip 76821–0617; tel. 325/365–2531 **A**9 10 18 **F**3 7 11 29 34 40 43 53 57 64 65 68 77 93 107 114 127 130 133 **P**5
Primary Contact: Grady Hooper, Chief Executive Officer
CFO: Josilyn Peterson, Chief Financial Officer
CHR: Roselyn Hudgens, Director Human Resources
Web address: www.ballingerhospital.org
Control: Hospital district or authority, Government, nonfederal **Service:** General Medical and Surgical

Staffed Beds: 16 **Admissions:** 171 **Census:** 3 **Outpatient Visits:** 17142 **Births:** 0 **Total Expense ($000):** 8197 **Payroll Expense ($000):** 3442 **Personnel:** 78

BAY CITY—Matagorda County

✠ **MATAGORDA REGIONAL MEDICAL CENTER (450465)**, 104 7th Street, Zip 77414–4853; tel. 979/245–6383 **A**1 9 10 20 **F**3 11 13 15 18 20 22 28 29 30 32 34 38 39 40 43 46 47 50 51 53 56 57 59 64 65 66 68 70 75 76 77 79 81 82 85 86 89 93 98 103 107 108 110 111 114 119 130 132 135 146 147 148 **S** QHR, Brentwood, TN
Primary Contact: Steven L. Smith, Chief Executive Officer
CFO: Bryan Prochnow, Chief Financial Officer
CIO: Mary Ann Cervantes, District Director Management Information Systems
CHR: Cindy Krebs, District Director Human Resources
CNO: Mike Lee, R.N., Chief Nursing Officer
Web address: www.matagordaregional.org
Control: Hospital district or authority, Government, nonfederal **Service:** General Medical and Surgical

Staffed Beds: 58 **Admissions:** 2172 **Census:** 25 **Outpatient Visits:** 38661 **Births:** 415 **Total Expense ($000):** 48714 **Payroll Expense ($000):** 17547 **Personnel:** 282

BAYTOWN—Harris County

★ ◇ **HOUSTON METHODIST SAN JACINTO HOSPITAL (450424)**, 4401 Garth Road, Zip 77521–2122; tel. 281/420–8600, (Includes HOUSTON METHODIST SAN JACINTO HOSPITAL – ALEXANDER, 1700 James Bowie Drive, Zip 77520–3386; tel. 281/420–6100), (Total facility includes 30 beds in nursing home–type unit) **A**2 9 10 13 21 **F**3 8 10 20 22 24 26 28 29 30 31 34 35 38 40 44 48 49 50 53 57 59 61 64 65 70 71 73 74 75 76 78 79 80 81 82 85 86 87 90 91 97 98 102 103 107 108 110 111 114 115 116 117 118 119 120 121 123 124 126 128 129 130 132 145 146 147 148 **P**3 **S** Houston Methodist, Houston, TX
Primary Contact: Donna Gares, R.N., FACHE, MSN, President and Chief Executive Officer
CFO: Jonathan Sturgis, Chief Financial Officer
CMO: Bruce Kennedy, M.D., Chief Medical Officer
CHR: Sherri Davis–Sampson, Director Human Resources
CNO: Jane DeStefano, R.N., Chief Nursing Officer
Web address: www.houstonmethodist.org
Control: Other not–for–profit (including NFP Corporation) **Service:** General Medical and Surgical

Staffed Beds: 275 **Admissions:** 12360 **Census:** 170 **Outpatient Visits:** 110627 **Births:** 1654 **Total Expense ($000):** 205384 **Payroll Expense ($000):** 80273 **Personnel:** 1338

BEAUMONT—Jefferson County

★ ◇ **BAPTIST HOSPITALS OF SOUTHEAST TEXAS (450346)**, 3080 College Street, Zip 77701–4689, Mailing Address: P.O. Box 1591, Zip 77704–1591; tel. 409/212–5000, (Includes BAPTIST HOSPITALS OF SOUTHEAST TEXAS FANNIN BEHAVIORAL HEALTH CENTER, 3250 Fannin Street, Zip 77701; tel. 409/212–7000) **A**2 9 10 21 **F**3 4 5 11 13 15 17 18 20 22 24 26 28 29 30 31 34 35 37 40 41 43 45 48 49 51 55 57 59 60 64 70 72 73 74 75 76 77 78 79 81 82 84 85 86 87 88 89 90 93 96 98 99 100 101 102 103 104 105 107 108 110 111 114 115 117 118 119 120 121 123 124 130 132 135 144 146 147 **P**6 **S** Community Hospital Corporation, Plano, TX
Primary Contact: David N. Parmer, Chief Executive Officer
COO: Gerald W. Bryant, R.N., Chief Nursing Officer
CFO: Gary Troutman, CPA, Chief Financial Officer
CIO: William Toon, Chief Information Officer
CHR: Deborah Verret, JD, Chief Human Resources Officer
CNO: Gerald W. Bryant, R.N., Chief Nursing Officer
Web address: www.bhset.net
Control: Other not–for–profit (including NFP Corporation) **Service:** General Medical and Surgical

Staffed Beds: 394 **Admissions:** 16422 **Census:** 204 **Outpatient Visits:** 139668 **Births:** 1451 **Total Expense ($000):** 195201 **Payroll Expense ($000):** 77399 **Personnel:** 1491

BEAUMONT BONE AND JOINT INSTITUTE (670007), 3650 Laurel Street, Zip 77707–2216; tel. 409/838–0346, (Nonreporting) **A**9 10
Primary Contact: Duane N. Hill, Chief Executive Officer
Web address: www.orthodoc.aaos.org/bbji/
Control: Partnership, Investor–owned, for–profit **Service:** General Medical and Surgical

Staffed Beds: 6

✠ **CHRISTUS HOSPITAL–ST. ELIZABETH (450034)**, 2830 Calder Avenue, Zip 77702–1809, Mailing Address: P.O. Box 5405, Zip 77726–5405; tel. 409/892–7171, (Includes CHRISTUS HOSPITAL–ST. MARY, 3600 Gates Boulevard, Port Arthur, Zip 77642–3601, Mailing Address: P.O. Box 3696, Zip 77643–3696; tel. 409/985–7431; Wayne Moore, Administrator) **A**1 2 9 10 **F**3 11 13 15 17 18 20 22 24 26 28 29 30 31 34 35 36 38 40 43 44 49 50 51 53 54 57 59 60 64 70 72 74 75 76 77 78 79 81 82 83 85 86 87 88 89 93 94 107 108 111 114 118 119 124 126 129 130 132 144 146 147 148 **P**4 8 **S** CHRISTUS Health, Irving, TX
Primary Contact: Paul Trevino, Chief Executive Officer
CFO: Shawn Adams, Chief Financial Officer
CMO: Rick Tyler, M.D., Vice President Medical Affairs
CIO: Robert Jacobs, Regional Director Information Management
CHR: Charles Foster, Regional Director Human Resources
Web address: www.christushospital.org
Control: Church–operated, Nongovernment, not–for profit **Service:** General Medical and Surgical

Staffed Beds: 430 **Admissions:** 19527 **Census:** 244 **Outpatient Visits:** 370371 **Births:** 2248 **Total Expense ($000):** 319603 **Payroll Expense ($000):** 106605 **Personnel:** 1279

✠ **DUBUIS HOSPITAL OF BEAUMONT (452042)**, 2830 Calder Avenue, 4th Floor, Zip 77702–1809; tel. 409/899–8154 **A**1 9 10 **F**1 3 18 29 30 31 35 130 148 **S** Dubuis Health System, Houston, TX
Primary Contact: Jeffrey Livingston, Administrator
Web address: www.dubuis.org/BeaumontandPortArthurSystem–CHRISTUSDubuisHospitalofBeaumont
Control: Church–operated, Nongovernment, not–for profit **Service:** Long–Term Acute Care hospital

Staffed Beds: 51 **Admissions:** 458 **Census:** 35 **Outpatient Visits:** 0 **Births:** 0 **Total Expense ($000):** 15994 **Payroll Expense ($000):** 6062 **Personnel:** 103

HARBOR HOSPITAL OF SOUTHEAST TEXAS (452093), 860 South 8th Street, Zip 77701–4626; tel. 409/840–3200 **A**9 10 **F**1 3 29 30 35 45 85 130 148
Primary Contact: Ronald Hunt, Chief Executive Officer
Web address: www.communityhospitalcorp.com
Control: Partnership, Investor–owned, for–profit **Service:** Long–Term Acute Care hospital

Staffed Beds: 30 **Admissions:** 327 **Census:** 22 **Outpatient Visits:** 0 **Births:** 0 **Total Expense ($000):** 11633 **Payroll Expense ($000):** 5063 **Personnel:** 96

TX

Hospital, Medicare Provider Number, Address, Telephone, Approval, Facility, and Physician Codes, Health Care System

★ American Hospital Association (AHA) membership
□ The Joint Commission accreditation   ◇ DNV Healthcare Inc. accreditation
○ Healthcare Facilities Accreditation Program
△ Commission on Accreditation of Rehabilitation Facilities (CARF) accreditation

✠ **HEALTHSOUTH REHABILITATION HOSPITAL OF BEAUMONT (453048)**, 3340 Plaza 10 Boulevard, Zip 77707–2551; tel. 409/835–0835 **A**1 9 10 **F**3 28 29 30 62 64 74 75 77 79 87 90 91 93 95 96 131 132 148 **S** HEALTHSOUTH Corporation, Birmingham, AL
Primary Contact: H. J. Gaspard, Chief Executive Officer
CFO: David Pipkins, Controller
CMO: Linda C. Smith, M.D., Medical Director
CHR: Joanna Donica, Director Human Resource
CNO: Barbara Morris, R.N., Chief Nursing Officer
Web address: www.healthsouthbeaumont.com
Control: Corporation, Investor–owned, for–profit **Service:** Rehabilitation

Staffed Beds: 61 **Admissions:** 692 **Census:** 23 **Outpatient Visits:** 6494 **Births:** 0 **Total Expense ($000):** 11285 **Payroll Expense ($000):** 5678 **Personnel:** 114

MEMORIAL HERMANN BAPTIST FANNIN BEHAVIORAL HEALTH CENTER
See Baptist Hospitals of Southeast Texas Fannin Behavioral Health Center

VICTORY MEDICAL CENTER BEAUMONT, 6025 Metropolitan Drive, Zip 77706–2407; tel. 409/617–7700, (Data for 228 days) **F**3 8 15 29 35 40 45 49 79 81 82 85 86 97 107 110 111 114 119 120 143 **S** Victory Healthcare, The Woodlands, TX
Primary Contact: Becky Ames, Chief Executive Officer
Web address: www.victory–healthcare.com/beaumont
Control: Partnership, Investor–owned, for–profit **Service:** Surgical

Staffed Beds: 17 **Admissions:** 1344 **Census:** 8 **Outpatient Visits:** 3196 **Births:** 0 **Total Expense ($000):** 22800 **Payroll Expense ($000):** 5671 **Personnel:** 123

BEDFORD—Tarrant County

☐ **RELIANT REHABILITATION HOSPITAL MID–CITIES (673044)**, 2304 State Highway 121, Zip 76021–5985; tel. 817/684–2000 **A**1 9 10 **F**3 29 90 93 96 148
Primary Contact: Robert M. Smart, Chief Executive Officer
CFO: Mary Mwaniki, Chief Financial Officer
CMO: Toni Willis, M.D., Medical Director
CHR: Christie Moore, Director Human Resources
Web address: www.relianthcp.com
Control: Partnership, Investor–owned, for–profit **Service:** Rehabilitation

Staffed Beds: 60 **Admissions:** 1189 **Census:** 34 **Outpatient Visits:** 1718 **Births:** 0 **Total Expense ($000):** 13829 **Payroll Expense ($000):** 5946 **Personnel:** 128

✠ **TEXAS HEALTH HARRIS METHODIST HOSPITAL HURST–EULESS–BEDFORD (450639)**, 1600 Hospital Parkway, Zip 76022–6913, Mailing Address: P.O. Box 669, Zip 76095–0669; tel. 817/685–4000, (Includes HARRIS METHODIST–SPRINGWOOD, 1608 Hospital Parkway, Zip 76022; tel. 817/355–7700) **A**1 2 9 10 **F**9 11 12 13 15 18 20 22 24 26 28 29 30 31 34 35 40 43 47 49 50 53 60 64 70 72 74 75 76 78 79 80 81 82 86 87 93 107 108 111 114 118 119 126 130 131 132 134 135 146 147 148 **S** Texas Health Resources, Arlington, TX
Primary Contact: Deborah Paganelli, President
COO: Alice Landers, Administrative Director Operations
CFO: Shelly Miland, Vice President Finance and Chief Financial Officer
CMO: Bob Nowland, M.D., Chief of Staff
CHR: Dale Smith, Director Human Resources
Web address: www.texashealth.org
Control: Other not–for–profit (including NFP Corporation) **Service:** General Medical and Surgical

Staffed Beds: 190 **Admissions:** 14159 **Census:** 176 **Outpatient Visits:** 86097 **Births:** 1898 **Total Expense ($000):** 223177 **Payroll Expense ($000):** 94316 **Personnel:** 1324

BEEVILLE—Bee County

✠ **CHRISTUS SPOHN HOSPITAL BEEVILLE (450082)**, 1500 East Houston Street, Zip 78102–5312; tel. 361/354–2000 **A**1 9 10 20 **F**3 11 13 15 29 30 32 34 35 40 43 45 50 57 59 64 70 75 76 77 79 81 85 86 87 93 97 107 108 111 119 130 132 146 147 148 **P**8 **S** CHRISTUS Health, Irving, TX
Primary Contact: Nathan Tudor, Vice President and Chief Executive Officer
Web address: www.christusspohn.org
Control: Church–operated, Nongovernment, not–for profit **Service:** General Medical and Surgical

Staffed Beds: 49 **Admissions:** 2047 **Census:** 20 **Outpatient Visits:** 44204 **Births:** 350 **Total Expense ($000):** 27460 **Payroll Expense ($000):** 12144 **Personnel:** 169

BELLAIRE—Harris County

◇ **FIRST STREET HOSPITAL (670029)**, 4801 Bissonnet, Zip 77401–4028; tel. 713/275–1111 **A**9 10 21 **F**3 29 40 45 47 48 49 65 79 81 82 85 107 119 126 130
Primary Contact: Sharon McDonough, Chief Executive Officer
Web address: www.firststreethospital.com
Control: Corporation, Investor–owned, for–profit **Service:** General Medical and Surgical

Staffed Beds: 19 **Admissions:** 486 **Census:** 2 **Outpatient Visits:** 2284 **Births:** 0 **Total Expense ($000):** 28339 **Payroll Expense ($000):** 9436 **Personnel:** 110

☐ **HOUSTON ORTHOPEDIC AND SPINE HOSPITAL (670012)**, 5410 West Loop South, Zip 77401–2103; tel. 713/314–4500 **A**1 9 10 **F**3 29 37 40 57 64 74 77 79 81 82 85 91 93 107 111 114 119 126 130 131 **S** Foundation Surgical Hospital Affiliates, Oklahoma City, OK
Primary Contact: Andrew Knizley, Chief Executive Officer
CMO: L. V. Ansell, M.D., Medical Director
Web address: www.foundationsurgicalhospital.com
Control: Partnership, Investor–owned, for–profit **Service:** Surgical

Staffed Beds: 64 **Admissions:** 2090 **Census:** 15 **Outpatient Visits:** 10704 **Births:** 0 **Total Expense ($000):** 64780 **Payroll Expense ($000):** 14979 **Personnel:** 286

BELLVILLE—Austin County

BELLVILLE GENERAL HOSPITAL See Bellville St. Joseph Health Center

✠ **BELLVILLE ST. JOSEPH HEALTH CENTER (450253)**, 44 North Cummings Street, Zip 77418–1347; tel. 979/413–7400 **A**1 9 10 **F**3 11 15 29 40 43 45 50 57 59 64 65 68 75 81 93 107 110 111 114 119 127 130 133 146 **S** Sylvania Franciscan Health, Toledo, OH
Primary Contact: Mark Riggins, Administrator
CMO: Christophe Gay, M.D., Chief of Staff
CHR: Jacqueline McEuen, Coordinator Human Resources
Web address: www.st–joseph.org/body.cfm?id=773
Control: Other not–for–profit (including NFP Corporation) **Service:** General Medical and Surgical

Staffed Beds: 23 **Admissions:** 207 **Census:** 2 **Outpatient Visits:** 19891 **Births:** 0 **Total Expense ($000):** 10820 **Payroll Expense ($000):** 3748 **Personnel:** 80

BELTON—Bell County

☐ **CEDAR CREST HOSPITAL AND RESIDENTIAL TREATMENT CENTER (454114)**, 3500 I–35 South, Zip 76513; tel. 254/939–2100 **A**1 9 10 **F**29 34 35 59 68 86 87 98 99 100 101 103 104 105 106 130 143 **P**4 **S** Acadia Healthcare Company, Inc., Franklin, TN
Primary Contact: Rob Marsh, Chief Executive Officer
CFO: San Juana Garza, Chief Financial Officer
CMO: Taghi Shafie, M.D., Interim Medical Director
CIO: Cesar Osario, Specialist Information Technology
CHR: Tracy McHaney, Director Human Resources
CNO: Bonnie Kolb, Director of Nursing Services
Web address: www.cedarcresthospital.com
Control: Corporation, Investor–owned, for–profit **Service:** Psychiatric

Staffed Beds: 70 **Admissions:** 2246 **Census:** 53 **Outpatient Visits:** 2399 **Births:** 0 **Total Expense ($000):** 9728 **Payroll Expense ($000):** 4998 **Personnel:** 135

BIG LAKE—Reagan County

★ **REAGAN MEMORIAL HOSPITAL (451301)**, 805 North Main Street, Zip 76932–3999; tel. 325/884–2561 **A**9 10 18 **F**3 40 43 53 57 89 93 107 114 128 130 133 143 **P**5
Primary Contact: Pam Clark, Interim Administrator
CMO: Joseph Sudolcan, M.D., Medical Director
Control: Hospital district or authority, Government, nonfederal **Service:** General Medical and Surgical

Staffed Beds: 7 **Admissions:** 24 **Census:** 1 **Outpatient Visits:** 4564 **Births:** 0 **Total Expense ($000):** 5825 **Payroll Expense ($000):** 1876 **Personnel:** 41

BIG SPRING—Howard County

☐ **BIG SPRING STATE HOSPITAL (454000)**, 1901 North Highway 87,
Zip 79720–0283; tel. 432/267–8216 **A**1 3 5 10 **F**30 39 50 56 59 61 68 74
75 77 86 87 98 101 103 106 130 132 135 146 **P**6 **S** Texas Department of
State Health Services, Austin, TX
Primary Contact: Lorie Dunnam, Superintendent
CFO: Adrienne Bides, Assistant Chief Financial Officer and Budget Analyst
CMO: Ba Han, M.D., Clinical Director
CIO: Elizabeth Correa, Director Information Management
CHR: Lorie Couch, Assistant Superintendent
CNO: Stormy Ward, Chief Nurse Executive
Web address: www.dshs.state.tx.us/mhhospitals/BigSpringSH/default.shtm
Control: State–Government, nonfederal **Service:** Psychiatric

Staffed Beds: 200 **Admissions:** 846 **Census:** 189 **Outpatient Visits:** 0
Births: 0 **Total Expense ($000):** 42240 **Payroll Expense ($000):** 21548
Personnel: 559

✠ **SCENIC MOUNTAIN MEDICAL CENTER (450653)**, 1601 West 11th Place,
Zip 79720–4198; tel. 432/263–1211 **A**1 9 10 20 **F**3 8 11 13 15 18 20 29 30
34 35 39 40 43 47 50 51 57 59 64 65 68 69 70 75 76 77 79 81 85 87 93
107 108 110 111 114 119 129 130 133 146 147 148 **P**6 **S** Community Health
Systems, Inc., Franklin, TN
Primary Contact: Larry Rodgers, Chief Executive Officer
CFO: Rodger W. Bowen, M.P.H., Chief Financial Officer
CMO: Keith Ledford, M.D., Chief of Staff
CIO: Gene Mills, Director Information Technology
CHR: Dwight Linton, Director Human Resources
CNO: Judy Roever, MSN, Chief Nursing Officer
Web address: www.smmccares.com
Control: Corporation, Investor–owned, for–profit **Service:** General Medical and
Surgical

Staffed Beds: 75 **Admissions:** 2542 **Census:** 22 **Outpatient Visits:** 29412
Births: 275 **Total Expense ($000):** 38691 **Payroll Expense ($000):** 13957
Personnel: 234

✠ **WEST TEXAS VETERANS AFFAIRS HEALTH CARE SYSTEM**, 300 Veterans
Boulevard, Zip 79720–5500; Mailing Address: Big Springs, tel. 432/263–7361,
(Nonreporting) **A**1 3 5 9 **S** Department of Veterans Affairs, Washington,
DC
Primary Contact: Adam M. Welch, Interim Director
CFO: Ray Olivas, Chief Fiscal Service
CMO: Martin Schnier, D.O., Chief of Staff
CIO: Mike McKinley, Information Security Officer
CHR: Anna Osborne, Chief Human Resources Management Service
Web address: www.bigspring.va.gov/about/
Control: Veterans Affairs, Government, federal **Service:** General Medical and
Surgical

Staffed Beds: 149

BONHAM—Fannin County

★ ◇ **RED RIVER REGIONAL HOSPITAL (451370)**, 504 Lipscomb Street,
Zip 75418–4028; tel. 903/583–8585 **A**9 10 18 21 **F**3 11 15 28 29 30 34 35
40 46 50 57 59 64 65 70 75 81 87 93 107 108 110 111 118 119 130 133
135 146
Primary Contact: David Conejo, Chief Executive Officer
CFO: Jay Hodges, Chief Financial Officer
CMO: Michael Brown, D.O., Chief of Staff
CIO: Jack Farguson, Director Information Technology
CHR: Brenda Bagley, Director Human Resources
CNO: William Kiefer, Chief Nursing Officer
Web address: www.redriverregional.com/
Control: Hospital district or authority, Government, nonfederal **Service:** General
Medical and Surgical

Staffed Beds: 25 **Admissions:** 741 **Census:** 9 **Outpatient Visits:** 14283
Births: 0 **Total Expense ($000):** 14950 **Payroll Expense ($000):** 6101
Personnel: 121

SAM RAYBURN MEMORIAL VETERANS CENTER See Veterans Affairs North
Texas Health Care System, Dallas

BORGER—Hutchinson County

GOLDEN PLAINS COMMUNITY HOSPITAL (451369), 100 Medical Drive,
Zip 79007–7579; tel. 806/467–5700 **A**9 10 18 **F**11 13 15 29 30 34 35 40 43
45 50 54 57 59 62 64 65 66 68 70 75 76 77 79 81 85 86 87 93 107 108
115 119 127 130 131 132 133 146 147 148 **P**6
Primary Contact: Kevin Storey, Chief Executive Officer
COO: Melody Henderson, R.N., Chief Operating Officer and Chief Nursing Officer
CFO: Dennis P. Kilday, Chief Financial Officer
CMO: Bard Rogers, M.D., Chief of Staff
CHR: Sally Mason, Director Human Resources
Web address: www.goldenplains.org
Control: Corporation, Investor–owned, for–profit **Service:** General Medical and
Surgical

Staffed Beds: 25 **Admissions:** 748 **Census:** 7 **Outpatient Visits:** 55651
Births: 217 **Total Expense ($000):** 24248 **Payroll Expense ($000):** 7116
Personnel: 184

BOWIE—Montague County

BOWIE MEMORIAL HOSPITAL (450497), 705 East Greenwood Avenue,
Zip 76230–3199; tel. 940/872–1126 **A**9 10 **F**3 10 11 15 28 29 40 43 45 53
57 62 63 64 70 75 81 82 84 93 103 107 115 119 129 130 131 132 133
148 **P**4
Primary Contact: Michael L. McEachern, Chief Executive Officer
CFO: Kim Lee, Chief Financial Officer
CMO: Surinder Aujla, M.D., Chief of Staff
CIO: Randell Cox, Director Data Processing
CHR: Mary Bates, Director Human Resources
CNO: Pam Alexander, R.N., Chief Nursing Officer
Web address: www.bowiememorial.com
Control: Hospital district or authority, Government, nonfederal **Service:** General
Medical and Surgical

Staffed Beds: 44 **Admissions:** 684 **Census:** 11 **Outpatient Visits:** 42284
Births: 0 **Total Expense ($000):** 13630 **Payroll Expense ($000):** 5558
Personnel: 163

BRADY—Mcculloch County

HEART OF TEXAS MEMORIAL HOSPITAL (451348), 2008 Nine Road,
Zip 76825–7210, Mailing Address: P.O. Box 1150, Zip 76825–1150;
tel. 325/597–2901 **A**9 10 18 **F**11 15 28 40 43 45 64 81 93 107 111 114
119 127 133 **P**4
Primary Contact: Tim Jones, Chief Executive Officer
CFO: Brad Burnett, Chief Financial Officer
CMO: Pete Castro, D.O., Chief of Staff
Web address: www.bradyhospital.com/
Control: Other not–for–profit (including NFP Corporation) **Service:** General
Medical and Surgical

Staffed Beds: 25 **Admissions:** 383 **Census:** 4 **Outpatient Visits:** 29652
Births: 0 **Total Expense ($000):** 11177 **Payroll Expense ($000):** 3533
Personnel: 111

BRECKENRIDGE—Stephens County

STEPHENS MEMORIAL HOSPITAL (450498), 200 South Geneva Street,
Zip 76424–4799; tel. 254/559–2242 **A**9 10 20 **F**3 7 8 11 15 28 30 34 35 40
43 45 50 53 56 57 59 63 64 68 69 81 85 87 89 93 97 103 107 114 130
133 146 **P**6
Primary Contact: Matthew Kempton, Chief Executive Officer and Administrator
CFO: Samuel Grant, Chief Financial Officer
CMO: Cynthia Perry, M.D., Chief of Staff
CIO: Bobby Thompson, Director Information Technology
CHR: Michelle Funderburg, Director Human Resources
CNO: Alicia Whitt, R.N., Chief Nursing Officer
Web address: www.smhtx.com
Control: County–Government, nonfederal **Service:** General Medical and Surgical

Staffed Beds: 21 **Admissions:** 365 **Census:** 4 **Outpatient Visits:** 15781
Births: 0 **Total Expense ($000):** 9507 **Payroll Expense ($000):** 4494
Personnel: 110

TX

BRENHAM—Washington County

⊞ **SCOTT & WHITE HOSPITAL – BRENHAM (450187)**, 700 Medical Parkway, Zip 77833–5498; tel. 979/337–5000 **A**1 9 10 **F**3 11 13 15 29 30 32 34 35 40 43 44 50 51 53 56 57 59 64 65 70 75 76 77 78 79 80 81 82 85 86 87 93 107 108 110 111 114 119 127 129 130 132 133 135 146 **P**6 **S** Baylor Scott & White Health, Dallas, TX
Primary Contact: Michael Pittman, Chief Operating Officer and Chief Nursing Officer
CFO: Jane Wellmann, Chief Financial Officer
CMO: Michael Schlabach, M.D., Chief Medical Officer
CIO: Sharon Schwartz, Director Medical Records
CHR: Virginia Counts, Manager Human Resources
Web address: www.swbrenham.org
Control: Other not-for-profit (including NFP Corporation) **Service:** General Medical and Surgical

Staffed Beds: 60 **Admissions:** 1717 **Census:** 17 **Outpatient Visits:** 40264 **Births:** 365 **Total Expense ($000):** 29325 **Payroll Expense ($000):** 13594 **Personnel:** 198

BROWNFIELD—Terry County

★ **BROWNFIELD REGIONAL MEDICAL CENTER (450399)**, 705 East Felt Street, Zip 79316–3439; tel. 806/637–3551 **A**9 10 20 **F**3 7 13 28 29 30 34 40 43 45 50 53 57 59 62 64 65 68 75 76 80 81 85 86 87 90 93 97 102 107 119 127 130 135 148 **P**4
Primary Contact: Mike Click, Administrator
CFO: Josh Savage, Chief Financial Officer
CIO: Sheryl Holcombe, Administrative Assistant
CHR: Avis DePoyster, Director Human Resources
CNO: Melissa Richolson, R.N., Director of Nursing
Web address: www.brownfield–rmc.org
Control: Hospital district or authority, Government, nonfederal **Service:** General Medical and Surgical

Staffed Beds: 26 **Admissions:** 803 **Census:** 7 **Outpatient Visits:** 52285 **Births:** 135 **Total Expense ($000):** 15082 **Payroll Expense ($000):** 6678 **Personnel:** 190

BROWNSVILLE—Cameron County

☐ **SOUTH TEXAS REHABILITATION HOSPITAL (453092)**, 425 East Alton Gloor Boulevard, Zip 78526–3361; tel. 956/554–6000 **A**1 9 10 **F**3 28 29 34 35 59 64 75 77 86 87 90 93 94 96 130 132 148 **P**6 **S** Ernest Health, Inc., Albuquerque, NM
Primary Contact: Jessie Eason Smedley, Chief Executive Officer
COO: Mary Valdez, Chief Operating Officer
CFO: Sue Thomsen, Chief Financial Officer
CMO: Christopher Wilson, M.D., Inpatient Medical Director
CIO: Deborah Alcocer, Chief Information Officer
CHR: Tony Rodriguez, Director Human Resources
CNO: Cheryl Sexton, Director Nursing Operations
Web address: www.strh.ernesthealth.com
Control: Partnership, Investor-owned, for-profit **Service:** Rehabilitation

Staffed Beds: 40 **Admissions:** 825 **Census:** 32 **Outpatient Visits:** 4245 **Births:** 0 **Total Expense ($000):** 13867 **Payroll Expense ($000):** 6516 **Personnel:** 116

⊞ **VALLEY BAPTIST MEDICAL CENTER–BROWNSVILLE (450028)**, 1040 West Jefferson Street, Zip 78520–6338, Mailing Address: P.O. Box 3590, Zip 78523–3590; tel. 956/698–5400, (Total facility includes 11 beds in nursing home-type unit) **A**1 9 10 **F**3 11 12 15 18 20 22 24 26 28 29 30 34 35 39 40 43 44 45 49 50 54 56 57 59 60 63 64 65 70 72 73 74 75 76 77 79 81 82 84 85 86 87 89 93 98 100 101 102 103 104 105 106 107 109 110 111 112 114 115 119 128 129 130 132 146 147 148 **S** TENET Healthcare Corporation, Dallas, TX
Primary Contact: Leslie Bingham, Senior Vice President and Chief Executive Officer
COO: Marisa Aguilar, Chief Operating Officer
CFO: Harvey Torres, Chief Financial Officer
CMO: Jose L. Ayala, M.D., Chief Medical Officer
CIO: Mary Garrido, Vice President and Regional Chief Information Officer
CHR: Irma L. Pye, Chief Human Resource Officer
CNO: Aniceta Mendoza, R.N., Chief Nursing Officer
Web address: www.valleybaptist.net/brownsville/index.htm
Control: Corporation, Investor-owned, for-profit **Service:** General Medical and Surgical

Staffed Beds: 240 **Admissions:** 9847 **Census:** 141 **Outpatient Visits:** 67326 **Births:** 2172 **Total Expense ($000):** 115075 **Payroll Expense ($000):** 65894 **Personnel:** 690

⊞ **VALLEY REGIONAL MEDICAL CENTER (450662)**, 100A Alton Gloor Boulevard, Zip 78526–3354, Mailing Address: P.O. Box 3710, Zip 78523–3710; tel. 956/350–7101 **A**1 9 10 **F**3 11 13 15 18 20 22 24 26 29 30 31 32 34 35 40 43 44 45 47 49 50 53 57 59 60 61 64 65 68 70 72 73 74 75 76 77 78 79 81 82 84 85 86 87 89 93 107 108 110 111 115 118 119 124 130 132 135 146 147 148 **P**7 **S** HCA, Nashville, TN
Primary Contact: Susan Andrews, Chief Executive Officer
COO: Steven C. Hoelscher, Chief Operating Officer
CFO: Marcia Patterson, Chief Financial Officer
CIO: Carlos Leal, Director Information Technology
CHR: Vicky Kahl, Director Human Resources
CNO: Holley Tyler, R.N., Chief Nursing Officer
Web address: www.valleyregionalmedicalcenter.com
Control: Partnership, Investor-owned, for-profit **Service:** General Medical and Surgical

Staffed Beds: 214 **Admissions:** 9625 **Census:** 128 **Outpatient Visits:** 68066 **Births:** 2617 **Total Expense ($000):** 120694 **Payroll Expense ($000):** 47012 **Personnel:** 710

BROWNWOOD—Brown County

⊞ **BROWNWOOD REGIONAL MEDICAL CENTER (450587)**, 1501 Burnet Drive, Zip 76801–8520, Mailing Address: P.O. Box 760, Zip 76804–0760; tel. 325/646–8541, (Total facility includes 20 beds in nursing home-type unit) **A**1 9 10 20 **F**3 11 13 15 18 28 29 30 31 34 35 39 40 45 48 49 50 51 53 54 56 57 59 63 64 68 70 74 75 76 77 78 79 81 82 85 86 87 93 97 107 108 111 114 119 120 121 123 128 129 130 132 146 147 148 **P**3 8 **S** Community Health Systems, Inc., Franklin, TN
Primary Contact: Claude E. Camp, III, Chief Executive Officer
CFO: John D. Montois, Chief Financial Officer
CMO: Dan Locker, M.D., Chief of Staff
CIO: Jay Smith, Director Information Systems
CHR: Mikeana Bailey, Director Human Resources
CNO: Alicia Kayga, R.N., Chief Nursing Officer
Web address: www.brmc-cares.com
Control: Partnership, Investor-owned, for-profit **Service:** General Medical and Surgical

Staffed Beds: 168 **Admissions:** 4658 **Census:** 59 **Outpatient Visits:** 61670 **Births:** 631 **Total Expense ($000):** 61973 **Payroll Expense ($000):** 24598 **Personnel:** 473

BRYAN—Brazos County

⊞ **CHRISTUS DUBUIS HOSPITAL OF BRYAN (452113)**, 1600 Joseph Drive, 2nd Floor, Zip 77802–1502; tel. 979/821–5000 **A**1 9 10 **F**1 3 29 30 34 75 80 82 85 86 87 91 130 148 **P**8 **S** Dubuis Health System, Houston, TX
Primary Contact: Judy Wolfe, Chief Executive Officer
Web address: www.dubuis.org/CHRISTUSDubuisHospitalofBryan
Control: Church-operated, Nongovernment, not-for profit **Service:** Long-Term Acute Care hospital

Staffed Beds: 30 **Admissions:** 186 **Census:** 14 **Outpatient Visits:** 0 **Births:** 0 **Total Expense ($000):** 6500 **Payroll Expense ($000):** 2405 **Personnel:** 52

⊞ **ST. JOSEPH REGIONAL HEALTH CENTER (450011)**, 2801 Franciscan Drive, Zip 77802–2599; tel. 979/776–3777 **A**1 2 3 5 9 10 **F**3 7 11 12 13 15 17 18 20 22 24 28 29 30 31 32 34 35 37 40 42 43 44 45 46 48 49 50 53 54 57 59 64 65 68 70 74 75 76 77 78 79 80 81 84 85 86 87 89 90 93 96 107 110 111 114 118 119 121 123 124 126 127 129 130 131 132 135 143 144 146 148 **S** Sylvania Franciscan Health, Toledo, OH
Primary Contact: Kathleen R. Krusie, FACHE, Chief Executive Officer
CFO: Lisa McNair, CPA, Senior Vice President and Chief Financial Officer
CIO: John Phillips, Vice President Information Services
CHR: Michael G. Costa, Vice President Human Resources
Web address: www.st-joseph.org
Control: Church-operated, Nongovernment, not-for-profit **Service:** General Medical and Surgical

Staffed Beds: 233 **Admissions:** 15155 **Census:** 174 **Outpatient Visits:** 323291 **Births:** 1515 **Total Expense ($000):** 256143 **Payroll Expense ($000):** 91428 **Personnel:** 1656

☐ **THE PHYSICIANS CENTRE HOSPITAL (450834)**, 3131 University Drive East, Zip 77802–3473; tel. 979/731–3100 **A**1 9 10 **F**3 12 15 29 34 35 40 44 45 50 51 59 64 68 74 75 77 79 81 82 85 86 87 89 107 111 114 119 130 131 132 135
Primary Contact: Kori Rich, Chief Executive Officer
CFO: Paul Tannos, Chief Financial Officer
CMO: Barry Solcher, M.D., Chief of Staff
CIO: Shawn Clark, Director Information Systems
CHR: LeeAnn Ford, Director Human Resources and Imaging
CNO: Robert Raymond Lemay, R.N., Chief Nursing Officer
Web address: www.thephysicianscentre.com
Control: Corporation, Investor-owned, for-profit **Service:** General Medical and Surgical

Staffed Beds: 16 **Admissions:** 359 **Census:** 2 **Outpatient Visits:** 8664 **Births:** 0 **Total Expense ($000):** 14352 **Payroll Expense ($000):** 3870 **Personnel:** 84

Many Facility Codes have changed. Please refer to the AHA Guide Code Chart. © 2014 AHA Guide

BURNET—Burnet County

✠ **SETON HIGHLAND LAKES (451365)**, 3201 South Water Street, Zip 78611–4510, Mailing Address: P.O. Box 1219, Zip 78611–7219; tel. 512/715–3000 **A**1 9 10 18 **F**3 11 15 18 28 29 30 34 35 40 43 44 50 57 59 62 63 64 65 66 68 70 71 74 75 77 78 79 81 82 84 85 86 87 91 92 93 97 107 110 111 115 119 127 130 132 133 135 146 148 **P**3 8 **S** Ascension Health, Saint Louis, MO
Primary Contact: Michelle Robertson, R.N., President and Chief Executive Officer
CFO: Douglas D. Waite, Senior Vice President and Chief Financial Officer
CIO: Gerry Lewis, Chief Information Officer
Web address: www.seton.net
Control: Church–operated, Nongovernment, not–for profit **Service:** General Medical and Surgical

Staffed Beds: 23 **Admissions:** 1279 **Census:** 10 **Outpatient Visits:** 106922 **Births:** 0 **Total Expense ($000):** 41757 **Payroll Expense ($000):** 15827 **Personnel:** 248

CALDWELL—Burleson County

✠ **BURLESON ST. JOSEPH HEALTH CENTER (451305)**, 1101 Woodson Drive, Zip 77836–1052, Mailing Address: P.O. Box 360, Zip 77836–0360; tel. 979/567–3245 **A**1 9 10 18 **F**3 7 11 29 30 34 35 40 43 57 59 64 68 84 93 107 114 130 133 143 **S** Sylvania Franciscan Health, Toledo, OH
Primary Contact: John Hughson, Administrator
CFO: Lisa McNair, CPA, Senior Vice President and Chief Financial Officer
CMO: Kristel Leubner, D.O., Chief of Staff
CHR: Michael G. Costa, Vice President Human Resources
Web address: www.st-joseph.org/
Control: Church–operated, Nongovernment, not–for profit **Service:** General Medical and Surgical

Staffed Beds: 25 **Admissions:** 264 **Census:** 5 **Outpatient Visits:** 18510 **Births:** 0 **Total Expense ($000):** 9151 **Payroll Expense ($000):** 4139 **Personnel:** 71

CAMERON—Milam County

CENTRAL TEXAS HOSPITAL (450770), 806 North Crockett Avenue, Zip 76520–2553, Mailing Address: P.O. Box 947, Zip 76520–0947; tel. 254/697–6591, (Nonreporting) **A**9 10
Primary Contact: Tariq Mahmood, Chief Executive Officer
CFO: Joe White, Chief Financial Officer
Web address: www.centexhospital.com
Control: Corporation, Investor–owned, for–profit **Service:** General Medical and Surgical

Staffed Beds: 34

CANADIAN—Hemphill County

HEMPHILL COUNTY HOSPITAL (450578), 1020 South Fourth Street, Zip 79014–3315; tel. 806/323–6422 **A**9 10 20 **F**2 7 29 35 40 45 56 57 62 63 64 68 69 87 89 93 97 102 107 108 130 133 146 148
Primary Contact: Christy Francis, Chief Executive Officer
COO: Patrick Murfee, Chief Operating Officer
CFO: Bob Ericson, Chief Financial Officer
CMO: G. Anthony Cook, M.D., Medical Director
CIO: Brian Goza, Chief Information Officer
CHR: David Troublefield, Chief Communications Officer
CNO: Debra Sappenfield, R.N., Chief Nursing Officer
Web address: www.hchdst.org
Control: Hospital district or authority, Government, nonfederal **Service:** General Medical and Surgical

Staffed Beds: 19 **Admissions:** 196 **Census:** 3 **Outpatient Visits:** 12380 **Births:** 0 **Total Expense ($000):** 8013 **Payroll Expense ($000):** 3004 **Personnel:** 92

CARRIZO SPRINGS—Dimmit County

DIMMIT REGIONAL HOSPITAL (450620), 704 Hospital Drive, Zip 78834–3836, Mailing Address: P.O. Box 1016, Zip 78834–7016; tel. 830/876–2424 **A**9 10 20 **F**11 13 40 43 45 57 62 64 70 76 81 89 93 107 115 119
Primary Contact: James E. Buckner, Jr., FACHE, Interim Chief Executive Officer
CFO: Alma Melendez, Controller
Web address: www.dcmhospital.org
Control: Other not–for–profit (including NFP Corporation) **Service:** General Medical and Surgical

Staffed Beds: 35 **Admissions:** 1287 **Census:** 10 **Outpatient Visits:** 21664 **Births:** 269 **Total Expense ($000):** 11905 **Payroll Expense ($000):** 5786 **Personnel:** 155

CARROLLTON—Denton County

✠ **BAYLOR MEDICAL CENTER AT CARROLLTON (450730)**, 4343 North Josey Lane, Zip 75010–4691; tel. 972/492–1010 **A**1 9 10 **F**3 11 12 13 15 18 20 22 29 30 31 34 35 40 45 48 49 50 51 54 55 56 57 59 64 70 72 73 74 75 76 77 78 79 81 82 84 85 86 87 93 107 108 111 114 115 119 129 130 131 132 135 146 147 148
Primary Contact: Michael Sanborn, MS, FACHE, President
CFO: James McNatt, Chief Financial Officer
CMO: Matthew Smith, M.D., Vice President Medical Affairs and Chief Medical Officer
CIO: Paul Ratcliff, Director Information Services
CHR: Drew Smith, Director Human Resources
CNO: Barbara Vaughn, Chief Nursing Officer
Web address: www.baylorhealth.com
Control: Other not–for–profit (including NFP Corporation) **Service:** General Medical and Surgical

Staffed Beds: 123 **Admissions:** 6211 **Census:** 70 **Outpatient Visits:** 62746 **Births:** 1429 **Total Expense ($000):** 122853 **Payroll Expense ($000):** 43690 **Personnel:** 780

☐ **CARROLLTON SPRINGS (454119)**, 2225 Parker Road, Zip 75010–4711; tel. 972/242–4114 **A**1 9 10 **F**4 98 102 103 104 105
Primary Contact: Shanti Carter, Chief Executive Officer
Web address: www.carrolltonsprings.com
Control: Corporation, Investor–owned, for–profit **Service:** Psychiatric

Staffed Beds: 45 **Admissions:** 1387 **Census:** 30 **Outpatient Visits:** 6156 **Births:** 0 **Total Expense ($000):** 8685 **Payroll Expense ($000):** 5388 **Personnel:** 120

✠ **SELECT SPECIALTY HOSPITAL–DALLAS (452022)**, 2329 West Parker Road, Zip 75010–4713; tel. 469/892–1400 **A**1 9 10 **F**1 3 29 56 74 75 77 85 91 107 114 119 130 135 148 **S** Select Medical Corporation, Mechanicsburg, PA
Primary Contact: Barbara Mobley, Chief Executive Officer
Web address: www.selectspecialtyhospitals.com/company/locations/dallas.aspx
Control: Corporation, Investor–owned, for–profit **Service:** Long–Term Acute Care hospital

Staffed Beds: 60 **Admissions:** 547 **Census:** 40 **Outpatient Visits:** 0 **Births:** 0 **Total Expense ($000):** 22383 **Payroll Expense ($000):** 9970 **Personnel:** 172

CARTHAGE—Panola County

✠ **EAST TEXAS MEDICAL CENTER CARTHAGE (450210)**, 409 Cottage Road, Zip 75633–1466, Mailing Address: P.O. Box 549, Zip 75633–0549; tel. 903/693–3841 **A**1 9 10 20 **F**3 8 11 15 28 29 30 34 35 40 43 45 50 57 59 64 65 75 81 85 107 108 110 111 115 119 127 129 145 146 **S** East Texas Medical Center Regional Healthcare System, Tyler, TX
Primary Contact: Gary Mikeal Hudson, Administrator
COO: Gary Mikeal Hudson, Administrator
CFO: Phillip A. Caron, Chief Financial Officer
CMO: Salah Almohammed, Chief of Staff
CIO: Renee Lawhorn, Director Medical Records
CHR: Amber Cox, Director Human Resources
CNO: Judy Peterson, R.N., Chief Nursing Officer
Web address: www.etmc.org
Control: Other not–for–profit (including NFP Corporation) **Service:** General Medical and Surgical

Staffed Beds: 25 **Admissions:** 878 **Census:** 7 **Outpatient Visits:** 85487 **Births:** 0 **Total Expense ($000):** 21839 **Payroll Expense ($000):** 7767 **Personnel:** 178

CEDAR PARK—Williamson County

✠ **CEDAR PARK REGIONAL MEDICAL CENTER (670043)**, 1401 Medical Parkway, Zip 78613–7763; tel. 512/528–7000 **A**1 5 9 10 **F**3 12 13 15 18 20 22 29 34 35 40 45 47 49 50 54 57 59 64 68 70 73 74 75 76 77 78 79 81 82 85 87 93 107 108 110 111 114 115 119 126 130 132 135 146 147 148 **P**6 **S** Community Health Systems, Inc., Franklin, TN
Primary Contact: Brad D. Holland, Chief Executive Officer
COO: Megan Drake, Assistant Administrator
CFO: Erich Wallschlaeger, Chief Financial Officer
CIO: Brad Hoar, Director Information and Technology
CHR: Amy D. Reeves, Director Human Resources
CNO: Krista Baty, R.N., Chief Nursing Officer
Web address: www.cedarparkregional.com
Control: Corporation, Investor–owned, for–profit **Service:** General Medical and Surgical

Staffed Beds: 85 **Admissions:** 4230 **Census:** 37 **Outpatient Visits:** 40891 **Births:** 982 **Total Expense ($000):** 70369 **Payroll Expense ($000):** 26210 **Personnel:** 451

TX

Hospital, Medicare Provider Number, Address, Telephone, Approval, Facility, and Physician Codes, Health Care System

★ American Hospital Association (AHA) membership
☐ The Joint Commission accreditation
◇ DNV Healthcare Inc. accreditation
○ Healthcare Facilities Accreditation Program
△ Commission on Accreditation of Rehabilitation Facilities (CARF) accreditation

◇ **SCOTT & WHITE EMERGENCY HOSPITAL– CEDAR PARK (670087)**, 900 East Whitestone Boulevard, Zip 78613–9093; tel. 512/684–4911, (Data for 330 days) **A**10 21 **F**3 34 40 44 75 87 107 119 **P**5 **S** Baylor Scott & White Health, Dallas, TX
Primary Contact: John Wood, Administrator
Web address: www.sweh.org
Control: Partnership, Investor–owned, for–profit **Service:** General Medical and Surgical

Staffed Beds: 8 **Admissions:** 41 **Census:** 1 **Outpatient Visits:** 6140 **Births:** 0 **Total Expense ($000):** 5390 **Payroll Expense ($000):** 1734 **Personnel:** 26

CHANNELVIEW—Harris County

★ **KINDRED HOSPITAL EAST HOUSTON (452075)**, 15101 East Freeway, Zip 77530–4104; tel. 832/200–5500, (Includes KINDRED HOSPITAL BAYTOWN, 1700 James Bowie Drive, 3rd Floor, Baytown, Zip 77520; tel. 281/420–7800; Angel Gradney, Chief Executive Officer) **A**9 10 **F**1 3 29 45 57 64 75 77 81 85 93 96 107 130 148 **S** Kindred Healthcare, Louisville, KY
Primary Contact: Angel Gradney, Chief Executive Officer
Web address: www.kheasthouston.com
Control: Corporation, Investor–owned, for–profit **Service:** Long–Term Acute Care hospital

Staffed Beds: 230 **Admissions:** 1937 **Census:** 140 **Outpatient Visits:** 4741 **Births:** 0 **Total Expense ($000):** 80538 **Payroll Expense ($000):** 27336 **Personnel:** 434

CHILDRESS—Childress County

★ **CHILDRESS REGIONAL MEDICAL CENTER (450369)**, Highway 83 North, Zip 79201–5800, Mailing Address: P.O. Box 1030, Zip 79201–1030; tel. 940/937–6371 **A**9 10 20 **F**7 8 13 15 29 32 34 35 40 43 45 50 56 57 59 60 61 62 63 64 65 66 79 81 84 91 92 93 107 111 119 127 129 130 133
Primary Contact: John Henderson, Chief Executive Officer
COO: Holly Holcomb, R.N., Chief Operating Officer
CFO: Kathy McLain, Chief Financial Officer
CMO: Dustin Pratt, M.D., Chief of Staff
CIO: Holly Holcomb, R.N., Chie Operating Officer
CHR: Gayle Cannon, Director Human Resources
CNO: Sulynn Mester, R.N., Chief Nursing Officer
Web address: www.childresshospital.com
Control: Hospital district or authority, Government, nonfederal **Service:** General Medical and Surgical

Staffed Beds: 39 **Admissions:** 925 **Census:** 7 **Outpatient Visits:** 151739 **Births:** 205 **Total Expense ($000):** 22811 **Payroll Expense ($000):** 9463 **Personnel:** 257

CHILLICOTHE—Hardeman County

★ **CHILLICOTHE HOSPITAL DISTRICT (451326)**, 303 Avenue I, Zip 79225, Mailing Address: P.O. Box 370, Zip 79225–0370; tel. 940/852–5131 **A**9 10 18 **F**29 34 40 43 45 57 59 69 81 89 132 133 **P**5
Primary Contact: Linda Hall, Administrator and Chief Executive Officer
COO: Linda Hall, Administrator and Chief Executive Officer
CFO: Linda Hall, Administrator and Chief Executive Officer
CMO: Weldon Glidden, M.D., Chief of Staff
CIO: Kathy Busby, Medical Record Technician
CHR: Linda Hall, Administrator and Chief Executive Officer
CNO: Sonya Richardson, Chief Nursing Officer
Web address: www.chillhd.org
Control: Hospital district or authority, Government, nonfederal **Service:** General Medical and Surgical

Staffed Beds: 13 **Admissions:** 75 **Census:** 1 **Outpatient Visits:** 5083 **Births:** 0 **Total Expense ($000):** 2161 **Payroll Expense ($000):** 1254 **Personnel:** 24

CLARKSVILLE—Red River County

★ **EAST TEXAS MEDICAL CENTER CLARKSVILLE (450188)**, 3000 West Main Street, Zip 75426–3371, Mailing Address: P.O. Box 1270, Zip 75426–1270; tel. 903/427–6400 **A**9 10 **F**11 29 34 35 40 44 56 57 59 64 68 75 81 86 87 107 108 115 119 127 130 135 146 **P**6 **S** East Texas Medical Center Regional Healthcare System, Tyler, TX
Primary Contact: Matthew Wylie, Administrator
CFO: Samuel L. Brown, CPA, Chief Financial Officer
CMO: Ravi K. Sreerama, M.D., Chief of Staff
CHR: Kathy Shelton, Director Human Resources
Web address: www.etmc.org
Control: Other not–for–profit (including NFP Corporation) **Service:** General Medical and Surgical

Staffed Beds: 30 **Admissions:** 694 **Census:** 8 **Outpatient Visits:** 12534 **Births:** 0 **Total Expense ($000):** 10875 **Payroll Expense ($000):** 4090 **Personnel:** 69

CLEBURNE—Johnson County

✠ **TEXAS HEALTH HARRIS METHODIST HOSPITAL CLEBURNE (450148)**, 201 Walls Drive, Zip 76033–4007; tel. 817/641–2551 **A**1 9 10 **F**3 11 13 15 29 32 34 35 40 43 44 45 46 49 50 51 56 57 59 64 65 68 70 75 76 77 79 81 85 89 93 107 108 110 114 119 124 126 129 130 146 148 **P**6 **S** Texas Health Resources, Arlington, TX
Primary Contact: Blake Kretz, President
CFO: Richard Humphrey, Director Finance
CMO: Judy Laviolette, M.D., Chief Medical Officer
CIO: Brenda Taylor, Director Information Systems
CHR: Shelly Allain, Director
CNO: Lorrie Normand, R.N., Chief Nursing Officer
Web address: www.texashealth.org
Control: Other not–for–profit (including NFP Corporation) **Service:** General Medical and Surgical

Staffed Beds: 85 **Admissions:** 3831 **Census:** 41 **Outpatient Visits:** 46768 **Births:** 586 **Total Expense ($000):** 60078 **Payroll Expense ($000):** 24344 **Personnel:** 312

CLEVELAND—Liberty County

CLEVELAND REGIONAL MEDICAL CENTER (450296), 300 East Crockett Street, Zip 77327–4062, Mailing Address: P.O. Box 1688, Zip 77328–1688; tel. 281/593–1811 **A**9 10 **F**3 11 13 15 18 29 30 34 35 40 41 43 50 57 59 64 68 70 74 75 76 77 79 81 85 87 92 107 108 114 119 130 132 133 135 146 **P**6
Primary Contact: Vickie L. Newsome, Chief Executive Officer
Web address: www.clevelandregionalmedicalcenter.com
Control: Partnership, Investor–owned, for–profit **Service:** General Medical and Surgical

Staffed Beds: 98 **Admissions:** 556 **Census:** 6 **Outpatient Visits:** 17824 **Births:** 82 **Total Expense ($000):** 16105 **Payroll Expense ($000):** 7449 **Personnel:** 151

DOCTORS DIAGNOSTIC HOSPITAL (670018), 1017 South Travis Street, Zip 77327–5152; tel. 281/622–2900, (Nonreporting) **A**9 10
Primary Contact: Don Vickers, Chief Executive Officer
Web address: www.ddhclv.com
Control: Corporation, Investor–owned, for–profit **Service:** General Medical and Surgical

Staffed Beds: 6

CLIFTON—Bosque County

★ **GOODALL–WITCHER HOSPITAL AUTHORITY (450052)**, 101 South Avenue T, Zip 76634–1897, Mailing Address: P.O. Box 549, Zip 76634–0549; tel. 254/675–8322, (Data for 212 days) **A**9 10 20 **F**3 11 13 15 29 30 34 35 36 40 43 45 53 57 59 62 64 65 68 76 77 81 93 107 108 114 119 127 130 133 146 147 148 **P**3
Primary Contact: Adam Willmann, President and Chief Executive Officer
CFO: Vicki Gloff, Chief Financial Officer
CMO: Kevin Blanton, D.O., Chief of Staff
CHR: Jennie Oldham, Director Human Resources
CNO: Donna Nichols, R.N., Chief Nursing Officer
Web address: www.gwhf.org
Control: Hospital district or authority, Government, nonfederal **Service:** General Medical and Surgical

Staffed Beds: 33 **Admissions:** 287 **Census:** 7 **Outpatient Visits:** 22549 **Births:** 47 **Total Expense ($000):** 9399 **Payroll Expense ($000):** 3946 **Personnel:** 148

COLEMAN—Coleman County

COLEMAN COUNTY MEDICAL CENTER (451347), 310 South Pecos Street, Zip 76834–4159; tel. 325/625–2135 **A**9 10 18 **F**3 7 8 11 13 28 29 34 40 43 45 57 59 64 65 66 68 75 77 81 93 97 107 114 127 133 134 **S** Preferred Management Corporation, Shawnee, OK
Primary Contact: Michael W. Pruitt, Administrator and Chief Executive Officer
CMO: Paul Reynolds, M.D., Medical Director
CIO: Harvey Ramirez, Chief Information Officer
CHR: Sue Titsworth, Director Human Resources
CNO: Melissa Ereman, R.N., Chief Nursing Officer
Web address: www.colemantexas.org/hospital.html
Control: Hospital district or authority, Government, nonfederal **Service:** General Medical and Surgical

Staffed Beds: 25 **Admissions:** 627 **Census:** 7 **Outpatient Visits:** 24079 **Births:** 30 **Total Expense ($000):** 9938 **Payroll Expense ($000):** 4599 **Personnel:** 104

TX

COLLEGE STATION—Brazos County

✠ **COLLEGE STATION MEDICAL CENTER (450299)**, 1604 Rock Prairie Road, Zip 77845–8345, Mailing Address: P.O. Box 10000, Zip 77842–3500; tel. 979/764–5100 **A**1 2 3 5 9 10 **F**3 11 13 15 18 20 22 24 26 28 29 30 31 34 40 43 45 46 49 53 57 61 70 72 74 76 77 78 79 81 82 84 85 87 89 90 91 93 107 108 111 113 115 118 119 126 127 129 130 131 132 135 146 147 148 **P**7 **S** Community Health Systems, Inc., Franklin, TN
Primary Contact: Barry S. Schneider, Interim Chief Executive Officer
COO: Vicky Cha Bridier, Chief Operating Officer
CFO: Ken Pannell, Chief Financial Officer
CIO: Daphne Hartman, Director Information Systems
CHR: Sharon Bond, Director Human Resources
CNO: Sherri Welch, R.N., Chief Nursing Officer
Web address: www.csmedcenter.com
Control: Corporation, Investor–owned, for–profit **Service:** General Medical and Surgical

Staffed Beds: 85 **Admissions:** 7467 **Census:** 74 **Outpatient Visits:** 50294
Births: 1979 **Total Expense ($000):** 129252 **Payroll Expense ($000):** 52159 **Personnel:** 533

COLORADO CITY—Mitchell County

★ **MITCHELL COUNTY HOSPITAL (451342)**, 997 West Interstate 20, Zip 79512–2685; tel. 325/728–3431 **A**9 10 18 **F**3 7 11 28 29 40 43 45 50 57 59 64 68 81 93 107 119 133 146 **P**6
Primary Contact: Robbie Dewberry, Chief Executive Officer
CFO: Joe Wright, Chief Financial Officer
CMO: Dee A. Roach, M.D., Chief of Staff
CIO: Randy Myers, Chief Information Officer, Information Technology
CHR: Deana Overton, Director Human Resources
CNO: Donna Goebel, M.D., Chief Nursing Officer
Web address: www.mitchellcountyhospital.com
Control: Hospital district or authority, Government, nonfederal **Service:** General Medical and Surgical

Staffed Beds: 25 **Admissions:** 469 **Census:** 4 **Outpatient Visits:** 32400
Births: 0 **Total Expense ($000):** 18424 **Payroll Expense ($000):** 8875
Personnel: 226

COLUMBUS—Colorado County

★ **COLUMBUS COMMUNITY HOSPITAL (450370)**, 110 Shult Drive, Zip 78934–3010; tel. 979/732–2371 **A**5 6 9 10 **F**3 11 13 15 29 31 35 40 43 56 57 62 67 68 76 79 81 89 107 110 111 114 119 127 130 133 135
Primary Contact: Robert Thomas, Chief Executive Officer and Administrator
CFO: Regina Wicke, Chief Financial Officer
CMO: Jorge Duchicela, M.D., Chief of Staff
CIO: Ashley Mathis, Privacy Officer
CHR: Janie Hammonds, Human Resources Officer
CNO: Jeno Hargrove, R.N., Director of Nursing
Web address: www.columbusch.com
Control: Other not–for–profit (including NFP Corporation) **Service:** General Medical and Surgical

Staffed Beds: 40 **Admissions:** 1405 **Census:** 15 **Outpatient Visits:** 74319
Births: 246 **Total Expense ($000):** 23982 **Payroll Expense ($000):** 7962
Personnel: 148

COMANCHE—Comanche County

★ **COMANCHE COUNTY MEDICAL CENTER (451382)**, 10201 Highway 16, Zip 76442–4462; tel. 254/879–4900 **A**9 10 18 **F**3 11 15 28 29 30 34 35 40 43 45 50 57 59 64 65 68 70 75 77 79 81 85 89 93 97 107 108 110 111 115 119 127 129 130 131 132 133 135 145 146 148 **P**4
Primary Contact: Carl James Christensen, Chief Executive Officer
CFO: David Freshour, Chief Financial Officer
CMO: Guyle Donham, M.D., Chief of Staff
CIO: Ismelda Garza, Director Information Systems
CHR: Peggy Jordan, Director Human Resources
CNO: Mona Sloan, Chief Nursing Officer
Web address: www.comanchecmc.org
Control: Other not–for–profit (including NFP Corporation) **Service:** General Medical and Surgical

Staffed Beds: 25 **Admissions:** 713 **Census:** 9 **Outpatient Visits:** 52210
Births: 1 **Total Expense ($000):** 19468 **Payroll Expense ($000):** 6456
Personnel: 145

COMMERCE—Hunt County

✠ **HUNT REGIONAL COMMUNITY HOSPITAL (451321)**, 2900 Sterling Hart Drive, Zip 75428–3912; tel. 903/886–3161 **A**1 9 10 18 **F**3 11 29 30 40 41 57 75 85 87 93 105 107 114 119 130 133 135 146 **S** Hunt Regional Healthcare, Greenville, TX
Primary Contact: Michael R. Klepin, Administrator
COO: John Heatherly, Assistant Administrator Support Services
CFO: Jeri Rich, Assistant Administrator and Chief Financial Officer
CMO: Richard Selvaggi, M.D., Chief of Staff
CIO: Jonathan Schafft, Director Information Systems
CHR: Stacey Lane, Director Human Resources
CNO: Deborah Clack, Chief Nursing Officer
Web address: www.huntregional.org
Control: Hospital district or authority, Government, nonfederal **Service:** General Medical and Surgical

Staffed Beds: 15 **Admissions:** 246 **Census:** 4 **Outpatient Visits:** 7838
Births: 0 **Total Expense ($000):** 8254 **Payroll Expense ($000):** 2769
Personnel: 44

CONROE—Montgomery County

✠ **ASPIRE HOSPITAL (454112)**, 2006 South Loop 336 West, Suite 500, Zip 77304–3315; tel. 936/647–3500 **A**1 9 10 **F**3 5 15 34 40 56 57 59 64 78 98 102 103 104 105 107 108 110 111 116 117 118 119 120 121 123 124 129 130 147
Primary Contact: Jerry Nash, Chief Executive Officer
CFO: Bob Gray, Chief Financial Officer
CIO: John Heemann, Chief Information Officer
CHR: Angela Walker, Manager Human Resources
CNO: Troy Ryder, Director of Nursing
Web address: www.aspirehospital.com
Control: Partnership, Investor–owned, for–profit **Service:** Psychiatric

Staffed Beds: 24 **Admissions:** 768 **Census:** 18 **Outpatient Visits:** 2402
Births: 0 **Total Expense ($000):** 9089 **Payroll Expense ($000):** 2751
Personnel: 80

✠ **CONROE REGIONAL MEDICAL CENTER (450222)**, 504 Medical Boulevard, Zip 77304, Mailing Address: P.O. Box 1538, Zip 77305–1538; tel. 936/539–1111 **A**1 9 10 13 **F**3 11 12 13 15 17 18 20 22 24 26 28 29 31 34 35 40 43 45 46 53 54 57 59 64 68 70 72 73 74 75 76 78 79 81 82 85 86 89 90 91 93 107 108 111 114 115 118 119 121 124 129 130 132 135 146 147 148 **P**7 **S** HCA, Nashville, TN
Primary Contact: Matt Davis, Chief Executive Officer
COO: Tripp Montalbo, Chief Operating Officer
CFO: Thomas A. Holt, Chief Financial Officer
CIO: Jeremy Fuller, Director Information Systems
CHR: Diana Howell, Director Human Resources
CNO: Karen Tomsu, R.N., Chief Nursing Officer
Web address: www.conroeregional.com/
Control: Partnership, Investor–owned, for–profit **Service:** General Medical and Surgical

Staffed Beds: 312 **Admissions:** 13580 **Census:** 184 **Outpatient Visits:** 121279 **Births:** 788 **Total Expense ($000):** 201180 **Payroll Expense ($000):** 70336 **Personnel:** 1113

✠ **HEALTHSOUTH REHABILITATION HOSPITAL THE WOODLANDS (453059)**, 18550 'IH' 45 South, Zip 77384; tel. 281/364–2000 **A**1 10 **F**3 28 29 34 35 44 57 59 62 65 68 74 75 77 79 82 86 87 90 91 95 96 130 132 148 **S** HEALTHSOUTH Corporation, Birmingham, AL
Primary Contact: Krista Uselman, Chief Executive Officer
CMO: Ben Agana, M.D., Medical Director
CHR: Valerie Wells, Manager Human Resources
Web address: www.healthsouththewoodlands.com
Control: Corporation, Investor–owned, for–profit **Service:** Rehabilitation

Staffed Beds: 84 **Admissions:** 1171 **Census:** 39 **Outpatient Visits:** 10762
Births: 0 **Total Expense ($000):** 17065 **Payroll Expense ($000):** 8818
Personnel: 110

☐ **SOLARA HOSPITAL CONROE (452107)**, 1500 Grand Lake Drive, Zip 77304–2891; tel. 936/523–1800 **A**1 9 10 **F**1 3 29 34 39 40 74 75 79 85 86 87 91 130 148 **S** Cornerstone Healthcare Group, Dallas, TX
Primary Contact: Suzanne Kretschmer, Interim Hospital Administrator
Web address: www.chghospitals.com/conroe/
Control: Partnership, Investor–owned, for–profit **Service:** Long–Term Acute Care hospital

Staffed Beds: 41 **Admissions:** 513 **Census:** 36 **Outpatient Visits:** 10 **Births:** 0 **Total Expense ($000):** 16875 **Payroll Expense ($000):** 6525 **Personnel:** 114

TX

CORINTH—Denton County

☐ ◇ **ATRIUM MEDICAL CENTER OF CORINTH (452111)**, 3305 Corinth Parkway, Zip 76208–5380; tel. 940/270–4100 **A**1 9 10 21 **F**1 3 28 29 40 45 47 60 64 68 70 75 77 86 87 96 107 111 114 119 148 **P**2
Primary Contact: Dorothy J. Elford, Chief Executive Officer
COO: Kathy Mason, Chief Operating Officer
CFO: Anbu Nachimuthu, Chief Financial Officer
CMO: Jalil Kahn, M.D., Chief of Staff
CIO: Wendy Keller, Director Health Information Management
CHR: Melissa Dovel, Manager Human Resources
CNO: Michelle Gray, Nurse Executive
Web address: www.atriumhealthcare.net
Control: Corporation, Investor–owned, for–profit **Service:** Long–Term Acute Care hospital

Staffed Beds: 57 **Admissions:** 575 **Census:** 44 **Outpatient Visits:** 2753 **Births:** 0 **Total Expense ($000):** 25829 **Payroll Expense ($000):** 10482 **Personnel:** 189

CORPUS CHRISTI—Nueces County

✦ **CHRISTUS SPOHN HOSPITAL CORPUS CHRISTI MEMORIAL (450046)**, 2606 Hospital Boulevard, Zip 78405–1804, Mailing Address: P.O. Box 5280, Zip 78465–5280; tel. 361/902–4000, (Includes CHRISTUS SPOHN HOSPITAL CORPUS CHRISTI SHORELINE, 600 Elizabeth Street, Zip 78404–2235; tel. 361/881–3000; Xavier Villarreal, Chief Executive Officer; CHRISTUS SPOHN HOSPITAL CORPUS CHRISTUS SOUTH, 5950 Saratoga, Zip 78414–4100; tel. 361/985–5000), (Total facility includes 22 beds in nursing home–type unit) **A**1 2 3 5 9 10 **F**3 8 11 13 15 17 18 20 22 24 26 28 29 30 34 35 37 38 39 40 43 45 46 47 48 49 50 51 53 54 56 57 58 59 60 64 66 67 68 70 72 73 74 75 76 77 78 79 81 85 86 87 90 93 96 97 98 99 100 101 102 103 107 108 111 114 115 118 119 120 121 123 126 127 128 130 146 147 148 **P**8 **S** CHRISTUS Health, Irving, TX
Primary Contact: Xavier Villarreal, Chief Executive Officer
COO: Xavier Villarreal, Chief Operating Officer
CFO: Brower Pam, Chief Financial Officer
CMO: Charles T. Volk, M.D., Regional Chief Medical Officer
CHR: Mary LaFrancois, Vice President Human Resources
CNO: Jennifer Gentry, R.N., Chief Nursing Officer
Web address: www.christusspohn.org
Control: Church–operated, Nongovernment, not–for profit **Service:** General Medical and Surgical

Staffed Beds: 774 **Admissions:** 34373 **Census:** 537 **Outpatient Visits:** 305834 **Births:** 2929 **Total Expense ($000):** 550271 **Payroll Expense ($000):** 186001 **Personnel:** 3054

✦ **CORPUS CHRISTI MEDICAL CENTER (450788)**, 3315 South Alameda Street, Zip 78411–1883, Mailing Address: P.O. Box 8991, Zip 78468–8991; tel. 361/761–1400, (Includes BAYVIEW BEHAVIORAL HOSPITAL, 6629 Wooldridge Road, Zip 78414; tel. 361/986–9444; Jamie Molbert, Associate Administrator; CORPUS CHRISTI MEDICAL CENTER BAY AREA, 7101 South Padre Island Drive, Zip 78412–4999; tel. 361/985–1200) **A**1 9 10 12 13 **F**3 4 5 11 12 13 15 17 18 20 22 24 26 28 29 30 31 34 35 37 38 40 42 44 47 49 50 53 57 58 59 64 68 70 72 73 74 75 76 77 78 79 81 82 85 86 87 90 93 97 98 99 100 101 102 103 104 107 108 110 111 114 115 118 119 120 121 126 130 131 132 146 147 148 **P**3 8 **S** HCA, Nashville, TN
Primary Contact: Jay Woodall, Chief Executive Officer
COO: Michael Roussos, Chief Operating Officer
CFO: Chris Nicosia, Chief Financial Officer
CMO: Lawrence Brenner, M.D., Chief of Staff
CIO: Bryan Brown, Director Information Services and Technology
CHR: Michael Conwill, Director Human Resources
CNO: Kathleen A. Rubano, MSN, Chief Nursing Officer
Web address: www.ccmedicalcenter.com
Control: Partnership, Investor–owned, for–profit **Service:** General Medical and Surgical

Staffed Beds: 415 **Admissions:** 18657 **Census:** 244 **Outpatient Visits:** 114982 **Births:** 4014 **Total Expense ($000):** 246553 **Payroll Expense ($000):** 80762 **Personnel:** 1555

✦ **DRISCOLL CHILDREN'S HOSPITAL (453301)**, 3533 South Alameda Street, Zip 78411–1785, Mailing Address: P.O. Box 6530, Zip 78466–6530; tel. 361/694–5000 **A**1 3 5 9 10 13 **F**3 7 11 12 19 21 23 25 27 29 30 31 32 34 35 38 39 40 41 43 49 50 54 55 57 58 59 60 61 64 65 68 72 74 75 77 78 79 81 82 85 86 87 88 89 92 93 97 99 104 107 108 111 115 118 119 130 132 134 138 143 144 146 148
Primary Contact: Steve Woerner, President and Chief Executive Officer
COO: Donna Quinn, Vice President Operations and Quality
CFO: Eric Hamon, Chief Financial Officer
CIO: Miguel Perez, Director Information Systems
CHR: Bill Larsen, Vice President Human Resources
Web address: www.driscollchildrens.org
Control: Other not–for–profit (including NFP Corporation) **Service:** Children's general

Staffed Beds: 162 **Admissions:** 4698 **Census:** 72 **Outpatient Visits:** 130420 **Births:** 0 **Total Expense ($000):** 192918 **Payroll Expense ($000):** 80767 **Personnel:** 1439

✦ **DUBUIS HOSPITAL OF CORPUS CHRISTI (452086)**, 600 Elizabeth Street, 3rd Floor, Zip 78404–2235; tel. 361/881–3223 **A**1 9 10 **F**1 3 29 30 31 75 85 87 148 **P**5 **S** Dubuis Health System, Houston, TX
Primary Contact: Diane Kaiser, Administrator
Web address: www.dubuis.org/DubuisHospitalofCorpusChristi
Control: Church–operated, Nongovernment, not–for profit **Service:** Long–Term Acute Care hospital

Staffed Beds: 22 **Admissions:** 230 **Census:** 18 **Outpatient Visits:** 0 **Births:** 0 **Total Expense ($000):** 9156 **Payroll Expense ($000):** 3273 **Personnel:** 51

KINDRED HOSPITAL–CORPUS CHRISTI See Post Acute Medical Specialty Hospital of Corpus Christi

✦ **POST ACUTE MEDICAL SPECIALTY HOSPITAL OF CORPUS CHRISTI (452092)**, 6226 Saratoga Boulevard, Zip 78414–3421; tel. 361/986–1600 **A**1 9 10 **F**1 3 29 30 34 35 45 57 59 60 70 74 75 77 80 82 85 86 87 97 100 107 130 146 148 **S** Post Acute Medical, LLC, Enola, PA
Primary Contact: Jason Carter, Interim Chief Executive Officer
CFO: Eva De La Paz, Chief Financial Officer
CHR: Kasey Parkey, Coordinator Payroll and Benefits
Web address: www.postacutemedical.com
Control: Corporation, Investor–owned, for–profit **Service:** Long–Term Acute Care hospital

Staffed Beds: 86 **Admissions:** 760 **Census:** 44 **Outpatient Visits:** 0 **Births:** 0 **Total Expense ($000):** 19159 **Payroll Expense ($000):** 7184 **Personnel:** 179

☐ **SOUTH TEXAS SURGICAL HOSPITAL (670061)**, 6130 Parkway Drive, Zip 78414–2455; tel. 361/993–2000 **A**1 9 10 **F**3 29 40 45 54 64 68 75 79 81 82 85 119 130 **S** National Surgical Hospitals, Chicago, IL
Primary Contact: James Murphy, Chief Executive Officer
CFO: Julie Wittwer, Chief Financial Officer
CMO: Michael Mintz, M.D., Chief Medical Officer
CHR: Chelsea Abercrombie, Director Human Resources
CNO: Jan O'Donnell, Chief Nursing Officer
Web address: www.nshinc.com
Control: Partnership, Investor–owned, for–profit **Service:** General Medical and Surgical

Staffed Beds: 20 **Admissions:** 1010 **Census:** 9 **Outpatient Visits:** 4877 **Births:** 0 **Total Expense ($000):** 28256 **Payroll Expense ($000):** 5973 **Personnel:** 131

CORSICANA—Navarro County

✦ **NAVARRO REGIONAL HOSPITAL (450447)**, 3201 West State Highway 22, Zip 75110–2469; tel. 903/654–6800 **A**1 9 10 19 **F**3 11 13 14 15 18 29 30 34 35 39 40 43 45 47 49 50 51 57 59 60 64 68 70 75 76 79 81 82 85 93 107 108 110 111 114 119 129 132 135 146 148 **P**7 **S** Community Health Systems, Inc., Franklin, TN
Primary Contact: Michael K. Stewart, Chief Executive Officer
CFO: Joseph Woolridge, Chief Financial Officer
CIO: Bryan Chilton, Director Information Systems
CHR: Melodee Pugh, Director Human Resources
CNO: Angie K. Merrell, R.N., Chief Nursing Officer
Web address: www.navarrohospital.com
Control: Partnership, Investor–owned, for–profit **Service:** General Medical and Surgical

Staffed Beds: 148 **Admissions:** 3068 **Census:** 28 **Outpatient Visits:** 41780 **Births:** 482 **Total Expense ($000):** 41006 **Payroll Expense ($000):** 14888 **Personnel:** 258

CRANE—Crane County

★ **CRANE MEMORIAL HOSPITAL (451353)**, 1310 South Alford Street, Zip 79731–3899; tel. 432/558–3555 **A**9 10 18 **F**3 29 32 34 40 57 59 64 65 68 75 81 86 97 107 114 119 127 133 145 147 148 **P**6
Primary Contact: Dianne Yeager, Chief Executive Officer
CMO: Jay Sigel, M.D., Chief Medical Staff
Web address: www.cranememorial.org
Control: Hospital district or authority, Government, nonfederal **Service:** General Medical and Surgical

Staffed Beds: 25 **Admissions:** 125 **Census:** 1 **Outpatient Visits:** 12658 **Births:** 0 **Total Expense ($000):** 5629 **Payroll Expense ($000):** 2174 **Personnel:** 45

CROCKETT—Houston County

★ **EAST TEXAS MEDICAL CENTER CROCKETT (450580)**, 1100 Loop 304 East, Zip 75835–1810; tel. 936/546–3862 **A**9 10 20 **F**3 11 13 15 28 29 32 35 40 43 46 50 54 57 58 59 61 64 70 75 76 81 87 97 107 108 111 114 118 119 127 129 146 **P**7 **S** East Texas Medical Center Regional Healthcare System, Tyler, TX
Primary Contact: Terry Cutler, Administrator and Chief Executive Officer
Web address: www.etmc.org
Control: Other not–for–profit (including NFP Corporation) **Service:** General Medical and Surgical

Staffed Beds: 46 **Admissions:** 1304 **Census:** 12 **Outpatient Visits:** 57179 **Births:** 206 **Total Expense ($000):** 18086 **Payroll Expense ($000):** 7207 **Personnel:** 152

CROSBYTON—Crosby County

CROSBYTON CLINIC HOSPITAL (451345), 710 West Main Street, Zip 79322–2143; tel. 806/675–2382 **A**9 10 18 **F**7 10 29 34 40 50 57 59 63 64 68 87 93 111 119 127 130 133 148 **P**6
Primary Contact: Debra Miller, Administrator
CFO: Cherie Parkhill, Chief Financial Officer
CMO: Steve B. Alley, M.D., Chief of Staff
CHR: Janie Cantu, Director Human Resources
CNO: Anna Bradford, R.N., Chief Nursing Officer
Web address: www.crosbytonclinichospital.com
Control: Other not–for–profit (including NFP Corporation) **Service:** General Medical and Surgical

Staffed Beds: 25 **Admissions:** 249 **Census:** 4 **Outpatient Visits:** 15912 **Births:** 0 **Total Expense ($000):** 5918 **Payroll Expense ($000):** 2588 **Personnel:** 76

CUERO—Dewitt County

★ **CUERO COMMUNITY HOSPITAL (450597)**, 2550 North Esplanade Street, Zip 77954–4716; tel. 361/275–6191 **A**9 10 **F**3 7 11 13 15 29 34 40 43 45 57 59 62 64 68 70 75 76 77 79 81 85 86 93 103 107 108 111 115 118 119 129 130 131
Primary Contact: Skip Gjolberg, FACHE, Chief Executive Officer
CFO: Greg Pritchett, Controller
CIO: Arthur Mueller, Director Management Information Systems
CHR: Wanda Kolodziejcyk, Director Human Resources
CNO: Judith Krupala, R.N., Chief Nursing Officer
Web address: www.cuerohosp.org
Control: Hospital district or authority, Government, nonfederal **Service:** General Medical and Surgical

Staffed Beds: 29 **Admissions:** 1028 **Census:** 10 **Outpatient Visits:** 138164 **Births:** 75 **Total Expense ($000):** 27241 **Payroll Expense ($000):** 11713 **Personnel:** 317

CYPRESS—Harris County

☐ ◇ **LONE STAR BEHAVIORAL HEALTH (454118)**, 16303 Grant Road, Zip 77429–1253; tel. 281/516–6200 **A**1 9 10 21 **F**98 104 105 **P**5
Primary Contact: Nathan Daniel Ingram, Chief Executive Officer and Owner
Web address: www.lonestarbehavioralhealth.com
Control: Partnership, Investor–owned, for–profit **Service:** Psychiatric

Staffed Beds: 24 **Admissions:** 665 **Census:** 15 **Outpatient Visits:** 0 **Births:** 0 **Total Expense ($000):** 6750 **Payroll Expense ($000):** 3915 **Personnel:** 84

☐ **NORTH CYPRESS MEDICAL CENTER (670024)**, 21214 Northwest Freeway, Zip 77429–3373; tel. 832/912–3500 **A**1 9 10 **F**3 8 12 15 18 20 22 24 26 28 29 31 34 35 36 37 39 40 42 44 45 46 47 48 49 50 51 57 59 60 64 70 74 75 77 78 79 81 82 85 86 87 93 96 107 108 109 110 111 114 115 116 117 118 119 120 121 123 124 129 130 131 132 146 148
Primary Contact: Robert Behar, M.D., Chief Executive Officer
Web address: www.ncmc–hospital.com
Control: Partnership, Investor–owned, for–profit **Service:** General Medical and Surgical

Staffed Beds: 139 **Admissions:** 9152 **Census:** 118 **Outpatient Visits:** 208129 **Births:** 0 **Total Expense ($000):** 198057 **Payroll Expense ($000):** 69857 **Personnel:** 1309

DALHART—Hartley County

COON MEMORIAL HOSPITAL (451331), 1411 Denver Avenue, Zip 79022–4809, Mailing Address: P.O. Box 2014, Zip 79022–6014; tel. 806/244–4571 **A**9 10 18 **F**3 7 10 11 13 30 34 35 40 43 45 50 53 57 59 62 63 64 65 68 69 71 77 79 81 82 83 85 87 93 97 103 107 114 119 125 127 131 133 143 144 146 148 **P**5
Primary Contact: Leroy Schaffner, Chief Executive Officer
CFO: Donny Pettit, Chief Financial Officer
CMO: Randy Herring, M.D., Chief of Staff
CIO: Anthony Lovato, Director Information Technology
CHR: Dee Dawn McCormick, Director Personnel and Human Resources
Web address: www.coonmemorial.org
Control: Hospital district or authority, Government, nonfederal **Service:** General Medical and Surgical

Staffed Beds: 21 **Admissions:** 505 **Census:** 5 **Outpatient Visits:** 19331 **Births:** 149 **Total Expense ($000):** 24993 **Payroll Expense ($000):** 8576 **Personnel:** 174

DALLAS—Dallas County

A. WEBB ROBERTS HOSPITAL See Baylor University Medical Center

⊞ **BAYLOR INSTITUTE FOR REHABILITATION (453036)**, 909 North Washington Avenue, Zip 75246–1520; tel. 214/820–9300 **A**1 9 10 **F**3 29 30 35 44 62 64 65 68 74 77 85 86 87 90 92 93 94 96 130 131 132 135 143 148 **S** Baylor Scott & White Health, Dallas, TX
Primary Contact: Fabian Polo, Chief Executive Officer
CFO: Ted Bolcavage, Vice President and Division Controller
CMO: Amy Wilson, M.D., Medical Director
CHR: Karen Hill, Director Human Resources
CNO: Beth Hudson, Chief Nursing Officer
Web address: www.baylorhealth.com/PhysiciansLocations/BIR/Pages/Default.aspx
Control: Partnership, Investor–owned, for–profit **Service:** Rehabilitation

Staffed Beds: 89 **Admissions:** 1482 **Census:** 76 **Outpatient Visits:** 152 **Births:** 0 **Total Expense ($000):** 64224 **Payroll Expense ($000):** 37414 **Personnel:** 255

☐ **BAYLOR JACK AND JANE HAMILTON HEART AND VASCULAR HOSPITAL (450851)**, 621 North Hall Street, Zip 75226–1339; tel. 214/820–0600 **A**1 5 9 10 **F**3 11 18 20 21 22 26 28 29 30 34 35 57 58 59 64 68 75 81 85 86 87 93 96 100 107 115 119 132 135
Primary Contact: Nancy Vish, Ph.D., President
CFO: Julius Wicke, III, Vice President Finance and Hospital Financial Officer
CMO: Kevin Wheelan, M.D., Medical Director
CHR: Kim Krause, Director Human Resources
Web address: www.baylorhearthospital.com
Control: Partnership, Investor–owned, for–profit **Service:** General Medical and Surgical

Staffed Beds: 64 **Admissions:** 2225 **Census:** 23 **Outpatient Visits:** 20389 **Births:** 0 **Total Expense ($000):** 84706 **Payroll Expense ($000):** 24319 **Personnel:** 251

⊞ **BAYLOR MEDICAL CENTER AT UPTOWN (450422)**, 2727 East Lemmon Avenue, Zip 75204–2895; tel. 214/443–3000 **A**1 9 10 **F**29 40 68 79 81 82 85 107 111 **P**4 **S** United Surgical Partners International, Addison, TX
Primary Contact: Matt Chance, Chief Executive Officer
CFO: Colene Fielding, Manager Business Office
CMO: Mark Armstrong, M.D., Medical Director
CIO: Javier Vela, Director Information Technology
CHR: Emalie Sanchez, Director Human Resources
CNO: Verette Neeb, R.N., Chief Nursing Officer
Web address: www.bmcuptown.com
Control: Partnership, Investor–owned, for–profit **Service:** General Medical and Surgical

Staffed Beds: 24 **Admissions:** 880 **Census:** 6 **Outpatient Visits:** 10126 **Births:** 0 **Total Expense ($000):** 42665 **Payroll Expense ($000):** 8862 **Personnel:** 215

⊞ **BAYLOR SPECIALTY HOSPITAL (452017)**, 3504 Swiss Avenue, Zip 75204–6224; tel. 214/820–9700 **A**1 9 10 **F**1 30 50 75 77 85 130 148 **S** Baylor Scott & White Health, Dallas, TX
Primary Contact: Elizabeth Youngblood, President
COO: Melody Nagel, Executive Director Operations
CFO: Trey Wicke, Vice President
CMO: Michael Highbaugh, M.D., Medical Director
CHR: Stacie Roberts, Coordinator Human Resources
CNO: Kelli Terpstra, R.N., Chief Nursing Officer
Web address: www.baylorhealth.com/PhysiciansLocations/BSH/Pages/Default.aspx
Control: Other not–for–profit (including NFP Corporation) **Service:** Long–Term Acute Care hospital

Staffed Beds: 61 **Admissions:** 502 **Census:** 41 **Outpatient Visits:** 0 **Births:** 0 **Total Expense ($000):** 25677 **Payroll Expense ($000):** 10857 **Personnel:** 125

TX

Hospital, Medicare Provider Number, Address, Telephone, Approval, Facility, and Physician Codes, Health Care System

★ American Hospital Association (AHA) membership
☐ The Joint Commission accreditation   ◇ DNV Healthcare Inc. accreditation
○ Healthcare Facilities Accreditation Program
△ Commission on Accreditation of Rehabilitation Facilities (CARF) accreditation

✠ **BAYLOR UNIVERSITY MEDICAL CENTER (450021)**, 3500 Gaston Avenue, Zip 75246–2088; tel. 214/820–0111, (Includes A. WEBB ROBERTS HOSPITAL, Zip 75246; ERIK AND MARGARET JONSSON HOSPITAL, Zip 75246; GEORGE W. TRUETT MEMORIAL HOSPITAL, 3500 Gaston Avenue, Zip 75246; KARL AND ESTHER HOBLITZELLE MEMORIAL HOSPITAL, 3500 Gaston Avenue, Zip 75246) **A**1 2 3 5 8 9 10 **F**3 6 11 12 13 14 15 17 18 20 22 24 26 28 29 30 31 34 35 36 37 38 39 40 43 44 45 46 47 48 49 50 51 54 55 56 57 58 59 60 61 63 64 65 66 68 70 72 74 75 76 78 79 80 81 82 84 85 86 87 91 92 94 95 96 97 102 107 108 110 111 112 114 115 116 117 118 119 120 121 123 124 126 129 130 132 135 136 138 139 140 141 142 143 144 145 146 147 148 **S** Baylor Scott & White Health, Dallas, TX
Primary Contact: John B. McWhorter, III, President
COO: Doug Lawson, Chief Operating Officer
CFO: Jay Whitfield, Chief Financial Officer
CMO: Brad Lembcke, M.D., Vice President Medical Staff Affairs
CHR: Julie Strittmatter, Director Human Resources
CNO: Claudia Wilder, R.N., Chief Nursing Officer
Web address: www.baylorhealth.com/PhysiciansLocations/Dallas/Pages/Default.aspx
Control: Other not–for–profit (including NFP Corporation) **Service:** General Medical and Surgical

Staffed Beds: 874 **Admissions:** 35796 **Census:** 609 **Outpatient Visits:** 278165 **Births:** 4606 **Total Expense ($000):** 881878 **Payroll Expense ($000):** 307408 **Personnel:** 4108

✠ **CHILDREN'S MEDICAL CENTER OF DALLAS (453302)**, 1935 Medical District Drive, Zip 75235; tel. 214/456–7000 **A**1 3 5 8 9 10 **F**3 7 8 11 12 17 19 21 23 25 27 29 30 31 32 34 35 38 39 40 41 43 44 45 46 47 48 49 50 51 54 55 57 58 59 60 61 62 64 65 66 68 72 74 75 77 78 79 81 82 84 85 86 87 88 89 91 92 93 94 97 98 99 100 101 102 104 105 106 107 108 111 114 116 117 118 119 126 127 129 130 131 132 134 136 137 138 139 140 141 142 143 144 145 146 148
Primary Contact: Christopher J. Durovich, President and Chief Executive Officer
COO: Douglas G. Hock, Senior Vice President Operations
CFO: David Eager, Senior Vice President and Chief Financial Officer
CMO: W. Robert Morrow, M.D., Executive Vice President and Chief Medical Officer
CIO: Pamela Arora, Vice President Information Systems
CHR: Kim Besse, Senior Vice President and Chief Human Resource Officer
CNO: Mary Stowe, R.N., Senior Vice President and Chief Nursing Officer
Web address: www.childrens.com
Control: Other not–for–profit (including NFP Corporation) **Service:** Children's general

Staffed Beds: 418 **Admissions:** 27530 **Census:** 286 **Outpatient Visits:** 578089 **Births:** 0 **Total Expense ($000):** 944556 **Payroll Expense ($000):** 394931 **Personnel:** 4824

☐ **DALLAS MEDICAL CENTER (450379)**, Seven Medical Parkway, Zip 75234–7823, Mailing Address: P.O. Box 819094, Zip 75381–9094; tel. 972/247–1000 **A**1 10 **F**3 12 15 18 20 22 26 29 34 40 44 45 49 56 57 59 68 70 74 75 77 78 79 81 82 84 85 86 93 97 107 108 111 114 119 130 131 132 141 142 146 147 148 **S** Prime Healthcare Services, Ontario, CA
Primary Contact: Raji Kumar, Chief Executive Officer
CFO: Karen Bomersbach, Chief Financial Officer
CIO: Mary Jo Tallant–Ball, Director Health Information Systems
CHR: Sheila K. Richards, Human Resources Director
Web address: www.dallasmedcenter.com
Control: Corporation, Investor–owned, for–profit **Service:** General Medical and Surgical

Staffed Beds: 71 **Admissions:** 2730 **Census:** 34 **Outpatient Visits:** 33547 **Births:** 0 **Total Expense ($000):** 60198 **Payroll Expense ($000):** 19005 **Personnel:** 356

✠ **DOCTORS HOSPITAL AT WHITE ROCK LAKE (450678)**, 9440 Poppy Drive, Zip 75218–3694; tel. 214/324–6100 **A**1 9 10 **F**3 11 12 13 15 17 18 20 24 26 28 29 30 31 34 35 37 40 45 47 49 50 51 53 56 57 59 64 66 68 70 72 73 74 75 76 77 78 79 81 82 85 93 107 108 110 111 114 115 119 124 129 130 132 135 146 147 148 **S** TENET Healthcare Corporation, Dallas, TX
Primary Contact: Jaikumar Krishnaswamy, Chief Executive Officer
CFO: Drew Shea, Chief Financial Officer
CMO: Tom Jones, D.O., Chief Medical Officer
CHR: Lorinnsa Bridges–Kee, Chief Human Resources Officer
Web address: www.doctorshospitaldallas.com
Control: Partnership, Investor–owned, for–profit **Service:** General Medical and Surgical

Staffed Beds: 151 **Admissions:** 6451 **Census:** 73 **Outpatient Visits:** 62467 **Births:** 768 **Total Expense ($000):** 98420 **Payroll Expense ($000):** 35334 **Personnel:** 573

○ **FOREST PARK MEDICAL CENTER (670057)**, 11990 North Central Expressway, Zip 75243–3714; tel. 972/234–1900 **A**9 11 **F**3 8 12 29 34 35 37 40 45 47 48 49 59 64 65 70 75 77 79 81 82 85 86 87 91 92 107 111 115 119 126 129 130 132 **P**8 **S** Vibrant Healthcare, Dallas, TX
Primary Contact: Cindy Bledsoe, Chief Executive Officer
Web address: www.forestparkmc.com/
Control: Partnership, Investor–owned, for–profit **Service:** General Medical and Surgical

Staffed Beds: 84 **Admissions:** 3221 **Census:** 21 **Outpatient Visits:** 9730 **Births:** 0 **Personnel:** 343

★ **GLOBALREHAB HOSPITAL – DALLAS (673033)**, 1340 Empire Central Drive, Zip 75247–4022; tel. 214/879–7300 **A**10 **F**3 28 29 30 68 75 90 91 96 100 130 148 **S** GLOBALREHAB, Dallas, TX
Primary Contact: David Smith, Chief Executive Officer
Web address: www.baylorhealth.com/bir
Control: Partnership, Investor–owned, for–profit **Service:** Rehabilitation

Staffed Beds: 42 **Admissions:** 699 **Census:** 25 **Outpatient Visits:** 0 **Births:** 0 **Total Expense ($000):** 14805 **Payroll Expense ($000):** 6483 **Personnel:** 93

✠ **GREEN OAKS HOSPITAL (454094)**, 7808 Clodus Fields Drive, Zip 75251–2206; tel. 972/991–9504 **A**1 9 10 **F**4 5 29 54 87 98 99 102 103 104 105 130 132 **P**5 **S** HCA, Nashville, TN
Primary Contact: Thomas M. Collins, President, Chairman and Chief Executive Officer
COO: Pam Whitley, R.N., Chief Operating Officer and Chief Nursing Officer
CFO: Aaron Rowe, Chief Financial Officer
CMO: Joel Holiner, M.D., Executive Medical Director
CIO: Richard Fontenault, Director Information Systems
CHR: Kevin Adkins, Director Human Resources
CNO: Pam Whitley, R.N., Chief Nursing Officer and Chief Operating Officer
Web address: www.greenoakspsych.com
Control: Corporation, Investor–owned, for–profit **Service:** Psychiatric

Staffed Beds: 124 **Admissions:** 4581 **Census:** 110 **Outpatient Visits:** 33484 **Births:** 0 **Total Expense ($000):** 42471 **Payroll Expense ($000):** 19863 **Personnel:** 370

✠ **KINDRED HOSPITAL DALLAS CENTRAL (452108)**, 8050 Meadows Road, Zip 75231–3406; tel. 469/232–6500 **A**1 9 10 **F**1 3 29 75 77 85 87 96 107 114 148 **P**8 **S** Kindred Healthcare, Louisville, KY
Primary Contact: Stephanie Madrid, Chief Executive Officer
CFO: Joni Gonzalez, Controller
CNO: Jackie Gordon, Chief Clinical Officer
Web address: www.khdallascentral.com/
Control: Corporation, Investor–owned, for–profit **Service:** Long–Term Acute Care hospital

Staffed Beds: 60 **Admissions:** 495 **Census:** 33 **Outpatient Visits:** 300 **Births:** 0 **Total Expense ($000):** 22352 **Payroll Expense ($000):** 7299 **Personnel:** 127

KINDRED HOSPITAL DALLAS–WALNUT HILL See Kindred Hospital–Dallas

✠ **KINDRED HOSPITAL–DALLAS (452015)**, 9525 Greenville Avenue, Zip 75243–4116; tel. 214/355–2600, (Includes KINDRED HOSPITAL DALLAS–WALNUT HILL, 8200 Walnut Hill Lane, Zip 75231; tel. 214/345–6500) **A**1 9 10 **F**1 3 29 70 107 114 130 148 **S** Kindred Healthcare, Louisville, KY
Primary Contact: James Mendez, Chief Executive Officer
CFO: Jean McDowell, Chief Financial Officer
Web address: www.khdallas.com
Control: Partnership, Investor–owned, for–profit **Service:** Long–Term Acute Care hospital

Staffed Beds: 50 **Admissions:** 437 **Census:** 31 **Outpatient Visits:** 0 **Births:** 0 **Total Expense ($000):** 19402 **Payroll Expense ($000):** 7063 **Personnel:** 190

✠ **KINDRED HOSPITAL–WHITE ROCK (452071)**, 9440 Poppy Drive, 5th Floor, Zip 75218–3652; tel. 214/324–6562 **A**1 9 10 **F**1 29 85 86 87 130 148 **P**5 **S** Kindred Healthcare, Louisville, KY
Primary Contact: Kelly Bailey, Administrator
COO: Kim Chipman, Chief Clinical Officer
CFO: Jennifer Penland, Controller
CMO: Mark Ferris, M.D., Medical Director
CNO: Brenda Perez, R.N., Chief Clinical Officer
Web address: www.khwhiterock.com
Control: Corporation, Investor–owned, for–profit **Service:** Long–Term Acute Care hospital

Staffed Beds: 25 **Admissions:** 227 **Census:** 19 **Outpatient Visits:** 0 **Births:** 0 **Total Expense ($000):** 9719 **Payroll Expense ($000):** 4083 **Personnel:** 60

✠ **LIFECARE HOSPITALS OF DALLAS (452044)**, 1950 Record Crossing Road, Zip 75235–6223; tel. 214/640–9600 **A**1 9 10 **F**1 3 29 40 64 75 119 148 **S** LifeCare Management Services, Plano, TX
Primary Contact: Kevin S. Cooper, R.N., Chief Executive Officer
CFO: Amie Gratch, Director Financial Services
CMO: Jonathan Weissler, M.D., Chief Medical Officer
CHR: Linzie Riley, Interim Human Resource Manager
CNO: Kathy Mason, R.N., Chief Nursing Officer
Web address: www.lifecare–hospitals.com/hospital/dallas
Control: Corporation, Investor–owned, for–profit **Service:** Long–Term Acute Care hospital

Staffed Beds: 206 **Admissions:** 1527 **Census:** 112 **Outpatient Visits:** 13352 **Births:** 0 **Total Expense ($000):** 62027 **Payroll Expense ($000):** 26149 **Personnel:** 403

LIFECARE HOSPITALS OF NORTH TEXAS See LifeCare Hospitals of Dallas

MARY SHIELS HOSPITAL See Baylor Medical Center at Uptown

✠ **MEDICAL CITY DALLAS HOSPITAL (450647)**, 7777 Forest Lane,
Zip 75230–2598; tel. 972/566–7000, (Includes MEDICAL CITY CHILDREN'S
HOSPITAL, 7777 Forest Lane, Zip 75230–2505; tel. 972/566–7000; Keith
Zimmerman, Chief Executive Officer) **A**1 2 3 5 9 10 **F**3 8 11 12 13 15 17 18 19
20 21 22 23 24 25 26 27 28 29 30 31 34 35 37 40 41 44 45 46 47 49 50
51 55 56 57 58 59 60 63 64 65 68 70 72 73 74 75 76 77 78 79 81 82 84
85 86 87 88 89 93 97 105 107 108 110 111 114 115 116 117 118 119 126
129 130 132 135 136 137 138 141 142 143 144 146 147 148 **P**6 7 **S** HCA,
Nashville, TN
Primary Contact: Troy Villarreal, President and Chief Executive Officer
CFO: Mark Atchley, Vice President and Chief Financial Officer
CMO: Mark Hebert, M.D., President Medical Staff
CIO: Troy Sypien, Director Information Technology and Systems
CHR: Jenifer K. Tertel, Director Human Resources
Web address: www.medicalcityhospital.com
Control: Corporation, Investor–owned, for–profit **Service:** General Medical and
Surgical

> **Staffed Beds:** 544 **Admissions:** 24475 **Census:** 369 **Outpatient Visits:**
> 165585 **Births:** 3366 **Total Expense ($000):** 458018 **Payroll Expense**
> **($000):** 162795 **Personnel:** 2070

✠ **METHODIST CHARLTON MEDICAL CENTER (450723)**, 3500 West Wheatland
Road, Zip 75237–3460, Mailing Address: P.O. Box 225357, Zip 75222–5357;
tel. 214/947–7777 **A**1 9 10 13 **F**3 11 13 15 18 20 22 24 29 30 31 34 35 40
45 46 47 49 50 53 58 59 60 64 66 68 70 74 76 78 79 81 82 84 85 86 87
97 107 108 110 111 114 118 119 130 131 132 146 148 **P**1 7 **S** Methodist
Health System, Dallas, TX
Primary Contact: Jonathan S. Davis, FACHE, President
COO: Pamela Stoyanoff, Executive Vice President and Chief Operating Officer
CFO: Michael J. Schaefer, Executive Vice President and Chief Financial Officer
CIO: Pamela McNutt, Vice President Information Systems
CHR: Cheryl Flynn, Senior Vice President Human Resources
CNO: Fran Laukaitis, R.N., Vice President Nursing
Web address: www.methodisthealthsystem.org/charlton
Control: Other not–for–profit (including NFP Corporation) **Service:** General
Medical and Surgical

> **Staffed Beds:** 293 **Admissions:** 12888 **Census:** 173 **Outpatient Visits:**
> 154643 **Births:** 1962 **Total Expense ($000):** 202329 **Payroll Expense**
> **($000):** 96877 **Personnel:** 1410

✠ **METHODIST DALLAS MEDICAL CENTER (450051)**, 1441 North Beckley
Avenue, Zip 75203–1201, Mailing Address: P.O. Box 655999, Zip 75265–5999;
tel. 214/947–8181 **A**1 2 3 5 8 9 10 **F**3 11 12 13 15 18 20 22 24 26 28 29
30 31 34 35 37 40 43 45 46 47 48 50 53 54 58 59 60 64 66 68 70 72
74 76 78 79 81 82 84 85 87 92 93 97 107 108 110 111 118 119 126 130
132 138 139 142 146 148 **P**1 7 **S** Methodist Health System, Dallas, TX
Primary Contact: David D. Clark, President
COO: Pamela Stoyanoff, Executive Vice President and Chief Operating Officer
CFO: Randy Walker, Vice President
CIO: Pamela McNutt, Senior Vice President and Chief Information Officer
CHR: Jackie Middleton, Vice President Human Resources
Web address: www.methodisthealthsystem.org/Dallas
Control: Other not–for–profit (including NFP Corporation) **Service:** General
Medical and Surgical

> **Staffed Beds:** 408 **Admissions:** 18592 **Census:** 274 **Outpatient Visits:**
> 161321 **Births:** 3664 **Total Expense ($000):** 369355 **Payroll Expense**
> **($000):** 149880 **Personnel:** 2238

☐ **METHODIST REHABILITATION HOSPITAL (673031)**, 3020 West Wheatland
Road, Zip 75237–3537; tel. 972/708–8600 **A**1 9 10 **F**29 30 60 90 91 93 96
Primary Contact: Chris Ensmann, MS, Chief Executive Officer
Web address: www.methodist–rehab.com
Control: Partnership, Investor–owned, for–profit **Service:** Rehabilitation

> **Staffed Beds:** 40 **Admissions:** 957 **Census:** 32 **Outpatient Visits:** 10779
> **Births:** 0 **Total Expense ($000):** 15285 **Payroll Expense ($000):** 7905
> **Personnel:** 146

☐ **NORTH CENTRAL SURGICAL CENTER (670049)**, 9301 North Central
Expressway, Suite 100, Zip 75231–0802; tel. 214/265–2810 **A**1 9 10 **F**3 40 45
79 81 82 85 107 111 114 115 119
Primary Contact: Suzanne Greever, Chief Executive Officer
COO: Thanh Tran, Chief Operating Officer
CFO: Linda Fite, Chief Financial Officer
CMO: Stuart Simon, M.D., Medical Director
CNO: Katherine Martinez, Chief Nursing Officer
Web address: www.northcentralsurgical.com
Control: Partnership, Investor–owned, for–profit **Service:** Surgical

> **Staffed Beds:** 23 **Admissions:** 1116 **Census:** 7 **Outpatient Visits:** 19380
> **Births:** 0 **Total Expense ($000):** 59936 **Payroll Expense ($000):** 14055
> **Personnel:** 295

✠ **OUR CHILDREN'S HOUSE AT BAYLOR (453308)**, 1208 North Hall Street,
Zip 75204; tel. 214/820–9838 **A**1 3 5 9 10 **F**3 29 30 32 34 35 39 50 54 58
59 74 75 81 85 86 87 89 90 93 129 130 132 146 148 **S** Baylor Scott & White
Health, Dallas, TX
Primary Contact: Elizabeth Youngblood, President
CMO: Andrew Gelfand, M.D., Medical Director
CHR: Stacie Roberts, Coordinator Human Resources
CNO: Kelli Terpstra, R.N., Chief Nursing Officer
Web address: www.baylorhealth.com/PhysiciansLocations/OCH/Pages/Default.
aspx
Control: Other not–for–profit (including NFP Corporation) **Service:** Children's
general

> **Staffed Beds:** 54 **Admissions:** 380 **Census:** 23 **Outpatient Visits:** 118540
> **Births:** 0 **Total Expense ($000):** 33390 **Payroll Expense ($000):** 16924
> **Personnel:** 231

✠ **PARKLAND HEALTH & HOSPITAL SYSTEM (450015)**, 5201 Harry Hines
Boulevard, Zip 75235–7708; tel. 214/590–8000 **A**1 2 3 5 8 9 10 **F**3 8 9 11 12
13 15 16 17 18 20 22 26 28 29 30 31 34 35 38 39 40 43 46 47 48 49 50
51 54 55 56 57 58 59 60 61 64 65 66 68 70 71 72 74 75 76 77 78 79 81
82 84 85 86 87 90 91 92 93 94 97 98 99 100 101 102 103 104 105 107
108 110 111 115 118 119 129 130 131 132 134 135 138 141 143 144 146
147 148 **P**1
Primary Contact: Fred Cerise, M.D., Chief Executive Officer
CIO: Fernando Martinez, Senior Vice President and Chief Information Officer
CNO: Mary K. Eagen, R.N., Executive Vice President, Chief Nursing Officer
Web address: www.parklandhospital.com
Control: Hospital district or authority, Government, nonfederal **Service:** General
Medical and Surgical

> **Staffed Beds:** 831 **Admissions:** 43222 **Census:** 603 **Outpatient Visits:**
> 1258346 **Births:** 10258 **Total Expense ($000):** 1231608 **Payroll Expense**
> **($000):** 646213 **Personnel:** 10376

☐ **PINE CREEK MEDICAL CENTER (450894)**, 9032 Harry Hines Boulevard,
Zip 75235–1720; tel. 214/231–2273 **A**1 9 10 **F**3 12 29 30 34 40 42 45 49
51 64 79 81 82 85 93 107 111 114
Primary Contact: Corazon Ramirez, M.D., Chief Executive Officer
CFO: Michael Conroy, Chief Financial Officer
CIO: Kevin Carney, Senior Information Systems Analyst
Web address: www.pinecreekmedicalcenter.com
Control: Partnership, Investor–owned, for–profit **Service:** General Medical and
Surgical

> **Staffed Beds:** 18 **Admissions:** 1021 **Census:** 6 **Outpatient Visits:** 6172
> **Births:** 0 **Total Expense ($000):** 47502 **Payroll Expense ($000):** 9240
> **Personnel:** 146

☐ **PROMISE HOSPITAL OF DALLAS (452067)**, 7955 Harry Hines Boulevard,
Zip 75235–3305; tel. 214/637–0000 **A**1 9 10 **F**1 3 29 30 64 75 85 87 148
S Promise Healthcare, Boca Raton, FL
Primary Contact: Mary Alexander, Interim Chief Executive Officer
CFO: Diana B. Smith, Chief Financial Officer
CMO: Gary E. Goff, M.D., Medical Director
CHR: Ginger Davenport, Director Human Resources
Web address: www.promise–dallas.com/
Control: Corporation, Investor–owned, for–profit **Service:** Long–Term Acute Care
hospital

> **Staffed Beds:** 62 **Admissions:** 279 **Census:** 20 **Outpatient Visits:** 1481
> **Births:** 0 **Total Expense ($000):** 12463 **Payroll Expense ($000):** 3767
> **Personnel:** 74

☐ **RELIANT REHABILITATION HOSPITAL DALLAS (673043)**, 7930 Northaven
Road, Zip 75230–3331; tel. 214/706–8200 **A**1 9 10 **F**3 29 90 93 96 130 148
Primary Contact: Kasey Norman, Chief Executive Officer
CFO: Mary Mwaniki, Chief Financial Officer
CMO: Anna Freed–Sigurdsson, M.D., Medical Director
CIO: James E. King, Corporate Director Information Technology
CHR: Ieesha Cannida, Director Human Resources
CNO: Nancy Faas, R.N., Chief Nursing Officer
Web address: www.relianthcp.com
Control: Partnership, Investor–owned, for–profit **Service:** Rehabilitation

> **Staffed Beds:** 60 **Admissions:** 736 **Census:** 22 **Outpatient Visits:** 2214
> **Births:** 0 **Total Expense ($000):** 11858 **Payroll Expense ($000):** 4494
> **Personnel:** 130

TX

✠ **SELECT SPECIALTY HOSPITAL–SOUTH DALLAS (452078)**, 3500 West Wheatland Road, 4th Floor, Zip 75237–3460; tel. 972/780–6500 **A**1 9 10 **F**1 3 29 40 85 107 130 148 **S** Select Medical Corporation, Mechanicsburg, PA
Primary Contact: Richard Knowland, Chief Executive Officer
Web address: www.selectspecialtyhospitals.com/company/locations/southdallas.aspx
Control: Corporation, Investor–owned, for–profit **Service:** Long–Term Acute Care hospital

Staffed Beds: 69 **Admissions:** 498 **Census:** 36 **Outpatient Visits:** 0 **Births:** 0 **Total Expense ($000):** 20503 **Payroll Expense ($000):** 8070 **Personnel:** 149	

✠ △ **TEXAS HEALTH PRESBYTERIAN HOSPITAL DALLAS (450462)**, 8200 Walnut Hill Lane, Zip 75231–4426; tel. 214/345–6789 **A**1 2 3 5 7 9 10 **F**3 5 11 12 13 15 17 18 20 22 24 26 28 29 30 31 32 34 35 36 37 38 40 44 45 46 47 49 50 51 52 53 54 55 56 57 58 59 60 61 63 64 65 66 68 70 72 74 75 76 77 78 79 81 82 85 86 87 90 91 92 93 94 95 96 97 98 100 101 102 103 104 105 107 108 110 111 112 114 115 118 119 124 126 129 130 131 132 135 141 143 144 146 147 148 **P**6 **S** Texas Health Resources, Arlington, TX
Primary Contact: James A. Berg, Interim Chief Executive Officer
CFO: Brian Craft, Vice President Finance and Group Finance Officer
CMO: Aurora Estevez, M.D., Chief Medical Officer
CIO: Edward Marx, Senior Vice President and Chief Information Officer
CHR: Connie Wright, Director Human Resources
CNO: Cole Edmonson, R.N., Vice President and Chief Nursing Officer
Web address: www.texashealth.org
Control: Other not–for–profit (including NFP Corporation) **Service:** General Medical and Surgical

Staffed Beds: 621 **Admissions:** 28159 **Census:** 430 **Outpatient Visits:** 394857 **Births:** 5488 **Total Expense ($000):** 588969 **Payroll Expense ($000):** 193220 **Personnel:** 2647	

TEXAS HOSPITAL FOR ADVANCED MEDICINE See Dallas Medical Center

☐ **TEXAS INSTITUTE FOR SURGERY AT TEXAS HEALTH PRESBYTERIAN DALLAS (450889)**, 7115 Greenville Avenue, Zip 75231–5100; tel. 214/647–5300 **A**1 9 10 **F**40 51 64 79 81 82 107 129
Primary Contact: David Helfer, President
CFO: John S. Croley, Vice President Business Operations
CMO: Presley Mock, M.D., Chief of Staff
CHR: Jennifer Cherrnay, Director Human Resources
CNO: Joy Dier, R.N., Vice President Clinical Services and Chief Nursing Officer
Web address: www.texasinstituteforsurgery.com
Control: Partnership, Investor–owned, for–profit **Service:** General Medical and Surgical

Staffed Beds: 9 **Admissions:** 351 **Census:** 2 **Outpatient Visits:** 11171 **Births:** 0 **Total Expense ($000):** 47509 **Payroll Expense ($000):** 10918 **Personnel:** 163	

✠ **TEXAS SCOTTISH RITE HOSPITAL FOR CHILDREN (453314)**, 2222 Welborn Street, Zip 75219–3924, Mailing Address: P.O. Box 190567, Zip 75219–0567; tel. 214/559–5000 **A**1 3 5 10 **F**3 5 11 29 34 35 50 53 58 64 68 74 75 77 79 81 85 86 87 89 92 94 107 111 115 119 130 131 132 143 146 148 **P**6
Primary Contact: Robert L. Walker, President and Chief Executive Officer
CFO: William R. Huston, Senior Vice President and Chief Financial Officer
CMO: Daniel J. Sucato, M.D., Chief of Staff
CIO: Amy Bailey, Director Information Systems
CHR: James D. Sturgis, Associate Administrator
CNO: Debbie A. Sayles, R.N., Vice President and Chief Nursing Officer
Web address: www.tsrhc.org
Control: Other not–for–profit (including NFP Corporation) **Service:** Children's orthopedic

Staffed Beds: 52 **Admissions:** 1187 **Census:** 17 **Outpatient Visits:** 38337 **Births:** 0 **Total Expense ($000):** 128885 **Payroll Expense ($000):** 65825 **Personnel:** 791	

☐ **TIMBERLAWN MENTAL HEALTH SYSTEM (454081)**, 4600 Samuell Boulevard, Zip 75228–6800; tel. 214/381–7181 **A**1 9 10 **F**4 5 54 56 59 64 87 98 99 100 101 102 103 104 105 130 132 143 **S** Universal Health Services, Inc., King of Prussia, PA
Primary Contact: Shelah Adams, Chief Executive Officer
CFO: Lori Verbeke, Chief Financial Officer
CMO: John Pascoe, M.D., Executive Medical Director
CIO: Twila Ragar–Thomas, Director Health Information Management and Quality Improvement
CHR: Winnie Boehnke, Director Human Resources
CNO: Sarah Stonehouse, R.N., Director of Nursing
Web address: www.timberlawn.com
Control: Corporation, Investor–owned, for–profit **Service:** Psychiatric

Staffed Beds: 144 **Admissions:** 6166 **Census:** 122 **Outpatient Visits:** 15255 **Births:** 0 **Total Expense ($000):** 23289 **Payroll Expense ($000):** 10933 **Personnel:** 238	

UNIVERSITY GENERAL HOSPITAL–DALLAS (670002), 2929 South Hampton Road, Zip 75224–3026; tel. 214/623–4400 **A**9 10 **F**8 12 29 30 34 40 45 57 60 64 68 70 79 81 82 93 107 108 111 115 118 119 129 130 148 **S** University General Health System, Houston, TX
Primary Contact: Susie Edler, Chief Executive Officer
Web address: www.universitygeneralhospital.com
Control: Corporation, Investor–owned, for–profit **Service:** General Medical and Surgical

Staffed Beds: 111 **Admissions:** 1342 **Census:** 18 **Outpatient Visits:** 16631 **Births:** 0 **Total Expense ($000):** 31107 **Payroll Expense ($000):** 11538 **Personnel:** 220	

✠ △ **UNIVERSITY OF TEXAS SOUTHWESTERN MEDICAL CENTER (450766)**, 5323 Harry Hines Boulevard, Zip 75390–9265; tel. 214/645–5555, (Includes UNIVERSITY OF TEXAS SOUTHWESTERN MEDICAL CENTER – ST. PAUL, 5909 Harry Hines Boulevard, Zip 75390–9200; tel. 214/645–5555; UNIVERSITY OF TEXAS SOUTHWESTERN MEDICAL CENTER – ZALE LIPSHY, 5151 Harry Hines Boulevard, tel. 214/645–5555; Daniel Podolsky, M.D., President) **A**1 2 3 5 7 8 9 10 **F**3 6 7 8 9 11 12 13 15 17 18 20 22 24 26 28 29 30 31 34 35 36 38 39 40 44 45 46 47 48 49 50 52 53 54 55 58 59 60 61 62 64 65 68 70 71 72 74 75 76 77 78 79 80 81 82 84 85 86 87 90 91 92 93 94 95 96 97 98 99 100 101 102 103 104 107 108 109 110 111 114 115 116 117 118 119 120 121 123 124 126 129 130 131 132 135 136 137 138 139 140 141 142 143 145 146 147 148 **P**4 6
Primary Contact: John Warner, M.D., Chief Executive Officer
COO: Becky McCulley, Chief Operating Officer
CFO: Elizabeth S. Ward, Chief Financial Officer
CMO: Steven Leach, M.D., Chief Medical Officer
CIO: Suresh Gunasekaran, Assistant Vice President Information Resources
CHR: William Behrendt, Ph.D., Vice President Human Resources
CNO: Susan Hernandez, Chief Nursing Officer
Web address: www.utsouthwestern.edu
Control: State–Government, nonfederal **Service:** General Medical and Surgical

Staffed Beds: 459 **Admissions:** 22163 **Census:** 364 **Outpatient Visits:** 363144 **Births:** 1584 **Total Expense ($000):** 716332 **Payroll Expense ($000):** 252389 **Personnel:** 4165	

✠ △ **VETERANS AFFAIRS NORTH TEXAS HEALTH CARE SYSTEM**, 4500 South Lancaster Road, Zip 75216–7167; tel. 214/742–8387, (Includes SAM RAYBURN MEMORIAL VETERANS CENTER, 1201 East Ninth Street, Bonham, Zip 75418–4091; tel. 903/583–2111; Angela Nix, Administrator), (Nonreporting) **A**1 2 3 5 7 9 **S** Department of Veterans Affairs, Washington, DC
Primary Contact: Jeffrey Milligan, Director
CFO: Garry Martin, Chief Fiscal
CIO: Lucy Rogers, Chief Information Resource Management Systems
Web address: www.northtexas.va.gov/
Control: Veterans Affairs, Government, federal **Service:** General Medical and Surgical

Staffed Beds: 875	

WALNUT HILL MEDICAL CENTER, 7502 Greenville Avenue, Zip 75231–3802; tel. 972/863–6000, (Nonreporting)
Primary Contact: Cory Countryman, Chief Executive Officer
Web address: www.walnuthillmc.com
Control: Partnership, Investor–owned, for–profit **Service:** General Medical and Surgical

Staffed Beds: 100	

DECATUR—Wise County

✠ **WISE REGIONAL HEALTH SYSTEM (450271)**, 609 Medical Center Drive, Zip 76234–3836; tel. 940/627–5921, (Includes PARKWAY SURGICAL & CARDIOVASCULAR HOSPITAL, 3200 North Tarrant Parkway, Fort Worth, Zip 76177–8611; tel. 817/502–7300; WISE REGIONAL HEALTH SYSTEM – BRIDGEPORT CAMPUS, 1905 Doctors Hospital Drive, Bridgeport, Zip 76426–2260; tel. 940/683–0300; WISE REGIONAL HEALTH SYSTEM, EAST CAMPUS DECATUR, 609 Medical Center Drive, tel. 940/627–5921; WISE REGIONAL HEALTH SYSTEM, WEST CAMPUS DECATUR, 2000 South Fm 51, Zip 76234–3702; tel. 940/627–5921) **A**1 2 9 10 **F**3 11 12 13 15 17 18 20 22 24 26 28 29 30 31 32 34 40 43 45 47 49 51 53 54 56 57 59 60 64 70 74 75 76 77 78 79 81 85 87 89 90 93 96 97 98 103 104 107 108 110 111 114 115 116 118 119 129 130 131 132 135 147 148 **P**7
Primary Contact: Stephen M. Summers, CPA, FACHE, Chief Executive Officer
COO: Leon Fuqua, Chief Operating Officer
CFO: Jim Eaton, Chief Financial Officer
CMO: Jason Schuh, M.D., Chief of Staff
CIO: Joe Arispe, Director Information Systems
CHR: Mike McQuiston, Administrative Director Human Resources
CNO: Sue Sewell, Chief Nursing Officer
Web address: www.wiseregional.com
Control: Hospital district or authority, Government, nonfederal **Service:** General Medical and Surgical

Staffed Beds: 133 **Admissions:** 4972 **Census:** 62 **Outpatient Visits:** 227768 **Births:** 623 **Total Expense ($000):** 150127 **Payroll Expense ($000):** 53963 **Personnel:** 1161	

TX

DEL RIO—Val Verde County

✠ **VAL VERDE REGIONAL MEDICAL CENTER (450154)**, 801 Bedell Avenue,
Zip 78840–4112, Mailing Address: P.O. Box 1527, Zip 78841–1527;
tel. 830/775–8566 **A**1 9 10 20 **F**3 7 11 13 15 18 20 29 30 34 35 40 43 46
48 54 57 59 63 73 75 76 77 79 81 82 84 85 87 89 93 96 107 108 110 111
114 119 129 131 132 133 146 147
Primary Contact: Victoria Barnthouse, R.N., MS, Chief Executive Officer
CFO: Lisa Medovich, Chief Financial Officer
CMO: Mustafa Salama, M.D., Chief of Staff
CIO: Val King, Chief Information Officer
CHR: Leigh Ann Qualia, Director Human Resources
CNO: Keith Tucker, R.N., Chief Nursing Officer
Web address: www.vvrmc.org
Control: Hospital district or authority, Government, nonfederal **Service:** General
Medical and Surgical

> **Staffed Beds:** 80 **Admissions:** 3184 **Census:** 29 **Outpatient Visits:** 61875
> **Births:** 924 **Total Expense ($000):** 48450 **Payroll Expense ($000):** 20195
> **Personnel:** 544

DENISON—Grayson County

☐ **TEXOMA MEDICAL CENTER (450324)**, 5016 South U.S. Highway 75,
Zip 75020–4584, Mailing Address: P.O. Box 890, Zip 75021–0890;
tel. 903/416–4000 **A**1 9 10 **F**3 11 12 13 15 17 18 20 22 24 28 29 30 31 34
40 41 43 45 46 47 49 50 53 54 57 59 62 64 74 75 76 77 78 79 81 85
86 87 89 90 93 96 98 99 100 101 102 103 104 105 107 108 110 111 115
119 126 129 130 132 144 145 146 147 148 **P**6 7 **S** Universal Health Services,
Inc., King of Prussia, PA
Primary Contact: Ronald T. Seal, Chief Executive Officer
CFO: Gerard Hebert, Chief Financial Officer
CMO: Robert Sanders, M.D., Chief Medical Officer
CIO: Lisa Engle, Director Information Technology
CHR: Bill Heinzmann, Director Human Resources
CNO: Andrea Brenn, R.N., Chief Nursing Officer
Web address: www.texomamedicalcenter.net
Control: Corporation, Investor–owned, for–profit **Service:** General Medical and
Surgical

> **Staffed Beds:** 288 **Admissions:** 11649 **Census:** 168 **Outpatient Visits:**
> 95932 **Births:** 1126 **Total Expense ($000):** 201009 **Payroll Expense**
> **($000):** 64777 **Personnel:** 1393

DENTON—Denton County

✠ **DENTON REGIONAL MEDICAL CENTER (450634)**, 3535 South 1–35 East,
Zip 76210; tel. 940/384–3535 **A**1 9 10 **F**3 13 15 18 20 22 24 26 28 29 30
34 35 40 43 45 46 47 49 50 57 59 64 66 68 69 70 73 74 75 76 77 79 81
82 85 86 87 93 107 108 110 111 114 118 119 126 130 132 135 144 146
147 148 **S** HCA, Nashville, TN
Primary Contact: Caleb F. O'Rear, Chief Executive Officer
COO: Jeffrey T. Lawrence, Chief Operating Officer
CFO: Todd Gibson, Chief Financial Officer
CMO: Stanley Evans, M.D., Chief of Staff
CHR: Stacey Bravo, Vice President Human Resources
CNO: Nicki Roderman, Chief Nursing Officer
Web address: www.dentonregional.com
Control: Partnership, Investor–owned, for–profit **Service:** General Medical and
Surgical

> **Staffed Beds:** 208 **Admissions:** 10559 **Census:** 129 **Outpatient Visits:**
> 94114 **Births:** 1123 **Total Expense ($000):** 150595 **Payroll Expense**
> **($000):** 52634 **Personnel:** 658

☐ **INTEGRITY TRANSITIONAL HOSPITAL (452109)**, 2813 South Mayhill Road,
Zip 76208–5910; tel. 940/320–2300 **A**1 9 10 **F**1 3 29 40 42 77 84 86 87 91
130 148 **P**5
Primary Contact: Israel Navarro, Chief Executive Officer
CNO: Michele Andrews, Chief Clinical Officer
Web address: www.ithcare.com
Control: Partnership, Investor–owned, for–profit **Service:** General Medical and
Surgical

> **Staffed Beds:** 54 **Admissions:** 875 **Census:** 24 **Outpatient Visits:** 0 **Births:**
> 0 **Total Expense ($000):** 15283 **Payroll Expense ($000):** 5541 **Personnel:**
> 87

✠ **MAYHILL HOSPITAL (670010)**, 2809 South Mayhill Road, Zip 76208–5910;
tel. 940/239–3000 **A**1 9 10 **F**4 29 40 56 82 98 102 103 104 130 **S** Universal
Health Services, Inc., King of Prussia, PA
Primary Contact: Jason Toalson, Chief Executive Officer
CFO: Emmy Adams, Chief Financial Officer
CMO: Asad Islam, M.D., Chief Medical Officer
CIO: Kyle Murphy, Director Information Technology
CHR: Patricia Gloria–Barraza, Coordinator Human Resources
Web address: www.mayhillhospital.com
Control: Partnership, Investor–owned, for–profit **Service:** Psychiatric

> **Staffed Beds:** 59 **Admissions:** 1392 **Census:** 38 **Outpatient Visits:** 642
> **Births:** 0 **Total Expense ($000):** 8817 **Payroll Expense ($000):** 4159
> **Personnel:** 91

✠ **SELECT REHABILITATION HOSPITAL OF DENTON (673036)**, 2620 Scripture
Street, Zip 76201–4315; tel. 940/297–6500 **A**1 9 10 **F**3 29 40 60 64 68 74
75 77 79 86 87 90 93 96 132 135 148 **P**6 **S** Select Medical Corporation,
Mechanicsburg, PA
Primary Contact: Michelle Powell, Chief Executive Officer
CFO: Doug Selsor, Director Finance
CHR: Patsy Martin, Manager Human Resources
CNO: Lee Ann Elliott, R.N., Director of Nursing
Web address: www.selectrehab–denton.com/
Control: Corporation, Investor–owned, for–profit **Service:** Rehabilitation

> **Staffed Beds:** 44 **Admissions:** 613 **Census:** 22 **Outpatient Visits:** 5067
> **Births:** 0 **Total Expense ($000):** 11861 **Payroll Expense ($000):** 6060
> **Personnel:** 85

✠ **TEXAS HEALTH PRESBYTERIAN HOSPITAL DENTON (450743)**, 3000 North
I–35, Zip 76201–5119; tel. 940/898–7000 **A**1 9 10 **F**3 11 12 13 15 17 18 20
22 24 26 28 29 30 31 34 35 40 45 46 48 49 57 59 70 72 74 75 76 78 79
81 82 85 86 89 93 107 108 110 111 114 115 118 119 126 129 130 131
132 135 145 146 147 148 **S** Texas Health Resources, Arlington, TX
Primary Contact: Stan C. Morton, FACHE, President
CFO: David B. Meltzer, Chief Financial Officer
CMO: Timothy Harris, M.D., Chief Quality Officer
CIO: Melissa Smart, Communication ad Public Relations Specialist
CHR: Kathy Hardcastle, Director Human Resources
CNO: Deborah Bostic, R.N., Chief Nursing Officer
Web address: www.dentonhospital.com
Control: Other not–for–profit (including NFP Corporation) **Service:** General
Medical and Surgical

> **Staffed Beds:** 208 **Admissions:** 9194 **Census:** 114 **Outpatient Visits:** 62665
> **Births:** 1905 **Total Expense ($000):** 158455 **Payroll Expense ($000):**
> 58813 **Personnel:** 916

◇ **THE HEART HOSPITAL BAYLOR DENTON (450893)**, 2801 South Mayhill
Road, Zip 76208–5910; tel. 940/220–0600, (Nonreporting) **A**9 10 21
Primary Contact: Mark Valentine, President
COO: Bradley Morgan, Vice President of Operations
Web address: www.https://denton.thehearthospitalbaylor.com
Control: Partnership, Investor–owned, for–profit **Service:** Heart

> **Staffed Beds:** 16

✠ **UNIVERSITY BEHAVIORAL HEALTH OF DENTON (454104)**, 2026 West
University Drive, Zip 76201–0644; tel. 940/320–8100 **A**1 9 10 **F**4 5 54 98 100
102 103 104 105 **S** Universal Health Services, Inc., King of Prussia, PA
Primary Contact: Jason Toalson, Chief Executive Officer
CFO: Ed Sopiarz, Chief Financial Officer
CMO: Atique Khan, M.D., Medical Director
CIO: Marsh Smith, Manager Health Information
CHR: Dorie Atherton, Manager Human Resources
CNO: Vicki Stoker, Chief Nursing Officer
Web address: www.ubhdenton.com
Control: Partnership, Investor–owned, for–profit **Service:** Psychiatric

> **Staffed Beds:** 104 **Admissions:** 3137 **Census:** 80 **Outpatient Visits:** 12005
> **Births:** 0 **Total Expense ($000):** 16363 **Payroll Expense ($000):** 9185
> **Personnel:** 182

TX

Hospital, Medicare Provider Number, Address, Telephone, Approval, Facility, and Physician Codes, Health Care System

★ American Hospital Association (AHA) membership
☐ The Joint Commission accreditation   ◇ DNV Healthcare Inc. accreditation
○ Healthcare Facilities Accreditation Program
△ Commission on Accreditation of Rehabilitation Facilities (CARF) accreditation

DENVER CITY—Yoakum County

★ **YOAKUM COUNTY HOSPITAL (451308)**, 412 Mustang Avenue,
Zip 79323–2762, Mailing Address: P.O. Box 1130, Zip 79323–1130;
tel. 806/592–2121 **A**9 10 18 **F**3 11 13 28 34 35 40 43 50 53 57 59 60 62
64 76 81 87 89 93 107 114 119 127 129 133 **P**6
Primary Contact: Jerry Osburn, Chief Executive Officer
CFO: Suann Parrish, Chief Financial Officer
CMO: Dan Khan, M.D., Chief Medical Officer
CIO: Todd Carrillo, Chief Information Officer
CHR: Teresa Howard, Manager Human Resources
Web address: www.ych.us
Control: County–Government, nonfederal **Service:** General Medical and Surgical

Staffed Beds: 22 **Admissions:** 541 **Census:** 7 **Outpatient Visits:** 43534
Births: 161 **Total Expense ($000):** 21600 **Payroll Expense ($000):** 7438
Personnel: 172

DESOTO—Dallas County

☐ **HICKORY TRAIL HOSPITAL (454065)**, 2000 Old Hickory Trail,
Zip 75115–2242; tel. 972/298–7323 **A**1 9 10 **F**4 5 29 38 98 99 103 104 105
130 **S** Universal Health Services, Inc., King of Prussia, PA
Primary Contact: Lance Folske, Chief Executive Officer
CFO: Terri Logsdon, Chief Financial Officer
CMO: Manoochehr Khatami, M.D., Medical Director
CHR: Sarah Warren, Coordinator Human Resources
Web address: www.hickorytrail.com
Control: Corporation, Investor–owned, for–profit **Service:** Psychiatric

Staffed Beds: 86 **Admissions:** 2838 **Census:** 67 **Outpatient Visits:** 8653
Births: 0 **Total Expense ($000):** 15986 **Payroll Expense ($000):** 7744
Personnel: 184

⊞ **VIBRA SPECIALTY HOSPITAL AT DESOTO (452097)**, 2700 Walker Way,
Zip 75115–2088; tel. 972/298–1100 **A**1 10 **F**1 3 16 17 29 70 75 77 80 87
90 91 107 130 148 **S** Vibra Healthcare, Mechanicsburg, PA
Primary Contact: Greg Floyd, Chief Executive Officer
CFO: Donald Trimble, CPA, Chief Financial Officer
CMO: Ed Dominguez, President Medical Staff
CHR: Tim Lozier, Director Human Resources
CNO: Mae C. Weathersby, R.N., Chief Clinical Officer
Web address: www.vshdesoto.com
Control: Corporation, Investor–owned, for–profit **Service:** Long–Term Acute Care hospital

Staffed Beds: 40 **Admissions:** 453 **Census:** 35 **Outpatient Visits:** 0 **Births:**
0 **Total Expense ($000):** 17780 **Payroll Expense ($000):** 8971 **Personnel:**
140

DILLEY—Frio County

☐ **NIX COMMUNITY GENERAL HOSPITAL (670089)**, 230 West Miller,
Zip 78017–3818; tel. 830/965–2003, (Data for 168 days) **A**1 9 10 **F**34 40 57
97 107 127
Primary Contact: Rodrigo Gaona, Administrator
CFO: Lester Surrock, Chief Financial Officer
CHR: Blake W. Hubbard, FACHE, Senior Vice President and Chief Operating Officer
Medical Surgical Operations and Human Resources
CNO: Amy Lieck, Chief Nursing Officer
Control: Corporation, Investor–owned, for–profit **Service:** General Medical and Surgical

Staffed Beds: 6 **Admissions:** 79 **Census:** 1 **Outpatient Visits:** 3860 **Births:**
0 **Total Expense ($000):** 1835 **Payroll Expense ($000):** 864 **Personnel:** 41

DIMMITT—Castro County

★ **PLAINS MEMORIAL HOSPITAL (451350)**, 310 West Halsell Street,
Zip 79027–1846, Mailing Address: P.O. Box 278, Zip 79027–0278;
tel. 806/647–2191 **A**9 10 18 **F**7 32 34 35 40 43 53 57 59 64 65 69 75 77
85 86 87 93 97 107 114 115 119 127 130 133 135 **P**6
Primary Contact: Linda Rasor, R.N., Chief Executive Officer
CFO: Terri Martinez, Chief Financial Officer
CMO: Gary R. Hardee, M.D., Medical Director
CIO: Terry Young, Chief Information Officer
CHR: Debbie Underwood, Manager Human Resources
CNO: Renee Castillo, Chief Nursing Officer
Web address: www.plainsmemorial.com
Control: Hospital district or authority, Government, nonfederal **Service:** General Medical and Surgical

Staffed Beds: 25 **Admissions:** 234 **Census:** 4 **Outpatient Visits:** 24060
Births: 0 **Total Expense ($000):** 6026 **Payroll Expense ($000):** 3931
Personnel: 107

DUMAS—Moore County

☐ **MOORE COUNTY HOSPITAL DISTRICT (450221)**, 224 East Second Street,
Zip 79029–3808; tel. 806/935–7171 **A**1 9 10 20 **F**3 7 11 13 15 28 34 35 39
40 43 46 50 51 57 59 62 63 70 75 76 77 79 81 85 86 89 91 93 107 111
115 119 130 131 132 133 146 147 148
Primary Contact: Jeff Turner, FACHE, Chief Executive Officer
COO: Yvonne Blue, Chief Operations Officer
CFO: John E. Bailey, Chief Financial Officer
CHR: Ashleigh Wiswell, Director Human Resources
CNO: Stacey Cropley, M.D., Chief Nursing Officer
Web address: www.mchd.net
Control: Hospital district or authority, Government, nonfederal **Service:** General Medical and Surgical

Staffed Beds: 47 **Admissions:** 1556 **Census:** 8 **Outpatient Visits:** 18904
Births: 354 **Total Expense ($000):** 24287 **Payroll Expense ($000):** 12369
Personnel: 283

EAGLE LAKE—Colorado County

★ **RICE MEDICAL CENTER (451312)**, 600 South Austin Road, Zip 77434–3298,
Mailing Address: P.O. Box 277, Zip 77434–0277; tel. 979/234–5571 **A**9 10 18
F3 11 13 15 29 34 40 43 57 59 64 65 70 76 79 81 107 119 127 133 **P**6
Primary Contact: James D. Janek, Chief Executive Officer
CFO: Brian Mc Bride, Chief Financial Officer
CMO: Russell Thomas, M.D., Chief of Staff
CHR: Velma Loya, Administrative Human Resource Coordinator
CNO: Susan Hernandez, R.N., Chief Nursing Officer
Web address: www.ricemedicalcenter.net/
Control: Corporation, Investor–owned, for–profit **Service:** General Medical and Surgical

Staffed Beds: 15 **Admissions:** 256 **Census:** 3 **Outpatient Visits:** 23183
Births: 28 **Total Expense ($000):** 11069 **Payroll Expense ($000):** 3282
Personnel: 93

EAGLE PASS—Maverick County

☐ **FORT DUNCAN REGIONAL MEDICAL CENTER (450092)**, 3333 North Foster
Maldonado Boulevard, Zip 78852–5893; tel. 830/773–5321 **A**1 9 10 20 **F**3 13
15 18 29 35 40 43 45 46 47 49 53 57 60 64 65 68 70 75 76 77 79 81 85
86 87 89 90 91 93 107 108 110 111 114 118 119 129 130 146 147 148
S Universal Health Services, Inc., King of Prussia, PA
Primary Contact: Richard Prati, Chief Executive Officer
COO: Richard Prati, Chief Executive Officer
CFO: Joel Morales, Chief Financial Officer
CMO: David Land, D.O., Chief Medical Staff
CIO: Tony Hernandez, Director Information Technology
CHR: Daisy Rodriguez, Director Human Resources
CNO: Wilma Carbonel Mason, Chief Nursing Officer
Web address: www.fortduncanmedicalcenter.com
Control: Corporation, Investor–owned, for–profit **Service:** General Medical and Surgical

Staffed Beds: 101 **Admissions:** 4993 **Census:** 62 **Outpatient Visits:** 43294
Births: 1176 **Total Expense ($000):** 47393 **Payroll Expense ($000):** 21130
Personnel: 381

EASTLAND—Eastland County

EASTLAND MEMORIAL HOSPITAL (450411), 304 South Daugherty Street,
Zip 76448–2609, Mailing Address: P.O. Box 897, Zip 76448–0897;
tel. 254/629–2601 **A**9 10 20 **F**7 11 15 28 30 34 40 43 45 49 50 53 56 57
59 64 65 68 75 81 85 86 87 93 107 111 114 119 128 130 131 133
146 148
Primary Contact: Ted Matthews, Chief Executive Officer
CFO: Jamie Hayden, Chief Financial Officer
CHR: Leisha Hodges, Human Resources Officer
Web address: www.eastlandmemorial.com
Control: Hospital district or authority, Government, nonfederal **Service:** General Medical and Surgical

Staffed Beds: 36 **Admissions:** 682 **Census:** 8 **Outpatient Visits:** 21864
Births: 1 **Total Expense ($000):** 11840 **Payroll Expense ($000):** 5662
Personnel: 138

EDEN—Concho County

CONCHO COUNTY HOSPITAL (451325), 614 Eaker Street, Zip 76837–0359,
Mailing Address: P.O. Box 987, Zip 76837–0987; tel. 325/869–5911 **A**9 10 18
F3 40 43 50 57 59 77 87 107 133 146
Primary Contact: Dudley R. White, Administrator and Chief Executive Officer
CFO: Melanie Lozano, Chief Financial Officer
CNO: Toby Lehn, Director of Nurses
Web address: www.conchocountyhospital.com
Control: Hospital district or authority, Government, nonfederal **Service:** General Medical and Surgical

Staffed Beds: 16 **Admissions:** 133 **Census:** 2 **Outpatient Visits:** 4586
Births: 0 **Total Expense ($000):** 5470 **Payroll Expense ($000):** 1784
Personnel: 38

Many Facility Codes have changed. Please refer to the AHA Guide Code Chart. © 2014 AHA Guide

TX

EDINBURG—Hidalgo County

⊠ **CORNERSTONE REGIONAL HOSPITAL (450825)**, 2302 Cornerstone Boulevard, Zip 78539–8471; tel. 956/618–4444 **A**1 9 10 **F**3 8 29 35 37 39 40 45 46 51 57 64 74 79 81 82 85 87 119 **S** Universal Health Services, Inc., King of Prussia, PA
Primary Contact: Roxanna M. Godinez, Chief Executive Officer
CFO: Janie Alvarez, Accounting Director
CMO: Omar Gomez, M.D., Chief of Staff
CHR: Erika Betancourt, Coordinator Human Resources
CNO: Roxanne Reyes, Director of Nursing
Web address: www.cornerstoneregional.com
Control: Partnership, Investor–owned, for–profit **Service:** General Medical and Surgical

Staffed Beds: 14 **Admissions:** 577 **Census:** 4 **Outpatient Visits:** 2622 **Births:** 0 **Total Expense ($000):** 12003 **Payroll Expense ($000):** 3063 **Personnel:** 71

☐ **DOCTOR'S HOSPITAL AT RENAISSANCE (450869)**, 5501 South McColl Road, Zip 78539–9152; tel. 956/362–7360 **A**1 9 10 **F**3 4 12 13 15 17 18 19 20 22 24 26 28 29 30 31 34 35 38 39 40 43 45 46 47 48 49 50 51 54 55 56 57 58 59 60 64 65 70 72 73 74 75 76 77 78 79 80 81 82 84 85 87 88 89 90 91 92 93 96 98 99 100 101 102 103 104 107 108 110 111 112 113 114 115 116 117 118 119 120 121 123 124 126 130 132 145 146 147 148 **P**3 8
Primary Contact: Israel Rocha, Chief Executive Officer
COO: Marissa Castaneda, Chief Operating Officer and Director Marketing
CFO: Susan S. Turley, Chief Financial Officer
Web address: www.dhr–rgv.com
Control: Partnership, Investor–owned, for–profit **Service:** General Medical and Surgical

Staffed Beds: 525 **Admissions:** 29670 **Census:** 373 **Outpatient Visits:** 203323 **Births:** 8990 **Total Expense ($000):** 346236 **Payroll Expense ($000):** 153243 **Personnel:** 3026

SOUTH TEXAS HEALTH SYSTEM (450119), 1102 West Trenton Road, Zip 78539–9105; tel. 956/388–6000, (Includes EDINBURG CHILDREN'S HOSPITAL, 1400 West Trenton Road, Zip 78539; tel. 956/388–8000; EDINBURG REGIONAL MEDICAL CENTER, 1102 West Trenton Road, Zip 78539–6199; tel. 956/388–6000; MCALLEN HEART HOSPITAL, 1900 South D. Street, McAllen, Zip 78503; tel. 956/994–2000; MCALLEN MEDICAL CENTER, 301 West Expressway 83, McAllen, Zip 78503–3045; tel. 956/632–4000; SOUTH TEXAS BEHAVIORAL HEALTH CENTER, 2101 West Trenton Road, Zip 78539; tel. 956/388–1300; Joe Rodriguez, Chief Executive Officer) **A**9 10 **F**3 4 11 12 13 15 17 18 20 22 24 26 29 30 31 34 35 37 38 39 40 41 43 45 46 47 48 49 50 53 57 59 60 68 70 72 74 75 76 77 78 79 81 85 86 87 88 89 90 96 98 99 100 101 102 103 104 107 108 110 111 114 115 119 129 130 135 138 146 148 **P**6 8 **S** Universal Health Services, Inc., King of Prussia, PA
Primary Contact: Jennifer Garza, Chief Executive Officer
COO: Jerome M. Brooks, Chief Operating Officer
CFO: Carlos Guajardo, Chief Financial Officer
CMO: Yuri Bermudez, M.D., Chief of Staff
CIO: Rosie L. Mendiola–Balderas, Director Information Systems
CHR: Patricia Mcclelland, Director Human Resources
CNO: Catherine Domian, R.N., Chief Nursing Officer
Web address: www.southtexashealthsystem.com
Control: Partnership, Investor–owned, for–profit **Service:** General Medical and Surgical

Staffed Beds: 775 **Admissions:** 22943 **Census:** 306 **Outpatient Visits:** 108213 **Births:** 1326 **Total Expense ($000):** 197967 **Payroll Expense ($000):** 100504 **Personnel:** 1818

EDNA—Jackson County

★ **JACKSON COUNTY HOSPITAL DISTRICT (451363)**, 1013 South Wells Street, Zip 77957–4098; tel. 361/782–7800 **A**9 10 18 **F**7 15 34 40 43 45 50 56 57 59 62 64 65 68 75 81 87 93 103 104 107 110 111 114 119 127 129 130 131 133 146 148 **P**8
Primary Contact: Bill Jones, Chief Executive Officer
CFO: Lance Smiga, Chief Financial Officer
CMO: Francisco Ortiz, M.D., Chief of Staff
CIO: Jeff Prukop, Director Professional Services
CHR: Donna Coleman, Coordinator Human Resources
CNO: Tammy Zajicek, Director of Nursing
Web address: www.jchd.org
Control: Hospital district or authority, Government, nonfederal **Service:** General Medical and Surgical

Staffed Beds: 17 **Admissions:** 355 **Census:** 3 **Outpatient Visits:** 16386 **Births:** 0 **Total Expense ($000):** 16350 **Payroll Expense ($000):** 6562 **Personnel:** 155

EL CAMPO—Wharton County

EL CAMPO MEMORIAL HOSPITAL (450694), 303 Sandy Corner Road, Zip 77437–9535; tel. 979/543–6251 **A**9 10 **F**3 11 15 29 34 35 40 45 56 57 59 60 62 64 68 70 77 79 81 85 86 93 97 107 108 110 111 114 119 127 129 130 131 132 148 **P**6
Primary Contact: Tisha Zalman, Chief Executive Officer
CFO: Laurie Harvey, Controller
CMO: Laurie Hulsman, M.D., Chief of Staff
CIO: Bill Eller, Director Information Technology
CHR: Ginger Andreas, Coordinator Personnel and Credentialing
CNO: Desiree Cernoch, Director of Nurses
Web address: www.ecmh.org
Control: Other not–for–profit (including NFP Corporation) **Service:** General Medical and Surgical

Staffed Beds: 26 **Admissions:** 374 **Census:** 4 **Outpatient Visits:** 52689 **Births:** 0 **Total Expense ($000):** 18012 **Payroll Expense ($000):** 6796 **Personnel:** 117

EL PASO—El Paso County

EAST EL PASO PHYSICIANS MEDICAL CENTER See Foundation Surgical Hospital of El Paso

☐ **EL PASO CHILDREN'S HOSPITAL (453313)**, 4845 Alameda Avenue, Zip 79905–2705; tel. 915/298–5444 **A**1 3 5 9 10 **F**3 11 29 31 34 40 41 44 45 46 47 48 49 50 58 64 65 72 73 74 75 78 79 81 82 85 86 87 88 89 93 96 111 119 130 146 148 **P**6
Primary Contact: Ray R. Dziesinski, Chief Executive Officer
COO: Elias Armendariz, Chief Operating Officer and Chief Nursing Officer
CFO: David Mier, Chief Financial Officer
CMO: Bradley Fuhrman, M.D., Physician in Chief
CIO: Janina Prada, Director Information Technology
CHR: Natalia Chaparro, Manager Human Resources
CNO: Elias Armendariz, Chief Operating Officer and Chief Nursing Officer
Web address: www.elpasochildrens.org
Control: Other not–for–profit (including NFP Corporation) **Service:** Children's general

Staffed Beds: 122 **Admissions:** 4018 **Census:** 61 **Outpatient Visits:** 40084 **Births:** 0 **Total Expense ($000):** 99217 **Payroll Expense ($000):** 28311 **Personnel:** 529

EL PASO LTAC HOSPITAL (452103), 1221 North Cotton Street, 3rd Floor, Zip 79902–3015; tel. 915/496–9687 **A**9 10 **F**1 3 7 29 30 34 57 60 75 77 82 84 85 86 87 91 100 103 119 130 148
Primary Contact: Evelyn G. Stewart, Chief Executive Officer
Control: Partnership, Investor–owned, for–profit **Service:** Long–Term Acute Care hospital

Staffed Beds: 33 **Admissions:** 302 **Census:** 21 **Outpatient Visits:** 0 **Births:** 0 **Total Expense ($000):** 9616 **Payroll Expense ($000):** 3326 **Personnel:** 70

☐ **EL PASO PSYCHIATRIC CENTER (454100)**, 4615 Alameda Avenue, Zip 79905–2702; tel. 915/532–2202 **A**1 3 5 9 10 **F**29 98 99 103 130 135 **P**6 **S** Texas Department of State Health Services, Austin, TX
Primary Contact: Zulema Carrillo, Superintendent
CFO: David Osterhout, Assistant Superintendent and Chief Financial Officer
CMO: Nicolas Baida–Fragoso, M.D., Clinical Director
CNO: Raul D. Luna, Chief Nurse Executive
Web address: www.dshs.state.tx.us/mhhospitals/ElPasoPC/default.shtm
Control: State–Government, nonfederal **Service:** Psychiatric

Staffed Beds: 77 **Admissions:** 1120 **Census:** 69 **Outpatient Visits:** 0 **Births:** 0 **Total Expense ($000):** 19372 **Payroll Expense ($000):** 9621 **Personnel:** 259

☐ **EL PASO SPECIALTY HOSPITAL (450845)**, 1755 Curie Drive, Zip 79902–2919; tel. 915/544–3636 **A**1 9 10 **F**3 29 34 35 40 59 64 68 75 79 81 82 85 87 107 130 131 148 **S** National Surgical Hospitals, Chicago, IL
Primary Contact: James Wilcox, Chief Executive Officer
CFO: Greg Watters, Chief Financial Officer
CMO: David Mansfield, M.D., Chief of Staff
CNO: Anne Harvey, MSN, Chief Nursing Officer
Web address: www.elpasospecialtyhospital.com
Control: Partnership, Investor–owned, for–profit **Service:** Orthopedic

Staffed Beds: 27 **Admissions:** 671 **Census:** 5 **Outpatient Visits:** 17423 **Births:** 0 **Total Expense ($000):** 27144 **Payroll Expense ($000):** 7040 **Personnel:** 161

TX

Hospital, Medicare Provider Number, Address, Telephone, Approval, Facility, and Physician Codes, Health Care System

★ American Hospital Association (AHA) membership
☐ The Joint Commission accreditation
◇ DNV Healthcare Inc. accreditation
◯ Healthcare Facilities Accreditation Program
△ Commission on Accreditation of Rehabilitation Facilities (CARF) accreditation

◇ **FOUNDATION SURGICAL HOSPITAL OF EL PASO (450877)**, 1416 George Dieter Drive, Zip 79936–7601; tel. 915/598–4240 **A**9 10 21 **F**3 29 40 45 49 79 81 82 85 86 107 111 114 119 **S** Foundation Surgical Hospital Affiliates, Oklahoma City, OK
Primary Contact: Kane Dawson, Chief Executive Officer
COO: Marta Contreras, Chief Nursing Officer and Chief Operating Officer
CIO: Louie Aguilera, Director Information Technology
CHR: Grace Beltran, Director Human Resources
CNO: Marta Contreras, Chief Nursing Officer and Chief Operating Officer
Web address: www.physiciansmedcenter.com
Control: Corporation, Investor–owned, for–profit **Service:** Surgical

Staffed Beds: 20 **Admissions:** 1309 **Census:** 6 **Outpatient Visits:** 40776 **Births:** 0 **Total Expense ($000):** 46215 **Payroll Expense ($000):** 8568 **Personnel:** 84

☐ △ **HIGHLANDS REGIONAL REHABILITATION HOSPITAL (453086)**, 1395 George Dieter Drive, Zip 79936–7410; tel. 915/298–7222 **A**1 7 9 10 **F**3 29 30 34 57 59 64 74 75 79 86 87 90 93 96 100 130 132 143 146 148
Primary Contact: Mariaelena Carmona, Chief Executive Officer
Web address: www.highlandsrehab.com
Control: Partnership, Investor–owned, for–profit **Service:** Rehabilitation

Staffed Beds: 41 **Admissions:** 951 **Census:** 29 **Outpatient Visits:** 4688 **Births:** 0 **Total Expense ($000):** 8237 **Payroll Expense ($000):** 5942 **Personnel:** 118

✠ **KINDRED HOSPITAL EL PASO (452079)**, 1740 Curie Drive, Zip 79902–2901; tel. 915/351–9044 **A**1 9 10 **F**1 3 29 30 34 75 77 87 130 148 **S** Kindred Healthcare, Louisville, KY
Primary Contact: Diana Schultz, Chief Executive Officer
CFO: Melissa Campa, Controller
CMO: Edward Juarez, M.D., Chief Medical Officer
CHR: Laura Anchondo, Administrator Human Resources
Web address: www.khelpaso.com
Control: Corporation, Investor–owned, for–profit **Service:** Long–Term Acute Care hospital

Staffed Beds: 62 **Admissions:** 691 **Census:** 47 **Outpatient Visits:** 955 **Births:** 0 **Total Expense ($000):** 18738 **Payroll Expense ($000):** 8421 **Personnel:** 121

✠ △ **LAS PALMAS MEDICAL CENTER (450107)**, 1801 North Oregon Street, Zip 79902–3591; tel. 915/521–1200, (Includes DEL SOL MEDICAL CENTER, 10301 West Gateway Boulevard, Zip 79925–7798; tel. 915/595–9000; Jacob Cintron, FACHE, Chief Executive Officer; LAS PALMAS REHABILITATION HOSPITAL, 300 Waymore Drive, Zip 79902–1628; tel. 915/577–2600) **A**1 3 5 7 9 10 **F**3 12 13 15 17 18 20 22 24 26 27 28 29 30 31 34 35 36 37 38 40 41 43 45 46 47 48 49 50 51 53 54 55 56 61 64 68 70 72 73 74 75 76 77 78 79 81 82 85 86 87 88 89 90 91 92 93 107 108 109 110 111 112 114 115 117 119 120 121 122 126 129 130 132 134 138 143 146 147 148 **S** HCA, Nashville, TN
Primary Contact: Hank Hernandez, Chief Executive Officer
COO: Don Karl, Chief Operating Officer
Web address: www.laspalmashealth.com
Control: Partnership, Investor–owned, for–profit **Service:** General Medical and Surgical

Staffed Beds: 570 **Admissions:** 26630 **Census:** 355 **Outpatient Visits:** 208786 **Births:** 4725 **Total Expense ($000):** 344571 **Payroll Expense ($000):** 127177 **Personnel:** 2028

☐ **MESA HILLS SPECIALTY HOSPITAL (452035)**, 2311 North Oregon Street, Zip 79902–3216; tel. 915/545–1823 **A**1 9 10 **F**1 3 29 54 59 61 64 65 74 75 77 82 83 84 85 94 130 143 148 **S** Encore Healthcare, Columbia, MD
Primary Contact: Jesus Ruiz, Chief Executive Officer
COO: Elena Pino, Chief Operating Officer and Chief Nursing Officer
CFO: Priscilla Carter, Chief Financial Officer
Web address: www.mesahillsspecialtyhospital.com/mesa_hills/index.aspx
Control: Corporation, Investor–owned, for–profit **Service:** Long–Term Acute Care hospital

Staffed Beds: 32 **Admissions:** 277 **Census:** 20 **Outpatient Visits:** 3203 **Births:** 0 **Personnel:** 54

✠ **PROVIDENCE MEMORIAL HOSPITAL (450002)**, 2001 North Oregon Street, Zip 79902–3368; tel. 915/577–6625, (Includes CHILDREN'S HOSPITAL AT PROVIDENCE, 2001 North Oregon Street, Zip 79902–3320; tel. 915/577–7746) **A**1 9 10 **F**3 11 12 13 14 15 17 18 19 20 21 22 23 24 25 28 29 31 32 34 35 40 41 42 43 45 46 49 50 51 54 56 57 59 63 64 65 70 72 73 74 75 76 77 78 79 81 84 85 86 87 88 89 91 92 93 98 103 107 108 110 111 114 118 119 126 129 130 132 134 145 146 147 148 **P**1 **S** TENET Healthcare Corporation, Dallas, TX
Primary Contact: J. Eric Evans, Chief Executive Officer
COO: Monica Vargas, Chief Operating Officer
CFO: Charles Hondley, Chief Financial Officer
CIO: Ray Davis, Administrative Director
CHR: Stephanie S. Talley, Interim Chief Human Resource Officer
Web address: www.sphn.com
Control: Partnership, Investor–owned, for–profit **Service:** General Medical and Surgical

Staffed Beds: 351 **Admissions:** 16734 **Census:** 204 **Outpatient Visits:** 177642 **Total Expense ($000):** 236406 **Payroll Expense ($000):** 76098 **Personnel:** 1320

✠ **SIERRA MEDICAL CENTER (450668)**, 1625 Medical Center Drive, Zip 79902–5044; tel. 915/747–4000 **A**1 5 9 10 **F**3 8 11 13 15 17 18 20 22 24 26 29 30 31 34 37 40 42 43 45 47 48 49 50 54 55 57 58 59 60 61 64 68 69 70 72 74 75 76 77 78 79 81 82 85 86 90 107 110 111 114 115 118 119 124 126 130 132 134 144 145 146 147 148 **P**1 **S** TENET Healthcare Corporation, Dallas, TX
Primary Contact: J. Eric Evans, Chief Executive Officer
COO: Enrique Gallegos, Chief Operating Officer
CFO: David Byrd, Chief Financial Officer
CIO: Ray Davis, Administrative Director Information Systems
CHR: Stephanie S. Talley, Interim Chief Human Resource Officer
CNO: Katherine A. Doll, R.N., Chief Nursing Officer
Web address: www.sphn.com
Control: Partnership, Investor–owned, for–profit **Service:** General Medical and Surgical

Staffed Beds: 352 **Admissions:** 9668 **Census:** 128 **Outpatient Visits:** 99246 **Births:** 1702 **Total Expense ($000):** 151913 **Payroll Expense ($000):** 47075 **Personnel:** 790

✠ **SIERRA PROVIDENCE EAST MEDICAL CENTER (670047)**, 3280 Joe Battle Boulevard, Zip 79938–2622; tel. 915/832–2000 **A**1 2 5 9 10 **F**3 13 15 18 20 22 26 29 30 31 34 35 37 40 45 46 47 49 50 57 59 60 63 64 68 70 72 73 74 75 76 77 79 81 85 86 87 93 107 108 110 111 115 119 130 134 146 148 **P**4 **S** TENET Healthcare Corporation, Dallas, TX
Primary Contact: Sally A. Deitch, MSN, R.N., Chief Executive Officer
COO: Lauren Morton, Chief Operating Officer
CFO: Brandon May, Chief Financial Officer
Web address: www.sphn.com
Control: Individual, Investor–owned, for–profit **Service:** General Medical and Surgical

Staffed Beds: 110 **Admissions:** 8390 **Census:** 91 **Outpatient Visits:** 75270 **Births:** 1804 **Total Expense ($000):** 116264 **Payroll Expense ($000):** 36529 **Personnel:** 709

TRIUMPH HOSPITAL EL PASO See Kindred Hospital El Paso

☐ **UNIVERSITY BEHAVIORAL HEALTH OF EL PASO (454109)**, 1900 Denver Avenue, Zip 79902–3008; tel. 915/544–4000 **A**1 3 5 9 10 **F**4 56 57 75 86 87 98 99 101 102 103 104 105 130 **S** Universal Health Services, Inc., King of Prussia, PA
Primary Contact: David W. Morris, Chief Executive Officer
COO: Selene Q. Hammon, Chief Operating Officer
CFO: Phillip Sosa, Chief Financial Officer
CMO: Arthur L. Ramirez, M.D., Medical Director
CIO: Victor Torres, Information Technology Specialist Administrator
CHR: Brenda Holguin, Manager Human Resources
CNO: Susan Brown, Chief Nursing Officer
Web address: www.ubhelpaso.com/
Control: Corporation, Investor–owned, for–profit **Service:** Psychiatric

Staffed Beds: 163 **Admissions:** 4908 **Census:** 134 **Outpatient Visits:** 16498 **Births:** 0 **Total Expense ($000):** 22324 **Payroll Expense ($000):** 12967 **Personnel:** 307

✠ **UNIVERSITY MEDICAL CENTER OF EL PASO (450024)**, 4815 Alameda Avenue, Zip 79905–2794, Mailing Address: P.O. Box 20009, Zip 79998–0009; tel. 915/544–1200 **A**1 2 3 5 8 9 10 **F**3 8 11 15 17 18 20 22 24 26 28 29 30 31 34 35 37 40 43 45 46 47 48 49 50 51 53 54 56 57 59 60 61 64 65 68 70 74 75 76 77 79 81 82 85 86 87 92 93 94 96 97 100 102 107 108 110 111 112 114 118 119 126 127 130 131 134 143 144 145 146 147 148 **P**6
Primary Contact: James N. Valenti, FACHE, President and Chief Executive Officer
COO: Maria Zampini, Chief Operating Officer
CFO: Michael Nunez, Chief Financial Officer
CMO: Carmela Morales, M.D., Chief of Staff
CIO: Janina Prada, Director Information Services
CHR: Janice M. Harris, Director Human Resources
CNO: Diana Fancher, Chief Nursing Officer
Web address: www.thomasoncares.org
Control: Hospital district or authority, Government, nonfederal **Service:** General Medical and Surgical

Staffed Beds: 266 **Admissions:** 14898 **Census:** 182 **Outpatient Visits:** 720088 **Births:** 3496 **Total Expense ($000):** 472230 **Payroll Expense ($000):** 123726 **Personnel:** 2325

✠ **WILLIAM BEAUMONT ARMY MEDICAL CENTER**, 5005 North Piedras Street, Zip 79920–5001; tel. 915/742–2121, (Nonreporting) **A**1 2 3 5 9 **S** Department of the Army, Office of the Surgeon General, Falls Church, VA
Primary Contact: Colonel Michael S. Heimall, Commander
CIO: Major Rion Koon, Chief Information Management Division
Web address: www.wbamc.amedd.army.mil
Control: Army, Government, federal **Service:** General Medical and Surgical

Staffed Beds: 209

TX

ELDORADO—Schleicher County

★ **SCHLEICHER COUNTY MEDICAL CENTER (451304)**, 400 West Murchison, Zip 76936, Mailing Address: P.O. Box V., Zip 76936–1246; tel. 325/853–2507 **A**9 10 18 **F**11 34 40 57 59 64 65 66 68 93 107 127 133 **S** Preferred Management Corporation, Shawnee, OK
Primary Contact: Paul Burke, Administrator
CFO: Larry Stephens, Chief Financial Officer
CMO: Gordy Day, M.D., Medical Director
CHR: Beverly Minor, Chief Human Resources
Web address: www.scmc.us
Control: Corporation, Investor–owned, for–profit **Service:** General Medical and Surgical

Staffed Beds: 14 **Admissions:** 102 **Census:** 1 **Outpatient Visits:** 8246
Births: 0 **Total Expense ($000):** 4621 **Payroll Expense ($000):** 2001
Personnel: 45

ELECTRA—Wichita County

★ **ELECTRA MEMORIAL HOSPITAL (451343)**, 1207 South Bailey Street, Zip 76360–3221, Mailing Address: P.O. Box 1112, Zip 76360–1112; tel. 940/495–3981 **A**9 10 18 **F**3 7 11 32 40 43 53 59 62 64 65 66 75 77 93 97 107 114 119 129 130 131 133 147 148
Primary Contact: Jan A. Reed, CPA, Administrator and Chief Executive Officer
CFO: Rebecca McCain, Chief Financial Officer and Assistant Administrator
CIO: Brandon Huffstutler, Chief Information Officer
CNO: Kim Gilbert, R.N., Chief Nursing Officer
Web address: www.electrahospital.com
Control: Hospital district or authority, Government, nonfederal **Service:** General Medical and Surgical

Staffed Beds: 19 **Admissions:** 483 **Census:** 7 **Outpatient Visits:** 22543
Births: 0 **Total Expense ($000):** 12456 **Payroll Expense ($000):** 5969
Personnel: 111

ENNIS—Ellis County

⊞ **ENNIS REGIONAL MEDICAL CENTER (450833)**, 2201 West Lampasas Street, Zip 75119–5644; tel. 972/875–0900 **A**1 9 10 **F**3 11 13 15 18 29 34 40 43 45 50 51 57 59 70 75 76 77 79 81 82 85 93 107 108 110 111 115 119 146 **S** LifePoint Hospitals, Inc., Brentwood, TN
Primary Contact: Kevin Zachary, Chief Executive Officer
CFO: Jack Wilcox, Chief Financial Officer
CMO: Raymond W. Blair, Jr., M.D., Chief of Staff
CHR: Selena Cryer, Director Human Resources
CNO: Edwina A. Miner, R.N., Chief Nursing Officer
Web address: www.ennisregional.com
Control: Partnership, Investor–owned, for–profit **Service:** General Medical and Surgical

Staffed Beds: 58 **Admissions:** 1946 **Census:** 15 **Outpatient Visits:** 31080
Births: 617 **Total Expense ($000):** 23609 **Payroll Expense ($000):** 9896
Personnel: 183

FAIRFIELD—Freestone County

★ **EAST TEXAS MEDICAL CENTER FAIRFIELD (450658)**, 125 Newman Street, Zip 75840–1499; tel. 903/389–2121 **A**9 10 20 **F**15 28 34 40 43 45 50 57 59 68 75 81 82 107 110 115 119 127 130 132 **P**7 **S** East Texas Medical Center Regional Healthcare System, Tyler, TX
Primary Contact: Ruth Cook, Administrator
CFO: David A. Travis, Chief Financial Officer
CMO: J. Michael Orms, M.D., Chief of Staff
CHR: Jennifer Rummel, Director Human Resources
Web address: www.etmc.org
Control: Other not–for–profit (including NFP Corporation) **Service:** General Medical and Surgical

Staffed Beds: 44 **Admissions:** 437 **Census:** 3 **Outpatient Visits:** 40967
Births: 0 **Total Expense ($000):** 14094 **Payroll Expense ($000):** 4005
Personnel: 92

FLORESVILLE—Wilson County

CONNALLY MEMORIAL MEDICAL CENTER (450108), 499 10th Street, Zip 78114–3175; tel. 830/393–1300 **A**9 10 **F**3 15 18 29 34 35 40 43 45 47 54 57 59 62 64 70 75 81 82 85 86 87 107 111 114 119 130 132 133 146 148 **P**4
Primary Contact: Brian D. Burnside, FACHE, Chief Executive Officer
COO: Thomas Repino, Executive Director Ancillary Services
CFO: Jamie R. Jacoby, Chief Financial Officer
CMO: Carl Blond, M.D., Chief of Staff
CIO: Kim Schultz, Senior Application Analyst
CHR: Dane Bonecutter, Director Human Resources
CNO: Sue Tackitt, Chief Nursing Officer
Web address: www.connallymmc.org
Control: Hospital district or authority, Government, nonfederal **Service:** General Medical and Surgical

Staffed Beds: 17 **Admissions:** 882 **Census:** 9 **Outpatient Visits:** 71647
Births: 1 **Total Expense ($000):** 23476 **Payroll Expense ($000):** 8859
Personnel: 197

FLOWER MOUND—Denton County

◇ **CONTINUUM REHABILITATION HOSPITAL OF NORTH TEXAS (673047)**, 3100 Peters Colony Road, Zip 75022–2949; tel. 214/513–0310, (Total facility includes 12 beds in nursing home–type unit) **A**9 10 21 **F**3 34 57 59 64 90 93 96 128 130
Primary Contact: John M. Griffes, Chief Executive Officer
Web address: www.continuumhs.com
Control: Individual, Investor–owned, for–profit **Service:** Rehabilitation

Staffed Beds: 41 **Admissions:** 500 **Census:** 18 **Outpatient Visits:** 1382
Births: 0 **Total Expense ($000):** 8833 **Payroll Expense ($000):** 3877
Personnel: 70

□ ◇ **TEXAS HEALTH PRESBYTERIAN HOSPITAL FLOWER MOUND (670068)**, 4400 Long Prairie Road, Zip 75028–1892; tel. 469/322–7000 **A**1 9 10 21 **F**3 13 15 18 20 29 30 31 34 40 45 49 57 59 70 73 74 75 76 77 78 79 81 82 85 87 93 107 108 110 111 114 115 119 126 130 146 147
Primary Contact: Spencer Turner, Chief Executive Officer
COO: Shelley R. Tobey, R.N., Chief Operating Officer and Chief Nursing Officer
CFO: Tom Howard, Chief Financial Officer
CHR: Nicole Schweigert, Director Human Resources
CNO: Shelley R. Tobey, R.N., Chief Operating Officer and Chief Nursing Officer
Web address: www.phfmtexas.com/
Control: Partnership, Investor–owned, for–profit **Service:** General Medical and Surgical

Staffed Beds: 92 **Admissions:** 4407 **Census:** 47 **Outpatient Visits:** 32520
Births: 1421 **Total Expense ($000):** 89470 **Payroll Expense ($000):** 29245
Personnel: 607

FORT HOOD—Bell County

⊞ **CARL R. DARNALL ARMY MEDICAL CENTER**, 36000 Darnall Loop, Zip 76544–5095; tel. 254/288–8000, (Nonreporting) **A**1 2 3 5 9 **S** Department of the Army, Office of the Surgeon General, Falls Church, VA
Primary Contact: Colonel Patricia Darnauer, Medical Center Commander
CMO: Colonel Roger A. Gallup, Deputy Commander Clinical Service
CHR: Charles Burton, Chief Human Resources
Web address: www.crdamc.amedd.army.mil
Control: Army, Government, federal **Service:** General Medical and Surgical

Staffed Beds: 109

FORT SAM HOUSTON—Bexar County

BROOKE ARMY MEDICAL CENTER See San Antonio Military Medical Center

⊞ **SAN ANTONIO MILITARY MEDICAL CENTER**, 3851 Roger Brookes Drive, Zip 78234–4501; tel. 210/916–4141, (Nonreporting) **A**1 2 3 5 9 **S** Department of the Army, Office of the Surgeon General, Falls Church, VA
Primary Contact: Colonel Kyle D. Campbell, Commander
CMO: Colonel Joseph P. Chozinski, M.D., Deputy Commander Clinical Services
CIO: Lieutenant Colonel David Broyhill, Chief Information Management
CHR: Rose Juarez, Chief Civilian Personnel Branch
CNO: Colonel Sheri Howell, Deputy Commander Nursing
Web address: www.bamc.amedd.army.mil
Control: Army, Government, federal **Service:** General Medical and Surgical

Staffed Beds: 226

Hospital, Medicare Provider Number, Address, Telephone, Approval, Facility, and Physician Codes, Health Care System

★ American Hospital Association (AHA) membership
□ The Joint Commission accreditation   ◇ DNV Healthcare Inc. accreditation
○ Healthcare Facilities Accreditation Program
△ Commission on Accreditation of Rehabilitation Facilities (CARF) accreditation

FORT STOCKTON—Pecos County

★ **PECOS COUNTY MEMORIAL HOSPITAL (450178)**, 387 West I. H–10, Zip 79735–8912, Mailing Address: P.O. Box 1648, Zip 79735–1648; tel. 432/336–2004 **A**9 10 20 **F**3 11 13 28 29 30 32 34 35 40 43 53 57 59 62 63 64 65 75 76 81 93 107 111 119 127 129 130 146 148 **P**5 6
Primary Contact: Jim Horton, Chief Executive Officer
CFO: Leticia Fox, Chief Financial Officer
CMO: Larry Boyd, M.D., Chief of Staff
CHR: Malissa Trevino, Director Human Resources
CNO: Gina Kalka, R.N., Chief Nursing Officer
Web address: www.pcmhfs.com
Control: County–Government, nonfederal **Service:** General Medical and Surgical

> **Staffed Beds:** 27 **Admissions:** 1475 **Census:** 12 **Outpatient Visits:** 90785 **Births:** 173 **Total Expense ($000):** 31841 **Payroll Expense ($000):** 13642 **Personnel:** 276

FORT WORTH—Tarrant County

⊞ **BAYLOR ALL SAINTS MEDICAL CENTER AT FORT WORTH (450137)**, 1400 Eighth Avenue, Zip 76104–4192; tel. 817/926–2544 **A**1 2 9 10 **F**3 11 12 13 17 18 20 22 24 26 28 29 30 31 34 35 40 45 46 47 49 53 55 56 59 64 68 70 72 73 74 75 76 77 78 79 80 81 82 84 86 87 90 93 96 97 100 101 102 103 105 107 108 111 114 115 119 124 126 130 131 132 138 139 142 146 147 148 **S** Baylor Scott & White Health, Dallas, TX
Primary Contact: David G. Klein, M.D., President
COO: Janice L. Walker, R.N., Chief Operating Officer
CFO: Lucy Catala, Vice President Finance
CMO: Dahlia Hassani, Vice President of Medical Affairs
CIO: Sandy Vaughn, Director Information Services
CHR: Tracy Stanford, Director Human Resources
CNO: Ellen Pitcher, MSN, Vice President and Chief Nursing Officer
Web address: www.baylorhealth.com/PhysiciansLocations/AllSaints/Pages/Default.aspx
Control: Other not–for–profit (including NFP Corporation) **Service:** General Medical and Surgical

> **Staffed Beds:** 449 **Admissions:** 18444 **Census:** 228 **Outpatient Visits:** 80372 **Births:** 5598 **Total Expense ($000):** 310621 **Payroll Expense ($000):** 115426 **Personnel:** 1199

☐ **BAYLOR SURGICAL HOSPITAL AT FORT WORTH (450880)**, 750 12th Avenue, Zip 76104–2517; tel. 817/334–5050 **A**1 9 10 **F**3 29 40 75 79 81 82 85 87 107 111 114 119 120 130
Primary Contact: Roger Rhodes, Chief Executive Officer
CFO: Jane Mathis, Chief Financial Officer
CMO: Bruce Bollinger, Medical Director
CNO: Stacie Merrill, Chief Nursing Officer
Web address: www.mcsh-hospital.com
Control: Partnership, Investor–owned, for–profit **Service:** General Medical and Surgical

> **Staffed Beds:** 22 **Admissions:** 1070 **Census:** 7 **Outpatient Visits:** 10261 **Births:** 0 **Total Expense ($000):** 59786 **Payroll Expense ($000):** 10300 **Personnel:** 164

⊞ **COOK CHILDREN'S MEDICAL CENTER (453300)**, 801 Seventh Avenue, Zip 76104–2796; tel. 682/885–4000 **A**1 3 5 9 10 **F**3 7 8 19 21 23 25 27 29 30 31 32 34 35 38 39 40 41 43 44 45 48 50 51 54 55 57 58 59 60 61 64 68 72 74 75 77 78 79 80 81 82 84 85 86 87 88 89 90 93 97 98 99 100 101 102 104 105 106 107 108 111 112 113 114 118 119 129 130 131 132 134 136 138 143 144 146 148 **P**6
Primary Contact: Rick W. Merrill, President and Chief Executive Officer
CFO: Stephen Kimmel, Chief Financial Officer
CMO: James C. Cunningham, M.D., Chief Medical Officer
CIO: Theresa Meadows, Chief Information Officer
CHR: Keith Holtz, Chief Human Resources Officer
CNO: Teresa J. Clark, R.N., Chief Nursing Officer
Web address: www.cookchildrens.org
Control: Other not–for–profit (including NFP Corporation) **Service:** Children's general

> **Staffed Beds:** 353 **Admissions:** 12419 **Census:** 220 **Outpatient Visits:** 254177 **Births:** 0 **Total Expense ($000):** 645265 **Payroll Expense ($000):** 217440 **Personnel:** 3518

★ **GLOBALREHAB HOSPITAL – FORT WORTH (673035)**, 6601 Harris Parkway, Zip 76132–6108; tel. 817/433–9600 **A**10 **F**3 28 29 30 75 90 93 130 **S** GLOBALREHAB, Dallas, TX
Primary Contact: Jeffrey D. Thompson, Chief Executive Officer
CMO: Ade Adedokun, M.D., Medical Director
CHR: Lenae Romack, Manager Human Resources
CNO: Fred J. Andrews, Director of Nursing and Ancillary Services
Web address: www.globalrehabhospitals.com
Control: Partnership, Investor–owned, for–profit **Service:** Rehabilitation

> **Staffed Beds:** 42 **Admissions:** 1000 **Census:** 31 **Outpatient Visits:** 2821 **Births:** 0 **Total Expense ($000):** 15995 **Payroll Expense ($000):** 7070 **Personnel:** 93

⊞ **HEALTHSOUTH CITY VIEW REHABILITATION HOSPITAL (453042)**, 6701 Oakmont Boulevard, Zip 76132–2957; tel. 817/370–4700 **A**1 9 10 **F**3 29 62 77 82 90 91 93 94 95 96 118 130 148 **S** HEALTHSOUTH Corporation, Birmingham, AL
Primary Contact: Trent Pierce, R.N., Chief Executive Officer
Web address: www.healthsouthcityview.com
Control: Corporation, Investor–owned, for–profit **Service:** Rehabilitation

> **Staffed Beds:** 62 **Admissions:** 1062 **Census:** 38 **Outpatient Visits:** 10808 **Births:** 0 **Total Expense ($000):** 14933 **Payroll Expense ($000):** 8767 **Personnel:** 161

⊞ **HEALTHSOUTH REHABILITATION HOSPITAL OF FORT WORTH (453041)**, 1212 West Lancaster Avenue, Zip 76102–4510; tel. 817/870–2336 **A**1 9 10 **F**3 29 30 68 74 75 77 79 86 90 91 95 96 130 131 148 **S** HEALTHSOUTH Corporation, Birmingham, AL
Primary Contact: Trent Pierce, R.N., Chief Executive Officer
CFO: Sherry Hapney, Chief Financial Officer
CMO: Patrick Donovan, M.D., Director Medical Staff
CHR: Tara Kleas, Director Human Resources
Web address: www.healthsouthfortworth.com
Control: Corporation, Investor–owned, for–profit **Service:** Rehabilitation

> **Staffed Beds:** 60 **Admissions:** 1089 **Census:** 39 **Outpatient Visits:** 0 **Births:** 0 **Total Expense ($000):** 13537 **Payroll Expense ($000):** 7596 **Personnel:** 152

JOHN PETER SMITH HOSPITAL See JPS Health Network

★ **JPS HEALTH NETWORK (450039)**, 1500 South Main Street, Zip 76104–4917; tel. 817/921–3431, (Includes JOHN PETER SMITH HOSPITAL, 1500 South Main Street, Zip 76104; tel. 817/921–3431; TRINITY SPRINGS PAVILION, 1500 South Main Street, tel. 817/927–3636; Lily Wong, Director Psychiatry), (Total facility includes 15 beds in nursing home–type unit) **A**2 3 5 8 9 10 **F**3 8 11 13 15 17 18 20 22 24 26 28 29 30 31 32 34 35 36 37 38 39 40 43 44 45 47 49 50 54 55 56 57 58 59 60 61 64 65 66 68 70 73 74 75 76 77 78 79 80 81 82 84 85 86 87 89 91 92 93 97 98 99 100 101 102 103 104 105 107 108 110 111 114 115 118 119 120 121 123 124 126 128 130 131 132 134 135 142 143 144 146 147 148
Primary Contact: Robert Earley, President and Chief Executive Officer
COO: Bill Whitman, Chief Operating Officer
CIO: Melinda Custin, Chief Information Officer
CHR: Nikki Sumpter, Senior Vice President Human Resources
CNO: Wanda V. Peebles, Chief Nursing Officer
Web address: www.jpshealthnet.org
Control: Hospital district or authority, Government, nonfederal **Service:** General Medical and Surgical

> **Staffed Beds:** 517 **Admissions:** 25579 **Census:** 382 **Outpatient Visits:** 1020777 **Births:** 4741 **Total Expense ($000):** 720629 **Payroll Expense ($000):** 268681 **Personnel:** 4897

⊞ **KINDRED HOSPITAL–FORT WORTH (452088)**, 815 Eighth Avenue, Zip 76104–2609; tel. 817/332–4812, (Includes KINDRED HOSPITAL TARRANT COUNTY–FORT WORTH SOUTHWEST, 7800 Oakmont Boulevard, Zip 76132–4299; tel. 817/346–0094; Anna Rojas, Chief Executive Officer) **A**1 9 10 **F**3 29 46 48 60 70 77 79 82 85 107 114 130 148 **S** Kindred Healthcare, Louisville, KY
Primary Contact: Angela Harris, Chief Executive Officer
CFO: Susan Popp, Controller
CMO: Stuart McDonald, M.D., President Medical Staff
CIO: Norma Warner, Area Director Health Information Management
CHR: Nicole Newpower, Coordinator Human Resources
Web address: www.kindredfortworth.com/
Control: Corporation, Investor–owned, for–profit **Service:** Long–Term Acute Care hospital

> **Staffed Beds:** 54 **Admissions:** 652 **Census:** 46 **Outpatient Visits:** 0 **Births:** 0 **Total Expense ($000):** 23488 **Payroll Expense ($000):** 9499 **Personnel:** 162

MESA SPRINGS, 5560 Mesa Springs Drive, Zip 76123; tel. 817/292–4600, (Nonreporting)
Primary Contact: Barbara Schmidt, Chief Executive Officer
CFO: Jessica Knox, Chief Financial Officer
CMO: Stewart Keller, M.D., Medical Director
CHR: Jill Housand, Director Human Resources
CNO: Lisa Thames, Director of Nursing
Web address: www.springstone.com/hospitals.stmhl
Control: Corporation, Investor–owned, for–profit **Service:** Psychiatric

> **Staffed Beds:** 48

Many Facility Codes have changed. Please refer to the AHA Guide Code Chart. © 2014 AHA Guide

TX

PLAZA MEDICAL CENTER OF FORT WORTH (450672), 900 Eighth Avenue, Zip 76104–3902; tel. 817/336–2100 **A**1 2 9 10 12 13 **F**3 11 12 17 18 20 22 24 26 28 29 30 31 34 35 36 37 40 45 47 48 49 50 57 58 59 67 70 74 77 78 79 81 85 87 91 93 107 108 111 114 115 118 119 126 129 130 132 138 145 146 148 **P**8 **S** HCA, Nashville, TN
Primary Contact: Clay Franklin, Chief Executive Officer
COO: Gregory Haralson, Chief Operating Officer
CFO: Elia Stokes, Chief Financial Officer
CMO: Amir Malik, M.D., Cardiologist
CIO: Kelley Fredrickson, Director Information Services
CHR: Cyndi Roberts, Director Human Resources
Web address: www.plazamedicalcenter.com
Control: Partnership, Investor–owned, for–profit **Service:** General Medical and Surgical

Staffed Beds: 212 Admissions: 10324 Census: 145 Outpatient Visits: 35616 **Births:** 0 **Total Expense ($000):** 162342 **Payroll Expense ($000):** 52634 **Personnel:** 827

REGENCY HOSPITAL OF FORT WORTH (452099), 6801 Oakmont Boulevard, Zip 76132–3918; tel. 817/840–2500 **A**1 9 10 **F**1 3 29 45 75 77 85 86 87 107 130 148 **P**5 **S** Select Medical Corporation, Mechanicsburg, PA
Primary Contact: Natalie D. Lamberton, Chief Executive Officer
Web address: www.regencyhospital.com
Control: Corporation, Investor–owned, for–profit **Service:** Long–Term Acute Care hospital

Staffed Beds: 44 Admissions: 406 Census: 28 Outpatient Visits: 0 **Births:** 0 **Total Expense ($000):** 15641 **Payroll Expense ($000):** 7724 **Personnel:** 123

TEXAS HEALTH HARRIS METHODIST HOSPITAL ALLIANCE (670085), 10864 Texas Health Trail, Zip 76244–4897; tel. 682/212–2000 **A**1 9 10 **F**3 11 12 13 15 18 29 30 34 35 40 45 46 48 49 57 59 64 70 72 74 75 76 77 79 81 82 85 86 91 93 107 108 110 111 113 114 115 118 119 130 131 132 135 145 146 147 148 **S** Texas Health Resources, Arlington, TX
Primary Contact: Winjie Tang Miao, President
Control: Other not–for–profit (including NFP Corporation) **Service:** General Medical and Surgical

Staffed Beds: 58 Admissions: 2861 Census: 24 Outpatient Visits: 30486 **Births:** 927 **Total Expense ($000):** 58091 **Payroll Expense ($000):** 21927 **Personnel:** 406

△ **TEXAS HEALTH HARRIS METHODIST HOSPITAL FORT WORTH (450135)**, 1301 Pennsylvania Avenue, Zip 76104–2122; tel. 817/250–2000 **A**1 2 7 9 10 **F**3 11 12 13 15 17 18 20 22 24 26 28 29 30 31 34 35 36 40 42 43 45 46 47 48 49 53 56 57 58 59 60 61 64 65 68 70 71 72 74 75 76 77 78 79 81 82 83 84 85 86 87 91 92 93 94 95 96 107 108 110 111 112 114 115 116 117 118 119 120 126 130 131 132 135 146 147 148 **S** Texas Health Resources, Arlington, TX
Primary Contact: Lillie Biggins, R.N., President
CFO: Richard Humphrey, Vice President Finance
CMO: Joseph Prosser, M.D., Chief Medical Officer
CHR: Joseph Condon, Director Human Resources
CNO: Elaine Nelson, R.N., Chief Nursing Officer
Web address: www.texashealth.org
Control: Other not–for–profit (including NFP Corporation) **Service:** General Medical and Surgical

Staffed Beds: 633 Admissions: 33083 Census: 487 Outpatient Visits: 175626 **Births:** 3443 **Total Expense ($000):** 654862 **Payroll Expense ($000):** 242980 **Personnel:** 3862

TEXAS HEALTH HARRIS METHODIST HOSPITAL SOUTHWEST FORT WORTH (450779), 6100 Harris Parkway, Zip 76132–4199; tel. 817/433–5000 **A**1 9 10 **F**3 11 13 15 18 20 29 30 31 34 35 36 40 45 46 47 48 49 50 57 59 64 67 68 70 72 75 76 77 78 79 81 85 86 87 93 102 107 110 111 114 115 119 126 130 146 147 **S** Texas Health Resources, Arlington, TX
Primary Contact: Joseph DeLeon, President
CFO: Charlotte Ward, Entity Financial Officer
CMO: Mark Montgomery, M.D., Chief Medical Officer
CHR: Leanna W. Nalley, Director Human Resources
CNO: Mary Robinson, Chief Nursing Officer and Vice President Patient Care Services
Web address: www.texashealth.org
Control: Other not–for–profit (including NFP Corporation) **Service:** General Medical and Surgical

Staffed Beds: 180 Admissions: 11918 Census: 119 Outpatient Visits: 94593 **Births:** 3176 **Total Expense ($000):** 164688 **Payroll Expense ($000):** 60852 **Personnel:** 848

TEXAS HEALTH HUGULEY HOSPITAL FORT WORTH SOUTH (450677), 11801 South Freeway, Zip 76028–7021, Mailing Address: P.O. Box 6337, Zip 76115–0337; tel. 817/293–9110 **A**1 10 **F**3 5 8 11 13 15 17 18 20 22 24 28 29 30 31 32 34 35 38 40 44 45 49 51 53 54 56 57 59 60 64 65 68 70 71 74 75 76 77 78 79 80 81 82 85 86 87 89 93 98 100 101 102 103 104 105 107 108 110 111 114 118 119 120 121 126 130 132 135 146 147 148 **S** Adventist Health System Sunbelt Health Care Corporation, Altamonte Springs, FL
Primary Contact: Kenneth A. Finch, President and Chief Executive Officer
CFO: Penny Johnson, Chief Financial Officer
CMO: Edward Laue, M.D., Chief Medical Officer
CIO: David Smith, Manager Data Center
CHR: Laura Fisher, Director Human Resources
CNO: Tammy Collier, Vice President Patient Services
Web address: www.huguley.org
Control: Church–operated, Nongovernment, not–for profit **Service:** General Medical and Surgical

Staffed Beds: 192 Admissions: 9317 Census: 108 Outpatient Visits: 133422 **Births:** 1076 **Total Expense ($000):** 147510 **Payroll Expense ($000):** 58994 **Personnel:** 1018

TEXAS HEALTH SPECIALTY HOSPITAL (452018), 1301 Pennsylvania Avenue, 4th Floor, Zip 76104–2190; tel. 817/250–5500 **A**1 9 10 **F**1 3 42 44 65 87 130 148 **S** Texas Health Resources, Arlington, TX
Primary Contact: Cheryl Mobley, FACHE, President
CFO: Vicki L. Galati, Chief Financial Officer
CMO: Joseph Prosser, M.D., Chief Medical Officer
CHR: Joseph Condon, Director Human Resources
CNO: Pam Duffey, R.N., Chief Nursing Officer
Web address: www.texashealth.org
Control: Church–operated, Nongovernment, not–for profit **Service:** Long–Term Acute Care hospital

Staffed Beds: 10 Admissions: 79 Census: 8 Outpatient Visits: 0 **Births:** 0 **Total Expense ($000):** 6996 **Payroll Expense ($000):** 3092 **Personnel:** 42

□ △ **TEXAS REHABILITATION HOSPITAL OF FORT WORTH (673048)**, 425 Alabama Avenue, Zip 76104–1022; tel. 817/820–3400 **A**1 7 9 10 **F**3 29 74 79 90 91 96 130 132 148 **S** Centerre Healthcare, Brentwood, TN
Primary Contact: Russell Bailey, Chief Executive Officer
Web address: www.texasrehabhospital.com/
Control: Corporation, Investor–owned, for–profit **Service:** Rehabilitation

Staffed Beds: 66 Admissions: 1178 Census: 44 Outpatient Visits: 0 **Births:** 0 **Total Expense ($000):** 17306 **Payroll Expense ($000):** 8352 **Personnel:** 139

□ **USMD HOSPITAL AT FORT WORTH (670046)**, 5900 Dirks Road, Zip 76132–5473; tel. 817/433–9100 **A**1 9 10 **F**3 29 39 40 51 64 68 81 85 89 107 114 119 130 **S** USMD Inc., Irving, TX
Primary Contact: Stephanie Atkins–Guidry, Administrator
CHR: Alex Stefanowicz, Vice President Human Resources
CNO: Stephanie Atkins–Guidry, Administrator and Chief Nursing Officer
Web address: www.usmdfortworth.com/
Control: Partnership, Investor–owned, for–profit **Service:** Surgical

Staffed Beds: 8 Admissions: 426 Census: 3 Outpatient Visits: 5317 **Births:** 0 **Total Expense ($000):** 30785 **Payroll Expense ($000):** 4476 **Personnel:** 109

FREDERICKSBURG—Gillespie County

HILL COUNTRY MEMORIAL HOSPITAL (450604), 1020 South State Highway 16, Zip 78624–4471, Mailing Address: P.O. Box 835, Zip 78624–0835; tel. 830/997–4353 **A**1 9 10 **F**3 11 13 15 18 20 28 29 30 31 32 34 35 37 40 43 45 49 50 51 53 57 59 62 63 64 68 70 74 75 76 77 78 79 81 82 84 85 86 87 90 93 96 107 108 110 111 114 115 119 124 129 130 131 132 135 146 148 **P**8
Primary Contact: Jayne E. Pope, Chief Executive Officer
CFO: Mark Jones, Chief Financial Officer
CMO: Jose A. Lopez, M.D., Chief of Staff
CIO: Holly Schmidt, Chief Information Officer
CHR: Alysha Metzger, Director Human Resources
Web address: www.hcmhs.org
Control: Other not–for–profit (including NFP Corporation) **Service:** General Medical and Surgical

Staffed Beds: 57 Admissions: 2711 Census: 24 Outpatient Visits: 77582 **Births:** 483 **Total Expense ($000):** 65646 **Payroll Expense ($000):** 26531 **Personnel:** 483

FRIONA—Parmer County

PARMER COUNTY COMMUNITY HOSPITAL See Parmer Medical Center

TX

Hospital, Medicare Provider Number, Address, Telephone, Approval, Facility, and Physician Codes, Health Care System

★ American Hospital Association (AHA) membership
□ The Joint Commission accreditation
◇ DNV Healthcare Inc. accreditation
○ Healthcare Facilities Accreditation Program
△ Commission on Accreditation of Rehabilitation Facilities (CARF) accreditation

PARMER MEDICAL CENTER (451300), 1307 Cleveland Avenue, Zip 79035–1121; tel. 806/250–2754 **A**9 10 18 **F**11 30 34 40 43 57 64 75 77 89 93 107 119 127 130 133 148 **S** Preferred Management Corporation, Shawnee, OK
Primary Contact: Gayla Quillin, Administrator
Web address: www.parmermedicalcenter.com
Control: Other not-for-profit (including NFP Corporation) **Service:** General Medical and Surgical

Staffed Beds: 15 **Admissions:** 198 **Census:** 4 **Outpatient Visits:** 13943 **Births:** 0 **Total Expense ($000):** 9543 **Payroll Expense ($000):** 3495 **Personnel:** 86

FRISCO—Collin County

☒ **BAYLOR INSTITUTE FOR REHABILITATION AT FRISCO (673046)**, 2990 Legacy Drive, Zip 75034–6066; tel. 469/888–5100 **A**1 9 10 **F**29 30 34 36 75 90 91 93 96 130 132 148 **S** Select Medical Corporation, Mechanicsburg, PA
Primary Contact: Mark D. Boles, Chief Executive Officer
Web address: www.baylorhealth.com/bir
Control: Partnership, Investor-owned, for-profit **Service:** Rehabilitation

Staffed Beds: 44 **Admissions:** 791 **Census:** 26 **Outpatient Visits:** 5983 **Births:** 0 **Total Expense ($000):** 14948 **Payroll Expense ($000):** 6870 **Personnel:** 112

☐ **BAYLOR MEDICAL CENTER AT FRISCO (450853)**, 5601 Warren Parkway, Zip 75034–4069; tel. 214/407–5000 **A**1 9 10 **F**3 13 29 34 40 51 54 57 64 68 72 74 75 76 79 81 85 87 107 111 114 119 144 **S** United Surgical Partners International, Addison, TX
Primary Contact: William A. Keaton, Chief Executive Officer
COO: Kevin Coats, Chief Operating Officer and Chief Financial Officer
CFO: Kevin Coats, Chief Financial Officer
CMO: Jimmy Laferney, M.D., Vice President Medical Staff Affairs
CIO: Rick Barry, Director Information Systems
CHR: Margaret Garcia, Manager Human Resources
CNO: Randi Elliott MSN, Chief Nursing Officer
Web address: www.bmcf.com
Control: Partnership, Investor-owned, for-profit **Service:** General Medical and Surgical

Staffed Beds: 68 **Admissions:** 4477 **Census:** 39 **Outpatient Visits:** 28460 **Births:** 2528 **Total Expense ($000):** 115054 **Payroll Expense ($000):** 38333 **Personnel:** 559

☒ **CENTENNIAL MEDICAL CENTER (450885)**, 12505 Lebanon Road, Zip 75035–8298; tel. 972/963–3333 **A**1 9 10 **F**3 8 13 15 18 20 22 24 29 30 34 35 40 45 46 47 48 49 50 51 57 59 64 65 70 72 74 75 76 78 79 81 82 85 86 89 92 93 107 108 110 111 114 115 119 124 130 131 144 146 147 148 **S** TENET Healthcare Corporation, Dallas, TX
Primary Contact: Joe D. Thomason, Chief Executive Officer
COO: Reed Hammond, Chief Operating Officer
CFO: Blaise Bondi, Chief Financial Officer
CMO: Robert S. Hendler, M.D., Regional Chief Medical Officer
CIO: Dianne Yarborough, Director of Information Technology
CHR: Stephanie S. Talley, Director Human Resources
CNO: Calee Travis, R.N., Chief Nursing Officer
Web address: www.centennialmedcenter.com
Control: Corporation, Investor-owned, for-profit **Service:** General Medical and Surgical

Staffed Beds: 118 **Admissions:** 4081 **Census:** 48 **Outpatient Visits:** 34279 **Births:** 758 **Total Expense ($000):** 76718 **Payroll Expense ($000):** 27300 **Personnel:** 509

○ **FOREST PARK MEDICAL CENTER FRISCO**, 5500 Frisco Square Boulevard, Zip 75034–3305; tel. 214/618–0500 **A**11 **F**29 40 45 57 59 64 70 74 77 79 81 85 86 87 107 108 111 114 115 119 126 130 **P**5 **S** Vibrant Healthcare, Dallas, TX
Primary Contact: Julie A. Camp, R.N., Chief Executive Officer
COO: Kathryn Murphy, Chief Operating Officer and Chief Nursing Officer
CFO: Elisa Banigan, Chief Financial Officer
CMO: Robert Wyatt, M.D., Chief Medical Officer
CHR: Bryan Jewell, Director Human Resources
CNO: Kathryn Murphy, Chief Operating Officer and Chief Nursing Officer
Web address: www.forestparkfrisco.com/default.aspx
Control: Corporation, Investor-owned, for-profit **Service:** Surgical

Staffed Beds: 54 **Admissions:** 586 **Census:** 4 **Outpatient Visits:** 5233 **Births:** 0 **Total Expense ($000):** 65567 **Payroll Expense ($000):** 14074 **Personnel:** 220

GAINESVILLE—Cooke County

NORTH TEXAS MEDICAL CENTER (450090), 1900 Hospital Boulevard, Zip 76240–2002; tel. 940/665–1751 **A**9 10 20 **F**3 11 13 15 28 29 30 34 35 40 43 45 50 59 60 62 64 68 70 75 76 77 79 81 82 85 87 93 104 107 108 110 111 115 118 119 127 130 132 133 146 147
Primary Contact: Randy B. Bacus, FACHE, Chief Executive Officer
CFO: Kelly Hayes, Chief Financial Officer
CHR: Teresa Krebs, Director Human Resources
Web address: www.ntmconline.net
Control: Hospital district or authority, Government, nonfederal **Service:** General Medical and Surgical

Staffed Beds: 48 **Admissions:** 1496 **Census:** 15 **Outpatient Visits:** 58031 **Births:** 364 **Total Expense ($000):** 36101 **Payroll Expense ($000):** 15828 **Personnel:** 270

GALVESTON—Galveston County

☐ **SHRINERS HOSPITALS FOR CHILDREN–GALVESTON BURNS HOSPITAL (453311)**, (Burn Care), 815 Market Street, Zip 77550–2725; tel. 409/770–6600 **A**1 3 5 10 **F**3 11 16 29 30 32 34 35 38 64 68 75 77 81 82 85 86 93 99 100 101 104 119 130 132 146 148 **S** Shriners Hospitals for Children, Tampa, FL
Primary Contact: Mary Jaco, R.N., MSN, Administrator
CFO: Lona Pope, Director Financial Services
CMO: David N. Herndon, M.D., Chief of Staff
CHR: Lynn Clements, Director Human Resources
Web address: www.shrinershospitalsforchildren.org/Hospitals/Locations/Galveston.aspx
Control: Other not-for-profit (including NFP Corporation) **Service:** Children's other specialty

Staffed Beds: 15 **Admissions:** 240 **Census:** 9 **Outpatient Visits:** 8397 **Births:** 0 **Total Expense ($000):** 32002 **Payroll Expense ($000):** 11784 **Personnel:** 201

☒ **UNIVERSITY OF TEXAS MEDICAL BRANCH HOSPITALS (450018)**, 301 University Boulevard, Zip 77555–0128; tel. 409/772–1011 **A**1 2 5 8 9 10 13 **F**3 8 11 12 13 14 15 16 17 18 19 20 22 24 26 28 29 30 31 34 35 36 38 39 40 41 43 44 45 46 49 50 51 52 53 64 65 66 68 70 71 72 73 74 75 76 77 78 79 80 81 82 84 85 86 87 88 89 90 92 93 94 96 97 99 100 101 102 103 104 107 108 110 111 114 115 117 118 119 120 121 123 124 126 129 130 131 132 134 135 137 138 141 142 143 144 145 146 147 148 **P**6 **S** University of Texas System, Austin, TX
Primary Contact: Donna K. Sollenberger, Executive Vice President and Chief Executive Officer
COO: Deb McGrew, Chief Operating Officer
CMO: Oscar Brown, M.D., Interim Chief Medical Officer
CIO: Todd Leach, Chief Information Officer
CHR: Ronald McKinley, Ph.D., Vice President Human Resources and Employee Services
CNO: David R. Marshall, JD, Chief Nursing and Patient Care Services Officer
Web address: www.utmb.edu
Control: State-Government, nonfederal **Service:** General Medical and Surgical

Staffed Beds: 397 **Admissions:** 22410 **Census:** 318 **Outpatient Visits:** 730864 **Births:** 5315 **Total Expense ($000):** 643225 **Payroll Expense ($000):** 236692 **Personnel:** 3521

GARLAND—Dallas County

☒ **BAYLOR MEDICAL CENTER AT GARLAND (450280)**, 2300 Marie Curie Drive, Zip 75042–5706; tel. 972/487–5000 **A**1 2 3 5 9 10 **F**3 11 13 15 18 20 22 24 26 28 29 30 34 35 40 45 47 50 54 56 57 59 60 64 65 66 70 74 75 76 77 78 79 81 82 84 85 86 87 90 93 94 98 107 108 110 111 114 118 119 126 129 130 132 135 145 146 147 148 **S** Baylor Scott & White Health, Dallas, TX
Primary Contact: Thomas J. Trenary, President
COO: Janice L. Walker, R.N., Chief Nursing Officer and Chief Operating Officer
CFO: Robert Knowlton, Vice President and Chief Financial Officer
CMO: Steven Arze, M.D., Chief Medical Officer and Vice President Medical Affairs
CIO: Michael Larsen, Director Information Systems
CHR: Laura Settles, Director Human Resources
CNO: Janice L. Walker, R.N., Chief Nursing Officer and Chief Operating Officer
Web address: www.baylorhealth.com/PhysiciansLocations/Garland/Pages/Default.aspx
Control: Other not-for-profit (including NFP Corporation) **Service:** General Medical and Surgical

Staffed Beds: 220 **Admissions:** 10392 **Census:** 127 **Outpatient Visits:** 118701 **Births:** 1231 **Total Expense ($000):** 180819 **Payroll Expense ($000):** 70166 **Personnel:** 991

GATESVILLE—Coryell County

☐ **CORYELL MEMORIAL HOSPITAL (451379)**, 1507 West Main Street, Zip 76528–1098; tel. 254/865–8251 **A**1 9 10 18 **F**3 7 10 11 15 18 20 28 40 43 50 57 62 65 70 81 82 87 93 97 107 111 115 119 125 127 129 130 133 **P**6
Primary Contact: David Byrom, Chief Executive Officer
COO: David Byrom, Chief Executive Officer
CFO: Carol Jones, Controller and Manager Business Office
CMO: Diedra Wuenschel, D.O., President Medical Staff
CIO: Mike Huckabee, Network Administrator
CHR: Paula Smithhart, Director Human Resources
CNO: Jeanne Griffith, Chief Nursing Officer
Web address: www.cmhos.org
Control: Hospital district or authority, Government, nonfederal **Service:** General Medical and Surgical

Staffed Beds: 25 **Admissions:** 800 **Census:** 12 **Outpatient Visits:** 42147 **Births:** 0 **Total Expense ($000):** 25647 **Payroll Expense ($000):** 10907 **Personnel:** 320

GEORGETOWN—Williamson County

★ **ROCK SPRINGS**, 700 Southeast Inner Loop, Zip 78626; tel. 512/819–9400, (Nonreporting)
Primary Contact: Edgar E. Prettyman, PsyD, Chief Executive Officer
Web address: www.rockspringshealth.com/
Control: Corporation, Investor–owned, for–profit **Service:** Psychiatric

Staffed Beds: 48

GILMER—Upshur County

★ **EAST TEXAS MEDICAL CENTER–GILMER (450884)**, 712 North Wood Street, Zip 75644–1751; tel. 903/841–7100 **A**9 10 **F**3 11 29 30 40 43 50 57 59 68 85 87 97 107 108 111 115 119 127 **P**6 **S** East Texas Medical Center Regional Healthcare System, Tyler, TX
Primary Contact: James Warren Robicheaux, Administrator
CFO: Thomas O'Gorman, Jr., Chief Financial Officer
CHR: William Henry, Director Human Resources
CNO: Miguel Casas, R.N., Chief Nursing Officer
Web address: www.etmc.org
Control: Other not–for–profit (including NFP Corporation) **Service:** General Medical and Surgical

Staffed Beds: 35 **Admissions:** 450 **Census:** 4 **Outpatient Visits:** 25638 **Births:** 0 **Total Expense ($000):** 10488 **Payroll Expense ($000):** 3897 **Personnel:** 75

GLEN ROSE—Somervell County

☒ **GLEN ROSE MEDICAL CENTER (450451)**, 1021 Holden Street, Zip 76043–4937, Mailing Address: P.O. Box 2099, Zip 76043–2099; tel. 254/897–2215 **A**1 9 10 **F**2 15 29 34 40 43 45 48 51 56 57 59 65 79 81 93 103 104 107 108 110 111 119 129 130 132 133 143 146 **P**7
Primary Contact: Ray Reynolds, Chief Executive Officer
CFO: Michael Honea, Chief Financial Officer
CHR: Ladonna Green, Director Human Resources
CNO: Laura Hodnett, Interim Chief Nursing Officer
Web address: www.glenrosemedicalcenter.com
Control: Hospital district or authority, Government, nonfederal **Service:** General Medical and Surgical

Staffed Beds: 16 **Admissions:** 724 **Census:** 6 **Outpatient Visits:** 76870 **Births:** 0 **Total Expense ($000):** 14494 **Payroll Expense ($000):** 5582 **Personnel:** 187

GONZALES—Gonzales County

★ **MEMORIAL HOSPITAL (450235)**, 1110 Sarah Dewitt Drive, Zip 78629–3311, Mailing Address: P.O. Box 587, Zip 78629–0587; tel. 830/672–7581 **A**9 10 **F**3 11 13 15 29 34 35 38 40 43 53 57 59 62 64 65 68 70 75 76 77 81 85 87 93 97 107 110 111 115 119 127 129 130 132 148 **S** QHR, Brentwood, TN
Primary Contact: Charles Norris, Chief Executive Officer
CFO: Patty Stewart, Chief Financial Officer
CMO: Commie Hisey, D.O., Chief of Staff
CHR: Joni Leland, Director Human Resources
CNO: Valerie Hohenshell, Director of Clinical Services
Web address: www.gonzaleshealthcare.com
Control: Hospital district or authority, Government, nonfederal **Service:** General Medical and Surgical

Staffed Beds: 33 **Admissions:** 882 **Census:** 7 **Outpatient Visits:** 67675 **Births:** 215 **Total Expense ($000):** 25201 **Payroll Expense ($000):** 9766 **Personnel:** 251

GRAHAM—Young County

★ **GRAHAM REGIONAL MEDICAL CENTER (450085)**, 1301 Montgomery Road, Zip 76450–4240, Mailing Address: P.O. Box 1390, Zip 76450–1390; tel. 940/549–3400 **A**9 10 20 **F**7 11 13 15 28 29 40 43 53 57 59 62 63 70 75 76 79 81 85 89 93 104 107 111 115 119 127 130 133 135 **P**5
Primary Contact: Scott M. Landrum, Interim Administrator
CIO: Jeff Clark, Director Information Systems
CHR: Judy Guinn, Chief Human Resources Officer
Web address: www.grahamrmc.com
Control: City–Government, nonfederal **Service:** General Medical and Surgical

Staffed Beds: 37 **Admissions:** 1042 **Census:** 9 **Outpatient Visits:** 52389 **Births:** 224 **Total Expense ($000):** 22954 **Payroll Expense ($000):** 9315 **Personnel:** 200

GRANBURY—Hood County

☒ **LAKE GRANBURY MEDICAL CENTER (450596)**, 1310 Paluxy Road, Zip 76048–5655; tel. 817/573–2273 **A**1 9 10 **F**3 8 11 12 13 15 18 20 22 26 28 29 30 34 37 40 43 45 49 53 57 59 64 70 74 75 76 77 79 81 82 85 86 93 107 108 110 111 114 118 119 126 129 133 135 146 147 **S** Community Health Systems, Inc., Franklin, TN
Primary Contact: Derrick Cuenca, Chief Executive Officer
CFO: Noe Gutierrez, Chief Financial Officer
CIO: Kevin Myers, Director Information Systems
CHR: Brooke Montoya, Director Human Resources
Web address: www.lakegranburymedicalcenter.com
Control: Corporation, Investor–owned, for–profit **Service:** General Medical and Surgical

Staffed Beds: 83 **Admissions:** 2594 **Census:** 22 **Outpatient Visits:** 53732 **Births:** 519 **Total Expense ($000):** 52421 **Payroll Expense ($000):** 17207 **Personnel:** 323

GRAND PRAIRIE—Dallas County

◇ **TEXAS GENERAL HOSPITAL (670083)**, 2709 Hospital Boulevard, Zip 75051–1017; tel. 469/999–0000 **A**10 21 **F**3 12 18 20 22 34 35 40 45 49 50 57 59 64 70 79 81 82 85 87 107 108 111 115 119 148
Primary Contact: Suleman Hashmi, President and Chief Executive Officer
Web address: www.texasgeneralhospital.com
Control: Partnership, Investor–owned, for–profit **Service:** General Medical and Surgical

Staffed Beds: 41 **Admissions:** 544 **Census:** 4 **Outpatient Visits:** 10755 **Births:** 0 **Total Expense ($000):** 43733 **Payroll Expense ($000):** 8422 **Personnel:** 204

GRAPEVINE—Tarrant County

☒ **BAYLOR REGIONAL MEDICAL CENTER AT GRAPEVINE (450563)**, 1650 West College Street, Zip 76051–3565; tel. 817/481–1588 **A**1 2 9 10 **F**3 11 12 13 15 18 20 22 24 26 28 29 30 31 34 35 40 45 46 47 48 49 56 57 59 61 64 65 70 72 74 75 76 77 78 79 80 81 82 84 86 87 107 108 110 111 114 115 116 126 129 130 131 132 135 145 146 147 **S** Baylor Scott & White Health, Dallas, TX
Primary Contact: Steven R. Newton, President
CFO: Terri Foster, Hospital Finance Officer
CMO: Ron Jensen, D.O., Chief Medical Officer and Vice President
CIO: Sandy Vaughn, Director Information Systems
CHR: Donna Stark, Director Human Resources
CNO: Beth P. Houser, R.N., Chief Nursing Officer
Web address: www.https://www.baylorhealth.com/PhysiciansLocations/Grapevine/Pages/Default.aspx
Control: Other not–for–profit (including NFP Corporation) **Service:** General Medical and Surgical

Staffed Beds: 284 **Admissions:** 11583 **Census:** 139 **Outpatient Visits:** 79616 **Births:** 2589 **Total Expense ($000):** 195220 **Payroll Expense ($000):** 69061 **Personnel:** 1021

☐ **ETHICUS HOSPITAL – GRAPEVINE (452110)**, 4201 William D. Tate Avenue, Zip 76051–5736; tel. 817/288–1300 **A**1 9 10 **F**1 3 29 40 64 74 75 77 87 93 96 107 119 130 148
Primary Contact: Roger T. Jenkins, Chief Executive Officer
Web address: www.ethicusgrapevine.com
Control: Partnership, Investor–owned, for–profit **Service:** Long–Term Acute Care hospital

Staffed Beds: 48 **Admissions:** 447 **Census:** 34 **Outpatient Visits:** 17 **Births:** 0 **Total Expense ($000):** 22206 **Payroll Expense ($000):** 9919 **Personnel:** 186

Hospital, Medicare Provider Number, Address, Telephone, Approval, Facility, and Physician Codes, Health Care System

★ American Hospital Association (AHA) membership
☐ The Joint Commission accreditation
◇ DNV Healthcare Inc. accreditation
○ Healthcare Facilities Accreditation Program
△ Commission on Accreditation of Rehabilitation Facilities (CARF) accreditation

GREENVILLE—Hunt County

☐ **GLEN OAKS HOSPITAL (454050)**, 301 Division Street, Zip 75401–4101; tel. 903/454–6000 **A**1 9 10 **F**4 5 29 34 40 68 98 99 100 101 102 103 104 105 **S** Universal Health Services, Inc., King of Prussia, PA
Primary Contact: Joel Klein, Chief Executive Officer and Managing Director
CFO: Lowell K. Hudson, Chief Financial Officer
CMO: David Lucas, R.N., Director of Nursing
CHR: Joe Carson, Director Human Resources
Web address: www.glenoakshospital.com
Control: Corporation, Investor–owned, for–profit **Service:** Psychiatric

Staffed Beds: 54 **Admissions:** 1742 **Census:** 39 **Outpatient Visits:** 5235
Births: 0 **Total Expense ($000):** 7728 **Payroll Expense ($000):** 4090
Personnel: 96

✠ **HUNT REGIONAL MEDICAL CENTER (450352)**, 4215 Joe Ramsey Boulevard, Zip 75401–7899, Mailing Address: P.O. Box 1059, Zip 75403–1059; tel. 903/408–5000, (Includes HUNT REGIONAL MEDICAL CENTER, 4215 Joe Ramsey Boulevard, Zip 75403–1059, Mailing Address: Drawer 1059, Zip 75403–1059; tel. 903/408–5000) **A**1 9 10 **F**4 9 12 13 15 16 17 20 22 24 28 29 34 36 38 40 43 51 53 54 56 64 70 72 75 76 77 78 80 81 86 87 89 98 100 102 103 107 108 111 116 118 119 130 144 147 **P**2 **S** Hunt Regional Healthcare, Greenville, TX
Primary Contact: Richard Carter, District Chief Executive Officer
COO: Michael R. Klepin, Administrator
CFO: Jeri Rich, Assistant Administrator and Chief Financial Officer
CMO: James H. Sandin, M.D., Assistant Administrator Medical Affairs
CIO: Jonathan Schafft, Director Information Systems
CHR: John Heatherly, Assistant Administrator Support Services
CNO: Deborah Clack, Chief Nursing Officer
Web address: www.huntregional.org
Control: Church–operated, Nongovernment, not–for profit **Service:** General Medical and Surgical

Staffed Beds: 266 **Admissions:** 12225 **Census:** 162 **Outpatient Visits:** 234747 **Births:** 2761 **Total Expense ($000):** 272866 **Payroll Expense ($000):** 86294 **Personnel:** 1377

GROESBECK—Limestone County

LIMESTONE MEDICAL CENTER (451303), 701 Mcclintic Drive, Zip 76642–2128; tel. 254/729–3281 **A**9 10 18 **F**3 7 11 28 32 34 35 40 41 43 45 57 64 65 75 77 84 85 90 93 96 97 104 107 114 127 129 130 133 135 146 148
Primary Contact: Larry Price, Chief Executive Officer
CFO: Mike Williams, Accountant
CMO: Sheer Rahaman, M.D., Chief of Medical Staff
CIO: Byong Lee, Manager Information Technology and PACS Administrator
CHR: Jean Koester, Manager Human Resources
CNO: Jean Wragge, Director of Nurses
Web address: www.lmchospital.com
Control: Hospital district or authority, Government, nonfederal **Service:** General Medical and Surgical

Staffed Beds: 20 **Admissions:** 450 **Census:** 7 **Outpatient Visits:** 21075
Births: 0 **Total Expense ($000):** 17341 **Payroll Expense ($000):** 7460
Personnel: 201

HALLETTSVILLE—Lavaca County

LAVACA MEDICAL CENTER (451376), 1400 North Texana Street, Zip 77964–2099; tel. 361/798–3671 **A**9 10 18 **F**3 11 15 29 34 40 41 43 45 47 53 56 57 59 64 65 68 75 77 81 85 86 87 93 107 108 110 111 114 119 127 133 135 146 148
Primary Contact: James Vanek, Chief Executive Officer
Control: Hospital district or authority, Government, nonfederal **Service:** General Medical and Surgical

Staffed Beds: 25 **Admissions:** 650 **Census:** 8 **Outpatient Visits:** 32500
Births: 0 **Total Expense ($000):** 15226 **Payroll Expense ($000):** 5210
Personnel: 136

HAMILTON—Hamilton County

★ **HAMILTON GENERAL HOSPITAL (450754)**, 400 North Brown Street, Zip 76531–1518; tel. 254/386–1600 **A**9 10 20 **F**3 7 11 15 28 29 34 40 43 44 45 50 53 56 57 59 64 68 79 80 81 82 85 86 93 97 103 104 107 110 114 127 130 132
Primary Contact: Brian Roland, Chief Executive Officer
CFO: Brian Roland, Chief Financial Officer
CIO: Chad Reinert, Director Information Technology
CHR: Emily Dossey, Director Human Resources
CNO: Debra Martin, Director of Nursing
Web address: www.hamiltonhospital.org
Control: Hospital district or authority, Government, nonfederal **Service:** General Medical and Surgical

Staffed Beds: 42 **Admissions:** 1238 **Census:** 12 **Outpatient Visits:** 81648
Births: 0 **Total Expense ($000):** 19854 **Payroll Expense ($000):** 7643
Personnel: 256

HAMLIN—Jones County

HAMLIN MEMORIAL HOSPITAL (450243), 632 Northwest Second Street, Zip 79520–3831, Mailing Address: P.O. Box 400, Zip 79520–0400; tel. 325/576–3646 **A**9 10 **F**3 7 11 28 29 40 43 64 68 69 107 133 135 146 148 **P**5
Primary Contact: Keith L. Butler, Interim Chief Executive Officer
CMO: Krishna Sunkavalle, M.D., Chief Medical Officer
Control: Hospital district or authority, Government, nonfederal **Service:** General Medical and Surgical

Staffed Beds: 23 **Admissions:** 161 **Census:** 2 **Outpatient Visits:** 3953
Births: 0 **Total Expense ($000):** 3293 **Payroll Expense ($000):** 1807
Personnel: 65

HARKER HEIGHTS—Bell County

✠ **SETON MEDICAL CENTER HARKER HEIGHTS (670080)**, 850 West Central Texas Expressway, Zip 76548–1890; tel. 254/690–0900 **A**1 9 10 **F**3 13 15 18 20 22 26 28 29 30 34 35 40 45 49 50 51 56 57 59 60 64 70 74 75 76 77 79 81 91 97 107 108 110 111 115 119 129 130 135 146 147 148 **P**3 **S** LHP Hospital Group, Plano, TX
Primary Contact: Matt T. Maxfield, FACHE, Chief Executive Officer
CFO: John K. Sharp, Chief Financial Officer
CHR: Mona Tucker, Director Human Resources
CNO: Pamela Craig, R.N., Chief Nursing Officer
Web address: www.setonharkerheights.net
Control: Partnership, Investor–owned, for–profit **Service:** General Medical and Surgical

Staffed Beds: 58 **Admissions:** 3325 **Census:** 30 **Outpatient Visits:** 58302
Births: 729 **Total Expense ($000):** 73409 **Payroll Expense ($000):** 21657
Personnel: 357

HARLINGEN—Cameron County

✠ **HARLINGEN MEDICAL CENTER (450855)**, 5501 South Expressway 77, Zip 78550–3213; tel. 956/365–1000 **A**1 9 10 **F**3 12 13 15 17 18 20 22 24 29 30 40 43 49 50 51 57 59 64 68 70 74 75 79 81 85 86 89 107 108 110 111 114 115 118 119 129 130 146 147 148 **S** Prime Healthcare Services, Ontario, CA
Primary Contact: Brenda Ivory, Chief Executive Officer
CFO: David Glassburn, Vice President Finance and Chief Financial Officer
CMO: Elizabeth Juarez, M.D., Chief Medical Officer
CHR: Emmett Craig, Director Human Resources
CNO: Deborah Meeks, Chief Nursing Officer
Web address: www.harlingenmedicalcenter.com
Control: Partnership, Investor–owned, for–profit **Service:** General Medical and Surgical

Staffed Beds: 88 **Admissions:** 5092 **Census:** 46 **Outpatient Visits:** 86480
Births: 770 **Total Expense ($000):** 91664 **Payroll Expense ($000):** 29217
Personnel: 463

☐ **RIO GRANDE STATE CENTER/SOUTH TEXAS HEALTH CARE SYSTEM (454088)**, 1401 South Rangerville Road, Zip 78552–7638; tel. 956/364–8000, (Includes RIO GRANDE STATE CENTER, 1401 South Rangerville Road, tel. 956/364–8000; SOUTH TEXAS HEALTH CARE SYSTEM, 1401 Rangerville Road, Zip 78552–7609; tel. 956/364–8000) **A**1 10 **F**30 53 54 57 65 66 68 75 87 97 98 101 107 119 130 132 135 143 146 147 **P**6 **S** Texas Department of State Health Services, Austin, TX
Primary Contact: Sonia Hernandez–Keeble, Superintendent
CFO: Tom Garza, Director Fiscal and Support
CMO: David Moron, M.D., Clinical Director
CIO: Blas Ortiz, Jr., Assistant Superintendent and Public Information Officer
CHR: Irma Garcia, Job Coordinator
CNO: Maia Baker, MSN, Chief Nurse Executive
Web address: www.dshs.state.tx.us/mhhospitals/RioGrandeSC/default.shtm
Control: State–Government, nonfederal **Service:** Psychiatric

Staffed Beds: 128 **Admissions:** 953 **Census:** 47 **Outpatient Visits:** 34429
Births: 0 **Total Expense ($000):** 15322 **Payroll Expense ($000):** 5060
Personnel: 519

SOLARA HOSPITAL HARLINGEN (452101), 508 Victoria Lane, Zip 78550–3225; tel. 956/425–9600, (Includes SOLARA HOSPITAL – BROWNSVILLE CAMPUS, 333 Lorenaly Drive, Brownsville, Zip 78526–4333; tel. 956/546–0808) **A**9 10 **F**1 3 29 30 35 40 57 75 85 86 130 148 **S** Cornerstone Healthcare Group, Dallas, TX
Primary Contact: Cary L. Montalvo, Chief Executive Officer
CFO: Kurt Schultz, Chief Financial Officer
CIO: Adam Davis, Chief Information Officer
CHR: Dan Perkins, Vice President of Human Resources
Web address: www.chghospitals.com/harlingen/
Control: Partnership, Investor–owned, for–profit **Service:** Long–Term Acute Care hospital

Staffed Beds: 82 **Admissions:** 859 **Census:** 59 **Outpatient Visits:** 0 **Births:** 0 **Total Expense ($000):** 26421 **Payroll Expense ($000):** 10344
Personnel: 191

Many Facility Codes have changed. Please refer to the AHA Guide Code Chart. © 2014 AHA Guide

TX

VALLEY BAPTIST MEDICAL CENTER–HARLINGEN (450033), 2101 Pease Street, Zip 78550–8307, Mailing Address: P.O. Drawer 2588, Zip 78551–2588; tel. 956/389–1100 **A**1 3 5 9 10 **F**3 11 12 13 14 15 17 18 20 22 24 26 28 29 30 31 34 35 39 40 43 44 45 46 47 48 49 50 54 56 57 59 60 63 64 65 68 70 71 72 73 74 75 76 77 78 79 81 82 84 85 86 87 88 89 90 91 92 93 94 100 103 104 107 108 110 111 112 114 115 116 129 130 132 144 146 147 148 **S** TENET Healthcare Corporation, Dallas, TX
Primary Contact: Todd Mann, Senior Vice President and Chief Executive Officer
CHR: Irma L. Pye, Senior Vice President and Chief Human Resource Officer
CNO: Stephen Hill, Vice President and Chief Nursing Officer
Web address: www.valleybaptist.net/harlingen/index.htm
Control: Corporation, Investor–owned, for–profit **Service:** General Medical and Surgical

> **Staffed Beds:** 416 **Admissions:** 17076 **Census:** 230 **Outpatient Visits:** 110577 **Births:** 2610 **Total Expense ($000):** 244726 **Payroll Expense ($000):** 129562 **Personnel:** 1366

HASKELL—Haskell County

HASKELL MEMORIAL HOSPITAL (451341), 1 North Avenue N, Zip 79521–5499, Mailing Address: P.O. Box 1117, Zip 79521–1117; tel. 940/864–2621 **A**9 10 18 **F**11 28 29 34 35 40 53 56 57 59 68 75 77 86 87 93 119 130 131 133 146 **P**1
Primary Contact: Fran McCown, Administrator
CHR: Emily Moore, Director Human Resources and Information Technology
CNO: Charolotte Welch, Chief Nursing Officer
Control: Hospital district or authority, Government, nonfederal **Service:** General Medical and Surgical

> **Staffed Beds:** 15 **Admissions:** 283 **Census:** 3 **Outpatient Visits:** 8647 **Births:** 0 **Total Expense ($000):** 4452 **Payroll Expense ($000):** 2043 **Personnel:** 61

HEMPHILL—Sabine County

SABINE COUNTY HOSPITAL (451361), Highway 83 West, Zip 75948, Mailing Address: P.O. Box 750, Zip 75948–0750; tel. 409/787–3300 **A**1 9 10 18 **F**34 35 40 43 50 57 59 64 68 75 83 84 87 91 92 93 94 107 114 119 127 132 133 **S** Preferred Management Corporation, Shawnee, OK
Primary Contact: Diana Taylor, Administrator
COO: Deanna Lathrop, Assistant Administrator
CFO: Cindy Erickson, Chief Financial Officer
CMO: Grover C. Winslow, M.D., Chief of Staff
CIO: Margaret Moore, Manager Business Office
Web address: www.sabinecountyhospital.com/
Control: Corporation, Investor–owned, for–profit **Service:** General Medical and Surgical

> **Staffed Beds:** 25 **Admissions:** 323 **Census:** 4 **Outpatient Visits:** 20629 **Births:** 0 **Total Expense ($000):** 8090 **Payroll Expense ($000):** 2988 **Personnel:** 78

HENDERSON—Rusk County

EAST TEXAS MEDICAL CENTER HENDERSON (450475), 300 Wilson Street, Zip 75652–5956; tel. 903/655–3616 **A**1 9 10 **F**3 8 11 13 15 28 29 30 34 35 37 40 43 45 50 57 59 64 65 75 76 79 81 85 107 108 110 111 115 119 127 129 133 145 146 147 148 **S** East Texas Medical Center Regional Healthcare System, Tyler, TX
Primary Contact: Mark Leitner, Chief Executive Officer
CFO: Phillip A. Caron, Chief Financial Officer
CHR: William Henry, Director Human Resources
CNO: Miguel Casas, R.N., Chief Clinical Officer
Web address: www.etmc.org/etmchenderson/
Control: Other not–for–profit (including NFP Corporation) **Service:** General Medical and Surgical

> **Staffed Beds:** 41 **Admissions:** 1634 **Census:** 15 **Outpatient Visits:** 47224 **Births:** 280 **Total Expense ($000):** 27489 **Payroll Expense ($000):** 8651 **Personnel:** 160

HENRIETTA—Clay County

CLAY COUNTY MEMORIAL HOSPITAL (451362), 310 West South Street, Zip 76365–3346; tel. 940/538–5621 **A**9 10 18 **F**7 8 11 28 34 35 40 50 53 57 62 68 80 81 90 93 107 111 119 130 132 133 148 **P**5
Primary Contact: Jeff Huskey, Chief Executive Officer and Administrator
COO: Michael Clark, Director Operations
CFO: Debra Haehn, Chief Financial Officer
CMO: Mitchell Wolfe, M.D., Chief of Staff
CIO: Larry Evangelista, Supervisor Information Technology
CHR: Linda Burleson, Administrative Secretary
Web address: www.ccmhospital.com
Control: County–Government, nonfederal **Service:** General Medical and Surgical

> **Staffed Beds:** 25 **Admissions:** 200 **Census:** 3 **Outpatient Visits:** 7605 **Births:** 0 **Total Expense ($000):** 5122 **Payroll Expense ($000):** 2600 **Personnel:** 74

HEREFORD—Deaf Smith County

HEREFORD REGIONAL MEDICAL CENTER (450155), 540 West 15th Street, Zip 79045–2820; tel. 806/364–2141 **A**9 10 **F**3 7 11 13 15 29 35 40 43 50 57 59 62 65 70 76 77 81 85 93 107 111 114 119 127 130 133 147 **P**5
Primary Contact: Nathan A. Flood, Chief Executive Officer
COO: Meri Killingsworth, Chief Operating Officer
CFO: Greg Reinart, Chief Financial Officer
CNO: Anthony T. Jerina, Chief Nursing Officer
Web address: www.herefordregional.com
Control: Hospital district or authority, Government, nonfederal **Service:** General Medical and Surgical

> **Staffed Beds:** 39 **Admissions:** 854 **Census:** 8 **Outpatient Visits:** 60114 **Births:** 330 **Total Expense ($000):** 22433 **Payroll Expense ($000):** 7218 **Personnel:** 187

HILLSBORO—Hill County

HILL REGIONAL HOSPITAL (450192), 101 Circle Drive, Zip 76645–2670; tel. 254/580–8500 **A**1 9 10 **F**3 13 15 17 18 19 29 34 35 40 43 45 50 57 59 64 65 68 70 75 76 77 78 79 81 82 86 87 88 89 93 107 114 118 119 133 146 147 **S** Community Health Systems, Inc., Franklin, TN
Primary Contact: Jan McClure, Chief Executive Officer
CFO: Judy Culp, Chief Financial Officer
CHR: Becky Hale, Director Human Resources
Web address: www.chs.net
Control: Corporation, Investor–owned, for–profit **Service:** General Medical and Surgical

> **Staffed Beds:** 66 **Admissions:** 1474 **Census:** 14 **Outpatient Visits:** 22344 **Births:** 255 **Total Expense ($000):** 29698 **Payroll Expense ($000):** 8634 **Personnel:** 159

HONDO—Medina County

MEDINA COMMUNITY HOSPITAL See Medina Regional Hospital

MEDINA REGIONAL HOSPITAL (451330), 3100 Avenue E., Zip 78861–3599; tel. 830/426–7700 **A**9 10 18 **F**3 11 13 15 29 34 35 40 43 45 50 57 59 64 76 81 87 93 97 107 111 114 119 127 133 146 **P**4
Primary Contact: Janice Simons, FACHE, Chief Executive Officer
COO: Dale Semar, Controller
CFO: Kevin Frosch, Chief Financial Officer
CMO: Matthew Windrow, M.D., Chief of Staff
CIO: Michael Smith, Director Support Services and Information Technology
CHR: Sharon Garcia, Human Resources Representative
CNO: Rebecca Hinojoza, Chief Nursing Officer
Web address: www.medinahospital.net
Control: Hospital district or authority, Government, nonfederal **Service:** General Medical and Surgical

> **Staffed Beds:** 25 **Admissions:** 959 **Census:** 10 **Outpatient Visits:** 98454 **Births:** 133 **Total Expense ($000):** 22011 **Payroll Expense ($000):** 8395 **Personnel:** 219

HOUSTON—Harris County

BEHAVIORAL HOSPITAL OF BELLAIRE (454107), 5314 Dashwood Drive, Zip 77081–4603; tel. 713/600–9500 **A**1 9 10 **F**4 5 98 100 101 103 104 105 **S** Universal Health Services, Inc., King of Prussia, PA
Primary Contact: Drew Martin, Chief Executive Officer
Web address: www.bhbhospital.com
Control: Corporation, Investor–owned, for–profit **Service:** Psychiatric

> **Staffed Beds:** 76 **Admissions:** 2333 **Census:** 59 **Outpatient Visits:** 11465 **Births:** 0 **Total Expense ($000):** 15061 **Payroll Expense ($000):** 8051 **Personnel:** 163

BEN TAUB GENERAL HOSPITAL See Harris Health System

CAMBRIDGE HOSPITAL IN HOUSTON (454120), 7601 Fannin Street, Zip 77054–1905; tel. 713/795–5025 **A**1 9 10 **F**4 29 40 44 53 56 74 86 87 98 99 100 101 102 103 105 130 132 135 **P**8
Primary Contact: Trey Miller, Chief Executive Officer
Web address: www.cambridgehospitalhouston.com
Control: Corporation, Investor–owned, for–profit **Service:** Psychiatric

> **Staffed Beds:** 100 **Admissions:** 2074 **Census:** 19 **Outpatient Visits:** 0 **Births:** 0 **Total Expense ($000):** 4984 **Payroll Expense ($000):** 2648 **Personnel:** 98

CHILDREN'S MEMORIAL HERMANN HOSPITAL See Memorial Hermann – Texas Medical Center

TX

Hospital, Medicare Provider Number, Address, Telephone, Approval, Facility, and Physician Codes, Health Care System

★ American Hospital Association (AHA) membership
☐ The Joint Commission accreditation ◇ DNV Healthcare Inc. accreditation
◯ Healthcare Facilities Accreditation Program
△ Commission on Accreditation of Rehabilitation Facilities (CARF) accreditation

TX

☐ **CORNERSTONE HOSPITAL–MEDICAL CENTER OF HOUSTON (452055)**, 2001 Hermann Drive, Zip 77004; tel. 832/649–6200 **A**1 10 **F**1 3 29 31 65 77 85 86 87 119 130 148 **S** Cornerstone Healthcare Group, Dallas, TX
Primary Contact: Michael Higginbotham, Chief Executive Officer
Web address: www.chghospitals.com
Control: Corporation, Investor–owned, for–profit **Service:** Long–Term Acute Care hospital

Staffed Beds: 35 Admissions: 340 Census: 24 Outpatient Visits: 0 Births: 0 Total Expense ($000): 13527 Payroll Expense ($000): 5498 Personnel: 90

☐ **CYPRESS CREEK HOSPITAL (454108)**, 17750 Cali Drive, Zip 77090–2700; tel. 281/586–7600 **A**1 9 10 **F**4 5 29 30 64 87 98 99 100 102 104 105 130 132 **S** Universal Health Services, Inc., King of Prussia, PA
Primary Contact: Brian Brooker, Chief Executive Officer
CFO: Leslie Stuart, Chief Financial Officer
CMO: Marshall Lucas, M.D., Medical Director
CHR: Brenda Dominguez, Director Human Resources
CNO: Shazetta Richardson, Director of Nursing
Web address: www.cypresscreekhospital.com
Control: Corporation, Investor–owned, for–profit **Service:** Psychiatric

Staffed Beds: 96 Admissions: 4001 Census: 87 Outpatient Visits: 7898 Births: 0 Total Expense ($000): 21121 Payroll Expense ($000): 9975 Personnel: 186

✠ **CYPRESS FAIRBANKS MEDICAL CENTER (450716)**, 10655 Steepletop Drive, Zip 77065–4297; tel. 281/890–4285 **A**1 9 10 **F**3 11 12 13 15 18 20 22 24 29 30 31 34 40 42 45 46 47 49 50 53 57 59 64 70 72 74 75 76 77 78 79 81 82 85 87 89 93 107 108 110 111 114 115 118 119 120 121 129 130 131 132 144 145 146 147 148 **P**8 **S** TENET Healthcare Corporation, Dallas, TX
Primary Contact: Terry J. Wheeler, Chief Executive Officer
COO: Collin LeMaistre, Chief Operating Officer
CFO: James Wright, M.D., Chief Financial Officer
CMO: Arturo Bravo, M.D., Chief of Staff
CIO: Donna Cain, Director Information Systems Department
CHR: Linda Creswell, Director Human Resource
CNO: Lisa D. Cox, R.N., Chief Nursing Officer
Web address: www.cyfairhospital.com
Control: Corporation, Investor–owned, for–profit **Service:** General Medical and Surgical

Staffed Beds: 181 Admissions: 8166 Census: 88 Outpatient Visits: 112547 Births: 2854 Total Expense ($000): 124628 Payroll Expense ($000): 49194 Personnel: 629

☐ **DOCTOR'S HOSPITAL – TIDWELL (450803)**, 510 West Tidwell Road, Zip 77091–4399; tel. 713/691–1111, (Includes DOCTORS HOSPITAL PARKWAY, 233 West Parker Road, Zip 77076–2999; tel. 281/765–2600) **A**1 9 10 **F**22 29 40 43 50 64 68 70 75 79 81 92 107 114 119 130 148
Primary Contact: Farida Moeen, M.D., Interim Administrator
COO: Farida Moeen, M.D., Chief Operating Officer
CFO: Theresa Eatherly, Chief Financial Officer
CMO: Cesar Ortega, M.D., Chief of Staff
CIO: Dell Davis, Director Information Systems
CHR: Carolyn Washington, Director of Human Resources
Web address: www.dhthou.com/
Control: Partnership, Investor–owned, for–profit **Service:** General Medical and Surgical

Staffed Beds: 52 Admissions: 2765 Census: 26 Outpatient Visits: 18435 Births: 1195 Total Expense ($000): 32794 Payroll Expense ($000): 15113 Personnel: 303

DUBUIS HOSPITAL OF HOUSTON See Cornerstone Hospital–Medical Center of Houston

✠ △ ◇ **HARRIS HEALTH SYSTEM (450289)**, 2525 Holly Hall Street, Zip 77054–4108, Mailing Address: P.O. Box 66769, Zip 77266–6769; tel. 713/566–6403, (Includes BEN TAUB GENERAL HOSPITAL, 1504 Taub Loop, Zip 77030; tel. 713/873–2300; LYNDON B JOHNSON GENERAL HOSPITAL, 5656 Kelley, Zip 77026; tel. 713/566–5000; Jesse Lee Tucker, Administrator; QUENTIN MEASE HOSPITAL, 3601 North MacGregor, Zip 77004; tel. 713/873–3700; Jeffrey Webster, Administrator), (Total facility includes 24 beds in nursing home–type unit) **A**1 2 3 5 7 8 9 10 21 **F**3 5 7 13 15 17 18 20 22 24 26 29 30 31 33 34 35 39 40 41 43 45 46 49 50 51 54 55 56 57 58 59 60 61 64 65 68 70 71 72 73 74 75 76 77 78 79 81 82 84 87 89 90 91 92 93 94 97 98 99 100 101 102 103 104 107 110 111 112 114 115 118 119 120 121 124 128 129 130 132 134 135 143 144 145 146 147 148 **P**6
Primary Contact: George V. Masi, Chief Executive Officer
CFO: Michael Norby, Chief Financial Officer
CMO: Fred Sutton, M.D., Chief Medical Officer
CIO: Tim Tindle, Chief Information Officer
CHR: Diane Poirot, Vice President Human Resources
CNO: Elizabeth Cloyd, R.N., Chief Nurse Executive and Executive Vice President
Web address: www.hchdonline.com
Control: Hospital district or authority, Government, nonfederal **Service:** General Medical and Surgical

Staffed Beds: 809 Admissions: 34538 Census: 540 Outpatient Visits: 1742429 Births: 6676 Total Expense ($000): 1160666 Payroll Expense ($000): 488597 Personnel: 6946

◇ **HEALTHBRIDGE CHILDREN'S HOSPITAL OF HOUSTON (453309)**, 2929 Woodland Park Drive, Zip 77082–2687; tel. 281/293–7774 **A**9 10 21 **F**3 29 74 75 79 85 87 93 100 130 146 148 **S** Nexus Health Systems, Houston, TX
Primary Contact: Ronell Myburgh, Chief Executive Officer
CMO: Robert Yetman, M.D., Medical Director
CHR: Guy Murdock, Vice President Human Resources
Web address: www.healthbridgehouston.com/
Control: Partnership, Investor–owned, for–profit **Service:** Children's general

Staffed Beds: 40 Admissions: 211 Census: 20 Outpatient Visits: 999 Births: 0 Total Expense ($000): 12020 Payroll Expense ($000): 4917 Personnel: 120

✠ **HEALTHSOUTH REHABILITATION HOSPITAL OF CYPRESS (673050)**, 13031 Wortham Center Drive, Zip 77065–5662; tel. 832/280–2500 **A**1 10 **F**3 29 34 57 60 62 64 68 75 77 87 90 91 93 94 95 96 100 130 132 146 148 **S** HEALTHSOUTH Corporation, Birmingham, AL
Primary Contact: Sheila A. Bollier, Chief Executive Officer
CFO: Melissa Haddox, Controller
CMO: Ignazio LaChina, M.D., Medical Director
CHR: Keisha Pittman, Director Human Resources
CNO: Roshonda Henry, Chief Nursing Officer
Web address: www.healthsouthcypress.com
Control: Corporation, Investor–owned, for–profit **Service:** Rehabilitation

Staffed Beds: 40 Admissions: 997 Census: 35 Outpatient Visits: 3519 Births: 0 Total Expense ($000): 13248 Payroll Expense ($000): 7390 Personnel: 128

☐ **HOUSTON HOSPITAL FOR SPECIALIZED SURGERY (450797)**, 5445 La Branch Street, Zip 77004–6835; tel. 713/528–6800 **A**1 3 5 9 10 **F**3 8 40 45 46 47 48 49 79 81 82
Primary Contact: Gary Williams, Administrator
CFO: Deborah Jones, Controller
Web address: www.scasurgery.com
Control: Partnership, Investor–owned, for–profit **Service:** General Medical and Surgical

Staffed Beds: 7 Admissions: 151 Census: 1 Outpatient Visits: 4959 Births: 0 Total Expense ($000): 12419 Payroll Expense ($000): 3426 Personnel: 55

★ △ ◇ **HOUSTON METHODIST HOSPITAL (450358)**, 6565 Fannin Street, Zip 77030–2707; tel. 713/790–3311, (Total facility includes 25 beds in nursing home–type unit) **A**2 3 5 7 8 9 10 21 **F**3 6 8 9 11 12 13 14 15 17 18 20 22 24 26 28 29 30 31 33 34 35 36 37 40 42 44 45 46 47 48 49 50 51 52 53 54 55 56 57 58 59 60 61 63 64 65 68 70 72 73 74 75 76 77 78 79 81 82 84 85 86 87 90 91 92 93 94 96 97 98 100 101 102 103 104 105 107 108 110 111 114 115 116 117 118 119 120 121 123 124 126 128 129 130 131 132 135 136 137 138 139 140 141 142 143 145 146 147 148 **P**8 **S** Houston Methodist, Houston, TX
Primary Contact: Roberta Schwartz, Executive Vice President
CMO: Dirk Sostman, M.D., Executive Vice President, Chief Medical Officer and Chief Academic Officer
CIO: Timothy L. Thompson, Sr., Senior Vice President and Chief Information Officer
CHR: Lauren P. Rykert, Senior Vice President
Web address: www.methodisthealth.com
Control: Other not–for–profit (including NFP Corporation) **Service:** General Medical and Surgical

Staffed Beds: 849 Admissions: 36310 Census: 635 Outpatient Visits: 362521 Births: 1058 Total Expense ($000): 1287490 Payroll Expense ($000): 354440 Personnel: 6413

★ ◇ **HOUSTON METHODIST WEST HOSPITAL (670077)**, 18500 Katy Freeway, Zip 77094–1110; tel. 832/522–1000 **A**3 5 9 10 21 **F**3 12 13 15 18 20 22 24 26 28 29 30 31 34 35 40 45 49 50 51 57 59 64 68 70 73 74 75 76 77 78 79 81 82 85 93 107 108 109 110 111 114 115 119 120 121 123 124 126 130 131 132 135 146 147 **P**1 **S** Houston Methodist, Houston, TX
Primary Contact: Wayne M. Voss, Chief Executive Officer
Web address: www.methodisthealth.com
Control: Other not–for–profit (including NFP Corporation) **Service:** General Medical and Surgical

Staffed Beds: 146 Admissions: 8338 Census: 83 Outpatient Visits: 77572 Births: 1944 Total Expense ($000): 142464 Payroll Expense ($000): 51414 Personnel: 868

★ ◇ **HOUSTON METHODIST WILLOWBROOK HOSPITAL (450844)**, 18220 Tomball Parkway, Zip 77070–4347; tel. 281/477–1000 **A**3 5 9 10 21 **F**3 8 12 13 15 17 18 20 22 24 26 28 29 30 31 34 35 37 40 44 45 49 53 57 59 64 65 70 72 73 74 75 76 77 78 79 81 85 86 87 93 96 102 107 108 110 111 115 119 120 121 123 126 129 130 131 132 135 146 147 **S** Houston Methodist, Houston, TX
Primary Contact: Beryl O. Ramsey, FACHE, Chief Executive Officer
CHR: Sherene Thompson, Director Human Resources
Web address: www.methodisthealth.com
Control: Other not–for–profit (including NFP Corporation) **Service:** General Medical and Surgical

Staffed Beds: 241 Admissions: 14471 Census: 160 Outpatient Visits: 135798 Births: 3174 Total Expense ($000): 230599 Payroll Expense ($000): 83513 Personnel: 1336

Many Facility Codes have changed. Please refer to the AHA Guide Code Chart.   © 2014 AHA Guide

✠ **HOUSTON NORTHWEST MEDICAL CENTER (450638)**, 710 FM 1960 Road West, Zip 77090–3402; tel. 281/440–1000 **A**1 2 3 5 9 10 **F**3 8 11 12 13 15 18 20 22 24 26 28 29 30 31 34 40 42 43 45 46 49 50 54 59 64 65 70 72 74 75 76 77 78 79 81 82 84 85 86 87 89 91 92 93 96 102 107 108 109 110 111 112 113 114 115 116 117 118 119 126 129 130 132 135 144 145 146 147 148 **S** TENET Healthcare Corporation, Dallas, TX
Primary Contact: Timothy Puthoff, Chief Executive Officer
COO: Juan Fresquez, Chief Operating Officer
CFO: Bryan Forry, Chief Financial Officer
CIO: Ed Roberson, Director Information Systems
CHR: Melanie R. Webb, Director Human Resources
CNO: Cindy Henning, R.N., Chief Nursing Officer
Web address: www.hnmc.com
Control: Partnership, Investor–owned, for–profit **Service:** General Medical and Surgical

Staffed Beds: 339 **Admissions:** 14903 **Census:** 185 **Outpatient Visits:** 141549 **Births:** 3293 **Total Expense ($000):** 280388 **Payroll Expense ($000):** 82150 **Personnel:** 1192

☐ **INTRACARE NORTH HOSPITAL (454083)**, 1120 Cypress Station Drive, Zip 77090–3031; tel. 281/893–7200 **A**1 9 10 **F**5 98 99 100 101 103 104 105
Primary Contact: Terry Scovill, Chief Executive Officer
CFO: Fred Chan, Chief Financial Officer
CMO: Javier Ruiz, M.D., Medical Director
Web address: www.intracare.org
Control: Other not–for–profit (including NFP Corporation) **Service:** Psychiatric

Staffed Beds: 68 **Admissions:** 3171 **Census:** 59 **Outpatient Visits:** 61056 **Births:** 0 **Total Expense ($000):** 18785 **Payroll Expense ($000):** 8605 **Personnel:** 264

✠ **KINDRED HOSPITAL MIDTOWN**, 105 Drew Avenue, Zip 77006–1527; tel. 713/529–8922, (Nonreporting) **A**1 9 **S** Kindred Healthcare, Louisville, KY
Primary Contact: Robert Stein, Chief Executive Officer
Web address: www.khmidtown.com
Control: Corporation, Investor–owned, for–profit **Service:** Long–Term Acute Care hospital

Staffed Beds: 40

✠ **KINDRED HOSPITAL–HOUSTON (452023)**, 6441 Main Street, Zip 77030–1596; tel. 713/790–0500 **A**1 5 9 10 **F**1 3 29 30 70 75 77 85 107 130 148 **S** Kindred Healthcare, Louisville, KY
Primary Contact: Robert Stein, Chief Executive Officer
CFO: Sara Langlitz, Controller
Web address: www.khhouston.com/
Control: Corporation, Investor–owned, for–profit **Service:** Long–Term Acute Care hospital

Staffed Beds: 105 **Admissions:** 979 **Census:** 83 **Outpatient Visits:** 0 **Births:** 0 **Total Expense ($000):** 41573 **Payroll Expense ($000):** 17681 **Personnel:** 273

✠ **KINDRED HOSPITAL–HOUSTON NORTHWEST (452039)**, 11297 Fallbrook Drive, Zip 77065–4292; tel. 281/897–8114 **A**1 9 10 **F**1 3 29 49 57 64 70 77 85 87 107 114 130 148 **P**5 **S** Kindred Healthcare, Louisville, KY
Primary Contact: Larkin Virden, Chief Executive Officer
Web address: www.khhoustonnw.com/
Control: Corporation, Investor–owned, for–profit **Service:** Long–Term Acute Care hospital

Staffed Beds: 84 **Admissions:** 680 **Census:** 47 **Outpatient Visits:** 450 **Births:** 0 **Total Expense ($000):** 28595 **Payroll Expense ($000):** 10662 **Personnel:** 164

LYNDON B JOHNSON GENERAL HOSPITAL See Harris Health System

✠ **MEMORIAL HERMANN – TEXAS MEDICAL CENTER (450068)**, 6411 Fannin Street, Zip 77030–1501; tel. 713/704–4000, (Includes CHILDREN'S MEMORIAL HERMANN HOSPITAL, 6411 Fannin, Zip 77030; tel. 713/704–5437), (Total facility includes 8 beds in nursing home–type unit) **A**1 2 3 5 8 9 10 **F**3 7 12 13 15 16 17 18 19 20 21 22 23 24 25 26 27 28 29 30 31 32 34 35 36 37 40 41 43 44 45 46 47 48 49 50 51 55 56 57 58 59 60 61 64 68 70 72 73 74 75 76 77 78 79 81 82 84 85 86 87 88 89 90 91 92 93 96 97 100 102 107 108 109 110 111 113 114 115 116 117 118 119 120 121 123 124 126 128 129 130 131 132 135 137 138 139 141 142 144 146 147 148 **P**1 5 6 **S** Memorial Hermann Healthcare System, Houston, TX
Primary Contact: Craig Cordola, Chief Executive Officer
COO: Tom Flanagan, Chief Operating Officer
CFO: William Pack, Chief Financial Officer
CMO: Jeffrey Katz, M.D., Chief Medical Officer
CIO: David Bradshaw, Chief Information Officer
CHR: Vivian Kardow, Chief Human Resources Officer
Web address: www.mhhs.org
Control: Other not–for–profit (including NFP Corporation) **Service:** General Medical and Surgical

Staffed Beds: 897 **Admissions:** 34565 **Census:** 622 **Outpatient Visits:** 180181 **Births:** 4112 **Total Expense ($000):** 1021205 **Payroll Expense ($000):** 313572 **Personnel:** 4367

✠ **MEMORIAL HERMANN MEMORIAL CITY MEDICAL CENTER (450610)**, 921 Gessner Road, Zip 77024–2501; tel. 713/242–3000 **A**1 2 9 10 **F**3 12 13 15 18 20 22 24 26 28 29 30 31 34 35 37 40 41 43 46 49 51 56 57 59 60 65 70 72 74 75 76 77 78 79 80 81 82 84 85 87 89 107 108 110 111 114 115 117 118 119 120 121 123 124 126 129 130 131 132 135 146 147 148 **P**1 5 6 **S** Memorial Hermann Healthcare System, Houston, TX
Primary Contact: Keith N. Alexander, Chief Executive Officer
COO: Allen Tseng, Chief Operations Officer
CFO: Lisa Kendler, Chief Financial Officer
CMO: Harold Gottlieb, M.D., Chief Medical Officer
CIO: David Bradshaw, Chief Information, Planning and Marketing Officer
CHR: Suzanne S. Meier, System Director, Compensation and Human Resources Technology
CNO: Dan Kelly, R.N., Chief Nursing Officer
Web address: www.memorialhermann.org
Control: Other not–for–profit (including NFP Corporation) **Service:** General Medical and Surgical

Staffed Beds: 386 **Admissions:** 19434 **Census:** 223 **Outpatient Visits:** 226315 **Births:** 2963 **Total Expense ($000):** 384263 **Payroll Expense ($000):** 105002 **Personnel:** 1492

✠ **MEMORIAL HERMANN NORTHWEST HOSPITAL (450184)**, 1635 North Loop West, Zip 77008–1532; tel. 713/867–3380, (Includes MEMORIAL HERMANN SOUTHEAST HOSPITAL, 11800 Astoria Boulevard, Zip 77089–6041; tel. 281/929–6100; Erin Asprec, Chief Executive Officer; MEMORIAL HERMANN SOUTHWEST HOSPITAL, 7600 Beechnut, Zip 77074–1850; tel. 713/456–5000; Gary Kerr, Chief Executive Officer; MEMORIAL HERMANN THE WOODLANDS HOSPITAL, 9250 Pinecroft Drive, The Woodlands, Zip 77380–3225; tel. 281/364–2300) **A**1 2 3 5 9 10 **F**3 8 9 11 12 13 15 17 18 20 22 24 26 28 29 30 31 34 35 36 37 40 41 42 43 44 45 46 47 48 49 50 51 53 54 55 56 57 58 59 60 61 62 63 64 65 68 69 70 72 73 74 75 76 77 78 79 80 81 82 83 84 85 86 87 89 90 91 92 93 96 97 98 100 101 102 103 105 107 108 109 110 111 114 115 116 117 118 119 120 121 123 124 126 129 130 131 132 135 143 146 147 148 **P**1 5 6 **S** Memorial Hermann Healthcare System, Houston, TX
Primary Contact: Susan Jadlowski, MSN, R.N., Chief Executive Officer
COO: Wesley Tidwell, Chief Operating Officer
CFO: James R. Shallock, Chief Financial Officer
CMO: Maurice Leibman, M.D., Chief Medical Officer
CIO: David Bradshaw, Chief Information Officer
CNO: Melody Ford Dickerson, Chief Nursing Officer
Web address: www.mhbh.org
Control: Other not–for–profit (including NFP Corporation) **Service:** General Medical and Surgical

Staffed Beds: 1200 **Admissions:** 56666 **Census:** 714 **Outpatient Visits:** 485771 **Births:** 12074 **Total Expense ($000):** 967480 **Payroll Expense ($000):** 333281 **Personnel:** 4984

MEMORIAL HERMANN SOUTHEAST HOSPITAL See Memorial Hermann Northwest Hospital

MEMORIAL HERMANN SOUTHWEST HOSPITAL See Memorial Hermann Northwest Hospital

TX

Hospital, Medicare Provider Number, Address, Telephone, Approval, Facility, and Physician Codes, Health Care System

★ American Hospital Association (AHA) membership
☐ The Joint Commission accreditation
◇ DNV Healthcare Inc. accreditation
○ Healthcare Facilities Accreditation Program
△ Commission on Accreditation of Rehabilitation Facilities (CARF) accreditation

☐ **MENNINGER CLINIC**, 12301 Main Street, Zip 77035–6207; tel. 713/275–5000 **A**1 3 5 **F**30 35 98 99 101 104 106 130 132
Primary Contact: Ian Aitken, President and Chief Executive Officer
COO: Shawna Morris, Senior Vice President Operations and Chief Operating Officer
CFO: Kenneth Klein, CPA, Senior Vice President Finance and Chief Financial Officer
CMO: John M. Oldham, M.D., Senior Vice President and Chief of Staff
CIO: Kenneth Klein, CPA, Senior Vice President Finance and Chief Financial Officer
CHR: Shawna Morris, Senior Vice President Operations and Chief Operating Officer
Web address: www.menningerclinic.com
Control: Other not–for–profit (including NFP Corporation) **Service:** Psychiatric

> **Staffed Beds:** 102 **Admissions:** 831 **Census:** 92 **Outpatient Visits:** 1277 **Births:** 0 **Total Expense ($000):** 51436 **Payroll Expense ($000):** 22688 **Personnel:** 380

METHODIST WEST HOUSTON HOSPITAL See Houston Methodist West Hospital

METHODIST WILLOWBROOK HOSPITAL See Houston Methodist Willowbrook Hospital

⊠ △ **MICHAEL E. DEBAKEY VETERANS AFFAIRS MEDICAL CENTER**, 2002 Holcombe Boulevard, Zip 77030–4298; tel. 713/791–1414, (Nonreporting) **A**1 2 3 5 7 8 9 **S** Department of Veterans Affairs, Washington, DC
Primary Contact: Adam C. Walmus, Director
COO: Christopher Sandles, Associate Director
CFO: Alisa Cooper, Manager Financial Resources
CMO: Jagadeesh S. Kalavar, M.D., Chief of Staff
CIO: Kevin Lenamond, Information Management Service Line Executive
CHR: Mark Muhammad, Manager Human Resources
CNO: Kelly Ann Irving, MSN, RN–B, Associate Director for Patient Care Services
Web address: www.houston.va.gov
Control: Veterans Affairs, Government, federal **Service:** General Medical and Surgical

> **Staffed Beds:** 479

⊠ **PARK PLAZA HOSPITAL (450659)**, 1313 Hermann Drive, Zip 77004–7092; tel. 713/527–5000 **A**1 2 9 10 **F**3 12 15 18 20 22 29 31 34 35 40 45 49 50 56 57 59 70 74 78 79 81 85 92 107 108 110 111 114 115 118 119 120 121 123 129 130 132 146 147 148 **S** TENET Healthcare Corporation, Dallas, TX
Primary Contact: John Tressa, R.N., MSN, Chief Executive Officer
COO: Mary Jo Goodman, Chief Operating Officer
CMO: Robert Brown, M.D., Chief Medical Officer
CIO: Terry Janis, Assistant Vice President
CHR: Melanie R. Webb, Chief Human Resources Officer
CNO: Martha M. Smith, R.N., Chief Nursing Officer
Web address: www.parkplazahospital.com
Control: Partnership, Investor–owned, for–profit **Service:** General Medical and Surgical

> **Staffed Beds:** 157 **Admissions:** 4551 **Census:** 65 **Outpatient Visits:** 36427 **Births:** 309 **Total Expense ($000):** 88053 **Payroll Expense ($000):** 31695 **Personnel:** 493

⊠ **PLAZA SPECIALTY HOSPITAL (452046)**, 1300 Binz, Zip 77004–7016; tel. 713/285–1000 **A**1 9 10 **F**1 3 29 31 56 63 68 70 75 77 78 82 84 85 87 130 148 **P**8 **S** TENET Healthcare Corporation, Dallas, TX
Primary Contact: Steven Barr, R.N., MSN, Chief Executive Officer
CFO: Charles R. Handley, Chief Financial Officer
CMO: Wasae S. Tabibi, M.D., President Medical Staff
CIO: Steve Peacock, Assistant Vice President
Web address: www.plazaspecialtyhospital.com
Control: Corporation, Investor–owned, for–profit **Service:** Long–Term Acute Care hospital

> **Staffed Beds:** 39 **Admissions:** 346 **Census:** 26 **Outpatient Visits:** 0 **Births:** 0 **Total Expense ($000):** 21606 **Payroll Expense ($000):** 5662 **Personnel:** 74

☐ **PROMISE HOSPITAL OF HOUSTON (452043)**, 6160 South Loop East, Zip 77087–1010; tel. 713/640–2400 **A**1 9 10 **F**1 3 29 70 75 77 85 87 130 148 **S** Promise Healthcare, Boca Raton, FL
Primary Contact: Tom Omondi, Interim Chief Executive Officer
CFO: Betty Priestley, Manager Business Office
CMO: Alfred Louis, M.D., Chief Medical Staff
CHR: Laura Garza, Director Human Resources
Web address: www.promise–houston.com
Control: Corporation, Investor–owned, for–profit **Service:** Long–Term Acute Care hospital

> **Staffed Beds:** 25 **Admissions:** 230 **Census:** 15 **Outpatient Visits:** 0 **Births:** 0 **Total Expense ($000):** 9544 **Payroll Expense ($000):** 2996 **Personnel:** 53

QUENTIN MEASE HOSPITAL See Harris Health System

☐ **RELIANT NORTHWEST HOUSTON (673052)**, 20180 Chasewood Park Drive, Zip 77070–1436; tel. 281/205–5100 **A**1 9 10 **F**3 29 65 90 96 130 148
Primary Contact: Jeff Crawford, Chief Executive Officer
CNO: Stanley F. Kiebzak, R.N., Chief Nursing Officer
Web address: www.reliantnwhouston.com
Control: Partnership, Investor–owned, for–profit **Service:** Rehabilitation

> **Staffed Beds:** 60 **Admissions:** 859 **Census:** 27 **Outpatient Visits:** 0 **Births:** 0 **Total Expense ($000):** 12106 **Payroll Expense ($000):** 5116 **Personnel:** 130

RENAISSANCE HOSPITAL – HOUSTON See St. Anthony's Hospital

☐ **RIVERSIDE GENERAL HOSPITAL (450446)**, 3204 Ennis Street, Zip 77004–3299; tel. 713/526–2441 **A**1 10 **F**4 5 29 35 40 43 57 61 98 99 100 101 105 130 132 146 **P**5
Primary Contact: Pamela Cashaw, President
CFO: Manny Ignacio, Controller
Web address: www.riversidegeneral.org
Control: Other not–for–profit (including NFP Corporation) **Service:** Psychiatric

> **Staffed Beds:** 88 **Admissions:** 114 **Census:** 4 **Outpatient Visits:** 7 **Births:** 0 **Total Expense ($000):** 10662 **Payroll Expense ($000):** 4994 **Personnel:** 146

⊠ **SELECT SPECIALTY HOSPITAL–HOUSTON HEIGHTS (452049)**, 1917 Ashland Street, Zip 77008–3994; tel. 713/861–6161, (Includes SELECT SPECIALTY HOSPITAL–HOUSTON MEDICAL CENTER, 2130 West Holcombe, Zip 77030–1502; tel. 713/218–2300; Michael A. Anaya, FACHE, Chief Executive Officer; SELECT SPECIALTY HOSPITAL–HOUSTON WEST, 9430 Old Katy Road, Zip 77055; tel. 713/984–2273; Mitali Paul, Chief Executive Officer) **A**1 9 10 **F**1 3 29 34 45 50 57 59 60 64 70 85 87 91 130 148 **S** Select Medical Corporation, Mechanicsburg, PA
Primary Contact: Naman Mahajan, Chief Operating Officer
CFO: Traci Jameson, Manager Finance
CMO: Chi C. Mao, M.D., Medical Director
CHR: Pamela Simpson, Director Human Resources
Web address: www.selectspecialtyhospitals.com/company/locations/houstonheights.aspx
Control: Partnership, Investor–owned, for–profit **Service:** Long–Term Acute Care hospital

> **Staffed Beds:** 182 **Admissions:** 1453 **Census:** 113 **Outpatient Visits:** 1799 **Births:** 0 **Total Expense ($000):** 67762 **Payroll Expense ($000):** 29772 **Personnel:** 549

SELECT SPECIALTY HOSPITAL–HOUSTON MEDICAL CENTER See Select Specialty Hospital–Houston Heights

SELECT SPECIALTY HOSPITAL–HOUSTON WEST See Select Specialty Hospital–Houston Heights

☐ **SHRINERS HOSPITALS FOR CHILDREN–HOUSTON (453312)**, 6977 Main Street, Zip 77030–3701; tel. 713/797–1616 **A**1 3 5 10 **F**3 29 30 35 50 59 64 68 74 75 77 79 81 86 87 93 94 96 130 131 132 134 143 146 148 **S** Shriners Hospitals for Children, Tampa, FL
Primary Contact: David A. Ferrell, Regional Administrator
COO: Cathy Moniaci, Chief Operating Officer
CFO: Lona Pope, Director Fiscal Services
CMO: Douglas A. Barnes, M.D., Chief of Staff
CHR: Lynn Clements, Director Human Resources
Web address: www.shrinershospitalsforchildren.org/Hospitals/Locations/Houston.aspx
Control: Other not–for–profit (including NFP Corporation) **Service:** Children's orthopedic

> **Staffed Beds:** 40 **Admissions:** 469 **Census:** 8 **Outpatient Visits:** 6763 **Births:** 0 **Total Expense ($000):** 25363 **Payroll Expense ($000):** 12043 **Personnel:** 175

◇ **ST. ANTHONY'S HOSPITAL (450795)**, 2807 Little York Road, Zip 77093–3495; tel. 713/697–7777, (Nonreporting) **A**9 10 21
Primary Contact: Jason LeDay, Chief Executive Officer
COO: Nora Peralta, Chief Nursing Officer
CFO: John Lucia, Chief Financial Officer
CMO: Rafael Borges, M.D., Chief of Staff
CIO: Bill DuBrul, Director Information Technology
CHR: Cathy McCue, Director Human Resources
Web address: www.stanthonyshouston.com
Control: Partnership, Investor–owned, for–profit **Service:** General Medical and Surgical

> **Staffed Beds:** 39

Many Facility Codes have changed. Please refer to the AHA Guide Code Chart. © 2014 AHA Guide

TX

◇ **ST. JOSEPH MEDICAL CENTER (450035)**, 1401 St. Joseph Parkway, Zip 77002–8301; tel. 713/757–1000, (Total facility includes 18 beds in nursing home–type unit) **A**3 5 9 10 21 **F**3 11 12 13 15 18 20 22 24 26 29 30 31 34 35 40 42 43 47 49 50 51 53 55 57 58 59 60 64 68 70 72 74 75 76 77 78 79 81 82 84 85 86 87 90 93 94 97 98 101 102 103 105 107 108 110 111 114 115 116 117 118 119 121 123 124 126 128 129 130 131 132 135 143 144 146 147 148 **P**8 **S** IASIS Healthcare, Franklin, TN
Primary Contact: Mark L. Bernard, Chief Executive Officer
COO: Laura Fortin, R.N., Chief Operating Officer
CIO: Robin Brown, Chief Information Officer and Compliance Officer
CHR: Kris Clatanoff, Director Human Resources
Web address: www.sjmctx.com
Control: Partnership, Investor–owned, for–profit **Service:** General Medical and Surgical

Staffed Beds: 374 **Admissions:** 16060 **Census:** 227 **Outpatient Visits:** 111071 **Births:** 4673 **Total Expense ($000):** 196761 **Payroll Expense ($000):** 90812 **Personnel:** 1381

★ ◇ **ST. LUKE'S HOSPITAL – THE VINTAGE HOSPITAL (670075)**, 20171 Chasewood Park Drive, Zip 77070–1437; tel. 832/534–5000 **A**9 10 21 **F**3 11 12 13 15 18 20 22 24 26 29 30 34 35 40 45 49 50 57 59 60 64 68 70 72 75 76 77 79 81 82 85 87 107 108 110 111 114 115 118 119 130 146 147 **P**5 **S** Catholic Health Initiatives, Englewood, CO
Primary Contact: Norman F. Stephens, Chief Executive Officer
Web address: www.stlukesvintage.com/
Control: Church–operated, Nongovernment, not–for profit **Service:** General Medical and Surgical

Staffed Beds: 78 **Admissions:** 3241 **Census:** 36 **Outpatient Visits:** 25795 **Births:** 518 **Total Expense ($000):** 81098 **Payroll Expense ($000):** 25591 **Personnel:** 438

★ ◇ **ST. LUKE'S MEDICAL CENTER (450193)**, 6720 Bertner Avenue, Zip 77030–2697, Mailing Address: P.O. Box 20269, Zip 77225–0269; tel. 832/355–1000 **A**2 3 5 8 9 10 21 **F**3 11 14 15 17 18 20 22 24 26 28 29 30 31 34 35 36 39 40 42 44 45 46 47 48 49 50 51 54 56 57 58 59 60 61 64 65 66 68 70 71 74 75 76 77 79 81 82 84 85 86 87 90 91 92 96 97 100 107 108 110 111 114 115 116 117 118 119 120 121 123 124 126 129 130 132 135 137 138 139 140 142 145 146 147 148 **P**5 6 8 **S** Catholic Health Initiatives, Englewood, CO
Primary Contact: Wayne Keathley, M.P.H., President
CFO: William Brosius, Vice President and Chief Financial Officer
CIO: James Albin, Chief Information Officer
CHR: Susan Bailey–Newell, Vice President Human Resources
CNO: Karen K. Myers, MSN, Vice President and Chief Nursing Officer
Web address: www.stlukestexas.com
Control: Church–operated, Nongovernment, not–for profit **Service:** General Medical and Surgical

Staffed Beds: 690 **Admissions:** 26367 **Census:** 477 **Outpatient Visits:** 263510 **Births:** 0 **Total Expense ($000):** 763341 **Payroll Expense ($000):** 300871 **Personnel:** 3356

☐ **TEXAS CHILDREN'S HOSPITAL (453304)**, 6621 Fannin Street, Zip 77030–2399, Mailing Address: Box 300630, Zip 77230–0630; tel. 832/824–1000, (Includes TEXAS CHILDREN'S HOSPITAL WEST CAMPUS, 18200 Katy Freeway, Zip 77094–1285; tel. 832/227–1000) **A**1 3 5 8 9 10 **F**3 7 11 12 13 17 19 21 23 25 27 29 30 31 32 34 35 38 39 40 41 43 48 49 50 52 55 57 58 59 60 61 64 65 68 71 72 73 74 75 76 77 78 79 80 81 84 85 86 87 88 89 90 92 93 94 95 96 97 99 100 101 104 107 108 111 114 115 116 117 118 119 129 130 131 132 134 136 137 138 139 140 143 144 146 147 148
Primary Contact: Mark A. Wallace, President and Chief Executive Officer
CFO: Benjamin B. Melson, CPA, Executive Vice President and Chief Financial Officer
CMO: Mark W. Kline, M.D., Physician in Chief
CHR: Linda W. Aldred, Senior Vice President
Web address: www.texaschildrenshospital.org
Control: Other not–for–profit (including NFP Corporation) **Service:** Children's general

Staffed Beds: 592 **Admissions:** 31223 **Census:** 493 **Outpatient Visits:** 947639 **Births:** 5075 **Total Expense ($000):** 1343597 **Payroll Expense ($000):** 515229 **Personnel:** 6944

⊠ **TEXAS ORTHOPEDIC HOSPITAL (450804)**, 7401 South Main Street, Zip 77030–4509; tel. 713/799–8600 **A**1 3 5 9 10 **F**3 29 30 40 59 64 68 70 79 81 82 85 86 87 93 94 97 107 111 115 119 146 **S** HCA, Nashville, TN
Primary Contact: Trent Lind, Chief Executive Officer
CFO: Blair Callaway, Chief Financial Officer
CMO: Gregory Stocks, M.D., Chief of Staff
CNO: Troy Sarver, R.N., Chief Nursing Officer
Web address: www.texasorthopedic.com
Control: Partnership, Investor–owned, for–profit **Service:** Orthopedic

Staffed Beds: 49 **Admissions:** 3200 **Census:** 24 **Outpatient Visits:** 34033 **Births:** 0 **Total Expense ($000):** 73431 **Payroll Expense ($000):** 22815 **Personnel:** 373

THE METHODIST HOSPITAL See Houston Methodist Hospital

⊠ △ **TIRR MEMORIAL HERMANN (453025)**, 1333 Moursund Street, Zip 77030–3405; tel. 713/799–5000 **A**1 3 5 7 9 10 **F**11 29 30 34 35 44 50 52 54 58 59 60 64 68 74 75 77 79 82 86 87 90 91 93 95 96 97 100 104 107 114 119 129 130 131 132 146 148 **P**1 5 6 **S** Memorial Hermann Healthcare System, Houston, TX
Primary Contact: Carl E. Josehart, Chief Executive Officer
COO: Mary Ann Euliarte, R.N., Chief Operating Officer and Chief Nursing Officer
CFO: William Pack, Chief Financial Officer
CMO: Gerard E. Francisco, M.D., Chief Medical Officer
CIO: Gina Tripp, Director Information Systems
CHR: Vivian Kardow, Chief Human Resources Officer
CNO: Mary Ann Euliarte, R.N., Chief Operating Officer and Chief Nursing Officer
Web address: www.memorialhermann.org/locations/tirr.html
Control: Other not–for–profit (including NFP Corporation) **Service:** Rehabilitation

Staffed Beds: 119 **Admissions:** 1175 **Census:** 85 **Outpatient Visits:** 18322 **Births:** 0 **Total Expense ($000):** 79920 **Payroll Expense ($000):** 39203 **Personnel:** 670

TOPS SURGICAL SPECIALTY HOSPITAL (450774), 17080 Red Oak Drive, Zip 77090–2602; tel. 281/539–2900 **A**9 10 **F**3 15 29 37 39 40 45 51 64 68 79 81 85 91 107 110 111 114 119 142 **P**2 **S** United Surgical Partners International, Addison, TX
Primary Contact: Daniel Smith, Interim Chief Executive Officer
CFO: Daniel Smith, Chief Financial Officer
CMO: Thomas Barton, M.D., Medical Director
CIO: Maud Jones, Manager Medical Records
CHR: Ashley Monzingo, Human Resources, Accounts Payable and Payroll
CNO: Andrea Wappelhorst, Chief Nursing Officer
Web address: www.tops–hospital.com
Control: Partnership, Investor–owned, for–profit **Service:** General Medical and Surgical

Staffed Beds: 15 **Admissions:** 587 **Census:** 4 **Births:** 0 **Total Expense ($000):** 30523 **Payroll Expense ($000):** 8308 **Personnel:** 154

TRIUMPH HOSPITAL CENTRAL See Kindred Hospital Midtown

TRIUMPH HOSPITAL NORTHWEST See Kindred Hospital Spring

☐ **UNIVERSITY GENERAL HOSPITAL (670019)**, 7501 Fannin Street, Zip 77054–1938; tel. 713/375–7000 **A**1 9 10 **F**8 12 18 20 22 29 31 40 45 47 49 54 57 59 75 79 81 82 85 86 107 108 111 114 119 130 132 148 **S** University General Health System, Houston, TX
Primary Contact: David Kreye, Chief Executive Officer
Web address: www.ughospital.com
Control: Partnership, Investor–owned, for–profit **Service:** General Medical and Surgical

Staffed Beds: 69 **Admissions:** 3411 **Census:** 40 **Births:** 0 **Total Expense ($000):** 109582 **Payroll Expense ($000):** 28955 **Personnel:** 503

⊠ **UNIVERSITY OF TEXAS HARRIS COUNTY PSYCHIATRIC CENTER (454076)**, 2800 South MacGregor Way, Zip 77021–1000, Mailing Address: P.O. Box 20249, Zip 77225–0249; tel. 713/741–7870 **A**1 5 9 10 **F**29 30 34 35 57 58 68 75 86 87 98 99 100 101 103 106 130 146 **P**6 **S** University of Texas System, Austin, TX
Primary Contact: Jair C. Soares, M.D., Executive Director
COO: Stephen Glazier, Chief Operating Officer
CFO: Lois K. Pierson, Chief Financial Officer
CMO: R. Andrew Harper, M.D., Medical Director
CHR: Jill Strutton, Director Personnel Systems
CNO: Margaret Pung, R.N., Chief Nursing Officer
Web address: www.hcpc.uth.tmc.edu
Control: State–Government, nonfederal **Service:** Psychiatric

Staffed Beds: 204 **Admissions:** 8164 **Census:** 178 **Outpatient Visits:** 0 **Births:** 0 **Total Expense ($000):** 45102 **Payroll Expense ($000):** 29221 **Personnel:** 468

TX

✠ **UNIVERSITY OF TEXAS M.D. ANDERSON CANCER CENTER (450076)**, 1515 Holcombe Boulevard, Box 91, Zip 77030–4000; tel. 713/792–2121 **A**1 2 3 5 8 9 10 **F**3 8 11 14 15 18 20 26 29 30 31 32 34 35 36 37 38 39 40 44 45 46 47 49 50 54 55 57 58 59 60 63 64 66 68 70 71 74 75 77 78 79 80 81 82 83 84 85 86 87 88 89 92 93 94 96 97 99 100 101 102 104 107 108 110 111 112 114 115 117 118 119 120 121 122 123 124 126 129 130 132 134 135 136 141 145 146 147 148 **P**6 **S** University of Texas System, Austin, TX
Primary Contact: Ronald A. DePinho, M.D., President
CMO: Thomas Buchholz, M.D., Physician–in–Chief and Executive Vice President
CIO: Chris Belmont, Chief Information Officer and Vice President
CHR: Shibu Varghese, Vice President Human Resources
CNO: Barbara L. Summers, Ph.D., Vice President Nursing Practice and Chief Nursing Officer
Web address: www.mdanderson.org
Control: State–Government, nonfederal **Service:** Cancer

> **Staffed Beds:** 656 **Admissions:** 27905 **Census:** 555 **Outpatient Visits:** 1349956 **Births:** 0 **Total Expense ($000):** 3685644 **Payroll Expense ($000):** 1641513 **Personnel:** 19079

☐ **VICTORY MEDICAL CENTER HOUSTON**, 2001 Hermann Drive, Zip 77004–7643; tel. 713/285–5500 **A**1 **F**3 8 12 29 40 68 81 85 86 107 114 **S** Victory Healthcare, The Woodlands, TX
Primary Contact: Nicholas Crafts, Chief Executive Officer
Web address: www.victory–healthcare.com
Control: Hospital district or authority, Government, nonfederal **Service:** Surgical

> **Staffed Beds:** 25 **Admissions:** 471 **Census:** 3 **Outpatient Visits:** 2223 **Births:** 0 **Total Expense ($000):** 38287 **Payroll Expense ($000):** 6082 **Personnel:** 89

☐ **VICTORY SURGICAL HOSPITAL EAST HOUSTON**, 12950 East Freeway, Zip 77015–5710; tel. 713/330–3887, (Nonreporting) **A**1 **S** Victory Healthcare, The Woodlands, TX
Primary Contact: Steve Winnett, Chief Executive Officer
CFO: Carol Files, Chief Financial Officer
CMO: Ian Reynolds, Chief Medical Officer
CIO: Yobi Kasper, Chief Information Officer
CHR: Gabby Myers, Human Resources Director
CNO: Angelo Carrambas, Chief Clinical Officer
Web address: www.victory–healthcare.com/easthouston
Control: Other not–for–profit (including NFP Corporation) **Service:** Surgical

> **Staffed Beds:** 42

✠ **WEST HOUSTON MEDICAL CENTER (450644)**, 12141 Richmond Avenue, Zip 77082–2499; tel. 281/558–3444 **A**1 9 10 **F**3 11 12 13 15 18 20 22 24 26 28 29 30 31 39 40 42 45 46 47 48 49 50 51 56 57 59 60 64 70 73 74 75 76 77 78 79 80 81 82 85 90 93 96 98 102 103 107 110 111 115 116 117 118 119 121 124 129 130 132 145 146 147 148 **S** HCA, Nashville, TN
Primary Contact: Todd Caliva, Chief Executive Officer
CFO: Stanley K. Nord, Chief Financial Officer
CMO: Magdy Rizk, M.D., Chief of Staff
CIO: Sergio Almeida, Director Information Systems
CHR: Carol Melville, Director Human Resources
Web address: www.westhoustonmedical.com
Control: Partnership, Investor–owned, for–profit **Service:** General Medical and Surgical

> **Staffed Beds:** 238 **Admissions:** 11565 **Census:** 169 **Outpatient Visits:** 107576 **Births:** 2588 **Total Expense ($000):** 150304 **Payroll Expense ($000):** 68264 **Personnel:** 985

☐ **WEST OAKS HOSPITAL (454026)**, 6500 Hornwood Drive, Zip 77074–5095; tel. 713/995–0909 **A**1 3 5 9 10 **F**5 29 54 56 64 68 98 99 100 101 103 104 105 132 **S** Universal Health Services, Inc., King of Prussia, PA
Primary Contact: Gregory Drummond, Chief Executive Officer
CFO: Rob Tyler, Chief Financial Officer
CMO: Vernon Walling, M.D., Executive Medical Director
CIO: James Harmon, Network Administrator
CHR: Janice Webster, Director Human Resources
CNO: Israel Ahaine, Chief Nursing Officer
Web address: www.westoakshospital.com
Control: Corporation, Investor–owned, for–profit **Service:** Psychiatric

> **Staffed Beds:** 144 **Admissions:** 6105 **Census:** 110 **Outpatient Visits:** 25613 **Births:** 0 **Total Expense ($000):** 22666 **Payroll Expense ($000):** 13290 **Personnel:** 286

◇ **WESTBURY COMMUNITY HOSPITAL (670072)**, 5556 Gasmer Drive, Zip 77035–4502; tel. 713/422–2625 **A**9 10 21 **F**3 29 35 38 64 68 98 99 100 101 103 104 105 130
Primary Contact: Tim C. Simmons, Chief Executive Officer
Control: Corporation, Investor–owned, for–profit **Service:** Psychiatric

> **Staffed Beds:** 85 **Admissions:** 2865 **Census:** 52 **Outpatient Visits:** 43689 **Births:** 0 **Total Expense ($000):** 19609 **Payroll Expense ($000):** 9902 **Personnel:** 206

★ **WESTSIDE SURGICAL HOSPITAL**, 4200 Twelve Oaks Drive, Zip 77027; tel. 713/621–5010, (Data for 338 days) **F**3 15 20 29 35 40 45 64 75 79 81 82 85 86 107 119 126 131
Primary Contact: James Witt, Interim Chief Executive Officer
Control: Partnership, Investor–owned, for–profit **Service:** Surgical

> **Staffed Beds:** 12 **Admissions:** 202 **Census:** 2 **Outpatient Visits:** 2340 **Births:** 0 **Total Expense ($000):** 29853 **Payroll Expense ($000):** 5069 **Personnel:** 108

✠ **WOMAN'S HOSPITAL OF TEXAS (450674)**, 7600 Fannin Street, Zip 77054–1906; tel. 713/790–1234 **A**1 3 5 9 10 **F**3 7 13 15 29 30 34 40 46 50 53 58 68 70 72 73 75 76 77 81 85 86 87 93 107 108 110 111 118 119 126 130 132 146 147 **S** HCA, Nashville, TN
Primary Contact: Linda B. Russell, Chief Executive Officer
COO: Eric Evans, Chief Operating Officer
CFO: Scott Bentley, Chief Financial Officer
CMO: Eberhard Lotze, M.D., Chief Medical Officer
CIO: Emily Le, Director Information Technology and Services
CHR: Arnita Crawford, Director Human Resources
CNO: Andrea Harrow, Chief Nursing Officer
Web address: www.womanshospital.com
Control: Partnership, Investor–owned, for–profit **Service:** Obstetrics and gynecology

> **Staffed Beds:** 367 **Admissions:** 13997 **Census:** 218 **Outpatient Visits:** 45540 **Births:** 10094 **Total Expense ($000):** 168145 **Payroll Expense ($000):** 85501 **Personnel:** 1117

HUMBLE—Harris County

✠ **HEALTHSOUTH REHABILITATION HOSPITAL (453029)**, 19002 McKay Drive, Zip 77338–5701; tel. 281/446–6148 **A**1 9 10 **F**29 56 64 75 77 82 86 87 90 91 92 93 95 96 130 132 143 148 **S** HEALTHSOUTH Corporation, Birmingham, AL
Primary Contact: Angela L. Simmons, Chief Executive Officer
CFO: Sheila Shepard, Controller
CMO: Emile Mathurin, Jr., M.D., Medical Director
CHR: Christy Dixon, Chief Human Resources Officer
CNO: Anita L. Marban, R.N., Chief Nursing Officer
Web address: www.healthsouthhumble.com
Control: Corporation, Investor–owned, for–profit **Service:** Rehabilitation

> **Staffed Beds:** 60 **Admissions:** 1075 **Census:** 41 **Outpatient Visits:** 5550 **Births:** 0 **Total Expense ($000):** 14375 **Payroll Expense ($000):** 8233 **Personnel:** 156

✠ **ICON HOSPITAL (452112)**, 19211 McKay Boulevard, Zip 77338–5502; tel. 281/883–5500 **A**1 9 10 **F**1 3 29 40 45 64 77 82 85 107 114 119 130 146 148 **S** AcuityHealthcare, LP, Charlotte, NC
Primary Contact: Hilda Long, Chief Executive Officer
Web address: www.acuityhealthcare.net
Control: Partnership, Investor–owned, for–profit **Service:** Long–Term Acute Care hospital

> **Staffed Beds:** 32 **Admissions:** 521 **Census:** 34 **Outpatient Visits:** 508 **Births:** 0 **Total Expense ($000):** 19758 **Payroll Expense ($000):** 8786 **Personnel:** 159

✠ **KINDRED REHABILITATION HOSPITAL NORTHEAST HOUSTON (673051)**, 18839 McKay Road, Zip 77338–5721; tel. 281/964–6600 **A**1 9 10 **F**3 29 64 77 90 91 93 130 148 **S** Kindred Healthcare, Louisville, KY
Primary Contact: Reagan Simpson, Chief Executive Officer
CFO: Cheryl Csepke, Controller
CMO: Helen Schilling, M.D., Medical Director
CHR: Stephanie Williams, Coordinator Human Resources
CNO: Albert J. Chapple, R.N., Chief Clinical Officer
Web address: www.khrehabnortheasthouston.com
Control: Corporation, Investor–owned, for–profit **Service:** Rehabilitation

> **Staffed Beds:** 46 **Admissions:** 632 **Census:** 24 **Outpatient Visits:** 832 **Births:** 0 **Total Expense ($000):** 13802 **Payroll Expense ($000):** 5522 **Personnel:** 107

✠ **MEMORIAL HERMANN NORTHEAST (450684)**, 18951 North Memorial Drive, Zip 77338–4297; tel. 281/540–7700 **A**1 2 9 10 **F**3 11 12 13 15 18 20 22 29 30 31 34 35 36 37 40 42 45 46 49 53 54 56 57 59 64 70 72 73 74 75 76 77 78 79 80 81 85 86 87 89 93 107 108 109 110 111 114 115 119 120 121 123 126 129 130 131 132 135 146 147 148 **P**1 5 6 **S** Memorial Hermann Healthcare System, Houston, TX
Primary Contact: Louis G. Smith, Jr., Chief Executive Officer
COO: Heath Rushing, Chief Operating Officer
CFO: Rebecca Tucker, Chief Financial Officer
CMO: Susan Curling, M.D., Chief Medical Officer
CHR: Monica Baisden, Director Human Resources
CNO: Linda Stephens, R.N., Chief Nursing Officer
Web address: www.memorialhermann.org
Control: Other not–for–profit (including NFP Corporation) **Service:** General Medical and Surgical

> **Staffed Beds:** 227 **Admissions:** 10914 **Census:** 136 **Outpatient Visits:** 97653 **Births:** 1285 **Total Expense ($000):** 166003 **Payroll Expense ($000):** 60827 **Personnel:** 831

TX

Many Facility Codes have changed. Please refer to the AHA Guide Code Chart. © 2014 AHA Guide

HUNTSVILLE—Walker County

✠ **HUNTSVILLE MEMORIAL HOSPITAL (450347)**, 110 Memorial Hospital Drive, Zip 77340–4940, Mailing Address: P.O. Box 4001, Zip 77342–4001; tel. 936/291–3411 **A**1 9 10 **F**3 8 11 12 13 15 26 28 29 31 32 34 35 39 40 42 43 45 46 50 53 54 56 57 59 62 64 65 66 67 68 70 75 76 77 78 79 81 82 85 86 87 89 90 91 92 93 97 100 101 107 108 110 111 114 115 118 119 127 130 131 132 135 141 142 146 147 148
Primary Contact: Shannon Brown, Chief Executive Officer
CFO: Guy Gyros, Chief Financial Officer
CIO: Raul Velez, Director Information Systems
CHR: Brenda Ray, Director Human Resources
CNO: Sheila Ard, Chief Nursing Officer
Web address: www.huntsvillememorial.com
Control: Other not–for–profit (including NFP Corporation) **Service:** General Medical and Surgical

Staffed Beds: 97 **Admissions:** 4201 **Census:** 45 **Outpatient Visits:** 94859 **Births:** 439 **Total Expense ($000):** 71826 **Payroll Expense ($000):** 30090 **Personnel:** 463

HURST—Tarrant County

☐ **COOK CHILDREN'S NORTHEAST HOSPITAL (670045)**, 6316 Precinct Line Road, Zip 76054–2766; tel. 817/605–2500 **A**1 9 10 **F**3 39 40 41 45 48 64 68 79 81 85 89 107 111 114 119 144
Primary Contact: Jan Milligan, Chief Executive Officer
CMO: Christopher Mann, M.D., Medical Director
CNO: Jan Milligan, Chief Nursing Officer
Web address: www.cookchildrens.org/AboutUs/Companies/Pages/NortheastHospital.aspx
Control: Corporation, Investor–owned, for–profit **Service:** Children's general

Staffed Beds: 3 **Admissions:** 12 **Census:** 1 **Outpatient Visits:** 51189 **Births:** 0 **Total Expense ($000):** 12702 **Payroll Expense ($000):** 8848 **Personnel:** 162

☐ **VICTORY MEDICAL CENTER MID–CITIES (450886)**, 1612 Hurst Town Center Drive, Zip 76054–6236; tel. 817/345–4100 **A**1 9 10 **F**3 12 29 40 45 46 48 49 77 79 81 82 85 86 87 107 108 114 **S** Victory Healthcare, The Woodlands, TX
Primary Contact: Barbara Millwood, Chief Executive Officer
CFO: Michelle Brost, Financial Officer
CMO: Dale Brancel, D.O., Chief of Staff
CHR: Donna Irvin, Director Human Resources
Web address: www.victory–healthcare.com
Control: Partnership, Investor–owned, for–profit **Service:** Surgical

Staffed Beds: 16 **Admissions:** 482 **Census:** 2 **Outpatient Visits:** 1930 **Births:** 0 **Total Expense ($000):** 43815 **Payroll Expense ($000):** 7591 **Personnel:** 118

IRAAN—Pecos County

IRAAN GENERAL HOSPITAL (451307), 600 349 North, Zip 79744, Mailing Address: P.O. Box 665, Zip 79744–0665; tel. 432/639–2871 **A**9 10 18 **F**28 40 43 56 57 59 64 65 75 86 93 104 107 119 127 130 133
Primary Contact: Teresa Callahan, R.N., MSN, Chief Executive Officer
CFO: Tami Burks, Chief Fiscal Services
CMO: Robert W. Garcia, M.D., Chief Medical Officer
CHR: Cathy Tucker, Director Human Resources
Web address: www.igh–hospital.com
Control: Hospital district or authority, Government, nonfederal **Service:** General Medical and Surgical

Staffed Beds: 13 **Admissions:** 61 **Census:** 1 **Outpatient Visits:** 17571 **Births:** 0 **Total Expense ($000):** 6722 **Payroll Expense ($000):** 2758 **Personnel:** 47

IRVING—Dallas County

✠ **BAYLOR MEDICAL CENTER AT IRVING (450079)**, 1901 North MacArthur Boulevard, Zip 75061–2220; tel. 972/579–8100 **A**1 2 9 10 **F**3 11 12 13 15 17 18 20 22 24 26 28 29 30 31 34 35 40 45 46 47 49 54 55 57 58 59 64 65 70 73 74 75 76 77 78 79 80 81 82 84 85 86 87 90 93 94 98 100 107 108 110 111 114 115 116 117 118 119 120 121 122 126 129 130 141 143 146 147 148 **S** Baylor Scott & White Health, Dallas, TX
Primary Contact: Cindy K. Schamp, President
COO: Brenda K. Blain, FACHE, Chief Nursing Officer and Chief Operating Officer
CMO: Jeffrey Embrey, M.D., Vice President Medical Affairs
CIO: Catherine Shisler, Director Information Services
CHR: Donna Stark, Director Human Resources
CNO: Brenda K. Blain, FACHE, Chief Nursing Officer and Chief Operating Officer
Web address: www.baylorhealth.com/PhysiciansLocations/Irving/Pages/Default.aspx
Control: Other not–for–profit (including NFP Corporation) **Service:** General Medical and Surgical

Staffed Beds: 242 **Admissions:** 10483 **Census:** 138 **Outpatient Visits:** 104977 **Births:** 1971 **Total Expense ($000):** 187237 **Payroll Expense ($000):** 72562 **Personnel:** 1089

✠ **IRVING COPPELL SURGICAL HOSPITAL (450874)**, 400 West Interstate 635, Zip 75063; tel. 972/868–4000 **A**1 9 10 **F**3 29 39 40 51 64 68 75 81 87 100 107 111 112 114 119 **P**2 **S** United Surgical Partners International, Addison, TX
Primary Contact: Deonna Unell, Chief Executive Officer
CFO: Gabrielle Holland, Chief Financial Officer
CMO: Scott McGraw, M.D., Medical Director
Web address: www.ic–sh.com
Control: Partnership, Investor–owned, for–profit **Service:** General Medical and Surgical

Staffed Beds: 12 **Admissions:** 507 **Census:** 3 **Outpatient Visits:** 10554 **Births:** 0 **Total Expense ($000):** 33401 **Payroll Expense ($000):** 6755 **Personnel:** 86

✠ **LAS COLINAS MEDICAL CENTER (450822)**, 6800 North MacArthur Boulevard, Zip 75039–2422; tel. 972/969–2000 **A**1 9 10 **F**3 8 13 15 18 20 22 24 29 30 31 34 35 37 40 45 46 47 48 49 50 57 59 60 64 68 70 72 73 74 75 76 77 78 79 81 87 93 100 102 107 108 110 111 114 118 119 126 129 130 147 148 **S** HCA, Nashville, TN
Primary Contact: Daniela Decell, Chief Executive Officer
COO: Chip Zahn, Chief Operating Officer
CFO: Nick Galt, Chief Financial Officer
Web address: www.lascolinasmedical.com
Control: Corporation, Investor–owned, for–profit **Service:** General Medical and Surgical

Staffed Beds: 90 **Admissions:** 4936 **Census:** 47 **Outpatient Visits:** 53665 **Births:** 1681 **Total Expense ($000):** 75647 **Payroll Expense ($000):** 25305 **Personnel:** 384

JACKSBORO—Jack County

FAITH COMMUNITY HOSPITAL (450241), 717 Magnolia Street, Zip 76458–1111; tel. 940/567–6633 **A**9 10 20 **F**7 11 28 34 35 40 43 57 59 76 77 93 107 114 119 127 130 133 **P**6
Primary Contact: Frank Beaman, Administrator
CFO: James Bartlett, Chief Financial Officer
CMO: Sushil Chokshi, M.D., Chief Medical Officer
CIO: Bradlee Landis, Chief Information Officer
CHR: James Bartlett, Human Resources
CNO: Joy Henry, R.N., Director Nurses
Web address: www.faithcommunityhospital.com
Control: Hospital district or authority, Government, nonfederal **Service:** General Medical and Surgical

Staffed Beds: 17 **Admissions:** 175 **Census:** 2 **Outpatient Visits:** 18642 **Births:** 3 **Total Expense ($000):** 7612 **Payroll Expense ($000):** 3397 **Personnel:** 89

TX

Hospital, Medicare Provider Number, Address, Telephone, Approval, Facility, and Physician Codes, Health Care System

★ American Hospital Association (AHA) membership
☐ The Joint Commission accreditation   ◇ DNV Healthcare Inc. accreditation
○ Healthcare Facilities Accreditation Program
△ Commission on Accreditation of Rehabilitation Facilities (CARF) accreditation

JACKSONVILLE—Cherokee County

EAST TEXAS MEDICAL CENTER JACKSONVILLE (450194), 501 South Ragsdale Street, Zip 75766–2413; tel. 903/541–5000 **A**1 9 10 20 **F**3 8 11 13 15 18 26 29 34 35 37 39 40 43 45 50 57 59 64 65 70 75 76 79 81 82 85 97 107 108 110 111 115 119 127 129 145 146 147 148 **S** East Texas Medical Center Regional Healthcare System, Tyler, TX
Primary Contact: Jack R. Endres, JD, FACHE, Administrator
CFO: Phillip A. Caron, Chief Financial Officer
CMO: Sharlet Slough, D.O., Chief of Staff
CHR: Elysia Epperson, Director Human Resources
CNO: Jana Bateman, R.N., Chief Nursing Officer
Web address: www.etmc.org
Control: Other not-for-profit (including NFP Corporation) **Service:** General Medical and Surgical

Staffed Beds: 38 **Admissions:** 1741 **Census:** 15 **Outpatient Visits:** 79865 **Births:** 447 **Total Expense ($000):** 32986 **Payroll Expense ($000):** 10318 **Personnel:** 187

MOTHER FRANCES HOSPITAL – JACKSONVILLE (451319), 2026 South Jackson, Zip 75766–5822; tel. 903/541–4500 **A**1 9 10 18 **F**3 8 15 18 29 30 32 34 35 40 43 45 50 53 56 57 59 64 65 68 77 79 81 82 85 93 97 107 108 110 111 114 119 129 130 133 145 147 **P**5 6 7 8 **S** Trinity Mother Frances Hospitals and Clinics, Tyler, TX
Primary Contact: Thomas N. Cammack, Jr., Chief Administrative Officer
COO: Michael Lewis, Chief Operating Officer
CFO: Elizabeth Pulliam, Chief Financial Officer
CMO: Matthew Vierkant, M.D., President Medical Staff
CIO: Jeff Pearson, Chief Information Officer
CHR: Denise Abrams, Human Resources
CNO: Kerry F. Bolin, Chief Nursing Officer
Web address: www.tmfhs.org/jacksonville
Control: Other not-for-profit (including NFP Corporation) **Service:** General Medical and Surgical

Staffed Beds: 21 **Admissions:** 1096 **Census:** 9 **Outpatient Visits:** 69129 **Births:** 0 **Total Expense ($000):** 30893 **Payroll Expense ($000):** 7996 **Personnel:** 174

JASPER—Jasper County

CHRISTUS JASPER MEMORIAL HOSPITAL (450573), 1275 Marvin Hancock Drive, Zip 75951–4995; tel. 409/384–5461 **A**1 9 10 **F**3 11 13 15 29 30 34 40 43 50 51 57 59 64 70 76 77 79 81 82 83 89 90 107 111 119 127 130 135 146 **P**8 **S** CHRISTUS Health, Irving, TX
Primary Contact: Deborah Mecom, R.N., Administrator
COO: Mark Durand, Assistant Administrator Operations
CFO: Nikki Martin, Chief Financial Officer
CIO: Robert Jacobs, Regional Information Management Executive
CHR: Kay Powell, Director Human Resources
CNO: Deborah Mecom, R.N., Chief Nursing Officer
Web address: www.christusjasper.org
Control: Church-operated, Nongovernment, not-for profit **Service:** General Medical and Surgical

Staffed Beds: 50 **Admissions:** 1671 **Census:** 16 **Outpatient Visits:** 58926 **Births:** 386 **Total Expense ($000):** 26552 **Payroll Expense ($000):** 11296 **Personnel:** 188

JOURDANTON—Atascosa County

SOUTH TEXAS REGIONAL MEDICAL CENTER (450165), 1905 Highway 97 East, Zip 78026–1504; tel. 830/769–3515 **A**1 9 10 20 **F**3 11 13 15 18 20 29 30 34 35 39 40 43 45 57 59 64 68 70 75 76 77 79 81 82 85 93 107 108 110 111 114 119 127 129 130 132 133 144 146 147 148 **P**6 **S** Community Health Systems, Inc., Franklin, TN
Primary Contact: James R. Resendez, Chief Executive Officer
CFO: Gary Redmon, Chief Financial Officer
CIO: Rita S. Castillo, R.N., Chief Quality Officer and Risk Management
Web address: www.strmc.com
Control: Corporation, Investor-owned, for-profit **Service:** General Medical and Surgical

Staffed Beds: 67 **Admissions:** 1644 **Census:** 16 **Outpatient Visits:** 37406 **Births:** 260 **Total Expense ($000):** 32655 **Payroll Expense ($000):** 13148 **Personnel:** 259

JUNCTION—Kimble County

★ **KIMBLE HOSPITAL (451306)**, 349 Reid Road, Zip 76849–3049; tel. 325/446–3321 **A**9 10 18 **F**3 11 29 34 35 40 43 45 47 56 57 59 65 66 68 75 77 81 93 97 107 114 127 133 146 **S** Preferred Management Corporation, Shawnee, OK
Primary Contact: Steve Bowen, Administrator
COO: Teena Hagood, Chief Nursing Officer
CFO: Larry Stephens, Chief Financial Officer
CMO: Ben Udall, M.D., Chief of Staff
CIO: Anna Henry, Chief Information Officer
CHR: Hope Lamb, Manager Human Resources
Web address: www.kimblehospital.org/
Control: Corporation, Investor-owned, for-profit **Service:** General Medical and Surgical

Staffed Beds: 15 **Admissions:** 245 **Census:** 2 **Outpatient Visits:** 12434 **Births:** 0 **Total Expense ($000):** 6712 **Payroll Expense ($000):** 2733 **Personnel:** 65

KATY—Harris County

CHRISTUS ST. CATHERINE HOSPITAL See Houston Methodist St. Catherine Hospital

HOUSTON METHODIST ST. CATHERINE HOSPITAL (450832), 701 Fry Road, Zip 77450–2255; tel. 281/599–5700 **A**1 2 9 10 **F**3 11 12 13 15 17 18 29 30 34 35 40 54 57 59 61 64 69 70 75 76 77 78 79 81 82 84 86 87 89 90 93 107 108 110 111 114 115 117 119 124 129 130 131 132 135 146 147 148 **S** Houston Methodist, Houston, TX
Primary Contact: Gary L. Kempf, Administrator
CFO: Nancy Brock, Chief Financial Officer
CHR: James A. Fitch, Director Human Resources
Web address: www.houstonmethodist.org/katy-st-catherine-hospital
Control: Church-operated, Nongovernment, not-for profit **Service:** General Medical and Surgical

Staffed Beds: 102 **Admissions:** 3722 **Census:** 39 **Outpatient Visits:** 61971 **Births:** 942 **Total Expense ($000):** 77053 **Payroll Expense ($000):** 27524 **Personnel:** 451

MEMORIAL HERMANN KATY HOSPITAL (450847), 23900 Katy Freeway, Zip 77494–1323; tel. 281/644–7000 **A**1 9 10 **F**3 8 11 13 15 18 20 29 30 35 39 40 43 45 46 49 50 57 59 61 64 65 68 69 70 73 74 75 76 77 79 81 85 89 93 102 107 108 111 114 118 119 126 130 131 132 145 146 147 **P**1 5 6 **S** Memorial Hermann Healthcare System, Houston, TX
Primary Contact: Brian S. Barbe, Chief Executive Officer
CFO: Linda Kulhanek, Chief Financial Officer
Web address: www.memorialhermann.org/locations/katy/
Control: Other not-for-profit (including NFP Corporation) **Service:** General Medical and Surgical

Staffed Beds: 142 **Admissions:** 9227 **Census:** 86 **Outpatient Visits:** 81540 **Births:** 2455 **Total Expense ($000):** 139045 **Payroll Expense ($000):** 48959 **Personnel:** 635

MEMORIAL HERMANN REHABILITATION HOSPITAL – KATY (673038), 21720 Kingsland Boulevard, Zip 77450–2550; tel. 281/579–5555 **A**1 9 10 **F**3 29 64 79 90 92 93 107 111 114 119 130 131 148 **P**1 5 6 **S** Memorial Hermann Healthcare System, Houston, TX
Primary Contact: Carl E. Josehart, Chief Executive Officer
COO: Mary Ann Euliarte, R.N., Chief Operating Officer
CFO: Wayne Gordon, Chief Financial Officer
CMO: Shalin Patel, M.D., Chief Medical Officer
CIO: David Bradshaw, Chief Information Officer
CHR: Joyce Williams, Consultant Human Resources and Organizational Development
CNO: Mary Ann Euliarte, R.N., Chief Nursing Officer
Web address: www.memorialhermann.com
Control: Partnership, Investor-owned, for-profit **Service:** Rehabilitation

Staffed Beds: 35 **Admissions:** 601 **Census:** 23 **Outpatient Visits:** 10114 **Births:** 0 **Total Expense ($000):** 18127 **Payroll Expense ($000):** 6784 **Personnel:** 113

KAUFMAN—Kaufman County

TEXAS HEALTH PRESBYTERIAN HOSPITAL KAUFMAN (450292), 850 Ed Hall Drive, Zip 75142–1861, Mailing Address: P.O. Box 1108, Zip 75142–5401; tel. 972/932–7200 **A**1 9 10 **F**3 11 13 15 29 30 34 35 40 43 45 50 53 57 59 65 68 70 75 76 79 81 85 86 87 93 102 107 108 111 114 118 119 130 132 135 146 148 **P**5 **S** Texas Health Resources, Arlington, TX
Primary Contact: Patsy Youngs, President
CMO: Benjamin Bradshaw, M.D., President Medical Staff
CHR: Mark J. Rainey, Director Human Resources
CNO: Denise Claussen, R.N., Chief Nursing Officer
Web address: www.texashealth.org/Kaufman
Control: Other not-for-profit (including NFP Corporation) **Service:** General Medical and Surgical

Staffed Beds: 68 **Admissions:** 2189 **Census:** 19 **Outpatient Visits:** 71138 **Births:** 295 **Total Expense ($000):** 33308 **Payroll Expense ($000):** 13852 **Personnel:** 202

TX

KENEDY—Karnes County

★ **OTTO KAISER MEMORIAL HOSPITAL (451364)**, 3349 South Highway 181, Zip 78119–5247; tel. 830/583–3401 **A**9 10 18 **F**3 11 15 29 30 34 40 43 45 46 57 62 64 68 77 81 93 107 111 114 119 133 135 148 **P**8
Primary Contact: David Lee, Chief Executive Officer
CIO: Shaneece Pieprzyca, Director Information Technology
CHR: Christina Benavides, Director Employee Services
CNO: Vincent Sowell, Chief Nursing Officer
Web address: www.okmh.org/
Control: Hospital district or authority, Government, nonfederal **Service:** General Medical and Surgical

Staffed Beds: 25 **Admissions:** 425 **Census:** 6 **Outpatient Visits:** 27744 **Births:** 0 **Total Expense ($000):** 15515 **Payroll Expense ($000):** 6552 **Personnel:** 134	

KERMIT—Winkler County

WINKLER COUNTY MEMORIAL HOSPITAL (451314), 821 Jeffee Drive, Zip 79745–4696, Mailing Address: P.O. Box H., Zip 79745–6008; tel. 432/586–5864 **A**9 10 18 **F**3 32 34 36 40 57 59 64 65 69 93 97 107 114 119 127 133
Primary Contact: John Clark, Interim Administrator
CFO: Wannah Hartley, Controller
CMO: K. Pham, M.D., Chief of Staff
CIO: Keith Palmer, Assistant Administrator
Control: County–Government, nonfederal **Service:** General Medical and Surgical

Staffed Beds: 19 **Admissions:** 166 **Census:** 2 **Outpatient Visits:** 7435 **Births:** 0 **Total Expense ($000):** 8856 **Payroll Expense ($000):** 2982 **Personnel:** 69	

KERRVILLE—Kerr County

KERRVILLE DIVISION See South Texas Veterans Health Care System, San Antonio

☐ **KERRVILLE STATE HOSPITAL (454014)**, 721 Thompson Drive, Zip 78028–5154; tel. 830/896–2211 **A**1 3 5 10 **F**11 30 34 39 44 50 56 65 68 75 86 87 97 98 101 103 130 132 135 146 **S** Texas Department of State Health Services, Austin, TX
Primary Contact: Leigh Ann Fitzpatrick, Superintendent
CMO: Matthew Faubion, M.D., Clinical Director
CNO: Lee McGuire, Chief Nurse Executive
Web address: www.dshs.state.tx.us/mhhospitals/KerrvilleSH/default.shtm
Control: State–Government, nonfederal **Service:** Psychiatric

Staffed Beds: 202 **Admissions:** 82 **Census:** 185 **Outpatient Visits:** 0 **Births:** 0 **Total Expense ($000):** 38694 **Payroll Expense ($000):** 20301 **Personnel:** 549	

☒ **PETERSON REGIONAL MEDICAL CENTER (450007)**, 551 Hill Country Drive, Zip 78028–6085; tel. 830/896–4200 **A**1 9 10 19 **F**3 8 11 13 15 18 20 26 29 30 31 34 35 39 40 44 45 49 54 57 59 62 63 64 65 68 70 74 75 76 77 78 79 80 81 82 84 85 86 87 90 93 96 97 100 107 108 110 111 114 115 118 119 126 130 131 132 135 145 146 147 148 **P**1 6
Primary Contact: James Patrick Murray, FACHE, Chief Executive Officer
COO: Stephen Pautler, FACHE, Chief Operating Officer
CFO: Julie Johnson, Chief Financial Officer
CMO: Kerri Truelock, M.D., Chief of Staff
CIO: Richard Cruthirds, Director Information Systems
CHR: Buddy Volpe, Director Human Resources
CNO: Kaeli Dressler, R.N., Chief Nursing Officer
Web address: www.petersonrmc.com
Control: Other not–for–profit (including NFP Corporation) **Service:** General Medical and Surgical

Staffed Beds: 124 **Admissions:** 4768 **Census:** 59 **Outpatient Visits:** 139915 **Births:** 422 **Total Expense ($000):** 94814 **Payroll Expense ($000):** 39176 **Personnel:** 743	

KILGORE—Gregg County

◇ **ALLEGIANCE SPECIALTY HOSPITAL OF KILGORE (450488)**, 1612 South Henderson Boulevard, Zip 75662–3594; tel. 903/984–3505 **A**9 10 21 **F**3 29 34 35 56 59 98 101 103 104 130 **S** Allegiance Health Management, Shreveport, LA
Primary Contact: Sherry Bustin, Chief Executive Officer
CHR: Becky Wilson, Manager Human Resources
Web address: www.ahmgt.com
Control: Corporation, Investor–owned, for–profit **Service:** Psychiatric

Staffed Beds: 60 **Admissions:** 717 **Census:** 21 **Outpatient Visits:** 25261 **Births:** 0 **Total Expense ($000):** 8777 **Payroll Expense ($000):** 3910 **Personnel:** 159	

KILLEEN—Bell County

☒ **METROPLEX ADVENTIST HOSPITAL (450152)**, 2201 South Clear Creek Road, Zip 76549–4110; tel. 254/526–7523 **A**1 9 10 **F**3 8 11 12 13 15 18 20 22 26 28 29 30 34 35 39 40 43 45 46 48 49 54 57 59 62 65 68 70 71 74 75 76 77 78 79 81 82 83 85 86 87 89 91 93 98 99 100 101 102 103 104 105 107 108 110 111 114 115 118 119 129 130 131 132 135 146 147 148 **P**8
S Adventist Health System Sunbelt Health Care Corporation, Altamonte Springs, FL
Primary Contact: Carlyle L. E. Walton, FACHE, Chief Executive Officer
CFO: Penny Johnson, Chief Financial Officer
CMO: Frederick Barnett, M.D., Chief of Staff
CIO: Dale Koebnick, Director Management Information Systems and Patient Access
CHR: Brenda Coley, Executive Director
Web address: www.mplex.org
Control: Church–operated, Nongovernment, not–for profit **Service:** General Medical and Surgical

Staffed Beds: 177 **Admissions:** 6422 **Census:** 66 **Outpatient Visits:** 108505 **Births:** 1376 **Total Expense ($000):** 101178 **Payroll Expense ($000):** 40282 **Personnel:** 1000	

KINGSVILLE—Kleberg County

☒ **CHRISTUS SPOHN HOSPITAL KLEBERG (450163)**, 1311 General Cavazos Boulevard, Zip 78363–7130; tel. 361/595–1661 **A**1 9 10 20 **F**3 11 13 15 29 30 34 35 40 43 53 54 57 59 64 65 70 75 76 77 79 81 85 86 87 89 93 102 108 110 111 119 130 146 **S** CHRISTUS Health, Irving, TX
Primary Contact: David LeMonte, Vice President and Chief Operating Officer
CFO: Lauralinda Moore, Manager Finance
CHR: Candace Jefferson, Manager Human Resources
Web address: www.christusspohn.org
Control: Church–operated, Nongovernment, not–for profit **Service:** General Medical and Surgical

Staffed Beds: 79 **Admissions:** 3697 **Census:** 44 **Outpatient Visits:** 47339 **Births:** 327 **Total Expense ($000):** 39605 **Payroll Expense ($000):** 16603 **Personnel:** 236	

KINGWOOD—Montgomery County

☒ **KINGWOOD MEDICAL CENTER (450775)**, 22999 U.S. Highway 59 North, Zip 77339; tel. 281/348–8000 **A**1 9 10 **F**3 13 15 18 20 22 24 26 28 29 31 34 35 40 42 45 49 57 58 59 61 64 70 72 74 76 78 79 81 85 86 87 89 90 96 107 108 110 111 115 119 126 129 130 132 146 147 **P**7 **S** HCA, Nashville, TN
Primary Contact: Melinda Stephenson, Chief Executive Officer
COO: Megan Marietta, Chief Operating Officer
CFO: Daniel E. Davis, Chief Financial Officer
CMO: Eugene Ogrod, M.D., Chief Medical Officer
CNO: Lisa Hoyle, R.N., Chief Nursing Officer
Web address: www.kingwoodmedical.com
Control: Corporation, Investor–owned, for–profit **Service:** General Medical and Surgical

Staffed Beds: 262 **Admissions:** 15053 **Census:** 208 **Outpatient Visits:** 96536 **Births:** 2593 **Total Expense ($000):** 169600 **Payroll Expense ($000):** 65994 **Personnel:** 845	

☐ **KINGWOOD PINES HOSPITAL (454103)**, 2001 Ladbrook Drive, Zip 77339–3004; tel. 281/404–1001 **A**1 9 10 **F**4 5 29 75 86 87 98 99 101 103 104 105 130 132 **S** Universal Health Services, Inc., King of Prussia, PA
Primary Contact: James Burroughs, Chief Executive Officer
COO: Grey Mc Kellar, Chief Operating Officer and Director of Performance Improvement and Risk
CFO: Sharon Corum, Chief Financial Officer
CMO: Javier Ruiz, M.D., Medical Director
CNO: Kim Wheeler, R.N., Director of Nursing
Web address: www.kingwoodpines.com
Control: Corporation, Investor–owned, for–profit **Service:** Psychiatric

Staffed Beds: 116 **Admissions:** 4090 **Census:** 90 **Outpatient Visits:** 3444 **Births:** 0 **Total Expense ($000):** 20448 **Payroll Expense ($000):** 10148 **Personnel:** 203	

KINGWOOD SPECIALTY HOSPITAL See Memorial Hermann Surgical Hospital Kingwood

TX

☐ **MEMORIAL HERMANN SURGICAL HOSPITAL KINGWOOD (670005)**, 300 Kingwood Medical Drive, Zip 77339–6400; tel. 281/312–4000 **A**1 9 10 **F**3 29 40 45 51 64 68 79 81 82 85 86 87
Primary Contact: Teal Holden, Chief Executive Officer
Web address: www.memorialhermannkingwood.com
Control: Corporation, Investor–owned, for–profit **Service:** General Medical and Surgical

Staffed Beds: 10 **Admissions:** 174 **Census:** 1 **Outpatient Visits:** 6341
Births: 0 **Total Expense ($000):** 17809 **Payroll Expense ($000):** 4073
Personnel: 100

KNOX CITY—Knox County

KNOX COUNTY HOSPITAL (450746), 701 South Fifth Street, Zip 79529–2107, Mailing Address: P.O. Box 608, Zip 79529–0608; tel. 940/657–3535, (Total facility includes 56 beds in nursing home–type unit) **A**9 10 20 **F**7 11 28 34 40 43 57 59 62 127 133 **P**6
Primary Contact: Stephan A. Kuehler, Administrator
CFO: Dan Offutt, Manager Finance
CMO: Kevin Finley, D.O., Chief of Staff
CIO: Sue Marion, Manager Business Office
CNO: Sheila Kuehler, R.N., Director of Nursing
Web address: www.knoxcountyhospital–texas.com
Control: Hospital district or authority, Government, nonfederal **Service:** General Medical and Surgical

Staffed Beds: 70 **Admissions:** 173 **Census:** 35 **Outpatient Visits:** 34800
Births: 0 **Total Expense ($000):** 8712 **Payroll Expense ($000):** 3825
Personnel: 117

KYLE—Hays County

✣ **SETON MEDICAL CENTER HAYS (670056)**, 6001 Kyle Parkway, Zip 78640–6112, Mailing Address: 6001 Kyle Prkway, Zip 78640–6112; tel. 512/504–5000 **A**1 3 5 9 10 **F**3 11 13 15 18 20 22 24 28 29 30 31 34 35 40 43 44 45 46 49 50 57 60 64 65 68 70 72 74 75 76 77 78 79 81 82 85 87 107 108 110 111 114 115 118 119 129 130 131 135 146 148 **P**3 8 **S** Ascension Health, Saint Louis, MO
Primary Contact: Christopher L. Hartle, President
COO: Neal Kelley, Vice President and Chief Operating Officer
Web address: www.seton.net/locations/seton_medical_center_hays/
Control: Church–operated, Nongovernment, not–for profit **Service:** General Medical and Surgical

Staffed Beds: 96 **Admissions:** 6037 **Census:** 71 **Outpatient Visits:** 49090
Births: 735 **Total Expense ($000):** 102987 **Payroll Expense ($000):** 34939
Personnel: 637

LA GRANGE—Fayette County

★ **ST. MARK'S MEDICAL CENTER (670004)**, One St. Mark's Place, Zip 78945; tel. 979/242–2200 **A**3 5 9 10 **F**3 8 11 12 13 15 17 29 30 34 40 43 45 50 56 57 59 68 70 74 75 76 79 81 82 84 85 87 89 93 107 110 111 114 119 128 129 130 133 145 146 147 **P**6 **S** Community Hospital Corporation, Plano, TX
Primary Contact: Shane Kernell, Chief Executive Officer
COO: Carol Drozd, Chief Operating Officer
CFO: Dennis Boyd, Chief Financial Officer
CMO: Russell Juno, M.D., Chief of Staff
CHR: Tammy Oehlke, Director Human Resources
Web address: www.smmctx.org
Control: Other not–for–profit (including NFP Corporation) **Service:** General Medical and Surgical

Staffed Beds: 44 **Admissions:** 1931 **Census:** 17 **Outpatient Visits:** 52829
Births: 243 **Total Expense ($000):** 26023 **Payroll Expense ($000):** 10405
Personnel: 186

LAKE JACKSON—Brazoria County

✣ **BRAZOSPORT REGIONAL HEALTH SYSTEM (450072)**, 100 Medical Drive, Zip 77566–5674; tel. 979/297–4411 **A**1 2 9 10 **F**3 11 12 13 15 18 20 22 28 29 30 31 34 37 40 41 43 45 47 48 49 50 51 57 59 60 62 64 65 68 70 74 75 76 78 79 81 82 85 86 87 89 90 91 93 94 107 108 110 111 114 117 118 119 120 121 123 129 130 131 132 146 147 148 **P**8 **S** QHR, Brentwood, TN
Primary Contact: Al Guevara, FACHE, President and Chief Executive Officer
CFO: Chuck Jeffress, Vice President Fiscal Services
CMO: Michael Gilliand, M.D., Chief of Staff
CIO: Todd Edwards, Director Information Management Systems
CHR: Christopher Calia, Director Human Resources
CNO: Jerrie Patterson, Chief Nursing Officer
Web address: www.brhstx.org
Control: Other not–for–profit (including NFP Corporation) **Service:** General Medical and Surgical

Staffed Beds: 103 **Admissions:** 4796 **Census:** 51 **Outpatient Visits:** 147708
Births: 645 **Total Expense ($000):** 76504 **Payroll Expense ($000):** 30268
Personnel: 576

LAKEWAY—Travis County

✣ **LAKEWAY REGIONAL MEDICAL CENTER (670079)**, 100 Medical Parkway, Zip 78738–5621; tel. 512/571–5000 **A**1 9 10 **F**3 13 15 17 18 20 22 24 29 30 34 38 40 45 46 49 50 51 54 57 59 60 64 69 70 72 74 75 76 78 79 81 82 85 86 87 91 92 93 107 108 110 111 115 116 117 118 119 129 130 146 147 148 **P**6
Primary Contact: Susan MacLeod, Chief Executive Officer
CFO: Thomas Marshall, Chief Financial Officer
CIO: Matt Pace, Information Technology Director
CHR: Ron Morrison, Chief Human Resources Officer
CNO: Laura L. Miller, MSN, Chief Nursing Officer
Web address: www.lakewayregional.com
Control: Corporation, Investor–owned, for–profit **Service:** General Medical and Surgical

Staffed Beds: 48 **Admissions:** 1721 **Census:** 18 **Outpatient Visits:** 17384
Births: 229 **Total Expense ($000):** 83149 **Payroll Expense ($000):** 17870
Personnel: 295

LAMESA—Dawson County

MEDICAL ARTS HOSPITAL (450489), 2200 North Bryan Avenue, Zip 79331–2451; tel. 806/872–2183 **A**9 10 20 **F**3 11 13 28 29 30 35 40 43 45 50 57 59 62 64 75 76 81 87 93 97 107 111 114 119 127 130 133 146 148 **P**6
Primary Contact: Letha Stokes, Chief Executive Officer
COO: JoBeth Smith, Chief Operating Officer and Director of Human Resources
CFO: Jeff Weaver, Chief Financial Officer
CMO: Mark Key, M.D., Chief of Staff
CHR: Traci Brown, Human Resources Generalist
CNO: Heidi Cobb, R.N., Chief Nursing Officer
Web address: www.medicalartshospital.org
Control: Hospital district or authority, Government, nonfederal **Service:** General Medical and Surgical

Staffed Beds: 22 **Admissions:** 401 **Census:** 4 **Outpatient Visits:** 72180
Births: 101 **Total Expense ($000):** 22425 **Payroll Expense ($000):** 7794
Personnel: 208

LAMPASAS—Lampasas County

✣ **ROLLINS–BROOK COMMUNITY HOSPITAL (451323)**, 608 North Key Avenue, Zip 76550–1106, Mailing Address: P.O. Box 589, Zip 76550–0032; tel. 512/556–3682 **A**1 9 10 18 **F**3 8 15 29 35 40 43 45 46 61 81 85 87 93 97 107 110 111 114 119 130 131 133 146 **P**4 8 **S** Adventist Health System Sunbelt Health Care Corporation, Altamonte Springs, FL
Primary Contact: Ashley Underwood, Administrator and Director of Nursing
CFO: Robert Brock, Chief Financial Officer and Vice President
CMO: Don Daniels, M.D., Chief Medical Officer
CIO: Carl Elkins, Director Information Technology
CHR: Brenda Coley, Executive Director
CNO: Tammy Rodriguez, Vice President of Patient Care Services
Web address: www.mplex.org
Control: Church–operated, Nongovernment, not–for profit **Service:** General Medical and Surgical

Staffed Beds: 35 **Admissions:** 726 **Census:** 10 **Outpatient Visits:** 18043
Births: 0 **Total Expense ($000):** 13587 **Payroll Expense ($000):** 4560
Personnel: 81

LANCASTER—Dallas County

◇ **CRESCENT MEDICAL CENTER LANCASTER**, 2600 West Pleasant Run Road, Zip 75146–1114; tel. 972/230–8888, (Nonreporting) **A**21
Primary Contact: Susie Elder, Interim Chief Executive Officer
Control: Partnership, Investor–owned, for–profit **Service:** General Medical and Surgical

Staffed Beds: 84

LAREDO—Webb County

☐ **DOCTORS HOSPITAL OF LAREDO (450643)**, 10700 McPherson Road, Zip 78045–6268; tel. 956/523–2000 **A**1 2 9 10 **F**3 11 12 13 15 18 20 22 26 29 30 31 32 34 37 39 40 43 45 48 49 50 54 57 59 60 63 64 70 71 72 74 75 76 77 78 79 81 85 87 89 90 91 93 107 108 111 114 119 121 129 130 132 146 147 148 **P**5 **S** Universal Health Services, Inc., King of Prussia, PA
Primary Contact: Rene Lopez, Chief Executive Officer
COO: Eladio Montalvo, Chief Operating Officer
CFO: Jorge Latibeaudiere, Chief Financial Officer
CMO: Ralph Nimchan, M.D., Chief of Staff
CIO: Maribel Mata, Director Information Services
CHR: Roseann Figueroa, Director Human Resources
CNO: Daniel Cabrera, Chief Nursing Officer
Web address: www.doctorshoslaredo.com
Control: Partnership, Investor–owned, for–profit **Service:** General Medical and Surgical

Staffed Beds: 183 **Admissions:** 8023 **Census:** 96 **Outpatient Visits:** 96505
Births: 2641 **Total Expense ($000):** 83917 **Payroll Expense ($000):** 34661
Personnel: 621

Many Facility Codes have changed. Please refer to the AHA Guide Code Chart. © 2014 AHA Guide

✠ **LAREDO MEDICAL CENTER (450029)**, 1700 East Saunders Avenue, Zip 78041–5474, Mailing Address: P.O. Box 2068, Zip 78044–2068; tel. 956/796–5000, (Total facility includes 18 beds in nursing home–type unit) **A**1 9 10 **F**3 8 11 12 13 15 18 20 22 24 26 28 29 30 31 34 37 40 43 45 46 49 50 51 53 54 56 57 59 60 64 68 70 72 74 75 76 77 78 79 81 85 86 87 89 90 91 92 93 96 107 108 110 111 114 119 120 121 123 128 132 135 146 147 148 **S** Community Health Systems, Inc., Franklin, TN
Primary Contact: Timothy E. Schmidt, Chief Executive Officer
COO: John E. Ulbricht, Chief Operating Officer
CFO: Ed Romero, Chief Financial Officer
CIO: Joe Rivera, Chief Information Technology Officer
Web address: www.laredomedical.com
Control: Corporation, Investor–owned, for–profit **Service:** General Medical and Surgical

Staffed Beds: 326 Admissions: 15795 Census: 221 Outpatient Visits: 171896 Births: 3465 Total Expense ($000): 264054 Payroll Expense ($000): 56016 Personnel: 1299

☐ **LAREDO SPECIALTY HOSPITAL (452096)**, 2005 Bustamente Street, Zip 78041–5470; tel. 956/753–5353 **A**1 10 **F**3 29 30 70 75 77 85 91 96 130 148 **S** Ernest Health, Inc., Albuquerque, NM
Primary Contact: Mario Rodriguez, Chief Executive Officer
CFO: Robert Voss, Chief Financial Officer
CMO: Marisa Guerrero, Director Human Resources
Web address: www.lsh.ernesthealth.com
Control: Partnership, Investor–owned, for–profit **Service:** General Medical and Surgical

Staffed Beds: 60 Admissions: 490 Census: 34 Outpatient Visits: 0 Births: 0 Total Expense ($000): 18349 Payroll Expense ($000): 7290 Personnel: 149

LEAGUE CITY—Galveston County

☐ **DEVEREUX TEXAS TREATMENT NETWORK (454085)**, 1150 Devereux Drive, Zip 77573–2043; tel. 281/335–1000 **A**1 9 10 **F**4 5 29 32 35 38 53 54 59 64 75 86 87 98 99 100 101 102 103 104 105 106 130 132 134 **S** Devereux, Villanova, PA
Primary Contact: Pamela E. Helm, Executive Director
Web address: www.devereux.org
Control: Other not–for–profit (including NFP Corporation) **Service:** Children's hospital psychiatric

Staffed Beds: 39 Admissions: 321 Census: 51 Outpatient Visits: 3652 Births: 0 Total Expense ($000): 10009 Payroll Expense ($000): 3384 Personnel: 65

LEVELLAND—Hockley County

★ **COVENANT HOSPITAL–LEVELLAND (450755)**, 1900 South College Avenue, Zip 79336–6508; tel. 806/894–4963 **A**9 10 **F**11 13 15 29 30 34 40 43 45 50 54 57 59 64 65 68 75 76 77 81 82 85 86 87 89 90 91 93 97 107 110 111 114 115 119 127 130 133 146 **P**4 **S** Covenant Health System, Lubbock, TX
Primary Contact: Bruce White, Administrator
CFO: Newman Wheeler, Chief Financial Officer and Chief Operating Officer
CMO: Harry Weaver, M.D., Chief of Staff
CIO: Kevin Elmore, Chief Information Officer
CHR: Tammy Franklin, Manager Personnel and Marketing
CNO: Connie Thomman, Director of Nursing
Web address: www.covenanthospitallevelland.com/
Control: Church–operated, Nongovernment, not–for profit **Service:** General Medical and Surgical

Staffed Beds: 22 Admissions: 1266 Census: 9 Outpatient Visits: 41301 Births: 290 Total Expense ($000): 20193 Payroll Expense ($000): 7976 Personnel: 188

LEWISVILLE—Denton County

✠ **MEDICAL CENTER OF LEWISVILLE (450669)**, 500 West Main, Zip 75057–3699; tel. 972/420–1000 **A**1 9 10 **F**3 13 15 18 20 22 24 26 28 29 30 31 34 35 40 42 43 46 49 50 56 57 59 68 70 72 74 75 76 78 79 81 85 87 89 90 93 96 107 108 110 111 114 118 119 129 130 131 132 135 146 147 148 **S** HCA, Nashville, TN
Primary Contact: Ashley McClellan, Chief Executive Officer
COO: James G. Russell, Chief Operating Officer
CFO: Lisa Brodbeck, Chief Financial Officer
CIO: Shirley Archambeault, Chief Information Officer
CHR: Dara Biegert, Vice President Human Resources
CNO: Lynn O'Neill, R.N., Chief Nursing Officer
Web address: www.lewisvillemedical.com
Control: Corporation, Investor–owned, for–profit **Service:** General Medical and Surgical

Staffed Beds: 166 Admissions: 7262 Census: 90 Outpatient Visits: 67452 Births: 1291 Total Expense ($000): 126763 Payroll Expense ($000): 47102 Personnel: 677

LIBERTY—Liberty County

☐ **LIBERTY DAYTON REGIONAL MEDICAL CENTER (451375)**, 1353 North Travis, Zip 77575–3549; tel. 936/336–7316 **A**1 9 10 18 **F**3 29 40 45 64 81 85 107 115 119 130 133
Primary Contact: James E. Koulovatos, Chief Executive Officer
CFO: Hal Mayo, Chief Financial Officer
CMO: Don Callens, M.D., Chief Medical Officer
CNO: Mark Nichols, R.N., Director of Nurses
Web address: www.libertydaytonrmc.com
Control: Other not–for–profit (including NFP Corporation) **Service:** General Medical and Surgical

Staffed Beds: 14 Admissions: 286 Census: 2 Outpatient Visits: 14363 Births: 0 Total Expense ($000): 7743 Payroll Expense ($000): 3623 Personnel: 74

LITTLEFIELD—Lamb County

★ **LAMB HEALTHCARE CENTER (450698)**, 1500 South Sunset, Zip 79339–4899; tel. 806/385–6411 **A**9 10 20 **F**13 29 35 40 43 45 57 59 64 66 75 76 81 86 87 89 107 114 119 127 132 133 134 147 **P**6
Primary Contact: Jo Nell Wischkaemper, Administrator and Chief Executive Officer
CFO: Cindy Klein, Chief Financial Officer
CMO: Isabel Molina, M.D., Chief Medical Officer
CHR: Joan Williams, Administrative Assistant/Human Resources
CNO: Stacie Styron, Chief Nursing Officer
Control: County–Government, nonfederal **Service:** General Medical and Surgical

Staffed Beds: 41 Admissions: 427 Census: 5 Outpatient Visits: 20599 Births: 96 Total Expense ($000): 11771 Payroll Expense ($000): 4158 Personnel: 134

LIVINGSTON—Polk County

☐ **MEMORIAL MEDICAL CENTER – LIVINGSTON (450395)**, 1717 Highway 59 Bypass, Zip 77351–1257, Mailing Address: P.O. Box 1257, Zip 77351–0022; tel. 936/329–8700 **A**1 9 10 **F**3 11 13 15 29 34 35 40 43 45 46 50 57 59 62 64 68 70 74 75 76 79 81 85 87 89 107 108 110 111 114 119 129 130 132 146 **S** Memorial Health System of East Texas, Lufkin, TX
Primary Contact: Randy Slack, Interim Chief Executive Officer
CFO: Ken Miller, Chief Financial Officer
CMO: Shane Shaw, M.D., Chief of Staff
CIO: Mark Clifton, Interim Chief Financial Officer
CHR: Donald Morris, System Vice President Human Resources
CNO: Jacqueline Gordon, R.N., Chief Nursing Officer
Web address: www.memorialhealth.org
Control: Other not–for–profit (including NFP Corporation) **Service:** General Medical and Surgical

Staffed Beds: 66 Admissions: 2758 Census: 26 Outpatient Visits: 50408 Births: 454 Total Expense ($000): 43586 Payroll Expense ($000): 17873 Personnel: 286

LLANO—Llano County

★ **SCOTT & WHITE HOSPITAL – LLANO (450219)**, 200 West Ollie Street, Zip 78643–2628; tel. 325/247–5040 **A**5 9 10 20 **F**3 7 11 12 13 15 32 34 35 40 43 45 57 59 75 76 77 79 81 85 87 93 107 114 119 127 129 130 135 146 **P**6 **S** Baylor Scott & White Health, Dallas, TX
Primary Contact: Eric N. Looper, Chief Executive Officer
COO: Linda Meredith, MSN, Chief Operating Officer
CFO: Jason Cole, Director Finance
CMO: Kim Russell, M.D., Chief of Staff
CIO: Rodney Lott, Director Management Information Systems and Facility Operations
CHR: Pearl Oestreich, Director Human Resources
CNO: Reta Hunt, Director of Nursing
Web address: www.llanomemorial.org
Control: Other not–for–profit (including NFP Corporation) **Service:** General Medical and Surgical

Staffed Beds: 22 Admissions: 706 Census: 5 Outpatient Visits: 116658 Births: 219 Total Expense ($000): 33707 Payroll Expense ($000): 19107 Personnel: 340

TX

LOCKNEY—Floyd County

★ **W. J. MANGOLD MEMORIAL HOSPITAL (451337)**, 320 North Main Street, Zip 79241–0037, Mailing Address: Box 37, Zip 79241–0037; tel. 806/652–3373 **A**9 10 18 **F**1 3 4 13 16 17 35 40 43 45 53 57 59 62 64 65 67 70 72 73 76 80 81 85 88 90 93 97 98 107 111 119 127 128 130 133 148 **P**4
Primary Contact: Larry Mullins, Chief Executive Officer
CFO: Alyssa McCarter, Chief Financial Officer
CMO: Kevin T. Stennett, M.D., Chief of Staff
CIO: Sam Vanderbeek, Chief Information Officer
CHR: Janice Yearwood, Director Human Resources
CNO: Billie Hendrix, R.N., Director of Nursing
Web address: www.mangoldmemorial.org
Control: Hospital district or authority, Government, nonfederal **Service:** General Medical and Surgical

> **Staffed Beds:** 25 **Admissions:** 546 **Census:** 6 **Outpatient Visits:** 31665 **Births:** 50 **Total Expense ($000):** 10360 **Payroll Expense ($000):** 4671 **Personnel:** 124

LONGVIEW—Gregg County

☐ **BEHAVIORAL HOSPITAL OF LONGVIEW (454105)**, 22 Bermuda Lane, Zip 75605–2902; tel. 903/291–3456 **A**1 9 10 **F**98 100 101 130 **P**6
Primary Contact: Andre Deshong, Administrator
Web address: www.longviewhospital.com
Control: Corporation, Investor–owned, for–profit **Service:** Psychiatric

> **Staffed Beds:** 60 **Admissions:** 855 **Census:** 38 **Outpatient Visits:** 0 **Births:** 0 **Total Expense ($000):** 8794 **Payroll Expense ($000):** 4903 **Personnel:** 109

⊞ △ **GOOD SHEPHERD MEDICAL CENTER (450037)**, 700 East Marshall Avenue, Zip 75601–5580; tel. 903/315–2000 **A**1 7 9 10 **F**3 7 11 12 13 15 18 20 22 24 26 28 29 30 31 32 34 35 37 40 42 43 45 46 49 50 51 53 54 56 57 59 60 61 63 64 68 70 71 72 73 74 75 76 77 78 79 80 81 82 84 85 86 87 89 90 92 93 97 102 107 108 111 114 115 118 119 129 130 131 132 135 143 144 146 147 148 **P**8 **S** Good Shepherd Health System, Longview, TX
Primary Contact: Steve Altmiller, President and Chief Executive Officer
CFO: Tim Pileggi, Interim Chief Financial Officer
CMO: Larry Verfurth, D.O., Chief Medical Officer and Senior Vice President
CIO: Chris Blakemore, Interim Chief Information Officer
CHR: Ginger Morrow, Executive Vice President Human Resources
CNO: Patti Bennett, Chief Nursing Officer and Senior Vice President
Web address: www.gsmc.org
Control: Other not–for–profit (including NFP Corporation) **Service:** General Medical and Surgical

> **Staffed Beds:** 399 **Admissions:** 18901 **Census:** 244 **Outpatient Visits:** 192539 **Births:** 2386 **Total Expense ($000):** 276415 **Payroll Expense ($000):** 97869 **Personnel:** 1420

⊞ **LONGVIEW REGIONAL MEDICAL CENTER (450702)**, 2901 North Fourth Street, Zip 75605–5191, Mailing Address: P.O. Box 14000, Zip 75607–4000; tel. 903/758–1818, (Total facility includes 15 beds in nursing home–type unit) **A**1 9 10 **F**3 8 11 12 13 15 18 20 22 24 26 28 29 30 31 34 35 37 39 40 43 45 46 47 49 50 57 59 61 64 65 67 70 74 75 76 77 78 79 81 85 86 87 89 91 93 107 108 110 111 114 115 118 119 126 128 130 146 148 **P**8 **S** Community Health Systems, Inc., Franklin, TN
Primary Contact: Jim R. Kendrick, Chief Executive Officer
COO: Roy Finch, Chief Operating Officer
CFO: Todd Johnson, Chief Financial Officer
CMO: Kenneth McClure, M.D., Chief of Staff
CIO: Keith Jarvis, Director Information Systems
CHR: Terry Hardan, Director Human Resources
CNO: Stephanie Foster, MSN, Chief Nursing Officer
Web address: www.longviewregional.com
Control: Partnership, Investor–owned, for–profit **Service:** General Medical and Surgical

> **Staffed Beds:** 189 **Admissions:** 6892 **Census:** 77 **Outpatient Visits:** 77417 **Births:** 1073 **Total Expense ($000):** 113875 **Payroll Expense ($000):** 42514 **Personnel:** 731

☐ **OCEANS BEHAVIORAL HOSPITAL LONGVIEW (454117)**, 615 Clinic Drive, Zip 75605–5172; tel. 903/212–3105, (Nonreporting) **A**1 10 **S** Audubon Behavioral Healthcare, Longview, TX
Primary Contact: Lauren Weber, Administrator
Web address: www.oceanslongview.com/
Control: Partnership, Investor–owned, for–profit **Service:** Psychiatric

> **Staffed Beds:** 24

⊞ **SELECT SPECIALTY HOSPITAL–LONGVIEW (452087)**, 700 East Marshall Avenue, 1st Floor, Zip 75601–5580; tel. 903/315–1100 **A**1 9 10 **F**1 3 28 29 40 75 77 85 91 92 130 148 **S** Select Medical Corporation, Mechanicsburg, PA
Primary Contact: Dennis Baker, Chief Executive Officer
Web address: www.selectspecialtyhospitals.com/company/locations/longview.aspx
Control: Corporation, Investor–owned, for–profit **Service:** Long–Term Acute Care hospital

> **Staffed Beds:** 32 **Admissions:** 430 **Census:** 31 **Outpatient Visits:** 0 **Births:** 0 **Total Expense ($000):** 14573 **Payroll Expense ($000):** 6759 **Personnel:** 96

LUBBOCK—Lubbock County

⊞ **COVENANT CHILDREN'S HOSPITAL (453306)**, 4015 22nd Place, Zip 79410; tel. 806/725–1011 **A**1 3 5 9 10 **F**3 19 21 23 25 27 30 31 32 40 41 43 50 59 72 73 81 89 **P**8 **S** Covenant Health System, Lubbock, TX
Primary Contact: Christopher J. Dougherty, Chief Executive Officer
CMO: Scott Robins, M.D., Chief Medical Officer
CIO: Jim Reid, Vice President and Chief Information Officer
CHR: Rodney Cates, Senior Vice President Human Resources
Web address: www.covenanthealth.org/About–Us/Facilities/Childrens–Hospital.aspx
Control: Other not–for–profit (including NFP Corporation) **Service:** Children's general

> **Staffed Beds:** 73 **Admissions:** 2300 **Census:** 47 **Outpatient Visits:** 31946 **Births:** 0 **Total Expense ($000):** 61232 **Payroll Expense ($000):** 20246 **Personnel:** 205

⊞ **COVENANT MEDICAL CENTER (450040)**, 3615 19th Street, Zip 79410–1203, Mailing Address: P.O. Box 1201, Zip 79408–1201; tel. 806/725–0000, (Includes COVENANT MEDICAL CENTER–LAKESIDE, 4000 24th Street, Zip 79410–1894; tel. 806/725–0000) **A**1 3 5 6 9 10 **F**5 7 11 12 13 15 17 18 20 22 24 26 28 29 30 31 34 35 39 40 43 46 47 48 49 50 51 53 54 55 57 58 59 60 61 63 64 65 68 70 71 73 74 75 76 77 78 79 80 81 82 83 84 85 86 87 90 91 93 94 95 96 98 102 105 107 108 109 111 114 115 116 117 119 120 121 123 129 130 131 132 135 143 144 146 147 148 **P**6 8 **S** Covenant Health System, Lubbock, TX
Primary Contact: Troy Thibodeaux, Chief Executive Officer
COO: Walt Cathey, Chief Operating Officer
CFO: John A. Grigson, Vice President and Chief Financial Officer
CMO: Craig Rhyne, M.D., Chief Medical Officer
CIO: Troy Pratt, Information Technology Site Director
CHR: Chris Shaver, Vice President Human Resources
CNO: Karen Baggerly, Chief Nursing Officer and Vice President
Web address: www.covenanthealth.org
Control: Other not–for–profit (including NFP Corporation) **Service:** General Medical and Surgical

> **Staffed Beds:** 605 **Admissions:** 26059 **Census:** 333 **Outpatient Visits:** 332266 **Births:** 2924 **Total Expense ($000):** 513145 **Payroll Expense ($000):** 155253 **Personnel:** 3123

COVENANT SPECIALTY HOSPITAL (452102), 3815 20th Street, Zip 79410–1235; tel. 806/725–9200 **A**10 **F**1 3 29 30 31 60 63 68 75 77 78 79 87 119 130 143 148 **S** Covenant Health System, Lubbock, TX
Primary Contact: Stuart Oertli, Executive Director
CFO: John Carigson, Chief Financial Officer
CMO: Naidu Chekuru, M.D., Chief Medical Officer
CHR: Chris Shaver, Vice President Human Resources
CNO: Julie Bell, Director of Nursing
Web address: www.covenanthealth.org/view/Facilities/Specialty_Hospital
Control: Partnership, Investor–owned, for–profit **Service:** Long–Term Acute Care hospital

> **Staffed Beds:** 56 **Admissions:** 538 **Census:** 35 **Outpatient Visits:** 0 **Births:** 0 **Total Expense ($000):** 17450 **Payroll Expense ($000):** 6167 **Personnel:** 107

⊞ **GRACE MEDICAL CENTER (450162)**, 2412 50th Street, Zip 79412–2494; tel. 806/788–4100 **A**1 3 5 9 10 **F**3 8 11 12 15 29 34 35 40 44 45 47 49 50 51 59 64 70 75 79 81 82 85 87 107 108 110 111 114 115 118 119 135 146
Primary Contact: Vanessa Reasoner, Chief Executive Officer
CMO: Howard Beck, M.D., Chief of Staff
CIO: Jason Derouen, Director Management Information Systems
CHR: Sally Charles, Coordinator Human Resources
Web address: www.gracehealthsystem.com
Control: Partnership, Investor–owned, for–profit **Service:** General Medical and Surgical

> **Staffed Beds:** 43 **Admissions:** 855 **Census:** 7 **Outpatient Visits:** 64103 **Births:** 0 **Total Expense ($000):** 37200 **Payroll Expense ($000):** 8481 **Personnel:** 180

Many Facility Codes have changed. Please refer to the AHA Guide Code Chart. © 2014 AHA Guide

☐ **LLANO SPECIALTY HOSPITAL OF LUBBOCK (452050)**, 1409 9th Street, Zip 79401–2601; tel. 806/767–9133 **A**1 9 10 **F**1 12 29 60 65 75 92 107 119 130 148 **S** Fundamental Long Term Care Holdings, LLC, Sparks Glencoe, MD
Primary Contact: Dennis Fleenor, R.N., Chief Executive Officer
CFO: Robert Stanley, Chief Financial Officer
CMO: Enrique Rodriguez, M.D., Medical Director
CHR: Jerrie Yoakum, Director Human Resources
CNO: Charalene Ruble, Chief Nursing Officer
Web address: www.fundltc.com/Healthcare%2OFacility%2OLocator/facility_page.aspx?locationID=190
Control: Corporation, Investor–owned, for–profit **Service:** Long–Term Acute Care hospital

Staffed Beds: 15 **Admissions:** 69 **Census:** 4 **Outpatient Visits:** 0 **Births:** 0 **Total Expense ($000):** 2967 **Payroll Expense ($000):** 1266 **Personnel:** 31

LUBBOCK HEART HOSPITAL (450876), 4810 North Loop 289, Zip 79416–3025; tel. 806/687–7777 **A**3 5 9 10 **F**3 17 18 20 22 24 26 29 34 40 45 57 59 79 81 82 85 107 108 115 119 130 131 148
Primary Contact: Charley O. Trimble, Chief Executive Officer
Web address: www.lubbockhearthospital.com
Control: Partnership, Investor–owned, for–profit **Service:** General Medical and Surgical

Staffed Beds: 74 **Admissions:** 3377 **Census:** 30 **Outpatient Visits:** 30578 **Births:** 0 **Total Expense ($000):** 54768 **Payroll Expense ($000):** 17356 **Personnel:** 297

☐ **SUNRISE CANYON HOSPITAL (454093)**, 1950 Aspen Avenue, Zip 79404–1211, Mailing Address: P.O. Box 2828, Zip 79408–2828; tel. 806/740–1420 **A**1 10 **F**29 35 38 42 53 56 61 86 98 99 101 103 130 132 143 146 **P**5
Primary Contact: Eileen C. Barker, Administrator
CFO: Jerome Flores, Chief Financial Officer
CMO: Dana Butler, M.D., Medical Director
CIO: Wendy Potitadkui, Chief Information Officer
CHR: Barbara McCann, Director Human Resources
Web address: www.starcarelubbock.org
Control: Other not–for–profit (including NFP Corporation) **Service:** Psychiatric

Staffed Beds: 30 **Admissions:** 521 **Census:** 22 **Outpatient Visits:** 0 **Births:** 0 **Total Expense ($000):** 4733 **Payroll Expense ($000):** 1946 **Personnel:** 38

☐ **TEXAS SPECIALTY HOSPITAL AT LUBBOCK (452116)**, 4302 Princeton Street, Zip 79415–1304; tel. 806/723–8700 **A**1 9 10 **F**1 3 12 29 60 92 148 **S** Fundamental Long Term Care Holdings, LLC, Sparks Glencoe, MD
Primary Contact: Deanna Graves, Chief Executive Officer
CFO: Robert Stanley, Chief Financial Officer
CMO: Michael Ragain, M.D., Chief Medical Officer
CNO: Bernadette Hernandez, R.N., Chief Nursing Officer
Control: Corporation, Investor–owned, for–profit **Service:** Long–Term Acute Care hospital

Staffed Beds: 35 **Admissions:** 387 **Census:** 28 **Outpatient Visits:** 0 **Births:** 0 **Total Expense ($000):** 9747 **Payroll Expense ($000):** 3860 **Personnel:** 81

☐ **TRUSTPOINT HOSPITAL (670050)**, 4302 Princeton Street, Zip 79415–1304; tel. 806/749–2222 **A**1 3 5 9 10 **F**3 29 34 35 40 56 57 64 68 74 75 77 79 85 86 87 90 91 93 94 96 98 101 103 130 135 148 **S** Polaris Hospital Company, Brentwood, TN
Primary Contact: Craig Bragg, Chief Executive Officer
CFO: Crystal Roach, Chief Financial Officer
CNO: John Parsons, R.N., Chief Nursing Officer
Web address: www.trustpointhospital.com/
Control: Partnership, Investor–owned, for–profit **Service:** Rehabilitation

Staffed Beds: 64 **Admissions:** 1362 **Census:** 47 **Outpatient Visits:** 1 **Births:** 0 **Total Expense ($000):** 18682 **Payroll Expense ($000):** 7564 **Personnel:** 172

★ ◇ **UNIVERSITY MEDICAL CENTER (450686)**, 602 Indiana Avenue, Zip 79415–3364, Mailing Address: P.O. Box 5980, Zip 79408–5980; tel. 806/775–8200 **A**2 3 5 8 9 10 21 **F**3 7 8 11 12 13 15 16 17 18 19 20 22 24 26 27 28 29 30 31 34 35 36 40 41 43 45 46 47 48 49 50 54 57 58 59 60 62 64 65 66 68 70 72 74 75 76 77 78 79 80 81 83 84 85 86 87 88 89 93 94 96 97 102 107 108 110 111 114 115 116 117 118 119 120 121 123 124 126 127 130 131 132 135 136 141 142 143 144 146 147 148
Primary Contact: David G. Allison, President and Chief Executive Officer
COO: Mark Funderburk, Executive Vice President and Administrator
CFO: Jeff Dane, Executive Vice President and Chief Financial Officer
CMO: Michael Ragain, M.D., Chief Medical Officer and Senior Vice President
CIO: Bill Eubanks, Senior Vice President and Chief Information Officer
CHR: Adrienne Cozart, Vice President Human Resources
CNO: Tammy J. Williams, R.N., Chief Nursing Officer and Senior Vice President
Web address: www.umchealthsystem.com
Control: Hospital district or authority, Government, nonfederal **Service:** General Medical and Surgical

Staffed Beds: 446 **Admissions:** 25143 **Census:** 306 **Outpatient Visits:** 279816 **Births:** 2708 **Total Expense ($000):** 420966 **Payroll Expense ($000):** 158653 **Personnel:** 2686

LUFKIN—Angelina County

✠ **MEMORIAL MEDICAL CENTER – LUFKIN (450211)**, 1201 West Frank Avenue, Zip 75904–3357, Mailing Address: P.O. Box 1447, Zip 75902–1447; tel. 936/634–8111 **A**1 2 9 10 19 **F**3 11 12 13 14 15 17 18 20 21 22 23 24 26 28 29 30 31 34 35 37 38 40 44 45 46 47 48 49 50 51 56 57 59 60 61 62 63 64 68 70 71 74 75 76 77 78 79 81 82 83 84 85 86 87 90 91 92 93 97 100 101 102 107 108 110 111 112 114 115 116 117 119 121 126 129 130 132 135 143 144 146 147 148 **S** Memorial Health System of East Texas, Lufkin, TX
Primary Contact: Gary N. Looper, Chief Executive Officer
CFO: Kristi Gay, Chief Financial Officer
CHR: Tanya Tyler, Vice President Human Resources
Web address: www.memorialhealth.us/centers/lufkin
Control: Other not–for–profit (including NFP Corporation) **Service:** General Medical and Surgical

Staffed Beds: 217 **Admissions:** 7295 **Census:** 98 **Outpatient Visits:** 92534 **Births:** 580 **Total Expense ($000):** 125379 **Payroll Expense ($000):** 36099 **Personnel:** 862

MEMORIAL SPECIALTY HOSPITAL (452031), 1201 West Frank Avenue, Zip 75904–3357; tel. 936/639–7975 **A**9 10 **F**1 3 29 31 50 61 68 74 75 85 86 130 145 **S** Memorial Health System of East Texas, Lufkin, TX
Primary Contact: Leslie Leach, Administrator
CFO: Kristi Gay, Chief Financial Officer
CMO: David Todd, M.D., President Medical Staff
CHR: Tanya Tyler, Vice President Human Resources
Web address: www.memorialhealth.org
Control: Other not–for–profit (including NFP Corporation) **Service:** Long–Term Acute Care hospital

Staffed Beds: 26 **Admissions:** 247 **Census:** 19 **Outpatient Visits:** 0 **Births:** 0 **Total Expense ($000):** 9484 **Payroll Expense ($000):** 5913 **Personnel:** 48

☐ **OCEANS BEHAVIORAL HOSPITAL LUFKIN**, 302 Gobblers Knob, Zip 75904–5419; tel. 936/632–2276, (Data for 346 days) **A**1 **F**29 56 74 75 98 100 101 103 104 130 **P**6 **S** Audubon Behavioral Healthcare, Longview, TX
Primary Contact: Ronald E. Hand, Administrator
Web address: www.oceanslufkin.com/
Control: Individual, Investor–owned, for–profit **Service:** Psychiatric

Staffed Beds: 24 **Admissions:** 480 **Census:** 21 **Outpatient Visits:** 3600 **Births:** 0 **Total Expense ($000):** 3698 **Payroll Expense ($000):** 2400 **Personnel:** 91

TX

✠ **WOODLAND HEIGHTS MEDICAL CENTER (450484)**, 505 South John Redditt Drive, Zip 75904–3157, Mailing Address: P.O. Box 150610, Zip 75904; tel. 936/634–8311, (Total facility includes 15 beds in nursing home–type unit) **A**1 9 10 19 **F**3 8 11 12 13 15 17 18 20 22 24 26 28 29 30 34 35 40 41 46 49 50 51 53 57 59 64 68 70 74 75 76 77 78 79 81 82 85 86 87 93 102 107 108 111 114 115 118 119 128 129 130 131 146 147 148 **S** Community Health Systems, Inc., Franklin, TN
Primary Contact: Casey Robertson, Chief Executive Officer
COO: Conner Hickey, Chief Operating Officer
CFO: William Whiddon, Chief Financial Officer
CMO: William Strinden, M.D., Chief of Staff
CIO: Kalvin Buckley, Director Information Systems
CHR: Emilie Hobbs, Director Human Resources
Web address: www.woodlandheights.net
Control: Partnership, Investor–owned, for–profit **Service:** General Medical and Surgical

Staffed Beds: 115 Admissions: 5094 Census: 65 Outpatient Visits: 44874 Births: 791 Total Expense ($000): 77003 Payroll Expense ($000): 29361 Personnel: 522

LULING—Caldwell County

✠ **POST ACUTE/WARM SPRINGS SPECIALTY HOSPITAL OF LULING (452062)**, 200 Memorial Drive, Zip 78648–3213; tel. 830/875–8400 **A**1 9 10 **F**1 3 29 53 64 93 96 130 133 148 **S** Post Acute Medical, LLC, Enola, PA
Primary Contact: Jason Carter, Chief Executive Officer
CFO: James Asberry, Chief Financial Officer
Web address: www.warmsprings.org
Control: Partnership, Investor–owned, for–profit **Service:** Long–Term Acute Care hospital

Staffed Beds: 34 Admissions: 426 Census: 33 Outpatient Visits: 9734 Births: 0 Total Expense ($000): 15174 Payroll Expense ($000): 6659 Personnel: 152

✠ **SETON EDGAR B. DAVIS HOSPITAL (451371)**, 130 Hays Street, Zip 78648–3207; tel. 830/875–7000 **A**1 9 10 18 **F**3 11 15 18 29 30 35 40 43 44 45 50 56 68 71 75 77 78 79 81 84 85 87 93 97 103 107 110 111 114 119 127 130 133 135 143 146 **P**3 8 **S** Ascension Health, Saint Louis, MO
Primary Contact: Apryl Haynes, R.N., Vice President, Chief Operating Officer, Chief Nursing Officer and Administrator
CFO: Thomas E. Gallagher, Chief Financial Officer
CMO: Martin E. Weiner, M.D., Chief of Staff
CIO: Mike Minks, Chief Information Officer
CHR: Joe Canales, Director Human Resources
CNO: Apryl Haynes, R.N., Vice President, Chief Operating Officer, Chief Nursing Officer and Administrator
Web address: www.seton.net/locations/edgar_davis/
Control: Church–operated, Nongovernment, not–for profit **Service:** General Medical and Surgical

Staffed Beds: 25 Admissions: 1149 Census: 13 Outpatient Visits: 63796 Births: 0 Total Expense ($000): 22698 Payroll Expense ($000): 9749 Personnel: 141

WARM SPRINGS SPECIALTY HOSPITAL OF LULING See Post Acute/Warm Springs Specialty Hospital of Luling

MADISONVILLE—Madison County

✠ **MADISON ST. JOSEPH HEALTH CENTER (451316)**, 100 West Cross Street, Zip 77864–2432, Mailing Address: Box 698, Zip 77864–0698; tel. 936/348–2631 **A**1 9 10 18 **F**3 7 11 15 30 40 43 57 59 64 68 75 77 93 103 107 108 110 119 130 133 135 146 148 **S** Sylvania Franciscan Health, Toledo, OH
Primary Contact: Reed Edmundson, Administrator
COO: Reed Edmundson, Administrator
CFO: Kris Smith, Controller
CMO: Grover Hubley, M.D., President Medical Staff
CIO: Maurita Turner, Team Leader Health Information Systems Services
CHR: Marybeth Murphy, Director Human Resources
CNO: Roxanne Hass, Director of Nursing
Web address: www.st–joseph.org
Control: Church–operated, Nongovernment, not–for profit **Service:** General Medical and Surgical

Staffed Beds: 25 Admissions: 347 Census: 7 Outpatient Visits: 19883 Births: 0 Total Expense ($000): 10063 Payroll Expense ($000): 4803 Personnel: 91

MANSFIELD—Tarrant County

✠ **KINDRED HOSPITAL–MANSFIELD (452019)**, 1802 Highway 157 North, Zip 76063–3923; tel. 817/473–6101 **A**1 9 10 **F**1 3 29 30 45 46 60 70 75 82 85 107 130 132 148 **S** Kindred Healthcare, Louisville, KY
Primary Contact: Susan Schaetti, Administrator
CFO: Judy Baker, Chief Financial Officer
Web address: www.kindredmansfield.com
Control: Corporation, Investor–owned, for–profit **Service:** Long–Term Acute Care hospital

Staffed Beds: 55 Admissions: 407 Census: 28 Outpatient Visits: 80 Births: 0 Total Expense ($000): 14010 Payroll Expense ($000): 6559 Personnel: 108

✠ **METHODIST MANSFIELD MEDICAL CENTER (670023)**, 2700 East Broad Street, Zip 76063–5899; tel. 682/622–2000 **A**1 9 10 **F**3 11 13 15 18 20 22 24 29 30 31 34 35 37 40 45 46 48 49 50 58 59 60 64 68 70 72 74 76 78 79 81 82 85 87 93 97 107 108 110 111 115 118 119 126 130 132 146 148 **P**1 7 **S** Methodist Health System, Dallas, TX
Primary Contact: John E. Phillips, FACHE, President
CFO: Jary Ganske, Chief Financial Officer
CMO: Sam Bagchi, Chief Medical Officer
CIO: Pamela McNutt, Senior Vice President and Chief Information Officer
CHR: Judy K. Laister, Director, Human Resources
CNO: Nora Frasier, R.N., Chief Nursing Officer
Web address: www.methodisthealthsystem.org/mansfield
Control: Other not–for–profit (including NFP Corporation) **Service:** General Medical and Surgical

Staffed Beds: 175 Admissions: 9782 Census: 108 Outpatient Visits: 83844 Births: 2148 Total Expense ($000): 123160 Payroll Expense ($000): 57296 Personnel: 735

MARLIN—Falls County

★ **FALLS COMMUNITY HOSPITAL AND CLINIC (450348)**, 322 Coleman Street, Zip 76661–2358, Mailing Address: P.O. Box 60, Zip 76661–0060; tel. 254/803–3561 **A**9 10 20 **F**3 11 32 33 34 35 36 40 43 45 53 56 57 59 64 65 66 68 75 82 87 91 93 97 99 103 104 107 114 127 129 131 133 135 146 148
Primary Contact: Willis L. Reese, Administrator
COO: Becca Brewer, Chief Operations Officer
CFO: Willis L. Reese, Administrator
CMO: James Scott Crockett, M.D., Chief of Staff
CIO: Chris Smith, Chief Information Officer
CHR: Peggy Polster, Manager Personnel and Administrative Assistant
CNO: Tasha Burnett, Director of Nursing
Web address: www.fallshospital.com
Control: Other not–for–profit (including NFP Corporation) **Service:** General Medical and Surgical

Staffed Beds: 32 Admissions: 457 Census: 5 Outpatient Visits: 75389 Births: 0 Total Expense ($000): 17962 Payroll Expense ($000): 5607 Personnel: 156

MARSHALL—Harrison County

☐ **GOOD SHEPHERD MEDICAL CENTER–MARSHALL (450032)**, 811 South Washington Avenue, Zip 75670–5336, Mailing Address: P.O. Box 1599, Zip 75671–1599; tel. 903/927–6000 **A**1 9 10 **F**3 11 13 15 18 28 29 30 34 35 40 43 49 50 53 54 57 59 60 64 65 68 70 75 77 79 80 81 86 87 89 90 93 97 102 103 107 110 115 119 127 129 130 131 132 145 146 147 148 **P**7 8 **S** Good Shepherd Health System, Longview, TX
Primary Contact: Russell J. Collier, FACHE, President and Chief Executive Officer
COO: Keith Creel, Vice President Operations
CFO: Tim Pileggi, Interim Chief Financial Officer
CMO: Larry Verfurth, D.O., Executive Vice President and Chief Medical Officer
CIO: Walter Grimes, Director Information Technology
CHR: Ginger Morrow, Executive Vice President Human Resources
CNO: Keith Kirbow, R.N., Vice President and Chief Nursing Officer
Web address: www.gsmcmarshall.org
Control: Other not–for–profit (including NFP Corporation) **Service:** General Medical and Surgical

Staffed Beds: 140 Admissions: 4208 Census: 43 Outpatient Visits: 92181 Births: 545 Total Expense ($000): 64681 Payroll Expense ($000): 22527 Personnel: 418

MCALLEN—Hidalgo County

LIFECARE HOSPITALS OF SOUTH TEXAS–MCALLEN See Lifecare Hospitals of South Texas–North McAllen

✠ **LIFECARE HOSPITALS OF SOUTH TEXAS–NORTH MCALLEN (452063)**, 5101 North Jackson, Zip 78504–6343; tel. 956/926–7000, (Includes LIFECARE HOSPITALS OF SOUTH TEXAS–MCALLEN, 2001 South M Street, Zip 78503; tel. 956/688–4300) **A**1 9 10 **F**1 3 29 57 75 77 85 87 148 **S** LifeCare Management Services, Plano, TX
Primary Contact: Michelle Lozano, Chief Executive Officer
Web address: www.lifecare–hospitals.com/hospital/southtexas
Control: Corporation, Investor–owned, for–profit **Service:** Long–Term Acute Care hospital

Staffed Beds: 84 Admissions: 735 Census: 58 Outpatient Visits: 0 Births: 0 Total Expense ($000): 24864 Payroll Expense ($000): 10522 Personnel: 200

⊞ RIO GRANDE REGIONAL HOSPITAL (450711), 101 East Ridge Road, Zip 78503–1299; tel. 956/632–6000 **A**1 3 5 9 10 **F**3 8 11 12 13 15 18 19 20 21 22 23 24 25 26 27 29 30 31 34 35 39 40 42 43 45 46 49 50 54 56 57 59 60 64 68 70 71 72 73 74 75 76 78 79 81 85 87 88 89 93 107 108 110 111 114 118 119 130 132 146 147 148 **P**7 **S** HCA, Nashville, TN
Primary Contact: Cristina Rivera, Chief Executive Officer
COO: David Elgarico, Chief Operating Officer
CFO: William Saller, Chief Financial Officer
CHR: Marjorie Whittemore, Director Human Resources
Web address: www.riohealth.com
Control: Partnership, Investor–owned, for–profit **Service:** General Medical and Surgical

Staffed Beds: 320 **Admissions:** 14773 **Census:** 181 **Outpatient Visits:** 94217 **Births:** 2762 **Total Expense ($000):** 144629 **Payroll Expense ($000):** 60409 **Personnel:** 810

☐ SOLARA HOSPITAL MCALLEN (452095), 301 West Expressway 83, Zip 78503–3045; tel. 956/632–4880 **A**1 9 10 **F**1 3 29 30 40 56 57 68 70 75 77 85 86 87 91 130 148 **S** Cornerstone Healthcare Group, Dallas, TX
Primary Contact: Chris Chizek, Chief Executive Officer
Web address: www.chghospitals.com/mcallen/
Control: Corporation, Investor–owned, for–profit **Service:** Long–Term Acute Care hospital

Staffed Beds: 78 **Admissions:** 634 **Census:** 48 **Outpatient Visits:** 0 **Births:** 0 **Total Expense ($000):** 18841 **Payroll Expense ($000):** 9139 **Personnel:** 166

MCCAMEY—Upton County

★ MCCAMEY COUNTY HOSPITAL DISTRICT (451309), 2500 Highway 305 South, Zip 79752, Mailing Address: P.O. Box 1200, Zip 79752–1200; tel. 432/652–8626, (Total facility includes 30 beds in nursing home–type unit) **A**9 10 18 **F**3 40 53 59 64 65 66 93 127 128 133
Primary Contact: Jaime Ramirez, Chief Executive Officer
COO: Tana Robertson, Chief Operating Officer
CFO: Judith Gulihur, Director Human Resources and Chief Financial Officer
CMO: Ramon Domingo, M.D., Chief of Staff
CIO: Larry Rollins, Supervisor Information Technology
CHR: Judith Gulihur, Director Human Resources and Chief Financial Officer
CNO: Cheryl Roberts, Chief Nursing Officer
Web address: www.mccameyhospital.org
Control: Hospital district or authority, Government, nonfederal **Service:** General Medical and Surgical

Staffed Beds: 44 **Admissions:** 61 **Census:** 23 **Outpatient Visits:** 7847 **Births:** 0 **Total Expense ($000):** 8664 **Payroll Expense ($000):** 4773 **Personnel:** 73

MCKINNEY—Collin County

⊞ BAYLOR MEDICAL CENTER AT MCKINNEY (670082), 5252 West University Drive, Zip 75071–7822; tel. 469/764–1000 **A**1 9 10 **F**3 13 15 18 20 22 26 29 30 31 34 35 40 45 46 47 49 50 51 57 67 70 72 73 74 75 76 77 78 79 81 85 87 107 110 111 114 115 119 126 130 131 132 146 147 148 **S** Baylor Scott & White Health, Dallas, TX
Primary Contact: Scott Peek, FACHE, President
COO: Melissa Winter, R.N., Chief Operating Officer and Chief Nursing Officer
CFO: Steve Roussel, Chief Financial Officer
CMO: Jeff Kerr, M.D., Chief Medical Officer
CNO: Melissa Winter, R.N., Chief Operating Officer and Chief Nursing Officer
Web address: www.baylorhealth.com/PhysiciansLocations/McKinney/Pages/Default.aspx
Control: Other not–for–profit (including NFP Corporation) **Service:** General Medical and Surgical

Staffed Beds: 91 **Admissions:** 4686 **Census:** 48 **Outpatient Visits:** 34687 **Births:** 1240 **Total Expense ($000):** 101137 **Payroll Expense ($000):** 34308 **Personnel:** 652

⊞ MEDICAL CENTER OF MCKINNEY (450403), 4500 Medical Center Drive, Zip 75069–1650; tel. 972/547–8000, (Includes WYSONG CAMPUS, 130 South Central Expressway, Zip 75070; tel. 972/548–5300) **A**1 9 10 **F**3 4 11 13 15 18 20 22 24 26 28 29 30 34 37 40 45 49 50 56 57 59 60 64 68 70 72 74 75 76 77 78 79 81 82 85 87 90 91 92 93 94 96 97 98 102 103 107 108 109 110 111 114 115 119 126 129 130 131 132 146 147 148 **S** HCA, Nashville, TN
Primary Contact: Ernest C. Lynch, III, Chief Executive Officer
COO: LaSharndra Barbarin, Chief Operating Officer
CFO: Dwayne Ray, Chief Financial Officer
CIO: Kevin Fletcher, Director Information Systems
CHR: Senta Miles, Director Human Resources
CNO: Kimberly Kay Hatchel, Chief Nursing Officer
Web address: www.medicalcenterofmckinney.com
Control: Partnership, Investor–owned, for–profit **Service:** General Medical and Surgical

Staffed Beds: 217 **Admissions:** 10432 **Census:** 157 **Outpatient Visits:** 57064 **Births:** 814 **Total Expense ($000):** 116378 **Payroll Expense ($000):** 50403 **Personnel:** 792

☐ METHODIST MCKINNEY HOSPITAL (670069), 8000 West Eldorado Parkway, Zip 75070–5940; tel. 972/569–2700 **A**1 9 10 **F**3 15 29 34 40 45 51 70 75 79 81 82 85 93 107 111 119 126 129 130 131
Primary Contact: Joseph Minissale, President
CFO: Mike Mayden, Chief Financial Officer
CIO: Sharon Stark, R.N., Manager Clinical Information Systems
CHR: Diana Hume, Manager Human Resources
CNO: Staci Jones, R.N., Chief Nursing Officer
Web address: www.methodistmckinneyhospital.com
Control: Partnership, Investor–owned, for–profit **Service:** General Medical and Surgical

Staffed Beds: 21 **Admissions:** 709 **Census:** 5 **Outpatient Visits:** 19283 **Births:** 0 **Total Expense ($000):** 29761 **Payroll Expense ($000):** 7036 **Personnel:** 146

VICTORY MEDICAL CENTER CRAIG RANCH, 6045 Alma Road, Zip 75070–2188; tel. 972/908–1215, (Nonreporting) **S** Victory Healthcare, The Woodlands, TX
Primary Contact: Ashley Anson, Chief Executive Officer
CFO: Ron Collins, Chief Financial Officer
CHR: Dorie Alston, Manager Human Resources
CNO: Cathy Woodard, R.N., Chief Clinical Officer
Web address: www.victory–healthcare.com/craig–ranch/
Control: Corporation, Investor–owned, for–profit **Service:** Surgical

Staffed Beds: 24

MESQUITE—Dallas County

⊞ DALLAS REGIONAL MEDICAL CENTER (450688), 1011 North Galloway Avenue, Zip 75149–2433; tel. 214/320–7000 **A**1 9 10 **F**3 12 15 18 20 22 24 26 29 30 34 35 40 43 45 46 47 48 49 50 54 56 57 59 64 68 70 74 75 79 80 81 85 86 87 97 107 108 110 111 114 119 126 130 131 135 146 148 **S** Community Health Systems, Inc., Franklin, TN
Primary Contact: Tina Pollock, Chief Executive Officer
CMO: Srinivas Gunukula, M.D., Chief of Staff
Web address: www.dallasregionalmedicalcenter.com
Control: Corporation, Investor–owned, for–profit **Service:** General Medical and Surgical

Staffed Beds: 85 **Admissions:** 3739 **Census:** 44 **Outpatient Visits:** 54490 **Births:** 0 **Total Expense ($000):** 64303 **Payroll Expense ($000):** 22395 **Personnel:** 380

☐ MESQUITE REHABILITATION INSTITUTE (673045), 1023 North Belt Line Road, Zip 75149–1788; tel. 972/216–2400 **A**1 9 10 **F**3 28 29 30 34 35 57 59 64 82 90 91 93 96 148 **S** Ernest Health, Inc., Albuquerque, NM
Primary Contact: Brian Abraham, Chief Operating Officer
Web address: www.mesquiterehab.ernesthealth.com/
Control: Corporation, Investor–owned, for–profit **Service:** Rehabilitation

Staffed Beds: 20 **Admissions:** 437 **Census:** 17 **Outpatient Visits:** 1507 **Births:** 0 **Total Expense ($000):** 5465 **Payroll Expense ($000):** 3456 **Personnel:** 43

☐ MESQUITE SPECIALTY HOSPITAL (452100), 1024 North Galloway Avenue, Zip 75149–2434; tel. 972/216–2300 **A**1 9 10 **F**1 3 29 74 75 77 79 85 87 130 135 148 **S** Ernest Health, Inc., Albuquerque, NM
Primary Contact: Louis Bradley, Chief Executive Officer
Web address: www.msh.ernesthealth.com
Control: Partnership, Investor–owned, for–profit **Service:** Long–Term Acute Care hospital

Staffed Beds: 40 **Admissions:** 493 **Census:** 34 **Outpatient Visits:** 0 **Births:** 0 **Total Expense ($000):** 18392 **Payroll Expense ($000):** 7288 **Personnel:** 126

TX

Hospital, Medicare Provider Number, Address, Telephone, Approval, Facility, and Physician Codes, Health Care System

★ American Hospital Association (AHA) membership
☐ The Joint Commission accreditation   ◇ DNV Healthcare Inc. accreditation

○ Healthcare Facilities Accreditation Program
△ Commission on Accreditation of Rehabilitation Facilities (CARF) accreditation

MEXIA—Limestone County

✠ **PARKVIEW REGIONAL HOSPITAL (450400)**, 600 South Bonham,
Zip 76667–3603; tel. 254/562–5332 **A**1 9 10 20 **F**3 11 15 29 30 34 35 40
43 45 51 53 56 57 59 64 65 70 75 77 78 79 81 85 86 87 93 97 98 103
107 108 110 111 114 119 127 130 132 133 146 **P**5 6 **S** LifePoint Hospitals,
Inc., Brentwood, TN
Primary Contact: Kevin Zachary, Chief Executive Officer
Web address: www.parkviewregional.com
Control: Partnership, Investor–owned, for–profit **Service:** General Medical and
Surgical

Staffed Beds: 58 **Admissions:** 828 **Census:** 10 **Outpatient Visits:** 21534
Births: 0 **Total Expense ($000):** 18030 **Payroll Expense ($000):** 8015
Personnel: 168

MIDLAND—Midland County

☐ **BCA PERMIAN BASIN (454110)**, 3300 South FM 1788, Zip 79706–2601;
tel. 432/561–5915, (Nonreporting) **A**1 9 10
Primary Contact: William E. Ernst, Chief Executive Officer
Web address: www.bcapermianbasin.com/
Control: Corporation, Investor–owned, for–profit **Service:** Psychiatric

Staffed Beds: 64

BEHAVIORAL HEALTH CENTER OF THE PERMIAN BASIN (454110), 3300
South FM 1788, Zip 79706–2601; tel. 432/561–5915, (Nonreporting) **A**10
S Allegiance Health Management, Shreveport, LA
Primary Contact: Cheryl Rayl, Chief Executive Officer
Web address: www.ahmgt.com
Control: Corporation, Investor–owned, for–profit **Service:** Psychiatric

Staffed Beds: 48

✠ **HEALTHSOUTH REHABILITATION HOSPITAL MIDLAND–ODESSA (453057)**,
1800 Heritage Boulevard, Zip 79707–9750; tel. 432/520–1600 **A**1 5 9 10 **F**3
29 57 59 62 74 75 77 90 91 130 143 148 **S** HEALTHSOUTH Corporation,
Birmingham, AL
Primary Contact: Christopher Wortham, Chief Executive Officer
CFO: Vivian Irwin, Chief Financial Officer and Controller
CMO: Mark A. Fredrickson, M.D., Medical Director
CHR: Tina Parker, Director Human Resources
Web address: www.healthsouthmidland.com
Control: Corporation, Investor–owned, for–profit **Service:** Rehabilitation

Staffed Beds: 60 **Admissions:** 1281 **Census:** 46 **Outpatient Visits:** 0 **Births:**
0 **Total Expense ($000):** 16036 **Payroll Expense ($000):** 9761 **Personnel:**
174

★ ◇ **MIDLAND MEMORIAL HOSPITAL (450133)**, 400 Rosalind Redfern Grover
Parkway, Zip 79701–6499; tel. 432/221–1111, (Includes CONTINUECARE
HOSPITAL AT MIDLAND MEMORIAL, 4214 Andrews Highway, 3rd Floor,
Zip 79703–4822; tel. 432/221–3563; MIDLAND MEMORIAL HOSPITAL, 4214
Andrews Highway, Zip 79703–4822; tel. 432/685–1584) **A**2 3 5 9 10 21 **F**3 8
11 12 13 15 17 18 20 22 24 28 29 30 31 32 34 35 40 43 45 49 50 56 57
59 61 64 68 70 73 74 75 76 77 78 79 81 82 83 84 85 86 87 88 89 93 97
107 108 111 114 115 116 117 118 119 124 126 129 130 131 132 135 145
146 147 148 **P**8
Primary Contact: Russell Meyers, President and Chief Executive Officer
COO: Cory Edmondson, Chief Operating Officer
CFO: Stephen Bowerman, Chief Financial Officer
CIO: Taylor Weems, Director Information Systems
CNO: Robert L. Dent, R.N., Chief Nursing Officer
Web address: www.midland–memorial.com
Control: Hospital district or authority, Government, nonfederal **Service:** General
Medical and Surgical

Staffed Beds: 234 **Admissions:** 11280 **Census:** 141 **Outpatient Visits:**
143799 **Births:** 2325 **Total Expense ($000):** 219918 **Payroll Expense**
($000): 89391 **Personnel:** 1564

MINERAL WELLS—Palo Pinto County

✠ **PALO PINTO GENERAL HOSPITAL (450565)**, 400 S.W. 25th Avenue,
Zip 76067–8246; tel. 940/328–6403 **A**1 9 10 **F**11 13 15 17 18 28 29 32 34
40 43 45 46 51 53 54 57 59 62 63 64 65 66 68 69 71 74 75 76 77 79 81
84 86 87 91 93 107 108 110 111 114 119 127 129 130 131 133 135 146
147 **P**1
Primary Contact: Harris W. Brooks, Administrator and Chief Executive Officer
CFO: Dee Waldow, Chief Financial Officer
CMO: Alice Ramsey, M.D., Chief of Staff
CHR: Mary B. Braddock, Director Human Resources
CNO: Cheryl Kirby, Chief Nursing Officer
Web address: www.ppgh.com
Control: Hospital district or authority, Government, nonfederal **Service:** General
Medical and Surgical

Staffed Beds: 42 **Admissions:** 1983 **Census:** 18 **Outpatient Visits:** 93243
Births: 396 **Total Expense ($000):** 36188 **Payroll Expense ($000):** 16340
Personnel: 289

MISSION—Hidalgo County

✠ △ **MISSION REGIONAL MEDICAL CENTER (450176)**, 900 South Bryan
Road, Zip 78572–6613; tel. 956/323–9103 **A**1 7 9 10 **F**3 11 12 13 15 18 20
22 29 30 31 34 35 40 43 45 46 49 50 51 57 59 60 64 65 66 68 70 72 74
75 76 77 79 81 85 87 89 90 93 96 107 108 110 111 115 119 130 132 146
147 148 **P**8
Primary Contact: Javier Iruegas, FACHE, Chief Executive Officer
COO: Carlos Trevino, Chief Operating Officer
CFO: Timothy J. McVey, Chief Financial Officer
CHR: Susan Willars, Vice President Human Resources
Web address: www.missionrmc.org
Control: Other not–for–profit (including NFP Corporation) **Service:** General
Medical and Surgical

Staffed Beds: 245 **Admissions:** 9632 **Census:** 136 **Outpatient Visits:** 75784
Births: 2319 **Total Expense ($000):** 110762 **Payroll Expense ($000):**
52631 **Personnel:** 974

MONAHANS—Ward County

WARD MEMORIAL HOSPITAL (451373), 406 South Gary Street,
Zip 79756–4798, Mailing Address: P.O. Box 40, Zip 79756–0040;
tel. 432/943–2511 **A**9 10 18 **F**3 11 40 43 45 64 65 66 81 82 93 107 114
119 127 131 133 148 **P**6
Primary Contact: Padraic White, Administrator, Chief Executive Officer and Chief
Financial Officer
CFO: Leticia Rodriguez, Controller
CHR: Donna Lemon, Director Human Resources
Web address: www.wardmemorial.org
Control: County–Government, nonfederal **Service:** General Medical and Surgical

Staffed Beds: 25 **Admissions:** 373 **Census:** 4 **Outpatient Visits:** 23350
Births: 0 **Total Expense ($000):** 10057 **Payroll Expense ($000):** 5160
Personnel: 88

MORTON—Cochran County

COCHRAN MEMORIAL HOSPITAL (451366), 201 East Grant Street,
Zip 79346–3444; tel. 806/266–5565 **A**9 10 18 **F**34 40 57 59 65 127 **P**6
Primary Contact: Larry Turney, Administrator
CHR: Niona Tunney, Director Human Resources
Control: Hospital district or authority, Government, nonfederal **Service:** General
Medical and Surgical

Staffed Beds: 13 **Admissions:** 36 **Census:** 1 **Outpatient Visits:** 5191 **Births:**
0 **Total Expense ($000):** 3683 **Payroll Expense ($000):** 1768 **Personnel:**
41

MOUNT PLEASANT—Titus County

✠ **TITUS REGIONAL MEDICAL CENTER (450080)**, 2001 North Jefferson Avenue,
Zip 75455–2398; tel. 903/577–6000, (Total facility includes 7 beds in nursing
home–type unit) **A**1 9 10 19 **F**3 7 11 12 13 15 18 19 20 24 26 28 29 30 34
35 39 40 43 45 47 50 51 53 54 56 57 58 59 64 68 70 73 74 75 76 78 79
81 82 85 89 90 93 97 98 103 108 110 111 114 115 117 118 119 121 123
127 128 129 130 132 135 147 148 **P**7
Primary Contact: Ronald D. Davis, Chief Executive Officer
CFO: Terry Scoggin, Chief Financial Officer
CMO: Chris Burling, M.D., Chief of Staff
CIO: Kevin Harris, Director Information Systems
CHR: Tony Piazza, Director Human Resources
CNO: Carol Slider, Chief Nursing Officer
Web address: www.titusregional.com
Control: Hospital district or authority, Government, nonfederal **Service:** General
Medical and Surgical

Staffed Beds: 74 **Admissions:** 4287 **Census:** 47 **Outpatient Visits:** 211126
Births: 1088 **Total Expense ($000):** 66944 **Payroll Expense ($000):** 26475
Personnel: 518

MOUNT VERNON—Franklin County

★ **EAST TEXAS MEDICAL CENTER–MOUNT VERNON (450373)**, 500 Highway
37 South, Zip 75457–6550, Mailing Address: P.O. Box 477, Zip 75457–0477;
tel. 903/537–8000 **A**9 10 **F**3 29 34 35 40 43 50 57 63 64 65 68 75 82 84
85 86 87 97 102 107 114 119 127 **P**6 **S** East Texas Medical Center Regional
Healthcare System, Tyler, TX
Primary Contact: Jamie–Crystal Wylie, Chief Executive Officer
CFO: Margaret Haak–Muse, Chief Financial Officer and Assistant Administrator
CMO: Michael Walker, D.O., Chief of Staff
CHR: Kathy Shelton, Director Human Resources
Web address: www.etmc.org/etmcmountvernon/
Control: Other not–for–profit (including NFP Corporation) **Service:** General
Medical and Surgical

Staffed Beds: 30 **Admissions:** 526 **Census:** 5 **Outpatient Visits:** 20047
Births: 0 **Total Expense ($000):** 7487 **Payroll Expense ($000):** 2719
Personnel: 55

Many Facility Codes have changed. Please refer to the AHA Guide Code Chart. © 2014 AHA Guide

TX

MUENSTER—Cooke County

MUENSTER MEMORIAL HOSPITAL (451335), 605 North Maple Street, Zip 76252–2424, Mailing Address: P.O. Box 370, Zip 76252–0370; tel. 940/759–2271 **A**9 10 18 **F**11 35 40 43 45 53 57 59 62 64 65 75 77 81 93 107 114 119 127 130 133 146 **P**8
Primary Contact: Michael Kent, Chief Executive Officer
CFO: Richard Teeter, Chief Financial Officer
CMO: J. Stephen Jones, M.D., Chief of Staff
CIO: Sheri Hutchins, Director Health Information Management
Control: Hospital district or authority, Government, nonfederal **Service:** General Medical and Surgical

Staffed Beds: 18 **Admissions:** 318 **Census:** 11 **Outpatient Visits:** 4048
Births: 0 **Total Expense ($000):** 9613 **Payroll Expense ($000):** 4292
Personnel: 104

MULESHOE—Bailey County

★ **MULESHOE AREA MEDICAL CENTER (451372)**, 708 South First Street, Zip 79347–3627; tel. 806/272–4524 **A**9 10 18 **F**3 11 29 34 35 40 43 50 59 64 65 68 69 75 77 81 93 107 114 119 127 130 133
Primary Contact: David Burke, Administrator and Chief Executive Officer
CMO: Bruce Purdy, M.D., Chief of Staff
CHR: Suzanne Nichols, Director Human Resources
Web address: www.mahdtx.org
Control: Hospital district or authority, Government, nonfederal **Service:** General Medical and Surgical

Staffed Beds: 25 **Admissions:** 439 **Census:** 6 **Outpatient Visits:** 29501
Births: 1 **Total Expense ($000):** 8138 **Payroll Expense ($000):** 3417
Personnel: 125

NACOGDOCHES—Nacogdoches County

☒ **NACOGDOCHES MEDICAL CENTER (450656)**, 4920 N.E. Stallings Drive, Zip 75965–1200; tel. 936/569–9481 **A**1 2 9 10 19 **F**13 15 18 20 22 23 24 26 29 31 34 35 39 40 45 46 47 48 49 50 51 56 57 59 60 64 70 74 75 76 77 78 79 81 82 85 86 87 93 107 108 110 111 114 115 116 117 118 119 120 121 123 129 130 131 132 135 146 147 148 **S** TENET Healthcare Corporation, Dallas, TX
Primary Contact: Gary L. Stokes, Chief Executive Officer
COO: Clay Farell, Chief Operating Officer
CFO: Frank Malek, Chief Financial Officer
CMO: Charles Thompson, M.D., Chief Medical Officer
CIO: Teresa Simon, Director Information Systems
CHR: Teresa Farrell, Chief Human Resources Officer
CNO: Mario B. Estrella, R.N., Chief Nursing Officer
Web address: www.nacmedicalcenter.com
Control: Partnership, Investor–owned, for–profit **Service:** General Medical and Surgical

Staffed Beds: 109 **Admissions:** 3847 **Census:** 38 **Outpatient Visits:** 45682
Births: 629 **Total Expense ($000):** 52525 **Payroll Expense ($000):** 18083
Personnel: 327

☐ **NACOGDOCHES MEMORIAL HOSPITAL (450508)**, 1204 North Mound Street, Zip 75961–4061; tel. 936/564–4611 **A**1 9 10 19 **F**3 7 11 13 15 18 20 22 24 26 28 29 30 31 34 35 40 43 46 47 49 50 57 59 61 64 68 70 74 76 77 78 79 80 81 85 86 89 90 93 96 107 108 110 111 114 118 119 126 130 132 146 147 148
Primary Contact: Scott Street, Chief Executive Officer
CFO: Jane Ann Bridges, Chief Financial Officer
CNO: Beth Knight, Chief Nursing Officer
Web address: www.nacmem.org
Control: Hospital district or authority, Government, nonfederal **Service:** General Medical and Surgical

Staffed Beds: 118 **Admissions:** 4525 **Census:** 65 **Outpatient Visits:** 65744
Births: 755 **Total Expense ($000):** 84325 **Payroll Expense ($000):** 31501
Personnel: 701

NASSAU BAY—Harris County

★ **HOUSTON METHODIST ST. JOHN HOSPITAL (450709)**, 18300 St. John Drive, Zip 77058–6302; tel. 281/333–5503 **A**2 3 5 10 **F**3 8 11 13 15 18 20 22 24 26 28 29 30 34 35 40 44 45 49 51 53 54 57 59 60 62 63 64 65 66 68 69 70 71 73 74 75 76 77 78 79 81 82 83 84 85 86 87 93 107 108 110 111 114 115 119 130 131 132 146 147 148 **P**8 **S** Houston Methodist, Houston, TX
Primary Contact: Dan Newman, Interim Chief Executive Officer
COO: Nancy Pittman, MS, Vice President, Nursing
CFO: David A. Witt, Vice President Finances
CHR: Becky A. Merritt, Director Human Resources
CNO: Nancy Pittman, MS, Vice President, Nursing
Web address: www.houstonmethodist.org/st-john/clear-lake
Control: Other not–for–profit (including NFP Corporation) **Service:** General Medical and Surgical

Staffed Beds: 137 **Admissions:** 6412 **Census:** 70 **Outpatient Visits:** 146680
Births: 503 **Total Expense ($000):** 102181 **Payroll Expense ($000):** 40192
Personnel: 625

NAVASOTA—Grimes County

☒ **GRIMES ST. JOSEPH HEALTH CENTER (451322)**, 210 South Judson Street, Zip 77868–3704; tel. 936/825–6585 **A**1 9 10 18 **F**3 29 34 40 43 56 57 59 75 77 81 93 103 107 111 119 130 132 133 135 146 **S** Sylvania Franciscan Health, Toledo, OH
Primary Contact: Reed Edmundson, Regional Administrator
CFO: Dan Goggin, Senior Vice President and Chief Financial Officer
CMO: Luke P. Scamardo, II, M.D., Chief of Staff
CIO: Mike Russo, Vice President Information Systems
CHR: Michael G. Costa, Director Human Resources
CNO: Cesar Lopez, R.N., Director of Nurses
Web address: www.st–joseph.org
Control: Church–operated, Nongovernment, not–for profit **Service:** General Medical and Surgical

Staffed Beds: 18 **Admissions:** 418 **Census:** 8 **Outpatient Visits:** 18665
Births: 0 **Total Expense ($000):** 9716 **Payroll Expense ($000):** 4549
Personnel: 95

NEDERLAND—Jefferson County

MID–JEFFERSON EXTENDED CARE HOSPITAL (452083), 2600 Highway 365, Zip 77627–6237; tel. 409/726–8700 **A**9 10 **F**1 3 29 30 34 35 40 70 74 75 77 79 85 130 148
Primary Contact: Mark Rice, Administrator
COO: Wade K. Lester, Chief Nursing and Operations Officer
Web address: www.midjeffextendedcare.com/index.php
Control: Corporation, Investor–owned, for–profit **Service:** Long–Term Acute Care hospital

Staffed Beds: 48 **Admissions:** 503 **Census:** 34 **Outpatient Visits:** 0 **Births:** 0 **Total Expense ($000):** 14350 **Payroll Expense ($000):** 6685 **Personnel:** 116

NEW BRAUNFELS—Comal County

GULF STATES LONG TERM ACUTE CARE OF NEW BRAUNFELS See Post Acute/Warm Springs Specialty Hospital of New Braunfels

☐ **NEW BRAUNFELS REGIONAL REHABILITATION HOSPITAL (673049)**, 2041 Sundance Parkway, Zip 78130–2779; tel. 830/625–6700 **A**1 9 10 **F**29 34 57 64 90 91 93 130 132 148 **S** Ernest Health, Inc., Albuquerque, NM
Primary Contact: Jennifer Malatek, Chief Executive Officer
CFO: Sue Thomsen, Chief Financial Officer
CMO: Maria R. Lomba, Medical Director
CHR: Cheryl Smith, Manager Human Resources
CNO: Peggy Schmits, Director, Nursing Operations
Web address: www.nbrrh.ernesthealth.com
Control: Corporation, Investor–owned, for–profit **Service:** Rehabilitation

Staffed Beds: 40 **Admissions:** 690 **Census:** 28 **Outpatient Visits:** 3434
Births: 0 **Total Expense ($000):** 11799 **Payroll Expense ($000):** 5747
Personnel: 114

☒ **POST ACUTE/WARM SPRINGS SPECIALTY HOSPITAL OF NEW BRAUNFELS (452106)**, 1445 Hanz Drive, Zip 78130–2567; tel. 830/627–7600 **A**1 9 10 **F**1 3 29 30 34 85 130 148 **S** Post Acute Medical, LLC, Enola, PA
Primary Contact: Shayne Goode, Administrator
Web address: www.warmsprings.org/locations/hos/h1/
Control: Partnership, Investor–owned, for–profit **Service:** Long–Term Acute Care hospital

Staffed Beds: 40 **Admissions:** 392 **Census:** 27 **Outpatient Visits:** 0 **Births:** 0 **Total Expense ($000):** 14036 **Payroll Expense ($000):** 5485 **Personnel:** 88

TX

NOCONA—Montague County

NOCONA GENERAL HOSPITAL (450641), 100 Park Road, Zip 76255–3616; tel. 940/825–3235 **A**9 10 **F**7 11 28 29 30 34 35 40 43 45 50 53 57 59 62 64 66 75 81 82 83 84 86 87 93 107 108 114 119 130 133 146 148 **P**5
Primary Contact: Lance Meekins, Administrator
CFO: Lance Meekins, Administrator
CMO: Chance Dingler, M.D., Chief Medical Officer
CHR: Paula Monkres, Administrative Assistant and Director Human Resources
Web address: www.noconageneral.com/
Control: Hospital district or authority, Government, nonfederal **Service:** General Medical and Surgical

> **Staffed Beds:** 25 **Admissions:** 556 **Census:** 9 **Outpatient Visits:** 12452
> **Births:** 0 **Total Expense ($000):** 7439 **Payroll Expense ($000):** 3805
> **Personnel:** 102

NORTH RICHLAND HILLS—Tarrant County

⊞ **NORTH HILLS HOSPITAL (450087)**, 4401 Booth Calloway Road, Zip 76180–7399; tel. 817/255–1000 **A**1 9 10 **F**3 8 12 13 15 17 18 20 22 24 28 29 30 31 34 37 40 42 45 49 53 56 57 59 64 70 74 75 76 77 78 79 81 85 86 87 93 107 108 110 111 115 118 119 126 130 132 135 146 147 148 **P**3 **S** HCA, Nashville, TN
Primary Contact: Randy Moresi, Chief Executive Officer
COO: Nancy L. Hill, R.N., Chief Operating Officer
CFO: Nick Galt, Chief Financial Officer
CMO: John McDonald, M.D., Chief Medical Officer
CIO: Jason Sims, Facility Information Security Officer
CHR: Cynthia Dang, Vice President Human Resources
CNO: Tracey Smithson, Chief Nursing Officer
Web address: www.northhillshospital.com
Control: Partnership, Investor–owned, for–profit **Service:** General Medical and Surgical

> **Staffed Beds:** 176 **Admissions:** 7457 **Census:** 84 **Outpatient Visits:** 85902
> **Births:** 580 **Total Expense ($000):** 105798 **Payroll Expense ($000):** 41078
> **Personnel:** 573

ODESSA—Ector County

☐ **BASIN HEALTHCARE CENTER (670066)**, 900 East 4th Street, Zip 79761–5255; tel. 432/362–9900, (Nonreporting) **A**1 9 10
Primary Contact: Gail Knous, Interim Administrator
CFO: Carl J. Flanagan, CPA, Chief Financial Officer
CMO: Richard Bartlett, M.D., Chief Medical Officer
CIO: Carl J. Flanagan, CPA, Chief Financial Officer
CHR: Gail Knous, Chief Executive Officer and Chief Compliance Officer
Web address: www.bhcodessa.com/
Control: Partnership, Investor–owned, for–profit **Service:** General Medical and Surgical

> **Staffed Beds:** 12

⊞ **MEDICAL CENTER HEALTH SYSTEM (450132)**, 500 West Fourth Street, Zip 79761–5059, Mailing Address: P.O. Drawer 7239, Zip 79760–7239; tel. 432/640–4000 **A**1 2 3 5 8 9 10 **F**3 8 11 12 13 15 17 18 20 22 24 26 28 29 30 31 34 35 39 40 43 46 47 48 49 50 53 54 57 59 64 65 66 68 70 71 72 74 75 76 77 78 79 81 85 87 89 90 93 107 111 114 115 116 117 118 119 126 129 130 131 132 135 144 146 147 148 **P**6 8
Primary Contact: William W. Webster, FACHE, Chief Executive Officer
COO: Tony Ruiz, Chief Operating Officer
CFO: Jon Riggs, Chief Financial Officer
CMO: Bruce Becker, M.D., Chief Medical Officer
CIO: Gary Barnes, Chief Information Officer
CHR: Robbi Banks, Executive Director Human Resources
CNO: Chad Dunavan, R.N., Interim Chief Nursing Officer
Web address: www.mchodessa.com
Control: Hospital district or authority, Government, nonfederal **Service:** General Medical and Surgical

> **Staffed Beds:** 355 **Admissions:** 13525 **Census:** 190 **Outpatient Visits:** 299980 **Births:** 1586 **Total Expense ($000):** 240189 **Payroll Expense ($000):** 89847 **Personnel:** 1986

MEDICAL CENTER HOSPITAL See Medical Center Health System

◇ **ODESSA REGIONAL MEDICAL CENTER (450661)**, 520 East Sixth Street, Zip 79760–4565, Mailing Address: P.O. Box 4859, Zip 79760–4859; tel. 432/582–8000 **A**5 9 10 21 **F**3 12 13 15 17 18 20 22 23 24 25 29 34 35 40 43 46 49 50 51 52 55 57 59 60 64 72 74 75 76 79 80 81 82 85 86 87 89 90 91 107 108 111 115 119 124 130 132 146 147 148 **P**8 **S** IASIS Healthcare, Franklin, TN
Primary Contact: Stacey L. Gerig, Chief Executive Officer
CIO: Jimmy Diaz, Director Information Technology
CHR: Jill Sparkman, Director Human Resources
CNO: Levi Stone, R.N., Chief Nursing Officer
Web address: www.odessaregionalmedicalcenter.com
Control: Partnership, Investor–owned, for–profit **Service:** General Medical and Surgical

> **Staffed Beds:** 213 **Admissions:** 6237 **Census:** 86 **Outpatient Visits:** 44847
> **Births:** 2540 **Total Expense ($000):** 97294 **Payroll Expense ($000):** 35265
> **Personnel:** 570

OLNEY—Young County

★ **HAMILTON HOSPITAL (451354)**, 901 West Hamilton Street, Zip 76374–1725, Mailing Address: P.O. Box 158, Zip 76374–0158; tel. 940/564–5521 **A**9 10 18 **F**7 11 13 28 29 30 34 40 43 53 57 76 77 81 86 89 93 107 114 119 127 133 146 148
Primary Contact: Michael H. Huff, Chief Executive Officer
CFO: Coy Noles, Chief Financial Officer Consultant
CMO: Mark L. Mankins, M.D., Chief of Staff
CIO: Rick Oliver, Information Technology
CHR: Amy Moore, Human Resources
CNO: Samantha Isbell, R.N., Chief Nursing Officer
Web address: www.olneyhamiltonhospital.com
Control: Hospital district or authority, Government, nonfederal **Service:** General Medical and Surgical

> **Staffed Beds:** 25 **Admissions:** 713 **Census:** 9 **Outpatient Visits:** 13930
> **Births:** 36 **Total Expense ($000):** 11194 **Payroll Expense ($000):** 5124
> **Personnel:** 124

ORANGE—Orange County

★ ◇ **BAPTIST ORANGE HOSPITAL (450005)**, 608 Strickland Drive, Zip 77630–4717; tel. 409/883–9361 **A**9 10 21 **F**3 13 15 18 29 30 34 35 40 45 57 59 64 70 76 79 81 85 89 93 107 108 111 115 118 119 130 146 147 **S** Community Hospital Corporation, Plano, TX
Primary Contact: Jarren Garrett, Chief Administrative Officer
COO: Gerald W. Bryant, R.N., Chief Operating Officer and Chief Nursing Officer
CFO: Gary Troutman, CPA, Chief Financial Officer
CMO: Calvin Parker, M.D., Chief of Staff
CIO: William Toon, Director
CHR: Deborah Verret, JD, Chief Human Resources Officer and Risk Manager
CNO: Shannon Forrest, R.N., Administrative Director of Nursing Services
Web address: www.bhset.net
Control: Other not–for–profit (including NFP Corporation) **Service:** General Medical and Surgical

> **Staffed Beds:** 40 **Admissions:** 1940 **Census:** 18 **Outpatient Visits:** 34866
> **Births:** 213 **Total Expense ($000):** 27894 **Payroll Expense ($000):** 9363
> **Personnel:** 160

MEMORIAL HERMANN BAPTIST ORANGE HOSPITAL See Baptist Orange Hospital

PALACIOS—Matagorda County

PALACIOS COMMUNITY MEDICAL CENTER (451332), 311 Green Street, Zip 77465–3213; tel. 361/972–2511 **A**9 10 18 **F**11 29 30 34 35 38 40 41 54 56 57 59 63 64 65 68 87 91 93 107 114 119 127 128 133 146 148
Primary Contact: Alden M. Vandeveer, Jr., FACHE, Chief Executive Officer
COO: Lisa Henderson, Chief Operating Officer
CFO: Cherri Waites, Chief Financial Officer
CIO: Angela Yeager, Director Information Technology
CHR: Lisa Henderson, Chief Operations Officer
CNO: Kandance Hyde, R.N., Chief Nursing Officer
Web address: www.palacioshospital.net/
Control: Other not–for–profit (including NFP Corporation) **Service:** General Medical and Surgical

> **Staffed Beds:** 6 **Admissions:** 190 **Census:** 2 **Outpatient Visits:** 10646
> **Births:** 0 **Total Expense ($000):** 5191 **Payroll Expense ($000):** 2515
> **Personnel:** 57

PALESTINE—Anderson County

⊞ **PALESTINE REGIONAL MEDICAL CENTER (453089)**, 2900 South Loop 256, Zip 75801–6958; tel. 903/731–1000, (Nonreporting) **A**1 **S** LifePoint Hospitals, Inc., Brentwood, TN
Primary Contact: Alan E. George, Chief Executive Officer
CFO: Louis D. Ferguson, Chief Financial Officer
CIO: Rebecca Chou, Directory Information Systems
CHR: Rhonda Beard, Director Human Resources
CNO: Christi Watkins, R.N., Chief Operating Officer
Web address: www.palestineregional.com
Control: Corporation, Investor–owned, for–profit **Service:** Rehabilitation

> **Staffed Beds:** 12

★ **PALESTINE REGIONAL MEDICAL CENTER–EAST (450747)**, 2900 South Loop 256, Zip 75801–6958; tel. 903/731–1000 **A**9 10 19 20 **F**3 7 11 13 15 18 20 22 26 28 29 30 34 40 43 44 47 48 49 50 51 56 57 59 63 70 76 79 81 82 85 86 87 89 90 93 96 97 98 100 101 102 103 104 107 108 110 111 114 118 119 129 130 131 133 143 146 147 148 **S** LifePoint Hospitals, Inc., Brentwood, TN
Primary Contact: Alan E. George, Chief Executive Officer
CFO: Louis D. Ferguson, Chief Financial Officer
CIO: Rebecca Chou, Director Information Systems
CHR: Rhonda Beard, Director Human Resources
Web address: www.palestineregional.com
Control: Partnership, Investor–owned, for–profit **Service:** General Medical and Surgical

> **Staffed Beds:** 139 **Admissions:** 5589 **Census:** 59 **Outpatient Visits:** 82134
> **Births:** 716 **Total Expense ($000):** 56893 **Payroll Expense ($000):** 26618
> **Personnel:** 491

Many Facility Codes have changed. Please refer to the AHA Guide Code Chart. © 2014 AHA Guide

TX

PAMPA—Gray County

✠ **PAMPA REGIONAL MEDICAL CENTER (450099)**, One Medical Plaza, Zip 79065; tel. 806/665–3721 **A**1 9 10 20 **F**3 11 12 13 15 16 18 20 22 29 30 34 40 45 46 47 48 49 50 51 52 54 56 57 58 59 60 61 63 64 65 66 68 70 75 76 77 79 81 83 84 85 86 87 91 92 93 96 97 98 100 101 103 104 107 108 110 111 114 115 119 130 132 134 135 146 147 148 **P**7 **S** Prime Healthcare Services, Ontario, CA
Primary Contact: Brad S. Morse, Chief Executive Officer
CFO: Paul Christenson, Chief Financial Officer
CMO: David Hampton, M.D., Chief Medical Staff
CIO: Joy Patton, Chief Information Services
CHR: Debbie Dixon, Director Human Resources
CNO: Catherine Kenney, Chief Nursing Officer
Web address: www.prmctx.com
Control: Corporation, Investor–owned, for–profit **Service:** General Medical and Surgical

Staffed Beds: 50 **Admissions:** 1659 **Census:** 15 **Outpatient Visits:** 35653 **Births:** 254 **Total Expense ($000):** 31780 **Payroll Expense ($000):** 11780 **Personnel:** 276

PARIS—Lamar County

✠ **DUBUIS HOSPITAL OF PARIS (452082)**, 865 Deshong Drive, 5th Floor, Zip 75460–9313; tel. 903/782–2961 **A**1 9 10 **F**1 3 29 30 85 148 **S** Dubuis Health System, Houston, TX
Primary Contact: Kathie Reese, Administrator
CMO: James E. Gulde, M.D., Medical Director
CNO: Janice Cochran, R.N., Director of Patient Care
Web address: www.dubuis.org/CHRISTUSDubuisHospitalofParis
Control: Church–operated, Nongovernment, not–for profit **Service:** Long–Term Acute Care hospital

Staffed Beds: 25 **Admissions:** 200 **Census:** 14 **Outpatient Visits:** 0 **Births:** 0 **Total Expense ($000):** 5431 **Payroll Expense ($000):** 1778 **Personnel:** 33

☐ **PARIS REGIONAL MEDICAL CENTER (450196)**, 820 Clarksville Street, Zip 75460–6027, Mailing Address: P.O. Box 9070, Zip 75461–9070; tel. 903/785–4521, (Includes PARIS REGIONAL MEDICAL CENTER, 865 Deshong Drive, Zip 75462–2097; tel. 903/785–4521; PARIS REGIONAL MEDICAL CENTER–SOUTH CAMPUS, 820 Clarksville Street, Zip 75460–9070, Mailing Address: P.O. Box 9070, Zip 75461–9070; tel. 903/785–4521) **A**1 9 10 19 **F**3 8 11 13 15 17 18 20 22 24 26 28 29 30 31 34 35 36 39 40 45 49 50 51 55 57 59 60 64 65 66 68 70 72 74 75 76 77 78 79 81 82 85 86 87 89 90 91 93 97 98 102 103 107 108 111 115 119 126 127 130 132 135 144 145 146 147 148 **P**5 **S** RegionalCare Hospital Partners, Brentwood, TN
Primary Contact: Stephen Grubbs, Chief Executive Officer
CFO: Janet Montel, Chief Financial Officer
CMO: Richard Bercher, M.D., Chief Medical Officer
CHR: Cheryl Perry, Director Human Resources
CNO: Debra Taylor, Chief Nursing Officer
Web address: www.parisrmc.com
Control: Partnership, Investor–owned, for–profit **Service:** General Medical and Surgical

Staffed Beds: 192 **Admissions:** 7038 **Census:** 90 **Outpatient Visits:** 76077 **Births:** 748 **Total Expense ($000):** 97785 **Payroll Expense ($000):** 31645 **Personnel:** 729

PASADENA—Harris County

✠ **BAYSHORE MEDICAL CENTER (450097)**, 4000 Spencer Highway, Zip 77504–1202; tel. 713/359–2000, (Includes EAST HOUSTON REGIONAL MEDICAL CENTER, 13111 East Freeway, Houston, Zip 77015–5820; tel. 713/393–2000; Alice G. Adams, R.N., Chief Executive Officer) **A**1 2 3 5 9 10 **F**3 6 12 13 15 17 18 20 22 24 26 28 29 31 34 35 39 40 41 42 43 47 49 51 55 56 57 59 60 64 70 72 74 75 76 77 78 79 81 82 84 86 89 90 91 93 98 100 102 103 107 108 111 114 115 116 117 118 119 120 121 123 129 130 131 144 146 147 148 **S** HCA, Nashville, TN
Primary Contact: Jeanna Barnard, Chief Executive Officer
CFO: John Armour, Chief Financial Officer
CMO: Harold Walton, M.D., Chief of Staff
CIO: Clifford Ferguson, Director Information Technology and Systems
Web address: www.bayshoremedical.com
Control: Partnership, Investor–owned, for–profit **Service:** General Medical and Surgical

Staffed Beds: 481 **Admissions:** 20747 **Census:** 281 **Outpatient Visits:** 182783 **Births:** 4131 **Total Expense ($000):** 251483 **Payroll Expense ($000):** 102152 **Personnel:** 1801

★ **KINDRED HOSPITAL–BAY AREA**, 4801 East Sam Houston Parkway South, Zip 77505–3955; tel. 281/991–5463 **A**9 **F**1 3 29 30 34 45 46 47 60 64 70 77 93 107 114 130 132 146 148 **S** Kindred Healthcare, Louisville, KY
Primary Contact: Laura Cedillo–Rodriguez, Chief Executive Officer
CHR: Nellie Moen, Coordinator Human Resources
Web address: www.khbayareahouston.com/
Control: Corporation, Investor–owned, for–profit **Service:** Long–Term Acute Care hospital

Staffed Beds: 74 **Admissions:** 873 **Census:** 61 **Outpatient Visits:** 19 **Births:** 0 **Total Expense ($000):** 29565 **Payroll Expense ($000):** 10968 **Personnel:** 149

PATIENTS MEDICAL CENTER See St. Luke's Patients Medical Center

★ ◇ **ST. LUKE'S PATIENTS MEDICAL CENTER (670031)**, 4600 East Sam Houston Parkway South, Zip 77505–3948; tel. 713/948–7000 **A**9 10 21 **F**15 18 20 22 24 29 30 31 35 40 45 46 54 64 70 74 77 81 82 91 93 94 107 111 114 115 116 117 119 129 130 135 146 147 148 **S** Catholic Health Initiatives, Englewood, CO
Primary Contact: William Simmons, Chief Executive Officer
Web address: www.stlukestexas.com
Control: Corporation, Investor–owned, for–profit **Service:** General Medical and Surgical

Staffed Beds: 61 **Admissions:** 3914 **Census:** 52 **Outpatient Visits:** 46300 **Births:** 0 **Total Expense ($000):** 64133 **Payroll Expense ($000):** 24520 **Personnel:** 385

○ **SURGERY SPECIALTY HOSPITALS OF AMERICA (450831)**, 4301B Vista Road, Zip 77504; tel. 713/378–3000 **A**10 11 **F**3 12 29 40 45 70 75 79 81 85 107 119 129 132
Primary Contact: Dana Drummond, Chief Nursing Officer and Administrator
COO: Hemant Khemka, Chief Operating Officer
CFO: Hemant Khemka, Chief Financial Officer
CMO: Xiao H. Li, M.D., Chief of Staff
CIO: Ringo Cheng, Director Information Technology
CNO: Dana Drummond, Chief Nursing Officer and Administrator
Web address: www.surgeryspecialty.com/
Control: Partnership, Investor–owned, for–profit **Service:** General Medical and Surgical

Staffed Beds: 37 **Admissions:** 115 **Census:** 1 **Outpatient Visits:** 1412 **Births:** 0 **Total Expense ($000):** 13064 **Payroll Expense ($000):** 3333 **Personnel:** 84

PEARSALL—Frio County

★ **FRIO REGIONAL HOSPITAL (450293)**, 200 South I. H. 35, Zip 78061–3998; tel. 830/334–3617 **A**9 10 **F**3 8 15 29 35 40 43 45 53 59 62 64 68 76 77 81 87 93 107 114 119 130 133 148 **P**6
Primary Contact: Michael S. Thompson, Chief Executive Officer
CFO: Rhett D. Fricke, Chief Financial Officer
CMO: Oscar Garza, M.D., Chief of Medical Staff
CIO: Jacob Flores, Chief Information Officer
CHR: Amparo Garcia, Administrative Assistant
CNO: Louisa Martinez, Director of Nursing
Web address: www.frioregionalhospital.com
Control: Other not–for–profit (including NFP Corporation) **Service:** General Medical and Surgical

Staffed Beds: 22 **Admissions:** 324 **Census:** 3 **Outpatient Visits:** 16182 **Births:** 127 **Total Expense ($000):** 11277 **Payroll Expense ($000):** 4487 **Personnel:** 125

PECOS—Reeves County

REEVES COUNTY HOSPITAL (451377), 2323 Texas Street, Zip 79772–7338; tel. 432/447–3551 **A**9 10 18 **F**3 11 13 35 40 43 57 60 64 68 70 81 87 93 107 110 114 119 127 130 131 133 146 147 148
Primary Contact: Albert LaRochelle, Chief Executive Officer
CFO: Brenda Mckinney, Chief Financial Officer
CMO: W. J. Bang, M.D., Chief of Staff
CHR: Nadine Smith, Director Human Resources
CNO: Faye Lease, Director of Nursing
Web address: www.reevescountyhospital.com
Control: Hospital district or authority, Government, nonfederal **Service:** General Medical and Surgical

Staffed Beds: 25 **Admissions:** 1022 **Census:** 11 **Outpatient Visits:** 54081 **Births:** 98 **Total Expense ($000):** 20373 **Payroll Expense ($000):** 7944 **Personnel:** 199

TX

PERRYTON—Ochiltree County

OCHILTREE GENERAL HOSPITAL (451359), 3101 Garrett Drive,
Zip 79070–5323; tel. 806/435–3606 **A**9 10 18 **F**10 11 13 15 30 35 40 43 57
59 62 63 64 69 76 81 85 89 93 107 108 114 119 127 130 133 143 146
147 **P**1
Primary Contact: Nathan Staggs, Chief Executive Officer
CFO: Debbie Blodgett, Director of Fiscal Services
CIO: Dyan Harrison, Manager Health Information
CNO: Judy Russell, Director of Nurses
Web address: www.ochiltreehospital.com
Control: Hospital district or authority, Government, nonfederal **Service:** General
Medical and Surgical

Staffed Beds: 25 **Admissions:** 664 **Census:** 8 **Outpatient Visits:** 32659
Births: 172 **Total Expense ($000):** 13278 **Payroll Expense ($000):** 5802
Personnel: 166

PITTSBURG—Camp County

★ **EAST TEXAS MEDICAL CENTER PITTSBURG (451367)**, 2701 Highway 271
North, Zip 75686–1032; tel. 903/946–5000 **A**9 10 18 **F**3 11 12 28 29 35 40
43 45 50 53 57 59 64 68 70 75 77 81 85 87 89 92 93 97 104 107 108 111
115 119 127 129 130 133 **P**6 **S** East Texas Medical Center Regional Healthcare
System, Tyler, TX
Primary Contact: James Warren Robicheaux, Senior Administrator
CFO: Steve Miller, Chief Financial Officer
CMO: W. R. Christensen, M.D., Chief of Staff
CIO: Paula Anthony, Vice President Information Services
CHR: Kathy Shelton, Director Human Resources
CNO: Casey Mayben, Chief Nursing Officer
Web address: www.etmc.org/newpittsburg.htm
Control: Other not–for–profit (including NFP Corporation) **Service:** General
Medical and Surgical

Staffed Beds: 25 **Admissions:** 1006 **Census:** 11 **Outpatient Visits:** 80588
Births: 0 **Total Expense ($000):** 28978 **Payroll Expense ($000):** 9115
Personnel: 192

PLAINVIEW—Hale County

ALLEGIANCE BEHAVIORAL HEALTH CENTER OF PLAINVIEW (454101),
2601 Dimmit Road, 4th Floor, Zip 79072–1833; tel. 806/296–9191 **A**10 **F**29 35
56 64 98 101 103 104 **S** Allegiance Health Management, Shreveport, LA
Primary Contact: Angie Alexander, Chief Executive Officer
COO: Don Cameron, Chief Operating Officer
CFO: Jim Turgeon, Vice President Finance
CMO: Victor A. Gutierrez, M.D., Medical Director
CIO: Richard Merk, Executive Vice President
CHR: Rob Lindsey, Jr., Vice President Human Resources
Web address: www.ahmgt.com
Control: Corporation, Investor–owned, for–profit **Service:** Psychiatric

Staffed Beds: 20 **Admissions:** 300 **Census:** 12 **Outpatient Visits:** 31168
Births: 0 **Total Expense ($000):** 4624 **Payroll Expense ($000):** 2013
Personnel: 31

⊞ **COVENANT HOSPITAL PLAINVIEW (450539)**, 2601 Dimmitt Road,
Zip 79072–1833; tel. 806/296–5531 **A**1 9 10 20 **F**3 11 12 13 15 18 29 30
32 34 35 38 40 41 43 44 45 46 48 50 51 54 56 57 59 61 64 65 68 70 75
76 77 79 80 81 85 86 87 97 107 108 110 114 119 127 129 130 131 132
135 146 147 148 **S** Covenant Health System, Lubbock, TX
Primary Contact: Clay Taylor, Chief Executive Officer
COO: Mike McNutt, Assistant Administrator
CFO: Cassie Mogg, Chief Financial Officer
CMO: Sergio Lara, M.D., Chief Medical Officer
CIO: Tim Branch, Manager Information Technology
CNO: Leslie Hackett, Chief Nursing Officer
Web address: www.covenantplainview.org
Control: Church–operated, Nongovernment, not–for profit **Service:** General
Medical and Surgical

Staffed Beds: 68 **Admissions:** 2208 **Census:** 23 **Outpatient Visits:** 93722
Births: 520 **Total Expense ($000):** 34652 **Payroll Expense ($000):** 11787
Personnel: 319

PLANO—Collin County

✠ **BAYLOR REGIONAL MEDICAL CENTER AT PLANO (450890)**, 4700 Alliance
Boulevard, Zip 75093–5323; tel. 469/814–2000 **A**1 2 9 10 **F**3 12 15 29 30 31
34 35 40 45 46 47 49 54 57 59 64 70 74 75 77 78 79 80 81 82 84 85 86
87 107 108 110 111 114 118 119 126 129 130 131 132 145 146 147 148
S Baylor Scott & White Health, Dallas, TX
Primary Contact: Jerri Garison, R.N., President
COO: Joseph Brown, Vice President Operations
CFO: Deanne Kindered, Vice President Finance
CMO: John Marcucci, M.D., Vice President Medical Affairs
CHR: Kriss Gamez, Director Human Resources
Web address: www.baylorhealth.com/PhysiciansLocations/Plano/Pages/Default.
aspx
Control: Other not–for–profit (including NFP Corporation) **Service:** General
Medical and Surgical

Staffed Beds: 108 **Admissions:** 5925 **Census:** 85 **Outpatient Visits:** 55447
Births: 1 **Total Expense ($000):** 159521 **Payroll Expense ($000):** 50322
Personnel: 770

✠ **HEALTHSOUTH PLANO REHABILITATION HOSPITAL (453047)**, 2800 West
15th Street, Zip 75075–7526; tel. 972/612–9000 **A**1 9 10 **F**34 57 59 62 90
93 95 96 129 130 132 148 **S** HEALTHSOUTH Corporation, Birmingham, AL
Primary Contact: Jennifer Lynn Brewer, Chief Executive Officer
CFO: Catrina Madkins, Controller and Chief Financial Officer
CMO: Omar Colon, M.D., Medical Director
Web address: www.healthsouthplano.com
Control: Corporation, Investor–owned, for–profit **Service:** Rehabilitation

Staffed Beds: 83 **Admissions:** 1442 **Census:** 51 **Outpatient Visits:** 11723
Births: 0 **Total Expense ($000):** 19114 **Payroll Expense ($000):** 10617
Personnel: 230

✠ ◇ **MEDICAL CENTER OF PLANO (450651)**, 3901 West 15th Street,
Zip 75075–7738; tel. 972/596–6800 **A**1 2 9 10 21 **F**3 12 13 15 18 19 20 22
24 26 28 29 30 31 34 35 40 43 45 46 47 48 49 51 54 55 57 58 59 60 64
70 72 74 75 76 78 79 81 82 84 85 86 87 91 93 107 108 110 111 112 114
115 117 118 119 124 126 130 132 135 145 146 147 148 **P**5 **S** HCA,
Nashville, TN
Primary Contact: Charles Gressle, Chief Executive Officer
COO: Glenn Wallace, Chief Operating Officer
CFO: W. Patrick Whitmore, Chief Financial Officer
CMO: Ann Arnold, M.D., Medical Director
CIO: Michael Gfeller, Director Information Systems
CHR: Shanna Warren, Director Human Resources
Web address: www.medicalcenterplano.com
Control: Partnership, Investor–owned, for–profit **Service:** General Medical and
Surgical

Staffed Beds: 312 **Admissions:** 17250 **Census:** 245 **Outpatient Visits:**
113716 **Births:** 2470 **Total Expense ($000):** 271312 **Payroll Expense
($000):** 91842 **Personnel:** 1322

☐ **PLANO SPECIALTY HOSPITAL (452054)**, 1621 Coit Road, Zip 75075–6141;
tel. 972/758–5200 **A**1 9 10 **F**1 3 29 45 75 82 84 85 86 87 96 130 135 148
S Encore Healthcare, Columbia, MD
Primary Contact: Jay Lindsey, Chief Executive Officer
CFO: Deanna Lankford, Business Office Manager
CHR: Robbie McCranie, Director Human Resources
Web address: www.specialtyhospital–plano.com
Control: Corporation, Investor–owned, for–profit **Service:** Long–Term Acute Care
hospital

Staffed Beds: 43 **Admissions:** 287 **Census:** 22 **Outpatient Visits:** 0 **Births:**
0 **Total Expense ($000):** 12606 **Payroll Expense ($000):** 3944 **Personnel:**
89

☐ **TEXAS HEALTH CENTER FOR DIAGNOSTIC & SURGERY (450891)**, 6020
West Parker Road, Zip 75093–8171; tel. 972/403–2700 **A**1 2 9 10 **F**3 29 40
45 54 64 79 81 82 85 87 107 111 114 119 126 129
Primary Contact: Larry Robertson, President
CFO: Douglas Browning, Chief Financial Officer
CHR: Cookie Tedder, Human Resources Manager
CNO: Ellen Baldwin, R.N., Chief Nursing Officer
Web address: www.thcds.com
Control: Partnership, Investor–owned, for–profit **Service:** General Medical and
Surgical

Staffed Beds: 18 **Admissions:** 623 **Census:** 4 **Outpatient Visits:** 18726
Births: 0 **Total Expense ($000):** 51960 **Payroll Expense ($000):** 10754
Personnel: 147

TX

Many Facility Codes have changed. Please refer to the AHA Guide Code Chart. © 2014 AHA Guide

⊠ **TEXAS HEALTH PRESBYTERIAN HOSPITAL PLANO (450771)**, 6200 West Parker Road, Zip 75093–8185; tel. 972/981–8000 **A**1 9 10 **F**3 12 13 15 18 20 22 24 26 29 30 31 32 34 35 37 38 40 43 44 45 46 48 49 50 52 54 55 57 58 59 60 63 64 65 68 70 72 74 75 76 77 78 79 81 85 86 87 89 93 107 108 110 111 114 115 118 119 126 130 132 135 141 145 146 147 148 **P**6 **S** Texas Health Resources, Arlington, TX
Primary Contact: Mike Evans, R.N., MS, President
CFO: Lisa Gildon, Vice President and Chief Financial Officer
CMO: Gwen Webster, M.D., President Medical Staff
CIO: Susan Anderson, Director Information Systems
CHR: Kelly K. Martin, Human Resource Officer
CNO: Raymond Kelly, R.N., Chief Nursing Officer
Web address: www.texashealth.org
Control: Other not–for–profit (including NFP Corporation) **Service:** General Medical and Surgical

Staffed Beds: 338 **Admissions:** 14672 **Census:** 190 **Outpatient Visits:** 89799 **Births:** 3445 **Total Expense ($000):** 349114 **Payroll Expense ($000):** 121126 **Personnel:** 1168

☐ **THE HEART HOSPITAL BAYLOR PLANO (670025)**, 1100 Allied Drive, Zip 75093–5348; tel. 469/814–3278 **A**1 9 10 **F**3 18 20 22 24 26 28 29 30 34 40 54 57 59 64 75 81 84 85 86 87 91 92 93 96 97 107 108 111 112 114 115 116 117 118 119 120 121 123 124 126 130 146 147
Primary Contact: Mark Valentine, President
CFO: Bryan Nichols, Chief Financial Officer
CMO: Trent Pettijohn, M.D., Chief Medical Officer
CIO: Nayan Patel, Director Information Systems
CHR: Kriss Gamez, Director Human Resources
CNO: Susan Moats, R.N., Vice President of Patient Care Services and Chief Nursing Officer
Web address: www.thehearthospital.com
Control: Partnership, Investor–owned, for–profit **Service:** General Medical and Surgical

Staffed Beds: 122 **Admissions:** 3861 **Census:** 59 **Outpatient Visits:** 18930 **Births:** 0 **Total Expense ($000):** 163296 **Payroll Expense ($000):** 50072 **Personnel:** 723

☐ **VICTORY MEDICAL CENTER PLANO**, 2301 Marsh Lane, Zip 75093–8497; tel. 972/820–2600 **A**1 **F**3 8 29 40 45 46 49 68 81 82 85 86 87 130 144 **P**6 **S** Victory Healthcare, The Woodlands, TX
Primary Contact: Steve Williams, Chief Executive Officer
Web address: www.victory–healthcare.com/plano
Control: Partnership, Investor–owned, for–profit **Service:** Surgical

Staffed Beds: 20 **Admissions:** 714 **Census:** 3 **Outpatient Visits:** 3311 **Births:** 0 **Total Expense ($000):** 57796 **Payroll Expense ($000):** 8674 **Personnel:** 169

PORT ARTHUR—Jefferson County

★ **CHRISTUS DUBUIS HOSPITAL OF PORT ARTHUR (452042)**, 3600 Gates Boulevard, Zip 77642–3858; tel. 409/989–5300, (Nonreporting) **A**9 10 **S** Dubuis Health System, Houston, TX
Primary Contact: Jeffrey Livingston, Administrator
Web address: www.dubuis.org/CHRISTUSDubuisHospitalofPortArthur
Control: Church–operated, Nongovernment, not–for profit **Service:** Other specialty

Staffed Beds: 15

DUBUIS HOSPITAL OF PORT ARTHUR See Christus Dubuis Hospital of Port Arthur

◇ **THE MEDICAL CENTER OF SOUTHEAST TEXAS (450518)**, 2555 Jimmy Johnson Boulevard, Zip 77640–2007; tel. 409/724–7389 **A**9 10 21 **F**3 8 11 13 15 17 18 20 22 24 28 29 30 34 35 40 44 45 47 49 50 56 57 59 64 72 74 76 77 78 79 81 82 85 86 87 89 90 91 92 93 94 98 101 102 103 104 105 107 108 110 111 114 115 119 121 129 130 132 135 146 147 148 **P**2 **S** IASIS Healthcare, Franklin, TN
Primary Contact: Richard Gonzalez, Interim Chief Executive Officer
COO: Chris McMahon, Chief Operating Officer
CFO: Phillip Hacker, Chief Financial Officer
CMO: Nidal Buheis, M.D., Chief of Staff
CIO: Bryan Hebert, Director Information Systems
CHR: Carol Hebert, Director Human Resources
Web address: www.medicalcentersetexas.com
Control: Partnership, Investor–owned, for–profit **Service:** General Medical and Surgical

Staffed Beds: 185 **Admissions:** 8384 **Census:** 103 **Outpatient Visits:** 61738 **Births:** 1248 **Total Expense ($000):** 125651 **Payroll Expense ($000):** 39154 **Personnel:** 667

PORT LAVACA—Calhoun County

★ **MEMORIAL MEDICAL CENTER (451356)**, 815 North Virginia Street, Zip 77979–3025, Mailing Address: P.O. Box 25, Zip 77979–0025; tel. 361/552–6713 **A**9 10 18 **F**3 11 13 15 18 29 30 32 34 35 40 43 44 45 46 49 50 57 59 64 65 68 70 75 76 77 78 79 81 84 85 86 87 93 107 108 111 115 118 119 129 130 132 133 134 135 146 147 148
Primary Contact: Jason Anglin, Chief Executive Officer
COO: Roshanda Gray, Assistant Administrator
CFO: Diane Moore, Chief Financial Officer
CMO: Jeannine Griffin, M.D., Chief of Staff
CIO: Adam Besio, Chief Information Officer
CNO: Erin R. Clevenger, Chief Nursing Officer and Director of Quality
Web address: www.mmcportlavaca.com
Control: County–Government, nonfederal **Service:** General Medical and Surgical

Staffed Beds: 25 **Admissions:** 1086 **Census:** 13 **Outpatient Visits:** 38516 **Births:** 123 **Total Expense ($000):** 21664 **Payroll Expense ($000):** 8187 **Personnel:** 169

QUANAH—Hardeman County

HARDEMAN COUNTY MEMORIAL HOSPITAL (451352), 402 Mercer Street, Zip 79252–4026, Mailing Address: P.O. Box 90, Zip 79252–0090; tel. 940/663–2795 **A**9 10 18 **F**3 11 28 29 30 34 40 43 50 56 57 59 62 63 64 75 77 87 93 100 101 103 104 107 127 130 133 147 **P**5
Primary Contact: Dave Clark, Interim Chief Executive Officer
CFO: Tracy Betts, Chief Financial Officer
CMO: Kevin Lane, D.O., Chief of Staff
CNO: Dennis Thomas, Chief Nursing Officer
Web address: www.hcmhosp.com/
Control: Hospital district or authority, Government, nonfederal **Service:** General Medical and Surgical

Staffed Beds: 18 **Admissions:** 346 **Census:** 5 **Outpatient Visits:** 16442 **Births:** 0 **Total Expense ($000):** 7672 **Payroll Expense ($000):** 3766 **Personnel:** 77

QUITMAN—Wood County

★ **EAST TEXAS MEDICAL CENTER–QUITMAN (451380)**, 117 Winnsboro Street, Zip 75783–2144, Mailing Address: P.O. Box 1000, Zip 75783–1000; tel. 903/763–6300 **A**9 10 18 **F**3 11 15 29 30 35 40 43 45 50 57 59 64 65 68 79 81 85 87 107 108 110 111 115 119 127 129 130 133 **P**7 **S** East Texas Medical Center Regional Healthcare System, Tyler, TX
Primary Contact: James Warren Robicheaux, Interim Administrator
CNO: Teresa Meeks, Chief Nursing Officer
Web address: www.etmc.org/etmcquitman/
Control: Other not–for–profit (including NFP Corporation) **Service:** General Medical and Surgical

Staffed Beds: 25 **Admissions:** 934 **Census:** 11 **Outpatient Visits:** 36362 **Births:** 0 **Total Expense ($000):** 17158 **Payroll Expense ($000):** 5823 **Personnel:** 121

RANKIN—Upton County

★ **RANKIN HOSPITAL DISTRICT (451329)**, 1105 Elizabeth Street, Zip 79778, Mailing Address: P.O. Box 327, Zip 79778–0327; tel. 432/693–2443 **A**9 10 18 **F**7 35 40 59 64 65 68 89 93 97 119 133
Primary Contact: Tommy Johnson, Chief Executive Officer
CFO: Tami Burks, Comptroller
CMO: Thomas J. Curvin, M.D., Chief of Staff
Control: Hospital district or authority, Government, nonfederal **Service:** General Medical and Surgical

Staffed Beds: 10 **Admissions:** 75 **Census:** 1 **Outpatient Visits:** 3156 **Births:** 0 **Total Expense ($000):** 5804 **Payroll Expense ($000):** 2707 **Personnel:** 48

REFUGIO—Refugio County

REFUGIO COUNTY MEMORIAL HOSPITAL (451317), 107 Swift Street, Zip 78377–2425; tel. 361/526–2321 **A**9 10 18 **F**3 7 29 40 43 57 61 64 75 81 86 87 93 97 107 119 127 133 **P**6
Primary Contact: Louis R. Willeke, Administrator
Web address: www.refugiohospital.com/
Control: Hospital district or authority, Government, nonfederal **Service:** General Medical and Surgical

Staffed Beds: 20 **Admissions:** 152 **Census:** 2 **Outpatient Visits:** 25685 **Births:** 0 **Total Expense ($000):** 12320 **Payroll Expense ($000):** 4951 **Personnel:** 125

TX

Hospital, Medicare Provider Number, Address, Telephone, Approval, Facility, and Physician Codes, Health Care System

★ American Hospital Association (AHA) membership
☐ The Joint Commission accreditation   ◇ DNV Healthcare Inc. accreditation
○ Healthcare Facilities Accreditation Program
△ Commission on Accreditation of Rehabilitation Facilities (CARF) accreditation

RICHARDSON—Collin County

✈ **METHODIST RICHARDSON MEDICAL CENTER (450537)**, 2831 East President George Bush Highway, Zip 75082–3561; tel. 469/204–1000 **A**1 2 9 10 **F**3 5 11 13 15 18 20 22 24 29 30 31 34 35 38 40 42 45 46 49 54 55 56 57 59 64 65 68 70 74 75 76 77 78 79 81 82 85 86 87 93 97 98 100 101 102 103 104 105 107 108 109 110 111 112 115 116 117 119 120 121 123 124 126 129 130 131 132 135 146 147 148 **P**1 7 **S** Methodist Health System, Dallas, TX
Primary Contact: E. Kenneth Hutchenrider, President
COO: Robert Simpson, Vice President Operations
CFO: Amy Bodwell, Vice President Finance
CMO: Mark Smith, M.D., Chief Medical Officer
CIO: Terri Morris, Director Information Systems
CHR: Chris Loyd, Director Human Resources
CNO: Irene Strejc, Vice President, Nursing
Web address: www.methodisthealthsystem.org/richardson
Control: Other not–for–profit (including NFP Corporation) **Service:** General Medical and Surgical

Staffed Beds: 145 **Admissions:** 5912 **Census:** 77 **Outpatient Visits:** 80077
Births: 479 **Total Expense ($000):** 120794 **Payroll Expense ($000):** 54293
Personnel: 684

✈ **RELIANT REHABILITATION HOSPITAL NORTH TEXAS (673029)**, 3351 Waterview Parkway, Zip 75080–1449; tel. 972/398–5700 **A**1 9 10 **F**3 29 90 93 96 148 **S** Reliant Healthcare Partners, Richardson, TX
Primary Contact: Jim Ransom, Chief Executive Officer
CFO: Nichole Dykes, Chief Financial Officer
CMO: Richard Jones, M.D., Medical Director
CNO: Pam Smith, Chief Nursing Officer
Web address: www.relianthcp.com
Control: Partnership, Investor–owned, for–profit **Service:** Rehabilitation

Staffed Beds: 50 **Admissions:** 1134 **Census:** 36 **Outpatient Visits:** 6855
Births: 0 **Total Expense ($000):** 13894 **Payroll Expense ($000):** 6832
Personnel: 202

RICHMOND—Fort Bend County

☐ △ **OAKBEND MEDICAL CENTER (450330)**, 1705 Jackson Street, Zip 77469–3289; tel. 281/341–3000, (Total facility includes 26 beds in nursing home–type unit) **A**1 7 9 10 **F**3 11 13 15 18 20 22 24 26 29 30 31 34 35 40 42 43 45 46 47 49 50 56 57 59 64 65 70 72 74 75 76 78 79 81 82 85 87 89 93 98 102 103 107 108 109 110 111 114 118 119 128 129 130 132 146 147 148 **P**6
Primary Contact: Joe Freudenberger, Chief Executive Officer
CFO: Rodney Lenfant, Chief Financial Officer
CMO: Douglas Thibodeaux, M.D., Chief Medical Officer
CHR: Nancy Retzlaff, Director Human Resources
Web address: www.oakbendmedcenter.org
Control: Hospital district or authority, Government, nonfederal **Service:** General Medical and Surgical

Staffed Beds: 201 **Admissions:** 5323 **Census:** 73 **Outpatient Visits:** 60447
Births: 1447 **Total Expense ($000):** 89431 **Payroll Expense ($000):** 28428
Personnel: 652

RIO GRANDE CITY—Starr County

★ **STARR COUNTY MEMORIAL HOSPITAL (450654)**, 2753 Hospital Court, Zip 78582–6859, Mailing Address: P.O. Box 78, Zip 78582–0078; tel. 956/487–5561 **A**9 10 20 **F**7 11 13 15 29 30 34 40 43 45 46 50 57 59 64 65 66 68 75 76 81 89 107 110 111 114 119 127 130 135 145 148 **P**5
Primary Contact: Thalia H. Munoz, R.N., MS, Hospital Administrator
CFO: Rafael Olivares, Controller
CHR: Amaro Salinas, Assistant Administrator and Human Resource Officer
CNO: Mario Segura, Director of Nursing
Web address: www.starrcountyhospital.com
Control: Hospital district or authority, Government, nonfederal **Service:** General Medical and Surgical

Staffed Beds: 47 **Admissions:** 1406 **Census:** 13 **Outpatient Visits:** 45783
Births: 318 **Total Expense ($000):** 24998 **Payroll Expense ($000):** 11924
Personnel: 263

ROCKDALE—Milam County

◇ **LITTLE RIVER HEALTHCARE (451357)**, 1700 Brazos Street, Zip 76567–2517, Mailing Address: Drawer 1010, Zip 76567–1010; tel. 512/446–4500 **A**9 10 18 21 **F**11 15 18 20 22 26 28 29 40 64 65 68 75 77 79 81 82 83 84 85 87 93 96 97 107 110 111 114 119 127 130 131 133 148
Primary Contact: Jeffrey Madison, Chief Executive Officer
CMO: John Weed, III, M.D., Medical Director
CHR: Crystal Foley, Director Human Resources
Web address: www.lrhealthcare.com
Control: Corporation, Investor–owned, for–profit **Service:** General Medical and Surgical

Staffed Beds: 21 **Admissions:** 452 **Census:** 4 **Outpatient Visits:** 82961
Births: 2 **Total Expense ($000):** 46633 **Payroll Expense ($000):** 18413
Personnel: 381

ROCKWALL—Rockwall County

✈ **TEXAS HEALTH PRESBYTERIAN HOSPITAL OF ROCKWALL (670044)**, 3150 Horizon Road, Zip 75032–7805; tel. 469/698–1000 **A**1 9 10 **F**3 12 13 15 29 30 34 40 45 46 47 49 50 54 68 70 75 76 77 79 81 85 87 93 107 108 110 111 115 119 130 146 147 148
Primary Contact: Cindy Paris, R.N., President
CIO: Kenneth Huckaby, Senior Director Information Technology Systems Operations
Web address: www.phrtexas.com
Control: Corporation, Investor–owned, for–profit **Service:** General Medical and Surgical

Staffed Beds: 50 **Admissions:** 4117 **Census:** 38 **Outpatient Visits:** 49618
Births: 839 **Total Expense ($000):** 99412 **Payroll Expense ($000):** 31243
Personnel: 520

ROTAN—Fisher County

FISHER COUNTY HOSPITAL DISTRICT (451313), 774 State Highway 70 North, Zip 79546–6918, Mailing Address: P.O. Drawer F, Zip 79546–4019; tel. 325/735–2256 **A**9 10 18 **F**7 28 32 34 35 40 43 50 53 56 57 59 64 66 75 93 97 107 119 127 133 **P**6
Primary Contact: Steve Lefevre, Chief Executive Officer and Administrator
CFO: Debbie Hull, Chief Financial Officer
CMO: C. M. Callan, M.D., Chief of Staff
Web address: www.fishercountyhospital.com
Control: Hospital district or authority, Government, nonfederal **Service:** General Medical and Surgical

Staffed Beds: 12 **Admissions:** 103 **Census:** 1 **Outpatient Visits:** 18065
Births: 0 **Total Expense ($000):** 8468 **Payroll Expense ($000):** 3485
Personnel: 73

ROUND ROCK—Williamson County

CORNERSTONE HOSPITAL OF ROUND ROCK (452034), 4681 College Park Drive, Zip 78655; tel. 512/533–2525, (Nonreporting) **S** Cornerstone Healthcare Group, Dallas, TX
Primary Contact: Edward L. Dyer, Chief Executive Officer
Web address: www.chghospitals.com/roundrock
Control: **Service:** Long–Term Acute Care hospital

Staffed Beds: 54

☐ **RELIANT REHABILITATION HOSPITAL CENTRAL TEXAS (673032)**, 1400 Hester's Crossing, Zip 78681–8025; tel. 512/244–4400, (Total facility includes 25 beds in nursing home–type unit) **A**1 9 10 **F**3 29 90 93 96 128 130 148 **S** Reliant Healthcare Partners, Richardson, TX
Primary Contact: Eric Mueller, Chief Executive Officer
CNO: Vidette J. Forbes, R.N., Chief Nursing Officer and Chief Operating officer
Web address: www.reliantcentraltx.com/
Control: Partnership, Investor–owned, for–profit **Service:** Rehabilitation

Staffed Beds: 75 **Admissions:** 1669 **Census:** 55 **Outpatient Visits:** 5704
Births: 0 **Total Expense ($000):** 16973 **Payroll Expense ($000):** 7873
Personnel: 181

✈ **SCOTT & WHITE HOSPITAL AT ROUND ROCK (670034)**, 300 University Boulevard, Zip 78665–1032; tel. 512/509–0100 **A**1 5 9 10 **F**3 13 15 18 20 22 24 28 29 30 31 34 35 40 43 45 46 47 49 50 51 52 54 59 60 64 68 70 74 75 76 78 79 81 82 85 87 93 97 99 100 104 107 110 111 115 116 119 130 131 144 146 147 148 **P**6 **S** Baylor Scott & White Health, Dallas, TX
Primary Contact: Jay Fox, Chief Executive Officer
COO: Kevin E. Smith, Chief Operating Officer
CFO: Jason Cole, Senior Director Finance
CMO: Rob Watson, M.D., Chief Medical Officer
CIO: Matthew Chambers, Chief Information Officer
CHR: Mark A. Sherry, Director Human Resources
CNO: Leslie Gembol, MSN, Chief Nursing Officer
Web address: www.sw.org
Control: Other not–for–profit (including NFP Corporation) **Service:** General Medical and Surgical

Staffed Beds: 101 **Admissions:** 4925 **Census:** 47 **Outpatient Visits:** 342944
Births: 568 **Total Expense ($000):** 129675 **Payroll Expense ($000):** 43351
Personnel: 971

TX

Many Facility Codes have changed. Please refer to the AHA Guide Code Chart. © 2014 AHA Guide

✠ **SETON MEDICAL CENTER WILLIAMSON (670041)**, 201 Seton Parkway, Zip 78665–8000; tel. 512/324–4000 **A**1 5 9 10 **F**3 11 12 13 15 18 20 22 24 26 28 29 30 31 34 35 37 40 43 44 45 46 49 50 51 53 54 57 58 59 60 64 68 70 72 74 75 76 77 78 79 81 82 84 85 86 87 93 96 107 108 110 111 114 115 119 124 126 130 131 132 135 146 147 148 **P**3 8 **S** Ascension Health, Saint Louis, MO
Primary Contact: Michelle Robertson, R.N., President and Chief Executive Officer
CFO: Douglas D. Waite, Senior Vice President and Chief Financial Officer
CMO: Hugh V. Gilmore, M.D., Vice President Medical Affairs
CIO: Gerry Lewis, Chief Information Officer
CHR: Thomas Wilken, Vice President Human Resources
Web address: www.seton.net/williamson
Control: Church–operated, Nongovernment, not–for profit **Service:** General Medical and Surgical

Staffed Beds: 143 Admissions: 7443 Census: 88 Outpatient Visits: 64857 **Births:** 890 **Total Expense ($000):** 148572 **Payroll Expense ($000):** 46179 **Personnel:** 820

✠ **ST. DAVID'S ROUND ROCK MEDICAL CENTER (450718)**, 2400 Round Rock Avenue, Zip 78681–4097; tel. 512/341–1000 **A**1 2 5 9 10 **F**3 11 12 13 15 18 22 24 26 28 29 30 31 34 35 40 43 47 49 57 59 66 68 70 73 74 75 76 77 78 79 81 85 86 87 90 93 107 108 110 111 115 118 119 126 129 130 132 144 146 147 148 **P**3 6 8 **S** HCA, Nashville, TN
Primary Contact: Deborah L. Ryle, Administrator and Chief Executive Officer
COO: Tad Hatton, Chief Operating Officer
CFO: Cindy Sexton, Chief Financial Officer
CHR: Amy Noak, Director Human Resources
Web address: www.stdavids.com
Control: Other not–for–profit (including NFP Corporation) **Service:** General Medical and Surgical

Staffed Beds: 159 Admissions: 8084 Census: 95 Outpatient Visits: 64881 **Births:** 1889 **Total Expense ($000):** 116438 **Payroll Expense ($000):** 40337 **Personnel:** 610

ROWLETT—Rockwall County

✠ **LAKE POINTE MEDICAL CENTER (450742)**, 6800 Scenic Drive, Zip 75088–4552, Mailing Address: P.O. Box 1550, Zip 75030–1550; tel. 972/412–2273 **A**1 9 10 **F**3 12 13 15 18 20 22 24 28 29 30 34 35 40 42 45 46 49 50 53 54 57 59 60 64 65 70 72 73 74 75 77 78 79 81 82 85 86 87 93 107 108 110 111 114 115 118 119 120 121 126 129 130 131 132 144 146 147 148 **S** TENET Healthcare Corporation, Dallas, TX
Primary Contact: Brett D. Lee, Chief Executive Officer
COO: Debbie A. Moeller, R.N., Chief Operating Officer
CFO: Becky Speight, Chief Financial Officer
CMO: Larry Dencklau, D.O., Chief of Staff
CIO: Mark Slater, Director Information Systems
CHR: David Olmstead, Associate Administrator and Director Human Resources
CNO: Patti Gilliano, Chief Nursing Officer
Web address: www.lakepointemedical.com
Control: Corporation, Investor–owned, for–profit **Service:** General Medical and Surgical

Staffed Beds: 112 Admissions: 6867 Census: 63 Outpatient Visits: 95765 **Births:** 1439 **Total Expense ($000):** 95005 **Payroll Expense ($000):** 35802 **Personnel:** 579

RUSK—Cherokee County

☐ **RUSK STATE HOSPITAL (454009)**, 805 North Dickinson, Zip 75785–2333, Mailing Address: P.O. Box 318, Zip 75785–0318; tel. 903/683–3421 **A**1 10 **F**3 30 39 44 50 68 75 86 87 98 103 106 130 135 146 148 **P**6 **S** Texas Department of State Health Services, Austin, TX
Primary Contact: Brenda Slaton, Administrator
COO: Lynda Roberson, Senior Program Director
CFO: Rhonda Transier, Financial Officer
CMO: Joe Bates, M.D., Clinical Director
CHR: Kendra Brown, Job Requisition Coordinator
Web address: www.dshs.state.tx.us/mhhospitals/RuskSH/default.shtm
Control: State–Government, nonfederal **Service:** Psychiatric

Staffed Beds: 365 Admissions: 694 Census: 322 Outpatient Visits: 0 **Births:** 0 **Total Expense ($000):** 74144 **Payroll Expense ($000):** 32341 **Personnel:** 1028

SAN ANGELO—Tom Green County

☐ **RIVER CREST HOSPITAL (454064)**, 1636 Hunters Glen Road, Zip 76901–5016; tel. 325/949–5722 **A**1 9 10 **F**4 5 29 64 87 98 99 100 101 102 103 104 105 130 132 **S** Universal Health Services, Inc., King of Prussia, PA
Primary Contact: Mandy Westerman, Chief Executive Officer
CFO: Frank Urban, Chief Financial Officer
CMO: John Crowley, M.D., Medical Director
CHR: Brenda Coats, Director Human Resources
Web address: www.rivercresthospital.com
Control: Corporation, Investor–owned, for–profit **Service:** Psychiatric

Staffed Beds: 80 Admissions: 2743 Census: 52 Outpatient Visits: 2439 **Births:** 0 **Total Expense ($000):** 10154 **Payroll Expense ($000):** 5063 **Personnel:** 129

✠ △ **SAN ANGELO COMMUNITY MEDICAL CENTER (450340)**, 3501 Knickerbocker Road, Zip 76904–7698; tel. 325/949–9511 **A**1 7 9 10 **F**3 8 11 13 15 18 20 22 24 28 29 30 31 34 37 40 43 45 49 51 53 54 57 59 60 63 64 68 70 72 74 75 76 77 78 79 81 82 85 89 90 93 107 108 110 111 118 119 129 130 131 135 144 145 146 148 **P**8 **S** Community Health Systems, Inc., Franklin, TN
Primary Contact: Jeremy Riney, Chief Executive Officer
CHR: Lisa Bibb, Director Human Resources
Web address: www.sacmc.com
Control: Partnership, Investor–owned, for–profit **Service:** General Medical and Surgical

Staffed Beds: 131 Admissions: 5010 Census: 59 Outpatient Visits: 82770 **Births:** 790 **Total Expense ($000):** 83049 **Payroll Expense ($000):** 31256 **Personnel:** 503

✠ △ **SHANNON MEDICAL CENTER (450571)**, 120 East Harris Street, Zip 76903–5976, Mailing Address: P.O. Box 1879, Zip 76902–1879; tel. 325/653–6741, (Includes SHANNON MEDICAL CENTER– ST. JOHN'S CAMPUS, 2018 Pulliam Street, Zip 76905–5197; tel. 915/659–7100), (Total facility includes 24 beds in nursing home–type unit) **A**1 2 3 5 7 9 10 **F**3 7 8 11 13 15 18 20 22 24 26 28 29 30 31 32 34 35 37 38 40 43 45 49 50 51 53 54 56 57 58 59 60 61 62 64 68 70 72 73 74 75 76 77 78 79 80 81 82 84 85 86 87 89 90 92 93 94 96 98 100 101 102 103 107 108 110 111 114 115 117 119 128 129 130 132 145 146 147 148 **P**6
Primary Contact: Bryan Horner, President and Chief Executive Officer
CFO: Shane Plymell, Chief Financial Officer
CMO: Irvin Zeitler, D.O., Vice President Medical Affairs
CIO: Tom Perkins, Chief Information Officer
CHR: Teresa Morgan, Assistant Vice President Human Resources
CNO: Wilma P. Stuart, Ph.D., Chief Nursing Officer
Web address: www.shannonhealth.com
Control: Other not–for–profit (including NFP Corporation) **Service:** General Medical and Surgical

Staffed Beds: 289 Admissions: 11793 Census: 152 Outpatient Visits: 111804 **Births:** 1192 **Total Expense ($000):** 231453 **Payroll Expense ($000):** 74347 **Personnel:** 1487

SAN ANTONIO—Bexar County

✠ **ACUITY HOSPITAL OF SOUTH TEXAS (452040)**, 718 Lexington Avenue, Zip 78212–4768; tel. 210/572–4600 **A**1 9 10 **F**1 3 29 45 85 87 91 107 119 148 **S** AcuityHealthcare, LP, Charlotte, NC
Primary Contact: Kris Karns, Ph.D., FACHE, Chief Executive Officer
CFO: Wayne Hegwood, Chief Financial Officer
CMO: Qasim Butt, M.D., Chief Medical Officer
CHR: Sheree Allstrom, Director Human Resources
CNO: Danny Fraley, Chief Clinical Officer
Web address: www.acuitysouthtexas.com
Control: Corporation, Investor–owned, for–profit **Service:** Long–Term Acute Care hospital

Staffed Beds: 30 Admissions: 322 Census: 25 Outpatient Visits: 0 **Births:** 0 **Total Expense ($000):** 15655 **Payroll Expense ($000):** 6816 **Personnel:** 103

◇ **BAPTIST EMERGENCY HOSPITAL (670078)**, 16088 San Pedro, Zip 78232–2249; tel. 210/402–4092 **A**10 21 **F**3 40 41 75 107 108 **P**5
Primary Contact: Laura Salgado, Administrator
Web address: www.baptistemergencyhospital.com
Control: Corporation, Investor–owned, for–profit **Service:** General Medical and Surgical

Staffed Beds: 42 Admissions: 472 Census: 3 Outpatient Visits: 51366 **Births:** 1 **Total Expense ($000):** 30294 **Payroll Expense ($000):** 10748 **Personnel:** 188

Hospital, Medicare Provider Number, Address, Telephone, Approval, Facility, and Physician Codes, Health Care System

★ American Hospital Association (AHA) membership
☐ The Joint Commission accreditation
◇ DNV Healthcare Inc. accreditation
◯ Healthcare Facilities Accreditation Program
△ Commission on Accreditation of Rehabilitation Facilities (CARF) accreditation

TX

✠ △ **BAPTIST MEDICAL CENTER (450058)**, 111 Dallas Street, Zip 78205–1230; tel. 210/297–7000, (Includes MISSION TRAIL BAPTIST HOSPITAL, 3333 Research Plaza, Zip 78235–5154; tel. 210/297–3000; Andrew M. Harris, Chief Executive Officer; NORTH CENTRAL BAPTIST HOSPITAL, 520 Madison Oak Drive, Zip 78258–3912; tel. 210/297–4000; NORTHEAST BAPTIST HOSPITAL, 8811 Village Drive, Zip 78217–5440; tel. 210/297–2000; Matthew Stone, Chief Executive Officer; ST. LUKE'S BAPTIST HOSPITAL, 7930 Floyd Curl Drive, Zip 78229–0100; tel. 210/297–5000; John E. Knox, FACHE, Chief Executive Officer) **A**1 2 3 5 7 9 10 **F**1 3 11 12 13 14 15 17 18 19 20 22 24 26 28 29 30 31 35 37 38 40 41 42 43 44 45 46 47 50 54 55 56 57 59 60 64 65 68 70 72 73 74 75 76 77 78 79 80 81 82 85 86 87 88 89 90 91 92 93 95 96 98 101 102 103 107 108 111 114 115 116 117 119 124 126 129 130 132 135 145 146 147 148 **P**8 **S** TENET Healthcare Corporation, Dallas, TX
Primary Contact: Jonathan Turton, FACHE, Interim President
COO: Sandy Ethridge, Interim Chief Operating Officer
CFO: Linda Kirks, Chief Financial Officer
CMO: Richard Marple, M.D., Chief Medical Officer
CIO: Gary Davis, Vice President Information Systems
CHR: Sarah Spinharney, Senior Vice President
CNO: Nelson Tuazon, Chief Nursing Officer
Web address: www.baptisthealthsystem.com
Control: Partnership, Investor–owned, for–profit **Service:** General Medical and Surgical

Staffed Beds: 1527 **Admissions:** 66926 **Census:** 806 **Outpatient Visits:** 315134 **Births:** 10724 **Total Expense ($000):** 808040 **Payroll Expense ($000):** 332043 **Personnel:** 4831

✠ **CHRISTUS SANTA ROSA HEALTH SYSTEM (450237)**, 333 North Santa Rosa Street, Zip 78207–3108; tel. 210/704–4184, (Includes CHILDREN'S HOSPITAL OF SAN ANTONIO, 333 North Santa Rosa Street, Zip 78207; tel. 210/704–2011; Elias Neujahr, Administrator; CHRISTUS SANTA ROSA HOSPITAL – NEW BRAUNFELS, 600 North Union Avenue, New Braunfels, Zip 78130–4191; tel. 830/606–9111; Jim D. Wesson, Vice President and Administrator; CHRISTUS SANTA ROSA–MEDICAL CENTER, 2827 Babcock Road, Zip 78229–4813; tel. 210/705–6300; Christopher Bowe, Vice President and Administrator), (Nonreporting) **A**1 3 5 9 10 **S** CHRISTUS Health, Irving, TX
Primary Contact: Patrick Brian Carrier, President and Chief Executive Officer
CFO: Shawn Barnett, Vice President and Chief Financial Officer
CMO: James C. Martin, M.D., Vice President and Chief Medical Officer
CHR: Crystal H. Kohanke, Vice President Human Resources
CNO: Patty Toney, R.N., Chief Nurse Executive
Web address: www.christussantarosa.org
Control: Church–operated, Nongovernment, not–for profit **Service:** General Medical and Surgical

Staffed Beds: 560

☐ **CLARITY CHILD GUIDANCE CENTER**, 8535 Tom Slick, Zip 78229–3363; tel. 210/616–0300 **A**1 3 5 9 **F**29 41 98 99 101 102 104 105 106 130
Primary Contact: Frederick W. Hines, President and Chief Executive Officer
CFO: Michael Bernick, Vice President Finance
CMO: Graham Rogeness, M.D., Medical Director
CHR: Gina Massey, Vice President Human Resources
Web address: www.claritycgc.org
Control: Other not–for–profit (including NFP Corporation) **Service:** Children's hospital psychiatric

Staffed Beds: 52 **Admissions:** 1587 **Census:** 47 **Outpatient Visits:** 16142 **Births:** 0 **Total Expense ($000):** 15231 **Payroll Expense ($000):** 10295 **Personnel:** 228

◇ **FOUNDATION SURGICAL HOSPITAL OF SAN ANTONIO (670054)**, 9522 Huebner Road, Zip 78240–1548; tel. 210/478–5400 **A**9 10 21 **F**3 12 29 30 35 37 40 44 45 51 53 68 74 75 77 79 81 85 86 87 107 114 119 129 130 132 135 148 **S** Foundation Surgical Hospital Affiliates, Oklahoma City, OK
Primary Contact: Robert Trussell, Chief Executive Officer
Web address: www.fshsanantonio.com/bariatric–foundation–surgical.html
Control: Corporation, Investor–owned, for–profit **Service:** Surgical

Staffed Beds: 20 **Admissions:** 942 **Census:** 6 **Outpatient Visits:** 2047 **Births:** 0 **Total Expense ($000):** 29552 **Payroll Expense ($000):** 5431 **Personnel:** 88

✠ **HEALTHSOUTH REHABILITATION INSTITUTE OF SAN ANTONIO (453031)**, 9119 Cinnamon Hill, Zip 78240–5401; tel. 210/691–0737 **A**1 9 10 **F**29 62 64 75 90 91 93 96 130 132 148 **P**5 **S** HEALTHSOUTH Corporation, Birmingham, AL
Primary Contact: Scott Butcher, Chief Executive Officer
CFO: Larry Spriggs, Controller
CMO: Richard Senelick, M.D., Medical Director
CHR: Vanessa Tejada, Director Human Resources
CNO: Felipe Gregorio, Chief Nursing Officer
Web address: www.hsriosa.com
Control: Corporation, Investor–owned, for–profit **Service:** Rehabilitation

Staffed Beds: 96 **Admissions:** 1193 **Census:** 54 **Outpatient Visits:** 9239 **Births:** 0 **Total Expense ($000):** 20436 **Payroll Expense ($000):** 10368 **Personnel:** 196

✠ **KINDRED HOSPITAL–SAN ANTONIO (452016)**, 3636 Medical Drive, Zip 78229–2183; tel. 210/616–0616 **A**1 9 10 **F**1 3 29 30 70 75 77 85 87 107 130 148 **S** Kindred Healthcare, Louisville, KY
Primary Contact: Katherine Eskew, Chief Executive Officer
CFO: Erin Russell, Controller
CMO: Charles Duncan, M.D., Medical Director
CHR: Stanley Richardson, Coordinator Human Resources and Payroll Benefits
Web address: www.khsanantonio.com/
Control: Corporation, Investor–owned, for–profit **Service:** Long–Term Acute Care hospital

Staffed Beds: 59 **Admissions:** 417 **Census:** 29 **Outpatient Visits:** 29 **Births:** 0 **Total Expense ($000):** 18643 **Payroll Expense ($000):** 6741 **Personnel:** 109

✠ **LAUREL RIDGE TREATMENT CENTER (454060)**, 17720 Corporate Woods Drive, Zip 78259–3500; tel. 210/491–9400 **A**1 3 5 9 10 **F**5 29 35 38 75 77 98 99 100 101 103 105 106 130 132 **S** Universal Health Services, Inc., King of Prussia, PA
Primary Contact: Jacob Cuellar, M.D., Chief Executive Officer
COO: Debra Ward, Chief Operating Officer
CFO: Linda Maenius, Chief Financial Officer
CMO: Benigno J. Fernandez, M.D., Executive Medical Director
CHR: Brenda Frederick, Director Human Resources
CNO: Kathy Rosetta, Chief Nursing Officer
Web address: www.laurelridgetc.com
Control: Partnership, Investor–owned, for–profit **Service:** Psychiatric

Staffed Beds: 208 **Admissions:** 6323 **Census:** 165 **Outpatient Visits:** 17474 **Births:** 0 **Total Expense ($000):** 44908 **Payroll Expense ($000):** 18642 **Personnel:** 357

✠ **LIFECARE HOSPITALS OF SAN ANTONIO (452059)**, 8902 Floyd Curl Drive, Zip 78240–1681; tel. 210/690–7000 **A**1 9 10 **F**1 3 29 45 75 77 85 86 87 96 97 107 114 130 148 **S** LifeCare Management Services, Plano, TX
Primary Contact: Randell G. Stokes, Chief Executive Officer
CMO: Randall C. Bell, M.D., Medical Director
CIO: Mike Wattenbarger, Chief Information Officer
Web address: www.lifecare–hospitals.com
Control: Corporation, Investor–owned, for–profit **Service:** Long–Term Acute Care hospital

Staffed Beds: 62 **Admissions:** 630 **Census:** 53 **Outpatient Visits:** 0 **Births:** 0 **Total Expense ($000):** 26581 **Payroll Expense ($000):** 12085 **Personnel:** 223

✠ **METHODIST AMBULATORY SURGERY HOSPITAL – NORTHWEST (450780)**, 9150 Huebner Road, Suite 100, Zip 78240–1545; tel. 210/575–5000 **A**1 9 10 **F**3 29 40 68 79 81 85 87 **P**8 **S** HCA, Nashville, TN
Primary Contact: Andrew Williams, Chief Executive Officer
CFO: Tim Carr, Chief Financial Officer
CHR: Barry Burns, Vice President
CNO: Cathy Bump, R.N., Chief Nursing Officer
Web address: www.sahealth.com
Control: Partnership, Investor–owned, for–profit **Service:** General Medical and Surgical

Staffed Beds: 23 **Admissions:** 590 **Census:** 4 **Outpatient Visits:** 7552 **Births:** 0 **Total Expense ($000):** 22695 **Payroll Expense ($000):** 6704 **Personnel:** 108

✠ **METHODIST HOSPITAL (450388)**, 7700 Floyd Curl Drive, Zip 78229–3993; tel. 210/575–4000, (Includes METHODIST CHILDREN'S HOSPITAL, 7700 Floyd Curl Drive, Zip 78229–3383; tel. 210/575–7000; METHODIST SPECIALTY AND TRANSPLANT HOSPITAL, 8026 Floyd Curl Drive, Zip 78229–3915; tel. 210/575–8090; David Handley, Chief Executive Officer; METHODIST TEXSAN HOSPITAL, 6700 IH–10 West, Zip 78201; tel. 210/736–6700; Marc Strode, Chief Executive Officer; METROPOLITAN METHODIST HOSPITAL, 1310 McCullough Avenue, Zip 78212–2617; tel. 210/757–2909; Gregory A. Seiler, Chief Executive Officer; NORTHEAST METHODIST HOSPITAL, 12412 Judson Road, Live Oak, Zip 78233–3255; tel. 210/757–5000; Michael D. Beaver, Chief Executive Officer) **A**1 2 3 5 9 10 **F**3 4 5 8 11 12 13 15 17 18 19 20 21 22 23 24 25 26 27 28 29 30 31 34 35 38 40 41 42 43 44 45 46 47 48 49 51 53 54 56 57 58 59 60 64 65 68 70 72 74 75 76 77 78 79 80 81 82 84 85 86 87 88 89 90 93 95 96 98 100 101 102 103 104 105 107 108 111 114 115 119 121 124 126 127 129 130 132 135 136 137 138 139 142 143 145 146 147 148 **P**7 **S** HCA, Nashville, TN
Primary Contact: Gay Nord, Chief Executive Officer
CFO: Nancy Meadows, Chief Financial Officer
CMO: Russell Woodward, M.D., Chief Medical Officer
CIO: Eddie Cuellar, Vice President Information Systems
CHR: Nancy Edgar, Vice President Human Resources
Web address: www.sahealth.com
Control: Partnership, Investor–owned, for–profit **Service:** General Medical and Surgical

Staffed Beds: 1589 **Admissions:** 74866 **Census:** 1058 **Outpatient Visits:** 436401 **Births:** 9694 **Total Expense ($000):** 1044001 **Payroll Expense ($000):** 389911 **Personnel:** 5670

TX

Many Facility Codes have changed. Please refer to the AHA Guide Code Chart. © 2014 AHA Guide

✠ **METHODIST STONE OAK HOSPITAL (670055)**, 1139 East Sonterra Boulevard, Zip 78258–4347; tel. 210/638–2100 **A**1 9 10 **F**3 13 15 18 20 22 24 29 30 31 34 38 40 44 45 46 47 49 57 59 60 64 65 68 70 72 74 75 76 77 78 79 80 81 82 85 86 87 107 108 111 115 118 119 126 130 145 146 147 **S** HCA, Nashville, TN
Primary Contact: Dominic J. Dominguez, Interim Chief Executive Officer
COO: Candie Starr, Chief Operating Officer and Ethics and Compliance Officer
CFO: Gabriel Marrufo, Chief Financial Officer
CNO: Ann Winn, M.D., Chief Nursing Officer
Web address: www.stoneoakhealth.com
Control: Partnership, Investor–owned, for–profit **Service:** General Medical and Surgical

Staffed Beds: 140 **Admissions:** 8962 **Census:** 97 **Outpatient Visits:** 37582 **Births:** 1644 **Total Expense ($000):** 128280 **Payroll Expense ($000):** 35853 **Personnel:** 460

◇ **NIX HEALTH CARE SYSTEM (450130)**, 414 Navarro Street, Zip 78205–2516; tel. 210/271–1800 **A**3 5 9 10 21 **F**3 5 12 15 18 20 22 24 26 29 30 31 35 40 44 45 49 56 57 59 60 62 64 68 70 74 75 78 79 81 82 85 87 90 93 97 98 99 103 107 108 110 111 114 118 119 129 130 132 142 143 146 147 148
Primary Contact: John F. Strieby, Chief Executive Officer
COO: Blake W. Hubbard, FACHE, Senior Vice President and Chief Operating Officer
CFO: Lester Surrock, Chief Financial Officer
CMO: Dina Goytia–Leos, M.D., Chief of Staff
CIO: Adrian Dickreiter, Vice President Technology
CHR: Blake W. Hubbard, FACHE, Senior Vice President and Chief Operating Officer
CNO: Maria Rose Lopez, R.N., Chief of Nursing
Web address: www.nixhealth.com
Control: Corporation, Investor–owned, for–profit **Service:** General Medical and Surgical

Staffed Beds: 181 **Admissions:** 8019 **Census:** 125 **Outpatient Visits:** 136337 **Births:** 0 **Total Expense ($000):** 114283 **Payroll Expense ($000):** 37057 **Personnel:** 770

✠ **POST ACUTE/WARM SPRINGS REHABILITATION HOSPITAL OF SAN ANTONIO (453035)**, 5101 Medical Drive, Zip 78229–4801; tel. 210/616–0100, (Includes WARM SPRINGS REHABILITATION HOSPITAL OF THOUSAND OAKS, 14747 Jones Maltsberger Road, Zip 78247–3713; tel. 210/581–5300; Debra Bormann, Chief Executive Officer; WARM SPRINGS REHABILITATION HOSPITAL OF WESTOVER HILLS, 10323 State Highway 151, Zip 78251–4557; tel. 210/581–5306), (Total facility includes 4 beds in nursing home–type unit) **A**1 3 5 9 10 **F**3 11 29 30 57 64 68 74 75 79 82 90 91 93 94 96 128 130 132 146 148 **S** Post Acute Medical, LLC, Enola, PA
Primary Contact: Steve Flaherty, Chief Executive Officer
CFO: James Asberry, Chief Financial Officer
CMO: Alex Willingham, M.D., Medical Director
CIO: Rick Marek, Vice President Medical Information Systems
CHR: Waynea Finley, System Director Human Resources
Web address: www.warmsprings.org
Control: Partnership, Investor–owned, for–profit **Service:** Rehabilitation

Staffed Beds: 138 **Admissions:** 2570 **Census:** 103 **Outpatient Visits:** 23830 **Births:** 0 **Total Expense ($000):** 45634 **Payroll Expense ($000):** 20922 **Personnel:** 440

✠ **POST ACUTE/WARM SPRINGS SPECIALTY HOSPITAL OF SAN ANTONIO (452090)**, 7400 Barlite Boulevard, 2nd Floor, Zip 78224–1308; tel. 210/921–3550 **A**1 9 10 **F**1 3 29 30 148 **S** Post Acute Medical, LLC, Enola, PA
Primary Contact: Karen Pitcher, Chief Executive Officer
CNO: Carrie Nims, Director of Nursing
Web address: www.postacutemedical.com
Control: Partnership, Investor–owned, for–profit **Service:** Long–Term Acute Care hospital

Staffed Beds: 20 **Admissions:** 210 **Census:** 15 **Outpatient Visits:** 0 **Births:** 0 **Total Expense ($000):** 7845 **Payroll Expense ($000):** 3493 **Personnel:** 65

☐ **SAN ANTONIO STATE HOSPITAL (454011)**, 6711 South New Braunfels, Suite 100, Zip 78223–3006; tel. 210/531–7711 **A**1 5 10 **F**30 39 53 56 57 59 68 75 77 86 87 91 98 99 100 101 103 106 130 132 135 146 **P**1 **S** Texas Department of State Health Services, Austin, TX
Primary Contact: Robert C. Arizpe, Superintendent
CFO: Janie Rabago, Chief Accountant
CMO: Terresa Stallworth, M.D., Clinical Director
CIO: Chris Stanush, Director Information Management
CHR: Renee Bourland, Human Resources Specialist
CNO: Maria DC Ostrander, R.N., Chief Nurse Executive
Web address: www.dshs.state.tx.us/mhhospitals/SanAntonioSH/default.shtm
Control: State–Government, nonfederal **Service:** Psychiatric

Staffed Beds: 302 **Admissions:** 1892 **Census:** 263 **Outpatient Visits:** 0 **Births:** 0 **Total Expense ($000):** 64610 **Payroll Expense ($000):** 33437 **Personnel:** 836

★ ○ **SELECT REHABILITATION HOSPITAL OF SAN ANTONIO (673040)**, 19126 Stonehue Road, Zip 78258–3490; tel. 210/482–3400 **A**9 10 11 **F**3 29 30 75 90 96 130 148 **S** GLOBALREHAB, Dallas, TX
Primary Contact: Robert Ward, Chief Executive Officer
Web address: www.globalrehabhospitals.com
Control: Partnership, Investor–owned, for–profit **Service:** Rehabilitation

Staffed Beds: 42 **Admissions:** 809 **Census:** 29 **Outpatient Visits:** 0 **Births:** 0 **Total Expense ($000):** 13226 **Payroll Expense ($000):** 6038 **Personnel:** 125

✠ **SELECT SPECIALTY HOSPITAL–SAN ANTONIO (452073)**, 111 Dallas Street, 4th Floor, Zip 78205–1201; tel. 210/297–7185 **A**1 9 10 **F**1 29 148 **P**8 **S** Select Medical Corporation, Mechanicsburg, PA
Primary Contact: Sean Stricker, Chief Executive Officer
Web address: www.selectspecialtyhospitals.com/company/locations/sanantonio.aspx
Control: Corporation, Investor–owned, for–profit **Service:** Long–Term Acute Care hospital

Staffed Beds: 44 **Admissions:** 465 **Census:** 38 **Outpatient Visits:** 0 **Births:** 0 **Total Expense ($000):** 19637 **Payroll Expense ($000):** 7629 **Personnel:** 127

☐ **SOUTH TEXAS SPINE AND SURGICAL HOSPITAL (450856)**, 18600 Hardy Oak Boulevard, Zip 78258–4206; tel. 210/507–4090 **A**1 5 9 10 **F**3 29 40 41 64 70 75 77 79 81 85 86 87 89 **S** National Surgical Hospitals, Chicago, IL
Primary Contact: Debbie Kelly, Chief Executive Officer
CFO: Sylvia Garcia, Chief Accounting Officer
CHR: Sally Hall, Manager Human Resources
CNO: Jennifer West, Chief Nursing Officer
Web address: www.southtexassurgical.com
Control: Partnership, Investor–owned, for–profit **Service:** General Medical and Surgical

Staffed Beds: 30 **Admissions:** 1012 **Census:** 7 **Outpatient Visits:** 1961 **Births:** 0 **Total Expense ($000):** 24909 **Payroll Expense ($000):** 5419 **Personnel:** 99

✠ △ **SOUTH TEXAS VETERANS HEALTH CARE SYSTEM**, 7400 Merton Minter Boulevard, Zip 78229–4404; tel. 210/617–5300, (Includes KERRVILLE DIVISION, 3600 Memorial Boulevard, Kerrville, Zip 78028; tel. 210/896–2020; SAN ANTONIO DIVISION, 7400 Merton Minter Boulevard, Zip 78284–5799; tel. 210/617–5300), (Nonreporting) **A**1 3 5 7 8 **S** Department of Veterans Affairs, Washington, DC
Primary Contact: Marie L. Weldon, FACHE, Director
CFO: I. M. Rachal, Chief Fiscal Service
CMO: Richard Bauer, M.D., Chief of Staff
CIO: Simon Willett, Director Administrative Operations
CHR: Leslie Cruthirds, Chief Human Resource Management Service
Web address: www.southtexas.va.gov/
Control: Veterans Affairs, Government, federal **Service:** General Medical and Surgical

Staffed Beds: 838

SOUTHWEST GENERAL HOSPITAL (450697), 7400 Barlite Boulevard, Zip 78224–1399; tel. 210/921–2000 **A**9 10 **F**3 12 13 15 18 20 22 24 26 29 30 35 37 40 43 44 45 46 49 50 51 56 57 59 60 64 65 70 72 74 75 76 77 78 79 80 81 85 87 90 93 98 100 102 103 105 107 108 110 111 114 115 119 126 129 130 132 135 146 147 148 **S** IASIS Healthcare, Franklin, TN
Primary Contact: P. Craig Desmond, Chief Executive Officer
COO: Sarah Humme, MSN, Chief Operating Officer
CFO: Joe Sereno, Chief Financial Officer
CIO: Matthew D'Ambrosio, Director Information Systems
CHR: Christina Rivera, Director Human Resources
CNO: Sarah Humme, MSN, Chief Nursing Officer
Web address: www.swgeneralhospital.com
Control: Corporation, Investor–owned, for–profit **Service:** General Medical and Surgical

Staffed Beds: 265 **Admissions:** 9577 **Census:** 129 **Outpatient Visits:** 71834 **Births:** 1795 **Total Expense ($000):** 110340 **Payroll Expense ($000):** 43897 **Personnel:** 616

ST. LUKE'S BAPTIST HOSPITAL See Baptist Medical Center

TX

Hospital, Medicare Provider Number, Address, Telephone, Approval, Facility, and Physician Codes, Health Care System

★ American Hospital Association (AHA) membership
☐ The Joint Commission accreditation
◇ DNV Healthcare Inc. accreditation
○ Healthcare Facilities Accreditation Program
△ Commission on Accreditation of Rehabilitation Facilities (CARF) accreditation

☐ **TEXAS CENTER FOR INFECTIOUS DISEASE (452033)**, 2303 S.E. Military Drive, Zip 78223–3597; tel. 210/534–8857 **A**1 10 **F**1 3 29 30 50 53 54 61 64 68 75 87 130 132 135 143 146 **P**6 **S** Texas Department of State Health Services, Austin, TX
Primary Contact: James N. Elkins, FACHE, Superintendent
CFO: Glenda Armstrong–Huff, Assistant Superintendent
CMO: David Griffith, M.D., Medical Director
CIO: Andre Avant, Facility Automation Manager
CHR: Gerald Shackelford, Staff Support Specialist
CNO: Rebecca Sanchez, R.N., Director of Nursing
Web address: www.dshs.state.tx.us/tcid/default.shtm
Control: State–Government, nonfederal **Service:** Tuberculosis and other respiratory diseases

Staffed Beds: 40 **Admissions:** 69 **Census:** 37 **Outpatient Visits:** 793 **Births:** 0 **Total Expense ($000):** 14539 **Payroll Expense ($000):** 6329 **Personnel:** 163

✠ **UNIVERSITY HEALTH SYSTEM (450213)**, 4502 Medical Drive, Zip 78229–4493; tel. 210/358–2000, (Includes UNIVERSITY HEALTH CENTER – DOWNTOWN, 4502 Medical Drive, tel. 210/358–3400; UNIVERSITY HOSPITAL, 4502 Medical Drive, tel. 210/358–4000) **A**1 2 3 5 8 9 10 **F**3 4 7 11 13 14 15 16 17 18 19 20 21 22 23 24 25 26 27 29 30 31 32 34 35 38 40 41 43 44 45 46 47 48 49 50 51 52 54 55 56 57 58 59 60 61 64 65 66 68 70 72 73 74 75 76 77 78 79 80 81 82 84 85 86 87 88 89 90 92 93 95 96 98 100 101 107 108 110 111 115 118 119 124 126 129 130 132 135 138 139 140 141 142 143 144 145 146 147 148 **P**6
Primary Contact: George B. Hernandez, Jr., President and Chief Executive Officer
COO: Christann Vasquez, Executive Vice President and Chief Operating Officer
CFO: Peggy Deming, Executive Vice President and Chief Financial Officer
CMO: Bryan Alsip, M.D., Executive Vice President, Chief Medical Officer
CIO: Bill Phillips, Vice President Information Services
CHR: Theresa Scepanski, Vice President People and Organizational Development
CNO: Nancy L. Ray, R.N., Executive Vice President, Chief Nursing Executive
Web address: www.universityhealthsystem.com
Control: Hospital district or authority, Government, nonfederal **Service:** General Medical and Surgical

Staffed Beds: 377 **Admissions:** 21741 **Census:** 358 **Outpatient Visits:** 2211079 **Births:** 2895 **Total Expense ($000):** 1034526 **Payroll Expense ($000):** 289116 **Personnel:** 6065

☐ **VICTORY MEDICAL CENTER – SOUTHCROSS (670021)**, 5330 N. Loop 1604 W., Zip 78249; tel. 210/877–8000 **A**1 10 **F**3 12 29 40 45 75 79 81 82 86 132 **S** Victory Healthcare, The Woodlands, TX
Primary Contact: Louis O. Garcia, Chief Executive Officer
COO: Leroy Bernal, Chief Operating Officer
CFO: Julie Churchill, Chief Financial Officer
CHR: Regina Woolridge, Director Human Resources
CNO: Adam Apolinar, Chief Clinical Officer
Web address: www.victory–healthcare.com/san–antonio–location/
Control: Corporation, Investor–owned, for–profit **Service:** Surgical

Staffed Beds: 9 **Admissions:** 463 **Census:** 3 **Outpatient Visits:** 1539 **Births:** 0 **Total Expense ($000):** 42377 **Payroll Expense ($000):** 5120 **Personnel:** 90

VICTORY MEDICAL CENTER LANDMARK, 5330 North Loop 1604 West, Zip 78249–1371; tel. 210/877–8000, (Nonreporting) **S** Victory Healthcare, The Woodlands, TX
Primary Contact: Alex Garcia, Chief Executive Officer
Web address: www.victory–healthcare.com/sanantoniolandmark
Control: Other not–for–profit (including NFP Corporation) **Service:** Surgical

Staffed Beds: 25

SAN AUGUSTINE—San Augustine County

MEMORIAL MEDICAL CENTER – SAN AUGUSTINE (451360), 511 East Hospital Street, Zip 75972–2121, Mailing Address: P.O. Box 658, Zip 75972–0658; tel. 936/275–3446 **A**9 10 18 **F**29 35 40 57 59 64 102 107 119 132 133 **S** Memorial Health System of East Texas, Lufkin, TX
Primary Contact: Darlene Williams, R.N., Administrator
CFO: Kristi Gay, Chief Financial Officer
Web address: www.memorialhealth.org
Control: Other not–for–profit (including NFP Corporation) **Service:** General Medical and Surgical

Staffed Beds: 18 **Admissions:** 342 **Census:** 4 **Outpatient Visits:** 13215 **Births:** 0 **Total Expense ($000):** 5749 **Payroll Expense ($000):** 2877 **Personnel:** 48

SAN MARCOS—Hays County

✠ **CENTRAL TEXAS MEDICAL CENTER (450272)**, 1301 Wonder World Drive, Zip 78666–7544; tel. 512/353–8979 **A**1 9 10 **F**3 11 13 15 18 20 29 30 32 34 35 39 43 44 45 47 50 51 56 57 59 60 62 63 64 65 66 68 70 72 75 76 77 79 80 81 82 85 86 87 92 93 94 107 108 109 110 111 114 116 117 118 119 126 129 130 131 132 146 147 148 **P**6 8 **S** Adventist Health System Sunbelt Health Care Corporation, Altamonte Springs, FL
Primary Contact: Sam Huenergardt, President and Chief Executive Officer
CFO: Jesse Sutton, Chief Financial Officer
CHR: Debbie D. Cox, Administrative Director Human Resources
CNO: Lana Cameron, Chief Nursing Officer
Web address: www.ctmc.org
Control: Church–operated, Nongovernment, not–for profit **Service:** General Medical and Surgical

Staffed Beds: 140 **Admissions:** 4531 **Census:** 40 **Outpatient Visits:** 72625 **Births:** 1022 **Total Expense ($000):** 82452 **Payroll Expense ($000):** 30188 **Personnel:** 546

SEGUIN—Guadalupe County

✠ **GUADALUPE REGIONAL MEDICAL CENTER (450104)**, 1215 East Court Street, Zip 78155–5189; tel. 830/379–2411 **A**1 9 10 **F**3 5 8 11 13 15 18 20 28 29 30 31 34 35 40 43 45 46 49 50 51 53 56 57 59 60 62 63 64 66 68 70 74 75 76 77 78 79 81 82 85 86 87 90 93 96 103 104 107 108 110 111 112 114 118 119 129 130 132 143 145 146 148 **P**1
Primary Contact: Robert Haynes, FACHE, Chief Executive Officer
COO: Michelle Rumbaut, Chief Strategy Officer
CFO: Penny Wallace, Chief Financial Officer
CMO: Robert Ryan, M.D., Chief Medical Officer
CIO: Steve Ratliff, Director Information Technology
CHR: Fay Bennett, Vice President Employee Services
CNO: Daphne Blake, R.N., Chief Nursing Officer
Web address: www.grmedcenter.com
Control: City–County, Government, nonfederal **Service:** General Medical and Surgical

Staffed Beds: 90 **Admissions:** 3906 **Census:** 40 **Outpatient Visits:** 134518 **Births:** 821 **Total Expense ($000):** 82932 **Payroll Expense ($000):** 30945 **Personnel:** 619

SEMINOLE—Gaines County

★ **MEMORIAL HOSPITAL (451358)**, 209 N.W. Eighth Street, Zip 79360–3447; tel. 432/758–5811 **A**9 10 18 **F**3 10 11 13 28 29 30 32 34 35 40 43 45 53 56 57 59 62 63 64 65 75 76 81 87 93 97 102 107 114 119 130 131 132 133 143 146 147 148
Primary Contact: Betsy Briscoe, Chief Executive Officer
COO: Heath Mitchell, Chief Operating Officer
CFO: Traci Anderson, Chief Financial Officer
CMO: Michael Watson, M.D., Chief of Staff
Web address: www.seminolehospitaldistrict.com
Control: Hospital district or authority, Government, nonfederal **Service:** General Medical and Surgical

Staffed Beds: 25 **Admissions:** 853 **Census:** 10 **Outpatient Visits:** 62694 **Births:** 252 **Total Expense ($000):** 31397 **Payroll Expense ($000):** 7866 **Personnel:** 186

SEYMOUR—Baylor County

SEYMOUR HOSPITAL (450586), 200 Stadium Drive, Zip 76380–2344; tel. 940/889–5572 **A**9 10 20 **F**3 7 8 11 13 14 28 29 34 36 40 43 45 50 53 56 57 59 62 64 65 66 68 70 75 76 81 85 86 87 93 94 100 102 103 104 107 119 127 130 133 135 146 147 148 **P**1
Primary Contact: Leslie Hardin, Chief Executive Officer and Chief Financial Officer
CFO: Leslie Hardin, Chief Executive Officer and Chief Financial Officer
CMO: Kory Lann Martin, M.D., Chief of Staff
CHR: Linda Moore, Manager Human Resources
CNO: Julie Smajstrla, Director Nursing
Web address: www.seymourhospital.com/
Control: Hospital district or authority, Government, nonfederal **Service:** General Medical and Surgical

Staffed Beds: 38 **Admissions:** 501 **Census:** 6 **Outpatient Visits:** 38365 **Births:** 42 **Total Expense ($000):** 10480 **Payroll Expense ($000):** 4993 **Personnel:** 117

SHAMROCK—Wheeler County

SHAMROCK GENERAL HOSPITAL (451340), 1000 South Main Street, Zip 79079–2896, Mailing Address: P. O. Box 511, Zip 79079–0511; tel. 806/256–2114 **A**9 10 18 **F**7 11 29 32 34 40 43 63 65 68 93 107 119 127 130 133 **P**4
Primary Contact: Wiley M. Fires, Administrator
CFO: Wiley M. Fires, Administrator
CHR: Cecille Williams, Assistant Administrator
CNO: Jeanne Crossland, Director of Nursing
Control: Hospital district or authority, Government, nonfederal **Service:** General Medical and Surgical

Staffed Beds: 13 **Admissions:** 86 **Census:** 1 **Outpatient Visits:** 12683 **Births:** 0 **Total Expense ($000):** 5420 **Payroll Expense ($000):** 2807 **Personnel:** 74

TX

Many Facility Codes have changed. Please refer to the AHA Guide Code Chart. © 2014 AHA Guide

SHENANDOAH—Montgomery County

◇ **NEXUS SPECIALTY HOSPITAL**, 123 Vision Park Boulevard, Zip 77384–3001;
tel. 281/364–0317 **A**9 21 **F**1 3 70 74 75 77 82 84 85 91 92 93 100 101 107
119 130 132 135 148 **S** Nexus Health Systems, Houston, TX
Primary Contact: Judith Butryn, Chief Executive Officer
COO: Guido J. Cubellis, Chief Operating Officer
CFO: Julia Hatton, Chief Financial Officer
CMO: Ather Siddiqi, M.D., Medical Director
CIO: Deepak Chaudhry, Vice President Information Technology
CHR: Marc Leighton, Vice President Human Resources
CNO: Patrick Laird, Chief Clinical Officer
Web address: www.nexusspecialty.com
Control: Partnership, Investor–owned, for–profit **Service:** Long–Term Acute Care hospital

Staffed Beds: 75 **Admissions:** 546 **Census:** 50 **Outpatient Visits:** 395
Births: 0 **Total Expense ($000):** 27073 **Payroll Expense ($000):** 11416
Personnel: 258

☐ **RELIANT REHABILITATION HOSPITAL NORTH HOUSTON (673034)**, 117
Vision Park Boulevard, Zip 77384–3001; tel. 936/444–1700 **A**1 9 10 **F**3 29 65
90 93 96 130 148 **S** Reliant Healthcare Partners, Richardson, TX
Primary Contact: Abraham Sims, Chief Executive Officer
CFO: Terri Weiss, Chief Financial Officer
Web address: www.reliantnorthhouston.com/
Control: Partnership, Investor–owned, for–profit **Service:** Rehabilitation

Staffed Beds: 60 **Admissions:** 1726 **Census:** 49 **Outpatient Visits:** 12877
Births: 0 **Total Expense ($000):** 18445 **Payroll Expense ($000):** 8932
Personnel: 213

SHERMAN—Grayson County

◇ **CARRUS REHABILITATION HOSPITAL (673041)**, 1810 West U.S. Highway 82,
Suite 100, Zip 75092–7069; tel. 903/870–2600 **A**9 10 21 **F**3 29 40 41 44 65
74 75 77 79 85 86 87 90 91 96 130 **P**4 **S** Carrus Hospitals, Sherman, TX
Primary Contact: Jon Michael Rains, Chief Executive Officer
CFO: Michael Exline, Chief Financial Officer
CMO: Jose Matus, M.D., Director Medical
CIO: Gary Glenn, Director Information Technology
CHR: Charlene Shupert, Director Staff Services
CNO: Marie Johnson, Chief Nursing Officer
Web address: www.carrushospital.com
Control: Corporation, Investor–owned, for–profit **Service:** Rehabilitation

Staffed Beds: 24 **Admissions:** 432 **Census:** 14 **Outpatient Visits:** 0 **Births:**
0 **Total Expense ($000):** 5738 **Payroll Expense ($000):** 3001 **Personnel:**
30

◇ **CARRUS SPECIALTY HOSPITAL (452041)**, 1810 West U.S. Highway 82,
Zip 75092–7069; tel. 903/870–2600 **A**9 10 21 **F**1 3 29 40 41 44 56 65 74
75 77 78 79 83 85 86 87 91 107 114 129 130 148 **P**4 **S** Carrus Hospitals,
Sherman, TX
Primary Contact: Jon Michael Rains, Chief Executive Officer
CFO: Michael Exline, Chief Financial Officer
CMO: Nathan Watson, Jr., M.D., Chief of Staff
CIO: Gary Glenn, Director Information Technology
CHR: Charlene Shupert, Director Staff Services
CNO: Marie Johnson, Chief Nursing Officer
Web address: www.carrushospital.com
Control: Corporation, Investor–owned, for–profit **Service:** Long–Term Acute Care hospital

Staffed Beds: 16 **Admissions:** 159 **Census:** 11 **Outpatient Visits:** 3713
Births: 0 **Total Expense ($000):** 8166 **Payroll Expense ($000):** 2712
Personnel: 63

◇ **HERITAGE PARK SURGICAL HOSPITAL (670076)**, 3601 North Calais Street,
Zip 75090–1785; tel. 903/870–0999 **A**9 10 21 **F**3 8 29 34 39 40 45 49 54
57 64 75 79 81 82 85 86 87 107 111 114 119 131 135 **S** Foundation Surgical
Hospital Affiliates, Oklahoma City, OK
Primary Contact: Raymond Ford, Chief Executive Officer
CMO: Curtis Holbrook, M.D., Chief Medical Officer
CIO: Grant Hulsey, Director Information Technology
CHR: Terrie Langford, Director Human Resources
CNO: Teresa Dutton, R.N., Chief Nursing Officer
Web address: www.heritageparksurgicalhospital.com
Control: Corporation, Investor–owned, for–profit **Service:** General Medical and
Surgical

Staffed Beds: 10 **Admissions:** 325 **Census:** 2 **Outpatient Visits:** 28773
Births: 0 **Total Expense ($000):** 27371 **Payroll Expense ($000):** 7735
Personnel: 147

LIFE CENTER SPECIALTY HOSPITAL, 1111 Gallagher Drive, Zip 75090–1713;
tel. 903/870–7000, (Nonreporting) **A**9
Primary Contact: Lou Bradley, Chief Executive Officer
Web address: www.lifecenterhospital.org
Control: Other not–for–profit (including NFP Corporation) **Service:** Other specialty

Staffed Beds: 59

✖ **TEXAS HEALTH PRESBYTERIAN HOSPITAL–WNJ (450469)**, 500 North
Highland Avenue, Zip 75092–7354; tel. 903/870–4611 **A**1 9 10 **F**3 11 13 15
17 18 20 22 24 26 28 29 30 31 35 40 41 45 49 53 54 56 57 58 59 61 64
70 74 76 77 78 79 80 81 84 86 87 89 93 96 98 100 103 106 107 108 111
118 119 129 130 132 146 147 148 **S** LHP Hospital Group, Plano, TX
Primary Contact: Vance V. Reynolds, FACHE, CPA, Chief Executive Officer
CFO: Laura Allen, Chief Financial Officer
CMO: Al Cardenas, M.D., President Medical Staff
CIO: Michael Wooton, Manager Information Technology Service Delivery
CHR: Tammy Dawn Johnson, Vice President Human Resources
CNO: Tonya Price, Chief Nursing Officer
Web address: www.wnj.org
Control: Partnership, Investor–owned, for–profit **Service:** General Medical and
Surgical

Staffed Beds: 235 **Admissions:** 6391 **Census:** 84 **Outpatient Visits:** 45054
Births: 321 **Total Expense ($000):** 151229 **Payroll Expense ($000):** 29255
Personnel: 450

WILSON N. JONES MEDICAL CENTER See Texas Health Presbyterian
Hospital–WNJ

SMITHVILLE—Bastrop County

✖ **SETON SMITHVILLE REGIONAL HOSPITAL (450143)**, 800 East Highway 71,
Zip 78957–1730; tel. 512/237–3214 **A**1 9 10 **F**3 11 15 29 34 40 43 53 57
62 64 68 77 79 81 87 93 107 110 111 114 119 146 148 **P**3 8 **S** Ascension
Health, Saint Louis, MO
Primary Contact: Larry Mejia, Vice President and Chief Operating Officer
CFO: Melissa Nordyke, Chief Financial Officer
CHR: Sara Rodriguez, Human Resources
CNO: Christine Laflamme, R.N., Chief Nursing Officer
Web address: www.seton.org
Control: Church–operated, Nongovernment, not–for profit **Service:** General
Medical and Surgical

Staffed Beds: 10 **Admissions:** 429 **Census:** 4 **Outpatient Visits:** 34951
Births: 0 **Total Expense ($000):** 20451 **Payroll Expense ($000):** 8376
Personnel: 135

SNYDER—Scurry County

COGDELL MEMORIAL HOSPITAL (450073), 1700 Cogdell Boulevard,
Zip 79549–6198; tel. 325/573–6374 **A**9 10 20 **F**8 11 13 15 18 19 29 30 34
40 43 45 46 47 48 49 50 53 56 57 59 62 64 65 69 73 75 76 77 79 81 85 86
87 91 92 93 97 107 108 111 115 119 127 130 131 132 133 145 146 147
148 **P**6
Primary Contact: William W. Weldon, Ph.D., Interim Chief Executive Officer
CFO: John Everett, Chief Financial Officer
CMO: Robert Rakov, M.D., Chief Medical Officer
CHR: Linda Warren, Director Human Resources
Web address: www.cogdellhospital.com
Control: Hospital district or authority, Government, nonfederal **Service:** General
Medical and Surgical

Staffed Beds: 49 **Admissions:** 653 **Census:** 6 **Outpatient Visits:** 59314
Births: 160 **Total Expense ($000):** 28849 **Payroll Expense ($000):** 9994
Personnel: 211

SONORA—Sutton County

★ **LILLIAN M. HUDSPETH MEMORIAL HOSPITAL (451324)**, 308 Hudspeth
Avenue, Zip 76950–8003, Mailing Address: P.O. Box 455, Zip 76950–0455;
tel. 325/387–2521 **A**9 10 18 **F**3 7 11 12 15 18 28 29 30 32 34 35 40 43 44
45 50 53 57 59 64 65 66 68 74 75 79 86 87 90 93 96 97 107 110 111 115
119 127 128 131 132 133 134 135 147 148
Primary Contact: Robert A. Pascasio, FACHE, Chief Executive Officer
CFO: Michelle Schaefer, Chief Financial Officer
CMO: Kristy Edwards, M.D., Chief Medical Officer
CNO: Jon–Michael Parker, R.N., Chief Nursing Officer
Web address: www.sonora–hospital.org
Control: Hospital district or authority, Government, nonfederal **Service:** General
Medical and Surgical

Staffed Beds: 12 **Admissions:** 263 **Census:** 3 **Outpatient Visits:** 8232
Births: 0 **Total Expense ($000):** 9104 **Payroll Expense ($000):** 4820
Personnel: 77

TX

Hospital, Medicare Provider Number, Address, Telephone, Approval, Facility, and Physician Codes, Health Care System

★ American Hospital Association (AHA) membership
☐ The Joint Commission accreditation
◇ DNV Healthcare Inc. accreditation
○ Healthcare Facilities Accreditation Program
△ Commission on Accreditation of Rehabilitation Facilities (CARF) accreditation

SOUTHLAKE—Tarrant County

FOREST PARK MEDICAL CENTER–SOUTHLAKE, 421 East State Highway 114, Zip 76092; tel. 817/865–4400, (Nonreporting) **S** Vibrant Healthcare, Dallas, TX
Primary Contact: Dawn Beljin, R.N., Chief Operating Officer
COO: Dawn Beljin, R.N., Chief Operating Officer
Web address: www.forestparksouthlake.com
Control: Corporation, Investor–owned, for–profit **Service:** General Medical and Surgical

Staffed Beds: 15

☐ **TEXAS HEALTH HARRIS METHODIST HOSPITAL SOUTHLAKE (450888)**, 1545 East Southlake Boulevard, Zip 76092–6422; tel. 817/748–8700 **A**1 9 10 **F**3 29 30 40 64 74 79 81 85 107 111 113 114 119 130 146 **P**2
Primary Contact: Traci Bernard, President
CFO: Douglas Browning, Group Financial Officer
CMO: David Taunton, M.D., Chief of Staff
CHR: Tasha Sledge, Director Human Resources
CNO: Jessica Hill, Vice President, Chief Nursing Officer
Web address: www.texashealthsouthlake.com
Control: Corporation, Investor–owned, for–profit **Service:** General Medical and Surgical

Staffed Beds: 18 Admissions: 913 Census: 7 Outpatient Visits: 11380 Births: 0 Total Expense ($000): 49462 Payroll Expense ($000): 11652 Personnel: 140

SPEARMAN—Hansford County

★ **HANSFORD HOSPITAL (451344)**, 707 South Roland Street, Zip 79081–3441; tel. 806/659–2535 **A**9 10 18 **F**3 11 31 32 34 40 43 56 57 59 62 63 64 65 68 69 78 93 107 114 127 130 133 **P**6
Primary Contact: Jonathan D. Bailey, Chief Executive Officer and Administrator
CFO: Scott Beedy, Chief Financial Officer
CMO: Mark Garnett, M.D., Chief of Staff
CHR: Jackie Nelson, Director Human Resources
Web address: www.hchd.net
Control: Hospital district or authority, Government, nonfederal **Service:** General Medical and Surgical

Staffed Beds: 14 Admissions: 198 Census: 2 Outpatient Visits: 24205 Births: 0 Total Expense ($000): 9533 Payroll Expense ($000): 3774 Personnel: 82

SPRING—Montgomery County

NEXUS SPECIALTY HOSPITAL THE WOODLANDS (452057), 9182 Six Pines Drive, Zip 77380–3670; tel. 281/364–0317, (Nonreporting) **A**10
Primary Contact: Judith Butryn, Chief Executive Officer
COO: Guido J. Cubellis, Chief Operating Officer
CFO: Julia Hatton, Chief Financial Officer
CMO: Ather Siddiqi, M.D., Medical Director
CIO: Deepak Chaudhry, Vice President Information Technology
CHR: Marc Leighton, Vice President Human Resources
CNO: Patrick Laird, Chief Clinical Officer
Web address: www.nexusspecialty.com
Control: Partnership, Investor–owned, for–profit **Service:** Long–Term Acute Care hospital

Staffed Beds: 21

STAFFORD—Fort Bend County

◇ **ATRIUM MEDICAL CENTER (452114)**, 11929 West Airport Boulevard, Zip 77477–2451; tel. 281/207–8200 **A**9 10 21 **F**1 3 29 45 46 56 60 70 82 83 85 90 107 114 119 148
Primary Contact: Ahmad Zaid, Chief Executive Officer
Web address: www.atriummedicalcenter.com
Control: Partnership, Investor–owned, for–profit **Service:** Long–Term Acute Care hospital

Staffed Beds: 68 Admissions: 505 Census: 33 Outpatient Visits: 24 Births: 0 Total Expense ($000): 15498 Payroll Expense ($000): 6871 Personnel: 151

STAMFORD—Jones County

STAMFORD MEMORIAL HOSPITAL (450306), 1601 Columbia Street, Zip 79553–6863, Mailing Address: P.O. Box 911, Zip 79553–0911; tel. 325/773–2725 **A**9 10 **F**1 10 11 28 30 34 35 36 40 41 43 50 53 57 59 62 64 65 67 68 81 89 93 107 114 119 127 128 133 144 146 148 **P**4
Primary Contact: Richard G. DeFoore, FACHE, Chief Executive Officer
CFO: Elizabeth Miller, CPA, Chief Financial Officer
CMO: Michael Hart, M.D., Medical Director
CHR: Cheryl Hertel, Coordinator Human Resources
CNO: Angela Gass, Chief Nursing Officer
Web address: www.stamfordhosp.com/
Control: Other not–for–profit (including NFP Corporation) **Service:** General Medical and Surgical

Staffed Beds: 12 Admissions: 272 Census: 5 Outpatient Visits: 22400 Births: 1 Total Expense ($000): 9668 Payroll Expense ($000): 4151 Personnel: 122

STANTON—Martin County

MARTIN COUNTY HOSPITAL DISTRICT (451333), 600 Interstate 20E, Zip 79782, Mailing Address: P.O. Box 640, Zip 79782–0640; tel. 432/756–3345 **A**9 10 18 **F**7 40 57 62 81 91 93 107 119 127 133
Primary Contact: Paul McKinney, Administrator
CFO: Alison Israel, Controller
Control: Hospital district or authority, Government, nonfederal **Service:** General Medical and Surgical

Staffed Beds: 18 Admissions: 80 Census: 1 Outpatient Visits: 9442 Births: 0 Total Expense ($000): 14856 Payroll Expense ($000): 4120 Personnel: 90

STEPHENVILLE—Erath County

⊞ **TEXAS HEALTH HARRIS METHODIST HOSPITAL STEPHENVILLE (450351)**, 411 North Belknap Street, Zip 76401–3415; tel. 254/965–1500 **A**1 9 10 20 **F**3 8 13 15 29 30 34 35 39 40 41 43 45 50 57 59 65 68 70 75 76 77 79 81 86 89 107 108 111 114 118 119 129 130 135 145 146 147 148 **S** Texas Health Resources, Arlington, TX
Primary Contact: Christopher Leu, President
CFO: Carol Cross, Chief Financial Officer
CMO: Jeffrey Edwards, M.D., Chief of Staff
CHR: Kimberly Leondar, Director Human Resources
Web address: www.texashealth.org/landing.cfm?id=108
Control: Other not–for–profit (including NFP Corporation) **Service:** General Medical and Surgical

Staffed Beds: 54 Admissions: 1804 Census: 16 Outpatient Visits: 31031 Births: 442 Total Expense ($000): 35480 Payroll Expense ($000): 14627 Personnel: 182

SUGAR LAND—Fort Bend County

◇ **EMERUS (670058)**, 16000 Southwest Freeway, Suite 100, Zip 77479–2674; tel. 281/277–0911 **A**10 21 **F**3 4 40 63 75 107 114 119 **P**5 **S** Emerus, The Woodlands, TX
Primary Contact: Mike Kohler, Chief Executive Officer
Web address: www.emerus.com
Control: Corporation, Investor–owned, for–profit **Service:** General Medical and Surgical

Staffed Beds: 7 Admissions: 133 Census: 1 Outpatient Visits: 8282 Births: 0 Total Expense ($000): 5399 Payroll Expense ($000): 1853 Personnel: 29

⊞ **HEALTHSOUTH SUGAR LAND REHABILITATION HOSPITAL (673042)**, 1325 Highway 6, Zip 77478–4906; tel. 281/276–7574 **A**1 9 10 **F**3 29 34 75 87 90 95 96 130 132 146 148 **S** HEALTHSOUTH Corporation, Birmingham, AL
Primary Contact: Nicholas Hardin, Chief Executive Officer
Web address: www.healthsouthsugarland.com
Control: Corporation, Investor–owned, for–profit **Service:** Rehabilitation

Staffed Beds: 50 Admissions: 1068 Census: 38 Outpatient Visits: 0 Births: 0 Total Expense ($000): 15707 Payroll Expense ($000): 7473 Personnel: 178

⊞ ◇ **HOUSTON METHODIST SUGAR LAND HOSPITAL (450820)**, 16655 S.W. Freeway, Zip 77479–2329; tel. 281/274–7000 **A**1 9 10 21 **F**3 12 13 15 18 20 22 24 26 29 30 31 33 34 35 36 37 39 40 41 44 45 46 47 49 50 51 53 54 57 58 59 60 61 64 65 68 70 73 74 75 76 77 78 79 81 82 85 86 87 92 93 94 96 102 107 108 110 111 114 115 119 120 121 123 124 126 130 131 132 135 145 146 147 148 **S** Houston Methodist, Houston, TX
Primary Contact: Christopher Siebenaler, Chief Executive Officer
CFO: Lowell Stanton, Chief Financial Officer
CMO: Jeffrey Jackson, M.D., Medical Director
CHR: Luis Mario Garcia, Jr., Director Human Resources
Web address: www.methodisthealth.com
Control: Other not–for–profit (including NFP Corporation) **Service:** General Medical and Surgical

Staffed Beds: 235 Admissions: 13563 Census: 154 Outpatient Visits: 164743 Births: 2672 Total Expense ($000): 248170 Payroll Expense ($000): 84657 Personnel: 1547

⊞ **KINDRED HOSPITAL SUGAR LAND (452080)**, 1550 First Colony Boulevard, Zip 77479–4000; tel. 281/275–6000 **A**1 9 10 **F**1 3 29 31 35 45 57 65 75 77 85 87 91 107 130 148 **S** Kindred Healthcare, Louisville, KY
Primary Contact: Lorene Perona, Market Chief Executive Officer
CFO: Sara Rodriguez, Chief Financial Officer
CMO: Subodh Bhuchar, M.D., Chief of Staff
CIO: Artie Dmello, Director Case Management
CHR: Craig King, Coordinator Human Resources
CNO: Laura Jane Griffin, M.D., Chief Nursing Executive
Web address: www.khsugarland.com
Control: Corporation, Investor–owned, for–profit **Service:** Long–Term Acute Care hospital

Staffed Beds: 171 Admissions: 1713 Census: 122 Outpatient Visits: 405 Births: 0 Total Expense ($000): 66244 Payroll Expense ($000): 22961 Personnel: 304

✠ **MEMORIAL HERMANN SUGAR LAND HOSPITAL (450848)**, 17500 West Grand Parkway South, Zip 77479–2562; tel. 281/725–5000 **A**1 3 5 9 10 **F**3 8 13 14 15 17 20 22 29 30 34 35 36 37 39 40 41 43 44 45 46 47 48 49 50 51 53 54 55 56 57 59 60 62 63 64 68 70 72 74 75 76 77 78 79 81 82 85 86 87 89 91 92 93 97 107 108 109 110 111 112 114 116 117 119 124 129 130 131 146 147 148 **P**1 5 6 **S** Memorial Hermann Healthcare System, Houston, TX
Primary Contact: Gregory Haralson, Chief Executive Officer
CFO: Lisa Kendler, Chief Financial Officer
CMO: William Riley, Jr., M.D., Chief of Staff
CHR: Robert Blake, Chief Human Resources Officer Southwest Market
Web address: www.memorialhermann.org
Control: Other not–for–profit (including NFP Corporation) **Service:** General Medical and Surgical

Staffed Beds: 81 **Admissions:** 4793 **Census:** 47 **Outpatient Visits:** 73056
Births: 1252 **Total Expense ($000):** 94475 **Payroll Expense ($000):** 30150
Personnel: 400

METHODIST SUGAR LAND HOSPITAL See Houston Methodist Sugar Land Hospital

✠ ◇ **ST. LUKE'S SUGAR LAND HOSPITAL (670053)**, 1317 Lake Pointe Parkway, Zip 77478–3997; tel. 281/637–7000 **A**1 9 10 21 **F**3 15 18 20 22 26 29 30 34 35 37 39 40 41 44 45 46 49 50 57 60 64 68 70 74 75 79 81 82 85 107 108 110 111 115 119 129 130 146 147 148 **P**5 **S** Catholic Health Initiatives, Englewood, CO
Primary Contact: Robert A. Heifner, Chief Executive Officer
CFO: Bill Beauchamp, Chief Financial Officer
CNO: Wes Garrison
Web address: www.stlukessugarland.com
Control: Church–operated, Nongovernment, not–for profit **Service:** General Medical and Surgical

Staffed Beds: 58 **Admissions:** 3032 **Census:** 36 **Outpatient Visits:** 23020
Births: 0 **Total Expense ($000):** 66475 **Payroll Expense ($000):** 20051
Personnel: 302

SUGAR LAND REHABILITATION HOSPITAL See HEALTHSOUTH Sugar Land Rehabilitation Hospital

☐ **SUGAR LAND SURGICAL HOSPITAL (450860)**, 16906 Southwest Freeway, Zip 77479–2350; tel. 281/243–1000 **A**1 9 10 **F**3 29 40 45 59 64 75 79 81 82 85 86 87 92 107 111 119 130 **P**2 **S** United Surgical Partners International, Addison, TX
Primary Contact: Daniel Smith, Interim Chief Executive Officer
CFO: Raquel Hebert, Business Manager
CMO: Ken Thomson, M.D., Medical Director
Web address: www.sugarlandsurgicalhospital.com/
Control: Partnership, Investor–owned, for–profit **Service:** General Medical and Surgical

Staffed Beds: 6 **Admissions:** 230 **Census:** 2 **Outpatient Visits:** 8658 **Births:** 0 **Total Expense ($000):** 22351 **Payroll Expense ($000):** 5631 **Personnel:** 130

TRIUMPH HOSPITAL SOUTHWEST See Kindred Hospital Sugar Land

SULPHUR SPRINGS—Hopkins County

★ **HOPKINS COUNTY MEMORIAL HOSPITAL (450236)**, 115 Airport Road, Zip 75482–2105; tel. 903/885–7671 **A**9 10 **F**1 7 11 13 15 28 29 34 35 40 43 56 59 63 70 73 76 79 80 81 93 96 107 108 110 111 115 118 119 127 130 146 **P**6
Primary Contact: Michael McAndrew, Chief Executive Officer
COO: Donna Geiken Wallace, Chief Operating Officer and Chief Financial Officer
CFO: Donna Geiken Wallace, Chief Operating Officer and Chief Financial Officer
CMO: Scott McDearmont, M.D., Chief Medical Staff
CIO: Brandon Gauntt, Director Information Systems
CHR: Donna Rudzik, Director Human Resources
CNO: Terri Bunch, R.N., Chief Nursing Officer
Web address: www.hcmh.com
Control: Hospital district or authority, Government, nonfederal **Service:** General Medical and Surgical

Staffed Beds: 50 **Admissions:** 3356 **Census:** 31 **Outpatient Visits:** 61868
Births: 716 **Total Expense ($000):** 50008 **Payroll Expense ($000):** 18852
Personnel: 449

SUNNYVALE—Dallas County

☐ **TEXAS REGIONAL MEDICAL CENTER AT SUNNYVALE (670060)**, 231 South Collins Road, Zip 75182–4624; tel. 972/892–3000 **A**1 9 10 **F**3 13 15 18 20 22 24 29 34 35 40 45 49 57 59 64 70 74 75 76 79 80 81 82 85 87 107 108 110 111 114 115 119 130 135 146 147 148
Primary Contact: Stephen Garrison, Interim Chief Executive Officer
CFO: Ben Dunford, Chief Financial Officer
Web address: www.texasregionalmedicalcenter.com
Control: Partnership, Investor–owned, for–profit **Service:** General Medical and Surgical

Staffed Beds: 70 **Admissions:** 6377 **Census:** 50 **Outpatient Visits:** 41939
Births: 1367 **Total Expense ($000):** 73334 **Payroll Expense ($000):** 25351
Personnel: 377

SWEENY—Brazoria County

SWEENY COMMUNITY HOSPITAL (451311), 305 North McKinney Street, Zip 77480–2895; tel. 979/548–1500 **A**9 10 18 **F**3 7 10 11 15 29 34 35 40 43 45 53 56 57 59 65 69 70 75 81 85 93 103 104 107 110 114 119 130 132 133 143 145 148
Primary Contact: William H. Barnes, Administrator
CFO: Hong Wade, Chief Financial Officer
CMO: Fabio Aglieco, D.O., Chief of Staff
CIO: Stuart Butler, Director Information Technology
CHR: Grace Baty, Director Human Resources
Web address: www.sweenyhospital.org
Control: Hospital district or authority, Government, nonfederal **Service:** General Medical and Surgical

Staffed Beds: 14 **Admissions:** 291 **Census:** 2 **Outpatient Visits:** 16565
Births: 1 **Total Expense ($000):** 15947 **Payroll Expense ($000):** 6652
Personnel: 165

SWEETWATER—Nolan County

✠ **ROLLING PLAINS MEMORIAL HOSPITAL (450055)**, 200 East Arizona Street, Zip 79556–7199, Mailing Address: P.O. Box 690, Zip 79556–0690; tel. 325/235–1701 **A**1 9 10 20 **F**3 11 13 15 28 29 34 35 40 43 59 62 70 76 79 81 85 89 93 97 107 108 110 114 119 130 132 133 135 146 **P**6
Primary Contact: Donna Boatright, MSN, Administrator
COO: Rhonda Guelker, Senior Director Finance
CFO: Rhonda Guelker, Senior Director Finance
CMO: Ronnie Dennis, Chief of Staff
CIO: Rhonda Guelker, Senior Director Finance
CHR: Ame Monroe, Director Human Resources
CNO: Rosa Best, Chief Nursing Officer
Web address: www.rpmh.net
Control: Hospital district or authority, Government, nonfederal **Service:** General Medical and Surgical

Staffed Beds: 52 **Admissions:** 1347 **Census:** 16 **Outpatient Visits:** 77864
Births: 216 **Total Expense ($000):** 24060 **Payroll Expense ($000):** 12169
Personnel: 252

TAHOKA—Lynn County

★ **LYNN COUNTY HOSPITAL DISTRICT (451351)**, 2600 Lockwood, Zip 79373–4118, Mailing Address: Box 1310, Zip 79373–1310; tel. 806/998–4533 **A**9 10 18 **F**3 7 10 13 29 32 34 35 40 43 44 53 54 56 57 59 64 65 66 75 86 89 93 97 107 133 147 148 **P**5
Primary Contact: Stace D. Holland, Chief Executive Officer
CFO: Donna Raindl, Manager Business Office
CMO: Donald Freitag, M.D., Chief Medical Officer
CIO: Jim Brown, Director Information Technology
CHR: Jill Stone, Manager Human Resources
CNO: Vera Reno, Chief Nursing Officer
Web address: www.lchdhealthcare.org
Control: Hospital district or authority, Government, nonfederal **Service:** General Medical and Surgical

Staffed Beds: 24 **Admissions:** 154 **Census:** 1 **Outpatient Visits:** 15044
Births: 0 **Total Expense ($000):** 7095 **Payroll Expense ($000):** 2871
Personnel: 96

TAYLOR—Williamson County

JOHNS COMMUNITY HOSPITAL See Scott & White Hospital – Taylor

TX

✠ **SCOTT & WHITE HOSPITAL – TAYLOR (451374)**, 305 Mallard Lane, Zip 76574–1208; tel. 512/352–7611 **A**1 9 10 18 **F**3 11 15 18 29 34 40 41 43 45 57 59 62 64 81 85 86 93 97 107 108 110 114 119 129 130 132 133 148 **P**6 **S** Baylor Scott & White Health, Dallas, TX
Primary Contact: Jay Fox, Chief Executive Officer, Round Rock Region
CIO: Tim Tarbell, Assistant Administrator Support Services
Web address: www.swtaylor.org
Control: Other not–for–profit (including NFP Corporation) **Service:** General Medical and Surgical

Staffed Beds: 25 **Admissions:** 471 **Census:** 10 **Outpatient Visits:** 9975 **Births:** 0 **Total Expense ($000):** 14490 **Payroll Expense ($000):** 7493 **Personnel:** 104

TEMPLE—Bell County

✠ △ **CENTRAL TEXAS VETERANS HEALTHCARE SYSTEM**, 1901 Veterans Memorial Drive, Zip 76504–7493; tel. 254/778–4811, (Includes OLIN E. TEAGUE VETERANS' CENTER, 1901 South First Street, Zip 76504; tel. 817/778–4811; WACO VETERANS AFFAIRS HOSPITAL, 4800 Memorial Drive, Waco, Zip 76711–1397; tel. 254/752–6581), (Nonreporting) **A**1 2 3 5 7 8 9 **S** Department of Veterans Affairs, Washington, DC
Primary Contact: Sallie Houser–Hanfelder, FACHE, Director
CFO: Amy Maynard, Acting Chief Finance Service
CIO: Victor Vitolas, Acting Chief Information Technology Services
CHR: Mary P. Doerfler, Chief Human Resources Officer
CNO: Bryan W. Sisk, Associate Director Patient and Nursing Services
Web address: www.centraltexas.va.gov/
Control: Veterans Affairs, Government, federal **Service:** General Medical and Surgical

Staffed Beds: 1532

MCLANE CHILDREN'S HOSPITAL SCOTT & WHITE See Scott & White Memorial Hospital

OLIN E. TEAGUE VETERANS' CENTER See Central Texas Veterans Healthcare System

✠ **SCOTT & WHITE MEMORIAL HOSPITAL (450054)**, 2401 South 31st Street, Zip 76508–0002; tel. 254/724–2111, (Includes MCLANE CHILDREN'S HOSPITAL SCOTT & WHITE, 2401 South 31st Street, Zip 76508–0001; tel. 877/724–5437; John Boyd, III, M.D., Chief Executive Officer and Chief Medical Officer; MCLANE CHILDREN'S HOSPITAL SCOTT & WHITE, 1901 S.W. H. K. Dodgen Loop, Zip 76502–1896; tel. 254/771–8600; John Boyd, III, M.D., Chief Executive Officer), (Total facility includes 49 beds in nursing home–type unit) **A**1 2 3 5 8 9 10 **F**3 5 7 9 11 12 13 14 15 17 18 19 20 21 22 24 26 27 28 29 30 31 32 34 35 36 37 38 39 40 41 43 44 45 46 47 48 49 50 51 52 54 55 56 57 58 59 60 61 62 63 64 65 66 68 70 72 73 74 75 76 77 78 79 81 82 84 85 86 87 88 89 91 92 93 96 97 98 100 102 103 104 105 107 108 110 111 113 114 115 116 117 118 119 120 121 123 124 126 128 129 130 131 132 134 135 136 137 138 140 141 142 144 145 146 147 148 **P**6 **S** Baylor Scott & White Health, Dallas, TX
Primary Contact: Shahin Motakef, Chief Executive Officer
CFO: Alita Prosser, Chief Financial Officer
CMO: Stephen Sibbitt, M.D., Chief Medical Officer
CIO: Matthew Chambers, Chief Information Officer
CHR: Lorraine Bell, Vice President Operations Human Resources
CNO: Cyndy Dunlap, R.N., Chief Nursing Officer
Web address: www.sw.org/location/temple–hospital
Control: Other not–for–profit (including NFP Corporation) **Service:** General Medical and Surgical

Staffed Beds: 638 **Admissions:** 31858 **Census:** 436 **Outpatient Visits:** 1386996 **Births:** 2740 **Total Expense ($000):** 775712 **Payroll Expense ($000):** 313485 **Personnel:** 6761

★ **SCOTT AND WHITE CONTINUING CARE HOSPITAL (452105)**, 546 North Kegley Road, Zip 76502–4069; tel. 254/215–0900 **A**9 10 **F**1 3 29 30 60 68 85 107 119 130 148 **P**6 **S** Baylor Scott & White Health, Dallas, TX
Primary Contact: Kimberly K. Langston, R.N., Chief Executive Officer
CMO: David P. Ciceri, M.D., Chief Medical Officer
Web address: www.sw.org/location/temple–cch
Control: Other not–for–profit (including NFP Corporation) **Service:** Long–Term Acute Care hospital

Staffed Beds: 50 **Admissions:** 428 **Census:** 35 **Outpatient Visits:** 0 **Births:** 0 **Total Expense ($000):** 20059 **Payroll Expense ($000):** 9054 **Personnel:** 111

TERRELL—Kaufman County

☐ **TERRELL STATE HOSPITAL (454006)**, 1200 East Brin Street, Zip 75160–2938, Mailing Address: P.O. Box 70, Zip 75160–9000; tel. 972/524–6452 **A**1 5 9 10 **F**30 34 39 57 68 75 86 87 98 99 100 101 103 130 132 135 146 **P**6 **S** Texas Department of State Health Services, Austin, TX
Primary Contact: Dorothy Floyd, Ph.D., Superintendent
CFO: Mike Verseckes, Financial Officer
CMO: Anthony Claxton, M.D., Clinical Director
CIO: Sims Anderson, Manager Facility Automation
Web address: www.dshs.state.tx.us/mhhospitals/terrellsh
Control: State–Government, nonfederal **Service:** Psychiatric

Staffed Beds: 288 **Admissions:** 2507 **Census:** 283 **Outpatient Visits:** 0 **Births:** 0 **Total Expense ($000):** 57590 **Payroll Expense ($000):** 34830 **Personnel:** 854

TEXARKANA—Bowie County

✠ **CHRISTUS ST. MICHAEL HEALTH SYSTEM (450801)**, 2600 St. Michael Drive, Zip 75503–5220; tel. 903/614–1000, (Includes CHRISTUS ST. MICHAEL'S HOSPITAL–ATLANTA, 1007 South William Street, Atlanta, Zip 75551–3245; tel. 903/799–3000; Thomas McKinney, Administrator) **A**1 2 9 10 **F**3 11 13 15 17 18 20 22 24 28 29 30 31 34 35 40 41 43 45 48 49 51 53 55 56 57 59 60 64 65 68 70 71 72 74 75 76 77 78 79 80 81 82 84 85 86 87 89 92 97 98 107 108 109 110 111 114 115 118 119 120 121 122 123 124 126 129 130 131 132 135 143 144 146 147 148 **P**8 **S** CHRISTUS Health, Irving, TX
Primary Contact: Chris Karam, President and Chief Executive Officer
COO: Jason Rounds, Chief Operating Officer and Administrator
CFO: Glen Boles, Vice President and Chief Financial Officer
CMO: Mike Finley, M.D., Chief Medical Officer
CIO: Alana Higgins, Regional Information Management Executive
CHR: Pam Kennedy, Vice President Regional Human Resources and Organizational Department
CNO: Nancy C. Keenan, R.N., Chief Nursing Officer
Web address: www.christusstmichael.org
Control: Church–operated, Nongovernment, not–for profit **Service:** General Medical and Surgical

Staffed Beds: 376 **Admissions:** 14690 **Census:** 174 **Outpatient Visits:** 138338 **Births:** 1494 **Total Expense ($000):** 210513 **Payroll Expense ($000):** 70406 **Personnel:** 1630

✠ △ **CHRISTUS ST. MICHAEL REHABILITATION HOSPITAL (453065)**, 2400 St. Michael Drive, Zip 75503–2374; tel. 903/614–4000 **A**1 7 9 10 **F**3 11 18 28 29 30 34 35 57 59 65 68 75 77 79 82 87 90 93 96 132 135 143 148 **S** CHRISTUS Health, Irving, TX
Primary Contact: Aloma Gender, R.N., MSN, Administrator and Chief Nursing Officer
CFO: Glen Boles, Vice President and Chief Financial Officer
CMO: Richard Sharp, M.D., Medical Director
CIO: Alana Higgins, Regional Information Management Executive
CHR: Pam Kennedy, Director Human Resources
CNO: Aloma Gender, R.N., Administrator and Chief Nursing Officer
Web address: www.christusstmichael.org/rehab
Control: Church–operated, Nongovernment, not–for profit **Service:** Rehabilitation

Staffed Beds: 50 **Admissions:** 1170 **Census:** 36 **Outpatient Visits:** 44844 **Births:** 0 **Total Expense ($000):** 19375 **Payroll Expense ($000):** 9024 **Personnel:** 159

✠ **DUBUIS HOSPITAL OF TEXARKANA (452061)**, 2400 St. Michael Drive, 2nd Floor, Zip 75503–2372; tel. 903/614–7600 **A**1 9 10 **F**1 3 29 77 82 84 86 87 130 148 **S** Dubuis Health System, Houston, TX
Primary Contact: Holly Powell, Administrator
Web address: www.dubuis.org/DubuisHospitalofTexarkanaSystem
Control: Church–operated, Nongovernment, not–for profit **Service:** Long–Term Acute Care hospital

Staffed Beds: 49 **Admissions:** 476 **Census:** 34 **Outpatient Visits:** 0 **Births:** 0 **Total Expense ($000):** 13796 **Payroll Expense ($000):** 4889 **Personnel:** 95

✠ **HEALTHSOUTH REHABILITATION HOSPITAL OF TEXARKANA (453053)**, 515 West 12th Street, Zip 75501–4416; tel. 903/735–5000 **A**1 9 10 **F**3 28 29 42 62 64 74 77 79 90 91 93 95 96 130 131 132 143 148 **P**5 **S** HEALTHSOUTH Corporation, Birmingham, AL
Primary Contact: Michael G. Treadway, Interim Chief Executive Officer
CFO: Phylis Buck, Controller
CMO: Mark A. Wren, M.D., Medical Director
CHR: Ann R. Clapp, Director Human Resources
CNO: Lametria Griffie, Interim Chief Nursing Officer
Web address: www.healthsouthtexarkana.com
Control: Corporation, Investor–owned, for–profit **Service:** Rehabilitation

Staffed Beds: 60 **Admissions:** 1097 **Census:** 43 **Outpatient Visits:** 10492 **Births:** 0 **Total Expense ($000):** 13204 **Payroll Expense ($000):** 7584 **Personnel:** 159

Many Facility Codes have changed. Please refer to the AHA Guide Code Chart. © 2014 AHA Guide

☐ **WADLEY REGIONAL MEDICAL CENTER (450200)**, 1000 Pine Street, Zip 75501–5170; tel. 903/798–8000 **A**1 9 10 **F**3 11 12 13 15 18 20 22 24 28 29 30 31 34 35 40 43 45 49 50 56 57 59 60 64 65 70 71 73 74 75 76 77 78 79 81 85 86 87 89 98 103 107 108 110 111 114 115 119 126 130 146 147 **S** IASIS Healthcare, Franklin, TN
Primary Contact: Thomas D. Gilbert, FACHE, Chief Executive Officer
CFO: Bonny Sorensen, Chief Financial Officer
CIO: Matt Kesterson, Director Information Services
CHR: Debby Butler, Director Human Resources
CNO: Shelly Strayhorn, R.N., Chief Nursing Officer
Web address: www.wadleyhealth.com
Control: Corporation, Investor–owned, for–profit **Service:** General Medical and Surgical

Staffed Beds: 179 **Admissions:** 7432 **Census:** 91 **Outpatient Visits:** 78631 **Births:** 1327 **Total Expense ($000):** 91884 **Payroll Expense ($000):** 33033 **Personnel:** 622

THE WOODLANDS—Montgomery County

MEMORIAL HERMANN THE WOODLANDS HOSPITAL See Memorial Hermann Northwest Hospital, Houston

★ ◇ **ST. LUKE'S LAKESIDE HOSPITAL (670059)**, 17400 St. Luke's Way, Zip 77384–8036; tel. 936/266–9000 **A**9 10 21 **F**3 18 20 22 26 29 30 34 35 40 50 57 59 64 68 75 79 81 87 94 107 111 115 119 130 131 135 **P**5 **S** Catholic Health Initiatives, Englewood, CO
Primary Contact: Debra F. Sukin, Chief Executive Officer
CFO: Mary Sue Lipham, Chief Financial Officer
CMO: Bruce Lachterman, M.D., Chief of Medical Staff
CIO: Paul Solverson, Chief Information Officer
CHR: Debra Roberts, Director of Human Resources
CNO: Diane Freeman, R.N., Assistant Vice President and Chief Nursing Officer
Web address: www.stlukeslakeside.com/
Control: Corporation, Investor–owned, for–profit **Service:** General Medical and Surgical

Staffed Beds: 30 **Admissions:** 881 **Census:** 6 **Outpatient Visits:** 12503 **Births:** 0 **Total Expense ($000):** 41111 **Payroll Expense ($000):** 7430 **Personnel:** 125

★ ◇ **ST. LUKE'S THE WOODLANDS HOSPITAL (450862)**, 17200 St. Luke's Way, Zip 77384–8007; tel. 936/266–2000 **A**9 10 21 **F**3 11 12 13 15 18 20 22 24 26 28 29 30 34 35 38 40 41 45 49 50 57 58 59 64 68 70 72 74 75 76 78 79 81 82 85 86 87 89 93 107 108 109 110 111 114 118 119 124 126 129 130 131 135 145 146 147 148 **P**5 6 **S** Catholic Health Initiatives, Englewood, CO
Primary Contact: Debra F. Sukin, Chief Executive Officer
CFO: Mary Sue Lipham, Controller
CMO: Jefy Mathew, M.D., Chief of Staff
Web address: www.stlukeswoodlands.com
Control: Church–operated, Nongovernment, not–for profit **Service:** General Medical and Surgical

Staffed Beds: 184 **Admissions:** 10907 **Census:** 117 **Outpatient Visits:** 65729 **Births:** 1924 **Total Expense ($000):** 152207 **Payroll Expense ($000):** 52651 **Personnel:** 859

THROCKMORTON—Throckmorton County

★ **THROCKMORTON COUNTY MEMORIAL HOSPITAL (451339)**, 802 North Minter Street, Zip 76483–5357, Mailing Address: P.O. Box 729, Zip 76483–0729; tel. 940/849–2151 **A**9 10 18 **F**7 40 41 43 50 64 65 68 75 87 90 127 128 133 148 **P**5 6
Primary Contact: Kirby Gober, Chief Executive Officer
CFO: Cindy Parker, Chief Financial Officer and Director Human Resources
CMO: Ruth Ebangit, M.D., Chief of Staff and Medical Officer
CIO: Amber Myer, Director Medical Technology
CHR: Cindy Parker, Chief Financial Officer and Director Human Resources
CNO: Pam Stamm, Chief Nursing Officer
Control: County–Government, nonfederal **Service:** General Medical and Surgical

Staffed Beds: 14 **Admissions:** 206 **Census:** 2 **Outpatient Visits:** 7801 **Births:** 0 **Total Expense ($000):** 3428 **Payroll Expense ($000):** 1399 **Personnel:** 33

TOMBALL—Harris County

⊠ **KINDRED HOSPITAL TOMBALL (452074)**, 505 Graham Drive, Zip 77375–3368; tel. 281/255–5600, (Includes KINDRED HOSPITAL SPRING, 205 Hollow Tree Lane, Houston, Zip 77090; tel. 832/249–2700; Tracy Kohler, Chief Executive Officer), (Nonreporting) **A**1 9 **S** Kindred Healthcare, Louisville, KY
Primary Contact: Eric Cantrell, Chief Executive Officer
Web address: www.khtomball.com/
Control: Corporation, Investor–owned, for–profit **Service:** Long–Term Acute Care hospital

Staffed Beds: 74

⊠ **TOMBALL REGIONAL MEDICAL CENTER (450670)**, 605 Holderrieth Street, Zip 77375–6445; tel. 281/401–7500 **A**1 9 10 **F**3 8 13 15 18 20 22 24 26 28 29 30 34 40 44 45 46 47 48 49 50 51 53 54 57 59 60 64 70 72 74 75 76 78 79 80 81 82 85 86 87 90 91 94 96 98 102 103 107 108 110 111 114 115 119 120 121 123 124 126 129 130 131 132 146 148 **P**6 **S** Community Health Systems, Inc., Franklin, TN
Primary Contact: Thomas W. Jackson, Chief Executive Officer
COO: Brett Kinman, Chief Operating Officer
CFO: Richard Ervin, Chief Financial Officer
CMO: Ian Glass, M.D., Chief Medical Officer
CIO: Marisa Smith, Director
CHR: Vanessa Anyaso, Chief Human Resources
Web address: www.tomballregionalmedicalcenter.com
Control: Corporation, Investor–owned, for–profit **Service:** General Medical and Surgical

Staffed Beds: 200 **Admissions:** 9892 **Census:** 143 **Outpatient Visits:** 74466 **Births:** 741 **Total Expense ($000):** 169516 **Payroll Expense ($000):** 60454 **Personnel:** 907

TRINITY—Trinity County

★ **EAST TEXAS MEDICAL CENTER TRINITY (450749)**, 317 Prospect Drive, Zip 75862–6202, Mailing Address: P.O. Box 3169, Zip 75862–3169; tel. 936/744–1100 **A**9 10 **F**11 29 40 43 45 64 81 97 107 114 115 119 127 146 **P**7 **S** East Texas Medical Center Regional Healthcare System, Tyler, TX
Primary Contact: Terry Cutler, Interim Chief Executive Officer
CFO: Jerry A. Dominguez, CPA, Chief Financial Officer
CMO: David Mandel, M.D., Chief of Staff
CHR: Kathy Turner, Director Human Resources
CNO: Roxann Langston, Chief Nursing Officer
Web address: www.etmc.org
Control: Other not–for–profit (including NFP Corporation) **Service:** General Medical and Surgical

Staffed Beds: 22 **Admissions:** 547 **Census:** 5 **Outpatient Visits:** 34508 **Births:** 0 **Total Expense ($000):** 9720 **Payroll Expense ($000):** 3607 **Personnel:** 55

TROPHY CLUB—Denton County

☐ **BAYLOR MEDICAL CENTER AT TROPHY CLUB (450883)**, 2850 East State Highway 114, Zip 76262–5302; tel. 817/837–4600 **A**1 9 10 **F**3 12 29 40 64 70 75 79 81 85 87 107 108 111 114 118 121 123 141
Primary Contact: Melanie Chick, Chief Executive Officer
CFO: Jonathan Saunders, Chief Financial Officer
CMO: Mike Stanton, D.O., Medical Director
CIO: Scot Bradford, Chief Information Officer
CHR: Donna Irvin, Director Human Resources
CNO: Tina Huddleston, Chief Nursing Officer
Web address: www.baylortrophyclub.com
Control: Partnership, Investor–owned, for–profit **Service:** General Medical and Surgical

Staffed Beds: 20 **Admissions:** 675 **Census:** 5 **Outpatient Visits:** 13481 **Births:** 0 **Total Expense ($000):** 38004 **Payroll Expense ($000):** 8144 **Personnel:** 139

TULIA—Swisher County

SWISHER MEMORIAL HOSPITAL DISTRICT (451349), 539 Southeast Second, Zip 79088–2400, Mailing Address: P.O. Box 808, Zip 79088–0808; tel. 806/995–3581 **A**9 10 18 **F**3 7 10 11 29 34 35 40 43 50 53 59 62 64 65 68 77 93 107 114 127 129 130 133 **P**4
Primary Contact: Ryan Barnard, Chief Executive Officer
CFO: Connie Wilhelm, Chief Financial Officer
CIO: Brad Roberts, Network Administrator
Web address: www.swisherhospital.com
Control: Other not–for–profit (including NFP Corporation) **Service:** General Medical and Surgical

Staffed Beds: 20 **Admissions:** 281 **Census:** 2 **Outpatient Visits:** 23341 **Births:** 0 **Total Expense ($000):** 9324 **Payroll Expense ($000):** 4083 **Personnel:** 95

TX

Hospital, Medicare Provider Number, Address, Telephone, Approval, Facility, and Physician Codes, Health Care System

★ American Hospital Association (AHA) membership
☐ The Joint Commission accreditation ◇ DNV Healthcare Inc. accreditation
○ Healthcare Facilities Accreditation Program
△ Commission on Accreditation of Rehabilitation Facilities (CARF) accreditation

---

TYLER—Smith County

△ EAST TEXAS MEDICAL CENTER REHABILITATION HOSPITAL (453072), 701 Olympic Plaza Circle, Zip 75701–1950, Mailing Address: P.O. Box 7530, Zip 75711–7530; tel. 903/596–3000 **A**1 7 9 10 **F**3 28 29 30 34 53 57 75 86 90 91 93 96 130 131 132 148 **S** East Texas Medical Center Regional Healthcare System, Tyler, TX
Primary Contact: Eddie L. Howard, Vice President and Chief Operating Officer
COO: Eddie L. Howard, Chief Operating Officer
CFO: James Blanton, Chief Financial Officer
CMO: Jerry Schwarzbach, M.D., Medical Director
CIO: Paula Anthony, Vice President Information Services
CHR: David L. Langston, Corporate Vice President Human Resources
CNO: Laurie Lehnhof–Watts, Assistant Administrator Patient Services
Web address: www.etmc.org
Control: Other not–for–profit (including NFP Corporation) **Service:** Rehabilitation

Staffed Beds: 49 **Admissions:** 1008 **Census:** 37 **Outpatient Visits:** 70794 **Births:** 0 **Total Expense ($000):** 25557 **Payroll Expense ($000):** 11969 **Personnel:** 188

EAST TEXAS MEDICAL CENTER SPECIALTY HOSPITAL (452051), 1000 South Beckham, 5th Floor, Zip 75701–1908, Mailing Address: P.O. Box 7018, Zip 75711–7018; tel. 903/596–3600 **A**1 9 10 **F**1 3 29 30 75 84 130 148 **S** East Texas Medical Center Regional Healthcare System, Tyler, TX
Primary Contact: Eddie L. Howard, Vice President and Chief Operating Officer
CFO: James Blanton, Chief Financial Officer
CMO: J. David Johnson, M.D., Chief of Staff
CIO: Paula Anthony, Vice President Information Services
CHR: David L. Langston, Corporate Vice President Human Resources
CNO: Laurie Lehnhof–Watts, Assistant Administrator Risk Management Performance Improvement and Education
Web address: www.etmc.org
Control: Other not–for–profit (including NFP Corporation) **Service:** Long–Term Acute Care hospital

Staffed Beds: 36 **Admissions:** 386 **Census:** 29 **Outpatient Visits:** 0 **Births:** 0 **Total Expense ($000):** 15713 **Payroll Expense ($000):** 4853 **Personnel:** 80

EAST TEXAS MEDICAL CENTER TYLER (450083), 1000 South Beckham Street, Zip 75701–1908, Mailing Address: Box 6400, Zip 75711–6400; tel. 903/597–0351, (Includes EAST TEXAS MEDICAL CENTER BEHAVIORAL HEALTH CENTER, 4101 University Boulevard, Zip 75701–6600; tel. 903/566–8668; Jerry W. Echols, Administrator and Chief Executive Officer) **A**1 2 3 5 9 10 **F**3 5 8 11 12 13 15 17 18 20 22 24 26 28 29 30 31 34 35 37 38 40 42 43 44 45 46 47 48 49 51 56 58 59 60 61 64 65 68 70 71 73 74 75 76 78 79 80 81 82 84 85 86 87 89 93 98 99 100 101 102 103 104 105 107 110 111 115 117 118 119 120 121 123 124 126 129 130 132 138 141 145 146 147 148 **P**3 **S** East Texas Medical Center Regional Healthcare System, Tyler, TX
Primary Contact: Robert B. Evans, Administrator and Chief Executive Officer
CFO: Byron Hale, Chief Financial Officer
CMO: John Andrews, M.D., Chief of Staff
CIO: Paula Anthony, Vice President Information Services
CHR: Mike Gray, Corporate Vice President Human Resources
CNO: Mariarose Kulma, R.N., Vice President Patient Services
Web address: www.etmc.org
Control: Other not–for–profit (including NFP Corporation) **Service:** General Medical and Surgical

Staffed Beds: 437 **Admissions:** 21638 **Census:** 322 **Outpatient Visits:** 136862 **Births:** 834 **Total Expense ($000):** 396970 **Payroll Expense ($000):** 132539 **Personnel:** 1980

MOTHER FRANCES HOSPITAL – TYLER (450102), 800 East Dawson Street, Zip 75701–2036; tel. 903/593–8441, (Includes LOUIS & PEACHES OWEN HEART HOSPITAL, 703 South Fleishel Avenue, Zip 75701–2015; tel. 903/606–3000; John McGreevy, Chief Executive Officer) **A**1 2 9 10 **F**3 7 8 11 12 13 15 17 18 19 20 22 24 26 28 29 30 31 32 34 37 40 43 45 46 47 48 49 50 51 53 54 55 59 60 64 66 68 70 72 73 74 75 76 77 78 79 80 81 82 83 84 85 86 87 89 93 107 108 110 111 114 115 119 124 126 127 129 130 131 132 134 144 146 147 148 **P**5 6 7 8 **S** Trinity Mother Frances Hospitals and Clinics, Tyler, TX
Primary Contact: John McGreevy, Chief Executive Officer
COO: Todd Hancock, Senior Vice President and Chief Operating Officer
CFO: Joyce Hester, CPA, Senior Vice President and Chief Financial Officer
CMO: Barbara Allen, M.D., Vice President Medical Affairs
CIO: Jeff Pearson, Vice President and Chief Information Officer
CHR: Thomas Wilken, Senior Vice President and Chief Human Resources Officer
CNO: Robert Rose, R.N., Senior Vice President and System Chief Nursing Officer
Web address: www.tmfhs.org
Control: Other not–for–profit (including NFP Corporation) **Service:** General Medical and Surgical

Staffed Beds: 458 **Admissions:** 23567 **Census:** 292 **Outpatient Visits:** 500578 **Births:** 2553 **Total Expense ($000):** 480219 **Payroll Expense ($000):** 143072 **Personnel:** 3358

TEXAS SPINE & JOINT HOSPITAL (450864), 1814 Roseland Boulevard, Suite 100, Zip 75701–4262; tel. 903/525–3300 **A**1 10 **F**8 29 39 40 77 79 81 82 85 107 111 114 119 144
Primary Contact: Tony Wahl, Chief Executive Officer
CFO: Greg Cummings, Chief Financial Officer
CMO: Kim Foreman, M.D., Chief of Staff
CNO: Deborah Pelton, R.N., Chief Nursing Officer
Web address: www.tsjh.org
Control: Partnership, Investor–owned, for–profit **Service:** Orthopedic

Staffed Beds: 18 **Admissions:** 1576 **Census:** 10 **Outpatient Visits:** 31891 **Births:** 0 **Total Expense ($000):** 61414 **Payroll Expense ($000):** 14984 **Personnel:** 284

TRINITY MOTHER FRANCES REHABILITATION HOSPITAL (453056), 3131 Troup Highway, Zip 75701–8352; tel. 903/510–7000 **A**1 9 10 **F**3 9 28 29 56 62 64 74 75 77 79 82 87 90 91 93 95 96 130 131 132 143 147 148 **S** HEALTHSOUTH Corporation, Birmingham, AL
Primary Contact: Sharla Anderson, Chief Executive Officer
CFO: Michael G. Treadway, Controller
CMO: Bradley Merritt, M.D., Medical Director
Web address: www.tmfrehabhospital.com
Control: Partnership, Investor–owned, for–profit **Service:** Rehabilitation

Staffed Beds: 74 **Admissions:** 1737 **Census:** 61 **Outpatient Visits:** 15335 **Births:** 0 **Total Expense ($000):** 18517 **Payroll Expense ($000):** 10458 **Personnel:** 186

TYLER CONTINUECARE HOSPITAL AT MOTHER FRANCES (452091), 800 East Dawson, 4th Floor, Zip 75701–2036; tel. 903/531–4080 **A**9 10 **F**1 3 29 34 49 74 75 77 85 86 87 130 135 148 **P**4 **S** Trinity Mother Frances Hospitals and Clinics, Tyler, TX
Primary Contact: Stephanie Hyde, Chief Executive Officer
Web address: www.continuecare.org
Control: Other not–for–profit (including NFP Corporation) **Service:** Long--Term Acute Care hospital

Staffed Beds: 51 **Admissions:** 610 **Census:** 46 **Outpatient Visits:** 0 **Births:** 0 **Total Expense ($000):** 21985 **Payroll Expense ($000):** 8853 **Personnel:** 134

UNIVERSITY OF TEXAS HEALTH SCIENCE CENTER AT TYLER (450690), 11937 Highway 271, Zip 75708–3154; tel. 903/877–7777 **A**1 5 9 10 **F**3 8 11 15 18 20 22 24 26 28 29 30 31 32 34 35 40 43 45 46 47 48 49 50 53 55 56 57 58 59 64 65 68 70 75 77 78 79 81 85 86 87 93 97 107 108 110 111 114 118 119 120 121 123 124 129 130 135 146 147 148 **P**6 **S** University of Texas System, Austin, TX
Primary Contact: Kirk A. Calhoun, M.D., President
COO: Joe Woelkers, Executive Vice President and Chief Staff
CFO: Vernon Moore, Senior Vice President Chief Business and Finance
CMO: Steven Cox, M.D., Chief Medical Officer
CIO: Vernon Moore, Senior Vice President Chief Business and Finance
CHR: Jesse Gomez, Vice President Human Resources
CNO: Don Hunt, M.D., Vice President Patient Centered Care and Chief Nursing Officer
Web address: www.uthct.edu
Control: State–Government, nonfederal **Service:** General Medical and Surgical

Staffed Beds: 111 **Admissions:** 1637 **Census:** 21 **Outpatient Visits:** 218787 **Births:** 0 **Total Expense ($000):** 136745 **Payroll Expense ($000):** 62908 **Personnel:** 917

UVALDE—Uvalde County

UVALDE COUNTY HOSPITAL AUTHORITY (450177), 1025 Garner Field Road, Zip 78801–4809; tel. 830/278–6251 **A**1 9 10 20 **F**3 11 13 15 17 18 29 30 39 40 43 45 50 56 57 59 63 64 68 70 76 81 85 86 87 89 90 93 104 107 108 111 115 119 127 130 132 133 146 147 148 **P**3
Primary Contact: Thomas Nordwick, Chief Executive Officer
CFO: Valerie Lopez, CPA, Chief Financial Officer
CMO: Clifford White, M.D., Chief of Staff
CIO: Carolina Velasquez, Director Information Services
CHR: Charla Carter, Human Resource Officer
CNO: Jeanne E. Leake, R.N., Chief Nursing Officer
Web address: www.umhtx.org
Control: Hospital district or authority, Government, nonfederal **Service:** General Medical and Surgical

Staffed Beds: 48 **Admissions:** 2017 **Census:** 20 **Outpatient Visits:** 68940 **Births:** 421 **Total Expense ($000):** 49547 **Payroll Expense ($000):** 20644 **Personnel:** 460

Many Facility Codes have changed. Please refer to the AHA Guide Code Chart. © 2014 AHA Guide

VAN HORN—Culberson County

★ **CULBERSON HOSPITAL (451338)**, Eisenhower–Farm Market Road 2185,
Zip 79855, Mailing Address: P.O. Box 609, Zip 79855–0609; tel. 432/283–2760
A9 10 18 **F**3 7 34 40 43 57 59 65 66 68 93 107 114 119 127 133 148 **P**6
S Preferred Management Corporation, Shawnee, OK
Primary Contact: Jared Chanski, Administrator
CMO: John A. Thomas, M.D., Chief Medical Staff
Web address: www.culbersonhospital.org
Control: Corporation, Investor–owned, for–profit **Service:** General Medical and
Surgical

> **Staffed Beds:** 14 **Admissions:** 74 **Census:** 3 **Outpatient Visits:** 9897 **Births:**
> 0 **Total Expense ($000):** 5786 **Payroll Expense ($000):** 2376 **Personnel:**
> 59

VERNON—Wilbarger County

☐ **NORTH TEXAS STATE HOSPITAL**, Highway 70 Northwest, Zip 76384, Mailing
Address: P.O. Box 2231, Zip 76385–2231; tel. 940/552–9901 **A**1 **F**11 30 34
39 44 50 56 57 68 75 86 87 96 97 98 99 103 130 132 135 146 **P**6 **S** Texas
Department of State Health Services, Austin, TX
Primary Contact: James E. Smith, Superintendent
CFO: William Lowery, Financial Officer
CIO: Chad Hughes, Information Officer
Web address: www.dshs.state.tx.us/mhhospitals/NorthTexasSH/default.shtm
Control: State–Government, nonfederal **Service:** Psychiatric

> **Staffed Beds:** 640 **Admissions:** 2195 **Census:** 597 **Outpatient Visits:** 0
> **Births:** 0 **Personnel:** 2345

WILBARGER GENERAL HOSPITAL (450584), 920 Hillcrest Drive,
Zip 76384–3196; tel. 940/552–9351 **A**9 10 20 **F**3 11 15 29 34 35 40 43 45
54 56 57 60 62 75 81 85 86 87 93 98 101 103 104 107 111 115 119 124
127 130 132 133 143 146 148
Primary Contact: Jonathon Voelkel, Chief Executive Officer
CFO: Kim Fenter, Chief Financial Officer
CMO: Randall Schaffner, M.D., Chief of Staff and Medical Director
CIO: Ed Nary, Director Information Technology and Chief Compliance Officer
CHR: Cathie Bristo, Director Human Resources
CNO: Pam Akin, Interim Chief Nursing Officer
Web address: www.wghospital.com
Control: Hospital district or authority, Government, nonfederal **Service:** General
Medical and Surgical

> **Staffed Beds:** 27 **Admissions:** 452 **Census:** 11 **Outpatient Visits:** 13197
> **Births:** 0 **Total Expense ($000):** 20144 **Payroll Expense ($000):** 9520
> **Personnel:** 179

VICTORIA—Victoria County

★ ◇ **CITIZENS MEDICAL CENTER (450023)**, 2701 Hospital Drive,
Zip 77901–5749; tel. 361/573–9181, (Total facility includes 20 beds in nursing
home–type unit) **A**2 9 10 21 **F**1 3 4 11 12 13 15 16 17 18 20 22 24 28 29 30
31 34 35 38 40 41 42 43 45 49 50 51 53 54 56 57 59 62 64 65 67 70 72
73 74 75 76 77 78 79 80 81 82 85 86 87 88 89 90 93 94 97 98 102 107
108 109 110 111 113 114 115 116 117 118 119 120 121 124 126 128 129
130 131 132 135 144 146 147 148 **P**6
Primary Contact: Stephen Thames, Chief Executive Officer
COO: Caren Adamson, Chief Operating Officer
CFO: Carolyn Zafereo, Controller
CHR: Kathleen C. Mosmeyer, Director Human Resources
Web address: www.citizensmedicalcenter.org
Control: County–Government, nonfederal **Service:** General Medical and Surgical

> **Staffed Beds:** 296 **Admissions:** 8171 **Census:** 112 **Outpatient Visits:**
> 110402 **Births:** 822 **Total Expense ($000):** 139643 **Payroll Expense**
> **($000):** 55127 **Personnel:** 1091

⊠ **DETAR HEALTHCARE SYSTEM (450147)**, 506 East San Antonio Street,
Zip 77901–6060, Mailing Address: P.O. Box 2089, Zip 77902–2089;
tel. 361/575–7441, (Includes DETAR HOSPITAL NORTH, 101 Medical Drive,
Zip 77904–3198; tel. 361/573–6100; William R. Blanchard, Chief Executive
Officer), (Total facility includes 16 beds in nursing home–type unit) **A**1 9 10 **F**3 12
13 15 18 20 22 24 28 29 30 31 39 40 41 43 47 49 50 51 53 56 64 70 72
74 75 76 77 78 79 81 82 85 86 87 89 90 91 93 98 103 104 105 107 108
110 111 114 118 119 126 128 130 132 146 147 148 **P**3 5 8 **S** Community
Health Systems, Inc., Franklin, TN
Primary Contact: William R. Blanchard, Chief Executive Officer
CFO: Donald E. Hagan, Chief Financial Officer
CMO: James R. Brand, M.D., Chief of Staff
CIO: Kim Tompkins, Director Information Services
CHR: Kristina Elsik, Director Human Resources
Web address: www.detar.com
Control: Corporation, Investor–owned, for–profit **Service:** General Medical and
Surgical

> **Staffed Beds:** 245 **Admissions:** 8267 **Census:** 106 **Outpatient Visits:** 83089
> **Total Expense ($000):** 113045 **Payroll Expense ($000):** 45680 **Personnel:**
> 848

⊠ **POST ACUTE MEDICAL SPECIALTY HOSPITAL OF VICTORIA (452056)**, 506
East San Antonio Street, 3rd Floor, Zip 77901–6060; tel. 361/575–1445 **A**1 9
10 **F**1 3 29 30 31 82 85 86 87 97 130 148 **S** Post Acute Medical, LLC,
Enola, PA
Primary Contact: Portlyn Brogger, Chief Executive Officer
CHR: Rachel Reeves, Manager Human Resources
Web address: www.khvictoria.com
Control: Corporation, Investor–owned, for–profit **Service:** Long–Term Acute Care
hospital

> **Staffed Beds:** 23 **Admissions:** 288 **Census:** 22 **Outpatient Visits:** 0 **Births:**
> 0 **Total Expense ($000):** 10220 **Payroll Expense ($000):** 3991 **Personnel:**
> 100

⊠ **POST ACUTE/WARM SPRINGS SPECIALTY HOSPITAL OF VICTORIA**
(452094), 102 Medical Drive, Zip 77904–3101; tel. 361/576–6200 **A**1 9 10 **F**1
3 29 75 77 85 93 94 96 148 **S** Post Acute Medical, LLC, Enola, PA
Primary Contact: Portlyn Brogger, Chief Executive Officer
CFO: James Asberry, Chief Financial Officer
CMO: Behram Khan, M.D., Medical Director
CHR: Waynea Finley, Corporate Director Human Resources
Web address: www.warmsprings.org
Control: Partnership, Investor–owned, for–profit **Service:** Long–Term Acute Care
hospital

> **Staffed Beds:** 26 **Admissions:** 362 **Census:** 25 **Outpatient Visits:** 6954
> **Births:** 0 **Total Expense ($000):** 12756 **Payroll Expense ($000):** 5292
> **Personnel:** 110

WACO—Mclennan County

⊠ **HILLCREST BAPTIST MEDICAL CENTER (450101)**, 100 Hillcrest Medical
Boulevard, Zip 76712–8897, Mailing Address: P.O. Box 21146,
Zip 76702–1146; tel. 254/202–2000, (Includes HILLCREST BAPTIST MEDICAL
CENTER – HERRING AVENUE CAMPUS, 3000 HERRING AVENUE, ZIP 76708),
(Total facility includes 20 beds in nursing home–type unit) **A**1 2 3 5 9 10 **F**3 11
13 15 18 20 22 24 26 28 29 30 31 34 40 43 44 45 46 47 48 49 50 51 53
54 56 57 59 60 61 64 68 70 72 74 75 76 78 79 81 82 84 85 86 87 89 90
93 96 97 107 108 110 111 113 114 115 116 117 118 119 128 129 130
131 132 134 135 145 146 147 148 **S** Baylor Scott & White Health, Dallas, TX
Primary Contact: Glenn A. Robinson, Chief Executive Officer
CFO: Richard Perkins, Chief Financial Officer
CMO: J. E. Morrison, M.D., Chief Medical Officer
CIO: Richard Warren, Chief Information Officer
Web address: www.hillcrest.net
Control: Other not–for–profit (including NFP Corporation) **Service:** General
Medical and Surgical

> **Staffed Beds:** 263 **Admissions:** 12998 **Census:** 168 **Outpatient Visits:**
> 176010 **Births:** 2682 **Total Expense ($000):** 253275 **Payroll Expense**
> **($000):** 70758 **Personnel:** 1388

TX

Hospital, Medicare Provider Number, Address, Telephone, Approval, Facility, and Physician Codes, Health Care System

★ American Hospital Association (AHA) membership
☐ The Joint Commission accreditation   ◇ DNV Healthcare Inc. accreditation

○ Healthcare Facilities Accreditation Program
△ Commission on Accreditation of Rehabilitation Facilities (CARF) accreditation

---

✠ **PROVIDENCE HEALTH CENTER (450042)**, 6901 Medical Parkway, Zip 76712–7998, Mailing Address: P.O. Box 2589, Zip 76702–2589; tel. 254/751–4000, (Includes DEPAUL CENTER, 301 Londonderry Drive, Zip 76712; tel. 254/776–5970; Vicky Campbell, Vice President), (Total facility includes 336 beds in nursing home–type unit) **A**1 2 3 5 9 10 **F**2 3 4 5 6 8 9 10 11 12 13 14 15 18 20 22 24 26 28 29 30 31 34 35 38 40 41 44 45 46 48 49 50 53 54 56 57 58 59 61 62 64 67 68 70 74 75 76 77 78 79 81 82 84 85 86 87 89 93 97 98 99 100 101 102 103 104 105 107 108 110 114 115 119 125 128 130 132 135 144 146 147 148 **P**5 6 **S** Ascension Health, Saint Louis, MO
Primary Contact: Brett A. Esrock, President and Chief Executive Officer
COO: Steven Province, Senior Vice President and Chief Operating Officer
CFO: Karen K. Richardson, Vice President Finance and Chief Information Officer
CMO: T. Marc Barrett, M.D., Senior Vice President Medical Affairs
CIO: Jay Scherler, Director Information Systems and Vice President Business Services
CHR: Chuck Sivess, Vice President Human Resources
CNO: Christine Courtney, R.N., Vice President and Chief Nursing Officer
Web address: www.providence.net
Control: Church–operated, Nongovernment, not–for profit **Service:** General Medical and Surgical

Staffed Beds: 620 **Admissions:** 16704 **Census:** 484 **Outpatient Visits:** 393552 **Births:** 1443 **Total Expense ($000):** 264719 **Payroll Expense ($000):** 110711 **Personnel:** 2007

WACO VETERANS AFFAIRS HOSPITAL See Central Texas Veterans Healthcare System, Temple

WAXAHACHIE—Ellis County

✠ **BAYLOR MEDICAL CENTER AT WAXAHACHIE (450372)**, 1405 West Jefferson Street, Zip 75165–2275; tel. 972/923–7000 **A**1 2 9 10 **F**3 11 12 15 28 29 30 34 35 40 41 53 57 59 64 65 68 70 71 74 75 77 78 79 81 82 84 85 93 107 108 110 111 114 119 124 129 130 135 147 148 **S** Baylor Scott & White Health, Dallas, TX
Primary Contact: Christopher York, FACHE, President
COO: Cindy Murray, R.N., Chief Nursing Officer and Chief Operating Officer
CFO: Steve Roussel, Vice President Finance
CMO: Valerie Goman, M.D., President Medical Staff
CIO: Gary Beazley, Coordinator Information Systems
CHR: Marcos A. Ramirez, Human Resources Business Partner
Web address: www.baylorhealth.com/PhysiciansLocations/Waxahachie/Pages/Default.aspx
Control: Other not–for–profit (including NFP Corporation) **Service:** General Medical and Surgical

Staffed Beds: 54 **Admissions:** 3069 **Census:** 33 **Outpatient Visits:** 66451 **Births:** 0 **Total Expense ($000):** 60757 **Payroll Expense ($000):** 23477 **Personnel:** 338

WEATHERFORD—Parker County

✠ **WEATHERFORD REGIONAL MEDICAL CENTER (450203)**, 713 East Anderson Street, Zip 76086–5705; tel. 817/596–8751 **A**1 9 10 **F**3 8 13 15 17 18 20 22 28 29 34 35 40 43 49 51 57 59 68 70 74 75 76 77 79 81 82 85 93 107 111 114 115 119 130 131 132 133 135 146 148 **P**8 **S** Community Health Systems, Inc., Franklin, TN
Primary Contact: David Orcutt, Chief Executive Officer
CFO: Nancy Cooke, Chief Financial Officer
CMO: Scott Walker, M.D., Chief Medical Staff
CIO: Merri Roy, Director Information Services
CHR: Kristin Lawyer, Director Human Resources
CNO: Donna Boone, R.N., Chief Nursing Officer
Web address: www.weatherfordregional.com
Control: Corporation, Investor–owned, for–profit **Service:** General Medical and Surgical

Staffed Beds: 86 **Admissions:** 4652 **Census:** 46 **Outpatient Visits:** 65588 **Births:** 565 **Total Expense ($000):** 77454 **Payroll Expense ($000):** 23814 **Personnel:** 449

WEBSTER—Harris County

✠ **CLEAR LAKE REGIONAL MEDICAL CENTER (450617)**, 500 Medical Center Boulevard, Zip 77598–4220; tel. 281/332–2511, (Includes ALVIN DIAGNOSTIC AND URGENT CARE CENTER, 301 Medic Lane, Alvin, Zip 77511–5597; tel. 281/331–6141; MAINLAND MEDICAL CENTER, 6801 E F Lowry Expressway, Texas City, Zip 77591; tel. 409/938–5000; Michael Ehrat, Chief Executive Officer) **A**1 3 5 9 10 **F**3 11 13 15 17 18 20 22 24 26 28 29 30 31 34 35 40 41 42 43 44 45 46 47 49 50 51 54 56 57 59 60 64 70 72 73 74 75 76 77 78 79 81 83 85 86 87 88 89 90 93 94 96 98 100 101 103 104 107 108 110 111 114 115 119 124 126 129 130 132 135 146 147 148 **S** HCA, Nashville, TN
Primary Contact: Stephen K. Jones, Jr., FACHE, Chief Executive Officer
CFO: Jeff Sliwinski, Chief Financial Officer
CMO: Richard Marietta, M.D., Medical Director
CIO: Ley Samson, Director Management Information Systems
CHR: Brad Horst, Director Human Resources
Web address: www.clearlakermc.com
Control: Partnership, Investor–owned, for–profit **Service:** General Medical and Surgical

Staffed Beds: 699 **Admissions:** 28985 **Census:** 391 **Outpatient Visits:** 220642 **Births:** 3976 **Total Expense ($000):** 383465 **Payroll Expense ($000):** 158011 **Personnel:** 2209

CLEAR LAKE REHABILITATION HOSPITAL See Kindred Rehabilitation Hospital Clear Lake

☐ **CORNERSTONE HOSPITAL OF HOUSTON AT CLEARLAKE (452032)**, 709 Medical Center Boulevard, Zip 77598; tel. 281/332–3322, (Includes CORNERSTONE HOSPITAL OF HOUSTON – BELLAIRE, 5314 Dashwood, Houston, Zip 77081–4603; tel. 713/295–5300; James Camp, R.N., Chief Executive Officer) **A**1 9 10 **F**1 3 29 56 85 86 87 91 130 148 **S** Cornerstone Healthcare Group, Dallas, TX
Primary Contact: James Camp, R.N., Regional Chief Executive Officer, Houston Market
COO: Brenda Lucero, Chief Clinical Officer
CFO: A. Shane Wells, Chief Financial Officer
CMO: Mark Barlow, M.D., Chief Medical Officer and President Medical Staff
CIO: Jerald Harris, Chief Information Officer
CHR: Yolanda Jacobs, Coordinator Human Resources
Web address: www.cornerstonehealthcaregroup.com
Control: Partnership, Investor–owned, for–profit **Service:** Long–Term Acute Care hospital

Staffed Beds: 134 **Admissions:** 1240 **Census:** 88 **Outpatient Visits:** 0 **Births:** 0 **Total Expense ($000):** 37688 **Payroll Expense ($000):** 16006 **Personnel:** 295

◇ **HOUSTON PHYSICIANS HOSPITAL (670008)**, 333 North Texas Avenue, Zip 77598–4966; tel. 281/557–5620 **A**5 9 10 21 **F**3 29 40 51 64 68 74 79 81 82 85 86 91 93 107 111 114 141
Primary Contact: Michele Dionne, Chief Executive Officer
Web address: www.houstonphysicianshospital.com
Control: Corporation, Investor–owned, for–profit **Service:** Surgical

Staffed Beds: 21 **Admissions:** 642 **Census:** 4 **Outpatient Visits:** 12182 **Births:** 0 **Total Expense ($000):** 39119 **Payroll Expense ($000):** 9322 **Personnel:** 146

✠ **KINDRED REHABILITATION HOSPITAL CLEAR LAKE (453052)**, 655 East Medical Center Boulevard, Zip 77598–4328; tel. 281/286–1500 **A**1 9 10 **F**3 29 64 74 75 79 90 93 95 130 131 132 143 146 148 **S** Kindred Healthcare, Louisville, KY
Primary Contact: Dale R. Mulder, Chief Executive Officer
CFO: Michael McFall, Chief Financial Officer
CMO: Michael Rosenblatt, M.D., Medical Director
CHR: Monica Little, Coordinator Human Resources
CNO: Kathy Hutchins–Otero, Chief Clinical Officer
Web address: www.khrehabclearlake.com/
Control: Corporation, Investor–owned, for–profit **Service:** Rehabilitation

Staffed Beds: 60 **Admissions:** 998 **Census:** 36 **Outpatient Visits:** 4532 **Births:** 0 **Total Expense ($000):** 15489 **Payroll Expense ($000):** 7610 **Personnel:** 123

WELLINGTON—Collingsworth County

COLLINGSWORTH GENERAL HOSPITAL (451355), 1013 15th Street, Zip 79095–3703, Mailing Address: P.O. Box 1112, Zip 79095–1112; tel. 806/447–2521 **A**9 10 18 **F**3 16 40 43 57 59 68 93 97 107 114 127 133 **S** Preferred Management Corporation, Shawnee, OK
Primary Contact: Candy Powell, Administrator
CFO: Larry Stephens, Chief Financial Officer
CMO: Wesley Nickens, M.D., Chief of Staff
CIO: Thomas T. Ng, Chief Information Officer
CHR: April Wright, Human Resources Officer
CNO: Vikki Barton, R.N., Chief Nursing Officer
Web address: www.collingsworthgeneral.net
Control: Corporation, Investor–owned, for–profit **Service:** General Medical and Surgical

Staffed Beds: 13 **Admissions:** 277 **Census:** 4 **Outpatient Visits:** 13340 **Births:** 0 **Total Expense ($000):** 5791 **Payroll Expense ($000):** 2375 **Personnel:** 57

TX

WESLACO—Hidalgo County

☒ **KNAPP MEDICAL CENTER (450128)**, 1401 East Eighth Street,
Zip 78596–6640, Mailing Address: P.O. Box 1110, Zip 78599–1110;
tel. 956/968–8567 **A**1 9 10 **F**3 8 11 12 13 15 20 22 29 30 31 34 35 39 40
43 44 46 47 49 50 51 56 57 59 60 63 64 70 73 74 75 76 77 78 79 81 82
84 85 86 87 89 93 107 108 110 111 114 115 119 130 131 132 134 135
141 142 143 146 147 148 **P**8 **S** Prime Healthcare Services, Ontario, CA
Primary Contact: William D. Adams, Chief Executive Officer
CFO: Dinah L. Gonzalez, Chief Financial Officer
CIO: Teri Garza, Director Health Information Services
CHR: Emmett Craig, Chief Human Resources Officer
CNO: Anna Hinojosa, MSN, Interim Chief Nursing Officer
Web address: www.knappmed.org
Control: Other not–for–profit (including NFP Corporation) **Service:** General
Medical and Surgical

Staffed Beds: 190 **Admissions:** 9365 **Census:** 85 **Outpatient Visits:** 73580
Births: 1919 **Total Expense ($000):** 94501 **Payroll Expense ($000):** 39021
Personnel: 746

△ **WESLACO REHABILITATION HOSPITAL (453091)**, 906 South James Street,
Zip 78596–9840; tel. 956/969–2222 **A**7 9 10 **F**3 29 30 90 130 **P**5
Primary Contact: Maggie E. Barreiro, Administrator
CFO: Annette Garza, Controller
CMO: Daisy Arce, Chief of Medical Staff
CHR: Debbie Pendleton, Human Resources Specialist
CNO: Rita Mata–Guerrero, Nurse Director
Web address: www.weslacorehabhospital.com
Control: Partnership, Investor–owned, for–profit **Service:** Rehabilitation

Staffed Beds: 32 **Admissions:** 639 **Census:** 21 **Outpatient Visits:** 0 **Births:**
0 **Total Expense ($000):** 7619 **Payroll Expense ($000):** 4727 **Personnel:**
82

WHARTON—Wharton County

☐ **GULF COAST MEDICAL CENTER (450214)**, 10141 Highway 59,
Zip 77488–3004; tel. 979/282–6100 **A**1 9 10 **F**11 29 40 43 49 64 70 77 81
82 93 98 103 107 108 114 118 119 121 130 146 148 **S** Southwest
Healthcare System, Scottsdale, AZ
Primary Contact: Loretta Flynn, Chief Executive Officer
CFO: Barbara Starling, Chief Financial Officer
CHR: Loretta Flynn, Director Human Resources
Web address: www.gulfcoastmedical.com
Control: Partnership, Investor–owned, for–profit **Service:** General Medical and
Surgical

Staffed Beds: 129 **Admissions:** 846 **Census:** 13 **Outpatient Visits:** 16683
Births: 29 **Total Expense ($000):** 18534 **Payroll Expense ($000):** 8042
Personnel: 146

WHEELER—Wheeler County

PARKVIEW HOSPITAL (451334), 901 Sweetwater Street, Zip 79096–2421,
Mailing Address: P.O. Box 1030, Zip 79096–1030; tel. 806/826–5581 **A**9 10 18
F3 7 10 40 43 59 62 65 68 93 107 114 128 130 133 148
Primary Contact: Monica Kidd, R.N., MSN, Administrator
CFO: Jace Henderson, Chief Financial Officer
CMO: John P. Lavelle, M.D., Chief Medical Officer
CNO: Melisa Scales, Director of Nursing
Web address: www.parkviewhosp.org
Control: Hospital district or authority, Government, nonfederal **Service:** General
Medical and Surgical

Staffed Beds: 16 **Admissions:** 142 **Census:** 2 **Outpatient Visits:** 2711
Births: 0 **Total Expense ($000):** 6965 **Payroll Expense ($000):** 2802
Personnel: 96

WHITNEY—Hill County

LAKE WHITNEY MEDICAL CENTER (450270), 200 North San Jacinto Street,
Zip 76692–2388, Mailing Address: P.O. Box 458, Zip 76692–0458;
tel. 254/694–3165, (Nonreporting) **A**9 10
Primary Contact: Ruth Ann Crow, Administrator
COO: Tariq Mahmood, Chief Executive Officer
CFO: Joe White, Chief Financial Officer
CMO: Aman Ali Shah, M.D., Chief Medical Staff
CIO: Patricia Daniel, Chief Information Officer
CHR: Darleen Towers, Director Human Resources
Web address: www.lakewhitneychamber.com/lake–whitney–medical–center.html
Control: Corporation, Investor–owned, for–profit **Service:** General Medical and
Surgical

Staffed Beds: 28

WICHITA FALLS—Wichita County

☒ **HEALTHSOUTH REHABILITATION HOSPITAL–WICHITA FALLS (453054)**,
3901 Armory Road, Zip 76302–2204; tel. 940/720–5700 **A**1 9 10 **F**3 28 29 44
50 53 62 64 68 74 75 77 79 82 86 87 90 91 92 93 95 96 132 143 146 148
S HEALTHSOUTH Corporation, Birmingham, AL
Primary Contact: Michael L. Bullitt, Chief Executive Officer
CFO: Tom Box, CPA, Chief Financial Officer
CMO: Virgil Frardo, M.D., Medical Director
CIO: Mary Walker, Manager Information Technology
CHR: Kathleen Pirtle, Director Human Resources
CNO: Karla Dwyer, R.N., Chief Nursing Officer
Web address: www.healthsouthwichitafalls.com
Control: Partnership, Investor–owned, for–profit **Service:** Rehabilitation

Staffed Beds: 63 **Admissions:** 1201 **Census:** 43 **Outpatient Visits:** 10768
Births: 0 **Total Expense ($000):** 14815 **Payroll Expense ($000):** 7794
Personnel: 171

☐ **KELL WEST REGIONAL HOSPITAL (450827)**, 5420 Kell West Boulevard,
Zip 76310–1610; tel. 940/692–5888 **A**1 9 10 **F**3 31 39 40 49 50 51 74 75
78 79 81 82 85 87 91 93 107 108 111 114 119 129 130 **P**5
Primary Contact: Jerry Myers, M.D., Chief Executive Officer
CFO: Fran Lindemann, Director Finance
Web address: www.kellwest.com
Control: Partnership, Investor–owned, for–profit **Service:** General Medical and
Surgical

Staffed Beds: 41 **Admissions:** 914 **Census:** 8 **Outpatient Visits:** 25448
Births: 0 **Total Expense ($000):** 27967 **Payroll Expense ($000):** 8677
Personnel: 217

☐ **NORTH TEXAS STATE HOSPITAL, WICHITA FALLS CAMPUS (454008)**,
6515 Lake Road, Zip 76308–5419, Mailing Address: Box 300, Zip 76307–0300;
tel. 940/692–1220, (Nonreporting) **A**1 5 10
Primary Contact: James E. Smith, Superintendent
CFO: Bill Lowery, Chief Financial Officer
CMO: Lauren Parsons, M.D., Clinical Director
CIO: Crystal Dennstedt, Chief Information Officer
Web address: www.mhmr.state.tx.us
Control: State–Government, nonfederal **Service:** Psychiatric

Staffed Beds: 381

☐ **PROMISE HOSPITAL OF WICHITA FALLS (452068)**, 1103 Grace Street,
Zip 76301–4414; tel. 940/720–6633 **A**1 9 10 **F**1 3 29 30 31 56 75 77 82 85
86 87 91 100 130 143 148 **S** Promise Healthcare, Boca Raton, FL
Primary Contact: Delnita Bray, Administrator
CFO: Debbie Herder, Controller
CMO: Robert McBroom, M.D., Medical Director
CIO: Gail McIlroy, Director Medical Records
CNO: Deanna Dowling, R.N., Chief Nursing Officer
Web address: www.promise–wichitafalls.com
Control: Corporation, Investor–owned, for–profit **Service:** Long–Term Acute Care
hospital

Staffed Beds: 31 **Admissions:** 252 **Census:** 19 **Outpatient Visits:** 0 **Births:**
0 **Total Expense ($000):** 5875 **Payroll Expense ($000):** 2574 **Personnel:**
58

☐ **RED RIVER HOSPITAL (454018)**, 1505 Eighth Street, Zip 76301–3106;
tel. 940/322–3171 **A**1 9 10 **F**4 5 29 75 86 87 98 99 101 102 103 104 105
130 132 **S** Acadia Healthcare Company, Inc., Franklin, TN
Primary Contact: Rob Marsh, Chief Executive Officer
CFO: Lee Mitchell, Chief Financial Officer
CMO: Harvey C. Martin, M.D., Medical Director
CIO: Fay Helton, Director Medical Records
CHR: Tracy Fehr, Executive Assistant and Director Human Resources
CNO: Amy Frate, Director of Nursing
Web address: www.redriverhospital.com
Control: Corporation, Investor–owned, for–profit **Service:** Psychiatric

Staffed Beds: 74 **Admissions:** 1906 **Census:** 63 **Outpatient Visits:** 4347
Births: 0 **Total Expense ($000):** 9902 **Payroll Expense ($000):** 5750
Personnel: 193

TX

Hospital, Medicare Provider Number, Address, Telephone, Approval, Facility, and Physician Codes, Health Care System

★ American Hospital Association (AHA) membership
☐ The Joint Commission accreditation   ◇ DNV Healthcare Inc. accreditation

○ Healthcare Facilities Accreditation Program
△ Commission on Accreditation of Rehabilitation Facilities (CARF) accreditation

---

✠ **UNITED REGIONAL HEALTH CARE SYSTEM (450010)**, 1600 11th Street, Zip 76301–4300; tel. 940/764–7000, (Includes UNITED REGIONAL HEALTH CARE SYSTEM–EIGHTH STREET CAMPUS, 1600 Eighth Street, Zip 76301–3164; UNITED REGIONAL HEALTH CARE SYSTEM–ELEVENTH STREET CAMPUS, 1600 11th Street, Zip 76301–9988; tel. 940/764–0055) **A**1 2 3 5 9 10 20 **F**3 11 12 13 15 17 18 20 21 22 24 26 28 29 30 31 32 34 35 37 39 40 43 44 45 46 47 48 49 50 51 53 57 59 60 61 64 65 68 70 73 74 75 76 77 78 79 80 81 82 84 85 86 87 89 92 93 102 107 110 111 114 115 116 117 118 119 126 130 131 132 134 146 147 148 **P**3
Primary Contact: Phyllis A. Cowling, CPA, President and Chief Executive Officer
COO: Nancy Townley, R.N., Senior Vice President Operations
CFO: Robert M. Pert, Vice President Finance and Chief Financial Officer
CMO: Scott Hoyer, M.D., Vice President Quality and Chief Medical Officer
CIO: Jerry Marshall, Director Information Systems
CHR: Kristi Faulkner, Director Human Resources
Web address: www.urhcs.org
Control: Other not–for–profit (including NFP Corporation) **Service:** General Medical and Surgical

Staffed Beds: 304 **Admissions:** 14163 **Census:** 164 **Outpatient Visits:** 132647 **Births:** 2104 **Total Expense ($000):** 266414 **Payroll Expense ($000):** 111430 **Personnel:** 1776

WINNIE—Chambers County

WINNIE COMMUNITY HOSPITAL (451328), 538 Broadway, Zip 77665–7600, Mailing Address: P.O. Box 1249, Zip 77665–1249; tel. 409/296–6000 **A**9 10 18 **F**3 29 34 40 59 65 107 119 127 133 146 **P**6
Primary Contact: Daniel Yancy, Administrator and Chief Executive Officer
CFO: Julie Harris, Chief Financial Officer
CMO: Leonidas Andres, M.D., Chief of Staff
CHR: Anha Simon, Director Human Resources
Web address: www.winniehospital.com
Control: Partnership, Investor–owned, for–profit **Service:** General Medical and Surgical

Staffed Beds: 25 **Admissions:** 358 **Census:** 3 **Outpatient Visits:** 30201 **Births:** 0 **Total Expense ($000):** 10796 **Payroll Expense ($000):** 3652 **Personnel:** 79

WINNSBORO—Wood County

✠ **MOTHER FRANCES HOSPITAL – WINNSBORO (451381)**, 719 West Coke Road, Zip 75494–3011, Mailing Address: P.O. Box 628, Zip 75494–0628; tel. 903/342–5227 **A**1 9 10 18 **F**3 18 29 30 34 40 43 45 57 59 64 68 70 75 79 81 82 85 87 93 107 108 111 114 118 119 127 129 130 131 132 133 146 148 **P**5 6 7 8 **S** Trinity Mother Frances Hospitals and Clinics, Tyler, TX
Primary Contact: Janet E. Coates, R.N., President and Chief Executive Officer
CFO: Glenn Peltier, Chief Financial Officer
CNO: Kevin Jablonski, Chief Nursing Officer
Web address: www.tmfhs.org
Control: Other not–for–profit (including NFP Corporation) **Service:** General Medical and Surgical

Staffed Beds: 23 **Admissions:** 701 **Census:** 6 **Outpatient Visits:** 16320 **Births:** 0 **Total Expense ($000):** 17452 **Payroll Expense ($000):** 5125 **Personnel:** 126

TEXAS HEALTH PRESBYTERIAN HOSPITAL WINNSBORO See Mother Frances Hospital – Winnsboro

WINTERS—Runnels County

NORTH RUNNELS HOSPITAL (451315), 7821 Texas 153, Zip 79567, Mailing Address: P.O. Box 185, Zip 79567–0185; tel. 325/754–5551 **A**9 10 18 **F**7 11 40 57 59 62 65 66 68 97 119 127 133 **P**5
Primary Contact: Sidney Tucker, Chief Executive Officer
CFO: Judy Espitia, Chief Financial Officer
CMO: Mark McKinnon, M.D., Chief of Staff
CHR: Judy Espitia, Chief Financial Officer
CNO: Bobbie Collom, Nursing Director
Control: Hospital district or authority, Government, nonfederal **Service:** General Medical and Surgical

Staffed Beds: 21 **Admissions:** 155 **Census:** 2 **Outpatient Visits:** 4002 **Births:** 0 **Total Expense ($000):** 4315 **Payroll Expense ($000):** 2319 **Personnel:** 47

WOODVILLE—Tyler County

★ **TYLER COUNTY HOSPITAL (450460)**, 1100 West Bluff Street, Zip 75979–4799, Mailing Address: P.O. Box 549, Zip 75979–0549; tel. 409/283–8141 **A**9 10 20 **F**3 11 30 35 40 43 46 57 59 64 81 107 114 119 127 146 **P**5
Primary Contact: Sandra Gayle Wright, R.N., Ed.D., Chief Executive Officer
CFO: Chris Torres, Assistant Administrator Chief Financial Officer and Controller
CMO: Paula Denson, M.D., President
CIO: Rachel Haygood, Director Information Technology
CHR: Ken Jobe, Director Human Resources
CNO: Sondra Wilson, R.N., Chief Nursing Officer
Web address: www.tchospital.us
Control: Hospital district or authority, Government, nonfederal **Service:** General Medical and Surgical

Staffed Beds: 25 **Admissions:** 704 **Census:** 6 **Outpatient Visits:** 23700 **Births:** 0 **Total Expense ($000):** 10566 **Payroll Expense ($000):** 4551 **Personnel:** 120

YOAKUM—Lavaca County

★ **YOAKUM COMMUNITY HOSPITAL (451346)**, 1200 Carl Ramert Drive, Zip 77995–4868; tel. 361/293–2321 **A**9 10 18 **F**3 11 13 15 29 34 35 40 43 56 57 59 64 70 76 79 81 85 86 93 107 108 111 114 119 129 132 133 134 146 148 **S** Community Hospital Corporation, Plano, TX
Primary Contact: Karen Barber, R.N., Chief Executive Officer
CFO: Robert Foret, Chief Financial Officer
CMO: Timothy Wagner, M.D., Chief Medical Staff
CIO: Barbara Vasek, Director Information Technology
CHR: Karen Roznovsky, Director Human Resources
CNO: Jennifer Franklin, R.N., Chief Clinical Officer
Web address: www.yoakumhospital.org
Control: Other not–for–profit (including NFP Corporation) **Service:** General Medical and Surgical

Staffed Beds: 25 **Admissions:** 912 **Census:** 12 **Outpatient Visits:** 18748 **Births:** 77 **Total Expense ($000):** 15648 **Payroll Expense ($000):** 6757 **Personnel:** 116

TX

UTAH

AMERICAN FORK—Utah County

☒ **AMERICAN FORK HOSPITAL (460023)**, 170 North 1100 East, Zip 84003–2096; tel. 801/855–3300 **A**1 10 **F**3 13 15 29 31 32 34 38 39 40 43 44 45 48 54 57 59 62 64 70 72 75 76 77 78 81 82 85 86 87 89 107 110 111 114 116 117 119 123 128 130 131 132 134 144 146 147 148 **S** Intermountain Healthcare, Inc., Salt Lake City, UT
Primary Contact: Michael R. Olson, Administrator
CMO: Paul H. Robinson, M.D., Medical Director
CIO: Mary Gathers, Manager Information Systems
CHR: Luke P. Morris, Regional Director Human Resources
CNO: Maria Black, MSN, Nurse Administrator
Web address: www.intermountainhealthcare.org
Control: Other not–for–profit (including NFP Corporation) **Service:** General Medical and Surgical

Staffed Beds: 90 **Admissions:** 6363 **Census:** 47 **Births:** 3026 **Total Expense ($000):** 96596 **Payroll Expense ($000):** 30926 **Personnel:** 652

BEAVER—Beaver County

BEAVER VALLEY HOSPITAL (460035), 1109 North 100 West, Zip 84713, Mailing Address: P.O. Box 1670, Zip 84713–1670; tel. 435/438–7100, (Nonreporting) **A**9 10 20
Primary Contact: Craig Val Davidson, Chief Executive Officer and Administrator
Web address: www.bvhospital.com/
Control: City–Government, nonfederal **Service:** General Medical and Surgical

Staffed Beds: 49

BLANDING—San Juan County

☒ **BLUE MOUNTAIN HOSPITAL (461310)**, 802 South 200 West, Zip 84511–3910; tel. 435/678–3993 **A**1 9 10 18 **F**13 15 40 41 60 81 89 107 110 133
Primary Contact: Jeremy Lyman, Chief Executive Officer
COO: Donna Jensen, Director Clinical Services
CMO: L. Val Jones, M.D., Medical Director
CIO: Billy Xaochay, Manager Information Technology
CHR: Gail M. Northern, Director Human Resources
Web address: www.bmhutah.org/
Control: Other not–for–profit (including NFP Corporation) **Service:** General Medical and Surgical

Staffed Beds: 11 **Admissions:** 226 **Census:** 2 **Outpatient Visits:** 2321 **Births:** 127 **Total Expense ($000):** 8961 **Payroll Expense ($000):** 3425 **Personnel:** 69

BOUNTIFUL—Davis County

☒ **LAKEVIEW HOSPITAL (460042)**, 630 East Medical Drive, Zip 84010–4908; tel. 801/299–2200 **A**1 9 10 **F**3 8 11 13 15 18 20 22 26 28 29 30 34 37 38 40 44 45 49 50 51 53 56 57 59 60 64 65 67 68 70 72 74 75 76 77 79 81 82 85 86 87 91 93 96 97 98 100 101 102 103 107 108 110 111 114 118 119 126 129 130 132 135 146 147 148 **P**6 **S** HCA, Nashville, TN
Primary Contact: Rand Kerr, Chief Executive Officer
COO: Brian Lines, Chief Operating Officer
CFO: Wayne Dalton, Chief Financial Officer
CIO: Eric Peterson, Director Information Technology
CHR: Julie Isom, Director Human Resources
CNO: Marilyn Mariani, R.N., Chief Nursing Officer
Web address: www.lakeviewhospital.com
Control: Corporation, Investor–owned, for–profit **Service:** General Medical and Surgical

Staffed Beds: 119 **Admissions:** 4298 **Census:** 47 **Births:** 439 **Personnel:** 435

SOUTH DAVIS COMMUNITY HOSPITAL (462003), 401 South 400 East, Zip 84010–4933; tel. 801/295–2361, (Nonreporting) **A**9 10
Primary Contact: David Bland, Chief Executive Officer
CFO: Daniel J. Foster, Chief Financial Officer
CMO: Scott Southworth, M.D., Medical Director
CHR: Jamey Sulser, Director Human Resources
Web address: www.sdch.com
Control: Other not–for–profit (including NFP Corporation) **Service:** Long–Term Acute Care hospital

Staffed Beds: 176

BRIGHAM CITY—Box Elder County

☒ **BRIGHAM CITY COMMUNITY HOSPITAL (460017)**, 950 South Medical Drive, Zip 84302–4724; tel. 435/734–9471, (Nonreporting) **A**1 9 10 **S** HCA, Nashville, TN
Primary Contact: Richard Spuhler, Chief Executive Officer
CMO: Lance Bryce, M.D., Chief Medical Officer
CIO: Steve Reichard, Manager Information Systems
CHR: Jordan Lang, Director Human Resources
CNO: Jerry Bushman, Chief Nursing Officer
Web address: www.brighamcityhospital.com
Control: Corporation, Investor–owned, for–profit **Service:** General Medical and Surgical

Staffed Beds: 39

CEDAR CITY—Iron County

☒ **VALLEY VIEW MEDICAL CENTER (460007)**, 1303 North Main Street, Zip 84721–9746; tel. 435/868–5000 **A**1 9 10 20 **F**8 11 13 15 18 28 29 31 35 70 76 89 **S** Intermountain Healthcare, Inc., Salt Lake City, UT
Primary Contact: Jason Wilson, Administrator
CFO: Reed Sargent, Assistant Administrator Finance
Web address: www.ihc.com
Control: Other not–for–profit (including NFP Corporation) **Service:** General Medical and Surgical

Staffed Beds: 48 **Admissions:** 2718 **Census:** 18 **Outpatient Visits:** 134949 **Total Expense ($000):** 56586

DELTA—Millard County

★ **DELTA COMMUNITY MEDICAL CENTER (461300)**, 126 South White Sage Avenue, Zip 84624–8937; tel. 435/864–5591 **A**9 10 18 **F**3 8 11 13 15 29 31 34 40 41 42 45 54 57 59 68 75 81 82 86 87 107 110 111 114 128 133 144 145 146 147 148 **P**5 8 **S** Intermountain Healthcare, Inc., Salt Lake City, UT
Primary Contact: Lenny Lyons, Administrator
CFO: Chris Thompson, Chief Financial Officer
Web address: www.ihc.com
Control: Other not–for–profit (including NFP Corporation) **Service:** General Medical and Surgical

Staffed Beds: 18 **Admissions:** 220 **Census:** 1 **Outpatient Visits:** 17555 **Births:** 89 **Total Expense ($000):** 7816 **Payroll Expense ($000):** 2815 **Personnel:** 47

DRAPER—Salt Lake County

☒ **LONE PEAK HOSPITAL (460060)**, 1925 South State Street, Zip 84020; tel. 801/545–8000, (Data for 153 days) **A**1 10 **F**3 13 15 18 29 40 49 51 67 76 79 81 85 102 107 110 111 115 119 147 **S** HCA, Nashville, TN
Primary Contact: Mark Meadows, Chief Executive Officer
Web address: www.lonepeakhospital.com
Control: Corporation, Investor–owned, for–profit **Service:** General Medical and Surgical

Staffed Beds: 30 **Admissions:** 302 **Census:** 5 **Outpatient Visits:** 8578 **Births:** 139 **Total Expense ($000):** 18791 **Payroll Expense ($000):** 4667 **Personnel:** 129

FILLMORE—Millard County

★ **FILLMORE COMMUNITY MEDICAL CENTER (461301)**, 674 South Highway 99, Zip 84631–5013; tel. 435/743–5591 **A**9 10 18 **F**3 8 11 13 15 29 31 34 38 40 41 50 56 57 59 62 63 64 67 68 75 81 82 86 87 93 107 110 119 128 133 145 146 147 148 **S** Intermountain Healthcare, Inc., Salt Lake City, UT
Primary Contact: Lenny Lyons, Administrator
CFO: Chris Thompson, Chief Financial Officer
Web address: www.ihc.com
Control: Other not–for–profit (including NFP Corporation) **Service:** General Medical and Surgical

Staffed Beds: 19 **Admissions:** 147 **Census:** 12 **Outpatient Visits:** 10452 **Total Expense ($000):** 7344 **Payroll Expense ($000):** 2568 **Personnel:** 43

UT

GUNNISON—Sanpete County

★ **GUNNISON VALLEY HOSPITAL (461306)**, 64 East 100 North, Zip 84634, Mailing Address: P.O. Box 759, Zip 84634–0759; tel. 435/528–7246 **A**9 10 18 **F**7 11 13 15 18 34 35 39 40 56 57 59 62 63 64 65 76 79 81 82 85 97 107 115 119 129 130 133 135 146 147 148
Primary Contact: Mark F. Dalley, Administrator
CFO: Brian Murray, Chief Financial Officer
CIO: Mike Ryan, Director of Information Services
CHR: Liz Brown, Manager Human Resources
CNO: Brenda Bartholomew, Chief Nursing Officer
Web address: www.gvhospital.org
Control: County–Government, nonfederal **Service:** General Medical and Surgical

Staffed Beds: 25 **Admissions:** 888 **Census:** 10 **Outpatient Visits:** 29701 **Births:** 178 **Total Expense ($000):** 16668 **Payroll Expense ($000):** 6305 **Personnel:** 171

HEBER CITY—Wasatch County

★ **HEBER VALLEY MEDICAL CENTER (461307)**, 1485 South Highway 40, Zip 84032–3522; tel. 435/654–2500, (Nonreporting) **A**9 10 18 **S** Intermountain Healthcare, Inc., Salt Lake City, UT
Primary Contact: Shawn Morrow, Administrator
CFO: Craig Mills, Chief Financial Officer
CMO: Stanton B. McDonald, M.D., Medical Director
CHR: Bruce Dent, Human Resources Director
CNO: Gayle Sturgis, Nurse Administrator
Web address: www.intermountainhealthcare.org
Control: Other not–for–profit (including NFP Corporation) **Service:** General Medical and Surgical

Staffed Beds: 19

KANAB—Kane County

KANE COUNTY HOSPITAL (461309), 355 North Main Street, Zip 84741–3260; tel. 435/644–5811, (Nonreporting) **A**9 10 18
Primary Contact: Sherrie Pandya, Administrator
CFO: Stephen Howells, Chief Financial Officer
CMO: Darin Ott, D.O., Chief of Staff
CHR: Laurali Noteman, Director Human Resources
CNO: Charlene Kelly, Chief Nursing Officer
Web address: www.kanecountyhospital.net
Control: Hospital district or authority, Government, nonfederal **Service:** General Medical and Surgical

Staffed Beds: 25

LAYTON—Davis County

★ ◇ **DAVIS HOSPITAL AND MEDICAL CENTER (460041)**, 1600 West Antelope Drive, Zip 84041–1142; tel. 801/807–1000 **A**9 10 21 **F**3 11 12 13 15 17 18 20 22 26 28 29 31 34 35 40 45 46 47 48 49 55 57 59 64 65 68 70 72 73 74 75 76 77 78 79 81 82 85 86 87 89 90 93 94 98 102 105 107 108 109 110 111 114 115 116 117 119 120 129 130 146 147 148 **S** IASIS Healthcare, Franklin, TN
Primary Contact: Michael E. Jensen, Chief Executive Officer
COO: Derek Vance, Chief Operating Officer
CFO: Jared Spackman, Chief Financial Officer
CMO: Jason Hoagland, M.D., President, Medical Staff
CIO: Shane Williams, Director Information Systems
CHR: Matthew Anderson, Director Human Resources
CNO: Debbie Sprague, R.N., Chief Nursing Officer
Web address: www.davishospital.com
Control: Corporation, Investor–owned, for–profit **Service:** General Medical and Surgical

Staffed Beds: 200 **Admissions:** 6020 **Census:** 59 **Outpatient Visits:** 147320 **Births:** 1795 **Personnel:** 666

LOGAN—Cache County

⊞ **LOGAN REGIONAL HOSPITAL (460015)**, 1400 North 500 East, Zip 84341–2455; tel. 435/716–1000, (Total facility includes 10 beds in nursing home–type unit) **A**1 9 10 **F**3 8 11 13 14 15 18 20 22 28 29 31 32 34 35 36 37 40 43 45 46 49 50 51 57 59 60 64 66 68 70 72 74 75 76 77 78 79 81 82 85 86 87 89 91 93 97 98 99 100 101 102 103 104 105 107 108 109 110 111 114 115 119 120 121 123 128 129 130 131 132 135 146 147 148 **P**6 **S** Intermountain Healthcare, Inc., Salt Lake City, UT
Primary Contact: Michael A. Clark, Administrator and Chief Executive Officer
COO: Brandon McBride, Operations Officer
CFO: Alan Robinson, Chief Financial Officer
CMO: Todd A. Brown, M.D., Medical Director
CIO: Dave Felts, Chief Information Systems
CHR: Jolene Clonts, Director Human Resources
CNO: Neil C. Perkes, Operations Officer
Web address: www.loganregionalhospital.org
Control: Other not–for–profit (including NFP Corporation) **Service:** General Medical and Surgical

Staffed Beds: 135 **Admissions:** 6790 **Census:** 52 **Outpatient Visits:** 292993 **Births:** 2554 **Total Expense ($000):** 125297 **Payroll Expense ($000):** 41744 **Personnel:** 912

MILFORD—Beaver County

★ **MILFORD VALLEY MEMORIAL HOSPITAL (461305)**, 850 North Main Street, Zip 84751–0640, Mailing Address: P.O. Box 640, Zip 84751–0640; tel. 435/387–2411, (Nonreporting) **A**9 10 18
Primary Contact: Craig Val Davidson, Chief Executive Officer
Web address: www.bvhospital.com/directions–2.htm
Control: Hospital district or authority, Government, nonfederal **Service:** General Medical and Surgical

Staffed Beds: 25

MOAB—Grand County

★ **MOAB REGIONAL HOSPITAL (461302)**, 450 West Williams Way, Zip 84532–2065, Mailing Address: P.O. Box 998, Zip 84532–0998; tel. 435/719–3500 **A**9 10 18 **F**3 13 15 29 30 31 34 35 40 43 45 57 59 63 64 65 66 68 75 76 79 81 82 85 86 89 90 97 107 110 111 115 119 128 130 131 132 133 144 148
Primary Contact: Robert Austin, Chief Executive Officer
COO: Vicki Gigliotti, Chief Clinical Officer
CFO: Craig M. Daniels, Chief Financial Officer
CMO: J.C. Vasquez, M.D., Chief Medical Staff
CIO: Mike Foster, Manager Information Systems
CHR: Dianne H. Hanson, Director Human Resources
Web address: www.amhmoab.org
Control: Other not–for–profit (including NFP Corporation) **Service:** General Medical and Surgical

Staffed Beds: 17 **Admissions:** 582 **Census:** 5 **Outpatient Visits:** 18880 **Births:** 96 **Total Expense ($000):** 21737 **Payroll Expense ($000):** 7786 **Personnel:** 150

MONTICELLO—San Juan County

SAN JUAN HOSPITAL (461308), 380 West 100 North, Zip 84535, Mailing Address: P.O. Box 308, Zip 84535–0308; tel. 435/587–2116 **A**9 10 18 **F**3 13 15 29 31 32 34 35 40 41 45 56 59 64 65 66 68 76 79 81 82 89 107 110 119 127 128 133 **P**6
Primary Contact: Laurie Schafer, Interim Chief Executive Officer
CFO: Lyman Duncan, Chief Financial Officer
CMO: Kelly Jeppesen, Chief Medical Officer
CIO: Julie Bingham, IT Supervisor
CHR: Deana Dalton, Human Resources
CNO: Laurie Schafer, Chief Nursing Officer
Web address: www.sanjuanhealthservices.org/
Control: Hospital district or authority, Government, nonfederal **Service:** General Medical and Surgical

Staffed Beds: 25 **Admissions:** 482 **Census:** 3 **Outpatient Visits:** 7659

MOUNT PLEASANT—Sanpete County

★ **SANPETE VALLEY HOSPITAL (461303)**, 1100 South Medical Drive, Zip 84647–2222; tel. 435/462–2441, (Nonreporting) **A**9 10 18 **S** Intermountain Healthcare, Inc., Salt Lake City, UT
Primary Contact: Aaron Wood, Administrator
COO: Jody Green, Chief Quality Manager
CFO: Chris Thompson, Chief Financial Officer
CMO: Eileen Jackson, M.D., President Medical Staff
CIO: Michael Ence, Computer Specialist
CNO: Ryan Robison, Chief Nursing Officer
Web address: www.intermountainhealthcare.com
Control: Other not–for–profit (including NFP Corporation) **Service:** General Medical and Surgical

Staffed Beds: 15

MURRAY—Salt Lake County

□ △ **INTERMOUNTAIN MEDICAL CENTER (460010)**, 5121 South Cottonwood Street, Zip 84107–5701; tel. 801/507–7000 **A**1 2 3 5 7 10 **F**3 7 8 12 13 15 17 18 20 22 24 26 28 29 30 31 34 35 37 38 39 40 43 44 45 46 47 48 49 50 51 52 53 54 55 56 57 58 59 60 61 63 64 68 70 72 74 75 76 77 78 79 81 82 84 85 86 87 90 91 92 93 94 95 96 97 100 102 107 108 109 110 111 112 114 115 116 117 118 119 120 121 122 123 124 126 129 130 131 132 137 138 139 141 142 146 147 148 **P**6 **S** Intermountain Healthcare, Inc., Salt Lake City, UT
Primary Contact: David Grauer, Chief Executive Officer and Administrator
COO: Kelly L. Duffin, Operations Officer
CFO: Jeff Jensen, Finance Director
CMO: William L. Hamilton, M.D., Urban Central Region Medical Director
CIO: David Baird, Director of Information Systems
CHR: Cari Vande Veegaete, Human Resources Manager
CNO: Suzanne P. Anderson, Nurse Administrator
Web address: www.intermountainhealthcare.org
Control: Other not–for–profit (including NFP Corporation) **Service:** General Medical and Surgical

Staffed Beds: 464 **Admissions:** 25417 **Census:** 306 **Outpatient Visits:** 673963 **Births:** 4683 **Total Expense ($000):** 693221 **Payroll Expense ($000):** 211114 **Personnel:** 3588

UT

✠ **THE ORTHOPEDIC SPECIALTY HOSPITAL (460049)**, 5848 South 300 East, Zip 84107–6121; tel. 801/314–4100 **A**1 10 **F**3 9 29 32 34 35 37 53 57 58 59 64 68 74 75 77 79 81 85 86 87 91 93 94 100 107 111 114 115 119 130 131 132 134 135 146 **S** Intermountain Healthcare, Inc., Salt Lake City, UT
Primary Contact: Barbara Ohm, Administrator
CFO: Ronald Jensen, Manager Finance
CMO: Jon Sundin, M.D., Medical Director
CIO: David Baird, Chief Information Officer
CHR: Tina Tasso, Manager Human Resources
Web address: www.intermountainhealthcare.org
Control: Other not–for–profit (including NFP Corporation) **Service:** Orthopedic

> **Staffed Beds:** 40 **Admissions:** 1845 **Census:** 12 **Outpatient Visits:** 56621 **Births:** 0 **Total Expense ($000):** 63679 **Payroll Expense ($000):** 16930 **Personnel:** 340

NEPHI—Juab County

★ **CENTRAL VALLEY MEDICAL CENTER (461304)**, 48 West 1500 North, Zip 84648–8900; tel. 435/623–3000 **A**9 10 18 **F**3 13 15 34 35 40 41 43 45 50 57 62 63 64 65 75 76 77 79 81 82 85 86 89 93 94 97 107 110 114 119 128 129 130 131 133 147 148 **P**6 **S** Rural Health Group, Nephi, UT
Primary Contact: Mark R. Stoddard, President
CFO: Brent Davis, Chief Financial Officer
CMO: Joel Holman, Chief of Staff
CIO: Ken Richens, Chief Information Officer
CHR: Brian Allsop, Director Human Resources
CNO: Randy Allinson, R.N., Patient Care Services Director
Web address: www.cvmed.net
Control: Other not–for–profit (including NFP Corporation) **Service:** General Medical and Surgical

> **Staffed Beds:** 27 **Admissions:** 1236 **Census:** 12 **Outpatient Visits:** 31707 **Births:** 138 **Total Expense ($000):** 27385 **Payroll Expense ($000):** 8119 **Personnel:** 254

NORTH LOGAN—Cache County

☐ **CACHE VALLEY HOSPITAL (460054)**, 2380 North 400 East, Zip 84341–6000; tel. 435/713–9700 **A**1 10 **F**3 7 8 11 14 15 25 29 34 35 39 40 41 42 43 51 57 59 62 67 68 70 77 78 79 81 83 84 87 91 92 93 96 97 107 110 111 112 130 131 143 148 **S** National Surgical Hospitals, Chicago, IL
Primary Contact: John C. Worley, III, Chief Executive Officer
CFO: David S. Geary, Chief Financial Officer
CMO: Matt Welter, Chief Medical Officer
Web address: www.cvsh.com
Control: Partnership, Investor–owned, for–profit **Service:** General Medical and Surgical

> **Staffed Beds:** 22 **Admissions:** 634 **Census:** 5 **Outpatient Visits:** 68329 **Births:** 0 **Total Expense ($000):** 30579 **Payroll Expense ($000):** 11447 **Personnel:** 240

OGDEN—Weber County

✠ **MCKAY–DEE HOSPITAL CENTER (460004)**, 4401 Harrison Boulevard, Zip 84403–3195; tel. 801/387–2800 **A**1 2 10 **F**3 8 11 12 13 15 17 18 20 22 24 26 28 29 30 31 34 35 38 39 40 43 44 45 46 49 50 51 53 54 55 57 58 59 60 61 64 65 66 67 68 70 72 74 75 76 77 78 79 81 82 84 85 86 87 89 90 91 93 97 98 99 100 101 102 103 104 105 106 107 108 110 111 114 115 116 117 119 120 121 123 126 129 130 131 132 134 135 144 146 147 148 **P**6 **S** Intermountain Healthcare, Inc., Salt Lake City, UT
Primary Contact: Timothy T. Pehrson, Chief Executive Officer
CFO: Doug Smith, Chief Financial Officer
CMO: Christine Nefcy, M.D., Chief Medical Officer
CIO: Mary Gathers, Director Information Systems
CHR: Lee Lorimer, IV, Regional Director Human Resources
CNO: Bonnie Jacklin, R.N., Chief Nursing Officer
Web address: www.mckay–dee.org
Control: Other not–for–profit (including NFP Corporation) **Service:** General Medical and Surgical

> **Staffed Beds:** 294 **Admissions:** 18133 **Census:** 185 **Outpatient Visits:** 253159 **Births:** 3909 **Total Expense ($000):** 343048 **Payroll Expense ($000):** 109674 **Personnel:** 2105

✠ **OGDEN REGIONAL MEDICAL CENTER (460005)**, 5475 South 500 East, Zip 84405–6905; tel. 801/479–2111, (Nonreporting) **A**1 9 10 **S** HCA, Nashville, TN
Primary Contact: Mark B. Adams, Chief Executive Officer
COO: Scott Davis, Chief Operating Officer
CFO: Judd Taylor, Chief Financial Officer
CMO: Jeffrey Abel, M.D., Chief Medical Officer
CIO: Eric Peterson, Director
CHR: Chris Bissenden, Director Human Resources
CNO: Elizabeth B. Later, R.N., Chief Nursing Officer
Web address: www.ogdenregional.com
Control: Corporation, Investor–owned, for–profit **Service:** General Medical and Surgical

> **Staffed Beds:** 167

OREM—Utah County

✠ **OREM COMMUNITY HOSPITAL (460043)**, 331 North 400 West, Zip 84057–1999; tel. 801/224–4080 **A**1 10 **F**3 11 13 15 29 32 35 38 39 40 43 44 54 59 64 75 76 81 82 86 87 93 97 107 111 119 132 135 146 **S** Intermountain Healthcare, Inc., Salt Lake City, UT
Primary Contact: Steven Badger, R.N., FACHE, Administrator
CMO: Neil Whitaker, M.D., Chief Medical Director
CIO: Diane Rindlisbacher, Manager Information Systems
CHR: Pamela S. Niece, Director Human Resources
Web address: www.intermountainhealthcare.org
Control: Other not–for–profit (including NFP Corporation) **Service:** General Medical and Surgical

> **Staffed Beds:** 18 **Admissions:** 1281 **Census:** 7 **Births:** 1209 **Total Expense ($000):** 23895 **Payroll Expense ($000):** 8688 **Personnel:** 189

☐ **PROVO CANYON BEHAVIORAL HOSPITAL (464014)**, 1350 East 750 North, Zip 84097–4345; tel. 801/852–2273, (Nonreporting) **A**1 10 **S** Universal Health Services, Inc., King of Prussia, PA
Primary Contact: Jeremy Cottle, Ph.D., Chief Executive Officer
Web address: www.pcbh.com
Control: Corporation, Investor–owned, for–profit **Service:** Psychiatric

> **Staffed Beds:** 80

✠ **TIMPANOGOS REGIONAL HOSPITAL (460052)**, 750 West 800 North, Zip 84057–3660; tel. 801/714–6000, (Nonreporting) **A**1 9 10 **S** HCA, Nashville, TN
Primary Contact: Keith D. Tintle, Chief Executive Officer
COO: Kyle Brostrom, Chief Operating Officer
CFO: Zandra Anderson, Chief Financial Officer
CMO: David K. Anderson, M.D., Chief of Staff
CIO: Richard Neilson, Director of Information Services
CHR: Kelly Brimhall, Director of Human Resources
CNO: Sandy Ewell, Chief Nursing Officer
Web address: www.timpanogosregionalhospital.com
Control: Corporation, Investor–owned, for–profit **Service:** General Medical and Surgical

> **Staffed Beds:** 105

PANGUITCH—Garfield County

★ **GARFIELD MEMORIAL HOSPITAL AND CLINICS (460033)**, 200 North 400 East, Zip 84759, Mailing Address: P.O. Box 389, Zip 84759–0389; tel. 435/676–8811, (Total facility includes 27 beds in nursing home–type unit) **A**9 10 20 **F**2 13 15 17 28 29 32 34 35 40 45 56 57 59 64 65 67 70 72 75 76 81 82 87 88 97 107 110 119 127 128 129 130 132 133 148 **P**6 **S** Intermountain Healthcare, Inc., Salt Lake City, UT
Primary Contact: Alberto Vasquez, Administrator
CFO: Reed Sargent, Assistant Administrator Finance
Web address: www.ihc.com/hospitals/garfield
Control: Other not–for–profit (including NFP Corporation) **Service:** General Medical and Surgical

> **Staffed Beds:** 41 **Admissions:** 555 **Census:** 25 **Births:** 28 **Total Expense ($000):** 11031 **Payroll Expense ($000):** 5663

UT

Hospital, Medicare Provider Number, Address, Telephone, Approval, Facility, and Physician Codes, Health Care System
★ American Hospital Association (AHA) membership
☐ The Joint Commission accreditation   ◇ DNV Healthcare Inc. accreditation
○ Healthcare Facilities Accreditation Program
△ Commission on Accreditation of Rehabilitation Facilities (CARF) accreditation

© 2014 AHA Guide   *Many Facility Codes have changed. Please refer to the AHA Guide Code Chart.*   Hospitals **A661**

PARK CITY—Summit County

✠ **PARK CITY MEDICAL CENTER (460057)**, 900 Round Valley Drive, Zip 84060–7552; tel. 435/658–7000 **A**1 9 10 **F**3 13 15 18 29 34 35 36 38 40 43 45 48 50 51 53 57 59 65 68 74 75 76 79 81 82 85 87 89 93 96 102 107 108 110 111 115 119 129 130 131 135 146 147 **P**6 **S** Intermountain Healthcare, Inc., Salt Lake City, UT
Primary Contact: Robert W. Allen, FACHE, Chief Executive Officer
CFO: Craig Mills, Senior Financial Advisor
CMO: Wain Allen, M.D., Medical Director
CHR: Bruce Dent, Director Human Resources
CNO: Dan Davis, R.N., Nurse Administrator
Web address: www.intermountainhealthcare.org
Control: Other not–for–profit (including NFP Corporation) **Service:** General Medical and Surgical

Staffed Beds: 26 Admissions: 1803 Census: 11 Personnel: 294

PAYSON—Utah County

✠ **MOUNTAIN VIEW HOSPITAL (460013)**, 1000 East 100 North, Zip 84651–1600; tel. 801/465–7000, (Nonreporting) **A**1 9 10 **S** HCA, Nashville, TN
Primary Contact: Kevin Johnson, Chief Executive Officer
COO: Ric Johnson, Associate Administrator
CFO: Steven R. Schramm, Chief Financial Officer
CMO: Max Crouch, M.D., Chief Medical Staff
CIO: Cindy Mecham, Health Information Director
CHR: Wally Trotter, Director Human Resources
CNO: Lisa Taylor, Director of Nursing
Web address: www.mvhpayson.com
Control: Corporation, Investor–owned, for–profit **Service:** General Medical and Surgical

Staffed Beds: 114

PRICE—Carbon County

✠ **CASTLEVIEW HOSPITAL (460011)**, 300 North Hospital Drive, Zip 84501–4200; tel. 435/637–4800 **A**1 9 10 20 **F**3 8 11 12 13 15 29 31 34 39 40 41 45 47 48 50 51 57 59 68 70 75 76 77 78 79 81 82 85 86 87 89 93 107 108 110 111 114 119 127 130 131 133 146 147 148 **S** LifePoint Hospitals, Inc., Brentwood, TN
Primary Contact: Mark Holyoak, Chief Executive Officer
CFO: Greg Cook, Chief Financial Officer
CMO: Scott Justesen, M.D., Chief of Staff
CIO: Keenan Johnson, Director Information Systems
CHR: Misty Birch, Director Human Resources
CNO: Terri Watkins, R.N., Chief Nursing Officer
Web address: www.castleviewhospital.net
Control: Corporation, Investor–owned, for–profit **Service:** General Medical and Surgical

Staffed Beds: 49 Admissions: 1762 Census: 15 Outpatient Visits: 46144 Births: 315 Total Expense ($000): 31611 Payroll Expense ($000): 13424 Personnel: 300

PROVO—Utah County

☐ **UTAH STATE HOSPITAL (464001)**, 1300 East Center Street, Zip 84606–3554, Mailing Address: P.O. Box 270, Zip 84603–0270; tel. 801/344–4400 **A**1 10 **F**30 34 56 75 77 86 87 91 98 99 100 101 103 130 135 143 146 **P**6
Primary Contact: Dallas Earnshaw, Superintendent
COO: Dallas Earnshaw, Superintendent
CFO: Robert Burton, Manager Finance
CMO: Madhu Gundlapalli, M.D., Clinical Director
CIO: Jill Hill, Director Information Technology
CHR: Devin Patrick, Manager Human Resources
CNO: Chris Metcalf, Director of Nursing
Web address: www.ush.utah.gov
Control: State–Government, nonfederal **Service:** Psychiatric

Staffed Beds: 329 Admissions: 372 Census: 287 Outpatient Visits: 0 Births: 0 Total Expense ($000): 53539 Payroll Expense ($000): 27809 Personnel: 745

✠ △ **UTAH VALLEY REGIONAL MEDICAL CENTER (460001)**, 1034 North 500 West, Zip 84604–3337; tel. 801/357–7850 **A**1 2 7 10 **F**3 11 13 15 17 18 20 21 22 23 24 25 28 29 30 31 32 34 35 38 39 40 43 44 45 48 49 50 51 53 54 56 57 58 59 60 61 62 63 64 68 69 70 72 74 75 76 77 78 81 82 84 85 86 87 88 89 90 91 92 93 94 97 98 99 100 101 102 103 104 105 107 108 110 111 114 115 116 117 118 119 121 123 128 129 130 131 132 133 134 144 146 147 148 **P**6 **S** Intermountain Healthcare, Inc., Salt Lake City, UT
Primary Contact: Steve Smoot, Administrator
CFO: Rod Lisonbee, Chief Financial Officer
CIO: Mary Gathers, Director Information Systems
CHR: Luke P. Morris, Regional Director Human Resources
CNO: Lisa A. Paletta, R.N., Chief Nursing Officer
Web address: www.utahvalleyregional.org
Control: Other not–for–profit (including NFP Corporation) **Service:** General Medical and Surgical

Staffed Beds: 373 Admissions: 18999 Census: 226 Births: 4112 Total Expense ($000): 391384 Payroll Expense ($000): 130562 Personnel: 2796

☐ **UTAH VALLEY SPECIALTY HOSPITAL (462005)**, 306 River Bend Lane, Zip 84604–5625; tel. 801/226–8880, (Nonreporting) **A**1 9 10 **S** Ernest Health, Inc., Albuquerque, NM
Primary Contact: Ginger Fisher, Interim Chief Executive Officer
Web address: www.uvsh.ernesthealth.com
Control: Corporation, Investor–owned, for–profit **Service:** Long–Term Acute Care hospital

Staffed Beds: 40

RICHFIELD—Sevier County

✠ **SEVIER VALLEY MEDICAL CENTER (460026)**, 1000 North Main Street, Zip 84701–1857; tel. 435/893–4100, (Nonreporting) **A**1 9 10 20 **S** Intermountain Healthcare, Inc., Salt Lake City, UT
Primary Contact: Gary E. Beck, Administrator
CFO: Chris Thompson, Chief Financial Officer
CMO: Justin Abbott, M.D., Medical Director
CHR: Katey Nelson, Director Human Resources
CNO: Cami Blackham, R.N., Nurse Administrator
Web address: www.sevierhospital.org
Control: Other not–for–profit (including NFP Corporation) **Service:** General Medical and Surgical

Staffed Beds: 27

RIVERTON—Salt Lake County

✠ **RIVERTON HOSPITAL (460058)**, 3741 West 12600 South, Zip 84065–7215; tel. 801/285–4000 **A**1 9 10 **F**3 13 15 29 31 34 35 39 40 43 44 45 46 47 48 49 50 51 57 59 64 68 70 76 78 79 81 85 86 87 89 91 93 94 97 107 108 110 111 114 115 118 119 129 130 131 146 147 148 **S** Intermountain Healthcare, Inc., Salt Lake City, UT
Primary Contact: Blair Kent, Administrator
CFO: Royce Stephens, Chief Financial Officer
CMO: David Haselton, Chief Medical Officer
CNO: Judy Williamson, R.N., Chief Nursing Officer
Web address: www.intermountainhealthcare.org/
Control: Other not–for–profit (including NFP Corporation) **Service:** General Medical and Surgical

Staffed Beds: 88 Admissions: 4789 Census: 31 Outpatient Visits: 127187 Births: 2408 Total Expense ($000): 80206 Payroll Expense ($000): 23222 Personnel: 426

ROOSEVELT—Duchesne County

★ **UINTAH BASIN MEDICAL CENTER (460019)**, 250 West 300 North, 75–2, Zip 84066–2336; tel. 435/722–6163, (Total facility includes 90 beds in nursing home–type unit) **A**9 10 20 **F**6 7 11 13 15 17 35 40 43 45 50 52 53 54 57 59 60 62 63 70 73 76 77 79 81 82 84 85 87 89 93 107 110 111 114 118 119 128 129 130 131 132 135 144 146 147 148 **P**7
Primary Contact: James L. Marshall, President and Chief Executive Officer
CFO: Brent Hales, Chief Financial Officer
CMO: Gary B. White, M.D., Chief Medical Staff
CHR: Randall Bennett, Assistant Administrator
Web address: www.ubmc.org
Control: Other not–for–profit (including NFP Corporation) **Service:** General Medical and Surgical

Staffed Beds: 124 Admissions: 1912 Census: 77 Outpatient Visits: 62294 Births: 654 Total Expense ($000): 65289 Payroll Expense ($000): 21797 Personnel: 510

SAINT GEORGE—Washington County

✠ △ **DIXIE REGIONAL MEDICAL CENTER (460021)**, 1380 East Medical Center Drive, Zip 84790–2123; tel. 435/251–1000, (Includes DIXIE REGIONAL MEDICAL CENTER, 544 South 400 East, St. George, Zip 84770) **A**1 2 7 9 10 19 20 **F**3 7 11 12 13 15 18 19 20 21 22 23 24 25 28 29 31 34 35 38 40 43 45 46 50 53 54 57 59 64 67 68 70 72 74 75 76 77 78 79 80 81 82 83 84 85 89 90 93 98 102 107 108 110 111 114 115 117 119 120 121 127 129 130 131 132 135 146 147 148 **P**5 **S** Intermountain Healthcare, Inc., Salt Lake City, UT
Primary Contact: Terri Kane, Chief Executive Officer
CFO: Steven Vance, Chief Financial Officer
CMO: Steven Van Norman, M.D., Medical Director
CIO: Lance Bedingfield, Director Information Services
CHR: Vicki Wilson, Human Resources Director
CNO: Gary Cunningham, Chief Nursing Officer
Web address: www.intermountainhealthcare.org
Control: Other not–for–profit (including NFP Corporation) **Service:** General Medical and Surgical

Staffed Beds: 261 Admissions: 14331 Census: 136 Outpatient Visits: 473097 Births: 2241 Total Expense ($000): 345924 Payroll Expense ($000): 93274 Personnel: 1808

Many Facility Codes have changed. Please refer to the AHA Guide Code Chart. © 2014 AHA Guide

UT

SALT LAKE CITY—Salt Lake County

⊞ **LDS HOSPITAL (460006)**, Eighth Avenue and C Street, Zip 84143–0001;
tel. 801/408–1100 **A**1 3 5 10 **F**3 4 5 7 8 12 13 15 18 28 29 30 31 34 35 38
39 40 43 44 45 46 48 50 51 52 53 54 55 56 57 58 59 60 61 63 64 65 66
68 70 73 74 75 76 77 78 79 81 84 85 86 87 91 92 93 94 98 100 101 102
103 104 105 107 108 109 110 111 114 115 117 119 120 121 129 130 131
132 136 146 147 148 **S** Intermountain Healthcare, Inc., Salt Lake City, UT
Primary Contact: Jim Sheets, Chief Executive Officer and Administrator
COO: David Gardiner, Operations Officer
CFO: Dave M. Larsen, Chief Financial Officer
CMO: William L. Hamilton, M.D., Chief Medical Officer
CIO: David Baird, Chief Information Officer
CHR: Pamela S. Niece, Chief Human Resources Officer
CNO: Todd Neubert, Nurse Administrator
Web address: www.intermountainhealthcare.org
Control: Other not–for–profit (including NFP Corporation) **Service:** General
Medical and Surgical

Staffed Beds: 253 **Admissions:** 10356 **Census:** 118 **Outpatient Visits:**
222180 **Births:** 2463 **Total Expense ($000):** 220779 **Payroll Expense
($000):** 62261 **Personnel:** 1191

⊞ **MARIAN CENTER (464012)**, 451 East Bishop Federal Lane, Zip 84115–2357;
tel. 801/487–7557, (Nonreporting) **A**1 10
Primary Contact: Brad Albrechtsen, Chief Executive Officer
Web address: www.stjosephvilla.com
Control: Partnership, Investor–owned, for–profit **Service:** Psychiatric

Staffed Beds: 14

☐ **PRIMARY CHILDREN'S MEDICAL CENTER (463301)**, 100 North Mario
Capecchi Drive, Zip 84113–1100; tel. 801/662–1000 **A**1 3 5 9 10 **F**3 4 5 8 9
11 17 19 21 23 25 27 29 30 31 32 34 35 36 38 39 40 41 43 44 45 48 49
50 54 55 57 58 59 60 61 63 64 65 68 72 73 74 75 77 78 79 80 81 82 84
85 86 87 88 89 90 92 93 96 98 99 100 101 102 104 105 106 107 108 111
113 114 115 116 117 118 119 124 130 131 132 134 135 136 137 138 139
141 142 146 148 **S** Intermountain Healthcare, Inc., Salt Lake City, UT
Primary Contact: Katy Welkie, R.N., Chief Executive Officer
CFO: Jeremiah Radandt, Chief Financial Officer
CMO: Ed Clark, M.D., Chief Medical Officer
CIO: Joe Hales, Director Information Systems
CHR: Albert Bennett Buckworth, Director Human Resources
CNO: Judy Geiger, R.N., Chief Nursing Officer
Web address: www.intermountainhealthcare.org
Control: Other not–for–profit (including NFP Corporation) **Service:** Children's
general

Staffed Beds: 289 **Admissions:** 13810 **Census:** 185 **Outpatient Visits:**
387951 **Births:** 0 **Total Expense ($000):** 389359 **Payroll Expense ($000):**
146191 **Personnel:** 2489

PROMISE HOSPITAL OF SALT LAKE (462004), 8 Avenue, C. Street,
Zip 84143; tel. 801/408–7110, (Nonreporting) **A**9 10 **S** Promise Healthcare,
Boca Raton, FL
Primary Contact: Wayne Kinsey, Chief Executive Officer
CMO: Geoff Harding, Chief Clinical Officer
Web address: www.promise–saltlake.com
Control: Corporation, Investor–owned, for–profit **Service:** Long–Term Acute Care
hospital

Staffed Beds: 32

☐ **SALT LAKE BEHAVIORAL HEALTH (464013)**, 3802 South 700 East,
Zip 84106–1182; tel. 801/264–6000, (Nonreporting) **A**1 9 10 **S** Universal Health
Services, Inc., King of Prussia, PA
Primary Contact: Kreg Gillman, Chief Executive Officer
CFO: Nancy MacGregor, Chief Financial Officer
CHR: Robyn Holsten, Human Resources Director
CNO: Brooke Cline, Director of Nursing
Web address: www.saltlakebehavioralhealth.com
Control: Corporation, Investor–owned, for–profit **Service:** Psychiatric

Staffed Beds: 118

★ ◇ **SALT LAKE REGIONAL MEDICAL CENTER (460003)**, 1050 East South
Temple, Zip 84102–1507; tel. 801/350–4111, (Nonreporting) **A**3 5 9 10 21
S IASIS Healthcare, Franklin, TN
Primary Contact: Dale Johns, Chief Executive Officer
CFO: Scott Banks, Chief Financial Officer
CMO: Ben Howard, D.O., Chief of Staff
CIO: Mark Runyan, Director Information Services
CHR: Carolyn Livingston, Director Human Resources
CNO: Terron Arbon, R.N., Chief Nursing Officer
Web address: www.saltlakeregional.com
Control: Corporation, Investor–owned, for–profit **Service:** General Medical and
Surgical

Staffed Beds: 132

☐ **SHRINERS HOSPITALS FOR CHILDREN–SALT LAKE CITY (463302)**, Fairfax
Road & Virginia Street, Zip 84103–4399; tel. 801/536–3500 **A**1 3 5 10 **F**3 29
34 35 50 58 64 68 74 75 79 80 81 82 85 87 89 93 94 119 130 131 132
143 146 **S** Shriners Hospitals for Children, Tampa, FL
Primary Contact: Kevin Martin, M.P.H., R.N., Administrator
CFO: Randy Lindberg, Director Fiscal Services
CMO: Suzanne Yandow, M.D., Chief of Staff
CIO: Mike Allen, Director Information Technology
CHR: Russ Crockett, Director Human Resources
CNO: Gail McGuill, R.N., Chief Nursing Officer and Administrative Director of
Patient Care Services
Web address: www.shrinershospitalsforchildren.org/Hospitals/Locations/
SaltLakeCity.aspx
Control: Other not–for–profit (including NFP Corporation) **Service:** Children's
orthopedic

Staffed Beds: 18 **Admissions:** 441 **Census:** 4 **Outpatient Visits:** 11391
Births: 0 **Personnel:** 180

⊞ **ST. MARK'S HOSPITAL (460047)**, 1200 East 3900 South, Zip 84124–1390;
tel. 801/268–7111 **A**1 2 9 10 **F**3 8 11 12 13 14 15 17 18 20 22 24 26 28 29
30 31 34 35 36 38 40 42 46 49 50 53 56 57 58 59 60 64 65 67 70 72 73
74 75 76 77 78 79 80 81 82 84 85 86 87 102 107 108 110 111 114 115
118 119 124 126 128 129 130 132 135 145 146 147 148 **S** HCA,
Nashville, TN
Primary Contact: Steven B. Bateman, Chief Executive Officer
COO: Matt Dixon, Chief Operating Officer
CFO: Bryan McKinley, Chief Financial Officer
CMO: J. Eric Vanderhooft, M.D., President Medical Staff
CIO: Jesse Trujillo, Chief Information Officer
CHR: Robyn Opheikens, Assistant Administrator Human Resources
Web address: www.stmarkshospital.com
Control: Corporation, Investor–owned, for–profit **Service:** General Medical and
Surgical

Staffed Beds: 317 **Admissions:** 15323 **Census:** 175 **Outpatient Visits:**
96746 **Total Expense ($000):** 255810

★ △ ◇ **UNIVERSITY OF UTAH HEALTH CARE – HOSPITAL AND CLINICS
(460009)**, 50 North Medical Drive, Zip 84132–0002; tel. 801/587–3572 **A**3 5
7 8 9 10 21 **F**3 5 6 7 8 9 11 12 13 15 16 17 18 20 22 24 26 28 29 30 31
33 34 35 36 37 38 39 40 42 43 44 45 46 47 48 49 50 51 52 53 54 55 56
57 58 59 60 61 62 64 65 68 70 71 72 73 74 75 76 77 78 79 80 81 82 83
84 85 86 87 90 91 92 93 94 95 96 97 98 100 101 102 103 104 107 108
109 110 111 112 113 114 115 116 117 118 119 120 121 123 124 126 129
130 131 132 134 135 136 137 138 139 140 141 142 143 144 145 146 147
148 **P**1
Primary Contact: David Entwistle, Chief Executive Officer
COO: Quinn McKenna, Chief Operating Officer
CFO: Gordon Crabtree, Chief Financial Officer
CMO: Thomas Miller, M.D., Medical Director
CIO: James Turnbull, Chief Information Officer
CHR: Dale A. Spartz, Chief Human Resources Officer
CNO: Margaret Pearce, R.N., Chief Nursing Officer
Web address: www.uuhsc.utah.edu
Control: State–Government, nonfederal **Service:** General Medical and Surgical

Staffed Beds: 530 **Admissions:** 22612 **Census:** 382 **Outpatient Visits:**
1410400 **Births:** 3070 **Total Expense ($000):** 1012300 **Payroll Expense
($000):** 364620 **Personnel:** 8185

◇ **UNIVERSITY OF UTAH NEUROPSYCHIATRIC INSTITUTE (464009)**, 501
South Chipeta Way, Zip 84108–1222; tel. 801/583–2500 **A**3 5 9 10 21 **F**4 5
30 34 35 38 54 57 64 68 75 87 98 99 100 101 103 104 105 106 130
132 **P**1
Primary Contact: Ross Van Vranken, Executive Director
CFO: Becky Schaefer, Chief Financial Officer
CMO: Michael Lowry, M.D., Medical Director
Web address: www.med.utah.edu/uni
Control: State–Government, nonfederal **Service:** Psychiatric

Staffed Beds: 94 **Admissions:** 4126 **Census:** 101 **Outpatient Visits:** 35021
Births: 0 **Total Expense ($000):** 53721

Hospital, Medicare Provider Number, Address, Telephone, Approval, Facility, and Physician Codes, Health Care System

★ American Hospital Association (AHA) membership
☐ The Joint Commission accreditation   ◇ DNV Healthcare Inc. accreditation

○ Healthcare Facilities Accreditation Program
△ Commission on Accreditation of Rehabilitation Facilities (CARF) accreditation

UT

✠ △ **VETERANS AFFAIRS SALT LAKE CITY HEALTH CARE SYSTEM**, 500 Foothill Drive, Zip 84148–0002; tel. 801/582–1565 **A**1 3 5 7 **F**3 4 5 8 12 18 20 22 24 28 29 30 34 35 36 38 39 40 44 45 46 47 48 49 50 53 54 56 57 58 59 60 61 62 64 65 70 71 74 75 77 78 79 81 82 83 84 85 86 87 90 92 93 94 96 97 98 100 101 102 103 104 105 106 107 108 109 111 114 115 116 117 118 119 127 129 130 132 133 135 137 143 144 146 147 148 **P**6 **S** Department of Veterans Affairs, Washington, DC
Primary Contact: Steven W. Young, Director
COO: Roy L. Hawkins, Jr., Acting Associate Director
CFO: Val Martin, Director Financial Management Services Center
CMO: Ronald J. Gebhart, M.D., Chief of Staff
CIO: Lisa Leonelis, Chief Information Officer
CHR: Lisa Porter, Director Human Resources, Leadership and Education
Web address: www.saltlakecity.va.gov/
Control: Veterans Affairs, Government, federal **Service:** General Medical and Surgical

Staffed Beds: 121 **Admissions:** 5713 **Census:** 92 **Outpatient Visits:** 636197 **Births:** 0

SANDY—Salt Lake County

✠ **ALTA VIEW HOSPITAL (460044)**, 9660 South 1300 East, Zip 84094–3793; tel. 801/501–2600 **A**1 10 **F**3 8 12 13 15 29 31 34 35 38 39 40 44 45 46 47 48 49 50 53 54 56 57 59 64 68 70 75 76 78 79 81 85 86 87 92 93 102 107 108 110 111 115 119 129 130 131 132 135 146 147 **S** Intermountain Healthcare, Inc., Salt Lake City, UT
Primary Contact: Bryan L. Johnson, Administrator
CFO: Chris Hargis, Manager Finance
CHR: Leslie Bates, Manager Human Resources
Web address: www.intermountainhealthcare.org
Control: Other not-for-profit (including NFP Corporation) **Service:** General Medical and Surgical

Staffed Beds: 69 **Admissions:** 3619 **Census:** 25 **Outpatient Visits:** 129976 **Births:** 1354 **Total Expense ($000):** 86184 **Payroll Expense ($000):** 24028 **Personnel:** 431

✠ **HEALTHSOUTH REHABILITATION HOSPITAL OF UTAH (463025)**, 8074 South 1300 East, Zip 84094–0743; tel. 801/561–3400, (Nonreporting) **A**1 10 **S** HEALTHSOUTH Corporation, Birmingham, AL
Primary Contact: Jeff Frandsen, Chief Executive Officer
CFO: Daren Woolstenhulme, Chief Financial Officer
CMO: Joseph VickRoy, M.D., Medical Director
CHR: Troy Jensen, Director Human Resources
Web address: www.healthsouthutah.com
Control: Corporation, Investor-owned, for-profit **Service:** Rehabilitation

Staffed Beds: 105

TOOELE—Tooele County

✠ **MOUNTAIN WEST MEDICAL CENTER (460014)**, 2055 North Main Street, Zip 84074–9819; tel. 435/843–3600 **A**1 9 10 **F**3 8 12 13 15 18 20 29 30 34 37 38 40 45 49 50 51 57 59 64 68 70 72 74 75 76 77 79 81 85 93 102 107 108 109 110 111 114 115 118 119 133 143 146 147 **S** Community Health Systems, Inc., Franklin, TN
Primary Contact: Philip Eaton, Interim Chief Executive Officer
CMO: James Antinori, M.D., Chief of Staff
CIO: Marc Taylor, IS Director
CHR: Matthew Flygare, Director Human Resources
CNO: Yvonne Nielson, Chief Nursing Officer, Director Quality Management and Regulatory Compliance
Web address: www.mountainwestmc.com
Control: Corporation, Investor-owned, for-profit **Service:** General Medical and Surgical

Staffed Beds: 44 **Admissions:** 1953 **Census:** 13 **Outpatient Visits:** 33418 **Births:** 478 **Personnel:** 317

TREMONTON—Box Elder County

★ **BEAR RIVER VALLEY HOSPITAL (460039)**, 905 North 1000 West, Zip 84337–2497; tel. 435/207–4500, (Nonreporting) **A**9 10 **S** Intermountain Healthcare, Inc., Salt Lake City, UT
Primary Contact: Eric Packer, Administrator
CHR: Joy Sadler, Director Human Resources
CNO: Penny Marshall, Chief Nursing Officer
Web address: www.intermountainhealthcare.org/hospitals/bearriver
Control: Other not-for-profit (including NFP Corporation) **Service:** General Medical and Surgical

Staffed Beds: 14

VERNAL—Uintah County

✠ **ASHLEY REGIONAL MEDICAL CENTER (460030)**, 150 West 100 North, Zip 84078–2036; tel. 435/789–3342, (Nonreporting) **A**1 9 10 20 **S** LifePoint Hospitals, Inc., Brentwood, TN
Primary Contact: Ben Cluff, Chief Executive Officer
CFO: Chad Labrum, Chief Financial Officer
CMO: Aaron Bradbury, D.O., Chief of Staff
CIO: Mark Rich, Director Information Services
CHR: Deena Mansfield, Director Human Resources
CNO: Greg Gardiner, Chief Clinical Officer
Web address: www.ashleyregional.com
Control: Corporation, Investor-owned, for-profit **Service:** General Medical and Surgical

Staffed Beds: 39

WEST JORDAN—Salt Lake County

★ ◇ **JORDAN VALLEY MEDICAL CENTER (460051)**, 3580 West 9000 South, Zip 84088–8812; tel. 801/561–8888, (Nonreporting) **A**9 10 21 **S** IASIS Healthcare, Franklin, TN
Primary Contact: Steven Anderson, Chief Executive Officer
COO: Jon Butterfield, Chief Operating Officer
CFO: Kurt Shipley, Chief Financial Officer
CMO: B. Dee Allred, M.D., President Medical Staff
Web address: www.jordanvalleymc.com
Control: Partnership, Investor-owned, for-profit **Service:** General Medical and Surgical

Staffed Beds: 284

WEST VALLEY CITY—Salt Lake County

★ **PIONEER VALLEY HOSPITAL**, 3460 South Pioneer Parkway, Zip 84120–2049; tel. 801/561–8888, (Nonreporting) **S** IASIS Healthcare, Franklin, TN
Primary Contact: Steven Anderson, Chief Executive Officer
COO: Jon Butterfield, Administrator and Chief Operating Officer
CFO: Steven Payne, Chief Financial Officer
CMO: Justin Parkinson, M.D., President Medical Staff
CIO: Mark Runyan, Director Information Systems
CHR: Rob Burnett, Director Human Resources
CNO: Chris Johnson, R.N., Director of Nursing
Web address: www.pioneervalleyhospital.com
Control: Corporation, Investor-owned, for-profit **Service:** General Medical and Surgical

Staffed Beds: 101

UT

VERMONT

BENNINGTON—Bennington County

SOUTHWESTERN VERMONT MEDICAL CENTER (470012), 100 Hospital Drive, Zip 05201–5004; tel. 802/442–6361, (Nonreporting) **A**1 2 9 10 19
Primary Contact: Thomas A. Dee, Chief Executive Officer
CFO: Stephen D. Majetich, CPA, Chief Financial Officer
CMO: Trey Dobson, M.D., Chief Medical Officer
CIO: Richard Ogilvie, Chief Information Officer
CHR: Rudolph D. Weaver, Vice President Human Resources
CNO: Carol Conroy, R.N., Chief Nursing Officer
Web address: www.svhealthcare.org
Control: Other not–for–profit (including NFP Corporation) **Service:** General Medical and Surgical

Staffed Beds: 85

BERLIN—Washington County

CENTRAL VERMONT MEDICAL CENTER (470001), 130 Fisher Road, Zip 05602–9516, Mailing Address: P.O. Box 547, Barre, Zip 05641–0547; tel. 802/371–4100, (Total facility includes 153 beds in nursing home–type unit) **A**1 2 9 10 19 20 **F**3 8 11 13 15 28 29 30 31 34 35 36 40 43 44 45 46 49 50 51 52 53 57 58 59 64 65 74 75 77 78 79 81 82 83 84 85 87 93 94 96 97 98 99 100 102 103 104 107 108 110 111 114 115 116 117 118 119 128 130 131 132 135 143 146 147 148
Primary Contact: Judith C. Tartaglia, President and Chief Executive Officer
COO: Nancy Lothian, Chief Operating Officer and Chief Information Officer
CFO: Cheyenne Follard, Chief Financial Officer
CMO: Philip Brown, D.O., Vice President Medicai Affairs
CIO: Nancy Lothian, Chief Operating Officer and Chief Information Officer
CHR: Robert Patterson, Vice President Human Resources and Rehabilitation Services
Web address: www.cvmc.org/
Control: Other not–for–profit (including NFP Corporation) **Service:** General Medical and Surgical

Staffed Beds: 241 **Admissions:** 3659 **Census:** 178 **Outpatient Visits:** 318507 **Births:** 376 **Total Expense ($000):** 119439 **Payroll Expense ($000):** 55560 **Personnel:** 871

BRATTLEBORO—Windham County

★ **BRATTLEBORO MEMORIAL HOSPITAL (470011)**, 17 Belmont Avenue, Zip 05301–3498; tel. 802/257–0341 **A**9 10 **F**3 11 13 14 15 17 18 28 29 30 31 34 35 39 40 45 49 51 53 55 57 59 64 68 70 74 75 76 77 78 79 81 85 87 93 107 108 110 111 115 118 119 130 131 132 135 146 147 148
Primary Contact: Steven R. Gordon, President and Chief Executive Officer
CFO: Michael Rogers, Vice President Fiscal Services
CMO: David Albright, M.D., Chief Medical Officer
CIO: Jonathan Farina, Chief Information Officer
CHR: Robin R. Heald, Director Human Resources
CNO: Mary Urquhart, R.N., Vice President Patient Care
Web address: www.bmhvt.org
Control: Other not–for–profit (including NFP Corporation) **Service:** General Medical and Surgical

Staffed Beds: 32 **Admissions:** 1655 **Census:** 15 **Outpatient Visits:** 74679 **Births:** 367 **Total Expense ($000):** 67115 **Payroll Expense ($000):** 28238 **Personnel:** 371

BRATTLEBORO RETREAT (474001), Anna Marsh Lane, Zip 05301, Mailing Address: P.O. Box 803, Zip 05302–0803; tel. 802/257–7785 **A**1 5 9 10 **F**29 34 35 50 68 98 99 100 101 102 103 104 105 106
Primary Contact: Robert E. Simpson, Jr., M.P.H., President and Chief Executive Officer
COO: Gerri Cote, Vice President Operations
CFO: John E. Blaha, Vice President Finance and Chief Financial Officer
CMO: Frederick Engstrom, M.D., Chief Medical Officer
CHR: Jeffrey T. Corrigan, Vice President Human Resources
CNO: Linda J. Nagy, MSN, Chief Nursing Officer
Web address: www.brattlebororetreat.org
Control: Other not–for–profit (including NFP Corporation) **Service:** Psychiatric

Staffed Beds: 118 **Admissions:** 3580 **Census:** 99 **Outpatient Visits:** 32369 **Births:** 0 **Total Expense ($000):** 58889 **Payroll Expense ($000):** 37895 **Personnel:** 496

BURLINGTON--Chittenden County

FLETCHER ALLEN HEALTH CARE (470003), 111 Colchester Avenue, Zip 05401–1473; tel. 802/847–0000, (Includes FANNY ALLEN CAMPUS, 101 College Parkway, Colchester, Zip 05446–3035; tel. 802/655–1234; MEDICAL CENTER HOSPITAL CAMPUS, Colchester Avenue, Zip 05401; tel. 802/847–2345; VERMONT CHILDREN'S HOSPITAL, 111 Colchester Avenue, tel. 802/847–0000) **A**1 2 3 5 8 9 10 **F**3 4 5 6 7 9 11 12 13 15 16 17 18 19 20 21 22 23 24 25 26 28 29 30 31 32 34 35 36 37 39 40 43 44 45 46 47 48 49 50 51 52 54 55 56 57 58 59 60 61 63 64 65 66 68 70 72 73 74 75 76 77 78 79 81 82 84 85 86 87 88 89 90 91 92 93 94 96 97 98 99 100 101 102 103 104 105 107 108 110 111 114 115 116 117 118 119 120 121 123 124 126 128 129 130 131 132 135 136 138 141 142 143 144 145 146 147 148 **P**6
Primary Contact: John R. Brumsted, M.D., President and Chief Executive Officer
COO: Sandra L. Felis, R.N., Senior Vice President Patient Care Services and Chief Nursing Officer
CFO: Todd Keating, Chief Financial Officer
CMO: Stephen Leffler, Chief Medical Officer
CIO: Charles H. Podesta, Vice President Information Services
CHR: Paul Macuga, Chief Human Resources Officer
Web address: www.fletcherallen.org
Control: Other not–for–profit (including NFP Corporation) **Service:** General Medical and Surgical

Staffed Beds: 426 **Admissions:** 20216 **Census:** 322 **Outpatient Visits:** 1347985 **Births:** 2208 **Total Expense ($000):** 1000480 **Payroll Expense ($000):** 468713 **Personnel:** 6351

MIDDLEBURY--Addison County

★ **PORTER MEDICAL CENTER (471307)**, 115 Porter Drive, Zip 05753–8423; tel. 802/388–4701 **A**9 10 18 **F**3 8 11 13 15 18 26 29 40 43 45 50 59 64 68 70 75 76 79 81 85 86 93 97 107 108 111 114 115 119 130 133 146 **P**6
Primary Contact: James L. Daily, President
CFO: Steve Ciampa, Vice President Finance
CMO: Fred Kniffin, M.D., Chief Medical Officer
CIO: Rebecca Woods, Chief Information Officer
CHR: David Fuller, Director Human Resources
CNO: Lorraina Smith–Zuba, R.N., Chief Nursing Officer
Web address: www.portermedical.org
Control: Other not–for–profit (including NFP Corporation) **Service:** General Medical and Surgical

Staffed Beds: 25 **Admissions:** 1590 **Census:** 15 **Outpatient Visits:** 86320 **Births:** 331 **Personnel:** 484

MORRISVILLE--Lamoille County

★ **COPLEY HOSPITAL (471305)**, 528 Washington Highway, Zip 05661–8973; tel. 802/888–8888 **A**9 10 18 **F**13 15 18 28 29 30 31 34 35 39 40 58 59 64 65 70 74 75 76 77 78 79 81 85 86 93 107 110 111 119 129 130 131 133 135 146 147
Primary Contact: Melvyn Patashnick, President and Chief Executive Officer
COO: Greg Ward, Vice President Operations
CFO: Rassoul Rangaviz, Chief Financial Officer
CMO: Joel Silverstein, M.D., Chief Medical Officer
CIO: Greg Ward, Vice President Operations
CHR: Jennifer Archambault, Vice President Human Resources and Compliance
CNO: Carolyn J. Roe, R.N., Chief Nursing Officer
Web address: www.copleyvt.org
Control: Other not–for–profit (including NFP Corporation) **Service:** General Medical and Surgical

Staffed Beds: 25 **Admissions:** 1474 **Census:** 12 **Outpatient Visits:** 78150 **Births:** 210 **Total Expense ($000):** 53576 **Payroll Expense ($000):** 26684 **Personnel:** 341

VT

Hospital, Medicare Provider Number, Address, Telephone, Approval, Facility, and Physician Codes, Health Care System

★ American Hospital Association (AHA) membership
□ The Joint Commission accreditation   ◇ DNV Healthcare Inc. accreditation
○ Healthcare Facilities Accreditation Program
△ Commission on Accreditation of Rehabilitation Facilities (CARF) accreditation

NEWPORT—Orleans County

★ **NORTH COUNTRY HOSPITAL AND HEALTH CENTER (471304)**, 189 Prouty Drive, Zip 05855–9326; tel. 802/334–7331 **A**9 10 18 **F**11 13 15 28 29 30 31 34 40 45 53 70 74 75 76 77 78 79 81 82 84 89 93 104 107 108 110 111 114 118 119 127 129 130 131 133 135 146 148
Primary Contact: Claudio D. Fort, President and Chief Executive Officer
COO: Thomas Frank, Chief Operating Officer
CFO: Andre Bissonnette, Chief Financial Officer
CHR: William Perket, Vice President Human Resources
CNO: Brenda Neff, MSN, Vice President Patient Care Services and Chief Nursing Officer
Web address: www.nchsi.org
Control: Other not–for–profit (including NFP Corporation) **Service:** General Medical and Surgical

Staffed Beds: 25 **Admissions:** 1372 **Census:** 15 **Outpatient Visits:** 73765 **Births:** 206 **Total Expense ($000):** 77543 **Payroll Expense ($000):** 35783 **Personnel:** 447

RANDOLPH—Orange County

★ **GIFFORD MEDICAL CENTER (471301)**, 44 South Main Street, Zip 05060–1381, Mailing Address: P.O. Box 2000, Zip 05060–2000; tel. 802/728–7000, (Nonreporting) **A**2 9 10 18
Primary Contact: Joseph L. Woodin, President and Chief Executive Officer
CFO: Jeff Hebert, Interim Vice President Finance
CMO: Joshua Plavin, M.D., Medical Director Medicine Division
CIO: Sean Patrick, Director Information Systems
CHR: Janice Davis, Interim Director Human Resources
CNO: Linda Minsinger, Vice President Hospital Division
Web address: www.giffordmed.org
Control: Other not–for–profit (including NFP Corporation) **Service:** General Medical and Surgical

Staffed Beds: 52

RUTLAND—Rutland County

✠ **RUTLAND REGIONAL MEDICAL CENTER (470005)**, 160 Allen Street, Zip 05701–4595; tel. 802/775–7111 **A**1 2 9 10 19 20 **F**13 15 18 20 22 23 24 28 29 31 34 36 38 40 45 47 48 49 51 55 57 59 61 64 65 70 76 77 78 79 81 82 83 84 85 87 90 92 93 94 98 100 101 102 103 104 107 108 111 115 116 117 118 119 128 129 130 132 133 135 146 147 148
Primary Contact: Thomas W. Huebner, President
CFO: Ed Ogorzalek, Chief Financial Officer
CMO: Baxter C. Holland, M.D., Chief Medical Officer
CHR: Allison Wollen, Vice President Human Resources
CNO: Carol Egen, R.N., Chief Nursing Officer
Web address: www.rrmc.org
Control: Other not–for–profit (including NFP Corporation) **Service:** General Medical and Surgical

Staffed Beds: 129 **Admissions:** 5908 **Census:** 79 **Outpatient Visits:** 228980 **Births:** 388 **Total Expense ($000):** 211893 **Payroll Expense ($000):** 69635 **Personnel:** 1066

SAINT ALBANS—Franklin County

✠ **NORTHWESTERN MEDICAL CENTER (470024)**, 133 Fairfield Street, Zip 05478–1726; tel. 802/524–5911 **A**1 2 9 10 20 **F**3 11 13 15 28 29 30 31 32 34 35 36 37 38 40 43 44 45 50 51 57 58 59 63 69 76 77 78 79 80 81 82 84 85 86 87 89 93 96 107 108 111 114 119 130 131 132 133 134 135 143 146 147 148 **S** QHR, Brentwood, TN
Primary Contact: Jill Berry Bowen, President and Chief Executive Officer
COO: Jane Catton, R.N., Chief Operating Officer and Chief Nursing Officer
CFO: Ted D. Sirotta, Chief Financial Officer
CMO: Lowery Sullivan, M.D., Chief Medical Officer
CIO: Joel Benware, Vice President Information Technology and Compliance
CHR: Joy L. Sylvester, Vice President Human Resources and Organization Development
CNO: Jane Catton, R.N., Chief Operating Officer and Chief Nursing Officer
Web address: www.northwesternmedicalcenter.org
Control: Other not–for–profit (including NFP Corporation) **Service:** General Medical and Surgical

Staffed Beds: 55 **Admissions:** 2319 **Census:** 21

SAINT JOHNSBURY—Caledonia County

★ **NORTHEASTERN VERMONT REGIONAL HOSPITAL (471303)**, 1315 Hospital Drive, Zip 05819–9210, Mailing Address: PO Box 905, Zip 05819–0905; tel. 802/748–8141 **A**9 10 18 **F**3 11 13 15 18 26 28 29 30 34 35 40 44 45 50 51 59 64 68 70 74 75 76 77 78 79 81 82 84 86 87 89 93 104 107 108 110 111 115 118 119 127 130 131 132 133 135 146 147 **P**6
Primary Contact: Paul R. Bengtson, Chief Executive Officer
CFO: Robert Hersey, Chief Financial Officer
CIO: Andrea Lott, Vice President Information Services
CHR: Betty Ann Gwatkin, Vice President Human Resources
CNO: Seleem Choudhury, R.N., Chief Nursing Officer
Web address: www.nvrh.org
Control: Other not–for–profit (including NFP Corporation) **Service:** General Medical and Surgical

Staffed Beds: 25 **Admissions:** 1461 **Census:** 12 **Outpatient Visits:** 151682 **Births:** 184 **Total Expense ($000):** 63532 **Payroll Expense ($000):** 28974 **Personnel:** 349

SPRINGFIELD—Windsor County

SPRINGFIELD HOSPITAL (471306), 25 Ridgewood Road, Zip 05156–3050, Mailing Address: P.O. Box 2003, Zip 05156–2003; tel. 802/885–2151 **A**9 10 18 **F**2 3 5 13 15 29 31 34 35 36 37 38 39 40 45 48 50 53 54 55 56 57 59 61 64 65 66 75 76 77 79 81 85 86 87 89 93 97 98 100 101 102 103 104 106 107 108 110 111 115 118 119 127 130 131 132 133 135 144 145 146 147 148
Primary Contact: Timothy R. Ford, President and Chief Executive Officer
CFO: Andrew Majka, Chief Financial Officer and Chief Strategy Officer
CMO: Katrina Harris, D.O., President Medical Staff
CIO: Kyle Peoples, Director Technology Management Services
CHR: Janet Lyle, Chief Human Resources and Allied Health Services
CNO: Janet L. Sherer, Chief of Patient Care Services
Web address: www.springfieldhospital.org
Control: Other not–for–profit (including NFP Corporation) **Service:** General Medical and Surgical

Staffed Beds: 35 **Admissions:** 1945 **Census:** 25 **Outpatient Visits:** 149105 **Births:** 165 **Total Expense ($000):** 34347 **Payroll Expense ($000):** 17986 **Personnel:** 426

TOWNSHEND—Windham County

★ **GRACE COTTAGE HOSPITAL (471300)**, 185 Grafton Road, Zip 05353–0216, Mailing Address: P.O. Box 216, Zip 05353–0216; tel. 802/365–7357 **A**9 10 18 **F**3 11 29 30 34 40 50 53 56 57 59 64 68 75 77 85 87 93 97 102 104 107 114 119 127 128 130 131 132 133 135 146 148 **P**6
Primary Contact: Roger Allbee, Chief Executive Officer and Administrator
COO: Jeanne M. Fortier, R.N., Chief Nursing Officer and Interim Chief Operating Officer
CFO: Stephen A. Brown, Chief Financial Officer
CMO: Timothy Shafer, M.D., Medical Director
CIO: Tony Marques, Director Information Systems
CHR: Christopher J. Lackney, Director Human Resources
CNO: Jeanne M. Fortier, R.N., Chief Nursing Officer and Interim Chief Operating Officer
Web address: www.gracecottage.org
Control: Other not–for–profit (including NFP Corporation) **Service:** General Medical and Surgical

Staffed Beds: 19 **Admissions:** 415 **Census:** 10 **Outpatient Visits:** 39648 **Births:** 0

WHITE RIVER JUNCTION—Windsor County

✠ **WHITE RIVER JUNCTION VETERANS AFFAIRS MEDICAL CENTER**, 215 North Main Street, Zip 05009–0001; tel. 802/295–9363 **A**1 3 5 8 **F**3 4 5 8 9 12 18 20 29 30 31 34 35 36 38 40 44 45 46 49 50 53 54 55 56 57 58 59 60 61 62 63 64 65 70 74 75 77 78 79 81 82 83 84 85 86 87 93 94 95 96 97 98 100 101 102 103 104 105 106 107 108 111 115 118 119 127 130 132 135 141 143 144 146 147 148 **P**1 6 **S** Department of Veterans Affairs, Washington, DC
Primary Contact: Danielle Ocker, R.N., Acting Director
CFO: Joan Wilmot, Chief Finance Officer
CMO: M. Ganga Hematillake, M.D., Chief of Staff
CIO: Matthew Rafus, Chief Information Officer
CHR: Barbara Nadeau, Chief Human Resources Management Service
Web address: www.whiteriver.va.gov/
Control: Veterans Affairs, Government, federal **Service:** General Medical and Surgical

Staffed Beds: 60 **Admissions:** 2525 **Census:** 50 **Outpatient Visits:** 369531 **Births:** 0 **Total Expense ($000):** 172426 **Payroll Expense ($000):** 69852 **Personnel:** 870

VT

Many Facility Codes have changed. Please refer to the AHA Guide Code Chart. © 2014 AHA Guide

★ **MT. ASCUTNEY HOSPITAL AND HEALTH CENTER (471302)**, 289 County Road, Zip 05089–9000; tel. 802/674–6711 **A**9 10 18 **F**3 8 10 11 15 28 29 30 31 32 34 35 36 40 41 44 45 49 50 54 56 57 59 63 64 65 66 68 69 70 71 75 77 78 79 81 82 84 85 86 87 90 91 92 93 94 96 97 100 104 107 110 111 114 119 125 130 131 132 133 134 135 143 146 148 **P**6
Primary Contact: Kevin Donovan, Chief Executive Officer
COO: Paul Calandrella, Chief Operating Officer
CFO: David Sanville, Chief Financial Officer
CMO: Catherine Schneider, M.D., Chief Medical Officer
CIO: Brenna Heighes, Manager Information Technology
CHR: Jean Martaniuk, Director Human Resources
CNO: Jill Lord, MS, Director Patient Care Services
Web address: www.mtascutneyhospital.org
Control: Other not–for–profit (including NFP Corporation) **Service:** General Medical and Surgical

Staffed Beds: 35 **Admissions:** 990 **Census:** 41 **Outpatient Visits:** 86313 **Births:** 0 **Total Expense ($000):** 48695 **Payroll Expense ($000):** 22457 **Personnel:** 372

VT

VIRGINIA

ABINGDON—Washington County

✠ **JOHNSTON MEMORIAL HOSPITAL (490053)**, 16000 Johnston Memorial Drive, Zip 24211–7659; tel. 276/676–7000 **A**1 2 9 10 **F**3 7 8 11 13 15 18 20 28 29 30 31 34 35 39 40 44 45 48 49 50 51 54 57 59 60 62 63 64 68 70 74 75 76 77 78 79 81 82 84 85 87 92 93 97 100 107 108 109 110 111 115 118 119 120 121 123 129 130 132 133 135 143 144 146 147 148 **P**6 8 **S** Mountain States Health Alliance, Johnson City, TN
Primary Contact: Sean S. McMurray, FACHE, Vice President and Chief Executive Officer
CFO: John Jeter, Assistant Administrator and Chief Financial Officer
CIO: Jackson Dale, Director Management Information Services
CHR: Jackie G. Phipps, Director Human Resources
Web address: www.jmh.org
Control: Other not-for-profit (including NFP Corporation) **Service:** General Medical and Surgical

Staffed Beds: 116 **Admissions:** 7310 **Census:** 65 **Outpatient Visits:** 130865 **Births:** 744 **Total Expense ($000):** 78792 **Payroll Expense ($000):** 35605 **Personnel:** 651

ALDIE—Loudoun County

✠ **HEALTHSOUTH REHABILITATION HOSPITAL OF NORTHERN VIRGINIA (493033)**, 24430 Millstream Drive, Zip 20105–3098; tel. 703/957–2000, (Nonreporting) **A**1 10 **S** HEALTHSOUTH Corporation, Birmingham, AL
Primary Contact: Gary J. Herbek, Chief Executive Officer
Web address: www.healthsouthnorthernvirginia.com
Control: Corporation, Investor–owned, for–profit **Service:** Rehabilitation

Staffed Beds: 40

ALEXANDRIA—Alexandria City County

✠ **INOVA ALEXANDRIA HOSPITAL (490040)**, 4320 Seminary Road, Zip 22304–1535; tel. 703/504–3167 **A**1 2 5 9 10 **F**3 11 13 14 15 17 18 20 22 24 26 28 29 30 31 34 35 38 39 40 42 44 45 48 49 50 51 54 55 57 59 60 61 63 64 65 66 68 69 70 72 74 75 76 77 78 79 80 81 83 84 85 86 87 89 91 92 93 100 101 102 107 108 110 111 114 115 117 118 119 120 121 123 124 129 130 131 132 135 145 146 147 148 **P**6 **S** Inova Health System, Falls Church, VA
Primary Contact: Christine Candio, Chief Executive Officer
CFO: Todd Lockcuff, Chief Financial Officer
CMO: John R. Audett, M.D., Chief Medical Officer
CIO: Geoffrey Brown, Senior Vice President Information Services
CHR: Hugo Aguas, Vice President Human Resources
CNO: Mary Dixon, R.N., Chief Nursing Officer
Web address: www.inova.org
Control: Other not-for-profit (including NFP Corporation) **Service:** General Medical and Surgical

Staffed Beds: 334 **Admissions:** 17285 **Census:** 214 **Outpatient Visits:** 223228 **Births:** 3755 **Total Expense ($000):** 289518 **Payroll Expense ($000):** 103849 **Personnel:** 1467

✠ △ **INOVA MOUNT VERNON HOSPITAL (490122)**, 2501 Parker's Lane, Zip 22306–3209; tel. 703/664–7000 **A**1 2 3 5 7 9 10 **F**3 5 11 14 15 18 26 28 29 30 31 34 35 37 38 39 40 42 44 45 48 49 50 51 54 55 57 58 59 60 61 63 64 65 66 68 69 70 74 75 77 78 79 80 81 82 84 85 86 87 90 91 92 93 94 96 98 100 101 102 103 104 105 107 108 110 111 114 115 118 119 130 131 132 135 145 146 147 148 **P**6 **S** Inova Health System, Falls Church, VA
Primary Contact: Donald Brideau, M.D., Interim Chief Executive Officer
CFO: Tammy Razmic, Associate Administrator Finance and Chief Financial Officer
CMO: Donald Brideau, M.D., Chief Medical Officer
CHR: Bev Sugar, Associate Administrator and Director Human Resources
Web address: www.inova.org
Control: Other not-for-profit (including NFP Corporation) **Service:** General Medical and Surgical

Staffed Beds: 237 **Admissions:** 8624 **Census:** 140 **Outpatient Visits:** 79206 **Births:** 0 **Total Expense ($000):** 164982 **Payroll Expense ($000):** 60657 **Personnel:** 776

ARLINGTON—Arlington County

CAPITAL HOSPICE (490129), 4715 15th Street North, Zip 22205–2640; tel. 703/538–2065, (Nonreporting) **A**3 10
Primary Contact: Malene S. Davis, R.N., President and Chief Executive Officer
CFO: David Schwind, Chief Financial Officer
CIO: Diane Rigsby, Chief Information Officer
Web address: www.capitalhospice.org
Control: Other not-for-profit (including NFP Corporation) **Service:** Other specialty

Staffed Beds: 15

✠ △ **VIRGINIA HOSPITAL CENTER – ARLINGTON (490050)**, 1701 North George Mason Drive, Zip 22205–3698; tel. 703/558–5000 **A**1 2 3 5 7 9 10 **F**3 4 5 8 11 12 13 15 17 18 20 22 24 26 28 29 30 31 34 35 37 38 40 45 46 47 48 49 50 51 54 57 59 60 61 62 64 65 66 68 70 72 73 74 75 76 78 79 81 84 85 86 87 89 90 91 92 93 94 95 96 97 98 100 102 103 104 105 107 110 111 114 115 116 117 118 119 120 121 123 124 126 129 130 132 135 144 145 146 147 148 **P**6
Primary Contact: James B. Cole, Chief Executive Officer
COO: Carl Bahnlein, Executive Vice President and Chief Operating Officer
CFO: Robin Norman, Senior Vice President and Chief Financial Officer
CMO: Jeffrey P. DiLisi, Vice President and Chief Medical Officer
CIO: Russ McWey, M.D., Vice President and Chief Information Officer
CHR: Michael Malone, Vice President and Chief Human Resources Officer
CNO: Darlene Vrotsos, R.N., Vice President and Chief Nursing Officer
Web address: www.virginiahospitalcenter.com
Control: Other not-for-profit (including NFP Corporation) **Service:** General Medical and Surgical

Staffed Beds: 357 **Admissions:** 22978 **Census:** 267 **Outpatient Visits:** 331002 **Births:** 5685 **Total Expense ($000):** 349473 **Payroll Expense ($000):** 140309 **Personnel:** 2115

BEDFORD—Bedford City County

✠ **BEDFORD MEMORIAL HOSPITAL (490088)**, 1613 Oakwood Street, Zip 24523–1213, Mailing Address: P.O. Box 688, Zip 24523–0688; tel. 540/586–2441, (Total facility includes 111 beds in nursing home–type unit) **A**1 9 10 **F**2 3 11 15 18 19 28 29 30 34 35 40 42 46 53 57 59 63 67 70 81 84 85 93 97 107 119 128 129 130 134 143 145 146 148 **S** Centra Health, Inc., Lynchburg, VA
Primary Contact: Patti Jurkus, Vice President, Regional Hospital
CFO: Donald E. Lorton, Executive Vice President
CMO: E. Allen Joslyn, M.D., Chief Medical Officer
Web address: www.bmhva.com
Control: Other not-for-profit (including NFP Corporation) **Service:** General Medical and Surgical

Staffed Beds: 127 **Admissions:** 1849 **Census:** 112 **Outpatient Visits:** 25689 **Births:** 0 **Total Expense ($000):** 32736 **Payroll Expense ($000):** 13943 **Personnel:** 307

BIG STONE GAP—Wise County

✠ **WELLMONT LONESOME PINE HOSPITAL (490114)**, 1990 Holton Avenue East, Zip 24219–3350; tel. 276/523–3111 **A**1 9 10 13 **F**3 11 13 15 18 29 30 31 34 35 40 49 50 57 59 63 68 76 77 78 79 81 82 85 87 89 93 97 107 108 110 111 116 117 118 119 120 121 129 130 146 148 **S** Wellmont Health System, Kingsport, TN
Primary Contact: Fred L. Pelle, FACHE, Interim President and Chief Executive Officer
CFO: Regina Day, Executive Director Finance
CMO: Michael Vacco, M.D., Chief Medical Officer
CHR: Bobby Collins, Director Human Resources
CNO: Sheri Ives, R.N., Vice President Care Services
Web address: www.wellmont.org
Control: Other not-for-profit (including NFP Corporation) **Service:** General Medical and Surgical

Staffed Beds: 30 **Admissions:** 1497 **Census:** 10 **Outpatient Visits:** 31295 **Births:** 287 **Total Expense ($000):** 35177 **Payroll Expense ($000):** 7993 **Personnel:** 200

BLACKSBURG—Montgomery County

✠ **LEWISGALE HOSPITAL MONTGOMERY (490110)**, 3700 South Main Street, Zip 24060–7081, Mailing Address: P.O. Box 90004, Zip 24062–9004; tel. 540/951–1111, (Nonreporting) **A**1 9 10 12 13 **S** HCA, Nashville, TN
Primary Contact: Alan J. Fabian, Chief Executive Officer
COO: Matt Mathias, Chief Operating Officer
CFO: Timothy W. Haasken, Chief Financial Officer
CIO: Diron Lane, Director Information Systems
CHR: Kristie Walker, Director Human Resources
Web address: www.lewisgale.com
Control: Corporation, Investor–owned, for–profit **Service:** General Medical and Surgical

Staffed Beds: 89

BRISTOL—Bristol City County

✠ **REHABILITATION HOSPITAL OF SOUTHWEST VIRGINIA (493034)**, 103 North Street, Zip 24201–3201; tel. 276/642–7900, (Nonreporting) **A**1 10 **S** HEALTHSOUTH Corporation, Birmingham, AL
Primary Contact: Georgeanne Cole, Chief Executive Officer
Web address: www.rehabilitationhospitalswvirginia.com
Control: Corporation, Investor–owned, for–profit **Service:** Rehabilitation

Staffed Beds: 25

VA

BURKEVILLE—Nottoway County

☐ **PIEDMONT GERIATRIC HOSPITAL (490134)**, 5001 East Patrick Henry Highway, Zip 23922–3460, Mailing Address: P.O. Box 427, Zip 23922–0427; tel. 434/767–4401, (Nonreporting) **A**1 9 10 **S** Virginia Department of Mental Health, Richmond, VA
Primary Contact: Stephen M. Herrick, Ph.D., Director
CFO: James G. Ayers, Chief Financial Officer
CMO: Hugo Falcon, M.D., Director Medical Services
CHR: Michael Wimsatt, Director Human Resources
Web address: www.pgh.dmhmrsas.virginia.gov
Control: State–Government, nonfederal **Service:** Other specialty

Staffed Beds: 150

CATAWBA—Roanoke County

☐ **CATAWBA HOSPITAL (490135)**, 5525 Catawba Hospital Drive, Zip 24070–2115, Mailing Address: P.O. Box 200, Zip 24070–0200; tel. 540/375–4200 **A**1 9 10 **F**29 30 35 38 39 44 50 68 75 77 98 103 130 146 **P**6 **S** Virginia Department of Mental Health, Richmond, VA
Primary Contact: Walton F. Mitchell, III, Director
COO: Charles Law, Ph.D., Chief Operating Officer
CFO: Cecil Hardin, CPA, Chief Financial Officer
CMO: Yad Jabbarpour, M.D., Chief of Staff
CIO: Charles Law, Ph.D., Chief Operating Officer
CHR: Patricia Ebbett, Chief Human Resources Officer
CNO: Vicky Fisher, Ph.D., Chief Nurse Executive
Web address: www.catawba.dbhds.virginia.gov
Control: State–Government, nonfederal **Service:** Psychiatric

Staffed Beds: 110 **Admissions:** 249 **Census:** 92 **Outpatient Visits:** 0 **Births:** 0 **Total Expense ($000):** 20545 **Payroll Expense ($000):** 12096 **Personnel:** 257

CHARLOTTESVILLE—Charlottesville City County

★ ◇ **MARTHA JEFFERSON HOSPITAL (490077)**, 500 Martha Jefferson Drive, Zip 22911–4668; tel. 434/654–7000 **A**2 3 5 9 10 21 **F**3 8 12 13 15 18 20 22 26 28 29 30 31 34 35 36 40 42 45 46 47 48 49 50 64 66 68 70 74 75 76 78 79 81 82 84 85 86 87 89 92 93 94 97 107 108 110 111 114 115 116 117 118 119 120 121 123 124 129 130 132 135 145 146 147 148 **P**1 **S** Sentara Healthcare, Norfolk, VA
Primary Contact: James E. Haden, President and Chief Executive Officer
COO: Elliot H. Kuida, Vice President and Chief Operating Officer
CFO: J. Michael Burris, Vice President Corporate Services and Chief Financial Officer
CMO: F. Michael Ashby, M.D., Vice President and Medical Director
CIO: Marijo Lecker, Vice President
CHR: Debbie Desmond, Director Human Resources
CNO: Amy Black, R.N., Vice President Chief Nurse Executive
Web address: www.marthajefferson.org
Control: Other not–for–profit (including NFP Corporation) **Service:** General Medical and Surgical

Staffed Beds: 139 **Admissions:** 10464 **Census:** 97 **Outpatient Visits:** 448892 **Births:** 1783 **Total Expense ($000):** 235489 **Payroll Expense ($000):** 104388 **Personnel:** 1496

⊞ △ **UNIVERSITY OF VIRGINIA MEDICAL CENTER (490009)**, 1215 Lee Street, Zip 22908–0001, Mailing Address: P.O. Box 800809, Zip 22908–0809; tel. 434/924–0211, (Includes UNIVERSITY OF VIRGINIA CHILDREN'S HOSPITAL, PO Box 800566, Zip 22901; tel. 434/982–4453) **A**1 2 3 5 7 8 9 10 **F**3 4 5 6 7 8 9 11 12 13 15 16 17 18 19 20 21 22 23 24 25 26 27 28 29 30 31 32 34 35 36 37 38 39 40 41 43 44 45 46 47 48 49 50 51 52 54 55 56 57 58 59 60 61 62 64 65 66 68 70 71 72 73 74 75 76 77 78 79 80 81 82 83 84 85 86 87 88 89 90 91 92 93 94 97 98 99 100 101 102 103 104 107 108 110 111 112 114 115 116 117 118 119 120 121 123 124 126 129 130 131 132 134 135 136 137 138 139 140 141 142 143 145 146 147 148 **P**3 4 **S** UVA Health System, Charlottesville, VA
Primary Contact: Pamela Sutton–Wallace, Chief Executive Officer
COO: Robert Cofield, Dr.PH, Associate Vice President and Chief Operating Officer
CFO: Larry Fitzgerald, Associate Vice President Business Development and Finance
CMO: Chris A. Ghaemmaghami, M.D., Chief Medical Officer
CIO: Richard Skinner, Chief Information Technology Officer
CHR: John Boswell, Chief Human Resources Officer
CNO: Lorna M. Facteau, Ph.D., Chief Nursing Officer
Web address: www.healthsystem.virginia.edu
Control: State–Government, nonfederal **Service:** General Medical and Surgical

Staffed Beds: 570 **Admissions:** 28802 **Census:** 442 **Outpatient Visits:** 1772010 **Births:** 1572 **Total Expense ($000):** 1121967 **Payroll Expense ($000):** 394582 **Personnel:** 6422

UVA TRANSITIONAL CARE HOSPITAL (492011), 2965 Ivy Road (250 West), Zip 22903–9330; tel. 434/924–7897 **A**10 **F**1 3 29 30 60 77 85 94 114 130 146 148 **P**3 4 **S** UVA Health System, Charlottesville, VA
Primary Contact: Michelle Hereford, Chief
Web address: www.uvahealth.com/services/transitional–care–hospital
Control: State–Government, nonfederal **Service:** Long–Term Acute Care hospital

Staffed Beds: 40 **Admissions:** 315 **Census:** 23 **Outpatient Visits:** 0 **Births:** 0 **Total Expense ($000):** 16892 **Payroll Expense ($000):** 6725 **Personnel:** 110

⊞ **UVA–HEALTHSOUTH REHABILITATION HOSPITAL (493029)**, 515 Ray C. Hunt Drive, Zip 22903–2981; tel. 434/244–2000 **A**1 3 5 10 **F**28 29 54 64 74 77 90 91 93 94 96 131 148 **P**5 **S** HEALTHSOUTH Corporation, Birmingham, AL
Primary Contact: Thomas J. Cook, Chief Executive Officer
Web address: www.uvahealthsouth.com
Control: Corporation, Investor–owned, for–profit **Service:** Rehabilitation

Staffed Beds: 50 **Admissions:** 1171 **Census:** 39 **Outpatient Visits:** 25163 **Births:** 0 **Total Expense ($000):** 19668 **Payroll Expense ($000):** 11953 **Personnel:** 213

CHESAPEAKE—Chesapeake City County

★ ○ **CHESAPEAKE REGIONAL MEDICAL CENTER (490120)**, 736 Battlefield Boulevard North, Zip 23320–4941, Mailing Address: P.O. Box 2028, Zip 23327–2028; tel. 757/312–8121 **A**2 9 10 11 **F**3 6 8 10 11 12 13 15 18 20 22 26 28 29 30 31 34 35 40 44 45 46 49 50 53 54 57 58 59 61 62 63 64 65 66 68 69 70 71 73 74 75 76 77 78 79 81 83 84 85 86 87 89 91 93 100 101 102 103 107 108 110 111 114 115 118 119 120 121 123 126 129 130 132 135 141 142 143 146 147 148 **P**6 8
Primary Contact: Peter F. Bastone, Chief Executive Officer
CFO: John L. Skeans, Chief Financial Officer
CMO: Paul Brainstein, M.D., Interim Chief Medical Officer
CIO: Ken Deans, Chief Information Officer
CHR: Deborah L. Rosenburg, Vice President Human Resources
CNO: Elaine Griffiths, R.N., Chief Nursing Officer
Web address: www.chesapeakeregional.com
Control: Hospital district or authority, Government, nonfederal **Service:** General Medical and Surgical

Staffed Beds: 309 **Admissions:** 15268 **Census:** 204 **Outpatient Visits:** 187822 **Births:** 2531 **Total Expense ($000):** 250110 **Payroll Expense ($000):** 98576 **Personnel:** 1806

CHRISTIANSBURG—Montgomery County

⊞ **CARILION NEW RIVER VALLEY MEDICAL CENTER (490042)**, 2900 Lamb Circle, Zip 24073–6344, Mailing Address: P.O. Box 5, Radford, Zip 24143–0005; tel. 540/731–2000, (Includes CARILION CLINIC SAINT ALBANS HOSPITAL, 2900 Lamb Circle, tel. 540/731–2000) **A**1 9 10 **F**3 5 12 13 15 18 24 28 29 30 31 34 35 36 40 43 45 47 48 49 50 51 57 59 62 63 64 68 70 74 75 76 77 79 81 84 85 86 87 89 93 96 98 99 102 103 104 105 107 108 110 111 114 115 117 119 126 129 130 135 146 147 148 **S** Carilion Clinic, Roanoke, VA
Primary Contact: Melina Dee Perdue, R.N., Executive Vice President
CFO: Rob Vaughan, Chief Financial Officer
CMO: Dennis Means, M.D., Vice President Medical Affairs
CIO: Daniel Borchi, Chief Information Officer
CHR: Patti Jurkus, Director Human Resources
Web address: www.carilionclinic.org/Carilion/cnrv
Control: Other not–for–profit (including NFP Corporation) **Service:** General Medical and Surgical

Staffed Beds: 94 **Admissions:** 7930 **Census:** 81 **Outpatient Visits:** 88866 **Births:** 1233 **Total Expense ($000):** 135002 **Payroll Expense ($000):** 50053 **Personnel:** 840

CLINTWOOD—Dickenson County

DICKENSON COMMUNITY HOSPITAL (491303), 312 Hospital Drive, Zip 24228, Mailing Address: P.O. Box 1440, Zip 24228–1440; tel. 276/926–0300 **A**9 10 18 **F**3 29 40 44 64 87 97 107 119 148 **P**6 8 **S** Mountain States Health Alliance, Johnson City, TN
Primary Contact: Mark T. Leonard, Chief Executive Officer
CFO: Kevin Morrison, Chief Financial Officer
CMO: Erin Mullins, D.O., Chief Medical Staff
CHR: Valeri J. Colyer, Director Human Resources
CNO: Terri Roop, Director Patient Care Services
Web address: www.msha.com/dch
Control: Other not–for–profit (including NFP Corporation) **Service:** General Medical and Surgical

Staffed Beds: 25 **Admissions:** 9 **Census:** 1 **Outpatient Visits:** 21089 **Births:** 0 **Total Expense ($000):** 6120 **Payroll Expense ($000):** 2586 **Personnel:** 35

VA

Hospital, Medicare Provider Number, Address, Telephone, Approval, Facility, and Physician Codes, Health Care System

★ American Hospital Association (AHA) membership
☐ The Joint Commission accreditation　　◇ DNV Healthcare Inc. accreditation
○ Healthcare Facilities Accreditation Program
△ Commission on Accreditation of Rehabilitation Facilities (CARF) accreditation

CULPEPER—Culpeper County

⊞ **CULPEPER REGIONAL HOSPITAL (490019)**, 501 Sunset Lane, Zip 22701–3917, Mailing Address: P.O. Box 592, Zip 22701–0500; tel. 540/829–4100 **A**1 3 5 9 10 **F**3 7 8 11 13 15 18 28 29 30 34 35 36 37 38 40 45 50 54 57 59 64 68 70 74 75 76 77 78 79 81 82 85 87 93 97 102 107 108 110 111 114 115 119 120 121 123 130 132 133 135 143 146 148 **P**8
Primary Contact: Greg Napps, Acting Chief Executive Officer
COO: Greg Napps, Acting Chief Executive Officer
CFO: David J. Plaviak, Interim Chief Financial Officer
CMO: Morton Chiles, M.D., Chief Medical Officer
CIO: Steven Speelman, Director Information Systems
CHR: Susan Edwards, Vice President Human Resources
Web address: www.culpeperhealth.org
Control: Other not-for-profit (including NFP Corporation) **Service:** General Medical and Surgical

Staffed Beds: 68 **Admissions:** 3182 **Census:** 33 **Outpatient Visits:** 80667 **Births:** 358 **Total Expense ($000):** 73811 **Payroll Expense ($000):** 30512 **Personnel:** 524

DANVILLE—Danville City County

⊞ **DANVILLE REGIONAL MEDICAL CENTER (490075)**, 142 South Main Street, Zip 24541–2922; tel. 434/799–2100, (Nonreporting) **A**1 2 6 9 10 12 13 **S** LifePoint Hospitals, Inc., Brentwood, TN
Primary Contact: Eric Deaton, Chief Executive Officer
CFO: Mark T. Anderson, Chief Financial Officer
CMO: James F. Starling, M.D., Chief Medical Officer
CIO: David Cartwright, Director Management Information Systems
Web address: www.danvilleregional.org
Control: Other not-for-profit (including NFP Corporation) **Service:** General Medical and Surgical

Staffed Beds: 151

☐ **SOUTHERN VIRGINIA MENTAL HEALTH INSTITUTE (494017)**, 382 Taylor Drive, Zip 24541–4023; tel. 434/799–6220 **A**1 9 10 **F**34 38 50 57 68 75 77 86 87 98 100 101 102 106 130 132 146 **P**6 **S** Virginia Department of Mental Health, Richmond, VA
Primary Contact: William Cook, Director
CFO: Wayne Peters, Administrator
CMO: Pravin Patel, M.D., Acting President and Chief Executive Officer
CIO: Larry Hays, Director Information Technology
CHR: Stephanie Haywood, Director Human Resources
CNO: Kathy M. Dodd, Director of Nursing
Web address: www.svmhi.dbhds.virginia.gov
Control: State-Government, nonfederal **Service:** Psychiatric

Staffed Beds: 72 **Admissions:** 275 **Census:** 72 **Outpatient Visits:** 0 **Births:** 0 **Total Expense ($000):** 12916 **Payroll Expense ($000):** 7687

EMPORIA—Emporia City County

⊞ **SOUTHERN VIRGINIA REGIONAL MEDICAL CENTER (490097)**, 727 North Main Street, Zip 23847–1274; tel. 434/348–4400 **A**1 9 10 **F**3 11 15 26 28 29 30 31 39 40 45 49 57 59 62 64 70 77 78 79 81 82 85 89 93 98 103 107 115 119 124 129 130 133 146 148 **S** Community Health Systems, Inc., Franklin, TN
Primary Contact: Linda Burnette, R.N., Interim Chief Executive Officer
CMO: Michael S. Anderson, M.D., Chief of Staff
CIO: Brian Hopkins, Director Management Information Systems
CHR: Becky Parrish, Director Human Resources
CNO: Linda Burnette, R.N., Chief Nursing Officer
Web address: www.svrmc.com
Control: Corporation, Investor-owned, for-profit **Service:** General Medical and Surgical

Staffed Beds: 80 **Admissions:** 2121 **Census:** 28 **Outpatient Visits:** 24644 **Births:** 0 **Total Expense ($000):** 33360 **Payroll Expense ($000):** 11958 **Personnel:** 285

FAIRFAX—Fairfax County

⊞ **INOVA FAIR OAKS HOSPITAL (490101)**, 3600 Joseph Siewick Drive, Zip 22033–1798; tel. 703/391–3600 **A**1 2 3 5 9 10 **F**3 11 12 13 14 15 18 29 30 31 32 34 35 37 38 39 40 44 45 47 48 49 50 51 54 55 57 59 60 61 63 64 65 66 68 69 70 72 74 75 76 77 78 79 80 81 82 84 85 86 87 89 91 92 93 100 101 102 107 108 110 111 114 115 118 119 126 129 130 131 132 135 145 146 147 148 **S** Inova Health System, Falls Church, VA
Primary Contact: John L. Fitzgerald, Chief Executive Officer
CFO: Jerry Seager, Assistant Vice President and Chief Financial Officer
CMO: G. Michael Lynch, M.D., Chief Medical Officer
CIO: Geoffrey Brown, Chief Information Officer
CHR: Jeanne Robinson, Director Human Resources
CNO: Cheri Goll, MSN, Chief Nursing Officer
Web address: www.inova.org
Control: Other not-for-profit (including NFP Corporation) **Service:** General Medical and Surgical

Staffed Beds: 196 **Admissions:** 14149 **Census:** 129 **Outpatient Visits:** 111710 **Births:** 3853 **Total Expense ($000):** 226354 **Payroll Expense ($000):** 71677 **Personnel:** 976

FALLS CHURCH—Fairfax County

⊞ **DOMINION HOSPITAL (494023)**, 2960 Sleepy Hollow Road, Zip 22044–2030; tel. 703/536–2000 **A**1 9 10 **F**98 99 100 101 102 104 105 130 **S** HCA, Nashville, TN
Primary Contact: Cynthia A. Meyer, Chief Executive Officer
CFO: Edward R. Stojakovich, Chief Financial Officer
CMO: Gary Litovitz, M.D., Medical Director
CIO: Leslie Gilliam, Director Health Information Management
CHR: Lesley Channell, Vice President Human Resources
CNO: Teresa Brooke, Chief Nursing Officer
Web address: www.dominionhospital.com
Control: Corporation, Investor-owned, for-profit **Service:** Psychiatric

Staffed Beds: 100 **Admissions:** 2750 **Census:** 70 **Outpatient Visits:** 500 **Births:** 0

⊞ **INOVA FAIRFAX HOSPITAL (490063)**, 3300 Gallows Road, Zip 22042–3300; tel. 703/776–4001, (Includes INOVA FAIRFAX HOSPITAL FOR CHILDREN, 3300 Gallows Road, Zip 22042–3307; tel. 703/776–4002) **A**1 2 3 5 8 9 10 **F**3 4 5 6 8 9 11 12 13 14 15 17 18 19 20 21 22 23 24 25 26 27 28 29 30 31 32 34 35 36 37 38 39 40 41 42 43 44 45 46 47 48 49 50 51 54 55 56 57 58 59 60 61 63 64 65 66 68 69 70 71 72 74 75 76 77 78 79 80 81 82 83 84 85 86 87 88 89 91 92 93 94 96 97 98 99 100 101 102 103 104 105 107 108 109 110 111 114 115 118 119 120 121 123 124 126 129 130 131 132 134 135 136 137 138 140 141 142 145 146 147 148 **P**6 **S** Inova Health System, Falls Church, VA
Primary Contact: Patrick Christiansen, Ph.D., Chief Executive Officer
COO: Maureen Swick, R.N., Senior Vice President, Chief Operating Officer
CFO: Ronald Ewald, Chief Financial Officer
CMO: Joseph Hallal, M.D., Chief Medical Officer
CIO: Geoffrey Brown, Vice President Information Systems
CHR: Ken Hull, Director Human Resources
Web address: www.inova.org
Control: Other not-for-profit (including NFP Corporation) **Service:** General Medical and Surgical

Staffed Beds: 926 **Admissions:** 45767 **Census:** 667 **Outpatient Visits:** 280457 **Births:** 8535 **Total Expense ($000):** 1117926 **Payroll Expense ($000):** 390475 **Personnel:** 5042

☐ **NORTHERN VIRGINIA MENTAL HEALTH INSTITUTE (494010)**, 3302 Gallows Road, Zip 22042–3398; tel. 703/207–7110 **A**1 3 5 9 10 **F**29 30 98 101 130 132 **S** Virginia Department of Mental Health, Richmond, VA
Primary Contact: James R. Newton, Facility Director
CFO: John Poffenbarger, Director Fiscal Services
CMO: R. Maxilimien del Rio, M.D., Medical Director
CHR: Cynthia Lott, Director Human Resources
Web address: www.nvmhi.dmhmrsas.virginia.gov
Control: State-Government, nonfederal **Service:** Psychiatric

Staffed Beds: 123 **Admissions:** 693 **Census:** 116 **Outpatient Visits:** 0 **Births:** 0 **Total Expense ($000):** 28992 **Personnel:** 293

FARMVILLE—Prince Edward County

⊞ **CENTRA SOUTHSIDE COMMUNITY HOSPITAL (490090)**, 800 Oak Street, Zip 23901–1199; tel. 434/392–8811 **A**1 5 9 10 20 **F**3 11 13 15 28 29 30 34 35 40 44 45 49 50 57 59 62 64 70 75 76 77 79 81 85 86 87 89 93 107 108 110 115 118 119 129 130 132 133 146 147 148 **P**6 **S** Centra Health, Inc., Lynchburg, VA
Primary Contact: William L. Bass, Jr., Vice President and Chief Executive Officer
Web address: www.sch.centrahealth.com/
Control: Other not-for-profit (including NFP Corporation) **Service:** General Medical and Surgical

Staffed Beds: 86 **Admissions:** 4460 **Census:** 39 **Outpatient Visits:** 120546 **Births:** 413 **Total Expense ($000):** 67975 **Payroll Expense ($000):** 31760 **Personnel:** 442

SOUTHSIDE COMMUNITY HOSPITAL See Centra Southside Community Hospital

FISHERSVILLE—Augusta County

⊞ **AUGUSTA HEALTH (490018)**, 78 Medical Center Drive, Zip 22939–2332, Mailing Address: P.O. Box 1000, Zip 22939–1000; tel. 540/932–4000 **A**1 2 3 5 9 10 19 20 **F**3 5 7 11 13 15 18 20 22 28 29 30 31 34 35 36 39 40 45 46 48 49 50 51 53 54 56 57 58 59 61 62 63 68 73 74 75 76 77 78 79 81 82 85 86 87 89 90 91 92 93 96 97 98 100 101 102 103 104 107 108 110 111 114 115 118 119 120 121 123 128 129 130 131 132 135 144 145 146 147 148 **P**6
Primary Contact: Mary N. Mannix, FACHE, President and Chief Executive Officer
CFO: John R. Heider, Vice President Finance
CMO: Fred Castello, M.D., Chief Medical Officer
CIO: Velma Carroll, Chief Information Officer
CHR: Sue Krzastek, Vice President Human Resources
Web address: www.augustahealth.com
Control: Other not-for-profit (including NFP Corporation) **Service:** General Medical and Surgical

Staffed Beds: 224 **Admissions:** 11044 **Census:** 121 **Outpatient Visits:** 598719 **Births:** 1135 **Total Expense ($000):** 243386 **Payroll Expense ($000):** 107757 **Personnel:** 1884

WOODROW WILSON REHABILITATION CENTER, 243 Woodrow Wilson Avenue, Zip 22939, Mailing Address: P.O. Box 1500, Zip 22939–1500; tel. 540/332–7000, (Nonreporting) **A**5
Primary Contact: Richard Luck, Ed.D., Facility Director
COO: Richard Luck, Ed.D., Facility Director
CFO: Ernie Steidle, Chief Operating Officer
CMO: Mammen Mathew, M.D., Chief Rehabilitation Medicine
CIO: Keith Burt, Director Marketing
CHR: Debbie Mitchell, Director Human Resources
Web address: www.wwrc.net
Control: State–Government, nonfederal **Service:** Rehabilitation

Staffed Beds: 30

FORT BELVOIR—Fairfax County

⊞ **FORT BELVOIR COMMUNITY HOSPITAL**, 9300 Dewitt Loop, Zip 22060–5285; tel. 571/231–3224, (Nonreporting) **A**1 3 5 9 **S** Department of the Army, Office of the Surgeon General, Falls Church, VA
Primary Contact: Captain Jennifer Vedral–Baron, Commander
CMO: Lieutenant Colonel Mark D. Harris, Deputy Commander Clinical Services
CIO: Terrance Branch, Chief Information Management
Web address: www.fbch.capmed.mil/SitePages/Home.aspx
Control: Army, Government, federal **Service:** General Medical and Surgical

Staffed Beds: 46

FRANKLIN—Franklin City County

⊞ **SOUTHAMPTON MEMORIAL HOSPITAL (490092)**, 100 Fairview Drive, Zip 23851–1238, Mailing Address: P.O. Box 817, Zip 23851–0817; tel. 757/569–6100, (Nonreporting) **A**1 9 10 20 **S** Community Health Systems, Inc., Franklin, TN
Primary Contact: Kimberly W. Marks, Interim Chief Executive Officer
CFO: Steve Ramey, Chief Financial Officer
CMO: Donald Bowling, M.D., Chief Medical Staff
CIO: Kristie Howell, System Information Technology Director
CHR: Kimberly W. Marks, Director Human Resources
CNO: Laurie Ross, Chief Nursing Officer
Web address: www.smhfranklin.com
Control: Corporation, Investor–owned, for–profit **Service:** General Medical and Surgical

Staffed Beds: 72

FREDERICKSBURG—Fredericksburg City County

⊞ **HEALTHSOUTH REHABILITATION HOSPITAL OF FREDERICKSBURG (493032)**, 300 Park Hill Drive, Zip 22401–3387; tel. 540/368–7300, (Nonreporting) **A**1 10 **S** HEALTHSOUTH Corporation, Birmingham, AL
Primary Contact: Donna Z. Phillips, M.D., Chief Executive Officer
Web address: www.fredericksburgrehabhospital.com
Control: Corporation, Investor–owned, for–profit **Service:** Rehabilitation

Staffed Beds: 40

⊞ **MARY WASHINGTON HOSPITAL (490022)**, 1001 Sam Perry Boulevard, Zip 22401–3354; tel. 540/741–1100 **A**1 2 9 10 **F**5 13 15 18 20 22 24 26 28 29 30 31 34 35 40 42 43 44 45 46 48 49 50 54 57 58 59 61 62 64 68 70 74 75 77 78 79 81 82 83 84 85 86 87 92 93 96 98 99 100 101 102 104 105 107 108 111 114 115 118 119 120 121 124 126 129 130 131 132 135 146 147 148 **P**6 **S** Mary Washington Healthcare, Fredericksburg, VA
Primary Contact: Fred M. Rankin, III, President and Chief Executive Officer
CFO: Sean Barden, Executive Vice President and Chief Financial Officer
CMO: Rebecca Bigoney, M.D., Executive Vice President and Chief Medical Officer
CIO: Joyce Hanscome, Senior Vice President and Chief Information Officer
CHR: Kathryn S. Wall, Executive Vice President Human Resources and Organizational Development
CNO: Marianna Bedway, R.N., Senior Vice President and Chief Nursing Officer
Web address: www.marywashingtonhealthcare.com/locations/mary–washington–hospital
Control: Other not–for–profit (including NFP Corporation) **Service:** General Medical and Surgical

Staffed Beds: 437 Admissions: 23185 Census: 283 Outpatient Visits: 385717 Births: 2871 Total Expense ($000): 408769 Payroll Expense ($000): 141904 Personnel: 2248

SNOWDEN AT FREDERICKSBURG, 1200 Sam Perry Boulevard, Zip 22401–4456; tel. 540/741–3900, (Nonreporting) **A**9
Primary Contact: Charles Scercy, Chief Executive Officer
Web address: www.snowdenmentalhealth.com
Control: Other not–for–profit (including NFP Corporation) **Service:** Psychiatric

Staffed Beds: 30

⊞ **SPOTSYLVANIA REGIONAL MEDICAL CENTER (490141)**, 4600 Spotsylvania Parkway, Zip 22408–7762; tel. 540/834–1500, (Nonreporting) **A**1 9 10 **S** HCA, Nashville, TN
Primary Contact: Greg T. Madsen, Chief Executive Officer
COO: Terika Richardson, M.P.H., Associate Administrator
CFO: Sean Thomson, CPA, Chief Financial Officer
Web address: www.spotsrmc.com
Control: Corporation, Investor–owned, for–profit **Service:** General Medical and Surgical

Staffed Beds: 100

FRONT ROYAL—Warren County

⊞ **WARREN MEMORIAL HOSPITAL (490033)**, 1000 North Shenandoah Avenue, Zip 22630–3598; tel. 540/636–0300, (Total facility includes 120 beds in nursing home–type unit) **A**1 9 10 13 **F**3 11 13 15 28 29 30 34 35 36 40 50 53 54 56 57 59 64 65 67 70 75 76 77 79 81 82 85 86 87 93 96 107 108 111 114 118 119 128 130 132 135 144 146 147 148 **P**6 **S** Valley Health System, Winchester, VA
Primary Contact: Patrick B. Nolan, President and Chief Executive Officer
CFO: Phillip Graybeal, Chief Financial Officer
CMO: Robert Meltvedt, Jr., M.D., Vice President Medical Affairs
Web address: www.valleyhealthlink.com/WMH
Control: Other not–for–profit (including NFP Corporation) **Service:** General Medical and Surgical

Staffed Beds: 166 Admissions: 2750 Census: 138 Outpatient Visits: 62447 Births: 344 Total Expense ($000): 64885 Payroll Expense ($000): 24120 Personnel: 468

GALAX—Galax City County

⊞ **TWIN COUNTY REGIONAL HOSPITAL (490115)**, 200 Hospital Drive, Zip 24333–2227; tel. 276/236–8181, (Nonreporting) **A**1 9 10 20 **S** Duke LifePoint Healthcare, Brentwood, TN
Primary Contact: Jon D. Applebaum, Chief Executive Officer
CFO: Michael Widener, Chief Financial Officer
CIO: Jack Roberts, Director Information Systems
CHR: Kristal Harrington, Director Human Resources
CNO: Agnes A. Smith, R.N., Chief Nursing Officer
Web address: www.tcrh.org
Control: Other not–for–profit (including NFP Corporation) **Service:** General Medical and Surgical

Staffed Beds: 86

GLOUCESTER—Gloucester County

⊞ **RIVERSIDE WALTER REED HOSPITAL (490130)**, 7519 Hospital Drive, Zip 23061–4178, Mailing Address: P.O. Box 1130, Zip 23061–1130; tel. 804/693–8800 **A**1 2 9 10 **F**3 11 15 28 29 35 40 43 44 45 49 50 51 57 59 63 64 70 75 77 79 81 85 86 87 107 108 110 111 114 118 119 120 121 123 130 132 146 **P**6 **S** Riverside Health System, Newport News, VA
Primary Contact: Megan Kleckner, Vice President and Administrator
CHR: Kent Taylor, Director Human Resources
Web address: www.riversideonline.com
Control: Other not–for–profit (including NFP Corporation) **Service:** General Medical and Surgical

Staffed Beds: 31 Admissions: 2746 Census: 30 Outpatient Visits: 116051 Births: 0 Total Expense ($000): 54835 Payroll Expense ($000): 16923 Personnel: 297

GRUNDY—Buchanan County

⊞ **BUCHANAN GENERAL HOSPITAL (490127)**, 1535 Slate Creek Road, Zip 24614–6974; tel. 276/935–1000 **A**1 9 10 20 **F**3 15 18 29 34 35 40 41 45 57 59 62 64 68 70 81 82 85 87 93 107 108 110 115 119 130 132 135 146
Primary Contact: Robert D. Ruchti, Chief Executive Officer
CFO: Kim Boyd, Chief Financial Officer
CIO: Rita Ramey, Director Information Systems
CHR: Wanda Stiltner, Director Human Resources
CNO: Patty Dorton, Director of Nursing
Web address: www.bgh.org
Control: Other not–for–profit (including NFP Corporation) **Service:** General Medical and Surgical

Staffed Beds: 49 Admissions: 1307 Census: 14 Outpatient Visits: 41801 Births: 3 Total Expense ($000): 21118 Payroll Expense ($000): 8709 Personnel: 206

VA

Hospital, Medicare Provider Number, Address, Telephone, Approval, Facility, and Physician Codes, Health Care System

★ American Hospital Association (AHA) membership
□ The Joint Commission accreditation   ◇ DNV Healthcare Inc. accreditation
○ Healthcare Facilities Accreditation Program
△ Commission on Accreditation of Rehabilitation Facilities (CARF) accreditation

HAMPTON—Hampton City County

⊞ **HAMPTON VETERANS AFFAIRS MEDICAL CENTER**, 100 Emancipation Drive, Zip 23667–0001; tel. 757/722–9961, (Nonreporting) **A**1 3 5 **S** Department of Veterans Affairs, Washington, DC
Primary Contact: Michael H. Dunfee, Director
COO: Lorraine B. Price, Associate Director
CFO: Terry Grew, Chief Business Office
CMO: Val Gibberman, M.D., Acting Chief of Staff
CIO: Cary Parks, Chief Information Resource Management
Web address: www.hampton.va.gov/
Control: Veterans Affairs, Government, federal **Service:** General Medical and Surgical

Staffed Beds: 468

☐ **RIVERSIDE BEHAVIORAL HEALTH CENTER (494001)**, 2244 Executive Drive, Zip 23666–2430; tel. 757/827–1001, (Nonreporting) **A**1 5 9 10 **S** Riverside Health System, Newport News, VA
Primary Contact: Debra Campbell, R.N., Administrator
COO: Wade Broughman, Chief Operating Officer
CFO: W. William Austin, Jr., Senior Vice President Finance
CMO: Gary Starkey, M.D., Medical Director
CHR: Ashleigh Andrews, Director Human Resources
CNO: Terris Kennedy, Ph.D., Chief Nursing Officer
Web address: www.riversideonline.com
Control: Other not–for–profit (including NFP Corporation) **Service:** Psychiatric

Staffed Beds: 79

★ ◇ **SENTARA CAREPLEX HOSPITAL (490093)**, 3000 Coliseum Drive, Zip 23666–5963; tel. 757/736–1000 **A**2 3 5 9 10 21 **F**3 8 11 12 15 18 20 22 26 28 29 30 31 34 35 36 37 39 40 41 42 43 44 45 47 49 50 54 57 58 59 60 61 64 65 68 70 71 74 75 77 78 79 80 81 82 83 84 85 86 87 92 93 94 96 97 100 107 108 110 111 114 117 118 119 120 121 123 129 130 131 132 144 146 147 148 **S** Sentara Healthcare, Norfolk, VA
Primary Contact: Debra A. Flores, R.N., MS, President and Administrator
COO: Chet Hart, Vice President Operations
CFO: Cheryl Larner, Chief Financial Officer
CMO: Arthur Greene, M.D., Vice President Medical Affairs
CIO: Thomas Ewing, Director Information Technology
CHR: David Kidd, Manager Human Resources
Web address: www.sentara.com
Control: Other not–for–profit (including NFP Corporation) **Service:** General Medical and Surgical

Staffed Beds: 136 **Admissions:** 8873 **Census:** 124 **Outpatient Visits:** 434750 **Births:** 0 **Total Expense ($000):** 207908 **Payroll Expense ($000):** 79302 **Personnel:** 1212

⊞ **U. S. AIR FORCE HOSPITAL**, 77 Nealy Avenue, Zip 23665–2040; tel. 757/764–6969, (Nonreporting) **A**1 **S** Department of the Air Force, Washington, DC
Primary Contact: Colonel Wayne M. Pritt, Commander
COO: Colonel Michael Dietz, Administrator
CFO: Major Steven Dadd, Flight Commander Resource Management
CMO: Colonel Paul Gourley, M.D., Chief Hospital Services
CIO: Major Merlinda Vergonio, Chief Information Management and Technology
CHR: Major Steven Dadd, Flight Commander Resource Management
CNO: Colonel Marlene Kerchenski, Chief Nurse
Web address: www.jble.af.mil
Control: Air Force, Government, federal **Service:** General Medical and Surgical

Staffed Beds: 65

HARRISONBURG—Harrisonburg City County

⊞ ◇ **SENTARA RMH MEDICAL CENTER (490004)**, 2010 Health Campus Drive, Zip 22801–3293; tel. 540/689–1000 **A**1 2 5 9 10 19 20 21 **F**3 5 8 11 12 13 15 17 18 20 22 24 26 28 29 30 31 32 34 35 36 40 44 45 49 50 53 54 55 56 57 59 62 63 64 68 70 71 73 74 76 77 78 79 81 82 84 85 86 87 89 93 97 98 99 102 104 105 107 108 110 111 114 115 118 119 120 121 129 130 131 132 135 145 146 147 148 **P**6 8 **S** Sentara Healthcare, Norfolk, VA
Primary Contact: James D. Krauss, President
COO: Richard L. Haushalter, Senior Vice President Operations and Chief Operating Officer
CFO: J. Michael Burris, Chief Financial Officer
CMO: Dale Carroll, M.D., Senior Vice President Medical Affairs and Performance Improvement
CIO: Mike Rozmus, Director Information Systems
CHR: Mark Zimmerman, Regional Vice President Human Resources
CNO: Donna S. Hahn, DNP, RN, NEA–BC, R.N., Vice President Acute Care and Chief Nurse Executive
Web address: www.rmhonline.com
Control: Other not–for–profit (including NFP Corporation) **Service:** General Medical and Surgical

Staffed Beds: 244 **Admissions:** 12763 **Census:** 129 **Outpatient Visits:** 383385 **Births:** 1695 **Total Expense ($000):** 333811 **Payroll Expense ($000):** 139700 **Personnel:** 2278

HAYMARKET—Prince William County

NOVANT HEALTH HAYMARKET MEDICAL CENTER, 15225 Heathcote Boulevard, Zip 20155–4023, Mailing Address: 14535 John Marshall Highway, Gainesville, Zip 20155–4023; tel. 571/284–1000, (Nonreporting) **S** Novant Health, Winston Salem, NC
Primary Contact: Don Sedgley, President
CNO: Jason Jenkins, Senior Director of Nursing
Web address: www.novanthealth.org
Control: Other not–for–profit (including NFP Corporation) **Service:** General Medical and Surgical

Staffed Beds: 60

HOPEWELL—Hopewell City County

⊞ **JOHN RANDOLPH MEDICAL CENTER (490020)**, 411 West Randolph Road, Zip 23860–2938; tel. 804/541–1600 **A**1 2 9 10 **F**3 5 11 15 17 18 20 28 29 30 31 34 38 40 44 45 49 50 54 57 59 61 63 64 70 74 75 77 78 79 81 85 86 87 92 93 96 98 100 101 102 103 105 106 107 108 110 111 114 115 118 119 130 131 132 135 144 146 148 **S** HCA, Nashville, TN
Primary Contact: Suzanne B. Jackson, FACHE, Chief Executive Officer
CFO: Chigger Bynum, Chief Financial Officer
CHR: MaDena DuChemin, Assistant Administrator Human Resources
Web address: www.johnrandolphmed.com
Control: Corporation, Investor–owned, for–profit **Service:** General Medical and Surgical

Staffed Beds: 118 **Admissions:** 5094 **Census:** 71 **Outpatient Visits:** 68248 **Births:** 0 **Personnel:** 474

HOT SPRINGS—Bath County

⊞ **BATH COMMUNITY HOSPITAL (491300)**, 83 Park Drive, Zip 24445–2788, Mailing Address: P.O. Box Z., Zip 24445–0750; tel. 540/839–7000 **A**1 9 10 18 **F**3 7 15 28 30 35 40 45 49 50 53 57 59 64 75 77 81 92 93 102 107 111 119 127 129 130 133 135 143
Primary Contact: Jason Paret, Chief Executive Officer
COO: Mitzi Grey, Chief Operating Officer
CMO: James Redington, M.D., Chief of Staff
CIO: Tracy Bartley, Manager Information Technology
CHR: Patricia Foutz, Director Human Resources
CNO: Kyna Moore, R.N., Director of Nursing
Web address: www.bcchospital.org
Control: Other not–for–profit (including NFP Corporation) **Service:** General Medical and Surgical

Staffed Beds: 25 **Admissions:** 422 **Census:** 6 **Outpatient Visits:** 16468 **Births:** 1 **Total Expense ($000):** 15008 **Payroll Expense ($000):** 7016 **Personnel:** 134

KILMARNOCK—Lancaster County

⊞ **RAPPAHANNOCK GENERAL HOSPITAL (490123)**, 101 Harris Drive, Zip 22482–3880, Mailing Address: P.O. Box 1449, Zip 22482–1449; tel. 804/435–8000, (Nonreporting) **A**1 9 10 20
Primary Contact: James M. Holmes, Jr., President and Chief Executive Officer
Web address: www.rgh–hospital.com
Control: Other not–for–profit (including NFP Corporation) **Service:** General Medical and Surgical

Staffed Beds: 76

LEBANON—Russell County

☐ **RUSSELL COUNTY MEDICAL CENTER (490002)**, 58 Carroll Street, Zip 24266, Mailing Address: P.O. Box 3600, Zip 24266–0200; tel. 276/883–8000 **A**1 9 10 **F**3 11 15 29 30 34 35 40 44 45 50 56 57 59 62 63 64 68 70 75 81 85 87 93 98 107 108 110 111 114 118 119 127 129 130 133 146 147 148 **P**6 8 **S** Mountain States Health Alliance, Johnson City, TN
Primary Contact: Stephen K. Givens, Assistant Vice President and Administrator
CFO: John Jeter, Chief Financial Officer
CMO: Samuel Hughes Melton, M.D., Vice President Chief Medical Officer, Virginia Operations Medical Staff Services
CHR: Beth Hill, Director Human Resources
CNO: Melanie Paige Horton, Chief Nursing Officer
Web address: www.msha.com/rcmc
Control: Other not–for–profit (including NFP Corporation) **Service:** General Medical and Surgical

Staffed Beds: 78 **Admissions:** 2456 **Census:** 29 **Outpatient Visits:** 30789 **Births:** 0 **Total Expense ($000):** 24060 **Payroll Expense ($000):** 9662 **Personnel:** 167

Many Facility Codes have changed. Please refer to the AHA Guide Code Chart. © 2014 AHA Guide

VA

LEESBURG—Loudoun County

☒ **INOVA LOUDOUN HOSPITAL (490043)**, 44045 Riverside Parkway, Zip 20176–5101, Mailing Address: P.O. Box 6000, Zip 20177–0600; tel. 703/858–6000, (Total facility includes 100 beds in nursing home–type unit) **A**1 2 5 9 10 **F**3 5 11 13 14 15 18 20 22 26 28 29 30 31 34 35 37 38 39 40 41 42 44 45 48 49 50 54 55 57 59 60 61 63 64 65 66 67 68 69 70 71 72 74 75 76 77 78 79 80 81 82 84 85 86 87 89 91 92 93 96 98 100 101 102 103 104 105 107 108 110 111 114 115 118 119 120 121 123 126 128 130 131 132 135 145 146 147 148 **P**6 **S** Inova Health System, Falls Church, VA
Primary Contact: Patrick Walters, Chief Executive Officer
CFO: William Bane, Chief Financial Officer
CMO: Christopher Chiantella, M.D., Chief Medical Officer
CHR: Sarah Pavik, Director Human Resources and Guest Services
CNO: Elizabeth Dugan, Ph.D., Chief Nursing Officer
Web address: www.inova.org
Control: Other not–for–profit (including NFP Corporation) **Service:** General Medical and Surgical

Staffed Beds: 286 **Admissions:** 12435 **Census:** 214 **Outpatient Visits:** 148661 **Births:** 2628 **Total Expense ($000):** 229044 **Payroll Expense ($000):** 81884 **Personnel:** 1350

LEXINGTON—Lexington City County

☒ **CARILION STONEWALL JACKSON HOSPITAL (491304)**, 1 Health Circle, Zip 24450–2492; tel. 540/458–3300 **A**1 9 10 18 **F**3 8 11 15 18 28 29 34 35 40 42 45 50 53 56 57 59 65 70 75 77 79 81 85 87 93 107 108 110 111 115 119 129 130 132 133 135 146 148 **S** Carilion Clinic, Roanoke, VA
Primary Contact: Charles E. Carr, Vice President, Regional Hospital
CMO: Lyle McClung, M.D., Chief of Staff
Web address: www.carilionclinic.org/Carilion/csjh
Control: Other not–for–profit (including NFP Corporation) **Service:** General Medical and Surgical

Staffed Beds: 14 **Admissions:** 1250 **Census:** 13 **Outpatient Visits:** 30126 **Births:** 0 **Total Expense ($000):** 27960 **Payroll Expense ($000):** 10124 **Personnel:** 185

LOW MOOR—Alleghany County

☒ **LEWISGALE HOSPITAL ALLEGHANY (490126)**, One ARH Lane, Zip 24457, Mailing Address: P.O. Box 7, Zip 24457–0007; tel. 540/862–6011, (Nonreporting) **A**1 9 10 20 **S** HCA, Nashville, TN
Primary Contact: Charlotte C. Tyson, Chief Executive Officer
CMO: Michele Ballou, M.D., Chief Medical Staff
CIO: Jeffrey Steelman, Director Information Systems
CHR: Bernard M. Campbell, Administrator Human Resources
CNO: Robin Broughman, R.N., Chief Nursing Officer
Web address: www.alleghanyregional.com
Control: Corporation, Investor–owned, for–profit **Service:** General Medical and Surgical

Staffed Beds: 146

LURAY—Page County

☒ **PAGE MEMORIAL HOSPITAL (491307)**, 200 Memorial Drive, Zip 22835–1005; tel. 540/743–4561 **A**1 9 10 18 **F**3 7 8 11 15 28 29 30 34 35 40 53 56 57 59 60 64 66 68 74 75 77 79 81 85 90 93 107 108 110 111 114 119 127 128 129 130 133 135 143 146 **P**2 **S** Valley Health System, Winchester, VA
Primary Contact: N. Travis Clark, President
CFO: Phillip Graybeal, Chief Financial Officer
Web address: www.valleyhealthlink.com/page
Control: Other not–for–profit (including NFP Corporation) **Service:** General Medical and Surgical

Staffed Beds: 25 **Admissions:** 675 **Census:** 10 **Outpatient Visits:** 103479 **Births:** 0 **Total Expense ($000):** 23625 **Payroll Expense ($000):** 11480 **Personnel:** 180

LYNCHBURG—Lynchburg City County

CENTER FOR RESTORATIVE CARE AND REHABILITATION (492010), 3300 Rivermont Avenue, Zip 24503–2030; tel. 434/200–1799 **A**10 **F**1 3 29 31 82 85 130 132 148
Primary Contact: Kay Bowling, Chief Executive Officer
Control: Other not–for–profit (including NFP Corporation) **Service:** Long–Term Acute Care hospital

Staffed Beds: 36 **Admissions:** 326 **Census:** 25 **Births:** 0

CENTRA HEALTH See Centra Lynchburg General Hospital

CENTRA LYNCHBURG GENERAL HOSPITAL (490021)

☐ **CENTRA LYNCHBURG GENERAL HOSPITAL (490021)**, 1920 Atherholt Road, Zip 24501–1104; tel. 434/200–4700, (Includes CENTRA VIRGINIA BAPTIST HOSPITAL, 3300 Rivermont Avenue, Zip 24503–2053; tel. 434/200–4000; LYNCHBURG GENERAL HOSPITAL, 1901 Tate Springs Road, Zip 24501–1167; tel. 434/200–3000), (Total facility includes 433 beds in nursing home–type unit) **A**1 2 3 5 6 9 10 20 **F**1 2 3 5 7 10 11 13 15 17 18 19 20 22 24 26 28 29 30 31 32 34 35 37 38 40 43 44 45 46 47 48 49 50 53 54 55 56 57 59 60 61 62 63 64 67 68 70 71 72 73 74 75 76 77 78 79 80 81 82 84 85 86 87 89 90 93 94 98 99 100 102 103 104 105 106 107 108 109 110 111 114 115 117 118 119 120 121 123 124 125 126 127 128 129 130 131 132 133 135 143 144 146 147 148 **P**7 **S** Centra Health, Inc., Lynchburg, VA
Primary Contact: E. W. Tibbs, President and Chief Executive Officer
CFO: Lewis C. Addison, Senior Vice President and Chief Financial Officer
CMO: Chalmers Nunn, M.D., Chief Medical Officer and Senior Vice President
CIO: Ben Clark, Vice President and Chief Information Officer
CHR: Jan Walker, Director Human Resources
Web address: www.centrahealth.com
Control: Other not–for–profit (including NFP Corporation) **Service:** General Medical and Surgical

Staffed Beds: 1061 **Admissions:** 29509 **Census:** 759 **Outpatient Visits:** 486782 **Births:** 2559 **Total Expense ($000):** 599381 **Payroll Expense ($000):** 270085 **Personnel:** 4276

MADISON HEIGHTS—Amherst County

CENTRAL VIRGINIA TRAINING CENTER (490108), 210 East Colony Road, Zip 24572–2005, Mailing Address: P.O. Box 1098, Lynchburg, Zip 24505–1098; tel. 434/947–6326, (Nonreporting) **A**10 **S** Virginia Department of Mental Health, Richmond, VA
Primary Contact: Denise D. Micheletti, R.N., Director
COO: Denise D. Micheletti, R.N., Director
CFO: Charles Felmlee, Assistant Director Fiscal Services
CMO: Balraj Bawa, M.D., Assistant Director Medical Services
CHR: Burchkhard Blob, Manager Human Resources
Web address: www.cvtc.dmhmrsas.virginia.gov/
Control: State–Government, nonfederal **Service:** Institution for mental retardation

Staffed Beds: 1112

MANASSAS—Manassas City County

☒ **NOVANT HEALTH PRINCE WILLIAM MEDICAL CENTER (490045)**, 8700 Sudley Road, Zip 20110–4418, Mailing Address: P.O. Box 2610, Zip 20108–0867; tel. 703/369–8000 **A**1 2 9 10 **F**3 5 8 10 11 13 15 18 19 20 22 26 28 29 30 31 32 34 35 36 37 38 39 40 44 45 46 47 48 49 50 51 53 54 57 59 64 65 68 70 72 74 75 76 77 78 79 81 82 84 85 86 87 89 93 97 98 99 100 102 103 104 107 110 111 114 115 118 119 126 129 130 132 134 135 146 147 148 **P**6 **S** Novant Health, Winston Salem, NC
Primary Contact: Melissa Robson, President
COO: Bebe Holt, Vice President Chief Operating Officer
CMO: Doug Wall, M.D., Vice President Medical Affairs
CHR: Tracy Bowers, Director Human Resources
CNO: Bebe Holt, Vice President and Chief Nursing Officer
Web address: www.pwhs.org
Control: Other not–for–profit (including NFP Corporation) **Service:** General Medical and Surgical

Staffed Beds: 168 **Admissions:** 9900 **Census:** 99 **Outpatient Visits:** 202197 **Births:** 2015 **Total Expense ($000):** 150439 **Payroll Expense ($000):** 71717 **Personnel:** 924

MARION—Smyth County

☐ **SMYTH COUNTY COMMUNITY HOSPITAL (490038)**, 245 Medical Park Drive, Zip 24354, Mailing Address: P.O. Box 880, Zip 24354–0880; tel. 276/378–1000, (Total facility includes 109 beds in nursing home–type unit) **A**1 9 10 **F**2 3 8 11 15 18 28 29 30 31 34 35 40 45 50 51 54 57 59 62 64 67 68 70 75 77 78 79 81 84 85 87 90 91 93 97 107 110 111 115 118 119 128 129 130 131 132 133 135 146 147 148 **P**6 8 **S** Mountain States Health Alliance, Johnson City, TN
Primary Contact: Cathy Loving Maine, MSN, RN–B, Interim Chief Executive Officer
Web address: www.msha.com/scch
Control: Other not–for–profit (including NFP Corporation) **Service:** General Medical and Surgical

Staffed Beds: 153 **Admissions:** 2002 **Census:** 119 **Outpatient Visits:** 58970 **Births:** 0 **Total Expense ($000):** 45251 **Payroll Expense ($000):** 17651 **Personnel:** 230

VA

Hospital, Medicare Provider Number, Address, Telephone, Approval, Facility, and Physician Codes, Health Care System

★ American Hospital Association (AHA) membership
☐ The Joint Commission accreditation   ◇ DNV Healthcare Inc. accreditation
○ Healthcare Facilities Accreditation Program
△ Commission on Accreditation of Rehabilitation Facilities (CARF) accreditation

☐ **SOUTHWESTERN VIRGINIA MENTAL HEALTH INSTITUTE (490105)**, 340 Bagley Circle, Zip 24354–3390; tel. 276/783–1200, (Nonreporting) **A**1 9 10 **S** Virginia Department of Mental Health, Richmond, VA
Primary Contact: Cynthia McClaskey, Ph.D., Director
CIO: Kim Ratliff, Director Health Information Management
Web address: www.swvmhi.dmhmrsas.virginia.gov/
Control: State–Government, nonfederal **Service:** Psychiatric

Staffed Beds: 266

MARTINSVILLE—Martinsville City County

✠ **MEMORIAL HOSPITAL (490079)**, 320 Hospital Drive, Zip 24112–1981, Mailing Address: P.O. Box 4788, Zip 24115–4788; tel. 276/666–7200 **A**1 2 9 10 19 **F**3 8 11 13 14 15 18 20 22 24 26 28 29 30 31 34 38 40 41 45 46 50 51 56 57 59 60 62 63 70 74 76 77 78 79 81 82 85 86 87 93 97 98 103 107 111 116 118 119 129 130 133 145 146 147 148 **S** LifePoint Hospitals, Inc., Brentwood, TN
Primary Contact: Eric Deaton, Interim Chief Executive Officer
COO: John Maxwell, Chief Operating Officer
CFO: Brandy Hanners, Chief Financial Officer
CIO: Jeff Butker, Chief Information Officer
CHR: Sherry Schofield, Director Human Resources
CNO: Michael Pittman, Chief Nursing Officer
Web address: www.martinsvillehospital.com
Control: Corporation, Investor–owned, for–profit **Service:** General Medical and Surgical

Staffed Beds: 220 **Admissions:** 5948 **Census:** 64 **Outpatient Visits:** 52003 **Births:** 422 **Total Expense ($000):** 124237 **Payroll Expense ($000):** 48454 **Personnel:** 951

MECHANICSVILLE—Hanover County

✠ **BON SECOURS MEMORIAL REGIONAL MEDICAL CENTER (490069)**, 8260 Atlee Road, Zip 23116–1844; tel. 804/764–6000 **A**1 2 5 9 10 **F**3 7 8 11 13 15 17 18 20 22 24 26 28 29 30 31 33 34 35 38 40 46 48 49 50 54 57 58 59 60 63 64 65 66 68 70 72 74 75 76 77 78 79 81 84 86 87 100 104 107 108 109 110 111 114 115 119 126 129 130 131 132 133 144 146 147 148 **P**6 **S** Bon Secours Health System, Inc., Marriottsville, MD
Primary Contact: Michael Robinson, Chief Executive Officer
COO: Gary A. Welch, Assistant to the Chief Executive Officer and Administrative Director Support Systems
CFO: Stephan F. Quiriconi, Vice President Finance
CMO: Sunil K. Sinha, M.D., Chief Medical Officer
CIO: Gwen Harding, Site Manager Information Systems
CHR: Rebecca Kamguia, Administrative Director Human Resources
CNO: Jill M. Kennedy, R.N., Vice President Patient Care Services and Chief Nursing Officer
Web address: www.bonsecours.com
Control: Other not–for–profit (including NFP Corporation) **Service:** General Medical and Surgical

Staffed Beds: 225 **Admissions:** 10136 **Census:** 177 **Outpatient Visits:** 139256 **Births:** 1582 **Total Expense ($000):** 269917 **Payroll Expense ($000):** 74283 **Personnel:** 1361

✠ **SHELTERING ARMS REHABILITATION HOSPITAL (493025)**, 8254 Atlee Road, Zip 23116–1844; tel. 804/764–1000 **A**1 10 **F**29 30 34 53 54 57 59 64 68 75 77 79 82 86 87 90 91 92 93 95 96 130 131 132 143 146 148 **P**6
Primary Contact: James E. Sok, FACHE, President and Chief Executive Officer
COO: Mary A. Zweifel, Chief Operating Officer
CFO: Michael E. Dacus, Vice President and Chief Financial Officer
CMO: Hillary Hawkins, M.D., Medical Director
CIO: Chris Sorenson, Chief Information Officer
CHR: Ellen B. Vance, Chief Human Resource Officer
CNO: Sandra Eyler, MS, Chief Nursing Officer
Web address: www.shelteringarms.com
Control: Other not–for–profit (including NFP Corporation) **Service:** Rehabilitation

Staffed Beds: 68 **Admissions:** 1686 **Census:** 59 **Outpatient Visits:** 78148 **Births:** 0 **Total Expense ($000):** 52920 **Payroll Expense ($000):** 30358 **Personnel:** 545

MIDLOTHIAN—Chesterfield County

✠ **BON SECOURS ST. FRANCIS MEDICAL CENTER (490136)**, 13710 St. Francis Boulevard, Zip 23114–3267; tel. 804/594–7300, (Nonreporting) **A**1 2 9 10 **S** Bon Secours Health System, Inc., Marriottsville, MD
Primary Contact: Mark M. Gordon, Chief Executive Officer
COO: Peter J. Bernard, Chief Executive Officer
CIO: Mike Lokie, Project Director
CHR: Paul Catucci, Administrative Director Human Resources
Web address: www.bonsecours.com/sfmc/default.asp
Control: Other not–for–profit (including NFP Corporation) **Service:** General Medical and Surgical

Staffed Beds: 130

☐ **SHELTERING ARMS HOSPITAL SOUTH (493030)**, 13700 St. Francis Boulevard, Suite 400, Zip 23114–3222; tel. 804/764–1000 **A**1 10 **F**29 30 34 57 59 64 75 77 79 82 86 87 90 91 92 93 95 96 130 132 143 146 148
Primary Contact: James E. Sok, FACHE, President and Chief Executive Officer
COO: Mary A. Zweifel, Chief Operating Officer
CFO: Michael E. Dacus, Vice President and Chief Financial Officer
CMO: Timothy Silver, M.D., Medical Director
CIO: Chris Sorenson, Chief Information Officer
CHR: Ellen B. Vance, Chief Human Resources Officer
CNO: Sandra Eyler, MS, Chief Nursing Officer
Web address: www.shelteringarms.com
Control: Other not–for–profit (including NFP Corporation) **Service:** Rehabilitation

Staffed Beds: 28 **Admissions:** 714 **Census:** 22 **Outpatient Visits:** 5599 **Births:** 0 **Total Expense ($000):** 10984 **Payroll Expense ($000):** 5530 **Personnel:** 78

NASSAWADOX—Northampton County

☐ **RIVERSIDE SHORE MEMORIAL HOSPITAL (490037)**, 9507 Hospital Avenue, Zip 23413–1821, Mailing Address: P.O. Box 17, Zip 23413–0017; tel. 757/414–8000 **A**1 2 9 10 20 **F**2 3 11 15 28 29 30 31 34 40 45 50 59 62 70 75 76 77 78 79 81 82 85 93 102 103 105 107 110 111 118 119 128 129 130 132 133 135 146 148 **P**1 6 **S** Riverside Health System, Newport News, VA
Primary Contact: Susan McAndrews, Vice President and Administrator
CFO: W. William Austin, Jr., Senior Vice President Finance
CMO: Charles Goldstein, M.D., President Medical Staff
CIO: Andrew Woughter, Information Systems
CHR: Nicole Miller, Director Human Resources
Web address: www.riversideonline.com
Control: Other not–for–profit (including NFP Corporation) **Service:** General Medical and Surgical

Staffed Beds: 31 **Admissions:** 3011 **Census:** 30 **Outpatient Visits:** 82999 **Births:** 317 **Total Expense ($000):** 58995 **Payroll Expense ($000):** 17624 **Personnel:** 282

SHORE MEMORIAL HOSPITAL See Riverside Shore Memorial Hospital

NEW KENT—New Kent County

☐ **CUMBERLAND HOSPITAL (493300)**, 9407 Cumberland Road, Zip 23124–2029; tel. 804/966–2242, (Nonreporting) **A**1 10 **S** Universal Health Services, Inc., King of Prussia, PA
Primary Contact: Patrice Gay Brooks, Chief Executive Officer
CFO: Joanne Rial, Chief Financial Officer
CMO: Daniel N. Davidow, M.D., Medical Director
CIO: Towanda Brown, Director Standards and Regulatory Compliance
CHR: Lauren Bonner, Director Human Resources
Web address: www.cumberlandhospital.com
Control: Corporation, Investor–owned, for–profit **Service:** Children's rehabilitation

Staffed Beds: 132

NEWPORT NEWS—Newport News City County

☐ **HAMPTON ROADS SPECIALTY HOSPITAL (492008)**, 245 Chesapeake Avenue, Zip 23607–6038; tel. 757/534–5000, (Nonreporting) **A**1 10 **S** Riverside Health System, Newport News, VA
Primary Contact: Courtney Detwiler, R.N., Administrator
Web address: www.hamptonroadsspecialtyhospital.com
Control: Other not–for–profit (including NFP Corporation) **Service:** Long–Term Acute Care hospital

Staffed Beds: 25

KEYSTONE NEWPORT NEWS, 17579 Warwick Boulevard, Zip 23603–1343; tel. 757/888–0400 **F**29 30 32 50 75 99 101 106 132 143
Primary Contact: Paul Kirkham, Chief Executive Officer
COO: Paul Kirkham, Chief Executive Officer
CFO: Joe Brooks, Chief Financial Officer
CMO: Avtar Dhillon, M.D., Medical Director
CIO: Gene Yelton, Director Support Services
CHR: Shawn Marston, Director Human Resources
CNO: Karen Bruce, Director of Nursing
Web address: www.newportnewsbhc.com/
Control: Corporation, Investor–owned, for–profit **Service:** Psychiatric

Staffed Beds: 108 **Admissions:** 197 **Census:** 93 **Outpatient Visits:** 0 **Births:** 0 **Total Expense ($000):** 15257 **Payroll Expense ($000):** 7402 **Personnel:** 176

✠ **MARY IMMACULATE HOSPITAL (490041)**, 2 Bernardine Drive, Zip 23602–4499; tel. 757/886–6000, (Includes ST. FRANCIS NURSING CENTER), (Total facility includes 115 beds in nursing home–type unit) **A**1 9 10 **F**3 5 11 12 13 15 18 20 22 24 26 28 29 30 31 32 34 35 36 38 40 44 45 46 50 51 57 59 61 63 64 67 68 70 71 73 74 75 76 77 78 79 81 82 84 85 86 87 91 93 102 107 108 111 114 118 119 130 131 132 143 145 146 147 148 **P**6 **S** Bon Secours Health System, Inc., Marriottsville, MD
Primary Contact: Patricia L. Robertson, Executive Vice President
COO: Darlene Stephenson, Vice President Operations
CIO: Terri Spence, Vice President Information Services
CHR: Vickie Witcher Humphries, Vice President Human Resources
CNO: Jeffrey N. Doucette, MS, Chief Nursing Officer
Web address: www.bonsecourshamptonroads.com
Control: Other not–for–profit (including NFP Corporation) **Service:** General Medical and Surgical

Staffed Beds: 232 Admissions: 8834 Census: 180 Outpatient Visits: 68434 Births: 1527 Total Expense ($000): 163691 Payroll Expense ($000): 44987 Personnel: 794

☐ **RIVERSIDE REGIONAL MEDICAL CENTER (490052)**, 500 J. Clyde Morris Boulevard, Zip 23601–1929; tel. 757/594–2000, (Includes RIVERSIDE PSYCHIATRIC INSTITUTE) **A**1 2 3 5 6 9 10 13 **F**3 11 12 13 15 17 18 20 22 24 26 28 29 30 31 32 35 38 39 40 43 44 45 49 50 51 54 55 56 57 58 59 60 61 62 63 64 70 72 74 75 76 77 78 79 81 82 85 86 87 89 92 93 97 107 108 110 111 114 115 116 117 118 119 120 121 123 124 126 129 130 132 141 142 144 146 147 148 **P**6 **S** Riverside Health System, Newport News, VA
Primary Contact: Michael J. Doucette, Senior Vice President and Administrator
COO: William B. Downey, Chief Operating Officer
CFO: Wade Broughman, Executive Vice President and Chief Financial Officer
CMO: Barry L. Gross, M.D., Executive Vice President and Chief Medical Officer
CIO: John T. Stanley, Vice President Planning and Information Systems
CHR: Larry Boyles, Senior Vice President
Web address: www.riverside–online.com
Control: Other not–for–profit (including NFP Corporation) **Service:** General Medical and Surgical

Staffed Beds: 192 Admissions: 17108 Census: 203 Outpatient Visits: 497232 Births: 2657 Total Expense ($000): 523878 Payroll Expense ($000): 159137 Personnel: 1296

✠ **RIVERSIDE REHABILITATION INSTITUTE (493027)**, 245 Chesapeake Avenue, Zip 23607–6038; tel. 757/928–8000, (Nonreporting) **A**1 10 **S** Riverside Health System, Newport News, VA
Primary Contact: Edward Heckler, Administrator
COO: William B. Downey, President and Chief Executive Officer
CFO: Wade Broughman, Executive Vice President and Chief Financial Officer
CMO: C. Renee Moss, M.D., Chief Medical Officer
CIO: John T. Stanley, Vice President Planning and Information Systems
CHR: Ashleigh Andrews, Manager Human Resources
CNO: Debbie Outlaw, R.N., Director Patient Care Services
Web address: www.riverside–online.com
Control: Other not–for–profit (including NFP Corporation) **Service:** Rehabilitation

Staffed Beds: 25

NORFOLK—Norfolk City County

✠ **BON SECOURS–DEPAUL MEDICAL CENTER (490011)**, 150 Kingsley Lane, Zip 23505–4650; tel. 757/889–5000, (Total facility includes 24 beds in nursing home–type unit) **A**1 2 3 5 9 10 **F**3 11 13 15 18 20 22 29 30 31 34 40 43 45 46 50 51 54 57 59 61 64 68 70 71 74 75 76 78 79 81 82 84 85 86 87 93 97 102 107 108 110 111 114 115 118 119 120 121 128 129 130 131 132 143 145 146 147 148 **P**6 **S** Bon Secours Health System, Inc., Marriottsville, MD
Primary Contact: John E. Barrett, III, Chief Executive Officer
CFO: Charmaine Rochester, Vice President Finance
CMO: Raymond McCue, M.D., Chief Medical Officer
CIO: Lynne Zultanky, Director Corporate Communications and Media Relations
CHR: Vickie Witcher Humphries, Vice President Human Resources
CNO: Michael J. Bratton, R.N., Chief Nurse Executive and Vice President Patient Care Services
Web address: www.bonsecourshamptonroads.com
Control: Other not–for–profit (including NFP Corporation) **Service:** General Medical and Surgical

Staffed Beds: 204 Admissions: 7266 Census: 98 Outpatient Visits: 160304 Births: 1162 Total Expense ($000): 174357 Payroll Expense ($000): 55860 Personnel: 866

☐ **CHILDREN'S HOSPITAL OF THE KING'S DAUGHTERS (493301)**, 601 Children's Lane, Zip 23507–1910; tel. 757/668–7000 **A**1 3 5 9 10 **F**3 7 8 9 12 16 17 19 21 23 25 27 29 30 31 32 34 35 39 40 41 44 45 48 49 50 54 55 57 58 59 60 64 65 66 68 72 73 74 75 77 78 79 80 81 82 84 85 86 87 88 89 90 91 92 93 94 97 99 100 102 107 111 115 118 119 129 130 131 132 134 138 145 146 148 **P**8
Primary Contact: James D. Dahling, President and Chief Executive Officer
CFO: Dennis Ryan, Senior Vice President and Chief Financial Officer
CMO: Arno Zaritsky, M.D., Senior Vice President Clinical Services
CIO: Deborah Barnes, Vice President and Chief Information Officer
CHR: David Bowers, Vice President Human Resources and Support Services
CNO: Jo–Ann Burke, R.N., Vice President Patient Care Services
Web address: www.chkd.org
Control: Other not–for–profit (including NFP Corporation) **Service:** Children's general

Staffed Beds: 206 Admissions: 5177 Census: 135 Outpatient Visits: 210799 Births: 1 Total Expense ($000): 282473 Payroll Expense ($000): 122001 Personnel: 2292

HOSPITAL FOR EXTENDED RECOVERY (492007), 600 Gresham Drive, Suite 700, Zip 23507–1904; tel. 757/388–1700, (Nonreporting) **A**9 10
Primary Contact: Linda B. O'Neil, R.N., Chief Executive Officer
Control: Other not–for–profit (including NFP Corporation) **Service:** Long–Term Acute Care hospital

Staffed Beds: 35

☐ **KEMPSVILLE CENTER FOR BEHAVIORAL HEALTH**, 860 Kempsville Road, Zip 23502–3980; tel. 757/461–4565, (Nonreporting) **A**1
Primary Contact: Matt Ours, Chief Executive Officer
Control: Corporation, Investor–owned, for–profit **Service:** Psychiatric

Staffed Beds: 77

LAKE TAYLOR TRANSITIONAL CARE HOSPITAL (492001), 1309 Kempsville Road, Zip 23502–2286; tel. 757/461–5001, (Nonreporting) **A**3 5 10
Primary Contact: Thomas J. Orsini, President and Chief Executive Officer
CFO: Robert W. Fogg, Director Finance
CMO: Kevin Murray, M.D., Director Medical Services
CIO: Mark Davis, Director Information Systems
CHR: LeeAnn Lowman, Director Human Resources
Web address: www.laketaylor.org
Control: Hospital district or authority, Government, nonfederal **Service:** Long–Term Acute Care hospital

Staffed Beds: 293

★ ◇ **SENTARA LEIGH HOSPITAL (490046)**, 830 Kempsville Road, Zip 23502–3920; tel. 757/261–6000 **A**2 3 5 9 10 21 **F**3 8 9 13 15 18 20 22 26 28 29 30 31 34 35 36 37 38 39 40 43 44 45 46 47 48 49 50 51 54 57 58 59 60 61 63 64 68 70 71 74 75 76 77 78 79 81 82 84 85 86 87 92 93 94 96 97 100 102 107 108 110 111 114 119 126 130 131 132 141 144 146 147 148 **P**6 **S** Sentara Healthcare, Norfolk, VA
Primary Contact: Teresa L. Edwards, President and Administrator
COO: Howard P. Kern, President and Chief Operating Officer
CFO: Robert Broermann, Senior Vice President and Chief Financial Officer
CMO: Terry Gilliland, M.D., Chief Medical Officer
CIO: Bert Reese, Chief Information Officer
CHR: Michael V. Taylor, Senior Vice President Human Resources
CNO: Genemarie McGee, R.N., Chief Nursing Officer
Web address: www.sentara.com
Control: Other not–for–profit (including NFP Corporation) **Service:** General Medical and Surgical

Staffed Beds: 238 Admissions: 13830 Census: 167 Outpatient Visits: 460103 Births: 1813 Total Expense ($000): 231340 Payroll Expense ($000): 89161 Personnel: 1335

★ ◇ **SENTARA NORFOLK GENERAL HOSPITAL (490007)**, 600 Gresham Drive, Zip 23507–1904; tel. 757/388–3000 **A**2 3 5 6 9 10 21 **F**3 7 11 12 13 15 16 17 18 20 22 24 26 28 29 30 31 34 35 36 38 39 40 41 43 44 45 46 47 48 49 50 51 54 56 57 58 59 60 61 63 64 65 66 68 70 71 72 74 75 76 77 78 79 81 82 84 85 86 87 90 91 93 94 97 98 100 101 102 103 105 107 108 110 111 114 115 116 117 118 119 120 121 123 124 126 129 130 131 132 135 136 137 138 141 142 144 146 147 148 **P**6 **S** Sentara Healthcare, Norfolk, VA
Primary Contact: Kurt T. Hofelich, President
CFO: Robert Broermann, Senior Vice President and Chief Financial Officer
CIO: Bert Reese, Chief Information Officer
Web address: www.sentara.com
Control: Other not–for–profit (including NFP Corporation) **Service:** General Medical and Surgical

Staffed Beds: 495 Admissions: 25723 Census: 409 Outpatient Visits: 860393 Births: 2670 Total Expense ($000): 650824 Payroll Expense ($000): 220731 Personnel: 3430

VA

Hospital, Medicare Provider Number, Address, Telephone, Approval, Facility, and Physician Codes, Health Care System	
★ American Hospital Association (AHA) membership	○ Healthcare Facilities Accreditation Program
☐ The Joint Commission accreditation ◇ DNV Healthcare Inc. accreditation	△ Commission on Accreditation of Rehabilitation Facilities (CARF) accreditation

NORTON—Norton City County

★ **MOUNTAIN VIEW REGIONAL MEDICAL CENTER (490027)**, 310 Third Street N.E., Zip 24273–1137; tel. 276/679–9100, (Total facility includes 44 beds in nursing home–type unit) **A**9 **F**3 11 15 29 30 34 35 40 48 49 50 57 59 63 68 70 77 79 81 85 87 92 93 97 107 108 115 117 118 119 130 131 146 **S** Wellmont Health System, Kingsport, TN
Primary Contact: Fred L. Pelle, FACHE, President
CFO: Regina Day, Executive Director Finance
CMO: Souhail Shamiyeh, M.D., Chief of Staff
CHR: Bobby Collins, Director Human Resources
CNO: Sheri Ives, R.N., Vice President Patient Care Services
Web address: www.wellmont.org
Control: Other not–for–profit (including NFP Corporation) **Service:** General Medical and Surgical

| Staffed Beds: 72 | Admissions: 1809 | Census: 51 | Outpatient Visits: 38897 |
Births: 0 Total Expense ($000): 27920 Payroll Expense ($000): 7688
Personnel: 214

○ △ **NORTON COMMUNITY HOSPITAL (490001)**, 100 15th Street N.W., Zip 24273–1616; tel. 276/679–9600 **A**7 9 10 11 13 **F**3 8 11 13 15 18 28 29 30 34 35 40 44 45 46 51 53 57 62 63 64 68 70 75 76 77 79 81 84 87 90 91 93 107 108 110 111 112 115 116 118 119 122 123 124 129 130 131 133 135 146 147 148 **P**6 8 **S** Mountain States Health Alliance, Johnson City, TN
Primary Contact: Mark T. Leonard, Chief Executive Officer
CFO: Stephen Sawyer, Chief Financial Officer
CMO: Allen Mullens, M.D., Chief Medical Staff
CIO: Judy Lawson, Director Information Services
CHR: Valeri J. Colyer, Director Human Resources
Web address: www.msha.com/nch
Control: Other not–for–profit (including NFP Corporation) **Service:** General Medical and Surgical

Staffed Beds: 50 Admissions: 3695 Census: 35 Outpatient Visits: 75919
Births: 273 Total Expense ($000): 47699 Payroll Expense ($000): 20093
Personnel: 335

PEARISBURG—Giles County

✠ **CARILION GILES COMMUNITY HOSPITAL (491302)**, 159 Hartley Way, Zip 24134–2471; tel. 540/921–6000 **A**1 9 10 18 **F**3 11 15 28 29 34 35 36 40 45 50 57 59 64 65 68 70 75 77 79 81 82 85 86 87 93 96 107 108 110 111 115 119 130 133 135 146 147 148 **S** Carilion Clinic, Roanoke, VA
Primary Contact: Richard Mastalski, Senior Director Operations
CMO: John Tamminen, M.D., President Medical Staff
CHR: Carrie Boggess, Human Resource Generalist
CNO: Veronica Stump, Chief Nursing Officer
Web address: www.carilionclinic.org/Carilion/cgch
Control: Other not–for–profit (including NFP Corporation) **Service:** General Medical and Surgical

Staffed Beds: 17 Admissions: 1132 Census: 14 Outpatient Visits: 24420
Births: 0 Total Expense ($000): 24675 Payroll Expense ($000): 8756
Personnel: 164

PETERSBURG—Petersburg City County

☐ **CENTRAL STATE HOSPITAL**, 26317 West Washington Street, Zip 23803–2727, Mailing Address: P.O. Box 4030, Zip 23803–0030; tel. 804/524–7000, (Nonreporting) **A**1 9 **S** Virginia Department of Mental Health, Richmond, VA
Primary Contact: Vicki Montgomery, Director and Chief Executive Officer
COO: Ann Bailey, Assistant Director Administration
CFO: Robert Kaufman, Director Financial Services
CMO: Ronald O. Forbes, M.D., Medical Director
CIO: Jonathan Baber, Director Information Technology
CHR: Tracy Salisbury, Regional Manager Human Resources
CNO: Eva Parham, R.N., Chief Nurse Executive
Web address: www.csh.dbhds.virginia.gov
Control: State–Government, nonfederal **Service:** Psychiatric

Staffed Beds: 277

✠ **HEALTHSOUTH REHABILITATION HOSPITAL OF PETERSBURG (493031)**, 95 Pinehill Boulevard, Zip 23805–9233; tel. 804/504–8100 **A**1 10 **F**28 29 34 35 44 50 56 59 60 61 65 68 74 75 77 82 86 90 91 93 94 96 130 132 135 148 **S** HEALTHSOUTH Corporation, Birmingham, AL
Primary Contact: Tracy Penn Turman, Chief Executive Officer
Web address: www.healthsouthpetersburg.com
Control: Corporation, Investor–owned, for–profit **Service:** Rehabilitation

Staffed Beds: 64 Admissions: 1302 Census: 48 Outpatient Visits: 2009
Births: 0

☐ **HIRAM W. DAVIS MEDICAL CENTER (490104)**, 26317 West Washington Street, Zip 23803–2727, Mailing Address: P.O. Box 4030, Zip 23803–0030; tel. 804/524–7344, (Nonreporting) **A**1 10 **S** Virginia Department of Mental Health, Richmond, VA
Primary Contact: Bill Hawkins, Director
COO: Brenda Buenvenida, Facility Administrator
CFO: Robert Kaufman, Fiscal Officer
CHR: Tracy Salisbury, Director Human Resources
Control: State–Government, nonfederal **Service:** Other specialty

Staffed Beds: 10

✠ **POPLAR SPRINGS HOSPITAL (494022)**, 350 Poplar Drive, Zip 23805–9367; tel. 804/733–6874 **A**1 9 10 **F**4 29 64 87 98 99 100 101 102 103 104 105 106 130 143 **P**5 6 **S** Universal Health Services, Inc., King of Prussia, PA
Primary Contact: Joseph Trapani, Chief Executive Officer
COO: Kate McBride, Chief Operating Officer
CFO: Bettie Hill, Chief Financial Officer
CMO: Thresa Simon, M.D., Medical Director
CHR: Morris Mitchell, Director Human Resources
Web address: www.poplarsprings.com
Control: Corporation, Investor–owned, for–profit **Service:** Psychiatric

Staffed Beds: 180 Admissions: 3051 Census: 139 Outpatient Visits: 913
Births: 0 Total Expense ($000): 37467 Payroll Expense ($000): 13386
Personnel: 288

✠ **SOUTHSIDE REGIONAL MEDICAL CENTER (490067)**, 200 Medical Park Boulevard, Zip 23805–9274; tel. 804/765–5000 **A**1 2 6 9 10 **F**3 12 13 15 18 20 22 26 28 29 30 31 34 35 40 43 45 46 47 48 49 50 54 56 57 59 60 64 70 72 74 75 76 77 78 79 81 82 85 86 87 89 93 96 97 98 101 102 105 107 108 110 111 114 115 118 119 121 124 130 131 132 135 146 147 148 **P**6 **S** Community Health Systems, Inc., Franklin, TN
Primary Contact: Douglas J. Moyer, Chief Executive Officer
COO: Jerad Hanlon, Chief Operating Officer
CFO: Charles Coder, Chief Financial Officer
CMO: Boyd Wickizer, Jr., M.D., Chief Medical Officer
CIO: Eric Synnestvedt, Director Information Technology
CHR: Irene Buskey, Director Human Resources
CNO: Beverly Bzdek Smith, Chief Nursing Officer
Web address: www.srmconline.com
Control: Corporation, Investor–owned, for–profit **Service:** General Medical and Surgical

Staffed Beds: 300 Admissions: 12676 Census: 169 Outpatient Visits: 186546 Births: 1355 Total Expense ($000): 153211 Payroll Expense ($000): 78216 Personnel: 1193

PORTSMOUTH—Portsmouth City County

✠ **BON SECOURS MARYVIEW MEDICAL CENTER (490017)**, 3636 High Street, Zip 23707–3270; tel. 757/398–2200, (Total facility includes 120 beds in nursing home–type unit) **A**1 2 3 5 9 10 **F**3 4 5 11 12 13 15 17 18 20 22 24 26 28 29 30 31 34 35 36 38 40 42 44 45 50 51 54 57 59 61 62 63 64 70 71 73 74 75 76 77 78 79 81 82 84 85 86 87 90 91 93 96 97 98 99 100 101 102 103 104 105 106 107 108 110 111 114 115 118 119 121 126 128 129 130 131 132 134 135 143 145 146 147 **P**6 **S** Bon Secours Health System, Inc., Marriottsville, MD
Primary Contact: Joseph M. Oddis, Chief Executive Officer
CFO: Ernest C. Padden, Chief Financial Officer
CMO: Warren Austin, M.D., Vice President Medical Affairs
CIO: Terri Spence, Chief Information Officer
CHR: Vickie Witcher Humphries, Director Human Resources
CNO: Leana Fox, MSN, Interim Chief Nurse Executive
Web address: www.bonsecourshamptonroads.com
Control: Other not–for–profit (including NFP Corporation) **Service:** General Medical and Surgical

Staffed Beds: 473 Admissions: 12755 Census: 273 Outpatient Visits: 399222 Births: 986 Total Expense ($000): 314104 Payroll Expense ($000): 110392 Personnel: 2159

✠ **NAVAL MEDICAL CENTER**, 620 John Paul Jones Circle, Zip 23708–2197; tel. 757/953–0700, (Nonreporting) **A**1 2 3 5 **S** Bureau of Medicine and Surgery, Department of the Navy, Washington, DC
Primary Contact: Captain David Collins, Director Administration
COO: Captain David Collins, Director Administration
CFO: Commander Carlos J. Martinez, Director Resource Management
CMO: Commander Thomas Mooney, M.D., President Executive Committee Medical Staff
CIO: Lieutenant Colonel Karen Albany, Chief Information Officer
CHR: Jane Ackiss, Site Manager Human Resources
Web address: www.nmcphc.med.navy.mil/
Control: Navy, Government, federal **Service:** General Medical and Surgical

Staffed Beds: 274

PULASKI—Pulaski County

✠ **LEWISGALE HOSPITAL PULASKI (490116)**, 2400 Lee Highway, Zip 24301–2326, Mailing Address: P.O. Box 759, Zip 24301–0759; tel. 540/994–8100, (Nonreporting) **A**1 2 9 10 **S** HCA, Nashville, TN
Primary Contact: Mark Nichols, FACHE, Chief Executive Officer
CFO: Jeff Kurcab, Chief Financial Officer
CMO: Karanita Ojomo, M.D., Chief of Staff
CIO: Diron Lane, Director Information Systems
CHR: Jana Beckner, Director Human Resources
CNO: Linda M. Shepherd, RN, BSN, Chief Nursing Officer
Web address: www.lewisgale.com/
Control: Corporation, Investor–owned, for–profit **Service:** General Medical and Surgical

Staffed Beds: 54

Many Facility Codes have changed. Please refer to the AHA Guide Code Chart.

VA

RESTON—Fairfax County

✠ **RESTON HOSPITAL CENTER (490107)**, 1850 Town Center Parkway, Zip 20190–3219; tel. 703/689–9000 **A**1 2 9 10 **F**3 6 8 12 13 14 15 18 20 22 26 29 30 31 34 35 39 40 41 42 44 45 46 47 48 50 51 53 54 57 58 59 60 63 64 65 68 69 70 72 74 75 76 77 78 79 81 82 84 85 87 89 91 93 94 96 97 107 108 110 111 114 115 116 119 120 121 123 124 126 130 131 132 135 145 146 147 148 **S** HCA, Nashville, TN
Primary Contact: John A. Deardorff, Chief Executive Officer
COO: Jane Raymond, Vice President and Chief Operating Officer
CFO: Edward R. Stojakovich, Chief Financial Officer
CMO: Walter R. Zolkiwsky, M.D., Chief Medical Officer
CIO: Paresh Shah, Director Information Systems
CHR: Lesley Channell, Vice President Human Resources
CNO: Cynthia Glover, R.N., Vice President and Chief Nursing Officer
Web address: www.restonhospital.com
Control: Corporation, Investor–owned, for–profit **Service:** General Medical and Surgical

Staffed Beds: 199 **Admissions:** 12414 **Census:** 130 **Outpatient Visits:** 105420 **Births:** 3360 **Personnel:** 986

RICHLANDS—Tazewell County

✠ **CLINCH VALLEY MEDICAL CENTER (490060)**, 6801 Governor G. C. Peery Highway, Zip 24641–2194; tel. 276/596–6000, (Total facility includes 14 beds in nursing home–type unit) **A**1 9 10 **F**3 12 13 14 15 17 18 20 22 28 29 30 31 34 35 39 40 41 45 49 50 56 57 59 64 70 74 75 76 77 78 79 81 85 86 87 89 90 93 94 97 107 108 110 111 114 115 118 119 120 121 128 129 130 132 134 135 143 146 147 148 **S** LifePoint Hospitals, Inc., Brentwood, TN
Primary Contact: Peter Mulkey, Chief Executive Officer
CFO: Bob Barrett, Chief Financial Officer
CMO: Larry Mitchell, M.D., Chief of Staff
CIO: Chris Perkins, Director Information Services
CHR: John Knowles, Director Human Resources
Web address: www.clinchvalleymedicalcenter.com
Control: Corporation, Investor–owned, for–profit **Service:** General Medical and Surgical

Staffed Beds: 111 **Admissions:** 4438 **Census:** 48 **Outpatient Visits:** 71517 **Births:** 382 **Personnel:** 574

RICHMOND—Henrico County

✠ **BON SECOURS ST. MARY'S HOSPITAL (490059)**, 5801 Bremo Road, Zip 23226–1907; tel. 804/285–2011, (Includes BON SECOURS ST. MARY'S CHILDREN'S SERVICES, 5801 Bremo Road, tel. 804/285–2011) **A**1 2 3 5 9 10 **F**3 8 11 12 13 15 17 18 20 22 24 26 28 29 30 31 34 36 37 40 41 44 45 46 47 49 50 51 56 57 59 60 63 64 70 72 73 74 75 76 78 79 80 81 82 84 85 86 87 88 89 98 102 103 107 108 110 111 114 115 116 117 118 119 120 121 123 124 126 131 132 145 146 147 148 **P**6 8 **S** Bon Secours Health System, Inc., Marriottsville, MD
Primary Contact: Toni R. Ardabell, R.N., Chief Executive Officer
COO: Francine Barr, R.N., Vice President and Chief Operating Officer
CFO: Stephan F. Quiriconi, Chief Financial Officer
CMO: Khiet Trinh, M.D., Chief Medical Officer
CIO: Terri Spence, Chief Information Officer
CHR: Kristin Crandall, Director Human Resources
Web address: www.bonsecours.com
Control: Church–operated, Nongovernment, not–for profit **Service:** General Medical and Surgical

Staffed Beds: 391 **Admissions:** 20479 **Census:** 262 **Outpatient Visits:** 160587 **Births:** 2072 **Total Expense ($000):** 470003 **Payroll Expense ($000):** 153071 **Personnel:** 2111

✠ **BON SECOURS–RICHMOND COMMUNITY HOSPITAL (490094)**, 1500 North 28th Street, Zip 23223–5396, Mailing Address: P.O. Box 27184, Zip 23261–7184; tel. 804/225–1700, (Nonreporting) **A**1 6 9 10 **S** Bon Secours Health System, Inc., Marriottsville, MD
Primary Contact: Michael Robinson, Executive Vice President and Administrator
CIO: Jeff Burke, Chief Information Officer
CHR: Shelia White, Director Human Resources
Web address: www.bonsecours.com
Control: Church–operated, Nongovernment, not–for profit **Service:** General Medical and Surgical

Staffed Beds: 101

★ **CHILDREN'S HOSPITAL OF RICHMOND AT VCU–BROOK ROAD CAMPUS (493302)**, 2924 Brook Road, Zip 23220–1298; tel. 804/321–7474, (Nonreporting) **A**3 5 9 10
Primary Contact: Leslie G. Wyatt, Senior Vice President Children's Services and Executive Director
COO: Leslie G. Wyatt, Senior Vice President Children's Services and Executive Director
CFO: James A. Deyarmin, Controller
CMO: Eugene A. Monasterio, M.D., Medical Director
CIO: Greg Friedman, Director Information Technology
CNO: Sharon Darby, R.N., Vice President, Clinical Operations
Web address: www.chrichmond.org
Control: Other not–for–profit (including NFP Corporation) **Service:** Children's rehabilitation

Staffed Beds: 36

✠ **CJW MEDICAL CENTER (490112)**, 7101 Jahnke Road, Zip 23225–4044; tel. 804/320–3911, (Includes CHIPPENHAM MEDICAL CENTER, 7101 Jahnke Road, Zip 23225; tel. 804/320–3911; JOHNSTON–WILLIS HOSPITAL, 1401 Johnston–Willis Drive, Zip 23235; tel. 804/330–2000; Brandon Haushalter, Chief Executive Officer) **A**1 2 3 5 9 10 **F**3 4 8 13 15 17 18 19 20 22 24 26 28 29 30 31 34 35 37 38 40 41 42 43 45 46 47 49 50 51 52 55 56 57 58 59 60 63 64 65 68 70 72 73 74 75 76 77 78 79 80 81 82 84 85 86 87 88 89 90 96 98 99 100 101 102 103 105 107 108 109 110 111 114 115 116 117 118 119 120 121 123 124 126 127 129 130 131 132 133 135 141 146 147 148 **S** HCA, Nashville, TN
Primary Contact: Tim McManus, President and Chief Executive Officer
COO: Betsy Blair, R.N., Chief Operating Officer
CFO: Lynn Strader, Chief Financial Officer
CMO: Georgean DeBlois, M.D., Chairman Medical Staff
CIO: Tracy Hechler, Healthcare Director Information Services
CHR: Kris Lukish, Human Resources Officer
Web address: www.cjwmedical.com
Control: Corporation, Investor–owned, for–profit **Service:** General Medical and Surgical

Staffed Beds: 741 **Admissions:** 32607 **Census:** 465 **Outpatient Visits:** 166403 **Births:** 2778 **Personnel:** 2547

HALLMARK YOUTHCARE – RICHMOND, 12800 West Creek Parkway, Zip 23238–1116; tel. 804/784–2200, (Nonreporting)
Primary Contact: Di Hayes, Chief Executive Officer
Web address: www.hallmarkyouthcare.org
Control: State–Government, nonfederal **Service:** Children's hospital psychiatric

Staffed Beds: 84

✠ **HEALTHSOUTH REHABILITATION HOSPITAL OF VIRGINIA (493028)**, 5700 Fitzhugh Avenue, Zip 23226–1800; tel. 804/288–5700 **A**1 9 10 **F**28 29 30 31 34 35 50 57 59 64 65 68 74 75 78 79 80 81 92 93 95 96 97 130 132 148 **S** HEALTHSOUTH Corporation, Birmingham, AL
Primary Contact: David Cashwell, Chief Executive Officer
CMO: Roger Giordano, M.D., Medical Director
CIO: Faye Encke, Director Information Management
CHR: Tonya Ferguson, Director Human Resources
CNO: Michelle Anthony, Chief Nursing Officer
Web address: www.healthsouthrichmond.com
Control: Corporation, Investor–owned, for–profit **Service:** Rehabilitation

Staffed Beds: 40 **Admissions:** 645 **Census:** 27 **Outpatient Visits:** 1800 **Births:** 0 **Total Expense ($000):** 17765 **Payroll Expense ($000):** 6288 **Personnel:** 107

✠ **HENRICO DOCTORS' HOSPITAL (490118)**, 1602 Skipwith Road, Zip 23229–5205; tel. 804/289–4500, (Includes HENRICO DOCTORS' HOSPITAL – FOREST, 1602 Skipwith Road, Zip 23229–5298; tel. 804/289–4500; HENRICO DOCTORS' HOSPITAL – PARHAM, 7700 East Parham Road, Zip 23294–4301; tel. 804/747–5600; William Wagnon, Chief Executive Officer; HENRICO DOCTORS' HOSPITAL – RETREAT CAMPUS, 2621 Grove Avenue, Zip 23220–4308; tel. 804/254–5100; William Wagnon, Chief Executive Officer) **A**1 2 9 10 **F**3 8 12 13 15 17 18 20 22 24 26 28 29 30 31 34 35 37 40 42 44 45 46 49 50 51 54 55 56 57 64 65 68 70 71 72 73 74 75 76 77 78 79 81 85 86 87 88 89 90 93 96 97 98 107 108 109 110 111 112 114 115 119 120 121 123 126 129 130 131 132 135 138 141 144 146 147 148 **S** HCA, Nashville, TN
Primary Contact: William Wagnon, Chief Executive Officer
COO: Lisa R. Valentine, Chief Operating Officer
CFO: Christopher Denton, Chief Financial Officer
CIO: Daniel Patton, Director Information Systems
CHR: Steven Burgess, Administrator Human Resources
Web address: www.henricodoctorshospital.com
Control: Corporation, Investor–owned, for–profit **Service:** General Medical and Surgical

Staffed Beds: 571 **Admissions:** 19284 **Census:** 288 **Outpatient Visits:** 132247 **Births:** 3485

VA

Hospital, Medicare Provider Number, Address, Telephone, Approval, Facility, and Physician Codes, Health Care System

★ American Hospital Association (AHA) membership
☐ The Joint Commission accreditation   ◇ DNV Healthcare Inc. accreditation
○ Healthcare Facilities Accreditation Program
△ Commission on Accreditation of Rehabilitation Facilities (CARF) accreditation

✠ △ **HUNTER HOLMES MCGUIRE VETERANS AFFAIRS MEDICAL CENTER**, 1201 Broad Rock Boulevard, Zip 23249–0002; tel. 804/675–5000, (Total facility includes 98 beds in nursing home–type unit) **A**1 2 3 5 7 8 **F**3 4 5 7 8 12 15 17 18 20 22 24 26 28 29 30 31 34 35 36 38 39 40 44 45 46 47 48 49 50 51 53 54 56 57 58 59 60 61 62 63 64 65 66 68 70 71 74 75 77 78 79 81 82 83 84 85 86 87 90 91 92 93 94 95 96 97 98 100 102 103 104 106 107 108 110 111 115 116 117 118 119 120 121 124 126 127 128 129 130 131 132 135 137 141 143 144 145 146 147 148 **P**6 **S** Department of Veterans Affairs, Washington, DC
Primary Contact: John A. Brandecker, Director
COO: David P. Budinger, Associate Director
CFO: Roger T. Vergne, Chief Fiscal Service
CMO: Judy Brannen, MD, Interim Chief of Staff
CIO: David Dahlstrand, Associate Chief of Staff Information Technology
CHR: Heather Moody, Chief Human Resource Management
Web address: www.richmond.va.gov/
Control: Veterans Affairs, Government, federal **Service:** General Medical and Surgical

Staffed Beds: 387 Admissions: 7852 Census: 244 Outpatient Visits: 560376 **Births:** 0 **Total Expense ($000):** 382438 **Payroll Expense ($000):** 242633 **Personnel:** 2755

JOHNSTON–WILLIS HOSPITAL See CJW Medical Center
KINDRED HOSPITAL RICHMOND See Vibra Hospital of Richmond

✠ **VCU MEDICAL CENTER (490032)**, 1250 East Marshall Street, Zip 23298–5051, Mailing Address: P.O. Box 980510, Zip 23298–0510; tel. 804/828–9000, (Includes VCU HEALTH SYSTEM CHILDREN'S MEDICAL CENTER, 1001 East Marshall Street, Zip 23219–1918, Mailing Address: PO Box 980646, Zip 23298–0646; tel. 804/828–9602) **A**1 3 5 8 9 10 **F**2 3 4 6 8 9 10 11 12 13 15 16 17 18 19 20 21 22 23 24 25 26 27 28 29 30 31 32 34 35 36 37 38 39 40 41 43 44 45 46 47 48 49 50 51 52 54 55 56 57 58 59 60 61 62 64 65 66 68 70 71 72 73 74 75 76 78 79 80 81 82 83 84 85 86 87 88 89 90 92 93 95 96 97 98 99 100 101 102 103 104 105 107 108 109 110 111 114 115 116 117 118 119 120 121 123 124 126 129 130 131 132 134 135 136 137 138 139 141 142 143 145 146 147 148 **P**6 **S** VCU Health System, Richmond, VA
Primary Contact: John Duval, Chief Executive Officer
COO: Deborah W. Davis, Chief Operating Officer
CFO: Dominic J. Pulco, Executive Vice President Finance and Chief Financial Officer
CMO: Ron Clark, M.D., Vice President Clinical Activities and Chief Medical Officer
CIO: Richard Pollack, Vice President Information Services
CHR: Maria Curran, Vice President Human Resources
CNO: Deborah Zimmerman, R.N., Chief Nursing Officer and Vice President Patient Care Services
Web address: www.vcuhealth.org
Control: Hospital district or authority, Government, nonfederal **Service:** General Medical and Surgical

Staffed Beds: 758 Admissions: 31990 Census: 562 Outpatient Visits: 674339 **Births:** 2173 **Total Expense ($000):** 1026325 **Payroll Expense ($000):** 375019 **Personnel:** 7835

✠ **VIBRA HOSPITAL OF RICHMOND (492009)**, 2220 Edward Holland Drive, Zip 23230–2519; tel. 804/678–7000, (Data for 122 days) **A**1 10 **F**1 3 29 75 107 148 **P**6 **S** Vibra Healthcare, Mechanicsburg, PA
Primary Contact: Timothy C. Deaton, Chief Executive Officer
Web address: www.vhrichmond.com
Control: Corporation, Investor–owned, for–profit **Service:** Long–Term Acute Care hospital

Staffed Beds: 60 Admissions: 169 Census: 38 Outpatient Visits: 0 **Births:** 0 **Total Expense ($000):** 7206 **Payroll Expense ($000):** 3238 **Personnel:** 122

ROANOKE—Roanoke County

✠ **CARILION ROANOKE MEMORIAL HOSPITAL (490024)**, Belleview at Jefferson Street, Zip 24014, Mailing Address: P.O. Box 13367, Zip 24033–3367; tel. 540/981–7000, (Includes CARILION CLINIC CHILDREN'S HOSPITAL, 1906 Belleview Avenue, S.E., Zip 24014–1838; tel. 540/981–7000; CARILION ROANOKE COMMUNITY HOSPITAL, 101 Elm Avenue S.E., Zip 24013–2230, Mailing Address: P.O. Box 12946, Zip 24029–2946; tel. 540/985–8000; ROANOKE MEMORIAL REHABILITATION CENTER, South Jefferson and McClanahan Streets, Mailing Address: P.O. Box 13367, Zip 24033; tel. 703/342–4541) **A**1 2 3 5 8 9 10 12 13 **F**3 5 7 8 9 10 11 12 13 15 17 18 19 20 22 24 26 28 29 30 31 32 33 34 35 36 37 38 39 40 41 42 43 44 45 46 47 48 49 50 51 52 53 54 55 56 57 58 59 60 61 62 63 64 66 68 70 71 72 73 74 75 76 77 78 79 81 82 83 84 85 86 87 88 89 90 92 93 96 97 98 99 100 101 102 103 104 106 107 108 110 111 113 114 115 117 118 119 120 121 123 124 126 129 130 131 132 134 135 143 144 146 147 148 **P**6 **S** Carilion Clinic, Roanoke, VA
Primary Contact: Steven C. Arner, President
COO: Steven C. Arner, President
CFO: Donald Halliwill, Executive Vice President and Chief Financial Officer
CHR: Heather Shepardson, Vice President Human Resources
Web address: www.carilionclinic.org
Control: Other not–for–profit (including NFP Corporation) **Service:** General Medical and Surgical

Staffed Beds: 646 Admissions: 36564 Census: 499 Outpatient Visits: 234574 **Births:** 3408 **Total Expense ($000):** 938295 **Payroll Expense ($000):** 415452 **Personnel:** 5768

ROCKY MOUNT—Franklin County

✠ **CARILION FRANKLIN MEMORIAL HOSPITAL (490089)**, 180 Floyd Avenue, Zip 24151–1389; tel. 540/483–5277 **A**1 9 10 **F**11 15 18 28 29 30 34 35 40 45 50 59 62 63 68 70 75 77 81 84 85 93 96 107 110 115 119 130 132 135 146 **S** Carilion Clinic, Roanoke, VA
Primary Contact: William D. Jacobsen, Vice President and Administrator
Web address: www.carilionclinic.org/Carilion/Franklin+Memorial+Hospital
Control: Other not–for–profit (including NFP Corporation) **Service:** General Medical and Surgical

Staffed Beds: 15 Admissions: 1611 Census: 15 Outpatient Visits: 39216 **Births:** 0 **Total Expense ($000):** 33872 **Payroll Expense ($000):** 13199 **Personnel:** 247

SALEM—Salem City County

✠ **LEWIS–GALE MEDICAL CENTER (490048)**, 1900 Electric Road, Zip 24153–7494; tel. 540/776–4000, (Includes LEWIS–GALE PAVILION, 1902 Braeburn Drive, Zip 24153–7391; tel. 703/772–2800), (Nonreporting) **A**1 2 9 10 **S** HCA, Nashville, TN
Primary Contact: Charlotte C. Tyson, Chief Executive Officer
CFO: Angela D. Reynolds, Chief Financial Officer
CMO: Joseph Nelson, M.D., President Medical Staff
CIO: Beth Cole, Director Information Services
CHR: Dale Beaudoin, Vice President Human Resources
Web address: www.lewis-gale.com
Control: Corporation, Investor–owned, for–profit **Service:** General Medical and Surgical

Staffed Beds: 521

✠ **SALEM VETERANS AFFAIRS MEDICAL CENTER**, 1970 Roanoke Boulevard, Zip 24153–6478; tel. 540/982–2463, (Nonreporting) **A**1 2 3 5 8 **S** Department of Veterans Affairs, Washington, DC
Primary Contact: Miguel H. LaPuz, M.D., Director
CFO: Codie Walker, Chief Financial Officer
CMO: Anne Hutchins, M.D., Chief of Staff
CIO: Sharon Collins, Chief Information Officer
CHR: Brian Zeman, Chief Human Resources
CNO: Teresa England, R.N., Nurse Executive
Web address: www.salem.va.gov
Control: Veterans Affairs, Government, federal **Service:** General Medical and Surgical

Staffed Beds: 298

SOUTH BOSTON—Halifax County

✠ **HALIFAX REGIONAL HEALTH SYSTEM (490013)**, 2204 Wilborn Avenue, Zip 24592–1638; tel. 434/517–3100, (Total facility includes 348 beds in nursing home–type unit) **A**1 9 10 19 20 **F**3 13 14 15 17 18 20 28 29 30 31 35 36 38 40 44 45 46 47 48 57 60 62 63 64 65 67 68 70 74 75 76 77 78 79 81 82 84 85 86 87 89 92 93 94 96 97 100 101 102 103 104 107 108 110 111 114 115 116 117 118 119 127 128 129 130 131 132 135 146 147 148 **P**1 7 **S** Sentara Healthcare, Norfolk, VA
Primary Contact: Chris A. Lumsden, Chief Executive Officer
COO: Thomas S. Kluge, Chief Operating Officer
CFO: Stewart R. Nelson, Chief Financial Officer
CMO: Said Iskandar, M.D., Chief Medical Officer
CIO: William Zirkle, Manager Information Systems
CHR: Catherine Howard, Director Human Resources
CNO: Patricia F. Thomas, Chief Nursing Officer
Web address: www.hrhs.org
Control: Other not–for–profit (including NFP Corporation) **Service:** General Medical and Surgical

Staffed Beds: 438 Admissions: 4887 Census: 401 Outpatient Visits: 86321 **Births:** 411 **Total Expense ($000):** 125180 **Payroll Expense ($000):** 52537 **Personnel:** 633

SOUTH HILL—Mecklenburg County

✠ **VCU COMMUNITY MEMORIAL HOSPITAL (490098)**, 125 Buena Vista Circle, Zip 23970–1431, Mailing Address: P.O. Box 90, Zip 23970–0090; tel. 434/447–3151, (Total facility includes 110 beds in nursing home–type unit) **A**1 2 9 10 20 **F**3 11 15 18 28 29 30 31 34 35 39 40 45 46 49 50 53 54 56 57 59 61 62 63 64 65 70 74 75 77 78 79 81 82 84 85 87 93 96 97 107 108 110 111 114 118 119 127 130 131 132 133 135 146 147 148 **P**8 **S** VCU Health System, Richmond, VA
Primary Contact: W. Scott Burnette, President and Chief Executive Officer
COO: Edward M. Brandenburg, FACHE, Vice President Professional Services
CFO: Kenneth Libby, Vice President Finance
CMO: Manhal Saleeby, M.D., Associate Chief of Staff, Geriatrics and Extended Care
CHR: Maria Stephens, PHR, Director Human Resources, Education and Occupational Health and Wellness
Web address: www.cmh–sh.org
Control: Other not–for–profit (including NFP Corporation) **Service:** General Medical and Surgical

Staffed Beds: 178 Admissions: 4011 Census: 158 Outpatient Visits: 123176 **Births:** 0 **Total Expense ($000):** 70810 **Payroll Expense ($000):** 31481 **Personnel:** 631

VA

Many Facility Codes have changed. Please refer to the AHA Guide Code Chart. © 2014 AHA Guide

STAFFORD—Stafford County

⊞ **STAFFORD HOSPITAL (490140)**, 101 Hospital Center Boulevard, Zip 22554–6200; tel. 540/741–9000 **A**1 9 10 **F**3 13 15 18 20 22 29 30 31 34 35 40 44 45 46 48 49 50 55 57 59 60 61 64 68 70 74 75 77 78 79 81 85 86 87 93 96 107 108 111 115 118 119 120 131 132 146 **P**6 **S** Mary Washington Healthcare, Fredericksburg, VA
Primary Contact: Fred M. Rankin, III, President and Chief Executive Officer
CFO: Sean Barden, Executive Vice President and Chief Financial Officer
CMO: Rebecca Bigoney, M.D., Executive Vice President and Chief Medical Officer
CIO: Joyce Hanscome, Senior Vice President and Chief Information Officer
CHR: Kathryn S. Wall, Executive Vice President Human Resources and Organizational Development
CNO: Marianna Bedway, R.N., Senior Vice President and Chief Nursing Officer
Web address: www.mwhc.com
Control: Other not–for–profit (including NFP Corporation) **Service:** General Medical and Surgical

Staffed Beds: 100 **Admissions:** 3771 **Census:** 38 **Outpatient Visits:** 66883 **Births:** 576 **Total Expense ($000):** 79131 **Payroll Expense ($000):** 26620 **Personnel:** 411

STAUNTON—Staunton City County

COMMONWEALTH CENTER FOR CHILDREN AND ADOLESCENTS, 1355 Richmond Road, Zip 24401–9146, Mailing Address: Box 4000, Zip 24402–4000; tel. 540/332–2100, (Nonreporting) **A**3 5 9 **S** Virginia Department of Mental Health, Richmond, VA
Primary Contact: William J. Tuell, MSN, Facility Director
Web address: www.ccca.dbhds.virginia.gov
Control: State–Government, nonfederal **Service:** Children's other specialty

Staffed Beds: 60

☐ **WESTERN STATE HOSPITAL (490106)**, 1301 Richmond Avenue, Zip 24401–9146, Mailing Address: P.O. Box 2500, Zip 24402–2500; tel. 540/332–8000, (Nonreporting) **A**1 3 5 9 10 **S** Virginia Department of Mental Health, Richmond, VA
Primary Contact: Jack W. Barber, M.D., Director
CFO: David Mawyer, Chief Financial Officer
CMO: Mary Clare Smith, M.D., Medical Director
CIO: Sharon Johnson, Director Health Information Management
CHR: Kimberly Harman, Regional Manager Human Resources
Web address: www.dbhds.virginia.gov
Control: State–Government, nonfederal **Service:** Psychiatric

Staffed Beds: 260

STUART—Patrick County

★ ◇ **PIONEER COMMUNITY HOSPITAL OF PATRICK COUNTY (491306)**, 18688 Jeb Stuart Highway, Zip 24171–1559; tel. 276/694–3151, (Nonreporting) **A**9 10 18 21 **S** Pioneer Health Services, Magee, MS
Primary Contact: Jeanette Filpi, Chief Executive Officer
CFO: Julie Gieger, Chief Financial Officer
CMO: Nicholas Kipreos, M.D., Chief Medical Staff
CIO: Eddie Pope, Director Information Systems
CHR: Donn Paul, Vice President Human Resources
Web address: www.phscorporate.com
Control: Corporation, Investor–owned, for–profit **Service:** General Medical and Surgical

Staffed Beds: 25

SUFFOLK—Suffolk City County

⊞ ◇ **SENTARA OBICI HOSPITAL (490044)**, 2800 Godwin Boulevard, Zip 23434–8038; tel. 757/934–4000 **A**1 2 3 5 9 10 21 **F**3 11 13 15 18 20 26 28 29 30 31 34 35 36 37 40 45 47 48 49 50 51 54 56 57 58 59 64 68 70 73 74 75 76 77 78 79 81 85 86 87 92 93 94 96 97 98 107 108 110 111 117 118 119 120 121 123 128 129 130 131 132 144 146 147 148 **P**6 **S** Sentara Healthcare, Norfolk, VA
Primary Contact: Steve Julian, M.D., President
CFO: Mike Mounie, Director Finance
CMO: Steve Julian, M.D., Vice President Medical Affairs
CIO: Alice Oxton, Director Information Technology
CHR: Deborah Ferguson, Human Resources Consultant
Web address: www.sentara.com
Control: Other not–for–profit (including NFP Corporation) **Service:** General Medical and Surgical

Staffed Beds: 176 **Admissions:** 9029 **Census:** 102 **Outpatient Visits:** 328528 **Births:** 1266 **Total Expense ($000):** 165928 **Payroll Expense ($000):** 64206 **Personnel:** 1031

TAPPAHANNOCK—Essex County

☐ **RIVERSIDE TAPPAHANNOCK HOSPITAL (490084)**, 618 Hospital Road, Zip 22560–5000; tel. 804/443–3311 **A**1 9 10 20 **F**3 11 15 29 31 34 35 38 40 43 44 45 49 50 51 56 57 59 62 63 64 70 75 77 78 79 81 82 85 86 87 92 93 97 107 108 111 114 116 117 118 119 130 131 132 133 135 146 148 **P**6 **S** Riverside Health System, Newport News, VA
Primary Contact: John Peterman, Vice President and Administrator
CFO: Jeri Sibley, Director Revenue Cycle
CMO: Randy Ferrance, M.D., President Medical Staff
CHR: Jaime Cook, Director Human Resources
Web address: www.riverside–online.com
Control: Other not–for–profit (including NFP Corporation) **Service:** General Medical and Surgical

Staffed Beds: 16 **Admissions:** 1714 **Census:** 15 **Outpatient Visits:** 67482 **Births:** 0 **Total Expense ($000):** 44201 **Payroll Expense ($000):** 12807 **Personnel:** 183

TAZEWELL—Tazewell County

⊞ **CARILION TAZEWELL COMMUNITY HOSPITAL (490117)**, 141 Ben Bolt Avenue, Zip 24651–9700; tel. 276/988–8700 **A**1 9 10 **F**3 11 15 29 30 34 39 40 44 45 50 59 62 64 68 75 79 81 85 87 107 111 114 119 133 135 146 **S** Carilion Clinic, Roanoke, VA
Primary Contact: Kathren Dowdy, MSN, Regional Hospital Senior Director
CMO: Kerry Moore, M.D., Chief of Staff
CHR: Carrie Boggess, Human Resources Generalist
Web address: www.carilionclinic.org/Carilion/Carilion+Tazewell+Community+Hospital
Control: Other not–for–profit (including NFP Corporation) **Service:** General Medical and Surgical

Staffed Beds: 7 **Admissions:** 643 **Census:** 5 **Outpatient Visits:** 14293 **Births:** 0 **Total Expense ($000):** 13185 **Payroll Expense ($000):** 4658 **Personnel:** 96

VIRGINIA BEACH—Virginia Beach City County

★ ◇ **SENTARA PRINCESS ANNE HOSPITAL (490119)**, 2025 Glenn Mitchell Drive, Zip 23456–0178; tel. 757/507–1000 **A**2 3 5 9 10 21 **F**3 11 13 15 18 20 22 26 29 30 31 34 35 36 38 39 40 41 43 44 45 46 47 49 50 54 57 58 59 60 61 64 65 68 70 71 72 73 74 75 76 77 78 79 81 82 85 86 87 92 93 94 96 97 100 102 107 108 110 111 114 115 118 119 129 130 131 132 144 145 146 147 148 **P**6 **S** Sentara Healthcare, Norfolk, VA
Primary Contact: Thomas B. Thames, M.D., President
COO: Howard P. Kern, Chief Operating Officer
CFO: Robert Broermann, Senior Vice President and Chief Financial Officer
CMO: Terry Gilliland, M.D., Senior Vice President and Chief Medical Officer
CIO: Bert Reese, Chief Information Officer
CHR: Michael V. Taylor, Vice President Human Resources
CNO: Grace Myers, MSN, Vice President, Nurse Executive
Web address: www.sentara.com
Control: Other not–for–profit (including NFP Corporation) **Service:** General Medical and Surgical

Staffed Beds: 160 **Admissions:** 10745 **Census:** 132 **Outpatient Visits:** 313527 **Births:** 2575 **Total Expense ($000):** 156961 **Payroll Expense ($000):** 59690 **Personnel:** 1112

★ ◇ **SENTARA VIRGINIA BEACH GENERAL HOSPITAL (490057)**, 1060 First Colonial Road, Zip 23454–3002; tel. 757/395–8000 **A**2 3 5 9 10 21 **F**3 11 15 17 18 20 22 24 26 28 29 30 31 34 36 37 38 39 40 41 43 44 45 46 47 49 50 51 53 54 57 58 59 60 61 63 64 65 68 70 74 75 77 78 79 80 81 82 84 85 86 87 90 92 93 94 96 97 98 100 101 102 103 107 108 109 110 111 114 115 118 119 120 121 123 126 129 131 132 141 142 144 145 146 147 148 **P**6 **S** Sentara Healthcare, Norfolk, VA
Primary Contact: Elwood Bernard Boone, III, FACHE, President
COO: Joanne Inman, Vice President Operations
CFO: Marley Nacey, Director Finance
CHR: Michelle Meekins, Manager Human Resources
CNO: Peggy Braun, R.N., Vice President Patient Care Services and Chief Nurse Executive
Web address: www.sentara.com
Control: Other not–for–profit (including NFP Corporation) **Service:** General Medical and Surgical

Staffed Beds: 259 **Admissions:** 12389 **Census:** 190 **Outpatient Visits:** 414425 **Births:** 0 **Total Expense ($000):** 239742 **Payroll Expense ($000):** 94554 **Personnel:** 1472

VA

☐ **VIRGINIA BEACH PSYCHIATRIC CENTER (494025)**, 1100 First Colonial Road, Zip 23454–2403; tel. 757/496–6000 **A**1 9 10 **F**4 5 29 38 50 68 98 99 102 103 105 135 **S** Universal Health Services, Inc., King of Prussia, PA
Primary Contact: Frank Gallagher, Chief Executive Officer
Web address: www.absfirst.com
Control: Corporation, Investor–owned, for–profit **Service:** Psychiatric

Staffed Beds: 100 **Admissions:** 3600 **Census:** 75 **Outpatient Visits:** 0
Births: 0

WARRENTON—Fauquier County

⊠ △ **FAUQUIER HOSPITAL (490023)**, 500 Hospital Drive, Zip 20186–3099; tel. 540/316–5000 **A**1 7 9 10 **F**3 11 13 15 18 28 29 30 31 32 34 35 36 37 40 45 47 48 49 53 57 59 62 64 70 74 75 76 77 78 79 81 85 86 87 93 107 108 110 111 115 118 119 129 130 131 132 135 146 148 **S** LifePoint Hospitals, Inc., Brentwood, TN
Primary Contact: Rodger H. Baker, President and Chief Executive Officer
CFO: Lionel J. Phillips, Vice President Financial Services
CMO: Anhtai H. Nguyen, M.D., Vice President Medical Affairs and Chief Medical Officer
CIO: Donna Staton, Chief Information Officer
CHR: Katy Reeves, Vice President Human Resources
CNO: Linda Sharkey, R.N., Vice President Patient Care Services and Chief Nurse Executive
Web address: www.fauquierhospital.org
Control: Other not–for–profit (including NFP Corporation) **Service:** General Medical and Surgical

Staffed Beds: 86 **Admissions:** 5717 **Census:** 59 **Outpatient Visits:** 97055
Births: 823 **Total Expense ($000):** 126982 **Payroll Expense ($000):** 52991
Personnel: 781

WILLIAMSBURG—James City County

☐ **EASTERN STATE HOSPITAL (490109)**, 4601 Ironbound Road, Zip 23188–2652; tel. 757/253–5161, (Nonreporting) **A**1 3 5 9 10 **S** Virginia Department of Mental Health, Richmond, VA
Primary Contact: John M. Favret, Director
CFO: E. Clifford Love, Director Fiscal Services
CMO: Guillermo Schrader, M.D., Acting Medical Director
CIO: Barbara Lambert, Director Healthcare Compliance
CHR: Edie Rogan, Manager Human Resources
Web address: www.esh.dmhmrsas.virginia.gov/
Control: State–Government, nonfederal **Service:** Psychiatric

Staffed Beds: 334

☐ **RIVERSIDE DOCTORS' HOSPITAL (490143)**, 1500 Commonwealth Avenue, Zip 23185–5229; tel. 757/585–2200, (Data for 245 days) **A**1 **F**3 11 28 29 34 35 40 44 45 50 57 59 64 70 74 75 77 79 81 82 85 86 87 91 92 107 108 115 118 119 120 121 123 130 132 146 148 **P**6 **S** Riverside Health System, Newport News, VA
Primary Contact: Steve C. McCary, Administrator
CNO: Arlene Messina, R.N., Director of Nursing
Web address: www.riversideonline.com
Control: Other not–for–profit (including NFP Corporation) **Service:** General Medical and Surgical

Staffed Beds: 12 **Admissions:** 811 **Census:** 11 **Outpatient Visits:** 10926
Births: 0 **Total Expense ($000):** 28619 **Payroll Expense ($000):** 8240
Personnel: 174

★ ◇ **SENTARA WILLIAMSBURG REGIONAL MEDICAL CENTER (490066)**, 100 Sentara Circle, Zip 23188–5713; tel. 757/984–6000 **A**9 10 21 **F**3 8 11 13 15 18 20 22 28 29 30 31 34 35 36 37 39 40 41 43 44 45 46 47 48 49 50 51 54 56 57 58 59 60 63 64 65 68 70 74 75 76 77 78 79 81 83 84 85 86 87 89 90 92 93 94 96 97 100 102 103 104 107 108 110 111 114 115 116 117 118 119 129 130 131 132 135 144 146 147 148 **P**6 **S** Sentara Healthcare, Norfolk, VA
Primary Contact: David J. Masterson, President
CFO: Andreas Roehrle, Director Finance
CMO: Joe Robbins, M.D., Vice President Medical Affairs
CIO: Mike Freeman, Director Information Technology
CHR: Lois B. Demerich, Director Human Resources
CNO: Donna Wilmoth, Vice President Patient Care Services and Chief Nursing Officer
Web address: www.sentara.com
Control: Other not–for–profit (including NFP Corporation) **Service:** General Medical and Surgical

Staffed Beds: 145 **Admissions:** 7303 **Census:** 80 **Outpatient Visits:** 296989
Births: 913 **Total Expense ($000):** 145188 **Payroll Expense ($000):** 55172
Personnel: 747

☐ **THE PAVILION AT WILLIAMSBURG PLACE (490032)**, 5483 Mooretown Road, Zip 23188–2108; tel. 757/565–0106, (Nonreporting) **A**1 10
Primary Contact: Chris Ruble, Executive Director
Web address: www.pavilionwp.com
Control: Corporation, Investor–owned, for–profit **Service:** Psychiatric

Staffed Beds: 57

WINCHESTER—Winchester City County

⊠ **WINCHESTER MEDICAL CENTER (490005)**, 1840 Amherst Street, Zip 22601–2808, Mailing Address: P.O. Box 3340, Zip 22604–2540; tel. 540/536–8000 **A**1 2 3 5 9 10 19 20 **F**3 5 11 12 13 15 17 18 20 22 24 26 28 29 30 31 32 34 35 38 39 40 41 43 44 45 47 49 50 51 54 56 57 58 59 61 62 64 65 68 70 71 72 74 75 76 77 78 79 80 81 82 84 85 86 87 89 90 91 92 93 97 98 100 101 102 103 107 108 110 111 114 115 116 117 118 119 120 121 123 124 129 130 131 132 135 136 146 147 148 **P**5 **S** Valley Health System, Winchester, VA
Primary Contact: Mark H. Merrill, President
COO: Grady W. Philips, III, Senior Vice President and Chief Operating Officer
CFO: Robert Amos, Vice President and Chief Financial Officer
CMO: Nicolas Restrepo, M.D., Vice President Medical Affairs
CIO: Joan Roscoe, Chief Information Officer
CHR: Elizabeth Savage–Tracy, Vice President and Human Resources Officer
CNO: Anne Whiteside, Vice President Nursing
Web address: www.valleyhealthlink.com/WMC
Control: Other not–for–profit (including NFP Corporation) **Service:** General Medical and Surgical

Staffed Beds: 475 **Admissions:** 23410 **Census:** 312 **Outpatient Visits:** 278832 **Births:** 2301 **Total Expense ($000):** 471071 **Payroll Expense ($000):** 149788 **Personnel:** 2883

WOODBRIDGE—Prince William County

★ ◇ **SENTARA NORTHERN VIRGINIA MEDICAL CENTER (490113)**, 2300 Opitz Boulevard, Zip 22191–3399; tel. 703/523–1000 **A**2 9 10 21 **F**3 7 8 11 12 13 15 18 20 22 28 29 30 31 34 35 36 40 41 42 45 49 51 54 57 59 60 63 65 68 70 71 74 75 76 77 78 79 80 81 82 84 85 87 89 97 102 107 108 110 111 114 115 119 121 126 129 130 132 135 146 147 148 **P**6 **S** Sentara Healthcare, Norfolk, VA
Primary Contact: Stephen D. Porter, President
COO: Valerie E. Keane, FACHE, Vice President Operations
CMO: David M. Schwartz, D.O., Vice President, Medical Affairs
CIO: Thomas Ewing, Director Information Technology
CHR: Brett Willsie, Vice President Human Resources
CNO: Patricia Hill, Senior Director Nurse Executive
Web address: www.sentara.com/northernvirginia
Control: Other not–for–profit (including NFP Corporation) **Service:** General Medical and Surgical

Staffed Beds: 180 **Admissions:** 10005 **Census:** 107 **Outpatient Visits:** 322289 **Births:** 1977 **Total Expense ($000):** 205978 **Payroll Expense ($000):** 91128 **Personnel:** 1252

WOODSTOCK—Shenandoah County

⊠ **SHENANDOAH MEMORIAL HOSPITAL (491305)**, 759 South Main Street, Zip 22664–1127; tel. 540/459–1100 **A**1 9 10 18 **F**3 11 15 28 29 30 35 40 45 50 53 57 59 64 65 68 69 70 75 77 79 81 82 87 92 93 97 107 108 110 114 118 119 130 132 133 135 146 148 **S** Valley Health System, Winchester, VA
Primary Contact: Floyd Heater, President
CMO: James Kleinschmidt, M.D., Vice President Medical Affairs
CIO: Joan Roscoe, Chief Information Officer
CNO: Lisa Stokes, R.N., Vice President Patient Care Services
Web address: www.valleyhealthlink.com/shenandoah
Control: Other not–for–profit (including NFP Corporation) **Service:** General Medical and Surgical

Staffed Beds: 25 **Admissions:** 1709 **Census:** 18 **Outpatient Visits:** 73269
Births: 0 **Total Expense ($000):** 47266 **Payroll Expense ($000):** 15287
Personnel: 302

WYTHEVILLE—Wythe County

⊠ **WYTHE COUNTY COMMUNITY HOSPITAL (490111)**, 600 West Ridge Road, Zip 24382–1099; tel. 276/228–0200, (Nonreporting) **A**1 2 9 10 20 **S** LifePoint Hospitals, Inc., Brentwood, TN
Primary Contact: Timothy A. Bess, Chief Executive Officer
COO: Dale Clark, Chief Operating Officer
CFO: John D. White, Chief Financial Officer
CMO: George Farrell, M.D., Chief of Staff
CIO: Andrea Harless, Director Information Services
CNO: Theresa Dix, R.N., Chief Nursing Officer
Web address: www.wcchcares.com
Control: Corporation, Investor–owned, for–profit **Service:** General Medical and Surgical

Staffed Beds: 90

VA

WASHINGTON

ABERDEEN—Grays Harbor County

☐ **GRAYS HARBOR COMMUNITY HOSPITAL (500031)**, 915 Anderson Drive, Zip 98520–1097; tel. 360/532–8330 **A**1 9 10 20 **F**1 3 15 32 34 35 40 43 50 54 59 64 65 67 75 82 86 90 97 107 110 119 127 128 130 146
Primary Contact: Tom Jensen, Chief Executive Officer
COO: Thomas Hightower, R.N., Chief Operating Officer
CFO: Tim Howden, Interim Chief Financial Officer
CMO: Bill Hofmann, M.D., Chief Medical Staff
CIO: Scott Quigley, Director Information Services
CHR: Julie Feller, Director Human Resources
Web address: www.ghchwa.org
Control: Other not–for–profit (including NFP Corporation) **Service:** General Medical and Surgical

Staffed Beds: 105 **Admissions:** 4551 **Census:** 48 **Births:** 562 **Total Expense ($000):** 98900 **Payroll Expense ($000):** 37760

ANACORTES—Skagit County

★ ◇ **ISLAND HOSPITAL (500007)**, 1211 24th Street, Zip 98221–2562; tel. 360/299–1300 **A**2 9 10 21 **F**3 7 8 11 13 15 28 29 30 31 34 35 40 43 45 50 53 57 59 62 64 70 75 76 77 78 79 81 82 85 86 89 93 99 100 102 104 107 108 110 111 114 115 116 119 127 129 130 132 134 135 144 146 147 148 **P**6 8
Primary Contact: Vincent Oliver, Administrator
CFO: Elise Cutter, Chief Financial Officer
CIO: Tom Bluhm, Director Information Systems
CHR: Bill Horn, Human Resources Director
CNO: Lois Pate, R.N., Chief Nursing Officer
Web address: www.islandhospital.org
Control: Hospital district or authority, Government, nonfederal **Service:** General Medical and Surgical

Staffed Beds: 43 **Admissions:** 3014 **Census:** 29 **Outpatient Visits:** 195535 **Births:** 414 **Total Expense ($000):** 87865 **Payroll Expense ($000):** 36663 **Personnel:** 436

ARLINGTON—Snohomish County

◇ **CASCADE VALLEY HOSPITAL AND CLINICS (500060)**, 330 South Stillaguamish Avenue, Zip 98223–1642; tel. 360/435–2133, (Nonreporting) **A**9 10 21
Primary Contact: W. Clark Jones, Superintendent and Administrator
CFO: Ardis Schmiege, Chief Financial Officer
CMO: Edward Eissmann, M.D., President Medical Staff
CIO: Heather Logan, Assistant Administrator Diagnostic and Support Services
CHR: Barbara White, Director Human Resources
CNO: Michelle Sand, R.N., Assistant Administrator Patient Care
Web address: www.cascadevalley.org
Control: Hospital district or authority, Government, nonfederal **Service:** General Medical and Surgical

Staffed Beds: 48

AUBURN—King County

☐ △ **MULTICARE AUBURN MEDICAL CENTER (500015)**, 202 North Division, Plaza One, Zip 98001–4908; tel. 253/833–7711 **A**1 7 9 10 **F**3 13 15 18 20 22 29 30 34 35 40 41 42 43 45 49 50 51 52 53 57 64 65 68 70 72 74 75 76 77 79 81 84 85 87 90 91 93 96 97 102 103 107 108 110 111 114 119 124 126 129 130 134 135 141 146 148 **S** MultiCare Health System, Tacoma, WA
Primary Contact: David Nicewonger, Chief Operating Officer
COO: David Nicewonger, Chief Operating Officer
Web address: www.auburnregional.com
Control: Other not–for–profit (including NFP Corporation) **Service:** General Medical and Surgical

Staffed Beds: 195 **Admissions:** 6526 **Census:** 89 **Outpatient Visits:** 39818 **Births:** 694 **Total Expense ($000):** 108122 **Payroll Expense ($000):** 55529 **Personnel:** 593

BELLEVUE—King County

⊞ **OVERLAKE MEDICAL CENTER (500051)**, 1035 116th Avenue N.E., Zip 98004–4604; tel. 425/688–5000 **A**1 2 9 10 **F**3 11 12 13 15 17 18 20 22 24 26 29 30 31 34 35 40 43 44 45 46 48 49 56 57 58 59 64 68 70 72 74 75 76 77 78 79 81 84 85 86 87 91 92 93 97 98 100 102 104 105 107 108 110 111 114 115 116 117 118 119 120 121 123 124 126 130 132 134 144 145 146 147 148 **P**6
Primary Contact: J. Michael Marsh, President and Chief Executive Officer
COO: David W. Schultz, FACHE, Executive Vice President and Chief Operating Officer
CFO: Gary McLaughlin, Executive Vice President Finance and Chief Financial Officer
CHR: Lisa M. Brock, Vice President Human Resources
CNO: Julie Clayton, R.N., Chief Nursing Officer and Vice President Patient Care Services
Web address: www.overlakehospital.org
Control: Other not–for–profit (including NFP Corporation) **Service:** General Medical and Surgical

Staffed Beds: 297 **Admissions:** 18093 **Census:** 172 **Outpatient Visits:** 253859 **Births:** 3656 **Total Expense ($000):** 417016 **Payroll Expense ($000):** 180321 **Personnel:** 1995

BELLINGHAM—Whatcom County

★ △ ◇ **PEACEHEALTH ST. JOSEPH MEDICAL CENTER (500030)**, 2901 Squalicum Parkway, Zip 98225–1851; tel. 360/734–5400 **A**2 5 7 9 10 20 21 **F**2 3 13 17 18 20 22 24 26 28 29 30 31 34 35 40 41 43 45 46 47 48 49 50 51 54 57 58 59 63 64 65 70 74 75 76 77 78 79 81 84 85 86 87 89 90 92 93 94 96 97 98 106 107 108 109 114 115 118 119 120 121 123 129 130 131 132 135 141 146 148 **S** PeaceHealth, Vancouver, WA
Primary Contact: Nancy Steiger, R.N., FACHE, Chief Executive Officer and Chief Mission Officer, Northwest Network
COO: Stephen R. Omta, Chief Operating Officer
CFO: Dale Zender, Regional Vice President Finance and Chief Financial Officer
CMO: Chris Sprowl, M.D., Vice President
CIO: Marc Pierson, M.D., Vice President Clinical Information and Quality
CHR: Cindy C. Klein, Vice President Human Resources
Web address: www.peacehealth.org
Control: Church–operated, Nongovernment, not–for profit **Service:** General Medical and Surgical

Staffed Beds: 253 **Admissions:** 15138 **Census:** 163 **Births:** 1818 **Total Expense ($000):** 424082 **Payroll Expense ($000):** 159444

ST. JOSEPH HOSPITAL See PeaceHealth St. Joseph Medical Center

BREMERTON—Kitsap County

⊞ **HARRISON MEDICAL CENTER (500039)**, 2520 Cherry Avenue, Zip 98310–4229; tel. 360/744–3911 **A**1 2 9 10 **F**3 11 12 13 18 20 22 24 26 29 30 31 34 35 36 37 38 39 40 43 44 45 46 48 49 50 53 54 56 57 59 61 62 64 65 68 70 74 75 76 77 78 79 81 82 84 85 86 87 89 93 94 96 97 99 100 101 102 103 107 108 114 118 119 120 121 123 126 129 130 132 135 144 146 147 148 **P**6
Primary Contact: Joseph M. Kortum, Interim President
COO: Adar Palis, Executive Vice President and Chief Operating Officer
CFO: Mike Fitzgerald, Chief Financial Officer
CMO: Michael Anderson, M.D., Senior Vice President Quality and Chief Medical Officer
CIO: Rand Strobel, Regional Chief Information Officer, Information Technology Services
CHR: Marie LaMarche, Executive Director, Human Resources, Organizational Development, Employee Health
CNO: Jeanell Rasmussen, R.N., Senior Vice President and Chief Nursing Officer
Web address: www.harrisonmedical.org
Control: Other not–for–profit (including NFP Corporation) **Service:** General Medical and Surgical

Staffed Beds: 262 **Admissions:** 13466 **Census:** 152 **Births:** 1882 **Total Expense ($000):** 371826 **Payroll Expense ($000):** 140582

WA

Hospital, Medicare Provider Number, Address, Telephone, Approval, Facility, and Physician Codes, Health Care System

★ American Hospital Association (AHA) membership
☐ The Joint Commission accreditation
◇ DNV Healthcare Inc. accreditation
○ Healthcare Facilities Accreditation Program
△ Commission on Accreditation of Rehabilitation Facilities (CARF) accreditation

✠ **NAVAL HOSPITAL BREMERTON**, One Boone Road, Zip 98312–1898; tel. 360/475–4000 **A**1 3 5 **F**3 5 8 13 15 18 29 30 32 33 34 35 38 39 40 43 45 46 47 50 53 54 57 58 59 64 65 70 74 75 76 77 79 81 82 85 86 87 92 93 97 99 100 101 104 107 108 110 111 114 115 119 130 131 132 134 135 146 147 **S** Bureau of Medicine and Surgery, Department of the Navy, Washington, DC
Primary Contact: Commander Jeffrey Klinger, Director for Administration
CFO: Judith Hogan, Comptroller and Director Resources and Logistics
CIO: Patrick Flaherty, Director Management Information
Web address: www.med.navy.mil/sites/nhbrem/Pages/default.aspx
Control: Navy, Government, federal **Service:** General Medical and Surgical

> **Staffed Beds:** 40 **Admissions:** 2006 **Census:** 11 **Outpatient Visits:** 302390
> **Births:** 709 **Personnel:** 1440

BREWSTER—Okanogan County

THREE RIVERS HOSPITAL (501324), 507 Hospital Way, Zip 98812–0577, Mailing Address: P.O. Box 577, Zip 98812–0577; tel. 509/689–2517, (Nonreporting) **A**9 10 18
Primary Contact: Scott Graham, Chief Executive Officer
CFO: Jennifer Munson, Chief Financial Officer
CMO: Gordon Tagge, M.D., President Medical Staff
CIO: Edgar Alejandro Arellano, Chief Information Technologist
CHR: Anita Fisk, Director Human Resources
CNO: Gretchen Aguilar, Director Patient Care and Chief Nursing Officer
Web address: www.threerivershospital.net
Control: Hospital district or authority, Government, nonfederal **Service:** General Medical and Surgical

> **Staffed Beds:** 20

BURIEN—King County

✠ △ **HIGHLINE MEDICAL CENTER (500011)**, 16251 Sylvester Road S.W., Zip 98166–3052; tel. 206/244–9970, (Includes HIGHLINE SPECIALTY CENTER, 12844 MILITARY ROAD FORK, TUKWILA, ZIP 98168; MARK BENEDUM, ADMINISTRATOR), (Nonreporting) **A**1 2 7 9 10
Primary Contact: Mark Benedum, Chief Executive Officer
CMO: Dennis De Leon, M.D., Associate Chief Medical Officer and Vice President Medical Affairs
CHR: Grace M. Henley, Assistant Administrator Human Resources
CNO: Kim Baisch, R.N., Associate Vice President Patient Care Services
Web address: www.hchnet.org
Control: Other not–for–profit (including NFP Corporation) **Service:** General Medical and Surgical

> **Staffed Beds:** 179

CENTRALIA—Lewis County

✠ **PROVIDENCE CENTRALIA HOSPITAL (500019)**, 914 South Scheuber Road, Zip 98531–9027; tel. 360/736–2803 **A**1 9 10 20 **F**3 5 8 11 13 15 17 30 31 32 34 35 40 43 45 51 57 58 59 64 67 68 70 75 76 77 78 79 81 86 87 93 102 107 108 110 111 114 115 116 117 118 119 129 130 131 132 146 147 148 **P**6 **S** Providence Health & Services, Renton, WA
Primary Contact: Jill Cooper, Site Administrator
CFO: Denise Marroni, Chief Financial Officer
CMO: Kevin Caserta, M.D., Chief Medical Officer
CIO: Kerry Miles, Site Director
CHR: Susan Meenk, Vice President Service Area
Web address: www.providence.org
Control: Church–operated, Nongovernment, not–for profit **Service:** General Medical and Surgical

> **Staffed Beds:** 97 **Admissions:** 5229 **Census:** 48 **Outpatient Visits:** 186613
> **Births:** 633 **Total Expense ($000):** 120268 **Payroll Expense ($000):** 44835
> **Personnel:** 585

CHELAN—Chelan County

★ **LAKE CHELAN COMMUNITY HOSPITAL (501334)**, 503 East Highland Avenue, Zip 98816–8631, Mailing Address: P.O. Box 908, Zip 98816–0908; tel. 509/682–3300 **A**9 10 18 **F**4 5 7 8 11 13 15 18 29 30 32 34 35 36 38 39 40 41 43 44 45 50 56 57 59 62 63 64 65 66 68 71 74 75 76 77 79 81 84 85 86 87 91 92 93 94 96 99 100 101 102 103 104 106 107 108 110 111 119 126 130 131 132 133 135 143 146 147 148 **P**6
Primary Contact: Kevin Abel, Chief Executive Officer
COO: Brad Hankins, Chief Operating Quality Officer
CFO: Robert Wiegenstein, Chief Financial Officer
CIO: Ross Hurd, Chief Information Officer
CHR: DeLynn K. Cook, Director Human Resources
CNO: Carol Nunley Velasquez, R.N., Chief Nursing Officer
Web address: www.lakechelancommunityhospital.com
Control: Hospital district or authority, Government, nonfederal **Service:** General Medical and Surgical

> **Staffed Beds:** 25 **Admissions:** 820 **Census:** 17 **Outpatient Visits:** 25928
> **Births:** 97 **Total Expense ($000):** 21511 **Payroll Expense ($000):** 12522
> **Personnel:** 205

CHEWELAH—Stevens County

✠ **PROVIDENCE ST. JOSEPH'S HOSPITAL (501309)**, 500 East Webster Street, Zip 99109–9523; tel. 509/935–8211, (Total facility includes 40 beds in nursing home–type unit) **A**1 9 10 18 **F**3 8 10 11 13 15 29 30 34 35 40 43 44 45 57 59 65 75 79 81 82 84 87 91 93 107 114 119 128 133 146 148 **P**6 **S** Providence Health & Services, Renton, WA
Primary Contact: Robert D. Campbell, Jr., Chief Executive
COO: Ronald G. Rehn, Chief Operating Officer
CFO: Tony Lawrence, Chief Financial Officer
CMO: Patrick A. Barker, M.D., Chief Medical Officer
CIO: Theron DePaulo, Director Information Technology
CNO: Deborah Watson, R.N., Chief Nursing Officer
Web address: www.sjhospital.org
Control: Church–operated, Nongovernment, not–for profit **Service:** General Medical and Surgical

> **Staffed Beds:** 65 **Admissions:** 377 **Census:** 44 **Outpatient Visits:** 18951
> **Births:** 0 **Total Expense ($000):** 19684 **Payroll Expense ($000):** 9316
> **Personnel:** 141

CLARKSTON—Asotin County

✠ **TRI–STATE MEMORIAL HOSPITAL (501332)**, 1221 Highland Avenue, Zip 99403–2829, Mailing Address: P.O. Box 189, Zip 99403–0189; tel. 509/758–5511 **A**1 9 10 18 **F**10 11 15 29 34 35 37 40 45 49 60 64 65 70 75 79 81 82 85 97 107 111 115 119 124 125 129 130 131 132 133 144 146 147 148
Primary Contact: Donald Wee, Chief Executive Officer
CFO: Alex Town, Vice President Finance
CMO: Don Greggain, M.D., Physician Network Director
CIO: Joleen Carper, Vice President Quality and Risk
CHR: Gana Davis, Vice President Human Resources
CNO: Rhonda Mason, Vice President of Patient Care Services
Web address: www.tristatehospital.org
Control: Other not–for–profit (including NFP Corporation) **Service:** General Medical and Surgical

> **Staffed Beds:** 25 **Admissions:** 1294 **Census:** 12 **Outpatient Visits:** 128655
> **Births:** 0 **Total Expense ($000):** 58615 **Payroll Expense ($000):** 22746

COLFAX—Whitman County

★ **WHITMAN HOSPITAL AND MEDICAL CENTER (501327)**, 1200 West Fairview Street, Zip 99111–9579; tel. 509/397–3435 **A**9 10 18 **F**29 30 34 35 40 45 59 64 65 68 69 76 77 79 81 85 93 107 110 111 119 130 133 135 148 **S** Providence Health & Services, Renton, WA
Primary Contact: Gary V. Peck, Interim Chief Executive Officer
CFO: Jim Heilsberg, Chief Financial Officer and Chief Information Officer
CMO: W. Kimball Mellor, M.D., Chief Medical Officer
CIO: Jim Heilsberg, Chief Financial Officer and Chief Information Officer
CHR: Michelle Ellis, Director Human Resources
CNO: Denise Fowler, R.N., Chief Clinical Officer
Web address: www.whitmanhospital.com
Control: Hospital district or authority, Government, nonfederal **Service:** General Medical and Surgical

> **Staffed Beds:** 25 **Admissions:** 539 **Census:** 6 **Outpatient Visits:** 15805
> **Births:** 41 **Total Expense ($000):** 22454 **Payroll Expense ($000):** 8906

COLVILLE—Stevens County

✠ **PROVIDENCE MOUNT CARMEL HOSPITAL (501326)**, 982 East Columbia Avenue, Zip 99114–3352; tel. 509/685–5100 **A**1 9 10 18 **F**3 11 13 15 29 30 34 40 43 44 45 57 59 64 70 75 76 77 79 81 82 84 85 86 87 93 107 108 115 118 119 123 129 131 132 133 135 146 148 **P**6 **S** Providence Health & Services, Renton, WA
Primary Contact: Robert D. Campbell, Jr., Chief Executive
COO: Ronald G. Rehn, Chief Operating Officer
CFO: Helen Andrus, Chief Financial Officer
CMO: Deborah Montowski, M.D., Chief Medical Officer
CIO: Theron DePaulo, Manager Information Systems
CHR: Lori Johanson–Fogle, Vice President Human Resources
CNO: Deborah Watson, R.N., Senior Director of Nursing and Vice President, Patient Care Services
Web address: www.mtcarmelhospital.org
Control: Church–operated, Nongovernment, not–for profit **Service:** General Medical and Surgical

> **Staffed Beds:** 25 **Admissions:** 1122 **Census:** 11 **Outpatient Visits:** 49317
> **Births:** 212 **Total Expense ($000):** 38730 **Payroll Expense ($000):** 15236
> **Personnel:** 217

COUPEVILLE—Island County

★ **WHIDBEY GENERAL HOSPITAL (501339)**, 101 North Main Street, Zip 98239–3413; tel. 360/678–5151, (Nonreporting) **A**2 9 10 18
Primary Contact: Tom Tomasino, Administrator and Chief Executive Officer
COO: Hank Hanigan, Chief Operating Officer
CMO: Gabe Barrio, M.D., Chief of Staff
CNO: Linda Stephens Gipson, MSN, Chief Nursing Officer
Web address: www.whidbeygen.org
Control: Hospital district or authority, Government, nonfederal **Service:** General Medical and Surgical

> **Staffed Beds:** 25

WA

Many Facility Codes have changed. Please refer to the AHA Guide Code Chart.
© 2014 AHA Guide

DAVENPORT—Lincoln County

★ **LINCOLN HOSPITAL (501305)**, 10 Nicholls Street, Zip 99122–9729;
tel. 509/725–7101, (Nonreporting) **A**9 10 18
Primary Contact: Thomas J. Martin, Administrator
CFO: Tyson Lacy, Chief Financial Officer
CMO: Fred Reed, M.D., Chief of Staff
CIO: Elliott Donson, Chief Information Specialist
CHR: Becky Bailey, Director Human Resources
Web address: www.lincolnhospital.org
Control: Hospital district or authority, Government, nonfederal **Service:** General Medical and Surgical

Staffed Beds: 60

DAYTON—Columbia County

COLUMBIA COUNTY HEALTH SYSTEM (501302), 1012 South Third Street,
Zip 99328–1696; tel. 509/382–2531, (Total facility includes 34 beds in nursing home–type unit) **A**9 10 18 **F**40 93 107 127 133
Primary Contact: Jon D. Smiley, Interim Chief Executive Officer
COO: Shane McGuire, Chief Operations Officer and Information Technology Director
CFO: Steve Geidl, Chief Financial Officer
CIO: Shane McGuire, Chief Operations Officer and Information Technology Director
CHR: Steven J. Stahl, Director Human Resources
CNO: Stephanie Carpenter, Director of Nursing Services
Web address: www.cchd–wa.org
Control: Hospital district or authority, Government, nonfederal **Service:** General Medical and Surgical

Staffed Beds: 44 **Admissions:** 278 **Census:** 61 **Total Expense ($000):** 12218 **Payroll Expense ($000):** 5593 **Personnel:** 122

EDMONDS—Snohomish County

STEVENS HEALTHCARE See Swedish/Edmonds

⊞ **SWEDISH/EDMONDS (500026)**, 21601 76th Avenue West, Zip 98026–7506;
tel. 425/640–4000, (Nonreporting) **A**1 2 9 10 **S** Swedish Health Services, Seattle, WA
Primary Contact: David E. Jaffe, Chief Executive
CMO: Tim Roddy, M.D., Vice President Medical Affairs
CIO: Robert Pageler, Director Information Services
Web address: www.swedish.org
Control: Other not–for–profit (including NFP Corporation) **Service:** General Medical and Surgical

Staffed Beds: 139

ELLENSBURG—Kittitas County

★ **KITTITAS VALLEY HEALTHCARE (501333)**, 603 South Chestnut Street,
Zip 98926–3875; tel. 509/962–7302, (Nonreporting) **A**9 10 18
Primary Contact: Paul E. Nurick, Chief Executive Officer
COO: Catherine Bambrick, Chief Operating Officer
CFO: Libby Allgood, Chief Financial Officer
CMO: Don Solberg, M.D., Chief Medical Officer
CNO: Rhonda C. Holden, R.N., Chief Nursing Officer
Web address: www.kvhealthcare.org
Control: Hospital district or authority, Government, nonfederal **Service:** General Medical and Surgical

Staffed Beds: 25

ELMA—Grays Harbor County

SUMMIT PACIFIC MEDICAL CENTER (501304), 600 East Main Street,
Zip 98541–9560; tel. 360/346–2222, (Nonreporting) **A**9 10
Primary Contact: Renee K. Jensen, Chief Executive Officer
CFO: William Callicoat, Chief Financial Officer
CMO: William Hurley, M.D., Chief Medical Officer
CIO: Jeff Painter, Manager Information Technology
CHR: Mindy Portchy, Manager Human Resources
CNO: Brenda West, R.N., Chief Nursing Officer
Web address: www.markreed.org
Control: Corporation, Investor–owned, for–profit **Service:** General Medical and Surgical

Staffed Beds: 6

ENUMCLAW—King County

★ **ST. ELIZABETH HOSPITAL (501335)**, 1455 Battersby Avenue,
Zip 98022–3634, Mailing Address: P.O. Box 218, Zip 98022–0218;
tel. 360/284–4171 **A**9 10 18 **F**3 13 15 29 30 34 35 38 40 43 45 50 57 64 66 68 70 74 76 79 81 85 107 108 110 111 114 119 146 **P**3 6 **S** Catholic Health Initiatives, Englewood, CO
Primary Contact: Donna Russell–Cook, FACHE, President
COO: Joseph Wilczek, Chief Executive Officer
CFO: Philip Hjembo, Chief Financial Officer
CHR: Jerilyn Ray, Manager Human Resources
Web address: www.fhshealth.org
Control: Church–operated, Nongovernment, not–for profit **Service:** General Medical and Surgical

Staffed Beds: 38 **Admissions:** 1374 **Census:** 12 **Outpatient Visits:** 30327 **Births:** 276 **Total Expense ($000):** 46324 **Payroll Expense ($000):** 17984 **Personnel:** 224

EPHRATA—Grant County

★ **COLUMBIA BASIN HOSPITAL (501317)**, 200 Nat Washington Way,
Zip 98823–1982; tel. 509/754–4631, (Total facility includes 16 beds in nursing home–type unit) **A**9 10 18 **F**3 10 11 15 34 40 50 54 56 57 59 64 68 75 87 93 96 97 107 119 127 130 133 135 143 146 148 **P**6
Primary Contact: Rosalinda Kibby, Superintendent and Administrator
CFO: Rhonda Handley, Chief Financial Officer
CMO: Lowell C. Allred, M.D., Chief of Staff
CHR: Suzanne Little, Human Resources Specialist
Web address: www.columbiabasinhospital.org
Control: Hospital district or authority, Government, nonfederal **Service:** General Medical and Surgical

Staffed Beds: 25 **Admissions:** 267 **Census:** 33 **Outpatient Visits:** 34556 **Births:** 0 **Total Expense ($000):** 14008 **Payroll Expense ($000):** 5996 **Personnel:** 144

EVERETT—Snohomish County

⊞ △ **PROVIDENCE REGIONAL MEDICAL CENTER EVERETT (500014)**, 1321 Colby Avenue, Zip 98201–1665, Mailing Address: P.O. Box 1147, Zip 98206–1147; tel. 425/261–2000, (Includes PROVIDENCE EVERETT MEDICAL CENTER – COLBY CAMPUS, 1321 Colby Avenue, Zip 98206, Mailing Address: P.O. Box 1147, Zip 98206; tel. 425/261–2000; PROVIDENCE EVERETT MEDICAL CENTER – PACIFIC CAMPUS, Pacific and Nassau Streets, Zip 98201, Mailing Address: P.O. Box 1067, Zip 98206–1067; tel. 206/258–7123) **A**1 2 3 5 7 9 10 **F**3 4 5 8 11 12 13 15 17 18 20 22 24 26 28 29 30 31 32 34 35 36 38 40 43 44 45 46 47 48 49 50 53 54 55 56 57 58 59 60 61 64 65 66 68 70 72 73 74 75 76 77 78 79 80 81 82 84 85 86 87 89 90 93 94 96 97 100 107 108 109 111 114 115 116 117 118 119 120 121 123 124 126 129 130 131 132 135 144 145 146 147 148 **P**6 8 **S** Providence Health & Services, Renton, WA
Primary Contact: Preston M. Simmons, FACHE, Chief Executive Officer
COO: Kim Williams, R.N., Chief Operating Officer
CFO: Sheri Feeney, Chief Financial Officer
CMO: Joanne Roberts, M.D., Chief Medical Officer
CIO: Matt Wonser, Director, Information Services
CHR: Lori A. Vocca, Vice President Human Resources
CNO: Barbara M. Hyland–Hill, R.N., Chief Nursing Officer
Web address: www.providence.org
Control: Church–operated, Nongovernment, not–for–profit **Service:** General Medical and Surgical

Staffed Beds: 491 **Admissions:** 28439 **Census:** 338 **Outpatient Visits:** 415990 **Births:** 4325 **Total Expense ($000):** 557511 **Payroll Expense ($000):** 196249 **Personnel:** 3194

FEDERAL WAY—King County

⊞ **ST. FRANCIS HOSPITAL (500141)**, 34515 Ninth Avenue South,
Zip 98003–6799; tel. 253/944–8100 **A**1 9 10 **F**3 8 11 12 13 15 18 20 22 29 30 31 32 34 35 38 40 43 44 45 49 50 51 54 55 57 59 64 65 66 70 73 74 75 76 77 78 79 80 81 82 84 85 86 87 92 93 107 108 110 111 114 115 117 119 126 129 130 132 134 135 145 146 147 **P**3 6 **S** Catholic Health Initiatives, Englewood, CO
Primary Contact: Anthony McLean, President
CFO: Mike Fitzgerald, Chief Financial Officer
CMO: Mark C. Adams, M.D., Chief Medical Officer
CIO: Rand Strobel, Regional Chief Information Officer
CHR: Sharon Royne, Interim Senior Vice President Human Resources
CNO: Laurie Brown, R.N., Chief Nursing Officer
Web address: www.fhshealth.org
Control: Church–operated, Nongovernment, not–for profit **Service:** General Medical and Surgical

Staffed Beds: 124 **Admissions:** 8624 **Census:** 82 **Outpatient Visits:** 121638 **Births:** 1178 **Total Expense ($000):** 205407 **Payroll Expense ($000):** 70918 **Personnel:** 954

WA

Hospital, Medicare Provider Number, Address, Telephone, Approval, Facility, and Physician Codes, Health Care System

★ American Hospital Association (AHA) membership
□ The Joint Commission accreditation
◇ DNV Healthcare Inc. accreditation
○ Healthcare Facilities Accreditation Program
△ Commission on Accreditation of Rehabilitation Facilities (CARF) accreditation

FORKS—Clallam County

◇ **FORKS COMMUNITY HOSPITAL (501325)**, 530 Bogachiel Way,
Zip 98331–9120; tel. 360/374–6271, (Nonreporting) **A**9 10 18 21
Primary Contact: James Chaney, Interim Administrator
COO: John Sherrett, Chief Financial Officer and Chief Operating Officer
CFO: James Chaney, Chief Financial Officer
CIO: Andrea Perkins–Peppers, Manager Information Services
Web address: www.forkshospital.org
Control: Hospital district or authority, Government, nonfederal **Service:** General Medical and Surgical

Staffed Beds: 45

FRIDAY HARBOR—San Juan County

★ ◇ **PEACEHEALTH PEACE ISLAND MEDICAL CENTER (501340)**, 1117
Spring Street, Zip 98250–9782; tel. 360/378–2141 **A**9 10 18 21 **F**3 11 15 29
30 31 35 40 44 45 46 47 48 49 50 57 59 65 68 77 78 81 84 85 87 97 102
107 108 110 114 119 130 133 135 146 148 **S** PeaceHealth, Vancouver, WA
Primary Contact: James R. Barnhart, Chief Administrator Officer
Web address: www.peacehealth.org
Control: Other not–for–profit (including NFP Corporation) **Service:** General Medical and Surgical

**Staffed Beds: 10 Admissions: 105 Census: 1 Outpatient Visits: 2825
Births: 0 Total Expense ($000): 11269 Payroll Expense ($000): 4718
Personnel: 58**

GIG HARBOR—Pierce County

⊞ **ST. ANTHONY HOSPITAL (500151)**, 11567 Canterwood Boulevard N.W.,
Zip 98332–5812; tel. 253/530–2000 **A**1 9 10 **F**3 11 12 15 20 22 29 30 31
34 35 38 40 45 46 49 50 51 56 57 59 60 64 65 66 68 70 74 75 77 78 79
81 82 84 85 87 93 107 108 111 114 115 121 123 126 129 130 132 146
147 **S** Catholic Health Initiatives, Englewood, CO
Primary Contact: Kurt Schley, President
Web address: www.fhshealth.org/
Control: Church–operated, Nongovernment, not–for profit **Service:** General Medical and Surgical

**Staffed Beds: 80 Admissions: 5218 Census: 57 Outpatient Visits: 58359
Births: 0 Total Expense ($000): 120754 Payroll Expense ($000): 38057
Personnel: 520**

GOLDENDALE—Klickitat County

★ **KLICKITAT VALLEY HEALTH (501316)**, 310 South Roosevelt Avenue,
Zip 98620–9201; tel. 509/773–4022 **A**9 10 18 **F**3 7 8 15 18 29 30 34 35 40
43 45 57 59 62 63 64 65 68 75 77 81 83 84 85 97 107 119 127 128 130
133 135 146 148
Primary Contact: Leslie Hiebert, Chief Executive Officer
CFO: Jamie Eldred, Controller
CMO: Rod Krehbiel, M.D., Chief of Staff
CIO: Jonathan Hatfield, Supervisor Information Technology
CHR: Herbert Hill, Director Human Resources
CNO: Gwen Cox, Director Nursing Services
Web address: www.kvhealth.net
Control: Hospital district or authority, Government, nonfederal **Service:** General Medical and Surgical

**Staffed Beds: 17 Admissions: 271 Census: 5 Outpatient Visits: 4424
Births: 2 Total Expense ($000): 19333 Payroll Expense ($000): 8962
Personnel: 163**

GRAND COULEE—Grant County

COULEE COMMUNITY HOSPITAL See Coulee Medical Center

COULEE MEDICAL CENTER (501308), 411 Fortuyn Road, Zip 99133–8718;
tel. 509/633–1753, (Nonreporting) **A**9 10 18
Primary Contact: Debbie Bigelow, Interim Chief Executive Officer
COO: Alan Wagner, Chief Operating Officer
CFO: Debbie Bigelow, Chief Financial Officer
CMO: Jacob Chaffee, M.D., Chief Medical Officer
CHR: Julie D. Bjorklund, Director Human Resources
Web address: www.cmccares.org
Control: Hospital district or authority, Government, nonfederal **Service:** General Medical and Surgical

Staffed Beds: 25

ILWACO—Pacific County

★ **OCEAN BEACH HOSPITAL (501314)**, 174 First Avenue North,
Zip 98624–9137, Mailing Address: P.O. Box H., Zip 98624–0258;
tel. 360/642–3181 **A**9 10 18 **F**3 11 15 28 29 30 31 34 35 40 43 45 50 57
59 68 75 77 78 81 85 86 87 93 97 107 111 114 119 127 128 130 132 133
135 147 **P**6
Primary Contact: Kendall Sawa, R.N., Chief Executive Officer
CFO: Kathy Hubbard, Controller
CMO: Patty Malone, M.D., Chief Medical Officer
CIO: Julie P. Oakes, R.N., Manager Risk and Quality
CHR: Beth Whitton, Director Human Resources
CNO: Linda Kaino, Chief Nursing Officer
Web address: www.oceanbeachhospital.com
Control: Hospital district or authority, Government, nonfederal **Service:** General Medical and Surgical

**Staffed Beds: 15 Admissions: 400 Census: 4 Outpatient Visits: 24672
Births: 0 Total Expense ($000): 16010 Payroll Expense ($000): 8989
Personnel: 45**

iSSAQUAH—King County

★ ◇ **SWEDISH/ISSAQUAH (500152)**, 751 N.E. Blakely Drive, Zip 98029–6201;
tel. 425/313–4000 **A**9 10 21 **F**3 12 15 18 20 22 29 30 31 34 35 37 38
40 41 45 48 49 50 56 57 58 59 60 61 64 65 68 70 73 74 75 76 77 78 79
81 82 85 86 87 89 92 93 96 97 102 107 108 110 111 115 119 120 121
126 129 130 131 132 134 135 143 146 147 **S** Swedish Health Services,
Seattle, WA
Primary Contact: Rayburn Lewis, M.D., Chief Executive Officer
Web address: www.swedish.org/issaquah
Control: Other not–for–profit (including NFP Corporation) **Service:** General Medical and Surgical

**Staffed Beds: 80 Admissions: 5728 Census: 36 Outpatient Visits: 89667
Births: 1136 Total Expense ($000): 151103 Payroll Expense ($000):
42505**

KENNEWICK—Benton County

⊞ **TRIOS HEALTH (500053)**, 900 South Auburn Street, Zip 99336–5621, Mailing
Address: P.O. Box 6128, Zip 99336–0128; tel. 509/586–6111 **A**1 2 9 10 **F**2 8
11 13 15 18 20 28 29 30 31 34 35 40 45 49 50 54 56 57 59 62 64 70 73
74 75 76 77 78 79 80 81 85 86 87 89 93 97 107 108 110 111 114 119 129
130 144 146 147
Primary Contact: Glen Marshall, Chief Executive Officer
CFO: Tony Sudduth, Chief Financial Officer
CIO: Michael Cloutier, Director Information Services
CHR: Russ Keefer, Chief Human Resources Officer
CNO: Diane M. Sanders, Chief Nursing Officer
Web address: www.trioshealth.org
Control: Hospital district or authority, Government, nonfederal **Service:** General Medical and Surgical

**Staffed Beds: 111 Admissions: 5196 Census: 47 Outpatient Visits: 294805
Births: 1344 Total Expense ($000): 150178 Payroll Expense ($000):
72890**

KIRKLAND—King County

EVERGREEN HEALTHCARE See EvergreenHealth

⊞ **EVERGREENHEALTH (500124)**, 12040 N.E. 128th Street, Zip 98034–3013;
tel. 425/899–1000 **A**1 2 5 9 10 **F**3 11 12 13 15 18 20 22 28 29 30 34 35 37
38 40 42 43 44 45 46 49 50 51 53 54 55 56 57 58 59 62 63 64 65 68 70
71 72 73 74 75 76 78 79 80 81 82 84 85 86 87 89 90 91 92 93 94 95 96
97 100 102 103 107 108 110 111 114 115 119 120 121 123 124 126 129
130 131 132 134 135 144 146 147 148 **P**4 6
Primary Contact: Robert H. Malte, Chief Executive Officer
COO: David S. Danielson, Senior Vice President Operations
CFO: Chrissy Yamada, CPA, Senior Vice President Finance
CMO: Mitch Weinberg, M.D., Chief of Staff
CIO: Tom Martin, Vice President and Chief Information Officer
Web address: www.evergreenhealthcare.org
Control: Hospital district or authority, Government, nonfederal **Service:** General Medical and Surgical

**Staffed Beds: 278 Admissions: 14441 Census: 144 Outpatient Visits:
519318 Births: 4464 Total Expense ($000): 487055 Payroll Expense
($000): 243818 Personnel: 3516**

☐ **FAIRFAX HOSPITAL (504002)**, 10200 N.E. 132nd Street, Zip 98034–2899;
tel. 425/821–2000 **A**1 9 10 **F**4 29 35 38 98 99 100 101 102 105 130 132
S Universal Health Services, Inc., King of Prussia, PA
Primary Contact: Ron Escarda, Chief Executive Officer
COO: Todd Thama, Chief Operating Officer
CFO: Pam Rhoads, Chief Financial Officer
CMO: Samir Aziz, M.D., Medical Director
CHR: Anne Schreiber, Manager Human Resources
Web address: www.fairfaxhospital.com
Control: Corporation, Investor–owned, for–profit **Service:** Psychiatric

**Staffed Beds: 103 Admissions: 3442 Census: 91 Outpatient Visits: 2777
Births: 0 Total Expense ($000): 23393 Payroll Expense ($000): 13167**

Many Facility Codes have changed. Please refer to the AHA Guide Code Chart. © 2014 AHA Guide

WA

LAKEWOOD—Pierce County

☒ △ **ST. CLARE HOSPITAL (500021)**, 11315 Bridgeport Way S.W., Zip 98499–3004; tel. 253/985–1711 **A**1 7 9 10 **F**3 8 29 30 31 34 35 37 38 40 41 43 44 45 49 50 51 54 57 59 60 64 65 66 70 74 75 77 78 79 81 82 84 87 92 93 107 108 111 114 119 126 129 130 132 133 134 135 146 147 **P**3 6 **S** Catholic Health Initiatives, Englewood, CO
Primary Contact: Kathy Bressler, R.N., President
COO: Kathy Bressler, R.N., President
CFO: Mike Fitzgerald, Chief Financial Officer
CIO: Bruce Elkington, Regional Chief Information Officer
CHR: David C. Lawson, Senior Vice President Human Resources
Web address: www.fhshealth.org
Control: Church–operated, Nongovernment, not–for profit **Service:** General Medical and Surgical

Staffed Beds: 106 **Admissions:** 7035 **Census:** 79 **Outpatient Visits:** 100497 **Births:** 0 **Total Expense ($000):** 163822 **Payroll Expense ($000):** 51658 **Personnel:** 779

LEAVENWORTH—Chelan County

★ **CASCADE MEDICAL CENTER (501313)**, 817 Commercial Street, Zip 98826–1316; tel. 509/548–5815 **A**9 10 18 **F**3 7 15 30 34 40 43 45 59 63 64 65 68 77 93 97 104 107 110 114 127 130 131 133 148
Primary Contact: Diane Blake, Chief Executive Officer
COO: Amy Webb, Chief Operating Officer
CFO: John Hennessy, Chief Financial Officer
CMO: Emily Johnston, M.D., Chief Medical Officer
CHR: Adrianne Wiegenstein, Director Human Resources
Web address: www.cascademedical.org
Control: Hospital district or authority, Government, nonfederal **Service:** General Medical and Surgical

Staffed Beds: 9 **Admissions:** 161 **Census:** 3 **Births:** 0 **Total Expense ($000):** 14122 **Payroll Expense ($000):** 7019

LONGVIEW—Cowlitz County

☒ **PEACEHEALTH ST. JOHN MEDICAL CENTER (500041)**, 1615 Delaware Street, Zip 98632–2367, Mailing Address: P.O. Box 3002, Zip 98632–0302; tel. 360/414–2000 **A**1 2 9 10 19 **F**13 15 29 30 31 33 35 40 50 60 70 76 77 78 79 81 82 84 85 97 98 107 111 129 130 144 146 147 148 **P**3 **S** PeaceHealth, Vancouver, WA
Primary Contact: Kirk Raboin, Chief Administrative Officer
Web address: www.peacehealth.org
Control: Hospital district or authority, Government, nonfederal **Service:** General Medical and Surgical

Staffed Beds: 200 **Admissions:** 8558 **Census:** 93 **Outpatient Visits:** 182081 **Births:** 981 **Total Expense ($000):** 241666 **Payroll Expense ($000):** 99422 **Personnel:** 1370

MEDICAL LAKE—Spokane County

☐ **EASTERN STATE HOSPITAL (504004)**, Maple Street, Zip 99022–0045, Mailing Address: P.O. Box 800, Zip 99022–0800; tel. 509/565–4705 **A**1 9 10 **F**30 39 75 77 98 100 101 102 103 104 105 106 130
Primary Contact: Dorothy Sawyer, Chief Executive Officer
Web address: www.dshs.wa.gov/mhsystems/esh.shtml
Control: State–Government, nonfederal **Service:** Psychiatric

Staffed Beds: 287 **Admissions:** 743 **Census:** 269 **Births:** 0

MONROE—Snohomish County

★ ◇ **VALLEY GENERAL HOSPITAL (500084)**, 14701 179th S.E., Zip 98272–1108, Mailing Address: P.O. Box 646, Zip 98272–0646; tel. 360/794–7497, (Nonreporting) **A**9 10 21
Primary Contact: Eric Jensen, Chief Executive Officer
CFO: Malisa Westland, Chief Financial Officer
CIO: Scott Crader, Director Information Systems
CHR: Jessika A. Groce, Director Human Resources
CNO: Debbie T. Brown, R.N., Chief Clinical Officer
Web address: www.valleygeneral.com
Control: Hospital district or authority, Government, nonfederal **Service:** General Medical and Surgical

Staffed Beds: 68

MORTON—Lewis County

★ **MORTON GENERAL HOSPITAL (501319)**, 521 Adams Avenue, Zip 98356–9323, Mailing Address: P.O. Box 1138, Zip 98356–0019; tel. 360/496–5112 **A**9 10 18 **F**3 34 40 45 85 87 97 107 110 114 119 127 129 148
Primary Contact: Seth Whitmer, Administrator
CFO: Tim Cournyer, Chief Financial Officer
CIO: Mitch Walter, Director Information Technology
CHR: Shannon Kelly, Director Human Resources
Web address: www.mortongeneral.org
Control: Hospital district or authority, Government, nonfederal **Service:** General Medical and Surgical

Staffed Beds: 25 **Admissions:** 266 **Census:** 15 **Births:** 0 **Total Expense ($000):** 23643 **Payroll Expense ($000):** 12243 **Personnel:** 188

MOSES LAKE—Grant County

★ **SAMARITAN HEALTHCARE (500033)**, 801 East Wheeler Road, Zip 98837–1899; tel. 509/765–5606 **A**5 9 10 20 **F**3 8 13 15 29 34 35 40 43 45 50 57 59 64 65 68 70 75 76 79 81 86 87 93 97 107 108 110 111 114 118 119 127 130 132 135 144 146 147
Primary Contact: Thomas R. Thompson, Chief Executive Officer
CFO: Tom Legel, Chief Financial Officer and Chief Operating Officer
CMO: James Irwin, M.D., Chief Medical Officer
CHR: Lisa A. McDaniel, Chief Human Resources Officer
CNO: Kathryn E. Trumbull, R.N., Chief Nursing Officer and Vice President Patient Care Services
Web address: www.samaritanhealthcare.com
Control: Hospital district or authority, Government, nonfederal **Service:** General Medical and Surgical

Staffed Beds: 50 **Admissions:** 2873 **Census:** 20 **Outpatient Visits:** 94416 **Births:** 1006 **Total Expense ($000):** 66983 **Payroll Expense ($000):** 28291 **Personnel:** 433

MOUNT VERNON—Skagit County

★ ◇ **SKAGIT VALLEY HOSPITAL (500003)**, 1415 East Kincaid Street, Zip 98274–4126, Mailing Address: P.O. Box 1376, Zip 98273–1376; tel. 360/424–4111 **A**2 5 9 10 19 21 **F**3 9 11 13 18 20 22 26 28 29 30 31 32 34 35 36 40 41 43 45 47 48 49 50 51 54 56 57 58 59 60 62 63 64 68 70 73 74 76 77 78 79 80 81 82 84 85 86 87 89 92 93 97 98 100 102 103 107 108 111 114 115 116 117 118 120 121 123 124 127 129 130 144 146 147 148 **P**6
Primary Contact: Gregg A. Davidson, FACHE, Chief Executive Officer
COO: Michael T. Liepman, Chief Operating Officer
CFO: Thomas Litaker, Chief Financial Officer
CMO: Connie L. Davis, M.D., Chief Medical Officer
CIO: Doug Riley, Director Information Services
CHR: Deborah Martin, Assistant Administrator Human Resources
CNO: Barb Jensen, R.N., Interim Chief Nursing Executive
Web address: www.skagitvalleyhospital.org
Control: Hospital district or authority, Government, nonfederal **Service:** General Medical and Surgical

Staffed Beds: 137 **Admissions:** 7392 **Census:** 76 **Outpatient Visits:** 493731 **Births:** 1121 **Total Expense ($000):** 255031 **Payroll Expense ($000):** 103047 **Personnel:** 2002

NEWPORT—Pend Oreille County

NEWPORT HOSPITAL AND HEALTH SERVICES (501310), 714 West Pine Street, Zip 99156–9046; tel. 509/447–2441, (Nonreporting) **A**9 10 18
Primary Contact: Thomas W. Wilbur, Chief Executive Officer and Superintendent
COO: Shelley Froehlich, R.N., Director Nursing Services
CMO: Shannon Radke, M.D., Chief Medical Staff
CIO: Walter Price, Director Information Technology
CHR: Joseph Clouse, Chief Administrative Officer
Web address: www.phd1.org
Control: Hospital district or authority, Government, nonfederal **Service:** General Medical and Surgical

Staffed Beds: 25

Hospital, Medicare Provider Number, Address, Telephone, Approval, Facility, and Physician Codes, Health Care System

★ American Hospital Association (AHA) membership
☐ The Joint Commission accreditation
◇ DNV Healthcare Inc. accreditation
○ Healthcare Facilities Accreditation Program
△ Commission on Accreditation of Rehabilitation Facilities (CARF) accreditation

---

WA

OAK HARBOR—Island County

✠ **NAVAL HOSPITAL OAK HARBOR**, 3475 North Saratoga Street, Zip 98278–8800; tel. 360/257–9500, (Nonreporting) **A**1 **S** Bureau of Medicine and Surgery, Department of the Navy, Washington, DC
Primary Contact: Captain Edward D. Simmer, MC, USN, Commanding Officer, General and Forensic Psychiatrist
COO: Lieutenant Michael Bowers, Interim Director for Administration
CFO: Lieutenant Matthew Martin, Director Resource Management
CMO: Lieutenant Commander Catherine Borja, M.D., Chairman Executive Committee Medical Staff
CIO: Gregory Carruth, Head Information Management
CHR: Lieutenant Michael Bowers, Head Human Resources
CNO: Captain Karen Pruett–Baer, Senior Nurse Executive
Web address: www.med.navy.mil/sites/nhoh/Pages/default.aspx
Control: Navy, Government, federal **Service:** General Medical and Surgical

Staffed Beds: 29

ODESSA—Lincoln County

★ **ODESSA MEMORIAL HEALTHCARE CENTER (501307)**, 502 East Amende Drive, Zip 99159–7003, Mailing Address: P.O. Box 368, Zip 99159–0368; tel. 509/982–2611 **A**9 10 18 **F**3 7 10 29 30 34 40 43 45 50 57 59 65 77 93 127 128 130 133 **P**6
Primary Contact: Mo P. Sheldon, Administrator
COO: Alyssa Oestreich, Chief Operating Officer
CFO: Annette Edwards, Chief Financial Officer
CMO: Linda J. Powel, M.D., Medical Director
CHR: Jodi J. Bailey, Human Resources Director
CNO: Megan Shepard, Director Clinical Services
Web address: www.omhc.org
Control: Hospital district or authority, Government, nonfederal **Service:** General Medical and Surgical

Staffed Beds: 25 **Admissions:** 49 **Census:** 22 **Births:** 0 **Total Expense ($000):** 7000 **Payroll Expense ($000):** 3102

OLYMPIA—Thurston County

☐ **CAPITAL MEDICAL CENTER (500139)**, 3900 Capital Mall Drive S.W., Zip 98502–5026, Mailing Address: P.O. Box 19002, Zip 98507–0013; tel. 360/754–5858, (Nonreporting) **A**1 9 10 **S** Capella Healthcare, Franklin, TN
Primary Contact: Jim Geist, Chief Executive Officer
CFO: Brian Anderson, Chief Financial Officer
CMO: Rojesh Sharangpani, M.D., Chief of Staff
CIO: Renee Crotty, Coordinator Marketing and Public Relations
CHR: Dana Vandewege, Director Human Resources
Web address: www.capitalmedical.com
Control: Partnership, Investor–owned, for–profit **Service:** General Medical and Surgical

Staffed Beds: 110

✠ △ **PROVIDENCE ST. PETER HOSPITAL (500024)**, 413 Lilly Road N.E., Zip 98506–5166; tel. 360/491–9480 **A**1 7 9 10 **F**3 4 5 11 12 13 15 17 18 20 22 24 26 28 29 30 34 35 36 38 40 43 44 45 46 48 49 51 53 56 57 58 59 60 61 64 66 70 73 74 75 76 77 78 79 80 81 83 84 85 86 87 89 90 92 93 97 98 99 100 101 102 104 105 107 108 110 111 114 115 116 117 118 119 129 130 131 132 134 135 143 146 147 148 **P**6 **S** Providence Health & Services, Renton, WA
Primary Contact: Medrice Coluccio, R.N., Chief Executive Officer
COO: Paul G. Wilkinson, Chief Operating Officer
CFO: Denise Marroni, Chief Financial Officer
CMO: Kevin Caserta, M.D., Chief Medical Officer
CIO: Kerry Miles, Chief Information Officer
CHR: Susan Meenk, Vice President Human Resources
CNO: Michelle James, Chief Nursing Officer
Web address: www.providence.org/swsa/facilities/st_peter_hospital
Control: Church–operated, Nongovernment, not–for profit **Service:** General Medical and Surgical

Staffed Beds: 371 **Admissions:** 20665 **Census:** 259 **Outpatient Visits:** 295290 **Births:** 2089 **Total Expense ($000):** 359096 **Payroll Expense ($000):** 137054 **Personnel:** 1349

OMAK—Okanogan County

MID–VALLEY HOSPITAL (501328), 810 Jasmine, Zip 98841–9578, Mailing Address: P.O. Box 793, Zip 98841–0793; tel. 509/826–1760 **A**9 10 18 **F**11 13 15 29 34 40 43 45 57 59 64 65 68 70 76 81 82 87 89 93 107 115 119 127 133 135
Primary Contact: Michael D. Billing, Administrator
CFO: Scott Attridge, Chief Financial Officer
CMO: Jennifer Thill, Chief of Staff
CIO: Ethan Harris, Manager Information Systems
CHR: Randy Coffell, Manager Human Resources
CNO: Rebecca Christoph, Director Nursing and Patient Care Services
Web address: www.mvhealth.org
Control: Hospital district or authority, Government, nonfederal **Service:** General Medical and Surgical

Staffed Beds: 30 **Admissions:** 986 **Census:** 8 **Births:** 244 **Total Expense ($000):** 30487 **Payroll Expense ($000):** 14666

OTHELLO—Adams County

★ **OTHELLO COMMUNITY HOSPITAL (501318)**, 315 North 14th Avenue, Zip 99344–1297; tel. 509/488–2636 **A**9 10 18 **F**3 7 11 13 15 30 34 35 39 40 43 57 64 65 68 76 81 93 107 110 111 114 119 133 135 145
Primary Contact: Connie Agenbroad, Chief Executive Officer
CFO: Mark Bunch, Director Finance
CHR: Cheryl Olson, Chief Human Resources Officer
Web address: www.othellocommunityhospital.org
Control: Hospital district or authority, Government, nonfederal **Service:** General Medical and Surgical

Staffed Beds: 25 **Admissions:** 686 **Census:** 3 **Outpatient Visits:** 31333 **Births:** 515 **Total Expense ($000):** 14667 **Payroll Expense ($000):** 8534 **Personnel:** 118

PASCO—Franklin County

✠ △ **LOURDES MEDICAL CENTER (501337)**, 520 North Fourth Avenue, Zip 99301–5257, Mailing Address: P.O. Box 2568, Zip 99302–2568; tel. 509/547–7704 **A**1 7 9 10 18 **F**8 13 15 18 29 30 34 35 37 40 41 42 45 46 50 52 56 57 59 68 70 74 75 76 77 79 80 81 84 90 91 96 97 107 108 110 111 114 118 126 129 130 131 143 144 145 146 147 **S** Ascension Health, Saint Louis, MO
Primary Contact: John Serle, FACHE, President and Chief Executive Officer
CFO: Frank Becker, Chief Financial Officer
CMO: Venkataraman Sambasivan, M.D., Chief Medical Officer
CIO: Deb Carpenter, Director Information Technology
CHR: Barbara Blood, Executive Director Human Resources
CNO: Denise Clapp, Chief Nursing Officer
Web address: www.lourdeshealth.net
Control: Church–operated, Nongovernment, not–for profit **Service:** General Medical and Surgical

Staffed Beds: 53 **Admissions:** 1966 **Census:** 19 **Outpatient Visits:** 188779 **Total Expense ($000):** 85903 **Payroll Expense ($000):** 34653

POMEROY—Garfield County

★ **GARFIELD COUNTY PUBLIC HOSPITAL DISTRICT (501301)**, 66 North 6th Street, Zip 99347–9705; tel. 509/843–1591 **A**9 10 18 **F**7 11 29 34 35 38 40 41 44 50 56 57 59 64 65 75 77 86 87 91 93 94 96 97 99 100 101 102 103 104 127 130 131 133 146 148 **P**6
Primary Contact: Andrew Craigie, Chief Executive Officer
CFO: Andrew Craigie, Chief Executive Officer
CMO: Glenn Houser, M.D., Chief Medical Officer
CIO: Nevelyn Schooler, Health Information Manager
CHR: Alicia Scharnhorst, Human Resources and Business Office Manager
CNO: Susan Morrow, R.N., Chief Nursing Officer
Web address: www.garfieldcountyphd.org
Control: Hospital district or authority, Government, nonfederal **Service:** General Medical and Surgical

Staffed Beds: 25 **Admissions:** 104 **Census:** 21 **Outpatient Visits:** 8685 **Births:** 0 **Total Expense ($000):** 6259 **Payroll Expense ($000):** 3719 **Personnel:** 62

PORT ANGELES—Clallam County

★ **OLYMPIC MEDICAL CENTER (500072)**, 939 Caroline Street, Zip 98362–3997; tel. 360/417–7000 **A**2 5 9 10 19 20 **F**3 13 15 18 28 29 31 34 40 54 57 59 62 64 70 74 75 76 78 79 81 85 89 93 97 107 108 110 111 114 119 121 123 127 129 131 132 144 146 147 148 **P**6
Primary Contact: Eric Lewis, Chief Executive Officer
CFO: Julie Rukstad, Chief Financial Officer
CMO: R. Scott Kennedy, M.D., Assistant Administrator and Chief Medical Officer
CIO: Linda Brown, Chief Information Officer
CHR: Richard Neuman, Assistant Administrator and Chief Human Resources Officer
Web address: www.olympicmedical.org
Control: Hospital district or authority, Government, nonfederal **Service:** General Medical and Surgical

Staffed Beds: 78 **Admissions:** 4253 **Census:** 40 **Outpatient Visits:** 245246 **Births:** 453 **Total Expense ($000):** 141505 **Payroll Expense ($000):** 66518 **Personnel:** 966

PORT TOWNSEND—Jefferson County

★ ◇ **JEFFERSON HEALTHCARE (501323)**, 834 Sheridan Street, Zip 98368–2443; tel. 360/385–2200 **A**9 10 18 21 **F**13 15 18 28 29 31 34 35 40 45 46 50 62 63 65 70 76 81 87 93 107 110 111 114 119 127 129 130 135 146 148
Primary Contact: Mike Glenn, Chief Executive Officer
COO: Paula Dowdle, Chief Operating Officer
CFO: Hilary Whittington, Chief Financial Officer
CMO: Joe Mattern, M.D., Chief Medical Officer
CHR: Heather Bailey, Chief Human Resources Officer
CNO: Joyce Cardinal, Chief Nursing Executive
Web address: www.jeffersonhealthcare.org
Control: Hospital district or authority, Government, nonfederal **Service:** General Medical and Surgical

Staffed Beds: 25 **Admissions:** 1435 **Census:** 14 **Births:** 112 **Total Expense ($000):** 77515 **Payroll Expense ($000):** 35494

WA

★ **PMH MEDICAL CENTER (501312)**, 723 Memorial Street, Zip 99350–1593;
tel. 509/786–2222 **A**9 10 18 **F**7 11 13 15 29 34 35 37 40 43 45 54 56 57
59 62 64 68 75 76 77 79 81 85 89 97 107 108 110 114 119 127 130 131
133 135 143 146 148
Primary Contact: Julie Petersen, Chief Executive Officer
CFO: Tim Cooper, Chief Financial Officer
CMO: Keith Butvilas, M.D., Chief Medical Officer
CIO: Dan Harter, Manager Information Systems
CHR: Pamela S. Healea, Director Human Resources
CNO: Tina Glockner, Chief Nursing Officer
Web address: www.pmhmedicalcenter.com/
Control: Hospital district or authority, Government, nonfederal **Service:** General
Medical and Surgical

Staffed Beds: 25 **Admissions:** 705 **Census:** 9 **Births:** 289

☐ **PULLMAN REGIONAL HOSPITAL (501331)**, 835 S.E. Bishop Boulevard,
Zip 99163–5512; tel. 509/332–2541 **A**1 9 10 18 **F**3 13 15 28 29 30 34 35
36 37 38 40 43 44 45 47 50 51 53 55 57 59 64 68 70 74 75 76 77 78 79
81 86 87 89 93 98 101 102 104 105 107 108 110 111 114 118 119 126
129 130 131 132 133 144 146
Primary Contact: Scott K. Adams, Chief Executive Officer
CFO: Steven Febus, Chief Financial Officer
CMO: Richard Caggiano, M.D., Chief Medical Officer
CHR: Bernadette Berney, Director Human Resources
Web address: www.pullmanhospital.org
Control: Hospital district or authority, Government, nonfederal **Service:** General
Medical and Surgical

Staffed Beds: 25 **Admissions:** 1256 **Census:** 10 **Births:** 426 **Total Expense**
($000): 49838 **Payroll Expense ($000):** 23649

GOOD SAMARITAN COMMUNITY HEALTHCARE See MultiCare Good Samaritan
Hospital

☐ △ **MULTICARE GOOD SAMARITAN HOSPITAL (500079)**, 401 15th Avenue
S.E., Zip 98372–3770, Mailing Address: P.O. Box 1247, Zip 98371–0192;
tel. 253/697–4000 **A**1 2 7 9 10 **F**3 11 13 17 18 20 22 24 28 29 30 31 34 35
38 40 41 43 45 47 48 50 51 55 56 57 58 59 61 64 65 66 68 70 73 74 75
76 78 79 81 82 84 85 87 89 90 91 93 96 97 99 100 101 102 103 104 106
107 108 111 114 115 117 118 119 126 129 130 132 146 147 148
S MultiCare Health System, Tacoma, WA
Primary Contact: Glenn Kasman, President, East Pierce Region
COO: Marcia L. Johnson, R.N., Chief Operating Officer
CFO: Anna Loomis, Interim Vice President
CMO: David Chen, M.D., Vice President Medical Affairs
CIO: Florence Chang, Executive Vice President
CHR: Sarah Horsman, Vice President Human Resources
CNO: Kate Bechtold, R.N., Senior Vice President and Chief Nurse Executive
Web address: www.goodsamhealth.org
Control: Other not–for–profit (including NFP Corporation) **Service:** General
Medical and Surgical

Staffed Beds: 265 **Admissions:** 18044 **Census:** 199 **Outpatient Visits:**
128199 **Births:** 2267 **Total Expense ($000):** 311688 **Payroll Expense**
($000): 142651 **Personnel:** 1739

★ **QUINCY VALLEY MEDICAL CENTER (501320)**, 908 10th Avenue S.W.,
Zip 98848–1376; tel. 509/787–3531, (Nonreporting) **A**9 10 18
Primary Contact: Mehdi Merred, Chief Executive Officer
CFO: Dean Taplett, Controller
CMO: Mark Vance, M.D., Chief Medical Officer
CIO: Ruth Vance, Director Information Systems
CHR: Alene Walker, Director Human Resources
Web address: www.quincyhospital.org
Control: County–Government, nonfederal **Service:** General Medical and Surgical

Staffed Beds: 47

✉ **UW MEDICINE/VALLEY MEDICAL CENTER (500088)**, 400 South 43rd Street,
Zip 98055–5714, Mailing Address: P.O. Box 50010, Zip 98058–5010;
tel. 425/228–3450 **A**1 2 3 5 9 10 **F**3 8 11 13 15 18 19 20 22 26 28 29 30
31 32 34 35 36 37 38 40 43 44 45 48 49 50 51 53 54 55 57 58 59 60 64
65 66 68 70 72 74 75 76 77 78 79 81 82 83 84 85 86 87 89 91 92 93 94
96 97 100 101 102 104 107 110 114 115 118 119 120 121 123 124 126
129 130 131 132 135 144 146 147 148 **P**6 **S** UW Medicine, Seattle, WA
Primary Contact: Richard D. Roodman, Chief Executive Officer
COO: Paul Hayes, Executive Vice President and Chief Operating Officer
CFO: Larry Smith, Senior Vice President and Chief Financial Officer
CMO: Kathryn Beattie, M.D., Senior Vice President and Chief Medical Officer
CHR: Barbara Mitchell, Senior Vice President Marketing and Human Resources
CNO: Scott Alleman, Senior Vice President Patient Care Services and Chief
Nursing Officer
Web address: www.valleymed.org
Control: Hospital district or authority, Government, nonfederal **Service:** General
Medical and Surgical

Staffed Beds: 182 **Admissions:** 17477 **Census:** 180 **Outpatient Visits:**
632189 **Births:** 4356 **Total Expense ($000):** 461436 **Payroll Expense**
($000): 203577 **Personnel:** 2423

★ **FERRY COUNTY MEMORIAL HOSPITAL (501322)**, 36 Klondike Road,
Zip 99166–9701; tel. 509/775–3333, (Nonreporting) **A**9 10 18
Primary Contact: Gary W. Robertson, Chief Executive Officer
CFO: Kelly Leslie, Chief Financial Officer
CMO: Farhad H. Alrashedy, M.D., Chief Medical Officer
CIO: James Davidson, Director of Information Services
CHR: Michelle Loftis, Human Resources Officer
CNO: Thomas Durham, Chief Nursing Officer
Web address: www.fcphd.org
Control: Hospital district or authority, Government, nonfederal **Service:** General
Medical and Surgical

Staffed Beds: 25

✉ △ **KADLEC REGIONAL MEDICAL CENTER (500058)**, 888 Swift Boulevard,
Zip 99352–3514; tel. 509/946–4611 **A**1 2 7 9 10 **F**3 11 13 15 18 20 22 24
26 28 29 30 31 34 36 40 43 46 47 48 49 50 51 54 55 57 59 64 68 70 72
74 75 76 77 78 79 81 82 85 86 87 89 90 93 96 97 107 108 110 111 114
115 116 117 118 119 127 130 144 146 147 148 **S** QHR, Brentwood, TN
Primary Contact: Rand J. Wortman, Chief Executive Officer
COO: Rand J. Wortman, Chief Executive Officer
CFO: Julie Meek, Vice President Finance
CMO: Dale Hoekema, M.D., Vice President Medical Affairs and Chief Medical
Officer
CIO: David Roach, Vice President Information Systems
CHR: Jeff Clark, Vice President Human Resources
CNO: Kirk Harper, R.N., Vice President, Nursing
Web address: www.kadlecmed.org
Control: Other not–for–profit (including NFP Corporation) **Service:** General
Medical and Surgical

Staffed Beds: 251 **Admissions:** 14808 **Census:** 169 **Outpatient Visits:**
242787 **Births:** 2695 **Total Expense ($000):** 364761 **Payroll Expense**
($000): 161822 **Personnel:** 1750

★ **LOURDES COUNSELING CENTER (504008)**, 1175 Carondelet Drive,
Zip 99354–3300; tel. 509/943–9104, (Nonreporting) **A**9 10 **S** Ascension Health,
Saint Louis, MO
Primary Contact: Barbara Mead, Vice President Behavioral Health and Physician
Clinics
CFO: Frank Becker, Chief Financial Officer
CIO: Jared Fleming, Director, Information Services
CHR: Barbara Blood, Director Human Resources
CNO: Denise Clapp, Chief Nursing Officer
Web address: www.lourdeshealth.net
Control: Church–operated, Nongovernment, not–for profit **Service:** Psychiatric

Staffed Beds: 32

WA

Hospital, Medicare Provider Number, Address, Telephone, Approval, Facility, and Physician Codes, Health Care System

★ American Hospital Association (AHA) membership
☐ The Joint Commission accreditation
◇ DNV Healthcare Inc. accreditation
○ Healthcare Facilities Accreditation Program
△ Commission on Accreditation of Rehabilitation Facilities (CARF) accreditation

© 2014 AHA Guide   *Many Facility Codes have changed. Please refer to the AHA Guide Code Chart.*   Hospitals **A687**

RITZVILLE—Adams County

★ **EAST ADAMS RURAL HOSPITAL (501311)**, 903 South Adams Street, Zip 99169–2298; tel. 509/659–1200 **A**9 10 18 **F**7 40 43 57 65 82 84 93 97 107 127 133 143 148
Primary Contact: Gary Bostrom, Chief Executive Officer and Chief Financial Officer
COO: Dina McBride, Chief Operating Officer and Director Human Resources
CFO: Gary Bostrom, Chief Executive Officer and Chief Financial Officer
CMO: Valerie Eckley, M.D., Chief of Staff
CIO: Kellie Ottmar, Manager Information Services
CHR: Dina McBride, Chief Operating Officer and Director Human Resources
CNO: Brenda Herr, Chief Nursing Officer
Web address: www.earh.com
Control: Hospital district or authority, Government, nonfederal **Service:** General Medical and Surgical

Staffed Beds: 8 **Admissions:** 46 **Census:** 1 **Births:** 0 **Total Expense ($000):** 5024 **Payroll Expense ($000):** 2480

SEATTLE—King County

◇ **GROUP HEALTH COOPERATIVE CENTRAL HOSPITAL (500052)**, 201 16th Avenue East, Zip 98112–5226; tel. 206/326–3000, (Nonreporting) **A**3 5 9 10 21
Primary Contact: Jane Hutcheson, Administrator and Director Clinical Operations
Web address: www.https://www.ghc.org
Control: Corporation, Investor–owned, for–profit **Service:** General Medical and Surgical

Staffed Beds: 306

⊞ **KINDRED HOSPITAL SEATTLE–NORTHGATE (502002)**, 10631 8th Avenue N.E., Zip 98125–7213; tel. 206/364–2050, (Includes KINDRED HOSPITAL SEATTLE–FIRST HILL, 1334 Terry Avenue, Zip 98101–2747; tel. 206/682–2661), (Nonreporting) **A**1 9 10 **S** Kindred Healthcare, Louisville, KY
Primary Contact: Jean Clark, Administrator
CFO: David Stob, Chief Financial Officer
Web address: www.kindredhospitalseattle.com/
Control: Corporation, Investor–owned, for–profit **Service:** Long–Term Acute Care hospital

Staffed Beds: 42

☐ **NAVOS (504009)**, 2600 S.W. Holden Street, Zip 98126–3505; tel. 206/933–7299 **A**1 9 10 **F**29 98 99 100 101 102 103 104
Primary Contact: David Johnson, Chief Executive Officer
COO: Cassie Undlin, Chief Administrative Officer
CFO: Cassie Undlin, Chief Administrative Officer
CMO: Carlos Andarsio, M.D., Chief Medical Officer
CIO: Jim Rudnick, Vice President Information Technology
CHR: Judi Mitchell, Vice President Administrative Services
CNO: Terry McInerney, Director of Nursing, Inpatient
Web address: www.navos.org
Control: Other not–for–profit (including NFP Corporation) **Service:** Surgical

Staffed Beds: 69 **Admissions:** 1457 **Census:** 37 **Births:** 0

☐ **REGIONAL HOSPITAL FOR RESPIRATORY AND COMPLEX CARE (502001)**, 12844 Military Road South, Zip 98168–3045; tel. 206/248–4548 **A**1 10 **F**1 29 30 50 85 87 130 148 **P**1 4 5
Primary Contact: Anne McBride, Chief Executive Officer
CMO: Embra Roper, Chief Medical Officer
CHR: Valerie Albano, Director, Human Resources
CNO: Christi Sifri, Chief Nursing Executive
Web address: www.regionalhospital.org
Control: Other not–for–profit (including NFP Corporation) **Service:** Long–Term Acute Care hospital

Staffed Beds: 31 **Admissions:** 239 **Census:** 21 **Outpatient Visits:** 0 **Births:** 0 **Total Expense ($000):** 18715 **Payroll Expense ($000):** 7216

SCHICK SHADEL HOSPITAL, 12101 Ambaum Boulevard S.W., Zip 98146–2651, Mailing Address: P.O. Box 48149, Zip 98148–0149; tel. 206/244–8100, (Nonreporting) **A**9
Primary Contact: Bruce Brandler, Administrator
CFO: Troy Cherry, Chief Financial Officer
CMO: Kayyan Danbdala, M.D., Medical Director
CIO: Peter Vermulen, Director Information Technology
CHR: Elaine Oksendahl, Director Human Resources and Risk Management
Web address: www.schickshadel.com
Control: Corporation, Investor–owned, for–profit **Service:** Alcoholism and other chemical dependency

Staffed Beds: 48

⊞ **SEATTLE CANCER CARE ALLIANCE (500138)**, 825 Eastlake Avenue East, Zip 98109–4405, Mailing Address: P.O. Box 19023, Zip 98109–1023; tel. 206/288–1400 **A**1 9 10 **F**3 8 15 30 31 34 35 39 46 50 57 59 64 65 68 75 78 80 82 84 86 87 93 107 108 110 111 115 117 119 120 121 123 130 132 135 136 142 143 146 147
Primary Contact: Norm Hubbard, Executive Vice President
CFO: Jonathan Tingstad, Vice President and Chief Financial Officer
CMO: Marc Stewart, M.D., Vice President and Medical Director
CIO: David Ackerson, Chief Information Officer
CHR: Han Nachtrieb, Vice President Human Resources
Web address: www.seattlecca.org
Control: Other not–for–profit (including NFP Corporation) **Service:** Cancer

Staffed Beds: 20 **Admissions:** 579 **Census:** 17 **Outpatient Visits:** 82598 **Births:** 0 **Total Expense ($000):** 363820 **Payroll Expense ($000):** 73140 **Personnel:** 1020

☐ △ ◇ **SEATTLE CHILDREN'S HOSPITAL (503300)**, 4800 Sand Point Way N.E., Zip 98105–3901, Mailing Address: P.O. Box 5371, Zip 98145–5005; tel. 206/987–2000 **A**1 2 3 5 7 9 10 21 **F**3 7 8 9 21 23 25 27 29 30 31 32 34 35 36 38 39 40 43 46 53 54 55 57 58 60 61 62 64 65 66 68 71 72 74 75 77 78 79 81 82 84 85 86 87 88 89 90 93 97 98 99 100 102 104 105 107 108 111 115 116 117 119 126 129 130 131 132 134 136 137 138 139 141 142 143 144 146 148
Primary Contact: Thomas N. Hansen, M.D., Chief Executive Officer
COO: Cindy Gazecki, Senior Vice President, Hospital Operations
CFO: Kelly Wallace, Senior Vice President and Chief Financial Officer
CMO: David Fisher, M.D., Senior Vice President and Chief Medical Officer
CIO: Wes Wright, Senior Vice President and Chief Information Officer
CHR: Steven Hurwitz, Senior Vice President Shared Services
CNO: Susan Heath, R.N., Senior Vice President and Chief Nursing Officer
Web address: www.seattlechildrens.org
Control: Other not–for–profit (including NFP Corporation) **Service:** Children's general

Staffed Beds: 250 **Admissions:** 14494 **Census:** 202 **Births:** 0 **Total Expense ($000):** 892848 **Payroll Expense ($000):** 352979

⊞ △ **SWEDISH MEDICAL CENTER–CHERRY HILL CAMPUS (500025)**, 500 17th Avenue, Zip 98122–5711; tel. 206/320–2000 **A**1 2 3 5 7 9 10 **F**3 5 8 11 17 18 20 22 24 26 27 28 29 30 31 33 34 35 37 38 40 41 46 53 56 57 58 59 60 61 64 65 68 71 74 75 77 78 79 80 81 82 85 87 90 92 93 94 95 96 97 98 100 102 105 107 108 109 110 111 112 113 114 115 119 120 121 123 124 126 129 130 131 132 135 141 143 144 146 148 **P**2 6 **S** Swedish Health Services, Seattle, WA
Primary Contact: Todd Strumwasser, M.D., Chief Executive
CFO: Jeffrey Veilleux, Senior Vice President and Chief Financial Officer
CMO: John Vassall, M.D., Chief Medical Officer
CIO: Janice Newell, Chief Information Officer
Web address: www.swedish.org
Control: Other not–for–profit (including NFP Corporation) **Service:** General Medical and Surgical

Staffed Beds: 189 **Admissions:** 9445 **Census:** 130 **Outpatient Visits:** 131646 **Births:** 0 **Total Expense ($000):** 346321 **Payroll Expense ($000):** 96683

⊞ **SWEDISH MEDICAL CENTER–FIRST HILL (500027)**, 747 Broadway, Zip 98122–4307; tel. 206/386–6000, (Includes SWEDISH MEDICAL CENTER–BALLARD, 5300 Tallman Avenue N.W., Zip 98107–3932; tel. 206/782–2700; Jennifer Graves, R.N., MS, Chief Executive) **A**1 2 3 5 9 10 **F**3 4 5 8 11 12 13 15 18 20 21 22 29 30 31 32 34 35 36 37 38 39 40 41 42 45 46 47 48 49 52 54 55 56 57 58 59 60 61 64 65 66 68 70 71 72 73 74 75 76 77 78 79 80 81 82 83 84 85 86 87 88 89 91 92 93 94 95 96 97 99 100 101 102 104 107 108 109 110 111 112 114 115 116 117 118 119 120 121 123 126 127 129 130 131 132 134 135 136 138 139 141 143 144 146 147 148 **P**2 6 **S** Swedish Health Services, Seattle, WA
Primary Contact: Todd Strumwasser, M.D., Chief Executive
CFO: Jeffrey Veilleux, Executive Vice President and Chief Financial Officer
CMO: John Vassall, M.D., Chief Medical Officer
CIO: Janice Newell, Chief Information Officer
Web address: www.swedish.org
Control: Other not–for–profit (including NFP Corporation) **Service:** General Medical and Surgical

Staffed Beds: 631 **Admissions:** 33268 **Census:** 359 **Outpatient Visits:** 555574 **Births:** 6703

Many Facility Codes have changed. Please refer to the AHA Guide Code Chart. © 2014 AHA Guide

✠ △ **UNIVERSITY OF WASHINGTON MEDICAL CENTER (500008)**, 1959 N.E. Pacific Street, Zip 98195–6151; tel. 206/598–3300 **A**1 2 3 5 7 8 9 10 **F**3 8 9 11 12 13 15 17 18 20 22 24 26 28 29 30 31 34 35 36 39 40 44 45 46 47 48 49 50 51 52 54 55 56 57 58 59 60 61 64 65 68 70 72 74 75 76 77 78 79 81 82 84 85 86 87 90 91 92 93 94 96 97 98 100 101 102 103 104 106 107 108 110 111 114 115 116 117 118 119 120 121 123 124 126 130 131 132 136 137 138 139 140 141 142 144 145 146 147 148 **P**6 **S** UW Medicine, Seattle, WA
Primary Contact: Stephen P. Zieniewicz, FACHE, Executive Director
CFO: Lori J. Mitchell, Chief Financial Officer
CMO: Tom Staiger, M.D., Medical Director
CHR: Jennifer J. Petritz, Director Human Resources
CNO: Grace E. Parker, R.N., Chief Nursing Officer
Web address: www.uwmedicine.org/Patient–Care/Locations/UWMC/Pages/default.aspx
Control: State–Government, nonfederal **Service:** General Medical and Surgical

Staffed Beds: 419 **Admissions:** 17728 **Census:** 337 **Outpatient Visits:** 315465 **Births:** 2010 **Total Expense ($000):** 928186 **Payroll Expense ($000):** 328393 **Personnel:** 5503

✠ △ **UW MEDICINE/HARBORVIEW MEDICAL CENTER (500064)**, 325 Ninth Avenue, Zip 98104–2499, Mailing Address: P.O. Box 359717, Zip 98195–9717; tel. 206/744–3000 **A**1 3 5 7 8 9 10 **F**3 5 9 16 17 18 20 22 26 29 30 31 32 34 35 36 37 38 40 41 43 45 46 47 48 49 50 56 58 59 60 61 64 65 66 68 70 72 73 74 75 77 78 79 80 81 82 84 85 86 87 88 89 90 91 92 93 94 96 97 98 100 101 102 103 104 105 107 108 111 114 115 117 118 119 124 126 129 130 131 132 133 135 146 147 148 **P**6 **S** UW Medicine, Seattle, WA
Primary Contact: Johnese Spisso, Interim Executive Director
CFO: Kera Rabbit, Assistant Administrator, Finance
CMO: J. Richard Goss, M.D., Medical Director
CIO: James Fine, M.D., Chief Information Officer
CHR: Nicki McCraw, Assistant Vice President Human Resources
CNO: Darcy Jaffe, R.N., Interim Chief Nursing Officer
Web address: www.uwmedicine.org/Patient–Care/Locations/HMC/Pages/default.aspx
Control: County–Government, nonfederal **Service:** General Medical and Surgical

Staffed Beds: 413 **Admissions:** 17999 **Census:** 372 **Outpatient Visits:** 347510 **Births:** 0 **Total Expense ($000):** 807853 **Payroll Expense ($000):** 363096 **Personnel:** 5327

✠ **UW MEDICINE/NORTHWEST HOSPITAL & MEDICAL CENTER (500001)**, 1550 North 115th Street, Zip 98133–8401; tel. 206/364–0500 **A**1 2 3 5 9 10 **F**3 8 9 11 13 15 17 18 20 22 24 26 28 29 30 31 34 40 43 45 46 49 50 51 53 54 56 59 64 67 68 70 71 73 74 76 77 78 79 81 82 83 84 85 92 93 96 97 98 103 104 105 107 108 110 111 114 115 119 126 129 130 131 135 146 147 148 **S** UW Medicine, Seattle, WA
Primary Contact: Cynthia Hecker, R.N., Executive Director
CFO: Ketty Hsieh, Senior Director Finance
CMO: Greg Schroedl, M.D., Vice President, Medical and Chief Medical Officer
CIO: Eric Neil, Interim Chief Information Officer
CHR: Linda Olmstead, Director, Human Resources
CNO: Susan Manfredi, R.N., Vice President and Chief Nursing Officer
Web address: www.uwmedicine.org/Patient–Care/Locations/nwh/Pages/default.aspx
Control: Other not–for–profit (including NFP Corporation) **Service:** General Medical and Surgical

Staffed Beds: 177 **Admissions:** 9974 **Census:** 121 **Outpatient Visits:** 234884 **Births:** 1303 **Total Expense ($000):** 323557 **Payroll Expense ($000):** 132624 **Personnel:** 1597

✠ △ **VETERANS AFFAIRS PUGET SOUND HEALTH CARE SYSTEM**, 1660 South Columbian Way, Zip 98108–1597; tel. 206/762–1010, (Includes VETERANS AFFAIRS PUGET SOUND HEALTH CARE SYSTEM–AMERICAN LAKE DIVISION, Tacoma, Zip 98493; tel. 253/582–8440), (Nonreporting) **A**1 2 3 5 7 8 9 **S** Department of Veterans Affairs, Washington, DC
Primary Contact: Michael J. Murphy, FACHE, Chief Executive Officer
CFO: Kenneth J. Hudson, Chief Financial Officer
CMO: Gordon Starkebaum, M.D., Chief of Staff
CIO: Glenn Zwinger, Manager Information Systems Services
Web address: www.pugetsound.va.gov/
Control: Veterans Affairs, Government, federal **Service:** General Medical and Surgical

Staffed Beds: 358

✠ △ **VIRGINIA MASON MEDICAL CENTER (500005)**, 1100 Ninth Avenue, Zip 98101–2756, Mailing Address: P.O. Box 900, Zip 98111–0900; tel. 206/223–6600, (Total facility includes 35 beds in nursing home–type unit) **A**1 2 3 5 7 8 9 10 **F**2 3 5 8 9 12 15 17 18 20 22 24 26 28 29 30 31 32 34 35 36 37 38 40 44 45 46 47 48 49 50 51 54 55 56 57 58 59 60 61 63 64 65 66 68 70 71 74 75 77 78 79 80 81 82 83 84 85 86 87 90 91 92 93 94 96 97 100 101 102 103 104 105 107 108 110 111 114 115 116 117 118 119 120 121 123 124 126 128 129 130 131 132 135 136 138 141 142 143 145 146 147 148 **P**6
Primary Contact: Gary Kaplan, M.D., FACHE, Chairman and Chief Executive Officer
COO: Sarah Patterson, Executive Vice President and Chief Operating Officer
CFO: Sue Anderson, Senior Vice President, Chief Financial Officer and Chief Information Officer
CMO: Andrew Jacobs, M.D., Chief Medical Officer
CIO: Sue Anderson, Senior Vice President, Chief Financial Officer and Chief Information Officer
CHR: Kathy J. Shingleton, Ed.D., Vice President, Human Resources
CNO: Charleen Tachibana, R.N., Senior Vice President and Hospital Administrator
Web address: www.vmmc.org
Control: Other not–for–profit (including NFP Corporation) **Service:** General Medical and Surgical

Staffed Beds: 288 **Admissions:** 16437 **Census:** 232 **Outpatient Visits:** 896497 **Births:** 0 **Total Expense ($000):** 938243 **Payroll Expense ($000):** 454026 **Personnel:** 5030

SEDRO–WOOLLEY—Skagit County

✠ **PEACEHEALTH UNITED GENERAL HOSPITAL (501329)**, 2000 Hospital Drive, Zip 98284–4327; tel. 360/856–6021 **A**1 2 9 10 18 **F**3 11 15 29 30 31 34 35 40 43 45 50 53 57 59 64 68 70 75 77 78 79 81 85 89 92 93 107 108 110 111 115 118 119 120 121 123 129 130 133 134 135 143 146 **P**6 **S** PeaceHealth, Vancouver, WA
Primary Contact: James R. Barnhart, Chief Administrative Officer
CFO: Michael W. Bonthuis, Chief Financial Officer
CMO: Randy Anderson, DPM, Chief Medical Officer
CHR: Tracie Skrinde, Director Human Resources
Web address: www.peacehealth.org/united–general/Pages/default.aspx
Control: Hospital district or authority, Government, nonfederal **Service:** General Medical and Surgical

Staffed Beds: 25 **Admissions:** 796 **Census:** 6 **Outpatient Visits:** 94135 **Births:** 0 **Total Expense ($000):** 45466 **Payroll Expense ($000):** 17244 **Personnel:** 263

SHELTON—Mason County

✠ **MASON GENERAL HOSPITAL (501336)**, 901 Mountain View Drive, Zip 98584–4401, Mailing Address: P.O. Box 1668, Zip 98584–5001; tel. 360/426–1611 **A**1 9 10 18 **F**11 13 15 29 30 40 57 68 70 75 79 81 83 85 107 110 130 132 147
Primary Contact: Eric Moll, Chief Executive Officer
COO: Eileen Branscome, Chief Operating Officer
CFO: Merle Brandt, Chief Financial Officer
CMO: Dean Gushee, M.D., Medical Director
CIO: Tom Hornburg, Director Information Systems
CHR: Claudia Hawley, Director Human Resources
Web address: www.masongeneral.com
Control: Hospital district or authority, Government, nonfederal **Service:** General Medical and Surgical

Staffed Beds: 25 **Admissions:** 1608 **Census:** 14 **Births:** 261

SNOQUALMIE—King County

SNOQUALMIE VALLEY HOSPITAL (501338), 9575 Ethan Wade Way S.E., Zip 98065–9577, Mailing Address: 9801 Frontier Avenue S.E., Zip 98065–5200; tel. 425/831–2300, (Nonreporting) **A**9 10 18
Primary Contact: Rodger McCollum, Chief Executive Officer
CHR: Kimberly D. Washburn, Director Human Resources
Web address: www.snoqualmiehospital.org/
Control: Hospital district or authority, Government, nonfederal **Service:** General Medical and Surgical

Staffed Beds: 18

WA

Hospital, Medicare Provider Number, Address, Telephone, Approval, Facility, and Physician Codes, Health Care System
★ American Hospital Association (AHA) membership   ○ Healthcare Facilities Accreditation Program
□ The Joint Commission accreditation   ◇ DNV Healthcare Inc. accreditation   △ Commission on Accreditation of Rehabilitation Facilities (CARF) accreditation

SOUTH BEND—Pacific County

WILLAPA HARBOR HOSPITAL (501303), 800 Alder Street, Zip 98586–4900, Mailing Address: P.O. Box 438, Zip 98586–0438; tel. 360/875–5526 **A**9 10 18 **F**3 8 11 15 34 35 40 41 45 46 50 81 85 87 92 97 107 110 113 119 127 133 145
Primary Contact: Carole Halsan, R.N., Chief Executive Officer
CFO: Terry Stone, Chief Financial Officer and Chief Information Officer
CIO: Terry Stone, Chief Financial Officer and Chief Information Officer
CHR: Krisy L. Funkhouser, Manager Human Resources
Web address: www.willapaharborhospital.com
Control: Hospital district or authority, Government, nonfederal **Service:** General Medical and Surgical

Staffed Beds: 20 **Admissions:** 236 **Census:** 2 **Births:** 0 **Total Expense ($000):** 16319 **Payroll Expense ($000):** 8081

SPOKANE—Spokane County

☒ **DEACONESS HOSPITAL (500044)**, 800 West Fifth Avenue, Zip 99204–2803, Mailing Address: P.O. Box 248, Zip 99210–0248; tel. 509/458–5800, (Nonreporting) **A**1 2 3 5 9 10 **S** Community Health Systems, Inc., Franklin, TN
Primary Contact: Maurine Cate, Chief Executive Officer
CFO: Rodney Higgins, Chief Financial Officer
CIO: Richard DeRoche, Manager Information Technology
CHR: Melinda Moore, Director Human Resources
CNO: Jennifer Petrik, Interim Chief Nursing Officer
Web address: www.deaconessspokane.com/Deaconess–Hospital/home.aspx
Control: Other not–for–profit (including NFP Corporation) **Service:** General Medical and Surgical

Staffed Beds: 388

☒ **MANN–GRANDSTAFF VETERANS AFFAIRS MEDICAL CENTER**, 4815 North Assembly Street, Zip 99205–6197; tel. 509/434–7000, (Total facility includes 34 beds in nursing home–type unit) **A**1 5 9 **F**40 62 63 **S** Department of Veterans Affairs, Washington, DC
Primary Contact: Linda K. Reynolds, FACHE, Director
COO: Perry Klein, Chief Engineering
CFO: Michael Stuhlmiller, Chief Financial Officer
CIO: Rob Fortenberry, Chief Information Officer
CHR: Jacqueline Ross, Chief Human Resources Officer
CNO: Nancy Benton, Assistant Director Patient Care Services
Web address: www.spokane.va.gov/
Control: Veterans Affairs, Government, federal **Service:** General Medical and Surgical

Staffed Beds: 70 **Admissions:** 1159 **Census:** 20 **Outpatient Visits:** 330595 **Births:** 0 **Total Expense ($000):** 168000 **Personnel:** 877

☒ △ **PROVIDENCE HOLY FAMILY HOSPITAL (500077)**, 5633 North Lidgerwood Street, Zip 99208–1224; tel. 509/482–0111 **A**1 2 5 7 9 10 **F**3 4 8 11 12 13 15 18 20 22 29 30 31 34 35 37 38 39 40 41 43 45 46 47 48 49 50 53 56 57 58 59 60 61 64 68 70 73 74 75 76 77 78 79 81 82 84 85 86 87 89 92 100 107 108 121 123 129 130 131 132 135 143 145 146 147 148 **P**6 **S** Providence Health & Services, Renton, WA
Primary Contact: Alex Jackson, Chief Executive
COO: Cathy J. Simchuk, Chief Operating Officer
CIO: Mark Vogelsang, Director Information Services
CHR: Patrick M. Clarry, Vice President Human Resources
Web address: www.providence.org
Control: Church–operated, Nongovernment, not–for profit **Service:** General Medical and Surgical

Staffed Beds: 189 **Admissions:** 9288 **Census:** 96 **Outpatient Visits:** 122974 **Births:** 1254 **Total Expense ($000):** 169029 **Payroll Expense ($000):** 54735 **Personnel:** 804

☒ **PROVIDENCE SACRED HEART MEDICAL CENTER & CHILDREN'S HOSPITAL (500054)**, 101 West Eighth Avenue, Zip 99204–2364, Mailing Address: P.O. Box 2555, Zip 99220–2555; tel. 509/474–3131, (Includes SACRED HEART CHILDREN'S HOSPITAL, 101 West Eight Avenue, Zip 99204–2307, Mailing Address: PO Box 2555, Zip 99220–2555; tel. 509/474–4841) **A**1 2 3 5 9 10 **F**3 8 13 15 17 18 19 20 21 22 23 24 25 26 27 28 29 30 31 35 36 37 40 41 42 43 45 46 47 48 49 50 56 57 58 60 64 68 70 71 72 74 75 76 78 79 81 82 83 84 85 86 87 88 89 92 96 100 102 103 104 105 106 107 108 110 111 112 114 115 118 119 120 121 123 124 126 130 132 137 138 141 145 146 147 148 **P**6 **S** Providence Health & Services, Renton, WA
Primary Contact: Alex Jackson, Chief Executive
CMO: Jeff Collins, Chief Medical Officer
CHR: Patrick Clary, Vice President Human Resources
Web address: www.shmc.org
Control: Church–operated, Nongovernment, not–for profit **Service:** General Medical and Surgical

Staffed Beds: 642 **Admissions:** 28183 **Census:** 401 **Outpatient Visits:** 206701 **Births:** 2945 **Total Expense ($000):** 710163 **Payroll Expense ($000):** 254856 **Personnel:** 3044

☐ **SHRINERS HOSPITALS FOR CHILDREN–SPOKANE (503302)**, 911 West Fifth Avenue, Zip 99204–2901, Mailing Address: P.O. Box 2472, Zip 99210–2472; tel. 509/455–7844, (Nonreporting) **A**1 9 10 **S** Shriners Hospitals for Children, Tampa, FL
Primary Contact: Peter G. Brewer, Administrator
CFO: Monica Hickman, Director Fiscal Services
CMO: Paul Caskey, M.D., Chief of Staff
CIO: Mike Allen, Director Information Services
CHR: Russ Crockett, Director Human Resources
CNO: Lynda Vilanova, Director Patient Care Services
Web address: www.shrinershospitalsforchildren.org/Hospitals/Locations/Spokane.aspx
Control: Other not–for–profit (including NFP Corporation) **Service:** Children's orthopedic

Staffed Beds: 30

☒ △ **ST. LUKE'S REHABILITATION INSTITUTE (503025)**, 711 South Cowley Street, Zip 99202–1388; tel. 509/473–6000 **A**1 7 9 10 **F**28 29 30 36 38 50 53 58 64 68 74 75 77 79 82 86 87 90 91 92 93 94 95 96 130 131 132 135 146 **P**6
Primary Contact: Thomas M. Fritz, Chief Executive Officer
COO: Ulrike Berzau, FACHE, Administrator
CFO: John D. Craig, Chief Financial Officer
CMO: Stefan Humphries, M.D., Medical Director
CIO: Fred Galusha, Chief Information Officer
CHR: Phyllis Gabel, Chief Human Resource Officer
CNO: Ginger Cohen, Chief Nurse Executive
Web address: www.st–lukes.org
Control: Other not–for–profit (including NFP Corporation) **Service:** Rehabilitation

Staffed Beds: 72 **Admissions:** 1503 **Census:** 57 **Outpatient Visits:** 59589 **Births:** 0 **Total Expense ($000):** 37938 **Payroll Expense ($000):** 22323 **Personnel:** 438

VETERANS AFFAIRS MEDICAL CENTER See Mann–Grandstaff Veterans Affairs Medical Center

SPOKANE VALLEY—Spokane County

☒ **VALLEY HOSPITAL (500119)**, 12606 East Mission Avenue, Zip 99216–1090; tel. 509/924–6650 **A**1 2 9 10 **F**15 18 29 30 31 34 40 43 45 49 50 60 64 68 70 74 75 76 77 78 79 81 85 87 107 111 114 119 146 147 148 **S** Community Health Systems, Inc., Franklin, TN
Primary Contact: Gregory Repetti, Interim Chief Executive Officer
COO: David Martin, Assistant Administrator
CFO: Justin Voelker, Chief Financial Officer
Web address: www.valleyhospital.org
Control: Corporation, Investor–owned, for–profit **Service:** General Medical and Surgical

Staffed Beds: 123 **Admissions:** 6283 **Census:** 61 **Births:** 718 **Total Expense ($000):** 107223 **Payroll Expense ($000):** 41391

SUNNYSIDE—Yakima County

★ **SUNNYSIDE COMMUNITY HOSPITAL AND CLINICS (501330)**, 1016 Tacoma Avenue, Zip 98944–2263, Mailing Address: P.O. Box 719, Zip 98944–0719; tel. 509/837–1500 **A**9 10 18 **F**3 13 15 18 26 29 30 32 34 35 40 43 45 46 50 55 56 57 59 64 65 68 70 75 76 77 79 81 82 85 86 87 97 107 108 110 111 114 119 127 130 131 133 146 147 148 **S** HealthTech Management Services, Brentwood, TN
Primary Contact: John Gallagher, Chief Executive Officer
CFO: Cary Rowan, Chief Financial Officer
CIO: John Andersen, Manager Information Systems
CHR: Elaina Wagner, Director Human Resources
CNO: Mary Beth Tubbs, Chief Nursing Officer
Web address: www.sunnysidehospital.com
Control: Other not–for–profit (including NFP Corporation) **Service:** General Medical and Surgical

Staffed Beds: 25 **Admissions:** 1561 **Census:** 12 **Outpatient Visits:** 57068 **Births:** 512 **Total Expense ($000):** 49351 **Payroll Expense ($000):** 22417 **Personnel:** 331

TACOMA—Pierce County

ALLENMORE HOSPITAL See MultiCare Tacoma General Hospital

☒ **MADIGAN HEALTHCARE SYSTEM**, Fitzsimmons Drive, Building 9040, Zip 98431–1100; tel. 253/968–1110, (Nonreporting) **A**1 2 3 5 **S** Department of the Army, Office of the Surgeon General, Falls Church, VA
Primary Contact: Colonel Dallas Homas, Commander
COO: Colonel R. Neal David, Administrator and Chief of Staff
CFO: Lieutenant Colonel Bryan Longmuir, Chief Resource Management
CIO: Lieutenant Colonel Andrew Smith, Chief Information Management
CHR: David Aiken, Chief Human Resources Officer
Web address: www.mamc.amedd.army.mil
Control: Army, Government, federal **Service:** General Medical and Surgical

Staffed Beds: 207

WA

Many Facility Codes have changed. Please refer to the AHA Guide Code Chart. © 2014 AHA Guide

☐ **MULTICARE MARY BRIDGE CHILDREN'S HOSPITAL AND HEALTH CENTER (503301)**, 317 Martin Luther King Jr. Way, Zip 98405–4234, Mailing Address: P.O. Box 5299, Zip 98415–0299; tel. 253/403–1400 **A**1 9 10 **F**3 7 8 12 19 21 23 25 27 29 30 31 32 34 35 40 41 43 48 50 54 55 57 58 59 62 63 64 65 66 71 74 75 78 79 81 82 84 85 86 87 88 89 91 92 93 96 97 99 102 104 107 108 110 111 114 115 116 117 119 120 121 123 124 129 130 131 132 134 135 143 144 146 148 **S** MultiCare Health System, Tacoma, WA
Primary Contact: Robert Lenza, Chief Operating Officer and Administrator
CFO: Vince Schmitz, Senior Vice President and Chief Financial Officer
CMO: Lester Reed, M.D., Vice President Medical Affairs and Acute Care
CIO: Florence Chang, Executive Vice President
CHR: Sarah Horsman, Senior Vice President Human Potential
CNO: Kate Bechtold, R.N., Senior Vice President and Chief Nurse Executive
Web address: www.multicare.org/marybridge
Control: Other not–for–profit (including NFP Corporation) **Service:** Children's general

Staffed Beds: 72 **Admissions:** 4506 **Census:** 37 **Outpatient Visits:** 101619 **Births:** 0 **Total Expense ($000):** 126466 **Payroll Expense ($000):** 57269 **Personnel:** 496

☒ **MULTICARE TACOMA GENERAL HOSPITAL (500129)**, 315 Martin Luther King Jr. Way, Zip 98405–4234, Mailing Address: P.O. Box 5299, Zip 98415–0299; tel. 253/403–1000, (Includes ALLENMORE HOSPITAL, South 19th and Union Avenue, Zip 98405, Mailing Address: P.O. Box 11414, Zip 98411–0414; tel. 253/403–2323) **A**1 2 9 10 **F**2 3 8 13 15 17 18 19 20 21 22 23 24 25 26 27 28 29 30 31 34 35 36 40 42 43 45 46 47 48 49 50 51 54 55 57 58 59 62 63 64 65 70 71 72 73 74 75 76 77 78 79 80 81 82 83 84 85 86 87 93 97 102 107 108 109 110 111 114 115 116 117 119 120 121 123 124 126 127 129 130 131 132 135 144 146 147 148 **S** MultiCare Health System, Tacoma, WA
Primary Contact: William G. Robertson, President and Chief Executive Officer
COO: Lisa Strom, R.N., Chief Operating Officer
CFO: Anna Loomis, Interim Chief Financial Officer
CMO: Claire Spain–Remy, M.D., Senior Vice President, MultiCare Medical Associates
CIO: Florence Chang, Executive Vice President
CHR: Sarah Horsman, Senior Vice President Human Potential
CNO: Kate Bechtold, R.N., Senior Vice President and Chief Nurse Executive
Web address: www.multicare.org
Control: Other not–for–profit (including NFP Corporation) **Service:** General Medical and Surgical

Staffed Beds: 385 **Admissions:** 18062 **Census:** 233 **Outpatient Visits:** 218558 **Births:** 2856 **Total Expense ($000):** 462529 **Payroll Expense ($000):** 220704 **Personnel:** 2179

☒ △ **ST. JOSEPH MEDICAL CENTER (500108)**, 1717 South J Street, Zip 98405–3004, Mailing Address: P.O. Box 2197, Zip 98401–2197; tel. 253/426–4101 **A**1 2 7 9 10 **F**3 8 12 13 17 18 20 22 24 26 28 29 30 31 32 34 35 38 40 43 44 45 46 47 48 49 50 51 53 54 55 57 58 59 60 63 64 65 66 68 70 72 73 74 75 76 77 78 79 80 81 82 84 85 86 87 90 92 93 98 102 107 108 111 114 115 120 130 132 134 135 145 146 147 148 **S** Catholic Health Initiatives, Englewood, CO
Primary Contact: Syd Bersante, R.N., President
COO: Syd Bersante, R.N., President
CFO: Mike Fitzgerald, Chief Financial Officer
CIO: Rand Strobel, Vice President Information Technology and Compliance
CHR: Sharon Royne, Interim Senior Vice President Human Resources
CNO: Laurie Brown, R.N., Chief Nursing Officer
Web address: www.fhshealth.org
Control: Church–operated, Nongovernment, not–for profit **Service:** General Medical and Surgical

Staffed Beds: 366 **Admissions:** 22213 **Census:** 286 **Outpatient Visits:** 255513 **Births:** 3750 **Total Expense ($000):** 600882 **Payroll Expense ($000):** 223409 **Personnel:** 3063

VETERANS AFFAIRS PUGET SOUND HEALTH CARE SYSTEM–AMERICAN LAKE DIVISION See Veterans Affairs Puget Sound Health Care System, Seattle

WESTERN STATE HOSPITAL (504003), 9601 Steilacom Boulevard S.W., Zip 98498–7213; tel. 253/582–8900, (Nonreporting) **A**5 9 10
Primary Contact: Jess Jamieson, Chief Executive Officer
COO: Dale Thompson, Chief Operating Officer
CFO: Charm Reimer, Chief Financial Officer
CMO: John Chiles, M.D., Medical Director
CHR: Lori Manning, Administrator Human Resources
Web address: www.dshs.wa.gov/mentalhealth/wsh.shtml
Control: State–Government, nonfederal **Service:** Psychiatric

Staffed Beds: 867

TONASKET—Okanogan County

★ **NORTH VALLEY HOSPITAL (501321)**, 203 South Western Avenue, Zip 98855–8803; tel. 509/486–2151, (Total facility includes 58 beds in nursing home–type unit) **A**9 10 18 **F**3 13 15 26 29 34 35 40 43 45 50 59 64 75 77 81 82 85 87 93 94 96 97 107 110 111 114 119 128 130 131 132 133 135 148 **P**6
Primary Contact: Linda Michel, Administrator
CFO: Helen Verhasselt, Chief Financial Officer
CMO: Paul Lacey, M.D., Chief Medical Staff
CIO: Kelly Cariker, Chief Information Officer
CHR: Jan Gonzales, Director Human Resources
Web address: www.nvhospital.org
Control: Hospital district or authority, Government, nonfederal **Service:** General Medical and Surgical

Staffed Beds: 83 **Admissions:** 490 **Census:** 65 **Outpatient Visits:** 13980 **Births:** 98 **Total Expense ($000):** 21322 **Payroll Expense ($000):** 9777 **Personnel:** 208

TOPPENISH—Yakima County

☒ **TOPPENISH COMMUNITY HOSPITAL (500037)**, 502 West Fourth Avenue, Zip 98948–1616, Mailing Address: P.O. Box 672, Zip 98948–0672; tel. 509/865–3105 **A**1 9 10 **F**3 8 13 15 18 20 22 24 28 29 30 40 45 50 57 59 68 70 76 79 81 89 98 107 111 114 119 133 146 **S** Community Health Systems, Inc., Franklin, TN
Primary Contact: Perry Gay, Chief Executive Officer
CFO: Curtis Herrin, Chief Financial Officer
CHR: Rosa Solorzano, Interim Director Human Resources
Web address: www.toppenishhospital.com
Control: Corporation, Investor–owned, for–profit **Service:** General Medical and Surgical

Staffed Beds: 63 **Admissions:** 1730 **Census:** 8 **Births:** 447

TUKWILA—King County

☐ **CASCADE BEHAVIORAL HOSPITAL (504011)**, 12844 Military Road South, Zip 98168–3045; tel. 206/244–0180, (Nonreporting) **A**1 **S** Acadia Healthcare Company, Inc., Franklin, TN
Primary Contact: Michael Uradnik, Chief Executive Officer
COO: Michelle Curry, Chief Operating Officer
CFO: Gregg Terreson, Chief Financial Officer
CHR: Sherry Cochran, Manager Human Resources
CNO: Nadine Tranquilla, Chief Nursing Officer
Web address: www.cascadebh.com
Control: Corporation, Investor–owned, for–profit **Service:** Psychiatric

Staffed Beds: 63

VANCOUVER—Clark County

LEGACY SALMON CREEK HOSPITAL See Legacy Salmon Creek Medical Center

☒ **LEGACY SALMON CREEK MEDICAL CENTER (500150)**, 2211 N.E. 139th Street, Zip 98686–2742; tel. 360/487–1000 **A**1 9 10 **F**3 11 13 15 18 20 26 28 29 30 31 32 34 35 38 39 40 44 45 46 47 50 51 57 59 60 64 65 68 70 72 74 75 76 77 78 79 80 81 82 84 85 87 89 93 96 97 101 107 108 110 111 114 116 117 118 119 120 121 126 129 130 132 146 147 148 **P**6 **S** Legacy Health, Portland, OR
Primary Contact: Bryce R. Helgerson, Chief Executive Officer
COO: Michael Newcomb, D.O., Senior Vice President and Chief Operating Officer
CMO: Lewis Low, M.D., Senior Vice President and Chief Medical Officer
CHR: Sonja Steves, Senior Vice President Human Resources
CNO: Carol Bradley, MSN, Senior Vice President and Chief Nursing Officer
Web address: www.legacyhealth.org
Control: Other not–for–profit (including NFP Corporation) **Service:** General Medical and Surgical

Staffed Beds: 198 **Admissions:** 11042 **Census:** 111 **Outpatient Visits:** 195844 **Births:** 2301 **Total Expense ($000):** 199281 **Payroll Expense ($000):** 105283 **Personnel:** 1404

WA

Hospital, Medicare Provider Number, Address, Telephone, Approval, Facility, and Physician Codes, Health Care System

★ American Hospital Association (AHA) membership
☐ The Joint Commission accreditation ◇ DNV Healthcare Inc. accreditation
○ Healthcare Facilities Accreditation Program
△ Commission on Accreditation of Rehabilitation Facilities (CARF) accreditation

★ △ ◇ **PEACEHEALTH SOUTHWEST MEDICAL CENTER (500050)**, 400 N.E. Mother Joseph Place, Zip 98664–3200, Mailing Address: P.O. Box 1600, Zip 98668–1600; tel. 360/256–2000, (Includes VANCOUVER MEMORIAL CAMPUS, 3400 Main Street, Zip 98663; tel. 206/696–5000) **A**2 3 5 7 9 10 21 **F**3 11 12 13 15 17 18 20 24 26 28 29 30 31 34 35 40 43 44 45 46 49 50 51 54 57 58 59 60 61 62 63 64 65 68 70 72 74 75 76 77 78 79 81 82 84 85 86 87 89 90 92 93 96 97 98 100 101 102 103 104 105 107 108 109 110 111 113 114 115 116 119 120 121 122 124 126 129 130 131 132 135 144 145 146 147 148 **S** PeaceHealth, Vancouver, WA
Primary Contact: Sy Johnson, Chief Administrative Officer and Chief Operating Officer, PeaceHealth Columbia Network
COO: Joanne Owen, Interim Vice President Operations
CFO: Gordon Edwards, System Vice President and Chief Financial Officer, Columbia Network
CMO: Alden Roberts, M.D., Chief Medical Officer
CIO: Don McMillan, Chief Information Officer
CHR: Laurie Lemieux, Vice President People and Culture
Web address: www.swmedicalcenter.org
Control: Other not–for–profit (including NFP Corporation) **Service:** General Medical and Surgical

Staffed Beds: 450 **Admissions:** 24486 **Census:** 268 **Births:** 2954 **Total Expense ($000):** 609063 **Payroll Expense ($000):** 206423

SOUTHWEST WASHINGTON MEDICAL CENTER See PeaceHealth Southwest Medical Center

WALLA WALLA—Walla Walla County

★ **JONATHAN M. WAINWRIGHT MEMORIAL VETERANS AFFAIRS MEDICAL CENTER**, 77 Wainwright Drive, Zip 99362–3994; tel. 509/525–5200, (Nonreporting) **A**9 **S** Department of Veterans Affairs, Washington, DC
Primary Contact: Brian W. Westfield, MSN, Director
CFO: Debra Pearson, Chief Financial Officer
CMO: Charles Beleny, D.O., Chief of Staff
CIO: Gary Ramer, Manager Information Management
CHR: Mary C. Lee, Manager Human Resources
CNO: Diana Nelson, R.N., Associate Director for Patient Care Services/Nurse Executive
Web address: www.wallawalla.va.gov
Control: Veterans Affairs, Government, federal **Service:** General Medical and Surgical

Staffed Beds: 14

⊞ △ **PROVIDENCE ST. MARY MEDICAL CENTER (500002)**, 401 West Poplar Street, Zip 99362–2846, Mailing Address: P.O. Box 1477, Zip 99362–0312; tel. 509/525–3320 **A**1 2 7 9 10 19 **F**3 8 11 13 15 18 20 28 29 30 31 34 35 40 43 45 46 49 57 58 59 62 64 65 70 73 74 75 76 77 78 79 81 82 84 85 87 89 90 93 96 97 107 110 111 114 115 118 119 121 129 130 135 144 146 147 148 **P**2 **S** Providence Health & Services, Renton, WA
Primary Contact: Steven A. Burdick, Chief Executive Officer
COO: Susan Blackburn, Chief Operating Officer
CMO: Tim Davidson, M.D., Chief Executive Physician Services
CIO: Martin Manny, Director, I.S.
CNO: Yvonne M. Strader, Chief Nursing Officer
Web address: www.washington.providence.org/hospitals/st–mary/
Control: Church–operated, Nongovernment, not–for profit **Service:** General Medical and Surgical

Staffed Beds: 79 **Admissions:** 3926 **Census:** 38 **Outpatient Visits:** 115218 **Births:** 572 **Total Expense ($000):** 149184 **Payroll Expense ($000):** 59750 **Personnel:** 1005

STATE PENITENTIARY HOSPITAL, 1313 North 13th Street, Zip 99362–8817; tel. 509/525–3610, (Nonreporting)
Primary Contact: Pat Rima, Health Care Manager
Control: State–Government, nonfederal **Service:** Hospital unit of an institution (prison hospital, college infimary, etc.)

Staffed Beds: 36

⊞ **WALLA WALLA GENERAL HOSPITAL (500049)**, 1025 South Second Avenue, Zip 99362–4116, Mailing Address: P.O. Box 1398, Zip 99362–0309; tel. 509/525–0480 **A**1 9 10 **F**13 15 20 28 29 30 34 35 40 43 45 49 52 56 57 59 62 64 68 69 70 73 74 75 76 79 81 83 85 87 89 93 97 107 110 111 115 119 127 129 130 132 133 135 146 147 **S** Adventist Health, Roseville, CA
Primary Contact: Monty E. Knittel, President and Chief Executive Officer
CFO: Duane Meidinger, Vice President Finance
CIO: Gary Dietz, Director Information Technology Services
CHR: Barbara Blood, Director Human Resources
Web address: www.wwgh.com
Control: Church–operated, Nongovernment, not–for profit **Service:** General Medical and Surgical

Staffed Beds: 37 **Admissions:** 1346 **Census:** 10 **Births:** 280

WENATCHEE—Chelan County

⊞ **CENTRAL WASHINGTON HOSPITAL (500016)**, 1201 South Miller Street, Zip 98801–3201, Mailing Address: P.O. Box 1887, Zip 98807–1887; tel. 509/662–1511 **A**1 9 10 13 19 **F**3 13 17 18 20 22 24 26 28 29 30 31 34 35 40 43 45 46 47 49 50 62 63 64 68 69 70 73 74 75 76 78 79 81 83 84 85 86 89 91 93 94 107 111 114 115 119 128 130 146 148 **P**3
Primary Contact: Peter Rutherford, M.D., Chief Executive Officer
COO: Richard L. Canning, Chief Operating Officer
CFO: John Doyle, Chief Financial Officer
CMO: Stuart Freed, M.D., Chief Medical Officer
CIO: Robert Pageler, Chief Information Officer
CHR: Jim Wood, Chief Human Resources Officer
CNO: Tracey A. Kasnic, R.N., Chief Nursing Officer
Web address: www.cwhs.com
Control: Other not–for–profit (including NFP Corporation) **Service:** General Medical and Surgical

Staffed Beds: 198 **Admissions:** 9896 **Census:** 102 **Outpatient Visits:** 158360 **Births:** 1327 **Total Expense ($000):** 224346 **Payroll Expense ($000):** 75019 **Personnel:** 1052

△ **WENATCHEE VALLEY MEDICAL CENTER (500148)**, 820 North Chelan Avenue, Zip 98801–2028; tel. 509/663–8711, (Nonreporting) **A**2 7 9 10
Primary Contact: Peter Rutherford, M.D., Chief Executive Officer
COO: Kevin Gilbert, R.N., Vice President
CFO: John Doyle, Chief Financial Officer
CMO: Stuart Freed, M.D., Medical Director
CIO: Robert Pageler, Chief Information Officer
CHR: Jim Wood, Chief Human Resources Officer
CNO: Tracey A. Kasnic, R.N., Chief Nursing Officer
Web address: www.wvmedical.com
Control: Partnership, Investor–owned, for–profit **Service:** General Medical and Surgical

Staffed Beds: 20

WHITE SALMON—Klickitat County

SKYLINE HOSPITAL (501315), 211 Skyline Drive, Zip 98672–1918, Mailing Address: P.O. Box 99, Zip 98672–0099; tel. 509/493–1101 **A**9 10 18 **F**17 34 40 43 57 64 67 81 89 93 97 107 114 119 128 131 133 145 146 **P**5
Primary Contact: Robert P. Kimmes, Chief Executive Officer
CFO: Brenda Schneider, Chief Financial Officer
CMO: Troy Witherrite, M.D., Chief Medical Officer
CIO: Steve Opbroek, Manager Information Technology
CHR: Jessie Ramos, Manager Human Resources
CNO: Stefanie Boen, Chief Nursing Officer
Web address: www.skylinehospital.com
Control: Hospital district or authority, Government, nonfederal **Service:** General Medical and Surgical

Staffed Beds: 25 **Admissions:** 294 **Census:** 2 **Outpatient Visits:** 17987 **Births:** 0 **Total Expense ($000):** 18629 **Payroll Expense ($000):** 8166 **Personnel:** 133

YAKIMA—Yakima County

⊞ △ **YAKIMA REGIONAL MEDICAL AND CARDIAC CENTER (500012)**, 110 South Ninth Avenue, Zip 98902–3315; tel. 509/575–5000, (Nonreporting) **A**1 2 7 9 10 **S** Community Health Systems, Inc., Franklin, TN
Primary Contact: Veronica Knudson, Chief Executive Officer
CMO: Dave Atteberry, M.D., Chief of Staff
CHR: Ralph L. Lundberg, Director Human Resources
CNO: Sara H. Williamson, MSN, Chief Nursing Officer
Web address: www.yakimaregional.net
Control: Corporation, Investor–owned, for–profit **Service:** General Medical and Surgical

Staffed Beds: 214

⊞ **YAKIMA VALLEY MEMORIAL HOSPITAL (500036)**, 2811 Tieton Drive, Zip 98902–3761; tel. 509/575–8000 **A**1 2 3 5 9 10 **F**3 8 11 13 15 17 18 20 22 26 28 29 30 31 32 34 35 36 40 41 42 43 44 45 46 47 49 50 51 55 57 59 60 62 63 65 68 70 72 73 74 75 76 77 78 79 81 82 84 85 86 87 89 92 93 96 98 100 102 104 107 108 110 111 114 116 117 119 120 121 123 124 129 130 131 132 135 144 146 147 148 **P**4 6 7
Primary Contact: Russ Myers, Chief Executive Officer
COO: James Aberle, Vice President, Chief Operating Officer
CFO: Tim Reed, Vice President and Chief Financial Officer
CIO: Jeff Yamada, Vice President
CHR: Jolene R. Seda, Administrative Director
CNO: Sandy J. Dahl, Senior Vice President, Chief Clinical Officer
Web address: www.yakimamemorial.org
Control: Other not–for–profit (including NFP Corporation) **Service:** General Medical and Surgical

Staffed Beds: 226 **Admissions:** 12530 **Census:** 133 **Outpatient Visits:** 424530 **Births:** 2722 **Total Expense ($000):** 287779 **Payroll Expense ($000):** 114735 **Personnel:** 1849

WA

Many Facility Codes have changed. Please refer to the AHA Guide Code Chart. © 2014 AHA Guide

WEST VIRGINIA

BECKLEY—Raleigh County

☐ **BECKLEY ARH HOSPITAL (510062)**, 306 Stanaford Road, Zip 25801–3142; tel. 304/255–3000 **A**1 9 10 **F**3 11 12 15 17 18 20 28 29 30 31 34 35 38 39 40 43 44 45 46 47 48 49 50 51 54 57 59 60 61 62 64 65 70 74 75 77 78 79 81 82 85 86 87 89 90 93 97 98 99 100 101 102 103 107 108 110 111 115 116 118 119 129 130 146 148 **P**6 **S** Appalachian Regional Healthcare, Inc., Lexington, KY
Primary Contact: Rocco K. Massey, Community Chief Executive Officer
CMO: Ali Suleiman, M.D., Chief of Staff
CHR: Sue Thomas, Manager Human Resources
CNO: Rosalina Dunford–Boothe, Community Chief Nursing Officer
Web address: www.arh.org
Control: Other not–for–profit (including NFP Corporation) **Service:** General Medical and Surgical

Staffed Beds: 170 **Admissions:** 6782 **Census:** 115 **Outpatient Visits:** 70389
Births: 0 **Total Expense ($000):** 85891 **Payroll Expense ($000):** 25946
Personnel: 522

⊞ **BECKLEY VETERANS AFFAIRS MEDICAL CENTER**, 200 Veterans Avenue, Zip 25801–6499; tel. 304/255–2121, (Nonreporting) **A**1 **S** Department of Veterans Affairs, Washington, DC
Primary Contact: Karin L. McGraw, MSN, FACHE, Director
CFO: Terry Massey, Chief Fiscal Services
CMO: John David Berryman, M.D., Chief of Staff
CIO: Sherry Gregg, Chief Information Technology Officer
CNO: Debra Lynn Legg, Associate Director Patient Care Services and Nurse Executive
Web address: www.beckley.va.gov/
Control: Veterans Affairs, Government, federal **Service:** General Medical and Surgical

Staffed Beds: 40

⊞ **RALEIGH GENERAL HOSPITAL (510070)**, 1710 Harper Road, Zip 25801–3397; tel. 304/256–4100 **A**1 9 10 19 **F**3 13 15 17 18 20 22 29 30 31 34 35 40 43 45 49 57 59 60 64 70 74 75 76 78 79 81 85 87 89 93 107 110 111 114 115 117 119 126 130 131 132 146 147 **S** LifePoint Hospitals, Inc., Brentwood, TN
Primary Contact: David B. Darden, Chief Executive Officer
COO: Reba Celsor, Chief Operating Officer
CFO: Randy Harrison, Chief Financial Officer
CMO: Syed Siddiqi, M.D., President Medical Staff
CIO: Kevin Sexton, Director Information Systems
CHR: Chris T. Beebe, Director Human Resources
CNO: Alene Lewis, R.N., Chief Nursing Officer
Web address: www.raleighgeneral.com
Control: Corporation, Investor–owned, for–profit **Service:** General Medical and Surgical

Staffed Beds: 229 **Admissions:** 12001 **Census:** 145 **Outpatient Visits:** 107609 **Births:** 1303 **Total Expense ($000):** 138640 **Payroll Expense ($000):** 46916 **Personnel:** 905

BERKELEY SPRINGS—Morgan County

★ **WAR MEMORIAL HOSPITAL (511309)**, One Healthy Way, Zip 25411–7463; tel. 304/258–1234, (Total facility includes 16 beds in nursing home–type unit) **A**9 10 18 **F**3 11 15 28 29 30 34 35 40 45 50 53 54 57 59 64 65 77 79 81 85 86 93 97 107 119 129 130 133 **P**6 **S** Valley Health System, Winchester, VA
Primary Contact: Neil R. McLaughlin, R.N., President
CFO: Christine Lowman, Vice President Finance
Web address: www.valleyhealthlink.com/war
Control: Other not–for–profit (including NFP Corporation) **Service:** General Medical and Surgical

Staffed Beds: 41 **Admissions:** 521 **Census:** 28 **Outpatient Visits:** 45863
Births: 0 **Total Expense ($000):** 20941 **Payroll Expense ($000):** 8328
Personnel: 171

BLUEFIELD—Mercer County

⊞ **BLUEFIELD REGIONAL MEDICAL CENTER (510071)**, 500 Cherry Street, Zip 24701–3390; tel. 304/327–1100 **A**1 9 10 12 13 19 **F**3 8 13 15 17 18 20 22 28 29 31 34 40 43 45 46 47 49 50 56 57 59 60 64 68 70 74 75 76 77 78 79 81 85 86 89 96 107 108 110 115 118 119 121 124 127 129 130 132 144 146 147 **P**8 **S** Community Health Systems, Inc., Franklin, TN
Primary Contact: David Henry, Chief Executive Officer
CMO: Joel Shor, M.D., Chief of Staff
CIO: Rose Lasker, Director Information Services
CHR: Sandee Cheynet, Vice President Administrative Services
Web address: www.bluefield.org
Control: Corporation, Investor–owned, for–profit **Service:** General Medical and Surgical

Staffed Beds: 240 **Admissions:** 4743 **Census:** 49 **Outpatient Visits:** 71680
Births: 614 **Total Expense ($000):** 84650 **Payroll Expense ($000):** 26521
Personnel: 598

BRIDGEPORT—Harrison County

⊞ **UNITED HOSPITAL CENTER (510006)**, 327 Medical Park Drive, Zip 26330–9006; tel. 681/342–1000 **A**1 2 3 5 9 10 12 13 19 20 **F**3 5 11 13 15 17 18 20 22 28 29 30 31 34 36 38 39 40 45 46 48 49 51 54 57 58 59 60 62 63 64 65 68 70 74 75 76 77 78 79 81 82 84 85 86 87 89 93 97 98 99 100 101 102 103 104 107 108 109 110 111 114 115 116 117 118 119 120 121 123 126 128 129 130 131 132 146 148 **P**6 7 8 **S** West Virginia United Health System, Fairmont, WV
Primary Contact: Bruce C. Carter, President and Chief Executive Officer
COO: Michael Tillman, Vice President Patient Services and Chief Operating Officer
CFO: Douglas Coffman, Vice President and Chief Financial Officer
CMO: Eric Radcliffe, M.D., Medical Director
CIO: Brian Cottrill, Chief Information Officer
CHR: Timothy M. Allen, Vice President Human Resources
Web address: www.thenewuhc.com
Control: Other not–for–profit (including NFP Corporation) **Service:** General Medical and Surgical

Staffed Beds: 264 **Admissions:** 12261 **Census:** 182 **Outpatient Visits:** 430984 **Births:** 1034 **Total Expense ($000):** 238007 **Payroll Expense ($000):** 93808 **Personnel:** 1689

BUCKEYE—Pocahontas County

★ **POCAHONTAS MEMORIAL HOSPITAL (511314)**, 150 Duncan Road, Zip 24924, Mailing Address: Rural Route 2, Box 52 W, Zip 24924; tel. 304/799–7400 **A**9 10 18 **F**3 7 11 29 30 34 35 40 43 56 57 59 64 65 68 86 87 93 97 107 108 119 127 128 130 132 133 135 144 146 **P**4
Primary Contact: Barbara Lay, Chief Executive Officer
COO: Terry Wagner, R.N., Chief Operating Officer
CFO: Melissa Kane, Chief Financial Officer
CMO: Frank Puckett, M.D., Chief Medical Officer
CIO: Aaron Vaughan, Coordinator Information Systems
CHR: Katie Brown, Coordinator Human Resources
CNO: Kerrie Ridgeway, R.N., Chief Nursing Officer
Web address: www.pmhwv.org/
Control: County–Government, nonfederal **Service:** General Medical and Surgical

Staffed Beds: 25 **Admissions:** 309 **Census:** 4 **Outpatient Visits:** 17558
Births: 0 **Total Expense ($000):** 10107 **Payroll Expense ($000):** 4889
Personnel: 119

BUCKHANNON—Upshur County

☒ **ST. JOSEPH'S HOSPITAL OF BUCKHANNON (510053)**, 1 Amalia Drive, Zip 26201–2276; tel. 304/473–2000, (Total facility includes 16 beds in nursing home–type unit) **A**1 9 10 **F**3 11 13 15 18 28 29 30 31 34 35 40 43 44 45 50 57 59 62 63 64 65 70 75 76 79 81 83 84 85 87 89 107 110 114 119 128 129 130 132 133 135 144 146 **P**6 8 **S** Pallottine Health Services, Huntington, WV
Primary Contact: Sue E. Johnson–Phillippe, FACHE, President and Chief Executive Officer
CFO: Renee Hofer, Controller
CMO: Robert Blake, M.D., Chief of Staff
CIO: Brian Williams, Service Leader Corporate Information Systems
CHR: Anissa Hite–Davis, Vice President Human Resources
CNO: Eric Rice, Vice President Patient Care Services
Web address: www.stj.net
Control: Other not–for–profit (including NFP Corporation) **Service:** General Medical and Surgical

Staffed Beds: 69 **Admissions:** 1358 **Census:** 29 **Outpatient Visits:** 94583 **Births:** 267 **Total Expense ($000):** 41930 **Payroll Expense ($000):** 20010 **Personnel:** 352

CHARLESTON—Kanawha County

☒ △ **CHARLESTON AREA MEDICAL CENTER (510022)**, 501 Morris Street, Zip 25301–1300, Mailing Address: P.O. Box 1547, Zip 25326–1547; tel. 304/388–5432, (Includes GENERAL HOSPITAL, 501 Morris Street, Zip 25301, Mailing Address: Box 1393, Zip 25325; tel. 304/388–5432; Michael D. Williams, Vice President and Administrator; MEMORIAL HOSPITAL, 3200 MacCorkle Avenue S.E., Zip 25304; tel. 304/388–5973; Jeffrey L. Oskin, Vice President and Administrator; WOMEN AND CHILDREN'S HOSPITAL, 800 Pennsylvania Avenue, Zip 25302, Mailing Address: P.O. Box 6669, Zip 25362; tel. 304/388–5432; Andrew Weber, Vice President and Administrator) **A**1 2 3 5 7 8 9 10 12 13 **F**3 8 11 12 13 15 17 18 19 20 22 24 26 28 29 30 31 32 34 35 38 40 41 43 44 45 46 47 48 49 50 51 52 54 55 56 57 59 60 61 64 65 68 70 72 74 75 76 77 78 79 81 82 84 85 86 88 89 90 92 93 94 96 97 98 99 100 101 102 103 104 107 108 110 111 114 115 116 117 118 119 124 126 129 130 131 132 134 135 138 141 143 144 145 146 147 148 **P**6 **S** Charleston Area Medical Center Health System, Inc., Charleston, WV
Primary Contact: David L. Ramsey, President and Chief Executive Officer
COO: Glenn Crotty, Jr., M.D., Executive Vice President and Chief Operating Officer
CFO: Larry C. Hudson, Executive Vice President and Chief Financial Officer
CMO: T. Pinckney McIlwain, M.D., Vice President and Chief Medical Officer
CIO: Gregory M. Veltri, Vice President Information Services and Chief Information Officer
CHR: Kristi Snyder, Vice President Human Resources
CNO: Ronald E. Moore, R.N., Vice President Professional Practice and Chief Nursing Officer
Web address: www.camc.org
Control: Other not–for–profit (including NFP Corporation) **Service:** General Medical and Surgical

Staffed Beds: 795 **Admissions:** 35142 **Census:** 530 **Outpatient Visits:** 551512 **Births:** 2718 **Total Expense ($000):** 823057 **Payroll Expense ($000):** 277967 **Personnel:** 5679

☐ **EYE AND EAR CLINIC OF CHARLESTON (510059)**, 1306 Kanawha Boulevard East, Zip 25301–3001, Mailing Address: P.O. Box 2271, Zip 25328–2271; tel. 304/343–4371 **A**1 10 **F**39 45 57 79 81 89 107 111 119 141
Primary Contact: Christina Arvon, Administrator and Chief Executive Officer
CMO: James W. Candill, M.D., President Medical Staff
Web address: www.eyeandearclinicwv.org
Control: Corporation, Investor–owned, for–profit **Service:** General Medical and Surgical

Staffed Beds: 17 **Admissions:** 1 **Census:** 1 **Outpatient Visits:** 12312 **Births:** 0 **Total Expense ($000):** 12876 **Payroll Expense ($000):** 4494 **Personnel:** 131

GENERAL HOSPITAL See Charleston Area Medical Center

☒ **HIGHLAND HOSPITAL (514001)**, 300 56th Street S.E., Zip 25304–2361, Mailing Address: P.O. Box 4107, Zip 25364–4107; tel. 304/926–1600 **A**1 9 10 **F**4 34 35 50 54 57 59 97 98 99 101 103 104 130 135 **P**6
Primary Contact: Cynthia A. Persily, Ph.D., R.N., President and Chief Executive Officer
COO: Lisa Layden, Chief Operating Officer
CFO: Lisa Layden, Director of Finance
CMO: Kiran Devaraj, Medical Director
CIO: Pearl McWatters, Director Information Services
CNO: Carla Hall, Director of Nursing
Web address: www.highlandhosp.com
Control: Other not–for–profit (including NFP Corporation) **Service:** Psychiatric

Staffed Beds: 80 **Admissions:** 2195 **Census:** 60 **Outpatient Visits:** 637 **Births:** 0 **Total Expense ($000):** 18203 **Payroll Expense ($000):** 8979 **Personnel:** 269

MEMORIAL HOSPITAL See Charleston Area Medical Center

☒ **SAINT FRANCIS HOSPITAL (510031)**, 333 Laidley Street, Zip 25301–1628, Mailing Address: P.O. Box 471, Zip 25322–0471; tel. 304/347–6500, (Total facility includes 25 beds in nursing home–type unit) **A**1 9 10 **F**3 11 15 18 20 22 29 30 34 37 40 45 48 49 51 57 58 59 60 64 68 69 70 74 75 79 81 82 84 86 87 93 107 108 110 111 115 119 128 130 131 143 146 147 148 **S** Thomas Health System, Inc., South Charleston, WV
Primary Contact: Stephen P. Dexter, President and Chief Executive Officer
COO: Daniel Lauffer, FACHE, Executive Vice President and Chief Operating Officer
CFO: Charles O. Covert, Chief Financial Officer
CMO: Paul Legg, M.D., President Medical Staff
CIO: Jeremy Taylor, Director Information Services
CHR: Marybeth Smith, Director Human Resources
CNO: Rebecca Brannon, R.N., Chief Nursing Officer
Web address: www.stfrancishospital.com
Control: Other not–for–profit (including NFP Corporation) **Service:** General Medical and Surgical

Staffed Beds: 111 **Admissions:** 3704 **Census:** 51 **Outpatient Visits:** 91488 **Births:** 0 **Total Expense ($000):** 101845 **Payroll Expense ($000):** 31969 **Personnel:** 642

☒ **SELECT SPECIALTY HOSPITAL–CHARLESTON (512002)**, 333 Laidley Street, 3rd Floor East, Zip 25301–1614; tel. 304/720–7234 **A**1 9 10 **F**1 29 74 75 79 85 130 148 **S** Select Medical Corporation, Mechanicsburg, PA
Primary Contact: Frank Weber, Chief Executive Officer
CHR: Sabrina White, Coordinator Human Resources
Web address: www.selectspecialtyhospitals.com/company/locations/charleston.aspx
Control: Corporation, Investor–owned, for–profit **Service:** Long–Term Acute Care hospital

Staffed Beds: 32 **Admissions:** 422 **Census:** 30 **Outpatient Visits:** 0 **Births:** 0 **Total Expense ($000):** 15799 **Payroll Expense ($000):** 5850 **Personnel:** 103

WOMEN AND CHILDREN'S HOSPITAL See Charleston Area Medical Center

CLARKSBURG—Harrison County

☐ **HIGHLAND–CLARKSBURG HOSPITAL (514011)**, 3 Hospital Drive, Zip 26301–9316; tel. 304/969–3100, (Data for 43 days) **A**1 10 **F**86 87 98 99
Primary Contact: James H. Dissen, President and Chairman
CFO: Shelly Giaguinto, Controller
CMO: Marilou Patalinjug Tyner, M.D., Medical Director
CHR: Cynthia Drury, Coordinator Human Resources
CNO: Paula Herndon, R.N., Nurse Executive
Web address: www.highlandhosp.com
Control: Other not–for–profit (including NFP Corporation) **Service:** Psychiatric

Staffed Beds: 35 **Admissions:** 65 **Census:** 8 **Outpatient Visits:** 0 **Births:** 0 **Total Expense ($000):** 2189 **Payroll Expense ($000):** 716 **Personnel:** 77

☒ **LOUIS A. JOHNSON VETERANS AFFAIRS MEDICAL CENTER**, 1 Medical Center Drive, Zip 26301–4199; tel. 304/623–3461, (Nonreporting) **A**1 3 5 **S** Department of Veterans Affairs, Washington, DC
Primary Contact: Beth Brown, Medical Center Director
CMO: Glenn R. Snider, M.D., Chief of Staff
CIO: Michael Matthey, Facility Chief Information Officer
CHR: Ian Jacobs, Chief, Human Resource Management Service
Web address: www.clarksburg.va.gov
Control: Veterans Affairs, Government, federal **Service:** General Medical and Surgical

Staffed Beds: 71

ELKINS—Randolph County

☒ **DAVIS MEMORIAL HOSPITAL (510030)**, Gorman Avenue and Reed Street, Zip 26241, Mailing Address: P.O. Box 1484, Zip 26241–1484; tel. 304/636–3300 **A**1 2 9 10 20 **F**11 13 15 20 28 29 30 31 34 35 40 49 50 51 54 57 59 64 68 69 70 71 74 75 77 78 79 81 82 85 86 87 89 92 93 107 108 109 110 111 115 116 117 118 119 121 123 129 130 132 135 146 147 148 **P**8 **S** Davis Health System, Elkins, WV
Primary Contact: Mark Doak, Chief Executive Officer
CFO: Rebecca J. Hammer, Chief Financial Officer
CMO: Charles Kirkland, D.O., Chief Medical Officer
CHR: Jon Steen, Director Human Resources
Web address: www.davishealthsystem.com
Control: Other not–for–profit (including NFP Corporation) **Service:** General Medical and Surgical

Staffed Beds: 90 **Admissions:** 3826 **Census:** 36 **Outpatient Visits:** 143275 **Births:** 338 **Total Expense ($000):** 80078 **Payroll Expense ($000):** 36176 **Personnel:** 555

WV

Many Facility Codes have changed. Please refer to the AHA Guide Code Chart. © 2014 AHA Guide

FAIRMONT—Marion County

✠ **FAIRMONT GENERAL HOSPITAL (510047)**, 1325 Locust Avenue, Zip 26554–1435; tel. 304/367–7100 **A**1 2 9 10 19 **F**3 11 12 13 14 15 18 20 28 29 30 31 34 35 38 39 40 41 43 45 46 47 48 49 50 51 53 54 56 57 59 60 62 64 68 69 70 75 76 77 78 79 81 84 85 86 87 89 91 92 93 97 98 100 102 103 104 107 108 110 111 114 115 116 118 119 129 130 132 135 146 147 148 **P**6
Primary Contact: Margaret C. Coster, R.N., MSN, President and Chief Executive Officer
CFO: Daniel Honerbrink, Vice President Finance and Chief Financial Officer
CMO: Wes Steele, M.D., Chief of Staff
CIO: Mike Wooddell, Director Information Services
CHR: Jim Harris, Vice President Human Resources
CNO: Margaret C. Coster, R.N., Vice President Patient Services
Web address: www.fghi.com
Control: Other not–for–profit (including NFP Corporation) **Service:** General Medical and Surgical

Staffed Beds: 140 **Admissions:** 4547 **Census:** 73 **Outpatient Visits:** 165624 **Births:** 395 **Total Expense ($000):** 79213 **Payroll Expense ($000):** 27329 **Personnel:** 677

GASSAWAY—Braxton County

BRAXTON COUNTY MEMORIAL HOSPITAL (511308), 100 Hoylman Drive, Zip 26624–9318; tel. 304/364–5156 **A**9 10 18 **F**1 3 4 8 11 15 30 32 34 35 40 43 45 57 59 62 64 67 75 81 89 90 97 98 107 108 114 116 127 128 130 133 146 147 **P**6
Primary Contact: Ben Vincent, FACHE, Chief Executive Officer
CFO: Kimber Knight, Chief Financial Officer
CMO: Russell L. Stewart, M.D., Chief Medical Officer
Web address: www.braxtonmemorial.org
Control: Other not–for–profit (including NFP Corporation) **Service:** General Medical and Surgical

Staffed Beds: 25 **Admissions:** 264 **Census:** 2 **Outpatient Visits:** 41470 **Births:** 0 **Total Expense ($000):** 15012 **Payroll Expense ($000):** 6502 **Personnel:** 161

GLEN DALE—Marshall County

✠ **REYNOLDS MEMORIAL HOSPITAL (510013)**, 800 Wheeling Avenue, Zip 26038–1697; tel. 304/845–3211, (Total facility includes 20 beds in nursing home–type unit) **A**1 9 10 **F**3 11 13 15 18 20 28 30 34 39 40 43 53 56 57 59 62 64 65 70 74 75 76 77 78 79 80 81 82 85 86 89 92 93 107 108 110 111 114 118 119 128 130 132 135 146 148 **P**8
Primary Contact: Jay E. Prager, Chief Executive Officer
COO: Kevin Britt, Chief Operating Officer
CFO: William Robert Hunt, Chief Financial Officer
CMO: David F. Hess, M.D., President Medical Staff
CIO: Warren Kelley, Chief Information Officer
CHR: R. Craig Madden, Director Employee Relations
CNO: Carol R. Miller, R.N., Chief Nursing Officer
Web address: www.reynoldsmemorial.com
Control: Other not–for–profit (including NFP Corporation) **Service:** General Medical and Surgical

Staffed Beds: 99 **Admissions:** 2361 **Census:** 41 **Outpatient Visits:** 82463 **Births:** 121 **Total Expense ($000):** 36802 **Payroll Expense ($000):** 18295 **Personnel:** 350

GRAFTON—Taylor County

GRAFTON CITY HOSPITAL (511307), 1 Hospital Plaza, Zip 26354–1283; tel. 304/265–0400, (Total facility includes 76 beds in nursing home–type unit) **A**9 10 18 **F**11 15 28 29 30 31 32 34 35 38 39 40 43 53 54 56 57 59 61 64 65 67 75 77 78 79 81 84 86 87 91 93 97 100 101 103 104 107 108 111 114 119 127 128 129 130 131 132 133 135 144 146 147 148 **P**6
Primary Contact: Patrick Shaw, Chief Executive Officer
CFO: Susie Higgins, Chief Financial Officer
CMO: Christopher Villaraza, II, M.D., Chief Medical Staff
CIO: Ann Rexroad, Director Information Technology
CHR: Missey Kimbrew, Director Human Resources
CNO: Violet Shaw, R.N., Director of Nursing
Web address: www.graftonhospital.com
Control: City–Government, nonfederal **Service:** General Medical and Surgical

Staffed Beds: 101 **Admissions:** 404 **Census:** 73 **Outpatient Visits:** 39288 **Births:** 0 **Total Expense ($000):** 17836 **Payroll Expense ($000):** 10017 **Personnel:** 304

GRANTSVILLE—Calhoun County

★ **MINNIE HAMILTON HEALTHCARE CENTER (511303)**, 186 Hospital Drive, Zip 26147–7100; tel. 304/354–9244, (Total facility includes 24 beds in nursing home–type unit) **A**9 10 18 **F**3 7 11 15 29 30 32 34 35 36 39 40 41 43 44 50 53 56 57 59 61 64 65 66 68 75 82 84 86 87 93 97 99 101 107 108 119 127 130 132 133 134 135 143 144 146 147 148 **P**6
Primary Contact: Steve Whited, Chief Executive Officer
CFO: Kyle Pierson, Chief Financial Officer
CMO: Suresh Balasubramony, M.D., Chief Medical Officer
CIO: Brent Barr, Chief Information Officer
CHR: Sheila Gherke, Director Human Resources
CNO: Kim Houchin, Chief Nursing Officer
Web address: www.mhhcc.com
Control: Other not–for–profit (including NFP Corporation) **Service:** General Medical and Surgical

Staffed Beds: 42 **Admissions:** 273 **Census:** 25 **Outpatient Visits:** 61162 **Births:** 0 **Total Expense ($000):** 17741 **Payroll Expense ($000):** 10868 **Personnel:** 258

HINTON—Summers County

SUMMERS COUNTY ARH HOSPITAL (511310), Terrace Street, Zip 25951–2407, Mailing Address: Drawer 940, Zip 25951–0940; tel. 304/466–1000 **A**9 10 18 **F**11 15 29 30 32 34 35 40 43 44 50 54 57 59 62 64 65 71 81 82 86 87 93 97 107 114 119 127 130 133 146 147 148 **P**6 **S** Appalachian Regional Healthcare, Inc., Lexington, KY
Primary Contact: Wesley Dangerfield, Community Chief Executive Officer
CMO: Waheed Khan, M.D., President Medical Staff
CIO: Brent Styer, Chief Information Officer
CHR: Beth Elswick, Administrative Assistant
CNO: Sharon Milburn, Chief Nursing Officer
Web address: www.arh.org
Control: Other not–for–profit (including NFP Corporation) **Service:** General Medical and Surgical

Staffed Beds: 25 **Admissions:** 660 **Census:** 9 **Outpatient Visits:** 22606 **Births:** 0 **Total Expense ($000):** 15755 **Payroll Expense ($000):** 4996 **Personnel:** 114

HUNTINGTON—Cabell County

✠ **CABELL HUNTINGTON HOSPITAL (510055)**, 1340 Hal Greer Boulevard, Zip 25701–0195; tel. 304/526–2000, (Includes HOOPS FAMILY CHILDREN'S HOSPITAL, 1340 Hal Greer Boulevard, Zip 25701–3800; tel. 304/526–2000), (Total facility includes 15 beds in nursing home–type unit) **A**1 2 3 5 9 10 12 13 **F**3 7 11 12 13 15 16 17 18 20 22 26 28 29 30 31 32 34 35 37 38 39 40 41 43 44 45 46 47 48 49 50 51 52 54 55 56 57 58 59 60 61 62 64 65 66 70 72 73 74 75 76 77 78 79 81 82 84 85 86 87 88 89 92 93 94 96 97 107 108 110 111 114 115 117 118 119 120 121 123 126 128 129 130 131 132 134 135 144 145 146 147 148
Primary Contact: Brent A. Marsteller, President and Chief Executive Officer
COO: Kevin N. Fowler, Senior Vice President and Chief Operating Officer
CFO: David M. Ward, Senior Vice President and Chief Financial Officer
CMO: Hoyt J. Burdick, M.D., Vice President Medical Affairs
CIO: Dennis Lee, Vice President and Chief Information Officer
CHR: Barry Tourigny, Vice President Human Resources and Organizational Development
CNO: Joy S. Pelfrey, R.N., Vice President and Chief Nursing Officer
Web address: www.cabellhuntington.org
Control: Other not–for–profit (including NFP Corporation) **Service:** General Medical and Surgical

Staffed Beds: 303 **Admissions:** 26068 **Census:** 250 **Outpatient Visits:** 491265 **Births:** 2788 **Total Expense ($000):** 400078 **Payroll Expense ($000):** 136953 **Personnel:** 2191

☐ **CORNERSTONE HOSPITAL OF HUNTINGTON (512003)**, 2900 First Avenue, Two East, Zip 25702–1241; tel. 304/399–2600, (Nonreporting) **A**1 9 10 **S** Cornerstone Healthcare Group, Dallas, TX
Primary Contact: Cynthia Isaacs, Chief Executive Officer
CFO: Frank Carter, Chief Financial Officer
CMO: William Beam, M.D., Chief of Staff
Web address: www.chghospitals.com
Control: Corporation, Investor–owned, for–profit **Service:** Long–Term Acute Care hospital

Staffed Beds: 28

WV

✠ **HEALTHSOUTH HUNTINGTON REHABILITATION HOSPITAL (513028)**, 6900 West Country Club Drive, Zip 25705–2000; tel. 304/733–1060 **A**1 10 **F**29 34 59 90 95 96 146 **S** HEALTHSOUTH Corporation, Birmingham, AL
Primary Contact: Michael E. Zuliani, Chief Executive Officer
CHR: Jenny Overcash, Director Human Resources
CNO: Ann Evans, Chief Nursing Officer
Web address: www.healthsouthhuntington.com
Control: Corporation, Investor–owned, for–profit **Service:** Rehabilitation

Staffed Beds: 52 **Admissions:** 1192 **Census:** 46 **Outpatient Visits:** 0 **Births:** 0 **Total Expense ($000):** 13235 **Payroll Expense ($000):** 7114 **Personnel:** 150

✠ **HUNTINGTON VETERANS AFFAIRS MEDICAL CENTER**, 1540 Spring Valley Drive, Zip 25704–9300; tel. 304/429–6741 **A**1 3 5 **F**3 7 11 12 15 18 28 29 30 31 34 38 45 54 56 57 58 59 62 63 64 70 74 75 77 78 79 81 82 84 85 87 93 97 104 107 111 114 115 119 130 132 135 143 146 147 148 **S** Department of Veterans Affairs, Washington, DC
Primary Contact: Brian Nimmo, Director
CIO: Gary Henderson, Chief Information Resources Management Services
Web address: www.huntington.va.gov/
Control: Veterans Affairs, Government, federal **Service:** General Medical and Surgical

Staffed Beds: 80 **Admissions:** 3784 **Census:** 44 **Births:** 0

☐ **MILDRED MITCHELL–BATEMAN HOSPITAL (514009)**, 1530 Norway Avenue, Zip 25705–1358, Mailing Address: P.O. Box 448, Zip 25709–0448; tel. 304/525–7801 **A**1 9 10 **F**3 4 11 30 86 87 97 98 103 106 130 135 143 146 **P**6
Primary Contact: Craig A. Richards, Chief Executive Officer
CFO: Lucille Gedies, Chief Financial Officer
CMO: Shahid Masood, M.D., Clinical Director
CIO: Elias Majdalani, Director Management Information Systems
CHR: Kieth Anne Worden, Director Human Resources
CNO: Patricia Hamilton, R.N., Director of Nursing
Web address: www.batemanhospital.org
Control: State–Government, nonfederal **Service:** Psychiatric

Staffed Beds: 110 **Admissions:** 472 **Census:** 106 **Outpatient Visits:** 0 **Births:** 0 **Total Expense ($000):** 34502 **Payroll Expense ($000):** 13912 **Personnel:** 393

☐ **RIVER PARK HOSPITAL (514008)**, 1230 Sixth Avenue, Zip 25701–2312, Mailing Address: P.O. Box 1875, Zip 25719–1875; tel. 304/526–9111 **A**1 9 10 **F**29 34 35 38 98 99 100 101 102 103 106 130 143 **P**4 5 6 **S** Universal Health Services, Inc., King of Prussia, PA
Primary Contact: Terry A. Stephens, Chief Executive Officer
CFO: Steve Kuhn, Chief Financial Officer
CMO: Mark A. Hughes, M.D., Medical Director
CIO: Tony Radenheimer, Network Administrator
CHR: Mary Stratton, Director Human Resources
CNO: Charles Christopher Whitt, Chief Nursing Officer
Web address: www.riverparkhospital.net
Control: Corporation, Investor–owned, for–profit **Service:** Psychiatric

Staffed Beds: 173 **Admissions:** 1610 **Census:** 143 **Outpatient Visits:** 0 **Births:** 0 **Total Expense ($000):** 20122 **Payroll Expense ($000):** 11284 **Personnel:** 300

✠ **ST. MARY'S MEDICAL CENTER (510007)**, 2900 First Avenue, Zip 25702–1272; tel. 304/526–1234, (Total facility includes 19 beds in nursing home–type unit) **A**1 2 3 5 9 10 **F**3 9 11 12 13 15 17 18 20 22 24 26 28 29 30 31 32 34 35 36 40 42 43 44 45 46 47 48 49 50 53 55 57 58 59 60 61 62 64 65 66 67 68 70 74 75 76 77 78 79 81 82 84 85 86 87 89 92 93 96 97 98 100 101 102 103 107 108 110 111 114 115 118 119 120 121 123 124 126 128 129 130 132 133 135 145 146 147 148 **P**8 **S** Pallottine Health Services, Huntington, WV
Primary Contact: Michael G. Sellards, President and Chief Executive Officer
COO: Todd Campbell, Senior Vice President and Chief Operating Officer
CFO: Angela Swearingen, Vice President Finance
CMO: Ernest Lee Taylor, M.D., Vice President Medical Affairs
CIO: Michael House, Director Information Systems
CHR: Susan Beth Robinson, Vice President Human Resources
CNO: Elizabeth Bosley, R.N., Vice President Patient Services
Web address: www.st–marys.org
Control: Church–operated, Nongovernment, not–for profit **Service:** General Medical and Surgical

Staffed Beds: 393 **Admissions:** 18158 **Census:** 276 **Outpatient Visits:** 243332 **Births:** 389 **Total Expense ($000):** 347446 **Payroll Expense ($000):** 117401 **Personnel:** 2207

HURRICANE—Putnam County

★ **CAMC TEAYS VALLEY HOSPITAL (510085)**, 1400 Hospital Drive, Zip 25526–9202; tel. 304/757–1700 **A**9 10 **F**3 11 15 28 29 34 35 39 40 45 46 47 50 54 56 57 59 64 65 70 74 75 77 79 81 82 85 87 93 97 100 102 107 108 110 111 115 118 119 130 131 132 135 145 146 148 **S** Charleston Area Medical Center Health System, Inc., Charleston, WV
Primary Contact: Randall H. Hodges, FACHE, President and Chief Executive Officer
CFO: Larry C. Hudson, Executive Vice President and Chief Financial Officer
CMO: T. Pinckney McIlwain, M.D., Vice President Medical Affairs and Chief Medical Officer
CIO: Gregory M. Veltri, Vice President, Information Services and Chief Information Officer
CNO: Mary Beth Mullins, Associate Administrator and Chief Nursing Officer
Web address: www.camc.org
Control: Other not–for–profit (including NFP Corporation) **Service:** General Medical and Surgical

Staffed Beds: 70 **Admissions:** 2297 **Census:** 30 **Outpatient Visits:** 89472 **Births:** 0 **Total Expense ($000):** 51958 **Payroll Expense ($000):** 17783 **Personnel:** 328

KEYSER—Mineral County

✠ **POTOMAC VALLEY HOSPITAL (511315)**, 100 Pin Oak Lane, Zip 26726–5908; tel. 304/597–3500 **A**1 9 10 18 **F**3 15 18 28 29 30 34 40 45 57 59 63 64 70 75 79 81 85 87 88 93 107 108 110 111 114 119 127 128 130 132 133 135 146 **S** West Virginia United Health System, Fairmont, WV
Primary Contact: Linda K. Shroyer, Administrator
CFO: Marian Cardwell, Chief Financial Officer
CMO: Charles Bess, M.D., Medical Director
CIO: Micah Reel, Director of Bio–Med
CHR: Dianne Smith, Director Personnel and Human Resources
CNO: Mary Ann Billings, Director of Nursing
Web address: www.potomacvalleyhospital.com
Control: Corporation, Investor–owned, for–profit **Service:** General Medical and Surgical

Staffed Beds: 25 **Admissions:** 793 **Census:** 9 **Outpatient Visits:** 51173 **Births:** 0 **Total Expense ($000):** 20620 **Payroll Expense ($000):** 7127 **Personnel:** 190

KINGWOOD—Preston County

★ **PRESTON MEMORIAL HOSPITAL (511312)**, 300 South Price Street, Zip 26537–1495; tel. 304/329–1400 **A**9 10 18 **F**3 11 12 15 18 29 30 34 35 40 43 45 47 48 50 53 57 59 64 65 70 74 75 76 77 81 92 93 107 108 111 114 119 129 132 133 135 146 147 **P**6
Primary Contact: Melissa Lockwood, Chief Executive Officer
CFO: Robert W. Milvet, Jr., Chief Financial Officer
CIO: Beth Horne, System Administrator Information Technology
CHR: Michele Batiste, Director Human Resources
Web address: www.prestonmemorial.com
Control: Other not–for–profit (including NFP Corporation) **Service:** General Medical and Surgical

Staffed Beds: 25 **Admissions:** 644 **Census:** 6 **Outpatient Visits:** 56350 **Births:** 0 **Total Expense ($000):** 25067 **Payroll Expense ($000):** 11649 **Personnel:** 307

LOGAN—Logan County

✠ **LOGAN REGIONAL MEDICAL CENTER (510048)**, 20 Hospital Drive, Zip 25601–3452; tel. 304/831–1101 **A**1 9 10 20 **F**3 11 13 15 18 20 28 29 31 34 35 40 43 45 49 51 54 57 59 64 65 70 74 75 76 77 78 79 81 86 87 89 90 92 93 97 107 108 110 111 114 115 118 119 129 130 133 135 146 147 **P**6 **S** LifePoint Hospitals, Inc., Brentwood, TN
Primary Contact: Gerald C. Dooley, Interim Chief Executive Officer
COO: Brian Springate, Interim Chief Operating Officer
CFO: Tim Matney, Chief Financial Officer
CMO: Kathy Harvey, D.O., Chief Medical Officer
CIO: Barry Hensley, Director Information Systems
CHR: Jessica Martin, Director Human Resources
CNO: Karen Barnes, Interim Chief Nursing Officer
Web address: www.loganregionalmedicalcenter.com
Control: Corporation, Investor–owned, for–profit **Service:** General Medical and Surgical

Staffed Beds: 129 **Admissions:** 5092 **Census:** 65 **Outpatient Visits:** 92415 **Births:** 309 **Total Expense ($000):** 74435 **Payroll Expense ($000):** 24730 **Personnel:** 596

WV

MADISON—Boone County

⊞ **BOONE MEMORIAL HOSPITAL (511313)**, 701 Madison Avenue,
Zip 25130–1699; tel. 304/369–1230 **A**1 9 10 18 **F**3 11 15 28 34 35 40 43
45 50 53 54 57 59 64 65 75 77 81 87 97 107 108 111 119 127 128 129
130 131 133 135 146 147
Primary Contact: Tommy H. Mullins, Administrator
CFO: Randy Foxx, Chief Financial Officer
CMO: Ziad Chanaa, M.D., Chief of Staff
CIO: Susan Shreve, Executive Director Information Technology
CHR: Sheliah Cook, Director Human Resources
CNO: Teresa Meade, R.N., Chief Nursing Officer
Web address: www.bmh.org
Control: Other not–for–profit (including NFP Corporation) **Service:** General
Medical and Surgical

Staffed Beds: 25 **Admissions:** 621 **Census:** 13 **Outpatient Visits:** 53959
Births: 0 **Total Expense ($000):** 20694 **Payroll Expense ($000):** 7400
Personnel: 200

MARTINSBURG—Berkeley County

⊞ **BERKELEY MEDICAL CENTER (510008)**, 2500 Hospital Drive,
Zip 25401–3402; tel. 304/264–1000 **A**1 2 3 5 9 10 **F**3 11 12 13 15 18 20 22
28 29 30 31 34 35 38 40 43 44 45 47 49 51 53 57 59 62 64 70 74 75 76
77 78 79 81 82 85 86 87 89 92 93 98 102 103 107 108 110 111 115 118
119 124 129 130 131 132 135 145 146 148 **S** West Virginia United Health
System, Fairmont, WV
Primary Contact: Anthony Zelenka, President and Chief Operating Officer
CFO: Kathleen Quinones, Interim Vice President Finance
CIO: Mark Combs, Interim Director System Information Technology
CHR: Michelle Thomas, Vice President Human Resources
CNO: Donna Clews, Ph.D., Vice President Patient Care Services
Web address: www.cityhospital.org
Control: Other not–for–profit (including NFP Corporation) **Service:** General
Medical and Surgical

Staffed Beds: 170 **Admissions:** 7875 **Census:** 96 **Outpatient Visits:** 219190
Births: 955 **Total Expense ($000):** 147764 **Payroll Expense ($000):** 56342
Personnel: 1116

⊞ **MARTINSBURG VETERANS AFFAIRS MEDICAL CENTER**, 510 Butler Avenue,
Zip 25405–9990; tel. 304/263–0811, (Total facility includes 121 beds in nursing
home–type unit) **A**1 3 5 9 **F**3 4 5 7 18 26 29 30 31 33 34 35 38 39 40 45 54
56 57 58 59 68 70 74 75 77 78 79 81 82 83 84 85 87 90 91 92 93 94 97
98 102 103 104 105 106 107 108 111 114 115 119 128 129 130 135 143
146 147 148 **S** Department of Veterans Affairs, Washington, DC
Primary Contact: Timothy J. Cooke, Medical Center Director and Chief Executive
Officer
COO: Timothy J. Cooke, Medical Center Director and Chief Executive Officer
CFO: Eric C. Sorenson, Chief Fiscal Office
CMO: Jonathan Fierer, M.D., Chief of Staff
CIO: Mary Ann Creel, Chief Information Resource Management
CHR: Brenda Byrd–Pelaez, Chief Human Resources Management Office
CNO: Susan George, R.N., Associate Director Patient Care Services
Web address: www.martinsburg.va.gov/
Control: Veterans Affairs, Government, federal **Service:** General Medical and
Surgical

Staffed Beds: 192 **Admissions:** 3459 **Census:** 148 **Outpatient Visits:**
456497 **Births:** 0 **Total Expense ($000):** 275957 **Payroll Expense ($000):**
116253 **Personnel:** 1810

MONTGOMERY—Fayette County

⊞ **MONTGOMERY GENERAL HOSPITAL (511318)**, 401 Sixth Avenue,
Zip 25136–2116, Mailing Address: P.O. Box 270, Zip 25136–0270;
tel. 304/442–5151, (Total facility includes 44 beds in nursing home–type unit) **A**1
9 10 18 **F**3 11 15 29 30 34 35 40 45 49 50 53 57 59 64 67 68 77 81 87 93
97 107 111 114 119 128 129 130 131 133 135 146 147 **P**6 8
Primary Contact: Vickie Gay, Chief Executive Officer
CFO: Sherri Murray, Chief Financial Officer
CMO: Traci Acklin, M.D., Chief of Staff
CIO: Denzil Blevins, Director Information Systems
CHR: Kelly D. Frye, Director Human Resources
Web address: www.mghwv.com
Control: Other not–for–profit (including NFP Corporation) **Service:** General
Medical and Surgical

Staffed Beds: 69 **Admissions:** 753 **Census:** 42 **Outpatient Visits:** 61139
Births: 0 **Total Expense ($000):** 21502 **Payroll Expense ($000):** 10858
Personnel: 226

MORGANTOWN—Monongalia County

CHESTNUT RIDGE HOSPITAL See West Virginia University Hospitals

⊞ **HEALTHSOUTH MOUNTAINVIEW REGIONAL REHABILITATION HOSPITAL**
(513030), 1160 Van Voorhis Road, Zip 26505–3437; tel. 304/598–1100 **A**1 3
5 10 **F**3 29 34 35 57 59 60 64 74 75 77 79 82 86 90 91 93 94 95 96 100
103 130 131 132 135 146 148 **S** HEALTHSOUTH Corporation, Birmingham, AL
Primary Contact: Vickie Demers, Chief Executive Officer
CFO: Jason Gizzi, Controller
CMO: Govind Patel, M.D., Medical Director
CIO: Robin Wherry, Risk Manager and Director Quality Assurance and Health
Information Management
CHR: Shannon Hyde, Director Human Resources
CNO: Stacy Jones, Chief Nursing Officer
Web address: www.healthsouthmountainview.com
Control: Corporation, Investor–owned, for–profit **Service:** Rehabilitation

Staffed Beds: 96 **Admissions:** 1865 **Census:** 75 **Outpatient Visits:** 8710
Births: 0 **Total Expense ($000):** 24798 **Payroll Expense ($000):** 12282
Personnel: 314

⊞ **MONONGALIA GENERAL HOSPITAL (510024)**, 1200 J. D. Anderson Drive,
Zip 26505–3486; tel. 304/598–1200 **A**1 2 9 10 19 **F**3 13 15 17 18 20 22 24
26 28 29 30 31 32 34 35 40 43 45 46 49 50 51 54 57 59 60 63 64 65 68
70 74 75 76 77 78 79 81 82 84 85 86 87 89 97 107 108 111 114 115 116
118 119 126 129 130 132 135 144 145 146 147 148 **P**6 8
Primary Contact: Darryl L. Duncan, President and Chief Executive Officer
COO: Linda Neu Ollis, FACHE, Chief Operating Officer
CFO: Daris Rosencrance, Chief Financial Officer
CMO: Mike Ferrebee, M.D., Vice President Medical Affairs
CIO: Linda Allen, Vice President Quality and Information Systems
CHR: Melissa Shreves, Director Human Resources
Web address: www.mongeneral.com
Control: Other not–for–profit (including NFP Corporation) **Service:** General
Medical and Surgical

Staffed Beds: 175 **Admissions:** 8494 **Census:** 95 **Outpatient Visits:** 173135
Births: 1020 **Total Expense ($000):** 208533 **Payroll Expense ($000):**
69769 **Personnel:** 1269

⊞ **WEST VIRGINIA UNIVERSITY HOSPITALS (510001)**, 1 Medical Center Drive,
Zip 26506–4749; tel. 304/598–4000, (Includes CHESTNUT RIDGE HOSPITAL,
930 Chestnut Ridge Road, Zip 26505–2854; tel. 304/293–4000; WEST VIRGINIA
UNIVERSITY CHILDREN'S HOSPITAL, Medical Center Drive, Zip 26506–8111;
tel. 800/982–6277) **A**1 3 5 8 9 10 12 13 19 **F**3 4 5 9 11 12 13 15 17 18 19
20 21 22 23 24 25 26 27 28 29 30 31 35 36 37 38 39 40 43 45 46 47 48
49 50 51 54 55 56 57 59 60 61 64 68 70 72 74 75 76 77 78 79 80 81 82
84 85 86 87 88 89 92 98 99 100 101 102 103 105 106 107 108 110 111
114 115 118 119 120 121 123 124 126 129 130 132 136 141 145 146 147
148 **P**6 **S** West Virginia United Health System, Fairmont, WV
CFO: Mary Jo Shahan, Vice President and Chief Financial Officer
CMO: Michelle Nuss, M.D., Chief Medical Officer
CIO: Rich King, Vice President Information Technology
CHR: Charlotte Bennett, Vice President Human Resources
Web address: www.health.wvu.edu
Control: Other not–for–profit (including NFP Corporation) **Service:** General
Medical and Surgical

Staffed Beds: 514 **Admissions:** 25772 **Census:** 421 **Outpatient Visits:**
657026 **Births:** 1460 **Total Expense ($000):** 672782 **Payroll Expense**
($000): 244717 **Personnel:** 4850

NEW MARTINSVILLE—Wetzel County

⊞ **WETZEL COUNTY HOSPITAL (510072)**, 3 East Benjamin Drive,
Zip 26155–2758; tel. 304/455–8000 **A**1 9 10 20 **F**3 8 15 28 30 31 34 40 43
45 57 59 64 65 70 75 77 81 85 93 94 107 108 114 118 119 127 130 132
133 135 146 148 **P**6
Primary Contact: Brian K. Felici, Chief Executive Officer
CFO: Edwin Szewczyk, Chief Financial Officer
CMO: Donald A. Blum, M.D., Chief of Staff
CIO: Amy Frazier, Supervisor Management Information Systems
CHR: Sarah Boley, Director Human Resources
Web address: www.wetzelcountyhospital.com
Control: County–Government, nonfederal **Service:** General Medical and Surgical

Staffed Beds: 44 **Admissions:** 738 **Census:** 9 **Outpatient Visits:** 86524
Births: 0 **Total Expense ($000):** 23648 **Payroll Expense ($000):** 9802
Personnel: 227

Hospital, Medicare Provider Number, Address, Telephone, Approval, Facility, and Physician Codes, Health Care System

★ American Hospital Association (AHA) membership   ○ Healthcare Facilities Accreditation Program
□ The Joint Commission accreditation   ◇ DNV Healthcare Inc. accreditation   △ Commission on Accreditation of Rehabilitation Facilities (CARF) accreditation

OAK HILL—Fayette County

✠ **PLATEAU MEDICAL CENTER (511317)**, 430 Main Street, Zip 25901–3455;
tel. 304/469–8600 **A**1 9 10 18 **F**3 8 15 18 29 30 34 35 40 45 46 50 57 59
64 68 70 75 77 79 81 85 87 91 93 97 107 108 110 111 114 119 129 146
S Community Health Systems, Inc., Franklin, TN
Primary Contact: Derek W. Cimala, Interim Chief Executive Officer
CFO: Heather Hylton, Chief Financial Officer
CMO: Jacob McNeel, D.O., Chief of Staff
CIO: Nick Stover, Director Information Systems
CHR: Tammie Chinn, Director Marketing and Public Relations
CNO: Randell Thompson, Chief Nursing Officer
Web address: www.plateaumedicalcenter.com
Control: Corporation, Investor–owned, for–profit **Service:** General Medical and
Surgical

> **Staffed Beds:** 25 **Admissions:** 1397 **Census:** 14 **Outpatient Visits:** 49765
> **Births:** 0 **Total Expense ($000):** 30855 **Payroll Expense ($000):** 13256
> **Personnel:** 254

PARKERSBURG—Wood County

✠ **CAMDEN CLARK MEDICAL CENTER (510058)**, 800 Garfield Avenue,
Zip 26101–5378, Mailing Address: P.O. Box 718, Zip 26102–0718;
tel. 304/424–2111, (Includes ST. JOSEPH'S HOSPITAL, 1824 Murdoch Avenue,
Zip 26101–3246, Mailing Address: P.O. Box 327, Zip 26102–0327;
tel. 304/424–4111), (Total facility includes 25 beds in nursing home–type unit)
A1 9 10 13 **F**1 3 7 8 11 12 13 15 17 18 20 22 24 28 29 30 31 34 35 40 43
45 50 51 53 54 57 58 59 64 65 66 67 68 70 74 75 76 78 79 81 84 85 86
87 89 92 97 98 100 101 102 107 108 110 111 114 115 116 117 118 119
120 121 123 124 128 129 130 132 135 146 147 148 **P**6 8 **S** West Virginia
United Health System, Fairmont, WV
Primary Contact: David K. McClure, President and Chief Executive Officer
COO: David K. McClure, President and Chief Executive Officer
CMO: David Gnegy, M.D., President Medical Staff
CIO: Josh Woods, Director Information Systems
CHR: Tom Heller, Vice President Human Resources
CNO: Sherry Simmons, Vice President Patient Care Services and Chief Nursing
Officer
Web address: www.camdenclark.org
Control: Other not–for–profit (including NFP Corporation) **Service:** General
Medical and Surgical

> **Staffed Beds:** 255 **Admissions:** 14097 **Census:** 162 **Outpatient Visits:**
> 317050 **Births:** 1562 **Total Expense ($000):** 239445 **Payroll Expense**
> **($000):** 75919 **Personnel:** 1882

✠ **HEALTHSOUTH WESTERN HILLS REHABILITATION HOSPITAL (513027)**, 3
Western Hills Drive, Zip 26105–8122; tel. 304/420–1300 **A**1 10 **F**29 64 90 93
94 96 130 146 148 **S** HEALTHSOUTH Corporation, Birmingham, AL
Primary Contact: Alvin R. Lawson, JD, FACHE, Chief Executive Officer
CFO: Jessica Walkup, Controller
CMO: Kalapala Rao, M.D., Medical Director
CHR: Candace Ross, Coordinator Human Resources
CNO: Tanda Hockenberry, Chief Nursing Officer
Web address: www.healthsouthwesternhills.com
Control: Corporation, Investor–owned, for–profit **Service:** Rehabilitation

> **Staffed Beds:** 40 **Admissions:** 922 **Census:** 34 **Outpatient Visits:** 8157
> **Births:** 0 **Total Expense ($000):** 13070 **Payroll Expense ($000):** 5510
> **Personnel:** 103

PETERSBURG—Grant County

★ **GRANT MEMORIAL HOSPITAL (511316)**, 117 Hospital Drive,
Zip 26847–9566, Mailing Address: P.O. Box 1019, Zip 26847–1019;
tel. 304/257–1026, (Total facility includes 20 beds in nursing home–type unit) **A**9
10 18 **F**3 11 13 15 18 28 29 30 34 35 40 45 50 57 59 64 65 67 68 70 75
76 77 79 81 84 85 86 87 93 102 107 108 110 114 119 128 130 132 133
146 148 **P**6
Primary Contact: Mary Beth Barr, R.N., Chief Executive Officer
CFO: Joe Barnes, Chief Financial Officer
CMO: Stephen Thompson, D.O., Chief of Staff
CIO: Derek Nesselrodt, Director Information Systems
CHR: Ronnie Arbaugh, Director Human Resources
CNO: Kimberly Linville, Chief Nursing Officer
Web address: www.grantmemorial.com
Control: County–Government, nonfederal **Service:** General Medical and Surgical

> **Staffed Beds:** 45 **Admissions:** 1463 **Census:** 15 **Outpatient Visits:** 48348
> **Births:** 244 **Total Expense ($000):** 30318 **Payroll Expense ($000):** 10364
> **Personnel:** 266

PHILIPPI—Barbour County

★ **BROADDUS HOSPITAL (511300)**, 1 Healthcare Drive, Zip 26416–9405, Mailing
Address: P.O. Box 930, Zip 26416–0930; tel. 304/457–1760, (Total facility
includes 60 beds in nursing home–type unit) **A**9 10 18 **F**3 15 29 30 34 35 40
57 59 64 65 75 85 87 97 107 110 114 119 128 130 133 143 146 **S** Davis
Health System, Elkins, WV
Primary Contact: Jeffrey A. Powelson, Chief Executive Officer
CFO: Cathy Kalar, Chief Financial Officer
CHR: Penny D. Brown, Director of Human Resources
Web address: www.davishealthsystem.org/
Control: Other not–for–profit (including NFP Corporation) **Service:** General
Medical and Surgical

> **Staffed Beds:** 72 **Admissions:** 313 **Census:** 63 **Outpatient Visits:** 22429
> **Births:** 0 **Total Expense ($000):** 15531 **Payroll Expense ($000):** 6508
> **Personnel:** 161

POINT PLEASANT—Mason County

✠ **PLEASANT VALLEY HOSPITAL (510012)**, 2520 Valley Drive,
Zip 25550–2031; tel. 304/675–4340, (Total facility includes 100 beds in nursing
home–type unit) **A**1 9 10 **F**3 11 13 15 17 18 28 29 30 33 34 35 39 40 43 48
50 53 56 57 59 62 63 68 70 74 75 76 77 78 79 81 85 86 87 89 93 107
108 110 111 114 115 118 119 128 129 130 131 132 143 144 146 147
148 **P**6
Primary Contact: Glen A. Washington, Chief Executive Officer
COO: William A. Barker, Jr., Vice President Administration
CFO: Richard Hogan, Chief Financial Officer
CMO: Agnes Enrico–Simon, M.D., President Medical Staff
CIO: Paula Brooker, Director Information Services
CHR: David A. Brown, Director Human Resources and Corporate Compliance
CNO: Amber Findley, Senior Director Nursing Services and NRC Administrator
Web address: www.pvalley.org
Control: Other not–for–profit (including NFP Corporation) **Service:** General
Medical and Surgical

> **Staffed Beds:** 201 **Admissions:** 2473 **Census:** 112 **Outpatient Visits:**
> 201452 **Births:** 156 **Total Expense ($000):** 64669 **Payroll Expense ($000):**
> 27897 **Personnel:** 573

PRINCETON—Mercer County

✠ **HEALTHSOUTH SOUTHERN HILLS REHABILITATION HOSPITAL (513026)**,
120 Twelfth Street, Zip 24740–2352; tel. 304/487–8000 **A**1 10 **F**29 56 57 59
60 64 74 75 77 79 87 90 93 94 130 132 148 **S** HEALTHSOUTH Corporation,
Birmingham, AL
Primary Contact: Robert Williams, Chief Executive Officer
CFO: Melinda Fanning, Chief Financial Officer and Controller
CMO: Robert Walker, M.D., Medical Director
CIO: Brian Bales, Director Plant Operations
CHR: Jan Thibodeau, Director Human Resources
CNO: Lisa Lester, Chief Nursing Officer
Web address: www.healthsouthsouthernhills.com
Control: Corporation, Investor–owned, for–profit **Service:** Rehabilitation

> **Staffed Beds:** 45 **Admissions:** 863 **Census:** 28 **Births:** 0 **Personnel:** 105

✠ **PRINCETON COMMUNITY HOSPITAL (510046)**, 122 12th Street,
Zip 24740–2352, Mailing Address: P.O. Box 1369, Zip 24740–1369;
tel. 304/487–7000 **A**1 2 9 10 19 **F**3 11 12 13 15 17 29 30 31 32 34 35 39
40 44 45 46 48 49 50 51 53 57 59 64 65 70 74 75 76 77 78 79 81 85 86
87 89 93 98 100 101 102 103 104 107 108 110 111 114 115 118 119 127
129 130 131 132 135 141 142 144 146 147 **P**1
Primary Contact: Wayne B. Griffith, FACHE, Chief Executive Officer
COO: Jeffrey Lilley, CPA, Chief Operating Officer
CFO: Frank J. Sinicrope, Jr., Vice President Financial Services
CMO: Wesley Asbury, M.D., President Medical Staff
CIO: Stephen A. Curry, Director Information Services
CHR: Heather Poff, Director Human Resources
CNO: Rose Morgan, R.N., Vice President Patient Care Services
Web address: www.pchonline.org
Control: City–Government, nonfederal **Service:** General Medical and Surgical

> **Staffed Beds:** 230 **Admissions:** 8724 **Census:** 124 **Outpatient Visits:**
> 217904 **Births:** 647 **Total Expense ($000):** 118790 **Payroll Expense**
> **($000):** 44258 **Personnel:** 1000

WV

Many Facility Codes have changed. Please refer to the AHA Guide Code Chart.

RANSON—Jefferson County

☒ **JEFFERSON MEDICAL CENTER (511319)**, 300 South Preston Street,
Zip 25438–1631; tel. 304/728–1600 **A**1 3 5 9 10 18 **F**3 11 13 15 29 30 34
35 38 40 43 44 45 57 59 64 70 74 75 76 77 79 81 82 85 86 87 92 93 107
108 110 111 115 118 119 129 130 132 135 146 148 **S** West Virginia United
Health System, Fairmont, WV
Primary Contact: Christina DeRosa, Ph.D., Chief Administrative Officer
CFO: Kathleen Quinones, Interim Vice President Finance
CMO: David A. Baltierra, M.D., President Medical Staff
CIO: Mark Combs, Chief Information Security Officer
CNO: Linda Blanc, R.N., Administrative Director of Nursing
Web address: www.wvuniversityhealthcare.com/locations/Jefferson–Medical–
Center.aspx
Control: Other not–for–profit (including NFP Corporation) **Service:** General
Medical and Surgical

Staffed Beds: 25 **Admissions:** 1410 **Census:** 11 **Outpatient Visits:** 80312
Births: 258 **Total Expense ($000):** 46400 **Payroll Expense ($000):** 17756
Personnel: 305

RIPLEY—Jackson County

☐ **JACKSON GENERAL HOSPITAL (511320)**, 122 Pinnell Street,
Zip 25271–9101, Mailing Address: P.O. Box 720, Zip 25271–0720;
tel. 304/372–2731 **A**1 9 10 18 **F**3 11 15 17 29 30 34 35 40 50 57 59 64 68
75 79 81 85 93 107 114 119 127 132 133 **P**6
Primary Contact: Stephanie McCoy, President and Chief Executive Officer
CFO: Angela Frame, Chief Financial Officer
CMO: James G. Gaal, M.D., Chief of Medical Staff
CIO: John Manley, Director Information Systems
CHR: Jeffrey Tabor, Director Human Resources
Web address: www.jacksongeneral.com
Control: Other not–for–profit (including NFP Corporation) **Service:** General
Medical and Surgical

Staffed Beds: 25 **Admissions:** 1047 **Census:** 12 **Outpatient Visits:** 45639
Births: 0 **Total Expense ($000):** 21748 **Payroll Expense ($000):** 11021
Personnel: 231

ROMNEY—Hampshire County

☒ **HAMPSHIRE MEMORIAL HOSPITAL (511311)**, 363 Sunrise Boulevard,
Zip 26757–4607; tel. 304/822–4561, (Total facility includes 30 beds in nursing
home–type unit) **A**1 9 10 18 **F**3 15 29 30 40 45 54 59 64 65 71 77 79 81 85
93 97 107 119 127 128 129 130 133 148 **P**6 **S** Valley Health System,
Winchester, VA
Primary Contact: Neil R. McLaughlin, R.N., President
CFO: Christine Lowman, Vice President Finance
CMO: Vijay K. Chowdhary, M.D., Medical Director
CHR: Cindy Combs, Supervisor Human Resources
CNO: Gena Swisher, Vice President Nursing
Web address: www.valleyhealthlink.com/hampshire
Control: Other not–for–profit (including NFP Corporation) **Service:** General
Medical and Surgical

Staffed Beds: 44 **Admissions:** 448 **Census:** 38 **Outpatient Visits:** 43457
Births: 0 **Total Expense ($000):** 22978 **Payroll Expense ($000):** 8138
Personnel: 163

RONCEVERTE—Greenbrier County

★ ○ **GREENBRIER VALLEY MEDICAL CENTER (510002)**, 202 Maplewood
Avenue, Zip 24970–1334, Mailing Address: P.O. Box 497, Zip 24970–0497;
tel. 304/647–4411 **A**9 10 11 12 13 19 20 **F**8 13 15 18 20 29 31 34 40 45
49 51 57 59 60 68 70 75 76 78 79 81 82 85 86 87 89 107 108 110 111
114 116 119 120 129 133 135 146 148 **P**6 **S** Community Health Systems,
Inc., Franklin, TN
Primary Contact: Robert Calhoun, Chief Executive Officer
CFO: Paige Adkins, Chief Financial Officer
CMO: John Johnson, M.D., Chief of Staff
CIO: Matt Turley, Interim Director Information Systems
CHR: Melissa Wickline, Director Marketing
CNO: Charlene Warren, R.N., Chief Nursing Officer
Web address: www.gvmc.com
Control: Corporation, Investor–owned, for–profit **Service:** General Medical and
Surgical

Staffed Beds: 113 **Admissions:** 3676 **Census:** 38 **Outpatient Visits:** 56042
Births: 648 **Total Expense ($000):** 54241 **Payroll Expense ($000):** 20003
Personnel: 465

SISTERSVILLE—Tyler County

★ **SISTERSVILLE GENERAL HOSPITAL (511304)**, 314 South Wells Street,
Zip 26175–1098; tel. 304/652–2611 **A**9 10 18 **F**3 7 11 15 28 29 30 32 35
40 43 50 53 57 59 63 64 65 79 83 84 87 93 97 107 119 127 128 129 130
132 133 135 146 147 148 **P**6
Primary Contact: John May, Chief Executive Officer
COO: Brandon Chadock, Director of Operations
CFO: Carl Worrell, Chief Financial Officer
CMO: Amanda Nichols, M.D., Chief of Staff
CIO: Casey Blake, Director Information Technology
CHR: Mary Beth Neff, Director Human Resources
CNO: Shelly West, Chief Nursing Officer
Web address: www.sistersvillehospital.com
Control: City–Government, nonfederal **Service:** General Medical and Surgical

Staffed Beds: 12 **Admissions:** 187 **Census:** 2 **Outpatient Visits:** 33328
Births: 0 **Total Expense ($000):** 10676 **Payroll Expense ($000):** 5977
Personnel: 126

SOUTH CHARLESTON—Kanawha County

☒ **THOMAS MEMORIAL HOSPITAL (510029)**, 4605 MacCorkle Avenue S.W.,
Zip 25309–1398; tel. 304/766–3600 **A**1 3 5 9 10 **F**3 5 8 11 13 15 17 18 20
22 29 30 31 32 34 35 38 40 43 45 46 47 48 49 50 53 54 57 59 60 62 64
65 68 69 70 72 74 75 76 77 78 79 81 84 85 86 87 89 92 93 98 99 100
101 102 103 104 105 107 108 110 111 114 115 118 119 120 121 123 124
126 129 130 131 132 143 144 146 147 **S** Thomas Health System, Inc., South
Charleston, WV
Primary Contact: Stephen P. Dexter, President and Chief Executive Officer
COO: Daniel Lauffer, FACHE, Senior Vice President and Chief Operating Officer
CFO: Charles O. Covert, Vice President Finance
CIO: Charles O. Covert, Vice President Finance
CHR: Marybeth Smith, Director Human Resources
CNO: Rebecca Brannon, R.N., Vice President Patient Services
Web address: www.thomaswv.org
Control: Other not–for–profit (including NFP Corporation) **Service:** General
Medical and Surgical

Staffed Beds: 215 **Admissions:** 8744 **Census:** 123 **Outpatient Visits:**
182684 **Births:** 1128 **Total Expense ($000):** 165025 **Payroll Expense
($000):** 55238 **Personnel:** 1010

SPENCER—Roane County

☒ **ROANE GENERAL HOSPITAL (511306)**, 200 Hospital Drive, Zip 25276–1050;
tel. 304/927–4444, (Total facility includes 35 beds in nursing home–type unit) **A**1
9 10 18 **F**1 3 15 28 29 34 35 40 43 45 53 57 59 64 65 67 81 89 90 93 97
107 108 119 127 128 130 133 148 **P**6
Primary Contact: Douglas E. Bentz, Chief Executive Officer
CFO: Louise Ward, Vice President Financial and Support Services
CMO: Brent Watson, M.D., Chief Medical Staff
CIO: Tony Keaton, Director Information Systems
CHR: Jeff Beane, Director Human Resources
Web address: www.roanegeneralhospital.com
Control: Other not–for–profit (including NFP Corporation) **Service:** General
Medical and Surgical

Staffed Beds: 60 **Admissions:** 445 **Census:** 42 **Outpatient Visits:** 68876
Births: 0 **Total Expense ($000):** 24798 **Payroll Expense ($000):** 11718
Personnel: 261

SUMMERSVILLE—Nicholas County

☒ **SUMMERSVILLE REGIONAL MEDICAL CENTER (510082)**, 400 Fairview
Heights Road, Zip 26651–9308; tel. 304/872–2891, (Total facility includes 52
beds in nursing home–type unit) **A**1 9 10 **F**1 3 13 15 28 30 34 35 40 43 57 59
64 65 67 68 70 75 76 77 79 81 83 84 85 89 91 93 97 107 108 110 111
115 119 127 128 129 130 131 133 135 146 147 148
Primary Contact: Randy Simmons, Interim Chief Executive Officer
CFO: Brian Kelbaugh, Chief Financial Officer
CMO: Bandy Mullins, M.D., Chief of Staff
CIO: Mike Ellison, Information Systems Lead
CHR: David M. Henderson, Director Human Resources
CNO: Jennifer McCue, Director Patient Care
Web address: www.https://www.summersvilleregional.org/
Control: City–Government, nonfederal **Service:** General Medical and Surgical

Staffed Beds: 105 **Admissions:** 1508 **Census:** 70 **Outpatient Visits:** 119522
Births: 328 **Total Expense ($000):** 46425 **Payroll Expense ($000):** 23358
Personnel: 580

Hospital, Medicare Provider Number, Address, Telephone, Approval, Facility, and Physician Codes, Health Care System

★ American Hospital Association (AHA) membership
☐ The Joint Commission accreditation   ◇ DNV Healthcare Inc. accreditation
○ Healthcare Facilities Accreditation Program
△ Commission on Accreditation of Rehabilitation Facilities (CARF) accreditation

WEBSTER SPRINGS—Webster County

★ **WEBSTER COUNTY MEMORIAL HOSPITAL (511301)**, 324 Miller Mountain Drive, Zip 26288–1087, Mailing Address: P.O. Box 312, Zip 26288–0312; tel. 304/847–5682 **A**9 10 18 **F**7 15 28 30 34 35 40 57 59 64 75 87 93 97 107 114 119 127 130 133 135 146 147 148
Primary Contact: Annette M. Keenan, Chief Executive Officer
CMO: Robert Mace, M.D., Chief of Staff
CIO: Margaret W. Short, Coordinator Information Technology
CHR: Deborah Bragg, Director Human Resources
Web address: www.wcmhwv.com
Control: Other not–for–profit (including NFP Corporation) **Service:** General Medical and Surgical

Staffed Beds: 15 **Admissions:** 180 **Census:** 2 **Outpatient Visits:** 43641
Births: 0 **Total Expense ($000):** 12508 **Payroll Expense ($000):** 6300
Personnel: 130

WEIRTON—Brooke County

⊠ **WEIRTON MEDICAL CENTER (510023)**, 601 Colliers Way, Zip 26062–5091; tel. 304/797–6000, (Total facility includes 33 beds in nursing home–type unit) **A**1 9 10 **F**3 5 9 11 13 15 17 18 20 22 26 29 30 32 34 35 37 39 40 41 43 45 46 47 48 49 50 51 53 54 56 57 59 60 61 62 64 68 70 74 75 76 77 78 79 81 82 85 86 89 90 92 93 96 97 99 100 101 102 103 104 107 108 110 111 114 115 116 118 119 124 126 128 129 130 131 132 135 143 145 146 147 148 **P**6
Primary Contact: Charles M. O'Brien, Jr., President and Chief Executive Officer
CFO: Robert A. Frank, Chief Financial Officer
CIO: Dave Angalich, Director Information Services
CHR: Barbara Coalter, Director Human Resources
CNO: Sherry L. Zisk, Chief Nursing Officer
Web address: www.weirtonmedical.com
Control: Other not–for–profit (including NFP Corporation) **Service:** General Medical and Surgical

Staffed Beds: 168 **Admissions:** 6151 **Census:** 98 **Outpatient Visits:** 213819
Births: 383 **Total Expense ($000):** 102552 **Payroll Expense ($000):** 44188
Personnel: 995

WELCH—Mcdowell County

WELCH COMMUNITY HOSPITAL (510086), 454 McDowell Street, Zip 24801–2097; tel. 304/436–8461, (Total facility includes 59 beds in nursing home–type unit) **A**9 10 20 **F**3 13 15 29 35 40 45 50 57 59 64 65 66 67 68 70 75 76 81 86 87 97 107 110 114 119 127 130 135 146 147 148 **P**6
Primary Contact: Walter J. Garrett, Chief Executive Officer
COO: Heather Smith, Chief Operating Officer
CFO: Johnny Brant, Chief Financial Officer
CMO: Chandra Sharma, M.D., Chief of Staff
CHR: Diana Blankenship, Director Human Resources
CNO: Mark Simpson, Director of Nursing
Control: State–Government, nonfederal **Service:** General Medical and Surgical

Staffed Beds: 108 **Admissions:** 743 **Census:** 52 **Outpatient Visits:** 34119
Births: 68 **Total Expense ($000):** 27476 **Payroll Expense ($000):** 9404
Personnel: 313

WESTON—Lewis County

⊠ **STONEWALL JACKSON MEMORIAL HOSPITAL (510038)**, 230 Hospital Plaza, Zip 26452–8558; tel. 304/269–8000 **A**1 9 10 **F**3 11 13 15 28 29 30 31 35 40 43 45 48 50 56 57 59 62 64 68 70 75 76 79 81 85 86 87 93 94 97 107 108 111 114 118 119 129 130 131 132 133 135 145 146 147 148 **P**6
Primary Contact: Avah Stalnaker, Chief Executive Officer
COO: Kevin P. Stalnaker, CPA, Chief Operating Officer
CFO: Dodie Arbogest, Chief Financial Officer
CMO: Jeremy Williams, M.D., President Medical Staff
CIO: Kay Butcher, Director Health Information Management
CHR: Rhonda M. Hager, Director Human Resources
CNO: David R. Courson, MSN, Chief Nursing Officer
Web address: www.stonewallhospital.com
Control: Other not–for–profit (including NFP Corporation) **Service:** General Medical and Surgical

Staffed Beds: 70 **Admissions:** 2287 **Census:** 24 **Outpatient Visits:** 82188
Births: 316 **Total Expense ($000):** 41777 **Payroll Expense ($000):** 21776
Personnel: 420

☐ **WILLIAM R. SHARPE, JR. HOSPITAL (514010)**, 936 Sharpe Hospital Road, Zip 26452–8550; tel. 304/269–1210 **A**1 5 9 10 **F**11 30 53 56 75 86 87 98 100 101 103 130 132 143 146 **P**6
Primary Contact: Parker Haddix, Chief Executive Officer
COO: Terry L. Small, Assistant Chief Executive Officer
CFO: Robert J. Kimble, Chief Financial Officer
CIO: Pam Lewis, Chief Compliance Officer
CNO: Cheryl France, M.D., Chief Medical Officer
Web address: www.wvdhhr.org/sharpe
Control: State–Government, nonfederal **Service:** Psychiatric

Staffed Beds: 150 **Admissions:** 469 **Census:** 145 **Outpatient Visits:** 0
Births: 0 **Total Expense ($000):** 40206 **Payroll Expense ($000):** 14336
Personnel: 457

WHEELING—Ohio County

☐ ○ **OHIO VALLEY MEDICAL CENTER (510039)**, 2000 Eoff Street, Zip 26003–3870; tel. 304/234–0123 **A**1 2 5 9 10 11 12 13 19 **F**3 5 9 11 13 15 18 20 28 29 30 31 34 35 38 40 43 44 48 49 50 51 53 55 56 57 58 59 60 61 64 65 68 70 74 75 76 77 78 79 81 82 84 85 86 87 89 93 97 98 99 100 101 102 103 104 105 107 108 110 111 114 115 116 117 119 121 123 129 130 131 132 134 135 146 147 148 **P**6 **S** Ohio Valley Health Services and Education Corporation, Wheeling, WV
Primary Contact: Michael J. Caruso, President and Chief Executive Officer
COO: Kelly Bettem, Chief Administrative Officer
CFO: Lisa M. Simon, Senior Vice President and Chief Financial Officer
CIO: Lisa M. Simon, Senior Vice President and Chief Financial Officer
CHR: Robert Wright, Senior Human Resource Advisor
CNO: Patsy George, R.N., Chief Nursing Officer
Web address: www.ovmc-eorh.com
Control: Other not–for–profit (including NFP Corporation) **Service:** General Medical and Surgical

Staffed Beds: 189 **Admissions:** 6166 **Census:** 92 **Outpatient Visits:** 135793
Births: 283 **Total Expense ($000):** 98626 **Payroll Expense ($000):** 38969
Personnel: 803

★ **PETERSON REHABILITATION HOSPITAL (513025)**, Homestead Avenue, Zip 26003; tel. 304/234–0500, (Total facility includes 150 beds in nursing home–type unit) **A**10 **F**29 34 50 56 57 59 75 77 86 87 90 93 96 128 130 131 132 143 148
Primary Contact: Barbara Sisarcick, Administrator
COO: Tom Barr, Director Operational Support Services
CFO: Tammy Parasida, Manager Business Office
CMO: William Mercer, M.D., Director
CIO: Jolene Nagle, Director Medical Records
CHR: Annie Barton, Director Human Resources
Web address: www.weat.com/site6/
Control: Corporation, Investor–owned, for–profit **Service:** Rehabilitation

Staffed Beds: 172 **Admissions:** 875 **Census:** 151 **Outpatient Visits:** 3179
Births: 0 **Total Expense ($000):** 18435 **Payroll Expense ($000):** 5727
Personnel: 148

☐ **WHEELING HOSPITAL (510050)**, 1 Medical Park, Zip 26003–6379; tel. 304/243–3000, (Total facility includes 24 beds in nursing home–type unit) **A**1 2 9 10 13 **F**3 11 13 15 17 18 20 22 24 26 28 29 30 31 32 34 35 36 40 43 44 45 46 49 50 53 54 57 58 59 61 62 64 65 66 70 74 75 76 77 78 79 81 85 86 87 89 92 93 96 97 99 107 108 110 114 115 117 118 119 120 121 123 128 129 130 131 132 135 143 146 147 148 **P**5
Primary Contact: Ronald L. Violi, Chief Executive Officer
CMO: Angelo Georges, M.D., President Medical and Dental Staff
CIO: David Rapp, Chief Information Officer
CHR: Susan Falbo, Vice President Human Resources
Web address: www.wheelinghospital.org
Control: Other not–for–profit (including NFP Corporation) **Service:** General Medical and Surgical

Staffed Beds: 247 **Admissions:** 9844 **Census:** 118 **Outpatient Visits:** 553071 **Births:** 1228 **Total Expense ($000):** 263577 **Payroll Expense ($000):** 115065 **Personnel:** 3087

WILLIAMSON—Mingo County

⊠ **WILLIAMSON MEMORIAL HOSPITAL (510077)**, 859 Alderson Street, Zip 25661–3215, Mailing Address: P.O. Box 1980, Zip 25661–1980; tel. 304/235–2500, (Nonreporting) **A**1 9 10 **S** Community Health Systems, Inc., Franklin, TN
Primary Contact: Cindy Segar–Miller, R.N., MS, Interim Chief Executive Officer
CMO: Manuel Angco, M.D., Chief of Staff
CHR: Tina Jackson, Manager Human Resources
Web address: www.williamsonmemorial.net
Control: Corporation, Investor–owned, for–profit **Service:** General Medical and Surgical

Staffed Beds: 76

Many Facility Codes have changed. Please refer to the AHA Guide Code Chart. © 2014 AHA Guide

WISCONSIN

AMERY—Polk County

★ **AMERY REGIONAL MEDICAL CENTER (521308)**, 265 Griffin Street East,
Zip 54001–1439; tel. 715/268–8000 **A**9 10 18 **F**3 11 13 15 18 28 29 31 32
33 34 35 36 40 43 44 45 47 50 53 54 56 57 59 64 65 75 76 77 78 79 80
81 82 85 86 87 89 92 93 97 98 100 101 102 103 104 105 107 110 111
115 119 127 129 130 131 132 133 135 143 144 145 146 148 **P**6 **S** QHR,
Brentwood, TN
Primary Contact: Michael Karuschak, Jr., Chief Executive Officer
CFO: Scott D. Edin, Chief Financial Officer
CMO: James Quenan, M.D., Chief Medical Officer
CIO: Patrice P. Wolff, Director Management Information Systems
CHR: Joanne Jackson, Administrator Human Resources, Community Relations and
Quality Improvement
Web address: www.amerymedicalcenter.org
Control: Other not–for–profit (including NFP Corporation) **Service:** General
Medical and Surgical

Staffed Beds: 11 **Admissions:** 1127 **Census:** 11 **Outpatient Visits:** 97987
Births: 127 **Total Expense ($000):** 50272 **Payroll Expense ($000):** 16790
Personnel: 301

ANTIGO—Langlade County

☐ **LANGLADE HOSPITAL (521350)**, 112 East Fifth Avenue, Zip 54409–2796;
tel. 715/623–2331 **A**1 5 9 10 18 **F**2 3 8 10 11 13 15 28 29 30 31 34 35 40
43 50 53 54 56 57 59 60 63 64 65 68 69 70 74 75 76 77 78 79 81 82 84
85 86 87 89 92 93 96 97 107 108 109 110 111 114 116 118 119 121 129
130 131 132 133 144 146 148
Primary Contact: David R. Schneider, Executive Director
CFO: Pat Tincher, Director Finance
CMO: Renee Smith, M.D., Chief Medical Staff
CHR: Janelle K. Markgraf, Director Human Resources
CNO: Sherry Bunten, Director Patient Care Services
Web address: www.langladehospital.org
Control: Church–operated, Nongovernment, not–for profit **Service:** General
Medical and Surgical

Staffed Beds: 9 **Admissions:** 829 **Census:** 9 **Outpatient Visits:** 115150
Births: 215 **Total Expense ($000):** 66779 **Payroll Expense ($000):** 30057
Personnel: 412

APPLETON—Outagamie County

☐ **APPLETON MEDICAL CENTER (520160)**, 1818 North Meade Street,
Zip 54911–3496; tel. 920/731–4101 **A**1 3 5 9 10 **F**3 4 8 9 11 13 15 17 18
19 20 21 22 23 24 25 26 28 29 30 31 32 34 35 36 37 40 43 44 45 46 49
50 51 53 55 56 59 60 64 68 69 70 74 75 76 78 79 80 81 82 84 85 86 87
88 89 93 107 108 110 111 114 116 117 118 119 120 121 123 124 130
132 135 143 144 146 147 148 **S** ThedaCare, Inc., Appleton, WI
Primary Contact: Brian Burmeister, Senior Vice President
COO: MaryJeanne Schaffmeyer, Chief Operating Officer
CFO: Tim Olson, Senior Vice President Finance
CMO: Gregory L. Long, M.D., Chief Medical Officer
CIO: Keith Livingston, Senior Vice President and Chief Information Officer
CHR: Maureen Pistone, Senior Vice President Talent Development and Human
Resources
Web address: www.thedacare.org
Control: Other not–for–profit (including NFP Corporation) **Service:** General
Medical and Surgical

Staffed Beds: 149 **Admissions:** 8055 **Census:** 83 **Outpatient Visits:** 123690
Births: 1261 **Total Expense ($000):** 210465 **Payroll Expense ($000):**
88157 **Personnel:** 1145

✠ **ST. ELIZABETH HOSPITAL (520009)**, 1506 South Oneida Street,
Zip 54915–1305; tel. 920/738–2000 **A**1 2 3 5 9 10 **F**3 4 5 6 8 9 11 13 15 17
18 20 22 24 26 28 29 30 31 32 35 36 37 40 43 44 45 46 47 48 49 50 56
59 66 68 69 70 72 74 75 76 77 78 79 80 81 82 84 85 86 87 88 89 93 97
98 99 100 102 103 104 105 106 107 108 110 111 114 115 117 118 119
120 121 123 124 126 129 130 131 132 135 144 145 146 147 148
S Ascension Health, Saint Louis, MO
Primary Contact: Daniel Neufelder, Interim Chief Executive Officer
CFO: Jeff Badger, Chief Financial Officer
CMO: Lawrence Donatelle, M.D., Vice President Medical Affairs
CIO: Will Weider, Chief Information Officer
CHR: Vince Gallucci, Senior Vice President Human Resources
Web address: www.affinityhealth.org
Control: Church–operated, Nongovernment, not–for profit **Service:** General
Medical and Surgical

Staffed Beds: 211 **Admissions:** 8003 **Census:** 94 **Outpatient Visits:** 149466
Births: 1095 **Total Expense ($000):** 148565 **Payroll Expense ($000):**
60406 **Personnel:** 864

ASHLAND—Ashland County

✠ **MEMORIAL MEDICAL CENTER – ASHLAND (521359)**, 1615 Maple Lane,
Zip 54806–3689; tel. 715/685–5500 **A**1 9 10 18 **F**3 5 8 13 15 28 30 34 40
41 43 45 46 47 48 49 57 59 64 65 76 79 81 85 86 93 94 97 98 99 100
101 102 103 104 105 107 108 110 111 115 118 119 130 132 135 144 145
146 148
Primary Contact: Jason T. Douglas, Chief Executive Officer
COO: Karen Hansen, Vice President and Chief Operating Officer
CFO: Kent Dumonseau, Vice President Finance and Information Services
CIO: Todd Reynolds, Chief Information Officer
CHR: Diane Lulich, Director Human Resources
CNO: Kathryn Tuttle, R.N., Director of Nursing
Web address: www.ashlandmmc.com
Control: Other not–for–profit (including NFP Corporation) **Service:** General
Medical and Surgical

Staffed Beds: 35 **Admissions:** 1833 **Census:** 16 **Outpatient Visits:** 48466
Births: 241 **Total Expense ($000):** 46360 **Payroll Expense ($000):** 21112
Personnel: 359

BALDWIN—St. Croix County

★ **BALDWIN AREA MEDICAL CENTER (521347)**, 730 10th Avenue,
Zip 54002–9416; tel. 715/684–3311 **A**9 10 18 **F**3 11 13 15 17 28 29 31 32
34 35 36 40 41 43 45 48 49 50 53 57 58 59 64 65 68 70 75 76 77 78 79
80 81 85 86 87 89 90 91 92 93 96 97 106 107 108 110 115 119 127 129
130 131 132 133 143 144 146 147 148
Primary Contact: Alison Page, Chief Executive Officer
CFO: Brian A. Lovdahl, Chief Financial Officer
CMO: Clint Semrau, Chief of Staff
CIO: Kendra Shaw, Chief Information Officer
CHR: Chris Riba, Director Human Resources
Web address: www.baldwinhospital.com
Control: Other not–for–profit (including NFP Corporation) **Service:** General
Medical and Surgical

Staffed Beds: 25 **Admissions:** 485 **Census:** 5 **Outpatient Visits:** 31402
Births: 63 **Total Expense ($000):** 27208 **Payroll Expense ($000):** 14437
Personnel: 226

WI

Hospital, Medicare Provider Number, Address, Telephone, Approval, Facility, and Physician Codes, Health Care System

★ American Hospital Association (AHA) membership
☐ The Joint Commission accreditation
◇ DNV Healthcare Inc. accreditation
○ Healthcare Facilities Accreditation Program
△ Commission on Accreditation of Rehabilitation Facilities (CARF) accreditation

BARABOO—Sauk County

✦ **ST. CLARE HOSPITAL (520057)**, 707 14th Street, Zip 53913–1597; tel. 608/356–1400 **A**1 3 5 10 **F**5 8 11 12 13 15 28 29 30 31 34 35 36 38 40 45 46 50 56 57 59 60 64 69 70 75 76 77 78 79 81 82 84 85 86 93 97 107 108 115 116 118 119 121 129 130 131 132 144 146 **S** SSM Health, Saint Louis, MO
Primary Contact: Sandra L. Anderson, President
COO: Laura Jelle, Executive Vice President and Chief Operating Officer
CFO: Troy Walker, Director Finance
CMO: Maureen Murphy, M.D., Director of Medical Affairs
CIO: Alan Steevens, Director Information Management
CHR: Jason Stelzer, Director Human Resources
CNO: Ginger Selle, Vice President Patient Care Services
Web address: www.stclare.com
Control: Church–operated, Nongovernment, not–for profit **Service:** General Medical and Surgical

Staffed Beds: 60 **Admissions:** 2673 **Census:** 18 **Outpatient Visits:** 82387 **Births:** 272 **Total Expense ($000):** 52304 **Payroll Expense ($000):** 21986 **Personnel:** 303

BARRON—Barron County

☐ **MAYO CLINIC HEALTH SYSTEM – NORTHLAND IN BARRON (521315)**, 1222 Woodland Avenue, Zip 54812–1798; tel. 715/537–3186, (Total facility includes 20 beds in nursing home–type unit) **A**1 9 10 18 **F**3 7 8 10 13 15 18 28 29 30 31 32 34 35 36 40 43 44 45 50 53 54 55 56 57 59 60 63 64 65 67 68 69 75 76 77 78 79 80 81 82 84 85 86 87 89 90 93 97 103 104 107 110 114 118 125 127 128 130 131 132 133 135 144 145 146 147 148 **P**6 **S** Mayo Clinic, Rochester, MN
Primary Contact: Maurita Sullivan, Vice President
COO: Karolyn Bartlett, Assistant Administrator
CFO: Paul Bammel, Vice President
CMO: Richard Nagler, M.D., Chief of Staff
CIO: Todd Muden, Section Head Information Management
CHR: Blythe Rinaldi, Vice President
CNO: Patricia Keller, MSN, Nurse Administrator
Web address: www.luthermidelfortnorthland.org
Control: Other not–for–profit (including NFP Corporation) **Service:** General Medical and Surgical

Staffed Beds: 38 **Admissions:** 770 **Census:** 29 **Outpatient Visits:** 83576 **Births:** 102 **Total Expense ($000):** 51109 **Payroll Expense ($000):** 24354 **Personnel:** 378

BEAVER DAM—Dodge County

✦ **BEAVER DAM COMMUNITY HOSPITALS (520076)**, 707 South University Avenue, Zip 53916–3089; tel. 920/887–7181, (Total facility includes 123 beds in nursing home–type unit) **A**1 9 10 19 **F**3 6 8 10 11 13 15 17 18 26 28 29 31 34 36 37 40 43 44 45 47 48 53 56 57 59 62 63 64 65 69 70 74 75 76 77 78 79 80 81 82 85 86 87 89 93 94 96 97 107 108 110 111 114 115 118 119 128 129 130 131 132 135 143 144 146 147 148 **P**6
Primary Contact: Kimberly J. Miller, FACHE, Chief Executive Officer
COO: David Corso, Chief Operating Officer
CFO: Donna Hutchinson, Chief Financial Officer
CMO: Richard Tovar, M.D., Chief of Staff
CHR: Bridget Sheridan, Chief Human Resources Officer
CNO: Mike Murphy, Chief Patient Care Officer
Web address: www.bdch.com
Control: Other not–for–profit (including NFP Corporation) **Service:** General Medical and Surgical

Staffed Beds: 171 **Admissions:** 2385 **Census:** 127 **Outpatient Visits:** 90977 **Births:** 357 **Total Expense ($000):** 78781 **Payroll Expense ($000):** 27705 **Personnel:** 550

BELOIT—Rock County

☐ **BELOIT HEALTH SYSTEM (520100)**, 1969 West Hart Road, Zip 53511–2299; tel. 608/364–5011 **A**1 9 10 **F**3 5 6 9 10 11 12 13 14 15 17 20 22 24 28 29 30 36 40 43 47 51 53 54 56 60 62 68 70 75 76 77 78 80 81 82 84 86 87 89 93 99 100 101 102 103 104 108 111 116 117 118 119 124 130 131 144 147 **P**1
Primary Contact: Timothy M. McKevett, President and Chief Executive Officer
CFO: William E. Groeper, Vice President Finance
CMO: Kenneth Klein, M.D., Vice President Medical Affairs
CHR: Thomas J. McCawley, Vice President Human Resources
CNO: Doris Mulder, Vice President Nursing
Web address: www.beloithealthsystem.org
Control: Other not–for–profit (including NFP Corporation) **Service:** General Medical and Surgical

Staffed Beds: 103 **Admissions:** 3898 **Census:** 43 **Outpatient Visits:** 364109 **Births:** 531 **Total Expense ($000):** 176554 **Payroll Expense ($000):** 83966 **Personnel:** 1164

BERLIN—Green Lake County

☐ **BERLIN MEMORIAL HOSPITAL (521355)**, 225 Memorial Drive, Zip 54923–1295; tel. 920/361–1313, (Includes JULIETTE MANOR NURSING HOME, COMMUNITY CLINICS), (Total facility includes 54 beds in nursing home–type unit) **A**1 9 10 18 **F**3 8 10 11 13 15 17 28 29 34 35 37 40 43 45 51 54 56 57 59 62 64 65 66 68 69 70 75 76 77 78 79 80 81 82 83 84 85 86 88 89 91 92 93 94 96 97 107 108 111 116 119 125 128 129 130 131 132 135 144 145 146 147 148
Primary Contact: John Feeney, President and Chief Executive Officer
CFO: Thomas P. Krystowiak, Chief Financial Officer
Web address: www.chnwi.org
Control: Other not–for–profit (including NFP Corporation) **Service:** General Medical and Surgical

Staffed Beds: 75 **Admissions:** 1908 **Census:** 53 **Outpatient Visits:** 60026 **Births:** 171 **Total Expense ($000):** 66894 **Payroll Expense ($000):** 33839 **Personnel:** 329

BLACK RIVER FALLS—Jackson County

☐ **BLACK RIVER MEMORIAL HOSPITAL (521333)**, 711 West Adams Street, Zip 54615–9113; tel. 715/284–5361 **A**1 9 10 18 **F**3 8 11 13 29 30 34 40 50 53 56 62 63 65 69 75 76 77 80 81 85 86 87 89 90 93 107 111 112 115 116 118 119 129 130 131 132 133 135 144 146 148
Primary Contact: Mary Beth White–Jacobs, R.N., FACHE, President and Chief Executive Officer
CFO: Robert Daley, Vice President Fiscal and Information Technology Services
CMO: Lea Coville, Chief of Staff
CIO: Robert Daley, Vice President Fiscal and Information Technology Services
CHR: Holly Winn, Vice President Human Resources and Ancillary Services
CNO: Melissa Bergerson, R.N., Vice President Patient Care Services
Web address: www.brmh.net
Control: Other not–for–profit (including NFP Corporation) **Service:** General Medical and Surgical

Staffed Beds: 25 **Admissions:** 857 **Census:** 7 **Outpatient Visits:** 18884 **Births:** 135 **Total Expense ($000):** 35332 **Payroll Expense ($000):** 16602 **Personnel:** 272

BLOOMER—Chippewa County

☐ **MAYO CLINIC HEALTH SYSTEM – CHIPPEWA VALLEY IN BLOOMER (521314)**, 1501 Thompson Street, Zip 54724–1299; tel. 715/568–2000, (Total facility includes 30 beds in nursing home–type unit) **A**1 9 10 18 **F**3 8 15 18 28 29 30 31 32 34 35 40 43 44 45 50 53 54 56 57 59 63 64 65 68 75 77 78 80 81 84 85 86 87 90 93 96 97 107 110 114 119 128 130 132 133 135 144 146 147 148 **P**6 **S** Mayo Clinic, Rochester, MN
Primary Contact: Edward A. Wittrock, Vice President Regional System
Web address: www.bloomermedicalcenter.org
Control: Other not–for–profit (including NFP Corporation) **Service:** General Medical and Surgical

Staffed Beds: 49 **Admissions:** 475 **Census:** 41 **Outpatient Visits:** 68452 **Births:** 0 **Total Expense ($000):** 32515 **Payroll Expense ($000):** 16777 **Personnel:** 259

BOSCOBEL—Grant County

GUNDERSEN BOSCOBEL AREA HOSPITAL AND CLINICS (521344), 205 Parker Street, Zip 53805–1698; tel. 608/375–4112 **A**9 10 18 **F**3 8 11 15 28 29 34 35 38 40 41 42 43 50 56 57 59 62 64 65 68 70 74 75 77 78 79 80 81 82 83 84 85 86 87 89 90 92 93 96 97 101 102 107 110 111 114 119 127 129 130 131 132 133 135 144 148 **P**6
Primary Contact: David Hartberg, Administrator
CFO: Melissa Uselman, Director Finance
CMO: Marilu Bintz, M.D., Chief of Staff
CIO: Scott Pauls, Manager Information Systems
CHR: Jennifer Dax, Director Human Resources
CNO: Theresa Lynn Braudt, Chief Nursing Officer
Web address: www.gundersenhealth.org/boscobel
Control: Other not–for–profit (including NFP Corporation) **Service:** General Medical and Surgical

Staffed Beds: 20 **Admissions:** 289 **Census:** 3 **Outpatient Visits:** 11953 **Births:** 1 **Total Expense ($000):** 14543 **Payroll Expense ($000):** 5311 **Personnel:** 97

WI

Many Facility Codes have changed. Please refer to the AHA Guide Code Chart. © 2014 AHA Guide

BROOKFIELD—Waukesha County

★ **WHEATON FRANCISCAN HEALTHCARE – ELMBROOK MEMORIAL (520170)**, 19333 West North Avenue, Zip 53045–4198; tel. 262/785–2000 **A**9 **F**3 4 8 11 12 13 15 17 18 20 22 24 26 28 29 30 31 33 34 36 40 42 43 45 46 47 49 54 56 58 59 64 65 68 70 72 74 75 76 77 78 79 80 81 82 84 85 86 87 89 90 91 92 93 97 99 100 107 108 109 110 111 112 114 115 117 118 119 120 121 122 123 124 126 130 131 132 135 143 145 146 147 **S** Wheaton Franciscan Healthcare, Wheaton, IL
Primary Contact: Debra K. Standridge, President
CFO: Michael Petitt, Director of Finance
CMO: Rita Hanson, M.D., Vice President Medical Affairs
CIO: Andrew Donovan, Director Information Technology
CHR: Christopher Morris, Director Human Resources
CNO: Sharon Baughman, R.N., Vice President Patient Services and Chief Nursing Officer
Web address: www.wfhealthcare.org
Control: Church–operated, Nongovernment, not–for profit **Service:** General Medical and Surgical

Staffed Beds: 100 **Admissions:** 5185 **Census:** 57 **Outpatient Visits:** 71233
Births: 470 **Total Expense ($000):** 110859 **Payroll Expense ($000):** 35681
Personnel: 456

BURLINGTON—Racine County

⊞ **AURORA MEMORIAL HOSPITAL OF BURLINGTON (520059)**, 252 McHenry Street, Zip 53105–1828; tel. 262/767–6000 **A**1 2 9 10 **F**3 11 15 17 18 20 26 28 29 30 31 32 34 35 36 40 44 45 46 47 48 49 50 51 53 56 57 58 59 68 70 74 75 79 80 81 82 84 85 86 87 89 93 94 96 107 108 109 110 111 115 116 118 119 130 131 132 134 135 146 148 **P**6 **S** Aurora Health Care, Milwaukee, WI
Primary Contact: Lisa Just, President
CFO: Stuart Arnett, Vice President Finance and Chief Financial Officer
CIO: Jean Chase, Regional Manager Information Services
CHR: Gene Krauklis, Regional Vice President Human Resources
Web address: www.aurorahealthcare.org
Control: Other not–for–profit (including NFP Corporation) **Service:** General Medical and Surgical

Staffed Beds: 55 **Admissions:** 2822 **Census:** 28 **Outpatient Visits:** 61607
Births: 174 **Total Expense ($000):** 59118 **Payroll Expense ($000):** 24111
Personnel: 407

CHILTON—Calumet County

⊞ **CALUMET MEDICAL CENTER (521317)**, 614 Memorial Drive, Zip 53014–1597; tel. 920/849–2386 **A**1 9 10 18 **F**3 7 15 28 29 34 35 40 43 45 54 56 57 59 64 65 75 77 78 79 80 81 82 85 86 87 89 92 93 97 102 107 110 114 119 126 127 129 130 131 132 133 144 145 146 148 **S** Ascension Health, Saint Louis, MO
Primary Contact: Timothy Richman, President
CFO: Jeff Badger, Chief Financial Officer
CMO: Mark W. Kehrberg, M.D., Chief Medical Officer
CIO: Will Weider, Chief Information Officer
CHR: Beth O'laire, Manager Human Resources
CNO: Tom Veeser, R.N., Chief Nursing Officer
Web address: www.affinityhealth.org
Control: Other not–for–profit (including NFP Corporation) **Service:** General Medical and Surgical

Staffed Beds: 15 **Admissions:** 553 **Census:** 6 **Outpatient Visits:** 39765
Births: 0 **Total Expense ($000):** 20412 **Payroll Expense ($000):** 8620
Personnel: 112

CHIPPEWA FALLS—Chippewa County

⊞ **ST. JOSEPH'S HOSPITAL (520017)**, 2661 County Highway I, Zip 54729–1498; tel. 715/723–1811 **A**1 9 10 **F**3 4 5 15 17 28 29 30 34 35 44 45 50 56 57 59 62 63 64 65 68 69 70 71 74 75 76 77 79 80 81 82 84 86 87 88 89 93 100 101 102 104 105 106 107 110 111 114 119 129 130 132 135 144 146 147 148 **P**6 **S** Hospital Sisters Health System, Springfield, IL
Primary Contact: Joan Coffman, President and Chief Executive Officer
CFO: David Nelson, Divisional Chief Financial Officer
CMO: Humayun Khan, M.D., Divisional Chief Medical Officer
CIO: Kevin Groskreutz, Chief Information Officer
CHR: Denise McMahon, Director People Services
CNO: Stella Clark, Chief Nursing Officer
Web address: www.stjoeschipfalls.com
Control: Other not–for–profit (including NFP Corporation) **Service:** General Medical and Surgical

Staffed Beds: 102 **Admissions:** 3135 **Census:** 35 **Outpatient Visits:** 80550
Births: 388 **Total Expense ($000):** 63561 **Payroll Expense ($000):** 27605
Personnel: 416

COLUMBUS—Columbia County

⊞ **COLUMBUS COMMUNITY HOSPITAL (521338)**, 1515 Park Avenue, Zip 53925–2402; tel. 920/623–2200 **A**1 9 10 18 **F**3 8 13 15 16 17 18 28 29 34 40 45 46 51 56 57 64 70 75 76 77 78 79 80 81 85 86 88 89 91 93 96 107 110 114 115 118 119 129 130 132 133 135 144 146 147
Primary Contact: John D. Russell, President and Chief Executive Officer
CFO: Phillip Roberts, Vice President Finance and Chief Financial Officer
CMO: Gary Galvin, M.D., Chief of Staff
CIO: Phillip Roberts, Vice President Finance and Chief Financial Officer
CHR: Ann Roundy, Vice President Employee Services
CNO: Jamie Hendrix, Vice President Patient Care Services
Web address: www.cch–inc.com
Control: Other not–for–profit (including NFP Corporation) **Service:** General Medical and Surgical

Staffed Beds: 18 **Admissions:** 824 **Census:** 9 **Outpatient Visits:** 30538
Births: 53 **Total Expense ($000):** 27592 **Payroll Expense ($000):** 10951
Personnel: 166

CUBA CITY—Grant County

SOUTHWEST HEALTH CENTER NURSING HOME See Southwest Health Center, Platteville

CUDAHY—Milwaukee County

AURORA ST. LUKE'S SOUTH SHORE See Aurora St. Luke's Medical Center, Milwaukee

CUMBERLAND—Barron County

☐ **CUMBERLAND MEMORIAL HOSPITAL (521353)**, 1110 Seventh Avenue, Zip 54829–9138; tel. 715/822–2741, (Total facility includes 50 beds in nursing home–type unit) **A**1 9 10 18 **F**11 13 28 29 34 40 43 53 56 67 75 76 77 81 82 86 87 89 93 98 107 125 128 130 131 144 **P**8
Primary Contact: Michael Gutsch, Chief Executive Officer
COO: Bob Lindberg, Chief Operating Officer
CFO: Angela Martens, Chief Financial Officer
CMO: Tom Lingen, M.D., Chief of Staff
CIO: Jason Morse, Director Information Technology
CHR: Hilary Butzler, Director Human Resources
Web address: www.cumberlandhealthcare.com
Control: Other not–for–profit (including NFP Corporation) **Service:** General Medical and Surgical

Staffed Beds: 75 **Admissions:** 750 **Census:** 49 **Outpatient Visits:** 9508
Births: 32 **Total Expense ($000):** 18685 **Payroll Expense ($000):** 7466
Personnel: 136

DARLINGTON—Lafayette County

MEMORIAL HOSPITAL OF LAFAYETTE COUNTY (521312), 800 Clay Street, Zip 53530–1228, Mailing Address: P.O. Box 70, Zip 53530–0070; tel. 608/776–4466 **A**9 10 18 **F**1 3 11 13 15 18 26 28 29 32 35 40 43 45 46 47 48 54 56 57 60 64 68 74 75 76 79 80 81 82 86 89 90 93 102 105 107 111 116 117 119 130 131 133 144
Primary Contact: Julie Chikowski, Administrator
CFO: Marie Wamsley, Chief Financial Officer
Web address: www.memorialhospitaloflafayettecounty.org
Control: County–Government, nonfederal **Service:** General Medical and Surgical

Staffed Beds: 23 **Admissions:** 418 **Census:** 5 **Outpatient Visits:** 19442
Births: 36 **Total Expense ($000):** 12392 **Payroll Expense ($000):** 3862
Personnel: 86

DODGEVILLE—Iowa County

⊞ **UPLAND HILLS HEALTH (521352)**, 800 Compassion Way, Zip 53533–1956, Mailing Address: P.O. Box 800, Zip 53533–0800; tel. 608/930–8000, (Total facility includes 44 beds in nursing home–type unit) **A**1 9 10 18 **F**3 11 13 15 17 28 29 31 32 34 35 36 40 43 53 54 56 57 59 60 62 63 64 67 70 75 76 77 78 80 81 82 85 86 87 88 89 90 92 93 96 107 114 119 128 129 130 131 132 133 144 146 147 148 **P**6
Primary Contact: Lisa W. Schnedler, FACHE, President and Chief Executive Officer
CFO: Karl Pustina, Vice President Finance
CIO: Karen Thuli, Coordinator Information Systems
CHR: Troy Marx, Director Human Resources
CNO: Lynn Hebgen, Vice President Nursing
Web address: www.uplandhillshealth.org
Control: Other not–for–profit (including NFP Corporation) **Service:** General Medical and Surgical

Staffed Beds: 69 **Admissions:** 1184 **Census:** 51 **Outpatient Visits:** 47321
Births: 286 **Total Expense ($000):** 36465 **Payroll Expense ($000):** 16380
Personnel: 245

WI

Hospital, Medicare Provider Number, Address, Telephone, Approval, Facility, and Physician Codes, Health Care System

★ American Hospital Association (AHA) membership
☐ The Joint Commission accreditation
◇ DNV Healthcare Inc. accreditation
○ Healthcare Facilities Accreditation Program
△ Commission on Accreditation of Rehabilitation Facilities (CARF) accreditation

DURAND—Pepin County

★ **CHIPPEWA VALLEY HOSPITAL AND OAKVIEW CARE CENTER (521307)**, 1220 Third Avenue West, Zip 54736–1600, Mailing Address: P.O. Box 224, Zip 54736–0224; tel. 715/672–4211, (Total facility includes 50 beds in nursing home–type unit) **A**9 10 18 **F**8 15 18 28 29 34 35 40 45 50 56 57 59 65 69 71 75 79 81 86 87 97 107 127 128 129 130 133 **S** Adventist Health System Sunbelt Health Care Corporation, Altamonte Springs, FL
Primary Contact: Douglas R. Peterson, President and Chief Executive Officer
Web address: www.chippewavalleyhospital.com/
Control: Church–operated, Nongovernment, not–for profit **Service:** General Medical and Surgical

Staffed Beds: 75 **Admissions:** 375 **Census:** 50 **Outpatient Visits:** 31382 **Births:** 0 **Total Expense ($000):** 15759 **Payroll Expense ($000):** 6539 **Personnel:** 101

EAGLE RIVER—Vilas County

★ **MINISTRY EAGLE RIVER MEMORIAL HOSPITAL (521300)**, 201 Hospital Road, Zip 54521–8835; tel. 715/479–7411 **A**9 10 18 **F**3 11 15 28 29 30 35 40 45 47 50 57 59 68 75 80 81 82 84 85 86 87 89 93 107 108 110 115 119 130 133 146 148 **S** Ascension Health, Saint Louis, MO
Primary Contact: Monica Hilt, President
CFO: Cathy Bukowski, Regional Chief Financial Officer
CMO: Richard Brodhead, M.D., President Medical Staff
CIO: Howard Dobizl, Director Information Technology Services
CHR: Michelle Cornelius, Director Human Resources for Northern Region
CNO: Deborah Karow, R.N., Vice President Patient Care Services
Web address: www.ministryhealth.org
Control: Church–operated, Nongovernment, not–for profit **Service:** General Medical and Surgical

Staffed Beds: 7 **Admissions:** 466 **Census:** 5 **Outpatient Visits:** 20409 **Births:** 0 **Total Expense ($000):** 13022 **Payroll Expense ($000):** 6942 **Personnel:** 105

EAU CLAIRE—Eau Claire County

☐ **MAYO CLINIC HEALTH SYSTEM IN EAU CLAIRE (520070)**, 1221 Whipple Street, Zip 54703–5270, Mailing Address: P.O. Box 4105, Zip 54702–4105; tel. 715/838–3311 **A**1 2 3 5 9 10 **F**3 4 5 7 8 12 13 15 17 18 20 22 24 26 28 29 30 31 32 34 35 36 37 40 43 44 45 46 48 49 50 53 54 55 57 58 59 60 63 64 65 68 70 71 72 74 75 76 77 78 79 80 81 82 83 84 85 86 87 89 90 92 93 96 97 98 99 100 101 102 103 104 105 107 108 110 111 114 115 118 119 120 121 124 126 129 130 131 132 135 144 145 146 147 148 **P**2 6 **S** Mayo Clinic, Rochester, MN
Primary Contact: Randall L. Linton, M.D., President and Chief Executive Officer
COO: John M. Dickey, Chief Administrative Officer
CFO: Paul Bammel, Vice President
CMO: Robert C. Peck, M.D., Chief Medical Officer
CHR: Blythe Loyd, Vice President
CNO: Pamela K. White, R.N., Chief Nursing Officer
Web address: www.mhs.mayo.edu
Control: Other not–for–profit (including NFP Corporation) **Service:** General Medical and Surgical

Staffed Beds: 204 **Admissions:** 10271 **Census:** 121 **Outpatient Visits:** 170648 **Births:** 1020 **Total Expense ($000):** 230917 **Payroll Expense ($000):** 96859 **Personnel:** 1562

☐ **OAKLEAF SURGICAL HOSPITAL (520196)**, 3802 West Oakwood Mall Drive, Zip 54701–3016; tel. 715/831–8130 **A**1 9 10 **F**3 37 45 47 48 51 64 75 79 80 81 82 85 119 130 145 148 **S** National Surgical Hospitals, Chicago, IL
Primary Contact: Anne Hargrave–Thomas, Chief Executive Officer
COO: Erma Radke, Director of Operations
CFO: Denise Freid–Scheppke, Chief Accounting Officer
CHR: Dorothy Conroy, Director Human Resources
CNO: Jacquelyn Maki, Chief Nursing Officer
Web address: www.oakleafmedical.com
Control: Corporation, Investor–owned, for–profit **Service:** General Medical and Surgical

Staffed Beds: 13 **Admissions:** 473 **Census:** 4 **Outpatient Visits:** 9547 **Births:** 0 **Total Expense ($000):** 29535 **Payroll Expense ($000):** 8949 **Personnel:** 131

✚ △ **SACRED HEART HOSPITAL (520013)**, 900 West Clairemont Avenue, Zip 54701–6122; tel. 715/717–4121 **A**1 2 3 5 7 9 10 **F**3 6 8 11 12 13 15 17 18 20 22 24 28 29 30 32 34 35 38 40 41 43 44 45 46 47 48 49 50 51 53 56 57 58 59 60 64 68 69 70 72 74 75 76 78 79 80 81 82 84 85 86 87 88 89 90 92 93 94 96 97 98 99 100 101 102 103 104 107 108 110 111 112 114 115 116 117 118 119 120 121 123 124 126 129 130 132 135 141 144 145 146 147 148 **P**6 **S** Hospital Sisters Health System, Springfield, IL
Primary Contact: Julie Manas, President and Chief Executive Officer
COO: Faye L. Deich, R.N., Chief Operating Officer
CFO: David Nelson, Chief Financial Officer
CMO: Humayun Khan, M.D., Chief Medical Officer
CIO: Kevin Groskreutz, Chief Information Officer
CHR: Craig Brenholt, Division Director People Services
CNO: Amy L. Dwyer, R.N., Chief Nursing Officer
Web address: www.sacredhearteauclaire.org
Control: Other not–for–profit (including NFP Corporation) **Service:** General Medical and Surgical

Staffed Beds: 206 **Admissions:** 9854 **Census:** 128 **Outpatient Visits:** 111024 **Births:** 903 **Total Expense ($000):** 183184 **Payroll Expense ($000):** 72264 **Personnel:** 1058

EDGERTON—Rock County

✚ **EDGERTON HOSPITAL AND HEALTH SERVICES (521319)**, 11101 North Sherman Road, Zip 53534–9002; tel. 608/884–3441 **A**1 9 10 18 **F**3 8 11 15 18 28 34 40 41 43 44 45 48 49 59 64 65 75 77 81 85 86 90 92 93 97 108 110 111 115 119 129 130 132 133 134 135 144 146 148
Primary Contact: Sherry Paulson, Executive Assistant
CFO: Charles Roader, Vice President Finance
CMO: William West, M.D., Chief of Staff
CIO: Sheryl Rucker, Chief Information Officer
CHR: Brad Olm, Director Human Resources
Web address: www.edgertonhospital.com
Control: Other not–for–profit (including NFP Corporation) **Service:** General Medical and Surgical

Staffed Beds: 18 **Admissions:** 383 **Census:** 8 **Outpatient Visits:** 14768 **Births:** 0 **Total Expense ($000):** 18718 **Payroll Expense ($000):** 7690 **Personnel:** 133

ELKHORN—Walworth County

✚ △ **AURORA LAKELAND MEDICAL CENTER (520102)**, W3985 County Road NN, Zip 53121–4389; tel. 262/741–2000 **A**1 2 7 9 10 **F**3 11 13 15 17 18 29 30 31 32 34 35 36 40 43 44 45 46 47 48 49 50 51 56 57 58 59 64 68 70 74 75 76 78 79 80 81 82 84 85 86 87 89 90 93 94 96 100 107 108 110 111 115 116 118 119 129 130 131 132 135 146 148 **P**6 **S** Aurora Health Care, Milwaukee, WI
Primary Contact: Lisa Just, President
CFO: Stuart Arnett, Regional Vice President Finance
CMO: Greg Gerber, M.D., Chief Medical Officer
CIO: Jean Chase, Regional Manager Information Services
CHR: Gene Krauklis, Regional Vice President Human Resources
Web address: www.aurorahealthcare.org
Control: Other not–for–profit (including NFP Corporation) **Service:** General Medical and Surgical

Staffed Beds: 67 **Admissions:** 3174 **Census:** 31 **Outpatient Visits:** 65713 **Births:** 656 **Total Expense ($000):** 61546 **Payroll Expense ($000):** 22263 **Personnel:** 378

FOND DU LAC—Fond Du Lac County

✚ △ **AGNESIAN HEALTHCARE (520088)**, 430 East Division Street, Zip 54935–4560, Mailing Address: P.O. Box 385, Zip 54936–0385; tel. 920/929–2300 **A**1 2 7 9 10 20 **F**2 3 5 6 11 13 15 18 20 22 24 26 28 29 30 31 34 35 36 38 40 42 43 44 45 46 47 48 49 50 51 53 54 55 56 57 59 62 63 64 66 67 68 69 71 74 75 76 77 78 79 80 81 82 83 84 85 86 87 90 92 93 94 96 97 98 99 100 101 102 103 104 105 106 107 108 109 110 111 114 115 117 118 119 120 121 123 124 126 129 130 131 132 134 135 143 144 146 147 148 **P**3 6
Primary Contact: Steven N. Little, President and Chief Executive Officer
COO: James Mugan, Senior Vice President for Clinical Services and Chief Operating Officer
CFO: Bonnie Schmitz, Vice President and Chief Financial Officer
CMO: Derek Colmenares, M.D., Chief Medical Officer
CIO: Nancy Birschbach, Assistant Vice President Information Services
CHR: Sue Edminster, Vice President Human Resources
Web address: www.agnesian.com
Control: Church–operated, Nongovernment, not–for profit **Service:** General Medical and Surgical

Staffed Beds: 160 **Admissions:** 6899 **Census:** 78 **Outpatient Visits:** 701005 **Births:** 867 **Total Expense ($000):** 290022 **Payroll Expense ($000):** 106808 **Personnel:** 1706

WI

FOND DU LAC COUNTY MENTAL HEALTH CENTER (524025), 459 East First Street, Zip 54935–4599; tel. 920/929–3571 **A**10 **F**4 38 98 99 102 103 130 **P**6
Primary Contact: Don Stout, Administrator
Web address: www.fdlco.wi.gov
Control: County–Government, nonfederal **Service:** Psychiatric

> **Staffed Beds:** 25 **Admissions:** 1020 **Census:** 14 **Outpatient Visits:** 512
> **Births:** 0 **Total Expense ($000):** 3513 **Payroll Expense ($000):** 2050
> **Personnel:** 43

FORT ATKINSON—Jefferson County

☒ **FORT HEALTHCARE (520071)**, 611 East Sherman Avenue, Zip 53538–1998; tel. 920/568–5000 **A**1 9 10 **F**3 11 12 13 15 28 29 34 35 40 50 53 55 56 57 59 62 68 75 76 77 79 80 81 85 86 87 89 90 93 94 96 107 108 110 111 115 118 119 129 130 132 135 144 145 146 147 **P**1 5
Primary Contact: Michael S. Wallace, President and Chief Executive Officer
CFO: James J. Nelson, Senior Vice President Finance and Strategic Planning
CHR: Nancy Alstad, Director Human Resources
CNO: Renee Clark, R.N., Vice President Nursing Services and Performance Improvement
Web address: www.forthealthcare.com
Control: Other not–for–profit (including NFP Corporation) **Service:** General Medical and Surgical

> **Staffed Beds:** 72 **Admissions:** 2499 **Census:** 20 **Outpatient Visits:** 286245
> **Births:** 460 **Total Expense ($000):** 120016 **Payroll Expense ($000):** 42207
> **Personnel:** 621

FRANKLIN—Milwaukee County

☒ **MIDWEST ORTHOPEDIC SPECIALTY HOSPITAL (520205)**, 10101 South 27th Street, 2nd Floor, Zip 53132–7209; tel. 414/817–5800 **A**1 9 10 **F**3 29 30 34 50 57 65 68 79 81 82 85 86 91 92 94 96 114 130 131 **S** Wheaton Franciscan Healthcare, Wheaton, IL
Primary Contact: Coreen Dicus–Johnson, President
CFO: Aaron Bridgeland, Director Finance
CMO: Daniel Guehlstorf, M.D., Chief of Staff
CIO: Gregory Smith, Senior Vice President and Chief Information Officer
CHR: Robert Bauer, Vice President Human Resources
CNO: Sheila Gansemer, R.N., Vice President Patient Care Services
Web address: www.mymosh.com/
Control: Partnership, Investor–owned, for–profit **Service:** General Medical and Surgical

> **Staffed Beds:** 16 **Admissions:** 1463 **Census:** 9 **Outpatient Visits:** 8669
> **Births:** 0 **Total Expense ($000):** 39031 **Payroll Expense ($000):** 6488
> **Personnel:** 108

☒ **WHEATON FRANCISCAN HEALTHCARE – FRANKLIN (520204)**, 10101 South 27th Street, Zip 53132–7209; tel. 414/325–4700 **A**1 9 10 **F**3 15 18 29 30 34 35 40 45 47 49 50 57 64 65 68 70 74 75 77 79 81 82 84 85 86 87 91 92 93 94 96 107 108 110 111 114 117 119 130 131 144 145 146 147 148 **S** Wheaton Franciscan Healthcare, Wheaton, IL
Primary Contact: Coreen Dicus–Johnson, President
CFO: Aaron Bridgeland, Director Finance
CMO: Michelle Graham, M.D., Vice President Medical Affairs
CIO: Gregory Smith, Senior Vice President and Chief Information Officer
CHR: Robert Bauer, Vice President Human Resources
CNO: Sheila Gansemer, R.N., Vice President Patient Care Services
Web address: www.mywheaton.org/
Control: Church–operated, Nongovernment, not–for profit **Service:** General Medical and Surgical

> **Staffed Beds:** 32 **Admissions:** 1946 **Census:** 20 **Outpatient Visits:** 76556
> **Births:** 0 **Total Expense ($000):** 56756 **Payroll Expense ($000):** 19426
> **Personnel:** 315

FRIENDSHIP—Adams County

MOUNDVIEW MEMORIAL HOSPITAL & CLINICS (521309), 402 West Lake Street, Zip 53934–9699, Mailing Address: P.O. Box 40, Zip 53934–0040; tel. 608/339–3331 **A**9 10 18 **F**6 11 15 18 28 29 31 34 35 36 40 43 50 56 57 59 64 77 79 81 82 84 86 87 93 97 107 108 111 115 119 127 129 130 133 144 146 **P**6
Primary Contact: Jeremy Normington–Slay, FACHE, Chief Executive Officer
Web address: www.moundview.org
Control: Other not–for–profit (including NFP Corporation) **Service:** General Medical and Surgical

> **Staffed Beds:** 25 **Admissions:** 187 **Census:** 2 **Outpatient Visits:** 22004
> **Births:** 0 **Total Expense ($000):** 13968 **Payroll Expense ($000):** 6333
> **Personnel:** 131

GRAFTON—Ozaukee County

☒ **AURORA MEDICAL CENTER GRAFTON (520207)**, 975 Port Washington Road, Zip 53024–9201; tel. 262/329–1000 **A**1 2 9 10 **F**3 6 8 13 15 17 18 20 22 24 26 28 29 30 31 32 35 36 37 40 43 44 45 46 48 49 50 51 53 54 56 64 65 68 69 70 72 74 75 76 78 79 80 81 82 85 86 87 89 91 93 96 107 108 109 110 111 114 115 116 117 118 119 120 121 123 126 130 131 132 135 146 148 **P**6 **S** Aurora Health Care, Milwaukee, WI
Primary Contact: Carrie Killoran, Interim President
CMO: Doug McManus, Chief Medical Officer
CNO: Terry Kabitzke–Groth, R.N., Vice President Nursing
Web address: www.aurorahealthcare.org
Control: Other not–for–profit (including NFP Corporation) **Service:** General Medical and Surgical

> **Staffed Beds:** 101 **Admissions:** 6403 **Census:** 61 **Outpatient Visits:** 86299
> **Births:** 738 **Total Expense ($000):** 143508 **Payroll Expense ($000):** 41908
> **Personnel:** 769

GRANTSBURG—Burnett County

★ **BURNETT MEDICAL CENTER (521331)**, 257 West St. George Avenue, Zip 54840–7827; tel. 715/463–5353, (Total facility includes 50 beds in nursing home–type unit) **A**9 10 18 **F**2 3 13 15 28 29 30 31 34 35 40 43 45 56 57 59 64 67 68 75 76 77 78 80 81 84 85 86 87 89 90 93 97 107 114 127 128 130 131 132 133 135 144 148 **P**6
Primary Contact: Gordon Lewis, Chief Executive Officer
CFO: Charles J. Faught, Chief Financial Officer
CMO: Hans Rechsteiner, M.D., Chief of Staff
CIO: Andy Douglas, Manager Information Technology
CHR: Sandy Hinrichs, Director Human Resources
Web address: www.burnettmedicalcenter.com
Control: Other not–for–profit (including NFP Corporation) **Service:** General Medical and Surgical

> **Staffed Beds:** 67 **Admissions:** 536 **Census:** 51 **Outpatient Visits:** 31118
> **Births:** 35 **Total Expense ($000):** 14915 **Payroll Expense ($000):** 7022
> **Personnel:** 126

GREEN BAY—Brown County

☒ △ **AURORA BAYCARE MEDICAL CENTER (520193)**, 2845 Greenbrier Road, Zip 54311–6519, Mailing Address: P.O. Box 8900, Zip 54308–8900; tel. 920/288–8000 **A**1 2 7 9 10 **F**3 8 12 13 15 17 18 19 20 22 24 26 28 29 30 31 32 34 35 36 40 43 44 45 46 47 48 49 50 53 54 57 58 59 64 65 70 72 74 75 76 78 79 80 81 82 85 86 87 89 90 93 94 96 107 108 109 110 111 114 115 116 117 118 119 120 121 123 124 126 129 130 131 132 135 144 146 147 148 **P**6 **S** Aurora Health Care, Milwaukee, WI
Primary Contact: Daniel T. Meyer, President
COO: Daniel T. Meyer, President
CFO: Gwen Christensen, Vice President Finance
CMO: Stephen Brada, Chief of Staff
CIO: Chuck Geurts, Manager Management Information Services
CHR: Elizabeth A. Kirby, Director Human Resources
CNO: Heather Schroeder, R.N., Chief Nurse Executive and Vice President of Nursing
Web address: www.aurorabaycare.com
Control: Partnership, Investor–owned, for–profit **Service:** General Medical and Surgical

> **Staffed Beds:** 167 **Admissions:** 8119 **Census:** 88 **Outpatient Visits:** 222330
> **Births:** 1752 **Total Expense ($000):** 201869 **Payroll Expense ($000):** 69677 **Personnel:** 1175

★ ◇ **BELLIN MEMORIAL HOSPITAL (520049)**, 744 South Webster Avenue, Zip 54301–3581, Mailing Address: P.O. Box 23400, Zip 54305–3400; tel. 920/433–3500 **A**9 10 21 **F**3 12 13 15 17 18 20 22 24 26 28 29 30 31 32 34 35 36 37 40 42 43 44 45 46 47 49 50 51 53 54 57 58 59 62 64 65 68 71 74 75 76 77 78 79 80 81 82 85 86 87 89 90 91 92 96 97 106 108 111 115 116 118 119 120 121 123 124 127 130 131 133 135 144 145 **P**2 6 8
Primary Contact: George Kerwin, President
CFO: Jim Dietsche, Chief Financial Officer
CMO: Ed Millermaier, M.D., Chief Medical Officer
CIO: John Rocheleau, Vice President Business Support and Information Technology
CHR: Troy L. Koebke, Director Human Resources Management
CNO: Laura Hieb, R.N., Chief Nursing Officer
Web address: www.bellin.org
Control: Church–operated, Nongovernment, not–for profit **Service:** General Medical and Surgical

> **Staffed Beds:** 167 **Admissions:** 8396 **Census:** 86 **Outpatient Visits:** 742481
> **Births:** 1231 **Total Expense ($000):** 345314 **Payroll Expense ($000):** 159416 **Personnel:** 2167

WI

Hospital, Medicare Provider Number, Address, Telephone, Approval, Facility, and Physician Codes, Health Care System

★ American Hospital Association (AHA) membership
☐ The Joint Commission accreditation   ◇ DNV Healthcare Inc. accreditation
◯ Healthcare Facilities Accreditation Program
△ Commission on Accreditation of Rehabilitation Facilities (CARF) accreditation

---

◇ **BELLIN PSYCHIATRIC CENTER (524038)**, 301 East St. Joseph Street,
Zip 54305–3725, Mailing Address: P.O. Box 23725, Zip 54305–3725;
tel. 920/433–3630 **A**9 10 21 **F**4 5 6 29 34 36 38 53 54 56 64 75 86 87 98
99 100 101 102 103 104 105 130 **P**2 6
Primary Contact: Sharla Baenen, President
CFO: Kevin McGurk, Controller
CMO: Ed Millermaier, M.D., Chief Medical Officer
CIO: Troy Schiesl, Director Information Services
CHR: Troy L. Koebke, Director Human Resources
CNO: Ray Bork, Team Leader Nursing
Web address: www.bellin.org
Control: Church–operated, Nongovernment, not–for profit **Service:** Psychiatric

Staffed Beds: 53 **Admissions:** 1693 **Census:** 19 **Outpatient Visits:** 59453
Births: 0 **Total Expense ($000):** 16948 **Payroll Expense ($000):** 10782
Personnel: 117

BROWN COUNTY COMMUNITY TREATMENT CENTER (524014), 3150
Gershwin Drive, Zip 54311–5899; tel. 920/391–4700 **A**10 **F**4 98 102 130
Primary Contact: Roberta Morschauser, Administrator
CFO: Margaret Hoff, Account Manager
CMO: Yogesh Pareek, M.D., Clinical Director
CIO: Dawn LaPlant, Manager Health Information Management
CHR: Brent R. Miller, Manager Human Resources
Web address: www.co.brown.wi.us/
Control: County–Government, nonfederal **Service:** Psychiatric

Staffed Beds: 10 **Admissions:** 1094 **Census:** 10 **Outpatient Visits:** 5613
Births: 0 **Total Expense ($000):** 5030 **Payroll Expense ($000):** 2810
Personnel: 74

BROWN COUNTY HUMAN SERVICES MENTAL HEALTH CENTER See Brown
County Community Treatment Center

⊞ **ST. MARY'S HOSPITAL MEDICAL CENTER (520097)**, 1726 Shawano Avenue,
Zip 54303–3282; tel. 920/498–4200 **A**1 9 10 **F**3 13 15 17 18 20 22 26 28
29 30 31 34 35 40 43 44 45 46 47 48 49 50 51 53 55 57 59 64 65 68 69
70 74 75 76 77 78 79 80 81 82 84 85 86 87 92 93 94 96 102 107 108 110
111 114 115 116 117 118 119 130 132 143 145 146 147 148 **P**2 **S** Hospital
Sisters Health System, Springfield, IL
Primary Contact: Therese B. Pandl, President and Chief Executive Officer
COO: Lawrence J. Connors, Chief Operating Officer
CFO: Greg Simia, Chief Financial Officer
CMO: Kenneth Johnson, M.D., Chief Physician Executive
CIO: Shane Miller, Chief Information Officer
CHR: Christine Jensema, Chief People Officer
CNO: Paula Hafeman, R.N., Chief Nursing Officer
Web address: www.stmgb.org
Control: Church–operated, Nongovernment, not–for profit **Service:** General
Medical and Surgical

Staffed Beds: 83 **Admissions:** 5184 **Census:** 41 **Outpatient Visits:** 117409
Births: 701 **Total Expense ($000):** 108009 **Payroll Expense ($000):** 34141
Personnel: 391

⊞ **ST. VINCENT HOSPITAL (520075)**, 835 South Van Buren Street,
Zip 54301–3526, Mailing Address: P.O. Box 13508, Zip 54307–3508;
tel. 920/433–0111 **A**1 2 9 10 **F**3 9 11 12 13 15 17 18 20 22 24 29 30 31 34
35 36 40 43 44 45 49 50 51 56 57 58 59 60 62 64 65 68 70 72 74 75 76
77 78 79 80 81 83 84 85 86 87 88 89 90 91 92 93 94 96 107 108 110 111
114 115 116 117 118 119 120 121 123 124 126 129 130 132 135 143 144
146 147 148 **P**2 **S** Hospital Sisters Health System, Springfield, IL
Primary Contact: Therese B. Pandl, President and Chief Executive Officer
COO: Lawrence J. Connors, Chief Operating Officer
CFO: Kelly Gigot, Vice President Finance
CMO: Kenneth Johnson, M.D., Chief Physician Executive
CIO: Shane Miller, Chief Information Officer
CHR: Christine Jensema, Chief People Officer
CNO: Paula Hafeman, R.N., Chief Nursing Officer
Web address: www.stvincenthospital.org
Control: Church–operated, Nongovernment, not–for profit **Service:** General
Medical and Surgical

Staffed Beds: 255 **Admissions:** 10371 **Census:** 128 **Outpatient Visits:**
125075 **Births:** 847 **Total Expense ($000):** 239146 **Payroll Expense**
($000): 77894 **Personnel:** 1263

GREENFIELD—Milwaukee County

KINDRED HOSPITAL–MILWAUKEE See Post Acute Medical Specialty Hospital of
Milwaukee

⊞ **POST ACUTE MEDICAL SPECIALTY HOSPITAL OF MILWAUKEE (522004)**,
5017 South 110Th Street, Zip 53228–3131; tel. 414/427–8282 **A**1 9 10 **F**1 3
29 34 56 65 75 80 85 86 87 90 96 100 130 **S** Post Acute Medical, LLC,
Enola, PA
Primary Contact: Terry W. Kepler, Chief Executive Officer
COO: Christine Ninu, Chief Clinical Officer
CMO: Alok Goyal, M.D., Medical Director
Web address: www.khmilwaukee.com/
Control: Corporation, Investor–owned, for–profit **Service:** Long–Term Acute Care
hospital

Staffed Beds: 56 **Admissions:** 466 **Census:** 34 **Outpatient Visits:** 0 **Births:**
0 **Total Expense ($000):** 15577 **Payroll Expense ($000):** 6278 **Personnel:**
134

HARTFORD—Washington County

⊞ **AURORA MEDICAL CENTER IN WASHINGTON COUNTY (520038)**, 1032
East Sumner Street, Zip 53027–1698; tel. 262/673–2300 **A**1 9 10 **F**2 3 8 11
15 17 28 29 30 31 32 34 35 37 40 43 44 45 46 47 48 49 50 53 54 56 59
60 64 65 68 70 74 75 79 80 81 82 85 87 89 90 93 107 111 118 119 129
130 131 132 135 146 148 **P**6 **S** Aurora Health Care, Milwaukee, WI
Primary Contact: Carrie Killoran, Interim President
CIO: John Sipek, Supervisor Client Services
CNO: Terry Kabitzke–Groth, R.N., Chief Nursing Officer
Web address: www.aurorahealthcare.org
Control: Other not–for–profit (including NFP Corporation) **Service:** General
Medical and Surgical

Staffed Beds: 34 **Admissions:** 1779 **Census:** 17 **Outpatient Visits:** 69673
Births: 0 **Total Expense ($000):** 49343 **Payroll Expense ($000):** 17679
Personnel: 289

HAYWARD—Sawyer County

★ **HAYWARD AREA MEMORIAL HOSPITAL AND NURSING HOME (521336)**,
11040 North State Road 77, Zip 54843–6391; tel. 715/934–4321, (Total facility
includes 70 beds in nursing home–type unit) **A**9 10 18 **F**3 8 10 11 13 15 31 34
35 40 43 45 51 64 75 76 77 78 81 82 85 86 93 97 107 111 115 119 128
130 132 133 134 135 145 146 148
Primary Contact: Timothy M. Gullingsrud, Chief Executive Officer
COO: Brad Zeller, Vice President Operations
CFO: Kent Dumonseau, Vice President Finance and Information Services
CHR: Rose Gates, Director Human Resources
Web address: www.hamhnh.com
Control: Other not–for–profit (including NFP Corporation) **Service:** General
Medical and Surgical

Staffed Beds: 75 **Admissions:** 1080 **Census:** 75 **Outpatient Visits:** 22311
Births: 157 **Total Expense ($000):** 27807 **Payroll Expense ($000):** 12461
Personnel: 157

HILLSBORO—Vernon County

★ **GUNDERSEN ST. JOSEPH'S HOSPITAL AND CLINICS (521304)**, 400 Water
Avenue, Zip 54634–9054, Mailing Address: P.O. Box 527, Zip 54634–0527;
tel. 608/489–8000 **A**9 10 18 **F**3 8 11 15 28 29 30 34 35 40 42 43 50 53 54
56 57 59 64 65 68 69 75 77 80 81 82 85 86 87 89 90 91 92 93 96 97 107
109 110 114 127 129 130 131 132 133 135 144 147 148 **P**6
Primary Contact: Debra Smith, Chief Executive Officer
CFO: Robin Nelson, Chief Financial Officer
CMO: William Cooke, M.D., Chief of Staff
CIO: Danial Phetteplace, Director Information Technology
CHR: Kristie McCoic, Clinic Operations Officer and Director Human Resources
Web address: www.stjhealthcare.org
Control: Other not–for–profit (including NFP Corporation) **Service:** General
Medical and Surgical

Staffed Beds: 15 **Admissions:** 226 **Census:** 2 **Outpatient Visits:** 2326
Births: 0 **Total Expense ($000):** 16219 **Payroll Expense ($000):** 6158
Personnel: 146

HUDSON—St. Croix County

☐ **HUDSON HOSPITAL AND CLINIC (521335)**, 405 Stageline Road,
Zip 54016–7848; tel. 715/531–6000 **A**1 9 10 18 **F**3 5 13 15 28 29 31 34 35
36 37 38 40 43 44 45 46 50 53 56 57 59 64 68 74 75 76 77 78 79 80 81
85 86 87 89 93 94 96 97 107 110 111 115 117 119 129 130 132 133 135
143 146 148
Primary Contact: Marian M. Furlong, R.N., FACHE, Chief Executive Officer
CFO: Douglas E. Johnson, Vice President and Chief Financial Officer
CMO: Paul Scott, M.D., Chief of Staff
CHR: Scott J. Allen, Director Human Resources
CNO: Robbi Hagelberg, R.N., Vice President Operations and Chief Nursing Officer
Web address: www.hudsonhospital.org
Control: Other not–for–profit (including NFP Corporation) **Service:** General
Medical and Surgical

Staffed Beds: 16 **Admissions:** 1540 **Census:** 12 **Outpatient Visits:** 43867
Births: 673 **Total Expense ($000):** 49291 **Payroll Expense ($000):** 19107
Personnel: 302

WI

JANESVILLE—Rock County

✠ **MERCY HOSPITAL AND TRAUMA CENTER (520066)**, 1000 Mineral Point Avenue, Zip 53548–2982, Mailing Address: P.O. Box 5003, Zip 53547–5003; tel. 608/756–6000, (Total facility includes 26 beds in nursing home–type unit) **A**1 2 9 10 **F**3 4 5 9 11 12 13 15 17 18 20 22 24 26 28 29 30 31 33 34 35 36 37 38 40 42 43 44 45 49 50 54 55 56 57 58 59 60 61 64 65 66 68 69 70 74 75 76 77 78 79 80 81 82 84 85 86 87 88 89 90 92 93 94 96 97 98 100 101 102 103 104 105 107 108 110 111 114 115 116 118 119 120 121 126 128 129 130 131 132 135 144 146 147 148 **P**6 **S** Mercy Health System, Janesville, WI
Primary Contact: Javon R. Bea, President and Chief Executive Officer
CFO: John Cook, Vice President and Chief Financial Officer
CMO: Mark L. Goelzer, M.D., Director Medical Affairs
CHR: Kathy Harris, Vice President
CNO: Sue Ripsch, R.N., Vice President and Chief Nursing Officer
Web address: www.mercyhealthsystem.org
Control: Other not–for–profit (including NFP Corporation) **Service:** General Medical and Surgical

Staffed Beds: 124 **Admissions:** 6612 **Census:** 89 **Outpatient Visits:** 1037167 **Births:** 732 **Total Expense ($000):** 375901 **Payroll Expense ($000):** 111386 **Personnel:** 2473

✠ **ST. MARY'S JANESVILLE HOSPITAL (520208)**, 3400 East Racine Steeet, Zip 53546–2344; tel. 608/373–8000 **A**1 10 **F**3 8 11 13 28 29 30 34 35 38 40 44 45 46 47 49 50 57 59 65 68 70 74 75 76 77 79 80 81 82 84 85 86 87 89 90 93 107 108 111 118 119 129 130 132 135 146 **S** SSM Health, Saint Louis, MO
Primary Contact: Kerry Swanson, President
Web address: www.stmarysjanesville.com
Control: Church–operated, Nongovernment, not–for profit **Service:** General Medical and Surgical

Staffed Beds: 50 **Admissions:** 3024 **Census:** 28 **Outpatient Visits:** 26007 **Births:** 469 **Total Expense ($000):** 56148 **Payroll Expense ($000):** 19185 **Personnel:** 239

KENOSHA—Kenosha County

✠ **AURORA MEDICAL CENTER (520189)**, 10400 South 75th Street, Zip 53142–7884; tel. 262/948–5600 **A**1 2 9 10 **F**3 8 11 13 15 17 18 20 28 29 30 31 32 34 35 36 40 43 44 45 46 47 48 49 50 51 54 57 64 68 70 74 75 76 79 80 81 82 84 85 86 87 89 93 94 96 100 107 108 110 111 114 115 116 118 119 120 121 123 129 130 131 132 135 148 **P**6 **S** Aurora Health Care, Milwaukee, WI
Primary Contact: Doug Koch, Market President
CFO: David Yeager, Vice President Finance
CMO: James Santarelli, M.D., President Medical Staff
CIO: Jean Chase, Regional Manager Information Services
CHR: Gene Krauklis, Regional Vice President Human Resources
Web address: www.aurorahealthcare.org
Control: Other not–for–profit (including NFP Corporation) **Service:** General Medical and Surgical

Staffed Beds: 74 **Admissions:** 4782 **Census:** 46 **Outpatient Visits:** 156417 **Births:** 860 **Total Expense ($000):** 104715 **Payroll Expense ($000):** 34562 **Personnel:** 634

☐ **UNITED HEALTH SYSTEM–KENOSHA CAMPUS (520021)**, 6308 Eighth Avenue, Zip 53143–5082; tel. 262/656–2011 **A**1 2 9 10 **F**1 11 12 13 15 17 20 22 24 28 29 34 40 43 51 53 60 64 70 72 75 76 77 78 80 81 86 87 89 90 93 100 102 107 108 111 118 119 130 131 144 147 **P**6
Primary Contact: Richard O. Schmidt, Jr., President and Chief Executive Officer
Web address: www.unitedhospitalsystem.org/
Control: Other not–for–profit (including NFP Corporation) **Service:** General Medical and Surgical

Staffed Beds: 247 **Admissions:** 9018 **Census:** 102 **Outpatient Visits:** 342240 **Births:** 1033 **Total Expense ($000):** 243485 **Payroll Expense ($000):** 115093 **Personnel:** 1664

LA CROSSE—La Crosse County

✠ △ **GUNDERSEN HEALTH SYSTEM (520087)**, 1900 South Avenue, Zip 54601–5467; tel. 608/782–7300 **A**1 2 3 5 7 8 9 10 **F**3 4 5 9 11 13 18 19 20 22 24 28 29 30 31 32 35 36 38 40 43 45 46 47 48 49 50 51 56 60 61 63 68 72 74 76 78 79 80 81 82 83 85 86 87 88 89 90 91 92 93 94 96 98 99 100 101 102 103 104 105 106 110 114 115 117 120 121 123 124 126 129 130 134 144 145 146 147 148
Primary Contact: Jeffrey E. Thompson, M.D., Chief Executive Officer
COO: Kathy Klock, R.N., Senior Vice President Clinical Operations and Human Resources
CFO: Michael Allen, Chief Financial Officer
CMO: Greg Thompson, Chief Medical Officer
CIO: Deb Rislow, Chief Information Officer
CHR: Kathy Klock, R.N., Senior Vice President Clinical Operations and Human Resources
CNO: Mary Lu Gerke, R.N., Vice President Nursing Systems
Web address: www.gundluth.org
Control: Other not–for–profit (including NFP Corporation) **Service:** General Medical and Surgical

Staffed Beds: 258 **Admissions:** 13314 **Census:** 159 **Outpatient Visits:** 590243 **Births:** 1432 **Total Expense ($000):** 466713 **Payroll Expense ($000):** 193147 **Personnel:** 2231

☐ **MAYO CLINIC HEALTH SYSTEM – FRANCISCAN HEALTHCARE IN LA CROSSE (520004)**, 700 West Avenue South, Zip 54601–4783; tel. 608/785–0940 **A**1 2 3 5 9 10 **F**1 3 4 5 6 8 9 11 13 16 17 18 19 20 21 22 23 25 26 27 28 29 30 31 32 34 35 36 40 42 43 50 52 53 54 55 56 57 58 59 61 64 65 66 68 69 70 71 72 74 75 76 77 78 79 80 81 82 84 86 87 88 89 90 93 94 97 98 99 100 101 102 103 104 105 107 108 110 111 114 115 117 118 119 120 121 123 124 127 129 130 131 132 134 135 143 144 145 146 147 148 **S** Mayo Clinic, Rochester, MN
Primary Contact: Timothy J. Johnson, President and Chief Executive Officer
COO: Joseph J. Kruse, Executive Vice President
CFO: Tom Tiggelaar, Vice President Finance
CMO: David Rushlow, Vice President Medical Affairs
CIO: Neal Sanger, Vice President Information Services
CHR: Lisa Radtke, Regional Administrator Human Resources
CNO: Diane Holmay, R.N., Vice President and Chief Nursing Officer
Web address: www.franciscanskemp.org
Control: Church–operated, Nongovernment, not–for profit **Service:** General Medical and Surgical

Staffed Beds: 155 **Admissions:** 7419 **Census:** 70 **Outpatient Visits:** 87017 **Births:** 955 **Total Expense ($000):** 164603 **Payroll Expense ($000):** 74262 **Personnel:** 1539

LADYSMITH—Rusk County

★ **RUSK COUNTY MEMORIAL HOSPITAL (521328)**, 900 College Avenue West, Zip 54848–2116; tel. 715/532–5561, (Total facility includes 50 beds in nursing home–type unit) **A**9 10 18 **F**3 13 15 28 29 30 40 45 47 53 56 57 59 64 68 70 76 77 81 85 87 89 90 93 107 110 111 115 117 119 128 133 144 146 147 148
Primary Contact: Charisse S. Oland, FACHE, Chief Executive Officer
CFO: David Kuehn, Chief Financial Officer
CMO: Ganesh Pawar, M.D., Chief of Staff
CHR: Rita Telitz, Chief Administrative Officer
CNO: Debra Frenn, FACHE, Chief Patient Care Officer
Web address: www.ruskhospital.org
Control: County–Government, nonfederal **Service:** General Medical and Surgical

Staffed Beds: 75 **Admissions:** 567 **Census:** 49 **Outpatient Visits:** 31770 **Births:** 58 **Total Expense ($000):** 17550 **Payroll Expense ($000):** 6703 **Personnel:** 114

LAKE GENEVA—Walworth County

MERCY WALWORTH HOSPITAL AND MEDICAL CENTER (521357), N2950 State Road 67, Zip 53147–2655; tel. 262/245–0535 **A**9 10 18 **F**3 5 9 11 13 15 18 26 29 30 31 34 35 40 44 45 50 54 55 57 59 64 65 70 74 75 76 77 78 79 81 82 85 86 92 93 94 96 97 100 101 103 104 107 108 110 111 114 118 119 130 131 132 135 144 146 148 **P**6 **S** Mercy Health System, Janesville, WI
Primary Contact: Jennifer Hallatt, Chief Operating Officer
Web address: www.mercyhealthsystem.org
Control: Other not–for–profit (including NFP Corporation) **Service:** General Medical and Surgical

Staffed Beds: 15 **Admissions:** 1145 **Census:** 9 **Outpatient Visits:** 130074 **Births:** 127 **Total Expense ($000):** 47447 **Payroll Expense ($000):** 12718 **Personnel:** 280

WI

Hospital, Medicare Provider Number, Address, Telephone, Approval, Facility, and Physician Codes, Health Care System

★ American Hospital Association (AHA) membership
☐ The Joint Commission accreditation   ◇ DNV Healthcare Inc. accreditation
○ Healthcare Facilities Accreditation Program
△ Commission on Accreditation of Rehabilitation Facilities (CARF) accreditation

LANCASTER—Grant County

⊞ **GRANT REGIONAL HEALTH CENTER (521322)**, 507 South Monroe Street, Zip 53813–2054; tel. 608/723–2143 **A**1 9 10 18 **F**3 8 11 13 15 28 29 34 35 36 40 43 53 56 57 59 64 65 68 69 75 76 77 78 80 81 82 84 85 86 87 89 90 93 97 107 110 119 129 130 131 132 133 135 144 146 148 **P**6
S HealthTech Management Services, Brentwood, TN
Primary Contact: Nicole Clapp, R.N., MSN, FACHE, President and Chief Executive Officer
CFO: Dawn Bandy, Chief Financial Officer
CMO: Sheirlie Lamantia, M.D., Chief of Staff
CIO: Kevin Ruchti, Coordinator Information Systems
CHR: Stacy L. Martin, Director Human Resources
CNO: Jennifer Rutkowski, R.N., Vice President Professional Services
Web address: www.grantregional.com
Control: Other not–for–profit (including NFP Corporation) **Service:** General Medical and Surgical

Staffed Beds: 4 **Admissions:** 705 **Census:** 4 **Outpatient Visits:** 27406 **Births:** 164 **Total Expense ($000):** 19278 **Payroll Expense ($000):** 8945 **Personnel:** 146	

MADISON—Dane County

☐ **MENDOTA MENTAL HEALTH INSTITUTE (524008)**, 301 Troy Drive, Zip 53704–1599; tel. 608/301–1000 **A**1 3 5 9 10 **F**6 29 30 38 44 50 56 68 75 82 86 87 98 100 101 103 104 105 130 143 **P**6
Primary Contact: Greg Van Rybroek, Chief Executive Officer
CFO: Stacie Schiereck, Director Management Services
CMO: Molli Martha Rolli, M.D., Medical Director
CNO: Jane Walters, Director of Nursing
Web address: www.dhfs.state.wi.us
Control: State–Government, nonfederal **Service:** Psychiatric

Staffed Beds: 257 **Admissions:** 782 **Census:** 228 **Outpatient Visits:** 18535 **Births:** 0 **Total Expense ($000):** 55620 **Payroll Expense ($000):** 36074 **Personnel:** 707	

⊞ △ **MERITER HOSPITAL (520089)**, 202 South Park Street, Zip 53715–1507; tel. 608/417–6000 **A**1 3 5 7 9 10 **F**3 4 5 9 11 12 13 15 17 18 20 22 24 26 28 29 30 31 32 34 35 36 37 40 41 43 45 46 48 49 50 53 56 57 58 59 64 65 66 68 70 71 72 74 75 76 78 79 80 81 84 85 86 87 89 90 92 93 97 98 99 100 101 102 103 104 105 106 107 108 111 115 117 118 119 126 130 132 135 145 146 147 148 **P**6
Primary Contact: Peter W. Thoreen, FACHE, Interim Chief Executive Officer
CFO: Beth Erdman, Chief Financial Officer
CMO: Geoff Priest, M.D., Chief Medical Officer
CIO: Denise Gomez, Assistant Vice President Information Systems
CHR: James Arnett, Vice President Human Resources
CNO: Pat Grunwald, MSN, Chief Nursing Officer
Web address: www.meriter.com
Control: Other not–for–profit (including NFP Corporation) **Service:** General Medical and Surgical

Staffed Beds: 315 **Admissions:** 16848 **Census:** 197 **Outpatient Visits:** 190475 **Births:** 3697 **Total Expense ($000):** 422239 **Payroll Expense ($000):** 192744 **Personnel:** 2516	

⊞ **SELECT SPECIALTY HOSPITAL–MADISON (522008)**, 801 Braxton Place, 2nd Floor, Zip 53715–1415; tel. 608/260–2700 **A**1 10 **F**1 3 18 29 30 34 50 60 65 68 74 75 79 80 84 85 86 90 97 107 114 130 148 **P**2 8 **S** Select Medical Corporation, Mechanicsburg, PA
Primary Contact: Raymond F. Carnevale, Chief Executive Officer
CHR: Mallary Stramowski, Chief Human Resources Officer
CNO: Dana McKinney, Chief Nursing Officer
Web address: www.madison.selectspecialtyhospitals.com
Control: Corporation, Investor–owned, for–profit **Service:** Long–Term Acute Care hospital

Staffed Beds: 58 **Admissions:** 529 **Census:** 43 **Outpatient Visits:** 0 **Births:** 0 **Total Expense ($000):** 27000 **Payroll Expense ($000):** 10649 **Personnel:** 167	

⊞ **ST. MARY'S HOSPITAL (520083)**, 700 South Park Street, Zip 53715–1830; tel. 608/251–6100 **A**1 3 5 10 **F**2 11 13 15 17 20 22 24 28 29 34 38 40 43 51 53 54 56 60 64 70 72 75 76 77 78 80 81 89 98 103 107 108 118 119 130 **S** SSM Health, Saint Louis, MO
Primary Contact: Frank D. Byrne, M.D., President
COO: Kristin McManmon, Chief Operating Officer
CFO: Steve Caldwell, Vice President Finance and Chief Financial Officer
CHR: Linda Taplin Statz, System Vice President Human Resources
CNO: Ginger Malone, MSN, RN–B, Chief Nursing Officer
Web address: www.stmarysmadison.com
Control: Other not–for–profit (including NFP Corporation) **Service:** General Medical and Surgical

Staffed Beds: 364 **Admissions:** 20272 **Census:** 237 **Outpatient Visits:** 129679 **Births:** 3270 **Total Expense ($000):** 368180 **Payroll Expense ($000):** 137352 **Personnel:** 1815	

⊞ △ **UNIVERSITY OF WISCONSIN HOSPITAL AND CLINICS (520098)**, 600 Highland Avenue, Zip 53792–0002; tel. 608/263–6400, (Includes UNIVERSITY OF WISCONSIN CHILDREN'S HOSPITAL ; AMERICAN FAMILY CHILDREN'S HOSPITAL, 1675 Highland Avenue, Zip 53705; tel. 608/890–5437) **A**1 3 5 7 8 9 10 13 **F**3 5 6 8 9 12 15 16 17 18 19 20 21 22 23 24 25 26 27 28 29 30 31 32 34 35 36 37 40 41 43 44 45 46 47 48 49 50 51 52 53 54 55 56 57 58 59 60 61 62 64 68 70 71 74 75 77 78 79 80 81 82 83 84 85 86 87 88 89 90 92 93 94 96 97 98 100 102 103 104 107 108 109 110 111 112 114 115 116 117 118 119 120 121 123 124 126 129 130 131 132 134 135 136 137 138 139 140 141 142 143 145 146 147 148 **P**3
Primary Contact: Donna Katen–Bahensky, President and Chief Executive Officer
COO: Ron Sliwinski, Chief Operations Officer
CFO: Michael D. Buhl, Senior Vice President and Chief Financial Officer
CMO: Christopher Green, M.D., Senior Vice President Medical Affairs and Associate Dean Hospital Affairs
CIO: Jocelyn DeWitt, Ph.D., Vice President and Chief Information Officer
CHR: Janice K. Bultema, MSN, Senior Vice President Human Resources
CNO: Beth Houlahan, MSN, Senior Vice President and Chief Nursing Officer
Web address: www.uwhospital.org
Control: Other not–for–profit (including NFP Corporation) **Service:** General Medical and Surgical

Staffed Beds: 530 **Admissions:** 28120 **Census:** 393 **Outpatient Visits:** 957346 **Births:** 0 **Total Expense ($000):** 1175793 **Payroll Expense ($000):** 429924 **Personnel:** 7207	

⊞ **WILLIAM S. MIDDLETON MEMORIAL VETERANS HOSPITAL**, 2500 Overlook Terrace, Zip 53705–2286; tel. 608/256–1901, (Nonreporting) **A**1 3 5
S Department of Veterans Affairs, Washington, DC
Primary Contact: Judy McKee, FACHE, Director
COO: Allen R. Ackers, Associate Director
CFO: Abraham Rabinowitz, Assistant Finance Officer
CMO: Alan J. Bridges, M.D., Chief of Staff
CIO: Randall Margenau, Chief Information Officer
CHR: Stuart Souders, Coordinator Human Resources
Web address: www.madison.va.gov
Control: Veterans Affairs, Government, federal **Service:** General Medical and Surgical

Staffed Beds: 87	

MANITOWOC—Manitowoc County

⊞ **HOLY FAMILY MEMORIAL (520107)**, 2300 Western Avenue, Zip 54220–3712, Mailing Address: P.O. Box 1450, Zip 54221–1450; tel. 920/320–2011 **A**1 2 9 10 **F**3 4 5 8 11 13 15 17 20 22 26 28 29 30 31 34 36 40 45 46 47 48 49 50 51 53 54 56 57 58 59 62 63 64 65 68 70 74 75 76 77 78 79 80 81 82 84 85 86 89 93 97 99 100 101 102 103 104 107 108 110 111 115 116 118 119 121 129 130 131 132 135 144 146 147 148 **P**6 8 **S** Franciscan Sisters of Christian Charity Sponsored Ministries, Inc., Manitowoc, WI
Primary Contact: Mark P. Herzog, President and Chief Executive Officer
COO: Jane Curran–Meuli, Chief Operating Officer
CFO: Patricia Huettl, Vice President Finance and Chief Financial Officer
CMO: Steve Driggers, M.D., Chief Medical Officer
CIO: Theron Pappas, Director Management Information Systems
CHR: Laura M. Fielding, Administrative Director Organizational Development
CNO: Bonny Range, MSN, Chief Nursing Officer
Web address: www.hfmhealth.org
Control: Church–operated, Nongovernment, not–for profit **Service:** General Medical and Surgical

Staffed Beds: 62 **Admissions:** 2254 **Census:** 26 **Outpatient Visits:** 227363 **Births:** 233 **Total Expense ($000):** 128376 **Payroll Expense ($000):** 64604 **Personnel:** 743	

MARINETTE—Marinette County

⊞ **BAY AREA MEDICAL CENTER (520113)**, 3100 Shore Drive, Zip 54143–4242; tel. 715/735–6621 **A**1 9 10 20 **F**3 7 8 11 13 15 17 18 20 22 28 29 30 31 34 40 42 43 45 46 48 50 57 59 60 64 68 70 74 75 76 77 78 79 80 81 85 86 87 89 93 96 107 108 110 111 115 119 130 131 143 146 147 148 **P**8
Primary Contact: Edward A. Harding, FACHE, President and Chief Executive Officer
COO: Bernie VanCourt, Chief Operating Officer
CFO: C. Daniel Carlson, Chief Financial Officer
CMO: Richard Stein, M.D., Chief Medical Officer
CIO: Pete Eisenzoph, Director Information Technology
CHR: Ken Joyner, Vice President of Employee Services
CNO: Rooney Freimund, R.N., Chief Nurse Executive
Web address: www.bamc.org
Control: Other not–for–profit (including NFP Corporation) **Service:** General Medical and Surgical

Staffed Beds: 32 **Admissions:** 3642 **Census:** 32 **Outpatient Visits:** 62081 **Births:** 312 **Total Expense ($000):** 102319 **Payroll Expense ($000):** 44204 **Personnel:** 486	

WI

Many Facility Codes have changed. Please refer to the AHA Guide Code Chart. © 2014 AHA Guide

MARSHFIELD—Wood County

⊠ △ **MINISTRY SAINT JOSEPH'S HOSPITAL (520037)**, 611 St. Joseph Avenue, Zip 54449–1898; tel. 715/387–1713, (Includes SAINT JOSEPH'S CHILDEN'S HOSPITAL, 611 Saint Joseph Avenue, Zip 54449–1832; tel. 715/387–1713) **A**1 2 3 5 7 9 10 20 **F**3 4 5 6 7 9 11 12 13 16 17 18 19 20 22 24 26 27 28 29 30 31 34 35 36 38 40 41 43 44 49 50 56 57 59 61 64 68 69 70 72 74 75 76 77 78 79 80 81 82 83 84 85 86 87 88 89 90 93 96 98 100 101 102 103 108 111 112 116 117 118 119 120 121 123 124 126 130 132 135 136 144 146 147 148 **S** Ascension Health, Saint Louis, MO
Primary Contact: Brian Kief, Regional Vice President Ministry Health Care and President Ministry Saint Joseph's Hospital
CFO: William J. Hinner, Vice President Financial Analysis and Planning Ministry Health Care
CMO: Peter Stamas, M.D., Vice President Medical Affairs
CIO: Will Weider, Chief Information Officer
CHR: Cheryl F. Zima, Vice President Human Resources Ministry Health Care
CNO: Robin Kretschman, MSN, Vice President Patient Care Services
Web address: www.stjosephs–marshfield.org
Control: Church–operated, Nongovernment, not–for profit **Service:** General Medical and Surgical

Staffed Beds: 319 **Admissions:** 17572 **Census:** 262 **Outpatient Visits:** 51811 **Births:** 1001 **Total Expense ($000):** 298150 **Payroll Expense ($000):** 105946 **Personnel:** 1560

NORWOOD HEALTH CENTER (524019), 1600 North Chestnut Avenue, Zip 54449–1499; tel. 715/384–2188, (Total facility includes 24 beds in nursing home–type unit) **A**9 10 **F**3 4 30 34 98 99 100 101 102 103 128 130 143 146 148 **P**6
Primary Contact: Rhonda Kozik, Administrator
CFO: Jo Timmerman, Manager Accounting
CHR: Larry Shear, Administrative Assistant
Web address: www.co.wood.wi.us/norwood/index.htm
Control: County–Government, nonfederal **Service:** Psychiatric

Staffed Beds: 40 **Admissions:** 682 **Census:** 30 **Outpatient Visits:** 0 **Births:** 0 **Total Expense ($000):** 3181 **Payroll Expense ($000):** 1744 **Personnel:** 41

MAUSTON—Juneau County

☐ **MILE BLUFF MEDICAL CENTER (520109)**, 1050 Division Street, Zip 53948–1997; tel. 608/847–6161, (Total facility includes 104 beds in nursing home–type unit) **A**1 9 10 20 **F**3 10 11 13 15 28 29 30 31 34 35 36 40 41 43 44 50 56 57 59 60 62 64 65 66 69 75 76 77 78 79 80 81 82 85 86 87 89 92 93 94 96 97 107 108 110 111 115 118 119 125 127 128 129 130 131 132 135 143 144 145 146 148
Primary Contact: James M. O'Keefe, President and Chief Executive Officer
Web address: www.milebluff.com
Control: Other not–for–profit (including NFP Corporation) **Service:** General Medical and Surgical

Staffed Beds: 117 **Admissions:** 1466 **Census:** 117 **Outpatient Visits:** 90255 **Births:** 183 **Total Expense ($000):** 63889 **Payroll Expense ($000):** 35198 **Personnel:** 447

MEDFORD—Taylor County

⊠ **ASPIRUS MEDFORD HOSPITAL (521324)**, 135 South Gibson Street, Zip 54451–1696; tel. 715/748–8100, (Includes MEMORIAL NURSING HOME), (Total facility includes 109 beds in nursing home–type unit) **A**1 9 10 18 **F**1 3 10 11 13 15 28 29 31 32 34 35 36 40 43 50 53 57 59 60 64 65 75 76 77 78 79 81 82 85 86 87 89 90 93 96 97 107 110 111 116 118 119 125 127 128 129 130 131 132 133 135 144 146 147 148 **S** Aspirus, Inc., Wausau, WI
Primary Contact: Gregory A. Olson, President and Chief Executive Officer
COO: Kaaron Keene, Vice President Patient Care Services
CFO: Lori Peck, Vice President Finance
CMO: Alecia Hylton, M.D., Chief of Staff
CIO: Helen Volger, Director of Information Services
CHR: Angela C. Hupf, Vice President Human Resources and Community Relations
CNO: Kaaron Keene, Vice President Patient Care Services
Web address: www.memhc.com
Control: Other not–for–profit (including NFP Corporation) **Service:** General Medical and Surgical

Staffed Beds: 124 **Admissions:** 874 **Census:** 93 **Outpatient Visits:** 68324 **Births:** 200 **Total Expense ($000):** 47271 **Payroll Expense ($000):** 22667 **Personnel:** 384

MENOMONEE FALLS—Waukesha County

⊠ △ **COMMUNITY MEMORIAL HOSPITAL (520103)**, W180 N8085 Town Hall Road, Zip 53051–3518, Mailing Address: P.O. Box 408, Zip 53052–0408; tel. 262/251–1000 **A**1 2 3 5 7 9 10 **F**3 4 5 11 13 15 17 18 20 22 24 26 28 29 30 31 34 35 36 38 40 43 44 45 46 47 48 49 50 51 56 57 58 59 60 64 65 66 70 72 74 75 76 77 78 79 80 81 82 84 85 86 87 88 89 90 92 93 94 96 97 98 100 101 102 103 104 106 107 108 110 111 115 116 117 118 119 120 121 123 126 129 130 131 132 135 143 145 146 147 148
Primary Contact: Dennis Pollard, President
COO: Allen Ericson, Chief Operating Officer CHD
CFO: Thomas Knoll, Site Director Finance
CMO: David Goldberg, M.D., Vice President Medical Affairs
CIO: Robert DeGrand, Vice President Information Systems, Chief Information Officer
CHR: Keith Allen, Senior Vice President and Chief Human Resources Officer
CNO: Teri Lux, R.N., Vice President Patient Care Services and Chief Nursing Officer
Web address: www.communitymemorial.com
Control: Other not–for–profit (including NFP Corporation) **Service:** General Medical and Surgical

Staffed Beds: 198 **Admissions:** 8663 **Census:** 111 **Outpatient Visits:** 95989 **Births:** 1010 **Total Expense ($000):** 163311 **Payroll Expense ($000):** 61439 **Personnel:** 976

MENOMONIE—Dunn County

☐ **MAYO CLINIC HEALTH SYSTEM – RED CEDAR IN MENOMONIE (521340)**, 2321 Stout Road, Zip 54751–2397; tel. 715/235–5531 **A**1 5 9 10 18 **F**3 8 11 13 15 18 28 29 30 31 32 34 35 36 40 43 44 45 50 53 54 55 57 60 63 64 65 68 75 76 77 78 79 80 81 82 84 85 86 87 89 90 93 97 99 100 101 102 103 104 107 108 110 111 115 119 127 129 130 131 132 133 135 144 146 147 148 **P**6 **S** Mayo Clinic, Rochester, MN
Primary Contact: Steven Lindberg, Chief Administrative Officer
CFO: Jeanie Lubinsky, Chief Financial Officer
CMO: Mark Deyo Svendsen, M.D., Medical Director
CIO: Frank Wrogg, Director Information Technology
CHR: Leann Wurtzel, Director Human Resources
Web address: www.rcmc–mhs.org
Control: Other not–for–profit (including NFP Corporation) **Service:** General Medical and Surgical

Staffed Beds: 21 **Admissions:** 1584 **Census:** 16 **Outpatient Visits:** 110857 **Births:** 310 **Total Expense ($000):** 78270 **Payroll Expense ($000):** 41593 **Personnel:** 584

RED CEDAR MEDICAL CENTER–MAYO HEALTH SYSTEM See Mayo Clinic Health System – Red Cedar in Menomonie

MEQUON—Ozaukee County

COLUMBIA CENTER (520195), 13125 North Port Washington Road, Zip 53097–2416; tel. 262/243–7408 **A**9 10 **F**3 8 13 34 35 64 71 76 81 85 86 87 104 133
Primary Contact: Candy J. Casey, R.N., MS, President and Chief Executive Officer
CMO: Daniel Hagerman, M.D., President Medical Staff
Web address: www.columbiacenter.org
Control: Other not–for–profit (including NFP Corporation) **Service:** General Medical and Surgical

Staffed Beds: 6 **Admissions:** 507 **Census:** 4 **Outpatient Visits:** 223 **Births:** 502 **Total Expense ($000):** 6394 **Payroll Expense ($000):** 3000 **Personnel:** 43

⊠ **COLUMBIA ST. MARY'S OZAUKEE HOSPITAL (520027)**, 13111 North Port Washington Road, Zip 53097–2416; tel. 262/243–7300 **A**1 2 9 10 **F**4 5 9 15 17 20 22 24 28 29 34 36 38 40 43 51 53 54 56 64 70 75 77 78 80 81 86 89 90 93 98 100 102 103 107 108 111 116 118 119 130 144 147 **P**6 **S** Ascension Health, Saint Louis, MO
Primary Contact: Travis Andersen, President and Chief Executive Officer
CFO: Rhonda Anderson, Executive Vice President Finance and Chief Financial Officer
CMO: David Shapiro, M.D., Vice President Medical Affairs and Chief Medical Officer
CIO: Mary Paul, Chief Information Officer
CHR: Cheryl Hill, Vice President Human Resources
Web address: www.columbia–stmarys.org
Control: Church–operated, Nongovernment, not–for profit **Service:** General Medical and Surgical

Staffed Beds: 102 **Admissions:** 4814 **Census:** 54 **Outpatient Visits:** 231685 **Births:** 0 **Total Expense ($000):** 110349 **Payroll Expense ($000):** 32700 **Personnel:** 462

WI

Hospital, Medicare Provider Number, Address, Telephone, Approval, Facility, and Physician Codes, Health Care System

★ American Hospital Association (AHA) membership
☐ The Joint Commission accreditation
◇ DNV Healthcare Inc. accreditation
○ Healthcare Facilities Accreditation Program
△ Commission on Accreditation of Rehabilitation Facilities (CARF) accreditation

MERRILL—Lincoln County

GOOD SAMARITAN HEALTH CENTER OF MERRILL See Ministry Good Samaritan Health Center

☒ **MINISTRY GOOD SAMARITAN HEALTH CENTER (521339)**, 601 South Center Avenue, Zip 54452–3404; tel. 715/536–5511 **A**1 9 10 18 **F**3 15 18 28 29 30 31 34 40 43 45 50 56 60 64 75 78 79 80 81 82 85 86 **87** 89 93 107 108 111 114 118 119 130 132 133 144 146 147 **P**2 **S** Ascension Health, Saint Louis, MO
Primary Contact: Mary T. Krueger, President
CFO: David Jirovec, Director Finance
CHR: Nancy Kwiesielewicz, Human Resources Manager
CNO: Kristine McGarigle, R.N., Vice President Patient Care
Web address: www.ministryhealth.org
Control: Church–operated, Nongovernment, not–for profit **Service:** General Medical and Surgical

Staffed Beds: 10 **Admissions:** 587 **Census:** 5 **Outpatient Visits:** 25653 **Births:** 0 **Total Expense ($000):** 22186 **Payroll Expense ($000):** 11827 **Personnel:** 112

MILWAUKEE—Milwaukee County

★ △ **AURORA SINAI MEDICAL CENTER (520064)**, 945 North 12th Street, Zip 53233–1337, Mailing Address: P.O. Box 342, Zip 53201–0342; tel. 414/219–2000 **A**3 5 7 8 9 **F**1 3 5 6 8 11 12 13 15 17 18 20 22 24 28 29 30 31 32 34 35 36 37 38 40 42 43 44 45 46 49 50 51 54 55 56 57 59 64 65 70 72 75 76 77 78 79 80 81 82 84 85 86 87 89 90 93 96 100 102 103 104 107 108 110 111 114 118 119 123 126 129 130 131 132 135 144 146 147 148 **P**6 **S** Aurora Health Care, Milwaukee, WI
Primary Contact: Carolynn Glocka, R.N., President
CHR: Heidi Grow, Director Human Resources
CNO: Ania Horner, R.N., Chief Nurse Executive
Web address: www.aurorahealthcare.org
Control: Other not–for–profit (including NFP Corporation) **Service:** General Medical and Surgical

Staffed Beds: 189 **Admissions:** 8324 **Census:** 102 **Outpatient Visits:** 249343 **Births:** 2250 **Total Expense ($000):** 168212 **Payroll Expense ($000):** 57906 **Personnel:** 940

☒ △ **AURORA ST. LUKE'S MEDICAL CENTER (520138)**, 2900 West Oklahoma Avenue, Zip 53215–4330, Mailing Address: P.O. Box 2901, Zip 53201–2901; tel. 414/649–6000, (Includes AURORA ST. LUKE'S SOUTH SHORE, 5900 South Lake Drive, Cudahy, Zip 53110–8903; tel. 414/769–9000) **A**1 2 3 5 7 8 9 10 **F**1 2 3 4 5 6 8 11 12 15 17 18 20 22 24 26 28 29 30 31 32 34 35 36 37 38 40 43 44 45 46 47 49 50 51 54 56 57 58 59 64 65 66 68 69 70 72 74 75 78 79 80 81 82 84 85 86 87 89 90 91 92 93 94 96 97 98 100 101 102 103 104 105 107 108 110 111 114 115 116 117 118 119 120 121 123 124 126 129 130 132 135 136 137 138 139 140 142 143 144 145 146 148 **P**6 **S** Aurora Health Care, Milwaukee, WI
Primary Contact: Marie Golanowski, R.N., MS, President
CFO: Nan Nelson, Senior Vice President Finance
CMO: Jeffrey A. Smith, M.D., Senior Vice President and Chief Medical Officer
CIO: Philip Loftus, Ph.D., Vice President and Chief Information Officer
CHR: Thomas C. Ter Horst, Vice President Human Resources
CNO: Faye Zwieg, Vice President and Chief Nursing Officer
Web address: www.aurorahealthcare.org
Control: Other not–for–profit (including NFP Corporation) **Service:** General Medical and Surgical

Staffed Beds: 709 **Admissions:** 35317 **Census:** 537 **Outpatient Visits:** 496454 **Births:** 0 **Total Expense ($000):** 870973 **Payroll Expense ($000):** 263006 **Personnel:** 4297

☒ **CHILDREN'S HOSPITAL OF WISCONSIN (523300)**, 9000 West Wisconsin Avenue, Zip 53226–4810, Mailing Address: P.O. Box 1997, Zip 53201–1997; tel. 414/266–2000 **A**1 3 5 8 9 10 **F**7 9 12 17 20 22 24 28 29 34 36 38 40 43 51 60 61 64 72 75 77 78 81 82 87 88 89 93 99 100 102 104 107 108 111 116 119 130 131 137 138 140 141 144 **S** Children's Hospital and Health System, Milwaukee, WI
Primary Contact: Peggy N. Troy, President and Chief Executive Officer
COO: Cinthia S. Christensen, JD, Executive Vice President and Chief Operating Officer
CMO: Michael Gutzeit, M.D., Chief Medical Officer
CIO: Michael Jones, Vice President and Chief Information Officer
CHR: Peggy Niemer, Vice President Human Resources
Web address: www.chw.org
Control: Other not–for–profit (including NFP Corporation) **Service:** Children's general

Staffed Beds: 296 **Admissions:** 23945 **Census:** 229 **Outpatient Visits:** 339218 **Births:** 0 **Total Expense ($000):** 522827 **Payroll Expense ($000):** 152276 **Personnel:** 2321

☒ △ **CLEMENT J. ZABLOCKI VETERANS AFFAIRS MEDICAL CENTER**, 5000 West National Avenue, Zip 53295–0001; tel. 414/384–2000, (Nonreporting) **A**1 2 3 5 7 **S** Department of Veterans Affairs, Washington, DC
Primary Contact: Robert H. Beller, FACHE, Director
COO: James McClain, Deputy Director
CFO: John Lasota, Assistant Finance Officer
CMO: Michael Erdmann, M.D., Chief of Staff
CIO: Bryan Vail, Chief Information Officer
CHR: Kay Schwieger, Chief Human Resources Officer
CNO: Mary E. Brunn, R.N., Acting Associate Director Nursing
Web address: www.milwaukee.va.gov/
Control: Veterans Affairs, Government, federal **Service:** General Medical and Surgical

Staffed Beds: 637

☒ **COLUMBIA ST. MARY'S HOSPITAL MILWAUKEE (520051)**, 2301 North Lake Drive, Zip 53211–4508; tel. 414/291–1000, (Includes COLUMBIA ST. MARY'S COLUMBIA HOSPITAL, 2025 East Newport Avenue, Zip 53211–2990; tel. 414/961–3300; COLUMBIA ST. MARY'S MILWAUKEE HOSPITAL, 2323 North Lake Drive, Zip 53211–9682, Mailing Address: P.O. Box 503, Zip 53201–0503; tel. 414/291–1000) **A**1 2 3 5 9 10 **F**4 9 12 13 15 16 17 20 22 24 28 29 34 36 38 40 43 51 53 54 56 64 70 72 75 76 77 78 80 81 86 87 89 98 100 102 103 107 108 111 116 118 119 130 144 147 **P**2 **S** Ascension Health, Saint Louis, MO
Primary Contact: Travis Andersen, President and Chief Executive Officer
CFO: Rhonda Anderson, Executive Vice President Finance and Chief Financial Officer
CMO: David Shapiro, M.D., Vice President Medical Affairs and Chief Medical Officer
CIO: Mary Paul, Chief Information Officer
CHR: Cheryl Hill, Vice President Human Resources
Web address: www.columbia–stmarys.org
Control: Church–operated, Nongovernment, not–for profit **Service:** General Medical and Surgical

Staffed Beds: 266 **Admissions:** 12225 **Census:** 162 **Outpatient Visits:** 234747 **Births:** 2761 **Total Expense ($000):** 272866 **Payroll Expense ($000):** 86294 **Personnel:** 1363

☒ △ **FROEDTERT MEMORIAL LUTHERAN HOSPITAL (520177)**, 9200 West Wisconsin Avenue, Zip 53226–3596, Mailing Address: P.O. Box 26099, Zip 53226–0099; tel. 414/805–3000 **A**1 2 3 5 7 8 9 10 **F**3 6 12 13 15 17 18 20 22 24 26 29 30 31 33 34 35 38 40 43 44 45 46 47 48 49 50 51 52 55 56 57 58 59 60 64 68 70 74 75 76 77 78 79 80 81 84 85 86 87 90 91 92 93 94 96 97 98 100 107 108 110 111 113 114 115 116 117 118 119 120 121 123 124 126 129 130 131 132 134 135 136 137 138 139 140 141 142 144 145 146 147 148
Primary Contact: Catherine Buck, President
CFO: Scott Hawig, Chief Financial Officer and Senior Vice President Finance and Treasurer
CMO: Lee Biblo, M.D., Chief Medical Officer
CIO: Robert DeGrand, Chief Information Officer
CHR: Keith Allen, Senior Vice President and Chief Human Resources Officer
CNO: Kathleen Bechtel, MSN, Vice President Patient Care Services and Chief Nursing Officer
Web address: www.froedtert.com
Control: Other not–for–profit (including NFP Corporation) **Service:** General Medical and Surgical

Staffed Beds: 500 **Admissions:** 26112 **Census:** 394 **Outpatient Visits:** 713487 **Births:** 2052 **Total Expense ($000):** 915319 **Payroll Expense ($000):** 265903 **Personnel:** 4524

★ **MILWAUKEE COUNTY BEHAVIORAL HEALTH DIVISION (524001)**, 9455 Watertown Plank Road, Zip 53226–3559; tel. 414/257–6995, (Total facility includes 94 beds in nursing home–type unit) **A**3 5 10 **F**30 42 66 67 71 77 87 98 99 100 102 103 104 105 128 130 146 **P**3 6
Primary Contact: Jim Kubicek, Interim Chief Executive Officer
COO: Steve Delgado, Operations Coordinator
CFO: Randy Oleszak, Director Fiscal Services
CMO: John Schneider, M.D., Medical Director
CIO: Chris Lindberg, Chief Information Officer
CHR: Ara Garcia, Manager Human Resources
CNO: Nancy Ann Marigomen, R.N., Director of Nursing
Web address: www.milwaukeecounty.com
Control: County–Government, nonfederal **Service:** Psychiatric

Staffed Beds: 190 **Admissions:** 2288 **Census:** 177 **Outpatient Visits:** 12812 **Births:** 0 **Total Expense ($000):** 156360 **Payroll Expense ($000):** 33812 **Personnel:** 487

WI

Many Facility Codes have changed. Please refer to the AHA Guide Code Chart. © 2014 AHA Guide

ORTHOPAEDIC HOSPITAL OF WISCONSIN – GLENDALE (520194), 475 West River Woods Parkway, Zip 53212–1081; tel. 414/961–6800 **A**9 10 **F**3 29 38 53 64 79 80 81 82 85 86 93 94 107 111 112 114 119 130 131 135
Primary Contact: Brian J. Cramer, Chief Executive Officer
CFO: Tom Swiderski, Chief Financial Officer
CMO: Rory Wright, M.D., President Medical Staff
CIO: Todd Heikkinen, Director Rehabilitation Services
Web address: www.ohow.org
Control: Partnership, Investor–owned, for–profit **Service:** General Medical and Surgical

> **Staffed Beds:** 30 **Admissions:** 1160 **Census:** 9 **Outpatient Visits:** 28681 **Births:** 0 **Total Expense ($000):** 34207 **Payroll Expense ($000):** 10811 **Personnel:** 165

⊠ △ **SACRED HEART REHABILITATION INSTITUTE (523025)**, 2323 North Lake Drive, Zip 53211–4508; tel. 414/298–6750 **A**1 7 9 10 **F**9 29 34 54 56 64 75 77 86 90 93 100 102 103 130 131 **P**6 **S** Ascension Health, Saint Louis, MO
Primary Contact: Allan M. Spooner, President
CFO: Rhonda Anderson, Executive Vice President Finance and Chief Financial Officer
CMO: David Shapiro, M.D., Vice President Medical Affairs and Chief Medical Officer
CIO: Mary Paul, Vice President and Chief Information Officer
CHR: Cheryl Hill, Vice President Human Resources
Web address: www.columbia-stmarys.org/SHRI
Control: Church–operated, Nongovernment, not–for profit **Service:** Rehabilitation

> **Staffed Beds:** 31 **Admissions:** 371 **Census:** 17 **Outpatient Visits:** 9733 **Births:** 0 **Total Expense ($000):** 11231 **Payroll Expense ($000):** 5234 **Personnel:** 79

⊠ **SELECT SPECIALTY HOSPITAL–MILWAUKEE (522006)**, 8901 West Lincoln Avenue, 2nd Floor, Zip 53227–2409; tel. 414/328–7700 **A**1 9 10 **F**1 3 17 29 70 77 78 80 82 87 90 100 103 130 **S** Select Medical Corporation, Mechanicsburg, PA
Primary Contact: Richard Keddington, Chief Executive Officer
CMO: Matt Mathai, M.D., Medical Director
CHR: Chris Froh, Senior Coordinator Human Resources
CNO: Jane Cerra, Market Nurse Executive and Chief Nursing Officer
Web address: www.selectspecialtyhospitals.com/company/locations/milwaukee.aspx
Control: Corporation, Investor–owned, for–profit **Service:** Long–Term Acute Care hospital

> **Staffed Beds:** 34 **Admissions:** 415 **Census:** 31 **Outpatient Visits:** 0 **Births:** 0 **Total Expense ($000):** 17939 **Payroll Expense ($000):** 5975 **Personnel:** 110

⊠ **WHEATON FRANCISCAN HEALTHCARE – ST. FRANCIS (520078)**, 3237 South 16th Street, Zip 53215–4592; tel. 414/647–5000 **A**1 2 9 10 **F**3 9 13 15 18 20 22 24 26 28 29 30 31 34 35 38 40 45 46 47 48 49 50 54 56 57 64 65 68 72 74 75 76 77 78 79 80 81 82 84 85 86 87 91 92 93 94 96 98 100 101 102 103 104 107 108 110 111 114 115 118 119 120 121 122 123 129 130 131 132 144 145 146 147 148 **S** Wheaton Franciscan Healthcare, Wheaton, IL
Primary Contact: Coreen Dicus–Johnson, President
CFO: Aaron Bridgeland, Director Finance
CMO: Michelle Graham, M.D., Vice President Medical Affairs
CIO: Gregory Smith, Senior Vice President and Chief Information Officer
CHR: Robert Bauer, Vice President Human Resources
CNO: Marilyn Spenner, R.N., Vice President Patient Care Services
Web address: www.mywheaton.org/stfrancis
Control: Church–operated, Nongovernment, not–for profit **Service:** General Medical and Surgical

> **Staffed Beds:** 165 **Admissions:** 8234 **Census:** 110 **Outpatient Visits:** 164031 **Births:** 1073 **Total Expense ($000):** 167460 **Payroll Expense ($000):** 61585 **Personnel:** 922

⊠ **WHEATON FRANCISCAN HEALTHCARE – ST. JOSEPH'S (520136)**, 5000 West Chambers Street, Zip 53210–1650; tel. 414/447–2000 **A**1 2 3 5 9 10 **F**3 6 8 11 13 15 17 18 20 22 24 26 28 29 30 31 33 35 37 40 41 42 43 45 46 47 48 53 54 55 64 66 68 70 72 74 75 76 77 78 79 80 81 82 83 84 85 87 89 90 91 92 93 94 97 107 108 109 110 111 112 113 114 115 116 118 119 121 123 124 129 130 131 133 143 144 145 146 147 148 **P**6 **S** Wheaton Franciscan Healthcare, Wheaton, IL
Primary Contact: Debra K. Standridge, President
CFO: Michael Petitt, Director of Finance
CMO: Rita Hanson, M.D., Vice President Medical Affairs
CIO: Andrew Donovan, Regional Director Information Services
CHR: Christopher Morris, Vice President Human Resources
CNO: Sharon Baughman, R.N., Senior Vice President Patient Services and Chief Nursing Officer
Web address: www.mywheaton.org/stjoseph
Control: Church–operated, Nongovernment, not–for profit **Service:** General Medical and Surgical

> **Staffed Beds:** 316 **Admissions:** 10895 **Census:** 131 **Outpatient Visits:** 426530 **Births:** 2618 **Total Expense ($000):** 252787 **Payroll Expense ($000):** 94811 **Personnel:** 1507

MONROE—Green County

☐ **MONROE CLINIC (520028)**, 515 22nd Avenue, Zip 53566–1598; tel. 608/324–1000 **A**1 9 10 **F**3 5 6 8 9 11 13 15 17 18 20 22 26 28 29 30 31 32 34 35 36 37 38 40 43 44 45 46 49 50 55 56 57 59 62 63 65 68 70 74 75 76 77 79 80 81 84 85 86 87 90 93 97 99 100 101 102 103 104 107 108 110 111 112 115 117 119 126 129 130 131 132 135 142 144 145 146 147 148 **P**6
Primary Contact: Michael B. Sanders, President and Chief Executive Officer
COO: Julie Wilke, Vice President
CFO: Jim Nemeth, Chief Financial Officer
CMO: Mark Thompson, M.D., Chief Medical Officer
CIO: Carrie Blum, Chief Information Officer
CHR: Jane Monahan, Vice President Ministry and Human Resources
CNO: Paula Elmer, R.N., Vice President and Chief Nursing Officer
Web address: www.monroeclinic.org
Control: Other not–for–profit (including NFP Corporation) **Service:** General Medical and Surgical

> **Staffed Beds:** 50 **Admissions:** 2790 **Census:** 27 **Outpatient Visits:** 271423 **Births:** 446 **Total Expense ($000):** 159413 **Payroll Expense ($000):** 79302 **Personnel:** 1047

NEENAH—Winnebago County

☐ **CHILDREN'S HOSPITAL OF WISCONSIN–FOX VALLEY (523302)**, 130 Second Avenue, 3rd Floor South, Zip 54956–2883; tel. 920/969–7900 **A**1 9 10 **F**7 29 34 38 72 75 86 89 93 100 130 **P**6 **S** Children's Hospital and Health System, Milwaukee, WI
Primary Contact: Peggy N. Troy, President and Chief Executive Officer
COO: Tim Klunk, Executive Director
CMO: Paul Myers, M.D., Neonatologist and Chief Medical Officer
Web address: www.chw.org
Control: Other not–for–profit (including NFP Corporation) **Service:** Children's general

> **Staffed Beds:** 42 **Admissions:** 1731 **Census:** 20 **Outpatient Visits:** 9301 **Births:** 0 **Total Expense ($000):** 21918 **Payroll Expense ($000):** 8238 **Personnel:** 107

☐ △ **THEDA CLARK MEDICAL CENTER (520045)**, 130 Second Street, Zip 54956–2883, Mailing Address: P.O. Box 2021, Zip 54957–2021; tel. 920/729–3100 **A**1 2 7 9 10 **F**3 4 5 7 8 9 11 12 13 15 17 18 19 20 21 22 23 25 28 29 30 31 32 34 35 36 40 43 44 45 46 47 48 49 50 51 53 55 56 59 60 64 68 69 70 74 75 76 78 79 80 82 84 85 86 87 88 90 93 98 99 101 102 103 104 105 106 107 108 110 111 112 114 115 118 119 126 130 132 134 135 144 146 147 148 **S** ThedaCare, Inc., Appleton, WI
Primary Contact: Brian Burmeister, Senior Vice President
COO: MaryJeanne Schaffmeyer, Chief Operating Officer
CFO: Tim Olson, Senior Vice President Finance
CMO: Gregory L. Long, M.D., Chief Medical Officer
CIO: Keith Livingston, Senior Vice President and Chief Information Officer
CHR: Maureen Pistone, Senior Vice President Human Resources
Web address: www.thedacare.org
Control: Other not–for–profit (including NFP Corporation) **Service:** General Medical and Surgical

> **Staffed Beds:** 151 **Admissions:** 7319 **Census:** 78 **Outpatient Visits:** 89188 **Births:** 1185 **Total Expense ($000):** 153474 **Payroll Expense ($000):** 63582 **Personnel:** 841

WI

NEILLSVILLE—Clark County

★ **MEMORIAL MEDICAL CENTER – NEILLSVILLE (521323)**, 216 Sunset Place, Zip 54456–1799; tel. 715/743–3101, (Includes NEILLSVILLE MEMORIAL HOME) **A**9 10 18 **F**3 6 10 11 13 15 28 40 43 45 56 59 62 64 75 76 77 79 80 81 82 85 86 89 97 107 108 110 114 119 127 130 131 132 133 135 144 146 **P**2 6
Primary Contact: Ryan T. Neville, FACHE, President and Chief Executive Officer
CFO: Roger Sneath, Chief Financial Officer
CMO: Timothy Meyer, M.D., Chief of Staff
CIO: Derrick Longdo, Director Information Systems
CHR: Tamie Zarak, Director Human Resources
Web address: www.memorialmedcenter.org
Control: Other not–for–profit (including NFP Corporation) **Service:** General Medical and Surgical

Staffed Beds: 18 **Admissions:** 309 **Census:** 2 **Outpatient Visits:** 14840 **Births:** 29 **Total Expense ($000):** 23131 **Payroll Expense ($000):** 12308 **Personnel:** 194

NEW LONDON—Outagamie County

☐ **NEW LONDON FAMILY MEDICAL CENTER (521326)**, 1405 Mill Street, Zip 54961–2155, Mailing Address: P.O. Box 307, Zip 54961–0307; tel. 920/531–2000 **A**1 9 10 18 **F**3 7 8 11 13 15 28 29 34 40 43 45 47 56 57 59 64 65 66 68 71 75 76 79 80 81 82 83 85 86 87 89 90 93 96 97 107 108 110 111 115 119 124 127 131 132 133 135 141 146 148 **S** ThedaCare, Inc., Appleton, WI
Primary Contact: William Schmidt, President and Chief Executive Officer
CFO: Kerry Lee Blanke, Vice President Finance
CMO: Paul Hoell, M.D., President Medical Staff
Web address: www.thedacare.org
Control: Other not–for–profit (including NFP Corporation) **Service:** General Medical and Surgical

Staffed Beds: 25 **Admissions:** 924 **Census:** 12 **Outpatient Visits:** 30911 **Births:** 133 **Total Expense ($000):** 24576 **Payroll Expense ($000):** 11903 **Personnel:** 158

NEW RICHMOND—St. Croix County

★ **WESTFIELDS HOSPITAL (521345)**, 535 Hospital Road, Zip 54017–1449; tel. 715/243–2600 **A**9 10 18 **F**1 3 13 15 18 26 27 28 29 30 31 34 38 40 42 43 45 46 50 56 57 59 64 65 66 70 71 74 75 76 77 78 79 80 81 82 86 87 89 90 93 97 104 107 110 111 112 113 114 117 119 129 130 131 132 133 146 148 **P**5 **S** HealthPartners, Bloomington, MN
Primary Contact: Steven Massey, President and Chief Executive Officer
CFO: Jason J. Luhrs, Vice President Fiscal Services
CMO: David O. DeGear, M.D., Vice President Medical Affairs
CIO: Patrice P. Wolff, Director Information Services
CHR: Chad P. Engstrom, Director Human Resources
Web address: www.westfieldshospital.com
Control: Other not–for–profit (including NFP Corporation) **Service:** General Medical and Surgical

Staffed Beds: 25 **Admissions:** 776 **Census:** 7 **Outpatient Visits:** 45838 **Births:** 127 **Total Expense ($000):** 36630 **Payroll Expense ($000):** 13515 **Personnel:** 277

OCONOMOWOC—Waukesha County

⊞ **OCONOMOWOC MEMORIAL HOSPITAL (520062)**, 791 Summit Avenue, Zip 53066–3896; tel. 262/569–9400 **A**1 2 9 10 **F**3 11 13 15 18 20 22 28 29 30 31 35 37 40 45 46 47 48 49 64 74 75 76 78 79 80 81 82 84 85 87 89 92 93 107 108 110 111 114 115 118 119 120 121 126 130 132 135 146 147 148 **S** ProHealth Care, Inc., Waukesha, WI
Primary Contact: John R. Robertstad, FACHE, President
COO: Mary Jo O'Malley, R.N., Vice President Diagnostics and Support Services
CMO: Brian Lipman, M.D., Medical Director and Medical Staff Services
CIO: Christine Bessler, Vice President Information Services
CHR: Edward Malindzak, Chief Human Resources Officer
CNO: Catherine Rapp, R.N., Vice President Nursing
Web address: www.prohealthcare.org/locations/locations–v2–detail/?id=1123
Control: Other not–for–profit (including NFP Corporation) **Service:** General Medical and Surgical

Staffed Beds: 58 **Admissions:** 3131 **Census:** 27 **Outpatient Visits:** 68587 **Births:** 430 **Total Expense ($000):** 96689 **Payroll Expense ($000):** 22968 **Personnel:** 372

⊞ **ROGERS MEMORIAL HOSPITAL (524018)**, 34700 Valley Road, Zip 53066–4599; tel. 262/646–4411 **A**1 3 5 9 10 **F**3 5 29 30 34 35 38 42 57 58 59 75 86 87 98 99 100 101 102 103 104 105 106 130 132 134
Primary Contact: Paul A. Mueller, Chief Executive Officer
COO: Paul A. Mueller, Chief Operating Officer
CFO: Gerald A. Noll, Chief Financial Officer
CMO: Peter M. Lake, M.D., Chief Medical Officer
CIO: Wayne Mattson, Management Information Systems Specialist
CHR: Renee A. Patterson, Vice President Employment and Training Services
CNO: Teresa L. Schultz, R.N., Vice President of Patient Care
Web address: www.rogershospital.org **Service:** Psychiatric
Control: Other not–for–profit (including NFP Corporation)

Staffed Beds: 58 **Admissions:** 2183 **Census:** 40 **Outpatient Visits:** 44286 **Births:** 0 **Total Expense ($000):** 45516 **Payroll Expense ($000):** 25708 **Personnel:** 440

OCONTO—Oconto County

◇ **BELLIN HEALTH OCONTO HOSPITAL (521356)**, 820 Arbutus Avenue, Zip 54153–2004, Mailing Address: P.O. Box 357, Zip 54153–0357; tel. 920/835–1100 **A**9 10 18 21 **F**3 8 18 29 31 32 34 35 40 43 44 45 46 47 59 62 64 65 68 71 78 79 80 81 85 92 97 99 100 101 104 107 111 115 119 127 129 135 144 **P**8
Primary Contact: Laura Cormier, Director
Web address: www.bellin.org/facilities_amenities/oconto_hospital_medical_center/
Control: Other not–for–profit (including NFP Corporation) **Service:** General Medical and Surgical

Staffed Beds: 10 **Admissions:** 183 **Census:** 2 **Outpatient Visits:** 10949 **Births:** 0 **Total Expense ($000):** 10473 **Payroll Expense ($000):** 4091 **Personnel:** 58

OCONTO FALLS—Oconto County

★ **COMMUNITY MEMORIAL HOSPITAL (521310)**, 855 South Main Street, Zip 54154–1296; tel. 920/846–3444 **A**9 10 18 **F**3 8 11 15 28 29 34 40 41 43 45 56 57 64 75 77 80 81 85 86 87 89 90 93 96 97 107 108 110 111 114 119 127 132 133 144 145 146 147 **P**4 5 6
Primary Contact: Daniel DeGroot, Chief Executive Officer
CFO: Michele Miller–Campbell, Chief Financial Officer
CMO: Isaias Cupino, Chief of Staff
CIO: Jared Alfson, Chief Information Officer
CHR: Laura Majewski, Director Human Resources
CNO: Kay Baranczyk, R.N., Chief Nursing Officer
Web address: www.cmhospital.org
Control: Other not–for–profit (including NFP Corporation) **Service:** General Medical and Surgical

Staffed Beds: 10 **Admissions:** 709 **Census:** 8 **Outpatient Visits:** 31775 **Births:** 0 **Total Expense ($000):** 31566 **Payroll Expense ($000):** 14884 **Personnel:** 228

OSCEOLA—Polk County

OSCEOLA MEDICAL CENTER (521318), 2600 65th Avenue, Zip 54020–4370, Mailing Address: P.O. Box 218, Zip 54020–0218; tel. 715/294–2111 **A**9 10 18 **F**8 11 13 15 18 28 29 30 31 34 40 41 42 43 45 50 53 56 57 58 59 64 65 68 70 74 75 76 77 78 79 81 86 87 89 93 97 107 110 111 119 129 133 135 144 **P**6
Primary Contact: Tom G. Geskermann, Chief Executive Officer
CMO: Rene Milner, Chief Medical Officer
CIO: Shawn Kammerud, Manager Information Services
CHR: Margie Evenson, Manager Human Resources
Web address: www.osceolamedicalcenter.com
Control: Other not–for–profit (including NFP Corporation) **Service:** General Medical and Surgical

Staffed Beds: 18 **Admissions:** 509 **Census:** 4 **Outpatient Visits:** 15379 **Births:** 66 **Total Expense ($000):** 28723 **Payroll Expense ($000):** 10386 **Personnel:** 222

OSHKOSH—Winnebago County

⊞ **AURORA MEDICAL CENTER OF OSHKOSH (520198)**, 855 North Westhaven Drive, Zip 54904–7668; tel. 920/456–6000 **A**1 2 9 10 **F**3 8 11 12 13 15 17 18 20 22 26 29 30 31 32 34 35 37 40 43 47 49 53 54 56 64 68 70 71 74 75 76 78 79 80 81 82 85 86 87 89 92 93 94 107 108 109 110 111 113 114 115 118 119 120 121 122 123 129 130 131 132 135 145 146 147 148 **P**6 **S** Aurora Health Care, Milwaukee, WI
Primary Contact: Jeffrey Bard, President
CFO: Sandra Ewald, Vice President Finance
CMO: Bruce L. Van Cleave, M.D., Senior Vice President and Chief Medical Officer
CIO: Philip Loftus, Ph.D., Vice President and Chief Information Officer
CHR: Linda Mingus, Director Human Resources
CNO: Mary Beth Kingston, R.N., Executive Vice President and Chief Nursing Officer
Web address: www.aurorahealthcare.com
Control: Other not–for–profit (including NFP Corporation) **Service:** General Medical and Surgical

Staffed Beds: 61 **Admissions:** 3018 **Census:** 27 **Outpatient Visits:** 99756 **Births:** 640 **Total Expense ($000):** 77473 **Payroll Expense ($000):** 26461 **Personnel:** 486

⊠ △ **MERCY MEDICAL CENTER (520048)**, 500 South Oakwood Road, Zip 54904–7944; tel. 920/223–2000 **A**1 2 7 9 10 **F**3 4 5 11 13 15 16 17 18 20 22 26 28 29 30 31 34 35 38 40 43 44 46 47 48 49 50 51 53 56 57 59 64 65 68 70 75 76 78 80 81 82 86 87 88 89 90 92 93 96 98 103 104 107 108 110 111 112 114 117 119 120 121 122 123 126 129 130 131 132 134 144 146 147 148 **S** Ascension Health, Saint Louis, MO
Primary Contact: William Calhoun, President
CFO: Jeff Badger, Chief Financial Officer
CMO: Mark W. Kehrberg, M.D., Senior Vice President and Chief Medical Officer
CIO: Will Weider, Chief Information Officer
CHR: Vince Gallucci, Senior Vice President Human Resources
Web address: www.affinityhealth.org
Control: Church–operated, Nongovernment, not–for profit **Service:** General Medical and Surgical

> **Staffed Beds:** 122 **Admissions:** 5713 **Census:** 63 **Outpatient Visits:** 91046 **Births:** 663 **Total Expense ($000):** 102025 **Payroll Expense ($000):** 41075 **Personnel:** 539

OSSEO—Trempealeau County

☐ **MAYO CLINIC HEALTH SYSTEM – OAKRIDGE IN OSSEO (521302)**, 13025 Eighth Street, Zip 54758–7634, Mailing Address: P.O. Box 70, Zip 54758–0070; tel. 715/597–3121, (Total facility includes 35 beds in nursing home–type unit) **A**1 9 10 18 **F**3 7 10 15 18 28 29 30 32 34 35 40 43 44 50 54 56 57 59 63 64 65 68 75 77 80 84 85 86 87 90 93 97 107 110 115 125 128 130 132 133 135 144 146 148 **P**6 **S** Mayo Clinic, Rochester, MN
Primary Contact: Dean Eide, Vice President
Web address: www.mayoclinichealthsystem.org/locations/osseo
Control: Other not–for–profit (including NFP Corporation) **Service:** General Medical and Surgical

> **Staffed Beds:** 39 **Admissions:** 358 **Census:** 43 **Outpatient Visits:** 28428 **Births:** 0 **Total Expense ($000):** 19941 **Payroll Expense ($000):** 11013 **Personnel:** 172

PARK FALLS—Price County

★ **FLAMBEAU HOSPITAL (521325)**, 98 Sherry Avenue, Zip 54552–1467, Mailing Address: P.O. Box 310, Zip 54552–0310; tel. 715/762–2484 **A**9 10 18 **F**3 11 15 17 28 29 30 31 34 35 40 44 45 50 53 56 57 59 62 63 64 65 68 69 70 75 77 79 80 81 82 84 85 86 87 89 90 93 96 97 107 108 110 119 130 131 132 133 143 144 146 148 **S** Ascension Health, Saint Louis, MO
Primary Contact: David A. Grundstrom, Chief Administrative Officer
CFO: James R. Braun, Chief Financial Officer
CMO: Yusuf Kasirye, M.D., Chief of Staff
CHR: Paul Rybak, Director Human Resources
CNO: Elizabeth Schreiber, R.N., Director Patient Care Services
Web address: www.flambeauhospital.org
Control: Other not–for–profit (including NFP Corporation) **Service:** General Medical and Surgical

> **Staffed Beds:** 25 **Admissions:** 563 **Census:** 4 **Outpatient Visits:** 21225 **Births:** 0 **Total Expense ($000):** 14059 **Payroll Expense ($000):** 6136 **Personnel:** 172

PEWAUKEE—Waukesha County

⊠ **LIFECARE HOSPITALS OF WISCONSIN (522007)**, 2400 Golf Road, Zip 53072–5590; tel. 262/524–2600 **A**1 9 10 **F**1 3 29 77 86 90 107 148 **P**2 5 **S** LifeCare Management Services, Plano, TX
Primary Contact: Dennis Mattes, Chief Executive Officer
CMO: John Daniels, M.D., Medical Director
CHR: Jill Schuetz, Director Human Resources
CNO: Cathy Batzner, MSN, Chief Nursing Officer
Web address: www.lifecare–hospitals.com
Control: Corporation, Investor–owned, for–profit **Service:** Long–Term Acute Care hospital

> **Staffed Beds:** 26 **Admissions:** 321 **Census:** 26 **Outpatient Visits:** 0 **Births:** 0 **Total Expense ($000):** 20606 **Payroll Expense ($000):** 8485 **Personnel:** 104

PLATTEVILLE—Grant County

⊠ **SOUTHWEST HEALTH CENTER (521354)**, 1400 Eastside Road, Zip 53818–9800; tel. 608/348–2331, (Includes SOUTHWEST HEALTH CENTER NURSING HOME, 808 South Washington Street, Cuba City, Zip 53807; tel. 608/744–2161), (Total facility includes 84 beds in nursing home–type unit) **A**1 9 10 18 **F**2 3 6 8 13 15 28 29 31 34 40 43 45 46 47 48 49 50 56 57 59 64 74 75 76 77 79 81 82 83 84 85 86 87 93 96 97 98 100 101 102 103 104 105 106 107 110 111 112 115 117 119 128 129 130 132 133 143 144 146 148
Primary Contact: Dan D. Rohrbach, President and Chief Executive Officer
CFO: Matthew Streeter, Chief Financial Officer
CMO: Andrew Klann, D.O., Chief of Staff
CIO: Todd Lull, Director Information Technology
CHR: Holly Beehn, Director Human Resources
CNO: Suzi Okey, Director of Nursing
Web address: www.southwesthealth.org
Control: Other not–for–profit (including NFP Corporation) **Service:** General Medical and Surgical

> **Staffed Beds:** 119 **Admissions:** 913 **Census:** 86 **Outpatient Visits:** 38494 **Births:** 116 **Total Expense ($000):** 25343 **Payroll Expense ($000):** 8645 **Personnel:** 185

PLEASANT PRAIRIE—Kenosha County

★ **UNITED HOSPITAL SYSTEM, ST. CATHERINE'S MEDICAL CENTER CAMPUS**, 9555 76th Street, Zip 53158–1984; tel. 262/656–2011, (Nonreporting) **A**2 9 **S** Wheaton Franciscan Healthcare, Wheaton, IL
Primary Contact: Richard O. Schmidt, Jr., President and Chief Executive Officer
Web address: www.uhsi.org
Control: Other not–for–profit (including NFP Corporation) **Service:** General Medical and Surgical

> **Staffed Beds:** 202

PORTAGE—Columbia County

☐ **DIVINE SAVIOR HEALTHCARE (520041)**, 2817 New Pinery Road, Zip 53901–9240, Mailing Address: P.O. Box 387, Zip 53901–0387; tel. 608/742–4131, (Total facility includes 123 beds in nursing home–type unit) **A**1 9 10 **F**3 4 7 11 12 13 15 28 30 31 34 35 36 40 43 44 45 50 54 55 57 59 60 62 64 68 69 70 74 75 76 77 78 79 80 81 82 85 86 87 89 90 91 92 93 94 96 97 107 108 110 111 115 117 118 119 128 129 130 131 132 133 143 144 145 146 147 148 **P**6
Primary Contact: Michael Decker, President and Chief Executive Officer
CFO: Marlin Pete Nelson, Vice President Fiscal Services
CMO: Elizabeth Strabel, M.D., Chief Medical Staff
CHR: Carol J. Bank, Vice President Human Resources
Web address: www.dshealthcare.com
Control: Church–operated, Nongovernment, not–for profit **Service:** General Medical and Surgical

> **Staffed Beds:** 133 **Admissions:** 2197 **Census:** 112 **Outpatient Visits:** 146346 **Births:** 276 **Total Expense ($000):** 62668 **Payroll Expense ($000):** 34460 **Personnel:** 547

PRAIRIE DU CHIEN—Crawford County

⊠ **PRAIRIE DU CHIEN MEMORIAL HOSPITAL (521330)**, 705 East Taylor Street, Zip 53821–2196; tel. 608/357–2000 **A**1 9 10 18 **F**10 11 13 15 17 28 29 30 34 35 36 40 41 45 48 50 53 56 57 59 62 63 64 65 68 69 70 75 76 77 79 80 81 82 83 84 86 87 93 107 108 110 115 119 129 130 131 132 133 135 142 144 146 147 148
Primary Contact: William P. Sexton, Chief Executive Officer
CFO: Dave Breitbach, Chief Financial Officer
CMO: Steven Bush, Chief Medical Officer
CIO: John Daane, Information Systems Officer
CHR: Gabriel Oosthuysen, Director Human Resources
Web address: www.pdcmemorialhospital.org
Control: Other not–for–profit (including NFP Corporation) **Service:** General Medical and Surgical

> **Staffed Beds:** 13 **Admissions:** 1055 **Census:** 11 **Outpatient Visits:** 10078 **Births:** 103 **Total Expense ($000):** 32541 **Payroll Expense ($000):** 15243 **Personnel:** 251

WI

Hospital, Medicare Provider Number, Address, Telephone, Approval, Facility, and Physician Codes, Health Care System

★ American Hospital Association (AHA) membership
☐ The Joint Commission accreditation   ◇ DNV Healthcare Inc. accreditation
◯ Healthcare Facilities Accreditation Program
△ Commission on Accreditation of Rehabilitation Facilities (CARF) accreditation

PRAIRIE DU SAC—Sauk County

★ ○ **SAUK PRAIRIE HEALTHCARE (520095)**, 260 26th Street,
Zip 53578–1599; tel. 608/643–3311 **A**9 10 11 **F**3 11 13 15 28 29 32 34 35
36 40 43 45 47 48 53 56 57 58 59 69 75 76 77 79 80 81 83 84 85 86 90
93 96 97 107 108 111 115 118 119 124 127 129 130 131 132 133 135
144 146 148 **P**6
Primary Contact: Larry Schroeder, Chief Executive Officer
CFO: Carol May, Chief Financial Officer, Vice President Finance and Operations
CMO: John McAuliffe, M.D., Medical Director
CIO: Marybeth Bay, Director Information Technology
CHR: Robbi E. Bos, Vice President Human Resources
CNO: Margaret Sheeks, R.N., Vice President Patient Services
Web address: www.saukprairiehealthcare.org/
Control: Other not–for–profit (including NFP Corporation) **Service:** General
Medical and Surgical

Staffed Beds: 36 **Admissions:** 1697 **Census:** 11 **Outpatient Visits:** 110279
Births: 258 **Total Expense ($000):** 66762 **Payroll Expense ($000):** 31118
Personnel: 404

RACINE—Racine County

⊞ △ **WHEATON FRANCISCAN HEALTHCARE – ALL SAINTS (520096)**, 3801
Spring Street, Zip 53405–1690; tel. 262/687–4011, (Total facility includes 50
beds in nursing home–type unit) **A**1 2 7 9 10 **F**3 4 5 6 13 15 17 18 20 22 24
26 28 29 30 31 33 34 35 38 40 43 44 45 46 48 49 50 51 53 55 56 57 58
59 64 65 68 70 72 74 75 76 77 78 79 80 81 85 86 87 89 90 91 92 93 96
97 98 99 100 101 102 103 104 105 107 108 110 111 112 115 116 118
119 120 121 123 124 126 128 129 130 131 132 134 135 146 147 148 **P**6
S Wheaton Franciscan Healthcare, Wheaton, IL
Primary Contact: Susan Boland, R.N., MSN, President and Chief Executive Officer
CFO: Jeanne Gramza, Director Finance
CMO: Jerry Hardacre, M.D., Chief of Staff
CIO: Joanne Bisterfeldt, Chief Information Officer
CHR: Mary Jo Wodicka, Vice President Human Resources
CNO: Mary Elizabeth Ouimet, MSN, Senior Vice President and Chief Nursing
Officer
Web address: www.allsaintshealth.com
Control: Church–operated, Nongovernment, not–for profit **Service:** General
Medical and Surgical

Staffed Beds: 405 **Admissions:** 15381 **Census:** 256 **Outpatient Visits:**
420421 **Births:** 1648 **Total Expense ($000):** 331718 **Payroll Expense**
($000): 128088 **Personnel:** 2470

REEDSBURG—Sauk County

⊞ **REEDSBURG AREA MEDICAL CENTER (521351)**, 2000 North Dewey Street,
Zip 53959–1097; tel. 608/524–6487 **A**1 9 10 18 **F**3 8 11 13 15 18 28 30 31
34 35 40 41 43 45 48 50 53 54 57 59 64 66 75 76 77 78 79 80 81 82 85
86 87 89 93 97 107 110 111 114 115 129 130 131 132 133 135 144 146
147 148
Primary Contact: Robert Van Meeteren, President and Chief Executive Officer
COO: Dale Turner, Chief Operating Officer
CFO: Barry Borchert, Vice President Finance
CNO: Dena Jarog, R.N., Vice President Patient Care
Web address: www.ramchealth.com
Control: Other not–for–profit (including NFP Corporation) **Service:** General
Medical and Surgical

Staffed Beds: 25 **Admissions:** 1357 **Census:** 14 **Outpatient Visits:** 55084
Births: 279 **Total Expense ($000):** 43450 **Payroll Expense ($000):** 18869
Personnel: 363

RHINELANDER—Oneida County

⊞ **MINISTRY SAINT MARY'S HOSPITALS (520019)**, 2251 North Shore Drive,
Zip 54501–6710; tel. 715/361–2000, (Includes ST. MARY'S HOSPITAL, 1044
Kabel Avenue, Zip 54501; tel. 715/369–6600) **A**1 9 10 20 **F**3 4 5 13 15 18 28
29 30 31 34 35 40 43 44 45 49 50 54 57 59 64 65 68 69 74 75 76 77 78
79 80 81 82 84 85 86 87 89 91 92 93 94 96 98 99 100 101 103 104 107
108 109 110 111 112 115 116 117 119 130 131 132 144 146 148
S Ascension Health, Saint Louis, MO
Primary Contact: Monica Hilt, President
COO: Laurie Oungst, Vice President and Chief Operating Officer
CFO: Cathy Bukowski, Regional Chief Financial Officer
CMO: Dean Pollnow, M.D., President Medical Staff
CIO: Howard Dobizl, Director Information Services for the Northern Region
CHR: Michelle Cornelius, Director Human Resources for the Northern Region
CNO: Ann Zenk, Vice President Patient Care Services
Web address: www.ministryhealth.org
Control: Church–operated, Nongovernment, not–for profit **Service:** General
Medical and Surgical

Staffed Beds: 51 **Admissions:** 3149 **Census:** 30 **Outpatient Visits:** 87529
Births: 314 **Total Expense ($000):** 107852 **Payroll Expense ($000):** 62774
Personnel: 530

RICE LAKE—Barron County

⊞ **LAKEVIEW MEDICAL CENTER (520011)**, 1700 West Stout Street,
Zip 54868–5000; tel. 715/234–1515 **A**1 9 10 20 **F**7 11 13 15 18 28 29 34
36 40 43 45 51 53 54 56 57 59 60 62 63 64 65 68 69 70 75 76 77 79 80
81 82 83 84 85 86 87 89 93 107 111 114 119 120 124 129 130 132 135
146 147 **P**8
Primary Contact: Edward H. Wolf, President and Chief Executive Officer
COO: Cindy Arts–Strenke, R.N., Chief Operating Officer and Chief Nursing Officer
CFO: Jacqueline Klein, Chief Financial Officer
CMO: John L. Olson, M.D., Medical Director
CIO: Brad Gerrits, Director Information Systems
CHR: Kathy Mitchell, Director Human Resources
Web address: www.lakeviewmedical.com
Control: Other not–for–profit (including NFP Corporation) **Service:** General
Medical and Surgical

Staffed Beds: 40 **Admissions:** 2194 **Census:** 18 **Outpatient Visits:** 152945
Births: 468 **Total Expense ($000):** 57989 **Payroll Expense ($000):** 21917
Personnel: 391

RICHLAND CENTER—Richland County

☐ **RICHLAND HOSPITAL (521341)**, 333 East Second Street, Zip 53581–1914;
tel. 608/647–6321 **A**1 9 10 18 **F**2 8 12 13 15 18 28 30 31 34 35 40 43 45
46 50 56 57 58 59 64 65 66 70 74 76 78 79 80 81 86 89 93 97 107 110
112 115 119 127 129 130 131 132 133 143 144 146 148
Primary Contact: Michael Delfs, Chief Executive Officer
CFO: Karen Traynor, Chief Financial Officer
CMO: Kay M. Balink, M.D., Chief of Staff
CIO: Jerry Cooper, Manager Data Processing
CHR: Rhonda Sutton, Director Human Resources
Web address: www.richlandhospital.com
Control: Other not–for–profit (including NFP Corporation) **Service:** General
Medical and Surgical

Staffed Beds: 25 **Admissions:** 1232 **Census:** 11 **Outpatient Visits:** 37775
Births: 176 **Total Expense ($000):** 32804 **Payroll Expense ($000):** 14487
Personnel: 245

RIPON—Fond Du Lac County

☐ **RIPON MEDICAL CENTER (521321)**, 933 Newbury Street, Zip 54971–1798,
Mailing Address: P.O. Box 390, Zip 54971–0390; tel. 920/748–3101 **A**1 9 10
18 **F**3 8 11 15 17 26 28 29 30 32 34 35 37 40 43 45 46 49 53 56 57 59 64
68 69 70 74 75 77 78 79 80 81 85 86 87 88 89 93 96 97 100 104 107 108
110 114 118 119 130 131 132 133 135 144 146 148 **P**6
Primary Contact: Katherine Vergos, Chief Operating Officer
COO: Katherine Vergos, Chief Operating Officer
CFO: Bonnie Schmitz, Chief Financial Officer
CIO: Nancy Birschbach, Vice President and Chief Information Officer
CHR: Sue Edminster, Vice President Human Resources
Web address: www.agnesian.com
Control: Other not–for–profit (including NFP Corporation) **Service:** General
Medical and Surgical

Staffed Beds: 25 **Admissions:** 533 **Census:** 5 **Outpatient Visits:** 24895
Births: 0 **Total Expense ($000):** 20281 **Payroll Expense ($000):** 8821
Personnel: 135

RIVER FALLS—St. Croix County

⊞ **RIVER FALLS AREA HOSPITAL (521349)**, 1629 East Division Street,
Zip 54022–1571; tel. 715/425–6155 **A**1 2 9 10 18 **F**3 13 14 15 28 29 30 31
34 35 40 41 43 44 45 50 53 64 68 76 77 78 79 80 81 82 84 86 87 89 90
91 93 94 107 112 114 119 126 129 130 131 133 146 147 148 **S** Allina
Health, Minneapolis, MN
Primary Contact: David R. Miller, President
COO: William Frommelt, Director Operations and Finance
CFO: William Frommelt, Director Operations and Finance
CHR: Kristen Novak, Manager Human Resources
Web address: www.allina.com
Control: Other not–for–profit (including NFP Corporation) **Service:** General
Medical and Surgical

Staffed Beds: 8 **Admissions:** 953 **Census:** 8 **Outpatient Visits:** 20580
Births: 158 **Total Expense ($000):** 34093 **Payroll Expense ($000):** 12450
Personnel: 181

WI

SHAWANO—Shawano County

⌧ **SHAWANO MEDICAL CENTER (521346)**, 309 North Bartlette Street, Zip 54166–2127; tel. 715/526–2111 **A1** 9 10 18 **F3** 11 13 18 28 29 31 34 35 40 45 46 50 53 56 57 59 64 65 68 74 75 76 77 79 80 81 82 84 85 86 87 90 93 94 97 102 107 108 111 114 119 129 131 132 133 135 143 145 146 148 **P5 S** ThedaCare, Inc., Appleton, WI
Primary Contact: Dorothy Erdmann, Chief Executive Officer
CFO: Kerry Lee Blanke, Chief Financial Officer
CMO: Mindy Frimodig, D.O., President Medical Staff ThedaCare Physicians Shawano
CIO: Jennifer Quinn, Quality and Safety Coordinator
CNO: Patricia A. Angelucci, MS, Director Patient Care Services
Web address: www.shawanomed.org
Control: Other not–for–profit (including NFP Corporation) **Service:** General Medical and Surgical

Staffed Beds: 25 **Admissions:** 1707 **Census:** 14 **Outpatient Visits:** 36092 **Births:** 306 **Total Expense ($000):** 38506 **Payroll Expense ($000):** 16473 **Personnel:** 215

SHEBOYGAN—Sheboygan County

⌧ **AURORA SHEBOYGAN MEMORIAL MEDICAL CENTER (520035)**, 2629 North Seventh Street, Zip 53083–4998; tel. 920/451–5000 **A1** 2 9 10 **F3** 4 8 13 17 18 20 22 26 28 29 30 31 32 34 35 36 40 41 43 44 45 49 50 53 54 56 57 59 64 65 68 70 72 74 75 76 78 79 80 81 82 85 86 87 89 93 94 96 98 99 100 102 103 107 108 111 112 114 115 118 119 120 121 123 129 130 131 132 135 146 147 148 **P6 S** Aurora Health Care, Milwaukee, WI
Primary Contact: David Graebner, President
CFO: Pamela Ott, Vice President Finance
CMO: Andrea Gavin, M.D., Chief Medical officer
CIO: Steve Serketich, Manager Information Services
CHR: Stacie A. Schneider, Director Human Resources
CNO: Lori Knitt, Chief Nursing Officer
Web address: www.aurorahealthcare.org
Control: Other not–for–profit (including NFP Corporation) **Service:** General Medical and Surgical

Staffed Beds: 136 **Admissions:** 5486 **Census:** 54 **Outpatient Visits:** 87306 **Births:** 879 **Total Expense ($000):** 107569 **Payroll Expense ($000):** 32748 **Personnel:** 558

⌧ **ST. NICHOLAS HOSPITAL (520044)**, 3100 Superior Avenue, Zip 53081–1948; tel. 920/459–8300 **A1** 2 9 10 **F3** 11 13 15 17 18 20 22 28 29 30 31 34 35 36 38 40 43 44 48 49 50 53 57 59 60 62 63 64 65 68 70 71 74 75 76 79 80 81 84 86 87 89 90 93 96 107 108 110 111 115 116 117 118 119 120 121 123 129 130 132 146 **P2 5 S** Hospital Sisters Health System, Springfield, IL
Primary Contact: Andrew Bagnall, President and Chief Executive Officer
CFO: Greg Simia, Chief Financial Officer
CMO: Jeffrey Herold, M.D., President Medical Staff
CIO: Shane Miller, Chief Information Officer
CHR: Christine Jensema, Chief People Officer
CNO: Mary Martin, MSN, Chief Nursing Officer
Web address: www.stnicholashospital.org
Control: Church–operated, Nongovernment, not–for profit **Service:** General Medical and Surgical

Staffed Beds: 53 **Admissions:** 3112 **Census:** 27 **Outpatient Visits:** 75515 **Births:** 313 **Total Expense ($000):** 64410 **Payroll Expense ($000):** 20005 **Personnel:** 310

SHELL LAKE—Washburn County

☐ **INDIANHEAD MEDICAL CENTER (521342)**, 113 Fourth Avenue, Zip 54871–4457, Mailing Address: P.O. Box 300, Zip 54871–0300; tel. 715/468–7833 **A1** 9 10 18 **F3** 15 17 18 28 31 34 35 40 43 45 47 48 50 56 57 59 62 64 65 66 70 76 80 81 83 84 85 86 89 93 96 97 107 114 119 127 130 133 143 144 148 **P5**
Primary Contact: Paul Naglosky, Administrator
CFO: Michael Elliott, Controller
CMO: Allan Haesemeyer, M.D., Chief of Staff
CHR: Gwen Nielsen, Manager Human Resources
Web address: www.indianheadmedicalcenter.com
Control: Corporation, Investor–owned, for–profit **Service:** General Medical and Surgical

Staffed Beds: 25 **Admissions:** 339 **Census:** 4 **Outpatient Visits:** 9374 **Births:** 6 **Total Expense ($000):** 6288 **Payroll Expense ($000):** 2730 **Personnel:** 65

SPARTA—Monroe County

MAYO CLINIC HEALTH SYSTEM – FRANCISCAN HEALTHCARE IN SPARTA (521305), 310 West Main Street, Zip 54656–2171; tel. 608/269–2132 **A9** 10 18 **F5** 11 15 28 29 30 34 35 40 42 43 53 56 57 59 64 65 66 68 75 77 80 81 86 87 93 97 107 108 119 127 130 132 133 143 144 146 **P2 S** Mayo Clinic, Rochester, MN
Primary Contact: Kimberly Hawthorne, Administrator
COO: Joseph J. Kruse, Chief Administrative Officer
CFO: Tom Tiggelaar, Vice President Finance ad Chief Financial Officer
CMO: Tracy Warsing, M.D., Site Leader Chief of Staff
CHR: Lisa Radtke, Regional Administrator Human Resources
CNO: Diane Holmay, R.N., Chief Nursing Officer
Web address: www.mayohealthsystem.com
Control: Church–operated, Nongovernment, not–for profit **Service:** General Medical and Surgical

Staffed Beds: 13 **Admissions:** 381 **Census:** 9 **Outpatient Visits:** 23337 **Births:** 0 **Total Expense ($000):** 13644 **Payroll Expense ($000):** 7560 **Personnel:** 114

SPOONER—Washburn County

★ **SPOONER HEALTH SYSTEM (521332)**, 819 Ash Street, Zip 54801–1299; tel. 715/635–2111 **A9** 10 18 **F3** 13 15 17 29 31 34 35 40 43 45 50 56 57 59 62 63 64 65 68 70 76 78 80 81 85 86 87 89 90 93 107 111 115 119 130 132 133 135 146 148 **S** HealthTech Management Services, Brentwood, TN
Primary Contact: Michael Schafer, Chief Executive Officer and Administrator
CFO: Rebecca Busch, Chief Financial Officer
CHR: Cindy Rouzer, Director Human Resources
Web address: www.spoonerhealthsystem.com
Control: Other not–for–profit (including NFP Corporation) **Service:** General Medical and Surgical

Staffed Beds: 25 **Admissions:** 624 **Census:** 8 **Outpatient Visits:** 21250 **Births:** 57 **Total Expense ($000):** 14660 **Payroll Expense ($000):** 6691 **Personnel:** 107

ST. CROIX FALLS—Polk County

ST. CROIX REGIONAL MEDICAL CENTER (521337), 235 State Street, Zip 54024–4117; tel. 715/483–3261 **A9** 10 18 **F3** 6 8 11 13 15 18 26 28 29 31 32 34 35 36 40 41 43 45 48 50 51 55 56 57 64 65 66 70 74 75 76 77 78 79 80 81 82 83 85 86 87 92 93 94 97 99 100 101 104 107 108 110 111 115 116 117 118 119 127 129 131 132 133 135 144 146 148 **P5** 6
Primary Contact: Dave Dobosenski, Chief Executive Officer
CFO: John Tremble, Chief Financial Officer
CMO: Jeffrey Hall, DPM, Chief Medical Officer
CIO: Brent McCurdy, Director Management Information
CHR: Lee Ann Vitalis, Executive Director Human Resources
CNO: Laura J. Jensen, Vice President Patient Care Services
Web address: www.scrmc.org
Control: Other not–for–profit (including NFP Corporation) **Service:** General Medical and Surgical

Staffed Beds: 25 **Admissions:** 1681 **Census:** 15 **Outpatient Visits:** 183252 **Births:** 275 **Total Expense ($000):** 59114 **Payroll Expense ($000):** 22979 **Personnel:** 402

STANLEY—Chippewa County

★ **MINISTRY OUR LADY OF VICTORY HOSPITAL (521311)**, 1120 Pine Street, Zip 54768–1297; tel. 715/644–5571 **A9** 10 18 **F3** 15 28 29 30 34 35 40 41 45 50 59 65 75 77 80 81 84 85 86 87 89 90 93 94 96 97 107 109 110 114 127 130 131 133 144 146 148 **P6 S** Ascension Health, Saint Louis, MO
Primary Contact: Vanessa Freitag, President
CFO: Terri Lewandowski, Director Financial Services
Web address: www.ministryhealth.org
Control: Other not–for–profit (including NFP Corporation) **Service:** General Medical and Surgical

Staffed Beds: 12 **Admissions:** 357 **Census:** 6 **Outpatient Visits:** 30300 **Births:** 0 **Total Expense ($000):** 17705 **Payroll Expense ($000):** 8305 **Personnel:** 101

WI

Hospital, Medicare Provider Number, Address, Telephone, Approval, Facility, and Physician Codes, Health Care System

★ American Hospital Association (AHA) membership
☐ The Joint Commission accreditation   ◇ DNV Healthcare Inc. accreditation
○ Healthcare Facilities Accreditation Program
△ Commission on Accreditation of Rehabilitation Facilities (CARF) accreditation

STEVENS POINT—Portage County

✠ **MINISTRY SAINT MICHAEL'S HOSPITAL (520002)**, 900 Illinois Avenue, Zip 54481–3196; tel. 715/346–5000 **A**1 9 10 19 **F**3 4 5 12 13 15 17 20 28 29 30 34 35 40 43 44 45 47 48 50 51 56 57 59 64 65 68 70 72 74 75 76 77 79 80 81 82 84 85 86 87 88 89 93 94 98 99 100 101 102 103 104 105 106 107 108 110 111 115 116 118 119 120 121 129 130 131 132 135 144 146 147 148 **S** Ascension Health, Saint Louis, MO
Primary Contact: Jeffrey L. Martin, President
CFO: William J. Hinner, Vice President Financial Analysis and Planning
CIO: Will Weider, Chief Information Officer
CHR: Cheryl F. Zima, Vice President Human Resources
Web address: www.ministryhealth.org/SMH/home.nws
Control: Church–operated, Nongovernment, not–for profit **Service:** General Medical and Surgical

Staffed Beds: 50 Admissions: 4841 Census: 45 Outpatient Visits: 305435 Births: 473 Total Expense ($000): 154808 Payroll Expense ($000): 89390 Personnel: 623

SAINT MICHAEL'S HOSPITAL See Ministry Saint Michael's Hospital

STOUGHTON—Dane County

☐ **STOUGHTON HOSPITAL ASSOCIATION (521343)**, 900 Ridge Street, Zip 53589–1864; tel. 608/873–6611 **A**1 9 10 18 **F**3 4 6 8 15 28 29 30 34 35 36 40 41 42 45 53 54 56 57 59 62 64 65 68 70 75 77 79 80 81 85 86 89 90 91 92 93 96 98 100 103 107 110 115 129 130 131 132 133 135 144 146 147 148
Primary Contact: Terrence Brenny, President and Chief Executive Officer
CFO: Karen Myers, Vice President Financial Services
CMO: Dean Kresge, M.D., Chief of Staff
CIO: Karen Myers, Vice President Financial Services
CHR: Christopher Schmitz, Director Human Resources
Web address: www.stoughtonhospital.com
Control: Other not–for–profit (including NFP Corporation) **Service:** General Medical and Surgical

Staffed Beds: 32 Admissions: 984 Census: 16 Outpatient Visits: 51560 Births: 0 Total Expense ($000): 35489 Payroll Expense ($000): 15509 Personnel: 342

STURGEON BAY—Door County

DOOR COUNTY MEMORIAL HOSPITAL See Ministry Door County Medical Center

★ **MINISTRY DOOR COUNTY MEDICAL CENTER (521358)**, 323 South 18th Avenue, Zip 54235–1495; tel. 920/743–5566, (Total facility includes 30 beds in nursing home–type unit) **A**9 10 18 **F**2 3 11 13 15 17 28 29 30 31 32 34 35 36 40 43 55 56 57 59 61 64 65 66 68 70 75 76 77 78 79 80 81 82 84 85 86 87 89 90 93 107 108 110 111 114 117 118 119 127 128 129 130 132 133 135 144 145 147 148 **P**6 **S** Ascension Health, Saint Louis, MO
Primary Contact: Gerald M. Worrick, President and Chief Executive Officer
CFO: Brian Stephens, Chief Financial Officer
CIO: Mary Lopas, Chief Information Officer
CHR: Kelli Bowling, Chief Culture Officer
CNO: Jody Boes, Vice President Patient Care Services
Web address: www.ministryhealth.org
Control: Church–operated, Nongovernment, not–for profit **Service:** General Medical and Surgical

Staffed Beds: 55 Admissions: 1538 Census: 35 Outpatient Visits: 89498 Births: 129 Total Expense ($000): 63283 Payroll Expense ($000): 33463 Personnel: 466

SUMMIT—Waukesha County

✠ **AURORA MEDICAL CENTER SUMMIT (520206)**, 36500 Aurora Drive, Zip 53066–4899; tel. 262/434–1000 **A**1 2 9 10 **F**3 8 11 12 13 15 17 18 20 22 24 26 28 29 30 31 32 34 35 36 37 40 41 43 44 45 46 47 48 49 50 53 54 55 59 64 68 70 72 74 75 76 79 80 81 82 85 86 87 89 90 93 94 96 107 108 110 111 114 115 116 117 118 119 120 121 123 124 126 129 130 131 132 135 146 147 148 **P**6 **S** Aurora Health Care, Milwaukee, WI
Primary Contact: Michael Bergman, President
Web address: www.aurorahealthcare.org
Control: Other not–for–profit (including NFP Corporation) **Service:** General Medical and Surgical

Staffed Beds: 85 Admissions: 2827 Census: 28 Outpatient Visits: 76842 Births: 441 Total Expense ($000): 90488 Payroll Expense ($000): 28310 Personnel: 520

SUPERIOR—Douglas County

✠ **ESSENTIA HEALTH ST. MARY'S HOSPITAL OF SUPERIOR (521329)**, 3500 Tower Avenue, Zip 54880–5395; tel. 715/817–7000 **A**1 9 10 18 **F**3 11 15 28 29 30 40 41 42 56 59 64 65 75 77 78 80 81 82 86 87 90 93 96 97 107 110 119 130 133 135 142 146 148 **S** Essentia Health, Duluth, MN
Primary Contact: Terry Jacobson, Administrator and Chief Executive Officer
Web address: www.essentiahealth.org/EssentiaHealthStMarysHospitalofSuperiorFoundation/overview.aspx
Control: Other not–for–profit (including NFP Corporation) **Service:** General Medical and Surgical

Staffed Beds: 25 Admissions: 467 Census: 9 Outpatient Visits: 48444 Births: 0 Total Expense ($000): 29227 Payroll Expense ($000): 15676 Personnel: 201

TOMAH—Monroe County

✠ **TOMAH MEMORIAL HOSPITAL (521320)**, 321 Butts Avenue, Zip 54660–1412; tel. 608/372–2181 **A**1 9 10 18 **F**3 11 12 13 18 28 30 31 34 35 40 43 50 56 57 59 63 64 68 76 77 79 80 81 82 84 85 86 87 89 90 93 107 111 115 119 129 130 132 133 135 144 148 **P**5 **S** HealthTech Management Services, Brentwood, TN
Primary Contact: Philip J. Stuart, Administrator and Chief Executive Officer
CFO: Joseph Zeps, Vice President Finance
CIO: LaVonne Smith, Director Health Information Technology
CHR: Brenda Reinert, Director Human Resources
CNO: Tracy Myhrz, Chief Nursing Officer
Web address: www.tomahhospital.org
Control: Other not–for–profit (including NFP Corporation) **Service:** General Medical and Surgical

Staffed Beds: 25 Admissions: 1027 Census: 8 Outpatient Visits: 29500 Births: 318 Total Expense ($000): 32056 Payroll Expense ($000): 14798 Personnel: 230

✠ **TOMAH VETERANS AFFAIRS MEDICAL CENTER**, 500 East Veterans Street, Zip 54660–3105; tel. 608/372–3971, (Nonreporting) **A**1 **S** Department of Veterans Affairs, Washington, DC
Primary Contact: Mario DeSanctis, FACHE, Director
CFO: Jane Mashak–Ekern, Fiscal Officer
CMO: David Houlihan, M.D., Chief of Staff
CIO: Edward Hensel, Chief Information Officer
CHR: David Dechant, Chief Human Resources Officer
Web address: www.tomah.va.gov
Control: Veterans Affairs, Government, federal **Service:** General Medical and Surgical

Staffed Beds: 71

TOMAHAWK—Lincoln County

★ **MINISTRY SACRED HEART HOSPITAL (521313)**, 401 West Mohawk Drive, Zip 54487–2274; tel. 715/453–7700 **A**9 10 18 **F**3 5 15 28 29 30 34 35 40 44 45 49 50 57 59 65 68 75 77 80 81 84 86 87 89 91 92 93 96 99 100 101 104 107 109 115 119 130 131 133 146 **S** Ascension Health, Saint Louis, MO
Primary Contact: Monica Hilt, President
Web address: www.ministryhealth.org
Control: Church–operated, Nongovernment, not–for profit **Service:** General Medical and Surgical

Staffed Beds: 6 Admissions: 348 Census: 3 Outpatient Visits: 9859 Births: 0 Total Expense ($000): 11995 Payroll Expense ($000): 7875 Personnel: 89

TWO RIVERS—Manitowoc County

✠ **AURORA MEDICAL CENTER – MANITOWOC COUNTY (520034)**, 5000 Memorial Drive, Zip 54241–3900; tel. 920/794–5000 **A**1 2 9 10 **F**3 11 13 28 29 30 31 32 34 35 36 37 40 43 44 45 47 48 49 50 54 56 57 59 64 75 76 78 79 80 81 82 85 86 87 93 94 107 108 111 114 119 121 123 129 130 132 133 134 135 143 146 147 148 **P**6 **S** Aurora Health Care, Milwaukee, WI
Primary Contact: Cathie A. Kocourek, President
COO: Carrie L. Penovich, Chief Clinical Services Officer
CFO: Sandra Ewald, Vice President Finance
CMO: Paul Mihalakakos, M.D., Chief of Staff
CIO: Philip Loftus, Ph.D., Chief Information Officer
CHR: Stacie A. Schneider, Director Human Resources
CNO: Betsy Benz, R.N., Chief Nursing Officer
Web address: www.aurorahealthcare.org
Control: Other not–for–profit (including NFP Corporation) **Service:** General Medical and Surgical

Staffed Beds: 63 Admissions: 2112 Census: 18 Outpatient Visits: 59345 Births: 410 Total Expense ($000): 47062 Payroll Expense ($000): 16063 Personnel: 326

WI

VIROQUA—Vernon County

VERNON MEMORIAL HEALTHCARE (521348), 507 South Main Street, Zip 54665–2096; tel. 608/637–2101 **A**9 10 18 **F**3 5 13 15 28 29 34 35 36 37 40 43 45 53 56 57 59 62 63 68 75 76 77 80 81 82 85 86 87 89 93 97 107 110 115 127 130 131 132 133 135 144 146 148 **P**6
Primary Contact: Kyle Bakkum, Chief Executive Officer and Administrator
COO: Kristy Wiltrout, R.N., Chief Operating Officer
CFO: Mary Koenig, Chief Financial Officer
CIO: Scott Adkins, Manager Information Technology
CHR: Kay Starr, Manager Human Resources
Web address: www.vmh.org
Control: Other not–for–profit (including NFP Corporation) **Service:** General Medical and Surgical

Staffed Beds: 24 **Admissions:** 1357 **Census:** 10 **Outpatient Visits:** 122143 **Births:** 178 **Total Expense ($000):** 59184 **Payroll Expense ($000):** 24935 **Personnel:** 356

WATERFORD—Racine County

☐ △ **LAKEVIEW SPECIALTY HOSPITAL AND REHABILITATION CENTER (522005)**, 1701 Sharp Road, Zip 53185–5214; tel. 262/534–7297 **A**1 7 9 10 **F**1 12 28 29 30 34 36 38 53 62 64 75 82 85 86 87 90 91 92 93 94 97 99 100 101 104 106 127 130 143 148 **P**6
Primary Contact: Robyn Rushing, Administrator
Web address: www.lakeviewsystem.com
Control: Corporation, Investor–owned, for–profit **Service:** Long–Term Acute Care hospital

Staffed Beds: 39 **Admissions:** 264 **Census:** 25 **Outpatient Visits:** 4110 **Births:** 0 **Total Expense ($000):** 15094 **Payroll Expense ($000):** 6555 **Personnel:** 165

WATERTOWN—Dodge County

⊞ **WATERTOWN REGIONAL MEDICAL CENTER (520116)**, 125 Hospital Drive, Zip 53098–3303; tel. 920/261–4210 **A**1 9 10 **F**3 8 10 11 13 15 18 20 22 26 27 28 29 30 34 35 36 40 41 42 44 45 46 47 48 50 53 54 56 57 59 64 65 66 68 69 74 75 76 77 78 79 80 81 82 85 86 87 89 90 92 93 94 96 97 104 107 108 110 111 114 118 119 125 129 130 131 132 135 144 146 147 **P**8
Primary Contact: John P. Kosanovich, President
COO: John P. Kosanovich, President
CFO: John Graf, Senior Vice President
CHR: Duane Floyd, Vice President Human Resources and Professional Services
CNO: Mary Kay Diderrich, Vice President Patient Services
Web address: www.uwphwatertown.com
Control: Other not–for–profit (including NFP Corporation) **Service:** General Medical and Surgical

Staffed Beds: 55 **Admissions:** 1716 **Census:** 15 **Outpatient Visits:** 194617 **Births:** 280 **Total Expense ($000):** 85051 **Payroll Expense ($000):** 40406 **Personnel:** 554

WAUKESHA—Waukesha County

☐ **REHABILITATION HOSPITAL OF WISCONSIN (523027)**, 1625 Coldwater Creek Drive, Zip 53188–8028; tel. 262/521–8800 **A**1 9 10 **F**3 29 34 35 57 64 65 74 75 79 86 90 91 93 96 97 130 148 **S** Centerre Healthcare, Brentwood, TN
Primary Contact: Linda Newberry–Ferguson, Chief Executive Officer
CFO: Mary Reeves, Controller
CMO: Yechiel Kleen, M.D., Medical Director
CHR: Annette Hahn, Director Human Resources
Web address: www.rehabhospitalwi.com
Control: Partnership, Investor–owned, for–profit **Service:** Rehabilitation

Staffed Beds: 40 **Admissions:** 669 **Census:** 26 **Outpatient Visits:** 5059 **Births:** 0 **Total Expense ($000):** 12372 **Payroll Expense ($000):** 5942 **Personnel:** 105

WAUKESHA COUNTY MENTAL HEALTH CENTER (524026), 2501 Airport Road, Zip 53188; tel. 262/548–7950 **A**10 **F**4 98 130 132
Primary Contact: Michele A. Cusatis, Ph.D., Administrator
Web address: www.waukeshacounty.gov/
Control: County–Government, nonfederal **Service:** Psychiatric

Staffed Beds: 28 **Admissions:** 862 **Census:** 17 **Outpatient Visits:** 0 **Births:** 0 **Total Expense ($000):** 6401 **Payroll Expense ($000):** 3362 **Personnel:** 48

⊞ **WAUKESHA MEMORIAL HOSPITAL (520008)**, 725 American Avenue, Zip 53188–5099; tel. 262/928–1000 **A**1 2 3 5 9 10 **F**3 4 5 6 11 12 13 15 18 20 22 24 26 28 29 30 31 32 34 35 37 40 44 45 46 47 49 50 56 57 58 59 64 68 72 74 75 76 78 79 80 81 82 84 85 87 89 92 93 97 98 100 101 102 103 105 107 108 110 111 114 115 116 117 118 119 120 121 123 124 126 129 130 132 135 146 147 148 **S** ProHealth Care, Inc., Waukesha, WI
Primary Contact: John R. Robertstad, FACHE, President
CMO: James D. Gardner, M.D., Vice President and Chief Medical Officer
CIO: Rodney Dykehouse, Senior Vice President Information Services
CHR: Nadine T. Guirl, Senior Vice President Human Resources
Web address: www.prohealthcare.org/locations/locations–v2–detail/?id=1119
Control: Other not–for–profit (including NFP Corporation) **Service:** General Medical and Surgical

Staffed Beds: 290 **Admissions:** 14820 **Census:** 167 **Outpatient Visits:** 283666 **Births:** 1681 **Total Expense ($000):** 396973 **Payroll Expense ($000):** 106409 **Personnel:** 1856

WAUPACA—Waupaca County

☐ **RIVERSIDE MEDICAL CENTER (521334)**, 800 Riverside Drive, Zip 54981–1999; tel. 715/258–1000 **A**1 9 10 18 **F**3 8 11 13 17 28 29 34 35 40 44 45 57 59 64 68 70 76 78 80 81 82 85 86 87 88 89 90 97 107 111 112 114 119 130 133 135 144 146 147 148 **S** ThedaCare, Inc., Appleton, WI
Primary Contact: Craig A. Kantos, Chief Executive Officer
CFO: Kerry Lee Blanke, Director Financial Services
CMO: James Williams, M.D., Chief of Staff
CHR: Kevin Gossens, Director Human Resources
Web address: www.riversidemedical.org
Control: Other not–for–profit (including NFP Corporation) **Service:** General Medical and Surgical

Staffed Beds: 25 **Admissions:** 1022 **Census:** 10 **Outpatient Visits:** 41813 **Births:** 145 **Total Expense ($000):** 28620 **Payroll Expense ($000):** 15021 **Personnel:** 209

WAUPUN—Dodge County

☐ **WAUPUN MEMORIAL HOSPITAL (521327)**, 620 West Brown Street, Zip 53963–1799; tel. 920/324–5581 **A**1 9 10 18 **F**3 11 13 15 28 29 30 31 34 35 36 40 43 44 50 51 57 59 60 66 68 69 70 71 74 75 76 77 79 81 82 84 85 86 87 93 97 107 108 110 114 118 119 130 131 132 133 134 143 144 146 147 148 **P**6
Primary Contact: DeAnn Thurmer, Chief Operating Officer
COO: DeAnn Thurmer, Chief Operating Officer
CFO: Bonnie Schmitz, Chief Financial Officer
CMO: Derek Colmenares, M.D., Chief Medical Officer
CIO: Nancy Birschbach, Vice President and Chief Information Officer
CHR: Sue Edminster, Vice President Human Resources
CNO: DeAnn Thurmer, Chief Nursing Officer
Web address: www.agnesian.com
Control: Church–operated, Nongovernment, not–for profit **Service:** General Medical and Surgical

Staffed Beds: 25 **Admissions:** 931 **Census:** 8 **Outpatient Visits:** 58025 **Births:** 142 **Total Expense ($000):** 32492 **Payroll Expense ($000):** 13811 **Personnel:** 195

WAUSAU—Marathon County

⊞ △ **ASPIRUS WAUSAU HOSPITAL (520030)**, 333 Pine Ridge Boulevard, Zip 54401–4187; tel. 715/847–2121 **A**1 2 3 5 7 9 10 **F**3 5 6 7 8 11 12 13 15 17 18 20 22 24 26 28 29 30 31 34 35 36 40 43 44 45 46 47 49 50 51 54 55 56 58 59 60 62 63 64 65 68 69 70 71 72 74 75 76 78 79 80 81 82 83 84 85 86 87 89 90 92 93 96 97 100 102 103 104 107 108 110 111 114 115 116 117 118 119 120 121 123 124 126 129 130 132 135 143 144 145 146 147 148 **P**8 **S** Aspirus, Inc., Wausau, WI
Primary Contact: Darrell Lentz, Interim President
COO: Marita Hattem, Interim President and Chief Operating Officer
CFO: Sidney C. Sczygelski, Senior Vice President Finance and Chief Financial Officer
CHR: Roger V. Lucas, Vice President, Human Resources
Web address: www.aspirus.org
Control: Other not–for–profit (including NFP Corporation) **Service:** General Medical and Surgical

Staffed Beds: 257 **Admissions:** 12072 **Census:** 136 **Outpatient Visits:** 105846 **Births:** 1281 **Total Expense ($000):** 321290 **Payroll Expense ($000):** 111364 **Personnel:** 2013

WI

NORTH CENTRAL HEALTH CARE (524017), 1100 Lake View Drive, Zip 54403–6785; tel. 715/848–4600, (Total facility includes 228 beds in nursing home–type unit) **A**9 10 **F**3 4 5 6 29 34 35 38 56 57 66 75 83 84 86 93 98 99 100 101 102 103 104 105 106 128 132 134 135 146
Primary Contact: Gary Bezucha, FACHE, Chief Executive Officer
CFO: Brenda Glodowski, Chief Financial Officer
CHR: Michael Loy, Director Human Resources
Web address: www.norcen.org
Control: County–Government, nonfederal **Service:** Psychiatric

Staffed Beds: 244 **Admissions:** 1249 **Census:** 243 **Outpatient Visits:** 166601 **Births:** 0 **Total Expense ($000):** 28224 **Payroll Expense ($000):** 16079 **Personnel:** 196

NORTH CENTRAL HEALTH CARE FACILITIES See North Central Health Care

WAUWATOSA—Milwaukee County

✠ **AURORA PSYCHIATRIC HOSPITAL (524000)**, 1220 Dewey Avenue, Zip 53213–2598; tel. 414/454–6600 **A**1 9 10 **F**3 4 5 30 32 35 38 44 50 54 59 64 68 75 86 87 98 99 100 101 102 104 105 106 130 132 135 **P**6 **S** Aurora Health Care, Milwaukee, WI
Primary Contact: Peter Carlson, Administrator
CFO: Susan Dwyer, Vice President Finance
CMO: Anthony Meyer, M.D., Medical Director
CIO: Philip Loftus, Ph.D., Vice President and Chief Information Officer
CHR: Pamela Gamb, Manager Human Resources
CNO: Jamie Lewiston, R.N., Chief Nursing Officer
Web address: www.aurorahealthcare.org
Control: Other not–for–profit (including NFP Corporation) **Service:** Psychiatric

Staffed Beds: 80 **Admissions:** 3491 **Census:** 47 **Outpatient Visits:** 56018 **Births:** 0 **Total Expense ($000):** 23853 **Payroll Expense ($000):** 13126 **Personnel:** 239

★ **WHEATON FRANCISCAN HEALTHCARE – THE WISCONSIN HEART HOSPITAL (520199)**, 10000 West Bluemound Road, Zip 53226–4321; tel. 414/778–7800 **A**9 **F**3 8 18 20 22 24 26 29 31 37 40 42 43 70 72 74 75 77 79 81 85 86 87 92 94 107 108 115 118 119 123 126 130 135 143 146 **P**6 **S** Wheaton Franciscan Healthcare, Wheaton, IL
Primary Contact: Debra K. Standridge, President
CFO: Michael Petitt, Director of Finance
CMO: Rita Hanson, M.D., Vice President Medical Affairs
CIO: Gregory Smith, Senior Vice President and Chief Information Officer
CHR: Christopher Morris, Director Human Resources
CNO: Sharon Baughman, R.N., Vice President Patient Services and Chief Nursing Officer
Web address: www.mywheaton.org/hearthospital
Control: Church–operated, Nongovernment, not–for profit **Service:** General Medical and Surgical

Staffed Beds: 30 **Admissions:** 1671 **Census:** 13 **Outpatient Visits:** 10808 **Births:** 0 **Total Expense ($000):** 48527 **Payroll Expense ($000):** 10776 **Personnel:** 131

WEST ALLIS—Milwaukee County

✠ **AURORA WEST ALLIS MEDICAL CENTER (520139)**, 8901 West Lincoln Avenue, Zip 53227–2409, Mailing Address: P.O. Box 27901, Zip 53227–0901; tel. 414/328–6000 **A**1 9 10 **F**2 3 8 11 12 13 15 29 30 31 32 34 35 37 38 40 41 43 44 45 49 50 52 54 55 56 57 59 64 65 68 70 72 74 75 76 78 79 80 81 82 84 85 86 87 91 93 94 95 96 97 107 108 110 111 114 115 116 118 119 120 121 123 126 130 132 133 135 146 147 148 **P**6 **S** Aurora Health Care, Milwaukee, WI
Primary Contact: Richard A. Kellar, President
COO: Gerard Colman, Chief Operating Officer
CFO: Chris Hemmer, Director Finance
CMO: Andrew McDonagh, M.D., Chief Medical Officer
CIO: Philip Loftus, Ph.D., Chief Information Officer
CHR: Shannon Christenson, Director Human Resources
CNO: Kathy Becker, Ph.D., Vice President and Chief Nursing Officer
Web address: www.aurorahealthcare.org
Control: Other not–for–profit (including NFP Corporation) **Service:** General Medical and Surgical

Staffed Beds: 220 **Admissions:** 12901 **Census:** 146 **Outpatient Visits:** 137585 **Births:** 3352 **Total Expense ($000):** 177842 **Payroll Expense ($000):** 59442 **Personnel:** 1094

WEST BEND—Washington County

✠ **ST. JOSEPH'S HOSPITAL (520063)**, 3200 Pleasant Valley Road, Zip 53095–9274; tel. 262/334–5533 **A**1 2 9 10 **F**3 4 13 15 17 28 29 30 31 34 35 43 44 45 46 47 48 49 50 56 57 59 60 63 64 70 74 75 76 77 78 79 80 81 85 86 87 89 98 100 101 107 108 110 111 114 115 116 118 119 120 121 129 130 132 135 146 147 148
Primary Contact: Allen Ericson, President
CFO: Scott Hawig, Chief Financial Officer
CMO: Patrick Gardner, M.D., Vice President Medical Affairs
CHR: Keith Allen, Senior Vice President Human Resources
CNO: Teri Lux, R.N., Vice President Patient Care Services and Chief Nursing Officer
Web address: www.froedtert.com
Control: Other not–for–profit (including NFP Corporation) **Service:** General Medical and Surgical

Staffed Beds: 78 **Admissions:** 3630 **Census:** 41 **Outpatient Visits:** 79935 **Births:** 716 **Total Expense ($000):** 84578 **Payroll Expense ($000):** 27516 **Personnel:** 421

WESTON—Marathon County

✠ **MINISTRY SAINT CLARE'S HOSPITAL (520202)**, 3400 Ministry Parkway, Zip 54476–5220; tel. 715/393–3000 **A**1 9 10 **F**3 11 13 17 18 20 22 24 26 29 30 31 34 35 37 40 43 44 50 51 57 59 64 68 70 72 74 75 76 78 79 80 81 82 84 85 86 87 89 115 120 121 126 130 132 135 143 146 148 **P**6 **S** Ascension Health, Saint Louis, MO
Primary Contact: Mary T. Krueger, President
CFO: Charlotte Esselman, Director Finance
CMO: Larry T. Hegland, M.D., Chief Medical Officer
CIO: Tammy Hawkey, Manager Information Technology Client Services
CHR: Nancy Kwiesielewicz, Human Resources Manager
CNO: Kristine McGarigle, R.N., Vice President Patient Care
Web address: www.ministryhealth.org
Control: Church–operated, Nongovernment, not–for profit **Service:** General Medical and Surgical

Staffed Beds: 77 **Admissions:** 5449 **Census:** 48 **Outpatient Visits:** 17133 **Births:** 612 **Total Expense ($000):** 92175 **Payroll Expense ($000):** 32309 **Personnel:** 380

WHITEHALL—Trempealeau County

★ **GUNDERSEN TRI–COUNTY HOSPITAL AND CLINICS (521316)**, 18601 Lincoln Street, Zip 54773–8605; tel. 715/538–4361, (Total facility includes 47 beds in nursing home–type unit) **A**9 10 18 **F**3 10 11 15 28 31 34 35 40 43 45 46 53 56 57 59 64 66 68 71 75 78 81 86 90 93 97 107 108 110 114 128 129 130 132 133 144 146 148
Primary Contact: Brian Theiler, President and Chief Executive Officer
COO: Brian Theiler, President and Chief Executive Officer
CFO: Vince Studer, Director Finance
CMO: Katrina Hammel, M.D., Chief Medical Officer
CIO: John Waldera, Director Information Technology
CHR: Jill Wesener Dieck, Director Human Resources
CNO: Emily Anderson, Director of Nursing Emergency Room
Web address: www.gundersenhealth.org/tri–county
Control: Other not–for–profit (including NFP Corporation) **Service:** General Medical and Surgical

Staffed Beds: 50 **Admissions:** 352 **Census:** 47 **Outpatient Visits:** 24428 **Births:** 0 **Total Expense ($000):** 14375 **Payroll Expense ($000):** 6778 **Personnel:** 121

WILD ROSE—Waushara County

WILD ROSE COMMUNITY MEMORIAL HOSPITAL (521303), 601 Grove Avenue, Zip 54984–6903, Mailing Address: P.O. Box 243, Zip 54984–0243; tel. 920/622–3257 **A**9 10 18 **F**11 15 28 29 34 40 43 56 64 75 77 80 81 86 87 89 90 93 99 100 101 102 103 104 107 111 119 131 144 147 **P**7
Primary Contact: Donald Caves, President
CFO: Thomas P. Krystowiak, Vice President Finance
CMO: Reginaldo Arboleda, M.D., Chief of Staff
CHR: Karen M. West, Administrator Support Services
Web address: www.wildrosehospital.org
Control: Other not–for–profit (including NFP Corporation) **Service:** General Medical and Surgical

Staffed Beds: 25 **Admissions:** 441 **Census:** 8 **Outpatient Visits:** 13343 **Births:** 0 **Total Expense ($000):** 11684 **Payroll Expense ($000):** 5104 **Personnel:** 113

WI

Many Facility Codes have changed. Please refer to the AHA Guide Code Chart. © 2014 AHA Guide

WINNEBAGO—Winnebago County

☐ **WINNEBAGO MENTAL HEALTH INSTITUTE (524002)**, 1300 South Drive,
Zip 54985, Mailing Address: Box 9, Zip 54985–0009; tel. 920/235–4910 **A**1 9
10 **F**3 4 5 29 75 82 87 92 98 99 103 130 143 146 **P**7
Primary Contact: Thomas Speech, Ph.D., Director
COO: Chris Craggs, Deputy Director
CFO: Lisa Spanbauer, Financial Program Supervisor
CMO: Randy Kerswill, M.D., Medical Director
CIO: Terrance J. Sweet, Director Information Technology
CHR: Mary Howard, Director Human Resources
CNO: Lori Monroe, Director of Nursing
Web address: www.dhfs.state.wi.us/mh_winnebago
Control: State–Government, nonfederal **Service:** Psychiatric

Staffed Beds: 180 **Admissions:** 1827 **Census:** 120 **Outpatient Visits:** 0
Births: 0 **Total Expense ($000):** 46546 **Payroll Expense ($000):** 29495
Personnel: 582

WISCONSIN RAPIDS—Wood County

✦ **RIVERVIEW HOSPITAL ASSOCIATION (520033)**, 410 Dewey Street,
Zip 54494–4715, Mailing Address: P.O. Box 8080, Zip 54495–8080;
tel. 715/423–6060 **A**1 9 10 **F**3 4 8 13 14 15 17 28 30 31 34 35 40 43 56 59
64 65 68 69 70 74 75 76 77 78 79 80 81 84 85 86 88 89 90 93 97 98 100
107 108 110 111 115 117 118 119 120 121 124 127 129 130 131 132 135
146 148
Primary Contact: Celse A. Berard, President
CFO: Michael Bovee, Vice President Finance
CMO: Timothy K. Huebner, M.D., President Medical Affairs
CIO: Marjorie Tell, Vice President Information Technology
CHR: Tom Hunsberger, Vice President Human Resources
Web address: www.riverviewhospital.org
Control: Other not–for–profit (including NFP Corporation) **Service:** General
Medical and Surgical

Staffed Beds: 69 **Admissions:** 3000 **Census:** 23 **Outpatient Visits:** 52767
Births: 481 **Total Expense ($000):** 83607 **Payroll Expense ($000):** 34894
Personnel: 464

WOODRUFF—Oneida County

✦ **HOWARD YOUNG MEDICAL CENTER (520091)**, 240 Maple Street,
Zip 54568–9190, Mailing Address: P.O. Box 470, Zip 54568–0470;
tel. 715/356–8000 **A**1 9 10 20 **F**3 8 11 13 15 18 28 29 30 35 40 43 45 47
48 49 50 57 59 68 75 76 77 80 81 82 84 85 86 87 88 89 93 96 107 108
110 115 119 126 129 130 133 146 148 **P**6 **S** Ascension Health, Saint
Louis, MO
Primary Contact: Monica Hilt, President
CFO: Cathy Bukowski, Chief Financial Officer
CMO: Mark Rassier, M.D., President Howard Young Medical Center Staff
CIO: Howard Dobizl, Director Information Technology Services
CHR: Michelle Cornelius, Director Human Resources
CNO: Deborah Karow, R.N., Vice President Patient Care Services
Web address: www.ministryhealth.org
Control: Church–operated, Nongovernment, not–for profit **Service:** General
Medical and Surgical

Staffed Beds: 53 **Admissions:** 2848 **Census:** 29 **Outpatient Visits:** 40795
Births: 284 **Total Expense ($000):** 49377 **Payroll Expense ($000):** 24883
Personnel: 340

WI

Hospital, Medicare Provider Number, Address, Telephone, Approval, Facility, and Physician Codes, Health Care System

★ American Hospital Association (AHA) membership
☐ The Joint Commission accreditation　◇ DNV Healthcare Inc. accreditation
○ Healthcare Facilities Accreditation Program
△ Commission on Accreditation of Rehabilitation Facilities (CARF) accreditation

WYOMING

AFTON—Lincoln County

★ **STAR VALLEY MEDICAL CENTER (531313)**, 901 Adams Street,
Zip 83110–9621, Mailing Address: P.O. Box 579, Zip 83110–0579;
tel. 307/885–5800, (Total facility includes 24 beds in nursing home–type unit) **A**9
10 18 **F**3 7 11 12 13 15 29 31 34 40 43 45 57 59 64 65 67 74 75 76 77 78
79 81 82 85 86 87 89 93 97 102 107 110 111 114 118 119 128 129 130
131 132 133 135 144 146 147 148 **P**6
Primary Contact: Charlie A. Button, President and Chief Executive Officer
CFO: Chad Turner, Chief Financial Officer
CMO: Christian Morgan, M.D., Chief of Staff
CIO: Denise Wheeler, Chief Information Officer
CHR: Trevor Merritt, Director Human Resources
CNO: Dave Dunn, Director of Nursing
Web address: www.svmcwy.org
Control: Hospital district or authority, Government, nonfederal **Service:** General
Medical and Surgical

Staffed Beds: 44 **Admissions:** 677 **Census:** 29 **Outpatient Visits:** 21428
Births: 87 **Total Expense ($000):** 25283 **Payroll Expense ($000):** 12238
Personnel: 218

BASIN—Big Horn County

SOUTH BIG HORN COUNTY HOSPITAL (531301), 388 South U.S. Highway
20, Zip 82410–8902; tel. 307/568–3311, (Total facility includes 37 beds in
nursing home–type unit) **A**9 10 18 **F**32 34 35 40 56 57 59 64 82 93 97 107
110 119 127 128 130 133 **P**4
Primary Contact: Jackie Claudson, Administrator
Web address: www.midwayclinic.com
Control: Hospital district or authority, Government, nonfederal **Service:** General
Medical and Surgical

Staffed Beds: 43 **Admissions:** 122 **Census:** 36 **Outpatient Visits:** 1943
Births: 1 **Total Expense ($000):** 6057 **Payroll Expense ($000):** 3105
Personnel: 90

BUFFALO—Johnson County

★ **JOHNSON COUNTY HEALTHCARE CENTER (531308)**, 497 West Lott Street,
Zip 82834–1691; tel. 307/684–5521, (Total facility includes 50 beds in nursing
home–type unit) **A**9 10 18 **F**11 13 15 28 31 40 57 62 63 67 70 76 78 79 81
89 93 107 119 130 133
Primary Contact: Sandy Ward, Administrator
CFO: Sandy Ward, Administrator
CMO: Brian Darnell, D.O., Chief of Staff
CIO: Laurie Hansen, Director Administrative Services
CHR: Karen Ferguson, Director Human Resources
CNO: Mary Whaley, Director of Acute Care
Web address: www.jchealthcare.com
Control: Hospital district or authority, Government, nonfederal **Service:** General
Medical and Surgical

Staffed Beds: 75 **Admissions:** 401 **Census:** 44 **Outpatient Visits:** 17193
Births: 58 **Total Expense ($000):** 18070 **Payroll Expense ($000):** 9068
Personnel: 171

CASPER—Natrona County

☐ **ELKHORN VALLEY REHABILITATION HOSPITAL (533027)**, 5715 East 2nd
Street, Zip 82609–4322; tel. 307/265–0005, (Nonreporting) **A**1 10 **S** Ernest
Health, Inc., Albuquerque, NM
Primary Contact: Michael Phillips, Chief Executive Officer
Web address: www.evrh.ernesthealth.com/
Control: Corporation, Investor–owned, for–profit **Service:** Rehabilitation

Staffed Beds: 40

○ **MOUNTAIN VIEW REGIONAL HOSPITAL (530033)**, 6550 East Second Street,
Zip 82609–4321, Mailing Address: P.O. Box 51888, Zip 82605–1888;
tel. 307/995–8100, (Nonreporting) **A**10 11 **S** National Surgical Hospitals,
Chicago, IL
Primary Contact: Jeff Van Horn, Chief Executive Officer
Web address: www.mountainviewregionalhospital.com
Control: Partnership, Investor–owned, for–profit **Service:** Surgical

Staffed Beds: 23

☐ **WYOMING BEHAVIORAL INSTITUTE (534004)**, 2521 East 15th Street,
Zip 82609–4126; tel. 307/237–7444 **A**1 10 **F**34 56 57 59 98 99 100 101 102
103 104 105 106 130 **S** Universal Health Services, Inc., King of Prussia, PA
Primary Contact: Joseph Gallagher, Chief Executive Officer
CFO: Carmel Bickford, Chief Financial Officer
CMO: Steven Brown, M.D., Medical Director
CHR: Jon Barra, Director Human Resources
Web address: www.wbihelp.com
Control: Corporation, Investor–owned, for–profit **Service:** Psychiatric

Staffed Beds: 129 **Admissions:** 1972 **Census:** 80 **Outpatient Visits:** 2338
Births: 0 **Total Expense ($000):** 18480 **Payroll Expense ($000):** 9364
Personnel: 170

⊞ **WYOMING MEDICAL CENTER (530012)**, 1233 East Second Street,
Zip 82601–2988; tel. 307/577–7201 **A**1 9 10 **F**3 7 11 12 13 18 20 22 24 28
29 30 31 34 35 40 41 43 45 46 48 49 50 51 57 59 60 61 68 70 74 76 79
81 82 85 86 87 89 97 102 107 108 111 114 118 119 120 121 123 124 126
129 130 132 135 144 146 147 148 **P**6
Primary Contact: Vickie L. Diamond, R.N., MS, President and Chief Executive
Officer
COO: Julie Cann–Taylor, R.N., Chief Operating Officer, Senior Vice President
Patient Care Services and Chief Nursing Officer
CFO: Yvonne Wigington, Vice President, Chief Financial Officer
CMO: Carol M. Solie, M.D., Chief Medical Officer
CIO: Rob Pettigrew, Director Information Technology
CNO: Julie Cann–Taylor, R.N., Chief Operating Officer, Senior Vice President
Patient Care Services and Chief Nursing Officer
Web address: www.wmcnet.org
Control: Other not–for–profit (including NFP Corporation) **Service:** General
Medical and Surgical

Staffed Beds: 191 **Admissions:** 9080 **Census:** 94 **Outpatient Visits:** 80027
Births: 1138 **Total Expense ($000):** 180164 **Payroll Expense ($000):**
63144 **Personnel:** 1053

CHEYENNE—Laramie County

⊞ △ **CHEYENNE REGIONAL MEDICAL CENTER (530014)**, 214 East 23rd
Street, Zip 82001–3790; tel. 307/634–2273 **A**1 2 7 9 10 20 **F**3 5 11 12 13 15
18 20 22 24 26 28 29 30 31 34 35 37 38 40 43 44 45 46 47 48 49 50 51
53 57 59 60 62 63 64 65 66 68 69 70 71 72 74 75 77 78 79 81 82 83 84
85 86 87 90 93 94 96 97 98 99 100 101 102 103 104 107 108 110 111
114 116 117 118 119 120 121 123 124 128 129 130 131 132 135 143 144
146 147 148 **P**5 6 7
Primary Contact: Margo Karsten, Ph.D., MSN, Chief Executive Officer
COO: Jason Shenefield, Chief Operating Officer
CFO: Kerry Warburton, Chief Financial Officer
CMO: David Lind, M.D., Chief Medical Officer
CIO: Ashutosh Goel, M.D., Chief Information Technology Officer
CHR: Craig Luzinski, MSN, Chief Human Resources Officer
CNO: Constance Schmidt, R.N., Chief Nursing Officer
Web address: www.cheyenneregional.org/
Control: County–Government, nonfederal **Service:** General Medical and Surgical

Staffed Beds: 238 **Admissions:** 10683 **Census:** 133 **Outpatient Visits:**
214245 **Births:** 1196 **Total Expense ($000):** 245529 **Payroll Expense
($000):** 104336 **Personnel:** 2003

⊞ **CHEYENNE VETERANS AFFAIRS MEDICAL CENTER**, 2360 East Pershing
Boulevard, Zip 82001–5392; tel. 307/778–7550, (Total facility includes 42 beds
in nursing home–type unit) **A**1 9 **F**3 5 8 18 29 30 31 34 35 38 39 40 44 45 54
59 62 63 64 65 68 70 71 74 75 77 78 79 81 82 84 85 86 87 91 92 93 94
97 100 101 102 103 104 107 108 109 111 115 119 128 129 130 132 135
143 144 145 146 147 148 **P**6 **S** Department of Veterans Affairs,
Washington, DC
Primary Contact: Cynthia McCormack, MS, Director
CFO: Melvin Cranford, Chief Fiscal Services
CMO: Roger Johnson, M.D., Chief of Staff
CIO: Liz McCulloch, Chief Information Resource Management Systems
CHR: Ron Lester, Chief Human Resources
Web address: www.cheyenne.va.gov/
Control: Veterans Affairs, Government, federal **Service:** General Medical and
Surgical

Staffed Beds: 61 **Admissions:** 1114 **Census:** 45 **Outpatient Visits:** 240271
Births: 0 **Total Expense ($000):** 121222 **Payroll Expense ($000):** 43816
Personnel: 488

Many Facility Codes have changed. Please refer to the AHA Guide Code Chart. © 2014 AHA Guide

WY

CODY—Park County

★ **WEST PARK HOSPITAL (531312)**, 707 Sheridan Avenue, Zip 82414–3409;
tel. 307/527–7501, (Total facility includes 97 beds in nursing home–type unit) **A**9
10 18 **F**3 4 5 6 7 11 13 15 18 24 26 28 29 30 31 34 35 36 38 40 43 45 46
50 56 57 59 62 63 64 65 68 70 75 76 78 79 81 84 85 86 87 93 97 99 102
103 104 105 107 108 110 111 114 119 120 128 130 131 132 133 135 143
144 145 146 147 148 **S** QHR, Brentwood, TN
Primary Contact: Douglas A. McMillan, Administrator and Chief Executive Officer
CFO: Patrick G. McConnell, Chief Financial Officer
CHR: Dick Smith, Director Human Resources
Web address: www.westparkhospital.org
Control: Hospital district or authority, Government, nonfederal **Service:** General
Medical and Surgical

Staffed Beds: 140 **Admissions:** 1553 **Census:** 86 **Outpatient Visits:** 63288
Births: 228 **Total Expense ($000):** 68556 **Payroll Expense ($000):** 29148
Personnel: 469

DOUGLAS—Converse County

★ **MEMORIAL HOSPITAL OF CONVERSE COUNTY (531302)**, 111 South Fifth
Street, Zip 82633–2434, Mailing Address: P.O. Box 1450, Zip 82633–1450;
tel. 307/358–2122 **A**10 18 **F**3 7 8 13 15 28 29 32 34 35 40 43 45 46 50 57
59 64 70 75 76 79 81 82 85 86 87 94 107 110 115 119 126 127 129 131
133 135 144 146 147 148 **P**6
Primary Contact: Ryan K. Smith, Chief Executive Officer
CFO: Curtis R. Dugger, Chief Financial Officer
CMO: Deanne Engle, M.D., Chief of Staff
CIO: Dave Patterson, Information Systems Manager
CHR: Linda York, Manager Human Resources
CNO: Christy Dicklich–Cobb, Chief Nursing Officer
Web address: www.conversehospital.com
Control: County–Government, nonfederal **Service:** General Medical and Surgical

Staffed Beds: 25 **Admissions:** 821 **Census:** 6 **Outpatient Visits:** 35069
Births: 145 **Total Expense ($000):** 41517 **Payroll Expense ($000):** 18814
Personnel: 340

EVANSTON—Uinta County

⊞ **EVANSTON REGIONAL HOSPITAL (530032)**, 190 Arrowhead Drive,
Zip 82930–9266; tel. 307/789–3636 **A**1 9 10 20 **F**3 11 13 15 29 34 35 40
43 45 48 60 65 70 74 75 76 77 79 81 82 85 86 87 89 93 107 108 111 114
119 128 129 133 134 146 **P**6 **S** Community Health Systems, Inc., Franklin, TN
Primary Contact: George Winn, Chief Executive Officer
CFO: Terry W. Shambles, Chief Financial Officer
CHR: Joshua Jones, Director of Human Resources
CNO: Cheri Willard, R.N., Chief Nursing Officer
Web address: www.evanstonregionalhospital.com
Control: Corporation, Investor–owned, for–profit **Service:** General Medical and
Surgical

Staffed Beds: 42 **Admissions:** 995 **Census:** 6 **Outpatient Visits:** 25063
Births: 279 **Total Expense ($000):** 26467 **Payroll Expense ($000):** 11666
Personnel: 158

WYOMING STATE HOSPITAL (534001), 830 Highway 150 South,
Zip 82931–5341, Mailing Address: P.O. Box 177, Zip 82931–0177;
tel. 307/789–3464 **A**9 10 **F**29 30 50 56 77 98 100 101 102 103 130 132
135 **P**6
Primary Contact: William J. Sexton, Administrator
CFO: Paul Mullenax, Business Manager
CIO: Steve Baldwin, Manager Information Technology
Web address: www.health.wyo.gov/statehospital/index.html
Control: State–Government, nonfederal **Service:** Psychiatric

Staffed Beds: 183 **Admissions:** 251 **Census:** 86 **Outpatient Visits:** 0 **Births:**
0 **Total Expense ($000):** 36002

GILLETTE—Campbell County

★ ◇ **CAMPBELL COUNTY MEMORIAL HOSPITAL (530002)**, 501 South Burma
Avenue, Zip 82716–3426, Mailing Address: P.O. Box 3011, Zip 82717–3011;
tel. 307/682–8811, (Total facility includes 125 beds in nursing home–type unit)
A9 10 20 21 **F**3 5 6 7 11 13 15 28 29 30 31 34 35 38 40 43 45 51 53 54
56 59 60 62 63 64 65 66 68 69 70 71 73 74 75 76 77 78 79 81 82 84 85
86 87 88 93 94 96 97 98 99 100 101 102 103 104 105 107 108 109 110
111 114 115 116 118 119 120 121 125 129 130 131 132 133 134 135 143
144 146 147 148 **P**6
Primary Contact: Andy Fitzgerald, Chief Executive Officer
CFO: Dalton Huber, Chief Financial Officer
CIO: Chris Harrison, Manager Information Systems
CHR: John A. Fitch, Vice President Human Resources
CNO: Deb L. Tonn, Vice President Patient Care
Web address: www.ccmh.net
Control: Hospital district or authority, Government, nonfederal **Service:** General
Medical and Surgical

Staffed Beds: 197 **Admissions:** 3124 **Census:** 142 **Outpatient Visits:**
253403 **Births:** 752 **Total Expense ($000):** 140696 **Payroll Expense
($000):** 73240 **Personnel:** 983

JACKSON—Teton County

⊞ **ST. JOHN'S MEDICAL CENTER AND LIVING CENTER (530015)**, 625 East
Broadway Street, Zip 83001–8642, Mailing Address: P.O. Box 428,
Zip 83001–0428; tel. 307/733–3636, (Total facility includes 60 beds in nursing
home–type unit) **A**1 9 10 20 **F**3 11 13 15 29 30 31 34 35 40 43 44 45 46 51
53 54 57 59 62 63 67 68 70 74 75 76 77 78 81 82 84 86 87 97 107 108
110 111 115 119 129 130 132 133 135 144 145 146 148 **P**5
Primary Contact: Lou Hochheiser, M.D., Chief Executive Officer
COO: Gary Tauner, Chief Operating Officer
CFO: John Kren, Chief Financial Officer
CIO: David Witton, Manager Information Systems
CNO: Lynn Kirman, R.N., Chief Nursing Officer
Web address: www.tetonhospital.org
Control: Hospital district or authority, Government, nonfederal **Service:** General
Medical and Surgical

Staffed Beds: 100 **Admissions:** 2249 **Census:** 66 **Outpatient Visits:** 64778
Births: 445 **Total Expense ($000):** 78661 **Payroll Expense ($000):** 31251
Personnel: 474

KEMMERER—Lincoln County

★ **SOUTH LINCOLN MEDICAL CENTER (531315)**, 711 Onyx Street,
Zip 83101–3214; tel. 307/877–4401, (Total facility includes 24 beds in nursing
home–type unit) **A**9 10 18 **F**3 7 13 15 31 32 34 35 40 43 57 59 65 68 75 76
77 79 81 93 97 107 111 114 119 128 129 130 133 135 146 148 **P**6
Primary Contact: Eric Boley, Administrator and Chief Executive Officer
COO: Lou Ann Carmichael, Director Operations
CFO: Curtis Nielson, Director Finance
CMO: G. Christopher Krell, M.D., Chief of Staff
CIO: Kristin Housley, Chief Management Information Systems
CHR: Armand Drummond, Manager Human Resources
CNO: Kathi Parks, Director of Nursing
Web address: www.southlincolnmedical.com
Control: Hospital district or authority, Government, nonfederal **Service:** General
Medical and Surgical

Staffed Beds: 40 **Admissions:** 125 **Census:** 20 **Outpatient Visits:** 21790
Births: 34 **Total Expense ($000):** 12686 **Payroll Expense ($000):** 6703
Personnel: 126

LANDER—Fremont County

⊞ **SAGEWEST HEALTHCARE–LANDER (530010)**, 1320 Bishop Randall Drive,
Zip 82520–3996; tel. 307/332–4420 **A**1 9 10 20 **F**3 11 13 15 28 29 34 35
38 39 40 43 57 59 70 74 76 77 79 80 81 85 87 90 91 93 96 98 103 106
107 108 110 111 114 119 128 130 131 133 135 147 **P**5 **S** LifePoint
Hospitals, Inc., Brentwood, TN
Primary Contact: Stephen M. Erixon, Chief Executive Officer
COO: Derrick Brumfield, Chief Operating Officer
CFO: Ann Huhnke, Chief Financial Officer
CMO: Paul Ebbert, Chief of Staff
CIO: Keith Blair, M.D., Manager Information Systems
CHR: Dawn Nelson, Manager Human Resources
Web address: www.sagewesthealthcare.com
Control: Corporation, Investor–owned, for–profit **Service:** General Medical and
Surgical

Staffed Beds: 89 **Admissions:** 1984 **Census:** 27 **Outpatient Visits:** 31643
Births: 277 **Total Expense ($000):** 34628 **Payroll Expense ($000):** 11729
Personnel: 208

LARAMIE—Albany County

✠ **IVINSON MEMORIAL HOSPITAL (530025)**, 255 North 30th Street,
Zip 82072–5140; tel. 307/742–2141, (Total facility includes 9 beds in nursing
home–type unit) **A**1 10 20 **F**11 13 15 28 29 30 31 34 38 40 45 50 56 57 59
60 64 70 73 75 76 77 78 79 81 85 89 98 99 102 107 108 111 115 119 121
128 129 130 132 133 146 147 **P**8
Primary Contact: Doug Faus, FACHE, Chief Executive Officer
COO: Holly Zajic, Chief Operating Officer
CFO: Bryan Chalmers, Chief Financial Officer
CMO: Lawrence Jenkins, M.D., Chief of Staff
CIO: Brandon Lewis, Director of Information Technology
CHR: Becky Kosach, Director Human Resources
CNO: Sharon Gern, R.N., Chief Nursing Officer
Web address: www.ivinsonhospital.org
Control: Hospital district or authority, Government, nonfederal **Service:** General
Medical and Surgical

Staffed Beds: 99 **Admissions:** 2852 **Census:** 25 **Outpatient Visits:** 41142
Births: 413 **Total Expense ($000):** 56666 **Payroll Expense ($000):** 21895
Personnel: 382

LOVELL—Big Horn County

★ **NORTH BIG HORN HOSPITAL DISTRICT (531309)**, 1115 Lane 12,
Zip 82431–9537; tel. 307/548–5203, (Total facility includes 85 beds in nursing
home–type unit) **A**9 10 18 **F**3 6 7 10 15 28 29 34 40 41 45 56 57 59 62 64
65 66 68 75 79 81 85 86 87 93 97 107 110 114 119 127 128 130 131 132
133 135 143 146 147 148 **P**6 8
Primary Contact: Rick Schroeder, Chief Executive Officer
CFO: Lori Smith, Chief Financial Officer
CMO: Richard Jay, D.O., Chief of Staff
CIO: Lisa Strom, Director Information Systems
CHR: Barbara Shumway, Director Human Resources
CNO: Tina Toner, Director of Nursing
Web address: www.nbhh.com
Control: Hospital district or authority, Government, nonfederal **Service:** General
Medical and Surgical

Staffed Beds: 100 **Admissions:** 267 **Census:** 78 **Outpatient Visits:** 19643
Births: 1 **Total Expense ($000):** 14457 **Payroll Expense ($000):** 8300
Personnel: 172

LUSK—Niobrara County

NIOBRARA HEALTH AND LIFE CENTER (531314), 921 Ballencee Avenue,
Zip 82225, Mailing Address: P.O. Box 780, Zip 82225–0780; tel. 307/334–4000
A9 10 18 **F**3 40 41 82 91 107 128 135
Primary Contact: Gary R. Poquette, FACHE, Chief Executive Officer
Web address: www.niobrarahospital.com
Control: County–Government, nonfederal **Service:** General Medical and Surgical

Staffed Beds: 24 **Admissions:** 57 **Census:** 1 **Outpatient Visits:** 3000 **Births:**
0 **Total Expense ($000):** 6061 **Payroll Expense ($000):** 2886 **Personnel:**
47

NEWCASTLE—Weston County

★ **WESTON COUNTY HEALTH SERVICES (531303)**, 1124 Washington
Boulevard, Zip 82701–2972; tel. 307/746–4491, (Total facility includes 54 beds
in nursing home–type unit) **A**9 10 18 **F**28 29 40 41 56 57 59 62 64 77 91 93
107 119 130 133 **S** Regional Health, Rapid City, SD
Primary Contact: Maureen K. Cadwell, Chief Executive Officer
CFO: Lynn Moller, Chief Financial Officer
CMO: Chuck Franklin, M.D., Chief Medical Staff
CIO: Terri Frye, Information Technology Officer
CHR: Julie A. Sindlinger, Director of Human Resources
Web address: www.wchs–wy.org
Control: Hospital district or authority, Government, nonfederal **Service:** General
Medical and Surgical

Staffed Beds: 75 **Admissions:** 229 **Census:** 59 **Outpatient Visits:** 8361
Births: 0 **Total Expense ($000):** 11006 **Payroll Expense ($000):** 5484
Personnel: 130

POWELL—Park County

★ **POWELL VALLEY HEALTHCARE (531310)**, 777 Avenue H, Zip 82435–2296;
tel. 307/754–2267, (Total facility includes 100 beds in nursing home–type unit)
A9 10 18 **F**3 7 10 11 13 15 18 28 29 34 35 36 40 43 45 56 57 59 62 63 64
67 70 76 79 81 85 87 97 107 110 111 115 119 130 131 132 133 135 144
146 147 148 **P**1 6 **S** HealthTech Management Services, Brentwood, TN
Primary Contact: Bill D. Patten, Jr., Chief Executive Officer
CFO: Mike Long, Chief Financial Officer
CMO: Valerie Lengfelder, M.D., Chief of Staff
CIO: Joshua Baxter, Director, Information Systems
CHR: Cassie Tinsley, Director, Human Resources
CNO: Arleen Campeau, R.N., Vice President of Patient Care Services, Chief
Nursing Officer
Web address: www.pvhc.org
Control: Other not–for–profit (including NFP Corporation) **Service:** General
Medical and Surgical

Staffed Beds: 125 **Admissions:** 702 **Census:** 92 **Outpatient Visits:** 33027
Births: 187 **Total Expense ($000):** 45710 **Payroll Expense ($000):** 23012
Personnel: 375

RAWLINS—Carbon County

★ **MEMORIAL HOSPITAL OF CARBON COUNTY (531316)**, 2221 West Elm
Street, Zip 82301–5108, Mailing Address: P.O. Box 460, Zip 82301–0460;
tel. 307/324–2221 **A**9 10 18 **F**3 7 11 13 15 18 28 29 31 34 35 39 40 45 50
57 59 65 68 70 76 79 81 85 93 105 107 110 111 114 119 129 130 133
135 146 147 148 **S** QHR, Brentwood, TN
Primary Contact: Ned Hill, Chief Executive Officer
CFO: David Pike, Interim Chief Financial Officer
CMO: David Cesko, M.D., Chief of Staff
CIO: Toby Schaef, Director Information Technology
CHR: Julia Nelson, Director Human Resources
CNO: Amber Green, R.N., Chief Clinical Officer
Web address: www.imhcc.com
Control: County–Government, nonfederal **Service:** General Medical and Surgical

Staffed Beds: 25 **Admissions:** 630 **Census:** 5 **Outpatient Visits:** 19439
Births: 80 **Total Expense ($000):** 21726 **Payroll Expense ($000):** 10905
Personnel: 145

RIVERTON—Fremont County

✠ **RIVERTON MEMORIAL HOSPITAL (530008)**, 2100 West Sunset Drive,
Zip 82501–2274; tel. 307/856–4161 **A**1 9 10 20 **F**3 11 13 15 29 34 35 40
43 45 46 47 48 49 50 51 57 59 64 68 70 74 75 76 77 79 81 85 87 93 107
108 110 111 114 119 129 130 131 132 133 145 147 **P**7 **S** LifePoint
Hospitals, Inc., Brentwood, TN
Primary Contact: Stephen M. Erixon, Interim Chief Executive Officer
CFO: Susan Goetzinger, Chief Financial Officer
CMO: Cielette Karn, M.D., Chief of Staff
CIO: Linda Tice, Director Information Systems
CHR: Dawn Nelson, Director Human Resources
Web address: www.riverton–hospital.com
Control: Corporation, Investor–owned, for–profit **Service:** General Medical and
Surgical

Staffed Beds: 37 **Admissions:** 1571 **Census:** 11 **Outpatient Visits:** 28413
Births: 289 **Total Expense ($000):** 23206 **Payroll Expense ($000):** 9074
Personnel: 143

ROCK SPRINGS—Sweetwater County

✠ **MEMORIAL HOSPITAL OF SWEETWATER COUNTY (530011)**, 1200 College
Drive, Zip 82901–5868, Mailing Address: P.O. Box 1359, Zip 82902–1359;
tel. 307/362–3711 **A**1 9 10 20 **F**3 5 8 11 13 15 28 29 30 31 34 35 40 43 48
57 59 60 70 75 76 77 78 79 81 82 87 93 97 99 100 102 103 104 105 107
110 111 114 115 116 118 119 129 130 131 135 146 147
Primary Contact: Gerard D. Klein, Chief Executive Officer
CFO: Irene Richardson, Chief Financial Officer
CMO: Melinda Poyer, D.O., President, Medical Staff
CHR: Keri Chorazewitz, Vice President Compliance and Employee Relations
CNO: Deborah L. Gaspar, R.N., Chief Nursing Officer
Web address: www.sweetwatermedicalcenter.com
Control: County–Government, nonfederal **Service:** General Medical and Surgical

Staffed Beds: 58 **Admissions:** 1904 **Census:** 14 **Outpatient Visits:** 105306
Births: 492 **Total Expense ($000):** 57620 **Payroll Expense ($000):** 23808
Personnel: 373

SHERIDAN—Sheridan County

☐ **SHERIDAN MEMORIAL HOSPITAL (530006)**, 1401 West Fifth Street,
Zip 82801–2799; tel. 307/672–1000, (Nonreporting) **A**1 9 10 20
Primary Contact: Michael McCafferty, Chief Executive Officer
CFO: Charlotte Marie Mather, Chief Nursing Officer
CMO: John Addlesperger, D.O., Chief Medical Officer
CIO: Nyle Morgan, Chief Information Officer
CHR: Len Gross, Chief Human Resources Officer
Web address: www.sheridanhospital.org
Control: County–Government, nonfederal **Service:** General Medical and Surgical

Staffed Beds: 72

✠ △ **SHERIDAN VETERANS AFFAIRS MEDICAL CENTER**, 1898 Fort Road,
Zip 82801–8320; tel. 307/672–3473, (Nonreporting) **A**1 7 9 **S** Department of
Veterans Affairs, Washington, DC
Primary Contact: Debra L. Hirschman, R.N., MSN, Director
COO: Chandra Lake, Associate Director
CFO: Donna Fuerstenberg, Fiscal Chief
CMO: Wendell Robison, M.D., Chief of Staff
CIO: Anthony Giljum, Chief Information Officer
CHR: James Hardin, Human Resources Officer
CNO: Kathy Berger, R.N., Associate Director, Nursing and Patient Support
Services
Web address: www.sheridan.va.gov/
Control: Veterans Affairs, Government, federal **Service:** Psychiatric

Staffed Beds: 208

Many Facility Codes have changed. Please refer to the AHA Guide Code Chart. © 2014 AHA Guide

WY

Hospitals, U.S. / WYOMING

SUNDANCE—Crook County

★ **CROOK COUNTY MEDICAL SERVICES DISTRICT (531311)**, 713 Oak Street, Zip 82729, Mailing Address: P.O. Box 517, Zip 82729–0517; tel. 307/283–3501, (Nonreporting) **A**9 10 18 **S** Regional Health, Rapid City, SD
Primary Contact: Jan VanBeek, Chief Executive Officer
CFO: Betty Meyers, Chief Financial Officer
CMO: Jeremi Villano, M.D., Chief of Staff
CHR: Patricia Feist, Manager Human Resources
Web address: www.crookcountymedical.com
Control: Hospital district or authority, Government, nonfederal **Service:** General Medical and Surgical

Staffed Beds: 48

THERMOPOLIS—Hot Springs County

★ **HOT SPRINGS COUNTY MEMORIAL HOSPITAL (531304)**, 150 East Arapahoe Street, Zip 82443–2498; tel. 307/864–3121 **A**10 18 **F**3 11 13 15 28 29 31 34 40 43 45 64 75 76 78 79 81 82 85 86 89 107 108 110 111 115 119 127 129 130 133 135 145 146 **S** HealthTech Management Services, Brentwood, TN
Primary Contact: Robin Roling, Chief Executive Officer
CFO: Shelly Larson, Chief Financial Officer
CHR: Patti Jeunehomme, Director Human Resources
Web address: www.hscmh.org
Control: County–Government, nonfederal **Service:** General Medical and Surgical

Staffed Beds: 25 **Admissions:** 491 **Census:** 5 **Outpatient Visits:** 19130
Births: 59 **Total Expense ($000):** 13963 **Payroll Expense ($000):** 5060
Personnel: 88

TORRINGTON—Goshen County

★ **COMMUNITY HOSPITAL (531307)**, 2000 Campbell Drive, Zip 82240–1597; tel. 307/532–4181 **A**9 10 18 **F**3 11 13 15 28 29 30 31 35 36 40 43 45 46 57 59 64 68 70 75 77 79 81 84 87 93 107 114 119 128 129 130 131 132 133 135 146 148 **P**6 **S** Banner Health, Phoenix, AZ
Primary Contact: Vincent B. DiFranco, Chief Executive Officer
CMO: Bonnie Randolph, M.D., Chief of Staff
CIO: Rod Miller, Chief Information Technology
CHR: Sandy Dugger, Chief Human Resources Officer
Web address: www.bannerhealth.com/Locations/Wyoming/Community+Hospital/
Control: Other not–for–profit (including NFP Corporation) **Service:** General Medical and Surgical

Staffed Beds: 25 **Admissions:** 647 **Census:** 6 **Outpatient Visits:** 33085
Births: 80 **Total Expense ($000):** 17465 **Payroll Expense ($000):** 7009
Personnel: 137

WHEATLAND—Platte County

⊞ **PLATTE COUNTY MEMORIAL HOSPITAL (531305)**, 201 14th Street, Zip 82201–3201, Mailing Address: P.O. Box 848, Zip 82201–0848; tel. 307/322–3636 **A**1 9 10 18 **F**3 13 15 29 30 40 43 46 47 48 49 59 64 70 75 76 81 107 110 114 119 128 129 130 132 133 **S** Banner Health, Phoenix, AZ
Primary Contact: Shelby Nelson, Chief Executive Officer
CFO: James Cussins, Chief Financial Officer
CMO: James Hawley, M.D., Chief of Staff
CIO: Robin May, Director Information Systems
CHR: Jennifer L. Sherwood, Chief Human Resources Officer
Web address: www.bannerhealth.com/Locations/Wyoming/Platte+County+Memorial+Hospital
Control: Other not–for–profit (including NFP Corporation) **Service:** General Medical and Surgical

Staffed Beds: 25 **Admissions:** 451 **Census:** 4 **Outpatient Visits:** 21403
Births: 66 **Total Expense ($000):** 13920 **Payroll Expense ($000):** 6358

WORLAND—Washakie County

★ **WASHAKIE MEDICAL CENTER (531306)**, 400 South 15th Street, Zip 82401–3531, Mailing Address: P.O. Box 700, Zip 82401–0700; tel. 307/347–3221 **A**9 10 18 **F**3 11 13 15 28 29 31 34 35 40 43 45 57 59 64 68 70 75 76 77 79 81 82 85 87 89 93 97 107 110 111 114 119 129 131 133 135 145 146 148 **P**6 **S** Banner Health, Phoenix, AZ
Primary Contact: Margie Molitor, R.N., Chief Executive Officer
CFO: Jennifer Montgomery, Chief Financial Officer
CMO: Ryan Clifford, M.D., Chief of Staff
CHR: Jerry Clipp, Manager Human Resources
Web address: www.washakiemedicalcenter.com
Control: Other not–for–profit (including NFP Corporation) **Service:** General Medical and Surgical

Staffed Beds: 25 **Admissions:** 692 **Census:** 7 **Outpatient Visits:** 43148
Births: 39

Hospital, Medicare Provider Number, Address, Telephone, Approval, Facility, and Physician Codes, Health Care System

★ American Hospital Association (AHA) membership
☐ The Joint Commission accreditation   ◇ DNV Healthcare Inc. accreditation
○ Healthcare Facilities Accreditation Program
△ Commission on Accreditation of Rehabilitation Facilities (CARF) accreditation

WY

© 2014 AHA Guide   *Many Facility Codes have changed. Please refer to the AHA Guide Code Chart.*   Hospitals **A723**

Hospitals in Areas Associated with the United States, by Area

AMERICAN SAMOA

PAGO PAGO— County

LYNDON B. JOHNSON TROPICAL MEDICAL CENTER (640001), Faga'alu Village, Zip 96799, Mailing Address: P.O. Box LBJ, Zip 96799; tel. 684/633–1222, (Nonreporting) **A**10
Primary Contact: Patricia Tindall, Chief Executive Officer
Web address: www.asmca.org
Control: State-Government, nonfederal **Service:** General Medical and Surgical

Staffed Beds: 125

GUAM

AGANA—Guam County

✠ **U. S. NAVAL HOSPITAL GUAM**, Zip 96910; Mailing Address: FPO, tel. 671/344–9340, (Nonreporting) **A**1 **S** Bureau of Medicine and Surgery, Department of the Navy, Washington, DC
Primary Contact: Lieutenant Commander Rona Green
Web address: www.med.navy.mil/sites/usnhguam/Pages/default.aspx
Control: Navy, Government, federal **Service:** General Medical and Surgical

Staffed Beds: 55

TAMUNING—Guam County

✠ **GUAM MEMORIAL HOSPITAL AUTHORITY (650001)**, 850 Governor Carlos G. Camacho Road, Zip 96913; tel. 671/647–2108, (Nonreporting) **A**1 10
Primary Contact: Joseph P. Verga, FACHE, Chief Executive Officer
CFO: Alan Ulrich, Chief Financial Officer
CMO: James J. Stadler, M.D., Associate Administrator Medical Services
CIO: Vince Quichocho, Manager Information Systems
CHR: Elizabeth Claros, Administrator Personnel Services
Web address: www.gmha.org
Control: Hospital district or authority, Government, nonfederal **Service:** General Medical and Surgical

Staffed Beds: 104

MARSHALL ISLANDS

KWAJALEIN ISLAND— County

KWAJALEIN HOSPITAL, U.S. Army Kwajalein Atoll, Zip 96960, Mailing Address: Box 1702, APO, UNIT, Zip 96555–5000; tel. 805/355–2225, (Nonreporting) **S** Department of the Army, Office of the Surgeon General, Falls Church, VA
Primary Contact: Elaine McMahon, Administrator
Control: Army, Government, federal **Service:** General Medical and Surgical

Staffed Beds: 14

PUERTO RICO

AGUADILLA—Aguadilla County

✠ **HOSPITAL BUEN SAMARITANO (400079)**, Carr #2 Km 141–1 Avenue Severiano Cuevas, Zip 00603, Mailing Address: P.O. Box 4055, Zip 00605–4055; tel. 787/658–0000, (Nonreporting) **A**1 5 9 10
Primary Contact: Elyonel Ponton Cruz, Executive Director
CFO: Taira Valentin Borges, Comptroller
CMO: Arturo Cedeno Llorens, M.D., Medical Director
CHR: Jose Garcia Rivera, Director Human Resources
CNO: Eneida Alicea Perez, Interim Nursing Director
Web address: www.hbspr.org
Control: Other not–for–profit (including NFP Corporation) **Service:** General Medical and Surgical

Staffed Beds: 150

AIBONITO—Aibonito County

✠ **CENTRO DE SALUD CONDUCTUAL MENONITA–CIMA (404009)**, Carretera Estatal 14 Interior, Zip 00705, Mailing Address: CIMA Calle Sargento Gerardo Santiago, Zip 00705; tel. 787/714–2462, (Nonreporting) **A**1 9 10
Primary Contact: Pedro Melendez, Chief Executive Officer
Control: Other not–for–profit (including NFP Corporation) **Service:** Psychiatric

Staffed Beds: 32

✠ **MENNONITE GENERAL HOSPITAL (400018)**, Calle Jose C. Vasquez, Zip 00705, Mailing Address: P.O. Box 372800, Cayey, Zip 00737–2800; tel. 787/535–1001 **A**1 9 10 **F**7 8 13 15 17 29 30 31 34 35 40 41 42 46 47 57 59 62 63 64 65 68 70 72 74 75 76 78 79 81 82 89 107 111 114 115 119 124 130 143 144 145 146 147 148 **P**5
Primary Contact: Pedro Melendez, Chief Executive Officer
COO: Marta R Mercado Suro, Chief Operating Officer
CFO: Jose E. Solivan, Chief Financial Officer
CMO: Victor Hernandez Miranda, M.D., Chief of Staff
CIO: Daniza Morales, Manager Information System
CHR: Evelyn Padilla Ortiz, Director Human Resources
CNO: Gloria Mercado, Director of Nursing
Web address: www.hospitalmenonita.com
Control: Other not–for–profit (including NFP Corporation) **Service:** General Medical and Surgical

Staffed Beds: 143 Admissions: 8270 Census: 96 Births: 869 Total Expense ($000): 55123 Payroll Expense ($000): 22279 Personnel: 856

ARECIBO—Arecibo County

✠ **HOSPITAL DR. CAYETANO COLL Y TOSTE (400087)**, 129 San Luis Avenue, Zip 00612, Mailing Address: P.O. Box 659, Zip 00613; tel. 787/650–7272, (Nonreporting) **A**1 9 10
Primary Contact: Homar Perez, Chief Executive Officer and Vice President Administration
COO: Jamie Rivera, Chief Financial Officer
CFO: Agustin Gonzalez, Director Finance
CMO: Antoine Pavia, M.D., Medical Director
CIO: David Valle, Chief Information Officer
CHR: Yesenia Natal, Coordinator Human Resources
CNO: Iris Toledo, Chief Nursing Officer
Web address: www.cayetano@xsn.net
Control: Corporation, Investor–owned, for–profit **Service:** General Medical and Surgical

Staffed Beds: 188

★ **HOSPITAL METROPOLITANO DR. SUSONI (400117)**, Calle Palma #55, Zip 00612, Mailing Address: P.O. Box 145200, Zip 00614; tel. 787/650–1030 **A**9 10 **F**18 29 30 31 45 49 70 74 75 78 79 81 82 89 93 107 110 111 114 119 130 148
Primary Contact: Astrid J. Abreu, Executive Director
CFO: Hector Ortiz, Financial Director
CMO: Ada S. Miranda, M.D., Medical Director
CIO: Mayra Montano, Director Information Systems
CHR: Janiva Hernandez, Coordinator Human Resources
CNO: Carmen G. Fuster, Nursing Director
Web address: www.metropavia.com/DrSusoni.cfm
Control: Corporation, Investor–owned, for–profit **Service:** General Medical and Surgical

Staffed Beds: 134 Admissions: 8069 Census: 101 Outpatient Visits: 60927 Births: 0 Total Expense ($000): 36544 Payroll Expense ($000): 13014

ARROYO—Arroyo County

★ **LAFAYETTE HOSPITAL (400026)**, Central Lafayette, Zip 00714, Mailing Address: P.O. Box 207, Zip 00714; tel. 787/839–3232, (Nonreporting) **A**9 10
Primary Contact: Ruth M. Ortiz Vargas, Administrator
CMO: Jose L. Pimentel Fernandez, Medical Director
Control: Corporation, Investor–owned, for–profit **Service:** General Medical and Surgical

Staffed Beds: 38

BAYAMON—Bayamon County

★ **DOCTOR'S CENTER OF BAYAMON (400102)**, Extension Hermanas Davila, Zip 00960, Mailing Address: P.O. Box 2957, Zip 00960; tel. 787/622–5420, (Nonreporting) **A**10
Primary Contact: Carlos Blanco, M.D., Administrator
Control: Corporation, Investor–owned, for–profit **Service:** General Medical and Surgical

Staffed Beds: 91

Many Facility Codes have changed. Please refer to the AHA Guide Code Chart.

⊞ HOSPITAL HERMANOS MELENDEZ (400032), Route 2, KM 11–7, Zip 00960, Mailing Address: P.O. Box 306, Zip 00960; tel. 787/620–8181, (Nonreporting) **A**1 9 10
Primary Contact: Maria T. Machado, Administrator
CFO: Luz D. Medina, Controller
CMO: Norma Ortiz, M.D., Medical Director
CIO: Leticia Santana, Administrator Medical Records
Web address: www.hospitalhermanosmelendez.net
Control: Corporation, Investor–owned, for–profit **Service:** General Medical and Surgical

Staffed Beds: 211

⊞ HOSPITAL SAN PABLO (400109), Calle Santa Cruz 70, Zip 00961–7020, Mailing Address: P.O. Box 236, Zip 00960–0236; tel. 787/740–4747 **A**1 3 5 9 10 **F**3 8 13 17 18 19 20 22 24 26 29 30 31 34 40 41 44 45 46 47 49 51 59 70 72 73 74 75 76 78 79 80 81 86 87 88 89 92 93 107 110 111 114 115 119 126 145 146 148 **P**1
Primary Contact: Jose E. Carballo, Chief Executive Officer and Managing Director
Web address: www.sanpablo.com
Control: Corporation, Investor–owned, for–profit **Service:** General Medical and Surgical

Staffed Beds: 394 **Admissions:** 16027 **Census:** 299 **Outpatient Visits:** 10666 **Births:** 762 **Total Expense ($000):** 149852 **Payroll Expense ($000):** 52391 **Personnel:** 1643

⊞ HOSPITAL UNIVERSITARIO DR. RAMON RUIZ ARNAU (400105), Avenue Laurel, Santa Juanita, Zip 00956; tel. 787/787–5151, (Nonreporting) **A**1 3 5 10 **S** Puerto Rico Department of Health, San Juan, PR
Primary Contact: Humberto M. Monserrate, Chief Executive Officer
CFO: Elsie Morales, Chief Financial Officer
CMO: Hector Cintron Principe, M.D., Director
CIO: Irma Duprey, Administrator Medical Records
CHR: Aurea De Leon, Chief Human Resources Officer
Control: State–Government, nonfederal **Service:** General Medical and Surgical

Staffed Beds: 101

CABO ROJO—Cabo Rojo County

★ HOSPITAL PSIQUIATRICO METROPOLITANO (404007), 108 Munoz Rivera Street, Zip 00623–4060, Mailing Address: P.O. Box 910, Zip 00623–0910; tel. 787/851–2025, (Nonreporting) **A**9 10
Primary Contact: Elizabeth De Santiago, Director
Control: Other not–for–profit (including NFP Corporation) **Service:** General Medical and Surgical

Staffed Beds: 39

CAGUAS—Caguas County

⊞ HOSPITAL HIMA SAN PABLO CAGUAS (400120), Avenida Munoz Marin, Zip 00726, Mailing Address: P.O. Box 4980, Zip 00726; tel. 787/653–3434, (Nonreporting) **A**1 2 5 9 10
Primary Contact: Claudia V. Guzman, Executive Director
CFO: Luis A. Arroyo, Chief Financial Officer
CMO: Ivan E. Del Toro, M.D., Medical Director
CIO: Giovanni Piereschi, Vice President Enterprise Information and Chief Information Officer
CHR: Elena Robinson, Chief Human Resources Officer
CNO: Elenia Berrios, Chief Nursing Officer
Control: Partnership, Investor–owned, for–profit **Service:** General Medical and Surgical

Staffed Beds: 300

CAROLINA—Carolina County

⊞ HOSPITAL DE LA UNIVERSIDAD DE PUERTO RICO/DR. FEDERICO TRILLA (400112), 65th Infanteria, KM 8 3, Zip 00984, Mailing Address: P.O. Box 6021, Zip 00984; tel. 787/757–1800, (Nonreporting) **A**1 3 5 9 10
Primary Contact: Diraida Maldonado, Chief Executive Officer
COO: Diraida Maldonado, Chief Executive Officer
CFO: Yolanda Quinonez, Chief Financial Officer
CMO: Marina Roman, M.D., Medical Director
CIO: Francisco Perez, Manager Management Information Systems
CHR: Betzaida Jimenez, Director Human Resources
Web address: www.hospitalupr.org
Control: Corporation, Investor–owned, for–profit **Service:** General Medical and Surgical

Staffed Beds: 196

CASTANER—Lares County

★ CASTANER GENERAL HOSPITAL (400010), KM 64–2, Route 135, Zip 00631, Mailing Address: P.O. Box 1003, Zip 00631; tel. 787/829–5010, (Nonreporting) **A**3 5 10
Primary Contact: Domingo Monroig, Executive Director
COO: Agustin Ponce, Supervisor Maintenance
CFO: Guillermo Jimenez, Director Finance
CMO: Jose O. Rodriguez, M.D., Medical Director
CIO: Domingo Monroig, Executive Director
CHR: Nydimar Salcedo, Chief Human Resources Officer
CNO: Margarita Rentas, R.N., Nursing Director
Control: Other not–for–profit (including NFP Corporation) **Service:** General Medical and Surgical

Staffed Beds: 24

CAYEY—Cayey County

⊞ HOSPITAL MENONITA DE CAYEY (400013), 4 H. Mendoza Street, Zip 00736–3801, Mailing Address: P.O. Box 373130, Zip 00737–3130; tel. 787/263–1001, (Nonreporting) **A**1 9 10
Primary Contact: Pedro Melendez, Chief Executive Director
COO: Leda Marta R Mercado, Chief Operating Officer
CFO: Jose E. Solivan, Chief Financial Officer
CMO: Luis J Rodriquez Saenz, M.D., Medical Director
CIO: Daniza Morales, Chief Information Officer
CHR: Evelyn Padilla Ortiz, Director Human Resources
Web address: www.hospitalmenonita.com
Control: Other not–for–profit (including NFP Corporation) **Service:** General Medical and Surgical

Staffed Beds: 145

CIDRA—Cidra County

⊞ FIRST HOSPITAL PANAMERICANO (404004), State Road 787 KM 1 5, Zip 00739, Mailing Address: P.O. Box 1400, Zip 00739; tel. 787/739–5555, (Nonreporting) **A**1 3 5 9 10 **S** Universal Health Services, Inc., King of Prussia, PA
Primary Contact: Astro Munoz, Executive Director
COO: Tim McCarthy, President Puerto Rico Division
CFO: Arthur Fernandez, Chief Financial Officer
CMO: Arlene Martinez–Nieto, M.D., Chief Medical Officer
CIO: Tomas Rodriguez, Chief Information Technology Officer
CHR: Shirley Ayala, Director Human Resources
Web address: www.hospitalpanamericano.com
Control: Corporation, Investor–owned, for–profit **Service:** Psychiatric

Staffed Beds: 153

COTO LAUREL—Ponce County

★ HOSPITAL SAN CRISTOBAL (400113), 506 Carr Road, Zip 00780; tel. 787/848–2100, (Nonreporting) **A**3 5 9 10
Primary Contact: Pedro L. Benetti–Loyola, Administrator
COO: Pedro L. Benetti–Loyola, Senior Executive and Vice President
CFO: Marian Collazo, Director Finance
CMO: Ramon Rodriguez Rivas, M.D., Medical Director
CIO: Ramon Acevedo, Supervisor Information Systems
CHR: Candie Rodriguez, Director Human Resources
Web address: www.hospitalsancristobal.com
Control: Corporation, Investor–owned, for–profit **Service:** Other specialty

Staffed Beds: 103

FAJARDO—Fajardo County

★ CARIBBEAN MEDICAL CENTER (400131), 151 Avenue Osvaldo Molina, Zip 00738–4013, Mailing Address: Call Box 70006, Zip 00738–7006; tel. 787/801–0081 **A**9 10 **F**3 30 40 41 60 70 76 79 81 89 107 119 130 **P**1
Primary Contact: Eduardo Sotomayor, Executive Director
CMO: Miguel Rodriguez, Medical Director
Control: Other not–for–profit (including NFP Corporation) **Service:** General Medical and Surgical

Staffed Beds: 39 **Admissions:** 3350 **Census:** 40 **Outpatient Visits:** 33316 **Births:** 313 **Total Expense ($000):** 14605 **Payroll Expense ($000):** 3972 **Personnel:** 219

Hospital, Medicare Provider Number, Address, Telephone, Approval, Facility, and Physician Codes, Health Care System

★ American Hospital Association (AHA) membership
□ The Joint Commission accreditation
◇ DNV Healthcare Inc. accreditation
○ Healthcare Facilities Accreditation Program
△ Commission on Accreditation of Rehabilitation Facilities (CARF) accreditation

Other Associated Areas

✠ **HOSPITAL SAN PABLO DEL ESTE (400125)**, Avenida General Valero, 404, Zip 00738, Mailing Address: P.O. Box 1028, Zip 00738–1028; tel. 787/863–0505, (Nonreporting) **A**1 9 10
Primary Contact: Aixa Irizarry, Executive Director
CFO: Luis A. Arroyo, Chief Financial Officer
CMO: Manuel Navas, M.D., Medical Director
CHR: Vilma Rodriguez, Director Human Resources
Web address: www.sanpablo.com
Control: Corporation, Investor–owned, for–profit **Service:** General Medical and Surgical

Staffed Beds: 136

GUAYAMA—Guayama County

✠ **HOSPITAL EPISCOPAL SAN LUCAS GUAYAMA (400048)**, Avenue Pedro Albizu Campos, Zip 00784, Mailing Address: PO Box 10011, Zip 00785–1006; tel. 787/864–4300, (Nonreporting) **A**1 3 5 9 10
Primary Contact: Julio Colon, CPA, Chief Executive Officer
COO: Arnaldo Rodriguez Sanchez, M.D., Chief Operating Officer
CFO: Rosemary De La Cruz, Chief Financial Officer
CMO: Gerson Jimenez, M.D., Medical Director
CHR: Ivette Lacot, Director Human Resources
Web address: www.ssepr.com
Control: Church–operated, Nongovernment, not–for profit **Service:** General Medical and Surgical

Staffed Beds: 115

★ **HOSPITAL SANTA ROSA (400009)**, Veterans Avenue, Zip 00784, Mailing Address: P.O. Box 10008, Zip 00785; tel. 787/864–0101 **A**9 10 **F**18 20 40 45 46 70 76 81 89 107 111 119
Primary Contact: Gloria Diaz, Executive Director
CFO: Edwin De Jesus, Comptroller
CMO: Ausberto Alejandro, M.D., President
CIO: Waleska Rolon, Manager
Control: Other not–for–profit (including NFP Corporation) **Service:** General Medical and Surgical

Staffed Beds: 89 **Admissions:** 3220 **Census:** 31 **Outpatient Visits:** 43494 **Births:** 193 **Total Expense ($000):** 14282 **Payroll Expense ($000):** 3994 **Personnel:** 190

GUAYNABO—Guaynabo County

PROFESSIONAL HOSPITAL GUAYNABO (400122), Carretera 199 Km 1.2 Avenue, Zip 00969, Mailing Address: PO Box 1609, Zip 00970; tel. 787/708–6560, (Nonreporting) **A**10
Primary Contact: Leonardo Valentin, Chief Executive Officer
Web address: www.professionalhospital.com
Control: Other not–for–profit (including NFP Corporation) **Service:** Psychiatric

Staffed Beds: 54

HATO REY—San Juan County, See San Juan

HUMACAO—Humacao County

HOSPITAL DR. DOMINGUEZ See Hospital Oriente

✠ **HOSPITAL HMA DE HUMACAO (400005)**, 3 Font Martelo Street, Zip 00791–3342, Mailing Address: P.O. Box 639, Zip 00792–0639; tel. 787/656–2424, (Nonreporting) **A**1 9 10
Primary Contact: Aixa Irizarry, Executive Director
COO: Carlos M. Pineiro, President
CFO: Luis A. Arroyo, Chief Financial Officer
CMO: Francisco R. Carballo, M.D., Medical Director
CIO: Giovanni Piereschi, Vice President Management Information Systems
CHR: Iris Abreu, Supervisor Human Resources
Control: Corporation, Investor–owned, for–profit **Service:** General Medical and Surgical

Staffed Beds: 64

★ **HOSPITAL ORIENTE (400011)**, 300 Font Martelo Street, Zip 00791–3230, Mailing Address: P.O. Box 699, Zip 00792–0699; tel. 787/852–0505, (Nonreporting) **A**9 10
Primary Contact: Juan Carlos Latorre, Administrator
CFO: Ivonne Rivera, Director Finance
CMO: Carmelo Herrero, M.D., Medical Director
CHR: Ivonne Lopez, Director Human Resources
Control: Corporation, Investor–owned, for–profit **Service:** General Medical and Surgical

Staffed Beds: 60

★ **RYDER MEMORIAL HOSPITAL (400007)**, 355 Font Martelo Street, Zip 00791–3249, Mailing Address: P.O. Box 859, Zip 00792–0859; tel. 787/852–0768, (Total facility includes 62 beds in nursing home–type unit) **A**9 10 **F**6 8 10 13 15 20 26 30 31 34 35 39 40 41 42 54 56 57 59 61 62 63 64 65 68 70 72 75 76 77 78 81 87 89 93 94 107 110 111 115 119 124 125 128 130 144 146 147 **P**5 8
Primary Contact: Jose R. Feliciano, Chief Executive Officer
CFO: Jose O. Ortiz, Chief Financial Officer
CMO: Raul Ramos Pereira, M.D., Medical Director
CIO: Joseph V. Cruz, Chief Information Officer
CHR: Maria Figueroa, Director Human Resources
CNO: Aurelis Burgus, Nursing Director
Web address: www.hryder@prtc.net
Control: Other not–for–profit (including NFP Corporation) **Service:** General Medical and Surgical

Staffed Beds: 165 **Admissions:** 7443 **Census:** 106 **Outpatient Visits:** 147421 **Births:** 395 **Total Expense ($000):** 56427 **Payroll Expense ($000):** 22804 **Personnel:** 945

MANATI—Manati County

✠ **DOCTORS CENTER (400118)**, KM 47–7, Zip 00674, Mailing Address: P.O. Box 30532, Zip 00674; tel. 787/854–3322, (Nonreporting) **A**1 9 10
Primary Contact: Carlos Blanco, M.D., Administrator
Control: Corporation, Investor–owned, for–profit **Service:** General Medical and Surgical

Staffed Beds: 150

★ **HEALTHSOUTH HOSPITAL OF MANATI (403026)**, Carretera 2, Kilometro 47 7, Zip 00674; tel. 787/621–3800 **A**9 10 **F**90 91 96 130 **S** HEALTHSOUTH Corporation, Birmingham, AL
Primary Contact: Enrique A. Vicens–Rivera, Jr., JD, Chief Executive Officer
CFO: Jesus M. Corazon, Controller
CMO: Jamie L. Marrero, M.D., Medical Director
CHR: Erika Landrau, Director Human Resources
CNO: Evelyn Diaz, R.N., Chief Nursing Officer
Web address: www.healthsouth.com
Control: Corporation, Investor–owned, for–profit **Service:** Rehabilitation

Staffed Beds: 40 **Admissions:** 1038 **Census:** 35 **Births:** 0

✠ **HOSPITAL MANATI MEDICAL CENTER (400114)**, Calle Hernandez, Carrion 668, Zip 00674, Mailing Address: P.O. Box 1142, Zip 00674–1142; tel. 787/621–3700 **A**1 3 5 9 10 **F**3 8 13 14 15 17 18 19 20 22 26 29 30 34 40 41 45 46 47 48 49 51 60 69 70 73 74 75 76 78 79 80 87 89 93 107 110 111 113 114 115 119 130 145 146 **P**8
Primary Contact: Alfonso Vazquez, Executive Director
CFO: Noriselle Rivera–Pol, Vice President Finance
CMO: Luis R. Rosa–Toledo, M.D., Medical Director
CIO: Alberto Medina, Information Technology Senior Consultant
CHR: Nilda Paravisini, Director Human Resources
Web address: www.manatimedical.com
Control: Corporation, Investor–owned, for–profit **Service:** General Medical and Surgical

Staffed Beds: 235 **Admissions:** 17114 **Census:** 221 **Outpatient Visits:** 54232 **Births:** 1853 **Personnel:** 1590

MAYAGUEZ—Mayaguez County

✠ **BELLA VISTA HOSPITAL (400014)**, State Road 349, Zip 00680, Mailing Address: P.O. Box 1750, Zip 00681; tel. 787/834–6000, (Nonreporting) **A**1 3 5 9 10
Primary Contact: Jesus Nieves, Chief Executive Officer
CFO: Enrique Rivera, Chief Financial Officer
CMO: Miguel Cruz, M.D., Medical Director
CHR: Benjamin Astacio, Director Human Resources
Web address: www.bvhpr.org
Control: Church–operated, Nongovernment, not–for profit **Service:** General Medical and Surgical

Staffed Beds: 157

✠ **DR. RAMON E. BETANCES HOSPITAL–MAYAGUEZ MEDICAL CENTER BRANCH (400103)**, 410 Hostos Avenue, Zip 00680–1501, Mailing Address: P.O. Box 600, Zip 00681–0600; tel. 787/652–9200, (Nonreporting) **A**1 3 5 9 10
Primary Contact: Jaime Maestre, Chief Executive Officer
CMO: Milton D. Carrero, M.D., Medical Director
CHR: Betsmari Medina, Director Human Resources
Control: State–Government, nonfederal **Service:** General Medical and Surgical

Staffed Beds: 144

Many Facility Codes have changed. Please refer to the AHA Guide Code Chart. © 2014 AHA Guide

★ **HOSPITAL PEREA (400123)**, 15 Basora Street, Zip 00681, Mailing Address: P.O. Box 170, Zip 00681; tel. 787/834–0101, (Nonreporting) **A**10 **S** United Medical Corporation, Windermere, FL
Primary Contact: Jorge I. Martinez, Executive Director
CFO: Joannie Garcia, CPA, Director Finance
CMO: Humberto Olivencia, M.D., Medical Director
Web address: www.paviahealth.com/perea_hospital.htm
Control: Corporation, Investor–owned, for–profit **Service:** General Medical and Surgical

Staffed Beds: 103

MOCA—Moca County

★ **HOSPITAL SAN CARLOS BORROMEO (400111)**, 550 Concepcion Vera Ayala, Zip 00676; tel. 787/877–8000 **A**9 10 **F**8 15 29 30 34 40 45 65 70 74 75 76 79 81 89 107 111 115 119 130 133 145 146 148 **P**8
Primary Contact: Rosaida M. Crespo, Executive Director
COO: Rosaida M. Crespo, Executive Director
CFO: Irma Cabrera, Finance Director
CMO: Erick Nieves, M.D., Medical Director
CIO: Juan Carlos Soto, Director Information Systems
CHR: Migdalia Ortiz, Director Human Resources
CNO: Luz M. Velez, Director–Administration of Nursing Services
Web address: www.hscbpr.org
Control: Other not–for–profit (including NFP Corporation) **Service:** General Medical and Surgical

Staffed Beds: 106 Admissions: 5195 Census: 69 Outpatient Visits: 41125 Births: 707 Total Expense ($000): 26216 Payroll Expense ($000): 8898 Personnel: 371

PONCE—Ponce County

✠ **DR. PILA'S HOSPITAL (400003)**, Avenida Las Americas, Zip 00731, Mailing Address: P.O. Box 1910, Zip 00733–1910; tel. 787/848–5600, (Nonreporting) **A**1 3 5 9 10
Primary Contact: Rafael Alvarado, Chief Executive Officer
Web address: www.drpila.com
Control: Other not–for–profit (including NFP Corporation) **Service:** General Medical and Surgical

Staffed Beds: 115

✠ **HOSPITAL DE DAMAS (400022)**, Ponce by Pass, Zip 00731; tel. 787/840–8686, (Nonreporting) **A**1 3 5 9 10
Primary Contact: Edwin Sueiro, Administrator
CFO: Julio Colon, Financial Director
CMO: Pedro Benitez, M.D., Medical Director
CIO: Bienvenido Ortiz, Coordinator Information Systems
CHR: Gilberto Cuevas, Director Human Resources
CNO: Sandra Dominicci, Nursing Director
Web address: www.hospitaldamas.com
Control: Other not–for–profit (including NFP Corporation) **Service:** General Medical and Surgical

Staffed Beds: 225

★ **HOSPITAL ONCOLOGICO ANDRES GRILLASCA (400028)**, Centro Medico De Ponce, Zip 00733, Mailing Address: P.O. Box 331324, Zip 00733–1324; tel. 787/848–0800, (Nonreporting) **A**3 5 9
Primary Contact: Manuel J. Vazquez, Executive Administrator
CMO: Roberto Velasquez, M.D., Medical Director
CIO: Maria T. Teissonniere, Director Public Relations
CHR: Carlos T. Santiago, Director Human Resources
Control: Other not–for–profit (including NFP Corporation) **Service:** Cancer

Staffed Beds: 49

★ **INSPIRA PONCE (404008)**, Calle Guadalupe, #184, Piso2, Zip 00730; tel. 787/079–4130, (Nonreporting) **A**10
Primary Contact: Alberto M. Varela, M.D., President
Web address: www.inspirapr.com
Control: Corporation, Investor–owned, for–profit **Service:** Psychiatric

Staffed Beds: 30

✠ **ST. LUKE'S EPISCOPAL HOSPITAL (400044)**, 917 Tito Castro Avenue, Zip 00731–4717, Mailing Address: P.O. Box 336810, Zip 00733–6810; tel. 787/844–2080 **A**1 3 5 9 10 **F**7 13 17 18 20 22 24 26 30 35 40 41 42 43 45 46 47 48 49 51 57 58 64 67 70 72 73 75 76 79 81 82 85 87 88 89 92 93 107 111 114 115 119 124 130 131 144 145 147 148
Primary Contact: Julio Colon, Interim President and Chief Executive Officer
CFO: Julio Colon, Chief Financial Officer
CMO: Jenaro Scarano, M.D., Medical Director
CHR: Juan Salazar, Director Human Resources
Web address: www.sanlucaspr.com
Control: Church–operated, Nongovernment, not–for profit **Service:** General Medical and Surgical

Staffed Beds: 334 Admissions: 17176 Census: 275 Outpatient Visits: 88891 Births: 2052 Total Expense ($000): 112793 Payroll Expense ($000): 32513 Personnel: 1203

RIO PIEDRAS—San Juan County, See San Juan

SAN GERMAN—San German County

✠ **HOSPITAL DE LA CONCEPCION (400021)**, Carr 2, Km 173, Bo Cain Alto, Zip 00683–3920, Mailing Address: P.O. Box 285, Zip 00683–0285; tel. 787/892–1860, (Nonreporting) **A**1 3 5 9 10
Primary Contact: Felicita Bonilla, Administrator
COO: Gustavo Almodovar, Executive Director
CFO: Lizmari Calderon, Director Finance
CMO: Ivan Acosta, M.D., Medical Director
CIO: Daniel Ferreira, Director Management Information Systems
CHR: Ada Bermudez, Director Human Resources
CNO: Amanda Caraballo, Nursing Director
Web address: www.hospitalconcepcion.org
Control: Church–operated, Nongovernment, not–for profit **Service:** General Medical and Surgical

Staffed Beds: 167

★ **HOSPITAL METROPOLITANO SAN GERMAN (400126)**, Calle Javilla Al Costado Parque de Bombas, Zip 00683; tel. 787/892–5300, (Nonreporting) **A**9 10
Primary Contact: Nannete Acosta, Chief Executive Officer
Control: Corporation, Investor–owned, for–profit **Service:** Other specialty

Staffed Beds: 40

SAN JUAN—San Juan County
(Mailing Addresses - Hato Rey, Rio Piedras)

✠ **ASHFORD PRESBYTERIAN COMMUNITY HOSPITAL (400001)**, 1451 Avenue Ashford, Zip 00907–1511, Mailing Address: P.O. Box 9020032, Zip 00902–0032; tel. 787/721–2160 **A**1 9 10 **F**3 8 11 13 15 17 18 30 40 41 43 45 46 49 51 53 59 65 70 72 75 76 79 80 81 82 87 88 89 91 93 97 107 110 111 114 119 130 131 146 147 148 **P**5
Primary Contact: Pedro J. Gonzalez, FACHE, Chief Executive Officer
COO: Obdulia Medina, MSN, Associate Director for Administrative Support, Clinical Management and Ambulatory Care
CFO: Mayra Torres, Chief Financial Officer
CMO: Francisco de Torres, M.D., Medical Director
CIO: Gerald Lopez, Chief Information Officer
CHR: Irma Carrillo, Director Human Resources
CNO: Itza Soto, MSN, Nursing Executive
Web address: www.presbypr.com
Control: Other not–for–profit (including NFP Corporation) **Service:** General Medical and Surgical

Staffed Beds: 191 Admissions: 11022 Census: 142 Outpatient Visits: 41055 Births: 3371 Total Expense ($000): 75467 Payroll Expense ($000): 27034 Personnel: 801

✠ **AUXILIO MUTUO HOSPITAL (400016)**, Ponce De Leon Avenue, Zip 00918–1000, Mailing Address: P.O. Box 191227, Zip 00919–1227; tel. 787/758–2000, (Nonreporting) **A**1 3 5 9 10
Primary Contact: Jorge L. Matta Serrano, Administrator
COO: Carmen Martin, Associate Administrator
CFO: Maria L. Marti, Director Fiscal Services
CMO: Jose Isado, M.D., Medical Director
CIO: Edgardo Rodriguez, Director Management Information Systems
CHR: Maria Vega, Director Human Resources
Web address: www.auxiliomutuo.com
Control: Other not–for–profit (including NFP Corporation) **Service:** General Medical and Surgical

Staffed Beds: 483

Hospital, Medicare Provider Number, Address, Telephone, Approval, Facility, and Physician Codes, Health Care System

★ American Hospital Association (AHA) membership
□ The Joint Commission accreditation   ◇ DNV Healthcare Inc. accreditation
○ Healthcare Facilities Accreditation Program
△ Commission on Accreditation of Rehabilitation Facilities (CARF) accreditation

✠ **CARDIOVASCULAR CENTER OF PUERTO RICO AND THE CARIBBEAN (400124)**, Americo Miranda Centro Medico, Zip 00936, Mailing Address: P.O. Box 366528, Zip 00936–6528; tel. 787/754–8500, (Nonreporting) **A**1 3 5 10 **S** Puerto Rico Department of Health, San Juan, PR
Primary Contact: Waleska Crespo, Executive Director
COO: Wilfredo Rabelo Millan, Chief Operating Officer
CFO: Arthur J. Fernandez del Valle, Chief Financial Officer
CMO: Jose E. Novoa Loyola, M.D., Medical Director
CIO: Eugenio Torres Ayala, Director Information Systems
CHR: Myriam T. Rodriguez Schmidt, Director Human Resources
CNO: Pedro Laureano Cantre, Chief Nursing Officer
Web address: www.cardiovascular.gobierno.pr
Control: State–Government, nonfederal **Service:** General Medical and Surgical

Staffed Beds: 146

★ **DOCTORS' CENTER HOSPITAL SAN JUAN (400006)**, 1395 San Rafael Street, Zip 00909–2518, Mailing Address: Box 11338, Santurce Station, Zip 00910–3428; tel. 787/999–7620 **A**9 10 **F**29 40 41 45 46 70 74 76 77 78 81 89 107 119 130 148
Primary Contact: Norma Marrero, Executive Administrator
COO: Norma Marrero, Executive Administrator
CFO: Alejandro Santiago, Director Finance
CMO: Ubaldo Santiago, M.D., Chairman
CIO: Luis Alicea, Chief Information Officer
CHR: Carmen Perez, Director Human Resources
CNO: Lesbia Lopez, Chief Nursing Officer
Web address: www.tuhospitalfamiliar.com
Control: Corporation, Investor–owned, for–profit **Service:** General Medical and Surgical

Staffed Beds: 125 **Admissions:** 6155 **Census:** 101 **Outpatient Visits:** 23393 **Births:** 243 **Total Expense ($000):** 28452 **Payroll Expense ($000):** 8741 **Personnel:** 422

★ **HEALTHSOUTH REHABILITATION HOSPITAL OF SAN JUAN (403025)**, University Hospital, 3rd Floor, Zip 00923, Mailing Address: P.O. Box 70344, Zip 00923; tel. 787/274–5100 **A**3 5 9 10 **F**7 29 77 90 93 **P**1 **S** HEALTHSOUTH Corporation, Birmingham, AL
Primary Contact: Daniel Del Castillo, Chief Executive Officer
CFO: Jesus M. Corazon, Controller
CMO: Eduardo Ramos, M.D., Medical Director
CHR: Frances Fuentes, Coordinator Human Resources
CNO: Zamarys Rivera, R.N., Chief Nursing Officer
Web address: www.healthsouthsanjuan.com
Control: Corporation, Investor–owned, for–profit **Service:** Rehabilitation

Staffed Beds: 32 **Admissions:** 885 **Census:** 31 **Outpatient Visits:** 5025 **Births:** 0 **Total Expense ($000):** 6894 **Payroll Expense ($000):** 3267 **Personnel:** 101

★ **HOSPITAL DE PSIQUIATRIA (404006)**, Dr. Ramon Fernandez Marina, P.O. Box 2100, Zip 00936; tel. 787/766–4646, (Nonreporting) **A**3 5
Primary Contact: Miguel J. Bustelo, Executive Director
CMO: Brunilda Vazquez, Medical Director
CHR: Idalia Garcia, Chief Human Resources Officer
Control: State–Government, nonfederal **Service:** Psychiatric

Staffed Beds: 153

✠ **HOSPITAL DEL MAESTRO (400004)**, 550 Sergio Cuevas, Zip 00918–3741, Mailing Address: P.O. Box 364708, Zip 00936–4708; tel. 787/758–8383, (Nonreporting) **A**1 9 10
Primary Contact: Jorge Torres Otero, Executive Director
CFO: Marisol Vargas, Director Finance
CMO: Jose Montalvo, M.D., Medical Director
CIO: Laura Rodriguez, Director Medical Records
CHR: Orlando Santiago, Human Resources Officer
Control: Corporation, Investor–owned, for–profit **Service:** General Medical and Surgical

Staffed Beds: 250

✠ **HOSPITAL METROPOLITAN (400106)**, 1785 Carr 21, Zip 00921–3399, Mailing Address: P.O. Box 11981, Zip 00922; tel. 787/782–9999, (Nonreporting) **A**1 9 10
Primary Contact: Jose Rosado, Chief Executive Officer
CFO: Maritza Rodriguez, Chief Financial Officer
CMO: Maria de los Angeles Correa, M.D., Medical Director
CIO: Manuel Santiago, Chief Information Officer
Control: Corporation, Investor–owned, for–profit **Service:** General Medical and Surgical

Staffed Beds: 122

✠ **HOSPITAL PAVIA–HATO REY (400128)**, 435 Ponce De Leon Avenue, Zip 00917–3428; tel. 787/641–2323, (Nonreporting) **A**1 3 5 9 10 **S** United Medical Corporation, Windermere, FL
Primary Contact: Guillermo Pastrana, Executive Director
Web address: www.paviahealth.com
Control: Corporation, Investor–owned, for–profit **Service:** General Medical and Surgical

Staffed Beds: 180

✠ **HOSPITAL PAVIA–SANTURCE (400019)**, 1462 Asia Street, Zip 00909–2143, Mailing Address: Box 11137, Santurce Station, Zip 00910–1137; tel. 787/727–6060, (Nonreporting) **A**1 10 **S** United Medical Corporation, Windermere, FL
Primary Contact: Jose Luis Rodriguez, Chief Executive Officer
CFO: Francisco Espina, Director Finance
Web address: www.paviahealth.com
Control: Corporation, Investor–owned, for–profit **Service:** General Medical and Surgical

Staffed Beds: 215

✠ **HOSPITAL SAN FRANCISCO (400098)**, 371 Avenida De Diego, Zip 00923–1711, Mailing Address: P.O. Box 29025, Zip 00929–0025; tel. 787/767–5100, (Nonreporting) **A**1 10
Primary Contact: Marcos Aguila, Chief Executive Officer
CFO: Lizzette Rodriguez, Director Finance
CMO: Hector L. Cotto, M.D., Medical Director
CIO: Deborah Nieves, Director Management Information Systems
CHR: Sugehi Santiago, Director
Web address: www.sanpablo.com
Control: Corporation, Investor–owned, for–profit **Service:** General Medical and Surgical

Staffed Beds: 150

★ **HOSPITAL SAN GERARDO (400121)**, 138 Avenue Winston Churchill, Zip 00926–6013; tel. 787/761–8383, (Nonreporting) **A**9 10
Primary Contact: Henry Ruberte, Administrator
Control: Other not–for–profit (including NFP Corporation) **Service:** Chronic disease

Staffed Beds: 60

✠ **I. GONZALEZ MARTINEZ ONCOLOGIC HOSPITAL (400012)**, Puerto Rico Medical Center, Hato Rey, Zip 00935, Mailing Address: P.O. Box 191811, Zip 00919–1811; tel. 787/765–2382 **A**1 2 3 5 10 **F**3 8 15 18 29 30 31 34 35 45 54 57 58 59 63 64 65 66 70 75 78 79 81 86 87 93 100 107 110 111 114 115 117 118 119 124 130 132 133 136 141 146 148 **P**5
Primary Contact: Jorge De Jesus, Executive Director
COO: Felix Ortiz, Administrator
CFO: Yolanda Quinones, Director Finance
CMO: Carlos Chevere, M.D., Medical Director
CHR: Luz Maria Hernandez, Director Human Resources
Control: Other not–for–profit (including NFP Corporation) **Service:** Cancer

Staffed Beds: 57 **Admissions:** 1156 **Census:** 16 **Outpatient Visits:** 20469 **Births:** 0 **Total Expense ($000):** 11467 **Payroll Expense ($000):** 4572 **Personnel:** 129

★ **INDUSTRIAL HOSPITAL**, Puerto Rico Medical Center, Zip 00936, Mailing Address: P.O. Box 365028, Zip 00936; tel. 787/754–2525, (Nonreporting) **A**9
Primary Contact: Carlos Cabrera, Executive Director
CFO: Robert Bernier Casanova, Chief Financial Officer
CMO: Carmen Carrasquillo, M.D., Medical Director
CHR: Sonia M. Lebron, Human Resources Specialist
Control: State–Government, nonfederal **Service:** General Medical and Surgical

Staffed Beds: 121

✠ **SAN JORGE CHILDREN'S HOSPITAL**, 252 San Jorge Street, Santurce, Zip 00912–3310; tel. 787/727–1000, (Nonreporting) **A**1 3 5 9 **S** United Medical Corporation, Windermere, FL
Primary Contact: Domingo Cruz, Senior Vice President Operations
CFO: Jose Marrero, Director Finance
CMO: Luis Clavell, M.D., Medical Director
CIO: Rogelio Caballero, Chief Information Systems
CHR: Odette Burgos, Supervisor Human Resources
CNO: Leticia Fuentes, Nursing Director
Web address: www.sanjorgechildrenshospital.com
Control: Corporation, Investor–owned, for–profit **Service:** Children's general

Staffed Beds: 125

✠ **SAN JUAN CAPESTRANO HOSPITAL (404005)**, Rural Route 2, Box 11, Zip 00926; tel. 787/625–2900, (Nonreporting) **A**1 9 10
Primary Contact: Marta Rivera Plaza, Chief Executive Officer and Managing Director
CFO: Julia Cruz, Chief Financial Officer
CMO: Jose' Alonso, M.D., Medical Director
CIO: Ana Morandeira, Director Marketing
CHR: Luis Rivera, Director Human Resources
Web address: www.sjcapestrano.com
Control: Corporation, Investor–owned, for–profit **Service:** Psychiatric

Staffed Beds: 108

Many Facility Codes have changed. Please refer to the AHA Guide Code Chart. © 2014 AHA Guide

⊞ **SAN JUAN CITY HOSPITAL (400015)**, Puerto Rico Medical Center, Zip 00928, Mailing Address: PMB 79, P.O. Box 70344, Zip 00936–8344; tel. 787/766–2222, (Nonreporting) **A**1 3 5 10
Primary Contact: Ramon Lopez Maldonado, Executive Director
COO: Norma Marcano, Chief Operating Officer
CFO: Jaime Rodriguez, Chief Financial Officer
CMO: Raul Reyes, M.D., Medical Director
CIO: Gustavo Mesa, Chief Information Officer
CHR: Jose Garcia, Chief Human Resources Officer
Web address: www.massalud.com
Control: City-Government, nonfederal **Service:** General Medical and Surgical

Staffed Beds: 267

★ **UNIVERSITY HOSPITAL (400061)**, Nineyas 869 Rio Piedras, Zip 00922, Mailing Address: P.O. Box 2116, Zip 00922; tel. 787/754–0101, (Nonreporting) **A**3 5 9 10 **S** Puerto Rico Department of Health, San Juan, PR
Primary Contact: Jorge Matta Gonzalez, Executive Director
CFO: Janet Baez, Director
CMO: Ricardo Moscoso, M.D., Medical Director
CIO: Josue Martinez, Coordinator Information Systems
CHR: Ramomita Navarro, Director Human Resources
Control: State-Government, nonfederal **Service:** General Medical and Surgical

Staffed Beds: 262

⊞ **UNIVERSITY PEDIATRIC HOSPITAL (403301)**, Barrio Monacenno, Carretera 22, Rio Piedras, Zip 00935, Mailing Address: P.O. Box 191079, San Juan, Zip 00910–1070; tel. 787/777–3535, (Nonreporting) **A**1 3 5 9 10 **S** Puerto Rico Department of Health, San Juan, PR
Primary Contact: Gloria Hernandez, Executive Director
CMO: Myrna Quinones Feliciano, M.D., Medical Director
Web address: www.md.rcm.upr.edu/pediatrics/university_pediatric_hospital.php
Control: State-Government, nonfederal **Service:** Children's general

Staffed Beds: 145

⊞ △ **VETERANS AFFAIRS CARIBBEAN HEALTHCARE SYSTEM**, 10 Casia Street, Zip 00921–3201; tel. 787/641–7582, (Nonreporting) **A**1 2 3 5 7 9 **S** Department of Veterans Affairs, Washington, DC
Primary Contact: DeWayne Hamlin, Director
CFO: Oscar Rodriguez, Chief Fiscal Officer
CMO: Antonio Sanchez, M.D., Chief of Staff
CIO: Manuel Negron, Chief Information Technology Service
CHR: Omar Ahmed, Acting Manager Human Resources
CNO: Kathleen Ruiz, M.D., Associate Director Patient Care Services
Web address: www.caribbean.va.gov/
Control: Veterans Affairs, Government, federal **Service:** General Medical and Surgical

Staffed Beds: 330

UTUADO— County

★ **METROPOLITANO DE LA MONTANA (400130)**, Calle Issac Gonzalez, Zip 00641, Mailing Address: P.O. Box 2600, Zip 00641; tel. 787/933–1100, (Nonreporting) **A**10
Primary Contact: Waleska Marrero, Administrator
Control: Corporation, Investor-owned, for-profit **Service:** General Medical and Surgical

Staffed Beds: 25

VEGA BAJA—Vega Alta County

★ **WILMA N. VAZQUEZ MEDICAL CENTER (400115)**, KM 39 1/2 Road 2, Call Box 7001, Zip 00694; tel. 787/858–1580, (Nonreporting) **A**9 10
Primary Contact: Ramon J. Vilar, Administrator
COO: Jose O. Pabon, Director Operations
CFO: Youdie Reynolds-Gossette, Controller
CMO: Jorge Feria, M.D., President Medical Staff
CIO: Miguel Aponte, Supervisor Management Information Systems
CHR: Aymette Garcia, Manager Human Resources
Control: Corporation, Investor-owned, for-profit **Service:** General Medical and Surgical

Staffed Beds: 110

YAUCO—Yauco County

⊞ **HOSPITAL METROPOLITANO DR. TITO MATTEI (400110)**, Carretera 128 KM 1, Zip 00698, Mailing Address: P.O. Box 5643, Zip 00698; tel. 787/856–1000, (Nonreporting) **A**1 5 9 10
Primary Contact: Marco Reyes, Vice President of Operations
CFO: Elizabeth Gonzalez, Chief Financial Officer
CMO: Manuel Ramirez Soto, M.D., Medical Director
CIO: Edson Ortiz, Chief Information Officer
Web address: www.hmyauco.com
Control: Corporation, Investor-owned, for-profit **Service:** General Medical and Surgical

Staffed Beds: 105

VIRGIN ISLANDS

CHRISTIANSTED—St. Croix County

⊞ **GOVERNOR JUAN F. LOUIS HOSPITAL (480002)**, 4007 Estate Diamond Ruby, Zip 00820–4421; tel. 340/778–6311, (Nonreporting) **A**1 9 10
Primary Contact: Darice S. Plaskett, R.N., FACHE, Interim Chief Executive Officer
CFO: Rosalie Javois, Chief Financial Officer
CMO: Robert Centeno, M.D., Chief Medical Officer
CIO: Reuben D. Molloy, Chief Information Officer
CHR: Joan Jean-Baptiste, Vice President Human Resources
Web address: www.jflusvi.org
Control: State-Government, nonfederal **Service:** General Medical and Surgical

Staffed Beds: 165

SAINT THOMAS—St. Thomas County

⊞ **SCHNEIDER REGIONAL MEDICAL CENTER (480001)**, 9048 Sugar Estate, Charlotte Amalie, Zip 00802; tel. 340/776–8311, (Nonreporting) **A**1 10
Primary Contact: Bernard Wheatley, FACHE, Chief Executive Officer
CMO: Thelma Ruth Watson, M.D., Medical Director
CIO: J. C. Creque, Director Management Information Systems
CHR: Marlene J. Adams, Director Human Resources
Web address: www.rlshospital.org
Control: State-Government, nonfederal **Service:** General Medical and Surgical

Staffed Beds: 123

Hospital, Medicare Provider Number, Address, Telephone, Approval, Facility, and Physician Codes, Health Care System

★ American Hospital Association (AHA) membership
□ The Joint Commission accreditation   ◇ DNV Healthcare Inc. accreditation
○ Healthcare Facilities Accreditation Program
△ Commission on Accreditation of Rehabilitation Facilities (CARF) accreditation

U.S. Government Hospitals
Outside the United States, by Area

GERMANY
Heidelberg: ★ Heidelberg Army Community Hospital, APO, CMR 242, AE 09042
Landstuhl: ★ Landstuhl Army Regional Medical Center, APO, CMR 402, AE 09180
Wuerzburg: ★ Wuerzburg Army Community Hospital, APO, USAMEDDAC Wuerzburg, Ut 26610, AE 09244

ITALY
Naples: ★ U. S. Naval Hospital, FPO, none, AE 09619

JAPAN
Yokosuka: ★ U. S. Naval Hospital, Box 1487, UNIT 96350

SOUTH KOREA
Seoul: ★ Brian Allgood Army Community Hospital, 121st General Hospital, UNIT 96205
Yongsan: Medcom 18th Commander, Facilities Division Eamc L EM, UNIT 96205

SPAIN
Rota: ★ U. S. Naval Hospital, Rota, FPO, PSC 819, Box 18, AE 09645–2500

TAIWAN
Taipei: ★ U. S. Naval Hospital Taipei, No 300 Shin–Pai Road, Sec 2

Notes

Notes

Notes

Notes

Indexes

Index of Hospitals

This section is an index of all hospitals in alphabetical order by hospital name, followed by the city, state, and page reference to the hospital's listing in Section A.

A

A. WEBB ROBERTS HOSPITAL, DALLAS, TEXAS (*see* BAYLOR UNIVERSITY MEDICAL CENTER), p. A610
ABBEVILLE AREA MEDICAL CENTER, ABBEVILLE, SC, p. A562
ABBEVILLE GENERAL HOSPITAL, ABBEVILLE, LA, p. A272
ABBOTT NORTHWESTERN HOSPITAL, MINNEAPOLIS, MN, p. A347
ABILENE BEHAVIORAL HEALTH, ABILENE, TX, p. A595
ABILENE REGIONAL MEDICAL CENTER, ABILENE, TX, p. A595
ABINGTON HEALTH LANSDALE HOSPITAL, LANSDALE, PA, p. A542
ABINGTON MEMORIAL HOSPITAL, ABINGTON, PA, p. A532
ABRAHAM LINCOLN MEMORIAL HOSPITAL, LINCOLN, IL, p. A195
ABROM KAPLAN MEMORIAL HOSPITAL, KAPLAN, LA, p. A280
ACADIA GENERAL HOSPITAL, CROWLEY, LA, p. A276
ACADIA OPTIMA HOSPITAL, LAFAYETTE, LA, p. A280
ACADIA VERMILION HOSPITAL, LAFAYETTE, LA, p. A281
ACADIA–ST. LANDRY HOSPITAL, CHURCH POINT, LA, p. A275
ACADIAN MEDICAL CENTER, EUNICE, LOUISIANA (*see* MERCY REGIONAL MEDICAL CENTER), p. A290
ACCESS HOSPITAL DAYTON, DAYTON, OH, p. A491
ACMH HOSPITAL, KITTANNING, PA, p. A542
ACOMA–CANONCITO–LAGUNA HOSPITAL, ACOMA, NM, p. A426
ACUITY HOSPITAL OF SOUTH TEXAS, SAN ANTONIO, TX, p. A645
ACUITY SPECIALTY HOSPITAL OF NEW JERSEY, ATLANTIC CITY, NJ, p. A413
ACUITY SPECIALTY HOSPITALS OHIO VALLEY, STEUBENVILLE, OH, p. A502
ACUITY SPECIALTY HOSPITALS OHIO VALLEY AT BELMONT, BELLAIRE, OHIO (*see* ACUITY SPECIALTY HOSPITALS OHIO VALLEY), p. A502
ACUTE CARE SPECIALTY HOSPITAL OF AULTMAN, CANTON, OH, p. A485
ACUTE GENERAL HOSPITAL, MERWICK UNIT–EXTENDED CARE AND REHABILITATION, PRINCETON HOUSE UNIT–COMMUNITY MENTAL HEALTH AND SUBSTANCE ABUSE (*see* UNIVERSITY MEDICAL CENTER OF PRINCETON AT PLAINSBORO), p. A421
ADAIR COUNTY MEMORIAL HOSPITAL, GREENFIELD, IA, p. A231
ADAMS COUNTY REGIONAL MEDICAL CENTER, SEAMAN, OH, p. A501
ADAMS MEMORIAL HOSPITAL, DECATUR, IN, p. A209
ADCARE HOSPITAL OF WORCESTER, WORCESTER, MA, p. A316
ADDISON GILBERT HOSPITAL, GLOUCESTER, MASSACHUSETTS (*see* BEVERLY HOSPITAL), p. A305
ADENA GREENFIELD MEDICAL CENTER, GREENFIELD, OH, p. A495
ADENA MEDICAL CENTER, CHILLICOTHE, OH, p. A486
ADENA PIKE MEDICAL CENTER, WAVERLY, OH, p. A505
ADIRONDACK MEDICAL CENTER, SARANAC LAKE, NY, p. A454
ADVANCE CARE HOSPITAL OF FORT SMITH, FORT SMITH, AR, p. A46
ADVANCE CARE HOSPITAL OF HOT SPRINGS, HOT SPRINGS NATIONAL PARK, AR, p. A47
ADVANCED CARE HOSPITAL OF MONTANA, BILLINGS, MT, p. A385
ADVANCED CARE HOSPITAL OF SOUTHERN NEW MEXICO, LAS CRUCES, NM, p. A428
ADVANCED CARE HOSPITAL OF WHITE COUNTY, SEARCY, AR, p. A52
ADVANCED SPECIALTY HOSPITAL OF TOLEDO, TOLEDO, OH, p. A503
ADVANCED SURGICAL HOSPITAL, WASHINGTON, PA, p. A557
ADVENTIST BEHAVIORAL HEALTH ROCKVILLE, ROCKVILLE, MD, p. A303
ADVENTIST BOLINGBROOK HOSPITAL, BOLINGBROOK, IL, p. A182
ADVENTIST GLENOAKS HOSPITAL, GLENDALE HEIGHTS, IL, p. A191
ADVENTIST HINSDALE HOSPITAL, HINSDALE, IL, p. A193
ADVENTIST LA GRANGE MEMORIAL HOSPITAL, LA GRANGE, IL, p. A194
ADVENTIST MEDICAL CENTER – HANFORD, HANFORD, CA, p. A66

ADVENTIST MEDICAL CENTER–PORTLAND, PORTLAND, OR, p. A528
ADVENTIST MEDICAL CENTER–REEDLEY, REEDLEY, CA, p. A86
ADVENTIST MEDICAL CENTER–SELMA, SELMA, CALIFORNIA (*see* ADVENTIST MEDICAL CENTER – HANFORD), p. A66
ADVENTIST REHABILITATION HOSPITAL OF MARYLAND, ROCKVILLE, MD, p. A303
ADVOCATE BROMENN MEDICAL CENTER, NORMAL, IL, p. A198
ADVOCATE CHRIST MEDICAL CENTER, OAK LAWN, IL, p. A198
ADVOCATE CONDELL MEDICAL CENTER, LIBERTYVILLE, IL, p. A194
ADVOCATE EUREKA HOSPITAL, EUREKA, IL, p. A189
ADVOCATE GOOD SAMARITAN HOSPITAL, DOWNERS GROVE, IL, p. A188
ADVOCATE GOOD SHEPHERD HOSPITAL, BARRINGTON, IL, p. A181
ADVOCATE HOPE CHILDREN'S HOSPITAL, OAK LAWN, ILLINOIS (*see* ADVOCATE CHRIST MEDICAL CENTER), p. A198
ADVOCATE ILLINOIS MASONIC MEDICAL CENTER, CHICAGO, IL, p. A183
ADVOCATE LUTHERAN GENERAL HOSPITAL, PARK RIDGE, IL, p. A199
ADVOCATE SHERMAN HOSPITAL, ELGIN, IL, p. A189
ADVOCATE SOUTH SUBURBAN HOSPITAL, HAZEL CREST, IL, p. A192
ADVOCATE TRINITY HOSPITAL, CHICAGO, IL, p. A183
AFFINITY MEDICAL CENTER, MASSILLON, OH, p. A498
AGNESIAN HEALTHCARE, FOND DU LAC, WI, p. A704
AHMC ANAHEIM REGIONAL MEDICAL CENTER, ANAHEIM, CA, p. A55
AIKEN REGIONAL MEDICAL CENTERS, AIKEN, SC, p. A562
AKRON CHILDREN'S HOSPITAL, AKRON, OH, p. A482
AKRON GENERAL MEDICAL CENTER, AKRON, OH, p. A482
ALAMANCE REGIONAL MEDICAL CENTER, BURLINGTON, NC, p. A461
ALAMEDA COUNTY MEDICAL CENTER, OAKLAND, CA, p. A80
ALAMEDA COUNTY MEDICAL CENTER–FAIRMONT CAMPUS, SAN LEANDRO, CALIFORNIA (*see* ALAMEDA COUNTY MEDICAL CENTER), p. A80
ALAMEDA HOSPITAL, ALAMEDA, CA, p. A55
ALASKA NATIVE MEDICAL CENTER, ANCHORAGE, AK, p. A28
ALASKA PSYCHIATRIC INSTITUTE, ANCHORAGE, AK, p. A28
ALASKA REGIONAL HOSPITAL, ANCHORAGE, AK, p. A28
ALBANY AREA HOSPITAL AND MEDICAL CENTER, ALBANY, MN, p. A339
ALBANY MEDICAL CENTER, ALBANY, NY, p. A432
ALBANY MEDICAL CENTER SOUTH–CLINICAL CAMPUS, ALBANY, NEW YORK (*see* ALBANY MEDICAL CENTER), p. A432
ALBANY MEMORIAL HOSPITAL, ALBANY, NY, p. A432
ALBANY STRATTON VETERANS AFFAIRS MEDICAL CENTER, ALBANY, NY, p. A432
ALBERT J. SOLNIT PSYCHIATRIC CENTER – SOUTH CAMPUS, MIDDLETOWN, CT, p. A115
ALCOHOL AND DRUG ABUSE TREATMENT CENTER, BUTNER, NORTH CAROLINA (*see* JOHN UMSTEAD HOSPITAL), p. A461
ALEDA E. LUTZ VETERANS AFFAIRS MEDICAL CENTER, SAGINAW, MI, p. A333
ALEXANDRIA VETERANS AFFAIRS HEALTH CARE SYSTEM, PINEVILLE, LA, p. A287
ALEXIAN BROTHERS BEHAVIORAL HEALTH HOSPITAL, HOFFMAN ESTATES, IL, p. A193
ALEXIAN BROTHERS MEDICAL CENTER, ELK GROVE VILLAGE, IL, p. A189
ALEXIAN BROTHERS WOMEN & CHILDREN'S HOSPITAL, HOFFMAN ESTATES, ILLINOIS (*see* ALEXIAN BROTHERS MEDICAL CENTER), p. A189
ALEXIAN REHABILITATION HOSPITAL, ELK GROVE VILLAGE, ILLINOIS (*see* ALEXIAN BROTHERS MEDICAL CENTER), p. A189
ALFRED AND NORMA LERNER TOWER, BOLWELL HEALTH CENTER, HANNA PAVILION, LAKESIDE HOSPITAL, SAMUEL MATHER PAVILION, HANNA HOUSE SKILLED NURSING FACILITY, CLEVELAND, OHIO (*see* UNIVERSITY HOSPITALS CASE MEDICAL CENTER), p. A489
RAINBOW BABIES AND CHILDREN'S HOSPITAL, CLEVELAND, OHIO (*see* UNIVERSITY HOSPITALS CASE MEDICAL CENTER), p. A489

UNIVERSITY MACDONALD WOMEN'S HOSPITAL, CLEVELAND, OHIO (*see* UNIVERSITY HOSPITALS CASE MEDICAL CENTER), p. A489
ALFRED I. DUPONT HOSPITAL FOR CHILDREN, WILMINGTON, DE, p. A120
ALHAMBRA HOSPITAL MEDICAL CENTER, ALHAMBRA, CA, p. A55
ALICE HYDE MEDICAL CENTER, MALONE, NY, p. A440
ALICE PECK DAY MEMORIAL HOSPITAL, LEBANON, NH, p. A410
ALL CHILDREN'S HOSPITAL JOHNS HOPKINS MEDICINE, SAINT PETERSBURG, FL, p. A144
ALLEGAN GENERAL HOSPITAL, ALLEGAN, MI, p. A318
ALLEGHANY MEMORIAL HOSPITAL, SPARTA, NC, p. A473
ALLEGHENY GENERAL HOSPITAL, PITTSBURGH, PA, p. A550
ALLEGHENY VALLEY HOSPITAL, NATRONA HEIGHTS, PA, p. A546
ALLEGIANCE BEHAVIORAL HEALTH CENTER OF PLAINVIEW, PLAINVIEW, TX, p. A642
ALLEGIANCE HEALTH, JACKSON, MI, p. A327
ALLEGIANCE HEALTH CENTER OF RUSTON, RUSTON, LA, p. A287
ALLEGIANCE SPECIALTY HOSPITAL OF GREENVILLE, GREENVILLE, MS, p. A358
ALLEGIANCE SPECIALTY HOSPITAL OF KILGORE, KILGORE, TX, p. A631
ALLEN COUNTY REGIONAL HOSPITAL, IOLA, KS, p. A246
ALLEN PARISH HOSPITAL, KINDER, LA, p. A280
ALLENDALE COUNTY HOSPITAL, FAIRFAX, SC, p. A565
ALLENMORE HOSPITAL, TACOMA, WASHINGTON (*see* MULTICARE TACOMA GENERAL HOSPITAL), p. A691
ALLIANCE COMMUNITY HOSPITAL, ALLIANCE, OH, p. A482
ALLIANCE HEALTH CENTER, MERIDIAN, MS, p. A362
ALLIANCE HEALTHCARE SYSTEM, HOLLY SPRINGS, MS, p. A359
ALLIED SERVICES REHABILITATION HOSPITAL, SCRANTON, PA, p. A554
ALPENA REGIONAL MEDICAL CENTER, ALPENA, MI, p. A318
ALTA BATES MEDICAL CENTER–HERRICK CAMPUS, BERKELEY, CALIFORNIA (*see* ALTA BATES SUMMIT MEDICAL CENTER), p. A58
ALTA BATES SUMMIT MEDICAL CENTER, BERKELEY, CA, p. A58
ALTA BATES SUMMIT MEDICAL CENTER – SUMMIT CAMPUS, OAKLAND, CA, p. A80
ALTA VIEW HOSPITAL, SANDY, UT, p. A664
ALTA VISTA REGIONAL HOSPITAL, LAS VEGAS, NM, p. A429
ALTON MEMORIAL HOSPITAL, ALTON, IL, p. A180
ALTON MENTAL HEALTH CENTER, ALTON, IL, p. A180
ALTRU HEALTH SYSTEM, GRAND FORKS, ND, p. A478
ALTRU HOSPITAL, GRAND FORKS, NORTH DAKOTA (*see* ALTRU HEALTH SYSTEM), p. A478
ALTRU REHABILITATION CENTER, GRAND FORKS, NORTH DAKOTA (*see* ALTRU HEALTH SYSTEM), p. A478
ALVARADO HOSPITAL MEDICAL CENTER, SAN DIEGO, CA, p. A89
ALVARADO PARKWAY INSTITUTE BEHAVIORAL HEALTH SYSTEM, LA MESA, CA, p. A68
ALVIN C. YORK CAMPUS, MURFREESBORO, TENNESSEE (*see* TENNESSEE VALLEY HEALTHCARE SYSTEM), p. A591
ALVIN DIAGNOSTIC AND URGENT CARE CENTER, ALVIN, TEXAS (*see* CLEAR LAKE REGIONAL MEDICAL CENTER), p. A656
AMARILLO VETERANS AFFAIRS HEALTH CARE SYSTEM, AMARILLO, TX, p. A596
AMERICAN FORK HOSPITAL, AMERICAN FORK, UT, p. A659
AMERY REGIONAL MEDICAL CENTER, AMERY, WI, p. A701
AMG SPECIALTY HOSPITAL – BOGALUSA, BOGALUSA, LOUISIANA (*see* OUR LADY OF THE ANGELS HOSPITAL), p. A274
AMG SPECIALTY HOSPITAL – MUNCIE, MUNCIE, IN, p. A219
AMG SPECIALTY HOSPITAL–ALBUQUERQUE, ALBUQUERQUE, NM, p. A426
AMG SPECIALTY HOSPITAL–DENHAM SPRINGS, DENHAM SPRINGS, LA, p. A277
AMG SPECIALTY HOSPITAL–EDMOND, EDMOND, OK, p. A510
AMG SPECIALTY HOSPITAL–FELICIANA, CLINTON, LA, p. A275
AMG SPECIALTY HOSPITAL–GREENWOOD, GREENWOOD, MS, p. A358
AMG SPECIALTY HOSPITAL–HOUMA, HOUMA, LA, p. A278
AMG SPECIALTY HOSPITAL–LAFAYETTE, LAFAYETTE, LA, p. A281
AMG SPECIALTY HOSPITAL–SLIDELL, SLIDELL, LA, p. A288

B

BAPTIST HEALTH LA GRANGE, LA GRANGE, KY, p. A263
BAPTIST HEALTH LEXINGTON, LEXINGTON, KY, p. A264
BAPTIST HEALTH LOUISVILLE, LOUISVILLE, KY, p. A265
BAPTIST HEALTH MADISONVILLE, MADISONVILLE, KY, p. A267
BAPTIST HEALTH MEDICAL CENTER – NORTH LITTLE ROCK,
    NORTH LITTLE ROCK, AR, p. A51
BAPTIST HEALTH MEDICAL CENTER–ARKADELPHIA,
    ARKADELPHIA, AR, p. A43
BAPTIST HEALTH MEDICAL CENTER–HEBER SPRINGS, HEBER
    SPRINGS, AR, p. A47
BAPTIST HEALTH MEDICAL CENTER–HOT SPRING COUNTY,
    MALVERN, AR, p. A50
BAPTIST HEALTH MEDICAL CENTER–LITTLE ROCK, LITTLE
    ROCK, AR, p. A49
BAPTIST HEALTH MEDICAL CENTER–STUTTGART, STUTTGART,
    AR, p. A53
BAPTIST HEALTH PADUCAH, PADUCAH, KY, p. A269
BAPTIST HEALTH REHABILITATION INSTITUTE, LITTLE ROCK,
    AR, p. A49
BAPTIST HEALTH RICHMOND, RICHMOND, KY, p. A270
BAPTIST HEALTH SOUTH FLORIDA, BAPTIST HOSPITAL OF
    MIAMI, MIAMI, FL, p. A136
BAPTIST HEALTH SOUTH FLORIDA, DOCTORS HOSPITAL,
    CORAL GABLES, FL, p. A126
BAPTIST HEALTH SOUTH FLORIDA, HOMESTEAD HOSPITAL,
    HOMESTEAD, FL, p. A131
BAPTIST HEALTH SOUTH FLORIDA, MARINERS HOSPITAL,
    TAVERNIER, FL, p. A148
BAPTIST HEALTH SOUTH FLORIDA, SOUTH MIAMI HOSPITAL,
    MIAMI, FL, p. A136
BAPTIST HEALTH SOUTH FLORIDA, WEST KENDALL BAPTIST
    HOSPITAL, MIAMI, FL, p. A136
BAPTIST HOSPITAL, PENSACOLA, FL, p.A142
BAPTIST HOSPITALS OF SOUTHEAST TEXAS, BEAUMONT, TX,
    p. A601
BAPTIST HOSPITALS OF SOUTHEAST TEXAS FANNIN
    BEHAVIORAL HEALTH CENTER, BEAUMONT, TEXAS (see
    BAPTIST HOSPITALS OF SOUTHEAST TEXAS), p. A601
BAPTIST MEDICAL CENTER, SAN ANTONIO, TX, p. A646
BAPTIST MEDICAL CENTER BEACHES, JACKSONVILLE BEACH,
    FL, p. A132
BAPTIST MEDICAL CENTER EAST, MONTGOMERY, AL, p. A23
BAPTIST MEDICAL CENTER JACKSONVILLE, JACKSONVILLE, FL,
    p. A131
BAPTIST MEDICAL CENTER LEAKE, CARTHAGE, MS, p. A356
BAPTIST MEDICAL CENTER NASSAU, FERNANDINA BEACH, FL,
    p. A128
BAPTIST MEDICAL CENTER SOUTH, JACKSONVILLE, FLORIDA
    (see BAPTIST MEDICAL CENTER JACKSONVILLE), p. A131
BAPTIST MEDICAL CENTER SOUTH, MONTGOMERY, AL, p. A23
BAPTIST MEMORIAL HOSPITAL – MEMPHIS, MEMPHIS, TN,
    p. A588
BAPTIST MEMORIAL HOSPITAL FOR WOMEN, MEMPHIS, TN,
    p. A588
BAPTIST MEMORIAL HOSPITAL–BOONEVILLE, BOONEVILLE, MS,
    p. A356
BAPTIST MEMORIAL HOSPITAL–COLLIERVILLE, COLLIERVILLE,
    TN, p. A581
BAPTIST MEMORIAL HOSPITAL–DESOTO, SOUTHAVEN, MS,
    p. A365
BAPTIST MEMORIAL HOSPITAL–GOLDEN TRIANGLE,
    COLUMBUS, MS, p. A357
BAPTIST MEMORIAL HOSPITAL–HUNTINGDON, HUNTINGDON,
    TN, p. A584
BAPTIST MEMORIAL HOSPITAL–NORTH MISSISSIPPI, OXFORD,
    MS, p. A364
BAPTIST MEMORIAL HOSPITAL–TIPTON, COVINGTON, TN,
    p. A582
BAPTIST MEMORIAL HOSPITAL–UNION CITY, UNION CITY, TN,
    p. A594
BAPTIST MEMORIAL HOSPITAL–UNION COUNTY, NEW ALBANY,
    MS, p. A363
BAPTIST MEMORIAL RESTORATIVE CARE HOSPITAL, MEMPHIS,
    TN, p. A588
BAPTIST ORANGE HOSPITAL, ORANGE, TX, p. A640
BAPTIST REHABILITATION–GERMANTOWN, GERMANTOWN, TN,
    p. A583
BAPTIST ST. ANTHONY HEALTH SYSTEM, AMARILLO, TX,
    p. A596
BARAGA COUNTY MEMORIAL HOSPITAL, L'ANSE, MI, p. A328
BARBARA BUSH CHILDREN'S HOSPITAL, PORTLAND, MAINE
    (see MAINE MEDICAL CENTER), p. A294
BARIX CLINICS OF PENNSYLVANIA, LANGHORNE, PA, p. A542
BARLOW RESPIRATORY HOSPITAL, LOS ANGELES, CA, p. A71
BARNABAS HEALTH BEHAVIORAL HEALTH CENTER, TOMS
    RIVER, NJ, p. A423
BARNES–JEWISH HOSPITAL, SAINT LOUIS, MO, p. A380
BARNES–JEWISH ST. PETERS HOSPITAL, SAINT PETERS, MO,
    p. A382

BARNES–JEWISH WEST COUNTY HOSPITAL, SAINT LOUIS, MO,
    p. A380
BARNES–KASSON COUNTY HOSPITAL, SUSQUEHANNA, PA,
    p. A555
BARNESVILLE HOSPITAL, BARNESVILLE, OH, p. A483
BARRETT HOSPITAL & HEALTHCARE, DILLON, MT, p. A387
BARROW REGIONAL MEDICAL CENTER, WINDER, GA, p. A169
BARSTOW COMMUNITY HOSPITAL, BARSTOW, CA, p. A58
BARTLETT REGIONAL HOSPITAL, JUNEAU, AK, p. A29
BARTON COUNTY MEMORIAL HOSPITAL, LAMAR, MO, p. A375
BARTON MEMORIAL HOSPITAL, SOUTH LAKE TAHOE, CA,
    p. A96
BARTOW REGIONAL MEDICAL CENTER, BARTOW, FL, p. A123
BASCOM PALMER EYE INSTITUTE–ANNE BATES LEACH EYE
    HOSPITAL, MIAMI, FL, p. A136
BASIN HEALTHCARE CENTER, ODESSA, TX, p. A640
BASSETT ARMY COMMUNITY HOSPITAL, FORT WAINWRIGHT,
    AK, p. A29
BASSETT MEDICAL CENTER, COOPERSTOWN, NY, p. A436
BATES COUNTY MEMORIAL HOSPITAL, BUTLER, MO, p. A368
BATESVILLE SPECIALTY HOSPITAL, BATESVILLE, MS, p. A355
BATH COMMUNITY HOSPITAL, HOT SPRINGS, VA, p. A672
BATH VETERANS AFFAIRS MEDICAL CENTER, BATH, NY,
    p. A433
BATON ROUGE BEHAVIORAL HOSPITAL, BATON ROUGE, LA,
    p. A273
BATON ROUGE GENERAL MEDICAL CENTER, BATON ROUGE,
    LA, p. A273
BATON ROUGE GENERAL MEDICAL CENTER–BLUEBONNET,
    BATON ROUGE, LOUISIANA (see BATON ROUGE GENERAL
    MEDICAL CENTER), p. A273
BATON ROUGE REHABILITATION HOSPITAL, BATON ROUGE, LA,
    p. A273
BATTLE CREEK VETERANS AFFAIRS MEDICAL CENTER, BATTLE
    CREEK, MI, p. A319
BATTLE MOUNTAIN GENERAL HOSPITAL, BATTLE MOUNTAIN,
    NV, p. A404
BAUM HARMON MERCY HOSPITAL, PRIMGHAR, IA, p. A236
BAXTER REGIONAL MEDICAL CENTER, MOUNTAIN HOME, AR,
    p. A50
BAY AREA HOSPITAL, COOS BAY, OR, p. A524
BAY AREA MEDICAL CENTER, MARINETTE, WI, p. A708
BAY MEDICAL CENTER SACRED HEART, PANAMA CITY, FL,
    p. A141
BAY PINES VETERANS AFFAIRS MEDICAL CENTER, BAY PINES,
    FL, p. A123
BAY REGIONAL MEDICAL CENTER–WEST CAMPUS, BAY CITY,
    MICHIGAN (see MCLAREN BAY REGION), p. A319
BAYCARE ALLIANT HOSPITAL, DUNEDIN, FL, p. A127
BAYFRONT HEALTH BROOKSVILLE, BROOKSVILLE, FL, p. A125
BAYFRONT HEALTH DADE CITY, DADE CITY, FL, p. A126
BAYFRONT HEALTH PORT CHARLOTTE, PORT CHARLOTTE, FL,
    p. A143
BAYFRONT HEALTH PUNTA GORDA, PUNTA GORDA, FL,
    p. A143
BAYFRONT HEALTH SPRING HILL, SPRING HILL, FLORIDA (see
    BAYFRONT HEALTH BROOKSVILLE), p. A125
BAYFRONT HEALTH ST. PETERSBURG, SAINT PETERSBURG, FL,
    p. A144
BAYHEALTH MEDICAL CENTER, DOVER, DE, p. A119
BAYHEALTH MEDICAL CENTER AT KENT GENERAL, DOVER,
    DELAWARE (see BAYHEALTH MEDICAL CENTER), p. A119
BAYHEALTH MEDICAL CENTER, MILFORD MEMORIAL HOSPITAL,
    MILFORD, DELAWARE (see BAYHEALTH MEDICAL CENTER),
    p. A119
BAYLOR ALL SAINTS MEDICAL CENTER AT FORT WORTH, FORT
    WORTH, TX, p. A618
BAYLOR EMERGENCY MEDICAL CENTER AT AUBREY, AUBREY,
    TX, p. A598
BAYLOR INSTITUTE FOR REHABILITATION, DALLAS, TX, p. A609
BAYLOR INSTITUTE FOR REHABILITATION AT FRISCO, FRISCO,
    TX, p. A620
BAYLOR JACK AND JANE HAMILTON HEART AND VASCULAR
    HOSPITAL, DALLAS, TX, p. A609
BAYLOR MEDICAL CENTER AT CARROLLTON, CARROLLTON,
    TX, p. A605
BAYLOR MEDICAL CENTER AT FRISCO, FRISCO, TX, p. A620
BAYLOR MEDICAL CENTER AT GARLAND, GARLAND, TX,
    p. A620
BAYLOR MEDICAL CENTER AT IRVING, IRVING, TX, p. A629
BAYLOR MEDICAL CENTER AT MCKINNEY, MCKINNEY, TX,
    p. A637
BAYLOR MEDICAL CENTER AT TROPHY CLUB, TROPHY CLUB,
    TX, p. A653
BAYLOR MEDICAL CENTER AT UPTOWN, DALLAS, TX, p. A609
BAYLOR MEDICAL CENTER AT WAXAHACHIE, WAXAHACHIE, TX,
    p. A656
BAYLOR ORTHOPEDIC AND SPINE HOSPITAL AT ARLINGTON,
    ARLINGTON, TX, p. A597

BAYLOR REGIONAL MEDICAL CENTER AT GRAPEVINE,
    GRAPEVINE, TX, p. A621
BAYLOR REGIONAL MEDICAL CENTER AT PLANO, PLANO, TX,
    p. A642
BAYLOR SPECIALTY HOSPITAL, DALLAS, TX, p. A609
BAYLOR SURGICAL HOSPITAL AT FORT WORTH, FORT WORTH,
    TX, p. A618
BAYLOR UNIVERSITY MEDICAL CENTER, DALLAS, TX, p. A610
BAYNE–JONES ARMY COMMUNITY HOSPITAL, FORT POLK, LA,
    p. A277
BAYONNE MEDICAL CENTER, BAYONNE, NJ, p. A413
BAYPOINTE BEHAVIORAL HEALTH, MOBILE, AL, p. A22
BAYSHORE COMMUNITY HOSPITAL, HOLMDEL, NJ, p. A417
BAYSHORE MEDICAL CENTER, PASADENA, TX, p. A641
BAYSTATE CHILDREN'S HOSPITAL, SPRINGFIELD,
    MASSACHUSETTS (see BAYSTATE MEDICAL CENTER),
    p. A314
BAYSTATE FRANKLIN MEDICAL CENTER, GREENFIELD, MA,
    p. A310
BAYSTATE MARY LANE HOSPITAL, WARE, MA, p. A316
BAYSTATE MEDICAL CENTER, SPRINGFIELD, MA, p. A314
BAYVIEW BEHAVIORAL HEALTH CAMPUS, CHULA VISTA,
    CALIFORNIA (see PARADISE VALLEY HOSPITAL), p. A79
BAYVIEW BEHAVIORAL HOSPITAL, CORPUS CHRISTI, TEXAS
    (see CORPUS CHRISTI MEDICAL CENTER), p. A608
BCA PERMIAN BASIN, MIDLAND, TX, p. A638
BEACHAM MEMORIAL HOSPITAL, MAGNOLIA, MS, p. A361
BEACON BEHAVIORAL HOSPITAL – NEW ORLEANS, NEW
    ORLEANS, LA, p. A285
BEACON CHILDREN'S HOSPITAL, LUVERNE, AL, p. A22
BEAR LAKE MEMORIAL HOSPITAL, MONTPELIER, ID, p. A177
BEAR RIVER VALLEY HOSPITAL, TREMONTON, UT, p. A664
BEAR VALLEY COMMUNITY HOSPITAL, BIG BEAR LAKE, CA,
    p. A58
BEARTOOTH BILLINGS CLINIC, RED LODGE, MT, p. A390
BEATRICE COMMUNITY HOSPITAL AND HEALTH CENTER,
    BEATRICE, NE, p. A394
BEAUFORT MEMORIAL HOSPITAL, BEAUFORT, SC, p. A562
BEAUMONT BONE AND JOINT INSTITUTE, BEAUMONT, TX,
    p. A601
BEAUMONT CHILDREN'S HOSPITAL, ROYAL OAK, MICHIGAN
    (see BEAUMONT HOSPITAL – ROYAL OAK), p. A333
BEAUMONT HOSPITAL – ROYAL OAK, ROYAL OAK, MI, p. A333
BEAUMONT HOSPITAL – TROY, TROY, MI, p. A336
BEAUMONT HOSPITAL GROSSE POINTE, GROSSE POINTE, MI,
    p. A326
BEAUREGARD MEMORIAL HOSPITAL, DE RIDDER, LA, p. A276
BEAVER COUNTY MEMORIAL HOSPITAL, BEAVER, OK, p. A508
BEAVER DAM COMMUNITY HOSPITALS, BEAVER DAM, WI,
    p. A702
BEAVER VALLEY HOSPITAL, BEAVER, UT, p. A659
BECKETT SPRINGS, WEST CHESTER, OH, p. A505
BECKLEY ARH HOSPITAL, BECKLEY, WV, p. A693
BECKLEY VETERANS AFFAIRS MEDICAL CENTER, BECKLEY,
    WV, p. A693
BEDFORD MEMORIAL HOSPITAL, BEDFORD, VA, p. A668
BEDFORD VETERANS AFFAIRS MEDICAL CENTER, EDITH
    NOURSE ROGERS MEMORIAL VETERANS HOSPITAL,
    BEDFORD, MA, p. A305
BEEBE HEALTHCARE, LEWES, DE, p. A119
BEHAVIORAL CENTER OF MICHIGAN, WARREN, MI, p. A336
BEHAVIORAL HEALTH CENTER, WINFIELD, ILLINOIS (see
    CENTRAL DUPAGE HOSPITAL), p. A205
BEHAVIORAL HEALTH CENTER, GREENSBORO, NORTH
    CAROLINA (see MOSES H. CONE MEMORIAL HOSPITAL),
    p. A465
BEHAVIORAL HEALTH CENTER OF THE PERMIAN BASIN,
    MIDLAND, TX, p. A638
BEHAVIORAL HEALTHCARE CENTER AT CLARKSVILLE,
    CLARKSVILLE, TN, p. A581
BEHAVIORAL HEALTHCARE CENTER AT COLUMBIA, COLUMBIA,
    TN, p. A581
BEHAVIORAL HEALTHCARE CENTER AT HUNTSVILLE,
    HUNTSVILLE, AL, p. A21
BEHAVIORAL HEALTHCARE CENTER AT MARTIN, MARTIN, TN,
    p. A587
BEHAVIORAL HOSPITAL OF BELLAIRE, HOUSTON, TX, p. A623
BEHAVIORAL HOSPITAL OF LONGVIEW, LONGVIEW, TX, p. A634
BELL HOSPITAL, ISHPEMING, MI, p. A327
BELLA VISTA HOSPITAL, MAYAGUEZ, PR, p. A726
BELLEVUE HOSPITAL, BELLEVUE, OH, p. A484
BELLEVUE HOSPITAL CENTER, NEW YORK, NY, p. A442
BELLEVUE MEDICAL CENTER, BELLEVUE, NE, p. A394
BELLEVUE WOMAN'S CARE CENTER, SCHENECTADY, NEW
    YORK (see ELLIS HOSPITAL), p. A454
BELLIN HEALTH OCONTO HOSPITAL, OCONTO, WI, p. A712
BELLIN MEMORIAL HOSPITAL, GREEN BAY, WI, p. A705
BELLIN PSYCHIATRIC CENTER, GREEN BAY, WI, p. A706
BELLVILLE ST. JOSEPH HEALTH CENTER, BELLVILLE, TX,
    p. A602

BELMONT CENTER FOR COMPREHENSIVE TREATMENT, PHILADELPHIA, PA, p. A547
BELMONT COMMUNITY HOSPITAL, BELLAIRE, OH, p. A483
BELMONT PINES HOSPITAL, YOUNGSTOWN, OH, p. A506
BELOIT HEALTH SYSTEM, BELOIT, WI, p. A702
BELTON REGIONAL MEDICAL CENTER, BELTON, MO, p. A367
BEN TAUB GENERAL HOSPITAL, HOUSTON, TEXAS (see HARRIS HEALTH SYSTEM), p. A624
BENEFIS HEALTH CARE–EAST CAMPUS, GREAT FALLS, MONTANA (see BENEFIS HOSPITALS), p. A388
BENEFIS HEALTH CARE–WEST CAMPUS, GREAT FALLS, MONTANA (see BENEFIS HOSPITALS), p. A388
BENEFIS HOSPITALS, GREAT FALLS, MT, p. A388
BENEWAH COMMUNITY HOSPITAL, SAINT MARIES, ID, p. A178
BENNETT COUNTY HOSPITAL AND NURSING HOME, MARTIN, SD, p. A574
BENSON HOSPITAL, BENSON, AZ, p. A31
BERGEN REGIONAL MEDICAL CENTER, PARAMUS, NJ, p. A420
BERGER HEALTH SYSTEM, CIRCLEVILLE, OH, p. A488
BERKELEY MEDICAL CENTER, MARTINSBURG, WV, p. A697
BERKSHIRE MEDICAL CENTER, PITTSFIELD, MA, p. A313
BERLIN MEMORIAL HOSPITAL, BERLIN, WI, p. A702
BERNARD MITCHELL HOSPITAL, CHICAGO, ILLINOIS (see UNIVERSITY OF CHICAGO MEDICAL CENTER), p. A187
BERT FISH MEDICAL CENTER, NEW SMYRNA BEACH, FL, p. A139
BERTRAND CHAFFEE HOSPITAL, SPRINGVILLE, NY, p. A455
BERWICK HOSPITAL CENTER, BERWICK, PA, p. A533
BETH ISRAEL DEACONESS HOSPITAL PLYMOUTH, PLYMOUTH, MA, p. A314
BETH ISRAEL DEACONESS HOSPITAL–MILTON, MILTON, MA, p. A312
BETH ISRAEL DEACONESS HOSPITAL–NEEDHAM CAMPUS, NEEDHAM, MASSACHUSETTS (see BETH ISRAEL DEACONESS MEDICAL CENTER), p. A306
BETH ISRAEL DEACONESS MEDICAL CENTER, BOSTON, MA, p. A306
BETHESDA BUTLER COUNTY HOSPITAL, HAMILTON, OHIO (see BETHESDA NORTH HOSPITAL), p. A486
BETHESDA BUTLER HOSPITAL, HAMILTON, OH, p. A495
BETHESDA HOSPITAL, SAINT PAUL, MN, p. A351
BETHESDA HOSPITAL, ZANESVILLE, OHIO (see GENESIS HEALTHCARE SYSTEM), p. A506
BETHESDA HOSPITAL EAST, BOYNTON BEACH, FL, p. A124
BETHESDA NORTH HOSPITAL, CINCINNATI, OH, p. A486
BETHESDA REHABILITATION HOSPITAL, BATON ROUGE, LA, p. A273
BEVERLY HOSPITAL, MONTEBELLO, CA, p. A78
BEVERLY HOSPITAL, BEVERLY, MA, p. A305
BHC ALHAMBRA HOSPITAL, ROSEMEAD, CA, p. A86
BIBB MEDICAL CENTER, CENTREVILLE, AL, p. A18
BIENVILLE MEDICAL CENTER, ARCADIA, LA, p. A272
BIG BEND REGIONAL MEDICAL CENTER, ALPINE, TX, p. A596
BIG HORN COUNTY MEMORIAL HOSPITAL, HARDIN, MT, p. A388
BIG SANDY MEDICAL CENTER, BIG SANDY, MT, p. A385
BIG SPRING STATE HOSPITAL, BIG SPRING, TX, p. A603
BIGFORK VALLEY HOSPITAL, BIGFORK, MN, p. A340
BILLINGS CLINIC, BILLINGS, MT, p. A385
BILOXI REGIONAL MEDICAL CENTER, BILOXI, MS, p. A355
BINGHAM MEMORIAL HOSPITAL, BLACKFOOT, ID, p. A174
BINGHAMTON GENERAL HOSPITAL, BINGHAMTON, NEW YORK (see UNITED HEALTH SERVICES HOSPITALS–BINGHAMTON), p. A434
BIRMINGHAM VETERANS AFFAIRS MEDICAL CENTER, BIRMINGHAM, AL, p. A16
BLACK HILLS SURGERY CENTER, RAPID CITY, SD, p. A575
BLACK RIVER MEDICAL CENTER, POPLAR BLUFF, MO, p. A378
BLACK RIVER MEMORIAL HOSPITAL, BLACK RIVER FALLS, WI, p. A702
BLAIR E. BATSON HOSPITAL FOR CHILDREN, JACKSON, MISSISSIPPI (see UNIVERSITY HOSPITAL), p. A360
BLAKE MEDICAL CENTER, BRADENTON, FL, p. A124
BLANCHARD VALLEY HOSPITAL, FINDLAY, OH, p. A494
BLANCHARD VALLEY HOSPITAL, FINDLAY, OHIO (see BLANCHARD VALLEY HOSPITAL), p. A494
BLECKLEY MEMORIAL HOSPITAL, COCHRAN, GA, p. A156
BLESSING HOSPITAL, QUINCY, IL, p. A201
BLESSING HOSPITAL, QUINCY, ILLINOIS (see BLESSING HOSPITAL), p. A201
BLOOMINGTON MEADOWS HOSPITAL, BLOOMINGTON, IN, p. A207
BLOUNT MEMORIAL HOSPITAL, MARYVILLE, TN, p. A588
BLUE HILL MEMORIAL HOSPITAL, BLUE HILL, ME, p. A292
BLUE MOUNTAIN HOSPITAL, JOHN DAY, OR, p. A526
BLUE MOUNTAIN HOSPITAL, BLANDING, UT, p. A659
BLUE RIDGE HEALTHCARE HOSPITALS, MORGANTON, NC, p. A469

BLUE RIDGE MEDICAL CENTER – YANCEY CAMPUS, BURNSVILLE, NORTH CAROLINA (see BLUE RIDGE REGIONAL HOSPITAL), p. A473
BLUE RIDGE REGIONAL HOSPITAL, SPRUCE PINE, NC, p. A473
BLUEFIELD REGIONAL MEDICAL CENTER, BLUEFIELD, WV, p. A693
BLUEGRASS COMMUNITY HOSPITAL, VERSAILLES, KY, p. A271
BLUFFTON HOSPITAL, BLUFFTON, OH, p. A484
BLUFFTON REGIONAL MEDICAL CENTER, BLUFFTON, IN, p. A207
BLYTHEDALE CHILDREN'S HOSPITAL, VALHALLA, NY, p. A457
BOB WILSON MEMORIAL GRANT COUNTY HOSPITAL, ULYSSES, KS, p. A255
BOCA RATON REGIONAL HOSPITAL, BOCA RATON, FL, p. A124
BOGALUSA COMMUNITY MEDICAL CENTER, BOGALUSA, LOUISIANA (see OUR LADY OF THE ANGELS HOSPITAL), p. A274
BOISE VETERANS AFFAIRS MEDICAL CENTER, BOISE, ID, p. A174
BOLIVAR GENERAL HOSPITAL, BOLIVAR, TN, p. A579
BOLIVAR MEDICAL CENTER, CLEVELAND, MS, p. A357
BON SECOURS BALTIMORE HEALTH SYSTEM, BALTIMORE, MD, p. A296
BON SECOURS COMMUNITY HOSPITAL, PORT JERVIS, NY, p. A452
BON SECOURS MARYVIEW MEDICAL CENTER, PORTSMOUTH, VA, p. A676
BON SECOURS MEMORIAL REGIONAL MEDICAL CENTER, MECHANICSVILLE, VA, p. A674
BON SECOURS ST. FRANCIS HEALTH SYSTEM, GREENVILLE, SC, p. A566
BON SECOURS ST. FRANCIS MEDICAL CENTER, MIDLOTHIAN, VA, p. A674
BON SECOURS ST. FRANCIS XAVIER HOSPITAL, CHARLESTON, SC, p. A563
BON SECOURS ST. MARY'S CHILDREN'S SERVICES, RICHMOND, VIRGINIA (see BON SECOURS ST. MARY'S HOSPITAL), p. A677
BON SECOURS ST. MARY'S HOSPITAL, RICHMOND, VA, p. A677
BON SECOURS–DEPAUL MEDICAL CENTER, NORFOLK, VA, p. A675
BON SECOURS–RICHMOND COMMUNITY HOSPITAL, RICHMOND, VA, p. A677
BONE AND JOINT HOSPITAL, OKLAHOMA CITY, OKLAHOMA (see ST. ANTHONY HOSPITAL), p. A516
BONNER GENERAL HOSPITAL, SANDPOINT, ID, p. A178
BOONE COUNTY HEALTH CENTER, ALBION, NE, p. A393
BOONE COUNTY HOSPITAL, BOONE, IA, p. A226
BOONE MEMORIAL HOSPITAL, MADISON, WV, p. A697
BOONEVILLE COMMUNITY HOSPITAL, BOONEVILLE, AR, p. A44
BORGESS MEDICAL CENTER, KALAMAZOO, MI, p. A328
BORGESS–LEE MEMORIAL HOSPITAL, DOWAGIAC, MI, p. A323
BORGESS–PIPP HOSPITAL, PLAINWELL, MI, p. A332
BOSTON CHILDREN'S HOSPITAL, BOSTON, MA, p. A306
BOSTON MEDICAL CENTER, BOSTON, MA, p. A306
BOTHWELL REGIONAL HEALTH CENTER, SEDALIA, MO, p. A382
BOTSFORD HOSPITAL, FARMINGTON HILLS, MI, p. A323
BOULDER CITY HOSPITAL, BOULDER CITY, NV, p. A404
BOULDER COMMUNITY FOOTHILLS HOSPITAL, BOULDER, COLORADO (see BOULDER COMMUNITY HOSPITAL), p. A102
BOULDER COMMUNITY HOSPITAL, BOULDER, CO, p. A102
BOUNDARY COMMUNITY HOSPITAL, BONNERS FERRY, ID, p. A175
BOUNDARY COUNTY NURSING HOME (see BOUNDARY COMMUNITY HOSPITAL), p. A175
BOURBON COMMUNITY HOSPITAL, PARIS, KY, p. A269
BOURNEWOOD HEALTH SYSTEMS, BROOKLINE, MA, p. A308
BOWDLE HOSPITAL, BOWDLE, SD, p. A572
BOWIE MEMORIAL HOSPITAL, BOWIE, TX, p. A603
BOX BUTTE GENERAL HOSPITAL, ALLIANCE, NE, p. A393
BOYS TOWN NATIONAL RESEARCH HOSPITAL, OMAHA, NE, p. A399
BOZEMAN DEACONESS HOSPITAL, BOZEMAN, MT, p. A385
BRADFORD HEALTH SERVICES AT HUNTSVILLE, MADISON, AL, p. A22
BRADFORD HEALTH SERVICES AT WARRIOR LODGE, WARRIOR, AL, p. A26
BRADFORD REGIONAL MEDICAL CENTER, BRADFORD, PA, p. A534
BRADLEY CENTER OF ST. FRANCIS, COLUMBUS, GEORGIA (see ST. FRANCIS HOSPITAL), p. A156
BRADLEY COUNTY MEDICAL CENTER, WARREN, AR, p. A53
BRADLEY MEMORIAL, SOUTHINGTON, CONNECTICUT (see THE HOSPITAL OF CENTRAL CONNECTICUT), p. A115
BRAINTREE REHABILITATION HOSPITAL, BRAINTREE, MA, p. A308
BRANDON REGIONAL HOSPITAL, BRANDON, FL, p. A124
BRANDYWINE HOSPITAL, COATESVILLE, PA, p. A536
BRATTLEBORO MEMORIAL HOSPITAL, BRATTLEBORO, VT, p. A665

BRATTLEBORO RETREAT, BRATTLEBORO, VT, p. A665
BRAXTON COUNTY MEMORIAL HOSPITAL, GASSAWAY, WV, p. A695
BRAZOSPORT REGIONAL HEALTH SYSTEM, LAKE JACKSON, TX, p. A632
BRECKINRIDGE MEMORIAL HOSPITAL, HARDINSBURG, KY, p. A262
BRENNER CHILDREN'S HOSPITAL & HEALTH SERVICES, WINSTON SALEM, NORTH CAROLINA (see WAKE FOREST BAPTIST MEDICAL CENTER), p. A475
BRENTWOOD BEHAVIORAL HEALTHCARE OF MISSISSIPPI, JACKSON, MS, p. A359
BRENTWOOD HOSPITAL, SHREVEPORT, LA, p. A288
BRENTWOOD MEADOWS, NEWBURGH, IN, p. A220
BRIDGEPORT HOSPITAL, BRIDGEPORT, CT, p. A113
BRIDGETON HEALTH CENTER, BRIDGETON, NEW JERSEY (see INSPIRA MEDICAL CENTER–VINELAND), p. A424
BRIDGEWATER STATE HOSPITAL, BRIDGEWATER, MA, p. A308
BRIDGEWELL HOSPITAL OF CINCINNATI, CINCINNATI, OH, p. A486
BRIDGTON HOSPITAL, BRIDGTON, ME, p. A292
BRIGHAM AND WOMEN'S FAULKNER HOSPITAL, BOSTON, MA, p. A306
BRIGHAM AND WOMEN'S HOSPITAL, BOSTON, MA, p. A306
BRIGHAM CITY COMMUNITY HOSPITAL, BRIGHAM CITY, UT, p. A659
BRIGHTON CENTER FOR RECOVERY, BRIGHTON, MI, p. A320
BRISTOL BAY AREA HEALTH CORPORATION, DILLINGHAM, AK, p. A28
BRISTOL HOSPITAL, BRISTOL, CT, p. A113
BRISTOL–MYERS SQUIBB CHILDREN'S HOSPITAL, NEW BRUNSWICK, NEW JERSEY (see ROBERT WOOD JOHNSON UNIVERSITY HOSPITAL), p. A419
BRISTOW MEDICAL CENTER, BRISTOW, OK, p. A508
BROADDUS HOSPITAL, PHILIPPI, WV, p. A698
BROADLAWNS MEDICAL CENTER, DES MOINES, IA, p. A229
BROADWATER HEALTH CENTER, TOWNSEND, MT, p. A391
BROCKTON VETERANS AFFAIRS MEDICAL CENTER, BROCKTON, MA, p. A308
BRODSTONE MEMORIAL HOSPITAL, SUPERIOR, NE, p. A402
BROMENN REGIONAL MEDICAL CENTER, NORMAL, ILLINOIS (see ADVOCATE BROMENN MEDICAL CENTER), p. A198
BRONSON BATTLE CREEK, BATTLE CREEK, MI, p. A319
BRONSON LAKEVIEW HOSPITAL, PAW PAW, MI, p. A332
BRONSON METHODIST HOSPITAL, KALAMAZOO, MI, p. A328
BRONSON VICKSBURG HOSPITAL, VICKSBURG, MICHIGAN (see BRONSON METHODIST HOSPITAL), p. A328
BRONX CHILDREN'S PSYCHIATRIC CENTER,, NEW YORK (see NEW YORK CITY CHILDREN'S CENTER), p. A446
BRONX PSYCHIATRIC CENTER,, NY, p. A442
BRONX–LEBANON HOSPITAL CENTER HEALTH CARE SYSTEM,, NY, p. A442
BRONX–LEBANON SPECIAL CARE CENTER,, NEW YORK (see BRONX–LEBANON HOSPITAL CENTER HEALTH CARE SYSTEM), p. A442
BROOK LANE HEALTH SERVICES, HAGERSTOWN, MD, p. A301
BROOKDALE HOSPITAL MEDICAL CENTER,, NY, p. A443
BROOKE GLEN BEHAVIORAL HOSPITAL, FORT WASHINGTON, PA, p. A539
BROOKHAVEN HOSPITAL, TULSA, OK, p. A520
BROOKHAVEN MEMORIAL HOSPITAL MEDICAL CENTER, PATCHOGUE, NY, p. A451
BROOKINGS HEALTH SYSTEM, BROOKINGS, SD, p. A572
BROOKLYN CHILDREN'S PSYCHIATRIC CENTER,, NEW YORK (see NEW YORK CITY CHILDREN'S CENTER), p. A446
BROOKLYN HOSPITAL CENTER,, NY, p. A443
BROOKS COUNTY HOSPITAL, QUITMAN, GA, p. A165
BROOKS MEMORIAL HOSPITAL, DUNKIRK, NY, p. A436
BROOKS REHABILITATION HOSPITAL, JACKSONVILLE, FL, p. A131
BROOKWOOD MEDICAL CENTER, BIRMINGHAM, AL, p. A16
BROUGHTON HOSPITAL, MORGANTON, NC, p. A469
BROWARD HEALTH CORAL SPRINGS, CORAL SPRINGS, FL, p. A126
BROWARD HEALTH IMPERIAL POINT, FORT LAUDERDALE, FL, p. A128
BROWARD HEALTH MEDICAL CENTER, FORT LAUDERDALE, FL, p. A128
BROWARD HEALTH NORTH, DEERFIELD BEACH, FL, p. A127
BROWN COUNTY COMMUNITY TREATMENT CENTER, GREEN BAY, WI, p. A706
BROWN COUNTY HOSPITAL, AINSWORTH, NE, p. A393
BROWNFIELD REGIONAL MEDICAL CENTER, BROWNFIELD, TX, p. A604
BROWNWOOD REGIONAL MEDICAL CENTER, BROWNWOOD, TX, p. A604
BRUNSWICK PSYCH CENTER, AMITYVILLE, NY, p. A432
BRYAN HOSPITAL, BRYAN, OHIO (see COMMUNITY HOSPITALS AND WELLNESS CENTERS), p. A484
BRYAN MEDICAL CENTER, LINCOLN, NE, p. A397

CHILDREN'S MERCY HOSPITALS AND CLINICS, KANSAS CITY, MO, p. A373
CHILDREN'S MERCY SOUTH, OVERLAND PARK, KS, p. A252
CHILDREN'S NATIONAL MEDICAL CENTER, WASHINGTON, DC, p. A121
CHILDREN'S SPECIALIZED HOSPITAL, MOUNTAINSIDE, NEW JERSEY (see CHILDREN'S SPECIALIZED HOSPITAL–PSE&G), p. A419
CHILDREN'S SPECIALIZED HOSPITAL–PSE&G, NEW BRUNSWICK, NJ, p. A419
CHILDRENS CARE HOSPITAL AND SCHOOL, SIOUX FALLS, SD, p. A576
CHILDRESS REGIONAL MEDICAL CENTER, CHILDRESS, TX, p. A606
CHILLICOTHE HOSPITAL DISTRICT, CHILLICOTHE, TX, p. A606
CHILLICOTHE VETERANS AFFAIRS MEDICAL CENTER, CHILLICOTHE, OH, p. A486
CHILTON MEDICAL CENTER, POMPTON PLAINS, NJ, p. A421
CHINESE HOSPITAL, SAN FRANCISCO, CA, p. A90
CHINLE COMPREHENSIVE HEALTH CARE FACILITY, CHINLE, AZ, p. A31
CHINO VALLEY MEDICAL CENTER, CHINO, CA, p. A59
CHIPPENHAM MEDICAL CENTER, RICHMOND, VIRGINIA (see CJW MEDICAL CENTER), p. A677
CHIPPEWA COUNTY–MONTEVIDEO HOSPITAL, MONTEVIDEO, MN, p. A348
CHIPPEWA VALLEY HOSPITAL AND OAKVIEW CARE CENTER, DURAND, WI, p. A704
CHOATE MENTAL HEALTH CENTER, ANNA, IL, p. A180
CHOCTAW COUNTY HOSPITAL, ACKERMAN, MS, p. A355
CHOCTAW GENERAL HOSPITAL, BUTLER, AL, p. A17
CHOCTAW HEALTH CENTER, PHILADELPHIA, MS, p. A364
CHOCTAW MEMORIAL HOSPITAL, HUGO, OK, p. A512
CHOCTAW NATION HEALTH CARE CENTER, TALIHINA, OK, p. A519
CHRIS EVERT CHILDRENS HOSPITAL, FORT LAUDERDALE, FLORIDA (see BROWARD HEALTH MEDICAL CENTER), p. A128
CHRIST HOSPITAL, JERSEY CITY, NJ, p. A417
CHRIST HOSPITAL, CINCINNATI, OH, p. A486
CHRISTIAN HEALTH CARE CENTER, WYCKOFF, NJ, p. A425
CHRISTIAN HOSPITAL, SAINT LOUIS, MO, p. A380
CHRISTIANA CARE HEALTH SYSTEM, NEWARK, DE, p. A119
CHRISTIANA HOSPITAL, WILMINGTON, DELAWARE (see CHRISTIANA CARE HEALTH SYSTEM), p. A119
CHRISTUS COUSHATTA HEALTH CARE CENTER, COUSHATTA, LA, p. A275
CHRISTUS DUBUIS HOSPITAL OF BRYAN, BRYAN, TX, p. A604
CHRISTUS DUBUIS HOSPITAL OF PORT ARTHUR, PORT ARTHUR, TX, p. A643
CHRISTUS HIGHLAND MEDICAL CENTER, SHREVEPORT, LA, p. A288
CHRISTUS HIGHLAND MEDICAL CENTER, SHREVEPORT, LOUISIANA (see CHRISTUS HIGHLAND MEDICAL CENTER), p. A288
CHRISTUS HOSPITAL–ST. ELIZABETH, BEAUMONT, TX, p. A601
CHRISTUS HOSPITAL–ST. MARY, PORT ARTHUR, TEXAS (see CHRISTUS HOSPITAL–ST. ELIZABETH), p. A601
CHRISTUS JASPER MEMORIAL HOSPITAL, JASPER, TX, p. A630
CHRISTUS SANTA ROSA HEALTH SYSTEM, SAN ANTONIO, TX, p. A646
CHRISTUS SANTA ROSA HOSPITAL – NEW BRAUNFELS, NEW BRAUNFELS, TEXAS (see CHRISTUS SANTA ROSA HEALTH SYSTEM), p. A646
CHRISTUS SANTA ROSA–MEDICAL CENTER, SAN ANTONIO, TEXAS (see CHRISTUS SANTA ROSA HEALTH SYSTEM), p. A646
CHRISTUS SPOHN HOSPITAL ALICE, ALICE, TX, p. A595
CHRISTUS SPOHN HOSPITAL BEEVILLE, BEEVILLE, TX, p. A602
CHRISTUS SPOHN HOSPITAL CORPUS CHRISTI MEMORIAL, CORPUS CHRISTI, TX, p. A608
CHRISTUS SPOHN HOSPITAL CORPUS CHRISTI SHORELINE, CORPUS CHRISTI, TEXAS (see CHRISTUS SPOHN HOSPITAL CORPUS CHRISTI MEMORIAL), p. A608
CHRISTUS SPOHN HOSPITAL CORPUS CHRISTUS SOUTH, CORPUS CHRISTI, TEXAS (see CHRISTUS SPOHN HOSPITAL CORPUS CHRISTI MEMORIAL), p. A608
CHRISTUS SPOHN HOSPITAL KLEBERG, KINGSVILLE, TX, p. A631
CHRISTUS ST. FRANCES CABRINI HOSPITAL, ALEXANDRIA, LA, p. A272
CHRISTUS ST. MICHAEL HEALTH SYSTEM, TEXARKANA, TX, p. A652
CHRISTUS ST. MICHAEL REHABILITATION HOSPITAL, TEXARKANA, TX, p. A652
CHRISTUS ST. MICHAEL'S HOSPITAL–ATLANTA, ATLANTA, TEXAS (see CHRISTUS ST. MICHAEL HEALTH SYSTEM), p. A652
CHRISTUS ST. PATRICK HOSPITAL OF LAKE CHARLES, LAKE CHARLES, LA, p. A282

CHRISTUS ST. VINCENT PHYSICIANS MEDICAL CENTER, SANTA FE, NEW MEXICO (see CHRISTUS ST. VINCENT REGIONAL MEDICAL CENTER), p. A430
CHRISTUS ST. VINCENT REGIONAL MEDICAL CENTER, SANTA FE, NM, p. A430
CIBOLA GENERAL HOSPITAL, GRANTS, NM, p. A428
CIMARRON MEMORIAL HOSPITAL, BOISE CITY, OK, p. A508
CINCINNATI CHILDREN'S HOSPITAL MEDICAL CENTER, CINCINNATI, OH, p. A486
CINCINNATI VETERANS AFFAIRS MEDICAL CENTER, CINCINNATI, OH, p. A486
CIRCLES OF CARE, MELBOURNE, FL, p. A135
CITIZENS BAPTIST MEDICAL CENTER, TALLADEGA, AL, p. A25
CITIZENS MEDICAL CENTER, COLBY, KS, p. A242
CITIZENS MEDICAL CENTER, COLUMBIA, LA, p. A275
CITIZENS MEDICAL CENTER, VICTORIA, TX, p. A655
CITIZENS MEMORIAL HOSPITAL, BOLIVAR, MO, p. A367
CITRUS MEMORIAL HEALTH SYSTEM, INVERNESS, FL, p. A131
CITRUS VALLEY MEDICAL CENTER–INTER COMMUNITY CAMPUS, COVINA, CA, p. A61
CITRUS VALLEY MEDICAL CENTER–INTER–COMMUNITY CAMPUS, COVINA, CALIFORNIA (see CITRUS VALLEY MEDICAL CENTER–INTER COMMUNITY CAMPUS), p. A61
CITRUS VALLEY MEDICAL CENTER–QUEEN OF THE VALLEY CAMPUS, WEST COVINA, CALIFORNIA (see CITRUS VALLEY MEDICAL CENTER–INTER COMMUNITY CAMPUS), p. A61
CITY OF HOPE'S HELFORD CLINICAL RESEARCH HOSPITAL, DUARTE, CA, p. A62
CJW MEDICAL CENTER, RICHMOND, VA, p. A677
CLAIBORNE COUNTY MEDICAL CENTER, PORT GIBSON, MS, p. A364
CLAIBORNE MEDICAL CENTER, TAZEWELL, TN, p. A593
CLARA BARTON HOSPITAL, HOISINGTON, KS, p. A245
CLARA MAASS MEDICAL CENTER, BELLEVILLE, NJ, p. A413
CLAREMORE INDIAN HOSPITAL, CLAREMORE, OK, p. A509
CLARENDON MEMORIAL HOSPITAL, MANNING, SC, p. A568
CLARINDA REGIONAL HEALTH CENTER, CLARINDA, IA, p. A227
CLARION HOSPITAL, CLARION, PA, p. A535
CLARION PSYCHIATRIC CENTER, CLARION, PA, p. A535
CLARITY CHILD GUIDANCE CENTER, SAN ANTONIO, TX, p. A646
CLARK FORK VALLEY HOSPITAL, PLAINS, MT, p. A390
CLARK MEMORIAL HOSPITAL, JEFFERSONVILLE, IN, p. A215
CLARK REGIONAL MEDICAL CENTER, WINCHESTER, KY, p. A271
CLARKE COUNTY HOSPITAL, OSCEOLA, IA, p. A236
CLARKS SUMMIT STATE HOSPITAL, CLARKS SUMMIT, PA, p. A535
CLAXTON–HEPBURN MEDICAL CENTER, OGDENSBURG, NY, p. A450
CLAY COUNTY HOSPITAL, ASHLAND, AL, p. A15
CLAY COUNTY HOSPITAL, FLORA, IL, p. A190
CLAY COUNTY MEDICAL CENTER, CLAY CENTER, KS, p. A242
CLAY COUNTY MEMORIAL HOSPITAL, HENRIETTA, TX, p. A623
CLEAR BROOK LODGE, SHICKSHINNY, PA, p. A555
CLEAR BROOK MANOR, WILKES–BARRE, PA, p. A558
CLEAR LAKE REGIONAL MEDICAL CENTER, WEBSTER, TX, p. A656
CLEARFIELD HOSPITAL, CLEARFIELD, PA, p. A536
CLEARVIEW REGIONAL MEDICAL CENTER, MONROE, GA, p. A164
CLEARWATER VALLEY HOSPITAL AND CLINICS, OROFINO, ID, p. A177
CLEMENT J. ZABLOCKI VETERANS AFFAIRS MEDICAL CENTER, MILWAUKEE, WI, p. A710
CLEO WALLACE CENTERS HOSPITAL, WESTMINSTER, CO, p. A112
CLEVELAND AREA HOSPITAL, CLEVELAND, OK, p. A509
CLEVELAND CAMPUS, CLEVELAND, OHIO (see NORTHCOAST BEHAVIORAL HEALTHCARE SYSTEM), p. A499
CLEVELAND CLINIC, CLEVELAND, OH, p. A488
CLEVELAND CLINIC CHILDREN'S HOSPITAL, CLEVELAND, OHIO (see CLEVELAND CLINIC), p. A488
CLEVELAND CLINIC CHILDREN'S HOSPITAL FOR REHABILITATION, CLEVELAND, OH, p. A488
CLEVELAND CLINIC FLORIDA, WESTON, FL, p. A150
CLEVELAND REGIONAL MEDICAL CENTER, SHELBY, NC, p. A472
CLEVELAND REGIONAL MEDICAL CENTER, CLEVELAND, TX, p. A606
CLIFTON SPRINGS HOSPITAL AND CLINIC, CLIFTON SPRINGS, NY, p. A435
CLIFTON T. PERKINS HOSPITAL CENTER, JESSUP, MD, p. A301
CLIFTON–FINE HOSPITAL, STAR LAKE, NY, p. A455
CLINCH MEMORIAL HOSPITAL, HOMERVILLE, GA, p. A161
CLINCH VALLEY MEDICAL CENTER, RICHLANDS, VA, p. A677
CLINTON COUNTY HOSPITAL, ALBANY, KY, p. A258
CLINTON HOSPITAL, CLINTON, MA, p. A309
CLINTON MEMORIAL HOSPITAL, WILMINGTON, OH, p. A505
CLOUD COUNTY HEALTH CENTER, CONCORDIA, KS, p. A242

CLOVIS COMMUNITY MEDICAL CENTER, CLOVIS, CA, p. A60
COAL COUNTY GENERAL HOSPITAL, COALGATE, OK, p. A509
COALINGA REGIONAL MEDICAL CENTER, COALINGA, CA, p. A60
COAST PLAZA HOSPITAL, NORWALK, CA, p. A80
COASTAL CAROLINA HOSPITAL, HARDEEVILLE, SC, p. A567
COASTAL COMMUNITIES HOSPITAL, SANTA ANA, CA, p. A93
COASTAL HARBOR TREATMENT CENTER, SAVANNAH, GA, p. A166
COATESVILLE VETERANS AFFAIRS MEDICAL CENTER, COATESVILLE, PA, p. A536
COBLESKILL REGIONAL HOSPITAL, COBLESKILL, NY, p. A436
COBRE VALLEY REGIONAL MEDICAL CENTER, GLOBE, AZ, p. A33
COCHRAN MEMORIAL HOSPITAL, MORTON, TX, p. A638
COFFEE REGIONAL MEDICAL CENTER, DOUGLAS, GA, p. A158
COFFEY COUNTY HOSPITAL, BURLINGTON, KS, p. A242
COFFEYVILLE REGIONAL MEDICAL CENTER, COFFEYVILLE, KS, p. A242
COGDELL MEMORIAL HOSPITAL, SNYDER, TX, p. A649
COLE MEMORIAL, COUDERSPORT, PA, p. A536
COLEMAN COUNTY MEDICAL CENTER, COLEMAN, TX, p. A606
COLER MEMORIAL HOSPITAL, NEW YORK, NEW YORK (see HENRY J. CARTER SPECIALTY HOSPITAL AND NURSING FACILITY), p. A444
COLISEUM CENTER FOR BEHAVIORAL HEALTH, MACON, GA, p. A162
COLISEUM MEDICAL CENTERS, MACON, GA, p. A162
COLISEUM NORTHSIDE HOSPITAL, MACON, GA, p. A162
COLLEGE HOSPITAL CERRITOS, CERRITOS, CA, p. A59
COLLEGE HOSPITAL COSTA MESA, COSTA MESA, CA, p. A60
COLLEGE STATION MEDICAL CENTER, COLLEGE STATION, TX, p. A607
COLLETON MEDICAL CENTER, WALTERBORO, SC, p. A570
COLLINGSWORTH GENERAL HOSPITAL, WELLINGTON, TX, p. A656
COLMERY–O'NEIL VETERANS AFFAIRS MEDICAL CENTER, TOPEKA, KANSAS (see VETERANS AFFAIRS EASTERN KANSAS HEALTH CARE SYSTEM), p. A255
COLONEL FLORENCE A. BLANCHFIELD ARMY COMMUNITY HOSPITAL, FORT CAMPBELL, KY, p. A261
COLORADO ACUTE LONG TERM HOSPITAL, DENVER, CO, p. A104
COLORADO MENTAL HEALTH INSTITUTE AT FORT LOGAN, DENVER, CO, p. A104
COLORADO MENTAL HEALTH INSTITUTE AT PUEBLO, PUEBLO, CO, p. A110
COLORADO PLAINS MEDICAL CENTER, FORT MORGAN, CO, p. A106
COLORADO RIVER MEDICAL CENTER, NEEDLES, CA, p. A79
COLQUITT REGIONAL MEDICAL CENTER, MOULTRIE, GA, p. A164
COLUMBIA BASIN HOSPITAL, EPHRATA, WA, p. A683
COLUMBIA CENTER, MEQUON, WI, p. A709
COLUMBIA COUNTY HEALTH SYSTEM, DAYTON, WA, p. A683
COLUMBIA MEMORIAL HOSPITAL, HUDSON, NY, p. A439
COLUMBIA MEMORIAL HOSPITAL, ASTORIA, OR, p. A523
COLUMBIA ST. MARY'S COLUMBIA HOSPITAL, MILWAUKEE, WISCONSIN (see COLUMBIA ST. MARY'S HOSPITAL MILWAUKEE), p. A710
COLUMBIA ST. MARY'S HOSPITAL MILWAUKEE, MILWAUKEE, WI, p. A710
COLUMBIA ST. MARY'S MILWAUKEE HOSPITAL, MILWAUKEE, WISCONSIN (see COLUMBIA ST. MARY'S HOSPITAL MILWAUKEE), p. A710
COLUMBIA ST. MARY'S OZAUKEE HOSPITAL, MEQUON, WI, p. A709
COLUMBUS COMMUNITY HOSPITAL, COLUMBUS, NE, p. A395
COLUMBUS COMMUNITY HOSPITAL, COLUMBUS, TX, p. A607
COLUMBUS COMMUNITY HOSPITAL, COLUMBUS, WI, p. A703
COLUMBUS HOSPITAL LTACH, NEWARK, NJ, p. A419
COLUMBUS REGIONAL HEALTHCARE SYSTEM, WHITEVILLE, NC, p. A474
COLUMBUS REGIONAL HOSPITAL, COLUMBUS, IN, p. A208
COLUMBUS SPECIALTY HOSPITAL, COLUMBUS, GA, p. A156
COLUSA REGIONAL MEDICAL CENTER, COLUSA, CA, p. A60
COMANCHE COUNTY HOSPITAL, COLDWATER, KS, p. A242
COMANCHE COUNTY MEDICAL CENTER, COMANCHE, TX, p. A607
COMANCHE COUNTY MEMORIAL HOSPITAL, LAWTON, OK, p. A512
COMMONWEALTH CENTER FOR CHILDREN AND ADOLESCENTS, STAUNTON, VA, p. A679
COMMONWEALTH REGIONAL SPECIALTY HOSPITAL, BOWLING GREEN, KY, p. A258
COMMUNITY BEHAVIORAL HEALTH CENTER, FRESNO, CA, p. A64
COMMUNITY BEHAVIORAL HEALTH HOSPITAL – ALEXANDRIA, ALEXANDRIA, MN, p. A339
COMMUNITY BEHAVIORAL HEALTH HOSPITAL – ANNANDALE, ANNANDALE, MN, p. A339

COMMUNITY BEHAVIORAL HEALTH HOSPITAL – BAXTER, BAXTER, MN, p. A340

COMMUNITY BEHAVIORAL HEALTH HOSPITAL – BEMIDJI, BEMIDJI, MN, p. A340

COMMUNITY BEHAVIORAL HEALTH HOSPITAL – FERGUS FALLS, FERGUS FALLS, MN, p. A343

COMMUNITY BEHAVIORAL HEALTH HOSPITAL – ROCHESTER, ROCHESTER, MN, p. A350

COMMUNITY BEHAVIORAL HEALTH HOSPITAL – ST. PETER, SAINT PETER, MN, p. A352

COMMUNITY CARE HOSPITAL, NEW ORLEANS, LA, A285

COMMUNITY GENERAL HEALTH CENTER, FORT FAIRFIELD, MAINE (see THE AROOSTOOK MEDICAL CENTER), p. A295

COMMUNITY HEALTH CENTER OF BRANCH COUNTY, COLDWATER, MI, p. A321

COMMUNITY HEALTHCARE SYSTEM, ONAGA, KS, p. A251

COMMUNITY HEART AND VASCULAR HOSPITAL, INDIANAPOLIS, IN, p. A213

COMMUNITY HOSPITAL, TALLASSEE, AL, p. A26

COMMUNITY HOSPITAL, GRAND JUNCTION, CO, p. A107

COMMUNITY HOSPITAL, MUNSTER, IN, p. A219

COMMUNITY HOSPITAL, MCCOOK, NE, p. A398

COMMUNITY HOSPITAL, OKLAHOMA CITY, OK, p. A515

COMMUNITY HOSPITAL, TORRINGTON, WY, p. A723

COMMUNITY HOSPITAL, HARRISBURG, PENNSYLVANIA (see PINNACLE HEALTH SYSTEM), p. A540

COMMUNITY HOSPITAL EAST, INDIANAPOLIS, IN, p. A213

COMMUNITY HOSPITAL NORTH, INDIANAPOLIS, IN, p. A213

COMMUNITY HOSPITAL OF ANACONDA, ANACONDA, MT, p. A385

COMMUNITY HOSPITAL OF ANDERSON AND MADISON COUNTY, ANDERSON, IN, p. A206

COMMUNITY HOSPITAL OF BREMEN, BREMEN, IN, p. A207

COMMUNITY HOSPITAL OF HUNTINGTON PARK, HUNTINGTON PARK, CA, p. A67

COMMUNITY HOSPITAL OF LONG BEACH, LONG BEACH, CA, p. A70

COMMUNITY HOSPITAL OF SAN BERNARDINO, SAN BERNARDINO, CA, p. A88

COMMUNITY HOSPITAL OF THE MONTEREY PENINSULA, MONTEREY, CA, p. A78

COMMUNITY HOSPITAL SOUTH, INDIANAPOLIS, IN, p. A213

COMMUNITY HOSPITAL–FAIRFAX, FAIRFAX, MO, p. A371

COMMUNITY HOSPITALS AND WELLNESS CENTERS, BRYAN, OH, p. A484

COMMUNITY HOSPITALS AND WELLNESS CENTERS–MONTPELIER, MONTPELIER, OH, p. A499

COMMUNITY HOWARD REGIONAL HEALTH, KOKOMO, IN, p. A216

COMMUNITY HOWARD SPECIALTY HOSPITAL, KOKOMO, IN, p. A216

COMMUNITY MEDICAL CENTER, MISSOULA, MT, p. A389

COMMUNITY MEDICAL CENTER, FALLS CITY, NE, p. A395

COMMUNITY MEDICAL CENTER, TOMS RIVER, NJ, p. A423

COMMUNITY MEDICAL CENTER OF IZARD COUNTY, CALICO ROCK, AR, p. A44

COMMUNITY MEMORIAL HEALTH SYSTEM, VENTURA, CA, p. A99

COMMUNITY MEMORIAL HEALTHCARE, MARYSVILLE, KS, p. A249

COMMUNITY MEMORIAL HOSPITAL, VENTURA, CALIFORNIA (see COMMUNITY MEMORIAL HEALTH SYSTEM), p. A99

COMMUNITY MEMORIAL HOSPITAL, STAUNTON, IL, p. A203

COMMUNITY MEMORIAL HOSPITAL, SUMNER, IA, p. A238

COMMUNITY MEMORIAL HOSPITAL, CLOQUET, MN, p. A341

COMMUNITY MEMORIAL HOSPITAL, SYRACUSE, NE, p. A402

COMMUNITY MEMORIAL HOSPITAL, HAMILTON, NY, p. A438

COMMUNITY MEMORIAL HOSPITAL, TURTLE LAKE, ND, p. A480

COMMUNITY MEMORIAL HOSPITAL, HICKSVILLE, OH, p. A495

COMMUNITY MEMORIAL HOSPITAL, BURKE, SD, p. A572

COMMUNITY MEMORIAL HOSPITAL, REDFIELD, SD, p. A576

COMMUNITY MEMORIAL HOSPITAL, MENOMONEE FALLS, WI, p. A709

COMMUNITY MEMORIAL HOSPITAL, OCONTO FALLS, WI, p. A712

COMMUNITY MENTAL HEALTH CENTER, LAWRENCEBURG, IN, p. A217

COMMUNITY REGIONAL MEDICAL CENTER, FRESNO, CA, p. A64

COMMUNITY SPECIALTY HOSPITAL, LAFAYETTE, LA, p. A281

COMMUNITY WESTVIEW HOSPITAL, INDIANAPOLIS, IN, p. A213

COMPASS BEHAVIORAL CENTER OF ALEXANDRIA, ALEXANDRIA, LA, p. A272

COMPASS BEHAVIORAL CENTER OF CROWLEY, CROWLEY, LA, p. A276

COMPASS BEHAVIORAL CENTER OF HOUMA, HOUMA, LA, p. A278

COMPLEX CARE HOSPITAL AT RIDGELAKE, SARASOTA, FL, p. A145

COMPLEX CARE HOSPITAL AT TENAYA, LAS VEGAS, NV, p. A405

CONCHO COUNTY HOSPITAL, EDEN, TX, p. A614

CONCORD HOSPITAL, CONCORD, NH, p. A409

CONCOURSE DIVISION,, NEW YORK (see BRONX–LEBANON HOSPITAL CENTER HEALTH CARE SYSTEM), p. A442

CONEMAUGH MEMORIAL MEDICAL CENTER, JOHNSTOWN, PA, p. A541

CONEMAUGH MEYERSDALE MEDICAL CENTER, MEYERSDALE, PA, A545

CONEMAUGH MINERS MEDICAL CENTER, HASTINGS, PA, p. A540

CONEY ISLAND HOSPITAL,, NY, p. A443

CONIFER PARK, GLENVILLE, NY, p. A438

CONNALLY MEMORIAL MEDICAL CENTER, FLORESVILLE, TX, p. A617

CONNECTICUT CHILDREN'S MEDICAL CENTER, HARTFORD, CT, p. A114

CONNECTICUT DEPARTMENT OF CORRECTION'S HOSPITAL, SOMERS, CT, p. A117

CONNECTICUT MENTAL HEALTH CENTER, NEW HAVEN, CT, p. A116

CONNECTICUT VALLEY HOSPITAL, MIDDLETOWN, CT, p. A115

CONROE REGIONAL MEDICAL CENTER, CONROE, TX, p. A607

CONTINUE CARE HOSPITAL AT HENDRICK MEDICAL CENTER, ABILENE, TX, p. A595

CONTINUECARE HOSPITAL AT MIDLAND MEMORIAL, MIDLAND, TEXAS (see MIDLAND MEMORIAL HOSPITAL), p. A638

CONTINUING CARE HOSPITAL, LEXINGTON, KY, p. A264

CONTINUING CARE HOSPITAL AT ST. LUKE'S, CEDAR RAPIDS, IA, p. A226

CONTINUOUS CARE CENTERS OF OKLAHOMA, TULSA, OKLAHOMA (see AMG SPECIALTY HOSPITAL–TULSA), p. A520

CONTINUUM REHABILITATION HOSPITAL OF NORTH TEXAS, FLOWER MOUND, TX, p. A617

CONTRA COSTA REGIONAL MEDICAL CENTER, MARTINEZ, CA, p. A77

CONWAY MEDICAL CENTER, CONWAY, SC, p. A565

CONWAY REGIONAL MEDICAL CENTER, CONWAY, AR, p. A44

CONWAY REGIONAL REHAB HOSPITAL, CONWAY, AR, p. A44

COOK CHILDREN'S MEDICAL CENTER, FORT WORTH, TX, p. A618

COOK CHILDREN'S NORTHEAST HOSPITAL, HURST, TX, p. A629

COOK COUNTY NORTH SHORE HOSPITAL, GRAND MARAIS, MN, p. A344

COOK HOSPITAL AND CONVALESCENT NURSING CARE UNIT, COOK, MN, p. A341

COOK MEDICAL CENTER–A CAMPUS OF TIFT REGIONAL MEDICAL CENTER, ADEL, GA, p. A151

COOKEVILLE REGIONAL MEDICAL CENTER, COOKEVILLE, TN, p. A581

COOLEY DICKINSON HOSPITAL, NORTHAMPTON, MA, p. A313

COON MEMORIAL HOSPITAL, DALHART, TX, p. A609

COOPER COUNTY MEMORIAL HOSPITAL, BOONVILLE, MO, p. A368

COOPER UNIVERSITY HEALTH CARE, CAMDEN, NJ, p. A414

COOPERSTOWN MEDICAL CENTER, COOPERSTOWN, ND, p. A477

COORDINATED HEALTH–BETHLEHEM, BETHLEHEM, PA, p. A533

COOSA VALLEY MEDICAL CENTER, SYLACAUGA, AL, p. A25

COPLEY HOSPITAL, MORRISVILLE, VT, p. A665

COPPER BASIN MEDICAL CENTER, COPPERHILL, TN, p. A581

COPPER QUEEN COMMUNITY HOSPITAL, BISBEE, AZ, p. A31

COQUILLE VALLEY HOSPITAL, COQUILLE, OR, p. A524

CORAL GABLES HOSPITAL, CORAL GABLES, FL, p. A126

CORDELL MEMORIAL HOSPITAL, CORDELL, OK, p. A509

CORDOVA COMMUNITY MEDICAL CENTER, CORDOVA, AK, p. A28

CORNERSTONE HOSPITAL OF AUSTIN, AUSTIN, TX, p. A599

CORNERSTONE HOSPITAL OF AUSTIN, AUSTIN, TEXAS (see CORNERSTONE HOSPITAL OF AUSTIN), p. A599

CORNERSTONE HOSPITAL OF BOSSIER CITY, BOSSIER CITY, LA, p. A274

CORNERSTONE HOSPITAL OF HOUSTON – BELLAIRE, HOUSTON, TEXAS (see CORNERSTONE HOSPITAL OF HOUSTON AT CLEARLAKE), p. A656

CORNERSTONE HOSPITAL OF HOUSTON AT CLEARLAKE, WEBSTER, TX, p. A656

CORNERSTONE HOSPITAL OF HUNTINGTON, HUNTINGTON, WV, p. A695

CORNERSTONE HOSPITAL OF NORTH LITTLE ROCK, JACKSONVILLE, AR, p. A48

CORNERSTONE HOSPITAL OF ROUND ROCK, ROUND ROCK, TX, p. A644

CORNERSTONE HOSPITAL OF SOUTHEAST ARIZONA, TUCSON, AZ, p. A40

CORNERSTONE HOSPITAL OF SOUTHWEST LOUISIANA, SULPHUR, LA, p. A289

CORNERSTONE HOSPITAL–MEDICAL CENTER OF HOUSTON, HOUSTON, TX, p. A624

CORNERSTONE HOSPITAL–WEST MONROE, WEST MONROE, LA, p. A290

CORNERSTONE OF MEDICAL ARTS CENTER HOSPITAL, FRESH MEADOWS, NY, p. A437

CORNERSTONE REGIONAL HOSPITAL, EDINBURG, TX, p. A615

CORNING HOSPITAL, CORNING, NY, p. A436

CORONA REGIONAL MEDICAL CENTER, CORONA, CA, p. A60

CORONA REGIONAL MEDICAL CENTER–REHABILITATION, CORONA, CALIFORNIA (see CORONA REGIONAL MEDICAL CENTER), p. A60

CORPUS CHRISTI MEDICAL CENTER, CORPUS CHRISTI, TX, p. A608

CORPUS CHRISTI MEDICAL CENTER BAY AREA, CORPUS CHRISTI, TEXAS (see CORPUS CHRISTI MEDICAL CENTER), p. A608

CORRY MEMORIAL HOSPITAL, CORRY, PA, p. A536

CORTLAND REGIONAL MEDICAL CENTER, CORTLAND, NY, p. A436

CORYELL MEMORIAL HOSPITAL, GATESVILLE, TX, p. A621

COSHOCTON COUNTY MEMORIAL HOSPITAL, COSHOCTON, OH, p. A491

COTEAU DES PRAIRIES HOSPITAL, SISSETON, SD, p. A577

COTTAGE CHILDREN'S HOSPITAL, SANTA BARBARA, CALIFORNIA (see SANTA BARBARA COTTAGE HOSPITAL), p. A94

COTTAGE HOSPITAL, WOODSVILLE, NH, p. A412

COTTAGE REHABILITATION HOSPITAL, SANTA BARBARA, CALIFORNIA (see SANTA BARBARA COTTAGE HOSPITAL), p. A94

COULEE MEDICAL CENTER, GRAND COULEE, WA, p. A684

COVENANT CHILDREN'S HOSPITAL, LUBBOCK, TX, p. A634

COVENANT HOSPITAL PLAINVIEW, PLAINVIEW, TX, p. A642

COVENANT HOSPITAL–LEVELLAND, LEVELLAND, TX, p. A633

COVENANT MEDICAL CENTER, WATERLOO, IA, p. A239

COVENANT MEDICAL CENTER, SAGINAW, MI, p. A333

COVENANT MEDICAL CENTER, LUBBOCK, TX, p. A634

COVENANT MEDICAL CENTER–COOPER, SAGINAW, MICHIGAN (see COVENANT MEDICAL CENTER), p. A333

COVENANT MEDICAL CENTER–HARRISON, SAGINAW, MICHIGAN (see COVENANT MEDICAL CENTER), p. A333

COVENANT MEDICAL CENTER–LAKESIDE, LUBBOCK, TEXAS (see COVENANT MEDICAL CENTER), p. A634

COVENANT SPECIALTY HOSPITAL, LUBBOCK, TX, p. A634

COVINGTON COUNTY HOSPITAL, COLLINS, MS, p. A357

COX MEDICAL CENTER BRANSON, BRANSON, MO, p. A368

COX MEDICAL CENTER NORTH, SPRINGFIELD, MISSOURI (see COX MEDICAL CENTERS), p. A383

COX MEDICAL CENTER SOUTH, SPRINGFIELD, MISSOURI (see COX MEDICAL CENTERS), p. A383

COX MEDICAL CENTERS, SPRINGFIELD, MO, p. A383

COX MONETT, MONETT, MO, p. A377

COZAD COMMUNITY HOSPITAL, COZAD, NE, p. A395

CRAIG GENERAL HOSPITAL, VINITA, OK, p. A521

CRAIG HOSPITAL, ENGLEWOOD, CO, p. A106

CRANE MEMORIAL HOSPITAL, CRANE, TX, p. A608

CRAWFORD COUNTY MEMORIAL HOSPITAL, DENISON, IA, p. A229

CRAWFORD MEMORIAL HOSPITAL, ROBINSON, IL, p. A201

CRAWLEY MEMORIAL HOSPITAL, SHELBY, NC, p. A472

CREEDMOOR PSYCHIATRIC CENTER,, NY, p. A443

CREEK NATION COMMUNITY HOSPITAL, OKEMAH, OK, p. A514

CRENSHAW COMMUNITY HOSPITAL, LUVERNE, AL, p. A22

CRESCENT MEDICAL CENTER LANCASTER, LANCASTER, TX, p. A632

CRESTWOOD MEDICAL CENTER, HUNTSVILLE, AL, p. A21

CRETE AREA MEDICAL CENTER, CRETE, NE, p. A395

CRISP REGIONAL HOSPITAL, CORDELE, GA, p. A157

CRITTENDEN COUNTY HOSPITAL, MARION, KY, p. A267

CRITTENTON CHILDREN'S CENTER, KANSAS CITY, MO, p. A373

CRITTENTON HOSPITAL MEDICAL CENTER, ROCHESTER, MI, p. A333

CROOK COUNTY MEDICAL SERVICES DISTRICT, SUNDANCE, WY, p. A723

CROSBYTON CLINIC HOSPITAL, CROSBYTON, TX, p. A609

CROSSGATES RIVER OAKS HOSPITAL, BRANDON, MS, p. A356

CROSSRIDGE COMMUNITY HOSPITAL, WYNNE, AR, p. A54

CROSSROADS COMMUNITY HOSPITAL, MOUNT VERNON, IL, p. A197

CROTCHED MOUNTAIN REHABILITATION CENTER, GREENFIELD, NH, p. A410

CROUSE HOSPITAL, SYRACUSE, NY, p. A455

CROW/NORTHERN CHEYENNE HOSPITAL, CROW AGENCY, MT, p. A386

CROZER–CHESTER MEDICAL CENTER, UPLAND, PA, p. A556

CUBA MEMORIAL HOSPITAL, CUBA, NY, p. A436

CUERO COMMUNITY HOSPITAL, CUERO, TX, p. A609

CULBERSON HOSPITAL, VAN HORN, TX, p. A655

CULLMAN REGIONAL MEDICAL CENTER, CULLMAN, AL, p. A18

EYE AND EAR CLINIC OF CHARLESTON, CHARLESTON, WV, p. A694

EYE AND EAR HOSPITAL OF PITTSBURGH, PITTSBURGH, PENNSYLVANIA (see UPMC PRESBYTERIAN SHADYSIDE), p. A552

F

F. F. THOMPSON HOSPITAL, CANANDAIGUA, NY, p. A435
F. W. HUSTON MEDICAL CENTER, WINCHESTER, KS, p. A257
FAIR OAKS (see GREENVILLE REGIONAL HOSPITAL), p. A191
FAIR OAKS PAVILION, DELRAY BEACH, FLORIDA (see DELRAY MEDICAL CENTER), p. A127
FAIRBANKS, INDIANAPOLIS, IN, p. A214
FAIRBANKS MEMORIAL HOSPITAL, FAIRBANKS, AK, p. A29
FAIRCHILD MEDICAL CENTER, YREKA, CA, p. A101
FAIRFAX COMMUNITY HOSPITAL, FAIRFAX, OK, p. A511
FAIRFAX HOSPITAL, KIRKLAND, WA, p. A684
FAIRFIELD MEDICAL CENTER, LANCASTER, OH, p. A496
FAIRFIELD MEMORIAL HOSPITAL, FAIRFIELD, IL, p. A190
FAIRFIELD MEMORIAL HOSPITAL, WINNSBORO, SC, p. A571
FAIRLAWN REHABILITATION HOSPITAL, WORCESTER, MA, p. A316
FAIRMONT GENERAL HOSPITAL, FAIRMONT, WV, p. A695
FAIRMOUNT BEHAVIORAL HEALTH SYSTEM, PHILADELPHIA, PA, p. A548
FAIRVIEW HOSPITAL, GREAT BARRINGTON, MA, p. A310
FAIRVIEW HOSPITAL, CLEVELAND, OH, p. A488
FAIRVIEW LAKES HEALTH SERVICES, WYOMING, MN, p. A354
FAIRVIEW NORTHLAND MEDICAL CENTER, PRINCETON, MN, p. A349
FAIRVIEW PARK HOSPITAL, DUBLIN, GA, p. A159
FAIRVIEW REGIONAL MEDICAL CENTER, FAIRVIEW, OK, p. A511
FAIRVIEW RIDGES HOSPITAL, BURNSVILLE, MN, p. A341
FAIRVIEW RIVERSIDE HOSPITAL, MINNEAPOLIS, MINNESOTA (see UNIVERSITY OF MINNESOTA MEDICAL CENTER, FAIRVIEW), p. A348
FAIRVIEW SOUTHDALE HOSPITAL, EDINA, MN, p. A343
FAIRWAY MEDICAL CENTER, COVINGTON, LA, p. A276
FAITH COMMUNITY HOSPITAL, JACKSBORO, TX, p. A629
FAITH REGIONAL HEALTH SERVICES, NORFOLK, NE, p. A398
FALL RIVER HOSPITAL, HOT SPRINGS, SD, p. A574
FALLBROOK HOSPITAL, FALLBROOK, CA, p. A63
FALLON MEDICAL COMPLEX, BAKER, MT, p. A385
FALLS COMMUNITY HOSPITAL AND CLINIC, MARLIN, TX, p. A636
FALMOUTH HOSPITAL, FALMOUTH, MA, p. A310
FAMILY HEALTH WEST, FRUITA, CO, p. A106
FANNIN REGIONAL HOSPITAL, BLUE RIDGE, GA, p. A154
FANNY ALLEN CAMPUS, COLCHESTER, VERMONT (see FLETCHER ALLEN HEALTH CARE), p. A665
FARGO VETERANS AFFAIRS HEALTH CARE SYSTEM, FARGO, ND, p. A477
FAULKTON AREA MEDICAL CENTER, FAULKTON, SD, p. A573
FAUQUIER HOSPITAL, WARRENTON, VA, p. A680
FAWCETT MEMORIAL HOSPITAL, PORT CHARLOTTE, FL, p. A143
FAXTON CAMPUS, UTICA, NEW YORK (see FAXTON–ST. LUKE'S HEALTHCARE), p. A456
FAXTON–ST. LUKE'S HEALTHCARE, UTICA, NY, p. A456
FAYETTE COUNTY HOSPITAL, VANDALIA, IL, p. A204
FAYETTE COUNTY MEMORIAL HOSPITAL, WASHINGTON COURT HOUSE, OH, p. A504
FAYETTE MEDICAL CENTER, FAYETTE, AL, p. A20
FAYETTE REGIONAL HEALTH SYSTEM, CONNERSVILLE, IN, p. A208
FAYETTEVILLE VETERANS AFFAIRS MEDICAL CENTER, FAYETTEVILLE, NC, p. A464
FEATHER RIVER HOSPITAL, PARADISE, CA, p. A82
FEDERAL CORRECTIONAL INSTITUTE HOSPITAL, LITTLETON, CO, p. A109
FEDERAL MEDICAL CENTER, LEXINGTON, KY, p. A264
FERRELL HOSPITAL, ELDORADO, IL, p. A188
FERRY COUNTY MEMORIAL HOSPITAL, REPUBLIC, WA, p. A687
FHN MEMORIAL HOSPITAL, FREEPORT, IL, p. A190
FIELD MEMORIAL COMMUNITY HOSPITAL, CENTREVILLE, MS, p. A356
FIELDSTONE CENTER, BATTLE CREEK, MICHIGAN (see BRONSON BATTLE CREEK), p. A319
FILLMORE COMMUNITY MEDICAL CENTER, FILLMORE, UT, p. A659
FILLMORE COUNTY HOSPITAL, GENEVA, NE, p. A396
FIRELANDS REGIONAL HEALTH SYSTEM, SANDUSKY, OH, p. A501
FIRELANDS REGIONAL MEDICAL CENTER – MAIN CAMPUS, SANDUSKY, OHIO (see FIRELANDS REGIONAL HEALTH SYSTEM), p. A501

FIRELANDS REGIONAL MEDICAL CENTER SOUTH CAMPUS, SANDUSKY, OHIO (see FIRELANDS REGIONAL HEALTH SYSTEM), p. A501
FIRST CARE HEALTH CENTER, PARK RIVER, ND, p. A480
FIRST HOSPITAL PANAMERICANO, CIDRA, PR, p. A725
FIRST HOSPITAL WYOMING VALLEY, KINGSTON, PA, p. A541
FIRST STREET HOSPITAL, BELLAIRE, TX, p. A602
FIRSTHEALTH MONTGOMERY MEMORIAL HOSPITAL, TROY, NC, p. A474
FIRSTHEALTH MOORE REGIONAL HOSPITAL, PINEHURST, NC, p. A470
FIRSTHEALTH RICHMOND MEMORIAL HOSPITAL, ROCKINGHAM, NC, p. A471
FIRSTLIGHT HEALTH SYSTEM, MORA, MN, p. A348
FISHER COUNTY HOSPITAL DISTRICT, ROTAN, TX, p. A644
FISHER–TITUS MEDICAL CENTER, NORWALK, OH, p. A500
FISHERMEN'S HOSPITAL, MARATHON, FL, p. A135
FITZGIBBON HOSPITAL, MARSHALL, MO, p. A376
FIVE RIVERS MEDICAL CENTER, POCAHONTAS, AR, p. A52
FLAGET MEMORIAL HOSPITAL, BARDSTOWN, KY, p. A258
FLAGLER HOSPITAL, SAINT AUGUSTINE, FL, p. A144
FLAGSTAFF MEDICAL CENTER, FLAGSTAFF, AZ, p. A32
FLAMBEAU HOSPITAL, PARK FALLS, WI, p. A713
FLEMING COUNTY HOSPITAL, FLEMINGSBURG, KY, p. A260
FLETCHER ALLEN HEALTH CARE, BURLINGTON, VT, p. A665
FLINT RIVER COMMUNITY HOSPITAL, MONTEZUMA, GA, p. A164
FLORENCE HOSPITAL AT ANTHEM, FLORENCE, AZ, p. A32
FLORIDA HOSPITAL, ORLANDO, FL, p. A140
FLORIDA HOSPITAL AT CONNERTON LONG TERM ACUTE CARE, LAND O'LAKES, FL, p. A134
FLORIDA HOSPITAL CARROLLWOOD, TAMPA, FL, p. A147
FLORIDA HOSPITAL CELEBRATION HEALTH, CELEBRATION, FLORIDA (see FLORIDA HOSPITAL), p. A140
FLORIDA HOSPITAL DELAND, DELAND, FL, p. A127
FLORIDA HOSPITAL EAST ORLANDO, ORLANDO, FLORIDA (see FLORIDA HOSPITAL), p. A140
FLORIDA HOSPITAL FISH MEMORIAL, ORANGE CITY, FL, p. A140
FLORIDA HOSPITAL FOR CHILDREN–WALT DISNEY PAVILION, ORLANDO, FLORIDA (see FLORIDA HOSPITAL), p. A140
FLORIDA HOSPITAL HEARTLAND MEDICAL CENTER, SEBRING, FL, p. A145
FLORIDA HOSPITAL KISSIMMEE, KISSIMMEE, FLORIDA (see FLORIDA HOSPITAL), p. A140
FLORIDA HOSPITAL MEMORIAL MEDICAL CENTER, DAYTONA BEACH, FL, p. A127
FLORIDA HOSPITAL NORTH PINELLAS, TARPON SPRINGS, FL, p. A148
FLORIDA HOSPITAL TAMPA, TAMPA, FL, p. A147
FLORIDA HOSPITAL WATERMAN, TAVARES, FL, p. A148
FLORIDA HOSPITAL WAUCHULA, WAUCHULA, FL, p. A149
FLORIDA HOSPITAL WESLEY CHAPEL, WESLEY CHAPEL, FL, p. A149
FLORIDA HOSPITAL ZEPHYRHILLS, ZEPHYRHILLS, FL, p. A150
FLORIDA HOSPITAL–ALTAMONTE, ALTAMONTE SPRINGS, FLORIDA (see FLORIDA HOSPITAL), p. A140
FLORIDA HOSPITAL–APOPKA, APOPKA, FLORIDA (see FLORIDA HOSPITAL), p. A140
FLORIDA HOSPITAL–FLAGLER, PALM COAST, FL, p. A141
FLORIDA HOSPITAL–OCEANSIDE, ORMOND BEACH, FLORIDA (see FLORIDA HOSPITAL MEMORIAL MEDICAL CENTER), p. A127
FLORIDA STATE HOSPITAL, CHATTAHOOCHEE, FL, p. A125
FLOWERS HOSPITAL, DOTHAN, AL, p. A19
FLOYD COUNTY MEDICAL CENTER, CHARLES CITY, IA, p. A227
FLOYD MEDICAL CENTER, ROME, GA, p. A165
FLOYD MEMORIAL HOSPITAL AND HEALTH SERVICES, NEW ALBANY, IN, p. A220
FLOYD VALLEY HOSPITAL, LE MARS, IA, p. A233
FLUSHING HOSPITAL MEDICAL CENTER,, NY, p. A443
FOND DU LAC COUNTY MENTAL HEALTH CENTER, FOND DU LAC, WI, p. A705
FOOTHILL PRESBYTERIAN HOSPITAL, GLENDORA, CA, p. A66
FORBES REGIONAL HOSPITAL, MONROEVILLE, PA, p. A545
FOREST HEALTH MEDICAL CENTER, YPSILANTI, MI, p. A337
FOREST HILLS HOSPITAL,, NY, p. A443
FOREST PARK MEDICAL CENTER, DALLAS, TX, p. A610
FOREST PARK MEDICAL CENTER FRISCO, FRISCO, TX, p. A620
FOREST PARK MEDICAL CENTER–SOUTHLAKE, SOUTHLAKE, TX, p. A650
FOREST VIEW PSYCHIATRIC HOSPITAL, GRAND RAPIDS, MI, p. A325
FORKS COMMUNITY HOSPITAL, FORKS, WA, p. A684
FORREST CITY MEDICAL CENTER, FORREST CITY, AR, p. A46
FORREST GENERAL HOSPITAL, HATTIESBURG, MS, p. A359
FORT BELKNAP U. S. PUBLIC HEALTH SERVICE INDIAN HOSPITAL, HARLEM, MT, p. A388
FORT BELVOIR COMMUNITY HOSPITAL, FORT BELVOIR, VA, p. A671

FORT DUNCAN REGIONAL MEDICAL CENTER, EAGLE PASS, TX, p. A614
FORT HAMILTON HOSPITAL, HAMILTON, OH, p. A495
FORT HEALTHCARE, FORT ATKINSON, WI, p. A705
FORT LAUDERDALE HOSPITAL, FORT LAUDERDALE, FL, p. A128
FORT LOUDOUN MEDICAL CENTER, LENOIR CITY, TN, p. A586
FORT MADISON COMMUNITY HOSPITAL, FORT MADISON, IA, p. A231
FORT SANDERS REGIONAL MEDICAL CENTER, KNOXVILLE, TN, p. A585
FORT WALTON BEACH MEDICAL CENTER, FORT WALTON BEACH, FL, p. A129
FORT WASHINGTON MEDICAL CENTER, FORT WASHINGTON, MD, p. A301
FOUNDATION SURGICAL HOSPITAL OF EL PASO, EL PASO, TX, p. A616
FOUNDATION SURGICAL HOSPITAL OF SAN ANTONIO, SAN ANTONIO, TX, p. A646
FOUNDATIONS BEHAVIORAL HEALTH, DOYLESTOWN, PA, p. A537
FOUNTAIN VALLEY REGIONAL HOSPITAL AND MEDICAL CENTER, FOUNTAIN VALLEY, CA, p. A63
FOUR COUNTY COUNSELING CENTER, LOGANSPORT, IN, p. A217
FOUR WINDS HOSPITAL, KATONAH, NY, p. A439
FOUR WINDS HOSPITAL, SARATOGA SPRINGS, NY, p. A454
FOX CHASE CANCER CENTER–AMERICAN ONCOLOGIC HOSPITAL, PHILADELPHIA, PA, p. A548
FRAMINGHAM UNION HOSPITAL, FRAMINGHAM, MASSACHUSETTS (see METROWEST MEDICAL CENTER), p. A310
FRANCES MAHON DEACONESS HOSPITAL, GLASGOW, MT, p. A387
FRANCISCAN HEALTHCARE – MUNSTER, MUNSTER, IN, p. A219
FRANCISCAN HOSPITAL FOR CHILDREN, BOSTON, MA, p. A306
FRANCISCAN ST. ANTHONY HEALTH – CROWN POINT, CROWN POINT, IN, p. A209
FRANCISCAN ST. ANTHONY HEALTH – MICHIGAN CITY, MICHIGAN CITY, IN, p. A218
FRANCISCAN ST. ELIZABETH HEALTH – CRAWFORDSVILLE, CRAWFORDSVILLE, IN, p. A209
FRANCISCAN ST. ELIZABETH HEALTH – LAFAYETTE CENTRAL, LAFAYETTE, IN, p. A216
FRANCISCAN ST. ELIZABETH HEALTH – LAFAYETTE EAST, LAFAYETTE, IN, p. A216
FRANCISCAN ST. FRANCIS HEALTH – INDIANAPOLIS, INDIANAPOLIS, IN, p. A214
FRANCISCAN ST. FRANCIS HEALTH – MOORESVILLE, MOORESVILLE, IN, p. A219
FRANCISCAN ST. FRANCIS HEALTH–CARMEL, CARMEL, IN, p. A208
FRANCISCAN ST. JAMES HOSPITAL AND HEALTH CENTERS, OLYMPIA FIELDS, IL, p. A199
FRANCISCAN ST. MARGARET HEALTH – DYER, DYER, INDIANA (see FRANCISCAN ST. MARGARET HEALTH – HAMMOND), p. A212
FRANCISCAN ST. MARGARET HEALTH – HAMMOND, HAMMOND, IN, p. A212
FRANK R. HOWARD MEMORIAL HOSPITAL, WILLITS, CA, p. A100
FRANKFORD CAMPUS, PHILADELPHIA, PENNSYLVANIA (see ARIA HEALTH), p. A547
FRANKFORT REGIONAL MEDICAL CENTER, FRANKFORT, KY, p. A261
FRANKLIN COUNTY MEDICAL CENTER, PRESTON, ID, p. A178
FRANKLIN COUNTY MEMORIAL HOSPITAL, MEADVILLE, MS, p. A362
FRANKLIN COUNTY MEMORIAL HOSPITAL, FRANKLIN, NE, p. A395
FRANKLIN FOUNDATION HOSPITAL, FRANKLIN, LA, p. A277
FRANKLIN GENERAL HOSPITAL, HAMPTON, IA, p. A231
FRANKLIN HOSPITAL, VALLEY STREAM, NY, p. A457
FRANKLIN HOSPITAL DISTRICT, BENTON, IL, p. A181
FRANKLIN MEDICAL CENTER, WINNSBORO, LA, p. A290
FRANKLIN MEMORIAL HOSPITAL, FARMINGTON, ME, p. A293
FRANKLIN REGIONAL HOSPITAL, FRANKLIN, NH, p. A410
FRANKLIN WOODS COMMUNITY HOSPITAL, JOHNSON CITY, TN, p. A585
FRAZIER REHAB INSTITUTE, LOUISVILLE, KY, p. A265
FREDERICK MEMORIAL HOSPITAL, FREDERICK, MD, p. A301
FREDONIA REGIONAL HOSPITAL, FREDONIA, KS, p. A244
FREEDOM PAIN HOSPITAL, SCOTTSDALE, AZ, p. A38
FREEMAN HOSPITAL EAST, JOPLIN, MISSOURI (see FREEMAN HOSPITAL WEST), p. A373
FREEMAN HOSPITAL WEST, JOPLIN, MO, p. A373
FREEMAN NEOSHO HOSPITAL, NEOSHO, MO, p. A377
FREEMAN REGIONAL HEALTH SERVICES, FREEMAN, SD, p. A574
FREMONT HEALTH, FREMONT, NE, p. A395
FREMONT HOSPITAL, FREMONT, CA, p. A64

G

H

HEALTHPARK MEDICAL CENTER, FORT MYERS, FLORIDA (see LEE MEMORIAL HOSPITAL), p. A129
HEALTHSOURCE SAGINAW, SAGINAW, MI, p. A334
HEALTHSOUTH BAKERSFIELD REHABILITATION HOSPITAL, BAKERSFIELD, CA, p. A57
HEALTHSOUTH CANE CREEK REHABILITATION HOSPITAL, MARTIN, TN, p. A587
HEALTHSOUTH CHATTANOOGA REHABILITATION HOSPITAL, CHATTANOOGA, TN, p. A580
HEALTHSOUTH CHESAPEAKE REHABILITATION HOSPITAL, SALISBURY, MD, p. A303
HEALTHSOUTH CITY VIEW REHABILITATION HOSPITAL, FORT WORTH, TX, p. A618
HEALTHSOUTH DEACONESS REHABILITATION HOSPITAL, EVANSVILLE, IN, p. A210
HEALTHSOUTH DESERT CANYON REHABILITATION HOSPITAL, LAS VEGAS, NV, p. A405
HEALTHSOUTH EAST VALLEY REHABILITATION HOSPITAL, MESA, AZ, p. A34
HEALTHSOUTH EMERALD COAST REHABILITATION HOSPITAL, PANAMA CITY, FL, p. A142
HEALTHSOUTH HARMARVILLE REHABILITATION HOSPITAL, PITTSBURGH, PA, p. A551
HEALTHSOUTH HOSPITAL OF MANATI, MANATI, PR, p. A726
HEALTHSOUTH HUNTINGTON REHABILITATION HOSPITAL, HUNTINGTON, WV, p. A696
HEALTHSOUTH LAKESHORE REHABILITATION HOSPITAL, BIRMINGHAM, AL, p. A16
HEALTHSOUTH LAKEVIEW REHABILITATION HOSPITAL, ELIZABETHTOWN, KY, p. A260
HEALTHSOUTH MOUNTAINVIEW REGIONAL REHABILITATION HOSPITAL, MORGANTOWN, WV, p. A697
HEALTHSOUTH NITTANY VALLEY REHABILITATION HOSPITAL, PLEASANT GAP, PA, p. A552
HEALTHSOUTH NORTHERN KENTUCKY REHABILITATION HOSPITAL, EDGEWOOD, KY, p. A260
HEALTHSOUTH PLANO REHABILITATION HOSPITAL, PLANO, TX, p. A642
HEALTHSOUTH READING REHABILITATION HOSPITAL, READING, PA, p. A553
HEALTHSOUTH REHABILITATION HOSPITAL, DOTHAN, AL, p. A19
HEALTHSOUTH REHABILITATION HOSPITAL, FAYETTEVILLE, AR, p. A45
HEALTHSOUTH REHABILITATION HOSPITAL, LARGO, FL, p. A134
HEALTHSOUTH REHABILITATION HOSPITAL, CONCORD, NH, p. A409
HEALTHSOUTH REHABILITATION HOSPITAL, ALBUQUERQUE, NM, p. A426
HEALTHSOUTH REHABILITATION HOSPITAL, SEWICKLEY, PA, p. A555
HEALTHSOUTH REHABILITATION HOSPITAL, KINGSPORT, TN, p. A585
HEALTHSOUTH REHABILITATION HOSPITAL, HUMBLE, TX, p. A628
HEALTHSOUTH REHABILITATION HOSPITAL – HENDERSON, HENDERSON, NV, p. A405
HEALTHSOUTH REHABILITATION HOSPITAL AT DRAKE, CINCINNATI, OH, p. A487
HEALTHSOUTH REHABILITATION HOSPITAL AT MARTIN HEALTH, STUART, FL, p. A146
HEALTHSOUTH REHABILITATION HOSPITAL MEMPHIS–NORTH, MEMPHIS, TN, p. A588
HEALTHSOUTH REHABILITATION HOSPITAL MIDLAND–ODESSA, MIDLAND, TX, p. A638
HEALTHSOUTH REHABILITATION HOSPITAL OF ALEXANDRIA, ALEXANDRIA, LA, p. A272
HEALTHSOUTH REHABILITATION HOSPITAL OF ALTOONA, ALTOONA, PA, p. A532
HEALTHSOUTH REHABILITATION HOSPITAL OF ARLINGTON, ARLINGTON, TX, p. A597
HEALTHSOUTH REHABILITATION HOSPITAL OF AUSTIN, AUSTIN, TX, p. A599
HEALTHSOUTH REHABILITATION HOSPITAL OF BEAUMONT, BEAUMONT, TX, p. A602
HEALTHSOUTH REHABILITATION HOSPITAL OF CHARLESTON, CHARLESTON, SC, p. A563
HEALTHSOUTH REHABILITATION HOSPITAL OF COLORADO SPRINGS, COLORADO SPRINGS, CO, p. A103
HEALTHSOUTH REHABILITATION HOSPITAL OF COLUMBIA, COLUMBIA, SC, p. A564
HEALTHSOUTH REHABILITATION HOSPITAL OF CYPRESS, HOUSTON, TX, p. A624
HEALTHSOUTH REHABILITATION HOSPITAL OF DENVER, LITTLETON, CO, p. A109
HEALTHSOUTH REHABILITATION HOSPITAL OF ERIE, ERIE, PA, p. A538
HEALTHSOUTH REHABILITATION HOSPITAL OF FLORENCE, FLORENCE, SC, p. A565

HEALTHSOUTH REHABILITATION HOSPITAL OF FORT SMITH, FORT SMITH, AR, p. A46
HEALTHSOUTH REHABILITATION HOSPITAL OF FORT WORTH, FORT WORTH, TX, p. A618
HEALTHSOUTH REHABILITATION HOSPITAL OF FREDERICKSBURG, FREDERICKSBURG, VA, p. A671
HEALTHSOUTH REHABILITATION HOSPITAL OF JONESBORO, JONESBORO, AR, p. A48
HEALTHSOUTH REHABILITATION HOSPITAL OF MECHANICSBURG, MECHANICSBURG, PA, p. A544
HEALTHSOUTH REHABILITATION HOSPITAL OF MEMPHIS, MEMPHIS, TN, p. A588
HEALTHSOUTH REHABILITATION HOSPITAL OF MIAMI, CUTLER BAY, FL, p. A126
HEALTHSOUTH REHABILITATION HOSPITAL OF MONTGOMERY, MONTGOMERY, AL, p. A23
HEALTHSOUTH REHABILITATION HOSPITAL OF NORTH ALABAMA, HUNTSVILLE, AL, p. A21
HEALTHSOUTH REHABILITATION HOSPITAL OF NORTHERN VIRGINIA, ALDIE, VA, p. A668
HEALTHSOUTH REHABILITATION HOSPITAL OF OCALA, OCALA, FL, p. A139
HEALTHSOUTH REHABILITATION HOSPITAL OF PETERSBURG, PETERSBURG, VA, p. A676
HEALTHSOUTH REHABILITATION HOSPITAL OF ROCK HILL, ROCK HILL, SC, p. A569
HEALTHSOUTH REHABILITATION HOSPITAL OF SAN JUAN, SAN JUAN, PR, p. A728
HEALTHSOUTH REHABILITATION HOSPITAL OF SARASOTA, SARASOTA, FL, p. A145
HEALTHSOUTH REHABILITATION HOSPITAL OF SOUTHERN ARIZONA, TUCSON, AZ, p. A40
HEALTHSOUTH REHABILITATION HOSPITAL OF SPRING HILL, BROOKSVILLE, FL, p. A125
HEALTHSOUTH REHABILITATION HOSPITAL OF TALLAHASSEE, TALLAHASSEE, FL, p. A147
HEALTHSOUTH REHABILITATION HOSPITAL OF TEXARKANA, TEXARKANA, TX, p. A652
HEALTHSOUTH REHABILITATION HOSPITAL OF TOMS RIVER, TOMS RIVER, NJ, p. A423
HEALTHSOUTH REHABILITATION HOSPITAL OF UTAH, SANDY, UT, p. A664
HEALTHSOUTH REHABILITATION HOSPITAL OF VINELAND, VINELAND, NJ, p. A424
HEALTHSOUTH REHABILITATION HOSPITAL OF VIRGINIA, RICHMOND, VA, p. A677
HEALTHSOUTH REHABILITATION HOSPITAL OF WESTERN MASSACHUSETTS, LUDLOW, MA, p. A311
HEALTHSOUTH REHABILITATION HOSPITAL OF YORK, YORK, PA, p. A559
HEALTHSOUTH REHABILITATION HOSPITAL THE WOODLANDS, CONROE, TX, p. A607
HEALTHSOUTH REHABILITATION HOSPITAL–LAS VEGAS, LAS VEGAS, NV, p. A405
HEALTHSOUTH REHABILITATION HOSPITAL–WICHITA FALLS, WICHITA FALLS, TX, p. A657
HEALTHSOUTH REHABILITATION INSTITUTE OF SAN ANTONIO, SAN ANTONIO, TX, p. A646
HEALTHSOUTH REHABILITATION INSTITUTE OF TUCSON, TUCSON, AZ, p. A40
HEALTHSOUTH REHABILITATION OF GADSDEN, GADSDEN, AL, p. A20
HEALTHSOUTH SCOTTSDALE REHABILITATION HOSPITAL, SCOTTSDALE, AZ, p. A38
HEALTHSOUTH SEA PINES REHABILITATION HOSPITAL, MELBOURNE, FL, p. A136
HEALTHSOUTH SOUTHERN HILLS REHABILITATION HOSPITAL, PRINCETON, WV, p. A698
HEALTHSOUTH SUGAR LAND REHABILITATION HOSPITAL, SUGAR LAND, TX, p. A650
HEALTHSOUTH SUNRISE REHABILITATION HOSPITAL, SUNRISE, FL, p. A146
HEALTHSOUTH TREASURE COAST REHABILITATION HOSPITAL, VERO BEACH, FL, p. A149
HEALTHSOUTH TUSTIN REHABILITATION HOSPITAL, TUSTIN, CA, p. A98
HEALTHSOUTH VALLEY OF THE SUN REHABILITATION HOSPITAL, GLENDALE, AZ, p. A33
HEALTHSOUTH WALTON REHABILITATION HOSPITAL, AUGUSTA, GA, p. A153
HEALTHSOUTH WESTERN HILLS REHABILITATION HOSPITAL, PARKERSBURG, WV, p. A698
HEART HOSPITAL OF AUSTIN, AUSTIN, TEXAS (see ST. DAVID'S MEDICAL CENTER), p. A600
HEART HOSPITAL OF LAFAYETTE, LAFAYETTE, LA, p. A281
HEART HOSPITAL OF NEW MEXICO, ALBUQUERQUE, NEW MEXICO (see LOVELACE MEDICAL CENTER), p. A426
HEART OF AMERICA MEDICAL CENTER, RUGBY, ND, p. A480
HEART OF FLORIDA REGIONAL MEDICAL CENTER, DAVENPORT, FL, p. A127

HEART OF LANCASTER REGIONAL MEDICAL CENTER, LITITZ, PA, p. A543
HEART OF TEXAS MEMORIAL HOSPITAL, BRADY, TX, p. A603
HEART OF THE ROCKIES REGIONAL MEDICAL CENTER, SALIDA, CO, p. A111
HEARTLAND BEHAVIORAL HEALTH SERVICES, NEVADA, MO, p. A377
HEARTLAND BEHAVIORAL HEALTHCARE, MASSILLON, OH, p. A498
HEARTLAND LONG TERM ACUTE CARE HOSPITAL, SAINT JOSEPH, MO, p. A379
HEARTLAND REGIONAL MEDICAL CENTER, MARION, IL, p. A195
HEARTLAND REGIONAL MEDICAL CENTER, SAINT JOSEPH, MO, p. A379
HEATHERHILL CARE COMMUNITIES, CHARDON, OH, p. A485
HEBER VALLEY MEDICAL CENTER, HEBER CITY, UT, p. A660
HEBREW REHABILITATION CENTER, BOSTON, MA, p. A307
HEDRICK MEDICAL CENTER, CHILLICOTHE, MO, p. A369
HEGG MEMORIAL HEALTH CENTER AVERA, ROCK VALLEY, IA, p. A237
HELEN DEVOS CHILDREN'S HOSPITAL, GRAND RAPIDS, MICHIGAN (see SPECTRUM HEALTH – BUTTERWORTH HOSPITAL), p. A325
HELEN HAYES HOSPITAL, WEST HAVERSTRAW, NY, p. A457
HELEN KELLER HOSPITAL, SHEFFIELD, AL, p. A25
HELEN NEWBERRY JOY HOSPITAL, NEWBERRY, MI, p. A331
HELEN NEWBERRY JOY HOSPITAL ANNEX (see HELEN NEWBERRY JOY HOSPITAL), p. A331
HELENA REGIONAL MEDICAL CENTER, HELENA, AR, p. A47
HEMET VALLEY MEDICAL CENTER, HEMET, CA, p. A67
HEMPHILL COUNTY HOSPITAL, CANADIAN, TX, p. A605
HENDERSON COUNTY COMMUNITY HOSPITAL, LEXINGTON, TN, p. A587
HENDERSON HEALTH CARE SERVICES, HENDERSON, NE, p. A396
HENDRICK HEALTH SYSTEM, ABILENE, TX, p. A595
HENDRICKS COMMUNITY HOSPITAL, HENDRICKS, MN, p. A345
HENDRICKS REGIONAL HEALTH, DANVILLE, IN, p. A209
HENDRY REGIONAL MEDICAL CENTER, CLEWISTON, FL, p. A126
HENNEPIN COUNTY MEDICAL CENTER, MINNEAPOLIS, MN, p. A347
HENRICO DOCTORS' HOSPITAL, RICHMOND, VA, p. A677
HENRICO DOCTORS' HOSPITAL – FOREST, RICHMOND, VIRGINIA (see HENRICO DOCTORS' HOSPITAL), p. A677
HENRICO DOCTORS' HOSPITAL – PARHAM, RICHMOND, VIRGINIA (see HENRICO DOCTORS' HOSPITAL), p. A677
HENRICO DOCTORS' HOSPITAL – RETREAT CAMPUS, RICHMOND, VIRGINIA (see HENRICO DOCTORS' HOSPITAL), p. A677
HENRY COUNTY HEALTH CENTER, MOUNT PLEASANT, IA, p. A234
HENRY COUNTY HOSPITAL, NEW CASTLE, IN, p. A220
HENRY COUNTY HOSPITAL, NAPOLEON, OH, p. A499
HENRY COUNTY MEDICAL CENTER, PARIS, TN, p. A592
HENRY FORD HOSPITAL, DETROIT, MI, p. A322
HENRY FORD KINGSWOOD HOSPITAL, FERNDALE, MI, p. A323
HENRY FORD MACOMB HOSPITAL – MOUNT CLEMENS CAMPUS, MOUNT CLEMENS, MICHIGAN (see HENRY FORD MACOMB HOSPITALS), p. A321
HENRY FORD MACOMB HOSPITALS, CLINTON TOWNSHIP, MI, p. A321
HENRY FORD WEST BLOOMFIELD HOSPITAL, WEST BLOOMFIELD, MI, p. A337
HENRY FORD WYANDOTTE HOSPITAL, WYANDOTTE, MI, p. A337
HENRY J. CARTER SPECIALTY HOSPITAL AND NURSING FACILITY, NEW YORK, NY, p. A444
HENRY MAYO NEWHALL MEMORIAL HOSPITAL, VALENCIA, CA, p. A98
HENRY MEDICAL CENTER, STOCKBRIDGE, GA, p. A167
HEREFORD REGIONAL MEDICAL CENTER, HEREFORD, TX, p. A623
HERINGTON MUNICIPAL HOSPITAL, HERINGTON, KS, p. A245
HERITAGE MEDICAL CENTER, SHELBYVILLE, TN, p. A593
HERITAGE OAKS HOSPITAL, SACRAMENTO, CA, p. A87
HERITAGE PARK SURGICAL HOSPITAL, SHERMAN, TX, p. A649
HERITAGE VALLEY HEALTH SYSTEM, BEAVER, PA, p. A533
HERMANN AREA DISTRICT HOSPITAL, HERMANN, MO, p. A372
HERRIN HOSPITAL, HERRIN, IL, p. A192
HEYWOOD HOSPITAL, GARDNER, MA, p. A310
HI-DESERT MEDICAL CENTER, JOSHUA TREE, CA, p. A67
HIALEAH HOSPITAL, HIALEAH, FL, p. A130
HIAWATHA COMMUNITY HOSPITAL, HIAWATHA, KS, p. A245
HICKORY TRAIL HOSPITAL, DESOTO, TX, p. A614
HIGGINS GENERAL HOSPITAL, BREMEN, GA, p. A154
HIGH POINT REGIONAL HEALTH SYSTEM, HIGH POINT, NC, p. A466

© 2014 AHA Guide

HIGHBRIDGE WOODYCREST CENTER,, NEW YORK (see BRONX–LEBANON HOSPITAL CENTER HEALTH CARE SYSTEM), p. A442
HIGHLAND COMMUNITY HOSPITAL, PICAYUNE, MS, p. A364
HIGHLAND DISTRICT HOSPITAL, HILLSBORO, OH, p. A495
HIGHLAND HOSPITAL, CHARLESTON, WV, p. A694
HIGHLAND HOSPITAL OF ROCHESTER, ROCHESTER, NY, p. A453
HIGHLAND PARK HOSPITAL, MIAMI, FLORIDA (see JACKSON HEALTH SYSTEM), p. A137
HIGHLAND–CLARKSBURG HOSPITAL, CLARKSBURG, WV, p. A694
HIGHLANDS BEHAVIORAL HEALTH SYSTEM, LITTLETON, CO, p. A109
HIGHLANDS HOSPITAL, CONNELLSVILLE, PA, p. A536
HIGHLANDS MEDICAL CENTER, SCOTTSBORO, AL, p. A25
HIGHLANDS MEDICAL CENTER, SPARTA, TN, p. A593
HIGHLANDS REGIONAL MEDICAL CENTER, SEBRING, FL, p. A146
HIGHLANDS REGIONAL MEDICAL CENTER, PRESTONSBURG, KY, p. A269
HIGHLANDS REGIONAL REHABILITATION HOSPITAL, EL PASO, TX, p. A616
HIGHLANDS–CASHIERS HOSPITAL, HIGHLANDS, NC, p. A466
HIGHLINE MEDICAL CENTER, BURIEN, WA, p. A682
HIGHLINE SPECIALTY CENTER, 12844 MILITARY ROAD FORK, TUKWILA, ZIP 98168; MARK BENEDUM, ADMINISTRATOR (see HIGHLINE MEDICAL CENTER), p. A682
HIGHSMITH–RAINEY SPECIALTY HOSPITAL, FAYETTEVILLE, NC, p. A464
HILL COUNTRY MEMORIAL HOSPITAL, FREDERICKSBURG, TX, p. A619
HILL CREST BEHAVIORAL HEALTH SERVICES, BIRMINGHAM, AL, p. A16
HILL HOSPITAL OF SUMTER COUNTY, YORK, AL, p. A27
HILL REGIONAL HOSPITAL, HILLSBORO, TX, p. A623
HILLCREST BAPTIST MEDICAL CENTER, WACO, TX, p. A655
HILLCREST BAPTIST MEDICAL CENTER – HERRING AVENUE CAMPUS, 3000 HERRING AVENUE, ZIP 76708 (see HILLCREST BAPTIST MEDICAL CENTER), p. A655
HILLCREST HOSPITAL, PITTSFIELD, MASSACHUSETTS (see BERKSHIRE MEDICAL CENTER), p. A313
HILLCREST HOSPITAL, CLEVELAND, OH, p. A488
HILLCREST HOSPITAL – SOUTH, TULSA, OK, p. A520
HILLCREST HOSPITAL CLAREMORE, CLAREMORE, OK, p. A509
HILLCREST HOSPITAL CUSHING, CUSHING, OK, p. A509
HILLCREST HOSPITAL HENRYETTA, HENRYETTA, OK, p. A511
HILLCREST MEDICAL CENTER, TULSA, OK, p. A520
HILLCREST MEMORIAL HOSPITAL, SIMPSONVILLE, SC, p. A569
HILLS & DALES GENERAL HOSPITAL, CASS CITY, MI, p. A320
HILLSBORO AREA HOSPITAL, HILLSBORO, IL, p. A192
HILLSBORO COMMUNITY HOSPITAL, HILLSBORO, KS, p. A245
HILLSDALE COMMUNITY HEALTH CENTER, HILLSDALE, MI, p. A326
HILLSIDE REHABILITATION HOSPITAL, WARREN, OH, p. A504
HILO MEDICAL CENTER, HILO, HI, p. A170
HILTON HEAD HOSPITAL, HILTON HEAD ISLAND, SC, p. A567
HIND GENERAL HOSPITAL, HOBART, IN, p. A213
HIRAM W. DAVIS MEDICAL CENTER, PETERSBURG, VA, p. A676
HOAG HOSPITAL IRVINE, IRVINE, CALIFORNIA (see HOAG MEMORIAL HOSPITAL PRESBYTERIAN), p. A80
HOAG MEMORIAL HOSPITAL PRESBYTERIAN, NEWPORT BEACH, CA, p. A80
HOAG ORTHOPEDIC INSTITUTE, IRVINE, CA, p. A67
HOBOKEN UNIVERSITY MEDICAL CENTER, HOBOKEN, NJ, p. A417
HOCKING VALLEY COMMUNITY HOSPITAL, LOGAN, OH, p. A496
HODGEMAN COUNTY HEALTH CENTER, JETMORE, KS, p. A246
HOLDENVILLE GENERAL HOSPITAL, HOLDENVILLE, OK, p. A512
HOLLAND HOSPITAL, HOLLAND, MI, p. A326
HOLLY HILL HOSPITAL, RALEIGH, NC, p. A471
HOLLYWOOD PAVILION,, FL, p. A130
HOLLYWOOD PRESBYTERIAN MEDICAL CENTER, LOS ANGELES, CA, p. A72
HOLMES COUNTY HOSPITAL AND CLINICS, LEXINGTON, MS, p. A361
HOLTON COMMUNITY HOSPITAL, HOLTON, KS, p. A245
HOLTZ CHILDREN'S HOSPITAL, MIAMI, FLORIDA (see JACKSON HEALTH SYSTEM), p. A137
HOLY CROSS HOSPITAL, FORT LAUDERDALE, FL, p. A128
HOLY CROSS HOSPITAL, CHICAGO, IL, p. A184
HOLY CROSS HOSPITAL, SILVER SPRING, MD, p. A303
HOLY CROSS HOSPITAL, TAOS, NM, p. A431
HCLY FAMILY HOSPITAL AND MEDICAL CENTER, METHUEN, MA, p. A312
HOLY FAMILY MEMORIAL, MANITOWOC, WI, p. A708
HOLY NAME MEDICAL CENTER, TEANECK, NJ, p. A423
HOLY REDEEMER HOSPITAL, MEADOWBROOK, PA, p. A544
HOLY ROSARY HEALTHCARE, MILES CITY, MT, p. A389
HOLY SPIRIT HOSPITAL, CAMP HILL, PA, p. A535

HOLYOKE MEDICAL CENTER, HOLYOKE, MA, p. A311
HOLZER MEDICAL CENTER, GALLIPOLIS, OH, p. A494
HOLZER MEDICAL CENTER – JACKSON, JACKSON, OH, p. A495
HOMER MEMORIAL HOSPITAL, HOMER, LA, p. A278
HOOD MEMORIAL HOSPITAL, AMITE, LA, p. A272
HOOPS FAMILY CHILDREN'S HOSPITAL, HUNTINGTON, WEST VIRGINIA (see CABELL HUNTINGTON HOSPITAL), p. A695
HOPEDALE MEDICAL COMPLEX, HOPEDALE, IL, p. A193
HOPI HEALTH CARE CENTER, KEAMS CANYON, AZ, p. A33
HOPKINS COUNTY MEMORIAL HOSPITAL, SULPHUR SPRINGS, TX, p. A651
HORIZON SPECIALTY HOSPITAL, LAS VEGAS, NV, p. A406
HORN MEMORIAL HOSPITAL, IDA GROVE, IA, p. A232
HORSHAM CLINIC, AMBLER, PA, p. A533
HORTON COMMUNITY HOSPITAL, HORTON, KS, p. A246
HOSPITAL BUEN SAMARITANO, AGUADILLA, PR, p. A724
HOSPITAL DE DAMAS, PONCE, PR, p. A727
HOSPITAL DE LA CONCEPCION, SAN GERMAN, PR, p. A727
HOSPITAL DE LA UNIVERSIDAD DE PUERTO RICO/DR. FEDERICO TRILLA, CAROLINA, PR, p. A725
HOSPITAL DE PSIQUIATRIA, SAN JUAN, PR, p. A728
HOSPITAL DEL MAESTRO, SAN JUAN, PR, p. A728
HOSPITAL DR. CAYETANO COLL Y TOSTE, ARECIBO, PR, p. A724
HOSPITAL EPISCOPAL SAN LUCAS GUAYAMA, GUAYAMA, PR, p. A726
HOSPITAL FOR EXTENDED RECOVERY, NORFOLK, VA, p. A675
HOSPITAL FOR SPECIAL CARE, NEW BRITAIN, CT, p. A115
HOSPITAL FOR SPECIAL SURGERY, NEW YORK, NY, p. A444
HOSPITAL HERMANOS MELENDEZ, BAYAMON, PR, p. A725
HOSPITAL HIMA SAN PABLO CAGUAS, CAGUAS, PR, p. A725
HOSPITAL HMA DE HUMACAO, HUMACAO, PR, p. A726
HOSPITAL MANATI MEDICAL CENTER, MANATI, PR, p. A726
HOSPITAL MENONITA DE CAYEY, CAYEY, PR, p. A725
HOSPITAL METROPOLITAN, SAN JUAN, PR, p. A728
HOSPITAL METROPOLITANO DR. SUSONI, ARECIBO, PR, p. A724
HOSPITAL METROPOLITANO DR. TITO MATTEI, YAUCO, PR, p. A729
HOSPITAL METROPOLITANO SAN GERMAN, SAN GERMAN, PR, p. A727
HOSPITAL OF THE UNIVERSITY OF PENNSYLVANIA, PHILADELPHIA, PA, p. A548
HOSPITAL ONCOLOGICO ANDRES GRILLASCA, PONCE, PR, p. A727
HOSPITAL ORIENTE, HUMACAO, PR, p. A726
HOSPITAL PAVIA–HATO REY, SAN JUAN, PR, p. A728
HOSPITAL PAVIA–SANTURCE, SAN JUAN, PR, p. A728
HOSPITAL PEREA, MAYAGUEZ, PR, p. A727
HOSPITAL PSIQUIATRICO METROPOLITANO, CABO ROJO, PR, p. A725
HOSPITAL SAN CARLOS BORROMEO, MOCA, PR, p. A727
HOSPITAL SAN CRISTOBAL, COTO LAUREL, PR, p. A725
HOSPITAL SAN FRANCISCO, SAN JUAN, PR, p. A728
HOSPITAL SAN GERARDO, SAN JUAN, PR, p. A728
HOSPITAL SAN PABLO, BAYAMON, PR, p. A725
HOSPITAL SAN PABLO DEL ESTE, FAJARDO, PR, p. A726
HOSPITAL SANTA ROSA, GUAYAMA, PR, p. A726
HOSPITAL UNIVERSITARIO DR. RAMON RUIZ ARNAU, BAYAMON, PR, p. A725
HOT SPRINGS COUNTY MEMORIAL HOSPITAL, THERMOPOLIS, WY, p. A723
HOULTON REGIONAL HOSPITAL, HOULTON, ME, p. A293
HOUSTON COUNTY COMMUNITY HOSPITAL, ERIN, TN, p. A582
HOUSTON HOSPITAL FOR SPECIALIZED SURGERY, HOUSTON, TX, p. A624
HOUSTON MEDICAL CENTER, WARNER ROBINS, GA, p. A169
HOUSTON METHODIST HOSPITAL, HOUSTON, TX, p. A624
HOUSTON METHODIST SAN JACINTO HOSPITAL, BAYTOWN, TX, p. A601
HOUSTON METHODIST SAN JACINTO HOSPITAL – ALEXANDER, BAYTOWN, TEXAS (see HOUSTON METHODIST SAN JACINTO HOSPITAL), p. A601
HOUSTON METHODIST ST. CATHERINE HOSPITAL, KATY, TX, p. A630
HOUSTON METHODIST ST. JOHN HOSPITAL, NASSAU BAY, TX, p. A639
HOUSTON METHODIST SUGAR LAND HOSPITAL, SUGAR LAND, TX, p. A650
HOUSTON METHODIST WEST HOSPITAL, HOUSTON, TX, p. A624
HOUSTON METHODIST WILLOWBROOK HOSPITAL, HOUSTON, TX, p. A624
HOUSTON NORTHWEST MEDICAL CENTER, HOUSTON, TX, p. A625
HOUSTON ORTHOPEDIC AND SPINE HOSPITAL, BELLAIRE, TX, p. A602
HOUSTON PHYSICIANS HOSPITAL, WEBSTER, TX, p. A656
HOWARD A. RUSK REHABILITATION CENTER, COLUMBIA, MO, p. A370

HOWARD COUNTY GENERAL HOSPITAL, COLUMBIA, MD, p. A300
HOWARD COUNTY MEDICAL CENTER, SAINT PAUL, NE, p. A401
HOWARD MEMORIAL HOSPITAL, NASHVILLE, AR, p. A50
HOWARD UNIVERSITY HOSPITAL, WASHINGTON, DC, p. A121
HOWARD YOUNG MEDICAL CENTER, WOODRUFF, WI, p. A719
HUDSON HOSPITAL AND CLINIC, HUDSON, WI, p. A706
HUDSON VALLEY HOSPITAL CENTER, CORTLANDT MANOR, NY, p. A436
HUGGINS HOSPITAL, WOLFEBORO, NH, p. A412
HUGH CHATHAM MEMORIAL HOSPITAL, ELKIN, NC, p. A464
HUHUKAM MEMORIAL HOSPITAL, SACATON, AZ, p. A38
HUMBOLDT COUNTY MEMORIAL HOSPITAL, HUMBOLDT, IA, p. A232
HUMBOLDT COUNTY MENTAL HEALTH, EUREKA, CA, p. A62
HUMBOLDT GENERAL HOSPITAL, WINNEMUCCA, NV, p. A408
HUNT REGIONAL COMMUNITY HOSPITAL, COMMERCE, TX, p. A607
HUNT REGIONAL MEDICAL CENTER, GREENVILLE, TX, p. A622
HUNT REGIONAL MEDICAL CENTER, GREENVILLE, TEXAS (see HUNT REGIONAL MEDICAL CENTER), p. A622
HUNTER HOLMES MCGUIRE VETERANS AFFAIRS MEDICAL CENTER, RICHMOND, VA, p. A678
HUNTERDON MEDICAL CENTER, FLEMINGTON, NJ, p. A416
HUNTINGTON BEACH HOSPITAL, HUNTINGTON BEACH, CA, p. A67
HUNTINGTON HOSPITAL, HUNTINGTON, NY, p. A439
HUNTINGTON MEMORIAL HOSPITAL, PASADENA, CA, p. A83
HUNTINGTON VETERANS AFFAIRS MEDICAL CENTER, HUNTINGTON, WV, p. A696
HUNTSVILLE HOSPITAL, HUNTSVILLE, AL, p. A22
HUNTSVILLE HOSPITAL FOR WOMEN AND CHILDREN, HUNTSVILLE, ALABAMA (see HUNTSVILLE HOSPITAL), p. A22
HUNTSVILLE MEMORIAL HOSPITAL, HUNTSVILLE, TX, p. A629
HURLEY CHILDREN'S HOSPITAL, FLINT, MICHIGAN (see HURLEY MEDICAL CENTER), p. A323
HURLEY MEDICAL CENTER, FLINT, MI, p. A323
HURON MEDICAL CENTER, BAD AXE, MI, p. A318
HURON REGIONAL MEDICAL CENTER, HURON, SD, p. A574
HUTCHESON MEDICAL CENTER, FORT OGLETHORPE, GA, p. A160
HUTCHINSON HEALTH, HUTCHINSON, MN, p. A345
HUTCHINSON REGIONAL MEDICAL CENTER, HUTCHINSON, KS, p. A246

I

I–70 COMMUNITY HOSPITAL, SWEET SPRINGS, MO, p. A383
I. GONZALEZ MARTINEZ ONCOLOGIC HOSPITAL,, PR, p. A728
IBERIA EXTENDED CARE HOSPITAL, NEW IBERIA, LOUISIANA (see LOUISIANA EXTENDED CARE HOSPITAL OF LAFAYETTE), p. A281
IBERIA MEDICAL CENTER, NEW IBERIA, LA, p. A285
IBERIA REHABILITATION HOSPITAL, NEW IBERIA, LA, p. A285
ICON HOSPITAL, HUMBLE, TX, p. A628
ILLINI COMMUNITY HOSPITAL, PITTSFIELD, IL, p. A200
ILLINOIS VALLEY COMMUNITY HOSPITAL, PERU, IL, p. A200
INCLINE VILLAGE COMMUNITY HOSPITAL, INCLINE VILLAGE, NV, p. A405
INDIAN HEALTH SERVICE HOSPITAL, RAPID CITY, SD, p. A575
INDIAN PATH MEDICAL CENTER, KINGSPORT, TN, p. A585
INDIAN RIVER MEDICAL CENTER, VERO BEACH, FL, p. A149
INDIANA ORTHOPAEDIC HOSPITAL, INDIANAPOLIS, IN, p. A214
INDIANA REGIONAL MEDICAL CENTER, INDIANA, PA, p. A541
INDIANA UNIVERSITY HEALTH ARNETT HOSPITAL, LAFAYETTE, IN, p. A217
INDIANA UNIVERSITY HEALTH BALL MEMORIAL HOSPITAL, MUNCIE, IN, p. A219
INDIANA UNIVERSITY HEALTH BEDFORD HOSPITAL, BEDFORD, IN, p. A206
INDIANA UNIVERSITY HEALTH BLACKFORD HOSPITAL, HARTFORD CITY, IN, p. A213
INDIANA UNIVERSITY HEALTH BLOOMINGTON HOSPITAL, BLOOMINGTON, IN, p. A207
INDIANA UNIVERSITY HEALTH GOSHEN HOSPITAL, GOSHEN, IN, p. A212
INDIANA UNIVERSITY HEALTH LA PORTE HOSPITAL, LA PORTE, IN, p. A216
INDIANA UNIVERSITY HEALTH METHODIST HOSPITAL, INDIANAPOLIS, INDIANA (see INDIANA UNIVERSITY HEALTH UNIVERSITY HOSPITAL), p. A214
INDIANA UNIVERSITY HEALTH MORGAN HOSPITAL, MARTINSVILLE, IN, p. A218
INDIANA UNIVERSITY HEALTH NORTH HOSPITAL, CARMEL, IN, p. A208
INDIANA UNIVERSITY HEALTH PAOLI HOSPITAL, PAOLI, IN, p. A221

INDIANA UNIVERSITY HEALTH STARKE HOSPITAL, KNOX, IN, p. A216
INDIANA UNIVERSITY HEALTH TIPTON HOSPITAL, TIPTON, IN, p. A223
INDIANA UNIVERSITY HEALTH UNIVERSITY HOSPITAL, INDIANAPOLIS, IN, p. A214
INDIANA UNIVERSITY HEALTH WEST HOSPITAL, AVON, IN, p. A206
INDIANA UNIVERSITY HEALTH WHITE MEMORIAL HOSPITAL, MONTICELLO, IN, p. A219
INDIANA UNIVERSITY HOSPITAL, INDIANAPOLIS, INDIANA (see INDIANA UNIVERSITY HEALTH UNIVERSITY HOSPITAL), p. A214
INDIANHEAD MEDICAL CENTER, SHELL LAKE, WI, p. A715
INDUSTRIAL HOSPITAL, SAN JUAN, PR, p. A728
INFIRMARY LONG TERM ACUTE CARE HOSPITAL, MOBILE, AL, p. A22
INGALLS MEMORIAL HOSPITAL, HARVEY, IL, p. A192
INGHAM REGIONAL MEDICAL CENTER, GREENLAWN CAMPUS, LANSING, MICHIGAN (see MCLAREN GREATER LANSING), p. A328
INLAND HOSPITAL, WATERVILLE, ME, p. A295
INLAND VALLEY MEDICAL CENTER, WILDOMAR, CALIFORNIA (see SOUTHWEST HEALTHCARE SYSTEM), p. A79
INOVA ALEXANDRIA HOSPITAL, ALEXANDRIA, VA, p. A668
INOVA FAIR OAKS HOSPITAL, FAIRFAX, VA, p. A670
INOVA FAIRFAX HOSPITAL, FALLS CHURCH, VA, p. A670
INOVA FAIRFAX HOSPITAL FOR CHILDREN, FALLS CHURCH, VIRGINIA (see INOVA FAIRFAX HOSPITAL), p. A670
INOVA LOUDOUN HOSPITAL, LEESBURG, VA, p. A673
INOVA MOUNT VERNON HOSPITAL, ALEXANDRIA, VA, p. A668
INSPIRA MEDICAL CENTER–ELMER, ELMER, NJ, p. A416
INSPIRA MEDICAL CENTER–VINELAND, VINELAND, NJ, p. A424
INSPIRA MEDICAL CENTER–WOODBURY, WOODBURY, NJ, p. A425
INSPIRA PONCE, PONCE, PR, p. A727
INSTITUTE FOR ORTHOPAEDIC SURGERY, LIMA, OH, p. A496
INSTITUTE OF LIVING, HARTFORD, CONNECTICUT (see HARTFORD HOSPITAL), p. A114
INTEGRIS BAPTIST MEDICAL CENTER, OKLAHOMA CITY, OK, p. A515
INTEGRIS BAPTIST REGIONAL HEALTH CENTER, MIAMI, OK, p. A513
INTEGRIS BASS BAPTIST HEALTH CENTER, ENID, OK, p. A510
INTEGRIS BASS PAVILION, ENID, OK, p. A510
INTEGRIS BLACKWELL REGIONAL HOSPITAL, BLACKWELL, OK, p. A508
INTEGRIS CANADIAN VALLEY HOSPITAL, YUKON, OK, p. A522
INTEGRIS CLINTON REGIONAL HOSPITAL, CLINTON, OK, p. A509
INTEGRIS GROVE HOSPITAL, GROVE, OK, p. A511
INTEGRIS HEALTH EDMOND, EDMOND, OK, p. A510
INTEGRIS MARSHALL COUNTY MEDICAL CENTER, MADILL, OK, p. A513
INTEGRIS MAYES COUNTY MEDICAL CENTER, PRYOR, OK, p. A518
INTEGRIS MENTAL HEALTH SYSTEM–SPENCER, SPENCER, OKLAHOMA (see INTEGRIS BAPTIST MEDICAL CENTER), p. A515
INTEGRIS SEMINOLE MEDICAL CENTER, SEMINOLE, OK, p. A518
INTEGRIS SOUTHWEST MEDICAL CENTER, OKLAHOMA CITY, OK, p. A515
INTEGRITY TRANSITIONAL HOSPITAL, DENTON, TX, p. A613
INTERFAITH MEDICAL CENTER,, NY, p. A444
INTERIM LSU PUBLIC HOSPITAL, NEW ORLEANS, LA, p. A285
INTERMEDICAL HOSPITAL OF SOUTH CAROLINA, COLUMBIA, SC, p. A564
INTERMOUNTAIN HOSPITAL, BOISE, ID, p. A174
INTERMOUNTAIN MEDICAL CENTER, MURRAY, UT, p. A660
INTRACARE NORTH HOSPITAL, HOUSTON, TX, p. A625
IOWA CITY VETERANS AFFAIRS HEALTH CARE SYSTEM, IOWA CITY, IA, p. A232
IOWA MEDICAL AND CLASSIFICATION CENTER, CORALVILLE, IA, p. A228
IOWA SPECIALTY HOSPITAL–BELMOND, BELMOND, IA, p. A225
IOWA SPECIALTY HOSPITAL–CLARION, CLARION, IA, p. A227
IRA DAVENPORT MEMORIAL HOSPITAL, BATH, NY, p. A433
IRAAN GENERAL HOSPITAL, IRAAN, TX, p. A629
IREDELL MEMORIAL HOSPITAL, STATESVILLE, NC, p. A473
IRELAND ARMY COMMUNITY HOSPITAL, FORT KNOX, KY, p. A261
IRON COUNTY MEDICAL CENTER, PILOT KNOB, MO, p. A378
IROQUOIS MEMORIAL HOSPITAL AND RESIDENT HOME, WATSEKA, IL, p. A204
IRVING COPPELL SURGICAL HOSPITAL, IRVING, TX, p. A629
IRWIN ARMY COMMUNITY HOSPITAL, JUNCTION CITY, KS, p. A247
IRWIN COUNTY HOSPITAL, OCILLA, GA, p. A164
ISLAND HOSPITAL, ANACORTES, WA, p. A681

IU HEALTH SAXONY HOSPITAL, FISHERS, INDIANA (see INDIANA UNIVERSITY HEALTH UNIVERSITY HOSPITAL), p. A214
IVINSON MEMORIAL HOSPITAL, LARAMIE, WY, p. A722

J

J. ARTHUR DOSHER MEMORIAL HOSPITAL, SOUTHPORT, NC, p. A473
J. C. BLAIR MEMORIAL HOSPITAL, HUNTINGDON, PA, p. A541
J. D. MCCARTY CENTER FOR CHILDREN WITH DEVELOPMENTAL DISABILITIES, NORMAN, OK, p. A514
J. PAUL JONES HOSPITAL, CAMDEN, AL, p. A18
JACK C. MONTGOMERY VETERANS AFFAIRS MEDICAL CENTER, MUSKOGEE, OK, p. A514
JACK D WEILER HOSPITAL OF ALBERT EINSTEIN COLLEGE OF MEDICINE,, NEW YORK (see MONTEFIORE MEDICAL CENTER), p. A446
JACK HUGHSTON MEMORIAL HOSPITAL, PHENIX CITY, AL, p. A25
JACKSON COUNTY HOSPITAL DISTRICT, EDNA, TX, p. A615
JACKSON COUNTY MEMORIAL HOSPITAL, ALTUS, OK, p. A507
JACKSON COUNTY REGIONAL HEALTH CENTER, MAQUOKETA, IA, p. A234
JACKSON GENERAL HOSPITAL, RIPLEY, WV, p. A699
JACKSON HEALTH SYSTEM, MIAMI, FL, p. A137
JACKSON HOSPITAL, MARIANNA, FL, p. A135
JACKSON HOSPITAL AND CLINIC, MONTGOMERY, AL, p. A24
JACKSON MEDICAL CENTER, JACKSON, AL, p. A22
JACKSON MEMORIAL HOSPITAL, MIAMI, FLORIDA (see JACKSON HEALTH SYSTEM), p. A137
JACKSON NORTH MEDICAL CENTER, NORTH MIAMI BEACH, FLORIDA (see JACKSON HEALTH SYSTEM), p. A137
JACKSON PARISH HOSPITAL, JONESBORO, LA, p. A280
JACKSON PARK HOSPITAL AND MEDICAL CENTER, CHICAGO, IL, p. A184
JACKSON PURCHASE MEDICAL CENTER, MAYFIELD, KY, p. A267
JACKSON SOUTH COMMUNITY HOSPITAL, MIAMI, FLORIDA (see JACKSON HEALTH SYSTEM), p. A137
JACKSON–MADISON COUNTY GENERAL HOSPITAL, JACKSON, TN, p. A584
JACOBI MEDICAL CENTER,, NY, p. A444
JACOBSON MEMORIAL HOSPITAL CARE CENTER, ELGIN, ND, p. A477
JAMAICA HOSPITAL MEDICAL CENTER,, NY, p. A444
JAMES A. HALEY VETERANS' HOSPITAL, TAMPA, FL, p. A147
JAMES AND CONNIE MAYNARD CHILDREN'S HOSPITAL, GREENVILLE, NORTH CAROLINA (see VIDANT MEDICAL CENTER), p. A465
JAMES B. HAGGIN MEMORIAL HOSPITAL, HARRODSBURG, KY, p. A262
JAMES CANCER HOSPITAL AND SOLOVE RESEARCH INSTITUTE, COLUMBUS, OH, p. A489
JAMES E. VAN ZANDT VETERANS AFFAIRS MEDICAL CENTER, ALTOONA, PA, p. A532
JAMES H. QUILLEN VETERANS AFFAIRS MEDICAL CENTER, MOUNTAIN HOME, TN, p. A590
JAMES J. PETERS VETERANS AFFAIRS MEDICAL CENTER,, NY, p. A444
JAMESON HOSPITAL, NEW CASTLE, PA, p. A546
JAMESTOWN REGIONAL MEDICAL CENTER, JAMESTOWN, ND, p. A478
JAMESTOWN REGIONAL MEDICAL CENTER, JAMESTOWN, TN, p. A584
JANE PHILLIPS MEDICAL CENTER, BARTLESVILLE, OK, p. A508
JANE PHILLIPS NOWATA HEALTH CENTER, NOWATA, OK, p. A514
JANE TODD CRAWFORD HOSPITAL, GREENSBURG, KY, p. A262
JASPER COUNTY HOSPITAL, RENSSELAER, IN, p. A221
JASPER COUNTY NURSING HOME (see JASPER GENERAL HOSPITAL), p. A355
JASPER GENERAL HOSPITAL, BAY SPRINGS, MS, p. A355
JASPER MEMORIAL HOSPITAL, MONTICELLO, GA, p. A164
JAY COUNTY HOSPITAL, PORTLAND, IN, p. A221
JAY HOSPITAL, JAY, FL, p. A132
JEANES HOSPITAL, PHILADELPHIA, PA, p. A548
JEFF DAVIS HOSPITAL, HAZLEHURST, GA, p. A160
JEFFERSON COMMUNITY HEALTH CENTER, FAIRBURY, NE, p. A395
JEFFERSON COUNTY HEALTH CENTER, FAIRFIELD, IA, p. A230
JEFFERSON COUNTY HOSPITAL, FAYETTE, MS, p. A357
JEFFERSON COUNTY HOSPITAL, WAURIKA, OK, p. A522
JEFFERSON DAVIS COMMUNITY HOSPITAL, PRENTISS, MS, p. A364
JEFFERSON HEALTHCARE, PORT TOWNSEND, WA, p. A686
JEFFERSON HOSPITAL, LOUISVILLE, GA, p. A162
JEFFERSON HOSPITAL, JEFFERSON HILLS, PA, p. A541

JEFFERSON MEDICAL CENTER, RANSON, WV, p. A699
JEFFERSON REGIONAL MEDICAL CENTER, PINE BLUFF, AR, p. A52
JELLICO COMMUNITY HOSPITAL, JELLICO, TN, p. A585
JENKINS COUNTY HOSPITAL, MILLEN, GA, p. A163
JENNERSVILLE REGIONAL HOSPITAL, WEST GROVE, PA, p. A558
JENNIE M. MELHAM MEMORIAL MEDICAL CENTER, BROKEN BOW, NE, p. A394
JENNIE STUART MEDICAL CENTER, HOPKINSVILLE, KY, p. A263
JENNINGS AMERICAN LEGION HOSPITAL, JENNINGS, LA, p. A279
JENNINGS SENIOR CARE HOSPITAL, JENNINGS, LA, p. A279
JEROLD PHELPS COMMUNITY HOSPITAL, GARBERVILLE, CA, p. A65
JEROME GOLDEN CENTER FOR BEHAVIORAL HEALTH, INC., WEST PALM BEACH, FL, p. A150
JERSEY CITY MEDICAL CENTER, JERSEY CITY, NJ, p. A417
JERSEY COMMUNITY HOSPITAL, JERSEYVILLE, IL, p. A193
JERSEY SHORE HOSPITAL, JERSEY SHORE, PA, p. A541
JERSEY SHORE UNIVERSITY MEDICAL CENTER, NEPTUNE, NJ, p. A419
JESSE BROWN VETERANS AFFAIRS MEDICAL CENTER, CHICAGO, IL, p. A184
JEWELL COUNTY HOSPITAL, MANKATO, KS, p. A249
JEWISH HOME OF SAN FRANCISCO, SAN FRANCISCO, CA, p. A90
JEWISH HOSPITAL, LOUISVILLE, KY, p. A265
JEWISH HOSPITAL–SHELBYVILLE, SHELBYVILLE, KY, p. A270
JFK JOHNSON REHABILITATION INSTITUTE, EDISON, NJ, p. A415
JFK MEDICAL CENTER, ATLANTIS, FL, p. A123
JFK MEDICAL CENTER, EDISON, NJ, p. A415
JIM TALIAFERRO COMMUNITY MENTAL HEALTH, LAWTON, OK, p. A512
JOE DIMAGGIO CHILDREN'S HOSPITAL,, FLORIDA (see MEMORIAL REGIONAL HOSPITAL SOUTH), p. A131
JOHN C. FREMONT HEALTHCARE DISTRICT, MARIPOSA, CA, p. A76
JOHN C. LINCOLN DEER VALLEY HOSPITAL, PHOENIX, AZ, p. A36
JOHN C. LINCOLN NORTH MOUNTAIN HOSPITAL, PHOENIX, AZ, p. A36
JOHN C. STENNIS MEMORIAL HOSPITAL, DE KALB, MS, p. A357
JOHN D. ARCHBOLD MEMORIAL HOSPITAL, THOMASVILLE, GA, p. A168
JOHN D. DINGELL VETERANS AFFAIRS MEDICAL CENTER, DETROIT, MI, p. A322
JOHN F. KENNEDY MEMORIAL HOSPITAL, INDIO, CA, p. A67
JOHN H. STROGER JR. HOSPITAL OF COOK COUNTY, CHICAGO, IL, p. A184
JOHN HEINZ INSTITUTE OF REHABILITATION MEDICINE, WILKES-BARRE, PA, p. A558
JOHN J. MADDEN MENTAL HEALTH CENTER, HINES, IL, p. A192
JOHN J. PERSHING VETERANS AFFAIRS MEDICAL CENTER, POPLAR BLUFF, MO, p. A378
JOHN MUIR BEHAVIORAL HEALTH CENTER, CONCORD, CA, p. A60
JOHN MUIR MEDICAL CENTER, CONCORD, CONCORD, CA, p. A60
JOHN MUIR MEDICAL CENTER, WALNUT CREEK, WALNUT CREEK, CA, p. A100
JOHN PETER SMITH HOSPITAL, FORT WORTH, TEXAS (see JPS HEALTH NETWORK), p. A618
JOHN RANDOLPH MEDICAL CENTER, HOPEWELL, VA, p. A672
JOHN T. MATHER MEMORIAL HOSPITAL, PORT JEFFERSON, NY, p. A452
JOHN UMSTEAD HOSPITAL, BUTNER, NC, p. A461
JOHNS HOPKINS BAYVIEW MEDICAL CENTER, BALTIMORE, MD, p. A296
JOHNS HOPKINS CHILDREN'S CENTER, BALTIMORE, MARYLAND (see JOHNS HOPKINS HOSPITAL), p. A296
JOHNS HOPKINS HOSPITAL, BALTIMORE, MD, p. A296
JOHNSON CITY MEDICAL CENTER, JOHNSON CITY, TN, p. A585
JOHNSON COUNTY COMMUNITY HOSPITAL, MOUNTAIN CITY, TN, p. A590
JOHNSON COUNTY HEALTHCARE CENTER, BUFFALO, WY, p. A720
JOHNSON COUNTY HOSPITAL, TECUMSEH, NE, p. A402
JOHNSON MEMORIAL HEALTH SERVICES, DAWSON, MN, p. A342
JOHNSON MEMORIAL HOSPITAL, STAFFORD SPRINGS, CT, p. A117
JOHNSON MEMORIAL HOSPITAL, FRANKLIN, IN, p. A212
JOHNSON REGIONAL MEDICAL CENTER, CLARKSVILLE, AR, p. A44
JOHNSON–MATHERS NURSING HOME (see NICHOLAS COUNTY HOSPITAL), p. A259

JOHNSTON MEMORIAL HOSPITAL, ABINGDON, VA, p. A668
JOHNSTON R. BOWMAN HEALTH CENTER, CHICAGO, ILLINOIS (see RUSH UNIVERSITY MEDICAL CENTER), p. A186
JOHNSTON UNC HEALTH CARE, SMITHFIELD, NC, p. A473
JOHNSTON–WILLIS HOSPITAL, RICHMOND, VIRGINIA (see CJW MEDICAL CENTER), p. A677
JOINT TOWNSHIP DISTRICT MEMORIAL HOSPITAL, SAINT MARYS, OH, p. A501
JONATHAN M. WAINWRIGHT MEMORIAL VETERANS AFFAIRS MEDICAL CENTER, WALLA WALLA, WA, p. A692
JONES MEMORIAL HOSPITAL, WELLSVILLE, NY, p. A457
JORDAN VALLEY MEDICAL CENTER, WEST JORDAN, UT, p. A664
JOYCE EISENBERG–KEEFER MEDICAL CENTER, RESEDA, CA, p. A86
JPS HEALTH NETWORK, FORT WORTH, TX, p. A618
JULIAN F. KEITH ALCOHOL AND DRUG ABUSE TREATMENT CENTER, BLACK MOUNTAIN, NC, p. A460
JULIETTE MANOR NURSING HOME, COMMUNITY CLINICS (see BERLIN MEMORIAL HOSPITAL), p. A702
JUPITER MEDICAL CENTER, JUPITER, FL, p. A132

K

K. HOVNANIAN CHILDREN'S HOSPITAL, NEPTUNE, NEW JERSEY (see JERSEY SHORE UNIVERSITY MEDICAL CENTER), p. A419
KAATERSKILL CARE, CATSKILL, NEW YORK (see COLUMBIA MEMORIAL HOSPITAL), p. A439
KADLEC REGIONAL MEDICAL CENTER, RICHLAND, WA, p. A687
KAHI MOHALA BEHAVIORAL HEALTH, EWA BEACH, HI, p. A170
KAHUKU MEDICAL CENTER, KAHUKU, HI, p. A171
KAILO LTAC HOSPITAL, CROWLEY, LA, p. A276
KAISER FOUNDATION HOSPITAL, MARTINEZ, CALIFORNIA (see KAISER PERMANENTE WALNUT CREEK MEDICAL CENTER), p. A100
KAISER FOUNDATION HOSPITAL WESTSIDE MEDICAL CENTER, HILLSBORO, OR, p. A525
KAISER FOUNDATION MENTAL HEALTH CENTER, LOS ANGELES, CALIFORNIA (see KAISER PERMANENTE LOS ANGELES MEDICAL CENTER), p. A72
KAISER PERMANENTE ANTIOCH MEDICAL CENTER, ANTIOCH, CA, p. A55
KAISER PERMANENTE BALDWIN PARK MEDICAL CENTER, BALDWIN PARK, CA, p. A57
KAISER PERMANENTE DOWNEY MEDICAL CENTER, DOWNEY, CA, p. A61
KAISER PERMANENTE FONTANA MEDICAL CENTER, FONTANA, CA, p. A63
KAISER PERMANENTE FRESNO MEDICAL CENTER, FRESNO, CA, p. A64
KAISER PERMANENTE HAYWARD MEDICAL CENTER, HAYWARD, CA, p. A66
KAISER PERMANENTE LOS ANGELES MEDICAL CENTER, LOS ANGELES, CA, p. A72
KAISER PERMANENTE MANTECA MEDICAL CENTER, MANTECA, CA, p. A76
KAISER PERMANENTE MEDICAL CENTER, HONOLULU, HI, p. A170
KAISER PERMANENTE MORENO VALLEY MEDICAL CENTER, MORENO VALLEY, CA, p. A78
KAISER PERMANENTE OAKLAND MEDICAL CENTER, OAKLAND, CA, p. A80
KAISER PERMANENTE ONTARIO MEDICAL CENTER, ONTARIO, CA, p. A81
KAISER PERMANENTE ORANGE COUNTY ANAHEIM MEDICAL CENTER, ANAHEIM, CA, p. A55
KAISER PERMANENTE PANORAMA CITY MEDICAL CENTER,, CA, p. A72
KAISER PERMANENTE REDWOOD CITY MEDICAL CENTER, REDWOOD CITY, CA, p. A85
KAISER PERMANENTE RICHMOND MEDICAL CENTER, RICHMOND, CALIFORNIA (see KAISER PERMANENTE OAKLAND MEDICAL CENTER), p. A80
KAISER PERMANENTE RIVERSIDE MEDICAL CENTER, RIVERSIDE, CA, p. A86
KAISER PERMANENTE ROSEVILLE MEDICAL CENTER, ROSEVILLE, CA, p. A87
KAISER PERMANENTE SACRAMENTO MEDICAL CENTER, SACRAMENTO, CA, p. A87
KAISER PERMANENTE SAN DIEGO MEDICAL CENTER, SAN DIEGO, CA, p. A89
KAISER PERMANENTE SAN FRANCISCO MEDICAL CENTER, SAN FRANCISCO, CA, p. A91
KAISER PERMANENTE SAN JOSE MEDICAL CENTER, SAN JOSE, CA, p. A92
KAISER PERMANENTE SAN RAFAEL MEDICAL CENTER, SAN RAFAEL, CA, p. A93

KAISER PERMANENTE SANTA CLARA MEDICAL CENTER, SANTA CLARA, CA, p. A94
KAISER PERMANENTE SANTA ROSA MEDICAL CENTER, SANTA ROSA, CA, p. A95
KAISER PERMANENTE SOUTH BAY MEDICAL CENTER,, CA, p. A72
KAISER PERMANENTE SOUTH SACRAMENTO MEDICAL CENTER, SACRAMENTO, CA, p. A87
KAISER PERMANENTE SOUTH SAN FRANCISCO, SOUTH SAN FRANCISCO, CA, p. A96
KAISER PERMANENTE SUNNYSIDE MEDICAL CENTER, CLACKAMAS, OR, p. A523
KAISER PERMANENTE VACAVILLE MEDICAL CENTER, VACAVILLE, CA, p. A98
KAISER PERMANENTE VALLEJO MEDICAL CENTER, VALLEJO, CA, p. A99
KAISER PERMANENTE WALNUT CREEK MEDICAL CENTER, WALNUT CREEK, CA, p. A100
KAISER PERMANENTE WEST LOS ANGELES MEDICAL CENTER, LOS ANGELES, CA, p. A72
KAISER PERMANENTE WOODLAND HILLS MEDICAL CENTER,, CA, p. A72
KALAMAZOO PSYCHIATRIC HOSPITAL, KALAMAZOO, MI, p. A328
KALEIDA HEALTH, BUFFALO, NY, p. A434
KALISPELL REGIONAL MEDICAL CENTER, KALISPELL, MT, p. A389
KALKASKA MEMORIAL HEALTH CENTER, KALKASKA, MI, p. A328
KANE COMMUNITY HOSPITAL, KANE, PA, p. A541
KANE COUNTY HOSPITAL, KANAB, UT, p. A660
KANSAS CITY ORTHOPAEDIC INSTITUTE, LEAWOOD, KS, p. A248
KANSAS CITY VETERANS AFFAIRS MEDICAL CENTER, KANSAS CITY, MO, p. A373
KANSAS HEART HOSPITAL, WICHITA, KS, p. A256
KANSAS MEDICAL CENTER, ANDOVER, KS, p. A241
KANSAS NEUROLOGICAL INSTITUTE, TOPEKA, KS, p. A255
KANSAS REHABILITATION HOSPITAL, TOPEKA, KS, p. A255
KANSAS SPINE AND SPECIALTY HOSPITAL, WICHITA, KS, p. A256
KANSAS SURGERY AND RECOVERY CENTER, WICHITA, KS, p. A256
KAPIOLANI MEDICAL CENTER FOR WOMEN & CHILDREN, HONOLULU, HI, p. A170
KARL AND ESTHER HOBLITZELLE MEMORIAL HOSPITAL, DALLAS, TEXAS (see BAYLOR UNIVERSITY MEDICAL CENTER), p. A610
KARMANOS CANCER CENTER, DETROIT, MI, p. A322
KATHERINE SHAW BETHEA HOSPITAL, DIXON, IL, p. A188
KAU HOSPITAL, PAHALA, HI, p. A172
KAUAI VETERANS MEMORIAL HOSPITAL, WAIMEA, HI, p. A173
KAWEAH DELTA MEDICAL CENTER, VISALIA, CA, p. A99
KEARNEY COUNTY HEALTH SERVICES, MINDEN, NE, p. A398
KEARNEY REGIONAL MEDICAL CENTER, KEARNEY, NE, p. A397
KEARNY COUNTY HOSPITAL, LAKIN, KS, p. A248
KECK HOSPITAL OF USC, LOS ANGELES, CA, p. A72
KEDREN COMMUNITY MENTAL HEALTH CENTER, LOS ANGELES, CA, p. A73
KEEFE MEMORIAL HOSPITAL, CHEYENNE WELLS, CO, p. A103
KELL WEST REGIONAL HOSPITAL, WICHITA FALLS, TX, p. A657
KELLER ARMY COMMUNITY HOSPITAL, WEST POINT, NY, p. A458
KEMPSVILLE CENTER FOR BEHAVIORAL HEALTH, NORFOLK, VA, p. A675
KENDALL REGIONAL MEDICAL CENTER, MIAMI, FL, p. A137
KENMARE COMMUNITY HOSPITAL, KENMARE, ND, p. A479
KENMORE MERCY HOSPITAL, KENMORE, NY, p. A439
KENNEDY HEALTH SYSTEM, CHERRY HILL, NJ, p. A414
KENNEDY KRIEGER INSTITUTE, BALTIMORE, MD, p. A296
KENNEDY UNIVERSITY HOSPITAL – STRATFORD, STRATFORD, NEW JERSEY (see KENNEDY HEALTH SYSTEM), p. A414
KENNEDY UNIVERSITY HOSPITAL – WASHINGTON TOWNSHIP, TURNERSVILLE, NEW JERSEY (see KENNEDY HEALTH SYSTEM), p. A414
KENSINGTON HOSPITAL, PHILADELPHIA, PA, p. A549
KENT COUNTY MEMORIAL HOSPITAL, WARWICK, RI, p. A561
KENTFIELD REHABILITATION AND SPECIALTY HOSPITAL, KENTFIELD, CA, p. A68
KENTUCKIANA MEDICAL CENTER, CLARKSVILLE, IN, p. A208
KENTUCKY CHILDREN'S HOSPITAL, LEXINGTON, KENTUCKY (see UNIVERSITY OF KENTUCKY ALBERT B. CHANDLER HOSPITAL), p. A265
KENTUCKY RIVER MEDICAL CENTER, JACKSON, KY, p. A263
KEOKUK AREA HOSPITAL, KEOKUK, IA, p. A233
KEOKUK COUNTY HEALTH CENTER, SIGOURNEY, IA, p. A237
KERN MEDICAL CENTER, BAKERSFIELD, CA, p. A57
KERN VALLEY HEALTHCARE DISTRICT, LAKE ISABELLA, CA, p. A69

KERNERSVILLE MEDICAL CENTER, KERNERSVILLE, NORTH CAROLINA (see NOVANT HEALTH FORSYTH MEDICAL CENTER), p. A475
KERRVILLE DIVISION, KERRVILLE, TEXAS (see SOUTH TEXAS VETERANS HEALTH CARE SYSTEM), p. A647
KERRVILLE STATE HOSPITAL, KERRVILLE, TX, p. A631
KERSHAWHEALTH, CAMDEN, SC, p. A562
KESSLER INSTITUTE FOR REHABILITATION, WEST ORANGE, NJ, p. A424
KESSLER INSTITUTE FOR REHABILITATION, CHESTER, NEW JERSEY (see KESSLER INSTITUTE FOR REHABILITATION), p. A424
KESSLER INSTITUTE FOR REHABILITATION, SADDLE BROOK, NEW JERSEY (see KESSLER INSTITUTE FOR REHABILITATION), p. A424
KESSLER INSTITUTE FOR REHABILITATION, WEST ORANGE, NEW JERSEY (see KESSLER INSTITUTE FOR REHABILITATION), p. A424
KETTERING MEDICAL CENTER, KETTERING, OH, p. A495
KEYSTONE NEWPORT NEWS, NEWPORT NEWS, VA, p. A674
KIDSPEACE CHILDREN'S HOSPITAL, OREFIELD, PA, p. A547
KILMICHAEL HOSPITAL, KILMICHAEL, MS, p. A361
KIMBALL HEALTH SERVICES, KIMBALL, NE, p. A397
KIMBALL–RIDGE CENTER, WATERLOO, IOWA (see COVENANT MEDICAL CENTER), p. A239
KIMBLE HOSPITAL, JUNCTION, TX, p. A630
KINDRED CHICAGO LAKESHORE, CHICAGO, ILLINOIS (see KINDRED CHICAGO–CENTRAL HOSPITAL), p. A184
KINDRED CHICAGO–CENTRAL HOSPITAL, CHICAGO, IL, p. A184
KINDRED HOSPITAL ARIZONA–NORTHWEST PHOENIX, PEORIA, ARIZONA (see KINDRED HOSPITAL ARIZONA–PHOENIX), p. A36
KINDRED HOSPITAL ARIZONA–PHOENIX, PHOENIX, AZ, p. A36
KINDRED HOSPITAL BAY AREA–TAMPA, TAMPA, FL, p. A147
KINDRED HOSPITAL BAYTOWN, BAYTOWN, TEXAS (see KINDRED HOSPITAL EAST HOUSTON), p. A606
KINDRED HOSPITAL BOSTON–NORTH SHORE, PEABODY, MA, p. A313
KINDRED HOSPITAL CENTRAL TAMPA, TAMPA, FL, p. A148
KINDRED HOSPITAL CHICAGO NORTH, CHICAGO, ILLINOIS (see KINDRED CHICAGO–CENTRAL HOSPITAL), p. A184
KINDRED HOSPITAL CHICAGO–NORTHLAKE, NORTHLAKE, IL, p. A198
KINDRED HOSPITAL CLEVELAND–GATEWAY, CLEVELAND, OH, p. A488
KINDRED HOSPITAL DALLAS CENTRAL, DALLAS, TX, p. A610
KINDRED HOSPITAL DALLAS–WALNUT HILL, DALLAS, TEXAS (see KINDRED HOSPITAL–DALLAS), p. A610
KINDRED HOSPITAL DETROIT, DETROIT, MI, p. A322
KINDRED HOSPITAL EAST HOUSTON, CHANNELVIEW, TX, p. A606
KINDRED HOSPITAL EL PASO, EL PASO, TX, p. A616
KINDRED HOSPITAL INDIANAPOLIS SOUTH, GREENWOOD, IN, p. A212
KINDRED HOSPITAL KANSAS CITY, KANSAS CITY, MO, p. A373
KINDRED HOSPITAL LAS VEGAS, DESERT SPRINGS CAMPUS, LAS VEGAS, NEVADA (see KINDRED HOSPITAL LAS VEGAS–SAHARA), p. A406
KINDRED HOSPITAL LAS VEGAS–SAHARA, LAS VEGAS, NV, p. A406
KINDRED HOSPITAL LIMA, LIMA, OH, p. A496
KINDRED HOSPITAL LOUISVILLE AT JEWISH HOSPITAL, LOUISVILLE, KENTUCKY (see KINDRED HOSPITAL–LOUISVILLE), p. A265
KINDRED HOSPITAL MELBOURNE, MELBOURNE, FL, p. A136
KINDRED HOSPITAL MIDTOWN, HOUSTON, TX, p. A625
KINDRED HOSPITAL NEW JERSEY – RAHWAY, RAHWAY, NEW JERSEY (see KINDRED HOSPITAL–NEW JERSEY MORRIS COUNTY), p. A415
KINDRED HOSPITAL NEW JERSEY – WAYNE, WAYNE, NEW JERSEY (see KINDRED HOSPITAL–NEW JERSEY MORRIS COUNTY), p. A415
KINDRED HOSPITAL NORTH FLORIDA, GREEN COVE SPRINGS, FL, p. A130
KINDRED HOSPITAL NORTHEAST–STOUGHTON, STOUGHTON, MA, p. A315
KINDRED HOSPITAL NORTHLAND, KANSAS CITY, MO, p. A373
KINDRED HOSPITAL NORTHWEST INDIANA, HAMMOND, IN, p. A213
KINDRED HOSPITAL OCALA, OCALA, FL, p. A139
KINDRED HOSPITAL OF CENTRAL OHIO, MANSFIELD, OH, p. A497
KINDRED HOSPITAL OF CLEVELAND, CLEVELAND, OHIO (see KINDRED HOSPITAL CLEVELAND–GATEWAY), p. A488
KINDRED HOSPITAL OF NORTHERN INDIANA, MISHAWAKA, IN, p. A218
KINDRED HOSPITAL PEORIA, PEORIA, IL, p. A199
KINDRED HOSPITAL PITTSBURGH–NORTH SHORE, PITTSBURGH, PA, p. A551

© 2014 AHA Guide

LOS ANGELES COUNTY CENTRAL JAIL HOSPITAL, LOS ANGELES, CA, p. A73
LOS NINOS HOSPITAL, PHOENIX, AZ, p. A36
LOS ROBLES HOSPITAL AND MEDICAL CENTER, THOUSAND OAKS, CA, p. A97
LOST RIVERS MEDICAL CENTER, ARCO, ID, p. A174
LOUIS & PEACHES OWEN HEART HOSPITAL, TYLER, TEXAS (see MOTHER FRANCES HOSPITAL – TYLER), p. A654
LOUIS A. JOHNSON VETERANS AFFAIRS MEDICAL CENTER, CLARKSBURG, WV, p. A694
LOUIS A. WEISS MEMORIAL HOSPITAL, CHICAGO, IL, p. A184
LOUIS STOKES CLEVELAND VETERANS AFFAIRS MEDICAL CENTER, CLEVELAND, OH, p. A488
LOUISIANA CONTINUING CARE HOSPITAL, MARRERO, LA, p. A283
LOUISIANA EXTENDED CARE HOSPITAL OF LAFAYETTE, LAFAYETTE, LA, p. A281
LOUISIANA EXTENDED CARE HOSPITAL OF NATCHITOCHES, NATCHITOCHES, LA, p. A285
LOUISIANA EXTENDED CARE HOSPITAL WEST MONROE, WEST MONROE, LA, p. A290
LOUISIANA HEART HOSPITAL, LACOMBE, LA, p. A280
LOURDES COUNSELING CENTER, RICHLAND, WA, p. A687
LOURDES HOSPITAL, PADUCAH, KY, p. A269
LOURDES MEDICAL CENTER, PASCO, WA, p. A686
LOURDES MEDICAL CENTER OF BURLINGTON COUNTY, WILLINGBORO, NJ, p. A424
LOURDES SPECIALTY HOSPITAL OF SOUTHERN NEW JERSEY, WILLINGBORO, NJ, p. A425
LOVELACE MEDICAL CENTER, ALBUQUERQUE, NM, p. A426
LOVELACE REGIONAL HOSPITAL – ROSWELL, ROSWELL, NM, p. A430
LOVELACE REHABILITATION HOSPITAL, ALBUQUERQUE, NM, p. A426
LOVELACE WESTSIDE HOSPITAL, ALBUQUERQUE, NM, p. A426
LOVELACE WOMEN'S HOSPITAL, ALBUQUERQUE, NM, p. A426
LOWELL GENERAL HOSPITAL, LOWELL, MA, p. A311
LOWELL GENERAL HOSPITAL, SAINTS CAMPUS, LOWELL, MASSACHUSETTS (see LOWELL GENERAL HOSPITAL), p. A311
LOWER BUCKS HOSPITAL, BRISTOL, PA, p. A534
LOWER KEYS MEDICAL CENTER, KEY WEST, FL, p. A133
LOWER UMPQUA HOSPITAL DISTRICT, REEDSPORT, OR, p. A529
LOYOLA UNIVERSITY MEDICAL CENTER, MAYWOOD, IL, p. A195
LUBBOCK HEART HOSPITAL, LUBBOCK, TX, p. A635
LUCAS COUNTY HEALTH CENTER, CHARITON, IA, p. A227
LUCILE SALTER PACKARD CHILDREN'S HOSPITAL AT STANFORD, PALO ALTO, CA, p. A82
LUTHERAN HOSPITAL, CLEVELAND, OH, p. A488
LUTHERAN HOSPITAL OF INDIANA, FORT WAYNE, IN, p. A211
LUTHERAN MEDICAL CENTER, WHEAT RIDGE, CO, p. A112
LUTHERAN MEDICAL CENTER,, NY, p. A445
LUTZ WING CONVALESCENT AND NURSING CARE UNIT (see MAYO CLINIC HEALTH SYSTEM IN FAIRMONT), p. A343
LYNCHBURG GENERAL HOSPITAL, LYNCHBURG, VIRGINIA (see CENTRA LYNCHBURG GENERAL HOSPITAL), p. A673
LYNDON B JOHNSON GENERAL HOSPITAL, HOUSTON, TEXAS (see HARRIS HEALTH SYSTEM), p. A624
LYNDON B. JOHNSON TROPICAL MEDICAL CENTER, PAGO PAGO, AS, p. A724
LYNN COUNTY HOSPITAL DISTRICT, TAHOKA, TX, p. A651
LYONS DIVISION, LYONS, NEW JERSEY (see VETERANS AFFAIRS NEW JERSEY HEALTH CARE SYSTEM), p. A415

M

MACKINAC STRAITS HEALTH SYSTEM, SAINT IGNACE, MI, p. A334
MACNEAL HOSPITAL, BERWYN, IL, p. A181
MACON COUNTY GENERAL HOSPITAL, LAFAYETTE, TN, p. A586
MAD RIVER COMMUNITY HOSPITAL, ARCATA, CA, p. A56
MADELIA COMMUNITY HOSPITAL, MADELIA, MN, p. A346
MADERA COMMUNITY HOSPITAL, MADERA, CA, p. A76
MADIGAN HEALTHCARE SYSTEM, TACOMA, WA, p. A690
MADISON COMMUNITY HOSPITAL, MADISON, SD, p. A574
MADISON COUNTY HEALTH CARE SYSTEM, WINTERSET, IA, p. A240
MADISON COUNTY HOSPITAL, LONDON, OH, p. A496
MADISON COUNTY MEMORIAL HOSPITAL, MADISON, FL, p. A135
MADISON HOSPITAL, MADISON, ALABAMA (see HUNTSVILLE HOSPITAL), p. A22
MADISON HOSPITAL, MADISON, MN, p. A346
MADISON MEDICAL CENTER, FREDERICKTOWN, MO, p. A371
MADISON MEMORIAL HOSPITAL, REXBURG, ID, p. A178
MADISON PARISH HOSPITAL, TALLULAH, LA, p. A289

MADISON RIVER OAKS MEDICAL CENTER, CANTON, MS, p. A356
MADISON ST. JOSEPH HEALTH CENTER, MADISONVILLE, TX, p. A636
MADISON STATE HOSPITAL, MADISON, IN, p. A218
MADISON VALLEY MEDICAL CENTER, ENNIS, MT, p. A387
MADONNA REHABILITATION HOSPITAL, LINCOLN, NE, p. A398
MAGEE GENERAL HOSPITAL, MAGEE, MS, p. A361
MAGEE REHABILITATION HOSPITAL, PHILADELPHIA, PA, p. A549
MAGEE–WOMENS HOSPITAL OF UPMC, PITTSBURGH, PA, p. A551
MAGNOLIA BEHAVIORAL HEALTHCARE, LACOMBE, LA, p. A280
MAGNOLIA REGIONAL HEALTH CENTER, CORINTH, MS, p. A357
MAGNOLIA REGIONAL MEDICAL CENTER, MAGNOLIA, AR, p. A49
MAGRUDER MEMORIAL HOSPITAL, PORT CLINTON, OH, p. A500
MAHASKA HEALTH PARTNERSHIP, OSKALOOSA, IA, p. A236
MAHNOMEN HEALTH CENTER, MAHNOMEN, MN, p. A346
MAIMONIDES INFANTS AND CHILDREN'S HOSPITAL OF BROOKLYN, NEW YORK (see MAIMONIDES MEDICAL CENTER), p. A445
MAIMONIDES MEDICAL CENTER,, NY, p. A445
MAIN CAMPUS, BATTLE CREEK, MICHIGAN (see BRONSON BATTLE CREEK), p. A319
MAINE COAST MEMORIAL HOSPITAL, ELLSWORTH, ME, p. A293
MAINE MEDICAL CENTER, PORTLAND, ME, p. A294
MAINE MEDICAL CENTER, BRIGHTON CAMPUS, PORTLAND, MAINE (see MAINE MEDICAL CENTER), p. A294
MAINE VETERANS AFFAIRS MEDICAL CENTER, AUGUSTA, ME, p. A291
MAINEGENERAL MEDICAL CENTER, AUGUSTA, ME, p. A291
MAINEGENERAL MEDICAL CENTER–AUGUSTA CAMPUS, AUGUSTA, MAINE (see MAINEGENERAL MEDICAL CENTER), p. A291
MAINLAND MEDICAL CENTER, TEXAS CITY, TEXAS (see CLEAR LAKE REGIONAL MEDICAL CENTER), p. A656
MAJOR HOSPITAL, SHELBYVILLE, IN, p. A222
MALCOM RANDALL VETERANS AFFAIRS MEDICAL CENTER, GAINESVILLE, FL, p. A129
MALVERN INSTITUTE, MALVERN, PA, p. A544
MAMMOTH HOSPITAL, MAMMOTH LAKES, CA, p. A76
MANATEE GLENS HOSPITAL AND ADDICTION CENTER, BRADENTON, FL, p. A124
MANATEE MEMORIAL HOSPITAL, BRADENTON, FL, p. A124
MANATEE PALMS YOUTH SERVICES, BRADENTON, FL, p. A124
MANCHESTER MEMORIAL HOSPITAL, MANCHESTER, CT, p. A114
MANCHESTER MEMORIAL HOSPITAL, MANCHESTER, KY, p. A267
MANCHESTER VETERANS AFFAIRS MEDICAL CENTER, MANCHESTER, NH, p. A411
MANHASSET AMBULATORY CARE PAVILION, MANHASSET, NEW YORK (see LONG ISLAND JEWISH MEDICAL CENTER), p. A445
MANHATTAN EYE, EAR AND THROAT HOSPITAL, NEW YORK, NEW YORK (see LENOX HILL HOSPITAL), p. A445
MANHATTAN PSYCHIATRIC CENTER–WARD'S ISLAND, NEW YORK, NY, p. A445
MANHATTAN SURGICAL CENTER,, KS, p. A249
MANIILAQ HEALTH CENTER, KOTZEBUE, AK, p. A29
MANN–GRANDSTAFF VETERANS AFFAIRS MEDICAL CENTER, SPOKANE, WA, p. A690
MANNING REGIONAL HEALTHCARE CENTER, MANNING, IA, p. A234
MANSFIELD HOSPITAL, MANSFIELD, OHIO (see OHIOHEALTH MEDCENTRAL MANSFIELD HOSPITAL), p. A497
MAPLE GROVE HOSPITAL, MAPLE GROVE, MN, p. A346
MARCUM AND WALLACE MEMORIAL HOSPITAL, IRVINE, KY, p. A263
MARCUS DALY MEMORIAL HOSPITAL, HAMILTON, MT, p. A388
MARENGO MEMORIAL HOSPITAL, UNITYPOINT HEALTH, MARENGO, IA, p. A234
MARGARET MARY HEALTH, BATESVILLE, IN, p. A206
MARGARET R. PARDEE MEMORIAL HOSPITAL, HENDERSONVILLE, NC, p. A466
MARGARETVILLE HOSPITAL, MARGARETVILLE, NY, p. A441
MARIA FARERI CHILDREN'S HOSPITAL, VALHALLA, NEW YORK (see WESTCHESTER MEDICAL CENTER), p. A457
MARIA PARHAM MEDICAL CENTER, HENDERSON, NC, p. A466
MARIAN CENTER, SALT LAKE CITY, UT, p. A663
MARIAN REGIONAL MEDICAL CENTER, SANTA MARIA, CA, p. A94
MARIANJOY REHABILITATION HOSPITAL, WHEATON, IL, p. A205
MARIAS MEDICAL CENTER, SHELBY, MT, p. A391
MARICOPA INTEGRATED HEALTH SYSTEM, PHOENIX, AZ, p. A36
MARIETTA MEMORIAL HOSPITAL, MARIETTA, OH, p. A497
MARIN GENERAL HOSPITAL, GREENBRAE, CA, p. A66
MARINA DEL REY HOSPITAL, MARINA DEL REY, CA, p. A76
MARION GENERAL HOSPITAL, MARION, IN, p. A218

MARION GENERAL HOSPITAL, COLUMBIA, MS, p. A357
MARION REGIONAL MEDICAL CENTER, HAMILTON, AL, p. A21
MARION VETERANS AFFAIRS MEDICAL CENTER, MARION, IL, p. A195
MARK TWAIN MEDICAL CENTER, SAN ANDREAS, CA, p. A88
MARLBORO PARK HOSPITAL, BENNETTSVILLE, SC, p. A562
MARLETTE REGIONAL HOSPITAL, MARLETTE, MI, p. A330
MARLTON REHABILITATION HOSPITAL, MARLTON, NJ, p. A418
MARQUETTE GENERAL HOSPITAL, MARQUETTE, MI, p. A330
MARSHALL BROWNING HOSPITAL, DU QUOIN, IL, p. A188
MARSHALL COUNTY HEALTHCARE CENTER AVERA, BRITTON, SD, p. A572
MARSHALL COUNTY HOSPITAL, BENTON, KY, p. A258
MARSHALL I. PICKENS HOSPITAL, GREENVILLE, SOUTH CAROLINA (see GREENVILLE MEMORIAL HOSPITAL), p. A566
MARSHALL MEDICAL CENTER, PLACERVILLE, CA, p. A83
MARSHALL MEDICAL CENTER, LEWISBURG, TN, p. A587
MARSHALL MEDICAL CENTER NORTH, GUNTERSVILLE, AL, p. A21
MARSHALL MEDICAL CENTER SOUTH, BOAZ, AL, p. A17
MARSHALLTOWN MEDICAL & SURGICAL CENTER, MARSHALLTOWN, IA, p. A234
MARTHA JEFFERSON HOSPITAL, CHARLOTTESVILLE, VA, p. A669
MARTHA'S VINEYARD HOSPITAL, OAK BLUFFS, MA, p. A313
MARTIN ARMY COMMUNITY HOSPITAL, FORT BENNING, GA, p. A160
MARTIN COUNTY HOSPITAL DISTRICT, STANTON, TX, p. A650
MARTIN GENERAL HOSPITAL, WILLIAMSTON, NC, p. A474
MARTIN HEALTH SYSTEM, STUART, FL, p. A146
MARTIN MEMORIAL HOSPITAL SOUTH, STUART, FLORIDA (see MARTIN HEALTH SYSTEM), p. A146
MARTINSBURG VETERANS AFFAIRS MEDICAL CENTER, MARTINSBURG, WV, p. A697
MARY BLACK MEMORIAL HOSPITAL, SPARTANBURG, SC, p. A570
MARY BRECKINRIDGE ARH HOSPITAL, HYDEN, KY, p. A263
MARY FREE BED REHABILITATION HOSPITAL, GRAND RAPIDS, MI, p. A325
MARY GREELEY MEDICAL CENTER, AMES, IA, p. A225
MARY IMMACULATE HOSPITAL, NEWPORT NEWS, VA, p. A675
MARY LANNING HEALTHCARE, HASTINGS, NE, p. A396
MARY RUTAN HOSPITAL, BELLEFONTAINE, OH, p. A483
MARY S HARPER GERIATRIC PSYCHIATRY CENTER, TUSCALOOSA, AL, p. A26
MARY WASHINGTON HOSPITAL, FREDERICKSBURG, VA, p. A671
MARYMOUNT HOSPITAL, GARFIELD HEIGHTS, OH, p. A494
MARYVALE HOSPITAL MEDICAL CENTER, PHOENIX, AZ, p. A36
MASON DISTRICT HOSPITAL, HAVANA, IL, p. A192
MASON GENERAL HOSPITAL, SHELTON, WA, p. A689
MASONICARE HEALTH CENTER, WALLINGFORD, CT, p. A117
MASSAC MEMORIAL HOSPITAL, METROPOLIS, IL, p. A196
MASSACHUSETTS EYE AND EAR INFIRMARY, BOSTON, MA, p. A307
MASSACHUSETTS GENERAL HOSPITAL, BOSTON, MA, p. A307
MASSACHUSETTS HOSPITAL SCHOOL, CANTON, MA, p. A309
MASSENA MEMORIAL HOSPITAL, MASSENA, NY, p. A441
MASSGENERAL FOR CHILDREN AT NEWTON–WELLESLEY HOSPITAL, NEWTON, MASSACHUSETTS (see NEWTON–WELLESLEY HOSPITAL), p. A313
MASSGENERAL FOR CHILDREN AT NORTH SHORE MEDICAL CENTER, SALEM, MASSACHUSETTS (see NORTH SHORE MEDICAL CENTER), p. A314
MASSGENERAL HOSPITAL FOR CHILDREN, BOSTON, MASSACHUSETTS (see MASSACHUSETTS GENERAL HOSPITAL), p. A307
MAT–SU REGIONAL MEDICAL CENTER, PALMER, AK, p. A30
MATAGORDA REGIONAL MEDICAL CENTER, BAY CITY, TX, p. A601
MATHENY MEDICAL AND EDUCATIONAL CENTER, PEAPACK, NJ, p. A420
MATTEL CHILDREN'S HOSPITAL, LOS ANGELES, CALIFORNIA (see RONALD REAGAN UNIVERSITY OF CALIFORNIA LOS ANGELES MEDICAL CENTER), p. A74
MAUI MEMORIAL MEDICAL CENTER, WAILUKU, HI, p. A172
MAURY REGIONAL HOSPITAL, COLUMBIA, TN, p. A581
MAYERS MEMORIAL HOSPITAL DISTRICT, FALL RIVER MILLS, CA, p. A63
MAYHILL HOSPITAL, DENTON, TX, p. A613
MAYO CLINIC – SAINT MARYS HOSPITAL, ROCHESTER, MINNESOTA (see MAYO CLINIC HOSPITAL – ROCHESTER), p. A350
MAYO CLINIC HEALTH SYSTEM – CHIPPEWA VALLEY IN BLOOMER, BLOOMER, WI, p. A702
MAYO CLINIC HEALTH SYSTEM – FRANCISCAN HEALTHCARE IN LA CROSSE, LA CROSSE, WI, p. A707
MAYO CLINIC HEALTH SYSTEM – FRANCISCAN HEALTHCARE IN SPARTA, SPARTA, WI, p. A715
MAYO CLINIC HEALTH SYSTEM – NORTHLAND IN BARRON, BARRON, WI, p. A702

MAYO CLINIC HEALTH SYSTEM – OAKRIDGE IN OSSEO, OSSEO, WI, p. A713

MAYO CLINIC HEALTH SYSTEM – RED CEDAR IN MENOMONIE, MENOMONIE, WI, p. A709

MAYO CLINIC HEALTH SYSTEM IN ALBERT LEA, ALBERT LEA, MN, p. A339

MAYO CLINIC HEALTH SYSTEM IN AUSTIN, AUSTIN, MN, p. A340

MAYO CLINIC HEALTH SYSTEM IN CANNON FALLS, CANNON FALLS, MN, p. A341

MAYO CLINIC HEALTH SYSTEM IN EAU CLAIRE, EAU CLAIRE, WI, p. A704

MAYO CLINIC HEALTH SYSTEM IN FAIRMONT, FAIRMONT, MN, p. A343

MAYO CLINIC HEALTH SYSTEM IN LAKE CITY, LAKE CITY, MN, p. A345

MAYO CLINIC HEALTH SYSTEM IN MANKATO, MANKATO, MN, p. A346

MAYO CLINIC HEALTH SYSTEM IN NEW PRAGUE, NEW PRAGUE, MN, p. A348

MAYO CLINIC HEALTH SYSTEM IN RED WING, RED WING, MN, p. A350

MAYO CLINIC HEALTH SYSTEM IN SAINT JAMES, SAINT JAMES, MN, p. A351

MAYO CLINIC HEALTH SYSTEM IN SPRINGFIELD, SPRINGFIELD, MN, p. A352

MAYO CLINIC HEALTH SYSTEM IN WASECA, WASECA, MN, p. A353

MAYO CLINIC HEALTH SYSTEM IN WAYCROSS, WAYCROSS, GA, p. A169

MAYO CLINIC HOSPITAL, PHOENIX, AZ, p. A36

MAYO CLINIC HOSPITAL – ROCHESTER, ROCHESTER, MN, p. A350

MAYO CLINIC JACKSONVILLE, JACKSONVILLE, FL, p. A131

MAYO REGIONAL HOSPITAL, DOVER-FOXCROFT, ME, p. A293

MCALESTER REGIONAL HEALTH CENTER, MCALESTER, OK, p. A513

MCALLEN HEART HOSPITAL, MCALLEN, TEXAS (see SOUTH TEXAS HEALTH SYSTEM), p. A615

MCALLEN MEDICAL CENTER, MCALLEN, TEXAS (see SOUTH TEXAS HEALTH SYSTEM), p. A615

MCBRIDE CLINIC ORTHOPEDIC HOSPITAL, OKLAHOMA CITY, OK, p. A515

MCCAMEY COUNTY HOSPITAL DISTRICT, MCCAMEY, TX, p. A637

MCCONE COUNTY HEALTH CENTER, CIRCLE, MT, p. A386

MCCREADY FOUNDATION, CRISFIELD, MD, p. A300

MCCULLOUGH–HYDE MEMORIAL HOSPITAL, OXFORD, OH, p. A500

MCCURTAIN MEMORIAL HOSPITAL, IDABEL, OK, p. A512

MCDONOUGH DISTRICT HOSPITAL, MACOMB, IL, p. A195

MCDOWELL ARH HOSPITAL, MCDOWELL, KY, p. A267

MCDOWELL HOSPITAL, MARION, NC, p. A468

MCFARLAND SPECIALTY HOSPITAL, LEBANON, TENNESSEE (see UNIVERSITY MEDICAL CENTER), p. A586

MCGEHEE–DESHA COUNTY HOSPITAL, MCGEHEE, AR, p. A50

MCKAY–DEE HOSPITAL CENTER, OGDEN, UT, p. A661

MCKEE MEDICAL CENTER, LOVELAND, CO, p. A109

MCKENZIE COUNTY HEALTHCARE SYSTEM, WATFORD CITY, ND, p. A480

MCKENZIE HEALTH SYSTEM, SANDUSKY, MI, p. A334

MCKENZIE REGIONAL HOSPITAL, MCKENZIE, TN, p. A588

MCKENZIE–WILLAMETTE MEDICAL CENTER, SPRINGFIELD, OR, p. A530

MCLANE CHILDREN'S HOSPITAL SCOTT & WHITE, TEMPLE, TEXAS (see SCOTT & WHITE MEMORIAL HOSPITAL), p. A652

MCLANE CHILDREN'S HOSPITAL SCOTT & WHITE, TEMPLE, TEXAS (see SCOTT & WHITE MEMORIAL HOSPITAL), p. A652

MCLAREN BAY REGION, BAY CITY, MI, p. A319

MCLAREN BAY SPECIAL CARE, BAY CITY, MI, p. A319

MCLAREN CENTRAL MICHIGAN, MOUNT PLEASANT, MI, p. A330

MCLAREN FLINT, FLINT, MI, p. A323

MCLAREN GREATER LANSING, LANSING, MI, p. A328

MCLAREN LAPEER REGION, LAPEER, MI, p. A329

MCLAREN MACOMB, MOUNT CLEMENS, MI, p. A330

MCLAREN NORTHERN MICHIGAN, PETOSKEY, MI, p. A332

MCLAREN OAKLAND, PONTIAC, MI, p. A332

MCLAREN ORTHOPEDIC HOSPITAL, LANSING, MICHIGAN (see MCLAREN GREATER LANSING), p. A328

MCLEAN HOSPITAL, BELMONT, MA, p. A305

MCLEOD LORIS SEACOAST HOSPITAL, LORIS, SC, p. A568

MCLEOD MEDICAL CENTER DILLON, DILLON, SC, p. A565

MCLEOD MEDICAL CENTER–DARLINGTON, DARLINGTON, SC, p. A565

MCLEOD REGIONAL MEDICAL CENTER, FLORENCE, SC, p. A566

MCLEOD SEACOAST, LITTLE RIVER, SOUTH CAROLINA (see MCLEOD LORIS SEACOAST HOSPITAL), p. A568

MCNAIRY REGIONAL HOSPITAL, SELMER, TN, p. A592

MCPHERSON HOSPITAL, MCPHERSON, KS, p. A250

MCREYNOLDS HALL (see OTSEGO MEMORIAL HOSPITAL), p. A324

MEADE DISTRICT HOSPITAL, MEADE, KS, p. A250

MEADOW WOOD BEHAVIORAL HEALTH SYSTEM, NEW CASTLE, DE, p. A119

MEADOWBROOK REHABILITATION HOSPITAL, GARDNER, KS, p. A244

MEADOWLANDS HOSPITAL MEDICAL CENTER, SECAUCUS, NJ, p. A422

MEADOWS PSYCHIATRIC CENTER, CENTRE HALL, PA, p. A535

MEADOWS REGIONAL MEDICAL CENTER, VIDALIA, GA, p. A168

MEADOWVIEW REGIONAL MEDICAL CENTER, MAYSVILLE, KY, p. A267

MEADVILLE MEDICAL CENTER, MEADVILLE, PA, p. A544

MEASE COUNTRYSIDE HOSPITAL, SAFETY HARBOR, FL, p. A144

MEASE DUNEDIN HOSPITAL, DUNEDIN, FL, p. A128

MEDICAL ARTS HOSPITAL, LAMESA, TX, p. A632

MEDICAL CENTER AT BOWLING GREEN, BOWLING GREEN, KY, p. A259

MEDICAL CENTER AT FRANKLIN, FRANKLIN, KY, p. A261

MEDICAL CENTER AT SCOTTSVILLE, SCOTTSVILLE, KY, p. A270

MEDICAL CENTER BARBOUR, EUFAULA, AL, p. A19

MEDICAL CENTER ENTERPRISE, ENTERPRISE, AL, p. A19

MEDICAL CENTER HEALTH SYSTEM, ODESSA, TX, p. A640

MEDICAL CENTER HOSPITAL CAMPUS, BURLINGTON, VERMONT (see FLETCHER ALLEN HEALTH CARE), p. A665

MEDICAL CENTER OF ARLINGTON, ARLINGTON, TX, p. A598

MEDICAL CENTER OF AURORA, AURORA, CO, p. A102

MEDICAL CENTER OF AURORA NORTH, AURORA, COLORADO (see MEDICAL CENTER OF AURORA), p. A102

MEDICAL CENTER OF LEWISVILLE, LEWISVILLE, TX, p. A633

MEDICAL CENTER OF MANCHESTER, MANCHESTER, TN, p. A587

MEDICAL CENTER OF MCKINNEY, MCKINNEY, TX, p. A637

MEDICAL CENTER OF PEACH COUNTY, NAVICENT HEALTH, FORT VALLEY, GA, p. A160

MEDICAL CENTER OF PLANO, PLANO, TX, p. A642

MEDICAL CENTER OF SOUTH ARKANSAS, EL DORADO, AR, p. A45

MEDICAL CENTER OF SOUTHEASTERN OKLAHOMA, DURANT, OK, p. A510

MEDICAL CENTER OF THE ROCKIES, LOVELAND, CO, p. A110

MEDICAL CENTER OF TRINITY, TRINITY, FL, p. A149

MEDICAL CENTER, NAVICENT HEALTH, MACON, GA, p. A163

MEDICAL CITY CHILDREN'S HOSPITAL, DALLAS, TEXAS (see MEDICAL CITY DALLAS HOSPITAL), p. A611

MEDICAL CITY DALLAS HOSPITAL, DALLAS, TX, p. A611

MEDICAL WEST, BESSEMER, AL, p. A16

MEDICINE LODGE MEMORIAL HOSPITAL, MEDICINE LODGE, KS, p. A250

MEDINA HOSPITAL, MEDINA, OH, p. A498

MEDINA MEMORIAL HOSPITAL, MEDINA, NY, p. A441

MEDINA REGIONAL HOSPITAL, HONDO, TX, p. A623

MEDSTAR FRANKLIN SQUARE MEDICAL CENTER, BALTIMORE, MD, p. A297

MEDSTAR GEORGETOWN UNIVERSITY HOSPITAL, WASHINGTON, DC, p. A121

MEDSTAR GOOD SAMARITAN HOSPITAL, BALTIMORE, MD, p. A297

MEDSTAR HARBOR HOSPITAL, BALTIMORE, MD, p. A297

MEDSTAR MONTGOMERY MEDICAL CENTER, OLNEY, MD, p. A302

MEDSTAR NATIONAL REHABILITATION HOSPITAL, WASHINGTON, DC, p. A121

MEDSTAR SOUTHERN MARYLAND HOSPITAL CENTER, CLINTON, MD, p. A300

MEDSTAR ST. MARY'S HOSPITAL, LEONARDTOWN, MD, p. A302

MEDSTAR UNION MEMORIAL HOSPITAL, BALTIMORE, MD, p. A297

MEDSTAR WASHINGTON HOSPITAL CENTER, WASHINGTON, DC, p. A121

MEE MEMORIAL HOSPITAL, KING CITY, CA, p. A68

MEEKER MEMORIAL HOSPITAL, LITCHFIELD, MN, p. A345

MELISSA MEMORIAL HOSPITAL, HOLYOKE, CO, p. A107

MELROSE–WAKEFIELD HOSPITAL, MELROSE, MASSACHUSETTS (see HALLMARK HEALTH SYSTEM), p. A312

MEMORIAL BEHAVIORAL HEALTH, GULFPORT, MISSISSIPPI (see MEMORIAL HOSPITAL AT GULFPORT), p. A358

MEMORIAL CAMPUS, WORCESTER, MASSACHUSETTS (see UMASS MEMORIAL MEDICAL CENTER), p. A317

MEMORIAL CHILDREN'S HOSPITAL, SAVANNAH, GEORGIA (see MEMORIAL HEALTH), p. A166

MEMORIAL CHILDREN'S HOSPITAL, SOUTH BEND, INDIANA (see MEMORIAL HOSPITAL OF SOUTH BEND), p. A222

MEMORIAL COMMUNITY HEALTH, AURORA, NE, p. A393

MEMORIAL COMMUNITY HOSPITAL AND HEALTH SYSTEM, BLAIR, NE, p. A394

MEMORIAL HEALTH, SAVANNAH, GA, p. A166

MEMORIAL HEALTH CARE SYSTEM, CHATTANOOGA, TN, p. A580

MEMORIAL HEALTH CARE SYSTEMS, SEWARD, NE, p. A402

MEMORIAL HEALTH SYSTEM, ABILENE, KS, p. A241

MEMORIAL HEALTHCARE, OWOSSO, MI, p. A331

MEMORIAL HERMANN – TEXAS MEDICAL CENTER, HOUSTON, TX, p. A625

MEMORIAL HERMANN KATY HOSPITAL, KATY, TX, p. A630

MEMORIAL HERMANN MEMORIAL CITY MEDICAL CENTER, HOUSTON, TX, p. A625

MEMORIAL HERMANN NORTHEAST, HUMBLE, TX, p. A628

MEMORIAL HERMANN NORTHWEST HOSPITAL, HOUSTON, TX, p. A625

MEMORIAL HERMANN REHABILITATION HOSPITAL – KATY, KATY, TX, p. A630

MEMORIAL HERMANN SOUTHEAST HOSPITAL, HOUSTON, TEXAS (see MEMORIAL HERMANN NORTHWEST HOSPITAL), p. A625

MEMORIAL HERMANN SOUTHWEST HOSPITAL, HOUSTON, TEXAS (see MEMORIAL HERMANN NORTHWEST HOSPITAL), p. A625

MEMORIAL HERMANN SUGAR LAND HOSPITAL, SUGAR LAND, TX, p. A651

MEMORIAL HERMANN SURGICAL HOSPITAL KINGWOOD, KINGWOOD, TX, p. A632

MEMORIAL HERMANN THE WOODLANDS HOSPITAL, THE WOODLANDS, TEXAS (see MEMORIAL HERMANN NORTHWEST HOSPITAL), p. A625

MEMORIAL HOSPITAL, CHARLESTON, WEST VIRGINIA (see CHARLESTON AREA MEDICAL CENTER), p. A694

MEMORIAL HOSPITAL, COLORADO SPRINGS, CO, p. A103

MEMORIAL HOSPITAL, BELLEVILLE, IL, p. A181

MEMORIAL HOSPITAL, CARTHAGE, IL, p. A182

MEMORIAL HOSPITAL, CHESTER, IL, p. A183

MEMORIAL HOSPITAL, NORTH CONWAY, NH, p. A412

MEMORIAL HOSPITAL, FREMONT, OH, p. A494

MEMORIAL HOSPITAL, STILWELL, OK, p. A519

MEMORIAL HOSPITAL, TOWANDA, PA, p. A556

MEMORIAL HOSPITAL, YORK, PA, p. A559

MEMORIAL HOSPITAL, GONZALES, TX, p. A621

MEMORIAL HOSPITAL, SEMINOLE, TX, p. A648

MEMORIAL HOSPITAL, MARTINSVILLE, VA, p. A674

MEMORIAL HOSPITAL AND HEALTH CARE CENTER, JASPER, IN, p. A215

MEMORIAL HOSPITAL AND MANOR, BAINBRIDGE, GA, p. A154

MEMORIAL HOSPITAL AND PHYSICIAN GROUP, FREDERICK, OK, p. A511

MEMORIAL HOSPITAL AT CRAIG, CRAIG, CO, p. A104

MEMORIAL HOSPITAL AT GULFPORT, GULFPORT, MS, p. A358

MEMORIAL HOSPITAL HIXSON, HIXSON, TENNESSEE (see MEMORIAL HEALTH CARE SYSTEM), p. A580

MEMORIAL HOSPITAL JACKSONVILLE, JACKSONVILLE, FL, p. A131

MEMORIAL HOSPITAL LOS BANOS, LOS BANOS, CA, p. A76

MEMORIAL HOSPITAL MIRAMAR, MIRAMAR, FL, p. A138

MEMORIAL HOSPITAL OF CARBON COUNTY, RAWLINS, WY, p. A722

MEMORIAL HOSPITAL OF CARBONDALE, CARBONDALE, IL, p. A182

MEMORIAL HOSPITAL OF CONVERSE COUNTY, DOUGLAS, WY, p. A721

MEMORIAL HOSPITAL OF GARDENA, GARDENA, CA, p. A65

MEMORIAL HOSPITAL OF LAFAYETTE COUNTY, DARLINGTON, WI, p. A703

MEMORIAL HOSPITAL OF RHODE ISLAND, PAWTUCKET, RI, p. A560

MEMORIAL HOSPITAL OF SALEM COUNTY, SALEM, NJ, p. A422

MEMORIAL HOSPITAL OF SOUTH BEND, SOUTH BEND, IN, p. A222

MEMORIAL HOSPITAL OF SWEETWATER COUNTY, ROCK SPRINGS, WY, p. A722

MEMORIAL HOSPITAL OF TAMPA, TAMPA, FL, p. A148

MEMORIAL HOSPITAL OF TEXAS COUNTY, GUYMON, OK, p. A511

MEMORIAL HOSPITAL OF UNION COUNTY, MARYSVILLE, OH, p. A497

MEMORIAL HOSPITAL PEMBROKE, PEMBROKE PINES, FL, p. A142

MEMORIAL HOSPITAL WEST, PEMBROKE PINES, FL, p. A142

MEMORIAL MEDICAL CENTER, MODESTO, CA, p. A78

MEMORIAL MEDICAL CENTER, MODESTO, CALIFORNIA (see MEMORIAL MEDICAL CENTER), p. A78

MEMORIAL MEDICAL CENTER, SPRINGFIELD, IL, p. A203

MEMORIAL MEDICAL CENTER, LAS CRUCES, NM, p. A429

MEMORIAL MEDICAL CENTER, PORT LAVACA, TX, p. A643

MEMORIAL MEDICAL CENTER – ASHLAND, ASHLAND, WI, p. A701

MEMORIAL MEDICAL CENTER – LEE CAMPUS, JOHNSTOWN, PENNSYLVANIA (see CONEMAUGH MEMORIAL MEDICAL CENTER), p. A541

MEMORIAL MEDICAL CENTER – LIVINGSTON, LIVINGSTON, TX, p. A633
MEMORIAL MEDICAL CENTER – LUFKIN, LUFKIN, TX, p. A635
MEMORIAL MEDICAL CENTER – NEILLSVILLE, NEILLSVILLE, WI, p. A712
MEMORIAL MEDICAL CENTER – SAN AUGUSTINE, SAN AUGUSTINE, TX, p. A648
MEMORIAL MISSION HOSPITAL, ASHEVILLE, NORTH CAROLINA (see MISSION HOSPITAL), p. A460
MEMORIAL NURSING HOME (see ASPIRUS MEDFORD HOSPITAL), p. A709
MEMORIAL REGIONAL HOSPITAL,, FL, p. A130
MEMORIAL REGIONAL HOSPITAL SOUTH,, FL, p. A131
MEMORIAL SLOAN–KETTERING CANCER CENTER, NEW YORK, NY, p. A445
MEMORIAL SPECIALTY HOSPITAL, LUFKIN, TX, p. A635
MEMPHIS MENTAL HEALTH INSTITUTE, MEMPHIS, TN, p. A589
MEMPHIS VETERANS AFFAIRS MEDICAL CENTER, MEMPHIS, TN, p. A589
MENA REGIONAL HEALTH SYSTEM, MENA, AR, p. A50
MENDOCINO COAST DISTRICT HOSPITAL, FORT BRAGG, CA, p. A63
MENDOTA COMMUNITY HOSPITAL, MENDOTA, IL, p. A196
MENDOTA MENTAL HEALTH INSTITUTE, MADISON, WI, p. A708
MENIFEE VALLEY MEDICAL CENTER, SUN CITY, CA, p. A96
MENLO PARK SURGICAL HOSPITAL, MENLO PARK, CA, p. A77
MENNINGER CLINIC, HOUSTON, TX, p. A626
MENNONITE GENERAL HOSPITAL, AIBONITO, PR, p. A724
MENORAH MEDICAL CENTER, OVERLAND PARK, KS, p. A252
MENTAL HEALTH CENTER, ALBUQUERQUE, NEW MEXICO (see UNIVERSITY OF NEW MEXICO HOSPITALS), p. A427
MENTAL HEALTH INSTITUTE, CHEROKEE, IA, p. A227
MENTAL HEALTH INSTITUTE, CLARINDA, IA, p. A227
MENTAL HEALTH INSTITUTE, INDEPENDENCE, IA, p. A232
MENTAL HEALTH INSTITUTE, MOUNT PLEASANT, IA, p. A235
MENTAL HEALTH SERVICES FOR CLARK AND MADISON COUNTIES, SPRINGFIELD, OH, p. A502
MERCER HEALTH, COLDWATER, OH, p. A489
MERCY ALLEN HOSPITAL, OBERLIN, OH, p. A500
MERCY CHILDREN'S HOSPITAL, TOLEDO, OHIO (see MERCY ST. VINCENT MEDICAL CENTER), p. A503
MERCY CHILDREN'S HOSPITAL SPRINGFIELD, SPRINGFIELD, MISSOURI (see MERCY HOSPITAL SPRINGFIELD), p. A383
MERCY CHILDREN'S HOSPITAL ST. LOUIS, SAINT LOUIS, MISSOURI (see MERCY HOSPITAL ST. LOUIS), p. A380
MERCY FITZGERALD HOSPITAL, DARBY, PENNSYLVANIA (see MERCY FITZGERALD HOSPITAL), p. A537
MERCY FITZGERALD HOSPITAL, DARBY, PA, p. A537
MERCY FRANKLIN CENTER, DES MOINES, IOWA (see MERCY MEDICAL CENTER–DES MOINES), p. A229
MERCY GENERAL HOSPITAL, SACRAMENTO, CA, p. A87
MERCY GILBERT MEDICAL CENTER, GILBERT, AZ, p. A33
MERCY HARVARD HOSPITAL, HARVARD, IL, p. A191
MERCY HEALTH – ANDERSON HOSPITAL, CINCINNATI, OH, p. A487
MERCY HEALTH – CLERMONT HOSPITAL, BATAVIA, OH, p. A483
MERCY HEALTH – FAIRFIELD HOSPITAL, FAIRFIELD, OH, p. A493
MERCY HEALTH – WEST HOSPITAL, CINCINNATI, OH, p. A487
MERCY HEALTH LOVE COUNTY, MARIETTA, OK, p. A513
MERCY HEALTH PARTNERS, LAKESHORE CAMPUS, SHELBY, MI, p. A334
MERCY HEALTH SAINT MARY'S, GRAND RAPIDS, MI, p. A325
MERCY HEALTH, GENERAL CAMPUS, MUSKEGON, MICHIGAN (see MERCY HEALTH, MERCY CAMPUS), p. A331
MERCY HEALTH, HACKLEY CAMPUS, MUSKEGON, MI, p. A331
MERCY HEALTH, MERCY CAMPUS, MUSKEGON, MI, p. A331
MERCY HOSPITAL, MOUNDRIDGE, KS, p. A250
MERCY HOSPITAL, COON RAPIDS, MN, p. A342
MERCY HOSPITAL, MOOSE LAKE, MN, p. A348
MERCY HOSPITAL, BUFFALO, NY, p. A434
MERCY HOSPITAL, DEVILS LAKE, ND, p. A477
MERCY HOSPITAL, VALLEY CITY, ND, p. A480
MERCY HOSPITAL – A CAMPUS OF PLANTATION GENERAL HOSPITAL, MIAMI, FLORIDA (see PLANTATION GENERAL HOSPITAL), p. A143
MERCY HOSPITAL ADA, ADA, OK, p. A507
MERCY HOSPITAL AND MEDICAL CENTER, CHICAGO, IL, p. A185
MERCY HOSPITAL AND TRAUMA CENTER, JANESVILLE, WI, p. A707
MERCY HOSPITAL ARDMORE, ARDMORE, OK, p. A507
MERCY HOSPITAL AURORA, AURORA, MO, p. A367
MERCY HOSPITAL BERRYVILLE, BERRYVILLE, AR, p. A43
MERCY HOSPITAL CADILLAC, CADILLAC, MI, p. A320
MERCY HOSPITAL CARTHAGE, CARTHAGE, MO, p. A369
MERCY HOSPITAL CASSVILLE, CASSVILLE, MO, p. A369
MERCY HOSPITAL EL RENO, EL RENO, OK, p. A510
MERCY HOSPITAL FORT SCOTT, FORT SCOTT, KS, p. A244

MERCY HOSPITAL FORT SMITH, FORT SMITH, AR, p. A46
MERCY HOSPITAL GRAYLING, GRAYLING, MI, p. A325
MERCY HOSPITAL HEALDTON, HEALDTON, OK, p. A511
MERCY HOSPITAL HOT SPRINGS, HOT SPRINGS NATIONAL PARK, AR, p. A48
MERCY HOSPITAL INDEPENDENCE, INDEPENDENCE, KS, p. A246
MERCY HOSPITAL JEFFERSON, CRYSTAL CITY, MO, p. A370
MERCY HOSPITAL JOPLIN, JOPLIN, MO, p. A373
MERCY HOSPITAL KINGFISHER, KINGFISHER, OK, p. A512
MERCY HOSPITAL LEBANON, LEBANON, MO, p. A375
MERCY HOSPITAL LOGAN COUNTY, GUTHRIE, OK, p. A511
MERCY HOSPITAL OF DEFIANCE, DEFIANCE, OH, p. A492
MERCY HOSPITAL OF FOLSOM, FOLSOM, CA, p. A63
MERCY HOSPITAL OF FRANCISCAN SISTERS, OELWEIN, IA, p. A235
MERCY HOSPITAL OF PORTLAND, PORTLAND, ME, p. A294
MERCY HOSPITAL OKLAHOMA CITY, OKLAHOMA CITY, OK, p. A515
MERCY HOSPITAL OZARK, OZARK, AR, p. A51
MERCY HOSPITAL PARIS, PARIS, AR, p. A51
MERCY HOSPITAL ROGERS, ROGERS, AR, p. A52
MERCY HOSPITAL SPRINGFIELD, SPRINGFIELD, MO, p. A383
MERCY HOSPITAL ST. LOUIS, SAINT LOUIS, MO, p. A380
MERCY HOSPITAL TISHOMINGO, TISHOMINGO, OK, p. A520
MERCY HOSPITAL WALDRON, WALDRON, AR, p. A53
MERCY HOSPITAL WASHINGTON, WASHINGTON, MO, p. A384
MERCY HOSPITAL WATONGA, WATONGA, OK, p. A522
MERCY HOSPITALS OF BAKERSFIELD, BAKERSFIELD, CA, p. A57
MERCY IOWA CITY, IOWA CITY, IA, p. A232
MERCY MAUDE NORTON HOSPITAL, COLUMBUS, KS, p. A242
MERCY MEDICAL CENTER, BALTIMORE, MD, p. A297
MERCY MEDICAL CENTER, SPRINGFIELD, MA, p. A315
MERCY MEDICAL CENTER, ROCKVILLE CENTRE, NY, p. A453
MERCY MEDICAL CENTER, WILLISTON, ND, p. A480
MERCY MEDICAL CENTER, CANTON, OH, p. A485
MERCY MEDICAL CENTER, ROSEBURG, OR, p. A529
MERCY MEDICAL CENTER, OSHKOSH, WI, p. A713
MERCY MEDICAL CENTER – WEST LAKES, WEST DES MOINES, IA, p. A239
MERCY MEDICAL CENTER MERCED, MERCED, CA, p. A77
MERCY MEDICAL CENTER MERCED–DOMINICAN CAMPUS, MERCED, CALIFORNIA (see MERCY MEDICAL CENTER MERCED), p. A77
MERCY MEDICAL CENTER MOUNT SHASTA, MOUNT SHASTA, CA, p. A79
MERCY MEDICAL CENTER REDDING, REDDING, CA, p. A85
MERCY MEDICAL CENTER–CEDAR RAPIDS, CEDAR RAPIDS, IA, p. A226
MERCY MEDICAL CENTER–CENTERVILLE, CENTERVILLE, IA, p. A227
MERCY MEDICAL CENTER–CLINTON, CLINTON, IA, p. A227
MERCY MEDICAL CENTER–DES MOINES, DES MOINES, IA, p. A229
MERCY MEDICAL CENTER–DUBUQUE, DUBUQUE, IA, p. A230
MERCY MEDICAL CENTER–DYERSVILLE, DYERSVILLE, IA, p. A230
MERCY MEDICAL CENTER–NEW HAMPTON, NEW HAMPTON, IA, p. A235
MERCY MEDICAL CENTER–NORTH IOWA, MASON CITY, IA, p. A234
MERCY MEDICAL CENTER–SIOUX CITY, SIOUX CITY, IA, p. A238
MERCY MEMORIAL HOSPITAL, URBANA, OH, p. A504
MERCY MEMORIAL HOSPITAL SYSTEM, MONROE, MI, p. A330
MERCY ORTHOPEDIC HOSPITAL SPRINGFIELD, OZARK, MISSOURI (see MERCY HOSPITAL SPRINGFIELD), p. A383
MERCY PHILADELPHIA HOSPITAL, PHILADELPHIA, PENNSYLVANIA (see MERCY FITZGERALD HOSPITAL), p. A537
MERCY REGIONAL HEALTH CENTER,, KS, p. A249
MERCY REGIONAL MEDICAL CENTER, DURANGO, CO, p. A105
MERCY REGIONAL MEDICAL CENTER, VILLE PLATTE, LA, p. A290
MERCY REGIONAL MEDICAL CENTER, LORAIN, OH, p. A497
MERCY REHABILITATION HOSPITAL, CHESTERFIELD, MO, p. A369
MERCY REHABILITATION HOSPITAL OKLAHOMA CITY, OKLAHOMA CITY, OK, p. A515
MERCY REHABILITION HOSPITAL SPRINGFIELD, SPRINGFIELD, MO, p. A383
MERCY SAN JUAN MEDICAL CENTER, CARMICHAEL, CA, p. A59
MERCY SERVICES FOR AGING, CLINTON, IOWA (see MERCY MEDICAL CENTER–CLINTON), p. A227
MERCY SOUTHWEST HOSPITAL, BAKERSFIELD, CALIFORNIA (see MERCY HOSPITALS OF BAKERSFIELD), p. A57
MERCY ST. ANNE HOSPITAL, TOLEDO, OH, p. A503
MERCY ST. CHARLES HOSPITAL, OREGON, OH, p. A500
MERCY ST. FRANCIS HOSPITAL, MOUNTAIN VIEW, MO, p. A377
MERCY ST. VINCENT MEDICAL CENTER, TOLEDO, OH, p. A503

MERCY SUBURBAN HOSPITAL, NORRISTOWN, PA, p. A546
MERCY TIFFIN HOSPITAL, TIFFIN, OH, p. A503
MERCY WALWORTH HOSPITAL AND MEDICAL CENTER, LAKE GENEVA, WI, p. A707
MERCY WILLARD HOSPITAL, WILLARD, OH, p. A505
MERIDIAN HEALTH SERVICES, MUNCIE, IN, p. A219
MERITER HOSPITAL, MADISON, WI, p. A708
MERITUS MEDICAL CENTER, HAGERSTOWN, MD, p. A301
MERRIMACK VALLEY HOSPITAL, HAVERHILL, MA, p. A310
MESA HILLS SPECIALTY HOSPITAL, EL PASO, TX, p. A616
MESA SPRINGS, FORT WORTH, TX, p. A618
MESA VIEW REGIONAL HOSPITAL, MESQUITE, NV, p. A407
MESCALERO PUBLIC HEALTH SERVICE INDIAN HOSPITAL, MESCALERO, NM, p. A429
MESILLA VALLEY HOSPITAL, LAS CRUCES, NM, p. A429
MESQUITE REHABILITATION INSTITUTE, MESQUITE, TX, p. A637
MESQUITE SPECIALTY HOSPITAL, MESQUITE, TX, p. A637
METHODIST AMBULATORY SURGERY HOSPITAL – NORTHWEST, SAN ANTONIO, TX, p. A646
METHODIST BEHAVIORAL HOSPITAL OF ARKANSAS, MAUMELLE, AR, p. A50
METHODIST CHARLTON MEDICAL CENTER, DALLAS, TX, p. A611
METHODIST CHILDREN'S HOSPITAL, SAN ANTONIO, TEXAS (see METHODIST HOSPITAL), p. A646
METHODIST DALLAS MEDICAL CENTER, DALLAS, TX, p. A611
METHODIST EXTENDED CARE HOSPITAL, MEMPHIS, TN, p. A589
METHODIST HEALTHCARE MEMPHIS HOSPITALS, MEMPHIS, TN, p. A589
METHODIST HEALTHCARE–FAYETTE HOSPITAL, SOMERVILLE, TN, p. A593
METHODIST HEALTHCARE–NORTH HOSPITAL, MEMPHIS, TENNESSEE (see METHODIST HEALTHCARE MEMPHIS HOSPITALS), p. A589
METHODIST HEALTHCARE–SOUTH HOSPITAL, MEMPHIS, TENNESSEE (see METHODIST HEALTHCARE MEMPHIS HOSPITALS), p. A589
METHODIST HOSPITAL, HENDERSON, KY, p. A262
METHODIST HOSPITAL, SAN ANTONIO, TX, p. A646
METHODIST HOSPITAL, PHILADELPHIA, PENNSYLVANIA (see THOMAS JEFFERSON UNIVERSITY HOSPITAL), p. A550
METHODIST HOSPITAL FOR SURGERY, ADDISON, TX, p. A595
METHODIST HOSPITAL OF CHICAGO, CHICAGO, IL, p. A185
METHODIST HOSPITAL OF SACRAMENTO, SACRAMENTO, CA, p. A87
METHODIST HOSPITAL OF SOUTHERN CALIFORNIA, ARCADIA, CA, p. A56
METHODIST HOSPITAL UNION COUNTY, MORGANFIELD, KY, p. A268
METHODIST HOSPITALS, GARY, IN, p. A212
METHODIST JENNIE EDMUNDSON HOSPITAL, COUNCIL BLUFFS, IA, p. A228
METHODIST LE BONHEUR GERMANTOWN HOSPITAL, GERMANTOWN, TENNESSEE (see METHODIST HEALTHCARE MEMPHIS HOSPITALS), p. A589
METHODIST MANSFIELD MEDICAL CENTER, MANSFIELD, TX, p. A636
METHODIST MCKINNEY HOSPITAL, MCKINNEY, TX, p. A637
METHODIST MEDICAL CENTER OF OAK RIDGE, OAK RIDGE, TN, p. A591
METHODIST OLIVE BRANCH HOSPITAL, OLIVE BRANCH, MS, p. A363
METHODIST REHABILITATION CENTER, JACKSON, MS, p. A360
METHODIST REHABILITATION HOSPITAL, DALLAS, TX, p. A611
METHODIST RICHARDSON MEDICAL CENTER, RICHARDSON, TX, p. A644
METHODIST SPECIALTY AND TRANSPLANT HOSPITAL, SAN ANTONIO, TEXAS (see METHODIST HOSPITAL), p. A646
METHODIST STONE OAK HOSPITAL, SAN ANTONIO, TX, p. A647
METHODIST TEXSAN HOSPITAL, SAN ANTONIO, TEXAS (see METHODIST HOSPITAL), p. A646
METHODIST WOMEN'S HOSPITAL, ELKHORN, NEBRASKA (see NEBRASKA METHODIST HOSPITAL), p. A400
METRO HEALTH HOSPITAL, WYOMING, MI, p. A337
METROHEALTH MEDICAL CENTER, CLEVELAND, OH, p. A489
METROPLEX ADVENTIST HOSPITAL, KILLEEN, TX, p. A631
METROPOLITAN GENERAL CARE UNIT, METROPOLITAN DRUG DETOXIFICATION AND METROPOLITAN PSYCHIATRIC UNIT (see METROPOLITAN HOSPITAL CENTER), p. A446
METROPOLITAN HOSPITAL CENTER, NEW YORK, NY, p. A446
METROPOLITAN METHODIST HOSPITAL, SAN ANTONIO, TEXAS (see METHODIST HOSPITAL), p. A646
METROPOLITAN ST. LOUIS PSYCHIATRIC CENTER, SAINT LOUIS, MO, p. A381
METROPOLITAN STATE HOSPITAL, NORWALK, CA, p. A80
METROPOLITANO DE LA MONTANA, UTUADO, PR, p. A729
METROSOUTH MEDICAL CENTER, BLUE ISLAND, IL, p. A182
METROWEST MEDICAL CENTER, FRAMINGHAM, MA, p. A310

N

O

P

PARK RIDGE HEALTH, HENDERSONVILLE, NC, p. A466
PARK ROYAL HOSPITAL, FORT MYERS, FL, p. A129
PARKCARE PAVILION, YONKERS, NEW YORK (see ST. JOHN'S RIVERSIDE HOSPITAL), p. A458
PARKER ADVENTIST HOSPITAL, PARKER, CO, p. A110
PARKLAND HEALTH & HOSPITAL SYSTEM, DALLAS, TX, p. A611
PARKLAND HEALTH CENTER, FARMINGTON, MO, p. A371
PARKLAND HEALTH CENTER-BONNE TERRE, BONNE TERRE, MO, p. A367
PARKLAND MEDICAL CENTER, DERRY, NH, p. A409
PARKRIDGE EAST HOSPITAL, CHATTANOOGA, TENNESSEE (see PARKRIDGE MEDICAL CENTER), p. A580
PARKRIDGE MEDICAL CENTER, CHATTANOOGA, TN, p. A580
PARKRIDGE VALLEY CHILD AND ADOLESCENT CAMPUS, CHATTANOOGA, TENNESSEE (see PARKRIDGE MEDICAL CENTER), p. A580
PARKRIDGE WEST HOSPITAL, JASPER, TN, p. A584
PARKSIDE HOSPITAL, TULSA, OK, p. A520
PARKVIEW ORTHO HOSPITAL, FORT WAYNE, IN, p. A211
PARKVIEW ADVENTIST MEDICAL CENTER, BRUNSWICK, ME, p. A292
PARKVIEW COMMUNITY HOSPITAL MEDICAL CENTER, RIVERSIDE, CA, p. A86
PARKVIEW HOSPITAL, WHEELER, TX, p. A657
PARKVIEW HOSPITAL RANDALLIA, FORT WAYNE, INDIANA (see PARKVIEW REGIONAL MEDICAL CENTER), p. A211
PARKVIEW HUNTINGTON HOSPITAL, HUNTINGTON, IN, p. A213
PARKVIEW LAGRANGE HOSPITAL, LAGRANGE, IN, p. A217
PARKVIEW MEDICAL CENTER, PUEBLO, CO, p. A110
PARKVIEW NOBLE HOSPITAL, KENDALLVILLE, IN, p. A216
PARKVIEW REGIONAL HOSPITAL, MEXIA, TX, p. A638
PARKVIEW REGIONAL MEDICAL CENTER, FORT WAYNE, IN, p. A211
PARKVIEW WHITLEY HOSPITAL, COLUMBIA CITY, IN, p. A208
PARKWAY REGIONAL HOSPITAL, FULTON, KY, p. A261
PARKWAY SURGICAL & CARDIOVASCULAR HOSPITAL, FORT WORTH, TEXAS (see WISE REGIONAL HEALTH SYSTEM), p. A612
PARKWEST MEDICAL CENTER, KNOXVILLE, TN, p. A586
PARKWOOD BEHAVIORAL HEALTH SYSTEM, OLIVE BRANCH, MS, p. A363
PARMER MEDICAL CENTER, FRIONA, TX, p. A620
PARRISH MEDICAL CENTER, TITUSVILLE, FL, p. A149
PARSONS STATE HOSPITAL AND TRAINING CENTER, PARSONS, KS, p. A252
PASSAVANT AREA HOSPITAL, JACKSONVILLE, IL, p. A193
PATEWOOD MEMORIAL HOSPITAL, GREENVILLE, SC, p. A566
PATHWAY REHABILITATION HOSPITAL, BOSSIER CITY, LA, p. A274
PATHWAYS OF TENNESSEE, JACKSON, TN, p. A584
PATHWAYS TREATMENT CENTER, KALISPELL, MONTANA (see KALISPELL REGIONAL MEDICAL CENTER), p. A389
PATIENT'S CHOICE MEDICAL CENTER OF HUMPHREYS COUNTY, BELZONI, MS, p. A355
PATIENTS CHOICE MEDICAL CENTER OF SMITH COUNTY, RALEIGH, MS, p. A365
PATIENTS' HOSPITAL OF REDDING, REDDING, CA, p. A85
PATRICK B. HARRIS PSYCHIATRIC HOSPITAL, ANDERSON, SC, p. A562
PATTON STATE HOSPITAL, PATTON, CA, p. A83
PAUL B. HALL REGIONAL MEDICAL CENTER, PAINTSVILLE, KY, p. A269
PAUL OLIVER MEMORIAL HOSPITAL, FRANKFORT, MI, p. A324
PAULDING COUNTY HOSPITAL, PAULDING, OH, p. A500
PAULS VALLEY GENERAL HOSPITAL, PAULS VALLEY, OK, p. A517
PAWHUSKA HOSPITAL, PAWHUSKA, OK, p. A517
PAWNEE COUNTY MEMORIAL HOSPITAL AND RURAL HEALTH CLINIC, PAWNEE CITY, NE, p. A401
PAWNEE VALLEY COMMUNITY HOSPITAL, LARNED, KS, p. A248
PAYNE WHITNEY PSYCHIATRIC CLINIC, NEW YORK, NEW YORK (see NEW YORK-PRESBYTERIAN HOSPITAL), p. A447
PAYSON REGIONAL MEDICAL CENTER, PAYSON, AZ, p. A35
PEACEHEALTH COTTAGE GROVE COMMUNITY MEDICAL CENTER, COTTAGE GROVE, OR, p. A524
PEACEHEALTH KETCHIKAN MEDICAL CENTER, KETCHIKAN, AK, p. A29
PEACEHEALTH PEACE HARBOR MEDICAL CENTER, FLORENCE, OR, p. A524
PEACEHEALTH PEACE ISLAND MEDICAL CENTER, FRIDAY HARBOR, WA, p. A684
PEACEHEALTH SACRED HEART MEDICAL CENTER AT RIVERBEND, SPRINGFIELD, OR, p. A530
PEACEHEALTH SACRED HEART MEDICAL CENTER, UNIVERSITY DISTRICT, EUGENE, OR, p. A524
PEACEHEALTH SOUTHWEST MEDICAL CENTER, VANCOUVER, WA, p. A692
PEACEHEALTH ST. JOHN MEDICAL CENTER, LONGVIEW, WA, p. A685

PEACEHEALTH ST. JOSEPH MEDICAL CENTER, BELLINGHAM, WA. p. A681
PEACEHEALTH UNITED GENERAL HOSPITAL, SEDRO-WOOLLEY, WA, p. A689
PEACHFORD BEHAVIORAL HEALTH SYSTEM, ATLANTA, GA, p. A153
PEAK BEHAVIORAL HEALTH SERVICES, SANTA TERESA, NM, p. A430
PEAK VIEW BEHAVIORAL HEALTH, COLORADO SPRINGS, CO, p. A103
PEARL RIVER COUNTY HOSPITAL, POPLARVILLE, MS, p. A364
PECONIC BAY MEDICAL CENTER, RIVERHEAD, NY, p. A452
PECOS COUNTY MEMORIAL HOSPITAL, FORT STOCKTON, TX, p. A618
PECOS VALLEY LODGE, ROSWELL, NEW MEXICO (see NEW MEXICO REHABILITATION CENTER), p. A430
PEKIN HOSPITAL, PEKIN, IL, p. A199
PELLA REGIONAL HEALTH CENTER, PELLA, IA, p. A236
PEMBINA COUNTY MEMORIAL HOSPITAL AND WEDGEWOOD MANOR, CAVALIER, ND, p. A476
PEMBROKE HOSPITAL, PEMBROKE, MA, p. A313
PEMISCOT MEMORIAL HEALTH SYSTEM, HAYTI, MO, p. A372
PEN BAY MEDICAL CENTER, ROCKPORT, ME, p. A295
PENDER COMMUNITY HOSPITAL, PENDER, NE, p. A401
PENDER MEMORIAL HOSPITAL, BURGAW, NC, p. A460
PENINSULA HOSPITAL, BURLINGAME, CALIFORNIA (see MILLS-PENINSULA HEALTH SERVICES), p. A58
PENINSULA HOSPITAL, LOUISVILLE, TN, p. A587
PENINSULA REGIONAL MEDICAL CENTER, SALISBURY, MD, p. A303
PENN HIGHLANDS BROOKVILLE, BROOKVILLE, PA, p. A534
PENN PRESBYTERIAN MEDICAL CENTER, PHILADELPHIA, PA, p. A549
PENN STATE CHILDREN'S HOSPITAL, HERSHEY, PENNSYLVANIA (see PENN STATE MILTON S. HERSHEY MEDICAL CENTER), p. A540
PENN STATE HERSHEY REHABILITATION HOSPITAL, HUMMELSTOWN, PA, p. A541
PENN STATE MILTON S. HERSHEY MEDICAL CENTER, HERSHEY, PA, p. A540
PENNOCK HOSPITAL, HASTINGS, MI, p. A326
PENNSYLVANIA HOSPITAL, PHILADELPHIA, PA, p. A549
PENNSYLVANIA PSYCHIATRIC INSTITUTE, HARRISBURG, PA, p. A540
PENOBSCOT VALLEY HOSPITAL, LINCOLN, ME, p. A294
PENROSE HOSPITAL, COLORADO SPRINGS, COLORADO (see PENROSE-ST. FRANCIS HEALTH SERVICES), p. A104
PENROSE-ST. FRANCIS HEALTH SERVICES, COLORADO SPRINGS, CO, p. A104
PERHAM HEALTH, PERHAM, MN, p. A349
PERKINS COUNTY HEALTH SERVICES, GRANT, NE, p. A396
PERMIAN REGIONAL MEDICAL CENTER, ANDREWS, TX, p. A597
PERRY COMMUNITY HOSPITAL, LINDEN, TN, p. A587
PERRY COUNTY GENERAL HOSPITAL, RICHTON, MS, p. A365
PERRY COUNTY MEMORIAL HOSPITAL, TELL CITY, IN, p. A222
PERRY COUNTY MEMORIAL HOSPITAL, PERRYVILLE, MO, p. A378
PERRY HOSPITAL, PERRY, GA, p. A164
PERRY MEMORIAL HOSPITAL, PRINCETON, IL, p. A200
PERRY MEMORIAL HOSPITAL, PERRY, OK, p. A517
PERSHING GENERAL HOSPITAL, LOVELOCK, NV, p. A407
PERSON MEMORIAL HOSPITAL, ROXBORO, NC, p. A472
PERTH AMBOY DIVISION, PERTH AMBOY, NEW JERSEY (see RARITAN BAY MEDICAL CENTER), p. A421
PETALUMA VALLEY HOSPITAL, PETALUMA, CA, p. A83
PETERSBURG MEDICAL CENTER, PETERSBURG, AK, p. A30
PETERSON REGIONAL MEDICAL CENTER, KERRVILLE, TX, p. A631
PETERSON REHABILITATION HOSPITAL, WHEELING, WV, p. A700
PEYTON MANNING CHILDREN'S HOSPITAL, INDIANAPOLIS, INDIANA (see ST. VINCENT INDIANAPOLIS HOSPITAL), p. A215
PEYTON MANNING CHILDREN'S HOSPITAL AT ST. VINCENT, INDIANAPOLIS, INDIANA (see ST. VINCENT INDIANAPOLIS HOSPITAL), p. A215
PHELPS COUNTY REGIONAL MEDICAL CENTER, ROLLA, MO, p. A379
PHELPS MEMORIAL HEALTH CENTER, HOLDREGE, NE, p. A396
PHELPS MEMORIAL HOSPITAL CENTER, SLEEPY HOLLOW, NY, p. A454
PHILADELPHIA VETERANS AFFAIRS MEDICAL CENTER, PHILADELPHIA, PA, p. A549
PHILHAVEN, MOUNT GRETNA, PA, p. A545
PHILIP HEALTH SERVICES, PHILIP, SD, p. A575
PHILLIPS COUNTY HOSPITAL, PHILLIPSBURG, KS, p. A252
PHILLIPS COUNTY HOSPITAL, MALTA, MT, p. A389
PHILLIPS EYE INSTITUTE, MINNEAPOLIS, MN. p. A347
PHOEBE NORTH, ALBANY, GEORGIA (see PHOEBE PUTNEY MEMORIAL HOSPITAL), p. A151

PHOEBE PUTNEY MEMORIAL HOSPITAL, ALBANY, GA, p. A151
PHOEBE SUMTER MEDICAL CENTER, AMERICUS, GA, p. A151
PHOEBE WORTH MEDICAL CENTER, SYLVESTER, GA, p. A167
PHOENIX BAPTIST HOSPITAL, PHOENIX, AZ, p. A36
PHOENIX BEHAVIORAL HOSPITAL, RAYNE, LA, p. A287
PHOENIX CHILDREN'S HOSPITAL, PHOENIX, AZ, p. A36
PHOENIX VETERANS AFFAIRS HEALTH CARE SYSTEM, PHOENIX, AZ, p. A36
PHOENIXVILLE HOSPITAL, PHOENIXVILLE, PA, p. A550
PHS SANTA FE INDIAN HOSPITAL, SANTA FE, NM, p. A430
PHYLLIS AND DAVID KOMANSKY CENTER FOR CHILDREN'S HEALTH, NEW YORK, NEW YORK (see NEW YORK-PRESBYTERIAN HOSPITAL), p. A447
PHYSICIAN'S CHOICE HOSPITAL - FREMONT, FREMONT, OH, p. A494
PHYSICIANS BEHAVIORAL HOSPITAL, SHREVEPORT, LA, p. A288
PHYSICIANS CARE SURGICAL HOSPITAL, ROYERSFORD, PA, p. A554
PHYSICIANS MEDICAL CENTER, HOUMA, LA, p. A279
PHYSICIANS REGIONAL, NAPLES, FLORIDA (see PHYSICIANS REGIONAL - PINE RIDGE), p. A139
PHYSICIANS REGIONAL - PINE RIDGE, NAPLES, FL, p. A139
PHYSICIANS SURGICAL HOSPITAL - PANHANDLE CAMPUS, AMARILLO, TX, p. A596
PHYSICIANS SURGICAL HOSPITAL - QUAIL CREEK, AMARILLO, TX, p. A596
PHYSICIANS' HOSPITAL IN ANADARKO, ANADARKO, OK, p. A507
PHYSICIANS' MEDICAL CENTER, NEW ALBANY, IN, p. A220
PHYSICIANS' SPECIALTY HOSPITAL, FAYETTEVILLE, AR, p. A45
PICKENS COUNTY MEDICAL CENTER, CARROLLTON, AL, p. A18
PIEDMONT FAYETTE HOSPITAL, FAYETTEVILLE, GA, p. A159
PIEDMONT GERIATRIC HOSPITAL, BURKEVILLE, VA, p. A669
PIEDMONT HOSPITAL, ATLANTA, GA, p. A153
PIEDMONT MEDICAL CENTER, ROCK HILL, SC, p. A569
PIEDMONT MOUNTAINSIDE HOSPITAL, JASPER, GA, p. A161
PIEDMONT NEWNAN HOSPITAL, NEWNAN, GA, p. A164
PIGGOTT COMMUNITY HOSPITAL, PIGGOTT, AR, p. A51
PIKE COUNTY MEMORIAL HOSPITAL, LOUISIANA, MO, p. A376
PIKES PEAK REGIONAL HOSPITAL, WOODLAND PARK, CO, p. A112
PIKEVILLE MEDICAL CENTER, PIKEVILLE, KY, p. A269
PILGRIM PSYCHIATRIC CENTER, BRENTWOOD, NY, p. A434
PINCKNEYVILLE COMMUNITY HOSPITAL, PINCKNEYVILLE, IL, p. A200
PINE CREEK MEDICAL CENTER, DALLAS, TX, p. A611
PINE REST CHRISTIAN MENTAL HEALTH SERVICES, GRAND RAPIDS, MI, p. A325
PINECREST REHABILITATION HOSPITAL, DELRAY BEACH, FLORIDA (see DELRAY MEDICAL CENTER), p. A127
PINEVILLE COMMUNITY HOSPITAL ASSOCIATION, PINEVILLE, KY, p. A269
PINNACLE HEALTH SYSTEM, HARRISBURG, PA, p. A540
PINNACLE HOSPITAL, CROWN POINT, IN, p. A209
PINNACLE POINTE HOSPITAL, LITTLE ROCK, AR, p. A49
PINNACLE SPECIALTY HOSPITAL, TULSA, OK, p. A520
PIONEER COMMUNITY HOSPITAL OF ABERDEEN, ABERDEEN, MS, p. A355
PIONEER COMMUNITY HOSPITAL OF EARLY, BLAKELY, GA, p. A154
PIONEER COMMUNITY HOSPITAL OF NEWTON, NEWTON, MS, p. A363
PIONEER COMMUNITY HOSPITAL OF PATRICK COUNTY, STUART, VA, p. A679
PIONEER COMMUNITY HOSPITAL OF STOKES, DANBURY, NC, p. A463
PIONEER MEDICAL CENTER, BIG TIMBER, MT, p. A385
PIONEER MEMORIAL HOSPITAL, HEPPNER, OR, p. A525
PIONEER MEMORIAL HOSPITAL, PRINEVILLE, OR, p. A529
PIONEER MEMORIAL HOSPITAL AND HEALTH SERVICES, VIBORG, SD, p. A577
PIONEER VALLEY HOSPITAL, WEST VALLEY CITY, UT, p. A664
PIONEERS MEDICAL CENTER, MEEKER, CO, p. A110
PIONEERS MEMORIAL HEALTHCARE DISTRICT, BRAWLEY, CA, p. A58
PIPESTONE COUNTY MEDICAL CENTER AVERA, PIPESTONE, MN, p. A349
PLACENTIA-LINDA HOSPITAL, PLACENTIA, CA, p. A83
PLAINS MEMORIAL HOSPITAL, DIMMITT, TX, p. A614
PLAINS REGIONAL MEDICAL CENTER, CLOVIS, NM, p. A427
PLAINVIEW HOSPITAL, PLAINVIEW, NY, p. A451
PLANO SPECIALTY HOSPITAL, PLANO, TX, p. A642
PLANTATION GENERAL HOSPITAL, PLANTATION, FL, p. A143
PLATEAU MEDICAL CENTER, OAK HILL, WV, p. A698
PLATTE COUNTY MEMORIAL HOSPITAL, WHEATLAND, WY, p. A723
PLATTE HEALTH CENTER AVERA, PLATTE, SD, p. A575
PLATTE VALLEY MEDICAL CENTER, BRIGHTON, CO, p. A103

PUTNAM COUNTY HOSPITAL, GREENCASTLE, IN, p. A212
PUTNAM COUNTY MEMORIAL HOSPITAL, UNIONVILLE, MO, p. A384
PUTNAM GENERAL HOSPITAL, EATONTON, GA, p. A159
PUTNAM HOSPITAL CENTER, CARMEL, NY, p. A435

Q

QUARTZ MOUNTAIN MEDICAL CENTER, MANGUM, OK, p. A513
QUEEN OF THE VALLEY MEDICAL CENTER, NAPA, CA, p. A79
QUEEN'S MEDICAL CENTER, HONOLULU, HI, p. A171
QUEENS HOSPITAL CENTER,, NY, p. A448
QUENTIN MEASE HOSPITAL, HOUSTON, TEXAS (see HARRIS HEALTH SYSTEM), p. A624
QUILLEN REHABILITATION HOSPITAL, JOHNSON CITY, TENNESSEE (see JOHNSON CITY MEDICAL CENTER), p. A585
QUINCY MEDICAL CENTER, QUINCY, MA, p. A314
QUINCY VALLEY MEDICAL CENTER, QUINCY, WA, p. A687
QUITMAN COUNTY HOSPITAL, MARKS, MS, p. A362

R

RADIUS SPECIALTY HOSPITAL BOSTON, BOSTON, MA, p. A307
RADY CHILDREN'S HOSPITAL – SAN DIEGO, SAN DIEGO, CA, p. A89
RAINBOW MENTAL HEALTH FACILITY, KANSAS CITY, KS, p. A247
RAINY LAKE MEDICAL CENTER, INTERNATIONAL FALLS, MN, p. A345
RALEIGH GENERAL HOSPITAL, BECKLEY, WV, p. A693
RALPH H. JOHNSON VETERANS AFFAIRS MEDICAL CENTER, CHARLESTON, SC, p. A563
RANCHO LOS AMIGOS NATIONAL REHABILITATION CENTER, DOWNEY, CA, p. A62
RANCHO SPRINGS MEDICAL CENTER, MURRIETA, CALIFORNIA (see SOUTHWEST HEALTHCARE SYSTEM), p. A79
RANDALL CHILDREN'S HOSPITAL, PORTLAND, OREGON (see LEGACY EMANUEL HOSPITAL AND HEALTH CENTER), p. A528
RANDOLPH HOSPITAL, ASHEBORO, NC, p. A459
RANGE REGIONAL HEALTH SERVICES, HIBBING, MN, p. A345
RANGELY DISTRICT HOSPITAL, RANGELY, CO, p. A110
RANKEN JORDAN PEDIATRIC BRIDGE HOSPITAL, MARYLAND HEIGHTS, MO, p. A376
RANKIN HOSPITAL DISTRICT, RANKIN, TX, p. A643
RANSOM MEMORIAL HOSPITAL, OTTAWA, KS, p. A251
RAPID CITY REGIONAL HOSPITAL, RAPID CITY, SD, p. A576
RAPIDES REGIONAL MEDICAL CENTER, ALEXANDRIA, LA, p. A272
RAPPAHANNOCK GENERAL HOSPITAL, KILMARNOCK, VA, p. A672
RARITAN BAY MEDICAL CENTER, PERTH AMBOY, NJ, p. A421
RAULERSON HOSPITAL, OKEECHOBEE, FL, p. A140
RAWLINS COUNTY HEALTH CENTER, ATWOOD, KS, p. A241
RAY COUNTY MEMORIAL HOSPITAL, RICHMOND, MO, p. A379
RAYMOND BLANK MEMORIAL HOSPITAL FOR CHILDREN, DES MOINES, IOWA (see UNITYPOINT HEALTH – IOWA METHODIST MEDICAL CENTER), p. A229
RC HOSPITAL AND CLINICS, OLIVIA, MN, p. A349
READING HOSPITAL AND MEDICAL CENTER, WEST READING, PA, p. A558
REAGAN MEMORIAL HOSPITAL, BIG LAKE, TX, p. A602
RECEPTION AND MEDICAL CENTER, LAKE BUTLER, FL, p. A133
RED BAY HOSPITAL, RED BAY, AL, p. A25
RED BUD REGIONAL HOSPITAL, RED BUD, IL, p. A201
RED RIVER BEHAVIORAL CENTER, BOSSIER CITY, LA, p. A274
RED RIVER HOSPITAL, WICHITA FALLS, TX, p. A657
RED RIVER REGIONAL HOSPITAL, BONHAM, TX, p. A603
RED ROCK BEHAVIORAL HOSPITAL, LAS VEGAS, NV, p. A406
REDINGTON–FAIRVIEW GENERAL HOSPITAL, SKOWHEGAN, ME, p. A295
REDLANDS COMMUNITY HOSPITAL, REDLANDS, CA, p. A85
REDMOND REGIONAL MEDICAL CENTER, ROME, GA, p. A165
REDWOOD AREA HOSPITAL, REDWOOD FALLS, MN, p. A350
REDWOOD MEMORIAL HOSPITAL, FORTUNA, CA, p. A63
REEDSBURG AREA MEDICAL CENTER, REEDSBURG, WI, p. A714
REEVES COUNTY HOSPITAL, PECOS, TX, p. A641
REEVES MEMORIAL MEDICAL CENTER, BERNICE, LA, p. A274
REFUGIO COUNTY MEMORIAL HOSPITAL, REFUGIO, TX, p. A643
REGENCY HOSPITAL CLEVELAND EAST, WARRENSVILLE HEIGHTS, OH, p. A504

REGENCY HOSPITAL OF AKRON, BARBERTON, OHIO (see REGENCY HOSPITAL CLEVELAND EAST), p. A504
REGENCY HOSPITAL OF CENTRAL GEORGIA, MACON, GA, p. A163
REGENCY HOSPITAL OF CLEVELAND – WEST, MIDDLEBURG HEIGHTS, OHIO (see REGENCY HOSPITAL CLEVELAND EAST), p. A504
REGENCY HOSPITAL OF COLUMBUS, COLUMBUS, OH, p. A490
REGENCY HOSPITAL OF COVINGTON, COVINGTON, LA, p. A276
REGENCY HOSPITAL OF FLORENCE, FLORENCE, SC, p. A566
REGENCY HOSPITAL OF FORT WORTH, FORT WORTH, TX, p. A619
REGENCY HOSPITAL OF GREENVILLE, GREENVILLE, SC, p. A566
REGENCY HOSPITAL OF HATTIESBURG, HATTIESBURG, MS, p. A359
REGENCY HOSPITAL OF JACKSON, JACKSON, MS, p. A360
REGENCY HOSPITAL OF MERIDIAN, MERIDIAN, MS, p. A362
REGENCY HOSPITAL OF MINNEAPOLIS, GOLDEN VALLEY, MN, p. A344
REGENCY HOSPITAL OF NORTHWEST ARKANSAS, FAYETTEVILLE, AR, p. A45
REGENCY HOSPITAL OF NORTHWEST ARKANSAS – SPRINGDALE, SPRINGDALE, ARKANSAS (see REGENCY HOSPITAL OF NORTHWEST ARKANSAS), p. A45
REGENCY HOSPITAL OF NORTHWEST INDIANA, EAST CHICAGO, IN, p. A209
REGENCY HOSPITAL OF PORTER COUNTY, PORTAGE, INDIANA (see REGENCY HOSPITAL OF NORTHWEST INDIANA), p. A209
REGENCY HOSPITAL OF SOUTH ATLANTA, EAST POINT, GA, p. A159
REGENCY HOSPITAL OF TOLEDO, SYLVANIA, OH, p. A502
REGINA HOSPITAL, HASTINGS, MN, p. A345
REGIONAL GENERAL HOSPITAL, WILLISTON, FL, p. A150
REGIONAL HEALTH SERVICES OF HOWARD COUNTY, CRESCO, IA, p. A228
REGIONAL HOSPITAL FOR RESPIRATORY AND COMPLEX CARE, SEATTLE, WA, p. A688
REGIONAL HOSPITAL OF JACKSON, JACKSON, TN, p. A584
REGIONAL HOSPITAL OF SCRANTON, SCRANTON, PA, p. A554
REGIONAL MEDICAL CENTER, MANCHESTER, IA, p. A234
REGIONAL MEDICAL CENTER, ORANGEBURG, SC, p. A569
REGIONAL MEDICAL CENTER BAYONET POINT, HUDSON, FL, p. A131
REGIONAL MEDICAL CENTER OF ACADIANA, LAFAYETTE, LA, p. A282
REGIONAL MEDICAL CENTER OF SAN JOSE, SAN JOSE, CA, p. A92
REGIONAL MENTAL HEALTH CENTER, MERRILLVILLE, IN, p. A218
REGIONAL ONE HEALTH, MEMPHIS, TN, p. A589
REGIONAL REHABILITATION CENTER, SALEM, OREGON (see SALEM HOSPITAL), p. A530
REGIONAL REHABILITATION HOSPITAL, PHENIX CITY, AL, p. A25
REGIONAL WEST MEDICAL CENTER, SCOTTSBLUFF, NE, p. A402
REGIONS HOSPITAL, SAINT PAUL, MN, p. A351
REHABILITATION HOSPITAL OF FORT WAYNE, FORT WAYNE, IN, p. A211
REHABILITATION HOSPITAL OF INDIANA, INDIANAPOLIS, IN, p. A214
REHABILITATION HOSPITAL OF JENNINGS, JENNINGS, LA, p. A279
REHABILITATION HOSPITAL OF RHODE ISLAND, NORTH SMITHFIELD, RI, p. A560
REHABILITATION HOSPITAL OF SOUTHERN NEW MEXICO, LAS CRUCES, NM, p. A429
REHABILITATION HOSPITAL OF SOUTHWEST VIRGINIA, BRISTOL, VA, p. A668
REHABILITATION HOSPITAL OF THE PACIFIC, HONOLULU, HI, p. A171
REHABILITATION HOSPITAL OF TINTON FALLS, TINTON FALLS, NJ, p. A423
REHABILITATION HOSPITAL OF WISCONSIN, WAUKESHA, WI, p. A717
REHABILITATION HOSPITAL, NAVICENT HEALTH, MACON, GA, p. A163
REHABILITATION INSTITUTE AT THE MOUNT KEMBLE DIVISION, GORYEB CHILDREN'S HOSPITAL, MORRISTOWN, NEW JERSEY (see MORRISTOWN MEDICAL CENTER), p. A418
REHABILITATION INSTITUTE OF CHICAGO, CHICAGO, IL, p. A186
REHABILITATION INSTITUTE OF MICHIGAN, DETROIT, MI, p. A322
REHABILITATION INSTITUTE OF OREGON, PORTLAND, OREGON (see LEGACY GOOD SAMARITAN HOSPITAL AND MEDICAL CENTER), p. A528
REHABILITATION INSTITUTE OF WEST FLORIDA, PENSACOLA, FLORIDA (see WEST FLORIDA HOSPITAL), p. A142
REHOBOTH MCKINLEY CHRISTIAN HEALTH CARE SERVICES, GALLUP, NM, p. A428

REID HOSPITAL AND HEALTH CARE SERVICES, RICHMOND, IN, p. A221
REISCH MEMORIAL NURSING HOME (see THOMAS H. BOYD MEMORIAL HOSPITAL), p. A182
RELIANT AUSTIN, AUSTIN, TX, p. A599
RELIANT NORTHWEST HOUSTON, HOUSTON, TX, p. A626
RELIANT REHABILITATION HOSPITAL ABILENE, ABILENE, TX, p. A595
RELIANT REHABILITATION HOSPITAL CENTRAL TEXAS, ROUND ROCK, TX, p. A644
RELIANT REHABILITATION HOSPITAL DALLAS, DALLAS, TX, p. A611
RELIANT REHABILITATION HOSPITAL MID–CITIES, BEDFORD, TX, p. A602
RELIANT REHABILITATION HOSPITAL NORTH HOUSTON, SHENANDOAH, TX, p. A649
RELIANT REHABILITATION HOSPITAL NORTH TEXAS, RICHARDSON, TX, p. A644
RENOWN CHILDREN'S HOSPITAL, RENO, NEVADA (see RENOWN REGIONAL MEDICAL CENTER), p. A407
RENOWN REGIONAL MEDICAL CENTER, RENO, NV, p. A407
RENOWN REHABILITATION HOSPITAL, RENO, NV, p. A408
RENOWN SOUTH MEADOWS MEDICAL CENTER, RENO, NV, p. A408
REPUBLIC COUNTY HOSPITAL, BELLEVILLE, KS, p. A241
RESEARCH MEDICAL CENTER, KANSAS CITY, MO, p. A374
RESEARCH PSYCHIATRIC CENTER, KANSAS CITY, MO, p. A374
RESTON HOSPITAL CENTER, RESTON, VA, p. A677
RESTORA HOSPITAL OF MESA, MESA, AZ, p. A34
RESTORA HOSPITAL OF SUN CITY, SUN CITY, AZ, p. A39
REX HEALTHCARE, RALEIGH, NC, p. A471
REYNOLDS ARMY COMMUNITY HOSPITAL, FORT SILL, OK, p. A511
REYNOLDS MEMORIAL HOSPITAL, GLEN DALE, WV, p. A695
RHEA MEDICAL CENTER, DAYTON, TN, p. A582
RHODE ISLAND HOSPITAL, PROVIDENCE, RI, p. A561
RICE COUNTY DISTRICT HOSPITAL, LYONS, KS, p. A249
RICE MEDICAL CENTER, EAGLE LAKE, TX, p. A614
RICE MEMORIAL HOSPITAL, WILLMAR, MN, p. A354
RICHARD H. HUTCHINGS PSYCHIATRIC CENTER, SYRACUSE, NY, p. A455
RICHARD H. YOUNG BEHAVIORAL HEALTH CENTER, KEARNEY, NEBRASKA (see CHI HEALTH GOOD SAMARITAN), p. A397
RICHARD L. ROUDEBUSH VETERANS AFFAIRS MEDICAL CENTER, INDIANAPOLIS, IN, p. A215
RICHARD P. STADTER PSYCHIATRIC CENTER, GRAND FORKS, ND, p. A478
RICHARDSON MEDICAL CENTER, RAYVILLE, LA, p. A287
RICHLAND HOSPITAL, RICHLAND CENTER, WI, p. A714
RICHLAND MEMORIAL HOSPITAL, OLNEY, IL, p. A198
RICHLAND PARISH HOSPITAL, DELHI, LA, p. A276
RICHMOND STATE HOSPITAL, RICHMOND, IN, p. A222
RICHMOND UNIVERSITY MEDICAL CENTER,, NY, p. A448
RIDDLE HOSPITAL, MEDIA, PA, p. A545
RIDGE BEHAVIORAL HEALTH SYSTEM, LEXINGTON, KY, p. A264
RIDGECREST REGIONAL HOSPITAL, RIDGECREST, CA, p. A86
RIDGEVIEW BEHAVIORAL HOSPITAL, MIDDLE POINT, OH, p. A498
RIDGEVIEW INSTITUTE, SMYRNA, GA, p. A167
RIDGEVIEW MEDICAL CENTER, WACONIA, MN, p. A353
RIDGEVIEW PSYCHIATRIC HOSPITAL AND CENTER, OAK RIDGE, TN, p. A592
RILEY HOSPITAL FOR CHILDREN AT INDIANA UNIVERSITY HEALTH, INDIANAPOLIS, INDIANA (see INDIANA UNIVERSITY HEALTH UNIVERSITY HOSPITAL), p. A214
RINGGOLD COUNTY HOSPITAL, MOUNT AYR, IA, p. A234
RIO GRANDE HOSPITAL, DEL NORTE, CO, p. A104
RIO GRANDE REGIONAL HOSPITAL, MCALLEN, TX, p. A637
RIO GRANDE STATE CENTER, HARLINGEN, TEXAS (see RIO GRANDE STATE CENTER/SOUTH TEXAS HEALTH CARE SYSTEM), p. A622
RIO GRANDE STATE CENTER/SOUTH TEXAS HEALTH CARE SYSTEM, HARLINGEN, TX, p. A622
RIPON MEDICAL CENTER, RIPON, WI, p. A714
RIVENDELL BEHAVIORAL HEALTH, BOWLING GREEN, KY, p. A259
RIVENDELL BEHAVIORAL HEALTH SERVICES OF ARKANSAS, BENTON, AR, p. A43
RIVER BEND HOSPITAL, WEST LAFAYETTE, IN, p. A224
RIVER CREST HOSPITAL, SAN ANGELO, TX, p. A645
RIVER FALLS AREA HOSPITAL, RIVER FALLS, WI, p. A714
RIVER HOSPITAL, ALEXANDRIA BAY, NY, p. A432
RIVER OAKS CHILD AND ADOLESCENT HOSPITAL, NEW ORLEANS, LOUISIANA (see RIVER OAKS HOSPITAL), p. A286
RIVER OAKS HOSPITAL, NEW ORLEANS, LA, p. A286
RIVER OAKS HOSPITAL, FLOWOOD, MS, p. A357
RIVER PARISHES HOSPITAL, LA PLACE, LA, p. A280
RIVER PARK HOSPITAL, MC MINNVILLE, TN, p. A588
RIVER PARK HOSPITAL, HUNTINGTON, WV, p. A696

S

SHRINERS HOSPITALS FOR CHILDREN–BOSTON, BOSTON, MA, p. A307
SHRINERS HOSPITALS FOR CHILDREN–CHICAGO, CHICAGO, IL, p. A186
SHRINERS HOSPITALS FOR CHILDREN–CINCINNATI BURNS HOSPITAL, CINCINNATI, OH, p. A487
SHRINERS HOSPITALS FOR CHILDREN–GALVESTON BURNS HOSPITAL, GALVESTON, TX, p. A620
SHRINERS HOSPITALS FOR CHILDREN–GREENVILLE, GREENVILLE, SC, p. A566
SHRINERS HOSPITALS FOR CHILDREN–HONOLULU, HONOLULU, HI, p. A171
SHRINERS HOSPITALS FOR CHILDREN–HOUSTON, HOUSTON, TX, p. A626
SHRINERS HOSPITALS FOR CHILDREN–LEXINGTON, LEXINGTON, KY, p. A264
SHRINERS HOSPITALS FOR CHILDREN–LOS ANGELES, LOS ANGELES, CA, p. A74
SHRINERS HOSPITALS FOR CHILDREN–NORTHERN CALIFORNIA, SACRAMENTO, CA, p. A87
SHRINERS HOSPITALS FOR CHILDREN–PHILADELPHIA, PHILADELPHIA, PA, p. A550
SHRINERS HOSPITALS FOR CHILDREN–PORTLAND, PORTLAND, OR, p. A529
SHRINERS HOSPITALS FOR CHILDREN–SALT LAKE CITY, SALT LAKE CITY, UT, p. A663
SHRINERS HOSPITALS FOR CHILDREN–SHREVEPORT, SHREVEPORT, LA, p. A288
SHRINERS HOSPITALS FOR CHILDREN–SPOKANE, SPOKANE, WA, p. A690
SHRINERS HOSPITALS FOR CHILDREN–SPRINGFIELD, SPRINGFIELD, MA, p. A315
SHRINERS HOSPITALS FOR CHILDREN–ST. LOUIS, SAINT LOUIS, MO, p. A381
SHRINERS HOSPITALS FOR CHILDREN–TAMPA, TAMPA, FL, p. A148
SHRINERS HOSPITALS FOR CHILDREN–TWIN CITIES, MINNEAPOLIS, MN, p. A347
SIBLEY MEDICAL CENTER, ARLINGTON, MN, p. A339
SIBLEY MEMORIAL HOSPITAL, WASHINGTON, DC, p. A122
SIDNEY HEALTH CENTER, SIDNEY, MT, p. A391
SIDNEY REGIONAL MEDICAL CENTER, SIDNEY, NE, p. A402
SIERRA MEDICAL CENTER, EL PASO, TX, p. A616
SIERRA NEVADA MEMORIAL HOSPITAL, GRASS VALLEY, CA, p. A66
SIERRA PROVIDENCE EAST MEDICAL CENTER, EL PASO, TX, p. A616
SIERRA SURGERY HOSPITAL, CARSON CITY, NV, p. A404
SIERRA TUCSON, TUCSON, AZ, p. A40
SIERRA VIEW DISTRICT HOSPITAL, PORTERVILLE, CA, p. A84
SIERRA VISTA HOSPITAL, SACRAMENTO, CA, p. A87
SIERRA VISTA HOSPITAL, TRUTH OR CONSEQUENCES, NM, p. A431
SIERRA VISTA REGIONAL HEALTH CENTER, SIERRA VISTA, AZ, p. A39
SIERRA VISTA REGIONAL MEDICAL CENTER, SAN LUIS OBISPO, CA, p. A93
SIGNATURE HEALTHCARE BROCKTON HOSPITAL, BROCKTON, MA, p. A308
SIGNATURE PSYCHIATRIC HOSPITAL, KANSAS CITY, MO, p. A374
SILOAM SPRINGS REGIONAL HOSPITAL, SILOAM SPRINGS, AR, p. A53
SILVER CROSS HOSPITAL, NEW LENOX, IL, p. A198
SILVER HILL HOSPITAL, NEW CANAAN, CT, p. A116
SILVER LAKE MEDICAL CENTER, LOS ANGELES, CA, p. A74
SILVER LAKE MEDICAL CENTER-INGLESIDE HOSPITAL, ROSEMEAD, CALIFORNIA (see SILVER LAKE MEDICAL CENTER), p. A74
SILVERTON HOSPITAL, SILVERTON, OR, p. A530
SIMI VALLEY HOSPITAL AND HEALTH CARE SERVICES, SIMI VALLEY, CA, p. A95
SIMPSON GENERAL HOSPITAL, MENDENHALL, MS, p. A362
SINAI CHILDREN'S HOSPITAL, CHICAGO, ILLINOIS (see MOUNT SINAI HOSPITAL), p. A185
SINAI HOSPITAL OF BALTIMORE, BALTIMORE, MD, p. A298
SINAI-GRACE HOSPITAL, DETROIT, MI, p. A322
SINGING RIVER HEALTH SYSTEM, PASCAGOULA, MS, p. A364
SINGING RIVER HOSPITAL, PASCAGOULA, MISSISSIPPI (see SINGING RIVER HEALTH SYSTEM), p. A364
SIOUX CENTER HEALTH, SIOUX CENTER, IA, p. A237
SIOUX FALLS SPECIALTY HOSPITAL, SIOUX FALLS, SD, p. A576
SIOUX FALLS VETERANS AFFAIRS HEALTH CARE SYSTEM, SIOUX FALLS, SD, p. A577
SIOUXLAND SURGERY CENTER, DAKOTA DUNES, SD, p. A573
SISKIN HOSPITAL FOR PHYSICAL REHABILITATION, CHATTANOOGA, TN, p. A580
SISTER EMMANUEL HOSPITAL, MIAMI, FL, p. A137

SISTER KENNY REHABILITATION INSTITUTE, MINNEAPOLIS, MINNESOTA (see ABBOTT NORTHWESTERN HOSPITAL), p. A347
SISTERS OF CHARITY HOSPITAL OF BUFFALO, BUFFALO, NY, p. A435
SISTERSVILLE GENERAL HOSPITAL, SISTERSVILLE, WV, p. A699
SITKA COMMUNITY HOSPITAL, SITKA, AK, p. A30
SKAGIT VALLEY HOSPITAL, MOUNT VERNON, WA, p. A685
SKIFF MEDICAL CENTER, NEWTON, IA, p. A235
SKY LAKES MEDICAL CENTER, KLAMATH FALLS, OR, p. A526
SKY RIDGE MEDICAL CENTER, LONE TREE, CO, p. A109
SKYLINE HOSPITAL, WHITE SALMON, WA, p. A692
SKYRIDGE MEDICAL CENTER, CLEVELAND, TN, p. A581
SKYRIDGE MEDICAL CENTER – WESTSIDE CAMPUS, CLEVELAND, TENNESSEE (see SKYRIDGE MEDICAL CENTER), p. A581
SLEEPY EYE MEDICAL CENTER, SLEEPY EYE, MN, p. A352
SLIDELL MEMORIAL HOSPITAL, SLIDELL, LA, p. A289
SMITH COUNTY MEMORIAL HOSPITAL, SMITH CENTER, KS, p. A254
SMITH NORTHVIEW HOSPITAL, VALDOSTA, GEORGIA (see SOUTH GEORGIA MEDICAL CENTER), p. A168
SMYTH COUNTY COMMUNITY HOSPITAL, MARION, VA, p. A673
SNOQUALMIE VALLEY HOSPITAL, SNOQUALMIE, WA, p. A689
SNOWDEN AT FREDERICKSBURG, FREDERICKSBURG, VA, p. A671
SOCORRO GENERAL HOSPITAL, SOCORRO, NM, p. A431
SOIN MEDICAL CENTER, BEAVERCREEK, OH, p. A483
SOLARA HOSPITAL – BROWNSVILLE CAMPUS, BROWNSVILLE, TEXAS (see SOLARA HOSPITAL HARLINGEN), p. A622
SOLARA HOSPITAL CONROE, CONROE, TX, p. A607
SOLARA HOSPITAL HARLINGEN, HARLINGEN, TX, p. A622
SOLARA HOSPITAL MCALLEN, MCALLEN, TX, p. A637
SOLARA HOSPITAL OF MUSKOGEE, MUSKOGEE, OK, p. A514
SOLARA HOSPITAL OF SHAWNEE, SHAWNEE, OK, p. A518
SOLDIERS AND SAILORS MEMORIAL HOSPITAL, WELLSBORO, PA, p. A557
SOLDIERS AND SAILORS MEMORIAL HOSPITAL OF YATES COUNTY, PENN YAN, NY, p. A451
SOMERSET HOSPITAL, SOMERSET, PA, p. A555
SOMERVILLE HOSPITAL, SOMERVILLE, MASSACHUSETTS (see CAMBRIDGE HEALTH ALLIANCE), p. A309
SONOMA DEVELOPMENTAL CENTER, ELDRIDGE, CA, p. A62
SONOMA VALLEY HOSPITAL, SONOMA, CA, p. A95
SONORA BEHAVIORAL HEALTH HOSPITAL, TUCSON, AZ, p. A40
SONORA REGIONAL MEDICAL CENTER, SONORA, CA, p. A95
SOUTH BALDWIN REGIONAL MEDICAL CENTER, FOLEY, AL, p. A20
SOUTH BAY HOSPITAL, SUN CITY CENTER, FL, p. A146
SOUTH BEACH PSYCHIATRIC CENTER,, NY, p. A448
SOUTH BIG HORN COUNTY HOSPITAL, BASIN, WY, p. A720
SOUTH CAMERON MEMORIAL HOSPITAL, CAMERON, LA, p. A275
SOUTH CAMPUS, VISALIA, CALIFORNIA (see KAWEAH DELTA MEDICAL CENTER), p. A99
SOUTH CAMPUS, AURORA, COLORADO (see MEDICAL CENTER OF AURORA), p. A102
SOUTH CAROLINA DEPARTMENT OF CORRECTIONS HOSPITAL, COLUMBIA, SC, p. A564
SOUTH CENTRAL KANSAS MEDICAL CENTER, ARKANSAS CITY, KS, p. A241
SOUTH CENTRAL REGIONAL MEDICAL CENTER, LAUREL, MS, p. A361
SOUTH COUNTY HOSPITAL, WAKEFIELD, RI, p. A561
SOUTH DAVIS COMMUNITY HOSPITAL, BOUNTIFUL, UT, p. A659
SOUTH FLORIDA BAPTIST HOSPITAL, PLANT CITY, FL, p. A143
SOUTH FLORIDA STATE HOSPITAL,, FL, p. A131
SOUTH GEORGIA MEDICAL CENTER, VALDOSTA, GA, p. A168
SOUTH GEORGIA MEDICAL CENTER BERRIEN CAMPUS, NASHVILLE, GA, p. A164
SOUTH GEORGIA MEDICAL CENTER LANIER CAMPUS, LAKELAND, GA, p. A162
SOUTH HAVEN HEALTH SYSTEM, SOUTH HAVEN, MI, p. A335
SOUTH LAKE HOSPITAL, CLERMONT, FL, p. A125
SOUTH LINCOLN MEDICAL CENTER, KEMMERER, WY, p. A721
SOUTH LYON MEDICAL CENTER, YERINGTON, NV, p. A408
SOUTH MISSISSIPPI COUNTY REGIONAL MEDICAL CENTER, OSCEOLA, AR, p. A51
SOUTH MISSISSIPPI STATE HOSPITAL, PURVIS, MS, p. A364
SOUTH NASSAU COMMUNITIES HOSPITAL, OCEANSIDE, NY, p. A450
SOUTH OAKS HOSPITAL, AMITYVILLE, NY, p. A432
SOUTH PENINSULA HOSPITAL, HOMER, AK, p. A29
SOUTH POINTE HOSPITAL, WARRENSVILLE HEIGHTS, OH, p. A504
SOUTH SHORE HOSPITAL, CHICAGO, IL, p. A186
SOUTH SHORE HOSPITAL, SOUTH WEYMOUTH, MA, p. A314
SOUTH SUNFLOWER COUNTY HOSPITAL, INDIANOLA, MS, p. A359

SOUTH TEXAS BEHAVIORAL HEALTH CENTER, EDINBURG, TEXAS (see SOUTH TEXAS HEALTH SYSTEM), p. A615
SOUTH TEXAS HEALTH CARE SYSTEM, HARLINGEN, TEXAS (see RIO GRANDE STATE CENTER/SOUTH TEXAS HEALTH CARE SYSTEM), p. A622
SOUTH TEXAS HEALTH SYSTEM, EDINBURG, TX, p. A615
SOUTH TEXAS REGIONAL MEDICAL CENTER, JOURDANTON, TX, p. A630
SOUTH TEXAS REHABILITATION HOSPITAL, BROWNSVILLE, TX, p. A604
SOUTH TEXAS SPINE AND SURGICAL HOSPITAL, SAN ANTONIO, TX, p. A647
SOUTH TEXAS SURGICAL HOSPITAL, CORPUS CHRISTI, TX, p. A608
SOUTH TEXAS VETERANS HEALTH CARE SYSTEM, SAN ANTONIO, TX, p. A647
SOUTHAMPTON HOSPITAL, SOUTHAMPTON, NY, p. A455
SOUTHAMPTON MEMORIAL HOSPITAL, FRANKLIN, VA, p. A671
SOUTHCOAST HOSPITALS GROUP, FALL RIVER, MA, p. A310
SOUTHEAST ALABAMA MEDICAL CENTER, DOTHAN, AL, p. A19
SOUTHEAST ARIZONA MEDICAL CENTER, DOUGLAS, AZ, p. A32
SOUTHEAST COLORADO HOSPITAL DISTRICT, SPRINGFIELD, CO, p. A111
SOUTHEAST GEORGIA HEALTH SYSTEM BRUNSWICK CAMPUS, BRUNSWICK, GA, p. A155
SOUTHEAST GEORGIA HEALTH SYSTEM CAMDEN CAMPUS, SAINT MARYS, GA, p. A166
SOUTHEAST HEALTH CENTER OF REYNOLDS COUNTY, ELLINGTON, MO, p. A370
SOUTHEAST HEALTH CENTER OF RIPLEY COUNTY, DONIPHAN, MO, p. A370
SOUTHEAST HEALTH CENTER OF STODDARD COUNTY, DEXTER, MO, p. A370
SOUTHEAST HOSPITAL, CAPE GIRARDEAU, MO, p. A369
SOUTHEAST MICHIGAN SURGICAL HOSPITAL, WARREN, MI, p. A336
SOUTHEAST MISSOURI MENTAL HEALTH CENTER, FARMINGTON, MO, p. A371
SOUTHEAST REGIONAL MEDICAL CENTER, KENTWOOD, LA, p. A280
SOUTHEAST REHABILITATION HOSPITAL, LAKE VILLAGE, AR, p. A48
SOUTHEASTERN HEALTH, LUMBERTON, NC, p. A468
SOUTHEASTERN OHIO REGIONAL MEDICAL CENTER, CAMBRIDGE, OH, p. A485
SOUTHEASTERN REGIONAL MEDICAL CENTER, NEWNAN, GA, p. A164
SOUTHEASTERN REGIONAL REHABILITATION CENTER, BEHAVIORAL HEALTH CARE OF CAPE FEAR VALLEY HEALTH SYSTEM, FAYETTEVILLE, NORTH CAROLINA (see CAPE FEAR VALLEY MEDICAL CENTER), p. A464
SOUTHEASTERN REGIONAL REHABILITATION CENTER, FAYETTEVILLE, NORTH CAROLINA (see CAPE FEAR VALLEY MEDICAL CENTER), p. A464
SOUTHERN ARIZONA VETERANS AFFAIRS HEALTH CARE SYSTEM, TUCSON, AZ, p. A41
SOUTHERN CALIFORNIA HOSPITAL AT CULVER CITY, CULVER CITY, CA, p. A61
SOUTHERN CALIFORNIA HOSPITAL AT HOLLYWOOD, LOS ANGELES, CA, p. A75
SOUTHERN CALIFORNIA HOSPITAL AT VAN NUYS,, CALIFORNIA (see SOUTHERN CALIFORNIA HOSPITAL AT HOLLYWOOD), p. A75
SOUTHERN COOS HOSPITAL AND HEALTH CENTER, BANDON, OR, p. A523
SOUTHERN CRESCENT HOSPITAL FOR SPECIALTY CARE, RIVERDALE, GA, p. A165
SOUTHERN HILLS HOSPITAL AND MEDICAL CENTER, LAS VEGAS, NV, p. A406
SOUTHERN INDIANA REHABILITATION HOSPITAL, NEW ALBANY, IN, p. A220
SOUTHERN INYO HEALTHCARE DISTRICT, LONE PINE, CA, p. A70
SOUTHERN KENTUCKY REHABILITATION HOSPITAL, BOWLING GREEN, KY, p. A259
SOUTHERN MAINE HEALTH CARE – BIDDEFORD MEDICAL CENTER, BIDDEFORD, MAINE (see SOUTHERN MAINE HEALTH CARE – BIDDEFORD MEDICAL CENTER X), p. A292
SOUTHERN MAINE HEALTH CARE – BIDDEFORD MEDICAL CENTER X, BIDDEFORD, ME, p. A292
SOUTHERN MAINE HEALTH CARE – SANFORD MEDICAL CENTER, SANFORD, MAINE (see SOUTHERN MAINE HEALTH CARE – BIDDEFORD MEDICAL CENTER X), p. A292
SOUTHERN NEVADA ADULT MENTAL HEALTH SERVICES, LAS VEGAS, NV, p. A406
SOUTHERN NEW HAMPSHIRE MEDICAL CENTER, NASHUA, NH, p. A411
SOUTHERN OCEAN MEDICAL CENTER, MANAHAWKIN, NJ, p. A418

SOUTHERN OHIO MEDICAL CENTER, PORTSMOUTH, OH, p. A501
SOUTHERN PALMETTO HOSPITAL, BARNWELL, SC, p. A562
SOUTHERN REGIONAL MEDICAL CENTER, RIVERDALE, GA, p. A165
SOUTHERN SURGICAL HOSPITAL, SLIDELL, LA, p. A289
SOUTHERN TENNESSEE REGIONAL HEALTH SYSTEM–LAWRENCEBURG, LAWRENCEBURG, TN, p. A586
SOUTHERN TENNESSEE REGIONAL HEALTH SYSTEM–PULASKI, PULASKI, TN, p. A592
SOUTHERN TENNESSEE REGIONAL HEALTH SYSTEM–SEWANEE, SEWANEE, TENNESSEE (see SOUTHERN TENNESSEE REGIONAL HEALTH SYSTEM–WINCHESTER), p. A594
SOUTHERN TENNESSEE REGIONAL HEALTH SYSTEM–WINCHESTER, WINCHESTER, TN, p. A594
SOUTHERN VIRGINIA MENTAL HEALTH INSTITUTE, DANVILLE, VA, p. A670
SOUTHERN VIRGINIA REGIONAL MEDICAL CENTER, EMPORIA, VA, p. A670
SOUTHERN WINDS HOSPITAL, HIALEAH, FLORIDA (see WESTCHESTER GENERAL HOSPITAL), p. A138
SOUTHLAKE CAMPUS, MERRILLVILLE, INDIANA (see METHODIST HOSPITALS), p. A212
SOUTHPOINTE HOSPITAL, SAINT LOUIS, MISSOURI (see ST. ALEXIUS HOSPITAL – BROADWAY CAMPUS), p. A381
SOUTHSIDE HOSPITAL, BAY SHORE, NY, p. A433
SOUTHSIDE REGIONAL MEDICAL CENTER, PETERSBURG, VA, p. A676
SOUTHVIEW HOSPITAL AND FAMILY HEALTH CENTER, DAYTON, OHIO (see GRANDVIEW MEDICAL CENTER), p. A492
SOUTHWEST CONNECTICUT MENTAL HEALTH SYSTEM, BRIDGEPORT, CT, p. A113
SOUTHWEST GENERAL HEALTH CENTER, MIDDLEBURG HEIGHTS, OH, p. A498
SOUTHWEST GENERAL HOSPITAL, SAN ANTONIO, TX, p. A647
SOUTHWEST GEORGIA REGIONAL MEDICAL CENTER, CUTHBERT, GA, p. A157
SOUTHWEST HEALTH CENTER, PLATTEVILLE, WI, p. A713
SOUTHWEST HEALTH CENTER NURSING HOME, CUBA CITY, WISCONSIN (see SOUTHWEST HEALTH CENTER), p. A713
SOUTHWEST HEALTHCARE SERVICES, BOWMAN, ND, p. A476
SOUTHWEST HEALTHCARE SYSTEM, MURRIETA, CA, p. A79
SOUTHWEST IDAHO ADVANCED CARE HOSPITAL, BOISE, ID, p. A174
SOUTHWEST MEDICAL CENTER, LIBERAL, KS, p. A249
SOUTHWEST MEMORIAL HOSPITAL, CORTEZ, CO, p. A104
SOUTHWEST MISSISSIPPI REGIONAL MEDICAL CENTER, MCCOMB, MS, p. A362
SOUTHWEST REGIONAL MEDICAL CENTER, GEORGETOWN, OH, p. A494
SOUTHWEST REGIONAL MEDICAL CENTER, WAYNESBURG, PA, p. A557
SOUTHWEST REGIONAL REHABILITATION CENTER, BATTLE CREEK, MI, p. A319
SOUTHWESTERN MEDICAL CENTER, LAWTON, OK, p. A512
SOUTHWESTERN REGIONAL MEDICAL CENTER, TULSA, OK, p. A521
SOUTHWESTERN STATE HOSPITAL, THOMASVILLE, GA, p. A168
SOUTHWESTERN VERMONT MEDICAL CENTER, BENNINGTON, VT, p. A665
SOUTHWESTERN VIRGINIA MENTAL HEALTH INSTITUTE, MARION, VA, p. A674
SOUTHWOOD PSYCHIATRIC HOSPITAL, PITTSBURGH, PA, p. A551
SPALDING REGIONAL MEDICAL CENTER, GRIFFIN, GA, p. A160
SPALDING REHABILITATION HOSPITAL, AURORA, CO, p. A102
SPANISH PEAKS REGIONAL HEALTH CENTER, WALSENBURG, CO, p. A112
SPARKS REGIONAL MEDICAL CENTER, FORT SMITH, AR, p. A46
SPARROW CLINTON HOSPITAL, SAINT JOHNS, MI, p. A334
SPARROW HOSPITAL, LANSING, MI, p. A328
SPARROW IONIA HOSPITAL, IONIA, MI, p. A327
SPARROW REGIONAL CHILDREN'S CENTER, LANSING, MICHIGAN (see SPARROW HOSPITAL), p. A328
SPARROW SPECIALTY HOSPITAL, LANSING, MI, p. A329
SPARTA COMMUNITY HOSPITAL, SPARTA, IL, p. A202
SPARTANBURG HOSPITAL FOR RESTORATIVE CARE, SPARTANBURG, SC, p. A570
SPARTANBURG REGIONAL MEDICAL CENTER, SPARTANBURG, SC, p. A570
SPAULDING HOSPITAL FOR CONTINUING MEDICAL CARE NORTH SHORE, SALEM, MA, p. A314
SPAULDING HOSPITAL FOR CONTINUING MEDICAL CARE CAMBRIDGE, CAMBRIDGE, MA, p. A309
SPAULDING REHABILITATION HOSPITAL, CHARLESTOWN, MA, p. A309
SPAULDING REHABILITATION HOSPITAL CAPE COD, EAST SANDWICH, MA, p. A309
SPEARE MEMORIAL HOSPITAL, PLYMOUTH, NH, p. A412

SPEARFISH REGIONAL HOSPITAL, SPEARFISH, SD, p. A577
SPEARFISH REGIONAL SURGERY CENTER, SPEARFISH, SD, p. A577
SPECIAL CARE HOSPITAL, NANTICOKE, PA, p. A546
SPECIALISTS HOSPITAL – SHREVEPORT, SHREVEPORT, LA, p. A288
SPECIALTY EXTENDED CARE HOSPITAL OF MONROE, MONROE, LA, p. A284
SPECIALTY HOSPITAL JACKSONVILLE, JACKSONVILLE, FL, p. A132
SPECIALTY HOSPITAL OF CENTRAL JERSEY, LAKEWOOD, NJ, p. A417
SPECIALTY HOSPITAL OF LORAIN, AMHERST, OH, p. A482
SPECIALTY HOSPITAL OF MERIDIAN, MERIDIAN, MS, p. A363
SPECIALTY HOSPITAL OF MIDWEST CITY, MIDWEST CITY, OK, p. A513
SPECIALTY HOSPITAL OF WASHINGTON, WASHINGTON, DC, p. A122
SPECIALTY HOSPITAL OF WASHINGTON–HADLEY, WASHINGTON, DC, p. A122
SPECIALTY HOSPITAL OF WINNFIELD, WINNFIELD, LA, p. A290
SPECIALTY REHABILITATION HOSPITAL OF COUSHATTA, COUSHATTA, LA, p. A275
SPECTRUM HEALTH, GRAND RAPIDS, MICHIGAN (see SPECTRUM HEALTH – BUTTERWORTH HOSPITAL), p. A325
SPECTRUM HEALTH – BLODGETT CAMPUS, GRAND RAPIDS, MICHIGAN (see SPECTRUM HEALTH – BUTTERWORTH HOSPITAL), p. A325
SPECTRUM HEALTH – BUTTERWORTH HOSPITAL, GRAND RAPIDS, MI, p. A325
SPECTRUM HEALTH BIG RAPIDS HOSPITAL, BIG RAPIDS, MI, p. A319
SPECTRUM HEALTH GERBER MEMORIAL, FREMONT, MI, p. A324
SPECTRUM HEALTH KELSEY HOSPITAL, LAKEVIEW, MICHIGAN (see SPECTRUM HEALTH UNITED HOSPITAL), p. A326
SPECTRUM HEALTH LUDINGTON HOSPITAL, LUDINGTON, MI, p. A329
SPECTRUM HEALTH REED CITY HOSPITAL, REED CITY, MI, p. A333
SPECTRUM HEALTH SPECIAL CARE HOSPITAL, GRAND RAPIDS, MI, p. A325
SPECTRUM HEALTH UNITED HOSPITAL, GREENVILLE, MI, p. A326
SPECTRUM HEALTH ZEELAND COMMUNITY HOSPITAL, ZEELAND, MI, p. A338
SPENCER HOSPITAL, SPENCER, IA, p. A238
SPINE HOSPITAL OF LOUISIANA, BATON ROUGE, LA, p. A274
SPOONER HEALTH SYSTEM, SPOONER, WI, p. A715
SPOTSYLVANIA REGIONAL MEDICAL CENTER, FREDERICKSBURG, VA, p. A671
SPRING GROVE HOSPITAL CENTER, BALTIMORE, MD, p. A298
SPRING HARBOR HOSPITAL, WESTBROOK, ME, p. A295
SPRING MOUNTAIN SAHARA, LAS VEGAS, NV, p. A406
SPRING MOUNTAIN TREATMENT CENTER, LAS VEGAS, NV, p. A406
SPRING VALLEY HOSPITAL MEDICAL CENTER, LAS VEGAS, NV, p. A406
SPRING VIEW HOSPITAL, LEBANON, KY, p. A263
SPRINGBROOK BEHAVIORAL HEALTH SYSTEM, TRAVELERS REST, SC, p. A570
SPRINGBROOK HOSPITAL, BROOKSVILLE, FL, p. A125
SPRINGFIELD HOSPITAL, SPRINGFIELD, PENNSYLVANIA (see CROZER–CHESTER MEDICAL CENTER), p. A556
SPRINGFIELD HOSPITAL, SPRINGFIELD, VT, p. A666
SPRINGFIELD HOSPITAL CENTER, SYKESVILLE, MD, p. A303
SPRINGFIELD IMAGING CENTER, SPRINGFIELD, OHIO (see SPRINGFIELD REGIONAL MEDICAL CENTER), p. A502
SPRINGFIELD REGIONAL MEDICAL CENTER, SPRINGFIELD, OH, p. A502
SPRINGHILL MEDICAL CENTER, SPRINGHILL, LA, p. A289
SPRINGHILL MEMORIAL HOSPITAL, MOBILE, AL, p. A23
SPRINGS MEMORIAL HOSPITAL, LANCASTER, SC, p. A568
SPRINGWOODS BEHAVIORAL HEALTH HOSPITAL, FAYETTEVILLE, AR, p. A45
SSM CARDINAL GLENNON CHILDREN'S MEDICAL CENTER, SAINT LOUIS, MO, p. A381
SSM DEPAUL HEALTH CENTER, BRIDGETON, MO, p. A368
SSM SELECT REHABILITATION HOSPITAL, RICHMOND HEIGHTS, MO, p. A379
SSM SELECT REHABILITATION HOSPITAL, BRIDGETON, MISSOURI (see SSM SELECT REHABILITATION HOSPITAL), p. A379
SSM ST. CLARE HEALTH CENTER, FENTON, MO, p. A371
SSM ST. JOSEPH HEALTH CENTER, SAINT CHARLES, MO, p. A379
SSM ST. JOSEPH HEALTH CENTER – WENTZVILLE, WENTZVILLE, MISSOURI (see SSM ST. JOSEPH HEALTH CENTER), p. A379

SSM ST. JOSEPH HOSPITAL WEST, LAKE SAINT LOUIS, MO, p. A375
SSM ST. MARY'S HEALTH CENTER, SAINT LOUIS, MO, p. A381
ST LUKE'S HOSPITAL – ALLENTOWN CAMPUS, ALLENTOWN, PENNSYLVANIA (see ST. LUKE'S UNIVERSITY HOSPITAL – BETHLEHEM CAMPUS), p. A534
ST. ALEXIUS HOSPITAL – BROADWAY CAMPUS, SAINT LOUIS, MO, p. A381
ST. ALEXIUS HOSPITAL – FOREST PARK CAMPUS, SAINT LOUIS, MISSOURI (see ST. ALEXIUS HOSPITAL – BROADWAY CAMPUS), p. A381
ST. ALEXIUS MEDICAL CENTER, HOFFMAN ESTATES, IL, p. A193
ST. ALEXIUS MEDICAL CENTER, BISMARCK, ND, p. A476
ST. ALOISIUS MEDICAL CENTER, HARVEY, ND, p. A478
ST. ANDREW'S HEALTH CENTER, BOTTINEAU, ND, p. A476
ST. ANDREWS HOSPITAL AND HEALTHCARE CENTER, BOOTHBAY HARBOR, MAINE (see LINCOLN HEALTH), p. A293
ST. ANTHONY COMMUNITY HOSPITAL, WARWICK, NY, p. A457
ST. ANTHONY HOSPITAL, LAKEWOOD, CO, p. A108
ST. ANTHONY HOSPITAL, OKLAHOMA CITY, OK, p. A516
ST. ANTHONY HOSPITAL, PENDLETON, OR, p. A527
ST. ANTHONY HOSPITAL, GIG HARBOR, WA, p. A684
ST. ANTHONY NORTH HOSPITAL, WESTMINSTER, CO, p. A112
ST. ANTHONY REGIONAL HOSPITAL, CARROLL, IA, p. A226
ST. ANTHONY SHAWNEE HOSPITAL, SHAWNEE, OK, p. A519
ST. ANTHONY SUMMIT MEDICAL CENTER, FRISCO, CO, p. A106
ST. ANTHONY'S HOSPITAL, SAINT PETERSBURG, FL, p. A145
ST. ANTHONY'S HOSPITAL, HOUSTON, TX, p. A626
ST. ANTHONY'S MEDICAL CENTER, SAINT LOUIS, MO, p. A381
ST. ANTHONY'S MEMORIAL HOSPITAL, EFFINGHAM, IL, p. A188
ST. ANTHONY'S REHABILITATION HOSPITAL, LAUDERDALE LAKES, FL, p. A134
ST. BARNABAS HOSPITAL,, NY, p. A448
ST. BERNARD HOSPITAL AND HEALTH CARE CENTER, CHICAGO, IL, p. A187
ST. BERNARD PARISH HOSPITAL, CHALMETTE, LA, p. A275
ST. BERNARDINE MEDICAL CENTER, SAN BERNARDINO, CA, p. A88
ST. BERNARDS MEDICAL CENTER, JONESBORO, AR, p. A48
ST. CATHERINE HOSPITAL, EAST CHICAGO, IN, p. A209
ST. CATHERINE HOSPITAL, GARDEN CITY, KS, p. A244
ST. CATHERINE MEMORIAL HOSPITAL, NEW ORLEANS, LA, p. A286
ST. CATHERINE OF SIENA MEDICAL CENTER, SMITHTOWN, NY, p. A454
ST. CATHERINE'S REHABILITATION HOSPITAL, NORTH MIAMI, FL, p. A139
ST. CHARLES HOSPITAL, PORT JEFFERSON, NY, p. A452
ST. CHARLES MADRAS, MADRAS, OR, p. A526
ST. CHARLES MEDICAL CENTER – BEND, BEND, OR, p. A523
ST. CHARLES MEDICAL CENTER – REDMOND, REDMOND, OR, p. A529
ST. CHARLES PARISH HOSPITAL, LULING, LA, p. A283
ST. CHARLES SURGICAL HOSPITAL, NEW ORLEANS, LA, p. A286
ST. CHRISTOPHER'S HOSPITAL FOR CHILDREN, PHILADELPHIA, PA, p. A550
ST. CLAIR HOSPITAL, PITTSBURGH, PA, p. A551
ST. CLAIRE REGIONAL MEDICAL CENTER, MOREHEAD, KY, p. A268
ST. CLARE HOSPITAL, LAKEWOOD, WA, p. A685
ST. CLARE HOSPITAL, BARABOO, WI, p. A702
ST. CLOUD HOSPITAL, SAINT CLOUD, MN, p. A350
ST. CLOUD REGIONAL MEDICAL CENTER, SAINT CLOUD, FL, p. A144
ST. CLOUD VETERANS AFFAIRS HEALTH CARE SYSTEM, SAINT CLOUD, MN, p. A351
ST. CROIX REGIONAL MEDICAL CENTER, ST. CROIX FALLS, WI, p. A715
ST. DAVID'S GEORGETOWN HOSPITAL, GEORGETOWN, TEXAS (see ST. DAVID'S MEDICAL CENTER), p. A600
ST. DAVID'S MEDICAL CENTER, AUSTIN, TX, p. A600
ST. DAVID'S NORTH AUSTIN MEDICAL CENTER, AUSTIN, TX, p. A600
ST. DAVID'S REHABILITATION CENTER, AUSTIN, TX, p. A600
ST. DAVID'S ROUND ROCK MEDICAL CENTER, ROUND ROCK, TX, p. A645
ST. DAVID'S SOUTH AUSTIN MEDICAL CENTER, AUSTIN, TX, p. A600
ST. DOMINIC–JACKSON MEMORIAL HOSPITAL, JACKSON, MS, p. A360
ST. ELIAS SPECIALTY HOSPITAL, ANCHORAGE, AK, p. A28
ST. ELIZABETH BOARDMAN HEALTH CENTER, BOARDMAN, OH, p. A484
ST. ELIZABETH COMMUNITY HOSPITAL, RED BLUFF, CA, p. A85
ST. ELIZABETH COVINGTON, COVINGTON, KENTUCKY (see ST. ELIZABETH EDGEWOOD), p. A260
ST. ELIZABETH EDGEWOOD, EDGEWOOD, KY, p. A260
ST. ELIZABETH FLORENCE, FLORENCE, KY, p. A261

SWEDISH COVENANT HOSPITAL, CHICAGO, IL, p. A187
SWEDISH MEDICAL CENTER, ENGLEWOOD, CO, p. A106
SWEDISH MEDICAL CENTER–BALLARD, SEATTLE, WASHINGTON (see SWEDISH MEDICAL CENTER–FIRST HILL), p. A688
SWEDISH MEDICAL CENTER–CHERRY HILL CAMPUS, SEATTLE, WA, p. A688
SWEDISH MEDICAL CENTER–FIRST HILL, SEATTLE, WA, p. A688
SWEDISH/EDMONDS, EDMONDS, WA, p. A683
SWEDISH/ISSAQUAH, ISSAQUAH, WA, p. A684
SWEDISHAMERICAN HOSPITAL, ROCKFORD, IL, p. A202
SWEENY COMMUNITY HOSPITAL, SWEENY, TX, p. A651
SWEETWATER HOSPITAL, SWEETWATER, TN, p. A593
SWIFT COUNTY–BENSON HOSPITAL, BENSON, MN, p. A340
SWISHER MEMORIAL HOSPITAL DISTRICT, TULIA, TX, p. A653
SYCAMORE MEDICAL CENTER, MIAMISBURG, OH, p. A498
SYCAMORE SHOALS HOSPITAL, ELIZABETHTON, TN, p. A582
SYCAMORE SPRINGS HOSPITAL, LAFAYETTE, IN, p. A217
SYLVAN GROVE HOSPITAL, JACKSON, GA, p. A161
SYOSSET HOSPITAL, SYOSSET, NY, p. A455
SYRACUSE VETERANS AFFAIRS MEDICAL CENTER, SYRACUSE, NY, p. A456
SYRINGA HOSPITAL AND CLINICS, GRANGEVILLE, ID, p. A176

T

T. C. THOMPSON CHILDREN'S HOSPITAL, CHATTANOOGA, TENNESSEE (see ERLANGER MEDICAL CENTER), p. A580
T. J. SAMSON COMMUNITY HOSPITAL, GLASGOW, KY, p. A262
TAHOE FOREST HOSPITAL DISTRICT, TRUCKEE, CA, p. A97
TAHOE PACIFIC HOSPITALS, RENO, NV, p. A408
TAHOE PACIFIC HOSPITALS – WEST, RENO, NEVADA (see TAHOE PACIFIC HOSPITALS), p. A408
TAKOMA REGIONAL HOSPITAL, GREENEVILLE, TN, p. A583
TALLAHASSEE MEMORIAL HEALTHCARE, TALLAHASSEE, FL, p. A147
TALLAHATCHIE GENERAL HOSPITAL, CHARLESTON, MS, p. A356
TAMPA COMMUNITY HOSPITAL, TAMPA, FL, p. A148
TAMPA GENERAL HOSPITAL, TAMPA, FL, p. A148
TAMPA GENERAL HOSPITAL CHILDREN'S MEDICAL CENTER, TAMPA, FLORIDA (see TAMPA GENERAL HOSPITAL), p. A148
TANNER MEDICAL CENTER–CARROLLTON, CARROLLTON, GA, p. A155
TANNER MEDICAL CENTER–VILLA RICA, VILLA RICA, GA, p. A168
TAUNTON STATE HOSPITAL, TAUNTON, MA, p. A315
TAYLOR HARDIN SECURE MEDICAL FACILITY, TUSCALOOSA, AL, p. A26
TAYLOR HOSPITAL, RIDLEY PARK, PENNSYLVANIA (see CROZER–CHESTER MEDICAL CENTER), p. A556
TAYLOR REGIONAL HOSPITAL, HAWKINSVILLE, GA, p. A160
TAYLOR REGIONAL HOSPITAL, CAMPBELLSVILLE, KY, p. A259
TAYLORVILLE MEMORIAL HOSPITAL, TAYLORVILLE, IL, p. A204
TECHE REGIONAL MEDICAL CENTER, MORGAN CITY, LA, p. A284
TEHACHAPI VALLEY HEALTHCARE DISTRICT, TEHACHAPI, CA, p. A96
TELECARE HERITAGE PSYCHIATRIC HEALTH CENTER, OAKLAND, CA, p. A81
TEMPE ST. LUKE'S HOSPITAL, TEMPE, ARIZONA (see ST. LUKE'S MEDICAL CENTER), p. A37
TEMPLE COMMUNITY HOSPITAL, LOS ANGELES, CA, p. A75
TEMPLE UNIVERSITY HOSPITAL, PHILADELPHIA, PA, p. A550
TEMPLE UNIVERSITY HOSPITAL – EPISCOPAL DIVISION, PHILADELPHIA, PENNSYLVANIA (see TEMPLE UNIVERSITY HOSPITAL), p. A550
TEN BROECK TENNESSEE TREATMENT FACILITY, COOKEVILLE, TN, p. A581
TEN LAKES CENTER, DENNISON, OH, p. A493
TENNESSEE VALLEY HEALTHCARE SYSTEM, NASHVILLE, TN, p. A591
TENNOVA HEALTHCARE–JEFFERSON MEMORIAL HOSPITAL, JEFFERSON CITY, TN, p. A584
TENNOVA HEALTHCARE–LAFOLLETTE MEDICAL CENTER, LA FOLLETTE, TN, p. A586
TENNOVA NEWPORT MEDICAL CENTER, NEWPORT, TN, p. A591
TENNOVA NORTH KNOXVILLE MEDICAL CENTER, POWELL, TENNESSEE (see TENNOVA PHYSICIANS REGIONAL MEDICAL CENTER), p. A586
TENNOVA PHYSICIANS REGIONAL MEDICAL CENTER, KNOXVILLE, TN, p. A586
TENNOVA TURKEY CREEK MEDICAL CENTER, KNOXVILLE, TENNESSEE (see TENNOVA PHYSICIANS REGIONAL MEDICAL CENTER), p. A586

TERENCE CARDINAL COOKE HEALTH CARE CENTER, NEW YORK, NY, p. A449
TERRE HAUTE REGIONAL HOSPITAL, TERRE HAUTE, IN, p. A223
TERREBONNE GENERAL MEDICAL CENTER, HOUMA, LA, p. A279
TERRELL STATE HOSPITAL, TERRELL, TX, p. A652
TETON MEDICAL CENTER, CHOTEAU, MT, p. A386
TETON VALLEY HEALTH CARE, DRIGGS, ID, p. A176
TEWKSBURY HOSPITAL, TEWKSBURY, MA, p. A315
TEXAS CENTER FOR INFECTIOUS DISEASE, SAN ANTONIO, TX, p. A648
TEXAS CHILDREN'S HOSPITAL, HOUSTON, TX, p. A627
TEXAS CHILDREN'S HOSPITAL WEST CAMPUS, HOUSTON, TEXAS (see TEXAS CHILDREN'S HOSPITAL), p. A627
TEXAS COUNTY MEMORIAL HOSPITAL, HOUSTON, MO, p. A372
TEXAS GENERAL HOSPITAL, GRAND PRAIRIE, TX, p. A621
TEXAS HEALTH ARLINGTON MEMORIAL HOSPITAL, ARLINGTON, TX, p. A598
TEXAS HEALTH CENTER FOR DIAGNOSTIC & SURGERY, PLANO, TX, p. A642
TEXAS HEALTH HARRIS METHODIST HOSPITAL ALLIANCE, FORT WORTH, TX, p. A619
TEXAS HEALTH HARRIS METHODIST HOSPITAL AZLE, AZLE, TX, p. A601
TEXAS HEALTH HARRIS METHODIST HOSPITAL CLEBURNE, CLEBURNE, TX, p. A606
TEXAS HEALTH HARRIS METHODIST HOSPITAL FORT WORTH, FORT WORTH, TX, p. A619
TEXAS HEALTH HARRIS METHODIST HOSPITAL HURST–EULESS–BEDFORD, BEDFORD, TX, p. A602
TEXAS HEALTH HARRIS METHODIST HOSPITAL SOUTHLAKE, SOUTHLAKE, TX, p. A650
TEXAS HEALTH HARRIS METHODIST HOSPITAL SOUTHWEST FORT WORTH, FORT WORTH, TX, p. A619
TEXAS HEALTH HARRIS METHODIST HOSPITAL STEPHENVILLE, STEPHENVILLE, TX, p. A650
TEXAS HEALTH HEART & VASCULAR HOSPITAL ARLINGTON, ARLINGTON, TX, p. A598
TEXAS HEALTH HUGULEY HOSPITAL FORT WORTH SOUTH, FORT WORTH, TX, p. A619
TEXAS HEALTH PRESBYTERIAN HOSPITAL ALLEN, ALLEN, TX, p. A596
TEXAS HEALTH PRESBYTERIAN HOSPITAL DALLAS, DALLAS, TX, p. A612
TEXAS HEALTH PRESBYTERIAN HOSPITAL DENTON, DENTON, TX, p. A613
TEXAS HEALTH PRESBYTERIAN HOSPITAL FLOWER MOUND, FLOWER MOUND, TX, p. A617
TEXAS HEALTH PRESBYTERIAN HOSPITAL KAUFMAN, KAUFMAN, TX, p. A630
TEXAS HEALTH PRESBYTERIAN HOSPITAL OF ROCKWALL, ROCKWALL, TX, p. A644
TEXAS HEALTH PRESBYTERIAN HOSPITAL PLANO, PLANO, TX, p. A643
TEXAS HEALTH PRESBYTERIAN HOSPITAL–WNJ, SHERMAN, TX, p. A649
TEXAS HEALTH SPECIALTY HOSPITAL, FORT WORTH, TX, p. A619
TEXAS INSTITUTE FOR SURGERY AT TEXAS HEALTH PRESBYTERIAN DALLAS, DALLAS, TX, p. A612
TEXAS NEUROREHAB CENTER, AUSTIN, TX, p. A600
TEXAS ORTHOPEDIC HOSPITAL, HOUSTON, TX, p. A627
TEXAS REGIONAL MEDICAL CENTER AT SUNNYVALE, SUNNYVALE, TX, p. A651
TEXAS REHABILITATION HOSPITAL OF FORT WORTH, FORT WORTH, TX, p. A619
TEXAS SCOTTISH RITE HOSPITAL FOR CHILDREN, DALLAS, TX, p. A612
TEXAS SPECIALTY HOSPITAL AT LUBBOCK, LUBBOCK, TX, p. A635
TEXAS SPINE & JOINT HOSPITAL, TYLER, TX, p. A654
TEXAS STAR RECOVERY, AUSTIN, TX, p. A600
TEXOMA MEDICAL CENTER, DENISON, TX, p. A613
THAYER COUNTY HEALTH SERVICES, HEBRON, NE, p. A396
THE ACADIA HOSPITAL, BANGOR, ME, p. A291
THE ALLEN PAVILION, NEW YORK, NEW YORK (see NEW YORK–PRESBYTERIAN HOSPITAL), p. A447
THE AROOSTOOK MEDICAL CENTER, PRESQUE ISLE, ME, p. A295
THE BRIDGEWAY, NORTH LITTLE ROCK, AR, p. A51
THE BROOK AT DUPONT, LOUISVILLE, KY, p. A266
THE BROOK HOSPITAL – KMI, LOUISVILLE, KY, p. A266
THE CENTERS, OCALA, FL, p. A139
THE CHARLOTTE HUNGERFORD HOSPITAL, TORRINGTON, CT, p. A117
THE CHILDREN'S CENTER, BETHANY, OK, p. A508
THE CHILDREN'S CENTER AT WESLEY, WICHITA, KANSAS (see WESLEY MEDICAL CENTER), p. A257
THE CHILDREN'S HOME OF PITTSBURGH, PITTSBURGH, PA, p. A551

THE CHILDREN'S HOSPITAL AT SAINT PETER'S UNIVERSITY, NEW BRUNSWICK, NEW JERSEY (see SAINT PETER'S UNIVERSITY HOSPITAL), p. A419
THE CHILDREN'S HOSPITAL AT SUNY DOWNSTATE,, NEW YORK (see SUNY DOWNSTATE MEDICAL CENTER UNIVERSITY HOSPITAL), p. A448
THE CHILDREN'S HOSPITAL OF ALABAMA, BIRMINGHAM, AL, p. A17
THE CHILDREN'S INSTITUTE OF PITTSBURGH, PITTSBURGH, PA, p. A551
THE CONNECTICUT HOSPICE, BRANFORD, CT, p. A113
THE GOOD SAMARITAN HOSPITAL, LEBANON, PA, p. A543
THE HEALTHCENTER, KALISPELL, MT, p. A389
THE HEART HOSPITAL AT DEACONESS GATEWAY, NEWBURGH, IN, p. A220
THE HEART HOSPITAL BAYLOR DENTON, DENTON, TX, p. A613
THE HEART HOSPITAL BAYLOR PLANO, PLANO, TX, p. A643
THE HOSPITAL AT HEBREW HEALTH CARE, WEST HARTFORD, CT, p. A118
THE HOSPITAL AT WESTLAKE MEDICAL CENTER, AUSTIN, TX, p. A600
THE HOSPITAL OF CENTRAL CONNECTICUT, NEW BRITAIN, CT, p. A115
THE HSC PEDIATRIC CENTER, WASHINGTON, DC, p. A122
THE JEWISH HOSPITAL – MERCY HEALTH, CINCINNATI, OH, p. A487
THE JOSEPH M. SANZARI CHILDREN'S HOSPITAL, HACKENSACK, NEW JERSEY (see HACKENSACK UNIVERSITY MEDICAL CENTER), p. A416
THE KING'S DAUGHTERS HOSPITAL, GREENVILLE, MISSISSIPPI (see DELTA REGIONAL MEDICAL CENTER), p. A358
THE MEDICAL CENTER, COLUMBUS, GA, p. A156
THE MEDICAL CENTER AT ELIZABETH PLACE, DAYTON, OH, p. A492
THE MEDICAL CENTER OF SOUTHEAST TEXAS, PORT ARTHUR, TX, p. A643
THE NEUROMEDICAL CENTER REHABILITATION HOSPITAL, BATON ROUGE, LA, p. A274
THE ORTHOPEDIC SPECIALTY HOSPITAL, MURRAY, UT, p. A661
THE OUTER BANKS HOSPITAL, NAGS HEAD, NC, p. A470
THE PAVILION, CHAMPAIGN, IL, p. A183
THE PAVILION, PENSACOLA, FLORIDA (see WEST FLORIDA HOSPITAL), p. A142
THE PAVILION AT WILLIAMSBURG PLACE, WILLIAMSBURG, VA, p. A680
THE PHYSICIANS CENTRE HOSPITAL, BRYAN, TX, p. A604
THE REHABILITATION HOSPITAL, FORT MYERS, FLORIDA (see LEE MEMORIAL HOSPITAL), p. A129
THE REHABILITATION INSTITUTE OF ST. LOUIS, SAINT LOUIS, MO, p. A382
THE SURGICAL HOSPITAL OF PHOENIX, PHOENIX, AZ, p. A37
THE UNIVERSITY OF KANSAS HOSPITAL, KANSAS CITY, KS, p. A247
THE UNIVERSITY OF KANSAS HOSPITAL – INDIAN CREEK CAMPUS, OVERLAND PARK, KANSAS (see THE UNIVERSITY OF KANSAS HOSPITAL), p. A247
THE UNIVERSITY OF TOLEDO MEDICAL CENTER, TOLEDO, OH, p. A503
THE VILLAGES REGIONAL HOSPITAL, THE VILLAGES, FL, p. A149
THE VINES, OCALA, FL, p. A140
THE WILLIAM W. BACKUS HOSPITAL, NORWICH, CT, p. A116
THE WOMEN'S HOSPITAL, NEWBURGH, IN, p. A220
THE WOODS AT PARKSIDE, GAHANNA, OH, p. A494
THEDA CLARK MEDICAL CENTER, NEENAH, WI, p. A711
THIBODAUX REGIONAL MEDICAL CENTER, THIBODAUX, LA, p. A289
THOMAS B. FINAN CENTER, CUMBERLAND, MD, p. A300
THOMAS H. BOYD MEMORIAL HOSPITAL, CARROLLTON, IL, p. A182
THOMAS HOSPITAL, FAIRHOPE, AL, p. A20
THOMAS JEFFERSON UNIVERSITY HOSPITAL, PHILADELPHIA, PA, p. A550
THOMAS MEMORIAL HOSPITAL, SOUTH CHARLESTON, WV, p. A699
THOREK MEMORIAL HOSPITAL, CHICAGO, IL, p. A187
THOUSAND OAKS SURGICAL HOSPITAL, THOUSAND OAKS, CA, p. A97
THREE GABLES SURGERY CENTER, PROCTORVILLE, OH, p. A501
THREE RIVERS BEHAVIORAL HEALTH, WEST COLUMBIA, SC, p. A571
THREE RIVERS HEALTH, THREE RIVERS, MI, p. A336
THREE RIVERS HOSPITAL, WAVERLY, TN, p. A594
THREE RIVERS HOSPITAL, BREWSTER, WA, p. A682
THREE RIVERS MEDICAL CENTER, LOUISA, KY, p. A265
THROCKMORTON COUNTY MEMORIAL HOSPITAL, THROCKMORTON, TX, p. A653
TIFT REGIONAL MEDICAL CENTER, TIFTON, GA, p. A168

U

W

W. G. (BILL) HEFFNER VETERANS AFFAIRS MEDICAL CENTER, SALISBURY, NC, p. A472
W. J. MANGOLD MEMORIAL HOSPITAL, LOCKNEY, TX, p. A634
WABASH COUNTY HOSPITAL, WABASH, IN, p. A224
WABASH GENERAL HOSPITAL, MOUNT CARMEL, IL, p. A197
WACCAMAW COMMUNITY HOSPITAL, MURRELLS INLET, SC, p. A569
WACO VETERANS AFFAIRS HOSPITAL, WACO, TEXAS (see CENTRAL TEXAS VETERANS HEALTHCARE SYSTEM), p. A652
WADLEY REGIONAL MEDICAL CENTER, TEXARKANA, TX, p. A653
WADLEY REGIONAL MEDICAL CENTER AT HOPE, HOPE, AR, p. A47
WAGNER COMMUNITY MEMORIAL HOSPITAL AVERA, WAGNER, SD, p. A578
WAGONER COMMUNITY HOSPITAL, WAGONER, OK, p. A522
WAHIAWA GENERAL HOSPITAL, WAHIAWA, HI, p. A172
WAKE FOREST BAPTIST HEALTH–DAVIE HOSPITAL, MOCKSVILLE, NC, p. A469
WAKE FOREST BAPTIST HEALTH–LEXINGTON MEDICAL CENTER, LEXINGTON, NC, p. A468
WAKE FOREST BAPTIST MEDICAL CENTER, WINSTON–SALEM, NC, p. A475
WAKE FOREST UNIVERSITY HEALTH SERVICE, WINSTON–SALEM, NC, p. A475
WAKEMED CARY HOSPITAL, CARY, NC, p. A461
WAKEMED RALEIGH CAMPUS, RALEIGH, NC, p. A471
WALBRIDGE MEMORIAL CONVALESCENT WING (see PIONEERS MEDICAL CENTER), p. A110
WALDEN PSYCHIATRIC CARE, WALTHAM, MA, p. A316
WALDO COUNTY GENERAL HOSPITAL, BELFAST, ME, p. A292
WALKER BAPTIST MEDICAL CENTER, JASPER, AL, p. A22
WALLA WALLA GENERAL HOSPITAL, WALLA WALLA, WA, p. A692
WALLACE THOMSON HOSPITAL, UNION, SC, p. A570
WALLOWA MEMORIAL HOSPITAL, ENTERPRISE, OR, p. A524
WALNUT HILL MEDICAL CENTER, DALLAS, TX, p. A612
WALTER B. JONES ALCOHOL AND DRUG ABUSE TREATMENT CENTER, GREENVILLE, NC, p. A465
WALTER KNOX MEMORIAL HOSPITAL, EMMETT, ID, p. A176
WALTER P. REUTHER PSYCHIATRIC HOSPITAL, WESTLAND, MI, p. A337
WALTER REED NATIONAL MILITARY MEDICAL CENTER, BETHESDA, MD, p. A299
WALTHALL COUNTY GENERAL HOSPITAL, TYLERTOWN, MS, p. A365
WAMEGO HEALTH CENTER, WAMEGO, KS, p. A256
WAR MEMORIAL HOSPITAL, SAULT SAINTE MARIE, MI, p. A334
WAR MEMORIAL HOSPITAL, BERKELEY SPRINGS, WV, p. A693
WARD MEMORIAL HOSPITAL, MONAHANS, TX, p. A638
WARM SPRINGS MEDICAL CENTER, WARM SPRINGS, GA, p. A169
WARM SPRINGS REHABILITATION HOSPITAL OF THOUSAND OAKS, SAN ANTONIO, TEXAS (see POST ACUTE/WARM SPRINGS REHABILITATION HOSPITAL OF SAN ANTONIO), p. A647
WARM SPRINGS REHABILITATION HOSPITAL OF WESTOVER HILLS, SAN ANTONIO, TEXAS (see POST ACUTE/WARM SPRINGS REHABILITATION HOSPITAL OF SAN ANTONIO), p. A647
WARRACK CAMPUS, SANTA ROSA, CALIFORNIA (see SUTTER MEDICAL CENTER OF SANTA ROSA, CHANATE CAMPUS), p. A95
WARREN GENERAL HOSPITAL, WARREN, PA, p. A557
WARREN MEMORIAL HOSPITAL, FRIEND, NE, p. A395
WARREN MEMORIAL HOSPITAL, FRONT ROYAL, VA, p. A671
WARREN STATE HOSPITAL, WARREN, PA, p. A557
WARWICK MANOR BEHAVIORAL HEALTH, EAST NEW MARKET, MD, p. A300
WASHAKIE MEDICAL CENTER, WORLAND, WY, p. A723
WASHINGTON ADVENTIST HOSPITAL, TAKOMA PARK, MD, p. A303
WASHINGTON COUNTY HOSPITAL, NASHVILLE, IL, p. A197
WASHINGTON COUNTY HOSPITAL, WASHINGTON, KS, p. A256
WASHINGTON COUNTY HOSPITAL, PLYMOUTH, NC, p. A470
WASHINGTON COUNTY HOSPITAL AND CLINICS, WASHINGTON, IA, p. A238
WASHINGTON COUNTY HOSPITAL AND NURSING HOME, CHATOM, AL, p. A18
WASHINGTON COUNTY MEMORIAL HOSPITAL, POTOSI, MO, p. A379
WASHINGTON COUNTY REGIONAL MEDICAL CENTER, SANDERSVILLE, GA, p. A166
WASHINGTON DC VETERANS AFFAIRS MEDICAL CENTER, WASHINGTON, DC, p. A122

WASHINGTON HOSPITAL, WASHINGTON, PA, p. A557
WASHINGTON HOSPITAL HEALTHCARE SYSTEM, FREMONT, CA, p. A64
WASHINGTON REGIONAL MEDICAL CENTER, FAYETTEVILLE, AR, p. A46
WATAUGA MEDICAL CENTER, BOONE, NC, p. A460
WATERBURY HOSPITAL, WATERBURY, CT, p. A118
WATERTOWN REGIONAL MEDICAL CENTER, WATERTOWN, WI, p. A717
WATSONVILLE COMMUNITY HOSPITAL, WATSONVILLE, CA, p. A100
WAUKESHA COUNTY MENTAL HEALTH CENTER, WAUKESHA, WI, p. A717
WAUKESHA MEMORIAL HOSPITAL, WAUKESHA, WI, p. A717
WAUPUN MEMORIAL HOSPITAL, WAUPUN, WI, p. A717
WAVERLY HEALTH CENTER, WAVERLY, IA, p. A239
WAYNE COUNTY HOSPITAL, CORYDON, IA, p. A228
WAYNE COUNTY HOSPITAL, MONTICELLO, KY, p. A267
WAYNE GENERAL HOSPITAL, WAYNESBORO, MS, p. A366
WAYNE HOSPITAL, GREENVILLE, OH, p. A495
WAYNE MEDICAL CENTER, WAYNESBORO, TN, p. A594
WAYNE MEMORIAL HOSPITAL, JESUP, GA, p. A161
WAYNE MEMORIAL HOSPITAL, GOLDSBORO, NC, p. A465
WAYNE MEMORIAL HOSPITAL, HONESDALE, PA, p. A540
WAYNESBORO HOSPITAL, WAYNESBORO, PA, p. A557
WEATHERFORD REGIONAL HOSPITAL, WEATHERFORD, OK, p. A522
WEATHERFORD REGIONAL MEDICAL CENTER, WEATHERFORD, TX, p. A656
WEBSTER COUNTY COMMUNITY HOSPITAL, RED CLOUD, NE, p. A401
WEBSTER COUNTY MEMORIAL HOSPITAL, WEBSTER SPRINGS, WV, p. A700
WEDOWEE HOSPITAL, WEDOWEE, AL, p. A26
WEED ARMY COMMUNITY HOSPITAL, FORT IRWIN, CA, p. A63
WEEKS MEDICAL CENTER, LANCASTER, NH, p. A410
WEIRTON MEDICAL CENTER, WEIRTON, WV, p. A700
WEISBROD MEMORIAL COUNTY HOSPITAL, EADS, CO, p. A105
WEISER MEMORIAL HOSPITAL, WEISER, ID, p. A179
WEISMAN CHILDREN'S REHABILITATION HOSPITAL, MARLTON, NJ, p. A418
WEKIVA SPRINGS CENTER FOR WOMEN, JACKSONVILLE, FL, p. A132
WELCH COMMUNITY HOSPITAL, WELCH, WV, p. A700
WELLINGTON REGIONAL MEDICAL CENTER, WEST PALM BEACH, FL, p. A150
WELLMONT BRISTOL REGIONAL MEDICAL CENTER, BRISTOL, TN, p. A579
WELLMONT HANCOCK COUNTY HOSPITAL, SNEEDVILLE, TN, p. A593
WELLMONT HAWKINS COUNTY MEMORIAL HOSPITAL, ROGERSVILLE, TN, p. A592
WELLMONT HOLSTON VALLEY MEDICAL CENTER, KINGSPORT, TN, p. A585
WELLMONT LONESOME PINE HOSPITAL, BIG STONE GAP, VA, p. A668
WELLSPAN SURGERY AND REHABILLITATION HOSPITAL, YORK, PENNSYLVANIA (see YORK HOSPITAL), p. A559
WELLSPRING FOUNDATION, BETHLEHEM, CT, p. A113
WELLSTAR COBB HOSPITAL, AUSTELL, GA, p. A154
WELLSTAR DOUGLAS HOSPITAL, DOUGLASVILLE, GA, p. A158
WELLSTAR KENNESTONE HOSPITAL, MARIETTA, GA, p. A163
WELLSTAR PAULDING HOSPITAL, DALLAS, GA, p. A157
WELLSTAR WINDY HILL HOSPITAL, MARIETTA, GA, p. A163
WELLSTONE REGIONAL HOSPITAL, JEFFERSONVILLE, IN, p. A215
WENATCHEE VALLEY MEDICAL CENTER, WENATCHEE, WA, p. A692
WENTWORTH–DOUGLASS HOSPITAL, DOVER, NH, p. A410
WERNERSVILLE STATE HOSPITAL, WERNERSVILLE, PA, p. A557
WESLACO REHABILITATION HOSPITAL, WESLACO, TX, p. A657
WESLEY LONG COMMUNITY HOSPITAL, GREENSBORO, NORTH CAROLINA (see MOSES H. CONE MEMORIAL HOSPITAL), p. A465
WESLEY MEDICAL CENTER, WICHITA, KS, p. A257
WESLEY MEDICAL CENTER, HATTIESBURG, MS, p. A359
WESLEY REHABILITATION HOSPITAL, WICHITA, KS, p. A257
WEST ANAHEIM MEDICAL CENTER, ANAHEIM, CA, p. A55
WEST BOCA MEDICAL CENTER, BOCA RATON, FL, p. A124
WEST BRANCH REGIONAL MEDICAL CENTER, WEST BRANCH, MI, p. A337
WEST CALCASIEU CAMERON HOSPITAL, SULPHUR, LA, p. A289
WEST CAMPUS, NORFOLK, NEBRASKA (see FAITH REGIONAL HEALTH SERVICES), p. A398
WEST CARROLL MEMORIAL HOSPITAL, OAK GROVE, LA, p. A286
WEST CENTRAL GEORGIA REGIONAL HOSPITAL, COLUMBUS, GA, p. A156
WEST CHESTER HOSPITAL, WEST CHESTER, OH, p. A505

WEST FELICIANA PARISH HOSPITAL, SAINT FRANCISVILLE, LA, p. A288
WEST FLORIDA COMMUNITY CARE CENTER, MILTON, FL, p. A138
WEST FLORIDA HOSPITAL, PENSACOLA, FL, p. A142
WEST GABLES REHABILITATION HOSPITAL, MIAMI, FL, p. A138
WEST GEORGIA HEALTH, LA GRANGE, GA, p. A162
WEST HAVEN DIVISION, WEST HAVEN, CONNECTICUT (see VETERANS AFFAIRS CONNECTICUT HEALTHCARE SYSTEM), p. A118
WEST HILLS HOSPITAL, RENO, NV, p. A408
WEST HILLS HOSPITAL AND MEDICAL CENTER,, CA, p. A75
WEST HOLT MEMORIAL HOSPITAL, ATKINSON, NE, p. A393
WEST HOUSTON MEDICAL CENTER, HOUSTON, TX, p. A628
WEST JEFFERSON MEDICAL CENTER, MARRERO, LA, p. A284
WEST MARION COMMUNITY HOSPITAL, OCALA, FLORIDA (see OCALA REGIONAL MEDICAL CENTER), p. A139
WEST OAKS HOSPITAL, HOUSTON, TX, p. A628
WEST PALM BEACH VETERANS AFFAIRS MEDICAL CENTER, WEST PALM BEACH, FL, p. A150
WEST PALM HOSPITAL, WEST PALM BEACH, FL, p. A150
WEST PARK HOSPITAL, CODY, WY, p. A721
WEST PENN HOSPITAL, PITTSBURGH, PA, p. A552
WEST RIVER REGIONAL MEDICAL CENTER, HETTINGER, ND, p. A478
WEST SHORE MEDICAL CENTER, MANISTEE, MI, p. A329
WEST SPRINGS HOSPITAL, GRAND JUNCTION, CO, p. A107
WEST SUBURBAN MEDICAL CENTER, OAK PARK, IL, p. A198
WEST TEXAS VETERANS AFFAIRS HEALTH CARE SYSTEM, BIG SPRING, TX, p. A603
WEST VALLEY HOSPITAL, GOODYEAR, AZ, p. A33
WEST VALLEY HOSPITAL, DALLAS, OR, p. A524
WEST VALLEY MEDICAL CENTER, CALDWELL, ID, p. A175
WEST VIRGINIA UNIVERSITY CHILDREN'S HOSPITAL, MORGANTOWN, WEST VIRGINIA (see WEST VIRGINIA UNIVERSITY HOSPITALS), p. A697
WEST VIRGINIA UNIVERSITY HOSPITALS, MORGANTOWN, WV, p. A697
WESTBURY COMMUNITY HOSPITAL, HOUSTON, TX, p. A628
WESTCHESTER GENERAL HOSPITAL, MIAMI, FL, p. A138
WESTCHESTER MEDICAL CENTER, VALHALLA, NY, p. A457
WESTERLY HOSPITAL, WESTERLY, RI, p. A561
WESTERN ARIZONA REGIONAL MEDICAL CENTER, BULLHEAD CITY, AZ, p. A31
WESTERN MARYLAND HOSPITAL CENTER, HAGERSTOWN, MD, p. A301
WESTERN MARYLAND REGIONAL MEDICAL CENTER, CUMBERLAND, MD, p. A300
WESTERN MASSACHUSETTS HOSPITAL, WESTFIELD, MA, p. A316
WESTERN MEDICAL CENTER ANAHEIM, ANAHEIM, CA, p. A55
WESTERN MEDICAL CENTER–SANTA ANA, SANTA ANA, CA, p. A93
WESTERN MENTAL HEALTH INSTITUTE, BOLIVAR, TN, p. A579
WESTERN MISSOURI MEDICAL CENTER, WARRENSBURG, MO, p. A384
WESTERN NEW YORK CHILDREN'S PSYCHIATRIC CENTER, WEST SENECA, NY, p. A458
WESTERN PLAINS MEDICAL COMPLEX, DODGE CITY, KS, p. A243
WESTERN PSYCHIATRIC INSTITUTE AND CLINIC, PITTSBURGH, PENNSYLVANIA (see UPMC PRESBYTERIAN SHADYSIDE), p. A552
WESTERN REGIONAL MEDICAL CENTER, GOODYEAR, AZ, p. A33
WESTERN STATE HOSPITAL, HOPKINSVILLE, KY, p. A263
WESTERN STATE HOSPITAL, STAUNTON, VA, p. A679
WESTERN STATE HOSPITAL, TACOMA, WA, p. A691
WESTFIELD HOSPITAL, ALLENTOWN, PA, p. A532
WESTFIELD MEMORIAL HOSPITAL, WESTFIELD, NY, p. A458
WESTFIELDS HOSPITAL, NEW RICHMOND, WI, p. A712
WESTLAKE HOSPITAL, MELROSE PARK, IL, p. A196
WESTLAKE REGIONAL HOSPITAL, COLUMBIA, KY, p. A259
WESTON COUNTY HEALTH SERVICES, NEWCASTLE, WY, p. A722
WESTSIDE REGIONAL MEDICAL CENTER, PLANTATION, FL, p. A143
WESTSIDE SURGICAL HOSPITAL, HOUSTON, TX, p. A628
WESTWOOD LODGE HOSPITAL, WESTWOOD, MA, p. A316
WETZEL COUNTY HOSPITAL, NEW MARTINSVILLE, WV, p. A697
WHEATLAND MEMORIAL HEALTHCARE, HARLOWTON, MT, p. A388
WHEATON FRANCISCAN HEALTHCARE – ALL SAINTS, RACINE, WI, p. A714
WHEATON FRANCISCAN HEALTHCARE – ELMBROOK MEMORIAL, BROOKFIELD, WI, p. A703
WHEATON FRANCISCAN HEALTHCARE – FRANKLIN, FRANKLIN, WI, p. A705
WHEATON FRANCISCAN HEALTHCARE – ST. FRANCIS, MILWAUKEE, WI, p. A711

WHEATON FRANCISCAN HEALTHCARE – ST. JOSEPH'S, MILWAUKEE, WI, p. A711

WHEATON FRANCISCAN HEALTHCARE – THE WISCONSIN HEART HOSPITAL, WAUWATOSA, WI, p. A718

WHEELING HOSPITAL, WHEELING, WV, p. A700

WHIDBEY GENERAL HOSPITAL, COUPEVILLE, WA, p. A682

WHIDDEN MEMORIAL HOSPITAL, EVERETT, MASSACHUSETTS (see CAMBRIDGE HEALTH ALLIANCE), p. A309

WHITE COUNTY MEDICAL CENTER, SEARCY, AR, p. A52

WHITE COUNTY MEDICAL CENTER – SOUTH CAMPUS, SEARCY, ARKANSAS (see WHITE COUNTY MEDICAL CENTER), p. A52

WHITE MEMORIAL MEDICAL CENTER, LOS ANGELES, CA, p. A75

WHITE MOUNTAIN REGIONAL MEDICAL CENTER, SPRINGERVILLE, AZ, p. A39

WHITE PLAINS HOSPITAL CENTER, WHITE PLAINS, NY, p. A458

WHITE RIVER JUNCTION VETERANS AFFAIRS MEDICAL CENTER, WHITE RIVER JUNCTION, VT, p. A666

WHITE RIVER MEDICAL CENTER, BATESVILLE, AR, p. A43

WHITESBURG ARH HOSPITAL, WHITESBURG, KY, p. A271

WHITFIELD MEDICAL SURGICAL HOSPITAL, WHITFIELD, MISSISSIPPI (see MISSISSIPPI STATE HOSPITAL), p. A366

WHITING FORENSIC DIVISION OF CONNECTICUT VALLEY HOSPITAL, MIDDLETOWN, CONNECTICUT (see CONNECTICUT VALLEY HOSPITAL), p. A115

WHITINSVILLE MEDICAL CENTER, WHITINSVILLE, MASSACHUSETTS (see MILFORD REGIONAL MEDICAL CENTER), p. A312

WHITMAN HOSPITAL AND MEDICAL CENTER, COLFAX, WA, p. A682

WHITTEN CENTER, CLINTON, SC, p. A564

WHITTIER HOSPITAL MEDICAL CENTER, WHITTIER, CA, p. A100

WHITTIER PAVILION, HAVERHILL, MA, p. A310

WHITTIER REHABILITATION HOSPITAL, BRADFORD, MA, p. A307

WHITTIER REHABILITATION HOSPITAL, WESTBOROUGH, MA, p. A316

WICHITA COUNTY HEALTH CENTER, LEOTI, KS, p. A248

WICKENBURG COMMUNITY HOSPITAL, WICKENBURG, AZ, p. A41

WILBARGER GENERAL HOSPITAL, VERNON, TX, p. A655

WILCOX MEMORIAL HOSPITAL, LIHUE, HI, p. A172

WILD ROSE COMMUNITY MEMORIAL HOSPITAL, WILD ROSE, WI, p. A718

WILKES REGIONAL MEDICAL CENTER, NORTH WILKESBORO, NC, p. A470

WILKES–BARRE GENERAL HOSPITAL, WILKES–BARRE, PA, p. A558

WILKES–BARRE GENERAL HOSPITAL, WILKES–BARRE, PENNSYLVANIA (see WILKES–BARRE GENERAL HOSPITAL), p. A558

WILKES–BARRE VETERANS AFFAIRS MEDICAL CENTER, WILKES–BARRE, PA, p. A558

WILLAMETTE VALLEY MEDICAL CENTER, MCMINNVILLE, OR, p. A526

WILLAPA HARBOR HOSPITAL, SOUTH BEND, WA, p. A690

WILLIAM AND INEZ MABIE SKILLED NURSING FACILITY, HOLLISTER, CALIFORNIA (see HAZEL HAWKINS MEMORIAL HOSPITAL), p. A67

WILLIAM BEAUMONT ARMY MEDICAL CENTER, EL PASO, TX, p. A616

WILLIAM BEE RIRIE HOSPITAL, ELY, NV, p. A404

WILLIAM J. MCCORD ADOLESCENT AND TREATMENT CENTER, ORANGEBURG, SC, p. A569

WILLIAM NEWTON HOSPITAL, WINFIELD, KS, p. A257

WILLIAM R. SHARPE, JR. HOSPITAL, WESTON, WV, p. A700

WILLIAM S. HALL PSYCHIATRIC INSTITUTE, COLUMBIA, SC, p. A564

WILLIAM S. MIDDLETON MEMORIAL VETERANS HOSPITAL, MADISON, WI, p. A708

WILLIAMSBURG REGIONAL HOSPITAL, KINGSTREE, SC, p. A567

WILLIAMSON ARH HOSPITAL, SOUTH WILLIAMSON, KY, p. A270

WILLIAMSON MEDICAL CENTER, FRANKLIN, TN, p. A583

WILLIAMSON MEMORIAL HOSPITAL, WILLIAMSON, WV, p. A700

WILLIAMSPORT REGIONAL MEDICAL CENTER, WILLIAMSPORT, PA, p. A559

WILLIE D. MILLER EYE CENTER, CHATTANOOGA, TENNESSEE (see ERLANGER MEDICAL CENTER), p. A580

WILLINGWAY HOSPITAL, STATESBORO, GA, p. A167

WILLIS–KNIGHTON MEDICAL CENTER, SHREVEPORT, LA, p. A288

WILLIS–KNIGHTON PIERREMONT HEALTH CENTER, SHREVEPORT, LOUISIANA (see WILLIS–KNIGHTON MEDICAL CENTER), p. A288

WILLIS–KNIGHTON SOUTH – THE CENTER FOR WOMEN'S HEALTH, SHREVEPORT, LOUISIANA (see WILLIS–KNIGHTON MEDICAL CENTER), p. A288

WILLOUGH HEALTHCARE SYSTEM, NAPLES, FL, p. A139

WILLOW CREEK WOMEN'S HOSPITAL, JOHNSON, ARKANSAS (see NORTHWEST MEDICAL CENTER – SPRINGDALE), p. A53

WILLOW CREST HOSPITAL, MIAMI, OK, p. A513

WILLOW ROCK CENTER, SAN LEANDRO, CA, p. A92

WILLOW SPRINGS CENTER, RENO, NV, p. A408

WILLS MEMORIAL HOSPITAL, WASHINGTON, GA, p. A169

WILMA N. VAZQUEZ MEDICAL CENTER, VEGA BAJA, PR, p. A729

WILMINGTON HOSPITAL, WILMINGTON, DELAWARE (see CHRISTIANA CARE HEALTH SYSTEM), p. A119

WILMINGTON TREATMENT CENTER, WILMINGTON, NC, p. A474

WILSON MEDICAL CENTER, NEODESHA, KS, p. A250

WILSON MEDICAL CENTER, WILSON, NC, p. A475

WILSON MEMORIAL HOSPITAL, SIDNEY, OH, p. A502

WILSON MEMORIAL REGIONAL MEDICAL CENTER, JOHNSON CITY, NEW YORK (see UNITED HEALTH SERVICES HOSPITALS–BINGHAMTON), p. A434

WINCHESTER HOSPITAL, WINCHESTER, MA, p. A316

WINCHESTER MEDICAL CENTER, WINCHESTER, VA, p. A680

WINDBER MEDICAL CENTER, WINDBER, PA, p. A559

WINDHAM HOSPITAL, WILLIMANTIC, CT, p. A118

WINDHAVEN PSYCHIATRIC HOSPITAL, PRESCOTT VALLEY, AZ, p. A37

WINDMOOR HEALTHCARE OF CLEARWATER, CLEARWATER, FL, p. A125

WINDOM AREA HOSPITAL, WINDOM, MN, p. A354

WINDSOR–LAURELWOOD CENTER FOR BEHAVIORAL MEDICINE, WILLOUGHBY, OH, p. A505

WING MEMORIAL HOSPITAL, PALMER, MA, p. A313

WINKLER COUNTY MEMORIAL HOSPITAL, KERMIT, TX, p. A631

WINN ARMY COMMUNITY HOSPITAL, HINESVILLE, GA, p. A161

WINN PARISH MEDICAL CENTER, WINNFIELD, LA, p. A290

WINNEBAGO MENTAL HEALTH INSTITUTE, WINNEBAGO, WI, p. A719

WINNER REGIONAL HEALTHCARE CENTER, WINNER, SD, p. A578

WINNESHIEK MEDICAL CENTER, DECORAH, IA, p. A229

WINNIE COMMUNITY HOSPITAL, WINNIE, TX, p. A658

WINNIE PALMER HOSPITAL FOR WOMEN AND BABIES, ORLANDO, FLORIDA (see ORLANDO REGIONAL MEDICAL CENTER), p. A141

WINONA HEALTH, WINONA, MN, p. A354

WINSTON MEDICAL CENTER, LOUISVILLE, MS, p. A361

WINTER HAVEN HOSPITAL, WINTER HAVEN, FL, p. A150

WINTER PARK MEMORIAL HOSPITAL, WINTER PARK, FLORIDA (see FLORIDA HOSPITAL), p. A140

WINTHROP–UNIVERSITY HOSPITAL, MINEOLA, NY, p. A441

WIREGRASS MEDICAL CENTER, GENEVA, AL, p. A20

WISE REGIONAL HEALTH SYSTEM, DECATUR, TX, p. A612

WISE REGIONAL HEALTH SYSTEM – BRIDGEPORT CAMPUS, BRIDGEPORT, TEXAS (see WISE REGIONAL HEALTH SYSTEM), p. A612

WISE REGIONAL HEALTH SYSTEM, EAST CAMPUS DECATUR, DECATUR, TEXAS (see WISE REGIONAL HEALTH SYSTEM), p. A612

WISE REGIONAL HEALTH SYSTEM, WEST CAMPUS DECATUR, DECATUR, TEXAS (see WISE REGIONAL HEALTH SYSTEM), p. A612

WISHEK COMMUNITY HOSPITAL AND CLINICS, WISHEK, ND, p. A481

WITHAM MEMORIAL HOSPITAL, LEBANON, IN, p. A217

WK BOSSIER HEALTH CENTER, BOSSIER CITY, LA, p. A274

WM. JENNINGS BRYAN DORN VETERANS AFFAIRS MEDICAL CENTER, COLUMBIA, SC, p. A565

WOLFSON CHILDREN'S HOSPITAL, JACKSONVILLE, FLORIDA (see BAPTIST MEDICAL CENTER JACKSONVILLE), p. A131

WOMACK ARMY MEDICAL CENTER, FORT BRAGG, NC, p. A464

WOMAN'S CHRISTIAN ASSOCIATION HOSPITAL, JAMESTOWN, NY, p. A439

WOMAN'S HOSPITAL, BATON ROUGE, LA, p. A274

WOMAN'S HOSPITAL, FLOWOOD, MS, p. A358

WOMAN'S HOSPITAL OF TEXAS, HOUSTON, TX, p. A628

WOMEN & INFANTS HOSPITAL OF RHODE ISLAND, PROVIDENCE, RI, p. A561

WOMEN AND CHILDREN'S HOSPITAL, CHARLESTON, WEST VIRGINIA (see CHARLESTON AREA MEDICAL CENTER), p. A694

WOMEN AND CHILDREN'S HOSPITAL, BUFFALO, NEW YORK (see KALEIDA HEALTH), p. A434

WOMEN'S AND CHILDREN'S HOSPITAL, LOS ANGELES, CALIFORNIA (see LAC/UNIVERSITY OF SOUTHERN CALIFORNIA MEDICAL CENTER), p. A73

WOMEN'S AND CHILDREN'S HOSPITAL, LAFAYETTE, LOUISIANA (see REGIONAL MEDICAL CENTER OF ACADIANA), p. A282

WOMEN'S AND CHILDREN'S HOSPITAL, COLUMBIA, MISSOURI (see UNIVERSITY OF MISSOURI HOSPITALS AND CLINICS), p. A370

WOMEN'S HOSPITAL OF GREENSBORO, GREENSBORO, NORTH CAROLINA (see MOSES H. CONE MEMORIAL HOSPITAL), p. A465

WOOD COUNTY HOSPITAL, BOWLING GREEN, OH, p. A484

WOODBRIDGE DEVELOPMENT CENTER, WOODBRIDGE, NJ, p. A425

WOODHULL MEDICAL AND MENTAL HEALTH CENTER,, NY, p. A449

WOODLAND HEALTHCARE, WOODLAND, CA, p. A101

WOODLAND HEIGHTS MEDICAL CENTER, LUFKIN, TX, p. A636

WOODLAWN HOSPITAL, ROCHESTER, IN, p. A222

WOODRIDGE HOSPITAL, JOHNSON CITY, TENNESSEE (see JOHNSON CITY MEDICAL CENTER), p. A585

WOODROW WILSON REHABILITATION CENTER, FISHERSVILLE, VA, p. A671

WOODWARD REGIONAL HOSPITAL, WOODWARD, OK, p. A522

WOODWINDS HEALTH CAMPUS, WOODBURY, MN, p. A354

WOOSTER COMMUNITY HOSPITAL, WOOSTER, OH, p. A505

WORCESTER RECOVERY CENTER AND HOSPITAL, WORCESTER, MA, p. A317

WRANGELL MEDICAL CENTER, WRANGELL, AK, p. A30

WRAY COMMUNITY DISTRICT HOSPITAL, WRAY, CO, p. A112

WRIGHT MEMORIAL HOSPITAL, TRENTON, MO, p. A384

WRIGHT PATTERSON MEDICAL CENTER, WRIGHT–PATTERSON AFB, OH, p. A505

WUESTHOFF MEDICAL CENTER – MELBOURNE, MELBOURNE, FL, p. A136

WUESTHOFF MEDICAL CENTER – ROCKLEDGE, ROCKLEDGE, FL, p. A144

WYANDOT MEMORIAL HOSPITAL, UPPER SANDUSKY, OH, p. A503

WYCKOFF HEIGHTS MEDICAL CENTER,, NY, p. A449

WYOMING BEHAVIORAL INSTITUTE, CASPER, WY, p. A720

WYOMING COUNTY COMMUNITY HOSPITAL, WARSAW, NY, p. A457

WYOMING MEDICAL CENTER, CASPER, WY, p. A720

WYOMING STATE HOSPITAL, EVANSTON, WY, p. A721

WYSONG CAMPUS, MCKINNEY, TEXAS (see MEDICAL CENTER OF MCKINNEY), p. A637

WYTHE COUNTY COMMUNITY HOSPITAL, WYTHEVILLE, VA, p. A680

Y

YADKIN VALLEY COMMUNITY HOSPITAL, YADKINVILLE, NC, p. A475

YAKIMA REGIONAL MEDICAL AND CARDIAC CENTER, YAKIMA, WA, p. A692

YAKIMA VALLEY MEMORIAL HOSPITAL, YAKIMA, WA, p. A692

YALE–NEW HAVEN CHILDREN'S HOSPITAL, NEW HAVEN, CONNECTICUT (see YALE–NEW HAVEN HOSPITAL), p. A116

YALE–NEW HAVEN HOSPITAL, NEW HAVEN, CT, p. A116

YALE–NEW HAVEN HOSPITAL–SAINT RAPHAEL CAMPUS, NEW HAVEN, CONNECTICUT (see YALE–NEW HAVEN HOSPITAL), p. A116

YALE–NEW HAVEN PSYCHIATRIC HOSPITAL, NEW HAVEN, CONNECTICUT (see YALE–NEW HAVEN HOSPITAL), p. A116

YALOBUSHA GENERAL HOSPITAL, WATER VALLEY, MS, p. A366

YAMPA VALLEY MEDICAL CENTER, STEAMBOAT SPRINGS, CO, p. A111

YAVAPAI REGIONAL MEDICAL CENTER – EAST, PRESCOTT VALLEY, AZ, p. A37

YAVAPAI REGIONAL MEDICAL CENTER, PRESCOTT, AZ, p. A37

YOAKUM COMMUNITY HOSPITAL, YOAKUM, TX, p. A658

YOAKUM COUNTY HOSPITAL, DENVER CITY, TX, p. A614

YORK GENERAL HOSPITAL, YORK, NE, p. A403

YORK HOSPITAL, YORK, ME, p. A295

YORK HOSPITAL, YORK, PA, p. A559

YOUNKER MEMORIAL REHABILITATION CENTER, DES MOINES, IOWA (see UNITYPOINT HEALTH – IOWA METHODIST MEDICAL CENTER), p. A229

YOUTH VILLAGES INNER HARBOUR CAMPUS, DOUGLASVILLE, GA, p. A158

YUKON–KUSKOKWIM DELTA REGIONAL HOSPITAL, BETHEL, AK, p. A28

YUMA DISTRICT HOSPITAL, YUMA, CO, p. A112

YUMA REGIONAL MEDICAL CENTER, YUMA, AZ, p. A42

YUMA REHABILITATION HOSPITAL, YUMA, AZ, p. A42

Z

ZUCKER HILLSIDE HOSPITAL,, NEW YORK (see LONG ISLAND JEWISH MEDICAL CENTER), p. A445

Index of Health Care Professionals

This section is an index of the key health care professionals for the hospitals and/or health care systems listed in this publication. The index is in alphabetical order, by individual, followed by the title, institutional affiliation, city, state and page reference to the hospital and/or health care system listing in section A and/or B.

A

AAGARD, Kim, Chief Financial Officer, Tri–County Hospital, Wadena, MN, p. A353

AARON, Tracey, Director Human Resources, Novant Health Rowan Medical Center, Salisbury, NC, p. A472

ABAD, Ann, Vice President Operations, Barnes–Jewish St. Peters Hospital, Saint Peters, MO, p. A382

ABAIR, Cynthia, Associate Director, Veterans Affairs San Diego Healthcare System, San Diego, CA, p. A90

ABANG, Toni, M.D. Medical Director, HEALTHSOUTH Lakeview Rehabilitation Hospital, Elizabethtown, KY, p. A260

ABBATIELLO, Michael, Chief Financial Officer, Spring Harbor Hospital, Westbrook, ME, p. A295

ABBOTT, Alan, Vice President Patient Care Services, St. Joseph Regional Medical Center, Lewiston, ID, p. A176

ABBOTT, Jody, Senior Vice President and Chief Operating Officer, North Kansas City Hospital, North Kansas City, MO, p. A378

ABBOTT, Joe, Director Information Systems, North Ottawa Community Hospital, Grand Haven, MI, p. A324

ABBOTT, Justin, M.D. Medical Director, Sevier Valley Medical Center, Richfield, UT, p. A662

ABBOTT, Lisa, Chief Human Resources Officer, Penn State Milton S. Hershey Medical Center, Hershey, PA, p. A540

ABBOTT, Peggy L., President and Chief Executive Officer, Ouachita County Medical Center, Camden, AR, p. A44

ABDA, William, Chief Human Resources Officer, Clarks Summit State Hospital, Clarks Summit, PA, p. A535

ABDELNASER, Mohammad, Chief Nursing Officer, Centinela Hospital Medical Center, Inglewood, CA, p. A67

ABEL, Barbara J., Vice President Human Resources, Heart of the Rockies Regional Medical Center, Salida, CO, p. A111

ABEL, Jeffrey, M.D. Chief Medical Officer, Ogden Regional Medical Center, Ogden, UT, p. A661

ABEL, Kevin, Chief Executive Officer, Lake Chelan Community Hospital, Chelan, WA, p. A682

ABEL, Stacy L., Director Human Resources, Craig Hospital, Englewood, CO, p. A106

ABELLERA, Roland, Chief Quality Officer and Vice President Clinical Operations, St. Bernard Hospital and Health Care Center, Chicago, IL, p. A187

ABELSON, David, M.D., President and Chief Executive Officer, Park Nicollet Methodist Hospital, Minneapolis, MN, p. A347

ABELY, Susan Cerrone, Vice President and Chief Information Officer, Roger Williams Medical Center, Providence, RI, p. A561

ABERCROMBIE, Chelsea, Director Human Resources, South Texas Surgical Hospital, Corpus Christi, TX, p. A608

ABERCROMBIE, David, Chief Executive Officer, Madison County Memorial Hospital, Madison, FL, p. A135

ABERCROMBIE, Zach, Chief Financial Officer, Citizens Baptist Medical Center, Talladega, AL, p. A25

ABERLE, James, Vice President, Chief Operating Officer, Yakima Valley Memorial Hospital, Yakima, WA, p. A692

ABEYTA, Mary Anna, R.N. Chief Nursing/Clinical Services Officer, Holy Cross Hospital, Taos, NM, p. A431

ABINSAY, Alvin, M.D. Chief Medical Staff, Carolinas Hospital System Marion, Mullins, SC, p. A568

ABNEY, Stuart, Controller, Jasper Memorial Hospital, Monticello, GA, p. A164

ABOUD, Al, Chief Financial Officer, East Orange General Hospital, East Orange, NJ, p. A415

ABRAHAM, Akram, M.D. Chief of Staff, Harmon Memorial Hospital, Hollis, OK, p. A512

ABRAHAM, Brian, Chief Operating Officer, Mesquite Rehabilitation Institute, Mesquite, TX, p. A637

ABRAHAMSON–BATY, Sherri, Director Patient Care Services, Cambridge Medical Center, Cambridge, MN, p. A341

ABRAHAMY, Ran, Chief of Staff, University Hospital and Medical Center, Tamarac, FL, p. A147

ABRAMOVITZ, Alan L., Director Human Resources, Saint Luke's North Hospital – Barry Road, Kansas City, MO, p. A374

ABRAMS, Danielle, Manager Human Resources, Marketing and Executive Assistant, St. Vincent Clay Hospital, Brazil, IN, p. A207

ABRAMS, David, Vice President Human Resources, North Memorial Medical Center, Robbinsdale, MN, p. A350

ABRAMS, Denise, Human Resources, Mother Frances Hospital – Jacksonville, Jacksonville, TX, p. A630

ABREU, Astrid J., Executive Director, Hospital Metropolitano Dr. Susoni, Arecibo, PR, p. A724

ABREU, Iris, Supervisor Human Resources, Hospital HMA de Humacao, Humacao, PR, p. A726

ABREU, John, Vice President and Chief Financial Officer, Portneuf Medical Center, Pocatello, ID, p. A177

ABRINA, Sofia
Administrator and Chief Nursing Officer, Garden Grove Hospital and Medical Center, Garden Grove, CA, p. A65
Administrator and Chief Nursing Officer, Huntington Beach Hospital, Huntington Beach, CA, p. A67

ABROMOVICH, Sari, Chief Executive Officer, Harbor Oaks Hospital, New Baltimore, MI, p. A331

ABRUTZ Jr., Joseph F., Administrator, Cameron Regional Medical Center, Cameron, MO, p. A368

ABUIN, Jack, Director Management Information Systems, Mount Sinai Queens, New Rochelle, NY, p. A446

ABUNDO, Manuel, M.D. Chief of Staff, Wahiawa General Hospital, Wahiawa, HI, p. A172

ABY, Sherry, Director Information Management, Carlisle Regional Medical Center, Carlisle, PA, p. A535

ACCASHIAN, Chris, Chief Executive Officer, Parkland Medical Center, Derry, NH, p. A409

ACETO, Anthony, Vice President Human Resources, Norwalk Hospital, Norwalk, CT, p. A116

ACEVEDO, Jose, M.D., President and Chief Executive Officer, Finger Lakes Health, Geneva, NY, p. B58

ACEVEDO, Jose, M.D.,
President and Chief Executive Officer, Geneva General Hospital, Geneva, NY, p. A437
President and Chief Executive Officer, Soldiers and Sailors Memorial Hospital of Yates County, Penn Yan, NY, p. A451

ACEVEDO, Ramon, Supervisor Information Systems, Hospital San Cristobal, Coto Laurel, PR, p. A725

ACHAMALLAH, Nagui, M.D. Chief of Staff, John Muir Behavioral Health Center, Concord, CA, p. A60

ACHEBE, James Bob, M.D. President Medical Staff, South Shore Hospital, Chicago, IL, p. A186

ACHTER, Dick, Chief Financial Officer, Barrett Hospital & HealthCare, Dillon, MT, p. A387

ACKER, Carmen, Chief Financial Officer, Morton Hospital and Medical Center, Taunton, MA, p. A315

ACKER, David B., FACHE, President and CEO, Canton–Potsdam Hospital, Potsdam, NY, p. A452

ACKER, David B., FACHE, President and CEO, St. Lawrence Health System, Potsdam, NY, p. B128

ACKER, Peter W., President, Carolinas Medical Center–Lincoln, Lincolnton, NC, p. A468

ACKERMAN, Sigurd H., M.D., President and Chief Executive Officer, Silver Hill Hospital, New Canaan, CT, p. A116

ACKERS, Allen R., Associate Director, William S. Middleton Memorial Veterans Hospital, Madison, WI, p. A708

ACKERSON, David, Chief Information Officer, Seattle Cancer Care Alliance, Seattle, WA, p. A688

ACKERT, Sara, Associate Director, Sioux Falls Veterans Affairs Health Care System, Sioux Falls, SD, p. A577

ACKISS, Jane, Site Manager Human Resources, Naval Medical Center, Portsmouth, VA, p. A676

ACKLAND, Jeanne, Director of Finance, Fillmore County Hospital, Geneva, NE, p. A396

ACKLEY, Michael
Chief Financial Officer, Kentucky River Medical Center, Jackson, KY, p. A263
Chief Financial Officer, Three Rivers Medical Center, Louisa, KY, p. A265

ACKLIN, Traci, M.D. Chief of Staff, Montgomery General Hospital, Montgomery, WV, p. A697

ACKMAN, Jeffrey D., M.D. Chief of Staff, Shriners Hospitals for Children–Chicago, Chicago, IL, p. A186

ACKMAN, Laura, Chief Operating Officer and Administrator, Essentia Health Northern Pines, Aurora, MN, p. A340

ACOSTA, Ivan, M.D. Medical Director, Hospital De La Concepcion, San German, PR, p. A727

ACOSTA, Louis, M.D. Chief of Staff, Silver Lake Medical Center, Los Angeles, CA, p. A74

ACOSTA, Nannete, Chief Executive Officer, Hospital Metropolitano San German, San German, PR, p. A727

ACOSTA–CARLSON, Francisca, M.D. Chief of Staff, Lexington Regional Health Center, Lexington, NE, p. A397

ACOSTA–CRUZ, Maridel, Chief Executive Officer, Eastern New Mexico Medical Center, Roswell, NM, p. A430

ACREE, Charis, Senior Vice President, West Georgia Health, La Grange, GA, p. A162

ADAIR, Dale K., M.D. Chief Medical Officer, Wernersville State Hospital, Wernersville, PA, p. A557

ADAIR, Julie, Interim Corporate Chief Human Resources Officer, Fresno Heart and Surgical Hospital, Fresno, CA, p. A64

ADAM, Sheryl, Chief Financial Officer, Hanover Hospital, Hanover, PA, p. A245

ADAMO, James D., M.D. Medical Director, Harbor Oaks Hospital, New Baltimore, MI, p. A331

ADAMO, Peter J.
Chief Executive Officer, Lower Bucks Hospital, Bristol, PA, p. A534
Chief Executive Officer, Roxborough Memorial Hospital, Philadelphia, PA, p. A550

ADAMS, Alan L., President, Memorial Hospital, Stilwell, OK, p. A519

ADAMS, Amy B.
Executive Director Human Resources, Laureate Psychiatric Clinic and Hospital, Tulsa, OK, p. A520
Executive Director Human Resources, Saint Francis Hospital, Tulsa, OK, p. A521
Executive Director Human Resources, Saint Francis Hospital South, Tulsa, OK, p. A521

ADAMS, Bob, Director Information Services, Bay Area Hospital, Coos Bay, OR, p. A524

ADAMS, Brian
President and Chief Executive Officer, Florida Hospital at Connerton Long Term Acute Care, Land O'Lakes, FL, p. A134
President and CEO, Florida Hospital Tampa, Tampa, FL, p. A147

ADAMS, Carla A., Chief Nursing Officer and Chief Operating Officer, French Hospital Medical Center, San Luis Obispo, CA, p. A93

ADAMS, Charlotte, Director Associate Resources, Carolina Pines Regional Medical Center, Hartsville, SC, p. A567

ADAMS, Chris, Vice President Operations, Good Samaritan Regional Health Center, Mount Vernon, IL, p. A197

ADAMS, Cynthia, Vice President Human Resources, TriStar StoneCrest Medical Center, Smyrna, TN, p. A593

ADAMS, Cynthia D., R.N. Network Chief Nursing Officer, Community Hospital North, Indianapolis, IN, p. A213

ADAMS, Diane, Director Business Services, Temple Community Hospital, Los Angeles, CA, p. A75

ADAMS, Earl, Chief Information Officer, Indiana University Health La Porte Hospital, La Porte, IN, p. A216

ADAMS, Emmy, Chief Financial Officer, Mayhill Hospital, Denton, TX, p. A613

ADAMS, Essie, Director of Nursing, Kedren Community Mental Health Center, Los Angeles, CA, p. A73

ADAMS, Gini, Director Employee and Public Relations, Yuma District Hospital, Yuma, CO, p. A112

ADAMS, Jason, Chief Operating Officer, Christus St. Vincent Regional Medical Center, Santa Fe, NM, p. A430

ADAMS, Jennifer B., Chief Operating Officer and Chief Financial Officer, Lake City Medical Center, Lake City, FL, p. A133

ADAMS, Jo, Director Human Resources, Donalsonville Hospital, Donalsonville, GA, p. A158

ADAMS, John, Administrator, Willow Rock Center, San Leandro, CA, p. A92

ADAMS, Karen, Vice President Human Resources, Baxter Regional Medical Center, Mountain Home, AR, p. A50

ADAMS, Kelly H., Chief Executive Officer, Desert View Hospital, Pahrump, NV, p. A407

ADAMS, Kimberly, Manager Human Resources, Carroll County Memorial Hospital, Carrollton, KY, p. A259

ADAMS, Mark A., President and Chief Executive Officer, Methodist Rehabilitation Center, Jackson, MS, p. A360

ADAMS, Mark B., Chief Executive Officer, Ogden Regional Medical Center, Ogden, UT, p. A661

ADAMS, Mark C., M.D. Chief Medical Officer, St. Francis Hospital, Federal Way, WA, p. A683

ADAMS, Marlene J., Director Human Resources, Schneider Regional Medical Center, Saint Thomas, VI, p. A729

ADAMS, Mary Jane, R.N. Senior Vice President and Chief Nursing Officer, University of Louisville Hospital, Louisville, KY, p. A266

ADAMS, Mike, M.D. Chief Medical Officer, Gateway Regional Medical Center, Granite City, IL, p. A191

ADAMS, Nancy D., R.N. Senior Vice President and Chief Operating Officer and Chief Nurse Executive, Western Maryland Regional Medical Center, Cumberland, MD, p. A300

ADAMS, Norma, Director Human Resources, Southern Regional Medical Center, Riverdale, GA, p. A165

ADAMS, Patricia, Chief Executive Officer, Select Specialty Hospital–Flint, Flint, MI, p. A324

ADAMS, Patsy, Vice President Human Resources, Redmond Regional Medical Center, Rome, GA, p. A165

ADAMS, Renee, Director Information Technology, Windber Medical Center, Windber, PA, p. A559

ADAMS, Robert H., Vice President Operations, Jersey Shore University Medical Center, Neptune, NJ, p. A419

ADAMS, Robin, Director Human Resources, Reeves Memorial Medical Center, Bernice, LA, p. A274

ADAMS, Scott K., Chief Executive Officer, Pullman Regional Hospital, Pullman, WA, p. A687

ADAMS, Shannon, Chief Financial Officer, Avera Holy Family Hospital, Estherville, IA, p. A230

ADAMS, Sharon, R.N. Senior Vice President Patient Care Services and Chief Quality Officer, Mercy Medical Center, Springfield, MA, p. A315

ADAMS, Shaun, Chief Financial Officer, Harton Regional Medical Center, Tullahoma, TN, p. A593

ADAMS, Shawn, Chief Financial Officer, CHRISTUS Hospital–St. Elizabeth, Beaumont, TX, p. A601

ADAMS, Shelah, Chief Executive Officer, Timberlawn Mental Health System, Dallas, TX, p. A612

ADAMS, Stanley
  Chief Financial Officer, Banner Baywood Medical Center, Mesa, AZ, p. A34
  Chief Financial Officer, Banner Heart Hospital, Mesa, AZ, p. A34

ADAMS, Stephen D., Executive Vice President and Chief Information Officer, UPMC Mercy, Pittsburgh, PA, p. A551

ADAMS, William D., Chief Executive Officer, Knapp Medical Center, Weslaco, TX, p. A657

ADAMSKI, Joseph, Chief Nursing Officer, HEALTHSOUTH Rehabilitation Hospital, Concord, NH, p. A409

ADAMSON, Caren, Chief Operating Officer, Citizens Medical Center, Victoria, TX, p. A655

ADAMSON, James, Chief Executive Officer, Mountain View Hospital, Idaho Falls, ID, p. A176

ADAMSON, Kandi, R.N. Chief Nursing Officer, Indiana University Health Blackford Hospital, Hartford City, IN, p. A213

ADAMSON, Nancy, R.N. Chief Nursing Officer, Banner Estrella Medical Center, Phoenix, AZ, p. A35

ADCOCK, William, Chief Financial Officer, Union General Hospital, Farmerville, LA, p. A277

ADDINGTON, Tom, Chief Information Officer, Saint Michael's Medical Center, Newark, NJ, p. A420

ADDISON, Holland M., M.D. Medical Director, Mississippi Hospital for Restorative Care, Jackson, MS, p. A360

ADDISON, Lenora, Vice President Patient Care and Nursing, MedStar Harbor Hospital, Baltimore, MD, p. A297

ADDISON, Lewis C., Senior Vice President and Chief Financial Officer, Centra Lynchburg General Hospital, Lynchburg, VA, p. A673

ADDLESPERGER, John, D.O. Chief Medical Officer, Sheridan Memorial Hospital, Sheridan, WY, p. A722

ADEDOKUN, Ade, M.D. Medical Director, GLOBALREHAB Hospital – Fort Worth, Fort Worth, TX, p. A618

ADELMAN, Michael, M.D., Director, Erie Veterans Affairs Medical Center, Erie, PA, p. A538

ADEN, Susie, Director of IP Services, Pocahontas Community Hospital, Pocahontas, IA, p. A236

ADER, Michael H., M.D. Vice President Medical Affairs, Hanover Hospital, Hanover, PA, p. A540

ADERHOLD, Pat, Director Human Resources, J. Arthur Dosher Memorial Hospital, Southport, NC, p. A473

ADERHOLDT, Elizabeth, President and Chief Executive Officer, Genesys Regional Medical Center, Grand Blanc, MI, p. A324

ADKINS, Gary W., Chief Executive Officer, Parkview Noble Hospital, Kendallville, IN, p. A216

ADKINS, Kedrick D., Chief Financial Officer, Mayo Clinic Hospital -- Rochester, Rochester, MN, p. A350

ADKINS, Kevin, Director Human Resources, Green Oaks Hospital, Dallas, TX, p. A610

ADKINS, Paige, Chief Financial Officer, Greenbrier Valley Medical Center, Ronceverte, WV, p. A699

ADKINS, Raymond, Chief Information Officer, Peninsula Regional Medical Center, Salisbury, MD, p. A303

ADKINS, Scott, Manager Information Technology, Vernon Memorial Healthcare, Viroqua, WI, p. A717

ADKINSON, Jessica, Administrator, MMO WestEnd Hospital, Jennings, LA, p. A279

ADLER, Josh, M.D. Chief Medical Officer, UCSF Medical Center, San Francisco, CA, p. A91

ADLER, Kenneth, M.D. Medical Director, Arrowhead Behavioral Health Hospital, Maumee, OH, p. A498

ADLER, Maurita, Director Information Services, Gottlieb Memorial Hospital, Melrose Park, IL, p. A196

ADLER–MARKS, Cathy
  Director Information Technology, Vista Medical Center East, Waukegan, IL, p. A205
  Director Information Technology, Vista Medical Center West, Waukegan, IL, p. A205

ADMA, Vishal, M.D. Medical Director, KVC Prairie Ridge Psychiatric Hospital, Kansas City, KS, p. A247

ADORNATO, Sara F., Executive Director, Barnes–Kasson County Hospital, Susquehanna, PA, p. A555

ADOUR, Sandra, Acting Administrator, Runnells Specialized Hospital of Union County, Berkeley Heights, NJ, p. A413

ADRIAANSE, Steven W., Vice President and Chief Human Resources Officer, Tallahassee Memorial HealthCare, Tallahassee, FL, p. A147

ADUDDELL, Chad S., President, St. Vincent Infirmary Medical Center, Little Rock, AR, p. A49

ADVEY, Linda, Manager Information Systems, Glenbeigh Hospital and Outpatient Centers, Rock Creek, OH, p. A501

AFANEH, Bassam, M.D. Chief of Staff, Deckerville Community Hospital, Deckerville, MI, p. A321

AFENYA, Kenneth, M.D. Chief of Staff, Baptist Memorial Hospital–Tipton, Covington, TN, p. A582

AFLAK, Ziba, Chief Financial Officer, Kindred Hospital–San Francisco Bay Area, San Leandro, CA, p. A92

AFONYA, Idatonye I., M.D. Chief of Staff, RiverView Health, Crookston, MN, p. A342

AFZAL, Muhammed, M.D. Chief of Staff, Sutter Medical Center, Sacramento, Sacramento, CA, p. A88

AGANA, Ben, M.D. Medical Director, HEALTHSOUTH Rehabilitation Hospital The Woodlands, Conroe, TX, p. A607

AGBA, C. Okey, Senior Vice President, Chief Financial Officer and Treasurer, Tufts Medical Center, Boston, MA, p. A307

AGEE, Nancy Howell, President and Chief Executive Officer, Carilion Clinic, Roanoke, VA, p. B27

AGENBROAD, Connie, Chief Executive Officer, Othello Community Hospital, Othello, WA, p. A686

AGLIECO, Fabio, D.O. Chief of Staff, Sweeny Community Hospital, Sweeny, TX, p. A651

AGLOINGA, Roy, Chief Administrative Officer, Norton Sound Regional Hospital, Nome, AK, p. A29

AGNEW, Claire, Chief Financial Officer, Banner Gateway Medical Center, Gilbert, AZ, p. A32

AGNEW, Mary Christine, R.N. Vice President and Chief Nursing Officer, Reading Hospital and Medical Center, West Reading, PA, p. A558

AGOSTINI, Scott, Director, Magee Rehabilitation Hospital, Philadelphia, PA, p. A549

AGOSTO, Paula M., R.N. Senior Vice President and Chief Nursing Officer, Children's Hospital of Philadelphia, Philadelphia, PA, p. A547

AGRAWAL, Abha, M.D. Vice President Medical Administration and Chief Operating Officer, Norwegian American Hospital, Chicago, IL, p. A185

AGRESTI, Katie, R.N. Director Patient Care Services, Millcreek Community Hospital, Erie, PA, p. A538

AGUAS, Hugo, Vice President Human Resources, Inova Alexandria Hospital, Alexandria, VA, p. A668

AGUIAR–OLSEN, Rinely, M.D. Medical Director, Yuma Rehabilitation Hospital, Yuma, AZ, p. A42

AGUILA, Marcos, Chief Executive Officer, Hospital San Francisco, San Juan, PR, p. A728

AGUILAR, Gretchen, Director Patient Care and Chief Nursing Officer, Three Rivers Hospital, Brewster, WA, p. A682

AGUILAR, Marisa, Chief Operating Officer, Valley Baptist Medical Center–Brownsville, Brownsville, TX, p. A604

AGUILERA, Louie, Director Information Technology, Foundation Surgical Hospital of El Paso, El Paso, TX, p. A616

AGUINAGA, Miguel, M.D. Medical Director, Advanced Care Hospital of White County, Searcy, AR, p. A52

AGUIRRE, Jose, M.D. Medical Director, Carson Tahoe Continuing Care Hospital, Carson City, NV, p. A404

AHAINE, Israel, Chief Nursing Officer, West Oaks Hospital, Houston, TX, p. A628

AHEARN, Patrick, Chief Operating Officer and Senior Vice President, Saint Barnabas Medical Center, Livingston, NJ, p. A417

AHL, Dennis, Director Information Technology, Jefferson Community Health Center, Fairbury, NE, p. A395

AHLBERG, Suzanne, Director of Nursing, Clay County Medical Center, Clay Center, KS, p. A242

AHLERS, Timothy, Chief Executive Officer, Story County Medical Center, Nevada, IA, p. A235

AHMAD, Yousuf, Divisional Senior Vice President and Chief Network Transformation Officer, Mercy Health – Fairfield Hospital, Fairfield, OH, p. A493

AHMED, Ashraf, M.D. Senior Vice President Physician and Hospital Services, Alliance Community Hospital, Alliance, OH, p. A482

AHMED, Imtiaz, Chief of Staff, Mercy Hospital Ada, Ada, OK, p. A507

AHMED, Mohammed Shafeeq, M.D., Interim President, Baystate Mary Lane Hospital, Ware, MA, p. A316

AHMED, Omar, Acting Manager Human Resources, Veterans Affairs Caribbean Healthcare System, San Juan, PR, p. A729

AHMED, Shabeer A., M.D. Clinical Director, Community Behavioral Health Hospital – Annandale, Annandale, MN, p. A339

AHNER, Dawn, Chief Financial Officer, Renown Rehabilitation Hospital, Reno, NV, p. A408

AHRENS, Dustin, Chief Executive Officer, Liberty Medical Center, Chester, MT, p. A386

AIELLO, Joseph, M.D. Chief of Staff, Asheville Specialty Hospital, Asheville, NC, p. A459

AIELLO, Louis
  Senior Vice President and Chief Financial Officer, Faxton–St. Luke's Healthcare, Utica, NY, p. A456
  Chief Financial Officer, St. Elizabeth Medical Center, Utica, NY, p. A456

AIKEN, Carnel, Director Information Systems, Coastal Carolina Hospital, Hardeeville, SC, p. A567

AIKEN, David, Chief Human Resources Officer, Madigan Healthcare System, Tacoma, WA, p. A690

AIKEN, Richard, M.D. Medical Director, Lakeland Behavioral Health System, Springfield, MO, p. A383

AINSLEY, Howard N., Chief Executive Officer, Morehead Memorial Hospital, Eden, NC, p. A463

AIONA, Michael, M.D. Chief of Staff, Shriners Hospitals for Children–Portland, Portland, OR, p. A529

AIRHART, Steven, Chief Executive Officer, Hartgrove Hospital, Chicago, IL, p. A184

AIROSUS, Diane, Chief Financial Officer, Pembroke Hospital, Pembroke, MA, p. A313

AISEN, Mindy, M.D. Chief Medical Officer, Rancho Los Amigos National Rehabilitation Center, Downey, CA, p. A62

AISENBREY, Lisa, Administrator Human Resources and Support Services, Sidney Health Center, Sidney, MT, p. A391

AITI, Tamer, M.D. Chief of Staff, Union County Hospital, Anna, IL, p. A180

AITKEN, Ian, President and Chief Executive Officer, Menninger Clinic, Houston, TX, p. A626

AJANAH, Muhammed, M.D. Clinical Director, Clifton T. Perkins Hospital Center, Jessup, MD, p. A301

AJMAL, Farooq, Vice President and Chief Information Officer, Nassau University Medical Center, East Meadow, NY, p. A437

AKBARIAN, M., M.D. Medical Director, Kindred Hospital Boston–North Shore, Peabody, MA, p. A313

AKENS, Rick, Director Human Resources, Methodist Medical Center of Oak Ridge, Oak Ridge, TN, p. A591

AKERS, Earl, Supervisor Information Technology, Salina Surgical Hospital, Salina, KS, p. A254

AKERS, Sandra, Bureau Director, Public Health Hospitals, Massachusetts Department of Public Health, Boston, MA, p. B88

AKHRAS, Omar, M.D. Chief of Staff, Putnam General Hospital, Eatonton, GA, p. A159

AKHTAR, Jabir, M.D. Chief of Staff, Marlette Regional Hospital, Marlette, MI, p. A330

AKIN, Pam, Interim Chief Nursing Officer, Wilbarger General Hospital, Vernon, TX, p. A655

AKIN, Pat, Chief Human Resource Officer, Spearfish Regional Surgery Center, Spearfish, SD, p. A577

AKIN, Terry, President and Chief Operating Officer, Moses H. Cone Memorial Hospital, Greensboro, NC, p. A465

AKINS, Tina, Director Human Resources, Lost Rivers Medical Center, Arco, ID, p. A174

AKOPYAN, George, Director Human Resources, Centinela Hospital Medical Center, Inglewood, CA, p. A67

AL–HASHMI, Samer, M.D. Chief Medical Staff, Stevens County Hospital, Hugoton, KS, p. A246

AL–KHOURI, Samir, M.D. Medical Director, Specialty Hospital of Washington–Hadley, Washington, DC, p. A122

ALAGAR, Ravi, M.D. Medical Director, Kindred Hospital–Pittsburgh, Oakdale, PA, p. A547

ALASZEWSKI, Lydia, Chief Nursing Officer, Select Specialty Hospital–Macomb County, Mount Clemens, MI, p. A330

ALBAN, John, Director Information Systems, Advocate Illinois Masonic Medical Center, Chicago, IL, p. A183

ALBANO, Valerie, Director, Human Resources, Regional Hospital for Respiratory and Complex Care, Seattle, WA, p. A688

ALBANY, Karen, Chief Information Officer, Naval Medical Center, Portsmouth, VA, p. A676

ALBARANO, Francis G.
Administrator, St. Vincent Mercy Hospital, Elwood, IN, p. A210
Administrator, St. Vincent Randolph Hospital, Winchester, IN, p. A224

ALBAUGH, Jolene, R.N. Vice President and Chief Nursing Officer, Adventist Bolingbrook Hospital, Bolingbrook, IL, p. A182

ALBAUGH, Rick, Manager Information Services, Southwest Regional Rehabilitation Center, Battle Creek, MI, p. A319

ALBAUM, Michael, M.D. Senior Vice President and Chief Medical Officer, Southern Maine Health Care – Biddeford Medical Center X, Biddeford, ME, p. A292

ALBERG, Ellen, Director Human Resources, Johnson Memorial Health Services, Dawson, MN, p. A342

ALBERT, Debra, MSN Senior Vice President Patient Care and Chief Nursing Officer, University of Chicago Medical Center, Chicago, IL, p. A187

ALBERT, Kristine, Personnel Officer, Riverview Psychiatric Center, Augusta, ME, p. A291

ALBERT, Todd, M.D. Surgeon–in–Chief and Medical Director, Hospital for Special Surgery, New York, NY, p. A444

ALBERTI, Harry, M.D. Chief Medical Officer and Vice President Medical Affairs, Verde Valley Medical Center, Cottonwood, AZ, p. A32

ALBERTINI, Bernie, Chief Administrative Officer, East Ohio Regional Hospital, Martins Ferry, OH, p. A497

ALBERTS, Patrick J., Senior Vice President and Chief Operating Officer, Monongahela Valley Hospital, Monongahela, PA, p. A545

ALBERTS, W. Michael, M.D. Vice President Medical Affairs, H. Lee Moffitt Cancer Center and Research Institute, Tampa, FL, p. A147

ALBERTSON, Robert, M.D. Chief Medical Officer, CareLink of Jackson, Jackson, MI, p. A328

ALBIN, James, Chief Information Officer, St. Luke's Medical Center, Houston, TX, p. A627

ALBRECHT, David L., President, Owatonna Hospital, Owatonna, MN, p. A349

ALBRECHTSEN, Brad, Chief Executive Officer, Marian Center, Salt Lake City, UT, p. A663

ALBRIGHT, Bill, Director Human Resources, Stewart Memorial Community Hospital, Lake City, IA, p. A233

ALBRIGHT, David, M.D. Chief Medical Officer, Brattleboro Memorial Hospital, Brattleboro, VT, p. A665

ALBRIGHT, Leslie, Vice President Information Systems, Bethesda Hospital East, Boynton Beach, FL, p. A124

ALBRIGHT, Sara Z., Vice President Human Resources, Bassett Medical Center, Cooperstown, NY, p. A436

ALBRIGHT, Tammy, Chief Nursing Officer, Takoma Regional Hospital, Greeneville, TN, p. A583

ALBRIGHT, Tina, Vice President Human Resources and Consumer Advocacy, Arkansas Surgical Hospital, North Little Rock, AR, p. A51

ALCALA, Paul, Vice President and Chief Information Officer, NorthBay Medical Center, Fairfield, CA, p. A62

ALCOCER, Deborah, Chief Information Officer, South Texas Rehabilitation Hospital, Brownsville, TX, p. A604

ALDANA, Eladio, Manager Information Systems, College Hospital Costa Mesa, Costa Mesa, CA, p. A60

ALDERFER, Jennifer, Chief Executive Officer, North Suburban Medical Center, Thornton, CO, p. A111

ALDERSON, Charles
Chief Financial Officer, Summa Barberton Citizens Hospital, Barberton, OH, p. A483
Chief Financial Officer, Summa Wadsworth–Rittman Hospital, Wadsworth, OH, p. A504

ALDIS, Karen, Director of Nursing, Harper Hospital District Five, Harper, KS, p. A245

ALDRED, Linda W., Senior Vice President, Texas Children's Hospital, Houston, TX, p. A627

ALDREDGE, Sarah, M.D. Chief Medical Officer, Essentia Health Sandstone, Sandstone, MN, p. A352

ALDRICH, Alan, Chief Financial Officer, Central Montana Medical Center, Lewistown, MT, p. A389

ALDRIDGE, Kenneth, M.D
Vice President Medical Affairs, DCH Regional Medical Center, Tuscaloosa, AL, p. A26
Vice President Medical Affairs, Northport Medical Center, Northport, AL, p. A24

ALEEM, Asaf, M.D. Medical Director, Peachford Behavioral Health System, Atlanta, GA, p. A153

ALEJANDRO, Ausberto, M.D. President, Hospital Santa Rosa, Guayama, PR, p. A726

ALEMAN, Ralph A., President and Chief Executive Officer, Citrus Memorial Health System, Inverness, FL, p. A131

ALEXANDA, Lisa, M.D. Vice President Medical Affairs, Parrish Medical Center, Titusville, FL, p. A149

ALEXANDER, Alan B., Chief Executive Officer, Caverna Memorial Hospital, Horse Cave, KY, p. A263

ALEXANDER, Angie, Chief Executive Officer, Allegiance Behavioral Health Center of Plainview, Plainview, TX, p. A642

ALEXANDER, April, Director Human Resources, Metropolitan Hospital Center, New York, NY, p. A446

ALEXANDER, Bobby, Chief Nursing Officer, Pinnacle Pointe Hospital, Little Rock, AR, p. A49

ALEXANDER, Brian, Chief Administrative Officer, Novato Community Hospital, Novato, CA, p. A80

ALEXANDER, Craig, Fiscal Specialist, Thomas B. Finan Center, Cumberland, MD, p. A300

ALEXANDER, Debra, Chief Information Officer, Safe Haven Hospital of Treasure Valley, Boise, ID, p. A174

ALEXANDER, Fred, M.D. Medical Director, Kaiser Permanente West Los Angeles Medical Center, Los Angeles, CA, p. A72

ALEXANDER, Gene, Chief Financial Officer, MountainView Regional Medical Center, Las Cruces, NM, p. A429

ALEXANDER, Jack, M.D. Chief Medical Officer, Mayo Clinic Health System in Red Wing, Red Wing, MN, p. A350

ALEXANDER, Jane, Director Facility Administrative Services, Sagamore Children's Psychiatric Center, Dix Hills, NY, p. A436

ALEXANDER, Jason P., FACHE, Chief Executive Officer, East Cooper Medical Center, Mount Pleasant, SC, p. A568

ALEXANDER, Jeffrey, Chief Executive Officer, Select Specialty Hospital–Western Missouri, Kansas City, MO, p. A374

ALEXANDER, Jerry, Chief Executive Officer, Regency Hospital of Northwest Arkansas, Fayetteville, AR, p. A45

ALEXANDER, Jr., John, M.D. Chief of Staff, Magnolia Regional Medical Center, Magnolia, AR, p. A49

ALEXANDER, Keith N., Chief Executive Officer, Memorial Hermann Memorial City Medical Center, Houston, TX, p. A625

ALEXANDER, Mary, Interim Chief Executive Officer, Promise Hospital of Dallas, Dallas, TX, p. A611

ALEXANDER, Michael D., MS,
Administrator, Higgins General Hospital, Bremen, GA, p. A154
Interim Chief Executive Officer, Wedowee Hospital, Wedowee, AL, p. A26

ALEXANDER, Pam, R.N. Chief Nursing Officer, Bowie Memorial Hospital, Bowie, TX, p. A603

ALEXANDER, Peter H.
Administrator, St. Vincent Seton Specialty Hospital, Indianapolis, IN, p. A215
Administrator, St. Vincent Seton Specialty Hospital, Lafayette, IN, p. A217

ALEXANDER, Richmond, M.D. President Medical Staff, Specialty Hospital of Meridian, Meridian, MS, p. A363

ALEXANDER, Steven, Executive Director, Bellevue Hospital Center, New York, NY, p. A442

ALEXANDER, Wendy F., Director Human Resources, Louisiana Heart Hospital, Lacombe, LA, p. A280

ALEXANDER–HINES, Joyce, R.N. Associate Director, Patient Care Services, Fayetteville Veterans Affairs Medical Center, Fayetteville, NC, p. A464

ALEXANDER–LANE, Victoria, Chief Executive Officer, Northern Inyo Hospital, Bishop, CA, p. A58

ALFANO, Anthony J., President and Chief Executive Officer, Montefiore New Rochelle, New Rochelle, NY, p. A442

ALFONSO, Eduardo, M.D. Chairman Ophthalmology, Bascom Palmer Eye Institute–Anne Bates Leach Eye Hospital, Miami, FL, p. A136

ALFORD, Charles
Vice President Finance, Vidant Beaufort Hospital, Washington, NC, p. A474
Vice President Financial Services, Vidant Edgecombe Hospital, Tarboro, NC, p. A473

ALFORD, Karla, Chief Information Officer, Greater Regional Medical Center, Creston, IA, p. A228

ALFORD, Michelle, R.N. Director of Nursing, Washington County Hospital and Nursing Home, Chatom, AL, p. A18

ALFRED, Lorrie, Director Human Resources, Southern Surgical Hospital, Slidell, LA, p. A289

ALFSON, Jared, Chief Information Officer, Community Memorial Hospital, Oconto Falls, WI, p. A712

ALGER, Steve, Senior Vice President and Chief Financial Officer, Lakes Regional Healthcare, Spirit Lake, IA, p. A238

ALHADEFF, Joseph, M.D. President, OSS Orthopaedic Specialty Hospital, York, PA, p. A559

ALI, Irfan, Director Information Services, Saint Agnes Medical Center, Fresno, CA, p. A64

ALI, Mahmood, President Medical Staff, Saint Francis Hospital–Bartlett, Bartlett, TN, p. A579

ALI, Mirza Z., M.D. Chief of Staff, Wilkes–Barre Veterans Affairs Medical Center, Wilkes–Barre, PA, p. A558

ALI, Muhammad, M.D. Chief Medical Officer, Sanford Tracy Medical Center, Tracy, MN, p. A353

ALI, Solomon, M.D. Chief of Staff, Fairview Regional Medical Center, Fairview, OK, p. A511

ALI–KHAN, Mir, M.D. Medical Director, Canyon Ridge Hospital, Chino, CA, p. A59

ALICEA, Luis, Chief Information Officer, Doctors' Center Hospital San Juan, San Juan, PR, p. A728

ALICEA PEREZ, Eneida, Interim Nursing Director, Hospital Buen Samaritano, Aguadilla, PR, p. A724

ALIFF, Sarah, Vice President Patient Care Service and Chief Nursing Officer, Mercy Hospital, Devils Lake, ND, p. A477

ALKHOULI, Hassan, M.D
Chief Medical Officer, Garden Grove Hospital and Medical Center, Garden Grove, CA, p. A65
Medical Director, Huntington Beach Hospital, Huntington Beach, CA, p. A67
Chief Medical Officer, West Anaheim Medical Center, Anaheim, CA, p. A55

ALLAIN, Shelly, Director, Texas Health Harris Methodist Hospital Cleburne, Cleburne, TX, p. A606

ALLARD, Joan, Director Human Resources, Heart of Florida Regional Medical Center, Davenport, FL, p. A127

ALLATT, Richard, M.D. Medical Director, HEALTHSOUTH Nittany Valley Rehabilitation Hospital, Pleasant Gap, PA, p. A552

ALLBEE, Roger, Chief Executive Officer and Administrator, Grace Cottage Hospital, Townshend, VT, p. A666

ALLBRITTON, James, Chief Financial Officer, Morehouse General Hospital, Bastrop, LA, p. A273

ALLDREDGE, Kim, Director Human Resources, Lawrence County Memorial Hospital, Lawrenceville, IL, p. A194

ALLEE, Erin, R.N. Director Nursing Services, Royal Oaks Hospital, Windsor, MO, p. A384

ALLEMAN, Scott, Senior Vice President Patient Care Services and Chief Nursing Officer, UW Medicine/Valley Medical Center, Renton, WA, p. A687

ALLEN, Audrey, Coordinator Benefits, Dallas County Medical Center, Fordyce, AR, p. A46

ALLEN, Barbara, M.D. Vice President Medical Affairs, Mother Frances Hospital – Tyler, Tyler, TX, p. A654

ALLEN, Brian, M.D. President Medical Staff, Georgetown Community Hospital, Georgetown, KY, p. A262

ALLEN, Carolyn, Chief Financial Officer, Sharon Hospital, Sharon, CT, p. A117

ALLEN, Claudia, Chief Information Officer, St. John Hospital and Medical Center, Detroit, MI, p. A322

ALLEN, Cyril, M.D. Chief Medical Officer, United Medical Center, Washington, DC, p. A122

ALLEN, David B., Chief Executive Officer, Richland Memorial Hospital, Olney, IL, p. A198

ALLEN, Dawn, R.N. Chief Clinical Officer, Redwood Area Hospital, Redwood Falls, MN, p. A350

ALLEN, Devon, M.D. Chief of Medical Staff, Samuel Simmonds Memorial Hospital, Barrow, AK, p. A28

ALLEN, Donald, Chief Operating Officer, Unity Medical & Surgical Hospital, Mishawaka, IN, p. A219

ALLEN, Douglas H., Senior Vice President Human Resources, Cooper University Health Care, Camden, NJ, p. A414

ALLEN, Elms, M.D
Senior Vice President Medical Affairs, Novant Health Forsyth Medical Center, Winston–Salem, NC, p. A475
Senior Vice President Medical Affairs, Novant Health Medical Park Hospital, Winston–Salem, NC, p. A475

ALLEN, Jane, Director Human Resources and Payroll, Liberty Medical Center, Chester, MT, p. A386

ALLEN, Jason, Director of Nursing, Brook Lane Health Services, Hagerstown, MD, p. A301

ALLEN, Jennifer, Vice President Human Resources, Plantation General Hospital, Plantation, FL, p. A143

ALLEN, Joanne E., President and Chief Executive Officer, Seton Medical Center, Daly City, CA, p. A61

ALLEN, John, Chief Information Officer, Holzer Medical Center, Gallipolis, OH, p. A494

ALLEN, John P., Chief Executive Officer, Regency Hospital of Minneapolis, Golden Valley, MN, p. A344

ALLEN, Judy, Human Resource Specialist, Carl Albert Community Mental Health Center, McAlester, OK, p. A513

ALLEN, Kandice K., R.N., Chief Executive Officer, Share Medical Center, Alva, OK, p. A507

ALLEN, Karen A., R.N. Chief Nursing Officer, Butler Health System, Butler, PA, p. A534

ALLEN, Keith
Senior Vice President and Chief Human Resources Officer, Community Memorial Hospital, Menomonee Falls, WI, p. A709
Senior Vice President and Chief Human Resources Officer, Froedtert Memorial Lutheran Hospital, Milwaukee, WI, p. A710
Senior Vice President Human Resources, St. Joseph's Hospital, West Bend, WI, p. A718

ALLEN, Kent, Director Human Resources, West Branch Regional Medical Center, West Branch, MI, p. A337

ALLEN, Laura
  Chief Financial Officer, Dauterive Hospital, New Iberia, LA, p. A285
  Chief Financial Officer, Texas Health Presbyterian Hospital–WNJ, Sherman, TX, p. A649
ALLEN, Linda, MSN Chief Nursing Officer, Johnston UNC Health Care, Smithfield, NC, p. A473
ALLEN, Linda, Vice President Quality and Information Systems, Monongalia General Hospital, Morgantown, WV, p. A697
ALLEN, Linda M., Vice President Human Resources, The Children's Institute of Pittsburgh, Pittsburgh, PA, p. A551
ALLEN, Lori, Chief Financial Officer, Anthony Medical Center, Anthony, KS, p. A241
ALLEN, Mary Beth, Vice President Human Resources, Emory University Hospital, Atlanta, GA, p. A152
ALLEN, Michael, Chief Financial Officer, Gundersen Health System, La Crosse, WI, p. A707
ALLEN, Mike
  Director Information Services, Shawnee Mission Medical Center, Shawnee Mission, KS, p. A254
  Director Information Technology, Shriners Hospitals for Children–Salt Lake City, Salt Lake City, UT, p. A663
  Director Information Services, Shriners Hospitals for Children–Spokane, Spokane, WA, p. A690
ALLEN, Nancy, R.N. Director, Patient Services and Chief Nursing Executive, Advocate Eureka Hospital, Eureka, IL, p. A189
ALLEN, Nikki, Patient Care Executive, Sutter Amador Hospital, Jackson, CA, p. A67
ALLEN, R. Keith, Senior Vice President Human Resources, University of Maryland Medical Center, Baltimore, MD, p. A298
ALLEN, Richard, Chief Executive Officer, Palmdale Regional Medical Center, Palmdale, CA, p. A82
ALLEN, Robert
  Chief Financial Officer, Keck Hospital of USC, Los Angeles, CA, p. A72
  Chief Financial Officer, University of Southern California–Norris Cancer Hospital, Los Angeles, CA, p. A75
ALLEN, Robert W., FACHE, Chief Executive Officer, Park City Medical Center, Park City, UT, p. A662
ALLEN, Scott J., Director Human Resources, Hudson Hospital and Clinic, Hudson, WI, p. A706
ALLEN, Steve, M.D. Chief Executive Officer, Nationwide Children's Hospital, Columbus, OH, p. A490
ALLEN, Timothy J., FACHE, Chief Executive Officer, Ochsner St. Anne General Hospital, Raceland, LA, p. A287
ALLEN, Timothy M., Vice President Human Resources, United Hospital Center, Bridgeport, WV, p. A693
ALLEN, Tracey, Controller, Central Texas Rehabilitation Hospital, Austin, TX, p. A599
ALLEN, Vicki, Chief Financial Officer, Chicot Memorial Medical Center, Lake Village, AR, p. A48
ALLEN, Vicki, R.N. Vice President Patient Care Services and Chief Nursing Officer, Harnett Health System, Dunn, NC, p. A463
ALLEN, Wain, M.D. Medical Director, Park City Medical Center, Park City, UT, p. A662
ALLEN, Wayne
  Acting Chief Operating Officer, Brooklyn Hospital Center, NY, p. A443
  Interim Chief Executive Officer, Mendocino Coast District Hospital, Fort Bragg, CA, p. A63
  Chief Financial Officer, Mendocino Coast District Hospital, Fort Bragg, CA, p. A63
ALLEN, Zac, CPA Chief Financial Officer, Cherokee Medical Center, Centre, AL, p. A18
ALLEN–JOHNSON, Angela, Director Information Services, Ephraim McDowell Regional Medical Center, Danville, KY, p. A260
ALLENSWORTH, Ed, M.D. Medical Director, Craig General Hospital, Vinita, OK, p. A521
ALLEY, David
  Chief Financial Officer, Starr Regional Medical Center, Athens, TN, p. A579
  Chief Financial Officer, Starr Regional Medical Center–Etowah, Etowah, TN, p. A582
ALLEY, John L., Chief Executive Officer, Woodlawn Hospital, Rochester, IN, p. A222
ALLEY, Steve B., M.D. Chief of Staff, Crosbyton Clinic Hospital, Crosbyton, TX, p. A609
ALLGOOD, Libby, Chief Financial Officer, Kittitas Valley Healthcare, Ellensburg, WA, p. A683
ALLICON, Keary T., Vice President Finance and Chief Financial Officer, Wing Memorial Hospital, Palmer, MA, p. A313
ALLIES, Karla, Director Human Resources, Rosebud Health Care Center, Forsyth, MT, p. A387
ALLINSON, Randy, R.N. Patient Care Services Director, Central Valley Medical Center, Nephi, UT, p. A661

ALLISON, David G., President and Chief Executive Officer, University Medical Center, Lubbock, TX, p. A635
ALLISON, Joel T., Chief Executive Officer, Baylor Scott & White Health, Dallas, TX, p. B22
ALLISON, Shannon, Chief Financial Officer, Houston County Community Hospital, Erin, TN, p. A582
ALLISON, Steve, Director Human Resources, Logan County Hospital, Oakley, KS, p. A251
ALLMAN, Rex, M.D. President Medical Staff, Pulaski Memorial Hospital, Winamac, IN, p. A224
ALLORE, Gary
  Chief Financial Officer, Mercy Health, Hackley Campus, Muskegon, MI, p. A331
  Chief Financial Officer, Mercy Health, Mercy Campus, Muskegon, MI, p. A331
ALLOWAY, Cindy
  President, CHI Health Lakeside, Omaha, NE, p. A399
  President, CHI Health Midlands, Papillion, NE, p. A401
ALLPHIN, Allan, M.D. Chief of Staff, Mercy Hospital Springfield, Springfield, MO, p. A383
ALLPORT, Jeff, Vice President, Chief Information Officer, Valley Presbyterian Hospital, CA, p. A75
ALLRED, Al W., Chief Financial Officer, Bert Fish Medical Center, New Smyrna Beach, FL, p. A139
ALLRED, B. Dee, M.D. President Medical Staff, Jordan Valley Medical Center, West Jordan, UT, p. A664
ALLRED, Lowell C., M.D. Chief of Staff, Columbia Basin Hospital, Ephrata, WA, p. A683
ALLRED, William, M.D. Vice President Medical Affairs, St. John Medical Center, Tulsa, OK, p. A521
ALLSOP, Brian, Director Human Resources, Central Valley Medical Center, Nephi, UT, p. A661
ALLSTOTT, Patti, Administrative Coordinator Human Resources and Grant Writer, Pioneer Memorial Hospital, Heppner, OR, p. A525
ALLSTROM, Sheree, Director Human Resources, Acuity Hospital of South Texas, San Antonio, TX, p. A645
ALLUMS, Allyson, Director Medical Records, North Caddo Medical Center, Vivian, LA, p. A290
ALMANZA, Rhonda, Administrator, Reception and Medical Center, Lake Butler, FL, p. A133
ALMEIDA, Sergio, Director Information Systems, West Houston Medical Center, Houston, TX, p. A628
ALMEIDA–SUAREZ, Mario, M.D. Chief of Staff, Larkin Community Hospital, South Miami, FL, p. A146
ALMENDAREZ, Frank, Chief Operating Officer, Willamette Valley Medical Center, McMinnville, OR, p. A526
ALMENDINGER, J. Todd, President and Chief Executive Officer, Magruder Memorial Hospital, Port Clinton, OH, p. A500
ALMODOVAR, Gustavo, Executive Director, Hospital De La Concepcion, San German, PR, p. A727
ALMOHAMMED, Salah, Chief of Staff, East Texas Medical Center Carthage, Carthage, TX, p. A605
ALO, Kathleen, R.N. Chief Nursing Officer, Mammoth Hospital, Mammoth Lakes, CA, p. A76
ALONSO, Gwen, Chief Nursing Officer, Florida Hospital Zephyrhills, Zephyrhills, FL, p. A150
ALONSO, Jose', M.D. Medical Director, San Juan Capestrano Hospital, San Juan, PR, p. A728
ALONSO, Nancy, Vice President Human Resources, Vista Medical Center East, Waukegan, IL, p. A205
ALONZO, Patti, Manager Human Resources, Pacifica Hospital of the Valley, CA, p. A74
ALPERT, Jeffrey, M.D. Medical Director, Wichita County Health Center, Leoti, KS, p. A248
ALPERT, Len, Director Human Resources, Hollywood Pavilion, FL, p. A130
ALRASHEDY, Farhad H., M.D. Chief Medical Officer, Ferry County Memorial Hospital, Republic, WA, p. A687
ALSIP, Bryan, M.D. Executive Vice President, Chief Medical Officer, University Health System, San Antonio, TX, p. A648
ALSLEBEN, Tony, Director Information Technology, Glencoe Regional Health Services, Glencoe, MN, p. A344
ALSTAD, Nancy, Director Human Resources, Fort HealthCare, Fort Atkinson, WI, p. A705
ALSTON, Dorie, Manager Human Resources, Victory Medical Center Craig Ranch, McKinney, TX, p. A637
ALT, Melinda, Chief Financial Officer, Guthrie County Hospital, Guthrie Center, IA, p. A231
ALTEBARMAKIAN, Varouj, M.D. Physician in Chief, Kaiser Permanente Fresno Medical Center, Fresno, CA, p. A64
ALTENBURGER, Andy, Chief Information Officer, Marietta Memorial Hospital, Marietta, OH, p. A497
ALTENDORF, Amanda, Chief Human Resources and Quality Management, Richard P. Stadter Psychiatric Center, Grand Forks, ND, p. A478
ALTHOEN, David, Director Financial Planning and Analysis, Forest Health Medical Center, Ypsilanti, MI, p. A337
ALTMAN, III, Alexander B., Chief Financial Officer, Union County General Hospital, Clayton, NM, p. A427

ALTMAN, Angela, Market Human Resources Director, Shands Live Oak Regional Medical Center, Live Oak, FL, p. A134
ALTMAN, Brett, President and Chief Executive Officer, Skiff Medical Center, Newton, IA, p. A235
ALTMAN, Harold, M.D. Chief Medical Officer, ACMH Hospital, Kittanning, PA, p. A542
ALTMILLER, Steve, President and Chief Executive Officer, Good Shepherd Health System, Longview, TX, p. B61
ALTMILLER, Steve, President and Chief Executive Officer, Good Shepherd Medical Center, Longview, TX, p. A634
ALTOE, Ann, Senior Director Information Systems and Security Officer, Alfred I. duPont Hospital for Children, Wilmington, DE, p. A120
ALTOM, Andy, Chief Executive Officer, Methodist Behavioral Hospital of Arkansas, Maumelle, AR, p. A50
ALTON, Aaron K., President and Chief Executive Officer, Sisters of Mary of the Presentation Health System, Fargo, ND, p. B125
ALTON, Guy, Chief Financial Officer, St. Bernard Hospital and Health Care Center, Chicago, IL, p. A187
ALTOSE, Murray, M.D. Chief of Staff, Louis Stokes Cleveland Veterans Affairs Medical Center, Cleveland, OH, p. A488
ALTSCHULER, Steven M., M.D., President and Chief Executive Officer, Children's Hospital of Philadelphia, Philadelphia, PA, p. A547
ALTSHULER, Keith, President and Chief Administrative Officer, Fort Sanders Regional Medical Center, Knoxville, TN, p. A585
ALUISE, Tony, Chief Executive Officer, Three Gables Surgery Center, Proctorville, OH, p. A501
ALVARADO, Rafael, Chief Executive Officer, Dr. Pila's Hospital, Ponce, PR, p. A727
ALVARADO, Ramona, Interim Manager Human Resources, Adventist Medical Center–Reedley, Reedley, CA, p. A86
ALVAREZ, Dena C., R.N. COO & Chief Compliance Officer, Brodstone Memorial Hospital, Superior, NE, p. A402
ALVAREZ, Janie, Accounting Director, Cornerstone Regional Hospital, Edinburg, TX, p. A615
ALVAREZ, Jose, M.D. Chief Medical Staff, Circles of Care, Melbourne, FL, p. A135
ALVAREZ, Maria Charlotte, M.D. Chief of Staff, Sheridan Community Hospital, Sheridan, MI, p. A335
ALVAREZ, Mike, M.D. Chief Medical Officer, Dauterive Hospital, New Iberia, LA, p. A285
ALVAREZ, Valerie, Executive Assistant, Adventist Medical Center–Reedley, Reedley, CA, p. A86
ALVERSON, Tammy S., M.D. Chief of Staff, Coshocton County Memorial Hospital, Coshocton, OH, p. A491
ALVES, Richard, Chief Financial Officer, Kaiser Permanente Fresno Medical Center, Fresno, CA, p. A64
ALVEY, Raymond, Chief Financial Officer, Saint Louis University Hospital, Saint Louis, MO, p. A381
ALVIS, Darlene, Chief Human Resources Officer, Banner Churchill Community Hospital, Fallon, NV, p. A404
ALWARD, Dale, Chief Executive Officer, Englewood Community Hospital, Englewood, FL, p. A128
ALWINE, Steven, Chief Executive Officer, HEALTHSOUTH Rehabilitation Hospital of York, York, PA, p. A559
AMADO, Mitchell, Senior Vice President Finance and Chief Financial Officer, Glens Falls Hospital, Glens Falls, NY, p. A438
AMANTEA, Paul, Director Finance, University Hospitals Geauga Medical Center, Chardon, OH, p. A485
AMAR Jr., Eugene, Administrator, Kohala Hospital, Kohala, HI, p. A172
AMBACHER, Linda, Interim Chief Nursing Officer, Hackettstown Regional Medical Center, Hackettstown, NJ, p. A416
AMBROSE, Sherie, Vice President Patient Care Services, Mercy Medical Center Mount Shasta, Mount Shasta, CA, p. A79
AMBROSIANI, Michael, Chief Financial Officer, Knox Community Hospital, Mount Vernon, OH, p. A499
AMEEN, David J., President and Chief Executive Officer, Logansport Memorial Hospital, Logansport, IN, p. A218
AMERSON, Jeff, Director Information System, West Florida Hospital, Pensacola, FL, p. A142
AMES, Becky, Chief Executive Officer, Victory Medical Center Beaumont, Beaumont, TX, p. A602
AMES, Julie
  Chief Information Officer, RML Specialty Hospital, Chicago, IL, p. A186
  Chief Information Officer, RML Specialty Hospital, Hinsdale, IL, p. A193
AMES, Laura, Chief Executive Officer, Arbour Hospital, Boston, MA, p. A305
AMEY, Mark, Chief Information Officer, Keck Hospital of USC, Los Angeles, CA, p. A72
AMIN, Yogesh, M.D. Medical Director, Select Specialty Hospital–Fort Wayne, Fort Wayne, IN, p. A211
AMIRNENI, Vamsee, M.D. Chief of Staff, Mercy Allen Hospital, Oberlin, OH, p. A500

AMMAZZALORSO, Michael, M.D. Chief Medical Officer, Winthrop–University Hospital, Mineola, NY, p. A441

AMMONS, Eric, President, Mercy Hospital Jefferson, Crystal City, MO, p. A370

AMODEO, Jeffrey, M.D. Chief of Staff, Indiana University Health Morgan Hospital, Martinsville, IN, p. A218

AMODO, Mitch, Vice President and Chief Financial Officer, Orange Regional Medical Center, Middletown, NY, p. A441

AMONS, Gene, Administrator, Oceans Behavioral Hospital of Alexandria, Alexandria, LA, p. A272

AMOROSE, Carl, Vice President Finance, Norton Hospital, Louisville, KY, p. A266

AMOROSO, Mitze, Chief Information Officer, Terence Cardinal Cooke Health Care Center, New York, NY, p. A449

AMOS, John
  Chief Executive Officer, Yavapai Regional Medical Center – East, Prescott Valley, AZ, p. A37
  President and Chief Executive Officer, Yavapai Regional Medical Center, Prescott, AZ, p. A37

AMOS, Robert, Vice President and Chief Financial Officer, Winchester Medical Center, Winchester, VA, p. A680

AMROM, George, M.D. Vice President Medical Affairs, Hahnemann University Hospital, Philadelphia, PA, p. A548

AMSBERRY, Shelly, Director of Nursing, Jennie M. Melham Memorial Medical Center, Broken Bow, NE, p. A394

AMSTUTZ, Terry L., FACHE, Vice President and Administrator, Baptist Health Medical Center–Stuttgart, Stuttgart, AR, p. A53

AMYX, Maleigha, Chief Information Officer, Rockcastle Regional Hospital and Respiratory Care Center, Mount Vernon, KY, p. A268

ANASTASI, Frank, Chief Financial Officer, Pennsylvania Hospital, Philadelphia, PA, p. A549

ANAYA, Sandra J., R.N., Chief Executive Officer, Palo Verde Hospital, Blythe, CA, p. A58

ANCHONDO, Laura, Administrator Human Resources, Kindred Hospital El Paso, El Paso, TX, p. A616

ANDARSIO, Carlos, M.D. Chief Medical Officer, Navos, Seattle, WA, p. A688

ANDERMAN, Steven, Chief Operating Officer, Bronx–Lebanon Hospital Center Health Care System, NY, p. A442

ANDERS, Anna, Interim Vice President Patient Care, Carson Tahoe Regional Medical Center, Carson City, NV, p. A404

ANDERS, Jr., James M., Administrator and Chief Operating Officer, Kennedy Krieger Institute, Baltimore, MD, p. A296

ANDERS, Mark, Administrator, Villa Feliciana Medical Complex, Jackson, LA, p. A279

ANDERS, Robert, Chief Financial Officer, Ouachita County Medical Center, Camden, AR, p. A44

ANDERSEN, John, Manager Information Systems, Sunnyside Community Hospital and Clinics, Sunnyside, WA, p. A690

ANDERSEN, Sue
  Chief Financial Officer, French Hospital Medical Center, San Luis Obispo, CA, p. A93
  Chief Financial Officer, Marian Regional Medical Center, Santa Maria, CA, p. A94

ANDERSEN, Toni, R.N. Chief Nurse Executive, Kaiser Permanente Fontana Medical Center, Fontana, CA, p. A63

ANDERSEN, Travis
  President and Chief Executive Officer, Columbia St. Mary's Hospital Milwaukee, Milwaukee, WI, p. A710
  President and Chief Executive Officer, Columbia St. Mary's Ozaukee Hospital, Mequon, WI, p. A709

ANDERSEN, Wendy, Director Human Resources, Eastern Idaho Regional Medical Center, Idaho Falls, ID, p. A176

ANDERSON, A. Elizabeth, Administrator, University of South Alabama Medical Center, Mobile, AL, p. A23

ANDERSON, Allyson, Chief Administrative Officer, Legacy Meridian Park Medical Center, Tualatin, OR, p. A531

ANDERSON, Angie, Director Information Technology, Crawford County Memorial Hospital, Denison, IA, p. A229

ANDERSON, Ashley, Manager Human Resources, Winona Health, Winona, MN, p. A354

ANDERSON, Barbara, Chief Financial Officer, Stanton County Hospital, Johnson, KS, p. A246

ANDERSON, Benjamin, Chief Executive Officer and Administrator, Kearny County Hospital, Lakin, KS, p. A248

ANDERSON, Blake, M.D. Chief of Staff, Parkland Health Center–Bonne Terre, Bonne Terre, MO, p. A367

ANDERSON, Brad, Chief Financial Officer, Community Memorial Hospital, Cloquet, MN, p. A341

ANDERSON, Brian, Chief Financial Officer, Capital Medical Center, Olympia, WA, p. A686

ANDERSON, Cherri, Chief Nursing Officer, Banner Behavioral Health Hospital – Scottsdale, Scottsdale, AZ, p. A38

ANDERSON, Chris, Chief Executive Officer, Mississippi Baptist Health System, Jackson, MS, p. B95

ANDERSON, Craig, Director Management Information Systems, River Bend Hospital, West Lafayette, IN, p. A224

ANDERSON, Darla, Chief Financial Officer, Sibley Medical Center, Arlington, MN, p. A339

ANDERSON, Dave, FACHE Vice President Administration, Carolinas Medical Center–Union, Monroe, NC, p. A469

ANDERSON, David, Chief Executive Officer, Jackson Purchase Medical Center, Mayfield, KY, p. A267

ANDERSON, David K., M.D. Chief of Staff, Timpanogos Regional Hospital, Orem, UT, p. A661

ANDERSON, Debra, Manager Patient Financial Services, Norman Specialty Hospital, Norman, OK, p. A514

ANDERSON, Dianne J., R.N., President and Chief Executive Officer, Lawrence General Hospital, Lawrence, MA, p. A311

ANDERSON, Donna K., R.N. Chief Nursing Officer, Cannon Memorial Hospital, Pickens, SC, p. A569

ANDERSON, Duke, President and Chief Executive Officer, Hillsdale Community Health Center, Hillsdale, MI, p. A326

ANDERSON, Edward, Chief Financial Officer, Johnson Regional Medical Center, Clarksville, AR, p. A44

ANDERSON, Edwin, M.D. Chief of Staff and Chief Medical Officer, Bigfork Valley Hospital, Bigfork, MN, p. A340

ANDERSON, Emily, Director of Nursing Emergency Room, Gundersen Tri–County Hospital and Clinics, Whitehall, WI, p. A718

ANDERSON, Gaynell, M.D. Medical Director, St. Anthony Shawnee Hospital, Shawnee, OK, p. A519

ANDERSON, Gina
  Chief Financial Officer, Mercy Medical Center Mount Shasta, Mount Shasta, CA, p. A79
  Human Resources Officer, Riverview Regional Medical Center, Carthage, TN, p. A579
  Chief Financial Officer, St. Elizabeth Community Hospital, Red Bluff, CA, p. A85

ANDERSON, Gladys, Chief Executive Officer, Houston County Community Hospital, Erin, TN, p. A582

ANDERSON, Greg E., Chief Financial Officer, Emory Health System, Emory University Hospital, Atlanta, GA, p. A152

ANDERSON, Holly, Supervisor Human Resources, Sanford Hospital Rock Rapids, Rock Rapids, IA, p. A237

ANDERSON, J. Bryant, Administrator and Chief Executive Officer, Anthony Medical Center, Anthony, KS, p. A241

ANDERSON, Jason, Chief Financial Officer, Mackinac Straits Health System, Saint Ignace, MI, p. A334

ANDERSON, Jimmy, Director of Information Systems, Regional Hospital of Jackson, Jackson, TN, p. A584

ANDERSON, Joann, President and Chief Executive Officer, Southeastern Health, Lumberton, NC, p. A468

ANDERSON, Jodie, Director Human Resources, Mitchell County Regional Health Center, Osage, IA, p. A236

ANDERSON, John D., FACHE, Administrator, Marshall Medical Center South, Boaz, AL, p. A17

ANDERSON, John G., Vice President, Administrator, Anderson Regional Medical Center–South Campus, Meridian, MS, p. A362

ANDERSON, Kenneth, M.D. Vice President and Chief Medical Officer, Baptist Health Louisville, Louisville, KY, p. A265

ANDERSON, Kimball, FACHE, Chief Executive Officer, Southern Hills Hospital and Medical Center, Las Vegas, NV, p. A406

ANDERSON, Libby, Chief Financial Officer, Satanta District Hospital, Satanta, KS, p. A254

ANDERSON, Lisa, Vice President Nursing, Ferrell Hospital, Eldorado, IL, p. A188

ANDERSON, Lisa K., Vice President Finance, Unity Hospital, Fridley, MN, p. A344

ANDERSON, Lucia E., Senior Vice President Nursing and Chief Nurse Executive, Lake Region Healthcare, Fergus Falls, MN, p. A343

ANDERSON, Mark, Chief Financial Officer, Lane Regional Medical Center, Zachary, LA, p. A290

ANDERSON, Mark T., Chief Financial Officer, Danville Regional Medical Center, Danville, VA, p. A670

ANDERSON, Matthew, Director Human Resources, Davis Hospital and Medical Center, Layton, UT, p. A660

ANDERSON, Michael, M.D. Senior Vice President Quality and Chief Medical Officer, Harrison Medical Center, Bremerton, WA, p. A681

ANDERSON, Michael, Ph.D. Chief Operating Officer, Metropolitan St. Louis Psychiatric Center, Saint Louis, MO, p. A381

ANDERSON, Michael, M.D. Chief Medical Officer, University Hospitals Case Medical Center, Cleveland, OH, p. A489

ANDERSON, Michael S., M.D. Chief of Staff, Southern Virginia Regional Medical Center, Emporia, VA, p. A670

ANDERSON, Patrick, Chief Information Officer, Memorial Medical Center, Modesto, CA, p. A78

ANDERSON, Paula, Administrative Director Human Resources, Endless Mountain Health Systems, Montrose, PA, p. A545

ANDERSON, Randy, DPM Chief Medical Officer, PeaceHealth United General Hospital, Sedro–Woolley, WA, p. A689

ANDERSON, Rhonda
  Executive Vice President Finance and Chief Financial Officer, Columbia St. Mary's Hospital Milwaukee, Milwaukee, WI, p. A710
  Executive Vice President Finance and Chief Financial Officer, Columbia St. Mary's Ozaukee Hospital, Mequon, WI, p. A709
  Executive Vice President Finance and Chief Financial Officer, Sacred Heart Rehabilitation Institute, Milwaukee, WI, p. A711

ANDERSON, Richard A., President and Chief Executive Officer, St. Luke's University Health Network, Bethlehem, PA, p. B128

ANDERSON, Richard A., President and Chief Executive Officer, St. Luke's University Hospital – Bethlehem Campus, Bethlehem, PA, p. A534

ANDERSON, Rick, M.D. Senior Vice President and Chief Medical Officer, TMC Healthcare, Tucson, AZ, p. A41

ANDERSON, Robert C., Interim Chief Financial Officer, Alameda Hospital, Alameda, CA, p. A55

ANDERSON, Rohan, Chief Information Officer, Doctors Memorial Hospital, Bonifay, FL, p. A124

ANDERSON, Roland, M.D., Medical Director, Arkansas Department of Correction Hospital, Pine Bluff, AR, p. A52

ANDERSON, Sandra L., President, St. Clare Hospital, Baraboo, WI, p. A702

ANDERSON, Sharla, Chief Executive Officer, Trinity Mother Frances Rehabilitation Hospital, Tyler, TX, p. A654

ANDERSON, Shawn, Chief Operating Officer, Cary Medical Center, Caribou, ME, p. A292

ANDERSON, Sims, Manager Facility Automation, Terrell State Hospital, Terrell, TX, p. A652

ANDERSON, Stephanie, Executive Vice President and Chief Operating Officer, Woman's Hospital, Baton Rouge, LA, p. A274

ANDERSON, Stephen, M.D
  Chief Medical Officer, Saint Joseph Regional Medical Center, Mishawaka, IN, p. A219
  Chief Medical Officer, Saint Joseph Regional Medical Center–Plymouth Campus, Plymouth, IN, p. A221

ANDERSON, Steven
  Chief Executive Officer, Jordan Valley Medical Center, West Jordan, UT, p. A664
  Chief Executive Officer, Pioneer Valley Hospital, West Valley City, UT, p. A664

ANDERSON, Sue, Senior Vice President, Chief Financial Officer and Chief Information Officer, Virginia Mason Medical Center, Seattle, WA, p. A689

ANDERSON, Susan, Director Information Systems, Texas Health Presbyterian Hospital Plano, Plano, TX, p. A643

ANDERSON, Suzanne P., Nurse Administrator, Intermountain Medical Center, Murray, UT, p. A660

ANDERSON, Thomas, M.D. Vice President Medical Affairs, Chambersburg Hospital, Chambersburg, PA, p. A535

ANDERSON, Thomas, Vice President Medical Affairs, Lakeview Hospital, Stillwater, MN, p. A352

ANDERSON, Thomas, M.D
  Chief of Staff, Portland Veterans Affairs Medical Center, Portland, OR, p. A528
  Vice President Medical Affairs, Waynesboro Hospital, Waynesboro, PA, p. A557

ANDERSON, Jr., Timothy Craig, Chief Nursing Officer, Wellmont Bristol Regional Medical Center, Bristol, TN, p. A579

ANDERSON, Todd, Chief Financial Officer, Grandview Medical Center, Dayton, OH, p. A492

ANDERSON, Traci, Chief Financial Officer, Memorial Hospital, Seminole, TX, p. A648

ANDERSON, Tracy, Chief Information Officer, St. Mary's Regional Medical Center, Enid, OK, p. A510

ANDERSON, William, M.D. Medical Director, Rosebud Health Care Center, Forsyth, MT, p. A387

ANDERSON, Zandra, Chief Financial Officer, Timpanogos Regional Hospital, Orem, UT, p. A661

ANDERT, Nancy, Director Human Resources, Murray County Medical Center, Slayton, MN, p. A352

ANDERT, Vicki, Chief Nursing Officer, Eureka Springs Hospital, Eureka Springs, AR, p. A45

ANDESON, Charles, Chief Medical Officer, Desert Regional Medical Center, Palm Springs, CA, p. A82

ANDRADA, Sally, Chief Information Officer, Los Alamitos Medical Center, Los Alamitos, CA, p. A71

ANDRAE, Andrea
  Chief Financial Officer, Gnaden Huetten Memorial Hospital, Lehighton, PA, p. A543
  Chief Financial Officer, Palmerton Hospital, Palmerton, PA, p. A547

ANDRE, Katelyn, Human Resource Coordinator, Select Specialty Hospital–Macomb County, Mount Clemens, MI, p. A330

ANDREAS, Ginger, Coordinator Personnel and Credentialing, El Campo Memorial Hospital, El Campo, TX, p. A615

ANDREAS, Lori, Director Patient Care Services, Johnson Memorial Health Services, Dawson, MN, p. A342

ANDREASEN, Raymond, M.D. Chief Medical Officer–Inpatient, California Medical Facility, Vacaville, CA, p. A98

ANDRES, Elizabeth, Director Human Resources, Atascadero State Hospital, Atascadero, CA, p. A56

ANDRES, Leonidas, M.D. Chief of Staff, Winnie Community Hospital, Winnie, TX, p. A658

ANDRESEN, Daniel, Chief information Officer, Mercy Medical Center Merced, Merced, CA, p. A77

ANDREW, Larry, M.D. Deputy Commander Clinical Services, Moncrief Army Community Hospital, Fort Jackson, SC, p. A566

ANDREWS, Ashleigh
  Director Human Resources, Riverside Behavioral Health Center, Hampton, VA, p. A672
  Manager Human Resources, Riverside Rehabilitation Institute, Newport News, VA, p. A675

ANDREWS, Callie, Chief Operating Officer, Eastside Medical Center, Snellville, GA, p. A167

ANDREWS, Carolle, Interim Chief Human Resources Officer, University of Connecticut Health Center, John Dempsey Hospital, Farmington, CT, p. A114

ANDREWS, David, Manager Information Systems, Chicot Memorial Medical Center, Lake Village, AR, p. A48

ANDREWS, Fred J., Director of Nursing and Ancillary Services, GLOBALREHAB Hospital – Fort Worth, Fort Worth, TX, p. A618

ANDREWS, Jade, Chief Financial Officer, Methodist Hospital for Surgery, Addison, TX, p. A595

ANDREWS, Jim, Chief Financial Officer, North Okaloosa Medical Center, Crestview, FL, p. A126

ANDREWS, John, M.D. Chief of Staff, East Texas Medical Center Tyler, Tyler, TX, p. A654

ANDREWS, Laurie, Chief Human Resources Officer, Memorial Community Health, Aurora, NE, p. A393

ANDREWS, Lisa, Director Human Resources, Lancaster Rehabilitation Hospital, Lancaster, PA, p. A542

ANDREWS, Maria, MS, Director, Tuscaloosa Veterans Affairs Medical Center, Tuscaloosa, AL, p. A26

ANDREWS, Michael, Coordinator Information Systems, Harlan County Health System, Alma, NE, p. A393

ANDREWS, Michele, Chief Clinical Officer, Integrity Transitional Hospital, Denton, TX, p. A613

ANDREWS, Mike, Administrator and Chief Operating Officer, OCH Regional Medical Center, Starkville, MS, p. A365

ANDREWS, Paul
  Chief Executive Officer, The Brook at Dupont, Louisville, KY, p. A266
  Chief Executive Officer, The Brook Hospital – KMI, Louisville, KY, p. A266

ANDREWS, Rebecca, Chief Financial Officer, Vibra Hospital of Northern California, Redding, CA, p. A85

ANDREWS, Steve, Chief Financial Officer, Three Rivers Health, Three Rivers, MI, p. A336

ANDREWS, Susan, Chief Executive Officer, Valley Regional Medical Center, Brownsville, TX, p. A604

ANDREWS, Terri, Director Information Technology, Alamance Regional Medical Center, Burlington, NC, p. A461

ANDREWS, Terry, Manager Information Technology, Aultman Orrville Hospital, Orrville, OH, p. A500

ANDRITSCH, Scott, Vice President and Chief Financial Officer, Indiana University Health Morgan Hospital, Martinsville, IN, p. A218

ANDRO, Ronald J., Chief Operating Officer, Allegheny General Hospital, Pittsburgh, PA, p. A550

ANDRUS, Helen, Chief Financial Officer, Providence Mount Carmel Hospital, Colville, WA, p. A682

ANDRUS, Jonathon, Chief Executive Officer, Fairchild Medical Center, Yreka, CA, p. A101

ANDRUS, Michael G., Administrator and Chief Executive Officer, Franklin County Medical Center, Preston, ID, p. A178

ANDRUS, Terry W., President, East Alabama Medical Center, Opelika, AL, p. A24

ANDURSKY, John, Chief Financial Officer, Highlands Hospital, Connellsville, PA, p. A536

ANFINSON, Julie, Director Human Resources, Mercy Medical Center–Sioux City, Sioux City, IA, p. A238

ANGALICH, Dave, Director Information Services, Weirton Medical Center, Weirton, WV, p. A700

ANGCO, Manuel, M.D. Chief of Staff, Williamson Memorial Hospital, Williamson, WV, p. A700

ANGELL, Nancy, Associate Administrator Personnel, Sagamore Children's Psychiatric Center, Dix Hills, NY, p. A436

ANGELO, Gregory, Chief Fiscal Program, James J. Peters Veterans Affairs Medical Center, NY, p. A444

ANGELUCCI, Patricia A., MS Director Patient Care Services, Shawano Medical Center, Shawano, WI, p. A715

ANGERAMI, Deborah, Chief Operating Officer, Health First Viera Hospital, Melbourne, FL, p. A136

ANGERMEIER, Elizabeth, Director of Nursing, Evansville Psychiatric Children Center, Evansville, IN, p. A210

ANGLE, Gregory R., Chief Executive Officer, Thousand Oaks Surgical Hospital, Thousand Oaks, CA, p. A97

ANGLE, James L., FACHE,
  Chief Executive Officer, St. Luke's Jerome, Jerome, ID, p. A176
  Regional Chief Executive Officer, St. Luke's Magic Valley Medical Center, Twin Falls, ID, p. A178

ANGLE, Mary Ann, R.N. Chief Nursing Officer, TriStar Summit Medical Center, Hermitage, TN, p. A584

ANGLIN, Jason, Chief Executive Officer, Memorial Medical Center, Port Lavaca, TX, p. A643

ANGUS, Jolyn M., R.N. Chief Nursing Officer, Miami Valley Hospital, Dayton, OH, p. A492

ANHALT, Joel, D.O. Chief of Staff, West Shore Medical Center, Manistee, MI, p. A329

ANKIN, Michael G., M.D
  Vice President Medical Affairs & Chief Medical Officer, Northwestern Lake Forest Hospital, Lake Forest, IL, p. A194
  Vice President Medical Affairs & Chief Medical Officer, Northwestern Memorial Hospital, Chicago, IL, p. A185

ANMUTH, Craig, M.D. Medical Director, Bacharach Institute for Rehabilitation, Pomona, NJ, p. A421

ANNARINO, Phillip, Vice President Human Resources, Fisher–Titus Medical Center, Norwalk, OH, p. A500

ANNECHARICO, Mary Alice
  Chief Information Officer, Henry Ford Hospital, Detroit, MI, p. A322
  Senior VP and CIO, Henry Ford Health System, Henry Ford Wyandotte Hospital, Wyandotte, MI, p. A337

ANNESSER, Sue
  Chief Information Officer, Freeman Hospital West, Joplin, MO, p. A373
  Director Information Systems, Freeman Neosho Hospital, Neosho, MO, p. A377

ANNIS, Donald E., Chief Executive Officer, Crawford Memorial Hospital, Robinson, IL, p. A201

ANOLIK, Adam, Chief Financial Officer, Highland Hospital of Rochester, Rochester, NY, p. A453

ANSELL, David A., M.D. Senior Vice President Clinical Affairs and Chief Medical Officer, Rush University Medical Center, Chicago, IL, p. A186

ANSELL, L. V., M.D. Medical Director, Houston Orthopedic and Spine Hospital, Bellaire, TX, p. A602

ANSELMA, M., Chief Operating Officer, Saint Anthony's Health Center, Alton, IL, p. A180

ANSI, Azena, Manager Health Information Management, Horizon Specialty Hospital, Las Vegas, NV, p. A406

ANSLEY, Pamela, Director Finance, Sutter Center for Psychiatry, Sacramento, CA, p. A87

ANSON, Ashley, Chief Executive Officer, Victory Medical Center Craig Ranch, McKinney, TX, p. A637

ANSON, Crystal, Director Health Information, Fairlawn Rehabilitation Hospital, Worcester, MA, p. A316

ANTCZAK, Kenneth, Vice President Human Resources, St. Mary Mercy Hospital, Livonia, MI, p. A329

ANTES, John, President, Missouri Baptist Medical Center, Saint Louis, MO, p. A381

ANTHONY, Anne G., FACHE, President and Chief Executive Officer, Willow Crest Hospital, Miami, OK, p. A513

ANTHONY, Jean, R.N., President and Chief Executive Officer, Hills & Dales General Hospital, Cass City, MI, p. A320

ANTHONY, Kenneth J., Chief Executive Officer, HEALTHSOUTH Harmarville Rehabilitation Hospital, Pittsburgh, PA, p. A551

ANTHONY, Mark, Executive Vice President and Chief Operating Officer, Borgess Medical Center, Kalamazoo, MI, p. A328

ANTHONY, Michelle, Chief Nursing Officer, HEALTHSOUTH Rehabilitation Hospital of Virginia, Richmond, VA, p. A677

ANTHONY, Paula
  Vice President Information Services, East Texas Medical Center Pittsburg, Pittsburg, TX, p. A642
  Vice President Information Services, East Texas Medical Center Rehabilitation Hospital, Tyler, TX, p. A654
  Vice President Information Services, East Texas Medical Center Specialty Hospital, Tyler, TX, p. A654
  Vice President Information Services, East Texas Medical Center Tyler, Tyler, TX, p. A654

ANTHONY, Sharon, Chief Executive Officer, Select Specialty Hospital–Phoenix, Phoenix, AZ, p. A37

ANTINELLI, Mark, Manager Human Resources, Syracuse Veterans Affairs Medical Center, Syracuse, NY, p. A456

ANTINORI, James, M.D. Chief of Staff, Mountain West Medical Center, Tooele, UT, p. A664

ANTOINE, Greg, M.D. Chief of Staff, Fayetteville Veterans Affairs Medical Center, Fayetteville, NC, p. A464

ANTON, Lourdes, Director Human Resources, Palm Springs General Hospital, Hialeah, FL, p. A130

ANTONACCI, Amy, MSN Vice President Nursing Services, Alliance Community Hospital, Alliance, OH, p. A482

ANTONECCHIA, Paul, M.D. Vice President Medical Affairs, St. John's Riverside Hospital, Yonkers, NY, p. A458

ANTONIADES, Michael A., Executive Vice President and Chief Operating Officer, Robert Wood Johnson University Hospital, New Brunswick, NJ, p. A419

ANTONSON, Pete, Chief Executive Officer, Northwood Deaconess Health Center, Northwood, ND, p. A479

ANTONUCCI, Lawrence, M.D
  Chief Operating Officer, Cape Coral Hospital, Cape Coral, FL, p. A125
  Chief Operating Officer, Gulf Coast Medical Center, Fort Myers, FL, p. A129
  Chief Operating Officer, Lee Memorial Hospital, Fort Myers, FL, p. A129

ANTRUM, Sheila, R.N. Chief Nursing Officer, Director Patient Care Services, UCSF Medical Center, San Francisco, CA, p. A91

ANWAR, Muhammad, M.D. Chief Medical Officer, Encino Hospital Medical Center, CA, p. A71

ANYASO, Vanessa, Chief Human Resources, Tomball Regional Medical Center, Tomball, TX, p. A653

ANZEVENO, Jim, Chief Information Officer, Brigham and Women's Faulkner Hospital, Boston, MA, p. A306

APELES, Neil Christopher R., MSN Chief Nursing Officer, Providence Tarzana Medical Center, CA, p. A74

APIKI, Zessica L., Accountant, Molokai General Hospital, Kaunakakai, HI, p. A172

APLAND, Wendy
  Regional Vice President of Finance/Chief Financial Officer, PeaceHealth Sacred Heart Medical Center at RiverBend, Springfield, OR, p. A530
  Interim Chief Financial Officer, PeaceHealth Sacred Heart Medical Center, University District, Eugene, OR, p. A524

APOLINAR, Adam, Chief Clinical Officer, Victory Medical Center – Southcross, San Antonio, TX, p. A648

APOLIONA, Nicole, M.D. Medical Director, Kula Hospital, Kula, HI, p. A172

APONTE, Miguel, Supervisor Management Information Systems, Wilma N. Vazquez Medical Center, Vega Baja, PR, p. A729

APPENHEIMER, Tim, M.D. Vice President and Chief Medical Officer, Katherine Shaw Bethea Hospital, Dixon, IL, p. A188

APPLE, Donald L., Chief Financial Officer, St. Vincent Anderson Regional Hospital, Anderson, IN, p. A206

APPLEBAUM, Jon D., Chief Executive Officer, Twin County Regional Hospital, Galax, VA, p. A671

APPLEGATE, Amanda, M.D. Chief of Staff, Fleming County Hospital, Flemingsburg, KY, p. A260

APPLEGATE, Mary Jane, Chief Nursing Officer, Knoxville Hospital & Clinics, Knoxville, IA, p. A233

APPLETON, Joe, M.D. Chief of Surgery, Milan General Hospital, Milan, TN, p. A589

APRILE, Patricia, Senior Vice President and Chief Operating Officer, Southern Maine Health Care – Biddeford Medical Center X, Biddeford, ME, p. A292

AQUILINA, Anthony, D.O., Interim Chief Executive Officer, Geisinger–Community Medical Center, Scranton, PA, p. A554

AQUILINA, Joanne, Vice President Finance and Chief Financial Officer, Bethesda Hospital East, Boynton Beach, FL, p. A124

ARAD, Lana
  Chief Financial Officer, Good Samaritan Hospital, San Jose, CA, p. A92
  Chief Financial Officer, MountainView Hospital, Las Vegas, NV, p. A406

ARAGON, Juliette, Finance Director, Turquoise Lodge Hospital, Albuquerque, NM, p. A427

ARAGON, Liz, R.N. Vice President, Chief Nursing Officer, San Antonio Community Hospital, Upland, CA, p. A98

ARAIR, Sohaib, M.D. Chairman of Medical Staff, Pioneer Community Hospital of Newton, Newton, MS, p. A363

ARAMBULA, Frank, Chief Financial Officer, Arrowhead Regional Medical Center, Colton, CA, p. A60

ARAN, Peter P., M.D
  Senior Vice President and Chief Medical Officer, Saint Francis Hospital, Tulsa, OK, p. A521
  Senior Vice President and Chief Medical Officer, Saint Francis Hospital South, Tulsa, OK, p. A521

ARANDA, Heather R., R.N. Chief Nursing Officer, F. W. Huston Medical Center, Winchester, KS, p. A257

ARANIO, Lani, Regional Director Human Resources, Samuel Mahelona Memorial Hospital, Kapaa, HI, p. A172

ARATOW, Michael, M.D. Chief Information Officer, San Mateo Medical Center, San Mateo, CA, p. A93

ARAUJO, Marianne D., R.N. Vice President Nursing and Chief Nurse Executive, Advocate Good Shepherd Hospital, Barrington, IL, p. A181

ARAUJO, Markeeta, Chief Nursing Officer, Desert View Hospital, Pahrump, NV, p. A407

ARBAUGH, Ronnie, Director Human Resources, Grant Memorial Hospital, Petersburg, WV, p. A698

ARBOGEST, Dodie, Chief Financial Officer, Stonewall Jackson Memorial Hospital, Weston, WV, p. A700

ARBOLEDA, Reginaldo, M.D. Chief of Staff, Wild Rose Community Memorial Hospital, Wild Rose, WI, p. A718

ARBON, Don, Vice President Finance, Mid–Columbia Medical Center, The Dalles, OR, p. A530

ARBON, Terron, R.N. Chief Nursing Officer, Salt Lake Regional Medical Center, Salt Lake City, UT, p. A663

ARBONEAUX, Jane, Chief Financial Officer, Prevost Memorial Hospital, Donaldsonville, LA, p. A277

ARBONEAUX, Wayne M., Chief Executive Officer, Assumption Community Hospital, Napoleonville, LA, p. A285

ARBUCKLE, Barry S., Ph.D., President and Chief Executive Officer, MemorialCare, Fountain Valley, CA, p. B91

ARBUTHNOT, Rena, Director Human Resources, Shriners Hospitals for Children–Shreveport, Shreveport, LA, p. A288

ARCANGELI, Barbara J., Vice President Human Resources, Newport Hospital, Newport, RI, p. A560

ARCE, Daisy, Chief of Medical Staff, Weslaco Rehabilitation Hospital, Weslaco, TX, p. A657

ARCENEAUX, Larrie, Chief Clinical Officer, Promise Hospital Baton Rouge – Main Campus, Baton Rouge, LA, p. A273

ARCENEAUX, Susan, R.N. Coordinator Information Technology, Leonard J. Chabert Medical Center, Houma, LA, p. A279

ARCENEAUX, Trina, Assistant Chief Financial Officer, Promise Hospital Baton Rouge – Main Campus, Baton Rouge, LA, p. A273

ARCH, Chrissy, Chief Financial Officer, Cherokee Indian Hospital, Cherokee, NC, p. A462

ARCH, John K., FACHE, Director, Boys Town National Research Hospital, Omaha, NE, p. A399

ARCHAMBAULT, Jennifer, Vice President Human Resources and Compliance, Copley Hospital, Morrisville, VT, p. A665

ARCHAMBEAULT, Shirley, Chief Information Officer, Medical Center of Lewisville, Lewisville, TX, p. A633

ARCHER, David, Director Information Systems, Tristar Centennial Medical Center at Ashland City, Ashland City, TN, p. A579

ARCHER, David L., Chief Executive Officer, Saint Francis Hospital, Memphis, TN, p. A589

ARCHER, Doug, Assistant Administrator, Sutter Tracy Community Hospital, Tracy, CA, p. A97

ARCHER, Joe, Chief Information Officer, Victor Valley Global Medical Center, Victorville, CA, p. A99

ARCHER–DUSTE, Helen, Chief Operating Officer, Kaiser Permanente San Francisco Medical Center, San Francisco, CA, p. A91

ARCHEY, Eugene, Chief Information Technology, Veterans Affairs Greater Los Angeles Healthcare System, Los Angeles, CA, p. A75

ARCHIBOLD, Robert, Director, Human Resources, St. Anthony North Hospital, Westminster, CO, p. A112

ARCHULETA, Michael, Chief Information Technology Officer, Mt. San Rafael Hospital, Trinidad, CO, p. A111

ARCIDI, Alfred J., M.D.,
Senior Vice President, Whittier Rehabilitation Hospital, Bradford, MA, p. A307
Senior Vice President, Whittier Rehabilitation Hospital, Westborough, MA, p. A316

ARCIDI, Alfred L., M.D., President, Whittier Health Network, Haverhill, MA, p. B153

ARCIDI, Alfred L., M.D., Chief Executive Officer, Whittier Pavilion, Haverhill, MA, p. A310

ARCILLA, Jelden, R.N. Vice President and Chief Nursing Officer, John C. Lincoln North Mountain Hospital, Phoenix, AZ, p. A36

ARD, Sheila, Chief Nursing Officer, Huntsville Memorial Hospital, Huntsville, TX, p. A629

ARDABELL, Toni R., R.N., Chief Executive Officer, Bon Secours St. Mary's Hospital, Richmond, VA, p. A677

ARDEMAGNI, Jeff, Chief Financial Officer, Medical Center of Arlington, Arlington, TX, p. A598

ARDION, Doug, M.D. Chief Medical Officer, NCH Downtown Naples Hospital, Naples, FL, p. A138

ARDOIN, Candice, Director Human Resources, Dauterive Hospital, New Iberia, LA, p. A285

ARDOIN, Cody, Director Human Resources, Mercy Regional Medical Center, Ville Platte, LA, p. A290

ARDOIN, Stan, M.D. Medical Director, Griffin Memorial Hospital, Norman, OK, p. A514

ARELLANO, Edgar Alejandro, Chief Information Technologist, Three Rivers Hospital, Brewster, WA, p. A682

ARGIRO, Don
Regional Director Human Resources, Summa Barberton Citizens Hospital, Barberton, OH, p. A483
Regional Director Human Resources, Summa Wadsworth–Rittman Hospital, Wadsworth, OH, p. A504

ARGYROS, Gregory J., M.D. Interim Vice President Medical Affairs, MedStar Washington Hospital Center, Washington, DC, p. A121

ARIAS, Taffy J., R.N. Chief Nursing Officer, Porter Regional Hospital, Valparaiso, IN, p. A223

ARIGLIO, Basil, President and Chief Executive Officer, Rome Memorial Hospital, Rome, NY, p. A453

ARISPE, Joe, Director Information Systems, Wise Regional Health System, Decatur, TX, p. A612

ARIZPE, Robert C., Superintendent, San Antonio State Hospital, San Antonio, TX, p. A647

ARKFELD, Diane, R.N. Vice President, Clinical Nursing, Crawford County Memorial Hospital, Denison, IA, p. A229

ARLEDGE, Amy, Vice President Support Services, St. Luke's Hospital, Columbus, NC, p. A462

ARLEDGE, Denton
Vice President and Chief Information Officer, WakeMed Cary Hospital, Cary, NC, p. A461
Vice President and Chief Information Officer, WakeMed Raleigh Campus, Raleigh, NC, p. A471

ARLEDGE, Will, Administrator, Genesis Behavioral Hospital, Breaux Bridge, LA, p. A275

ARLIEN, Dana, M.D. Chief Medical Officer, Willow Springs Center, Reno, NV, p. A408

ARMADA, Anthony A., Chief Executive, Swedish Health Services, Seattle, WA, p. B131

ARMATO, Carl S., President and Chief Executive Officer, Novant Health, Winston Salem, NC, p. B101

ARMBRUSTER, Kent A W., M.D. Vice President Medical Affairs, Little Company of Mary Hospital and Health Care Centers, Evergreen Park, IL, p. A190

ARMENDARIZ, Elias, Chief Operating Officer and Chief Nursing Officer, El Paso Children's Hospital, El Paso, TX, p. A615

ARMENTROUT, Rich, Chief Financial Officer, Meadows Psychiatric Center, Centre Hall, PA, p. A535

ARMFIELD, Ben, Chief Financial Officer, Fresno Heart and Surgical Hospital, Fresno, CA, p. A64

ARMISTEAD, Russell, Chief Executive Officer, UF Health Jacksonville, Jacksonville, FL, p. A132

ARMOUR, John, Chief Financial Officer, Bayshore Medical Center, Pasadena, TX, p. A641

ARMSTRONG, Alan, M.D. Chief Medical Officer, Pine Rest Christian Mental Health Services, Grand Rapids, MI, p. A325

ARMSTRONG, Deborah, Chief Executive Officer, Rockdale Medical Center, Conyers, GA, p. A157

ARMSTRONG, Evelyn, Chief Nursing Officer, HEALTHSOUTH Rehabilitation Hospital of Erie, Erie, PA, p. A538

ARMSTRONG, Gary, Executive Vice President, Methodist Rehabilitation Center, Jackson, MS, p. A360

ARMSTRONG, James, Manager Information Technology, Delaware Valley Hospital, Walton, NY, p. A457

ARMSTRONG, Jeffrey, CPA Chief Financial Officer, Granville Health System, Oxford, NC, p. A470

ARMSTRONG, Jeremy, FACHE, Chief Executive Officer, Mitchell County Hospital Health Systems, Beloit, KS, p. A242

ARMSTRONG, Karen M., FACHE Senior Vice President and Chief Information Officer, Muncy Valley Hospital, Muncy, PA, p. A546

ARMSTRONG, Ken, Senior Vice President Information, ProMedica Flower Hospital, Sylvania, OH, p. A502

ARMSTRONG, Kim, Chief Financial Officer, Windom Area Hospital, Windom, MN, p. A354

ARMSTRONG, Kyle E., Administrator and Chief Executive Officer, Baptist Memorial Hospital–Collierville, Collierville, TN, p. A581

ARMSTRONG, Marcus, Chief Financial Officer, Bear Valley Community Hospital, Big Bear Lake, CA, p. A58

ARMSTRONG, Mark, M.D. Medical Director, Baylor Medical Center at Uptown, Dallas, TX, p. A609

ARMSTRONG, Neil G., FACHE Vice President and Chief Operating Officer, Divine Providence Hospital, Williamsport, PA, p. A558

ARMSTRONG, Robert, Senior Vice President and Chief Operating Officer, Lima Memorial Health System, Lima, OH, p. A496

ARMSTRONG, Roger
Interim Chief Financial Officer, Pioneers Memorial Healthcare District, Brawley, CA, p. A58
Vice President Finance and Chief Financial Officer, Proctor Hospital, Peoria, IL, p. A200

ARMSTRONG, Sandra, Chief Information Officer, University of Connecticut Health Center, John Dempsey Hospital, Farmington, CT, p. A114

ARMSTRONG, William C.
Senior Vice President and Chief Financial Officer, Mercy Medical Center, Rockville Centre, NY, p. A453
Vice President and Chief Financial Officer, St. Francis Hospital, Roslyn, NY, p. A454

ARMSTRONG–HUFF, Glenda, Assistant Superintendent, Texas Center for Infectious Disease, San Antonio, TX, p. A648

ARNAU, Barbara, R.N. Chief Nursing Officer, Chestatee Regional Hospital, Dahlonega, GA, p. A157

ARNAU, Dede, R.N. Chief Nursing Officer, Elbert Memorial Hospital, Elberton, GA, p. A159

ARNDELL, Scott, Chief Financial Officer, Twin Lakes Regional Medical Center, Leitchfield, KY, p. A264

ARNER, Steven C., President, Carilion Roanoke Memorial Hospital, Roanoke, VA, p. A678

ARNESON, Brenda, Administrative Assistant, St. Andrew's Health Center, Bottineau, ND, p. A476

ARNESON, Garrett
Chief Executive Officer, LifeCare Hospitals of Chester County, West Chester, PA, p. A558
Chief Executive Officer, LifeCare Hospitals of Mechanicsburg, Mechanicsburg, PA, p. A545

ARNETT, Gayle, President and Chief Executive Officer, Susan B. Allen Memorial Hospital, El Dorado, KS, p. A243

ARNETT, Jacob, Chief Information Technology Officer, Lakeside Behavioral Health System, Memphis, TN, p. A588

ARNETT, James, Vice President Human Resources, Meriter Hospital, Madison, WI, p. A708

ARNETT, Randal M., President and Chief Executive Officer, Southern Ohio Medical Center, Portsmouth, OH, p. A501

ARNETT, Sallie, Vice President Information Systems, Licking Memorial Hospital, Newark, OH, p. A499

ARNETT, Stuart
Regional Vice President Finance, Aurora Lakeland Medical Center, Elkhorn, WI, p. A704
Vice President Finance and Chief Financial Officer, Aurora Memorial Hospital of Burlington, Burlington, WI, p. A703

ARNHART, Carol, Controller and Chief Financial Officer, Siskin Hospital for Physical Rehabilitation, Chattanooga, TN, p. A580

ARNOLD, Ann, M.D. Medical Director, Medical Center of Plano, Plano, TX, p. A642

ARNOLD, Bill, Chief Operating Officer, Monmouth Medical Center, Long Branch Campus, Long Branch, NJ, p. A418

ARNOLD, Bobby, President and Chief Executive Officer, Jackson–Madison County General Hospital, Jackson, TN, p. A584

ARNOLD, Bobby, President and Chief Executive Officer, West Tennessee Healthcare, Jackson, TN, p. B152

ARNOLD, Dustin, D.O. Vice President and Chief Medical Officer, UnityPoint Health – St. Luke's Hospital, Cedar Rapids, IA, p. A226

ARNOLD, Jeffrey, M.D. Chief Medical Officer, Santa Clara Valley Medical Center, San Jose, CA, p. A92

ARNOLD, Kevin, President and Chief Executive Officer, Southwest Regional Rehabilitation Center, Battle Creek, MI, p. A319

ARNOLD, Kimberly N., R.N. Chief Nursing Officer and Interim Chief Quality Officer, Woodward Regional Hospital, Woodward, OK, p. A522

ARNOLD, Leslie, Chief Executive Officer and Administrator, St. Vincent Morrilton, Morrilton, AR, p. A50

ARNOLD, Paul, M.D. Chief of Medical Staff, Florida Hospital North Pinellas, Tarpon Springs, FL, p. A148

ARNOLD, Pauline, MSN Chief Nursing and Quality Officer and Vice President Clinical Operations, Indiana University Health La Porte Hospital, La Porte, IN, p. A216

ARNOLD, Scott, Senior Vice President Information Systems, Tampa General Hospital, Tampa, FL, p. A148

ARNOLD, Thomas, Chief Financial Officer, Piedmont Hospital, Atlanta, GA, p. A153

ARNOLD, W. Douglas, President and Chief Executive Officer, Helen Keller Hospital, Sheffield, AL, p. A25

ARNOW, Debra, R.N. VP Patient Care & Chief Nursing Officer, Children's Hospital and Medical Center, Omaha, NE, p. A400

ARNSTON, Hanz, R.N., Chief Executive Officer, Garfield County Health Center, Jordan, MT, p. A388

ARNTZ, Mary, Manager Business Office and Executive Assistant, Physicians' Medical Center, New Albany, IN, p. A220

AROCHO, Jacqueline, Administrator, BayCare Alliant Hospital, Dunedin, FL, p. A127

ARONS, Bernard, M.D. Director Medical Affairs, St. Elizabeths Hospital, Washington, DC, p. A122

ARORA, Gaurau, M.D. Chief Medical Officer, Indiana University Health Tipton Hospital, Tipton, IN, p. A223

ARORA, Pamela, Vice President Information Systerns, Children's Medical Center of Dallas, Dallas, TX, p. A610

ARORA, Sat, M.D. President Medical and Dental Staff, Crozer–Chester Medical Center, Upland, PA, p. A556

ARRINGTON, Rex, Chief Information Officer, Laughlin Memorial Hospital, Greeneville, TN, p. A583

ARROWOOD, Al, Chief Financial Officer, Washington County Hospital, Plymouth, NC, p. A470

ARROYO, Luis A.
Chief Financial Officer, Hospital HIMA San Pablo Caguas, Caguas, PR, p. A725
Chief Financial Officer, Hospital HMA de Humacao, Humacao, PR, p. A726
Chief Financial Officer, Hospital San Pablo Del Este, Fajardo, PR, p. A726

ARSENAULT, Donna, Director Human Resources, Baystate Mary Lane Hospital, Ware, MA, p. A316

ARSENAULT, Lisa, Vice President Human Resources and Compliance, Millinocket Regional Hospital, Millinocket, ME, p. A294

ARSENAULT, Rebecca L., MS, President and Chief Executive Officer, Franklin Memorial Hospital, Farmington, ME, p. A293

ARSLANPAY, Robin, Director Human Resources, LifeCare Hospitals of Pittsburgh, Pittsburgh, PA, p. A551

ARSURA, Edward, M.D. Chief Medical Officer, Richmond University Medical Center, NY, p. A448

ART, Steve, Senior Vice President and Chief Information Officer, Lutheran Medical Center, NY, p. A445

ARTERBURN, Catherine T., R.N. Vice President Human Resources, Sidney Regional Medical Center, Sidney, NE, p. A402

ARTHUR, John
Chief Financial Officer, St. Vincent Mercy Hospital, Elwood, IN, p. A210
Chief Financial Officer, St. Vincent Randolph Hospital, Winchester, IN, p. A224

ARTHUR, Lawrence J., President, Rural Community Hospitals of America, Kansas City, MO, p. B115

ARTHUR, Rita K., Director Human Resources, Littleton Adventist Hospital, Littleton, CO, p. A109

ARTIS, Cornelius, M.D. Chief Medical Officer, Our Community Hospital, Scotland Neck, NC, p. A472

ARTS–STRENKE, Cindy, R.N. Chief Operating Officer and Chief Nursing Officer, Lakeview Medical Center, Rice Lake, WI, p. A714

ARUMUGAM, Roger, M.D. Chief Medical Officer, Highlands Regional Medical Center, Sebring, FL, p. A146

ARUNAMATA, Peti, Interim Area Director Information Technology, Kaiser Permanente San Francisco Medical Center, San Francisco, CA, p. A91

ARVIDSON, Betty, Chief Financial Officer, RiverView Health, Crookston, MN, p. A342

ARVIN, Jon A., M.D. Chief Medical Officer, Rockcastle Regional Hospital and Respiratory Care Center, Mount Vernon, KY, p. A268

ARVON, Christina, Administrator and Chief Executive Officer, Eye and Ear Clinic of Charleston, Charleston, WV, p. A694

ARZE, Steven, M.D. Chief Medical Officer and Vice President Medical Affairs, Baylor Medical Center at Garland, Garland, TX, p. A620

ASADA, Bonnie, Director of Nursing, Alvarado Parkway Institute Behavioral Health System, La Mesa, CA, p. A68

ASAFTEI, Laura, Administrative Director, Florida Hospital Zephyrhills, Zephyrhills, FL, p. A150

ASAOKA, Danny, Executive Director Information Systems, Long Beach Memorial Medical Center, Long Beach, CA, p. A70

ASBERRY, James
Chief Financial Officer, Post Acute/Warm Springs Rehabilitation Hospital of San Antonio, San Antonio, TX, p. A647
Chief Financial Officer, Post Acute/Warm Springs Specialty Hospital of Luling, Luling, TX, p. A636
Chief Financial Officer, Post Acute/Warm Springs Specialty Hospital of Victoria, Victoria, TX, p. A655

ASBURY, Wesley, M.D. President Medical Staff, Princeton Community Hospital, Princeton, WV, p. A698

ASCHOFF, Jodi, Chief Financial Officer, Osmond General Hospital, Osmond, NE, p. A401

ASH, Richard M., Chief Executive Officer, Ortonville Area Health Services, Ortonville, MN, p. A349

ASHBY, F. Michael, M.D. Vice President and Medical Director, Martha Jefferson Hospital, Charlottesville, VA, p. A669

ASHBY, Fred, Director Information Technology, Fort Washington Medical Center, Fort Washington, MD, p. A301

ASHBY, Pamela, Vice President Human Resources, MedStar National Rehabilitation Hospital, Washington, DC, p. A121

ASHCOM, Thomas L., Ph.D., Chief Executive Officer, Kansas Heart Hospital, Wichita, KS, p. A256

ASHE, Patricia, R.N. Chief Nursing Officer, Margaret R. Pardee Memorial Hospital, Hendersonville, NC, p. A466

ASHENFELTER, Kathy, Chief Financial Officer, Swedish Medical Center, Englewood, CO, p. A106

ASHFORD, Michael, Administrator, DeQuincy Memorial Hospital, DeQuincy, LA, p. A277

ASHLEY, Clint, Director, South Mississippi State Hospital, Purvis, MS, p. A364

ASHLEY, Dennis H.
Vice President Human Resources, Montefiore Mount Vernon, Mount Vernon, NY, p. A442
Vice President Human Resources, Montefiore New Rochelle, New Rochelle, NY, p. A442

ASHLEY, Sharon, MSN Chief Nursing Officer, Adams County Regional Medical Center, Seaman, OH, p. A501

ASHLEY, Stanley, M.D. Chief Medical Officer, Brigham and Women's Hospital, Boston, MA, p. A306

ASHMENT, Kerry, Chief Executive Officer, Vibra Hospital of Fort Wayne, Fort Wayne, IN, p. A211

ASHRAF, Mirza, M.D. Medical Director, Carthage Area Hospital, Carthage, NY, p. A435

ASHWORTH, Fred, Chief Financial Officer, Orange Park Medical Center, Orange Park, FL, p. A140

ASKARI, Hasan, M.D. Chief of Staff, Sunbury Community Hospital and Outpatient Center, Sunbury, PA, p. A555

ASKEW, Pam, R.N. Vice President Patient Care Services, UnityPoint Health – Trinity Muscatine, Muscatine, IA, p. A235

ASKEY, Raymond C., CPA, Acting Chief Executive Officer, Nason Hospital, Roaring Spring, PA, p. A553

ASKINAZI, Murray, Senior Vice President and Chief Financial Officer, Lawrence Hospital Center, Bronxville, NY, p. A434

ASKINS, Stephen, M.D. Chief of Staff, Lake City Community Hospital, Lake City, SC, p. A568

ASLIN, Judy, MSN Vice President and Chief Nursing Officer, Southeast Hospital, Cape Girardeau, MO, p. A369

ASPLUND, David, Chief Operating Officer, Motion Picture and Television Fund Hospital and Residential Services, CA, p. A73

ASSAAD, Haney, Vice President Medical Affairs, North Ottawa Community Hospital, Grand Haven, MI, p. A324

ASSAVAPISITKUL, Colleen, Chief Nursing Officer, St. Helena Hospital Clear Lake, Clearlake, CA, p. A60

ASSESSOR, Peggy, Director Information Services, St. Joseph Mercy Port Huron, Port Huron, MI, p. A333

ASTACIO, Benjamin, Director Human Resources, Bella Vista Hospital, Mayaguez, PR, p. A726

ASTLEFORD, Daniel, Vice President Operations, Lafayette Regional Health Center, Lexington, MO, p. A376

ASTON, Brian W., Chief Operating Officer, Mission Hospital, Asheville, NC, p. A460

ATCHLEY, Mark, Vice President and Chief Financial Officer, Medical City Dallas Hospital, Dallas, TX, p. A611

ATEIA, Nashat, M.D. Chief of Staff, Doctors Hospital of West Covina, West Covina, CA, p. A100

ATEN, Byron, Controller, HEALTHSOUTH Rehabilitation Hospital, Albuquerque, NM, p. A426

ATHA, Shannon M., Director Finance, OhioHealth Doctors Hospital Nelsonville, Nelsonville, OH, p. A499

ATHENAIS, Dierdre, Director Human Resources, Colusa Regional Medical Center, Colusa, CA, p. A60

ATHERTON, Dorie, Manager Human Resources, University Behavioral Health of Denton, Denton, TX, p. A613

ATIENZA, Terry S., Director, Grand Junction Veterans Affairs Medical Center, Grand Junction, CO, p. A107

ATKIN, Suzanne, M.D. Chief of Staff and Associate Dean Clinical Affairs, University Hospital, Newark, NJ, p. A420

ATKINS, James
Interim Chief Executive Officer, Bolivar Medical Center, Cleveland, MS, p. A357
Chief Operating Officer, Rockdale Medical Center, Conyers, GA, p. A157

ATKINS, Jim, Director Employee Services, Elks Rehab Hospital, Boise, ID, p. A174

ATKINS, Jodi, Human Resources Specialist, Baptist Medical Center Nassau, Fernandina Beach, FL, p. A128

ATKINS, Melissa, CPA, Chief Executive Officer, Graham County Hospital, Hill City, KS, p. A245

ATKINS, Stephen R., M.D. Medical Director, Southwest Connecticut Mental Health System, Bridgeport, CT, p. A113

ATKINS, Tracy, Chief Operating and Nursing Officer, Orchard Hospital, Gridley, CA, p. A64

ATKINS–GUIDRY, Stephanie, Administrator, USMD Hospital at Fort Worth, Fort Worth, TX, p. A619

ATKINSON, James, M.D. Medical Director, Santa Monica–UCLA Medical Center and Orthopaedic Hospital, Santa Monica, CA, p. A95

ATKINSON, Jodi, President and Chief Executive Officer, St. Andrew's Health Center, Bottineau, ND, p. A476

ATKINSON, Johnie M., Chief Human Resources Officer, Saint Vincent Health Center, Erie, PA, p. A539

ATKINSON, William, Vice President Patient Care Services and Chief Nursing Officer, Christ Hospital, Jersey City, NJ, p. A417

ATTEBERRY, Dave, M.D. Chief of Staff, Yakima Regional Medical and Cardiac Center, Yakima, WA, p. A692

ATTEBERY, Tim, Chief Executive Officer, Wellmont Holston Valley Medical Center, Kingsport, TN, p. A585

ATTEBURY, Mary, Chief Operating Officer, Northwest Missouri Psychiatric Rehabilitation Center, Saint Joseph, MO, p. A380

ATTERBERG, Linda, Chief Information Officer, Keokuk Area Hospital, Keokuk, IA, p. A233

ATTI, Lucretia, Chief Executive Officer, HEALTHSOUTH Rehabilitation Hospital of Erie, Erie, PA, p. A538

ATTLESEY–PRIES, Jacqueline M., R.N. Chief Nursing Officer, Vice President, Boulder Community Hospital, Boulder, CO, p. A102

ATTRIDGE, Scott, Chief Financial Officer, Mid–Valley Hospital, Omak, WA, p. A686

ATTY, James, Chief Executive Officer, Humboldt County Memorial Hospital, Humboldt, IA, p. A232

ATWAL, Money
Chief Financial Officer, Hilo Medical Center, Hilo, HI, p. A170
Chief Financial Officer, Kau Hospital, Pahala, HI, p. A172

ATWELL, Denaye, Manager Human Resources, Muscogee Creek Nation Physical Rehabilitation Center, Okmulgee, OK, p. A517

ATWOOD, Julie, Director Human Resources, San Bernardino Mountains Community Hospital District, Lake Arrowhead, CA, p. A69

ATWOOD, Sheila, R.N. Chief Operating Officer, Kalkaska Memorial Health Center, Kalkaska, MI, p. A328

AUAH, Deb, Supervisor Information Technology, Memorial Community Health, Aurora, NE, p. A393

AUBE–WARREN, Robin C., Director, Veterans Affairs Medical Center, Wilmington, DE, p. A120

AUBEL, Eugenia, President, St. Elizabeth Boardman Health Center, Boardman, OH, p. A484

AUBEL, James, Chief Financial Officer, Jameson Hospital, New Castle, PA, p. A546

AUBRY, Michael, Director Information Systems, Adventist Medical Center – Hanford, Hanford, CA, p. A66

AUBUCHON, Christy, Director Personnel, Washington County Memorial Hospital, Potosi, MO, p. A379

AUBUT, Richard H., R.N., President and Chief Executive Officer, South Shore Hospital, South Weymouth, MA, p. A314

AUCKER, Kendra A., Vice President Operations, Evangelical Community Hospital, Lewisburg, PA, p. A543

AUDET, Stefanie, Director Human Resources, Florida Hospital DeLand, DeLand, FL, p. A127

AUDETT, John R., M.D
Chief Medical Officer, Inova Alexandria Hospital, Alexandria, VA, p. A668
Medical Director Clinical Affairs, Overlook Medical Center, Summit, NJ, p. A423

AUDIRSCH, Lanell, Administrative Assistant, North Caddo Medical Center, Vivian, LA, p. A290

AUER, Kenneth E., Director Human Resources, Unity Hospital, Fridley, MN, p. A344

AUERBACH, Bruce S., President and Chief Executive Officer, Sturdy Memorial Hospital, Attleboro, MA, p. A305

AUERBACH, Jeffrey, D.O. Medical Director, Bon Secours Community Hospital, Port Jervis, NY, p. A452

AUERBACH, Lorraine P., FACHE, President and Chief Executive Officer, Dameron Hospital, Stockton, CA, p. A96

AUFDERHEIDE, Allen D., Chief Executive Officer, Callaway Community Hospital, Fulton, MO, p. A371

AUGSBURGER, Marc, President and Chief Executive Officer, Caro Community Hospital, Caro, MI, p. A320

AUGSBURGER, Tod, Senior Vice President and Chief Operating Officer, Lexington Medical Center, West Columbia, SC, p. A571

AUGUST, Prudence, Chief Information Officer, Palomar Medical Center, Escondido, CA, p. A62

AUGUSTIN, Robert, Director Human Resources, Southern Tennessee Regional Health System–Lawrenceburg, Lawrenceburg, TN, p. A586

AUGUSTIN, III, W. Walter, CPA Vice President Financial Services and Chief Financial Officer, University of Maryland Rehabilitation and Orthopaedic Institute, Baltimore, MD, p. A298

AUGUSTINE, David, Interim Chief Executive Officer, Trego County–Lemke Memorial Hospital, Wakeeney, KS, p. A256

AUGUSTUS, Richard, M.D. Chief Medical Officer, West Valley Medical Center, Caldwell, ID, p. A175

AUGUSTYNIAK, Becky, Director Human Resources, Northside Medical Center, Columbus, GA, p. A156

AUJLA, Surinder, M.D. Chief of Staff, Bowie Memorial Hospital, Bowie, TX, p. A603

AUKES, Amy, Human Resources Analyst, Avera Flandreau Hospital, Flandreau, SD, p. A573

AUNAN, II, Milton E., CPA Senior Vice President and Chief Financial Officer, UnityPoint Health – St. Luke's Hospital, Cedar Rapids, IA, p. A226

AURILIO, Lisa, R.N. Vice President Patient Services and Chief Nursing Officer, Akron Children's Hospital, Akron, OH, p. A482

AUSMAN, Dan F., President and Chief Executive Officer, Methodist Hospital of Southern California, Arcadia, CA, p. A56

AUSTELLI, Oscar, Chief Information Officer, LAC/University of Southern California Medical Center, Los Angeles, CA, p. A73

AUSTERLITZ, Michael, M.D. Chief of Staff, East Los Angeles Doctors Hospital, Los Angeles, CA, p. A71

AUSTIN, Arthur, M.D. Vice President Medical Affairs, Gerald Champion Regional Medical Center, Alamogordo, NM, p. A426

AUSTIN, Cheryse, Vice President Patient Care Services and Chief Nursing Officer, Banner Casa Grande Medical Center, Casa Grande, AZ, p. A31

AUSTIN, Dan, Manager Data Processing, Ashley County Medical Center, Crossett, AR, p. A44

AUSTIN, Debbie W., R.N. Vice President Patient Care Services, P & S Surgical Hospital, Monroe, LA, p. A284

AUSTIN, Deborah, Chief People Officer, Physicians' Specialty Hospital, Fayetteville, AR, p. A45

AUSTIN, Joe, Executive Vice President and Chief Operating Officer, Phoebe Putney Memorial Hospital, Albany, GA, p. A151

AUSTIN, Judith J., MSN Chief Nursing Officer and Chief Operating Officer, Hi–Desert Medical Center, Joshua Tree, CA, p. A67

AUSTIN, Judy, Director Human Resources, Campbellton Graceville Hospital, Graceville, FL, p. A130

AUSTIN, Laura, Chief Financial Officer and Chief Operating Officer, Community Hospital of Anaconda, Anaconda, MT, p. A385

AUSTIN, Robert, Chief Executive Officer, Moab Regional Hospital, Moab, UT, p. A660

AUSTIN, Jr., W. William
Senior Vice President Finance, Riverside Behavioral Health Center, Hampton, VA, p. A672
Senior Vice President Finance, Riverside Shore Memorial Hospital, Nassawadox, VA, p. A674

AUSTIN, Warren, M.D. Vice President Medical Affairs, Bon Secours Maryview Medical Center, Portsmouth, VA, p. A676

AUSTIN–MOORE, Gale, Director Area Technology, Kaiser Permanente Vallejo Medical Center, Vallejo, CA, p. A99

AUTREY, Pamela Spencer, R.N. Chief Nursing Officer, Medical West, Bessemer, AL, p. A16

AVANT, Andre, Facility Automation Manager, Texas Center for Infectious Disease, San Antonio, TX, p. A648

AVATO, Rich, Director, St. Mary's Medical Center, West Palm Beach, FL, p. A150

AVENEL, William, Assistant Vice President Information Services, Medical Center, Navicent Health, Macon, GA, p. A163

AVERETT, Elaine, Chief Financial Officer, Grove Hill Memorial Hospital, Grove Hill, AL, p. A21

AVERILL, Clark, Director Information Technology, St. Luke's Hospital, Duluth, MN, p. A343

AVERNA, Russell, Director Human Resources, Spaulding Rehabilitation Hospital, Charlestown, MA, p. A309

AVERY, Baret H., Chief Information Officer, Siskin Hospital for Physical Rehabilitation, Chattanooga, TN, p. A580

AVERY, Danny, Chief Financial Officer and Chief Operating Officer, Quartz Mountain Medical Center, Mangum, OK, p. A513

AVERY, Donald R., FACHE, President and Chief Executive Officer, Fairview Park Hospital, Dublin, GA, p. A159

AVERY III, John B., Administrator, Perry Community Hospital, Linden, TN, p. A587

AVERY, Jonathan, Chief Administrative Officer, Legacy Good Samaritan Hospital and Medical Center, Portland, OR, p. A528

AVERY, Scott B., Commander, Martin Army Community Hospital, Fort Benning, GA, p. A160

AVIADO, Gail, Chief Nursing Officer, Montclair Hospital Medical Center, Montclair, CA, p. A78

AVVISATO, Michael, Senior Vice President and Chief Financial Officer, Allied Services Rehabilitation Hospital, Scranton, PA, p. A554

AVVISATO, Mike, Vice President and Chief Financial Officer, John Heinz Institute of Rehabilitation Medicine, Wilkes–Barre, PA, p. A558

AWALD, Tamara, Chief Nursing Officer and Chief Operating Officer, Saint Joseph Regional Medical Center–Plymouth Campus, Plymouth, IN, p. A221

AWALT, Scott, Chief Financial Officer, Sanford Hillsboro Medical Center, Hillsboro, ND, p. A478

AWAN, Naveed, FACHE, Chief Executive Officer, St. Helena Parish Hospital, Greensburg, LA, p. A278

AWOLOWO, Yinusa, Business Officer, Kingsboro Psychiatric Center, NY, p. A444

AWWAD, Emad, Director Care Delivery Sites Information Systems and Technology, Lakeview Hospital, Stillwater, MN, p. A352

AYALA, Jose L., M.D. Chief Medical Officer, Valley Baptist Medical Center–Brownsville, Brownsville, TX, p. A604

AYALA, Lisa, R.N. Director Human Resources, Specialty Hospital Jacksonville, Jacksonville, FL, p. A132

AYALA, Shirley, Director Human Resources, First Hospital Panamericano, Cidra, PR, p. A725

AYCOCK, Jean, President and Chief Executive Officer, Oconee Regional Health Systems, Milledgeville, GA, p. B102

AYCOCK, Jean, President and Chief Executive Officer, Oconee Regional Medical Center, Milledgeville, GA, p. A163

AYCOCK, Mark, Chief Operating Officer, Spartanburg Regional Medical Center, Spartanburg, SC, p. A570

AYERS, James G., Chief Financial Officer, Piedmont Geriatric Hospital, Burkeville, VA, p. A669

AYERS, Jessi, Chief Financial Officer, Person Memorial Hospital, Roxboro, NC, p. A472

AYERS, Matthew, Chief Executive Officer, Norton Hospital, Louisville, KY, p. A266

AYKUL, Nikki, Manager Business Office, LifeCare Hospitals of Pittsburgh, Pittsburgh, PA, p. A551

AYOUB, John J., FACHE, Chief Executive Officer, Melissa Memorial Hospital, Holyoke, CO, p. A107

AYRES, Daniel M., Chief Executive Officer, O'Connor Hospital, Delhi, NY, p. A436

AYRES, Michael, Senior Vice President and Chief Financial Officer, Maricopa Integrated Health System, Phoenix, AZ, p. A36

AYRES, Robert, Director Information Systems, Firelands Regional Health System, Sandusky, OH, p. A501

AYRES, Shane, Chief Financial Officer, Sanford Wheaton Medical Center, Wheaton, MN, p. A354

AYSCUE, Charles F., Senior Vice President Finance and Chief Financial Officer, Mission Hospital, Asheville, NC, p. A460

AZAR, Jennifer, Director Human Resources, Turning Point Hospital, Moultrie, GA, p. A164

AZCONA, Alain, Director Business Development, Aurora San Diego Hospital, San Diego, CA, p. A89

AZEVEDO, Michael, M.D. Medical Director, San Joaquin Valley Rehabilitation Hospital, Fresno, CA, p. A64

AZIZ, Samir, M.D. Medical Director, Fairfax Hospital, Kirkland, WA, p. A684

AZURE, Vernon, Clinical Director, Public Health Service Indian Hospital – Quentin N. Burdick Memorial Health Facility, Belcourt, ND, p. A476

B

BAACKE, II, George C., M.D. Acting Clinical Director, Northern Navajo Medical Center, Shiprock, NM, p. A431

BAADE, Leigh, Director Human Resources, New England Rehabilitation Hospital of Portland, Portland, ME, p. A295

BAAS, Daniel, R.N. Chief Nursing Officer, Baylor Emergency Medical Center at Aubrey, Aubrey, TX, p. A598

BAAS, Dina, Director Financial Services, Orange City Area Health System, Orange City, IA, p. A235

BABAKANIAN, Ed, Chief Information Officer, UC San Diego Health System, San Diego, CA, p. A90

BABB, Cindy, Executive Director Human Resources and Organizational Effectiveness, St. Joseph Hospital & Health Center, Kokomo, IN, p. A216

BABB, Daniel R., Chief Executive Officer, Oakland Regional Hospital, Southfield, MI, p. A335

BABB, Donald J., Chief Executive Officer, Citizens Memorial Hospital, Bolivar, MO, p. A367

BABB, Kathy, Manager Human Resources, Clifton Springs Hospital and Clinic, Clifton Springs, NY, p. A435

BABCOCK, Daniel, Chief Executive Officer, Marlette Regional Hospital, Marlette, MI, p. A330

BABCOCK, Kimberly, Administrator Human Resources, Kalkaska Memorial Health Center, Kalkaska, MI, p. A328

BABCOCK, Robert, M.D. Chief of Staff, Canandaigua Veterans Affairs Medical Center, Canandaigua, NY, p. A435

BABCOCK, Timothy, Chief Information Officer, Ralph H. Johnson Veterans Affairs Medical Center, Charleston, SC, p. A563

BABER, Jonathan, Director Information Technology, Central State Hospital, Petersburg, VA, p. A676

BABICH, Eli, Chief Nursing Officer, Select Specialty Hospital–Pittsburgh/UPMC, Pittsburgh, PA, p. A551

BABINEAU, Timothy J., M.D., President and Chief Executive Officer, Lifespan Corporation, Providence, RI, p. B87

BABINEAU, Timothy J., M.D., President and Chief Executive Officer, Rhode Island Hospital, Providence, RI, p. A561

BABUSCIO, Cathy, Director Human Resources, Mat–Su Regional Medical Center, Palmer, AK, p. A30

BACA, Modesto, Chief Information Officer, Amarillo Veterans Affairs Health Care System, Amarillo, TX, p. A596

BACH, Dawn M., MS Chief Clinical Officer, Buena Vista Regional Medical Center, Storm Lake, IA, p. A238

BACH, Terrance, M.D. Director Medical Affairs, Bay Area Hospital, Coos Bay, OR, p. A524

BACHA, Fadi, M.D. Chief Medical Officer, Select Specialty Hospital–Lexington, Lexington, KY, p. A264

BACHE–WIIG, Ben, M.D., President, Abbott Northwestern Hospital, Minneapolis, MN, p. A347

BACHELDOR, H. Lee, D.O. Medical Director, St. John River District Hospital, East China, MI, p. A323

BACHER, Beth, Chief Executive Officer, HEALTHSOUTH Valley of the Sun Rehabilitation Hospital, Glendale, AZ, p. A33

BACHER, Katherine, Interim Senior Vice President and Chief Financial Officer, Vassar Brothers Medical Center, Poughkeepsie, NY, p. A452

BACHMAN, John Page, Corporate Vice President, St. John Medical Center, Tulsa, OK, p. A521

BACHMAN, Judith Lynn
Chief Operating Officer, Fox Chase Cancer Center–American Oncologic Hospital, Philadelphia, PA, p. A548
Chief Operating Officer, Jeanes Hospital, Philadelphia, PA, p. A548

BACHMAN, Robert J., Chief Executive Officer, Emory University Hospital, Atlanta, GA, p. A152

BACHMAN, Roberta, Director Human Resources, Riverview Behavioral Health, Texarkana, AR, p. A53

BACK, Barbara, Manager Human Resources, Encino Hospital Medical Center, CA, p. A71

BACK, Bill, M.D. Chief of Staff, Mercy Willard Hospital, Willard, OH, p. A505

BACK, V. Richard, M.D. Chief Medical Officer, Columbia Memorial Hospital, Hudson, NY, p. A439

BACKER, Jackie, Director Human Resources, Providence Medical Center, Wayne, NE, p. A402

BACON, James S., Director Team Resources, St. Anthony's Hospital, Saint Petersburg, FL, p. A145

BACON, Jeff, D.O. Medical Director, Sterling Regional MedCenter, Sterling, CO, p. A111

BACON, Ken J., President and Chief Executive Officer, Shawnee Mission Medical Center, Shawnee Mission, KS, p. A254

BACUS, Randy B., FACHE, Chief Executive Officer, North Texas Medical Center, Gainesville, TX, p. A620

BADALIAN, B. Joseph, Chief Executive Officer, Fountain Valley Regional Hospital and Medical Center, Fountain Valley, CA, p. A63

BADBERG, Amy, M.D. Physician, Sanford Sheldon Medical Center, Sheldon, IA, p. A237

BADEN, Robert M., Chief Financial Officer, Lompoc Valley Medical Center, Lompoc, CA, p. A70

BADEN, Jr., Thomas, Chief Information Officer, Community Behavioral Health Hospital – Rochester, Rochester, MN, p. A350

BADGER, Jeff
Chief Financial Officer, Calumet Medical Center, Chilton, WI, p. A703
Chief Financial Officer, Mercy Medical Center, Oshkosh, WI, p. A713
Chief Financial Officer, St. Elizabeth Hospital, Appleton, WI, p. A701

BADGER, Steven, FACHE, Administrator, Orem Community Hospital, Orem, UT, p. A661

BADILLO, Linda, M.D. Chief of Medical Staff, Medical Center of Trinity, Trinity, FL, p. A149

BADINGER, Sandy, Chief Financial Officer, Slidell Memorial Hospital, Slidell, LA, p. A289

BADR, Safwan, M.D. Executive Vice President and Chief Medical Officer, Detroit Receiving Hospital/University Health Center, Detroit, MI, p. A321

BAEHLER, Amy, Director Nursing, Greeley County Health Services, Tribune, KS, p. A255

BAEHSER, Deborah, Vice President Patient Care Services, Cape Regional Medical Center, Cape May Court House, NJ, p. A414

BAENEN, Sharla, President, Bellin Psychiatric Center, Green Bay, WI, p. A706

BAER, Douglas, Chief Executive Officer, Brooks Rehabilitation Hospital, Jacksonville, FL, p. A131

BAER, James E., FACHE, President and Chief Executive Officer, Highland District Hospital, Hillsboro, OH, p. A495

BAEZ, Janet, Director, University Hospital, San Juan, PR, p. A729

BAGALIO, Sharon, R.N. Chief Nursing Officer, Parkview Adventist Medical Center, Brunswick, ME, p. A292

BAGCHI, Sam, Chief Medical Officer, Methodist Mansfield Medical Center, Mansfield, TX, p. A636

BAGGERLY, Karen, Chief Nursing Officer and Vice President, Covenant Medical Center, Lubbock, TX, p. A634

BAGGETT, Al, M.D. Interim Chief of Staff, Taylor Regional Hospital, Hawkinsville, GA, p. A160

BAGGETT, Margarita, MSN Interim Chief Operating Officer, UC San Diego Health System, San Diego, CA, p. A90

BAGLEY, Brenda, Director Human Resources, Red River Regional Hospital, Bonham, TX, p. A603

BAGLEY, Peter, M.D. Medical Director, Fairlawn Rehabilitation Hospital, Worcester, MA, p. A316

BAGNALL, Andrew, President and Chief Executive Officer, St. Nicholas Hospital, Sheboygan, WI, p. A715

BAGNELL, Kelly, M.D. Chief of Staff, Providence St. Joseph Medical Center, Polson, MT, p. A390

BAHL, Barry I., Director, St. Cloud Veterans Affairs Health Care System, Saint Cloud, MN, p. A351

BAHLS, Fredrick, M.D. Chief of Staff, Veterans Affairs Central Iowa Health Care System, Des Moines, IA, p. A230

BAHNLEIN, Carl, Executive Vice President and Chief Operating Officer, Virginia Hospital Center – Arlington, Arlington, VA, p. A668

BAIDA–FRAGOSO, Nicolas, M.D. Clinical Director, El Paso Psychiatric Center, El Paso, TX, p. A615

BAIER, Roger, Chief Executive Officer, Sanford Mayville Medical Center, Mayville, ND, p. A479

BAILEY, Amy, Director Information Systems, Texas Scottish Rite Hospital for Children, Dallas, TX, p. A612

BAILEY, Ann, Assistant Director Administration, Central State Hospital, Petersburg, VA, p. A676

BAILEY, Becky, R.N. Director Nursing, Kansas Surgery and Recovery Center, Wichita, KS, p. A256

BAILEY, Becky, Director Human Resources, Lincoln Hospital, Davenport, WA, p. A683

BAILEY, Bruce P., President and Chief Executive Officer, Georgetown Hospital System, Georgetown, SC, p. B61

BAILEY, Cheryl, R.N., Interim President, Cullman Regional Medical Center, Cullman, AL, p. A18

BAILEY, Cindy, R.N. Chief Nursing Officer, Richland Memorial Hospital, Olney, IL, p. A198

BAILEY, Cori, Accountant, Tyler Holmes Memorial Hospital, Winona, MS, p. A366

BAILEY, Craig, MS, Administrator, Colorado Acute Long Term Hospital, Denver, CO, p. A104

BAILEY, Dan, Director Information Systems, Norton Sound Regional Hospital, Nome, AK, p. A29

BAILEY, Dan, M.D. Vice President Medical Affairs and Chief Medical Officer, Upper Valley Medical Center, Troy, OH, p. A503

BAILEY, David, FACHE, Chief Executive Officer, Community Hospital of Bremen, Bremen, IN, p. A207

BAILEY, David J., M.D., President and Chief Executive Officer, Nemours, Jacksonville, FL, p. B97

BAILEY, Dawn A., R.N. Vice President Nursing and Chief Nursing Officer, Euclid Hospital, Euclid, OH, p. A493

BAILEY, Dianne, Coordinator Information Systems, Pana Community Hospital, Pana, IL, p. A199

BAILEY, Heather, Chief Human Resources Officer, Jefferson Healthcare, Port Townsend, WA, p. A686

BAILEY, Jim, M.D. Chief Medical Officer, Northeast Georgia Medical Center, Gainesville, GA, p. A160

BAILEY, Jodi J., Human Resources Director, Odessa Memorial Healthcare Center, Odessa, WA, p. A686

BAILEY, John E., Chief Financial Officer, Moore County Hospital District, Dumas, TX, p. A614

BAILEY, Jonathan D., Chief Executive Officer and Administrator, Hansford Hospital, Spearman, TX, p. A650

BAILEY, Joy, Director Information Technology, Sutter Amador Hospital, Jackson, CA, p. A67

BAILEY, Kathy C., FACHE, President and Chief Executive Officer, Blue Ridge Healthcare Hospitals, Morganton, NC, p. A469

BAILEY, Kelly, Administrator, Kindred Hospital–White Rock, Dallas, TX, p. A610

BAILEY, Larry, Chief Executive Officer, Indiana University Health Paoli Hospital, Paoli, IN, p. A221

BAILEY, Leisa, M.D. Chief of Staff, Doctors Memorial Hospital, Bonifay, FL, p. A124

BAILEY, Lynn, M.D. Director Primary Care and Medical Services, Naval Hospital Camp Pendleton, Camp Pendleton, CA, p. A59

BAILEY, Marquita, Chief Nursing Officer, DeKalb Regional Medical Center, Fort Payne, AL, p. A20

BAILEY, Matthew D., FACHE, President and Chief Executive Officer, Indiana University Health West Hospital, Avon, IN, p. A206

BAILEY, Mikeana, Director Human Resources, Brownwood Regional Medical Center, Brownwood, TX, p. A604

BAILEY, Owen, Administrator, University of South Alabama Children's and Women's Hospital, Mobile, AL, p. A23

BAILEY, Robert W., Chief Information Officer, Hawthorn Center, Northville, MI, p. A331

BAILEY, Ron, Chief Financial Officer, Franklin Foundation Hospital, Franklin, LA, p. A277

BAILEY, Russell, Chief Executive Officer, Texas Rehabilitation Hospital of Fort Worth, Fort Worth, TX, p. A619

BAILEY, Scott, Chief Financial Officer, EASTAR Health System, Muskogee, OK, p. A514

BAILEY, Susan P., R.N., Chief Executive Officer, Specialty Hospital of Washington, Washington, DC, p. A122

BAILEY, Travis A., Vice President Administration, St. Claire Regional Medical Center, Morehead, KY, p. A268

BAILEY–DELEEUW, Sandra, Chief Executive Officer, Methodist Extended Care Hospital, Memphis, TN, p. A589

BAILEY–NEWELL, Susan, Vice President Human Resources, St. Luke's Medical Center, Houston, TX, p. A627

BAILEY–OETKER, Jessica, Director Quality and Medical Staff, Providence Willamette Falls Medical Center, Oregon City, OR, p. A527

BAILON, Amy R., M.D., Medical Director, Woodbridge Development Center, Woodbridge, NJ, p. A425

BAIN, Brad, Information Systems Leader, Kaiser Permanente Fresno Medical Center, Fresno, CA, p. A64

BAIN, Holly, Chief Nursing Officer, Integris Marshall County Medical Center, Madill, OK, p. A513

BAIN, Joel, Director Information Services, TriStar Summit Medical Center, Hermitage, TN, p. A584

BAIN, Mark, Chief Human Resources, Veterans Affairs Connecticut Healthcare System, West Haven, CT, p. A118

BAIN, Pat, Chief Nursing Officer, Lower Bucks Hospital, Bristol, PA, p. A534

BAIOCCO, Jeffrey D., Chief Financial Officer, Eastern Idaho Regional Medical Center, Idaho Falls, ID, p. A176

BAIR, Ada, Chief Executive Officer, Memorial Hospital, Carthage, IL, p. A182

BAIR, Andrew P., Chief Executive Officer, Curry General Hospital, Gold Beach, OR, p. A525

BAIR, Connie, Human Resources Assistant, Pike County Memorial Hospital, Louisiana, MO, p. A376

BAIRD, Brenda, Senior Vice President and Chief Nursing Officer, St. Vincent Infirmary Medical Center, Little Rock, AR, p. A49

BAIRD, David
Director of Information Systems, Intermountain Medical Center, Murray, UT, p. A660
Chief Information Officer, LDS Hospital, Salt Lake City, UT, p. A663
Chief Information Officer, The Orthopedic Specialty Hospital, Murray, UT, p. A661

BAIRD, Donna, Vice President Corporate Services, Bay Medical Center Sacred Heart, Panama City, FL, p. A141

BAIRD, John D.
President and Chief Executive Officer, Presence Holy Family Medical Center, Des Plaines, IL, p. A188
Regional President and Chief Executive Officer, Presence Our Lady of the Resurrection Medical Center, Chicago, IL, p. A185
Regional President and Chief Executive Officer, Presence Resurrection Medical Center, Chicago, IL, p. A185

BAIRD, Nancy, Director Human Resources, Galesburg Cottage Hospital, Galesburg, IL, p. A190

BAISCH, Kim, R.N. Associate Vice President Patient Care Services, Highline Medical Center, Burien, WA, p. A682

BAISDEN, Monica, Director Human Resources, Memorial Hermann Northeast, Humble, TX, p. A628

BAJARI, Pamela R., R.N. Nurse Executive MHSATS, Community Behavioral Health Hospital – Rochester, Rochester, MN, p. A350

BAKAR, Anne L., President and Chief Executive Officer, Telecare Heritage Psychiatric Health Center, Oakland, CA, p. A81

BAKER, Amy, Associate Director Finance Services, Missouri Rehabilitation Center, Mount Vernon, MO, p. A377

BAKER, Bonnie, Vice President Finance and Chief Financial Officer, Butler Hospital, Providence, RI, p. A560

BAKER, Bonnie, M.D. Chief Medical Services, Veterans Health Care System of the Ozarks, Fayetteville, AR, p. A46

BAKER, Brenda, Chief Financial Officer, Riverview Hospital, Noblesville, IN, p. A220

BAKER, Chuck, R.N. Chief Operating Officer and Chief Nursing Officer, Callaway Community Hospital, Fulton, MO, p. A371

BAKER, Damon, D.O. Chief Medical Officer, Oklahoma State University Medical Center, Tulsa, OK, p. A520

BAKER, Denis, Chief Information Officer, Sarasota Memorial Health Care System, Sarasota, FL, p. A145

BAKER, Dennis, Chief Executive Officer, Select Specialty Hospital–Longview, Longview, TX, p. A634

BAKER, Frank, Chief Information Officer, Mary Breckinridge ARH Hospital, Hyden, KY, p. A263

BAKER, Gary A., President, Memorial Hospital, Towanda, PA, p. A556

BAKER, Gary E.
Senior Vice President and Chief Executive Officer, Scottsdale Healthcare Shea Medical Center, Scottsdale, AZ, p. A38
Senior Vice President and Administrator, Scottsdale Healthcare–Osborn Medical Center, Scottsdale, AZ, p. A38

BAKER, Harlan T., Department Leader Information Systems, McDonough District Hospital, Macomb, IL, p. A195

BAKER, Holli, Chief Executive Officer, Valley Behavioral Health System, Barling, AR, p. A43

BAKER, J. Matthew, M.D. President Medical Staff, Bertrand Chaffee Hospital, Springville, NY, p. A455

BAKER, Joann, Administrator, Doctors Memorial Hospital, Bonifay, FL, p. A124

BAKER, Joel, D.O. Chief Medical Officer, Wayne County Hospital, Corydon, IA, p. A228

BAKER, John
Interim Chief Executive Officer, Haven Behavioral Health of Eastern Pennsylvania, Reading, PA, p. A553
Interim Chief Executive Officer, Haven Behavioral Senior Care of Albuquerque, Albuquerque, NM, p. A426

BAKER, Judy, Chief Information Officer, Kindred Hospital–Mansfield, Mansfield, TX, p. A636

BAKER, Linda, Director Human Resources, St. Alexius Medical Center, Hoffman Estates, IL, p. A193

BAKER, Maia, MSN Chief Nurse Executive, Rio Grande State Center/South Texas Health Care System, Harlingen, TX, p. A622

BAKER, Maribel, Director Human Resources, Johnson Regional Medical Center, Clarksville, AR, p. A44

BAKER, Mark A., Chief Executive Officer, Jack Hughston Memorial Hospital, Phenix City, AL, p. A25

BAKER, Meredith, Business Manager, Mental Health Institute, Clarinda, IA, p. A227

BAKER, Michael, D.O. Chief of Staff, Daviess Community Hospital, Washington, IN, p. A224

BAKER, Michelle, Director Information Systems, Indiana University Health White Memorial Hospital, Monticello, IN, p. A219

BAKER, Nichelle A., Chair Human Resources, Mayo Clinic Hospital, Phoenix, AZ, p. A36

BAKER, Paula F., President and Chief Executive Officer, Freeman Health System, Joplin, MO, p. B60

BAKER, Paula F.
President and Chief Executive Officer, Freeman Hospital West, Joplin, MO, p. A373
President and Chief Executive Officer, Freeman Neosho Hospital, Neosho, MO, p. A377

BAKER, Phillip, Vice President and Chief Financial Officer, Fawcett Memorial Hospital, Port Charlotte, FL, p. A143

BAKER, R. Hal, M.D. Vice President and Chief Information Officer, York Hospital, York, PA, p. A559

BAKER, Reese, Director Information Systems, Crittenden County Hospital, Marion, KY, p. A267

BAKER, Reta K., President, Mercy Hospital Fort Scott, Fort Scott, KS, p. A244

BAKER, Rodger H., President and Chief Executive Officer, Fauquier Hospital, Warrenton, VA, p. A680

BAKER, Ron, Chief Executive Officer, Allen County Regional Hospital, Iola, KS, p. A246

BAKER, Ronald L., Chief Executive Officer, Saint Luke's East Hospital, Lee's Summit, MO, p. A375

BAKER, Shari
Director Human Resources, Orange City Area Health System, Orange City, IA, p. A235
Chief Executive Officer, Palmetto Lowcountry Behavioral Health, Charleston, SC, p. A563

BAKER, Sharon, Director Support Services, Fairbanks, Indianapolis, IN, p. A214

BAKER, Shawna, M.D. Chief of Staff, Community Hospital of Anaconda, Anaconda, MT, p. A385

BAKER, Steve, Chief Information Officer, East Jefferson General Hospital, Metairie, LA, p. A284

BAKER, Vanya, Director, Wilkes Regional Medical Center, North Wilkesboro, NC, p. A470

BAKER, W. Douglas, Director, Julian F. Keith Alcohol and Drug Abuse Treatment Center, Black Mountain, NC, p. A460

BAKER Jr., Wendell H., President, Vidant Edgecombe Hospital, Tarboro, NC, p. A473

BAKHTIER, Hasan, M.D. Medical Director, Community Mental Health Center, Lawrenceburg, IN, p. A217

BAKICH, Sandy, Director Information Management, Delano Regional Medical Center, Delano, CA, p. A61

BAKKEN, Mary, Executive Vice President and Chief Operating Officer, Silver Cross Hospital, New Lenox, IL, p. A198

BAKKUM, Kyle, Chief Executive Officer and Administrator, Vernon Memorial Healthcare, Viroqua, WI, p. A717

BALASUBRAMONY, Suresh, M.D. Chief Medical Officer, Minnie Hamilton HealthCare Center, Grantsville, WV, p. A695

BALAZY, Thomas E., M.D. Medical Director, Craig Hospital, Englewood, CO, p. A106

BALCAVAGE, Thomas, Vice President Information Systems and Chief Information Officer Technology, Kennedy Health System, Cherry Hill, NJ, p. A414

BALCH, Jackson, IT Director, Garden Park Medical Center, Gulfport, MS, p. A358

BALCITIS, Judith, MS Vice President, Nursing and Chief Nursing Officer, Advocate Sherman Hospital, Elgin, IL, p. A189

BALDAUF, Robb, Coordinator Information Systems, Lodi Community Hospital, Lodi, OH, p. A496

BALDERRAMA, Jose, Vice President Human Resources, Nationwide Children's Hospital, Columbus, OH, p. A490

BALDOSARO, Thomas
Chief Financial Officer, Inspira Medical Center–Elmer, Elmer, NJ, p. A416
Chief Financial Officer, inspira Medical Center–Vineland, Vineland, NJ, p. A424

BALDRICA, Joyce, Chief Executive Officer, Kindred Hospital Melbourne, Melbourne, FL, p. A136

BALDRIDGE, Dava, R.N. Chief Nursing Officer, Hillcrest Hospital – South, Tulsa, OK, p. A520

BALDWIN, Barbara, Chief Information Officer, Anne Arundel Medical Center, Annapolis, MD, p. A296

BALDWIN, David, Chief Information Officer, Robinson Memorial Hospital, Ravenna, OH, p. A501

BALDWIN, Ellen, R.N. Chief Nursing Officer, Texas Health Center for Diagnostic & Surgery, Plano, TX, p. A642

BALDWIN, Erin, M.P.H. Chief Operating Officer, Mahaska Health Partnership, Oskaloosa, IA, p. A236

BALDWIN, Genny, R.N. Chief Nursing Officer, Santiam Memorial Hospital, Stayton, OR, p. A530

BALDWIN, Gilda, Chief Executive Officer, Westchester General Hospital, Miami, FL, p. A138

BALDWIN, Nathan, M.D. President Medical Staff, Baptist Memorial Hospital–Booneville, Booneville, MS, p. A356

BALDWIN, Steve
Vice President Finance, Willough Healthcare System, Naples, FL, p. A139
Manager Information Technology, Wyoming State Hospital, Evanston, WY, p. A721

BALDWIN, William, Chief Information Officer, Ashe Memorial Hospital, Jefferson, NC, p. A467

BALENTINE, Jerry, D.O. Executive Vice President and Chief Medical Director, St. Barnabas Hospital, NY, p. A448

BALES, Brian, Director Plant Operations, HEALTHSOUTH Southern Hills Rehabilitation Hospital, Princeton, WV, p. A698

BALES, Glenn, Chief Financial Officer, Providence Saint Joseph Medical Center, Burbank, CA, p. A58

BALES–CHUBB, Denyse, Chief Executive Officer, Florida Hospital Wesley Chapel, Wesley Chapel, FL, p. A149

BALFOUR, Ann M., R.N., President, St. Joseph Health System, Tawas City, MI, p. A335

BALINK, Kay M., M.D. Chief of Staff, Richland Hospital, Richland Center, WI, p. A714

BALKO, Tom, Manager Information Systems, Redwood Area Hospital, Redwood Falls, MN, p. A350

BALL, Cassie, Chief Financial Officer, Hilton Head Hospital, Hilton Head Island, SC, p. A567

BALL, Charlie, Chief Operating Officer, Specialty Rehabilitation Hospital of Coushatta, Coushatta, LA, p. A275

BALL, Jim, Chief Operating Officer, St. Catherine's Rehabilitation Hospital, North Miami, FL, p. A139

BALL, III, Johnny Percy, Assistant Administrator Human Resources, South Georgia Medical Center, Valdosta, GA, p. A168

BALLA, Matt, Chief Executive Officer, St. Vincent Dunn Hospital, Bedford, IN, p. A207

BALLANCE, William, M.D. Chief of Medical Staff, Vidant Bertie Hospital, Windsor, NC, p. A475

BALLARD, Annette, Director Information Systems, Murray–Calloway County Hospital, Murray, KY, p. A268

BALLARD, Christine A.
Vice President Human Resources, Muncy Valley Hospital, Muncy, PA, p. A546
Vice President Human Resources, Soldiers and Sailors Memorial Hospital, Wellsboro, PA, p. A557
Senior Vice President Human Resources, Williamsport Regional Medical Center, Williamsport, PA, p. A559

BALLARD, Jerry, Director Information Systems, Central Florida Regional Hospital, Sanford, FL, p. A145

BALLARD, John, Ph.D., Chief Executive Officer, Parkway Regional Hospital, Fulton, KY, p. A261

BALLARD, Lorraine L., Director Human Resources, St. Helena Parish Hospital, Greensburg, LA, p. A278

BALLARD, Richard R., Chief Executive Officer and Administrator, University of Miami Hospital and Clinics, Miami, FL, p. A138

BALLARD, Terri, Chief Nursing Officer, HEALTHSOUTH Northern Kentucky Rehabilitation Hospital, Edgewood, KY, p. A260

BALLECK, Michelle, Director Public Relations, Middle Park Medical Center–Kremmling, Kremmling, CO, p. A108

BALLESTERO, Susan, Vice President and Chief Human Resources Officer, Saint Peter's University Hospital, New Brunswick, NJ, p. A419

BALLIETT, Matt, Chief Information Officer, Coal County General Hospital, Coalgate, OK, p. A509

BALLINGHOFF, James R., MSN Chief Nursing Officer and Associate Executive Director, Penn Presbyterian Medical Center, Philadelphia, PA, p. A549

BALLMAN, Patricia, Director, Westfield Memorial Hospital, Westfield, NY, p. A458

BALLOU, Michele, M.D. Chief Medical Staff, LewisGale Hospital Alleghany, Low Moor, VA, p. A673

BALOGH, Tamas, M.D. Chief of Staff, Northern Hospital of Surry County, Mount Airy, NC, p. A469

BALON, Stanley, M.D. President Medical Staff, Landmark Medical Center, Woonsocket, RI, p. A561

BALSANO, Tony, Vice President Finance, Saint Francis Medical Center, Cape Girardeau, MO, p. A368

BALT, David, D.O. Chief Medical Officer, Avera Queen of Peace Hospital, Mitchell, SD, p. A575

BALTIERRA, David A., M.D. President Medical Staff, Jefferson Medical Center, Ranson, WV, p. A699

BALUTANSKI, Brian, CPA Chief Financial Officer, Chestnut Hill Hospital, Philadelphia, PA, p. A547

BALZANO, Janice, Chief Operating Officer, Brandon Regional Hospital, Brandon, FL, p. A124

BAMAN, Raj, D.O. President Medical Staff, Samaritan North Lincoln Hospital, Lincoln City, OR, p. A526

BAMBRICK, Catherine, Chief Operating Officer, Kittitas Valley Healthcare, Ellensburg, WA, p. A683

BAMMEL, Paul
Vice President, Mayo Clinic Health System – Northland in Barron, Barron, WI, p. A702
Vice President, Mayo Clinic Health System in Eau Claire, Eau Claire, WI, p. A704

BANBURY, Brian, Director Site Information Systems, Advocate Christ Medical Center, Oak Lawn, IL, p. A198

BANCO, Leonard, M.D. Senior Vice President and Chief Medical Officer, Bristol Hospital, Bristol, CT, p. A113

BANDA, Venkat, M.D. President Medical Staff, Promise Hospital of Baton Rouge – Ochsner Campus, Baton Rouge, LA, p. A274

BANDLA, H., M.D. Chief Clinical Affairs, Walter P. Reuther Psychiatric Hospital, Westland, MI, p. A337

BANDY, Dawn, Chief Financial Officer, Grant Regional Health Center, Lancaster, WI, p. A708

BANDY, Don, Director Information Technology, Deaconess Hospital, Oklahoma City, OK, p. A515

BANDY, P. Ross, M.D. Chief Medical Officer and Chief of Staff, Levi Hospital, Hot Springs National Park, AR, p. A47

BANE, William, Chief Financial Officer, Inova Loudoun Hospital, Leesburg, VA, p. A673

BANG, W. J., M.D. Chief of Staff, Reeves County Hospital, Pecos, TX, p. A641

BANGERT, Rick, Chief Executive Officer, Options Behavioral Health System, Indianapolis, IN, p. A214

BANIGAN, Elisa, Chief Financial Officer, Forest Park Medical Center Frisco, Frisco, TX, p. A620

BANK, Carol J., Vice President Human Resources, Divine Savior Healthcare, Portage, WI, p. A713

BANKER, Julie G., R.N. Chief Nursing Officer, Lehigh Regional Medical Center, Lehigh Acres, FL, p. A134

BANKERS, Diane, Director of Nursing, FirstLight Health System, Mora, MN, p. A348

BANKS, Chester, Director Human Resources, East Orange General Hospital, East Orange, NJ, p. A415

BANKS, Elizabeth, Chief Executive Officer, Summit Behavioral Healthcare, Cincinnati, OH, p. A487

BANKS, Maureen, MS,
President, Spaulding Hospital for Continuing Medical Care North Shore, Salem, MA, p. A314
President, Spaulding Hospital for Continuing Medical Care Cambridge, Cambridge, MA, p. A309

BANKS, Maureen, R.N. Chief Operating Officer, Spaulding Rehabilitation Hospital, Charlestown, MA, p. A309

BANKS, Maureen, MS, President, Spaulding Rehabilitation Hospital Cape Cod, East Sandwich, MA, p. A309

BANKS, Robbi, Executive Director Human Resources, Medical Center Health System, Odessa, TX, p. A640

BANKS, Scott, Chief Financial Officer, Salt Lake Regional Medical Center, Salt Lake City, UT, p. A663

BANKS, Walter, Director Human Resources, Baptist Memorial Hospital–Desoto, Southaven, MS, p. A365

BANKTSON, Julie, Manager Human Resources, Paul Oliver Memorial Hospital, Frankfort, MI, p. A324

BANNER, Fred, Chief Information Officer, Shore Medical Center, Somers Point, NJ, p. A422

BANOS, Edward D., Chief Executive Officer, Marquette General Hospital, Marquette, MI, p. A330

BANSBACH, Steven, M.D. Medical Director, Thousand Oaks Surgical Hospital, Thousand Oaks, CA, p. A97

BANUEDOS, Jorge, Director Human Resources, Metropolitan State Hospital, Norwalk, CA, p. A80

BANVILLE, Carol Anne, Chief Nursing Officer, HEALTHSOUTH Rehabilitation Hospital of Denver, Littleton, CO, p. A109

BAPTISTE, Ernest, Executive Director, Kings County Hospital Center, NY, p. A444

BAQUET, Shawn, Chief of Staff, Iberia Medical Center, New Iberia, LA, p. A285

BARANCZYK, Kay, R.N. Chief Nursing Officer, Community Memorial Hospital, Oconto Falls, WI, p. A712

BARANSKI, David J., Vice President Human Resources, Phoebe Putney Memorial Hospital, Albany, GA, p. A151

BARANSKI, Kenneth, Chief Financial Officer, Hills & Dales General Hospital, Cass City, MI, p. A320

BARBA, James J., President and Chief Executive Officer, Albany Medical Center, Albany, NY, p. A432

BARBADIAN, John, Vice President Human Resources, Tulare Regional Medical Center, Tulare, CA, p. A98

BARBAGLIA, J. Joseph, Vice President Financial Services, Columbus Community Hospital, Columbus, NE, p. A395

BARBAREE, Jerry, Director Human Resources, Baptist Memorial Hospital – Memphis, Memphis, TN, p. A588

BARBARIN, LaSharndra
Chief Operating Officer, Medical Center of Arlington, Arlington, TX, p. A598
Chief Operating Officer, Medical Center of McKinney, McKinney, TX, p. A637

BARBAROTTA, Ann Marie, Executive Director, Creedmoor Psychiatric Center, NY, p. A443

BARBE, Brian S., Chief Executive Officer, Memorial Hermann Katy Hospital, Katy, TX, p. A630

BARBEE, Daniel, Vice President Clinical Affairs, The University of Toledo Medical Center, Toledo, OH, p. A503

BARBER, Chris B., FACHE, President and Chief Executive Officer, St. Bernards Medical Center, Jonesboro, AR, p. A48

BARBER, Eric A., President and Chief Executive Officer, Mary Lanning Healthcare, Hastings, NE, p. A396

BARBER, Jack W., M.D., Director, Western State Hospital, Staunton, VA, p. A679

BARBER, Karen, R.N., Chief Executive Officer, Yoakum Community Hospital, Yoakum, TX, p. A658

BARBER, Michael, System Chief Operating Officer, Chester County Hospital, West Chester, PA, p. A558

BARBER, Richard, M.D. Chief Medical Officer, Wilkes Regional Medical Center, North Wilkesboro, NC, p. A470

BARBER, Scott, Chief Executive Officer, Decatur County General Hospital, Parsons, TN, p. A592

BARBER, Teresa Rini, Vice President Support Services, Southwest General Health Center, Middleburg Heights, OH, p. A498

BARBER, Wendi, Vice President Finance and Chief Financial Officer, Park Ridge Health, Hendersonville, NC, p. A466

BARBINI, Gerald J., President and Chief Executive Officer, Allegan General Hospital, Allegan, MI, p. A318

BARBO, Steve, R.N., Administrator, Citizens Medical Center, Columbia, LA, p. A275

BARBOSA, Robert, D.O. Chief Medical Officer, Oakland Regional Hospital, Southfield, MI, p. A335

BARBOUR, Alexis, Director Finance, Dublin Springs, Dublin, OH, p. A493

BARBUAT, James P., Chief Financial Officer, Gunnison Valley Hospital, Gunnison, CO, p. A107

BARCHI, Daniel
Senior Vice President, Technical Services and Chief Information Officer, Bridgeport Hospital, Bridgeport, CT, p. A113
Senior Vice President Information Systems and Chief Information Officer, Yale–New Haven Hospital, New Haven, CT, p. A116

BARCLAY, Duane, D.O. Chief Medical Officer, DeKalb Medical at Hillandale, Lithonia, GA, p. A162

BARCLAY, Emily, Vice President Human Resources, Dana–Farber Cancer Institute, Boston, MA, p. A306

BARCLAY, Rick, Vice President Support Services, Mercy Hospital Rogers, Rogers, AR, p. A52

BARCLIFT, Larry, Chief Financial Officer, Yuma Rehabilitation Hospital, Yuma, AZ, p. A42

BARD, Jeffrey, President, Aurora Medical Center of Oshkosh, Oshkosh, WI, p. A712

BARDEN, Marlana, Director Human Resources, Benewah Community Hospital, Saint Maries, ID, p. A178

BARDEN, Sean
Executive Vice President and Chief Financial Officer, Mary Washington Hospital, Fredericksburg, VA, p. A671
Executive Vice President and Chief Financial Officer, Stafford Hospital, Stafford, VA, p. A679

BARDIER, Catherine, Vice President, Human Resources, Elliot Hospital, Manchester, NH, p. A411

BARDWELL, Carol A., R.N. Chief Nurse Executive, Martha's Vineyard Hospital, Oak Bluffs, MA, p. A313

BARDWELL, Jean, Vice President and Chief Financial Officer, Ranken Jordan Pediatric Bridge Hospital, Maryland Heights, MO, p. A376

BARDWELL, Sheila, Director Information Systems, Baptist Memorial Hospital–Golden Triangle, Columbus, MS, p. A357

BARDWELL, Tom, Vice President Human Resources, Hills & Dales General Hospital, Cass City, MI, p. A320

BAREFOOT, Denise, Director Health Information Systems, Carolina Pines Regional Medical Center, Hartsville, SC, p. A567

BAREIS, Charles, M.D. Medical Director, MacNeal Hospital, Berwyn, IL, p. A181

BARELA, Barbara, Director Human Resources, Gila Regional Medical Center, Silver City, NM, p. A431

BARFIELD, Donna, Chief Nursing Officer, Volunteer Community Hospital, Martin, TN, p. A587

BARGINERE, Cynthia, MSN Vice President Clinical Nursing and Chief Nursing Officer, Rush University Medical Center, Chicago, IL, p. A186

BARIOLA, Christopher L.
Chief Executive Officer, Eureka Springs Hospital, Eureka Springs, AR, p. A45
Chief Executive Officer, River Valley Medical Center, Dardanelle, AR, p. A44
BARISANO, Nancy, Chief Information Officer, Monadnock Community Hospital, Peterborough, NH, p. A412
BARKEMA, Annette, Chief Financial Officer, Portland Veterans Affairs Medical Center, Portland, OR, p. A528
BARKER, Eileen C., Administrator, Sunrise Canyon Hospital, Lubbock, TX, p. A635
BARKER, Jaime, M.D. Medical Director, Manatee Palms Youth Services, Bradenton, FL, p. A124
BARKER, James, President, West Shore Medical Center, Manistee, MI, p. A329
BARKER, Karen, Vice President and Chief Information Officer, Sinai Hospital of Baltimore, Baltimore, MD, p. A298
BARKER, Kathryn L., Chief Human Resources Management, Veterans Health Care System of the Ozarks, Fayetteville, AR, p. A46
BARKER, Larry, Chief Operating Officer, Clearwater Valley Hospital and Clinics, Orofino, ID, p. A177
BARKER, Louise, R.N., Chief Executive Officer, Central Louisiana Surgical Hospital, Alexandria, LA, p. A272
BARKER, M. Debby, Director Human Resources, Siskin Hospital for Physical Rehabilitation, Chattanooga, TN, p. A580
BARKER, Patrick A., M.D. Chief Medical Officer, Providence St. Joseph's Hospital, Chewelah, WA, p. A682
BARKER, Richard, Administrator, Mercy Health Love County, Marietta, OK, p. A513
BARKER, Russell
Community Chief Executive Officer, McDowell ARH Hospital, McDowell, KY, p. A267
Information Officer, U. S. Public Health Service Indian Hospital–Whiteriver, Whiteriver, AZ, p. A41
BARKER, Thomas, Director Information, Southeast Health Center of Reynolds County, Ellington, MO, p. A370
BARKER, Jr., William A., Vice President Administration, Pleasant Valley Hospital, Point Pleasant, WV, p. A698
BARKHYMER, Mary C., R.N. Vice President Patient Care Services and Chief Nursing Officer, UPMC St. Margaret, Pittsburgh, PA, p. A552
BARKMAN, Joseph, Vice President Financial Services, Oaklawn Psychiatric Center, Goshen, IN, p. A212
BARKSDALE, Mary, Director Human Resources, Person Memorial Hospital, Roxboro, NC, p. A472
BARKSDALE, Vickie, Manager Human Resources, North Oak Regional Medical Center, Senatobia, MS, p. A365
BARLAGE, Seth, Associate Medical Center Director, John J. Pershing Veterans Affairs Medical Center, Poplar Bluff, MO, p. A378
BARLEY, Leonard, M.D. Chief Medical Officer, Windsor–Laurelwood Center for Behavioral Medicine, Willoughby, OH, p. A505
BARLEY, Tammy, Director, Human Resources, HEALTHSOUTH Rehabilitation Hospital of Jonesboro, Jonesboro, AR, p. A48
BARLOW, Mark, M.D. Chief Medical Officer and President Medical Staff, Cornerstone Hospital of Houston at Clearlake, Webster, TX, p. A656
BARLOW, Teresa, Medical Records Administrator, Mental Health Institute, Clarinda, IA, p. A227
BARMECHA, Jitendra, M.D. Senior Vice President and Chief Information Officer, St. Barnabas Hospital, NY, p. A448
BARNARD, Jeanna, Chief Executive Officer, Bayshore Medical Center, Pasadena, TX, p. A641
BARNARD, Kerri, Director Human Resources, Larned State Hospital, Larned, KS, p. A248
BARNARD, Lawrence, Chief Executive Officer, University Medical Center, Las Vegas, NV, p. A407
BARNARD, Ryan, Chief Executive Officer, Swisher Memorial Hospital District, Tulia, TX, p. A653
BARNCORD, Sharon
Business Partner Human Resources, Kaiser Permanente Redwood City Medical Center, Redwood City, CA, p. A85
Human Resource Business Partner, Kaiser Permanente South San Francisco, South San Francisco, CA, p. A96
BARNES, Alan, Chief Financial Officer, North Star Behavioral Health System, Anchorage, AK, p. A28
BARNES, Becky, Chief Operating Officer, Rapides Regional Medical Center, Alexandria, LA, p. A272
BARNES, Chenell, Administrator, Premier Rehabilitation, Luling, LA, p. A283
BARNES, Deborah, Vice President and Chief Information Officer, Children's Hospital of The King's Daughters, Norfolk, VA, p. A675
BARNES, Donald K., Chief Human Resources Officer, Duke Raleigh Hospital, Raleigh, NC, p. A472
BARNES, Douglas A., M.D. Chief of Staff, Shriners Hospitals for Children–Houston, Houston, TX, p. A626

BARNES, Gary, Chief Information Officer, Medical Center Health System, Odessa, TX, p. A640
BARNES, George, M.D. Medical Director, Lakeview Regional Medical Center, Covington, LA, p. A276
BARNES, Gloria V., MSN Assistant Vice President Patient Care Services, Southeastern Regional Medical Center, Newnan, GA, p. A164
BARNES, Jacqueline, Manager Health Information, Select Specialty Hospital–Jackson, Jackson, MS, p. A360
BARNES, James, Director Information Technology, Crossroads Community Hospital, Mount Vernon, IL, p. A197
BARNES, Jeff, Director Information Technology, Girard Medical Center, Girard, KS, p. A244
BARNES, Joe, Chief Financial Officer, Grant Memorial Hospital, Petersburg, WV, p. A698
BARNES, John, Administrative Director Human Resources, Beverly Hospital, Montebello, CA, p. A78
BARNES, Karen, Interim Chief Nursing Officer, Logan Regional Medical Center, Logan, WV, p. A696
BARNES, Larry, Vice President Information Technology, Salina Regional Health Center, Salina, KS, p. A254
BARNES, Laura P., MSN Vice President Patient Care Services and Chief Nursing Officer, East Tennessee Children's Hospital, Knoxville, TN, p. A585
BARNES, Leslie, Chief Financial Officer, Parkview Medical Center, Pueblo, CO, p. A110
BARNES, Marla, Director of Nursing, Pushmataha Hospital & Home Health, Antlers, OK, p. A507
BARNES, Maryann, MS Vice President and Chief Nursing Officer East Region, St. John Hospital and Medical Center, Detroit, MI, p. A322
BARNES, Michael, Chief Information Officer, North Valley Hospital, Whitefish, MT, p. A392
BARNES, P. Marie, Director, Human Resources, North Mississippi Medical Center–Pontotoc, Pontotoc, MS, p. A364
BARNES, Sherry, Director Health Information and Quality Management, Rolling Hills Hospital, Ada, OK, p. A507
BARNES, Sheryl L., MSN Senior Director Clinical Services, Mercy Medical Center – West Lakes, West Des Moines, IA, p. A239
BARNES, William H., Administrator, Sweeny Community Hospital, Sweeny, TX, p. A651
BARNETT, Barbara, M.D. Medical Director, Glen Cove Hospital, Glen Cove, NY, p. A438
BARNETT, Carol, Chief Human Resources Officer, Fairbanks Memorial Hospital, Fairbanks, AK, p. A29
BARNETT, Frederick, M.D. Chief of Staff, Metroplex Adventist Hospital, Killeen, TX, p. A631
BARNETT, Julia, Chief Nursing Officer, Union General Hospital, Blairsville, GA, p. A154
BARNETT, Laura, Executive Director, Human Resources, Brigham and Women's Faulkner Hospital, Boston, MA, p. A306
BARNETT, Lori, R.N. Chief Nursing Officer, Troy Community Hospital, Troy, PA, p. A556
BARNETT, Shawn, Vice President and Chief Financial Officer, CHRISTUS Santa Rosa Health System, San Antonio, TX, p. A646
BARNETT, Steve, MS, President and Chief Executive Officer, McKenzie Health System, Sandusky, MI, p. A334
BARNHARDT, Bonnie, Executive Director Human Resources, Minnesota Valley Health Center, Le Sueur, MN, p. A345
BARNHART, Ann, Chief Executive Officer, Heart of Florida Regional Medical Center, Davenport, FL, p. A127
BARNHART, David, Director Information Systems, Wuesthoff Medical Center – Rockledge, Rockledge, FL, p. A144
BARNHART, James R.
Chief Administrator Officer, PeaceHealth Peace Island Medical Center, Friday Harbor, WA, p. A684
Chief Administrative Officer, PeaceHealth United General Hospital, Sedro–Woolley, WA, p. A689
BARNHART, Jeff, Administrator, Northwest Texas Surgery Center, Amarillo, TX, p. A596
BARNHART, Roger, Chief Executive Officer, Ashland Health Center, Ashland, KS, p. A241
BARNTHOUSE, Victoria, MS, Chief Executive Officer, Val Verde Regional Medical Center, Del Rio, TX, p. A613
BARONE, Nancy, Vice President and Executive Director Operations and Strategic Planning, University of Cincinnati Medical Center, Cincinnati, OH, p. A487
BARONE, Richard, M.D. Medical Director, Montefiore New Rochelle, New Rochelle, NY, p. A442
BARONOFF, Peter R.
Chief Executive Officer, Promise Healthcare, Boca Raton, FL, p. B109
President and Chief Executive Officer, Success Healthcare, Boca Raton, FL, p. B129
BARR, Annette, Chief Nursing Officer, HEALTHSOUTH Rehabilitation Hospital of Southern Arizona, Tucson, AZ, p. A40

BARR, Brant, M.D. Chief Medical Officer, District One Hospital, Faribault, MN, p. A343
BARR, Brent, Chief Information Officer, Minnie Hamilton HealthCare Center, Grantsville, WV, p. A695
BARR, Bret, Vice President Fiscal Services, Conway Medical Center, Conway, SC, p. A565
BARR, Catherine, Senior Vice President and President, Bethesda Hospital, Bethesda Hospital, Saint Paul, MN, p. A351
BARR, Francine, R.N. Vice President and Chief Operating Officer, Bon Secours St. Mary's Hospital, Richmond, VA, p. A677
BARR, Kristine, Vice President Communication Services, O'Bleness Memorial Hospital, Athens, OH, p. A483
BARR, Laurie C.
Vice President Human Resources, Salem Hospital, Salem, OR, p. A530
Vice President Human Resources, West Valley Hospital, Dallas, OR, p. A524
BARR, Mary Beth, R.N., Chief Executive Officer, Grant Memorial Hospital, Petersburg, WV, p. A698
BARR, Steven, MSN, Chief Executive Officer, Plaza Specialty Hospital, Houston, TX, p. A626
BARR, Tom, Director Operational Support Services, Peterson Rehabilitation Hospital, Wheeling, WV, p. A700
BARR, Vivian C.
Director Human Resources, Higgins General Hospital, Bremen, GA, p. A154
Director Human Resources, Tanner Medical Center–Carrollton, Carrollton, GA, p. A155
BARRA, Jon, Director Human Resources, Wyoming Behavioral Institute, Casper, WY, p. A720
BARRACO, Dennis, D.O. Medical Director, Wickenburg Community Hospital, Wickenburg, AZ, p. A41
BARRALL, Audrey, Director Human Resources, St. Helena Hospital Clear Lake, Clearlake, CA, p. A60
BARRAMEDA, Maricar, Chief Information Officer, Lincoln Medical and Mental Health Center, NY, p. A445
BARREIRO, Maggie E., Administrator, Weslaco Rehabilitation Hospital, Weslaco, TX, p. A657
BARRERA, Edward, Director Communications, Encino Hospital Medical Center, CA, p. A71
BARRERE, Davie Ann, Coordinator Information Technology, Dahl Memorial Healthcare Association, Ekalaka, MT, p. A387
BARRETT, Anne J., Associate Executive Director Human Resources, Southside Hospital, Bay Shore, NY, p. A433
BARRETT, Bob, Chief Financial Officer, Clinch Valley Medical Center, Richlands, VA, p. A677
BARRETT, Cindy, Administrative Assistant, Patton State Hospital, Patton, CA, p. A83
BARRETT Jr., James W., Chief Executive Officer, Richardson Medical Center, Rayville, LA, p. A287
BARRETT, Jason P., Chief Operating Officer, Flagler Hospital, Saint Augustine, FL, p. A144
BARRETT, John, Regional Director Human Resources, Franciscan St. Anthony Health – Michigan City, Michigan City, IN, p. A218
BARRETT III, John E., Chief Executive Officer, Bon Secours–DePaul Medical Center, Norfolk, VA, p. A675
BARRETT, Kerry Flynn, Vice President Human Resources, Northern Westchester Hospital, Mount Kisco, NY, p. A442
BARRETT, Linda, Vice President of Information Services, Community Hospital of Bremen, Bremen, IN, p. A207
BARRETT, Lynn, Chief Nursing Officer, Centerpoint Medical Center, Independence, MO, p. A372
BARRETT, Pam, Human Resources Director, Colorado River Medical Center, Needles, CA, p. A79
BARRETT, Peggy, R.N., Chief Executive Officer, Central Texas Rehabilitation Hospital, Austin, TX, p. A599
BARRETT, T. Marc, M.D. Senior Vice President Medical Affairs, Providence Health Center, Waco, TX, p. A656
BARRICK, Lisa, Controller, HEALTHSOUTH Scottsdale Rehabilitation Hospital, Scottsdale, AZ, p. A38
BARRIO, Gabe, M.D. Chief of Staff, Whidbey General Hospital, Coupeville, WA, p. A682
BARRON, Lee, Chief Executive Officer, Southern Inyo Healthcare District, Lone Pine, CA, p. A70
BARRON, Steven R., President, St. Bernardine Medical Center, San Bernardino, CA, p. A88
BARROW, Robert, Chief Executive Officer, Doctors' Hospital of Michigan, Pontiac, MI, p. A332
BARROW II, William F., President and Chief Executive Officer, Our Lady of Lourdes Regional Medical Center, Lafayette, LA, p. A281
BARROWS, Cheryl, Vice President Human Resources, Sturdy Memorial Hospital, Attleboro, MA, p. A305
BARRY, Amy C., Senior Vice President and Chief Human Resources Officer, Lakeland Regional Medical Center, Lakeland, FL, p. A134
BARRY, Anne, Deputy Commissioner, Minnesota Department of Human Services, Saint Paul, MN, p. B94

BARRY, Rick, Director Information Systems, Baylor Medical Center at Frisco, Frisco, TX, p. A620

BARRY, Thomas, Chief Executive Officer, Pulaski Memorial Hospital, Winamac, IN, p. A224

BARSOM, Michael, M.D., Executive Director, Metropolitan State Hospital, Norwalk, CA, p. A80

BARSOUM, Wael, Interim Chief Executive Officer, Cleveland Clinic Florida, Weston, FL, p. A150

BARSTAD, Stacy
Chief Executive Officer, Sanford Tracy Medical Center, Tracy, MN, p. A353
Chief Executive Officer, Sanford Westbrook Medical Center, Westbrook, MN, p. A354

BARTAL, Ely, M.D., Chief Executive Officer, Kansas Surgery and Recovery Center, Wichita, KS, p. A256

BARTELS, Jennifer, Director Human Resources, Pawnee County Memorial Hospital and Rural Health Clinic, Pawnee City, NE, p. A401

BARTH, Marci, Chief Nursing Officer, Fayette County Hospital, Vandalia, IL, p. A204

BARTHEL, Gayle, Coordinator Human Resources, Select Specialty Hospital–Flint, Flint, MI, p. A324

BARTHOLOMEW, Brenda, Chief Nursing Officer, Gunnison Valley Hospital, Gunnison, UT, p. A660

BARTHOLOMEW, K. A., M.D. Medical Director, Faulkton Area Medical Center, Faulkton, SD, p. A573

BARTHOLOMEW, Shelley, Director Human Resources, Decatur County General Hospital, Parsons, TN, p. A592

BARTILSON, Jim, Manager Information Systems, South Peninsula Hospital, Homer, AK, p. A9

BARTINGALE, Robert, Administrator, Mayo Clinic Health System in Fairmont, Fairmont, MN, p. A343

BARTLETT, Beth, Vice President Nursing, CHI Health Saint Francis, Grand Island, NE, p. A396

BARTLETT, James, Chief Financial Officer, Faith Community Hospital, Jacksboro, TX, p. A629

BARTLETT, Karolyn, Assistant Administrator, Mayo Clinic Health System – Northland in Barron, Barron, WI, p. A702

BARTLETT, Regina, Chief Executive Officer, TriStar Hendersonville Medical Center, Hendersonville, TN, p. A584

BARTLETT, Richard, M.D. Chief Medical Officer, Basin Healthcare Center, Odessa, TX, p. A640

BARTLETT, Ronald E., Chief Financial Officer, Boston Medical Center, Boston, MA, p. A306

BARTLETT, Taci, Chief Financial Officer, Gothenburg Memorial Hospital, Gothenburg, NE, p. A396

BARTLETT III, Thomas G., Administrator, Laird Hospital, Union, MS, p. A366

BARTLETT, Wayne, Director Information Systems, Alvarado Hospital Medical Center, San Diego, CA, p. A89

BARTLEY, Tracy, Manager Information Technology, Bath Community Hospital, Hot Springs, VA, p. A672

BARTO Jr., John K., President and Chief Executive Officer, New Hanover Regional Medical Center, Wilmington, NC, p. A474

BARTO Jr., John K., President and Chief Executive Officer, New Hanover Regional Medical Center, Wilmington, NC, p. B98

BARTOLOTTA, Carmen J., Chief Nursing Officer, Missouri Baptist Sullivan Hospital, Sullivan, MO, p. A383

BARTON, Annie, Director Human Resources, Peterson Rehabilitation Hospital, Wheeling, WV, p. A700

BARTON, Charles, Business Manager, Southwestern State Hospital, Thomasville, GA, p. A168

BARTON, Gratia, Chief Financial Officer, Sequoia Hospital, Redwood City, CA, p. A86

BARTON, Rod, Administrator, Cassia Regional Medical Center, Burley, ID, p. A175

BARTON, Thomas, M.D. Medical Director, TOPS Surgical Specialty Hospital, Houston, TX, p. A627

BARTON, Vikki, R.N. Chief Nursing Officer, Collingsworth General Hospital, Wellington, TX, p. A656

BARTON, Wendy, Manager Business Office, Fredonia Regional Hospital, Fredonia, KS, p. A244

BARTOS, John M., Chief Executive Officer, Marcus Daly Memorial Hospital, Hamilton, MT, p. A388

BARTS, Dennis, Chief Executive Officer, Avista Adventist Hospital, Louisville, CO, p. A109

BARTZ, Ryan, D.O. Chief of Staff, McNairy Regional Hospital, Selmer, TN, p. A592

BARWICK, Kim, Vice President Human Resources, Anthony Medical Center, Anthony, KS, p. A241

BARWIS, Kurt A., FACHE, President and Chief Executive Officer, Bristol Hospital, Bristol, CT, p. A113

BASA, Rhea, Director Human Resources, Morrill County Community Hospital, Bridgeport, NE, p. A394

BASCOM, Steven, M.D. Chief Medical Officer, Guthrie County Hospital, Guthrie Center, IA, p. A231

BASELGA, Jose, M.D. Physician–in–Chief, Memorial Sloan–Kettering Cancer Center, New York, NY, p. A445

BASEY, Marjorie, Chief Financial Officer, Rehabilitation Hospital of Indiana, Indianapolis, IN, p. A214

BASH, Camille, Chief Financial Officer, Doctors Community Hospital, Lanham, MD, p. A302

BASLER, Cyndi, Chief Operating Officer, Iron County Medical Center, Pilot Knob, MO, p. A378

BASQUILL, Debra, Director Human Resources, Jennersville Regional Hospital, West Grove, PA, p. A558

BASS, Andrew C., M.D. Medical Director, Shands Live Oak Regional Medical Center, Live Oak, FL, p. A134

BASS, Anne, Chief Financial Officer, Fairfield Memorial Hospital, Winnsboro, SC, p. A571

BASS, Gordon B., Chief Operating Officer, Ann & Robert H. Lurie Children's Hospital of Chicago, Chicago, IL, p. A183

BASS, Louis A., Vice President Finance, Northeast Alabama Regional Medical Center, Anniston, AL, p. A15

BASS, Sonya, MS Chief Nursing Officer, Colorado Plains Medical Center, Fort Morgan, CO, p. A106

BASS Jr., William L., Vice President and Chief Executive Officer, Centra Southside Community Hospital, Farmville, VA, p. A670

BASSETT, Annie, Director Finance, McBride Clinic Orthopedic Hospital, Oklahoma City, OK, p. A515

BASSETT, Eugene, President and Chief Executive Officer, Methodist Hospital of Sacramento, Sacramento, CA, p. A87

BASSETT, Kimberly S., R.N., President, Morton Hospital and Medical Center, Taunton, MA, p. A315

BASSO, Marty
Chief Financial Officer, Sibley Memorial Hospital, Washington, DC, p. A122
Senior Vice President Finance, Suburban Hospital, Bethesda, MD, p. A299

BASTIANELLO, Carol, Director Employee Services, NORTHSTAR Health System, Iron River, MI, p. A327

BASTIEN IV, Samuel A., Ph.D., Chief Executive Officer, Four Winds Hospital, Saratoga Springs, NY, p. A454

BASTING, Gregory, M.D
Vice President Medical Affairs, Allied Services Rehabilitation Hospital, Scranton, PA, p. A554
Vice President Medical Affairs, John Heinz Institute of Rehabilitation Medicine, Wilkes–Barre, PA, p. A558

BASTONE, Peter F., Chief Executive Officer, Chesapeake Regional Medical Center, Chesapeake, VA, p. A669

BATA, Katie
Vice President Human Resources, Advocate Illinois Masonic Medical Center, Chicago, IL, p. A183
Vice President Human Resources, Advocate Lutheran General Hospital, Park Ridge, IL, p. A199

BATAL, Lucille M., Administrator, Baldpate Hospital, Haverhill, MA, p. A310

BATCHELOR, Cheryl, Chief Financial Officer, Coffeyville Regional Medical Center, Coffeyville, KS, p. A242

BATCHELOR, Dale, M.D. Chief Medical Officer, Saint Thomas West Hospital, Nashville, TN, p. A590

BATCHELOR, Daniela, Director Human Resources, Springhill Memorial Hospital, Mobile, AL, p. A23

BATCHELOR, Diana, Chief Nursing Officer, UnityPoint Health – Finley Hospital, Dubuque, IA, p. A230

BATCHELOR, Michael, Chief Executive Officer, Baptist Easley Hospital, Easley, SC, p. A565

BATDORF, Beth E., Director People Services, St. Mary's Hospital, Streator, IL, p. A204

BATEMAN, Bryan S., Chief Executive Officer, Lake Area Medical Center, Lake Charles, LA, p. A282

BATEMAN, Jana, R.N. Chief Nursing Officer, East Texas Medical Center Jacksonville, Jacksonville, TX, p. A630

BATEMAN, Mark T., Interim Chief Operating Officer, Saint Agnes Medical Center, Fresno, CA, p. A64

BATEMAN, Steven B., Chief Executive Officer, St. Mark's Hospital, Salt Lake City, UT, p. A663

BATES, Beth, Chief Nursing Officer, Shoshone Medical Center, Kellogg, ID, p. A176

BATES, Don, President and Chief Executive Officer, Cloud County Health Center, Concordia, KS, p. A242

BATES, Earl, Director Information Technology, Western Mental Health Institute, Bolivar, TN, p. A579

BATES, Joe, M.D. Clinical Director, Rusk State Hospital, Rusk, TX, p. A645

BATES, Leslie, Manager Human Resources, Alta View Hospital, Sandy, UT, p. A664

BATES, Mary, Director Human Resources, Bowie Memorial Hospital, Bowie, TX, p. A603

BATES, Ondrea, Senior Vice President Patient Care Continuum and Chief Nursing Officer, Allegiance Health, Jackson, MI, p. A327

BATES, Peter, M.D. Vice President Medical Affairs and Chief Medical Officer, Maine Medical Center, Portland, ME, p. A294

BATES, Robert A., Executive Director Finance and Chief Financial Officer, St. Vincent Carmel Hospital, Carmel, IN, p. A208

BATH, Harneet, M.D. Vice President, Chief Medicine Officer, OSF Saint Anthony Medical Center, Rockford, IL, p. A201

BATISTA, David J., Chief Executive Officer, Garfield Medical Center, Monterey Park, CA, p. A78

BATISTE, Michele, Director Human Resources, Preston Memorial Hospital, Kingwood, WV, p. A696

BATORY, Robert J., Vice President Human Resources, York Hospital, York, PA, p. A559

BATSHAW, Mark L., M.D. Physician–in–Chief, Executive Vice President and Chief Academic Officer, Children's National Medical Center, Washington, DC, p. A121

BATTISTA, Edward
Vice President Human Resources, Good Samaritan Hospital, San Jose, CA, p. A92
Vice President Human Resources, West Hills Hospital and Medical Center, CA, p. A75

BATTLE, Joe, Director, G.V. (Sonny) Montgomery Veterans Affairs Medical Center, Jackson, MS, p. A360

BATTLES, Ruth, Administrative Director Human Resources, Corona Regional Medical Center, Corona, CA, p. A60

BATTY, Jill I., Chief Financial Officer, Cambridge Health Alliance, Cambridge, MA, p. A309

BATTY, Mark, Chief Executive Officer, Rochelle Community Hospital, Rochelle, IL, p. A201

BATULIS, Scott, President and Chief Executive Officer, Greater Hudson Valley Health System, Middletown, NY, p. B62

BATULIS, Scott, President and Chief Executive Officer, Orange Regional Medical Center, Middletown, NY, p. A441

BATY, Grace, Director Human Resources, Sweeny Community Hospital, Sweeny, TX, p. A651

BATY, Krista, R.N. Chief Nursing Officer, Cedar Park Regional Medical Center, Cedar Park, TX, p. A605

BATZEL, Linnane, M.D. Senior Vice President Quality and Medical Affairs and Chief Medical Officer, UPMC Altoona, Altoona, PA, p. A532

BATZNER, Cathy, MSN Chief Nursing Officer, LifeCare Hospitals of Wisconsin, Pewaukee, WI, p. A713

BAUER, Brian, Chief Executive Officer, Lutheran Hospital of Indiana, Fort Wayne, IN, p. A211

BAUER, John, Chief Operating Officer, Post Acute Northshore Specialty Hospital, Covington, LA, p. A276

BAUER, Jonathan, Director Information Systems, Somerset Hospital, Somerset, PA, p. A555

BAUER, Kyle, Chief Financial Officer, Cuyuna Regional Medical Center, Crosby, MN, p. A342

BAUER, Richard, M.D. Chief of Staff, South Texas Veterans Health Care System, San Antonio, TX, p. A647

BAUER, Robert
Vice President Human Resources, Midwest Orthopedic Specialty Hospital, Franklin, WI, p. A705
Vice President Human Resources, Wheaton Franciscan Healthcare – Franklin, Franklin, WI, p. A705
Vice President Human Resources, Wheaton Franciscan Healthcare – St. Francis, Milwaukee, WI, p. A711

BAUER, Roberta, M.D. Acting Chair Medical Staff, Cleveland Clinic Children's Hospital for Rehabilitation, Cleveland, OH, p. A488

BAUER, Sandra A., Director Human Resources, Jefferson Community Health Center, Fairbury, NE, p. A395

BAUER, Shar, Executive Secretary, Wishek Community Hospital and Clinics, Wishek, ND, p. A481

BAUER, Tracy, Chief Executive Officer, Midwest Medical Center, Galena, IL, p. A190

BAUER, William, Vice President Finance and Chief Financial Officer, Lehigh Valley Hospital – Hazleton, Hazleton, PA, p. A540

BAUER, William, M.D. Medical Director, Montevista Hospital, Las Vegas, NV, p. A406

BAUGHMAN, Sharon, R.N
Vice President Patient Services and Chief Nursing Officer, Wheaton Franciscan Healthcare – Elmbrook Memorial, Brookfield, WI, p. A703
Senior Vice President Patient Services and Chief Nursing Officer, Wheaton Franciscan Healthcare – St. Joseph's, Milwaukee, WI, p. A711
Vice President Patient Services and Chief Nursing Officer, Wheaton Franciscan Healthcare – The Wisconsin Heart Hospital, Wauwatosa, WI, p. A718

BAUM, David, M.D. Senior Vice President Medical Services, F. F. Thompson Hospital, Canandaigua, NY, p. A435

BAUM, Judy, Chief Executive Officer, Mountain Valley Regional Rehabilitation Hospital, Prescott Valley, AZ, p. A37

BAUMAN, Chris, Director of Nursing, Ballard Rehabilitation Hospital, San Bernardino, CA, p. A88

BAUMAN, Jonathan, M.D. Chief Medical Officer, Four Winds Hospital, Katonah, NY, p. A439

BAUMEIER, Mark, M.D. Chief of Staff, St. Joseph Mercy Livingston Hospital, Howell, MI, p. A327

BAUMERT, Steven P., President and Chief Executive Officer, Methodist Jennie Edmundson Hospital, Council Bluffs, IA, p. A228

BAUMGARDNER, Brian, Chief Executive Officer, West Florida Hospital, Pensacola, FL, p. A142

BAUMGARDNER, Charles J., President and Chief Executive Officer, Psychiatric Institute of Washington, Washington, DC, p. A122

BAUMGARDNER, David, Director Information Management, Union Hospital, Dover, OH, p. A493

BAUMGARTNER, Jennifer, Chief Information Officer, Perkins County Health Services, Grant, NE, p. A396

BAUMGARTNER, Michael A., President, Baptist Health Madisonville, Madisonville, KY, p. A267

BAUNCHALK, James M., Deputy Chief Clinical Services, Dwight David Eisenhower Army Medical Center, Fort Gordon, GA, p. A160

BAUR, Heidi, R.N. Chief Nursing Officer, St. Christopher's Hospital for Children, Philadelphia, PA, p. A550

BAUSCHKA, Martha F., R.N. Vice President and Chief Nursing Officer, Southwest General Health Center, Middleburg Heights, OH, p. A498

BAUTE, Corey, Vice President Human Resources, Franciscan St. Francis Health – Indianapolis, Indianapolis, IN, p. A214

BAUTISTA, Veronica, Chief Financial Officer, Memorial Regional Hospital South, FL, p. A131

BAVA, Michele, Director Human Resources, Doctors Medical Center, Modesto, CA, p. A77

BAVERSO, Lou, Vice President Operations, Magee–Womens Hospital of UPMC, Pittsburgh, PA, p. A551

BAW, Joseph, Director Human Resources, Riveredge Hospital, Forest Park, IL, p. A190

BAWA, Balraj, M.D. Assistant Director Medical Services, Central Virginia Training Center, Madison Heights, VA, p. A673

BAXLEY, Russell, Chief Operating Officer, Lancaster Regional Medical Center, Lancaster, PA, p. A542

BAXTER, Greg, M.D. Senior Vice President Medical Affairs and Chief Medical Officer, Elliot Hospital, Manchester, NH, p. A411

BAXTER, Joshua, Director, Information Systems, Powell Valley Healthcare, Powell, WY, p. A722

BAXTER, Michael T., Chief Executive Officer, Parkview Medical Center, Pueblo, CO, p. A110

BAXTER, Robert O., President and Chief Executive Officer, St. Rita's Medical Center, Lima, OH, p. A496

BAY, Marybeth, Director Information Technology, Sauk Prairie Healthcare, Prairie Du Sac, WI, p. A714

BAYARDO, Fernando, M.D. Chief Medical Officer, Espanola Hospital, Espanola, NM, p. A428

BAYLESS, Victoria, President and Chief Executive Officer, Anne Arundel Medical Center, Annapolis, MD, p. A296

BAYTOS, David G., Chief Executive Officer, Methodist Olive Branch Hospital, Olive Branch, MS, p. A363

BAYUS, Robin, Chief Financial Officer, Rancho Los Amigos National Rehabilitation Center, Downey, CA, p. A62

BAZELEY, Stephen, M.D. Vice President Medical Affairs, ProMedica St. Luke's Hospital, Maumee, OH, p. A498

BAZEMORE, Webster Carl, M.D. Interim Chief of Staff, Charles George Veterans Affairs Medical Center, Asheville, NC, p. A459

BEA, Javon R., President and Chief Executive Officer, Mercy Health System, Janesville, WI, p. B93

BEA, Javon R., President and Chief Executive Officer, Mercy Hospital and Trauma Center, Janesville, WI, p. A707

BEACH, David, Vice President Human Resources, Spectrum Health – Butterworth Hospital, Grand Rapids, MI, p. A325

BEACH, Karrie, Director Human Resources, Community Memorial Hospital, Syracuse, NE, p. A402

BEACH, Misty, Chief Financial Officer, Grisell Memorial Hospital District One, Ransom, KS, p. A253

BEACH, Sarah, Director of Nursing, Jerold Phelps Community Hospital, Garberville, CA, p. A65

BEACHMAN, Michelle, Chief Financial Officer, Twin Rivers Regional Medical Center, Kennett, MO, p. A375

BEADLE, Walter, Chief Information Officer, Physicians' Specialty Hospital, Fayetteville, AR, p. A45

BEADMAN, Cindi, Director Medical Records, Harper Hospital District Five, Harper, KS, p. A245

BEAL, Christopher, M.D. Chief of Staff, Sparrow Clinton Hospital, Saint Johns, MI, p. A334

BEAL, Dwight, Chief Fiscal Services, Jack C. Montgomery Veterans Affairs Medical Center, Muskogee, OK, p. A514

BEALE, Robert, M.D. Chief of Staff, Marshall County Hospital, Benton, KY, p. A258

BEALER, Shirley, Medical Center Director, Overton Brooks Veterans Affairs Medical Center, Shreveport, LA, p. A288

BEAM, William, M.D. Chief of Staff, Cornerstone Hospital of Huntington, Huntington, WV, p. A695

BEAMAN Jr., Charles D., Chief Executive Officer, Palmetto Health, Columbia, SC, p. B105

BEAMAN, Frank, Administrator, Faith Community Hospital, Jacksboro, TX, p. A629

BEAMES, Bo, Interim Administrator, Plains Regional Medical Center, Clovis, NM, p. A427

BEAN, Howard, M.D. Chief Medical Officer, Mary Black Memorial Hospital, Spartanburg, SC, p. A570

BEAN, Roberta, R.N. Interim Chief Nursing Officer, East Morgan County Hospital, Brush, CO, p. A103

BEANE, Jeff, Director Human Resources, Roane General Hospital, Spencer, WV, p. A699

BEAR, John, Hospital Administrator Officer and Supervisor Human Resources, Lawton Indian Hospital, Lawton, OK, p. A512

BEARD, Angie, Chief Nursing Officer, Northcrest Medical Center, Springfield, TN, p. A593

BEARD, Bert, Chief Operating Officer, Wilson Medical Center, Wilson, NC, p. A475

BEARD, Bradley, President, Fairview Southdale Hospital, Edina, MN, p. A343

BEARD, Edward L., R.N. Chief Operating Officer and Chief Nursing Officer, Catawba Valley Medical Center, Hickory, NC, p. A466

BEARD, Gerald C., Chief Operating Officer, Healthmark Regional Medical Center, DeFuniak Springs, FL, p. A127

BEARD, Joan, Chief Nursing Officer, Northwest Florida Community Hospital, Chipley, FL, p. A125

BEARD, Pat, Director Human Resources, Clinton County Hospital, Albany, KY, p. A258

BEARD, Rhonda
  Director Human Resources, Palestine Regional Medical Center, Palestine, TX, p. A640
  Director Human Resources, Palestine Regional Medical Center–East, Palestine, TX, p. A640

BEARD, Robert, Chief Clinical Officer, Vibra Hospital of Northwestern Indiana, Crown Point, IN, p. A209

BEARD, Tim, Interim Chief Executive Officer, Cimarron Memorial Hospital, Boise City, OK, p. A508

BEARDEN, Amy, R.N. Vice President Patient Care Services and Chief Nursing Officer, St. Luke's Magic Valley Medical Center, Twin Falls, ID, p. A178

BEASLEY, Carla, Director of Nursing, Mitchell County Hospital, Camilla, GA, p. A155

BEASLEY, Leslie, Director Human Resources, Temple Community Hospital, Los Angeles, CA, p. A75

BEASLEY, Lynn W., FACHE, Interim Chief Executive Officer, Penobscot Valley Hospital, Lincoln, ME, p. A294

BEASLEY, Ruth, Director Human Resources, Vanderbilt Stallworth Rehabilitation Hospital, Nashville, TN, p. A591

BEASLEY, Tareka, Director Human Resources, RiverWoods Behavioral Health System, Riverdale, GA, p. A165

BEASLEY, Terry, R.N. Chief Nursing Officer, Columbus Regional Healthcare System, Whiteville, NC, p. A474

BEATTIE, Kathryn, M.D. Senior Vice President and Chief Medical Officer, UW Medicine/Valley Medical Center, Renton, WA, p. A687

BEATTIE, Mac, Computer Network Specialist, Deer's Head Hospital Center, Salisbury, MD, p. A303

BEATTY, Alan, Vice President Human Resources, Shore Medical Center, Somers Point, NJ, p. A422

BEATTY, Ann, Director Human Resources, Fairview Hospital, Cleveland, OH, p. A488

BEATTY, Dale E., MSN Chief Nursing Officer, Sharp Grossmont Hospital, La Mesa, CA, p. A68

BEATTY, John, Vice President Human Resources, Barnes–Jewish Hospital, Saint Louis, MO, p. A380

BEATTY, Talia, Director Human Resources, Sunbury Community Hospital and Outpatient Center, Sunbury, PA, p. A555

BEATY, Holly, Chief Financial Officer, South Central Kansas Medical Center, Arkansas City, KS, p. A241

BEATY, Ralph E., Chief Executive Officer, Great River Medical Center, Blytheville, AR, p. A43

BEATY, Ralph E., Chief Executive Officer, Mississippi County Hospital System, Blytheville, AR, p. B95

BEATY, Ralph E., Chief Executive Officer, South Mississippi County Regional Medical Center, Osceola, AR, p. A51

BEATY, Shannon, Nursing Director, Ten Broeck Tennessee Treatment Facility, Cookeville, TN, p. A581

BEAUBIEN, Troy, Director Information Services, Manatee Memorial Hospital, Bradenton, FL, p. A124

BEAUCHAMP, Bill, Chief Financial Officer, St. Luke's Sugar Land Hospital, Sugar Land, TX, p. A651

BEAUDOIN, Dale, Vice President Human Resources, Lewis–Gale Medical Center, Salem, VA, p. A678

BEAUDOIN, Paul
  Senior Vice President Finance and Chief Financial Officer, Kent County Memorial Hospital, Warwick, RI, p. A561
  Chief Financial Officer, Memorial Hospital of Rhode Island, Pawtucket, RI, p. A560

BEAUDRY, Lisa, M.P.H. Director, Patient Care, Baystate Mary Lane Hospital, Ware, MA, p. A316

BEAULAC, Gary, Chief Operating Officer, Henry Ford Macomb Hospitals, Clinton Township, MI, p. A321

BEAULIEU, Lynn, R.N. Chief Nursing Officer, HEALTHSOUTH Walton Rehabilitation Hospital, Augusta, GA, p. A153

BEAULIEU, Sue, Chief Nurse Executive, Massena Memorial Hospital, Massena, NY, p. A441

BEAUPRE, Paul, M.D., Chief Executive Officer, Good Samaritan Hospital, San Jose, CA, p. A92

BEAUVAIS, Richard E., Ph.D., Chief Executive Officer, Wellspring Foundation, Bethlehem, CT, p. A113

BEAVEN, Stacey, R.N. Chief Nursing Officer, Saint Thomas Rutherford Hospital, Murfreesboro, TN, p. A590

BEAVER, Patrick, Chief Nursing Officer, North Shore Medical Center, Miami, FL, p. A137

BEAVER, Randy, Chief Information Officer, Palo Alto County Health System, Emmetsburg, IA, p. A230

BEAVER, Rhonda, Chief Operating Officer, Creek Nation Community Hospital, Okemah, OK, p. A514

BEAZLEY, Gary, Coordinator Information Systems, Baylor Medical Center at Waxahachie, Waxahachie, TX, p. A656

BEBOW, Gary, FACHE, Administrator and Chief Executive Officer, White River Health System, Batesville, AR, p. B153

BEBOW, Gary, FACHE, Administrator and Chief Executive Officer, White River Medical Center, Batesville, AR, p. A43

BECHTEL, Kathleen, MSN Vice President Patient Care Services and Chief Nursing Officer, Froedtert Memorial Lutheran Hospital, Milwaukee, WI, p. A710

BECHTLE, Mavis, MSN Senior Vice President and Chief Nursing Officer, MetroHealth Medical Center, Cleveland, OH, p. A489

BECHTOLD, Kate, R.N
  Senior Vice President and Chief Nurse Executive, MultiCare Good Samaritan Hospital, Puyallup, WA, p. A687
  Senior Vice President and Chief Nurse Executive, MultiCare Mary Bridge Children's Hospital and Health Center, Tacoma, WA, p. A691
  Senior Vice President and Chief Nurse Executive, MultiCare Tacoma General Hospital, Tacoma, WA, p. A691

BECHTOLD, Polly, MSN Chief Nursing Officer, Baptist Health Paducah, Paducah, KY, p. A269

BECK, Allan, Chief Executive Officer, Baylor Orthopedic and Spine Hospital at Arlington, Arlington, TX, p. A597

BECK, Ann
  Vice President and Chief Financial Officer, Carson Tahoe Continuing Care Hospital, Carson City, NV, p. A404
  Vice President Finance, Carson Tahoe Regional Medical Center, Carson City, NV, p. A404

BECK, Brian, Vice President Human Resources, Oak Valley Hospital District, Oakdale, CA, p. A80

BECK, David, Chief Operating Officer and Director Human Resources, Lane Regional Medical Center, Zachary, LA, p. A290

BECK, Gary E., Administrator, Sevier Valley Medical Center, Richfield, UT, p. A662

BECK, Howard, M.D. Chief of Staff, Grace Medical Center, Lubbock, TX, p. A634

BECK, J. Christopher, D.O. President Medical Staff, Aspen Valley Hospital District, Aspen, CO, p. A102

BECK, J. Robert, M.D. Chief Medical Officer, Fox Chase Cancer Center–American Oncologic Hospital, Philadelphia, PA, p. A548

BECK, James, Interim President and Chief Executive Officer, Loring Hospital, Sac City, IA, p. A237

BECK, Joyce, Chief Executive Officer, St. Vincent General Hospital District, Leadville, CO, p. A108

BECK, Kathy, R.N. Chief Nursing Officer, University of Mississippi Medical Center Grenada, Grenada, MS, p. A358

BECK, Michael D., Vice President Operations, Mission Hospital, Mission Viejo, CA, p. A77

BECK, Nina, Interim Chief Executive Officer, HEALTHSOUTH Rehabilitation Hospital – Henderson, Henderson, NV, p. A405

BECK, Steve, MS Manager Human Resources, Kearney Regional Medical Center, Kearney, NE, p. A397

BECK, Walter G., Chief Executive Officer, Colusa Regional Medical Center, Colusa, CA, p. A60

BECKER, Bernard H., Vice President and Chief Human Resources Officer, Stormont–Vail HealthCare, Topeka, KS, p. A255

BECKER, Bruce, M.D. Chief Medical Officer, Medical Center Health System, Odessa, TX, p. A640

BECKER, Bryan, Associate Vice President for Operations and Chief Executive Officer, University of Illinois Hospital & Health Sciences System, Chicago, IL, p. A187

BECKER, Cindy, Vice President and Chief Operating Officer, Highland Hospital of Rochester, Rochester, NY, p. A453

BECKER, Eric, Chief Operating Officer, Research Medical Center, Kansas City, MO, p. A374

BECKER, Frank
  Chief Financial Officer, Lourdes Counseling Center, Richland, WA, p. A687
  Chief Financial Officer, Lourdes Medical Center, Pasco, WA, p. A686

© 2014 AHA Guide

BECKER, Kathleen R., JD,
Interim Chief Executive Officer, SSM Cardinal Glennon
Children's Medical Center, Saint Louis, MO, p. A381
President, SSM St. Mary's Health Center, Saint Louis, MO,
p. A381

BECKER, Kathy, Ph.D. Vice President and Chief Nursing Officer,
Aurora West Allis Medical Center, West Allis, WI, p. A718

BECKER, Kelly, Administrative Coordinator Human Resources,
Select Specialty Hospital–Indianapolis, Indianapolis, IN,
p. A215

BECKER, Preston, Chief Financial Officer, Gritman Medical
Center, Moscow, ID, p. A177

BECKER, Ralph W., Vice President, Chief Financial Officer, Saint
Mary's Hospital, Waterbury, CT, p. A118

BECKER, Richard B., M.D., President, Chief Executive Officer
and Interim Chief Medical Officer, Brooklyn Hospital Center,
NY, p. A443

BECKES, Hap, Director Information Systems, Sullivan County
Community Hospital, Sullivan, IN, p. A222

BECKETT, Jason, Director Information Services, San Dimas
Community Hospital, San Dimas, CA, p. A90

BECKHAM, Steve, Director Human Resources, Magee General
Hospital, Magee, MS, p. A361

BECKMANN, Gregory, Finance Controller, Avera Creighton
Hospital, Creighton, NE, p. A395

BECKNER, Jana, Director Human Resources, LewisGale Hospital
Pulaski, Pulaski, VA, p. A676

BECKSVOORT, Jennifer F., Senior Human Resource Business
Partner, Spectrum Health Zeeland Community Hospital,
Zeeland, MI, p. A338

BEDARD, Lori, Chief Executive Officer, HEALTHSOUTH
Rehabilitation Hospital of Spring Hill, Brooksville, FL, p. A125

BEDELL, Diane, R.N. Director of Nursing, Kahi Mohala
Behavioral Health, Ewa Beach, HI, p. A170

BEDELL, Julie, Manager Human Resources, Perkins County
Health Services, Grant, NE, p. A396

BEDELL, Mikael, M.D. Medical Director, Cascade Medical
Center, Cascade, ID, p. A175

BEDFORD, Jeff, Executive Vice President and Chief Financial
Officer, Woman's Hospital, Flowood, MS, p. A358

BEDFORD, Tim, Chief Executive Officer, Emerald Coast
Behavioral Hospital, Panama City, FL, p. A141

BEDGER, Kathy, Chief Nursing Officer, Clearfield Hospital,
Clearfield, PA, p. A536

BEDICK, Jennifer L., Deputy Commander Nursing, Tripler Army
Medical Center, Honolulu, HI, p. A171

BEDINGFIELD, Lance, Director Information Services, Dixie
Regional Medical Center, Saint George, UT, p. A662

BEDWAY, Marianna, R.N
Senior Vice President and Chief Nursing Officer, Mary
Washington Hospital, Fredericksburg, VA, p. A671
Senior Vice President and Chief Nursing Officer, Stafford
Hospital, Stafford, VA, p. A679

BEDZYK, J. Paul, Deputy Director Administration, Elmira
Psychiatric Center, Elmira, NY, p. A437

BEEBE, Chris T., Director Human Resources, Raleigh General
Hospital, Beckley, WV, p. A693

BEEBY, Lori, Director Information Systems, Community Hospital,
McCook, NE, p. A398

BEECHLER, Jane, Director Healthcare Information Systems,
Wyoming County Community Hospital, Warsaw, NY, p. A457

BEECHY, Andrew, Manager Information Technology Systems,
Lee's Summit Medical Center, Lee's Summit, MO, p. A375

BEED, Donna E., Chief Information Management Division, Tripler
Army Medical Center, Honolulu, HI, p. A171

BEEDLE, Chester
Chief Financial Officer, Kern Valley Healthcare District, Lake
Isabella, CA, p. A69
Interim Chief Financial Officer, Tehachapi Valley Healthcare
District, Tehachapi, CA, p. A96

BEEDY, Scott, Chief Financial Officer, Hansford Hospital,
Spearman, TX, p. A650

BEEG, Gregg, Chief Financial Officer, McLaren Central Michigan,
Mount Pleasant, MI, p. A330

BEEG, Gregg M., FACHE Chief Financial Officer, Oaklawn
Hospital, Marshall, MI, p. A330

BEEHLER, Darryl, D.O. Chief of Staff, CHI St. Joseph's Health,
Park Rapids, MN, p. A349

BEEHN, Holly, Director Human Resources, Southwest Health
Center, Platteville, WI, p. A713

BEEMAN, Thomas E., FACHE, President and Chief Executive
Officer, Lancaster General Health, Lancaster, PA, p. A542

BEENE, Nikia, Assistant Chief Executive Officer, Ponca City
Medical Center, Ponca City, OK, p. A517

BEER, Ronald R., FACHE, Vice President, Clinical Operations,
Geisinger Wyoming Valley Medical Center, Wilkes Barre, PA,
p. A558

BEESON, John C., M.D. Chief Medical Officer, Christus St.
Vincent Regional Medical Center, Santa Fe, NM, p. A430

BEGALSKE, Kathy, Chief Nursing Officer, Palmer Lutheran
Health Center, West Union, IA, p. A239

BEGAN, Victoria D., R.N
Chief Nursing Officer, University of Arizona Medical Center –
South Campus, Tucson, AZ, p. A41
Chief Nursing Officer, Vice President Patient Services,
University of Arizona Medical Center – University Campus,
Tucson, AZ, p. A41

BEGAY, Trudy, Human Resources Specialist, Hopi Health Care
Center, Keams Canyon, AZ, p. A33

BEGGANE, Thomas, Manager Human Resources, LAC–Olive
View–UCLA Medical Center, CA, p. A73

BEGGS, Shaun, Chief Financial Officer, OneCore Health,
Oklahoma City, OK, p. A516

BEGIN, James, Director Information Technology, Golden Valley
Memorial Healthcare, Clinton, MO, p. A369

BEGLEY, Bruce D., Executive Director, Methodist Hospital,
Henderson, KY, p. A262

BEGLEY, Robyn, R.N. Chief Nursing Officer, AtlantiCare Regional
Medical Center, Atlantic City, NJ, p. A413

BEGUIN, Shelley, Director Human Resources, Gordon Memorial
Hospital, Gordon, NE, p. A396

BEHAN, Lawrence, Vice President Administration and Finance,
Chief Financial Officer, Walden Psychiatric Care, Waltham,
MA, p. A316

BEHAR, Robert, M.D., Chief Executive Officer, North Cypress
Medical Center, Cypress, TX, p. A609

BEHM, Anthony, D.O. Chief of Staff, Erie Veterans Affairs
Medical Center, Erie, PA, p. A538

BEHNE, Carl P., Administrator and Chief Executive Officer,
Greene County Medical Center, Jefferson, IA, p. A233

BEHNER, Bruce M., Chief Operating Officer, Knox Community
Hospital, Mount Vernon, OH, p. A499

BEHNKEN, Nick, Supervisor Information Technology, Red Bud
Regional Hospital, Red Bud, IL, p. A201

BEHR, Richard A., Deputy Commander for Health Services,
Reynolds Army Community Hospital, Fort Sill, OK, p. A511

BEHRENDT, Darcy, R.N. Vice President, Patient Care Services,
CHI Health Missouri Valley, Missouri Valley, IA, p. A234

BEHRENDT, William, Ph.D. Vice President Human Resources,
University of Texas Southwestern Medical Center, Dallas, TX,
p. A612

BEHRENDTSEN, Ole, M.D. Medical Director, Santa Barbara
County Psychiatric Health Facility, Santa Barbara, CA, p. A94

BEHRENS, Colleen, Director Information Technology, Community
Memorial Healthcare, Marysville, KS, p. A249

BEHRENS, Karen, Director Technology Services, Perry Memorial
Hospital, Princeton, IL, p. A200

BEIDELSCHIES, Sandra, MS
Chief Nursing Officer, Knox Community Hospital, Mount
Vernon, OH, p. A499
Vice President Patient Services, Wood County Hospital,
Bowling Green, OH, p. A484

BEIERMAN, Jennifer, Director Human Resources, Boone County
Health Center, Albion, NE, p. A393

BEIGHLE, John, Flight Chief Medical Information Systems, Wright
Patterson Medical Center, Wright–Patterson AFB, OH,
p. A505

BEILER, Jeffrey
Associate Director, Philadelphia Veterans Affairs Medical
Center, Philadelphia, PA, p. A549
Interim Director, Wilkes–Barre Veterans Affairs Medical
Center, Wilkes–Barre, PA, p. A558

BEINDIT, Dawn, Director Work Life Services, St. John River
District Hospital, East China, MI, p. A323

BEIRNE, Frank T., FACHE,
Senior Vice President and Area Manager, Kaiser Permanente
Redwood City Medical Center, Redwood City, CA, p. A85
Senior Vice President and Area Manager, Kaiser Permanente
South San Francisco, South San Francisco, CA, p. A96

BEISSEL, Debbie, Chief Executive Officer, Surgical Institute of
Reading, Wyomissing, PA, p. A559

BEISWENGER, Joel, Chief Executive Officer, Tri–County Hospital,
Wadena, MN, p. A353

BEITCHER, Bob, Chief Executive Officer, Motion Picture and
Television Fund Hospital and Residential Services, CA, p. A73

BEITER, Amy, M.D., President and Chief Executive Officer,
Carondelet St. Mary's Hospital, Tucson, AZ, p. A40

BEITER, Donna M., MSN, Director, Veterans Affairs Greater Los
Angeles Healthcare System, Los Angeles, CA, p. A75

BEITING, Mark, Vice President Human Resources, Alta Bates
Summit Medical Center – Summit Campus, Oakland, CA,
p. A80

BEITZEL, Mark, Director Information Systems, Advocate
Lutheran General Hospital, Park Ridge, IL, p. A199

BEJARINO, Paul, M.D. Chief of Staff, Oro Valley Hospital, Oro
Valley, AZ, p. A35

BEJNAR, Darla, M.D. Chief Medical Officer, Socorro General
Hospital, Socorro, NM, p. A431

BELAIR, Norman, Senior Vice President and Chief Financial
Officer, Southern Maine Health Care – Biddeford Medical
Center X, Biddeford, ME, p. A292

BELBECK, Michael, President and Chief Administrative Officer,
Methodist Medical Center of Oak Ridge, Oak Ridge, TN,
p. A591

BELCHER, Debbie, Director Human Resources, HEALTHSOUTH
Rehabilitation Hospital of Austin, Austin, TX, p. A599

BELCHER, Kenneth H., Chief Executive Officer, CharterCare
Health Partners, Providence, RI, p. B34

BELDECOS, Athena, M.D. Medical Director, Vibra Hospital of
Charleston, Mt. Pleasant, SC, p. A568

BELENY, Charles, D.O. Chief of Staff, Jonathan M. Wainwright
Memorial Veterans Affairs Medical Center, Walla Walla, WA,
p. A692

BELGARDE, Donna, Human Resources Specialist, Public Health
Service Indian Hospital – Quentin N. Burdick Memorial Health
Facility, Belcourt, ND, p. A476

BELHASEN, F. K., M.D. Medical Director, Paul B. Hall Regional
Medical Center, Paintsville, KY, p. A269

BELJIN, Dawn, R.N., Chief Operating Officer, Forest Park
Medical Center–Southlake, Southlake, TX, p. A650

BELKOSKI, Dave, Chief Financial Officer, University Hospital
McDuffie, Thomson, GA, p. A168

BELKOSKI, David, Executive Vice President and Chief Financial
Officer, University Hospital, Augusta, GA, p. A154

BELL, Brian, Associate Administrator and Chief Operating
Officer, National Park Medical Center, Hot Springs, AR,
p. A47

BELL, Cindy, Director Finance, Willow Crest Hospital, Miami, OK,
p. A513

BELL, Gordon, M.D. Chief of Staff, Frances Mahon Deaconess
Hospital, Glasgow, MT, p. A387

BELL, Heath
Chief Information Officer, Kishwaukee Hospital, DeKalb, IL,
p. A188
Chief Information Officer, Valley West Hospital, Sandwich, IL,
p. A202

BELL, Hollis, M.D. Medical Director, Mercy Rehabilitation Hospital
Springfield, Springfield, MO, p. A383

BELL, Julie, Director of Nursing, Covenant Specialty Hospital,
Lubbock, TX, p. A634

BELL, Kae, Chief Financial Officer, Brentwood Hospital,
Shreveport, LA, p. A288

BELL, Kristen, Director Human Resources, UPMC Mercy,
Pittsburgh, PA, p. A551

BELL, Lorraine, Vice President Operations Human Resources,
Scott & White Memorial Hospital, Temple, TX, p. A652

BELL, Madeline, President and Chief Operating Officer,
Children's Hospital of Philadelphia, Philadelphia, PA, p. A547

BELL, Randall C., M.D. Medical Director, LifeCare Hospitals of
San Antonio, San Antonio, TX, p. A646

BELL, Roderick, Chief Financial Officer, College Hospital
Cerritos, Cerritos, CA, p. A59

BELL, Rodric, M.D. Medical Director, HEALTHSOUTH Tustin
Rehabilitation Hospital, Tustin, CA, p. A98

BELL, Roni Sue, Director Nursing Services, Ohio Valley General
Hospital, McKees Rocks, PA, p. A544

BELL, Jr., Sammie, Chief Financial Officer, Tallahatchie General
Hospital, Charleston, MS, p. A356

BELL, Scot, Chief Medical Officer, Anderson Regional Medical
Center, Meridian, MS, p. A362

BELL, Sonja, Coordinator Human Resources, Sedgwick County
Health Center, Julesburg, CO, p. A108

BELL, Stuart, M.D. Vice President Medical Affairs, MedStar
Union Memorial Hospital, Baltimore, MD, p. A297

BELL, Talana, Chief Financial Officer, Flowers Hospital, Dothan,
AL, p. A19

BELL, Tammie
Director Human Resources, McKenzie Regional Hospital,
McKenzie, TN, p. A588
Director Human Resources, Volunteer Community Hospital,
Martin, TN, p. A587

BELL, Tanya, Public Information Officer, Penrose–St. Francis
Health Services, Colorado Springs, CO, p. A104

BELL, Thomas, Deputy Commander Administration, Keller Army
Community Hospital, West Point, NY, p. A458

BELL, Tony, Manager Personnel, Tippah County Hospital, Ripley,
MS, p. A365

BELL, W. Scot, M.D. Chief Medical Officer, Rush Foundation
Hospital, Meridian, MS, p. A362

BELLAMY, David, Chief Financial Officer, McLaren Northern
Michigan, Petoskey, MI, p. A332

BELLAND, Patrick, Vice President Operations, Unity Hospital,
Fridley, MN, p. A344

BELLEAU, Christopher, M.D. Medical Director, Sage
Rehabilitation Hospital, Baton Rouge, LA, p. A274

BELLEAU, Donella, Director Human Resources, Graham County
Hospital, Hill City, KS, p. A245

BELLER, Robert H., FACHE, Director, Clement J. Zablocki Veterans Affairs Medical Center, Milwaukee, WI, p. A710

BELLUCCI, Alessandro, M.D., Executive Director, North Shore University Hospital, Manhasset, NY, p. A440

BELLWAY, Regina, Vice President Human Resources, Bethesda Hospital East, Boynton Beach, FL, p. A124

BELMONT, Chris, Chief Information Officer and Vice President, University of Texas M.D. Anderson Cancer Center, Houston, TX, p. A628

BELMONT, James, Associate Director, Northern Arizona Veterans Affairs Health Care System, Prescott, AZ, p. A37

BELMONT, Terry A., Chief Executive Officer, UC Irvine Medical Center, Orange, CA, p. A81

BELT, Katrina, Chief Financial Officer, Baptist Medical Center East, Montgomery, AL, p. A23

BELTRAN, Grace, Director Human Resources, Foundation Surgical Hospital of El Paso, El Paso, TX, p. A616

BELTZ, John, Chief Financial Officer, Hendry Regional Medical Center, Clewiston, FL, p. A126

BELVINS, Pam, Director Information Technology Member Hospitals Mission, McDowell Hospital, Marion, NC, p. A468

BELYEU, Peggy, Controller, Vanderbilt Stallworth Rehabilitation Hospital, Nashville, TN, p. A591

BELZER, Michael, M.D. Medical Director, Hennepin County Medical Center, Minneapolis, MN, p. A347

BEMENT, Douglas J., Chief Financial Officer, Kosciusko Community Hospital, Warsaw, IN, p. A224

BEN, Sabrina, Director Human Resources, North Star Behavioral Health System, Anchorage, AK, p. A28

BENAVIDES, Christina, Director Employee Services, Otto Kaiser Memorial Hospital, Kenedy, TX, p. A631

BENCOMO, Dionisio, Chief Executive Officer, Select Specialty Hospital–Miami, Miami, FL, p. A137

BENDER, Brad, M.D. Chief of Staff, Malcom Randall Veterans Affairs Medical Center, Gainesville, FL, p. A129

BENDER, Janette, Chief Financial Officer, Arkansas Valley Regional Medical Center, La Junta, CO, p. A108

BENDER, Ron, Chief Executive Officer, Clay County Medical Center, Clay Center, KS, p. A242

BENDER, Roxanna, Interim Administrator, Bryce Hospital, Tuscaloosa, AL, p. A26

BENDER, Steve, Chief Financial Officer, Wuesthoff Medical Center – Melbourne, Melbourne, FL, p. A136

BENDINELLI, Emily, Director of Nurses, Ashley County Medical Center, Crossett, AR, p. A44

RENEDICT, Eva, R.N., President and Chief Executive Officer, Jones Memorial Hospital, Wellsville, NY, p. A457

BENEDICT, Joy M., Director Human Resources, Baptist Health Richmond, Richmond, KY, p. A270

BENEDUM, Mark, Chief Executive Officer, Highline Medical Center, Burien, WA, p. A682

BENEFIELD, Marlene, Director Human Resources, Cherokee Medical Center, Centre, AL, p. A18

BENEPAL, Jaspreet, Chief Nursing Officer, Contra Costa Regional Medical Center, Martinez, CA, p. A77

BENETTI–LOYOLA, Pedro L., Administrator, Hospital San Cristobal, Coto Laurel, PR, p. A725

BENFIELD, Ronald K., Chief Operating Officer, Adventist Medical Center–Portland, Portland, OR, p. A528

BENGALI, Abdul, Chief Information Officer, Via Christi Hospital on St. Francis, Wichita, KS, p. A257

BENGSTON, Jennifer, M.D. Chief Medical Officer, Valley County Health System, Ord, NE, p. A400

BENGTSON, Paul R., Chief Executive Officer, Northeastern Vermont Regional Hospital, Saint Johnsbury, VT, p. A666

BENINK, Eric, M.D. Chief Medical Officer, Northwest Community Hospital, Arlington Heights, IL, p. A180

BENITEZ, Pedro, M.D. Medical Director, Hospital De Damas, Ponce, PR, p. A727

BENJAMIN, Christian, MC, Commander, Mike O'Callaghan Federal Hospital, Nellis AFB, NV, p. A407

BENJAMIN, Kathleen, R.N. Chief Nursing Officer, MacNeal Hospital, Berwyn, IL, p. A181

BENJAMIN, Sunny J., Chief Human Resources Officer, Oklahoma State University Medical Center, Tulsa, OK, p. A520

BENNER, Brenda, Director Human Resources, HEALTHSOUTH Rehabilitation Hospital of Sarasota, Sarasota, FL, p. A145

BENNETT, Anthony, M.D. Chief Clinical Affairs, Baptist Health Medical Center–Little Rock, Little Rock, AR, p. A49

BENNETT, Bart, Chief Financial Officer, Springbrook Behavioral Health System, Travelers Rest, SC, p. A570

BENNETT, Charlotte, Vice President Human Resources, West Virginia University Hospitals, Morgantown, WV, p. A697

BENNETT, Christin, Administrator, Oceans Behavioral Hospital of Lake Charles, Lake Charles, LA, p. A282

BENNETT, Dan, Director Operations, Waldo County General Hospital, Belfast, ME, p. A292

BENNETT, Darnell, Director Finance, Horizon Specialty Hospital, Las Vegas, NV, p. A406

BENNETT, E. Kyle, Executive Vice President and Chief Operating Officer, Memorial Hospital and Health Care Center, Jasper, IN, p. A215

BENNETT, Edwin, Controller, Turning Point Hospital, Moultrie, GA, p. A164

BENNETT, Fay, Vice President Employee Services, Guadalupe Regional Medical Center, Seguin, TX, p. A648

BENNETT, Kay

Vice President Human Resources, Baptist Medical Center East, Montgomery, AL, p. A23

System Director Human Resources, Baptist Medical Center South, Montgomery, AL, p. A23

BENNETT, Kimberly, Director Patient Care, Dubuis Hospital of Alexandria, Alexandria, LA, p. A272

BENNETT, Kris, Chief Operating Officer, Lutheran Hospital, Cleveland, OH, p. A488

BENNETT, Laurie, Director Human Resources, Sarasota Memorial Health Care System, Sarasota, FL, p. A145

BENNETT, Lee W., Chief Financial Officer, Sitka Community Hospital, Sitka, AK, p. A30

BENNETT, Leo, M.D. Deputy Commander Clinical Services, Bassett Army Community Hospital, Fort Wainwright, AK, p. A29

BENNETT, Lisa, Interim CEO and Chief Financial Officer, Waverly Health Center, Waverly, IA, p. A239

BENNETT, Mary Ann, R.N. Chief Operating Officer and Chief Nursing Officer, Springbrook Behavioral Health System, Travelers Rest, SC, p. A570

BENNETT, Melissa, Chief Nursing Officer, Trumbull Memorial Hospital, Warren, OH, p. A504

BENNETT, Nathan, M.D. Chief Medical Officer, Mercy Hospital Waldron, Waldron, AR, p. A53

BENNETT, Patti, Chief Nursing Officer and Senior Vice President, Good Shepherd Medical Center, Longview, TX, p. A634

BENNETT, Randall, Assistant Administrator, Uintah Basin Medical Center, Roosevelt, UT, p. A662

BENNETT, Richard G., M.D., President, Johns Hopkins Bayview Medical Center, Baltimore, MD, p. A296

BENNETT, Richard I., Senior Vice President and Chief Financial Officer, Delaware County Memorial Hospital, Drexel Hill, PA, p. A537

BENNETT, Rick, Administrator, St. James Behavioral Health Hospital, Gonzales, LA, p. A278

BENNETT, Ron, Chief Financial Officer, Abilene Regional Medical Center, Abilene, TX, p. A595

BENNETT, Sharon, Manager Information Systems, Cobre Valley Regional Medical Center, Globe, AZ, p. A33

BENNETT, Sheila, R.N. Vice President & Chief Nursing Officer, Floyd Medical Center, Rome, GA, p. A165

BENNETT, Tony N., Chief Executive Officer, HEALTHSOUTH Emerald Coast Rehabilitation Hospital, Panama City, FL, p. A142

BENNETT, W. Bradley, President and Chief Executive Officer, Fundamental Long Term Care Holdings, LLC, Sparks Glencoe, MD, p. B60

BENNETT, Wayne, Chief Financial Officer, Franklin Memorial Hospital, Farmington, ME, p. A293

BENOIT, Paul, Associate Administrator, Central Louisiana State Hospital, Pineville, LA, p. A287

BENOIT, Rebecca, R.N. Chief Nursing Officer, Lafayette General Medical Center, Lafayette, LA, p. A281

BENSEMA, David, Chief Information Officer, Baptist Health La Grange, La Grange, KY, p. A263

BENSON, Annie, Chief Executive Officer, Southeast Arizona Medical Center, Douglas, AZ, p. A32

BENSON, Cheryl, Chief Operating Officer, Wernersville State Hospital, Wernersville, PA, p. A557

BENSON, Eric, Vice President Human Resources, Sarah Bush Lincoln Health Center, Mattoon, IL, p. A195

BENSON, Kevin, Chief Financial Officer, Ortonville Area Health Services, Ortonville, MN, p. A349

BENTLEY, Scott, Chief Financial Officer, Woman's Hospital of Texas, Houston, TX, p. A628

BENTON, Dennis C., Executive Director, Kaiser Permanente Panorama City Medical Center, CA, p. A72

BENTON, Nancy, Assistant Director Patient Care Services, Mann–Grandstaff Veterans Affairs Medical Center, Spokane, WA, p. A690

BENTON, Tony, Interim Chief Executive Officer Washington County Hospitals, Johnson City Medical Center, Johnson City, TN, p. A585

BENTZ, Douglas E., Chief Executive Officer, Roane General Hospital, Spencer, WV, p. A699

BENVENUTTI, Cathy, Human Resource Director, Hancock Medical Center, Bay Saint Louis, MS, p. A355

BENWARE, Joel, Vice President Information Technology and Compliance, Northwestern Medical Center, Saint Albans, VT, p. A666

BENZ, Betsy, R.N. Chief Nursing Officer, Aurora Medical Center – Manitowoc County, Two Rivers, WI, p. A716

BENZ Jr., Edward J., M.D., President and Chief Executive Officer, Dana–Farber Cancer Institute, Boston, MA, p. A306

BENZEL, Cindy, Manager Human Resources, Sanford Vermillion Medical Center, Vermillion, SD, p. A577

BEPLER, Gerold, Ph.D., President and Chief Executive Officer, Karmanos Cancer Center, Detroit, MI, p. A322

BERAN, Richard, Director Information Technology and Chief Information Officer, Fremont Health, Fremont, NE, p. A395

BERARD, Celse A., President, Riverview Hospital Association, Wisconsin Rapids, WI, p. A719

BERARDI, Paula, Manager Human Resources, Bournewood Health Systems, Brookline, MA, p. A308

BERCHER, Richard, M.D. Chief Medical Officer, Paris Regional Medical Center, Paris, TX, p. A641

BERCI, Haya, Executive Director of Nursing, Joyce Eisenberg–Keefer Medical Center, Reseda, CA, p. A86

BERDAN, Barclay E., FACHE, Chief Executive Officer, Texas Health Resources, Arlington, TX, p. B135

BERENS, Jeff, MS Chief Nursing Officer, Sanford Vermillion Medical Center, Vermillion, SD, p. A577

BERENTES, Amy, R.N. Vice President Patient Care Services, Mercy Medical Center–Clinton, Clinton, IA, p. A227

BERETTA, Dante, M.D. Chief of Staff, CentraCare Health–Melrose, Melrose, MN, p. A346

BERG, Gary L., D.O. Chief Medical Officer, St. John Macomb–Oakland Hospital, Warren, MI, p. A336

BERG, James A., Interim Chief Executive Officer, Texas Health Presbyterian Hospital Dallas, Dallas, TX, p. A612

BERG, Jon, M.D. Chief of Staff, Northwood Deaconess Health Center, Northwood, ND, p. A479

BERG, Tony L., M.D. Chief of Staff, Winner Regional Healthcare Center, Winner, SD, p. A578

BERG, William, Chief Information Officer, Naval Hospital Pensacola, Pensacola, FL, p. A142

BERGE, Ron, Executive Vice President and Chief Operating Officer, National Jewish Health, Denver, CO, p. A105

BERGEAUX, Scott, M.D. Chief Medical Staff, Abrom Kaplan Memorial Hospital, Kaplan, LA, p. A280

BERGEMANN, John, Director Human Resources, Crouse Hospital, Syracuse, NY, p. A455

BERGEN, Sharon A., Chief Operating Officer, Belmont Center for Comprehensive Treatment, Philadelphia, PA, p. A547

BERGENFELD, Joel

Chief Executive Officer, Hemet Valley Medical Center, Hemet, CA, p. A67

Chief Hospital Executive Officer, Menifee Valley Medical Center, Sun City, CA, p. A96

BERGENFELD, Joel, Chief Executive Officer, Physicians for Healthy Hospitals, Hemet, CA, p. B106

BERGER, George, Controller, HEALTHSOUTH Rehabilitation Hospital of Altoona, Altoona, PA, p. A532

BERGER, Jeffrey, M.D. Chief Medical Officer, Brighton Center for Recovery, Brighton, MI, p. A320

BERGER, Kathy, R.N. Associate Director, Nursing and Patient Support Services, Sheridan Veterans Affairs Medical Center, Sheridan, WY, p. A722

BERGERON, Johnny, Chief Information Officer, Bunkie General Hospital, Bunkie, LA, p. A275

BERGERON, Pierre, Director Information Services, Wellington Regional Medical Center, West Palm Beach, FL, p. A150

BERGERON, Timothy, Deputy Commander, Administration, Bassett Army Community Hospital, Fort Wainwright, AK, p. A29

BERGERSON, Melissa, R.N. Vice President Patient Care Services, Black River Memorial Hospital, Black River Falls, WI, p. A702

BERGFORT, Joe, Chief Information Officer, UCSF Medical Center, San Francisco, CA, p. A91

BERGH, Roger, Director Human Resources, Helen Newberry Joy Hospital, Newberry, MI, p. A331

BERGHERM, Bruce, Chief Executive Officer, Florida Hospital North Pinellas, Tarpon Springs, FL, p. A148

BERGHOLM, Brenda, MSN Chief Nursing Officer, Caribou Memorial Hospital and Living Center, Soda Springs, ID, p. A178

BERGLING, Richard Q., Chief Executive Officer, Gove County Medical Center, Quinter, KS, p. A253

BERGMAN, Angela, Director Health Information Management, Van Matre HEALTHSOUTH Rehabilitation Hospital, Rockford, IL, p. A202

BERGMAN, Chris, Chief Financial Officer, Christ Hospital, Cincinnati, OH, p. A486

BERGMAN, Jim, Director Human Resources, Northeast Regional Medical Center, Kirksville, MO, p. A375

BERGMANN, Daniel, M.D. Chief Medical Officer, Barnes–Jewish St. Peters Hospital, Saint Peters, MO, p. A382

BERGMANN, Michael, President, Aurora Medical Center Summit, Summit, WI, p. A716

BERGMANN, Peter U., President and Chief Executive Officer, Sisters of Charity Hospital of Buffalo, Buffalo, NY, p. A435

BERGQUIST, Susan, Human Resources Generalist, Kindred Hospital–La Mirada, La Mirada, CA, p. A68

BERGSENG, John H., D.O. Vice President Medical Affairs, Glencoe Regional Health Services, Glencoe, MN, p. A344

BERGSTEDT, Sharon, Director of Nursing, Alaska Psychiatric Institute, Anchorage, AK, p. A28

BERGSTROM, Jenny, Project Manager Information Technology, Cloud County Health Center, Concordia, KS, p. A242

BERKOWITZ, David J., Vice President and Chief Operating Officer, Palisades Medical Center, North Bergen, NJ, p. A420

BERKRAM, Treasure, Chief Financial Officer, Northern Rockies Medical Center, Cut Bank, MT, p. A386

BERLINGHOFF, Kathleen, Director Human Resources, Sharon Hospital, Sharon, CT, p. A117

BERLOT, Alvin, M.D. Medical Director, Bucktail Medical Center, Renovo, PA, p. A553

BERLOWITZ, Dan, M.D. Acting Chief of Staff, Bedford Veterans Affairs Medical Center, Edith Nourse Rogers Memorial Veterans Hospital, Bedford, MA, p. A305

BERLUCCHI, Scott A., FACHE, President and Chief Executive Officer, Auburn Community Hospital, Auburn, NY, p. A433

BERLYN, Maria, Assistant Vice President Nursing Services, John Heinz Institute of Rehabilitation Medicine, Wilkes–Barre, PA, p. A558

BERMAN, Manuel S., President and Chief Executive Officer, Tuality Healthcare, Hillsboro, OR, p. A525

BERMAN, Ronald, M.D. Chief of Staff, Mad River Community Hospital, Arcata, CA, p. A56

BERMUDEZ, Ada, Director Human Resources, Hospital De La Concepcion, San German, PR, p. A727

BERMUDEZ, Armand, M.D. Medical Director, Select Specialty Hospital–Zanesville, Zanesville, OH, p. A506

BERMUDEZ, Yuri, M.D. Chief of Staff, South Texas Health System, Edinburg, TX, p. A615

BERNAL, Leroy, Chief Operating Officer, Victory Medical Center – Southcross, San Antonio, TX, p. A648

BERNARD, Donald P.
Chief Financial Officer, Kaiser Permanente Fontana Medical Center, Fontana, CA, p. A63
Area Chief Finance Officer, Kaiser Permanente Ontario Medical Center, Ontario, CA, p. A81

BERNARD, Doug, M.D. Chief Medical Officer, White River Medical Center, Batesville, AR, p. A43

BERNARD, Duane, President, Chief Financial Officer and Chief Operating Officer, Freedom Pain Hospital, Scottsdale, AZ, p. A38

BERNARD, Joseph, Chief Executive Officer, Highlands Regional Medical Center, Sebring, FL, p. A146

BERNARD, Mark L., Chief Executive Officer, St. Joseph Medical Center, Houston, TX, p. A627

BERNARD, Peter J., Chief Executive Officer, Bon Secours St. Francis Medical Center, Midlothian, VA, p. A674

BERNARD, Robert, M.D. Chief of Staff, Alexandria Veterans Affairs Health Care System, Pineville, LA, p. A287

BERNARD, Traci, President, Texas Health Harris Methodist Hospital Southlake, Southlake, TX, p. A650

BERNARDI, Barbara, R.N. Nurse Executive, Jameson Hospital, New Castle, PA, p. A546

BERNARDO, Maria, M.D. Chief of Staff, Bullock County Hospital, Union Springs, AL, p. A26

BERNATIS, Terry D., Director Human Resources, Community HealthCare System, Onaga, KS, p. A251

BERND, David L., Chief Executive Officer, Sentara Healthcare, Norfolk, VA, p. B123

BERNDT, Julia L., Chief Financial Officer, Logansport Memorial Hospital, Logansport, IN, p. A218

BERNERT–YAP, Kellie, Director Human Resources, Vibra Specialty Hospital of Portland, Portland, OR, p. A529

BERNEY, Bernadette, Director Human Resources, Pullman Regional Hospital, Pullman, WA, p. A687

BERNICK, Michael, Vice President Finance, Clarity Child Guidance Center, San Antonio, TX, p. A646

BERNINI, A. Susan, Chief Operating Officer, Einstein Medical Center Philadelphia, Philadelphia, PA, p. A548

BERNS, Erin, Director Human Resources, Veterans Memorial Hospital, Waukon, IA, p. A239

BERNSTEIN, Lee
Regional Executive Vice President and Chief Operating Officer, SSM St. Clare Health Center, Fenton, MO, p. A371
Regional Executive Vice President and Chief Operating Officer, SSM St. Joseph Health Center, Saint Charles, MO, p. A379

BERNSTEIN, Les, Chief Information Officer, Cookeville Regional Medical Center, Cookeville, TN, p. A581

BERNSTEIN, Michael, Chief Financial Officer, Tulare Regional Medical Center, Tulare, CA, p. A98

BERNSTEIN, Paul E., M.D. Area Medical Director, Kaiser Permanente San Diego Medical Center, San Diego, CA, p. A89

BERRIGAN, Mary, Chief Operating Officer, Medical Center of Aurora, Aurora, CO, p. A102

BERRIOS, Elenia, Chief Nursing Officer, Hospital HIMA San Pablo Caguas, Caguas, PR, p. A725

BERRONG, Barbara, R.N. Chief Nursing Officer, Parkland Health Center, Farmington, MO, p. A371

BERRY, Cheryl Furdge, Chief Nursing Officer, Baptist Memorial Hospital–Tipton, Covington, TN, p. A582

BERRY, David, Senior Vice President and Chief Operating Officer, Arkansas Children's Hospital, Little Rock, AR, p. A48

BERRY, Deborah, Director of Operations, Greene County Hospital, Leakesville, MS, p. A361

BERRY, Dennis, Chief Executive Officer, Tennessee Health Management, Parsons, TN, p. B134

BERRY, Eilleen, Manager Information Technology, Webster County Community Hospital, Red Cloud, NE, p. A401

BERRY, Greg, Chief Financial Officer, Doctors Medical Center, Modesto, CA, p. A77

BERRY, Linda, Vice President Human Resources, Memorial Hospital, Towanda, PA, p. A556

BERRY, Lisa, Director, Saint Anne's Hospital, Fall River, MA, p. A310

BERRY, Rebecca
Senior Director Human Resources, Pioneer Memorial Hospital, Prineville, OR, p. A529
Senior Director Human Resources, St. Charles Medical Center – Bend, Bend, OR, p. A523
Senior Director Human Resources, St. Charles Medical Center – Redmond, Redmond, OR, p. A529

BERRY, Robert F., Chief Executive Officer, Lane Frost Health and Rehabilitation Center, Hugo, OK, p. A512

BERRY, Roberta, Manager Human Resources, Southeast Arizona Medical Center, Douglas, AZ, p. A32

BERRY, Wesley, Chief Financial Officer, Nicholas County Hospital, Carlisle, KY, p. A259

BERRYMAN, John David, M.D. Chief of Staff, Beckley Veterans Affairs Medical Center, Beckley, WV, p. A693

BERRYMAN, William R., M.D. Chief of Staff, Grand Junction Veterans Affairs Medical Center, Grand Junction, CO, p. A107

BERSANTE, Syd, R.N., President, St. Joseph Medical Center, Tacoma, WA, p. A691

BERSHAD, Joshua M., M.D. Senior Vice President Medical Affairs and Chief Medical Officer, Robert Wood Johnson University Hospital, New Brunswick, NJ, p. A419

BERSINGER, David, M.D. Chief of Staff, Chesterfield General Hospital, Cheraw, SC, p. A563

BERSTLER, Michael T., Chief Medical Officer, Waverly Health Center, Waverly, IA, p. A239

BERT, Alisa, Chief Financial Officer, Aventura Hospital and Medical Center, Aventura, FL, p. A123

BERTHIL, Emmanuel, Chief Clinical Officer, New Bedford Rehabilitation Hospital, New Bedford, MA, p. A312

BERTKE, Bradley J., President and Chief Executive Officer, Mercy St. Anne Hospital, Toledo, OH, p. A503

BERTRAM, Jo, Vice President Finance, SSM St. Mary's Health Center, Saint Louis, MO, p. A381

BERTRAND, Joan L., Vice President Human Resources, Adcare Hospital of Worcester, Worcester, MA, p. A316

BERTRAND, Neil W., Chief Financial Officer, Longmont United Hospital, Longmont, CO, p. A109

BERTSCH, Darrold, Chief Executive Officer, Sakakawea Medical Center, Hazen, ND, p. A478

BERZ, Derek, Chief Operating Officer, Kaiser Permanente Los Angeles Medical Center, Los Angeles, CA, p. A72

BERZAU, Ulrike, FACHE Administrator, St. Luke's Rehabilitation Institute, Spokane, WA, p. A690

BESCOE, Bradley, Chief Financial Officer, Straith Hospital for Special Surgery, Southfield, MI, p. A335

BESHEL, Michael, R.N. Vice President Patient Care and Chief Nursing Officer, Nazareth Hospital, Philadelphia, PA, p. A549

BESIO, Adam, Chief Information Officer, Memorial Medical Center, Port Lavaca, TX, p. A643

BESS, Amy, Chief Financial Officer, Mizell Memorial Hospital, Opp, AL, p. A24

BESS, Charles, M.D. Medical Director, Potomac Valley Hospital, Keyser, WV, p. A696

BESS, Timothy A.
Chief Executive Officer, Lake Cumberland Regional Hospital, Somerset, KY, p. A270
Chief Executive Officer, Wythe County Community Hospital, Wytheville, VA, p. A680

BESSE, Kim, Senior Vice President and Chief Human Resource Officer, Children's Medical Center of Dallas, Dallas, TX, p. A610

BESSEL, Marjorie, M.D. Chief Medical Officer, Banner Desert Medical Center, Mesa, AZ, p. A34

BESSER, Sherry L., R.N. Vice President Quality, Risk Management and Chief Nursing Officer, Pratt Regional Medical Center, Pratt, KS, p. A253

BESSET, Kerry, Senior Vice President Human Resources, Memorial Sloan–Kettering Cancer Center, New York, NY, p. A445

BESSLER, Christine, Vice President Information Services, Oconomowoc Memorial Hospital, Oconomowoc, WI, p. A712

BESSLER, September, Manager Human Resources, Brookings Health System, Brookings, SD, p. A572

BESSON, Kathleen, Executive Vice President and Chief Operating Officer, Caromont Regional Medical Center, Gastonia, NC, p. A465

BESST, Kara, President and Chief Executive Officer, Gritman Medical Center, Moscow, ID, p. A177

BEST, Rosa, Chief Nursing Officer, Rolling Plains Memorial Hospital, Sweetwater, TX, p. A651

BESTEN, Robert, Chief Financial Officer, Mary Breckinridge ARH Hospital, Hyden, KY, p. A263

BESTGEN, Pat, Manager Human Resources, Cameron Regional Medical Center, Cameron, MO, p. A368

BESWICK, Elizabeth, Vice President Human Resources and Public Relations, Carteret General Hospital, Morehead City, NC, p. A469

BETANCOURT, Erika, Coordinator Human Resources, Cornerstone Regional Hospital, Edinburg, TX, p. A615

BETHON, Celeste Ann, MS Chief Nursing Officer, Nyack Hospital, Nyack, NY, p. A450

BETKE, Bryce, Chief Financial Officer, Crete Area Medical Center, Crete, NE, p. A395

BETKE–MENA, Rachel, Director Health Information Management, Colusa Regional Medical Center, Colusa, CA, p. A60

BETTCHER, Sue, R.N. Vice President of Nursing Services, Community Hospital of Bremen, Bremen, IN, p. A207

BETTEM, Kelly, Chief Administrative Officer, Ohio Valley Medical Center, Wheeling, WV, p. A700

BETTS, Brooks
Vice President and Chief Information Officer, Lincoln Health, Damariscotta, ME, p. A293
Director Information Systems and Chief Information Officer, Pen Bay Medical Center, Rockport, ME, p. A295

BETTS, Crystal
Chief Financial Officer, Incline Village Community Hospital, Incline Village, NV, p. A405
Chief Financial Officer, Tahoe Forest Hospital District, Truckee, CA, p. A97

BETTS, Nicholas, Director Information Technology, Grundy County Memorial Hospital, Grundy Center, IA, p. A231

BETTS, Tracy, Chief Financial Officer, Hardeman County Memorial Hospital, Quanah, TX, p. A643

BETZ, Paul, FACHE Chief Operating Officer and Senior Vice President, Maury Regional Hospital, Columbia, TN, p. A581

BETZ, Paul, FACHE, Interim Chief Executive Officer, Wayne Medical Center, Waynesboro, TN, p. A594

BEUTKE, Kenneth, Vice President Organization Development and Planning, OSF Saint James – John W. Albrecht Medical Center, Pontiac, IL, p. A200

BEVEL, John, Manager Information Systems, Shriners Hospitals for Children–Northern California, Sacramento, CA, p. A87

BEVERLEY, Tracey, M.D. Chief Medical Staff, Sweetwater Hospital, Sweetwater, TN, p. A593

BEVERLY, DeAnna, Chief Operating Officer, Seven Rivers Regional Medical Center, Crystal River, FL, p. A126

BEVERLY, Douglas H., Chief Executive Officer, HEALTHSOUTH Rehabilitation Hospital of North Alabama, Huntsville, AL, p. A21

BEVERLY, Esther, Vice President Human Resources, Tri–City Medical Center, Oceanside, CA, p. A81

BEVERS, Donald, Chief Financial Officer, Memorial Hospital of Salem County, Salem, NJ, p. A422

BEYER, Jim, Director Human Resources, Norman Regional Health System, Norman, OK, p. A514

BEYER, Laurie, Senior Vice President and Chief Financial Officer, Union Hospital, Elkton, MD, p. A300

BEYER, Teri, Chief Information Officer, Rice Memorial Hospital, Willmar, MN, p. A354

BEZUCHA, Gary, FACHE, Chief Executive Officer, North Central Health Care, Wausau, WI, p. A718

BHAMBI, Brijesh, M.D. Chief Medical Officer, Bakersfield Heart Hospital, Bakersfield, CA, p. A56

BHAMBRA, Jody, Chief Nursing Officer, Hartgrove Hospital, Chicago, IL, p. A184

BHANDARI, Raj, M.D. Physician–in–Chief, Kaiser Permanente San Jose Medical Center, San Jose, CA, p. A92

BHATEJA, Renu, M.D. President Medical Staff, Ridgeview Psychiatric Hospital and Center, Oak Ridge, TN, p. A592

BHATIA, Sanjay, Chief Medicai Officer, Lower Bucks Hospital, Bristol, PA, p. A534

BHAYANI, Sam B., M.D. Chief Medical Officer, Barnes–Jewish West County Hospital, Saint Louis, MO, p. A380

BHOORASINGH, Merlene, Administrator, Kindred Hospital Ocala, Ocala, FL, p. A139

BHUCHAR, Subodh, M.D. Chief of Staff, Kindred Hospital Sugar Land, Sugar Land, TX, p. A650

BIAGIONI, Donna K., R.N. Director of Nursing, Maniilaq Health Center, Kotzebue, AK, p. A29

BIANCAMANO, John, Chief Financial Officer, University of Connecticut Health Center, John Dempsey Hospital, Farmington, CT, p. A114

BIANCHI, Cynthia, Chief Information Officer, Woodhull Medical and Mental Health Center, NY, p. A449

BIANCHI, Patty, Interim Chief Executive Officer and Administrator, Pershing General Hospital, Lovelock, NV, p. A407

BIAS, Richard R., Chief Operating Officer, Lahey Hospital & Medical Center, Burlington, Burlington, MA, p. A308

BIBAL, Antoinette, Director Human Resources, Kindred Hospital–Baldwin Park, Baldwin Park, CA, p. A57

BIBB, Lisa, Director Human Resources, San Angelo Community Medical Center, San Angelo, TX, p. A645

BIBBO, Karen, R.N. Chief Nursing Officer, Aventura Hospital and Medical Center, Aventura, FL, p. A123

BIBEAU, Roland R., FACHE, President, Novant Health Matthews Medical Center, Matthews, NC, p. A469

BIBER, Carl, Chief Financial Officer, Columbus Regional Healthcare System, Whiteville, NC, p. A474

BIBLO, Lee, M.D. Chief Medical Officer, Froedtert Memorial Lutheran Hospital, Milwaukee, WI, p. A710

BIBY, Thom, Chief Financial Officer, Tulsa Spine and Specialty Hospital, Tulsa, OK, p. A521

BICE, Rodney, R.N. Chief Nursing Officer, Pikes Peak Regional Hospital, Woodland Park, CO, p. A112

BICHIMER, Michael, Acting Vice President of Finance, OhioHealth MedCentral Mansfield Hospital, Mansfield, OH, p. A497

BICKEL, George, Director, Information Systems, Biloxi Regional Medical Center, Biloxi, MS, p. A355

BICKEL, James, Chief Executive Officer, Columbus Regional Hospital, Columbus, IN, p. A208

BICKFORD, Carmel, Chief Financial Officer, Wyoming Behavioral Institute, Casper, WY, p. A720

BIDDLE, Kenneth, Controller, Kensington Hospital, Philadelphia, PA, p. A549

BIDES, Adrienne, Assistant Chief Financial Officer and Budget Analyst, Big Spring State Hospital, Big Spring, TX, p. A603

BIDLEMAN, Angela, R.N. Chief Nursing Officer, Integris Grove Hospital, Grove, OK, p. A511

BIE, Gary E., CPA Chief Financial Officer, Stony Brook University Medical Center, Stony Brook, NY, p. A455

BIEBER, Courtney, Director Information Systems, Mercy Regional Medical Center, Ville Platte, LA, p. A290

BIEBER, Julie, Senior Vice President Human Resources, Beth Israel Deaconess Medical Center, Boston, MA, p. A306

BIEDIGER, Daniel F., Vice President Human Resources, FirstHealth Moore Regional Hospital, Pinehurst, NC, p. A470

BIEDIGER, Michael J., FACHE, President and Chief Executive Officer, Lexington Medical Center, West Columbia, SC, p. A571

BIEDRON, Janet, R.N., Chief Executive Officer, Vibra Hospital of Sacramento, Folsom, CA, p. A63

BIEGERT, Dara, Vice President Human Resources, Medical Center of Lewisville, Lewisville, TX, p. A633

BIEGLER, Elizabeth Anne, R.N
Chief Nursing Officer, OhioHealth Dublin Methodist Hospital, Dublin, OH, p. A493
Chief Nursing Officer, OhioHealth Grady Memorial Hospital, Delaware, OH, p. A492

BIEHL, Albert, M.D. Vice President Medical Affairs, Bethesda Hospital East, Boynton Beach, FL, p. A124

BIEL, Christopher, Chief Information Officer, Goodland Regional Medical Center, Goodland, KS, p. A244

BIELECKI, Thomas A., Chief Financial Officer, Geisinger Wyoming Valley Medical Center, Wilkes Barre, PA, p. A558

BIEN, Jim, M.D. Vice President Quality and Patient Safety, Indiana University Health Arnett Hospital, Lafayette, IN, p. A217

BIEN, John, Vice President Finance, United Hospital, Saint Paul, MN, p. A351

BIER, Alan, M.D. Executive Vice President and Chief Medical Officer, Gwinnett Hospital System, Lawrenceville, GA, p. A162

BIERI, Bryan, Manager Finance, Kansas City Veterans Affairs Medical Center, Kansas City, MO, p. A373

BIERMAN, Debra, Associate Executive Director Human Resources, North Shore University Hospital, Manhasset, NY, p. A440

BIERMAN, Joan, Vice President Finance, Cherokee Regional Medical Center, Cherokee, IA, p. A227

BIERMAN, Marcia, M.D. Chief of Staff, North Shore Medical Center, Miami, FL, p. A137

BIERMAN, Ronald L., Chief Executive Officer, Affinity Medical Center, Massillon, OH, p. A498

BIERSCHENK, Kevin, Chief Executive Officer, Dodge County Hospital, Eastman, GA, p. A159

BIERUT, Barbara, Chief Financial Officer, HEALTHSOUTH Rehabilitation Hospital of Sarasota, Sarasota, FL, p. A145

BIFFLE, Sandra, Personnel Clerk, Quitman County Hospital, Marks, MS, p. A362

BIGELOW, Barbara, Administrator, Providence Valdez Medical Center, Valdez, AK, p. A30

BIGELOW, David C., PharmD, Chief Executive Officer, Samaritan Pacific Communities Hospital, Newport, OR, p. A527

BIGELOW, Debbie, Interim Chief Executive Officer, Coulee Medical Center, Grand Coulee, WA, p. A684

BIGELOW, Timothy, Director Human Resources, Butler Hospital, Providence, RI, p. A560

BIGGINS, Lillie, R.N., President, Texas Health Harris Methodist Hospital Fort Worth, Fort Worth, TX, p. A619

BIGGS, Carol, Interim Vice President Nursing and Patient Care Services, Iredell Memorial Hospital, Statesville, NC, p. A473

BIGGS, Daniel, Director Human Resources, Valley View Hospital, Glenwood Springs, CO, p. A106

BIGGS, Jeremy, President and Chief Administrative Officer, Cumberland Medical Center, Crossville, TN, p. A582

BIGGS, Kelly, M.D. Chief Medical Officer, Tyrone Hospital, Tyrone, PA, p. A556

BIGHAM, Laurie S., R.N. Chief Nursing Officer, Lovelace Medical Center, Albuquerque, NM, p. A426

BIGLER, Nathan, Vice President Human Relations, Riverside Community Hospital, Riverside, CA, p. A86

BIGLER, Pamela, R.N. Senior Vice President Chief Nursing Officer, Carle Foundation Hospital, Urbana, IL, p. A204

BIGLEY, John, M.D. Medical Director, Kaiser Permanente Baldwin Park Medical Center, Baldwin Park, CA, p. A57

BIGLEY, Robert F., President and Chief Executive Officer, East Georgia Regional Medical Center, Statesboro, GA, p. A167

BIGNAULT, Jon, M.D. Chief of Staff, Athens–Limestone Hospital, Athens, AL, p. A16

BIGONEY, Rebecca, M.D
Executive Vice President and Chief Medical Officer, Mary Washington Hospital, Fredericksburg, VA, p. A671
Executive Vice President and Chief Medical Officer, Stafford Hospital, Stafford, VA, p. A679

BIHUNIAK, Peter, Vice President Finance, Robert Wood Johnson University Hospital Rahway, Rahway, NJ, p. A422

BIITTNER, Sallie, Vice President Human Resources, St. Joseph's Hospital Health Center, Syracuse, NY, p. A456

BIK, Lymar, M.D. Medical Director, Coalinga Regional Medical Center, Coalinga, CA, p. A60

BILBREY, Mickey, President and Chief Executive Officer, QHR, Brentwood, TN, p. B111

BILL, Charles E., Chief Executive Officer, Bartlett Regional Hospital, Juneau, AK, p. A29

BILLECI, Theresa, Executive Director, Porterville Developmental Center, Porterville, CA, p. A84

BILLIG, Samantha, Chief Executive Officer, Gateway Rehabilitation Hospital, Florence, KY, p. A261

BILLING, Michael D., Administrator, Mid–Valley Hospital, Omak, WA, p. A686

BILLING, Tommye, Vice President and Chief Information Officer, St. Vincent Medical Center–North, Sherwood, AR, p. A52

BILLINGS, Mary Ann, Director of Nursing, Potomac Valley Hospital, Keyser, WV, p. A696

BILLINGS, Robert E., Chief Financial Officer, Largo Medical Center, Largo, FL, p. A134

BILLINGSLEA, Anidra, Health Insurance Management, HEALTHSOUTH Rehabilitation Hospital of Montgomery, Montgomery, AL, p. A23

BILLINGSLEY, Angela, Director Human Resources, Intermountain Hospital, Boise, ID, p. A174

BILLINGSLEY, Margaret, R.N. Chief Nursing Officer, T. J. Samson Community Hospital, Glasgow, KY, p. A262

BILLINGSLEY, Richard A., MSN Chief Operating Officer and Chief Nursing Officer, Mena Regional Health System, Mena, AR, p. A50

BILLINGTON, Carole, R.N. Vice President Patient Care Services, Saint Anne's Hospital, Fall River, MA, p. A310

BILLMEYER, Joe, Director, Information Services, Mercy Medical Center–Dubuque, Dubuque, IA, p. A230

BILLS, James, Chief Executive Officer, Logan Memorial Hospital, Russellville, KY, p. A270

BILLY, Frank, Chief Financial Officer, Kindred Hospital Bay Area–Tampa, Tampa, FL, p. A147

BILUNKA, Dianne C., Director Human Resources, Clarion Psychiatric Center, Clarion, PA, p. A535

BINDER, Buzz, Vice President Finance, Exempla Saint Joseph Hospital, Denver, CO, p. A104

BINDERMAN, Judi, Chief Information Technology Officer and Chief Medical Informatics Officer, St. Francis Medical Center, Lynwood, CA, p. A76

BINDRA, Pavel, M.D. Chief Medical Officer and Chief Information Officer, Citrus Valley Medical Center–Inter Community Campus, Covina, CA, p. A61

BINGHAM, Julie, IT Supervisor, San Juan Hospital, Monticello, UT, p. A660

BINGHAM, Leslie, Senior Vice President and Chief Executive Officer, Valley Baptist Medical Center–Brownsville, Brownsville, TX, p. A604

BINGHAM, Roxane, Director Marketing, Baton Rouge Rehabilitation Hospital, Baton Rouge, LA, p. A273

BINGMAN, Ryan, Director Operations, Grundy County Memorial Hospital, Grundy Center, IA, p. A231

BINKLEY, Sharon, Director Human Resources, Fairfax Community Hospital, Fairfax, OK, p. A511

BINTZ, Marilu, M.D. Chief of Staff, Gundersen Boscobel Area Hospital and Clinics, Boscobel, WI, p. A702

BIRA, Patrick G., JD, Chief Executive Officer, Lincoln County Medical Center, Troy, MO, p. A384

BIRCH, Misty, Director Human Resources, Castleview Hospital, Price, UT, p. A662

BIRCHMEIER, Kevin, Director Human Resources, Covenant Medical Center, Saginaw, MI, p. A333

BIRD, Chris, Chief Operating Officer, Phoenix Baptist Hospital, Phoenix, AZ, p. A36

BIRD, Gregory A., R.N. Interim Chief Nursing Officer, Cooley Dickinson Hospital, Northampton, MA, p. A313

BIRD, Jeffrey C., M.D. Chief Medical Officer, Indiana University Health Ball Memorial Hospital, Muncie, IN, p. A219

BIRD, Lindsay, Director Finance, South Pointe Hospital, Warrensville Heights, OH, p. A504

BIRD, Michele
Chief Human Resources Officer, Hemet Valley Medical Center, Hemet, CA, p. A67
Chief Human Resources Officer, Menifee Valley Medical Center, Sun City, CA, p. A96

BIRD, Suzanne C., R.N. Chief Nursing Officer, Mobile Infirmary Medical Center, Mobile, AL, p. A22

BIRDZELL, JoAnn, Chief Executive Officer and Administrator, St. Catherine Hospital, East Chicago, IN, p. A209

BIREN, David, Chief Financial Officer, Mayo Clinic Health System in Lake City, Lake City, MN, p. A345

BIRENBERG, Allan, Vice President Medical Affairs, MedStar Harbor Hospital, Baltimore, MD, p. A297

BIRK, Deborah L., Ph.D. Vice President Patient Care Services, Saint Anthony's Health Center, Alton, IL, p. A184

BIRKEL, Sue M., R.N. Director of Nursing, Butler County Health Care Center, David City, NE, p. A395

BIRKENSTOCK, Timothy L., Chief Financial Officer, Miami Children's Hospital, Miami, FL, p. A137

BIRKHOFER, Colleen, Chief Nursing Officer, Trenton Psychiatric Hospital, Trenton, NJ, p. A424

BIRNBAUM, Bernard, M.D. Senior Vice President, Vice Dean and Chief Hospital Operations, NYU Langone Medical Center, New York, NY, p. A448

BIRSCHBACH, Nancy
Assistant Vice President Information Services, Agnesian HealthCare, Fond Du Lac, WI, p. A704
Vice President and Chief Information Officer, Ripon Medical Center, Ripon, WI, p. A714
Vice President and Chief Information Officer, Waupun Memorial Hospital, Waupun, WI, p. A717

BISAL, Yasmir, Vice President Finance, Clara Maass Medical Center, Belleville, NJ, p. A413

BISCHALANEY, George, President and Chief Executive Officer, Eden Medical Center, Castro Valley, CA, p. A59

BISCONE, Mark A.
Interim Chief Executive Officer, Pen Bay Medical Center, Rockport, ME, p. A295
Executive Director, Waldo County General Hospital, Belfast, ME, p. A292

BISDORF, Jonathan, Director Information Technology, Ohio Valley Surgical Hospital, Springfield, OH, p. A502

BISH, Carol, Human Resources Coordinator, North Greenville Hospital, Travelers Rest, SC, p. A570

BISHARA, Reemon, M.D. Medical Director, Coastal Harbor Treatment Center, Savannah, GA, p. A166

BISHKU, Dilek, M.D. Vice President Medical Affairs, La Rabida Children's Hospital, Chicago, IL, p. A184

BISHOP, Amy Leigh, Director Human Resources, Red Bay Hospital, Red Bay, AL, p. A25

BISHOP, Bill, Chief Information Officer, Colquitt Regional Medical Center, Moultrie, GA, p. A164

BISHOP, Bryan, Chief Financial Officer, Heartland Behavioral Health Services, Nevada, MO, p. A377

BISHOP, Clint, Program Manager, Marion Veterans Affairs Medical Center, Marion, IL, p. A195

BISHOP, Elizabeth, Manager Business Office, Salina Surgical Hospital, Salina, KS, p. A254

BISHOP, Janice E., R.N. Chief Nursing Officer, Tewksbury Hospital, Tewksbury, MA, p. A315

BISHOP, Jim, Chief Executive Officer, Harney District Hospital, Burns, OR, p. A523
BISHOP, John
Chief Financial Officer, Long Beach Memorial Medical Center, Long Beach, CA, p. A70
Chief Executive Officer and Chief Financial Officer, Madison Valley Medical Center, Ennis, MT, p. A387
Chief Executive Officer and Chief Financial Officer, Madison Valley Medical Center, Ennis, MT, p. A387
BISIGNANI, Thomas, Chief Financial Officer, Moses Taylor Hospital, Scranton, PA, p. A554
BISSEL, Jane, Chief Financial Officer, Wabash County Hospital, Wabash, IN, p. A224
BISSELL, John, Chief Information Officer, Hutchinson Regional Medical Center, Hutchinson, KS, p. A246
BISSENDEN, Chris, Director Human Resources, Ogden Regional Medical Center, Ogden, UT, p. A661
BISSONETTE, Christine, R.N. Chief Nursing Officer, Kalkaska Memorial Health Center, Kalkaska, MI, p. A328
BISSONNETTE, Andre, Chief Financial Officer, North Country Hospital and Health Center, Newport, VT, p. A666
BISTERFELDT, Joanne, Chief Information Officer, Wheaton Franciscan Healthcare – All Saints, Racine, WI, p. A714
BITAR, Adib, M.D. Medical Director, Aurora Charter Oak Hospital, Covina, CA, p. A61
BITAR, Ali, M.D. Vice President Medical Affairs, Rehabilitation Institute of Michigan, Detroit, MI, p. A322
BITHER, Dean, Chief Financial Officer, Inland Hospital, Waterville, ME, p. A295
BITNER, Janet
Interim Chief Executive Officer, Texas NeuroRehab Center, Austin, TX, p. A600
Chief Operating Officer, Texas Star Recovery, Austin, TX, p. A600
BITSILLY, Christina, Human Resource Specialist, U. S. Public Health Service Indian Hospital, Crownpoint, NM, p. A428
BITSOLI, Deborah, Chief Operating Officer, Saint Vincent Hospital, Worcester, MA, p. A317
BITTNER, Augustine, Chief Information Officer, Robley Rex Veterans Affairs Medical Center, Louisville, KY, p. A266
BIUSO, Joseph, M.D. Vice President and Chief of Medical Affairs, Floyd Medical Center, Rome, GA, p. A165
BIVIN, Richard, M.D. President Medical Staff, Abraham Lincoln Memorial Hospital, Lincoln, IL, p. A195
BIXLER, David, Chief Executive Officer, Daviess Community Hospital, Washington, IN, p. A224
BIXLER, Jacquelyn, Vice President Human Resources, BryLin Hospitals, Buffalo, NY, p. A434
BJARNASON, Dana, R.N. Vice President and Chief Nursing Officer, OHSU Hospital, Portland, OR, p. A528
BJELICH, Steven C., President and Chief Executive Officer, Saint Francis Medical Center, Cape Girardeau, MO, p. A368
BJELLA, Karmon T., Chief Executive Officer, Alpena Regional Medical Center, Alpena, MI, p. A318
BJERKE, Carolyn, Director Human Resources, Mercy Hospital Kingfisher, Kingfisher, OK, p. A512
BJERKNES, Dan, Director Human Resources, Mercy Medical Center, Williston, ND, p. A480
BJORDAHL, Kevin, M.D. Chief Medical Officer, Milbank Area Hospital Avera, Milbank, SD, p. A574
BJORGUM, Deb, Manager Data Processing, Johnson Regional Medical Center, Clarksville, AR, p. A44
BJORK, David, M.D. Chief Medical Officer, Prairie Ridge Hospital and Health Services, Elbow Lake, MN, p. A343
BJORKLUND, Julie D., Director Human Resources, Coulee Medical Center, Grand Coulee, WA, p. A684
BJORNBERG, Christopher R., Chief Executive Officer, Warren Memorial Hospital, Friend, NE, p. A395
BJORNSTAD, Brad, M.D. Vice President and Chief Medical Officer, Florida Hospital Tampa, Tampa, FL, p. A147
BLABON, Gary, Director Operations, Novant Health Rowan Medical Center, Salisbury, NC, p. A472
BLACK, Jr., Albert P., Chief Operating Officer, Hospital of the University of Pennsylvania, Philadelphia, PA, p. A548
BLACK, Amy, R.N. Vice President Chief Nurse Executive, Martha Jefferson Hospital, Charlottesville, VA, p. A669
BLACK, Jr., Charles, Chief Financial Officer, Rockcastle Regional Hospital and Respiratory Care Center, Mount Vernon, KY, p. A268
BLACK, Doug, President, Barnes–Jewish West County Hospital, Saint Louis, MO, p. A380
BLACK, Gary E., President and Chief Executive Officer, Lenoir Memorial Hospital, Kinston, NC, p. A467
BLACK, Marcey, Chief Financial Officer, Northwest Florida Community Hospital, Chipley, FL, p. A125
BLACK, Maria, MSN Nurse Administrator, American Fork Hospital, American Fork, UT, p. A659
BLACK, Marilynn, Chief Information Officer, Verde Valley Medical Center, Cottonwood, AZ, p. A32

BLACK, Michael, Director Human Resources, East Georgia Regional Medical Center, Statesboro, GA, p. A167
BLACK, Paul S.
Controller, H. C. Watkins Memorial Hospital, Quitman, MS, p. A364
Chief Financial Officer, Scott Regional Hospital, Morton, MS, p. A363
BLACK, Robert O., Chief Executive Officer, Linton Hospital, Linton, ND, p. A479
BLACK, Ronald, M.D. Chief of Staff, Clark Fork Valley Hospital, Plains, MT, p. A390
BLACK, Terri, Network Manager, Lucas County Health Center, Chariton, IA, p. A227
BLACKBEAR, Annabelle, Human Resources Specialist, U. S. Public Health Service Indian Hospital, Pine Ridge, SD, p. A575
BLACKBURN, Lisa R., Director Human Resources, St. Margaret's Hospital, Spring Valley, IL, p. A203
BLACKBURN, Mary, Vice President Operations and Chief Practice Officer, Hugh Chatham Memorial Hospital, Elkin, NC, p. A464
BLACKBURN, Susan, Chief Operating Officer, Providence St. Mary Medical Center, Walla Walla, WA, p. A692
BLACKFORD, Nate, Chief Operating Officer, Northwest Medical Center, Albany, MO, p. A367
BLACKHAM, Cami, R.N. Nurse Administrator, Sevier Valley Medical Center, Richfield, UT, p. A662
BLACKMAN, Jay H., Senior Vice President and Chief Operating Officer, Howard County General Hospital, Columbia, MD, p. A300
BLACKMON, Jenean
Assistant Vice President and Chief Information Officer, McLeod Medical Center Dillon, Dillon, SC, p. A565
Associate Vice President and Chief Information Officer, McLeod Regional Medical Center, Florence, SC, p. A566
BLACKMON, Tanya S., President, Novant Health Huntersville Medical Center, Huntersville, NC, p. A467
BLACKWELL, Dawn, R.N. VP, Patient Care Services, Memorial Healthcare, Owosso, MI, p. A331
BLACKWELL, Jack, Chief Financial Officer, Highlands Regional Medical Center, Prestonsburg, KY, p. A269
BLACKWELL, James, Vice President and Chief Financial Officer, Clara Barton Hospital, Hoisington, KS, p. A245
BLACKWELL, Lenore, Director Human Resources, Harton Regional Medical Center, Tullahoma, TN, p. A593
BLACKWELL, Timothy, Manager Human Resources, Rolling Hills Hospital, Ada, OK, p. A507
BLACKWOOD, Jim, Chief Executive Officer, Tallahatchie General Hospital, Charleston, MS, p. A356
BLAD, Nathan, Chief Executive Officer, RC Hospital and Clinics, Olivia, MN, p. A349
BLADEN, Anthony M., Vice President Human Resources, Calvert Memorial Hospital, Prince Frederick, MD, p. A302
BLAHA, Bill, Manager Information Technology, Tri–County Hospital, Wadena, MN, p. A353
BLAHA, John E., Vice President Finance and Chief Financial Officer, Brattleboro Retreat, Brattleboro, VT, p. A665
BLAHNIK, David, Chief Operating Officer, Twin Valley Behavioral Healthcare, Columbus, OH, p. A491
BLAIN, Brenda K., FACHE Chief Nursing Officer and Chief Operating Officer, Baylor Medical Center at Irving, Irving, TX, p. A629
BLAIR, Betsy, R.N. Chief Operating Officer, CJW Medical Center, Richmond, VA, p. A677
BLAIR, Brenda, Vice President Human Resources, Alice Peck Day Memorial Hospital, Lebanon, NH, p. A410
BLAIR, Diane, Human Resources and Admissions, CHI Health Plainview, Plainview, NE, p. A401
BLAIR, Heidi L., Vice President Administration, Manatee Glens Hospital and Addiction Center, Bradenton, FL, p. A124
BLAIR, Janet M., Director Human Resources, Clinton Memorial Hospital, Wilmington, OH, p. A505
BLAIR, Judy, Senior Vice President Clinical Services and Chief Nursing Officer, Glendale Adventist Medical Center, Glendale, CA, p. A65
BLAIR, Keith, M.D. Manager Information Systems, SageWest Healthcare–Lander, Lander, WY, p. A721
BLAIR, Mark, M.D. Medical Director, Dublin Springs, Dublin, OH, p. A493
BLAIR, Jr., Raymond W., M.D. Chief of Staff, Ennis Regional Medical Center, Ennis, TX, p. A617
BLAIR, Robert D., Chief Executive Officer, Spine Hospital of Louisiana, Baton Rouge, LA, p. A274
BLAIS, Samantha, Manager Human Resource, Parkview Adventist Medical Center, Brunswick, ME, p. A292
BLAKE, Alan, M.D. President Medical Staff, Samaritan Lebanon Community Hospital, Lebanon, OR, p. A526
BLAKE, Casey, Director Information Technology, Sistersville General Hospital, Sistersville, WV, p. A699
BLAKE, Daphne, R.N. Chief Nursing Officer, Guadalupe Regional Medical Center, Seguin, TX, p. A648

BLAKE, Diane, Chief Executive Officer, Cascade Medical Center, Leavenworth, WA, p. A685
BLAKE, Kelly, Chief Executive Officer, Select Specialty Hospital–Johnstown, Johnstown, PA, p. A541
BLAKE, Robert, Chief Human Resources Officer Southwest Market, Memorial Hermann Sugar Land Hospital, Sugar Land, TX, p. A651
BLAKE, Robert, M.D
Chief of Staff, St. Joseph's Hospital of Buckhannon, Buckhannon, WV, p. A694
Chief Medical Officer, The HSC Pediatric Center, Washington, DC, p. A122
BLAKE, Sheryl Lewis, FACHE, Chief Executive Officer, Pennock Hospital, Hastings, MI, p. A326
BLAKELY, Michelle, Associate Director, Jesse Brown Veterans Affairs Medical Center, Chicago, IL, p. A184
BLAKEMORE, Chris, Interim Chief Information Officer, Good Shepherd Medical Center, Longview, TX, p. A634
BLAKEY GORMAN, Mary, Director Human Resources, Northwest Missouri Psychiatric Rehabilitation Center, Saint Joseph, MO, p. A380
BLALOCK, Andy, M.D. Physician Executive, Our Lady of Lourdes Regional Medical Center, Lafayette, LA, p. A281
BLALOCK, Cam, Senior Vice President Corporate Services, Nash Health Care Systems, Rocky Mount, NC, p. A471
BLALOCK, Tracey, Chief Nursing Officer, Medical Center, Navicent Health, Macon, GA, p. A163
BLANC, Linda, R.N. Administrative Director of Nursing, Jefferson Medical Center, Ranson, WV, p. A699
BLANCHARD, Timothy D., Chief Financial Officer, Kingman Regional Medical Center, Kingman, AZ, p. A33
BLANCHARD, Wayne, Market Chief Executive Officer, Kindred Hospital–Louisville, Louisville, KY, p. A265
BLANCHARD, William R., Chief Executive Officer, DeTar Healthcare System, Victoria, TX, p. A655
BLANCHETTE, Edward A., M.D., Director, Connecticut Department of Correction's Hospital, Somers, CT, p. A117
BLANCO, Andres, Director Management Information Systems, Westside Regional Medical Center, Plantation, FL, p. A143
BLANCO, Carlos, M.D.,
Administrator, Doctor's Center of Bayamon, Bayamon, PR, p. A724
Administrator, Doctors Center, Manati, PR, p. A726
BLAND, David, Chief Executive Officer, South Davis Community Hospital, Bountiful, UT, p. A659
BLAND, Douglas, Manager Information Services, Spring View Hospital, Lebanon, KY, p. A263
BLAND, James G., M.D. Chief of Staff, Jane Todd Crawford Hospital, Greensburg, KY, p. A262
BLANK, Arthur J., President and Chief Executive Officer, Mount Desert Island Hospital, Bar Harbor, ME, p. A291
BLANKE, Kerry Lee
Vice President Finance, New London Family Medical Center, New London, WI, p. A712
Director Financial Services, Riverside Medical Center, Waupaca, WI, p. A717
Chief Financial Officer, Shawano Medical Center, Shawano, WI, p. A715
BLANKENSHIP, Beth, Coordinator Human Resources, Norman Specialty Hospital, Norman, OK, p. A514
BLANKENSHIP, Diana, Director Human Resources, Welch Community Hospital, Welch, WV, p. A700
BLANKENSHIP, Jeff, CPA Vice President and Chief Financial Officer, Jackson–Madison County General Hospital, Jackson, TN, p. A584
BLANKENSHIP, Stacy, Chief Nursing Officer, Mercy Hospital Washington, Washington, MO, p. A384
BLANTON, Christina, Administrative Assistant and Human Resources Coordinator, Select Specialty Hospital–Knoxville, Knoxville, TN, p. A586
BLANTON, Forest
Senior VP and Chief Information Officer, Memorial Hospital Miramar, Miramar, FL, p. A138
Chief Information Officer, Memorial Hospital Pembroke, Pembroke Pines, FL, p. A142
Chief Information Officer, Memorial Hospital West, Pembroke Pines, FL, p. A142
Administrator Process Engineering, Memorial Regional Hospital, FL, p. A130
BLANTON, James
Chief Financial Officer, East Texas Medical Center Rehabilitation Hospital, Tyler, TX, p. A654
Chief Financial Officer, East Texas Medical Center Specialty Hospital, Tyler, TX, p. A654
BLANTON, Kevin, D.O. Chief of Staff, Goodall–Witcher Hospital Authority, Clifton, TX, p. A606
BLANTON, Marion, Chief Financial Officer, Minneola District Hospital, Minneola, KS, p. A250
BLANTON, Ron, Chief Fiscal Services, Boise Veterans Affairs Medical Center, Boise, ID, p. A174

BLAS, Phil, Chief Information Officer, John C. Fremont Healthcare District, Mariposa, CA, p. A76

BLASER, Karla, Director Human Resources, UnityPoint Health – Trinity Muscatine, Muscatine, IA, p. A235

BLASINGAME, Billy, Chief Executive Officer, Plum Creek Specialty Hospital, Amarillo, TX, p. A596

BLASIUS, Rita, Assistant Administrator and Chief Financial Officer, Avera St. Benedict Health Center, Parkston, SD, p. A575

BLAUER, Michael, Chief Executive Officer, Providence Seaside Hospital, Seaside, OR, p. A530

BLAUWET, Judy, M.P.H. Senior Vice President Operations and Chief Nursing Officer, Avera McKennan Hospital and University Health Center, Sioux Falls, SD, p. A576

BLAYLOCK, Darrell, Chief Executive Officer, Volunteer Community Hospital, Martin, TN, p. A587

BLAYLOCK, Kevin, Chief Executive Officer, Oklahoma Spine Hospital, Oklahoma City, OK, p. A516

BLAYLOCK, L. Dwayne, Chief Executive Officer, River Oaks Hospital, Flowood, MS, p. A357

BLAZEK, Dennis, Chief Information Officer, Clarke County Hospital, Osceola, IA, p. A236

BLAZIER, Patty, Chief Nursing Officer, Hamilton Memorial Hospital District, McLeansboro, IL, p. A196

BLEAK, Jason, Administrator and Chief Executive Officer, Grover C. Dils Medical Center, Caliente, NV, p. A404

BLEAKNEY, David A., Chief Executive Officer and Administrator, Angleton Danbury Medical Center, Angleton, TX, p. A597

BLECHA, Timothy, M.D. Medical Director, Brodstone Memorial Hospital, Superior, NE, p. A402

BLEDSOE, Cindy, Chief Executive Officer, Forest Park Medical Center, Dallas, TX, p. A610

BLEDSOE, Richard, Director Information Systems, Novant Health Gaffney Medical Center, Gaffney, SC, p. A566

BLESI, Michael, Director Information Technology, Rainy Lake Medical Center, International Falls, MN, p. A345

BLESSING, Brian, Chief Financial Officer, Texas Health Harris Methodist Hospital Azle, Azle, TX, p. A601

BLEVINS, Denzil, Director Information Systems, Montgomery General Hospital, Montgomery, WV, p. A697

BLEVINS, Heather, Director Human Resources, HEALTHSOUTH Rehabilitation of Gadsden, Gadsden, AL, p. A20

BLEVINS, Matthew H., Chief Executive Officer, Select Specialty Hospital–Kansas City, Kansas City, KS, p. A247

BLEVINS, Pam, R.N. Director, Clinical Informatics, Blue Ridge Regional Hospital, Spruce Pine, NC, p. A473

BLIGHTON, Gordon, Director Resource Management, Naval Hospital Camp Pendleton, Camp Pendleton, CA, p. A59

BLISE, Catherine, R.N. Chief Nursing Officer, Wesley Medical Center, Wichita, KS, p. A257

BLISS, Ann, Manager Computer Services, Southeast Arizona Medical Center, Douglas, AZ, p. A32

BLIVEN, Donna, Vice President Patient Care Services and Chief Nursing Officer, Jones Memorial Hospital, Wellsville, NY, p. A457

BLOB, Burchkhard, Manager Human Resources, Central Virginia Training Center, Madison Heights, VA, p. A673

BLOCHLINGER, Pamela, Acting Vice President Finance, Cloud County Health Center, Concordia, KS, p. A242

BLOCK, Annie, Director Human Resources, Poplar Community Hospital, Poplar, MT, p. A390

BLOCK, Deborah, Vice President Nursing and Chief Nursing Officer, Oconee Regional Medical Center, Milledgeville, GA, p. A163

BLOCK, George, M.D. Chief Medical Officer, O'Connor Hospital, San Jose, CA, p. A92

BLOCK, Sherri, Chief Operating Officer, Aurora Vista Del Mar Hospital, Ventura, CA, p. A99

BLODGETT, Debbie, Director of Fiscal Services, Ochiltree General Hospital, Perryton, TX, p. A642

BLOEMER, Brad, Vice President Finance and Chief Financial Officer, Arkansas Methodist Medical Center, Paragould, AR, p. A51

BLOM, David P., President and Chief Executive Officer, OhioHealth, Columbus, OH, p. B103

BLOMELEY, Geoff, Interim Chief Financial Officer, Ponca City Medical Center, Ponca City, OK, p. A517

BLOMQUIST, David, Director Information Technology, McKenzie–Willamette Medical Center, Springfield, OR, p. A530

BLOND, Carl, M.D. Chief of Staff, Connally Memorial Medical Center, Floresville, TX, p. A617

BLOOD, Barbara
Director Human Resources, Lourdes Counseling Center, Richland, WA, p. A687
Executive Director Human Resources, Lourdes Medical Center, Pasco, WA, p. A686
Director Human Resources, Walla Walla General Hospital, Walla Walla, WA, p. A692

BLOOM, Irwin, President and Chief Executive Officer, Flagstaff Medical Center, Flagstaff, AZ, p. A32

BLOOM, Jane, Ph.D. Chief Nursing Officer, Austen Riggs Center, Stockbridge, MA, p. A315

BLOOM, Kerry, Director Human Resources, Kalamazoo Psychiatric Hospital, Kalamazoo, MI, p. A328

BLOOM, Laura, Director Human Resources, Coffee Regional Medical Center, Douglas, GA, p. A158

BLOOM, Stephanie L., FACHE, President and Chief Executive Officer, Community Medical Center, Toms River, NJ, p. A423

BLOOMQUIST, Trudy, Director of Nursing, Warren General Hospital, Warren, PA, p. A557

BLOUGH Jr., Daniel D., Chief Executive Officer, Punxsutawney Area Hospital, Punxsutawney, PA, p. A553

BLUE, Gaea, R.N., Administrator and Chief Executive Officer, Avera Weskota Memorial Hospital, Wessington Springs, SD, p. A578

BLUE, Jan L., Vice President Human Resources, Hoag Memorial Hospital Presbyterian, Newport Beach, CA, p. A80

BLUE, Lawrence, Administrator and Chief Executive Officer, Cavalier County Memorial Hospital, Langdon, ND, p. A479

BLUE, Lee Ann, MSN Chief Nursing Officer and Executive Vice President Patient Care Services, Eskenazi Health, Indianapolis, IN, p. A214

BLUE, Yvonne, Chief Operations Officer, Moore County Hospital District, Dumas, TX, p. A614

BLUHM, Tom, Director Information Systems, Island Hospital, Anacortes, WA, p. A681

BLUM, Carrie, Chief Information Officer, Monroe Clinic, Monroe, WI, p. A711

BLUM, Donald A., M.D. Chief of Staff, Wetzel County Hospital, New Martinsville, WV, p. A697

BLUM, Walter B., M.D. Chief of Staff, McLeod Medical Center Dillon, Dillon, SC, p. A565

BLUMENFELD, Barry, M.D. Chief Information Officer, Maine Medical Center, Portland, ME, p. A294

BLUNK, Jim, D.O. Chief Medical Officer, Sumner County Hospital District One, Caldwell, KS, p. A242

BLURTON, Cheri
Director Human Resources, HIPAA Privacy Officer, Great River Medical Center, Blytheville, AR, p. A43
Director Human Resources, South Mississippi County Regional Medical Center, Osceola, AR, p. A51

BLYTHE, Thomas W.
Regional Vice President Human Resources, Good Samaritan Regional Health Center, Mount Vernon, IL, p. A197
Vice President Human Resources, St. Mary's Hospital, Centralia, IL, p. A182

BOAL, Jeremy, M.D
Executive Vice President and Chief Medical Officer, Mount Sinai Beth Israel, New York, NY, p. A446
Executive Vice President and Chief Medical Officer, Mount Sinai St. Luke's, New York, NY, p. A446
Executive Vice President and Chief Medical Officer, New York Eye and Ear Infirmary of Mount Sinai, New York, NY, p. A447

BOALDIN, Gail, R.N. Director Nursing, Phillips County Hospital, Phillipsburg, KS, p. A252

BOARD, Gloria, Director Human Resources, Liberty Healthcare Systems, Bastrop, LA, p. A272

BOARD, Patricia, Vice President Human Resources, Community Hospital of Bremen, Bremen, IN, p. A207

BOARDMAN, Debra K., FACHE, President and Chief Executive Officer, Range Regional Health Services, Hibbing, MN, p. A345

BOAS, Erik, Vice President Finance, University of Maryland Charles Regional Medical Center, La Plata, MD, p. A302

BOATMAN, Daniel W., Chief Executive Officer, Granite County Medical Center, Philipsburg, MT, p. A390

BOATMAN, James, Chief Financial Officer, Doctors Medical Center, San Pablo, CA, p. A93

BOATMAN, Robert, Director Information Technology, Richmond State Hospital, Richmond, IN, p. A222

BOATRIGHT, Donna, MSN, Administrator, Rolling Plains Memorial Hospital, Sweetwater, TX, p. A651

BOBBITT, James, Vice President Human Resources, Saint Agnes Hospital, Baltimore, MD, p. A297

BOBBS, Kathy J., FACHE, President Chief Executive Officer, Regional Medical Center of Acadiana, Lafayette, LA, p. A282

BOBO, Matt, Chief Information Officer, Meade District Hospital, Meade, KS, p. A250

BOCCELLATO, Judy, R.N. Chief Nursing Officer, Specialty Hospital of Central Jersey, Lakewood, NJ, p. A417

BOCKENEK, William, M.D. Chief Medical Officer, Carolinas Rehabilitation, Charlotte, NC, p. A462

BOCKMANN, Rick, Chief Executive Officer, Frank R. Howard Memorial Hospital, Willits, CA, p. A100

BOCKNEK, Marc, D.O. Vice President Medical Affairs, DMC Huron Valley–Sinai Hospital, Commerce Township, MI, p. A321

BODEMAN, Gabe, Director of Nursing, Howard County Medical Center, Saint Paul, NE, p. A401

BODENHAM, Steve, Senior Manager Clinical Engineering, Indiana University Health North Hospital, Carmel, IN, p. A208

BODENMANN, Linda, Chief Operating Officer, Southcoast Hospitals Group, Fall River, MA, p. A310

BODENNER, Nancy, Director Human Resources, St. Joseph Health System, Tawas City, MI, p. A335

BODENSTEINER, Kim, Chief Financial Officer, Essentia Health Fosston, Fosston, MN, p. A343

BODIN, Donna L., Vice President, Woman's Hospital, Baton Rouge, LA, p. A274

BODINE, Maureen, Chief Clinical Officer, Kindred Hospital–San Diego, San Diego, CA, p. A89

BODLOVIC, Kirk
Vice President and Chief Financial Officer, Providence St. Joseph Medical Center, Polson, MT, p. A390
Regional Chief Financial Officer, St. Patrick Hospital, Missoula, MT, p. A390

BODNAR, Darrell, Director Information, Weeks Medical Center, Lancaster, NH, p. A410

BODWELL, Amy, Vice President Finance, Methodist Richardson Medical Center, Richardson, TX, p. A644

BOECKMANN, Patricia, R.N. Vice President Operations and Chief Nursing Officer, Straub Clinic & Hospital, Honolulu, HI, p. A171

BOEHLER, Richard, M.D., President and Chief Executive Officer, St. Joseph Hospital, Nashua, NH, p. A411

BOEHM, Scott D., Executive Vice President Human Resources and Facilities, Sanford Bismarck, Bismarck, ND, p. A476

BOEHNKE, Winnie, Director Human Resources, Timberlawn Mental Health System, Dallas, TX, p. A612

BOEMER, Sally Mason
Senior Vice President Finance, Massachusetts General Hospital, Boston, MA, p. A307
Chief Financial Officer, North Shore Medical Center, Salem, MA, p. A314

BOEMMEL, Michael, Vice President and Chief Financial Officer, MedStar National Rehabilitation Hospital, Washington, DC, p. A121

BOEN, Stefanie, Chief Nursing Officer, Skyline Hospital, White Salmon, WA, p. A692

BOER, Jeff, Director Information Technology, Pulaski Memorial Hospital, Winamac, IN, p. A224

BOES, Jody, Vice President Patient Care Services, Ministry Door County Medical Center, Sturgeon Bay, WI, p. A716

BOESE, Chris, Vice President and Chief Nursing Officer, Regions Hospital, Saint Paul, MN, p. A351

BOGARD, Tim, Manager Information Technology, Highland District Hospital, Hillsboro, OH, p. A495

BOGEDAIN, Carol, FACHE, Director, Veterans Affairs Roseburg Healthcare System, Roseburg, OR, p. A529

BOGEN, Mark A., Senior Vice President and Chief Financial Officer, South Nassau Communities Hospital, Oceanside, NY, p. A450

BOGERS, Christina, Chief Clinical Officer, North Valley Hospital, Whitefish, MT, p. A392

BOGGESS, Carrie
Human Resource Generalist, Carilion Giles Community Hospital, Pearisburg, VA, p. A676
Human Resources Generalist, Carilion Tazewell Community Hospital, Tazewell, VA, p. A679

BOGGESS, Jack, Chief Executive Officer, Reliant Austin, Austin, TX, p. A599

BOGGS, Danny L., President and Chief Executive Officer, Samaritan Regional Health System, Ashland, OH, p. A482

BOGGS, Lynn Ingram
President and Chief Executive Officer, Blue Ridge Regional Hospital, Spruce Pine, NC, p. A473
President, McDowell Hospital, Marion, NC, p. A468

BOGGS, Michael S., Chief Executive Officer, Regency Hospital of Central Georgia, Macon, GA, p. A163

BOGLE, Bryan, Chief Executive Officer, Madison River Oaks Medical Center, Canton, MS, p. A356

BOGLE, William J., Director Information Systems, North Arkansas Regional Medical Center, Harrison, AR, p. A47

BOGOLIN, Lore, Chief Nursing Officer and Vice President Care Services, Vassar Brothers Medical Center, Poughkeepsie, NY, p. A452

BOHALL, Karen, Director Human Resources, Woman's Christian Association Hospital, Jamestown, NY, p. A439

BOHANNON, Michelle, Director of Nursing Operations and Risk, Compliance, Quality and Safety, Wilson Medical Center, Neodesha, KS, p. A250

BOHATY, Richard, Director Information Technology, CHI Health St Elizabeth, Lincoln, NE, p. A397

BOHLMANN, Charles, President and Chief Executive Officer, Iroquois Memorial Hospital and Resident Home, Watseka, IL, p. A204

BOHNENKAMP, Russ, Director Finance, Chadron Community Hospital and Health Services, Chadron, NE, p. A394

BOICE, Sandra, Chief Nursing Officer, RiverView Health, Crookston, MN, p. A342

BOICE, Sheila, Director Human Resources, Barton County Memorial Hospital, Lamar, MO, p. A375

BOIKE, Darlene, Chief Financial Officer, Chippewa County–Montevideo Hospital, Montevideo, MN, p. A348

BOILEAU, Michel, M.D
Chief Clinical Officer, Pioneer Memorial Hospital, Prineville, OR, p. A529
Chief Clinical Officer, St. Charles Medical Center – Bend, Bend, OR, p. A523
Chief Clinical Officer, St. Charles Medical Center – Redmond, Redmond, OR, p. A529

BOILY, Cindy, MSN Senior Vice President and Chief Nursing Officer, WakeMed Cary Hospital, Cary, NC, p. A461

BOIS, Alain, R.N. Director of Nursing, Northern Maine Medical Center, Fort Kent, ME, p. A293

BOISVERT, Gerald J., Vice President and Chief Financial Officer, Connecticut Children's Medical Center, Hartford, CT, p. A114

BOJO, Rolland, R.N. Chief Nursing Officer, Administrator Patient Care and Services, Catskill Regional Medical Center, Harris, NY, p. A438

BOKA, Darin, Chief Information Officer, McLaren Oakland, Pontiac, MI, p. A332

BOKERN, Bob, Director Human Resources, St. Mary Medical Center, Long Beach, CA, p. A70

BOKHARI, Syed, M.D. Chief Medical Officer, Presence St. Mary's Hospital, Kankakee, IL, p. A194

BOKOVITZ, Beverly, R.N. Chief Nursing Officer, St. Anthony's Medical Center, Saint Louis, MO, p. A381

BOLAND, E. Kay, R.N. Vice President and Chief Nursing Officer, United Health Services Hospitals–Binghamton, Binghamton, NY, p. A434

BOLAND, Susan, MSN, President and Chief Executive Officer, Wheaton Franciscan Healthcare – All Saints, Racine, WI, p. A714

BOLANDER, Patrick C., Chief Financial Officer, Georgetown Community Hospital, Georgetown, KY, p. A262

BOLANO, Odette, R.N., Senior Vice President and Area Manager, Kaiser Permanente Oakland Medical Center, Oakland, CA, p. A80

BOLCAVAGE, Ted, Vice President and Division Controller, Baylor Institute for Rehabilitation, Dallas, TX, p. A609

BOLD, Harry, Administrator, Big Sandy Medical Center, Big Sandy, MT, p. A385

BOLDA, Craig, Chief Operating Officer, St. Catherine Hospital, East Chicago, IN, p. A209

BOLDING, Kay, R.N. Vice President Patient Care Services and Chief Nursing Officer, Jackson County Memorial Hospital, Altus, OK, p. A507

BOLDUC, Tiana, Chief Information Officer, Mercy Hospital Ozark, Ozark, AR, p. A51

BOLEN, David, Vice President and Chief Financial Officer, Passavant Area Hospital, Jacksonville, IL, p. A193

BOLEN, Shannon, Director Human Resources, Baptist Memorial Hospital–Booneville, Booneville, MS, p. A356

BOLES, Glen
Vice President and Chief Financial Officer, CHRISTUS St. Michael Health System, Texarkana, TX, p. A652
Vice President and Chief Financial Officer, CHRISTUS St. Michael Rehabilitation Hospital, Texarkana, TX, p. A652

BOLES, Mark D., Chief Executive Officer, Baylor Institute for Rehabilitation at Frisco, Frisco, TX, p. A620

BOLEWARE, Mike, Administrator, Franklin County Memorial Hospital, Meadville, MS, p. A362

BOLEY, Eric, Administrator and Chief Executive Officer, South Lincoln Medical Center, Kemmerer, WY, p. A721

BOLEY, Sarah, Director Human Resources, Wetzel County Hospital, New Martinsville, WV, p. A697

BOLGER, Thomas, Chief Financial Officer, Chinese Hospital, San Francisco, CA, p. A90

BOLIN, Angie, Executive Administrative Assistant and Human Resources Manager, Black River Medical Center, Poplar Bluff, MO, p. A378

BOLIN, Cris, Chief Executive Officer, Delta Memorial Hospital, Dumas, AR, p. A45

BOLIN, Kerry F., Chief Nursing Officer, Mother Frances Hospital – Jacksonville, Jacksonville, TX, p. A630

BOLIN, Paul, Vice President Human Resources, The Acadia Hospital, Bangor, ME, p. A291

BOLINGER, John, M.D. Vice President Medical Affairs, Union Hospital, Terre Haute, IN, p. A223

BOLLARD, Robert, Chief Financial Officer, HEALTHSOUTH Rehabilitation Hospital – Henderson, Henderson, NV, p. A405

BOLLICH, Mary, Director of Nurses, AMG Specialty Hospital–Lafayette, Lafayette, LA, p. A281

BOLLIER, Sheila A., Chief Executive Officer, HEALTHSOUTH Rehabilitation Hospital of Cypress, Houston, TX, p. A624

BOLLINGER, Bruce, Medical Director, Baylor Surgical Hospital at Fort Worth, Fort Worth, TX, p. A618

BOLLINGER, Candace, Director of Nursing, Booneville Community Hospital, Booneville, AR, p. A44

BOLLMANN, Brett, Administrator, Memorial Hospital, Chester, IL, p. A183

BOLOGNANI, Laurie, Human Resources Officer, Speare Memorial Hospital, Plymouth, NH, p. A412

BOLOR, Erlinda, R.N. Chief Nursing Officer, San Joaquin General Hospital, French Camp, CA, p. A64

BOLTER, Cindy, Chief Nursing and Operations Officer, John Muir Behavioral Health Center, Concord, CA, p. A60

BOMAR, Jacob, Director Information Technology, Hardin Medical Center, Savannah, TN, p. A592

BOMBA, Douglas, Chief Financial Officer, Cameron Memorial Community Hospital, Angola, IN, p. A206

BOMERSBACH, Karen, Chief Financial Officer, Dallas Medical Center, Dallas, TX, p. A610

BOMSTAD, Heather, R.N. Chief Nursing Officer, Mendota Community Hospital, Mendota, IL, p. A196

BONAMASE, Karen, R.N., Chief Executive Officer, The Surgical Hospital of Phoenix, Phoenix, AZ, p. A37

BONAMO, John F., MS, President and Chief Executive Officer, Saint Barnabas Medical Center, Livingston, NJ, p. A417

BONAR, Carrie, Chief Information Officer, Southern California Hospital at Culver City, Culver City, CA, p. A61

BONAR, Lynette, Chief Support Services, Tuba City Regional Health Care Corporation, Tuba City, AZ, p. A40

BONAR Jr., Robert I., Chief Executive Officer, Dell Children's Medical Center of Central Texas, Austin, TX, p. A599

BONCZEK, Mary Ellen, R.N. Chief Nursing Executive, New Hanover Regional Medical Center, Wilmington, NC, p. A474

BOND, Lee, Chief Financial Officer, Singing River Health System, Pascagoula, MS, p. A364

BOND, Sharon, Director Human Resources, College Station Medical Center, College Station, TX, p. A607

BOND, Troy, Chief Human Resources Officer, Atlanta Medical Center, Atlanta, GA, p. A152

BONDI, Blaise, Chief Financial Officer, Centennial Medical Center, Frisco, TX, p. A620

BONDS, Cyrilia, Administrator, United Medical Rehabilitation Hospital, Hammond, LA, p. A278

BONDURANT, Barry, Administrator and Chief Executive Officer, Baptist Memorial Hospital–Union City, Union City, TN, p. A594

BONDURANT, Charles, Chief Information Officer, Meadows Regional Medical Center, Vidalia, GA, p. A168

BONE, Janice, Director Human Resources, Parkway Regional Hospital, Fulton, KY, p. A261

BONECUTTER, Dane, Director Human Resources, Connally Memorial Medical Center, Floresville, TX, p. A617

BONFILIO, Nicholas, M.D. Chief of Staff, Great Falls Clinic Medical Center, Great Falls, MT, p. A388

BONI, Shirley M., Administrative Officer, U. S. Public Health Service Indian Hospital, San Carlos, AZ, p. A38

BONILLA, Felicita, Administrator, Hospital De La Concepcion, San German, PR, p. A727

BONILLA, Jose A., Deputy Commander Administration, Winn Army Community Hospital, Hinesville, GA, p. A161

BONK, Daniel J., Chief Executive Officer, Aspen Valley Hospital District, Aspen, CO, p. A102

BONNELL, Jay, Controller, Oakwood Hospital–Wayne, Wayne, MI, p. A337

BONNER, Daphne, Administrator, Greenbriar Rehabilitation Hospital, Boardman, OH, p. A484

BONNER, Gwen, Chief Operating Officer, Saint Francis Hospital–Bartlett, Bartlett, TN, p. A579

BONNER, Lauren, Director Human Resources, Cumberland Hospital, New Kent, VA, p. A674

BONNER, Lenne
Chief Financial Officer, Clearwater Valley Hospital and Clinics, Orofino, ID, p. A177
Chief Financial Officer, St. Mary's Hospital, Cottonwood, ID, p. A175

BONNER, Robert
Chief Financial Officer, Montclair Hospital Medical Center, Montclair, CA, p. A78
Chief Financial Officer, San Dimas Community Hospital, San Dimas, CA, p. A90

BONNETTE, James C., M.D. Chief Clinical Officer, Genesys Regional Medical Center, Grand Blanc, MI, p. A324

BONNICHSEN, Daniel G., Deputy Commander for Administration, Irwin Army Community Hospital, Junction City, KS, p. A247

BONSER, Kathleen, R.N. Vice President Nursing and Chief Nursing Officer, SSM DePaul Health Center, Bridgeton, MO, p. A368

BONTHUIS, Michael W., Chief Financial Officer, PeaceHealth United General Hospital, Sedro-Woolley, WA, p. A689

BONZO, Kelly, Director, Baptist Health Richmond, Richmond, KY, p. A270

BOO, Thomas, M.D. Chief of Staff, Northern Inyo Hospital, Bishop, CA, p. A58

BOOHER, Terresa O., Vice President of Patient Care Services, Highlands Regional Medical Center, Prestonsburg, KY, p. A269

BOOKER, Angela, Director of Nursing Services, Teton Valley Health Care, Driggs, ID, p. A176

BOOKMAN, Larry, D.O. Chief Medical Officer, Yampa Valley Medical Center, Steamboat Springs, CO, p. A111

BOOM, Marc L., M.D., Chief Executive Officer, Houston Methodist, Houston, TX, p. B74

BOONE, Bradley, M.D. Chief Medical Staff, Anderson Regional Medical Center–South Campus, Meridian, MS, p. A362

BOONE, David J., Senior Vice President, Finance, Catawba Valley Medical Center, Hickory, NC, p. A466

BOONE, Donna, R.N. Chief Nursing Officer, Weatherford Regional Medical Center, Weatherford, TX, p. A656

BOONE III, Elwood Bernard, FACHE, President, Sentara Virginia Beach General Hospital, Virginia Beach, VA, p. A679

BOONE, Margie, Registered Health Information Technician, Cumberland River Hospital, Celina, TN, p. A580

BOONE, Richard, Chief Financial Officer, Sparks Regional Medical Center, Fort Smith, AR, p. A46

BOONE, Sherry, Chief Information Resource Management, Veterans Affairs Illiana Health Care System, Danville, IL, p. A187

BOORAS, Laura
Vice President Human Resources, Coliseum Medical Centers, Macon, GA, p. A162
Director of Human Resources, Coliseum Northside Hospital, Macon, GA, p. A162

BOORE, Chad, President and Chief Executive Officer, OSF St. Joseph Medical Center, Bloomington, IL, p. A181

BOORNAZIAN, John, M.D. Chief Medical Officer, Huggins Hospital, Wolfeboro, NH, p. A412

BOOTH, Christy, Chief Human Resources Officer, Doctors Memorial Hospital, Bonifay, FL, p. A124

BOOTH, Daniel, Vice President Operations and Chief Human Resources Officer, Inland Hospital, Waterville, ME, p. A295

BOOTH, Patrick M., Chief Executive Officer, Fremont Health, Fremont, NE, p. A395

BOOTH-MILLS, Megan, Director Planning and Marketing, Vidant Bertie Hospital, Windsor, NC, p. A475

BORCHERT, Barry, Vice President Finance, Reedsburg Area Medical Center, Reedsburg, WI, p. A714

BORCHI, Daniel, Chief Information Officer, Carilion New River Valley Medical Center, Christiansburg, VA, p. A669

BORDELON, Rock, President and Chief Executive Officer, Allegiance Health Management, Shreveport, LA, p. B8

BORDEN, Eric, Chief Operating Officer and Chief Financial Officer, Jewell County Hospital, Mankato, KS, p. A249

BORDEN, Sandy, Chief Financial Officer, Brodstone Memorial Hospital, Superior, NE, p. A402

BORDENKIRCHER, Kimberly Hupp, Chief Executive Officer, Henry County Hospital, Napoleon, OH, p. A499

BORDO, David, M.D
Chief Medical Officer, Presence Holy Family Medical Center, Des Plaines, IL, p. A188
Vice President and Chief Medical Officer, Presence Our Lady of the Resurrection Medical Center, Chicago, IL, p. A185

BOREL, Patricia, Chief Financial Officer, Central Community Hospital, Elkader, IA, p. A230

BOREN, Kevin, Chief Financial Officer, Essentia Health Duluth, Duluth, MN, p. A342

BOREN, Shed, Administrator and Chief Executive Officer, Sister Emmanuel Hospital, Miami, FL, p. A137

BORENGASSER, Connie, Chief Executive Officer, Vantage Point of Northwest Arkansas, Fayetteville, AR, p. A46

BORENS, Dwan, Director of Nursing, St. John Broken Arrow, Broken Arrow, OK, p. A508

BORER, Tom, Vice President Operations, ProMedica Fostoria Community Hospital, Fostoria, OH, p. A494

BORGERSON, Carol, Business Office Manager and Chief Financial Officer, Madison Hospital, Madison, MN, p. A346

BORGERT, Karen, Vice President Human Resources, Grandview Medical Center, Dayton, OH, p. A492

BORGES, Rafael, M.D. Chief of Staff, St. Anthony's Hospital, Houston, TX, p. A626

BORGSTROM, Marna P., President and Chief Executive Officer, Yale New Haven Health System, New Haven, CT, p. B153

BORGSTROM, Marna P., Chief Executive Officer, Yale–New Haven Hospital, New Haven, CT, p. A116

BORING, Ronald L., Senior Vice President and Chief Operating Officer, McLeod Regional Medical Center, Florence, SC, p. A566

BORIS, Diane
Vice President and Chief Financial Officer, Schuylkill Medical Center – East Norwegian Street, Pottsville, PA, p. A553
Chief Financial Officer, Schuylkill Medical Center – South Jackson Street, Pottsville, PA, p. A553

BORIS, Jamie, M.D. President Medical Staff, Southwest Regional Medical Center, Waynesburg, PA, p. A557

BORJA, Catherine, M.D. Chairman Executive Committee Medical Staff, Naval Hospital Oak Harbor, Oak Harbor, WA, p. A686

BORK, Ray, Team Leader Nursing, Bellin Psychiatric Center, Green Bay, WI, p. A706

BORLAND, Winston, FACHE, President and Chief Executive Officer, Medical Center of Arlington, Arlington, TX, p. A598

BORMANN, Jim, Director Human Resources, Passavant Area Hospital, Jacksonville, IL, p. A193

BORN, Michael, M.D. Chief Medical Officer and Chief Quality Officer, SwedishAmerican Hospital, Rockford, IL, p. A202

BOROWSKI, Thomas
  Chief Information Officer, Mayo Clinic Health System in Mankato, Mankato, MN, p. A346
  Chief Information Officer, Mayo Clinic Health System in Saint James, Saint James, MN, p. A351

BORRIS–HALE, Cathy, Chief Executive Officer, Specialty Hospital of Washington–Hadley, Washington, DC, p. A122

BORTEL, Karol, Vice President Financial Services, Wood County Hospital, Bowling Green, OH, p. A484

BORTKE, Todd, Director Information Systems, St. Alexius Medical Center, Bismarck, ND, p. A476

BORTOLAZZO, Tomi, M.D. Chief of Staff, Mammoth Hospital, Mammoth Lakes, CA, p. A76

BORZON, Eve, R.N. Chief Operating Officer, Woodhull Medical and Mental Health Center, NY, p. A449

BOS, Robbi E., Vice President Human Resources, Sauk Prairie Healthcare, Prairie Du Sac, WI, p. A714

BOSCIA, Michael, Chief Financial Officer, Bartow Regional Medical Center, Bartow, FL, p. A123

BOSCO, John
  Vice President and Chief Information Officer, Forest Hills Hospital, NY, p. A443
  Chief Information Officer, Franklin Hospital, Valley Stream, NY, p. A457

BOSCO, Maureen, Executive Director, Central New York Psychiatric Center, Marcy, NY, p. A441

BOSER, Andrew, Chief Executive Officer, Cuba Memorial Hospital, Cuba, NY, p. A436

BOSHUT, Sami, Director Management Information Systems, Jamaica Hospital Medical Center, NY, p. A444

BOSLEY, Elizabeth, R.N. Vice President Patient Services, St. Mary's Medical Center, Huntington, WV, p. A696

BOSS, Craig, M.D. Chief Medical Officer, Charlevoix Area Hospital, Charlevoix, MI, p. A320

BOSS, Virgil, Chief Executive Officer, Cascade Medical Center, Cascade, ID, p. A175

BOSSE, Doyle, M.D. Chief Medical Officer, Jackson Hospital, Marianna, FL, p. A135

BOST, Cecelia, Chief Operating Officer, Alliance HealthCare System, Holly Springs, MS, p. A359

BOST, Marcus, Director Information Services and Chief Information Officer, Adena Greenfield Medical Center, Greenfield, OH, p. A495

BOSTER, Brian, M.D. Medical Director, Select Specialty Hospital–Cincinnati, Cincinnati, OH, p. A487

BOSTIC, Deborah, MSN Senior Vice President Hospital Operations and Chief Nursing Officer, St. Francis Hospital, Columbus, GA, p. A156

BOSTIC, Deborah, R.N. Chief Nursing Officer, Texas Health Presbyterian Hospital Denton, Denton, TX, p. A613

BOSTIC, William, Administrative Assistant Human Resources, Surprise Valley Health Care District, Cedarville, CA, p. A59

BOSTON, Katie, Senior Vice President Patient Care Services, Union Hospital, Elkton, MD, p. A300

BOSTON III, Ward, Chief Executive Officer, North Florida Regional Medical Center, Gainesville, FL, p. A129

BOSTROM, Brenda, Director of Nursing, Coteau des Prairies Hospital, Sisseton, SD, p. A577

BOSTROM, Gary, Chief Executive Officer and Chief Financial Officer, East Adams Rural Hospital, Ritzville, WA, p. A688

BOSTROM, Stuart, M.D. Director Medical Affairs, Sutter Roseville Medical Center, Roseville, CA, p. A87

BOSTWICK, John, Interim Chief Financial Officer, Henderson County Community Hospital, Lexington, TN, p. A587

BOSTWICK, Monte J., Chief Executive Officer, Biloxi Regional Medical Center, Biloxi, MS, p. A355

BOSTWICK, Shari, Director Human Resources, New London Hospital, New London, NH, p. A411

BOSWELL, Debbie, Chief Operating Officer and Chief Nursing Officer, Mercy Medical Center, Roseburg, OR, p. A529

BOSWELL, Diane, Director Human Resources and Marketing, Salem Township Hospital, Salem, IL, p. A202

BOSWELL, John, Chief Human Resources Officer, University of Virginia Medical Center, Charlottesville, VA, p. A669

BOSWINKEL, Jan, M.D. Vice President Medical Operations and Chief Safety Officer, Children's Hospital of Philadelphia, Philadelphia, PA, p. A547

BOSWORTH, Dawn, Director Human Resources, Arrowhead Behavioral Health Hospital, Maumee, OH, p. A498

BOTAK, Geoff, Chief Executive Officer, Friends Hospital, Philadelphia, PA, p. A548

BOTHE, Jr., Albert, M.D. Chief Medical Officer, Geisinger Medical Center, Danville, PA, p. A537

BOTHNER, Joan, M.D. Chief Medical Officer, Children's Hospital Colorado, Aurora, CO, p. A102

BOTHUN, Crystal, Chief Financial Officer, Johnson Memorial Health Services, Dawson, MN, p. A342

BOTINE, Gary, Vice President, Chief Financial Officer, Mary Greeley Medical Center, Ames, IA, p. A225

BOTNEY, Mitchell, M.D. Vice President Medical Affairs and Chief Medical Officer, Missouri Baptist Medical Center, Saint Louis, MO, p. A381

BOTTCHER, Sharon A., R.N. Vice President Patient Care Services, MedStar Union Memorial Hospital, Baltimore, MD, p. A297

BOTTGER, Barry, Chief Financial Officer, Republic County Hospital, Belleville, KS, p. A241

BOTTICELLA, Mary, R.N. Chief Nursing Officer, Fountain Valley Regional Hospital and Medical Center, Fountain Valley, CA, p. A63

BOTTOM, Paige, Director Operations, Wilmington Treatment Center, Wilmington, NC, p. A474

BOUCK, Nancy, Director Human Resources, Huron Medical Center, Bad Axe, MI, p. A318

BOUCOT, Mark, President and Chief Executive Officer, Garrett County Memorial Hospital, Oakland, MD, p. A302

BOUGHAL, Ginni, Director Health Information and Information Technology, PeaceHealth Peace Harbor Medical Center, Florence, OR, p. A524

BOULA, Rodney C., Administrator and Chief Executive Officer, Elizabethtown Community Hospital, Elizabethtown, NY, p. A437

BOULENGER, Albert, Chief Executive Officer, Baptist Health South Florida, Baptist Hospital of Miami, Miami, FL, p. A136

BOULLION, Leona, Chief Operating Officer, Regional Medical Center of Acadiana, Lafayette, LA, p. A282

BOULLION, Robert A., Chief Financial Officer, Homer Memorial Hospital, Homer, LA, p. A278

BOUQUIO, George, Director Human Resources, South Beach Psychiatric Center, NY, p. A448

BOUR, Eric, M.D., President, Hillcrest Memorial Hospital, Simpsonville, SC, p. A569

BOURDEAU, Patricia, Director Human Resources, Brook Lane Health Services, Hagerstown, MD, p. A301

BOURGAULT, Catherine, Director Human Resources, Providence Hood River Memorial Hospital, Hood River, OR, p. A525

BOURLAND, Don, Vice President Human Resources, PeaceHealth Peace Harbor Medical Center, Florence, OR, p. A524

BOURLAND, Renee, Human Resources Specialist, San Antonio State Hospital, San Antonio, TX, p. A647

BOURN, Jennifer, Director Health Information Services, Performance Improvement and Medical Staff Services, CenterPointe Hospital, Saint Charles, MO, p. A379

BOURNE, Kara, R.N. Chief Nursing Officer and Chief Operating Officer, Newport Specialty Hospital, Tustin, CA, p. A98

BOURQUE, Teresa, Sr. Administrator for Nursing/Chief Nurse, Hurley Medical Center, Flint, MI, p. A323

BOUTROS, Akram, FACHE, President and Chief Executive Officer, MetroHealth Medical Center, Cleveland, OH, p. A489

BOUTROS, Nashaat, M.D. Clinical Director, Center for Behavioral Medicine, Kansas City, MO, p. A373

BOUYEA, Janine, Director Human Resources, Natividad Medical Center, Salinas, CA, p. A88

BOVEE, Michael, Vice President Finance, Riverview Hospital Association, Wisconsin Rapids, WI, p. A719

BOVIO Jr., Ernest L., Chief Executive Officer, High Point Regional Health System, High Point, NC, p. A466

BOWE, Christopher, M.D. Chief Operating Officer, St. Anthony's Medical Center, Saint Louis, MO, p. A381

BOWEN, Christine, R.N. Chief Nursing Officer, DMC Harper University Hospital, Detroit, MI, p. A322

BOWEN, Jill Berry, President and Chief Executive Officer, Northwestern Medical Center, Saint Albans, VT, p. A666

BOWEN, John, Assistant Vice President and Administrator, Baptist Health Medical Center–Arkadelphia, Arkadelphia, AR, p. A43

BOWEN, Mary Beth, R.N. Vice President Nursing and Chief Nursing Officer, United Memorial Medical Center, Batavia, NY, p. A433

BOWEN, Rodger W., M.P.H. Chief Financial Officer, Scenic Mountain Medical Center, Big Spring, TX, p. A603

BOWEN, Steve, Administrator, Kimble Hospital, Junction, TX, p. A630

BOWEN, Tim, Chief Executive Officer, Mena Regional Health System, Mena, AR, p. A50

BOWER, David, M.D. Chief of Staff, Atlanta Veterans Affairs Medical Center, Decatur, GA, p. A158

BOWER, James, M.D. Chief Medical Officer, Research Medical Center, Kansas City, MO, p. A374

BOWER, Kay, Associate Director for Patient Care Services, Battle Creek Veterans Affairs Medical Center, Battle Creek, MI, p. A319

BOWERMAN, Joeann, Director of Nursing Services, Chambers Memorial Hospital, Danville, AR, p. A44

BOWERMAN, Stephen, Chief Financial Officer, Midland Memorial Hospital, Midland, TX, p. A638

BOWERS, Daniel, Chief Operating Officer, Riverside Community Hospital, Riverside, CA, p. A86

BOWERS, David, Vice President Human Resources and Support Services, Children's Hospital of The King's Daughters, Norfolk, VA, p. A675

BOWERS, David N., M.D. Medical Director, Siskin Hospital for Physical Rehabilitation, Chattanooga, TN, p. A580

BOWERS, Gary, Chief Operating Officer, CarePartners Health Services, Asheville, NC, p. A459

BOWERS, Melodee, Director Human Resources, Carle Hoopeston Regional Health Center, Hoopeston, IL, p. A193

BOWERS, Michael, Interim Director for Administration, Naval Hospital Oak Harbor, Oak Harbor, WA, p. A686

BOWERS, Michael E., President, SSM St. Joseph Health Center, Saint Charles, MO, p. A379

BOWERS, Sharon, R.N. Manager of Community, Public and Employee Relations, Sheridan Community Hospital, Sheridan, MI, p. A335

BOWERS, Shelby, Director Marketing and Public Relations, Peninsula Hospital, Louisville, TN, p. A587

BOWERS, Susan, R.N., President, Mercy Allen Hospital, Oberlin, OH, p. A500

BOWERS, Tracy, Director Human Resources, Novant Health Prince William Medical Center, Manassas, VA, p. A673

BOWERSOX, Bruce D., Chief Executive Officer, Nelson County Health System, Mcville, ND, p. A479

BOWES, Arthur, Senior Vice President Human Resources, North Shore Medical Center, Salem, MA, p. A314

BOWES, William, Chief Financial Officer, UAMS Medical Center, Little Rock, AR, p. A49

BOWIE, Craig, Information Technology Manager, Pauls Valley General Hospital, Pauls Valley, OK, p. A517

BOWIE, Joshua, Chief Executive Officer, Yuma Rehabilitation Hospital, Yuma, AZ, p. A42

BOWLEG, Teresa, R.N. Chief Nursing Officer, Murphy Medical Center, Murphy, NC, p. A470

BOWLES, John, Medical Director, Neshoba County General Hospital, Philadelphia, MS, p. A364

BOWLES, Patrica, R.N. Chief Nursing Officer, Franklin County Medical Center, Preston, ID, p. A178

BOWLING, Donald, M.D. Chief Medical Staff, Southampton Memorial Hospital, Franklin, VA, p. A671

BOWLING, Judy, Director Human Resources, Southeast Health Center of Stoddard County, Dexter, MO, p. A459

BOWLING, Kay, Chief Executive Officer, Center for Restorative Care and Rehabilitation, Lynchburg, VA, p. A673

BOWLING, Kelli, Chief Culture Officer, Ministry Door County Medical Center, Sturgeon Bay, WI, p. A716

BOWLING, Nancy, Director Human Resources, Shoals Hospital, Muscle Shoals, AL, p. A24

BOWMAN, Barbara, Chief Human Resource Officer, Ann & Robert H. Lurie Children's Hospital of Chicago, Chicago, IL, p. A183

BOWMAN, Dyan, Director Human Resources, Newberry County Memorial Hospital, Newberry, SC, p. A569

BOWMAN, Joseph E., Chief Financial Officer, TriStar StoneCrest Medical Center, Smyrna, TN, p. A593

BOWMAN, Julie, Chief Nursing Officer, Havasu Regional Medical Center, Lake Havasu City, AZ, p. A34

BOWMAN, Ken, Chief Executive Officer, Van Matre HEALTHSOUTH Rehabilitation Hospital, Rockford, IL, p. A202

BOWMAN, Mark, M.D. President Medical Staff, Tillamook Regional Medical Center, Tillamook, OR, p. A530

BOWMAN, Maureen, Vice President of Nursing and Chief Nursing Officer, Beaumont Hospital – Royal Oak, Royal Oak, MI, p. A333

BOWMAN, Scott, Administrator, Sweetwater Hospital, Sweetwater, TN, p. A593

BOWMAN, William, M.D. Vice President Medical Affairs, Moses H. Cone Memorial Hospital, Greensboro, NC, p. A465

BOWSER, John, Vice President, Chief Financial Officer, OSF Saint Luke Medical Center, Kewanee, IL, p. A194

BOX, Darrel, Chief Executive Officer, Lafayette Regional Health Center, Lexington, MO, p. A376

BOX, Tom, CPA Chief Financial Officer, HEALTHSOUTH Rehabilitation Hospital–Wichita Falls, Wichita Falls, TX, p. A657

BRAMLIET, Charles, M.D. Medical Director, MMO WestEnd Hospital, Jennings, LA, p. A279

BRANAN, Annette
Chief Nursing Officer, Vice President Patient Care Services, Emory Wesley Woods Geriatric Hospital, Atlanta, GA, p. A152
Chief Nursing Officer and Vice President Patient Care Services, Select Specialty Hospital – Northeast Atlanta, Atlanta, GA, p. A153

BRANCATO, Joyce A., Chief Executive Officer, Seven Rivers Regional Medical Center, Crystal River, FL, p. A126

BRANCEL, Dale, D.O. Chief of Staff, Victory Medical Center Mid–Cities, Hurst, TX, p. A629

BRANCH, Cathryn, R.N., Chief Executive Officer, Kindred Hospital–San Diego, San Diego, CA, p. A89

BRANCH, Terrance, Chief Information Management, Fort Belvoir Community Hospital, Fort Belvoir, VA, p. A671

BRANCH, Tim, Manager Information Technology, Covenant Hospital Plainview, Plainview, TX, p. A642

BRANCHICK, James, MS, Executive Director, Kaiser Permanente Downey Medical Center, Downey, CA, p. A61

BRANCO, Patrick J.
President, Clearwater Valley Hospital and Clinics, Orofino, ID, p. A177
President, St. Mary's Hospital, Cottonwood, ID, p. A175

BRAND, Debbie, Chief Nurse Executive, Carolina Pines Regional Medical Center, Hartsville, SC, p. A567

BRAND, James R., M.D. Chief of Staff, DeTar Healthcare System, Victoria, TX, p. A655

BRANDECKER, John A., Director, Hunter Holmes McGuire Veterans Affairs Medical Center, Richmond, VA, p. A678

BRANDENBURG, Edward M., FACHE Vice President Professional Services, VCU Community Memorial Hospital, South Hill, VA, p. A678

BRANDENBURG, Valerie, Director Human Resources, Northwest Hospital, Randallstown, MD, p. A302

BRANDIS, Destin, Chief Information Officer, William Bee Ririe Hospital, Ely, NV, p. A404

BRANDLER, Bruce, Administrator, Schick Shadel Hospital, Seattle, WA, p. A688

BRANDNER, Nicholas R., Chief Executive Officer, Community Memorial Hospital, Redfield, SD, p. A576

BRANDON, David R., President and Chief Executive Officer, UnityPoint Health – Finley Hospital, Dubuque, IA, p. A230

BRANDON, Deborah, Director Total Quality Management, Eastern Louisiana Mental Health System, Jackson, LA, p. A279

BRANDON, Wendy H., Chief Executive Officer, Central Florida Regional Hospital, Sanford, FL, p. A145

BRANDT, Matthew, Chief Financial Officer, St. Alexius Hospital – Broadway Campus, Saint Louis, MO, p. A381

BRANDT, Merle, Chief Financial Officer, Mason General Hospital, Shelton, WA, p. A689

BRANDT, Steve, M.D. Chief of Staff, Dale Medical Center, Ozark, AL, p. A24

BRANNAN, Debbie
Chief Financial Officer, George Regional Hospital, Lucedale, MS, p. A361
Chief Financial Officer, Greene County Hospital, Leakesville, MS, p. A361

BRANNEN, Charles C., Senior Vice President and Chief Operating Officer, Southeast Alabama Medical Center, Dothan, AL, p. A19

BRANNEN, Judy, M.D. Interim Chief of Staff, Hunter Holmes McGuire Veterans Affairs Medical Center, Richmond, VA, p. A678

BRANNIGAN, Robert C., Administrator, West Valley Hospital, Dallas, OR, p. A524

BRANNMAN, Brian G., President and Chief Executive Officer, St. Rose Dominican Hospitals – Siena Campus, Henderson, NV, p. A405

BRANNON, Jeffrey M., Chief Executive Officer, Monroe County Hospital, Monroeville, AL, p. A23

BRANNON, Jim, Vice President Human Resources, Atlantic General Hospital, Berlin, MD, p. A298

BRANNON, Linda, Vice President Human Resources, Circles of Care, Melbourne, FL, p. A135

BRANNON, Rebecca, R.N
Chief Nursing Officer, Saint Francis Hospital, Charleston, WV, p. A694
Vice President Patient Services, Thomas Memorial Hospital, South Charleston, WV, p. A699

BRANSCOME, Eileen, Chief Operating Officer, Mason General Hospital, Shelton, WA, p. A689

BRANSON, Brett, M.D. Chief of Staff, TriStar Hendersonville Medical Center, Hendersonville, TN, p. A584

BRANSON, Jason, Chief Executive Officer, AMG Specialty Hospital–Lafayette, Lafayette, LA, p. A281

BRANSTETTER, Jon, Vice President Finance, Missouri Delta Medical Center, Sikeston, MO, p. A382

BRANT, Johnny, Chief Financial Officer, Welch Community Hospital, Welch, WV, p. A700

BRANT, Mick, FACHE, Chief Executive Officer, Gothenburg Memorial Hospital, Gothenburg, NE, p. A396

BRANTZ, Jerry, Chief Financial Officer, Shoshone Medical Center, Kellogg, ID, p. A176

BRASHER, Tanya, Administrator, Marion Regional Medical Center, Hamilton, AL, p. A21

BRASSER, Brian, President, Spectrum Health United Hospital, Greenville, MI, p. A326

BRASSINGER, Cindy, Chief Operating Officer, Vibra Hospital of Southeastern Michigan, Lincoln Park, MI, p. A329

BRASWELL, Gingie, Director Human Resources, DeKalb Community Hospital, Smithville, TN, p. A593

BRATCHER, Tammy
System Information Technology Director, Great River Medical Center, Blytheville, AR, p. A43
Director Information Technology, South Mississippi County Regional Medical Center, Osceola, AR, p. A51

BRATTON, Michael J., R.N. Chief Nurse Executive and Vice President Patient Care Services, Bon Secours–DePaul Medical Center, Norfolk, VA, p. A675

BRAUDT, Theresa Lynn, Chief Nursing Officer, Gundersen Boscobel Area Hospital and Clinics, Boscobel, WI, p. A702

BRAUN, James R., Chief Financial Officer, Flambeau Hospital, Park Falls, WI, p. A713

BRAUN, Norma, Vice President Human Resources, Hollywood Presbyterian Medical Center, Los Angeles, CA, p. A72

BRAUN, Peggy, R.N. Vice President Patient Care Services and Chief Nurse Executive, Sentara Virginia Beach General Hospital, Virginia Beach, VA, p. A679

BRAUN, Jr., Richard G., CP
Senior Vice President and Chief Financial Officer, Bradford Regional Medical Center, Bradford, PA, p. A534
Senior Vice President and Chief Financial Officer, Olean General Hospital, Olean, NY, p. A450

BRAUN, Sahlenia, Chief Financial Officer, Wishek Community Hospital and Clinics, Wishek, ND, p. A481

BRAVO, Arturo, M.D. Chief of Staff, Cypress Fairbanks Medical Center, Houston, TX, p. A624

BRAVO, Stacey, Vice President Human Resources, Denton Regional Medical Center, Denton, TX, p. A613

BRAWLEY, Carrie, Administrator, Behavioral HealthCare Center at Martin, Martin, TN, p. A587

BRAXTON, Edwin R., Director Human Resources, Lompoc Valley Medical Center, Lompoc, CA, p. A70

BRAY, Bob, Chief Information Officer, Jersey Community Hospital, Jerseyville, IL, p. A193

BRAY, Delnita, Administrator, Promise Hospital of Wichita Falls, Wichita Falls, TX, p. A657

BRAY, John, M.D. Medical Director, Select Specialty Hospital–Pensacola, Pensacola, FL, p. A142

BRAY, Karen A., R.N. Vice President Patient Care Services, Washington Hospital, Washington, PA, p. A557

BRAY, Pam, Director of Nursing and Director Inpatient Services, Kane Community Hospital, Kane, PA, p. A541

BRAYFORD, Amy, Chief Human Resources Officer, Geisinger Medical Center, Danville, PA, p. A537

BRAYTON, Jackie, Vice President Human Resources, Portsmouth Regional Hospital, Portsmouth, NH, p. A412

BRAYTON, Ranee C., MSN, Chief Executive Officer, Northeast Regional Medical Center, Kirksville, MO, p. A375

BRAZ, Marcus, Chief Executive Officer, HEALTHSOUTH Rehabilitation Hospital of Sarasota, Sarasota, FL, p. A145

BRAZASKI, Karrie, R.N. Chief Operating Officer and Chief Nursing Officer, Lovelace Westside Hospital, Albuquerque, NM, p. A426

BRAZEL, Gary, M.D
Chief Medical Officer, St. Vincent Anderson Regional Hospital, Anderson, IN, p. A206
Chief Medical Officer, St. Vincent Mercy Hospital, Elwood, IN, p. A210

BRAZIL, Bob, Chief Operating Officer, Memorial Health System, Abilene, KS, p. A241

BRAZIL, Wendy, Chief Operating Officer, Neosho Memorial Regional Medical Center, Chanute, KS, p. A242

BREA, Christie, Manager Human Resources, Promise Hospital of Phoenix, Mesa, AZ, p. A34

BREADY, Sharon, R.N., Chief Executive Officer, Care One at Raritan Bay Medical Center, Perth Amboy, NJ, p. A421

BREAKWELL, Michael, R.N. Nurse Executive, Twin Valley Behavioral Healthcare, Columbus, OH, p. A491

BRECHBILL, Alan L., Director and Chief Operating Officer, Penn State Milton S. Hershey Medical Center, Hershey, PA, p. A540

BREEDEN, Donetta, Chief Clinical Officer, Monroe Hospital, Bloomington, IN, p. A207

BREEDEN, Patricia, M.D. Chief of Staff, Veterans Affairs Medical Center–Lexington, Lexington, KY, p. A265

BREEDEN, Susan M., Administrator and Chief Executive Officer, Baptist Memorial Hospital–Huntingdon, Huntingdon, TN, p. A584

BREEDLOVE, Jean Ann
Chief Information Officer, Children's Mercy Hospitals and Clinics, Kansas City, MO, p. A373
Chief Information Officer, Children's Mercy South, Overland Park, KS, p. A252

BREEDLOVE, Kelly, Vice President of Nursing, Health First Holmes Regional Medical Center, Melbourne, FL, p. A135

BREEDLOVE, Laurie, Vice President Human Resources, Crawley Memorial Hospital, Shelby, NC, p. A472

BREEDLOVE, Linda, Vice President of Patient Care Services and Chief Nursing Officer, Robinson Memorial Hospital, Ravenna, OH, p. A501

BREEDVELD, Stacey, R.N. Associate Director for Patient Care, Veterans Affairs Ann Arbor Healthcare System, Ann Arbor, MI, p. A318

BREEN, Charles J., M.D. Medical Director, Sanford Hillsboro Medical Center, Hillsboro, ND, p. A478

BREEN, Thomas, Vice President and Chief Financial Officer, South County Hospital, Wakefield, RI, p. A561

BREHM, Robert, Division President, Kessler Institute for Rehabilitation, West Orange, NJ, p. A424

BREIDSTER, Cara, Chief Financial Officer, Indiana University Health Arnett Hospital, Lafayette, IN, p. A217

BREILAND, Keith, M.D. Medical Director, Seven Hills Behavioral Institute, Henderson, NV, p. A405

BREITBACH, Dave, Chief Financial Officer, Prairie du Chien Memorial Hospital, Prairie Du Chien, WI, p. A713

BREITENBACH, Ray, M.D. Chief of Staff, Doctors' Hospital of Michigan, Pontiac, MI, p. A332

BREITFELDER, Michelle, Chief Operating Officer, Northside Medical Center, Columbus, GA, p. A156

BREITLING, Bryan, Administrator, Avera Hand County Memorial Hospital, Miller, SD, p. A574

BREKKE, Erin, Director Human Resources, Burgess Health Center, Onawa, IA, p. A235

BRELAND, Kelly R., CPA Director Support Services, Mississippi State Hospital, Whitfield, MS, p. A366

BREMER, David, D.O. Chief of Staff, MidMichigan Medical Center–Clare, Clare, MI, p. A321

BREMER Jr., Louis H., President and Chief Executive Officer, St. Francis Medical Center, Monroe, LA, p. A284

BRENAN, Kevin, Chief Financial Officer, Emory Saint Joseph's Hospital of Atlanta, Atlanta, GA, p. A152

BRENDLE, Judi, Vice President Clinical Support and Chief Nursing Officer, Bassett Medical Center, Cooperstown, NY, p. A436

BRENDLER, Stephen, Director Information Systems, Hilton Head Hospital, Hilton Head Island, SC, p. A567

BRENHOLT, Craig, Division Director People Services, Sacred Heart Hospital, Eau Claire, WI, p. A704

BRENKLE, George, Chief Information Officer, UMass Memorial Medical Center, Worcester, MA, p. A317

BRENN, Andrea, R.N. Chief Nursing Officer, Texoma Medical Center, Denison, TX, p. A613

BRENNAN, Angela, M.D. Chief of Staff, Howard County Medical Center, Saint Paul, NE, p. A401

BRENNAN, John A., M.P.H., President and Chief Executive Officer, Newark Beth Israel Medical Center, Newark, NJ, p. A419

BRENNAN, Kevin F., CPA Executive Vice President and Chief Financial Officer, Geisinger Medical Center, Danville, PA, p. A537

BRENNAN, Maria, R.N. Vice President and Chief Nursing Officer, St. Joseph's Regional Medical Center, Paterson, NJ, p. A420

BRENNAN, Patrick, Director Information System Technology, Saint Louis University Hospital, Saint Louis, MO, p. A381

BRENNAN, Patrick J., M.D. Senior Vice President and Chief Medical Officer, Hospital of the University of Pennsylvania, Philadelphia, PA, p. A548

BRENNAN, Theresa, M.D. Chief Medical Officer, University of Iowa Hospitals and Clinics, Iowa City, IA, p. A232

BRENNER, Lawrence, M.D. Chief of Staff, Corpus Christi Medical Center, Corpus Christi, TX, p. A608

BRENNER, Pattie, R.N. Chief Nursing Officer, HEALTHSOUTH Rehabilitation Hospital, Largo, FL, p. A134

BRENNER, William
Chief Financial Officer, Kindred Hospital Indianapolis South, Greenwood, IN, p. A212
Chief Financial Officer, Kindred Hospital–Indianapolis, Indianapolis, IN, p. A214

BRENNY, Terrence, President and Chief Executive Officer, Stoughton Hospital Association, Stoughton, WI, p. A716

BRENTANO, Gregory
Chief Financial Officer, Chino Valley Medical Center, Chino, CA, p. A59
Chief Executive Officer, Montclair Hospital Medical Center, Montclair, CA, p. A78

BREON, Richard C., President and Chief Executive Officer, Spectrum Health, Grand Rapids, MI, p. B126

BRES, Thomas, Vice President and Chief Administrative Officer, Sparrow Hospital, Lansing, MI, p. A328

BRESCIA, Michael J., M.D. Executive Medical Director, Calvary Hospital, NY, p. A443

BRESLIN, Michael P., Senior Vice President Finance, New York Methodist Hospital, NY, p. A447

BRESLIN, Susan, R.N. Vice President Patient Care Services and Chief Nursing Officer, DeKalb Medical at North Decatur, Decatur, GA, p. A158

BRESNAHAN, Christine, Manager Human Resources, Radius Specialty Hospital Boston, Boston, MA, p. A307

BRESNAHAN, Jacky, Director Human Resources, Mahaska Health Partnership, Oskaloosa, IA, p. A236

BRESNAHAN, Patti, Director Human Resources, Mercy Medical Center, Canton, OH, p. A485

BRESSLER, Kathy, R.N., President, St. Clare Hospital, Lakewood, WA, p. A685

BRETTNER, Eric, Vice President and Chief Financial Officer, St. Mary's Medical Center, San Francisco, CA, p. A91

BREUDER, Andrew, M.D. Chief of Staff, Manchester Veterans Affairs Medical Center, Manchester, NH, p. A411

BREUER, Jason, President, LakeWood Health Center, Baudette, MN, p. A340

BREUER, Rick, Chief Executive Officer and Administrator, Community Memorial Hospital, Cloquet, MN, p. A341

BREUM, Linda G., R.N. Chief Nursing Officer, Bert Fish Medical Center, New Smyrna Beach, FL, p. A139

BREWER, Becca, Chief Operations Officer, Falls Community Hospital and Clinic, Marlin, TX, p. A636

BREWER, David, Chief Financial Officer, Memorial Hospital, Fremont, OH, p. A494

BREWER, Gary L., Chief Executive Officer, Valley View Hospital, Glenwood Springs, CO, p. A106

BREWER, Jennifer, R.N. Chief Nursing Officer and Vice President Nursing Services, Verde Valley Medical Center, Cottonwood, AZ, p. A32

BREWER, Jennifer Lynn, Chief Executive Officer, HEALTHSOUTH Plano Rehabilitation Hospital, Plano, TX, p. A642

BREWER, Jim, M.P.H. Chief Financial Officer, Healthmark Regional Medical Center, DeFuniak Springs, FL, p. A127

BREWER, Kaye, Vice President Human Resources, Maury Regional Hospital, Columbia, TN, p. A581

BREWER, Kelley, MSN, President, Lakeside Women's Hospital, Oklahoma City, OK, p. A515

BREWER, Peter G., Administrator, Shriners Hospitals for Children–Spokane, Spokane, WA, p. A690

BREWER, Rebecca, FACHE, Interim Chief Executive Officer, Andalusia Regional Hospital, Andalusia, AL, p. A15

BREWER, RN, Ruby, Senior Vice President and Chief Quality Officer, East Jefferson General Hospital, Metairie, LA, p. A284

BREWINGTON, Kenneth C., M.D., Administrator, Mobile Infirmary Medical Center, Mobile, AL, p. A22

BREWINGTON, Yvonne, Director Human Resources, Belton Regional Medical Center, Belton, MO, p. A367

BREWSTER, Melvin, Chief Information Officer, LAC–Olive View–UCLA Medical Center, CA, p. A73

BREXLER, James L., President and Chief Executive Officer, Doylestown Hospital, Doylestown, PA, p. A537

BREYFOGLE, Cynthia, FACHE, Director, Charles George Veterans Affairs Medical Center, Asheville, NC, p. A459

BREZA, Lisa, R.N. Vice President and Chief Nursing Officer, Robert Wood Johnson University Hospital at Hamilton, Hamilton, NJ, p. A416

BREZNY, Angie, Director Human Resources, Prague Community Hospital, Prague, OK, p. A518

BRIAN, David, Director Information Services, Shriners Hospitals for Children–Lexington, Lexington, KY, p. A264

BRICHER, Joan
Senior Vice President Finance and Chief Financial Officer, Goleta Valley Cottage Hospital, Santa Barbara, CA, p. A94
Senior Vice President Finance and Chief Financial Officer, Santa Barbara Cottage Hospital, Santa Barbara, CA, p. A94
Senior Vice President Finance and Chief Financial Officer, Santa Ynez Valley Cottage Hospital, Solvang, CA, p. A95

BRICKER, Tim
President and Chief Executive Officer, Chandler Regional Medical Center, Chandler, AZ, p. A31
President and Chief Executive Officer, Mercy Gilbert Medical Center, Gilbert, AZ, p. A33

BRICKMAN, Jeffrey, FACHE, President and Chief Executive Officer, St. Anthony Hospital, Lakewood, CO, p. A108

BRICKNER, Derek, Interim Medical Staff, Jamestown Regional Medical Center, Jamestown, ND, p. A478

BRIDEAU, Donald, M.D., Interim Chief Executive Officer, Inova Mount Vernon Hospital, Alexandria, VA, p. A668

BRIDEN, David, Chief Information Officer, Exeter Hospital, Exeter, NH, p. A410

BRIDGE, Elaine, R.N. Senior Vice President Patient Care Services and Chief Nursing Officer, Newton–Wellesley Hospital, Newton Lower Falls, MA, p. A313

BRIDGELAND, Aaron
Director Finance, Midwest Orthopedic Specialty Hospital, Franklin, WI, p. A705
Director Finance, Wheaton Franciscan Healthcare – Franklin, Franklin, WI, p. A705
Director Finance, Wheaton Franciscan Healthcare – St. Francis, Milwaukee, WI, p. A711

BRIDGES, Alan J., M.D. Chief of Staff, William S. Middleton Memorial Veterans Hospital, Madison, WI, p. A708

BRIDGES, James M., Executive Vice President and Chief Operating Officer, Palmetto Health Baptist, Columbia, SC, p. A564

BRIDGES, Jane Ann, Chief Financial Officer, Nacogdoches Memorial Hospital, Nacogdoches, TX, p. A639

BRIDGES, Mary, Director Human Resources, Ouachita County Medical Center, Camden, AR, p. A44

BRIDGES, Stephanie, Chief Executive Officer, Kindred Hospital–St. Louis, Saint Louis, MO, p. A380

BRIDGES–KEE, Lorinnsa, Chief Human Resources Officer, Doctors Hospital at White Rock Lake, Dallas, TX, p. A610

BRIDGEWATER, Melinda, Director, Information Services, Montana State Hospital, Warm Springs, MT, p. A391

BRIER, Pamela S., President and Chief Executive Officer, Maimonides Medical Center, NY, p. A445

BRIESEMEISTER, Eric, Chief Executive Officer, UnityPoint Health – Jones Regional Medical Center, Anamosa, IA, p. A225

BRIETE, Mark, M.D. Vice President Medical Affairs, Mercy Hospital Jefferson, Crystal City, MO, p. A370

BRIGGS, Deborah, Vice President Human Resources, Marketing, Volunteer Services and Community Relations, Ellenville Regional Hospital, Ellenville, NY, p. A437

BRIGGS, Gary, Director Human Resources, TriStar Southern Hills Medical Center, Nashville, TN, p. A591

BRIGGS, Michael, M.D. Chief Medical Officer, Essentia Health Fargo, Fargo, ND, p. A477

BRIGGS, Paul
Executive Vice President and Chief Operating Officer, Presbyterian Hospital, Albuquerque, NM, p. A426
Executive VP/Chief Operating Officer, Presbyterian Kaseman Hospital, Albuquerque, NM, p. A427

BRIGGS, Ronald O., FACHE, President and Chief Executive Officer, St. Francis Memorial Hospital, West Point, NE, p. A402

BRIGGS, Thomas, Chief Financial Officer, Integris Marshall County Medical Center, Madill, OK, p. A513

BRIGHT, Kim, M.D. Clinical Director, Springfield Hospital Center, Sykesville, MD, p. A303

BRIGHT, Shawn, Chief Executive Officer, Yadkin Valley Community Hospital, Yadkinville, NC, p. A475

BRIGHT, Tony, M.D. Administrator Medical Services, Caswell Center, Kinston, NC, p. A467

BRILEY, Jay, President, Vidant Duplin Hospital, Kenansville, NC, p. A467

BRILL, Beth K., Senior Director Human Resources, Barnesville Hospital, Barnesville, OH, p. A483

BRILLANTES, Dorothy, Senior Vice President Human Resources, Howard County General Hospital, Columbia, MD, p. A300

BRILLI, Richard, M.D. Chief Medical Officer, Nationwide Children's Hospital, Columbus, OH, p. A490

BRILLIANT, Patrick D., President and Chief Executive Officer, Riverside Community Hospital, Riverside, CA, p. A86

BRILLIANT, Steven, M.D. Chief of Staff, Veterans Affairs Sierra Nevada Health Care System, Reno, NV, p. A408

BRIMHALL, Kelly, Director of Human Resources, Timpanogos Regional Hospital, Orem, UT, p. A661

BRINDLE, Charles B., M.D. Chief Medical Staff, Iowa Specialty Hospital–Belmond, Belmond, IA, p. A225

BRINER, Junior, Chief Operating Officer, Lawrence Memorial Hospital, Walnut Ridge, AR, p. A53

BRINK, Jr., Bruce, D.O. Chief of Staff, Gibson General Hospital, Princeton, IN, p. A221

BRINKERHOFF, Cindy H., Director Human Resources, South Peninsula Hospital, Homer, AK, p. A29

BRINKERHOFF, Douglas, M.D. Clinical Director, U. S. Public Health Service Indian Hospital, San Carlos, AZ, p. A38

BRINKERHOFF, Robert, System Vice President, Palmetto Health Richland, Columbia, SC, p. A564

BRINKHAUS, Theresa, Chief Financial Officer, St. Helena Parish Hospital, Greensburg, LA, p. A278

BRINKLEY, Terry, Vice President Finance, Paris Community Hospital, Paris, IL, p. A199

BRINKMAN, Dan, R.N., Interim Chief Executive Officer, Hilo Medical Center, Hilo, HI, p. A170

BRINKMAN, Janet, Director Human Resources, Colorado Plains Medical Center, Fort Morgan, CO, p. A106

BRINSON, David, Director Information Technology, Wabash County Hospital, Wabash, IN, p. A224

BRINSON, Pam, Nurse Executive, South Mississippi State Hospital, Purvis, MS, p. A364

BRIONES, Melba, M.D. Medical Director, Evansville State Hospital, Evansville, IN, p. A210

BRISBOE, Mark
VP and Chief Financial Officer, Sparrow Clinton Hospital, Saint Johns, MI, p. A334
VP and Chief Financial Officer, Sparrow Ionia Hospital, Ionia, MI, p. A327

BRISCOE, Betsy, Chief Executive Officer, Memorial Hospital, Seminole, TX, p. A648

BRISCOE, Charles G., FACHE, Chief Executive Officer, Coliseum Medical Centers, Macon, GA, p. A162

BRISCOE, Mary Beth, Chief Financial Officer, University of Alabama Hospital, Birmingham, AL, p. A17

BRISENDINE, Chad
Vice President and Chief Information Officer, St. Luke's Hospital – Miners Campus, Coaldale, PA, p. A536
Chief Information Officer, St. Luke's Hospital – Quakertown Campus, Quakertown, PA, p. A553
Chief Information Officer, St. Luke's University Hospital – Bethlehem Campus, Bethlehem, PA, p. A534

BRISTER, Kim, Director Human Resources, Gettysburg Hospital, Gettysburg, PA, p. A539

BRISTO, Cathie, Director Human Resources, Wilbarger General Hospital, Vernon, TX, p. A655

BRISTOL, Michelle, Director of Nursing, Clifton–Fine Hospital, Star Lake, NY, p. A455

BRISTOLL, Holly L.
President, ProMedica Bay Park Hospital, Oregon, OH, p. A500
President, ProMedica Fostoria Community Hospital, Fostoria, OH, p. A494

BRISTOW, III, Clyde A., MSN Chief Nursing Officer, Wake Forest Baptist Health–Davie Hospital, Mocksville, NC, p. A469

BRITT, Kevin, Chief Operating Officer, Reynolds Memorial Hospital, Glen Dale, WV, p. A695

BRITT, Key, Associate Director, Greenwood Leflore Hospital, Greenwood, MS, p. A358

BRITT, Linda, Director Information Systems, Baptist Memorial Hospital–North Mississippi, Oxford, MS, p. A364

BRITT, Suzanne, Director Human Resources, Samaritan Memorial Hospital, Macon, MO, p. A376

BRITT, Tommy, Director Human Resources, West Georgia Health, La Grange, GA, p. A162

BRITTAIN, Libby, Director Human Resources, Steele Memorial Medical Center, Salmon, ID, p. A178

BRITTON, David, Interim Chief Financial Officer, Medina Memorial Hospital, Medina, NY, p. A441

BRITTON, John, Vice President Information Services, Fisher–Titus Medical Center, Norwalk, OH, p. A500

BRITTON, Lynn, President and Chief Executive Officer, Mercy Health, Chesterfield, MO, p. B92

BRITTON, Natalie J., Director Human Resources, Silverton Hospital, Silverton, OR, p. A530

BRITTON, William N., Associate Administrator Finance, Alfred I. duPont Hospital for Children, Wilmington, DE, p. A120

BROADDUS, Jackie, Business Partner, Taylorville Memorial Hospital, Taylorville, IL, p. A204

BROADNAX, Melissa, Supervisor Human Resources, Kindred Hospital Bay Area–Tampa, Tampa, FL, p. A147

BROADUS, Ronald, Assistant Administrator Human Resources, Interim LSU Public Hospital, New Orleans, LA, p. A285

BROADWATER, Gary W., Chief Financial Officer, McCready Foundation, Crisfield, MD, p. A300

BROADWAY, Chris, Manager Information Technology, Mayers Memorial Hospital District, Fall River Mills, CA, p. A63

BROADWAY, Marsha, Chief Nursing Officer, Hardin County General Hospital, Rosiclare, IL, p. A202

BROBBEY, Andrew, M.D. Chief of Staff, Euclid Hospital, Euclid, OH, p. A493

BROBERG, John R., FACHE, Senior Administrator, Mercy Regional Health Center, KS, p. A249

BROBST, Mary, R.N. Senior Vice President Patient Care Services and Chief Nursing Officer, Mercy Medical Center–Cedar Rapids, Cedar Rapids, IA, p. A226

BROCK, Berna, Vice President Human Resources, Adena Pike Medical Center, Waverly, OH, p. A505

BROCK, Jamie, Director Human Resources, Windber Medical Center, Windber, PA, p. A559

BROCK, Kyle, Vice President Human Resources, Glens Falls Hospital, Glens Falls, NY, p. A438

BROCK, Lisa M., Vice President Human Resources, Overlake Medical Center, Bellevue, WA, p. A681

BROCK, Melinda, Director Human Resources, Woodward Regional Hospital, Woodward, OK, p. A522

BROCK, Nancy, Chief Financial Officer, Houston Methodist St. Catherine Hospital, Katy, TX, p. A630

BROCK, Robert
Chief Financial Officer and Vice President, Rollins–Brook Community Hospital, Lampasas, TX, p. A632
Vice President Finance, Saint Joseph – Martin, Martin, KY, p. A267

BROCK, Sue, Chief Financial Officer, Indiana University Health Paoli Hospital, Paoli, IN, p. A221

BROCK, Theresa, Vice President Nursing, Good Shepherd Health Care System, Hermiston, OR, p. A525

BROCK, William, Chief Information Officer, Atlanta Veterans Affairs Medical Center, Decatur, GA, p. A158

BROCKETTE, Darby, Chief Executive Officer, Ernest Health, Inc., Albuquerque, NM, p. B57

BROCKHAUS, Jennifer, Chief Information Officer, Sidney Regional Medical Center, Sidney, NE, p. A402

BROCKMEYER, Heather, Human Resource Administrative Officer, Nevada Regional Medical Center, Nevada, MO, p. A377

BROCKMEYER, JoEllyn, Director Human Resources, Indiana University Health White Memorial Hospital, Monticello, IN, p. A219

BROCKUS, Harry, Chief Executive Officer, Carle Hoopeston Regional Health Center, Hoopeston, IL, p. A193

BROCKWELL, Linda, R.N. Chief Nursing Officer, Wickenburg Community Hospital, Wickenburg, AZ, p. A41

BRODALE, Sean, D.O. Chief Medical Staff, Davis County Hospital, Bloomfield, IA, p. A226

BRODBECK, MSN, RN–, Kathleen, Chief Nursing Officer, St. James Mercy Health System, Hornell, NY, p. A439

BRODBECK, Lisa, Chief Financial Officer, Medical Center of Lewisville, Lewisville, TX, p. A633

BRODERICK, John, M.D. Chief Medical Officer, Adirondack Medical Center, Saranac Lake, NY, p. A454

BRODEUR, Mark S., FACHE, Chief Executive Officer, Select Specialty Hospital – Cincinnati North, Cincinnati, OH, p. A487

BRODHEAD, Richard, M.D. President Medical Staff, Ministry Eagle River Memorial Hospital, Eagle River, WI, p. A704

BRODHEAD, Richard Ross, Director Human Resources, St. Vincent Randolph Hospital, Winchester, IN, p. A224

BRODHEAD, Ross, Manager Human Resources, St. Vincent Mercy Hospital, Elwood, IN, p. A210

BRODIAN, Craig R., Vice President Human Resources, Johns Hopkins Bayview Medical Center, Baltimore, MD, p. A296

BRODRICK, Theresa M., R.N
Chief Nursing Officer, Alamance Regional Medical Center, Burlington, NC, p. A461
Executive Vice President and Chief Nursing Officer, Moses H. Cone Memorial Hospital, Greensboro, NC, p. A465

BRODY, Anne Marie, Director Information Systems Customer Service, Providence Saint Joseph Medical Center, Burbank, CA, p. A58

BRODY, Robert J., President and Chief Executive Officer, Franciscan St. Francis Health – Indianapolis, Indianapolis, IN, p. A214

BROEKHUIS, Arlyn, Vice President and Chief Information Officer, Sanford USD Medical Center, Sioux Falls, SD, p. A576

BROEMELING, Richard, Information Systems Flight Commander, U. S. Air Force Clinic, Mountain Home AFB, ID, p. A177

BROERMANN, Robert
Senior Vice President and Chief Financial Officer, Sentara Leigh Hospital, Norfolk, VA, p. A675
Senior Vice President and Chief Financial Officer, Sentara Norfolk General Hospital, Norfolk, VA, p. A675
Senior Vice President and Chief Financial Officer, Sentara Princess Anne Hospital, Virginia Beach, VA, p. A679

BROFMAN, John, M.D. Medical Director, RML Specialty Hospital, Hinsdale, IL, p. A193

BROGGER, Portlyn
Chief Executive Officer, Post Acute Medical Specialty Hospital of Victoria, Victoria, TX, p. A655
Chief Executive Officer, Post Acute/Warm Springs Specialty Hospital of Victoria, Victoria, TX, p. A655

BROHAWN, Bill, Chief of Staff, Trace Regional Hospital, Houston, MS, p. A359

BROKAW, Sara, Vice President Patient Care Services, Bellevue Hospital, Bellevue, OH, p. A484

BROKENSHIRE, Shelia Kay, Vice President of Nursing, Van Wert County Hospital, Van Wert, OH, p. A504

BROMAN, Craig J., FACHE, President, St. Cloud Hospital, Saint Cloud, MN, p. A350

BROMLEY, Trudy, Vice President Human Resources, JFK Medical Center, Atlantis, FL, p. A123

BRONER, Eloise, President and Chief Executive Officer, Good Samaritan Hospital, Dayton, OH, p. A492

BRONHARD, John, Interim Chief Financial Officer, HealthAlliance Hospitals, Leominster, MA, p. A311

BROOCKS, Kelli C., Director Human Resources, Public Relations and Physician Recruitment, Beauregard Memorial Hospital, De Ridder, LA, p. A276

BROOKE, Teresa, Chief Nursing Officer, Dominion Hospital, Falls Church, VA, p. A670

BROOKE, William R., M.D. President Medical Staff, Pickens County Medical Center, Carrollton, AL, p. A18

BROOKER, Brian, Chief Executive Officer, Cypress Creek Hospital, Houston, TX, p. A624

BROOKER, Paula, Director Information Services, Pleasant Valley Hospital, Point Pleasant, WV, p. A698

BROOKER, Susan E., R.N. Chief Clinical Officer, Vibra Specialty Hospital of Portland, Portland, OR, p. A529

BROOKES, Jeffrey, M.D
Chief Medical Officer, Parkview LaGrange Hospital, LaGrange, IN, p. A217
Medical Director, Parkview Whitley Hospital, Columbia City, IN, p. A208

BROOKHYSER, Joan, Medical Center Director and Chief Executive Officer, University Medical Center, Las Vegas, NV, p. A407

BROOKS, Albert, M.D. Chief Medical Staff Services, Washington Hospital Healthcare System, Fremont, CA, p. A64

BROOKS, Ann Marie T., R.N. Vice President, Nursing, Riddle Hospital, Media, PA, p. A545

BROOKS, Anthony, Chief Information Officer, Miami Veterans Affairs Healthcare System, Miami, FL, p. A137

BROOKS, April, Chief Nursing Officer, HEALTHSOUTH Rehabilitation Hospital of Columbia, Columbia, SC, p. A564

BROOKS, David, President, St. John Hospital and Medical Center, Detroit, MI, p. A322

BROOKS, Harris W., Administrator and Chief Executive Officer, Palo Pinto General Hospital, Mineral Wells, TX, p. A638

BROOKS III, J. Milton, Administrator, Pineville Community Hospital Association, Pineville, KY, p. A269

BROOKS, Janet, Chief Nursing Officer, USC Verdugo Hills Hospital, Glendale, CA, p. A65

BROOKS, Janet, R.N. Vice President and Chief Nursing Officer, West Hills Hospital and Medical Center, CA, p. A75

BROOKS, Jeffrey, M.D. Medical Director, Parkview Huntington Hospital, Huntington, IN, p. A213

BROOKS, Jerome M., Chief Operating Officer, South Texas Health System, Edinburg, TX, p. A615

BROOKS, Joe, Chief Financial Officer, Keystone Newport News, Newport News, VA, p. A674

BROOKS, Lisa, Chief Financial Officer, Comanche County Hospital, Coldwater, KS, p. A242

BROOKS, Lori, Director Human Resources, Red Bud Regional Hospital, Red Bud, IL, p. A201

BROOKS, Nick, Director of Information Systems, Citrus Memorial Health System, Inverness, FL, p. A131

BROOKS, Patrice Gay, Chief Executive Officer, Cumberland Hospital, New Kent, VA, p. A674

BROOKS, Patti, Director Information Systems, Avera Queen of Peace Hospital, Mitchell, SD, p. A575

BROOKS, Robert E., FACHE Executive Vice President and Chief Operating Officer, Erlanger Medical Center, Chattanooga, TN, p. A580

BROOKS, Scott, Manager Information Technology, Boulder City Hospital, Boulder City, NV, p. A404

BROOKS, Steven, Vice President Human Resources, McAlester Regional Health Center, McAlester, OK, p. A513

BROOKS, Steven Michael, Vice President Human Resources, Southeastern Ohio Regional Medical Center, Cambridge, OH, p. A485

BROOKS, Troy, Assistant Administrator Fiscal Services, Newton Medical Center, Covington, GA, p. A157

BROOKS–WILLIAMS, Denise, President and Chief Executive Officer, Henry Ford Wyandotte Hospital, Wyandotte, MI, p. A337

BROOKSHIRE–HEAVIN, Keri S., Chief Nurse Executive, Phelps County Regional Medical Center, Rolla, MO, p. A379

BROPHY, Beth, Interim VP for Human Resources, Hurley Medical Center, Flint, MI, p. A323

BROSIUS, William, Vice President and Chief Financial Officer, St. Luke's Medical Center, Houston, TX, p. A627

BROSKEY, Steven, Associate Director, Veterans Affairs Roseburg Healthcare System, Roseburg, OR, p. A529

BROSNAHAN, Jan, Chief Financial Officer, Winona Health, Winona, MN, p. A354

BROSNAN, Kimberly, Director Human Resources, Norwood Hospital, Norwood, MA, p. A313

BROSS, James B., President and Chief Executive Officer, Angel Medical Center, Franklin, NC, p. A464

BROSS, Mary Ann, Vice President Human Resources, Robert Wood Johnson University Hospital Somerset, Somerville, NJ, p. A422

BROST, Michelle, Financial Officer, Victory Medical Center Mid–Cities, Hurst, TX, p. A629

BROSTROM, Kyle, Chief Operating Officer, Timpanogos Regional Hospital, Orem, UT, p. A661

BROTEN, Kurt, Chief Financial Officer, Palmdale Regional Medical Center, Palmdale, CA, p. A82

BROTHERS, John T., MS, Administrator, St. Joseph Memorial Hospital, Murphysboro, IL, p. A197

BROTHMAN, Daniel, Chief Executive Officer, Western Medical Center–Santa Ana, Santa Ana, CA, p. A93

BROTHMAN, Joe, Vice President Information Systems, MedStar Washington Hospital Center, Washington, DC, p. A121

BROUGHMAN, Robin, R.N. Chief Nursing Officer, LewisGale Hospital Alleghany, Low Moor, VA, p. A673

BROUGHMAN, Wade
Chief Operating Officer, Riverside Behavioral Health Center, Hampton, VA, p. A672
Executive Vice President and Chief Financial Officer, Riverside Regional Medical Center, Newport News, VA, p. A675
Executive Vice President and Chief Financial Officer, Riverside Rehabilitation Institute, Newport News, VA, p. A675

BROUILLETTE, Cindy, Chief Financial Officer, St. David's Rehabilitation Center, Austin, TX, p. A600

BROUSSARD, Clifford M., FACHE, Administrator, WK Bossier Health Center, Bossier City, LA, p. A274

BROUSSARD, E. Paul, Chief Executive Officer, Kailo LTAC Hospital, Crowley, LA, p. A276

BROUWER, Heath, Administrator, Douglas County Memorial Hospital, Armour, SD, p. A572

BROWDER, Renate, R.N. Director of Nursing, Lake City Community Hospital, Lake City, SC, p. A568

BROWER, Fred B., President and Chief Executive Officer, Trinity Health System, Steubenville, OH, p. A502

BROWER, Laura E., R.N. Chief Nursing Officer, Georgia Regents Medical Center, Augusta, GA, p. A153

BROWN, Ann R., FACHE, Director, Jesse Brown Veterans Affairs Medical Center, Chicago, IL, p. A184

BROWN, B. Blaine, Vice President and General Counsel, Prattville Baptist Hospital, Prattville, AL, p. A25

BROWN, Barbara, D.O. Chief of Staff, Osborne County Memorial Hospital, Osborne, KS, p. A251

BROWN, Beth, Medical Center Director, Louis A. Johnson Veterans Affairs Medical Center, Clarksburg, WV, p. A694

BROWN, Bryan
Director Information Services and Technology, Corpus Christi Medical Center, Corpus Christi, TX, p. A608
Executive Director, Mercy Hospital Fort Smith, Fort Smith, AR, p. A46

BROWN, Chad J., M.P.H., President, Wake Forest Baptist Health–Davie Hospital, Mocksville, NC, p. A469

BROWN, Cheryl, Administrator, Henderson Health Care Services, Henderson, NE, p. A396

BROWN, Chistiane, Assistant Vice President, MedStar Montgomery Medical Center, Olney, MD, p. A302

BROWN, Christi, Director Human Resources, Our Lady of the Angels Hospital, Bogalusa, LA, p. A274

BROWN, Christopher, M.D. Chief of Staff, Ellinwood District Hospital, Ellinwood, KS, p. A243

BROWN, Chuck, Administrator, Bethesda Butler Hospital, Hamilton, OH, p. A495

BROWN, Crystal, M.D. Medical Director, Medical Center of Peach County, Navicent Health, Fort Valley, GA, p. A160

BROWN, Cynthia, Director of Nursing, Hill Hospital of Sumter County, York, AL, p. A27

BROWN, Damon, Chief Executive Officer, Midwest Regional Medical Center, Midwest City, OK, p. A513

BROWN, Darin, Vice President Finance, Henry County Hospital, New Castle, IN, p. A220

BROWN, David A., Director Human Resources and Corporate Compliance, Pleasant Valley Hospital, Point Pleasant, WV, p. A698

BROWN, Deana, Director Administrative Services, Jasper County Hospital, Rensselaer, IN, p. A221

BROWN, Debbie T., R.N. Chief Clinical Officer, Valley General Hospital, Monroe, WA, p. A685

BROWN, Debra L., Area Financial Officer, Kaiser Permanente Manteca Medical Center, Manteca, CA, p. A76

BROWN, Denise, Vice President Human Resources, Presence Saint Joseph Hospital, Chicago, IL, p. A185

BROWN, Derek, Chief Information Officer, Jellico Community Hospital, Jellico, TN, p. A585

BROWN, Donald G., Interim President and Chief Executive Officer, Ferrell Hospital, Eldorado, IL, p. A188

BROWN, Ed, Interim Chief Financial Officer, Homer Memorial Hospital, Homer, LA, p. A278

BROWN, Eric, M.D. Physician Executive, Palmetto Health Richland, Columbia, SC, p. A564

BROWN, Eric, Senior Business Partner, Shady Grove Adventist Hospital, Rockville, MD, p. A303

BROWN, Frank, M.D. Chief Medical Officer, Emory Wesley Woods Geriatric Hospital, Atlanta, GA, p. A152

BROWN, Geoffrey
Senior Vice President Information Services, Inova Alexandria Hospital, Alexandria, VA, p. A668
Chief Information Officer, Inova Fair Oaks Hospital, Fairfax, VA, p. A670
Vice President Information Systems, Inova Fairfax Hospital, Falls Church, VA, p. A670

BRUCE, Bill, FACHE, Chief Executive Officer, Crawford County Memorial Hospital, Denison, IA, p. A229

BRUCE, Karen, Director of Nursing, Keystone Newport News, Newport News, VA, p. A674

BRUCE, Michael D., Chief Executive Officer, Lake Martin Community Hospital, Dadeville, AL, p. A18

BRUCE, Mike, Chief Financial Officer, Elmore Community Hospital, Wetumpka, AL, p. A26

BRUCE, Paul, Chief Nursing Officer, HEALTHSOUTH Rehabilitation Hospital of Austin, Austin, TX, p. A599

BRUCE, Sandra B., FACHE, President and Chief Executive Officer, Presence Health, Chicago, IL, p. B108

BRUCE, Scott, Vice President Operations, St. Mary's Healthcare, Amsterdam, NY, p. A432

BRUCE, Sheila, Director Information System, Baptist Health Madisonville, Madisonville, KY, p. A267

BRUCKEN, Keri, Director Health Information Management, Holton Community Hospital, Holton, KS, p. A245

BRUDNICKI, Gary F., Senior Executive Vice President, Chief Operating Officer and Chief Financial Officer, Westchester Medical Center, Valhalla, NY, p. A457

BRUFF, Edward, Executive Vice President and Chief Operating Officer, Covenant Medical Center, Saginaw, MI, p. A333

BRUGGEMAN, Chris, Chief Operating Officer, RiverView Health, Crookston, MN, p. A342

BRUHL, Elliot, M.D. Medical Director, SEARHC MT. Edgecumbe Hospital, Sitka, AK, p. A30

BRUHL, Lisa G., Chief Operating Officer, Lallie Kemp Medical Center, Independence, LA, p. A279

BRUHN, Julie, R.N. Associate Director Patient Care and Nurse Executive, Fargo Veterans Affairs Health Care System, Fargo, ND, p. A477

BRUI, Thomas M., Director Resource Management, Naval Hospital Lemoore, Lemoore, CA, p. A69

BRUMFIELD, Derrick, Chief Operating Officer, SageWest Healthcare–Lander, Lander, WY, p. A721

BRUMFIELD, Rita, R.N. Chief Nursing Officer, Ste. Genevieve County Memorial Hospital, Ste. Genevieve, MO, p. A383

BRUMMETT, Vince, Director Administrative Services, Tri–Lakes Medical Center, Batesville, MS, p. A355

BRUMMUND, Calvin J., Interim Chief Financial Officer, Neshoba County General Hospital, Philadelphia, MS, p. A364

BRUMSTED, John R., M.D., President and Chief Executive Officer, Fletcher Allen Health Care, Burlington, VT, p. A665

BRUNDISE, Cynthia, Vice President Human Resources, St. Anthony Hospital, Oklahoma City, OK, p. A516

BRUNELLE, Diane, MSN Vice President of Patient Care Services and Chief Nursing Officer, Noble Hospital, Westfield, MA, p. A316

BRUNER, Deborah, Chief Executive Officer and Administrator, Minneola District Hospital, Minneola, KS, p. A250

BRUNING, Troy, Director Information Technology, Meeker Memorial Hospital, Litchfield, MN, p. A345

BRUNKE, Renea, Vice President Human Resources, Chandler Regional Medical Center, Chandler, AZ, p. A31

BRUNN, Mary E., R.N. Acting Associate Director Nursing, Clement J. Zablocki Veterans Affairs Medical Center, Milwaukee, WI, p. A710

BRUNO, Catherine, FACHE Chief Information Officer, Eastern Maine Medical Center, Bangor, ME, p. A291

BRUNO, Frank, Chief Executive Officer, Gracie Square Hospital, New York, NY, p. A443

BRUNO, John, Vice President Human Resources, St. Joseph's Regional Medical Center, Paterson, NJ, p. A420

BRUNO, Judy, R.N. Vice President, Clinical Operations, The Outer Banks Hospital, Nags Head, NC, p. A470

BRUNO, Steve, Manager Business, Central Regional Hospital, Butner, NC, p. A461

BRUNO, Yolanda, M.D. Medical Director, Henry J. Carter Specialty Hospital and Nursing Facility, New York, NY, p. A444

BRUNS, Christine, Chief Human Resources Officer, Veterans Affairs Butler Healthcare, Butler, PA, p. A534

BRUNSON, Pam, Director Human Resources, South Baldwin Regional Medical Center, Foley, AL, p. A20

BRUNT, C. Hal, M.D. Medical Director, Lakeside Behavioral Health System, Memphis, TN, p. A588

BRUNTON, Hope, Chief Manpower Branch, Irwin Army Community Hospital, Junction City, KS, p. A247

BRUNTZ, Troy, Vice President Finance and Chief Financial Officer, Community Hospital, McCook, NE, p. A398

BRUS, Sarah, Director Human Resources, Doctor's Memorial Hospital, Perry, FL, p. A142

BRUSKI, Gayle, R.N. Chief Nursing Officer, Alpena Regional Medical Center, Alpena, MI, p. A318

BRUSSEAU, Margie, R.N
Chief Nursing Officer, Starr Regional Medical Center, Athens, TN, p. A579
Chief Nursing Officer, Starr Regional Medical Center–Etowah, Etowah, TN, p. A582

BRUTON, Jeff, Director Human Resources, Fairview Park Hospital, Dublin, GA, p. A159

BRUUN, Edward, President and Chief Executive Officer, Sparrow Clinton Hospital, Saint Johns, MI, p. A334

BRVENIK, Richard A., FACHE, President, Carteret General Hospital, Morehead City, NC, p. A469

BRYAN, Darlene, R.N. Chief Nursing Officer, Humboldt General Hospital, Winnemucca, NV, p. A408

BRYAN, Jason, Director Human Resources, Middle Park Medical Center–Kremmling, Kremmling, CO, p. A108

BRYAN, Jay, President and Chief Executive Officer, Mercy Health Partners, Lakeshore Campus, Shelby, MI, p. A334

BRYAN, Kenneth E., FACHE, President and Chief Executive Officer, Harnett Health System, Dunn, NC, p. A463

BRYAN, Lynda, Vice President Human Resources, Northwest Medical Center, Margate, FL, p. A135

BRYAN, Margaret, Administrator, Shriners Hospitals for Children–Northern California, Sacramento, CA, p. A87

BRYAN, Marilyn, Chief Executive Officer, Roger Mills Memorial Hospital, Cheyenne, OK, p. A508

BRYAN, Mark, Chief Executive Officer, Delray Medical Center, Delray Beach, FL, p. A127

BRYAN, Sarah, Manager Human Resources, The Heart Hospital at Deaconess Gateway, Newburgh, IN, p. A220

BRYAN–SMITH, Lissa, Chief Administrative Officer, Geisinger–Bloomsburg Hospital, Bloomsburg, PA, p. A534

BRYANT, Amy, Chief Financial Officer, Cornerstone Hospital of Southwest Louisiana, Sulphur, LA, p. A289

BRYANT, Dawn L., Senior Vice President and Chief Human Resource Officer, Saint Francis Hospital and Medical Center, Hartford, CT, p. A114

BRYANT, Gayla, R.N., Administrator, Sage Rehabilitation Hospital, Baton Rouge, LA, p. A274

BRYANT, Gerald W., R.N
Chief Nursing Officer, Baptist Hospitals of Southeast Texas, Beaumont, TX, p. A601
Chief Operating Officer and Chief Nursing Officer, Baptist Orange Hospital, Orange, TX, p. A640

BRYANT, Karen, Chief Support Services Officer, Prowers Medical Center, Lamar, CO, p. A108

BRYANT, Kay, Executive Director Human Resources, Saint Clare's Health System, Denville, NJ, p. A415

BRYANT, Kim, Chief Executive Officer, Highlands Medical Center, Scottsboro, AL, p. A25

BRYANT, Lisa G., Director Human Resources, Cannon Memorial Hospital, Pickens, SC, p. A569

BRYANT, Mandy, Chief Information Officer, Twin Lakes Regional Medical Center, Leitchfield, KY, p. A264

BRYANT, Maureen A., FACHE, President, Delnor Hospital, Geneva, IL, p. A191

BRYANT, Pam, Director Human Resources, Helen Keller Hospital, Sheffield, AL, p. A25

BRYANT, Ron, President and Chief Executive Officer, Noble Hospital, Westfield, MA, p. A316

BRYANT, Rusty, Director Information Technology, Drew Memorial Hospital, Monticello, AR, p. A50

BRYANT, Valerie, Chief Financial Officer, Deckerville Community Hospital, Deckerville, MI, p. A321

BRYANT, William J., Chief Executive Officer, Kindred Hospital–Chattanooga, Chattanooga, TN, p. A580

BRYANT–MOBLEY, Phyllis, M.D. Director Medical Services, William S. Hall Psychiatric Institute, Columbia, SC, p. A564

BRYCE, Keith, Chief Financial Officer, Mt. Graham Regional Medical Center, Safford, AZ, p. A38

BRYCE, Lance, M.D. Chief Medical Officer, Brigham City Community Hospital, Brigham City, UT, p. A659

BRYDON, Paul, Chief Financial Officer, Antelope Valley Hospital, Lancaster, CA, p. A69

BRYER, Alex, Director Information Management, Los Robles Hospital and Medical Center, Thousand Oaks, CA, p. A97

BRYNER, Jennifer, Chief Nursing Officer, Petersburg Medical Center, Petersburg, AK, p. A30

BRYSON, Kellie, Director Human Resources, The Hospital at Westlake Medical Center, Austin, TX, p. A600

BUBENIK, Oldrich, M.D. Chief of Staff, Rush County Memorial Hospital, La Crosse, KS, p. A248

BUCCI, Annette, Senior Administrator Human Resources, Burke Rehabilitation Hospital, White Plains, NY, p. A458

BUCCI, Barbara A., R.N. Vice President Patient Care and Chief Nursing Officer, Mount St. Mary's Hospital and Health Center, Lewiston, NY, p. A440

BUCCIARELLI, Brant, Chief Information Officer, Riverview Hospital, Noblesville, IN, p. A220

BUCCOLO, Martin A., Ph.D., Chief Executive Officer, Four Winds Hospital, Katonah, NY, p. A439

BUCCULATO, Vito, Chief Operating Officer, Coney Island Hospital, NY, p. A443

BUCH, David, M.D. Chief Medical Officer, Carrier Clinic, Belle Mead, NJ, p. A413

BUCH, Naishadh, Chief Operating Officer, Lompoc Valley Medical Center, Lompoc, CA, p. A70

BUCHANAN, Dennis, Vice President Human Resources, New York Methodist Hospital, NY, p. A447

BUCHANAN, Donald E.
Interim Chief Executive Officer, Haskell County Community Hospital, Stigler, OK, p. A519
Interim Chief Executive Officer, Seiling Community Hospital, Seiling, OK, p. A518

BUCHANAN, Donna, Director Nursing, Stroud Regional Medical Center, Stroud, OK, p. A519

BUCHANAN, Gary, Director of Nursing, Broadwater Health Center, Townsend, MT, p. A391

BUCHANAN, Herbert, President, Indiana University Health University Hospital, Indianapolis, IN, p. A214

BUCHANAN, Jean, Director Human Resources, Broughton Hospital, Morganton, NC, p. A469

BUCHANAN, Kevin, Chief Information Officer, Wake Forest Baptist Health–Lexington Medical Center, Lexington, NC, p. A468

BUCHANAN, Kyle, Chief Executive Officer, Lawrence Medical Center, Moulton, AL, p. A24

BUCHANAN, Robert, Chief Information Officer, Anna Jaques Hospital, Newburyport, MA, p. A312

BUCHANAN, Ron, Director Information Services, West Central Georgia Regional Hospital, Columbus, GA, p. A156

BUCHANAN, Toni, Chief Financial Officer, Unicoi County Memorial Hospital, Erwin, TN, p. A582

BUCHANAN, Tracy, Chief Executive Officer / President, CarePartners Health Services, Asheville, NC, p. A459

BUCHART, Phyllis, Chief Operating Officer, Marina Del Rey Hospital, Marina Del Rey, CA, p. A76

BUCHELE, Paula, Chief Human Resources, Bay Pines Veterans Affairs Medical Center, Bay Pines, FL, p. A123

BUCHERT, Charles, Director Human Resources, Lake Area Medical Center, Lake Charles, LA, p. A282

BUCHHEIT, Anne, Coordinator Mental Health Local Information Systems, Buffalo Psychiatric Center, Buffalo, NY, p. A434

BUCHHEIT, Joe, Chief Financial Officer, Our Lady of Bellefonte Hospital, Ashland, KY, p. A258

BUCHHOLZ, Kari, Director Health Information Management, Wishek Community Hospital and Clinics, Wishek, ND, p. A481

BUCHHOLZ, Thomas, M.D. Physician–in–Chief and Executive Vice President, University of Texas M.D. Anderson Cancer Center, Houston, TX, p. A628

BUCHNESS, Michael P., M.D. Director Medical, Deer's Head Hospital Center, Salisbury, MD, p. A303

BUCIENSKI, Jennifer C., Vice President Human Resources, Hayes Green Beach Memorial Hospital, Charlotte, MI, p. A320

BUCK, Catherine, President, Froedtert Memorial Lutheran Hospital, Milwaukee, WI, p. A710

BUCK, Cheryl, Vice President Human Resources, Lake Region Healthcare, Fergus Falls, MN, p. A343

BUCK, Cindy D., Chief Executive Officer, Rutherford Regional Health System, Rutherfordton, NC, p. A472

BUCK, Gwen, R.N. Chief Nursing Officer, Greater Regional Medical Center, Creston, IA, p. A228

BUCK, Linda K., Vice President Human Resources, Proctor Hospital, Peoria, IL, p. A200

BUCK, Nathan, R.N. Nursing Manager, Mountain River Birthing and Surgery Center, Blackfoot, ID, p. A174

BUCK, Phylis, Controller, HEALTHSOUTH Rehabilitation Hospital of Texarkana, Texarkana, TX, p. A652

BUCK, Tavia, Interim Chief Nursing Officer, Mount Pleasant Hospital, Mount Pleasant, SC, p. A568

BUCK, William G., Chief Executive Officer, Northwest Mississippi Regional Medical Center, Clarksdale, MS, p. A356

BUCKELEW, Rick, Chief Executive Officer, Austin Lakes Hospital, Austin, TX, p. A599

BUCKHOY, Sandra, Chief Clinical Officer, Kindred Hospital Chicago–Northlake, Northlake, IL, p. A198

BUCKINGHAM, Deborah, R.N. Director Human Resources, Redington–Fairview General Hospital, Skowhegan, ME, p. A295

BUCKLEY, David, Acting Chief Information Management Services, Oklahoma City Veterans Affairs Medical Center, Oklahoma City, OK, p. A516

BUCKLEY, Jeffrey L., Interim Chief Executive Officer, Breckinridge Memorial Hospital, Hardinsburg, KY, p. A262

BUCKLEY, John, M.D. President Medical Staff, Vibra Hospital of Denver, Thornton, CO, p. A111

BUCKLEY, Kalvin, Director Information Systems, Woodland Heights Medical Center, Lufkin, TX, p. A636

BUCKLEY, Karen, R.N. Chief Nursing Officer, Community Behavioral Health Center, Fresno, CA, p. A64

BUCKLEY, Patrick, Vice President Human Resources, St. Elizabeth Medical Center, Utica, NY, p. A456

BUCKLEY, Peter, M.D., Interim Chief Executive Officer, Georgia Regents Medical Center, Augusta, GA, p. A153

BUCKLEY, R. Michael, M.D., Executive Director, Pennsylvania Hospital, Philadelphia, PA, p. A549

BUCKLEY, William, M.D. Chief of Staff, Elkhart General Healthcare System, Elkhart, IN, p. A210

BUCKNER Jr., James E., FACHE, Interim Chief Executive Officer, Dimmit Regional Hospital, Carrizo Springs, TX, p. A605

BUCKNER, Marlys, Chief Nursing Officer, Barton County Memorial Hospital, Lamar, MO, p. A375

BUCKNER, Terry, Chief Executive Officer, Pikes Peak Regional Hospital, Woodland Park, CO, p. A112

BUCKWORTH, Albert Bennett, Director Human Resources, Primary Children's Medical Center, Salt Lake City, UT, p. A663

BUDA, Jeff, Chief Information Officer, Floyd Medical Center, Rome, GA, p. A165

BUDD, Edward, President and Chief Executive Officer, Thorek Memorial Hospital, Chicago, IL, p. A187

BUDDE, Rex P., President and Chief Executive Officer, Southern Illinois Hospital Services, Carbondale, IL, p. B125

BUDIG, Aletha, R.N. Director Nursing, Ellinwood District Hospital, Ellinwood, KS, p. A243

BUDINGER, David P., Associate Director, Hunter Holmes McGuire Veterans Affairs Medical Center, Richmond, VA, p. A678

BUDNICK, Michael J., FACHE Chief Operating Officer, Franklin Hospital District, Benton, IL, p. A181

BUDZINSKI, William, Vice President Human Resources, Methodist Hospital of Southern California, Arcadia, CA, p. A56

BUDZINSKY, Chris, R.N. Vice President Nursing/CNO Alexian Brothers Acute Care Ministries, St. Alexius Medical Center, Hoffman Estates, IL, p. A193

BUE, Cheryl, Health Information Transcriptionist, Faulkton Area Medical Center, Faulkton, SD, p. A573

BUEHLER, Bonnie, Chief Information Officer, St. Mary Medical Center, Langhorne, PA, p. A542

BUELL, Jack, Director Information Services, Sutter Lakeside Hospital, Lakeport, CA, p. A69

BUENVENIDA, Brenda, Facility Administrator, Hiram W. Davis Medical Center, Petersburg, VA, p. A676

BUER, Shane, Vice President, Human Resources, Mercy Medical Center–Clinton, Clinton, IA, p. A227

BUFFINGTON, John, Chief Operating Officer, San Juan Regional Medical Center, Farmington, NM, p. A428

BUFFINGTON, Mike, Manager Information Technology, Kansas Medical Center, Andover, KS, p. A241

BUGG, Robert, Chief Financial Officer, Broward Health North, Deerfield Beach, FL, p. A127

BUGNA, Eric, M.D. Chief of Staff, Eastern Plumas Health Care, Portola, CA, p. A84

BUHEIS, Nidal, M.D. Chief of Staff, The Medical Center of Southeast Texas, Port Arthur, TX, p. A643

BUHL, Michael D., Senior Vice President and Chief Financial Officer, University of Wisconsin Hospital and Clinics, Madison, WI, p. A708

BUHLKE, Brian, M.D. Medical Director, Genoa Community Hospital, Genoa, NE, p. A396

BUI, Kim, Director Human Resources, East Valley Hospital Medical Center, Glendora, CA, p. A65

BUKOWSKI, Cathy
Chief Financial Officer, Howard Young Medical Center, Woodruff, WI, p. A719
Regional Chief Financial Officer, Ministry Eagle River Memorial Hospital, Eagle River, WI, p. A704
Regional Chief Financial Officer, Ministry Saint Mary's Hospitals, Rhinelander, WI, p. A714

BULAU, Chris, Manager Information Technology, Sibley Medical Center, Arlington, MN, p. A339

BULEN, Susan, M.D. Medical Director, HEALTHSOUTH Rehabilitation Hospital of Southern Arizona, Tucson, AZ, p. A40

BULFIN, Joey, R.N. Chief Operating Officer, St. Mary's Medical Center, West Palm Beach, FL, p. A150

BULLARD, Brandon
Chief Financial Officer, Bailey Medical Center, Owasso, OK, p. A517
Chief Financial Officer, Hillcrest Hospital Claremore, Claremore, OK, p. A509

BULLARD, Elizabeth, Chief Operating Officer, Northern Colorado Rehabilitation Hospital, Johnstown, CO, p. A108

BULLARD, John, Director Information Technology, St. Mary's Hospital and Regional Medical Center, Grand Junction, CO, p. A107

BULLARD, Patrick, Chief Financial Officer, Fayetteville Veterans Affairs Medical Center, Fayetteville, NC, p. A464

BULLARD, Timothy, M.D. Chief of Staff, Orlando Regional Medical Center, Orlando, FL, p. A141

BULLINGTON, Benjamin P., M.D. Chief of Staff, Pioneer Medical Center, Big Timber, MT, p. A385

BULLINGTON, Gina, Chief Nursing Officer, TriStar Horizon Medical Center, Dickson, TN, p. A582

BULLITT, Michael L., Chief Executive Officer, HEALTHSOUTH Rehabilitation Hospital–Wichita Falls, Wichita Falls, TX, p. A657

BULLOCK, David, Director Information Services, Northwest Medical Center, Tucson, AZ, p. A40

BULLOCK, Lance, M.D. Medical Director, St. James Behavioral Health Hospital, Gonzales, LA, p. A278

BULLOCK, Scott, Director Information Systems, Barstow Community Hospital, Barstow, CA, p. A58

BULMAN, Laurie, Director Human Resources, Winneshiek Medical Center, Decorah, IA, p. A229

BULMASH, Jack, M.D. Chief of Staff, Edward Hines, Jr. Veterans Affairs Hospital, Hines, IL, p. A192

BULTEMA, Janice K., MSN Senior Vice President Human Resources, University of Wisconsin Hospital and Clinics, Madison, WI, p. A708

BUMAN, Karen, Chief Nurse Executive, Myrtue Medical Center, Harlan, IA, p. A232

BUMANN, Tim, D.O. Chief of Staff, Abilene Regional Medical Center, Abilene, TX, p. A595

BUMATAY, Susan C., R.N. Assistant Administrator, Sutter Delta Medical Center, Antioch, CA, p. A56

BUMBAUGH, Christopher, Executive Human Resources, Meritus Medical Center, Hagerstown, MD, p. A301

BUMGARDNER, Chuck
Director Information Systems, Southeast Georgia Health System Brunswick Campus, Brunswick, GA, p. A155
Director, Southeast Georgia Health System Camden Campus, Saint Marys, GA, p. A166

BUMGARNER, William J., President, Spencer Hospital, Spencer, IA, p. A238

BUMP, Cathy, R.N. Chief Nursing Officer, Methodist Ambulatory Surgery Hospital – Northwest, San Antonio, TX, p. A646

BUNCH, David V., Chief Executive Officer, Heritage Medical Center, Shelbyville, TN, p. A593

BUNCH, Elicia, Chief Executive Officer, Centennial Peaks Hospital, Louisville, CO, p. A109

BUNCH, Jimm, President and Chief Executive Officer, Park Ridge Health, Hendersonville, NC, p. A466

BUNCH, Kim, Director Information Technology, Marshall Medical Center North, Guntersville, AL, p. A21

BUNCH, Mark, Director Finance, Othello Community Hospital, Othello, WA, p. A686

BUNCH, Mike, Executive Vice President, Chief Operating Officer and Chief Financial Officer, KershawHealth, Camden, SC, p. A562

BUNCH, Terri, R.N. Chief Nursing Officer, Hopkins County Memorial Hospital, Sulphur Springs, TX, p. A651

BUND, Linda, Chief Information Officer and Director Education, James J. Peters Veterans Affairs Medical Center, NY, p. A444

BUNGER, Mary, R.N. Director Nursing Services, Kearney County Health Services, Minden, NE, p. A398

BUNING, Paula Jean, Chief Nursing Officer, Marlboro Park Hospital, Bennettsville, SC, p. A562

BUNKER, Marla, Vice President Nursing and Chief Operating Officer, War Memorial Hospital, Sault Sainte Marie, MI, p. A334

BUNN, Barry, M.D. Chief of Staff, Vidant Edgecombe Hospital, Tarboro, NC, p. A473

BUNSELMEYER, Becky, Director Information Services, Memorial Hospital, Chester, IL, p. A183

BUNTEN, Sherry, Director Patient Care Services, Langlade Hospital, Antigo, WI, p. A701

BUNTING, Katherine, Chief Executive Officer, Fairfield Memorial Hospital, Fairfield, IL, p. A190

BUNTON, William Ralph, Supervisor Information Technology, Marshall Browning Hospital, Du Quoin, IL, p. A188

BUNTYN, Diane, MSN Vice President Patient Care Services, Southeast Alabama Medical Center, Dothan, AL, p. A19

BUNYARD, Steve
Chief Operating Officer, OhioHealth Dublin Methodist Hospital, Dublin, OH, p. A493
Chief Operating Officer, OhioHealth Grady Memorial Hospital, Delaware, OH, p. A492

BUONGIORNO, Michael J.
Executive Vice President Finance and Chief Financial Officer, Bryn Mawr Hospital, Bryn Mawr, PA, p. A534
Vice President Finance, Lankenau Medical Center, Wynnewood, PA, p. A559

BUPP, Steven, M.D. Medical Director, Sonora Behavioral Health Hospital, Tucson, AZ, p. A40

BURASCO, Carmen, Director Human Resources, Siloam Springs Regional Hospital, Siloam Springs, AR, p. A53

BURBANK, Jimmy, Chief Information Officer, U. S. Public Health Service Indian Hospital, Crownpoint, NM, p. A428

BURCH, Eric, Chief Executive Officer, Lewis County General Hospital, Lowville, NY, p. A440

BURCH, Larry, M.D. Vice President Medical Affairs, Saint Anthony's Health Center, Alton, IL, p. A180

BURCH, Lee, Director Management Information Systems, Bayfront Health Brooksville, Brooksville, FL, p. A125

BURCHAM Sr., Michael G., Chief Executive Officer, Thayer County Health Services, Hebron, NE, p. A396

BURCHELL, Pam, Director Human Resources, Lawnwood Regional Medical Center & Heart Institute, Fort Pierce, FL, p. A129

BURCHETT, Claudia L., R.N. Vice President Patient Services, Southern Ohio Medical Center, Portsmouth, OH, p. A501

BURCHETT, Travis, Troop Commander Human Resources, Colonel Florence A. Blanchfield Army Community Hospital, Fort Campbell, KY, p. A261

BURCHILL, Kevin, Chief Executive Officer, Arbour–Fuller Hospital, Attleboro, MA, p. A305

BURCZEUSKI, Jason
Controller, Arms Acres, Carmel, NY, p. A435
Controller, Conifer Park, Glenville, NY, p. A438

BURD, Vanessa, R.N. Chief Nursing Officer, Caverna Memorial Hospital, Horse Cave, KY, p. A263

BURDEN, Jennifer, Human Resources Director, Tristar Centennial Medical Center, Nashville, TN, p. A591

BURDICK, Ginny
Senior Vice President and Chief Human Resources Officer, Clovis Community Medical Center, Clovis, CA, p. A60
Vice President Human Resources, Community Behavioral Health Center, Fresno, CA, p. A64
Vice President Human Resources, Community Regional Medical Center, Fresno, CA, p. A64

BURDICK, Hoyt J., M.D. Vice President Medical Affairs, Cabell Huntington Hospital, Huntington, WV, p. A695

BURDICK, Steven A., Chief Executive Officer, Providence St. Mary Medical Center, Walla Walla, WA, p. A692

BURG, Andrew, M.D. Chief of Staff, St. Mary Medical Center, Long Beach, CA, p. A70

BURGER, Janice, Chief Executive, Providence St. Vincent Medical Center, Portland, OR, p. A528

BURGESS, Angela, Chief Information Officer, Randolph Hospital, Asheboro, NC, p. A459

BURGESS, Daniel, Chief Information Officer, MaineGeneral Medical Center, Augusta, ME, p. A291

BURGESS, John, Director Information Services, Hocking Valley Community Hospital, Logan, OH, p. A496

BURGESS, Robert L., President and Chief Executive Officer, St. Elizabeth Hospital, Gonzales, LA, p. A278

BURGESS, Steven, Administrator Human Resources, Henrico Doctors' Hospital, Richmond, VA, p. A677

BURGIN, Kelli, Director Information Technology, Audubon County Memorial Hospital, Audubon, IA, p. A225

BURGOS, Odette, Supervisor Human Resources, San Jorge Children's Hospital, San Juan, PR, p. A728

BURGUILLOS, Richard, Chief Financial Officer, Care One at Raritan Bay Medical Center, Perth Amboy, NJ, p. A421

BURGUS, Aurelis, Nursing Director, Ryder Memorial Hospital, Humacao, PR, p. A726

BURICK, Adam, M.D. Chief Medical Officer, Post Acute Northshore Specialty Hospital, Covington, LA, p. A276

BURICK, Marsha, Chief Financial Officer, Central Florida Behavioral Hospital, Orlando, FL, p. A140

BURINGRUD, Duane, M.D. Chief Medical and Quality Officer, Palomar Medical Center, Escondido, CA, p. A62

BURISH, Brent, Chief Executive Officer, St. Cloud Regional Medical Center, Saint Cloud, FL, p. A144

BURK, Rachelle S., R.N. Vice President Patient Care Services and Chief Nursing Officer, Sparrow Ionia Hospital, Ionia, MI, p. A327

BURK, Thomas J., Chief Operating Officer, Danville State Hospital, Danville, PA, p. A536

BURKE, Brian, M.D. President Medical Staff, Fairview Hospital, Great Barrington, MA, p. A310

BURKE, David, Administrator and Chief Executive Officer, Muleshoe Area Medical Center, Muleshoe, TX, p. A639

BURKE, David J., Director Finance and Chief Financial Officer, Nantucket Cottage Hospital, Nantucket, MA, p. A312

BURKE, Dennis E., President and Chief Executive Officer, Good Shepherd Health Care System, Hermiston, OR, p. A525

BURKE, Dorothy, Chief Financial Officer, Southeast Colorado Hospital District, Springfield, CO, p. A111

BURKE, Drew, Director Human Resources, Willamette Valley Medical Center, McMinnville, OR, p. A526

BURKE, Ed, Chief Financial Officer, Interim LSU Public Hospital, New Orleans, LA, p. A285

BURKE, Greg, M.D. Medical Director, Geisinger HEALTHSOUTH Rehabilitation Hospital, Danville, PA, p. A536

BURKE, Jack J., MS Chief Operating Officer and Chief Nursing Officer, Antelope Valley Hospital, Lancaster, CA, p. A69

BURKE, James, M.D
Senior Vice President and Chief Medical Officer, Scottsdale Healthcare Shea Medical Center, Scottsdale, AZ, p. A38
Senior Vice President and Chief Medical Officer, Scottsdale Healthcare Thompson Peak Hospital, Scottsdale, AZ, p. A38
Senior Vice President and Chief Medical Officer, Scottsdale Healthcare–Osborn Medical Center, Scottsdale, AZ, p. A38
BURKE, James B., Chief Operating Officer, Hahnemann University Hospital, Philadelphia, PA, p. A548
BURKE, Jeff, Chief Information Officer, Bon Secours–Richmond Community Hospital, Richmond, VA, p. A677
BURKE, Jo-Ann, R.N. Vice President Patient Care Services, Children's Hospital of The King's Daughters, Norfolk, VA, p. A675
BURKE, John, Chief Financial Officer, Nyack Hospital, Nyack, NY, p. A450
BURKE, Julie, Director Human Resources, New England Sinai Hospital and Rehabilitation Center, Stoughton, MA, p. A315
BURKE, Kaye, Administrator, Noland Hospital Dothan, Dothan, AL, p. A19
BURKE, Marsha
Senior Vice President Financial Services, WellStar Paulding Hospital, Dallas, GA, p. A157
Senior Vice President and Chief Financial Officer, WellStar Windy Hill Hospital, Marietta, GA, p. A163
BURKE, Michael, Senior Vice President and Corporate Chief Financial Officer, NYU Langone Medical Center, New York, NY, p. A448
BURKE, Paul, Administrator, Schleicher County Medical Center, Eldorado, TX, p. A617
BURKE, Rebecca, R.N. Senior Vice President and Chief Nursing Officer, Kent County Memorial Hospital, Warwick, RI, p. A561
BURKE, Rose, Associate Director Patient Care Services, Marion Veterans Affairs Medical Center, Marion, IL, p. A195
BURKE, Timothy, M.D. Medical Director, The Brook Hospital – KMI, Louisville, KY, p. A266
BURKE, Timothy R., M.D. Chief of Staff, Veterans Affairs Butler Healthcare, Butler, PA, p. A534
BURKEL, Gregory, Chief Financial Officer, Mitchell County Regional Health Center, Osage, IA, p. A236
BURKET, Mark, Chief Executive Officer, Platte Health Center Avera, Platte, SD, p. A575
BURKETT, Doug, Manager Information Technology, L. V. Stabler Memorial Hospital, Greenville, AL, p. A21
BURKETT, Eric, M.D. Vice President Medical Affairs, Monmouth Medical Center, Long Branch Campus, Long Branch, NJ, p. A418
BURKETT, Evan, Chief Human Resource Officer, Sanford USD Medical Center, Sioux Falls, SD, p. A576
BURKEY, Brent, M.D. Chief Medical Officer, Fairview Hospital, Cleveland, OH, p. A488
BURKEY, Kathleen, R.N. Vice President of Nursing, Grand View Hospital, Sellersville, PA, p. A554
BURKHARDT, Raye, Chief Nursing Officer, St. John's Pleasant Valley Hospital, Camarillo, CA, p. A58
BURKHART, Brad, Assistant Administrator, Harlan ARH Hospital, Harlan, KY, p. A262
BURKHART, James R., FACHE, President and Chief Executive Officer, Tampa General Hospital, Tampa, FL, p. A148
BURKHART, Steven, M.D. Chief Medical Officer, Crittenden County Hospital, Marion, KY, p. A267
BURKHART, Tracy, Vice President Information Services, Sacred Heart Hospital, Allentown, PA, p. A532
BURKHOLDER, Adrienne, Director Human Resources, AMG Specialty Hospital–Wichita, Wichita, KS, p. A256
BURKHOLDER-MCNUTT, Kim, Chief Executive Officer, Advanced Specialty Hospital of Toledo, Toledo, OH, p. A503
BURKITT, David, Director Fiscal Services, Shriners Hospitals for Children–Los Angeles, Los Angeles, CA, p. A74
BURKLOW, Bryan, Chief Executive Officer, Brandywine Hospital, Coatesville, PA, p. A536
BURKS, Felicia, Chief Financial Officer, U. S. Air Force Regional Hospital, Elmendorf AFB, AK, p. A28
BURKS, Matt, Director Information Technology, United Regional Medical Center, Manchester, TN, p. A587
BURKS, Mel, Chief Executive Officer, Hamilton Center, Terre Haute, IN, p. A223
BURKS, Tami
Chief Fiscal Services, Iraan General Hospital, Iraan, TX, p. A629
Comptroller, Rankin Hospital District, Rankin, TX, p. A643
BURLESON, Linda, Administrative Secretary, Clay County Memorial Hospital, Henrietta, TX, p. A623
BURLESON, Stan, M.D. Chief Medical Staff, DeWitt Hospital, De Witt, AR, p. A45
BURLING, Chris, M.D. Chief of Staff, Titus Regional Medical Center, Mount Pleasant, TX, p. A638

BURMEISTER, Brian
Senior Vice President, Appleton Medical Center, Appleton, WI, p. A701
Senior Vice President, Theda Clark Medical Center, Neenah, WI, p. A711
BURMEISTER, Geraldine F., FACHE, Chief Executive Officer, Windom Area Hospital, Windom, MN, p. A354
BURMESTER, Mark A., Vice President Strategy and Communications, Kaiser Permanente Sunnyside Medical Center, Clackamas, OR, p. A523
BURNAM, Gregg, Chief Information Officer and Manager Business Office, Quartz Mountain Medical Center, Mangum, OK, p. A513
BURNELL, Lori, R.N. Senior Vice President and Chief Nursing Officer, Valley Presbyterian Hospital, CA, p. A75
BURNES BOLTON, Linda, R.N. Vice President and Chief Nursing Officer, Cedars–Sinai Medical Center, Los Angeles, CA, p. A71
BURNETT, Anthony, M.D. Medical Director, Julian F. Keith Alcohol and Drug Abuse Treatment Center, Black Mountain, NC, p. A460
BURNETT, Brad, Chief Financial Officer, Heart of Texas Memorial Hospital, Brady, TX, p. A603
BURNETT, Cindi, Chief Human Resources Officer, Madison County Memorial Hospital, Madison, FL, p. A135
BURNETT, Mark, President and Chief Executive Officer, Scott County Hospital, Scott City, KS, p. A254
BURNETT, Michael, Chief Operating Officer, Piedmont Fayette Hospital, Fayetteville, GA, p. A159
BURNETT, Rob, Director Human Resources, Pioneer Valley Hospital, West Valley City, UT, p. A664
BURNETT, Tasha, Director of Nursing, Falls Community Hospital and Clinic, Marlin, TX, p. A636
BURNETTE, Linda, R.N., Interim Chief Executive Officer, Southern Virginia Regional Medical Center, Emporia, VA, p. A670
BURNETTE, Peg, Chief Financial Officer, Denver Health, Denver, CO, p. A104
BURNETTE, Sheri, R.N., Chief Executive Officer and Administrator, Cornerstone Hospital of Bossier City, Bossier City, LA, p. A274
BURNETTE, W. Scott, President and Chief Executive Officer, VCU Community Memorial Hospital, South Hill, VA, p. A678
BURNEY, Sibte, M.D. Senior Vice President Medical Affairs and Chief Medical Officer, Kingsbrook Jewish Medical Center, NY, p. A445
BURNHAM, Sharon, Director of Nursing, Simpson General Hospital, Mendenhall, MS, p. A362
BURNS, Barry, Vice President, Methodist Ambulatory Surgery Hospital – Northwest, San Antonio, TX, p. A646
BURNS, Becky L., Manager Health Information Management, Ellinwood District Hospital, Ellinwood, KS, p. A243
BURNS, Bruce R., Chief Financial Officer, Concord Hospital, Concord, NH, p. A409
BURNS, Christal, R.N. Chief Nursing Officer, Care Regional Medical Center, Aransas Pass, TX, p. A597
BURNS, Coreg, Human Resources Lead, West Central Georgia Regional Hospital, Columbus, GA, p. A156
BURNS, Gregory T., President and Chief Executive Officer, Cameron Memorial Community Hospital, Angola, IN, p. A206
BURNS, Helen K., Ph.D
Senior Vice President and Chief Nursing Officer, Excela Frick Hospital, Mount Pleasant, PA, p. A546
Senior Vice President and Chief Nursing Officer, Excela Health Westmoreland Hospital, Greensburg, PA, p. A539
Senior Vice President and Chief Nursing Officer, Excela Latrobe Area Hospital, Latrobe, PA, p. A542
BURNS, Helene M., MSN Chief Nursing Executive, Kennedy Health System, Cherry Hill, NJ, p. A414
BURNS, Jared, Coordinator Human Resources, Regency Hospital of Hattiesburg, Hattiesburg, MS, p. A359
BURNS, Jeff, Manager of Information Technology, Mary Free Bed Rehabilitation Hospital, Grand Rapids, MI, p. A325
BURNS, Jon P.
Chief Information Officer, University of Maryland Medical Center, Baltimore, MD, p. A298
Senior Vice President and Chief Information Officer, University of Maryland Medical Center Midtown Campus, Baltimore, MD, p. A298
BURNS, Katherine, Vice President Human Resources, High Point Regional Health System, High Point, NC, p. A466
BURNS, Kathryn I., R.N. Director of Nursing, Medicine Lodge Memorial Hospital, Medicine Lodge, KS, p. A250
BURNS, Jr., Larry P., Chief Operating Officer, Yavapai Regional Medical Center, Prescott, AZ, p. A37
BURNS, Margaret, R.N. Vice President Patient Services and Chief Nursing Officer, Valley Regional Hospital, Claremont, NH, p. A409
BURNS, Melissa, Chief Nursing Officer, Inland Valley Medical Center, Southwest Healthcare System, Murrieta, CA, p. A79

BURNS, Patrick, Vice President Finance, ACMH Hospital, Kittanning, PA, p. A542
BURNS, Rhonda, Director Human Resources, Caldwell Medical Center, Princeton, KY, p. A269
BURNS, Sonda, Chief Executive Officer, Select Specialty Hospital–Akron, Akron, OH, p. A482
BURNS, Steven, Director Fiscal Services, Summit Behavioral Healthcare, Cincinnati, OH, p. A487
BURNS, Terry M.
President, Greene Memorial Hospital, Xenia, OH, p. A506
President, Soin Medical Center, Beavercreek, OH, p. A483
BURNS, Tom, M.D. Chief of Staff, The Hospital at Westlake Medical Center, Austin, TX, p. A600
BURNS–TISDALE, Susan, Senior Vice President Clinical Operations, Interim CNO, Exeter Hospital, Exeter, NH, p. A410
BURNSIDE, Brian D., FACHE, Chief Executive Officer, Connally Memorial Medical Center, Floresville, TX, p. A617
BURPEE, Scott, President, Safe Haven Health Care, Pocatello, ID, p. B116
BURRAGE, Chris, Manager Information Technology, Coalinga Regional Medical Center, Coalinga, CA, p. A60
BURRELL, Carol H., President and Chief Executive Officer, Northeast Georgia Medical Center, Gainesville, GA, p. A160
BURRESS, Lori, Chief Nursing Officer, Mt. Graham Regional Medical Center, Safford, AZ, p. A38
BURRIS, Bradley D., Chief Executive Officer, Pipestone County Medical Center Avera, Pipestone, MN, p. A349
BURRIS, Don, Chief Executive Officer, Haxtun Hospital District, Haxtun, CO, p. A107
BURRIS, J. Michael
Vice President Corporate Services and Chief Financial Officer, Martha Jefferson Hospital, Charlottesville, VA, p. A669
Chief Financial Officer, Sentara RMH Medical Center, Harrisonburg, VA, p. A672
BURRIS, Lisa
Manager Human Resources, Frazier Rehab Institute, Louisville, KY, p. A265
Director Human Resources, Southern Indiana Rehabilitation Hospital, New Albany, IN, p. A220
BURRISS, Jessica, Chief Financial Officer, HEALTHSOUTH Rehabilitation Hospital of Columbia, Columbia, SC, p. A564
BURRISS, Steve W., Chief Operating Officer, Rex Healthcare, Raleigh, NC, p. A471
BURRISS, Tracie, Chief Financial Officer, Wills Memorial Hospital, Washington, GA, p. A169
BURROUGHS, James, Chief Executive Officer, Kingwood Pines Hospital, Kingwood, TX, p. A631
BURROUGHS, Michael R., FACHE, Chief Executive Officer, Western Plains Medical Complex, Dodge City, KS, p. A243
BURROUGHS, Steven, Chief Financial Officer, Palms West Hospital, Loxahatchee, FL, p. A134
BURROUGHS, Valentine, M.D. Chief Medical Officer, East Orange General Hospital, East Orange, NJ, p. A415
BURROW, Debbie, R.N. Chief Nursing Officer, Saline Memorial Hospital, Benton, AR, p. A43
BURRUS, Gary, Director Information Technology, Winner Regional Healthcare Center, Winner, SD, p. A578
BURT, Alan, Director Information Services, Sunrise Hospital and Medical Center, Las Vegas, NV, p. A407
BURT, Gregory, M.D. Chief of Staff, Colusa Regional Medical Center, Colusa, CA, p. A60
BURT, Keith, Director Marketing, Woodrow Wilson Rehabilitation Center, Fishersville, VA, p. A671
BURT, Linda K.
Corporate Vice President Finance, Methodist Jennie Edmundson Hospital, Council Bluffs, IA, p. A228
Corporate Vice President Finance, Nebraska Methodist Hospital, Omaha, NE, p. A400
BURT, Noel F., Ph.D. Chief Human Resources Officer, Moses H. Cone Memorial Hospital, Greensboro, NC, p. A465
BURT, Timothy, Executive Vice President and Chief Financial Officer, Bellevue Hospital, Bellevue, OH, p. A484
BURT, Wilton M., Chief Executive Officer, Vibrant Healthcare, Dallas, TX, p. B149
BURTCH, Gloria, Director Human Resources, Cornerstone of Medical Arts Center Hospital, Fresh Meadows, NY, p. A437
BURTHAY, Darcy, MSN Chief Nursing Officer and Chief Operating Officer, St. Vincent Indianapolis Hospital, Indianapolis, IN, p. A215
BURTON, Carmella, Chief Nursing Officer, AnMed Health Rehabilitation Hospital, Anderson, SC, p. A562
BURTON, Charles, Chief Human Resources, Carl R. Darnall Army Medical Center, Fort Hood, TX, p. A617
BURTON, Cynthia, R.N. Chief Nursing Officer, Rockcastle Regional Hospital and Respiratory Care Center, Mount Vernon, KY, p. A268
BURTON, Faye, Director Health Information Management, Edgefield County Hospital, Edgefield, SC, p. A565

C

CABRAL, Joseph, Chief Human Resources Officer, Cleveland Clinic, Cleveland, OH, p. A488

CABRERA, Carlos, Executive Director, Industrial Hospital, San Juan, PR, p. A728

CABRERA, Daniel, Chief Nursing Officer, Doctors Hospital of Laredo, Laredo, TX, p. A632

CABRERA, Irma, Finance Director, Hospital San Carlos Borromeo, Moca, PR, p. A727

CACCIAMANI, John D., M.D., Chief Executive Officer, Chestnut Hill Hospital, Philadelphia, PA, p. A547

CACERES, Janet L., Chief Financial Officer, Paradise Valley Hospital, National City, CA, p. A79

CADE, Paul, Administrator and Chief Executive Officer, Baptist Memorial Hospital–Golden Triangle, Columbus, MS, p. A357

CADIGAN, Elizabeth, R.N. Senior Vice President Patient Care Services and Chief Nursing Officer, Cambridge Health Alliance, Cambridge, MA, p. A309

CADOGAN, David, Chief Medical Officer, Alaska Regional Hospital, Anchorage, AK, p. A28

CADWELL, Carrie, M.D. Chief Clinical Officer, Four County Counseling Center, Logansport, IN, p. A217

CADWELL, Maureen K., Chief Executive Officer, Weston County Health Services, Newcastle, WY, p. A722

CADY, Kathy, Coordinator Human Resources, Accounts Payable and Payroll, Safe Haven Hospital of Treasure Valley, Boise, ID, p. A174

CADY, Thomas, Vice President Human Resources, Heywood Hospital, Gardner, MA, p. A310

CADY, Tina, Controller, The Women's Hospital, Newburgh, IN, p. A220

CAFASSO, Michael, Vice President Operations, St. Mary–Corwin Medical Center, Pueblo, CO, p. A110

CAGEN, Richard M., President and Chief Executive Officer, Silverton Hospital, Silverton, OR, p. A530

CAGGIANO, Richard, M.D. Chief Medical Officer, Pullman Regional Hospital, Pullman, WA, p. A687

CAGLE, Jennifer, Director of Nursing, Marion Regional Medical Center, Hamilton, AL, p. A21

CAGLE, Karen, Chief Nursing Officer, Select Specialty Hospital–Nashville, Nashville, TN, p. A591

CAGNA, Ralph A.
Director Information Technology Operations, Cleveland Clinic Health System South Market, Marymount Hospital, Garfield Heights, OH, p. A494
Director Information Technology, South Pointe Hospital, Warrensville Heights, OH, p. A504

CAHALAN, Jay P., Chief Executive Officer, Columbia Memorial Hospital, Hudson, NY, p. A439

CAHILL, Donna, Vice President Human Resources, Palisades Medical Center, North Bergen, NJ, p. A420

CAHILL, Joseph, Executive Vice President and Chief Operating Officer, South Shore Hospital, South Weymouth, MA, p. A314

CAHILL, Marty, Chief Executive Officer, Samaritan North Lincoln Hospital, Lincoln City, OR, p. A526

CAHO–MOONEY, Linda, Chief Financial Officer, Claiborne County Medical Center, Port Gibson, MS, p. A364

CAHOJ, Lindsey, Chief Nursing Officer, Select Specialty Hospital–Wichita, Wichita, KS, p. A256

CAIN, Amy, District Director Human Resources, Kindred Hospital South Philadelphia, Philadelphia, PA, p. A549

CAIN, Donna, Director Information Systems Department, Cypress Fairbanks Medical Center, Houston, TX, p. A624

CAIN, Heather L., Chief Executive Officer, Stewart Memorial Community Hospital, Lake City, IA, p. A233

CAIN, Julie, Administrator, Stone County Hospital, Wiggins, MS, p. A366

CAIN, Mark, Chief Executive Officer, Tennova Healthcare–LaFollette Medical Center, La Follette, TN, p. A586

CAIN, Roxie, Chief Financial Officer, Big Horn County Memorial Hospital, Hardin, MT, p. A388

CAIN, William, Controller, Clearfield Hospital, Clearfield, PA, p. A536

CAINE, Claudia, President and Chief Operating Officer, Lutheran Medical Center, NY, p. A445

CAIRNS, Craig, M.D. Vice President Medical Affairs, Licking Memorial Hospital, Newark, OH, p. A499

CAISIP, Tess, Coordinator of Nursing Services, Lanterman Developmental Center, Pomona, CA, p. A84

CALABRESE, Joan L., Director Human Resources, Putnam Hospital Center, Carmel, NY, p. A435

CALABRESE, Steve, Executive Vice President and Chief Financial Officer, Sierra Vista Regional Health Center, Sierra Vista, AZ, p. A39

CALAIS, C. Matthew, Senior Vice President and Chief Information Officer, Legacy Good Samaritan Hospital and Medical Center, Portland, OR, p. A528

CALAMARI, Frank A., President and Chief Executive Officer, Calvary Hospital, NY, p. A443

CALAMARI, Jacquelyn, MSN Vice President and Chief Nursing Officer, Middlesex Hospital, Middletown, CT, p. A115

CALAME, Norma, Director Human Resources, Mount Sinai Queens, NY, p. A446

CALAMIA, Kenneth, Chair and Chief Executive Officer, Mayo Clinic Health System in Waycross, Waycross, GA, p. A169

CALANDRELLA, Paul, Chief Operating Officer, Mt. Ascutney Hospital and Health Center, Windsor, VT, p. A667

CALANDRIELLO, John, Vice President and Chief Financial Officer, Palisades Medical Center, North Bergen, NJ, p. A420

CALAWAY, Shearmaine, Director Human Resources, East Mississippi State Hospital, Meridian, MS, p. A362

CALBONE, Angelo G., President and Chief Executive Officer, Saratoga Hospital, Saratoga Springs, NY, p. A454

CALBY, Elizabeth, Vice President Human Resources, Advocate Good Samaritan Hospital, Downers Grove, IL, p. A188

CALDARI, Patricia, Vice President, Richmond University Medical Center, NY, p. A448

CALDAS, James, President, Putnam Hospital Center, Carmel, NY, p. A435

CALDAS, Robert, D.O. Chief Medical Officer, Southcoast Hospitals Group, Fall River, MA, p. A310

CALDEIRA, Amy, Director Information Technology and Systems, Fort Walton Beach Medical Center, Fort Walton Beach, FL, p. A129

CALDERA, Ken, Director Human Resources, Kessler Institute for Rehabilitation, West Orange, NJ, p. A424

CALDERON, Lizmari, Director Finance, Hospital De La Concepcion, San German, PR, p. A727

CALDERONE, John A., Ph.D., Chief Executive Officer, Olympia Medical Center, Los Angeles, CA, p. A73

CALDWELL, Bettie, Director Finance, Indiana University Health Blackford Hospital, Hartford City, IN, p. A213

CALDWELL, Carolyn W., Chief Executive Officer, Desert Regional Medical Center, Palm Springs, CA, p. A82

CALDWELL, Dari, FACHE, President, Novant Health Rowan Medical Center, Salisbury, NC, p. A472

CALDWELL, Darren
Chief Executive Officer, Delta Memorial Hospital, Dumas, AR, p. A45
Chief Executive Officer, DeWitt Hospital, De Witt, AR, p. A45

CALDWELL, Eric, Director Finance, Northside Hospital–Forsyth, Cumming, GA, p. A157

CALDWELL, James, R.N. Chief Nursing Officer, Henry County Medical Center, Paris, TN, p. A592

CALDWELL, Janice, Director Human Resources, Oak Tree Hospital, Corbin, KY, p. A260

CALDWELL, Matthew T., Chief Executive Officer, University Medical Center, Lebanon, TN, p. A586

CALDWELL, Paul, Facility Coordinator Information Technology Customer Relations, Page Hospital, Page, AZ, p. A35

CALDWELL, Steve, Vice President Finance and Chief Financial Officer, St. Mary's Hospital, Madison, WI, p. A708

CALDWELL Jr., William E., Chief Executive Officer, Wilson Medical Center, Wilson, NC, p. A475

CALEY, Carl, Chief Financial Officer, Spring Valley Hospital Medical Center, Las Vegas, NV, p. A406

CALHOUN, Cathy, Director Human Resources, River Point Behavioral Health, Jacksonville, FL, p. A132

CALHOUN, Joshua, M.D. Medical Director, Hawthorn Children Psychiatric Hospital, Saint Louis, MO, p. A380

CALHOUN, Kevin P., Chief Executive Officer, Munising Memorial Hospital, Munising, MI, p. A331

CALHOUN, Kirk A., M.D., President, University of Texas Health Science Center at Tyler, Tyler, TX, p. A654

CALHOUN, Robert, Chief Executive Officer, Greenbrier Valley Medical Center, Ronceverte, WV, p. A699

CALHOUN, Timothy, Vice President Finance and Chief Financial Officer, Lakeland Regional Medical Center–St. Joseph, Saint Joseph, MI, p. A334

CALHOUN, William, President, Mercy Medical Center, Oshkosh, WI, p. A713

CALIA, Christopher, Director Human Resources, Brazosport Regional Health System, Lake Jackson, TX, p. A632

CALIFORNIA, Randy, Interim Chief Executive Officer, Warren General Hospital, Warren, PA, p. A557

CALIGIURI, Michael, Chief Executive Officer, James Cancer Hospital and Solove Research Institute, Columbus, OH, p. A489

CALIVA, Todd, Chief Executive Officer, West Houston Medical Center, Houston, TX, p. A628

CALKIN, Steven, D.O. Vice President Medical Affairs, McLaren Oakland, Pontiac, MI, p. A332

CALKINS, Paul, M.D. Chief Medical Officer, Indiana University Health North Hospital, Carmel, IN, p. A208

CALL, Brett, D.O. Chief of Staff, Berger Health System, Circleville, OH, p. A488

CALL, Carie, Computer Support, Cassia Regional Medical Center, Burley, ID, p. A175

CALL, Dave, M.D. Medical Director, Select Long Term Care Hospital – Colorado Springs, Colorado Springs, CO, p. A104

CALL, Stacie, R.N. Vice President Patient Care and Chief Nursing Officer, East Liverpool City Hospital, East Liverpool, OH, p. A493

CALLAGHAN, Barbara, Chief Executive Officer, Kindred Hospital–New Jersey Morris County, Dover, NJ, p. A415

CALLAGHAN III, James, M.D., President, Franciscan St. Anthony Health – Michigan City, Michigan City, IN, p. A218

CALLAHAN, Ame, Acting Manager Resource Management Service, Northern Arizona Veterans Affairs Health Care System, Prescott, AZ, p. A37

CALLAHAN, Charles D., Ph.D. Executive Vice President and Chief Operating Officer, Memorial Medical Center, Springfield, IL, p. A203

CALLAHAN, Christopher M., Vice President Human Resources, Exeter Hospital, Exeter, NH, p. A410

CALLAHAN, Deanna, Director Information Systems, Titusville Area Hospital, Titusville, PA, p. A556

CALLAHAN, Jean, Manager Human Resources, Thousand Oaks Surgical Hospital, Thousand Oaks, CA, p. A97

CALLAHAN, Kelly, Public Information Officer, Elgin Mental Health Center, Elgin, IL, p. A189

CALLAHAN, Kevin J., President and Chief Executive Officer, Exeter Hospital, Exeter, NH, p. A410

CALLAHAN, Larry A., Senior Vice President Human Resources, Grady Memorial Hospital, Atlanta, GA, p. A152

CALLAHAN, Mark, Chief Operating Officer, Mary Lanning Healthcare, Hastings, NE, p. A396

CALLAHAN, Mary Beth, Chief Financial Officer, McLaren Lapeer Region, Lapeer, MI, p. A329

CALLAHAN, Neil, Chief Executive Officer, Brooke Glen Behavioral Hospital, Fort Washington, PA, p. A539

CALLAHAN Jr., Robert W., Director, Lebanon Veterans Affairs Medical Center, Lebanon, PA, p. A542

CALLAHAN, Teresa, MSN, Chief Executive Officer, Iraan General Hospital, Iraan, TX, p. A629

CALLAHAN, William, Chief Information Management Division, Bayne–Jones Army Community Hospital, Fort Polk, LA, p. A277

CALLAIS, Ronnie, Chief Financial Officer, MMO WestEnd Hospital, Jennings, LA, p. A279

CALLAN, C. M., M.D. Chief of Staff, Fisher County Hospital District, Rotan, TX, p. A644

CALLANAN, Patrick, Vice President Patient Care Services, Mercy Hospital Fort Scott, Fort Scott, KS, p. A244

CALLAS, Robin B., R.N. Vice President Human Resources, Rutherford Regional Health System, Rutherfordton, NC, p. A472

CALLAWAY, Blair, Chief Financial Officer, Texas Orthopedic Hospital, Houston, TX, p. A627

CALLECOD, David L., FACHE, President and CEO, Lafayette General Health, Lafayette, LA, p. B82

CALLENS, Don, M.D. Chief Medical Officer, Liberty Dayton Regional Medical Center, Liberty, TX, p. A633

CALLENS, Paul A., Ph.D., Director, North Mississippi State Hospital, Tupelo, MS, p. A365

CALLICOAT, William, Chief Financial Officer, Summit Pacific Medical Center, Elma, WA, p. A683

CALLISTER, T. Brian, M.D. Chief Medical Officer, Tahoe Pacific Hospitals, Reno, NV, p. A408

CALLOWAY, Jennifer, Human Resources Coordinator, Asheville Specialty Hospital, Asheville, NC, p. A459

CALLOWAY, Maria, R.N. Chief Nursing Officer, Central Florida Regional Hospital, Sanford, FL, p. A145

CALMAN, Kurt, Chief Information Officer, United Memorial Medical Center, Batavia, NY, p. A433

CALMET, Erick, M.D. Chief of Staff, Mineral Area Regional Medical Center, Farmington, MO, p. A371

CALUBAQUIB, Evelyn, Chief Nursing Officer, Greater El Monte Community Hospital, South El Monte, CA, p. A96

CALVARUSO, Gaspare, President, Capital Region Medical Center, Jefferson City, MO, p. A372

CALVERT, Heather, Director Human Resources, Carroll County Memorial Hospital, Carrollton, MO, p. A369

CALVERT, Mandy, Director Information Systems, Southern Coos Hospital and Health Center, Bandon, OR, p. A523

CALVERT, Regina, Chief Nursing Executive, Shelby Memorial Hospital, Shelbyville, IL, p. A202

CALVERT, Sarah, Chief Nursing Officer, McGehee–Desha County Hospital, McGehee, AR, p. A50

CALVIN, Jeff, Chief Financial Officer, Michiana Behavioral Health Center, Plymouth, IN, p. A221

CALVIN, Jr., Travis, M.D. Chief of Staff, Pioneers Memorial Healthcare District, Brawley, CA, p. A58

CAMA, Joseph, M.D. President Medical Staff, Memorial Hospital, Towanda, PA, p. A556

CAMARA, Robert, D.O. Chief Medical Officer, St. Joseph Mercy Port Huron, Port Huron, MI, p. A333

CAMARDELLO, Heidi, Vice President Patient Care Services and Chief Nursing Officer, Little Falls Hospital, Little Falls, NY, p. A440

CAMERON, Carl, Director Information Systems, Holyoke Medical Center, Holyoke, MA, p. A311

CAMERON, Don, Chief Operating Officer, Allegiance Behavioral Health Center of Plainview, Plainview, TX, p. A642

CAMERON, Kim, Manager Health Information Services, Patients' Hospital of Redding, Redding, CA, p. A85

CAMERON, Lana, Chief Nursing Officer, Central Texas Medical Center, San Marcos, TX, p. A648

CAMIRE, Patricia M., MS Senior Vice President Clinical Services and Chief Nursing Officer, Southern Maine Health Care – Biddeford Medical Center X, Biddeford, ME, p. A292

CAMMACK, Geri, R.N. Director of Nursing, Lost Rivers Medical Center, Arco, ID, p. A174

CAMMACK Jr., Thomas N., Chief Administrative Officer, Mother Frances Hospital – Jacksonville, Jacksonville, TX, p. A630

CAMMENGA, Randall, M.D. Vice President Medical Affairs, Indiana University Health Goshen Hospital, Goshen, IN, p. A212

CAMP III, Claude E., Chief Executive Officer, Brownwood Regional Medical Center, Brownwood, TX, p. A604

CAMP, David, Director Human Resources, Nor–Lea General Hospital, Lovington, NM, p. A429

CAMP, James, R.N., Regional Chief Executive Officer, Houston Market, Cornerstone Hospital of Houston at Clearlake, Webster, TX, p. A656

CAMP, Julie A., R.N., Chief Executive Officer, Forest Park Medical Center Frisco, Frisco, TX, p. A620

CAMP, Lea Ann, MSN Chief Nursing Officer, Greene County General Hospital, Linton, IN, p. A217

CAMPA, Melissa, Controller, Kindred Hospital El Paso, El Paso, TX, p. A616

CAMPAGNA, Paul, M.D. President Medical Staff, Good Shepherd Health Care System, Hermiston, OR, p. A525

CAMPANA, Thomas, M.D. Chief of Staff, Spectrum Health Reed City Hospital, Reed City, MI, p. A333

CAMPANELLA, Alfred
Vice President and Chief Information Officer, Virtua Berlin, Berlin, NJ, p. A413
Chief Information Officer, Virtua Voorhees, Voorhees, NJ, p. A424

CAMPAS, Janice, Chief Financial Officer, Wichita County Health Center, Leoti, KS, p. A248

CAMPBELL, Amy
Chief Financial Officer, Community Heart and Vascular Hospital, Indianapolis, IN, p. A213
Chief Financial Officer, Community Hospital North, Indianapolis, IN, p. A213

CAMPBELL, April, Director Human Resources, Broadwater Health Center, Townsend, MT, p. A391

CAMPBELL, Belinda H., Director Human Resources, Legal Compliance and Risk Management, University Hospital McDuffie, Thomson, GA, p. A168

CAMPBELL, Bernard M., Administrator Human Resources, LewisGale Hospital Alleghany, Low Moor, VA, p. A673

CAMPBELL, Brian, Director Professional Services, U. S. Public Health Service Indian Hospital–Whiteriver, Whiteriver, AZ, p. A41

CAMPBELL, C. Scott, Market Chief Executive Officer, Physicians Regional – Pine Ridge, Naples, FL, p. A139

CAMPBELL, Carla, R.N. Chief Nurse Officer, Mercy Hospital and Medical Center, Chicago, IL, p. A185

CAMPBELL, Chad, Chief Executive Officer, McKenzie–Willamette Medical Center, Springfield, OR, p. A530

CAMPBELL, Christopher, M.D. Chief of Staff, Ashe Memorial Hospital, Jefferson, NC, p. A467

CAMPBELL, Darrell, M.D. Chief Clinical Affairs, University of Michigan Hospitals and Health Centers, Ann Arbor, MI, p. A318

CAMPBELL, David, Administrator, Perry Hospital, Perry, GA, p. A164

CAMPBELL, David J., Executive Vice President Operations Systems Strategy and Growth, Oakwood Hospital–Southshore, Trenton, MI, p. A336

CAMPBELL, Dean, Vice President Information Services and Chief Information Officer, Good Samaritan Hospital, Los Angeles, CA, p. A72

CAMPBELL, Deborah, Administrator, Thomas H. Boyd Memorial Hospital, Carrollton, IL, p. A182

CAMPBELL, Debra, R.N., Administrator, Riverside Behavioral Health Center, Hampton, VA, p. A672

CAMPBELL, Emily, Director Human Resources, Alice Hyde Medical Center, Malone, NY, p. A440

CAMPBELL, Eric, Chief Financial Officer, Oswego Hospital, Oswego, NY, p. A451

CAMPBELL, Fritz, Director Information Systems, Olympia Medical Center, Los Angeles, CA, p. A73

CAMPBELL, Gina, Chief Operating Officer, Baystate Franklin Medical Center, Greenfield, MA, p. A310

CAMPBELL, Ivy, Director of Nursing, Community Medical Center, Falls City, NE, p. A395

CAMPBELL, John
Director Management Information Systems, Spaulding Rehabilitation Hospital, Charlestown, MA, p. A309
Chief Information Officer, Spaulding Rehabilitation Hospital Cape Cod, East Sandwich, MA, p. A309

CAMPBELL, Kathy, Interim Chief Nursing Officer, Wellmont Holston Valley Medical Center, Kingsport, TN, p. A585

CAMPBELL, Kyle D., Commander, San Antonio Military Medical Center, Fort Sam Houston, TX, p. A617

CAMPBELL, Melissa, Controller, Mercy Rehabilitation Hospital Springfield, Springfield, MO, p. A383

CAMPBELL, Melvin, M.D. Medical Staff Chairman, Brown County Hospital, Ainsworth, NE, p. A393

CAMPBELL, Pamela, M.D. Medical Director, Lincoln Prairie Behavioral Health Center, Springfield, IL, p. A203

CAMPBELL Jr., Robert D.
Chief Executive, Providence Mount Carmel Hospital, Colville, WA, p. A682
Chief Executive, Providence St. Joseph's Hospital, Chewelah, WA, p. A682

CAMPBELL, Rose, R.N., President, Elk Regional Health Center, Saint Marys, PA, p. A554

CAMPBELL, Sandra M., R.N. Chief Nursing Officer, Dodge County Hospital, Eastman, GA, p. A159

CAMPBELL, Stephen J., Chief Operating Officer, Pioneers Memorial Healthcare District, Brawley, CA, p. A58

CAMPBELL, Susie, Chief Executive Officer, Community Memorial Hospital, Staunton, IL, p. A203

CAMPBELL, Teresa, R.N. Chief Nursing Executive, Sutter Lakeside Hospital, Lakeport, CA, p. A69

CAMPBELL, Todd, Senior Vice President and Chief Operating Officer, St. Mary's Medical Center, Huntington, WV, p. A696

CAMPEAU, Arleen, R.N. Vice President of Patient Care Services, Chief Nursing Officer, Powell Valley Healthcare, Powell, WY, p. A722

CAMPION, John, Administrator, Essentia Health–Holy Trinity Hospital, Graceville, MN, p. A344

CAMPO, Mary Beth, MS Director of Nursing, Eastern Niagara Hospital, Lockport, NY, p. A440

CAMPOS, Christina, Administrator, Guadalupe County Hospital, Santa Rosa, NM, p. A430

CAMPOS–DIAZ, Evelyn, Director Human Resources, MedStar St. Mary's Hospital, Leonardtown, MD, p. A302

CAMPS, Lourdes, R.N. Chief Nursing Officer, Hialeah Hospital, Hialeah, FL, p. A130

CANADY, Carolyn, Chief Financial Officer, Sierra Nevada Memorial Hospital, Grass Valley, CA, p. A66

CANADY, Ray R., Chief Executive Officer and Administrator, Knox County Hospital, Barbourville, KY, p. A258

CANALE, Joseph, Business Manager, Trenton Psychiatric Hospital, Trenton, NJ, p. A424

CANALEJO, Donald, Director Human Resources, Lower Keys Medical Center, Key West, FL, p. A133

CANALES, Joe, Director Human Resources, Seton Edgar B. Davis Hospital, Luling, TX, p. A636

CANARIOS, Mike, Vice President and Chief Financial Officer, St. Jude Children's Research Hospital, Memphis, TN, p. A589

CANAVAN, Patrick J., PsyD, Chief Executive Officer, St. Elizabeths Hospital, Washington, DC, p. A122

CANCILLA, Deborah, Chief Information Officer, Grady Memorial Hospital, Atlanta, GA, p. A152

CANDIA, Gary R., FACHE, Chief Executive Officer, Abington Health Lansdale Hospital, Lansdale, PA, p. A542

CANDILL, James W., M.D. President Medical Staff, Eye and Ear Clinic of Charleston, Charleston, WV, p. A694

CANDIO, Christine, Chief Executive Officer, Inova Alexandria Hospital, Alexandria, VA, p. A668

CANDULLO, Carl, Chief Information Officer, Munroe Regional Medical Center, Ocala, FL, p. A139

CANEDO, Jim, Chief Financial Officer, Pacific Hospital of Long Beach, Long Beach, CA, p. A70

CANFIELD, Brian, Chief Operating Officer, FirstHealth Moore Regional Hospital, Pinehurst, NC, p. A470

CANIZARO, Tom, Vice President and Chief Financial Officer, South Central Regional Medical Center, Laurel, MS, p. A361

CANLAS, Emma, Chief Financial Officer, Los Alamos Medical Center, Los Alamos, NM, p. A429

CANN–TAYLOR, Julie, R.N. Chief Operating Officer, Senior Vice President Patient Care Services and Chief Nursing Officer, Wyoming Medical Center, Casper, WY, p. A720

CANNIDA, Ieesha, Director Human Resources, Reliant Rehabilitation Hospital Dallas, Dallas, TX, p. A611

CANNIFF, Christopher, Executive Director, Human Resources, Harrington Memorial Hospital, Southbridge, MA, p. A314

CANNING, John, Chief Financial Officer, Blythedale Children's Hospital, Valhalla, NY, p. A457

CANNING, Richard L., Chief Operating Officer, Central Washington Hospital, Wenatchee, WA, p. A692

CANNON, Brenda, R.N. Director of Nursing, Laughlin Memorial Hospital, Greeneville, TN, p. A583

CANNON, Gayle, Director Human Resources, Childress Regional Medical Center, Childress, TX, p. A606

CANNON, Linda, Chief Medical Records Services, San Diego County Psychiatric Hospital, San Diego, CA, p. A89

CANNON, Matthew, Chief Executive Officer, Select Specialty Hospital–Saginaw, Saginaw, MI, p. A334

CANNON, Pam
Chief Human Resources Officer, Banner Baywood Medical Center, Mesa, AZ, p. A34
Chief Human Resources Officer, Banner Heart Hospital, Mesa, AZ, p. A34

CANTER, Danny, Manager Information Systems, OhioHealth Doctors Hospital Nelsonville, Nelsonville, OH, p. A499

CANTEY, Larry D., M.D. Chief Medical Officer, Fairfield Memorial Hospital, Winnsboro, SC, p. A571

CANTLEY, J. Scott, President and Chief Executive Officer, Marietta Memorial Hospital, Marietta, OH, p. A497

CANTRE, Pedro Laureano, Chief Nursing Officer, Cardiovascular Center of Puerto Rico and the Caribbean, San Juan, PR, p. A728

CANTRELL, Dedra
Chief Information Officer, Emory Saint Joseph's Hospital of Atlanta, Atlanta, GA, p. A152
Chief Information Officer, Emory University Hospital, Atlanta, GA, p. A152
Chief Information Officer, Emory University Hospital Midtown, Atlanta, GA, p. A152
Chief Information Officer, Emory Wesley Woods Geriatric Hospital, Atlanta, GA, p. A152

CANTRELL, Eric, Chief Executive Officer, Kindred Hospital Tomball, Tomball, TX, p. A653

CANTU, Janie, Director Human Resources, Crosbyton Clinic Hospital, Crosbyton, TX, p. A609

CAPECE Jr., Vincent G., President and Chief Executive Officer, Middlesex Hospital, Middletown, CT, p. A115

CAPILI, Anthony, M.D. Chief of Staff, Chambers County Public Hospital District 1, Anahuac, TX, p. A597

CAPITELLI, Robert, M.D. Senior Vice President and Chief Medical Officer, St. Tammany Parish Hospital, Covington, LA, p. A276

CAPITULO, Kathleen, Ph.D. Chief Nurse Executive, James J. Peters Veterans Affairs Medical Center, NY, p. A444

CAPLAN, Margaret B., Director, Veterans Affairs Hudson Valley Health Care System–F.D. Roosevelt Hospital, Montrose, NY, p. A441

CAPLER, Glenda, Interim Director of Nursing, Gordon Memorial Hospital, Gordon, NE, p. A396

CAPLES, Greg, Chief Operating Officer, TriStar Summit Medical Center, Hermitage, TN, p. A584

CAPOTE, Henry, Interim Chief Financial Officer, Coral Gables Hospital, Coral Gables, FL, p. A126

CAPPEL, Blaine, Director Information Systems, Memorial Health System, Abilene, KS, p. A241

CAPPS, Kim, Chief Financial Officer, Hayes Green Beach Memorial Hospital, Charlotte, MI, p. A320

CAPPS, Melissa, Site Leader Information Technology, St. Luke's Magic Valley Medical Center, Twin Falls, ID, p. A178

CAPPS, Rick, Chief Financial Officer, Cumberland County Hospital, Burkesville, KY, p. A259

CAPUANO, Terry Ann, R.N
Chief Operating Officer, Lehigh Valley Hospital, Allentown, PA, p. A532
Chief Operating Officer, Lehigh Valley Hospital–Muhlenberg, Bethlehem, PA, p. A533

CAPUTO, Becky, Interim Director Human Resources, Cleveland Clinic Florida, Weston, FL, p. A150

CAPUTO, Louis, Chief Executive Officer, TriStar StoneCrest Medical Center, Smyrna, TN, p. A593

CARABALLO, Amanda, Nursing Director, Hospital De La Concepcion, San German, PR, p. A727

CARACCIOLO, Kevin, Chief Human Resources Officer, Palm Beach Gardens Medical Center, Palm Beach Gardens, FL, p. A141

CARACCIOLO, Mary Jo, Director Human Resources, Wellington Regional Medical Center, West Palm Beach, FL, p. A150

CARAMANICA, Laura J., Ph.D. Vice President and Chief Nursing Officer, WellStar Kennestone Hospital, Marietta, GA, p. A163

CARBALLO, Francisco R., M.D. Medical Director, Hospital HMA de Humacao, Humacao, PR, p. A726

CARBALLO, Jose E., Chief Executive Officer and Managing Director, Hospital San Pablo, Bayamon, PR, p. A725

CARBONE, Davide M., FACHE, Chief Executive Officer, St. Mary's Medical Center, West Palm Beach, FL, p. A150

CARBONE, Dominick, M.D. Chief of Staff, Hugh Chatham Memorial Hospital, Elkin, NC, p. A464

CARBONE, K., M.D. President, Wake Forest Baptist Medical Center, Winston-Salem, NC, p. A475

CARBONEL MASON, Wilma, Chief Nursing Officer, Fort Duncan Regional Medical Center, Eagle Pass, TX, p. A614

CARRELLI, Bobbie, Director Human Resources, Summit Behavioral Healthcare, Cincinnati, OH, p. A487

CARRERA, Lavern H., Senior Vice President Human Resources, Northside Medical Center, Youngstown, OH, p. A506

CARRERO, Milton D., M.D. Medical Director, Dr. Ramon E. Betances Hospital–Mayaguez Medical Center Branch, Mayaguez, PR, p. A724

CARRIER, Jeffrey, R.N. Chief Clinical Officer, Freeman Hospital West, Joplin, MO, p. A373

CARRIER, Lynn, Associate Director Administration and Support, Veterans Affairs Greater Los Angeles Healthcare System, Los Angeles, CA, p. A75

CARRIER, Patrick Brian, President and Chief Executive Officer, CHRISTUS Santa Rosa Health System, San Antonio, TX, p. A646

CARRIGG, John, Executive Vice President and Chief Operating Officer, United Health Services Hospitals–Binghamton, Binghamton, NY, p. A434

CARRILLO, Irma, Director Human Resources, Ashford Presbyterian Community Hospital, San Juan, PR, p. A727

CARRILLO, Todd, Chief Information Officer, Yoakum County Hospital, Denver City, TX, p. A614

CARRILLO, Zulema, Superintendent, El Paso Psychiatric Center, El Paso, TX, p. A615

CARRINGER, Rick, Vice President Finance and Support Services, LeConte Medical Center, Sevierville, TN, p. A592

CARRINGTON, Paul Henry, Chief Nursing Officer, Pawnee Valley Community Hospital, Larned, KS, p. A248

CARROCINO, Joanne, FACHE, President and Chief Executive Officer, Cape Regional Medical Center, Cape May Court House, NJ, p. A414

CARROLL, Allen P., Senior Vice President and Chief Executive Officer, Bon Secours St. Francis Xavier Hospital, Charleston, SC, p. A563

CARROLL, Candice R., Chief Nursing Officer, Coliseum Medical Centers, Macon, GA, p. A162

CARROLL, Dale, M.D. Senior Vice President Medical Affairs and Performance Improvement, Sentara RMH Medical Center, Harrisonburg, VA, p. A672

CARROLL, David W., Chief Financial Officer, O'Connor Hospital, San Jose, CA, p. A92

CARROLL, Eric, Chief Executive Officer, Select Specialty Hospital–Tri Cities, Bristol, TN, p. A579

CARROLL, Jack, Senior Director Human Resources, Spaulding Hospital for Continuing Medical Care Cambridge, Cambridge, MA, p. A309

CARROLL, Jack A., Ph.D., President and Chief Executive Officer, Magee Rehabilitation Hospital, Philadelphia, PA, p. A549

CARROLL, Jacqueline, Director Human Resources, Los Alamos Medical Center, Los Alamos, NM, p. A429

CARROLL, Jaime, Department Head, Walter Reed National Military Medical Center, Bethesda, MD, p. A299

CARROLL, James H., Chief Information Officer, St. John Medical Center, Westlake, OH, p. A505

CARROLL, John, M.D. Chief Medical Officer, St. James Mercy Health System, Hornell, NY, p. A439

CARROLL, Karen, MSN Vice President and Chief Nursing Officer, Beaufort Memorial Hospital, Beaufort, SC, p. A562

CARROLL, Marsha
Director of Fiscal Services, Jenkins County Hospital, Millen, GA, p. A163
Director Financial Services, Screven County Hospital, Sylvania, GA, p. A167

CARROLL, Michael W., Administrator, Richland Parish Hospital, Delhi, LA, p. A276

CARROLL, Peggy, Chief Information Officer, Palos Community Hospital, Palos Heights, IL, p. A199

CARROLL, Richard, M.D
Chief Medical officer, Adventist Bolingbrook Hospital, Bolingbrook, IL, p. A182
Chief Medical Officer, Adventist GlenOaks Hospital, Glendale Heights, IL, p. A191

CARROLL, Terrence, Ph.D. Vice President, Information Services, Dartmouth–Hitchcock Medical Center, Lebanon, NH, p. A411

CARROLL, Terri L., Vice President Financial Services, Hillsboro Area Hospital, Hillsboro, IL, p. A192

CARROLL, Velma, Chief Information Officer, Augusta Health, Fishersville, VA, p. A670

CARRON, Patrick E., FACHE, President and Chief Executive Officer, Perry County Memorial Hospital, Perryville, MO, p. A378

CARRUTH, Gregory, Head Information Management, Naval Hospital Oak Harbor, Oak Harbor, WA, p. A686

CARRUTH, Keith, Chief Executive Officer, AMG Specialty Hospital–Feliciana, Clinton, LA, p. A275

CARSON, Carole, Director of Nursing Operations, Rehabilitation Hospital of Southern New Mexico, Las Cruces, NM, p. A429

CARSON, Christine, Vice President Human Resources, St. Vincent Medical Center, Los Angeles, CA, p. A75

CARSON, Debbie, Director Human Resources, Promise Hospital of Vicksburg, Vicksburg, MS, p. A366

CARSON, Gregory W., Administrator, U. S. Air Force Clinic, Mountain Home AFB, ID, p. A177

CARSON, Jim, Director Human Resources, Henry County Health Center, Mount Pleasant, IA, p. A234

CARSON, Joe, Director Human Resources, Glen Oaks Hospital, Greenville, TX, p. A622

CARSON, Kara Jo, Chief Financial Officer, Pinckneyville Community Hospital, Pinckneyville, IL, p. A200

CARSON, Mitchell C., President and Chief Executive Officer, Longmont United Hospital, Longmont, CO, p. A109

CARSTENSEN, Karla, Director Patient Care, Avera Dells Area Hospital, Dell Rapids, SD, p. A573

CARTAGENA, Maria, M.D. Chief Medical Officer, BryLin Hospitals, Buffalo, NY, p. A434

CARTE, Theresa, Ph.D., Administrator and Chief Executive Officer, Cordova Community Medical Center, Cordova, AK, p. A28

CARTER, Billie, Chief Operating Officer and Assistant Administrator, Stonewall Memorial Hospital, Aspermont, TX, p. A598

CARTER, Bruce C., President and Chief Executive Officer, United Hospital Center, Bridgeport, WV, p. A693

CARTER, Charla, Human Resource Officer, Uvalde County Hospital Authority, Uvalde, TX, p. A654

CARTER, Christen, Director Public Relations, Roosevelt Warm Springs Rehabilitation and Specialty Hospitals, Warm Springs, GA, p. A169

CARTER, Cindy, Chief Nursing Officer, Northeast Regional Medical Center, Kirksville, MO, p. A375

CARTER, D. Montez, President, St. Mary's Good Samaritan Hospital, Greensboro, GA, p. A160

CARTER, Dennis, M.D. Chief of Staff, Eastern Oklahoma Medical Center, Poteau, OK, p. A517

CARTER, Donna, Director Human Resources, Lawrence Memorial Hospital, Walnut Ridge, AR, p. A53

CARTER, Donna, MSN Chief Nursing Officer, Minden Medical Center, Minden, LA, p. A284

CARTER, Doug, Chief Financial Officer, Brookwood Medical Center, Birmingham, AL, p. A16

CARTER, Douglas S., M.D. Vice President and Chief Medical Officer, Major Hospital, Shelbyville, IN, p. A222

CARTER, Frank, Chief Financial Officer, Cornerstone Hospital of Huntington, Huntington, WV, p. A695

CARTER, Gary L., M.D. Vice President and Chief Medical Officer, North Kansas City Hospital, North Kansas City, MO, p. A378

CARTER, Jr., James R., Chief Operating Officer, Methodist Healthcare Memphis Hospitals, Memphis, TN, p. A589

CARTER, Jason
Interim Chief Executive Officer, Post Acute Medical Specialty Hospital of Corpus Christi, Corpus Christi, TX, p. A608
Chief Executive Officer, Post Acute/Warm Springs Specialty Hospital of Luling, Luling, TX, p. A636

CARTER, Jessica Y., Chief Financial Officer, Crisp Regional Hospital, Cordele, GA, p. A157

CARTER, Leonard M., Vice President Human Resources, FHN Memorial Hospital, Freeport, IL, p. A190

CARTER, Malinda Yvonne, Chief Human Resource Manager, Saint Anthony Hospital, Chicago, IL, p. A186

CARTER, Marcia, Director Human Resources, Bluegrass Community Hospital, Versailles, KY, p. A271

CARTER, Michael, Administrator Information Technology, Northwest Ohio Psychiatric Hospital, Toledo, OH, p. A503

CARTER, Michael C., Executive Director, Kaiser Permanente Woodland Hills Medical Center, CA, p. A72

CARTER, Michael J., Chief Executive Officer, Eastern Oklahoma Medical Center, Poteau, OK, p. A517

CARTER, Misty, Director Human Resources and Chief Operating Officer, Great Plains Regional Medical Center, Elk City, OK, p. A510

CARTER, Priscilla, Chief Financial Officer, Mesa Hills Specialty Hospital, El Paso, TX, p. A616

CARTER, Rebecca W., MS
Chief Nursing Officer and Chief Operating Officer, Blue Ridge Regional Hospital, Spruce Pine, NC, p. A473
Vice President Patient Care and Chief Operating Officer, Transylvania Regional Hospital, Brevard, NC, p. A460

CARTER, Richard, Chief Executive Officer, Hunt Regional Healthcare, Greenville, TX, p. B74

CARTER, Richard, District Chief Executive Officer, Hunt Regional Medical Center, Greenville, TX, p. A622

CARTER, Richard, M.D. Chief of Staff, Tennova Healthcare–Jefferson Memorial Hospital, Jefferson City, TN, p. A584

CARTER, Richard G., Chief Executive Officer, Valley View Medical Center, Fort Mohave, AZ, p. A32

CARTER, Shanti, Chief Executive Officer, Carrollton Springs, Carrollton, TX, p. A605

CARTER, Teresa
Vice President and Chief Operating Officer, Novant Health Medical Park Hospital, Winston–Salem, NC, p. A475
Vice President Patient Care Services, OneCore Health, Oklahoma City, OK, p. A516

CARTER, Theodora, Administrative Director Human Resources, Hackensack University Medical Center at Pascack Valley, Westwood, NJ, p. A424

CARTER, Vickie, Information Systems Director, Sumner Regional Medical Center, Gallatin, TN, p. A583

CARTER-ROBERTSON, Kira, President and Chief Executive Officer, Sparrow Specialty Hospital, Lansing, MI, p. A329

CARTHEW, Edward, Chief Human Resources Officer, St. Anthony's Medical Center, Saint Louis, MO, p. A381

CARTWRIGHT, Bryan, Chief Information Technology Officer, Missouri River Medical Center, Fort Benton, MT, p. A387

CARTWRIGHT, David, Director Management Information Systems, Danville Regional Medical Center, Danville, VA, p. A670

CARTWRIGHT, David A., Vice President Finance, Advocate Condell Medical Center, Libertyville, IL, p. A194

CARTWRIGHT, Debra, Chief Financial Officer, St. Francis Health Center, Topeka, KS, p. A255

CARTWRIGHT, Kay B., R.N. Vice President and Chief Nursing Officer, Reid Hospital and Health Care Services, Richmond, IN, p. A221

CARUCCI, Dean, Chief Operating Officer, Overland Park Regional Medical Center, Overland Park, KS, p. A252

CARUGATI, Diane, Chief Operating Officer, Friends Hospital, Philadelphia, PA, p. A548

CARUSO, Diane M., MSN Chief Nursing Officer, HEALTHSOUTH Scottsdale Rehabilitation Hospital, Scottsdale, AZ, p. A38

CARUSO, Don, M.D. Chief Medical Officer, Cheshire Medical Center, Keene, NH, p. A410

CARUSO, Michael J., President and Chief Executive Officer, East Ohio Regional Hospital, Martins Ferry, OH, p. A497

CARUSO, Michael J., President and Chief Executive Officer, Ohio Valley Health Services and Education Corporation, Wheeling, WV, p. B103

CARUSO, Michael J., President and Chief Executive Officer, Ohio Valley Medical Center, Wheeling, WV, p. A700

CARVER, Deborah, R.N. Vice President Patient Care Services, Yuma Regional Medical Center, Yuma, AZ, p. A42

CARVOLTH, Richard, M.D. Chief Medical Officer, Santa Rosa Memorial Hospital, Santa Rosa, CA, p. A95

CARYNSKI, Paula A., R.N., President, OSF Saint Anthony Medical Center, Rockford, IL, p. A201

CASABONA, Nicholas, Chief Information Officer, Winthrop–University Hospital, Mineola, NY, p. A441

CASALOU, Robert F.
President and Chief Executive Officer, St. Joseph Mercy Hospital Ann Arbor, Ypsilanti, MI, p. A338
President and Chief Executive Officer, St. Joseph Mercy Livingston Hospital, Howell, MI, p. A327

CASALS, Patricia, MSN Chief Nursing Officer, Tyler Memorial Hospital, Tunkhannock, PA, p. A556

CASANOVA, Robert Bernier, Chief Financial Officer, Industrial Hospital, San Juan, PR, p. A728

CASAREZ, Margaret, Chief Financial Officer, San Joaquin Valley Rehabilitation Hospital, Fresno, CA, p. A64

CASAREZ, Teresa, Director Human Resources, New Mexico Rehabilitation Center, Roswell, NM, p. A430

CASAS, Miguel, R.N
Chief Clinical Officer, East Texas Medical Center Henderson, Henderson, TX, p. A623
Chief Nursing Officer, East Texas Medical Center–Gilmer, Gilmer, TX, p. A621

CASCIARI, Raymond, M.D. Chief Medical Officer, St. Joseph Hospital, Orange, CA, p. A81

CASE, Beth, Vice President Human Resources, St. Mary's Healthcare, Amsterdam, NY, p. A432

CASE, Cliff, Chief Financial Officer, Mineral Community Hospital, Superior, MT, p. A391

CASE, Ed, Executive Vice President and Chief Financial Officer, Rehabilitation Institute of Chicago, Chicago, IL, p. A186

CASE, Harvey
President, Vidant Beaufort Hospital, Washington, NC, p. A474
President, Vidant Pungo Hospital, Belhaven, NC, p. A460

CASE, Matthew, Director Administration, Naval Hospital Camp Lejeune, Camp Lejeune, NC, p. A461

CASERTA, Kevin, M.D
Chief Medical Officer, Providence Centralia Hospital, Centralia, WA, p. A682
Chief Medical Officer, Providence St. Peter Hospital, Olympia, WA, p. A686

CASEY, Candy J., MS, President and Chief Executive Officer, Columbia Center, Mequon, WI, p. A709

CASEY, Dina, Human Resources Officer, Lane County Hospital, Dighton, KS, p. A243

CASEY, John P., Administrator, Shodair Children's Hospital, Helena, MT, p. A388

CASEY, Joseph, Chief Financial Officer, Sturdy Memorial Hospital, Attleboro, MA, p. A305

CASEY, Rick, M.D. Chief Medical Staff, Cedar County Memorial Hospital, El Dorado Springs, MO, p. A370

CASH, Jeff, Senior Vice President and Chief Information Officer, Mercy Medical Center–Cedar Rapids, Cedar Rapids, IA, p. A226

CASH, Jimmie, R.N. Executive Director and Patient Care, Saint Francis Hospital South, Tulsa, OK, p. A521

CASH, Jordan, President, Integris Baptist Regional Health Center, Miami, OK, p. A513

CASHAW, Pamela, President, Riverside General Hospital, Houston, TX, p. A626

CASHWELL, David, Chief Executive Officer, HEALTHSOUTH Rehabilitation Hospital of Virginia, Richmond, VA, p. A677

CASIANO, Manuel, M.D. Vice President Medical Affairs, Frederick Memorial Hospital, Frederick, MD, p. A301

CASILLAS, Rosalind, Director of Nursing, Lawrence Memorial Hospital, Walnut Ridge, AR, p. A53

CASKEY, Paul, M.D. Chief of Staff, Shriners Hospitals for Children–Spokane, Spokane, WA, p. A690

CASNER, Trina, President and Chief Executive Officer, Pana Community Hospital, Pana, IL, p. A199

CASOLA, Frances, Senior Vice President Operations, St. Joseph's Medical Center, Yonkers, NY, p. A458

CASON, Amy, Chief Executive Officer and Chief Nursing Officer, Southwest Georgia Regional Medical Center, Cuthbert, GA, p. A157

CASON, Diane, Chief Information Officer, Controller and Director Human Resources, Lake Butler Hospital Hand Surgery Center, Lake Butler, FL, p. A133

CASON, Randall R., FACHE, President and Chief Executive Officer, Via Christi Hospital in Pittsburg, Pittsburg, KS, p. A253

CASON, Steven, Chief Information Officer, Putnam General Hospital, Eatonton, GA, p. A159

CASON, Will, Vice President Human Resources, St. Rita's Medical Center, Lima, OH, p. A496

CASPER, Rylee, R.N. Chief Nursing Officer, Newman Memorial Hospital, Shattuck, OK, p. A518

CASPERSON, William, M.D. Vice President Medical Affairs, Memorial Hospital, Belleville, IL, p. A181

CASS, Jinilinn, Director Medical Records, Lakeview Regional Medical Center, Covington, LA, p. A276

CASS, Julene J., R.N. Director of Nursing, Community Memorial Hospital, Redfield, SD, p. A576

CASS, Katherine, R.N. Nurse Manager, Kindred Hospital–Dayton, Dayton, OH, p. A492

CASS, Paul, D.O. Chief Medical & Clinical Integration Officer, Wentworth–Douglass Hospital, Dover, NH, p. A410

CASSADY, Craig, Director of Nursing, Wiregrass Medical Center, Geneva, AL, p. A20

CASSADY, Perry, M.D. Medical Director, Physicians' Medical Center, New Albany, IN, p. A220

CASSAGNE, Nancy R., FACHE, Chief Executive Officer, West Jefferson Medical Center, Marrero, LA, p. A284

CASSARA, Pamela, Chief Financial Officer, MetroSouth Medical Center, Blue Island, IL, p. A182

CASSEL, Asenath, Chief Nursing Officer, Wellington Regional Medical Center, West Palm Beach, FL, p. A150

CASSEL, Kari
  Senior Vice President and Chief Information Officer, UF Health Jacksonville, Jacksonville, FL, p. A132
  Senior Vice President and Chief Information Officer, UF Health Shands Hospital, Gainesville, FL, p. A130

CASSELL, Sally, Manager Human Resources, Ozark Health Medical Center, Clinton, AR, p. A44

CASSELMAN, Rebecca, Director of Nursing, Okmulgee Memorial Hospital, Okmulgee, OK, p. A517

CASSELS, William H., Administrator, DCH Regional Medical Center, Tuscaloosa, AL, p. A26

CASSIDAY, Cheryl, R.N. Director of Nursing, Chadron Community Hospital and Health Services, Chadron, NE, p. A394

CASSIDY, Doris B., Associate Director, Veterans Health Care System of the Ozarks, Fayetteville, AR, p. A46

CASSIDY, John W., M.D., President, Chief Executive Officer and Chief Medical Officer, Nexus Health Systems, Houston, TX, p. B99

CASSIDY, Joseph J., Vice President, Holy Redeemer Hospital, Meadowbrook, PA, p. A544

CASSIDY, Louise, Chief Executive Officer, Cornerstone Hospital of SouthEast Arizona, Tucson, AZ, p. A40

CASSLE, Susie, R.N. Assistant Vice President Nursing Services, Hendrick Health System, Abilene, TX, p. A595

CASTANEDA, Edmundo, President, Mercy General Hospital, Sacramento, CA, p. A87

CASTANEDA, Marissa, Chief Operating Officer and Director Marketing, Doctor's Hospital at Renaissance, Edinburg, TX, p. A615

CASTANEDA, Trevor, Chief Operating Officer, Harton Regional Medical Center, Tullahoma, TN, p. A593

CASTEEL, Brian, Information Technology Technician, Hardin County General Hospital, Rosiclare, IL, p. A202

CASTEEL, Karen, Director Human Resources, Palms of Pasadena Hospital, Saint Petersburg, FL, p. A144

CASTEEL, Lisa, Assistant Administrator and Chief Financial Officer, Henry County Medical Center, Paris, TN, p. A592

CASTEEL, Rick
  Vice President Management Information Systems and Chief Information Officer, Harford Memorial Hospital, Havre De Grace, MD, p. A301
  Vice President Management Information Systems and Chief Information Officer, Upper Chesapeake Medical Center, Bel Air, MD, p. A298

CASTELLO, Frank V., M.D. Medical Director, Children's Specialized Hospital–PSE&G, New Brunswick, NJ, p. A419

CASTELLO, Fred, M.D. Chief Medical Officer, Augusta Health, Fishersville, VA, p. A670

CASTILLO, Carol, Medical Director, Sonoma Developmental Center, Eldridge, CA, p. A62

CASTILLO, Dan, Chief Executive Officer, LAC/University of Southern California Medical Center, Los Angeles, CA, p. A73

CASTILLO, Edgar, Chief Financial Officer, Larkin Community Hospital, South Miami, FL, p. A146

CASTILLO, Paul, Chief Financial Officer, University of Michigan Hospitals and Health Centers, Ann Arbor, MI, p. A318

CASTILLO, Ralph A., CPA, Chief Executive Officer, Morgan Memorial Hospital, Madison, GA, p. A163

CASTILLO, Renee, Chief Nursing Officer, Plains Memorial Hospital, Dimmitt, TX, p. A614

CASTILLO, Rita S., R.N. Chief Quality Officer and Risk Management, South Texas Regional Medical Center, Jourdanton, TX, p. A630

CASTLE, Dorothy, Director Human Resources, North Mississippi Medical Center–Eupora, Eupora, MS, p. A357

CASTLE, Eric, Director Information Services, Lawnwood Regional Medical Center & Heart Institute, Fort Pierce, FL, p. A129

CASTLE, Kenneth, Chief Information Officer, Easton Hospital, Easton, PA, p. A538

CASTLE, Samantha, Chief Operating Officer, Ridge Behavioral Health System, Lexington, KY, p. A264

CASTLEBERRY, David L., FACHE, Chief Executive Officer, Upson Regional Medical Center, Thomaston, GA, p. A168

CASTLEBERRY, Debi, Director Information System, St. David's Rehabilitation Center, Austin, TX, p. A600

CASTLEBERRY, Ginger, Corporate Risk Manager, Quality and Patient Safety, Valir Rehabilitation Hospital, Oklahoma City, OK, p. A516

CASTLEMAN, Pam, MSN Chief Nursing Officer, Regional One Health, Memphis, TN, p. A589

CASTLEY, Karen, Medical Director, Summit Park Hospital and Nursing Care Center, Pomona, NY, p. A451

CASTOR, Susan, Chief Nursing Officer, HEALTHSOUTH Rehabilitation Hospital of Toms River, Toms River, NJ, p. A423

CASTRO, Ana, Director Information Services and Clinical Information Services, Gerald Champion Regional Medical Center, Alamogordo, NM, p. A426

CASTRO, Craig
  Chief Executive Officer, Clovis Community Medical Center, Clovis, CA, p. A60
  Chief Information Officer, Community Regional Medical Center, Fresno, CA, p. A64

CASTRO, Jill, M.D. Medical Director, HEALTHSOUTH Rehabilitation Hospital of Denver, Littleton, CO, p. A109

CASTRO, Pete, D.O. Chief of Staff, Heart of Texas Memorial Hospital, Brady, TX, p. A603

CASTRO, Richard, Chief Executive Officer, Whittier Hospital Medical Center, Whittier, CA, p. A100

CASTROMAN, Nellie, Chief Executive Officer, Select Specialty Hospital–Orlando, Orlando, FL, p. A141

CASTRONOVA, Paul, Chief Information Officer, North Canyon Medical Center, Gooding, ID, p. A176

CASTRONUEVO, Joseph, Director Information Management, St. Lawrence Rehabilitation Center, Lawrenceville, NJ, p. A417

CASWELL, Lori, Director Information Technology, Good Samaritan Medical Center, Brockton, MA, p. A308

CASWELL, Penny, Director of Nursing, Bloomington Meadows Hospital, Bloomington, IN, p. A207

CATALA, Lucy, Vice President Finance, Baylor All Saints Medical Center at Fort Worth, Fort Worth, TX, p. A618

CATALDO, Linda, Human Resources Secretary, Prevost Memorial Hospital, Donaldsonville, LA, p. A277

CATALIOTTI, Palmira, Senior Vice President, Chief Financial Officer and Treasurer, Winthrop–University Hospital, Mineola, NY, p. A441

CATANIA, Joseph M., President and Chief Executive Officer, Catholic Health Services, Lauderdale Lakes, FL, p. B32

CATANIA, Joseph M., Chief Executive Officer, St. Anthony's Rehabilitation Hospital, Lauderdale Lakes, FL, p. A134

CATAUDELLA, Mary, Corporate Director Human Resources, Jersey City Medical Center, Jersey City, NJ, p. A417

CATE, Maurine, Chief Executive Officer, Deaconess Hospital, Spokane, WA, p. A690

CATENA, Cornelio R., President and Chief Executive Officer, Wilkes–Barre General Hospital, Wilkes–Barre, PA, p. A558

CATES, Jessica, Fiscal Manager, Western State Hospital, Hopkinsville, KY, p. A263

CATES, Rodney, Senior Vice President Human Resources, Covenant Children's Hospital, Lubbock, TX, p. A634

CATHEY Jr., James E., Chief Executive Officer, North Oaks Health System, Hammond, LA, p. B100

CATHEY, Walt, Chief Operating Officer, Covenant Medical Center, Lubbock, TX, p. A634

CATINO, Anne, R.N. Vice President and Chief Nursing Officer, Holy Redeemer Hospital, Meadowbrook, PA, p. A544

CATLIN, Rexford, Chief Executive Officer, Endless Mountain Health Systems, Montrose, PA, p. A545

CATT, Robbin K., Chief Nursing Officer, Jackson Hospital, Marianna, FL, p. A135

CATTALANI, Mark, M.D. Clinical Director, Richard H. Hutchings Psychiatric Center, Syracuse, NY, p. A455

CATTELL, JoAnne, Chief Nursing Officer, St. Petersburg General Hospital, Saint Petersburg, FL, p. A145

CATTELL, Nancy E., Vice President Human Resources, Liberty Hospital, Liberty, MO, p. A376

CATTON, Jane, R.N. Chief Operating Officer and Chief Nursing Officer, Northwestern Medical Center, Saint Albans, VT, p. A666

CATUCCI, Paul, Administrative Director Human Resources, Bon Secours St. Francis Medical Center, Midlothian, VA, p. A674

CAUBLE, David, Chief Financial Officer, St. Vincent's Blount, Oneonta, AL, p. A24

CAUDEL, Katie, Controller, Southeast Health Center of Reynolds County, Ellington, MO, p. A370

CAUDILL, Allan, M.D. Chief of Staff, South Haven Health System, South Haven, MI, p. A335

CAUDILL, David, Director Human Resources, Rush County Memorial Hospital, La Crosse, KS, p. A248

CAUDILL, Ralph, Director Information Systems, St. Mary's Hospital, Centralia, IL, p. A182

CAUGHELL, David, M.D. Chief of Staff, Jane Phillips Nowata Health Center, Nowata, OK, p. A514

CAUGHEY, Michelle, M.D. Physician In Chief, Kaiser Permanente South San Francisco, South San Francisco, CA, p. A96

CAUSEY, Cynthia, Associate Administrator Human and Mission Services, McLeod Medical Center Dillon, Dillon, SC, p. A565

CAUSEY, Jack M., Administrator and Chief Executive Officer, Leesville Rehabilitation Hospital, Leesville, LA, p. A283

CAUSEY, Jennifer, Chief Executive Officer, Select Specialty Hospital–Nashville, Nashville, TN, p. A591

CAVA, Anthony V., Chief Operating Officer, Bayshore Community Hospital, Holmdel, NJ, p. A417

CAVAGNARO III, Charles E., M.D., President and Chief Executive Officer, Wing Memorial Hospital, Palmer, MA, p. A313

CAVANAUGH, Paul, Director Human Resources, Friends Hospital, Philadelphia, PA, p. A548

CAVE, Rogelio, M.D. Medical Director, Roseland Community Hospital, Chicago, IL, p. A186

CAVELL, Richard, M.D. Medical Director, University Health Conway, Monroe, LA, p. A284

CAVENEY, Timothy, President, South Shore Hospital, Chicago, IL, p. A186

CAVERNO, John
  Chief Human Resources Officer, Excela Frick Hospital, Mount Pleasant, PA, p. A546
  Chief Human Resources Officer, Excela Health Westmoreland Hospital, Greensburg, PA, p. A539

CAVES, Donald, President, Wild Rose Community Memorial Hospital, Wild Rose, WI, p. A718

CAWLEY, Patrick J., M.D., Vice President of Clinical Operations and Chief Executive Officer, MUSC Medical Center of Medical University of South Carolina, Charleston, SC, p. A563

CAWOOD, Marina, Administrative Assistant, Middlesboro ARH Hospital, Middlesboro, KY, p. A267

CAYER, Gerald, Executive Vice President and Chief Operating Officer, Franklin Memorial Hospital, Farmington, ME, p. A293

CAZAYOUX, John, Chief Financial Officer, Pointe Coupee General Hospital, New Roads, LA, p. A286

CEBRIK, Michael M., M.D. Director Medical Staff, Veterans Home and Hospital, Rocky Hill, CT, p. A117

CEBULA, Scott, Interim Chief Information Officer, UC Irvine Medical Center, Orange, CA, p. A81

CECCONI, Thomas E., President and Chief Executive Officer, Mercy Medical Center, Canton, OH, p. A485

CECIL, Bruce, Chief Financial Officer, Fresno Surgical Hospital, Fresno, CA, p. A64

CECIL, Janell, R.N. Senior Vice President and Chief Nursing Officer, University of Tennessee Medical Center, Knoxville, TN, p. A586

CECIL, Jason, Chief Information Officer, Capital Region Medical Center, Jefferson City, MO, p. A372

CECIL, Jon C.
  Chief Human Resource Officer, Cape Coral Hospital, Cape Coral, FL, p. A125
  Chief Human Resource Officer, Gulf Coast Medical Center, Fort Myers, FL, p. A129
  Chief Human Resource Officer, Lee Memorial Hospital, Fort Myers, FL, p. A129

CEDENO LLORENS, Arturo, M.D. Medical Director, Hospital Buen Samaritano, Aguadilla, PR, p. A724

CEDILLO-RODRIGUEZ, Laura, Chief Executive Officer, Kindred Hospital–Bay Area, Pasadena, TX, p. A641

CEDOTAL, Kiley P., Chief Executive Officer, Regency Hospital of Covington, Covington, LA, p. A276

CEHELYK, Bohdan, M.D. Chief Medical Officer, East Mountain Hospital, Belle Mead, NJ, p. A413

CEKALLA, Bernie, Manager Human Resources, Albany Area Hospital and Medical Center, Albany, MN, p. A339

CELANO, Julie, Vice President Human Resources, Brigham and Women's Hospital, Boston, MA, p. A306

CELLA, Ann S., R.N. Senior Vice President, Patient Care Services, St. Francis Hospital, Roslyn, NY, p. A454

CELLA, Robert, M.D
  Chief Medical Officer, Albany Memorial Hospital, Albany, NY, p. A432
  Vice President Medical Affairs, Berkshire Medical Center, Pittsfield, MA, p. A313
  Chief Medical Officer, St. Peter's Hospital, Albany, NY, p. A432

CELSOR, Reba, Chief Operating Officer, Raleigh General Hospital, Beckley, WV, p. A693

CELUCH, Paul
  Corporate Human Resources Director, Community Hospital of Huntington Park, Huntington Park, CA, p. A67
  Chief Human Resource Officer, East Los Angeles Doctors Hospital, Los Angeles, CA, p. A71

CEMATE, David D., FACHE Senior Vice President and Chief Operating Officer, Mercy Medical Center, Canton, OH, p. A485

CEMENO, Michael J., Chief Information Officer, Waterbury Hospital, Waterbury, CT, p. A118

CENTENO, Robert, M.D. Chief Medical Officer, Governor Juan F. Louis Hospital, Christiansted, VI, p. A729

CEPERO, Jesus, Ph.D. Vice President Chief Nursing Officer, Meritus Medical Center, Hagerstown, MD, p. A301

CERCEK, Robert
  Regional President of Operations, Clifton Springs Hospital and Clinic, Clifton Springs, NY, p. A435
  Regional President Operations, Newark–Wayne Community Hospital, Newark, NY, p. A449

CERCEO, Richard, Executive Vice President and Chief Operating Officer, Mercy Hospital and Medical Center, Chicago, IL, p. A185

CERIMELE, Leeann, Vice President Human Resources, UPMC Passavant, Pittsburgh, PA, p. A552

CERISE, Fred, M.D., Chief Executive Officer, Parkland Health & Hospital System, Dallas, TX, p. A611

CERNAVA, Joanne, Director Human Resources, Marlton Rehabilitation Hospital, Marlton, NJ, p. A418

CERNOCH, Desiree, Director of Nurses, El Campo Memorial Hospital, El Campo, TX, p. A615

CERONE, Shane, President, Beaumont Hospital – Royal Oak, Royal Oak, MI, p. A333

CERRA, Jane, Market Nurse Executive and Chief Nursing Officer, Select Specialty Hospital–Milwaukee, Milwaukee, WI, p. A711

CERRONE, Susan, Chief Information Officer, St. Joseph Health Services of Rhode Island, North Providence, RI, p. A560

CERULLO, Timothy J., Chief Executive Officer, Wuesthoff Medical Center – Rockledge, Rockledge, FL, p. A144

CERVANTES, Jason
  Corporate Chief Information Officer, Community Hospital of Huntington Park, Huntington Park, CA, p. A67
  Chief Information Officer, East Los Angeles Doctors Hospital, Los Angeles, CA, p. A71

CERVANTES, Mary Ann, District Director Management Information Systems, Matagorda Regional Medical Center, Bay City, TX, p. A601

CERVINO, Noel A., President and Chief Executive Officer, University of Maryland Charles Regional Medical Center, La Plata, MD, p. A302

CESAREZ, Margaret, Chief Financial Officer, Gateway Rehabilitation Hospital, Florence, KY, p. A261

CESCA, Ken, Vice President Human Resources, MidState Medical Center, Meriden, CT, p. A115

CESKO, David, M.D. Chief of Staff, Memorial Hospital of Carbon County, Rawlins, WY, p. A722

CHA BRIDIER, Vicky, Chief Operating Officer, College Station Medical Center, College Station, TX, p. A607

CHABALOWSKI, Edward, Chief Financial Officer, Geisinger–Community Medical Center, Scranton, PA, p. A554

CHABOT, Judy, R.N. Chief Nursing Officer, Placentia–Linda Hospital, Placentia, CA, p. A83

CHACKO, Benson, Chief Operating Officer, Des Peres Hospital, Saint Louis, MO, p. A380

CHADEK, Richard, M.D. Clinical Director, Lawton Indian Hospital, Lawton, OK, p. A512

CHADHA, Beenu, Chief Financial Officer, San Ramon Regional Medical Center, San Ramon, CA, p. A93

CHADOCK, Brandon, Director of Operations, Sistersville General Hospital, Sistersville, WV, p. A699

CHADWICK, Maureen C., R.N. Chief Nursing Officer, Saint Vincent Health Center, Erie, PA, p. A539

CHADWICK, Sharon M., Director Human Resources, Arrowhead Hospital, Glendale, AZ, p. A33

CHAFFEE, Jacob, M.D. Chief Medical Officer, Coulee Medical Center, Grand Coulee, WA, p. A684

CHAFFIN, Angela J., Director Human Resources, Cumberland Medical Center, Crossville, TN, p. A582

CHAFFIN, Linda, Director Medical Review, Baptist Memorial Hospital–Booneville, Booneville, MS, p. A356

CHAFFIN, Robert A., President and Chief Executive Officer, OSF Saint Elizabeth Medical Center, Ottawa, IL, p. A199

CHAHADEH, Hassan, M.D., Chief Executive Officer, University General Health System, Houston, TX, p. B144

CHAHANOVICH, Jen, Chief Executive Officer, Pali Momi Medical Center, Aiea, HI, p. A170

CHAILDIN, Roberta, Manager Human Resources, Parrish Medical Center, Titusville, FL, p. A149

CHALFANT, Cathie, Director Human Resources, Harrison County Community Hospital, Bethany, MO, p. A367

CHALIAN, Christopher, M.D. Medical Director, Casa Colina Hospital for Rehabilitative Medicine, Pomona, CA, p. A84

CHALK, Jackie, Director Human Resources, HEALTHSOUTH Rehabilitation Hospital, Largo, FL, p. A134

CHALKE, Dennis, Chief Financial Officer and Treasurer, Baystate Medical Center, Springfield, MA, p. A314

CHALMERS, Bryan, Chief Financial Officer, Ivinson Memorial Hospital, Laramie, WY, p. A722

CHALONER, Robert S., President and Chief Executive Officer, Southampton Hospital, Southampton, NY, p. A455

CHALPHANT, Steve, Director Information Management Service Line, Wm. Jennings Bryan Dorn Veterans Affairs Medical Center, Columbia, SC, p. A565

CHALTRY, Richard, M.D. Director Medical Staff, Aspirus Ontonagon Hospital, Ontonagon, MI, p. A331

CHAMBERLIN, Kim, Vice President Patient Services and Chief Nursing Officer, Mercy Medical Center–North Iowa, Mason City, IA, p. A234

CHAMBERS, Barbara, Chief Nursing Officer, Harney District Hospital, Burns, OR, p. A523

CHAMBERS, Bradley, President, MedStar Union Memorial Hospital, Baltimore, MD, p. A297

CHAMBERS, Erin, M.D. Chief Medical Officer, Houston County Community Hospital, Erin, TN, p. A582

CHAMBERS, Matthew
  Chief Information Officer, Scott & White Hospital at Round Rock, Round Rock, TX, p. A644
  Chief Information Officer, Scott & White Memorial Hospital, Temple, TX, p. A652

CHAMBERS, Regina, Vice President Human Resource, Rome Memorial Hospital, Rome, NY, p. A453

CHAMBLEE, Jane, Manager Human Resources, North Mississippi Medical Center–Iuka, Iuka, MS, p. A359

CHAMBLESS, Lesley
  Vice President Human Resources, Carolinas Medical Center–Lincoln, Lincolnton, NC, p. A468
  Assistant Vice President Workforce Relations, Carolinas Medical Center–NorthEast, Concord, NC, p. A462

CHAMBLISS, Crystal, Director of Nursing, Riverview Behavioral Health, Texarkana, AR, p. A53

CHAMBLISS, Robert, M.D. Chief Medical Officer, Breckinridge Memorial Hospital, Hardinsburg, KY, p. A262

CHAMPAGNE, Charles, Chief Financial Officer, Northeast Rehabilitation Hospital, Salem, NH, p. A412

CHAMPAGNE, Laurie, Controller, Kindred Hospital–New Orleans, New Orleans, LA, p. A285

CHAMPAVANNARATH, Vilakon, Director Information Systems, Bartow Regional Medical Center, Bartow, FL, p. A123

CHAMPION, Joshua I., Director, Florida Hospital–Flagler, Palm Coast, FL, p. A141

CHAN, Bruce, Director Business Planning and Marketing, Sonora Regional Medical Center, Sonora, CA, p. A95

CHAN, Fred, Chief Financial Officer, Intracare North Hospital, Houston, TX, p. A625

CHAN, Joyce, Chief Human Resources Officer, CentraCare Health–Melrose, Melrose, MN, p. A346

CHANAA, Ziad, M.D. Chief of Staff, Boone Memorial Hospital, Madison, WV, p. A697

CHANCE, Matt, Chief Executive Officer, Baylor Medical Center at Uptown, Dallas, TX, p. A609

CHANCE, Tammara, D.O. Chief of Staff, Boone County Hospital, Boone, IA, p. A226

CHANCELLOR, Jayme, Chief Operating Officer, Northside Hospital, Saint Petersburg, FL, p. A144

CHAND, Eric, Chief of Staff, East Georgia Regional Medical Center, Statesboro, GA, p. A167

CHAND, Parveen, Chief Operating Officer, Eskenazi Health, Indianapolis, IN, p. A214

CHANDLER, Aileen, Director of Nursing, Ogallala Community Hospital, Ogallala, NE, p. A399

CHANDLER, Laurie, Financial Officer, Prairie Community Hospital, Terry, MT, p. A391

CHANDLER, Loren, Interim, Vice President and Chief Financial Officer, Holy Cross Hospital, Chicago, IL, p. A184

CHANDLER, Ryan, President and Chief Executive Officer, The Medical Center, Columbus, GA, p. A156

CHANDLER, Vincent, Director Information Services, Porterville Developmental Center, Porterville, CA, p. A84

CHANDY, Joseph, Administrator, Methodist Hospital of Chicago, Chicago, IL, p. A185

CHANEY, James, Interim Administrator, Forks Community Hospital, Forks, WA, p. A684

CHANEZ, Adolfo, Vice President Finance and Chief Financial Officer, Saddleback Memorial Medical Center, Laguna Hills, CA, p. A68

CHANG, Alex, Chief Operating Officer, Englewood Community Hospital, Englewood, FL, p. A128

CHANG, C. Joseph, President and Chief Executive Officer, East Valley Hospital Medical Center, Glendora, CA, p. A65

CHANG, Colin, M.D. Chief of Staff, Monroe Hospital, Bloomington, IN, p. A207

CHANG, Florence
  Executive Vice President, MultiCare Good Samaritan Hospital, Puyallup, WA, p. A687
  Executive Vice President, MultiCare Mary Bridge Children's Hospital and Health Center, Tacoma, WA, p. A691
  Executive Vice President, MultiCare Tacoma General Hospital, Tacoma, WA, p. A691

CHANG, Jason, M.D. Chief Medical Director, Rehabilitation Hospital of the Pacific, Honolulu, HI, p. A171

CHANG, Myrna, Chief Nursing Executive, Sutter Davis Hospital, Davis, CA, p. A61

CHANG, Sang-ick, M.D. Chief Medical Officer, Alameda County Medical Center, Oakland, CA, p. A80

CHANNELL, Lesley
  Vice President Human Resources, Dominion Hospital, Falls Church, VA, p. A670
  Vice President Human Resources, Reston Hospital Center, Reston, VA, p. A677

CHANNING, Alan H., President and Chief Executive Officer, Schwab Rehabilitation Hospital, Chicago, IL, p. A186

CHANSKI, Jared, Administrator, Culberson Hospital, Van Horn, TX, p. A655

CHAPARRO, Natalia, Manager Human Resources, El Paso Children's Hospital, El Paso, TX, p. A615

CHAPLIN, Steven, M.D. Medical Director, Kahi Mohala Behavioral Health, Ewa Beach, HI, p. A170

CHAPMAN, Cully
  Chief Financial Officer, Lutheran Hospital of Indiana, Fort Wayne, IN, p. A211
  Chief Financial Officer, Rehabilitation Hospital of Fort Wayne, Fort Wayne, IN, p. A211

CHAPMAN, Glen, M.D. Medical Director, Moses Ludington Hospital, Ticonderoga, NY, p. A456

CHAPMAN, Judy, Interim Director Information Systems, Lock Haven Hospital, Lock Haven, PA, p. A543

CHAPMAN, Karen, Director Human Resources, Chester Regional Medical Center, Chester, SC, p. A564

CHAPMAN, Patrick, Assistant Vice President Operations, West Palm Hospital, West Palm Beach, FL, p. A150

CHAPMAN, Rachel, Nurse Manager, Noland Hospital Birmingham, Birmingham, AL, p. A16

CHAPMAN, Rick, Chief Information Officer, Kindred Hospital North Florida, Green Cove Springs, FL, p. A130

CHAPMAN, Roland, Chief Information Officer, Northern Navajo Medical Center, Shiprock, NM, p. A431

CHAPMAN, Scott, Administrator, Manhattan Surgical Center, KS, p. A249

CHAPMAN, Teresa, Vice President Human Resources, Marianjoy Rehabilitation Hospital, Wheaton, IL, p. A205

CHAPPELL, Brandee, Director of Nursing, LifeCare Hospitals of North Carolina, Rocky Mount, NC, p. A471

CHAPPELL, Robert, M.D. Chief Medical Officer and Chief Quality Officer, Huntsville Hospital, Huntsville, AL, p. A22

CHAPPELL, Teresa, Chief Information Officer, Johnston UNC Health Care, Smithfield, NC, p. A473

CHAPPLE, Albert J., R.N. Chief Clinical Officer, Kindred Rehabilitation Hospital Northeast Houston, Humble, TX, p. A628

CHAPPLE, Scott, Chief Operating Officer, Oroville Hospital, Oroville, CA, p. A82

CHAPRNKA, Karen, Senior Vice President and Chief Operating Officer, Allegiance Health, Jackson, MI, p. A327

CHARBONNEAU, Elissa, D.O. Medical Director, New England Rehabilitation Hospital of Portland, Portland, ME, p. A295

CHARDAVOYNE, Alan, Controller, Elizabethtown Community Hospital, Elizabethtown, NY, p. A437

CHAREST, Richard
President, Landmark Medical Center, Woonsocket, RI, p. A561
Chief Executive Officer, Rehabilitation Hospital of Rhode Island, North Smithfield, RI, p. A560

CHARETTE, Deborah, Director of Nursing, East Mountain Hospital, Belle Mead, NJ, p. A413

CHARI, Ganesh, M.D. Chief of Staff, Oak Hill Hospital, Brooksville, FL, p. A125

CHARLAT, Richard A., Chief of Staff, Iowa City Veterans Affairs Health Care System, Iowa City, IA, p. A232

CHARLES, Charlotte, Director Acute Patient Services, Madison Community Hospital, Madison, SD, p. A574

CHARLES, Sally, Coordinator Human Resources, Grace Medical Center, Lubbock, TX, p. A634

CHARLES, Timothy L., President and Chief Executive Officer, Mercy Medical Center–Cedar Rapids, Cedar Rapids, IA, p. A226

CHARLTON, Jr., Francis, M.D. Chief Medical Staff, St. Mary's Medical Center, San Francisco, CA, p. A91

CHARMEL, Patrick, President and Chief Executive Officer, Griffin Hospital, Derby, CT, p. A114

CHARRON, Robert M., Chief Executive Officer, Beauregard Memorial Hospital, De Ridder, LA, p. A276

CHARTIER, Bridgett, Director of Nursing, Beartooth Billings Clinic, Red Lodge, MT, p. A390

CHARTIER, Dianne, R.N., Interim Chief Executive Officer, Kindred Hospital–Albuquerque, Albuquerque, NM, p. A426

CHARTIER, Terry
Director, Information Systems, Mercy Medical Center–New Hampton, New Hampton, IA, p. A235
Director, Information Systems, Mercy Medical Center–North Iowa, Mason City, IA, p. A234

CHASE, Brenda, Chief Operating Officer, Mercy Hospital Rogers, Rogers, AR, p. A52

CHASE, Jean
Regional Manager Information Services, Aurora Lakeland Medical Center, Elkhorn, WI, p. A704
Regional Manager Information Services, Aurora Medical Center, Kenosha, WI, p. A707
Regional Manager Information Services, Aurora Memorial Hospital of Burlington, Burlington, WI, p. A703

CHASE, Kyle, Chief Financial Officer, Glacial Ridge Health System, Glenwood, MN, p. A344

CHASE, Layla, Chief Financial Officer, Springhill Medical Center, Springhill, LA, p. A289

CHASE, Pansy, Director Human Resources, Vidant Duplin Hospital, Kenansville, NC, p. A467

CHASE, Robert, M.D
Chief Medical Officer, West Suburban Medical Center, Oak Park, IL, p. A198
Chief Medical Officer, Westlake Hospital, Melrose Park, IL, p. A196

CHASE, Steven, Chief Executive Officer, Craig General Hospital, Vinita, OK, p. A521

CHASE, Susan, Vice President, Carolinas Rehabilitation, Charlotte, NC, p. A462

CHASE, Trudi, M.D. President Medical Staff, Parkview Adventist Medical Center, Brunswick, ME, p. A292

CHASIN, Marc, M.D. Chief Information Officer, St. Luke's Regional Medical Center, Boise, ID, p. A175

CHASON, Robert, Interim Chief Executive Officer, Fremont–Rideout Health Group, Marysville, CA, p. A77

CHASSE, Floyd, Vice President Human Resources, McLaren Greater Lansing, Lansing, MI, p. A328

CHASTAIN, James G., FACHE, Director, Mississippi State Hospital, Whitfield, MS, p. A366

CHASTAIN, Katherine L., R.N. Chief Nursing Officer, Sacred Heart Hospital on the Gulf, Port St. Joe, FL, p. A143

CHASTAIN, Stephen L., M.D. Chief Medical Officer, HEALTHSOUTH Rehabilitation Hospital at Martin Health, Stuart, FL, p. A146

CHASTANT, Lee, M.D., Chief Executive Officer, West Feliciana Parish Hospital, Saint Francisville, LA, p. A288

CHATANI, Kumar
Senior Vice President and Chief Information Officer Mount Sinai Health System, Mount Sinai Beth Israel, New York, NY, p. A446
Senior Vice President and Chief Information Officer Mount Sinai Health System, Mount Sinai Hospital, New York, NY, p. A446
Chief Information Officer, Mount Sinai Health System, Mount Sinai St. Luke's, New York, NY, p. A446
Chief Information Officer, Mount Sinai Health System, New York Eye and Ear Infirmary of Mount Sinai, New York, NY, p. A447

CHATELAIN, Vincent, Director Business Development, River Oaks Hospital, New Orleans, LA, p. A286

CHATLEY, Alice M., R.N. Vice President Acute Care Services, St. Marys Health Center, Jefferson City, MO, p. A372

CHATMAN, Hubert, Chief Civilian Personnel, Wright Patterson Medical Center, Wright–Patterson AFB, OH, p. A505

CHATMAN, Jim, Chief Financial Officer, Maria Parham Medical Center, Henderson, NC, p. A466

CHATMAN, Mary, Ph.D. Chief Operating Officer, Memorial Health, Savannah, GA, p. A166

CHATMAN, Rosie, R.N. Associate Director Patient and Nursing Services, Northport Veterans Affairs Medical Center, Northport, NY, p. A449

CHATTERJEE, Kanan, M.D. Chief of Staff, Lebanon Veterans Affairs Medical Center, Lebanon, PA, p. A542

CHAUDHARY, Shahid, M.D. Chief Medical Officer, Avera St. Luke's Hospital, Aberdeen, SD, p. A572

CHAUDHRY, Deepak
Vice President Information Technology, Nexus Specialty Hospital, Shenandoah, TX, p. A649
Vice President Information Technology, Nexus Specialty Hospital The Woodlands, Spring, TX, p. A650

CHAUSSARD, David, Chief Executive Officer, Hillcrest Hospital Claremore, Claremore, OK, p. A509

CHAVEZ, Irene, Senior Vice President and Area Manager, Kaiser Permanente San Jose Medical Center, San Jose, CA, p. A92

CHAVEZ, Shari, Chief Nursing Officer, Swedish Medical Center, Englewood, CO, p. A106

CHAVEZ, Virgil, Director Information Technology, Tsehootsooi Medical Center, Fort Defiance, AZ, p. A32

CHAVIS, Anthony D., M.D. Vice President Enterprise Medical Officer, Community Hospital Foundation, Community Hospital of the Monterey Peninsula, Monterey, CA, p. A78

CHAWLA, Nikki, M.D. Medical Director, Integris Seminole Medical Center, Seminole, OK, p. A518

CHAYER, Olivia, Lead Human Resources, York Hospital, York, ME, p. A295

CHAYKIN, Lee B., Chief Executive Officer, Westside Regional Medical Center, Plantation, FL, p. A143

CHEANEY, Theresa, Controller, Chambers County Public Hospital District 1, Anahuac, TX, p. A597

CHEATWOOD, Elizabeth, Human Resource Director and Administrative Assistant, Jackson Parish Hospital, Jonesboro, LA, p. A280

CHECKETTS, Lannie
Interim Assistant Chief Financial Officer, Saint Alphonsus Medical Center – Nampa, Nampa, ID, p. A177
Vice President Finance and Operations, Saint Alphonsus Medical Center – Ontario, Ontario, OR, p. A527

CHEEMA, Linde, Vice President Human Resources, Sequoia Hospital, Redwood City, CA, p. A86

CHEESEMAN, Karen, Executive Vice President, Mackinac Straits Health System, Saint Ignace, MI, p. A334

CHEEVER, Liz, Administrator, Miracle Mile Medical Center, Los Angeles, CA, p. A73

CHEKOURAS, Christopher A., Vice President and Chief Operating Officer, Virtua Berlin, Berlin, NJ, p. A413

CHEKURU, Naidu, M.D. Chief Medical Officer, Covenant Specialty Hospital, Lubbock, TX, p. A634

CHELLAPPA, Sheila, M.D. Chief of Staff, Coatesville Veterans Affairs Medical Center, Coatesville, PA, p. A536

CHEN, David, M.D. Vice President Medical Affairs, MultiCare Good Samaritan Hospital, Puyallup, WA, p. A687

CHEN, Helen, M.D. Chief Medical Officer, Hebrew Rehabilitation Center, Boston, MA, p. A307

CHEN, Stephen, M.D. Chief Medicare, Alhambra Hospital Medical Center, Alhambra, CA, p. A55

CHEN, Van, M.D. Medical Director, Ballard Rehabilitation Hospital, San Bernardino, CA, p. A88

CHENEY, David, Chief Executive Officer, Banner Boswell Medical Center, Sun City, AZ, p. A39

CHENG, Alice, Interim President and Chief Executive Officer, Beverly Hospital, Montebello, CA, p. A78

CHENG, Becky, Chief Financial Officer, Corona Regional Medical Center, Corona, CA, p. A60

CHENG, Rebecca
Chief Financial Officer, California Hospital Medical Center, Los Angeles, CA, p. A71
Chief Financial Officer, Glendale Memorial Hospital and Health Center, Glendale, CA, p. A65

CHENG, Ringo, Director Information Technology, Surgery Specialty Hospitals of America, Pasadena, TX, p. A641

CHENNAULT, Paula, Administrator, Behavioral HealthCare Center at Columbia, Columbia, TN, p. A581

CHENOWETH, Judy, Chief Nursing Officer, Russell County Hospital, Russell Springs, KY, p. A270

CHEPAK, Lois, R.N. Chief Clinical Officer, Eagleville Hospital, Eagleville, PA, p. A537

CHERMSIDE, Paula L., Chief Operating Officer, Aspirus Grand View Hospital, Ironwood, MI, p. A327

CHERNOW, David S., President and Chief Executive Officer, Select Medical Corporation, Mechanicsburg, PA, p. B119

CHERONE, Nancy, Executive Director and Administrator, Nazareth Hospital, Philadelphia, PA, p. A549

CHERRNAY, Jennifer, Director Human Resources, Texas Institute for Surgery at Texas Health Presbyterian Dallas, Dallas, TX, p. A612

CHERRY, Jean
Executive Vice President, Commonwealth Regional Specialty Hospital, Bowling Green, KY, p. A258
Executive Vice President and Chief Information Officer, Medical Center at Bowling Green, Bowling Green, KY, p. A259
Executive Vice President & Chief Information Officer, Medical Center at Franklin, Franklin, KY, p. A261
Chief Information Officer, Medical Center at Scottsville, Scottsville, KY, p. A270

CHERRY, Jonathan M., President and Chief Executive Officer, LifeStream Behavioral Center, Leesburg, FL, p. A134

CHERRY, Kris, Chief Nursing Officer, Saint Francis Hospital–Bartlett, Bartlett, TN, p. A579

CHERRY, Robert, M.D. Chief Medical Officer, Loyola University Medical Center, Maywood, IL, p. A195

CHERRY, Troy, Chief Financial Officer, Schick Shadel Hospital, Seattle, WA, p. A688

CHESLEK, Ingrid, R.N. Chief Nursing Officer, Metro Health Hospital, Wyoming, MI, p. A337

CHESLEY, Jeanine
Controller, HEALTHSOUTH Rehabilitation Hospital, Concord, NH, p. A409
Chief Executive Officer, New England Rehabilitation Hospital of Portland, Portland, ME, p. A295

CHESLEY, Stephen, Chief of Staff, Sanford Luverne Medical Center, Luverne, MN, p. A346

CHESLEY, Walter, Vice President Human Resources, Hennepin County Medical Center, Minneapolis, MN, p. A347

CHESNOS, Richard C., Senior Vice President Finance and Chief Financial Officer, St. Clair Hospital, Pittsburgh, PA, p. A551

CHESSARE, John B., FACHE, President and Chief Executive Officer, Greater Baltimore Medical Center, Baltimore, MD, p. A296

CHESSIN, Neil A., Vice President, Jameson Hospital, New Castle, PA, p. A546

CHESSUM, George
Senior Vice President and Chief Information Officer, Presence Our Lady of the Resurrection Medical Center, Chicago, IL, p. A185
Senior Vice President Information Systems and Chief Information Officer, Presence Resurrection Medical Center, Chicago, IL, p. A185
Vice President Information Systems, Presence Saint Francis Hospital, Evanston, IL, p. A190
Senior Vice President Information Systems and Chief Information Officer, Presence Saint Joseph Hospital, Chicago, IL, p. A185

CHESTER, Julie, Vice President Human Resources, University Hospitals Case Medical Center, Cleveland, OH, p. A489

CHESTER, Kate, Senior Coordinator Public Relations, Providence St. Vincent Medical Center, Portland, OR, p. A528

CHESTER, Linnes L., USAF Administrator, Mike O'Callaghan Federal Hospital, Nellis AFB, NV, p. A407

CHESTER, William, Manager Human Resources, Grand Junction Veterans Affairs Medical Center, Grand Junction, CO, p. A107

CHESTNUT–RAULS, Monica, Vice President Human Resources, Peconic Bay Medical Center, Riverhead, NY, p. A452

CHEUNG, Alan, M.D. Vice President Medical Affairs, Castle Medical Center, Kailua, HI, p. A171

CHEUNG, Anna, President, St. Mary's Medical Center, San Francisco, CA, p. A91

CHEUNG, Marilou, Assistant Administrator Finance, Kaiser Permanente Woodland Hills Medical Center, CA, p. A72

CHEVERE, Carlos, M.D. Medical Director, I. Gonzalez Martinez Oncologic Hospital, San Juan, PR, p. A728

CHEW, Roy G., Ph.D., President, Kettering Medical Center, Kettering, OH, p. A495

CHEWNING III, Larry H., President and Chief Executive Officer, Nash Health Care Systems, Rocky Mount, NC, p. A471
CHEYNET, Sandee, Vice President Administrative Services, Bluefield Regional Medical Center, Bluefield, WV, p. A693
CHHABRA, Ankit
Director Finance, Fairview Hospital, Cleveland, OH, p. A488
Director Finance, Lakewood Hospital, Lakewood, OH, p. A496
CHIACCHIARO, Peter, Vice President Human Resources, St. Joseph Hospital, Bethpage, NY, p. A433
CHIANTELLA, Christopher, M.D. Chief Medical Officer, Inova Loudoun Hospital, Leesburg, VA, p. A673
CHIANTELLO, Charmaine, Chief Financial Officer, Aspirus Grand View Hospital, ironwood, MI, p. A327
CHIARCHIARO, Martha, Vice President Human Resources, Clinton Hospital, Clinton, MA, p. A309
CHIAVETTA, Robert, Vice President Finance, United Memorial Medical Center, Batavia, NY, p. A433
CHICK, Melanie, Chief Executive Officer, Baylor Medical Center at Trophy Club, Trophy Club, TX, p. A653
CHICKEN, Kurt, Director Support Services, Palmer Lutheran Health Center, West Union, IA, p. A239
CHIEFFO, Ron, Chief Information Officer, Colorado River Medical Center, Needles, CA, p. A79
CHIKOWSKI, Julie, Administrator, Memorial Hospital of Lafayette County, Darlington, WI, p. A703
CHILCOTT, Stephen, Associate Director Human Resources, University of California, Davis Medical Center, Sacramento, CA, p. A88
CHILD, Clint L., R.N. Chief Nursing Officer, Saint Alphonsus Medical Center – Nampa, Nampa, ID, p. A177
CHILDERS, Bethany, Director Human Resources, Fremont Health, Fremont, NE, p. A395
CHILDERS, Christy, Director Information Technology, P & S Surgical Hospital, Monroe, LA, p. A284
CHILDERS, James R., Chief Financial Officer, Cobre Valley Regional Medical Center, Globe, AZ, p. A33
CHILDERS, Linda, Director Human Resources, Wallowa Memorial Hospital, Enterprise, OR, p. A524
CHILDRE Jr., Jimmy, Interim Chief Executive Officer, Washington County Regional Medical Center, Sandersville, GA, p. A166
CHILDS, Deborah, Chief Human Resources Officer, University of Michigan Hospitals and Health Centers, Ann Arbor, MI, p. A318
CHILDS, Joe, M.D. Vice President Medical Services, East Tennessee Children's Hospital, Knoxville, TN, p. A585
CHILDS, Michelle B., Senior Administrative Director Human Resources, Salinas Valley Memorial Healthcare System, Salinas, CA, p. A88
CHILES, John, M.D. Medical Director, Western State Hospital, Tacoma, WA, p. A691
CHILES, Kevin, Vice President Human Resources, Hutchinson Regional Medical Center, Hutchinson, KS, p. A246
CHILES, Morton, M.D. Chief Medical Officer, Culpeper Regional Hospital, Culpeper, VA, p. A670
CHILESKI, Andy, Chief Information Officer and Vice President Facilities, Berger Health System, Circleville, OH, p. A488
CHILSON, Terrance, Chief of Staff, Tyler Memorial Hospital, Tunkhannock, PA, p. A556
CHILTON, Alvin, Chief Financial Officer, Southeast Arizona Medical Center, Douglas, AZ, p. A32
CHILTON, Bryan, Director Information Systems, Navarro Regional Hospital, Corsicana, TX, p. A608
CHIN, Ellyn, Vice President Finance, Gottlieb Memorial Hospital, Melrose Park, IL, p. A196
CHINBURG, Paul, M.D. Medical Director, Lane County Hospital, Dighton, KS, p. A243
CHINERY, William, M.D. Chief of Staff, Marlboro Park Hospital, Bennettsville, SC, p. A562
CHING, Angelica, Director Information Systems, Monterey Park Hospital, Monterey Park, CA, p. A78
CHING, Geraldine, Assistant General Minister, Sisters of Saint Francis, Syracuse, NY, p. B125
CHINN, Mary, M.D. President Medical Staff, Mendota Community Hospital, Mendota, IL, p. A196
CHINN, Tammie, Director Marketing and Public Relations, Plateau Medical Center, Oak Hill, WV, p. A698
CHINN, Terri, Vice President Finance, St. Mary's Hospital and Regional Medical Center, Grand Junction, CO, p. A107
CHINNOCK, Rachel, Chief Human Resources Officer, Latimer County General Hospital, Wilburton, OK, p. A522
CHIOLO, Denise, Chief Human Resources Officer, Phoenixville Hospital, Phoenixville, PA, p. A550
CHIPMAN, Kim, Chief Clinical Officer, Kindred Hospital–White Rock, Dallas, TX, p. A610
CHIRICHELLA, Joseph P., President and Chief Executive Officer, Deborah Heart and Lung Center, Browns Mills, NJ, p. A414
CHIRICO, Cathy, Director Human Resources, Gouverneur Hospital, Gouverneur, NY, p. A438
CHISENSKI, Walter, Director Information Technology, Banner Casa Grande Medical Center, Casa Grande, AZ, p. A31

CHISHOLM, Ken, Director Human Resources, Martha's Vineyard Hospital, Oak Bluffs, MA, p. A313
CHISHOLM, Moody L.
President & Chief Executive Officer, St. Vincent's Medical Center Riverside, Jacksonville, FL, p. A132
President and Chief Executive Officer, St. Vincent's Medical Center Southside, Jacksonville, FL, p. A132
CHISHOLM, Sharon, Director Human Resources, Texas Health Presbyterian Hospital Allen, Allen, TX, p. A596
CHISSELL, Herbert G., M.D. Chief Medical Officer, Torrance State Hospital, Torrance, PA, p. A556
CHITAYAT, Ron, M.D. Chief Medical Staff, West Hills Hospital and Medical Center, CA, p. A75
CHITTENDEN, Michael D., President, St. Vincent Carmel Hospital, Carmel, IN, p. A208
CHITTOM, Tommy, Vice President Information Services, East Alabama Medical Center, Opelika, AL, p. A24
CHIVERS, John, Senior Vice President Finance, Sierra View District Hospital, Porterville, CA, p. A84
CHIZEK, Chris, Chief Executive Officer, Solara Hospital McAllen, McAllen, TX, p. A637
CHMIELEWSKI, Linda A., R.N. Vice President Operations, St. Cloud Hospital, Saint Cloud, MN, p. A350
CHMURA, David, Manager Management Information Systems, Copper Queen Community Hospital, Bisbee, AZ, p. A31
CHOATE, Charlotte, Director Information Systems, Trinity Hospital of Augusta, Augusta, GA, p. A154
CHODKOWSKI, Paul J., Chief Executive Officer, St. Anthony Summit Medical Center, Frisco, CO, p. A106
CHOINKA, Keith A., Vice President Information Systems and Chief Information Officer, St. Joseph Hospital, Nashua, NH, p. A411
CHOKSHI, Rajiv, M.D. Chief of Staff, Broward Health Medical Center, Fort Lauderdale, FL, p. A128
CHOKSHI, Sushil, M.D. Chief Medical Officer, Faith Community Hospital, Jacksboro, TX, p. A629
CHOLGER, Dave, Chief Financial Officer, Woodlawn Hospital, Rochester, IN, p. A222
CHONG, Johnnette, Chief Financial Officer, Los Angeles Community Hospital at Los Angeles, Los Angeles, CA, p. A73
CHOPRA, Praveen, Chief Information and Supply Chain Officer, Children's Healthcare of Atlanta, Atlanta, GA, p. A152
CHORAZEWITZ, Keri, Vice President Compliance and Employee Relations, Memorial Hospital of Sweetwater County, Rock Springs, WY, p. A722
CHORD, Ginger, Coordinator Human Resources, Sturgis Regional Hospital, Sturgis, SD, p. A577
CHOREY, Raymond M., President and Chief Executive Officer, Southeastern Ohio Regional Medical Center, Cambridge, OH, p. A485
CHOU, Rebecca
Directory Information Systems, Palestine Regional Medical Center, Palestine, TX, p. A640
Director Information Systems, Palestine Regional Medical Center–East, Palestine, TX, p. A640
CHOUDHURY, Seleem, R.N. Chief Nursing Officer, Northeastern Vermont Regional Hospital, Saint Johnsbury, VT, p. A666
CHOWDHARY, Vijay K., M.D. Medical Director, Hampshire Memorial Hospital, Romney, WV, p. A699
CHOY, Ann N., Manager Human Resources and Payroll, Kuakini Medical Center, Honolulu, HI, p. A170
CHOY, Rose, Chief Financial Officer, Kahi Mohala Behavioral Health, Ewa Beach, HI, p. A170
CHOZINSKI, Joseph P., M.D. Deputy Commander Clinical Services, San Antonio Military Medical Center, Fort Sam Houston, TX, p. A617
CHRENCIK, Robert A., President and Chief Executive Officer, University of Maryland Medical System, Baltimore, MD, p. B145
CHRISTENSEN, Carl James, Chief Executive Officer, Comanche County Medical Center, Comanche, TX, p. A607
CHRISTENSEN, Cinthia S., JD Executive Vice President and Chief Operating Officer, Children's Hospital of Wisconsin, Milwaukee, WI, p. A710
CHRISTENSEN, Connie, Chief Financial Officer, Morrill County Community Hospital, Bridgeport, NE, p. A394
CHRISTENSEN, David, M.D. Senior Vice President Medical Affairs and Chief Medical Officer, Children's Hospital Central California, Madera, CA, p. A76
CHRISTENSEN, Earlene, Director Human Resources, Fayette County Memorial Hospital, Washington Court House, OH, p. A504
CHRISTENSEN, Elizabeth B., Director Human Resources, Mercy Hospital of Portland, Portland, ME, p. A294
CHRISTENSEN, G. N., M.D. Chief Medical Officer, William Bee Ririe Hospital, Ely, NV, p. A404
CHRISTENSEN, Gwen, Vice President Finance, Aurora BayCare Medical Center, Green Bay, WI, p. A705
CHRISTENSEN, Jay, FACHE, Administrator, Mahaska Health Partnership, Oskaloosa, IA, p. A236

CHRISTENSEN, Jeffrey, Chief Executive Officer, HEALTHSOUTH Rehabilitation Institute of Tucson, Tucson, AZ, p. A40
CHRISTENSEN, Marilyn, Director Information Technology, Milford Hospital, Milford, CT, p. A115
CHRISTENSEN, Mark, Director, Finance, Cassia Regional Medical Center, Burley, ID, p. A175
CHRISTENSEN, Marti, Director of Psychiatric Nursing, Douglas County Community Mental Health Center, Omaha, NE, p. A400
CHRISTENSEN, Rodney, Director Information Systems, Caldwell Memorial Hospital, Lenoir, NC, p. A468
CHRISTENSEN, Sandra
Chief Financial Officer, Dallas County Hospital, Perry, IA, p. A236
Chief Executive Officer, Sheridan Memorial Hospital, Plentywood, MT, p. A390
CHRISTENSEN, Scott, Chief Executive Officer, Delta Regional Medical Center, Greenville, MS, p. A358
CHRISTENSEN, Todd, Chief Financial Officer, Kittson Memorial Healthcare Center, Hallock, MN, p. A344
CHRISTENSEN, Troy, Chief Financial Officer, Madison Memorial Hospital, Rexburg, ID, p. A178
CHRISTENSEN, W. R., M.D. Chief of Staff, East Texas Medical Center Pittsburg, Pittsburg, TX, p. A642
CHRISTENSEN–MORES, Donna, Director Human Resources, Myrtue Medical Center, Harlan, IA, p. A232
CHRISTENSON, Ann, Executive Vice President Human Resources and Support Services, Sanford Medical Center Fargo, Fargo, ND, p. A477
CHRISTENSON, Lee, Chief Executive Officer, Springwoods Behavioral Health Hospital, Fayetteville, AR, p. A45
CHRISTENSON, Paul, Chief Financial Officer, Pampa Regional Medical Center, Pampa, TX, p. A641
CHRISTENSON, Ron, Chief Financial Officer, Morris County Hospital, Council Grove, KS, p. A243
CHRISTENSON, Shannon, Director Human Resources, Aurora West Allis Medical Center, West Allis, WI, p. A718
CHRISTIAN, Bruce C., Chief Executive Officer, Adventist GlenOaks Hospital, Glendale Heights, IL, p. A191
CHRISTIAN, Chuck, Vice President Chief Information Officer, St. Francis Hospital, Columbus, GA, p. A156
CHRISTIAN, Glenn, Administrator, Mayo Clinic Health System in Cannon Falls, Cannon Falls, MN, p. A341
CHRISTIAN, Greg
Executive Director, Kaiser Permanente Fontana Medical Center, Fontana, CA, p. A63
Executive Director, Kaiser Permanente Ontario Medical Center, Ontario, CA, p. A81
CHRISTIAN, Karolyne, Director Human Resources, Byrd Regional Hospital, Leesville, LA, p. A282
CHRISTIAN, Patricia L., R.N., Chief Executive Officer, John Umstead Hospital, Butner, NC, p. A461
CHRISTIAN–AVERY, Sonya, Chief Information Officer, West Georgia Health, La Grange, GA, p. A162
CHRISTIANSEN, Anne, Chief Financial Officer, Pioneer Memorial Hospital and Health Services, Viborg, SD, p. A577
CHRISTIANSEN, Hilary, Chief Financial Officer, George C Grape Community Hospital, Hamburg, IA, p. A231
CHRISTIANSEN, Judy A., R.N., Interim Chief Executive Officer, Mendota Community Hospital, Mendota, IL, p. A196
CHRISTIANSEN, Keith, Chief Nursing Officer, Select Specialty Hospital–Erie, Erie, PA, p. A539
CHRISTIANSEN, Patrick, Ph.D., Chief Executive Officer, Inova Fairfax Hospital, Falls Church, VA, p. A670
CHRISTIANSEN, Sara, Interim Director Human Resources, Sibley Medical Center, Arlington, MN, p. A339
CHRISTIANSON, Clark P., President and Chief Executive Officer, Providence Hospital, Mobile, AL, p. A22
CHRISTIANSON, Clinton J., FACHE, President, Mercy Medical Center–Centerville, Centerville, IA, p. A227
CHRISTIANSON, Delano, Administrator, CentraCare Health–Sauk Centre, Sauk Centre, MN, p. A352
CHRISTIE, Andy, Chief Information Technology, Adair County Memorial Hospital, Greenfield, IA, p. A231
CHRISTIE, Janet L., Senior Vice President Human Resources, UF Health Shands Hospital, Gainesville, FL, p. A130
CHRISTINE, Gerald, Chief Financial Officer, Lakewood Ranch Medical Center, Bradenton, FL, p. A124
CHRISTION, Lydia, Director Human Resources, HEALTHSOUTH Rehabilitation Hospital, Dothan, AL, p. A19
CHRISTISON, George, M.D. Medical Director, Patton State Hospital, Patton, CA, p. A83
CHRISTMAN, Lawrence, Chief Financial Officer and Chief Operating Officer, Riverview Hospital, Noblesville, IN, p. A220
CHRISTMAN, Lyndon J., President and Chief Executive Officer, Fayette County Memorial Hospital, Washington Court House, OH, p. A504
CHRISTMAN, Thomas C., Director Plant Operations, Kindred Hospital–St. Louis, Saint Louis, MO, p. A380

CHRISTMANN, Linda, M.D. Chief of Staff, Manatee Memorial Hospital, Bradenton, FL, p. A124

CHRISTOPH, Rebecca, Director Nursing and Patient Care Services, Mid–Valley Hospital, Omak, WA, p. A686

CHRISTOPHEL, Randal, President and Chief Executive Officer, Indiana University Health Goshen Hospital, Goshen, IN, p. A212

CHROBAK, Jeffrey, Vice President Finance and Chief Financial Officer, Sharon Regional Health System, Sharon, PA, p. A555

CHROMIK, James R., Interim Chief Executive Officer, Coffeyville Regional Medical Center, Coffeyville, KS, p. A242

CHU, Edward, Chief Financial Officer, Leahi Hospital, Honolulu, HI, p. A170

CHUA, Jesus, M.D. Chief of Staff, Franklin Foundation Hospital, Franklin, LA, p. A277

CHUBB, Jack, Chief Executive Officer, Community Behavioral Health Center, Fresno, CA, p. A64

CHUBB, John M., Chief Executive Officer, Community Regional Medical Center, Fresno, CA, p. A64

CHUE, Bevins, M.D. Medical Director, HEALTHSOUTH Desert Canyon Rehabilitation Hospital, Las Vegas, NV, p. A405

CHUGHTAI, Omar, Vice President and Chief Operating Officer, West Hills Hospital and Medical Center, CA, p. A75

CHULACK, Peggy, Chief Administrative Officer and Chief Information Officer, Presbyterian Intercommunity Health Hospital, Whittier, CA, p. A100

CHULI, Judith, R.N. Chief Nursing Officer, Fairlawn Rehabilitation Hospital, Worcester, MA, p. A316

CHUN, Leslie, M.D. Vice President Medical Staff and Chief Quality Officer, Queen's Medical Center, Honolulu, HI, p. A171

CHUNG, Maria, CPA Director Fiscal Services, Shriners Hospitals for Children–Boston, Boston, MA, p. A307

CHUNG, Michael
  Chief Financial Officer, AHMC Anaheim Regional Medical Center, Anaheim, CA, p. A55
  Chief Financial Officer, Greater El Monte Community Hospital, South El Monte, CA, p. A96

CHUNG, Raymond, M.D. Chief of Staff, Phoenix Veterans Affairs Health Care System, Phoenix, AZ, p. A36

CHUNG, William, M.D. Chief of Staff, Chinese Hospital, San Francisco, CA, p. A90

CHUNN, Ashley, Director of Nursing, Atmore Community Hospital, Atmore, AL, p. A16

CHUNN, Debbie, Director Medical Records, Sterlington Rehabilitation Hospital, Bastrop, LA, p. A273

CHURCH, Kim
  Manager Human Resources, G. Werber Bryan Psychiatric Hospital, Columbia, SC, p. A564
  Manager Human Resources, William S. Hall Psychiatric Institute, Columbia, SC, p. A564

CHURCHILL, Brigitte, Director of Human Resources, Mayo Clinic Health System in Waycross, Waycross, GA, p. A169

CHURCHILL, Julie, Chief Financial Officer, Victory Medical Center – Southcross, San Antonio, TX, p. A648

CHURCHILL, Larry, Director Information Services, Woodward Regional Hospital, Woodward, OK, p. A522

CHURCHILL, Sandi, Vice President Business Development and Operations, Professional Services, Advocate Good Samaritan Hospital, Downers Grove, IL, p. A188

CHURCHILL, Timothy A., President, Stephens Memorial Hospital, Norway, ME, p. A294

CHURCHWELL, Kevin B., M.D. Chief Operating Officer and Executive Vice President of Health Affairs, Boston Children's Hospital, Boston, MA, p. A306

CIAMPA, Amy, Chief Financial Officer, Park Royal Hospital, Fort Myers, FL, p. A129

CIAMPA, Steve, Vice President Finance, Porter Medical Center, Middlebury, VT, p. A665

CIANCIOLO, Kirk, D.O. Chief Medical Officer, Blake Medical Center, Bradenton, FL, p. A124

CIANCIOTTO CROYLE, Allison, Vice President of Human Resources, Mercy Medical Center, Rockville Centre, NY, p. A453

CIANFLONE, Laura, Director Human Resources, Kenmore Mercy Hospital, Kenmore, NY, p. A439

CIANFRANI, Michelle, Director Information Technology, Gilbert Hospital, Gilbert, AZ, p. A32

CIAREFELLA, Donna, Director Human Resources, Vibra Hospital of Western Massachusetts, Springfield, MA, p. A315

CICCARELLI, John, Director Information Technology, Parkview Community Hospital Medical Center, Riverside, CA, p. A86

CICCARELLI, Thomas, Chief Information Officer, East Orange General Hospital, East Orange, NJ, p. A415

CICE, Donna, Vice President Human Resources, Huntington Hospital, Huntington, NY, p. A439

CICERI, David P., M.D. Chief Medical Officer, Scott and White Continuing Care Hospital, Temple, TX, p. A652

CICIRETTI, Mary Louise, Director Human Resources, Riddle Hospital, Media, PA, p. A545

CIENCEWICKI, Michael, M.D. Vice President Medical Affairs, Raritan Bay Medical Center, Perth Amboy, NJ, p. A421

CIHA, Clayton, President and Chief Executive Officer, Alexian Brothers Behavioral Health Hospital, Hoffman Estates, IL, p. A193

CIHAK, Scott A., Chief Executive Officer, Kendall Regional Medical Center, Miami, FL, p. A137

CILLO, Laura A., Chief Operating Officer, West Boca Medical Center, Boca Raton, FL, p. A124

CIMALA, Derek W., Interim Chief Executive Officer, Plateau Medical Center, Oak Hill, WV, p. A698

CIMINO, Jr., Michael A., Chief Financial Officer, Banner Behavioral Health Hospital – Scottsdale, Scottsdale, AZ, p. A38

CINICOLA, John, M.D
  Chief Medical Officer, Heritage Valley Health System, Beaver, PA, p. A533
  Chief Medical Officer, Sewickley Valley Hospital, (A Division of Valley Medical Facilities), Sewickley, PA, p. A555

CIOFFI, Cheryl, R.N. Vice President Patient Care Services and Chief Nursing Officer, Frederick Memorial Hospital, Frederick, MD, p. A301

CIOTA, Mark, M.D.,
  Chief Executive Officer, Mayo Clinic Health System in Albert Lea, Albert Lea, MN, p. A339
  Chief Executive Officer, Mayo Clinic Health System in Austin, Austin, MN, p. A340

CIRALDO, Lou, Information Services Representative, University Hospitals Geauga Medical Center, Chardon, OH, p. A485

CIRONE, Laura, Manager Human Resources, Rochelle Community Hospital, Rochelle, IL, p. A201

CITA, Bob, Director Information Services, SEARHC MT. Edgecumbe Hospital, Sitka, AK, p. A30

CITAK, Michael, M.D. Chief Medical Officer, Lake Cumberland Regional Hospital, Somerset, KY, p. A270

CIUFO, Donna, R.N. Vice President and Chief Nurse Executive, Southern Ocean Medical Center, Manahawkin, NJ, p. A418

CIVAN, Dino, Chief Information Officer, Kings County Hospital Center, NY, p. A444

CIVELLO, RN, Ralph Jay, MSN Associate Executive Director Patient Care Services, Franklin Hospital, Valley Stream, NY, p. A457

CIVIC, Dave, M.D. Associate Director Clinical Services, U. S. Public Health Service Phoenix Indian Medical Center, Phoenix, AZ, p. A37

CIVITELLO, Dean, Vice President Human Resources, Public Relations and Development, St. Joseph's Medical Center, Yonkers, NY, p. A458

CLABAUGH, John, Director Human Resources, Saint Luke's East Hospital, Lee's Summit, MO, p. A375

CLACK, Deborah
  Chief Nursing Officer, Hunt Regional Community Hospital, Commerce, TX, p. A607
  Chief Nursing Officer, Hunt Regional Medical Center, Greenville, TX, p. A622

CLACK, Lee, R.N. Chief Nursing Officer, Lake Wales Medical Center, Lake Wales, FL, p. A133

CLADOUHOS, Joseph, Chief Executive Officer, Syringa Hospital and Clinics, Grangeville, ID, p. A176

CLAIBORNE, Ronnie, M.D. Chief Medical Officer, Good Samaritan Hospital, Bakersfield, CA, p. A57

CLANCY, Karen, Manager Information Systems Operations, Bath Veterans Affairs Medical Center, Bath, NY, p. A433

CLANCY, Mikki, Chief Operating Officer, Miami Valley Hospital, Dayton, OH, p. A492

CLANCY, Patricia, M.D. Director Medical Services, Maniilaq Health Center, Kotzebue, AK, p. A29

CLAPP, Ann R., Director Human Resources, HEALTHSOUTH Rehabilitation Hospital of Texarkana, Texarkana, TX, p. A652

CLAPP, Denise
  Chief Nursing Officer, Lourdes Counseling Center, Richland, WA, p. A687
  Chief Nursing Officer, Lourdes Medical Center, Pasco, WA, p. A686

CLAPP, Mary, Controller, Henry County Hospital, Napoleon, OH, p. A499

CLAPP, Nicole, FACHE, President and Chief Executive Officer, Grant Regional Health Center, Lancaster, WI, p. A708

CLARK, Allan W., M.D. Medical Director, Southwood Psychiatric Hospital, Pittsburgh, PA, p. A551

CLARK, Andrew, M.D. Medical Director, KidsPeace Children's Hospital, Orefield, PA, p. A547

CLARK, Ashley, Coordinator Human Resources, Noland Hospital Birmingham, Birmingham, AL, p. A16

CLARK, Ben, Vice President and Chief Information Officer, Centra Lynchburg General Hospital, Lynchburg, VA, p. A673

CLARK, Chris, Chief Technology Officer, Elkview General Hospital, Hobart, OK, p. A512

CLARK, Chris, M.D. Senior Vice President Medical Affairs and Chief Medical Officer, Saint Vincent Health Center, Erie, PA, p. A539

CLARK, Dale, Chief Operating Officer, Wythe County Community Hospital, Wytheville, VA, p. A680

CLARK, Dave, Interim Chief Executive Officer, Hardeman County Memorial Hospital, Quanah, TX, p. A643

CLARK, David D., President, Methodist Dallas Medical Center, Dallas, TX, p. A611

CLARK, Denise C., R.N. Chief Clinical Officer, Mt. San Rafael Hospital, Trinidad, CO, p. A111

CLARK, Ed, M.D. Chief Medical Officer, Primary Children's Medical Center, Salt Lake City, UT, p. A663

CLARK, Ed, Vice President Finance, Specialty Hospital of Washington, Washington, DC, p. A122

CLARK, Eileen, Director Computer Services, University of Tennessee Medical Center, Knoxville, TN, p. A586

CLARK, Frank, Chief Information Officer, MUSC Medical Center of Medical University of South Carolina, Charleston, SC, p. A563

CLARK, Heather, Chief Executive Officer, Caldwell Memorial Hospital, Columbia, LA, p. A275

CLARK, Janice, Manager Human Resources, Garfield Park Hospital, Chicago, IL, p. A183

CLARK, Jason, Director Quality Improvement, Risk Management and Information System, Greenwood County Hospital, Eureka, KS, p. A244

CLARK, Jean, Administrator, Kindred Hospital Seattle–Northgate, Seattle, WA, p. A688

CLARK, Jeff
  Director Information Systems, Graham Regional Medical Center, Graham, TX, p. A621
  Vice President Human Resources, Kadlec Regional Medical Center, Richland, WA, p. A687

CLARK, Jeremy, Chief Executive Officer, Saint Francis Hospital–Bartlett, Bartlett, TN, p. A579

CLARK, John
  Chief Financial Officer, Childrens Care Hospital and School, Sioux Falls, SD, p. A576
  Interim Administrator, Winkler County Memorial Hospital, Kermit, TX, p. A631

CLARK, Karen, MS Vice President Operations, Advocate South Suburban Hospital, Hazel Crest, IL, p. A192

CLARK, Karen
  Director Administrative Services, Sonoma Developmental Center, Eldridge, CA, p. A62
  Vice President Patient Care Services, St. Mary's Regional Medical Center, Lewiston, ME, p. A294

CLARK, Karen S., Chief Financial Officer, St. Mary's Hospital, Streator, IL, p. A204

CLARK, Kathy, R.N., President and Chief Executive Officer, Wilcox Memorial Hospital, Lihue, HI, p. A172

CLARK, Kent, M.D. Chief Medical Affairs and Quality, Waldo County General Hospital, Belfast, ME, p. A292

CLARK, Lawrence, M.D. President Medical Staff, Riverside Community Hospital, Riverside, CA, p. A86

CLARK, Lisa, Human Resources Officer, Holy Cross Hospital, Taos, NM, p. A431

CLARK, M. Victoria, Chief Executive Officer, La Paz Regional Hospital, Parker, AZ, p. A35

CLARK, Mark
  Human Resources Liaison, U. S. Air Force Regional Hospital, Elmendorf AFB, AK, p. A28
  Vice President Information Services, Yampa Valley Medical Center, Steamboat Springs, CO, p. A111

CLARK, Mark A., Vice President Operations, St. Mary's Hospital, Centralia, IL, p. A182

CLARK, Megan, Coordinator Human Resources, Genesis Medical Center–Aledo, Aledo, IL, p. A180

CLARK, Michael
  Director Operations, Clay County Memorial Hospital, Henrietta, TX, p. A623
  Vice President Finance, FHN Memorial Hospital, Freeport, IL, p. A190
  Interim Chief Executive Officer, Putnam Community Medical Center, Palatka, FL, p. A141

CLARK, Michael A., Administrator and Chief Executive Officer, Logan Regional Hospital, Logan, UT, p. A660

CLARK, N. Travis, President, Page Memorial Hospital, Luray, VA, p. A673

CLARK, Nancy, Vice President Human Resources, Regional Medical Center of San Jose, San Jose, CA, p. A92

CLARK, Pam, Interim Administrator, Reagan Memorial Hospital, Big Lake, TX, p. A602

CLARK, Patrick, Manager Information Technology, Sunnyview Rehabilitation Hospital, Schenectady, NY, p. A454

CLARK Jr., Ralph H., FACHE, Chief Executive Officer, Medical Center Barbour, Eufaula, AL, p. A19

CLARK, Randal, Vice President Finance, Sebasticook Valley Health, Pittsfield, ME, p. A294

CLARK, Renee, R.N. Vice President Nursing Services and Performance Improvement, Fort HealthCare, Fort Atkinson, WI, p. A705

CLARK, Rhonda, Interim Chief Nursing Officer, Alta Vista Regional Hospital, Las Vegas, NM, p. A429

CLARK, Richard, Chief Executive Officer, Rolling Hills Hospital, Franklin, TN, p. A583

CLARK, Robert J., President and Chief Executive Officer, Bristol Bay Area Health Corporation, Dillingham, AK, p. A28

CLARK, Robin, Chief Nursing Officer, Select Specialty Hospital–Greensboro, Greensboro, NC, p. A465

CLARK, Ron, M.D. Vice President Clinical Activities and Chief Medical Officer, VCU Medical Center, Richmond, VA, p. A678

CLARK, Shannon, Chief Financial Officer, Drew Memorial Hospital, Monticello, AR, p. A50

CLARK, Sharon, Director Human Resources, Hillsboro Area Hospital, Hillsboro, IL, p. A192

CLARK, Shawn, Director Information Systems, The Physicians Centre Hospital, Bryan, TX, p. A604

CLARK, Stella, Chief Nursing Officer, St. Joseph's Hospital, Chippewa Falls, WI, p. A703

CLARK, Steve, Chief Information Officer, Sentara Albemarle Medical Center, Elizabeth City, NC, p. A464

CLARK, Teresa, Director of Nursing, Wichita County Health Center, Leoti, KS, p. A248

CLARK, Teresa J., R.N. Chief Nursing Officer, Cook Children's Medical Center, Fort Worth, TX, p. A618

CLARK, Theo, Director Financial Services, Promise Hospital of Phoenix, Mesa, AZ, p. A34

CLARK, Thomas A., Regional President and Chief Executive Officer, Avera Queen of Peace Hospital, Mitchell, SD, p. A575

CLARK, Tim
  Director Human Resources, Moberly Regional Medical Center, Moberly, MO, p. A377
  Chief Operating Officer and Chief Clinical Officer, Vibra Hospital of San Diego, San Diego, CA, p. A90

CLARK, Troy, Chief Operating Officer, Wellmont Holston Valley Medical Center, Kingsport, TN, p. A585

CLARK, William, M.D. Chief Clinical Affairs, Caro Center, Caro, MI, p. A320

CLARKE, James, M.D. Vice President Medical Affairs and Clinical Effectiveness, Ocean Medical Center, Brick Township, NJ, p. A414

CLARKIN, John, Director Human Resource, Abington Health Lansdale Hospital, Lansdale, PA, p. A542

CLAROS, Elizabeth, Administrator Personnel Services, Guam Memorial Hospital Authority, Tamuning, GU, p. A724

CLARRY, Patrick M., Vice President Human Resources, Providence Holy Family Hospital, Spokane, WA, p. A690

CLARY, Brandon, Chief Executive Officer, Edgefield County Hospital, Edgefield, SC, p. A565

CLARY, Elizabeth P., R.N., Vice President Behavioral Health, Peninsula Hospital, Louisville, TN, p. A587

CLARY, Patrick, Vice President Human Resources, Providence Sacred Heart Medical Center & Children's Hospital, Spokane, WA, p. A690

CLATANOFF, Kris, Director Human Resources, St. Joseph Medical Center, Houston, TX, p. A627

CLAUDSON, Jackie, Administrator, South Big Horn County Hospital, Basin, WY, p. A720

CLAUDY, Frank, M.D. Vice President Medical Staff Affairs, Genesis Medical Center–Davenport, Davenport, IA, p. A228

CLAUNCH, Jeremy, Chief Financial Officer, Power County Hospital District, American Falls, ID, p. A174

CLAUSEN, Patricia J., R.N. Chief Nurse Executive, Kaiser Permanente Downey Medical Center, Downey, CA, p. A61

CLAUSSEN, Denise, R.N. Chief Nursing Officer, Texas Health Presbyterian Hospital Kaufman, Kaufman, TX, p. A630

CLAUSSEN, Tammy, Human Resources Executive, Tri Valley Health System, Cambridge, NE, p. A394

CLAVELL, Luis, M.D. Medical Director, San Jorge Children's Hospital, San Juan, PR, p. A728

CLAVELLE, Joanne T., R.N. Senior Vice President and Chief Clinical Officer, Scottsdale Healthcare Shea Medical Center, Scottsdale, AZ, p. A38

CLAWSON, Tonya, Manager Human Resources, Mercy Medical Center–Centerville, Centerville, IA, p. A227

CLAXTON, Anthony, M.D. Clinical Director, Terrell State Hospital, Terrell, TX, p. A652

CLAXTON, Tracey, Chief Financial Officer, Chester Regional Medical Center, Chester, SC, p. A564

CLAY, David, Chief Operating Officer, Piedmont Medical Center, Rock Hill, SC, p. A569

CLAYMORE, Krystal, Chief Financial Officer, Great Plains Health, North Platte, NE, p. A398

CLAYPOOL, Blain, Chief Executive Officer, St. Vincent's Medical Center Clay County, Middleburg, FL, p. A138

CLAYTON, Edward, Chief Financial Officer, Phelps County Regional Medical Center, Rolla, MO, p. A379

CLAYTON, Julie, R.N. Chief Nursing Officer and Vice President Patient Care Services, Overlake Medical Center, Bellevue, WA, p. A681

CLAYTON, Kathy, Chief Financial Officer, Fairfield Memorial Hospital, Fairfield, IL, p. A190

CLAYTON, Kent G., Chief Executive Officer, Los Alamitos Medical Center, Los Alamitos, CA, p. A71

CLAYTON, Philip A., President and Chief Executive Officer, Conway Medical Center, Conway, SC, p. A565

CLEARY, Steven R.
  Vice President Finance, St. Joseph Medical Center, Kansas City, MO, p. A374
  Vice President Finance, St. Mary's Medical Center, Blue Springs, MO, p. A367

CLEAVER, Chuck, Vice President and Chief Financial Officer, Martin Health System, Stuart, FL, p. A146

CLECKLER, Jason, Chief Executive Officer, Delta County Memorial Hospital, Delta, CO, p. A104

CLELAND, Dub, Chief Financial Officer, Oklahoma Surgical Hospital, Tulsa, OK, p. A520

CLELAND, Richard C., FACHE, President and Chief Operating Officer and Interim Chief Executive Officer, Erie County Medical Center, Buffalo, NY, p. A434

CLELAND, William H., M.D. Chief Medical Officer, University Hospital, Jackson, MS, p. A360

CLEMEN, Linda, R.N. Vice President and Chief Nursing Officer, Katherine Shaw Bethea Hospital, Dixon, IL, p. A188

CLEMENS, Brian L.
  President and Chief Executive Officer, Community Hospital, Oklahoma City, OK, p. A515
  Chief Executive Officer, Northwest Surgical Hospital, Oklahoma City, OK, p. A515

CLEMENT, Bernie, Chief Information Officer, Thibodaux Regional Medical Center, Thibodaux, LA, p. A289

CLEMENT, Bruce, Chief Operating Officer, Slidell Memorial Hospital, Slidell, LA, p. A289

CLEMENT, Kevin J., Chief Executive Officer, Siloam Springs Regional Hospital, Siloam Springs, AR, p. A53

CLEMENT, Mark C., President and Chief Executive Officer, Rochester Regional Health System, Rochester, NY, p. B115

CLEMENT, Michelle, Executive Assistant/Human Resources Director, Roundup Memorial Healthcare, Roundup, MT, p. A390

CLEMENTS, John R., Vice President and Chief Financial Officer, McCullough–Hyde Memorial Hospital, Oxford, OH, p. A500

CLEMENTS, Lynn
  Director Human Resources, Shriners Hospitals for Children–Galveston Burns Hospital, Galveston, TX, p. A620
  Director Human Resources, Shriners Hospitals for Children–Houston, Houston, TX, p. A626

CLEMMENSEN, J. Scott
  Vice President Human Resources and Leadership Enhancement, Capital Health Medical Center–Hopewell, Pennington, NJ, p. A421
  Vice President Human Resources and Leadership Enhancement, Capital Health Regional Medical Center, Trenton, NJ, p. A423

CLEMMER, Deb, Vice President Human Resources, Bothwell Regional Health Center, Sedalia, MO, p. A382

CLEMONS, Deneace, Chief Operating Officer, Twin Lakes Regional Medical Center, Leitchfield, KY, p. A264

CLERE, Trevor, Director Information Technology, Mercy Medical Center, Canton, OH, p. A485

CLEVELAND, Austin B., Chief Executive Officer, Select Specialty Hospital–Quad Cities, Davenport, IA, p. A229

CLEVELAND, Cynthia, Ph.D. Associate Director for Patient Care Services and Nurse Executive, Birmingham Veterans Affairs Medical Center, Birmingham, AL, p. A16

CLEVENGER, Erin R., Chief Nursing Officer and Director of Quality, Memorial Medical Center, Port Lavaca, TX, p. A643

CLEWS, Donna, Ph.D. Vice President Patient Care Services, Berkeley Medical Center, Martinsburg, WV, p. A697

CLICK, Glenn, Chief Financial Officer, Sequoyah Memorial Hospital, Sallisaw, OK, p. A518

CLICK, Mike, Administrator, Brownfield Regional Medical Center, Brownfield, TX, p. A604

CLIFF, Tammy, R.N. Director Nursing Services, McKenzie Health System, Sandusky, MI, p. A334

CLIFFE, Peggy, Chief Executive Officer, Select Specialty Hospital–Wichita, Wichita, KS, p. A256

CLIFFORD, Michael J., Director Finance, Wayne Memorial Hospital, Honesdale, PA, p. A540

CLIFFORD, Ryan, M.D. Chief of Staff, Washakie Medical Center, Worland, WY, p. A723

CLIFTON, Mark, Interim Chief Financial Officer, Memorial Medical Center – Livingston, Livingston, TX, p. A633

CLINE, Brooke, Director of Nursing, Salt Lake Behavioral Health, Salt Lake City, UT, p. A663

CLINE, Richard, D.O. Chief of Staff, Lincoln County Health System, Fayetteville, TN, p. A583

CLINE, Vickie, Director Human Resources, Northwest Medical Center, Albany, MO, p. A367

CLINGENPEEL, Jeremy, Administrator, Satanta District Hospital, Satanta, KS, p. A254

CLINGER, Dallas, Administrator, Power County Hospital District, American Falls, ID, p. A174

CLINITE, Ed, D.O. Chief of Staff, Sonora Regional Medical Center, Sonora, CA, p. A95

CLINTON, Lee, FACHE Vice President Operations, Perry County Memorial Hospital, Perryville, MO, p. A378

CLINTON, Lori, Chief Nursing Officer, Sparta Community Hospital, Sparta, IL, p. A202

CLIPP, Jerry, Manager Human Resources, Washakie Medical Center, Worland, WY, p. A723

CLISTER, Martha L., Director Human Resources, Canonsburg General Hospital, Canonsburg, PA, p. A535

CLOHSEY, Maria, Director of Nursing, Shore Rehabilitation Institute, Brick, NJ, p. A413

CLONCH, Leslie, Vice President and Chief Information Officer, University Hospital, Augusta, GA, p. A154

CLONTS, Jolene, Director Human Resources, Logan Regional Hospital, Logan, UT, p. A660

CLOSE, Debra, Chief Executive Officer, Dukes Memorial Hospital, Peru, IN, p. A221

CLOUD, Avery, Vice President and Chief Information Officer, New Hanover Regional Medical Center, Wilmington, NC, p. A474

CLOUD, Sylvia, Director Human Resources, Silver Lake Medical Center, Los Angeles, CA, p. A74

CLOUGH, Jeanette G., President and Chief Executive Officer, Mount Auburn Hospital, Cambridge, MA, p. A309

CLOUGH, Sheila, Chief Executive Officer, Asante Ashland Community Hospital, Ashland, OR, p. A523

CLOUGH–BERRY, Cherie, Vice President, Finance, Hampstead Hospital, Hampstead, NH, p. A410

CLOUSE, Joseph, Chief Administrative Officer, Newport Hospital and Health Services, Newport, WA, p. A685

CLOUSE DAY, Sherry, Vice President Finance, Mercy Hospital Berryville, Berryville, AR, p. A43

CLOUTIER, Mary, Director Human Resources, Adventist Behavioral Health Rockville, Rockville, MD, p. A303

CLOUTIER, Michael, Director Information Services, Trios Health, Kennewick, WA, p. A684

CLOVER, Robert, Superintendent and Chief Executive Officer, Logansport State Hospital, Logansport, IN, p. A218

CLOWES, Jennifer, Chief Financial Officer, Broadwater Health Center, Townsend, MT, p. A391

CLOYD, Elizabeth, R.N. Chief Nurse Executive and Executive Vice President, Harris Health System, Houston, TX, p. A624

CLUCK, Robert N., M.D. Vice President and Medical Director, Texas Health Arlington Memorial Hospital, Arlington, TX, p. A598

CLUFF, Ben, Chief Executive Officer, Ashley Regional Medical Center, Vernal, UT, p. A664

CLUNE, T. Patrick, Chief Financial Officer, Florence Hospital at Anthem, Florence, AZ, p. A32

CLUNN, Amy, M.D. Medical Director, HEALTHSOUTH Rehabilitation Hospital of Ocala, Ocala, FL, p. A139

CLUTTS, Kathaleen, Chief Human Resources Officer, Des Peres Hospital, Saint Louis, MO, p. A380

CLYNE, Andrea, R.N. Chief Nursing Officer, Palms of Pasadena Hospital, Saint Petersburg, FL, p. A144

CLYNE, Mary Ellen, Ph.D., President and Chief Executive Officer, Clara Maass Medical Center, Belleville, NJ, p. A413

CMIEL, Peggy, R.N. Chief Nursing Officer, Chinese Hospital, San Francisco, CA, p. A90

COALTER, Barbara, Director Human Resources, Weirton Medical Center, Weirton, WV, p. A700

COATE, Mark, M.D. Chief of Staff, Madison County Hospital, London, OH, p. A496

COATES, Janet E., R.N., President and Chief Executive Officer, Mother Frances Hospital – Winnsboro, Winnsboro, TX, p. A658

COATES, Jennifer, Coordinator Information Technology, Purcell Municipal Hospital, Purcell, OK, p. A518

COATS, Brenda, Director Human Resources, River Crest Hospital, San Angelo, TX, p. A645

COATS, Daniel J., Vice President Operations, Mercy Hospital Ada, Ada, OK, p. A507

COATS, John, M.D. Chief Medical Staff, Morehouse General Hospital, Bastrop, LA, p. A273

COATS, Kevin, Chief Operating Officer and Chief Financial Officer, Baylor Medical Center at Frisco, Frisco, TX, p. A620

COBARRUBIAS, Samuel, M.D. Chief of Staff, Clinch Memorial Hospital, Homerville, GA, p. A161

COBB, April, Chief Nursing Officer, HEALTHSOUTH Lakeshore Rehabilitation Hospital, Birmingham, AL, p. A16

COBB, Heidi, R.N. Chief Nursing Officer, Medical Arts Hospital, Lamesa, TX, p. A632

COBB, Janice M., R.N. Chief Nursing Officer, Tennessee Valley Healthcare System, Nashville, TN, p. A591

COBB, Jason E., FACHE, Chief Executive Officer, Rapides Regional Medical Center, Alexandria, LA, p. A272

COBB, Jeff, Information Technologist, Guthrie County Hospital, Guthrie Center, IA, p. A231

COBB, Maura, R.N. Chief Nursing Officer, Northridge Medical Center, Commerce, GA, p. A157

COBB, Tammy, Chief Financial Officer, Northeast Regional Medical Center, Kirksville, MO, p. A375

COBBLE, Emlyn, Vice President and Chief Support Officer, Parkwest Medical Center, Knoxville, TN, p. A586

COBBS, Wendy, Director of Human Resources, Promise Hospital of Baton Rouge – Ochsner Campus, Baton Rouge, LA, p. A274

COBURN, Nate, Chief Financial Officer, Weiser Memorial Hospital, Weiser, ID, p. A179

COBURN, Paul, Chief Financial Officer, Liberty Healthcare Systems, Bastrop, LA, p. A272

COCCHI, Dean, Chief Financial Officer, Kindred Hospital Ocala, Ocala, FL, p. A139

COCHENNET, Bradley, Chief Executive Officer, Pagosa Springs Medical Center, Pagosa Springs, CO, p. A110

COCHRAN, Dan
 Chief Operating Officer, Bingham Memorial Hospital, Blackfoot, ID, p. A174
 Chief Operating Officer, Mountain River Birthing and Surgery Center, Blackfoot, ID, p. A174

COCHRAN, Daniel, Vice President and Chief Financial Officer, Shady Grove Adventist Hospital, Rockville, MD, p. A303

COCHRAN, Janice, R.N. Director of Patient Care, Dubuis Hospital of Paris, Paris, TX, p. A641

COCHRAN, Kenneth, FACHE, President and Chief Executive Officer, East Liverpool City Hospital, East Liverpool, OH, p. A493

COCHRAN, Sherry, Manager Human Resources, Cascade Behavioral Hospital, Tukwila, WA, p. A691

COCHRAN, Jr., Willie, M.D. Chief of Staff, Southern Regional Medical Center, Riverdale, GA, p. A165

COCHRANE, Andrew S., Chief Executive Officer, Maple Grove Hospital, Maple Grove, MN, p. A346

COCHRANE, Robert K., Interim Vice President, Finance, Cheshire Medical Center, Keene, NH, p. A410

COCKING, Kathy, R.N. Vice President Operations, Barton Memorial Hospital, South Lake Tahoe, CA, p. A96

COCKRELL, Christopher, Executive Director Human Resources, Providence Hospital, Mobile, AL, p. A22

COCKRELL, Dennis, Director Human Resources, Gritman Medical Center, Moscow, ID, p. A177

COCKRELL, Tim, Chief Executive Officer, Patients Choice Medical Center of Smith County, Raleigh, MS, p. A365

CODER, Charles, Chief Financial Officer, Southside Regional Medical Center, Petersburg, VA, p. A676

CODY, Carolyn, M.D. Vice President Medical Affairs, Bryan Medical Center, Lincoln, NE, p. A397

CODY, James, Director, Syracuse Veterans Affairs Medical Center, Syracuse, NY, p. A456

COE, Jason, M.D. Medical Director, MMO Greenbrier Hospital, Covington, LA, p. A276

COE, Jason C., President and Chief Executive Officer, Hackettstown Regional Medical Center, Hackettstown, NJ, p. A416

COE, Susan
 Vice President Human Resources, University of Maryland Shore Medical Center at Chestertown, Chestertown, MD, p. A299
 Regional Vice President Human Resources, University of Maryland Shore Medical Center at Dorchester, Cambridge, MD, p. A299
 Regional Vice President Human Resources, University of Maryland Shore Medical Center at Easton, Easton, MD, p. A300

COEN, Vickie, Chief Clinical Officer and Nurse Executive, Pana Community Hospital, Pana, IL, p. A199

COFFEE, Paula, Director Human Resources, St. Mary's of Michigan, Saginaw, MI, p. A334

COFFEE, Robert, Chief Information Officer, Creek Nation Community Hospital, Okemah, OK, p. A514

COFFELL, Randy, Manager Human Resources, Mid–Valley Hospital, Omak, WA, p. A686

COFFEY, Bryan D., Chief Executive Officer, Hamilton County Hospital, Syracuse, KS, p. A255

COFFEY, C. Edward, M.D., Chief Executive Officer and Director Behavioral Health Services, Henry Ford Kingswood Hospital, Ferndale, MI, p. A323

COFFEY, Daniel B., President and Chief Executive Officer, The Acadia Hospital, Bangor, ME, p. A291

COFFEY, Douglas W., R.N. Chief Nursing Officer, St. Mary's Regional Medical Center, Enid, OK, p. A510

COFFEY, Glenna, R.N., Chief Operating Officer, Bridgewell Hospital of Cincinnati, Cincinnati, OH, p. A486

COFFEY, Joseph, Director Facility Administration, Rochester Psychiatric Center, Rochester, NY, p. A453

COFFEY, Judy
 Senior Vice President and Area Manager, Kaiser Permanente San Rafael Medical Center, San Rafael, CA, p. A93
 Senior Vice President and Area Manager, Kaiser Permanente Santa Rosa Medical Center, Santa Rosa, CA, p. A95

COFFEY, Kevin, Chief Executive Officer, Winner Regional Healthcare Center, Winner, SD, p. A578

COFFEY, Timothy O., Senior Vice President Operations, Lake Charles Memorial Hospital, Lake Charles, LA, p. A282

COFFING, Sylvia K., R.N. Chief Nursing and Compliance Officer, Unity Medical & Surgical Hospital, Mishawaka, IN, p. A219

COFFMAN, Courtney, Chief Financial Officer, Lower Bucks Hospital, Bristol, PA, p. A534

COFFMAN, Douglas, Vice President and Chief Financial Officer, United Hospital Center, Bridgeport, WV, p. A693

COFFMAN, Joan, President and Chief Executive Officer, St. Joseph's Hospital, Chippewa Falls, WI, p. A703

COFFMAN BARNES, Julie, M.D. Chief Medical Officer, Redmond Regional Medical Center, Rome, GA, p. A165

COFIELD, Robert, Dr.PH Associate Vice President and Chief Operating Officer, University of Virginia Medical Center, Charlottesville, VA, p. A669

COFINAS, Rebecca, Vice President and Chief Operating Executive Operations, Scripps Memorial Hospital–Encinitas, Encinitas, CA, p. A62

COHEN, Aaron, Chief Financial Officer, Bellevue Hospital Center, New York, NY, p. A442

COHEN, Cindy, Director Human Resources, Stewart & Lynda Resnick Neuropsychiatric Hospital at UCLA, Los Angeles, CA, p. A75

COHEN, Ginger, Chief Nurse Executive, St. Luke's Rehabilitation Institute, Spokane, WA, p. A690

COHEN, Joe, M.D. Chief of Staff, Transylvania Regional Hospital, Brevard, NC, p. A460

COHEN, Kathleena, Director of Nursing, Hampton Behavioral Health Center, Westampton, NJ, p. A424

COHEN, Mark, M.D. Chief Medical Officer, Piedmont Hospital, Atlanta, GA, p. A153

COHEN, Philip A., Chief Executive Officer, Monterey Park Hospital, Monterey Park, CA, p. A78

COHEN, Robert, M.D. Chief Medical Officer, Sonoma Valley Hospital, Sonoma, CA, p. A95

COKER, Cindy, M.P.H. Vice President, Patient Care Services, Vidant Chowan Hospital, Edenton, NC, p. A464

COLADONATO, Angela, MSN Chief Nursing Officer, Chester County Hospital, West Chester, PA, p. A558

COLAGUORI, Ronald J., Vice President Operations, St. Anthony's Hospital, Saint Petersburg, FL, p. A145

COLAMARIA, James, Director of Nursing, Four Winds Hospital, Saratoga Springs, NY, p. A454

COLANGELO, Nicholas, Chief Executive Officer, Clear Brook Lodge, Shickshinny, PA, p. A555

COLAS, Chuck, M.D. Medical Director, Surprise Valley Health Care District, Cedarville, CA, p. A59

COLBERG, Gary R., FACHE, President and Chief Executive Officer, Southeast Georgia Health System, Brunswick, GA, p. B125

COLBERG, Gary R., FACHE, President and Chief Executive Officer, Southeast Georgia Health System Brunswick Campus, Brunswick, GA, p. A155

COLBURN, Douglas, Chief Information Officer, Northside Medical Center, Columbus, GA, p. A156

COLBURN, Tim, President and Chief Executive Officer, Berger Health System, Circleville, OH, p. A488

COLBY, Dennis, M.D. Chief of Staff, Iowa Specialty Hospital–Clarion, Clarion, IA, p. A227

COLCHER, Marian W., President and Chief Executive Officer, Valley Forge Medical Center and Hospital, Norristown, PA, p. A546

COLE, Annette E., R.N. Vice President and Chief Nursing Officer, Sky Lakes Medical Center, Klamath Falls, OR, p. A526

COLE, Bernadette Green, R.N. Chief Nursing Officer, Charlevoix Area Hospital, Charlevoix, MI, p. A320

COLE, Beth, Director Information Services, Lewis–Gale Medical Center, Salem, VA, p. A678

COLE, Cal, Director Information Systems, Winter Haven Hospital, Winter Haven, FL, p. A150

COLE, Carlene, Manager Human Resources, Kittson Memorial Healthcare Center, Hallock, MN, p. A344

COLE, Cyndie, MSN, Administrator, Ventura County Medical Center, Ventura, CA, p. A99

COLE, Eric, Director Information Technology, Coffey County Hospital, Burlington, KS, p. A242

COLE, F. Sessions, M.D. Chief Medical Officer, St. Louis Children's Hospital, Saint Louis, MO, p. A382

COLE, Georgeanne, Chief Executive Officer, Rehabilitation Hospital of Southwest Virginia, Bristol, VA, p. A668

COLE Jr., Harry, Administrator, Georgiana Hospital, Georgiana, AL, p. A21

COLE, James B., Chief Executive Officer, Virginia Hospital Center – Arlington, Arlington, VA, p. A668

COLE, Jason
 Director Finance, Scott & White Hospital – Llano, Llano, TX, p. A633
 Senior Director Finance, Scott & White Hospital at Round Rock, Round Rock, TX, p. A644

COLE, Karen S., FACHE, Chief Executive Officer, Shenandoah Medical Center, Shenandoah, IA, p. A237

COLE, Lori, Director Information Management, Wayne Memorial Hospital, Goldsboro, NC, p. A465

COLE, Missy, Director Human Resources, HEALTHSOUTH Rehabilitation Hospital, Fayetteville, AR, p. A45

COLE, Philip, M.D. Vice President Medical Affairs and Chief Medical Officer, CHRISTUS Highland Medical Center, Shreveport, LA, p. A288

COLE, Robert, Chief Operating Officer, Connecticut Mental Health Center, New Haven, CT, p. A116

COLE–HUDSON, Jan, R.N. Director Nursing Services, Dundy County Hospital, Benkelman, NE, p. A394

COLECCHI, Stephen, President and Chief Executive Officer, Robinson Memorial Hospital, Ravenna, OH, p. A501

COLEMAN, Alice, Blessing Corporate Controller, Illini Community Hospital, Pittsfield, IL, p. A200

COLEMAN, Alisa, Chief Executive Officer, Trigg County Hospital, Cadiz, KY, p. A259

COLEMAN, Amy, Director Human Resources, Loretto Hospital, Chicago, IL, p. A184

COLEMAN, Andrea C., Chief Operating Officer, Penrose–St. Francis Health Services, Colorado Springs, CO, p. A104

COLEMAN, Curt, FACHE,
 Administrator, Genesis Medical Center, DeWitt, De Witt, IA, p. A229
 Administrator, Jackson County Regional Health Center, Maquoketa, IA, p. A234

COLEMAN, D. Scott, Medical Director, Livingston Memorial Hospital, Livingston, MT, p. A389

COLEMAN, Donna, Coordinator Human Resources, Jackson County Hospital District, Edna, TX, p. A615

COLEMAN, James J., Ed.D., Director, Kalamazoo Psychiatric Hospital, Kalamazoo, MI, p. A328

COLEMAN, Jr., Jim L., Chief Operating Officer, Parkridge Medical Center, Chattanooga, TN, p. A580

COLEMAN, Judy, Chief Operating Officer and Chief Financial Officer, Indiana University Health West Hospital, Avon, IN, p. A206

COLEMAN, Karen, Director of Nursing, Grove Hill Memorial Hospital, Grove Hill, AL, p. A21

COLEMAN, Keith T., Chief Financial Officer, Mount Carmel, Columbus, OH, p. A490

COLEMAN, Melissa, Director Human Resources, HEALTHSOUTH Rehabilitation Hospital, Sewickley, PA, p. A555

COLENDA, Christopher, M.P.H., President and Chief Executive Officer, West Virginia United Health System, Fairmont, WV, p. B152

COLERICK, Steven, Chief Executive Officer, Buena Vista Regional Medical Center, Storm Lake, IA, p. A238

COLETTA, Antonio
 Vice President Human Resources, Advocate BroMenn Medical Center, Normal, IL, p. A198
 Vice President Human Resources, Advocate Eureka Hospital, Eureka, IL, p. A189

COLETTA, Diane, Director Human Resources, Royal Oaks Hospital, Windsor, MO, p. A384

COLEY, Brenda
 Executive Director, Metroplex Adventist Hospital, Killeen, TX, p. A631
 Executive Director, Rollins–Brook Community Hospital, Lampasas, TX, p. A632

COLGAN, Teresa, VP of Nursing, Great River Medical Center, West Burlington, IA, p. A239

COLINERI, Lori, MSN Senior Vice President Nursing and Chief Nursing Officer, Robert Wood Johnson University Hospital, New Brunswick, NJ, p. A419

COLKER, Rebecca, Chief Financial Officer, St. Mary's Hospital, Decatur, IL, p. A188

COLLAZO, Marian, Director Finance, Hospital San Cristobal, Coto Laurel, PR, p. A725

COLLETT, John, Vice President and Chief Financial Officer, Cayuga Medical Center at Ithaca, Ithaca, NY, p. A439

COLLETT, Josh, Director Human Resources, Pineville Community Hospital Association, Pineville, KY, p. A269

COLLEY, Sarah, Senior Vice President Human Resources, Regional One Health, Memphis, TN, p. A589

COLLIER, Brad, Director, Newton Medical Center, Covington, GA, p. A157

COLLIER, Jack, M.D. Chief of Staff, MountainView Hospital, Las Vegas, NV, p. A406

COLLIER, Margaret P., Chief Executive Officer and Managing Director, Anchor Hospital, Atlanta, GA, p. A151

COLLIER, Russell J., FACHE, President and Chief Executive Officer, Good Shepherd Medical Center–Marshall, Marshall, TX, p. A636

COLLIER, Scarlet, Chief Information Officer, Lane Regional Medical Center, Zachary, LA, p. A290

COLLIER, Shari, Chief Financial Officer, Overland Park Regional Medical Center, Overland Park, KS, p. A252

COLLIER, Tammy, Vice President Patient Services, Texas Health Huguley Hospital Fort Worth South, Fort Worth, TX, p. A619

COLLIER, Tom, Manager Information Systems, Missouri Rehabilitation Center, Mount Vernon, MO, p. A377

COLLINI, M. Patrick, M.D. President Medical Staff, USMD Hospital at Arlington, Arlington, TX, p. A598

COLLINS, Alesha Danielle, Chief Nursing Officer, Howard Memorial Hospital, Nashville, AR, p. A50

COLLINS, Barry, D.O. Chief of Staff, Hillsdale Community Health Center, Hillsdale, MI, p. A326

COLLINS, Bobby
  Director Human Resources, Mountain View Regional Medical Center, Norton, VA, p. A676
  Director Human Resources, Wellmont Lonesome Pine Hospital, Big Stone Gap, VA, p. A668

COLLINS, Chauncey, Director Operations and Finance, Austen Riggs Center, Stockbridge, MA, p. A315

COLLINS, David, Director Administration, Naval Medical Center, Portsmouth, VA, p. A676

COLLINS, Dennis, Chief Financial Officer, The Brook Hospital – KMI, Louisville, KY, p. A266

COLLINS, Edmund, Chief Information Officer, Martin Health System, Stuart, FL, p. A146

COLLINS, Frances, Director of Nursing, Andrew McFarland Mental Health Center, Springfield, IL, p. A203

COLLINS, Harold E., JD Chief Financial Officer, Franciscan Healthcare – Munster, Munster, IN, p. A219

COLLINS, James M., President and Chief Executive Officer, St. Clair Hospital, Pittsburgh, PA, p. A551

COLLINS, Jeff, Chief Medical Officer, Providence Sacred Heart Medical Center & Children's Hospital, Spokane, WA, p. A690

COLLINS, Jeffrey A., M.D., Senior Vice President and Area Manager, Kaiser Permanente Fresno Medical Center, Fresno, CA, p. A64

COLLINS, John F., President and Chief Executive Officer, Winthrop–University Hospital, Mineola, NY, p. A441

COLLINS, John R., Chief Financial Officer, Hemet Valley Medical Center, Hemet, CA, p. A67

COLLINS, Kandy, MSN, Director, Lafayette Behavioral Health, Lafayette, LA, p. A281

COLLINS, Karen S., R.N., Chief Executive Officer, Lady of the Sea General Hospital, Cut Off, LA, p. A276

COLLINS, Kathleen, M.D. Chief Medical Officer, Presence Covenant Medical Center, Urbana, IL, p. A204

COLLINS, Kevin J., M.D. Medical Director, St. Vincent Rehabilitation Hospital, Sherwood, AR, p. A52

COLLINS, Leonora, Chief Nursing Officer, Nashville General Hospital, Nashville, TN, p. A590

COLLINS, Michael F., Chief Executive Officer, Merrimack Valley Hospital, Haverhill, MA, p. A310

COLLINS, Pam, Director Human Resources, Fairway Medical Center, Covington, LA, p. A276

COLLINS, Pamela, Vice President Chief Patient Services Officer, McCullough–Hyde Memorial Hospital, Oxford, OH, p. A500

COLLINS, Richard F., M.D. Executive Vice President and Chief Medical Officer, Jefferson Hospital, Jefferson Hills, PA, p. A541

COLLINS, Ricky M., M.D. Chief of Staff, Whitesburg ARH Hospital, Whitesburg, KY, p. A271

COLLINS, Ron, Chief Financial Officer, Victory Medical Center Craig Ranch, McKinney, TX, p. A637

COLLINS, Rudy
  Human Resources Business Partner, Kaiser Permanente San Rafael Medical Center, San Rafael, CA, p. A93
  Human Resources Business Partner, Kaiser Permanente Santa Rosa Medical Center, Santa Rosa, CA, p. A95

COLLINS, Sandra, Chief Clinical Officer, Kindred Hospital–Philadelphia, Philadelphia, PA, p. A549

COLLINS, Sharon
  Director Human Resources and Executive Administrative Assistant, Russell Regional Hospital, Russell, KS, p. A253
  Chief Information Officer, Salem Veterans Affairs Medical Center, Salem, VA, p. A678

COLLINS, Shaw, Director Information Technology, Methodist Hospitals, Gary, IN, p. A212

COLLINS, Terry, Chief Financial Officer, Aspen Valley Hospital District, Aspen, CO, p. A102

COLLINS, Thomas M., President, Chairman and Chief Executive Officer, Green Oaks Hospital, Dallas, TX, p. A610

COLLIPP, Dan, M.D. Chief of Staff, Wayne Memorial Hospital, Jesup, GA, p. A161

COLLISON, June, President, Community Hospital of San Bernardino, San Bernardino, CA, p. A88

COLLOM, Bobbie, Nursing Director, North Runnels Hospital, Winters, TX, p. A658

COLLOTTA, Sharon
  Director Human Resources, Mease Countryside Hospital, Safety Harbor, FL, p. A144
  Director Human Resources, Mease Dunedin Hospital, Dunedin, FL, p. A128
  Director Human Resources, Morton Plant Hospital, Clearwater, FL, p. A125
  Director Team Resources, Morton Plant North Bay Hospital, New Port Richey, FL, p. A139

COLMAN, Gerard, Chief Operating Officer, Aurora West Allis Medical Center, West Allis, WI, p. A718

COLMENARES, Derek, M.D
  Chief Medical Officer, Agnesian HealthCare, Fond Du Lac, WI, p. A704
  Chief Medical Officer, Waupun Memorial Hospital, Waupun, WI, p. A717

COLOMBO, Armando, Chief Executive Officer, Intermedical Hospital of South Carolina, Columbia, SC, p. A564

COLOMBO, Lisa, R.N. Senior Vice President and Chief Nursing Officer, Lahey Hospital & Medical Center, Burlington, Burlington, MA, p. A308

COLON, Julio, Financial Director, Hospital De Damas, Ponce, PR, p. A727

COLON, Julio, CPA, Chief Executive Officer, Hospital Episcopal San Lucas Guayama, Guayama, PR, p. A726

COLON, Julio
  Interim President and Chief Executive Officer, St. Luke's Episcopal Hospital, Ponce, PR, p. A727
  Chief Financial Officer, St. Luke's Episcopal Hospital, Ponce, PR, p. A727

COLON, Omar, M.D. Medical Director, HEALTHSOUTH Plano Rehabilitation Hospital, Plano, TX, p. A642

COLONES, Robert L., President and Chief Executive Officer, McLeod Health, Florence, SC, p. B90

COLONES, Robert L., President and Chief Executive Officer, McLeod Regional Medical Center, Florence, SC, p. A566

COLORADO, Judy, R.N. Chief Nursing Officer and Chief Nursing Officer, Monmouth Medical Center, Southern Campus, Lakewood, NJ, p. A417

COLPITTS, Robert, Chief Human Resource Service, Bedford Veterans Affairs Medical Center, Edith Nourse Rogers Memorial Veterans Hospital, Bedford, MA, p. A305

COLPO, Susan T., Chief Executive Officer, Life Line Hospital, Steubenville, OH, p. A502

COLSON, Curt, President and Chief Executive Officer, Clara Barton Hospital, Hoisington, KS, p. A245

COLSON, Wayne, Chief Financial Officer, Southwestern Medical Center, Lawton, OK, p. A512

COLT, Darlene, R.N. Chief Nursing Officer, Spanish Peaks Regional Health Center, Walsenburg, CO, p. A112

COLTHARP, Missy, Director, Baptist Memorial Hospital–Union County, New Albany, MS, p. A363

COLTON, Jan, M.D. Acting Clinical Director, U. S. Public Health Service Indian Hospital, Pine Ridge, SD, p. A575

COLTRAIN, Penny, Director Human Resources, Vidant Beaufort Hospital, Washington, NC, p. A474

COLUCCI, Eugene, Vice President Finance, Greenwich Hospital, Greenwich, CT, p. A114

COLUCCIO, Medrice, R.N., Chief Executive Officer, Providence St. Peter Hospital, Olympia, WA, p. A686

COLVARD, Dusty, Manager Information Technology, Tehachapi Valley Healthcare District, Tehachapi, CA, p. A96

COLVERT, Richard, Chief Information Officer, Royal Oaks Hospital, Windsor, MO, p. A384

COLVIN, Garren
  Senior Vice President and Chief Financial Officer, St. Elizabeth Edgewood, Edgewood, KY, p. A260
  Senior Vice President Finance and Chief Financial Officer, St. Elizabeth Florence, Florence, KY, p. A261
  Senior Vice President and Chief Financial Officer, St. Elizabeth Fort Thomas, Fort Thomas, KY, p. A261

COLVIN, Robert L., Administrator, Ouachita Community Hospital, West Monroe, LA, p. A290

COLVIN, William, Human Resources Officer, Homer Memorial Hospital, Homer, LA, p. A278

COLWELL, Dean, D.O. Vice President Medical Affairs, OhioHealth Doctors Hospital, Columbus, OH, p. A490

COLYER, Valeri J.
  Director Human Resources, Dickenson Community Hospital, Clintwood, VA, p. A669
  Director Human Resources, Norton Community Hospital, Norton, VA, p. A676

COMAIANNI, Sheri, Vice President Human Resources, Bakersfield Memorial Hospital, Bakersfield, CA, p. A57

COMBEST, Felton, M.D. Vice President Medical Affairs, Magnolia Regional Health Center, Corinth, MS, p. A357

COMBS, Cindy, Supervisor Human Resources, Hampshire Memorial Hospital, Romney, WV, p. A699

COMBS, Mark
  Interim Director System Information Technology, Berkeley Medical Center, Martinsburg, WV, p. A697
  Chief Information Security Officer, Jefferson Medical Center, Ranson, WV, p. A699

COMBS, Meri, R.N. Vice President and Chief Nursing Officer, Madera Community Hospital, Madera, CA, p. A76

COMBS, Mike, Manager Information Technology, Holdenville General Hospital, Holdenville, OK, p. A512

COMBS, Will, Director Information Technology, Harrison Community Hospital, Cadiz, OH, p. A484

COMER, Fannessa, Chief Executive Officer, Northern Navajo Medical Center, Shiprock, NM, p. A431

COMER, Jennifer, M.D. Medical Director, Valle Vista Hospital, Greenwood, IN, p. A212

COMER, Randy, Chief Operating Officer, Athens–Limestone Hospital, Athens, AL, p. A16

COMER, Scott, Director Administrative Services, Marshall Medical Center, Placerville, CA, p. A83

COMERFORD, Jennifer, Manager Information Services, MidState Medical Center, Meriden, CT, p. A115

COMFORT, Jeff, Vice President Administration, Northcoast Behavioral Healthcare System, Northfield, OH, p. A499

COMITTO, Judy, Vice President Information Services and Chief Information Officer, Trinitas Regional Medical Center, Elizabeth, NJ, p. A415

COMPTON, Brenda, Manager Information Technology, Plumas District Hospital, Quincy, CA, p. A84

COMPTON, Mark, Chief Financial Officer, Laughlin Memorial Hospital, Greeneville, TN, p. A583

COMPTON–OGLE, Carri, Administrative Officer, Heartland Behavioral Health Services, Nevada, MO, p. A377

COMSTOCK, John M., Chief Executive Officer, Cherokee Regional Medical Center, Cherokee, IA, p. A227

CONALLEN, Kathryn
  Chief Executive Officer, Mercy Fitzgerald Hospital, Darby, PA, p. A537
  Interim Chief Executive Officer, Mercy Suburban Hospital, Norristown, PA, p. A546

CONANT, Cathy, Chief Human Resources and Personnel, Eastern Plumas Health Care, Portola, CA, p. A84

CONANT, Merrill, M.D. Chief of Staff, Western Plains Medical Complex, Dodge City, KS, p. A243

CONANT, Sonya, Senior Director Human Resources, Alaska Native Medical Center, Anchorage, AK, p. A28

CONATY, Robert B., Executive Vice President Operations, Montefiore Medical Center, NY, p. A446

CONAWAY, E. Edwin, M.D. Vice President Medical Affairs and Chief Medical Officer, Southeastern Ohio Regional Medical Center, Cambridge, OH, p. A485

CONAWAY, Keith, M.D. Chief Medical Officer, Solara Hospital of Shawnee, Shawnee, OK, p. A518

CONCANNON, Margaret, Administrator, Veterans Home and Hospital, Rocky Hill, CT, p. A117

CONCEPCION, Walter, Chief Executive Officer, West Gables Rehabilitation Hospital, Miami, FL, p. A138

CONDIT, Edward, President and Chief Executive Officer, St. Mary's Hospital, Passaic, NJ, p. A420

CONDOLUCI, David, M.D. Senior Vice President and Chief Medical Officer, Kennedy Health System, Cherry Hill, NJ, p. A414

CONDON, Joseph
  Director Human Resources, Texas Health Harris Methodist Hospital Fort Worth, Fort Worth, TX, p. A619
  Director Human Resources, Texas Health Specialty Hospital, Fort Worth, TX, p. A619

CONDON, William, Deputy Administrative Officer, U. S. Public Health Service Indian Hospital, Fort Yates, ND, p. A478

CONDRY, Donna, Director Human Resources, UnityPoint Health – Jones Regional Medical Center, Anamosa, IA, p. A225

CONE, Maryann, Chief Operating Officer, Sharp Grossmont Hospital, La Mesa, CA, p. A68

CONEJO, David, Chief Executive Officer, Red River Regional Hospital, Bonham, TX, p. A603

CONFALONE, Daniel, Chief Financial Officer and Vice President Finance, St. Mary Medical Center, Langhorne, PA, p. A542

CONFER, James, Manager Information Systems, Clarion Hospital, Clarion, PA, p. A535

CONGDON, James B., M.D. Medical Director, Horsham Clinic, Ambler, PA, p. A533

CONGER, Rex D., FACHE, President and Chief Executive Officer, Perry Memorial Hospital, Princeton, IL, p. A200

CONGER, Sue, Chief Operating Officer, Eastside Psychiatric Hospital, Tallahassee, FL, p. A146

CONKERTON, Lawrence, Administrator, Seaside Health System, Gonzales, LA, p. A277

COOKE, David, Chief Nursing Officer, Sutter Surgical Hospital – North Valley, Yuba City, CA, p. A101

COOKE, Jordan, Director Human Resources, Shadow Mountain Behavioral Health System, Tulsa, OK, p. A521

COOKE, Nancy, Chief Financial Officer, Weatherford Regional Medical Center, Weatherford, TX, p. A656

COOKE, Rebecca L., Director Human Resources, Kearney County Health Services, Minden, NE, p. A398

COOKE, Timothy J., Medical Center Director and Chief Executive Officer, Martinsburg Veterans Affairs Medical Center, Martinsburg, WV, p. A697

COOKE, William, M.D. Chief of Staff, Gundersen St. Joseph's Hospital and Clinics, Hillsboro, WI, p. A706

COOKSEY, Jill, Vice President Chief Nursing Officer, University Hospitals Elyria Medical Center, Elyria, OH, p. A493

COOLEY, Elizabeth A., R.N., Chief Executive Officer, St. Luke's Rehabilitation Hospital, Chesterfield, MO, p. A369

COOLEY, W. Carl, M.D. Chief Medical Officer, Crotched Mountain Rehabilitation Center, Greenfield, NH, p. A410

COOMBS, James, Chief Executive Officer, Grand River Hospital District, Rifle, CO, p. A111

COOMBS, Teri, R.N. Director Nursing Services, Cascade Medical Center, Cascade, ID, p. A175

COOMES, Larry, Chief Executive Officer, Palm Beach Gardens Medical Center, Palm Beach Gardens, FL, p. A141

COONER, Suzanne, MSN, Chief Executive Officer, Decatur County Hospital, Leon, IA, p. A233

COONEY, Darlene, Director Nursing, Sumner Regional Medical Center, Wellington, KS, p. A256

COONEY, Lauri Ann, Director Nursing, Wheatland Memorial Healthcare, Harlowton, MT, p. A388

COOPER, Alisa, Manager Financial Resources, Michael E. DeBakey Veterans Affairs Medical Center, Houston, TX, p. A626

COOPER, Casey, Chief Executive Officer, Cherokee Indian Hospital, Cherokee, NC, p. A462

COOPER, Chad D., Chief Executive Officer, Riverwood Healthcare Center, Aitkin, MN, p. A339

COOPER, Curtis, Manager Information Systems, Pioneers Medical Center, Meeker, CO, p. A110

COOPER, Dena, Chief Financial Officer, Campbellton Graceville Hospital, Graceville, FL, p. A130

COOPER, Donald, Director Information Systems, Harton Regional Medical Center, Tullahoma, TN, p. A593

COOPER, Douglas, M.D. Chief Medical Officer, Grundy County Memorial Hospital, Grundy Center, IA, p. A231

COOPER Jr., Edwin H., MS, President and Chief Executive Officer, AcuityHealthcare, LP, Charlotte, NC, p. B5

COOPER, Hunt, M.D. Chief of Staff, Siloam Springs Regional Hospital, Siloam Springs, AR, p. A53

COOPER, Ian, Chief Executive Officer, Hillside Rehabilitation Hospital, Warren, OH, p. A504

COOPER, Jeff, Chief Operating Officer, Henry Medical Center, Stockbridge, GA, p. A167

COOPER, Jerry, Manager Data Processing, Richland Hospital, Richland Center, WI, p. A714

COOPER, Jill, Site Administrator, Providence Centralia Hospital, Centralia, WA, p. A682

COOPER, John C., Chief Executive Officer, Fremont Hospital, Fremont, CA, p. A64

COOPER, Jon, President, Norton Audubon Hospital, Louisville, KY, p. A266

COOPER, Kevin S., R.N., Chief Executive Officer, LifeCare Hospitals of Dallas, Dallas, TX, p. A610

COOPER, Scott, M.D., Chief Executive Officer, St. Barnabas Hospital, NY, p. A448

COOPER, Sheri, Director Human Resources, Union General Hospital, Farmerville, LA, p. A277

COOPER, Tami, Acting Director of Nursing, Riverview Psychiatric Center, Augusta, ME, p. A291

COOPER, Tim, Chief Financial Officer, PMH Medical Center, Prosser, WA, p. A687

COOPER–LOHR, Willie, Chief Financial Officer, Barnesville Hospital, Barnesville, OH, p. A483

COOPERMAN, Todd, M.D. Medical Director, Rehabilitation Hospital of Tinton Falls, Tinton Falls, NJ, p. A423

COOPWOOD, Reginald W., M.D., President and Chief Executive Officer, Regional One Health, Memphis, TN, p. A589

COOTS, Aaron, Information Technology Director, Mason District Hospital, Havana, IL, p. A192

COOTS, Lawrence, M.D. Chief Medical Officer, Orange Park Medical Center, Orange Park, FL, p. A140

COPE, Brent A., Chief Executive Officer, Silver Lake Medical Center, Los Angeles, CA, p. A74

COPELAND, Carolyn, Business Administrator, Madison State Hospital, Madison, IN, p. A218

COPELAND, Darlinda, Chief Operating Officer, Florida Hospital Memorial Medical Center, Daytona Beach, FL, p. A127

COPELAND, Gail, Director Management Information Systems, CrossRidge Community Hospital, Wynne, AR, p. A54

COPELAND, Gearline, R.N. Chief Nursing Officer, Highlands Medical Center, Sparta, TN, p. A593

COPELAND Jr., Robert Y., FACHE, Chief Executive Officer, Mercy Hospital Carthage, Carthage, MO, p. A369

COPELAND, Willie Mae, Chief Financial Officer, Harmon Memorial Hospital, Hollis, OK, p. A512

COPELAND, Yolanda, R.N. Senior Vice President and Chief Nursing Officer, Saint Agnes Hospital, Baltimore, MD, p. A297

COPEN, Greg, Chief Information Officer, Haywood Regional Medical Center, Clyde, NC, p. A462

COPENHAVER, Kathy, Director Human Resources, Haven Behavioral Health of Eastern Pennsylvania, Reading, PA, p. A553

COPES, Tammy, Director Information Systems, St. Mary's of Michigan Standish Hospital, Standish, MI, p. A335

COPPLE, Brad
President, Kishwaukee Hospital, DeKalb, IL, p. A188
President, Kishwaukee Hospital, DeKalb, IL, p. A188
President, Valley West Hospital, Sandwich, IL, p. A202

COPPLE, Robert C., FACHE, President and CEO, Memorial Community Hospital and Health System, Blair, NE, p. A394

COPPOCK, R. Alan, FACHE, President, Oak Tree Hospital, Corbin, KY, p. A260

CORAZON, Jesus M.
Controller, HEALTHSOUTH Hospital of Manati, Manati, PR, p. A726
Controller, HEALTHSOUTH Rehabilitation Hospital of San Juan, San Juan, PR, p. A728

CORBET, Mark, Interim Chief Financial Officer, LAC/University of Southern California Medical Center, Los Angeles, CA, p. A73

CORBIN, Michelle, M.D. Chief of Staff, Deer Lodge Medical Center, Deer Lodge, MT, p. A386

CORCIMIGLIA, Michael, Chief Operating Officer, Wyoming County Community Hospital, Warsaw, NY, p. A457

CORCORAN, Joseph C., Chief Medical Officer, Brandon Regional Hospital, Brandon, FL, p. A124

CORCORAN, Kevin
Chief Financial Officer, Presbyterian–St. Luke's Medical Center, Denver, CO, p. A105
Chief Financial Officer, Westside Regional Medical Center, Plantation, FL, p. A143

CORCORAN, Nancy R., Senior Vice President Human Resources and Quality Service, Hackensack University Medical Center, Hackensack, NJ, p. A416

CORD, Jennifer
Assistant Vice President Operations, Presence Covenant Medical Center, Urbana, IL, p. A204
Vice President Operations, Presence United Samaritans Medical Center, Danville, IL, p. A187

CORDDRY, David, Chief Financial Officer, Ten Broeck Tennessee Treatment Facility, Cookeville, TN, p. A581

CORDER, Earline, Chief Fiscal, Charlie Norwood Veterans Affairs Medical Center, Augusta, GA, p. A153

CORDER, Scott, Controller, HEALTHSOUTH Rehabilitation Hospital at Drake, Cincinnati, OH, p. A487

CORDES, Debra, Chief Nursing Officer, Rehabilitation Hospital of Indiana, Indianapolis, IN, p. A214

CORDIA, Jennifer, Vice President and Chief Nursing Executive, Christian Hospital, Saint Louis, MO, p. A380

CORDOLA, Craig, Chief Executive Officer, Memorial Hermann – Texas Medical Center, Houston, TX, p. A625

CORDOVA, Martin, Director Information Services, Centinela Hospital Medical Center, Inglewood, CA, p. A67

CORDOVA, Richard D., FACHE, President and Chief Executive Officer, Children's Hospital Los Angeles, Los Angeles, CA, p. A71

CORDOVA, Sheila, Director Clinical Services and Chief Operating Officer, Aurora Charter Oak Hospital, Covina, CA, p. A61

CORDTS, Paul, Commander, Colonel Florence A. Blanchfield Army Community Hospital, Fort Campbell, KY, p. A261

CORDY, Roy, M.D. President Medical Staff, Presentation Medical Center, Rolla, ND, p. A480

COREA, Rohan, Director Healthcare Information Technology, Pacific Hospital of Long Beach, Long Beach, CA, p. A70

COREY, Mark, Chief Financial Officer, Behavioral Center of Michigan, Warren, MI, p. A336

CORFITS, Joe
Chief Financial Officer, UnityPoint Health – Des Moines, Des Moines, IA, p. A229
Senior Vice President Finance, UnityPoint Health – Iowa Methodist Medical Center, Des Moines, IA, p. A229

CORK, Ronald J., President and Chief Executive Officer, Avera St. Anthony's Hospital, O'Neill, NE, p. A399

CORKERY, Thomas B., D.O. Chief Medical Officer, Canonsburg General Hospital, Canonsburg, PA, p. A535

CORLEW, Scott, M.D. Chief Medical Officer, Saint Thomas Rutherford Hospital, Murfreesboro, TN, p. A590

CORLEY, Becky, Director Human Resources, Tyler Holmes Memorial Hospital, Winona, MS, p. A366

CORLEY, Craig, Chief Financial Officer, Thousand Oaks Surgical Hospital, Thousand Oaks, CA, p. A97

CORLEY, Janet, Accountant, Malvern Institute, Malvern, PA, p. A544

CORMIER, Laura, Director, Bellin Health Oconto Hospital, Oconto, WI, p. A712

CORN, Rick, Chief Information Officer, Huntsville Hospital, Huntsville, AL, p. A22

CORNEJO, C. Susan
Senior Vice President Finance and Chief Financial Officer, Providence Hospital, Mobile, AL, p. A22
Chief Financial Officer, Sacred Heart Hospital of Pensacola, Pensacola, FL, p. A142

CORNELIUS, David, Director Information Systems, Parkridge Medical Center, Chattanooga, TN, p. A580

CORNELIUS, Margaret E., Vice President Human Resources, Wyckoff Heights Medical Center, NY, p. A449

CORNELIUS, Michelle
Director Human Resources, Howard Young Medical Center, Woodruff, WI, p. A719
Director Human Resources for Northern Region, Ministry Eagle River Memorial Hospital, Eagle River, WI, p. A704
Director Human Resources for the Northern Region, Ministry Saint Mary's Hospitals, Rhinelander, WI, p. A714

CORNELIUS, Senta, Director Human Resources, West Valley Medical Center, Caldwell, ID, p. A175

CORNELL, John, Vice President Finance, Meadows Regional Medical Center, Vidalia, GA, p. A168

CORNETT, Sheila, Manager Human Resources, Hazard ARH Regional Medical Center, Hazard, KY, p. A262

CORNETT, Suzanne, Director Human Resources, Southern Kentucky Rehabilitation Hospital, Bowling Green, KY, p. A259

CORNICELLI, Kari, Chief Financial Officer, Sharp Grossmont Hospital, La Mesa, CA, p. A68

CORNWALL, Thomas, M.D. Medical Director, Holly Hill Hospital, Raleigh, NC, p. A471

CORNWELL, Cheryl, Chief Financial Officer, Great Falls Clinic Medical Center, Great Falls, MT, p. A388

CORNWELL, Cheryl J., Chief Financial Officer, Lake District Hospital, Lakeview, OR, p. A526

CORNWELL, James, M.D. Chief Medical Staff, Effingham Hospital, Springfield, GA, p. A167

CORONEL, Jorge, Chief Information Officer, Regional Hospital of Scranton, Scranton, PA, p. A554

CORPORA, Don, Executive Vice President and Chief Human Resources Officer, Akron General Medical Center, Akron, OH, p. A482

CORRADINO, Richard L., Chief Financial Officer, Spanish Peaks Regional Health Center, Walsenburg, CO, p. A112

CORRADO, Joseph, M.D. Chief of Staff, Audrain Medical Center, Mexico, MO, p. A376

CORRADO, Theresa, Director Finance, St. Luke's Hospital – Quakertown Campus, Quakertown, PA, p. A553

CORREA, Elizabeth, Director Information Management, Big Spring State Hospital, Big Spring, TX, p. A603

CORREA, Maria de los Angeles, M.D. Medical Director, Hospital Metropolitan, San Juan, PR, p. A728

CORREA, Omar, Chief Operating Officer, Texas NeuroRehab Center, Austin, TX, p. A600

CORREA, Sharon, Vice President and Chief Information Officer, Glendale Adventist Medical Center, Glendale, CA, p. A65

CORREIA, Antonio, Chief Financial Officer, Holyoke Medical Center, Holyoke, MA, p. A311

CORREIA, Kathryn G., President and Chief Executive Officer, HealthEast Care System, Saint Paul, MN, p. B69

CORRIDON, Fran, Vice President Human Resources and Shared Services, Hackensack University Medical Center Mountainside, Montclair, NJ, p. A418

CORRIGAN, Heidi, Manager Human Resources, Trinity Hospital, Weaverville, CA, p. A100

CORRIGAN, Jeffrey T., Vice President Human Resources, Brattleboro Retreat, Brattleboro, VT, p. A665

CORRIGAN, Paula, Vice President and Chief Financial Officer, OSF Saint James – John W. Albrecht Medical Center, Pontiac, IL, p. A200

CORRIGAN, Thomas L., Senior Vice President Finance, Managed Care and Chief Financial Officer, Christiana Care Health System, Newark, DE, p. A119

CORS, William K., M.D. Vice President and Chief Medical Quality Officer, Pocono Medical Center, East Stroudsburg, PA, p. A538

CORSO, David, Chief Operating Officer, Beaver Dam Community Hospitals, Beaver Dam, WI, p. A702

CORTEZ, Audrey, Chief Nursing Officer, Gunnison Valley Hospital, Gunnison, CO, p. A107

CORTEZ, Pamela, Director Clinical Operations, West Valley Hospital, Dallas, OR, p. A524

CORTI, Ronald, President and Chief Executive Officer, St. John's Riverside Hospital, Yonkers, NY, p. A458

CORUM, Sharon, Chief Financial Officer, Kingwood Pines Hospital, Kingwood, TX, p. A631

CORVINO, Frank A., President and Chief Executive Officer, Greenwich Hospital, Greenwich, CT, p. A114

CORWIN, Florence, Director for Administration, Pilgrim Psychiatric Center, Brentwood, NY, p. A434

CORWIN, Nancy, Chief Operating Officer, Summit Surgical, Hutchinson, KS, p. A246

CORWIN, R. William, M.D. Vice President and Chief Medical Officer, Miriam Hospital, Providence, RI, p. A560

CORWIN, Steven J., M.D., Chief Executive Officer, New York Presbyterian Healthcare System, New York, NY, p. B98

CORWIN, Steven J., M.D., Chief Executive Officer, New York–Presbyterian Hospital, New York, NY, p. A447

CORZINE, Judy, Administrative Director and Chief Information Officer, Stormont–Vail HealthCare, Topeka, KS, p. A255

COSBY, Dwan, Manager Human Resources, McLaren Oakland, Pontiac, MI, p. A332

COSBY, Ernestine Y., Vice President Clinical Services and Chief Nursing Officer, Sheppard Pratt Health System, Baltimore, MD, p. A297

COSGROVE, Delos, M.D., President and Chief Executive Officer, Cleveland Clinic, Cleveland, OH, p. A488

COSGROVE, Delos, M.D., President and Chief Executive Officer, Cleveland Clinic Health System, Cleveland, OH, p. B35

COSGROVE, Mila, Manager Human Resources, Bartlett Regional Hospital, Juneau, AK, p. A29

COSTA, Christopher P., M.D. Chief of Staff, Gordon Memorial Hospital, Gordon, NE, p. A396

COSTA, Joe
  Acting Chief Fiscal Officer, Brockton Veterans Affairs Medical Center, Brockton, MA, p. A308
  Chief Financial Officer, Veterans Affairs Boston Healthcare System, Boston, MA, p. A307

COSTA, Mark E., Executive Director, Kaiser Permanente Los Angeles Medical Center, Los Angeles, CA, p. A72

COSTA, Michael G.
  Vice President Human Resources, Burleson St. Joseph Health Center, Caldwell, TX, p. A605
  Director Human Resources, Grimes St. Joseph Health Center, Navasota, TX, p. A639
  Vice President Human Resources, St. Joseph Regional Health Center, Bryan, TX, p. A604

COSTA, Vivian, Director, Barix Clinics of Pennsylvania, Langhorne, PA, p. A542

COSTANTINO, Mark J., M.D. Interim Chief Medical Officer, Athens Regional Medical Center, Athens, GA, p. A151

COSTANTINO, Vincent, Vice President Operations and Human Resources, Raritan Bay Medical Center, Perth Amboy, NJ, p. A421

COSTELLA, Jeane L., Vice President, Hudson Valley Hospital Center, Cortlandt Manor, NY, p. A436

COSTELLO, Benny, Chief Executive Officer, Promise Hospital of Miss Lou, Vidalia, LA, p. A289

COSTELLO, Jeff
  Chief Financial Officer, Elkhart General Healthcare System, Elkhart, IN, p. A210
  Chief Financial Officer, Memorial Hospital of South Bend, South Bend, IN, p. A222

COSTELLO, Susan, Chief Nursing Officer, Lucile Salter Packard Children's Hospital at Stanford, Palo Alto, CA, p. A82

COSTER, Margaret C., MSN, President and Chief Executive Officer, Fairmont General Hospital, Fairmont, WV, p. A695

COSTIC, Andrew
  Regional Chief Financial Officer, Abraham Lincoln Memorial Hospital, Lincoln, IL, p. A195
  Regional Chief Financial Officer, Taylorville Memorial Hospital, Taylorville, IL, p. A204

COSTIE, Glenn A., FACHE, Director, Dayton Veterans Affairs Medical Center, Dayton, OH, p. A492

COTA, Scott, M.D. Director Medical Services, Naval Hospital Lemoore, Lemoore, CA, p. A69

COTE, Gerri, Vice President Operations, Brattleboro Retreat, Brattleboro, VT, p. A665

COTNOIR, Laurie, Director Nursing and Quality, Upper Connecticut Valley Hospital, Colebrook, NH, p. A409

COTT, Gary, M.D. Executive Vice President Medical and Clinical Services, National Jewish Health, Denver, CO, p. A105

COTTER, Brian, Chief Executive Officer, Healthbridge Children's Hospital, Orange, CA, p. A81

COTTER, Carole
  Senior Vice President and Chief Information Officer, Emma Pendleton Bradley Hospital, East Providence, RI, p. A560
  Vice President and Chief Information Officer, Miriam Hospital, Providence, RI, p. A560
  Senior Vice President and Chief Information Officer, Rhode Island Hospital, Providence, RI, p. A561

COTTERMAN, Rob, Assistant Superintendent Program Services, Moccasin Bend Mental Health Institute, Chattanooga, TN, p. A580

COTTI, Matthew, Chief Financial Officer, Rehabilitation Hospital of Rhode Island, North Smithfield, RI, p. A560

COTTINGHAM, Jerod, Director Information Systems, Carlinville Area Hospital, Carlinville, IL, p. A182

COTTLE, Gil, Chief Financial Officer, St. Christopher's Hospital for Children, Philadelphia, PA, p. A550

COTTLE, Jeremy, Ph.D., Chief Executive Officer, Provo Canyon Behavioral Hospital, Orem, UT, p. A661

COTTLE, Mike, Chief Information Officer, Newton Medical Center, Newton, KS, p. A250

COTTO, Hector L., M.D. Medical Director, Hospital San Francisco, San Juan, PR, p. A728

COTTON, C. Gerald, Interim Chief Operating Officer, Baptist Medical Center Leake, Carthage, MS, p. A356

COTTON, Michael, Chief Financial Officer, Gadsden Regional Medical Center, Gadsden, AL, p. A20

COTTREL, Doug, M.D. Chief Medical Officer, Madison Memorial Hospital, Rexburg, ID, p. A178

COTTRELL, Leslie, Nurse Lead, Iroquois Memorial Hospital and Resident Home, Watseka, IL, p. A204

COTTRILL, Brian, Chief Information Officer, United Hospital Center, Bridgeport, WV, p. A693

COUCH, Beulah, Director Human Resources, Mary Breckinridge ARH Hospital, Hyden, KY, p. A263

COUCH, Bill, Chief Financial Officer, Ashley County Medical Center, Crossett, AR, p. A44

COUCH, Lorie, Assistant Superintendent, Big Spring State Hospital, Big Spring, TX, p. A603

COUCH, Robert J., Chief Executive Officer, Medical Center of Manchester, Manchester, TN, p. A587

COUCHMAN, Diane, Vice President Patient Care Services and Chief Nursing Executive, Calvert Memorial Hospital, Prince Frederick, MD, p. A302

COUGHLIN, Ann, Director Human Resources, Boundary Community Hospital, Bonners Ferry, ID, p. A175

COUGHLIN, Cynthia, MS Chief Nursing Officer, Cheshire Medical Center, Keene, NH, p. A410

COULLIETTE, Edwina, Manager Human Resources, St. Vincent's Medical Center Southside, Jacksonville, FL, p. A132

COULTER, Barbara
  Director Information Systems, Franciscan St. Francis Health – Indianapolis, Indianapolis, IN, p. A214
  Director Information Systems, Franciscan St. Francis Health – Mooresville, Mooresville, IN, p. A219

COULTER, David C., Senior Vice President and Administrator, WakeMed Cary Hospital, Cary, NC, p. A461

COUNTRYMAN, Cory, Chief Executive Officer, Walnut Hill Medical Center, Dallas, TX, p. A612

COUNTS, Virginia, Manager Human Resources, Scott & White Hospital – Brenham, Brenham, TX, p. A604

COUNTY–TEEMER, Vickie, Coordinator Human Resources, Mitchell County Hospital, Camilla, GA, p. A155

COURIS, John D., President and Chief Executive Officer, Jupiter Medical Center, Jupiter, FL, p. A132

COURNYER, Tim, Chief Financial Officer, Morton General Hospital, Morton, WA, p. A685

COUROUNIS, Glenn, Vice President People and Patient Experience, St. Luke's Cornwall Hospital, Newburgh, NY, p. A449

COURREGE, Chad, Vice President Human Resources, Touro Infirmary, New Orleans, LA, p. A286

COURREGE, Gary, Chief Information Officer, Jennings American Legion Hospital, Jennings, LA, p. A279

COURSON, David R., MSN Chief Nursing Officer, Stonewall Jackson Memorial Hospital, Weston, WV, p. A700

COURTEMANCHE, Scott, Chief Financial Officer, Southwest Connecticut Mental Health System, Bridgeport, CT, p. A113

COURTNEY, Christine, R.N. Vice President and Chief Nursing Officer, Providence Health Center, Waco, TX, p. A656

COURTOIS, Harold, Chief Executive Officer, Russell Regional Hospital, Russell, KS, p. A253

COURTOIS, Robert, Vice President Finance, Otsego Memorial Hospital, Gaylord, MI, p. A324

COURTWAY, Peter, Chief Information Officer, New Milford Hospital, New Milford, CT, p. A116

COUSAR, Myra, Director Human Resources, Baptist Memorial Hospital–Tipton, Covington, TN, p. A582

COUSINEAU, Cathy, Director Human Resources, Kaiser Permanente Woodland Hills Medical Center, CA, p. A72

COUTURE, Jeannie, Manager Personnel, Riverland Medical Center, Ferriday, LA, p. A277

COUTURE, Maureen, Chief Nursing Officer and Vice President Nursing, Cardinal Hill Rehabilitation Hospital, Lexington, KY, p. A264

COVA, Charles, Interim Chief Executive Officer, St. John's Regional Medical Center, Oxnard, CA, p. A82

COVA, Charles J., President and Chief Executive Officer, Marian Regional Medical Center, Santa Maria, CA, p. A94

COVAULT, Julie, Vice President Finance, Wilson Memorial Hospital, Sidney, OH, p. A502

COVE, Netty S., R.N. Vice President Patient Services and Chief Nursing Officer, Spectrum Health Big Rapids Hospital, Big Rapids, MI, p. A319

COVELL, Nancy, Director Human Resources, Cameron Memorial Community Hospital, Angola, IN, p. A206

COVELLI, Margaret, R.N. Chief Nursing Officer, Spring Valley Hospital Medical Center, Las Vegas, NV, p. A406

COVER, Barry, M.D. Medical Director, Magruder Memorial Hospital, Port Clinton, OH, p. A500

COVERT, Charles O.
  Chief Financial Officer, Saint Francis Hospital, Charleston, WV, p. A694
  Vice President Finance, Thomas Memorial Hospital, South Charleston, WV, p. A699

COVERT, Kathy, Vice President Human Resources, Schneck Medical Center, Seymour, IN, p. A222

COVERT, Terri, Vice President Human Resources, Mission Hospital, Mission Viejo, CA, p. A77

COVEY, Staci, MS, President, Troy Community Hospital, Troy, PA, p. A556

COVILLE, Lea, Chief of Staff, Black River Memorial Hospital, Black River Falls, WI, p. A702

COVINGTON, Carmen, Chief Nursing Officer, Middle Park Medical Center–Kremmling, Kremmling, CO, p. A108

COVINGTON, Casey, M.D. President Elect, Medical Staff, Jennie Stuart Medical Center, Hopkinsville, KY, p. A263

COVINGTON, Celia, MSN Director of Nursing, St. Mary's Good Samaritan Hospital, Greensboro, GA, p. A160

COVINGTON, Jerome, M.D. Chief Medical Officer, Lower Keys Medical Center, Key West, FL, p. A133

COVONE, Ann Marie, Senior Vice President and Chief Financial Officer, Terence Cardinal Cooke Health Care Center, New York, NY, p. A449

COWAN, J. W., Administrator, Choctaw General Hospital, Butler, AL, p. A17

COWAN, Joshua, Chief Information Officer, St. Helena Hospital Clear Lake, Clearlake, CA, p. A60

COWAN, Ronald M., Vice President Information Systems, Geisinger–Lewistown Hospital, Lewistown, PA, p. A543

COWART, Mark, Chief Information Officer, Carl Vinson Veterans Affairs Medical Center, Dublin, GA, p. A159

COWART, Michelle, R.N. Chief Nursing Officer, HEALTHSOUTH Chattanooga Rehabilitation Hospital, Chattanooga, TN, p. A580

COWART, Timothy, Interim Chief Executive Officer, The Centers, Ocala, FL, p. A139

COWIE, Cynthia, Chief Executive Officer, Southwest Regional Medical Center, Waynesburg, PA, p. A557

COWLES, John, Chief Financial Officer, Silver Lake Medical Center, Los Angeles, CA, p. A74

COWLING, Phyllis A., CPA, President and Chief Executive Officer, United Regional Health Care System, Wichita Falls, TX, p. A658

COWPERTHWAIT, Cheri, R.N., Chief Executive Officer, Lourdes Specialty Hospital of Southern New Jersey, Willingboro, NJ, p. A425

COX, Amber, Director Human Resources, East Texas Medical Center Carthage, Carthage, TX, p. A605

COX, Brenda, Assistant Vice President Human Resources, North Florida Regional Medical Center, Gainesville, FL, p. A129

COX, Brian, Director Information Systems, Floyd Memorial Hospital and Health Services, New Albany, IN, p. A220

COX, Courtney, Vice President Human Resources, UPMC Northwest, Seneca, PA, p. A554

COX, David W., Chief Financial Officer, Marin General Hospital, Greenbrae, CA, p. A66

COX, Debbie D., Administrative Director Human Resources, Central Texas Medical Center, San Marcos, TX, p. A648

COX, Denida A., Chief Nursing Officer, Shoals Hospital, Muscle Shoals, AL, p. A24

COX, Dina, Director Human Resources, Kansas Rehabilitation Hospital, Topeka, KS, p. A255

COX, Dorothy, Manager Information Systems, Hackettstown Regional Medical Center, Hackettstown, NJ, p. A416

COX, Gray, President, St. Francis Hospital and Health Services, Maryville, MO, p. A376

COX, Gwen, Director Nursing Services, Klickitat Valley Health, Goldendale, WA, p. A684

COX, Jack, M.D. Senior Vice President and Chief Quality Officer, Hoag Memorial Hospital Presbyterian, Newport Beach, CA, p. A80

COX, Jason, Chief Executive Officer, Chestatee Regional Hospital, Dahlonega, GA, p. A157

COX, Jr., John A., M.D. President Medical Staff, Comanche County Memorial Hospital, Lawton, OK, p. A512

COX, Keith, Administrator, LifeCare Hospitals of Shreveport, Shreveport, LA, p. A288

COX, Kenneth, M.D. Chief Medical Officer, Lucile Salter Packard Children's Hospital at Stanford, Palo Alto, CA, p. A82

CRIBBS, Susan, D.O. Chief of Staff, Tehachapi Valley Healthcare District, Tehachapi, CA, p. A96

CRIDER, Terry, Information Technology Site Manager, NEA Baptist Memorial Hospital, Jonesboro, AR, p. A48

CRIGER, Sara J., President, Mercy Hospital, Coon Rapids, MN, p. A342

CRILLY, Tom, Executive Vice President and Chief Financial Officer, Unity Hospital, Rochester, NY, p. A453

CRIM, Marcia, MSN, Chief Executive Officer, USMD Hospital at Arlington, Arlington, TX, p. A598

CRIPE, Kimberly C.
President and Chief Executive Officer, Children's Hospital at Mission, Mission Viejo, CA, p. A77
President and Chief Executive Officer, Children's Hospital of Orange County, Orange, CA, p. A81

CRIPPS, Hugh Don, M.D. Chief of Staff, DeKalb Community Hospital, Smithville, TN, p. A593

CRISANTI, John, M.D. Vice President Medical Affairs, Community Medical Center, Toms River, NJ, p. A423

CRISLER, Catherine, Executive Director Human Resources, Piedmont Fayette Hospital, Fayetteville, GA, p. A159

CRISSEY, James E., President and Chief Executive Officer, Southern Regional Medical Center, Riverdale, GA, p. A165

CRIST, Chris, Director Information Technology, Nevada Regional Medical Center, Nevada, MO, p. A377

CRIST, Kathy, Director of Patient Care Services, Highlands–Cashiers Hospital, Highlands, NC, p. A466

CRISTY, Kirk, Chief Financial Officer, Sanford Bismarck, Bismarck, ND, p. A476

CRISWELL, Jodie, Vice President Fiscal Services, Hammond–Henry Hospital, Geneseo, IL, p. A190

CRITCHLEY, Dan
Chief Information Officer, University of Arizona Medical Center – South Campus, Tucson, AZ, p. A41
Chief Information Officer, University of Arizona Medical Center – University Campus, Tucson, AZ, p. A41

CRITTENDEN, Shana, Chief Operating Officer, North Shore Medical Center, Miami, FL, p. A137

CRNKOVIC, A. Elaine, Chief Executive Officer, Cedar Springs Hospital, Colorado Springs, CO, p. A103

CROCKER, Daniel, M.D. Chief Medical Officer, LifeCare Hospitals of North Carolina, Rocky Mount, NC, p. A471

CROCKER, Phillip, Accounting Specialist, Black River Medical Center, Poplar Bluff, MO, p. A378

CROCKETT, James Scott, M.D. Chief of Staff, Falls Community Hospital and Clinic, Marlin, TX, p. A636

CROCKETT, Kim, Director Management Information Systems, Shriners Hospitals for Children–Shreveport, Shreveport, LA, p. A288

CROCKETT, Mandy Lee
Director Human Resources, San Luis Valley Health, Alamosa, CO, p. A102
Director Human Resources, San Luis Valley Health Conejos County Hospital, La Jara, CO, p. A108

CROCKETT, Russ
Director Human Resources, Shriners Hospitals for Children–Salt Lake City, Salt Lake City, UT, p. A663
Director Human Resources, Shriners Hospitals for Children–Spokane, Spokane, WA, p. A690

CROFFORD, Patricia, Vice President Human Resources, Flagstaff Medical Center, Flagstaff, AZ, p. A32

CROFT, Kim, R.N. Executive Director Human Resources, Pomerene Hospital, Millersburg, OH, p. A499

CROFTON, Michael
Senior Vice President and Chief Financial Officer, Bethesda North Hospital, Cincinnati, OH, p. A486
Chief Financial Officer, Good Samaritan Hospital, Cincinnati, OH, p. A487
Chief Financial Officer, TriHealth Evendale Hospital, Cincinnati, OH, p. A487

CROKER, James, Director Information Systems, St. Bernardine Medical Center, San Bernardino, CA, p. A88

CROLEY, John S., Vice President Business Operations, Texas Institute for Surgery at Texas Health Presbyterian Dallas, Dallas, TX, p. A612

CRONER, Robert, Executive Vice President and Chief Human Resources Officer, Children's Hospital of Philadelphia, Philadelphia, PA, p. A547

CRONIN, Annamarie, Director Human Resources, New England Rehabilitation Hospital, Woburn, MA, p. A316

CRONIN, David J., Regional Vice President Human Resources, Good Samaritan Medical Center, Brockton, MA, p. A308

CROOKS, Heidi M., R.N. Senior Associate Director, Outpatient and Patient Care Services, Ronald Reagan University of California Los Angeles Medical Center, Los Angeles, CA, p. A74

CROOKS, John, Chairman Information Services, Mayo Clinic Jacksonville, Jacksonville, FL, p. A131

CROOM, Jon–Paul, Chief Operating Officer, Central Mississippi Medical Center, Jackson, MS, p. A360

CROOM Jr., Kennedy L., Administrator and Chief Executive Officer, Rhea Medical Center, Dayton, TN, p. A582

CROPLEY, Stacey, M.D. Chief Nursing Officer, Moore County Hospital District, Dumas, TX, p. A614

CROPPER, Douglas P., President and Chief Executive Officer, Genesis Health System, Davenport, IA, p. B60

CROPPER, Ronnie, Chief Operating Officer, Warren State Hospital, Warren, PA, p. A557

CROSBIE, John, Director Support Services, Indiana University Health Blackford Hospital, Hartford City, IN, p. A213

CROSBY, Evalie M., CPA Vice President Finance and Chief Financial Officer, Alice Peck Day Memorial Hospital, Lebanon, NH, p. A410

CROSBY, Robert
Chief Financial Officer, Athol Memorial Hospital, Athol, MA, p. A305
Senior Vice President and Chief Financial Officer, Heywood Hospital, Gardner, MA, p. A310

CROSHAW, Diane, Vice President Human Resources, Bacharach Institute for Rehabilitation, Pomona, NJ, p. A421

CROSS, Carol, Chief Financial Officer, Texas Health Harris Methodist Hospital Stephenville, Stephenville, TX, p. A650

CROSS, Lynda, R.N. Director of Nurses, Nemaha Valley Community Hospital, Seneca, KS, p. A254

CROSS, Mark A., Chief Executive Officer, Marias Medical Center, Shelby, MT, p. A391

CROSSER, Roxanna, President, OSF St. Mary Medical Center, Galesburg, IL, p. A190

CROSSEY, Robert, D.O. Chief Medical Officer, LifeCare Hospitals of Pittsburgh – Monroeville, Monroeville, PA, p. A545

CROSSLAND, Jeanne, Director of Nursing, Shamrock General Hospital, Shamrock, TX, p. A648

CROSSLEY, Beth, Director Information Systems, Chestnut Hill Hospital, Philadelphia, PA, p. A547

CROSSLEY, Kent, M.D. Acting Chief of Staff, Minneapolis Veterans Affairs Health Care System, Minneapolis, MN, p. A347

CROSSLEY, Rachel, R.N. Chief Patient Care Services, Veterans Affairs Sierra Nevada Health Care System, Reno, NV, p. A408

CROSTON, J. Kevin, M.D. Chief Medical Officer, North Memorial Medical Center, Robbinsdale, MN, p. A350

CROTEAU, Christine, Director, Bedford Veterans Affairs Medical Center, Edith Nourse Rogers Memorial Veterans Hospital, Bedford, MA, p. A305

CROTEAU, Gary, Assistant Vice President and Chief Information Officer, South County Hospital, Wakefield, RI, p. A561

CROTTY, Jr., Glenn, M.D. Executive Vice President and Chief Operating Officer, Charleston Area Medical Center, Charleston, WV, p. A694

CROTTY, Renee, Coordinator Marketing and Public Relations, Capital Medical Center, Olympia, WA, p. A686

CROUCH, Amy, Chief Financial Officer, DeKalb Health, Auburn, IN, p. A206

CROUCH, Chester, Chief Executive Officer, Reliant Healthcare Partners, Richardson, TX, p. B114

CROUCH, James, Vice President Technical Services, Northwest Medical Center, Albany, MO, p. A367

CROUCH, Matthew, Chief Executive Officer and Managing Director, Peachford Behavioral Health System, Atlanta, GA, p. A153

CROUCH, Max, M.D. Chief Medical Staff, Mountain View Hospital, Payson, UT, p. A662

CROUT, Tom, MS Director Human Resources, Central Louisiana State Hospital, Pineville, LA, p. A287

CROW, Angie, Director Finance, Saint Thomas Hospital for Spinal Surgery, Nashville, TN, p. A590

CROW, Regina W., R.N. Chief Nursing Officer, Bothwell Regional Health Center, Sedalia, MO, p. A382

CROW, Ruth Ann, Administrator, Lake Whitney Medical Center, Whitney, TX, p. A657

CROWDER, Jerry W., President and Chief Executive Officer, Bradford Health Services, Birmingham, AL, p. B24

CROWDER, Lonna, Director of Nursing, Phillips County Hospital, Malta, MT, p. A389

CROWE, Arthur, Director Information Systems, Peconic Bay Medical Center, Riverhead, NY, p. A452

CROWE, William R., President, Conemaugh Miners Medical Center, Hastings, PA, p. A540

CROWELL, Eric T.
President and Chief Executive Officer, UnityPoint Health – Des Moines, Des Moines, IA, p. A229
President and Chief Executive Officer, UnityPoint Health – Iowa Methodist Medical Center, Des Moines, IA, p. A229

CROWELL, Lynn, Chief Executive Officer, Arkansas Valley Regional Medical Center, La Junta, CO, p. A108

CROWELL, Robin, Chief Nursing Officer and Chief Operating Officer, Saint Thomas Hickman Hospital, Centerville, TN, p. A580

CROWL, Heather N., Chief Human Resources Officer, Kingman Regional Medical Center, Kingman, AZ, p. A33

CROWLEY, Cathleen, Chief Information Officer, Columbia Memorial Hospital, Hudson, NY, p. A439

CROWLEY, John, M.D. Medical Director, River Crest Hospital, San Angelo, TX, p. A645

CROWLEY, Thomas, President and Chief Executive Officer, Saint Elizabeth's Medical Center, Wabasha, MN, p. A353

CRUCETTI, Carol, R.N. Chief Nursing Officer, St. Mary's Hospital, Troy, NY, p. A456

CRUM, Dennis L., Senior Vice President and Chief Financial Officer, Tift Regional Medical Center, Tifton, GA, p. A168

CRUM, Jarett, Administrator, EastPointe Hospital, Daphne, AL, p. A18

CRUMB, Dennis, Chief Information Officer, Ellwood City Hospital, Ellwood City, PA, p. A538

CRUMLEY, Vickie L., Vice President Human Resources, Mary Rutan Hospital, Bellefontaine, OH, p. A483

CRUMP, Rick, Chief Financial Officer, Lakeland Behavioral Health System, Springfield, MO, p. A383

CRUMPTON, Althea H., Administrator, Magee General Hospital, Magee, MS, p. A361

CRUNK, Frances H., Vice President and Chief Financial Officer, Florida Hospital Waterman, Tavares, FL, p. A148

CRUNK, Tommy, M.D. Chief of Staff, Northcrest Medical Center, Springfield, TN, p. A593

CRUSE, Ray, Chief Executive Officer, Lakeland Community Hospital Watervliet, Watervliet, MI, p. A336

CRUTHIRDS, Leslie, Chief Human Resource Management Service, South Texas Veterans Health Care System, San Antonio, TX, p. A647

CRUTHIRDS, Richard, Director Information Systems, Peterson Regional Medical Center, Kerrville, TX, p. A631

CRUZ, Domingo, Senior Vice President Operations, San Jorge Children's Hospital, San Juan, PR, p. A728

CRUZ, Elyonel Ponton, Executive Director, Hospital Buen Samaritano, Aguadilla, PR, p. A724

CRUZ, Joseph V., Chief Information Officer, Ryder Memorial Hospital, Humacao, PR, p. A726

CRUZ, Julia, Chief Financial Officer, San Juan Capestrano Hospital, San Juan, PR, p. A728

CRUZ, Michael, Vice President Operations, Baptist St. Anthony Health System, Amarillo, TX, p. A596

CRUZ, Miguel, M.D. Medical Director, Bella Vista Hospital, Mayaguez, PR, p. A726

CRUZ, Miguel, Medical Staff Credentialing Coordinator, HEALTHSOUTH Rehabilitation Hospital of Miami, Cutler Bay, FL, p. A126

CRYER, Betty, Chief Nursing Officer, Anderson Regional Medical Center–South Campus, Meridian, MS, p. A362

CRYER, Selena, Director Human Resources, Ennis Regional Medical Center, Ennis, TX, p. A617

CSEPKE, Cheryl, Controller, Kindred Rehabilitation Hospital Northeast Houston, Humble, TX, p. A628

CUBELLIS, Guido J.
Chief Operating Officer, Nexus Specialty Hospital, Shenandoah, TX, p. A649
Chief Operating Officer, Nexus Specialty Hospital The Woodlands, Spring, TX, p. A650

CUBRE, Alan, M.D. Medical Director, Vibra Hospital of Sacramento, Folsom, CA, p. A63

CUDWORTH, Craig R., Interim Chief Executive Officer, Newberry County Memorial Hospital, Newberry, SC, p. A569

CUELLAR, Eddie, Vice President Information Systems, Methodist Hospital, San Antonio, TX, p. A646

CUELLAR, Jacob, M.D., Chief Executive Officer, Laurel Ridge Treatment Center, San Antonio, TX, p. A646

CUENCA, Derrick, Chief Executive Officer, Lake Granbury Medical Center, Granbury, TX, p. A621

CUERO, Liza, Coordinator Human Resources, Central Texas Rehabilitation Hospital, Austin, TX, p. A599

CUEVAS, Gilberto, Director Human Resources, Hospital De Damas, Ponce, PR, p. A727

CUEVAS, Jacki, Director Health Information Services, Regional Rehabilitation Hospital, Phenix City, AL, p. A25

CULBERSON, David K., Chief Executive Officer, San Joaquin General Hospital, French Camp, CA, p. A64

CULBERT, Devon, Controller, The Hospital at Westlake Medical Center, Austin, TX, p. A600

CULBERTSON, Laura, Director Human Resources, Southwest Healthcare System, Murrieta, CA, p. A79

CULBRETH, Lucile, Chief Nursing Officer, Abbeville Area Medical Center, Abbeville, SC, p. A562

CULLEN, John, M.D. Chief of Staff and Medical Director Long Term Care, Providence Valdez Medical Center, Valdez, AK, p. A30

CULLEN, John, Assistant Superintendent, Thomas B. Finan Center, Cumberland, MD, p. A300

CULLEN, Mark J., Chief Executive Officer, Compass Health, Crowley, LA, p. B43

CULLEN, Michael, Senior Vice President and Chief Financial Officer, South Shore Hospital, South Weymouth, MA, p. A314

CULLEN, Neil, Director Human Resources, HEALTHSOUTH Rehabilitation Hospital of Southern Arizona, Tucson, AZ, p. A40

CULLEN, Paul T., M.D. Vice President Medical Affairs, Washington Hospital, Washington, PA, p. A557

CULLEN, Scott, Chief Executive Officer, Northwest Hills Surgical Hospital, Austin, TX, p. A599

CULLITON, Gerald F., Medical Center Director, Veterans Affairs Connecticut Healthcare System, West Haven, CT, p. A118

CULLIVER, Sandra, Director Human Resources, National Park Medical Center, Hot Springs, AR, p. A47

CULLUM, Beth, Chief Operating Officer, Kindred Hospital Boston–North Shore, Peabody, MA, p. A313

CULP, Judith H., Chief Financial Officer, Mesilla Valley Hospital, Las Cruces, NM, p. A429

CULP, Judy, Chief Financial Officer, Hill Regional Hospital, Hillsboro, TX, p. A623

CULUMBER, Janene, Vice President and Chief Financial Officer, H. Lee Moffitt Cancer Center and Research Institute, Tampa, FL, p. A147

CULVER, Douglas, Chief Financial Officer, Mercy Hospital Carthage, Carthage, MO, p. A369

CULVER, Shawna, Director Information Systems, Western Plains Medical Complex, Dodge City, KS, p. A243

CUMBEE, Lib, Director Information Systems, Providence Hospital, Columbia, SC, p. A564

CUMBEST, Sheena
Assistant Vice President Human Resources, Lafayette General Medical Center, Lafayette, LA, p. A281
Assistant Vice President Human Resources, Lafayette General Surgical Hospital, Lafayette, LA, p. A281

CUMBIE, Dan L., Chief Nursing Officer, Flowers Hospital, Dothan, AL, p. A19

CUMBO, Adam, Chief Financial Officer, Dukes Memorial Hospital, Peru, IN, p. A221

CUMING, Richard, R.N. Vice President and Chief Nurse Executive, Einstein Medical Center Philadelphia, Philadelphia, PA, p. A548

CUMMINGS, Brooke, Chief Financial Officer, Our Lady of the Angels Hospital, Bogalusa, LA, p. A274

CUMMINGS, Bruce D., President and Chief Executive Officer, L+M Healthcare, New London, CT, p. B82

CUMMINGS, Bruce D.
President and Chief Executive Officer, Lawrence + Memorial Hospital, New London, CT, p. A116
President and Chief Executive Officer, Westerly Hospital, Westerly, RI, p. A561

CUMMINGS, Cindy, Chief Executive Officer, Putnam County Memorial Hospital, Unionville, MO, p. A384

CUMMINGS, Greg, Chief Financial Officer, Texas Spine & Joint Hospital, Tyler, TX, p. A654

CUMMINGS, Jerry, Chief Operating Officer, Putnam County Memorial Hospital, Unionville, MO, p. A384

CUMMINGS, Rae, Chief Operating Officer, Boulder City Hospital, Boulder City, NV, p. A404

CUMMINGS, Steve, M.D. Chief of Medical Staff, Stillwater Medical Center, Stillwater, OK, p. A519

CUMMINGS, Steven, Chief Operating Officer and Chief Information Officer, Noble Hospital, Westfield, MA, p. A316

CUMMINS, Frank L., Vice President Human Resources, John C. Lincoln Deer Valley Hospital, Phoenix, AZ, p. A36

CUMMINS, Thomas H., M.D. Senior Vice President and Chief Medical Officer, St. Vincent Infirmary Medical Center, Little Rock, AR, p. A49

CUNNIGHAM, James, D.O. Chief of Staff, Audubon County Memorial Hospital, Audubon, IA, p. A225

CUNNINGHAM, Becky, Controller, Salem Memorial District Hospital, Salem, MO, p. A382

CUNNINGHAM, Brian, Interim Chief Executive Officer, Gila Regional Medical Center, Silver City, NM, p. A431

CUNNINGHAM, Gail, Interim Chief Medical Officer, University of Maryland St. Joseph Medical Center, Towson, MD, p. A304

CUNNINGHAM, Gary, Chief Nursing Officer, Dixie Regional Medical Center, Saint George, UT, p. A662

CUNNINGHAM, James C., M.D. Chief Medical Officer, Cook Children's Medical Center, Fort Worth, TX, p. A618

CUNNINGHAM, Julie, Associate Administrator and Chief Human Resources Officer, Pioneers Memorial Healthcare District, Brawley, CA, p. A58

CUNNINGHAM, Keith W., M.D. Medical Director, HEALTHSOUTH Scottsdale Rehabilitation Hospital, Scottsdale, AZ, p. A38

CUNNINGHAM, Larmar, Chief Operating Officer, West Central Georgia Regional Hospital, Columbus, GA, p. A156

CUNNINGHAM, M. Edward, Chief Executive Officer, Gateway Regional Medical Center, Granite City, IL, p. A191

CUNNINGHAM, Michelle P., Chief Executive Officer, Highlands Hospital, Connellsville, PA, p. A536

CUNNINGHAM, Regina, Ph.D. Chief Nurse Executive, Hospital of the University of Pennsylvania, Philadelphia, PA, p. A548

CUPINO, Isaias, Chief of Staff, Community Memorial Hospital, Oconto Falls, WI, p. A712

CURCURUTO, James J., Senior Vice President Finance, St. Joseph's Medical Center, Yonkers, NY, p. A458

CURLEE, Robbin, Controller, RMC Jacksonville, Jacksonville, AL, p. A22

CURLING, Susan, M.D. Chief Medical Officer, Memorial Hermann Northeast, Humble, TX, p. A628

CURNEL, Robin, MSN Chief Operating Officer and Chief Nursing Officer, Crittenden County Hospital, Marion, KY, p. A267

CURNUTT, Ann, Director Information Systems, Garfield Medical Center, Monterey Park, CA, p. A78

CURPHY, Rona, President and Chief Executive Officer, Banner Casa Grande Medical Center, Casa Grande, AZ, p. A31

CURRAN, Dezerae, Director Human Resources, Osawatomie State Hospital, Osawatomie, KS, p. A251

CURRAN, Maria, Vice President Human Resources, VCU Medical Center, Richmond, VA, p. A678

CURRAN, Robert, Director Health Information Management, SSM St. Mary's Health Center, Saint Louis, MO, p. A381

CURRAN–MEULI, Jane, Chief Operating Officer, Holy Family Memorial, Manitowoc, WI, p. A708

CURRANCE, Lana, MSN, Chief Executive Officer, Peak View Behavioral Health, Colorado Springs, CO, p. A103

CURRANS, Sheila, Chief Executive Officer, Harrison Memorial Hospital, Cynthiana, KY, p. A260

CURREN, Robert
Director Information Technology, Center for Behavioral Medicine, Kansas City, MO, p. A373
Western Region Chief Information Technology Officer, Northwest Missouri Psychiatric Rehabilitation Center, Saint Joseph, MO, p. A380

CURRIE, Michelle, Chief Financial Officer, Richard P. Stadter Psychiatric Center, Grand Forks, ND, p. A478

CURRIE, Scott D., Vice President and Chief Financial Officer, MidMichigan Medical Center–Midland, Midland, MI, p. A330

CURRIER, Donald L., Vice President Human Resources, Piedmont Medical Center, Rock Hill, SC, p. A569

CURRIN, Sue, MS, Chief Executive Officer, San Francisco General Hospital and Trauma Center, San Francisco, CA, p. A91

CURRY, Cheryl, Chief Financial Officer, Littleton Adventist Hospital, Littleton, CO, p. A109

CURRY, Christopher, Chief Operating Officer, Iroquois Memorial Hospital and Resident Home, Watseka, IL, p. A204

CURRY, Jeffrey T.
Executive Vice President and Chief Financial Officer, Excela Frick Hospital, Mount Pleasant, PA, p. A546
Executive Vice President and Chief Financial Officer, Excela Health Westmoreland Hospital, Greensburg, PA, p. A539

CURRY, Lori, Regional Chief Human Resources Officer, Providence Holy Cross Medical Center, CA, p. A74

CURRY, Michelle, Chief Operating Officer, Cascade Behavioral Hospital, Tukwila, WA, p. A691

CURRY, Robert H., President and Chief Executive Officer, Citrus Valley Health Partners, Covina, CA, p. B35

CURRY, Robert H.
President and Chief Executive Officer, Citrus Valley Medical Center–Inter Community Campus, Covina, CA, p. A61
President and Chief Executive Officer, Foothill Presbyterian Hospital, Glendora, CA, p. A66

CURRY, Stephen A., Director Information Services, Princeton Community Hospital, Princeton, WV, p. A698

CURRY, Steve, Regional Director Human Resources, Four County Counseling Center, Logansport, IN, p. A217

CURRY, Thomas A., M.D
Vice President Medical Affairs for Clinical Effectiveness and Documentation, Schuylkill Medical Center – East Norwegian Street, Pottsville, PA, p. A553
Vice President Medical Affairs for Clinical Effectiveness and Documentation, Schuylkill Medical Center – South Jackson Street, Pottsville, PA, p. A553

CURRY–PELYAK, Mary Jane, R.N. Vice President and Chief Clinical Officer, The Villages Regional Hospital, The Villages, FL, p. A149

CURTIN, Sean, Chief Financial Officer, Alice Hyde Medical Center, Malone, NY, p. A440

CURTIS, Donald, Chief Executive Officer and Chief Financial Officer and Chief Operating Officer, Copper Basin Medical Center, Copperhill, TN, p. A581

CURTIS, Edgar J., FACHE, President and Chief Executive Officer, Memorial Health System, Springfield, IL, p. B90

CURTIS, Edgar J., FACHE, President and Chief Executive Officer, Memorial Medical Center, Springfield, IL, p. A203

CURTIS, George, Chief Information Officer, Houston Medical Center, Warner Robins, GA, p. A169

CURTIS, Janis, Interim Director Information Technology, Duke Raleigh Hospital, Raleigh, NC, p. A470

CURTIS, Joy U., Senior Vice President Human Resources, Cambridge Health Alliance, Cambridge, MA, p. A309

CURTIS, Lorna, Chief Financial Officer, Kaiser Permanente Riverside Medical Center, Riverside, CA, p. A86

CURTIS, Marilyn K., Vice President Professional Services, Saint Francis Medical Center, Cape Girardeau, MO, p. A368

CURTIS, Michael, Chief Operating Officer, McKenzie County Healthcare System, Watford City, ND, p. A480

CURTIS, Scott A., Administrator and Chief Executive Officer, Kossuth Regional Health Center, Algona, IA, p. A225

CURTIS, Tracie, Vice President Human Resources, Medina Hospital, Medina, OH, p. A498

CURVIN, Thomas J., M.D. Chief of Staff, Rankin Hospital District, Rankin, TX, p. A643

CUSANO, Susan, Director Human Resources, Four Winds Hospital, Katonah, NY, p. A439

CUSATIS, Michele A., Ph.D., Administrator, Waukesha County Mental Health Center, Waukesha, WI, p. A717

CUSENZ, Bruce J., M.D. Medical Director, Eastern Niagara Hospital, Lockport, NY, p. A440

CUSHING, Heidi, Director Finance, Gordon Memorial Hospital, Gordon, NE, p. A396

CUSSINS, James, Chief Financial Officer, Platte County Memorial Hospital, Wheatland, WY, p. A723

CUSTER, Cherie, Chief Nursing Officer, Cherry Hospital, Goldsboro, NC, p. A465

CUSTER, Joshua, Director Finance, St. Luke's Magic Valley Medical Center, Twin Falls, ID, p. A178

CUSTER–MITCHELL, Marilyn J., President and Chief Executive Officer, Wabash County Hospital, Wabash, IN, p. A224

CUSTIN, Melinda, Chief Information Officer, JPS Health Network, Fort Worth, TX, p. A618

CUTLER, RN, Nancy, R.N. Vice President Patient Services/CNO, FHN Memorial Hospital, Freeport, IL, p. A190

CUTLER, Terry
Administrator and Chief Executive Officer, East Texas Medical Center Crockett, Crockett, TX, p. A609
Interim Chief Executive Officer, East Texas Medical Center Trinity, Trinity, TX, p. A653

CUTOLO, Jr., Edward, M.D. Chief of Staff, James A. Haley Veterans' Hospital, Tampa, FL, p. A147

CUTRIGHT, Bruce E., MS Vice President Human Resources, Mary Lanning Healthcare, Hastings, NE, p. A396

CUTSFORTH, Shawn, Information Systems Officer, Pioneer Memorial Hospital, Heppner, OR, p. A525

CUTTER, Elise, Chief Financial Officer, Island Hospital, Anacortes, WA, p. A681

CUZZOLA, Anthony, Vice President Rehabilitation Services, JFK Johnson Rehabilitation Institute, Edison, NJ, p. A415

CYTLAK, David
Chief Financial Officer, Blanchard Valley Hospital, Findlay, OH, p. A494
Vice President Finance, Bluffton Hospital, Bluffton, OH, p. A484

CZAJKA, Paul M., Chief Operating Officer, USC Verdugo Hills Hospital, Glendale, CA, p. A65

CZEREW, Jane, Vice President Clinical Services and Quality, Spectrum Health Zeeland Community Hospital, Zeeland, MI, p. A338

CZINCILA, Robert, D.O. Medical Staff President, Einstein Medical Center Montgomery, East Norriton, PA, p. A538

CZYZ, AnneMarie, R.N. Vice President for Clinical and Educational Services, St. Joseph's Hospital Health Center, Syracuse, NY, p. A456

D

D'ACCURZIO, Albert, M.D. Medical Director, St. Elizabeth Medical Center, Utica, NY, p. A456

D'AGNES, Michael R., FACHE, President and Chief Executive Officer, Raritan Bay Medical Center, Perth Amboy, NJ, p. A421

D'ALBERTO, Richard E., FACHE, Campus President, Greenville Health System – Laurens County Memorial Hospital, Clinton, SC, p. A564

D'AMBROSIO, Matthew, Director Information Systems, Southwest General Hospital, San Antonio, TX, p. A647

D'AMBROSIO, Paul, Chief Operating Officer, Complex Care Hospital at Tenaya, Las Vegas, NV, p. A405

D'AMICO, Kenneth, Chief Executive Officer, Landmark Hospital of Joplin, Joplin, MO, p. A373

D'AMICO, Paul, M.D. Chief of Staff, Stanly Regional Medical Center, Albemarle, NC, p. A459

D'AMORE, Seanna, Director Human Resources, Elk Regional Health Center, Saint Marys, PA, p. A554

D'ANGELO, Elizabeth, M.D. Chief of Staff, Onslow Memorial Hospital, Jacksonville, NC, p. A467

D'ANGELO, Jennifer, Assistant Vice President Information Services, Christian Health Care Center, Wyckoff, NJ, p. A425

D'ANGINA, Joseph, Area Finance Officer, Kaiser Permanente Vallejo Medical Center, Vallejo, CA, p. A99

D'APOLLO, Julie, R.N. Director of Nursing, Hampstead Hospital, Hampstead, NH, p. A410

D'AQUILA, Richard, President and Chief Operating Officer, Yale–New Haven Hospital, New Haven, CT, p. A116

D'ELIA, Peter, Chief Financial Officer, Saint Vincent Hospital, Worcester, MA, p. A317

D'ENBEAU, Richard, Chief Operating Officer, Mount Carmel New Albany Surgical Hospital, New Albany, OH, p. A499

D'ESMOND, C. Thomas, FACHE, Administrator, Shriners Hospitals for Children–Boston, Boston, MA, p. A307

D'ETTORRE, Joseph A., Chief Executive Officer, Wyandot Memorial Hospital, Upper Sandusky, OH, p. A503

D'EVANO, John, Chief Operating Officer, Connecticut Valley Hospital, Middletown, CT, p. A115

D'SOUZA, Carol, Director Human Resources, Banner Casa Grande Medical Center, Casa Grande, AZ, p. A31

D'SOUZA, Gladys, Chief Nursing Officer, Barlow Respiratory Hospital, Los Angeles, CA, p. A71

DAANE, John, Information Systems Officer, Prairie du Chien Memorial Hospital, Prairie Du Chien, WI, p. A713

DABNEY, Ann, Manager Human Resources, Spring View Hospital, Lebanon, KY, p. A263

DABNEY, Janice, Chief Executive Officer, Springs Memorial Hospital, Lancaster, SC, p. A568

DACE, Linda, Vice President Finance, McDonough District Hospital, Macomb, IL, p. A195

DACEY, Michael J., MS, President and Chief Operating Officer, Kent County Memorial Hospital, Warwick, RI, p. A561

DACUS, Michael E.
Vice President and Chief Financial Officer, Sheltering Arms Hospital South, Midlothian, VA, p. A674
Vice President and Chief Financial Officer, Sheltering Arms Rehabilitation Hospital, Mechanicsville, VA, p. A674

DADD, Steven, Flight Commander Resource Management, U. S. Air Force Hospital, Hampton, VA, p. A672

DADEY, Mary Lee, R.N. Vice President of Nursing, Windber Medical Center, Windber, PA, p. A559

DADLEZ, Christopher M., President and Chief Executive Officer, Mount Sinai Rehabilitation Hospital, Hartford, CT, p. A114

DADLEZ, Christopher M., President and Chief Executive Officer, Saint Francis Care, Inc., Hartford, CT, p. B116

DADLEZ, Christopher M., President and Chief Executive Officer, Saint Francis Hospital and Medical Center, Hartford, CT, p. A114

DADO, Joseph, Chief Information Officer, Conemaugh Memorial Medical Center, Johnstown, PA, p. A541

DAECH, Ed, Director Human Resources, Heartland Regional Medical Center, Marion, IL, p. A195

DAEGER, Brian, Vice President Financial Services, Margaret Mary Health, Batesville, IN, p. A206

DAFOE, Joe, R.N. Chief Clinical Officer, Columbia Memorial Hospital, Astoria, OR, p. A523

DAGENBACH, Pete, Chief Financial Officer, Adams County Regional Medical Center, Seaman, OH, p. A501

DAGHER, Michel, D.O. Vice President and Chief Medical Officer, Banner Del E. Webb Medical Center, Sun City West, AZ, p. A39

DAGLIO, Michael, Chief Operating Officer, Danbury Hospital, Danbury, CT, p. A113

DAHDUL, Adnan, M.D. Medical Director, HEALTHSOUTH Rehabilitation Hospital of Western Massachusetts, Ludlow, MA, p. A311

DAHL, Sandy J., Senior Vice President, Chief Clinical Officer, Yakima Valley Memorial Hospital, Yakima, WA, p. A692

DAHLBERG, Connie, Director Business and Employee, Sleepy Eye Medical Center, Sleepy Eye, MN, p. A352

DAHLE, Dan, Chief of Staff, Mayers Memorial Hospital District, Fall River Mills, CA, p. A63

DAHLHAUSEN, Daniel J., M.D. President of Medical Staff/Chief Medical Officer, Cannon Memorial Hospital, Pickens, SC, p. A569

DAHLING, James D., President and Chief Executive Officer, Children's Hospital of The King's Daughters, Norfolk, VA, p. A675

DAHLSTRAND, David, Associate Chief of Staff Information Technology, Hunter Holmes McGuire Veterans Affairs Medical Center, Richmond, VA, p. A678

DAHLSTROM, Josiah, Administrator, Safe Haven Hospital of Pocatello, Pocatello, ID, p. A178

DAIGLE, Charles D.
Senior Vice President and Chief Operating Officer, Willis–Knighton Medical Center, Shreveport, LA, p. A288
Chief Operating Officer, WK Bossier Health Center, Bossier City, LA, p. A274

DAIGLE, Cindy, Chief Financial Officer, Northern Maine Medical Center, Fort Kent, ME, p. A293

DAIGLE, J. Barry, Manager Information Systems, University Hospital and Clinics, Lafayette, LA, p. A282

DAIKEN, Michael E., Chief Financial Officer, Highlands–Cashiers Hospital, Highlands, NC, p. A466

DAIKER, David, Chief Information Resource Management, Veterans Affairs Nebraska–Western Iowa Health Care System, Lincoln, NE, p. A398

DAILEY, Gina, Chief Financial Officer, Pinnacle Pointe Hospital, Little Rock, AR, p. A49

DAILEY, Jacqueline, Chief Information Officer, West Penn Hospital, Pittsburgh, PA, p. A552

DAILEY, Richard R., D.O. President Medical Staff, Ellett Memorial Hospital, Appleton City, MO, p. A367

DAILY, James L., President, Porter Medical Center, Middlebury, VT, p. A665

DAISLEY, Samuel, D.O. Vice President Medical Affairs, UPMC Horizon, Greenville, PA, p. A539

DAJCZAK, Stanislaw, M.D. Chief of Staff, ProMedica Defiance Regional Hospital, Defiance, OH, p. A492

DALBY, William, Director Fiscal Services, Shriners Hospitals for Children–Northern California, Sacramento, CA, p. A87

DALE, Jackson, Director Management Information Services, Johnston Memorial Hospital, Abingdon, VA, p. A668

DALE, Jae, Chief Executive Officer, Oro Valley Hospital, Oro Valley, AZ, p. A35

DALEBOUT, Kenneth, Administrator and Chief Executive Officer, Arroyo Grande Community Hospital, Arroyo Grande, CA, p. A56

DALEY, Chris, M.D. Chief of Staff, Estes Park Medical Center, Estes Park, CO, p. A106

DALEY, Linda, Vice President Human Resources, Oswego Hospital, Oswego, NY, p. A451

DALEY, Robert, Vice President Fiscal and Information Technology Services, Black River Memorial Hospital, Black River Falls, WI, p. A702

DALGAI, Netrisha, Director of Operations, Sage Memorial Hospital, Ganado, AZ, p. A32

DALL, Jamie, Chief Financial Officer, New Hampshire Hospital, Concord, NH, p. A409

DALLER, Sue, R.N. Assistant Administrator Nursing, Hermann Area District Hospital, Hermann, MO, p. A372

DALLEY, Mark F., Administrator, Gunnison Valley Hospital, Gunnison, UT, p. A660

DALLIS, Donna, R.N. Vice President Patient Care, Northeastern Health System, Tahlequah, OK, p. A519

DALPOAS, Dolan, President and Chief Executive Officer, Abraham Lincoln Memorial Hospital, Lincoln, IL, p. A195

DALTON, Deana, Human Resources, San Juan Hospital, Monticello, UT, p. A660

DALTON, Eric
Chief Financial Officer, Memorial Medical Center, Modesto, CA, p. A78
Chief Financial Officer, Sutter Tracy Community Hospital, Tracy, CA, p. A97

DALTON, John, President and Chief Executive Officer, Inland Hospital, Waterville, ME, p. A295

DALTON, Valerie, R.N., Administrator, Oceans Behavioral Hospital of Baton Rouge, Baton Rouge, LA, p. A273

DALTON, Wayne, Chief Financial Officer, Lakeview Hospital, Bountiful, UT, p. A659

DALY, Cindy, R.N. Director of Nursing, Syringa Hospital and Clinics, Grangeville, ID, p. A176

DALY, Gail, Chief Nursing Officer and Chief Operating Officer, St. Mary Medical Center, Long Beach, CA, p. A70

DALY, Sheila, President and Chief Executive Officer, Clinton Hospital, Clinton, MA, p. A309

DALY, Thomas M., Chief Financial Officer, University Hospital, Newark, NJ, p. A420

DALY, William, Chief Executive Officer, Pennsylvania Psychiatric Institute, Harrisburg, PA, p. A540

DAMA, Sunil, M.D. Medical Director, Select Specialty Hospital – Cincinnati North, Cincinnati, OH, p. A487

DAMBOISE, Robin, Director Human Resources, Northern Maine Medical Center, Fort Kent, ME, p. A293

DAMICO, Donna, Director Human Resources, Carolinas Hospital System, Florence, SC, p. A565

DAMM, Julie, Chief Financial Officer, Hancock County Health System, Britt, IA, p. A226

DAMMEYER, Matt, Ph.D. Chief Operating Officer, Central Peninsula General Hospital, Soldotna, AK, p. A30

DAMODARAN, A. N., M.D. President Medical Staff, Indiana University Health Starke Hospital, Knox, IN, p. A216

DAMON, Chad, Contractor, St. Vincent Dunn Hospital, Bedford, IN, p. A207

DAMON, Kerry, Director Human Resources, Baystate Franklin Medical Center, Greenfield, MA, p. A310

DAMRON, Greg, Vice President Finance and Chief Financial Officer, Georgia Regents Medical Center, Augusta, GA, p. A153

DAMSCHRODER, Robin
Chief Operating Officer, St. Joseph Mercy Hospital Ann Arbor, Ypsilanti, MI, p. A338
Chief Operating Officer, St. Joseph Mercy Livingston Hospital, Howell, MI, p. A327

DANBDALA, Kayyan, M.D. Medical Director, Schick Shadel Hospital, Seattle, WA, p. A688

DANCH, Stephen M., Chief Financial Officer, UPMC Hamot, Erie, PA, p. A539

DANDRIDGE, Thomas C., FACHE, President and Chief Executive Officer, Regional Medical Center, Orangeburg, SC, p. A569

DANE, Jeff, Executive Vice President and Chief Financial Officer, University Medical Center, Lubbock, TX, p. A635

DANELLO, Sherry, MSN Vice President Patient Care Services, St. Joseph's Hospital, Savannah, GA, p. A166

DANG, Cynthia, Vice President Human Resources, North Hills Hospital, North Richland Hills, TX, p. A640

DANG, Minh, Vice President Finance, Robert Packer Hospital, Sayre, PA, p. A554

DANG–DO, Mihn, Chief Financial Officer, Shands Live Oak Regional Medical Center, Live Oak, FL, p. A134

DANGERFIELD, Wesley, Community Chief Executive Officer, Summers County ARH Hospital, Hinton, WV, p. A695

DANIEL, Dena, Director Information Systems, Jackson County Memorial Hospital, Altus, OK, p. A507

DANIEL, Karen, Chief Executive Officer, Warm Springs Medical Center, Warm Springs, GA, p. A169

DANIEL, Lisa, Chief Executive Officer, Memphis Mental Health Institute, Memphis, TN, p. A589

DANIEL, Patricia, Chief Information Officer, Lake Whitney Medical Center, Whitney, TX, p. A657

DANIEL, Ron, Manager Information Systems, Matheny Medical and Educational Center, Peapack, NJ, p. A420

DANIEL, S., M.D. Chief Medical Officer, Spring Valley Hospital Medical Center, Las Vegas, NV, p. A406

DANIEL, Steven G., Senior Vice President and Chief Operating Officer, CHRISTUS Spohn Hospital Alice, Alice, TX, p. A595

DANIEL, Vera W., Chief Human Resources Officer, Saint Louis University Hospital, Saint Louis, MO, p. A381

DANIEL, W. D., D.O. Chief of Staff, Medical Center of Manchester, Manchester, TN, p. A587

DANIELS, Alex, Chief Nurse Executive, U. S. Public Health Service Indian Hospital, Crownpoint, NM, p. A428

DANIELS, Andy
Chief Operating Officer, Bucyrus Community Hospital, Bucyrus, OH, p. A484
Vice President Non–Clinical Operations and Information Systems, Galion Community Hospital, Galion, OH, p. A494

DANIELS, Anita
Acting Executive Director, New York City Children's Center, NY, p. A446
Executive Director, Rockland Children's Psychiatric Center, Orangeburg, NY, p. A451

DANIELS, Betty, M.D. Chief of Staff, St. Bernardine Medical Center, San Bernardino, CA, p. A88

DANIELS, Buddy, Chief Executive Officer, Helena Regional Medical Center, Helena, AR, p. A47

DANIELS, Craig M., Chief Financial Officer, Moab Regional Hospital, Moab, UT, p. A660

DANIELS, Don, M.D. Chief Medical Officer, Rollins–Brook Community Hospital, Lampasas, TX, p. A632

DANIELS, Don, Executive Vice President and Chief Operating Officer, SwedishAmerican Hospital, Rockford, IL, p. A202

DANIELS, Jeff
Chief Financial Officer, Bingham Memorial Hospital, Blackfoot, ID, p. A174
Chief Financial Officer, Mountain River Birthing and Surgery Center, Blackfoot, ID, p. A174

DANIELS, John, M.D. Medical Director, LifeCare Hospitals of Wisconsin, Pewaukee, WI, p. A713

DANIELS, Judy, Vice President Human Resources, Our Lady of Bellefonte Hospital, Ashland, KY, p. A258

DANIELS, Karen, MSN Chief Nursing Officer, Halifax Regional Medical Center, Roanoke Rapids, NC, p. A471

DANIELS, Kristin, Manager Human Resources, Sutter Center for Psychiatry, Sacramento, CA, p. A87

DANIELS, Mark, M.D. Vice President Physician Enterprise, Delnor Hospital, Geneva, IL, p. A191

DANIELS, S. Janette, Director Human Resources, HEALTHSOUTH Rehabilitation Hospital of Fort Smith, Fort Smith, AR, p. A46

DANIELS, Todd, M.D. Medical Director, HEALTHSOUTH Rehabilitation Hospital of Arlington, Arlington, TX, p. A597

DANIELS, W. Peter, Chief Operating Officer, John H. Stroger Jr. Hospital of Cook County, Chicago, IL, p. A184

DANIELSEN, Marsha, Director Information Systems, Good Samaritan Hospital, Vincennes, IN, p. A223

DANIELSON, Carol, R.N. Senior Vice President and Chief Nursing Officer, Gwinnett Hospital System, Lawrenceville, GA, p. A162

DANIELSON, David S., Senior Vice President Operations, EvergreenHealth, Kirkland, WA, p. A684

DANKER, Doug, Administrator, Mercy Hospital El Reno, El Reno, OK, p. A510

DANKERT, Sheri
Chief Financial Officer, Mayo Clinic Health System in Albert Lea, Albert Lea, MN, p. A339
Vice President Finance, Mayo Clinic Health System in Austin, Austin, MN, p. A340

DANKO, Douglas, President and Chief Executive Officer, Jameson Hospital, New Castle, PA, p. A546

DANN, Doreen, R.N. Chief Operating Officer, Victor Valley Global Medical Center, Victorville, CA, p. A99

DANOWSKI, Dale G., R.N. Senior Vice President Chief Operating Officer and Chief Nursing Officer, St. Vincent's Medical Center, Bridgeport, CT, p. A113

DANSBY, Tommy, Chief Medical Officer, Liberty Healthcare Systems, Bastrop, LA, p. A272

DANTIS, Gerry, Assistant Vice President Finance, SUNY Downstate Medical Center University Hospital, NY, p. A448

DANUSER, James, Chief Information Officer, Veterans Affairs Central Iowa Health Care System, Des Moines, IA, p. A230

DAOUD, Joudat, M.D. Chief of Staff, Community Health Center of Branch County, Coldwater, MI, p. A321

DAQUIOAG, Francis, Controller, Kahuku Medical Center, Kahuku, HI, p. A171

DARBONNE, Tina, Chief Financial Officer, Central Louisiana State Hospital, Pineville, LA, p. A287

DARBY, Kristin, Chief Information Officer, Eastern Regional Medical Center, Philadelphia, PA, p. A548

DARBY, Sharon, R.N. Vice President, Clinical Operations, Children's Hospital of Richmond at VCU–Brook Road Campus, Richmond, VA, p. A677

DARCEY, Patricia, R.N. Vice President/Chief Nursing Officer, Southampton Hospital, Southampton, NY, p. A455

DARDANO, Anthony, M.D. Chief Medical Officer, Delray Medical Center, Delray Beach, FL, p. A127

DARDEAU, Sean T., Chief Executive Officer, Mary Black Memorial Hospital, Spartanburg, SC, p. A570

DARDEN, David B., Chief Executive Officer, Raleigh General Hospital, Beckley, WV, p. A693

DAREY, Roland, M.D. Medical Director, Wamego Health Center, Wamego, KS, p. A256

DARLING, Cory, Chief Operating Officer, TriStar Hendersonville Medical Center, Hendersonville, TN, p. A584

DARLING, Rudy, Chief Operating Officer, Baxter Regional Medical Center, Mountain Home, AR, p. A50

DARNAUER, Patricia, Medical Center Commander, Carl R. Darnall Army Medical Center, Fort Hood, TX, p. A617

DARNELL, Brian, D.O. Chief of Staff, Johnson County Healthcare Center, Buffalo, WY, p. A720

DARNELL, Don, Chief Information Officer, Hamilton Memorial Hospital District, McLeansboro, IL, p. A196

DARNELL, Linda, Director Management Information Systems, King's Daughters' Health, Madison, IN, p. A218

DARNELL, Vicki A., MSN, President and Chief Executive Officer, Ephraim McDowell Regional Medical Center, Danville, KY, p. A260

DARRINGTON, Gilbert, Director Human Resources, Jackson Hospital and Clinic, Montgomery, AL, p. A24

DARVIN, Ken, M.D. Chief of Staff, Stroud Regional Medical Center, Stroud, OK, p. A519

DASARO, Lynda, Director Human Resources, Sutter Roseville Medical Center, Roseville, CA, p. A87

DASCANI, Jimmy, Chief Nursing Officer, HEALTHSOUTH Rehabilitation Hospital at Martin Health, Stuart, FL, p. A146

DASCHER Jr., Norman E.
Chief Executive Officer, Samaritan Hospital, Troy, NY, p. A456
Chief Executive Officer, St. Mary's Hospital, Troy, NY, p. A456

DASHIELD, Luanne G., Personnel Administrator, Deer's Head Hospital Center, Salisbury, MD, p. A303

DASHIELL, Stacy, M.D. Chief of Staff, Rice County District Hospital, Lyons, KS, p. A249

DASKALAKIS, Tom G., Chief Operating Officer, West Chester Hospital, West Chester, OH, p. A505

DASS, Karla, Director Human Resources, Regional General Hospital, Williston, FL, p. A150

DASSAU, Scott, Chief Nursing Officer, St. Bernard Parish Hospital, Chalmette, LA, p. A275

DASSENKO, Dennis, Chief Information Officer, Essentia Health Duluth, Duluth, MN, p. A342

DAUBERT, Stephanie
Chief Financial Officer, Bellevue Medical Center, Bellevue, NE, p. A394
Chief Financial Officer, Nebraska Medical Center, Omaha, NE, p. A400

DAUBY, Randall W., Chief Executive Officer, Hamilton Memorial Hospital District, McLeansboro, IL, p. A196

DAUGHDRILL, Diane, Director Human Resources, Jefferson Davis Community Hospital, Prentiss, MS, p. A364

DAUGHDRILL, Richard, R.N., Chief Executive Officer, AMG Specialty Hospital–Slidell, Slidell, LA, p. A288

DAUGHERTY, Angela, Chief Operating Officer, Okmulgee Memorial Hospital, Okmulgee, OK, p. A517

DAUGHERTY, Don, Director Information Systems, Fleming County Hospital, Flemingsburg, KY, p. A260

DAUGHERTY, Marney, Worklife Services Consultant, Brighton Center for Recovery, Brighton, MI, p. A320

DAUGHERTY, Stephen J., Chief Executive Officer, Coliseum Northside Hospital, Macon, GA, p. A162

DAUGHTERY, Beth, Chief Nursing Officer, Dukes Memorial Hospital, Peru, IN, p. A221

DAUGHTRY, Kaci, Director Human Resources, Andalusia Regional Hospital, Andalusia, AL, p. A15

DAUM, Karen, R.N. Vice President and Chief Nursing Officer, Passavant Area Hospital, Jacksonville, IL, p. A193

DAUTERIVE, F. Ralph, M.D. Vice President Medical Affairs, Ochsner Medical Center–Baton Rouge, Baton Rouge, LA, p. A273

DAUZ, Urbano, M.D. President Medical Staff, Shelby Memorial Hospital, Shelbyville, IL, p. A202

DAVE, Bhasker J., M.D., Superintendent, Mental Health Institute, Independence, IA, p. A232

DAVE', Rajesh J., M.D. Executive Vice President and Chief Medical Officer, United Health Services Hospitals–Binghamton, Binghamton, NY, p. A434

DAVENPORT, David, Director Human Resources, Washington County Hospital, Nashville, IL, p. A197

DAVENPORT, Douglas
Senior Vice President and Chief Financial Officer, St. John's Hospital, Saint Paul, MN, p. A351
Senior Vice President and Chief Financial Officer, Woodwinds Health Campus, Woodbury, MN, p. A354

DAVENPORT, Ginger, Director Human Resources, Promise Hospital of Dallas, Dallas, TX, p. A611

DAVENPORT, Julie, Chief Executive Officer, I–70 Community Hospital, Sweet Springs, MO, p. A383

DAVENPORT, Michael, M.D., President and Interim Chief Executive Officer, Methodist Hospitals, Gary, IN, p. A212

DAVENPORT, Polly J., R.N., Chief Executive Officer, Ochsner Medical Center – North Shore, Slidell, LA, p. A289

DAVENPORT, Sally M., MS Chief Nursing Officer and Chief Operating Officer, Ephraim McDowell Regional Medical Center, Danville, KY, p. A260

DAVENPORT, Sheilah, R.N., Chief Executive Officer and Superintendent, Clifton T. Perkins Hospital Center, Jessup, MD, p. A301

DAVENPORT, Terry, D.O. Chief of Staff, Benewah Community Hospital, Saint Maries, ID, p. A178

DAVES, Ronnie, Chief Executive Officer, Carolinas Hospital System Marion, Mullins, SC, p. A568

DAVID, Biff, Administrator, St. Landry Extended Care Hospital, Opelousas, LA, p. A287

DAVID, Daphne, Chief Operating Officer, Garden Park Medical Center, Gulfport, MS, p. A358

DAVID, Lim, Vice President Finance and Chief Financial Officer, St. Joseph Medical Center, Reading, PA, p. A553

DAVID, Michelle, Chief Executive Officer, Valley Hospital Phoenix, Phoenix, AZ, p. A37

DAVID, R. Neal, Administrator and Chief of Staff, Madigan Healthcare System, Tacoma, WA, p. A690

DAVID, Robert G., President, UH Regional Hospitals, Cleveland, OH, p. A489

DAVIDOFF, Ravin, M.D. Chief Medical Officer, Boston Medical Center, Boston, MA, p. A306

DAVIDOW, Daniel N., M.D. Medical Director, Cumberland Hospital, New Kent, VA, p. A674

DAVIDSON, Camille, Director Human Resources, Stanton County Hospital, Johnson, KS, p. A246

DAVIDSON, Charles O., M.D. Vice President Medical Affairs, Methodist Hospitals, Gary, IN, p. A212

DAVIDSON, Craig Val
Chief Executive Officer and Administrator, Beaver Valley Hospital, Beaver, UT, p. A659
Chief Executive Officer, Milford Valley Memorial Hospital, Milford, UT, p. A660

DAVIDSON, Diane, Senior Vice President Human Resources, Essentia Health Duluth, Duluth, MN, p. A342

DAVIDSON, Gary, Senior Vice President and Chief Information Officer, Lancaster General Health, Lancaster, PA, p. A542

DAVIDSON, Gary, M.D. Medical Director, Select Specialty Hospital–Johnstown, Johnstown, PA, p. A541

DAVIDSON, Gregg A., FACHE, Chief Executive Officer, Skagit Valley Hospital, Mount Vernon, WA, p. A685

DAVIDSON, James, Director of Information Services, Ferry County Memorial Hospital, Republic, WA, p. A687

DAVIDSON, James F., Chief Operating Officer, EASTAR Health System, Muskogee, OK, p. A514

DAVIDSON, James N., Troop Commander, Tripler Army Medical Center, Honolulu, HI, p. A171

DAVIDSON, John, Vice President Human Resources, Sharon Regional Health System, Sharon, PA, p. A555

DAVIDSON, Lezley, Chief Nursing Officer, Atoka County Medical Center, Atoka, OK, p. A508

DAVIDSON, Nancy, Senior Vice President and Chief Financial Officer, Jackson County Memorial Hospital, Altus, OK, p. A507

DAVIDSON, Paulette, FACHE Chief Operating Officer, Bellevue Medical Center, Bellevue, NE, p. A394

DAVIDSON, Rocky, Chief Financial Officer, Hollywood Pavilion, FL, p. A130

DAVIDSON, Rowena, Manager Business Office, AMG Specialty Hospital–Edmond, Edmond, OK, p. A510

DAVIDSON, Stephen, Director Human Resources, Lafayette Regional Health Center, Lexington, MO, p. A376

DAVIDSON, Tim, M.D. Chief Executive Physician Services, Providence St. Mary Medical Center, Walla Walla, WA, p. A692

DAVIDSON, Tori, R.N. Chief Nursing Officer, Tsehootsooi Medical Center, Fort Defiance, AZ, p. A32

DAVIDSON, Verno, R.N. Chief Nursing Officer, Bell Hospital, Ishpeming, MI, p. A327

DAVIES, Janie, Chief Financial Officer, New Mexico Rehabilitation Center, Roswell, NM, p. A430

DAVILA, Susan, Chief Executive Officer and Administrator, Carson Valley Medical Center, Gardnerville, NV, p. A404

DAVIN, Joni, Director Information and Business Management Service Line, Veterans Affairs Eastern Kansas Health Care System, Topeka, KS, p. A255

DAVINI, John, Vice President, St. Rose Hospital, Hayward, CA, p. A66

DAVIS, Adam
Director Information Technology, Cornerstone Hospital of SouthEast Arizona, Tucson, AZ, p. A40
Chief Information Officer, Cornerstone Hospital–West Monroe, West Monroe, LA, p. A290
Chief Information Officer, Solara Hospital Harlingen, Harlingen, TX, p. A622

DAVIS, Amelia, Director of Nursing, CrossRidge Community Hospital, Wynne, AR, p. A54

DAVIS, Amy, Chief Operating Officer, Southwest Regional Rehabilitation Center, Battle Creek, MI, p. A319

DAVIS, Andrea, Chief Executive Officer, HEALTHSOUTH Desert Canyon Rehabilitation Hospital, Las Vegas, NV, p. A405

DAVIS, Andrew, President, Carney Hospital, Boston, MA, p. A306

DAVIS, Andy, President, St. Vincent's Birmingham, Birmingham, AL, p. A17

DAVIS, Anne, Director Human Resources, Mason District Hospital, Havana, IL, p. A192

DAVIS, Astrid, R.N. Chief Nursing Officer, York Hospital, York, PA, p. A559

DAVIS, Autherine, Director Human Resources, D. W. McMillan Memorial Hospital, Brewton, AL, p. A17

DAVIS, Barry L., FACHE, President and Chief Executive Officer, Arkansas Methodist Medical Center, Paragould, AR, p. A51

DAVIS, Betty, Director Administrative Services, Porterville Developmental Center, Porterville, CA, p. A84

DAVIS, Brenda, R.N. Vice President of Patient Services, Indiana University Health Bedford Hospital, Bedford, IN, p. A206

DAVIS, Brent
Human Resources Team Leader, Arkansas Heart Hospital, Little Rock, AR, p. A48
Chief Financial Officer, Avista Adventist Hospital, Louisville, CO, p. A109
Chief Financial Officer, Central Valley Medical Center, Nephi, UT, p. A661

DAVIS, C.J., Chief Executive Officer/ Executive Director, Four County Counseling Center, Logansport, IN, p. A217

DAVIS, Cathy J.
Director Human Resources, ProMedica Bixby Hospital, Adrian, MI, p. A318
Director Human Resources, ProMedica Herrick Hospital, Tecumseh, MI, p. A336

DAVIS, Charlotte C., Director Human Resources, Lincoln Trail Behavioral Health System, Radcliff, KY, p. A269

DAVIS, Cheryl, M.D. Chief Medical Officer, Scotland Health Care System, Laurinburg, NC, p. A468

DAVIS, Clinton, M.D. Chief of Staff, Edward White Hospital, Saint Petersburg, FL, p. A144

DAVIS, Connie L., M.D. Chief Medical Officer, Skagit Valley Hospital, Mount Vernon, WA, p. A685

DAVIS, Curtis, Director Finance, Baystate Mary Lane Hospital, Ware, MA, p. A316

DAVIS, Dan, R.N. Nurse Administrator, Park City Medical Center, Park City, UT, p. A662

DAVIS, Daniel E., Chief Financial Officer, Kingwood Medical Center, Kingwood, TX, p. A631

DAVIS, Darcy, Chief Financial Officer, Lakeside Medical Center, Belle Glade, FL, p. A123

DAVIS, David, Chief Operating Officer, Western Maryland Hospital Center, Hagerstown, MD, p. A301

DAVIS, Deborah W., Chief Operating Officer, VCU Medical Center, Richmond, VA, p. A678

DAVIS, Debra K., Director of Operations, Winner Regional Healthcare Center, Winner, SD, p. A578

DAVIS, Deland, Chief Financial Officer, Public Health Service Indian Hospital – Quentin N. Burdick Memorial Health Facility, Belcourt, ND, p. A476

DAVIS, Dell, Director Information Systems, Doctor's Hospital – Tidwell, Houston, TX, p. A624

DAVIS, Elaine, Chief Nursing Officer and Vice President Patient Services, Northeast Alabama Regional Medical Center, Anniston, AL, p. A15

DAVIS, Ellen, Service Unit Director, U. S. Public Health Service Indian Hospital, Pine Ridge, SD, p. A575

DAVIS, Evan, Director Technology and Environmental Services, Knox County Hospital, Barbourville, KY, p. A258

DAVIS, Gana, Vice President Human Resources, Tri–State Memorial Hospital, Clarkston, WA, p. A682

DAVIS, Gannon, Director Human Resources, Medical West, Bessemer, AL, p. A16

DAVIS, Gary
 Vice President Information Systems, Baptist Medical Center, San Antonio, TX, p. A646
 Director Information Systems, Great River Medical Center, West Burlington, IA, p. A239

DAVIS, Hervey E., Chief Executive Officer, Franklin Hospital District, Benton, IL, p. A181

DAVIS, Howard, M.D. Vice President Medical Affairs, St. Joseph Medical Center, Reading, PA, p. A553

DAVIS, James, M.D. Chief Medical Staff, Chatham Hospital, Siler City, NC, p. A472

DAVIS, James R., President and Chief Executive Officer, University Health Care System, Augusta, GA, p. B144

DAVIS, James R., Chief Executive Officer, University Hospital, Augusta, GA, p. A154

DAVIS, Janet, R.N. Senior Vice President and Chief Nursing Officer, Tampa General Hospital, Tampa, FL, p. A148

DAVIS, Janice, Interim Director Human Resources, Gifford Medical Center, Randolph, VT, p. A666

DAVIS, Jeff
 Chief Financial Officer, Harrison County Hospital, Corydon, IN, p. A209
 Senior Vice President Human Resources, Massachusetts General Hospital, Boston, MA, p. A307

DAVIS, Jefferson, M.D. Medical Director, Perry Hospital, Perry, GA, p. A164

DAVIS, Jeffrey, D.O. Chief Medical Officer, St. Mary's Medical Center, West Palm Beach, FL, p. A150

DAVIS, Jimmy, Director Human Resources, Hardin Medical Center, Savannah, TN, p. A592

DAVIS, John, Chief Human Resources Officer, Bristol Bay Area Health Corporation, Dillingham, AK, p. A28

DAVIS, John William, Chief Executive Officer and Chief Financial Officer, Slidell Memorial Hospital, Slidell, LA, p. A289

DAVIS, Johnnie, Director Human Resources, Medicine Lodge Memorial Hospital, Medicine Lodge, KS, p. A250

DAVIS, Jon, Chief Financial Officer, Mahaska Health Partnership, Oskaloosa, IA, p. A236

DAVIS, Jonathan S., FACHE, President, Methodist Charlton Medical Center, Dallas, TX, p. A611

DAVIS, Justin, Chief Executive Officer, Moses Taylor Hospital, Scranton, PA, p. A554

DAVIS, Kassi, Director Patient Care Services, Willow Crest Hospital, Miami, OK, p. A513

DAVIS, Kenneth, Assistant Vice President Information Systems, Kennedy Krieger Institute, Baltimore, MD, p. A296

DAVIS, Kenneth L., M.D., President and Chief Executive, Mount Sinai Health System, New York, NY, p. B96

DAVIS, LaKeitha, Director Human Resources, Medical Center of South Arkansas, El Dorado, AR, p. A45

DAVIS, Leslie C., President, Magee–Womens Hospital of UPMC, Pittsburgh, PA, p. A551

DAVIS, Lisa, Vice President Finance, Saint Thomas West Hospital, Nashville, TN, p. A590

DAVIS, Lora, Chief Executive Officer, Select Specialty Hospital–Tallahassee, Tallahassee, FL, p. A147

DAVIS, Lorraine, Vice President Human Resources, Horn Memorial Hospital, Ida Grove, IA, p. A232

DAVIS, Lyle E., Administrator, Cozad Community Hospital, Cozad, NE, p. A395

DAVIS, Malene S., R.N., President and Chief Executive Officer, Capital Hospice, Arlington, VA, p. A668

DAVIS, Marcia, Vice President Patient Services, Mary Rutan Hospital, Bellefontaine, OH, p. A483

DAVIS, Mark, M.D. President Medical Staff, Galesburg Cottage Hospital, Galesburg, IL, p. A190

DAVIS, Mark, Director Information Systems, Lake Taylor Transitional Care Hospital, Norfolk, VA, p. A675

DAVIS, Mark, M.D. Chief of Staff, Newberry County Memorial Hospital, Newberry, SC, p. A569

DAVIS, Matt, Chief Executive Officer, Conroe Regional Medical Center, Conroe, TX, p. A607

DAVIS, Melissa, Chief Operating Officer, Andalusia Regional Hospital, Andalusia, AL, p. A15

DAVIS, Michael, Vice President Finance and Chief Financial Officer, United Medical Center, Washington, DC, p. A122

DAVIS, Myrna, Manager Human Resources, Palo Verde Hospital, Blythe, CA, p. A58

DAVIS, Natalie, R.N. Interim Chief Nursing Officer, Clarendon Memorial Hospital, Manning, SC, p. A568

DAVIS, Pamela M., System President and Chief Executive Officer, Edward Hospital, Naperville, IL, p. A197

DAVIS, Pamela M., System President and Chief Executive Officer, Edward–Elmhurst Healthcare, Naperville, IL, p. B56

DAVIS, Patricia, Chief Nursing Officer, South Central Kansas Medical Center, Arkansas City, KS, p. A241

DAVIS, Paula M., Chief Human Resources Officer, Sonoma Valley Hospital, Sonoma, CA, p. A95

DAVIS, Randy
 Director Information Technology, CGH Medical Center, Sterling, IL, p. A203
 Chief Executive Officer, Northcrest Medical Center, Springfield, TN, p. A593

DAVIS, Ray
 Administrative Director, Providence Memorial Hospital, El Paso, TX, p. A616
 Administrative Director Information Systems, Sierra Medical Center, El Paso, TX, p. A616

DAVIS, Richard
 Chief Executive Officer, Central Peninsula General Hospital, Soldotna, AK, p. A30
 Chief Financial Officer, George Washington University Hospital, Washington, DC, p. A121
 Chief Financial Officer, Saint Barnabas Medical Center, Livingston, NJ, p. A417

DAVIS, Richard O., Ph.D., President, Sibley Memorial Hospital, Washington, DC, p. A122

DAVIS, Rick, Chief Operating Officer and Support Services, Coshocton County Memorial Hospital, Coshocton, OH, p. A491

DAVIS, Roger K., Director Human Resources, Bourbon Community Hospital, Paris, KY, p. A269

DAVIS, Ronald, Chief Financial Officer, Specialty Hospital of Washington–Hadley, Washington, DC, p. A122

DAVIS, Ronald D., Chief Executive Officer, Titus Regional Medical Center, Mount Pleasant, TX, p. A638

DAVIS, Roy, M.D. Chief Medical Officer, Providence Alaska Medical Center, Anchorage, AK, p. A28

DAVIS, Rusty, Director Information Technology, J. C. Blair Memorial Hospital, Huntingdon, PA, p. A541

DAVIS, Scott
 Manager Information Technology, Arkansas Surgical Hospital, North Little Rock, AR, p. A51
 Chief Operating Officer, Ogden Regional Medical Center, Ogden, UT, p. A661

DAVIS, Sondra, Vice President Human Resources & System Development, Harnett Health System, Dunn, NC, p. A463

DAVIS, Stephen, Chief Financial Officer, Illinois Valley Community Hospital, Peru, IL, p. A200

DAVIS, Steve, M.D
 Chief Medical Officer, Campbellton Graceville Hospital, Graceville, FL, p. A130
 Chief of Staff, Henry County Health Center, Mount Pleasant, IA, p. A234

DAVIS, Steve W., Interim Chief Information Officer, Athens Regional Medical Center, Athens, GA, p. A151

DAVIS, Steven T., Chief Executive Officer, Lock Haven Hospital, Lock Haven, PA, p. A543

DAVIS, Terry, Chief Information Officer, Great Plains Regional Medical Center, Elk City, OK, p. A510

DAVIS, Teshia, Chief Clinical Officer, Carolinas Specialty Hospital, Charlotte, NC, p. A462

DAVIS, Toby, Chief Executive Officer, Red Rock Behavioral Hospital, Las Vegas, NV, p. A406

DAVIS, Todd, M.D. Vice President Medical Affairs, Patient Safety Officer, Caromont Regional Medical Center, Gastonia, NC, p. A465

DAVIS, Tommy, M.D. Chief of Staff, Oakdale Community Hospital, Oakdale, LA, p. A286

DAVIS, Trish, Chief Nursing Officer, Santa Rosa Medical Center, Milton, FL, p. A138

DAVIS, Verlene, Director Human Resources, Blue Mountain Hospital, John Day, OR, p. A526

DAVIS, Wayne, Manager Human Resources, Jesse Brown Veterans Affairs Medical Center, Chicago, IL, p. A184

DAVIS–HAGENS, Patricia, R.N., Chief Executive Officer, The Jewish Hospital – Mercy Health, Cincinnati, OH, p. A487

DAVIS–SAMPSON, Sherri, Director Human Resources, Houston Methodist San Jacinto Hospital, Baytown, TX, p. A601

DAVISON, Sandy, Personnel Assistant, Mental Health Institute, Clarinda, IA, p. A227

DAVY, Larry, Chief Executive Officer, Wallowa Memorial Hospital, Enterprise, OR, p. A524

DAWES, Christopher G., President and Chief Executive Officer, Lucile Salter Packard Children's Hospital at Stanford, Palo Alto, CA, p. A82

DAWES, John M., FACHE, Chief Executive Officer, Bothwell Regional Health Center, Sedalia, MO, p. A382

DAWKINS, Jeff, Chief Operating Officer, Detroit Receiving Hospital/University Health Center, Detroit, MI, p. A321

DAWSON, Amy S., Chief Clinical Officer, Manning Regional Healthcare Center, Manning, IA, p. A234

DAWSON, Anthony L., FACHE, Director, Veterans Affairs Gulf Coast Veterans Health Care System, Biloxi, MS, p. A356

DAWSON, Dave, Director Information Services, Van Diest Medical Center, Webster City, IA, p. A239

DAWSON, John, Chief Executive Officer, Montfort Jones Memorial Hospital, Kosciusko, MS, p. A361

DAWSON, Kane, Chief Executive Officer, Foundation Surgical Hospital of El Paso, El Paso, TX, p. A616

DAWSON, Kathy, R.N. Chief Nursing Officer, Saddleback Memorial Medical Center, Laguna Hills, CA, p. A68

DAWSON, Nancy, M.D. Medical Director, Mayo Clinic Jacksonville, Jacksonville, FL, p. A131

DAWSON, Trang, Chief Information Officer, Baylor Emergency Medical Center at Aubrey, Aubrey, TX, p. A598

DAWSON, Troy, M.D. President Medical Staff, Antelope Memorial Hospital, Neligh, NE, p. A398

DAX, Jennifer, Director Human Resources, Gundersen Boscobel Area Hospital and Clinics, Boscobel, WI, p. A702

DAY, Frank, Vice President Patient Services, Wood County Hospital, Bowling Green, OH, p. A484

DAY, Gordy, M.D. Medical Director, Schleicher County Medical Center, Eldorado, TX, p. A617

DAY, John M.
 Chief Operating Officer, Doctors NeuroMedical Hospital, Bremen, IN, p. A208
 Chief Executive Officer, Unity Medical & Surgical Hospital, Mishawaka, IN, p. A219

DAY, Kim, Interim President, Mercy Hospital Hot Springs, Hot Springs National Park, AR, p. A48

DAY, Mark, Chief Financial Officer, Twin Cities Hospital, Niceville, FL, p. A139

DAY, Regina
 Executive Director Finance, Mountain View Regional Medical Center, Norton, VA, p. A676
 Chief Financial Officer, Wellmont Hancock County Hospital, Sneedville, TN, p. A593
 Executive Director Finance, Wellmont Lonesome Pine Hospital, Big Stone Gap, VA, p. A668

DAY, Scott, Vice President Human Resources, Lutheran Medical Center, Wheat Ridge, CO, p. A112

DAY, Sherry Clouse, CP
 Vice President Finance and Regional Chief Financial Officer, Mercy Hospital Aurora, Aurora, MO, p. A367
 Chief Financial Officer, Mercy Hospital Cassville, Cassville, MO, p. A369
 Chief Financial Officer, Mercy St. Francis Hospital, Mountain View, MO, p. A377

DAY, Therese, Chief Financial Officer, UMass Memorial Medical Center, Worcester, MA, p. A317

DE FARIA, Ludmila, M.D. Chief Medical Officer, Eastside Psychiatric Hospital, Tallahassee, FL, p. A146

DE FUR, Kyle, FACHE, President, St. Vincent Indianapolis Hospital, Indianapolis, IN, p. A215

DE JEAN, Julie, Chief Executive Officer, Select Specialty Hospital–Springfield, Springfield, MO, p. A383

DE JESUS, Alexander, M.D. Medical Director, HEALTHSOUTH Rehabilitation Hospital of Sarasota, Sarasota, FL, p. A145

DE JESUS, Edwin, Comptroller, Hospital Santa Rosa, Guayama, PR, p. A726

DE JESUS, Hector M., Chief Operating Officer, Florida Hospital DeLand, DeLand, FL, p. A127

DE JESUS, Jorge, Executive Director, I. Gonzalez Martinez Oncologic Hospital, San Juan, PR, p. A728

DE LA CRUZ, Rosemary, Chief Financial Officer, Hospital Episcopal San Lucas Guayama, Guayama, PR, p. A726

DE LA PAZ, Christine, Director Human Resources, Aurora Charter Oak Hospital, Covina, CA, p. A61

DE LA PAZ, Eva, Chief Financial Officer, Post Acute Medical Specialty Hospital of Corpus Christi, Corpus Christi, TX, p. A608

DE LA PENA, Will, Chief Financial Officer, MidHudson Regional Hospital of Westchester Medical Center, Poughkeepsie, NY, p. A452

DE LA TORRE, Ralph, M.D., Chairman and Chief Executive Officer, Steward Health Care System, LLC, Boston, MA, p. B129

DE LEON, Aurea, Chief Human Resources Officer, Hospital Universitario Dr. Ramon Ruiz Arnau, Bayamon, PR, p. A725

DE LEON, Darcy, Director Human Resources, Frank R. Howard Memorial Hospital, Willits, CA, p. A100

DE LEON, Dennis, M.D. Associate Chief Medical Officer and Vice President Medical Affairs, Highline Medical Center, Burien, WA, p. A682

DE LOS REYES, Jay
   Chief Operating Officer, HEALTHSOUTH Sunrise Rehabilitation Hospital, Sunrise, FL, p. A146
   Chief Operating Officer, Trumbull Memorial Hospital, Warren, OH, p. A504

DE PALO, Vera, M.D. Chief Medical Officer, Signature Healthcare Brockton Hospital, Brockton, MA, p. A308

DE PASQUALE, Edward, Chief Financial Officer, Conemaugh Memorial Medical Center, Johnstown, PA, p. A541

DE PIANO, Linda, Ph.D., Chief Executive Officer, Jerome Golden Center for Behavioral Health, Inc., West Palm Beach, FL, p. A150

DE PREZ, Bernadette, Chief Operating Officer, Skyridge Medical Center, Cleveland, TN, p. A581

DE ROSA, James, Vice President Finance, Robert Wood Johnson University Hospital Somerset, Somerville, NJ, p. A422

DE ROSIER, Colleen, Coordinator Human Resource, Spearfish Regional Hospital, Spearfish, SD, p. A577

DE SANTIAGO, Elizabeth, Director, Hospital Psiquiatrico Metropolitano, Cabo Rojo, PR, p. A725

DE TORRES, Francisco, M.D. Medical Director, Ashford Presbyterian Community Hospital, San Juan, PR, p. A727

DE VOSS, Gerald, Acting Administrator, Duane L. Waters Hospital, Jackson, MI, p. A328

DEAK, Terry, Chief Financial Officer, Lodi Memorial Hospital, Lodi, CA, p. A69

DEAKYNE, John R., Chief Financial Officer, Saint Mary's Regional Medical Center, Reno, NV, p. A408

DEAL, Jennifer, Chief Financial Officer, Greeley County Health Services, Tribune, KS, p. A255

DEAL, Lisa, Budget Analyst, U. S. Public Health Service Indian Hospital, Eagle Butte, SD, p. A573

DEAN, Amanda, Human Resources Officer, Ralph H. Johnson Veterans Affairs Medical Center, Charleston, SC, p. A563

DEAN, Donna, Chief Financial Officer, Rainbow Mental Health Facility, Kansas City, KS, p. A247

DEAN, Douglas B., Chief Human Resources Officer, The Children's Hospital of Alabama, Birmingham, AL, p. A17

DEAN, Harrison M., FACHE, Senior Vice President and Administrator, Baptist Health Medical Center – North Little Rock, North Little Rock, AR, p. A51

DEAN, Joel, Director Information Services, Piedmont Medical Center, Rock Hill, SC, p. A569

DEAN, Laura, Director Human Resources, Wilson Medical Center, Neodesha, KS, p. A250

DEAN, Lloyd H., President and Chief Executive Officer, Dignity Health, San Francisco, CA, p. B52

DEAN, Megan, Director Human Resources, South Bay Hospital, Sun City Center, FL, p. A146

DEAN, Morre, Chief Executive Officer, Parker Adventist Hospital, Parker, CO, p. A110

DEAN, Russell, Administrator, LifeCare Hospital of Dayton, Miamisburg, OH, p. A498

DEAN, Thomas, M.D. Chief of Staff, Avera Weskota Memorial Hospital, Wessington Springs, SD, p. A578

DEANE, Leslie, Chief Executive Officer, Select Specialty Hospital–Winston–Salem, Winston–Salem, NC, p. A475

DEANS, Ken, Chief Information Officer, Chesapeake Regional Medical Center, Chesapeake, VA, p. A669

DEAO, Ellen, Director Information Services, CHI Health Creighton University Medical Center, Omaha, NE, p. A399

DEARDORFF, Chad, Chief Financial Officer, Cornerstone Hospital of Bossier City, Bossier City, LA, p. A274

DEARDORFF, John A., Chief Executive Officer, Reston Hospital Center, Reston, VA, p. A677

DEARMOND, Karl, Director Information Systems, Geary Community Hospital, Junction City, KS, p. A246

DEARY, Shirley, Director Human Resources, Glenbeigh Hospital and Outpatient Centers, Rock Creek, OH, p. A501

DEATER, Gary A., Vice President Administration, Human Resources and Risk Management, Witham Memorial Hospital, Lebanon, IN, p. A217

DEATHERAGE, Karen, Director of Nursing, Russell Regional Hospital, Russell, KS, p. A253

DEATON, David, Chief Executive Officer, Ozark Health Medical Center, Clinton, AR, p. A44

DEATON, Eric
   Chief Executive Officer, Danville Regional Medical Center, Danville, VA, p. A670
   Interim Chief Executive Officer, Memorial Hospital, Martinsville, VA, p. A674

DEATON, Mike, Chief Financial Officer, Ozark Health Medical Center, Clinton, AR, p. A44

DEATON, Susan Renodin, Chief Human Resources Officer, Cumberland River Hospital, Celina, TN, p. A580

DEATON, Timothy C., Chief Executive Officer, Vibra Hospital of Richmond, Richmond, VA, p. A678

DEBARBA Jr., Daniel J., President and Chief Executive Officer, Norwalk Hospital, Norwalk, CT, p. A116

DEBARROS, Paula, Director Human Resources, Southwest Connecticut Mental Health System, Bridgeport, CT, p. A113

DEBBAS, Elias, M.D. President Medical Staff, Fort Washington Medical Center, Fort Washington, MD, p. A301

DEBLASIS, John, Vice President, Belmont Community Hospital, Bellaire, OH, p. A483

DEBLIEUX, Dawna, Chief Nurse Executive, Natchitoches Regional Medical Center, Natchitoches, LA, p. A285

DEBLOIS, Georgean, M.D. Chairman Medical Staff, CJW Medical Center, Richmond, VA, p. A677

DEBOER, Cynthia D., Chief Financial Officer, Cedar Springs Hospital, Colorado Springs, CO, p. A103

DEBOER, K. C., President and Chief Executive Officer, Jamestown Regional Medical Center, Jamestown, ND, p. A478

DEBOOY, Ann, R.N. Chief Nursing Officer, Memorial Medical Center, Las Cruces, NM, p. A429

DEBORD, Thomas, President, Summa Wadsworth–Rittman Hospital, Wadsworth, OH, p. A504

DECELIS, Lori, Director Human Resources, Hampton Behavioral Health Center, Westampton, NJ, p. A424

DECELL, Daniela, Chief Executive Officer, Las Colinas Medical Center, Irving, TX, p. A629

DECHABERT, Rebecca, Acting Director Personnel, New York State Psychiatric Institute, New York, NY, p. A447

DECHAIRO–MARINO, Ann, R.N. Chief Nursing Officer, Providence Holy Cross Medical Center, CA, p. A74

DECHANT, David, Chief Human Resources Officer, Tomah Veterans Affairs Medical Center, Tomah, WI, p. A716

DECKARD, Rick, Chief Fiscal Service, Chillicothe Veterans Affairs Medical Center, Chillicothe, OH, p. A486

DECKARD, Steven D., Vice President Human Resources, Indiana University Health Bloomington Hospital, Bloomington, IN, p. A207

DECKER, Janet, Assistant Vice President, MedStar Union Memorial Hospital, Baltimore, MD, p. A297

DECKER, Jeanine, Manager Human Resources, Arizona State Hospital, Phoenix, AZ, p. A35

DECKER, Kathy, Interim Chief Nursing Officer, Northern Inyo Hospital, Bishop, CA, p. A58

DECKER, Kevin, Chief Executive Officer, Forrest City Medical Center, Forrest City, AR, p. A46

DECKER, Lisa K., Vice President Marketing, Franciscan St. Elizabeth Health – Lafayette Central, Lafayette, IN, p. A216

DECKER, Michael, President and Chief Executive Officer, Divine Savior Healthcare, Portage, WI, p. A713

DECORTE, Raymond P., M.D. Chief Medical Officer, East Jefferson General Hospital, Metairie, LA, p. A284

DECOUX, Bobby, Assistant Vice President Human Resources, WellStar Kennestone Hospital, Marietta, GA, p. A163

DECREMER, Dean, Chief Information Officer, Dickinson County Healthcare System, Iron Mountain, MI, p. A327

DEDECKER, Troy, Chief Executive Officer, Mid–America Rehabilitation Hospital, Shawnee Mission, KS, p. A254

DEE, Thomas A., Chief Executive Officer, Southwestern Vermont Medical Center, Bennington, VT, p. A665

DEEMER, Miriam
   Interim Chief Executive Officer, Select Specialty Hospital–Downriver, Wyandotte, MI, p. A337
   Chief Executive Officer, Select Specialty Hospital–Grosse Pointe, Grosse Pointe, MI, p. A326

DEER, Dolores, Director Human Resources, Northwest Texas Healthcare System, Amarillo, TX, p. A596

DEERING, Linda, R.N., President, Advocate Sherman Hospital, Elgin, IL, p. A189

DEERING, Lisa, Administrator, Heatherhill Care Communities, Chardon, OH, p. A485

DEES, Edith, Vice President Information Services and Chief Information Officer, Holy Spirit Hospital, Camp Hill, PA, p. A535

DEFAUW, Thomas D., FACHE, President and Chief Executive Officer, Blue Water Health Services Corporation, Port Huron, MI, p. B24

DEFAUW, Thomas D., FACHE, President and Chief Executive Officer, Port Huron Hospital, Port Huron, MI, p. A332

DEFAYE, Yael, Director, Information Technology, Rio Grande Hospital, Del Norte, CO, p. A104

DEFOORE, Richard G., FACHE, Chief Executive Officer, Stamford Memorial Hospital, Stamford, TX, p. A650

DEFORD, Drexel, Chief Information Officer, Scripps Mercy Hospital, San Diego, CA, p. A89

DEFRANCESCO, Anthony, Associate Director, Veterans Affairs Long Beach Healthcare System, Long Beach, CA, p. A70

DEFREECE, Todd, Vice President Operations, CHI Health Creighton University Medical Center, Omaha, NE, p. A399

DEFURIO, Anthony C., Vice President and Chief Financial Officer, University of Colorado Hospital, Aurora, CO, p. A102

DEFURIO, Ken, President and Chief Executive Officer, Butler Health System, Butler, PA, p. A534

DEGEAR, David O., M.D. Vice President Medical Affairs, Westfields Hospital, New Richmond, WI, p. A712

DEGENNARO, Vincent, M.D. Chief of Staff, Miami Veterans Affairs Healthcare System, Miami, FL, p. A137

DEGINA, Anthony M., President and Chief Executive Officer, Largo Medical Center, Largo, FL, p. A134

DEGLANDON, Frances, Chief Financial Officer, Bunkie General Hospital, Bunkie, LA, p. A275

DEGRAND, Robert
   Vice President Information Systems, Chief Information Officer, Community Memorial Hospital, Menomonee Falls, WI, p. A709
   Chief Information Officer, Froedtert Memorial Lutheran Hospital, Milwaukee, WI, p. A710

DEGRAVELLE, Eric, Director Human Resources, Thibodaux Regional Medical Center, Thibodaux, LA, p. A289

DEGROFF, James, Director Technology and Network Services, St. Mary's Healthcare, Amsterdam, NY, p. A432

DEGROOT, Daniel, Chief Executive Officer, Community Memorial Hospital, Oconto Falls, WI, p. A712

DEGROOT, Randy, President and Chief Executive Officer, Community Health Center of Branch County, Coldwater, MI, p. A321

DEHART, Kristen, Interim Administrator, Spalding Rehabilitation Hospital, Aurora, CO, p. A102

DEHAVEN, Bryce, Chief Financial Officer, Medical Center of Aurora, Aurora, CO, p. A102

DEHNING, Cielo, M.D. Medical Director, Mid–America Rehabilitation Hospital, Shawnee Mission, KS, p. A254

DEIBEL, Justin, Senior Vice President and Chief Financial Officer, Mercy Medical Center, Baltimore, MD, p. A297

DEICH, Faye L., R.N. Chief Operating Officer, Sacred Heart Hospital, Eau Claire, WI, p. A704

DEITCH, Sally A., R.N., Chief Executive Officer, Sierra Providence East Medical Center, El Paso, TX, p. A616

DEITRICK, Diana, Director Information Services, Devereux Hospital and Children's Center of Florida, Melbourne, FL, p. A135

DEITZEN, Denise M., Director, Veterans Affairs Northern Indiana Health Care System, Fort Wayne, IN, p. A211

DEJACO, Lynn S., Chief Financial Officer, FirstHealth Moore Regional Hospital, Pinehurst, NC, p. A470

DEJESUS, David, Senior Vice President Human Resources, Southcoast Hospitals Group, Fall River, MA, p. A310

DEKASTLE, Reuben J., Chief Nursing Officer, Weiser Memorial Hospital, Weiser, ID, p. A179

DEKEYZER, Ron, Regional Director Information Systems, Christus St. Vincent Regional Medical Center, Santa Fe, NM, p. A430

DEKOK, Joni, Chief Nursing Officer, Sanford Sheldon Medical Center, Sheldon, IA, p. A237

DEKONING, Bernard L., M.D. Chief of Staff, Wm. Jennings Bryan Dorn Veterans Affairs Medical Center, Columbia, SC, p. A565

DEKREY, Dale, MS Associate Director Operations and Resources, Fargo Veterans Affairs Health Care System, Fargo, ND, p. A477

DEKREY, Daniel, M.D. Chief of Staff, Sanford Bemidji Medical Center, Bemidji, MN, p. A340

DEKRUSE, Jet L., Administrator, Humboldt County Mental Health, Eureka, CA, p. A62

DEL BOCCIO, Suzanne, MS Chief Nursing Officer and Vice President Patient Care Services, Indiana University Health North Hospital, Carmel, IN, p. A208

DEL CASTILLO, Daniel, Chief Executive Officer, HEALTHSOUTH Rehabilitation Hospital of San Juan, San Juan, PR, p. A728

DEL GAUDIO, Frank J., Administrator, Essex County Hospital Center, Cedar Grove, NJ, p. A414

DEL RIO, R. Maximilien, M.D. Medical Director, Northern Virginia Mental Health Institute, Falls Church, VA, p. A670

DEL ROSARIO, Cris, M.D. President Medical Staff, Illini Community Hospital, Pittsfield, IL, p. A200

DEL TORO, Gustavo, M.D. Chief Medical Officer, Wyckoff Heights Medical Center, NY, p. A449

DEL TORO, Ivan E., M.D. Medical Director, Hospital HIMA San Pablo Caguas, Caguas, PR, p. A725

DELA TORRE, Victor, Command Legal Officer, Naval Hospital Lemoore, Lemoore, CA, p. A69

DELACROIX, Marc, Chief Information Officer, Signature Healthcare Brockton Hospital, Brockton, MA, p. A308

DELAGARDELLE, Pamela K., President and Chief Executive Officer, UnityPoint Health – Allen Hospital, Waterloo, IA, p. A239

DELANEY, Michael, Chief Financial Officer, Two Rivers Behavioral Health System, Kansas City, MO, p. A375

DELANO, John
  Vice President Chief Information Officer, Integris Baptist Medical Center, Oklahoma City, OK, p. A515
  Vice President and Chief Information Officer, Integris Southwest Medical Center, Oklahoma City, OK, p. A515

DELANO, Michael, Administrator, Spearfish Regional Surgery Center, Spearfish, SD, p. A577

DELATTE, Sandra, Director Human Resources, Villa Feliciana Medical Complex, Jackson, LA, p. A279

DELEDDA, John, M.D. Vice President Medical Affairs, University of Cincinnati Medical Center, Cincinnati, OH, p. A487

DELEEUW, John, M.D. Chief of Staff, Northeast Regional Medical Center, Kirksville, MO, p. A375

DELELLIS, Terry, R.N. Director of Nursing, Corry Memorial Hospital, Corry, PA, p. A536

DELEON, Arsenio V., M.D. Chief Medical Officer, Select Specialty Hospital–Macomb County, Mount Clemens, MI, p. A330

DELEON, Joseph, President, Texas Health Harris Methodist Hospital Southwest Fort Worth, Fort Worth, TX, p. A619

DELEON, Marcos
  Vice President Community Engagement, Truman Medical Center–Hospital Hill, Kansas City, MO, p. A374
  Vice President Community Engagement, Truman Medical Center–Lakewood, Kansas City, MO, p. A374

DELFF, Michael, Chief Executive Officer, Mercy Hospital, Moose Lake, MN, p. A348

DELFS, Michael, Chief Executive Officer, Richland Hospital, Richland Center, WI, p. A714

DELGADO, Eric, Chief Financial Officer, Lakewood Regional Medical Center, Lakewood, CA, p. A69

DELGADO, Pete, President and Chief Executive Officer, Salinas Valley Memorial Healthcare System, Salinas, CA, p. A88

DELGADO, Steve, Operations Coordinator, Milwaukee County Behavioral Health Division, Milwaukee, WI, p. A710

DELGRECO, Trish, Director of Nursing, OhioHealth MedCentral Shelby Hospital, Shelby, OH, p. A502

DELIEN, Rudie, Director Human Resources, Devereux Georgia Treatment Network, Kennesaw, GA, p. A161

DELISE, Donna, Associate Director Patient Care Services, Oklahoma City Veterans Affairs Medical Center, Oklahoma City, OK, p. A516

DELLA LANA, David, M.D. Chief of Staff, Fairchild Medical Center, Yreka, CA, p. A101

DELLA TORRE, Linda, Senior Vice President and Chief Operating Officer, Athens Regional Medical Center, Athens, GA, p. A151

DELLACECCA, Kathe, Chief Executive Officer, Garfield Park Hospital, Chicago, IL, p. A183

DELLASEGA, Dave, President and Chief Executive Officer, Great Plains Health Alliance, Inc., Wichita, KS, p. B61

DELLEA, Eugene A., President, Fairview Hospital, Great Barrington, MA, p. A310

DELLICK, Charles, Director Information Technology, Magruder Memorial Hospital, Port Clinton, OH, p. A500

DELLOCONO, John, Senior Vice President and Chief Financial Officer, CentraState Healthcare System, Freehold, NJ, p. A416

DELONE, Lori
  Senior Vice President Support Services and Chief Information Officer, Health First Cape Canaveral Hospital, Cocoa Beach, FL, p. A126
  Senior Vice President Information Technology, Health First Palm Bay Hospital, Melbourne, FL, p. A136
  Senior Vice President and Chief Information Officer, Health First Viera Hospital, Melbourne, FL, p. A136

DELONG, Patricia, Chief Nursing Officer, Essentia Health St. Joseph's Medical Center, Brainerd, MN, p. A340

DELORENZO, David, Senior Director Human Resources, Sisters of Charity Hospital of Buffalo, Buffalo, NY, p. A435

DELOS SANTOS, Edwin, Director Information Systems, Placentia–Linda Hospital, Placentia, CA, p. A83

DELPLEACHE, Michael, Specialist Information Technology, Anchor Hospital, Atlanta, GA, p. A151

DELVEAUX, Joe, Manager Information Services, St. Francis Regional Medical Center, Shakopee, MN, p. A352

DEMARCO, Victor, Chief Financial Officer, Bronx–Lebanon Hospital Center Health Care System, NY, p. A442

DEMAREST, Pamela, R.N. Chief Nursing Officer, UNM Sandoval Regional Medical Center, Rio Rancho, NM, p. A430

DEMARTINO, Pat, Chief Information Officer, Children's Specialized Hospital–PSE&G, New Brunswick, NJ, p. A419

DEMAS, Beth, Director Public Relations, Shriners Hospitals for Children–Tampa, Tampa, FL, p. A148

DEMASIE, Dennis, Vice President Information Systems and Chief Information Officer, Rush–Copley Medical Center, Aurora, IL, p. A181

DEMATTEO, Kathleen, Chief Information Officer, Danbury Hospital, Danbury, CT, p. A113

DEMAY, Paul, Chief Information Officer, Northwest Medical Center – Springdale, Springdale, AR, p. A53

DEMBER, Barbara, President and Chief Executive Officer, Verde Valley Medical Center, Cottonwood, AZ, p. A32

DEMBITSKAYA, Svetlana, Chief Operating Officer, Metro Health Hospital, Wyoming, MI, p. A337

DEMERICH, Lois B., Director Human Resources, Sentara Williamsburg Regional Medical Center, Williamsburg, VA, p. A680

DEMERS, Vickie, Chief Executive Officer, HEALTHSOUTH MountainView Regional Rehabilitation Hospital, Morgantown, WV, p. A697

DEMING, Mark, Controller, Oakwood Hospital–Taylor, Taylor, MI, p. A335

DEMING, Peggy, Executive Vice President and Chief Financial Officer, University Health System, San Antonio, TX, p. A648

DEMING, Terra, Director Human Resources, Otsego Memorial Hospital, Gaylord, MI, p. A324

DEMMEL, Ruth, M.D. Chief Medical Officer, Perkins County Health Services, Grant, NE, p. A396

DEMONTGORENCY, Tara, Director Business Development, HEALTHSOUTH Bakersfield Rehabilitation Hospital, Bakersfield, CA, p. A57

DEMORLIS, John, M.D. Chief Medical Staff, Salem Memorial District Hospital, Salem, MO, p. A382

DEMORROW, Dawn P., Chief Human Resources Service, Wilkes–Barre Veterans Affairs Medical Center, Wilkes–Barre, PA, p. A558

DEMPSEY, Jeffrey, President and Chief Executive Officer, Mercy St. Charles Hospital, Oregon, OH, p. A500

DEMPSEY, John, Vice President and Chief Financial Officer, Hardin Memorial Hospital, Elizabethtown, KY, p. A260

DEMURO, Rob, M.D. President Medical Staff, Elizabethtown Community Hospital, Elizabethtown, NY, p. A437

DENBO, John R., Chief Executive Officer, Phelps County Regional Medical Center, Rolla, MO, p. A379

DENCKLAU, Larry, D.O. Chief of Staff, Lake Pointe Medical Center, Rowlett, TX, p. A645

DENEFF, Randall, Vice President Finance, Mary Free Bed Rehabilitation Hospital, Grand Rapids, MI, p. A325

DENEGRI, David, Chief Financial Officer, Parkwood Behavioral Health System, Olive Branch, MS, p. A363

DENEN, Bruce, Manager Data Processing, Fayette County Memorial Hospital, Washington Court House, OH, p. A504

DENHAM, Stephanie, Chief Financial Officer and Human Resources Officer, Phillips County Hospital, Malta, MT, p. A389

DENIGRIS, Deborah, Chief Nursing Officer, Kingsboro Psychiatric Center, NY, p. A444

DENIO, Arthur E., Vice President and Chief Financial Officer, NorthBay Medical Center, Fairfield, CA, p. A62

DENIRO, Lori, Senior Director Nursing, St. Elizabeth Boardman Health Center, Boardman, OH, p. A484

DENISIENKO, Mary, Vice President Human Resources, Palos Community Hospital, Palos Heights, IL, p. A199

DENISON, Rita, Manager Information Systems, Sturgis Hospital, Sturgis, MI, p. A335

DENKER, Jill, Executive Director Human Resources, Lexington Regional Health Center, Lexington, NE, p. A397

DENMARK, Donald, M.D
  Chief Medical Officer, Carondelet St. Joseph's Hospital, Tucson, AZ, p. A40
  Chief Medical Officer, Carondelet St. Mary's Hospital, Tucson, AZ, p. A40

DENNETT, Bryan, M.D. Chief of Staff, William Newton Hospital, Winfield, KS, p. A257

DENNEY, Jeff, Administrator, Southern Crescent Hospital for Specialty Care, Riverdale, GA, p. A165

DENNING, Christine, Chief Operating Officer and Chief Nursing Officer, Silverton Hospital, Silverton, OR, p. A530

DENNIS, Bradley, M.D. Chief Medical Officer, Brookwood Medical Center, Birmingham, AL, p. A16

DENNIS, Michael, Director, William J. McCord Adolescent and Treatment Center, Orangeburg, SC, p. A569

DENNIS, Ronnie, Chief of Staff, Rolling Plains Memorial Hospital, Sweetwater, TX, p. A651

DENNISON, Cindy, Senior Director Rural Division, Mercy Willard Hospital, Willard, OH, p. A505

DENNO, Charles, Chief Financial Officer, Westwood Lodge Hospital, Westwood, MA, p. A316

DENNSTEDT, Crystal, Chief Information Officer, North Texas State Hospital, Wichita Falls Campus, Wichita Falls, TX, p. A657

DENO, Mark S., Chief Executive Officer, HEALTHSOUTH Rehabilitation Hospital of Arlington, Arlington, TX, p. A597

DENO, Mary, Vice President Human Resources, Community Medical Center, Toms River, NJ, p. A423

DENSON, Anna, Human Resources Specialist, Choctaw Health Center, Philadelphia, MS, p. A364

DENSON, Paula, M.D. President, Tyler County Hospital, Woodville, TX, p. A658

DENT, Bruce
  Human Resources Director, Heber Valley Medical Center, Heber City, UT, p. A660
  Director Human Resources, Park City Medical Center, Park City, UT, p. A662

DENT, Robert L., R.N. Chief Nursing Officer, Midland Memorial Hospital, Midland, TX, p. A638

DENTEN, Jane, MSN Vice President Nursing and Chief Nurse Executive, Advocate Lutheran General Hospital, Park Ridge, IL, p. A199

DENTON, Brian, Administrator, Mercy Hospital Kingfisher, Kingfisher, OK, p. A512

DENTON, Christopher, Chief Financial Officer, Henrico Doctors' Hospital, Richmond, VA, p. A677

DENTON, Genise, Manager Human Resources, John J. Pershing Veterans Affairs Medical Center, Poplar Bluff, MO, p. A378

DENTON, Joe, Executive Vice President and Chief Financial Officer, Mobile Infirmary Medical Center, Mobile, AL, p. A22

DENTON, Tony, JD, Interim Chief Executive Officer, University of Michigan Hospitals and Health Centers, Ann Arbor, MI, p. A318

DENUCCI, Alex, Chief Financial Officer, Franciscan Hospital for Children, Boston, MA, p. A306

DEPASQUALE, Joseph, M.D. Interim Chief Medical Officer, Saint Michael's Medical Center, Newark, NJ, p. A410

DEPAULIS, Hugh, Interim Vice President and Chief Financial Officer, Mercy Medical Center–Sioux City, Sioux City, IA, p. A238

DEPAULO, Theron
  Manager Information Systems, Providence Mount Carmel Hospital, Colville, WA, p. A682
  Director Information Technology, Providence St. Joseph's Hospital, Chewelah, WA, p. A682

DEPINHO, Ronald A., M.D., President, University of Texas M.D. Anderson Cancer Center, Houston, TX, p. A628

DEPKO, Mike, Director Information Technology, Brown County Hospital, Ainsworth, NE, p. A393

DEPOYSTER, Avis, Director Human Resources, Brownfield Regional Medical Center, Brownfield, TX, p. A604

DEPPERMAN, Kristi, Chief Financial Officer, Memphis Veterans Affairs Medical Center, Memphis, TN, p. A589

DEPRIEST, Marcia L., R.N. Chief Nursing Officer, St. Thomas More Hospital, Canon City, CO, p. A103

DEQUARDO, John R., M.D., Superintendent, Colorado Mental Health Institute at Pueblo, Pueblo, CO, p. A110

DERAMUS, Brenda, Manager Human Resources, Sutter Lakeside Hospital, Lakeport, CA, p. A69

DERBY, Richard P., Vice President Finance, Barton Memorial Hospital, South Lake Tahoe, CA, p. A96

DERENZIS, Vicki, Chief Financial Officer, Highlands Regional Medical Center, Sebring, FL, p. A146

DERFLINGER, Terri, Administrator, Mercy Hospital of Franciscan Sisters, Oelwein, IA, p. A235

DEROCHE, Richard, Manager Information Technology, Deaconess Hospital, Spokane, WA, p. A690

DERONCEREY, Josiane, Director Human Resources, Christ Hospital, Jersey City, NJ, p. A417

DEROSA, Christina, Ph.D., Chief Administrative Officer, Jefferson Medical Center, Ranson, WV, p. A699

DEROUEN, George Patrick, Chief Executive Officer, Savoy Medical Center, Mamou, LA, p. A283

DEROUEN, Jason, Director Management Information Systems, Grace Medical Center, Lubbock, TX, p. A634

DEROUSSE, Jacqueline, Assistant Vice President Talent, Midwestern Regional Medical Center, Zion, IL, p. A205

DERRICO, Patricia, FACHE Chief Nursing Officer, Coliseum Northside Hospital, Macon, GA, p. A162

DERRINGTON, Ken R., Chief Financial Officer, Northern Colorado Rehabilitation Hospital, Johnstown, CO, p. A108

DERSCH, Stephen, M.D. President Medical Staff, Regency Hospital of Florence, Florence, SC, p. A566

DERTZ, Donna, Director Human Resources, St. Bernard Hospital and Health Care Center, Chicago, IL, p. A187

DERUS, Charles, M.D. Vice President Medical Management, Advocate Good Samaritan Hospital, Downers Grove, IL, p. A188

DERUYTER, David N., M.D. President Medical Staff, Kindred Hospital–Atlanta, Atlanta, GA, p. A152

DESAI, Nimesh, M.D. Medical Director, Massena Memorial Hospital, Massena, NY, p. A441

DESAI, Shailesh, M.D. Chief of Staff, Baum Harmon Mercy Hospital, Primghar, IA, p. A236

DESALVO, Susan, Manager Human Resources, Bath Veterans Affairs Medical Center, Bath, NY, p. A433

DESANCTIS, Mario, FACHE, Director, Tomah Veterans Affairs Medical Center, Tomah, WI, p. A716
DESANTIS, John
Chief Financial Officer, Glenwood Regional Medical Center, West Monroe, LA, p. A290
Chief Financial Officer, Ouachita Community Hospital, West Monroe, LA, p. A290
DESANTIS, Vincent, Vice President Finance, Phelps Memorial Hospital Center, Sleepy Hollow, NY, p. A454
DESCHAMBEAU, Wayne G., President and Chief Executive Officer, Wayne Hospital, Greenville, OH, p. A495
DESCHENE, Normand E., FACHE, Chief Executive Officer, Lowell General Hospital, Lowell, MA, p. A311
DESCHRYVER, Joseph, Chief Executive Officer, Sierra Vista Regional Medical Center, San Luis Obispo, CA, p. A93
DESEI, Nitin, M.D. Medical Director, Regional Rehabilitation Hospital, Phenix City, AL, p. A25
DESHAZO, Sheri, Chief Operating Officer, Kings Mountain Hospital, Kings Mountain, NC, p. A467
DESHONG, Andre, Administrator, Behavioral Hospital of Longview, Longview, TX, p. A634
DESHPANDE, Jay, M.D. Chief Quality Officer and Chief Medical Officer, Arkansas Children's Hospital, Little Rock, AR, p. A48
DESIMONE, Maureen, Chief Operating Officer, Blythedale Children's Hospital, Valhalla, NY, p. A457
DESJEUNES, Carol, Vice President and Chief Operating Officer, Psychiatric Institute of Washington, Washington, DC, p. A122
DESKINS, Juanita, Chief Operating Officer, Pikeville Medical Center, Pikeville, KY, p. A269
DESMARAIS, John, M.D. Chief Medical Officer, Fayette County Memorial Hospital, Washington Court House, OH, p. A504
DESMARTEAU, Lisa Jo, Chief Financial Officer, Miami Jewish Home and Hospital for Aged, Miami, FL, p. A137
DESMOND, Debbie, Director Human Resources, Martha Jefferson Hospital, Charlottesville, VA, p. A669
DESMOND, Heather, Chief Financial Officer, Bibb Medical Center, Centreville, AL, p. A18
DESMOND, P. Craig, Chief Executive Officer, Southwest General Hospital, San Antonio, TX, p. A647
DESOTELLE, Robert C., President and Chief Executive Officer, Asheville Specialty Hospital, Asheville, NC, p. A459
DESOTO, David, M.D. Chief of Staff, National Park Medical Center, Hot Springs, AR, p. A47
DESOTO, James, M.D
Vice President Medical Affairs, Mercy Medical Center Redding, Redding, CA, p. A85
Vice President Medical Affairs, St. Elizabeth Community Hospital, Red Bluff, CA, p. A85
DESOUZA, Jacqueline, Chief Executive Officer, Research Medical Center, Kansas City, MO, p. A374
DESPRES, Paul J., Chief Executive Officer, Eleanor Slater Hospital, Cranston, RI, p. A560
DESROCHES, Jeff, Manager Information Systems, AHMC Anaheim Regional Medical Center, Anaheim, CA, p. A55
DESSIEUX, Guesly, D.O. Chief Medical Officer, Santiam Memorial Hospital, Stayton, OR, p. A530
DESTEFANO, Geraldine, R.N. Chief Nursing Officer, West Palm Hospital, West Palm Beach, FL, p. A150
DESTEFANO, Jane, R.N. Chief Nursing Officer, Houston Methodist San Jacinto Hospital, Baytown, TX, p. A601
DETER, Kevin, Chief Operating Officer, WellStar Cobb Hospital, Austell, GA, p. A154
DETOR, Robert E., Chief Executive Officer, South Oaks Hospital, Amityville, NY, p. A432
DETTERMAN, B. Lynn
President and Chief Executive Officer, Mercy Tiffin Hospital, Tiffin, OH, p. A503
President and Chief Executive Officer, Mercy Willard Hospital, Willard, OH, p. A505
DETTMER, Robert E., Deputy Commander for Health Services, Irwin Army Community Hospital, Junction City, KS, p. A247
DETWILER, Courtney, R.N., Administrator, Hampton Roads Specialty Hospital, Newport News, VA, p. A674
DETWILER, Eric, Director Information Technology, Barnes–Kasson County Hospital, Susquehanna, PA, p. A555
DEUEL, Teresa L., Chief Executive Officer, Hodgeman County Health Center, Jetmore, KS, p. A246
DEURMIER, Carol, Chief Executive Officer, St. Michael's Hospital Avera, Tyndall, SD, p. A577
DEVANATHAN, Raja, M.D. Chief Medical Officer, Vibra Hospital of Northwestern Indiana, Crown Point, IN, p. A209
DEVANEY, Catherine, Chief Executive Officer, HEALTHSOUTH Rehabilitation Hospital, Concord, NH, p. A409
DEVANSKY, Gary W., Director, Coatesville Veterans Affairs Medical Center, Coatesville, PA, p. A536
DEVARAJ, Kiran, Medical Director, Highland Hospital, Charleston, WV, p. A694
DEVARAJAN, Vadakkipalayam N., Chief Medical Staff, St. Charles Parish Hospital, Luling, LA, p. A283

DEVAUGHN, Michael D.
Executive Vice President and Chief Financial Officer, WakeMed Cary Hospital, Cary, NC, p. A461
Senior Vice President Finance and Chief Financial Officer, WakeMed Raleigh Campus, Raleigh, NC, p. A471
DEVAULT, Jennifer, Vice President Associate Services, F. F. Thompson Hospital, Canandaigua, NY, p. A435
DEVAULT, Rosanne, Chief Financial Officer, McKenzie–Willamette Medical Center, Springfield, OR, p. A530
DEVAULT, Roseann M., Chief Financial Officer, Tennova Healthcare–Jefferson Memorial Hospital, Jefferson City, TN, p. A584
DEVENUTO, Joseph, Vice President and Chief Information Officer, Norton Suburban Hospital, Louisville, KY, p. A266
DEVILLE, Linda F., Chief Executive Officer, Bunkie General Hospital, Bunkie, LA, p. A275
DEVIN, Brian V., Chief Executive Officer, Massachusetts Hospital School, Canton, MA, p. A309
DEVIN, Joseph, Chief Financial Officer, Boone County Hospital, Boone, IA, p. A226
DEVINE, Joseph W., President and Chief Executive Officer, Kennedy Health System, Cherry Hill, NJ, p. A414
DEVINE, Kathryn, Vice President Human Resources, UPMC Presbyterian Shadyside, Pittsburgh, PA, p. A552
DEVITA, James, M.D. Chief Medical Officer, Tewksbury Hospital, Tewksbury, MA, p. A315
DEVITO, Joseph M., Vice President Finance and Chief Operating Officer, Geisinger–Bloomsburg Hospital, Bloomsburg, PA, p. A534
DEVLIN, James, Director Information Systems, St. Cloud Regional Medical Center, Saint Cloud, FL, p. A144
DEVOCELLE, Frank H., President and Chief Executive Officer, Olathe Medical Center, Olathe, KS, p. A251
DEVOE, Andrew, Vice President Finance, Aria Health, Philadelphia, PA, p. A547
DEVOL, Marjorie, M.D. Chief of Staff, OhioHealth Doctors Hospital Nelsonville, Nelsonville, OH, p. A499
DEVORE, Kathy, R.N. Director Patient Services, Advanced Care Hospital of White County, Searcy, AR, p. A52
DEVORE, Pam, Financial Manager, Hillcrest Memorial Hospital, Simpsonville, SC, p. A569
DEVORE, Paul A., M.D. Medical Director, Gladys Spellman Specialty Hospital and Nursing Center, Cheverly, MD, p. A299
DEVRIES, Russell, Chief Business Operations, Keller Army Community Hospital, West Point, NY, p. A458
DEW, Douglas, M.D. President Medical Staff, Flagler Hospital, Saint Augustine, FL, p. A144
DEWALSCHE, Diane, R.N. Chief Operating Officer, Community Hospital of Long Beach, Long Beach, CA, p. A70
DEWAN, Vijay, M.D. Clinical Director, Lincoln Regional Center, Lincoln, NE, p. A397
DEWAR, William, M.D. Chief of Staff, Wayne Memorial Hospital, Honesdale, PA, p. A540
DEWBERRY, Robbie, Chief Executive Officer, Mitchell County Hospital, Colorado City, TX, p. A607
DEWERFF, Mike, Chief Financial Officer, UnityPoint Health – Trinity Regional Medical Center, Fort Dodge, IA, p. A230
DEWISPELARE, Cheryl M., Chief Human Resources Officer, Veterans Affairs – Western Iowa Healthcare System, Omaha, NE, p. A400
DEWITT, Jocelyn, Ph.D. Vice President and Chief Information Officer, University of Wisconsin Hospital and Clinics, Madison, WI, p. A708
DEWORTH, Gerald M., Associate Director, Carl Vinson Veterans Affairs Medical Center, Dublin, GA, p. A159
DEXTER, Stephen P., President and Chief Executive Officer, Saint Francis Hospital, Charleston, WV, p. A694
DEXTER, Stephen P., President and Chief Executive Officer, Thomas Health System, Inc., South Charleston, WV, p. B135
DEXTER, Stephen P., President and Chief Executive Officer, Thomas Memorial Hospital, South Charleston, WV, p. A699
DEXTER, Sue, Administrative Department Leader Human Resources, McDonough District Hospital, Macomb, IL, p. A195
DEYARMIN, James A., Controller, Children's Hospital of Richmond at VCU–Brook Road Campus, Richmond, VA, p. A677
DHILLON, Avtar, M.D. Medical Director, Keystone Newport News, Newport News, VA, p. A674
DHINGRA, Ashok, M.D. Executive Medical Director, HEALTHSOUTH Deaconess Rehabilitation Hospital, Evansville, IN, p. A210
DHULIPALA, Vasudeva, M.D. Medical Director, HEALTHSOUTH Rehabilitation Hospital of Alexandria, Alexandria, LA, p. A272
DI BACCO, David J., Chief Operating Officer, Eastern Niagara Hospital, Lockport, NY, p. A440
DI BERNARDO, Deborah, Chief Information Officer, St. Joseph's Medical Center, Yonkers, NY, p. A458
DI RIENZO, Louis, Chief Information Officer, Lake Shore Health Care Center, Irving, NY, p. A439

DIAL, Jeffery
Chief Operating Officer, Vidant Bertie Hospital, Windsor, NC, p. A475
Vice President Operations, Vidant Chowan Hospital, Edenton, NC, p. A464
DIALTO, Margaret, Vice President Human Resources, Staten Island University Hospital, NY, p. A448
DIAMOND, Anne, JD, Interim Chief Executive Officer, University of Connecticut Health Center, John Dempsey Hospital, Farmington, CT, p. A114
DIAMOND, Kevin, M.D. Chief of Staff, Lawrence Memorial Hospital, Walnut Ridge, AR, p. A53
DIAMOND, Lester K., President, St. Dominic–Jackson Memorial Hospital, Jackson, MS, p. A360
DIAMOND, Robert
Senior Vice President and Chief Information Officer, Northern Dutchess Hospital, Rhinebeck, NY, p. A452
Vice President and Chief Information Officer, Putnam Hospital Center, Carmel, NY, p. A435
Chief Information Officer, Vassar Brothers Medical Center, Poughkeepsie, NY, p. A452
DIAMOND, Timothy, Chief Information Officer, La Rabida Children's Hospital, Chicago, IL, p. A184
DIAMOND, Vickie L., MS, President and Chief Executive Officer, Wyoming Medical Center, Casper, WY, p. A720
DIANGELO, John A., President and Chief Executive Officer, Inspira Health Network, Mullica Hill, NJ, p. B76
DIANGELO, John A.
President and Chief Executive Officer, Inspira Medical Center–Elmer, Elmer, NJ, p. A416
President and Chief Executive Officer, Inspira Medical Center–Vineland, Vineland, NJ, p. A424
DIAS, Walter, Vice President and Chief Operating Officer, Butler Hospital, Providence, RI, p. A560
DIAZ, Alberto, Chief Financial Officer, Oak Valley Hospital District, Oakdale, CA, p. A80
DIAZ, Cristina, Director, Rush Oak Park Hospital, Oak Park, IL, p. A198
DIAZ, Evelyn, R.N. Chief Nursing Officer, HEALTHSOUTH Hospital of Manati, Manati, PR, p. A726
DIAZ, Felipe, M.D. Chief of Staff, Bath Veterans Affairs Medical Center, Bath, NY, p. A433
DIAZ, Georgina, Chief Operating Officer, Palmetto General Hospital, Hialeah, FL, p. A130
DIAZ, Gloria, Executive Director, Hospital Santa Rosa, Guayama, PR, p. A726
DIAZ, Jesse, Chief Information Officer, Phoebe Putney Memorial Hospital, Albany, GA, p. A151
DIAZ, Jimmy, Director Information Technology, Odessa Regional Medical Center, Odessa, TX, p. A640
DIAZ, Jose, Director Information Systems, St. Mary's Medical Center of Evansville, Evansville, IN, p. A210
DIAZ, Joseph, M.D. Chief Medical Officer, Memorial Hospital of Rhode Island, Pawtucket, RI, p. A560
DIAZ, Lillian, R.N. Chief Nursing Officer, Metropolitan Hospital Center, New York, NY, p. A446
DIAZ, Paul J., President and Chief Executive Officer, Kindred Healthcare, Louisville, KY, p. B80
DIAZ, Ron, Manager Operations, Albany Stratton Veterans Affairs Medical Center, Albany, NY, p. A432
DIAZ, Steve, M.D. Chief Medical Officer, MaineGeneral Medical Center, Augusta, ME, p. A291
DIBBLE, Lynn, Vice President Patient Care Services, Memorial Hospital, Towanda, PA, p. A556
DICESARE, Gayle, President and Chief Executive Officer, RiverValley Behavioral Health Hospital, Owensboro, KY, p. A268
DICESARE, Jan, Vice President Financial Operations, St. Vincent's East, Birmingham, AL, p. A17
DICICCO, Marilyn, Director Human Resources, Chestnut Hill Hospital, Philadelphia, PA, p. A547
DICK, Andy, Director Information Services, Saline Memorial Hospital, Benton, AR, p. A43
DICK, David, Chief Executive Officer, Huron Regional Medical Center, Huron, SD, p. A574
DICK, Landon, Chief Information Officer, Homer Memorial Hospital, Homer, LA, p. A278
DICK, Lynette, Director of Support Services, Ellsworth County Medical Center, Ellsworth, KS, p. A243
DICK, Mollie, Coordinator Human Resources, Wayne County Hospital, Monticello, KY, p. A267
DICK, Myra, Manager Business Office, AMG Specialty Hospital–Wichita, Wichita, KS, p. A256
DICKENS, Betty, Director Human Resources, Sierra Tucson, Tucson, AZ, p. A40
DICKENS, Shelby, Director, Patient Care Services, Fort Madison Community Hospital, Fort Madison, IA, p. A231
DICKERSON, Gene, M.D. Vice President Medical Affairs, Tuomey Healthcare System, Sumter, SC, p. A570

DICKERSON, Kathy, Chief Financial Officer, HEALTHSOUTH Rehabilitation Hospital of Arlington, Arlington, TX, p. A597

DICKERSON, Melody Ford, Chief Nursing Officer, Memorial Hermann Northwest Hospital, Houston, TX, p. A625

DICKERSON, Taylor, Chief Information Officer, Lake City Medical Center, Lake City, FL, p. A133

DICKERSON, Toby, Chief Information Resources Management Services, Durham Veterans Affairs Medical Center, Durham, NC, p. A463

DICKEY, John M., Chief Administrative Officer, Mayo Clinic Health System in Eau Claire, Eau Claire, WI, p. A704

DICKEY, Mark, Director Business Development, Valir Rehabilitation Hospital, Oklahoma City, OK, p. A516

DICKEY, Sarah J., Director Human Resources, Marshall Browning Hospital, Du Quoin, IL, p. A188

DICKINSON, Ashley, Chief Operating Officer, Porter Regional Hospital, Valparaiso, IN, p. A223

DICKINSON, Galen, Chief Financial Officer, Cary Medical Center, Caribou, ME, p. A292

DICKINSON, Lani, R.N. Chief Nursing Officer, Doctors Medical Center, Modesto, CA, p. A77

DICKLICH–COBB, Christy, Chief Nursing Officer, Memorial Hospital of Converse County, Douglas, WY, p. A721

DICKMAN, Kathy, Director Information Technology, McCullough–Hyde Memorial Hospital, Oxford, OH, p. A500

DICKREITER, Adrian, Vice President Technology, Nix Health Care System, San Antonio, TX, p. A647

DICKS, Mandy, Director of Nursing, Lake Butler Hospital Hand Surgery Center, Lake Butler, FL, p. A133

DICKSON, Eric, M.D., President and Chief Executive Officer, UMass Memorial Health Care, Inc., Worcester, MA, p. B138

DICKSON, James J., Administrator and Chief Executive Officer, Copper Queen Community Hospital, Bisbee, AZ, p. A31

DICKSON, Karen, Director, Human Resources, Maine Coast Memorial Hospital, Ellsworth, ME, p. A293

DICKSON, Lynette, Director Clinical Operations and Director of Nursing, District One Hospital, Faribault, MN, p. A343

DICKSON, Thomas C., Chief Executive Officer, Banner Thunderbird Medical Center, Glendale, AZ, p. A33

DICKSON, William, Acting Executive Director, Capital District Psychiatric Center, Albany, NY, p. A432

DICUS–JOHNSON, Coreen
President, Midwest Orthopedic Specialty Hospital, Franklin, WI, p. A705
President, Wheaton Franciscan Healthcare – Franklin, Franklin, WI, p. A705
President, Wheaton Franciscan Healthcare – St. Francis, Milwaukee, WI, p. A711

DIDENKO, Dima, Chief Financial Officer, Florida Hospital Tampa, Tampa, FL, p. A147

DIDERRICH, Mary Kay, Vice President Patient Services, Watertown Regional Medical Center, Watertown, WI, p. A717

DIDIER, Debra, Vice President and Chief Financial Officer, Katherine Shaw Bethea Hospital, Dixon, IL, p. A188

DIEBLING, Tara, Chief Executive Officer, The Rehabilitation Institute of St. Louis, Saint Louis, MO, p. A382

DIECKMANN, Holli, Director Health Information, Sabetha Community Hospital, Sabetha, KS, p. A253

DIEDERICH, John A., Senior Vice President Operations and Chief Operating Officer, Rush–Copley Medical Center, Aurora, IL, p. A181

DIEDERICH, Thomas, Senior Vice President Human Resources, Phoenix Children's Hospital, Phoenix, AZ, p. A36

DIEDRICH, Michele, R.N. Chief Nursing Officer, Mercy Hospital Rogers, Rogers, AR, p. A52

DIEFFENBACH, Todd, Chief Financial Officer, Tyrone Hospital, Tyrone, PA, p. A556

DIEGEL, James A., FACHE, President and Chief Executive Officer, St. Charles Health System, Inc., Bend, OR, p. B127

DIER, Joy, R.N. Vice President Clinical Services and Chief Nursing Officer, Texas Institute for Surgery at Texas Health Presbyterian Dallas, Dallas, TX, p. A612

DIERKENS, Janelle, Chief Administration Officer, New York State Psychiatric Institute, New York, NY, p. A447

DIERKER, Anne, Vice President Hospital Services, Pekin Hospital, Pekin, IL, p. A199

DIERS, Suzanne, R.N. Director Patient Care Services, Shriners Hospitals for Children–Portland, Portland, OR, p. A529

DIESTEL, Peter, Senior Vice President and Chief Operating Officer, Valley Hospital, Ridgewood, NJ, p. A422

DIETER, Brian, President and Chief Executive Officer, Mary Greeley Medical Center, Ames, IA, p. A225

DIETERICH, Kevin, Director Information Services, Inland Hospital, Waterville, ME, p. A295

DIETLIN, Steve, Chief Financial Officer, Tri–City Medical Center, Oceanside, CA, p. A81

DIETRICH, Brenda, Chief Human Resources Officer, Banner Boswell Medical Center, Sun City, AZ, p. A39

DIETRICK, Brian, Director Information Systems, Wilson Medical Center, Wilson, NC, p. A475

DIETSCHE, Jim, Chief Financial Officer, Bellin Memorial Hospital, Green Bay, WI, p. A705

DIETZ, Brian E., FACHE, Interim President and Chief Executive officer, St. Francis Hospital, Wilmington, DE, p. A120

DIETZ, Gary, Director Information Technology Services, Walla Walla General Hospital, Walla Walla, WA, p. A692

DIETZ, Mark, Chief Medical Officer, CentraCare Health–Monticello, Monticello, MN, p. A348

DIETZ, Michael, Administrator, U. S. Air Force Hospital, Hampton, VA, p. A672

DIEWALD, Wayne A., President, Genesis Medical Center–Davenport, Davenport, IA, p. A228

DIFRANCO, Vincent B., Chief Executive Officer, Community Hospital, Torrington, WY, p. A723

DIGEROLAMO, Anthony, R.N. Chief Nursing Officer, West Jefferson Medical Center, Marrero, LA, p. A284

DIGGINS, Dana, Chief Financial Officer, Landmark Medical Center, Woonsocket, RI, p. A561

DIIESO, Nicholas T., R.N. Chief Operating Officer, Mount Auburn Hospital, Cambridge, MA, p. A309

DIIORIO, Emil, M.D., Chief Executive Officer, Surgical Specialty Center at Coordinated Health, Allentown, PA, p. A532

DIKE, Charles, M.D. Chief of Staff, Sanford Worthington Medical Center, Worthington, MN, p. A354

DILALLO, Kevin, Chief Executive Officer, Manatee Memorial Hospital, Bradenton, FL, p. A124

DILISI, Jeffrey P., Vice President and Chief Medical Officer, Virginia Hospital Center – Arlington, Arlington, VA, p. A668

DILL, Cathy, R.N. Director Patient Services, Spearfish Regional Hospital, Spearfish, SD, p. A577

DILL, Stephen, M.D. Chief of Staff, LeConte Medical Center, Sevierville, TN, p. A592

DILLARD, Evan S., FACHE, President and Chief Executive Officer, Forrest General Hospital, Hattiesburg, MS, p. A359

DILLARD, Leigh, M.D. Chief of Staff, De Soto Regional Health System, Mansfield, LA, p. A283

DILLEHUNT, David B., Chief Information Officer, FirstHealth Moore Regional Hospital, Pinehurst, NC, p. A470

DILLION, Tim, Vice President of Human Resources, Devereux Hospital and Children's Center of Florida, Melbourne, FL, p. A135

DILLON, Jim, Chief Financial Officer, Rangely District Hospital, Rangely, CO, p. A110

DILLON, Lorie, Chief Executive Officer, Geisinger HEALTHSOUTH Rehabilitation Hospital, Danville, PA, p. A536

DILLON, Mary E., MS Vice President Patient Care Services, Sisters of Charity Hospital of Buffalo, Buffalo, NY, p. A435

DILORENZO, Randolph, M.D. Medical Director, Syosset Hospital, Syosset, NY, p. A455

DILORETO, David, M.D. Executive Vice President and Chief Medical Officer, Presence Saint Francis Hospital, Evanston, IL, p. A190

DIMARCO, Lisa, R.N. Vice President Patient Care Service and Chief Nursing Officer, Little Company of Mary Hospital and Health Care Centers, Evergreen Park, IL, p. A190

DIMARE, John, M.D. Medical Director, Foothill Presbyterian Hospital, Glendora, CA, p. A66

DIMAURO, Cynthia, M.D. Medical Director, Hillside Rehabilitation Hospital, Warren, OH, p. A504

DIMICHELE, Maria, Administrative Assistant, Kensington Hospital, Philadelphia, PA, p. A549

DIMITROVA, Gergana, M.D. Medical Director, Carolina Center for Behavioral Health, Greer, SC, p. A567

DIMMICK, Scott
Senior Vice President Human Resources, St. Elizabeth Boardman Health Center, Boardman, OH, p. A484
Senior Vice President Human Resources, St. Elizabeth Health Center, Youngstown, OH, p. A506

DIMMIG, Thomas, M.D. Medical Director, North Carolina Specialty Hospital, Durham, NC, p. A463

DINAN, Edward M., President and Chief Executive Officer, Lawrence Hospital Center, Bronxville, NY, p. A434

DINGES, Brenda, Director of Nursing, Ness County Hospital, Ness City, KS, p. A250

DINGILIAN, John, M.D. Chief Medical Officer, Simi Valley Hospital and Health Care Services, Simi Valley, CA, p. A95

DINGLE, Steve, M.D. Chief Medical Officer, Arizona State Hospital, Phoenix, AZ, p. A35

DINGLER, Chance, M.D. Chief Medical Officer, Nocona General Hospital, Nocona, TX, p. A640

DINGMAN, III, Vincent, Chief Financial Officer, Columbia Memorial Hospital, Hudson, NY, p. A439

DINHAM, Vilma L., R.N. Chief Nursing Officer, Encino Hospital Medical Center, CA, p. A71

DINKHA, Duncan, M.D. Chief of Staff, Morrison Community Hospital, Morrison, IL, p. A197

DINKINS, Vicki, Director Human Resources, South Georgia Medical Center Lanier Campus, Lakeland, GA, p. A162

DINON, Nancy
Vice President Human Resources, Health Central Hospital, Ocoee, FL, p. A140
Vice President Human Resources, Orlando Regional Medical Center, Orlando, FL, p. A141

DINSLAGE, Dennis, Vice President Finance and Chief Financial Officer, St. Francis Memorial Hospital, West Point, NE, p. A402

DINSMOOR, Deb, Director Human Resource Operations, Bellevue Medical Center, Bellevue, NE, p. A394

DINSMOOR, William S., Chief Executive Officer, Nebraska Medical Center, Omaha, NE, p. A400

DION, Jeffrey P., Vice President Finance, St. Elizabeth's Medical Center, Brighton, MA, p. A308

DIONISOPOULOF, Peter, Chief Medical Officer, CHI Health Nebraska Heart, Lincoln, NE, p. A397

DIONNE, Michele, Chief Executive Officer, Houston Physicians Hospital, Webster, TX, p. A656

DIPALMA, Maureen, Chief Financial Officer, Tewksbury Hospital, Tewksbury, MA, p. A315

DIPAOLO, Joseph, President, Newton Medical Center, Newton, NJ, p. A420

DIPIERO, Annette, Human Resource Director, HEALTHSOUTH Rehabilitation Hospital at Martin Health, Stuart, FL, p. A146

DIPIETRO, Sandra P., Chief Financial Officer, St. Tammany Parish Hospital, Covington, LA, p. A276

DIPILLA, Victor, Vice President and Chief Business Development Officer, Christ Hospital, Cincinnati, OH, p. A486

DISANTO, Larry
Executive Vice President and Chief Operating Officer, Capital Health Medical Center–Hopewell, Pennington, NJ, p. A421
Executive Vice President and Chief Operating Officer, Capital Health Regional Medical Center, Trenton, NJ, p. A423

DISANZO, Frank, Vice President and Chief Information Officer and Chief Strategy Officer, Saint Peter's University Hospital, New Brunswick, NJ, p. A419

DISHMAN, Leonardo, M.D. Chief Medical Officer, Alice Hyde Medical Center, Malone, NY, p. A440

DISPOTO, Martha, R.N. Chief Nursing Officer, Whittier Hospital Medical Center, Whittier, CA, p. A100

DISSEN, James H., President and Chairman, Highland–Clarksburg Hospital, Clarksburg, WV, p. A694

DISTASIO, Stephen R., Director, Veterans Affairs Black Hills Health Care System, Fort Meade, SD, p. A574

DISTEFANO, Guy, Chief Financial Officer, Hampton Behavioral Health Center, Westampton, NJ, p. A424

DISTEFANO, Lisa, M.D. President Medical Staff, St. Francis Hospital and Health Services, Maryville, MO, p. A376

DISWOOD, Lavenia, R.N. Chief Nurse Executive, Northern Navajo Medical Center, Shiprock, NM, p. A431

DITON, Gregg, Chief Financial Officer, CarePartners Health Services, Asheville, NC, p. A459

DITTMANN, Jerry, Vice President Human Resources, Mount Nittany Medical Center, State College, PA, p. A555

DITTO, Debbie, CPA Controller, Lincoln Trail Behavioral Health System, Radcliff, KY, p. A269

DITURO, Beth, Divisional Chief Information Officer, Lenox Hill Hospital, New York, NY, p. A445

DITZLER, Andru, Chief Information Officer, Lebanon Veterans Affairs Medical Center, Lebanon, PA, p. A542

DIVELLO, Douglas F., President and Chief Executive Officer, Alice Hyde Medical Center, Malone, NY, p. A440

DIVINS, Brooke, Manager Human Resources, Clarion Hospital, Clarion, PA, p. A535

DIVITO, Frank, Manager Information Systems, Jameson Hospital, New Castle, PA, p. A546

DIX, Roger J., Vice President Finance, Hannibal Regional Hospital, Hannibal, MO, p. A372

DIX, Theresa, R.N. Chief Nursing Officer, Wythe County Community Hospital, Wytheville, VA, p. A680

DIXON, Christy, Chief Human Resources Officer, HEALTHSOUTH Rehabilitation Hospital, Humble, TX, p. A628

DIXON, Debbie, Director Human Resources, Pampa Regional Medical Center, Pampa, TX, p. A641

DIXON, Del, Chief Information Officer, South Shore Hospital, South Weymouth, MA, p. A314

DIXON, Florine, Chief Operating Officer, Memorial Hospital, Carthage, IL, p. A182

DIXON, Gregg, CP
Chief Financial Officer, Asheville Specialty Hospital, Asheville, NC, p. A459
Chief Financial Officer, Interfaith Medical Center, NY, p. A444

DIXON, Mary, R.N. Chief Nursing Officer, Inova Alexandria Hospital, Alexandria, VA, p. A668

DIXON, Matt, Chief Operating Officer, St. Mark's Hospital, Salt Lake City, UT, p. A663

DIXON, Michael, Director Human Resources, Self Regional Healthcare, Greenwood, SC, p. A567

DIXON, Patricia J., R.N. Chief Clinical Officer, Kindred Hospital Kansas City, Kansas City, MO, p. A373

DIXON, Sally J., Chief Executive Officer, Memorial Hospital, York, PA, p. A559

DIXON, Shannon, Manager Business Office, Weisbrod Memorial County Hospital, Eads, CO, p. A105

DIXON, Todd, R.N
Chief Operating Officer, Coliseum Medical Centers, Macon, GA, p. A162
Chief Operating Officer, Coliseum Northside Hospital, Macon, GA, p. A162

DIXON, Willa, R.N. Chief Nursing Officer, MountainView Regional Medical Center, Las Cruces, NM, p. A429

DIZNEY, Donald R., Chairman and Chief Executive Officer, United Medical Corporation, Windermere, FL, p. B138

DJOGAN, Djogan, Chief Financial Officer, Muscogee Creek Nation Physical Rehabilitation Center, Okmulgee, OK, p. A517

DLWGOSH, Robert, M.D. Chief of Staff, Ashtabula County Medical Center, Ashtabula, OH, p. A482

DMELLO, Artie, Director Case Management, Kindred Hospital Sugar Land, Sugar Land, TX, p. A650

DOAK, Mark, President and Chief Executive Officer, Davis Health System, Elkins, WV, p. B46

DOAK, Mark, Chief Executive Officer, Davis Memorial Hospital, Elkins, WV, p. A694

DOAN, Angela, Chief Financial Officer, Scott Memorial Hospital, Scottsburg, IN, p. A222

DOANE, Peter, M.D
Chief Medical Officer, Franklin Regional Hospital, Franklin, NH, p. A410
Chief Medical Officer, Lakes Region General Hospital, Laconia, NH, p. A410

DOBALIAN, Derek, M.D. Chief of Staff, Tri–City Regional Medical Center, Hawaiian Gardens, CA, p. A66

DOBBINS, Jim, Vice President Human Resources, Lenoir Memorial Hospital, Kinston, NC, p. A467

DOBBS, Stephanie, Chief Nursing Officer, Sanford Clear Lake Medical Center, Clear Lake, SD, p. A573

DOBIN, Jennifer, Vice President Human Resources, Bayonne Medical Center, Bayonne, NJ, p. A413

DOBIZL, Howard
Director Information Technology Services, Howard Young Medical Center, Woodruff, WI, p. A719
Director Information Technology Services, Ministry Eagle River Memorial Hospital, Eagle River, WI, p. A704
Director Information Services for the Northern Region, Ministry Saint Mary's Hospitals, Rhinelander, WI, p. A714

DOBOSENSKI, Dave, Chief Executive Officer, St. Croix Regional Medical Center, St. Croix Falls, WI, p. A715

DOBOSH, Jr., Joseph J., Vice President and Chief Financial Officer, Children's Specialized Hospital–PSE&G, New Brunswick, NJ, p. A419

DOBRAWA, Stanley
Area Technology Director, Kaiser Permanente San Rafael Medical Center, San Rafael, CA, p. A93
Area Technology Director, Kaiser Permanente Santa Rosa Medical Center, Santa Rosa, CA, p. A95

DOBRINSKI, Sandra, Director of Nursing, Comanche County Hospital, Coldwater, KS, p. A242

DOBROVICH, Michael, M.D. Chief Medical Officer, St. John Medical Center, Westlake, OH, p. A505

DOBSON, Glenda, Vice President Clinical Services, Louisiana Heart Hospital, Lacombe, LA, p. A280

DOBSON, Glenn E., Chief Financial Officer, NORTHSTAR Health System, Iron River, MI, p. A327

DOBSON, Trey, M.D. Chief Medical Officer, Southwestern Vermont Medical Center, Bennington, VT, p. A665

DODD, John, Vice President Human Resources, Central Peninsula General Hospital, Soldotna, AK, p. A30

DODD, Kathy M., Director of Nursing, Southern Virginia Mental Health Institute, Danville, VA, p. A670

DODD, Pam, Chief Operating Officer, Harper County Community Hospital, Buffalo, OK, p. A508

DODDS, Cheryl, M.D. Medical Director, Three Rivers Behavioral Health, West Columbia, SC, p. A571

DODDS, Rick A., Vice President Human Resources, Sonora Regional Medical Center, Sonora, CA, p. A95

DODDS, Sheryl, Chief Clinical Officer, Florida Hospital, Orlando, FL, p. A140

DODERER, Marcella, FACHE, President and Chief Executive Officer, Arkansas Children's Hospital, Little Rock, AR, p. A48

DODGE, Terry, M.D. Chief of Staff, Chester Regional Medical Center, Chester, SC, p. A564

DODSON, Thomas, Executive Director, Buffalo Psychiatric Center, Buffalo, NY, p. A434

DODSWORTH, Richard, Vice President Human Resources, MacNeal Hospital, Berwyn, IL, p. A181

DOEHRING, Christopher, M.D. Vice President Medical Affairs, Franciscan St. Francis Health – Indianapolis, Indianapolis, IN, p. A214

DOELING, Mariann, R.N., President, Carrington Health Center, Carrington, ND, p. A476

DOERFLER, Mary P., Chief Human Resources Officer, Central Texas Veterans Healthcare System, Temple, TX, p. A652

DOERGE, Jean B., M
Chief Nursing Executive, UnityPoint Health – Trinity Bettendorf, Bettendorf, IA, p. A225
Chief Nursing Officer, UnityPoint Health – Trinity Rock Island, Rock Island, IL, p. A201

DOERR, Brian, Chief Information Officer, Crawley Memorial Hospital, Shelby, NC, p. A472

DOGGETT, Geri, Director Business, East Mississippi State Hospital, Meridian, MS, p. A362

DOGGETT, Sherri L., Vice President Patient Services, Mercy Medical Center–Centerville, Centerville, IA, p. A227

DOHERTY, Allison, Chief Financial Officer, Spine Hospital of Louisiana, Baton Rouge, LA, p. A274

DOHERTY, Bryan, Management Information Technology Services I, Sagamore Children's Psychiatric Center, Dix Hills, NY, p. A436

DOHERTY, Donna, R.N. Vice President of Nursing and Chief Nursing Officer, Beth Israel Deaconess Hospital Plymouth, Plymouth, MA, p. A314

DOHERTY, John, Vice President Finance, University of Minnesota Medical Center, Fairview, Minneapolis, MN, p. A348

DOHERTY, Randy, CPA, Chief Financial Officer, Braintree Rehabilitation Hospital, Braintree, MA, p. A308

DOHERTY, William J., M.D. Executive Vice President and Chief Operating Officer, Hallmark Health System, Melrose, MA, p. A312

DOHLZEL, Cheryl, Director Information Technology, Marcus Daly Memorial Hospital, Hamilton, MT, p. A388

DOHM, Thomas J., Interim Chief Operating Officer, Provident Hospital of Cook County, Chicago, IL, p. A186

DOI, Kathy, Executive Director Human Resources, AHMC Anaheim Regional Medical Center, Anaheim, CA, p. A55

DOIDGE, John C., Vice President Finance, Glencoe Regional Health Services, Glencoe, MN, p. A344

DOKSUM, Kathryn, Director Finance, Samaritan North Lincoln Hospital, Lincoln City, OR, p. A526

DOLAN, John, Chief Executive Officer, Pauls Valley General Hospital, Pauls Valley, OK, p. A517

DOLAN, Mary
Regional Director Information Services and HIPAA Security Official, Shriners Hospitals for Children–Boston, Boston, MA, p. A307
Director Information Services, Shriners Hospitals for Children–Springfield, Springfield, MA, p. A315

DOLAN, Patricia R., R.N. Vice President/ Chief Nursing Officer, Florida Hospital Waterman, Tavares, FL, p. A148

DOLAN, Paul, M.D. Chief Medical Affairs Officer, Benefis Hospitals, Great Falls, MT, p. A388

DOLAN, Steve, Chief Information Officer, EastPointe Hospital, Daphne, AL, p. A18

DOLBEE, Hilary, Chief Financial Officer, Marshalltown Medical & Surgical Center, Marshalltown, IA, p. A234

DOLEN, Cassie, Vice President Finance and Chief Financial Officer, Hutchinson Regional Medical Center, Hutchinson, KS, p. A246

DOLL, Katherine A., R.N. Chief Nursing Officer, Sierra Medical Center, El Paso, TX, p. A616

DOLLINGER, Michael, Chief Operating Officer and Assistant Superintendent, Deer's Head Hospital Center, Salisbury, MD, p. A303

DOLLINS, Gary, Director Management Information Systems, Poplar Bluff Regional Medical Center, Poplar Bluff, MO, p. A378

DOLLINS, Mandy, R.N. Chief Nursing Officer, Five Rivers Medical Center, Pocahontas, AR, p. A52

DOLOHANTY–JOHNSON, Bridget, R.N. Vice President Patient Care Services, Parkview Whitley Hospital, Columbia City, IN, p. A208

DOLORESCO, Arthur M., Chief Executive Officer, Florence Hospital at Anthem, Florence, AZ, p. A32

DOLORESCO, Laureen, R.N. Associate Director for Patient Care and Nursing Services, James A. Haley Veterans' Hospital, Tampa, FL, p. A147

DOMALESKI, Vareen O'Keefe, MS Vice Patient Care Services and Chief Nursing Officer, Emma Pendleton Bradley Hospital, East Providence, RI, p. A560

DOMANICO, Lee, Chief Executive Officer, Marin General Hospital, Greenbrae, CA, p. A66

DOMANSKY, John, Vice President Operations, Rutherford Regional Health System, Rutherfordton, NC, p. A472

DOMBROUSKI, Joyce, R.N. Regional Chief Nursing Officer, St. Patrick Hospital, Missoula, MT, p. A390

DOMEIER, Sandy, Director Patient Care Services, Sibley Medical Center, Arlington, MN, p. A339

DOMIAN, Catherine, R.N. Chief Nursing Officer, South Texas Health System, Edinburg, TX, p. A615

DOMINGO, Connie, M.D. Medical Director, Weisman Children's Rehabilitation Hospital, Marlton, NJ, p. A418

DOMINGO, Ramon, M.D. Chief of Staff, McCamey County Hospital District, McCamey, TX, p. A637

DOMINGUE, Buffy, Chief Executive Officer, Lafayette Surgical Specialty Hospital, Lafayette, LA, p. A281

DOMINGUEZ, Brenda, Director Human Resources, Cypress Creek Hospital, Houston, TX, p. A624

DOMINGUEZ, Dominic J., Interim Chief Executive Officer, Methodist Stone Oak Hospital, San Antonio, TX, p. A647

DOMINGUEZ, Ed, President Medical Staff, Vibra Specialty Hospital at DeSoto, Desoto, TX, p. A614

DOMINGUEZ, Isabel, Director Human Resources, Benson Hospital, Benson, AZ, p. A31

DOMINGUEZ, Jerry A., CPA Chief Financial Officer, East Texas Medical Center Trinity, Trinity, TX, p. A653

DOMINICCI, Sandra, Nursing Director, Hospital De Damas, Ponce, PR, p. A727

DOMINO, Laura, R.N. Vice President Patient Care Services, Hammond–Henry Hospital, Geneseo, IL, p. A190

DOMINSKI, Paul, Vice President Human Resources, Park Nicollet Methodist Hospital, Minneapolis, MN, p. A347

DOMMER, Matthew, M.D. Chief Medical Officer, Bronson LakeView Hospital, Paw Paw, MI, p. A332

DOMON, Steven, M.D. Medical Director, Arkansas State Hospital, Little Rock, AR, p. A49

DOMRES, Mary Jane, Director Materials Management and Administrator Information Technology, Cavalier County Memorial Hospital, Langdon, ND, p. A479

DONAGHY, Deirdre, M.D. Vice President Medical Affairs, St. Mary Medical Center, Langhorne, PA, p. A542

DONAHEY, Kenneth C., Chief Operating Officer, West Florida Hospital, Pensacola, FL, p. A142

DONAHUE, Brian, Chief Financial Officer, Portage Health, Hancock, MI, p. A326

DONAHUE, Debra, Senior Vice President and Chief Operating Officer, Champlain Valley Physicians Hospital Medical Center, Plattsburgh, NY, p. A451

DONAHUE, Elisabeth, Associate Director Human Resources, Jeanes Hospital, Philadelphia, PA, p. A548

DONAHUE, Leslie A., President and Chief Executive Officer, Piedmont Hospital, Atlanta, GA, p. A153

DONAHUE, Michael, M.D. Medical Director, Select Specialty Hospital–Pittsburgh/UPMC, Pittsburgh, PA, p. A551

DONAHUE, Moreen, R.N. Chief Nursing Executive, Danbury Hospital, Danbury, CT, p. A113

DONAHUE, Patrick, Vice President and Administrator, Methodist Hospital Union County, Morganfield, KY, p. A268

DONAHUE, Ruth, R.N. Chief Nursing Officer, Harrison County Hospital, Corydon, IN, p. A209

DONALDSON, Brooke G., Assistant Administrator Human Resources, Jackson Hospital, Marianna, FL, p. A135

DONALDSON, Jill, Vice President Operations, MedStar Harbor Hospital, Baltimore, MD, p. A297

DONALDSON, Les, M.D. Chief of Staff, Roosevelt General Hospital, Portales, NM, p. A429

DONALDSON, Lori, Chief Financial Officer, UC San Diego Health System, San Diego, CA, p. A90

DONALDSON, Nesha, Chief Financial Officer, Cullman Regional Medical Center, Cullman, AL, p. A18

DONALDSON, Sherry, Director Human Resources, Southern Palmetto Hospital, Barnwell, SC, p. A562

DONALDSON, Tammy, Director of Nursing, Highlands Hospital, Connellsville, PA, p. A536

DONATELLE, Lawrence, M.D. Vice President Medical Affairs, St. Elizabeth Hospital, Appleton, WI, p. A701

DONAWAY, Duane, Director Information Technology, Hendrick Health System, Abilene, TX, p. A595

DONELAN, Matthias B., M.D. Chief of Staff, Shriners Hospitals for Children–Boston, Boston, MA, p. A307

DONENWIRTH, Karl, Vice President Information Services, Northcoast Behavioral Healthcare System, Northfield, OH, p. A499

DONGILLI, Jr., Paul, Ph.D. Executive Vice President and Chief Operating Officer, Madonna Rehabilitation Hospital, Lincoln, NE, p. A398

DONHAM, Guyle, M.D. Chief of Staff, Comanche County Medical Center, Comanche, TX, p. A607

DONICA, Joanna, Director Human Resource, HEALTHSOUTH Rehabilitation Hospital of Beaumont, Beaumont, TX, p. A602

DONLEY, Linda, Vice President Operations, Ira Davenport Memorial Hospital, Bath, NY, p. A433

DONLIN, Bruce, Director Information Services, Mount Desert Island Hospital, Bar Harbor, ME, p. A291

DONLIN, John
Regional Director Human Resources – Boston, Erie, and Springfield, Shriners Hospitals for Children–Boston, Boston, MA, p. A307
Director Human Resources, Shriners Hospitals for Children–Springfield, Springfield, MA, p. A315

DONLIN, Michael T., FACHE, Administrator, Floyd Valley Hospital, Le Mars, IA, p. A233

DONNELL, Dan, M.D. Chief of Staff, Midwest Regional Medical Center, Midwest City, OK, p. A513
DONNELLY, Gloria, Director Human Resources, Euclid Hospital, Euclid, OH, p. A493
DONNELLY, James E., Chief Nursing Officer and Vice President Patient Care Services, UPMC Hamot, Erie, PA, p. A539
DONNELLY, Lane, M.D. Chief Medical Officer, Nemours Children's Hospital, Orlando, FL, p. A140
DONNELLY, Sheryl, Human Resources Specialist, State Hospital South, Blackfoot, ID, p. A174
DONNER, Larry, Administrator, University Health Conway, Monroe, LA, p. A284
DONOGHUE, Alicia, Director Human Resources, EastPointe Hospital, Daphne, AL, p. A18
DONOHUE, Carolyn Viall, MSN Vice President Nursing, Roper Hospital, Charleston, SC, p. A563
DONOHUE, Mary Ann T., Ph.D. Chief Patient Care Services Officer, Stony Brook University Medical Center, Stony Brook, NY, p. A455
DONOVAN, Andrew
    Director Information Technology, Wheaton Franciscan Healthcare – Elmbrook Memorial, Brookfield, WI, p. A703
    Regional Director Information Services, Wheaton Franciscan Healthcare – St. Joseph's, Milwaukee, WI, p. A711
DONOVAN, James W., President and Chief Executive Officer, Lincoln Health, Damariscotta, ME, p. A293
DONOVAN, Jenny, Director Human Resources, Wright Memorial Hospital, Trenton, MO, p. A384
DONOVAN, Kevin, Chief Executive Officer, Mt. Ascutney Hospital and Health Center, Windsor, VT, p. A667
DONOVAN, Mary, Controller, HEALTHSOUTH Rehabilitation Institute of Tucson, Tucson, AZ, p. A40
DONOVAN, Mike, Chief Financial Officer, Lemuel Shattuck Hospital, Jamaica Plain, MA, p. A311
DONOVAN, Patrick, M.D. Director Medical Staff, HEALTHSOUTH Rehabilitation Hospital of Fort Worth, Fort Worth, TX, p. A618
DONSON, Elliott, Chief Information Specialist, Lincoln Hospital, Davenport, WA, p. A683
DONZE, Richard D., D.O. Senior Vice President Medical Affairs, Chester County Hospital, West Chester, PA, p. A558
DOODY, Kris A., R.N., Chief Executive Officer, Cary Medical Center, Caribou, ME, p. A292
DOOLEY, Gerald C., Interim Chief Executive Officer, Logan Regional Medical Center, Logan, WV, p. A696
DOOLEY, Lisa, Health Information Officer, Middlesboro ARH Hospital, Middlesboro, KY, p. A267
DOOLEY, Mark J., Chief Executive Officer, Wilson Memorial Hospital, Sidney, OH, p. A502
DOOLING, Edward, Vice President, Human Resources, Masonicare Health Center, Wallingford, CT, p. A117
DOOLITTLE, Jon D., President and Chief Executive Officer, Northwest Medical Center, Albany, MO, p. A367
DOPLER, Lois, Interim Director Human Resources, Phoenix Baptist Hospital, Phoenix, AZ, p. A36
DORAK, John, Chief Information Officer, Nicholas H. Noyes Memorial Hospital, Dansville, NY, p. A436
DORAN, Judy, R.N. Vice President of Hospital Services and Chief Nurse Executive, Stanly Regional Medical Center, Albemarle, NC, p. A459
DORAN, Ken, Interim Chief Executive Officer, Sierra Surgery Hospital, Carson City, NV, p. A404
DORAN, T., Chief of Staff, Perry Memorial Hospital, Princeton, IL, p. A200
DORF, Jeffrey, M.D. Medical Director, Kindred Hospital–Albuquerque, Albuquerque, NM, p. A426
DORGAN, Amanda, Chief Nursing Officer, Central Regional Hospital, Butner, NC, p. A461
DORMAN, Christopher, Senior Vice President/Chief Operating Officer, Tift Regional Medical Center, Tifton, GA, p. A168
DORMAN, Stephen, M.D. Chief Medical Officer, New Mexico Rehabilitation Center, Roswell, NM, p. A430
DORNOFF, Edward G., Associate Director, Battle Creek Veterans Affairs Medical Center, Battle Creek, MI, p. A319
DOROGY, Sharon, Director Health Information Management, The Children's Institute of Pittsburgh, Pittsburgh, PA, p. A551
DOROTHY, Jonnie, Senior Director Human Resources, Massena Memorial Hospital, Massena, NY, p. A441
DORR, Amy, Vice President Human Resources, McLaren Lapeer Region, Lapeer, MI, p. A329
DORRIS, Patricia, Executive Director, Medical Center of Southeastern Oklahoma, Durant, OK, p. A510
DORRIS, Ronald E., Chief Executive Officer, Carrus Hospitals, Sherman, TX, p. B28
DORRIS, Steve, Chief Financial Officer, Poplar Bluff Regional Medical Center, Poplar Bluff, MO, p. A378
DORSCH, Anthony, Chief Financial Officer, Providence Alaska Medical Center, Anchorage, AK, p. A28

DORSEY, Michael A., FACHE,
    Chief Executive Officer, St. Joseph Medical Center, Kansas City, MO, p. A374
    Chief Executive Officer, St. Mary's Medical Center, Blue Springs, MO, p. A367
DORSEY, William, M.D., Board Chairman and Chief Executive Officer, Jackson Park Hospital and Medical Center, Chicago, IL, p. A184
DORST, Jake, Vice President and Chief Information Officer, Meritus Medical Center, Hagerstown, MD, p. A301
DORTON, Patty, Director of Nursing, Buchanan General Hospital, Grundy, VA, p. A671
DOSS, Mounir F.
    Executive Vice President and Chief Financial Officer, Flushing Hospital Medical Center, NY, p. A443
    Executive Vice President and Chief Financial Officer, Jamaica Hospital Medical Center, NY, p. A444
DOSSEY, Emily, Director Human Resources, Hamilton General Hospital, Hamilton, TX, p. A622
DOSTAL, Drew H., R.N. Vice President Operations, Spectrum Health Ludington Hospital, Ludington, MI, p. A329
DOTTS–MCCOOL, Michelle, Chief Nursing Officer, St. Vincent Dunn Hospital, Bedford, IN, p. A207
DOTY, Lisa, Manager Human Resources, Desert View Hospital, Pahrump, NV, p. A407
DOUBLE, Ron
    Chief Information Technology Officer, Parkview LaGrange Hospital, LaGrange, IN, p. A217
    Chief Information Officer, Parkview Noble Hospital, Kendallville, IN, p. A216
DOUCETTE, Elmer, Vice President and Chief Financial Officer, Eastern Maine Medical Center, Bangor, ME, p. A291
DOUCETTE, Jeffrey N., MS Chief Nursing Officer, Mary Immaculate Hospital, Newport News, VA, p. A675
DOUCETTE, Michael J., Senior Vice President and Administrator, Riverside Regional Medical Center, Newport News, VA, p. A675
DOUD, Tony, Controller, St. Mary's of Michigan Standish Hospital, Standish, MI, p. A335
DOUGH, Robert, M.D. Chief of Staff, Randolph Hospital, Asheboro, NC, p. A459
DOUGHERTY, Christopher J., Chief Executive Officer, Covenant Children's Hospital, Lubbock, TX, p. A634
DOUGHERTY, David, Chief Information Management Officer, Irwin Army Community Hospital, Junction City, KS, p. A247
DOUGHERTY, James, Commander, U. S. Air Force Medical Center Keesler, Keesler AFB, MS, p. A360
DOUGHERTY, Terry, Director Human Resources, Bryn Mawr Hospital, Bryn Mawr, PA, p. A534
DOUGHTY, Cathy, Vice President Human Resources, Sheppard Pratt Health System, Baltimore, MD, p. A297
DOUGHTY, Linda, Chief Nursing Officer, Alaska Regional Hospital, Anchorage, AK, p. A28
DOUGHTY, Stephanie
    Chief Financial Officer, Medical Center of the Rockies, Loveland, CO, p. A110
    Chief Financial Officer, Poudre Valley Hospital, Fort Collins, CO, p. A106
DOUGLAS, Andy, Manager Information Technology, Burnett Medical Center, Grantsburg, WI, p. A705
DOUGLAS, Bill, Senior Vice President and Chief Financial Officer, Riverside Medical Center, Kankakee, IL, p. A194
DOUGLAS, Debbie, Director Human Resources, Putnam County Memorial Hospital, Unionville, MO, p. A384
DOUGLAS, Doug, Vice President Human Resources, AnMed Health Medical Center, Anderson, SC, p. A562
DOUGLAS, Errol, Director Human Resources, University of Miami Hospital, Miami, FL, p. A137
DOUGLAS, Jason T., Chief Executive Officer, Memorial Medical Center – Ashland, Ashland, WI, p. A701
DOUGLAS, Lesia, R.N. Vice President Patient Care Services and Chief Nurse Executive, Bon Secours Baltimore Health System, Baltimore, MD, p. A296
DOUGLAS, Paul, Vice President Human Resources, Baton Rouge General Medical Center, Baton Rouge, LA, p. A273
DOUGLAS, Phillip B., Chairman and Chief Executive Officer, LifeCare Management Services, Plano, TX, p. B84
DOULAVERIS, Phyllis, MS
    Senior Vice President and Chief Nursing Officer, Covenant Medical Center, Waterloo, IA, p. A239
    Senior Vice President and Chief Nursing Officer, Mercy Hospital of Franciscan Sisters, Oelwein, IA, p. A235
DOVEL, Melissa, Manager Human Resources, Atrium Medical Center of Corinth, Corinth, TX, p. A608
DOVER, James F., FACHE,
    President and CEO, O'Connor Hospital, San Jose, CA, p. A92
    President and CEO, Saint Louise Regional Hospital, Gilroy, CA, p. A65
DOVER, Jerry, Chief Executive Officer, Sullivan County Memorial Hospital, Milan, MO, p. A377

DOVNARSKY, James, M.D. Director Pulmonary Medical, Kindred Hospital South Philadelphia, Philadelphia, PA, p. A549
DOW, Laura, Vice President, Finance, Memorial Health, Savannah, GA, p. A166
DOWDLE, Paula, Chief Operating Officer, Jefferson Healthcare, Port Townsend, WA, p. A686
DOWDY, Kathren, MSN, Regional Hospital Senior Director, Carilion Tazewell Community Hospital, Tazewell, VA, p. A679
DOWELL, James, Administrator and Chief Executive Officer, Little River Memorial Hospital, Ashdown, AR, p. A43
DOWELL, Wade, M.D. Chief of Staff, South Sunflower County Hospital, Indianola, MS, p. A359
DOWERS, Cindy, Chief Nursing Officer, Harsha Behavioral Center, Terre Haute, IN, p. A223
DOWGUN, Richard, Chief Information Officer, St. Francis Medical Center, Trenton, NJ, p. A423
DOWLING, Deanna, R.N. Chief Nursing Officer, Promise Hospital of Wichita Falls, Wichita Falls, TX, p. A657
DOWLING, Lisa, Manager Finance, Mercy Hospital Tishomingo, Tishomingo, OK, p. A520
DOWLING, Michael J., President and Chief Executive Officer, North Shore–Long Island Jewish Health System, Great Neck, NY, p. B100
DOWN, Melanie Falls, Site Manager, Crow/Northern Cheyenne Hospital, Crow Agency, MT, p. A386
DOWN, Philip B., Chief Executive Officer, Doctors Community Hospital, Lanham, MD, p. A302
DOWNARD, Diane, Chief Financial Officer, Coal County General Hospital, Coalgate, OK, p. A509
DOWNES, Patrick, Chief Operating Officer, Hialeah Hospital, Hialeah, FL, p. A130
DOWNEY, Brandon
    Chief Executive Officer, Bayfront Health Punta Gorda, Punta Gorda, FL, p. A143
    Chief Operating Officer, Mary Black Memorial Hospital, Spartanburg, SC, p. A570
DOWNEY, Daniel, Chief Fiscal Service, Veterans Administration New York Harbor Healthcare System, NY, p. A449
DOWNEY, Susan, MS, Chief Executive Officer, Kindred Hospital–Boston, Brighton, MA, p. A308
DOWNEY, William B., President and Chief Executive Officer, Riverside Health System, Newport News, VA, p. B114
DOWNEY, William B.
    Chief Operating Officer, Riverside Regional Medical Center, Newport News, VA, p. A675
    President and Chief Executive Officer, Riverside Rehabilitation Institute, Newport News, VA, p. A675
DOWNIE, Beth, Chief Information Officer, Newton–Wellesley Hospital, Newton Lower Falls, MA, p. A313
DOWNING, James, Chief Executive Officer, St. Jude Children's Research Hospital, Memphis, TN, p. A589
DOWNING, Jeff, R.N. Chief Nursing Officer, National Jewish Health, Denver, CO, p. A105
DOWNS, Beverly Sue, FACHE, President, Flaget Memorial Hospital, Bardstown, KY, p. A258
DOWNS, Bryan, Director Information Systems, Central Peninsula General Hospital, Soldotna, AK, p. A30
DOWNS, Connie, Chief Financial Officer, Pennock Hospital, Hastings, MI, p. A326
DOWNS, Lisa M., R.N. Chief Nursing Officer, Sarah D. Culbertson Memorial Hospital, Rushville, IL, p. A202
DOWNS, Nancy, M.D. Vice President Medical Affairs, Memorial Hospital at Gulfport, Gulfport, MS, p. A358
DOWNS, Patricia, Director Human Resources, Northern Nevada Medical Center, Sparks, NV, p. A408
DOWNS, Ray, Senior Staff Accountant, Healthmark Regional Medical Center, DeFuniak Springs, FL, p. A127
DOXTADER, Regina, Corporate Vice President and Chief Financial Officer, Botsford Hospital, Farmington Hills, MI, p. A323
DOYEL, Brenda K., Chief Financial Officer, Sayre Memorial Hospital, Sayre, OK, p. A518
DOYLE, Barbara J., MS, Chief Executive Officer, MetroWest Medical Center, Framingham, MA, p. A310
DOYLE, Ben, R.N. Director of Nursing, Jefferson Hospital, Louisville, GA, p. A162
DOYLE, Craig, Director and Chief Information Officer, St. Tammany Parish Hospital, Covington, LA, p. A276
DOYLE, Dennis D., Commanding Officer, Tripler Army Medical Center, Honolulu, HI, p. A171
DOYLE, Jay, Chief Financial Officer, St. James Healthcare, Butte, MT, p. A386
DOYLE, John
    Chief Financial Officer, Central Washington Hospital, Wenatchee, WA, p. A692
    Vice President Finance, Paoli Hospital, Paoli, PA, p. A547
    Chief Financial Officer, Wenatchee Valley Medical Center, Wenatchee, WA, p. A692
DOYLE, Kelly, Chief Executive Officer, Rothman Specialty Hospital, Bensalem, PA, p. A533

DOYLE, Michael, M.D. Deputy Commander Clinical Services, Keller Army Community Hospital, West Point, NY, p. A458

DOYLE, Patricia S., R.N. Chief Nursing Officer, Regional Medical Center, Manchester, IA, p. A234

DOZIER, Carol
President and Chief Executive Officer, King's Daughters' Health, Madison, IN, p. A218
Chief Financial Officer, LifeStream Behavioral Center, Leesburg, FL, p. A134

DOZIER, Mike, Chief Information Officer, Southeast Hospital, Cape Girardeau, MO, p. A369

DRABANT, Leah, Director of Finance, Complex Care Hospital at Ridgelake, Sarasota, FL, p. A145

DRAEGER, Anne, Chief Nursing Officer, Owatonna Hospital, Owatonna, MN, p. A349

DRAGE, Marcia, R.N. Chief Nursing Officer, Minidoka Memorial Hospital, Rupert, ID, p. A178

DRAGO, Susan, Chief Executive Officer, Kindred Hospital North Florida, Green Cove Springs, FL, p. A130

DRAKE, Bryan L., D.O. Chief of Staff, Weiser Memorial Hospital, Weiser, ID, p. A179

DRAKE, Carolyn, Director of Nursing, Milan General Hospital, Milan, TN, p. A589

DRAKE, Megan, Assistant Administrator, Cedar Park Regional Medical Center, Cedar Park, TX, p. A605

DRAPER, Jason, Chief Financial Officer, Volunteer Community Hospital, Martin, TN, p. A587

DRAPER, Vivian, Chief Financial Officer, U. S. Public Health Service Indian Hospital–Sells, Sells, AZ, p. A39

DREGNEY, Jim, Chief Financial Officer, Lakewood Health System, Staples, MN, p. A352

DREHER, Craig, Chief Information Officer, Mercy Hospital of Portland, Portland, ME, p. A294

DREHER, Ronald, Finance Officer, Robert J. Dole Veterans Affairs Medical Center, Wichita, KS, p. A256

DRENTH, Nancy E., Director Ancillary Services, Sanford Luverne Medical Center, Luverne, MN, p. A346

DRESSEL, Amy, M.D. Chief of Staff, Bartlett Regional Hospital, Juneau, AK, p. A29

DRESSER, Carol Ann, Vice President Information Services and Chief Information Officer, Hallmark Health System, Melrose, MA, p. A312

DRESSLER, Kaeli, R.N. Chief Nursing Officer, Peterson Regional Medical Center, Kerrville, TX, p. A631

DREUSSI, Rob, Interim Director Information Systems, Ponca City Medical Center, Ponca City, OK, p. A517

DREW, Jeff, Fiscal Officer, Aleda E. Lutz Veterans Affairs Medical Center, Saginaw, MI, p. A333

DREW, Jim, Chief Information Officer, Saint Thomas Midtown Hospital, Nashville, TN, p. A590

DREXLER, Diane, R.N
Chief Nursing Officer, Yavapai Regional Medical Center – East, Prescott Valley, AZ, p. A37
Chief Nursing Officer, Yavapai Regional Medical Center, Prescott, AZ, p. A37

DRIFTMIER, PHR, Tammie, Director Human Resources, Clarinda Regional Health Center, Clarinda, IA, p. A227

DRIGGERS, Gina, Manager Information Technology, Greenville Health System – Laurens County Memorial Hospital, Clinton, SC, p. A564

DRIGGERS, Steve, M.D. Chief Medical Officer, Holy Family Memorial, Manitowoc, WI, p. A708

DRIGGS, Christi, Chief Financial Officer, Phillips County Hospital, Phillipsburg, KS, p. A252

DRINKWATER, Jinia, R.N. Director Patient Care Services, Braintree Rehabilitation Hospital, Braintree, MA, p. A308

DRINKWATER, Linda, Chief Financial Officer, Waldo County General Hospital, Belfast, ME, p. A292

DRINKWITZ, Jeremy, Chief Operating Officer, Sparks Regional Medical Center, Fort Smith, AR, p. A46

DRISCOLL, Angie, Director Human Resources, Los Alamitos Medical Center, Los Alamitos, CA, p. A71

DRISCOLL, Nancy, R.N. Chief Nursing Officer, Longmont United Hospital, Longmont, CO, p. A109

DRIVER, Ramona, Director Human Resources, De Queen Medical Center, De Queen, AR, p. A45

DROBOT, Michael D., Chief Executive Officer, Pacific Hospital of Long Beach, Long Beach, CA, p. A70

DROEGE, Marie T., President, Robert Packer Hospital, Sayre, PA, p. A554

DRONE, Marilyn, R.N. Vice President, CNO, St. Mary Medical Center, Apple Valley, CA, p. A56

DROTTS, Jennifer, Manager Human Resources, Bigfork Valley Hospital, Bigfork, MN, p. A340

DROZD, Carol, Chief Operating Officer, St. Mark's Medical Center, La Grange, TX, p. A632

DRUCKENMILLER, Carol, R.N. Assistant Administrator and Chief Nursing Officer, University of South Alabama Children's and Women's Hospital, Mobile, AL, p. A23

DRUMMOND, Armand, Manager Human Resources, South Lincoln Medical Center, Kemmerer, WY, p. A721

DRUMMOND, Dana, Chief Nursing Officer and Administrator, Surgery Specialty Hospitals of America, Pasadena, TX, p. A641

DRUMMOND, Gregory, Chief Executive Officer, West Oaks Hospital, Houston, TX, p. A628

DRUMMOND, Michael, Chief Financial Officer, Runnells Specialized Hospital of Union County, Berkeley Heights, NJ, p. A413

DRURY, Cynthia, Coordinator Human Resources, Highland–Clarksburg Hospital, Clarksburg, WV, p. A694

DRURY, Dennis, Director Information Technology, Northern Cochise Community Hospital, Willcox, AZ, p. A41

DRVARIC, David M., M.D. Chief of Staff, Shriners Hospitals for Children–Springfield, Springfield, MA, p. A315

DRYBURGH, Louise, Chief Executive Officer, First Care Health Center, Park River, ND, p. A480

DRYMON, Lisa, Manager, Fairfax Community Hospital, Fairfax, OK, p. A511

DRZEWIECKI–BURGER, Mary Jo, Administrative Manager, Caro Center, Caro, MI, p. A320

DU PONT, Karen, Chief Human Resource Officer, Casa Colina Hospital for Rehabilitative Medicine, Pomona, CA, p. A84

DU RALL, Marty, Executive Director Human Resources, St. Vincent Indianapolis Hospital, Indianapolis, IN, p. A215

DUANE, Paul K.
Chief Financial Officer and Office of Health Reform, Palmetto Health Baptist, Columbia, SC, p. A564
Chief Financial Officer and Office of Health Reform, Palmetto Health Richland, Columbia, SC, p. A564

DUBE, Cynthia, M.D. Medical Director, Mayo Clinic Health System in Austin, Austin, MN, p. A340

DUBE, Sheri, Chief Operating Officer, St. David's North Austin Medical Center, Austin, TX, p. A600

DUBEN, Julie, Chief Clinical Officer, Kindred Hospital Northland, Kansas City, MO, p. A373

DUBICKI, Robert, Executive Vice President and Chief Operating Officer, Kingsbrook Jewish Medical Center, NY, p. A445

DUBIS, John S., FACHE, President and Chief Executive Officer, St. Elizabeth Edgewood, Edgewood, KY, p. A260

DUBIS, John S., FACHE President and Chief Executive Officer, St. Elizabeth Edgewood, Edgewood, KY, p. A260

DUBIS, John S., FACHE, President and Chief Executive Officer, St. Elizabeth Healthcare, Edgewood, KY, p. B127

DUBOIS, Brady, Chief Executive Officer, Northern Louisiana Medical Center, Ruston, LA, p. A287

DUBOSE, Alta, Chief Financial Officer, Carolinas Hospital System Marion, Mullins, SC, p. A568

DUBROCA, Darryl S.
Chief Executive Officer and Managing Director, Spring Mountain Sahara, Las Vegas, NV, p. A406
Chief Executive Officer and Managing Director, Spring Mountain Treatment Center, Las Vegas, NV, p. A406

DUBROW, Melissa, Chief Operating Officer, Waynesboro Hospital, Waynesboro, PA, p. A557

DUBRUL, Bill, Director Information Technology, St. Anthony's Hospital, Houston, TX, p. A626

DUBRUYNE, Sharon, Director Human Resources, College Hospital Costa Mesa, Costa Mesa, CA, p. A60

DUCEY, Ann, Chief Information Officer, Boys Town National Research Hospital, Omaha, NE, p. A399

DUCHARME, Adele, MSN, Chief Executive Officer, Saint Luke's Cushing Hospital, Leavenworth, KS, p. A248

DUCHARME, Maria, R.N. Interim Chief Nursing Officer, Miriam Hospital, Providence, RI, p. A560

DUCHEMIN, MaDena, Assistant Administrator Human Resources, John Randolph Medical Center, Hopewell, VA, p. A672

DUCHENE, Pam, R.N. Vice President Patient Care Services, St. Joseph Hospital, Nashua, NH, p. A411

DUCHESNEAU, Angy, Senior Director Human Resources, Lakeview Hospital, Stillwater, MN, p. A352

DUCHICELA, Jorge, M.D. Chief of Staff, Columbus Community Hospital, Columbus, TX, p. A607

DUCHMAN, Susan, R.N. Vice President and Chief Nursing Officer, Williamsport Regional Medical Center, Williamsport, PA, p. A559

DUCKOR, Steven, M.D. Chief of Staff, Chapman Medical Center, Orange, CA, p. A81

DUCKWORTH, Allison G., R.N. Chief Operating Officer and Chief Nursing Officer, FirstHealth Richmond Memorial Hospital, Rockingham, NC, p. A471

DUCKWORTH, Bob, Director Information Systems, Medical West, Bessemer, AL, p. A16

DUDA, David, Senior Vice President and Chief Operating Officer, Riverside Medical Center, Kankakee, IL, p. A194

DUDEK, Gerald, M.D. Chief of Staff, Mercy Hospital Cadillac, Cadillac, MI, p. A320

DUDLEY, III, Edward L., Executive Vice President and Chief Financial Officer, Catholic Medical Center, Manchester, NH, p. A411

DUDLEY, Heather, Director Administrative Services, Brookhaven Hospital, Tulsa, OK, p. A520

DUDLEY, James, M.D. Medical Director, Cordova Community Medical Center, Cordova, AK, p. A28

DUDLEY, Sarah, Chief Operating Officer, Princeton Baptist Medical Center, Birmingham, AL, p. A16

DUDLEY, Sharon, Chief Operating Officer, Comanche County Memorial Hospital, Lawton, OK, p. A512

DUDLEY, W. Steve, CPA Chief Financial Officer, Ed Fraser Memorial Hospital and Baker Community Health Center, MacClenny, FL, p. A135

DUERR, Joe, Chief Executive Officer, Morton County Health System, Elkhart, KS, p. A243

DUET, Angela, Director Information Technology, St. Charles Parish Hospital, Luling, LA, p. A283

DUETSCH, Stephen, Vice President Operations and Support, Spencer Hospital, Spencer, IA, p. A238

DUFF, Isabel, MS, Director, Veterans Affairs Southern Nevada Healthcare System, North Las Vegas, NV, p. A407

DUFF, Jim, Chief Financial Officer, Colorado Mental Health Institute at Pueblo, Pueblo, CO, p. A110

DUFF, Mary Claire, CPA Chief Financial Officer, Ridgeview Psychiatric Hospital and Center, Oak Ridge, TN, p. A592

DUFFEE, Patrick, Director Medical Information Systems, Delta Medical Center, Memphis, TN, p. A588

DUFFEY, David, D.O. Chief Medical Officer, Metro Health Hospital, Wyoming, MI, p. A337

DUFFEY, Pam, R.N. Chief Nursing Officer, Texas Health Specialty Hospital, Fort Worth, TX, p. A619

DUFFEY, Victoria, Director of Nursing, Citizens Medical Center, Colby, KS, p. A242

DUFFIELD, Douglas, President and Chief Executive Officer, San Joaquin Community Hospital, Bakersfield, CA, p. A57

DUFFIN, Kelly L., Operations Officer, Intermountain Medical Center, Murray, UT, p. A660

DUFFORD, Shawn, M.D. Vice President Medical Affairs and Chief Medical Officer, Exempla Saint Joseph Hospital, Denver, CO, p. A104

DUFFY, Beth, Chief Operating Officer, Einstein Medical Center Montgomery, East Norriton, PA, p. A538

DUFFY, Daniel, D.O. Chief Medical Director, HealthSource Saginaw, Saginaw, MI, p. A334

DUFFY, Delilah, Interim Chief Nurse Officer, Central Montana Medical Center, Lewistown, MT, p. A389

DUFFY, Karen, R.N. Director Patient Care Services, BayCare Alliant Hospital, Dunedin, FL, p. A127

DUFFY, Kenneth, M.D. Medical Director, Seiling Community Hospital, Seiling, OK, p. A518

DUFFY, Michelle, Director Human Resources, Franciscan St. Elizabeth Health – Lafayette Central, Lafayette, IN, p. A216

DUFFY, Pam, Vice President Human Resources, South Oaks Hospital, Amityville, NY, p. A432

DUFFY, Pamela
Vice President Patient Care Services and Chief Nursing Officer, Kishwaukee Hospital, DeKalb, IL, p. A188
Vice President Patient Services and CNO, Valley West Hospital, Sandwich, IL, p. A202

DUFOUR, Charles, Coordinator Information Systems, North Alabama Regional Hospital, Decatur, AL, p. A18

DUFT, Ryan, R.N. Chief Nursing Officer, Fredonia Regional Hospital, Fredonia, KS, p. A244

DUGAL, John Charles, M.D. Medical Director, Community Specialty Hospital, Lafayette, LA, p. A281

DUGAN, Elizabeth, Ph.D. Chief Nursing Officer, Inova Loudoun Hospital, Leesburg, VA, p. A673

DUGAN, Gary, M.D. Vice President Medical Affairs, DuBois Regional Medical Center, Du Bois, PA, p. A537

DUGAR, Edward, Interim Chief Executive Officer, Hood Memorial Hospital, Amite, LA, p. A272

DUGGAL, Harpreet, M.D. Medical Director, Department of Health and Human Services, Humboldt County Mental Health, Eureka, CA, p. A62

DUGGAN, Allison, M.D. Vice President and Chief Operating Officer, Oswego Hospital, Oswego, NY, p. A451

DUGGAN, Daniel, Chief Operating Officer, Bon Secours St. Francis Health System, Greenville, SC, p. A566

DUGGAN, Eileen, M.D. Medical Director, Crittenton Children's Center, Kansas City, MO, p. A373

DUGGAN, James E., Director Human Resources, Western Massachusetts Hospital, Westfield, MA, p. A316

DUGGAN, Margaret M., M.D. Chief Medical Officer, Brigham and Women's Faulkner Hospital, Boston, MA, p. A306

DUGGAN, Stephanie J., M.D. Vice President and Chief Medical Officer, Sacred Heart Hospital of Pensacola, Pensacola, FL, p. A142

DUGGAN, Tonya, Director Human Resources, Northern Louisiana Medical Center, Ruston, LA, p. A287

DUGGAR, Susan, R.N. Vice President Nursing, Spartanburg Regional Medical Center, Spartanburg, SC, p. A570

DUGGER, Curtis R., Chief Financial Officer, Memorial Hospital of Converse County, Douglas, WY, p. A721

DUGGER, Sandy, Chief Human Resources Officer, Community Hospital, Torrington, WY, p. A723

DUHAIME, Robert A., R.N. Senior Vice President Clinical Operations and Chief Nursing Officer, Catholic Medical Center, Manchester, NH, p. A411

DUHE, Louis, Senior Director Information Technology, George Washington University Hospital, Washington, DC, p. A121

DUHE, Suzette, Chief Financial Officer, Louisiana Heart Hospital, Lacombe, LA, p. A280

DUHON, Neal J., M.D. Chief of Staff, Acadia General Hospital, Crowley, LA, p. A276

DUHON, Susan, Director Medical Records, St. James Parish Hospital, Lutcher, LA, p. A283

DUHON, Thomas, Director Human Resources, Heart Hospital of Lafayette, Lafayette, LA, p. A281

DUKE, Kathleen, Chief Executive Officer, Taunton State Hospital, Taunton, MA, p. A315

DUKE, II, Lee M., M.D. Senior Vice President and Chief Physician Executive, Lancaster General Health, Lancaster, PA, p. A542

DUKES, Brenda, Director Human Resources, Sonoma Developmental Center, Eldridge, CA, p. A62

DUKOFF, Ruth, M.D. Medical Director, North Star Behavioral Health System, Anchorage, AK, p. A28

DULANEY, Paul, Chief of Staff, Troy Regional Medical Center, Troy, AL, p. A26

DULANEY, Thomas, M.D. Chief of Staff, St. Anthony Regional Hospital, Carroll, IA, p. A226

DULIT, Alan, M.D. Chief Medical Officer, St. Anthony Summit Medical Center, Frisco, CO, p. A106

DULNY, David
Chief Financial Officer, Providence Medical Center, Kansas City, KS, p. A247
Chief Financial Officer, Saint John Hospital, Leavenworth, KS, p. A248

DUMAL, Jennifer, R.N. Chief Operating Officer of Clinical and Chief Nursing Officer, Memorial Hospital at Gulfport, Gulfport, MS, p. A358

DUMONSEAU, Kent
Vice President Finance and Information Services, Hayward Area Memorial Hospital and Nursing Home, Hayward, WI, p. A706
Vice President Finance and Information Services, Memorial Medical Center – Ashland, Ashland, WI, p. A701

DUMONT, Rene, Vice President Strategic Growth, St. Mary's Regional Medical Center, Lewiston, ME, p. A294

DUNAVAN, Chad, R.N. Interim Chief Nursing Officer, Medical Center Health System, Odessa, TX, p. A640

DUNCAN, Allison, Chief Financial Officer, Arrowhead Behavioral Health Hospital, Maumee, OH, p. A498

DUNCAN, Barbara, Chief Financial Officer, Habersham Medical Center, Demorest, GA, p. A158

DUNCAN, Charles, M.D. Medical Director, Kindred Hospital–San Antonio, San Antonio, TX, p. A646

DUNCAN, Cindy
Administrator and Chief Executive Officer, Memorial Hospital and Physician Group, Frederick, OK, p. A511
Manager Human Resources, Plains Regional Medical Center, Clovis, NM, p. A427
Director Human Resources, Roosevelt General Hospital, Portales, NM, p. A429

DUNCAN, Darryl L., President and Chief Executive Officer, Monongalia General Hospital, Morgantown, WV, p. A697

DUNCAN, Erika, Vice President Human Resources, Metro Health Hospital, Wyoming, MI, p. A337

DUNCAN, Jeremy, Director Information Systems, Lawrence Medical Center, Moulton, AL, p. A24

DUNCAN, Leeann, Director Patient Care Services, Harbor Oaks Hospital, New Baltimore, MI, p. A331

DUNCAN, Linda, Director Human Resources, Lee's Summit Medical Center, Lee's Summit, MO, p. A375

DUNCAN, Lyman, Chief Financial Officer, San Juan Hospital, Monticello, UT, p. A660

DUNCAN, Michael J., System Chief Executive Officer, Chester County Hospital, West Chester, PA, p. A558

DUNCAN, Nathan, Chief Executive Officer, Lakeland Behavioral Health System, Springfield, MO, p. A383

DUNCAN, Thomas M., Executive Vice President and Chief Financial Officer, Miami Valley Hospital, Dayton, OH, p. A492

DUNFEE, Michael H., Director, Hampton Veterans Affairs Medical Center, Hampton, VA, p. A672

DUNFORD, Ben, Chief Financial Officer, Texas Regional Medical Center at Sunnyvale, Sunnyvale, TX, p. A651

DUNFORD, Bill, Manager, Northside Hospital–Cherokee, Canton, GA, p. A155

DUNFORD–BOOTHE, Rosalina, Community Chief Nursing Officer, Beckley ARH Hospital, Beckley, WV, p. A693

DUNGAN, Janice L., Senior Vice President Clinical Services, Lake Regional Health System, Osage Beach, MO, p. A378

DUNHAM, David S., President, Mercy Medical Center Merced, Merced, CA, p. A77

DUNHAM, Shelly, R.N., Chief Executive Officer, Okeene Municipal Hospital, Okeene, OK, p. A514

DUNIGAN, Linda, Chief Executive Officer, Claiborne County Medical Center, Port Gibson, MS, p. A364

DUNIO, Gina, Chief Human Resources, James E. Van Zandt Veterans Affairs Medical Center, Altoona, PA, p. A532

DUNKER, Karla, Director Finance, Sedgwick County Health Center, Julesburg, CO, p. A108

DUNKIEL, Barbara, Director Human Resources, HEALTHSOUTH Sunrise Rehabilitation Hospital, Sunrise, FL, p. A146

DUNKIN, Jackie J., Director Human Resources, Platte Valley Medical Center, Brighton, CO, p. A103

DUNKIN, Richard, Vice President and Chief Information Officer, Mount Sinai Hospital, Chicago, IL, p. A185

DUNLAP, Cyndy, R.N. Chief Nursing Officer, Scott & White Memorial Hospital, Temple, TX, p. A652

DUNLAP, DeeDee, Information Officer, Garden County Health Services, Oshkosh, NE, p. A401

DUNLAP, Mary Lou, Correctional Health Services Administrator, California Medical Facility, Vacaville, CA, p. A98

DUNLEY, Pamela L., R.N. Vice President Chief Nursing Officer and Chief Operating Officer, Elmhurst Memorial Hospital, IL, p. A189

DUNLOP, Jr., James H., CP
Senior Vice President and Chief Financial Officer, Kenmore Mercy Hospital, Kenmore, NY, p. A439
Senior Vice President Finance and Chief Financial Officer, Mercy Hospital, Buffalo, NY, p. A434
Chief Financial Officer, Sisters of Charity Hospital of Buffalo, Buffalo, NY, p. A435

DUNMAN, Robyn, Coordinator Human Resources, Kindred Hospital–Nashville, Nashville, TN, p. A590

DUNMYER, Daniel C., Chief Executive Officer, Carolinas Specialty Hospital, Charlotte, NC, p. A462

DUNN, Christopher, M.D. Vice President Medical Affairs, Sequoia Hospital, Redwood City, CA, p. A86

DUNN, Connie, Director Human Resources, Livingston Memorial Hospital, Livingston, MT, p. A389

DUNN, Daniel N., Vice President Operations, Wentworth–Douglass Hospital, Dover, NH, p. A410

DUNN, Dave, Director of Nursing, Star Valley Medical Center, Afton, WY, p. A720

DUNN, E. D., Vice President Human Resources, Virtua Memorial, Mount Holly, NJ, p. A419

DUNN, Edna, Chief Nursing Officer, Western Plains Medical Complex, Dodge City, KS, p. A243

DUNN, Hope, Chief Nursing Officer, HEALTHSOUTH East Valley Rehabilitation Hospital, Mesa, AZ, p. A34

DUNN, Jack, M.D. Chief of Staff, La Paz Regional Hospital, Parker, AZ, p. A35

DUNN, Janice, Chief Financial Officer, Saint Joseph Regional Medical Center–Plymouth Campus, Plymouth, IN, p. A221

DUNN, Leonard, M.D. Chief Medical Officer, BayCare Alliant Hospital, Dunedin, FL, p. A127

DUNN, Marcy
Vice President Information Services and Chief Information Officer, Good Samaritan Hospital Medical Center, West Islip, NY, p. A458
Vice President Information Services and Chief Information Officer, Mercy Medical Center, Rockville Centre, NY, p. A453
Vice President Information Services and Chief Information Officer, St. Francis Hospital, Roslyn, NY, p. A454

DUNN, Margie, Director Human Resources, Middle Tennessee Mental Health Institute, Nashville, TN, p. A590

DUNN, Nicholas, Director Information Systems, Mena Regional Health System, Mena, AR, p. A50

DUNN, Patrick A., R.N. Chief Nursing Officer, Lea Regional Medical Center, Hobbs, NM, p. A428

DUNN, Rosemary, R.N. Chief Nursing Officer, Hahnemann University Hospital, Philadelphia, PA, p. A548

DUNN, Shawn, M.D. Medical Director, Spine Hospital of Louisiana, Baton Rouge, LA, p. A274

DUNN, Sheila, Assistant Administrator Human Resources, Dale Medical Center, Ozark, AL, p. A24

DUNN, Tandra, Director of Nursing, San Luis Valley Health Conejos County Hospital, La Jara, CO, p. A108

DUNN, Terry, Director Information Technology, Battle Mountain General Hospital, Battle Mountain, NV, p. A404

DUNNAM, Lorie, Superintendent, Big Spring State Hospital, Big Spring, TX, p. A603

DUNNE, Elizabeth
Chief Executive, Providence Little Company of Mary Medical Center – Torrance, Torrance, CA, p. A97
Interim Chief Executive Officer, Providence Little Company of Mary Medical Center San Pedro, CA, p. A74

DUNNING, Shane, Administrator, Carnegie Tri–County Municipal Hospital, Carnegie, OK, p. A508

DUNWOODY, Robert, Chief Financial Officer, Lawnwood Regional Medical Center & Heart Institute, Fort Pierce, FL, p. A129

DUPLECHAN, Lloyd, Chief Operating Officer, Kaiser Permanente Ontario Medical Center, Ontario, CA, p. A81

DUPPER, Harold, Chief Financial Officer, Platte Valley Medical Center, Brighton, CO, p. A103

DUPPER, Larry L., Chief Financial Officer, Valley View Hospital, Glenwood Springs, CO, p. A106

DUPPSTADT, Edwin, M.D. Chief Medical Officer, Medical Center of Arlington, Arlington, TX, p. A598

DUPRE, Ritchie, Chief Executive Officer, Leonard J. Chabert Medical Center, Houma, LA, p. A279

DUPRE', Charlotte W., Chief Executive Officer, Central Mississippi Medical Center, Jackson, MS, p. A360

DUPREE, Lucy G., Director Human Resources, District One Hospital, Faribault, MN, p. A343

DUPREY, Irma, Administrator Medical Records, Hospital Universitario Dr. Ramon Ruiz Arnau, Bayamon, PR, p. A725

DUPUIS, Pamela M., R.N. Senior Vice President Patient Care Services, Montefiore New Rochelle, New Rochelle, NY, p. A442

DUQUETTE, Connie, Director Human Resources, Sharp Memorial Hospital, San Diego, CA, p. A90

DUQUETTE, William M., Chief Executive Officer, Baptist Health South Florida, Homestead Hospital, Homestead, FL, p. A131

DURAND, Mark, Assistant Administrator Operations, CHRISTUS Jasper Memorial Hospital, Jasper, TX, p. A630

DURBAK, Ivan, Chief Information Officer, Bronx–Lebanon Hospital Center Health Care System, NY, p. A442

DURBIN, Melissa, R.N. Chief Nursing Officer, Boca Raton Regional Hospital, Boca Raton, FL, p. A124

DURDEN, Rhonda, Chief Financial Officer, Emanuel Medical Center, Swainsboro, GA, p. A167

DURFLINGER, Kathy, Vice President Nursing, Magruder Memorial Hospital, Port Clinton, OH, p. A500

DURHAM, Bill, M.D. Chief Medical Officer, Oak Tree Hospital, Corbin, KY, p. A260

DURHAM, Linda
Director Human Resources, Henderson County Community Hospital, Lexington, TN, p. A587
Director Human Resources, McNairy Regional Hospital, Selmer, TN, p. A592

DURHAM, Thomas, Chief Nursing Officer, Ferry County Memorial Hospital, Republic, WA, p. A687

DURIS, Deb, Director of Nursing, Northwest Ohio Psychiatric Hospital, Toledo, OH, p. A503

DURNEY, Gerry, Chief Operating Officer, Good Samaritan Hospital, Suffern, NY, p. A455

DURNIOK, Brian, Vice President Human Resources, UPMC Hamot, Erie, PA, p. A539

DURON, Kety, Vice President Human Resources, Stanford Hospital and Clinics, Palo Alto, CA, p. A82

DUROSE, Galen, M.D. Chief of Staff, Trinity Hospital Twin City, Dennison, OH, p. A493

DUROVICH, Christopher J., President and Chief Executive Officer, Children's Medical Center of Dallas, Dallas, TX, p. A610

DURR, Amber, Director Human Resources, Community Hospital–Fairfax, Fairfax, MO, p. A371

DURR, Durinda, Vice President and Chief Nursing Officer, Rome Memorial Hospital, Rome, NY, p. A453

DURRENCE, Elizabeth, Chief Operating Officer, Kendall Regional Medical Center, Miami, FL, p. A137

DURST, Geoff, Vice President Finance, Avera St. Luke's Hospital, Aberdeen, SD, p. A572

DURST, Sue, R.N. Vice President Plant Operations, McLaren Macomb, Mount Clemens, MI, p. A330

DURSTELER, Courtney, Chief Human Resources Officer, Franklin County Medical Center, Preston, ID, p. A178

DURYEE, Edward E., Director Information Systems, Saint Francis Medical Center, Cape Girardeau, MO, p. A368

DUSANG, Nina
Vice President Finance and Chief Financial Officer, DCH Regional Medical Center, Tuscaloosa, AL, p. A26
Chief Financial Officer, Northport Medical Center, Northport, AL, p. A24

DUSENBERY, Jack, President and Chief Executive Officer, Covenant Medical Center, Waterloo, IA, p. A239

DUTCHER, Phillip C., Chief Operating Officer, NCH Downtown Naples Hospital, Naples, FL, p. A138

DUTHE, Robert J., Director Information Systems and Chief Information Officer, Cortland Regional Medical Center, Cortland, NY, p. A436

DUTLA, Nimal, M.D. Chief Medical Staff, Holzer Medical Center – Jackson, Jackson, OH, p. A495

DUTMERS, David, Manager Technology Information System, Spectrum Health United Hospital, Greenville, MI, p. A326

DUTTON, Angela, Chief Human Resources Management Service, Robley Rex Veterans Affairs Medical Center, Louisville, KY, p. A266

DUTTON, Rebecca, Director Human Resources, Larue D. Carter Memorial Hospital, Indianapolis, IN, p. A214

DUTTON, Teresa, R.N. Chief Nursing Officer, Heritage Park Surgical Hospital, Sherman, TX, p. A649

DUVAL, John, Chief Executive Officer, VCU Health System, Richmond, VA, p. B148

DUVAL, John, Chief Executive Officer, VCU Medical Center, Richmond, VA, p. A678

DUVAL, Rob, Chief Human Resources Officer, Emma Pendleton Bradley Hospital, East Providence, RI, p. A560

DUVALL, Richard, Chief Operating Officer, Carthage Area Hospital, Carthage, NY, p. A435

DUVALL, Wendy, Chief Executive Officer, Barton County Memorial Hospital, Lamar, MO, p. A375

DUVVURI, Vikas, M.D. Medical Director, Fremont Hospital, Fremont, CA, p. A64

DVORAK, Rebecca, Chief Nursing Officer, Two Rivers Behavioral Health System, Kansas City, MO, p. A375

DWORKIN, Darren, Senior Vice President and Chief Information Officer, Cedars–Sinai Medical Center, Los Angeles, CA, p. A71

DWORKIN, Jack H., M.D. Vice President Medical Affairs and Chief Medical Officer, CentraState Healthcare System, Freehold, NJ, p. A416

DWORKIN, Paul, M.D. Physician–in–Chief, Connecticut Children's Medical Center, Hartford, CT, p. A114

DWYER, Amy L., R.N. Chief Nursing Officer, Sacred Heart Hospital, Eau Claire, WI, p. A704

DWYER, Cathy, Senior Administrator Information Systems, Burke Rehabilitation Hospital, White Plains, NY, p. A458

DWYER, James P., D.O
  Executive Vice President and Chief Medical Officer, Virtua Memorial, Mount Holly, NJ, p. A419
  Executive Vice President and Chief Medical Officer, Virtua Voorhees, Voorhees, NJ, p. A424

DWYER, Karla, R.N. Chief Nursing Officer, HEALTHSOUTH Rehabilitation Hospital–Wichita Falls, Wichita Falls, TX, p. A657

DWYER, Nancy, Vice President Human Resources, Eastside Medical Center, Snellville, GA, p. A167

DWYER, Susan, Vice President Finance, Aurora Psychiatric Hospital, Wauwatosa, WI, p. A718

DWYER, William, Vice President Human Resources, Children's Specialized Hospital–PSE&G, New Brunswick, NJ, p. A419

DYCHE, Ginny, Director Community Relations, Aspen Valley Hospital District, Aspen, CO, p. A102

DYCUS, Steve, Director Marketing and Public Relations, Williamson Medical Center, Franklin, TN, p. A583

DYE, Blake A., President, St. Vincent Heart Center, Indianapolis, IN, p. A215

DYE, Chris, Director Information Systems, Saint Joseph – Martin, Martin, KY, p. A267

DYE, Emily, Vice President Human Resources, TriStar Summit Medical Center, Hermitage, TN, p. A584

DYE, Kathy, Interim Administrator, Adena Greenfield Medical Center, Greenfield, OH, p. A495

DYER, Dave, Vice President and Chief Information Officer, Robert Wood Johnson University Hospital Somerset, Somerville, NJ, p. A422

DYER, Edward L., Chief Executive Officer, Cornerstone Hospital of Round Rock, Round Rock, TX, p. A644

DYER, Kathleen, Vice President and Chief Information Officer, Adventist Behavioral Health Rockville, Rockville, MD, p. A303

DYGERT, John, D.O. Chief of Staff, Citizens Medical Center, Colby, KS, p. A242

DYKEHOUSE, Rod, Chief Information Officer, Penn State Milton S. Hershey Medical Center, Hershey, PA, p. A540

DYKEHOUSE, Rodney, Senior Vice President Information Services, Waukesha Memorial Hospital, Waukesha, WI, p. A717

DYKENS, Jeff, CPA Chief Operating Officer, Falmouth Hospital, Falmouth, MA, p. A310

DYKES, Bradford W., President and Chief Executive Officer, Indiana University Health Bedford Hospital, Bedford, IN, p. A206

DYKES, Jennifer, Director Human Resources, Russell County Hospital, Russell Springs, KY, p. A270

DYKES, Nichole, Chief Financial Officer, Reliant Rehabilitation Hospital North Texas, Richardson, TX, p. A644

DYKSTERHOUSE, Trevor J., President, Forest Health Medical Center, Ypsilanti, MI, p. A337

DYKSTRA, Janet H., Chief Executive Officer, Osceola Community Hospital, Sibley, IA, p. A237

DYLE, Amanda, Chief Financial Officer, Coastal Carolina Hospital, Hardeeville, SC, p. A567

DYRKACZ, Anna, Chief Financial Officer, Vibra Hospital of Western Massachusetts, Springfield, MA, p. A315

DYSART–CREDEUR, Amy, Administrator, Oceans Behavioral Hospital of Broussard, Broussard, LA, p. A275

DZIEDZICKI, Ron, R.N. Chief Operating Officer, University Hospitals Case Medical Center, Cleveland, OH, p. A489

DZIESINSKI, Ray R., Chief Executive Officer, El Paso Children's Hospital, El Paso, TX, p. A615

DZURENKO, Jeanne, M.P.H. Chief Nursing Officer and Senior Vice President Patient Care, Good Samaritan Hospital Medical Center, West Islip, NY, p. A458

E

EADIE, Reginald J., M.D.,
  Chief Executive Officer, DMC Harper University Hospital, Detroit, MI, p. A322
  Interim President, Sinai–Grace Hospital, Detroit, MI, p. A322

EADS, Barry, Chief Nursing Officer, HEALTHSOUTH Rehabilitation of Gadsden, Gadsden, AL, p. A20

EAGEN, Mary K., R.N. Executive Vice President, Chief Nursing Officer, Parkland Health & Hospital System, Dallas, TX, p. A611

EAGER, David, Senior Vice President and Chief Financial Officer, Children's Medical Center of Dallas, Dallas, TX, p. A610

EAGERTON, Gregory S., Ph.D. Nurse Executive, Durham Veterans Affairs Medical Center, Durham, NC, p. A463

EAKS, C. Alan, Chief Executive Officer, Aurora Chicago Lakeshore Hospital, Chicago, IL, p. A183

EARL, Anna, M.D. Chief of Staff, Liberty Medical Center, Chester, MT, p. A386

EARL, Mindy, Health Information Manager, Power County Hospital District, American Falls, ID, p. A174

EARLE, Audra, FACHE, Chief Executive Officer, Watsonville Community Hospital, Watsonville, CA, p. A100

EARLE, Cletis, Vice President and Chief Information Officer, St. Luke's Cornwall Hospital, Newburgh, NY, p. A449

EARLEY, Robert, President and Chief Executive Officer, JPS Health Network, Fort Worth, TX, p. A618

EARLEY, Tom, Chief Financial Officer, Woodward Regional Hospital, Woodward, OK, p. A522

EARLS, Sandra, Chief Financial Officer, Coalinga Regional Medical Center, Coalinga, CA, p. A60

EARLY, Elfie, Manager Data Services, Georgia Regional Hospital at Atlanta, Decatur, GA, p. A158

EARNSHAW, Dallas, Superintendent, Utah State Hospital, Provo, UT, p. A662

EASLEY, Evan, M.D. Chief Medical Officer, Carson Valley Medical Center, Gardnerville, NV, p. A404

EASON, Laurence, M.D. Chief Medical Officer, Providence Little Company of Mary Medical Center – Torrance, Torrance, CA, p. A97

EASON SMEDLEY, Jessie, Chief Executive Officer, South Texas Rehabilitation Hospital, Brownsville, TX, p. A604

EASTBURG, Mark C., Ph.D., President and Chief Executive Officer, Pine Rest Christian Mental Health Services, Grand Rapids, MI, p. A325

EASTER, Louise, R.N. Chief Operating Officer and Chief Nursing Officer, Wagoner Community Hospital, Wagoner, OK, p. A522

EASTERLING, Jamie, Executive Director, Operations, Good Samaritan Hospital, Cincinnati, OH, p. A487

EASTERWOOD, Diane J., Human Resources Business Partner, Kaiser Permanente San Francisco Medical Center, San Francisco, CA, p. A91

EASTMAN, David, Site Director, Ukiah Valley Medical Center, Ukiah, CA, p. A98

EASTMAN, Joseph F., Director Human Resources, Central Carolina Hospital, Sanford, NC, p. A472

EASTON, Laura S., R.N., President and Chief Executive Officer, Caldwell Memorial Hospital, Lenoir, NC, p. A468

EATHERLY, Theresa, Chief Financial Officer, Doctor's Hospital – Tidwell, Houston, TX, p. A624

EATON, Ellen, Vice President Human Resources, Tift Regional Medical Center, Tifton, GA, p. A168

EATON, Jim, Chief Financial Officer, Wise Regional Health System, Decatur, TX, p. A612

EATON, Philip, Interim Chief Executive Officer, Mountain West Medical Center, Tooele, UT, p. A664

EAVENSON, Steve, Vice President Finance, Mercy Health Saint Mary's, Grand Rapids, MI, p. A325

EAVES, Clinton, Administrator, H. C. Watkins Memorial Hospital, Quitman, MS, p. A364

EBANGIT, Ruth, M.D. Chief of Staff and Medical Officer, Throckmorton County Memorial Hospital, Throckmorton, TX, p. A653

EBAUGH, Matthew T., Area Information Officer, Kaiser Permanente San Diego Medical Center, San Diego, CA, p. A89

EBBERT, Paul, Chief of Staff, SageWest Healthcare–Lander, Lander, WY, p. A721

EBBETT, Patricia, Chief Human Resources Officer, Catawba Hospital, Catawba, VA, p. A669

EBERSOLE, Nathan, Controller, Calhoun–Liberty Hospital, Blountstown, FL, p. A123

EBERT, Cynthia, R.N. Chief Nursing Officer, Summit Healthcare Regional Medical Center, Show Low, AZ, p. A39

EBERT, Jr., Larry W., Chief Operating Officer and Chief Financial Officer, Northridge Medical Center, Commerce, GA, p. A157

EBERT, Michael, M.D. Chief of Staff, Veterans Affairs Connecticut Healthcare System, West Haven, CT, p. A118

EBERTH, Denise A., Director Human Resources, Allegan General Hospital, Allegan, MI, p. A318

EBLIN, Steven E., Chief Executive Officer / President, Randolph Hospital, Asheboro, NC, p. A459

EBNER, Carl, Vice President Finance, Robinson Memorial Hospital, Ravenna, OH, p. A501

EBNER, Joseph, M.D. Chief Medical Officer, Speare Memorial Hospital, Plymouth, NH, p. A412

EBRI, Patrick D., Ph.D
  Vice President, Human Resources, Southeast Georgia Health System Brunswick Campus, Brunswick, GA, p. A155
  Vice President Human Resources, Southeast Georgia Health System Camden Campus, Saint Marys, GA, p. A166

ECCLESTON, Julie, Vice President Human Resources, Hillcrest Medical Center, Tulsa, OK, p. A520

ECHOLS, Jane, Chief Executive Officer, Wills Memorial Hospital, Washington, GA, p. A169

ECK, Carol, President, Peak Behavioral Health Services, Santa Teresa, NM, p. A430

ECKELS, Dan, Chief Financial Officer, Washington Regional Medical Center, Fayetteville, AR, p. A46

ECKENFELS, Susan, Chief Financial Officer, Ste. Genevieve County Memorial Hospital, Ste. Genevieve, MO, p. A383

ECKERD, Gayle
  Chief Executive Officer, River Point Behavioral Health, Jacksonville, FL, p. A132
  Chief Executive Officer, Wekiva Springs Center for Women, Jacksonville, FL, p. A132

ECKERT, Mark, Vice President Finance, Ochsner Medical Center – Kenner, Kenner, LA, p. A280

ECKERT, Mary L., President and Chief Executive Officer, Millcreek Community Hospital, Erie, PA, p. A538

ECKERT, Susan E., R.N. Senior Vice President and Chief Nursing Officer, MedStar Washington Hospital Center, Washington, DC, p. A121

ECKES, Chad, Vice President Information Services and Chief Information Officer, Wake Forest Baptist Medical Center, Winston–Salem, NC, p. A475

ECKFORD, Marjorie, Chief Nursing Officer, Menlo Park Surgical Hospital, Menlo Park, CA, p. A77

ECKLEY, Valerie, M.D. Chief of Staff, East Adams Rural Hospital, Ritzville, WA, p. A688

ECKMANN, John, Director Information Systems, Shenandoah Medical Center, Shenandoah, IA, p. A237

ECKSTEIN, William, Chief Financial Officer, Columbus Specialty Hospital, Columbus, GA, p. A156

EDALATI, David, M.D. Medical Director, Meadowbrook Rehabilitation Hospital, Gardner, KS, p. A244

EDDEY, Gary E., M.D. Medical Director, Matheny Medical and Educational Center, Peapack, NJ, p. A420

EDDINGTON, Tonya, Coordinator Human Resources, Select Specialty Hospital–Springfield, Springfield, MO, p. A383

EDDLEMAN, Patricia, Fiscal Officer, Heartland Behavioral Healthcare, Massillon, OH, p. A498

EDELEN, Donald B., M.D. Vice President Medical Services and Quality Initiatives, Franciscan St. Elizabeth Health – Lafayette Central, Lafayette, IN, p. A216

EDELMAN, Marc D., Vice President Operations, Bristol Hospital, Bristol, CT, p. A113

EDEN, Tina M., Director of Nursing, Virginia Gay Hospital, Vinton, IA, p. A238

EDENFIELD, Janet, Director Financial Services, Georgia Regional Hospital at Savannah, Savannah, GA, p. A166

EDGAR, Joseph H., Senior Vice President Operations, Gettysburg Hospital, Gettysburg, PA, p. A539

EDGAR, Nancy, Vice President Human Resources, Methodist Hospital, San Antonio, TX, p. A646

EDGEWORTH, Mitch, Adult Enterprise Chief Operating Officer, Vanderbilt Hospital and Clinics, Nashville, TN, p. A591

EDIN, Scott D., Chief Financial Officer, Amery Regional Medical Center, Amery, WI, p. A701

EDLER, Susie, Chief Executive Officer, University General Hospital–Dallas, Dallas, TX, p. A612

EDMINSTER, Sue
Vice President Human Resources, Agnesian HealthCare, Fond Du Lac, WI, p. A704
Vice President Human Resources, Ripon Medical Center, Ripon, WI, p. A714
Vice President Human Resources, Waupun Memorial Hospital, Waupun, WI, p. A717
EDMISTON, Gena, R.N. Chief Nursing Officer, Fairbanks Memorial Hospital, Fairbanks, AK, p. A29
EDMONDS, Kelly, Chief Financial Officer, Western Maryland Hospital Center, Hagerstown, MD, p. A301
EDMONDSON, Bobby, Controller, Regional Rehabilitation Hospital, Phenix City, AL, p. A25
EDMONDSON, Cory, Chief Operating Officer, Midland Memorial Hospital, Midland, TX, p. A638
EDMONDSON, James H., Chief Executive Officer, Riverview Regional Medical Center, Gadsden, AL, p. A20
EDMONSON, Cole, R.N. Vice President and Chief Nursing Officer, Texas Health Presbyterian Hospital Dallas, Dallas, TX, p. A612
EDMUNDS, Liza, Director Human Resources, Gateway Medical Center, Clarksville, TN, p. A581
EDMUNDSON, Reed
Regional Administrator, Grimes St. Joseph Health Center, Navasota, TX, p. A639
Administrator, Madison St. Joseph Health Center, Madisonville, TX, p. A636
EDNEY, Daniel, M.D. Chief of Staff, Promise Hospital of Vicksburg, Vicksburg, MS, p. A366
EDRINGTON, Katherine, R.N. Administrator, Mercy Health – Anderson Hospital, Cincinnati, OH, p. A487
EDSON, Pamela A., Chief Executive Officer, Kindred Hospital of Central Ohio, Mansfield, OH, p. A497
EDWARD, Virginia, R.N. Administrator and Chief Nursing Officer, West Anaheim Medical Center, Anaheim, CA, p. A55
EDWARDS, Angela Imelda, R.N. Chief Nurse Executive, Woodhull Medical and Mental Health Center, NY, p. A449
EDWARDS, Annette, Chief Financial Officer, Odessa Memorial Healthcare Center, Odessa, WA, p. A686
EDWARDS, Becky, Manager Human Resources, Irwin County Hospital, Ocilla, GA, p. A164
EDWARDS, Bruce
Vice President Human Resources, Heritage Valley Health System, Beaver, PA, p. A533
Vice President Human Resources, Sewickley Valley Hospital, (A Division of Valley Medical Facilities), Sewickley, PA, p. A555
EDWARDS, Chris, M.D. Chief Medical Officer, Maury Regional Hospital, Columbia, TN, p. A581
EDWARDS, Dana, Chief Financial Officer, HEALTHSOUTH Sea Pines Rehabilitation Hospital, Melbourne, FL, p. A136
EDWARDS, Danny R., Administrator, Complex Care Hospital at Ridgelake, Sarasota, FL, p. A145
EDWARDS, David, M.D. Chief Medical Officer, Banner Gateway Medical Center, Gilbert, AZ, p. A32
EDWARDS, Dennis, M.D. Vice President Medical Affairs, CHI Health Good Samaritan, Kearney, NE, p. A397
EDWARDS, Elizabeth, R.N. Director, Nursing Services, Sheridan Community Hospital, Sheridan, MI, p. A335
EDWARDS, Frank, M.D. Medical Director, Jones Memorial Hospital, Wellsville, NY, p. A457
EDWARDS, Gordon, System Vice President and Chief Financial Officer, Columbia Network, PeaceHealth Southwest Medical Center, Vancouver, WA, p. A692
EDWARDS, Gregg
Vice President Human Resources, Asante Ashland Community Hospital, Ashland, OR, p. A523
Chief People Officer, Asante Rogue Regional Medical Center, Medford, OR, p. A527
Chief People Officer, Asante Three Rivers Medical Center, Grants Pass, OR, p. A525
EDWARDS, Jeff, Manager Information Services, Mendocino Coast District Hospital, Fort Bragg, CA, p. A63
EDWARDS, Jeffrey, M.D. Chief of Staff, Texas Health Harris Methodist Hospital Stephenville, Stephenville, TX, p. A650
EDWARDS, John R., Administrator and Chief Executive Officer, Pacific Alliance Medical Center, Los Angeles, CA, p. A74
EDWARDS, Kathleen, Manager Information Systems Operation, HEALTHSOUTH Rehabilitation Hospital of Altoona, Altoona, PA, p. A532
EDWARDS, Kristy, M.D. Chief Medical Officer, Lillian M. Hudspeth Memorial Hospital, Sonora, TX, p. A649
EDWARDS, Mark A., Chief Executive Officer, Livingston Hospital and Healthcare Services, Salem, KY, p. A270
EDWARDS, Matt, Vice President Nursing Services and Chief Nursing Officer, Anderson Regional Medical Center, Meridian, MS, p. A362
EDWARDS, Michael R., Administrator, Scott Regional Hospital, Morton, MS, p. A363

EDWARDS, Michelle, Executive Vice President Information Technology, Palmetto Health Baptist, Columbia, SC, p. A564
EDWARDS, Nicki E., Ph.D. Interim Chief Nursing Officer, Sierra Vista Regional Medical Center, San Luis Obispo, CA, p. A93
EDWARDS, Rebecca
Chief Nursing Officer, Greenwood Leflore Hospital, Greenwood, MS, p. A358
Director Human Resources, Martin General Hospital, Williamston, NC, p. A474
Chief Human Resources Officer, Penn Highlands Brookville, Brookville, PA, p. A534
EDWARDS, Rick
Vice President Finance Services, Hancock Regional Hospital, Greenfield, IN, p. A212
Director Information Systems, Howard County General Hospital, Columbia, MD, p. A300
EDWARDS, Samuel, M.D. Chief of Staff, Florida Hospital DeLand, DeLand, FL, p. A127
EDWARDS, Sondra, Human Resources Supervisor, Epic Medical Center, Eufaula, OK, p. A510
EDWARDS, Steven D., President and Chief Executive Officer, Cox Medical Centers, Springfield, MO, p. A383
EDWARDS, Steven D., President and Chief Executive Officer, CoxHealth, Springfield, MO, p. B45
EDWARDS, Susan, Vice President Human Resources, Culpeper Regional Hospital, Culpeper, VA, p. A670
EDWARDS, Susan A., President and Chief Executive Officer, ProHealth Care, Inc., Waukesha, WI, p. B109
EDWARDS, Teresa L., President and Administrator, Sentara Leigh Hospital, Norfolk, VA, p. A675
EDWARDS, Terry, Controller, Kings Mountain Hospital, Kings Mountain, NC, p. A467
EDWARDS, Todd, Director Information Management Systems, Brazosport Regional Health System, Lake Jackson, TX, p. A632
EDWARDS, William, Information Technology Generalist, Wernersville State Hospital, Wernersville, PA, p. A557
EESLEY, Michael S., Chief Executive Officer, Centegra Health System, Crystal Lake, IL, p. B33
EESLEY, Michael S.
Chief Executive Officer, Centegra Hospital – McHenry, McHenry, IL, p. A196
Chief Executive Officer, Centegra Hospital – Woodstock, Woodstock, IL, p. A205
EFFEREN, Linda, M.D. Senior Vice President and Chief Medical Officer, South Nassau Communities Hospital, Oceanside, NY, p. A450
EGAN, Kim, Executive Director Human Resources, Regions Hospital, Saint Paul, MN, p. A351
EGAN, Timothy, Chief Restructuring Officer and President, Roseland Community Hospital, Chicago, IL, p. A186
EGAN, Timothy C., Director, Human Resources, MountainView Regional Medical Center, Las Cruces, NM, p. A429
EGBERT, Jeff R., Interim Chief Executive Officer, Clinton Memorial Hospital, Wilmington, OH, p. A505
EGEN, Carol, R.N. Chief Nursing Officer, Rutland Regional Medical Center, Rutland, VT, p. A666
EGERTON, W. Eugene, M.D. Chief Medical Officer, University of Maryland Medical Center Midtown Campus, Baltimore, MD, p. A298
EGGEN, Caity, Senior Director Human Resources and Ancillary Services, Fairview Northland Medical Center, Princeton, MN, p. A349
EGGERS, Judy, Manager Human Resources, Alliance HealthCare System, Holly Springs, MS, p. A359
EGGLESTON, Kirk W., Commanding Officer, Winn Army Community Hospital, Hinesville, GA, p. A161
EGGLESTON, Ryan, Chief Financial Officer, Desert View Hospital, Pahrump, NV, p. A407
EGYUD, Amber, Vice President Chief Nursing Officer, Forbes Regional Hospital, Monroeville, PA, p. A545
EHASZ, James, Chief Financial Officer, Copper Queen Community Hospital, Bisbee, AZ, p. A31
EHLER, Phyllis, Director Human Resources, Avera St. Benedict Health Center, Parkston, SD, p. A575
EHLERS, Jeffrey, Chief Financial Officer, Memorial Hospital of Union County, Marysville, OH, p. A497
EHLKE, Ranae, Administrative Secretary and Coordinator Risk Management and Human Resources, Kenmare Community Hospital, Kenmare, ND, p. A479
EHLY, Ronda S., R.N. Chief Nursing Officer, Mary Lanning Healthcare, Hastings, NE, p. A396
EHN, Jerry, Chief Operating Officer, Northfield Hospital, Northfield, MN, p. A348
EHRENBERGER, David, M.D. Chief Medical Officer, Avista Adventist Hospital, Louisville, CO, p. A109
EHRET, Charlene S., FACHE, Director, James H. Quillen Veterans Affairs Medical Center, Mountain Home, TN, p. A590
EHRICH, Laurie, Chief Communications Officer, Wayne County Hospital, Corydon, IA, p. A228

EHRLICH, Frank, M.D
Chief Medical Officer, Health Alliance Hospital – Broadway Campus, Kingston, NY, p. A440
Chief Medical Officer, Health Alliance Hospital – Mary's Avenue Campus, Kingston, NY, p. A440
EHRLICH, Susan P., M.D., Chief Executive Officer, San Mateo Medical Center, San Mateo, CA, p. A93
EHTISHAM, Saad, R.N
Vice President and Chief Operating Officer, Leesburg Regional Medical Center, Leesburg, FL, p. A134
Vice President and Chief Operating Officer, The Villages Regional Hospital, The Villages, FL, p. A149
EICH, Gary, Interim Chief Financial Officer, Mendota Community Hospital, Mendota, IL, p. A196
EICHENAUER, Donald T., Chief Executive Officer, Wyoming County Community Hospital, Warsaw, NY, p. A457
EICHENBERGER, Daniel J., M.D. Medical Director, Floyd Memorial Hospital and Health Services, New Albany, IN, p. A220
EICHER, Kim D., Chief Executive Officer, St. Francis Health Care Centre, Green Springs, OH, p. A495
EICHMANN, Roger, Chief Fiscal Officer, Charles George Veterans Affairs Medical Center, Asheville, NC, p. A459
EIDAM, JoEllen, Chief Executive Officer, Adams Memorial Hospital, Decatur, IN, p. A209
EIDE, Dean, Vice President, Mayo Clinic Health System – Oakridge in Osseo, Osseo, WI, p. A713
EIDE, Tom, Chief Financial Officer, Prairie St. John's, Fargo, ND, p. A477
EIFFERT, Sarah, Director Human Resources, Mercy Rehabilitation Hospital Springfield, Springfield, MO, p. A383
EIG, Blair, M.D. Senior Vice President Medical Affairs, Holy Cross Hospital, Silver Spring, MD, p. A303
EIKE, Gail, Chief Financial Officer, Sanford Jackson Medical Center, Jackson, MN, p. A345
EILBRACHT, Hans, Chief Information Officer, Hamilton Center, Terre Haute, IN, p. A223
EILER, John M., President, St. Louis Regional Psychiatric Stabilization Center, Saint Louis, MO, p. A382
EIMERS, Katy, Human Resources Officer, Syringa Hospital and Clinics, Grangeville, ID, p. A176
EINHORN, George, Interim Chief Executive Officer, Kindred Hospital–St. Louis at Mercy, Saint Louis, MO, p. A380
EINSWEILER, Desiree, Chief Executive Officer, Palo Alto County Health System, Emmetsburg, IA, p. A230
EIPE, Joseph, M.D. Chief Medical Officer, Pacifica Hospital of the Valley, CA, p. A74
EISCHEID, Randy, Director Information Systems, St. Anthony Regional Hospital, Carroll, IA, p. A226
EISELE, Karla, M.D. Clinical Director, State Hospital North, Orofino, ID, p. A177
EISEMANN, Bradley
Administrator, Beacon Children's Hospital, Luverne, AL, p. A22
Administrator, Crenshaw Community Hospital, Luverne, AL, p. A22
EISEN, Robert A.
Vice President Human Resources, Northern California Region, Queen of the Valley Medical Center, Napa, CA, p. A79
Vice President Human Resources, Santa Rosa Memorial Hospital, Santa Rosa, CA, p. A95
EISENBERG, Barry, FACHE, Chief Operating Officer and Executive Director, Levindale Hebrew Geriatric Center and Hospital, Baltimore, MD, p. A296
EISENMAN, Edward, Chief Executive Officer, Sunnyview Rehabilitation Hospital, Schenectady, NY, p. A454
EISENMANN, Claudia Ann, Chief Executive Officer, Franklin Foundation Hospital, Franklin, LA, p. A277
EISENRING, Ric, Chief Financial Officer, St. Vincent General Hospital District, Leadville, CO, p. A108
EISENTRAGER, Steve, President, Ohio Valley Surgical Hospital, Springfield, OH, p. A502
EISENZOPH, Pete, Director Information Technology, Bay Area Medical Center, Marinette, WI, p. A708
EISMAN, Michael, M.D. Medical Director, Schuyler Hospital, Montour Falls, NY, p. A441
EISNER, Nina W., Chief Executive Officer and Managing Director, Ridge Behavioral Health System, Lexington, KY, p. A264
EISSMANN, Edward, M.D. President Medical Staff, Cascade Valley Hospital and Clinics, Arlington, WA, p. A681
EITZEN, Tamara, Chief Nursing Officer, Fairview Regional Medical Center, Fairview, OK, p. A511
EKENGREN, Francie H., M.D. Chief Medical Officer, Wesley Medical Center, Wichita, KS, p. A257
EKEREN, Douglas R., Interim Chief Executive Officer, Avera Sacred Heart Hospital, Yankton, SD, p. A578
EKLUND, Cynda, Chief Human Resources Officer, Sterling Regional MedCenter, Sterling, CO, p. A111

ENCE, Michael, Computer Specialist, Sanpete Valley Hospital, Mount Pleasant, UT, p. A660

ENCKE, Faye, Director Information Management, HEALTHSOUTH Rehabilitation Hospital of Virginia, Richmond, VA, p. A677

ENDEN, Jay, M.D. Medical Director, Southside Hospital, Bay Shore, NY, p. A433

ENDERELE, Mark A., M.D., Director, Veterans Health Care System of the Ozarks, Fayetteville, AR, p. A46

ENDERS Jr., Robert A., President, Chatham Hospital, Siler City, NC, p. A472

ENDOM, Beth W., R.N. Vice President and Chief Nursing Officer, South Central Regional Medical Center, Laurel, MS, p. A361

ENDRES, Jack R., FACHE, Administrator, East Texas Medical Center Jacksonville, Jacksonville, TX, p. A630

ENG, Bland, Chief Executive Officer, Brandon Regional Hospital, Brandon, FL, p. A124

ENG, Jeffrey, M.D. Medical Director, HEALTHSOUTH Rehabilitation Hospital of Montgomery, Montgomery, AL, p. A23

ENGBRECHT, Chad, Chief Financial Officer, Alvarado Parkway Institute Behavioral Health System, La Mesa, CA, p. A68

ENGEL, David, Chief Executive Officer, Phillips County Hospital, Phillipsburg, KS, p. A252

ENGEL, Dawn M., Chief Nursing Officer, Geary Community Hospital, Junction City, KS, p. A246

ENGEL, Marsha, Director Human Resources, Gothenburg Memorial Hospital, Gothenburg, NE, p. A396

ENGEL, Terry, Manager Information Technology, Oakes Community Hospital, Oakes, ND, p. A480

ENGELKE, Brian, Chief Financial Officer, Community Memorial Hospital, Staunton, IL, p. A203

ENGELKEN, Joseph T., Chief Executive Officer, Tuba City Regional Health Care Corporation, Tuba City, AZ, p. A40

ENGESSER, Edward, Chief Financial Officer and Chief Information Officer, Barlow Respiratory Hospital, Los Angeles, CA, p. A71

ENGFEHR, Tricia A., Chief Human Resources, Selby General Hospital, Marietta, OH, p. A497

ENGLAND, Dave, Director Human Resources, Lakeland Behavioral Health System, Springfield, MO, p. A383

ENGLAND, Donna, Director Medical Records, HEALTHSOUTH Rehabilitation Hospital of Fort Smith, Fort Smith, AR, p. A46

ENGLAND, Leslie, Chief of Staff, Natchez Regional Medical Center, Natchez, MS, p. A363

ENGLAND, Mary Ann, Chief Nurse Executive, Wilcox Memorial Hospital, Lihue, HI, p. A172

ENGLAND, Richard N., Chief Financial Officer, Palo Verde Mental Health Services, Tucson, AZ, p. A40

ENGLAND, Russell, Chief Medical Officer, Mental Health Institute, Mount Pleasant, IA, p. A235

ENGLAND, Stacy, Community Chief Nursing Officer, Middlesboro ARH Hospital, Middlesboro, KY, p. A267

ENGLAND, Teresa, R.N. Nurse Executive, Salem Veterans Affairs Medical Center, Salem, VA, p. A678

ENGLE, Dan, Chief Information Officer, Thayer County Health Services, Hebron, NE, p. A396

ENGLE, Dana E., Chief Executive Officer, Madison County Hospital, London, OH, p. A496

ENGLE, Deanne, M.D. Chief of Staff, Memorial Hospital of Converse County, Douglas, WY, p. A721

ENGLE, Heidi, Manager Information Technology, Glacial Ridge Health System, Glenwood, MN, p. A344

ENGLE, Lisa, Director Information Technology, Texoma Medical Center, Denison, TX, p. A613

ENGLE, Sharon, Director Clinical Services, Noland Hospital Birmingham, Birmingham, AL, p. A16

ENGLE, Steve, Chief Operations Officer, Mad River Community Hospital, Arcata, CA, p. A56

ENGLEHART, Jay, M.D. Medical Director, Southeast Missouri Mental Health Center, Farmington, MO, p. A371

ENGLEKING, David, M.D. Vice President Medical Affairs, CHRISTUS St. Patrick Hospital of Lake Charles, Lake Charles, LA, p. A282

ENGLERTH, LaDonna, Administrator, East Carroll Parish Hospital, Lake Providence, LA, p. A282

ENGLISH, Anne L., Director Human Resources, Chenango Memorial Hospital, Norwich, NY, p. A450

ENGLISH, Dennis, M.D. Vice President Medical Affairs, Magee–Womens Hospital of UPMC, Pittsburgh, PA, p. A551

ENGLISH, Jeff, Vice President Human Resources, St. Mary's Health Care System, Athens, GA, p. A151

ENGLISH, Julene, Director Human Resources, Kentfield Rehabilitation and Specialty Hospital, Kentfield, CA, p. A68

ENGLISH, Laurie, Senior Vice President and Chief Human Resource Officer, Excela Latrobe Area Hospital, Latrobe, PA, p. A542

ENGLISH, Mark E., M.D. Chief of Staff, McKenzie Health System, Sandusky, MI, p. A334

ENGSTROM, Chad P., Director Human Resources, Westfields Hospital, New Richmond, WI, p. A712

ENGSTROM, Frederick, M.D. Chief Medical Officer, Brattleboro Retreat, Brattleboro, VT, p. A665

ENICKS, Charles, Chief Information Officer, Georgia Regents Medical Center, Augusta, GA, p. A153

ENJADY, Rainey, Administrative Officer, Mescalero Public Health Service Indian Hospital, Mescalero, NM, p. A429

ENNEN, Philip L.
Vice President and Chief Executive Officer, Community Hospitals and Wellness Centers, Bryan, OH, p. A484
President and Chief Executive Officer, Community Hospitals and Wellness Centers–Montpelier, Montpelier, OH, p. A499

ENNIS, Virgil, Chief Information Officer, Helen Hayes Hospital, West Haverstraw, NY, p. A457

ENNS, Merle, Director Information Services, Prairie View, Newton, KS, p. A250

ENOCHS, Darren, Director Human Resources, Promise Hospital of Overland Park, Overland Park, KS, p. A252

ENOKA, Christina, Director Human Resources and Risk Management, Kahi Mohala Behavioral Health, Ewa Beach, HI, p. A170

ENRICO–SIMON, Agnes, M.D. President Medical Staff, Pleasant Valley Hospital, Point Pleasant, WV, p. A698

ENRIQUEZ, Kelly, Chief Executive Officer, Sebastian River Medical Center, Sebastian, FL, p. A145

ENRIQUEZ, Martha G., R.N. Vice President Patient Care Services and Chief Nursing Officer, Salem Hospital, Salem, OR, p. A530

ENSEY, Jeremy, Chief Executive Officer, St. Luke Hospital and Living Center, Marion, KS, p. A249

ENSLEY, Terrasina, Director Human Resources, Fannin Regional Hospital, Blue Ridge, GA, p. A154

ENSMANN, Chris, MS, Chief Executive Officer, Methodist Rehabilitation Hospital, Dallas, TX, p. A611

ENSMINGER, Jennifer, Chief Operating Officer, Pacific Hospital of Long Beach, Long Beach, CA, p. A70

ENSRUDE, Layne, Chief Financial Officer, First Care Health Center, Park River, ND, p. A480

ENTLER, Paul, D.O. Medical Director, Sparrow Specialty Hospital, Lansing, MI, p. A329

ENTWISTLE, David, Chief Executive Officer, University of Utah Health Care – Hospital and Clinics, Salt Lake City, UT, p. A663

ENTZMINGER, Julie, Manager Human Resources, Oakes Community Hospital, Oakes, ND, p. A480

EOLOFF, Eric J., Chief Operating Officer, Mercy Hospital St. Louis, Saint Louis, MO, p. A380

EPPERSON, Edward L., Chief Executive Officer, Carson Tahoe Regional Medical Center, Carson City, NV, p. A404

EPPERSON, Elysia, Director Human Resources, East Texas Medical Center Jacksonville, Jacksonville, TX, p. A630

EPPERSON, Jeff, Chief Financial Officer, Millwood Hospital, Arlington, TX, p. A598

EPPLER, Todd, FACHE, Chief Executive Officer, De Soto Regional Health System, Mansfield, LA, p. A283

EPPLEY, Doug, Director of Nursing, Bridgewell Hospital of Cincinnati, Cincinnati, OH, p. A486

EPPS, Donna, Vice President and Chief Human Resources Officer, Lawrence + Memorial Hospital, New London, CT, p. A116

EPSTEIN, Michael, M.D. Senior Vice President Medical Affairs, All Children's Hospital Johns Hopkins Medicine, Saint Petersburg, FL, p. A144

ERB, Judy, Vice President Patient Care Services and Chief Nursing Officer, Aultman Orrville Hospital, Orrville, OH, p. A500

ERDMAN, Beth, Chief Financial Officer, Meriter Hospital, Madison, WI, p. A708

ERDMAN, Donja, Chief Financial Officer, Marcus Daly Memorial Hospital, Hamilton, MT, p. A388

ERDMANN, Dorothy, Chief Executive Officer, Shawano Medical Center, Shawano, WI, p. A715

ERDMANN, Michael, M.D. Chief of Staff, Clement J. Zablocki Veterans Affairs Medical Center, Milwaukee, WI, p. A710

ERDOS, Joseph, M.D. Chief Information Officer, Veterans Affairs Connecticut Healthcare System, West Haven, CT, p. A118

EREMAN, Melissa, R.N. Chief Nursing Officer, Coleman County Medical Center, Coleman, TX, p. A606

ERGLE, Jeanine, Chief Financial Officer, Bay Pines Veterans Affairs Medical Center, Bay Pines, FL, p. A123

ERICH, Kevin R., President and Chief Executive Officer, Feather River Hospital, Paradise, CA, p. A82

ERICKSON, Brent, Administrator, Wright Patterson Medical Center, Wright-Patterson AFB, OH, p. A505

ERICKSON, Cheryl A., R.N. Director of Nursing, Memorial Community Health, Aurora, NE, p. A393

ERICKSON, Cindy, Chief Financial Officer, Sabine County Hospital, Hemphill, TX, p. A623

ERICKSON, Doug, Chief Financial Officer, Prague Community Hospital, Prague, OK, p. A518

ERICKSON, Karyn, Director Human Resources, Delta Medical Center, Memphis, TN, p. A588

ERICKSON, Nancy, Administrator Information Systems, Kossuth Regional Health Center, Algona, IA, p. A225

ERICKSON, Robert J., Chief Executive Officer, St. Francis Health Center, Topeka, KS, p. A255

ERICKSON, Ty W., President, Regina Hospital, Hastings, MN, p. A345

ERICSON, Allen
Chief Operating Officer CHD, Community Memorial Hospital, Menomonee Falls, WI, p. A709
President, St. Joseph's Hospital, West Bend, WI, p. A718

ERICSON, Bob, Chief Financial Officer, Hemphill County Hospital, Canadian, TX, p. A605

ERICSON, Kim
Vice President Finance, Fairview Lakes Health Services, Wyoming, MN, p. A354
Vice President Finance, Fairview Northland Medical Center, Princeton, MN, p. A349

ERIXON, Stephen M.
Interim Chief Executive Officer, Riverton Memorial Hospital, Riverton, WY, p. A722
Chief Executive Officer, SageWest Healthcare–Lander, Lander, WY, p. A721

ERKEN, Carole L., Human Resources Leader, Kaiser Permanente Panorama City Medical Center, CA, p. A72

ERLANDSON, Lesley
Human Resources, Carrington Health Center, Carrington, ND, p. A476
Human Resources Generalist, Mercy Hospital, Valley City, ND, p. A480

ERMANN, William, President and Chief Executive Officer, Southwest Medical Center, Liberal, KS, p. A249

ERNST, William E., Chief Executive Officer, BCA Permian Basin, Midland, TX, p. A638

ERRICHETTI, Ann, M.D.,
Chief Executive Officer, Albany Memorial Hospital, Albany, NY, p. A432
Chief Executive Officer, St. Peter's Hospital, Albany, NY, p. A432

ERTEL, David
Chief Financial Officer, Einstein Medical Center Montgomery, East Norriton, PA, p. A538
Chief Financial Officer, Einstein Medical Center Philadelphia, Philadelphia, PA, p. A548

ERUKHIMOU, Jeffrey, M.D. Medical Director, Kindred Hospital–Heritage Valley, Beaver, PA, p. A533

ERVIN, Fulton
Senior Vice President and Chief Financial Officer, McLeod Medical Center Dillon, Dillon, SC, p. A565
Chief Financial Officer, McLeod Regional Medical Center, Florence, SC, p. A566

ERVIN, Paul D., Chief Financial Officer, Valley Behavioral Health System, Barling, AR, p. A43

ERVIN, Richard, Chief Financial Officer, Tomball Regional Medical Center, Tomball, TX, p. A653

ERVING–MENGEL, Tammi, Vice President, Chief Nursing Officer, High Point Regional Health System, High Point, NC, p. A466

ERWAY, Robert, Director for Administration, Bronx Psychiatric Center, NY, p. A442

ERWIN, Connie, Manager, Samaritan Lebanon Community Hospital, Lebanon, OR, p. A526

ERWIN, Duane L., Interim Chief Executive Officer, Columbus Regional Healthcare System, Whiteville, NC, p. A474

ESCARDA, Ron, Chief Executive Officer, Fairfax Hospital, Kirkland, WA, p. A684

ESCHENBRENNER, Wade, Chief Financial Officer, Lexington Regional Health Center, Lexington, NE, p. A397

ESCUE, Richard S., Director Information Technology, Valley View Hospital, Glenwood Springs, CO, p. A106

ESFANDIARI, Seifolah, M.D. Chief of Staff, Western Medical Center–Santa Ana, Santa Ana, CA, p. A93

ESHLEMAN, James, D.O. President Medical Staff, Stephens Memorial Hospital, Norway, ME, p. A294

ESKEW, Katherine, Chief Executive Officer, Kindred Hospital–San Antonio, San Antonio, TX, p. A646

ESKILDSEN, Walter, M.D. Chief of Staff, Community Hospital, McCook, NE, p. A398

ESLINGER, Jennifer, Chief Operating Officer, Tulane Medical Center, New Orleans, LA, p. A286

ESPARZA, Caroline, Senior Vice President and Chief Nurse Executive, Simi Valley Hospital and Health Care Services, Simi Valley, CA, p. A95

ESPELAND, Darryl, D.O
Chief Nursing Officer, Dahl Memorial Healthcare Association, Ekalaka, MT, p. A387
Chief Medical Staff, Fallon Medical Complex, Baker, MT, p. A385

ESPINA, Francisco, Director Finance, Hospital Pavia–Santurce, San Juan, PR, p. A728

ESPINOZA, Ernest, Interim Chief Operating Officer, LAC–Olive View–UCLA Medical Center, CA, p. A73

ESPINOZA, John, Chief Human Resources Officer, University Medical Center, Las Vegas, NV, p. A407

ESPINOZA, Judy, Chief Human Resources Officer, Via Christi Hospital on St. Francis, Wichita, KS, p. A257

ESPITIA, Judy, Chief Financial Officer, North Runnels Hospital, Winters, TX, p. A658

ESPOSITO, Jr., Anthony M., CPA Vice President Chief Financial Officer, Hackensack University Medical Center Mountainside, Montclair, NJ, p. A418

ESPOSITO, Mary H., Assistant Executive Director, Devereux Georgia Treatment Network, Kennesaw, GA, p. A161

ESPOSITO, Pamela, Director Administration, Buffalo Psychiatric Center, Buffalo, NY, p. A434

ESPY, Christine, Director Human Resources, Mid–Columbia Medical Center, The Dalles, OR, p. A530

ESROCK, Brett A., President and Chief Executive Officer, Providence Health Center, Waco, TX, p. A656

ESSELMAN, Charlotte, Director Finance, Ministry Saint Clare's Hospital, Weston, WI, p. A718

ESSEX, Jeshahnton, Vice President of Administration, Riddle Hospital, Media, PA, p. A545

ESSEX, Thomas, M.D. Chief of Staff, Grady Memorial Hospital, Chickasha, OK, p. A509

ESTAY, Mike, Chief Financial Officer, Hood Memorial Hospital, Amite, LA, p. A272

ESTES, Barbara, M.D. Chief of Staff, Calvert Memorial Hospital, Prince Frederick, MD, p. A302

ESTES, Benton D., Materials Management, King's Daughters Hospital, Yazoo City, MS, p. A366

ESTES, Melinda, M.D., President and Chief Executive Officer, Saint Luke's Health System, Kansas City, MO, p. B117

ESTES, Michael, Director Human Resources, University Hospital, Jackson, MS, p. A360

ESTES, Stephen A., Chief Executive Officer, Rockcastle Regional Hospital and Respiratory Care Center, Mount Vernon, KY, p. A268

ESTEVEZ, Aurora, M.D. Chief Medical Officer, Texas Health Presbyterian Hospital Dallas, Dallas, TX, p. A612

ESTRADA, Luis, Director Multifacility Information Systems, North Shore Medical Center, Miami, FL, p. A137

ESTRELLA, Mario B., R.N. Chief Nursing Officer, Nacogdoches Medical Center, Nacogdoches, TX, p. A639

ESTREM, Kristy, FACHE, President, Mercy Hospital Berryville, Berryville, AR, p. A43

ETCHASON, Barbara, HR Manager, West Gables Rehabilitation Hospital, Miami, FL, p. A138

ETHERIDGE, Darold, Vice President and Chief Financial Officer, WellStar Cobb Hospital, Austell, GA, p. A154

ETHERINGTON, Betty, Chief Financial Officer, Humboldt County Memorial Hospital, Humboldt, IA, p. A232

ETHRIDGE, Sandy, Interim Chief Operating Officer, Baptist Medical Center, San Antonio, TX, p. A646

ETTESTAD, Donita, R.N. Chief Nursing Officer, Rainy Lake Medical Center, International Falls, MN, p. A345

EUBANKS, Bill, Senior Vice President and Chief Information Officer, University Medical Center, Lubbock, TX, p. A635

EUBANKS, Susan, Chief Nursing Officer, Page Hospital, Page, AZ, p. A35

EULER, Barbara, Director Human Resources, Regional Hospital of Jackson, Jackson, TN, p. A584

EULIARTE, Mary Ann, R.N
Chief Operating Officer, Memorial Hermann Rehabilitation Hospital – Katy, Katy, TX, p. A630
Chief Operating Officer and Chief Nursing Officer, TIRR Memorial Hermann, Houston, TX, p. A627

EURE, Thomas, Vice President Administration, Blue Ridge Healthcare Hospitals, Morganton, NC, p. A469

EUSEBIO, Barbara, R.N. Vice President, Chief Nurse Executive, St. Mary's Medical Center, San Francisco, CA, p. A91

EUSTACE, Scott, Director Health Information Technology, Trenton Psychiatric Hospital, Trenton, NJ, p. A424

EVANGELISTA, Larry, Supervisor Information Technology, Clay County Memorial Hospital, Henrietta, TX, p. A623

EVANOFF, John, M.D. Vice President Medical Affairs, ProMedica Flower Hospital, Sylvania, OH, p. A502

EVANS, Ann, Chief Nursing Officer, HEALTHSOUTH Huntington Rehabilitation Hospital, Huntington, WV, p. A696

EVANS, Arthur D., Assistant Administrator, Bryan W. Whitfield Memorial Hospital, Demopolis, AL, p. A19

EVANS, Bradford L., Director Human Resources, Regional West Medical Center, Scottsbluff, NE, p. A402

EVANS, Brian, M.D. Chief of Medicine, Sierra Nevada Memorial Hospital, Grass Valley, CA, p. A66

EVANS, Brian G., FACHE, Chief Executive Officer, Clarke County Hospital, Osceola, IA, p. A236

EVANS, Chris, Vice President Operations, CHI Health Bergan Mercy, Omaha, NE, p. A399

EVANS, Cindy, R.N. Chief Nursing Officer, Legacy Good Samaritan Hospital and Medical Center, Portland, OR, p. A528

EVANS Jr., Daniel F., JD, President and Chief Executive Officer, Indiana University Health, Indianapolis, IN, p. B75

EVANS, Dawn, Manager Information Technology, Audrain Medical Center, Mexico, MO, p. A376

EVANS, Dwight, M.D. Chief of Staff, Veterans Affairs Loma Linda Healthcare System, Loma Linda, CA, p. A70

EVANS, Eric, Chief Operating Officer, Woman's Hospital of Texas, Houston, TX, p. A628

EVANS, George, Vice President and Chief Information Officer, Candler Hospital, Savannah, GA, p. A166

EVANS, Heath, Assistant Chief Executive Officer, North Okaloosa Medical Center, Crestview, FL, p. A126

EVANS, J. Eric
Chief Executive Officer, Providence Memorial Hospital, El Paso, TX, p. A616
Chief Executive Officer, Sierra Medical Center, El Paso, TX, p. A616

EVANS, Janice, Chief Financial Officer, John J. Madden Mental Health Center, Hines, IL, p. A192

EVANS, Jeff W., Vice President Information and Technology, Hannibal Regional Hospital, Hannibal, MO, p. A372

EVANS, Jeremy, Vice President Operations, Kootenai Health, Coeur D'Alene, ID, p. A175

EVANS, John, M.D. Chief Medical Officer, Twin Lakes Regional Medical Center, Leitchfield, KY, p. A264

EVANS, Kelley, Chief Executive Officer, Beartooth Billings Clinic, Red Lodge, MT, p. A390

EVANS, Kirstie, Chief Financial Officer, Covington County Hospital, Collins, MS, p. A357

EVANS, Lorrie, Director Human Resources, Laurel Oaks Behavioral Health Center, Dothan, AL, p. A19

EVANS, Manuel J., Senior Vice President Finance and Chief Financial Officer, Holy Spirit Hospital, Camp Hill, PA, p. A535

EVANS, Melinda S.
Vice President Finance, Saint Joseph East, Lexington, KY, p. A264
Vice President Finance, Saint Joseph Hospital, Lexington, KY, p. A264

EVANS, Michael C., Chief Executive Officer and Deputy Director of Finance and Administration, Santa Barbara County Psychiatric Health Facility, Santa Barbara, CA, p. A94

EVANS, Michael K., Chief Executive Officer, Park Royal Hospital, Fort Myers, FL, p. A129

EVANS, Mike, MS, President, Texas Health Presbyterian Hospital Plano, Plano, TX, p. A643

EVANS, Nina, R.N. Vice President and Chief Nursing Officer, St. Mary's Health Care System, Athens, GA, p. A151

EVANS, Patsy, Chief Financial Officer, Citizens Medical Center, Colby, KS, p. A242

EVANS, Paulette, MSN, Interim President and Chief Executive Officer, St. Joseph's Hospital, Breese, IL, p. A182

EVANS, Robert B., Administrator and Chief Executive Officer, East Texas Medical Center Tyler, Tyler, TX, p. A654

EVANS, Rod, Chief Information Officer, Community HealthCare System, Onaga, KS, p. A251

EVANS, S. Lagina, R.N
Assistant Chief Nursing Officer, Jenkins County Hospital, Millen, GA, p. A163
Assistant Chief Nursing Officer, Screven County Hospital, Sylvania, GA, p. A167

EVANS, Sam, Chief Human Resources Management, G.V. (Sonny) Montgomery Veterans Affairs Medical Center, Jackson, MS, p. A360

EVANS, Scott, PharmD,
Chief Executive Officer, Keck Hospital of USC, Los Angeles, CA, p. A72
Chief Executive Officer, University of Southern California–Norris Cancer Hospital, Los Angeles, CA, p. A75

EVANS, Stanley, M.D. Chief of Staff, Denton Regional Medical Center, Denton, TX, p. A613

EVANS, Susan, Chief Nursing Officer, HEALTHSOUTH Nittany Valley Rehabilitation Hospital, Pleasant Gap, PA, p. A552

EVANS, Tim, Assistant Financial Director, Devereux Children's Behavioral Health Center, Malvern, PA, p. A544

EVANS, Timothy, Vice President and Chief Financial Officer, Self Regional Healthcare, Greenwood, SC, p. A567

EVANS–HARRISON, Martina, R.N. Chief Nurse Executive, Methodist Hospital of Sacramento, Sacramento, CA, p. A87

EVARO, Randall J., Chief Executive Officer, Vibra Hospital of Boise, Meridian, ID, p. A177

EVE, John R., Vice President Human Resources, Wilson Memorial Hospital, Sidney, OH, p. A502

EVELIUS, Karen, Director Human Resources, MedStar Harbor Hospital, Baltimore, MD, p. A297

EVELYN, David M., M.D. Vice President Medical Affairs, Cayuga Medical Center at Ithaca, Ithaca, NY, p. A439

EVENS, James, Executive Director Human Resources, Cole Memorial, Coudersport, PA, p. A536

EVENS, Richard R., Chief Executive Officer, HEALTHSOUTH Northern Kentucky Rehabilitation Hospital, Edgewood, KY, p. A260

EVENS, Tamara, Director Human Resources, Moses Ludington Hospital, Ticonderoga, NY, p. A456

EVENSON, Carolyn, R.N. Chief Nursing Officer, Gothenburg Memorial Hospital, Gothenburg, NE, p. A396

EVENSON, Margie, Manager Human Resources, Osceola Medical Center, Osceola, WI, p. A712

EVERDING, Dawn, Chief Financial Officer, Community Memorial Hospital, Sumner, IA, p. A238

EVERETT, John, Chief Financial Officer, Cogdell Memorial Hospital, Snyder, TX, p. A649

EVERETT, Michael, Chief Executive Officer, Scott Memorial Hospital, Scottsburg, IN, p. A222

EVERETT, Neil, Vice President Human Resources, Robinson Memorial Hospital, Ravenna, OH, p. A501

EVERHART, Carole, Administrative Director Human Resources, Downey Regional Medical Center, Downey, CA, p. A61

EVERHART, Martin S., Senior Vice President Human Resources, Robert Wood Johnson University Hospital, New Brunswick, NJ, p. A419

EVERLY, Nanette, Manager Human Resources and Administrative Assistant, Jefferson County Health Center, Fairfield, IA, p. A230

EVERSOLE, Matt, Regional Vice President Information Services, Mercy Health – Anderson Hospital, Cincinnati, OH, p. A487

EVERT, Barbara, M.D
Vice President Medical Affairs, OhioHealth Dublin Methodist Hospital, Dublin, OH, p. A493
Vice President Medical Affairs, OhioHealth Grady Memorial Hospital, Delaware, OH, p. A492

EVINS, Starling C., M.D. Chief of Staff, Williamson Medical Center, Franklin, TN, p. A583

EVOLGA, Nancy K., Executive Director Human Resources, Bert Fish Medical Center, New Smyrna Beach, FL, p. A139

EWALD, Ronald, Chief Financial Officer, Inova Fairfax Hospital, Falls Church, VA, p. A670

EWALD, Sandra
Vice President Finance, Aurora Medical Center – Manitowoc County, Two Rivers, WI, p. A716
Vice President Finance, Aurora Medical Center of Oshkosh, Oshkosh, WI, p. A712

EWELL, Dorene L., Director Human Relations Education, Harrisburg Medical Center, Harrisburg, IL, p. A191

EWELL, Sandy, Chief Nursing Officer, Timpanogos Regional Hospital, Orem, UT, p. A661

EWING, Brenda, Chief Nursing Officer, Sandhills Regional Medical Center, Hamlet, NC, p. A466

EWING, Chandler, Chief Executive Officer, Select Specialty Hospital–Jackson, Jackson, MS, p. A360

EWING, Corey, Chief Executive Officer, DeKalb Regional Medical Center, Fort Payne, AL, p. A20

EWING, Thomas
Director Information Technology, Sentara CarePlex Hospital, Hampton, VA, p. A672
Director Information Technology, Sentara Northern Virginia Medical Center, Woodbridge, VA, p. A680

EXLINE, Michael
Chief Financial Officer, Carrus Rehabilitation Hospital, Sherman, TX, p. A649
Chief Financial Officer, Carrus Specialty Hospital, Sherman, TX, p. A649

EYE, Jeffrey, R.N. Chief Nursing Officer, Saint Luke's North Hospital – Barry Road, Kansas City, MO, p. A374

EYER, Ron, Manager Information Services, Aspirus Grand View Hospital, Ironwood, MI, p. A327

EYLER, James W., FACHE, Chief Executive Officer, Coliseum Center for Behavioral Health, Macon, GA, p. A162

EYLER, Sandra, M
    Chief Nursing Officer, Sheltering Arms Hospital South, Midlothian, VA, p. A674
    Chief Nursing Officer, Sheltering Arms Rehabilitation Hospital, Mechanicsville, VA, p. A674

F

FAAS, Michael D., President and Chief Executive Officer, Metro Health Hospital, Wyoming, MI, p. A337
FAAS, Nancy, R.N. Chief Nursing Officer, Reliant Rehabilitation Hospital Dallas, Dallas, TX, p. A611
FABER, Chris, Human Resources Analyst, ValleyCare Medical Center, Pleasanton, CA, p. A83
FABER, Tammy, Director Human Resources, Hegg Memorial Health Center Avera, Rock Valley, IA, p. A237
FABIAN, Alan J., Chief Executive Officer, LewisGale Hospital Montgomery, Blacksburg, VA, p. A668
FABIAN, Roxanne, Director of Nursing–Acute Care, LifeCare Medical Center, Roseau, MN, p. A350
FABIANKE, Raynard, M.D. Chief of Staff, Red Bay Hospital, Red Bay, AL, p. A25
FABIANO, Tom, Director Human Resources, Mount Auburn Hospital, Cambridge, MA, p. A309
FABIN, Peggy, Director Human Resources, Phillips County Hospital, Phillipsburg, KS, p. A252
FABRICK, Peter, Vice President Clinical Operations, Mountain View Hospital, Idaho Falls, ID, p. A176
FABRY, Joseph, D.O. Chief of Staff, Sutter Maternity and Surgery Center of Santa Cruz, Santa Cruz, CA, p. A94
FACKRELL, Sherlyn, Finance Controller, Grover C. Dils Medical Center, Caliente, NV, p. A404
FACTEAU, Lorna M., Ph.D. Chief Nursing Officer, University of Virginia Medical Center, Charlottesville, VA, p. A669
FACTEAU, Patrick M., Chief Financial Officer, Auburn Community Hospital, Auburn, NY, p. A433
FADALE, Sean, President and Chief Executive Officer, Community Memorial Hospital, Hamilton, NY, p. A438
FADLER, Jeannie, R.N. Vice President Patient Care Services, Saint Francis Medical Center, Cape Girardeau, MO, p. A368
FAEHNLE, Steve, M.D. Vice President Medical Affairs, Hendrick Health System, Abilene, TX, p. A595
FAGAN, Erin, Manager Human Resources, George Washington University Hospital, Washington, DC, p. A121
FAGAN, Mary, MSN Chief Nursing Officer, Rady Children's Hospital – San Diego, San Diego, CA, p. A89
FAGAN, Michael, Chief Financial Officer, Huntington Hospital, Huntington, NY, p. A439
FAGBONGBE, Eniola, M.D. Chief Medical Staff, Grove Hill Memorial Hospital, Grove Hill, AL, p. A21
FAGERBERG, Lesley, Vice President Fiscal Services, Heart of the Rockies Regional Medical Center, Salida, CO, p. A111
FAGERSTROM, Joel, Executive Vice President and Chief Operating Officer, St. Luke's Hospital – Miners Campus, Coaldale, PA, p. A536
FAGG, Cindy, Fiscal Officer, Battle Mountain General Hospital, Battle Mountain, NV, p. A404
FAGIN, Beth, Manager Information Systems, St. Vincent's Medical Center Southside, Jacksonville, FL, p. A132
FAGO, Todd, M.D. Chief of Staff, York General Hospital, York, NE, p. A403
FAHD II, Charles F., Chief Executive Officer, Massena Memorial Hospital, Massena, NY, p. A441
FAHEY, Dana, Manager Management Information Systems, Santa Barbara County Psychiatric Health Facility, Santa Barbara, CA, p. A94
FAHEY, Linda L., R.N. Vice President and Chief Nurse Executive, Decatur Memorial Hospital, Decatur, IL, p. A188
FAHEY, Stephen P., Executive Director, Sierra Tucson, Tucson, AZ, p. A40
FAHEY, Walter, Chief Information Officer, Maimonides Medical Center,, NY, p. A445
FAHMY, Raef, DPM Chief Medical Officer and Medical Information Officer, Catholic Medical Center, Manchester, NH, p. A411
FAHRLANDER, Jason, FACHE,
    President, Community Heart and Vascular Hospital, Indianapolis, IN, p. A213
    President, Community Hospital North, Indianapolis, IN, p. A213
FAILE, J. Gene, Chief Executive Officer and President, Wilkes Regional Medical Center, North Wilkesboro, NC, p. A470
FAILLA, Richard, Chief Executive Officer, Montevista Hospital, Las Vegas, NV, p. A406
FAIN, Nona, Ph.D. Director of Nursing, Belmont Center for Comprehensive Treatment, Philadelphia, PA, p. A547

FAIRBANKS, Bruce, Vice President and Chief Financial Officer, Southeast Hospital, Cape Girardeau, MO, p. A369
FAIRCHILD, David, M.D. Chief Medical Officer, Tufts Medical Center, Boston, MA, p. A307
FAIRCHILD, Kathy, Director Site Information Systems, Advocate Condell Medical Center, Libertyville, IL, p. A194
FAIRCHILDS, Constance, R.N. Vice President Patient Care Services, Emanuel Medical Center, Turlock, CA, p. A98
FAIRCLOTH, Gerald, Chief Operating Officer, Poplar Bluff Regional Medical Center, Poplar Bluff, MO, p. A378
FAIRCLOTH, Karen, Chief Financial Officer, Memorial Hospital and Manor, Bainbridge, GA, p. A154
FAIRFAX, Tom, Director Information Systems, Bothwell Regional Health Center, Sedalia, MO, p. A382
FAIRFAX, Walter, M.D. Chief Medical Officer, Kootenai Health, Coeur D'Alene, ID, p. A175
FAIRLEY, Dawn Ann, M.D. Chief of Staff, Putnam County Memorial Hospital, Unionville, MO, p. A384
FALBO, Susan, Vice President Human Resources, Wheeling Hospital, Wheeling, WV, p. A700
FALCON, Hugo, M.D. Director Medical Services, Piedmont Geriatric Hospital, Burkeville, VA, p. A669
FALCONE, Robert E., M.D. Chief of Staff, Cincinnati Veterans Affairs Medical Center, Cincinnati, OH, p. A486
FALIVENA, Richard, D.O. Vice President and Chief Medical Officer, Saratoga Hospital, Saratoga Springs, NY, p. A454
FALK, Chelsie, Chief Nursing Officer, Sanford Wheaton Medical Center, Wheaton, MN, p. A354
FALKENBERRY, Jody, Director Information Systems, Monroe County Hospital, Monroeville, AL, p. A23
FALL, J. Mark, Chief Executive Officer, CareLink of Jackson, Jackson, MI, p. A328
FALLEN, Barbara, FACHE, Director, Veterans Affairs Loma Linda Healthcare System, Loma Linda, CA, p. A70
FALLIS, Susan, Chief Nursing Officer, Buffalo Psychiatric Center, Buffalo, NY, p. A434
FALLON, Jeanne M.
    Senior Vice President and Chief Information Officer, Cape Cod Hospital, Hyannis, MA, p. A311
    Chief Information Officer, Falmouth Hospital, Falmouth, MA, p. A310
FALLON, L. J., Executive Vice President, Chief Legal and Human Resources Officer, Carle Foundation Hospital, Urbana, IL, p. A204
FALSETTI, Domonic F., M.D. Chief of Staff and Medical Director, Mount St. Mary's Hospital and Health Center, Lewiston, NY, p. A440
FALSEY, Fran, Senior Vice President Site Operations, Kent County Memorial Hospital, Warwick, RI, p. A561
FALTERMAN, Jr., James B., M.D. Medical Director, University Hospital and Clinics, Lafayette, LA, p. A282
FAMAKINWA, Abiodun, M.D. Acting Clinical Director, West Central Georgia Regional Hospital, Columbus, GA, p. A156
FAMMARTINO, Gary, Administrator, St. Vincent Fishers Hospital, Fishers, IN, p. A210
FANALE, James E., M.D. Senior Vice President System Development, Beth Israel Deaconess Hospital Plymouth, Plymouth, MA, p. A314
FANCHER, Diana, Chief Nursing Officer, University Medical Center of El Paso, El Paso, TX, p. A616
FANNIN, Allyson, Director Human Resources, LaSalle General Hospital, Jena, LA, p. A279
FANNIN, Pam, Coordinator Human Resources, LifeCare Hospital of Dayton, Miamisburg, OH, p. A498
FANNING, Linda T., R.N. Chief Nursing Officer, Mercy Hospital Oklahoma City, Oklahoma City, OK, p. A515
FANNING, Melinda, Chief Financial Officer and Controller, HEALTHSOUTH Southern Hills Rehabilitation Hospital, Princeton, WV, p. A698
FANNING, Teresa E., Director of Patient Care, Avera Hand County Memorial Hospital, Miller, SD, p. A574
FANNON, Susan, Chief Nursing Officer, Indian Path Medical Center, Kingsport, TN, p. A585
FANSELAU, Michael G., District Director Human Resources, Vibra Hospital of Sacramento, Folsom, CA, p. A63
FANTANO, Gene, Chief Financial Officer, Aurora San Diego Hospital, San Diego, CA, p. A89
FARAH, Tony, M.D. President Medical Staff, Allegheny General Hospital, Pittsburgh, PA, p. A550
FARBER, Bobbi, M.D. Chief Medical Officer, St. Francis Hospital, Columbus, GA, p. A156
FARBER, Nancy D., Chief Executive Officer, Washington Hospital Healthcare System, Fremont, CA, p. A64
FARELL, Clay, Chief Operating Officer, Nacogdoches Medical Center, Nacogdoches, TX, p. A639
FARGASON, Crayton A., M.D. Medical Director, The Children's Hospital of Alabama, Birmingham, AL, p. A17
FARGUSON, Jack, Director Information Technology, Red River Regional Hospital, Bonham, TX, p. A603

FARIA, Karen, Executive Director, Sonoma Developmental Center, Eldridge, CA, p. A62
FARIA, Mary, FACHE, Administrator, Seton Southwest Hospital, Austin, TX, p. A600
FARICY, Patrick O., M.D. Chief Medical Officer, Memorial Hospital, Colorado Springs, CO, p. A103
FARINA, Albert M.
    Chief Financial Officer, Montefiore Mount Vernon, Mount Vernon, NY, p. A442
    Senior Vice President and Chief Financial Officer, Montefiore New Rochelle, New Rochelle, NY, p. A442
FARINA, Jonathan, Chief Information Officer, Brattleboro Memorial Hospital, Brattleboro, VT, p. A665
FARISH, Audra, Vice President Human Resources, Emory Saint Joseph's Hospital of Atlanta, Atlanta, GA, p. A152
FARKAS, Laura, Director Human Resources, Fairview Hospital, Great Barrington, MA, p. A310
FARLEY, H. Fred, FACHE,
    President and Chief Operating Officer, Arnot Ogden Medical Center, Elmira, NY, p. A437
    President and Chief Operating Officer, St. Joseph's Hospital, Elmira, NY, p. A437
FARMER, Carlos, R.N. Director Clinical Operations, RMC Jacksonville, Jacksonville, AL, p. A22
FARMER, Kathleen, Assistant Administrator Finance and Chief Financial Officer, El Centro Regional Medical Center, El Centro, CA, p. A62
FARMER, Pat, Coordinator Human Resources and Safety Officer, Institute for Orthopaedic Surgery, Lima, OH, p. A496
FARMER, William, M.D. Chief of Staff, Evergreen Medical Center, Evergreen, AL, p. A19
FARNHAM, Diane, Acting Director Human Resources, Lallie Kemp Medical Center, Independence, LA, p. A279
FARNHAM, Krista, Chief Operating Officer, Providence Portland Medical Center, Portland, OR, p. A528
FARO, Joan, M.D. Chief Medical Officer, John T. Mather Memorial Hospital, Port Jefferson, NY, p. A452
FARQUHAR, Steven, M.D. President Medical Staff, Beauregard Memorial Hospital, De Ridder, LA, p. A276
FARR, Lorraine, Manager Human Resources, Georgia Regional Hospital at Atlanta, Decatur, GA, p. A158
FARR, Ronald, Chief Financial Officer, Jewish Hospital, Louisville, KY, p. A265
FARR, William L., M.D. Chief Medical Officer, University Hospital, Augusta, GA, p. A154
FARRAGE, Jim, M.D. Medical Director, Southern Kentucky Rehabilitation Hospital, Bowling Green, KY, p. A259
FARRAUTO, Joseph, Director Human Resources, Eastern Niagara Hospital, Lockport, NY, p. A440
FARRELL, Amy, M.D. Chief of Staff, Flaget Memorial Hospital, Bardstown, KY, p. A258
FARRELL, Brenda, Vice President Finance, Brookhaven Memorial Hospital Medical Center, Patchogue, NY, p. A451
FARRELL, Coleen M., Vice President Human Resources, Mid Coast Hospital, Brunswick, ME, p. A292
FARRELL, Darin, Chief Executive Officer, Arbuckle Memorial Hospital, Sulphur, OK, p. A519
FARRELL, George, M.D. Chief of Staff, Wythe County Community Hospital, Wytheville, VA, p. A680
FARRELL, Katie, Chief Operating Officer, Abington Health Lansdale Hospital, Lansdale, PA, p. A542
FARRELL, Roy, M.D. Chief Medical Officer, Carondelet Holy Cross Hospital, Nogales, AZ, p. A34
FARRELL, Steven E., M.D. Chief Medical Officer, Forrest General Hospital, Hattiesburg, MS, p. A359
FARRELL, Terence, Vice President and Administrator, Herrin Hospital, Herrin, IL, p. A192
FARRELL, Teresa, Chief Human Resources Officer, Nacogdoches Medical Center, Nacogdoches, TX, p. A639
FARRELL, Timothy, Executive Director, St. Lawrence Psychiatric Center, Ogdensburg, NY, p. A450
FARRELLY, Irene, Vice President and Chief Information Officer, Brooklyn Hospital Center,, NY, p. A443
FARRIS, Bain J., President and Chief Executive Officer, Exempla Saint Joseph Hospital, Denver, CO, p. A104
FARRIS, James R., FACHE, Chief Executive Officer, Union County Hospital, Anna, IL, p. A180
FARRIS, Jason, Chief Nursing Officer, Specialty Hospital of Midwest City, Midwest City, OK, p. A513
FARROW, Diane, Manager Information Technology and Systems, Willamette Valley Medical Center, McMinnville, OR, p. A526
FARSHAO, Nosratian, M.D. Chief Medical Staff, Memorial Hospital of Gardena, Gardena, CA, p. A65
FARWELL, Brenda
    Director Human Resources, Providence Medical Center, Kansas City, KS, p. A247
    Director Human Resources, Saint John Hospital, Leavenworth, KS, p. A248
FASANO, Philip, Chief Information Officer, Kaiser Permanente Sacramento Medical Center, Sacramento, CA, p. A87

FASTHORSE, Lena, Supervisor Human Resource, U. S. Public Health Service Indian Hospital–Whiteriver, Whiteriver, AZ, p. A41

FATCH, Casey, Chief Operating Officer, Tri–City Medical Center, Oceanside, CA, p. A81

FATTIG, Marty, Chief Executive Officer, Nemaha County Hospital, Auburn, NE, p. A393

FATULA, Suzette
Chief Financial Officer, Avoyelles Hospital, Marksville, LA, p. A283
Chief Financial Officer and Compliance Officer, Oakdale Community Hospital, Oakdale, LA, p. A286

FAUBION, Matthew, M.D. Clinical Director, Kerrville State Hospital, Kerrville, TX, p. A631

FAUCHER, Kimberly, M.D. Chief Medical Officer, Frank R. Howard Memorial Hospital, Willits, CA, p. A100

FAUCHEUX, Lisa, Director Human Resources, St. James Parish Hospital, Lutcher, LA, p. A283

FAUGHT, Charles J., Chief Financial Officer, Burnett Medical Center, Grantsburg, WI, p. A705

FAUL, Jennifer, Chief Operating Officer, Prairie St. John's, Fargo, ND, p. A477

FAULIS, Karen, Chief Operating Officer, Palmdale Regional Medical Center, Palmdale, CA, p. A82

FAULK, Gordon, Administrator, Elmore Community Hospital, Wetumpka, AL, p. A26

FAULKNER, Cheryl, Chief Nursing Officer, McKenzie County Healthcare System, Watford City, ND, p. A480

FAULKNER, Cindy, Chief Nursing Officer, Maria Parham Medical Center, Henderson, NC, p. A466

FAULKNER, David M., Chief Executive Officer, Fleming County Hospital, Flemingsburg, KY, p. A260

FAULKNER, Kristi, Director Human Resources, United Regional Health Care System, Wichita Falls, TX, p. A658

FAULKNER, Laura, Chief Human Resource Management Service, Veterans Affairs Medical Center–Lexington, Lexington, KY, p. A265

FAULKNER, Mark T., President, Baptist Health Care Corporation, Pensacola, FL, p. B20

FAULKNER, Sharon, Chief Nursing Officer, AMG Specialty Hospital–Denham Springs, Denham Springs, LA, p. A277

FAUS, Doug, FACHE, Chief Executive Officer, Ivinson Memorial Hospital, Laramie, WY, p. A722

FAUST, Bill D., Administrator, Floyd County Medical Center, Charles City, IA, p. A227

FAUST, Bonnie H., R.N. Vice President Chief Nursing Officer, Caromont Regional Medical Center, Gastonia, NC, p. A465

FAVALE, Maria, FACHE Associate Director, Northport Veterans Affairs Medical Center, Northport, NY, p. A449

FAVATA, Valerie, R.N. Chief Nursing Officer, Oswego Hospital, Oswego, NY, p. A451

FAVRET, John M., Director, Eastern State Hospital, Williamsburg, VA, p. A680

FAWLEY, Kimberly, Chief Nursing Officer, Florence Hospital at Anthem, Florence, AZ, p. A32

FAWNS, Bill, Interim Manager Information Systems, Kern Medical Center, Bakersfield, CA, p. A57

FAY, Brian, Director Information Systems, Sidney Health Center, Sidney, MT, p. A391

FAYEN, Edward J., Associate Administrator Operations and Support, Washington Hospital Healthcare System, Fremont, CA, p. A64

FAYRE, Gail, M.D. Medical Director, Anna Jaques Hospital, Newburyport, MA, p. A312

FAZIO, Charles, Chief Health Officer and Medical Director Health Plan, Regions Hospital, Saint Paul, MN, p. A351

FEAK, Christina, Chief Information Officer, Onslow Memorial Hospital, Jacksonville, NC, p. A467

FEAR, Frank, Vice President Ancillary Services and Chief Information Officer, Memorial Healthcare, Owosso, MI, p. A331

FEASEL, Jeff, Chief Executive Officer, Halifax Health Medical Center of Daytona Beach, Daytona Beach, FL, p. A127

FEATHER, Leroy P., Vice President Finance, Community Hospitals and Wellness Centers, Bryan, OH, p. A484

FEAZELL, Kayla, Chief Executive Officer, HEALTHSOUTH Rehabilitation of Gadsden, Gadsden, AL, p. A20

FEBRY, Ricardo, M.D. Medical Director, St. Theresa Specialty Hospital, Kenner, LA, p. A280

FEBUS, Steven, Chief Financial Officer, Pullman Regional Hospital, Pullman, WA, p. A687

FEDELE, Jerry J., President and Chief Executive Officer, Boca Raton Regional Hospital, Boca Raton, FL, p. A124

FEDER, Diane, MSN Senior Vice President and Chief Operating Officer, Witham Memorial Hospital, Lebanon, IN, p. A217

FEDERICO, Skip, Director Information Systems, Fairway Medical Center, Covington, LA, p. A276

FEDERINKO, David, Chief Information Officer, Allegan General Hospital, Allegan, MI, p. A318

FEDERSPIEL, John C., President and Chief Executive Officer, Hudson Valley Hospital Center, Cortlandt Manor, NY, p. A436

FEDORA, Deborah, Director Human Resources, Paoli Hospital, Paoli, PA, p. A547

FEE, Jeff, Chief Executive Officer, St. Patrick Hospital, Missoula, MT, p. A390

FEEMAN, Kimberly, Senior Vice President and Chief Operating Officer, The Good Samaritan Hospital, Lebanon, PA, p. A543

FEENEY, Daniel, M.D. Medical Director, Brentwood Hospital, Shreveport, LA, p. A288

FEENEY, John, President and Chief Executive Officer, Berlin Memorial Hospital, Berlin, WI, p. A702

FEENEY, Sheri, Chief Financial Officer, Providence Regional Medical Center Everett, Everett, WA, p. A683

FEESS, David, President and Chief Executive Officer, Liberty Hospital, Liberty, MO, p. A376

FEGAN, Claudia, M.D. Chief Medical Officer, John H. Stroger Jr. Hospital of Cook County, Chicago, IL, p. A184

FEGAN, Theresa, R.N. Clinical Officer, Tahoe Pacific Hospitals, Reno, NV, p. A408

FEGHALI, Georges, M.D
Senior Vice President Quality and Chief Medical Officer, Bethesda North Hospital, Cincinnati, OH, p. A486
Senior Vice President Quality and Chief Medical Officer, Good Samaritan Hospital, Cincinnati, OH, p. A487

FEHLINGS, Michele, Controller, Hermann Area District Hospital, Hermann, MO, p. A372

FEHR, Tracy, Executive Assistant and Director Human Resources, Red River Hospital, Wichita Falls, TX, p. A657

FEHRING, Marcia, Chief Financial Officer, Horn Memorial Hospital, Ida Grove, IA, p. A232

FEIDT, Leslie, Chief Information Officer, Erie County Medical Center, Buffalo, NY, p. A434

FEIKE, Jeffrey, President and Chief Administrative Officer, Fort Loudoun Medical Center, Lenoir City, TN, p. A586

FEIL, Julie, Accountant, Cavalier County Memorial Hospital, Langdon, ND, p. A479

FEILER, Kenneth H., Chief Executive Officer, Rose Medical Center, Denver, CO, p. A105

FEILNER, Margaret, Director Information Services, SSM St. Joseph Health Center, Saint Charles, MO, p. A379

FEINBERG, Daniel, M.D. Chief Medical Officer, Pennsylvania Hospital, Philadelphia, PA, p. A549

FEINBERG, David, M.D., Chief Executive Officer, Ronald Reagan University of California Los Angeles Medical Center, Los Angeles, CA, p. A74

FEINBERG, Jason, M.D
Vice President Medical Affairs and Chief Medical Officer, Geneva General Hospital, Geneva, NY, p. A437
Vice President Medical Affairs and Chief Medical Officer, Soldiers and Sailors Memorial Hospital of Yates County, Penn Yan, NY, p. A451

FEINER, David, M.D. Chief Staff, Calais Regional Hospital, Calais, ME, p. A292

FEIRN, Greg, CPA, President and Chief Executive Officer, LCMC Health, New Orleans, LA, p. B83

FEIST, Patricia, Manager Human Resources, Crook County Medical Services District, Sundance, WY, p. A723

FEISTRITZER, Nancye R., Chief Nursing Officer, Emory University Hospital, Atlanta, GA, p. A152

FELBINGER, Richard, Senior Vice President and Chief Financial Officer, Borgess Medical Center, Kalamazoo, MI, p. A328

FELCZAK, Jr., Michael J., Finance Manager, Brighton Center for Recovery, Brighton, MI, p. A320

FELDMAN, David L., Executive Vice President and Treasurer, Circles of Care, Melbourne, FL, p. A135

FELDMAN, Deborah A., President and Chief Executive Officer, Children's Medical Center, Dayton, OH, p. A491

FELDMAN, Mitchell S., Chief Executive Officer, West Boca Medical Center, Boca Raton, FL, p. A124

FELDMANN, Scott, Director Information Technology, SSM DePaul Health Center, Bridgeton, MO, p. A368

FELDSTEIN, Charles S., M.D. Vice President Medical Affairs, St. Rose Hospital, Hayward, CA, p. A66

FELEGE, Lester, Controller, New England Rehabilitation Hospital, Woburn, MA, p. A316

FELGAR, Alvin D., President and Chief Executive Officer, Frisbie Memorial Hospital, Rochester, NH, p. A412

FELICE, Michael, Chief Financial Officer, Pennsylvania Psychiatric Institute, Harrisburg, PA, p. A540

FELICETTI, Jacqueline, Director Human Resources, Chester County Hospital, West Chester, PA, p. A558

FELICI, Brian K., Chief Executive Officer, Wetzel County Hospital, New Martinsville, WV, p. A697

FELICIANO, Jose R., Chief Executive Officer, Ryder Memorial Hospital, Humacao, PR, p. A726

FELICIANO, Myrna Quinones, M.D. Medical Director, University Pediatric Hospital,, PR, p. A729

FELICIANO, Pablo, Manager Human Resources, VA Central Western Massachusetts Healthcare System, Leeds, MA, p. A311

FELIS, Sandra L., R.N. Senior Vice President Patient Care Services and Chief Nursing Officer, Fletcher Allen Health Care, Burlington, VT, p. A665

FELIZ, Miriam, M.D. Medical Director, St. Catherine's Rehabilitation Hospital, North Miami, FL, p. A139

FELKNER, Joseph G.
Senior Vice President Finance and Chief Financial Officer, Health First Cape Canaveral Hospital, Cocoa Beach, FL, p. A126
Executive Vice President, Finance and Chief Financial Officer, Health First Holmes Regional Medical Center, Melbourne, FL, p. A135
Executive Vice President and Chief Financial Officer, Health First Palm Bay Hospital, Melbourne, FL, p. A136
Executive Vice President and Chief Financial Officer, Health First Viera Hospital, Melbourne, FL, p. A136

FELL, David, M.D. Chief Medical Officer, Tulsa Spine and Specialty Hospital, Tulsa, OK, p. A521

FELLER, Julie, Director Human Resources, Grays Harbor Community Hospital, Aberdeen, WA, p. A681

FELLOWS, James, M.D. Chief of Staff, Methodist Hospital, Henderson, KY, p. A262

FELLOWS, Steven A.
Executive Vice President and Chief Operating Officer, Goleta Valley Cottage Hospital, Santa Barbara, CA, p. A94
Executive Vice President and Chief Operating Officer, Santa Barbara Cottage Hospital, Santa Barbara, CA, p. A94
Executive Vice President and Chief Operating Officer, Santa Ynez Valley Cottage Hospital, Solvang, CA, p. A95

FELMLEE, Charles, Assistant Director Fiscal Services, Central Virginia Training Center, Madison Heights, VA, p. A673

FELTMAN, Steven, CPA Chief Financial Officer, Essentia Health–Virginia, Virginia, MN, p. A353

FELTON, David, Manager Information Systems, Waldo County General Hospital, Belfast, ME, p. A292

FELTS, Dave, Chief Information Systems, Logan Regional Hospital, Logan, UT, p. A660

FELTY, Craig, President, Indiana University Health Starke Hospital, Knox, IN, p. A216

FENDER, Tamra, Chief Nursing Officer, Marias Medical Center, Shelby, MT, p. A391

FENDT, Phil, Chief Financial Officer, Memorial Community Health, Aurora, NE, p. A393

FENELLO, Michael A., Chief Executive Officer, St. Luke's McCall, McCall, ID, p. A177

FENER, Michael
Executive Director, Plainview Hospital, Plainview, NY, p. A451
Executive Director, Syosset Hospital, Syosset, NY, p. A455

FENN, Mark, Director Human Resources, Pulaski Memorial Hospital, Winamac, IN, p. A224

FENNELL, Charles, Vice President Information Management, St. Joseph's Hospital Health Center, Syracuse, NY, p. A456

FENNELL, David, M.D. Acting Medical Director, Atascadero State Hospital, Atascadero, CA, p. A56

FENNELL, Dustin, Director Information Systems, Mission Community Hospital,, CA, p. A73

FENSKE, Bill, Chief Financial Officer, Rice Memorial Hospital, Willmar, MN, p. A354

FENSKE, Candace, Chief Executive Officer, Madelia Community Hospital, Madelia, MN, p. A346

FENSKE, Mary, Human Resource Business Partner, Spectrum Health United Hospital, Greenville, MI, p. A326

FENTER, Kim, Chief Financial Officer, Wilbarger General Hospital, Vernon, TX, p. A655

FENTON, Joanne, FACHE, Chief Executive Officer, Livingston Regional Hospital, Livingston, TN, p. A587

FENWICK, Sandra L., Chief Executive Officer and President, Boston Children's Hospital, Boston, MA, p. A306

FEOLA, Ferd, Chief Information Officer, Pocono Medical Center, East Stroudsburg, PA, p. A538

FERBER, Robert, M.D. Chief Clinical Innovation Officer, Nanticoke Memorial Hospital, Seaford, DE, p. A119

FERCH, Wayne
President and Chief Executive Officer, Adventist Medical Center – Hanford, Hanford, CA, p. A66
President and Chief Executive Officer, Adventist Medical Center–Reedley, Reedley, CA, p. A86
President and Chief Executive Officer, Central Valley General Hospital, Hanford, CA, p. A66

FERGIE, Joy, Chief Financial Officer, Delta Medical Center, Memphis, TN, p. A588

FERGUS, Janie
Director and Chief Information Officer, Saint Joseph East, Lexington, KY, p. A264
Director and Chief Information Officer, Saint Joseph Hospital, Lexington, KY, p. A264

FERGUS, Linda, Manager Information Technology, Allegheny Valley Hospital, Natrona Heights, PA, p. A546

FERGUSON, Allison, Director Human Resources, Avoyelles Hospital, Marksville, LA, p. A283

FERGUSON, Cathy, R.N. VP and Chief Nursing Officer, Hamilton Medical Center, Dalton, GA, p. A158

FERGUSON, Cheryl L., Associate Administrator, Sanford Canby Medical Center, Canby, MN, p. A341

FERGUSON, Clifford, Director Information Technology and Systems, Bayshore Medical Center, Pasadena, TX, p. A641

FERGUSON, Deborah, Human Resources Consultant, Sentara Obici Hospital, Suffolk, VA, p. A679

FERGUSON, Denise, Chief Nursing Officer, Baptist Memorial Hospital–Collierville, Collierville, TN, p. A581

FERGUSON, G. Thomas, Senior Vice President and Chief Human Resources Officer, New York–Presbyterian Hospital, New York, NY, p. A447

FERGUSON, Gary W., Executive Vice President and Chief Operating Officer, Christiana Care Health System, Newark, DE, p. A119

FERGUSON, Gordon B., President and Chief Executive Officer, Saint Thomas Rutherford Hospital, Murfreesboro, TN, p. A590

FERGUSON, Karen, Director Human Resources, Johnson County Healthcare Center, Buffalo, WY, p. A720

FERGUSON, Louis D.
Chief Financial Officer, Palestine Regional Medical Center, Palestine, TX, p. A640
Chief Financial Officer, Palestine Regional Medical Center–East, Palestine, TX, p. A640

FERGUSON, Michael, Chief Financial Officer, Harbor Oaks Hospital, New Baltimore, MI, p. A331

FERGUSON, Nina L., Director Human Resources, Little Colorado Medical Center, Winslow, AZ, p. A41

FERGUSON, Randy, Chief Information Officer, Ridgecrest Regional Hospital, Ridgecrest, CA, p. A86

FERGUSON, Rick, Chief Executive Officer, Oklahoma Surgical Hospital, Tulsa, OK, p. A520

FERGUSON, Tonya, Director Human Resources, HEALTHSOUTH Rehabilitation Hospital of Virginia, Richmond, VA, p. A677

FERGUSON, Zeta, Chief Human Resources, Atlanta Veterans Affairs Medical Center, Decatur, GA, p. A158

FERIA, Jorge, M.D. President Medical Staff, Wilma N. Vazquez Medical Center, Vega Baja, PR, p. A729

FERNANDES, Roxanne, R.N. Chief Nursing Officer, Children's Hospitals and Clinics of Minnesota, Minneapolis, MN, p. A347

FERNANDEZ, Alexander, Chief Financial Officer, Broward Health Medical Center, Fort Lauderdale, FL, p. A128

FERNANDEZ, Arthur, Chief Financial Officer, First Hospital Panamericano, Cidra, PR, p. A725

FERNANDEZ, Benigno J., M.D. Executive Medical Director, Laurel Ridge Treatment Center, San Antonio, TX, p. A646

FERNANDEZ, Darlene, Chief Financial Officer, UNM Sandoval Regional Medical Center, Rio Rancho, NM, p. A430

FERNANDEZ, Genaro, M.D. Chief of Staff, Paradise Valley Hospital, National City, CA, p. A79

FERNANDEZ, Jean, Chief Information Officer, Beth Israel Deaconess Hospital–Milton, Milton, MA, p. A312

FERNANDEZ, John R., President and Chief Executive Officer, Massachusetts Eye and Ear Infirmary, Boston, MA, p. A307

FERNANDEZ, Jose L. Pimentel, Medical Director, Lafayette Hospital, Arroyo, PR, p. A724

FERNANDEZ, Manuel, Vice President Nursing, Larkin Community Hospital, South Miami, FL, p. A146

FERNANDEZ, Mark, M.D. Chief of Staff and President Medical Staff, Illinois Valley Community Hospital, Peru, IL, p. A200

FERNANDEZ, Ruben D., R.N. Vice President and Chief Nursing Officer, Palisades Medical Center, North Bergen, NJ, p. A420

FERNANDEZ, Tracey, Chief Financial Officer, St. Mary Medical Center, Apple Valley, CA, p. A56

FERNANDEZ DEL VALLE, Arthur J., Chief Financial Officer, Cardiovascular Center of Puerto Rico and the Caribbean, San Juan, PR, p. A728

FERNANDEZ–BRAVO, Grisel, R.N. Chief Nursing Officer, Memorial Hospital West, Pembroke Pines, FL, p. A142

FERNAU, Chalee, Controller, Howard County Medical Center, Saint Paul, NE, p. A401

FERNIANY, William, Ph.D., Chief Executive Officer, UAB Health System, Birmingham, AL, p. B137

FERRACANE, Tony, Vice President Human Resources, St. Mary Medical Center, Hobart, IN, p. A213

FERRANCE, Randy, M.D. President Medical Staff, Riverside Tappahannock Hospital, Tappahannock, VA, p. A679

FERRANTI, Jeffrey, M.D. Chief Information Officer, Duke University Hospital, Durham, NC, p. A463

FERRAROTTI, Gianna, Director Human Resources North Region, OhioHealth Marion General Hospital, Marion, OH, p. A497

FERREBEE, Mike, M.D. Vice President Medical Affairs, Monongalia General Hospital, Morgantown, WV, p. A697

FERREIRA, Daniel, Director Management Information Systems, Hospital De La Concepcion, San German, PR, p. A727

FERRELL, Angie
Director Human Resources, Mercy Health – Anderson Hospital, Cincinnati, OH, p. A487
Director Human Resources, Mercy Health – Clermont Hospital, Batavia, OH, p. A483

FERRELL, David A., Regional Administrator, Shriners Hospitals for Children–Houston, Houston, TX, p. A626

FERRELL, Eileen Brennan, R.N. Vice President and Chief Nursing Officer, MedStar Georgetown University Hospital, Washington, DC, p. A121

FERRELL, Jennifer, Chief Nursing Officer, HEALTHSOUTH Rehabilitation Hospital of Memphis, Memphis, TN, p. A588

FERRELL, Ronald, Chief Information Officer, Veterans Affairs Medical Center, Albuquerque, NM, p. A427

FERREN, Alison, Vice President Information Technology and Chief Information Officer, Abington Memorial Hospital, Abington, PA, p. A532

FERRERI, Anthony C., President and Chief Executive Officer, Staten Island University Hospital,, NY, p. A448

FERRERO, Marcia L., MS Chief Nursing Officer, Heritage Valley Health System, Beaver, PA, p. A533

FERRIS, David, Chief Nursing Officer and Vice President Patient Care Services, Claxton–Hepburn Medical Center, Ogdensburg, NY, p. A450

FERRIS, Joseph, Chief Financial Officer, Veterans Affairs Black Hills Health Care System, Fort Meade, SD, p. A574

FERRIS, Mark, M.D. Medical Director, Kindred Hospital–White Rock, Dallas, TX, p. A610

FERRIS, Michael, M.D. Chief Medical Officer, CHI Health St Elizabeth, Lincoln, NE, p. A397

FERRONI, Karen, M.D. Medical Director, Holyoke Medical Center, Holyoke, MA, p. A311

FERRY, Jane, M.D. Vice President Medical Affairs, Grand View Hospital, Sellersville, PA, p. A554

FERRY, Thomas, Business Administrator, Oakwood Correctional Facility, Lima, OH, p. A496

FESKO, Donald P., Chief Executive Officer and Administrator, Community Hospital, Munster, IN, p. A219

FESTA, J. Keith, M.D. Vice President Medical Affairs, MidHudson Regional Hospital of Westchester Medical Center, Poughkeepsie, NY, p. A452

FETTER, Trevor, President and Chief Executive Officer, TENET Healthcare Corporation, Dallas, TX, p. B132

FETTERLEY, Kathy, Vice President and Chief Human Resources Officer, Hardin Memorial Hospital, Elizabethtown, KY, p. A260

FETTEROLF, Kim, R.N. Chief Clinical Officer, Lourdes Specialty Hospital of Southern New Jersey, Willingboro, NJ, p. A425

FETTERS, Valerie, Chief Financial Officer, Hillsdale Community Health Center, Hillsdale, MI, p. A326

FEUCHT, Jason, Chief Financial Officer, Kossuth Regional Health Center, Algona, IA, p. A225

FEUER, Tammy, Chief Executive Officer, HEALTHSOUTH Rehabilitation Hospital of Vineland, Vineland, NJ, p. A424

FEUNNING, Charles, M.D. President Medical Staff, Summa Western Reserve Hospital, Cuyahoga Falls, OH, p. A491

FICCHI, Adrienne, Vice President Information Management, Philadelphia Veterans Affairs Medical Center, Philadelphia, PA, p. A549

FICHTER, Craig R., Interim Chief Executive Officer, Martin General Hospital, Williamston, NC, p. A474

FICICCHY, Teri, R.N. Chief Nursing Officer, Bon Secours St. Francis Health System, Greenville, SC, p. A566

FICKES, Catherine, R.N., President and Chief Executive Officer, St. Vincent Medical Center, Los Angeles, CA, p. A75

FIDELI, Barbara, Chief Operating Officer, Non–clinical Services, MetroSouth Medical Center, Blue Island, IL, p. A182

FIDLER, Soniya, Chief Human Resources Officer, Yampa Valley Medical Center, Steamboat Springs, CO, p. A111

FIDUCIA, Karen A., FACHE, President, Hospital Division, USMD Inc., Irving, TX, p. B147

FIELD, Clifford, M.D. Medical Director, Kau Hospital, Pahala, HI, p. A172

FIELD, Kori, Director of Nursing, Brodstone Memorial Hospital, Superior, NE, p. A402

FIELD, Laurie, Director Human Resources, Eaton Rapids Medical Center, Eaton Rapids, MI, p. A323

FIELDER, Barb, Vice President Finance, Chelsea Community Hospital, Chelsea, MI, p. A320

FIELDER, Jaf, Vice President and Administrator, Willis–Knighton Medical Center, Shreveport, LA, p. A288

FIELDING, Colene, Manager Business Office, Baylor Medical Center at Uptown, Dallas, TX, p. A609

FIELDING, Laura M., Administrative Director Organizational Development, Holy Family Memorial, Manitowoc, WI, p. A708

FIELDS, Donald R., Senior Community Chief Executive Officer, Hazard ARH Regional Medical Center, Hazard, KY, p. A262

FIELDS, Glenn C., Vice President, Human Resources, St. Vincent Anderson Regional Hospital, Anderson, IN, p. A206

FIELDS, Greg, Director Information Technology, Elbert Memorial Hospital, Elberton, GA, p. A159

FIELDS, Sarah G., R.N. Vice President Nursing, North Kansas City Hospital, North Kansas City, MO, p. A378

FIERER, Jonathan, M.D. Chief of Staff, Martinsburg Veterans Affairs Medical Center, Martinsburg, WV, p. A697

FIERRO, Barbara, Director, Human Resources, St. Francis Hospital, Roslyn, NY, p. A454

FIGUEROA, Maria, Director Human Resources, Ryder Memorial Hospital, Humacao, PR, p. A726

FIGUEROA, Roseann, Director Human Resources, Doctors Hospital of Laredo, Laredo, TX, p. A632

FIKE, Ruthita J., Chief Executive Officer, Loma Linda University Behavioral Medicine Center, Redlands, CA, p. A85

FILBURN, Mandi, Director Human Resources, Twin Lakes Regional Medical Center, Leitchfield, KY, p. A264

FILER, Christine, Director Human Resources, HEALTHSOUTH Rehabilitation Hospital of Altoona, Altoona, PA, p. A532

FILES, Ashley S., Director Human Resources, Winn Parish Medical Center, Winnfield, LA, p. A290

FILES, Carol, Chief Financial Officer, Victory Surgical Hospital East Houston, Houston, TX, p. A628

FILIAK, Thomas, Vice President Administration, Auburn Community Hospital, Auburn, NY, p. A433

FILIPINI, Alfred, Manager Human Resources, Ancora Psychiatric Hospital, Hammonton, NJ, p. A416

FILIPOWICZ, Thomas, M.D. Medical Director, St. Luke's Hospital – Quakertown Campus, Quakertown, PA, p. A553

FILLER, Richard, Chief Financial Officer, Berger Health System, Circleville, OH, p. A488

FILLER, Scott, Chief Executive Officer, HEALTHSOUTH Rehabilitation Hospital of Altoona, Altoona, PA, p. A532

FILLINGIM, Jed, Acting Chief Operating Officer and Associate Director, G.V. (Sonny) Montgomery Veterans Affairs Medical Center, Jackson, MS, p. A360

FILLIPO, Brian, M.D. Chief Medical Officer, Robert Packer Hospital, Sayre, PA, p. A554

FILOSA, Frank, Fiscal Manager, Washington DC Veterans Affairs Medical Center, Washington, DC, p. A122

FILPI, Jeanette, Chief Executive Officer, Pioneer Community Hospital of Patrick County, Stuart, VA, p. A679

FILSON, Debbie, Chief Financial Officer, Ashland Health Center, Ashland, KS, p. A241

FINAN Jr.,, John J., FACHE, President and Chief Executive Officer, Franciscan Missionaries of Our Lady Health System, Inc., Baton Rouge, LA, p. B59

FINAN, Timothy J., FACHE,
President and Chief Executive Officer, Bradford Regional Medical Center, Bradford, PA, p. A534
President and Chief Executive Officer, Olean General Hospital, Olean, NY, p. A450

FINAN, Timothy J., FACHE, President and Chief Executive Officer, Upper Allegheny Health System, Olean, NY, p. B147

FINCH, John
Vice President Information Services, Health Alliance Hospital – Broadway Campus, Kingston, NY, p. A440
Chief Information and Community Officer, Health Alliance Hospital – Mary's Avenue Campus, Kingston, NY, p. A440

FINCH, Kenneth A., President and Chief Executive Officer, Texas Health Huguley Hospital Fort Worth South, Fort Worth, TX, p. A619

FINCH, Kim, Chief Nursing Officer, Kosciusko Community Hospital, Warsaw, IN, p. A224

FINCH, Roy, Chief Operating Officer, Longview Regional Medical Center, Longview, TX, p. A634

FINCH, Teresa, Chief Financial Officer, Trident Medical Center, Charleston, SC, p. A563

FINCHER, Jodi, Vice President Patient Care Services, Saint John Hospital, Leavenworth, KS, p. A248

FINDLAY, Andrew L., Deputy Commander Clinical Services, Tripler Army Medical Center, Honolulu, HI, p. A171

FINDLAY, Denice C., Director Human Resources, Community Hospital of San Bernardino, San Bernardino, CA, p. A88

FINDLEY, Amber, Senior Director Nursing Services and NRC Administrator, Pleasant Valley Hospital, Point Pleasant, WV, p. A698

FINE, Allan, Chief Operating Officer, New York Eye and Ear Infirmary of Mount Sinai, New York, NY, p. A447

FINE, James, M.D. Chief Information Officer, UW Medicine/Harborview Medical Center, Seattle, WA, p. A689

FINE, Mathew N., M.D. Chief Medical Officer, Oroville Hospital, Oroville, CA, p. A82

FINE, Peter S., FACHE, President and Chief Executive Officer, Banner Health, Phoenix, AZ, p. B18

FINELLI, Frederick, M.D. Vice President Medical Affairs, MedStar Montgomery Medical Center, Olney, MD, p. A302

FINELLI, Peter, Chief Financial Officer, Payson Regional Medical Center, Payson, AZ, p. A35

FINETTI, Yoany, R.N. Chief Nursing Officer, Barnes–Jewish West County Hospital, Saint Louis, MO, p. A380

FINK, Kelley, Coordinator Human Resources, Sitka Community Hospital, Sitka, AK, p. A30

FINK, Renee, CPA Chief Financial Officer, Chase County Community Hospital, Imperial, NE, p. A397

FINK, Tom, Vice President Regional Finance Officer, Range Regional Health Services, Hibbing, MN, p. A345

FINLAYSON, Susan D., R.N. Senior Vice President of Operations, Mercy Medical Center, Baltimore, MD, p. A297

FINLEY, Alan, Chief Operating Officer, Conway Regional Medical Center, Conway, AR, p. A44

FINLEY, Cindy, Chief Nursing Officer, Iron County Medical Center, Pilot Knob, MO, p. A378

FINLEY, Delvecchio, Chief Executive Officer, Harbor–UCLA Medical Center, Torrance, CA, p. A97

FINLEY, E. Jane, Senior Vice President and Executive Director, Kaiser Permanente San Diego Medical Center, San Diego, CA, p. A89

FINLEY, Edward, Administrator, Wray Community District Hospital, Wray, CO, p. A112

FINLEY, Kevin, D.O. Chief of Staff, Knox County Hospital, Knox City, TX, p. A632

FINLEY, Mike, M.D. Chief Medical Officer, CHRISTUS St. Michael Health System, Texarkana, TX, p. A652

FINLEY, Tommy, Chief Information Officer, Rutherford Regional Health System, Rutherfordton, NC, p. A472

FINLEY, Waynea
Senior Vice President Human Resources, Post Acute Medical Specialty Hospital of Lafayette, Lafayette, LA, p. A282
Senior Vice President Human Resources, Post Acute Northshore Specialty Hospital, Covington, LA, p. A276
System Director Human Resources, Post Acute/Warm Springs Rehabilitation Hospital of San Antonio, San Antonio, TX, p. A647
Corporate Director Human Resources, Post Acute/Warm Springs Specialty Hospital of Victoria, Victoria, TX, p. A655

FINLEY–HAZLE, Gabrielle, Chief Executive Officer, North Shore Medical Center, Florida Medical Center Campus, Fort Lauderdale, FL, p. A128

FINN, Barry C., President and Chief Executive Officer, Rush–Copley Medical Center, Aurora, IL, p. A181

FINN, Patti, Chief Executive Officer, Fulton County Health Center, Wauseon, OH, p. A504

FINNEGAN, Jay, Chief Executive Officer, St. Lucie Medical Center, Port St. Lucie, FL, p. A143

FINNEGAN, Patricia, Vice President, Columbia Memorial Hospital, Hudson, NY, p. A439

FINNELL, Ian, Business Manager, Essex County Hospital Center, Cedar Grove, NJ, p. A414

FINNEY, David, R.N. Vice President Nursing, Chenango Memorial Hospital, Norwich, NY, p. A450

FINSTAD, Gary A., M.D. Chief of Staff, Kern Valley Healthcare District, Lake Isabella, CA, p. A69

FIORE–LOPEZ, Nicolette, R.N. Chief Nursing Officer, St. Charles Hospital, Port Jefferson, NY, p. A452

FIORELLO, Tony, R.N. Chief Operating and Chief Nursing Officer, Kaiser Permanente San Rafael Medical Center, San Rafael, CA, p. A93

FIORENZO, V. James, President, UPMC Hamot, Erie, PA, p. A539

FIORET, Phil, M.D. Vice President Medical Affairs, King's Daughters Medical Center, Ashland, KY, p. A258

FIRES, Wiley M., Administrator, Shamrock General Hospital, Shamrock, TX, p. A648

FIRMAN, Julie, R.N
Vice President and Chief Nursing Officer, Memorial Hospital of Carbondale, Carbondale, IL, p. A182
Chief Nursing Officer, St. Joseph Memorial Hospital, Murphysboro, IL, p. A197

FISCHELS, Diane, Senior Vice President and Chief Operating Officer, Mercy Medical Center–North Iowa, Mason City, IA, p. A234

FISCHER, Angie, Chief Financial Officer, Loring Hospital, Sac City, IA, p. A237

FISCHER, James, R.N. Vice President Patient Care Services/Chief Nursing Officer, Munson Medical Center, Traverse City, MI, p. A336

FISCHER, JC, Director Human Resources, Mercy Regional Medical Center, Lorain, OH, p. A497

FISCHER, Linda, Director Information Services, Huntington Hospital, Huntington, NY, p. A439

FISCHER, Lisa, Director Human Resources, Brown County Hospital, Ainsworth, NE, p. A393

FISCHER, Lukas, Chief Nursing Officer, Linton Hospital, Linton, ND, p. A479

FISCHER, Sandra, Director Human Resources, W. G. (Bill) Heffner Veterans Affairs Medical Center, Salisbury, NC, p. A472

FISCHER, Steve, Chief Financial Officer, T. J. Samson Community Hospital, Glasgow, KY, p. A262

FISCHER, Steven P., Chief Financial Officer, Beth Israel Deaconess Medical Center, Boston, MA, p. A306

FISCHER, Tamara, Chief Nursing Officer, Okeene Municipal Hospital, Okeene, OK, p. A514

FISER, David, Vice President and Chief Information Officer, Akron General Medical Center, Akron, OH, p. A482

FISH, Carolyn, Director Human Resources, Mission Community Hospital,, CA, p. A73

FISH, Carrie L., Senior Vice President and Chief Operating Officer, Florida Hospital Waterman, Tavares, FL, p. A148

FISH, Elizabeth
Senior Director Site Executive and Information Technology, University of Maryland Shore Medical Center at Chestertown, Chestertown, MD, p. A299
Chief Information Officer, University of Maryland Shore Medical Center at Dorchester, Cambridge, MD, p. A299
Chief Information Officer, University of Maryland Shore Medical Center at Easton, Easton, MD, p. A300

FISHBAIN, Ken, Chief Operating Officer, Gottlieb Memorial Hospital, Melrose Park, IL, p. A196

FISHEL, Linda, Manager Information Services, Gouverneur Hospital, Gouverneur, NY, p. A438

FISHER, Carol, Director of Nursing, Old Vineyard Behavioral Health Services, Winston–Salem, NC, p. A475

FISHER, David, Director Information Systems, Heart of Lancaster Regional Medical Center, Lititz, PA, p. A543

FISHER, David, M.D. Senior Vice President and Chief Medical Officer, Seattle Children's Hospital, Seattle, WA, p. A688

FISHER, David, Vice President Human Resources, Signature Healthcare Brockton Hospital, Brockton, MA, p. A308

FISHER, Diana D., Chief Executive Officer, Regency Hospital of Toledo, Sylvania, OH, p. A502

FISHER, Diane, R.N. VP, Patient Care Services, Otsego Memorial Hospital, Gaylord, MI, p. A324

FISHER, Donna, MS Chief Nursing Officer, St. Mary–Corwin Medical Center, Pueblo, CO, p. A110

FISHER, Ebony, Chief Nurse Executive, Metropolitan St. Louis Psychiatric Center, Saint Louis, MO, p. A381

FISHER, Ginger, Interim Chief Executive Officer, Utah Valley Specialty Hospital, Provo, UT, p. A662

FISHER, Jacob, Chief Executive Officer, Tampa Community Hospital, Tampa, FL, p. A148

FISHER, Jan E., President, Williamsport Regional Medical Center, Williamsport, PA, p. A559

FISHER, Jennifer A., Manager Human Resources, Henry County Hospital, Napoleon, OH, p. A499

FISHER, Kenneth, Associate Vice President Finance and Chief Financial Officer, University of Iowa Hospitals and Clinics, Iowa City, IA, p. A232

FISHER, Laura, Director Human Resources, Texas Health Huguley Hospital Fort Worth South, Fort Worth, TX, p. A619

FISHER, Lynn, M.D. Chief of Staff, Rooks County Health Center, Plainville, KS, p. A253

FISHER, Margaret A., Executive Director Human Resources, Specialty Hospital of Washington, Washington, DC, p. A122

FISHER, Mathew, M.D. Medical Director, Springbrook Behavioral Health System, Travelers Rest, SC, p. A570

FISHER, Matt, Vice President Finance, St. Dominic–Jackson Memorial Hospital, Jackson, MS, p. A360

FISHER, Michael, President and Chief Executive Officer, Cincinnati Children's Hospital Medical Center, Cincinnati, OH, p. A486

FISHER, Michael W., Executive Director, Veterans Affairs Long Beach Healthcare System, Long Beach, CA, p. A70

FISHER, Richard, President and Chief Executive Officer, Fox Chase Cancer Center–American Oncologic Hospital, Philadelphia, PA, p. A548

FISHER, Ryan
Director Human Resources, Blanchard Valley Hospital, Findlay, OH, p. A494
Director Human Resources, Bluffton Hospital, Bluffton, OH, p. A484

FISHER, Sharon, R.N. Chief Nursing Officer, Tyrone Hospital, Tyrone, PA, p. A556

FISHER, Teresa, R.N. Chief Nursing Officer, Fort Loudoun Medical Center, Lenoir City, TN, p. A586

FISHER, Teresa, Chief Nursing Officer, Lakewood Health System, Staples, MN, p. A352

FISHER, Thomas, Senior Vice President and Chief Financial Officer, University of Tennessee Medical Center, Knoxville, TN, p. A586

FISHER, Tommie Ann, R.N. Director of Nursing, Clay County Hospital, Ashland, AL, p. A15

FISHER, Vicky, Ph.D. Chief Nurse Executive, Catawba Hospital, Catawba, VA, p. A669

FISHKIN, Edward, M.D. Medical Director, Woodhull Medical and Mental Health Center,, NY, p. A449

FISHMANN, Andrew, M.D. Chairman, Medical Staff, Good Samaritan Hospital, Los Angeles, CA, p. A72

FISK, Anita, Director Human Resources, Three Rivers Hospital, Brewster, WA, p. A682

FISK, Kathryn M., Chief Human Resources Officer, El Camino Hospital, Mountain View, CA, p. A79

FISK, Kellee J., Chief People Resources Executive, Altru Health System, Grand Forks, ND, p. A478

FISLER, Eileen, Chief Financial Officer, Pacifica Hospital of the Valley,, CA, p. A74

FITCH, James A., Director Human Resources, Houston Methodist St. Catherine Hospital, Katy, TX, p. A630

FITCH, John A., Vice President Human Resources, Campbell County Memorial Hospital, Gillette, WY, p. A721

FITE, David, Director Information Technology, Towner County Medical Center, Cando, ND, p. A476

FITE, Linda, Chief Financial Officer, North Central Surgical Center, Dallas, TX, p. A611

FITE, Theresa, Chief Financial Officer, Logan Memorial Hospital, Russellville, KY, p. A270

FITTON, Lenora, D.O. Chief of Staff, Fayette County Memorial Hospital, Washington Court House, OH, p. A504

FITTS, Barry, Chief Information Officer, Trumbull Memorial Hospital, Warren, OH, p. A504

FITZ, Bette, Chief Nursing Officer, Garden City Hospital, Garden City, MI, p. A324

FITZ–PATRICK, Christina, R.N. Executive Director, Mercy Suburban Hospital, Norristown, PA, p. A546

FITZGERALD, Andy, Chief Executive Officer, Campbell County Memorial Hospital, Gillette, WY, p. A721

FITZGERALD, George, Regional Director Information Systems, LifeCare Hospitals of Pittsburgh, Pittsburgh, PA, p. A551

FITZGERALD, John L., Chief Executive Officer, Inova Fair Oaks Hospital, Fairfax, VA, p. A670

FITZGERALD, Larry, Associate Vice President Business Development and Finance, University of Virginia Medical Center, Charlottesville, VA, p. A669

FITZGERALD, Mike
Chief Financial Officer, Harrison Medical Center, Bremerton, WA, p. A681
Chief Financial Officer, St. Clare Hospital, Lakewood, WA, p. A685
Chief Financial Officer, St. Francis Hospital, Federal Way, WA, p. A683
Chief Financial Officer, St. Joseph Medical Center, Tacoma, WA, p. A691

FITZGERALD, Patty, Staff Services, Charlevoix Area Hospital, Charlevoix, MI, p. A320

FITZMAURICE, Dennis, Vice President, Professional Services, Presence Our Lady of the Resurrection Medical Center, Chicago, IL, p. A185

FITZPATRICK, Anna, Director Human Resources, St. Anthony Regional Hospital, Carroll, IA, p. A226

FITZPATRICK, Daniel, Director Human Resources, Whitesburg ARH Hospital, Whitesburg, KY, p. A271

FITZPATRICK, James, M.D. Vice President Medical Affairs, Kenmore Mercy Hospital, Kenmore, NY, p. A439

FITZPATRICK, James G., President, Mercy Medical Center–Sioux City, Sioux City, IA, p. A238

FITZPATRICK, Leigh, Director Human Resources, Arkansas Valley Regional Medical Center, La Junta, CO, p. A108

FITZPATRICK, Leigh Ann, Superintendent, Kerrville State Hospital, Kerrville, TX, p. A631

FITZPATRICK, Sean, Area Finance Officer, Kaiser Permanente Santa Clara Medical Center, Santa Clara, CA, p. A94

FITZSIMMONS, Shawn, Director Information Technology Services, Community Medical Center, Toms River, NJ, p. A423

FITZSIMONS, Patricia Sue, R.N. Senior Vice President Patient Services, Yale–New Haven Hospital, New Haven, CT, p. A116

FIX, Judith A., R.N. Senior Vice President and Chief Nursing Officer, Long Beach Memorial Medical Center, Long Beach, CA, p. A70

FIX, Vicki, Director Human Resources, Dahl Memorial Healthcare Association, Ekalaka, MT, p. A387

FLACH, Shannan, Chief Executive Officer, Wamego Health Center, Wamego, KS, p. A256

FLADER, Steve, Chief Financial Officer, Northwest Medical Center – Springdale, Springdale, AR, p. A53

FLAHERTY, Daniel, M.D. Chief Medical Staff, Prairie Lakes Healthcare System, Watertown, SD, p. A578

FLAHERTY, John, Controller, Fairlawn Rehabilitation Hospital, Worcester, MA, p. A316

FLAHERTY, Linda, R.N. Senior Vice President, Patient Care Services, McLean Hospital, Belmont, MA, p. A305

FLAHERTY, Patrick, Director Management Information, Naval Hospital Bremerton, Bremerton, WA, p. A682

FLAHERTY, Scott, Chief Executive Officer, Post Acute/Warm Springs Rehabilitation Hospital of San Antonio, San Antonio, TX, p. A647

FLAHERTY, Tom, Assistant Administrator, Los Angeles County Central Jail Hospital, Los Angeles, CA, p. A73

FLAKE, Robert, Chief Financial Officer, Yampa Valley Medical Center, Steamboat Springs, CO, p. A111

FLAMM, Cindy, Manager Quality, Choate Mental Health Center, Anna, IL, p. A180

FLANAGAN, Carl J., CP
Chief Financial Officer, Basin Healthcare Center, Odessa, TX, p. A640
Chief Financial Officer, Blue Mountain Hospital, John Day, OR, p. A526

FLANAGAN, Michael J., Senior Vice President and Chief Operating Officer, St. Clair Hospital, Pittsburgh, PA, p. A551

FLANAGAN, Thomas, M.D. Medical Director, Aurora San Diego Hospital, San Diego, CA, p. A89

FLANAGAN, Tom, Chief Operating Officer, Memorial Hermann – Texas Medical Center, Houston, TX, p. A625

FLANARY, Tresha, R.N. Chief Clinical Services Officer, Wamego Health Center, Wamego, KS, p. A256

FLANDERS, Dave, Director Information Technology Systems, Emanuel Medical Center, Swainsboro, GA, p. A167

FLANDERS, John T., R.N., President and Chief Executive Officer, St. Mary's Hospital, Streator, IL, p. A204

FLANIGAN, Erin, Vice President Human Resources, Wentworth–Douglass Hospital, Dover, NH, p. A410

FLANNERY, Donna M., Chief Executive Officer, Mercy Rehabilitation Hospital, Chesterfield, MO, p. A369

FLANNERY, Lindsay, R.N.,
Administrator and Chief Executive Officer, Avera Dells Area Hospital, Dell Rapids, SD, p. A573
Administrator and Chief Executive Officer, Avera Flandreau Hospital, Flandreau, SD, p. A573

FLANNERY, Maureen, Vice President Clinic Operations, Straub Clinic & Hospital, Honolulu, HI, p. A171

FLANZ, Bruce J.
President and Chief Executive Officer, Flushing Hospital Medical Center, NY, p. A443
President and Chief Executive Officer, Jamaica Hospital Medical Center,, NY, p. A444

FLASCHENRIEM, Julie, Chief Information Officer, Park Nicollet Methodist Hospital, Minneapolis, MN, p. A347

FLASHER, Sara, Chief Nurse Executive, Warren State Hospital, Warren, PA, p. A557

FLATT, G. Wayne, D.O. Chief Medical Director, Pushmataha Hospital & Home Health, Antlers, OK, p. A507

FLECHSIG, Randolph K., Administrator, Sheridan Community Hospital, Sheridan, MI, p. A335

FLECK, Julie, Chief Operating Officer, Parkview Ortho Hospital, Fort Wayne, IN, p. A211

FLECKENSTEIN, Casey, Medical and Surgical Nurse Manager, Monroe County Hospital, Forsyth, GA, p. A160

FLEEGEL, Monica, Director Human Resources, Mayo Clinic Health System in Albert Lea, Albert Lea, MN, p. A339

FLEENOR, Dennis, R.N., Chief Executive Officer, Ilano Specialty Hospital of Lubbock, Lubbock, TX, p. A635

FLEISCHMANN, Katherine, Director of Nursing, Harlan County Health System, Alma, NE, p. A393

FLEISCHMANN, Tim, Chief Financial Officer, Tuality Healthcare, Hillsboro, OR, p. A525

FLEITES, Fernando, Senior Vice President Human Resources, Bon Secours St. Francis Health System, Greenville, SC, p. A566

FLEMER, Andrew, Chief Operating Officer, South Georgia Medical Center, Valdosta, GA, p. A168

FLEMING, Jared, Director, Information Services, Lourdes Counseling Center, Richland, WA, p. A687

FLEMING, Michael, Chief People Officer, Banner Good Samaritan Medical Center, Phoenix, AZ, p. A35

FLEMING, Michelle, Chief Nursing Officer, Essentia Health–Virginia, Virginia, MN, p. A353

FLEMING, Shane
Chief Financial Officer, Capital Health Medical Center–Hopewell, Pennington, NJ, p. A421
Chief Financial Officer, Capital Health Regional Medical Center, Trenton, NJ, p. A423

FLEMING, Valarie, R.N. Chief Nursing Officer, Providence Saint Joseph Medical Center, Burbank, CA, p. A58

FLEMING, William P., Chief Operating Officer, Norwood Hospital, Norwood, MA, p. A313

FLEMMING, Libby, Controller and Chief Information Officer, South Georgia Medical Center Lanier Campus, Lakeland, GA, p. A162

FLESNER, Lynn, Director of Nursing, Glacial Ridge Health System, Glenwood, MN, p. A344

FLETCHALL, Terry L., Administrator, Santiam Memorial Hospital, Stayton, OR, p. A530

FLETCHER, Audrey, Chief Operating Officer, Madison Memorial Hospital, Rexburg, ID, p. A178

FLETCHER, Bill, Director Information Technology, Cooper County Memorial Hospital, Boonville, MO, p. A368

FLETCHER, John, Chief Executive Officer, Patrick B. Harris Psychiatric Hospital, Anderson, SC, p. A562

FLETCHER, John R., President, Lehigh Valley Hospital – Hazleton, Hazleton, PA, p. A540

FLETCHER, Kevin, Director Information Systems, Medical Center of McKinney, McKinney, TX, p. A637

FLETCHER, Michael, M.D. President Medical Staff Services, Hancock Regional Hospital, Greenfield, IN, p. A212

FLETCHER, Stephanie L., CPA Chief Financial Officer, Union General Hospital, Blairsville, GA, p. A154

FLETCHER, Steven, M.D. Chief of Staff, Baptist Health South Florida, Homestead Hospital, Homestead, FL, p. A131

FLETCHER–JANZEN, David, Chief Executive Officer, Sycamore Springs Hospital, Lafayette, IN, p. A217

FLETT, Will, Vice President Finance and Chief Financial Officer, Avera Queen of Peace Hospital, Mitchell, SD, p. A575

FLICKINGER, Kenneth E., System Chief Financial Officer, Chester County Hospital, West Chester, PA, p. A558

FLINCHBAUGH, Robert, D.O. Chief Medical Officer, Winneshiek Medical Center, Decorah, IA, p. A229

FLINN, Charles, Vice President, Chief Operating Officer, Saint Mary's Hospital, Waterbury, CT, p. A118

FLINN, James, FACHE, Chief Executive Officer, Oasis Hospital, Phoenix, AZ, p. A36

FLINT, Jennifer, Chief Financial Officer, Laird Hospital, Union, MS, p. A366

FLIS, James D., Chief Financial Officer, Livengrin Foundation, Bensalem, PA, p. A533

FLODEN, Scott, Chief Executive Officer, Promise Hospital of Phoenix, Mesa, AZ, p. A34

FLOOD, James, Director Information Systems, Claxton–Hepburn Medical Center, Ogdensburg, NY, p. A450

FLOOD, Nathan A., Chief Executive Officer, Hereford Regional Medical Center, Hereford, TX, p. A623

FLOOD, Rebecca L., R.N. Senior Vice President Nursing, New York Methodist Hospital,, NY, p. A447

FLORENTINE, Erich
Chief People Officer, Inspira Medical Center–Elmer, Elmer, NJ, p. A416
Chief People Officer, Inspira Medical Center–Vineland, Vineland, NJ, p. A424

FLORES, Christopher, Chief Financial Officer, Havasu Regional Medical Center, Lake Havasu City, AZ, p. A34

FLORES, Debbie, Chief Executive Officer, Banner Del E. Webb Medical Center, Sun City West, AZ, p. A39

FLORES, Debra A., MS, President and Administrator, Sentara CarePlex Hospital, Hampton, VA, p. A672

FLORES, Ernest, M.D. Chief of Staff and Medical Director, Mesilla Valley Hospital, Las Cruces, NM, p. A429

FLORES, Jacob, Chief Information Officer, Frio Regional Hospital, Pearsall, TX, p. A641

FLORES, Jeanne, Senior Vice President Human Resources and Organizational Development, Cedars–Sinai Medical Center, Los Angeles, CA, p. A71

FLORES, Jerome, Chief Financial Officer, Sunrise Canyon Hospital, Lubbock, TX, p. A635

FLORES, Linda, R.N. Vice President Nursing Services, Parkview Medical Center, Pueblo, CO, p. A110

FLORES–RAMIREZ, Rosie, Director Fiscal Services, Lanterman Developmental Center, Pomona, CA, p. A84

FLORKOWSKI, Doug, Chief Executive Officer, Lawrence County Memorial Hospital, Lawrenceville, IL, p. A194

FLOWE, Kenneth, M.D. Chief Medical Officer, Rice Memorial Hospital, Willmar, MN, p. A354

FLOWERS, Deborah, Director Human Resources, Monroe County Hospital, Forsyth, GA, p. A160

FLOWERS, Michael, Director Information Management, Calhoun–Liberty Hospital, Blountstown, FL, p. A123

FLOWERS, Patricia, Interim Chief Executive Officer, Winn Parish Medical Center, Winnfield, LA, p. A290

FLOWERS, Scott, Vice President Professional Services, Thibodaux Regional Medical Center, Thibodaux, LA, p. A289

FLOYD, Bambi, Chief Nursing Officer, Williamsburg Regional Hospital, Kingstree, SC, p. A567

FLOYD, Dorothy, Ph.D., Superintendent, Terrell State Hospital, Terrell, TX, p. A652

FLOYD, Duane, Vice President Human Resources and Professional Services, Watertown Regional Medical Center, Watertown, WI, p. A717

FLOYD, Greg, Chief Executive Officer, Vibra Specialty Hospital at DeSoto, Desoto, TX, p. A614

FLOYD, Jacqueline, Chief Nursing Officer, HEALTHSOUTH Rehabilitation Hospital of Fort Smith, Fort Smith, AR, p. A46

FLOYD, James R., Director, Jack C. Montgomery Veterans Affairs Medical Center, Muskogee, OK, p. A514

FLOYD, Kay A., R.N., Chief Executive Officer, Monroe County Hospital, Forsyth, GA, p. A160

FLOYD, Kiley, Administrator, Osborne County Memorial Hospital, Osborne, KS, p. A251

FLOYD, Miranda, R.N. Chief Nursing Officer, Northwest Medical Center, Albany, MO, p. A367

FLOYD, Richard B., President, Advocate Lutheran General Hospital, Park Ridge, IL, p. A199

FLUKE, Cinda, R.N. Chief Nursing Officer, Saint Joseph Mount Sterling, Mount Sterling, KY, p. A268

FLUTY, Lisa, Director Information Services, Baptist Health Lexington, Lexington, KY, p. A264

FLYGARE, Matthew, Director Human Resources, Mountain West Medical Center, Tooele, UT, p. A664

FLYNN, Brian, Chief Human Resources Officer, Veterans Affairs Northern Indiana Health Care System, Fort Wayne, IN, p. A211

FLYNN, Chanda, R.N. Chief Nursing Officer, Mary Black Memorial Hospital, Spartanburg, SC, p. A570

FLYNN, Cheryl, Senior Vice President Human Resources, Methodist Charlton Medical Center, Dallas, TX, p. A611

FLYNN, Dixie, Chief Nursing Officer, Cedar County Memorial Hospital, El Dorado Springs, MO, p. A370

FLYNN, Gail, Interim Director Human Resources, Quincy Medical Center, Quincy, MA, p. A314

FLYNN, James, Chief Executive Officer, Heartland Regional Medical Center, Marion, IL, p. A195

FLYNN, Jerry, M.D. Chief of Staff, Southeast Colorado Hospital District, Springfield, CO, p. A111

FLYNN, Kristin, Chief Human Resources Officer, Sierra Vista Regional Medical Center, San Luis Obispo, CA, p. A93

FLYNN, Loretta, Chief Executive Officer, Gulf Coast Medical Center, Wharton, TX, p. A657

FLYNN, Matthew J., Senior Vice President and Chief Financial Officer, Northwestern Lake Forest Hospital, Lake Forest, IL, p. A194

FLYNN, Patrick, Chief Financial Officer, Warm Springs Medical Center, Warm Springs, GA, p. A169

FLYNN, Timothy C., M.D. Chief of Staff, UF Health Shands Hospital, Gainesville, FL, p. A130

FOARD, Mesa, Director Information technology, William S. Hall Psychiatric Institute, Columbia, SC, p. A564

FOELSCH, Paul
Vice President Information Services and Chief Information Officer, Mercy Iowa City, Iowa City, IA, p. A232
Vice President and Chief Information Technology Officer, North Kansas City Hospital, North Kansas City, MO, p. A378

FOELSKE, Loren
Vice President Finance, Kishwaukee Hospital, DeKalb, IL, p. A188
Vice President Finance, Valley West Hospital, Sandwich, IL, p. A202

FOGARTY, Kathleen R., Director, James A. Haley Veterans' Hospital, Tampa, FL, p. A147

FOGARTY, Larry, Chief Financial Officer, Methodist Olive Branch Hospital, Olive Branch, MS, p. A363

FOGG, Robert W., Director Finance, Lake Taylor Transitional Care Hospital, Norfolk, VA, p. A675

FOGLE, Dennis, Vice President of Human Resources, Rush Memorial Hospital, Rushville, IN, p. A222

FOJTASEK, Georgia R., President and Chief Executive Officer, Allegiance Health, Jackson, MI, p. A327

FOLEY, Crystal, Director Human Resources, Little River Healthcare, Rockdale, TX, p. A644

FOLEY, James T., CPA Vice President and Chief Financial Officer, Shore Medical Center, Somers Point, NJ, p. A422

FOLEY, Jay, Chief Operating Officer, Southwestern Regional Medical Center, Tulsa, OK, p. A521

FOLEY, John, Chief Information Officer, Allegheny General Hospital, Pittsburgh, PA, p. A550

FOLEY, John V., Chief Information Officer, University Hospitals Case Medical Center, Cleveland, OH, p. A489

FOLEY, Michael, M.D. Chief Medical Officer, North Okaloosa Medical Center, Crestview, FL, p. A126

FOLEY, Regina, R.N. Vice President Nursing and Operations, Ocean Medical Center, Brick Township, NJ, p. A414

FOLEY, William T., M.D., Administrator, Arrowhead Regional Medical Center, Colton, CA, p. A60

FOLK, Jeffrey R., M.D. Vice President Medical Affairs and Chief Medical Officer, Piedmont Newnan Hospital, Newnan, GA, p. A164

FOLKENBERG, Todd, Chief Executive Officer, Castle Rock Adventist Hospital, Castle Rock, CO, p. A103

FOLKS, David G., M.D. Chief Medical Officer, New Hampshire Hospital, Concord, NH, p. A409

FOLL, Gary R., Chief Financial Officer, Atchison Hospital, Atchison, KS, p. A241

FOLLARD, Cheyenne, Chief Financial Officer, Central Vermont Medical Center, Berlin, VT, p. A665

FOLLETT, Richard, Chief Information Officer, The Good Samaritan Hospital, Lebanon, PA, p. A543

FOLSKE, Lance, Chief Executive Officer, Hickory Trail Hospital, Desoto, TX, p. A614

FOLTZ, Jeffry E., R.N. Vice President for Nursing, St. Joseph's Medical Center, Yonkers, NY, p. A458

FOLTZ, JoAnn M., R.N., Chief Executive Officer, Sanford Wheaton Medical Center, Wheaton, MN, p. A354

FOLTZ, Jon, M.D. Chief of Staff, Otsego Memorial Hospital, Gaylord, MI, p. A324

FONDESSY, Terrence, M.D. Vice President Medical Affairs, ProMedica Fostoria Community Hospital, Fostoria, OH, p. A494

FONG, Joseph, Administrator, Providence Seward Medical Center, Seward, AK, p. A30

FONTAINE, Jane, Vice President Human Resources, UMass Memorial–Marlborough Hospital, Marlborough, MA, p. A312

FONTAINE, Melissa, Chief Operating Officer, UAMS Medical Center, Little Rock, AR, p. A49

FONTAINE, Tim, Chief Operating Officer, Pioneer Community Hospital of Stokes, Danbury, NC, p. A463

FONTAINE–WESTHART, Mark, Associate Director, Bedford Veterans Affairs Medical Center, Edith Nourse Rogers Memorial Veterans Hospital, Bedford, MA, p. A305

FONTENAULT, Richard, Director Information Systems, Green Oaks Hospital, Dallas, TX, p. A610

FONTENELLE, Mary, Executive Nurse Director, Eastern Louisiana Mental Health System, Jackson, LA, p. A279

FONTENOT, Brandon, M.D. Chief of Staff, Mercy Regional Medical Center, Ville Platte, LA, p. A290

FONTENOT, Cathi E., M.D. Medical Director, Interim LSU Public Hospital, New Orleans, LA, p. A285

FONTENOT, H. Jerrel, M.D. Medical Director, Ouachita Community Hospital, West Monroe, LA, p. A290

FONTENOT, Micheal, Chief Financial Officer, Mercy Regional Medical Center, Ville Platte, LA, p. A290

FONTENOT, Teri G., FACHE, President and Chief Executive Officer, Woman's Hospital, Baton Rouge, LA, p. A274

FONZE, Tony, President and Chief Executive Officer, Carondelet St. Joseph's Hospital, Tucson, AZ, p. A40

FONZIE, Juril, Director Human Resources, Helena Regional Medical Center, Helena, AR, p. A47

FOOTE, Donald E., Fiscal Officer, Wilkes–Barre Veterans Affairs Medical Center, Wilkes–Barre, PA, p. A558

FOOTE, John, Chief Information Officer, Manchester Veterans Affairs Medical Center, Manchester, NH, p. A411

FOOTE, Mark, Chief Financial Officer, Madera Community Hospital, Madera, CA, p. A76

FORAND, Angela, Director, William S. Hall Psychiatric Institute, Columbia, SC, p. A564

FORBES, Brenda, Controller, HEALTHSOUTH Rehabilitation Hospital of Fort Smith, Fort Smith, AR, p. A46

FORBES, Geri, Chief Executive Officer, Doctor's Memorial Hospital, Perry, FL, p. A142

FORBES, Ronald O., M.D. Medical Director, Central State Hospital, Petersburg, VA, p. A676

FORBES, Vidette J., R.N
Chief Nursing Officer and Chief Operating Officer, Reliant Austin, Austin, TX, p. A599
Chief Nursing Officer and Chief Operating officer, Reliant Rehabilitation Hospital Central Texas, Round Rock, TX, p. A644

FORBORT, Gordy, Chief Financial Officer, FirstLight Health System, Mora, MN, p. A348

FORD, Alisa, Vice President Human Resources, The University of Kansas Hospital, Kansas City, KS, p. A247

FORD, Angelique, Administrator Human Resources, Spring Valley Hospital Medical Center, Las Vegas, NV, p. A406

FORD, Cindy, R.N. Chief Nursing Officer, Harrisburg Medical Center, Harrisburg, IL, p. A191

FORD, Cora, Vice President Human Resources, Our Lady of the Lake Regional Medical Center, Baton Rouge, LA, p. A273

FORD, James, Director Human Resources, Summit Medical Center, Van Buren, AR, p. A53

FORD, Karen, Chief Nursing Officer, Sabine Medical Center, Many, LA, p. A283

FORD, LeeAnn, Director Human Resources and Imaging, The Physicians Centre Hospital, Bryan, TX, p. A604

FORD, Mike, Vice President Human Resources, Floyd Memorial Hospital and Health Services, New Albany, IN, p. A220

FORD, Raymond, Chief Executive Officer, Heritage Park Surgical Hospital, Sherman, TX, p. A649

FORD, Timothy R., President and Chief Executive Officer, Springfield Hospital, Springfield, VT, p. A666

FORDE, Steve, Chief Financial Officer, Nelson County Health System, Mcville, ND, p. A479

FORDHAM, Karen, Vice President Chief Operating Officer, DMC Huron Valley–Sinai Hospital, Commerce Township, MI, p. A321

FORDYCE, Brian, Director Information Technology, Roosevelt Medical Center, Culbertson, MT, p. A386

FORDYCE, Carol, Director Patient Care Services, Sullivan County Memorial Hospital, Milan, MO, p. A377

FORDYCE, Michael L., President and Chief Executive Officer, Craig Hospital, Englewood, CO, p. A106

FOREMAN, Christopher, Director Human Resources, Santa Rosa Medical Center, Milton, FL, p. A138

FOREMAN, Kim, M.D. Chief of Staff, Texas Spine & Joint Hospital, Tyler, TX, p. A654

FOREMAN, Lee Ann
Vice President Human Resources, Mississippi Baptist Medical Center, Jackson, MS, p. A360
Vice President Human Resources, Mississippi Hospital for Restorative Care, Jackson, MS, p. A360

FOREMAN, Nena, Chief Nursing Officer, Palo Verde Hospital, Blythe, CA, p. A58

FORESE, Laura, M.D. Senior Vice President and Chief Medical Officer, New York–Presbyterian Hospital, New York, NY, p. A447

FORESYTHE, Brad, Director Information Systems, Emory Johns Creek Hospital, Johns Creek, GA, p. A161

FORET, Chris, M.D. Chief of Staff, Riverside Medical Center, Franklinton, LA, p. A277

FORET, Robert, Chief Financial Officer, Yoakum Community Hospital, Yoakum, TX, p. A658

FORGE, Brenda J., Vice President Human Resources, St. Joseph Regional Medical Center, Lewiston, ID, p. A176

FORGEY, Warren, Executive Vice President and Chief Administrative and Operations Officer, Schneck Medical Center, Seymour, IN, p. A222

FORGUES, Daniel, Chief Financial Officer and Vice President Finance, Mayo Regional Hospital, Dover–Foxcroft, ME, p. A293

FORKEL, Todd, President and Chief Executive Officer, Avera St. Luke's Hospital, Aberdeen, SD, p. A572

FORKNER, Christine, Executive Vice President and Chief Financial Officer, National Jewish Health, Denver, CO, p. A105

FORMELLA, Nancy A., R.N. Chief Operating Officer, Beth Israel Deaconess Medical Center, Boston, MA, p. A306

FORNERIS, Lori, R.N. Chief Clinical Officer, Loring Hospital, Sac City, IA, p. A237

FORNIER–JOHNSON, Michelle, Group Vice President Human Resources, St. Anthony Hospital, Lakewood, CO, p. A108

FORREST, Brian K.
Director Human Resources, Arnot Ogden Medical Center, Elmira, NY, p. A437
Director Human Resources, Ira Davenport Memorial Hospital, Bath, NY, p. A433
Vice President Human Resources, St. Joseph's Hospital, Elmira, NY, p. A437

FORREST, Mary Helen, R.N. Chief Nursing Officer, UAMS Medical Center, Little Rock, AR, p. A49

FORREST, Shannon, R.N. Administrative Director of Nursing Services, Baptist Orange Hospital, Orange, TX, p. A640

FORRESTER, John M., Director Information Services, Hamilton Medical Center, Dalton, GA, p. A158

FORRY, Bryan, Chief Financial Officer, Houston Northwest Medical Center, Houston, TX, p. A625

FORSCH, Randall T., M.D. Chief Medical Officer, Chelsea Community Hospital, Chelsea, MI, p. A320

FORSYTH, Beth, Chief Operating Officer, Exempla Good Samaritan Medical Center, Lafayette, CO, p. A108

FORSYTH, Larry, Director Information Services, OU Medical Center, Oklahoma City, OK, p. A516

FORSYTH, Rhonda, President and Chief Executive Officer, John C. Lincoln Health Network, Phoenix, AZ, p. B78

FORT, Claudio D., President and Chief Executive Officer, North Country Hospital and Health Center, Newport, VT, p. A666

FORTENBERRY, Denise, Chief Nursing Officer and Chief Compliance Officer, Cypress Pointe Surgical Hospital, Hammond, LA, p. A278

FORTENBERRY, Doris, Coordinator Human Resources, Delta Memorial Hospital, Dumas, AR, p. A45

FORTENBERRY, Rob, Chief Information Officer, Mann–Grandstaff Veterans Affairs Medical Center, Spokane, WA, p. A690

FORTIER, Jeanne M., R.N. Chief Nursing Officer and Interim Chief Operating Officer, Grace Cottage Hospital, Townshend, VT, p. A666

FORTIN, Amanda, Manager Finance, Decatur Health Systems, Oberlin, KS, p. A251

FORTIN, Laura, R.N. Chief Operating Officer, St. Joseph Medical Center, Houston, TX, p. A627

FORTNEY, John, M.D. Chief Medical Officer, Adena Medical Center, Chillicothe, OH, p. A486

FOSINA, Michael, M.P.H. SVP and Chief Operating Officer, New York Presbyterian Lower Manhattan Hospital, New York, NY, p. A447

FOSNESS, Nick, Chief Executive Officer, Marshall County Healthcare Center Avera, Britton, SD, p. A572

FOSNOCHT, Kevin, M.D. Chief Medical Officer and Associate Executive Director, Penn Presbyterian Medical Center, Philadelphia, PA, p. A549

FOSS, David, Chief Information Officer, New London Hospital, New London, NH, p. A411

FOSS, R. Coleman, Chief Executive Officer, Skyridge Medical Center, Cleveland, TN, p. A581

FOSSUM, John, Chief Executive Officer and Administrator, Ely–Bloomenson Community Hospital, Ely, MN, p. A343

FOSTER, Barbara A., Regional Human Resources Director, Select Specialty Hospital–Wilmington, Wilmington, DE, p. A120

FOSTER, Becky
Manager Human Resources, Sanford Tracy Medical Center, Tracy, MN, p. A353
Manager Human Resources, Sanford Westbrook Medical Center, Westbrook, MN, p. A354

FOSTER, Beverly, Chief Executive Officer, Kindred Hospital Chicago–Northlake, Northlake, IL, p. A198

FOSTER, Bob, Chief Information Officer, South Georgia Medical Center, Valdosta, GA, p. A168

FOSTER, Brian, Chief Information Officer, Vail Valley Medical Center, Vail, CO, p. A111

FOSTER, Charles, Regional Director Human Resources, CHRISTUS Hospital–St. Elizabeth, Beaumont, TX, p. A601

FOSTER, Chris, Director Health Information Management, Deer Lodge Medical Center, Deer Lodge, MT, p. A386

FOSTER, Daniel J., Chief Financial Officer, South Davis Community Hospital, Bountiful, UT, p. A659

FOSTER, Gary, R.N. Assistant Administrator, Banner Estrella Medical Center, Phoenix, AZ, p. A35

FOSTER, Gary, Vice President and Chief Financial Officer, Saratoga Hospital, Saratoga Springs, NY, p. A454

FOSTER, Joel, Director Human Resources, Massac Memorial Hospital, Metropolis, IL, p. A196

FOSTER, Michael, Director Information Systems, East Cooper Medical Center, Mount Pleasant, SC, p. A568

FOSTER, Mickey, President, Moses H. Cone Memorial Hospital, Greensboro, NC, p. A465

FOSTER, Mike, Manager Information Systems, Moab Regional Hospital, Moab, UT, p. A660

FOSTER, Mitzi, Director Information Services, Southern Tennessee Regional Health System–Pulaski, Pulaski, TN, p. A592

FOSTER, Patrick A., President and Chief Executive Officer, Centerre Healthcare, Brentwood, TN, p. B33

FOSTER, Rebecca, Chief Nursing Officer, Cumberland Medical Center, Crossville, TN, p. A582

FOSTER, Richard, Chief Financial Officer, Integris Clinton Regional Hospital, Clinton, OK, p. A509

FOSTER, Robert, Director Human Resources, L. V. Stabler Memorial Hospital, Greenville, AL, p. A21

FOSTER, Stephanie, MSN Chief Nursing Officer, Longview Regional Medical Center, Longview, TX, p. A634

FOSTER, Steven, Chief Executive Officer, Barstow Community Hospital, Barstow, CA, p. A58

FOSTER, Terri, Hospital Finance Officer, Baylor Regional Medical Center at Grapevine, Grapevine, TX, p. A621

FOSTER, Wanda, R.N. Vice President Nursing, McDonough District Hospital, Macomb, IL, p. A195

FOTIADIS, George, M.D. Chief of Staff, Clarke County Hospital, Osceola, IA, p. A236

FOTTER, Robert L., Chief Financial Officer, Littleton Regional Hospital, Littleton, NH, p. A411

FOUGHT, Scott, Vice President Finance, ProMedica Bay Park Hospital, Oregon, OH, p. A500

FOULKE, Elvia, Executive Vice President and Chief Operating Officer, Foothill Presbyterian Hospital, Glendora, CA, p. A66

FOUNTAIN, Aaron, Chief Information Officer, Brandon Regional Hospital, Brandon, FL, p. A124

FOUNTAIN, Wesley D., Chief Financial Officer, St. David's South Austin Medical Center, Austin, TX, p. A600

FOUSE, Carla, Chief Nursing Officer, St. Vincent Randolph Hospital, Winchester, IN, p. A224

FOUSE, Sarah, Associate Director of Patient Services, Captain James A. Lovell Federal Health Care Center, North Chicago, IL, p. A198

FOUST, Lisa, Senior Vice President Human Resources, John Muir Medical Center, Concord, Concord, CA, p. A60

FOUTS, Phillip
Chief Financial Officer, Chesterfield General Hospital, Cheraw, SC, p. A563
Chief Financial Officer, Marlboro Park Hospital, Bennettsville, SC, p. A562

FOUTZ, Patricia, Director Human Resources, Bath Community Hospital, Hot Springs, VA, p. A672

FOWLER, Andrew, Vice President Information Services, Atlantic General Hospital, Berlin, MD, p. A298

FOWLER, Andy, Senior Vice President Information Systems, Methodist Healthcare Memphis Hospitals, Memphis, TN, p. A589

FOWLER, Barry, Director Human and System Resources, Clark Fork Valley Hospital, Plains, MT, p. A390

FOWLER, Denise, R.N. Chief Clinical Officer, Whitman Hospital and Medical Center, Colfax, WA, p. A682

FOWLER, Eileen, Clinical Director and Chief Nursing Officer, New Horizons Health Systems, Owenton, KY, p. A268

Index of Health Care Professionals / Frimodig

FREDERICK, Wayne A. I., Interim Chief Executive Officer, Howard University Hospital, Washington, DC, p. A121
FREDERICKS, Raymond F., President and Chief Executive Officer, JFK Health System, Edison, NJ, p. B78
FREDERICKS, Raymond F., President and CEO, JFK Medical Center, Edison, NJ, p. A415
FREDERICKSON, Kathy, Information Systems Site Lead, Sutter Delta Medical Center, Antioch, CA, p. A56
FREDETTE, Beth, Chief Information Officer, Children's Medical Center, Dayton, OH, p. A491
FREDRICH, Nancy, R.N. Chief Clinical Officer, Cooper County Memorial Hospital, Boonville, MO, p. A368
FREDRICK, Joyce, Associate Director, VA Central Western Massachusetts Healthcare System, Leeds, MA, p. A311
FREDRICK, Rick, Director Information Technology, Cottage Hospital, Woodsville, NH, p. A412
FREDRICKSON, Kelley, Director Information Services, Plaza Medical Center of Fort Worth, Fort Worth, TX, p. A619
FREDRICKSON, Mark A., M.D. Medical Director, HEALTHSOUTH Rehabilitation Hospital Midland–Odessa, Midland, TX, p. A638
FREEBURG, Rick, Chief Executive Officer, Baptist Health South Florida, Mariners Hospital, Tavernier, FL, p. A148
FREEBURN, Mark, Chief Executive Officer, HEALTHSOUTH Rehabilitation Hospital of Mechanicsburg, Mechanicsburg, PA, p. A544
FREED, David H., President and Chief Executive Officer, Nyack Hospital, Nyack, NY, p. A450
FREED, Glenn, D.O. Medical Director, St. Luke's Hospital – Miners Campus, Coaldale, PA, p. A536
FREED, Nancy, Chief Financial Officer, Seiling Community Hospital, Seiling, OK, p. A518
FREED, Stuart, M.D
  Chief Medical Officer, Central Washington Hospital, Wenatchee, WA, p. A692
  Medical Director, Wenatchee Valley Medical Center, Wenatchee, WA, p. A692
FREED–SIGURDSSON, Anna, M.D. Medical Director, Reliant Rehabilitation Hospital Dallas, Dallas, TX, p. A611
FREEDMAN, Barry R., President and Chief Executive Officer, Einstein Healthcare Network, Philadelphia, PA, p. B56
FREEDMAN, Barry R., President and Chief Executive Officer, Einstein Medical Center Philadelphia, Philadelphia, PA, p. A548
FREEDMAN, Kenneth, M.D. Chief Medical Officer, Lemuel Shattuck Hospital, Jamaica Plain, MA, p. A311
FREEDMAN, Liz, Director Human Resources, Mercy Health – West Hospital, Cincinnati, OH, p. A487
FREEHOF, Leonard, Chief Executive Officer and Managing Director, Spring Valley Hospital Medical Center, Las Vegas, NV, p. A406
FREELAND, R. Alan, M.D. Chief Clinical Officer, Twin Valley Behavioral Healthcare, Columbus, OH, p. A491
FREEMAN, Amy E., President and Chief Executive Officer, Providence Hospital, Washington, DC, p. A121
FREEMAN, Brian, Vice President of Operations, Stanly Regional Medical Center, Albemarle, NC, p. A459
FREEMAN, Diane, R.N. Assistant Vice President and Chief Nursing Officer, St. Luke's Lakeside Hospital, The Woodlands, TX, p. A653
FREEMAN, Donald, President and Chief Executive Officer, Preferred Management Corporation, Shawnee, OK, p. B107
FREEMAN, Elizabeth Joyce, FACHE, Director, Veterans Affairs Palo Alto Health Care System, Palo Alto, CA, p. A82
FREEMAN, Jerry, Chief, Human Resources Management Services, Durham Veterans Affairs Medical Center, Durham, NC, p. A463
FREEMAN, Kimberlee, R.N. Vice President Patient Care Services and Chief Nursing Officer, Wayne Hospital, Greenville, OH, p. A495
FREEMAN, Marianne, Vice President Human Resources, Rockdale Medical Center, Conyers, GA, p. A157
FREEMAN, Megan, Chief Nursing Officer, Trinity Hospital of Augusta, Augusta, GA, p. A154
FREEMAN, Michael
  Director Human Resources, Alta Vista Regional Hospital, Las Vegas, NM, p. A429
  Director Human Resources, Huhukam Memorial Hospital, Sacaton, AZ, p. A38
FREEMAN, Mike, Director Information Technology, Sentara Williamsburg Regional Medical Center, Williamsburg, VA, p. A680
FREEMAN, Nikki, Vice President Human Resources, Wesley Medical Center, Wichita, KS, p. A257
FREEMAN, Richard, President and Chief Executive Officer, Robert Wood Johnson University Hospital at Hamilton, Hamilton, NJ, p. A416
FREEMAN, Robert, Director Human Resources, Sparks Regional Medical Center, Fort Smith, AR, p. A46
FREEMAN, Susan, M.D. Chief Medical Officer, Temple University Hospital, Philadelphia, PA, p. A550

FREER, Carol V., M.D. Chief Medical Officer, Penn State Milton S. Hershey Medical Center, Hershey, PA, p. A540
FREESE–DECKER, Christina, President, Spectrum Health Hospital Group, Spectrum Health – Butterworth Hospital, Grand Rapids, MI, p. A325
FREID–SCHEPPKE, Denise, Chief Accounting Officer, Oakleaf Surgical Hospital, Eau Claire, WI, p. A704
FREIER, Toby, President, New Ulm Medical Center, New Ulm, MN, p. A348
FREIJ, Walid, M.D. Chief of Staff, Vaughan Regional Medical Center, Selma, AL, p. A25
FREIMARK, Jeffrey P., Chief Executive Officer, Miami Jewish Home and Hospital for Aged, Miami, FL, p. A137
FREIMUND, Rooney, R.N. Chief Nurse Executive, Bay Area Medical Center, Marinette, WI, p. A708
FREIN, Ethel, Chief Executive Officer, Bennett County Hospital and Nursing Home, Martin, SD, p. A574
FREIS, Leon, Chief Operating Officer, Northern Inyo Hospital, Bishop, CA, p. A58
FREITAG, Donald, M.D. Chief Medical Officer, Lynn County Hospital District, Tahoka, TX, p. A651
FREITAG, Vanessa, President, Ministry Our Lady of Victory Hospital, Stanley, WI, p. A715
FRELING, Eric, M.D. Director Medical Staff Affairs, Memorial Hospital West, Pembroke Pines, FL, p. A142
FRENCH, Adam, M.D. Chief Medical Officer, Saint Catherine Regional Hospital, Charlestown, IN, p. A208
FRENCH, Dean, M.D., Chief Executive Officer, Sierra Vista Regional Health Medical Center, Sierra Vista, AZ, p. A39
FRENCH, Dean O., M.D. Chief of Staff, Faith Regional Health Services, Norfolk, NE, p. A398
FRENCH III, George E., FACHE, Chief Executive Officer, Minden Medical Center, Minden, LA, p. A284
FRENCH, Holly, Chief Financial Officer, Newman Regional Health, Emporia, KS, p. A243
FRENCH, Michael, Interim Chief Executive Officer, Providence Hospital, Columbia, SC, p. A564
FRENCH, Tracy
  Chief Financial Officer, Banner Goldfield Medical Center, Apache Junction, AZ, p. A31
  Chief Financial Officer, Banner Ironwood Medical Center, San Tan Valley, AZ, p. A38
FRENCH, William Chad, Chief Executive Officer, Davis Regional Medical Center, Statesville, NC, p. A473
FRENN, Debra, FACHE Chief Patient Care Officer, Rusk County Memorial Hospital, Ladysmith, WI, p. A707
FRERER, Mary
  Chief Human Resources Officer, Freeman Hospital West, Joplin, MO, p. A373
  Chief Human Resources Officer, Freeman Neosho Hospital, Neosho, MO, p. A377
FRERICHS, Craig, Chief Information Technology Service, Grand Junction Veterans Affairs Medical Center, Grand Junction, CO, p. A107
FRESH, John, Vice President Human Resources, Conemaugh Miners Medical Center, Hastings, PA, p. A540
FRESHOUR, David, Chief Financial Officer, Comanche County Medical Center, Comanche, TX, p. A607
FRESQUEZ, Juan, Chief Operating Officer, Houston Northwest Medical Center, Houston, TX, p. A625
FREUDENBERG, Liz, Chief Financial Officer, HEALTHSOUTH Rehabilitation Hospital of Denver, Littleton, CO, p. A109
FREUDENBERGER, Joe, Chief Executive Officer, OakBend Medical Center, Richmond, TX, p. A644
FREY, Jack, Acting Business Manager, Greystone Park Psychiatric Hospital, Morris Plains, NJ, p. A418
FREY, Jeff, Business Administrator, Andrew McFarland Mental Health Center, Springfield, IL, p. A203
FREY, Paul, Director Information Technology Applications, Indiana Orthopaedic Hospital, Indianapolis, IN, p. A214
FREY, Rachel, Director Human Resources, Athens–Limestone Hospital, Athens, AL, p. A16
FREYER, Mary, Chief Operating Officer, Little Company of Mary Hospital and Health Care Centers, Evergreen Park, IL, p. A190
FREYER, Sharon, R.N. Chief Nursing Officer, Westlake Hospital, Melrose Park, IL, p. A196
FREYMULLER, Robert S., Chief Executive Officer, Summerlin Hospital Medical Center, Las Vegas, NV, p. A406
FREYSINGER, Edward E., Chief Executive Officer, Providence Hood River Memorial Hospital, Hood River, OR, p. A525
FREYTAG, Peter, Senior Vice President Finance and Chief Financial Officer, Bristol Hospital, Bristol, CT, p. A113
FRIARTE, Pedro, Director of Physician Services, Coral Gables Hospital, Coral Gables, FL, p. A126
FRIBBLEY, Charles, Director Information Services, Edward White Hospital, Saint Petersburg, FL, p. A144
FRICK, Mark P., Senior Vice President Human Resources, Somerset Hospital, Somerset, PA, p. A555

FRICK, Mary Jo, Director Finance, St. Catherine's Rehabilitation Hospital, North Miami, FL, p. A139
FRICKE, Rhett D., Chief Financial Officer, Frio Regional Hospital, Pearsall, TX, p. A641
FRICKS, Tom, Interim Senior Vice President of Information Technology, PeaceHealth Sacred Heart Medical Center at RiverBend, Springfield, OR, p. A530
FRIDAY, Jason, M.D. Medical Director, Aurora Tempe Hospital, Tempe, AZ, p. A39
FRIDOVICH, Mark, Ph.D., Administrator, Hawaii State Hospital, Kaneohe, HI, p. A172
FRIED, Guy, M.D. Chief Medical Officer, Magee Rehabilitation Hospital, Philadelphia, PA, p. A549
FRIED, Jeffrey M., FACHE, President and Chief Executive Officer, Beebe Healthcare, Lewes, DE, p. A119
FRIED, Tera, Manager Human Resources, West River Regional Medical Center, Hettinger, ND, p. A478
FRIEDBERG, Robert, President, Vassar Brothers Medical Center, Poughkeepsie, NY, p. A452
FRIEDELL, Benjamin, Vice President Medical Affairs, Aurelia Osborn Fox Memorial Hospital, Oneonta, NY, p. A450
FRIEDEN, Robert
  Vice President Information Systems, Genesis Medical Center, Illini Campus, Silvis, IL, p. A202
  Vice President Information Systems, Genesis Medical Center–Aledo, Aledo, IL, p. A180
  Vice President Information Systems, Genesis Medical Center–Davenport, Davenport, IA, p. A228
FRIEDENBACH, Daryl, Director Fiscal Services, Floyd Valley Hospital, Le Mars, IA, p. A233
FRIEDLINE, Jennifer, R.N. Director of Nursing, Mercy Rehabilitation Hospital Springfield, Springfield, MO, p. A383
FRIEDLY, Jennifer, Chief Operating Officer and Vice President, UnityPoint Health – Allen Hospital, Waterloo, IA, p. A239
FRIEDMAN, Greg, Director Information Technology, Children's Hospital of Richmond at VCU–Brook Road Campus, Richmond, VA, p. A677
FRIEDMAN, Jonathan, Public Affairs Officer, Captain James A. Lovell Federal Health Care Center, North Chicago, IL, p. A198
FRIEDMAN, Lloyd, M.D. Vice President Medical Affairs and Chief Operating Officer, Milford Hospital, Milford, CT, p. A115
FRIEDMAN, Ross, Chief Operating Officer, Greystone Park Psychiatric Hospital, Morris Plains, NJ, p. A418
FRIEDMAN, Steven G., M.D. Interim Chief Medical Officer and Chair, Department of Surgery, New York Presbyterian Lower Manhattan Hospital, New York, NY, p. A447
FRIEDRICH III, Daniel J., Chief Executive Officer, Blake Medical Center, Bradenton, FL, p. A124
FRIEL, Donald F., Executive Vice President, Holy Redeemer Hospital, Meadowbrook, PA, p. A544
FRIEL, John P., Chief Executive Officer, Catalina Island Medical Center, Avalon, CA, p. A56
FRIELING, Jeff
  Vice President Information Systems, Camden General Hospital, Camden, TN, p. A579
  Vice President and Chief Information Officer, Jackson–Madison County General Hospital, Jackson, TN, p. A584
  Chief Information Officer, Pathways of Tennessee, Jackson, TN, p. A584
FRIELING, Morris J., Chief Financial Officer, UC Irvine Medical Center, Orange, CA, p. A81
FRIEND, Lori
  Director Human Resources, Integris Marshall County Medical Center, Madill, OK, p. A513
  Human Resources Director, Integris Seminole Medical Center, Seminole, OK, p. A518
FRIER, Nancy, Chief Financial Officer, Eastern Oklahoma Medical Center, Poteau, OK, p. A517
FRIES, Bob, Director Fiscal Services, Colorado Mental Health Institute at Fort Logan, Denver, CO, p. A104
FRIESEN, Dale L., Chief Financial Officer, CareLink of Jackson, Jackson, MI, p. A328
FRIESEN, Lynette, Manager Human Resources, Henderson Health Care Services, Henderson, NE, p. A396
FRIESEN, Nancy, Chief Financial Officer, CentraCare Health–Monticello, Monticello, MN, p. A348
FRIESEN, Quinton J., Executive Vice President and Chief Operating Officer, Greenwich Hospital, Greenwich, CT, p. A114
FRIGEN, Karen, Director Human Resources, Shriners Hospitals for Children–Twin Cities, Minneapolis, MN, p. A347
FRIGON, Shelby, Chief Financial Officer, Saint Luke's South Hospital, Overland Park, KS, p. A252
FRIGY, Alan, M.D. President Medical Staff, Pana Community Hospital, Pana, IL, p. A199
FRIMODIG, Mindy, D.O. President Medical Staff ThedaCare Physicians Shawano, Shawano Medical Center, Shawano, WI, p. A715

FRISBEE, Kent, Director Human Resources, Highlands Medical Center, Sparta, TN, p. A593

FRITSCH, William, M.D. Medical Director, Landmark Hospital, Cape Girardeau, MO, p. A368

FRITSCHEN, James, Chief Executive Officer, Louisiana Continuing Care Hospital, Marrero, LA, p. A283

FRITTON, Amy, Controller, Sierra Tucson, Tucson, AZ, p. A40

FRITTS, Doris, R.N., Executive Director, Same Day Surgery Center, Rapid City, SD, p. A576

FRITTS, Robert G., Chief Financial Officer and Senior Vice President, Blue Ridge Healthcare Hospitals, Morganton, NC, p. A469

FRITZ, Thomas M., Chief Executive Officer, St. Luke's Rehabilitation Institute, Spokane, WA, p. A690

FROCHTZWAJG, Stanley, M.D. Chief Medical Officer, Community Memorial Health System, Ventura, CA, p. A99

FRODIN–WHITE, Karin, Chief Nursing Officer, North Canyon Medical Center, Gooding, ID, p. A176

FROEHLICH, Shelley, R.N. Director Nursing Services, Newport Hospital and Health Services, Newport, WA, p. A685

FROEMKE, Janet, Human Resources Officer, Lisbon Area Health Services, Lisbon, ND, p. A479

FROESE, Stacy
  Regional Director Human Resources, Integris Bass Pavilion, Enid, OK, p. A510
  Regional Director Human Resources, Integris Grove Hospital, Grove, OK, p. A511

FROH, Chris, Senior Coordinator Human Resources, Select Specialty Hospital–Milwaukee, Milwaukee, WI, p. A711

FROHNHOFER, Erin J., Director Human Resources, Southwood Psychiatric Hospital, Pittsburgh, PA, p. A551

FROIMSON, Mark, M.D., President, Euclid Hospital, Euclid, OH, p. A493

FROIO, Ann M., Interim Chief Executive Officer, Arizona State Hospital, Phoenix, AZ, p. A35

FROISLAND, Jeffrey R., Chief Financial Officer, Mayo Clinic Hospital, Phoenix, AZ, p. A36

FROMHOLD, John A., Chief Executive Officer, Hackensack University Medical Center Mountainside, Montclair, NJ, p. A418

FROMM, Robert, M.D. Chief Medical Officer, Maricopa Integrated Health System, Phoenix, AZ, p. A36

FROMME, Pete, Chief Financial Officer, Fayette County Hospital, Vandalia, IL, p. A204

FROMMELT, William, Director Operations and Finance, River Falls Area Hospital, River Falls, WI, p. A714

FROSCH, Kevin, Chief Financial Officer, Medina Regional Hospital, Hondo, TX, p. A623

FROST, Eric, Associate Vice President Human Resources, Upstate University Hospital, Syracuse, NY, p. A456

FROST, Joan, R.N. Chief Operating Officer, Mercy Hospital Washington, Washington, MO, p. A384

FROST, Mark I., M.D. Vice President Medical Staff Affairs, Laureate Psychiatric Clinic and Hospital, Tulsa, OK, p. A520

FROST, Sarah
  Administrator, University of Arizona Medical Center – South Campus, Tucson, AZ, p. A41
  Chief Operating Officer and Administrator, University of Arizona Medical Center – South Campus, University of Arizona Medical Center – University Campus, Tucson, AZ, p. A41

FROST–KUNNEN, Jacqueline C., R.N. Senior Vice President Operations, Mercy Medical Center–Des Moines, Des Moines, IA, p. A229

FRUGE, Janie, MSN, Chief Executive Officer, West Calcasieu Cameron Hospital, Sulphur, LA, p. A289

FRUM, Judy, R.N. Chief Nursing Officer, Memorial Hospital Pembroke, Pembroke Pines, FL, p. A142

FRUM, R. David
  President, Bridgton Hospital, Bridgton, ME, p. A292
  President, Rumford Hospital, Rumford, ME, p. A295

FRUSH, Wendy, R.N. Nursing Executive, Mackinac Straits Health System, Saint Ignace, MI, p. A334

FRY, David, Vice President of Operations, Decatur County Memorial Hospital, Greensburg, IN, p. A212

FRY, Patrick E., President and Chief Executive Officer, Sutter Health, Sacramento, CA, p. B130

FRYE, Kelly D., Director Human Resources, Montgomery General Hospital, Montgomery, WV, p. A697

FRYE, Terri, Information Technology Officer, Weston County Health Services, Newcastle, WY, p. A722

FRYER, Ramona D., Chief Financial Officer, WK Bossier Health Center, Bossier City, LA, p. A274

FUCCI, Thomas, Chief Operating Officer, Saint Vincent Health Center, Erie, PA, p. A539

FUCHS, Jonathan, Chief Information Officer, DeWitt Hospital, De Witt, AR, p. A45

FUCHS, Mary Ann, R.N. Chief Nursing Officer, Duke University Hospital, Durham, NC, p. A463

FUCILE, Joanne, MSN Vice President Patient Care Services, Spaulding Hospital for Continuing Medical Care North Shore, Salem, MA, p. A314

FUEHRER, Susan, Director, Louis Stokes Cleveland Veterans Affairs Medical Center, Cleveland, OH, p. A488

FUENTES, Frances, Coordinator Human Resources, HEALTHSOUTH Rehabilitation Hospital of San Juan, San Juan, PR, p. A728

FUENTES, Leticia, Nursing Director, San Jorge Children's Hospital, San Juan, PR, p. A728

FUENTES Jr., Miguel A., President and Chief Executive Officer, Bronx–Lebanon Hospital Center Health Care System,, NY, p. A442

FUERSTENBERG, Donna, Fiscal Chief, Sheridan Veterans Affairs Medical Center, Sheridan, WY, p. A722

FUGATTE, Cheryl, MSN Vice President and Chief Nursing Officer, Jewish Hospital, Louisville, KY, p. A265

FUGAZY, Christopher, Chief Operating Officer, Jacobi Medical Center,, NY, p. A444

FUGLEBERG, Jason, R.N. Vice President Patient Services and Chief Nursing Officer, Millinocket Regional Hospital, Millinocket, ME, p. A294

FUHRMAN, Bradley, M.D. Physician in Chief, El Paso Children's Hospital, El Paso, TX, p. A615

FUHRMAN, Dennis, Vice President Finance, Essentia Health Fargo, Fargo, ND, p. A477

FUHRMAN, Geri, Chief Nursing Officer, I–70 Community Hospital, Sweet Springs, MO, p. A383

FUHS, Veronica, Chief Executive Officer, Lucas County Health Center, Chariton, IA, p. A227

FUJINAKA, Jason, Manager Information System, Wahiawa General Hospital, Wahiawa, HI, p. A172

FULCHER, Cathe, Superintendent, Evansville State Hospital, Evansville, IN, p. A210

FULCHER, Kimberly, Chief Human Resources Officer, Halifax Health Medical Center of Daytona Beach, Daytona Beach, FL, p. A127

FULCHER, Martha, MSN Chief Nursing Officer, OCH Regional Medical Center, Starkville, MS, p. A365

FULKERSON, Judy, Director Human Resources, TriStar Greenview Regional Hospital, Bowling Green, KY, p. A259

FULKERSON, Richard, Director Fiscal Services, Shriners Hospitals for Children–Springfield, Springfield, MA, p. A315

FULKERSON, William J., M.D., Interim President and Chief Executive Officer, Duke University Health System, Durham, NC, p. B54

FULKS, Chris, Vice President Finance, St. Joseph Mercy Port Huron, Port Huron, MI, p. A333

FULKS, Gerald N., President and Chief Executive Officer, West Georgia Health, La Grange, GA, p. A162

FULLBRIGHT, Gary D., Comptroller, Citizens Memorial Hospital, Bolivar, MO, p. A367

FULLER, Cara
  Vice President Human Resources, UnityPoint Health – Trinity Bettendorf, Bettendorf, IA, p. A225
  Vice President Human Resources, UnityPoint Health – Trinity Rock Island, Rock Island, IL, p. A201

FULLER, Cheryl, Director Information Resources, Kansas Neurological Institute, Topeka, KS, p. A255

FULLER, Dale, Vice President and Chief Information Officer, UPMC Altoona, Altoona, PA, p. A532

FULLER, David, Director Human Resources, Porter Medical Center, Middlebury, VT, p. A665

FULLER, David W., Chief Executive Officer, North Okaloosa Medical Center, Crestview, FL, p. A126

FULLER, Debbie, Director Health Information Systems and Chief Information Officer, Doctors Medical Center, Modesto, CA, p. A77

FULLER, Jeremy, Director Information Systems, Conroe Regional Medical Center, Conroe, TX, p. A607

FULLER, Jill, Ph.D., President and Chief Executive Officer, Prairie Lakes Healthcare System, Watertown, SD, p. A578

FULLER, Lexie, Controller, Specialty Hospital of Meridian, Meridian, MS, p. A363

FULLER, Robert, Executive Vice President and Chief Operating Officer, Downey Regional Medical Center, Downey, CA, p. A61

FULLOP, Julko, M.D. Chief of Staff, Wabash General Hospital, Mount Carmel, IL, p. A197

FULTON, Diane, R.N. Chief Nursing Officer, Rapides Regional Medical Center, Alexandria, LA, p. A272

FULTON, Lorna, Director Human Resources, Vibra Hospital of Denver, Thornton, CO, p. A111

FULTON, Lynn, President, OSF Saint Luke Medical Center, Kewanee, IL, p. A194

FUNDERBURG, Michelle, Director Human Resources, Stephens Memorial Hospital, Breckenridge, TX, p. A603

FUNDERBURK, Mark, Executive Vice President and Administrator, University Medical Center, Lubbock, TX, p. A635

FUNG, Adrian, Director Information Systems, University Medical Center, Lebanon, TN, p. A586

FUNK, Luann, Administrative Assistant and Manager Human Resources, Pana Community Hospital, Pana, IL, p. A199

FUNKHOUSER, Krisy L., Manager Human Resources, Willapa Harbor Hospital, South Bend, WA, p. A690

FUNKHOUSER, Lana, Vice President Human Resources, Indiana University Health West Hospital, Avon, IN, p. A206

FUQUA, David, Director Human Resources Management, University Health Shreveport, Shreveport, LA, p. A288

FUQUA, David G., Chief Executive Officer, Marshall County Hospital, Benton, KY, p. A258

FUQUA, Leon, Chief Operating Officer, Wise Regional Health System, Decatur, TX, p. A612

FUQUA, William, Administrator, MMO Greenbrier Hospital, Covington, LA, p. A276

FURER, Darnell F., R.N., Acting Administrator, Schuylkill Health System, Pottsville, PA, p. B119

FURER, Darnell F., R.N., Acting Administrator, Schuylkill Medical Center – East Norwegian Street, Pottsville, PA, p. A553

FURER, Darnell F., MS Vice President of Patient Care Services, Schuylkill Medical Center – East Norwegian Street, Pottsville, PA, p. A553

FURER, Darnell F., R.N., Acting Administrator, Schuylkill Medical Center – South Jackson Street, Pottsville, PA, p. A553

FURER, Darnell F., MS Vice President Patient Care Services and Chief Nursing Officer, Schuylkill Medical Center – South Jackson Street, Pottsville, PA, p. A553

FURGURSON, Carol, Chief Operating Officer, Saint Louise Regional Hospital, Gilroy, CA, p. A65

FURLONG, Marian M., FACHE, Chief Executive Officer, Hudson Hospital and Clinic, Hudson, WI, p. A706

FURLOW, Pete, Director Information Technology Services, Northeast Alabama Regional Medical Center, Anniston, AL, p. A15

FURNAS, David, Chief Information Officer, Gila Regional Medical Center, Silver City, NM, p. A431

FURNEY, June, R.N. Director of Nursing, Brooks County Hospital, Quitman, GA, p. A165

FURNISS, Scott, Senior Vice President and Chief Financial Officer, Saint Agnes Hospital, Baltimore, MD, p. A297

FURR, Robert, Director Information Services, Cannon Memorial Hospital, Pickens, SC, p. A569

FUSCHILLO, Ronald, Chief Information Officer, Englewood Hospital and Medical Center, Englewood, NJ, p. A416

FUSCO, Kevin, Chief Operating Officer, Broward Health North, Deerfield Beach, FL, p. A127

FUSELIER, Gerald, Chief Operating Officer, Savoy Medical Center, Mamou, LA, p. A283

FUSELIER, Michael, FACHE Chief Financial Officer, Central Louisiana Surgical Hospital, Alexandria, LA, p. A272

FUSSELL, Eugene, M.D
  Chief Medical Officer, St. John's Pleasant Valley Hospital, Camarillo, CA, p. A58
  Chief Medical Officer, St. John's Regional Medical Center, Oxnard, CA, p. A82

FUSTER, Carmen G., Nursing Director, Hospital Metropolitano Dr. Susoni, Arecibo, PR, p. A724

FUSTO, Gregg, Chief Nursing Officer, University Medical Center, Las Vegas, NV, p. A407

FUTCH, Margaret A., Chief Executive Officer, HEALTHSOUTH Rehabilitation Hospital, Dothan, AL, p. A19

FUTCH, Sharon
  Interim Vice President Human Resources, Anderson Regional Medical Center, Meridian, MS, p. A362
  Interim Vice President Human Resources, Anderson Regional Medical Center–South Campus, Meridian, MS, p. A362

FUTRAL, Cindy, Director Human Resources, Elmore Community Hospital, Wetumpka, AL, p. A26

FUTRELL, Bradley, Chief Operating Officer, Hamilton Memorial Hospital District, McLeansboro, IL, p. A196

FYBEL, Gary G., Chief Executive, Senior Vice President, Scripps Memorial Hospital–La Jolla, La Jolla, CA, p. A68

G

GAAL, James G., M.D. Chief of Medical Staff, Jackson General Hospital, Ripley, WV, p. A699

GAAL, John M., Deputy Commander Administration, Walter Reed National Military Medical Center, Bethesda, MD, p. A299

GAASCH, Andrew
  Chief Financial Officer, Parker Adventist Hospital, Parker, CO, p. A110
  Chief Financial Officer, Porter Adventist Hospital, Denver, CO, p. A105

GABALDON, Karen, Chief Management Information Systems, West Palm Beach Veterans Affairs Medical Center, West Palm Beach, FL, p. A150

GABARRO, Ralph, Interim Chief Executive Officer, Down East Community Hospital, Machias, ME, p. A294

GABBE, Steven, M.D., Chief Executive Officer, Ohio State University Wexner Medical Center, Columbus, OH, p. A490

GABEL, Christopher, Chief Operating Officer, Hollywood Pavilion,, FL, p. A130

GABEL, Marcia, Chief Financial Officer, Lane County Hospital, Dighton, KS, p. A243

GABEL, Phyllis, Chief Human Resource Officer, St. Luke's Rehabilitation Institute, Spokane, WA, p. A690

GABLE, Beth, Administrative Assistant, Jasper General Hospital, Bay Springs, MS, p. A355

GABLENZ, Gordon, Vice President Finance, Ridgeview Medical Center, Waconia, MN, p. A353

GABORIAULT, Randall, Chief Information Officer, Christiana Care Health System, Newark, DE, p. A119

GABRIEL, Scott F., President, Parkview Whitley Hospital, Columbia City, IN, p. A208

GABRIELE, Joan, Deputy Executive Director, Queens Hospital Center,, NY, p. A448

GABRYEL, Timothy, M.D. Vice President Medical Affairs and Medical Director, Mercy Hospital, Buffalo, NY, p. A434

GADALLAH, Yousri, M.D. Chief Medical Officer, Pershing General Hospital, Lovelock, NV, p. A407

GADDIS, Cathryn, Director Human Resources, RiverValley Behavioral Health Hospital, Owensboro, KY, p. A268

GADE, Swami P., M.D. Medical Director, Tioga Medical Center, Tioga, ND, p. A480

GADEN, Paul, Chief Executive Officer, Providence Portland Medical Center, Portland, OR, p. A528

GADOMSKI, Veronica, R.N. Chief Nursing Officer, HEALTHSOUTH Rehabilitation Hospital, Albuquerque, NM, p. A426

GAEDE, John, Director Information Systems, El Centro Regional Medical Center, El Centro, CA, p. A62

GAENZLE, Jack, Senior Vice President Finance and Administration, UPMC Mercy, Pittsburgh, PA, p. A551

GAFFOLI, Jill, Director Human Resources, Physicians Regional – Pine Ridge, Naples, FL, p. A139

GAFFORD, Deborah, Chief Financial Officer, Menorah Medical Center, Overland Park, KS, p. A252

GAGE, Bobby, Director Information Technology, Wabash General Hospital, Mount Carmel, IL, p. A197

GAGE, Eileen, R.N
   Vice President Nursing, Geneva General Hospital, Geneva, NY, p. A437
   Vice President Nursing, Soldiers and Sailors Memorial Hospital of Yates County, Penn Yan, NY, p. A451

GAGE, Kevin, Chief Financial Officer, Stamford Hospital, Stamford, CT, p. A117

GAGE, Mark, D.O. Medical Director, Brookhaven Hospital, Tulsa, OK, p. A520

GAGE, Susan, Financial Manager, Veterans Affairs Western New York Healthcare System–Buffalo Division, Buffalo, NY, p. A435

GAGLIARDI, Teresa, R.N. Chief Nursing Officer, Trinity Hospital Twin City, Dennison, OH, p. A493

GAGLIO, Tony, Chief Financial Officer, Henry Ford Kingswood Hospital, Ferndale, MI, p. A323

GAGNON, Andy, Director Information Technology, Mercy Regional Health Center,, KS, p. A249

GAGNON, Lynne, R.N. Chief Nursing Officer, Mayo Regional Hospital, Dover–Foxcroft, ME, p. A293

GAINER, Rolf B., Chief Executive Officer and Administrator, Brookhaven Hospital, Tulsa, OK, p. A520

GAIRE, Susan, M.D. President Medical Staff, Frisbie Memorial Hospital, Rochester, NH, p. A412

GAITAN, Alberto, M.D. Medical Director, O'Connor Hospital, Delhi, NY, p. A436

GAITER, Thomas E., M.D. Chief Medical Officer, Howard University Hospital, Washington, DC, p. A121

GAJ, Steve, Facility Chief Information Officer, Louis Stokes Cleveland Veterans Affairs Medical Center, Cleveland, OH, p. A488

GAJARE, N., M.D. Chief Clinical Affairs, Kalamazoo Psychiatric Hospital, Kalamazoo, MI, p. A328

GAJEWSKI, Christie, Director Human Resources, Pinckneyville Community Hospital, Pinckneyville, IL, p. A200

GALANDA, Chris, Chief Information Officer, Wilkes–Barre General Hospital, Wilkes–Barre, PA, p. A558

GALANG, Michael, M.D
   Chief Information Officer, Mercy Hospital, Buffalo, NY, p. A434
   Chief Information Officer, Sisters of Charity Hospital of Buffalo, Buffalo, NY, p. A435

GALARNEAU, Gerard, M.D., Chief Executive Officer and Chief Medical Officer, Catskill Regional Medical Center, Harris, NY, p. A438

GALATI, John P., Interim Chief Executive Officer, Lake Shore Health Care Center, Irving, NY, p. A439

GALATI, Vicki L., Chief Financial Officer, Texas Health Specialty Hospital, Fort Worth, TX, p. A619

GALBRAITH, Kathleen B., President, Duke Regional Hospital, Durham, NC, p. A463

GALDIERI, Lou, R.N.,
   President, Mease Countryside Hospital, Safety Harbor, FL, p. A144
   President, Mease Dunedin Hospital, Dunedin, FL, p. A128

GALE, Brendan, Chief Financial Officer, Middle Park Medical Center–Kremmling, Kremmling, CO, p. A108

GALE, Donald I., M.D. Vice President Medical Affairs, Winter Haven Hospital, Winter Haven, FL, p. A150

GALE, Gabrielle, Chief Financial Officer, Lighthouse Care Center of Conway, Conway, SC, p. A565

GALE, Michael, Chief Financial Officer, Bournewood Health Systems, Brookline, MA, p. A308

GALFANO, Victor J., FACHE, Chief Executive Officer, Select Specialty Hospital–Northern Kentucky, Fort Thomas, KY, p. A261

GALIPEAU, Michelle, Director Human Resources, St. Vincent's Birmingham, Birmingham, AL, p. A17

GALKOWSKI, James, Associate Director for Operations, Fayetteville Veterans Affairs Medical Center, Fayetteville, NC, p. A464

GALLA, Bernie, Interim Director Management Information Systems, Howard University Hospital, Washington, DC, p. A121

GALLAGHER, Doug, Director Human Resources, Carolinas Specialty Hospital, Charlotte, NC, p. A462

GALLAGHER, Frank, Chief Executive Officer, Virginia Beach Psychiatric Center, Virginia Beach, VA, p. A680

GALLAGHER, J. P., Chief Operating Officer, NorthShore University Health System, Evanston, IL, p. A189

GALLAGHER, James P., Chief Executive Officer, Summit Oaks Hospital, Summit, NJ, p. A423

GALLAGHER, Jeannie
   jeanie.gallagher@bannerhealth.com, McKee Medical Center, Loveland, CO, p. A109
   Chief Human Resource Officer, North Colorado Medical Center, Greeley, CO, p. A107

GALLAGHER, John, Chief Executive Officer, Sunnyside Community Hospital and Clinics, Sunnyside, WA, p. A690

GALLAGHER, Joseph, Chief Executive Officer, Wyoming Behavioral Institute, Casper, WY, p. A720

GALLAGHER, Karen, Vice President Human Resources and Learning, Brooks Rehabilitation Hospital, Jacksonville, FL, p. A131

GALLAGHER, Keith W., FACHE, Administrator and Chief Executive Officer, Memorial Hospital Pembroke, Pembroke Pines, FL, p. A142

GALLAGHER, Pamela, Chief Financial Officer, Providence Hospital, Columbia, SC, p. A564

GALLAGHER, Regen, M.D. Chief Medical Officer, Cary Medical Center, Caribou, ME, p. A292

GALLAGHER, Sherry, Director Nursing, Department of Health and Human Services, Humboldt County Mental Health, Eureka, CA, p. A464

GALLAGHER, Thomas E., Chief Financial Officer, Seton Edgar B. Davis Hospital, Luling, TX, p. A636

GALLAGHER, Timothy, M.D. Chief of Staff, Lake District Hospital, Lakeview, OR, p. A526

GALLAHOM, Gerty, Director Human Resources, Maniilaq Health Center, Kotzebue, AK, p. A29

GALLARDO, Kathleen, Chief Nursing Officer, Select Specialty Hospital–Flint, Flint, MI, p. A324

GALLARDO, Ysidro, Associate Administrator Human Resources, Hazel Hawkins Memorial Hospital, Hollister, CA, p. A67

GALLATI, Todd, FACHE, President and Chief Executive Officer, Trident Medical Center, Charleston, SC, p. A563

GALLAY, Emily, Vice President and Chief Information Officer, Lakeland Regional Medical Center–St. Joseph, Saint Joseph, MI, p. A334

GALLEGOS, Colleen, Director Human Resources, Guadalupe County Hospital, Santa Rosa, NM, p. A430

GALLEGOS, Enrique, Chief Operating Officer, Sierra Medical Center, El Paso, TX, p. A616

GALLEGOS, Kelly, Administrator, San Luis Valley Health Conejos County Hospital, La Jara, CO, p. A108

GALLI, Jodi, Chief Nursing Officer, Eastern Maine Medical Center, Bangor, ME, p. A291

GALLIARDT, Scott, Chief Executive Officer, Cornerstone Hospital of Austin, Austin, TX, p. A599

GALLIART, Mark, Chief Executive Officer, McBride Clinic Orthopedic Hospital, Oklahoma City, OK, p. A515

GALLIK, Becky, Information Sytems Manager, FirstLight Health System, Mora, MN, p. A348

GALLIN, John I., M.D., Director, National Institutes of Health Clinical Center, Bethesda, MD, p. A299

GALLO, Ronald, Director Human Resources, Blythedale Children's Hospital, Valhalla, NY, p. A457

GALLOGLY–SIMON, Catherine A., R.N. Chief Nursing Officer, Wyckoff Heights Medical Center,, NY, p. A449

GALLUCCI, Kathleen, Chief Human Resources, Highland Hospital of Rochester, Rochester, NY, p. A453

GALLUCCI, Vince
   Senior Vice President Human Resources, Mercy Medical Center, Oshkosh, WI, p. A713
   Senior Vice President Human Resources, St. Elizabeth Hospital, Appleton, WI, p. A701

GALLUP, Roger A., Deputy Commander Clinical Service, Carl R. Darnall Army Medical Center, Fort Hood, TX, p. A617

GALONSKY, Ronald J., Chief Executive Officer, Lakewood Regional Medical Center, Lakewood, CA, p. A69

GALT, Nick
   Chief Financial Officer, Las Colinas Medical Center, Irving, TX, p. A629
   Chief Financial Officer, North Hills Hospital, North Richland Hills, TX, p. A640

GALUSHA, Fred, Chief Information Officer, St. Luke's Rehabilitation Institute, Spokane, WA, p. A690

GALVIN, Gary, M.D. Chief of Staff, Columbus Community Hospital, Columbus, WI, p. A703

GALYON, Darlene, Director Human Resources, Choctaw Memorial Hospital, Hugo, OK, p. A512

GAMACHE, Cynde, R.N. Vice President and Chief Nursing Officer, Baptist Hospital, Pensacola, FL, p. A142

GAMACHE, Edward L., President and Chief Executive Officer, Harbor Beach Community Hospital, Harbor Beach, MI, p. A326

GAMB, Pamela, Manager Human Resources, Aurora Psychiatric Hospital, Wauwatosa, WI, p. A718

GAMBLA, Kurt, D.O. Chief Medical Officer, Beaufort Memorial Hospital, Beaufort, SC, p. A562

GAMBLE, Allen J., Chief Executive Officer, Pioneer Community Hospital of Early, Blakely, GA, p. A154

GAMBLE, Kathleen, Fiscal Officer, Patton State Hospital, Patton, CA, p. A83

GAMBLE, Laura, Director Clinical Services, Providence Medical Center, Wayne, NE, p. A402

GAMBLE, Robert, M.D. Chief of Staff, Terrebonne General Medical Center, Houma, LA, p. A279

GAMBLE, Jr., Troy B., M.D. Chief Medical Staff, Williamsburg Regional Hospital, Kingstree, SC, p. A567

GAMBRELL Jr., Edward C., Administrator, Stephens County Hospital, Toccoa, GA, p. A168

GAMEL, Richard B., Operations Leader, CHI Health Plainview, Plainview, NE, p. A401

GAMET, Nicki, R.N
   Vice President and Chief Nursing Officer, Mercy Hospital Aurora, Aurora, MO, p. A367
   Chief Nursing Officer, Mercy Hospital Cassville, Cassville, MO, p. A369

GAMEZ, Kriss
   Director Human Resources, Baylor Regional Medical Center at Plano, Plano, TX, p. A642
   Director Human Resources, The Heart Hospital Baylor Plano, Plano, TX, p. A643

GAMINO, Randall, Director Perot Site, St. Joseph's Medical Center, Stockton, CA, p. A96

GAMMIERE, Thomas A., Chief Executive, Senior Vice President, Scripps Mercy Hospital, San Diego, CA, p. A89

GANCI, Alan A., Director Finance and Controller, Lodi Community Hospital, Lodi, OH, p. A496

GANDHI, Tejas, Chief Administrative Officer, Medical Center, Navicent Health, Macon, GA, p. A163

GANDY, Patrick W., CPA, Executive Vice President and Chief Executive Officer, Lafayette General Medical Center, Lafayette, LA, p. A281

GANEY, John, M.D. Chief of Staff, John Muir Medical Center, Concord, Concord, CA, p. A60

GANGAHAR, Deepak, President, CHI Health Nebraska Heart, Lincoln, NE, p. A397

GANN, Lisa, R.N. Chief Nursing Officer, TriStar Hendersonville Medical Center, Hendersonville, TN, p. A584

GANN, Michele, Vice President Patient Services, Mercy Hospital Berryville, Berryville, AR, p. A43

GANN, Sherry, Administrator, Conway Regional Rehab Hospital, Conway, AR, p. A44

GANNON, Ronnie, Director Information Services, TriStar Southern Hills Medical Center, Nashville, TN, p. A591

GANNON, William, Chief Financial Officer, Parkview Adventist Medical Center, Brunswick, ME, p. A292

GANONG, Richard, M.D. Chief of Staff, Tahoe Forest Hospital District, Truckee, CA, p. A97

GANS, Bruce M., M.D. Executive Vice President and Chief Medical Officer, Kessler Institute for Rehabilitation, West Orange, NJ, p. A424

GANSEMER, Sheila, R.N
Vice President Patient Care Services, Midwest Orthopedic Specialty Hospital, Franklin, WI, p. A705
Vice President Patient Care Services, Wheaton Franciscan Healthcare – Franklin, Franklin, WI, p. A705

GANSKE, Jary, Chief Financial Officer, Methodist Mansfield Medical Center, Mansfield, TX, p. A636

GANTNER, John, Executive Vice President Finance and Partner Company Operations, Jersey Shore University Medical Center, Neptune, NJ, p. A419

GANTT, Cynthia J., Commanding Officer, Naval Hospital Lemoore, Lemoore, CA, p. A69

GANTT, Marsha, Interim Chief Nursing Officer, Southern Palmetto Hospital, Barnwell, SC, p. A562

GANTZER, Ann M., Ph.D. Vice President Patient Services and Chief Nursing Officer, SwedishAmerican Hospital, Rockford, IL, p. A202

GAONA, Rodrigo, Administrator, Nix Community General Hospital, Dilley, TX, p. A614

GAPSTUR, Roxanna L., Ph.D. Chief Nursing Officer, Park Nicollet Methodist Hospital, Minneapolis, MN, p. A347

GARAY, Kenneth, M.D. Chief Medical Officer, Jersey City Medical Center, Jersey City, NJ, p. A417

GARBANZOS, Del, Director Human Resources, Delano Regional Medical Center, Delano, CA, p. A61

GARBARINO, James, Chief Financial Officer, Clay County Medical Center, Clay Center, KS, p. A242

GARBER, Jennifer Elizabeth, Vice President Human Resources, Emory Johns Creek Hospital, Johns Creek, GA, p. A161

GARBER, Mark E., Director Human Resources, Mary Black Memorial Hospital, Spartanburg, SC, p. A570

GARBER, Mary, Vice President Finance, Mercy Hospital Ada, Ada, OK, p. A507

GARCIA, Alex, Chief Executive Officer, Victory Medical Center Landmark, San Antonio, TX, p. A648

GARCIA, Amparo, Administrative Assistant, Frio Regional Hospital, Pearsall, TX, p. A641

GARCIA, Ara, Manager Human Resources, Milwaukee County Behavioral Health Division, Milwaukee, WI, p. A710

GARCIA, Aymette, Manager Human Resources, Wilma N. Vazquez Medical Center, Vega Baja, PR, p. A729

GARCIA, Danette, Director Human Resources, HEALTHSOUTH Valley of the Sun Rehabilitation Hospital, Glendale, AZ, p. A33

GARCIA, Estevan, M.D. Chief Medical Officer, Brookdale Hospital Medical Center, NY, p. A443

GARCIA, Evangeline, M.D. Clinical Director, Eastern Shore Hospital Center, Cambridge, MD, p. A299

GARCIA, Fernando, M.D. Chief of Staff, Avoyelles Hospital, Marksville, LA, p. A283

GARCIA, Georgina R., R.N., Executive Director, Kaiser Permanente West Los Angeles Medical Center, Los Angeles, CA, p. A72

GARCIA, Gerard, Acting Vice President Human Resources, University Hospital, Newark, NJ, p. A420

GARCIA, Idalia, Chief Human Resources Officer, Hospital de Psiquiatria, San Juan, PR, p. A728

GARCIA, Iris, Director, Information Services, Jerome Golden Center for Behavioral Health, Inc., West Palm Beach, FL, p. A150

GARCIA, Irma, Job Coordinator, Rio Grande State Center/South Texas Health Care System, Harlingen, TX, p. A622

GARCIA, Joanne, Chief Operating Officer, Kindred Chicago–Central Hospital, Chicago, IL, p. A184

GARCIA, Joannie, CPA Director Finance, Hospital Perea, Mayaguez, PR, p. A727

GARCIA, Jose, M.D. Chief Medical Staff, Dundy County Hospital, Benkelman, NE, p. A394

GARCIA, Jose, Chief Human Resources Officer, San Juan City Hospital, San Juan, PR, p. A729

GARCIA, Kathleen, Controller, St. John's Episcopal Hospital–South Shore,, NY, p. A448

GARCIA, Louis O., Chief Executive Officer, Victory Medical Center – Southcross, San Antonio, TX, p. A648

GARCIA, Jr., Luis Mario, Director Human Resources, Houston Methodist Sugar Land Hospital, Sugar Land, TX, p. A650

GARCIA, Margaret, Manager Human Resources, Baylor Medical Center at Frisco, Frisco, TX, p. A620

GARCIA, Michael, M.D. Medical Director, Leonard J. Chabert Medical Center, Houma, LA, p. A279

GARCIA, Orlando, M.D. Chief Medical Officer, Hialeah Hospital, Hialeah, FL, p. A130

GARCIA, Robert W., M.D. Chief Medical Officer, Iraan General Hospital, Iraan, TX, p. A629

GARCIA, Roland
Senior Vice President and Chief Information Officer, Baptist Medical Center Beaches, Jacksonville Beach, FL, p. A132
Senior Vice President and Chief Information Officer, Baptist Medical Center Jacksonville, Jacksonville, FL, p. A131

GARCIA, Sharon, Human Resources Representative, Medina Regional Hospital, Hondo, TX, p. A623

GARCIA, Shawn, Manager Human Resources, Memorial Hospital Los Banos, Los Banos, CA, p. A76

GARCIA, Sylvia, Chief Accounting Officer, South Texas Spine and Surgical Hospital, San Antonio, TX, p. A647

GARCIA, Vicki, Vice President Human Resources, Roswell Park Cancer Institute, Buffalo, NY, p. A434

GARD, Emily, Chief Clinical Officer, Kindred Hospital–San Francisco Bay Area, San Leandro, CA, p. A92

GARDINER, David, Operations Officer, LDS Hospital, Salt Lake City, UT, p. A663

GARDINER, Greg, Chief Clinical Officer, Ashley Regional Medical Center, Vernal, UT, p. A664

GARDINER, Karen, Human Resources Director, Bayfront Health Port Charlotte, Port Charlotte, FL, p. A143

GARDNER, Debra C., MSN, Administrator, Ten Lakes Center, Dennison, OH, p. A493

GARDNER, Donald F., Vice President Finance/Chief Financial Officer, Caldwell Memorial Hospital, Lenoir, NC, p. A468

GARDNER, Elizabeth C., R.N. Chief Nursing Officer, Hemet Valley Medical Center, Hemet, CA, p. A67

GARDNER, Greg, Senior Vice President and Chief Financial Officer, Indian River Medical Center, Vero Beach, FL, p. A149

GARDNER, Jacque, Administrative Assistant, Clinic Manager, Co–Chief Financial Officer and Chief Human Resources, McCone County Health Center, Circle, MT, p. A386

GARDNER, James D., M.D. Vice President and Chief Medical Officer, Waukesha Memorial Hospital, Waukesha, WI, p. A717

GARDNER, John, Chief Executive Officer, Yuma District Hospital, Yuma, CO, p. A112

GARDNER, Jonathan H., FACHE, Director, Southern Arizona Veterans Affairs Health Care System, Tucson, AZ, p. A41

GARDNER, Patrick, M.D. Vice President Medical Affairs, St. Joseph's Hospital, West Bend, WI, p. A718

GARDNER, Paul A., CPA, Administrator, George Regional Hospital, Lucedale, MS, p. A361

GARDNER, Robb, Chief Executive Officer, Henry County Health Center, Mount Pleasant, IA, p. A234

GARDNER, Sharon, Manager Information Systems, SSM St. Joseph Hospital West, Lake Saint Louis, MO, p. A375

GARDNER, Sharon R., Vice President Human Resources, Yuma Regional Medical Center, Yuma, AZ, p. A42

GARDNER, William, Chief Nursing Officer, Bartlett Regional Hospital, Juneau, AK, p. A29

GARDNER, Zoe, Manager Human Resources, Sharp Chula Vista Medical Center, Chula Vista, CA, p. A59

GARES, Donna, MSN, President and Chief Executive Officer, Houston Methodist San Jacinto Hospital, Baytown, TX, p. A601

GARISON, Jerri, R.N., President, Baylor Regional Medical Center at Plano, Plano, TX, p. A642

GARKO, Michael, Chief Financial Officer, St. Vincent Medical Center, Los Angeles, CA, p. A75

GARLAND, Scott, Chief Nursing Officer, Shenandoah Medical Center, Shenandoah, IA, p. A237

GARLETS, Mary, Director Human Resources, Mayo Clinic Health System in Cannon Falls, Cannon Falls, MN, p. A341

GARMAN, Denise M., Director Human Resources, The Good Samaritan Hospital, Lebanon, PA, p. A543

GARMAN, Mary E., R.N. Chief Operating Officer and Chief Nursing Officer, Good Samaritan Hospital, Dayton, OH, p. A492

GARMAN, Michael, Chief Financial Officer, Avera St. Anthony's Hospital, O'Neill, NE, p. A399

GARNAS, David, Chief Executive Officer, Sedgwick County Health Center, Julesburg, CO, p. A108

GARNER, David, Chief Operating Officer, Yampa Valley Medical Center, Steamboat Springs, CO, p. A111

GARNER, Douglas, Vice President, Thomas Hospital, Fairhope, AL, p. A20

GARNER, Ethnee, Vice President Nursing Services, Memorial Hospital, North Conway, NH, p. A412

GARNETT, Mark, M.D. Chief of Staff, Hansford Hospital, Spearman, TX, p. A650

GAROFOLA, Aaron, Chief Executive Officer, Bluffton Regional Medical Center, Bluffton, IN, p. A207

GARON, Jack, M.D. Chief Medical Officer, Mount Sinai Hospital, Chicago, IL, p. A185

GARONE, Marlene, M.D. Vice President Medical Affairs and Medical Director, Woman's Christian Association Hospital, Jamestown, NY, p. A439

GARRAMONE, Kathy
Chief Financial Officer, Jacobi Medical Center,, NY, p. A444
Chief Financial Officer, North Central Bronx Hospital,, NY, p. A447

GARRED, Sr., John, M.D. Chief Medical Officer, Burgess Health Center, Onawa, IA, p. A235

GARRETT, Alan H., Chief Executive Officer, St. Mary Medical Center, Apple Valley, CA, p. A56

GARRETT, Courtney, CPA Chief Financial Officer, Children's Hospital, New Orleans, LA, p. A285

GARRETT, Darlene, President, Parkview Huntington Hospital, Huntington, IN, p. A213

GARRETT, David B.
Chief Information Officer, Novant Health Forsyth Medical Center, Winston–Salem, NC, p. A475
Chief Information Officer, Novant Health Matthews Medical Center, Matthews, NC, p. A469
Senior Vice President Information Technology, Novant Health Presbyterian Medical Center, Charlotte, NC, p. A462

GARRETT, Jarren, Chief Administrative Officer, Baptist Orange Hospital, Orange, TX, p. A640

GARRETT, Mark, Chief Information Officer, Shriners Hospitals for Children–Los Angeles, Los Angeles, CA, p. A74

GARRETT, Matthew, Director Information Systems, Flowers Hospital, Dothan, AL, p. A19

GARRETT, Nancy, Chief Analytics and Information Technology Officer, Hennepin County Medical Center, Minneapolis, MN, p. A347

GARRETT, Robert C., FACHE, President and Chief Executive Officer, Hackensack University Health Network, Hackensack, NJ, p. B63

GARRETT, Robert C., FACHE, President and Chief Executive Officer, Hackensack University Medical Center, Hackensack, NJ, p. A416

GARRETT, Scott, Director of IS, Ottumwa Regional Health Center, Ottumwa, IA, p. A236

GARRETT, Walter J., Chief Executive Officer, Welch Community Hospital, Welch, WV, p. A700

GARRICK, Renee, M.D. Director, Executive Medical, Westchester Medical Center, Valhalla, NY, p. A457

GARRIDO, Mary, Vice President and Regional Chief Information Officer, Valley Baptist Medical Center–Brownsville, Brownsville, TX, p. A604

GARRISON, Cort, M.D
Chief Information Officer, Salem Hospital, Salem, OR, p. A530
Chief Information Officer, West Valley Hospital, Dallas, OR, p. A524

GARRISON, Mark, Chief of Staff, Glenn Medical Center, Willows, CA, p. A101

GARRISON, Stephen, Interim Chief Executive Officer, Texas Regional Medical Center at Sunnyvale, Sunnyvale, TX, p. A651

GARRISON, Tina, Vice President Operations, SSM DePaul Health Center, Bridgeton, MO, p. A368

GARRISON, Wes,St. Luke's Sugar Land Hospital, Sugar Land, TX, p. A651

GARRITY, Elizabeth, Director Human Resources, Meadowlands Hospital Medical Center, Secaucus, NJ, p. A422

GARRITY, Nerissa, Chief Financial Officer, Kula Hospital, Kula, HI, p. A172

GARROW, Dina, Chief Nursing Officer and Chief Operating Officer, Kindred Hospital–Baldwin Park, Baldwin Park, CA, p. A57

GARRY, William, Chief Financial Officer, Edgefield County Hospital, Edgefield, SC, p. A565

GARSKE, Tom, Director Information Systems, Wiregrass Medical Center, Geneva, AL, p. A20

GARTNER, Katie, Director Health Information Management, CHI Health Good Samaritan, Kearney, NE, p. A397

GARVEY, Heather, Chief Financial Officer, Raulerson Hospital, Okeechobee, FL, p. A140

GARVEY, James, Executive Vice President, Operations and Administrator, Essentia Health St. Mary's Medical Center, Duluth, MN, p. A342

GARVEY, Rita, Chief Nursing Officer, Lawrence County Memorial Hospital, Lawrenceville, IL, p. A194

GARVEY, Sheila
Vice President Human Resources, Flushing Hospital Medical Center,, NY, p. A443
Vice President Human Resources, Jamaica Hospital Medical Center,, NY, p. A444

GARVEY, Thomas J., Senior Vice President Operations and Chief Financial Officer, Swedish Covenant Hospital, Chicago, IL, p. A187

GARVIN, Jan, Vice President Human Resources, Bryan Medical Center, Lincoln, NE, p. A397

GARWOOD, III, William D., Associate Administrator and Chief Financial Officer, Angleton Danbury Medical Center, Angleton, TX, p. A597

GARY, Al, COO, Simpson General Hospital, Mendenhall, MS, p. A362

GARZA, Annette, Controller, Weslaco Rehabilitation Hospital, Weslaco, TX, p. A657

GARZA, Ismelda, Director Information Systems, Comanche County Medical Center, Comanche, TX, p. A607

GARZA, Jennifer, Chief Executive Officer, South Texas Health System, Edinburg, TX, p. A615

GARZA, Laura, Director Human Resources, Promise Hospital of Houston, Houston, TX, p. A626

GARZA, Oscar, M.D. Chief of Medical Staff, Frio Regional Hospital, Pearsall, TX, p. A641

GARZA, San Juana, Chief Financial Officer, Cedar Crest Hospital and Residential Treatment Center, Belton, TX, p. A602

GARZA, Teri, Director Health Information Services, Knapp Medical Center, Weslaco, TX, p. A657

GARZA, Tom, Director Fiscal and Support, Rio Grande State Center/South Texas Health Care System, Harlingen, TX, p. A622

GASAWAY, Rob, Chief Financial Officer, Galesburg Cottage Hospital, Galesburg, IL, p. A190

GASCHO, Dwight, President and Chief Executive Officer, Scheurer Hospital, Pigeon, MI, p. A332

GASH, Deborah
Vice President and Chief Information Officer, Crittenton Children's Center, Kansas City, MO, p. A373
Chief Information Officer, Saint Luke's Hospital of Kansas City, Kansas City, MO, p. A374
Chief Information Officer, Saint Luke's South Hospital, Overland Park, KS, p. A252

GASKILL, Michelle, R.N., President, Advocate Trinity Hospital, Chicago, IL, p. A183

GASKINS, Michael, Director Information Technology, Lincoln Community Hospital and Nursing Home, Hugo, CO, p. A107

GASKINS, Michael W., Executive Vice President and Chief Financial Officer, Hanover Hospital, Hanover, PA, p. A540

GASPAR, Deborah L., R.N. Chief Nursing Officer, Memorial Hospital of Sweetwater County, Rock Springs, WY, p. A722

GASPARD, H. J., Chief Executive Officer, HEALTHSOUTH Rehabilitation Hospital of Beaumont, Beaumont, TX, p. A602

GASPARINI, Michael L., Vice President Clinical Services and Chief Operating Officer, Western Missouri Medical Center, Warrensburg, MO, p. A384

GASQUE, James, M.D. Chief Hospital Services, U. S. Air Force Medical Center Keesler, Keesler AFB, MS, p. A360

GASS, Angela, Chief Nursing Officer, Stamford Memorial Hospital, Stamford, TX, p. A650

GASSMAN, Alicia, Director Human Resources, SEARHC MT. Edgecumbe Hospital, Sitka, AK, p. A30

GAST, Edwin A., Chief Executive Officer, Marshall Browning Hospital, Du Quoin, IL, p. A188

GASTON, Jan, Administrator, Jasper Memorial Hospital, Monticello, GA, p. A164

GASTON, Kathy, Chief Nursing Officer, Baptist Medical Center East, Montgomery, AL, p. A23

GASTON, Tammy, Chief Information Officer, Smith County Memorial Hospital, Smith Center, KS, p. A254

GATES, John
Vice President Finance and Chief Financial Officer, California Pacific Medical Center, San Francisco, CA, p. A90
Chief Financial Officer, St. Luke's Hospital, San Francisco, CA, p. A91

GATES, Margaret, Chief Human Resources, Harris Hospital, Newport, AR, p. A51

GATES, Philip E., M.D. Chief of Staff, Shriners Hospitals for Children–Shreveport, Shreveport, LA, p. A288

GATES, Robert, Director Information Technology, Hackensack University Medical Center Mountainside, Montclair, NJ, p. A418

GATES, Rose, Director Human Resources, Hayward Area Memorial Hospital and Nursing Home, Hayward, WI, p. A706

GATES, Tracy, Chief Financial Officer, Jones Memorial Hospital, Wellsville, NY, p. A457

GATHERS, Mary
Manager Information Systems, American Fork Hospital, American Fork, UT, p. A659
Director Information Systems, McKay–Dee Hospital Center, Ogden, UT, p. A661
Director Information Systems, Utah Valley Regional Medical Center, Provo, UT, p. A662

GATHRIGHT, Travis, Chief Information and Corporate Compliance Officer, Magee Rehabilitation Hospital, Philadelphia, PA, p. A549

GATI, Ken, M.D. Chief of Staff, Medical Center of South Arkansas, El Dorado, AR, p. A45

GATIEN, Lionel J., D.O. Chief of Staff, Kindred Hospital North Florida, Green Cove Springs, FL, p. A130

GATMAITAN, Alfonso W., Chief Executive Officer, Indiana University Health Arnett Hospital, Lafayette, IN, p. A217

GATTMAN, Gregory B., Acute Care Executive, Palmetto Health Baptist, Columbia, SC, p. A564

GATTO, Tony, Director Management Information Systems, Flushing Hospital Medical Center,, NY, p. A443

GAU, Kimberley A., FACHE, Chief Executive Officer, Guttenberg Municipal Hospital, Guttenberg, IA, p. A231

GAUBERT, Steve C., Chief Financial Officer, Thibodaux Regional Medical Center, Thibodaux, LA, p. A289

GAUER, Natalie, Administrator, Milbank Area Hospital Avera, Milbank, SD, p. A574

GAUGHAN, Thomas, M.D. Chief Medical Officer, Kingman Regional Medical Center, Kingman, AZ, p. A33

GAUL, Michael, Manager Information Systems, Atchison Hospital, Atchison, KS, p. A241

GAUL–HOUSER, Kelly, Director Human Resources, Ottumwa Regional Health Center, Ottumwa, IA, p. A236

GAULKE, Becky, Chief Nursing Officer, Ely–Bloomenson Community Hospital, Ely, MN, p. A343

GAUNTT, Brandon, Director Information Systems, Hopkins County Memorial Hospital, Sulphur Springs, TX, p. A651

GAURON, Patricia, Director Human Resources, Holy Family Hospital and Medical Center, Methuen, MA, p. A312

GAUSE, Garry L., President and Chief Executive Officer, Brookwood Medical Center, Birmingham, AL, p. A16

GAUTHIER, Bonnie B., President and Chief Executive Officer, The Hospital at Hebrew Health Care, West Hartford, CT, p. A118

GAUTHIER, Paul, Chief Information Resources Management, Veterans Affairs Montana Health Care System, Fort Harrison, MT, p. A387

GAUTNEY, Steven, Chief Executive Officer, Crisp Regional Hospital, Cordele, GA, p. A157

GAVALCHIK, Stephen M., FACHE, Community Chief Executive Officer, Morgan County ARH Hospital, West Liberty, KY, p. A271

GAVENS, Mark R., Senior Vice President Clinical Care Services and Chief Operating Officer, Cedars–Sinai Medical Center, Los Angeles, CA, p. A71

GAVIN, Andrea, M.D. Chief Medical officer, Aurora Sheboygan Memorial Medical Center, Sheboygan, WI, p. A715

GAVIN, Donald, Chief Financial Officer, Southern Tennessee Regional Health System–Pulaski, Pulaski, TN, p. A592

GAVIN, Linda, Associate Executive Director Marketing and Physician Recruitment, South Central Regional Medical Center, Laurel, MS, p. A361

GAVIN, Martin J., President and Chief Executive Officer, Connecticut Children's Medical Center, Hartford, CT, p. A114

GAVIN, Patrick J., President, Crozer–Chester Medical Center, Upland, PA, p. A556

GAVIN, Tammy, Assistant Administrator and Chief Operating Officer, White River Medical Center, Batesville, AR, p. A43

GAVIN, Todd, Chief Medical Officer, Madelia Community Hospital, Madelia, MN, p. A346

GAVINO, Rey, M.D. Chief of Staff, RMC Jacksonville, Jacksonville, AL, p. A22

GAVIS, Patricia, Chief Financial Officer, Ellenville Regional Hospital, Ellenville, NY, p. A437

GAVORA, George, Director Program Evaluation, Kingsboro Psychiatric Center,, NY, p. A444

GAVULIC, Melany, President & Chief Executive Officer, Hurley Medical Center, Flint, MI, p. A323

GAW, Kris, Chief Operating Officer, Renown Regional Medical Center, Reno, NV, p. A407

GAWALUCK, David
Vice President and Chief Information Officer, Excela Frick Hospital, Mount Pleasant, PA, p. A546
Vice President and Chief Information Officer, Excela Health Westmoreland Hospital, Greensburg, PA, p. A539
Vice President and Chief Information Officer, Excela Latrobe Area Hospital, Latrobe, PA, p. A542

GAWITH, Marlene, Director of Nursing, Ottawa County Health Center, Minneapolis, KS, p. A250

GAWLER, William, Chief Information Officer, Chillicothe Veterans Affairs Medical Center, Chillicothe, OH, p. A486

GAWNE, Bernard B., M.D. Vice President and Chief Medical Officer, Christ Hospital, Cincinnati, OH, p. A486

GAWORSKI, Mark, Vice President Finance, Chief Financial Officer, Spencer Hospital, Spencer, IA, p. A238

GAY, Christophe, M.D. Chief of Staff, Bellville St. Joseph Health Center, Bellville, TX, p. A602

GAY, Don, Director Human Resources, West Hills Hospital, Reno, NV, p. A408

GAY, Kristi
Chief Financial Officer, Memorial Medical Center – Lufkin, Lufkin, TX, p. A635
Chief Financial Officer, Memorial Medical Center – San Augustine, San Augustine, TX, p. A648
Chief Financial Officer, Memorial Specialty Hospital, Lufkin, TX, p. A635

GAY, Michael, Chief Operating Officer, Habersham Medical Center, Demorest, GA, p. A158

GAY, Perry, Chief Executive Officer, Toppenish Community Hospital, Toppenish, WA, p. A691

GAY, Vickie, Chief Executive Officer, Montgomery General Hospital, Montgomery, WV, p. A697

GAYDUSEK, Lori, Chief Nursing Officer, Goodland Regional Medical Center, Goodland, KS, p. A244

GAYLER, Lisa, Director Human Resources, Select Long Term Care Hospital – Colorado Springs, Colorado Springs, CO, p. A104

GAYLOR, Rosanne, M.D., Acting Executive Director, South Beach Psychiatric Center,, NY, p. A448

GAYNOR, Sheila, Director Human Resources, Perry County Memorial Hospital, Tell City, IN, p. A222

GAYTKO, Caren, Chief Nursing Officer, Regency Hospital of Minneapolis, Golden Valley, MN, p. A344

GAZECKI, Cindy, Senior Vice President, Hospital Operations, Seattle Children's Hospital, Seattle, WA, p. A688

GEARHARD, Cynthia, Chief Nursing Officer, St. Luke's Regional Medical Center, Boise, ID, p. A175

GEARHART, Danielle, Chief Executive Officer, Cooper County Memorial Hospital, Boonville, MO, p. A368

GEARY, David S., Chief Financial Officer, Cache Valley Hospital, North Logan, UT, p. A661

GEARY, Herb J., R.N. Vice President Patient Care Services and Chief Nursing Officer, Santa Barbara Cottage Hospital, Santa Barbara, CA, p. A94

GEBHARD, Scott, Executive VP and Chief Operating Officer, JFK Medical Center, Edison, NJ, p. A415

GEBHART, Cheryl, Director Human Resources Providence Health Plan and Providence Medical Group, Providence Newberg Medical Center, Newberg, OR, p. A527

GEBHART Jr., Jim, FACHE, President, Mercy Hospital Oklahoma City, Oklahoma City, OK, p. A515

GEBHART, Ronald J., M.D. Chief of Staff, Veterans Affairs Salt Lake City Health Care System, Salt Lake City, UT, p. A664

GEDDES, Jason, Chief Financial Officer, Franciscan St. Elizabeth Health – Lafayette Central, Lafayette, IN, p. A216

GEDDINGS, Toni, Director Human Resources, Cullman Regional Medical Center, Cullman, AL, p. A18

GEDIES, Lucille, Chief Financial Officer, Mildred Mitchell–Bateman Hospital, Huntington, WV, p. A696

GEE, Kyle
Chief Financial Officer, Beartooth Billings Clinic, Red Lodge, MT, p. A390
Chief Financial Officer, Pioneer Medical Center, Big Timber, MT, p. A385
Regional Vice President Financial Operations, Roundup Memorial Healthcare, Roundup, MT, p. A390

GEE, Thomas H., Administrator, Henry County Medical Center, Paris, TN, p. A592

GEERTS, Jodi, Chief Nursing Officer, Henry County Health Center, Mount Pleasant, IA, p. A234

GEHANT, David P., President and Chief Executive Officer, Boulder Community Hospital, Boulder, CO, p. A102

GEHLAUF, Dee Ann, Senior Vice President Business and Organization Development, Marietta Memorial Hospital, Marietta, OH, p. A497

GEHRIG, Ryan, President, Mercy Hospital Fort Smith, Fort Smith, AR, p. A46

GEHRING, Jay, Director Information Systems, Kingman Community Hospital, Kingman, KS, p. A247

GEHRING, Mikaela, Chief Operating Officer, Marengo Memorial Hospital, UnityPoint Health, Marengo, IA, p. A234

GEHRING, Sherry, R.N. Vice President Nursing, Inpatient Care and Chief Nursing Officer, Hancock Regional Hospital, Greenfield, IN, p. A212

GEHRING, Terri, Vice President Operations, McPherson Hospital, McPherson, KS, p. A250

GEIDL, Steve, Chief Financial Officer, Columbia County Health System, Dayton, WA, p. A683

GEIDT, Steve, Chief Executive Officer, Saddleback Memorial Medical Center, Laguna Hills, CA, p. A68

GEIER, Joyce, Director Nursing, Girard Medical Center, Girard, KS, p. A244

GEIER, Kathy, Director of Nursing, Chase County Community Hospital, Imperial, NE, p. A397

GEIER, Peter E., Chief Executive Officer, Ohio State University Health System, Columbus, OH, p. B103

GEIER, Peter E., Chief Operating Officer, Ohio State University Wexner Medical Center, Columbus, OH, p. A490

GEIGER, Deb, Executive Director of Acute Care, Harbor Beach Community Hospital, Harbor Beach, MI, p. A326

GEIGER, Judy, R.N. Chief Nursing Officer, Primary Children's Medical Center, Salt Lake City, UT, p. A663

GEIGER, Ralph, M.D. Chief of Staff, Sebastian River Medical Center, Sebastian, FL, p. A145

GEIGLE, Joseph, Director Human Resources, Fort Hamilton Hospital, Hamilton, OH, p. A495

GEIL, Kristie A., VP, Chief Nursing Officer, CGH Medical Center, Sterling, IL, p. A203

GEIMAN, Robert, Senior Financial Analyst, Maple Grove Hospital, Maple Grove, MN, p. A346

GEISLER, Linda W., R.N. Vice President Patient Services, CentraState Healthcare System, Freehold, NJ, p. A416

GEISSLER, Michael E., Chief Executive Officer, Acadia Optima Hospital, Lafayette, LA, p. A280

GEIST, Jim, Chief Executive Officer, Capital Medical Center, Olympia, WA, p. A686

GEIST, Tammy, Chief Financial Officer, Novant Health Charlotte Orthopaedic Hospital, Charlotte, NC, p. A462

GEITZ, Cheri, Director Human Resources, Hansen Family Hospital, Iowa Falls, IA, p. A233

GEITZ, James, M.D. Chief of Staff, Newman Regional Health, Emporia, KS, p. A243

GEIVER, Betsy, Chief Human Resources Officer, Sioux Falls Veterans Affairs Health Care System, Sioux Falls, SD, p. A577

GELDHOF, Jay
Director Information Systems, Greater El Monte Community Hospital, South El Monte, CA, p. A96
Director Information Systems, Whittier Hospital Medical Center, Whittier, CA, p. A100

GELFAND, Andrew, M.D. Medical Director, Our Children's House at Baylor, Dallas, TX, p. A611

GELL, Michael, Director Human Resources, Boys Town National Research Hospital, Omaha, NE, p. A399

GELLENBECK, Mary Ann, Chief Operating Officer, Bethesda Butler Hospital, Hamilton, OH, p. A495

GELLER, Guy, Administrator and Chief Executive Officer, Beacham Memorial Hospital, Magnolia, MS, p. A361

GELLER, Harold S., Chief Executive Officer, St. Anthony Hospital, Pendleton, OR, p. A527

GELLER, Robert D., M.D. Vice President Medical Affairs, FHN Memorial Hospital, Freeport, IL, p. A190

GELLER, Warren, President and Chief Executive Officer, Englewood Hospital and Medical Center, Englewood, NJ, p. A416

GELORMINI, Frank, Chief Operating Officer, Community Medical Center, Toms River, NJ, p. A423

GEMBOL, Leslie, MSN Chief Nursing Officer, Scott & White Hospital at Round Rock, Round Rock, TX, p. A644

GEMME, Donna T., R.N. Chief Nursing Officer, MetroWest Medical Center, Framingham, MA, p. A310

GENDER, Aloma, MSN, Administrator and Chief Nursing Officer, CHRISTUS St. Michael Rehabilitation Hospital, Texarkana, TX, p. A652

GENEVRO, Thomas A., Vice President Human Resources, Butler Health System, Butler, PA, p. A534

GENGLER, Laraine, Chief Financial Officer, Lindsborg Community Hospital, Lindsborg, KS, p. A249

GENNA, Nick, Administrator, Treasure Valley Hospital, Boise, ID, p. A175

GENNARO, John, FACHE, Director, Veterans Affairs Butler Healthcare, Butler, PA, p. A534

GENOVESE, Vincent P., M.D. President Medical Staff, Muhlenberg Community Hospital, Greenville, KY, p. A262

GENSERT, Kurt, R.N. Vice President Operations, Platte Valley Medical Center, Brighton, CO, p. A103

GENTHNER, Diane, Chief Nursing Officer, St. Mary's Hospital, Streator, IL, p. A204

GENTILE, John, M.D
Vice President Medical Affairs, Alta Bates Summit Medical Center, Berkeley, CA, p. A58
Vice President Medical Affairs, Alta Bates Summit Medical Center – Summit Campus, Oakland, CA, p. A80
Chief Medical Officer, Hollywood Presbyterian Medical Center, Los Angeles, CA, p. A72

GENTILE, Serge, Director Human Resources, Belmont Community Hospital, Bellaire, OH, p. A483

GENTNER, Rocky, Chief Financial Officer, Newport Bay Hospital, Newport Beach, CA, p. A80

GENTRY, Cheryl G., Chief Executive Officer, Select Specialty Hospital–Indianapolis, Indianapolis, IN, p. A215

GENTRY, Gregg, Senior Vice President Human Resources, Erlanger Medical Center, Chattanooga, TN, p. A580

GENTRY, Jeanine
Chief Executive Officer, Pioneer Memorial Hospital, Prineville, OR, p. A529
Chief Executive Officer, St. Charles Madras, Madras, OR, p. A526

GENTRY, Jennifer, R.N. Chief Nursing Officer, CHRISTUS Spohn Hospital Corpus Christi Memorial, Corpus Christi, TX, p. A608

GENTRY, Kristen, Chief Operating Officer, Venice Regional Bayfront Health, Venice, FL, p. A149

GENTRY, Lee, FACHE, Vice President and Administrator, Baptist Health Rehabilitation Institute, Little Rock, AR, p. A49

GENTRY, Margie, Controller, T. J. Samson Community Hospital, Glasgow, KY, p. A262

GENTRY, Steve, Manager Information Technology, Natchitoches Regional Medical Center, Natchitoches, LA, p. A285

GEORGE, Alan E.
Chief Executive Officer, Palestine Regional Medical Center, Palestine, TX, p. A640
Chief Executive Officer, Palestine Regional Medical Center–East, Palestine, TX, p. A640

GEORGE, Amanda, Assistant Controller, St. Vincent Morrilton, Morrilton, AR, p. A50

GEORGE, Brad, Director Information Systems, Parkland Medical Center, Derry, NH, p. A409

GEORGE, Carol, Chief Nursing Officer, Columbus Specialty Hospital, Columbus, GA, p. A156

GEORGE, Denise, R.N., President, Northern Dutchess Hospital, Rhinebeck, NY, p. A452

GEORGE, Doug, Chief Financial Officer, Veterans Affairs Butler Healthcare, Butler, PA, p. A534

GEORGE, Gary
Regional Vice President Human Resources, Mercy St. Anne Hospital, Toledo, OH, p. A503
Regional Vice President Human Resources, Mercy St. Charles Hospital, Oregon, OH, p. A500
Senior Vice President Human Resources, Mercy St. Vincent Medical Center, Toledo, OH, p. A503

GEORGE, Jane, Controller, Methodist Healthcare–Fayette Hospital, Somerville, TN, p. A593

GEORGE, P. A., M.D. Chief of Staff, Madison Medical Center, Fredericktown, MO, p. A371

GEORGE, Patricia, Chief Information Officer, North Shore Medical Center, Salem, MA, p. A314

GEORGE, Patsy, R.N. Chief Nursing Officer, Ohio Valley Medical Center, Wheeling, WV, p. A700

GEORGE, Saju, Chief Administrative Officer, Garden City Hospital, Garden City, MI, p. A324

GEORGE, Shayne, Chief Executive Officer, Regional Medical Center Bayonet Point, Hudson, FL, p. A131

GEORGE, Susan, R.N. Associate Director Patient Care Services, Martinsburg Veterans Affairs Medical Center, Martinsburg, WV, p. A697

GEORGE, Tracy L., Chief Financial Officer, St. James Parish Hospital, Lutcher, LA, p. A283

GEORGE, William, M.D. Chief of Staff, Beartooth Billings Clinic, Red Lodge, MT, p. A390

GEORGES, Angelo, M.D. President Medical and Dental Staff, Wheeling Hospital, Wheeling, WV, p. A700

GERARD, Alice M., President and Chief Executive Officer, McLaren Bay Region, Bay City, MI, p. A319

GERARD, Greg D., President, Saint Joseph – London, London, KY, p. A265

GERBER, Allen, M.D. Chief of Staff, Baptist Health Medical Center–Hot Spring County, Malvern, AR, p. A50

GERBER, Greg, M.D. Chief Medical Officer, Aurora Lakeland Medical Center, Elkhorn, WI, p. A704

GERBIG, Ralph, M.D. Chief of Staff, Johnson Memorial Health Services, Dawson, MN, p. A342

GERDTS, Elizabeth, Chief Nursing Officer, North Central Bronx Hospital,, NY, p. A447

GERETY, Meghan, M.D. Chief of Staff, Veterans Affairs Medical Center, Albuquerque, NM, p. A427

GERHART, Paul, Chief Financial Officer, Sanford Canton–Inwood Medical Center, Canton, SD, p. A572

GERIG, Stacey L., Chief Executive Officer, Odessa Regional Medical Center, Odessa, TX, p. A640

GERING, Jeffrey T., FACHE, Director, Veterans Affairs San Diego Healthcare System, San Diego, CA, p. A90

GERING, Paul, M.D. Vice President Medical Affairs, Saint Alphonsus Medical Center – Ontario, Ontario, OR, p. A527

GERKE, Daniel, Chief Nursing Officer, Wright Patterson Medical Center, Wright–Patterson AFB, OH, p. A505

GERKE, Mary Lu, R.N. Vice President Nursing Systems, Gundersen Health System, La Crosse, WI, p. A707

GERKE, Sarah, Manager Human Resources, Dr. John Warner Hospital, Clinton, IL, p. A187

GERLACH, George, Chief Executive Officer, Granite Falls Municipal Hospital and Manor, Granite Falls, MN, p. A344

GERLACH, Matthew S.
Chief Operating Officer, Children's Hospital at Mission, Mission Viejo, CA, p. A77
Chief Operating Officer, Children's Hospital of Orange County, Orange, CA, p. A81

GERMAN, Mike
Chief Financial Officer, Cape Coral Hospital, Cape Coral, FL, p. A125
Chief Financial Officer, Gulf Coast Medical Center, Fort Myers, FL, p. A129
Chief Financial Officer, Lee Memorial Hospital, Fort Myers, FL, p. A129

GERMANY, Alan, Interim Chief Financial Officer, Bartlett Regional Hospital, Juneau, AK, p. A29

GERMUSKA, Natalie, MSN, Chief Executive Officer, Vibra Hospital of San Diego, San Diego, CA, p. A90

GERN, Sharon, R.N. Chief Nursing Officer, Ivinson Memorial Hospital, Laramie, WY, p. A722

GERNDT, Angie, Human Resources Manager, Central Community Hospital, Elkader, IA, p. A230

GERNHART, Diana, Chief Financial Officer, OHSU Hospital, Portland, OR, p. A528

GERRIOR, Marilyn, R.N. Chief Nursing Executive, Saint Louise Regional Hospital, Gilroy, CA, p. A65

GERRITS, Brad, Director Information Systems, Lakeview Medical Center, Rice Lake, WI, p. A714

GERSCH, Aaron, M.D. Chief of Staff, Albany Area Hospital and Medical Center, Albany, MN, p. A339

GERSON, Elaine, Chief Clinical Officer and General Counsel, Aspen Valley Hospital District, Aspen, CO, p. A102

GERSTENBERGER, Linda
Vice President Human Resources, St. Rose Dominican Hospitals – San Martin Campus, Las Vegas, NV, p. A406
Vice President Human Resources, St. Rose Dominican Hospitals – Siena Campus, Henderson, NV, p. A405

GERSTNER, Nancy, Manager Human Resources, Robert J. Dole Veterans Affairs Medical Center, Wichita, KS, p. A256

GERTH, Kevin, M.D. Chief of Staff, Spectrum Health Gerber Memorial, Fremont, MI, p. A324

GERVELER, Patrick M., Vice President Finance and Chief Financial Officer, Blessing Hospital, Quincy, IL, p. A201

GESKERMANN, Tom G., Chief Executive Officer, Osceola Medical Center, Osceola, WI, p. A712

GESSEL, Thomas, FACHE, President and Chief Executive Officer, Mercy Regional Medical Center, Durango, CO, p. A105

GESSNER, Christopher, President, Children's Hospital of Pittsburgh of UPMC, Pittsburgh, PA, p. A550

GETMAN, Sylvia, President and Chief Executive Officer, The Aroostook Medical Center, Presque Isle, ME, p. A295

GETSAY, Timothy, Chief Information Officer, Gillette Children's Specialty Healthcare, Saint Paul, MN, p. A351

GETTINGER, Thomas
Chief Operating Officer and Executive Vice President, WakeMed Cary Hospital, Cary, NC, p. A461
Executive Vice President and Chief Operating Officer, WakeMed Raleigh Campus, Raleigh, NC, p. A471

GETTINGS, Scott, M.D
Senior Vice President and Chief Medical Affairs, Health First Palm Bay Hospital, Melbourne, FL, p. A136
Senior Vice President and Chief Medical Officer, Health First Viera Hospital, Melbourne, FL, p. A136

GETTYS, Sky, Interim President and Chief Executive Officer, Fairfield Medical Center, Lancaster, OH, p. A496

GETWOOD, Charles, Assistant Chief Executive Officer, Calcasieu Oaks Geriatric Psychiatric Hospital, Lake Charles, LA, p. A282

GETZ, Liz, Chief Information Officer, Aultman Hospital, Canton, OH, p. A485

GETZENDANER, Gail, Director of Nursing, Missouri Rehabilitation Center, Mount Vernon, MO, p. A377

GEUDER, Denise, Vice President Patient Care Service and Chief Nursing Officer, Southwestern Regional Medical Center, Tulsa, OK, p. A521

GEURTS, Chuck, Manager Management Information Services, Aurora BayCare Medical Center, Green Bay, WI, p. A705

GEWECKE, Tyler, Information Technology Technician, Fillmore County Hospital, Geneva, NE, p. A396

GFELLER, Michael, Director Information Systems, Medical Center of Plano, Plano, TX, p. A642

GHAEMMAGHAMI, Chris A., M.D. Chief Medical Officer, University of Virginia Medical Center, Charlottesville, VA, p. A669

GHAFFARI, Bahram, President, Delano Regional Medical Center, Delano, CA, p. A61

GHERINGHELLI, Thomas, Chief Financial Officer, New England Baptist Hospital, Boston, MA, p. A307

GHERKE, Sheila, Director Human Resources, Minnie Hamilton HealthCare Center, Grantsville, WV, p. A695

GHIDOTTI, Craig J., Vice President Human Resources, Lake Health, Concord Township, OH, p. A491

GHION, christopher, Vice President and Chief Information Officer, Shady Grove Adventist Hospital, Rockville, MD, p. A303

GHOSH, Tarun, Chief Information Officer, Fremont–Rideout Health Group, Marysville, CA, p. A77

GIAGUINTO, Shelly, Controller, Highland–Clarksburg Hospital, Clarksburg, WV, p. A694

GIAMALIS, John N., Senior Vice President and Chief Financial Officer, Saint Francis Hospital and Medical Center, Hartford, CT, p. A114

GIANCOLA, Louis R., President and Chief Executive Officer, South County Hospital, Wakefield, RI, p. A561

GIANELLI, Arthur A., M.P.H., President, Mount Sinai St. Luke's, New York, NY, p. A446

GIANGARDELLA, Mike, Vice President Finance and Administration, Salem Regional Medical Center, Salem, OH, p. A501

GIANNONE, John, M.D. Chief Medical Officer, Delaware Valley Hospital, Walton, NY, p. A457

GIANNOSA, Amy, Director Human Resources, Havenwyck Hospital, Auburn Hills, MI, p. A318

GIANNUZZI, Donna, R.N
Chief Patient Care Officer, Gulf Coast Medical Center, Fort Myers, FL, p. A129
Chief Nursing Officer, Lee Memorial Hospital, Fort Myers, FL, p. A129

GIANSANTE, Joseph, Vice President Human Resources, Ellis Hospital, Schenectady, NY, p. A454

GIARDINA, Deborah, Director Human Resources and Medical Staff Services, Rehabilitation Hospital of Fort Wayne, Fort Wayne, IN, p. A211

GIBB, Matthew, M.D. Executive Vice President and System Chief Medical Officer, Carle Foundation Hospital, Urbana, IL, p. A204

GIBB, Randall K., M.D. Chief Medical Officer, Billings Clinic, Billings, MT, p. A385

GIBBENS, Lori, Controller, HEALTHSOUTH Rehabilitation Hospital of Erie, Erie, PA, p. A538

GIBBERMAN, Val, M.D. Acting Chief of Staff, Hampton Veterans Affairs Medical Center, Hampton, VA, p. A672

GIBBONS, Barbara, Vice President Patient Care Services, St. Joseph Hospital, Bethpage, NY, p. A433

GIBBONS, David
Executive Vice President and Chief Operating Officer, UPMC Hamot, Erie, PA, p. A539
President, UPMC Northwest, Seneca, PA, p. A554

GIBBONS, H. Ray, FACHE, Chief Executive Officer, Saint Alphonsus Medical Center – Baker City, Baker City, OR, p. A523

GIBBONS, Jason, Chief Financial Officer, Minidoka Memorial Hospital, Rupert, ID, p. A178

GIBBS, Christopher Michael, Director Information Management Systems, Taylor Regional Hospital, Campbellsville, KY, p. A259

GIBBS, Mick, Chief Operating Officer, Rapid City Regional Hospital, Rapid City, SD, p. A576

GIBBS–MCELVY, Shelana, M.D. Medical Director, HEALTHSOUTH Rehabilitation Hospital, Sewickley, PA, p. A555

GIBNEY, Thomas, Senior Vice President and Chief Financial Officer, St. Luke's Cornwall Hospital, Newburgh, NY, p. A449

GIBSON, Amy, Chief Executive Officer, Jackson Medical Center, Jackson, AL, p. A22

GIBSON, Armetria, Human Resources Generalist, Kindred Hospital–Atlanta, Atlanta, GA, p. A152

GIBSON, Belinda D., R.N. Vice President Patient Services, Baptist St. Anthony Health System, Amarillo, TX, p. A596

GIBSON, Connie, R.N. Director Human Resources, Novant Health Gaffney Medical Center, Gaffney, SC, p. A566

GIBSON, Joel, Vice President Human Resources, Henry Ford Macomb Hospitals, Clinton Township, MI, p. A321

GIBSON, Mary Helen, Director Human Resources, Floyd Valley Hospital, Le Mars, IA, p. A233

GIBSON, Megan, Nurse Manager, River Bend Hospital, West Lafayette, IN, p. A224

GIBSON, Richard, Senior Vice President and Chief Information Officer, Legacy Emanuel Hospital and Health Center, Portland, OR, p. A528

GIBSON, Robert, Senior Director Operating Services, OSF Saint Elizabeth Medical Center, Ottawa, IL, p. A199

GIBSON, Todd, Chief Financial Officer, Denton Regional Medical Center, Denton, TX, p. A613

GIBSON, Valerie, Chief Operating Officer, DMC Harper University Hospital, Detroit, MI, p. A322

GIBSON, William R., Chief Executive Officer, Lincoln Regional Center, Lincoln, NE, p. A397

GICZI, Mary Beth, Director Human Resources, HEALTHSOUTH Scottsdale Rehabilitation Hospital, Scottsdale, AZ, p. A38

GIDDINGS, Claudia, R.N. Chief Nursing Officer, Our Community Hospital, Scotland Neck, NC, p. A472

GIDDINGS, Wayne, Manager Management Information Systems, East Valley Hospital Medical Center, Glendora, CA, p. A65

GIDEON, Dawn M., Interim Chief Executive Officer, Doctors Medical Center, San Pablo, CA, p. A93

GIEGER, Julie
Chief Financial Officer, Lackey Memorial Hospital, Forest, MS, p. A358
Chief Financial Officer, Pioneer Community Hospital of Aberdeen, Aberdeen, MS, p. A355
Chief Financial Officer, Pioneer Community Hospital of Newton, Newton, MS, p. A363
Chief Financial Officer, Pioneer Community Hospital of Patrick County, Stuart, VA, p. A679
Chief Financial Officer, Pioneer Community Hospital of Stokes, Danbury, NC, p. A463

GIENGER, Del, Director Financial Services, Frances Mahon Deaconess Hospital, Glasgow, MT, p. A387

GIER, Jennifer, Director Human Resources, Brynn Marr Hospital, Jacksonville, NC, p. A467

GIERTUGA, Garry, Site Manager Human Resources, Adventist La Grange Memorial Hospital, La Grange, IL, p. A194

GIESE, Angela C., Director Human Resources, Midwest Regional Medical Center, Midwest City, OK, p. A513

GIESE, Jon, Vice President and Chief Financial Officer, Simi Valley Hospital and Health Care Services, Simi Valley, CA, p. A95

GIESING, Belva, Chief Nursing Officer, Crittenton Children's Center, Kansas City, MO, p. A373

GIFFORD, Ellen, Director Human Resources, Deaconess Hospital, Oklahoma City, OK, p. A515

GIGLIOTTI, Vicki, Chief Clinical Officer, Moab Regional Hospital, Moab, UT, p. A660

GIGOT, Kelly, Vice President Finance, St. Vincent Hospital, Green Bay, WI, p. A706

GIL, Julio, Manager Information Services, Hazel Hawkins Memorial Hospital, Hollister, CA, p. A67

GILBERT, Andrea F., FACHE, President, Bryn Mawr Hospital, Bryn Mawr, PA, p. A534

GILBERT, Cameron R., Ph.D., President and Chief Executive Officer, Doctors NeuroPsychiatric Hospital and Research Institute, Bremen, IN, p. A208

GILBERT, Cameron R., Ph.D., President and Chief Executive Officer, NeuroPsychiatric Hospitals, Mishawaka, IN, p. B97

GILBERT, Cameron R., Ph.D., President and Chief Executive Officer, RiverCrest Specialty Hospital, Mishawaka, IN, p. A218

GILBERT, Carla, Director Finance, Cedar County Memorial Hospital, El Dorado Springs, MO, p. A370

GILBERT, Jack, Vice President Finance and Support Services, Advocate Illinois Masonic Medical Center, Chicago, IL, p. A183

GILBERT, James B., Chief Financial Officer, Palms of Pasadena Hospital, Saint Petersburg, FL, p. A144

GILBERT, Jeri, Director Human Resources, Watsonville Community Hospital, Watsonville, CA, p. A100

GILBERT, Kevin, R.N. Vice President, Wenatchee Valley Medical Center, Wenatchee, WA, p. A692

GILBERT, Kim, R.N. Chief Nursing Officer, Electra Memorial Hospital, Electra, TX, p. A617

GILBERT, Jr., Ronald, Chief Financial Officer, Soldiers and Sailors Memorial Hospital, Wellsboro, PA, p. A557

GILBERT, Thomas, Director Information Technology Services, Lake Cumberland Regional Hospital, Somerset, KY, p. A270

GILBERT, Thomas D., FACHE,
Chief Executive Officer, Wadley Regional Medical Center, Texarkana, TX, p. A653
Chief Executive Officer, Wadley Regional Medical Center at Hope, Hope, AR, p. A47

GILBERT, Valarie, R.N. Chief Nursing Officer, Texas Health Harris Methodist Hospital Azle, Azle, TX, p. A601

GILBERTSON, Gerry, FACHE, Administrator, CentraCare Health–Melrose, Melrose, MN, p. A346

GILCHRIST, Doug, Chief Operating Officer, Summit Healthcare Regional Medical Center, Show Low, AZ, p. A39

GILDEA, Stephen, Chief Executive Officer, Tyrone Hospital, Tyrone, PA, p. A556

GILDER, Kevin, Chief Financial Officer, Williamsburg Regional Hospital, Kingstree, SC, p. A567

GILDON, Lisa, Vice President and Chief Financial Officer, Texas Health Presbyterian Hospital Plano, Plano, TX, p. A643

GILENE, Joseph, President, Jewish Hospital, Louisville, KY, p. A265

GILES, Charles, M.D. President Medical Staff, Westlake Regional Hospital, Columbia, KY, p. A259

GILES, Jared, Chief Operating Officer, Southwest Healthcare System, Murrieta, CA, p. A79

GILES, Steve, Chief Information Officer, Hollywood Presbyterian Medical Center, Los Angeles, CA, p. A72

GILES, William, Interim Chief Executive Officer, Hardy Wilson Memorial Hospital, Hazlehurst, MS, p. A359

GILFILLAN, Richard J., M.D., President and Chief Executive Officer, Catholic Health East / Trinity Health, Livonia, MI, p. B28

GILG, Ronald, Assistant Vice President Talent, Eastern Regional Medical Center, Philadelphia, PA, p. A548

GILGEN, Steve, Chief Financial Officer, Murphy Medical Center, Murphy, NC, p. A470

GILHAM, Merlin, Chief Executive Officer, U. S. Public Health Service Blackfeet Community Hospital, Saint Mary, MT, p. A390

GILJUM, Anthony, Chief Information Officer, Sheridan Veterans Affairs Medical Center, Sheridan, WY, p. A722

GILKEY, Edward, M.D. Vice President Medical Affairs, St. Luke's Hospital – Warren Campus, Phillipsburg, NJ, p. A421

GILL, Alexander, Chief Executive Officer, Kindred Hospital Kansas City, Kansas City, MO, p. A373

GILL, Margaret, Chief Executive Officer, Memorial Health, Savannah, GA, p. A166

GILL, Mark, Vice President Finance and Chief Financial Officer, Cape Regional Medical Center, Cape May Court House, NJ, p. A414

GILLAM, Sally A., R.N. Chief Nursing Officer, St. David's South Austin Medical Center, Austin, TX, p. A600

GILLARD, Austin M., Chief Executive Officer, Genoa Community Hospital, Genoa, NE, p. A396

GILLEN, Mark T., Director Finance and Operations, Owatonna Hospital, Owatonna, MN, p. A349

GILLES, Ken
Chief Information Officer, Essentia Health Fargo, Fargo, ND, p. A477
Associate Chief Information Officer, Essentia Health St. Mary's – Detroit Lakes, Detroit Lakes, MN, p. A342

GILLESPIE, Anne, R.N. Associate Director Patient Care and Nursing Services, Veterans Affairs Loma Linda Healthcare System, Loma Linda, CA, p. A70

GILLESPIE, Karen, Director Human Resources, Anderson County Hospital, Garnett, KS, p. A244

GILLESPIE, Lisa, M.D. Chief Medical Officer, Rockdale Medical Center, Conyers, GA, p. A157

GILLESPIE, Lynn J., Vice President Human Resources and Organizational Development, OSF Saint Francis Medical Center, Peoria, IL, p. A200

GILLESPIE, Michele, Vice President of Operations, Southwest Medical Center, Liberal, KS, p. A249

GILLESPIE, Thomas, Chief Information Officer, Fulton State Hospital, Fulton, MO, p. A372

GILLESPIE, Tim, Manager Information Systems, Richland Memorial Hospital, Olney, IL, p. A198

GILLESPIE, Tina, Vice President and Chief Financial Officer, Northwest Medical Center, Albany, MO, p. A367

GILLETTE, Daniel, M.D., Clinical Director, Mental Health Institute, Cherokee, IA, p. A227

GILLETTE, Karen, Associate Director Patient Care Services, Memphis Veterans Affairs Medical Center, Memphis, TN, p. A589

GILLETTE, Kathryn, President and Chief Executive Officer, Bayfront Health St. Petersburg, Saint Petersburg, FL, p. A144

GILLETTE, Robert, Chief Information Officer, St. Elizabeth Medical Center, Utica, NY, p. A456

GILLETTE, Tom, Senior Vice President and Chief Information Officer, Mount Sinai Medical Center, Miami Beach, FL, p. A138

GILLIAM, David, M.D. Medical Director, Bloomington Meadows Hospital, Bloomington, IN, p. A207

GILLIAM, Eric
Chief Executive Officer, Saint Joseph Berea, Berea, KY, p. A258
President, Saint Joseph East, Lexington, KY, p. A264

GILLIAM, Leslie, Director Health Information Management, Dominion Hospital, Falls Church, VA, p. A670

GILLIAN, Tom, Chief Operating Officer, River Bend Hospital, West Lafayette, IN, p. A224

GILLIAND, Michael, M.D. Chief of Staff, Brazosport Regional Health System, Lake Jackson, TX, p. A632

GILLIANO, Patti, Chief Nursing Officer, Lake Pointe Medical Center, Rowlett, TX, p. A645

GILLILAND, Terry, M.D
Chief Medical Officer, Sentara Leigh Hospital, Norfolk, VA, p. A675
Senior Vice President and Chief Medical Officer, Sentara Princess Anne Hospital, Virginia Beach, VA, p. A679

GILLINGHAM, Bruce, Commander, Naval Medical Center San Diego, San Diego, CA, p. A89

GILLIS, Anne, Chief Financial Officer, Holy Cross Hospital, Silver Spring, MD, p. A303

GILLMAN, Kreg, Chief Executive Officer, Salt Lake Behavioral Health, Salt Lake City, UT, p. A663

GILLY, Mike, Chief Information Officer, Our Lady of the Angels Hospital, Bogalusa, LA, p. A274

GILMAN, Howard, M.D. Medical Executive, Christian Health Care Center, Wyckoff, NJ, p. A425

GILMAN, Kim, Chief Executive Officer, Phoebe Worth Medical Center, Sylvester, GA, p. A167

GILMORE, Hugh V., M.D. Vice President Medical Affairs, Seton Medical Center Williamson, Round Rock, TX, p. A645

GILMORE, Linda, Chief Nursing Officer/Chief Administrative Officer, Littleton Regional Hospital, Littleton, NH, p. A411

GILMORE, Phillip K., FACHE, Chief Executive Officer, Ashley County Medical Center, Crossett, AR, p. A44

GILPIN, Ann C., President and Chief Executive Officer, Oswego Hospital, Oswego, NY, p. A451

GILPIN, Michael W., Vice President Human Resources, Sampson Regional Medical Center, Clinton, NC, p. A462

GILROY, Robert, M.D. Chief of Staff, Jackson–Madison County General Hospital, Jackson, TN, p. A584

GILTNER, Michelle, Interim Chief Nursing Officer, UH Regional Hospitals, Cleveland, OH, p. A489

GIN, Nancy, M.D. Area Associate Medical Director, Kaiser Permanente Orange County Anaheim Medical Center, Anaheim, CA, p. A55

GINGHER, Barbara S., R.N. Assistant Administrator for Patient Care Services, Baptist Medical Center Nassau, Fernandina Beach, FL, p. A128

GINGRAS, Sean, CPA Chief Financial Officer, Manatee Glens Hospital and Addiction Center, Bradenton, FL, p. A124

GINN, Bobby, Chief Operating Officer, Crestwood Medical Center, Huntsville, AL, p. A21

GINN, Doug, Executive Vice President Operations, Peak Behavioral Health Services, Santa Teresa, NM, p. A430

GINSBERG, Ronald L., M.D. Vice President Medical Affairs, Northwest Hospital, Randallstown, MD, p. A302

GINSBURG, J. Lawrence, M.D. Vice President Medical Affairs, Evangelical Community Hospital, Lewisburg, PA, p. A543

GINTER, Gary, Senior Vice President and Chief Information Officer, Miami Valley Hospital, Dayton, OH, p. A492

GINTOLI, Eric, Hospital Administrator, Baton Rouge Behavioral Hospital, Baton Rouge, LA, p. A273

GINTY, Neil W.
Administrator, South Georgia Medical Center Berrien Campus, Nashville, GA, p. A164
Administrator, South Georgia Medical Center Lanier Campus, Lakeland, GA, p. A162

GINTZIG, Donald R., President and Chief Executive Officer, WakeMed Health & Hospitals, Raleigh, NC, p. B151

GINTZIG, Donald R., President and Chief Executive Officer, WakeMed Raleigh Campus, Raleigh, NC, p. A471

GIOIA, Anthony, Chief Financial Officer, Indiana Orthopaedic Hospital, Indianapolis, IN, p. A214

GIOIA, Gregory J., Chief Fiscal and Administrative Services, Veterans Home and Hospital, Rocky Hill, CT, p. A117

GIORDANO, Paul, Vice President Human Resources, South Nassau Communities Hospital, Oceanside, NY, p. A450

GIORDANO, Roger, M.D. Medical Director, HEALTHSOUTH Rehabilitation Hospital of Virginia, Richmond, VA, p. A677

GIORDANO, Susan, R.N. Chief Nursing Officer, Hackensack University Medical Center at Pascack Valley, Westwood, NJ, p. A424

GIPSON, David N., Senior Vice President and Chief Clinical Operations Officer, Union Hospital, Elkton, MD, p. A300

GIPSON, Linda Stephens, MSN Chief Nursing Officer, Whidbey General Hospital, Coupeville, WA, p. A682

GIRARD, Thomas R.
Vice President Human Resources, Lincoln Health, Damariscotta, ME, p. A293
Vice President Human Resources, Pen Bay Medical Center, Rockport, ME, p. A295

GIRARDIER, Cheryl, Director Information Technology, Millcreek Community Hospital, Erie, PA, p. A538

GIRARDY, James, M.D. Vice President, Chief Surgical Officer, OSF Saint Anthony Medical Center, Rockford, IL, p. A201

GIRTEN, David M.
Corporate Director Financial Services, St. Vincent Seton Specialty Hospital, Indianapolis, IN, p. A215
Corporate Director Financial Services, St. Vincent Seton Specialty Hospital, Lafayette, IN, p. A217

GIRTY, Tara, Director Human Resources, Kiowa District Hospital and Manor, Kiowa, KS, p. A247

GISH, Kevin, Administrator and Vice President, Essentia Health Fosston, Fosston, MN, p. A343

GISLESON, Joni. Director Finance, Palmer Lutheran Health Center, West Union, IA, p. A239

GISSEL, Betty, Vice President Human Resources, University of Tennessee Medical Center, Knoxville, TN, p. A586

GITMAN, Michael, M.D. Medical Director, North Shore University Hospital, Manhasset, NY, p. A440

GITTELMAN, Michael B., Administrator, Bascom Palmer Eye Institute–Anne Bates Leach Eye Hospital, Miami, FL, p. A136

GIUDICE, William A., Vice President and Chief Financial Officer, Tallahassee Memorial HealthCare, Tallahassee, FL, p. A147

GIULIANELLI, Victor, FACHE, President and Chief Executive Officer, St. Mary's Healthcare, Amsterdam, NY, p. A432

GIVENS, Michael K., FACHE Administrator, St. Bernards Medical Center, Jonesboro, AR, p. A48

GIVENS, Stephen K., Assistant Vice President and Administrator, Russell County Medical Center, Lebanon, VA, p. A672

GIZDIC, John H., Chief Operating Officer, New Hanover Regional Medical Center, Wilmington, NC, p. A474

GIZINSKI, Judy, Chief Operating Officer, Health First Palm Bay Hospital, Melbourne, FL, p. A136

GIZZI, Jason, Controller, HEALTHSOUTH MountainView Regional Rehabilitation Hospital, Morgantown, WV, p. A697

GJOLBERG, Skip, FACHE, Chief Executive Officer, Cuero Community Hospital, Cuero, TX, p. A609

GLADBACH, Brandyn, Chief Information Technology Officer, Carroll County Memorial Hospital, Carrollton, MO, p. A369

GLADE, James G., Director Human Resources, Clearfield Hospital, Clearfield, PA, p. A536

GLADEN, Tracy, Chief Financial Officer, Twin Valley Behavioral Healthcare, Columbus, OH, p. A491

GLADFELTER, Sharon, Health Information Officer, Brook Lane Health Services, Hagerstown, MD, p. A301

GLADNEY, Robert C., Interim Chief Executive Officer, Kindred Hospital– Oklahoma City, Oklahoma City, OK, p. A515

GLADSTONE, Art, R.N., Chief Executive Officer, Straub Clinic & Hospital, Honolulu, HI, p. A171

GLANVILLE, Tristan, Chief Financial Officer, Adirondack Medical Center, Saranac Lake, NY, p. A454

GLANZER, Elgin, Chief Financial Officer, Memorial Health System, Abilene, KS, p. A241

GLASBERG, Michael, Senior Vice President, Chief Operating Officer, Dameron Hospital, Stockton, CA, p. A96

GLASER, Elaine, Chief Executive Officer, Kindred Hospital Las Vegas–Sahara, Las Vegas, NV, p. A406

GLASER, Ruth, President, Pender Memorial Hospital, Burgaw, NC, p. A460

GLASNAPP, Sherry L., Director, Douglas County Community Mental Health Center, Omaha, NE, p. A400

GLASS, Gordon, Chief Financial Officer, Golden Valley Memorial Healthcare, Clinton, MO, p. A369

GLASS, Ian, M.D. Chief Medical Officer, Tomball Regional Medical Center, Tomball, TX, p. A653

GLASS, Steven, Chief Financial Officer, Cleveland Clinic, Cleveland, OH, p. A488

GLASS, Wendy, Director Human Resources, Colleton Medical Center, Walterboro, SC, p. A570

GLASSBURN, David, Vice President Finance and Chief Financial Officer, Harlingen Medical Center, Harlingen, TX, p. A622

GLASSCOCK, Gary M., President and Chief Executive Officer, Noland Health Services, Inc., Birmingham, AL, p. B99

GLASSCOCK, Sheryl, Chief Nursing Officer, Lake Cumberland Regional Hospital, Somerset, KY, p. A270

GLASSMAN, Kimberly S., Ph.D. Chief Nursing Officer, NYU Langone Medical Center, New York, NY, p. A448

GLASSMAN, Randy, Chief Financial Officer, Little Colorado Medical Center, Winslow, AZ, p. A41

GLATT, Aaron, M.D., Executive Vice President and Chief Administrative Officer, Mercy Medical Center, Rockville Centre, NY, p. A453

GLAVES, Ann, Vice President Human Resources, St. Francis Regional Medical Center, Shakopee, MN, p. A352

GLAVIN, Jolene, R.N. Director Nursing, Salina Surgical Hospital, Salina, KS, p. A254

GLAVIS, Edward S., Senior Vice President and Area Manager, Kaiser Permanente Roseville Medical Center, Roseville, CA, p. A87

GLAZIER, Douglas, Interim Chief Financial Officer, Day Kimball Hospital, Putnam, CT, p. A116

GLAZIER, Stephen, Chief Operating Officer, University of Texas Harris County Psychiatric Center, Houston, TX, p. A627

GLEASON, Jeffrey J., M.D. Chief Medical Officer, Cookeville Regional Medical Center, Cookeville, TN, p. A581

GLEASON, Mike, Vice President and Chief Financial Officer, UF Health Jacksonville, Jacksonville, FL, p. A132

GLECKLER, John, Chief Financial Officer, St. Vincent's Medical Center, Bridgeport, CT, p. A113

GLEESON, Gabrielle, Human Resources, Hermann Area District Hospital, Hermann, MO, p. A372

GLEN, Diane M., Assistant Administrator, Barnes–Jewish West County Hospital, Saint Louis, MO, p. A380

GLENN, Gary
Director Information Technology, Carrus Rehabilitation Hospital, Sherman, TX, p. A649
Director Information Technology, Carrus Specialty Hospital, Sherman, TX, p. A649

GLENN, Jeannette, Vice President Human Resources, Education and Training, McLeod Regional Medical Center, Florence, SC, p. A566

GLENN, Marie, M.D. Clinical Director, North Alabama Regional Hospital, Decatur, AL, p. A18

GLENN, Mike, Chief Executive Officer, Jefferson Healthcare, Port Townsend, WA, p. A686

GLENN, Sue, Director Administrative Services, Kalamazoo Psychiatric Hospital, Kalamazoo, MI, p. A328

GLENN, Susan, Chief Executive Officer, HEALTHSOUTH Rehabilitation Hospital, Kingsport, TN, p. A585

GLENN, Wil A., Director Communications, Larry B. Zieverink, Sr. Alcoholism Treatment Center, Raleigh, NC, p. A471

GLENNING, Robert, Executive Vice President Finance and Chief Financial Officer, Hackensack University Medical Center, Hackensack, NJ, p. A416

GLICK, Jennifer, Manager Clinical Informatics, Oaklawn Psychiatric Center, Goshen, IN, p. A212

GLICKMAN, Bobby, M.D. Chief of Staff, Sutter Delta Medical Center, Antioch, CA, p. A56

GLIDDEN, Nancy, Chief Financial Officer, Calais Regional Hospital, Calais, ME, p. A292

GLIDDEN, Weldon, M.D. Chief of Staff, Chillicothe Hospital District, Chillicothe, TX, p. A606

GLIDEWELL Jr., Calvin E., Chief Executive Officer, Broward Health Medical Center, Fort Lauderdale, FL, p. A128

GLIELMI, Vincent D., D.O. Senior Vice President Medical Affairs, Ephrata Community Hospital, Ephrata, PA, p. A538

GLIHA, Jennie, Vice President Human Resources, Aurelia Osborn Fox Memorial Hospital, Oneonta, NY, p. A450

GLOCKA, Carolynn, R.N., President, Aurora Sinai Medical Center, Milwaukee, WI, p. A710

GLOCKNER, Cheri, Director Development, Carson Tahoe Regional Medical Center, Carson City, NV, p. A404

GLOCKNER, Tina, Chief Nursing Officer, PMH Medical Center, Prosser, WA, p. A687

GLODOWSKI, Brenda, Chief Financial Officer, North Central Health Care, Wausau, WI, p. A718

GLOFF, Vicki, Chief Financial Officer, Goodall–Witcher Hospital Authority, Clifton, TX, p. A606

GLOGGNER, Peter, Chief Human Resources Officer, Jupiter Medical Center, Jupiter, FL, p. A132

GLONER, James, Senior Vice President, North Philadelphia Health System, Philadelphia, PA, p. A549

GLORIA–BARRAZA, Patricia, Coordinator Human Resources, Mayhill Hospital, Denton, TX, p. A613

GLOSEMEYER, Talitha, FACHE, Administrator, Norman Specialty Hospital, Norman, OK, p. A514

GLOSS, John, FACHE, Administrator, Shriners Hospitals for Children–St. Louis, Saint Louis, MO, p. A381

GLOTZBACK, Lee, Director Human Resources, Citrus Memorial Health System, Inverness, FL, p. A131

GLOVER, Cynthia, R.N. Vice President and Chief Nursing Officer, Reston Hospital Center, Reston, VA, p. A677

GLOVER, Doug, Controller, William S. Hall Psychiatric Institute, Columbia, SC, p. A564

GLOVER, Leslie, Director Operations, Novant Health Gaffney Medical Center, Gaffney, SC, p. A566

GLOWA, Meghan, Director Human Resources, Sunnyview Rehabilitation Hospital, Schenectady, NY, p. A454

GLUBKA, Theresa, Chief Executive Officer, Sutter Solano Medical Center, Vallejo, CA, p. A99

GLUCHOWSKI, Jeanne, Executive Director, Conifer Park, Glenville, NY, p. A438

GLUCK, Michael, M.D. Medical Director, LifeCare Hospitals of Mechanicsburg, Mechanicsburg, PA, p. A545

GLUECKERT, John W., Administrator, Montana State Hospital, Warm Springs, MT, p. A391

GLYER, David, Vice President Finance, Community Memorial Health System, Ventura, CA, p. A99

GLYNN, Cindy, Director Human Resources, Regional Rehabilitation Hospital, Phenix City, AL, p. A25

GLYNN, John, Senior Vice President and Chief Information Officer, Unity Hospital, Rochester, NY, p. A453

GLYNN, Kevin, Chief Information Officer, Northeast Rehabilitation Hospital, Salem, NH, p. A412

GLYNN, Margaret, M.D. Chief Medical Officer, North Mississippi Medical Center–Iuka, Iuka, MS, p. A359

GLYNN, Shari, Vice President Finance and Chief Financial Officer, Eaton Rapids Medical Center, Eaton Rapids, MI, p. A323

GNAGEY, Keith, Chief Executive Officer, Teton Valley Health Care, Driggs, ID, p. A176

GNAM, Gwen, R.N. Chief Nursing Officer, Henry Ford Hospital, Detroit, MI, p. A322

GNANN, Andrew, Vice President Operations, St. Vincent's East, Birmingham, AL, p. A17

GNEGY, David, M.D. President Medical Staff, Camden Clark Medical Center, Parkersburg, WV, p. A698

GOACHER, Brad, Vice President Administration, Alton Memorial Hospital, Alton, IL, p. A180

GOAD, Pat, Director Human Resources, Hillcrest Hospital Claremore, Claremore, OK, p. A509

GOBEL, Bret, Chief Financial Officer, Sierra Vista Hospital, Truth or Consequences, NM, p. A431

GOBELL, James, Chief Financial Officer, UnityPoint Health – St. Luke's, Sioux City, IA, p. A238

GOBER, Kirby, Chief Executive Officer, Throckmorton County Memorial Hospital, Throckmorton, TX, p. A653

GOBLE, Jonathan R., FACHE, President and Chief Executive Officer, Indiana University Health North Hospital, Carmel, IN, p. A208

GOBLE, Mandy C., President and Chief Executive Officer, Mary Rutan Hospital, Bellefontaine, OH, p. A483

GOCHENOUR, Julia, Manager Information Systems, West River Regional Medical Center, Hettinger, ND, p. A478

GOCHIS, Paul D., M.D. Chief of Staff, St. Luke Community Healthcare, Ronan, MT, p. A390

GODAMUNNE, Karim, M.D. Chief Medical Officer, North Fulton Regional Hospital, Roswell, GA, p. A165

GODBOLD, Pat, Administrator, McLeod Medical Center–Darlington, Darlington, SC, p. A565

GODDARD, Mark, M.D. Medical Director, HEALTHSOUTH Rehabilitation Hospital at Drake, Cincinnati, OH, p. A487

GODESKY, Susan, Director Information Technology, Nanticoke Memorial Hospital, Seaford, DE, p. A119

GODFREY, Katrina, Director Human Resources, Mercy Hospital Ada, Ada, OK, p. A507

GODFREY, Kristine, Director Human Resources, Skyridge Medical Center, Cleveland, TN, p. A581

GODINEZ, Roxanna M., Chief Executive Officer, Cornerstone Regional Hospital, Edinburg, TX, p. A615

GODLEY, Maria, R.N., Chief Executive Officer, Northern Idaho Advanced Care Hospital, Post Falls, ID, p. A178

GODLEY, Patrick, Chief Financial Officer, Contra Costa Regional Medical Center, Martinez, CA, p. A77

GODWIN, Jr., Herman A., M.D. Senior Vice President and Medical Director, Watauga Medical Center, Boone, NC, p. A460

GOEB–BURKETT, Michele, R.N. Chief Nursing Officer, Florida Hospital Memorial Medical Center, Daytona Beach, FL, p. A127

GOEBEL, Bret, Finance Officer, Guadalupe County Hospital, Santa Rosa, NM, p. A430

GOEBEL, Cecilia B., R.N. Vice President and Chief Nursing Officer, Susan B. Allen Memorial Hospital, El Dorado, KS, p. A243

GOEBEL, Donna, M.D. Chief Nursing Officer, Mitchell County Hospital, Colorado City, TX, p. A607

GOEBEL, Michael
Chief Executive Officer, Adventist Hinsdale Hospital, Hinsdale, IL, p. A193
Chief Executive Officer, Adventist La Grange Memorial Hospital, La Grange, IL, p. A194

GOEHRING, Lawanda, MSN Chief Nursing Officer, Good Shepherd Penn Partners Specialty Hospital at Rittenhouse, Philadelphia, PA, p. A548

GOEL, Amitabh, M.D. Chief Medical Officer, University Hospitals Geneva Medical Center, Geneva, OH, p. A494

GOEL, Ashutosh, M.D. Chief Information Technology Officer, Cheyenne Regional Medical Center, Cheyenne, WY, p. A720

GOELOE–ALSTON, Hendrina, Assistant Vice President Personnel, SUNY Downstate Medical Center University Hospital,, NY, p. A448

GOELZER, Mark L., M.D. Director Medical Affairs, Mercy Hospital and Trauma Center, Janesville, WI, p. A707

GOERTZ, Richard, Chief Financial Officer, Greenwood County Hospital, Eureka, KS, p. A244

GOESER, Stephen L., FACHE, President and Chief Executive Officer, Nebraska Methodist Hospital, Omaha, NE, p. A400

GOETTSCH, Barry, Chief Executive Officer, Marengo Memorial Hospital, UnityPoint Health, Marengo, IA, p. A234

GOETZINGER, Susan, Chief Financial Officer, Riverton Memorial Hospital, Riverton, WY, p. A722

GOFF, Gary E., M.D. Medical Director, Promise Hospital of Dallas, Dallas, TX, p. A611

GOFF, Mark, Owner and Administrator, Community Specialty Hospital, Lafayette, LA, p. A281

GOFORTH, Annette, Manager Administrative Services, Central Prison Hospital, Raleigh, NC, p. A470

GOGGIN, Dan, Senior Vice President and Chief Financial Officer, Grimes St. Joseph Health Center, Navasota, TX, p. A639

GOGGIN, Kathy, Director Administrative Services, Devereux Georgia Treatment Network, Kennesaw, GA, p. A161

GOGIA, Harmohinder, M.D. Chief Medical Officer, Western Medical Center Anaheim, Anaheim, CA, p. A55

GOGLIETTINO, Deborah
Senior Vice President Human Resources, Manchester Memorial Hospital, Manchester, CT, p. A114
Senior Vice President Human Resources, Rockville General Hospital, Vernon Rockville, CT, p. A117

GOINGS, Harold, Chief Human Resources, Veterans Affairs Greater Los Angeles Healthcare System, Los Angeles, CA, p. A75

GOKLI, Asit, M.D., Chief Executive Officer, Memorial Hospital Los Banos, Los Banos, CA, p. A76

GOLAN, Marc
Chief Financial Officer, Franciscan St. Anthony Health – Crown Point, Crown Point, IN, p. A209
Regional Chief Financial Officer, Franciscan St. Anthony Health – Michigan City, Michigan City, IN, p. A218

GOLANOWSKI, Marie, MS, President, Aurora St. Luke's Medical Center, Milwaukee, WI, p. A710

GOLD, Barbara, M.D. Chief Medical Officer, University of Minnesota Medical Center, Fairview, Minneapolis, MN, p. A348

GOLD, Joseph, M.D. Chief Medical Officer, McLean Hospital, Belmont, MA, p. A305

GOLD, Larry M., Chief Executive Officer, Children's Hospital of Michigan, Detroit, MI, p. A321

GOLD, Neal, Chief Executive Officer, Westlake Regional Hospital, Columbia, KY, p. A259

GOLDAMMER, Kyle, Chief Financial Officer, Sioux Falls Specialty Hospital, Sioux Falls, SD, p. A576

GOLDBERG, Andrew S., Associate Executive Director, Syosset Hospital, Syosset, NY, p. A455

GOLDBERG, David, President & Interim Chief Executive Officer, Allegheny Valley Hospital, Natrona Heights, PA, p. A546

GOLDBERG, David, M.D. Vice President Medical Affairs, Community Memorial Hospital, Menomonee Falls, WI, p. A709

GOLDBERG, Frederick, M.D. Vice President Medical Affairs and Chief Medical Officer, Nathan Littauer Hospital and Nursing Home, Gloversville, NY, p. A438

GOLDBERG, Jonathan
Chief Information Officer, Albany Memorial Hospital, Albany, NY, p. A432
Vice President and Chief Information Officer, St. Mary's Hospital, Troy, NY, p. A456
Chief Information Officer, St. Peter's Hospital, Albany, NY, p. A432

GOLDBERG, Larry M., President and Chief Executive Officer, Loyola University Medical Center, Maywood, IL, p. A195

GOLDBERG, Paul R., Chief Financial Officer, Jersey City Medical Center, Jersey City, NJ, p. A417

GOLDBERG, Richard L., M.D., President, MedStar Georgetown University Hospital, Washington, DC, p. A121

GOLDBERG, Stephanie J., MSN Senior Vice President and Chief Nursing Officer, Hospital for Special Surgery, New York, NY, p. A444

GOLDBERGER, Joseph, M.D
Chief Medical Officer, Yavapai Regional Medical Center – East, Prescott Valley, AZ, p. A37
Chief Medical Officer, Yavapai Regional Medical Center, Prescott, AZ, p. A37

GOLDBLOOM, Alan L., M.D., Chief Executive Officer, Children's Hospitals and Clinics of Minnesota, Minneapolis, MN, p. A347

GOLDEN, Joy, Chief Executive Officer, Lakeside Behavioral Health System, Memphis, TN, p. A588

GOLDENBERG, Dianne, Chief Executive Officer, Aventura Hospital and Medical Center, Aventura, FL, p. A123

GOLDENSTEIN, Rachel, R.N. Chief Nursing Officer, Buchanan County Health Center, Independence, IA, p. A232

GOLDFARB, I. William, Chief Medical Officer, West Penn Hospital, Pittsburgh, PA, p. A552

GOLDFISHER, Anne M., R.N. Chief Nursing Officer, Kaiser Permanente Santa Clara Medical Center, Santa Clara, CA, p. A94

GOLDHAGEN, Michele, M.D. Chief of Staff, Russell Medical Center, Alexander City, AL, p. A15

GOLDMAN, David, M.D. Vice President Medical Affairs and Education, Prince George's Hospital Center, Cheverly, MD, p. A299

GOLDMAN, Eric, Chief Executive Officer, Palms West Hospital, Loxahatchee, FL, p. A134

GOLDMAN, John S., Director, Carl Vinson Veterans Affairs Medical Center, Dublin, GA, p. A159

GOLDSCHMID, David, M.D. President Medical Staff, Seton Medical Center, Daly City, CA, p. A61

GOLDSCHMIDT, Pascal J., M.D., Chief Executive Officer, University of Miami Health System, Miami, FL, p. B146

GOLDSMITH, Cheri L.
Director Financial Services, Parkland Health Center, Farmington, MO, p. A371
Director Financial Services, Parkland Health Center–Bonne Terre, Bonne Terre, MO, p. A367

GOLDSMITH, Dana L., M.D. Vice President Medical Affairs, Pen Bay Medical Center, Rockport, ME, p. A295

GOLDSMITH, Debra, Regional Administrator, CHI Health Mercy Corning, Corning, IA, p. A228

GOLDSTEIN, Allan, M.D. Medical Director and Chief of Staff, Select Specialty Hospital–Birmingham, Birmingham, AL, p. A16

GOLDSTEIN, Brian, M.D. Executive Vice President and Chief Operating Officer, University of North Carolina Hospitals, Chapel Hill, NC, p. A461

GOLDSTEIN, Charles, M.D. President Medical Staff, Riverside Shore Memorial Hospital, Nassawadox, VA, p. A674

GOLDSTEIN, David, M.D. Chief Medical Officer, Contra Costa Regional Medical Center, Martinez, CA, p. A77

GOLDSTEIN, Gary W., M.D., President and Chief Executive Officer, Kennedy Krieger Institute, Baltimore, MD, p. A296

GOLDSTEIN, Gerald, M.D. Senior Vice President and Chief Medical Officer, Western Maryland Regional Medical Center, Cumberland, MD, p. A300

GOLDSTEIN, Lawrence, M.D. Chief Medical Officer, Vibra Hospital of Mahoning Valley, Boardman, OH, p. A484

GOLDSTEIN, Lisa, Executive Vice President and Chief Operating Officer, Hospital for Special Surgery, New York, NY, p. A444

GOLDSTEIN, Mark L., Chief Financial Officer, Anna Jaques Hospital, Newburyport, MA, p. A312

GOLDSTEIN, III, Nathan, M.D. Chief Medical Officer, Northwest Texas Healthcare System, Amarillo, TX, p. A596

GOLDSTEIN, Paul, Vice President Finance and Chief Financial Officer, Orlando Regional Medical Center, Orlando, FL, p. A141

GOLDSTEIN, Steven I.
President and Chief Executive Officer, Highland Hospital of Rochester, Rochester, NY, p. A453
President and Chief Executive Officer, Strong Memorial Hospital of the University of Rochester, Rochester, NY, p. A453

GOLDSTEIN, Steven I., General Director and Chief Executive Officer, University of Rochester Medical Center, Rochester, NY, p. B146

GOLDSTEIN, Wendy Z., President and Chief Executive Officer, Lutheran Medical Center,, NY, p. A445

GOLDSZER, Robert, M.D. Senior Vice President and Chief Medical Officer, Mount Sinai Medical Center, Miami Beach, FL, p. A138

GOLEN, Michael, M.D. Chief Medical Officer, Lake Health, Concord Township, OH, p. A491

GOLIGHTLY, Beverly, Director Information Technology, St. Vincent's East, Birmingham, AL, p. A17

GOLKE, Rynae, Director Human Resources, Jacobson Memorial Hospital Care Center, Elgin, ND, p. A477

GOLL, Cheri, MSN Chief Nursing Officer, Inova Fair Oaks Hospital, Fairfax, VA, p. A670

GOLLAHER, Jeffrey, Chief Executive Officer, Hendricks Community Hospital, Hendricks, MN, p. A345

GOLOVAN, Ronald, M.D. Vice President Medical Operations, Lutheran Hospital, Cleveland, OH, p. A488

GOMAN, Valerie, M.D. President Medical Staff, Baylor Medical Center at Waxahachie, Waxahachie, TX, p. A656

GOMBAR, Greg A.
Chief Financial Officer, Carolinas Medical Center, Charlotte, NC, p. A461
Chief Financial Officer, Carolinas Medical Center–University, Charlotte, NC, p. A461

GOMBERG, Sandra, Chief Operating Officer, Aria Health, Philadelphia, PA, p. A547

GOMES, Carol, FACHE Chief Operating Officer, Stony Brook University Medical Center, Stony Brook, NY, p. A455

GOMES, Robert, FACHE,
Chief Executive Officer, St. Charles Medical Center – Bend, Bend, OR, p. A523
Chief Executive Officer, St. Charles Medical Center – Redmond, Redmond, OR, p. A529

GOMEZ, Carmen, Director Human Resources, North Shore Medical Center, Miami, FL, p. A137

GOMEZ, Denise, Assistant Vice President Information Systems, Meriter Hospital, Madison, WI, p. A708

GOMEZ, Edward, Manager Information Systems, HEALTHSOUTH Deaconess Rehabilitation Hospital, Evansville, IN, p. A210

GOMEZ, Gloria, M.D. Medical Director, East Mississippi State Hospital, Meridian, MS, p. A362

GOMEZ, Jesse, Vice President Human Resources, University of Texas Health Science Center at Tyler, Tyler, TX, p. A654

GOMEZ, Lynn M., Executive Director Human Resources, San Gorgonio Memorial Hospital, Banning, CA, p. A57

GOMEZ, Mike, Site Manager Medical Information Systems, Our Lady of Bellefonte Hospital, Ashland, KY, p. A258

GOMEZ, Omar, M.D. Chief of Staff, Cornerstone Regional Hospital, Edinburg, TX, p. A615

GOMEZ, Robin, MSN, Administrator, Alvarado Hospital Medical Center, San Diego, CA, p. A89

GOMPF, Shelly, Director Human Resources, Douglas County Hospital, Alexandria, MN, p. A339

GONCZ, Gray, Vice President of Medical Affairs, Trinity Health System, Steubenville, OH, p. A502

GONDER, Christie, Chief Nursing Officer, Salinas Valley Memorial Healthcare System, Salinas, CA, p. A88

GONDRON, Elizabeth, R.N. Vice President and Chief Nursing Officer, Iberia Medical Center, New Iberia, LA, p. A285

GONG, Christopher, M.D. Chief Staff, Huron Medical Center, Bad Axe, MI, p. A318

GONGAWARE, Robert, Senior Vice President Finance, Indiana Regional Medical Center, Indiana, PA, p. A541

GONYEA, Sonja, Director Human Resources, United Memorial Medical Center, Batavia, NY, p. A433

GONZALES, Angela, Manager Human Resources, San Mateo Medical Center, San Mateo, CA, p. A93

GONZALES, D. V., Head Information Technology Management, Naval Medical Center San Diego, San Diego, CA, p. A89

GONZALES, Ed
  Vice President Human Resources, St. John's Pleasant Valley Hospital, Camarillo, CA, p. A58
  Vice President Human Resources, St. John's Regional Medical Center, Oxnard, CA, p. A82

GONZALES, Jan, Director Human Resources, North Valley Hospital, Tonasket, WA, p. A691

GONZALES, Mary Ann, M.D. Medical Director, Central Texas Rehabilitation Hospital, Austin, TX, p. A599

GONZALES, Mike, Chief Financial Officer, Vibra Hospital of San Diego, San Diego, CA, p. A90

GONZALES, Pamela, Chief Operating Officer, Anson General Hospital, Anson, TX, p. A597

GONZALES, Rachel Ann, R.N., Chief Executive Officer, Madison Memorial Hospital, Rexburg, ID, p. A178

GONZALEZ, Agustin, Director Finance, Hospital Dr. Cayetano Coll Y Toste, Arecibo, PR, p. A724

GONZALEZ, Arthur A., FACHE, Chief Executive Officer, Denver Health, Denver, CO, p. A104

GONZALEZ, Aurelio, Chief Financial Officer, University Hospital and Medical Center, Tamarac, FL, p. A147

GONZALEZ, David, M.D. Medical Director, Brook Lane Health Services, Hagerstown, MD, p. A301

GONZALEZ, Dinah L., Chief Financial Officer, Knapp Medical Center, Weslaco, TX, p. A657

GONZALEZ, Elizabeth, Chief Financial Officer, Hospital Metropolitano Dr. Tito Mattei, Yauco, PR, p. A729

GONZALEZ, Erin
  Director Human Resources and Education, Maryvale Hospital Medical Center, Phoenix, AZ, p. A36
  Director Human Resources, Paradise Valley Hospital, Phoenix, AZ, p. A36

GONZALEZ, Hugo, M.D. Chief Medical Officer, Sister Emmanuel Hospital, Miami, FL, p. A137

GONZALEZ, Jacqueline, Senior Vice President and Chief Nursing Officer, Miami Children's Hospital, Miami, FL, p. A137

GONZALEZ, Jaime, Administrator, St. Catherine's Rehabilitation Hospital, North Miami, FL, p. A139

GONZALEZ, James R., President and Chief Executive Officer, University Hospital, Newark, NJ, p. A420

GONZALEZ, Joni, Controller, Kindred Hospital Dallas Central, Dallas, TX, p. A610

GONZALEZ, Jorge F., M.D
  Chief Medical Officer, Florida Hospital Heartland Medical Center, Sebring, FL, p. A145
  Vice President and Chief Nursing Officer, Florida Hospital Wauchula, Wauchula, FL, p. A149

GONZALEZ, Jorge Matta, Executive Director, University Hospital, San Juan, PR, p. A729

GONZALEZ, Laura, Interim Chief Nurse Executive, South Shore Hospital, Chicago, IL, p. A186

GONZALEZ, Pedro J., FACHE, Chief Executive Officer, Ashford Presbyterian Community Hospital, San Juan, PR, p. A727

GONZALEZ, Rainier, Chairman and Chief Executive Officer, Pacer Health Corporation, Miami Lakes, FL, p. B104

GONZALEZ, Richard, Interim Chief Executive Officer, The Medical Center of Southeast Texas, Port Arthur, TX, p. A643

GONZALEZ, Roberto, Executive Director Human Resources, Hoboken University Medical Center, Hoboken, NJ, p. A417

GONZALEZ, Sonia I., R.N. Chief Operating Officer, Oak Hill Hospital, Brooksville, FL, p. A125

GONZALEZ, Susan, Director of Clinical Services, Stanislaus Surgical Hospital, Modesto, CA, p. A78

GONZALEZ-FAJARDO, Ana, Human Resources Director, Palmetto General Hospital, Hialeah, FL, p. A130

GOOCH, Chris, Information Technology Director, Hermann Area District Hospital, Hermann, MO, p. A372

GOOCH, Chris, M.D. Chief of Staff, Parkway Regional Hospital, Fulton, KY, p. A261

GOOCH, Mathew, Chief Executive Officer, Jennersville Regional Hospital, West Grove, PA, p. A558

GOOCH, Patricia R., MSN Chief Nursing Officer, Doctors Hospital of Manteca, Manteca, CA, p. A76

GOOD, Jo, Director of Nursing, Palmetto Lowcountry Behavioral Health, Charleston, SC, p. A563

GOOD, Scott, Manager Information Services, Kearny County Hospital, Lakin, KS, p. A248

GOOD, Vance A., M.D. Chief Medical Staff, Troy Community Hospital, Troy, PA, p. A556

GOODALL, David, M.D. Chief Medical Staff, Essentia Health–Deer River, Deer River, MN, p. A342

GOODBALIAN, Terry
  Vice President Finance and Chief Financial Officer, Henry Ford Macomb Hospitals, Clinton Township, MI, p. A321
  Vice President, Finance and Chief Financial Officer, Henry Ford Wyandotte Hospital, Wyandotte, MI, p. A337

GOODE, Lori, Director Human Resources, Baptist Memorial Hospital–Union County, New Albany, MS, p. A363

GOODE, Shayne, Administrator, Post Acute/Warm Springs Specialty Hospital of New Braunfels, New Braunfels, TX, p. A639

GOODE, Vicky, Director Human Resources, LifeCare Hospitals of North Carolina, Rocky Mount, NC, p. A471

GOODELL, Thomas, M.D. Chief of Staff, Mt. San Rafael Hospital, Trinidad, CO, p. A111

GOODENBERY, Jason, Administrative Assistant III, Alaska Psychiatric Institute, Anchorage, AK, p. A28

GOODHAND, Melony W.
  Regional Chief Financial Officer, Presence Saint Joseph Medical Center, Joliet, IL, p. A194
  Chief Financial Officer, Presence St. Mary's Hospital, Kankakee, IL, p. A194

GOODIN, Debbie, Vice President Human Resources, Mills–Peninsula Health Services, Burlingame, CA, p. A58

GOODISON, Sharon A., R.N. Chief Nursing Officer, Jackson Hospital and Clinic, Montgomery, AL, p. A24

GOODLETT, Lisa, Senior Vice President and Chief Financial Officer, Laurel Regional Hospital, Laurel, MD, p. A302

GOODMAN, Brenda, Chief Nursing Officer, Medical Center of Peach County, Navicent Health, Fort Valley, GA, p. A160

GOODMAN, David M., Ph.D. Chief Information Officer, Veterans Affairs Boston Healthcare System, Boston, MA, p. A307

GOODMAN, Doug, Vice President Human Resources, Brandon Regional Hospital, Brandon, FL, p. A124

GOODMAN, Josie, Associate Director, Central State Hospital, Louisville, KY, p. A265

GOODMAN, Larry J., M.D., Chief Executive Officer, Rush University Medical Center, Chicago, IL, p. A186

GOODMAN, Larry J., M.D., Chief Executive Officer, Rush University Medical Center, Chicago, IL, p. B116

GOODMAN, Louis, Senior Vice President Human Resources, Monongahela Valley Hospital, Monongahela, PA, p. A545

GOODMAN, Mary Jo, Chief Operating Officer, Park Plaza Hospital, Houston, TX, p. A626

GOODMAN, Steven, Chief Operating Officer, Willow Crest Hospital, Miami, OK, p. A513

GOODNO, Janell, Interim Chief Executive Officer, Kiowa District Hospital and Manor, Kiowa, KS, p. A247

GOODNOW, John H., Chief Executive Officer, Benefis Health System, Great Falls, MT, p. B23

GOODNOW, John H., Chief Executive Officer, Benefis Hospitals, Great Falls, MT, p. A388

GOODPASTER, Amber, Chief Financial Officer, Clark Regional Medical Center, Winchester, KY, p. A271

GOODRICH, C. Harlan, Vice President and Chief Information Officer, MidMichigan Medical Center–Midland, Midland, MI, p. A330

GOODRICH, Zane, Vice President Finance, East Tennessee Children's Hospital, Knoxville, TN, p. A585

GOODSON, David, Chief Executive Officer, Select Specialty Hospital–Pensacola, Pensacola, FL, p. A142

GOODSON, Jacob, Director Information Technology, North Oaks Medical Center, Hammond, LA, p. A278

GOODSPEED, Darwin, Director, Sioux Falls Veterans Affairs Health Care System, Sioux Falls, SD, p. A577

GOODSTEIN, Ruth, Controller, HEALTHSOUTH Sunrise Rehabilitation Hospital, Sunrise, FL, p. A146

GOODWIN, Jeremy, M.D. President, Medical Staff, Monroe County Hospital, Forsyth, GA, p. A160

GOODWIN, Keith D., President and Chief Executive Officer, East Tennessee Children's Hospital, Knoxville, TN, p. A585

GOODWIN, Linda, R.N. Chief Nursing Officer, Via Christi Hospital on St. Francis, Wichita, KS, p. A257

GOODWIN, W. Jarrad, M.D. Director, University of Miami Hospital and Clinics, Miami, FL, p. A138

GOOLSBY, Elizabeth, Director, Fayetteville Veterans Affairs Medical Center, Fayetteville, NC, p. A464

GOOSTREE, Amanda J., President, Clay County Hospital, Flora, IL, p. A190

GORANSON, Ken, Chief Financial Officer, Benson Hospital, Benson, AZ, p. A31

GORBACH, Debbie, Vice President and Treasurer, Edwin Shaw Rehab, Cuyahoga Falls, OH, p. A491

GORBY, David R., M.D. Vice President Quality and Patient Safety, Nash Health Care Systems, Rocky Mount, NC, p. A471

GORBY, Karen S., FACHE, Administrator and Chief Nursing Officer, Mercy Memorial Hospital, Urbana, OH, p. A504

GORCZYCA, Julie A., R.N. Chief Nursing Officer, Genesys Regional Medical Center, Grand Blanc, MI, p. A324

GORDDARD, Jeffrey, Chief Executive Officer, Select Specialty Hospital–McKeesport, McKeesport, PA, p. A544

GORDIAN, Michael, Chief Financial Officer, Western Plains Medical Complex, Dodge City, KS, p. A243

GORDON, Cynthia, R.N., Chief Executive Officer, Shasta Regional Medical Center, Redding, CA, p. A85

GORDON, Dan, Chief Financial Officer, Feather River Hospital, Paradise, CA, p. A82

GORDON, Jackie, Chief Clinical Officer, Kindred Hospital Dallas Central, Dallas, TX, p. A610

GORDON, Jacqueline, R.N. Chief Nursing Officer, Memorial Medical Center – Livingston, Livingston, TX, p. A633

GORDON, Kevin, M.D. Chief of Staff, Medical Center of Southeastern Oklahoma, Durant, OK, p. A510

GORDON, Leilani, Director Human Resources and Payroll, Nye Regional Medical Center, Tonopah, NV, p. A408

GORDON, Mark, Chief Nursing Officer, Kern Valley Healthcare District, Lake Isabella, CA, p. A69

GORDON, Mark M., Chief Executive Officer, Bon Secours St. Francis Medical Center, Midlothian, VA, p. A674

GORDON, Nancy Gail, R.N. CNO and VP of Nursing, Baptist Health South Florida, Homestead Hospital, Homestead, FL, p. A131

GORDON, Robert, Manager Information Systems, Halifax Regional Medical Center, Roanoke Rapids, NC, p. A471

GORDON, Steve, Director Human Resources, Lake City Medical Center, Lake City, FL, p. A133

GORDON, Steven R., President and Chief Executive Officer, Brattleboro Memorial Hospital, Brattleboro, VT, p. A665

GORDON, Susan, R.N. Chief Nursing Officer, Memorial Hospital, York, PA, p. A559

GORDON, Thomas, Chief Information Officer, Virtua Marlton, Marlton, NJ, p. A418

GORDON, Wayne, Chief Financial Officer, Memorial Hermann Rehabilitation Hospital – Katy, Katy, TX, p. A630

GORDY, Joseph S., President, Flagler Hospital, Saint Augustine, FL, p. A144

GORE, Gary R., Chief Executive Officer, Marshall Health System, Guntersville, AL, p. B88

GORE, Tim, Chief Financial Officer, Rivendell Behavioral Health, Bowling Green, KY, p. A259

GOREAU, Judy, R.N. Director of Nursing, Eastside Psychiatric Hospital, Tallahassee, FL, p. A146

GOREY, Peter, Administrative Coordinator, Rockland Children's Psychiatric Center, Orangeburg, NY, p. A451

GORHAM, Jennie, D.O. Co–Medical Director, Missouri Rehabilitation Center, Mount Vernon, MO, p. A377

GORIAH, Steve, Chief Information Officer, Hoboken University Medical Center, Hoboken, NJ, p. A417

GORLEWSKI, Todd, Senior Vice President and Chief Financial Officer, St. Barnabas Hospital, NY, p. A448

GORMAN, Brandon, Controller, Bradley County Medical Center, Warren, AR, p. A53

GORMAN, Jodie, Director Human Resources, Salem Memorial District Hospital, Salem, MO, p. A382

GORMAN, Kathleen, MSN Executive Vice President Patient Care Services and Chief Operating Officer, Children's National Medical Center, Washington, DC, p. A121

GORMAN, Kirk E., Interim President and Chief Executive Officer, Jefferson Health System, Radnor, PA, p. B77

GORMAN, Martha C., MSN, Administrator, New Mexico Rehabilitation Center, Roswell, NM, p. A430

GORMAN, Matt, Administrator, Polk Medical Center, Cedartown, GA, p. A155

GORMAN, Patricia, Chief Nurse Executive, Chinle Comprehensive Health Care Facility, Chinle, AZ, p. A31

GORMLEY, Ann H., Vice President Human Resources, Pinnacle Health System, Harrisburg, PA, p. A540

GORMLEY, Maureen E., R.N. Chief Operating Officer, National Institutes of Health Clinical Center, Bethesda, MD, p. A299

GORMSEN, David, D.O. Chief Medical Officer, Mercy Medical Center, Canton, OH, p. A485

GORN, Angela, Vice President, Norton Sound Regional Hospital, Nome, AK, p. A29

GORS, Ann, Chief Executive Officer, Kentfield Rehabilitation and Specialty Hospital, Kentfield, CA, p. A68

GORSKI, William R., M.D., President and Chief Executive Officer, SwedishAmerican Hospital, Rockford, IL, p. A202

GORSKI, Yara, M.D. Chief of Staff, Southwest Healthcare System, Murrieta, CA, p. A79

GORY, James, Chief Financial Officer, Northwest Medical Center, Winfield, AL, p. A27

GOSCH, Shawn, Chief Financial Officer, Burgess Health Center, Onawa, IA, p. A235

GOSEY, J., M.D. Medical Director, Southern Surgical Hospital, Slidell, LA, p. A289

GOSHE, Nick, Chief Executive Officer, Rangely District Hospital, Rangely, CO, p. A110

GOSHIA, Rob, Chief Financial Officer, Paulding County Hospital, Paulding, OH, p. A500

GOSLEE, Belle, Chief Nursing Officer, HEALTHSOUTH Chesapeake Rehabilitation Hospital, Salisbury, MD, p. A303

GOSLINE, Peter L., Chief Administrative Officer, Upper Connecticut Valley Hospital, Colebrook, NH, p. A409

GOSNELL, Dewey, Manager, Rush Oak Park Hospital, Oak Park, IL, p. A198

GOSNEY, Brett, Chief Executive Officer, Animas Surgical Hospital, Durango, CO, p. A105

GOSS, J. Richard, M.D. Medical Director, UW Medicine/Harborview Medical Center, Seattle, WA, p. A689

GOSS, Norma, R.N. Chief Operating Officer and Chief Nursing Officer, Flaget Memorial Hospital, Bardstown, KY, p. A258

GOSS, Roger, Director, Information Services, North Sunflower Medical Center, Ruleville, MS, p. A365

GOSSENS, Kevin, Director Human Resources, Riverside Medical Center, Waupaca, WI, p. A717

GOSSETT, Lisa, MSN Chief Nursing Officer, OhioHealth Riverside Methodist Hospital, Columbus, OH, p. A490

GOTTI, Sreekant, Director Information Systems, Desert Valley Hospital, Victorville, CA, p. A99

GOTTLIEB, Gary L., M.D., President and Chief Executive Officer, Partners HealthCare System, Inc., Boston, MA, p. B105

GOTTLIEB, Harold, M.D. Chief Medical Officer, Memorial Hermann Memorial City Medical Center, Houston, TX, p. A625

GOTTLIEB, Jonathan, M.D. Senior Vice President and Chief Medical Officer, University of Maryland Medical Center, Baltimore, MD, p. A298

GOUGEON, Michele L., Executive Vice President and Chief Operating Officer, McLean Hospital, Belmont, MA, p. A305

GOUGH, Galal S., M.D. Chief of Staff, Coast Plaza Hospital, Norwalk, CA, p. A80

GOUGH, MSN, RN–, Michelle Marie, Chief Nursing Officer, Adams Memorial Hospital, Decatur, IN, p. A209

GOULD, Brian, Director Information System, Carson Valley Medical Center, Gardnerville, NV, p. A404

GOULD, Jacquelyn M., MS Vice President Patient Care Services and Chief Nursing Officer, The Good Samaritan Hospital, Lebanon, PA, p. A543

GOULD, Robert, Chief Executive Officer, Banner Desert Medical Center, Mesa, AZ, p. A34

GOULD, Tamara, R.N. Director of Nursing, Wabash General Hospital, Mount Carmel, IL, p. A197

GOULD, William R., Vice President Human Resources, Exempla Saint Joseph Hospital, Denver, CO, p. A104

GOULET, James P., Vice President Operations, Columbus Community Hospital, Columbus, NE, p. A395

GOULSON, Dan, M.D. Chief Medical Officer, Our Lady of Bellefonte Hospital, Ashland, KY, p. A258

GOURLEY, Paul, M.D. Chief Hospital Services, U. S. Air Force Hospital, Hampton, VA, p. A672

GOVE, Cynthia A., Chief Operating Officer, Hampstead Hospital, Hampstead, NH, p. A410

GOVINDAIAH, Rajesh G., M.D. Chief Medical Officer, Memorial Medical Center, Springfield, IL, p. A203

GOVORCHIN, Pete, Vice President Operations, Midwestern Regional Medical Center, Zion, IL, p. A205

GOWDER, Mike, Chief Executive Officer, Union General Hospital, Blairsville, GA, p. A154

GOWDER, Mike, Chief Executive Officer, Union General Hospital, Inc., Blairsville, GA, p. B138

GOWEN, Tina, System Controller, Westfield Memorial Hospital, Westfield, NY, p. A458

GOWER, Gary, Chief Information Officer, Appling Healthcare System, Baxley, GA, p. A154

GOYAL, Alok, M.D. Medical Director, Post Acute Medical Specialty Hospital of Milwaukee, Greenfield, WI, p. A706

GOYAL, Deepak, M.D. Chief of Staff, Jacobson Memorial Hospital Care Center, Elgin, ND, p. A477

GOYTIA–LEOS, Dina, M.D. Chief of Staff, Nix Health Care System, San Antonio, TX, p. A647

GOZA, Brian, Chief Information Officer, Hemphill County Hospital, Canadian, TX, p. A605

GOZIAH, Vicky, Software Administrator, Select Specialty Hospital – Northeast Atlanta, Atlanta, GA, p. A153

GRABER, Donald, M.D. Medical Director, Richmond State Hospital, Richmond, IN, p. A222

GRABUS, Christina, R.N. Chief Nursing Officer, Novant Health Thomasville Medical Center, Thomasville, NC, p. A474

GRACE, Jeffery, M.D. Clinical Director, Buffalo Psychiatric Center, Buffalo, NY, p. A434

GRACE, Richard, Chief Administrative Officer, Mayo Clinic Health System in Saint James, Saint James, MN, p. A351

GRACE, Terry, Director Information Technology, Logan County Hospital, Oakley, KS, p. A251

GRACE, Walter, Chief Executive Officer and Administrator, Baptist Memorial Hospital–Union County, New Albany, MS, p. A363

GRACER, Erik, M.D. Chief of Staff, San Ramon Regional Medical Center, San Ramon, CA, p. A93

GRACIE, Michael, Chief Information Officer, Veterans Health Care System of the Ozarks, Fayetteville, AR, p. A46

GRADDY, Steve W.

Chief Financial Officer, Freeman Hospital West, Joplin, MO, p. A373

Chief Financial Officer, Freeman Neosho Hospital, Neosho, MO, p. A377

GRADNEY, Angel, Chief Executive Officer, Kindred Hospital East Houston, Channelview, TX, p. A606

GRADY, John M., Associate Director, Veterans Affairs Hudson Valley Health Care System–F.D. Roosevelt Hospital, Montrose, NY, p. A441

GRADY, Kevin, M.D. Chief Medical Officer, St. John Hospital and Medical Center, Detroit, MI, p. A322

GRAEBER, Lawrence, Chief Executive Officer, Neshoba County General Hospital, Philadelphia, MS, p. A364

GRAEBER, Tod

Administrator, Community Memorial Hospital, Turtle Lake, ND, p. A480

Administrator, Garrison Memorial Hospital, Garrison, ND, p. A478

GRAEBNER, David, President, Aurora Sheboygan Memorial Medical Center, Sheboygan, WI, p. A715

GRAEBNER, Nancy Kay, President and Chief Executive Officer, Chelsea Community Hospital, Chelsea, MI, p. A320

GRAF, John, Senior Vice President, Watertown Regional Medical Center, Watertown, WI, p. A717

GRAGG, Connie, Director Human Resources, Saint Mary's Regional Medical Center, Russellville, AR, p. A52

GRAH, John A., FACHE, Chief Executive Officer, Des Peres Hospital, Saint Louis, MO, p. A380

GRAHAM, Barry A., M.D. Vice President Medical Affairs, Avera Sacred Heart Hospital, Yankton, SD, p. A578

GRAHAM, Bonnie S., Director, San Francisco Veterans Affairs Medical Center, San Francisco, CA, p. A91

GRAHAM, Brenda, Chief Nursing Officer, Knox County Hospital, Barbourville, KY, p. A258

GRAHAM, Brooke, Human Resources Manager, Franklin Woods Community Hospital, Johnson City, TN, p. A585

GRAHAM, Connie, Public Information Officer, Mercy Health Love County, Marietta, OK, p. A513

GRAHAM, David B., M.D. Senior Vice President and Chief Information Officer, Memorial Medical Center, Springfield, IL, p. A203

GRAHAM, Gerry J., Director Human Resource Operations, Southern New Hampshire Medical Center, Nashua, NH, p. A411

GRAHAM, Jay, Interim Chief Financial Officer, Brandywine Hospital, Coatesville, PA, p. A536

GRAHAM, Jeff

Market Leader and President, Mercy Health – Anderson Hospital, Cincinnati, OH, p. A487

Market Leader and President, Mercy Health – Clermont Hospital, Batavia, OH, p. A483

GRAHAM, John, M.D. Vice President Medical Affairs, Day Kimball Hospital, Putnam, CT, p. A116

GRAHAM, John R.

President and Chief Executive Officer, St. Mary's of Michigan, Saginaw, MI, p. A334

President and Chief Executive Officer, St. Mary's of Michigan Standish Hospital, Standish, MI, p. A335

GRAHAM, John W., Executive Vice President and Chief Operating Officer, Inspira Medical Center–Woodbury, Woodbury, NJ, p. A425

GRAHAM, Jon, Chief Financial Officer, Vidant Roanoke–Chowan Hospital, Ahoskie, NC, p. A459

GRAHAM, Kathryn, Director Communications and Community Relations, Novato Community Hospital, Novato, CA, p. A80

GRAHAM, Kenneth D., FACHE, President, North Hawaii Community Hospital, Kamuela, HI, p. A171

GRAHAM, Kimberley, R.N. Chief Nursing Officer and Chief Operating Officer, Broward Health Coral Springs, Coral Springs, FL, p. A126

GRAHAM, Larry M., FACHE, President and Chief Executive Officer, Lake Charles Memorial Hospital, Lake Charles, LA, p. A282

GRAHAM, Michael, Director Human Resources, Community Hospital, Munster, IN, p. A219

GRAHAM, Michelle, M.D

Vice President Medical Affairs, Wheaton Franciscan Healthcare – Franklin, Franklin, WI, p. A705

Vice President Medical Affairs, Wheaton Franciscan Healthcare – St. Francis, Milwaukee, WI, p. A711

GRAHAM, Scott, Chief Executive Officer, Three Rivers Hospital, Brewster, WA, p. A682

GRAHAM, Shauna, Director of Professional Services Human Resources, Marketing Foundation, Litzenberg Memorial County Hospital, Central City, NE, p. A394

GRAHAM, Sheri

Director Human Resources and Administrative Services, Parkland Health Center, Farmington, MO, p. A371

Director Human Resources and Administrative Services, Parkland Health Center–Bonne Terre, Bonne Terre, MO, p. A367

GRAHAM, Sonja, Chief Executive Officer, North Oak Regional Medical Center, Senatobia, MS, p. A365

GRAHAM, Susan, R.N. Nurse Executive, HealthSource Saginaw, Saginaw, MI, p. A334

GRAHAM, Yolanda, M.D. Medical Director, Devereux Georgia Treatment Network, Kennesaw, GA, p. A161

GRAHE, Raymond A., Senior Vice President Strategic Ventures and Chief Financial Officer, Meritus Medical Center, Hagerstown, MD, p. A301

GRAMBY, Tiffany, Senior Director Information Management and Privacy Officer, Barnesville Hospital, Barnesville, OH, p. A483

GRAMER, Johanna, Director Human Resources, Mimbres Memorial Hospital, Deming, NM, p. A428

GRAMZA, Jeanne, Director Finance, Wheaton Franciscan Healthcare – All Saints, Racine, WI, p. A714

GRAN, Daniel, Chief Executive Officer, Freeman Regional Health Services, Freeman, SD, p. A574

GRANADO–VILLAR, Deise, M.D. Chief Medical Officer and Senior Vice President Medical Affairs, Miami Children's Hospital, Miami, FL, p. A137

GRANATO, Jerome, M.D

Senior Vice President and Chief Medical Officer, Excela Frick Hospital, Mount Pleasant, PA, p. A546

Senior Vice President and Chief Medical Officer, Excela Health Westmoreland Hospital, Greensburg, PA, p. A539

GRAND, Lawrence N., Executive Vice President and Chief Operating Officer, Hunterdon Medical Center, Flemington, NJ, p. A416

GRANDIOSI, Joe, Director Information Technology, Southern Hills Hospital and Medical Center, Las Vegas, NV, p. A406

GRANER, Terry J., R.N. Vice President Patient Care, Abbott Northwestern Hospital, Minneapolis, MN, p. A347

GRANGER, Keith, President and Chief Executive Officer, Trinity Medical Center, Birmingham, AL, p. A17

GRANGER, Robert P., President and Chief Executive Officer, St. Francis Hospital, Columbus, GA, p. A156

GRANT, Cathy, R.N. Associate Vice President, Patient Services, DMC Huron Valley–Sinai Hospital, Commerce Township, MI, p. A321

GRANT, Chad M., Chief Operating Officer, Children's Hospital of Michigan, Detroit, MI, p. A321

GRANT, Debra, R.N. Chief Nursing Officer, Kaiser Permanente Los Angeles Medical Center, Los Angeles, CA, p. A72

GRANT, Dianna, M.D. Vice President Medical Management, Advocate Trinity Hospital, Chicago, IL, p. A183

GRANT, Gail, Director Human Resources, CHI St. Francis Health, Breckenridge, MN, p. A341

GRANT, Howard R., M.D., President and Chief Executive Officer, Lahey Health, Burlington, MA, p. B82

GRANT, Mikki, Chief Information Officer, Fort Belknap U. S. Public Health Service Indian Hospital, Harlem, MT, p. A388

GRANT, Pauline, FACHE, Chief Executive Officer, Broward Health North, Deerfield Beach, FL, p. A127

GRANT, Samuel, Chief Financial Officer, Stephens Memorial Hospital, Breckenridge, TX, p. A603

GRANT, Tonya, Director Human Resources, Westlake Regional Hospital, Columbia, KY, p. A259

GRANT, Will, Chief Financial Officer, Cannon Memorial Hospital, Pickens, SC, p. A569

GRANTHAM, Charlie, Manager Information Systems, Carolinas Hospital System Marion, Mullins, SC, p. A568

GRANTHAM, James, Administrator and Chief Executive Officer, Baptist Memorial Hospital–Booneville, Booneville, MS, p. A356

GRANTHAM, Keith, Director Information Technology, Covenant Medical Center, Saginaw, MI, p. A333

GRANVILLE, Brian, Director Information Technology, Buena Vista Regional Medical Center, Storm Lake, IA, p. A238

GRANVILLE, Sabrina M., Senior Vice President and Chief Human Resources Officer, Lowell General Hospital, Lowell, MA, p. A311

GRANZOTTI, Maria, M.D. Chief Physician Executive, Central Illinois Division, St. Mary's Hospital, Streator, IL, p. A204

GRANZOW, Steven L., Chief Executive Officer, Lincoln County Hospital, Lincoln, KS, p. A249

GRASER, David, Vice President and Chief Information Officer, Hillcrest Hospital – South, Tulsa, OK, p. A520

GRASS, Linda J., President and Chief Executive Officer, Jeanes Hospital, Philadelphia, PA, p. A548

GRASSER, Tierney Lynn, Senior Vice President and Chief Financial Officer, Olathe Medical Center, Olathe, KS, p. A251

GRATCH, Amie, Director Financial Services, LifeCare Hospitals of Dallas, Dallas, TX, p. A610

GRATZ, Silvia, D.O. Chief Medical Officer, Fairmount Behavioral Health System, Philadelphia, PA, p. A548

GRAU, Leah, Director Human Resources, Tulane Medical Center, New Orleans, LA, p. A286

GRAUER, David, Chief Executive Officer and Administrator, Intermountain Medical Center, Murray, UT, p. A660

GRAUPENSPERGER, Robert, Executive Vice President, Ephrata Community Hospital, Ephrata, PA, p. A538

GRAVELY, Sean, D.O. Chief of Staff, Nevada Regional Medical Center, Nevada, MO, p. A377

GRAVES, Amanda, Chief Information Systems, Washington DC Veterans Affairs Medical Center, Washington, DC, p. A122

GRAVES, Bruce, M.D. Chief of Staff, Hale Ho'ola Hamakua, Honokaa, HI, p. A170

GRAVES, Buddy, Chief Information Officer, Southern Surgical Hospital, Slidell, LA, p. A289

GRAVES, Deanna, Chief Executive Officer, Texas Specialty Hospital at Lubbock, Lubbock, TX, p. A635

GRAVES, Jimmy, Interim Chief Executive Officer, Jefferson Davis Community Hospital, Prentiss, MS, p. A364

GRAVES, Virginia, R.N. Nurse Executive, Montgomery County Emergency Service, Norristown, PA, p. A546

GRAY, Albert, Chief Executive Officer, The Children's Center, Bethany, OK, p. A508

GRAY, Anthony, Chief Financial Officer, LAC–Olive View–UCLA Medical Center,, CA, p. A73

GRAY, Bob, Chief Financial Officer, Aspire Hospital, Conroe, TX, p. A607

GRAY, Clarence, Chief Financial Officer, TriStar Horizon Medical Center, Dickson, TN, p. A582

GRAY, David L., FACHE, President, Baptist Health Louisville, Louisville, KY, p. A265

GRAY, Eric, Chief Financial Officer, HEALTHSOUTH Rehabilitation Hospital of Memphis, Memphis, TN, p. A588

GRAY, Gary, D.O. Chief Medical Officer, Natividad Medical Center, Salinas, CA, p. A88

GRAY, James, M.D. Chief Medical Service, Amarillo Veterans Affairs Health Care System, Amarillo, TX, p. A596

GRAY, Jason, M.D. Chief Medical Officer, Mercy Medical Center, Roseburg, OR, p. A529

GRAY, Jeremy, Chief Operating Officer, Fort Walton Beach Medical Center, Fort Walton Beach, FL, p. A129

GRAY, John, Administrator, St. Catherine Memorial Hospital, New Orleans, LA, p. A286

GRAY, Judy
Vice President Human Resources, Albany Memorial Hospital, Albany, NY, p. A432
Vice President Human Resources, St. Peter's Hospital, Albany, NY, p. A432

GRAY, Karen D., Director Human Resources, Vibra Hospital of Southeastern Michigan, Lincoln Park, MI, p. A329

GRAY, Larry, President, Baptist Health Corbin, Corbin, KY, p. A260

GRAY, Marty, R.N. Director of Nursing, Wyandot Memorial Hospital, Upper Sandusky, OH, p. A503

GRAY, Mary, Director Human Resources, Lehigh Regional Medical Center, Lehigh Acres, FL, p. A134

GRAY, Michelle
Nurse Executive, Atrium Medical Center of Corinth, Corinth, TX, p. A608
Vice President and Regional Chief Information Officer, Rex Healthcare, Raleigh, NC, p. A471

GRAY, Mike, Corporate Vice President Human Resources, East Texas Medical Center Tyler, Tyler, TX, p. A654

GRAY, Patricia, Director Health Information Management, Cumberland Hall Hospital, Hopkinsville, KY, p. A263

GRAY, Roshanda, Assistant Administrator, Memorial Medical Center, Port Lavaca, TX, p. A643

GRAY, Stephen, Chief Administrative Officer, Sutter Maternity and Surgery Center of Santa Cruz, Santa Cruz, CA, p. A94

GRAY, Tami, Chief Financial Officer, Irwin County Hospital, Ocilla, GA, p. A164

GRAY, Teresa, Chief Nursing Officer and Assistant Vice President, INTEGRIS Canadian Valley Hospital, Yukon, OK, p. A522

GRAY, Terry, Vice President Human Resources, Emanuel Medical Center, Turlock, CA, p. A98

GRAY, Thomas, M.D. Medical Director, Montana State Hospital, Warm Springs, MT, p. A391

GRAY, Tracy
Chief Information Officer, Grady General Hospital, Cairo, GA, p. A155
Senior Vice President Information Services, John D. Archbold Memorial Hospital, Thomasville, GA, p. A168
Chief Information Officer, Mitchell County Hospital, Camilla, GA, p. A155

GRAYBEAL, Phillip
Chief Financial Officer, Page Memorial Hospital, Luray, VA, p. A673
Chief Financial Officer, Warren Memorial Hospital, Front Royal, VA, p. A671

GRAYBILL, Matthew P., Chief Operating Officer, Children's Medical Center, Dayton, OH, p. A491

GRAYSON, Barbara, Vice President Human Resources, Mercy Hospital Washington, Washington, MO, p. A384

GREASON, Linda, Vice President Human Resources, Milford Regional Medical Center, Milford, MA, p. A312

GREBOSKY, Jamie, M.D. Vice President of Medical Affairs, Asante Rogue Regional Medical Center, Medford, OR, p. A527

GRECO, Andrew, Chief Financial Officer, Calvary Hospital,, NY, p. A443

GRECO, Anthony C., Compliance Officer, Essex County Hospital Center, Cedar Grove, NJ, p. A414

GRECO, Margaret, Chief Human Resources, Keller Army Community Hospital, West Point, NY, p. A458

GREELEY, Donna, Director Human Resources, Spalding Rehabilitation Hospital, Aurora, CO, p. A102

GREEN, Amber, R.N. Chief Clinical Officer, Memorial Hospital of Carbon County, Rawlins, WY, p. A722

GREEN, Arnold, Senior Vice President and Chief Operating Officer, McLeod Loris Seacoast Hospital, Loris, SC, p. A568

GREEN, Barbara, Director Human Resources, O'Connor Hospital, Delhi, NY, p. A436

GREEN, Calvin, Chief Executive Officer, Oakdale Community Hospital, Oakdale, LA, p. A286

GREEN, Charles B., M.D., Surgeon General, Department of the Air Force, Washington, DC, p. B47

GREEN, Christine, Administrative Director Human Resources, Sutter Delta Medical Center, Antioch, CA, p. A56

GREEN, Christopher, M.D. Senior Vice President Medical Affairs and Associate Dean Hospital Affairs, University of Wisconsin Hospital and Clinics, Madison, WI, p. A708

GREEN, Darryl, Director Administration, Naval Hospital Jacksonville, Jacksonville, FL, p. A132

GREEN, David, Chief Human Resources, West Palm Beach Veterans Affairs Medical Center, West Palm Beach, FL, p. A150

GREEN, David F., M.D. Chief Medical Officer, Concord Hospital, Concord, NH, p. A409

GREEN, Debra Jane, R.N. Director of Nursing, Turquoise Lodge Hospital, Albuquerque, NM, p. A427

GREEN, Gail P., R.N. Chief Nursing Officer, St. Vincent's Medical Center Riverside, Jacksonville, FL, p. A132

GREEN, Garry Kim, FACHE, Administrator, Shriners Hospitals for Children–Shreveport, Shreveport, LA, p. A288

GREEN, Gene E., M.D., President, Suburban Hospital, Bethesda, MD, p. A299

GREEN, Jack W., Administrator, Antelope Memorial Hospital, Neligh, NE, p. A398

GREEN, Jody, Chief Quality Manager, Sanpete Valley Hospital, Mount Pleasant, UT, p. A660

GREEN, John
Vice President Professional Services and Facility Planning, Iredell Memorial Hospital, Statesville, NC, p. A473
Vice President Finance, St. Peter's Hospital, Helena, MT, p. A388

GREEN, Julie, Vice President Human Resources, Cheshire Medical Center, Keene, NH, p. A410

GREEN, Karen, Chief Information Officer, Brooks Rehabilitation Hospital, Jacksonville, FL, p. A131

GREEN, Kaye, FACHE, Director, W. G. (Bill) Heffner Veterans Affairs Medical Center, Salisbury, NC, p. A472

GREEN, Ladonna, Director Human Resources, Glen Rose Medical Center, Glen Rose, TX, p. A621

GREEN Jr., Larry D., Chief Executive Officer, Windhaven Psychiatric Hospital, Prescott Valley, AZ, p. A37

GREEN, Lorraine, MSN Chief Human Resources Officer, St. Elizabeths Hospital, Washington, DC, p. A122

GREEN, Patrick, Chief Operating Officer, St. Anthony Hospital, Lakewood, CO, p. A108

GREEN, Paul, Chief Clinical Officer, Kindred Hospital–Aurora, Aurora, CO, p. A102

GREEN, Ricky, Senior Human Resources Business Partner, Spectrum Health Big Rapids Hospital, Big Rapids, MI, p. A319

GREEN, Rona,U. S. Naval Hospital Guam, Agana, GU, p. A724

GREEN, Ronnie, Director Information Systems, McBride Clinic Orthopedic Hospital, Oklahoma City, OK, p. A515

GREEN, Rose Marie, Director Human Resources, Humboldt General Hospital, Winnemucca, NV, p. A408

GREEN, Scott, M.D. Chief of Staff, St. Francis Memorial Hospital, West Point, NE, p. A402

GREEN, Steve, Comptroller, Jasper General Hospital, Bay Springs, MS, p. A355

GREEN, Susan, Senior Vice President Finance, Chief Financial Officer, Lowell General Hospital, Lowell, MA, p. A311

GREEN, Tracy V., Chief Financial Officer, Metropolitan Hospital Center, New York, NY, p. A446

GREEN–LORENZEN, Susan, SVP, Operations, Montefiore Mount Vernon, Mount Vernon, NY, p. A442

GREENBERG, Mark, M.D
Chief Medical Officer, Cape Coral Hospital, Cape Coral, FL, p. A125
Medical Director, Gulf Coast Medical Center, Fort Myers, FL, p. A129

GREENBERG, Raymond, M.D., Executive Vice Chancellor, University of Texas System, Austin, TX, p. B147

GREENBLATT, James, M.D. Chief Medical Officer, Vice President Medical Clinical Services, Walden Psychiatric Care, Waltham, MA, p. A316

GREENE, Arthur, M.D. Vice President Medical Affairs, Sentara CarePlex Hospital, Hampton, VA, p. A672

GREENE, Barbara M., President, Franciscan Healthcare – Munster, Munster, IN, p. A219

GREENE, Beth, Chief Operating Officer, Cherokee Indian Hospital, Cherokee, NC, p. A462

GREENE, Bradley, Chief Financial Officer, WellStar Douglas Hospital, Douglasville, GA, p. A158

GREENE, Cora, Chief Nursing Officer, Novant Health Rowan Medical Center, Salisbury, NC, p. A472

GREENE, Dustin, Chief Operating Officer, TriStar Skyline Medical Center, Nashville, TN, p. A591

GREENE, Erin, Coordinator Human Resources, Kindred Hospital–San Francisco Bay Area, San Leandro, CA, p. A92

GREENE, Hugh, President and Chief Executive Officer, Baptist Health, Jacksonville, FL, p. B19

GREENE, Kathleen, Director Human Resources, Promise Hospital of San Diego, San Diego, CA, p. A89

GREENE, Melodi, R.N. Chief Nursing Officer, Community Howard Regional Health, Kokomo, IN, p. A216

GREENE, Palmer, R.N. Chief Nursing Officer, Sierra Vista Hospital, Truth or Consequences, NM, p. A431

GREENE, Robert, Director Information Technology, Promise Hospital of Miss Lou, Vidalia, LA, p. A289

GREENE, Russ, Chief Executive Officer, Physicians' Specialty Hospital, Fayetteville, AR, p. A45

GREENE, Scott, Chief Information Officer, Gateway Medical Center, Clarksville, TN, p. A581

GREENE, Terry, M.D. Chief of Staff, Habersham Medical Center, Demorest, GA, p. A158

GREENER, Angela, Chief Administrative Officer, West Jefferson Medical Center, Marrero, LA, p. A284

GREENFIELD, Tadd, Chief Nursing Officer, Great Plains Health, North Platte, NE, p. A398

GREENLEE, Kathryn M., R.N
Vice President, Clinical Services/CNO, ProMedica Bixby Hospital, Adrian, MI, p. A318
Vice President, Clinical Services/CNO, ProMedica Herrick Hospital, Tecumseh, MI, p. A336

GREENMAN, Sharon, Director Human Resources, Melissa Memorial Hospital, Holyoke, CO, p. A107

GREENWOOD, Sherri, Chief Nursing Officer, St. John's Hospital, Springfield, IL, p. A203

GREENWOOD, Susan, R.N. Vice President and Chief Nursing Officer, St. Bernards Medical Center, Jonesboro, AR, p. A48

GREER, Nancy, R.N. Vice President Nursing, Asante Three Rivers Medical Center, Grants Pass, OR, p. A525

GREER, Troy, Chief Executive Officer, Lovelace Medical Center, Albuquerque, NM, p. A426

GREEVER, Suzanne, Chief Executive Officer, North Central Surgical Center, Dallas, TX, p. A611

GREGERSEN, Glenn, Director Information Technology, District One Hospital, Faribault, MN, p. A343

GREGERSON, Scott, President and Chief Executive Officer, ValleyCare Medical Center, Pleasanton, CA, p. A83

GREGG, Richard, M.D. Medical Director, LifeCare Hospital of Dayton, Miamisburg, OH, p. A498

GREGG, Shawna, Director Human Resources, Porterville Developmental Center, Porterville, CA, p. A84

GREGG, Sherry, Chief Information Technology Officer, Beckley Veterans Affairs Medical Center, Beckley, WV, p. A693

GREGG, Thomas, Vice President Human Resources, St. Peter's Hospital, Helena, MT, p. A388

GREGG, Tom, Vice President Human Resources, St. Alexius Medical Center, Bismarck, ND, p. A476

GREGG, Travis, Director Support Services, Kearney Regional Medical Center, Kearney, NE, p. A397

GREGGAIN, Don, M.D. Physician Network Director, Tri–State Memorial Hospital, Clarkston, WA, p. A682

GREGONIS, Michael, Comptroller, Naval Hospital Jacksonville, Jacksonville, FL, p. A132

GREGOR, Brian, Manager Information Technology Operations, Glendale Memorial Hospital and Health Center, Glendale, CA, p. A65

GREGORIAN, Myra, Vice President Human Resources, Long Beach Memorial Medical Center, Long Beach, CA, p. A70

GREGORICH, Miki, Director Human Resources, Pioneer Medical Center, Big Timber, MT, p. A385

GREGORIO, Felipe, Chief Nursing Officer, HEALTHSOUTH Rehabilitation Institute of San Antonio, San Antonio, TX, p. A646

GREGORY, Adina, Chief Nursing Officer, Great Bend Regional Hospital, Great Bend, KS, p. A244

GREGORY, Audrey, R.N. Chief Operating Officer, Saint Francis Hospital, Memphis, TN, p. A589

GREGORY, Ben, Director, Walter B. Jones Alcohol and Drug Abuse Treatment Center, Greenville, NC, p. A465

GREGORY, Christine, R.N., Director, Veterans Affairs Montana Health Care System, Fort Harrison, MT, p. A387

GREGORY, Jan, Chief of Human Resources, Crittenden County Hospital, Marion, KY, p. A267

GREGORY, Jay, M.D. Chief Medical Officer, EASTAR Health System, Muskogee, OK, p. A514

GREGORY, Jim, Controller, Methodist Hospital of Chicago, Chicago, IL, p. A185

GREGORY, Sean, President, Health First Holmes Regional Medical Center, Melbourne, FL, p. A135

GREGORY, Shawn, Chief Financial Officer, South Bay Hospital, Sun City Center, FL, p. A146

GREGORY, Trip, Senior Vice President Human Resources, Palmetto Health Baptist, Columbia, SC, p. A564

GREGOS, Ruth, Director Finance, Shriners Hospitals for Children–Tampa, Tampa, FL, p. A148

GREIMAN, Alan W., Administrator, Royal Oaks Hospital, Windsor, MO, p. A384

GREINER, Walter, Chief Financial Officer, AtlantiCare Regional Medical Center, Atlantic City, NJ, p. A413

GREINER, William, M.D. Chief of Staff, F. W. Huston Medical Center, Winchester, KS, p. A257

GREMILLION, Karen, R.N. Chief Nursing Officer, Opelousas General Health System, Opelousas, LA, p. A287

GRENALDO, Paul, Executive Vice President and Chief Operating Officer, Doctors Community Hospital, Lanham, MD, p. A302

GRENDON, M. Todd, M.D. President Medical Staff, Presence Saint Joseph Hospital, Chicago, IL, p. A185

GRENNAN, Jr., M. Joseph, M.D. Senior Vice President and Chief Medical Officer, Reading Hospital and Medical Center, West Reading, PA, p. A558

GRESKOVICH, William, Chief Information Officer, Saint Agnes Hospital, Baltimore, MD, p. A297

GRESLA, Mark S., M.D. Chief of Staff, Adams Memorial Hospital, Decatur, IN, p. A209

GRESS, Jr., Harold M., Manager Management Information Systems, Fulton County Medical Center, Mc Connellsburg, PA, p. A544

GRESSLE, Charles, Chief Executive Officer, Medical Center of Plano, Plano, TX, p. A642

GREW, Kate, MSN Vice President/Chief Nurse Executive, Carolinas Medical Center–NorthEast, Concord, NC, p. A462

GREW, Terry, Chief Business Office, Hampton Veterans Affairs Medical Center, Hampton, VA, p. A672

GREY, Mitzi, Chief Operating Officer, Bath Community Hospital, Hot Springs, VA, p. A672

GRIBBIN, John, FACHE, President and Chief Executive Officer, CentraState Healthcare System, Freehold, NJ, p. A416

GRICUS, Peggy, R.N. Vice President, Patient Care Services and Chief Nursing Officer, Silver Cross Hospital, New Lenox, IL, p. A198

GRIDLEY, Mark, FACHE Executive Vice President and Chief Operating Officer, FHN Memorial Hospital, Freeport, IL, p. A190

GRIEB, Paula, R.N
Vice President Patient Care Service and Chief Nursing Officer, ProMedica Bay Park Hospital, Oregon, OH, p. A500
Chief Nursing Officer, ProMedica Fostoria Community Hospital, Fostoria, OH, p. A494

GRIEP, John, M.D. Chief Medical Director, St. Catherine Hospital, East Chicago, IN, p. A209

GRIESS, Dan, FACHE, Chief Executive Officer, Box Butte General Hospital, Alliance, NE, p. A393

GRIEST, Mary, Vice President Finance and Chief Financial Officer, Samaritan Regional Health System, Ashland, OH, p. A482

GRIFFES, John M., Chief Executive Officer, Continuum Rehabilitation Hospital of North Texas, Flower Mound, TX, p. A617

GRIFFIE, Lametria, Interim Chief Nursing Officer, HEALTHSOUTH Rehabilitation Hospital of Texarkana, Texarkana, TX, p. A652

GRIFFIN, Amy, Vice President Patient Care Services, John D. Archbold Memorial Hospital, Thomasville, GA, p. A168

GRIFFIN, Angela, Privacy Officer, Wayne County Hospital, Monticello, KY, p. A267

GRIFFIN, Betty, Interim Chief Nursing Officer, Chester Regional Medical Center, Chester, SC, p. A564

GRIFFIN, Brad, Chief Executive Officer, Colleton Medical Center, Walterboro, SC, p. A570

GRIFFIN, Brian, Director Information Services, Springhill Medical Center, Springhill, LA, p. A289

GRIFFIN, Caleigh, Vice President Human Resources, Ferrell Hospital, Eldorado, IL, p. A188

GRIFFIN, Christopher B., Chief Executive Officer, D. W. McMillan Memorial Hospital, Brewton, AL, p. A17

GRIFFIN, Cindy, Director Human Resources, Medical Center Barbour, Eufaula, AL, p. A19

GRIFFIN, Donald, CPA Chief Financial Officer, New London Hospital, New London, NH, p. A411

GRIFFIN, Holly, R.N. Chief Nursing Officer, Lady of the Sea General Hospital, Cut Off, LA, p. A276

GRIFFIN, James, Manager Information Systems, Martin General Hospital, Williamston, NC, p. A474

GRIFFIN, Jeannine, M.D. Chief of Staff, Memorial Medical Center, Port Lavaca, TX, p. A643

GRIFFIN, Laura Jane, M.D. Chief Nursing Executive, Kindred Hospital Sugar Land, Sugar Land, TX, p. A650

GRIFFIN, Margaret Elizabeth, Chief Executive Officer, John C. Lincoln North Mountain Hospital, Phoenix, AZ, p. A36

GRIFFIN, Matthew, M.D. Vice President Medical Affairs, Sinai–Grace Hospital, Detroit, MI, p. A322

GRIFFIN, Michael L., Chief Financial Officer, Bethesda Butler Hospital, Hamilton, OH, p. A495

GRIFFIN, Paulette
Vice President Human Resources, Detroit Receiving Hospital/University Health Center, Detroit, MI, p. A321
Director Human Resources, Sinai–Grace Hospital, Detroit, MI, p. A322

GRIFFIN, Susan E., R.N. Chief Nursing Officer, St. David's Medical Center, Austin, TX, p. A600

GRIFFIN–MAHON, Selena, Assistant Vice President Human Resources, Bronx–Lebanon Hospital Center Health Care System,, NY, p. A442

GRIFFIS, Daniel, M.D. Chief Medical Officer, Syringa Hospital and Clinics, Grangeville, ID, p. A176

GRIFFITH, Barbara, M.D. Chief Medical Officer, Duke Regional Hospital, Durham, NC, p. A463

GRIFFITH, David, M.D. Medical Director, Texas Center for Infectious Disease, San Antonio, TX, p. A648

GRIFFITH, Donna Herrin, FACHE Senior Vice President and Chief Patient Care Officer, Martin Health System, Stuart, FL, p. A146

GRIFFITH, Dusty, Director Information Systems, Bolivar Medical Center, Cleveland, MS, p. A357

GRIFFITH, James, Chief Operating Officer, Salinas Valley Memorial Healthcare System, Salinas, CA, p. A88

GRIFFITH, Jeanne, Chief Nursing Officer, Coryell Memorial Hospital, Gatesville, TX, p. A621

GRIFFITH, John H., Ph.D., President & Chief Executive Officer, Kedren Community Mental Health Center, Los Angeles, CA, p. A73

GRIFFITH, Keitha, Chief Nursing Officer, Medical Center of South Arkansas, El Dorado, AR, p. A45

GRIFFITH, Patti, R.N. Chief Nursing Officer, Methodist Hospital for Surgery, Addison, TX, p. A595

GRIFFITH, Susan M., Chief Operations Officer, Eastern State Hospital, Lexington, KY, p. A264

GRIFFITH, Ty, Vice President Operations and Planning, St. Francis Hospital and Health Services, Maryville, MO, p. A376

GRIFFITH, Wayne B., FACHE, Chief Executive Officer, Princeton Community Hospital, Princeton, WV, p. A698

GRIFFITH, Wes
IT Director, Hancock Medical Center, Bay Saint Louis, MS, p. A355
Chief Financial Officer, Tennova Healthcare–LaFollette Medical Center, La Follette, TN, p. A586

GRIFFITHS, David, Vice President and Chief Financial Officer, Regional West Medical Center, Scottsbluff, NE, p. A402

GRIFFITHS, Elaine, R.N. Chief Nursing Officer, Chesapeake Regional Medical Center, Chesapeake, VA, p. A669

GRIFFITHS, Mark
Director Management Information Systems, Incline Village Community Hospital, Incline Village, NV, p. A405
Chief Systems Innovation Officer, Tahoe Forest Hospital District, Truckee, CA, p. A97

GRIGG, Dan, Chief Executive Officer, Pioneer Memorial Hospital, Heppner, OR, p. A525

GRIGG, William E., Senior Vice President and Chief Financial Officer, Methodist Hospital of Southern California, Arcadia, CA, p. A56

GRIGGS, Stacie, MIS Analyst, North Mississippi Medical Center–West Point, West Point, MS, p. A366

GRIGSBY, Jan, Vice President and Chief Financial Officer, Springhill Memorial Hospital, Mobile, AL, p. A23

GRIGSON, John A., Vice President and Chief Financial Officer, Covenant Medical Center, Lubbock, TX, p. A634

GRILL, Laura D., R.N. Executive Vice President and Administrator, East Alabama Medical Center, Opelika, AL, p. A24

GRILLO, Jorge C., Chief Information Officer, Canton–Potsdam Hospital, Potsdam, NY, p. A452

GRIM, Andrew, Chief Financial Officer, San Gabriel Valley Medical Center, San Gabriel, CA, p. A92

GRIMALDI, Richard, President Medical Staff, Highlands Hospital, Connellsville, PA, p. A536

GRIMER, Ginny, Director Human Resources, George E. Weems Memorial Hospital, Apalachicola, FL, p. A123

GRIMES, Pam, Director Human Resources, AMG Specialty Hospital–Edmond, Edmond, OK, p. A510

GRIMES, Paula, R.N. Chief Nursing Officer, NEA Baptist Memorial Hospital, Jonesboro, AR, p. A48

GRIMES, Teresa G., Chief Executive Officer, Troy Regional Medical Center, Troy, AL, p. A26

GRIMES, Walter, Director Information Technology, Good Shepherd Medical Center-Marshall, Marshall, TX, p. A636

GRIMLEY, Karen A., R.N. Chief Nursing Officer, UC Irvine Medical Center, Orange, CA, p. A81

GRIMM, William, Director, Information Services, Marengo Memorial Hospital, UnityPoint Health, Marengo, IA, p. A234

GRIMMER, Michael, Chief Operating Officer, Athol Memorial Hospital, Athol, MA, p. A305

GRIMSHAW, Bruce P., Chief Executive Officer, Southern California Hospital at Hollywood, Los Angeles, CA, p. A75

GRIMSHAW, Matthew, President, Mercy Medical Center, Williston, ND, p. A480

GRIMSLEY, Denise, Administrator, Florida Hospital Wauchula, Wauchula, FL, p. A149

GRINNELL, Steven, President and Chief Executive Officer, Lourdes Hospital, Paducah, KY, p. A269

GRINNEY, Jay F., President and Chief Executive Officer, HEALTHSOUTH Corporation, Birmingham, AL, p. B69

GRIPPI, Michael, M.D. Chief Medical Officer, Good Shepherd Penn Partners Specialty Hospital at Rittenhouse, Philadelphia, PA, p. A548

GRISDELA, Michael, Chief Financial Officer, Karmanos Cancer Center, Detroit, MI, p. A322

GRISH, John, Chief Financial Officer, Johnson Memorial Hospital, Stafford Springs, CT, p. A117

GRISIER, Douglas, D.O. Medical Director, HEALTHSOUTH Rehabilitation Hospital of Erie, Erie, PA, p. A538

GRISNAK, Karen, R.N. Chief Operating Officer and Assistant Administrator Quality Services, Kaiser Permanente Vallejo Medical Center, Vallejo, CA, p. A99

GRISSINGER, Matthew, Site Manager Information Systems, Indian Path Medical Center, Kingsport, TN, p. A585

GRISSLER, Brian G., President and Chief Executive Officer, Stamford Hospital, Stamford, CT, p. A117

GRISSOM, Tina, Chief Information Technology Officer, Arkansas State Hospital, Little Rock, AR, p. A49

GRISWOLD, Barbara, Chief Nursing Officer, Washington County Hospital and Clinics, Washington, IA, p. A238

GRIX, Gary J., M.D. Chief of Staff, Parkland Health Center, Farmington, MO, p. A371

GROCE, Jessika A., Director Human Resources, Valley General Hospital, Monroe, WA, p. A685

GROCE, Vicky, Chief Nursing Officer, Lincoln County Health System, Fayetteville, TN, p. A583

GROCHALA, Eugene
Vice President Information Systems, Capital Health Medical Center–Hopewell, Pennington, NJ, p. A421
Vice President Information Systems, Capital Health Regional Medical Center, Trenton, NJ, p. A423

GROCHOLSKI, James F., FACHE, Chief Executive Officer, Wesley Rehabilitation Hospital, Wichita, KS, p. A257

GROENEWEG, Jennifer, R.N. Director of Nursing, Spectrum Health Special Care Hospital, Grand Rapids, MI, p. A325

GROENIG, Matt, Vice President Finance, St. Luke's McCall, McCall, ID, p. A177

GROEPER, William E., Vice President Finance, Beloit Health System, Beloit, WI, p. A702

GROEPPER, Ronald, Senior Vice President and Area Manager, Kaiser Permanente Sacramento Medical Center, Sacramento, CA, p. A87

GROESBECK, John
Area Finance Officer, Kaiser Permanente San Rafael Medical Center, San Rafael, CA, p. A93
Area Finance Officer, Kaiser Permanente Santa Rosa Medical Center, Santa Rosa, CA, p. A95

GROGAN, Ed, Vice President Information Services and Chief Information Officer, Calvert Memorial Hospital, Prince Frederick, MD, p. A302

GROGAN, Richard
Interim Chief Executive Officer, Starr Regional Medical Center, Athens, TN, p. A579
Interim Chief Executive Officer, Starr Regional Medical Center–Etowah, Etowah, TN, p. A582

GRONBACH, Sue, Director Human Resources, Providence Hospital, Southfield, MI, p. A335

GRONDA, Mark E., Vice President and Chief Financial Officer, Covenant Medical Center, Saginaw, MI, p. A333

GRONEWOLD, Russell, Chief Financial Officer, Bryan Medical Center, Lincoln, NE, p. A397

GRONSETH, Timothy L., Vice President and Chief Financial Officer, Northfield Hospital, Northfield, MN, p. A348

GROOM, Scott C., Vice President Information Services and Chief Information Officer, Bassett Medical Center, Cooperstown, NY, p. A436

GROS, Albert, M.D. Chief Medical Officer, St. David's South Austin Medical Center, Austin, TX, p. A600

GROS, Mark, Director Human Resources, United Medical Rehabilitation Hospital, Hammond, LA, p. A278

GROSE, Jana
  Chief Information Officer, Alice Hyde Medical Center, Malone, NY, p. A440
  Chief Information Officer, Massena Memorial Hospital, Massena, NY, p. A441

GROSKREUTZ, Kevin
  Chief Information Officer, Sacred Heart Hospital, Eau Claire, WI, p. A704
  Chief Information Officer, St. Joseph's Hospital, Chippewa Falls, WI, p. A703

GROSS, Barry L., M.D. Executive Vice President and Chief Medical Officer, Riverside Regional Medical Center, Newport News, VA, p. A675

GROSS, Cathy, Director Health Information Management Systems, Wrangell Medical Center, Wrangell, AK, p. A30

GROSS, Cindy, Assistant Administrator, Barnes–Jewish St. Peters Hospital, Saint Peters, MO, p. A382

GROSS, Denton, Director Information Services, Larue D. Carter Memorial Hospital, Indianapolis, IN, p. A214

GROSS, Kevin J., Interim Chief Executive Officer, Hillcrest Medical Center, Tulsa, OK, p. A520

GROSS, Kristin, Director Information Technology Center, Avera McKennan Hospital and University Health Center, Sioux Falls, SD, p. A576

GROSS, Lawrence, Executive Director, Griffin Memorial Hospital, Norman, OK, p. A514

GROSS, Len, Chief Human Resources Officer, Sheridan Memorial Hospital, Sheridan, WY, p. A722

GROSS, Mark
  Senior Business Director Finance, Mercy Health Partners, Lakeshore Campus, Shelby, MI, p. A334
  Executive Vice President and Chief Financial Officer, South Haven Health System, South Haven, MI, p. A335

GROSS, Paul, Human Services and Finance Officer, Larry B. Zieverink, Sr. Alcoholism Treatment Center, Raleigh, NC, p. A471

GROSS, Peter A., M.D. Senior Vice President and Chief Medical Officer, Hackensack University Medical Center, Hackensack, NJ, p. A416

GROSS, Randy, Chief Executive Officer, Plantation General Hospital, Plantation, FL, p. A143

GROSS, Tina, Director of Clinical Services, Sparrow Specialty Hospital, Lansing, MI, p. A329

GROSSMAN, Drew, Chief Executive Officer, Broward Health Coral Springs, Coral Springs, FL, p. A126

GROSSMAN, Hannah, M.D. Chief Medical Officer, Los Robles Hospital and Medical Center, Thousand Oaks, CA, p. A97

GROSSMAN, Ilana, Administrator, Joyce Eisenberg–Keefer Medical Center, Reseda, CA, p. A86

GROSSMAN, Joseph
  Chief Financial Officer, McDowell ARH Hospital, McDowell, KY, p. A267
  Vice President Fiscal Affairs, Whitesburg ARH Hospital, Whitesburg, KY, p. A271

GROSSMAN, Martin, Chief of Staff, Aventura Hospital and Medical Center, Aventura, FL, p. A123

GROSSMAN, Robert I., M.D., Chief Executive Officer, NYU Langone Medical Center, New York, NY, p. A448

GROSSO, Michael, M.D. Senior Vice President Medical Affairs, Huntington Hospital, Huntington, NY, p. A439

GROTELUSCHEN, Ronald, Chief Financial Officer, Central Carolina Hospital, Sanford, NC, p. A472

GROVE, Julia, Chief Nursing Officer, Jackson Purchase Medical Center, Mayfield, KY, p. A267

GROVE, Lyle, Human Resources Director, North Dakota State Hospital, Jamestown, ND, p. A479

GROVE, Wanda, Administrator, Surprise Valley Health Care District, Cedarville, CA, p. A59

GROVER, Amy, Director, Appalachian Behavioral Healthcare, Athens, OH, p. A483

GROVER, James, Manager Data Processing, Atascadero State Hospital, Atascadero, CA, p. A56

GROVES, Tandy, Coordinator Human Resources, Bailey Medical Center, Owasso, OK, p. A517

GROW, Heidi, Director Human Resources, Aurora Sinai Medical Center, Milwaukee, WI, p. A710

GROW, Julie E., Chief Financial Officer, Hocking Valley Community Hospital, Logan, OH, p. A496

GROWSE, Michael, M.D. Clinical Director, Federal Medical Center, Lexington, KY, p. A264

GRUBB, Amanda Mandy, M.D. Chief Medical Officer, Cumberland Medical Center, Crossville, TN, p. A582

GRUBB, Michael, Chief Operating Officer and Chief Financial Officer, Kindred Hospital South Bay, Gardena, CA, p. A65

GRUBB, Nora, Chief Financial Officer, Big Sandy Medical Center, Big Sandy, MT, p. A385

GRUBBS, Stephen, Chief Executive Officer, Paris Regional Medical Center, Paris, TX, p. A641

GRUBER, Kreg, President, Memorial Hospital of South Bend, South Bend, IN, p. A222

GRUBER, Norman F., President and Chief Executive Officer, Salem Health, Salem, OR, p. B117

GRUBER, Norman F., President and Chief Executive Officer, Salem Hospital, Salem, OR, p. A530

GRUBER, Scott, M.D. Chief of Staff, John D. Dingell Veterans Affairs Medical Center, Detroit, MI, p. A322

GRUEBER, Cynthia M., Chief Operating Officer, OHSU Hospital, Portland, OR, p. A528

GRUEN, Jeremy, Director Information Systems, Pike County Memorial Hospital, Louisiana, MO, p. A376

GRUHONJIC, Osman, Chief Financial Officer, Lehigh Regional Medical Center, Lehigh Acres, FL, p. A134

GRUN, Joseph, Chief Information Officer, New York State Psychiatric Institute, New York, NY, p. A447

GRUNDSTROM, David A., Chief Administrative Officer, Flambeau Hospital, Park Falls, WI, p. A713

GRUNER, Dean, M.D., President and Chief Executive Officer, ThedaCare, Inc., Appleton, WI, p. B135

GRUNWALD, Pat, MSN Chief Nursing Officer, Meriter Hospital, Madison, WI, p. A708

GRUVER, Laquita, Fiscal Officer, Grand Junction Veterans Affairs Medical Center, Grand Junction, CO, p. A107

GRUZENSKY, Denton, Director Human Resources, Feather River Hospital, Paradise, CA, p. A82

GRYZBEK, Thomas J., President, Franciscan St. Margaret Health – Hammond, Hammond, IN, p. A212

GRZYBOWSKI, John, M.D. Medical Director, Mayo Clinic Health System in Albert Lea, Albert Lea, MN, p. A339

GUACCIO, Anthony, Senior Vice President & Chief Operating Officer, Swedish Covenant Hospital, Chicago, IL, p. A187

GUADAGNOLI, Donald, M.D. Chief Medical Officer, Cape Cod Hospital, Hyannis, MA, p. A311

GUAJARDO, Carlos, Chief Financial Officer, South Texas Health System, Edinburg, TX, p. A615

GUAJARDO, Michael, Director Finance, CHRISTUS Spohn Hospital Alice, Alice, TX, p. A595

GUARDIPEE, Lisa, Director, U. S. Public Health Service Indian Hospital, Fort Yates, ND, p. A478

GUARINO, Celia, R.N. Vice President and Chief Nursing Officer, Holy Cross Hospital, Silver Spring, MD, p. A303

GUARINO, Kathleen, R.N. Vice President Patient Care Services, Mercy Hospital, Buffalo, NY, p. A434

GUARINO, Rick, M.D. Vice President Medical Affairs, Wilson Medical Center, Wilson, NC, p. A475

GUARNESCHELLI, Philip, Senior Vice President and Chief Operating Officer, Pinnacle Health System, Harrisburg, PA, p. A540

GUARNIERI, Candace, Chief Financial Officer, Phoebe Worth Medical Center, Sylvester, GA, p. A167

GUARRACINO, Joseph, Senior Vice President and Chief Financial Officer, Brooklyn Hospital Center,, NY, p. A443

GUARRERA, Frank, Executive Vice President and Chief Financial Officer, Motion Picture and Television Fund Hospital and Residential Services,, CA, p. A73

GUBERMAN, Wayne, Director Finance, Matheny Medical and Educational Center, Peapack, NJ, p. A420

GUDVANGEN, Richard, M.D. Medical Director and Chief of Staff, Brookings Health System, Brookings, SD, p. A572

GUEHLSTORF, Daniel, M.D. Chief of Staff, Midwest Orthopedic Specialty Hospital, Franklin, WI, p. A705

GUELKER, Rhonda, Senior Director Finance, Rolling Plains Memorial Hospital, Sweetwater, TX, p. A651

GUERCI, Alan D., M.D., President and Chief Executive Officer, Catholic Health Services of Long Island, Rockville Centre, NY, p. B33

GUERRA, Jillian, Chief Human Resources Officer, Tri–City Regional Medical Center, Hawaiian Gardens, CA, p. A66

GUERRANT, Eric, M.D. President Medical Staff, Ephraim McDowell Regional Medical Center, Danville, KY, p. A260

GUERRERO, Marisa, Director Human Resources, Laredo Specialty Hospital, Laredo, TX, p. A633

GUERRIERO, Marianne, Nurse Executive, Christian Health Care Center, Wyckoff, NJ, p. A425

GUEST, Leona, Chief Nursing Unit, Hawaii State Hospital, Kaneohe, HI, p. A172

GUEST, William, Senior Vice President and Chief Medical Officer, Tift Regional Medical Center, Tifton, GA, p. A168

GUEVARA, Al, FACHE, President and Chief Executive Officer, Brazosport Regional Health System, Lake Jackson, TX, p. A632

GUEVIN, Scott, Chief Executive Officer, Penn State Hershey Rehabilitation Hospital, Hummelstown, PA, p. A541

GUEZ, Roberta H., Director, Dr. J. Corrigan Mental Health Center, Fall River, MA, p. A309

GUFFEY, Dale, Chief Financial Officer, Lower Keys Medical Center, Key West, FL, p. A133

GUFFEY, Jay, Senior Vice President and Chief Operating Officer, Mercy Hospital Springfield, Springfield, MO, p. A383

GUGEL, Paul, Manager Information Technology, Marlette Regional Hospital, Marlette, MI, p. A330

GUGLIELMO, Elaine, Vice President Human Resources and Organizational Development, Stamford Hospital, Stamford, CT, p. A117

GUIDERA, Kenneth, M.D. Chief of Staff, Shriners Hospitals for Children–Twin Cities, Minneapolis, MN, p. A347

GUIDRY, Carolyn, Business Manager, Community Specialty Hospital, Lafayette, LA, p. A281

GUIDRY, Floyd, M.D. Medical Director, Lake Area Medical Center, Lake Charles, LA, p. A282

GUIDRY, Lloyd, Chief Operating Officer, Lady of the Sea General Hospital, Cut Off, LA, p. A276

GUIDRY, Selina, Chief Nursing Officer, Lafayette Surgical Specialty Hospital, Lafayette, LA, p. A281

GUIDRY, Trisha, Administrator, Baton Rouge Rehabilitation Hospital, Baton Rouge, LA, p. A273

GUIGNIER, Liz, Vice President Human Resources, Eisenhower Medical Center, Rancho Mirage, CA, p. A84

GUILFOIL, Thomas, Director Human Resources, Wing Memorial Hospital, Palmer, MA, p. A313

GUILLORY, Larry, Chief Human Resources Officer, Baylor Emergency Medical Center at Aubrey, Aubrey, TX, p. A598

GUIMARAES, Antonio, M.D. Clinical Director, U. S. Public Health Service Indian Hospital, Cass Lake, MN, p. A341

GUIMARAES, Valerie, Director Human Resources, Livingston Regional Hospital, Livingston, TN, p. A587

GUIN Jr., Jamie W., Chief Executive Officer, Lincoln County Health System, Fayetteville, TN, p. A583

GUINA, Michelle, Manager Human Resources, Sutter Surgical Hospital – North Valley, Yuba City, CA, p. A101

GUINANE, Gerard, Vice President Human Resources and Diversity Management, Lakeland Regional Medical Center–St. Joseph, Saint Joseph, MI, p. A334

GUINANE, Jerry, Vice President Human Resources, SwedishAmerican Hospital, Rockford, IL, p. A202

GUINLE, Mary Lou, FACHE, Chief Executive Officer, Select Specialty Hospital–Lexington, Lexington, KY, p. A264

GUINN, Judy, Chief Human Resources Officer, Graham Regional Medical Center, Graham, TX, p. A621

GUIRL, Nadine T., Senior Vice President Human Resources, Waukesha Memorial Hospital, Waukesha, WI, p. A717

GULARTE, Steven, Chief Executive Officer, Chambers County Public Hospital District 1, Anahuac, TX, p. A597

GULDE, James E., M.D. Medical Director, Dubuis Hospital of Paris, Paris, TX, p. A641

GULIHUR, Judith, Director Human Resources and Chief Financial Officer, McCamey County Hospital District, McCamey, TX, p. A637

GULL, Joann Bernadette, Chief Nursing Officer, Elmhurst Hospital Center,, NY, p. A443

GULLINGSRUD, Timothy M., Chief Executive Officer, Hayward Area Memorial Hospital and Nursing Home, Hayward, WI, p. A706

GULRICH, Erica, Chief Operating Officer, Northwest Medical Center, Margate, FL, p. A135

GUM, Gary, R.N. Chief Nursing Officer, Kindred Hospital–Albuquerque, Albuquerque, NM, p. A426

GUMBINER, Carl H., M.D. Senior Vice President Medical Affairs and Chief Medical Officer, Children's Hospital and Medical Center, Omaha, NE, p. A400

GUMBS, Milton A., M.D. Vice President and Medical Director, Bronx–Lebanon Hospital Center Health Care System,, NY, p. A442

GUMMADI, Subhaker, M.D
  Chief Medical Staff, Promise Hospital Baton Rouge – Main Campus, Baton Rouge, LA, p. A273
  President Medical Staff, Promise Hospital of Baton Rouge – Mid–City Campus, Baton Rouge, LA, p. A274

GUNABALAN, Ryan, Chief Executive Officer, Behavioral Center of Michigan, Warren, MI, p. A336

GUNASEKARAN, Suresh, Assistant Vice President Information Resources, University of Texas Southwestern Medical Center, Dallas, TX, p. A612

GUNDERSEN, Robert A., Market Chief Executive Officer, Kindred Hospital Northeast–Stoughton, Stoughton, MA, p. A315

GUNDLAPALLI, Madhu, M.D. Clinical Director, Utah State Hospital, Provo, UT, p. A662

GUNDT, Kristin, Chief Nursing Officer, Community Hospital, Grand Junction, CO, p. A107

GUNKEL, Jeff, Chief Information Officer, Jamestown Regional Medical Center, Jamestown, ND, p. A478

GUNN, Deborah, Chief Information Officer, W. G. (Bill) Heffner Veterans Affairs Medical Center, Salisbury, NC, p. A472

GUNN, Elizabeth, R.N. Vice President, Patient Care Services, Southeast Georgia Health System Brunswick Campus, Brunswick, GA, p. A155

GUNN, John R., Executive Vice President and Chief Operating Officer, Memorial Sloan–Kettering Cancer Center, New York, NY, p. A445

GUNN, Terry, Interim Chief Executive Officer, KershawHealth, Camden, SC, p. A562

GUNNELL, Nancy
Vice President Human Resources, West Suburban Medical Center, Oak Park, IL, p. A198
Vice President Human Resources, Westlake Hospital, Melrose Park, IL, p. A196

GUNNERSEN, Niis, Administrator, Bertrand Chaffee Hospital, Springville, NY, p. A455

GUNTHER, Anne, R.N. Chief Nursing Officer, Aultman Hospital, Canton, OH, p. A485

GUNUKULA, Srinivas, M.D. Chief of Staff, Dallas Regional Medical Center, Mesquite, TX, p. A637

GUPTA, Anil, M.D. Chief of Staff, Kindred Hospital–Baldwin Park, Baldwin Park, CA, p. A57

GUPTA, Arun, M.D. Vice President Medical Affairs, South Pointe Hospital, Warrensville Heights, OH, p. A504

GUPTA, Ashok K., M.D. Chief of Staff, Eaton Rapids Medical Center, Eaton Rapids, MI, p. A323

GUPTA, Vijay D., M.D. President and Chief Executive Officer, Franciscan Healthcare – Munster, Munster, IN, p. A219

GURR, Lory, Chief Human Resources Division, Evans U. S. Army Community Hospital, Fort Carson, CO, p. A106

GURRI, Joseph Albert, Vice President of Medical Affairs, Health First Holmes Regional Medical Center, Melbourne, FL, p. A135

GURTO, Barbara
Manager Human Resources, University Hospitals Conneaut Medical Center, Conneaut, OH, p. A491
Manager Human Resources, University Hospitals Geneva Medical Center, Geneva, OH, p. A494

GURULE, Eric, Chief Information Officer, Turquoise Lodge Hospital, Albuquerque, NM, p. A427

GURUNG, Anju, M.D. Chief Medical Officer, Mahnomen Health Center, Mahnomen, MN, p. A346

GUSHEE, Dean, M.D. Medical Director, Mason General Hospital, Shelton, WA, p. A689

GUSHO, Michael, Chief Financial Officer, St. Joseph Mercy Oakland, Pontiac, MI, p. A332

GUSSERT, Jeff, Director Operations, Dickinson County Healthcare System, Iron Mountain, MI, p. A327

GUSTAFSON, Brian, Chief Financial Officer, Veterans Affairs Montana Health Care System, Fort Harrison, MT, p. A387

GUSTAFSON, Michael, M.D., Chief Operating Officer, Brigham and Women's Faulkner Hospital, Boston, MA, p. A306

GUSTAFSON, Sarah S., Vice President of Finance, Grand Itasca Clinic and Hospital, Grand Rapids, MN, p. A344

GUSTILO, Maria, M.D
Medical Director, Osawatomie State Hospital, Osawatomie, KS, p. A251
Medical Director, Rainbow Mental Health Facility, Kansas City, KS, p. A247

GUTHMILLER, Martin W., Chief Executive Officer, Orange City Area Health System, Orange City, IA, p. A235

GUTHRIE, Deborah S., Chief Executive Officer, HEALTHSOUTH Walton Rehabilitation Hospital, Augusta, GA, p. A153

GUTHRIE, Pamela A., Chief Human Resources Officer, Integris Mayes County Medical Center, Pryor, OK, p. A518

GUTIERREZ, Albert, FACHE, President and Chief Executive Officer, Saint Joseph Regional Medical Center, Mishawaka, IN, p. A219

GUTIERREZ, Doris, Director Human Resources, Holy Cross Hospital, Chicago, IL, p. A184

GUTIERREZ, Lori, Chief Financial Officer, Rochelle Community Hospital, Rochelle, IL, p. A201

GUTIERREZ, Michelle, Executive Director Human Resources, Orange Coast Memorial Medical Center, Fountain Valley, CA, p. A63

GUTIERREZ, Noe, Chief Financial Officer, Lake Granbury Medical Center, Granbury, TX, p. A621

GUTIERREZ, Vickie, Director of Patient Care, Dr. Dan C. Trigg Memorial Hospital, Tucumcari, NM, p. A431

GUTIERREZ, Victor A., M.D. Medical Director, Allegiance Behavioral Health Center of Plainview, Plainview, TX, p. A642

GUTJAHR, Susan, Reimbursement Specialist, Sparta Community Hospital, Sparta, IL, p. A202

GUTKIN, Marty, Vice President Finance and Chief Financial Officer, WellStar Kennestone Hospital, Marietta, GA, p. A163

GUTMAN, Luisa, Senior Vice President and Chief Operating Officer, Holy Cross Hospital, Fort Lauderdale, FL, p. A128

GUTNICK, Michael, Senior Vice President Finance, Memorial Sloan–Kettering Cancer Center, New York, NY, p. A445

GUTOW, Andrew, M.D. Medical Director, Menlo Park Surgical Hospital, Menlo Park, CA, p. A77

GUTSCH, Michael, Chief Executive Officer, Cumberland Memorial Hospital, Cumberland, WI, p. A703

GUTSCHENRITTER, John, Chief Financial Officer, Wilson Medical Center, Neodesha, KS, p. A250

GUTTENBERG, Ellen, Chief Operating Officer, Frances Mahon Deaconess Hospital, Glasgow, MT, p. A387

GUTTIN, Enrique, M.D. Chief of Staff, Veterans Affairs Medical Center, Wilmington, DE, p. A117

GUTTMACHER, Laurence, M.D. Clinical Director, Rochester Psychiatric Center, Rochester, NY, p. A453

GUTZEIT, Michael, M.D. Chief Medical Officer, Children's Hospital of Wisconsin, Milwaukee, WI, p. A710

GUY, Patrick, Vice President Human Resources, Los Robles Hospital and Medical Center, Thousand Oaks, CA, p. A97

GUYETTE, William, M.D. President Medical Staff, Livingston Hospital and Healthcare Services, Salem, KY, p. A270

GUZ, Andy, Chief Operating Officer, Kosciusko Community Hospital, Warsaw, IN, p. A224

GUZMAN, Claudia V., Executive Director, Hospital HIMA San Pablo Caguas, Caguas, PR, p. A725

GUZMAN, Elizabeth, Chief Operating Officer, Metropolitan Hospital Center, New York, NY, p. A446

GUZMAN, Lisa, Director Human Resources, California Hospital Medical Center, Los Angeles, CA, p. A71

GWATKIN, Betty Ann, Vice President Human Resources, Northeastern Vermont Regional Hospital, Saint Johnsbury, VT, p. A666

GWYN, Brian
President and Chief Executive Officer, Cleveland Regional Medical Center, Shelby, NC, p. A472
President Chief Operating Officer, Cleveland Regional Medical Center, Shelby, NC, p. A472
President and Chief Executive Officer, Kings Mountain Hospital, Kings Mountain, NC, p. A467

GYROS, Guy, Chief Financial Officer, Huntsville Memorial Hospital, Huntsville, TX, p. A629

H

HAACK, Wanda, MSN Chief Nursing Officer, Genesis Medical Center, DeWitt, De Witt, IA, p. A229

HAAGENSON, Deb, R.N. Vice President of Patient Care, CHI St. Joseph's Health, Park Rapids, MN, p. A349

HAAK, Karen S., R.N. Chief Nursing Officer, Good Samaritan Hospital, Vincennes, IN, p. A223

HAAK, Thelma, Manager Health Information, Avera Dells Area Hospital, Dell Rapids, SD, p. A573

HAAK–MUSE, Margaret, Chief Financial Officer and Assistant Administrator, East Texas Medical Center–Mount Vernon, Mount Vernon, TX, p. A638

HAAR, Clare A., Chief Executive Officer, Eastern Niagara Hospital, Lockport, NY, p. A440

HAAS, Christine, Chief Information Officer, Jersey Shore Hospital, Jersey Shore, PA, p. A541

HAAS, Lorin, Chief Financial Officer, Rush County Memorial Hospital, La Crosse, KS, p. A248

HAAS, Scott A., M.D. Chief Medical Officer, Eastern State Hospital, Lexington, KY, p. A264

HAAS, Steven J.
Chief Financial Officer, Health Alliance Hospital – Broadway Campus, Kingston, NY, p. A440
Chief Financial Officer, Health Alliance Hospital – Mary's Avenue Campus, Kingston, NY, p. A440

HAAS, Susan, Director Human Resources, Aurora San Diego Hospital, San Diego, CA, p. A89

HAASE, Patricia, Director Information Technology and Communications, Marian Regional Medical Center, Santa Maria, CA, p. A94

HAASKEN, Timothy W., Chief Financial Officer, LewisGale Hospital Montgomery, Blacksburg, VA, p. A668

HABASHY, Hany Mounir, M.D. Chief Medical Director, Methodist Extended Care Hospital, Memphis, TN, p. A589

HABIB, Noel, M.D. Chief Medical Officer, Huhukam Memorial Hospital, Sacaton, AZ, p. A38

HABOWSKI, Michael J., President and Chief Executive Officer, Ashtabula County Medical Center, Ashtabula, OH, p. A482

HACHENBERG, Dennis A., FACHE, Chief Executive Officer, Anderson County Hospital, Garnett, KS, p. A244

HACHEY, Michael, Senior Vice President and Chief Financial Officer, Mercy Hospital of Portland, Portland, ME, p. A294

HACKBARTH, John, CPA Senior Vice President Finance and Chief Financial Officer, Owensboro Health Regional Hospital, Owensboro, KY, p. A268

HACKER, Leanne, Chief Financial Officer, Eastern New Mexico Medical Center, Roswell, NM, p. A430

HACKER, Mary Dee, R.N. Vice President, Patient Care Services and Chief Nursing Officer, Children's Hospital Los Angeles, Los Angeles, CA, p. A71

HACKER, Phillip, Chief Financial Officer, The Medical Center of Southeast Texas, Port Arthur, TX, p. A643

HACKER, Tina, Director Human Resources, Advanced Specialty Hospital of Toledo, Toledo, OH, p. A503

HACKETT, Leslie, Chief Nursing Officer, Covenant Hospital Plainview, Plainview, TX, p. A642

HACKETT, Sylvia D., Vice President Human Resources, Rex Healthcare, Raleigh, NC, p. A471

HACKMAN, Paul, Chief Executive Officer, Ridgeview Institute, Smyrna, GA, p. A167

HACKNEY, Hannah, Director Accounting and Human Resources, DeWitt Hospital, De Witt, AR, p. A45

HACKSTEDDE, Anita, M.D., President and Chief Executive Officer, Salem Regional Medical Center, Salem, OH, p. A501

HADDADIN, Maen, M.D. President Medical Staff, CHI Health Mercy Corning, Corning, IA, p. A228

HADDEN, Kim E., R.N. Chief Nurse Executive, Kaiser Permanente Riverside Medical Center, Riverside, CA, p. A86

HADDICAN, James, Vice President Finance, Gillette Children's Specialty Healthcare, Saint Paul, MN, p. A351

HADDIX, Parker, Chief Executive Officer, William R. Sharpe, Jr. Hospital, Weston, WV, p. A700

HADDOX, Melissa, Controller, HEALTHSOUTH Rehabilitation Hospital of Cypress, Houston, TX, p. A624

HADEN, James E., President and Chief Executive Officer, Martha Jefferson Hospital, Charlottesville, VA, p. A669

HADLEY, David R., Managing Director and Chief Financial Officer, Integris Baptist Medical Center, Oklahoma City, OK, p. A515

HADLEY, H. Roger, M.D. Vice President, Medical Affairs, Loma Linda University Medical Center, Loma Linda, CA, p. A69

HADLEY, Jerry, Interim Vice President Finance and Chief Financial Officer, Newton–Wellesley Hospital, Newton Lower Falls, MA, p. A313

HADLEY, Steven N., Chief Financial Officer, Kansas Medical Center, Andover, KS, p. A241

HADLEY, Susan, R.N. Director of Nursing, Dickinson County Healthcare System, Iron Mountain, MI, p. A327

HADZEGA, Angela, Chief Financial Officer, Kane Community Hospital, Kane, PA, p. A541

HAEHN, Debra, Chief Financial Officer, Clay County Memorial Hospital, Henrietta, TX, p. A623

HAENELT, Michael, Chief Information Management, Weed Army Community Hospital, Fort Irwin, CA, p. A63

HAESEMEYER, Allan, M.D. Chief of Staff, Indianhead Medical Center, Shell Lake, WI, p. A715

HAFEMAN, Paula, R.N
Chief Nursing Officer, St. Mary's Hospital Medical Center, Green Bay, WI, p. A706
Chief Nursing Officer, St. Vincent Hospital, Green Bay, WI, p. A706

HAFFEY, Robert, R.N., President, Delaware County Memorial Hospital, Drexel Hill, PA, p. A537

HAFFNER, Randall L., Ph.D., Chief Executive Officer, Porter Adventist Hospital, Denver, CO, p. A105

HAFFORD, Juliet, Director Human Resources, Oakwood Hospital–Southshore, Trenton, MI, p. A336

HAFIZ, Irfan
Vice President Medical Affairs, Centegra Hospital – McHenry, McHenry, IL, p. A196
Vice President Medical Affairs, Centegra Hospital – Woodstock, Woodstock, IL, p. A205

HAGAN, David J., M.D. Chief Medical Officer, Gibson Area Hospital and Health Services, Gibson City, IL, p. A191

HAGAN, Donald E., Chief Financial Officer, DeTar Healthcare System, Victoria, TX, p. A655

HAGAN, Eric, R.N.,
Vice President/Administrator, Medical Center at Franklin, Franklin, KY, p. A261
Vice President/Administrator, Medical Center at Scottsville, Scottsville, KY, p. A270

HAGELBERG, Robbi, R.N. Vice President Operations and Chief Nursing Officer, Hudson Hospital and Clinic, Hudson, WI, p. A706

HAGELTHORN, Diane, Human Resources Generalist, Modoc Medical Center, Alturas, CA, p. A55

HAGEN, Bruce P.
President, OhioHealth Dublin Methodist Hospital, Dublin, OH, p. A493
Regional Executive and President, OhioHealth Grady Memorial Hospital, Delaware, OH, p. A492

HAGEN, Lynne D., Human Resources Officer, Avera McKennan Hospital and University Health Center, Sioux Falls, SD, p. A576

HAGEN, Mary, R.N. VP and Chief Nursing Officer, UnityPoint Health – Allen Hospital, Waterloo, IA, p. A239

HAGEN, Paulette, Human Resources and Administrative Services Director, CentraCare Health–Paynesville, Paynesville, MN, p. A349

HAGENBUCH, Michelle, M.D. Chief of Staff, Greenville Health System – Laurens County Memorial Hospital, Clinton, SC, p. A564

HAGENS, Gary, Chief Operating Officer and Chief Medical Officer, Springfield Regional Medical Center, Springfield, OH, p. A502

HAGENS, Paul, Vice President Human Resources, Doctors Community Hospital, Lanham, MD, p. A302

HAGER, Rhonda M., Director Human Resources, Stonewall Jackson Memorial Hospital, Weston, WV, p. A700

HAGERMAN, Daniel, M.D. President Medical Staff, Columbia Center, Mequon, WI, p. A709

HAGERMAN, Roy, Site Manager Information Technology, St. Rose Dominican Hospitals – San Martin Campus, Las Vegas, NV, p. A406

HAGERSTROM, Paige A., Director Human Resources, St. Joseph Hospital, Bangor, ME, p. A291

HAGGARD, Tommy, Chief Executive Officer, Bluegrass Community Hospital, Versailles, KY, p. A271

HAGGART, Sandra, Chief Nursing Officer, St. Vincent Clay Hospital, Brazil, IN, p. A207

HAGGERTY, Bridget, Chief Information Officer, OHSU Hospital, Portland, OR, p. A528

HAGHIGHAT, Dennis, M.D. Vice President Medical Affairs, St. Mary Medical Center, Apple Valley, CA, p. A56

HAGLER, Dan, M.D. Vice President and Chief Medical Officer, Carolinas Medical Center–NorthEast, Concord, NC, p. A462

HAGOOD, Teena, Chief Nursing Officer, Kimble Hospital, Junction, TX, p. A630

HAGUE, Samuel, M.D. Chief of Staff, Integris Blackwell Regional Hospital, Blackwell, OK, p. A508

HAGY, Kelly, Director Human Resources, Cumberland Hall Hospital, Hopkinsville, KY, p. A263

HAGY, Michael, Chief Financial Officer, Pikeville Medical Center, Pikeville, KY, p. A269

HAHEY, Joanne A.
Vice President Finance and Chief Financial Officer, University of Maryland Shore Medical Center at Chestertown, Chestertown, MD, p. A299
Senior Vice President and Chief Financial Officer, University of Maryland Shore Medical Center at Dorchester, Cambridge, MD, p. A299
Senior Vice President and Chief Financial Officer, University of Maryland Shore Medical Center at Easton, Easton, MD, p. A300

HAHN, Annette, Director Human Resources, Rehabilitation Hospital of Wisconsin, Waukesha, WI, p. A717

HAHN, Bashirat, Chief Information Officer, MetroSouth Medical Center, Blue Island, IL, p. A182

HAHN, James W., Administrator, North Mississippi Medical Center–West Point, West Point, MS, p. A366

HAHN, Joseph, M.D. Chief of Staff, Cleveland Clinic, Cleveland, OH, p. A488

HAHN, Kurt, M.D. Acting Clinical Director, Elmira Psychiatric Center, Elmira, NY, p. A437

HAHN, Lori, Vice President Nursing Services, Mercy Medical Center, Williston, ND, p. A480

HAHN, Ray, Chief Operating Officer, Kaiser Permanente Fontana Medical Center, Fontana, CA, p. A63

HAHN, DNP, RN, NEA-BC, Donna S., R.N. Vice President Acute Care and Chief Nurse Executive, Sentara RMH Medical Center, Harrisonburg, VA, p. A672

HAIGH, Sara, Associate Director, Durham Veterans Affairs Medical Center, Durham, NC, p. A463

HAIL, Brian, Chief Executive Officer, Cherokee Nation W.W. Hastings Indian Hospital, Tahlequah, OK, p. A519

HAIN, Jim, Chief Operating Officer, Lexington Regional Health Center, Lexington, NE, p. A397

HAINES, Beverly J., R.N., President, Patewood Memorial Hospital, Greenville, SC, p. A566

HAIR, Kelly, Director Information Technology, Abbeville General Hospital, Abbeville, LA, p. A272

HAIRGROVE, Heath, Administrator, Tri Parish Rehabilitation Hospital, Leesville, LA, p. A283

HAIZLIP, Jr., Thomas M., M.D. Chief of Staff, Charles A. Cannon Memorial Hospital, Linville, NC, p. A468

HAJEK, Julie, Director Human Resources, St. David's Medical Center, Austin, TX, p. A600

HAKIM, Jamal, M.D., Interim President and Chief Executive Officer, Orlando Health, Orlando, FL, p. B104

HALAKAN, Catherine, Senior Vice President, Albany Medical Center, Albany, NY, p. A432

HALAMA, George, Vice President Finance, McPherson Hospital, McPherson, KS, p. A250

HALAMKA, John, M.D. Chief Information Officer, Beth Israel Deaconess Medical Center, Boston, MA, p. A306

HALDEMAN, Larry, M.D. Executive Vice President and Chief Medical Officer, WellStar Windy Hill Hospital, Marietta, GA, p. A163

HALDEMAN, Richard, President and Chief Executive Officer, Southwestern Regional Medical Center, Tulsa, OK, p. A521

HALDER, Ranjay, M.D. Chief Medical Director, Manatee Glens Hospital and Addiction Center, Bradenton, FL, p. A124

HALE, Becky, Director Human Resources, Hill Regional Hospital, Hillsboro, TX, p. A623

HALE, Byron, Chief Financial Officer, East Texas Medical Center Tyler, Tyler, TX, p. A654

HALE, Carol, Vice President Finance, Carolinas Medical Center–NorthEast, Concord, NC, p. A462

HALE, Danny, Director Human Resources, Southwestern Medical Center, Lawton, OK, p. A512

HALE, Donna, Chief Nursing Officer, Baptist Rehabilitation–Germantown, Germantown, TN, p. A583

HALE, Elizabeth, R.N. Vice President Patient Services and Chief Nursing Officer, Lawrence General Hospital, Lawrence, MA, p. A311

HALE, Kathleen A., MS Vice President and Chief Nursing Officer, Ellis Hospital, Schenectady, NY, p. A454

HALE, Margie, R.N. Director of Nursing, Baraga County Memorial Hospital, L'Anse, MI, p. A328

HALE, Pat, Chief Financial Officer, Indian Path Medical Center, Kingsport, TN, p. A585

HALE, Renae, Chief Nursing Officer, Lincoln Prairie Behavioral Health Center, Springfield, IL, p. A203

HALE, Ron, Administrator, Alaska Psychiatric Institute, Anchorage, AK, p. A28

HALE, Russell, Director Human Resources, MetroSouth Medical Center, Blue Island, IL, p. A182

HALE, Tonia, Chief Nursing Officer, Tennova Newport Medical Center, Newport, TN, p. A591

HALEN, Catherine, Vice President Human Resources, Beebe Healthcare, Lewes, DE, p. A119

HALES, Brent, Chief Financial Officer, Uintah Basin Medical Center, Roosevelt, UT, p. A662

HALES, Joe, Director Information Systems, Primary Children's Medical Center, Salt Lake City, UT, p. A663

HALEY, Bob J., Chief Executive Officer, Pekin Hospital, Pekin, IL, p. A199

HALEY, James, M.D. Senior Vice President and Chief Medical Officer, Unity Hospital, Rochester, NY, p. A453

HALEY, Kevin, Chief Financial Officer, Penn State Milton S. Hershey Medical Center, Hershey, PA, p. A540

HALEY, Michael E., President and Chief Executive Officer, Indiana University Health Ball Memorial Hospital, Muncie, IN, p. A219

HALFEN, John, M.D. Medical Director, Lakewood Health System, Staples, MN, p. A352

HALFHILL, Patrick, Chief Financial Officer, Madison County Memorial Hospital, Madison, FL, p. A135

HALFORD, Dianne, Chief Financial Officer, Saint Clare's Health System, Denville, NJ, p. A415

HALIMI, Hamid, M.D. Medical Director, Select Specialty Hospital–Ann Arbor, Ypsilanti, MI, p. A338

HALL, Alice, Acting President and Chief Executive Officer, Hawaii Health Systems Corporation, Honolulu, HI, p. B63

HALL, Becky, R.N. Director Nursing, Rumford Hospital, Rumford, ME, p. A295

HALL, Carla, Director of Nursing, Highland Hospital, Charleston, WV, p. A694

HALL, Catherine, Manager Human Resources, Jefferson Hospital, Louisville, GA, p. A162

HALL, Charlene, Vice President Human Resources and Guest Support Services, Indiana University Health Morgan Hospital, Martinsville, IN, p. A218

HALL, Clara Cordelia, Chief Human Resources Officer, Breckinridge Memorial Hospital, Hardinsburg, KY, p. A262

HALL, Dan, R.N. Director of Nursing, St. John Owasso, Owasso, OK, p. A517

HALL, Dana, Director of Nursing, Quitman County Hospital, Marks, MS, p. A362

HALL, David, Chief Information Officer, Pineville Community Hospital Association, Pineville, KY, p. A269

HALL, David, M.D. Senior Vice President and Chief Medical Officer, St. Vincent Medical Center–North, Sherwood, AR, p. A52

HALL, David
Chief Information Officer, Union County General Hospital, Clayton, NM, p. A427
Senior Vice President and Chief Operating Officer, University of Tennessee Medical Center, Knoxville, TN, p. A586

HALL, Doug, Director Information Systems, Tri Valley Health System, Cambridge, NE, p. A394

HALL, Gary, Vice President of Information Technology, Estes Park Medical Center, Estes Park, CO, p. A106

HALL, George, M.D
Vice President Medical Affairs, St. Elizabeth Florence, Florence, KY, p. A261
Vice President Medical Affairs, St. Elizabeth Fort Thomas, Fort Thomas, KY, p. A261

HALL, James, Information Technology Support, Black River Medical Center, Poplar Bluff, MO, p. A378

HALL, Jeanne, Director Information Systems, Shriners Hospitals for Children–St. Louis, Saint Louis, MO, p. A381

HALL, Jeffrey, DPM Chief Medical Officer, St. Croix Regional Medical Center, St. Croix Falls, WI, p. A715

HALL, Jeremy, Assistant Administrator and Chief Financial Officer, Middlesboro ARH Hospital, Middlesboro, KY, p. A267

HALL, Jim
Budget Officer, Caswell Center, Kinston, NC, p. A467
Acting Chief Information Officer, Central Arkansas Veterans Healthcare System, Little Rock, AR, p. A49

HALL, Kathy J., Administrator, St. Mary's Warrick Hospital, Boonville, IN, p. A207

HALL, Kenneth C., R.N. Chief Nursing Officer, Saint Joseph Regional Medical Center, Mishawaka, IN, p. A219

HALL, Kent, M.D. Vice President and Chief Medical Officer, Champlain Valley Physicians Hospital Medical Center, Plattsburgh, NY, p. A451

HALL, Leslie, R.N. Senior Vice President–Chief Nursing Officer, Nash Health Care Systems, Rocky Mount, NC, p. A471

HALL, Linda, Administrator and Chief Executive Officer, Chillicothe Hospital District, Chillicothe, TX, p. A606

HALL, Margaret, M.D. Chief Medical Officer, Lakeside Women's Hospital, Oklahoma City, OK, p. A515

HALL, Mary A., Chief Medical Staff, McDowell ARH Hospital, McDowell, KY, p. A267

HALL, Melissa
Chief Nursing Officer, Coffey County Hospital, Burlington, KS, p. A242
Human Resources, Munising Memorial Hospital, Munising, MI, p. A331

HALL, Michael, Interim Chief Executive Officer, Mountrail County Medical Center, Stanley, ND, p. A480

HALL, Morrison, Chief Financial Officer, Pender Memorial Hospital, Burgaw, NC, p. A460

HALL, Robert, Chief Information Officer, Northern Hospital of Surry County, Mount Airy, NC, p. A469

HALL, Roger L.
President, Sacred Heart Hospital on the Emerald Coast, Miramar Beach, FL, p. A138
President, Sacred Heart Hospital on the Gulf, Port St. Joe, FL, p. A143

HALL, Sally, Manager Human Resources, South Texas Spine and Surgical Hospital, San Antonio, TX, p. A647

HALL, Stephanie, M.D. Medical Director, University of Southern California–Norris Cancer Hospital, Los Angeles, CA, p. A75

HALL, Steve, Chief Financial Officer, Pekin Hospital, Pekin, IL, p. A199

HALL, Trudy, M.D. Vice President Medical Affairs, Laurel Regional Hospital, Laurel, MD, p. A302

HALL, Veronica, R.N. Chief Operating Officer, Henry Ford Hospital, Detroit, MI, p. A322

HALLADAY, Mark, Director Information Services, F. F. Thompson Hospital, Canandaigua, NY, p. A435

HALLAGIN, Virginia, Chief Executive Officer, Keefe Memorial Hospital, Cheyenne Wells, CO, p. A103

HALLAL, Joseph, M.D. Chief Medical Officer, Inova Fairfax Hospital, Falls Church, VA, p. A670

HALLATT, Jennifer
Chief Operating Officer, Mercy Harvard Hospital, Harvard, IL, p. A191
Chief Operating Officer, Mercy Walworth Hospital and Medical Center, Lake Geneva, WI, p. A707

HALLER, Karen B., Ph.D. Vice President Nursing and Patient Care Services, Johns Hopkins Hospital, Baltimore, MD, p. A296

HALLER, III, William, M.D. Chief of Staff, Gadsden Regional Medical Center, Gadsden, AL, p. A20

HALLEY, Andrea, Director Human Resources, Hopedale Medical Complex, Hopedale, IL, p. A193

HALLEY, Lisa B., Vice President Human Resources, Holzer Medical Center, Gallipolis, OH, p. A494

HALLGREN, Hugh R., Chief Executive Officer, Sitka Community Hospital, Sitka, AK, p. A30

HALLICK, Susan M., R.N. Executive Vice President and Chief Nursing Officer, Geisinger Medical Center, Danville, PA, p. A537

HALLIDAY, Lisa, Director Accounting Services, Taylor Regional Hospital, Hawkinsville, GA, p. A160

HALLIWILL, Donald, Executive Vice President and Chief Financial Officer, Carilion Roanoke Memorial Hospital, Roanoke, VA, p. A678

HALLMARK, Todd, Chief Operating Officer, Choctaw Nation Health Care Center, Talihina, OK, p. A519

HALPIN, Jean
President, OhioHealth MedCentral Mansfield Hospital, Mansfield, OH, p. A497
President, OhioHealth MedCentral Shelby Hospital, Shelby, OH, p. A502

HALPIN, Kim, Director Human Resources, Arms Acres, Carmel, NY, p. A435

HALSAN, Carole, R.N., Chief Executive Officer, Willapa Harbor Hospital, South Bend, WA, p. A690

HALSELL, David, Senior Vice President and Chief Financial Officer, Lake Regional Health System, Osage Beach, MO, p. A378

HALSTEAD, Lisa, Chief Nursing Officer, Integris Baptist Regional Health Center, Miami, OK, p. A513

HALTER, Kevin, Chief Executive Officer, Our Lady of Bellefonte Hospital, Ashland, KY, p. A258

HALTER, Michael P., Chief Executive Officer, Hahnemann University Hospital, Philadelphia, PA, p. A548

HALVORSEN, Lisa, Chief Nurse Executive, Providence Milwaukie Hospital, Milwaukie, OR, p. A527

HALVORSON, Marla, Director Human Resources, St. Luke's Hospital, Duluth, MN, p. A343

HAM, Mike, Chief Executive Officer, Greenleaf Center, Valdosta, GA, p. A168

HAMAM, Hisham, M.D. Chief of Staff, Northern Cochise Community Hospital, Willcox, AZ, p. A41

HAMB, Aaron, M.D. Chief Medical Officer, Provident Hospital of Cook County, Chicago, IL, p. A186

HAMBLEN, Jeffrey J., Chief Executive Officer, Little Colorado Medical Center, Winslow, AZ, p. A41

HAMBLIN, James, Chief Financial Officer, White Mountain Regional Medical Center, Springerville, AZ, p. A39

HAMEL, Cathleen, MS Vice President and Chief Nursing Officer, Baxter Regional Medical Center, Mountain Home, AR, p. A50

HAMEL, Loren, M.D., President and Chief Executive Officer, Lakeland Healthcare, Saint Joseph, MI, p. B83

HAMEL, Loren, M.D.,
President and Chief Executive Officer, Lakeland Regional Medical Center-St. Joseph, Saint Joseph, MI, p. A334
President and Chief Executive Officer, Lakeland Specialty Hospital-Berrien Center, Berrien Center, MI, p. A319

HAMEL, Susan, Chief Nursing Officer, St. Luke's Hospital, Duluth, MN, p. A343

HAMILL, Dave H., President and Chief Executive Officer, Hampton Regional Medical Center, Varnville, SC, p. A570

HAMILTON, Aggie, Chief Human Resources, Veterans Affairs Montana Health Care System, Fort Harrison, MT, p. A387

HAMILTON, Catherine, Chief Nursing Officer, Hedrick Medical Center, Chillicothe, MO, p. A369

HAMILTON, Chanda, Chief Information Officer, Clifton T. Perkins Hospital Center, Jessup, MD, p. A301

HAMILTON, Crystal, R.N., Chief Executive Officer, Maryvale Hospital Medical Center, Phoenix, AZ, p. A36

HAMILTON, Dan, Director Inpatient Services, Nor–Lea General Hospital, Lovington, NM, p. A429

HAMILTON, Geoffrey W., Interim Chief Financial Officer, McKenzie County Healthcare System, Watford City, ND, p. A480

HAMILTON, Kay A., MS, President and Chief Executive Officer, Geisinger–Lewistown Hospital, Lewistown, PA, p. A543

HAMILTON, Marci, Chief Nursing Officer, Orthopaedic Hospital of Lutheran Health Network, Fort Wayne, IN, p. A211

HAMILTON, Marilyn, Director Human Resources, Promise Hospital Baton Rouge – Main Campus, Baton Rouge, LA, p. A273

HAMILTON, Matthew, President and Chief Executive Officer, Columbus Hospital LTACH, Newark, NJ, p. A419

HAMILTON, Nancy, Chief Human and Learning Resources, Veterans Affairs New Jersey Health Care System, East Orange, NJ, p. A415

HAMILTON, Neal C., Chief Human Resources, James A. Haley Veterans' Hospital, Tampa, FL, p. A147

HAMILTON, Patricia, R.N. Director of Nursing, Mildred Mitchell–Bateman Hospital, Huntington, WV, p. A696

HAMILTON, Phil, R.N., Chief Executive Officer, General John J. Pershing Memorial Hospital, Brookfield, MO, p. A368

HAMILTON, Randal S., Chief Executive Officer, Select Specialty Hospital–Panama City, Panama City, FL, p. A142

HAMILTON, Richard C., Interim Chief Executive Officer, Harrison County Community Hospital, Bethany, MO, p. A367

HAMILTON, Robert U., Director, Charlie Norwood Veterans Affairs Medical Center, Augusta, GA, p. A153

HAMILTON, Scott
Vice President and Chief Financial Officer, Parkwest Medical Center, Knoxville, TN, p. A586
Chief Financial Officer, Peninsula Hospital, Louisville, TN, p. A587

HAMILTON, Terry, President, St. John Macomb–Oakland Hospital, Warren, MI, p. A336

HAMILTON, Thomas, D.O. Chief Medical Officer, St. Francis Health Center, Topeka, KS, p. A255

HAMILTON, Toby, Chief Executive Officer, Emerus, The Woodlands, TX, p. B56

HAMILTON, Tom, M.D. Chief of Staff, Decatur County General Hospital, Parsons, TN, p. A592

HAMILTON, William L., M.D
Urban Central Region Medical Director, Intermountain Medical Center, Murray, UT, p. A660
Chief Medical Officer, LDS Hospital, Salt Lake City, UT, p. A663

HAMILTON–BEYER, Maggie, Chief Financial Officer, Knoxville Hospital & Clinics, Knoxville, IA, p. A233

HAMLIN, DeWayne, Director, Veterans Affairs Caribbean Healthcare System, San Juan, PR, p. A729

HAMLIN, Faye, Manager Human Resources, Julian F. Keith Alcohol and Drug Abuse Treatment Center, Black Mountain, NC, p. A460

HAMLIN, Jeff, Director Finance, Oak Tree Hospital, Corbin, KY, p. A260

HAMLIN, Scott J., Chief Financial Officer, Cincinnati Children's Hospital Medical Center, Cincinnati, OH, p. A486

HAMM, David, President and Chief Executive Officer, Exempla Good Samaritan Medical Center, Lafayette, CO, p. A108

HAMM, Jay, R.N., Chief Acute Care Executive, Palmetto Health Richland, Columbia, SC, p. A564

HAMM, Joseph, Chief Medical Director, Mayo Clinic Health System in Springfield, Springfield, MN, p. A352

HAMMACK, Kathy, Chief Financial Officer, Western Medical Center–Santa Ana, Santa Ana, CA, p. A93

HAMMACK, Stanley K., Chief Executive Officer, University of South Alabama Hospitals, Mobile, AL, p. B146

HAMMAKER, Barry, M.D. Chief Medical Officer and Chief Clinical Officer, Vail Valley Medical Center, Vail, CO, p. A111

HAMMAN, Baron L., M.D., President, Texas Health Heart & Vascular Hospital Arlington, Arlington, TX, p. A598

HAMMEL, Katrina, M.D. Chief Medical Officer, Gundersen Tri–County Hospital and Clinics, Whitehall, WI, p. A718

HAMMEL, Leah, Acting Administrator, Chester Mental Health Center, Chester, IL, p. A183

HAMMER, Michael, Chief Executive Officer, Sanford Worthington Medical Center, Worthington, MN, p. A354

HAMMER, Rebecca J., Chief Financial Officer, Davis Memorial Hospital, Elkins, WV, p. A694

HAMMES, Chris, FACHE, Interim President, Integris Grove Hospital, Grove, OK, p. A511

HAMMES, Paul, Chief Executive Officer, Hugh Chatham Memorial Hospital, Elkin, NC, p. A464

HAMMETT, George, Director Human Resources, Carolina Center for Behavioral Health, Greer, SC, p. A567

HAMMETT, Richard A., Chief Executive Officer, Medical Center of Aurora, Aurora, CO, p. A102

HAMMETT, Ron, M.D. Chief of Staff, Glenwood Regional Medical Center, West Monroe, LA, p. A290

HAMMETT, Troy, Vice President and Chief Financial Officer, OhioHealth Doctors Hospital, Columbus, OH, p. A490

HAMMOCK, Preston W., President and Chief Executive Officer, Alamance Regional Medical Center, Burlington, NC, p. A461

HAMMON, Seiene Q., Chief Operating Officer, University Behavioral Health of El Paso, El Paso, TX, p. A616

HAMMOND, Flora, M.D. Chief Medical Affairs, Rehabilitation Hospital of Indiana, Indianapolis, IN, p. A214

HAMMOND, Michael
Chief Financial Officer, Lourdes Medical Center of Burlington County, Willingboro, NJ, p. A424
Chief Financial Officer, Our Lady of Lourdes Medical Center, Camden, NJ, p. A414

HAMMOND, Patti, Chief Operating Officer, Adirondack Medical Center, Saranac Lake, NY, p. A454

HAMMOND, Reed, Chief Operating Officer, Centennial Medical Center, Frisco, TX, p. A620

HAMMONDS, Janie, Human Resources Officer, Columbus Community Hospital, Columbus, TX, p. A607

HAMMONDS, Laura, Assistant Administrator, Jasper Memorial Hospital, Monticello, GA, p. A164

HAMNER, Candy, Vice President and Chief Nursing Officer, Levindale Hebrew Geriatric Center and Hospital, Baltimore, MD, p. A296

HAMON, Eric, Chief Financial Officer, Driscoll Children's Hospital, Corpus Christi, TX, p. A608

HAMONS, Spencer, Chief Information Officer and Chief Operating Officer, Holy Cross Hospital, Taos, NM, p. A431

HAMP, Matthew, Chief Operating Officer, Sisters of Charity Hospital of Buffalo, Buffalo, NY, p. A435

HAMPF, Carl, M.D. Chief Medical Officer, Saint Thomas Hospital for Spinal Surgery, Nashville, TN, p. A590

HAMPSHIRE, Misty, Chief Financial Officer, Ozarks Community Hospital, Springfield, MO, p. A383

HAMPTON, Angie, Director Human Resources, Porter Regional Hospital, Valparaiso, IN, p. A223

HAMPTON, David, M.D. Chief Medical Staff, Pampa Regional Medical Center, Pampa, TX, p. A641

HAMPTON, Debra C., Ph.D., Vice President, Administration and Chief Nursing Officer, Daniel Drake Center for Post Acute Care, Cincinnati, OH, p. A486

HAMPTON, James, Chief Information Officer, Southeastern Ohio Regional Medical Center, Cambridge, OH, p. A485

HAMPTON, Jeff, Director Information Systems, Lehigh Regional Medical Center, Lehigh Acres, FL, p. A134

HAMPTON, Mary Ann, R.N. Chief Nursing Officer, Des Peres Hospital, Saint Louis, MO, p. A380

HAMRICK, Jan, Chief Financial Officer, Dodge County Hospital, Eastman, GA, p. A159

HAN, Ba, M.D. Clinical Director, Big Spring State Hospital, Big Spring, TX, p. A603

HAN, Kevin, Vice President and Chief Financial Officer, Stormont–Vail HealthCare, Topeka, KS, p. A255

HANCOCK, Denise, Chief Financial Officer, Arbuckle Memorial Hospital, Sulphur, OK, p. A519

HANCOCK, J. Brian, M.D. Chief of Staff, Fargo Veterans Affairs Health Care System, Fargo, ND, p. A477

HANCOCK, Katherine, R.N. Executive Chief Nursing Officer, Cleveland Clinic, Cleveland, OH, p. A488

HANCOCK, Kerry, Director Human Resources, Bacon County Hospital and Health System, Alma, GA, p. A151

HANCOCK, Lori, Chief Business Officer, West Palm Beach Veterans Affairs Medical Center, West Palm Beach, FL, p. A150

HANCOCK, Melinda, Interim Chief Financial Officer, Good Samaritan Hospital, Suffern, NY, p. A455

HANCOCK, Myrna, Director Financial Services, Choctaw Health Center, Philadelphia, MS, p. A364

HANCOCK, Paul, M.D. Chief Medical Officer, Swedish Medical Center, Englewood, CO, p. A106

HANCOCK, Sharon, Director Human Resources, McCullough–Hyde Memorial Hospital, Oxford, OH, p. A500

HANCOCK, Todd, Senior Vice President and Chief Operating Officer, Mother Frances Hospital – Tyler, Tyler, TX, p. A654

HAND, Ronald E., Administrator, Oceans Behavioral Hospital Lufkin, Lufkin, TX, p. A635

HANDEL, Daniel, M.D. Chief Medical Officer, MUSC Medical Center of Medical University of South Carolina, Charleston, SC, p. A563

HANDLER, Michael, M.D. Vice President Medical Administration, SSM St. Joseph Hospital West, Lake Saint Louis, MO, p. A375

HANDLEY, Charles R., Chief Financial Officer, Plaza Specialty Hospital, Houston, TX, p. A626

HANDLEY, Rhonda, Chief Financial Officer, Columbia Basin Hospital, Ephrata, WA, p. A683

HANDOL, Nelson, M.D. Medical Director, Laurel Oaks Behavioral Health Center, Dothan, AL, p. A19

HANDRICK, Carolyn, Manager Public Relations, Corning Hospital, Corning, NY, p. A436

HANDY, Steven P., CPA, Interim Chief Executive Officer, Uniontown Hospital, Uniontown, PA, p. A556

HANEN, Marti, Director Human Resources, Providence Seaside Hospital, Seaside, OR, p. A530

HANENBURG, Thomas S., Senior Vice President, Kaiser Permanente Hayward Medical Center, Hayward, CA, p. A66

HANEY, Judy, Chief Nursing Officer, Harris Hospital, Newport, AR, p. A51

HANEY, Kathryn, Controller, HEALTHSOUTH Valley of the Sun Rehabilitation Hospital, Glendale, AZ, p. A33

HANEY, Mark, President, WellStar Paulding Hospital, Dallas, GA, p. A157

HANGER, Kelvin, Chief Executive Officer, TriHealth Evendale Hospital, Cincinnati, OH, p. A487

HANIGAN, Hank, Chief Operating Officer, Whidbey General Hospital, Coupeville, WA, p. A682

HANISCH, Denise, M.D. Chief of Staff, Avera St. Mary's Hospital, Pierre, SD, p. A575

HANKINS, Brad, Chief Operating Quality Officer, Lake Chelan Community Hospital, Chelan, WA, p. A682

HANKS, Claire H., R.N. Vice President and Chief Nursing Officer, Glendale Memorial Hospital and Health Center, Glendale, CA, p. A65

HANKS, John, Director Information Systems, East Tennessee Children's Hospital, Knoxville, TN, p. A585

HANKS, Tammy, Director Human Resources, Minidoka Memorial Hospital, Rupert, ID, p. A178

HANLEY, Darlene S., R.N., President and Chief Executive Officer, St. Lawrence Rehabilitation Center, Lawrenceville, NJ, p. A417

HANLEY, Kathleen S., Chief Financial Officer, ProMedica Flower Hospital, Sylvania, OH, p. A502

HANLEY, Robert, Chief Human Resources Officer, University of Chicago Medical Center, Chicago, IL, p. A187

HANLON, Jerad, Chief Operating Officer, Southside Regional Medical Center, Petersburg, VA, p. A676

HANLY, Donna, R.N. Senior Vice President and Chief Nursing Officer, OhioHealth Grant Medical Center, Columbus, OH, p. A490

HANNA, David, Ph.D., Interim Chief Executive Officer, Eastern State Hospital, Lexington, KY, p. A264

HANNA, Mitchell J.
Chief Executive Officer, Sutter Auburn Faith Hospital, Auburn, CA, p. A56
Interim Chief Executive Officer, Sutter Coast Hospital, Crescent City, CA, p. A61

HANNA, Philip S., Administrator and Chief Executive Officer, Battle Mountain General Hospital, Battle Mountain, NV, p. A404

HANNA, Robb, Executive Director Information Technology, Lexington Regional Health Center, Lexington, NE, p. A397

HANNAH, Eddy L., R.N. Chief Nursing Officer, Harton Regional Medical Center, Tullahoma, TN, p. A593

HANNAH, Jill, Director Human Resources, James Cancer Hospital and Solove Research Institute, Columbus, OH, p. A489

HANNAN, Barbara E., R.N., Chief Executive Officer, Select Specialty Hospital–Northeast New Jersey, Rochelle Park, NJ, p. A422

HANNERS, Brandy, Chief Financial Officer, Memorial Hospital, Martinsville, VA, p. A674

HANNERS, Rodney, Senior Vice President and Chief Operating Officer, Children's Hospital Los Angeles, Los Angeles, CA, p. A71

HANNIFAN, Kevin R., President, St. Elizabeth's Medical Center, Brighton, MA, p. A308

HANNON, Edward J., Chief Executive Officer, Bates County Memorial Hospital, Butler, MO, p. A368

HANNON, Jennifer, Director Human Resources, Madison County Health Care System, Winterset, IA, p. A240

HANNON, Kay, Director Information Systems, Des Peres Hospital, Saint Louis, MO, p. A380

HANNON, Trish, FACHE, President and Chief Executive Officer, New England Baptist Hospital, Boston, MA, p. A307

HANS, Christopher, Chief Financial Officer, Riverside County Regional Medical Center, Moreno Valley, CA, p. A78

HANSCOME, Joyce
Senior Vice President and Chief Information Officer, Mary Washington Hospital, Fredericksburg, VA, p. A671
Senior Vice President and Chief Information Officer, Stafford Hospital, Stafford, VA, p. A679

HANSEL, Jimmie W., Ph.D.,
Chief Executive Officer, Garden County Health Services, Oshkosh, NE, p. A401
Interim Chief Executive Officer, Gordon Memorial Hospital, Gordon, NE, p. A396

HANSEN, Bart, Chief Financial Officer, Rehoboth McKinley Christian Health Care Services, Gallup, NM, p. A428

HANSEN, Becky, Chief Executive Officer, Southwest Healthcare Services, Bowman, ND, p. A476

HANSEN, Carla L., R.N. Chief Nurse Executive, Sanford Medical Center Fargo, Fargo, ND, p. A477

HANSEN, Carolyn, Chief Nursing Officer, Bingham Memorial Hospital, Blackfoot, ID, p. A174

HANSEN, Chris, Senior Vice President Ambulatory Services and Chief Information Officer, The University of Kansas Hospital, Kansas City, KS, p. A247

HANSEN, Gayle B., R.N
Chief Operating Officer, Mayo Clinic Health System in Fairmont, Fairmont, MN, p. A343
Chief Integration Officer, Mayo Clinic Health System in Saint James, Saint James, MN, p. A351

HANSEN, Jay, Director Information Services, Oconee Medical Center, Seneca, SC, p. A569

HANSEN, Karen, Vice President and Chief Operating Officer, Memorial Medical Center – Ashland, Ashland, WI, p. A701

HANSEN, Kristy, Chief Financial Officer, Myrtue Medical Center, Harlan, IA, p. A232

HANSEN, Kyle, Corporate Director Information Systems, Riverside Medical Center, Kankakee, IL, p. A194

HANSEN, Laurie
Associate Administrator, Emory Johns Creek Hospital, Johns Creek, GA, p. A161
Director Administrative Services, Johnson County Healthcare Center, Buffalo, WY, p. A720

HANSEN, Linda, Director Human Resources, Bakersfield Heart Hospital, Bakersfield, CA, p. A56

HANSEN, Maggie, R.N. Chief Nursing Officer, Memorial Regional Hospital,, FL, p. A130

HANSEN, Marcia A., R.N. Vice President Patient Services and Chief Nursing Officer, Ephrata Community Hospital, Ephrata, PA, p. A538

HANSEN, Michael T., FACHE, President and Chief Executive Officer, Columbus Community Hospital, Columbus, NE, p. A395

HANSEN, Misty
Chief Financial Officer, University of Arizona Medical Center – South Campus, Tucson, AZ, p. A41
Chief Financial Officer, University of Arizona Medical Center – University Campus, Tucson, AZ, p. A41

HANSEN, Paul, Administrator, Maniilaq Health Center, Kotzebue, AK, p. A29

HANSEN, Steven, Director Information Technology, Healdsburg District Hospital, Healdsburg, CA, p. A66

HANSEN, Thomas N., M.D., Chief Executive Officer, Seattle Children's Hospital, Seattle, WA, p. A688

HANSON, Brent, Chief Executive Officer and HIPAA Security and Compliance Officer, Great Bend Regional Hospital, Great Bend, KS, p. A244

HANSON, Carl, Administrator, Minidoka Memorial Hospital, Rupert, ID, p. A178

HANSON, Denise, Information Technology Specialist, St. Cloud Veterans Affairs Health Care System, Saint Cloud, MN, p. A351

HANSON, Dianne H., Director Human Resources, Moab Regional Hospital, Moab, UT, p. A660

HANSON, Emily, M.D. President, Medical Staff, St. Joseph Memorial Hospital, Murphysboro, IL, p. A197

HANSON, Gregory S., M.D., Chief Executive Officer, Clark Fork Valley Hospital, Plains, MT, p. A390

HANSON, Jane E., R.N. Chief Operating Officer, Mercy Gilbert Medical Center, Gilbert, AZ, p. A33

HANSON, Jennifer, R.N., President and Chief Administrative Officer, LeConte Medical Center, Sevierville, TN, p. A592

HANSON, Jesica, Vice President and Chief Financial Officer, Bakersfield Memorial Hospital, Bakersfield, CA, p. A57

HANSON, Mary Ann, Director Personnel, Mental Health Institute, Cherokee, IA, p. A227

HANSON, Paul A., FACHE, President, Sanford USD Medical Center, Sioux Falls, SD, p. A576

HANSON, Rhonda, Director Human Resources, Huron Regional Medical Center, Huron, SD, p. A574

HANSON, Rita, M.D
Vice President Medical Affairs, Wheaton Franciscan Healthcare – Elmbrook Memorial, Brookfield, WI, p. A703
Vice President Medical Affairs, Wheaton Franciscan Healthcare – St. Joseph's, Milwaukee, WI, p. A711
Vice President Medical Affairs, Wheaton Franciscan Healthcare – The Wisconsin Heart Hospital, Wauwatosa, WI, p. A718

HANSON, Samantha, Chief Human Resources Officer, Children's Hospitals and Clinics of Minnesota, Minneapolis, MN, p. A347

HANSON, Stephen C., Chief Executive Officer, Baptist Health, Louisville, KY, p. B19

HANTOOT, Mark, M.D. Medical Director, Gateways Hospital and Mental Health Center, Los Angeles, CA, p. A72

HANYAK, Diana C., Chief Executive Officer, HEALTHSOUTH Tustin Rehabilitation Hospital, Tustin, CA, p. A98

HAPNEY, Sherry, Chief Financial Officer, HEALTHSOUTH Rehabilitation Hospital of Fort Worth, Fort Worth, TX, p. A618

HAPPEL, Terry J., M.D. Vice President and Chief Medical Officer, Chandler Regional Medical Center, Chandler, AZ, p. A31

HAQUE, Haroon, M.D. Medical Director, Cornerstone Hospital of SouthEast Arizona, Tucson, AZ, p. A40

HARA, Karen, Personnel Management Specialist, Hawaii State Hospital, Kaneohe, HI, p. A172

HARALDSON, Richard, Chief Executive Officer, Sidney Health Center, Sidney, MT, p. A391

HARALSON, Gregory
Chief Executive Officer, Memorial Hermann Sugar Land Hospital, Sugar Land, TX, p. A651
Chief Operating Officer, Plaza Medical Center of Fort Worth, Fort Worth, TX, p. A619

HARALSON, Robert, Chief Financial Officer, Breckinridge Memorial Hospital, Hardinsburg, KY, p. A262

HARARI, Jack L., M.D. Chief Medical Officer, West Boca Medical Center, Boca Raton, FL, p. A124

HARBAUGH, Charles, Director Human Resources, Mountain Lakes Medical Center, Clayton, GA, p. A156

HARBAUGH, Ken, Vice President and Chief Financial Officer, OSF Saint Francis Medical Center, Peoria, IL, p. A200

HARBERT, Jim, Chief Technology Officer, Anthony Medical Center, Anthony, KS, p. A241

HARBERTS, Jerry, Information Technologist, Madison Hospital, Madison, MN, p. A346

HARBISON, Linda, Chief Nursing Officer, Red Bud Regional Hospital, Red Bud, IL, p. A201

HARBOR, Michael, Chief Financial Officer, Lincoln County Health System, Fayetteville, TN, p. A583

HARCHENKO, Vern, M.D. Chief of Staff, Garrison Memorial Hospital, Garrison, ND, p. A478

HARCLERODE, Tim, Chief Operating Officer, Maria Parham Medical Center, Henderson, NC, p. A466

HARCOURT, Jenifer, Chief Operating Officer, RiverWoods Behavioral Health System, Riverdale, GA, p. A165

HARCUP, Craig, M.D. Hospital Medical Director, Complex Care Hospital at Ridgelake, Sarasota, FL, p. A145

HARDACRE, Jerry, M.D. Chief of Staff, Wheaton Franciscan Healthcare – All Saints, Racine, WI, p. A714

HARDAN, Terry, Director Human Resources, Longview Regional Medical Center, Longview, TX, p. A634

HARDCASTLE, Brad, Chief Financial Officer, South Baldwin Regional Medical Center, Foley, AL, p. A20

HARDCASTLE, Kathy, Director Human Resources, Texas Health Presbyterian Hospital Denton, Denton, TX, p. A613

HARDEE, Gary R., M.D. Medical Director, Plains Memorial Hospital, Dimmitt, TX, p. A614

HARDEMAN, Diane, Director Personnel, Stephens County Hospital, Toccoa, GA, p. A168

HARDEN, Diane P.
Chief Financial Officer, Leesburg Regional Medical Center, Leesburg, FL, p. A134
Senior Vice President and Chief Financial Officer, The Villages Regional Hospital, The Villages, FL, p. A149

HARDESTY, Keith, Chief Financial Officer, Springfield Hospital Center, Sykesville, MD, p. A303

HARDIN, Cecil, CPA Chief Financial Officer, Catawba Hospital, Catawba, VA, p. A669

HARDIN, Christy
Chief Executive Officer, Southeast Health Center of Reynolds County, Ellington, MO, p. A370
Chief Executive Officer, Southeast Health Center of Ripley County, Doniphan, MO, p. A370

HARDIN, James, Human Resources Officer, Sheridan Veterans Affairs Medical Center, Sheridan, WY, p. A722

HARDIN, Leslie, Chief Executive Officer and Chief Financial Officer, Seymour Hospital, Seymour, TX, p. A648

HARDIN, Mark, M.D. Medical Director, Ed Fraser Memorial Hospital and Baker Community Health Center, MacClenny, FL, p. A135

HARDIN, Nicholas, Chief Executive Officer, HEALTHSOUTH Sugar Land Rehabilitation Hospital, Sugar Land, TX, p. A650

HARDING, Christina, Vice President Finance, Mount Desert Island Hospital, Bar Harbor, ME, p. A291

HARDING, Denise, Director Human Resources, Plumas District Hospital, Quincy, CA, p. A84

HARDING, Edward A., FACHE, President and Chief Executive Officer, Bay Area Medical Center, Marinette, WI, p. A708

HARDING, Geoff, Chief Clinical Officer, Promise Hospital of Salt Lake, Salt Lake City, UT, p. A663

HARDING, Gwen, Site Manager Information Systems, Bon Secours Memorial Regional Medical Center, Mechanicsville, VA, p. A674

HARDING, John, Interim Chief Executive Officer, Phoebe Sumter Medical Center, Americus, GA, p. A151

HARDING, Rick, Chief Executive Officer, Sundance Hospital, Arlington, TX, p. A598

HARDISON, Gerald, Director Finance, Vidant Pungo Hospital, Belhaven, NC, p. A460

HARDMAN, Danny, Senior Vice President and Chief Nursing Officer, McAlester Regional Health Center, McAlester, OK, p. A513

HARDOBY, Greg, Director Personnel, Runnells Specialized Hospital of Union County, Berkeley Heights, NJ, p. A413

HARDWICK, Garry, R.N. Chief Operating Officer, Newport Bay Hospital, Newport Beach, CA, p. A80

HARDY, Bob, Chief Operating Officer, Opelousas General Health System, Opelousas, LA, p. A287

HARDY, Eric S., Chief Financial Officer, Mesa View Regional Hospital, Mesquite, NV, p. A407

HARDY, James, D.O. Chief of Staff, Dayton Veterans Affairs Medical Center, Dayton, OH, p. A492

HARDY, Janice, Chief Human Resource Management Service, Central Alabama Veterans Health Care System, Montgomery, AL, p. A23

HARDY, John, Vice President Human Resources, Doctors Medical Center, San Pablo, CA, p. A93

HARDY, Kevin, Chief Financial Officer, HEALTHSOUTH Treasure Coast Rehabilitation Hospital, Vero Beach, FL, p. A149

HARDY, Melanie, D.O. Chief of Staff, Marias Medical Center, Shelby, MT, p. A391

HARDY, Valonia, Chief Healthy Living Officer, Tsehootsooi Medical Center, Fort Defiance, AZ, p. A32

HARGER, Anita, Director Human Resources, Mercy Gilbert Medical Center, Gilbert, AZ, p. A33

HARGETT, Stephen, Administrator Finance and Support Services, MUSC Medical Center of Medical University of South Carolina, Charleston, SC, p. A563

HARGETT, Stephen A., Senior Vice President and Chief Financial Officer, Marina Del Rey Hospital, Marina Del Rey, CA, p. A76

HARGIS, Bryan J., FACHE, Chief Executive Officer, Gilbert Hospital, Gilbert, AZ, p. A32

HARGIS, Chris, Manager Finance, Alta View Hospital, Sandy, UT, p. A664

HARGRAVE-THOMAS, Anne, Chief Executive Officer, Oakleaf Surgical Hospital, Eau Claire, WI, p. A704

HARGRODER, Ty, M.D. Chief of Staff, Acadia–St. Landry Hospital, Church Point, LA, p. A275

HARGROVE, Ben, Human Resources Director, LifeStream Behavioral Center, Leesburg, FL, p. A134

HARGROVE, Jeno, R.N. Director of Nursing, Columbus Community Hospital, Columbus, TX, p. A607

HARGROVE, Tressa B., Director Human Resources, Jackson Purchase Medical Center, Mayfield, KY, p. A267

HARIHARAN, Parma, M.D. Chief of Staff, Mercy Health – Clermont Hospital, Batavia, OH, p. A483

HARING, Don, Vice President Finance and Treasurer, SwedishAmerican Hospital, Rockford, IL, p. A202

HARKEY, Shirley S., R.N. Vice President, Patient Services, Wayne Memorial Hospital, Goldsboro, NC, p. A465

HARKINS, Shelly, M.D. Chief Medical Officer, St. Elizabeth's Hospital, Belleville, IL, p. A181

HARKLEROAD, Rod, R.N.,
Administrator, Riverview Regional Medical Center, Carthage, TN, p. A579
Chief Executive Officer, Trousdale Medical Center, Hartsville, TN, p. A583

HARKNESS, Charles, D.O. Vice President Medical Affairs, Southeast Alabama Medical Center, Dothan, AL, p. A19

HARLAN, Kevin W., President, Joint Township District Memorial Hospital, Saint Marys, OH, p. A501

HARLAN, Tom, Chief Executive Officer, Continue Care Hospital at Hendrick Medical Center, Abilene, TX, p. A595

HARLE, Connie, Senior Vice President and Chief Nursing Officer, Range Regional Health Services, Hibbing, MN, p. A345

HARLESS, Andrea, Director Information Services, Wythe County Community Hospital, Wytheville, VA, p. A680

HARLOVIC, Michael, R.N., President and Chief Executive Officer, Allegheny General Hospital, Pittsburgh, PA, p. A550

HARLOW, Donald, Director of Information Services, MountainView Regional Medical Center, Las Cruces, NM, p. A429

HARLOW, Tammy, Chief Nurse Executive, Riverview Regional Medical Center, Gadsden, AL, p. A20

HARLOWE, Michael, President and Chief Executive Officer, Indiana University Health Tipton Hospital, Tipton, IN, p. A223

HARMAN, Kenneth, Chief Executive Officer, Pioneers Medical Center, Meeker, CO, p. A110

HARMAN, Kimberly, Regional Manager Human Resources, Western State Hospital, Staunton, VA, p. A679

HARMON, Cheryl A., Chief Financial Officer, Porter Regional Hospital, Valparaiso, IN, p. A223

HARMON, Clifford K., Chief Executive Officer, Harrison Community Hospital, Cadiz, OH, p. A484

HARMON, David, D.O. Vice President Medical Services, RiverValley Behavioral Health Hospital, Owensboro, KY, p. A268

HARMON, James, Network Administrator, West Oaks Hospital, Houston, TX, p. A628

HARMON, P. Mark, Chief Operating Officer, Carlisle Regional Medical Center, Carlisle, PA, p. A535

HARMON, Richard, Chief of Staff, Opelousas General Health System, Opelousas, LA, p. A287

HARMON, Thomas, M.D. Vice President Medical Affairs, OhioHealth Riverside Methodist Hospital, Columbus, OH, p. A490

HARMOND, Josh, Chief Financial Officer, Montfort Jones Memorial Hospital, Kosciusko, MS, p. A361

HARMS, Arlene, Chief Executive Officer, Rio Grande Hospital, Del Norte, CO, p. A104

HARMS, George
Chief Financial Officer, Hays Medical Center, Hays, KS, p. A245
Chief Financial Officer, Pawnee Valley Community Hospital, Larned, KS, p. A248

HARNED, Barbara, R.N. Chief Nursing Officer, Monroe County Hospital, Monroeville, AL, p. A23

HARNESS, Lorraine L., Administrator, Pike County Memorial Hospital, Louisiana, MO, p. A376

HARNESS, Phil, Chief Executive Officer, Doctor's Hospital, Leawood, KS, p. A248

HARNEY, Geraldine, Chief Financial Officer, U. S. Public Health Service Phoenix Indian Medical Center, Phoenix, AZ, p. A37

HARNEY, John P., President and Chief Executive Officer, University of Colorado Hospital, Aurora, CO, p. A102

HARNING, Richard, Vice President Finance and Chief Financial Officer, Allegan General Hospital, Allegan, MI, p. A318

HARPE, Michael, Vice President Human Resources, Community Hospital of Anderson and Madison County, Anderson, IN, p. A206

HARPER, Arlene, R.N. Chief Nursing Officer, Progressive Hospital, Las Vegas, NV, p. A406

HARPER, Carrin, M.D., Chief Executive Officer, Haven Behavioral War Heroes Hospital, Pueblo, CO, p. A110

HARPER, Cindy, Manager Patient Data, Westfield Memorial Hospital, Westfield, NY, p. A458

HARPER, Corwin N.
Senior Vice President and Area Manager, Kaiser Permanente Manteca Medical Center, Manteca, CA, p. A76
Senior Vice President and Area Manager, Kaiser Permanente Manteca Medical Center, Manteca, CA, p. A76
Senior Vice President and Area Manager, Kaiser Permanente Vallejo Medical Center, Vallejo, CA, p. A99

HARPER, David, Director, Site Information Systems, Advocate Eureka Hospital, Eureka, IL, p. A189

HARPER, Eric, Chief Information Officer, Southeastern Health, Lumberton, NC, p. A468

HARPER, Heather L., Chief Executive Officer, Acadia General Hospital, Crowley, LA, p. A276

HARPER, James F., Vice President and Chief Human Resources Officer, Georgetown Memorial Hospital, Georgetown, SC, p. A566

HARPER, Kirk, R.N. Vice President, Nursing, Kadlec Regional Medical Center, Richland, WA, p. A687

HARPER, R. Andrew, M.D. Medical Director, University of Texas Harris County Psychiatric Center, Houston, TX, p. A627

HARPER, Wally G., Vice President Human Resources, Gaylord Hospital, Wallingford, CT, p. A117

HARPER, William F., M.D. Chief of Staff, Birmingham Veterans Affairs Medical Center, Birmingham, AL, p. A16

HARR, Donald, Controller, Ray County Memorial Hospital, Richmond, MO, p. A379

HARREL, Mark, Chief Executive Officer, Phelps Memorial Health Center, Holdrege, NE, p. A396

HARRELL, Aaron, Director, Grove Hill Memorial Hospital, Grove Hill, AL, p. A21

HARRELL, Joy, R.N. Interim Chief Nursing Officer, Mimbres Memorial Hospital, Deming, NM, p. A428

HARRELL, Mike
Chief Financial Officer, Perry Memorial Hospital, Princeton, IL, p. A200
Chief Executive Officer, Promise Hospital of Vicksburg, Vicksburg, MS, p. A366

HARRELL, Steven W., FACHE, Interim Chief Executive Officer, Bert Fish Medical Center, New Smyrna Beach, FL, p. A139

HARRELL, Thomas, M.D., Commander, U. S. Air Force Medical Center Keesler, Keesler AFB, MS, p. A360

HARRELSON, Rick, M.D. President Medical Staff, Medical Center Enterprise, Enterprise, AL, p. A19

HARRIER, Margie, Medical Center Chief Operations Officer, Kaiser Permanente Orange County Anaheim Medical Center, Anaheim, CA, p. A55

HARRIGAN, Robert, President, Summa Hospitals, Summa Akron City Hospital, Akron, OH, p. A482

HARRIGER, Richard, Director of Emergency Services, Kimball Health Services, Kimball, NE, p. A397

HARRILSON, Annette, Chief Clinical Officer, Kindred Hospital–Atlanta, Atlanta, GA, p. A152

HARRINGTON, Dan, Chief Operating Officer and Director Human Resources, Williamsburg Regional Hospital, Kingstree, SC, p. A567

HARRINGTON, Hal, Vice President Human Resources, River Region Medical Center, Vicksburg, MS, p. A366

HARRINGTON, Jason, President and Chief Executive Officer, Lakes Regional Healthcare, Spirit Lake, IA, p. A238

HARRINGTON, Jeff, Chief Financial Officer, Children's Hospital Colorado, Aurora, CO, p. A102

HARRINGTON Jr., John L., FACHE, Chief Executive Officer, John C. Lincoln Deer Valley Hospital, Phoenix, AZ, p. A36

HARRINGTON, Joseph P., President and Chief Executive Officer, Lodi Memorial Hospital, Lodi, CA, p. A69

HARRINGTON, Kathleen, Vice President Human Resources, Beth Israel Deaconess Hospital–Milton, Milton, MA, p. A312

HARRINGTON, Kristal, Director Human Resources, Twin County Regional Hospital, Galax, VA, p. A671

HARRINGTON, Michael, Chief Executive Officer, CHRISTUS Coushatta Health Care Center, Coushatta, LA, p. A275

HARRINGTON, Ron, Vice President and Chief Financial Officer, Gibson General Hospital, Princeton, IN, p. A221

HARRIS, Alicia, Director Fiscal Services, Mississippi State Hospital, Whitfield, MS, p. A366

HARRIS, Allen, M.D. Clinical Director, South Mississippi State Hospital, Purvis, MS, p. A364

HARRIS, Andrew E., President and Chief Executive Officer, Blue Mountain Health System, Lehighton, PA, p. B24

HARRIS, Andrew E.
Chief Executive Officer, Gnaden Huetten Memorial Hospital, Lehighton, PA, p. A543
Chief Executive Officer, Palmerton Hospital, Palmerton, PA, p. A547

HARRIS, Angela, Chief Executive Officer, Kindred Hospital–Fort Worth, Fort Worth, TX, p. A618

HARRIS, Betty J., Director Human Resources, Southern California Hospital at Culver City, Culver City, CA, p. A61

HARRIS, Burt, Chief Financial Officer, Canyon Ridge Hospital, Chino, CA, p. A59

HARRIS, C. Martin, M.D
Chief Information Officer, Cleveland Clinic, Cleveland, OH, p. A488
Chief Information Officer, Cleveland Clinic Children's Hospital for Rehabilitation, Cleveland, OH, p. A488
Chief Information Officer, Fairview Hospital, Cleveland, OH, p. A488
Chief Information Officer, Lakewood Hospital, Lakewood, OH, p. A496
Chief Information Officer, Lutheran Hospital, Cleveland, OH, p. A488

HARRIS, David, M.D. President Medical Affairs, Biloxi Regional Medical Center, Biloxi, MS, p. A355

HARRIS, David, Director Information Systems, De Queen Medical Center, De Queen, AR, p. A45

HARRIS, Deatrice, Supervisor Human Resources and Employment, Phoebe Sumter Medical Center, Americus, GA, p. A151

HARRIS, Denise H., R.N. Chief Nursing Officer, Baptist Health South Florida, West Kendall Baptist Hospital, Miami, FL, p. A136

HARRIS, Donna, Chief Executive Officer, HEALTHSOUTH Rehabilitation Hospital of Jonesboro, Jonesboro, AR, p. A48

HARRIS, Dory, Director Human Resource, Teton Valley Health Care, Driggs, ID, p. A176

HARRIS, Ethan, Manager Information Systems, Mid–Valley Hospital, Omak, WA, p. A686

HARRIS, Howard, Vice President Human Resources, Regional Medical Center, Orangeburg, SC, p. A569

HARRIS, Jan, R.N. Director of Nursing, Stonewall Memorial Hospital, Aspermont, TX, p. A598

HARRIS, Janet Y., R.N. Chief Nursing Officer, University Hospital, Jackson, MS, p. A360

HARRIS, Janice M., Director Human Resources, University Medical Center of El Paso, El Paso, TX, p. A616

HARRIS, Jen, Director Health Information Management, Chase County Community Hospital, Imperial, NE, p. A397

HARRIS, Jerald, Chief Information Officer, Cornerstone Hospital of Houston at Clearlake, Webster, TX, p. A656

HARRIS, Jim, Vice President Human Resources, Fairmont General Hospital, Fairmont, WV, p. A695

HARRIS, Joanne, Director Human Resources, Mount Desert Island Hospital, Bar Harbor, ME, p. A291

HARRIS, John, Chief Executive Officer, Memorial Medical Center, Las Cruces, NM, p. A429

HARRIS, John B., Vice President Finance and Chief Financial Officer, Community Hospital of Anderson and Madison County, Anderson, IN, p. A206

HARRIS, Julie, Chief Financial Officer, Winnie Community Hospital, Winnie, TX, p. A658

HARRIS, Kathy, Vice President, Mercy Hospital and Trauma Center, Janesville, WI, p. A707

HARRIS, Katrina, D.O. President Medical Staff, Springfield Hospital, Springfield, VT, p. A666

HARRIS, Kelli, Chief Financial Officer, Crouse Hospital, Syracuse, NY, p. A455

HARRIS, Kevin, Director Information Systems, Titus Regional Medical Center, Mount Pleasant, TX, p. A638

HARRIS, Lee, Assistant Administrator Support Services, Memorial Hospital and Manor, Bainbridge, GA, p. A154

HARRIS, Lisa, M.D. Senior Vice President Medical Affairs, Our Lady of Lourdes Memorial Hospital, Inc., Binghamton, NY, p. A433

HARRIS, Lisa E., M.D., Chief Executive Officer and Medical Director, Eskenazi Health, Indianapolis, IN, p. A214

HARRIS, Mark D., Deputy Commander Clinical Services, Fort Belvoir Community Hospital, Fort Belvoir, VA, p. A671

HARRIS, Merilyn, Administrator, Kau Hospital, Pahala, HI, p. A172

HARRIS, Michael, M.D. Chief Medical Officer, Englewood Hospital and Medical Center, Englewood, NJ, p. A416

HARRIS, Mike, Chief Operating Officer, AMG Specialty Hospital–Tulsa, Tulsa, OK, p. A520

HARRIS, Miriam, Director Finance, Oklahoma Forensic Center, Vinita, OK, p. A521

HARRIS, Paul, Manager Information Systems, Habersham Medical Center, Demorest, GA, p. A158

HARRIS, R. Brian, M.D. Chief of Staff, Reeves Memorial Medical Center, Bernice, LA, p. A274

HARRIS, Robert M., M.D. President Medical and Dental Staff, Bergen Regional Medical Center, Paramus, NJ, p. A420

HARRIS, Sandra L., R.N. Senior Vice President and Chief Operating Officer, Texas Health Arlington Memorial Hospital, Arlington, TX, p. A598

HARRIS, Shelley, MSN Chief Nursing Officer, St. Elizabeth's Hospital, Belleville, IL, p. A181

HARRIS, Shelly, Chief Executive Officer, Public Health Service Indian Hospital – Quentin N. Burdick Memorial Health Facility, Belcourt, ND, p. A476

HARRIS, Stuart, M.D. Chief of Staff, Trigg County Hospital, Cadiz, KY, p. A259

HARRIS, Sue, Vice President and Chief Nursing Officer, Methodist Medical Center of Oak Ridge, Oak Ridge, TN, p. A591

HARRIS, Sylvia, Fiscal Director, Moccasin Bend Mental Health Institute, Chattanooga, TN, p. A580

HARRIS, Terri, R.N. Chief Nursing Officer, East Cooper Medical Center, Mount Pleasant, SC, p. A568

HARRIS, Timothy, M.D. Chief Quality Officer, Texas Health Presbyterian Hospital Denton, Denton, TX, p. A613

HARRIS, Vena, Director Human Resources, Minneola District Hospital, Minneola, KS, p. A250

HARRIS, William, Chief Information Resources Management, Veterans Affairs Central California Health Care System, Fresno, CA, p. A64

HARRIS, William R., Chief Information Officer, Lawton Indian Hospital, Lawton, OK, p. A512

HARRIS–BREKEL, Donna
 Director Human Resources, Hawthorn Children Psychiatric Hospital, Saint Louis, MO, p. A380
 Director Human Resources, Metropolitan St. Louis Psychiatric Center, Saint Louis, MO, p. A381
 Director Human Resources, St. Louis Psychiatric Rehabilitation Center, Saint Louis, MO, p. A382

HARRISON, Alicia, Data Management Officer, Excelsior Springs Hospital, Excelsior Springs, MO, p. A370

HARRISON, Allen, Chief Executive Officer, St. David's North Austin Medical Center, Austin, TX, p. A600

HARRISON, Ann, R.N. Director of Nursing, Wills Memorial Hospital, Washington, GA, p. A169

HARRISON, Charles, Chief Executive Officer, San Bernardino Mountains Community Hospital District, Lake Arrowhead, CA, p. A69

HARRISON, Chris, Manager Information Systems, Campbell County Memorial Hospital, Gillette, WY, p. A721

HARRISON, Dean M., President and Chief Executive Officer, Northwestern Memorial Healthcare, Chicago, IL, p. B101

HARRISON, Dean M., President and Chief Executive Officer, Northwestern Memorial Hospital, Chicago, IL, p. A185

HARRISON, Debra, MS Chief Nursing Officer, Mayo Clinic Jacksonville, Jacksonville, FL, p. A131

HARRISON, Denise, Associate Director, Veterans Affairs – Western Iowa Healthcare System, Omaha, NE, p. A400

HARRISON, Dyan, Manager Health Information, Ochiltree General Hospital, Perryton, TX, p. A642

HARRISON, Jo L., Vice President of Patient Care Services, Southwest Medical Center, Liberal, KS, p. A249

HARRISON, Marva, R.N. Vice President and Chief Nursing Officer, Integris Southwest Medical Center, Oklahoma City, OK, p. A515

HARRISON, Pamela, R.N. Chief Nursing Officer, East Georgia Regional Medical Center, Statesboro, GA, p. A167

HARRISON, Randy, Chief Financial Officer, Raleigh General Hospital, Beckley, WV, p. A693

HARRON, Rick, Chief Financial Officer, Dominican Hospital, Santa Cruz, CA, p. A94

HARROP, Phil, Executive Director Operations, Saint Alphonsus Medical Center – Nampa, Nampa, ID, p. A177

HARROW, Andrea, Chief Nursing Officer, Woman's Hospital of Texas, Houston, TX, p. A628

HARRY, Robert, M.D., Chief Executive Officer, U. S. Public Health Service Indian Hospital, San Carlos, AZ, p. A38

HARRYMAN, John D., Chief Administrative Officer, Norton Brownsboro Hospital, Louisville, KY, p. A266

HARSHAWAT, Paras, M.D. Medical Director, Harsha Behavioral Center, Terre Haute, IN, p. A223

HARSHBARGER, Catherine S., R.N., Chief Executive Officer, Banner Lassen Medical Center, Susanville, CA, p. A96

HARSY, Brice, Chief Financial Officer, Marshall Browning Hospital, Du Quoin, IL, p. A188

HART, Amy, Chief Operating Officer, Cuyuna Regional Medical Center, Crosby, MN, p. A342

HART, Bruce, Chief Financial Officer, Southwest Regional Rehabilitation Center, Battle Creek, MI, p. A319

HART, Charles E., MS, President and Chief Executive Officer, Regional Health, Rapid City, SD, p. B113

HART, Chet, Vice President Operations, Sentara CarePlex Hospital, Hampton, VA, p. A672

HART, Deborah, Chief Financial Officer, North Suburban Medical Center, Thornton, CO, p. A111

HART, Denise, Director Human Resources, Sullivan County Community Hospital, Sullivan, IN, p. A222

HART, Donna, Chief Information Officer, Provident Hospital of Cook County, Chicago, IL, p. A186

HART, Gary, M.D., Co–Interim CEO, Claxton–Hepburn Medical Center, Ogdensburg, NY, p. A450

HART, John, Chief Executive Officer, Fredonia Regional Hospital, Fredonia, KS, p. A244

HART, Joline, Vice President Human Resources, Franklin Memorial Hospital, Farmington, ME, p. A293

HART, Ken, Vice President Operations, Saint Alphonsus Medical Center – Ontario, Ontario, OR, p. A527

HART, Kevin, Senior Director Support Services and Facilities, Alice Hyde Medical Center, Malone, NY, p. A440

HART, Linda, Vice President Finance, Grady Memorial Hospital, Chickasha, OK, p. A509

HART, Lisa, Chief Executive Officer, Elkview General Hospital, Hobart, OK, p. A512

HART, Michael, M.D. Medical Director, Stamford Memorial Hospital, Stamford, TX, p. A650

HART, Monique, Chief Financial Officer, Baptist Memorial Hospital–Tipton, Covington, TN, p. A582

HART, Pat, Director Human Resources, Three Rivers Medical Center, Louisa, KY, p. A265

HART, Richard, Chief Financial Officer, Stanislaus Surgical Hospital, Modesto, CA, p. A78

HART, Richard H., M.D., President and Chief Executive Officer, Loma Linda University Adventist Health Sciences Center, Loma Linda, CA, p. B87

HART, Scott, Controller, HEALTHSOUTH Lakeview Rehabilitation Hospital, Elizabethtown, KY, p. A260

HART, Steve, Controller, Kindred Hospital North Florida, Green Cove Springs, FL, p. A130

HART–FLYNN, Wilma, Ph.D. Vice President Patient Care Services and Chief Nursing Officer, Illinois Valley Community Hospital, Peru, IL, p. A200

HARTBERG, David, Administrator, Gundersen Boscobel Area Hospital and Clinics, Boscobel, WI, p. A702

HARTE, Brian J., M.D., President, Hillcrest Hospital, Cleveland, OH, p. A488

HARTER, Dan, Manager Information Systems, PMH Medical Center, Prosser, WA, p. A687

HARTGRAVES, Steve L., President and Chief Executive Officer, Jackson County Memorial Hospital, Altus, OK, p. A507

HARTKE, Michael, Executive Vice President, Chief Operating Officer, Northwest Community Hospital, Arlington Heights, IL, p. A180

HARTLE, Christopher L., President, Seton Medical Center Hays, Kyle, TX, p. A632

HARTLEY, Diane L., R.N. Director of Patient Care Services, Oakwood Hospital–Wayne, Wayne, MI, p. A337

HARTLEY, H. William, FACHE, Chief Executive Officer, Massac Memorial Hospital, Metropolis, IL, p. A196

HARTLEY, Melinda D., R.N. Vice President Patient Care Services, Perry Hospital, Perry, GA, p. A164

HARTLEY, Norma, Director Human Resources, Power County Hospital District, American Falls, ID, p. A174

HARTLEY, Shauna, Hospital Administrator, Turquoise Lodge Hospital, Albuquerque, NM, p. A427

HARTLEY, Wannah, Controller, Winkler County Memorial Hospital, Kermit, TX, p. A631

HARTMAN, Daphne, Director Information Systems, College Station Medical Center, College Station, TX, p. A607

HARTMAN, David, M.D. Chief of Staff, Franklin Hospital District, Benton, IL, p. A181

HARTMAN, Dennis, Chief Financial Officer, Excelsior Springs Hospital, Excelsior Springs, MO, p. A370

HARTMAN, Don, Director Human Resources, Sutter Davis Hospital, Davis, CA, p. A61

HARTMAN, Kathleen, Chief Nursing Officer, MetroSouth Medical Center, Blue Island, IL, p. A182

HARTMAN, Susan, Chief Executive Officer, HEALTHSOUTH Nittany Valley Rehabilitation Hospital, Pleasant Gap, PA, p. A552

HARTMANN, Doreen, Chief Financial Officer, St. Joseph's Behavioral Health Center, Stockton, CA, p. A96

HARTMANN, Margot, Ph.D., President and Chief Executive Officer, Nantucket Cottage Hospital, Nantucket, MA, p. A312

HARTMANN, Peter M., M.D. Vice President Medical Affairs, York Hospital, York, PA, p. A559

HARTMANN, Rob, Assistant Director Human Resources Management, University Health Conway, Monroe, LA, p. A284

HARTNETT, Tammy, Employee Relations Manager, UnityPoint Health – St. Luke's, Sioux City, IA, p. A238

HARTSELL, Scott, Chief Operating Officer, Bayfront Health Brooksville, Brooksville, FL, p. A125

HARTTER, Lynn, Director Human Resources, Nemaha Valley Community Hospital, Seneca, KS, p. A254

HARTUNG, Andy, Director Information Systems, Self Regional Healthcare, Greenwood, SC, p. A567

HARTWICK, Bryan
 Vice President Human Resources, Alton Memorial Hospital, Alton, IL, p. A180
 Vice President Human Resources, Christian Hospital, Saint Louis, MO, p. A380

HARVEY, Alice, Director of Nursing, Heatherhill Care Communities, Chardon, OH, p. A485

HARVEY, Anne, MSN Chief Nursing Officer, El Paso Specialty Hospital, El Paso, TX, p. A615

HARVEY, John, M.D., President and Chief Executive Officer, Oklahoma Heart Hospital, Oklahoma City, OK, p. A516

HARVEY, John, M.D. President and Chief Executive Officer, Oklahoma Heart Hospital, Oklahoma City, OK, p. A516

HARVEY, John, M.D., President and Chief Executive Officer, Oklahoma Heart Hospital South Campus, Oklahoma City, OK, p. A516

HARVEY, Kathy, D.O. Chief Medical Officer, Logan Regional Medical Center, Logan, WV, p. A696

HARVEY, Kevin, Chief Financial Officer, McKenzie Regional Hospital, McKenzie, TN, p. A588

HARVEY, Laurie, Controller, El Campo Memorial Hospital, El Campo, TX, p. A615

HARVEY, Linda, Chief Financial Officer, West Feliciana Parish Hospital, Saint Francisville, LA, p. A288

HARVEY, Michael, President and Chief Executive Officer, Community Memorial Hospital, Syracuse, NE, p. A402

HARVILL, Brian
 Vice President Financial Services, Vidant Bertie Hospital, Windsor, NC, p. A475
 Vice President Financial Services, Vidant Chowan Hospital, Edenton, NC, p. A464

HARYASZ, Sandy, R.N., Chief Executive Officer, Page Hospital, Page, AZ, p. A35

HASBROUCK, Matthew Steven, Chief Operating Officer, Fairview Park Hospital, Dublin, GA, p. A159

HASELTON, David, Chief Medical Officer, Riverton Hospital, Riverton, UT, p. A662

HASHMI, Mubashir, Chief Information Officer, Pacifica Hospital of the Valley,, CA, p. A74

HASHMI, Suleman, President and Chief Executive Officer, Texas General Hospital, Grand Prairie, TX, p. A621

HASKELL, Jeffrey, M.D. Chief Medical Staff, Lost Rivers Medical Center, Arco, ID, p. A174

HASKINS, Don, Administrative Director Human Resources, Southwest Mississippi Regional Medical Center, McComb, MS, p. A362

HASLER, Marge, R.N. Vice President Patient Care Services and Chief Nursing Officer, Botsford Hospital, Farmington Hills, MI, p. A323

HASNI, Kamran, M.D. Chief of Medical Staff, Knox County Hospital, Barbourville, KY, p. A258

HASS, Roxanne, Director of Nursing, Madison St. Joseph Health Center, Madisonville, TX, p. A636

HASSAN, Tariq, M.D. Associate Director of Patient Care, Captain James A. Lovell Federal Health Care Center, North Chicago, IL, p. A198

HASSANI, Dahlia, Vice President of Medical Affairs, Baylor All Saints Medical Center at Fort Worth, Fort Worth, TX, p. A618

HASSELBARTH, William C., Chief Financial Officer, Albany Medical Center, Albany, NY, p. A432

HASSELBRACK, Jeni, Director Human Resources, Gordon Hospital, Calhoun, GA, p. A155

HASSLER, Robert, M.D. Director Medical Affairs, Novant Health Brunswick Medical Center, Bolivia, NC, p. A460

HAST, Anne S., R.N., Chief Executive Officer, Advanced Surgical Hospital, Washington, PA, p. A557

HASTIN, Kathy, Administrative Assistant Human Resources, River Valley Medical Center, Dardanelle, AR, p. A44

HASTINGS, Clare, R.N. Chief Nurse Officer, National Institutes of Health Clinical Center, Bethesda, MD, p. A299

HASTINGS, David, Director Information Technology, Baton Rouge General Medical Center, Baton Rouge, LA, p. A273

HASTINGS, Kirk, Chief Information Technology, Veterans Affairs Butler Healthcare, Butler, PA, p. A534

HASTINGS, Sarah M., Vice President Human Resources, Ridgeview Medical Center, Waconia, MN, p. A353

HASTINGS–SMITH, Julie, Chief Financial Officer, Maryvale Hospital Medical Center, Phoenix, AZ, p. A36

HATA, Marilynn, Vice President Finance and Operations, North Hawaii Community Hospital, Kamuela, HI, p. A171

HATALA, Alexander J., FACHE, President and Chief Executive Officer, Our Lady of Lourdes Medical Center, Camden, NJ, p. A414

HATCH, Tammy, Manager, Sebasticook Valley Health, Pittsfield, ME, p. A294

HATCHEL, Kimberly Kay, Chief Nursing Officer, Medical Center of McKinney, McKinney, TX, p. A637

HATCHER, Amy, Chief Financial Officer, Children's Hospital and Medical Center, Omaha, NE, p. A400

HATCHER, Julie, Vice President Human Resources, O'Connor Hospital, San Jose, CA, p. A92

HATFIELD, Chad, Chief Executive Officer, Barrow Regional Medical Center, Winder, GA, p. A169

HATFIELD, Jonathan, Supervisor Information Technology, Klickitat Valley Health, Goldendale, WA, p. A684

HATFIELD, Timothy A., Community Chief Executive Officer, Williamson ARH Hospital, South Williamson, KY, p. A270

HATHAWAY, William, M.D. Chief Medical Officer, Mission Hospital, Asheville, NC, p. A460

HATHAWAY, Woody, Chief Financial Officer, Trinity Hospital Twin City, Dennison, OH, p. A493

HATHCOCK, Claudette
Human Resources Director, Holmes County Hospital and Clinics, Lexington, MS, p. A361
Administrative Director Human Resources, University of Mississippi Medical Center Grenada, Grenada, MS, p. A358

HATIRAS, Spiros, FACHE, President and Chief Executive Officer, Holyoke Medical Center, Holyoke, MA, p. A311

HATLESTAD, Jill, Vice President Human Resources and Organizational Support, Glencoe Regional Health Services, Glencoe, MN, p. A344

HATSFELT, Annette Wyble, Chief Nursing Officer, Oakdale Community Hospital, Oakdale, LA, p. A286

HATTEM, Marita, Interim President and Chief Operating Officer, Aspirus Wausau Hospital, Wausau, WI, p. A717

HATTERER–HOAG, Dawn, Director Human Resources, Psychiatric Institute of Washington, Washington, DC, p. A122

HATTON, Julia
Chief Financial Officer, Nexus Specialty Hospital, Shenandoah, TX, p. A649
Chief Financial Officer, Nexus Specialty Hospital The Woodlands, Spring, TX, p. A650

HATTON, Tad, Chief Operating Officer, St. David's Round Rock Medical Center, Round Rock, TX, p. A645

HAUBL, Eileen, Senior Vice President and Chief Financial Officer, Mission Hospital, Mission Viejo, CA, p. A77

HAUG, Darin, D.O. Chief Medical Officer, Fitzgibbon Hospital, Marshall, MO, p. A376

HAUGE, Meri, R.N. Associate Director of Patient Care Services and Nurse Executive, St. Cloud Veterans Affairs Health Care System, Saint Cloud, MN, p. A351

HAUGEN, O. G., Director Resources, Naval Medical Center San Diego, San Diego, CA, p. A89

HAUGH, William, Administrator, Georgetown Community Hospital, Georgetown, KY, p. A262

HAUN, Richard, Chief Financial Officer, Wuesthoff Medical Center – Rockledge, Rockledge, FL, p. A144

HAUPERT, John M., FACHE, Chief Executive Officer, Grady Memorial Hospital, Atlanta, GA, p. A152

HAUSAUER, Patricia K., Director Finance, Baptist Medical Center Nassau, Fernandina Beach, FL, p. A128

HAUSE, Eileen, Chief Executive Officer, Kensington Hospital, Philadelphia, PA, p. A549

HAUSER, Mark J., M.D. Chief Medical Officer, Baptist Health South Florida, Baptist Hospital of Miami, Miami, FL, p. A136

HAUSER, Megan, Director Human Resources, Shriners Hospitals for Children–Philadelphia, Philadelphia, PA, p. A550

HAUSHALTER, Richard L., Senior Vice President Operations and Chief Operating Officer, Sentara RMH Medical Center, Harrisonburg, VA, p. A672

HAUSMANN, Jena, President and Chief Operating Officer, Children's Hospital Colorado, Aurora, CO, p. A102

HAUSMANN, Sherry, Senior Administrator, Via Christi Hospital on St. Francis, Wichita, KS, p. A257

HAUSWIRTH, Michael
Chief Operating Officer, Aspirus Keweenaw Hospital, Laurium, MI, o. A329
Chief Operating Officer, Aspirus Keweenaw Hospital, Laurium, MI, p. A329
Chief Operating Officer, Aspirus Ontonagon Hospital, Ontonagon, MI, p. A331
Chief Operating Officer, Aspirus Ontonagon Hospital, Ontonagon, MI, p. A331

HAUSWIRTH, Renay, Chief Financial Officer, Palo Alto County Health System, Emmetsburg, IA, p. A230

HAVEN, Adrian C., Site Manager, Gallup Indian Medical Center, Gallup, NM, p. A428

HAVERSTOCK, Loren, Manager Human Resources, Harrison County Hospital, Corydon, IN, p. A209

HAVRILLA, David A., Chief Financial Officer, MedStar Montgomery Medical Center, Olney, MD, p. A302

HAWIG, Scott
Chief Financial Officer and Senior Vice President Finance and Treasurer, Froedtert Memorial Lutheran Hospital, Milwaukee, WI, p. A710
Chief Financial Officer, St. Joseph's Hospital, West Bend, WI, p. A718

HAWK, Kevin, Chief Executive Officer, Hillcrest Hospital Cushing, Cushing, OK, p. A509

HAWKES, Reed, Chief Information Officer, Wills Memorial Hospital, Washington, GA, p. A169

HAWKEY, Tammy, Manager Information Technology Client Services, Ministry Saint Clare's Hospital, Weston, WI, p. A718

HAWKINS, Bill, Director, Hiram W. Davis Medical Center, Petersburg, VA, p. A676

HAWKINS, Brian A., Director, Washington DC Veterans Affairs Medical Center, Washington, DC, p. A122

HAWKINS, Bryan, Controller, FirstHealth Montgomery Memorial Hospital, Troy, NC, p. A474

HAWKINS, Carl, M.D. Chief of Staff, Mackinac Straits Health System, Saint Ignace, MI, p. A334

HAWKINS, Ellis, President, SSM St. Clare Health Center, Fenton, MO, p. A371

HAWKINS, Hillary, M.D. Medical Director, Sheltering Arms Rehabilitation Hospital, Mechanicsville, VA, p. A674

HAWKINS, Janine, R.N. Vice President Patient Care Services and Chief Nursing Officer, Dameron Hospital, Stockton, CA, p. A96

HAWKINS, Jason F., President and Chief Executive Officer, Fulton County Medical Center, Mc Connellsburg, PA, p. A544

HAWKINS, Jr., Roy L.
Deputy Director, James A. Haley Veterans' Hospital, Tampa, FL, p. A147
Acting Associate Director, Veterans Affairs Salt Lake City Health Care System, Salt Lake City, UT, p. A664

HAWKINS, Sheri, Chief Nursing Officer, Shawnee Mission Medical Center, Shawnee Mission, KS, p. A254

HAWKINS, Thomas J., Administrator, Central Prison Hospital, Raleigh, NC, p. A470

HAWKINSON, Curtis R., Chief Executive Officer, Community Memorial Healthcare, Marysville, KS, p. A249

HAWLEY, Candice, Chief Nursing Executive, Washington County Hospital, Nashville, IL, p. A197

HAWLEY, Claudia, Director Human Resources, Mason General Hospital, Shelton, WA, p. A689

HAWLEY, James, M.D. Chief of Staff, Platte County Memorial Hospital, Wheatland, WY, p. A723

HAWLEY, Jason, Manager Information Services, Yuma District Hospital, Yuma, CO, p. A112

HAWTHORNE, Kimberly, Administrator, Mayo Clinic Health System – Franciscan Healthcare in Sparta, Sparta, WI, p. A715

HAWTOF, Jeffrey, M.D. Vice President Medical Operations and Informatics, Beebe Healthcare, Lewes, DE, p. A119

HAXTON, Rita K., R.N. Vice President Patient Care Nursing, Rapid City Regional Hospital, Rapid City, SD, p. A576

HAY, Morgan, Chief Financial Officer, Gerald Champion Regional Medical Center, Alamogordo, NM, p. A426

HAYDEN, Crystal, MSN Chief Nursing Officer, Onslow Memorial Hospital, Jacksonville, NC, p. A467

HAYDEN, James, M.D. Chief Medical Officer, J. C. Blair Memorial Hospital, Huntingdon, PA, p. A541

HAYDEN, Jamie, Chief Financial Officer, Eastland Memorial Hospital, Eastland, TX, p. A614

HAYDEN, John
Senior Vice President and Human Resources Officer, Bronson Battle Creek, Battle Creek, MI, p. A319
Senior Vice President and Chief Human Resources Officer, Bronson LakeView Hospital, Paw Paw, MI, p. A332
Vice President and Chief Human Resources Officer, Bronson Methodist Hospital, Kalamazoo, MI, p. A328

HAYDEN, Karen, Director Health Information Services, Performance Improvement and Risk Management, Valle Vista Hospital, Greenwood, IN, p. A212

HAYDEN, Michelle, Chief Financial Officer, Baptist Health Paducah, Paducah, KY, p. A269

HAYDEN, Sheryl, Chief Financial Officer, Sierra Surgery Hospital, Carson City, NV, p. A404

HAYDEN–PUGH, Beverly P., R.N. Vice President and Chief Nursing Officer, Children's Hospital Central California, Madera, CA, p. A76

HAYEK, Anthony, D.O. Medical Director, Edwin Shaw Rehab, Cuyahoga Falls, OH, p. A491

HAYES, Brian T., Commander, David Grant USAF Medical Center, Travis AFB, CA, p. A97

HAYES, Cheryl
Vice President Patient Care Services, Kenmore Mercy Hospital, Kenmore, NY, p. A439
Chief Executive Officer, Select Specialty Hospital–Gainesville, Gainesville, FL, p. A129

HAYES, David R., Chief Financial Officer, Westlake Regional Hospital, Columbia, KY, p. A259

HAYES, Deborah Marie, R.N. Chief Hospital Officer and Chief Nursing Officer, Christ Hospital, Cincinnati, OH, p. A486

HAYES, Di, Chief Executive Officer, Hallmark Youthcare – Richmond, Richmond, VA, p. A677

HAYES, Donna, Controller, Decatur County General Hospital, Parsons, TN, p. A592

HAYES, Elaine, Controller, Sts. Mary & Elizabeth Hospital, Louisville, KY, p. A266

HAYES, Farrell, Interim Chief Executive Officer, Hutcheson Medical Center, Fort Oglethorpe, GA, p. A160

HAYES, George E., FACHE, President and Chief Executive Officer, Memorial Hospital, Colorado Springs, CO, p. A103

HAYES, James L., Director Human Resources, Western State Hospital, Hopkinsville, KY, p. A263

HAYES, James M., Chief Executive Officer, UnityPoint Health – Trinity Muscatine, Muscatine, IA, p. A235

HAYES, Judy M., R.N. Vice President Nursing and Chief Nursing Officer, Brigham and Women's Faulkner Hospital, Boston, MA, p. A306

HAYES, Kathe, Executive Director, Western New York Children's Psychiatric Center, West Seneca, NY, p. A458

HAYES, Kelly, Chief Financial Officer, North Texas Medical Center, Gainesville, TX, p. A620

HAYES, Kevin, M.D. Chief of Staff, Pioneer Community Hospital of Aberdeen, Aberdeen, MS, p. A355

HAYES, Kim, Director Human Resources, Bibb Medical Center, Centreville, AL, p. A18

HAYES, Pamela, Director Finance, Providence Seaside Hospital, Seaside, OR, p. A530

HAYES, Paul, Executive Vice President and Chief Operating Officer, UW Medicine/Valley Medical Center, Renton, WA, p. A687

HAYES, Ruth, Director Human Resources, Patient's Choice Medical Center of Humphreys County, Belzoni, MS, p. A355

HAYES, Sharon
Chief Executive Officer, Edward White Hospital, Saint Petersburg, FL, p. A144
Interim Chief Executive Officer, Palms of Pasadena Hospital, Saint Petersburg, FL, p. A144

HAYES, Stacy, R.N. Chief Nursing Officer, Arizona Spine and Joint Hospital, Mesa, AZ, p. A34

HAYES, Susan, Director Human Resources, Southeastern Health, Lumberton, NC, p. A468

HAYES, Tammy, Chief Nursing Officer and Long Term Care Administrator, Northfield Hospital, Northfield, MN, p. A348

HAYES, Thomas P., Chief Executive Officer, Eastern Plumas Health Care, Portola, CA, p. A84

HAYES, Warren, Chief of Staff, Montgomery County Memorial Hospital, Red Oak, IA, p. A236

HAYES, William M., Chief Executive Officer, Northside Hospital–Cherokee, Canton, GA, p. A155

HAYGOOD, Rachel, Director Information Technology, Tyler County Hospital, Woodville, TX, p. A658

HAYHURST, Leslie, Director Information Systems, Southwest Regional Medical Center, Waynesburg, PA, p. A557

HAYMON, Beverly, Chief Financial Officer, Princeton Baptist Medical Center, Birmingham, AL, p. A16

HAYNES, Apryl, R.N., Vice President, Chief Operating Officer, Chief Nursing Officer and Administrator, Seton Edgar B. Davis Hospital, Luling, TX, p. A636

HAYNES, Christopher, Chief Executive Officer, Kindred Hospital–Greensboro, Greensboro, NC, p. A465

HAYNES, Deatosha D., Interim Associates Director for Patient, Veterans Affairs Gulf Coast Veterans Health Care System, Biloxi, MS, p. A356

HAYNES, Jamil, Regional Director Human Resources, Integris Baptist Regional Health Center, Miami, OK, p. A513

HAYNES, Jerry, President and Chief Executive Officer, Appalachian Regional Healthcare, Inc., Lexington, KY, p. B11

HAYNES, Jill, Financial Coach, Bath Veterans Affairs Medical Center, Bath, NY, p. A433

HAYNES, Jr., John H., M.D. Chief of Medical Staff, North Caddo Medical Center, Vivian, LA, p. A290

HAYNES, Laurie, Chief Financial Officer, Gulf Coast Regional Medical Center, Panama City, FL, p. A141

HAYNES, Mark, M.D. Chief of Staff, Homer Memorial Hospital, Homer, LA, p. A278

HAYNES, Robert, FACHE, Chief Executive Officer, Guadalupe Regional Medical Center, Seguin, TX, p. A648

HAYNES, William, Director Information Technology, Central Louisiana State Hospital, Pineville, LA, p. A287

HAYS, Cheryl M., FACHE, Administrator, Marshall Medical Center North, Guntersville, AL, p. A21

HAYS, Chuck, President, MaineGeneral Medical Center, Augusta, ME, p. A291

HAYS, Larry, Director Information Technology, Southern Virginia Mental Health Institute, Danville, VA, p. A670

HAYS, Richard, M.D. Chief of Staff, Wellington Regional Medical Center, West Palm Beach, FL, p. A150

HAYS, Richard O., Chief Fiscal Service, Veterans Affairs Southern Nevada Healthcare System, North Las Vegas, NV, p. A407

HAYS, Timothy A., Vice President Human Resources, Johnston UNC Health Care, Smithfield, NC, p. A473

HAYTAIAN, Mike, Head Director Information Resources Management, Naval Hospital Jacksonville, Jacksonville, FL, p. A132

HAYTON, Gregg, Vice President Finance and Chief Financial Officer, Our Lady of Lourdes Memorial Hospital, Inc., Binghamton, NY, p. A433

HAYWARD, Ernest, M.D. Chief of Staff, Saddleback Memorial Medical Center, Laguna Hills, CA, p. A68

HAYWOOD, Nancy, Chief Financial Officer, Genesys Regional Medical Center, Grand Blanc, MI, p. A324

HAYWOOD, Stephanie, Director Human Resources, Southern Virginia Mental Health Institute, Danville, VA, p. A670

HAZELBAKER, Matthew, M.D. President Medical Staff, Memorial Hospital of Union County, Marysville, OH, p. A497

HAZEN, Carol, Vice President Finance, Emory–Adventist Hospital, Smyrna, GA, p. A166

HEAD, David, M.D. Chief Medical Staff, Norton Sound Regional Hospital, Nome, AK, p. A29

HEADLAND, Mark
  Chief Information Officer, Children's Hospital at Mission, Mission Viejo, CA, p. A77
  Chief Information Officer, Children's Hospital of Orange County, Orange, CA, p. A81

HEALD, Robin R., Director Human Resources, Brattleboro Memorial Hospital, Brattleboro, VT, p. A665

HEALEA, Pamela S., Director Human Resources, PMH Medical Center, Prosser, WA, p. A687

HEALY, John, Manager Information Technology, Friends Hospital, Philadelphia, PA, p. A548

HEALY, Peggi, Executive Director, Mid–Hudson Forensic Psychiatric Center, New Hampton, NY, p. A442

HEALY, Peter J., Chief Executive Officer, Beth Israel Deaconess Hospital–Milton, Milton, MA, p. A312

HEALY, Stan, Administrator, North Greenville Hospital, Travelers Rest, SC, p. A570

HEALY, Victoria, Chief Executive Officer, HEALTHSOUTH Rehabilitation Hospital of Western Massachusetts, Ludlow, MA, p. A311

HEARD, Heather, Director Human Resources, Holdenville General Hospital, Holdenville, OK, p. A512

HEARD, John E., Chief Executive Officer, McGehee–Desha County Hospital, McGehee, AR, p. A50

HEARD, M. Denise, Director Business Services, North Mississippi Medical Center–Pontotoc, Pontotoc, MS, p. A364

HEARN, Gregory K., Chief Executive Officer, Ty Cobb Healthcare System, Inc., Royston, GA, p. B136

HEARN, Gregory K., Chief Executive Officer, Ty Cobb Regional Medical Center, Lavonia, GA, p. A162

HEARNE, Diane, Director Human Resources, Arizona Spine and Joint Hospital, Mesa, AZ, p. A34

HEARNSBERGER, John, M.D. Chief of Staff, Howard Memorial Hospital, Nashville, AR, p. A50

HEARTSILL, Keith
  Vice President of Finance, Anderson Regional Medical Center, Meridian, MS, p. A362
  Vice President Finance, Anderson Regional Medical Center–South Campus, Meridian, MS, p. A362

HEATER, Floyd, President, Shenandoah Memorial Hospital, Woodstock, VA, p. A680

HEATH, Susan, R.N. Senior Vice President and Chief Nursing Officer, Seattle Children's Hospital, Seattle, WA, p. A688

HEATH, Susan, Chief Executive Officer, Vanderbilt Stallworth Rehabilitation Hospital, Nashville, TN, p. A591

HEATHERLY, John
  Assistant Administrator Support Services, Hunt Regional Community Hospital, Commerce, TX, p. A607
  Assistant Administrator Support Services, Hunt Regional Medical Center, Greenville, TX, p. A622

HEATHERLY, Steve
  Chief Executive Officer, Harris Regional Hospital, Sylva, NC, p. A473
  Chief Executive Officer, Swain County Hospital, Bryson City, NC, p. A460

HEATHERLY–LLOYD, Sara, Chief Operating Officer, Tennova Healthcare–LaFollette Medical Center, La Follette, TN, p. A586

HEATON, Crystal, Director of Finance, St. Mary's Warrick Hospital, Boonville, IN, p. A207

HEATON, John, M.D. Senior Vice President and Medical Director, Children's Hospital, New Orleans, LA, p. A285

HEBBELER, Gregory P., Chief Financial Officer, Methodist Hospital Union County, Morganfield, KY, p. A268

HEBBERD, Hilda, R.N. Senior Director Clinical Services, Marlette Regional Hospital, Marlette, MI, p. A330

HEBEL, Barbara, Vice President Human Resources, Doylestown Hospital, Doylestown, PA, p. A537

HEBERT, Jr., Bernie, Chief Financial Officer, Doctors NeuroMedical Hospital, Bremen, IN, p. A208

HEBERT, Bryan, Director Information Systems, The Medical Center of Southeast Texas, Port Arthur, TX, p. A643

HEBERT, Gerard, Chief Financial Officer, Texoma Medical Center, Denison, TX, p. A613

HEBERT, Jeff, Interim Vice President Finance, Gifford Medical Center, Randolph, VT, p. A666

HEBERT, Katherine D., Chief Executive Officer, St. Martin Hospital, Breaux Bridge, LA, p. A275

HEBERT, Mark, M.D. President Medical Staff, Medical City Dallas Hospital, Dallas, TX, p. A611

HEBERT, Rachel, Chief Financial Officer, Heart Hospital of Lafayette, Lafayette, LA, p. A281

HEBERT, Raquel, Business Manager, Sugar Land Surgical Hospital, Sugar Land, TX, p. A651

HEBERT, Timothy, Director Human Resources, Teche Regional Medical Center, Morgan City, LA, p. A284

HEBGEN, Lynn, Vice President Nursing, Upland Hills Health, Dodgeville, WI, p. A703

HECHLER, Tracy, Healthcare Director Information Services, CJW Medical Center, Richmond, VA, p. A677

HECHT, David, M.D. Chief of Staff, James H. Quillen Veterans Affairs Medical Center, Mountain Home, TN, p. A590

HECK, III, George L., President and Chief Executive Officer, Coffee Regional Medical Center, Douglas, GA, p. A158

HECKATHORNE, Daniel R.
  System Chief Financial Officer, East Los Angeles Doctors Hospital, Los Angeles, CA, p. A71
  Chief Financial Officer, Memorial Hospital of Gardena, Gardena, CA, p. A65

HECKER, Cynthia, R.N., Executive Director, UW Medicine/Northwest Hospital & Medical Center, Seattle, WA, p. A689

HECKER, Lisa, Director Human Resources, Hedrick Medical Center, Chillicothe, MO, p. A369

HECKERMAN, Ray, Chief Executive Officer and Managing Director, Coastal Harbor Treatment Center, Savannah, GA, p. A166

HECKERT Jr., Robert J., Chief Executive Officer, Gerald Champion Regional Medical Center, Alamogordo, NM, p. A426

HECKEY, Robert, M.D. Chief of Staff, Sutter Medical Center of Santa Rosa, Chanate Campus, Santa Rosa, CA, p. A95

HECKLE, Mark, Chief Information Officer, Charles A. Cannon Memorial Hospital, Linville, NC, p. A468

HECKLER, Edward, Administrator, Riverside Rehabilitation Institute, Newport News, VA, p. A675

HECKLER, Tura, Director Information Systems, Corona Regional Medical Center, Corona, CA, p. A60

HEDBERG, Beth, R.N. Director Nursing, Lindsborg Community Hospital, Lindsborg, KS, p. A249

HEDDE, Charles C., M.D. Chief Medical Officer, Good Samaritan Hospital, Vincennes, IN, p. A223

HEDDEN, Elizabeth A., Chief Financial Officer, Johnson Memorial Hospital, Franklin, IN, p. A212

HEDDERMAN, Michael, Senior Vice President Finance and Chief Financial Officer, Marianjoy Rehabilitation Hospital, Wheaton, IL, p. A205

HEDGES, David, Chief Financial Officer, Southwestern Regional Medical Center, Tulsa, OK, p. A521

HEDIGER, Joseph, Chief Financial Officer, Fox Chase Cancer Center–American Oncologic Hospital, Philadelphia, PA, p. A548

HEDLEY, Kristen, Controller, Huron Medical Center, Bad Axe, MI, p. A318

HEDLUND, Chris, Director Information Systems, Community Hospital–Fairfax, Fairfax, MO, p. A371

HEDRIX, Michael D., Interim Chief Executive Officer, Essentia Health Sandstone, Sandstone, MN, p. A352

HEDSTROM, Marjorie, Director, John J. Pershing Veterans Affairs Medical Center, Poplar Bluff, MO, p. A378

HEEMANN, John, Chief Information Officer, Aspire Hospital, Conroe, TX, p. A607

HEETER, Eric, Superintendent, Larue D. Carter Memorial Hospital, Indianapolis, IN, p. A214

HEFFERNAN, Paul F., Vice President Human Resources, Women & Infants Hospital of Rhode Island, Providence, RI, p. A561

HEFFERNAN, Rebecca, Director Human Resources, MetroWest Medical Center, Framingham, MA, p. A310

HEFFERS, Margaret, Assistant Vice President Human Resources, Geisinger Wyoming Valley Medical Center, Wilkes Barre, PA, p. A558

HEFFLINGER, Larry, Director Information Systems, Fulton County Health Center, Wauseon, OH, p. A504

HEFLIN, Clyde, M.D. Chief Medical Officer, Kindred Hospital–Nashville, Nashville, TN, p. A590

HEFNER, Donna J., R.N., President and Chief Executive Officer, Sierra View District Hospital, Porterville, CA, p. A84

HEFNER, Kathy, Vice President Clinical Operations, McDowell Hospital, Marion, NC, p. A468

HEGGEM, Mark, M.D. Chief Medical Officer, Riverwood Healthcare Center, Aitkin, MN, p. A339

HEGGEN, Karra, R.N. Vice President Nursing, Elkhart General Healthcare System, Elkhart, IN, p. A210

HEGGEN, Steve, Administrative Director Human Resources, St. Joseph Hospital, Fort Wayne, IN, p. A211

HEGGER, John, Director Information Systems, Union County Hospital, Anna, IL, p. A180

HEGLAND, Larry T., M.D. Chief Medical Officer, Ministry Saint Clare's Hospital, Weston, WI, p. A718

HEGLAND, Sandra, Chief Executive Officer, HEALTHSOUTH Rehabilitation Hospital of Austin, Austin, TX, p. A599

HEGWOOD, Wayne, Chief Financial Officer, Acuity Hospital of South Texas, San Antonio, TX, p. A645

HEHEMANN, Bryan D., President and Chief Executive Officer, McCullough–Hyde Memorial Hospital, Oxford, OH, p. A500

HEICHERT, Susan
  Senior Vice President and Chief Information Officer, Abbott Northwestern Hospital, Minneapolis, MN, p. A347
  Chief Information Officer, Mercy Hospital, Coon Rapids, MN, p. A342
  Senior Vice President, United Hospital, Saint Paul, MN, p. A351
  Chief Information Officer, Unity Hospital, Fridley, MN, p. A344

HEIDER, John R., Vice President Finance, Augusta Health, Fishersville, VA, p. A670

HEIDT, Robert, Director Information Systems, Pembina County Memorial Hospital and Wedgewood Manor, Cavalier, ND, p. A476

HEIFNER, Robert A., Chief Executive Officer, St. Luke's Sugar Land Hospital, Sugar Land, TX, p. A651

HEIGHES, Brenna, Manager Information Technology, Mt. Ascutney Hospital and Health Center, Windsor, VT, p. A667

HEIKKINEN, Todd, Director Rehabilitation Services, Orthopaedic Hospital of Wisconsin – Glendale, Milwaukee, WI, p. A711

HEILSBERG, Jim, Chief Financial Officer and Chief Information Officer, Whitman Hospital and Medical Center, Colfax, WA, p. A682

HEIM, Nicole, Chief Information Officer, Milford Regional Medical Center, Milford, MA, p. A312

HEIM, Richard, President, Advocate South Suburban Hospital, Hazel Crest, IL, p. A192

HEIM, Tonya, R.N. Vice President Patient Services and Chief Nursing Officer, Memorial Hospital and Health Care Center, Jasper, IN, p. A215

HEIMALL, Michael S., Commander, William Beaumont Army Medical Center, El Paso, TX, p. A616

HEIMAN, Thomas, Vice President Information Services and Chief Information Officer, John T. Mather Memorial Hospital, Port Jefferson, NY, p. A452

HEIN, Jodi, R.N. Chief Clinical Officer, Promise Hospital of East Los Angeles, Suburban Medical Center Campus, Paramount, CA, p. A82

HEIN, Michael, M.D. Vice President Medical Affairs, CHI Health Saint Francis, Grand Island, NE, p. A396

HEINECK, Susan, M.D. President Professional Staff, Providence Seaside Hospital, Seaside, OR, p. A530

HEINEMANN, Don, Administrator and Chief Executive Officer, Blount Memorial Hospital, Maryville, TN, p. A588

HEINEMEIER, Robert
  Chief Financial Officer, Chapman Medical Center, Orange, CA, p. A81
  Chief Financial Officer, Coastal Communities Hospital, Santa Ana, CA, p. A93

HEINISCH, Sheri, Compliance Officer, Lisbon Area Health Services, Lisbon, ND, p. A479

HEINRICH, Bill, Chief Financial Officer, Florida Hospital Zephyrhills, Zephyrhills, FL, p. A150

HEINRICH, Kerry, Interim Chief Executive Officer, Loma Linda University Medical Center, Loma Linda, CA, p. A69

HEINRICH, Michael G., Executive Vice President and Chief Financial Officer, Mercy Iowa City, Iowa City, IA, p. A232

HEINRICHS, Alice, CPA Chief Financial Officer, Van Diest Medical Center, Webster City, IA, p. A239

HEINS, Patrick, Vice President Patient Care Services, Vidant Edgecombe Hospital, Tarboro, NC, p. A473

HEINSOHN, Carmel, M.D. Medical Director, Bournewood Health Systems, Brookline, MA, p. A308

HEINTZ, Shirley, R.N. Vice President Patient Care, Liberty Hospital, Liberty, MO, p. A376

HEINTZELMAN, Gayle, R.N. Site Administrator and Chief Nursing Officer, Mercy Health – Clermont Hospital, Batavia, OH, p. A483

HEINZE, Kyle, Coordinator Information Technology, Riveredge Hospital, Forest Park, IL, p. A190

HEINZEROTH, Kevin, Chief Financial Officer, Adair County Memorial Hospital, Greenfield, IA, p. A231

HEINZMAN, Jerry, Senior Vice President and Chief Financial Officer, Sampson Regional Medical Center, Clinton, NC, p. A462

HEINZMANN, Bill, Director Human Resources, Texoma Medical Center, Denison, TX, p. A613

HENNESSEY, Ruth, Executive Vice President and Chief Administrative Officer, St. Francis Hospital, Roslyn, NY, p. A454

HENNESSEY, John, Chief Financial Officer, Cascade Medical Center, Leavenworth, WA, p. A685

HENNIGAN, Michael, M.D. Medical Director, HEALTHSOUTH Emerald Coast Rehabilitation Hospital, Panama City, FL, p. A142

HENNIKE, Michael, Chief Executive Officer, Central Regional Hospital, Butner, NC, p. A461

HENNING, Cindy, R.N. Chief Nursing Officer, Houston Northwest Medical Center, Houston, TX, p. A625

HENNING, William C., Administrator and Chief Executive Officer, Baptist Memorial Hospital–North Mississippi, Oxford, MS, p. A364

HENNIS, Michelle, Administrative Director Financial Services, Grace Hospital, Cleveland, OH, p. A488

HENOCH, Malcolm S., M.D. Chief Medical Officer, Oakwood Hospital–Dearborn, Dearborn, MI, p. A321

HENRICH, Christy, Controller, Kindred Hospital of Northern Indiana, Mishawaka, IN, p. A218

HENRICI, Michael, Associate Administrator, Roxborough Memorial Hospital, Philadelphia, PA, p. A550

HENRIKSON, Mary L., Chief Nursing Officer and Chief Operating Officer, St. Anthony Summit Medical Center, Frisco, CO, p. A106

HENRY, Andrea, Director of Nursing, Sweetwater Hospital, Sweetwater, TN, p. A593

HENRY, Anna, Chief Information Officer, Kimble Hospital, Junction, TX, p. A630

HENRY, Chris, Associate Administrator and Chief Financial Officer, Washington Hospital Healthcare System, Fremont, CA, p. A64

HENRY, Dane, Executive Vice President and Chief Operating Officer, DeKalb Medical at North Decatur, Decatur, GA, p. A158

HENRY, David
Chief Executive Officer, Bluefield Regional Medical Center, Bluefield, WV, p. A693
President and Chief Executive Officer, Northern Montana Hospital, Havre, MT, p. A388

HENRY, Debbie, Vice President Financial Services, North Arkansas Regional Medical Center, Harrison, AR, p. A47

HENRY, Don, M.D. President Medical and Dental Staff, Community Hospital, Munster, IN, p. A219

HENRY, Donna, Vice President of Nursing Services, Four County Counseling Center, Logansport, IN, p. A217

HENRY, Ginger. Chief Executive Officer, Prattville Baptist Hospital, Prattville, AL, p. A25

HENRY, Heather, Manager Information Systems, Hammond–Henry Hospital, Geneseo, IL, p. A190

HENRY Jr., Jake, President and Chief Executive Officer, Saint Francis Health System, Tulsa, OK, p. B116

HENRY, James L., Director Human Resources, HEALTHSOUTH Sea Pines Rehabilitation Hospital, Melbourne, FL, p. A136

HENRY, Joy, R.N. Director Nurses, Faith Community Hospital, Jacksboro, TX, p. A629

HENRY, Joyce, Controller, HEALTHSOUTH Rehabilitation Hospital of York, York, PA, p. A559

HENRY, Peter, M.D. Chief Medical Officer, Essentia Health St. Joseph's Medical Center, Brainerd, MN, p. A340

HENRY, Roshonda, Chief Nursing Officer, HEALTHSOUTH Rehabilitation Hospital of Cypress, Houston, TX, p. A624

HENRY, Tim, Accountant, Chatuge Regional Hospital and Nursing Home, Hiawassee, GA, p. A161

HENRY, William
Director Human Resources, East Texas Medical Center Henderson, Henderson, TX, p. A623
Director Human Resources, East Texas Medical Center–Gilmer, Gilmer, TX, p. A621

HENSEL, David, Director Financial Operations, OhioHealth Grady Memorial Hospital, Delaware, OH, p. A492

HENSEL, Edward, Chief Information Officer, Tomah Veterans Affairs Medical Center, Tomah, WI, p. A716

HENSLEY, Barry, Director Information Systems, Logan Regional Medical Center, Logan, WV, p. A696

HENSLEY, Kristy, Director Human Resources, Indiana Orthopaedic Hospital, Indianapolis, IN, p. A214

HENSON, Judith, Chief Nursing Officer, Adena Medical Center, Chillicothe, OH, p. A486

HENSON, Maureen, Vice President Human Resources, Rapid City Regional Hospital, Rapid City, SD, p. A576

HENSON, Pam, Executive Director, Pathways of Tennessee, Jackson, TN, p. A584

HENSON, Steve, Chief Executive Officer, Arkansas State Hospital, Little Rock, AR, p. A49

HENTHORN, Cheryl, Chief Executive Officer, Summa Rehab Hospital, Akron, OH, p. A482

HENTON, Thomas, Chief Executive Officer and Administrator, Greenwood County Hospital, Eureka, KS, p. A244

HENTZEN PAGE, Ann, M.D., Chief Executive Officer, Summit Surgical, Hutchinson, KS, p. A246

HENZE, Mary Kay, Chief Nursing Officer, Hutchinson Health, Hutchinson, MN, p. A345

HENZE, Michael E., Chief Executive Officer, Lake Regional Health System, Osage Beach, MO, p. A378

HEPKER, Wendy J., FACHE, Director, Chillicothe Veterans Affairs Medical Center, Chillicothe, OH, p. A486

HEPNER, Tim, M.D. Medical Director, St. John Owasso, Owasso, OK, p. A517

HERALD, Kathleen R., Vice President and Chief Information Officer, Lexington Medical Center, West Columbia, SC, p. A571

HERBECK, Marilyn, Coordinator Human Resources, Community Memorial Hospital, Staunton, IL, p. A203

HERBEK, Gary J., Chief Executive Officer, HEALTHSOUTH Rehabilitation Hospital of Northern Virginia, Aldie, VA, p. A668

HERBER, Matt, M.D. Chief of Staff, Avera Dells Area Hospital, Dell Rapids, SD, p. A573

HERBER, Steven, FACS, President and Chief Executive Officer, St. Helena Hospital Napa Valley, Saint Helena, CA, p. A88

HERBERGER, Eva, Administrator Human Resources, USC Verdugo Hills Hospital, Glendale, CA, p. A65

HERBERT, Daniel, M.D. Medical Administrative Officer, Millinocket Regional Hospital, Millinocket, ME, p. A294

HERBERT, Janet, R.N. Chief Operating Officer, McKenzie Health System, Sandusky, MI, p. A334

HERBERT, Janet, Vice President Operations and Chief Nursing Officer, St. Joseph Mercy Port Huron, Port Huron, MI, p. A333

HERBERT, Kevin, Chief Financial Officer, Oconee Medical Center, Seneca, SC, p. A569

HERBERT, Laurie, Vice President Operations, Three Rivers Health, Three Rivers, MI, p. A336

HERBERT, Peter N., M.D. Senior Vice President Medical Affairs and Chief of Staff, Yale–New Haven Hospital, New Haven, CT, p. A116

HERBOLD, Charlotte, Manager Business Officer, Garfield County Health Center, Jordan, MT, p. A388

HERBST, Gary, Senior Vice President and Chief Financial Officer, Kaweah Delta Medical Center, Visalia, CA, p. A99

HERDENER, Tony, Vice President Systems and Finance, Northeast Georgia Medical Center, Gainesville, GA, p. A160

HERDER, Debbie, Controller, Promise Hospital of Wichita Falls, Wichita Falls, TX, p. A657

HEREDIA, Paul, Chief Human Resources Officer, Citrus Valley Medical Center–Inter Community Campus, Covina, CA, p. A61

HEREFORD, James, Chief Operating Officer, Stanford Hospital and Clinics, Palo Alto, CA, p. A82

HEREFORD, Michelle, Chief, UVA Transitional Care Hospital, Charlottesville, VA, p. A669

HERFORT, Oliver, M.D. Chief Medical Officer, Valley Regional Hospital, Claremont, NH, p. A409

HERGET, Jordan, Chief Operating Officer, Good Samaritan Hospital, San Jose, CA, p. A92

HERING, Kristine, R.N. Chief Nursing Officer, Speare Memorial Hospital, Plymouth, NH, p. A412

HERMAN, David C., M.D., President and Chief Executive Officer, Vidant Health, Greenville, NC, p. B150

HERMAN, Jeffrey, Chief Executive Officer, Meadows Psychiatric Center, Centre Hall, PA, p. A535

HERMAN, John J., Chief Operating Officer, Mercy Hospital, Buffalo, NY, p. A434

HERMAN, John W.
Chief Executive Officer, Fairview Lakes Health Services, Wyoming, MN, p. A354
Chief Executive Officer, Fairview Northland Medical Center, Princeton, MN, p. A349

HERMAN, Michael, Chief Operating Officer, Sumner Regional Medical Center, Gallatin, TN, p. A583

HERMANN, Terri, R.N. Chief Nursing Officer, Franklin Hospital District, Benton, IL, p. A181

HERMANN, Tom, Chief of Staff, Sturgis Regional Hospital, Sturgis, SD, p. A577

HERMOSA, Mercy, Director of Information System, Coral Gables Hospital, Coral Gables, FL, p. A126

HERN, Warren, President and Chief Executive Officer, Unity Hospital, Rochester, NY, p. A453

HERNANDEZ, Ashley, Chief Information Technology Officer, Pender Memorial Hospital, Burgaw, NC, p. A460

HERNANDEZ, Bernadette, R.N. Chief Nursing Officer, Texas Specialty Hospital at Lubbock, Lubbock, TX, p. A635

HERNANDEZ Jr., George B., President and Chief Executive Officer, University Health System, San Antonio, TX, p. A648

HERNANDEZ, Gloria, Executive Director, University Pediatric Hospital,, PR, p. A729

HERNANDEZ, Hank, Chief Executive Officer, Las Palmas Medical Center, El Paso, TX, p. A616

HERNANDEZ, Hector, M.D., Chief Executive Officer, Community Hospital of Huntington Park, Huntington Park, CA, p. A67

HERNANDEZ, Janiva, Coordinator Human Resources, Hospital Metropolitano Dr. Susoni, Arecibo, PR, p. A724

HERNANDEZ, Kim
Chief Human Resources Officer, AMG Specialty Hospital–Denham Springs, Denham Springs, LA, p. A277
Director Human Resources, AMG Specialty Hospital–Slidell, Slidell, LA, p. A288

HERNANDEZ, Leonard, President and Chief Executive Officer, Sumner Regional Medical Center, Wellington, KS, p. A256

HERNANDEZ, Luz Maria, Director Human Resources, I. Gonzalez Martinez Oncologic Hospital,, PR, p. A728

HERNANDEZ, Reyna, Chief Financial Officer, HEALTHSOUTH Rehabilitation Hospital of Miami, Cutler Bay, FL, p. A126

HERNANDEZ, Sandi, Controller, Lafayette General Surgical Hospital, Lafayette, LA, p. A281

HERNANDEZ, Susan, R.N. Chief Nursing Officer, Rice Medical Center, Eagle Lake, TX, p. A614

HERNANDEZ, Susan, Chief Nursing Officer, University of Texas Southwestern Medical Center, Dallas, TX, p. A612

HERNANDEZ, Tony, Director Information Technology, Fort Duncan Regional Medical Center, Eagle Pass, TX, p. A614

HERNANDEZ DROZDOWICZ, Diana, M.D. Medical Director, Rogers City Rehabilitation Hospital, Rogers City, MI, p. A333

HERNANDEZ–KEEBLE, Sonia, Superintendent, Rio Grande State Center/South Texas Health Care System, Harlingen, TX, p. A622

HERNANDEZ–LICHTL, Javier, Chief Executive Officer, Baptist Health South Florida, West Kendall Baptist Hospital, Miami, FL, p. A136

HERNDON, Amy, Director Finance, Morristown–Hamblen Healthcare System, Morristown, TN, p. A590

HERNDON, David N., M.D. Chief of Staff, Shriners Hospitals for Children–Galveston Burns Hospital, Galveston, TX, p. A620

HERNDON, Lori, R.N., President and Chief Executive Officer, AtlantiCare Regional Medical Center, Atlantic City, NJ, p. A413

HERNDON, Paula, R.N. Nurse Executive, Highland–Clarksburg Hospital, Clarksburg, WV, p. A694

HERNDON, Scott, Chief Financial Officer, Kendall Regional Medical Center, Miami, FL, p. A137

HEROLD, Jeffrey, M.D. President Medical Staff, St. Nicholas Hospital, Sheboygan, WI, p. A715

HEROLD, Mary, Director Human Resources, Share Medical Center, Alva, OK, p. A507

HERR, Brenda, Chief Nursing Officer, East Adams Rural Hospital, Ritzville, WA, p. A688

HERRARA, Espie, Chief Financial Officer, Peak Behavioral Health Services, Santa Teresa, NM, p. A430

HERREN, Richenda Dawn, M.D. Chief of Staff, Mercy Hospital Independence, Independence, KS, p. A246

HERRERA, Jocelyn A., Director Human Resources, Kaiser Permanente Orange County Anaheim Medical Center, Anaheim, CA, p. A55

HERRERA, Veronica, Director Human Resources, Aurora Las Encinas Hospital, Pasadena, CA, p. A83

HERRERA, Yamila, Director Human Resources, Hialeah Hospital, Hialeah, FL, p. A130

HERRERO, Carmelo, M.D. Medical Director, Hospital Oriente, Humacao, PR, p. A726

HERRICK, Stephen M., Ph.D., Director, Piedmont Geriatric Hospital, Burkeville, VA, p. A669

HERRIN, Curtis, Chief Financial Officer, Toppenish Community Hospital, Toppenish, WA, p. A691

HERRING, Donnette, Chief Information Officer, Vidant Medical Center, Greenville, NC, p. A465

HERRING, Randy, M.D. Chief of Staff, Coon Memorial Hospital, Dalhart, TX, p. A609

HERRINGTON, Bruce, M.D. Chief Medical Officer, South Georgia Medical Center Lanier Campus, Lakeland, GA, p. A162

HERRINGTON, John
Chief Financial Officer, Holmes County Hospital and Clinics, Lexington, MS, p. A361
Chief Financial Officer, University of Mississippi Medical Center Grenada, Grenada, MS, p. A358

HERRIOTT, Sue A., Director Human Resources, OSF St. Joseph Medical Center, Bloomington, IL, p. A181

HERRMAN, Edward, R.N.,
President, Integris Bass Baptist Health Center, Enid, OK, p. A510
President, Integris Bass Pavilion, Enid, OK, p. A510

HERRMANN, Deborah, M.D. Chief of Staff, I–70 Community Hospital, Sweet Springs, MO, p. A383

HERRMANN, Lee, Chief Healthcare Technology Officer, Santa Clara Valley Medical Center, San Jose, CA, p. A92

HERRMANN, Marty, M.D. Medical Director, Mayo Clinic Health System in New Prague, New Prague, MN, p. A348

HERRMANN, Sarah, R.N. Chief Nursing Officer, Select Specialty Hospital–Topeka, Topeka, KS, p. A255

HERRON, Katherine, Director Human Resources, Richard H. Hutchings Psychiatric Center, Syracuse, NY, p. A455

HERRON, Mary Beth, Director of Human Resources, Illinois Valley Community Hospital, Peru, IL, p. A200

HERSEY, Robert, Chief Financial Officer, Northeastern Vermont Regional Hospital, Saint Johnsbury, VT, p. A666

HERSHBERGER, Scott, Acting Chief Information Management Services, Battle Creek Veterans Affairs Medical Center, Battle Creek, MI, p. A319

HERSOM, Deborah, Director Human Resources, HEALTHSOUTH Chattanooga Rehabilitation Hospital, Chattanooga, TN, p. A580

HERTEL, Cheryl, Coordinator Human Resources, Stamford Memorial Hospital, Stamford, TX, p. A650

HERTEL, Holly, Director Nursing, Larned State Hospital, Larned, KS, p. A248

HERTZ, Roger
Vice President, Methodist Jennie Edmundson Hospital, Council Bluffs, IA, p. A228
Vice President Information Technology, Nebraska Methodist Hospital, Omaha, NE, p. A400

HERTZLER, Barbara, Chief Operating Officer, St. Joseph Mercy Oakland, Pontiac, MI, p. A332

HERWIG, Brian J., Chief Executive Officer, Estes Park Medical Center, Estes Park, CO, p. A106

HERZBERG, Deborah L., FACHE, Chief Executive Officer, Davis County Hospital, Bloomfield, IA, p. A226

HERZBERG, Joseph W., Assistant Vice President Human Resources, WellStar Cobb Hospital, Austell, GA, p. A154

HERZOG, Dean, Chief Financial Officer, Kona Community Hospital, Kealakekua, HI, p. A172

HERZOG, Mark P., President and Chief Executive Officer, Holy Family Memorial, Manitowoc, WI, p. A708

HERZOG, Paul F., Chief Operating Officer, University of New Mexico Hospitals, Albuquerque, NM, p. A427

HERZOG, Vernail, Chief Executive Officer, Allegiance Specialty Hospital of Greenville, Greenville, MS, p. A358

HESCH, Dennis, Executive Vice President Finance and Chief Financial Officer, Carle Foundation Hospital, Urbana, IL, p. A204

HESS, Bob, Chief Information Officer, Bonner General Hospital, Sandpoint, ID, p. A178

HESS, Brian, Chief Financial Officer, Venice Regional Bayfront Health, Venice, FL, p. A149

HESS, David F., M.D. President Medical Staff, Reynolds Memorial Hospital, Glen Dale, WV, p. A695

HESS, Heidi, Chief Nursing Officer, Genesis Medical Center–Aledo, Aledo, IL, p. A180

HESS, Pamela, Chief Financial Officer, St. Joseph Hospital, Fort Wayne, IN, p. A211

HESS, Phil, Chief Executive Officer, Philhaven, Mount Gretna, PA, p. A545

HESS, Steve
Vice President & Chief Information Officer, Medical Center of the Rockies, Loveland, CO, p. A110
Vice President Information Services and Chief Information Officer, University of Colorado Hospital, Aurora, CO, p. A102

HESSE, Fred, M.D. Medical Director, Arms Acres, Carmel, NY, p. A435

HESSE, Nancy, R.N. Senior Vice President Patient Care Services, Eastern Regional Medical Center, Philadelphia, PA, p. A548

HESSELRODE, Renee, Director Health Information Management, Landmark Hospital, Cape Girardeau, MO, p. A368

HESSER, Jason, M.D. Chief of Staff, Crete Area Medical Center, Crete, NE, p. A395

HESSHEIMER, Susan, Director Human Resources, Johnson County Hospital, Tecumseh, NE, p. A402

HESSING, Jeffrey, M.D. Medical Director, Treasure Valley Hospital, Boise, ID, p. A175

HESSMAN, Mary Pat, Chief Fiscal, Northport Veterans Affairs Medical Center, Northport, NY, p. A449

HESTER, Janet, R.N. Chief Nurse Executive, Massac Memorial Hospital, Metropolis, IL, p. A196

HESTER, Joyce, CPA Senior Vice President and Chief Financial Officer, Mother Frances Hospital – Tyler, Tyler, TX, p. A654

HESTER, Kathy, Chief Nursing Officer, Orange Park Medical Center, Orange Park, FL, p. A140

HESTER, Steven, M.D. Vice President Medical Affairs, Norton Suburban Hospital, Louisville, KY, p. A266

HESTON, Thomas, M.D. Chief of Staff, Shoshone Medical Center, Kellogg, ID, p. A176

HETHERINGTON, Ray, Network Administrator, Wheatland Memorial Healthcare, Harlowton, MT, p. A388

HETHERINGTON, Thomas, M.D. Chief of Staff, Capital Region Medical Center, Jefferson City, MO, p. A372

HETLAGE, C. Kennon, FACHE, Administrator and Chief Executive Officer, Memorial Hospital West, Pembroke Pines, FL, p. A142

HETLETVED, Beth, Director of Nurses, Garrison Memorial Hospital, Garrison, ND, p. A478

HETRICK, Robert G., Vice President Finance and Chief Financial Officer, Morehead Memorial Hospital, Eden, NC, p. A463

HETT, Samantha, Manager Human Resources, Satanta District Hospital, Satanta, KS, p. A254

HETTICH, E. Paul, Chief Financial Officer, BryLin Hospitals, Buffalo, NY, p. A434

HETTINGER, JoAnn, R.N. Director of Patient Care Services, Avera Weskota Memorial Hospital, Wessington Springs, SD, p. A578

HETTINGER, MaryLou, Director Quality Management, Devereux Children's Behavioral Health Center, Malvern, PA, p. A544

HETTINGER, Tiffany Erin, Associate Chief Nursing Officer, North Colorado Medical Center, Greeley, CO, p. A107

HETU, Maureen, Chief Information Officer, Our Lady of Lourdes Medical Center, Camden, NJ, p. A414

HETZ, Mark
Chief Information Officer, Asante Ashland Community Hospital, Ashland, OR, p. A523
Chief Information Officer, Asante Rogue Regional Medical Center, Medford, OR, p. A527
Chief Information Officer, Asante Three Rivers Medical Center, Grants Pass, OR, p. A525

HEURING, Ron, Director Information Systems, Perry County Memorial Hospital, Perryville, MO, p. A378

HEURTIN, John, Chief Financial Officer, Lee's Summit Medical Center, Lee's Summit, MO, p. A375

HEUSER, Keith E., President, Mercy Hospital, Valley City, ND, p. A480

HEVER, Susan C., Director Human Resources, Brookhaven Memorial Hospital Medical Center, Patchogue, NY, p. A451

HEWITT, Caryn, Executive Partner Information Technology and Chief Information Officer, Sanford Medical Center Fargo, Fargo, ND, p. A477

HEXEM, Gregory, Chief Financial Officer, Steele Memorial Medical Center, Salmon, ID, p. A178

HEYDON, Larry, President and Chief Executive Officer, Johnson Memorial Hospital, Franklin, IN, p. A212

HEYN, Matthew M., Chief Executive Officer, Ransom Memorial Hospital, Ottawa, KS, p. A251

HEYWOOD, Matthew, Chief Executive Officer, Aspirus, Inc., Wausau, WI, p. B15

HIATT, M. K., Administrator, Allendale County Hospital, Fairfax, SC, p. A565

HIATT, Tim, Chief Information Officer, Brodstone Memorial Hospital, Superior, NE, p. A402

HIBBARD, Carrie, Human Resource Business Partner, Adventist Rehabilitation Hospital of Maryland, Rockville, MD, p. A303

HIBBS, Cathryn A., FACHE, Chief Executive Officer, Deaconess Hospital, Oklahoma City, OK, p. A515

HIBEN, Daniel, Chief Executive Officer, Oswego Community Hospital, Oswego, KS, p. A251

HICKETHIER, Julie, R.N. Senior Vice President, Benefis Hospitals, Great Falls, MT, p. A388

HICKEY, Conner, Chief Operating Officer, Woodland Heights Medical Center, Lufkin, TX, p. A636

HICKEY, Mairead, Ph.D. Executive Vice President and Chief Operating Officer, Brigham and Women's Hospital, Boston, MA, p. A306

HICKEY, Thomas P., Chief Executive Officer and Managing Director, Pembroke Hospital, Pembroke, MA, p. A313

HICKEY–BOYNTON, Meg, Director Human Resources and Marketing, Community Hospital of Anaconda, Anaconda, MT, p. A385

HICKLING, Andrea, Vice President Finance and Chief Finance Officer, Northern Hospital of Surry County, Mount Airy, NC, p. A469

HICKLING, Karen, Director Human Resources, Palmdale Regional Medical Center, Palmdale, CA, p. A82

HICKMAN, George, Executive Vice President and Chief Information Officer, Albany Medical Center, Albany, NY, p. A432

HICKMAN, Louise, R.N. Vice President of Patient Care Services, Jefferson Regional Medical Center, Pine Bluff, AR, p. A52

HICKMAN, Monica, Director Fiscal Services, Shriners Hospitals for Children–Spokane, Spokane, WA, p. A690

HICKMAN, Sherie C., Vice President Operations and Chief Operating Officer, Sequoia Hospital, Redwood City, CA, p. A86

HICKS, Angela, Controller, Our Community Hospital, Scotland Neck, NC, p. A472

HICKS, Christia, Vice President Human Resources, Eskenazi Health, Indianapolis, IN, p. A214

HICKS, Crystal, R.N. Chief Nursing Officer, Harrison County Community Hospital, Bethany, MO, p. A367

HICKS, Janelle, R.N. Vice President Patient Services, Hocking Valley Community Hospital, Logan, OH, p. A496

HICKS, Joan, Chief Information Officer, University of Alabama Hospital, Birmingham, AL, p. A17

HICKS, Joe, President and Chief Executive Officer, Barnabas Health Behavioral Health Center, Toms River, NJ, p. A423

HICKS, John R., President and Chief Executive Officer, Platte Valley Medical Center, Brighton, CO, p. A103

HICKS, Kevin J., President and CEO, Overland Park Regional Medical Center, Overland Park, KS, p. A252

HICKS, Scott, Vice President, Clark Memorial Hospital, Jeffersonville, IN, p. A215

HICKS, Shawnee, Director Human Resources, Magnolia Regional Medical Center, Magnolia, AR, p. A49

HICKS, Susan
Chief Operating Officer, Sky Ridge Medical Center, Lone Tree, CO, p. A109
Information Technology Director, Starr Regional Medical Center–Etowah, Etowah, TN, p. A582

HICKS, Terri, Chief Operating Officer and Chief Financial Officer, P & S Surgical Hospital, Monroe, LA, p. A284

HICKS, William, Chief Operating Officer, Bellevue Hospital Center, New York, NY, p. A442

HIEB, Dorothy, Director Human Resources, Sanford Chamberlain Medical Center, Chamberlain, SD, p. A572

HIEB, Laura, R.N. Chief Nursing Officer, Bellin Memorial Hospital, Green Bay, WI, p. A705

HIEBERT, Leslie, Chief Executive Officer, Klickitat Valley Health, Goldendale, WA, p. A684

HIGA, Russel, JD Regional Director Human Resources, Leahi Hospital, Honolulu, HI, p. A170

HIGDON, Karen, R.N. Vice President and Chief Nursing Officer, Baptist Health La Grange, La Grange, KY, p. A263

HIGDON, Mark L., Commander, Moncrief Army Community Hospital, Fort Jackson, SC, p. A566

HIGGINBOTHAM, G. Douglas, President and Chief Executive Officer, South Central Regional Medical Center, Laurel, MS, p. A361

HIGGINBOTHAM, Michael, Chief Executive Officer, Cornerstone Hospital–Medical Center of Houston, Houston, TX, p. A624

HIGGINS, Alana
Regional Information Management Executive, CHRISTUS St. Michael Health System, Texarkana, TX, p. A652
Regional Information Management Executive, CHRISTUS St. Michael Rehabilitation Hospital, Texarkana, TX, p. A652

HIGGINS, JoAnn, Chief Nursing Officer and Assistant Administrator, Palo Alto County Health System, Emmetsburg, IA, p. A230

HIGGINS, John, Vice President and Chief Financial Officer, Exempla Good Samaritan Medical Center, Lafayette, CO, p. A108

HIGGINS, Kevin A., Chief Financial Officer, Olmsted Medical Center, Rochester, MN, p. A350

HIGGINS, Larry, Vice President Human Resources, King's Daughters Medical Center, Ashland, KY, p. A258

HIGGINS, Rodney, Chief Financial Officer, Deaconess Hospital, Spokane, WA, p. A690

HIGGINS, Susie, Chief Financial Officer, Grafton City Hospital, Grafton, WV, p. A695

HIGGINS, William, M.D. Vice President Medical Affairs, Hudson Valley Hospital Center, Cortlandt Manor, NY, p. A436

HIGGINS–BOWERS, Shirley, Vice President Human Resources, JFK Medical Center, Edison, NJ, p. A415

HIGGINSON, David, Senior Vice President and Chief Information Officer, Phoenix Children's Hospital, Phoenix, AZ, p. A36

HIGH, Kim, Chief Financial Officer, Baptist Memorial Hospital–Union County, New Albany, MS, p. A363

HIGHBAUGH, Michael, M.D. Medical Director, Baylor Specialty Hospital, Dallas, TX, p. A609

HIGHSMITH, Cameron, Chief Executive Officer, Washington County Hospital, Plymouth, NC, p. A470

HIGHSMITH, Danette, Director Human Resources, Burke Medical Center, Waynesboro, GA, p. A169

HIGHTOWER, Bernita, Chief Human Resources, Martin Army Community Hospital, Fort Benning, GA, p. A160

HIGHTOWER, Skip
Chief Financial Officer, Brooks County Hospital, Quitman, GA, p. A165
Chief Financial Officer, Grady General Hospital, Cairo, GA, p. A155
Senior Vice President and Chief Financial Officer, John D. Archbold Memorial Hospital, Thomasville, GA, p. A168
Senior Vice President and Chief Financial Officer, Mitchell County Hospital, Camilla, GA, p. A155

HIGHTOWER, Thomas, R.N. Chief Operating Officer, Grays Harbor Community Hospital, Aberdeen, WA, p. A681

HIJECK, Thomas W., R.N. Vice President Nursing Services and Chief Nursing Officer, Harrington Memorial Hospital, Southbridge, MA, p. A314

HILAMAN, Brad L., M.D. Chief of Staff, J. Arthur Dosher Memorial Hospital, Southport, NC, p. A473

HILBERT, Frank, Senior Vice President and Chief Information Officer, McAlester Regional Health Center, McAlester, OK, p. A513

HILDEBRAND, Randall, M.D. Chief Medical Officer, Great Bend Regional Hospital, Great Bend, KS, p. A244

HILDEBRANDT, James, D.O. Vice President Medical Affairs, Sarah Bush Lincoln Health Center, Mattoon, IL, p. A195

HILDEN, Michael, M.D. President Medical Staff, Carlisle Regional Medical Center, Carlisle, PA, p. A535

HILDRETH, Beth, Vice President Human Resources, OhioHealth MedCentral Mansfield Hospital, Mansfield, OH, p. A497

HILDRETH, Joe, Director Information Technology, Three Rivers Hospital, Waverly, TN, p. A594

HILDWEIN, Robin, Chief Information Officer, Boca Raton Regional Hospital, Boca Raton, FL, p. A124

HILFIGER, Janie, President, Soldiers and Sailors Memorial Hospital, Wellsboro, PA, p. A557

HILL, Bart, M.D. Chief Medical Officer, St. Luke's Regional Medical Center, Boise, ID, p. A175

HILL, Beth, Director Human Resources, Russell County Medical Center, Lebanon, VA, p. A672

HILL, Bettie, Chief Financial Officer, Poplar Springs Hospital, Petersburg, VA, p. A676

HILL, Cheryl
Vice President Human Resources, Columbia St. Mary's Hospital Milwaukee, Milwaukee, WI, p. A710
Vice President Human Resources, Columbia St. Mary's Ozaukee Hospital, Mequon, WI, p. A709
Vice President Human Resources, Sacred Heart Rehabilitation Institute, Milwaukee, WI, p. A711

HILL, Chris, Chief Executive Officer, Arizona Spine and Joint Hospital, Mesa, AZ, p. A34

HILL, David, Regional Administrator, Booneville Community Hospital, Booneville, AR, p. A44

HILL, Duane N., Chief Executive Officer, Beaumont Bone and Joint Institute, Beaumont, TX, p. A601

HILL, Herbert, Director Human Resources, Klickitat Valley Health, Goldendale, WA, p. A684

HILL, Jack, Chief Operating Officer and Administrator, The Jewish Hospital – Mercy Health, Cincinnati, OH, p. A487

HILL, James P., Senior Vice President Administrative Services, MedStar Washington Hospital Center, Washington, DC, p. A121

HILL, Janice, President and Chief Executive Officer, Baptist Memorial Health Care Corporation, Memphis, TN, p. B21

HILL, Janice, R.N., Administrator, Baptist Memorial Restorative Care Hospital, Memphis, TN, p. A588

HILL, Janice, Chief Executive Officer and Administrator, Baptist Rehabilitation–Germantown, Germantown, TN, p. A583

HILL, Jason, M.D. Chief Medical Officer, Choctaw Nation Health Care Center, Talihina, OK, p. A519

HILL, Jean, Chief Nursing Officer and Chief Clinical Officer, St. Charles Parish Hospital, Luling, LA, p. A283

HILL, Jeff, Chief Executive Officer, Steele Memorial Medical Center, Salmon, ID, p. A178

HILL, Jessica, Vice President, Chief Nursing Officer, Texas Health Harris Methodist Hospital Southlake, Southlake, TX, p. A650

HILL, Jill, Director Information Technology, Utah State Hospital, Provo, UT, p. A662

HILL, Jr., Joe B., Vice President Human Resources, Trident Medical Center, Charleston, SC, p. A563

HILL, John G.
Chief Executive Officer, PeaceHealth Sacred Heart Medical Center at RiverBend, Springfield, OR, p. A530
Chief Executive Officer, PeaceHealth Sacred Heart Medical Center, University District, Eugene, OR, p. A524

HILL, Karen, Director Human Resources, Baylor Institute for Rehabilitation, Dallas, TX, p. A609

HILL, Karen S., R.N. Chief Operating Officer and Chief Nursing Officer, Baptist Health Lexington, Lexington, KY, p. A264

HILL, Kent D., Director, Kansas City Veterans Affairs Medical Center, Kansas City, MO, p. A373

HILL, Leo, Chief Information Officer, Massachusetts Eye and Ear Infirmary, Boston, MA, p. A307

HILL, Mary Beth, Coordinator Human Resources, Vidant Bertie Hospital, Windsor, NC, p. A475

HILL, Nancy L., R.N. Chief Operating Officer, North Hills Hospital, North Richland Hills, TX, p. A640

HILL, Ned, Chief Executive Officer, Memorial Hospital of Carbon County, Rawlins, WY, p. A722

HILL, Pam, Director Human Resources, Baptist Rehabilitation–Germantown, Germantown, TN, p. A583

HILL, Pamela German
Chief Financial Officer, Vista Medical Center East, Waukegan, IL, p. A205
Chief Financial Officer, Vista Medical Center West, Waukegan, IL, p. A205

HILL, Patricia, Senior Director Nurse Executive, Sentara Northern Virginia Medical Center, Woodbridge, VA, p. A680

HILL, Phillip, Chief Executive Officer, Calhoun–Liberty Hospital, Blountstown, FL, p. A123

HILL, Robert, M.D
Vice President Medical Staff Affairs, Borgess Medical Center, Kalamazoo, MI, p. A328
Chief Medical Officer, Borgess–Lee Memorial Hospital, Dowagiac, MI, p. A323

HILL, Ryan
Chief Executive Officer, Essentia Health Ada, Ada, MN, p. A339
Chief Financial Officer, Essentia Health St. Mary's – Detroit Lakes, Detroit Lakes, MN, p. A342

HILL, Scott, Interim Chief Executive Officer, Columbus Regional Healthcare System, Columbus, GA, p. B36

HILL, Stephen, Vice President and Chief Nursing Officer, Valley Baptist Medical Center–Harlingen, Harlingen, TX, p. A623

HILL, Stuart, Vice President and Treasurer, White County Medical Center, Searcy, AR, p. A52

HILL, Susan, R.N. Director of Nursing, Marcus Daly Memorial Hospital, Hamilton, MT, p. A388

HILL, Terri L., Vice President and Administrator, Union Hospital Clinton, Clinton, IN, p. A208

HILL, Todd, D.O. Medical Director, Signature Psychiatric Hospital, Kansas City, MO, p. A374

HILL–DAVIS, Nancy L., Vice President Human Resources and Risk Management, Mercy Hospital and Medical Center, Chicago, IL, p. A185

HILLARD, Mary, R.N. Vice President Patient Care Services, Advocate Condell Medical Center, Libertyville, IL, p. A194

HILLARY, Maureen, Chief Nursing Officer, Hayes Green Beach Memorial Hospital, Charlotte, MI, p. A320

HILLEGASS, Bonnie Essex, Chief Executive Officer, Harmon Medical and Rehabilitation Hospital, Las Vegas, NV, p. A405

HILLEMEIER, A. Craig, M.D., Chief Executive Officer, Penn State Milton S. Hershey Medical Center, Hershey, PA, p. A540

HILLESTAD, Tammy, Chief Nursing Officer, Brookings Health System, Brookings, SD, p. A572

HILLIARD, David J., D.O. Chief of Staff, Barnesville Hospital, Barnesville, OH, p. A483

HILLIS, David W., Chairman and Chief Executive Officer, Adcare Hospital of Worcester, Worcester, MA, p. A316

HILLJE, Kathryn, Human Resource and Marketing Partner, Avera St. Anthony's Hospital, O'Neill, NE, p. A399

HILLMAN, Annette, Director Human Resources, Doctor's Hospital of Deer Creek, Leesville, LA, p. A283

HILLS, Cindi, Director Human Resources, Riverwood Healthcare Center, Aitkin, MN, p. A339

HILLS, Edward, D.D.S. Interim Chief Operating Officer, MetroHealth Medical Center, Cleveland, OH, p. A489

HILT, Monica
President, Howard Young Medical Center, Woodruff, WI, p. A719
President, Ministry Eagle River Memorial Hospital, Eagle River, WI, p. A704
President, Ministry Sacred Heart Hospital, Tomahawk, WI, p. A716
President, Ministry Saint Mary's Hospitals, Rhinelander, WI, p. A714

HILTON, Craig, Chief Executive Officer, Hampton Behavioral Health Center, Westampton, NJ, p. A424

HILTON, Lois, Director Human Resources, DeSoto Memorial Hospital, Arcadia, FL, p. A123

HILTON, Richard G., Administrator and Chief Executive Officer, OCH Regional Medical Center, Starkville, MS, p. A365

HILTON, Shane, Vice President and Chief Financial Officer, Johnson City Medical Center, Johnson City, TN, p. A585

HILTON–SIEBERT, Stephanie, President and Chief Executive Officer, Salem Township Hospital, Salem, IL, p. A202

HILTUNEN, Theresa, Entity Information Officer, Penn Presbyterian Medical Center, Philadelphia, PA, p. A549

HILTZ, Paul C., FACHE, Market President and Chief Executive Officer, Springfield Regional Medical Center, Springfield, OH, p. A502

HIMES, Cathy, Director Human Resources, Starr Regional Medical Center–Etowah, Etowah, TN, p. A582

HINCHEY, Paul P.
President and Chief Executive Officer, Candler Hospital, Savannah, GA, p. A166
President and Chief Executive Officer, St. Joseph's Hospital, Savannah, GA, p. A166

HINCKLEY, Fran, Chief Information Officer, Hebrew Rehabilitation Center, Boston, MA, p. A307

HINDMAN, Robbie, Vice President Patient Care Services and Chief Nursing Officer, Walker Baptist Medical Center, Jasper, AL, p. A22

HINDS, Bob, Executive Director, Bradford Health Services at Huntsville, Madison, AL, p. A22

HINDS, Nigel, Chief Financial Officer, Florida Hospital DeLand, DeLand, FL, p. A127

HINE, Rhonda, R.N. Interim Chief Nursing Executive, Mason District Hospital, Havana, IL, p. A192

HINEMAN, Elizabeth, M.D. Chief Medical Staff, Scott County Hospital, Scott City, KS, p. A254

HINER, Jill, Vice President and Chief Financial Officer, Summa Western Reserve Hospital, Cuyahoga Falls, OH, p. A491

HINER, Peggy, Director Human Resources, Wheatland Memorial Healthcare, Harlowton, MT, p. A388

HINES, Frederick W., President and Chief Executive Officer, Clarity Child Guidance Center, San Antonio, TX, p. A646

HINES, Linda
Vice President and Site Executive, University of Maryland Baltimore Washington Medical Center, Glen Burnie, MD, p. A301
Vice President Information Technology and Information Systems, University of Maryland Rehabilitation and Orthopaedic Institute, Baltimore, MD, p. A298

HINES, Lisa, Director Nursing, Eastern Shore Hospital Center, Cambridge, MD, p. A299

HINES, Mary Beth, D.O. Chief Medical Officer, Portage Health, Hancock, MI, p. A326

HINES, Randall, Interim Administrator, Central State Hospital, Milledgeville, GA, p. A163

HINESLEY, Jay, Chief Executive Officer, Stringfellow Memorial Hospital, Anniston, AL, p. A15

HINKLE, David, Senior Vice President and Chief Information Officer, Nash Health Care Systems, Rocky Mount, NC, p. A471

HINKLE, Stacey, Director Information Technology, Banner Desert Medical Center, Mesa, AZ, p. A34

HINNER, William J.
Vice President Financial Analysis and Planning Ministry Health Care, Ministry Saint Joseph's Hospital, Marshfield, WI, p. A709
Vice President Financial Analysis and Planning, Ministry Saint Michael's Hospital, Stevens Point, WI, p. A716

HINO, Raymond T., Chief Executive Officer, Bear Valley Community Hospital, Big Bear Lake, CA, p. A58

HINOJOSA, Anna, MSN Interim Chief Nursing Officer, Knapp Medical Center, Weslaco, TX, p. A657

HINOJOZA, Rebecca, Chief Nursing Officer, Medina Regional Hospital, Hondo, TX, p. A623

HINRICHS, Becky, Vice President Human Resources, Riverside Medical Center, Kankakee, IL, p. A194

HINRICHS, Sandy, Director Human Resources, Burnett Medical Center, Grantsburg, WI, p. A705

HINSHAW, Bruce, Director Human Resources, Artesia General Hospital, Artesia, NM, p. A427

HINTON, James H., President and Chief Executive Officer, Presbyterian Healthcare Services, Albuquerque, NM, p. B107

HINTON, Tommye, R.N. Chief Nursing Officer, Highland Hospital of Rochester, Rochester, NY, p. A453

HINTZ, Lori, Coordinator Information Systems, Rochester Psychiatric Center, Rochester, NY, p. A453

HINTZE, Hart, Chief Nursing Officer, Payson Regional Medical Center, Payson, AZ, p. A35

HINTZE, Paul, M.D. Vice President Medical Affairs, Mercy Hospital St. Louis, Saint Louis, MO, p. A380

HIOTT, III, Jimmy O., Chief Financial Officer, Colleton Medical Center, Walterboro, SC, p. A570

HIPKISS, Tom, Vice President Finance, Forbes Regional Hospital, Monroeville, PA, p. A545

HIRKALER, Kim, Director Human Resources, Bon Secours Community Hospital, Port Jervis, NY, p. A452

HIROSE, Mivic, Executive Administrator, Laguna Honda Hospital and Rehabilitation Center, San Francisco, CA, p. A91

HIRSCH, Leslie D., FACHE, President and Chief Executive Officer, Saint Clare's Health System, Denville, NJ, p. A415

HIRSCH, Michel Y., M.D. Chief Medical Staff, Prevost Memorial Hospital, Donaldsonville, LA, p. A277

HIRSCH, Ted W., Senior Executive Director, Kalispell Regional Medical Center, Kalispell, MT, p. A389

HIRSCHMAN, Debra L., MSN, Director, Sheridan Veterans Affairs Medical Center, Sheridan, WY, p. A722

HIRSHBERG, Mark I., Chief Operating Officer, Bothwell Regional Health Center, Sedalia, MO, p. A382

HIRST, Barb, Vice President Human Resources and Chief Nursing Officer, Salem Regional Medical Center, Salem, OH, p. A501

HISE, Landon, Chief Executive Officer, Cordell Memorial Hospital, Cordell, OK, p. A509

HISERODT, James, Senior Vice President Operations, Geneva General Hospital, Geneva, NY, p. A437

HISEY, Commie, D.O. Chief of Staff, Memorial Hospital, Gonzales, TX, p. A621

HITE–DAVIS, Anissa, Vice President Human Resources, St. Joseph's Hospital of Buckhannon, Buckhannon, WV, p. A694

HITT, Patricia A., Associate Director, Grand Junction Veterans Affairs Medical Center, Grand Junction, CO, p. A107

HIXENBAUGH, Cynthia, Director Human Resources, Pershing General Hospital, Lovelock, NV, p. A407

HIXSON, Kim, Chief Financial Officer, Providence Medical Center, Wayne, NE, p. A402

HJEMBO, Philip, Chief Financial Officer, St. Elizabeth Hospital, Enumclaw, WA, p. A683

HLAHOL, Jan, Manager Human Resources, Cleveland Clinic Children's Hospital for Rehabilitation, Cleveland, OH, p. A488

HLUCHY, Nicholas, Business Analyst, Support Services Manager, Baton Rouge Rehabilitation Hospital, Baton Rouge, LA, p. A273

HO, David, Senior Vice President and Chief Financial Officer, White Plains Hospital Center, White Plains, NY, p. A458

HO, Sylvia, Director Information Services, Grady Memorial Hospital, Chickasha, OK, p. A509

HO–SHING, Viodelda, Deputy Director Administration, Creedmoor Psychiatric Center,, NY, p. A443

HOAG, Linda, Director Human Resources, St. Mary's Regional Medical Center, Enid, OK, p. A510

HOAGBIN, Joseph, M.D. Chief Quality Officer, CHI Health Mercy Council Bluffs, Council Bluffs, IA, p. A228

HOAGLAND, Jason, M.D. President, Medical Staff, Davis Hospital and Medical Center, Layton, UT, p. A660

HOAR, Brad, Director Information and Technology, Cedar Park Regional Medical Center, Cedar Park, TX, p. A605

HOAR, Tanya, Chief Executive Officer and Chief Financial Officer, Schoolcraft Memorial Hospital, Manistique, MI, p. A329

HOARD, Kaylee S., Chief Financial Officer, Cook Hospital and Convalescent Nursing Care Unit, Cook, MN, p. A341

HOBACK, Kim, Supervisor Information Systems, Athens–Limestone Hospital, Athens, AL, p. A16

HOBAN, Donna, M.D. Senior Vice President and Physician–in–Chief, Beaumont Hospital Grosse Pointe, Grosse Pointe, MI, p. A326

HOBAN, Douglas M., Vice President and Chief Financial Officer, Mercy Hospital Lebanon, Lebanon, MO, p. A375

HOBART, Robert, Director Management Information Systems, Heartland Behavioral Healthcare, Massillon, OH, p. A498

HOBBS, Donna, Nurse Executive, U. S. Public Health Service Indian Hospital–Sells, Sells, AZ, p. A39

HOBBS, Ed, Director Information Services, DeKalb Health, Auburn, IN, p. A206

HOBBS, Emilie, Director Human Resources, Woodland Heights Medical Center, Lufkin, TX, p. A636

HOBBS, Joey, Chief Information Officer, Community Hospital of Anderson and Madison County, Anderson, IN, p. A206

HOBBS, Mike, Chief Financial Officer, Clay County Hospital, Flora, IL, p. A190

HOBBS, Steve E.
Chief Financial Officer, Eliza Coffee Memorial Hospital, Florence, AL, p. A20
Chief Financial Officer, Shoals Hospital, Muscle Shoals, AL, p. A24

HOBBS, Tommy, Chief Executive Officer, Illinois Valley Community Hospital, Peru, IL, p. A200

HOBGOOD, Lisa, Chief Information Officer, The Heart Hospital at Deaconess Gateway, Newburgh, IN, p. A220

HOBGOOD, Marcus, Director Information Services, University Health Shreveport, Shreveport, LA, p. A288

HOBSON, Christopher, Chief Operating Officer, Wellmont Bristol Regional Medical Center, Bristol, TN, p. A579

HOBSON, James M., Chief Executive Officer, Memorial Health Care System, Chattanooga, TN, p. A580

HOCE, N. Kristopher, President, Morton Plant Hospital, Clearwater, FL, p. A125

HOCHENBERG, Paul S., Senior Vice President Human Resources, Westchester Medical Center, Valhalla, NY, p. A457

HOCHHEISER, Lou, M.D., Chief Executive Officer, St. John's Medical Center and Living Center, Jackson, WY, p. A721

HOCHMAN, Rodney F., M.D., President and Chief Executive Officer, Providence Health & Services, Renton, WA, p. B110

HOCHSTETLER, Amy, Chief Financial Officer, Orthopaedic Hospital of Lutheran Health Network, Fort Wayne, IN, p. A211

HOCK, Douglas G., Senior Vice President Operations, Children's Medical Center of Dallas, Dallas, TX, p. A610

HOCKENBERRY, Michael A., Vice President Operations, Hanover Hospital, Hanover, PA, p. A540

HOCKENBERRY, Tanda, Chief Nursing Officer, HEALTHSOUTH Western Hills Rehabilitation Hospital, Parkersburg, WV, p. A698

HOCKENBURY, Debbie, Assistant Administrator and Chief Financial Officer, William Newton Hospital, Winfield, KS, p. A257

HOCKERT, Steve, Chief Executive Officer, OneCore Health, Oklahoma City, OK, p. A516

HOCKING, Dale E., Chief Financial Officer, Jupiter Medical Center, Jupiter, FL, p. A132

HOCKING, Patrick
Chief Financial Officer, Asante Ashland Community Hospital, Ashland, OR, p. A523
Chief Financial Officer, Asante Rogue Regional Medical Center, Medford, OR, p. A527
Chief Financial Officer, Asante Three Rivers Medical Center, Grants Pass, OR, p. A525

HOCUM, Timothy, Chief Financial Officer, Providence Kodiak Island Medical Center, Kodiak, AK, p. A29

HODGE, Pamela, R.N. Chief Nursing Officer and Coordinator Performance Improvement, Jellico Community Hospital, Jellico, TN, p. A585

HODGES, Alan, Chief Operating Officer, Ochsner Medical Center – North Shore, Slidell, LA, p. A289

HODGES, Dawn, Director Human Resources, Grand River Hospital District, Rifle, CO, p. A111

HODGES, Jay, Chief Financial Officer, Red River Regional Hospital, Bonham, TX, p. A603

HODGES, Leisha, Human Resources Officer, Eastland Memorial Hospital, Eastland, TX, p. A614

HODGES, Randall H., FACHE, President and Chief Executive Officer, CAMC Teays Valley Hospital, Hurricane, WV, p. A696

HODGIN, Robin, R.N. Vice President of Patient Services and Chief Nursing Officer, Northern Hospital of Surry County, Mount Airy, NC, p. A469

HODGKINSON, Kimberly
Chief Financial Officer, St. Vincent's Medical Center Riverside, Jacksonville, FL, p. A132
Chief Financial Officer, St. Vincent's Medical Center Southside, Jacksonville, FL, p. A132

HODGSON, Judith Ann, Chief Nursing Officer, Cheyenne County Hospital, Saint Francis, KS, p. A253

HODGSON, Susan M., R.N. Vice President Patient Care Services and Chief Nursing Officer, Canton–Potsdam Hospital, Potsdam, NY, p. A452

HODNETT, Laura, Interim Chief Nursing Officer, Glen Rose Medical Center, Glen Rose, TX, p. A621

HODSON, Don, M.D. Chief Medical Officer, St. Luke Hospital and Living Center, Marion, KS, p. A249

HODZEDA, Angela, Chief Financial Officer, Jack Hughston Memorial Hospital, Phenix City, AL, p. A25

HOEFER, Robert William, FACHE Chief Operating Officer, Saint Louis University Hospital, Saint Louis, MO, p. A381

HOEFLE, Brian
Chief Financial Officer, Yavapai Regional Medical Center – East, Prescott Valley, AZ, p. A37
Chief Financial Officer, Yavapai Regional Medical Center, Prescott, AZ, p. A37

HOEFS, Dennis, Manager Information Technology, New Mexico Rehabilitation Center, Roswell, NM, p. A430

HOEKEMA, Dale, M.D. Vice President Medical Affairs and Chief Medical Officer, Kadlec Regional Medical Center, Richland, WA, p. A687

HOELL, Paul, M.D. President Medical Staff, New London Family Medical Center, New London, WI, p. A712

HOELSCHER, Steven C., Chief Operating Officer, Valley Regional Medical Center, Brownsville, TX, p. A604

HOERTZ, Joanne, Vice President of Nursing, Brooks Rehabilitation Hospital, Jacksonville, FL, p. A131

HOEY, Amy J., R.N. Executive Vice President and Chief Operating Officer, Lowell General Hospital, Lowell, MA, p. A311

HOFELICH, Kurt T., President, Sentara Norfolk General Hospital, Norfolk, VA, p. A675

HOFER, Maggie, Human Resources Representative, Hawarden Regional Healthcare, Hawarden, IA, p. A232

HOFER, Renee, Controller, St. Joseph's Hospital of Buckhannon, Buckhannon, WV, p. A694

HOFF, David L., Chief Executive Officer, Wayne Memorial Hospital, Honesdale, PA, p. A540

HOFF, Deanna, R.N. Director of Nursing, Bacon County Hospital and Health System, Alma, GA, p. A151

HOFF, Linda, Senior Vice President and Chief Financial Officer, Legacy Mount Hood Medical Center, Gresham, OR, p. A525

HOFF, Margaret, Account Manager, Brown County Community Treatment Center, Green Bay, WI, p. A706

HOFFBERGER, Darren, D.O. Chief of Staff, Broward Health North, Deerfield Beach, FL, p. A127

HOFFELD, Thomas, M.D. Chief of Staff, Spanish Peaks Regional Health Center, Walsenburg, CO, p. A112

HOFFER, Nolan, Chief Executive Officer, Southwest Idaho Advanced Care Hospital, Boise, ID, p. A174

HOFFMAN, Barbara, M.D. Chief Medical Officer, St. Christopher's Hospital for Children, Philadelphia, PA, p. A550

HOFFMAN, Brad, Administrative Director Human Resources, Shawnee Mission Medical Center, Shawnee Mission, KS, p. A254

HOFFMAN, Brian, Director Human Resources, Lancaster Regional Medical Center, Lancaster, PA, p. A542

HOFFMAN, Brian, M.D. Chief Medical Services, Veterans Affairs Boston Healthcare System, Boston, MA, p. A307

HOFFMAN, Carole, Vice President, Parkridge Medical Center, Chattanooga, TN, p. A580

HOFFMAN, Chris, Chief Operating Officer, Highlands Regional Medical Center, Prestonsburg, KY, p. A269

HOFFMAN, Daniel, M.D. Administrative Medical Director, Good Samaritan Regional Health Center, Mount Vernon, IL, p. A197

HOFFMAN, Debbie, Vice President Patient Services, St. Francis Hospital and Health Services, Maryville, MO, p. A376

HOFFMAN, Debra, Manager Human Resources, Kern Valley Healthcare District, Lake Isabella, CA, p. A69

HOFFMAN, Howard, M.D. Medical Director, Psychiatric Institute of Washington, Washington, DC, p. A122

HOFFMAN, Jeff, M.D. Chief Medical Officer, Atrium Medical Center, Middletown, OH, p. A498

HOFFMAN, Jerry, Chief Financial Officer, Platte Health Center Avera, Platte, SD, p. A575

HOFFMAN, III, Joseph E.
Executive Vice President and Chief Financial Officer, Harford Memorial Hospital, Havre De Grace, MD, p. A301
Executive Vice President and Chief Financial Officer, Upper Chesapeake Medical Center, Bel Air, MD, p. A298

HOFFMAN, Julie, Vice President Patient Care Services and Chief Nursing Officer, Mercy Gilbert Medical Center, Gilbert, AZ, p. A33

HOFFMAN, Marcus, Area Chief Financial Officer, Kaiser Permanente Orange County Anaheim Medical Center, Anaheim, CA, p. A55

HOFFMAN, Mark, Chief Financial Officer, Oro Valley Hospital, Oro Valley, AZ, p. A35

HOFFMAN, Mary
Chief Administrative Officer and Chief Financial Officer, Mayo Clinic Health System in Waycross, Waycross, GA, p. A169
Chief Financial Officer, Mayo Clinic Jacksonville, Jacksonville, FL, p. A131

HOFFMAN, Michael, M.D. Chief Medical Officer, South Baldwin Regional Medical Center, Foley, AL, p. A20

HOFFMAN, Pamela S., Director of Human Resources, Monroe Hospital, Bloomington, IN, p. A207

HOFFMAN, Robert P., Vice President and Director Patient Care Services, Wilkes–Barre General Hospital, Wilkes–Barre, PA, p. A558

HOFFMAN, Todd, M.D. Medical Director, St. John Broken Arrow, Broken Arrow, OK, p. A508

HOFFMAN, Tom, Manager Information Systems, Wayne Memorial Hospital, Honesdale, PA, p. A540

HOFFMAN, Trudy, Executive Director, Northwest Center for Behavioral Health, Fort Supply, OK, p. A511

HOFFMAN, Val, Chief Financial Officer, Granite Falls Municipal Hospital and Manor, Granite Falls, MN, p. A344

HOFFMANN, Jeffrey, D.O. Chief Medical Staff, Guttenberg Municipal Hospital, Guttenberg, IA, p. A231

HOFFMANN, Wanda, Director Human Resources, River Oaks Hospital, New Orleans, LA, p. A286

HOFFNER, Amy, Administrator, Kindred Rehabilitation Hospital Arlington, Arlington, TX, p. A597

HOFIUS, Chuck, Chief Executive Officer, Perham Health, Perham, MN, p. A349

HOFLER, Linda, Ph.D. Senior Vice President, Nurse Executive, Vidant Medical Center, Greenville, NC, p. A465

HOFMAN, William, Manager Information Technology, Wilkes Regional Medical Center, North Wilkesboro, NC, p. A470

HOFMANN, Bill, M.D. Chief Medical Staff, Grays Harbor Community Hospital, Aberdeen, WA, p. A681

HOFSTETTER, Peter A., Chief Executive Officer, Willamette Valley Medical Center, McMinnville, OR, p. A526

HOGAN, Dan, Chief Financial Officer, DeSoto Memorial Hospital, Arcadia, FL, p. A123

HOGAN, Judith, Comptroller and Director Resources and Logistics, Naval Hospital Bremerton, Bremerton, WA, p. A682

HOGAN, Michael, Chief Resource Management, General Leonard Wood Army Community Hospital, Fort Leonard Wood, MO, p. A371

HOGAN, Richard, Chief Financial Officer, Pleasant Valley Hospital, Point Pleasant, WV, p. A698

HOGAN, Richard H., CPA Chief Financial Officer, Landmark Hospital, Cape Girardeau, MO, p. A368

HOGAN, Ronald E.
Chief Financial Officer, Our Lady of Lourdes Regional Medical Center, Lafayette, LA, p. A281
Regional Chief Financial Officer, St. Francis Medical Center, Monroe, LA, p. A284

HOGAN, Sean, President, SSM DePaul Health Center, Bridgeton, MO, p. A368

HOGAN, Timothy J., FACHE,
Regional President, Bayshore Community Hospital, Holmdel, NJ, p. A417
Regional President, Riverview Medical Center, Red Bank, NJ, p. A422

HOGDSON, Judy, R.N. Chief Nursing Officer, Rice County District Hospital, Lyons, KS, p. A249

HOGG, Donna, Supervisor Medical Records, Monroe County Hospital, Forsyth, GA, p. A160

HOGGARD, Cindy, Chief Nursing Officer, Hutcheson Medical Center, Fort Oglethorpe, GA, p. A160

HOHENSHELL, Valerie, Director of Clinical Services, Memorial Hospital, Gonzales, TX, p. A621

HOHMAN, Jennifer, M.D. President Medical Staff, Van Wert County Hospital, Van Wert, OH, p. A504

HOLBERT, Brandon, Director, Information Services, Ocala Regional Medical Center, Ocala, FL, p. A139

HOLBROOK, Chip, M.D. Chief of Staff, Simpson General Hospital, Mendenhall, MS, p. A362

HOLBROOK, Curtis, M.D. Chief Medical Officer, Heritage Park Surgical Hospital, Sherman, TX, p. A649

HOLCOMB, Holly, R.N. Chief Operating Officer, Childress Regional Medical Center, Childress, TX, p. A606

HOLCOMB, Mark, Administrator, Great Lakes Specialty Hospital–Muskegon, Muskegon, MI, p. A331

HOLCOMB, Sheila, M.D. President Medical Staff, Floyd Valley Hospital, Le Mars, IA, p. A233

HOLCOMBE, Sheryl, Administrative Assistant, Brownfield Regional Medical Center, Brownfield, TX, p. A604

HOLDEMAN, Royce, Chief Financial Officer, Mercy Hospital, Moundridge, KS, p. A250

HOLDEN, Carol E., M.D., Director, Center for Forensic Psychiatry, Saline, MI, p. A334

HOLDEN, Jay T.
Senior Vice President Chief Human Resources Officer, Beaumont Hospital – Royal Oak, Royal Oak, MI, p. A333
Vice President, Human Resources, Beaumont Hospital Grosse Pointe, Grosse Pointe, MI, p. A326

HOLDEN, Patricia, Chief Executive Officer, Mesa View Regional Hospital, Mesquite, NV, p. A407

HOLDEN, Peter J., President and Chief Executive Officer, Beth Israel Deaconess Hospital Plymouth, Plymouth, MA, p. A314

HOLDEN, Rhonda C., R.N. Chief Nursing Officer, Kittitas Valley Healthcare, Ellensburg, WA, p. A683

HOLDEN, Tami, Director Human Resources, HEALTHSOUTH Bakersfield Rehabilitation Hospital, Bakersfield, CA, p. A57

HOLDEN, Teal, Chief Executive Officer, Memorial Hermann Surgical Hospital Kingwood, Kingwood, TX, p. A632

HOLDER, Gregory, Administrator and Chief Nursing Executive, Integris Marshall County Medical Center, Madill, OK, p. A513

HOLDER, Hal
Director Finance, SSM DePaul Health Center, Bridgeton, MO, p. A368
Director Finance, SSM St. Joseph Hospital West, Lake Saint Louis, MO, p. A375

HOLDER, Joanna, Director Human Resources, Novant Health Franklin Medical Center, Louisburg, NC, p. A468

HOLDER, Virgil, Human Resources Business Partner, Henry Medical Center, Stockbridge, GA, p. A167

HOLDERMAN, Wanda, R.N., Chief Executive Officer, Fresno Heart and Surgical Hospital, Fresno, CA, p. A64

HOLEKAMP, Nicholas, M.D. Chief Medical Officer, Ranken Jordan Pediatric Bridge Hospital, Maryland Heights, MO, p. A376

HOLGUIN, Brenda, Manager Human Resources, University Behavioral Health of El Paso, El Paso, TX, p. A616

HOLGUIN, Mindee, Manager Human Resources, Sierra Vista Hospital, Truth or Consequences, NM, p. A431

HOLINER, Joel, M.D. Executive Medical Director, Green Oaks Hospital, Dallas, TX, p. A610

HOLLAND, Baxter C., M.D. Chief Medical Officer, Rutland Regional Medical Center, Rutland, VT, p. A666

HOLLAND, Brad D., Chief Executive Officer, Cedar Park Regional Medical Center, Cedar Park, TX, p. A605

HOLLAND, Charles, President and Chief Executive Officer, St. Bernard Hospital and Health Care Center, Chicago, IL, p. A187

HOLLAND, David
Chief Information Officer, Herrin Hospital, Herrin, IL, p. A192
Vice President Chief Innovation Officer, Memorial Hospital of Carbondale, Carbondale, IL, p. A182
Vice President Information Services, St. Joseph Memorial Hospital, Murphysboro, IL, p. A197

HOLLAND, Gabrielle, Chief Financial Officer, Irving Coppell Surgical Hospital, Irving, TX, p. A629

HOLLAND, John F., Chief Executive Officer, LHP Hospital Group, Plano, TX, p. B84

HOLLAND, Kevin, Chief Executive Officer, Singing River Health System, Pascagoula, MS, p. A364

HOLLAND, Kim, Senior Director Nursing Services, Comanche County Memorial Hospital, Lawton, OK, p. A512

HOLLAND, Kwi, Vice President Information Services, Knox Community Hospital, Mount Vernon, OH, p. A499

HOLLAND, Michael, M.D., Chief Executive Officer, Rehabilitation Hospital of Jennings, Jennings, LA, p. A279

HOLLAND, Penny, Associate Director for Patient Care Services, Aleda E. Lutz Veterans Affairs Medical Center, Saginaw, MI, p. A333

HOLLAND, Shannon S., R.N. Vice President of Patient Care Service, St. James Healthcare, Butte, MT, p. A386

HOLLAND, Sharron, Chief Financial Officer, Baptist Memorial Hospital–Huntingdon, Huntingdon, TN, p. A584

HOLLAND, Stace D., Chief Executive Officer, Lynn County Hospital District, Tahoka, TX, p. A651

HOLLAND, Stephen, M.D. Vice President Chief Medical Officer and Medical Director, Gaylord Hospital, Wallingford, CT, p. A117

HOLLAND, Tiffany, Chief Nursing Officer, Bradley County Medical Center, Warren, AR, p. A53

HOLLAND, William, Chief Executive Officer, Prague Community Hospital, Prague, OK, p. A518

HOLLAND–BAK, Chelsea, Interim Administrator, PeaceHealth Cottage Grove Community Medical Center, Cottage Grove, OR, p. A524

HOLLEMAN, Ivan, Chief Financial Officer, Baxter Regional Medical Center, Mountain Home, AR, p. A584

HOLLEMAN, James, M.D. Chief of Staff, St. Luke's Hospital, Columbus, NC, p. A462

HOLLEMAN, Stephen B., Chief Financial Officer, Shepherd Center, Atlanta, GA, p. A153

HOLLEY, Jacqueline A., R.N. Vice President Nursing, Jamaica Hospital Medical Center,, NY, p. A444

HOLLIDAY, Jonathan, Manager Information Technology, Central Community Hospital, Elkader, IA, p. A230

HOLLIDAY, Michael T., Vice President Fiscal and Administrative Services, Van Wert County Hospital, Van Wert, OH, p. A504

HOLLIMAN, Emily L., President, Norwood Hospital, Norwood, MA, p. A313

HOLLINGER, Brad, Chairman and Chief Executive Officer, Vibra Healthcare, Mechanicsburg, PA, p. B148

HOLLINGER, Lori, Manager Human Resources, Fulton State Hospital, Fulton, MO, p. A372

HOLLINGER, Terry, Chief Executive Officer, Bucktail Medical Center, Renovo, PA, p. A553

HOLLINGSWORTH, Carl, Chief Financial Officer, Artesia General Hospital, Artesia, NM, p. A427

HOLLINGSWORTH, Christine, Chief Financial Officer, Phoenix Veterans Affairs Health Care System, Phoenix, AZ, p. A36

HOLLINGSWORTH, Nancy, MSN, President and Chief Executive Officer, Saint Agnes Medical Center, Fresno, CA, p. A64

HOLLIS, Gary W., Comptroller, Arkansas State Hospital, Little Rock, AR, p. A49

HOLLIS, Tom, Chief Financial Officer, Ellett Memorial Hospital, Appleton City, MO, p. A367

HOLLISTER, Jerry, Chief Executive Officer, NorthEastern Center, Auburn, IN, p. A206

HOLLISTER, Richard, President of Medical Staff, Exeter Hospital, Exeter, NH, p. A410

HOLLON, Kim Norton, FACHE, Chief Executive Officer, Signature Healthcare Brockton Hospital, Brockton, MA, p. A308

HOLLOWAY, Basil, Director Information Services, Medical Center of Arlington, Arlington, TX, p. A598

HOLLOWAY, Cheryl, Director of Nursing, Green Clinic Surgical Hospital, Ruston, LA, p. A287

HOLLOWAY, David, M.D. Chief Medical Officer, West Valley Hospital, Dallas, OR, p. A524

HOLLOWAY, Kristina, Chief Human Resources Officer, Healdsburg District Hospital, Healdsburg, CA, p. A66

HOLLOWAY, Myra, Director Human Resources Management, Central State Hospital, Milledgeville, GA, p. A163

HOLLOWAY, W. David, M.D. Chief Medical Officer, Salem Hospital, Salem, OR, p. A530

HOLLOWAY, Whitney, Chief Financial Officer, Berwick Hospital Center, Berwick, PA, p. A533

HOLM, Mary Ann, Office Clerk, Tioga Medical Center, Tioga, ND, p. A480

HOLM, Stan V., FACHE, Chief Executive Officer, West Valley Hospital, Goodyear, AZ, p. A33

HOLMAN, Joel, Chief of Staff, Central Valley Medical Center, Nephi, UT, p. A661

HOLMAN, Steve M., Chief Executive Officer, Union Hospital, Terre Haute, IN, p. A223

HOLMAY, Diane, R.N
Vice President and Chief Nursing Officer, Mayo Clinic Health System – Franciscan Healthcare in La Crosse, La Crosse, WI, p. A707
Chief Nursing Officer, Mayo Clinic Health System – Franciscan Healthcare in Sparta, Sparta, WI, p. A715

HOLMBERT, Daniel, Director of Medical Affairs, New Ulm Medical Center, New Ulm, MN, p. A348

HOLMES, Dawne, Chief Financial Officer, Greenwood Leflore Hospital, Greenwood, MS, p. A358

HOLMES, Heather, Director Health Information Systems, Crossgates River Oaks Hospital, Brandon, MS, p. A356

HOLMES, Heidi, Chief Information Officer, Oklahoma State University Medical Center, Tulsa, OK, p. A520

HOLMES Jr., James M., President and Chief Executive Officer, Rappahannock General Hospital, Kilmarnock, VA, p. A672

HOLMES, James R., President and Chief Executive Officer, Redlands Community Hospital, Redlands, CA, p. A85

HOLMES, Jeremy, D.O. Chief of Staff, Kalkaska Memorial Health Center, Kalkaska, MI, p. A328

HOLMES, John, Business Manager, Ancora Psychiatric Hospital, Hammonton, NJ, p. A416

HOLMES, John A., Chief Financial Officer, Ephrata Community Hospital, Ephrata, PA, p. A538

HOLMES, Mardy, Director Information Technology, Arkansas Methodist Medical Center, Paragould, AR, p. A51

HOLMES, Terry R., M.D. Clinical Director, Moccasin Bend Mental Health Institute, Chattanooga, TN, p. A580

HOLMES, Troy, Director Finance, Advanced Specialty Hospital of Toledo, Toledo, OH, p. A503

HOLOM, Randall G., Chief Executive Officer, Frances Mahon Deaconess Hospital, Glasgow, MT, p. A387

HOLSAPPLE, Kim, Human Resource Specialist, Chester Mental Health Center, Chester, IL, p. A183

HOLSCHBACH, Dennis, Chief Financial Officer and Director Human Resources, Ruby Valley Hospital, Sheridan, MT, p. A391

HOLSON, Debbie C., R.N. Vice President Patient Care Services and Chief Nursing Officer, The HSC Pediatric Center, Washington, DC, p. A122

HOLST, Ken, Chief Financial Officer, Borgess–Lee Memorial Hospital, Dowagiac, MI, p. A323

HOLSTEN, Robyn, Human Resources Director, Salt Lake Behavioral Health, Salt Lake City, UT, p. A663

HOLSTIEN, Bruce, President and Chief Executive Officer, Spartanburg Regional Healthcare System, Spartanburg, SC, p. B126

HOLSTIEN, Bruce, President and Chief Executive Officer, Spartanburg Regional Medical Center, Spartanburg, SC, p. A570

HOLSTON, James, M.D. Vice President and Chief Quality Officer, South Central Regional Medical Center, Laurel, MS, p. A361

HOLT, Bebe, Vice President Chief Operating Officer, Novant Health Prince William Medical Center, Manassas, VA, p. A673

HOLT, Brian, Chief Executive Officer, Post Acute Medical Specialty Hospital of Lafayette, Lafayette, LA, p. A282

HOLT, Kory
Division Controller Network Operations, Avera Dells Area Hospital, Dell Rapids, SD, p. A573
Assistant Vice President for Financial Integration, Avera Flandreau Hospital, Flandreau, SD, p. A573

HOLT, Mari J., R.N. Vice President Patient Care Services, Unity Hospital, Fridley, MN, p. A344

HOLT, Peter, M.D. Director Medical Affairs, Saint Luke's Hospital of Kansas City, Kansas City, MO, p. A374

HOLT, Richard, R.N. Associate Director Patient Care Services, Veterans Affairs St. Louis Health Care System, Saint Louis, MO, p. A382

HOLT, Sherry, Director Human Resources, United Regional Medical Center, Manchester, TN, p. A587

HOLT, Thomas A., Chief Financial Officer, Conroe Regional Medical Center, Conroe, TX, p. A607

HOLT, Will, Director Information Technology, Harrison County Community Hospital, Bethany, MO, p. A367

HOLTHAUS, Julie K., Director Human Resources, Sabetha Community Hospital, Sabetha, KS, p. A253

HOLTHAUS, Monica, Chief Financial Officer, Community HealthCare System, Onaga, KS, p. A251

HOLTMAN, Jean M., Vice President Human Resources, St. Tammany Parish Hospital, Covington, LA, p. A276

HOLTZ, George, Director Human Resources, Sharp Grossmont Hospital, La Mesa, CA, p. A68

HOLTZ, Keith, Chief Human Resources Officer, Cook Children's Medical Center, Fort Worth, TX, p. A618

HOLTZ, Mark
Chief Operating Officer, Coordinated Health–Bethlehem, Bethlehem, PA, p. A533
Senior Vice President Operations and Chief Operating Officer, Glens Falls Hospital, Glens Falls, NY, p. A438

HOLTZ, Noel, M.D. Chief Medical Officer, WellStar Douglas Hospital, Douglasville, GA, p. A158

HOLTZMAN, Michael, M.D. Medical Director, Kindred Hospital–St. Louis, Saint Louis, MO, p. A380

HOLYFIELD, Linda S., MSN, President and Chief Executive Officer, P & S Surgical Hospital, Monroe, LA, p. A284

HOLYOAK, Mark, Chief Executive Officer, Castleview Hospital, Price, UT, p. A662

HOLZER, Traci, Chief Human Resources Officer, Doctors Hospital of Manteca, Manteca, CA, p. A76

HOMA, Jim, Chief Executive Officer, Heatherhill Care Communities, Chardon, OH, p. A485

HOMAN, Cheryl, Administrative Director, Lima Memorial Health System, Lima, OH, p. A496

HOMAS, Dallas, Commander, Madigan Healthcare System, Tacoma, WA, p. A690

HOMER, Kenneth, M.D. Chief Medical Officer, Holy Cross Hospital, Fort Lauderdale, FL, p. A128

HOMER, Margie, President, Southern Plains Medical Group, Oklahoma City, OK, p. B126

HOMERSKI, James, Director Information Services, Conemaugh Miners Medical Center, Hastings, PA, p. A540

HOMYK, David, Vice President Human Resources, Beaufort Memorial Hospital, Beaufort, SC, p. A562

HOMYK, Linda, Chief Nursing Officer, Sewickley Valley Hospital, (A Division of Valley Medical Facilities), Sewickley, PA, p. A555

HONAHNIE, De Alva, Chief Executive Officer, Hopi Health Care Center, Kearns Canyon, AZ, p. A33

HONAKER, Linda, Vice President Financial Operations, Scripps Memorial Hospital–La Jolla, La Jolla, CA, p. A68

HONAN, Thomas, Interim Chief Financial Officer, Loyola University Medical Center, Maywood, IL, p. A195

HONDLEY, Charles, Chief Financial Officer, Providence Memorial Hospital, El Paso, TX, p. A616

HONEA, Bert, M.D. Medical Director, McKee Medical Center, Loveland, CO, p. A109

HONEA, Bruce, Director Information Services, CHRISTUS Coushatta Health Care Center, Coushatta, LA, p. A275

HONEA, Michael, Chief Financial Officer, Glen Rose Medical Center, Glen Rose, TX, p. A621

HONERBRINK, Daniel, Vice President Finance and Chief Financial Officer, Fairmont General Hospital, Fairmont, WV, p. A695

HONEYCUTT, Cynthia, Director Human Resources, Moccasin Bend Mental Health Institute, Chattanooga, TN, p. A580

HONEYCUTT, Robert C., FACHE, Chief Executive Officer, HEALTHSOUTH Rehabilitation Hospital of Southern Arizona, Tucson, AZ, p. A40

HONEYCUTT, Tammy, R.N. Director of Nursing, Jasper Memorial Hospital, Monticello, GA, p. A164

HONSINGER, Melissa, Chief Operating Officer, Elks Rehab Hospital, Boise, ID, p. A174

HONTS, Gary, Interim Chief Executive Officer, John F. Kennedy Memorial Hospital, Indio, CA, p. A67

HOO–YOU, Hilary, Regional Administrator, Southwestern State Hospital, Thomasville, GA, p. A168

HOOD, Cliff, Chief Operating Officer, Central Regional Hospital, Butner, NC, p. A461

HOOD, Fred B., FACHE, Administrator, North Mississippi Medical Center–Pontotoc, Pontotoc, MS, p. A364

HOOD, Kathy, Administrative Assistant Human Resources, Union General Hospital, Blairsville, GA, p. A154

HOOD, M. Michelle, FACHE, President and Chief Executive Officer, Eastern Maine Healthcare Systems, Brewer, ME, p. B55

HOOD, Ron, M.D. Chief of Staff, Sutter Amador Hospital, Jackson, CA, p. A67

HOOD, Tom, Chief Operating Officer, King's Daughters Medical Center, Brookhaven, MS, p. A356

HOOFMAN, Kevin, Director Management Information, White County Medical Center, Searcy, AR, p. A52

HOOK, Diane, Chief Financial Officer, Wayne County Hospital, Corydon, IA, p. A228

HOOKER, Melvin, Chief Human Resources, Veterans Affairs Medical Center, Albuquerque, NM, p. A427

HOOKER, Rita, Administrative Director Information Services, Bon Secours St. Francis Health System, Greenville, SC, p. A566

HOOKS, Al, Senior Vice President and Chief Financial Officer, Nash Health Care Systems, Rocky Mount, NC, p. A471

HOOKS Jr., Dwayne, R.N., Chief Executive Officer, Select Specialty Hospital–Atlanta, Atlanta, GA, p. A153

HOOLAHAN, Susan E., R.N. Vice President Patient Care Services and Chief Nursing Officer, UPMC Passavant, Pittsburgh, PA, p. A552

HOOP, Heather, Human Resources Generalist, Adams County Regional Medical Center, Seaman, OH, p. A501

HOOPER, Grady, Chief Executive Officer, Ballinger Memorial Hospital, Ballinger, TX, p. A601

HOOPER, Joseph, Chief Operating Officer, OhioHealth Marion General Hospital, Marion, OH, p. A497

HOOPER, Robert A.
Director Human Resources, TriStar Skyline Madison Campus, Madison, TN, p. A587
Director Human Resources, TriStar Skyline Medical Center, Nashville, TN, p. A591

HOOPES, John L., Chief Executive Officer, Caribou Memorial Hospital and Living Center, Soda Springs, ID, p. A178

HOOVER, Alvin, FACHE, Chief Executive Officer, King's Daughters Medical Center, Brookhaven, MS, p. A356

HOOVER, Garrett W., FACHE Chief Operating Officer, Olean General Hospital, Olean, NY, p. A450

HOOVER, Jeremy, Chief Information Officer, Kiowa County Memorial Hospital, Greensburg, KS, p. A244

HOOVER, Leon, Director Information Systems, Hendry Regional Medical Center, Clewiston, FL, p. A126

HOOVER, Tom, Director of Nursing, West Holt Memorial Hospital, Atkinson, NE, p. A393

HOPE, Joseph D., D.O. President Medical Staff, Riddle Hospital, Media, PA, p. A545

HOPE, Lisa R., Director Human Resources, Muhlenberg Community Hospital, Greenville, KY, p. A262

HOPE, Steve, Vice President Corporate Services, Methodist Rehabilitation Center, Jackson, MS, p. A360

HOPE, IV, William, M.D. Chief of Medical Staff, Vidant Chowan Hospital, Edenton, NC, p. A464

HOPKINS, Brian, Director Management Information Systems, Southern Virginia Regional Medical Center, Emporia, VA, p. A670

HOPKINS, Denver, Director of Human Resources, Aventura Hospital and Medical Center, Aventura, FL, p. A123

HOPKINS, Frances F., Chief Financial Officer, Sabine Medical Center, Many, LA, p. A283

HOPKINS, Jason, Director, Human Resources, Hamilton Medical Center, Dalton, GA, p. A158

HOPKINS, Joy, Vice President Patient Care Services, OSF St. Francis Hospital and Medical Group, Escanaba, MI, p. A323

HOPKINS, Kelli, Director Human Resources, Baptist Health Medical Center–Hot Spring County, Malvern, AR, p. A50

HOPKINS, Ken, Vice President Finance and Chief Financial Officer, Norman Regional Health System, Norman, OK, p. A514

HOPKINS, Maura, R.N. Chief Nursing Officer, RML Specialty Hospital, Hinsdale, IL, p. A193

HOPKINS, Ronald, D.O. Chief of Staff, Nor–Lea General Hospital, Lovington, NM, p. A429

HOPKINS, William, Director Finance, Carolinas Rehabilitation, Charlotte, NC, p. A462

HOPP, Eva, Chief Nurse Executive, Pinckneyville Community Hospital, Pinckneyville, IL, p. A200

HOPPE, Janice
Vice President Information Technology System, Banner Baywood Medical Center, Mesa, AZ, p. A34
Vice President, Information Technology System, Banner Heart Hospital, Mesa, AZ, p. A34

HOPPEN, Claudine N., MSN Interim Chief Nursing Officer, Children's Hospital of Michigan, Detroit, MI, p. A321

HOPSON, W. Briggs, M.D. Clinical Medical Director, River Region Medical Center, Vicksburg, MS, p. A366

HOPSTAD, Kyle, Chief Executive Officer, Broadwater Health Center, Townsend, MT, p. A391

HOPWOOD, James, Chief Financial Officer, Promise Hospital of Miss Lou, Vidalia, LA, p. A289

HORAN, Gary S., FACHE, President and Chief Executive Officer, Trinitas Regional Medical Center, Elizabeth, NJ, p. A415

HORAN, Jim, Chief Financial Officer, Horsham Clinic, Ambler, PA, p. A533

HORAN, Patrick, M.D. Chief of Staff, Tampa Community Hospital, Tampa, FL, p. A148

HORAN, Sandra A., Executive Director, Margaretville Hospital, Margaretville, NY, p. A441

HORATH, Kevin, Vice President Human Resources, Decatur Memorial Hospital, Decatur, IL, p. A188

HORECKA, Richard, Chief Medical Officer, Swift County–Benson Hospital, Benson, MN, p. A340

HORN, Bill, Human Resources Director, Island Hospital, Anacortes, WA, p. A681

HORN, Jeff, Coordinator Information Systems, Jay County Hospital, Portland, IN, p. A221

HORN, LeeAnn, Chief Nurse Executive, Providence Kodiak Island Medical Center, Kodiak, AK, p. A29

HORN, Syndi, Director Information Systems, Memorial Hospital, Carthage, IL, p. A182

HORNBURG, Tom, Director Information Systems, Mason General Hospital, Shelton, WA, p. A689

HORNE, Beth, System Administrator Information Technology, Preston Memorial Hospital, Kingwood, WV, p. A696

HORNE, Eilene, Manager Human Resources, Mountain View Hospital, Idaho Falls, ID, p. A176

HORNE, Harry, D.O. Chief of Staff, Cumberland River Hospital, Celina, TN, p. A580

HORNE, J. Mark, Senior Vice President and Chief Operating Officer, Grand View Hospital, Sellersville, PA, p. A554

HORNE, Theresa, MS Vice President Patient Care Services, St. Dominic–Jackson Memorial Hospital, Jackson, MS, p. A360

HORNER, Ania, R.N. Chief Nurse Executive, Aurora Sinai Medical Center, Milwaukee, WI, p. A710

HORNER, Bryan, President and Chief Executive Officer, Shannon Medical Center, San Angelo, TX, p. A645

HORNER, Cheryl, Supervisor Data Processing, Community Memorial Hospital, Staunton, IL, p. A203

HORNER, Eva, Assistant Executive Director Operations, Devereux Hospital and Children's Center of Florida, Melbourne, FL, p. A135

HORNER, James, Chief Information Officer, Portland Veterans Affairs Medical Center, Portland, OR, p. A528

HORNER, John M., President and Chief Executive Officer, Major Hospital, Shelbyville, IN, p. A222

HORNSBY, Donny, Director Fiscal Services, Memphis Mental Health Institute, Memphis, TN, p. A589

HORNUNG, Dona, Director Information and Technology Services, Doctors Hospital, Augusta, GA, p. A153

HORNUNG, Kurt, Director, Medical Center of Trinity, Trinity, FL, p. A149

HORNUUG, Joel, M.D. Chief Medical Officer, Morris County Hospital, Council Grove, KS, p. A243

HOROWITZ, Ira, M.D. Chief Medical Officer, Emory University Hospital, Atlanta, GA, p. A152

HORRIGAN, Timothy, Chief Medical Officer, UnityPoint Health – Allen Hospital, Waterloo, IA, p. A239

HORSLEY, Steve, Vice President and Chief Information Officer, Moses H. Cone Memorial Hospital, Greensboro, NC, p. A465

HORSMAN, Sarah
Vice President Human Resources, MultiCare Good Samaritan Hospital, Puyallup, WA, p. A687
Senior Vice President Human Potential, MultiCare Mary Bridge Children's Hospital and Health Center, Tacoma, WA, p. A691
Senior Vice President Human Potential, MultiCare Tacoma General Hospital, Tacoma, WA, p. A691

HORST, Brad, Director Human Resources, Clear Lake Regional Medical Center, Webster, TX, p. A656

HORSTMAN, Jennifer M., R.N. Chief Nursing Officer and Chief Information Officer, Fairbanks, Indianapolis, IN, p. A214

HORTILLOSA, Maria, M.D. Chief of Staff, Middlesboro ARH Hospital, Middlesboro, KY, p. A267

HORTON, Eileen M.
Vice President Patient Services and Chief Nursing Officer, Capital Health Medical Center–Hopewell, Pennington, NJ, p. A421
Vice President, Patient Services/Chief Nursing Officer, Capital Health Regional Medical Center, Trenton, NJ, p. A423

HORTON, Greg, Director Support Services, State Hospital South, Blackfoot, ID, p. A174

HORTON, Jim, Chief Executive Officer, Pecos County Memorial Hospital, Fort Stockton, TX, p. A618

HORTON, Kenny, Director Information Systems, Walker Baptist Medical Center, Jasper, AL, p. A22

HORTON, Marie, Director Associate Relations, Bartow Regional Medical Center, Bartow, FL, p. A123

HORTON, Melanie Paige, Chief Nursing Officer, Russell County Medical Center, Lebanon, VA, p. A672

HORTON, Michelle, Senior Director Human Resources Services, Scripps Memorial Hospital–La Jolla, La Jolla, CA, p. A68

HORTON, Warren, Information Technologist, Baptist Health Medical Center–Stuttgart, Stuttgart, AR, p. A53

HORVAT, Kami, Chief Financial Officer, Doctors Hospital of West Covina, West Covina, CA, p. A100

HORVATH, Dolores A., Chief Executive Officer, Medina Memorial Hospital, Medina, NY, p. A441

HORWITZ, Lee, M.D. Chief of Staff, Oak Valley Hospital District, Oakdale, CA, p. A80

HOSKINS, Pearly Graham, M.D. President Medical Staff, Cape Fear Valley – Bladen County Hospital, Elizabethtown, NC, p. A464

HOSKINS, Shirley, Chief Operating Officer, Meadows Regional Medical Center, Vidalia, GA, p. A168

HOSLER, Stephan, Vice President Human Resources, Mercy Medical Center Redding, Redding, CA, p. A85

HOSTEENEZ, Vivie, Chief Financial Officer, U. S. Public Health Service Indian Hospital, San Carlos, AZ, p. A38

HOSTETTER, Lynne, Vice President Human Resources, The HSC Pediatric Center, Washington, DC, p. A122

HOTA, Bala, Interim Chief Information Officer, John H. Stroger Jr. Hospital of Cook County, Chicago, IL, p. A184

HOTALING, Andrew, Chief Executive Officer, Forest View Psychiatric Hospital, Grand Rapids, MI, p. A325

HOTCHKISS, Kaleigh, Controller, HEALTHSOUTH Rehabilitation Hospital of Southern Arizona, Tucson, AZ, p. A40

HOTES, Lawrence S., M.D. Chief Medical Officer, New England Sinai Hospital and Rehabilitation Center, Stoughton, MA, p. A315

HOTT, Judith, Chief Executive Officer, Thomas B. Finan Center, Cumberland, MD, p. A300

HOTTENDORF, Catherine, MS, Executive Director, Franklin Hospital, Valley Stream, NY, p. A457

HOUCHIN, Kim, Chief Nursing Officer, Minnie Hamilton HealthCare Center, Grantsville, WV, p. A695

HOUGH, Jason, Medical Staff President, Spencer Hospital, Spencer, IA, p. A238

HOUGHTON, Roxan, Director Human Resources, Promise Hospital of Miss Lou, Vidalia, LA, p. A289

HOULAHAN, Beth, MSN Senior Vice President and Chief Nursing Officer, University of Wisconsin Hospital and Clinics, Madison, WI, p. A708

HOULE, David, Executive Vice President and Chief Financial Officer, The Hospital at Hebrew Health Care, West Hartford, CT, p. A118

HOULIHAN, David, M.D. Chief of Staff, Tomah Veterans Affairs Medical Center, Tomah, WI, p. A716

HOULIHAN, James, Chief Financial Officer, Warren Memorial Hospital, Friend, NE, p. A395

HOUMANN, Lars D., President, Florida Hospital, Orlando, FL, p. A140

HOURANY, Joseph, Chief Medical Officer, Montclair Hospital Medical Center, Montclair, CA, p. A78

HOUSAND, Jill, Director Human Resources, Mesa Springs, Fort Worth, TX, p. A618

HOUSE, Alan, Chief Financial Officer, Margaret R. Pardee Memorial Hospital, Hendersonville, NC, p. A466

HOUSE, David
  Vice President, Baptist Health Extended Care Hospital, Little Rock, AR, p. A49
  Vice President and Chief Information Officer, Baptist Health Medical Center – North Little Rock, North Little Rock, AR, p. A51
  Vice President and Chief Information Officer, Baptist Health Medical Center–Arkadelphia, Arkadelphia, AR, p. A43
  Vice President and Chief Information Officer, Baptist Health Medical Center–Little Rock, Little Rock, AR, p. A49
  Vice President and Chief Information Officer, Baptist Health Rehabilitation Institute, Little Rock, AR, p. A49

HOUSE, Jennifer R., Chief Operations and Readiness, Reynolds Army Community Hospital, Fort Sill, OK, p. A511

HOUSE, Michael, Director Information Systems, St. Mary's Medical Center, Huntington, WV, p. A696

HOUSER, Beth P., R.N. Chief Nursing Officer, Baylor Regional Medical Center at Grapevine, Grapevine, TX, p. A621

HOUSER, David, M.D. Vice President Medical Affairs, Rapid City Regional Hospital, Rapid City, SD, p. A576

HOUSER, Glenn, M.D. Chief Medical Officer, Garfield County Public Hospital District, Pomeroy, WA, p. A686

HOUSER, Robert, FACHE, Chief Executive Officer, Blue Mountain Hospital, John Day, OR, p. A526

HOUSER, Sara, Chief Nursing Officer, Ashe Memorial Hospital, Jefferson, NC, p. A467

HOUSER–HANFELDER, Sallie, FACHE, Director, Central Texas Veterans Healthcare System, Temple, TX, p. A652

HOUSH, Joe, District Director Human Resources, Kindred Hospital–Indianapolis, Indianapolis, IN, p. A214

HOUSLEY, Kristin, Chief Management Information Systems, South Lincoln Medical Center, Kemmerer, WY, p. A721

HOUSMAN, Bradley W., M.D. Chief Medical Officer, Baptist Health Paducah, Paducah, KY, p. A269

HOUSTON, Anthony, Executive Vice President, St. Marys Health Center, Jefferson City, MO, p. A372

HOUSTON, Jerry, Director Information Systems, Jennie Stuart Medical Center, Hopkinsville, KY, p. A263

HOUSTON, Sally, M.D. Executive Vice President and Chief Medical Officer, Tampa General Hospital, Tampa, FL, p. A148

HOUSTON, Steven P., Vice President Strategy and Technology, CHI Health Bergan Mercy, Omaha, NE, p. A399

HOUSTON, William J., M.D. Chief Medical Officer, Indiana University Health La Porte Hospital, La Porte, IN, p. A216

HOUT, Darla, Director Human Resources and Marketing, Clay County Hospital, Flora, IL, p. A190

HOVAN, Keith A., R.N. President and Chief Executive Officer, Southcoast Hospitals Group, Fall River, MA, p. A310

HOVENS, Michael R., M.D. Chief Medical Officer, Tri–Lakes Medical Center, Batesville, MS, p. A355

HOWALT, Lyra, Chief Financial Officer, North Fulton Regional Hospital, Roswell, GA, p. A165

HOWARD, Andrew, Interim Chief Executive Officer, Lake Wales Medical Center, Lake Wales, FL, p. A133

HOWARD, Ben, D.O. Chief of Staff, Salt Lake Regional Medical Center, Salt Lake City, UT, p. A663

HOWARD, Catherine, Director Human Resources, Halifax Regional Health System, South Boston, VA, p. A678

HOWARD, Charles, M.D. Chief of Staff, St. Vincent Morrilton, Morrilton, AR, p. A50

HOWARD, Cindy, Director Financial Services, Oneida County Hospital, Malad City, ID, p. A176

HOWARD, Craig, Director, Canandaigua Veterans Affairs Medical Center, Canandaigua, NY, p. A435

HOWARD, Daniel, Chief Financial Officer, Maine Veterans Affairs Medical Center, Augusta, ME, p. A291

HOWARD, Darcy, Interim Chief Executive Officer, Logan County Hospital, Oakley, KS, p. A251

HOWARD, Eddie L.
  Vice President and Chief Operating Officer, East Texas Medical Center Rehabilitation Hospital, Tyler, TX, p. A654
  Chief Operating Officer, East Texas Medical Center Rehabilitation Hospital, Tyler, TX, p. A654
  Vice President and Chief Operating Officer, East Texas Medical Center Specialty Hospital, Tyler, TX, p. A654

HOWARD, Gary L., Senior VP and Chief Financial Officer, Hamilton Medical Center, Dalton, GA, p. A158

HOWARD, Greg M.
  Director Human Resource, Health Alliance Hospital – Broadway Campus, Kingston, NY, p. A440
  Vice President Human Resources, Health Alliance Hospital – Mary's Avenue Campus, Kingston, NY, p. A440

HOWARD, Gwenyth, Vice President Finance, St. Thomas More Hospital, Canon City, CO, p. A103

HOWARD, Jill, R.N. Chief Operating Officer, TriStar Skyline Madison Campus, Madison, TN, p. A587

HOWARD, Katherine, Vice President Finance and Planning, Hebrew Rehabilitation Center, Boston, MA, p. A307

HOWARD, Lisa M., Acting Director, Veterans Affairs Sierra Nevada Health Care System, Reno, NV, p. A408

HOWARD, Loy M., President and Chief Executive Officer, Tanner Health System, Carrollton, GA, p. B132

HOWARD, Mary, Director Human Resources, Winnebago Mental Health Institute, Winnebago, WI, p. A719

HOWARD, Mike, Associate Administrator, Eliza Coffee Memorial Hospital, Florence, AL, p. A20

HOWARD, Norma N., Chief Executive Officer, Lindsay Municipal Hospital, Lindsay, OK, p. A513

HOWARD, Opal R., Executive Director Human Resources, Florida Hospital Memorial Medical Center, Daytona Beach, FL, p. A127

HOWARD, Pamela B., R.N., Chief Executive Officer, Administrator and Risk Manager, Lake Butler Hospital Hand Surgery Center, Lake Butler, FL, p. A133

HOWARD, Roger, M.D. Senior Vice President and Medical Director, Beaumont Hospital – Troy, Troy, MI, p. A336

HOWARD, Roger, President and Chief Executive Officer, Dearborn County Hospital, Lawrenceburg, IN, p. A217

HOWARD, Ron, Chief Financial Officer, Holly Hill Hospital, Raleigh, NC, p. A471

HOWARD, Sabra, Manager Human Resources, Harlan ARH Hospital, Harlan, KY, p. A262

HOWARD, Teresa, Manager Human Resources, Yoakum County Hospital, Denver City, TX, p. A614

HOWARD, Tim
  Chief Human Resources Officer, Fountain Valley Regional Hospital and Medical Center, Fountain Valley, CA, p. A63
  Interim Chief Financial Officer, Memorial Hospital at Craig, Craig, CO, p. A104

HOWARD, Tom, Chief Financial Officer, Texas Health Presbyterian Hospital Flower Mound, Flower Mound, TX, p. A617

HOWARD, Win, Chief Executive Officer, Asante Three Rivers Medical Center, Grants Pass, OR, p. A525

HOWARD–CROW, Dallis
  Chief Human Resources Officer, Emory University Hospital Midtown, Atlanta, GA, p. A152
  Chief Human Resources Officer, Emory Wesley Woods Geriatric Hospital, Atlanta, GA, p. A152

HOWAT, Greg, Vice President Human Resources, Eastern Maine Medical Center, Bangor, ME, p. A291

HOWDEN, Tim, Interim Chief Financial Officer, Grays Harbor Community Hospital, Aberdeen, WA, p. A681

HOWDEN, William, Vice President Nursing, Good Samaritan Regional Medical Center, Corvallis, OR, p. A524

HOWE, Debbie, Chief Executive Officer, Weatherford Regional Hospital, Weatherford, OK, p. A522

HOWE, James L., Director Human Resources, Pinnacle Pointe Hospital, Little Rock, AR, p. A49

HOWE, Mary Lenzini, Vice President Human Resources, Geisinger–Bloomsburg Hospital, Bloomsburg, PA, p. A534

HOWE, Scott W., Chief Executive Officer, Weeks Medical Center, Lancaster, NH, p. A410

HOWE, Vicki, Health Information Management, Ness County Hospital, Ness City, KS, p. A250

HOWELL, Amy M., Director Human Resources, St. Luke's Behavioral Health Center, Phoenix, AZ, p. A37

HOWELL, Bradley, Chief Executive Officer, Roundup Memorial Healthcare, Roundup, MT, p. A390

HOWELL, Carrie, Chief Financial Officer, Barstow Community Hospital, Barstow, CA, p. A58

HOWELL, Diana, Director Human Resources, Conroe Regional Medical Center, Conroe, TX, p. A607

HOWELL, Jill, Clinical Director and Chief Nursing Officer, St. Luke's Jerome, Jerome, ID, p. A176

HOWELL, Kathy A., Vice President Human Resources, Lexington Medical Center, West Columbia, SC, p. A571

HOWELL, Kristie, System Information Technology Director, Southampton Memorial Hospital, Franklin, VA, p. A671

HOWELL, Nathan, Chief Operating Officer, St. Elizabeth's Medical Center, Brighton, MA, p. A308

HOWELL, Pat, Chief Nursing Officer, Community Memorial Hospital, Syracuse, NE, p. A402

HOWELL, R. Edward, Vice President and Chief Executive Officer, UVA Health System, Charlottesville, VA, p. B147

HOWELL, Ronene, Director Health Information Management, Bryce Hospital, Tuscaloosa, AL, p. A26

HOWELL, Sheri, Deputy Commander Nursing, San Antonio Military Medical Center, Fort Sam Houston, TX, p. A617

HOWELLS, Stephen, Chief Financial Officer, Kane County Hospital, Kanab, UT, p. A660

HOWERTER, Mark, M.D. President Medical Staff, Columbus Community Hospital, Columbus, NE, p. A395

HOWERTON, Russell M., M.D. Chief Medical Officer, Wake Forest Baptist Medical Center, Winston–Salem, NC, p. A475

HOWERTON, Shawn, M.D., Chief Executive Officer and President, Medical Staff, Sampson Regional Medical Center, Clinton, NC, p. A462

HOWES, Julie, Director Finance, Carson Valley Medical Center, Gardnerville, NV, p. A404

HOWLAND, Carol, Chief Nursing Officer, Twin Cities Community Hospital, Templeton, CA, p. A97

HOY, Jonathan B., Chief Financial Officer, Duke Regional Hospital, Durham, NC, p. A463

HOYE, Kelly, M.D. Vice President Medical Affairs, Morton Hospital and Medical Center, Taunton, MA, p. A315

HOYER, Scott, M.D. Vice President Quality and Chief Medical Officer, United Regional Health Care System, Wichita Falls, TX, p. A658

HOYES, Garry W., Chief Executive Officer, Dublin Springs, Dublin, OH, p. A493

HOYLE, Lisa, R.N. Chief Nursing Officer, Kingwood Medical Center, Kingwood, TX, p. A631

HOYOS, Kent, Chief Information Officer, Pomona Valley Hospital Medical Center, Pomona, CA, p. A84

HOYT, Nancy, R.N. Vice President Operations/Clinical and Chief Nursing Officer, Mercy Regional Medical Center, Durango, CO, p. A105

HRITZ, Diane, Chief Financial Officer, Advanced Surgical Hospital, Washington, PA, p. A557

HRON, Janine, Chief Executive Officer, Crittenton Children's Center, Kansas City, MO, p. A373

HRUBIAK, Dan, Associate Computer Program Analyst, Western New York Children's Psychiatric Center, West Seneca, NY, p. A458

HRUBY, Deidre, Director of Patient Care, Madelia Community Hospital, Madelia, MN, p. A346

HSIEH, Ketty, Senior Director Finance, UW Medicine/Northwest Hospital & Medical Center, Seattle, WA, p. A689

HSING, Shirley, Senior Vice President and Chief Financial Officer, North Oaks Medical Center, Hammond, LA, p. A278

HSU, Wah Chung, Senior Vice President Finance, San Antonio Community Hospital, Upland, CA, p. A98

HUANG, Djogan, Assistant Chief Financial Officer, Okmulgee Memorial Hospital, Okmulgee, OK, p. A517

HUANG, Joseph, M.D. Chief Medical and Quality Officer, Silverton Hospital, Silverton, OR, p. A530

HUBBARD, Bill, Vice President, Operations, Carolinas Medical Center–NorthEast, Concord, NC, p. A462

HUBBARD, Blake W., FACH
  Senior Vice President and Chief Operating Officer Medical Surgical Operations and Human Resources, Nix Community General Hospital, Dilley, TX, p. A614
  Senior Vice President and Chief Operating Officer, Nix Health Care System, San Antonio, TX, p. A647

HUBBARD, Brent
  Chief Operating Officer, Mercy Hospital Fort Smith, Fort Smith, AR, p. A46
  Chief Operating Officer, Mercy Hospital Ozark, Ozark, AR, p. A51
  Chief Operating Officer, Mercy Hospital Paris, Paris, AR, p. A51
  Chief Operating Officer, Mercy Hospital Waldron, Waldron, AR, p. A53

HUBBARD, Daniel, Chief Financial Officer, Sioux Falls Veterans Affairs Health Care System, Sioux Falls, SD, p. A577

HUBBARD, David, Chief Executive Officer, Daniels Memorial Healthcare Center, Scobey, MT, p. A391

HUBBARD, Gwen, Director of Nursing, Sierra Vista Hospital, Sacramento, CA, p. A87

HUBBARD, Kathy
  Controller, Ocean Beach Hospital, Ilwaco, WA, p. A684
  Manager Human Resources, Oneida County Hospital, Malad City, ID, p. A176

HUBBARD, Lynn, R.N. Vice President and Chief Nursing Officer, Indian River Medical Center, Vero Beach, FL, p. A149

HUBBARD, Mark, Vice President Risk Management, Loma Linda University Behavioral Medicine Center, Redlands, CA, p. A85

HUBBARD, Norm, Executive Vice President, Seattle Cancer Care Alliance, Seattle, WA, p. A688

HUBBARD, Tyson, Director Human Resources, Stanislaus Surgical Hospital, Modesto, CA, p. A78

HUBBS III, Olas A., FACHE, President and Chief Executive Officer, Memorial Hospital of Union County, Marysville, OH, p. A497

HUBER, Dalton, Chief Financial Officer, Campbell County Memorial Hospital, Gillette, WY, p. A721

HUBER, Timothy, Manager Financial Support, Mercy Hospital of Franciscan Sisters, Oelwein, IA, p. A235

HUBER, Vicki Lynn, R.N. Chief Nursing Officer, Paradise Valley Hospital, Phoenix, AZ, p. A36

HUBERT, Michael F., Vice President Human Resources, J. C. Blair Memorial Hospital, Huntingdon, PA, p. A541

HUBL, Bryan, M.D. Chief of Staff, Thayer County Health Services, Hebron, NE, p. A396

HUBLEY, Grover, M.D. President Medical Staff, Madison St. Joseph Health Center, Madisonville, TX, p. A636

HUBSCHER, Rebecca, Associate Director Operations, Veterans Affairs Butler Healthcare, Butler, PA, p. A534

HUBSCHMAN, Gary
Administrative Director Finance, Sutter Auburn Faith Hospital, Auburn, CA, p. A56
Administrative Director Finance, Sutter Roseville Medical Center, Roseville, CA, p. A87

HUCK, Karma, Chief Operating Officer, Scott County Hospital, Scott City, KS, p. A254

HUCKABEE, Mike, Network Administrator, Coryell Memorial Hospital, Gatesville, TX, p. A621

HUCKABY, Don, Chief Information Management Service, Veterans Affairs Eastern Colorado Health Care System, Denver, CO, p. A105

HUCKABY, Kenneth, Senior Director Information Technology Systems Operations, Texas Health Presbyterian Hospital of Rockwall, Rockwall, TX, p. A644

HUCKSHORN, Kevin Ann, MSN, Director, Delaware Psychiatric Center, New Castle, DE, p. A119

HUDA, Edith, Director Human Resources, Daniels Memorial Healthcare Center, Scobey, MT, p. A391

HUDAK, Corey, Director Human Resources, Memorial Hospital, York, PA, p. A559

HUDDLESTON, Tina, Chief Nursing Officer, Baylor Medical Center at Trophy Club, Trophy Club, TX, p. A653

HUDGENS, Roselyn, Director Human Resources, Ballinger Memorial Hospital, Ballinger, TX, p. A601

HUDGINS, Paul
Associate Vice President Human Resources, Bascom Palmer Eye Institute–Anne Bates Leach Eye Hospital, Miami, FL, p. A136
Associate Vice President Human Resources, University of Miami Hospital and Clinics, Miami, FL, p. A138

HUDGINS, Thomas J., FACHE, Administrator and Chief Executive Officer, Pinckneyville Community Hospital, Pinckneyville, IL, p. A200

HUDNELL, Sharon, R.N. Chief Nursing Officer, WK Bossier Health Center, Bossier City, LA, p. A274

HUDSON, Angie, Administrator, Compass Behavioral Center of Alexandria, Alexandria, LA, p. A272

HUDSON, Beth, Chief Nursing Officer, Baylor Institute for Rehabilitation, Dallas, TX, p. A609

HUDSON, C. R., Senior Vice President and Chief Financial Officer, Henry Mayo Newhall Memorial Hospital, Valencia, CA, p. A98

HUDSON, Gary Mikeal, Administrator, East Texas Medical Center Carthage, Carthage, TX, p. A605

HUDSON, James, Assistant Chief Information Resource Management, Lake City Veterans Affairs Medical Center, Lake City, FL, p. A133

HUDSON, Janell, Chief Clinical Officer, Sanford Thief River Falls Medical Center, Thief River Falls, MN, p. A353

HUDSON, Kayce H., Executive Director Human Resources, Saddleback Memorial Medical Center, Laguna Hills, CA, p. A68

HUDSON, Kenneth J., Chief Financial Officer, Veterans Affairs Puget Sound Health Care System, Seattle, WA, p. A689

HUDSON, Kent, Chief Financial Officer, Kingman Community Hospital, Kingman, KS, p. A247

HUDSON, Larry C.
Executive Vice President and Chief Financial Officer, CAMC Teays Valley Hospital, Hurricane, WV, p. A696
Executive Vice President and Chief Financial Officer, Charleston Area Medical Center, Charleston, WV, p. A694

HUDSON, Lowell K., Chief Financial Officer, Glen Oaks Hospital, Greenville, TX, p. A622

HUDSON, Maggie, Chief Financial and Operations Officer, Santiam Memorial Hospital, Stayton, OR, p. A530

HUDSON, MeKinzie, Chief Financial Officer, Stafford County Hospital, Stafford, KS, p. A254

HUDSON, Mike, Administrator, Federal Correctional Institute Hospital, Littleton, CO, p. A109

HUDSON, Pamela, M.D., Chief Executive Officer, Crestwood Medical Center, Huntsville, AL, p. A21

HUDSON, Robbi, Chief Financial Officer, HEALTHSOUTH Rehabilitation Hospital, Fayetteville, AR, p. A45

HUDSON, Skip, Manager Information Technology, Community Mental Health Center, Lawrenceburg, IN, p. A217

HUDSON, Stephen, M.D. Chief of Staff, Conway Regional Medical Center, Conway, AR, p. A44

HUDSON–JINKS, Therese M., R.N. Chief Nursing Officer, Tufts Medical Center, Boston, MA, p. A307

HUDSPETH, Todd R., FACHE, Chief Executive Officer, Cass County Memorial Hospital, Atlantic, IA, p. A225

HUEBNER, Thomas W., President, Rutland Regional Medical Center, Rutland, VT, p. A666

HUEBNER, Timothy K., M.D. President Medical Affairs, Riverview Hospital Association, Wisconsin Rapids, WI, p. A719

HUELSKAMP, Donald P., Vice President Finance and Chief Financial Officer, Southeastern Ohio Regional Medical Center, Cambridge, OH, p. A485

HUENERGARDT, Sam, President and Chief Executive Officer, Central Texas Medical Center, San Marcos, TX, p. A648

HUERTA, Brad, Chief Executive Officer and Administrator, Lost Rivers Medical Center, Arco, ID, p. A174

HUERTA, Guillermo, M.D. Chief Medical Officer, Select Specialty Hospital–Omaha, Omaha, NE, p. A400

HUERTER, Holly
Vice President Human Resources, Methodist Jennie Edmundson Hospital, Council Bluffs, IA, p. A228
Vice President Human Resources, Nebraska Methodist Hospital, Omaha, NE, p. A400

HUETTL, Patricia, Vice President Finance and Chief Financial Officer, Holy Family Memorial, Manitowoc, WI, p. A708

HUFF, Jeff, Assistant Administrator Finance, Fayette Medical Center, Fayette, AL, p. A20

HUFF, Michael H., Chief Executive Officer, Hamilton Hospital, Olney, TX, p. A640

HUFF, Shelly E., Director Human Resources, Indiana University Health Tipton Hospital, Tipton, IN, p. A223

HUFFMAN, David, Vice President and Controller, Select Specialty Hospital–Wilmington, Wilmington, DE, p. A120

HUFFMAN, James, Chief Executive Officer and Administrator, Baptist Memorial Hospital–Desoto, Southaven, MS, p. A365

HUFFMAN, Sherry
Administrator Human Resources, Oakwood Hospital–Dearborn, Dearborn, MI, p. A321
Administrator Human Resources, Oakwood Hospital–Taylor, Taylor, MI, p. A335

HUFFMAN, Steve
Chief Information Officer, Elkhart General Healthcare System, Elkhart, IN, p. A210
Chief Information Officer, Memorial Hospital of South Bend, South Bend, IN, p. A222

HUFFNER, William, M.D
Vice President Medical Affairs, Arnot Ogden Medical Center, Elmira, NY, p. A437
Chief Medical Officer and Senior Vice President Medical Affairs, St. Joseph's Hospital, Elmira, NY, p. A437
Chief Medical Officer, University of Maryland Shore Medical Center at Chestertown, Chestertown, MD, p. A299
Vice President Medical Affairs, University of Maryland Shore Medical Center at Dorchester, Cambridge, MD, p. A299
Chief Medical Officer, University of Maryland Shore Medical Center at Easton, Easton, MD, p. A300

HUFFORD, Dustin, Chief Information Officer, Memorial Hospital, Fremont, OH, p. A494

HUFFSTUTLER, Brandon, Chief Information Officer, Electra Memorial Hospital, Electra, TX, p. A617

HUFNAGEL, Keith, Director Human Resources, Stillwater Medical Center, Stillwater, OK, p. A519

HUGGINS, Lois, Chief Human Resources Officer and Senior Vice President Human Resources, Rehabilitation Institute of Chicago, Chicago, IL, p. A186

HUGGINS, Michael C., Administrator Network System, Eastern Oklahoma Medical Center, Poteau, OK, p. A517

HUGHES, April, Chief Financial Officer, Peachford Behavioral Health System, Atlanta, GA, p. A153

HUGHES, Beth
President and Chief Executive Officer, Presence Saint Joseph Medical Center, Joliet, IL, p. A194
President and Chief Executive Officer, Presence St. Mary's Hospital, Kankakee, IL, p. A194

HUGHES, Beverly, R.N. Vice President Nursing, Fayette County Memorial Hospital, Washington Court House, OH, p. A504

HUGHES, Chad, Information Officer, North Texas State Hospital, Vernon, TX, p. A655

HUGHES, Constance, Director of Nursing, West Gables Rehabilitation Hospital, Miami, FL, p. A138

HUGHES, David S., Chief Financial Officer, Vidant Medical Center, Greenville, NC, p. A465

HUGHES, David T., FACHE Senior Vice President Operations and Chief Operating Officer, Good Shepherd Health Care System, Hermiston, OR, p. A525

HUGHES, Dustan, M.D. Vice President Medical Affairs, Saint Alphonsus Medical Center – Nampa, Nampa, ID, p. A177

HUGHES, Edith M., R.N., President, Oakwood Hospital–Southshore, Trenton, MI, p. A336

HUGHES, James, Director Human Resources, Lake Cumberland Regional Hospital, Somerset, KY, p. A270

HUGHES, Jessica, Director Finance, Hawarden Regional Healthcare, Hawarden, IA, p. A232

HUGHES, John, Administrator, Ellinwood District Hospital, Ellinwood, KS, p. A243

HUGHES, John, FACHE, President and Chief Executive Officer, Marshalltown Medical & Surgical Center, Marshalltown, IA, p. A234

HUGHES, R.N., Lee, Chief Nursing Officer, Flint River Community Hospital, Montezuma, GA, p. A164

HUGHES, Leigh Ann, Chief Financial Officer, Hardin Medical Center, Savannah, TN, p. A592

HUGHES, Lori, R.N. Chief Nursing Officer, Vice President Operations and Patient Care Services, Cottage Hospital, Woodsville, NH, p. A412

HUGHES, Mark A., M.D. Medical Director, River Park Hospital, Huntington, WV, p. A696

HUGHES, Michelle, Director Health Information Management, Madison River Oaks Medical Center, Canton, MS, p. A356

HUGHES, Robert K., Executive Director, Henry J. Carter Specialty Hospital and Nursing Facility, New York, NY, p. A444

HUGHES, Sandra, Chief Financial Officer, Clinch Memorial Hospital, Homerville, GA, p. A161

HUGHES, Susan, Interim Director Human Resources, Winner Regional Healthcare Center, Winner, SD, p. A578

HUGHES, Tena, R.N. Program Director and Director Nursing, Sterlington Rehabilitation Hospital, Bastrop, LA, p. A273

HUGHES, Terry, Director Information Systems, Nantucket Cottage Hospital, Nantucket, MA, p. A312

HUGHES, Thomas, President, St. Joseph Health Services of Rhode Island, North Providence, RI, p. A560

HUGHEY, Nick
Administrator, Kula Hospital, Kula, HI, p. A172
Administrator, Lanai Community Hospital, Lanai City, HI, p. A172

HUGHSON, John, Administrator, Burleson St. Joseph Health Center, Caldwell, TX, p. A605

HUGLE, Dana, Administrator, Latimer County General Hospital, Wilburton, OK, p. A522

HUGUELEY, Sandra, Assistant Administrator and Chief Nursing Officer, Methodist Extended Care Hospital, Memphis, TN, p. A589

HUHNKE, Ann, Chief Financial Officer, SageWest Healthcare–Lander, Lander, WY, p. A721

HULBERT, Kim, R.N. Chief Clinical Officer, Madison County Health Care System, Winterset, IA, p. A240

HULETT, Rachelle, Vice President Human Resources, McLaren Flint, Flint, MI, p. A323

HULETT, Wendi, Chief Nursing Officer, Artesia General Hospital, Artesia, NM, p. A427

HULL, Betty, R.N. Chief Nursing Officer, Coalinga Regional Medical Center, Coalinga, CA, p. A60

HULL, Brad, Chief Financial Officer, Dale Medical Center, Ozark, AL, p. A24

HULL, Debbie, Chief Financial Officer, Fisher County Hospital District, Rotan, TX, p. A644

HULL, Kathy, President and Chief Executive Officer, Illini Community Hospital, Pittsfield, IL, p. A200

HULL, Ken, Director Human Resources, Inova Fairfax Hospital, Falls Church, VA, p. A670

HULM, Laurie, Administrative Assistant, Sakakawea Medical Center, Hazen, ND, p. A478

HULSE, Mark, Vice President and Chief Information Officer, H. Lee Moffitt Cancer Center and Research Institute, Tampa, FL, p. A147

HULSEY, Grant, Director Information Technology, Heritage Park Surgical Hospital, Sherman, TX, p. A649

HULSEY, Kelly, Chief Nursing Officer, Piedmont Hospital, Atlanta, GA, p. A153

HULSMAN, Laurie, M.D. Chief of Staff, El Campo Memorial Hospital, El Campo, TX, p. A615

HUMBLE, Kathryn G., Chief Human Resources Officer, Beatrice Community Hospital and Health Center, Beatrice, NE, p. A394

HUMBLE, Linnea, Director of Finance, Sutter Lakeside Hospital, Lakeport, CA, p. A69

HUME, Craig P., Chief Executive Officer, Surgical Specialty Center of Baton Rouge, Baton Rouge, LA, p. A274

HUME, Diana, Manager Human Resources, Methodist McKinney Hospital, McKinney, TX, p. A637

HUMES, Ronny, President and Chief Executive Officer, Magnolia Regional Health Center, Corinth, MS, p. A357

HUMME, Sarah, MSN Chief Operating Officer, Southwest General Hospital, San Antonio, TX, p. A647

HUMMEL, Angela, Vice President Human Resources, Evangelical Community Hospital, Lewisburg, PA, p. A543

HUMMELKE, Arlita, Manager Human Resources, Mercy Hospital Tishomingo, Tishomingo, OK, p. A520

HUMMER, Christopher R., President, Carolinas Medical Center–Pineville, Charlotte, NC, p. A461

HUMPHREY, Dale, Chief Executive Officer, Henderson County Community Hospital, Lexington, TN, p. A587

HUMPHREY, James, Vice President Talent Resources and Human Resources for South Side Operating Group, Penrose–St. Francis Health Services, Colorado Springs, CO, p. A104

HUMPHREY, Randy, Chief Financial Officer, Wesley Medical Center, Hattiesburg, MS, p. A359

HUMPHREY, Richard
    Director Finance, Texas Health Harris Methodist Hospital Cleburne, Cleburne, TX, p. A606
    Vice President Finance, Texas Health Harris Methodist Hospital Fort Worth, Fort Worth, TX, p. A619

HUMPHREY, Suzy, Interim Chief Nursing Officer, Biloxi Regional Medical Center, Biloxi, MS, p. A355

HUMPHREYS, L. Ray, Chief Executive Officer, Anderson Regional Medical Center, Meridian, MS, p. A362

HUMPHRIES, Stefan, M.D. Medical Director, St. Luke's Rehabilitation Institute, Spokane, WA, p. A690

HUMPHRIES, Vickie Witcher
    Director Human Resources, Bon Secours Maryview Medical Center, Portsmouth, VA, p. A676
    Vice President Human Resources, Bon Secours–DePaul Medical Center, Norfolk, VA, p. A675
    Vice President Human Resources, Mary Immaculate Hospital, Newport News, VA, p. A675

HUNG, Lynelle, Director of Nursing, Public Health Service Indian Hospital – Quentin N. Burdick Memorial Health Facility, Belcourt, ND, p. A476

HUNGER, Dennis, Chief Executive Officer, Washington County Hospital and Clinics, Washington, IA, p. A238

HUNSBERGER, Tom, Vice President Human Resources, Riverview Hospital Association, Wisconsin Rapids, WI, p. A719

HUNSICKER, Elizabeth, Chief Executive Officer, West Valley Medical Center, Caldwell, ID, p. A175

HUNSTOCK, Leanne M., R.N., Interim Administrator, Kaiser Permanente Medical Center, Honolulu, HI, p. A170

HUNT, Amy, Director Human Resources, Menorah Medical Center, Overland Park, KS, p. A252

HUNT, Cheri, R.N. Vice President Patient Care Services and Chief Nursing Officer, Children's Mercy Hospitals and Clinics, Kansas City, MO, p. A373

HUNT, D. Deann, Director Human Resources, Gibson General Hospital, Princeton, IN, p. A221

HUNT, Deloris, Corporate Vice President Human Resources, DMC Harper University Hospital, Detroit, MI, p. A322

HUNT, Don, M.D. Vice President Patient Centered Care and Chief Nursing Officer, University of Texas Health Science Center at Tyler, Tyler, TX, p. A654

HUNT, Janet, R.N. Chief Nursing Officer, Methodist Healthcare–Fayette Hospital, Somerville, TN, p. A593

HUNT, Jeff, Chief Executive Officer, Sunbury Community Hospital and Outpatient Center, Sunbury, PA, p. A555

HUNT, Mary Miles, Chief Executive Officer, Ballard Rehabilitation Hospital, San Bernardino, CA, p. A88

HUNT, Pamela, MSN Vice President of Patient Services and Chief Nursing Executive, Community Heart and Vascular Hospital, Indianapolis, IN, p. A213

HUNT, Reta, Director of Nursing, Scott & White Hospital – Llano, Llano, TX, p. A633

HUNT, Ronald, Chief Executive Officer, Harbor Hospital of Southeast Texas, Beaumont, TX, p. A601

HUNT, Tad M., MS, President and Chief Executive Officer, Crete Area Medical Center, Crete, NE, p. A395

HUNT, William Robert, Chief Financial Officer, Reynolds Memorial Hospital, Glen Dale, WV, p. A695

HUNTER, Becky, R.N. Chief Nursing Officer, Baptist Memorial Hospital – Memphis, Memphis, TN, p. A588

HUNTER, Byron, Vice President Human Resources, Cape Regional Medical Center, Cape May Court House, NJ, p. A414

HUNTER, Diana, Director of Nursing, Fort Belknap U. S. Public Health Service Indian Hospital, Harlem, MT, p. A388

HUNTER, Fred, R.N., Chief Executive Officer, Desert Valley Hospital, Victorville, CA, p. A99

HUNTER, George A., Vice President Human Resources, Allegiance Health, Jackson, MI, p. A327

HUNTER, Jerry, Vice President, Information Technology, Crotched Mountain Rehabilitation Center, Greenfield, NH, p. A410

HUNTER, Ken, R.N., Chief Executive Officer, Kimball Health Services, Kimball, NE, p. A397

HUNTER, Linda, Chief Nursing Officer, Spring View Hospital, Lebanon, KY, p. A263

HUNTER, Mary Ann, Director Nursing Services, Baptist Easley Hospital, Easley, SC, p. A565

HUNTER, Shelly
    Chief Financial Officer, Mercy Hospital Fort Scott, Fort Scott, KS, p. A244
    Chief Financial Officer, Mercy Hospital Independence, Independence, KS, p. A246
    Chief Financial Officer, Mercy Hospital Joplin, Joplin, MO, p. A373

HUNTER, Stephanie, Chief Human Resources, Veterans Affairs Ann Arbor Healthcare System, Ann Arbor, MI, p. A318

HUNTER, Tracy, Chief Human Resources Officer, East Cooper Medical Center, Mount Pleasant, SC, p. A568

HUNTLEY, Adrienne, Director Human Resources, HEALTHSOUTH Rehabilitation Hospital Memphis–North, Memphis, TN, p. A588

HUNTLEY, Devin, Vice President Operations, Community Medical Center, Missoula, MT, p. A389

HUNTON, David, M.D. Chief Medical Officer, Mercy Hospital Fort Smith, Fort Smith, AR, p. A46

HUPF, Angela C., Vice President Human Resources and Community Relations, Aspirus Medford Hospital, Medford, WI, p. A709

HUPP, Diane, R.N. Vice President Patient Care Services and Chief Nursing Officer, Children's Hospital of Pittsburgh of UPMC, Pittsburgh, PA, p. A550

HURD, Debra J., R.N. Vice President Nursing Acute Care, St. John's Hospital, Saint Paul, MN, p. A351

HURD, Jacque, Vice President Human Resources, St. Bernards Medical Center, Jonesboro, AR, p. A48

HURD, Ross, Chief Information Officer, Lake Chelan Community Hospital, Chelan, WA, p. A682

HURLBUT, Marty, M.D. Medical Director, HEALTHSOUTH Rehabilitation Hospital, Fayetteville, AR, p. A45

HURLBUTT, Nichole, Director Human Resources, OSF St. Mary Medical Center, Galesburg, IL, p. A190

HURLEY, Al, Clinic Chief Operating Officer, Sanford Bismarck, Bismarck, ND, p. A476

HURLEY, Jeff, Vice President Human Resources, Flagler Hospital, Saint Augustine, FL, p. A144

HURLEY, Sandra, MS Chief Nursing Officer, Valley View Hospital, Glenwood Springs, CO, p. A106

HURLEY, William, M.D. Chief Medical Officer, Summit Pacific Medical Center, Elma, WA, p. A683

HURME, Elaine, Chief Nursing Officer, Pointe Coupee General Hospital, New Roads, LA, p. A286

HURSH, John, Vice President Human Resources, Cox Medical Centers, Springfield, MO, p. A383

HURST, Steve, Information Technology Specialist, Haskell County Community Hospital, Stigler, OK, p. A519

HURT, Christie, M.D. Chief of Staff and Medical Director, Mercy Hospital Aurora, Aurora, MO, p. A367

HURWITZ, Steven, Senior Vice President Shared Services, Seattle Children's Hospital, Seattle, WA, p. A688

HURZELER, Rosemary Johnson, President and Chief Executive Officer, The Connecticut Hospice, Branford, CT, p. A113

HUSAIN, Syed Arshad, M.D. Executive Vice President and Chief Medical Officer, Royal Oaks Hospital, Windsor, MO, p. A384

HUSEBY, Custer
    Interim Chief Executive Officer, Vibra Hospital of Central Dakotas, Mandan, ND, p. A479
    Chief Executive Officer, Vibra Hospital of Fargo, Fargo, ND, p. A478

HUSHER, Phil, Chief Financial Officer, Winner Regional Healthcare Center, Winner, SD, p. A578

HUSKEY, Jeff, Chief Executive Officer and Administrator, Clay County Memorial Hospital, Henrietta, TX, p. A623

HUSS, Cathy, Chief Financial Officer, LifeCare Medical Center, Roseau, MN, p. A350

HUSSAIN, Hamid, M.D. Medical Director, Our Lady of the Angels Hospital, Bogalusa, LA, p. A274

HUSSAIN, Iftikhar
    Chief Financial Officer, El Camino Hospital, Mountain View, CA, p. A79
    Chief Financial Officer, Mills–Peninsula Health Services, Burlingame, CA, p. A58

HUSTEDT, Dale, Administrator, Avera Holy Family Hospital, Estherville, IA, p. A230

HUSTON, Gary, D.O. Chief Medical Officer, University Hospitals Conneaut Medical Center, Conneaut, OH, p. A491

HUSTON, William R., Senior Vice President and Chief Financial Officer, Texas Scottish Rite Hospital for Children, Dallas, TX, p. A612

HUTCHENRIDER, E. Kenneth, President, Methodist Richardson Medical Center, Richardson, TX, p. A644

HUTCHENS, Zachary, M.D. Chief Medical Officer, Saint Thomas Hickman Hospital, Centerville, TN, p. A580

HUTCHES, Trampas, Interim Chief Executive Officer, Middle Park Medical Center–Kremmling, Kremmling, CO, p. A108

HUTCHESON, Jane, Administrator and Director Clinical Operations, Group Health Cooperative Central Hospital, Seattle, WA, p. A688

HUTCHESON, Lou Ellen, M.D. Chief of Staff, Bacon County Hospital and Health System, Alma, GA, p. A151

HUTCHINS, Anne, M.D. Chief of Staff, Salem Veterans Affairs Medical Center, Salem, VA, p. A678

HUTCHINS, Michael T., Administrator, Jay Hospital, Jay, FL, p. A132

HUTCHINS, Sheri, Director Health Information Management, Muenster Memorial Hospital, Muenster, TX, p. A639

HUTCHINS–OTERO, Kathy, Chief Clinical Officer, Kindred Rehabilitation Hospital Clear Lake, Webster, TX, p. A656

HUTCHINSON, Donna, Chief Financial Officer, Beaver Dam Community Hospitals, Beaver Dam, WI, p. A702

HUTCHINSON, James, CPA Chief Financial Officer, Affinity Medical Center, Massillon, OH, p. A498

HUTCHISON, Barbra, Director Medical Records, Richland Parish Hospital, Delhi, LA, p. A276

HUTCHISON, Dee, Chief Executive Officer, U. S. Public Health Service Indian Hospital, Parker, AZ, p. A35

HUTCHISON, Florence N., M.D. Chief of Staff, Ralph H. Johnson Veterans Affairs Medical Center, Charleston, SC, p. A563

HUTCHISON, Harry, Vice President Fiscal Services, St. Bernards Medical Center, Jonesboro, AR, p. A48

HUTH, Michael, Chief Financial Officer, Sycamore Springs Hospital, Lafayette, IN, p. A217

HUTH, Thomas, M.D. Vice President Medical Affairs, Reid Hospital and Health Care Services, Richmond, IN, p. A221

HUTSELL, Dick, Vice President Information Technology Services, Saint Louise Regional Hospital, Gilroy, CA, p. A65

HUTSELL, Richard, Vice President and Chief Information Officer, Daughters of Charity Health System, O'Connor Hospital, San Jose, CA, p. A92

HUTSON, Donald, Director, Marion Veterans Affairs Medical Center, Marion, IL, p. A195

HUTSON, Joy M., Director Human Resources, Crossgates River Oaks Hospital, Brandon, MS, p. A356

HUTSON, Mark S., Chief Information Officer, Greenwood Leflore Hospital, Greenwood, MS, p. A358

HUTSON, Marty, Chief Financial Officer, St. Mary's Health Care System, Athens, GA, p. A151

HUTSON, Wayne
    Executive Vice President and Chief Financial Officer, Union Hospital, Terre Haute, IN, p. A223
    Chief Financial Officer, Union Hospital Clinton, Clinton, IN, p. A208

HUTTER, George, M.D. Chief of Staff, Palms of Pasadena Hospital, Saint Petersburg, FL, p. A144

HUVAL, Shadelle, Director Finance, St. Martin Hospital, Breaux Bridge, LA, p. A275

HUYCKE, Mark, M.D. Chief of Staff, Oklahoma City Veterans Affairs Medical Center, Oklahoma City, OK, p. A516

HYATT, Charlotte, MSN Chief Operating Officer and Chief Nursing Officer, CareLink of Jackson, Jackson, MI, p. A328

HYATT, David W., Chief Executive Officer, Jay County Hospital, Portland, IN, p. A221

HYATT, Robert, M.D. Senior Vice President Medical Affairs, Lake Regional Health System, Osage Beach, MO, p. A378

HYATT, Ronnie, Senior Vice President Finance and Chief Financial Officer, Bon Secours St. Francis Health System, Greenville, SC, p. A566

HYBERGER, Trey, Director Information Technology, Hardin Memorial Hospital, Elizabethtown, KY, p. A260

HYDE, Elmer, Chief Executive Officer, Carlsbad Medical Center, Carlsbad, NM, p. A427

HYDE, Jane E., President, Gettysburg Hospital, Gettysburg, PA, p. A539

HYDE, Kandance, R.N. Chief Nursing Officer, Palacios Community Medical Center, Palacios, TX, p. A640

HYDE, Keith, Chief Executive Officer, Providence Milwaukie Hospital, Milwaukie, OR, p. A527

HYDE, Robert, Human Resources Business Partner, Kaiser Permanente Santa Clara Medical Center, Santa Clara, CA, p. A94

HYDE, Shannon, Director Human Resources, HEALTHSOUTH MountainView Regional Rehabilitation Hospital, Morgantown, WV, p. A697

HYDE, Stephanie, Chief Executive Officer, Tyler Continuecare Hospital at Mother Frances, Tyler, TX, p. A654

HYDE, Stephen O., FACHE, Chief Executive Officer, Southwestern Medical Center, Lawton, OK, p. A512

HYDER, LouAnn, Director Information Integrity Management, Cardinal Hill Rehabilitation Hospital, Lexington, KY, p. A264

HYDER, Shiraz, M.D. Director Medical Affairs, St. Alexius Medical Center, Bismarck, ND, p. A476

HYLAND, Donna W., President and Chief Executive Officer, Children's Healthcare of Atlanta, Atlanta, GA, p. A152

HYLAND–HILL, Barbara M., R.N. Chief Nursing Officer, Providence Regional Medical Center Everett, Everett, WA, p. A683

HYLTON, Alecia, M.D. Chief of Staff, Aspirus Medford Hospital, Medford, WI, p. A709

HYLTON, Heather, Chief Financial Officer, Plateau Medical Center, Oak Hill, WV, p. A698

HYMAN, Bruce, M.D. Vice President Clinical Performance, Advocate Sherman Hospital, Elgin, IL, p. A189

HYMBAUGH, Mitzi, Chief Personnel, Ringgold County Hospital, Mount Ayr, IA, p. A234

HYMER, DNP, RN, CENP, Regina J., MSN Vice President Patient Care Services and Chief Nursing Officer, Norton Brownsboro Hospital, Louisville, KY, p. A266

HYNOSKI, Michael, Chief Information Resource Management, James E. Van Zandt Veterans Affairs Medical Center, Altoona, PA, p. A532

I

IBRAHIM, Tajudeen, Interim Business Administrator, Elgin Mental Health Center, Elgin, IL, p. A189

IBRAHIM, Tommy, Chief Physician Officer, Mercy Medical Center–Des Moines, Des Moines, IA, p. A229

ICENHOWER, Jeremy, Administrator and Chief Executive Officer, De Queen Medical Center, De Queen, AR, p. A45

ICKOWSKI, Michael F., Chief Financial Officer, Eastern Niagara Hospital, Lockport, NY, p. A440

IDBEIS, Badr, M.D., Chief Executive Officer, Kansas Medical Center, Andover, KS, p. A241

IDSTEIN, Mary, Chief Financial Officer, Porter–Starke Services, Valparaiso, IN, p. A223

IERARDI, Joseph P., Chief Executive Officer, Wayne Memorial Hospital, Jesup, GA, p. A161

IERO, Tony, Director Management Information Systems, North Philadelphia Health System, Philadelphia, PA, p. A549

IFTINIUK, Alan, Chief Executive Officer, French Hospital Medical Center, San Luis Obispo, CA, p. A93

IGNACIO, Manny, Controller, Riverside General Hospital, Houston, TX, p. A626

IGNAS, Ann, R.N. Chief Nurse Executive, Fairfield Memorial Hospital, Fairfield, IL, p. A190

IMBIMBO, Richard, Chief Financial Officer, Hahnemann University Hospital, Philadelphia, PA, p. A548

IMHOFF, Sarah, Business Administrator, Chester Mental Health Center, Chester, IL, p. A183

IMLAY, Ralph, M.D. Chief of Staff, Harper Hospital District Five, Harper, KS, p. A245

IMLER, James R., Director Human Resources, Kimball Health Services, Kimball, NE, p. A397

IMSEIS, Mikhail, M.D. Chief of Staff, Ness County Hospital, Ness City, KS, p. A250

INCARNATI, Philip A., President and Chief Executive Officer, McLaren Health Care Corporation, Flint, MI, p. B90

INGALLS, Dawn, Regional Manager Human Resources, Avera Dells Area Hospital, Dell Rapids, SD, p. A573

INGE, Ray, Vice President Human Resources, Pomona Valley Hospital Medical Center, Pomona, CA, p. A84

INGHAM, Raymond V., Ph.D., President and Chief Executive Officer, Witham Memorial Hospital, Lebanon, IN, p. A217

INGLIS, Suzanne, MSN Senior Vice President Nursing Services, Fisher–Titus Medical Center, Norwalk, OH, p. A500

INGRAM, David, Director Management Information Systems, Medina Hospital, Medina, OH, p. A498

INGRAM, Karen, Director Human Resources, Baptist Memorial Hospital for Women, Memphis, TN, p. A588

INGRAM, Kim, Chief Executive Officer, Mountain Lakes Medical Center, Clayton, GA, p. A156

INGRAM, Nathan Daniel, Chief Executive Officer and Owner, Lone Star Behavioral Health, Cypress, TX, p. A609

INGRAM, Peter, Vice President and Chief Information Officer, Schwab Rehabilitation Hospital, Chicago, IL, p. A186

INGWERSON, Connie, Chief Financial Officer, Nemaha Valley Community Hospital, Seneca, KS, p. A254

INHOFE, Kyle, Chief Human Resources Officer, Oklahoma City Veterans Affairs Medical Center, Oklahoma City, OK, p. A516

INMAN, Debbie
Chief Nursing Officer, Physicians Surgical Hospital – Panhandle Campus, Amarillo, TX, p. A596
Chief Nursing Officer, Physicians Surgical Hospital – Quail Creek, Amarillo, TX, p. A596

INMAN, Joanne, Vice President Operations, Sentara Virginia Beach General Hospital, Virginia Beach, VA, p. A679

INMAN, Julie, Regional Executive Officer, Southeast Missouri Mental Health Center, Farmington, MO, p. A371

INNOCENTI Sr., John, President and Chief Executive Officer, UPMC Presbyterian Shadyside, Pittsburgh, PA, p. A552

INO, Alan, Chief Financial Officer, Good Samaritan Hospital, Los Angeles, CA, p. A72

INOUYE, Valerie, Chief Financial Officer, San Francisco General Hospital and Trauma Center, San Francisco, CA, p. A91

INSCHO, Kimberly, Vice President Community Relations and Human Resources, Margaret Mary Health, Batesville, IN, p. A206

INSERRA, Toni A., Interim Administrator, South Lyon Medical Center, Yerington, NV, p. A408

INSKEEP, Johnathan, Chief Information Officer, Caribou Memorial Hospital and Living Center, Soda Springs, ID, p. A178

INZANA, Lou, Senior Vice President and Chief Financial Officer, Maine Medical Center, Portland, ME, p. A294

INZANA, Lugene A., Vice President and Chief Financial and Support Services Officer, Lawrence + Memorial Hospital, New London, CT, p. A116

IPSAN, Charlotte, President, Norton Suburban Hospital, Louisville, KY, p. A266

IQBAL, Nayyar, M.D. Director Medical Staff, Western State Hospital, Hopkinsville, KY, p. A263

IRELAND, Amy, Chief Financial Officer, Carroll County Memorial Hospital, Carrollton, MO, p. A369

IRISH, Kevin
Chief Information Officer, Franklin Regional Hospital, Franklin, NH, p. A410
Chief Information Officer, Lakes Region General Hospital, Laconia, NH, p. A410

IRISH–CLARDY, Katherine, M.D. Chief Medical Officer, Sparks Regional Medical Center, Fort Smith, AR, p. A46

IRIZARRI, David, Director Information Technology, Northwest Medical Center, Margate, FL, p. A135

IRIZARRY, Aixa
Executive Director, Hospital HMA de Humacao, Humacao, PR, p. A726
Executive Director, Hospital San Pablo Del Este, Fajardo, PR, p. A726

IRIZARRY, Lourdes, M.D. Chief of Staff, Albany Stratton Veterans Affairs Medical Center, Albany, NY, p. A432

IRUEGAS, Javier, FACHE, Chief Executive Officer, Mission Regional Medical Center, Mission, TX, p. A638

IRVIN, Debbie, Director Health Information Management, BHC Alhambra Hospital, Rosemead, CA, p. A86

IRVIN, Donna
Director Human Resources, Baylor Medical Center at Trophy Club, Trophy Club, TX, p. A653
Director Human Resources, Victory Medical Center Mid–Cities, Hurst, TX, p. A629

IRVIN, Mary, R.N. Senior Vice President and Chief Nursing Officer, Bethesda North Hospital, Cincinnati, OH, p. A486

IRVIN, Miriam, CNO, HEALTHSOUTH Rehabilitation Hospital, Fayetteville, AR, p. A45

IRVIN, Thomas M., Administrator Human Resources, Ranken Jordan Pediatric Bridge Hospital, Maryland Heights, MO, p. A376

IRVING, Edith E., R.N. Chief Nursing Officer, West Valley Medical Center, Caldwell, ID, p. A175

IRVING, MSN, RN–, Kelly Ann, Associate Director for Patient Care Services, Michael E. DeBakey Veterans Affairs Medical Center, Houston, TX, p. A626

IRVING, Mark, Manager Management Information Systems, OSF St. Francis Hospital and Medical Group, Escanaba, MI, p. A323

IRWIN, James, M.D. Chief Medical Officer, Samaritan Healthcare, Moses Lake, WA, p. A685

IRWIN, Robert G., Vice President Information Systems, Robert Wood Johnson University Hospital, New Brunswick, NJ, p. A419

IRWIN, Ruth, Associate Director Clinical Operations, Stewart & Lynda Resnick Neuropsychiatric Hospital at UCLA, Los Angeles, CA, p. A75

IRWIN, Vivian, Chief Financial Officer and Controller, HEALTHSOUTH Rehabilitation Hospital Midland–Odessa, Midland, TX, p. A638

ISAAC, Regina, Director of Nursing, Choctaw Health Center, Philadelphia, MS, p. A364

ISAACKS, Scott R., Interim Director, Ralph H. Johnson Veterans Affairs Medical Center, Charleston, SC, p. A563

ISAACS, Cynthia, Chief Executive Officer, Cornerstone Hospital of Huntington, Huntington, WV, p. A695

ISAACS, Diane, Director of Nursing, Ouachita County Medical Center, Camden, AR, p. A44

ISAACS, Linda, Vice President Human Resources, St. Luke's Hospital, San Francisco, CA, p. A91

ISAACS, Michael, Director Human Resources, Streamwood Behavioral Health Center, Streamwood, IL, p. A204

ISAACSON, Alan, Vice President and Chief Operating Officer, Seton Shoal Creek Hospital, Austin, TX, p. A600

ISADO, Jose, M.D. Medical Director, Auxilio Mutuo Hospital, San Juan, PR, p. A727

ISBELL, Gina, Administrator, Oceans Behavioral Hospital of Kentwood, Kentwood, LA, p. A280

ISBELL, Samantha, R.N. Chief Nursing Officer, Hamilton Hospital, Olney, TX, p. A640

ISEKE, Richard, M.D. Vice President Medical Affairs, Winchester Hospital, Winchester, MA, p. A316

ISEMANN, William R., President and Chief Executive Officer, KidsPeace Children's Hospital, Orefield, PA, p. A547

ISENMANN, Debra, Human Resources Generalist, Cox Monett, Monett, MO, p. A377

ISHAQUE, Saleem, M.D. Executive Medical Director, Alvarado Parkway Institute Behavioral Health System, La Mesa, CA, p. A68

ISHKANIAN, Gary, M.D. Vice President Medical Affairs, Montefiore Mount Vernon, Mount Vernon, NY, p. A442

ISKANDAR, Said, M.D. Chief Medical Officer, Halifax Regional Health System, South Boston, VA, p. A678

ISLAM, Asad, M.D. Chief Medical Officer, Mayhill Hospital, Denton, TX, p. A613

ISLEY, L. Lee, FACHE, Chief Executive Officer, Granville Health System, Oxford, NC, p. A470

ISMAIL, Asad, M.D. Medical Director, Wellstone Regional Hospital, Jeffersonville, IN, p. A215

ISMAIL, Hummayun, M.D. Medical Director, Select Specialty Hospital–Wilmington, Wilmington, DE, p. A120

ISMAILOGLU, Mehmet, M.D. Medical Director, Southwest Regional Rehabilitation Center, Battle Creek, MI, p. A319

ISOM, Julie, Director Human Resources, Lakeview Hospital, Bountiful, UT, p. A659

ISON, Tamara
Chief Operating Officer, Spalding Regional Medical Center, Griffin, GA, p. A160
Chief Financial Officer, Sylvan Grove Hospital, Jackson, GA, p. A161

ISON, William G., Human Resources Manager, Select Specialty Hospital–Tri Cities, Bristol, TN, p. A579

ISRAEL, Alison, Controller, Martin County Hospital District, Stanton, TX, p. A650

ISRAEL, Corry, Director Human Resources, Western Plains Medical Complex, Dodge City, KS, p. A243

ISRAEL, Michael D., President and Chief Executive Officer, Westchester Medical Center, Valhalla, NY, p. A457

ISSAI, Alice H.
Business Strategy and Finance Leader, Kaiser Permanente West Los Angeles Medical Center, Los Angeles, CA, p. A72
Chief Operating Officer, UC Irvine Medical Center, Orange, CA, p. A81

ISSAI, Robert, President and Chief Executive Officer, Daughters of Charity Health System, Los Altos Hills, CA, p. B46

ISTRE, Tony, Director Information Technology Services, Regional Medical Center of Acadiana, Lafayette, LA, p. A282

ITEN, Tess, Director of Nursing and Chief Nursing Officer, Deer's Head Hospital Center, Salisbury, MD, p. A303

ITO, Derek, Director Human Resources, Shriners Hospitals for Children–Honolulu, Honolulu, HI, p. A171

IVES, Matthew, Interim Chief Executive Officer and Chief Financial Officer, Keokuk County Health Center, Sigourney, IA, p. A237

IVES, Sheri, R.N
Vice President Patient Care Services, Mountain View Regional Medical Center, Norton, VA, p. A676
Vice President Clinical Services, Wellmont Hancock County Hospital, Sneedville, TN, p. A593
Vice President Care Services, Wellmont Lonesome Pine Hospital, Big Stone Gap, VA, p. A668

IVES ERICKSON, Jeanette R., MS Senior Vice President Patient Care and Chief Nurse, Massachusetts General Hospital, Boston, MA, p. A307

IVESON, Jr., William D., Clinical Operations Officer and Director Human Resources, Barnes–Kasson County Hospital, Susquehanna, PA, p. A555

IVEY, Bobbie, Director Human Resources, Chicot Memorial Medical Center, Lake Village, AR, p. A48

IVEY, Mark J., M.D. Medical Director, Great Lakes Specialty Hospital–Grand Rapids Campus, Grand Rapids, MI, p. A325

IVIE, Brian K., President, Mercy San Juan Medical Center, Carmichael, CA, p. A59

IVIE, Jack, President, Glendale Memorial Hospital and Health Center, Glendale, CA, p. A65

IVORY, Brenda, Chief Executive Officer, Harlingen Medical Center, Harlingen, TX, p. A622

IVY, Jay, R.N., Chief Executive Officer, The NeuroMedical Center Rehabilitation Hospital, Baton Rouge, LA, p. A274

IVY, Michael, M.D. Senior Vice President for Medical Affairs and Chief Medical Officer, Bridgeport Hospital, Bridgeport, CT, p. A113

IWEIMRIN, Salvatore, R.N., Chief Executive Officer, Select Specialty Hospital–Battle Creek, Battle Creek, MI, p. A319

IYER, Raju, Chief Financial Officer, Regional Medical Center of San Jose, San Jose, CA, p. A92

IZAKOVIC, Martin, M.D. Vice President Medical Staff Affairs and Chief Medical Officer, Mercy Iowa City, Iowa City, IA, p. A232

IZQUIERDO, Elizabeth L., CPA, Chief Executive Officer, HEALTHSOUTH Rehabilitation Hospital of Miami, Cutler Bay, FL, p. A126

IZZI, Denine, Site Manager Information Systems, Robert Wood Johnson University Hospital Rahway, Rahway, NJ, p. A422

IZZO, Carolyn, President and Chief Executive Officer, Ellwood City Hospital, Ellwood City, PA, p. A538

J

JABBARPOUR, Yad, M.D. Chief of Staff, Catawba Hospital, Catawba, VA, p. A669

JABLONOVER, Michael, M.D., President and Chief Executive Officer, University of Maryland Rehabilitation and Orthopaedic Institute, Baltimore, MD, p. A298

JABLONSKI, Kevin, Chief Nursing Officer, Mother Frances Hospital – Winnsboro, Winnsboro, TX, p. A658

JABLONSKI, Mark, Vice President Mission Integration, St. Jude Medical Center, Fullerton, CA, p. A65

JABOUR, John, Chief Information Officer, Ephrata Community Hospital, Ephrata, PA, p. A538

JACK, Claudia L., Director Associate Relations, Bayfront Health Brooksville, Brooksville, FL, p. A125

JACKES, Frederick D., Assistant Administrator and Director Human Resources, Valley Forge Medical Center and Hospital, Norristown, PA, p. A546

JACKLIN, Bonnie, R.N. Chief Nursing Officer, McKay–Dee Hospital Center, Ogden, UT, p. A661

JACKS, Anthony, Director Human Resources, Howard University Hospital, Washington, DC, p. A121

JACKSON, Alex
  Chief Executive, Providence Holy Family Hospital, Spokane, WA, p. A690
  Chief Executive, Providence Sacred Heart Medical Center & Children's Hospital, Spokane, WA, p. A690

JACKSON, Barbara, Chief Executive Officer, North Alabama Regional Hospital, Decatur, AL, p. A18

JACKSON, Bryan G., Vice President and Chief Financial Officer, Jefferson Regional Medical Center, Pine Bluff, AR, p. A52

JACKSON, Carolyn, Chief Executive Officer, St. Christopher's Hospital for Children, Philadelphia, PA, p. A550

JACKSON, Cindy, Director Human Resources, Phelps Memorial Health Center, Holdrege, NE, p. A396

JACKSON, Collette, R.N. Director of Clinical Services, St. Theresa Specialty Hospital, Kenner, LA, p. A280

JACKSON, Courtney, Director Human Resources, Logan Memorial Hospital, Russellville, KY, p. A270

JACKSON, Darryl, D.O. Chief of Staff, Prague Community Hospital, Prague, OK, p. A518

JACKSON, David, Chief Financial Officer, Baptist Medical Center Leake, Carthage, MS, p. A356

JACKSON, Eileen, M.D. President Medical Staff, Sanpete Valley Hospital, Mount Pleasant, UT, p. A660

JACKSON, Gary, D.O. Medical Director, Lincoln County Medical Center, Ruidoso, NM, p. A430

JACKSON, Holly, Chief Operating Officer, Gulf Coast Regional Medical Center, Panama City, FL, p. A141

JACKSON, Jabez, M.D. Chief of Staff, Harris Hospital, Newport, AR, p. A51

JACKSON, James, M.D. Chief of Staff, Cornerstone Hospital of Bossier City, Bossier City, LA, p. A274

JACKSON, James E. T., M.P.H., Chief Administrative Officer, San Leandro Hospital, San Leandro, CA, p. A92

JACKSON Jr., James H., Executive Director, Greenwood Leflore Hospital, Greenwood, MS, p. A358

JACKSON, James V., Budget Director, St. Elizabeths Hospital, Washington, DC, p. A122

JACKSON, Janice, Director Human Resources, Shands Lake Shore Regional Medical Center, Lake City, FL, p. A133

JACKSON, Jeffrey, M.D. Medical Director, Houston Methodist Sugar Land Hospital, Sugar Land, TX, p. A650

JACKSON, Jennifer, R.N. Vice President and Chief Nursing Officer, University of Cincinnati Medical Center, Cincinnati, OH, p. A487

JACKSON, Joanne, Administrator Human Resources, Community Relations and Quality Improvement, Amery Regional Medical Center, Amery, WI, p. A701

JACKSON, John J., President, FirstHealth Richmond Memorial Hospital, Rockingham, NC, p. A471

JACKSON, Judy, Director Health Information Management and Privacy Officer, Shodair Children's Hospital, Helena, MT, p. A388

JACKSON, Kelvin, LAN Administrator, Holmes County Hospital and Clinics, Lexington, MS, p. A361

JACKSON, Kevin, On Site Administrator, Highsmith–Rainey Specialty Hospital, Fayetteville, NC, p. A464

JACKSON, Les, Manager Information Systems, Lower Keys Medical Center, Key West, FL, p. A133

JACKSON, Lori L., Director Human Resources, Verde Valley Medical Center, Cottonwood, AZ, p. A32

JACKSON, Lynn, Administrator, Northside Hospital–Forsyth, Cumming, GA, p. A157

JACKSON, Max, M.D. Chief Medical Officer, Renown South Meadows Medical Center, Reno, NV, p. A408

JACKSON, Meg, Director Biomedical and Management Information Systems, Beauregard Memorial Hospital, De Ridder, LA, p. A276

JACKSON, Melinda, Director Human Resources, Bates County Memorial Hospital, Butler, MO, p. A368

JACKSON, Michelle, Chief Financial Officer, BHC Alhambra Hospital, Rosemead, CA, p. A86

JACKSON, Mike, President and Chief Executive Officer, Ephraim McDowell Fort Logan Hospital, Stanford, KY, p. A270

JACKSON, Patsy, Director of Nursing, Jay Hospital, Jay, FL, p. A132

JACKSON, Reese, President and Chief Executive Officer, Forbes Regional Hospital, Monroeville, PA, p. A545

JACKSON, Robert
  Chief Financial Officer, Alliance Health Center, Meridian, MS, p. A362
  Interim Chief Executive Officer, Cedar Ridge Hospital, Oklahoma City, OK, p. A515

JACKSON Jr., Robert, Chief Executive Officer, Grove City Medical Center, Grove City, PA, p. A540

JACKSON, Samatha, M.D. Chief of Staff, Elkview General Hospital, Hobart, OK, p. A512

JACKSON, Stephen, M.D. Chief of Staff, Skyridge Medical Center, Cleveland, TN, p. A581

JACKSON, Suzanne B., FACHE, Chief Executive Officer, John Randolph Medical Center, Hopewell, VA, p. A672

JACKSON, Tamara L., FACHE,
  Chief Executive Officer, Doctors Specialty Hospital, Columbus, GA, p. A156
  Chief Executive Officer, Northside Medical Center, Columbus, GA, p. A156

JACKSON, Thomas, M.D. Chief of Staff, Missouri Baptist Sullivan Hospital, Sullivan, MO, p. A383

JACKSON, Thomas W., Chief Executive Officer, Tomball Regional Medical Center, Tomball, TX, p. A653

JACKSON, Tina
  Director Human Resources, Barrow Regional Medical Center, Winder, GA, p. A169
  Manager Human Resources, Williamson Memorial Hospital, Williamson, WV, p. A700

JACKSON, Tom, Chief Financial Officer, Parkridge Medical Center, Chattanooga, TN, p. A580

JACKSON, Tommy, Chief Executive Officer, Landmark Hospital of Athens, Athens, GA, p. A151

JACKSON, Vance, FACHE, Administrator and Chief Executive Officer, Hancock County Health System, Britt, IA, p. A226

JACKSON, W. Anthony, Chief Executive Officer, HEALTHSOUTH Rehabilitation Hospital of Columbia, Columbia, SC, p. A564

JACKSON, Wendy, Chief Operating Officer and Chief Nursing Officer, Medina Memorial Hospital, Medina, NY, p. A441

JACO, Mary, MSN, Administrator, Shriners Hospitals for Children–Galveston Burns Hospital, Galveston, TX, p. A620

JACOB, Cheryl, Chief Operating Officer, Saddleback Memorial Medical Center, Laguna Hills, CA, p. A68

JACOBI, Elizabeth
  Human Resources Director, LAC/University of Southern California Medical Center, Los Angeles, CA, p. A73
  Associate Director Human Resources, Rancho Los Amigos National Rehabilitation Center, Downey, CA, p. A62

JACOBI, Robert, Chief Financial Officer, Bob Wilson Memorial Grant County Hospital, Ulysses, KS, p. A255

JACOBS, Andrea, Chief Operating Officer, South Pointe Hospital, Warrensville Heights, OH, p. A504

JACOBS, Andrew, M.D. Chief Medical Officer, Virginia Mason Medical Center, Seattle, WA, p. A689

JACOBS, Barbara Stewart, MSN Chief Nurse Officer, Suburban Hospital, Bethesda, MD, p. A299

JACOBS, Brian, M.D. Vice President Chief Information Officer and Chief Medical Information Officer, Children's National Medical Center, Washington, DC, p. A121

JACOBS, Donna K., FACHE, Director, Northern Arizona Veterans Affairs Health Care System, Prescott, AZ, p. A37

JACOBS, Greg, Manager, McLaren Bay Special Care, Bay City, MI, p. A319

JACOBS, Ian, Chief, Human Resource Management Service, Louis A. Johnson Veterans Affairs Medical Center, Clarksburg, WV, p. A694

JACOBS, Jenny, Director Human Resources, OSF Holy Family Medical Center, Monmouth, IL, p. A196

JACOBS, Joey, Chairman and Chief Executive Officer, Acadia Healthcare Company, Inc., Franklin, TN, p. B4

JACOBS, Julie
  Director Human Resources, Oklahoma Forensic Center, Vinita, OK, p. A521
  Chief Financial Officer, Warren General Hospital, Warren, PA, p. A557

JACOBS, Mark, Director Information Services, Pomerene Hospital, Millersburg, OH, p. A499

JACOBS, Michael
  Vice President Human Resources, Gladys Spellman Specialty Hospital and Nursing Center, Cheverly, MD, p. A299
  Vice President Human Resources, Prince George's Hospital Center, Cheverly, MD, p. A299

JACOBS, Richard, Vice President Finance and Chief Financial Officer, Canton–Potsdam Hospital, Potsdam, NY, p. A452

JACOBS, Robert
  Regional Director Information Management, CHRISTUS Hospital–St. Elizabeth, Beaumont, TX, p. A601
  Regional Information Management Executive, CHRISTUS Jasper Memorial Hospital, Jasper, TX, p. A630

JACOBS, Trace, Director Information Technology, Santiam Memorial Hospital, Stayton, OR, p. A530

JACOBS, Yolanda, Coordinator Human Resources, Cornerstone Hospital of Houston at Clearlake, Webster, TX, p. A656

JACOBSEN, Barry, Chief Executive Officer, Myrtue Medical Center, Harlan, IA, p. A232

JACOBSEN, John, M.D. Chief of Staff, Fillmore County Hospital, Geneva, NE, p. A396

JACOBSEN, William D., Vice President and Administrator, Carilion Franklin Memorial Hospital, Rocky Mount, VA, p. A678

JACOBSON, Andrea, Human Resource Officer, Cavalier County Memorial Hospital, Langdon, ND, p. A479

JACOBSON, Becky, Vice President Finance, St. Vincent Heart Center, Indianapolis, IN, p. A215

JACOBSON, Carlton, Vice President, St. Helena Hospital Napa Valley, Saint Helena, CA, p. A88

JACOBSON, Gary, M.D. Chief Medical Officer, Pembroke Hospital, Pembroke, MA, p. A313

JACOBSON, Janet, Director Human Resources, Lakewood Health System, Staples, MN, p. A352

JACOBSON, Jenny, Manager Human Resources, Sanford Hillsboro Medical Center, Hillsboro, ND, p. A478

JACOBSON, John, Chief Financial Officer, Gibson Area Hospital and Health Services, Gibson City, IL, p. A191

JACOBSON, John L., Chief Executive Officer, Atchison Hospital, Atchison, KS, p. A241

JACOBSON, Lisa, Director of Nursing, Community Hospital of Huntington Park, Huntington Park, CA, p. A67

JACOBSON, Mary Jo, Chief Executive Officer, San Joaquin Valley Rehabilitation Hospital, Fresno, CA, p. A64

JACOBSON, Peter, President, Essentia Health St. Mary's – Detroit Lakes, Detroit Lakes, MN, p. A342

JACOBSON, Randolph
  Chief Financial Officer, Carrier Clinic, Belie Mead, NJ, p. A413
  Chief Financial Officer, East Mountain Hospital, Belle Mead, NJ, p. A413

JACOBSON, Rodney D., Administrator, Bear Lake Memorial Hospital, Montpelier, ID, p. A177

JACOBSON, Sam, Director Management Information Systems, Community Memorial Hospital, Cloquet, MN, p. A341

JACOBSON, Shirley
  Chief Financial Officer, Community Behavioral Health Hospital – Alexandria, Alexandria, MN, p. A339
  Chief Financial Officer, Community Behavioral Health Hospital – Rochester, Rochester, MN, p. A350
  Chief Financial Officer, Community Behavioral Health Hospital – St. Peter, Saint Peter, MN, p. A352

JACOBSON, Terry, Administrator and Chief Executive Officer, Essentia Health St. Mary's Hospital of Superior, Superior, WI, p. A716

JACOBY, Jamie R., Chief Financial Officer, Connally Memorial Medical Center, Floresville, TX, p. A617

JACQUES, Teresa, Interim Chief Financial Officer, Adventist Medical Center–Reedley, Reedley, CA, p. A86

JADCZAK, Audrey, R.N
  Vice President/Chief Nursing Officer, Lourdes Medical Center of Burlington County, Willingboro, NJ, p. A424
  Vice President Chief Nursing Officer, Our Lady of Lourdes Medical Center, Camden, NJ, p. A414

JADEJA, Neerav, Administrator, Paradise Valley Hospital, National City, CA, p. A79

JADLOWSKI, Susan, R.N., Chief Executive Officer, Memorial Hermann Northwest Hospital, Houston, TX, p. A625

JAFFE, Darcy, R.N. Interim Chief Nursing Officer, UW Medicine/Harborview Medical Center, Seattle, WA, p. A689

JAFFE, David E., Chief Executive, Swedish/Edmonds, Edmonds, WA, p. A683

JAFFE, Gabriel, M.D. Vice President Medical Affairs, Doctors Community Hospital, Lanham, MD, p. A302

JAFFE, Richard, M.D. Medical Director, Belmont Center for Comprehensive Treatment, Philadelphia, PA, p. A547

JAGER, Linda, Director Finance, Avera Weskota Memorial Hospital, Wessington Springs, SD, p. A578

JAGGI, Michael, D.O. Vice President and Chief Medical Officer, Hurley Medical Center, Flint, MI, p. A323

JAGODITZ, Chris, Chief Financial Officer, Cumberland Hall Hospital, Hopkinsville, KY, p. A263

JAGOE, Patricia, Assistant Vice President Patient Care, Johnson Memorial Hospital, Stafford Springs, CT, p. A117

JAHAN, Mohammad S., M.D. Clinical Director, Middle Tennessee Mental Health Institute, Nashville, TN, p. A590

JAHN, Andrew, President and Chief Executive Officer, Sonora Regional Medical Center, Sonora, CA, p. A95

JAHN, Barbara A., Chief Operating Officer, Exempla Saint Joseph Hospital, Denver, CO, p. A104

JAHN, David B., President and Chief Executive Officer, War Memorial Hospital, Sault Sainte Marie, MI, p. A334

JAHN, Gregory L., R.N., Chief Executive Officer, St. Luke's Behavioral Health Center, Phoenix, AZ, p. A37

JAHN, Kim C., Chief Plant Operations and Chief Information Officer, Manning Regional Healthcare Center, Manning, IA, p. A234

JAHNIG, Jay A., Chief Executive Officer, Faulkton Area Medical Center, Faulkton, SD, p. A573

JAHRE, Jeffrey, M.D. Vice President Medical and Academic Affairs, St. Luke's University Hospital – Bethlehem Campus, Bethlehem, PA, p. A534

JAIN, Ashok, M.D. Chief of Staff, Oakwood Hospital–Wayne, Wayne, MI, p. A337

JAIN, Sunita, M.D. Chief Medical Officer, Baptist Rehabilitation–Germantown, Germantown, TN, p. A583

JAKACKI, Timothy
President, ProMedica Bixby Hospital, Adrian, MI, p. A318
President, ProMedica Herrick Hospital, Tecumseh, MI, p. A336

JAKOUBECK, Denise, Director Human Resources, Hancock County Health System, Britt, IA, p. A226

JALBERT, Susan L., R.N. Vice President Patient Care Services and Chief Nursing Officer, Northwest Hospital, Randallstown, MD, p. A302

JAMALEDDINE, Ghassan, M.D. Medical Director, Kings County Hospital Center,, NY, p. A444

JAMES, Annette, Chief Nursing Officer, Creek Nation Community Hospital, Okemah, OK, p. A514

JAMES, Bruce, Chief Executive Officer, Union Hospital, Dover, OH, p. A493

JAMES, Craig B., FACHE, Chief Executive Officer, Highlands–Cashiers Hospital, Highlands, NC, p. A466

JAMES, Dawn, Director of Nursing, Wyoming County Community Hospital, Warsaw, NY, p. A457

JAMES, Diane R., Administrator, Florida State Hospital, Chattahoochee, FL, p. A125

JAMES, Donald, D.O. Chief Medical Officer, Phelps County Regional Medical Center, Rolla, MO, p. A379

JAMES, Douglas, Chief Nursing Officer, Caldwell Medical Center, Princeton, KY, p. A269

JAMES, Gregory L., D.O. Chief Medical Officer, St. Vincent's Birmingham, Birmingham, AL, p. A17

JAMES, Janet, Director Human Resources, Trigg County Hospital, Cadiz, KY, p. A259

JAMES, Jobie, Chief Financial Officer, West Calcasieu Cameron Hospital, Sulphur, LA, p. A289

JAMES, Kenneth, Chief Executive Officer, Poplar Bluff Regional Medical Center, Poplar Bluff, MO, p. A378

JAMES, Laura, Director Human Resources, St. Francis Medical Center, Trenton, NJ, p. A423

JAMES, Michael
Chief Operations Officer, Jackson Hospital and Clinic, Montgomery, AL, p. A24
Information Technology Technical Support Specialist 1, Villa Feliciana Medical Complex, Jackson, LA, p. A279

JAMES, Michelle, Chief Nursing Officer, Providence St. Peter Hospital, Olympia, WA, p. A686

JAMES, Naren, M.D. Chief of Staff, Ephraim McDowell Fort Logan Hospital, Stanford, KY, p. A270

JAMES, Robert L., Director Human Resources, Oakwood Hospital–Wayne, Wayne, MI, p. A337

JAMES, Sherrie, R.N. Director of Nursing, The BridgeWay, North Little Rock, AR, p. A51

JAMES, Stephanie, Chief Executive Officer, Regency Hospital of Greenville, Greenville, SC, p. A566

JAMES, Taya, Director, Mercy Hospital Berryville, Berryville, AR, p. A43

JAMES, Teri, Chief Financial Officer, Lafayette Regional Health Center, Lexington, MO, p. A376

JAMES, Thomas L., M.D. Chief Medical Officer, Trumbull Memorial Hospital, Warren, OH, p. A504

JAMES, Tim, Coordinator Human Resources, Cordova Community Medical Center, Cordova, AK, p. A28

JAMES, William B., FACHE, Chief Executive Officer, Wake Forest Baptist Health–Lexington Medical Center, Lexington, NC, p. A468

JAMESON, David, M.D. Chief of Staff, Annie Jeffrey Memorial County Health Center, Osceola, NE, p. A400

JAMESON, Traci, Manager Finance, Select Specialty Hospital–Houston Heights, Houston, TX, p. A626

JAMIESON, Anne, FACHE, Chief Executive Officer, Portsmouth Regional Hospital, Portsmouth, NH, p. A412

JAMIESON, Jess, Chief Executive Officer, Western State Hospital, Tacoma, WA, p. A691

JAMIESON, Pamela, Vice President Patient Care Services and Chief Nursing Officer, University of Maryland St. Joseph Medical Center, Towson, MD, p. A304

JAMIN, David, Chief Financial Officer, St. Mary's Regional Medical Center, Enid, OK, p. A510

JANATKA, Lucille A.
President and CEO, MidState Medical Center, Meriden, CT, p. A115
President and CEO, The Hospital of Central Connecticut, New Britain, CT, p. A115

JANEK, James D., Chief Executive Officer, Rice Medical Center, Eagle Lake, TX, p. A614

JANERELLA, Wendy, Controller, Bucktail Medical Center, Renovo, PA, p. A553

JANICAK, Dan, Chief Financial Officer, University Hospital, Jackson, MS, p. A360

JANIS, Terry, Assistant Vice President, Park Plaza Hospital, Houston, TX, p. A626

JANKE, Paul, FACHE, President and Chief Executive Officer, Bay Area Hospital, Coos Bay, OR, p. A524

JANKOWSKI, Stan, Vice President and Chief Information Officer, Hospital for Special Care, New Britain, CT, p. A115

JANLOO, Arman, M.D. Chief Medical Staff, Fairfax Community Hospital, Fairfax, OK, p. A511

JANOSO, John R., President and Chief Executive Officer, Sharon Regional Health System, Sharon, PA, p. A555

JANOWSKI, Kenneth, M.D. Chief Medical Officer, Hackettstown Regional Medical Center, Hackettstown, NJ, p. A416

JANOYAN, Jano, M.D. Medical Director, Select Specialty Hospital–Knoxville, Knoxville, TN, p. A586

JANSEN, David, Vice President Human Resources, Karmanos Cancer Center, Detroit, MI, p. A322

JANSEN, Eric, Director Information Systems, Clifton Springs Hospital and Clinic, Clifton Springs, NY, p. A435

JANSEN, John, Management Information Specialist, Hawaii State Hospital, Kaneohe, HI, p. A172

JANSSEN, Darin A., Chief Financial Officer, Cimarron Memorial Hospital, Boise City, OK, p. A508

JANSSEN, Kathy, Director Medical Records, Mountrail County Medical Center, Stanley, ND, p. A480

JANSSEN, Paul, President and Chief Executive Officer, Henry County Hospital, New Castle, IN, p. A220

JANSSEN, Thomas, M.D. Chief of Staff, McBride Clinic Orthopedic Hospital, Oklahoma City, OK, p. A515

JANUS, Tammy, Senior Vice President Human Resources, Mercy Medical Center, Baltimore, MD, p. A297

JANVRIN, Susan, R.N. Chief Operating and Chief Nursing Officer, Kaiser Permanente Santa Rosa Medical Center, Santa Rosa, CA, p. A95

JANZEN, Wes, Chief Information Officer, Wamego Health Center, Wamego, KS, p. A256

JAQUEZ, Jason, Director Human Resources, Greater El Monte Community Hospital, South El Monte, CA, p. A96

JARBOE, Joe, Director Human Resources, Kosciusko Community Hospital, Warsaw, IN, p. A224

JARBOE, Lori, Chief Executive Officer, HEALTHSOUTH Lakeview Rehabilitation Hospital, Elizabethtown, KY, p. A260

JARM, Timothy L., President and Chief Executive Officer, Alliant Management Services, Louisville, KY, p. B9

JARMAN, Amy, Director Human Resources, Mena Regional Health System, Mena, AR, p. A50

JARMAN, Wayne, M.D. President Medical Staff, Lenoir Memorial Hospital, Kinston, NC, p. A467

JAROG, Dena, R.N. Vice President Patient Care, Reedsburg Area Medical Center, Reedsburg, WI, p. A714

JAROPILLO, Erwin, Director Information Systems, Lake Wales Medical Center, Lake Wales, FL, p. A133

JARREAU, Jeff, Senior Vice President Human Resources, North Oaks Medical Center, Hammond, LA, p. A278

JARRELL, Lindsey, Vice President Information Services, St. Joseph's Hospital, Tampa, FL, p. A148

JARRETT, Adam D., M.D. Executive Vice President and Chief Medical Officer, Holy Name Medical Center, Teaneck, NJ, p. A423

JARRETT, Brenda, Chief Financial Officer, Putnam General Hospital, Eatonton, GA, p. A159

JARRETT, Mark, M.D. Chief Medical Officer, Staten Island University Hospital,, NY, p. A448

JARRY, Jacques, Administrator, Bullock County Hospital, Union Springs, AL, p. A26

JARRY, Patricia, Manager Human Resources, Crenshaw Community Hospital, Luverne, AL, p. A22

JARVIS, Dinah, Director of Nursing, Pineville Community Hospital Association, Pineville, KY, p. A269

JARVIS, Keith, Director Information Systems, Longview Regional Medical Center, Longview, TX, p. A634

JASOVSKY, Deborah A., Ph.D. Chief Nursing Officer, Norwegian American Hospital, Chicago, IL, p. A185

JASPER, Harry, Administrator, Jerold Phelps Community Hospital, Garberville, CA, p. A65

JASPER, Jerry, Chief Executive Officer and Administrator, Southeast Colorado Hospital District, Springfield, CO, p. A111

JASTREMSKI, Michael S., M.D. Vice President Medical Affairs and Director Emergency Services, Community Memorial Hospital, Hamilton, NY, p. A438

JATCZAK, Tracy E., CPA Chief Financial Officer, Box Butte General Hospital, Alliance, NE, p. A393

JAUERSACK, Dawn, Vice President and Chief Financial Officer, Boca Raton Regional Hospital, Boca Raton, FL, p. A124

JAVOIS, Laurent D.
Regional Executive Officer, Hawthorn Children Psychiatric Hospital, Saint Louis, MO, p. A380
Regional Executive Officer, Metropolitan St. Louis Psychiatric Center, Saint Louis, MO, p. A381
Regional Executive Officer, St. Louis Psychiatric Rehabilitation Center, Saint Louis, MO, p. A382

JAVOIS, Rosalie, Chief Financial Officer, Governor Juan F. Louis Hospital, Christiansted, VI, p. A729

JAY, Richard, D.O. Chief of Staff, North Big Horn Hospital District, Lovell, WY, p. A722

JEAN–BAPTISTE, Joan, Vice President Human Resources, Governor Juan F. Louis Hospital, Christiansted, VI, p. A729

JEANNETTE, Joanie, MSN, Chief Executive Officer, Lehigh Regional Medical Center, Lehigh Acres, FL, p. A134

JEANSONNE, Corey, Chief Nursing Officer, Bunkie General Hospital, Bunkie, LA, p. A275

JEANTY, Johanne, Director Human Resources, Aurora Chicago Lakeshore Hospital, Chicago, IL, p. A183

JEFFERIES, Michael, Vice President Information Systems, Longmont United Hospital, Longmont, CO, p. A109

JEFFERSON, Candace, Manager Human Resources, CHRISTUS Spohn Hospital Kleberg, Kingsville, TX, p. A631

JEFFERSON, Terrie, R.N. Chief Nursing Officer, South Bay Hospital, Sun City Center, FL, p. A146

JEFFRAS, Charles, Executive Director Human Resources, St. Vincent Carmel Hospital, Carmel, IN, p. A208

JEFFRESS, Chuck, Vice President Fiscal Services, Brazosport Regional Health System, Lake Jackson, TX, p. A632

JEFFREY, Roberta, Chief Executive Officer, Holdenville General Hospital, Holdenville, OK, p. A512

JEFFRIES, John, Director Finance, St. Joseph's Hospital, Breese, IL, p. A182

JEHAN, Sayed, M.D. Interim Medical Director, Larned State Hospital, Larned,, KS, p. A248

JELALIAN, Christine, M.D. Medical Director, St. Luke's Cornwall Hospital, Newburgh, NY, p. A449

JELDEN, Dennis, M.D. Chief of Staff, Melissa Memorial Hospital, Holyoke, CO, p. A107

JELESKY, Beth, Director of Nursing and Director Clinical Services, Aurora Chicago Lakeshore Hospital, Chicago, IL, p. A183

JELKS, Kim, Fiscal Officer, Villa Feliciana Medical Complex, Jackson, LA, p. A279

JELLE, Laura, Executive Vice President and Chief Operating Officer, St. Clare Hospital, Baraboo, WI, p. A702

JENE, Suzanne, Chief Operating Officer, Tennessee Valley Healthcare System, Nashville, TN, p. A591

JENEY, Martie, Director Human Resources, Callaway Community Hospital, Fulton, MO, p. A371

JENKINS, Bonnie, Chief Financial Officer, Methodist Hospital of Sacramento, Sacramento, CA, p. A87

JENKINS, Brian, Director Human Resources, Arbour–Fuller Hospital, Attleboro, MA, p. A305

JENKINS, Debbie, Chief Human Resources Management Service, Veterans Affairs Sierra Nevada Health Care System, Reno, NV, p. A408

JENKINS, Denise, Chief Clinical Officer, Kindred Hospital–Brea, Brea, CA, p. A58

JENKINS, Jason, Senior Director of Nursing, Novant Health Haymarket Medical Center, Haymarket, VA, p. A672

JENKINS, Laura, Director Operations Finance and Business Development, Buffalo Hospital, Buffalo, MN, p. A341

JENKINS, Lawrence, M.D. Chief of Staff, Ivinson Memorial Hospital, Laramie, WY, p. A722

JENKINS, Linda, R.N. Vice President Patient Care Services, St. Jude Medical Center, Fullerton, CA, p. A65

JENKINS, Michelle, M.D. President Medical Staff, Herrin Hospital, Herrin, IL, p. A192

JENKINS, Rebecca, Director Human Resources Management, Harrison Memorial Hospital, Cynthiana, KY, p. A260

JENKINS, Roger T., Chief Executive Officer, Ethicus Hospital – Grapevine, Grapevine, TX, p. A621

JENKINS, Scott, Administrator, Cheyenne County Hospital, Saint Francis, KS, p. A253

JENKS, Lyn, Chief Executive Officer, Charlevoix Area Hospital, Charlevoix, MI, p. A320

JENNER, Jody J., President and Chief Executive Officer, Broadlawns Medical Center, Des Moines, IA, p. A229

JENNETTE, Brian, Chief Financial Officer, Northside Hospital–Cherokee, Canton, GA, p. A155

JENNINGS, D. Arlo, Ph.D. Chief Information Officer, Mission Hospital, Asheville, NC, p. A460

JENNINGS, Jeff, FACHE, Chief Executive Officer, Shoals Hospital, Muscle Shoals, AL, p. A24

JENNINGS, Keith, Chief Information Officer, Massachusetts General Hospital, Boston, MA, p. A307

JENNINGS, Marilyn, Director Human Resources, Arise Austin Medical Center, Austin, TX, p. A598

JENNINGS, Mark
Director Information Systems, Northeast Georgia Medical Center, Gainesville, GA, p. A160
Chief Information Officer, Saint Anthony Hospital, Chicago, IL, p. A186

JENNINGS, Reynold J., President and Chief Executive Officer, WellStar Health System, Marietta, GA, p. B151

JENNINGS, Shayla, Human Resources Director, Montgomery County Memorial Hospital, Red Oak, IA, p. A236

JENNINGS, William M., President and Chief Executive Officer, Bridgeport Hospital, Bridgeport, CT, p. A113

JENSEMA, Christine
Chief People Officer, St. Mary's Hospital Medical Center, Green Bay, WI, p. A706
Chief People Officer, St. Nicholas Hospital, Sheboygan, WI, p. A715
Chief People Officer, St. Vincent Hospital, Green Bay, WI, p. A706

JENSEN, Alice J., Chief Operating Officer, Geary Community Hospital, Junction City, KS, p. A246

JENSEN, Amy, Director Human Resources, Community Health Center of Branch County, Coldwater, MI, p. A321

JENSEN, Annelise, Chief Nursing Officer, Methodist Olive Branch Hospital, Olive Branch, MS, p. A363

JENSEN, Barb, R.N. Interim Chief Nursing Executive, Skagit Valley Hospital, Mount Vernon, WA, p. A685

JENSEN, Beth, Director Clinic Operations, Mobridge Regional Hospital, Mobridge, SD, p. A575

JENSEN, Christopher, Chief Financial Officer, Three Rivers Behavioral Health, West Columbia, SC, p. A571

JENSEN, Dave, Director Human Resources, Performance Improvement and Risk Management, Mountain View Hospital, Gadsden, AL, p. A20

JENSEN, Donna, Director Clinical Services, Blue Mountain Hospital, Blanding, UT, p. A659

JENSEN, Eric, Chief Executive Officer, Valley General Hospital, Monroe, WA, p. A685

JENSEN, Gail, Chief Financial Officer, Trego County–Lemke Memorial Hospital, Wakeeney, KS, p. A256

JENSEN, Jan, R.N., Chief Executive Officer and Administrator, William Bee Ririe Hospital, Ely, NV, p. A404

JENSEN, Janette, Manager Human Resources, Avera Holy Family Hospital, Estherville, IA, p. A230

JENSEN, Jeff, Finance Director, Intermountain Medical Center, Murray, UT, p. A660

JENSEN, Jeff, M.D. Vice President, Medical Affairs, Morton Plant Hospital, Clearwater, FL, p. A125

JENSEN, Laura J., Vice President Patient Care Services, St. Croix Regional Medical Center, St. Croix Falls, WI, p. A715

JENSEN, Leanna, Vice President Finance and Chief Financial Officer, Cobleskill Regional Hospital, Cobleskill, NY, p. A436

JENSEN, Mary, Controller, Mountain View Hospital, Gadsden, AL, p. A20

JENSEN, Michael E., Chief Executive Officer, Davis Hospital and Medical Center, Layton, UT, p. A660

JENSEN, Neal, Chief Executive Officer, Cobre Valley Regional Medical Center, Globe, AZ, p. A33

JENSEN, Pamela, FACHE, President, Memorial Hospital, Fremont, OH, p. A494

JENSEN, Paul, M.D. Chief of Staff, Regional Health Services of Howard County, Cresco, IA, p. A228

JENSEN, Renee K., Chief Executive Officer, Summit Pacific Medical Center, Elma, WA, p. A683

JENSEN, Ron, D.O. Chief Medical Officer and Vice President, Baylor Regional Medical Center at Grapevine, Grapevine, TX, p. A621

JENSEN, Ronald, Manager Finance, The Orthopedic Specialty Hospital, Murray, UT, p. A661

JENSEN, Ryan, Chief Executive Officer, Memorial Hospital of Salem County, Salem, NJ, p. A422

JENSEN, Sherry, Chief Financial Officer, Halifax Regional Medical Center, Roanoke Rapids, NC, p. A471

JENSEN, Tom, Chief Executive Officer, Grays Harbor Community Hospital, Aberdeen, WA, p. A681

JENSEN, Troy, Director Human Resources, HEALTHSOUTH Rehabilitation Hospital of Utah, Sandy, UT, p. A664

JENSEN, Twyla, Director Human Resources, Pioneers Medical Center, Meeker, CO, p. A110

JENTZ, Amy, M.D. Chief of Staff, Sparrow Ionia Hospital, Ionia, MI, p. A327

JEPPESEN, Kelly, Chief Medical Officer, San Juan Hospital, Monticello, UT, p. A660

JEPPI, Jessi, Director Human Resources, Rockford Center, Newark, DE, p. A119

JEPSEN, Christinia, R.N. Chief Nursing Officer, Mineral Area Regional Medical Center, Farmington, MO, p. A371

JEPSON, Brian, Chief Operating Officer, OhioHealth Riverside Methodist Hospital, Columbus, OH, p. A490

JEPSON, Jeanne, Director Human Resources, Hackettstown Regional Medical Center, Hackettstown, NJ, p. A416

JEPSON, Mark, Vice President, Silver Cross Hospital, New Lenox, IL, p. A198

JERGER, Greg, Chief Financial Officer, Memorial Health Care Systems, Seward, NE, p. A402

JERINA, Anthony T., Chief Nursing Officer, Hereford Regional Medical Center, Hereford, TX, p. A623

JERNIGAN, Donald L., Ph.D., President and Chief Executive Officer, Adventist Health System Sunbelt Health Care Corporation, Altamonte Springs, FL, p. B6

JERNIGAN, Pam, Chief Financial Officer, United Regional Medical Center, Manchester, TN, p. A587

JERNIGAN Jr., Robert F., Chief Executive Officer, Select Specialty Hospital–Durham, Durham, NC, p. A463

JESCH, Doug, Director Human Resources, Indiana University Health Starke Hospital, Knox, IN, p. A216

JESIOLOWSKI, Craig A., FACHE, President, Saint Anne's Hospital, Fall River, MA, p. A310

JESSUP, Daniel L., Chief Financial Officer, Silverton Hospital, Silverton, OR, p. A530

JESTER, Denise, Chief Financial Officer, Nanticoke Memorial Hospital, Seaford, DE, p. A119

JESTILA–PELTOLA, Gail, Chief Financial Officer, Baraga County Memorial Hospital, L'Anse, MI, p. A328

JESURASA, Jebashini, Vice President, Chief Information Technology Officer, Wyckoff Heights Medical Center,, NY, p. A449

JETER, John
Assistant Administrator and Chief Financial Officer, Johnston Memorial Hospital, Abingdon, VA, p. A668
Chief Financial Officer, Russell County Medical Center, Lebanon, VA, p. A672

JETER, John H., M.D., President and Chief Executive Officer, Hays Medical Center, Hays, KS, p. A245

JETER, Larry R., Chief Executive Officer, Jamestown Regional Medical Center, Jamestown, TN, p. A584

JETT, Heather, Director Patient Care Services, Peninsula Hospital, Louisville, TN, p. A587

JETTERGREN, Tess, Director Clinical Informatics, Essentia Health St. Mary's Medical Center, Duluth, MN, p. A342

JETTON, Dana, Chief Information Officer, AMG Specialty Hospital–Tulsa, Tulsa, OK, p. A520

JEUNEHOMME, Patti, Director Human Resources, Hot Springs County Memorial Hospital, Thermopolis, WY, p. A723

JEWELL, Bryan, Director Human Resources, Forest Park Medical Center Frisco, Frisco, TX, p. A620

JEWELL, Keith, President, St. Mary's Medical Center of Evansville, Evansville, IN, p. A210

JEWETT, Sherri R., Chief Executive Officer, Valle Vista Hospital, Greenwood, IN, p. A212

JEZIORSKE, John J., Director Human Resources, Abilene Regional Medical Center, Abilene, TX, p. A595

JEZSU, Peggy, Chief Nursing Officer, Alvarado Hospital Medical Center, San Diego, CA, p. A89

JHA, Gautam, M.D. Chief of Staff, Salem Township Hospital, Salem, IL, p. A202

JILEK, Lea, Director Finance, Bethesda Hospital, Saint Paul, MN, p. A351

JIMENEZ, Betzaida, Director Human Resources, Hospital de la Universidad de Puerto Rico/Dr. Federico Trilla, Carolina, PR, p. A725

JIMENEZ, Cristina, Chief Operating Officer, Coral Gables Hospital, Coral Gables, FL, p. A126

JIMENEZ, Edward, Interim Chief Executive Officer, UF Health Shands, Gainesville, FL, p. B137

JIMENEZ, Edward, Interim Chief Executive Officer, UF Health Shands Hospital, Gainesville, FL, p. A130

JIMENEZ, Gerson, M.D. Medical Director, Hospital Episcopal San Lucas Guayama, Guayama, PR, p. A726

JIMENEZ, Guillermo, Director Finance, Castaner General Hospital, Castaner, PR, p. A725

JIMENEZ, Ron, M.D. Chief Medical Officer, Florida Hospital Memorial Medical Center, Daytona Beach, FL, p. A127

JIMESON, Jean–Marie, Manager Human Resources, Kansas Spine and Specialty Hospital, Wichita, KS, p. A256

JIMMERSON, Kevin, Business Manager, Mental Health Institute, Independence, IA, p. A232

JIN, Marvin, M.D. Medical Director, Parkside Hospital, Tulsa, OK, p. A520

JIRON, Feliciano, Chief Executive Officer, Los Alamos Medical Center, Los Alamos, NM, p. A429

JIROVEC, David, Director Finance, Ministry Good Samaritan Health Center, Merrill, WI, p. A710

JITH, Gayathri S., M.P.H. Senior Vice President Strategy and Operations, Valley Presbyterian Hospital,, CA, p. A75

JIVIDEN, Roxanne, Chief Executive Officer, Ohio Hospital for Psychiatry, Columbus, OH, p. A490

JOBBITT, Patty, Vice President Operations, Rehabilitation Institute of Michigan, Detroit, MI, p. A322

JOBE, Kathy, R.N. Chief Nursing Officer and Vice President Patient Care Services, Summa Barberton Citizens Hospital, Barberton, OH, p. A483

JOBE, Ken, Director Human Resources, Tyler County Hospital, Woodville, TX, p. A658

JOCHIM, Steven, Administrator, Cape Cod & Island Community Mental Health Center, Pocasset, MA, p. A314

JODWAY, Timothy, Chief Financial Officer, Garden City Hospital, Garden City, MI, p. A324

JOEL, Linda, Vice President Operations, Spectrum Health Special Care Hospital, Grand Rapids, MI, p. A325

JOERS, Barbara, President and Chief Executive Officer, Gillette Children's Specialty Healthcare, Saint Paul, MN, p. A351

JOGLAR, Francisco M., M.D., Secretary of Health, Puerto Rico Department of Health, San Juan, PR, p. B111

JOHANSON–FOGLE, Lori, Vice President Human Resources, Providence Mount Carmel Hospital, Colville, WA, p. A682

JOHE, David, M.D. President Medical Staff, Elk Regional Health Center, Saint Marys, PA, p. A554

JOHN, Aleyamma, R.N. Director of Nursing, Kensington Hospital, Philadelphia, PA, p. A549

JOHN, Julian, Chief Financial Officer, Kings County Hospital Center,, NY, p. A444

JOHN, M. Joseph, M.D. Chief of Staff, Berwick Hospital Center, Berwick, PA, p. A533

JOHNS, Dale, Chief Executive Officer, Salt Lake Regional Medical Center, Salt Lake City, UT, p. A663

JOHNS, Dawn, Director Human Resources, Colquitt Regional Medical Center, Moultrie, GA, p. A164

JOHNS, Jeffery, M.D. Medical Director, Vanderbilt Stallworth Rehabilitation Hospital, Nashville, TN, p. A591

JOHNS, Paul, Chief Operating Officer, South Lake Hospital, Clermont, FL, p. A125

JOHNS, Thomas Bradford, M.D. Medical Director, Ridgeview Institute, Smyrna, GA, p. A167

JOHNS, Timothy, M.D. Chief Medical Officer, Gilbert Hospital, Gilbert, AZ, p. A32

JOHNSEN, Timothy J., MS, President, Integris Baptist Medical Center, Oklahoma City, OK, p. A515

JOHNSON, Alan, Chief Information Officer, Doctors Community Hospital, Lanham, MD, p. A302

JOHNSON, Allen
Chief Financial Officer, Truman Medical Center–Hospital Hill, Kansas City, MO, p. A374
Chief Financial Officer, Truman Medical Center–Lakewood, Kansas City, MO, p. A374

JOHNSON, Amy, M.D. Chief of Staff, Longmont United Hospital, Longmont, CO, p. A109

JOHNSON, Arlan D., Chief Executive Officer, Howard County Medical Center, Saint Paul, NE, p. A401

JOHNSON, Barbara, Chief Financial Officer, Essentia Health Northern Pines, Aurora, MN, p. A340

JOHNSON, Barbara A.
Vice President Human Resources, Good Samaritan Hospital, Dayton, OH, p. A492
Vice President Human Resources, Miami Valley Hospital, Dayton, OH, p. A492

JOHNSON, Becky, Director Human Resources, Oakdale Community Hospital, Oakdale, LA, p. A286

JOHNSON, Belinda, R.N. Chief Nursing Officer/Chief Clinical Officer, Russellville Hospital, Russellville, AL, p. A25

JOHNSON, Betty, Associate Administrator, University Health Shreveport, Shreveport, LA, p. A288

JOHNSON, Beverly, Vice President Human Resources, North Kansas City Hospital, North Kansas City, MO, p. A378

JOHNSON, Billy, Chief Executive Officer, Coal County General Hospital, Coalgate, OK, p. A509

JOHNSON, Bonnie, R.N. Vice President of Patient Services, Perham Health, Perham, MN, p. A349

JOHNSON, Brandi, Site Manager Technology Information Systems, Spectrum Health Reed City Hospital, Reed City, MI, p. A333

JOHNSON, Brenda
Director Human Resources, Baptist Memorial Hospital–Collierville, Collierville, TN, p. A581
Director Human Resources, North Mississippi Medical Center–West Point, West Point, MS, p. A366

JOHNSON, Bret
Chief Financial Officer, Bon Secours St. Francis Xavier Hospital, Charleston, SC, p. A563
Chief Financial Officer, Mount Pleasant Hospital, Mount Pleasant, SC, p. A568
Chief Financial Officer, Roper Hospital, Charleston, SC, p. A563

JOHNSON, Bryan L., Administrator, Alta View Hospital, Sandy, UT, p. A664

JOHNSON, III, C. Thomas, Vice President Finance and Chief Financial Officer, Southeastern Health, Lumberton, NC, p. A468

JOHNSON, Calvin D., Administrator, Kilmichael Hospital, Kilmichael, MS, p. A361

JOHNSON, Casey R., Chief Financial Officer, Sanford Thief River Falls Medical Center, Thief River Falls, MN, p. A353

JOHNSON, Charles, M.D. Chief of Staff, Renown Regional Medical Center, Reno, NV, p. A407

JOHNSON, Chris, Assistant Administrator and Chief Financial Officer, Essentia Health Sandstone, Sandstone, MN, p. A352

JOHNSON, Chris, M.D. Chief of Staff, Mercy Hospital Rogers, Rogers, AR, p. A52

JOHNSON, Chris, R.N. Director of Nursing, Pioneer Valley Hospital, West Valley City, UT, p. A664

JOHNSON, Christina, M.D. Vice President and Chief Clinical and Quality Officer, Lutheran Medical Center, Wheat Ridge, CO, p. A112

JOHNSON, Craig, D.O. Medical Director, St. Vincent Clay Hospital, Brazil, IN, p. A207

JOHNSON, Craig A., Chief Executive Officer, Boundary Community Hospital, Bonners Ferry, ID, p. A175

JOHNSON, Craig L., FACHE, Resource Chief Executive Officer, Vibra Hospital of Denver, Thornton, CO, p. A111

JOHNSON, Cynthia J., R.N. Chief Nursing Officer, Los Robles Hospital and Medical Center, Thousand Oaks, CA, p. A97

JOHNSON, Danielle, Chief Operating Officer, Florida Hospital Fish Memorial, Orange City, FL, p. A140

JOHNSON, Darren, M.D. Chief of Staff, Dyersburg Regional Medical Center, Dyersburg, TN, p. A582

JOHNSON, David
Chief Executive Officer, Navos, Seattle, WA, p. A688
Manager Information Services, Providence Kodiak Island Medical Center, Kodiak, AK, p. A29

JOHNSON, David P., Director Human Resources, Olmsted Medical Center, Rochester, MN, p. A350

JOHNSON, Deborah Carey, R.N., President and Chief Executive Officer, Eastern Maine Medical Center, Bangor, ME, p. A291

JOHNSON, Deeann, Director Human Resources, River Park Hospital, Mc Minnville, TN, p. A588

JOHNSON, Denise, M.D. Medical Director, Meadville Medical Center, Meadville, PA, p. A544

JOHNSON, Dennis B., President & CEO, Hardin Memorial Hospital, Elizabethtown, KY, p. A260

JOHNSON, Derek, Chief Executive Officer, Laurel Oaks Behavioral Health Center, Dothan, AL, p. A19

JOHNSON, Dian I., MSN Chief Nurse Executive, Staten Island University Hospital,, NY, p. A448

JOHNSON, Diana G., Acting Chief Human Resources Officer, Novato Community Hospital, Novato, CA, p. A80

JOHNSON, Diane, R.N. Vice President Patient Care Services and Chief Nursing Officer, Sinai Hospital of Baltimore, Baltimore, MD, p. A298

JOHNSON, Dominica, Executive Administrative Assistant and Executive Assistant Human Resources and Payroll, Pioneer Community Hospital of Newton, Newton, MS, p. A363

JOHNSON, Donald D., Assistant Administrator Human Resources, Cass County Memorial Hospital, Atlantic, IA, p. A225

JOHNSON, Doreen C., FACHE Chief Nursing Officer, Indiana University Health Ball Memorial Hospital, Muncie, IN, p. A219

JOHNSON, Douglas E.
Vice President and Chief Financial Officer, Hudson Hospital and Clinic, Hudson, WI, p. A706
Chief Financial Officer, Lakeview Hospital, Stillwater, MN, p. A352

JOHNSON, Douglas V., Chief Executive Officer, Stanislaus Surgical Hospital, Modesto, CA, p. A78

JOHNSON, Doyle K., Administrator, Mercy Hospital, Moundridge, KS, p. A250

JOHNSON, Drew, Chief Financial Officer, Holdenville General Hospital, Holdenville, OK, p. A512

JOHNSON, Earle, Area Information Officer, Kaiser Permanente Panorama City Medical Center,, CA, p. A72

JOHNSON, Eddie, Chief Information Technology Officer, Kansas City Veterans Affairs Medical Center, Kansas City, MO, p. A373

JOHNSON, Eunice, M.D. Chief Medical Staff, Kentucky River Medical Center, Jackson, KY, p. A263

JOHNSON, Greg, IT Coordinator, Cook County North Shore Hospital, Grand Marais, MN, p. A344

JOHNSON, Gregory, D.D.S. Medical Director, Fairbanks Memorial Hospital, Fairbanks, AK, p. A29

JOHNSON, Helen, R.N. Vice President Patient Services, Spectrum Health Ludington Hospital, Ludington, MI, p. A329

JOHNSON, J. David, M.D. Chief of Staff, East Texas Medical Center Specialty Hospital, Tyler, TX, p. A654

JOHNSON, Jack, Chief Nursing Officer, Sanford Hospital Rock Rapids, Rock Rapids, IA, p. A237

JOHNSON, Jackie, Executive Vice President Human Resources, United Medical Center, Washington, DC, p. A122

JOHNSON, James, Chief Financial Officer, St. Joseph's Hospital, Highland, IL, p. A192

JOHNSON, Jamie, R.N. VP of Nursing, Community Hospital of Anaconda, Anaconda, MT, p. A385

JOHNSON, Jamie, Director Human Resources, Miners' Colfax Medical Center, Raton, NM, p. A429

JOHNSON, Jan, R.N. Chief Nursing Officer, Northside Hospital–Cherokee, Canton, GA, p. A155

JOHNSON, Jani L., President and Chief Executive Officer, Saint Luke's South Hospital, Overland Park, KS, p. A252

JOHNSON, Jason, Controller, F. W. Huston Medical Center, Winchester, KS, p. A257

JOHNSON, Jay R., FACHE, President and Chief Executive Officer, Duncan Regional Hospital, Duncan, OK, p. A509

JOHNSON, Jayne, Director of Human Resources, Great Plains Health, North Platte, NE, p. A398

JOHNSON, Jeff, Director Information Systems, River Park Hospital, Mc Minnville, TN, p. A588

JOHNSON, Jeffrey, Vice President, Memorial Hospital, Colorado Springs, CO, p. A103

JOHNSON, Jennifer S., R.N. Chief Nursing Officer, Lane Regional Medical Center, Zachary, LA, p. A290

JOHNSON, Jeremy, Director of Information Technology, OSF Saint Luke Medical Center, Kewanee, IL, p. A194

JOHNSON, Joe, Chief Executive Officer, Florida Hospital Carrollwood, Tampa, FL, p. A147

JOHNSON, Joel, M.D. Chief Medical Staff, First Care Health Center, Park River, ND, p. A480

JOHNSON, John, M.D
Chief of Staff, Greenbrier Valley Medical Center, Ronceverte, WV, p. A699
Clinical Director, U. S. Public Health Service Indian Hospital, Crownpoint, NM, p. A428

JOHNSON, Juantina, Chief of Staff, Choctaw Health Center, Philadelphia, MS, p. A364

JOHNSON, Judith, Controller, HEALTHSOUTH Rehabilitation Hospital, Largo, FL, p. A134

JOHNSON, Juli, R.N. Chief Nursing Officer, Parkview Huntington Hospital, Huntington, IN, p. A213

JOHNSON, Julie, Chief Financial Officer, Peterson Regional Medical Center, Kerrville, TX, p. A631

JOHNSON, Karolynne, R.N. Chief Nurse Executive, Anaheim Medical Center, Kaiser Permanente Orange County Anaheim Medical Center, Anaheim, CA, p. A55

JOHNSON, Kathie A., Ph.D., Chief Executive Officer, Novant Health Thomasville Medical Center, Thomasville, NC, p. A474

JOHNSON, Kathryn
Chief Nursing Officer, Casa Colina Hospital for Rehabilitative Medicine, Pomona, CA, p. A84
Manager Human Resources, Marketing and Public Relations, St. Vincent Jennings Hospital, North Vernon, IN, p. A220

JOHNSON, Kathy, Chief Executive Officer and Administrator, Johnson Memorial Health Services, Dawson, MN, p. A342

JOHNSON, Kawanda, Director of Nursing, Specialty Hospital of Meridian, Meridian, MS, p. A363

JOHNSON, Kay, M.D. Chief of Staff, Bluffton Regional Medical Center, Bluffton, IN, p. A207

JOHNSON, Kayla, R.N. Vice President Patient Care Services and Chief Nursing Officer, St. Francis Medical Center, Monroe, LA, p. A284

JOHNSON, Keenan, Director Information Systems, Castleview Hospital, Price, UT, p. A662

JOHNSON, Kelly, R.N. Chief Nursing Officer, St. John Sapulpa, Sapulpa, OK, p. A518

JOHNSON, Kelly Marie, R.N. Senior Vice President Patience Care Services and Chief Nursing Officer, Children's Hospital Colorado, Aurora, CO, p. A102

JOHNSON, Ken, Chief Operating Officer, Hutchinson Regional Medical Center, Hutchinson, KS, p. A246

JOHNSON, Kendall, Chief Financial Officer, Baton Rouge General Medical Center, Baton Rouge, LA, p. A273

JOHNSON, Kenneth, M.D
Chief Physician Executive, St. Mary's Hospital Medical Center, Green Bay, WI, p. A706
Chief Physician Executive, St. Vincent Hospital, Green Bay, WI, p. A706

JOHNSON, Kenneth, Vice President, Sts. Mary & Elizabeth Hospital, Louisville, KY, p. A266

JOHNSON, Kevin, Chief Executive Officer, Mountain View Hospital, Payson, UT, p. A662

JOHNSON, Kirby, Administrator, Sanford Bagley Medical Center, Bagley, MN, p. A340

JOHNSON, Kurt, M.D. Chief of Staff, Ogallala Community Hospital, Ogallala, NE, p. A399

JOHNSON, Kurt E., President and Chief Executive Officer, Ingalls Memorial Hospital, Harvey, IL, p. A192

JOHNSON, Kyle
Vice President Finance, East Liverpool City Hospital, East Liverpool, OH, p. A493
Chief Information Officer, The Aroostook Medical Center, Presque Isle, ME, p. A295

JOHNSON, Larry C., M.D. Medical Director Rural Health Clinic, New Horizons Health Systems, Owenton, KY, p. A268

JOHNSON, Linda, R.N
Vice President of Nursing, Heart of the Rockies Regional Medical Center, Salida, CO, p. A111
Chief Clinical Officer, Mission Hospital, Mission Viejo, CA, p. A77

JOHNSON, Lisa, Vice President Human Resources, Hillside Rehabilitation Hospital, Warren, OH, p. A504

JOHNSON, Lisa, R.N
Chief Nursing Executive, Morton Plant Hospital, Clearwater, FL, p. A125
Chief Nursing Executive, Morton Plant North Bay Hospital, New Port Richey, FL, p. A139

JOHNSON, Lois, Administrator Fiscal Services, Ridgecrest Regional Hospital, Ridgecrest, CA, p. A86

JOHNSON, Lowell W., LFACHE, Chief Executive Officer, Riverside County Regional Medical Center, Moreno Valley, CA, p. A78

JOHNSON, Ludwig, Vice President Information Technology, Middlesex Hospital, Middletown, CT, p. A115

JOHNSON, Marcia L., R.N. Chief Operating Officer, MultiCare Good Samaritan Hospital, Puyallup, WA, p. A687

JOHNSON, Marianne, Chief Nursing Officer, Trace Regional Hospital, Houston, MS, p. A359

JOHNSON, Marie
Chief Nursing Officer, Carrus Rehabilitation Hospital, Sherman, TX, p. A649
Chief Nursing Officer, Carrus Specialty Hospital, Sherman, TX, p. A649

JOHNSON, Mark, M.D. Chief Medical Officer, Mercy Hospital Oklahoma City, Oklahoma City, OK, p. A515

JOHNSON, Mark
Chief Financial Officer, Norwood Hospital, Norwood, MA, p. A313
Chief Information Officer, West Holt Memorial Hospital, Atkinson, NE, p. A393

JOHNSON, Melissa, Chief Financial Officer, Baptist Medical Center South, Montgomery, AL, p. A23

JOHNSON, Michael, M.D. Medical Director, Salina Surgical Hospital, Salina, KS, p. A254

JOHNSON, Michael A., M.D. Chief of Staff, Bucyrus Community Hospital, Bucyrus, OH, p. A484

JOHNSON, Michael T., Chief Executive Officer, Regional Medical Center of San Jose, San Jose, CA, p. A92

JOHNSON, Mike
Vice President, Chief Information Officer, Caromont Regional Medical Center, Gastonia, NC, p. A465
Chief Financial Officer, Lancaster Regional Medical Center, Lancaster, PA, p. A542

JOHNSON, Nancy, Chief Nursing Officer, Select Specialty Hospital–North Knoxville, Knoxville, TN, p. A586

JOHNSON, Nate, Chief Information Officer, Highlands Regional Medical Center, Sebring, FL, p. A146

JOHNSON, Nikki, Interim Chief Executive Officer, Cooperstown Medical Center, Cooperstown, ND, p. A477

JOHNSON, Pam, R.N. Chief Nursing Officer, McCurtain Memorial Hospital, Idabel, OK, p. A512

JOHNSON, Pamela
  Treasurer and Chief Financial Officer, Geneva General Hospital, Geneva, NY, p. A437
  Treasurer and Chief Financial Officer, Soldiers and Sailors Memorial Hospital of Yates County, Penn Yan, NY, p. A451
JOHNSON, Pamela O., MS Chief Nursing Officer, Mayo Clinic Hospital – Rochester, Rochester, MN, p. A350
JOHNSON, Patricia, R.N. Senior Vice President, Woman's Hospital, Baton Rouge, LA, p. A274
JOHNSON, Paul F., President, Greenville Memorial Hospital, Greenville, SC, p. A566
JOHNSON, Penny
  Chief Financial Officer, Metroplex Adventist Hospital, Killeen, TX, p. A631
  Chief Financial Officer, Texas Health Huguley Hospital Fort Worth South, Fort Worth, TX, p. A619
JOHNSON, R. Milton, President and Chief Executive Officer, HCA, Nashville, TN, p. B64
JOHNSON, Ralph, Chief Information Officer, Franklin Memorial Hospital, Farmington, ME, p. A293
JOHNSON, Ric, Associate Administrator, Mountain View Hospital, Payson, UT, p. A662
JOHNSON, Richard F., Senior Vice President and Chief Information Officer, Indiana University Health University Hospital, Indianapolis, IN, p. A214
JOHNSON, Robb, Director Operations, Hamilton Center, Terre Haute, IN, p. A223
JOHNSON, Roger, M.D. Chief of Staff, Cheyenne Veterans Affairs Medical Center, Cheyenne, WY, p. A720
JOHNSON, Roger L., Director, VA Central Western Massachusetts Healthcare System, Leeds, MA, p. A311
JOHNSON, Ronald W., FACHE, President and Chief Executive Officer, Shore Medical Center, Somers Point, NJ, p. A422
JOHNSON, Ronda Kirk, Manager Health Information Management, Methodist Hospital for Surgery, Addison, TX, p. A595
JOHNSON, Ryan K., Vice President Finance, Spectrum Health United Hospital, Greenville, MI, p. A326
JOHNSON, Sam, Chief Financial Officer, Liberty Regional Medical Center, Hinesville, GA, p. A161
JOHNSON, Scott, Vice President Finance, St. Luke's Hospital, Chesterfield, MO, p. A369
JOHNSON, Sean, Chief Executive Officer, King's Daughters Hospital, Yazoo City, MS, p. A366
JOHNSON, Sharon, Director Health Information Management, Western State Hospital, Staunton, VA, p. A679
JOHNSON, Sheryl, Chief Information Officer, SwedishAmerican Hospital, Rockford, IL, p. A202
JOHNSON, Shrea, Director Human Resources, Alliance Health Center, Meridian, MS, p. A362
JOHNSON, Steven P., Ph.D., President and Chief Executive Officer, Health First, Inc., Rockledge, FL, p. B68
JOHNSON, Steven P., FACHE, President and Chief Executive Officer, Susquehanna Health System, Williamsport, PA, p. B130
JOHNSON, Sy, Chief Administrative Officer and Chief Operating Officer, PeaceHealth Columbia Network, PeaceHealth Southwest Medical Center, Vancouver, WA, p. A692
JOHNSON, Tamatha, Director Human Resources, Stringfellow Memorial Hospital, Anniston, AL, p. A15
JOHNSON, Tammy Dawn, Vice President Human Resources, Texas Health Presbyterian Hospital–WNJ, Sherman, TX, p. A649
JOHNSON, Thomas, Director Information Systems, Penn Highlands Brookville, Brookville, PA, p. A534
JOHNSON, Timothy, President and Chief Executive Officer, Eaton Rapids Medical Center, Eaton Rapids, MI, p. A323
JOHNSON, Timothy J., President and Chief Executive Officer, Mayo Clinic Health System – Franciscan Healthcare in La Crosse, La Crosse, WI, p. A707
JOHNSON, Todd, Chief Financial Officer, Longview Regional Medical Center, Longview, TX, p. A634
JOHNSON, Tommy, Chief Executive Officer, Rankin Hospital District, Rankin, TX, p. A643
JOHNSON, Trudy, R.N. Chief Nursing Officer, Santa Clara Valley Medical Center, San Jose, CA, p. A92
JOHNSON, Vern, Director Information Technology, Sullivan County Memorial Hospital, Milan, MO, p. A377
JOHNSON, Vernon, Administrator, Dale Medical Center, Ozark, AL, p. A24
JOHNSON, Victoria, R.N. Nursing Director of Surgical and Medical Services, The HealthCenter, Kalispell, MT, p. A389
JOHNSON, Vincent, Chief Operating Officer, University of California, Davis Medical Center, Sacramento, CA, p. A88
JOHNSON, Wade C., FACHE, Chief Executive Officer, Walter Knox Memorial Hospital, Emmett, ID, p. A176
JOHNSON Jr., Walter E., President and Chief Executive Officer, Jefferson Regional Medical Center, Pine Bluff, AR, p. A52

JOHNSON, William
  Director Information Systems, Eliza Coffee Memorial Hospital, Florence, AL, p. A20
  Director Information Systems, Shoals Hospital, Muscle Shoals, AL, p. A24
JOHNSON–HATCHER, Dawn, Chief Financial Officer, Lake Area Medical Center, Lake Charles, LA, p. A282
JOHNSON–MEKOTA, Judith, Director, Veterans Affairs Central Iowa Health Care System, Des Moines, IA, p. A230
JOHNSON–PHILLIPPE, Sue E., FACHE, President and Chief Executive Officer, St. Joseph's Hospital of Buckhannon, Buckhannon, WV, p. A694
JOHNSRUD, Carolyn, Manager Human Resources, Missouri River Medical Center, Fort Benton, MT, p. A387
JOHNSRUD, Jill, Director of Nursing, Essentia Health–Holy Trinity Hospital, Graceville, MN, p. A344
JOHNSTON, Charles W., Chief Executive Officer, Southern Coos Hospital and Health Center, Bandon, OR, p. A523
JOHNSTON, Diann, Vice President of Patient Care Services, Monmouth Medical Center, Long Branch Campus, Long Branch, NJ, p. A418
JOHNSTON, Don, Chief Information Officer, San Joaquin General Hospital, French Camp, CA, p. A64
JOHNSTON, Emily, M.D. Chief Medical Officer, Cascade Medical Center, Leavenworth, WA, p. A685
JOHNSTON, Jeffrey A., President, Mercy Hospital St. Louis, Saint Louis, MO, p. A380
JOHNSTON, Kevin, M.D. Chief Medical Staff, Harney District Hospital, Burns, OR, p. A523
JOHNSTON, Michael V., M.D. Chief Medical Officer and Senior Vice President Medical Programs, Kennedy Krieger Institute, Baltimore, MD, p. A296
JOHNSTON, Mike, Director Facilities Operations, Union General Hospital, Blairsville, GA, p. A154
JOHNSTON, Monte, Manager Human Resources, Coquille Valley Hospital, Coquille, OR, p. A524
JOHNSTON, Phyllis, Vice President, Catawba Valley Medical Center, Hickory, NC, p. A466
JOHNSTON, Susan, Director Human Resources, East Alabama Medical Center, Opelika, AL, p. A24
JOHNSTON, Susanne, Manager Human Resources, Lincoln County Medical Center, Ruidoso, NM, p. A430
JOHNSTON, William C., Interim Vice President, Information System, Brigham and Women's Hospital, Boston, MA, p. A306
JOHNSTON, Word, Medical Director, Covington County Hospital, Collins, MS, p. A357
JOHNSTONE, Jennifer, Chief Clinical Officer, Kindred Hospital Rome, Rome, GA, p. A165
JOICE, Jason, M.D. Chief Medical Staff, Integris Mayes County Medical Center, Pryor, OK, p. A518
JOLLEY, Sherry, Chief Clinical Officer, Lawrence Medical Center, Moulton, AL, p. A24
JOLLY, Gaye, FACHE, President/Chief Administrative Officer, Roane Medical Center, Harriman, TN, p. A583
JONAS, Stanley W., Chief Executive Officer, Alliance Community Hospital, Alliance, OH, p. A482
JONASON, Anna, Ph.D. Chief Nursing Officer, Colleton Medical Center, Walterboro, SC, p. A570
JONES, Adrienne, Director Human Resources, Creedmoor Psychiatric Center,, NY, p. A443
JONES, Alesia, Chief Human Resources Officer, University of Alabama Hospital, Birmingham, AL, p. A17
JONES, Allan, Controller, HEALTHSOUTH Rehabilitation Hospital of Jonesboro, Jonesboro, AR, p. A48
JONES, Amelia, Chief Operating Officer, Oakland Regional Hospital, Southfield, MI, p. A335
JONES, Anthony K., M.D., Chief Restructuring Officer and Chief Executive Officer, Tulare Regional Medical Center, Tulare, CA, p. A98
JONES, Austin, CP
  Chief Financial Officer, Physicians Surgical Hospital – Panhandle Campus, Amarillo, TX, p. A596
  Chief Financial Officer, Physicians Surgical Hospital – Quail Creek, Amarillo, TX, p. A596
JONES, Beth, Chief Operating Officer, Reeves Memorial Medical Center, Bernice, LA, p. A274
JONES, Bill, Chief Executive Officer, Jackson County Hospital District, Edna, TX, p. A615
JONES, Carol, Controller and Manager Business Office, Coryell Memorial Hospital, Gatesville, TX, p. A621
JONES, Catherine, Chief Nursing Officer, Ancora Psychiatric Hospital, Hammonton, NJ, p. A416
JONES, Cheryl L., Director Human Resources and Organizational Development, Baptist St. Anthony Health System, Amarillo, TX, p. A596
JONES, Chris, Chief Executive Officer, Vibra Hospital of Northern California, Redding, CA, p. A85
JONES, Christian, Chief Executive Officer, Moberly Regional Medical Center, Moberly, MO, p. A377

JONES, Clay, Regional Director of Human Resources, Phoebe Worth Medical Center, Sylvester, GA, p. A167
JONES, Connie, Director Human Resources, Community Behavioral Health Hospital – Rochester, Rochester, MN, p. A350
JONES, Dale, Administrator, Noland Hospital Tuscaloosa, Tuscaloosa, AL, p. A26
JONES, Dana, R.N. Chief Nursing Officer, Springhill Medical Center, Springhill, LA, p. A289
JONES Jr., Danny L., FACHE, Chief Executive Officer, Phoenix Baptist Hospital, Phoenix, AZ, p. A36
JONES, Darrell, Chief Executive Officer, Vibra Hospital of Charleston, Mt. Pleasant, SC, p. A568
JONES, David
  Chief Financial Officer, Alexian Brothers Behavioral Health Hospital, Hoffman Estates, IL, p. A193
  Chief Nursing Officer, HEALTHSOUTH Rehabilitation Hospital of Arlington, Arlington, TX, p. A597
JONES, David C., Administrator, North Caddo Medical Center, Vivian, LA, p. A290
JONES, Deborah, Controller, Houston Hospital for Specialized Surgery, Houston, TX, p. A624
JONES, Derrick, Chief Executive Officer, Lovelace Rehabilitation Hospital, Albuquerque, NM, p. A426
JONES, Donald J., FACHE, Administrator, Fayette Medical Center, Fayette, AL, p. A20
JONES, Douglas A., Chief Operating Officer, Forrest General Hospital, Hattiesburg, MS, p. A359
JONES, Elaine, M.D. President Medical Staff, Roger Williams Medical Center, Providence, RI, p. A561
JONES, Evan, Chief Financial Officer, Lakeland Regional Medical Center, Lakeland, FL, p. A134
JONES, Evelyn, Director Human Resources, Choctaw Nation Health Care Center, Talihina, OK, p. A519
JONES, Evelyn, R.N. Vice President Nursing Services, St. Bernard Hospital and Health Care Center, Chicago, IL, p. A187
JONES, G.R. Sonny, Vice President Finance and Chief Financial Officer, St. Claire Regional Medical Center, Morehead, KY, p. A268
JONES, Glen M., Administrator, Red Bay Hospital, Red Bay, AL, p. A25
JONES, Greg, Chief Financial Officer, Wayne Memorial Hospital, Jesup, GA, p. A161
JONES, Gregory, M.D. Chief of Staff, Vidant Pungo Hospital, Belhaven, NC, p. A460
JONES, H. Roger, Chief Executive Officer, Straith Hospital for Special Surgery, Southfield, MI, p. A335
JONES, Holly A., Administrative Director Nursing Services, Illini Community Hospital, Pittsfield, IL, p. A200
JONES, J. Stephen, M.D. Chief of Staff, Muenster Memorial Hospital, Muenster, TX, p. A639
JONES, Jacqueline V., Chief Civilian Personnel Branch, Reynolds Army Community Hospital, Fort Sill, OK, p. A511
JONES, Jason L., R.N. Chief Nursing Officer, Fannin Regional Hospital, Blue Ridge, GA, p. A154
JONES, Jeffrey, Chief Financial Officer, Moses H. Cone Memorial Hospital, Greensboro, NC, p. A465
JONES, Jeremy A., Administrator, Mercy Hospital Healdton, Healdton, OK, p. A511
JONES, John, Chief Nursing Officer, Logan Memorial Hospital, Russellville, KY, p. A270
JONES, John, M.D. Chief Medical Staff, Sanford Chamberlain Medical Center, Chamberlain, SD, p. A572
JONES, John R., Administrator, North Mississippi Medical Center–Eupora, Eupora, MS, p. A357
JONES, Joshua, Director of Human Resources, Evanston Regional Hospital, Evanston, WY, p. A721
JONES, Joyce, Director Human Resources, HEALTHSOUTH Rehabilitation Hospital, Kingsport, TN, p. A585
JONES, Judy, Chief Clinical Officer, Arkansas Surgical Hospital, North Little Rock, AR, p. A51
JONES, Julie L., R.N. Chief Nursing Officer, Beatrice Community Hospital and Health Center, Beatrice, NE, p. A394
JONES, Karen, Administrative Director Human Resources, Marion General Hospital, Marion, IN, p. A218
JONES, Karin, Chief Nursing Officer, HEALTHSOUTH Rehabilitation Hospital of Alexandria, Alexandria, LA, p. A272
JONES, Karol, Chief Nursing Officer, Huntsville Hospital, Huntsville, AL, p. A22
JONES, Kathy, Director Human Resources, Jackson Medical Center, Jackson, AL, p. A22
JONES, Ken M., Chief Operating Officer, UCSF Medical Center, San Francisco, CA, p. A91
JONES, Kenneth
  Chief Executive Officer, Orthopaedic Hospital of Lutheran Health Network, Fort Wayne, IN, p. A211
  Chief Executive Officer, St. Joseph Hospital, Fort Wayne, IN, p. A211

JONES, Kyle, Controller, Marshall Medical Center, Lewisburg, TN, p. A587

JONES, L. Val, M.D. Medical Director, Blue Mountain Hospital, Blanding, UT, p. A659

JONES, Linda, Director Medical Records, Millwood Hospital, Arlington, TX, p. A598

JONES, Liston, M.D. Medical Director, Springhill Memorial Hospital, Mobile, AL, p. A23

JONES, Lorrie Rickman, Ph.D., Director, Division of Mental Health, Department of Human Services, Springfield, IL, p. B53

JONES, Louis, Director Management Information Systems, Heart of Florida Regional Medical Center, Davenport, FL, p. A127

JONES, M. Steven
President, University Hospitals Conneaut Medical Center, Conneaut, OH, p. A491
President, University Hospitals Geauga Medical Center, Chardon, OH, p. A485
President, University Hospitals Geauga Medical Center, Chardon, OH, p. A485
President, University Hospitals Geneva Medical Center, Geneva, OH, p. A494

JONES, Mark, Chief Financial Officer, Hill Country Memorial Hospital, Fredericksburg, TX, p. A619

JONES, Mark A., President, Orlando Regional Medical Center, Orlando, FL, p. A141

JONES, Marsha, R.N. Director Nursing, King's Daughters Hospital, Yazoo City, MS, p. A366

JONES, Marshall, Senior Vice President Human Resources, Maricopa Integrated Health System, Phoenix, AZ, p. A36

JONES, Mary Jane, R.N. Vice President Nursing Operations, Northridge Hospital Medical Center,, CA, p. A73

JONES, Maud, Manager Medical Records, TOPS Surgical Specialty Hospital, Houston, TX, p. A627

JONES, Melinda, R.N. Chief Nursing Officer, Morehouse General Hospital, Bastrop, LA, p. A273

JONES, Meredith, Chief Financial Officer, McNairy Regional Hospital, Selmer, TN, p. A592

JONES, Michael, Vice President and Chief Information Officer, Children's Hospital of Wisconsin, Milwaukee, WI, p. A710

JONES, Michael L., Ph.D. Chief Information Officer, Shepherd Center, Atlanta, GA, p. A153

JONES, Mike, Director Information Services, Marshall Medical Center, Placerville, CA, p. A83

JONES, Mitchell, Director Information Technology, Little River Memorial Hospital, Ashdown, AR, p. A43

JONES, Pam, MSN Associate Hospital Director and Chief Nursing Officer, Vanderbilt Hospital and Clinics, Nashville, TN, p. A591

JONES, Pat, Director Information Systems, River Oaks Hospital, Flowood, MS, p. A357

JONES, Patrice I., R.N. Vice President and Chief Nursing Officer, UF Health Jacksonville, Jacksonville, FL, p. A132

JONES, Percy E., M.D. Chief of Staff, Kindred Hospital–Greensboro, Greensboro, NC, p. A465

JONES, Philip L., Chief Financial Officer, Kindred Hospital–Nashville, Nashville, TN, p. A590

JONES, Phyllis, Chief Human Resources, Wm. Jennings Bryan Dorn Veterans Affairs Medical Center, Columbia, SC, p. A565

JONES, Ransom, Information Technology Director, Covington County Hospital, Collins, MS, p. A357

JONES, Reginald, Business Manager, Georgia Regional Hospital at Atlanta, Decatur, GA, p. A158

JONES, Rex, Chief Executive Officer, Bradley County Medical Center, Warren, AR, p. A53

JONES, Richard, Chief Financial Officer, Bon Secours Baltimore Health System, Baltimore, MD, p. A296

JONES, Richard, M.D. Medical Director, Reliant Rehabilitation Hospital North Texas, Richardson, TX, p. A644

JONES, Richard W., Chief Financial Officer, Reading Hospital and Medical Center, West Reading, PA, p. A558

JONES, Rita A., Chief Executive Officer, Dundy County Hospital, Benkelman, NE, p. A394

JONES, Rob, Chief Nursing Officer, Physicians' Medical Center, New Albany, IN, p. A220

JONES, Robert, Director Management Information Systems, St. Joseph Mercy Oakland, Pontiac, MI, p. A332

JONES, Roger, M.D. Interim Chief of Staff, Tennessee Valley Healthcare System, Nashville, TN, p. A591

JONES, Ron, Chief Financial Officer, Butler County Health Care Center, David City, NE, p. A395

JONES, Ruth, Chief Operating Officer, Regency Hospital of Northwest Arkansas, Fayetteville, AR, p. A45

JONES, Scott, Chief Executive Officer, Midwestern Regional Medical Center, Zion, IL, p. A205

JONES, Shannon, M.D. Medical Director and Attending Psychiatrist, Evansville Psychiatric Children Center, Evansville, IN, p. A210

JONES, Sharon, Chief Financial Officer, Evergreen Medical Center, Evergreen, AL, p. A19

JONES, Sherry J., Chief Financial Officer, Crestwood Medical Center, Huntsville, AL, p. A21

JONES, Staci, R.N. Chief Nursing Officer, Methodist McKinney Hospital, McKinney, TX, p. A637

JONES, Stacy, Chief Nursing Officer, HEALTHSOUTH MountainView Regional Rehabilitation Hospital, Morgantown, WV, p. A697

JONES, Stephen K., President and Chief Executive Officer, Robert Wood Johnson Health System & Network, New Brunswick, NJ, p. B115

JONES, Stephen K., President and Chief Executive Officer, Robert Wood Johnson University Hospital, New Brunswick, NJ, p. A419

JONES, Stephen K., M.D. Vice President Medical Staff Affairs, St. Rose Dominican Hospitals – Rose de Lima Campus, Henderson, NV, p. A405

JONES Jr., Stephen K., FACHE, Chief Executive Officer, Clear Lake Regional Medical Center, Webster, TX, p. A656

JONES, Steven K., M.D. Medical Director, Advocate Eureka Hospital, Eureka, IL, p. A189

JONES, Tammie R., R.N. Chief Nursing Officer, St. Mary Medical Center, Hobart, IN, p. A213

JONES, Theresa, Manager Human Resources, St. Luke Community Healthcare, Ronan, MT, p. A390

JONES, Tim, Chief Executive Officer, Heart of Texas Memorial Hospital, Brady, TX, p. A603

JONES, Todd, President, Baptist Health Richmond, Richmond, KY, p. A270

JONES, Tom, D.O. Chief Medical Officer, Doctors Hospital at White Rock Lake, Dallas, TX, p. A610

JONES, Tom, Manager Information Technology, Fitzgibbon Hospital, Marshall, MO, p. A376

JONES, Tonya A., Vice President Human Resources, Maria Parham Medical Center, Henderson, NC, p. A466

JONES, Tracey, Director Human Resources, Jackson Park Hospital and Medical Center, Chicago, IL, p. A184

JONES, Trennis, Senior Vice President and Chief Administrative Officer, Seton Northwest Hospital, Austin, TX, p. A599

JONES, Vernita, Site Manager, PHS Santa Fe Indian Hospital, Santa Fe, NM, p. A430

JONES, W. Clark, Superintendent and Administrator, Cascade Valley Hospital and Clinics, Arlington, WA, p. A681

JONES, Wendy, Interim Chief Financial Officer, Blue Hill Memorial Hospital, Blue Hill, ME, p. A292

JONES, Yameeka, Chief Executive Officer, Regency Hospital of South Atlanta, East Point, GA, p. A159

JONES, Yvette A., HIM Director, Putnam Community Medical Center, Palatka, FL, p. A141

JONES MONNETT, Anna, MS Associate Director Patient Care Services, Dayton Veterans Affairs Medical Center, Dayton, OH, p. A492

JONES–BENDEL, Trish, R.N. Chief Nursing Officer, Linden Oaks Hospital at Edward, Naperville, IL, p. A197

JONES–BROWNING, Debbie, Vice President Operations and Physician Services and Chief Operating Officer, Rush Memorial Hospital, Rushville, IN, p. A222

JONTZ, Doug, Senior Vice President Human Resources, Mercy Medical Center–Cedar Rapids, Cedar Rapids, IA, p. A226

JORDAN, R.N., Amy, Chief Nursing Officer/Vice President of Nursing, Gordon Hospital, Calhoun, GA, p. A155

JORDAN, Andrew, M.D. Chief of Staff, University Medical Center, Lebanon, TN, p. A586

JORDAN, Gary W., FACHE, Chief Executive Officer, Wright Memorial Hospital, Trenton, MO, p. A384

JORDAN, Jill, Chief Executive Officer, Regional Rehabilitation Hospital, Phenix City, AL, p. A25

JORDAN, Ken, Chief Financial Officer, Fountain Valley Regional Hospital and Medical Center, Fountain Valley, CA, p. A63

JORDAN, Linda U., Administrator, Clay County Hospital, Ashland, AL, p. A15

JORDAN, Lori, Chief Executive Officer, Oklahoma Forensic Center, Vinita, OK, p. A521

JORDAN, Michelle J., Administrator, Lewis and Clark Specialty Hospital, Yankton, SD, p. A578

JORDAN, III, Patrick, Chief Operating Officer, Newton–Wellesley Hospital, Newton Lower Falls, MA, p. A313

JORDAN, Peggy, Director Human Resources, Comanche County Medical Center, Comanche, TX, p. A607

JORDAN, Quincy, M.D. Chief of Staff, Flint River Community Hospital, Montezuma, GA, p. A164

JORDAN, Rhonda R., Chief Human Resources Officer, Virtua Marlton, Marlton, NJ, p. A418

JORDAN, Terry, M.D. Chief of Staff, Alliance Health Center, Meridian, MS, p. A362

JORDEN BEST, Rosemary, Director Human Resources, Tyrone Hospital, Tyrone, PA, p. A556

JORE, Bernie, Chief Nursing Officer, St. Mary's of Michigan, Saginaw, MI, p. A334

JORGENSEN, Deanna, Coordinator Human Resources, Regency Hospital of Covington, Covington, LA, p. A276

JOSEHART, Carl E.
Chief Executive Officer, Memorial Hermann Rehabilitation Hospital – Katy, Katy, TX, p. A630
Chief Executive Officer, TIRR Memorial Hermann, Houston, TX, p. A627

JOSEPH, Elliot T., President and Chief Executive Officer, Hartford HealthCare, Hartford, CT, p. B63

JOSEPH, Heather, Administrator, Baypointe Behavioral Health, Mobile, AL, p. A22

JOSEPH, James, M.D. President Medical Staff, Geisinger–Bloomsburg Hospital, Bloomsburg, PA, p. A534

JOSEPH, Kevin, M.D., Chief Executive Officer, West Chester Hospital, West Chester, OH, p. A505

JOSEPH, Vincent D., Interim Administrator, Robert Wood Johnson University Hospital Somerset, Somerville, NJ, p. A422

JOSEPH–TAYLOR, Terri, Chief Human Resource Manager, Ochsner Medical Center – North Shore, Slidell, LA, p. A289

JOSHI, Nirmal, M.D. Senior Vice President Medical Affairs and Chief Medical Officer, Pinnacle Health System, Harrisburg, PA, p. A540

JOSLIN, Tim A., President and Chief Executive Officer, Community Medical Centers, Fresno, CA, p. B43

JOSLYN, E. Allen, M.D. Chief Medical Officer, Bedford Memorial Hospital, Bedford, VA, p. A668

JOSLYN, J. Scott, Senior Vice President and Chief Information Officer, Saddleback Memorial Medical Center, Laguna Hills, CA, p. A68

JOST, Eric, Chief Financial Officer, Crossroads Community Hospital, Mount Vernon, IL, p. A197

JOUD, Mohammad A., M.D. Chief of Staff, Bayfront Health Brooksville, Brooksville, FL, p. A125

JOUDEH, Jalal, M.D
Chief of Staff, DeQuincy Memorial Hospital, DeQuincy, LA, p. A277
Chief Medical Officer, Specialty Rehabilitation Hospital of Coushatta, Coushatta, LA, p. A275

JOURDEN, Marti, FACHE Chief Quality Officer, St. Anthony Hospital, Oklahoma City, OK, p. A516

JOY, Michelle L., Chief Operating Officer, McKee Medical Center, Loveland, CO, p. A109

JOY, Mike, Chief Financial Officer, Via Christi Hospital in Pittsburg, Pittsburg, KS, p. A253

JOY, Jr., Roland Eugene, Vice President and Chief Nursing Officer, The Aroostook Medical Center, Presque Isle, ME, p. A295

JOYAL, Shirley, Director Information Systems, Regional Medical Center of San Jose, San Jose, CA, p. A92

JOYCE, Allyson, Vice President Human Resources, Caro Community Hospital, Caro, MI, p. A320

JOYCE, Jodi S., R.N. Interim Chief Nursing Officer, University of Illinois Hospital & Health Sciences System, Chicago, IL, p. A187

JOYCE, Maria, Chief Financial Officer, National Institutes of Health Clinical Center, Bethesda, MD, p. A299

JOYNER, Jeff, Vice President of Operations, St. Joseph's Regional Medical Center, Paterson, NJ, p. A420

JOYNER, Ken, Vice President of Employee Services, Bay Area Medical Center, Marinette, WI, p. A708

JOYNER, Thomas, Chief Financial Officer, Lakeside Behavioral Health System, Memphis, TN, p. A588

JUAREZ, Edward, M.D. Chief Medical Officer, Kindred Hospital El Paso, El Paso, TX, p. A616

JUAREZ, Elizabeth, M.D. Chief Medical Officer, Harlingen Medical Center, Harlingen, TX, p. A622

JUAREZ, Rose, Chief Civilian Personnel Branch, San Antonio Military Medical Center, Fort Sam Houston, TX, p. A617

JUCHNOWICZ, Jean E., Director Human Resources, Natchez Regional Medical Center, Natchez, MS, p. A363

JUDD, Martin H., President and Chief Executive Officer, Presence Saints Mary & Elizabeth Medical Center, Chicago, IL, p. A186

JUDGE, Leigh Ann, Manager Human Resources, Guttenberg Municipal Hospital, Guttenberg, IA, p. A231

JUDYCKI–CREPEAULT, Christine, Chief Financial Officer, Adcare Hospital of Worcester, Worcester, MA, p. A316

JUEL, De De, Director Human Resources, St. David's Rehabilitation Hospital, Austin, TX, p. A600

JUENGER, Jacqueline, R.N. Chief Nursing Officer, HEALTHSOUTH Rehabilitation Hospital of Sarasota, Sarasota, FL, p. A145

JUGE, Shannon, Human Resources Representative, Spine Hospital of Louisiana, Baton Rouge, LA, p. A274

JUHASZ, Robert S., D.O., President, South Pointe Hospital, Warrensville Heights, OH, p. A504

JUHL, Gregory, M.D. Medical Director, Norton Brownsboro Hospital, Louisville, KY, p. A266

JUHL, Valerie, Director of Health, Madelia Community Hospital, Madelia, MN, p. A346

JULIAN, Bell, Associate Executive Director and Chief Financial Officer, James Cancer Hospital and Solove Research Institute, Columbus, OH, p. A489

JULIAN, Steve, M.D., President, Sentara Obici Hospital, Suffolk, VA, p. A679

JULIANA, Rich, Director Human Resources, Silver Hill Hospital, New Canaan, CT, p. A116

JUMONVILLE, III, John E., Chief Operating Officer, Community Specialty Hospital, Lafayette, LA, p. A281

JUMP, Beth, Chief Information Officer, Logansport Memorial Hospital, Logansport, IN, p. A218

JUNEAU, Cindy K., Chief Nursing Officer, Avoyelles Hospital, Marksville, LA, p. A283

JUNEAU, James B., Chief Financial Officer, Opelousas General Health System, Opelousas, LA, p. A287

JUNEAU, Tina Louise, Director Human Resources, Bunkie General Hospital, Bunkie, LA, p. A275

JUNGELS, Trisha, Chief Nursing Officer and Vice President Clinical Services, Jamestown Regional Medical Center, Jamestown, ND, p. A478

JUNGWIRTH, Scott, Chief Human Resources Officer, Providence Alaska Medical Center, Anchorage, AK, p. A28

JUNIS, Jennifer, MSN Vice President Chief Nursing Officer, OSF Saint Luke Medical Center, Kewanee, IL, p. A194

JUNO, Russell, M.D. Chief of Staff, St. Mark's Medical Center, La Grange, TX, p. A632

JURCZYK, John A., FACHE, Interim President, Good Samaritan Medical Center, Brockton, MA, p. A308

JUREK, Charlie, Business Office Manager, Specialty Hospital of Winnfield, Winnfield, LA, p. A290

JURGENS, Chad, Chief Executive Officer, Jefferson Community Health Center, Fairbury, NE, p. A395

JURICA, John, M.D. Vice President Medical Affairs, Riverside Medical Center, Kankakee, IL, p. A194

JURIS, Susan V., President, University Hospitals Ahuja Medical Center, Beachwood, OH, p. A483

JURKAS, Wade A., Director Computer Information Systems, Lake Region Healthcare, Fergus Falls, MN, p. A343

JURKUS, Patti
   Vice President, Regional Hospital, Bedford Memorial Hospital, Bedford, VA, p. A668
   Director Human Resources, Carilion New River Valley Medical Center, Christiansburg, VA, p. A669

JURY, Tina M., MSN Executive Vice President Patient Care Services and Chief Nursing Officer, AnMed Health Medical Center, Anderson, SC, p. A562

JUST, Lisa
   President, Aurora Lakeland Medical Center, Elkhorn, WI, p. A704
   President, Aurora Memorial Hospital of Burlington, Burlington, WI, p. A703

JUST, Paula B.
   Vice President Human Resources, Health First Cape Canaveral Hospital, Cocoa Beach, FL, p. A126
   Chief Human Resources Officer, Health First Holmes Regional Medical Center, Melbourne, FL, p. A135
   Chief Human Resources Officer, Health First Palm Bay Hospital, Melbourne, FL, p. A136
   Chief Human Resources Officer, Health First Viera Hospital, Melbourne, FL, p. A136

JUSTESEN, Scott, M.D. Chief of Staff, Castleview Hospital, Price, UT, p. A662

JUSTICE, Kim, Vice President Planning and Operations, Atlantic General Hospital, Berlin, MD, p. A298

JUSTUS, Jason, Vice President Finance and Chief Financial Officer, Pomerene Hospital, Millersburg, OH, p. A499

JUTILA, Kathy, M.D. Chief of Staff, Wheatland Memorial Healthcare, Harlowton, MT, p. A388

K

KA'AKIMAKA, Holly, Director Human Resources, Hilo Medical Center, Hilo, HI, p. A170

KAATZ, Gary E., President and Chief Executive Officer, Rockford Memorial Hospital, Rockford, IL, p. A201

KABITZKE–GROTH, Terry, R.N
   Vice President Nursing, Aurora Medical Center Grafton, Grafton, WI, p. A705
   Chief Nursing Officer, Aurora Medical Center in Washington County, Hartford, WI, p. A706

KABLE, Mary Ellen, Chief Operating Officer, LifeCare Hospitals of Mechanicsburg, Mechanicsburg, PA, p. A545

KACHIGION, Claudia, M.D. Medical Director, Alton Mental Health Center, Alton, IL, p. A180

KADDOURI, Sami, M.D. Medical Director, Cornerstone of Medical Arts Center Hospital, Fresh Meadows, NY, p. A437

KADLICK, Pamela, Vice President Nursing, Mercy St. Anne Hospital, Toledo, OH, p. A503

KAELIN, Darryl, M.D. Medical Director, Frazier Rehab Institute, Louisville, KY, p. A265

KAEMS, Amanda, Manager Information Systems, Paradise Valley Hospital, National City, CA, p. A79

KAESE, James, Vice President Administration, Rush Oak Park Hospital, Oak Park, IL, p. A198

KAFKA, Rich, M.D. Chief Medical Officer, Avera Gregory Hospital, Gregory, SD, p. A574

KAGAN, Richard J., M.D. Chief of Staff, Shriners Hospitals for Children–Cincinnati Burns Hospital, Cincinnati, OH, p. A487

KAHL, Vicky, Director Human Resources, Valley Regional Medical Center, Brownsville, TX, p. A604

KAHLE, Ty, Director Human Resources, Methodist Hospital, Henderson, KY, p. A262

KAHLER, Ralph, M.D. Medical Director, Regency Hospital of Hattiesburg, Hattiesburg, MS, p. A359

KAHLY–MCMAHON, Heidi
   Vice President Human Resources, Genesis Medical Center, Illini Campus, Silvis, IL, p. A202
   Interim Vice President Human Resources, Genesis Medical Center–Davenport, Davenport, IA, p. A228

KAHN, Brian, M.D. Chief of Staff, St. Vincent Medical Center, Los Angeles, CA, p. A75

KAHN, Jalil, M.D. Chief of Staff, Atrium Medical Center of Corinth, Corinth, TX, p. A608

KAHN, Maureen A., R.N., President and Chief Executive Officer, Blessing Hospital, Quincy, IL, p. A201

KAHOOHANOHANO, Teana, Interim Administrator, Hale Ho'ola Hamakua, Honokaa, HI, p. A170

KAINO, Linda, Chief Nursing Officer, Ocean Beach Hospital, Ilwaco, WA, p. A684

KAISER, Diane, Administrator, Dubuis Hospital of Corpus Christi, Corpus Christi, TX, p. A608

KAISER, Janet, R.N. Chief Nursing Officer, Kansas Medical Center, Andover, KS, p. A241

KAISER, Ken, Director Information Technology, Guttenberg Municipal Hospital, Guttenberg, IA, p. A231

KAISER, Larry, M.D., President and Chief Executive Officer, Temple University Health System, Philadelphia, PA, p. B132

KAJIWARA, Gary K., President and Chief Executive Officer, Kuakini Medical Center, Honolulu, HI, p. A170

KAKAVAS, Connie, Chief Human Resources Officer, Summit Healthcare Regional Medical Center, Show Low, AZ, p. A39

KAKI, Karim, M.D. Chief Medical Director, Hendry Regional Medical Center, Clewiston, FL, p. A126

KAKUDA, James, M.D. Chief of Staff, Pali Momi Medical Center, Aiea, HI, p. A170

KALAJAINEN, Kimberly, Vice President and Chief Information Officer, Lawrence + Memorial Hospital, New London, CT, p. A116

KALANIHUIA, Janice, President, Molokai General Hospital, Kaunakakai, HI, p. A172

KALAR, Cathy, Chief Financial Officer, Broaddus Hospital, Philippi, WV, p. A698

KALAVAR, Jagadeesh S., M.D. Chief of Staff, Michael E. DeBakey Veterans Affairs Medical Center, Houston, TX, p. A626

KALCHIK, Kevin, Chief Financial Officer, War Memorial Hospital, Sault Sainte Marie, MI, p. A334

KALE, Debra
   Vice President Human Resources, Cleveland Regional Medical Center, Shelby, NC, p. A472
   Director Human Resources, Kings Mountain Hospital, Kings Mountain, NC, p. A467

KALEEL, Reza, Executive Vice President and Chief Operating Officer, St. Mary's Hospital and Regional Medical Center, Grand Junction, CO, p. A107

KALINA, Andrea, Vice President External Affairs and Chief Human Resources Officer, St. Clair Hospital, Pittsburgh, PA, p. A551

KALKA, Gina, R.N. Chief Nursing Officer, Pecos County Memorial Hospital, Fort Stockton, TX, p. A618

KALKOWSKI, Kelly, Chief Executive Officer, Niobrara Valley Hospital, Lynch, NE, p. A398

KALKUT, Gary, M.D. Senior Vice President and Chief Medical Officer, Montefiore Medical Center,, NY, p. A446

KALL, Greg, Chief Information Officer, Summa Akron City Hospital, Akron, OH, p. A482

KALLAL, Catherine, M.D. Chief Medical Officer, Holy Cross Hospital, Chicago, IL, p. A184

KALLAS, Diane, Vice President of Nursing Services, McLaren Flint, Flint, MI, p. A323

KALLEN–ZURY, Karen, Chief Executive Officer, Hollywood Pavilion,, FL, p. A130

KALLEVIG, Daryl, Chief Information Officer, Riverwood Healthcare Center, Aitkin, MN, p. A339

KALSMAN, Stephen L., Area Finance Officer, Kaiser Permanente San Jose Medical Center, San Jose, CA, p. A92

KALTENBACH, Gretchen, R.N. Chief Operating Officer, Genesis Behavioral Hospital, Breaux Bridge, LA, p. A275

KALUA, Patricia, Chief Nurse Executive, Kona Community Hospital, Kealakekua, HI, p. A172

KAMBEROS, Peter N., Chief Operating Officer, Thorek Memorial Hospital, Chicago, IL, p. A187

KAMBIC, Phillip M., Chief Executive Officer, Riverside Medical Center, Kankakee, IL, p. A194

KAMBOJ, Pradeep, M.D. Chief Medical Staff, Tulare Regional Medical Center, Tulare, CA, p. A98

KAMERMAYER, Angela K., MS Chief Nursing Officer, INTEGRIS Health Edmond, Edmond, OK, p. A510

KAMGUIA, Rebecca, Administrative Director Human Resources, Bon Secours Memorial Regional Medical Center, Mechanicsville, VA, p. A674

KAMIKAWA, Cynthia, R.N. Vice President Nursing Emergency Department and Trauma and Chief Nursing Officer, Queen's Medical Center, Honolulu, HI, p. A171

KAMINSKI, Gene, Vice President Human Resources, McLaren Northern Michigan, Petoskey, MI, p. A332

KAMINSKI, Tammy, Director Human Resources, Alaska Regional Hospital, Anchorage, AK, p. A28

KAMINSKI, Toni, Director Human Resources, Medical Center Enterprise, Enterprise, AL, p. A19

KAMMERER, James M., Vice President Support Services, Great River Medical Center, West Burlington, IA, p. A239

KAMMERUD, Shawn, Manager Information Services, Osceola Medical Center, Osceola, WI, p. A712

KAMMIRE, Gordon, M.D. Chief of Staff, Wake Forest Baptist Health–Lexington Medical Center, Lexington, NC, p. A468

KAMOWSKI, David, Vice President and Chief Information Officer, Temple University Hospital, Philadelphia, PA, p. A550

KAMP, Kent, Director Information Systems, Mineral Area Regional Medical Center, Farmington, MO, p. A371

KAMPHUIS, Jan, Ph.D. Executive Vice President and Chief Nurse Executive, Sanford Bismarck, Bismarck, ND, p. A476

KAMPS, Mary Jane, Chief Information Officer, Southern Maine Health Care – Biddeford Medical Center X, Biddeford, ME, p. A292

KAMPSCHNIEDER, Carol, Vice President Clinical and Regulatory Services, St. Francis Memorial Hospital, West Point, NE, p. A402

KAMPWERTH, Dennis, Director Management Information Systems, Gateway Regional Medical Center, Granite City, IL, p. A191

KAMRAN, Khurram, M.D. Vice President Medical Affairs, ProMedica Toledo Hospital, Toledo, OH, p. A503

KANE, Addy, Chief Financial Officer, Roger Williams Medical Center, Providence, RI, p. A561

KANE, Audrey, Interim Chief Financial Officer, Prowers Medical Center, Lamar, CO, p. A108

KANE, Daniel A., Board Chairman, CarePoint Health, Jersey City, NJ, p. B27

KANE, Melissa, Chief Financial Officer, Pocahontas Memorial Hospital, Buckeye, WV, p. A693

KANE, Nancy, Assistant Vice President Finance LifeBridge Health, Northwest Hospital, Randallstown, MD, p. A302

KANE, Robert E., President, Divine Providence Hospital, Williamsport, PA, p. A558

KANE, Steve, Director Information Technology, Lower Bucks Hospital, Bristol, PA, p. A534

KANE, Terri, Chief Executive Officer, Dixie Regional Medical Center, Saint George, UT, p. A662

KANE, Thomas, Vice President Patient Care, West Shore Medical Center, Manistee, MI, p. A329

KANIA, Kathy, Chief Information Officer, Staten Island University Hospital,, NY, p. A448

KANKEL, LeAnne, Vice President Human Relations, Barton Memorial Hospital, South Lake Tahoe, CA, p. A96

KANNADAY, Colleen, FACHE,
   President, Advocate BroMenn Medical Center, Normal, IL, p. A198
   President, Advocate Eureka Hospital, Eureka, IL, p. A189

KANSGEN, Mike, Director Information Services, Community Hospital, Grand Junction, CO, p. A107

KANTHILAL, S. K., M.D. President Medical Staff, Sarah D. Culbertson Memorial Hospital, Rushville, IL, p. A202

KANTO, William, M.D. Senior Vice President and Chief Medical Officer, Georgia Regents Medical Center, Augusta, GA, p. A153

KANTOS, Craig A., Chief Executive Officer, Riverside Medical Center, Waupaca, WI, p. A717

KANUCH, James A.
   Vice President Finance, Allegheny Valley Hospital, Natrona Heights, PA, p. A546
   Vice President Finance, West Penn Hospital, Pittsburgh, PA, p. A552

KANWAL, Neeraj, M.D., President, ProMedica Flower Hospital, Sylvania, OH, p. A502

KEEFE, Dennis D., President and Chief Executive Officer, Care New England Health System, Providence, RI, p. B27

KEEFE, Eileen, Chief Nursing Officer, Parkland Medical Center, Derry, NH, p. A409

KEEFER, Russ, Chief Human Resources Officer, Trios Health, Kennewick, WA, p. A684

KEEGAN, Julie, Vice President Finance, Craig Hospital, Englewood, CO, p. A106

KEEGAN, Justin, Director Support Services, Avera Gregory Hospital, Gregory, SD, p. A574

KEEL, Barry L., Chief Executive Officer, Bay Medical Center Sacred Heart, Panama City, FL, p. A141

KEEL, Deborah C., Chief Executive Officer, North Fulton Regional Hospital, Roswell, GA, p. A165

KEEL, Jeri, Vice President Chief Clinical Officer, Leesburg Regional Medical Center, Leesburg, FL, p. A134

KEELAN, John E., Administrator and Chief Executive Officer, Brodstone Memorial Hospital, Superior, NE, p. A402

KEELE, Paula
Manager Information Systems, Presence Covenant Medical Center, Urbana, IL, p. A204
Manager Information Systems, Presence United Samaritans Medical Center, Danville, IL, p. A187

KEELER, Dave, Chief Financial Officer, Pipestone County Medical Center Avera, Pipestone, MN, p. A349

KEELER, Jason, Executive Vice President and Chief Operating Officer, University of Chicago Medical Center, Chicago, IL, p. A187

KEELER, Jean, President and Chief Executive Officer, Grand View Hospital, Sellersville, PA, p. A554

KEELER, Karl
Chief Executive Officer, Saint Alphonsus Medical Center – Nampa, Nampa, ID, p. A177
Chief Executive Officer, Saint Alphonsus Medical Center – Ontario, Ontario, OR, p. A527

KEELEY, Brian E., President and Chief Executive Officer, Baptist Health South Florida, Coral Gables, FL, p. B20

KEELEY, Katherine, M.D. Chief of Staff, Sunrise Hospital and Medical Center, Las Vegas, NV, p. A407

KEELING, Kevin, Chief Financial Officer, St. Lucie Medical Center, Port St. Lucie, FL, p. A143

KEELING, Terri, Vice President Information Systems, UPMC McKeesport, McKeesport, PA, p. A544

KEEN, Michael, Senior Vice President and Chief Financial Officer, Grand View Hospital, Sellersville, PA, p. A554

KEENAN, Annette M., Chief Executive Officer, Webster County Memorial Hospital, Webster Springs, WV, p. A700

KEENAN, Harold, M.D. Chief Medical Officer, Garden County Health Services, Oshkosh, NE, p. A401

KEENAN, Nancy C., R.N. Chief Nursing Officer, CHRISTUS St. Michael Health System, Texarkana, TX, p. A652

KEENAN, Richard, Senior Vice President Finance and Chief Financial Officer, Valley Hospital, Ridgewood, NJ, p. A422

KEENE, Kaaron, Vice President Patient Care Services, Aspirus Medford Hospital, Medford, WI, p. A709

KEENE, Russell G., Chief Executive Officer, Androscoggin Valley Hospital, Berlin, NH, p. A409

KEENER, Vicki, Administrative Assistant and Director Human Resources, Little River Memorial Hospital, Ashdown, AR, p. A43

KEENEY, Mary Ellen, Vice President Human Resources, Thomas Jefferson University Hospital, Philadelphia, PA, p. A550

KEENUM, Patricia, Health Information Management Systems Officer, Northwest Mississippi Regional Medical Center, Clarksdale, MS, p. A356

KEETON, James, M.D., Vice Chancellor for Health Affairs, University Hospitals and Health System, Jackson, MS, p. B144

KEEVER, Jerry, Administrator, Sharkey–Issaquena Community Hospital, Rolling Fork, MS, p. A365

KEGLEY, Carl J., System Director Information Technology, Fairbanks Memorial Hospital, Fairbanks, AK, p. A29

KEGLEY, Shawn, Director Information Services, Research Medical Center, Kansas City, MO, p. A374

KEGLEY, Sue, Director Human Resources, Onslow Memorial Hospital, Jacksonville, NC, p. A467

KEHRBERG, Mark W., M.D
Chief Medical Officer, Calumet Medical Center, Chilton, WI, p. A703
Senior Vice President and Chief Medical Officer, Mercy Medical Center, Oshkosh, WI, p. A713

KEHUS, Frank, Associate Director for Operations, Marion Veterans Affairs Medical Center, Marion, IL, p. A195

KEILER, Susan, Chief Operating Officer, St. Mary's Regional Medical Center, Lewiston, ME, p. A294

KEIM, Richard, M.D. Chief Medical Officer, Spearfish Regional Surgery Center, Spearfish, SD, p. A577

KEIM, Thomas, Chief Executive Officer, Ste. Genevieve County Memorial Hospital, Ste. Genevieve, MO, p. A383

KEIR, Douglas C., Interim Chief Executive Officer, Burke Medical Center, Waynesboro, GA, p. A169

KEIRNS, Melody, Manager Human Resources, F. W. Huston Medical Center, Winchester, KS, p. A257

KEISER, Trish, Comptroller, Avera Gregory Hospital, Gregory, SD, p. A574

KEISTER, Catharine L., Chief Nursing Officer, Sunbury Community Hospital and Outpatient Center, Sunbury, PA, p. A555

KEITEL, SPHR, Kal, Executive Director Human Resources, Baptist Health Paducah, Paducah, KY, p. A269

KEITH, Bridgette, Director Human Resources, HEALTHSOUTH Northern Kentucky Rehabilitation Hospital, Edgewood, KY, p. A260

KEITH, Darlene, Chief Information Systems, Alleghany Memorial Hospital, Sparta, NC, p. A473

KEITH, David N., FACHE, President and Chief Executive Officer, McAlester Regional Health Center, McAlester, OK, p. A513

KEITH, Leesa–Lee, R.N. Chief Nursing Officer, Baystate Franklin Medical Center, Greenfield, MA, p. A310

KEITH, Lorraine, FACHE Chief Nursing Officer, St. Vincent's Medical Center Southside, Jacksonville, FL, p. A132

KELBAUGH, Brian, Chief Financial Officer, Summersville Regional Medical Center, Summersville, WV, p. A699

KELBLY, Kevin, Senior Vice President Finance and Corporate Fiscal Affairs, Carroll Hospital Center, Westminster, MD, p. A304

KELLAR, Brian, Chief Executive Officer, Grundy County Memorial Hospital, Grundy Center, IA, p. A231

KELLAR, Mark, R.N. Interim Chief Nursing Officer, Our Lady of the Angels Hospital, Bogalusa, LA, p. A274

KELLAR, Richard A., President, Aurora West Allis Medical Center, West Allis, WI, p. A718

KELLEHER, John, Vice President Information Technology and Chief Information Officer, Glens Falls Hospital, Glens Falls, NY, p. A438

KELLEHER, LaCinda, Director of Nursing, West Springs Hospital, Grand Junction, CO, p. A107

KELLEHER, Mary, Vice President Human Resources, Holyoke Medical Center, Holyoke, MA, p. A311

KELLEHER, Mary Lou, R.N. Vice President, Nursing, Franciscan Hospital for Children, Boston, MA, p. A306

KELLEHER, Michael, Chief Medical Officer, Ann & Robert H. Lurie Children's Hospital of Chicago, Chicago, IL, p. A183

KELLEHER, Patrick, M.D. Chief Medical Staff, Saint Joseph Berea, Berea, KY, p. A258

KELLENBARGER, Lance, Site Director Information Systems, St. Catherine Hospital, Garden City, KS, p. A244

KELLER, Allen, Director Human Resources, Sumner Regional Medical Center, Wellington, KS, p. A256

KELLER, Anita M., R.N. Chief Nursing Officer, Johnson Memorial Hospital, Franklin, IN, p. A212

KELLER, Ann, Supervisor Health Information Management, HEALTHSOUTH Walton Rehabilitation Hospital, Augusta, GA, p. A153

KELLER, Christine, Chief Administrative Officer, Bluffton Hospital, Bluffton, OH, p. A484

KELLER, Diane R., Chief Executive Officer, Memorial Community Health, Aurora, NE, p. A393

KELLER, Gretchen, Director Health Information, Neosho Memorial Regional Medical Center, Chanute, KS, p. A242

KELLER, J. Michael, Vice President Operations, Newton Medical Center, Newton, KS, p. A250

KELLER, Jack M., Chief Executive Officer, Saint Thomas Hickman Hospital, Centerville, TN, p. A580

KELLER, James, Director Human Resources, NEA Baptist Memorial Hospital, Jonesboro, AR, p. A48

KELLER, Jane, R.N., Chief Executive Officer, Indiana Orthopaedic Hospital, Indianapolis, IN, p. A214

KELLER, Jill, R.N. Vice President for Nursing Services, Quality and Risk Management, Waynesboro Hospital, Waynesboro, PA, p. A557

KELLER, Jim, Site Director Information Services, Mercy Health Saint Mary's, Grand Rapids, MI, p. A325

KELLER, Justin, Chief Information Officer, Murray County Medical Center, Slayton, MN, p. A352

KELLER, Marsha, Director Human Resources, Kane Community Hospital, Kane, PA, p. A541

KELLER, Maryalice, Vice President Brand and Talent Management, Unity Hospital, Rochester, NY, p. A453

KELLER, Patricia, MSN Nurse Administrator, Mayo Clinic Health System – Northland in Barron, Barron, WI, p. A702

KELLER, Ruey, Acting Chief Information Officer, Veterans Affairs San Diego Healthcare System, San Diego, CA, p. A90

KELLER, Stewart, M.D. Medical Director, Mesa Springs, Fort Worth, TX, p. A618

KELLER, Thomas, President and Chief Executive Officer, Ozarks Medical Center, West Plains, MO, p. A384

KELLER, Wendy, Director Health Information Management, Atrium Medical Center of Corinth, Corinth, TX, p. A608

KELLERMAN, Laurie, MSN Chief Nursing Officer, Marshall Browning Hospital, Du Quoin, IL, p. A188

KELLERMAN, Scott, Chief Financial Officer, Ely–Bloomenson Community Hospital, Ely, MN, p. A343

KELLEY, Brent, Director Information Technology, Nor–Lea General Hospital, Lovington, NM, p. A429

KELLEY, Jalinda, Secretary of Interior Services, Chickasaw Nation Medical Center, Ada, OK, p. A507

KELLEY, Janice, Chief Financial Officer, Marshall County Hospital, Benton, KY, p. A258

KELLEY, Jim, Vice President Finance, Advocate Lutheran General Hospital, Park Ridge, IL, p. A199

KELLEY, Julie, M.D. President Medical Staff, Red Bud Regional Hospital, Red Bud, IL, p. A201

KELLEY, Lewis, Chief Operating Officer, Union General Hospital, Blairsville, GA, p. A154

KELLEY, Mary, Director Human Resources, The Outer Banks Hospital, Nags Head, NC, p. A470

KELLEY, Neal, Vice President and Chief Operating Officer, Seton Medical Center Hays, Kyle, TX, p. A632

KELLEY, R. Lewis, Administrator, Chatuge Regional Hospital and Nursing Home, Hiawassee, GA, p. A161

KELLEY, Sarah Jo, Director Human Resources, Ste. Genevieve County Memorial Hospital, Ste. Genevieve, MO, p. A383

KELLEY, Sharon, Chief Financial Officer, Clifton Springs Hospital and Clinic, Clifton Springs, NY, p. A435

KELLEY, Steven L., President and Chief Executive Officer, Ellenville Regional Hospital, Ellenville, NY, p. A437

KELLEY, Sue, Chief Financial Officer, Cordell Memorial Hospital, Cordell, OK, p. A509

KELLEY, Suzanne, Director Human Resources, North Suburban Medical Center, Thornton, CO, p. A111

KELLEY, Vicky, Chief Financial Officer, DeQuincy Memorial Hospital, DeQuincy, LA, p. A277

KELLEY, Warren, Chief Information Officer, Reynolds Memorial Hospital, Glen Dale, WV, p. A695

KELLOGG, Jason, M.D. Chief of Staff, Newport Bay Hospital, Newport Beach, CA, p. A80

KELLOGG, Susan, Administrator Patient Care Services, Carthage Area Hospital, Carthage, NY, p. A435

KELLS, Anne, Interim Chief Financial Officer, Appleton Area Health Services, Appleton, MN, p. A339

KELLUM, Craig, Director Management Information Systems, Cape Fear Valley – Bladen County Hospital, Elizabethtown, NC, p. A464

KELLY, Ann Marie, Chief Nursing Officer, Ellenville Regional Hospital, Ellenville, NY, p. A437

KELLY, Brian
Vice President Finance, Advocate South Suburban Hospital, Hazel Crest, IL, p. A192
Acting Chief Fiscal Service, San Franciso Veterans Affairs Medical Center, San Francisco, CA, p. A91

KELLY, Brian E., M.D. President Medical Staff, Saint Elizabeth's Medical Center, Wabasha, MN, p. A353

KELLY, Bruce, Chief Information Officer, Mercy Memorial Hospital System, Monroe, MI, p. A330

KELLY, Charlene, Chief Nursing Officer, Kane County Hospital, Kanab, UT, p. A660

KELLY, Charles, D.O. Vice President Medical Affairs and Chief Medical Officer, Henry Ford Macomb Hospitals, Clinton Township, MI, p. A321

KELLY, Colan, Chief Financial Officer, Pineville Community Hospital Association, Pineville, KY, p. A269

KELLY, Dan, R.N. Chief Nursing Officer, Memorial Hermann Memorial City Medical Center, Houston, TX, p. A625

KELLY, Daniel J., President, CHI Health St. Mary's, Nebraska City, NE, p. A398

KELLY, Daniel R., Chief Executive Officer, McKenzie County Healthcare System, Watford City, ND, p. A480

KELLY, Debbie, Chief Executive Officer, South Texas Spine and Surgical Hospital, San Antonio, TX, p. A647

KELLY, Derek J., M.D. Vice President Transformation and Chief Medical Information Officer, Swedish Covenant Hospital, Chicago, IL, p. A187

KELLY, Diane, R.N. Chief Operating Officer, Berkshire Medical Center, Pittsfield, MA, p. A313

KELLY, Ed, Chief Executive Officer, Kindred Hospital–San Francisco Bay Area, San Leandro, CA, p. A92

KELLY, Jim, Chief Operating Officer, Nantucket Cottage Hospital, Nantucket, MA, p. A312

KELLY, John, Chief Nursing Officer and Chief Operating Officer, UMass Memorial–Marlborough Hospital, Marlborough, MA, p. A312

KELLY, John J., M.D. Chief of Staff, Abington Memorial Hospital, Abington, PA, p. A532

KELLY, Laurence E., President and Chief Executive Officer, Nathan Littauer Hospital and Nursing Home, Gloversville, NY, p. A438

KELLY, Leo, M.D. Vice President Medical Management, Advocate Lutheran General Hospital, Park Ridge, IL, p. A199

KELLY, Lynn, Vice President Human Resources, San Antonio Community Hospital, Upland, CA, p. A98
KELLY, Mark, Vice President Finance, St. Francis Medical Center, Trenton, NJ, p. A423
KELLY, Maura, Vice President Fiscal Services, Pen Bay Medical Center, Rockport, ME, p. A295
KELLY, Maureen, R.N. Chief Nursing Officer, Roswell Park Cancer Institute, Buffalo, NY, p. A434
KELLY, Melanie, Director of Nursing, Keokuk Area Hospital, Keokuk, IA, p. A233
KELLY, Melissa, Administrator, Pender Community Hospital, Pender, NE, p. A401
KELLY, Michael, Vice President, Christian Hospital, Saint Louis, MO, p. A380
KELLY, Patrick J., FACHE, Director, Minneapolis Veterans Affairs Health Care System, Minneapolis, MN, p. A347
KELLY, Raymond, R.N. Chief Nursing Officer, Texas Health Presbyterian Hospital Plano, Plano, TX, p. A643
KELLY, Robert E., M.D., President, New York Presbyterian Lower Manhattan Hospital, New York, NY, p. A447
KELLY, Roy, Facility Director, Hawthorn Center, Northville, MI, p. A331
KELLY, Scott A., Chief Executive Officer, Asante Rogue Regional Medical Center, Medford, OR, p. A527
KELLY, Shannon, Director Human Resources, Morton General Hospital, Morton, WA, p. A685
KELLY, Steven G., President and Chief Executive Officer, Newton Medical Center, Newton, KS, p. A250
KELLY, Sylvia K., Chief Executive Officer, HEALTHSOUTH Rehabilitation Hospital, Albuquerque, NM, p. A426
KELLY, Teresa M., MSN Chief Nursing Officer, Chestnut Hill Hospital, Philadelphia, PA, p. A547
KELLY, Vicky, Chief Financial Officer, De Queen Medical Center, De Queen, AR, p. A45
KELLY, Virginia, Chief Financial Officer, Eastside Psychiatric Hospital, Tallahassee, FL, p. A146
KEM, Mark, Vice President Finance and Chief Financial Officer, Chandler Regional Medical Center, Chandler, AZ, p. A31
KEMKA, Joseph, Chief Financial Officer, St. Bernard Parish Hospital, Chalmette, LA, p. A275
KEMKER, S. E., M.D. President Medical Staff, St. Vincent Salem Hospital, Salem, IN, p. A222
KEMMERER, Jan, Director of Nursing, Mitchell County Hospital Health Systems, Beloit, KS, p. A242
KEMP, Robin, R.N. Chief Nursing Officer, Craig General Hospital, Vinita, OK, p. A521
KEMP, Thomas, Chief Information Officer, New York Hospital Queens,, NY, p. A447
KEMPF, Gary L., Administrator, Houston Methodist St. Catherine Hospital, Katy, TX, p. A630
KEMPIAK, Matthew, Director Human Resources and Administrative Services, Memorial Hospital of Gardena, Gardena, CA, p. A65
KEMPINSKI, Paul D., Chief Operating Officer, Alfred I. duPont Hospital for Children, Wilmington, DE, p. A120
KEMPT, Brooke, Corporate Nursing Director, Hamilton Center, Terre Haute, IN, p. A223
KEMPTON, Dana, Associate Director and Chief Financial Officer, Redington–Fairview General Hospital, Skowhegan, ME, p. A295
KEMPTON, Matthew, Chief Executive Officer and Administrator, Stephens Memorial Hospital, Breckenridge, TX, p. A603
KENAGY, John Jay, Ph.D
Senior Vice President and Chief Information Officer, Legacy Meridian Park Medical Center, Tualatin, OR, p. A531
Senior Vice President and Chief Information Officer, Legacy Mount Hood Medical Center, Gresham, OR, p. A525
KENDALL, Anthony
Vice President Human Resources, Baptist Health Extended Care Hospital, Little Rock, AR, p. A49
Vice President Human Resources, Baptist Health Medical Center – North Little Rock, North Little Rock, AR, p. A51
Vice President Human Resources, Baptist Health Medical Center–Arkadelphia, Arkadelphia, AR, p. A43
Vice President Human Resources, Baptist Health Medical Center–Little Rock, Little Rock, AR, p. A49
Vice President Human Resources, Baptist Health Rehabilitation Institute, Little Rock, AR, p. A49
KENDLE, Melinda
Manager Business Office, Evansville Psychiatric Children Center, Evansville, IN, p. A210
Director Fiscal Management, Evansville State Hospital, Evansville, IN, p. A210
KENDLER, Lisa
Chief Financial Officer, Memorial Hermann Memorial City Medical Center, Houston, TX, p. A625
Chief Financial Officer, Memorial Hermann Sugar Land Hospital, Sugar Land, TX, p. A651
KENDRICK, Donovan, M.D. Chief Medical Officer, Baptist Medical Center South, Montgomery, AL, p. A23

KENDRICK, Jim R., Chief Executive Officer, Longview Regional Medical Center, Longview, TX, p. A634
KENDRICK, Ray
Chief Human Resources Officer, Memorial Hospital Miramar, Miramar, FL, p. A138
Chief Human Resources Officer, Memorial Regional Hospital,, FL, p. A130
KENDRICK, Robert, Chief Nursing Officer, Madison Memorial Hospital, Rexburg, ID, p. A178
KENLEY, William A., Chief Executive Officer, Methodist Healthcare–Fayette Hospital, Somerville, TN, p. A593
KENNEDY, Anita J., Vice President Operations, Methodist Hospital of Sacramento, Sacramento, CA, p. A87
KENNEDY, Brad, Chief Executive Officer, HEALTHSOUTH Rehabilitation Hospital at Drake, Cincinnati, OH, p. A487
KENNEDY, Bruce, M.D. Chief Medical Officer, Houston Methodist San Jacinto Hospital, Baytown, TX, p. A601
KENNEDY, Carol, Chief Clinical Officer, Barrett Hospital & HealthCare, Dillon, MT, p. A387
KENNEDY, Connie, Director Human Resources, Marlette Regional Hospital, Marlette, MI, p. A330
KENNEDY, Darla, Chief Information Officer, Newport Specialty Hospital, Tustin, CA, p. A98
KENNEDY, Diana, Director Human Resources, Meadowview Regional Medical Center, Maysville, KY, p. A267
KENNEDY, Elizabeth M., Administrator, J. Paul Jones Hospital, Camden, AL, p. A18
KENNEDY, Eric, Chief Executive Officer, Longleaf Hospital, Alexandria, LA, p. A272
KENNEDY, Jill M., R.N. Vice President Patient Care Services and Chief Nursing Officer, Bon Secours Memorial Regional Medical Center, Mechanicsville, VA, p. A674
KENNEDY, John, M.D. Vice President Medical Affairs, Mercy Health – Fairfield Hospital, Fairfield, OH, p. A493
KENNEDY, Kimberly, Manager Human Resources, Mendota Community Hospital, Mendota, IL, p. A196
KENNEDY, Mary, R.N. Chief Nursing Officer, Medina Hospital, Medina, OH, p. A498
KENNEDY, Pam
Vice President Regional Human Resources and Organizational Department, CHRISTUS St. Michael Health System, Texarkana, TX, p. A652
Director Human Resources, CHRISTUS St. Michael Rehabilitation Hospital, Texarkana, TX, p. A652
KENNEDY, Peggy S., R.N. Vice President and Chief Nurse Executive, Fremont Health, Fremont, NE, p. A395
KENNEDY, R. Scott, M.D. Assistant Administrator and Chief Medical Officer, Olympic Medical Center, Port Angeles, WA, p. A686
KENNEDY, ReChelle, Chief Financial Officer, Kearny County Hospital, Lakin, KS, p. A248
KENNEDY, Ryan
Chief Financial Officer, Holy Name Medical Center, Teaneck, NJ, p. A423
Chief Operating Officer, Kingman Regional Medical Center, Kingman, AZ, p. A33
KENNEDY, Susan, Manager Human Resources, Novant Health Matthews Medical Center, Matthews, NC, p. A469
KENNEDY, Terris, Ph.D. Chief Nursing Officer, Riverside Behavioral Health Center, Hampton, VA, p. A672
KENNEDY, Timea, Director Human Resources, St. Mary–Corwin Medical Center, Pueblo, CO, p. A110
KENNEDY, Todd S., Executive Vice President and Chief Operating Officer, Providence Hospital, Mobile, AL, p. A22
KENNETH, Ron, M.D. Chief Medical Officer, West Valley Hospital, Goodyear, AZ, p. A33
KENNEY, Catherine, Chief Nursing Officer, Pampa Regional Medical Center, Pampa, TX, p. A641
KENNEY, Louise, Director of Nursing, University Health Conway, Monroe, LA, p. A284
KENNEY, Mary Ellen, Chief Human Services, Manchester Veterans Affairs Medical Center, Manchester, NH, p. A411
KENNINGTON, Lynn, Chief Financial Officer, Alaska Regional Hospital, Anchorage, AK, p. A28
KENNINGTON, Milas H., Vice President, Human Resources, Western Medical Center–Santa Ana, Santa Ana, CA, p. A93
KENNISON, Barbara, Director Clinical Services, Aurora San Diego Hospital, San Diego, CA, p. A89
KENNY, Carolyn, Executive Vice President Clinical Care, Children's Healthcare of Atlanta, Atlanta, GA, p. A152
KENT, Alan, Chief Executive Officer, Meadows Regional Medical Center, Vidalia, GA, p. A168
KENT, Blair, Administrator, Riverton Hospital, Riverton, UT, p. A662
KENT, David, Director Human Resources, Bolivar Medical Center, Cleveland, MS, p. A357
KENT, David, M.D. Chief Medical Officer, Safe Haven Hospital of Treasure Valley, Boise, ID, p. A174
KENT, David, Chief Operating Officer, Southeastern Regional Medical Center, Newnan, GA, p. A164

KENT, Michael, Chief Executive Officer, Muenster Memorial Hospital, Muenster, TX, p. A639
KENT, Robert, D.O., President and Chief Executive Officer, Summa Western Reserve Hospital, Cuyahoga Falls, OH, p. A491
KENTERA, Amy, Chief Information Officer, Conifer Park, Glenville, NY, p. A438
KENTFIELD, Melinda Johanna, Chief Nursing Officer, Warren Memorial Hospital, Friend, NE, p. A395
KENWOOD, Linda S., R.N. Chief Nursing Officer and Chief Operating Officer, Shore Medical Center, Somers Point, NJ, p. A422
KEOWN, Janet, Vice President Human Resources, Behavioral Health Network, Natchaug Hospital, Mansfield Center, CT, p. A115
KEPLER, Andrea, Chief Executive Officer, Wernersville State Hospital, Wernersville, PA, p. A557
KEPLER, Terry W., Chief Executive Officer, Post Acute Medical Specialty Hospital of Milwaukee, Greenfield, WI, p. A706
KEPLINGER, Ron, Chief Information Officer, Western Maryland Hospital Center, Hagerstown, MD, p. A301
KEPNER, Donald L., Chief Financial Officer, Ashtabula County Medical Center, Ashtabula, OH, p. A482
KEPPLER, Edward L., M.D. Chief Medical Officer, Marion General Hospital, Marion, IN, p. A218
KEPPLER, Matthew, Market Chief Executive Officer, Kindred Hospital Indianapolis South, Greenwood, IN, p. A212
KERBS, Curtis, Vice President Information Services, Memorial Hospital, North Conway, NH, p. A412
KERCHENSKI, Marlene, Chief Nurse, U. S. Air Force Hospital, Hampton, VA, p. A672
KERCHER, Eugene, M.D. Chief Medical Officer, Kern Medical Center, Bakersfield, CA, p. A57
KERDEL, Francisco, M.D. President Medical Staff, University of Miami Hospital, Miami, FL, p. A137
KERI, Alison, Director Human Resources, Hiawatha Community Hospital, Hiawatha, KS, p. A245
KERIN, Doug, M.D. Chief of Staff, Saint Mary's Regional Medical Center, Russellville, AR, p. A52
KERLIN, Kerry, Vice President Information Technology, Roswell Park Cancer Institute, Buffalo, NY, p. A434
KERMEN, John, D.O. Chief Medical Staff, Mendocino Coast District Hospital, Fort Bragg, CA, p. A63
KERN, Douglas W., Chief Executive Officer, Northcoast Behavioral Healthcare System, Northfield, OH, p. A499
KERN, Erica, Director Human Resources, Keefe Memorial Hospital, Cheyenne Wells, CO, p. A103
KERN, Gordon, M.D. Medical Director, Oswego Community Hospital, Oswego, KS, p. A251
KERN, Howard P.
President and Chief Operating Officer, Sentara Leigh Hospital, Norfolk, VA, p. A675
Chief Operating Officer, Sentara Princess Anne Hospital, Virginia Beach, VA, p. A679
KERN, Sue, Director of Nursing, Keefe Memorial Hospital, Cheyenne Wells, CO, p. A103
KERNELL, Shane, Chief Executive Officer, St. Mark's Medical Center, La Grange, TX, p. A632
KERNIZAN, Lorna, Chief Operating Officer, Aventura Hospital and Medical Center, Aventura, FL, p. A123
KERNS, Elizabeth, Chief Information Officer, Lakeland Regional Medical Center, Lakeland, FL, p. A134
KEROACK, Mark A., M.D., President and Chief Executive Officer, Baystate Health, Inc., Springfield, MA, p. B22
KERR, Jeff, M.D. Chief Medical Officer, Baylor Medical Center at McKinney, McKinney, TX, p. A637
KERR, Karen, R.N., Interim President and Chief Executive Officer, South Florida Baptist Hospital, Plant City, FL, p. A143
KERR, Mark, Chief Executive Officer, Presentation Medical Center, Rolla, ND, p. A480
KERR, Michael D.
Chief Executive Officer, Promise Hospital of East Los Angeles, Los Angeles, CA, p. A74
Chief Executive Officer, Promise Hospital of East Los Angeles, Suburban Medical Center Campus, Paramount, CA, p. A82
KERR, Rand, Chief Executive Officer, Lakeview Hospital, Bountiful, UT, p. A659
KERRINS, David, Vice President Information Services and Chief Information Officer, Dameron Hospital, Stockton, CA, p. A96
KERSCHEN, Susan, MS Vice President and Chief Nursing Officer, Exempla Good Samaritan Medical Center, Lafayette, CO, p. A108
KERSEY, Jerry, Director Employee Relations, Eastern State Hospital, Lexington, KY, p. A264
KERSHNER, Kathy, Director of Nursing, Herington Municipal Hospital, Herington, KS, p. A245
KERSWILL, Randy, M.D. Medical Director, Winnebago Mental Health Institute, Winnebago, WI, p. A719

KERTIS, Robert, Vice President Finance, Calvert Memorial Hospital, Prince Frederick, MD, p. A302

KERWIN, George, President, Bellin Memorial Hospital, Green Bay, WI, p. A705

KERWOOD, Christine, Chief Nursing Officer, East Ohio Regional Hospital, Martins Ferry, OH, p. A497

KERWOOD, Lori A., Director Human Resources, Cooley Dickinson Hospital, Northampton, MA, p. A313

KESSEL, Jennifer, Director Human Resources, Aultman Orrville Hospital, Orrville, OH, p. A500

KESSEL-FOX, Teri, Director Clinical Services, Regency Hospital of Covington, Covington, LA, p. A276

KESSLER, Alexander, M.D. Chief of Staff, Northside Hospital-Cherokee, Canton, GA, p. A155

KESSLER, David, M.D. Clinical Director, U. S. Public Health Service Indian Hospital, Zuni, NM, p. A431

KESSLER, Dawn, Senior Vice President Human Resources, St. John's Hospital, Saint Paul, MN, p. A351

KESSLER, Jeffrey R., Vice President Information Services, Dana-Farber Cancer Institute, Boston, MA, p. A306

KESSLER, Joseph, Executive Vice President and Chief Financial Officer, KALEIDA Health, Buffalo, NY, p. A434

KESSLER, Mike, Director, Information Services, Indiana University Health Tipton Hospital, Tipton, IN, p. A223

KESSLER, Renee A., Chief Operating Officer, Saint Thomas Midtown Hospital, Nashville, TN, p. A590

KESSLER, Terrence, Interim President and Chief Executive Officer, Sisters of Charity Health System, Cleveland, OH, p. B124

KESSNER, Jennifer, Financial Director, Roosevelt Medical Center, Culbertson, MT, p. A386

KESTER, Bonnie J., R.N. Vice President Patient Care Services and Chief Nursing Officer, Nantucket Cottage Hospital, Nantucket, MA, p. A312

KESTERSON, Matt
  Director Information Services, Wadley Regional Medical Center, Texarkana, TX, p. A653
  Director Information Services, Wadley Regional Medical Center at Hope, Hope, AR, p. A47

KETCH, Lynn
  Human Resources Recruiter Generalist, INTEGRIS Canadian Valley Hospital, Yukon, OK, p. A522
  Director, Integris Southwest Medical Center, Oklahoma City, OK, p. A515

KETCHAM, Krista, Chief Financial Officer, Buena Vista Regional Medical Center, Storm Lake, IA, p. A238

KETCHER, Greg, Administrator, Lawton Indian Hospital, Lawton, OK, p. A512

KETTELLE, John, M.D. Chief Medical Officer, University of Arizona Medical Center – South Campus, Tucson, AZ, p. A41

KETTERHAGEN, James P., M.D. Senior Vice President and Chief Medical Officer, Jewish Hospital, Louisville, KY, p. A265

KETTLER, Paul, M.D. Vice President Medical Affairs, Unity Hospital, Fridley, MN, p. A344

KEUTER, Mary Beth, Director Patient Care, Continuing Care Hospital at St. Luke's, Cedar Rapids, IA, p. A226

KEY, Lora, Chief Executive Officer, Sabetha Community Hospital, Sabetha, KS, p. A253

KEY, Mark, M.D. Chief of Staff, Medical Arts Hospital, Lamesa, TX, p. A632

KEY, Ramona, Chief Executive Officer, Austin Oaks Hospital, Austin, TX, p. A599

KEYS, Janice Colleen, MSN Chief Nurse Executive, Erlanger Medical Center, Chattanooga, TN, p. A580

KHADE, Kashmira, Coordinator Non–Clinical Services, Behavioral Center of Michigan, Warren, MI, p. A336

KHALIQUE, Tamia, Director Human Resources, Vibra Hospital of San Diego, San Diego, CA, p. A90

KHAN, Atique, M.D. Medical Director, University Behavioral Health of Denton, Denton, TX, p. A613

KHAN, Behram, M.D. Medical Director, Post Acute/Warm Springs Specialty Hospital of Victoria, Victoria, TX, p. A655

KHAN, Dan, M.D. Chief Medical Officer, Yoakum County Hospital, Denver City, TX, p. A614

KHAN, Humayun, M.D
  Chief Medical Officer, Sacred Heart Hospital, Eau Claire, WI, p. A704
  Divisional Chief Medical Officer, St. Joseph's Hospital, Chippewa Falls, WI, p. A703

KHAN, Sarfraz, Medical Director, Meridian Health Services, Muncie, IN, p. A219

KHAN, Shahbaz, M.D. Medical Director, Two Rivers Behavioral Health System, Kansas City, MO, p. A375

KHAN, Waheed, M.D. President Medical Staff, Summers County ARH Hospital, Hinton, WV, p. A695

KHAN, Yasin N., M.D. Chief Executive Officer, Westfield Hospital, Allentown, PA, p. A532

KHANCHANDANI, Ashok, Chief Financial Officer, Oroville Hospital, Oroville, CA, p. A82

KHANNA, Rajive, Chief Executive Officer, Grace Hospital, Cleveland, OH, p. A488

KHANNA, Vijay, M.D. Chief of Staff, Oakwood Hospital–Taylor, Taylor, MI, p. A335

KHATAMI, Manoochehr, M.D. Medical Director, Hickory Trail Hospital, Desoto, TX, p. A614

KHDOUR, Adel, M.D. Chief Medical Officer, Indiana University Health White Memorial Hospital, Monticello, IN, p. A219

KHEMKA, Hemant, Chief Operating Officer, Surgery Specialty Hospitals of America, Pasadena, TX, p. A641

KHIM FUGATE, Guay, Chief Operations Officer, Kindred Hospital Riverside, Perris, CA, p. A83

KHOERL, Thomas, Vice President Finance, Spectrum Health Big Rapids Hospital, Big Rapids, MI, p. A319

KHOO, Alex, Interim Area Finance Officer, Kaiser Permanente San Francisco Medical Center, San Francisco, CA, p. A91

KHOURY, Anwar, M.D. Chief of Staff, Geary Community Hospital, Junction City, KS, p. A246

KHOW, Vida J., Chief Executive Officer, Gallup Indian Medical Center, Gallup, NM, p. A428

KIBAR, Nizar, M.D. Chief Medical Staff, Kiowa County Memorial Hospital, Greensburg, KS, p. A244

KIBBY, Rosalinda, Superintendent and Administrator, Columbia Basin Hospital, Ephrata, WA, p. A683

KIBLER, Doug, Management Information Systems Specialist, Tennova Healthcare–LaFollette Medical Center, La Follette, TN, p. A586

KIBORT, Phillip M., M.D. Vice President Medical Affairs and Chief Medical Officer, Children's Hospitals and Clinics of Minnesota, Minneapolis, MN, p. A347

KIDD, David, Manager Human Resources, Sentara CarePlex Hospital, Hampton, VA, p. A672

KIDD, Larry R., R.N. Vice President and Chief Nursing Officer, Henry Mayo Newhall Memorial Hospital, Valencia, CA, p. A98

KIDD, Monica, MSN, Administrator, Parkview Hospital, Wheeler, TX, p. A657

KIDD, Scott, Director Human Resources, Mendocino Coast District Hospital, Fort Bragg, CA, p. A63

KIDD, Sue, Chief Financial Officer, Horton Community Hospital, Horton, KS, p. A246

KIDD, Thomas J., Assistant Administrator and Chief Financial Officer, Macon County General Hospital, Lafayette, TN, p. A586

KIDDER, Allison, Administrator, Compass Behavioral Center of Crowley, Crowley, LA, p. A276

KIDDER, David M., D.O. Chief Medical Officer, Garfield County Health Center, Jordan, MT, p. A388

KIDDER, Suzanne F., Director Human Resources, Opelousas General Health System, Opelousas, LA, p. A287

KIEBZAK, Stanley F., R.N. Chief Nursing Officer, Reliant Northwest Houston, Houston, TX, p. A626

KIEDROWSKI, Brian, M.D. Chief Medical Director, Miami Jewish Home and Hospital for Aged, Miami, FL, p. A137

KIEF, Brian, Regional Vice President Ministry Health Care and President Ministry Saint Joseph's Hospital, Ministry Saint Joseph's Hospital, Marshfield, WI, p. A709

KIEFER, William, Chief Nursing Officer, Red River Regional Hospital, Bonham, TX, p. A603

KIEHLE, Jessica, R.N. Chief Nursing Officer, Abilene Regional Medical Center, Abilene, TX, p. A595

KIELY, Sharon, M.D. Senior Vice President Medical Affairs and Chief Medical Officer, Stamford Hospital, Stamford, CT, p. A117

KIERNAN, Richard, Vice President Human Resources, Monmouth Medical Center, Long Branch Campus, Long Branch, NJ, p. A418

KIFAIEH, Nizar, M.D., President and Chief Medical Officer, Christ Hospital, Jersey City, NJ, p. A417

KIFER, Debbie, Chief Nursing Officer, EASTAR Health System, Muskogee, OK, p. A514

KIGER, Tom, Director Information Systems, Trinity Health System, Steubenville, OH, p. A502

KIGHT, Sheila, Director Human Resources, TriStar Horizon Medical Center, Dickson, TN, p. A582

KIISKILA, Walt, Interim Chief Executive Officer, Aspirus Keweenaw Hospital, Laurium, MI, p. A329

KILARSKI, David J., Chief Executive Officer, FirstHealth Moore Regional Hospital, Pinehurst, NC, p. A470

KILARSKI, David J., Chief Executive Officer, FirstHealth of the Carolinas, Pinehurst, NC, p. B58

KILBORN, Mark, Director Information Systems, Springhill Memorial Hospital, Mobile, AL, p. A23

KILDAY, Dennis P., Chief Financial Officer, Golden Plains Community Hospital, Borger, TX, p. A603

KILDAY, Kevin, Vice President Finance, Holy Family Hospital and Medical Center, Methuen, MA, p. A312

KILE, Steven E., Director Human Resources, Springfield Regional Medical Center, Springfield, OH, p. A502

KILEY, Dennis, President, Emory–Adventist Hospital, Smyrna, GA, p. A166

KILFEATHER–MACKEY, Robin F., Chief Financial Officer, Dartmouth–Hitchcock Medical Center, Lebanon, NH, p. A411

KILGORE, Jeremie, Director Information Technology, Galesburg Cottage Hospital, Galesburg, IL, p. A190

KILGORE, Sherry, Chief Financial Management Service, John D. Dingell Veterans Affairs Medical Center, Detroit, MI, p. A322

KILLINGSWORTH, Meri, Chief Operating Officer, Hereford Regional Medical Center, Hereford, TX, p. A623

KILLION, Rosie, R.N. Chief Nursing Officer, DeWitt Hospital, De Witt, AR, p. A45

KILLORAN, Carrie
  Interim President, Aurora Medical Center Grafton, Grafton, WI, p. A705
  Interim President, Aurora Medical Center in Washington County, Hartford, WI, p. A706

KILO, Charles M., M.D. Chief Medical Officer, OHSU Hospital, Portland, OR, p. A528

KILPATRICK, Von, Chief Nursing Officer, St. Vincent General Hospital District, Leadville, CO, p. A108

KIM, Dong, M.D. Chief of Staff, Parkview Community Hospital Medical Center, Riverside, CA, p. A86

KIM, Eric, Chief Information Officer, Aurora Las Encinas Hospital, Pasadena, CA, p. A83

KIM, Soon K., M.D., President and Chief Executive Officer, Aurora Behavioral Health Care, Corona, CA, p. B16

KIMBALL, Amy, D.O. Chief of Staff, Madison County Health Care System, Winterset, IA, p. A240

KIMBALL, Mark E., Chief Executive Officer, Select Specialty Hospital–Memphis, Memphis, TN, p. A589

KIMBALL, Sharon M., R.N. Vice President and Chief Nursing Officer, Caldwell Memorial Hospital, Lenoir, NC, p. A468

KIMBLE, D. Gay, Director Human Resources, Susan B. Allen Memorial Hospital, El Dorado, KS, p. A243

KIMBLE, Robert J., Chief Financial Officer, William R. Sharpe, Jr. Hospital, Weston, WV, p. A700

KIMBREW, Missey, Director Human Resources, Grafton City Hospital, Grafton, WV, p. A695

KIMBRO, George, Vice President Finance, Angel Medical Center, Franklin, NC, p. A464

KIMBROUGH, Pam, M.D. Vice President Medical Affairs, Mercy Hospital Ardmore, Ardmore, OK, p. A507

KIMMEL, Arnold, Chief Executive Officer, Franciscan St. James Hospital and Health Centers, Olympia Fields, IL, p. A199

KIMMEL, Edra, M.D. Chief of Staff, Woman's Hospital, Flowood, MS, p. A358

KIMMEL, Kyle, Chief Financial Officer, Bacon County Hospital and Health System, Alma, GA, p. A151

KIMMEL, Stephen, Chief Financial Officer, Cook Children's Medical Center, Fort Worth, TX, p. A618

KIMMES, Robert P., Chief Executive Officer, Skyline Hospital, White Salmon, WA, p. A692

KIMMY, Sharon, Coordinator Human Resources, Corry Memorial Hospital, Corry, PA, p. A536

KIMPLE, Robin, Director Information Services, Gettysburg Hospital, Gettysburg, PA, p. A539

KIMZEY, Mike, Chief Executive Officer and Administrator, Oklahoma Center for Orthopedic and Multi–Specialty Surgery, Oklahoma City, OK, p. A516

KINCAID, Kevin, Chief Executive Officer, Knoxville Hospital & Clinics, Knoxville, IA, p. A233

KINDER, Barbara, R.N. Chief Clinical Officer, Clark Regional Medical Center, Winchester, KY, p. A271

KINDERED, Deanne, Vice President Finance, Baylor Regional Medical Center at Plano, Plano, TX, p. A642

KINDRED, Bryan N., FACHE, President and Chief Executive Officer, DCH Health System, Tuscaloosa, AL, p. B46

KING, Abner, Chief Operating Officer, Steele Memorial Medical Center, Salmon, ID, p. A178

KING, Amber, Director Human Resources, Northcrest Medical Center, Springfield, TN, p. A593

KING, Ashley, Chief Executive Officer, North Valley Health Center, Warren, MN, p. A353

KING, Beth, Chief Financial Officer, Jersey Community Hospital, Jerseyville, IL, p. A193

KING, Brent R., Chief Medical Officer and Chief Physician, Alfred I. duPont Hospital for Children, Wilmington, DE, p. A120

KING, Bruce, President and Chief Executive Officer, New London Hospital, New London, NH, p. A411

KING, Chris, Director Information Services, OhioHealth Marion General Hospital, Marion, OH, p. A497

KING, Christopher, Director Operations and Administrative Services, Matheny Medical and Educational Center, Peapack, NJ, p. A420

KING, Craig, Coordinator Human Resources, Kindred Hospital Sugar Land, Sugar Land, TX, p. A650

KING, Dennis P., Chief Executive Officer, Spring Harbor Hospital, Westbrook, ME, p. A295

KING, Don, Chief Operating Officer, Saint Thomas West Hospital, Nashville, TN, p. A590

KING, Donna J., R.N. Vice President Clinical Operations and Chief Nursing Executive, Advocate Illinois Masonic Medical Center, Chicago, IL, p. A183

KING, Doug, M.D
Medical Director, Pathways of Tennessee, Jackson, TN, p. A584
Director Clinical Services, Western Mental Health Institute, Bolivar, TN, p. A579

KING, Ed, Chief Financial Officer, Downey Regional Medical Center, Downey, CA, p. A61

KING, Elizabeth, Director, White Plains Hospital Center, White Plains, NY, p. A458

KING, Glenn, R.N
Vice President, Chief Nursing Officer, MidMichigan Medical Center–Clare, Clare, MI, p. A321
Vice President and Chief Nursing Officer, MidMichigan Medical Center–Gladwin, Gladwin, MI, p. A324

KING, Grace, Regional Director Human Resources, Broward Health North, Deerfield Beach, FL, p. A127

KING, Heath
Chief Financial Officer, Coliseum Medical Centers, Macon, GA, p. A162
Chief Financial Officer, Coliseum Northside Hospital, Macon, GA, p. A162

KING, James E., Corporate Director Information Technology, Reliant Rehabilitation Hospital Dallas, Dallas, TX, p. A611

KING, Jason, Chief Information Officer, RiverView Health, Crookston, MN, p. A342

KING, Jason M., Vice President Patient Care Services and Chief Nursing Officer, Indiana University Health Morgan Hospital, Martinsville, IN, p. A218

KING, Jay
Vice President Human Resources, Marian Regional Medical Center, Santa Maria, CA, p. A94
Vice President Human Resources, Mercy Hospitals of Bakersfield, Bakersfield, CA, p. A57

KING, Jim, Executive Vice President and Chief Operating Officer, Jackson County Memorial Hospital, Altus, OK, p. A507

KING, Joanie, Chief Financial Officer, Carteret General Hospital, Morehead City, NC, p. A469

KING, Kim, Director Human Resources and Public Relations, Baptist Memorial Hospital–Huntingdon, Huntingdon, TN, p. A584

KING, Kirk, FACHE, President, Texas Health Arlington Memorial Hospital, Arlington, TX, p. A598

KING, Lenetra S., Chief Operating Officer, Menorah Medical Center, Overland Park, KS, p. A252

KING, Louie, Chief Executive Officer, Teton Medical Center, Choteau, MT, p. A386

KING, Mike, Chief Operating Officer, Doctors Medical Center, Modesto, CA, p. A77

KING, Paul, M.D. Medical Director, Parkwood Behavioral Health System, Olive Branch, MS, p. A363

KING, Ray, M.D. Senior Vice President and Chief Medical Officer, Allegiance Health, Jackson, MI, p. A327

KING, Rich, Vice President Information Technology, West Virginia University Hospitals, Morgantown, WV, p. A697

KING, Sam, Chief Financial Officer, Renown Regional Medical Center, Reno, NV, p. A407

KING, Sammy, Controller, HEALTHSOUTH Rehabilitation Hospital of Ocala, Ocala, FL, p. A139

KING, Sandra, Chief Nursing Officer, Sagamore Children's Psychiatric Center, Dix Hills, NY, p. A436

KING, Tamara, R.N. Chief Nurse Executive, Shepherd Center, Atlanta, GA, p. A153

KING, Val, Chief Information Officer, Val Verde Regional Medical Center, Del Rio, TX, p. A613

KING, Victoria, M.D. Chief Medical Officer, St. Thomas More Hospital, Canon City, CO, p. A103

KING ROBINSON, Jan, Vice President, Operations, Sentara Albemarle Medical Center, Elizabeth City, NC, p. A464

KINGHAM, Darrell L., CPA Vice President Finance, Beauregard Memorial Hospital, De Ridder, LA, p. A276

KINGSLEY, Christi, Director Human Resources, West Calcasieu Cameron Hospital, Sulphur, LA, p. A289

KINGSTON, Eileen M., R.N. Nurse Executive, Associate Director Patient Care, Veterans Affairs – Western Iowa Healthcare System, Omaha, NE, p. A400

KINGSTON, Mary Beth, R.N. Executive Vice President and Chief Nursing Officer, Aurora Medical Center of Oshkosh, Oshkosh, WI, p. A712

KINGSTON, Peggy, Chief Executive Officer, Select Specialty Hospital–Pontiac, Pontiac, MI, p. A332

KINI, M. Narendra, M.D., President and Chief Executive Officer, Miami Children's Hospital, Miami, FL, p. A137

KINKAID, Steve
Director Information Systems, Gnaden Huetten Memorial Hospital, Lehighton, PA, p. A543
Director Information Systems, Palmerton Hospital, Palmerton, PA, p. A547

KINLEN, Thomas, Superintendent, Larned State Hospital, Larned, KS, p. A248

KINMAN, Amanda, Director of Finance, Saint Joseph Mount Sterling, Mount Sterling, KY, p. A268

KINMAN, Brett, Chief Operating Officer, Tomball Regional Medical Center, Tomball, TX, p. A653

KINNEER, James W., Vice President Organizational Development, Indiana Regional Medical Center, Indiana, PA, p. A541

KINNEMAN, Mary, R.N. Chief Nursing Officer, Vice President Patient Care Services, Norwood Hospital, Norwood, MA, p. A313

KINNEY, Janet, Chief Operating Officer, Northwest Florida Community Hospital, Chipley, FL, p. A125

KINSALA, Edeli, Chief Executive Officer, Sonora Behavioral Health Hospital, Tucson, AZ, p. A40

KINSEL, Mike, Controller, Federal Medical Center, Lexington, KY, p. A264

KINSELLA, Daniel F.
Vice President and Chief Information Officer, Central DuPage Hospital, Winfield, IL, p. A205
Executive Vice President Information Technology, Delnor Hospital, Geneva, IL, p. A191

KINSEY, Daniel, M.D. Medical Director, Oaklawn Psychiatric Center, Goshen, IN, p. A212

KINSEY, Wayne, Chief Executive Officer, Promise Hospital of Salt Lake, Salt Lake City, UT, p. A663

KINSLOW, Kathleen, Ed.D., President and Chief Executive Officer, Aria Health, Philadelphia, PA, p. A547

KINTZ, Ronald J.
Vice President and Treasurer, Arnot Ogden Medical Center, Elmira, NY, p. A437
Chief Financial Officer, Ira Davenport Memorial Hospital, Bath, NY, p. A433
Senior Vice President Finance and Chief Financial Officer, St. Joseph's Hospital, Elmira, NY, p. A437

KINYON, Craig C., President, Reid Hospital and Health Care Services, Richmond, IN, p. A221

KINYON, David, Vice President of Operations and Outpatient Services, Asante Three Rivers Medical Center, Grants Pass, OR, p. A525

KINZIC, Elizabeth, M.D. Chief of Staff, Share Medical Center, Alva, OK, p. A507

KINZIE, Wesley, M.D. Chief of Staff, Stanislaus Surgical Hospital, Modesto, CA, p. A78

KIO, Kenneth, Manager Human Resources, Albany Stratton Veterans Affairs Medical Center, Albany, NY, p. A432

KIPER, Valerie, MSN Chief Nursing Officer, Northwest Texas Healthcare System, Amarillo, TX, p. A596

KIPFER, Debra, Chief Financial Officer, Community Hospital of Bremen, Bremen, IN, p. A207

KIPP, Christine, R.N. Chief Nursing Officer, Christus St. Vincent Regional Medical Center, Santa Fe, NM, p. A430

KIPREOS, Nicholas, M.D. Chief Medical Staff, Pioneer Community Hospital of Patrick County, Stuart, VA, p. A679

KIRACOFE, Darin, Director Information Resource Management, Broughton Hospital, Morganton, NC, p. A469

KIRALY, Denise G., Director Human Resources, Western Maryland Regional Medical Center, Cumberland, MD, p. A300

KIRBOW, Keith, R.N. Vice President and Chief Nursing Officer, Good Shepherd Medical Center–Marshall, Marshall, TX, p. A636

KIRBY, Adrienne, Ph.D., President and CEO, Cooper University Health Care, Camden, NJ, p. A414

KIRBY, Cheryl, Chief Nursing Officer, Palo Pinto General Hospital, Mineral Wells, TX, p. A638

KIRBY, Elizabeth A., Director Human Resources, Aurora BayCare Medical Center, Green Bay, WI, p. A705

KIRBY II, James M., President and Chief Executive Officer, Margaret R. Pardee Memorial Hospital, Hendersonville, NC, p. A466

KIRBY, Jennifer, R.N. Chief Nursing Officer, George Washington University Hospital, Washington, DC, p. A121

KIRBY, Juliana Kay, R.N. Chief Nursing Officer, Tehachapi Valley Healthcare District, Tehachapi, CA, p. A96

KIRBY, Penny V., MSN Chief Nursing Officer, McKenzie Regional Hospital, McKenzie, TN, p. A588

KIRBY, Richard S., Executive Vice President and Chief Financial Officer, Community Memorial Hospital, Hamilton, NY, p. A438

KIRBY, Ruby, Administrator, Bolivar General Hospital, Bolivar, TN, p. A579

KIRBY, Sarah, Acute Care Executive, Palmetto Health Baptist Parkridge, Columbia, SC, p. A564

KIRCH, Cyndi
Vice President Human Resources, Mercy General Hospital, Sacramento, CA, p. A87
Vice President Human Resources, Methodist Hospital of Sacramento, Sacramento, CA, p. A87

KIRCHER, Janelle, R.N. Vice President, Patient Care Services, Community Hospital, McCook, NE, p. A398

KIRCHER, Mark, Associate Vice President Finance, Norton Suburban Hospital, Louisville, KY, p. A266

KIRCHHOFF, Stacy, Coordinator Human Resources, Warren Memorial Hospital, Friend, NE, p. A395

KIRCHNER, Doris, Chief Executive Officer, Vail Valley Medical Center, Vail, CO, p. A111

KIRCHNER, Kent, M.D. Chief of Staff, G.V. (Sonny) Montgomery Veterans Affairs Medical Center, Jackson, MS, p. A360

KIRCHNER, Susan M., Director Human Resources, Four Winds Hospital, Saratoga Springs, NY, p. A454

KIRISITS, Christopher, Chief Nursing Officer, Rochester Psychiatric Center, Rochester, NY, p. A453

KIRITANI, Tracy, Vice President and Chief Financial Officer, Clovis Community Medical Center, Clovis, CA, p. A60

KIRK, Brian T., Vice President Finance, University Hospital and Clinics, Lafayette, LA, p. A282

KIRK, Darlene, Manager Finance, U. S. Public Health Service Indian Hospital, Crownpoint, NM, p. A428

KIRK, J. Douglas, M.D. Chief Medical Officer, University of California, Davis Medical Center, Sacramento, CA, p. A88

KIRK, Jean, Chief Financial Officer, Bennett County Hospital and Nursing Home, Martin, SD, p. A574

KIRK, Paul, Vice President, Woman's Hospital, Baton Rouge, LA, p. A274

KIRK, Peggy, Senior Vice President Clinical Operations, Rehabilitation Institute of Chicago, Chicago, IL, p. A186

KIRK, Roger L., President and Chief Executive Officer, Bethesda Hospital East, Boynton Beach, FL, p. A124

KIRK, Stephanie, Chief Financial Officer, Iberia Medical Center, New Iberia, LA, p. A285

KIRK, Vanessa, Director of Nursing, Kiowa County Memorial Hospital, Greensburg, KS, p. A244

KIRK, Warren J., Chief Executive Officer, Doctors Medical Center, Modesto, CA, p. A77

KIRKBRIDE, Jim, Assistant Vice President Ancillary and Support Services, St. Charles Medical Center – Redmond, Redmond, OR, p. A529

KIRKER, Lynda I., Chief Financial Officer, Flagler Hospital, Saint Augustine, FL, p. A144

KIRKER NEA–BC, Donna, R.N. Vice President Patient Services and Chief Nursing Officer, Glens Falls Hospital, Glens Falls, NY, p. A438

KIRKHAM, Paul, Chief Executive Officer, Keystone Newport News, Newport News, VA, p. A674

KIRKLAND, Charles, D.O. Chief Medical Officer, Davis Memorial Hospital, Elkins, WV, p. A694

KIRKLAND–ROSE, Tina, Coordinator Human Resources, Select Specialty Hospital–Lexington, Lexington, KY, p. A264

KIRKS, Linda, Chief Financial Officer, Baptist Medical Center, San Antonio, TX, p. A646

KIRMAN, Lynn, R.N. Chief Nursing Officer, St. John's Medical Center and Living Center, Jackson, WY, p. A721

KIRSHNER, Arthur N., Chief Information Management, Winn Army Community Hospital, Hinesville, GA, p. A161

KIRSTEIN, Susan A., R.N. Chief Nursing Officer, Broadlawns Medical Center, Des Moines, IA, p. A229

KISER, Greg, Chief Executive Officer, Three Rivers Medical Center, Louisa, KY, p. A265

KISER II, James R., Chief Executive Officer, Providence St. Joseph Medical Center, Polson, MT, p. A390

KISER, Pamela, R.N. Chief Nursing Executive and Vice President of Nursing, St. John Medical Center, Tulsa, OK, p. A521

KISER, Terry L.
Vice President and Chief Financial Officer, Georgetown Memorial Hospital, Georgetown, SC, p. A566
Chief Financial Officer, Waccamaw Community Hospital, Murrells Inlet, SC, p. A569

KISKADDON, Robert, M.D. Chief Medical Officer, Margaret R. Pardee Memorial Hospital, Hendersonville, NC, p. A466

KISNER, Angela, Director Human Resources and Coordinator Medical Staff, Landmark Hospital, Cape Girardeau, MO, p. A368

KISSNER, Michael, Chief Executive Officer, HEALTHSOUTH Treasure Coast Rehabilitation Hospital, Vero Beach, FL, p. A149

KISTLER, Beckie, Director of Finance, Our Lady of Peace, Louisville, KY, p. A266

KISTLER, Mike, Chief Executive Officer, Shadow Mountain Behavioral Health System, Tulsa, OK, p. A521

KITCHEN, Randy J., Chief Executive Officer, Dayton Rehabilitation Institute, Dayton, OH, p. A491

KITTELL, Elisabeth, Chief Financial Officer, Syracuse Veterans Affairs Medical Center, Syracuse, NY, p. A456

KITTNER, Bonnie, R.N. Chief Nursing Officer, Mendocino Coast District Hospital, Fort Bragg, CA, p. A63

KITTOE, Michael, Chief Financial Officer, Lake Health, Concord Township, OH, p. A491

KJERGAARD, Holly, Chief Nursing Officer, Audubon County Memorial Hospital, Audubon, IA, p. A225

KLANN, Andrew, D.O. Chief of Staff, Southwest Health Center, Platteville, WI, p. A713

KLASEK, Chance, CPA Chief Financial Officer, Jefferson Community Health Center, Fairbury, NE, p. A395

KLASSEN, Brad, Information Technology Coordinator, Sanford Worthington Medical Center, Worthington, MN, p. A354

KLASSEN, Karen, Controller, HEALTHSOUTH Chattanooga Rehabilitation Hospital, Chattanooga, TN, p. A580

KLASSEN, Susan K., Chief Executive Officer and Administrator, Mahnomen Health Center, Mahnomen, MN, p. A346

KLAUKA, Floyd, Chief Financial Officer, Brook Lane Health Services, Hagerstown, MD, p. A301

KLAUSTERMEIER, Lisa, R.N. Chief Nursing Officer, Anderson Hospital, Maryville, IL, p. A195

KLAWITTER, Kyle, Vice President Human Resources, Summa Akron City Hospital, Akron, OH, p. A482

KLEAS, Tara, Director Human Resources, HEALTHSOUTH Rehabilitation Hospital of Fort Worth, Fort Worth, TX, p. A618

KLECKNER, Megan, Vice President and Administrator, Riverside Walter Reed Hospital, Gloucester, VA, p. A671

KLEEN, Kathy, Chief Nursing Officer, Tri-County Hospital, Wadena, MN, p. A353

KLEEN, Yechiel, M.D. Medical Director, Rehabilitation Hospital of Wisconsin, Waukesha, WI, p. A717

KLEHN, Paul, Chief Information Technology Officer, Liberty Hospital, Liberty, MO, p. A376

KLEIN, Aron
   Vice President Finance, Advocate BroMenn Medical Center, Normal, IL, p. A198
   Vice President of Finance, Advocate Eureka Hospital, Eureka, IL, p. A189

KLEIN, Barbara, R.N. Director of Nursing, Arms Acres, Carmel, NY, p. A435

KLEIN, Bernard, M.D., Chief Executive Officer, Providence Holy Cross Medical Center,, CA, p. A74

KLEIN, Cindy, Chief Financial Officer, Lamb Healthcare Center, Littlefield, TX, p. A633

KLEIN, Cindy C., Vice President Human Resources, PeaceHealth St. Joseph Medical Center, Bellingham, WA, p. A681

KLEIN, Colleen, Vice President, Chief Nursing Officer, OSF Saint Anthony Medical Center, Rockford, IL, p. A201

KLEIN, David, Ph.D. Vice President Operations, Behavioral Health Network, Natchaug Hospital, Mansfield Center, CT, p. A115

KLEIN, David G., M.D., President, Baylor All Saints Medical Center at Fort Worth, Fort Worth, TX, p. A618

KLEIN, Diany, Vice President Human Resources, Community Memorial Health System, Ventura, CA, p. A99

KLEIN, Edward A., Chief Financial Officer, Johnston UNC Health Care, Smithfield, NC, p. A473

KLEIN, Gerard D., Chief Executive Officer, Memorial Hospital of Sweetwater County, Rock Springs, WY, p. A722

KLEIN, Greg, Senior Director Finance, Novant Health Matthews Medical Center, Matthews, NC, p. A469

KLEIN, Jacqueline, Chief Financial Officer, Lakeview Medical Center, Rice Lake, WI, p. A714

KLEIN, Jerry, Interim Chief Financial Officer, Massac Memorial Hospital, Metropolis, IL, p. A196

KLEIN, Jillyn, Chief Operating Officer, Howard County Medical Center, Saint Paul, NE, p. A401

KLEIN, Joel, Chief Executive Officer and Managing Director, Glen Oaks Hospital, Greenville, TX, p. A622

KLEIN, Julie, Chief Executive Officer, Sterling Regional MedCenter, Sterling, CO, p. A111

KLEIN, Kenneth, M.D. Vice President Medical Affairs, Beloit Health System, Beloit, WI, p. A702

KLEIN, Kenneth, CPA Senior Vice President Finance and Chief Financial Officer, Menninger Clinic, Houston, TX, p. A626

KLEIN, Perry, Chief Engineering, Mann-Grandstaff Veterans Affairs Medical Center, Spokane, WA, p. A690

KLEIN, Terrence, Vice President and Chief Operating Officer, Franciscan St. Elizabeth Health - Crawfordsville, Crawfordsville, IN, p. A209

KLEINE, Doug, IT Director, St. Mary Medical Center, Apple Valley, CA, p. A56

KLEINHANZL, Thomas A., President and Chief Executive Officer, Frederick Memorial Hospital, Frederick, MD, p. A301

KLEINMAN, Richard, R.N. Manager Medical Informatics, Catalina Island Medical Center, Avalon, CA, p. A56

KLEINSASSER, Dustin, Information Technology and BioMed, Fall River Hospital, Hot Springs, SD, p. A574

KLEINSCHMIDT, James, M.D. Vice President Medical Affairs, Shenandoah Memorial Hospital, Woodstock, VA, p. A680

KLENKE, Lisa R., R.N., Chief Executive Officer and Chief Nursing Officer, Mercer Health, Coldwater, OH, p. A489

KLEPIN, Michael R.
   Administrator, Hunt Regional Community Hospital, Commerce, TX, p. A607
   Administrator, Hunt Regional Medical Center, Greenville, TX, p. A622

KLESS, Adam, Chief Nursing Officer, Highlands Regional Medical Center, Sebring, FL, p. A146

KLEVEN, Brian, Chief Financial Officer, Alvarado Hospital Medical Center, San Diego, CA, p. A89

KLEYMANN, Mark, Manager Information Technology, Hamilton County Hospital, Syracuse, KS, p. A255

KLICKSTEIN, Judith S., Chief Information Officer, Cambridge Health Alliance, Cambridge, MA, p. A309

KLIEWER, Chad, Information Technology Specialist, Mercy Hospital Kingfisher, Kingfisher, OK, p. A512

KLIMEK, David, Vice President Human Resources, Olathe Medical Center, Olathe, KS, p. A251

KLIMESH, Linda, Chief Nursing Officer, Winneshiek Medical Center, Decorah, IA, p. A229

KLIMP, Mary J., FACHE, Administrator, Mayo Clinic Health System in New Prague, New Prague, MN, p. A348

KLINE, Brian S., Vice President and Chief Financial Officer, DuBois Regional Medical Center, Du Bois, PA, p. A537

KLINE, Donald E., Senior Vice President Finance, St. Joseph Health Center, Warren, OH, p. A504

KLINE, Jack, M.D. Chief of Staff, Mercy Medical Center-New Hampton, New Hampton, IA, p. A235

KLINE, Julie, Senior Vice President Patient Services, Sonora Regional Medical Center, Sonora, CA, p. A95

KLINE, Mark W., M.D. Physician in Chief, Texas Children's Hospital, Houston, TX, p. A627

KLINGA, Maria, Director Management Information Systems, Silver Hill Hospital, New Canaan, CT, p. A116

KLINGEMAN, Jennifer, Director of Nursing, Chester Mental Health Center, Chester, IL, p. A183

KLINGENBERG, Pat, Director Human Resources, Towner County Medical Center, Cando, ND, p. A476

KLINGER, Jeffrey, Director for Administration, Naval Hospital Bremerton, Bremerton, WA, p. A682

KLINGLER, Stacie, R.N. Vice President of Patient Services, Jasper County Hospital, Rensselaer, IN, p. A221

KLINGSEIS, Robert
   Manager Information Systems, Community Hospital of Long Beach, Long Beach, CA, p. A70
   Director Information Systems, Desert Regional Medical Center, Palm Springs, CA, p. A82

KLINKER, Suzanne M., Director, Bay Pines Veterans Affairs Medical Center, Bay Pines, FL, p. A123

KLINKNER, Donna M., Chief Financial Officer, Madelia Community Hospital, Madelia, MN, p. A346

KLOCK, Kathy, R.N. Senior Vice President Clinical Operations and Human Resources, Gundersen Health System, La Crosse, WI, p. A707

KLOCKMAN, Dena, Chief Financial Officer, Ogallala Community Hospital, Ogallala, NE, p. A399

KLOCKO, Daniel, Vice President Human Resources, Kootenai Health, Coeur D'Alene, ID, p. A175

KLOECKNER, Vicki, Director Human Resources, Greenville Regional Hospital, Greenville, IL, p. A191

KLOEWER, Ron, Chief Information Officer, Montgomery County Memorial Hospital, Red Oak, IA, p. A236

KLOPFER, Anthony Rudy, FACHE, Director, Veterans Affairs Eastern Kansas Health Care System, Topeka, KS, p. A255

KLOSTERMAN, Mark D., FACHE, President and Chief Executive Officer, Faith Regional Health Services, Norfolk, NE, p. A398

KLOSTERMAN, Mark D., FACHE, President and Chief Executive Officer, Faith Regional Health Services, Norfolk, NE, p. B58

KLOTZ, Carol, Director Human Resources, LifeCare Medical Center, Roseau, MN, p. A350

KLOTZ, Ken, M.D. Chief of Staff, Richard L. Roudebush Veterans Affairs Medical Center, Indianapolis, IN, p. A215

KLUGE, Thomas S., Chief Operating Officer, Halifax Regional Health System, South Boston, VA, p. A678

KLUGHERZ, Greg, Vice President Corporate Services and Chief Financial Officer, St. Cloud Hospital, Saint Cloud, MN, p. A350

KLUNK, Tim, Executive Director, Children's Hospital of Wisconsin-Fox Valley, Neenah, WI, p. A711

KMETZ, Thomas D., President, Kosair Children's Hospital, Louisville, KY, p. A266

KNACHSTEDT, Cameron, D.O. Chief of Medical Staff, Harlan County Health System, Alma, NE, p. A393

KNACKSTEDT, Nathan, D.O. Chief of Staff, Clara Barton Hospital, Hoisington, KS, p. A245

KNAK, Roger, Administrator, Fairview Regional Medical Center, Fairview, OK, p. A511

KNAPHEIDE, Debbie, MSN, Site Administrator, Chief Nursing Officer and Chief Operating Officer, Carondelet Holy Cross Hospital, Nogales, AZ, p. A34

KNAPP, Brian A., Vice President Operations, Fairview Ridges Hospital, Burnsville, MN, p. A341

KNAPP, Merlyn E., President and Chief Executive Officer, Saint Catherine Regional Hospital, Charlestown, IN, p. A208

KNECHT, Brian J., Chief Operating Officer, Regional Medical Center of San Jose, San Jose, CA, p. A92

KNECHT, John, Chief Medical Staff, Linton Hospital, Linton, ND, p. A479

KNECHT, Maria, R.N. Vice President and Chief Nursing Officer, Adventist GlenOaks Hospital, Glendale Heights, IL, p. A191

KNEDLER, Marie E., FACHE,
   President, CHI Health Bergan Mercy, Omaha, NE, p. A399
   President, CHI Health Mercy Council Bluffs, Council Bluffs, IA, p. A228

KNEISEL, Kristin, Interim Director, Information Services, Alice Peck Day Memorial Hospital, Lebanon, NH, p. A410

KNEPP, Gary, D.O. Vice President Physician Integration and Chief Medical Officer, UnityPoint Health - Methodist, Peoria, IL, p. A200

KNIFFIN, Fred, M.D. Chief Medical Officer, Porter Medical Center, Middlebury, VT, p. A665

KNIGHT, Beth, Chief Nursing Officer, Nacogdoches Memorial Hospital, Nacogdoches, TX, p. A639

KNIGHT, Bethany, M.D. Chief of Staff, Community Medical Center of Izard County, Calico Rock, AR, p. A44

KNIGHT, C. Diane, M.D., Director and Chief Executive Officer, Memphis Veterans Affairs Medical Center, Memphis, TN, p. A589

KNIGHT, Calvin K., President and Chief Executive Officer, John Muir Health, Walnut Creek, CA, p. B78

KNIGHT, Deana, Chief Executive Officer, Select Specialty Hospital-Greensboro, Greensboro, NC, p. A465

KNIGHT, Don, Assistant Administrator and Risk Manager, Teche Regional Medical Center, Morgan City, LA, p. A284

KNIGHT, Jennifer, Manager Human Resources, Waynesboro Hospital, Waynesboro, PA, p. A557

KNIGHT, Kimber, Chief Financial Officer, Braxton County Memorial Hospital, Gassaway, WV, p. A695

KNIGHT, Mark T., Executive Vice President and Chief Financial Officer, Jackson Health System, Miami, FL, p. A137

KNIGHT, Michael, M.D. Medical Director, Hampstead Hospital, Hampstead, NH, p. A410

KNIGHT, Russell M.
   President and Chief Executive Officer, Mercy Medical Center-Dubuque, Dubuque, IA, p. A230
   President and Chief Executive Officer, Mercy Medical Center-Dyersville, Dyersville, IA, p. A230

KNIGHT, Sue, CPA Chief Operating Officer, St. Elizabeth Hospital, Gonzales, LA, p. A278

KNIGHT, Terry, Public Information Officer and Administrative Assistant, California Mens Colony Hospital, San Luis Obispo, CA, p. A92

KNIGHT, Wayne, Director Finance, St. Vincent Clay Hospital, Brazil, IN, p. A207

KNIGHT, Wesley, Chief Financial Officer, Carolina Pines Regional Medical Center, Hartsville, SC, p. A567

KNIGHTEN, Mary Lynne, R.N. Chief Nursing Officer and Vice President Patient Care Services, St. Francis Medical Center, Lynwood, CA, p. A76

KNIPP, Cindi, Director Human Resources, Rooks County Health Center, Plainville, KS, p. A253

KNITT, Lori, Chief Nursing Officer, Aurora Sheboygan Memorial Medical Center, Sheboygan, WI, p. A715

KNITTEL, Monty E., President and Chief Executive Officer, Walla Walla General Hospital, Walla Walla, WA, p. A692

KNIZLEY, Andrew, Chief Executive Officer, Houston Orthopedic and Spine Hospital, Bellaire, TX, p. A602

KNOBLOCH, Stanley
   Chief Financial Officer, Sanford Hospital Rock Rapids, Rock Rapids, IA, p. A237
   Chief Financial Officer, Sanford Luverne Medical Center, Luverne, MN, p. A346

KNOCKE, Michael, Chief Information Officer, Kansas Spine and Specialty Hospital, Wichita, KS, p. A256

KNODE, Scott, Chief Financial Officer, Veterans Memorial Hospital, Waukon, IA, p. A239

KNODEL, Shirley, R.N. Chief Nursing Officer, Regional West Medical Center, Scottsbluff, NE, p. A402

KNOEPFFLER, Susan, R.N. Vice President Nursing, Huntington Hospital, Huntington, NY, p. A439

KNOERL, Thomas, Vice President Finance, Spectrum Health Reed City Hospital, Reed City, MI, p. A333

KNOKE, Debra R., Chief Executive Officer, Sequoyah Memorial Hospital, Sallisaw, OK, p. A518

KNOLL, Charlotte, R.N. Chief Nursing Executive, CHRISTUS Highland Medical Center, Shreveport, LA, p. A288

KNOLL, Rolf W., M.D. Senior Vice President and Chief Medical Officer, Saint Francis Hospital and Medical Center, Hartford, CT, p. A114

KNOLL, Thomas, Site Director Finance, Community Memorial Hospital, Menomonee Falls, WI, p. A709

KNORR, Kelly, Chief Financial Officer, First Hospital Wyoming Valley, Kingston, PA, p. A541

KNOTT, Kerry, Chief Executive Officer, Manatee Palms Youth Services, Bradenton, FL, p. A124

KNOUP, Amy, Director Human Resources, Palo Alto County Health System, Emmetsburg, IA, p. A230

KNOUS, Gail, Interim Administrator, Basin Healthcare Center, Odessa, TX, p. A640

KNOWLAND, Richard, Chief Executive Officer, Select Specialty Hospital–South Dallas, Dallas, TX, p. A612

KNOWLES, B. K., D.O. Chief of Staff, General John J. Pershing Memorial Hospital, Brookfield, MO, p. A368

KNOWLES, Christy, Chief Human Resources Officer, Coosa Valley Medical Center, Sylacauga, AL, p. A25

KNOWLES, John, Director Human Resources, Clinch Valley Medical Center, Richlands, VA, p. A677

KNOWLES, Robert, M.D. Chief of Staff, Highlands Medical Center, Sparta, TN, p. A593

KNOWLES–SMITH, Peter, M.D. Medical Director, Bennett County Hospital and Nursing Home, Martin, SD, p. A574

KNOWLTON, Robert, Vice President and Chief Financial Officer, Baylor Medical Center at Garland, Garland, TX, p. A620

KNOX, Dennis M., Chief Executive Officer, Antelope Valley Hospital, Lancaster, CA, p. A69

KNOX, Jessica, Chief Financial Officer, Mesa Springs, Fort Worth, TX, p. A618

KNOX, Jody, Administrator, Kindred Hospital Rancho, Rancho Cucamonga, CA, p. A84

KNOX, John, Senior Vice President and Chief Information Officer, Carolinas Medical Center–University, Charlotte, NC, p. A461

KNOX, Jud, President, York Hospital, York, ME, p. A295

KNOX, Roland, Chief Executive Officer, Northern Cochise Community Hospital, Willcox, AZ, p. A41

KNOX, Stacey A., Administrator, Rock County Hospital, Bassett, NE, p. A393

KNOX, Ty, Chief Information Officer, Long Island Jewish Medical Center,, NY, p. A445

KNUDSEN, Mark, Director Fiscal Services, Shriners Hospitals for Children–Portland, Portland, OR, p. A529

KNUDSON, Jenny, Controller, Hiawatha Community Hospital, Hiawatha, KS, p. A245

KNUDSON, Veronica, Chief Executive Officer, Yakima Regional Medical and Cardiac Center, Yakima, WA, p. A692

KNUEVEN, Karen, Chief Nursing Officer, Olympia Medical Center, Los Angeles, CA, p. A73

KNUTH, Kerry, Chief Operating Officer, Mercy Hospital of Defiance, Defiance, OH, p. A492

KNUTSON, Holly, Manager Information Technology, Kittson Memorial Healthcare Center, Hallock, MN, p. A344

KNUTSON, John P., M.D. Chief Medical Staff, Delta County Memorial Hospital, Delta, CO, p. A104

KNUTSON, Larry, Director Finance, CentraCare Health–Long Prairie, Long Prairie, MN, p. A346

KNUTSON, Ruth, Chief Financial Officer, Progressive Hospital, Las Vegas, NV, p. A406

KOBELJA, Mark A., USN, Commanding Officer, Naval Hospital Camp Pendleton, Camp Pendleton, CA, p. A59

KOBIS, David A., Senior Vice President and Chief Operating Officer, Bradford Regional Medical Center, Bradford, PA, p. A534

KOCH, Amanda
Director Human Resources, Greene Memorial Hospital, Xenia, OH, p. A506
Director Human Resources, Soin Medical Center, Beavercreek, OH, p. A483

KOCH, Carol, Manager Human Resources, Callaway District Hospital, Callaway, NE, p. A394

KOCH, Cody, Director Human Resources, CHI Health St Elizabeth, Lincoln, NE, p. A397

KOCH, Doug, Market President, Aurora Medical Center, Kenosha, WI, p. A707

KOCH, Erich, Chief Financial Officer, West Hills Hospital, Reno, NV, p. A408

KOCH, Holly, Chief Financial Officer, Girard Medical Center, Girard, KS, p. A244

KOCH, Joseph G., Chief Executive Officer, Bourbon Community Hospital, Paris, KY, p. A269

KOCH, Melanie, R.N. Chief Nursing Officer, Union County Hospital, Anna, IL, p. A180

KOCHEVAR, Vanessa, Chief Financial Officer, St. Mary–Corwin Medical Center, Pueblo, CO, p. A110

KOCHIE, Daniel A., CP
Chief Financial Officer, Samaritan Hospital, Troy, NY, p. A456
Chief Financial Officer, St. Mary's Hospital, Troy, NY, p. A456

KOCIOLA, Matthew, Senior Vice President and Chief Financial Officer, Somerset Hospital, Somerset, PA, p. A555

KOCOUREK, Cathie A., President, Aurora Medical Center – Manitowoc County, Two Rivers, WI, p. A716

KOCSIS, Dana, R.N. Vice President Nursing and Operations, Lodi Community Hospital, Lodi, OH, p. A496

KOCSIS, Violet, Chief Human Resources Officer, Hunterdon Medical Center, Flemington, NJ, p. A416

KOCZENT, Kurt, Executive Vice President and Chief Operating Officer, F. F. Thompson Hospital, Canandaigua, NY, p. A435

KOEBKE, Troy L.
Director Human Resources Management, Bellin Memorial Hospital, Green Bay, WI, p. A705
Director Human Resources, Bellin Psychiatric Center, Green Bay, WI, p. A706

KOEBNICK, Dale, Director Management Information Systems and Patient Access, Metroplex Adventist Hospital, Killeen, TX, p. A631

KOEHLER, Amy, Director Human Resources, Shelby Memorial Hospital, Shelbyville, IL, p. A202

KOEHLER, Maggie, Senior Vice President and Chief Financial Officer, Wilkes–Barre General Hospital, Wilkes–Barre, PA, p. A558

KOELE, Craig, Chief Executive Officer, Solara Hospital of Muskogee, Muskogee, OK, p. A514

KOENIG, Jr., Donald E., Executive Vice President and Chief Operating Officer, St. Elizabeth Health Center, Youngstown, OH, p. A506

KOENIG, Harris F., President and Chief Executive Officer, San Antonio Community Hospital, Upland, CA, p. A98

KOENIG, Mary, Chief Financial Officer, Vernon Memorial Healthcare, Viroqua, WI, p. A717

KOEPKE, Eldon, Chief Financial Officer, Mitchell County Hospital Health Systems, Beloit, KS, p. A242

KOEPPEL–OLSEN, Carol, R.N. Vice President Patient Care Services, Fairview Ridges Hospital, Burnsville, MN, p. A341

KOERNER, Jill, Manager Employee Relations, Weisman Children's Rehabilitation Hospital, Marlton, NJ, p. A418

KOESSL, Brenda, R.N. Director of Nursing Services, Frances Mahon Deaconess Hospital, Glasgow, MT, p. A387

KOESTER, Jean, Manager Human Resources, Limestone Medical Center, Groesbeck, TX, p. A622

KOESTERER, Susan, Regional Director Finance, Alton Memorial Hospital, Alton, IL, p. A180

KOETTING, Edward, Chief Financial Officer, Bedford Veterans Affairs Medical Center, Edith Nourse Rogers Memorial Veterans Hospital, Bedford, MA, p. A305

KOHANKE, Crystal H., Vice President Human Resources, CHRISTUS Santa Rosa Health System, San Antonio, TX, p. A646

KOHLBRENNER, Janis, R.N. Vice President Clinical Services and Chief Nursing Officer, Oneida Healthcare, Oneida, NY, p. A450

KOHLENBERG, Chris, Chief Financial Officer, Jennings American Legion Hospital, Jennings, LA, p. A279

KOHLENBERG, Darnell, R.N. Director of Nursing, Abrom Kaplan Memorial Hospital, Kaplan, LA, p. A280

KOHLER, Douglas, M.D. Vice President Medical Operations, Marymount Hospital, Garfield Heights, OH, p. A494

KOHLER, Mike, Chief Executive Officer, Emerus, Sugar Land, TX, p. A650

KOINZAN, Leigh Jean, Director Finance, Boys Town National Research Hospital, Omaha, NE, p. A399

KOKJOHN, Bradley J., Chief Financial Officer, Fort Madison Community Hospital, Fort Madison, IA, p. A231

KOLACZ, Nicole, Vice President Patient Services, Pomerene Hospital, Millersburg, OH, p. A499

KOLAR, Stephen J., M.D
Vice President Medical Affairs, Bethesda Hospital, Saint Paul, MN, p. A351
Vice President Medical Affairs, St. John's Hospital, Saint Paul, MN, p. A351
Vice President Medical Affairs, St. Joseph's Hospital, Saint Paul, MN, p. A351

KOLB, Andy, Chief Executive Officer, Stonewall Memorial Hospital, Aspermont, TX, p. A598

KOLB, Bonnie, Director of Nursing Services, Cedar Crest Hospital and Residential Treatment Center, Belton, TX, p. A602

KOLB, Edward, M.D. Medical Director, Boys Town National Research Hospital, Omaha, NE, p. A399

KOLB, Pat, Manager Information Technology, Clarendon Memorial Hospital, Manning, SC, p. A568

KOLHEDE, Deborah, Vice President and Chief Operating Officer, St. Mary's Medical Center, San Francisco, CA, p. A91

KOLLARS, Tim, Chief Executive Officer, Good Samaritan Hospital, Bakersfield, CA, p. A57

KOLLMEYER, Sherry, Vice President Human Resources, Youth Villages Inner Harbour Campus, Douglasville, GA, p. A158

KOLMAN, Bret G., FACHE, Chief Executive Officer, Lakeview Regional Medical Center, Covington, LA, p. A276

KOLODZIEJCYK, Wanda, Director Human Resources, Cuero Community Hospital, Cuero, TX, p. A609

KOLODZIEJCZYK, Clayton, Chief Financial Officer, Meadowview Regional Medical Center, Maysville, KY, p. A267

KOLOSKY, John A., Executive Vice President and Chief Operating Officer, H. Lee Moffitt Cancer Center and Research Institute, Tampa, FL, p. A147

KOLSETH, Shelley V., Chief Financial Officer, Memorial Hospital of Tampa, Tampa, FL, p. A148

KOMAN, Stuart, Ph.D., President and Chief Executive Officer, Walden Psychiatric Care, Waltham, MA, p. A316

KOMANDURI, Ramanujam, M.D. Chief of Staff, Veterans Affairs Southern Nevada Healthcare System, North Las Vegas, NV, p. A407

KOMAR, Ellen M., R.N. Vice President Patient Care Services, Stamford Hospital, Stamford, CT, p. A117

KOME, Hunter, Chief Operating Officer, Oconee Medical Center, Seneca, SC, p. A569

KOMENDA, John, Chief Financial Officer, Hendricks Regional Health, Danville, IN, p. A209

KOMINS, Jeff, M.D. Chief Medical Officer, Mercy Fitzgerald Hospital, Darby, PA, p. A537

KOMORNIK, Jeffrey, Director Human Resources, Milford Hospital, Milford, CT, p. A115

KOMOROSKI, Patrice L., R.N., Chief Executive Officer, Select Specialty Hospital–St. Louis, Saint Charles, MO, p. A379

KONARSKI, Debbie, Interim Chief Financial Officer, Pottstown Memorial Medical Center, Pottstown, PA, p. A552

KONDASH, Dennis, D.O
Vice President Medical Affairs, Gnaden Huetten Memorial Hospital, Lehighton, PA, p. A543
Vice President Medical Affairs, Palmerton Hospital, Palmerton, PA, p. A547

KONDO, Reid, Interim Chief Executive Officer, Leahi Hospital, Honolulu, HI, p. A170

KONECNE, Robin, Manager Human Resources, Kit Carson County Health Service District, Burlington, CO, p. A103

KONGARA, Rama, Chief Financial Officer, St. James Behavioral Health Hospital, Gonzales, LA, p. A278

KONKEL, Robert, Manager Finance, James A. Haley Veterans' Hospital, Tampa, FL, p. A147

KONOPKO, Stan, Chief Financial Officer, St. James Mercy Health System, Hornell, NY, p. A439

KONSAVAGE, Christian, M.D. Chief of Staff, Cumberland County Hospital, Burkesville, KY, p. A259

KOOBATIAN, Thomas, M.D., Executive Director and Chief of Staff, New Milford Hospital, New Milford, CT, p. A116

KOOIMAN, Thomas, Chief Executive Officer, Prairie Ridge Hospital and Health Services, Elbow Lake, MN, p. A343

KOON, Rion, Chief Information Management Division, William Beaumont Army Medical Center, El Paso, TX, p. A616

KOOP, Steven, M.D. Medical Director, Gillette Children's Specialty Healthcare, Saint Paul, MN, p. A351

KOOY, Donald C., President and Chief Executive Officer, McLaren Flint, Flint, MI, p. A323

KOPEL, Samuel, M.D. Medical Director, Maimonides Medical Center,, NY, p. A445

KOPFLE, Sue, Chief Human Resources Officer, University of Missouri Hospitals and Clinics, Columbia, MO, p. A370

KOPINSKI, Donna, Chief Financial Officer, Crittenton Hospital Medical Center, Rochester, MI, p. A333

KOPPELMAN, Benjamin, President, CHI St. Joseph's Health, Park Rapids, MN, p. A349

KOPPELMAN, Catherine S., MSN Chief Nursing Officer, University Hospitals Case Medical Center, Cleveland, OH, p. A489

KOPPERUD, Gordon, Director Operations, Sanford Westbrook Medical Center, Westbrook, MN, p. A354

KORBEL, Tamara, Director Management Information Systems, Ridgeview Medical Center, Waconia, MN, p. A353

KORDUCKI, Stanley R., President, Wood County Hospital, Bowling Green, OH, p. A484

KORDUPEL, Maureen
Director Relationship Manager, St. Elizabeth Boardman Health Center, Boardman, OH, p. A484
Director Relationship Manager, St. Elizabeth Health Center, Youngstown, OH, p. A506

KORICH, Frank, Vice President and Site Administrator, Soldiers and Sailors Memorial Hospital of Yates County, Penn Yan, NY, p. A451

KORKMAS, Ross, Assistant Chief Executive Officer, Medical Center of South Arkansas, El Dorado, AR, p. A45

KORN, Larry, Manager Finance, Southern Arizona Veterans Affairs Health Care System, Tucson, AZ, p. A41

KORN, Roy, M.D. Medical Director, Cobleskill Regional Hospital, Cobleskill, NY, p. A436

KORNBLATT, Lynne R.
Chief Human Resources Officer, Einstein Medical Center Montgomery, East Norriton, PA, p. A538
Chief Human Resources Officer, Einstein Medical Center Philadelphia, Philadelphia, PA, p. A548

KORNFIELD, Lee, M.D. Medical Director, Elks Rehab Hospital, Boise, ID, p. A174

KOROLY, Marla, M.D. Chief Medical Officer and Senior Vice President Medical Affairs, Northern Westchester Hospital, Mount Kisco, NY, p. A442

KORPELA, Donita, R.N. Director of Patient Care Services, Mercy Hospital, Moose Lake, MN, p. A348

KORPIEL, Michael, President and Chief Operating Officer, St. Vincent's East, Birmingham, AL, p. A17

KORTE, Fred, Chief Financial Officer, McLaren Oakland, Pontiac, MI, p. A332

KORTEMEYER, Jay, Chief Executive Officer, Brynn Marr Hospital, Jacksonville, NC, p. A467

KORTH, Mark, President, Mercy Medical Center Redding, Redding, CA, p. A85

KORTH, Paul, Chief Executive Officer, Cookeville Regional Medical Center, Cookeville, TN, p. A581

KORTH–WHITE, Kirsten, Vice President Physician Network and Ambulatory Service, Mercy Hospital Grayling, Grayling, MI, p. A325

KORTUM, Joseph M., Interim President, Harrison Medical Center, Bremerton, WA, p. A681

KOSACH, Becky, Director Human Resources, Ivinson Memorial Hospital, Laramie, WY, p. A722

KOSANOVICH, John, M.D. Vice President Covenant Healthcare and Chief Executive Officer Covenant Medical Group, Covenant Medical Center, Saginaw, MI, p. A333

KOSANOVICH, John P., President, Watertown Regional Medical Center, Watertown, WI, p. A717

KOSE, William H., M.D
Senior Vice President Medical Affairs, Blanchard Valley Hospital, Findlay, OH, p. A494
Vice President Quality and Medical Affairs, Bluffton Hospital, Bluffton, OH, p. A484

KOSEK, Kevin, Associate Director Operations, Iowa City Veterans Affairs Health Care System, Iowa City, IA, p. A232

KOSLOW, Howard B., President and Chief Executive Officer, Promise Hospital of Miss Lou, Vidalia, LA, p. A289

KOSNOSKY, David, M.D. Chief Medical Officer, University Hospitals Geauga Medical Center, Chardon, OH, p. A485

KOSOWICZ, Scott T., Chief Financial Officer, Radius Specialty Hospital Boston, Boston, MA, p. A307

KOSSEFF, Christopher O., President and Chief Executive Officer, University Hospital, Piscataway, NJ, p. A421

KOSTER, Tracy, Director Human Resources, Carlinville Area Hospital, Carlinville, IL, p. A182

KOSTERS, Gregory J., D.O. Chief Medical Officer, Osceola Community Hospital, Sibley, IA, p. A237

KOSTOK, Barbara, Manager Human Resources, Punxsutawney Area Hospital, Punxsutawney, PA, p. A553

KOSTROUN, Deborah, Chief Operating Officer, Manatee Glens Hospital and Addiction Center, Bradenton, FL, p. A124

KOSTURKO, MaryEllen, R.N. Senior Vice President Patient Care Operations and Chief Nursing Officer, Bridgeport Hospital, Bridgeport, CT, p. A113

KOSYLA, Gail, Chief Financial Officer, Hunterdon Medical Center, Flemington, NJ, p. A416

KOSZTYO, Carol, R.N. Vice President, Patient Care Services, Carrier Clinic, Belle Mead, NJ, p. A413

KOTIN, Kathy, Chief Financial Officer, Banner Good Samaritan Medical Center, Phoenix, AZ, p. A35

KOTRBA, Mitchell, Chief Financial Officer, North Valley Health Center, Warren, MN, p. A353

KOTSONIS, Robert, Chief Operating Officer, Northeast Rehabilitation Hospital, Salem, NH, p. A412

KOTTENBROOK, Susan, Chief Executive Officer, Red River Behavioral Center, Bossier City, LA, p. A274

KOTZEN, Michael S., Vice President and Chief Operating Officer, Virtua Voorhees, Voorhees, NJ, p. A424

KOUKOS, Dean, M.D. Chief Medical Staff, Southern Palmetto Hospital, Barnwell, SC, p. A562

KOULOVATOS, James E., Chief Executive Officer, Liberty Dayton Regional Medical Center, Liberty, TX, p. A633

KOUNS, Nicholas, D.O. Chief of Staff, Clark Regional Medical Center, Winchester, KY, p. A271

KOUNTZ, David, M.D. Senior Vice President Medical Affairs, Jersey Shore University Medical Center, Neptune, NJ, p. A424

KOUSKOLEKAS, Anthony, FACHE, President, Village Hospital, Greer, SC, p. A567

KOUTOUZOS, Connie L., MSN, Chief Executive Officer and President, NORTHSTAR Health System, Iron River, MI, p. A327

KOVAC, John, Facility Chief Information Officer, Veterans Affairs Pittsburgh Healthcare System, Pittsburgh, PA, p. A552

KOVACH, Andrew L.
Vice President Human Resources and Chief Administrative Officer, Morristown Medical Center, Morristown, NJ, p. A418
Vice President Human Resources and Chief Administrative Officer, Newton Medical Center, Newton, NJ, p. A420
Vice President Human Resources and Chief Administrative Officer, Overlook Medical Center, Summit, NJ, p. A423

KOVACS, Amber R., Chief Human Resources Officer, Banner Gateway Medical Center, Gilbert, AZ, p. A32

KOVACS, Tina, Chief Financial Officer, Saint Francis Hospital–Bartlett, Bartlett, TN, p. A579

KOVASZNAY, Beatrice, M.D. Clinical Director, Capital District Psychiatric Center, Albany, NY, p. A432

KOVICH, Lynn, Assistant Commissioner, Division of Mental Health and Addiction Services, Department of Human Services, State of New Jersey, Trenton, NJ, p. B53

KOWALOFF, Harvey, M.D. Vice President Medical Affairs, Saint Anne's Hospital, Fall River, MA, p. A310

KOWALSKI, David, Chief Executive Officer, Kindred Hospital–Aurora, Aurora, CO, p. A102

KOWALSKI, Patrick A., Chief Financial Officer, Mercy Health – Anderson Hospital, Cincinnati, OH, p. A487

KOWNACKI, Dawn, Director Human Resources, Brooke Glen Behavioral Hospital, Fort Washington, PA, p. A539

KOZAI, Gerald T., President and Chief Executive Officer, St. Francis Medical Center, Lynwood, CA, p. A76

KOZAR, Michael A., Chief Executive Officer, Carroll County Memorial Hospital, Carrollton, KY, p. A259

KOZEL, Kenneth D., FACHE,
President and Chief Executive Officer, University of Maryland Shore Medical Center at Chestertown, Chestertown, MD, p. A299
President and Chief Executive Officer, University of Maryland Shore Medical Center at Dorchester, Cambridge, MD, p. A299
President and Chief Executive Officer, University of Maryland Shore Medical Center at Easton, Easton, MD, p. A300

KOZEL, Mary Ann, Chief Fiscal, Veterans Affairs Medical Center, Wilmington, DE, p. A120

KOZIK, Rhonda, Administrator, Norwood Health Center, Marshfield, WI, p. A709

KOZIKUSKI, Courtney, Chief Financial Officer, Perry Memorial Hospital, Perry, OK, p. A517

KOZIN, Scott, M.D. Chief of Staff, Shriners Hospitals for Children–Philadelphia, Philadelphia, PA, p. A550

KOZIOL, Michael J., Chief Financial Officer, MaineGeneral Medical Center, Augusta, ME, p. A291

KOZOROSKY, Laurie, Chief Executive Officer, Select Specialty Hospital–Laurel Highlands, Latrobe, PA, p. A542

KRABBENHOFT, Kelby K., President and Chief Executive Officer, Sanford Health, Sioux Falls, SD, p. B118

KRABLIN, Brett, M.D. Chief of Staff, Mercy Hospital Kingfisher, Kingfisher, OK, p. A512

KRAFT, Chris, Director Information Systems, York General Hospital, York, NE, p. A403

KRAGENBRING, Mark, Administrator, Child and Adolescent Behavioral Health Services, Willmar, MN, p. A354

KRAHNERT, John F., M.D. Chief Medical Officer, FirstHealth Moore Regional Hospital, Pinehurst, NC, p. A470

KRAJEWSKI, David, Senior Vice President and Chief Financial Officer, Sinai Hospital of Baltimore, Baltimore, MD, p. A298

KRAMER, Blake, Chief Executive Officer, Franklin Medical Center, Winnsboro, LA, p. A290

KRAMER, Chad, Chief Operating Officer, Berwick Hospital Center, Berwick, PA, p. A533

KRAMER, Danette, Chief Financial Officer, Regional Medical Center, Manchester, IA, p. A234

KRAMER, Janie, Chief Operating Officer, Sharp Memorial Hospital, San Diego, CA, p. A90

KRAMER, Karen, R.N. Vice President and System Chief Nursing Officer, Cox Medical Centers, Springfield, MO, p. A383

KRAMER, Kathryn, M.D. President Medical Staff, Pekin Hospital, Pekin, IL, p. A199

KRAMER, Kevin, Chief Executive Officer, Modoc Medical Center, Alturas, CA, p. A55

KRAMER, Michael, Chief Operating Officer, Mercy Health – West Hospital, Cincinnati, OH, p. A487

KRAMER, Richard, Interim Chief Executive Officer, Northlake Behavioral Hospital, Mandeville, LA, p. A283

KRAMER, Susan, Director of Human Resources, Levi Hospital, Hot Springs National Park, AR, p. A47

KRAML, Louis D., FACHE,
Chief Executive Officer, Bingham Memorial Hospital, Blackfoot, ID, p. A174
Chief Executive Officer, Mountain River Birthing and Surgery Center, Blackfoot, ID, p. A174

KRAMPITS, Carrie, Director Human Resources, McKenzie Health System, Sandusky, MI, p. A334

KRANZ, Marlene, Controller, Holton Community Hospital, Holton, KS, p. A245

KRASON, Jane E., R.N., Chief Executive Officer, Appalachian Behavioral Healthcare, Athens, OH, p. A483

KRASS, Todd, Chief Executive Officer, Belton Regional Medical Center, Belton, MO, p. A367

KRAUKLIS, Gene
Regional Vice President Human Resources, Aurora Lakeland Medical Center, Elkhorn, WI, p. A704
Regional Vice President Human Resources, Aurora Medical Center, Kenosha, WI, p. A707
Regional Vice President Human Resources, Aurora Memorial Hospital of Burlington, Burlington, WI, p. A703

KRAUS, Jason, Director Human Resources, Magruder Memorial Hospital, Port Clinton, OH, p. A500

KRAUS, John, M.D. Chief Medical Officer, Bryn Mawr Rehabilitation Hospital, Malvern, PA, p. A543

KRAUSE, Donna, Chief Information Officer, Harry S. Truman Memorial Veterans Hospital, Columbia, MO, p. A370

KRAUSE, Kim, Director Human Resources, Baylor Jack and Jane Hamilton Heart and Vascular Hospital, Dallas, TX, p. A609

KRAUSE, Steven, Manager Information Technology, Franciscan Healthcare – Munster, Munster, IN, p. A219

KRAUSS, James D., President, Sentara RMH Medical Center, Harrisonburg, VA, p. A672

KRAUTSCHEID, Steven P., Ancillary Services Administrator, Tuality Healthcare, Hillsboro, OR, p. A525

KRAVETZ, Michael, M.D. Medical Director, HEALTHSOUTH Valley of the Sun Rehabilitation Hospital, Glendale, AZ, p. A33

KRAYNAK, Joseph, M.D. Chief Medical Officer, Abington Health Lansdale Hospital, Lansdale, PA, p. A542

KREATSOULAS, Nicholas, M.D
Vice President Medical Affairs and Chief Quality Officer, St. Elizabeth Boardman Health Center, Boardman, OH, p. A484
Senior Vice President and Chief Medical Officer and Chief Quality Officer, St. Elizabeth Health Center, Youngstown, OH, p. A506
Vice President Medical Affairs, St. Joseph Health Center, Warren, OH, p. A504

KREBS, Anne, Chief Financial Officer, Butler Health System, Butler, PA, p. A534

KREBS, Cindy, District Director Human Resources, Matagorda Regional Medical Center, Bay City, TX, p. A601

KREBS, George, M.D. Chief Medical Officer, Broughton Hospital, Morganton, NC, p. A469

KREBS, Mary Jane, Senior Vice President Intensive Services and Chief Administrative Officer, Spring Harbor Hospital, Westbrook, ME, p. A295

KREBS, Teresa, Director Human Resources, North Texas Medical Center, Gainesville, TX, p. A620

KREBSBACH, Mayla, Chief Executive Officer, Aurora Vista Del Mar Hospital, Ventura, CA, p. A99

KREELEY, Chris, Director Nursing, Marlton Rehabilitation Hospital, Marlton, NJ, p. A418

KREHBIEL, Beth, FACHE, President and Chief Executive Officer, Fairview Ridges Hospital, Burnsville, MN, p. A341

KREHBIEL, Rod, M.D. Chief of Staff, Klickitat Valley Health, Goldendale, WA, p. A684

KREIDER, Robert Q., President and Chief Executive Officer, Devereux, Villanova, PA, p. B52

KREIDLER, Marlene, Executive Director Human Resources, San Joaquin Community Hospital, Bakersfield, CA, p. A57

KREIS, Katherine, Chief Clinical Officer, Kindred Rehabilitation Hospital Arlington, Arlington, TX, p. A597

KREITINGER, Tate J., Chief Executive Officer, The HealthCenter, Kalispell, MT, p. A389

KREITZ, Don, Chief Executive Officer, Chapman Medical Center, Orange, CA, p. A81

KREITZER, Teri, Director Human Resources, Saint Francis Medical Center, Cape Girardeau, MO, p. A368

KRELL, G. Christopher, M.D. Chief of Staff, South Lincoln Medical Center, Kemmerer, WY, p. A721

KRELSTEIN, Michael, M.D. Medical Director, San Diego County Psychiatric Hospital, San Diego, CA, p. A89

KREMER, Ruth, Director Information Services, CentraCare Health–Monticello, Monticello, MN, p. A348

KREN, John, Chief Financial Officer, St. John's Medical Center and Living Center, Jackson, WY, p. A721

KRENOS, Lori L., R.N. Chief Nursing Officer, Bay Area Hospital, Coos Bay, OR, p. A524

KREPPS, John, Senior Vice President Finance, Silver Cross Hospital, New Lenox, IL, p. A198

KRESGE, Dean, M.D. Chief of Staff, Stoughton Hospital Association, Stoughton, WI, p. A716

KRESSE, Gregory, M.D. Chairman Medical Staff, Eureka Springs Hospital, Eureka Springs, AR, p. A45

KRETSCHMAN, Robin, MSN Vice President Patient Care Services, Ministry Saint Joseph's Hospital, Marshfield, WI, p. A709

KRETSCHMER, Suzanne, Interim Hospital Administrator, Solara Hospital Conroe, Conroe, TX, p. A607

KRETZ, Blake, President, Texas Health Harris Methodist Hospital Cleburne, Cleburne, TX, p. A606

KRETZINGER, Curt, Chief Operating Officer, Heartland Regional Medical Center, Saint Joseph, MO, p. A379

KREUTNER, Ron, Chief Financial Officer, San Joaquin General Hospital, French Camp, CA, p. A64

KREUTZER, Kevin, Chief Financial Officer, Russell Regional Hospital, Russell, KS, p. A253

KREUZ, Betsy, Chief Financial Officer, UPMC Altoona, Altoona, PA, p. A532

KREUZER, Jay E., FACHE, Chief Executive Officer, Kona Community Hospital, Kealakekua, HI, p. A172

KREYE, David, Chief Executive Officer, University General Hospital, Houston, TX, p. A627

KRICKBAUM, Robert, Chief Executive Officer, Edwards County Hospital and Healthcare Center, Kinsley, KS, p. A247

KRIEGER, Cathy, Human Resources Director, Greene County Medical Center, Jefferson, IA, p. A233

KRIEGER, Mark, Vice President and Chief Financial Officer, Barnes–Jewish Hospital, Saint Louis, MO, p. A380

KRIEGER, Robert M., Chief Executive Officer, Osceola Regional Medical Center, Kissimmee, FL, p. A133

KRIEGER, Tim, Director Information Systems, Harnett Health System, Dunn, NC, p. A463

KRINKE, Susan, Chief Executive Officer, Kindred Hospital Lima, Lima, OH, p. A496

KRIPAKARAN, Kasturi, M.D. Medical Director, Andrew McFarland Mental Health Center, Springfield, IL, p. A203

KRISHNAN, Radha, M.D. Chief Medical Officer, Antelope Valley Hospital, Lancaster, CA, p. A69

KRISHNAN, Suresh, Vice President and Chief Information Officer, Loretto Hospital, Chicago, IL, p. A184

KRISHNASWAMY, Jaikumar, Chief Executive Officer, Doctors Hospital at White Rock Lake, Dallas, TX, p. A610

KRISTEL, John, President and Chief Executive Officer, Good Shepherd Rehabilitation Hospital, Allentown, PA, p. A532

KRISTEL, John, President and Chief Executive Officer, Good Shepherd Rehabilitation Network, Allentown, PA, p. B61

KRITZ, Howard
Director Human Resources, Bellevue Hospital Center, New York, NY, p. A442
Director, Henry J. Carter Specialty Hospital and Nursing Facility, New York, NY, p. A444

KRITZER, Tammy, Vice President Clinic Operations, Mayo Clinic Health System in Austin, Austin, MN, p. A340

KRIVENKO, Chuck, M.D. Chief Medical Officer, Clinical and Quality Services, Lee Memorial Hospital, Fort Myers, FL, p. A129

KRMPOTIC, Debra J., R.N., Chief Executive Officer, Banner Estrella Medical Center, Phoenix, AZ, p. A35

KRODEL, Scott, Vice President Information Systems, Johnson Memorial Hospital, Franklin, IN, p. A212

KROELL Jr., H. Scott, Chief Executive Officer, Liberty Regional Medical Center, Hinesville, GA, p. A161

KROESE, Robert D., FACHE, Chief Executive Officer, Pella Regional Health Center, Pella, IA, p. A236

KROGSTAD, Karen, M.D. Chief Medical Officer, Greater Regional Medical Center, Creston, IA, p. A228

KROK, Stan, Chief Information Officer, Ann & Robert H. Lurie Children's Hospital of Chicago, Chicago, IL, p. A183

KROLL, Ronald, Chief Financial Officer, Mercy General Hospital, Sacramento, CA, p. A87

KROPP, Richard P., Vice President Human Resources, Lourdes Medical Center of Burlington County, Willingboro, NJ, p. A424

KROSOFF, Mary June, Chief Human Resources Officer, Highlands Hospital, Connellsville, PA, p. A536

KROUSE, Donald, M.D. Chief of Staff, Trinity Hospital, Weaverville, CA, p. A100

KROUSE, Michael
Chief Information Officer, OhioHealth Doctors Hospital, Columbus, OH, p. A490
Senior Vice President Chief Information Officer, OhioHealth Dublin Methodist Hospital, Dublin, OH, p. A493
Chief Information Officer Information Services, OhioHealth Grady Memorial Hospital, Delaware, OH, p. A492
Chief Information Officer, OhioHealth Grant Medical Center, Columbus, OH, p. A490
Chief Information Officer, OhioHealth Riverside Methodist Hospital, Columbus, OH, p. A490

KROUSE, Stephen W., Chief Human Resource Officer, St. Christopher's Hospital for Children, Philadelphia, PA, p. A550

KRUCZEK, Richard, Chief Executive Officer, HEALTHSOUTH Reading Rehabilitation Hospital, Reading, PA, p. A553

KRUEGER, Albert, M.D. Chief of Staff, Pioneers Medical Center, Meeker, CO, p. A110

KRUEGER, Christine, M.D. Chief of Staff, Munising Memorial Hospital, Munising, MI, p. A331

KRUEGER, David, Associate Director, Bath Veterans Affairs Medical Center, Bath, NY, p. A433

KRUEGER, Ellen, Director Human Resources, Chadron Community Hospital and Health Services, Chadron, NE, p. A394

KRUEGER, Eric, Chief Financial Officer, Mercy Hospital and Medical Center, Chicago, IL, p. A185

KRUEGER Jr., Harold L., Chief Executive Officer, Chadron Community Hospital and Health Services, Chadron, NE, p. A394

KRUEGER, James G., Ph.D., Chief Executive Officer, Rockefeller University Hospital, New York, NY, p. A448

KRUEGER, Justin, Chief Operating Officer, Aiken Regional Medical Centers, Aiken, SC, p. A562

KRUEGER, Mary T.
President, Ministry Good Samaritan Health Center, Merrill, WI, p. A710
President, Ministry Saint Clare's Hospital, Weston, WI, p. A718

KRUEGER, Pete, Director Human Resources, Borgess–Lee Memorial Hospital, Dowagiac, MI, p. A323

KRUEGER, Tammy A., Acting Director, Manchester Veterans Affairs Medical Center, Manchester, NH, p. A411

KRUGEL, Gary M., Chief Financial Officer, Norwegian American Hospital, Chicago, IL, p. A185

KRUGER, Dale K., Chief Executive Officer and Chief Financial Officer, Tyler Healthcare Center Avera, Tyler, MN, p. A353

KRUMBERGER, Joanne, FACHE, Director, Portland Veterans Affairs Medical Center, Portland, OR, p. A528

KRUMMEL, Dere, Director Information Systems, Ochsner Medical Center – Kenner, Kenner, LA, p. A280

KRUMREY, Arthur J., Chief Information Officer, Loyola University Medical Center, Maywood, IL, p. A195

KRUMWIED, Robert D., President and Chief Executive Officer, Regional Mental Health Center, Merrillville, IN, p. A218

KRUPALA, Judith, R.N. Chief Nursing Officer, Cuero Community Hospital, Cuero, TX, p. A609

KRUSE, Joseph J.
Executive Vice President, Mayo Clinic Health System – Franciscan Healthcare in La Crosse, La Crosse, WI, p. A707
Chief Administrative Officer, Mayo Clinic Health System – Franciscan Healthcare in Sparta, Sparta, WI, p. A715

KRUSE, Marcia, R.N. Director Nursing, Logan County Hospital, Oakley, KS, p. A251

KRUSE, Victoria, Manager Human Resources, Franklin General Hospital, Hampton, IA, p. A231

KRUSH, Leanne, Chief Financial Officer, Phoenix Baptist Hospital, Phoenix, AZ, p. A36

KRUSIE, Kathleen R., FACHE, Chief Executive Officer, St. Joseph Regional Health Center, Bryan, TX, p. A604

KRUYER–COLLINS, Emyle
Director Human Resources, Doctors NeuroMedical Hospital, Bremen, IN, p. A208
Chief Human Resources Officer, Unity Medical & Surgical Hospital, Mishawaka, IN, p. A219

KRUZEL, Janet, Business Office Manager, CentraCare Health–Melrose, Melrose, MN, p. A346

KRUZICK, Michael, Acting Chief Financial Officer, Norwalk Hospital, Norwalk, CT, p. A116

KRUZNER, Melinda, Chief Financial Officer, Lexington Medical Center, West Columbia, SC, p. A571

KRYSTOF, Linda, Interim Chief Operating Officer, Kaiser Permanente Antioch Medical Center, Antioch, CA, p. A55

KRYSTOWIAK, Thomas P.
Chief Financial Officer, Berlin Memorial Hospital, Berlin, WI, p. A702
Vice President Finance, Wild Rose Community Memorial Hospital, Wild Rose, WI, p. A718

KRYZANIAK, Larry, Chief Financial Officer, Hennepin County Medical Center, Minneapolis, MN, p. A347

KRZASTEK, Sue, Vice President Human Resources, Augusta Health, Fishersville, VA, p. A670

KU, Evelyn, Chief Nursing Officer, Monterey Park Hospital, Monterey Park, CA, p. A78

KUANGPARICHAT, Manoch, M.D. President Medical Staff, Excelsior Springs Hospital, Excelsior Springs, MO, p. A370

KUBACKI, Clayton, Interim Controller, Kindred Hospital Detroit, Detroit, MI, p. A322

KUBALA, Joseph
Chief Financial Officer, St. Vincent Jennings Hospital, North Vernon, IN, p. A220
Director Financial and Support Services, St. Vincent Salem Hospital, Salem, IN, p. A222

KUBALL, Lana, Director Administrative Services, Lucas County Health Center, Chariton, IA, p. A227

KUBE, Don, M.D. Chief of Staff, Dickinson County Healthcare System, Iron Mountain, MI, p. A327

KUBIAK, Phillip J., President, Hampstead Hospital, Hampstead, NH, p. A410

KUBIAK, Richard, M.D. Vice President Medical Affairs, Peconic Bay Medical Center, Riverhead, NY, p. A452

KUBICEK, Jim, Interim Chief Executive Officer, Milwaukee County Behavioral Health Division, Milwaukee, WI, p. A710

KUBIK, James A., Administrator, Pawnee County Memorial Hospital and Rural Health Clinic, Pawnee City, NE, p. A401

KUBOTA, Andrea, R.N. Director Patient Care Services, Shriners Hospitals for Children–Honolulu, Honolulu, HI, p. A171

KUBOUSHEK, David, Chief, Fiscal Service, Durham Veterans Affairs Medical Center, Durham, NC, p. A463

KUCERA, Kim, Chief Operating Officer, Mille Lacs Health System, Onamia, MN, p. A349

KUCHARSKI, Kathy, Director Management Information Systems, Brooks Memorial Hospital, Dunkirk, NY, p. A436

KUCKEWICH, Mike, Director Information Systems, Terre Haute Regional Hospital, Terre Haute, IN, p. A223

KUCZORA, Paul, Chief Executive Officer, Grant–Blackford Mental Health Center, Marion, IN, p. A218

KUEHLER, Sheila, R.N. Director of Nursing, Knox County Hospital, Knox City, TX, p. A632

KUEHN, David, Chief Financial Officer, Rusk County Memorial Hospital, Ladysmith, WI, p. A707

KUEHNEMUND, Bonnie, Comptroller, Heart of America Medical Center, Rugby, ND, p. A480

KUENNEN, Connie, Director Human Resources and Community Relations, Regional Health Services of Howard County, Cresco, IA, p. A228

KUESTERSTEFFEN, Vicki, Chief Executive Officer, J. D. McCarty Center for Children With Developmental Disabilities, Norman, OK, p. A514

KUGHN, Yvonne, Chief Executive Officer, Southeast Michigan Surgical Hospital, Warren, MI, p. A336

KUHAR, Peggy A., R.N. Chief Nursing Officer, University Hospitals Geauga Medical Center, Chardon, OH, p. A485

KUHLE, Terri, Director Human Resources, St. Mary's Hospital, Decatur, IL, p. A188

KUHLMAN, Ian, Manager Information Technology, Shelby Memorial Hospital, Shelbyville, IL, p. A202

KUHLMANN, Chris, Chief Financial Officer, Lakeland Community Hospital Watervliet, Watervliet, MI, p. A336

KUHN, Anita, Controller, Texas County Memorial Hospital, Houston, MO, p. A372

KUHN, Brenda, Ph.D. Vice President Patient Care Services, Kettering Medical Center, Kettering, OH, p. A495

KUHN, Keith, Chief Executive Officer, Haven Behavioral Senior Care of Dayton, Dayton, OH, p. A492

KUHN, Margueritte, M.D. Vice President Medical Affairs, MidMichigan Medical Center–Midland, Midland, MI, p. A330

KUHN, Steve, Chief Financial Officer, River Park Hospital, Huntington, WV, p. A696

KUHNS, Jay, Vice President Human Resources, All Children's Hospital Johns Hopkins Medicine, Saint Petersburg, FL, p. A144

KUIDA, Elliot H., Vice President and Chief Operating Officer, Martha Jefferson Hospital, Charlottesville, VA, p. A669

KUKELHAN, Alison, Manager Human Resources, Adams Memorial Hospital, Decatur, IN, p. A209

KULHANEK, Linda, Chief Financial Officer, Memorial Hermann Katy Hospital, Katy, TX, p. A630

KULIK, Alec G., Administrator, Cleveland Clinic Children's Hospital for Rehabilitation, Cleveland, OH, p. A488

KULISZ, Michael, D.O
Chief Medical Officer, Kishwaukee Hospital, DeKalb, IL, p. A188
Chief Medical Officer, Valley West Hospital, Sandwich, IL, p. A202

KULLMAN, Betsy, R.N. Executive Vice President and Chief Nursing Officer, Medical Center at Bowling Green, Bowling Green, KY, p. A259

KULMA, Mariarose, R.N. Vice President Patient Services, East Texas Medical Center Tyler, Tyler, TX, p. A654

KUMAR, Daryn J., Chief Executive Officer, Memorial Medical Center, Modesto, CA, p. A78

KUMAR, Nanda, M.D. Chief of Staff, Vibra Hospital of Northern California, Redding, CA, p. A85

KUMAR, Raji, Chief Executive Officer, Dallas Medical Center, Dallas, TX, p. A610

KUMM, Mandy, Vice President Fiscal Services, Boone County Health Center, Albion, NE, p. A393

KUMMER, Margaret, Vice President Human Resources, Citizens Medical Center, Colby, KS, p. A242

KUNES, Courtney, Director Human Resources, Lock Haven Hospital, Lock Haven, PA, p. A543

KUNKLE, David, Chief Financial Officer, Havenwyck Hospital, Auburn Hills, MI, p. A318

KUNNAPPILLY, Chester, M.D. Chief Medical Officer and Chief Quality Officer, San Mateo Medical Center, San Mateo, CA, p. A93

KUNSTLING, Ted, M.D. Chief Medical Officer, Duke Raleigh Hospital, Raleigh, NC, p. A470

KUNZ, Donna
Director Human Resources, Saint Luke's Cushing Hospital, Leavenworth, KS, p. A248
Manager Human Resources, Saint Luke's South Hospital, Overland Park, KS, p. A252

KUNZA, Mary Kay, Manager Human Resources, Lincoln County Medical Center, Troy, MO, p. A384

KUPER, Kandi, Chief Nursing Officer, Kit Carson County Health Service District, Burlington, CO, p. A103

KUPFERSTEIN, Ron, Chief Executive Officer, Monrovia Memorial Hospital, Monrovia, CA, p. A78

KUPLEN, Carol, R.N. Chief Operating Officer and Chief Nursing Officer, St. Luke's University Hospital – Bethlehem Campus, Bethlehem, PA, p. A534

KURCAB, Jeff, Chief Financial Officer, LewisGale Hospital Pulaski, Pulaski, VA, p. A676

KURESKA, Kirk, Chief Executive Officer, RiverWoods Behavioral Health System, Riverdale, GA, p. A165

KURIAN, Santha, M.D. Chief of Staff, James E. Van Zandt Veterans Affairs Medical Center, Altoona, PA, p. A532

KURLE, Janet, Chief Financial Officer, Community Memorial Hospital, Turtle Lake, ND, p. A174

KURRA, Shankar, M.D. Senior Vice President Medical Affairs, Fisher–Titus Medical Center, Norwalk, OH, p. A500

KURTZ, Maria
  Director Human Resources, Lutheran Hospital of Indiana, Fort Wayne, IN, p. A211
  Director Human Resources, Orthopaedic Hospital of Lutheran Health Network, Fort Wayne, IN, p. A211

KURTZ, Marvin A., Chief Financial Officer, Florida Hospital Carrollwood, Tampa, FL, p. A147

KURTZ, Jr., Thomas F., Chief Operating Officer, Georgia Regional Hospital at Savannah, Savannah, GA, p. A166

KURTZ, Thomas M., President and Chief Executive Officer, Windber Medical Center, Windber, PA, p. A559

KURZ, Kenneth R., M.D. Chief of Staff, MidState Medical Center, Meriden, CT, p. A115

KURZ, Sharon H., Ph.D., Chief Executive Officer, St. Elias Specialty Hospital, Anchorage, AK, p. A28

KURZENDOERFER, Laura, R.N. Chief Nursing Officer, Great Plains Regional Medical Center, Elk City, OK, p. A510

KUSHNER, Michael S., Senior Vice President and Chief Talent Officer, Miami Children's Hospital, Miami, FL, p. A137

KUSLER, Julie, Manager Information Services, Avera St. Luke's Hospital, Aberdeen, SD, p. A572

KUSNIERZ, William J., Vice President and Chief Financial Officer, Springfield Regional Medical Center, Springfield, OH, p. A502

KUTA, Daniel, R.N. Director of Nursing, Power County Hospital District, American Falls, ID, p. A174

KUTCH, John M., President, Trinity Health, Minot, ND, p. A479

KUTCHER, Gregory, M.D., President and Chief Executive Officer, Mayo Clinic Health System in Mankato, Mankato, MN, p. A346

KUTILEK, Richard J., Chief Operating Officer, Calvary Hospital,, NY, p. A443

KUYKENDALL, Kari, Human Resources Specialist, Pauls Valley General Hospital, Pauls Valley, OK, p. A517

KUZAS, Betsy, Executive Vice President and Chief Operating Officer, Phoenix Children's Hospital, Phoenix, AZ, p. A36

KUZEE, Ann, Executive Director Human Resources, Riverview Hospital, Noblesville, IN, p. A220

KUZMA, Gregory
  Vice President and Chief Financial Officer, Flagstaff Medical Center, Flagstaff, AZ, p. A32
  Vice President and Chief Financial Officer, Verde Valley Medical Center, Cottonwood, AZ, p. A32

KVASNICKA, John, M.D. Medical Director Acute Care Services, Woodwinds Health Campus, Woodbury, MN, p. A354

KWASS, George, M.D. Chief of Staff, Merrimack Valley Hospital, Haverhill, MA, p. A310

KWATER, Sherry M., R.N. Chief Nursing Officer, Penn State Milton S. Hershey Medical Center, Hershey, PA, p. A540

KWIATEK, Susan, R.N., Executive Director, Glen Cove Hospital, Glen Cove, NY, p. A438

KWIESIELEWICZ, Nancy
  Human Resources Manager, Ministry Good Samaritan Health Center, Merrill, WI, p. A710
  Human Resources Manager, Ministry Saint Clare's Hospital, Weston, WI, p. A718

KYHNELL, Koreen H., Vice President Human Resources, Indiana University Health Arnett Hospital, Lafayette, IN, p. A217

KYLER, Yvonne
  Director Human Resources, Texas Health Arlington Memorial Hospital, Arlington, TX, p. A598
  Director Human Resources, Texas Health Heart & Vascular Hospital Arlington, Arlington, TX, p. A598

KYRIACOU, George M., President and Chief Executive Officer, Gaylord Hospital, Wallingford, CT, p. A117

KYWI, Alberto
  Chief Information Officer, Goleta Valley Cottage Hospital, Santa Barbara, CA, p. A94
  Chief Information Officer, Santa Barbara Cottage Hospital, Santa Barbara, CA, p. A94
  Chief Information Officer, Santa Ynez Valley Cottage Hospital, Solvang, CA, p. A95

L

L'HEUREUX, Dennis P., Chief Information Officer, Rockford Memorial Hospital, Rockford, IL, p. A201

L'ITALIEN, Mark, Director Information Services, Salem Regional Medical Center, Salem, OH, p. A501

LA CAVA, Joseph, Chief Nursing Officer and Director Of Anesthesia, DeSoto Memorial Hospital, Arcadia, FL, p. A123

LA CROIX, Kent, Supervisor Information Technology, Schoolcraft Memorial Hospital, Manistique, MI, p. A329

LA PORTE, Todd
  Chief Financial Officer, John C. Lincoln North Mountain Hospital, Phoenix, AZ, p. A36
  Senior Vice President and Chief Financial Officer, Scottsdale Healthcare Shea Medical Center, Scottsdale, AZ, p. A38
  Chief Financial Officer, Scottsdale Healthcare Thompson Peak Hospital, Scottsdale, AZ, p. A38
  Senior Vice President and Chief Financial Officer, Scottsdale Healthcare–Osborn Medical Center, Scottsdale, AZ, p. A38

LABAGNARA, James, M.D. Vice President Medical Affairs, St. Joseph's Regional Medical Center, Paterson, NJ, p. A420

LABAND, Andrew, Chief Information Officer, McLean Hospital, Belmont, MA, p. A305

LABARGE, Robert J., Chief Executive Officer, Sturgis Hospital, Sturgis, MI, p. A335

LABELLE, Douglas, M.D. Chief Medical Officer, Bell Hospital, Ishpeming, MI, p. A327

LABELLE, James, M.D
  Chief Medical Officer, Scripps Green Hospital, La Jolla, CA, p. A68
  Chief Medical Officer, Scripps Memorial Hospital–La Jolla, La Jolla, CA, p. A68

LABIAGA, Kimberly
  Human Resources Leader, Kaiser Permanente Fontana Medical Center, Fontana, CA, p. A63
  Human Resources Director, Kaiser Permanente Ontario Medical Center, Ontario, CA, p. A81

LABINE, Lance C., Administrator, Dr. Dan C. Trigg Memorial Hospital, Tucumcari, NM, p. A431

LABONTE, Robin, Leader Financial Care, York Hospital, York, ME, p. A295

LABORANTI, Sarah M., Interim Director Human Resources, Tennova Physicians Regional Medical Center, Knoxville, TN, p. A586

LABORIE, Sheree
  Director Human Resources, Lakewood Hospital, Lakewood, OH, p. A496
  Director Human Resources, Lutheran Hospital, Cleveland, OH, p. A488

LABOWITZ, Robert, Chief Nursing Officer, Cornerstone Hospital of SouthEast Arizona, Tucson, AZ, p. A40

LABRIOLA, Terri, Human Resources Officer, Sierra Nevada Memorial Hospital, Grass Valley, CA, p. A66

LABRUM, Chad, Chief Financial Officer, Ashley Regional Medical Center, Vernal, UT, p. A664

LACASSE, Paul E., D.O., President and Chief Executive Officer, Botsford Hospital, Farmington Hills, MI, p. A323

LACAZE, Todd, Chief Financial Officer, Tulane Medical Center, New Orleans, LA, p. A286

LACEFIELD, Gayla, Director Human Resources, Howard Memorial Hospital, Nashville, AR, p. A50

LACEY, Carmen, R.N., President, Charles A. Cannon Memorial Hospital, Linville, NC, p. A468

LACEY, III, John W., M.D. Senior Vice President and Chief Medical Officer, University of Tennessee Medical Center, Knoxville, TN, p. A586

LACEY, Paul, M.D. Chief Medical Staff, North Valley Hospital, Tonasket, WA, p. A691

LACHANCE, Eric, Chief Financial Officer, Munroe Regional Medical Center, Ocala, FL, p. A139

LACHANCE, Mary Kay, Director Information Systems, St. John Macomb–Oakland Hospital, Warren, MI, p. A336

LACHER, Paula A., MSN Chief Nursing Officer, West Penn Hospital, Pittsburgh, PA, p. A552

LACHINA, Ignazio, M.D. Medical Director, HEALTHSOUTH Rehabilitation Hospital of Cypress, Houston, TX, p. A624

LACHOWSKY, John, M.D. Chief Medical Officer, Mercy Hospital Ozark, Ozark, AR, p. A51

LACHTERMAN, Bruce, M.D. Chief of Medical Staff, St. Luke's Lakeside Hospital, The Woodlands, TX, p. A653

LACKEY, Lori, Chief Financial Officer, Sabetha Community Hospital, Sabetha, KS, p. A253

LACKEY, Thomas O., Administrator, Hale County Hospital, Greensboro, AL, p. A21

LACKNEY, Christopher J., Director Human Resources, Grace Cottage Hospital, Townshend, VT, p. A666

LACOT, Ivette, Director Human Resources, Hospital Episcopal San Lucas Guayama, Guayama, PR, p. A726

LACY, Angela, Director of Nursing, Bolivar General Hospital, Bolivar, TN, p. A579

LACY, Dwight A., Chief Executive Officer, Rivendell Behavioral Health Services of Arkansas, Benton, AR, p. A43

LACY, Edward L., FACHE, Vice President and Administrator, Baptist Health Medical Center–Heber Springs, Heber Springs, AR, p. A47

LACY, Tyson, Chief Financial Officer, Lincoln Hospital, Davenport, WA, p. A683

LADAROLA, Sandra, Chief Nursing Officer, Waterbury Hospital, Waterbury, CT, p. A118

LADD, Bill, Director Information Services, Western Missouri Medical Center, Warrensburg, MO, p. A384

LADNER, Warren, Chief Financial Officer, Bay Medical Center Sacred Heart, Panama City, FL, p. A141

LADWIG, Michael, M.D. Chief of Staff, Marion Veterans Affairs Medical Center, Marion, IL, p. A195

LAEL, Marielle, R.N. Chief Nursing Officer, Select Specialty Hospital–Fort Wayne, Fort Wayne, IN, p. A211

LAFERNEY, Jimmy, M.D. Vice President Medical Staff Affairs, Baylor Medical Center at Frisco, Frisco, TX, p. A620

LAFFERTY, Aline, Vice President Human Resources, Mercy Memorial Hospital System, Monroe, MI, p. A330

LAFFERTY, Douglas L., Chief Executive Officer, Plumas District Hospital, Quincy, CA, p. A84

LAFFEY, Leah, R.N., Chief Executive Officer, HEALTHSOUTH Rehabilitation Hospital, Sewickley, PA, p. A555

LAFLAMME, Christine, R.N. Chief Nursing Officer, Seton Smithville Regional Hospital, Smithville, TX, p. A649

LAFLEUR, Cindy, Senior Administrator, Via Christi Rehabilitation Hospital, Wichita, KS, p. A257

LAFONE, Ken, Director Human Resources, Caswell Center, Kinston, NC, p. A467

LAFRANCOIS, Gregory, Chief Executive Officer, Prairie St. John's, Fargo, ND, p. A477

LAFRANCOIS, Mary, Vice President Human Resources, CHRISTUS Spohn Hospital Corpus Christi Memorial, Corpus Christi, TX, p. A608

LAGANA, Gina, Director Human Resources, Merrimack Valley Hospital, Haverhill, MA, p. A310

LAGASSE, David A., Senior Vice President Fiscal Affairs, McLean Hospital, Belmont, MA, p. A305

LAGNESE, John, M.D. Vice President Medical Affairs, UPMC St. Margaret, Pittsburgh, PA, p. A552

LAGROU, Robert, D.O. Medical Director, Henry Ford Kingswood Hospital, Ferndale, MI, p. A323

LAHASKY, Doug, Chief Financial Officer, Acadia Vermilion Hospital, Lafayette, LA, p. A281

LAHAYE, Daniel, Manager, Savoy Medical Center, Mamou, LA, p. A283

LAHOUT, Brenda, Chief Nurse Executive, Danville State Hospital, Danville, PA, p. A536

LAHTI, Molly, Director Human Resources, Parkland Medical Center, Derry, NH, p. A409

LAI, Abel, Manager Information Systems, Chinese Hospital, San Francisco, CA, p. A90

LAI, Iris, Chief Executive Officer, Alhambra Hospital Medical Center, Alhambra, CA, p. A55

LAIBINIS, Walter, M.D. Chief Medical Officer, Soldiers and Sailors Memorial Hospital, Wellsboro, PA, p. A557

LAIGN, Michael B., President and Chief Executive Officer, Holy Redeemer Hospital, Meadowbrook, PA, p. A544

LAIRD, Carol, R.N. Chief Nursing Officer, Southern Tennessee Regional Health System–Lawrenceburg, Lawrenceburg, TN, p. A586

LAIRD, Jeff, Controller, Stephens County Hospital, Toccoa, GA, p. A168

LAIRD, Patrick
  Chief Clinical Officer, Nexus Specialty Hospital, Shenandoah, TX, p. A649
  Chief Clinical Officer, Nexus Specialty Hospital The Woodlands, Spring, TX, p. A650

LAIRD, Shaw, Chief Information Officer, Chester Regional Medical Center, Chester, SC, p. A564

LAISTER, Judy K., Director, Human Resources, Methodist Mansfield Medical Center, Mansfield, TX, p. A636

LAKE, Chandra, Associate Director, Sheridan Veterans Affairs Medical Center, Sheridan, WY, p. A722

LAKE, Nathan, Vice President Human Resources, Prairie Lakes Healthcare System, Watertown, SD, p. A578

LAKE, Peter M., M.D. Chief Medical Officer, Rogers Memorial Hospital, Oconomowoc, WI, p. A712

LAKE, Robin E., Chief Executive Officer, Integris Clinton Regional Hospital, Clinton, OK, p. A509

LAKEY, David L., M.D., Commissioner, Texas Department of State Health Services, Austin, TX, p. B134

LAKEY, Travis, Chief Financial Officer, Mayers Memorial Hospital District, Fall River Mills, CA, p. A63

LAKINS, Tom, Director Information Systems, Tennova Physicians Regional Medical Center, Knoxville, TN, p. A586

LAKSHMANAN, Rekha, M.D. Medical Director, Kindred Hospital–St. Louis at Mercy, Saint Louis, MO, p. A380

LALLY, James M., D.O., President and Chief Medical Officer, Chino Valley Medical Center, Chino, CA, p. A59

LALLY, Michael K., Chief Executive Officer, Calais Regional Hospital, Calais, ME, p. A292

LALLY, Jr., Robert P., Vice President Finance, MedStar Franklin Square Medical Center, Baltimore, MD, p. A297

LAM, Shiva, M.D. Executive Medical Director, Austin Lakes Hospital, Austin, TX, p. A599

LAMADELEINE, Joseph, Chief Financial Officer, Veterans Affairs Connecticut Healthcare System, West Haven, CT, p. A118

LAMANTEER, Mike, M.D. Vice President Medical Affairs, Baptist St. Anthony Health System, Amarillo, TX, p. A596

LAMANTIA, Joseph, Executive Vice President and Chief Operating Officer, South Nassau Communities Hospital, Oceanside, NY, p. A450

LAMANTIA, Sheirlie, M.D. Chief of Staff, Grant Regional Health Center, Lancaster, WI, p. A708

LAMARCHE, Heather, Manager Human Resources, AMG Specialty Hospital–Lafayette, Lafayette, LA, p. A281

LAMARCHE, Marie, Executive Director, Human Resources, Organizational Development, Employee Health, Harrison Medical Center, Bremerton, WA, p. A681

LAMARCHE, Maximo, M.D. Chief Medical Officer, AMG Specialty Hospital–Lafayette, Lafayette, LA, p. A281

LAMB, Andrew, M.D. Chief of Staff, Alamance Regional Medical Center, Burlington, NC, p. A461

LAMB, Cindy, Director Human Resources, Marias Medical Center, Shelby, MT, p. A391

LAMB, Hope, Manager Human Resources, Kimble Hospital, Junction, TX, p. A630

LAMB, Thomas, Director Information Systems, Monongahela Valley Hospital, Monongahela, PA, p. A545

LAMB–PAGONE, Jerilynn, Nurse Executive, Connecticut Valley Hospital, Middletown, CT, p. A115

LAMBERT, Amand, Director Human Resources, Allen Parish Hospital, Kinder, LA, p. A280

LAMBERT, Barbara, Director Healthcare Compliance, Eastern State Hospital, Williamsburg, VA, p. A680

LAMBERT, Chelcia, Chief Operating Officer and Chief Financial Officer, Kettering Medical Center, Kettering, OH, p. A495

LAMBERT, James M., FACHE, President and Chief Executive Officer, Conway Regional Medical Center, Conway, AR, p. A44

LAMBERT, Karen A., President, Advocate Good Shepherd Hospital, Barrington, IL, p. A181

LAMBERT, Lynn, Chief Financial Officer, Harnett Health System, Dunn, NC, p. A463

LAMBERT, Paul, M.D. Chief of Staff, Boise Veterans Affairs Medical Center, Boise, ID, p. A174

LAMBERT, Robert K., FACHE, President and Chief Executive Officer, Arnot Health, Elmira, NY, p. B12

LAMBERTON, Natalie D., Chief Executive Officer, Regency Hospital of Fort Worth, Fort Worth, TX, p. A619

LAMBETH, Laura, Chief Executive Officer, Ashe Memorial Hospital, Jefferson, NC, p. A467

LAMBKE, Michael, M.D. Medical Director, Redington–Fairview General Hospital, Skowhegan, ME, p. A295

LAMBRECHT, Craig, M.D., President, Sanford Bismarck, Bismarck, ND, p. A476

LAMBRECHT, Rebecca, Manager Finance, CHI Health Plainview, Plainview, NE, p. A401

LAMBRECHT, Sandra, Chief Financial Officer, Haxtun Hospital District, Haxtun, CO, p. A107

LAMEBULL, Charlotte, Administrative Officer, Fort Belknap U. S. Public Health Service Indian Hospital, Harlem, MT, p. A388

LAMEN, Drake M., M.D., President and Chief Executive Officer, Chenango Memorial Hospital, Norwich, NY, p. A450

LAMEY, Rebecca, Vice President Human Resources, MaineGeneral Medical Center, Augusta, ME, p. A291

LAMIS, Pano, M.D. Medical Director, Atlanta Medical Center, Atlanta, GA, p. A152

LAMLE, Sandra, Chief Financial Officer, Okeene Municipal Hospital, Okeene, OK, p. A514

LAMMERS, Brent R., Chief Executive Officer, Alleghany Memorial Hospital, Sparta, NC, p. A473

LAMMERS, Sandra, Coordinator Human Resources and Finance, CHI Health Mercy Corning, Corning, IA, p. A228

LAMORELLA, Vincent M., Chief Financial Officer, Clarion Hospital, Clarion, PA, p. A535

LAMOUREUX, Bruce, Vice President and Chief Executive Officer, Providence Alaska Medical Center, Anchorage, AK, p. A28

LAMOUREUX, John P., Commander, Dwight David Eisenhower Army Medical Center, Fort Gordon, GA, p. A160

LAMOUREUX, Laurie, Director of Finance, Cooley Dickinson Hospital, Northampton, MA, p. A313

LAMPE, Michael, M.D. Chief of Staff, Kossuth Regional Health Center, Algona, IA, p. A225

LAMPE, Tammy K., Director Human Resources, Edwards County Hospital and Healthcare Center, Kinsley, KS, p. A247

LAMPLEY, Danny, Chief Operating Officer, Harrisburg Medical Center, Harrisburg, IL, p. A191

LAMPTON, Lucius, M.D. Medical Director, Beacham Memorial Hospital, Magnolia, MS, p. A361

LANCASTER, Penny, Controller, Cascade Medical Center, Cascade, ID, p. A175

LANCASTER, Tim, FACHE, President and Chief Executive Officer, Hendrick Health System, Abilene, TX, p. A595

LANCEY, Katie, Chief Nursing Officer, North Georgia Medical Center, Ellijay, GA, p. A159

LAND, David, D.O. Chief Medical Staff, Fort Duncan Regional Medical Center, Eagle Pass, TX, p. A614

LANDAU, Kenneth G., Chief Operating Officer, Curry General Hospital, Gold Beach, OR, p. A525

LANDENBERGER, Jason, Director of Nursing, Community Memorial Hospital, Turtle Lake, ND, p. A480

LANDERS, Alice, Administrative Director Operations, Texas Health Harris Methodist Hospital Hurst–Euless–Bedford, Bedford, TX, p. A602

LANDERS, Kimberly A., MS Vice President Patient Care Services, Morris Hospital & Healthcare Centers, Morris, IL, p. A196

LANDGARTEN, Steven, M.D. Chief Medical Officer, Hillcrest Medical Center, Tulsa, OK, p. A520

LANDIS, Bradlee, Chief Information Officer, Faith Community Hospital, Jacksboro, TX, p. A629

LANDIS, Catherine, MS, President and Chief Nursing Officer, Transylvania Regional Hospital, Brevard, NC, p. A460

LANDMAN, Paul, Director Human Resources, Ellwood City Hospital, Ellwood City, PA, p. A538

LANDRAU, Erika, Director Human Resources, HEALTHSOUTH Hospital of Manati, Manati, PR, p. A726

LANDRENEAU, Derrick, Director of Nursing, Baton Rouge Rehabilitation Hospital, Baton Rouge, LA, p. A273

LANDRETH, Jonathan, Chief Executive Officer, Lafayette Physical Rehabilitation Hospital, Lafayette, LA, p. A281

LANDRETH, Sandy, Director Human Resources, Seiling Community Hospital, Seiling, OK, p. A518

LANDRETH, Shannan, Information Systems, Livingston Hospital and Healthcare Services, Salem, KY, p. B12

LANDRUM, David, Chief Police Services, Atascadero State Hospital, Atascadero, CA, p. A56

LANDRUM, Scott M., Interim Administrator, Graham Regional Medical Center, Graham, TX, p. A621

LANDRY, Adam, Coordinator Computer Systems, Northern Maine Medical Center, Fort Kent, ME, p. A293

LANDRY, Candy, Chief Human Resource Officer, Eastside Psychiatric Hospital, Tallahassee, FL, p. A146

LANDRY, Donna F., Chief Operating Officer, Our Lady of Lourdes Regional Medical Center, Lafayette, LA, p. A281

LANDRY, Patrick, Controller, HEALTHSOUTH Rehabilitation Hospital–Las Vegas, Las Vegas, NV, p. A405

LANDRY, Ray A., Chief Executive Officer, Abbeville General Hospital, Abbeville, LA, p. A272

LANDRY, Wayne J., Chief Executive Officer, St. Bernard Parish Hospital, Chalmette, LA, p. A275

LANDSMAN, Joseph, President and Chief Executive Officer, University of Tennessee Medical Center, Knoxville, TN, p. A586

LANDSTROM, Gay L., MS Chief Nursing Officer, Dartmouth–Hitchcock Medical Center, Lebanon, NH, p. A411

LANDSTROM, John
Vice President Human Resources and Operations, RML Specialty Hospital, Chicago, IL, p. A186
Director Human Resources, RML Specialty Hospital, Hinsdale, IL, p. A193

LANE, Diron
Director Information Systems, LewisGale Hospital Montgomery, Blacksburg, VA, p. A668
Director Information Systems, LewisGale Hospital Pulaski, Pulaski, VA, p. A676

LANE, Kathy, Leader–ICU, Home Care, MedSurg, York Hospital, York, ME, p. A295

LANE, Kevin, D.O. Chief of Staff, Hardeman County Memorial Hospital, Quanah, TX, p. A643

LANE, Kevin, Vice President Information Systems, Silver Cross Hospital, New Lenox, IL, p. A198

LANE, Kim, Chief Fiscal Service, Overton Brooks Veterans Affairs Medical Center, Shreveport, LA, p. A288

LANE, Mike, Chief Operating Officer, Twin Cities Community Hospital, Templeton, CA, p. A97

LANE, Richard, Chief Financial Officer, Mid–America Rehabilitation Hospital, Shawnee Mission, KS, p. A254

LANE, Stacey
Executive Assistant Human Resources, Chambers Memorial Hospital, Danville, AR, p. A44
Director Human Resources, Hunt Regional Community Hospital, Commerce, TX, p. A607

LANE, Tommy, Assistant Vice President, Finance and Operations, East Alabama Medical Center–Lanier, Valley, AL, p. A26

LANER, Jr., Richard, Manager Information Systems, Miners' Colfax Medical Center, Raton, NM, p. A429

LANEY, Samuel Mark, M.D., President and Chief Executive Officer, Heartland Regional Medical Center, Saint Joseph, MO, p. A379

LANG, Anne, Vice President Human Resources and Compliance and Privacy Officer, Winchester Hospital, Winchester, MA, p. A316

LANG, Cyndi, Director Information Services, French Hospital Medical Center, San Luis Obispo, CA, p. A93

LANG, David, Vice President Human Resources, Baptist Health Madisonville, Madisonville, KY, p. A267

LANG, Gordon, M.D. Chief of Staff, Trego County–Lemke Memorial Hospital, Wakeeney, KS, p. A256

LANG, Heidi, M.D. Chief Medical Officer, Rehabilitation Hospital of Fort Wayne, Fort Wayne, IN, p. A211

LANG, Jeffrey M., Chief Executive Officer, United Hospital District, Blue Earth, MN, p. A340

LANG, John Christopher, Chief Executive Officer, Cass Regional Medical Center, Harrisonville, MO, p. A372

LANG, Jordan, Director Human Resources, Brigham City Community Hospital, Brigham City, UT, p. A659

LANG, Joseph, M.D. Chief of Staff, Carolinas Specialty Hospital, Charlotte, NC, p. A462

LANG, Linda, Chief Human Resources Officer, Marin General Hospital, Greenbrae, CA, p. A66

LANG, Nicholas P., M.D. Chief Medical Officer, UAMS Medical Center, Little Rock, AR, p. A49

LANG, Paula, Chief Executive Officer, Patient's Choice Medical Center of Humphreys County, Belzoni, MS, p. A355

LANG, Richard, Ed.D. Vice President and Chief Information Officer, Doylestown Hospital, Doylestown, PA, p. A537

LANG, Richard T., Chief Financial Officer, Gouverneur Hospital, Gouverneur, NY, p. A438

LANGBEHN, Cody, Chief Executive Officer, St. Luke's Wood River Medical Center, Ketchum, ID, p. A176

LANGBEHN, Jennifer, Medical Director, Mayo Clinic Health System in Saint James, Saint James, MN, p. A351

LANGBERG, Michael L., M.D. Senior Vice President Medical Affairs and Chief Medical Officer, Cedars–Sinai Medical Center, Los Angeles, CA, p. A71

LANGDON, Ashlee, Controller, Yalobusha General Hospital, Water Valley, MS, p. A366

LANGDORF, Brad, R.N. Chief Nursing Officer, SEARHC MT. Edgecumbe Hospital, Sitka, AK, p. A30

LANGE, Connie, R.N. Vice President of Patient Care Services, Lakes Regional Healthcare, Spirit Lake, IA, p. A238

LANGENBERG, Shannon, Director Human Resources, Jackson County Regional Health Center, Maquoketa, IA, p. A234

LANGFELDER, Richard, Executive Vice President and Chief Financial Officer, Lutheran Medical Center,, NY, p. A445

LANGFORD, Terrie, Director Human Resources, Heritage Park Surgical Hospital, Sherman, TX, p. A649

LANGHAM, Raymond E., Vice President Human Resources, Regional Medical Center of Acadiana, Lafayette, LA, p. A282

LANGHOFF, Erik, Ph.D., Director, James J. Peters Veterans Affairs Medical Center,, NY, p. A444

LANGLITZ, Sara, Controller, Kindred Hospital–Houston, Houston, TX, p. A625

LANGLOIS, John, Chief Financial Officer, Walker Baptist Medical Center, Jasper, AL, p. A22

LANGMEAD, Paula A., Chief Executive Officer, Springfield Hospital Center, Sykesville, MD, p. A303

LANGSTON, David L.
Corporate Vice President Human Resources, East Texas Medical Center Rehabilitation Hospital, Tyler, TX, p. A654
Corporate Vice President Human Resources, East Texas Medical Center Specialty Hospital, Tyler, TX, p. A654

LANGSTON, Kimberly K., R.N., Chief Executive Officer, Scott and White Continuing Care Hospital, Temple, TX, p. A652

LANGSTON, Roxann, Chief Nursing Officer, East Texas Medical Center Trinity, Trinity, TX, p. A653

LANGSTON, Sheila, Administrator, Oceans Behavioral Hospital of De Ridder, Deridder, LA, p. A277

LANHAM, Gary, Chief Medical Officer, Parkridge Medical Center, Chattanooga, TN, p. A580

LANIG, Indria S., M.D. Medical Director, Northern Colorado Rehabilitation Hospital, Johnstown, CO, p. A108

LANKFORD, Deanna, Business Office Manager, Plano Specialty Hospital, Plano, TX, p. A642

LANNOYE, Craig, Vice President Operations, Wilson Memorial Hospital, Sidney, OH, p. A502

LANOUE, Cheryl, Chief Financial Officer, Ottawa County Health Center, Minneapolis, KS, p. A250

LANS, Sue, Comptroller, Harlan County Health System, Alma, NE, p. A393

LANSDOWNE, Lynn M., Vice President Human Resources, Pocono Medical Center, East Stroudsburg, PA, p. A538

LANSFORD, Georgene, Director Information Systems, St. Mary's Hospital, Streator, IL, p. A204

LANTOS, Phyllis R., Executive Vice President, Corporate Chief Financial Officer and Treasurer, New York–Presbyterian Hospital, New York, NY, p. A447

LANTZY, William, Vice President Finance, DMC Huron Valley–Sinai Hospital, Commerce Township, MI, p. A321

LANZA, Nicholas, Controller, St. Mary's Hospital, Passaic, NJ, p. A420

LANZA, Raymond, D.O. Medical Director, Runnells Specialized Hospital of Union County, Berkeley Heights, NJ, p. A413

LAPERLE, Linda M., Vice President Administrative Services, Androscoggin Valley Hospital, Berlin, NH, p. A409

LAPHAM, Lisa, Interim Chief Executive Officer, HealthSource Saginaw, Saginaw, MI, p. A334

LAPLANT, Dawn, Manager Health Information Management, Brown County Community Treatment Center, Green Bay, WI, p. A706

LAPOSTA, Mary Jo, Ph.D. Senior Vice President Patient Care and Organizational Execellence, Saratoga Hospital, Saratoga Springs, NY, p. A454

LAPUZ, Miguel H., M.D., Director, Salem Veterans Affairs Medical Center, Salem, VA, p. A678

LARA, Anne, Chief Information Officer, Union Hospital, Elkton, MD, p. A300

LARA, Sergio, M.D. Chief Medical Officer, Covenant Hospital Plainview, Plainview, TX, p. A642

LARAMIE, Robert, Chief Information Officer, Beverly Hospital, Beverly, MA, p. A305

LARAMIE, Wayne, Vice President Nursing, SSM St. Clare Health Center, Fenton, MO, p. A371

LARCAS, John, M.D. Acting Medical Director, Choate Mental Health Center, Anna, IL, p. A180

LARCEN, Stephen W., Ph.D., President and CEO, Natchaug Hospital, Mansfield Center, CT, p. A115

LAREAU, Daniel, Executive Director Operations and Information, St. Vincent Carmel Hospital, Carmel, IN, p. A208

LAREAU, Kim, Vice President and Chief Information Officer, Regions Hospital, Saint Paul, MN, p. A351

LARET, Mark R., Chief Executive Officer, UCSF Medical Center, San Francisco, CA, p. A91

LARIMER, Cynthia, M.D. Chief of Staff, Lake Butler Hospital Hand Surgery Center, Lake Butler, FL, p. A133

LARIMORE, Rhonda, Vice President Human Resources, Magee–Womens Hospital of UPMC, Pittsburgh, PA, p. A551

LARISCY, Robin Barton, M.D. Medical Director, Mary S Harper Geriatric Psychiatry Center, Tuscaloosa, AL, p. A26

LARIVIERE, Beckye, Controller, HEALTHSOUTH Rehabilitation Hospital of Charleston, Charleston, SC, p. A563

LARKIN, Kevin, Regional Chief Financial Officer, Presence Saint Joseph Hospital, Elgin, IL, p. A189

LARKIN, Kim, Chief Information Officer, Washington County Hospital, Nashville, IL, p. A197

LARKINS, Gloria, Vice President Finance, Detroit Receiving Hospital/University Health Center, Detroit, MI, p. A321

LARMON, Mary Jane, Chief Clinical Officer, Vibra Hospital of Mahoning Valley, Boardman, OH, p. A484

LARNER, Cheryl, Chief Financial Officer, Sentara CarePlex Hospital, Hampton, VA, p. A672

LAROCHELLE, Albert, Chief Executive Officer, Reeves County Hospital, Pecos, TX, p. A641

LARRISON Jr., Robert G., President, Carolinas Rehabilitation, Charlotte, NC, p. A462

LARSEN, Bill, Vice President Human Resources, Driscoll Children's Hospital, Corpus Christi, TX, p. A608

LARSEN, Catherine M., Director Marketing, Sutter Tracy Community Hospital, Tracy, CA, p. A97

LARSEN, Dave M., Chief Financial Officer, LDS Hospital, Salt Lake City, UT, p. A663

LARSEN, Donald, M.D
Chief Medical Officer, Keck Hospital of USC, Los Angeles, CA, p. A72
Chief Medical Officer, USC Verdugo Hills Hospital, Glendale, CA, p. A65

LARSEN, Michael, Director Information Systems, Baylor Medical Center at Garland, Garland, TX, p. A620

LARSEN, Ryan C., FACHE, Chief Executive Officer, Community Medical Center, Falls City, NE, p. A395

LARSON, Barbara, R.N. Vice President and Chief Nursing Officer, Ottumwa Regional Health Center, Ottumwa, IA, p. A236

LARSON, Barbara R., R.N. Vice President Patient Care Services, Avera Sacred Heart Hospital, Yankton, SD, p. A578

LARSON, Bill, Chief Financial Officer, Torrance Memorial Medical Center, Torrance, CA, p. A97

LARSON, Eric, Director Human Resources, HEALTHSOUTH Harmarville Rehabilitation Hospital, Pittsburgh, PA, p. A551

LARSON, Erick, Vice President and Chief Information Officer, Mid–Columbia Medical Center, The Dalles, OR, p. A530

LARSON, Gordon, Chief Executive Officer, Sanford Aberdeen Medical Center, Aberdeen, SD, p. A572

LARSON, Jennifer, M.D. Chief of Staff, Blue Ridge Regional Hospital, Spruce Pine, NC, p. A473

LARSON, Jon, M.D. Medical Director, HEALTHSOUTH Rehabilitation Institute of Tucson, Tucson, AZ, p. A40

LARSON, Karla, Director Human Resources, Stevens Community Medical Center, Morris, MN, p. A348

LARSON, Kay, R.N. Chief Nursing Officer, Essentia Health St. Mary's – Detroit Lakes, Detroit Lakes, MN, p. A342

LARSON, Kirk, Chief Information Officer, Natividad Medical Center, Salinas, CA, p. A88

LARSON, Larry, Management Analyst, Dorothea Dix Psychiatric Center, Bangor, ME, p. A291

LARSON, Michael, Vice President Chief Information Officer, MidMichigan Medical Center–Clare, Clare, MI, p. A321

LARSON, Mike, Chief Operating Officer, Essentia Health St. Joseph's Medical Center, Brainerd, MN, p. A340

LARSON, Pamela, Division Director Financial Services, Hutchinson Health, Hutchinson, MN, p. A345

LARSON, Peggy, R.N., Administrator, Lisbon Area Health Services, Lisbon, ND, p. A479

LARSON, Rodney, M.D. Medical Director, Fall River Hospital, Hot Springs, SD, p. A574

LARSON, Ronald, Chief Financial Officer, Veterans Affairs San Diego Healthcare System, San Diego, CA, p. A90

LARSON, Scott, M.D. Vice President Medical Affairs and Chief Medical Officer, Bronson Methodist Hospital, Kalamazoo, MI, p. A328

LARSON, Scott C., Chief Executive Officer, Sanford Canton–Inwood Medical Center, Canton, SD, p. A572

LARSON, Shelly, Chief Financial Officer, Hot Springs County Memorial Hospital, Thermopolis, WY, p. A723

LARSON, Steve, M.D. Director Information Systems, Mercy Medical Center–Sioux City, Sioux City, IA, p. A238

LARSON, Tammy, Chief Financial Officer, Towner County Medical Center, Cando, ND, p. A476

LARSON, Tracy, MS Vice President Patient Care Services and Chief Nursing Officer, Mercy Medical Center–Sioux City, Sioux City, IA, p. A238

LARSON, Walt, Vice President Finance, Tillamook Regional Medical Center, Tillamook, OR, p. A530

LARSON, Wendy, Chief Clinical Officer, Promise Hospital of Phoenix, Mesa, AZ, p. A34

LASALA, Frank, M.D. President Medical Staff, OSF Holy Family Medical Center, Monmouth, IL, p. A196

LASCANO, Terrance, Administrative Officer, U. S. Public Health Service Indian Hospital, Cass Lake, MN, p. A341

LASECKI, Matt, Interim Vice President Human Resources, Providence Hospital, Washington, DC, p. A121

LASH, Lashaunda, Manager Human Resources, Pioneer Community Hospital of Stokes, Danbury, NC, p. A463

LASHER, Karen, Chief Nursing Officer, Vanderbilt Stallworth Rehabilitation Hospital, Nashville, TN, p. A591

LASHLEY, Linde, Manager Information Management, East Alabama Medical Center–Lanier, Valley, AL, p. A26

LASHLEY, Michael, Network Administrator, Thousand Oaks Surgical Hospital, Thousand Oaks, CA, p. A97

LASKER, Rose, Director Information Services, Bluefield Regional Medical Center, Bluefield, WV, p. A693

LASKOWSKI, Robert J., M.D., President and Chief Executive Officer, Christiana Care Health System, Wilmington, DE, p. B35

LASKOWSKI, Robert J., M.D., President and Chief Executive Officer, Christiana Care Health System, Newark, DE, p. A119

LASKOWSKI, Rose, R.N., Director, Caro Center, Caro, MI, p. A320

LASKY, John, Vice President and Chief Human Resources Officer, Temple University Hospital, Philadelphia, PA, p. A550

LASOTA, John, Assistant Finance Officer, Clement J. Zablocki Veterans Affairs Medical Center, Milwaukee, WI, p. A710

LASSITER, Rick, President and Chief Administrative Officer, Parkwest Medical Center, Knoxville, TN, p. A586

LASSITER, Susan S., FACHE, President and Chief Executive Officer, Vidant Roanoke–Chowan Hospital, Ahoskie, NC, p. A459

LASSITER III, Wright L., Chief Executive Officer, Alameda County Medical Center, Oakland, CA, p. A80

LASSITER III,, Wright L., Chief Executive Officer, Alameda Health System, San Leandro, CA, p. B8

LASTER, Charles, Director Information Management, WK Bossier Health Center, Bossier City, LA, p. A274

LATER, Elizabeth B., R.N. Chief Nursing Officer, Ogden Regional Medical Center, Ogden, UT, p. A661

LATHROM, Sue, Director of Nursing/Patient Care System Leader, Scheurer Hospital, Pigeon, MI, p. A332

LATHROP, Deanna, Assistant Administrator, Sabine County Hospital, Hemphill, TX, p. A623

LATIBEAUDIERE, Jorge, Chief Financial Officer, Doctors Hospital of Laredo, Laredo, TX, p. A632

LATIMER, Timothy, Chief Financial Officer, Great Bend Regional Hospital, Great Bend, KS, p. A244

LATORRE, Juan Carlos, Administrator, Hospital Oriente, Humacao, PR, p. A726

LATTERNER, Renee, Director Human Resources, Lake Wales Medical Center, Lake Wales, FL, p. A133

LATTIMORE, Justin, Chief Financial Officer, Iron County Medical Center, Pilot Knob, MO, p. A378

LATTO, Janet B., Chief Nursing Officer and Disaster Officer, Pacifica Hospital of the Valley,, CA, p. A74

LATUCHIE, Richard, Vice President Business Development, Rapid City Regional Hospital, Rapid City, SD, p. A576

LATULIPPE, Steve, President Medical Staff, East Liverpool City Hospital, East Liverpool, OH, p. A493

LAUBENTHAL, Sherrie L., R.N. Chief Nursing Officer, Clarinda Regional Health Center, Clarinda, IA, p. A227

LAUDERBACH, Jr., C. W., Vice President Clinical Services, St. Mary Mercy Hospital, Livonia, MI, p. A329

LAUDON, Larry A., Administrator, Community Behavioral Health Hospital – Bemidji, Bemidji, MN, p. A340

LAUE, Edward, M.D. Chief Medical Officer, Texas Health Huguley Hospital Fort Worth South, Fort Worth, TX, p. A619

LAUE, Jerry, Administrator, St. Vincent Clay Hospital, Brazil, IN, p. A207

LAUER, Ann, Director Finance, River's Edge Hospital and Clinic, Saint Peter, MN, p. A352

LAUER, Bill, Chief Information Officer, Morris County Hospital, Council Grove, KS, p. A243

LAUF, Michael K., President and Chief Executive Officer, Cape Cod Healthcare, Inc., Hyannis, MA, p. B26

LAUF, Michael K., President and Chief Executive Officer, Cape Cod Hospital, Hyannis, MA, p. A311

LAUFFER, Daniel, FACH
Executive Vice President and Chief Operating Officer, Saint Francis Hospital, Charleston, WV, p. A694
Senior Vice President and Chief Operating Officer, Thomas Memorial Hospital, South Charleston, WV, p. A699

LAUFLE, Chuck, Director of Information Services, San Luis Valley Health, Alamosa, CO, p. A102

LAUGHLIN, Don, Director Information Services, Presbyterian–St. Luke's Medical Center, Denver, CO, p. A105

LAUGHLIN, Nancy, R.N. Chief Nursing Officer, Nebraska Orthopaedic Hospital, Omaha, NE, p. A400

LAUGHLIN, Rod, President and Chief Executive Officer, Restora Healthcare, Alpharetta, GA, p. B114

LAUGHLIN, Warren, Vice President Human Resources, Longmont United Hospital, Longmont, CO, p. A109

LAUGHNAN Jr., Woody J., Administrator, Glenn Medical Center, Willows, CA, p. A101

LAUKAITIS, Fran, R.N. Vice President Nursing, Methodist Charlton Medical Center, Dallas, TX, p. A611

LAUMAN, Joan, Manager Clinical Systems, Abington Health Lansdale Hospital, Lansdale, PA, p. A542

LAUNIUS, Billie, Director Business Finance, Dallas County Medical Center, Fordyce, AR, p. A46

LAURENT, Merrill, M.D. Medical Director, Regency Hospital of Covington, Covington, LA, p. A276

LAURETO, Rose Ann
Corporate Vice President Information Resources, ProMedica Bay Park Hospital, Oregon, OH, p. A500
Chief Information Officer, ProMedica Fostoria Community Hospital, Fostoria, OH, p. A494
Chief Information Officer, ProMedica Toledo Hospital, Toledo, OH, p. A503

LAURIN, George M., Interim Director Human Resources, Crisp Regional Hospital, Cordele, GA, p. A157

LAURO, Frank, M.D. Chief Medical Officer, Indian Path Medical Center, Kingsport, TN, p. A585

LAUTER, Keith A.
Vice President Finance, Franciscan St. Elizabeth Health – Crawfordsville, Crawfordsville, IN, p. A209
Regional Chief Financial Officer, Franciscan St. Francis Health – Indianapolis, Indianapolis, IN, p. A214

LAUTEREN, Mark
Chief Information Officer, University of South Alabama Children's and Women's Hospital, Mobile, AL, p. A23
Chief Information Officer, University of South Alabama Medical Center, Mobile, AL, p. A23

LAUTNER, Marty, Vice President Finance and Chief Financial Officer, Cardinal Hill Rehabilitation Hospital, Lexington, KY, p. A264

LAUVE, Lisa R., R.N. Regional Chief Nursing Executive and Chief Operating Officer, CHRISTUS St. Frances Cabrini Hospital, Alexandria, LA, p. A272

LAUVER, David, M.D. Chief Division Hospital Based Care, Central Maine Medical Center, Lewiston, ME, p. A293

LAUZAU, Paul, Controller, Oakwood Hospital–Southshore, Trenton, MI, p. A336

LAVALLEY, Marlinda L., Chief Executive Officer, Gouverneur Hospital, Gouverneur, NY, p. A438

LAVELLE, John P., M.D. Chief Medical Officer, Parkview Hospital, Wheeler, TX, p. A657

LAVELY, Patricia A., FACHE Senior Vice President and Chief Information Officer, Gwinnett Hospital System, Lawrenceville, GA, p. A162

LAVER, Joseph H., M.D. Chief Medical Officer, Stony Brook University Medical Center, Stony Brook, NY, p. A455

LAVERDIERE, Dana, Director Human Resources, St. Anthony Summit Medical Center, Frisco, CO, p. A106

LAVERY FRASCA, Denise Anne, MSN Senior Vice President Patient Care Services and Chief Nursing Officer, Jeanes Hospital, Philadelphia, PA, p. A548

LAVIGNETTE, Brooke, Director of Nursing, Sycamore Springs Hospital, Lafayette, IN, p. A217

LAVIOLETTE, Judy, M.D. Chief Medical Officer, Texas Health Harris Methodist Hospital Cleburne, Cleburne, TX, p. A606

LAVOIE, Brad, Chief Financial Officer, Coastal Harbor Treatment Center, Savannah, GA, p. A166

LAW, Charles, Ph.D. Chief Operating Officer, Catawba Hospital, Catawba, VA, p. A669

LAW, Johnny, Area Information Officer, Kaiser Permanente Oakland Medical Center, Oakland, CA, p. A80

LAW, Kate J., Director Human Resources, Maple Grove Hospital, Maple Grove, MN, p. A346

LAWATSCH, Frank, Chief Executive Officer, Swift County–Benson Hospital, Benson, MN, p. A340

LAWHORN, Renee, Director Medical Records, East Texas Medical Center Carthage, Carthage, TX, p. A605

LAWHORNE, Thomas, Chief Financial Officer, Regional Medical Center Bayonet Point, Hudson, FL, p. A131

LAWLER, Anne, Director Human Resources, Marion Regional Medical Center, Hamilton, AL, p. A21

LAWLER, Kay, Business Office Manager, North Mississippi Medical Center–West Point, West Point, MS, p. A366

LAWLER, Patrick, Chief Executive Officer, Youth Villages Inner Harbour Campus, Douglasville, GA, p. A158

LAWLER, Stephen, President, Vidant Medical Center, Greenville, NC, p. A465

LAWLESS, JoBeth, Chief Nursing Officer, Nursing Services and Director Emergency Management Services, Lucas County Health Center, Chariton, IA, p. A227

LAWLESS, Rosalie, Director Human Resources, Fairlawn Rehabilitation Hospital, Worcester, MA, p. A316

LAWLEY, Richard W., Vice President Human Resources, TMC Healthcare, Tucson, AZ, p. A41

LAWLOR, Kevin F., President and Chief Executive Officer, Huntington Hospital, Huntington, NY, p. A439

LAWONN, Kenneth
Senior Vice President and Chief Information Officer, CHI Health Mercy Corning, Corning, IA, p. A228
Senior Vice President and Chief Information Officer, CHI Health Midlands, Papillion, NE, p. A401
Senior Vice President and Chief Information Officer, CHI Health Schuyler, Schuyler, NE, p. A401
Senior Vice President and Chief Information Officer, Sharp Grossmont Hospital, La Mesa, CA, p. A68
Senior Vice President and Chief Information Officer, Sharp Memorial Hospital, San Diego, CA, p. A90
Senior Vice President Information Systems, Sharp Mesa Vista Hospital, San Diego, CA, p. A90

LAWRASON, Jock, M.D. Chief Medical Officer, Nantucket Cottage Hospital, Nantucket, MA, p. A312

LAWRENCE, Bruce, President and Chief Executive Officer, INTEGRIS Health, Oklahoma City, OK, p. B76

LAWRENCE, Dana, Chief Financial Officer, Parkway Regional Hospital, Fulton, KY, p. A261

LAWRENCE, Jeffrey T., Chief Operating Officer, Denton Regional Medical Center, Denton, TX, p. A613

LAWRENCE, Kathy, Interim Vice President of Patient Care Services, Sentara Albemarle Medical Center, Elizabeth City, NC, p. A464

LAWRENCE, Mark, Director Information Systems, Saint Francis Hospital–Bartlett, Bartlett, TN, p. A579

LAWRENCE, Michael A., Chief Financial Officer, MacNeal Hospital, Berwyn, IL, p. A181

LAWRENCE, Rita, Director of Nursing, Doctors Hospital of West Covina, West Covina, CA, p. A100

LAWRENCE, Sandra A J
Executive Vice President and Chief Financial Officer, Children's Mercy Hospitals and Clinics, Kansas City, MO, p. A373
Executive Vice President and Chief Financial Officer, Children's Mercy South, Overland Park, KS, p. A252

LAWRENCE, Stephanie
Chief Financial Officer, Kentfield Rehabilitation and Specialty Hospital, Kentfield, CA, p. A68
Chief Financial Officer, Vibra Specialty Hospital of Portland, Portland, OR, p. A529

LAWRENCE, Tiffany, Chief Financial Officer, Sanford Medical Center Fargo, Fargo, ND, p. A477

LAWRENCE, Tony, Chief Financial Officer, Providence St. Joseph's Hospital, Chewelah, WA, p. A682

LAWRENCE, Ursula, MSN Chief Nursing Officer, Piedmont Medical Center, Rock Hill, SC, p. A569

LAWRENCE, William P., President and Chief Executive Officer, McLaren Central Michigan, Mount Pleasant, MI, p. A330

LAWRENSON, Victoria
Chief Operating Officer, Bullock County Hospital, Union Springs, AL, p. A26
Chief Operating Officer, Crenshaw Community Hospital, Luverne, AL, p. A22

LAWSON, Alvin R., FACHE, Chief Executive Officer, HEALTHSOUTH Western Hills Rehabilitation Hospital, Parkersburg, WV, p. A698

LAWSON, David C., Senior Vice President Human Resources, St. Clare Hospital, Lakewood, WA, p. A685

LAWSON, Doug, Chief Operating Officer, Baylor University Medical Center, Dallas, TX, p. A610

LAWSON, Judy, Director Information Services, Norton Community Hospital, Norton, VA, p. A676

LAWSON, Michael, President and Chief Operating Officer, OhioHealth Grant Medical Center, Columbus, OH, p. A490

LAWSON, Ralph E., Executive Vice President and Chief Financial Officer, Baptist Health South Florida, Baptist Hospital of Miami, Miami, FL, p. A136

LAWSON, Sandra K., Interim Director Fiscal Services, Shriners Hospitals for Children–St. Louis, Saint Louis, MO, p. A381

LAWSON, West, M.D
Chief Medical Officer, WakeMed Cary Hospital, Cary, NC, p. A461
Chief Medical Officer, WakeMed Raleigh Campus, Raleigh, NC, p. A471

LAWTON, Geoff, Vice President Operations, Littleton Adventist Hospital, Littleton, CO, p. A109

LAWYER, Kristin, Director Human Resources, Weatherford Regional Medical Center, Weatherford, TX, p. A656

LAY, Jr., A. K., M.D. Chief Medical Officer, Jasper General Hospital, Bay Springs, MS, p. A355

LAY, Barbara, Chief Executive Officer, Pocahontas Memorial Hospital, Buckeye, WV, p. A693

LAYDEN, Lisa, Chief Operating Officer, Highland Hospital, Charleston, WV, p. A694

LAYMAN, Linda, Director Human Resources, MedStar Union Memorial Hospital, Baltimore, MD, p. A297

LAYNE, Kristine, R.N. Chief Nursing Officer, Riverwood Healthcare Center, Aitkin, MN, p. A339

LAYTON, Ann, M.D. Chief of Staff, North Metro Medical Center, Jacksonville, AR, p. A48

LAYUGAN, Melvin, Director Human Resources, Horizon Specialty Hospital, Las Vegas, NV, p. A406

LAZARUS, David, M.D. Medical Director Clinical Affairs, Newton Medical Center, Newton, NJ, p. A420

LAZO, Nelson, Chief Executive Officer, Baptist Health South Florida, Doctors Hospital, Coral Gables, FL, p. A126

LAZROFF, Gary, Vice President Human Resources, St. John Medical Center, Westlake, OH, p. A505

LAZURE, Lee A., Director Civil Service Commission, Douglas County Community Mental Health Center, Omaha, NE, p. A400

LAZZARO, III, Frank A., Chief Human Resources Officer, Phelps County Regional Medical Center, Rolla, MO, p. A379

LE, Emily, Director Information Technology and Services, Woman's Hospital of Texas, Houston, TX, p. A628

LE, Jennifer, Chief Financial Officer, Southern Hills Hospital and Medical Center, Las Vegas, NV, p. A406

LEA, Hampton P. S., Acting Chief Executive Officer, Eastern Louisiana Mental Health System, Jackson, LA, p. A279

LEA, Randy, M.D. Vice President and Chief Medical Officer, Alice Peck Day Memorial Hospital, Lebanon, NH, p. A410

LEA, Rich, Vice President Operations, Euclid Hospital, Euclid, OH, p. A493

LEACH, Craig, President and Chief Executive Officer, Torrance Memorial Medical Center, Torrance, CA, p. A97

LEACH, Leslie, Administrator, Memorial Specialty Hospital, Lufkin, TX, p. A635

LEACH, Mary Anne, Vice President and Chief Information Officer, Children's Hospital Colorado, Aurora, CO, p. A102

LEACH, Ryan, Chief Information Officer, St. John's Hospital, Springfield, IL, p. A203

LEACH, Steven, M.D. Chief Medical Officer, University of Texas Southwestern Medical Center, Dallas, TX, p. A612

LEACH, Thomas J., Administrator, Lakeside Medical Center, Belle Glade, FL, p. A123

LEACH, Todd, Chief Information Officer, University of Texas Medical Branch Hospitals, Galveston, TX, p. A620

LEADBETTER, Jr., Raymond J., Revenue Cycle Consultant, Appling Healthcare System, Baxley, GA, p. A154

LEADER, Skip, Chief Information Officer, Choctaw Nation Health Care Center, Talihina, OK, p. A519

LEAHY, Kevin D., President and Chief Executive Officer, Franciscan Alliance, Mishawaka, IN, p. B59

LEAHY, Mary, M.D., Chief Executive Officer, Good Samaritan Hospital, Suffern, NY, p. A455

LEAHY, Mary P., Vice President Human Resources, St. Joseph Hospital, Orange, CA, p. A81

LEAHY, Rosanne, Vice President Nursing Services, CarolinaEast Health System, New Bern, NC, p. A470

LEAKE, Jeanne E., R.N. Chief Nursing Officer, Uvalde County Hospital Authority, Uvalde, TX, p. A654

LEAKE, Neta F., Administrative Assistant Human Resources, West Feliciana Parish Hospital, Saint Francisville, LA, p. A288

LEAKE, Sandy, MSN Associate Director, Nursing and Patient Care Services, Atlanta Veterans Affairs Medical Center, Decatur, GA, p. A158

LEAKEY, Kim, R.N. Chief Nursing Officer, Lafayette Regional Health Center, Lexington, MO, p. A376

LEAL, Carlos, Director Information Technology, Valley Regional Medical Center, Brownsville, TX, p. A604

LEAL, Jr., Joseph M., M.D. Chief of Staff, Glendive Medical Center, Glendive, MT, p. A387

LEAMING, Larry E., FACHE, Chief Executive Officer, Roosevelt General Hospital, Portales, NM, p. A429

LEAMON, Jim, Chief Financial Officer, JFK Medical Center, Atlantis, FL, p. A123

LEAR, Richard
Director Information Systems, St. David's Medical Center, Austin, TX, p. A600
Director Information Systems, St. David's South Austin Medical Center, Austin, TX, p. A600

LEARSON, Jerome, Manager Information Technology and Chief Security Officer, Palo Verde Hospital, Blythe, CA, p. A58

LEARY, Edward B., Chief Executive Officer, New Bedford Rehabilitation Hospital, New Bedford, MA, p. A312

LEARY, Matt, Chief Financial Officer, Wesley Medical Center, Wichita, KS, p. A257

LEASE, Faye, Director of Nursing, Reeves County Hospital, Pecos, TX, p. A641

LEASE-HOMEYER, Cheryl, Lead Information Technology Business Partner, Mercy Hospital Carthage, Carthage, MO, p. A369

LEASURE, Sandie, Senior Vice President Human Resources, O'Bleness Memorial Hospital, Athens, OH, p. A483

LEATH, Gina, R.N. Chief Nursing Officer, Parkway Regional Hospital, Fulton, KY, p. A261

LEATHERS, Cynthia, R.N
Chief Nursing Officer, Integris Bass Baptist Health Center, Enid, OK, p. A510
Chief Nursing Officer, Integris Bass Pavilion, Enid, OK, p. A510

LEAVER, William B., President and Chief Executive Officer, UnityPoint Health, West Des Moines, IA, p. B139

LEAVITT, Cynthia, R.N. Senior Vice President, Hospital Operations, Lincoln Health, Damariscotta, ME, p. A293

LEAZER, Ronald, Chief Financial Officer, Gateway Regional Medical Center, Granite City, IL, p. A191

LEBEAU, Michelle, Vice President Human Resources, Champlain Valley Physicians Hospital Medical Center, Plattsburgh, NY, p. A451

LEBER, Ian, M.D. Chief Medical Officer, Bayshore Community Hospital, Holmdel, NJ, p. A417

LEBLANC, Ed, M.D. Vice President Medical Affairs, Seton Northwest Hospital, Austin, TX, p. A599

LEBLANC, Karen, Director, Applications, Samaritan Hospital, Troy, NY, p. A456

LEBOWITZ, Howard, M.D. Chief Medical Officer, Specialty Hospital of Central Jersey, Lakewood, NJ, p. A417

LEBRON, Juan, M.D. Medical Director, HEALTHSOUTH Sea Pines Rehabilitation Hospital, Melbourne, FL, p. A136

LEBRON, Sonia M., Human Resources Specialist, Industrial Hospital, San Juan, PR, p. A728

LEBRUN, James, Chief Executive Officer, Perkins County Health Services, Grant, NE, p. A396

LECATES, William W., M.D. Medical Director, Bassett Medical Center, Cooperstown, NY, p. A436

LECHICH, Anthony, M.D. Chief Medical Officer, Terence Cardinal Cooke Health Care Center, New York, NY, p. A449

LECHMAN, Brenda, Director Human Resources, Haxtun Hospital District, Haxtun, CO, p. A107

LECHNER, David, M.D. Chief Medical Officer and Vice President Innovation, Community Medical Center, Missoula, MT, p. A389

LECHOCO, Bing, Director Human Resources, Specialty Hospital of Washington–Hadley, Washington, DC, p. A122

LECHUGA, Mario, Director Human Resources, Turquoise Lodge Hospital, Albuquerque, NM, p. A427

LECKELT, Mitchell D.
Interim Chief Executive Officer, Bell Hospital, Ishpeming, MI, p. A327

Assistant Administrator, Marquette General Hospital, Marquette, MI, p. A330

LECKER, Marijo, Vice President, Martha Jefferson Hospital, Charlottesville, VA, p. A669

LEDAY, Jason, Chief Executive Officer, St. Anthony's Hospital, Houston, TX, p. A626

LEDBETTER, Joy, Vice President Employee and Patient Experience and Chief Human Resources Officer, UnityPoint Health – Methodist, Peoria, IL, p. A200

LEDDEN, Edwin L., Assistant Administrator and Director Human Resources, Henry County Medical Center, Paris, TN, p. A592

LEDERER, Jane, R.N. Vice President and Chief Nursing Officer, Kingsbrook Jewish Medical Center,, NY, p. A445

LEDERMAN, Joel, Director Information Systems, Community Health Center of Branch County, Coldwater, MI, p. A321

LEDERMAN, Mark, Chief Information Officer, Interfaith Medical Center,, NY, p. A444

LEDFORD, Keith, M.D. Chief of Staff, Scenic Mountain Medical Center, Big Spring, TX, p. A603

LEDOUX, Roger C., Chief Executive Officer, Byrd Regional Hospital, Leesville, LA, p. A282

LEDYARD, Robin, M.P.H., President, Community Hospital East, Indianapolis, IN, p. A213

LEE, Brett D., Chief Executive Officer, Lake Pointe Medical Center, Rowlett, TX, p. A645

LEE, Byong, Manager Information Technology and PACS Administrator, Limestone Medical Center, Groesbeck, TX, p. A622

LEE, Cheryl, Director Human Resources, Eliza Coffee Memorial Hospital, Florence, AL, p. A20

LEE, Cheryl D., R.N. Vice President of Patient Care Services and Chief Nursing Officer, University of Maryland Rehabilitation and Orthopaedic Institute, Baltimore, MD, p. A298

LEE, David, Chief Executive Officer, Otto Kaiser Memorial Hospital, Kenedy, TX, p. A631

LEE, Deborah, Chief Nursing Officer, Community Westview Hospital, Indianapolis, IN, p. A213

LEE, Dennis, Vice President and Chief Information Officer, Cabell Huntington Hospital, Huntington, WV, p. A695

LEE, Eric A., President and Chief Executive Officer, Jennie Stuart Medical Center, Hopkinsville, KY, p. A263

LEE, Gina, Chief Financial Officer, Fort Lauderdale Hospital, Fort Lauderdale, FL, p. A128

LEE, James, M.D. Chief of Staff, Winn Parish Medical Center, Winnfield, LA, p. A290

LEE, James Y., Executive Vice President and Chief Operating Officer, Lawrence Hospital Center, Bronxville, NY, p. A434

LEE, Jeannie, Director Human Resources, Marshall County Hospital, Benton, KY, p. A258

LEE, Jenny, Human Resources Generalist, Essentia Health–Holy Trinity Hospital, Graceville, MN, p. A344

LEE, John Paul, M.D. Chief of Staff, Lackey Memorial Hospital, Forest, MS, p. A358

LEE, John R., Chief Executive Officer, Mat–Su Regional Medical Center, Palmer, AK, p. A30

LEE, Joshua, Chief Information Officer, University of Southern California–Norris Cancer Hospital, Los Angeles, CA, p. A75

LEE, Karen, MSN Chief Nursing Officer, Belton Regional Medical Center, Belton, MO, p. A367

LEE, Karen, Director Human Resources, Gallup Indian Medical Center, Gallup, NM, p. A428

LEE, Kayleen R., Chief Executive Officer, Sioux Center Health, Sioux Center, IA, p. A237

LEE, Kevin D., Director and Chief Executive Officer, Polaris Hospital Company, Brentwood, TN, p. B107

LEE, Kim, Chief Financial Officer, Bowie Memorial Hospital, Bowie, TX, p. A603

LEE, Larry, Chief Financial Officer, United Hospital District, Blue Earth, MN, p. A340

LEE, Lori L., Assistant Vice President Nursing, Nanticoke Memorial Hospital, Seaford, DE, p. A119

LEE, Mary C., Manager Human Resources, Jonathan M. Wainwright Memorial Veterans Affairs Medical Center, Walla Walla, WA, p. A692

LEE, Michael D., Chief Human Resources Officer, Adirondack Medical Center, Saranac Lake, NY, p. A454

LEE, Mihi, Chief Financial Officer, Coast Plaza Hospital, Norwalk, CA, p. A80

LEE, Mike, R.N. Chief Nursing Officer, Matagorda Regional Medical Center, Bay City, TX, p. A601

LEE, Nancy, R.N. Vice President Patient Care Services and Chief Nursing Officer, Stanford Hospital and Clinics, Palo Alto, CA, p. A82

LEE, Nathan W., Chief Executive Officer, Mary Breckinridge ARH Hospital, Hyden, KY, p. A263

LEE, Pamela, Executive Vice President Operations and Chief Quality Officer, United Medical Center, Washington, DC, p. A122

LEE, Randall, Vice President and Chief Operating Officer, Baptist Health South Florida, Baptist Hospital of Miami, Miami, FL, p. A136

LEE, Reginald, Chief Executive Officer, Kindred Hospital Detroit, Detroit, MI, p. A322

LEE, Robbin, Chief Executive Officer, Wellington Regional Medical Center, West Palm Beach, FL, p. A150

LEE, Robert H., President, Raulerson Hospital, Okeechobee, FL, p. A140

LEE, Sherry, Chief Nurse Executive, Fulton State Hospital, Fulton, MO, p. A372

LEE, Stephen, FACHE, President, Baptist Medical Center Nassau, Fernandina Beach, FL, p. A128

LEE, Terry, M.D. Chief of Staff, Garfield Medical Center, Monterey Park, CA, p. A78

LEE, Thomas G., Chief Financial Officer, Medicine Lodge Memorial Hospital, Medicine Lodge, KS, p. A250

LEE, Thomas J., FACHE, Administrator/CEO, Providence Medical Center, Wayne, NE, p. A402

LEE, Victor N., FACHE, President and Chief Executive Officer, Boone County Health Center, Albion, NE, p. A393

LEE, Wayne, Director of Nursing, Clinch Memorial Hospital, Homerville, GA, p. A161

LEE, Wendy, Chief Nursing Officer, Regional Rehabilitation Hospital, Phenix City, AL, p. A25

LEEGSTRA, Ruurd, Chief Financial Officer, Silver Hill Hospital, New Canaan, CT, p. A116

LEEK, Dustin, Vice President of Enterprise Technical Services, Health First Holmes Regional Medical Center, Melbourne, FL, p. A135

LEEKA, Andrew B., President and Chief Executive Officer, Good Samaritan Hospital, Los Angeles, CA, p. A72

LEEMING, Rosemary, M.D. Chief Medical Officer, UH Regional Hospitals, Cleveland, OH, p. A489

LEEPER, Kevin, Chief Executive Officer, Nevada Regional Medical Center, Nevada, MO, p. A377

LEESMAN, Keenan, Director Information Systems, Abraham Lincoln Memorial Hospital, Lincoln, IL, p. A195

LEFEVRE, Denise, Chief Information Officer, Oroville Hospital, Oroville, CA, p. A82

LEFEVRE, Steve, Chief Executive Officer and Administrator, Fisher County Hospital District, Rotan, TX, p. A644

LEFF, Marc, Vice President Human Resources, St. John's Riverside Hospital, Yonkers, NY, p. A458

LEFFLER, Stephen, Chief Medical Officer, Fletcher Allen Health Care, Burlington, VT, p. A665

LEFKOW, Frances, Director Human Resources, La Rabida Children's Hospital, Chicago, IL, p. A184

LEFTWICH, Hal W., FACHE, Chief Executive Officer, Fishermen's Hospital, Marathon, FL, p. A135

LEGASPI, Johnson, Director Information Systems, Alhambra Hospital Medical Center, Alhambra, CA, p. A55

LEGAULT, Matt, Chief Financial Administrator, Oakwood Hospital–Dearborn, Dearborn, MI, p. A321

LEGEL, Tom, Chief Financial Officer and Chief Operating Officer, Samaritan Healthcare, Moses Lake, WA, p. A685

LEGER, Lynn, Director Information Systems, Ridgeview Institute, Smyrna, GA, p. A167

LEGERE, Tina, President, Central Maine Medical Center, Lewiston, ME, p. A293

LEGG, Alyce, Vice President Human Resources, Samaritan Regional Health System, Ashland, OH, p. A482

LEGG, Debra Lynn, Associate Director Patient Care Services and Nurse Executive, Beckley Veterans Affairs Medical Center, Beckley, WV, p. A693

LEGG, Paul, M.D. President Medical Staff, Saint Francis Hospital, Charleston, WV, p. A694

LEGG, Susan E., Interim Administrator, Noland Hospital Montgomery, Montgomery, AL, p. A24

LEGGETT III, G. Raymond, President and Chief Executive Officer, CarolinaEast Health System, New Bern, NC, p. A470

LEGGETT, Sandra, R.N. Chief Nursing Officer, Atchison Hospital, Atchison, KS, p. A241

LEGLEITER, Brenda, R.N., Chief Executive Officer, Rush County Memorial Hospital, La Crosse, KS, p. A248

LEGRAND, Daniel, M.D. Chief Medical Officer, St. Vincent Indianapolis Hospital, Indianapolis, IN, p. A215

LEGRAND III,, Edwin C., Executive Director, Mississippi State Department of Mental Health, Jackson, MS, p. B95

LEHMAN, Andy
Chief Information Officer, Greene Memorial Hospital, Xenia, OH, p. A506

Vice President Information Systems, Soin Medical Center, Beavercreek, OH, p. A483

LEHMAN, James A., M.D
Vice President Medical Affairs, Covenant Medical Center, Waterloo, IA, p. A239

Vice President Medical Affairs, Mercy Hospital of Franciscan Sisters, Oelwein, IA, p. A235

LEHMAN, Sandi, Chief Financial Officer, Humboldt General Hospital, Winnemucca, NV, p. A408

LEHN, Matt, Chief Operating Officer, Bluffton Regional Medical Center, Bluffton, IN, p. A207

LEHN, Toby, Director of Nurses, Concho County Hospital, Eden, TX, p. A614

LEHNHOF–WATTS, Laurie
Assistant Administrator Patient Services, East Texas Medical Center Rehabilitation Hospital, Tyler, TX, p. A654

Assistant Administrator Risk Management Performance Improvement and Education, East Texas Medical Center Specialty Hospital, Tyler, TX, p. A654

LEHRACH, Christopher, M.D. Chief Transformation Officer for Interim Operations, Westerly Hospital, Westerly, RI, p. A561

LEIBMAN, Maurice, M.D. Chief Medical Officer, Memorial Hermann Northwest Hospital, Houston, TX, p. A625

LEICHMAN, Ann Marie, R.N. Vice President Patient Care Services and Chief Nursing Officer, Valley Hospital, Ridgewood, NJ, p. A422

LEICHNER, Raymond, Director Finance, Abington Health Lansdale Hospital, Lansdale, PA, p. A542

LEIDY, R. Grant, Vice President Finance, Deborah Heart and Lung Center, Browns Mills, NJ, p. A414

LEIF, Sue, R.N. Director Human Resources, Annie Jeffrey Memorial County Health Center, Osceola, NE, p. A400

LEIGH, Jordan, Chief Financial Officer, Boundary Community Hospital, Bonners Ferry, ID, p. A175

LEIGHTON, Heather, Director, Revenue Cycle and Privacy Officer, Upper Connecticut Valley Hospital, Colebrook, NH, p. A409

LEIGHTON, Marc
Vice President Human Resources, Nexus Specialty Hospital, Shenandoah, TX, p. A649

Vice President Human Resources, Nexus Specialty Hospital The Woodlands, Spring, TX, p. A650

LEIGHTON, Richard, Financial Application Analyst, Unity Medical & Surgical Hospital, Mishawaka, IN, p. A219

LEINEN, Rick, Chief Financial Officer, Montgomery County Memorial Hospital, Red Oak, IA, p. A236

LEISE, Karen, Coordinator Human Resources, Saunders Medical Center, Wahoo, NE, p. A402

LEISHER, George, Chief Human Resources Officer, Antelope Valley Hospital, Lancaster, CA, p. A69

LEISHER, Karla, Business Office Manager, Beaver County Memorial Hospital, Beaver, OK, p. A508

LEIST, Vincent, President and Chief Executive Officer, North Arkansas Regional Medical Center, Harrison, AR, p. A47

LEITE, Dolores
Chief Human Resource Executive, Jacobi Medical Center,, NY, p. A444

Chief Human Resource Executive, North Central Bronx Hospital,, NY, p. A447

LEITNER, Mark, Chief Executive Officer, East Texas Medical Center Henderson, Henderson, TX, p. A623

LEJSEK, Shari, Administrator, Patients' Hospital of Redding, Redding, CA, p. A85

LELAND, Joni, Director Human Resources, Memorial Hospital, Gonzales, TX, p. A621

LEM, Alan
Vice President Finance, Fairview Ridges Hospital, Burnsville, MN, p. A341

Vice President Finance, Fairview Southdale Hospital, Edina, MN, p. A343

LEMAIRE, Joseph, Executive Vice President Finance, Riverview Medical Center, Red Bank, NJ, p. A422

LEMAIRE, Joseph M.
Executive Vice President Finance and Partner Company Operations, Bayshore Community Hospital, Holmdel, NJ, p. A417

Executive Vice President, Southern Ocean Medical Center, Manahawkin, NJ, p. A418

LEMAIRE, Suzanne, Manager Health Information Management Services and Corporate Compliance Officer, Scheurer Hospital, Pigeon, MI, p. A332

LEMAISTRE, Collin, Chief Operating Officer, Cypress Fairbanks Medical Center, Houston, TX, p. A624

LEMANSKI, Dennis R., D.O. Senior Vice President Medical Affairs and Medical Education/CMO, Henry Ford Wyandotte Hospital, Wyandotte, MI, p. A337

LEVY, Susan M., M.D. Vice President Medical Affairs, Levindale Hebrew Geriatric Center and Hospital, Baltimore, MD, p. A296

LEWANDOWSKI, Jim, Interim Director of Human Resources, Carson Tahoe Regional Medical Center, Carson City, NV, p. A404

LEWANDOWSKI, Terri, Director Financial Services, Ministry Our Lady of Victory Hospital, Stanley, WI, p. A715

LEWELLEN, Thomas, D.O. Chief of Staff, Delta Memorial Hospital, Dumas, AR, p. A45

LEWERKE, Jane, Manager Human Resources, Northern Arizona Veterans Affairs Health Care System, Prescott, AZ, p. A37

LEWGOOD, Tony
Interim Administrator, Shriners Hospitals for Children–Cincinnati Burns Hospital, Cincinnati, OH, p. A487
Administrator, Shriners Hospitals for Children–Lexington, Lexington, KY, p. A264

LEWIS, Alene, R.N. Chief Nursing Officer, Raleigh General Hospital, Beckley, WV, p. A693

LEWIS, Angel, Senior Vice President Administration, Cookeville Regional Medical Center, Cookeville, TN, p. A581

LEWIS, Barbara, Chief Nursing Officer, Integris Seminole Medical Center, Seminole, OK, p. A518

LEWIS, Brandon, Director of Information Technology, Ivinson Memorial Hospital, Laramie, WY, p. A722

LEWIS, III, Carlisle, Senior Vice President Legal and Human Resources, Sharp Mesa Vista Hospital, San Diego, CA, p. A90

LEWIS, Colleen, Director Human Resources, Texas NeuroRehab Center, Austin, TX, p. A600

LEWIS, Craig, Interim Chief Financial Officer, Sentara Albemarle Medical Center, Elizabeth City, NC, p. A464

LEWIS, Curtis, M.D. Chief of Staff, Grady Memorial Hospital, Atlanta, GA, p. A152

LEWIS, Cynthia, Chief Nursing Officer, Sierra Vista Regional Health Center, Sierra Vista, AZ, p. A39

LEWIS, Dana, Director Clinical Services, Southern Kentucky Rehabilitation Hospital, Bowling Green, KY, p. A259

LEWIS, Darlene, Vice President Human Resources, Canton–Potsdam Hospital, Potsdam, NY, p. A452

LEWIS, Dave, Director Information Services, St. Francis Hospital and Health Services, Maryville, MO, p. A376

LEWIS, Jr., Donald C., Vice President and Chief Financial Officer, Coffee Regional Medical Center, Douglas, GA, p. A158

LEWIS, Doug
Chief Financial Officer, Elks Rehab Hospital, Boise, ID, p. A174
Chief Financial Officer, Wheatland Memorial Healthcare, Harlowton, MT, p. A388

LEWIS, Eric, Chief Executive Officer, Olympic Medical Center, Port Angeles, WA, p. A686

LEWIS, Fred, Chief Financial Officer, Riverview Behavioral Health, Texarkana, AR, p. A53

LEWIS, George E., M.D., Medical Officer, Nebraska Penal and Correctional Hospital, Lincoln, NE, p. A398

LEWIS, Gerry
Chief Information Officer, Seton Highland Lakes, Burnet, TX, p. A605
Chief Information Officer, Seton Medical Center Austin, Austin, TX, p. A599
Chief Information Officer, Seton Medical Center Williamson, Round Rock, TX, p. A645
Chief Information Officer, Seton Northwest Hospital, Austin, TX, p. A599
Chief Information Officer, Seton Shoal Creek Hospital, Austin, TX, p. A600
Chief Information Officer, University Medical Center at Brackenridge, Austin, TX, p. A600

LEWIS, Gordon, Chief Executive Officer, Burnett Medical Center, Grantsburg, WI, p. A705

LEWIS, Irvan Wick, Vice President Human Resources and Clinic Management, Mt. Graham Regional Medical Center, Safford, AZ, p. A38

LEWIS, J. Steve, Director Finance, Youth Villages Inner Harbour Campus, Douglasville, GA, p. A158

LEWIS, Jacob, Chief Financial Officer, Mark Twain Medical Center, San Andreas, CA, p. A88

LEWIS, John I., President and Chief Executive Officer, ACMH Hospital, Kittanning, PA, p. A542

LEWIS, Kathy, Chief Nursing Officer and Vice President Clinical Services, Riverview Regional Medical Center, Carthage, TN, p. A579

LEWIS, Kenneth S., JD, President and Chief Executive Officer, Union Hospital, Elkton, MD, p. A300

LEWIS, Kent, Director Information Services, Southwestern Medical Center, Lawton, OK, p. A512

LEWIS, Kevin, M.D. Chief Medical Officer, Memorial Health Care System, Chattanooga, TN, p. A580

LEWIS, Larry, Chief Executive Officer, Pioneers Memorial Healthcare District, Brawley, CA, p. A58

LEWIS, Lisa F., MSN Vice President and Chief Nursing Officer, Holy Spirit Hospital, Camp Hill, PA, p. A535

LEWIS, Luther J., FACHE, Chief Executive Officer, Five Rivers Medical Center, Pocahontas, AR, p. A52

LEWIS, Marie, Human Resources Liaison, Veterans Affairs St. Louis Health Care System, Saint Louis, MO, p. A382

LEWIS, Michael, Chief Operating Officer, Mother Frances Hospital – Jacksonville, Jacksonville, TX, p. A630

LEWIS, Nan M., Administrator, East Central Regional Hospital, Augusta, GA, p. A153

LEWIS, Nicholas P., Chief Executive Officer, Hardin Medical Center, Savannah, TN, p. A592

LEWIS, Pam, Chief Compliance Officer, William R. Sharpe, Jr. Hospital, Weston, WV, p. A700

LEWIS, Paul, Chief Executive Officer, Holy Rosary Healthcare, Miles City, MT, p. A389

LEWIS, Rayburn, M.D., Chief Executive Officer, Swedish/Issaquah, Issaquah, WA, p. A684

LEWIS, Robin, Chief Financial Officer, Kiowa District Hospital and Manor, Kiowa, KS, p. A247

LEWIS, Ron, President and Chief Executive Officer, Community Howard Regional Health, Kokomo, IN, p. A216

LEWIS, Rosalind, R.N. Chief Nursing Officer, Community HealthCare System, Onaga, KS, p. A251

LEWIS, Sharon, Director Information Systems, Forbes Regional Hospital, Monroeville, PA, p. A545

LEWIS, Sheila, Administrator, Harmon Memorial Hospital, Hollis, OK, p. A512

LEWIS, Shirley, Administrative Officer, Chinle Comprehensive Health Care Facility, Chinle, AZ, p. A31

LEWIS, Steven, Chief Executive Officer, Chase County Community Hospital, Imperial, NE, p. A397

LEWIS, Steven, M.D. Senior Vice President and Chief Medical Officer, Flagstaff Medical Center, Flagstaff, AZ, p. A32

LEWIS, Vickie, Chief Executive Officer, Central Florida Behavioral Hospital, Orlando, FL, p. A140

LEWIS, Winifred, R.N. Chief Nursing Officer, Roseland Community Hospital, Chicago, IL, p. A186

LEWISTON, Jamie, R.N. Chief Nursing Officer, Aurora Psychiatric Hospital, Wauwatosa, WI, p. A718

LEWKOWSKI, William, Executive Vice President Information Services and Chief Information Officer, Metro Health Hospital, Wyoming, MI, p. A337

LI, Ronald, Vice President Management Information Systems, Bergen Regional Medical Center, Paramus, NJ, p. A420

LI, Stephen, Vice President Management Information Systems, Jersey City Medical Center, Jersey City, NJ, p. A417

LI, Xiao H., M.D. Chief of Staff, Surgery Specialty Hospitals of America, Pasadena, TX, p. A641

LIAGRE, Ruthann, Vice President Human Resources, Memorial Healthcare, Owosso, MI, p. A331

LIANG, Bonnie, Divisional Finance Officer, Sutter Maternity and Surgery Center of Santa Cruz, Santa Cruz, CA, p. A94

LIBBY, David, Vice President Operations, Winter Haven Hospital, Winter Haven, FL, p. A150

LIBBY, Kenneth, Vice President Finance, VCU Community Memorial Hospital, South Hill, VA, p. A678

LIBCKE, Julia, R.N. VP Patient Care Services, Rehabilitation Institute of Michigan, Detroit, MI, p. A322

LIBENGOOD, Mary L., President, Conemaugh Meyersdale Medical Center, Meyersdale, PA, p. A545

LIBERATORE, Kristi, Vice President and Chief Financial Officer, St. Joseph Hospital, Orange, CA, p. A81

LICHIUS, Sylvia Marie, R.N. Chief Nursing Officer, Morrill County Community Hospital, Bridgeport, NE, p. A394

LICHTENFELS, Suellen, Vice President and Chief Nursing Officer, Somerset Hospital, Somerset, PA, p. A555

LICHTENWALNER, Tom, Vice President Finance, St. Luke's University Hospital – Bethlehem Campus, Bethlehem, PA, p. A534

LICINA, Leonard, Chief Executive Officer, Kahi Mohala Behavioral Health, Ewa Beach, HI, p. A170

LICKTEIG, Teri, HR Director, Pella Regional Health Center, Pella, IA, p. A236

LIDDELL, Sean, Manager Regional Service Information Technology, UnityPoint Health – Trinity Muscatine, Muscatine, IA, p. A235

LIDHOLM, Helen, Chief Executive Officer, Saint Mary's Regional Medical Center, Reno, NV, p. A408

LIEBER, Alan R., President, Overlook Medical Center, Summit, NJ, p. A423

LIEBERMAN, Jeffrey A., M.D., Executive Director, New York State Psychiatric Institute, New York, NY, p. A447

LIEBERMAN, Steven L., M.D. Chief of Staff, Veterans Affairs New Jersey Health Care System, East Orange, NJ, p. A415

LIEBERS, David, M.D. Chief Medical Officer and Vice President Medical Affairs, Ellis Hospital, Schenectady, NY, p. A454

LIECK, Amy, Chief Nursing Officer, Nix Community General Hospital, Dilley, TX, p. A614

LIEFER, Alan, M.D. President Medical Staff, Memorial Hospital, Chester, IL, p. A183

LIEKWEG, Richard J., President, Barnes–Jewish Hospital, Saint Louis, MO, p. A380

LIEN, Ann, R.N. Chief Nursing Officer, Meeker Memorial Hospital, Litchfield, MN, p. A345

LIEPMAN, Michael T., Chief Operating Officer, Skagit Valley Hospital, Mount Vernon, WA, p. A685

LIESMANN, George, M.D. Chief Medical Officer, Blessing Hospital, Quincy, IL, p. A201

LIGHT, Gary, Vice President and Chief Information Officer, Memorial Hospital and Health Care Center, Jasper, IN, p. A215

LIGHT, Laura, Director Human Resources, St. David's North Austin Medical Center, Austin, TX, p. A600

LIGHTBOURNE, Olieth, Chief Nursing Officer, Streamwood Behavioral Health Center, Streamwood, IL, p. A204

LIGHTCAP, Deb, Director Human Resources, Mercy Medical Center, Roseburg, OR, p. A529

LIGHTFOOT, William M., M.D. Vice President Medical Services, Providence Hospital, Mobile, AL, p. A22

LIGHTNER, Becky, Director Information Systems, Phoebe Sumter Medical Center, Americus, GA, p. A151

LIGON, Kim
Director Information Services, DCH Regional Medical Center, Tuscaloosa, AL, p. A26
Director Information Services, Northport Medical Center, Northport, AL, p. A24

LIGON, Lynda, Chief Nursing Officer, Warm Springs Medical Center, Warm Springs, GA, p. A169

LILES, Jerry, D.O.CHRISTUS Spohn Hospital Alice, Alice, TX, p. A595

LILES, Richard A., M.D. Medical Director, HEALTHSOUTH Rehabilitation Hospital, Largo, FL, p. A134

LILIK, Dennis
Chief Information Officer, Gladys Spellman Specialty Hospital and Nursing Center, Cheverly, MD, p. A299
Chief Information Officer, Prince George's Hospital Center, Cheverly, MD, p. A299

LILLEBOE, Linda, R.N. Director Operations, Carson Valley Medical Center, Gardnerville, NV, p. A404

LILLEY, Jeffrey, CPA Chief Operating Officer, Princeton Community Hospital, Princeton, WV, p. A698

LILLY, Brian, Director Information Systems, Nason Hospital, Roaring Spring, PA, p. A553

LILLY, Ryan S., Acting Director, Maine Veterans Affairs Medical Center, Augusta, ME, p. A291

LILLY, Spencer, President, Carolinas Medical Center, Charlotte, NC, p. A461

LIMA, Robert, Director Information Systems, Massachusetts Hospital School, Canton, MA, p. A309

LIMBAGA, Aries, R.N. Chief Nursing Officer, Rancho Los Amigos National Rehabilitation Center, Downey, CA, p. A62

LIMBOCKER, Jeff, Chief Financial Officer, Our Lady of the Lake Regional Medical Center, Baton Rouge, LA, p. A273

LIN, Dean Q., FACHE, President, Ocean Medical Center, Brick Township, NJ, p. A414

LIN, George, M.D. Physician Advisor, Hackensack University Medical Center at Pascack Valley, Westwood, NJ, p. A424

LIN, James Y., D.O. Chief of Staff, Millcreek Community Hospital, Erie, PA, p. A538

LINAFELTER, Robb, Chief Executive Officer, Lincoln Surgical Hospital, Lincoln, NE, p. A398

LINARES, Manuel, Chief Executive Officer, North Shore Medical Center, Miami, FL, p. A137

LINCKS, Brad, R.N. Chief Nursing Officer and Vice President, Our Lady of Peace, Louisville, KY, p. A266

LINCOLN, David R., FACHE, President and Chief Executive Officer, Covenant Health Systems, Inc., Tewksbury, MA, p. B45

LINCOLN, Wendy, Chief Nursing Officer, Northside Hospital, Saint Petersburg, FL, p. A144

LIND, David, M.D. Chief Medical Officer, Cheyenne Regional Medical Center, Cheyenne, WY, p. A720

LIND, Linda Knudson, Senior Vice President and Chief Operating Officer, Siskin Hospital for Physical Rehabilitation, Chattanooga, TN, p. A580

LIND, Mark, Director Information Technology, Mammoth Hospital, Mammoth Lakes, CA, p. A76

LIND, Sharon, MSN, Chief Executive Officer, Ogallala Community Hospital, Ogallala, NE, p. A399

LIND, Trent, Chief Executive Officer, Texas Orthopedic Hospital, Houston, TX, p. A627

LINDAUER, Randy L., FACHE, Chief Executive Officer, Coffey County Hospital, Burlington, KS, p. A242

LINDBERG, Bob, Chief Operating Officer, Cumberland Memorial Hospital, Cumberland, WI, p. A703

LINDBERG, Bonita N., Director Human Resources, Cortland Regional Medical Center, Cortland, NY, p. A436

LINDBERG, Chris, Chief Information Officer, Milwaukee County Behavioral Health Division, Milwaukee, WI, p. A710

LINDBERG, Randy, Director Fiscal Services, Shriners Hospitals for Children–Salt Lake City, Salt Lake City, UT, p. A663

LINDBERG, Steven, Chief Administrative Officer, Mayo Clinic Health System – Red Cedar in Menomonie, Menomonie, WI, p. A709

LINDELL, Charles, Chief Operating Officer, St. Bernard Parish Hospital, Chalmette, LA, p. A275

LINDELL, Jonathan, Director Information Technology, Miracle Mile Medical Center, Los Angeles, CA, p. A73

LINDEMAN, Annette, Chief Clinical Officer, Kindred Hospital–Tucson, Tucson, AZ, p. A40

LINDEMAN, Barry K., Director Human Resources, Cardinal Hill Rehabilitation Hospital, Lexington, KY, p. A264

LINDEMANN, Fran, Director Finance, Kell West Regional Hospital, Wichita Falls, TX, p. A657

LINDEMOEN, Pamela, Chief Operating Officer, Kaiser Permanente Santa Clara Medical Center, Santa Clara, CA, p. A94

LINDEN, Kelly, Senior Vice President, Chief Operating Officer, St. Mary Medical Center, Apple Valley, CA, p. A56

LINDEN, Todd C., President and Chief Executive Officer, Grinnell Regional Medical Center, Grinnell, IA, p. A231

LINDENBOOM, Kristen, Chief Operating Officer, Plantation General Hospital, Plantation, FL, p. A143

LINDER, Lawrence, M.D. Senior Vice President and Chief Medical Officer, University of Maryland Baltimore Washington Medical Center, Glen Burnie, MD, p. A301

LINDLEY, Michael, Chief Executive Officer, Haven Behavioral Healthcare, Nashville, TN, p. B63

LINDQUIST, Gina, Director Human Resources, Schoolcraft Memorial Hospital, Manistique, MI, p. A329

LINDQUIST, Molly, Interim Chief Financial Officer, Chestatee Regional Hospital, Dahlonega, GA, p. A157

LINDQUIST, Peter, Vice President and Chief Nursing Officer, Providence Hospital, Mobile, AL, p. A22

LINDSAY, Diane, Chief Financial Officer, St. Francis Hospital, Litchfield, IL, p. A195

LINDSAY, Jeffery T., Executive Vice President and Chief Operating Officer, Novant Health Medical Park Hospital, Winston–Salem, NC, p. A475

LINDSEY, Craig, R.N. Vice President Clinical Services/Chief Nursing Officer, Park Ridge Health, Hendersonville, NC, p. A466

LINDSEY, Don, Vice President and Chief information Officer, Tallahassee Memorial HealthCare, Tallahassee, FL, p. A147

LINDSEY, Hugh, M.D. Chief Medical Officer, Hayes Green Beach Memorial Hospital, Charlotte, MI, p. A320

LINDSEY, Jay, Chief Executive Officer, Plano Specialty Hospital, Plano, TX, p. A642

LINDSEY, Jim, M.D. Senior Vice President Medical Affairs, University Medical Center at Brackenridge, Austin, TX, p. A600

LINDSEY, Kenneth, M.D. Vice President of Medical Affairs, Asante Three Rivers Medical Center, Grants Pass, OR, p. A525

LINDSEY, Kim, Chief Human Resources Officer, Lourdes Hospital, Paducah, KY, p. A269

LINDSEY, Jr., Rob, Vice President Human Resources, Allegiance Behavioral Health Center of Plainview, Plainview, TX, p. A642

LINDSEY, Tony, Chief of Staff, University of North Carolina Hospitals, Chapel Hill, NC, p. A461

LINDSTROM, Carol, Director Human Resources, CHI Health Good Samaritan, Kearney, NE, p. A397

LINDSTROM, David, M.D. Vice President Medical Affairs, ProMedica Bay Park Hospital, Oregon, OH, p. A500

LINES, Brian, Chief Operating Officer, Lakeview Hospital, Bountiful, UT, p. A659

LING, Lori, Information Technician, Windom Area Hospital, Windom, MN, p. A354

LINGEN, Tom, M.D. Chief of Staff, Cumberland Memorial Hospital, Cumberland, WI, p. A703

LINGERFELT, Jeff, Chief Executive Officer, Heart of America Medical Center, Rugby, ND, p. A480

LINHARES, James, Chief Executive Officer, Kindred Hospital Riverside, Perris, CA, p. A83

LINK, Kimberly, Manager Human Resources, LifeCare Hospitals of Mechanicsburg, Mechanicsburg, PA, p. A545

LINK, Nate, M.D. Medical Director, Bellevue Hospital Center, New York, NY, p. A442

LINN, Steven C., M.D
Chief Medical Officer, Inspira Medical Center–Elmer, Elmer, NJ, p. A416
Chief Medical Officer, Inspira Medical Center–Vineland, Vineland, NJ, p. A424

LINNA, Gina, Manager Human Resources, Aspirus Ontonagon Hospital, Ontonagon, MI, p. A331

LINSCHEID, Carol, Vice President Human Resources, Enloe Medical Center, Chico, CA, p. A59

LINSE, Margaret, Administrative Secretary and Director Human Resources, West Holt Memorial Hospital, Atkinson, NE, p. A393

LINSIN, Amy, Chief Human Resources Officer, Good Samaritan Medical Center, West Palm Beach, FL, p. A149

LINTON, Dwight, Director Human Resources. Scenic Mountain Medical Center, Big Spring, TX, p. A603

LINTON, Randall L., M.D., President and Chief Executive Officer, Mayo Clinic Health System in Eau Claire, Eau Claire, WI, p. A704

LINTZ, Gordon, Chief Administrative Officer, Morristown–Hamblen Healthcare System, Morristown, TN, p. A590

LINVILLE, Kimberly, Chief Nursing Officer, Grant Memorial Hospital, Petersburg, WV, p. A698

LINZMAN, Rob, D.O. Chief of Staff, Jefferson County Hospital, Waurika, OK, p. A522

LIPARI, Cheryl
Director Information Technology, River Parishes Hospital, La Place, LA, p. A280
Manager Information Systems, Teche Regional Medical Center, Morgan City, LA, p. A284

LIPE, Curt, Vice President, Chief Financial Officer, OSF St. Mary Medical Center, Galesburg, IL, p. A190

LIPHAM, Mary Sue
Chief Financial Officer, St. Luke's Lakeside Hospital, The Woodlands, TX, p. A653
Controller, St. Luke's The Woodlands Hospital, The Woodlands, TX, p. A653

LIPINSKI, Gary, M.D
Regional Vice President and Chief Medical Officer, Adventist Hinsdale Hospital, Hinsdale, IL, p. A193
Regional Vice President and Chief Medical Officer, Adventist La Grange Memorial Hospital, La Grange, IL, p. A194

LIPINSKI, Jim, Chief Financial Officer, Franciscan St. Margaret Health – Hammond, Hammond, IN, p. A212

LIPMAN, Brian, M.D. Medical Director and Medical Staff Services, Oconomowoc Memorial Hospital, Oconomowoc, WI, p. A712

LIPMAN, Henry D., Senior Vice President, Financial Strategy and External Relations, Lakes Region General Hospital, Laconia, NH, p. A410

LIPNER, Zach, Vice President Human Resources, Newark Beth Israel Medical Center, Newark, NJ, p. A419

LIPPERT, Brandt, Vice President Human Resources, Adena Greenfield Medical Center, Greenfield, OH, p. A495

LIPPINCOTT, Ken, Chief of Staff, North Mississippi State Hospital, Tupelo, MS, p. A365

LIPSCOMB, Teresa, Director Human Resources, Springbrook Behavioral Health System, Travelers Rest, SC, p. A570

LIPSCOMB, Tracy, Vice President Financial Services and Chief Financial Officer, Garrett County Memorial Hospital, Oakland, MD, p. A302

LIPSEY, Prentice, Chief Executive Officer, Kindred Hospital Cleveland–Gateway, Cleveland, OH, p. A488

LIPSKY, Janice G., R.N. System Vice President Human Resources and Organizational Development, St. Vincent's Medical Center Riverside, Jacksonville, FL, p. A132

LIPSTEIN, Steven H., President and Chief Executive Officer, BJC HealthCare, Saint Louis, MO, p. B23

LIRAKIS, Kathy, R.N. Chief Nursing Officer, Blue Hill Memorial Hospital, Blue Hill, ME, p. A292

LIRIO, Ruel R., M.D. Clinical Physician Advisor, Spectrum Health Zeeland Community Hospital, Zeeland, MI, p. A338

LISA, Mark P., FACHE, Chief Executive Officer, Twin Cities Community Hospital, Templeton, CA, p. A97

LISELL, Susan C., Vice President of Clinical Services, LifeCare Medical Center, Roseau, MN, p. A350

LISENBY, Michael, M.D. Vice President and Chief Medical Officer, East Alabama Medical Center, Opelika, AL, p. A24

LISKA, Lee Ann, President and Chief Executive Officer, University of Cincinnati Medical Center, Cincinnati, OH, p. A487

LISKE, Thomas, M.D. Chief Medical Officer, Kindred Hospital–Sycamore, Sycamore, IL, p. A204

LISKO, J. Stuart, Regional Director Operations, Critical Access Hospital Operations, Booneville Community Hospital, Booneville, AR, p. A44

LISKOV, David, M.D. Medical Director, First Hospital Wyoming Valley, Kingston, PA, p. A541

LISONBEE, Rod, Chief Financial Officer, Utah Valley Regional Medical Center, Provo, UT, p. A662

LIST, Alan F., M.D., President and Chief Executive Officer, H. Lee Moffitt Cancer Center and Research Institute, Tampa, FL, p. A147

LISTER, Jack, Director Human Resources, Takoma Regional Hospital, Greeneville, TN, p. A583

LISTON, John, Chief Financial Officer, Port Huron Hospital, Port Huron, MI, p. A332

LITAKER, Thomas, Chief Financial Officer, Skagit Valley Hospital, Mount Vernon, WA, p. A685

LITE, Myron, Director Human Resources, Fitzgibbon Hospital, Marshall, MO, p. A376

LITKA, Calvin, R.N. Director of Nursing, Horsham Clinic, Ambler, PA, p. A533

LITOVITZ, Gary, M.D. Medical Director, Dominion Hospital, Falls Church, VA, p. A670

LITSINGER, Jim, Chief Financial Officer, Adventist Rehabilitation Hospital of Maryland, Rockville, MD, p. A303

LITTLE, Bridget, Deputy Commander Nursing, Bayne–Jones Army Community Hospital, Fort Polk, LA, p. A277

LITTLE, Christopher M., Vice President and Chief Financial Officer, Ellwood City Hospital, Ellwood City, PA, p. A538

LITTLE. Denise, Director Human Resources, St. Elizabeth Community Hospital, Red Bluff, CA, p. A85

LITTLE, Gary, M.D. Medical Director, George Washington University Hcspital, Washington, DC, p. A121

LITTLE, James E., Chief Financial Officer, Siloam Springs Regional Hospital, Siloam Springs, AR, p. A53

LITTLE, James P., M.D. Medical Director, HEALTHSOUTH Rehabilitation Hospital, Kingsport, TN, p. A585

LITTLE, Lou, President, WellStar Windy Hill Hospital, Marietta, GA, p. A163

LITTLE, Marlene, Senior Director, Little Falls Hospital, Little Falls, NY, p. A440

LITTLE, Monica, Coordinator Human Resources, Kindred Rehabilitation Hospital Clear Lake, Webster, TX, p. A656

LITTLE, Norris, Chief of Staff, Newton Medical Center, Covington, GA, p. A157

LITTLE, Steven N., President and Chief Executive Officer, Agnesian HealthCare, Fond Du Lac, WI, p. A704

LITTLE, Suzanne, Human Resources Specialist, Columbia Basin Hospital, Ephrata, WA, p. A683

LITTLE, Vicky, Director Human Resources, Effingham Hospital, Springfield, GA, p. A167

LITTLE, William, Chief Executive Officer, Highlands Medical Center, Sparta, TN, p. A593

LITTLEDEER, Lenora, R.N. Director of Nursing, Lawton Indian Hospital, Lawton, OK, p. A512

LITTLEFIELD, Karen, Manager Human Resources, Waldo County General Hospital, Belfast, ME, p. A292

LITTLESON, Steven G., FACHE, President, Jersey Shore University Medical Center, Neptune, NJ, p. A419

LITTRELL, Angy, Chief Operating Officer, Fitzgibbon Hospital, Marshall, MO, p. A376

LITTRELL, Jeremy, Director Human Resources, Brodstone Memorial Hospital, Superior, NE, p. A402

LITTRELL, Mark, Chief Executive Officer, Lincoln Prairie Behavioral Health Center, Springfield, IL, p. A203

LIU, Marsha, Executive Vice President and Chief Financial Officer, Northwest Community Hospital, Arlington Heights, IL, p. A180

LIUZZA, Jed M., Chief Human Resources Officer, OU Medical Center, Oklahoma City, OK, p. A516

LIUZZO, Gary, Director Information Systems, Scotland Health Care System, Laurinburg, NC, p. A468

LIVELY, Corey, Chief Executive Officer, Great Plains Regional Medical Center, Elk City, OK, p. A510

LIVENGOOD, Annette, Vice President Human Resources, Garrett County Memorial Hospital, Oakland, MD, p. A302

LIVERMAN, Brett, Chief Financial Officer, Alleghany Memorial Hospital, Sparta, NC, p. A473

LIVERSAGE, Lavonne, Director, Fargo Veterans Affairs Health Care System, Fargo, ND, p. A477

LIVESAY, Jr., William, D.O. Medical Director, HEALTHSOUTH Rehabilitation Hospital of Charleston, Charleston, SC, p. A563

LIVINGSTON, Carolyn, Director Human Resources, Salt Lake Regional Medical Center, Salt Lake City, UT, p. A663

LIVINGSTON, Charles
Administrator, Dakota Plains Surgical Center, Aberdeen, SD, p. A572
Chief Executive Officer, Midwest Surgical Hospital, Omaha, NE, p. A400

LIVINGSTON, Denise, Director Human Resources, Promise Hospital of East Los Angeles, Suburban Medical Center Campus, Paramount, CA, p. A82

LIVINGSTON, Jeffrey
Administrator, Christus Dubuis Hospital of Port Arthur, Port Arthur, TX, p. A643
Administrator, Dubuis Hospital of Beaumont, Beaumont, TX, p. A601

LIVINGSTON, Keith
Senior Vice President and Chief Information Officer, Appleton Medical Center, Appleton, WI, p. A701
Senior Vice President and Chief Information Officer, Theda Clark Medical Center, Neenah, WI, p. A711

LIVINGSTON, Richard, M.D. Medical Director, Valley Behavioral Health System, Barling, AR, p. A43

LIVINGSTON, Sam, Information Resource Consultant, G. Werber Bryan Psychiatric Hospital, Columbia, SC, p. A564

LIVINGSTONE, Marie, R.N. Chief Nursing Officer, Effingham Hospital, Springfield, GA, p. A167

LIVSEY, Don, Vice President and Chief Information Officer, Children's Hospital and Research Center Oakland, Oakland, CA, p. A80

LIVVIX, Susan, R.N. Vice President Nursing Services, Paris Community Hospital, Paris, IL, p. A199

LIZZA, Beth, Chief Nursing Officer, Ohio Valley Surgical Hospital, Springfield, OH, p. A502

LJUNGQUIST, Diane, MS, Chief Executive Officer, Tyler Memorial Hospital, Tunkhannock, PA, p. A556

LLANO, Manuel R.
  Chief Executive Officer, Atlantic Shores Hospital, Fort Lauderdale, FL, p. A128
  Chief Executive Officer, Fort Lauderdale Hospital, Fort Lauderdale, FL, p. A128

LLEWELLYN, Michael R., Chief Operating Officer, Laguna Honda Hospital and Rehabilitation Center, San Francisco, CA, p. A91

LLOYD, Davie, FACHE, Chief Executive Officer, Regional General Hospital, Williston, FL, p. A150

LLOYD II, Donald H., Administrator, CHRISTUS St. Patrick Hospital of Lake Charles, Lake Charles, LA, p. A282

LLOYD, John K., President and Chief Executive Officer, Meridian Health, Neptune, NJ, p. B93

LLOYD, Richard, D.O. Chief of Staff, Harbor Beach Community Hospital, Harbor Beach, MI, p. A326

LLOYD, Russell E., Acting Director, Veterans Affairs Illiana Health Care System, Danville, IL, p. A187

LO, Eric, M.D. Chief Medical Staff, Bert Fish Medical Center, New Smyrna Beach, FL, p. A139

LO, Wesley, Regional Chief Executive Officer, Maui Memorial Medical Center, Wailuku, HI, p. A172

LOADER, Clifford, Chief Financial Officer, Banner Desert Medical Center, Mesa, AZ, p. A34

LOBBAN, Victoria, Vice President Finance, New England Sinai Hospital and Rehabilitation Center, Stoughton, MA, p. A315

LOBECK, Charles C., Administrator, Shriners Hospitals for Children–Twin Cities, Minneapolis, MN, p. A347

LOCHRIDGE, Angela, Director Human Resources, Bradley County Medical Center, Warren, AR, p. A53

LOCKARD, Dennis, Vice President Fiscal Services and Chief Financial Officer, Wayne Hospital, Greenville, OH, p. A495

LOCKCUFF, Todd, Chief Financial Officer, Inova Alexandria Hospital, Alexandria, VA, p. A668

LOCKE, Cheryl, Vice President and Chief Human Resource Officer, Wake Forest Baptist Medical Center, Winston–Salem, NC, p. A475

LOCKE, Christopher, Interim Chief Executive Officer, Atlanta Medical Center, Atlanta, GA, p. A152

LOCKE, Kirsten, Director of Nursing Services, Mineral Community Hospital, Superior, MT, p. A391

LOCKE, Marianne, R.N. Associate Director Patient Care Services, Northern Arizona Veterans Affairs Health Care System, Prescott, AZ, p. A37

LOCKE, Stuart, Chief Executive Officer, Southern Kentucky Rehabilitation Hospital, Bowling Green, KY, p. A259

LOCKEE, W. Brad, M.D. Chief of Staff, CHI Health Plainview, Plainview, NE, p. A401

LOCKER, Dan, M.D. Chief of Staff, Brownwood Regional Medical Center, Brownwood, TX, p. A604

LOCKERD, Marie Paul, M.D. Chief Medical Officer, Sanford Jackson Medical Center, Jackson, MN, p. A345

LOCKHART, Jimmy Wayne, M.D. Medical Director, HEALTHSOUTH Treasure Coast Rehabilitation Hospital, Vero Beach, FL, p. A149

LOCKLAIR, Deborah, FACHE, Administrator, McLeod Medical Center Dillon, Dillon, SC, p. A565

LOCKLEAR, Ann, Vice President, Human Resources, Scotland Health Care System, Laurinburg, NC, p. A468

LOCKWOOD, Melissa, Chief Executive Officer, Preston Memorial Hospital, Kingwood, WV, p. A696

LODGE, Heidi, Chief of Staff, Copper Queen Community Hospital, Bisbee, AZ, p. A31

LOE, Cindy, Director of Nursing, Essentia Health Northern Pines, Aurora, MN, p. A340

LOEB, Katherine, R.N. Interim Vice President, Patient Care Services, Holy Cross Hospital, Chicago, IL, p. A184

LOEFFELHOLZ, Tim, Account Executive Information Technology, UnityPoint Health – Finley Hospital, Dubuque, IA, p. A230

LOEPP Jr., Robert A., FACHE, Chief Executive Officer, AMG Specialty Hospital–Wichita, Wichita, KS, p. A256

LOERA, Arnold, M.D. Clinical Director, Bristol Bay Area Health Corporation, Dillingham, AK, p. A28

LOERINC, Albert, M.D. Medical Director, New Bedford Rehabilitation Hospital, New Bedford, MA, p. A312

LOEWENSTEIN, Howard, Chief Information Resource Management Services, Jesse Brown Veterans Affairs Medical Center, Chicago, IL, p. A184

LOFF, Thomas, Chief Financial Officer, East Morgan County Hospital, Brush, CO, p. A103

LOFFING, David, Chief Operating Officer, University of Illinois Hospital & Health Sciences System, Chicago, IL, p. A187

LOFGREN, Richard P., M.P.H., President and CEO, UC Health, Cincinnati, OH, p. B137

LOFTIS, Michelle, Human Resources Officer, Ferry County Memorial Hospital, Republic, WA, p. A687

LOFTON, Jason, M.D. Medical Director, De Queen Medical Center, De Queen, AR, p. A45

LOFTON, Kevin E., FACHE, President and Chief Executive Officer, Catholic Health Initiatives, Englewood, CO, p. B30

LOFTON, Veronica, Acting Chief Executive Officer, Twin Valley Behavioral Healthcare, Columbus, OH, p. A491

LOFTUS, John, M.D. Chief of Staff, Kaiser Permanente Oakland Medical Center, Oakland, CA, p. A80

LOFTUS, Philip, Ph.D
  Chief Information Officer, Aurora Medical Center – Manitowoc County, Two Rivers, WI, p. A716
  Vice President and Chief Information Officer, Aurora Medical Center of Oshkosh, Oshkosh, WI, p. A712
  Vice President and Chief Information Officer, Aurora Psychiatric Hospital, Wauwatosa, WI, p. A718
  Vice President and Chief Information Officer, Aurora St. Luke's Medical Center, Milwaukee, WI, p. A710
  Chief Information Officer, Aurora West Allis Medical Center, West Allis, WI, p. A718

LOFURNO, Justin A., Director Human Resources, Providence Hospital, Columbia, SC, p. A564

LOGAN, Ann, Chief Operating Officer and Chief Nursing Officer, Hoboken University Medical Center, Hoboken, NJ, p. A417

LOGAN, Bradley
  Chief Financial Officer, Franklin Woods Community Hospital, Johnson City, TN, p. A585
  Chief Financial Officer, Sycamore Shoals Hospital, Elizabethton, TN, p. A582

LOGAN, Brenda C., R.N. Chief Nursing Officer, TriStar Southern Hills Medical Center, Nashville, TN, p. A591

LOGAN, Denise, Director Human Resources, Specialty Rehabilitation Hospital of Coushatta, Coushatta, LA, p. A275

LOGAN, Heather, Assistant Administrator Diagnostic and Support Services, Cascade Valley Hospital and Clinics, Arlington, WA, p. A681

LOGAN, Michael, Chief Financial Officer, Russell County Hospital, Russell Springs, KY, p. A270

LOGAN, Renee, Chief Financial Officer, Murray County Medical Center, Slayton, MN, p. A352

LOGAR, Michael, Assistant Superintendent, Larue D. Carter Memorial Hospital, Indianapolis, IN, p. A214

LOGSDON, Diane, Vice President Planning and Development, Hardin Memorial Hospital, Elizabethtown, KY, p. A260

LOGSDON, Terri, Chief Financial Officer, Hickory Trail Hospital, Desoto, TX, p. A614

LOH, Marcel C., FACHE, Chief Executive Officer, Saint John's Health Center, Santa Monica, CA, p. A94

LOHMAN, Eric, M.D. Chief of Staff, Meadowview Regional Medical Center, Maysville, KY, p. A267

LOHMEIER, Justin, M.D. Chief of Staff, Baptist Memorial Hospital–Union County, New Albany, MS, p. A363

LOHN, Eric
  Chief Financial Officer, Lake View Memorial Hospital, Two Harbors, MN, p. A353
  Vice President and Chief Financial Officer, St. Luke's Hospital, Duluth, MN, p. A343

LOHR, Daniel E.
  Regional Vice President Finance, The William W. Backus Hospital, Norwich, CT, p. A116
  Regional Vice President Finance, Windham Hospital, Willimantic, CT, p. A118

LOHRMAN, Joseph W., Chief Executive Officer, Annie Jeffrey Memorial County Health Center, Osceola, NE, p. A400

LOHSTRETER, Thomas, M.D. Chief of Staff, Kittson Memorial Healthcare Center, Hallock, MN, p. A344

LOKIE, Mike, Project Director, Bon Secours St. Francis Medical Center, Midlothian, VA, p. A674

LOKKEN, Christine, Manager of Finance, Bigfork Valley Hospital, Bigfork, MN, p. A340

LOLLIS, Sylvia, Director Human Resources, Osceola Regional Medical Center, Kissimmee, FL, p. A133

LOMAN, Sarah, Director Human Resources, Penobscot Valley Hospital, Lincoln, ME, p. A294

LOMBA, Maria R., Medical Director, New Braunfels Regional Rehabilitation Hospital, New Braunfels, TX, p. A639

LOMBARD, Scott, Acting Chief Nursing Officer, Spectrum Health Reed City Hospital, Reed City, MI, p. A333

LOMBARDO, Kathryn, M.D., President, Olmsted Medical Center, Rochester, MN, p. A350

LOMEO, Jody, Interim CEO, KALEIDA Health, Buffalo, NY, p. A434

LOMMEL, Marsha, FACHE, President and Chief Executive Officer, Madonna Rehabilitation Hospital, Lincoln, NE, p. A398

LONERGAN, Araceli
  Chief Executive Officer, East Los Angeles Doctors Hospital, Los Angeles, CA, p. A71
  Chief Executive Officer, Memorial Hospital of Gardena, Gardena, CA, p. A65

LONERGAN, Thomas J., Chief Executive Officer, Weisman Children's Rehabilitation Hospital, Marlton, NJ, p. A418

LONEY, Chris, Director Personnel, Thomas B. Finan Center, Cumberland, MD, p. A300

LONG, Adrian, M.D. Executive Vice President and Chief Medical Officer, Saint Agnes Hospital, Baltimore, MD, p. A297

LONG, Angela S., Vice President Clinical Services and Chief Nursing Officer, Southeastern Ohio Regional Medical Center, Cambridge, OH, p. A485

LONG, Brian, FACHE, President and Chief Executive Officer, Memorial Healthcare, Owosso, MI, p. A331

LONG, Dennis, Director Human Resources, Western Missouri Medical Center, Warrensburg, MO, p. A384

LONG, DeWayne, Chief Executive Officer, Doctors NeuroMedical Hospital, Bremen, IN, p. A208

LONG, Douglas, President and Chief Executive Officer, West Hills Hospital and Medical Center,, CA, p. A75

LONG, Erik
  Controller, Baptist Health South Florida, Homestead Hospital, Homestead, FL, p. A131
  Controller, Baptist Health South Florida, Mariners Hospital, Tavernier, FL, p. A148

LONG, Gary L.
  Senior Vice President Population Management, Virtua Berlin, Berlin, NJ, p. A413
  Senior Vice President Population Management, Virtua Marlton, Marlton, NJ, p. A418
  Senior Vice President Population Management, Virtua Voorhees, Voorhees, NJ, p. A424

LONG, Greg, Chief Executive Officer, O'Bleness Memorial Hospital, Athens, OH, p. A483

LONG, Gregory L., M.D
  Chief Medical Officer, Appleton Medical Center, Appleton, WI, p. A701
  Chief Medical Officer, Theda Clark Medical Center, Neenah, WI, p. A711

LONG, Hilda, Chief Executive Officer, ICON Hospital, Humble, TX, p. A628

LONG, James K., CPA, Administrator and Chief Executive Officer, West River Regional Medical Center, Hettinger, ND, p. A478

LONG, Jeremy, Manager Information Systems, St. Vincent Salem Hospital, Salem, IN, p. A222

LONG, Jonathan Ray, M.D. Chief of Staff, Weatherford Regional Hospital, Weatherford, OK, p. A522

LONG, Judy M., R.N. Chief Nursing Officer and Chief Operating Officer, Appling Healthcare System, Baxley, GA, p. A154

LONG, Karen, R.N. Vice President Nursing, Bayfront Health St. Petersburg, Saint Petersburg, FL, p. A144

LONG, Matthew, Chief Operating Officer, Spearfish Regional Surgery Center, Spearfish, SD, p. A577

LONG, Michael, MS, Chief Executive Officer, Marlton Rehabilitation Hospital, Marlton, NJ, p. A418

LONG, Mike, Chief Financial Officer, Powell Valley Healthcare, Powell, WY, p. A722

LONG, Richard, M.D. Chief Medical Officer, UPMC Hamot, Erie, PA, p. A539

LONG, Stephanie, Chief Executive Officer, Indiana University Health White Memorial Hospital, Monticello, IN, p. A219

LONG, Steven V., FACHE, President and Chief Executive Officer, Hancock Regional Hospital, Greenfield, IN, p. A212

LONG, Terry, Interim Chief Executive Officer, Cherokee Medical Center, Centre, AL, p. A18

LONG, Theresa, Chief Executive Officer, Danville State Hospital, Danville, PA, p. A536

LONGACRE, Mark E., FACHE Chief Operating Officer, Nebraska Orthopaedic Hospital, Omaha, NE, p. A400

LONGBINE, Vicki, Director Human Resources, Harper Hospital District Five, Harper, KS, p. A245

LONGBRAKE, Jeffery, President and Chief Executive Officer, Huron Medical Center, Bad Axe, MI, p. A318

LONGDO, Derrick, Director Information Systems, Memorial Medical Center – Neillsville, Neillsville, WI, p. A712

LONGEST, Bruce, M.D. President Medical Staff, Calhoun Health Services, Calhoun City, MS, p. A356

LONGEST, Sarah, Chief Information Officer, University of Mississippi Medical Center Grenada, Grenada, MS, p. A358

LONGEST, Sonya, M.D. Clinical Director, Walter B. Jones Alcohol and Drug Abuse Treatment Center, Greenville, NC, p. A465

LONGMORE, David, Chief Information Officer, Wilkes–Barre Veterans Affairs Medical Center, Wilkes–Barre, PA, p. A558

LONGMUIR, Bryan, Chief Resource Management, Madigan Healthcare System, Tacoma, WA, p. A690

LONGMUIR, Marla, M.D. Chief Medical Officer, Mountrail County Medical Center, Stanley, ND, p. A480

LONGNECKER, Stacy, Chief of Staff, Ortonville Area Health Services, Ortonville, MN, p. A349

LONGO, Marybeth, Manager Human Resources, Trenton Psychiatric Hospital, Trenton, NJ, p. A424

LONGO, Robert J., FACHE, President and Chief Executive Officer, The Good Samaritan Hospital, Lebanon, PA, p. A543

LONGPRE, Donald J., Vice President Finance and Chief Financial Officer, North Ottawa Community Hospital, Grand Haven, MI, p. A324

LONGTIN, Brett, Chief Financial Officer, Lake Region Healthcare, Fergus Falls, MN, p. A343

LONIS, Robert, Interim Chief Financial Officer, Nashville General Hospital, Nashville, TN, p. A590

LOOMIS, Anna
Interim Vice President, MultiCare Good Samaritan Hospital, Puyallup, WA, p. A687
Interim Chief Financial Officer, MultiCare Tacoma General Hospital, Tacoma, WA, p. A691

LOOMIS, Greg
President, Mercy Health, Hackley Campus, Muskegon, MI, p. A331
President, Mercy Health, Mercy Campus, Muskegon, MI, p. A331

LOONEY, Zane, Chief Information Officer, St. Bernard Parish Hospital, Chalmette, LA, p. A275

LOOPER, Eric N., Chief Executive Officer, Scott & White Hospital – Llano, Llano, TX, p. A633

LOOPER, Gary N., President and Chief Executive Officer, Memorial Health System of East Texas, Lufkin, TX, p. B91

LOOPER, Gary N., Chief Executive Officer, Memorial Medical Center – Lufkin, Lufkin, TX, p. A635

LOOPER, Jeanne M., Chief Operating Officer, Ozarks Medical Center, West Plains, MO, p. A384

LOOS, William, M.D. Chief Medical Officer, LAC–Olive View–UCLA Medical Center,, CA, p. A73

LOOSBROCK, Tammy
Chief Executive Officer, Sanford Hospital Rock Rapids, Rock Rapids, IA, p. A237
Chief Executive Officer, Sanford Luverne Medical Center, Luverne, MN, p. A346

LOOSEMORE, Tim
Director, Franciscan St. Anthony Health – Crown Point, Crown Point, IN, p. A209
Regional Director Information Systems, Franciscan St. Anthony Health – Michigan City, Michigan City, IN, p. A218

LOPACHIN, Vicki, M.D. Chief Medical Officer, Mount Sinai Hospital, New York, NY, p. A446

LOPAS, Mary, Vice President Information Officer, Ministry Door County Medical Center, Sturgeon Bay, WI, p. A716

LOPEZ, Amparo, Region Executive Director, Elgin Mental Health Center, Elgin, IL, p. A189

LOPEZ, Augustine, Chief Financial Officer, Salinas Valley Memorial Healthcare System, Salinas, CA, p. A88

LOPEZ, Cesar, R.N. Director of Nurses, Grimes St. Joseph Health Center, Navasota, TX, p. A639

LOPEZ, Enrique, M.D. Medical Director, Larry B. Zieverink, Sr. Alcoholism Treatment Center, Raleigh, NC, p. A471

LOPEZ, Ericca, Director Human Resources, Canyon Ridge Hospital, Chino, CA, p. A59

LOPEZ, Gerald, Chief Information Officer, Ashford Presbyterian Community Hospital, San Juan, PR, p. A727

LOPEZ, Ivonne, Director Human Resources, Hospital Oriente, Humacao, PR, p. A726

LOPEZ, Jose A., M.D. Chief of Staff, Hill Country Memorial Hospital, Fredericksburg, TX, p. A619

LOPEZ, Leonard H., Chief Operating Officer, Hopi Health Care Center, Keams Canyon, AZ, p. A33

LOPEZ, Lesbia, Chief Nursing Officer, Doctors' Center Hospital San Juan, San Juan, PR, p. A728

LOPEZ, Lisa M., Director Human Resources, San Joaquin General Hospital, French Camp, CA, p. A64

LOPEZ, Lucia, Manager Human Resources, Coalinga Regional Medical Center, Coalinga, CA, p. A60

LOPEZ, Maria Rose, R.N. Chief of Nursing, Nix Health Care System, San Antonio, TX, p. A647

LOPEZ, Maritza, M.D. Chief of Staff, Sanford Canby Medical Center, Canby, MN, p. A341

LOPEZ, Rene, Chief Executive Officer, Doctors Hospital of Laredo, Laredo, TX, p. A632

LOPEZ, Robert, Chief Medical Officer, Highland Community Hospital, Picayune, MS, p. A364

LOPEZ, Rosalio J., M.D. Senior Vice President and Chief Medical Officer, Presbyterian Intercommunity Health Hospital, Whittier, CA, p. A100

LOPEZ, Steve, Chief Executive Officer, Colorado River Medical Center, Needles, CA, p. A79

LOPEZ, Steven, M.D. Chief Medical Officer, Palmetto Lowcountry Behavioral Health, Charleston, SC, p. A563

LOPEZ, Susan Nordstrom, President, Advocate Illinois Masonic Medical Center, Chicago, IL, p. A183

LOPEZ, Tony, Vice President and Chief Financial Officer, West Hills Hospital and Medical Center,, CA, p. A75

LOPEZ, Valerie, CPA Chief Financial Officer, Uvalde County Hospital Authority, Uvalde, TX, p. A654

LORD, David, President and Chief Executive Officer, OSF St. Francis Hospital and Medical Group, Escanaba, MI, p. A323

LORD, Gregory D., M.D
Medical Director, Doctor's Hospital of Deer Creek, Leesville, LA, p. A283
Chief Medical Officer, Leesville Rehabilitation Hospital, Leesville, LA, p. A283

LORD, Jill, MS Director Patient Care Services, Mt. Ascutney Hospital and Health Center, Windsor, VT, p. A667

LORD, Robert L., JD Senior Vice President and Chief Operating Officer, Martin Health System, Stuart, FL, p. A146

LORD, Todd M., Chief Executive Officer, OSS Orthopaedic Specialty Hospital, York, PA, p. A559

LORENZ, Holly, R.N. Chief Nurse Executive, UPMC Presbyterian Shadyside, Pittsburgh, PA, p. A552

LORENZ, Pat, Chief Operating Officer, Okeene Municipal Hospital, Okeene, OK, p. A514

LORENZ, Paul E., Chief Executive Officer, Santa Clara Valley Medical Center, San Jose, CA, p. A92

LORENZEN, Shelli, Director Human Resources, Manning Regional Healthcare Center, Manning, IA, p. A234

LORENZO, Heather, M.D. Vice President and Chief Medical Officer, Meritus Medical Center, Hagerstown, MD, p. A301

LORIMER, IV, Lee, Regional Director Human Resources, McKay–Dee Hospital Center, Ogden, UT, p. A661

LORMAN, William J., Ph.D. Clinical Director, Livengrin Foundation, Bensalem, PA, p. A533

LORMAND, Jared, Vice President Information Technology, Opelousas General Health System, Opelousas, LA, p. A287

LORTON, Donald E., Executive Vice President, Bedford Memorial Hospital, Bedford, VA, p. A668

LOSADA, Marcus, Controller, The Surgical Hospital of Phoenix, Phoenix, AZ, p. A37

LOSASSO, Greg, President, Elkhart General Healthcare System, Elkhart, IN, p. A210

LOSITO, Glenna, R.N. Chief Nursing Officer, Cibola General Hospital, Grants, NM, p. A428

LOTHE, Eric L., Vice President and Administrator, UnityPoint Health – Des Moines, Des Moines, IA, p. A229

LOTHIAN, Nancy, Chief Operating Officer and Chief Information Officer, Central Vermont Medical Center, Berlin, VT, p. A665

LOTHRIDGE, Pamela, Chief Executive Officer, Ten Broeck Tennessee Treatment Facility, Cookeville, TN, p. A581

LOTT, Andrea, Vice President Information Services, Northeastern Vermont Regional Hospital, Saint Johnsbury, VT, p. A666

LOTT, Ben, Vice President of Clinical Services, Riverside Medical Center, Franklinton, LA, p. A277

LOTT, Cynthia, Director Human Resources, Northern Virginia Mental Health Institute, Falls Church, VA, p. A670

LOTT, Jeff, Director Information Services, Touro Infirmary, New Orleans, LA, p. A286

LOTT, Laura, Administrative Director, Eastern Louisiana Mental Health System, Jackson, LA, p. A279

LOTT, Rodney, Director Management Information Systems and Facility Operations, Scott & White Hospital – Llano, Llano, TX, p. A633

LOTTS, Wendy, M.D. President Medical Staff, Vista Medical Center West, Waukegan, IL, p. A205

LOTZE, Eberhard, M.D. Chief Medical Officer, Woman's Hospital of Texas, Houston, TX, p. A628

LOUBERT, Cheryl, M.D. Chief Medical Staff, MidMichigan Medical Center–Gladwin, Gladwin, MI, p. A324

LOUDEN CORBETT, Jeanette L., Chief Human Resources Officer, Alameda County Medical Center, Oakland, CA, p. A80

LOUDERMILK, Kerry, Senior Vice President and Chief Financial Officer, Phoebe Putney Memorial Hospital, Albany, GA, p. A151

LOUDON, Cathy, Director Human Resources, Mid–America Rehabilitation Hospital, Shawnee Mission, KS, p. A254

LOUGHERY, Vicki, R.N. Chief Nursing Officer, Monadnock Community Hospital, Peterborough, NH, p. A412

LOUGHRAN, Michael, Vice President Human Resources, Kennedy Krieger Institute, Baltimore, MD, p. A296

LOUIS, Alfred, M.D. Chief Medical Staff, Promise Hospital of Houston, Houston, TX, p. A626

LOUK, Rodney, Vice President Information Systems, Washington Hospital, Washington, PA, p. A557

LOVALLO, Diane, R.N. Chief Nursing Officer, Merrimack Valley Hospital, Haverhill, MA, p. A310

LOVATO, Anthony, Director Information Technology, Coon Memorial Hospital, Dalhart, TX, p. A609

LOVDAHL, Brian A., Chief Financial Officer, Baldwin Area Medical Center, Baldwin, WI, p. A701

LOVE, Alex, Acting Manager Human Resources, Alexandria Veterans Affairs Health Care System, Pineville, LA, p. A287

LOVE, Bianca, Assistant Administrator Human Resources, Trinity Hospital Twin City, Dennison, OH, p. A493

LOVE, E. Clifford, Director Fiscal Services, Eastern State Hospital, Williamsburg, VA, p. A680

LOVE, Glenn Neil, M.D. Medical Director, Hilton Head Hospital, Hilton Head Island, SC, p. A567

LOVE, Jodi, R.N. Chief Nursing Officer, Helena Regional Medical Center, Helena, AR, p. A47

LOVE, Matt
Senior Vice President Finance, St. Elizabeth Boardman Health Center, Boardman, OH, p. A484
Senior Vice President Finance, St. Elizabeth Health Center, Youngstown, OH, p. A506

LOVE, Tim, Director Information Services, Reid Hospital and Health Care Services, Richmond, IN, p. A221

LOVE, Valerie, Manager Business Office, Heatherhill Care Communities, Chardon, OH, p. A485

LOVE–WATLER, Meylan, Chief Operating Officer, Lower Keys Medical Center, Key West, FL, p. A133

LOVEJOY, Leslie, R.N. Chief Nursing and Quality Officer, Sonoma Valley Hospital, Sonoma, CA, p. A95

LOVEJOY, Rob, Chief Operating Officer, Sanford Thief River Falls Medical Center, Thief River Falls, MN, p. A353

LOVELACE, Alan, Vice President and Chief Financial Officer, Stillwater Medical Center, Stillwater, OK, p. A519

LOVELACE, Christina, Director Human Resources, Gunnison Valley Hospital, Gunnison, CO, p. A107

LOVELACE, Donald, Chief Financial Officer, Bluffton Regional Medical Center, Bluffton, IN, p. A207

LOVELESS, Craig, Chief Executive Officer, Prowers Medical Center, Lamar, CO, p. A108

LOVELESS, Jane Doll, Vice President Information Services, Grand View Hospital, Sellersville, PA, p. A554

LOVELESS, Kurt, Chief Financial Officer, Summit Healthcare Regional Medical Center, Show Low, AZ, p. A39

LOVELESS, Steve, Acting President and Chief Executive Officer, St. Vincent Healthcare, Billings, MT, p. A385

LOVELL Jr., Charles D., FACHE, President and Chief Executive Officer, Caldwell Medical Center, Princeton, KY, p. A269

LOVELL, Mark, Vice President and Chief Financial Officer, Tuomey Healthcare System, Sumter, SC, p. A570

LOVELL, Stephanie, Vice President and General Counsel, Boston Medical Center, Boston, MA, p. A306

LOVELL, Terrence, Vice President Human Resources, Union Hospital, Elkton, MD, p. A300

LOVELLETTE, Teresa A., Manager Human Resources, Herrin Hospital, Herrin, IL, p. A192

LOVERA, Carlos, Director Information Systems, Montrose Memorial Hospital, Montrose, CO, p. A110

LOVERING, Keith, Information Technician, Miller County Hospital, Colquitt, GA, p. A156

LOVERING, Richard, Corporate Vice President Human Resources and Organizational Development, AtlantiCare Regional Medical Center, Atlantic City, NJ, p. A413

LOVERN, Ed, Chief Operating Officer, Piedmont Hospital, Atlanta, GA, p. A153

LOVERSO, Felice L., Ph.D., President and Chief Executive Officer, Casa Colina Hospital for Rehabilitative Medicine, Pomona, CA, p. A84

LOVETT, Chad, Chief Executive Officer, Kindred Hospital Rome, Rome, GA, p. A165

LOVING, David E., Chief Executive Officer, Central Carolina Hospital, Sanford, NC, p. A472

LOVINGOOD, Toni, Chief Operating Officer, Murphy Medical Center, Murphy, NC, p. A470

LOVRICH, John, Chief Financial Officer, Catalina Island Medical Center, Avalon, CA, p. A56

LOVSTAD, Corliss, Vice President Human Resources, Children's Hospital and Medical Center, Omaha, NE, p. A400

LOW, Lewis, M.D
Senior Vice President and Chief Medical Officer, Legacy Meridian Park Medical Center, Tualatin, OR, p. A531
Chief Medical Officer, Legacy Mount Hood Medical Center, Gresham, OR, p. A525
Senior Vice President and Chief Medical Officer, Legacy Salmon Creek Medical Center, Vancouver, WA, p. A691

LOWE, Brad, Director Information Systems, Caverna Memorial Hospital, Horse Cave, KY, p. A263

LOWE, Bren, Chief Executive Officer, Livingston Memorial Hospital, Livingston, MT, p. A389

LOWE, E. Rick, FACHE Operations Support Risk Management and Compliance, St. Francis Hospital, Columbus, GA, p. A156

LOWE, Elyssia, Chief Executive Officer, Three Rivers Behavioral Health, West Columbia, SC, p. A571

LOWE, Greg, Chief Executive Officer, Lawnwood Regional Medical Center & Heart Institute, Fort Pierce, FL, p. A129

LOWE, Joe, Director Management Information Systems, Cumberland Medical Center, Crossville, TN, p. A582

LOWE, Lavah, Executive Vice President and Chief Operating Officer, Bayfront Health St. Petersburg, Saint Petersburg, FL, p. A144

LOWE, Phillip W., Interim Chief Executive Officer, Holy Cross Hospital, Taos, NM, p. A431

LOWELL, David, M.D. Medical Director, Spaulding Rehabilitation Hospital Cape Cod, East Sandwich, MA, p. A309

LOWENTHAL, David, M.D. Clinical Director, New York State Psychiatric Institute, New York, NY, p. A447

LOWENTHAL, Steve, M.D. Vice President Medical Affairs, Capital Health Regional Medical Center, Trenton, NJ, p. A423

LOWENTHAL, Steve B., M.D. Senior Vice President Medical Affairs and Chief Medical Officer, Rush–Copley Medical Center, Aurora, IL, p. A181

LOWERY, Bill, Chief Financial Officer, North Texas State Hospital, Wichita Falls Campus, Wichita Falls, TX, p. A657

LOWERY, John, M.D. Deputy Commander Clinical Services, General Leonard Wood Army Community Hospital, Fort Leonard Wood, MO, p. A371

LOWERY, Linda, Manager Human Resources, Jay Hospital, Jay, FL, p. A132

LOWERY, William, Financial Officer, North Texas State Hospital, Vernon, TX, p. A655

LOWMAN, Christine
  Vice President Finance, Hampshire Memorial Hospital, Romney, WV, p. A699
  Vice President Finance, War Memorial Hospital, Berkeley Springs, WV, p. A693

LOWMAN, LeeAnn, Director Human Resources, Lake Taylor Transitional Care Hospital, Norfolk, VA, p. A675

LOWREY, Linda, Human Resources Officer, Atmore Community Hospital, Atmore, AL, p. A16

LOWRY, Claudia Jean, R.N. Director of Nursing, Community Howard Specialty Hospital, Kokomo, IN, p. A216

LOWRY, Michael, M.D. Medical Director, University of Utah Neuropsychiatric Institute, Salt Lake City, UT, p. A663

LOY, Michael, Director Human Resources, North Central Health Care, Wausau, WI, p. A718

LOYA, John R., Vice President Human Resources and Organizational Development, Columbus Regional Hospital, Columbus, IN, p. A208

LOYA, Theresa, R.N. Chief Nursing Officer, John C. Fremont Healthcare District, Mariposa, CA, p. A76

LOYA, Velma, Administrative Human Resource Coordinator, Rice Medical Center, Eagle Lake, TX, p. A614

LOYD, Blythe, Vice President, Mayo Clinic Health System in Eau Claire, Eau Claire, WI, p. A704

LOYD, Chris, Director Human Resources, Methodist Richardson Medical Center, Richardson, TX, p. A644

LOYO–RODRIGUEZ, Raul J., Administrative Analyst III, San Diego County Psychiatric Hospital, San Diego, CA, p. A89

LOZADA, Leonardo J., M.D. Chief Physician Executive, Saint Luke's North Hospital – Barry Road, Kansas City, MO, p. A374

LOZANO, Elias B., Executive Officer, Tripler Army Medical Center, Honolulu, HI, p. A171

LOZANO, Melanie, Chief Financial Officer, Concho County Hospital, Eden, TX, p. A614

LOZANO, Michelle, Chief Executive Officer, Lifecare Hospitals of South Texas–North McAllen, McAllen, TX, p. A636

LOZAR, Beverly, Chief Nursing Executive, St. Vincent Charity Medical Center, Cleveland, OH, p. A489

LOZIER, Tim, Director Human Resources, Vibra Specialty Hospital at DeSoto, Desoto, TX, p. A614

LUBARSKY, Neil, Senior Vice President Finance, Thomas Jefferson University Hospital, Philadelphia, PA, p. A550

LUBBRING, Kim, Director Financial Services, Missouri Baptist Sullivan Hospital, Sullivan, MO, p. A383

LUBIN, Bertram, M.D., President and Chief Executive Officer, Children's Hospital and Research Center Oakland, Oakland, CA, p. A80

LUBINSKY, Jeanie, Chief Financial Officer, Mayo Clinic Health System – Red Cedar in Menomonie, Menomonie, WI, p. A709

LUBITSKY, John, Chief Executive Officer, Ancora Psychiatric Hospital, Hammonton, NJ, p. A416

LUBITZ, Robert, M.D. Vice President of Medical Affairs, WellStar Kennestone Hospital, Marietta, GA, p. A163

LUCAS, Jr., Benny Lee, Chief Nursing Executive, St. Joseph's Behavioral Health Center, Stockton, CA, p. A96

LUCAS, Bob, Vice President Operations, King's Daughters Medical Center, Ashland, KY, p. A258

LUCAS, David, R.N. Director of Nursing, Glen Oaks Hospital, Greenville, TX, p. A622

LUCAS, Jackie, Vice President, Oak Tree Hospital, Corbin, KY, p. A260

LUCAS, III, John F., M.D. Chief of Staff, Greenwood Leflore Hospital, Greenwood, MS, p. A358

LUCAS, Kelly, Chief Information Officer, Sampson Regional Medical Center, Clinton, NC, p. A462

LUCAS, Marshall, M.D. Medical Director, Cypress Creek Hospital, Houston, TX, p. A624

LUCAS, Roger V., Vice President, Human Resources, Aspirus Wausau Hospital, Wausau, WI, p. A717

LUCCHESI, Michael, M.D. Interim Chief Medical Officer, SUNY Downstate Medical Center University Hospital,, NY, p. A448

LUCE, Glenda, Chief Nursing Officer, Memorial Hospital of Gardena, Gardena, CA, p. A65

LUCE, Jamie, Director Human Resources, Emory–Adventist Hospital, Smyrna, GA, p. A166

LUCE, John, M.D. Chief Medical Officer, San Francisco General Hospital and Trauma Center, San Francisco, CA, p. A91

LUCE, Paul W., MSN, Vice President Operations, Miami County Medical Center, Paola, KS, p. A252

LUCERO, Brenda, Chief Clinical Officer, Cornerstone Hospital of Houston at Clearlake, Webster, TX, p. A656

LUCERO, Lupe, Chief Financial Officer, Espanola Hospital, Espanola, NM, p. A428

LUCEY, Jeffery, M.D. Clinical Director, Kingsboro Psychiatric Center,, NY, p. A444

LUCIA, John, Chief Financial Officer, St. Anthony's Hospital, Houston, TX, p. A626

LUCIA, Sandra J., Director Health Information and Corporate Compliance Officer, Hampstead Hospital, Hampstead, NH, p. A410

LUCIANO, Lisa M., D.O. Medical Director, Shore Rehabilitation Institute, Brick, NJ, p. A413

LUCIER, Robbyn, Director Human Resources, Portage Health, Hancock, MI, p. A326

LUCK, Richard, Ed.D., Facility Director, Woodrow Wilson Rehabilitation Center, Fishersville, VA, p. A671

LUCKE, Kim, Vice President Finance, Northern Montana Hospital, Havre, MT, p. A388

LUCKETT, Douglas R., President and Chief Executive Officer, Caromont Regional Medical Center, Gastonia, NC, p. A465

LUCORE, Charles, M.D., President and Chief Executive Officer, St. John's Hospital, Springfield, IL, p. A203

LUDINGTON, Gail, Chief Financial Officer, Coquille Valley Hospital, Coquille, OR, p. A524

LUDWIG, John A., R.N. Vice President Operations, Bridgton Hospital, Bridgton, ME, p. A292

LUDWIG, Ted, Chief Medical Officer, War Memorial Hospital, Sault Sainte Marie, MI, p. A334

LUDWIG, Walter, Chief Operating Officer, Kenmore Mercy Hospital, Kenmore, NY, p. A439

LUDWIG–BEYMER, Patti, Ph.D. Vice President Chief Nursing Officer, Edward Hospital, Naperville, IL, p. A197

LUDWIGSEN, Kevin, Director Information Systems, Newman Regional Health, Emporia, KS, p. A243

LUEBBERING, Tom, Vice President Finance, Capital Region Medical Center, Jefferson City, MO, p. A372

LUEBCKE, Diane, R.N. Director Nursing, Community Memorial Healthcare, Marysville, KS, p. A249

LUECHT, Jackie
  Director, Human Resources, Mercy Medical Center–New Hampton, New Hampton, IA, p. A235
  Chief Human Resources Officer, Mercy Medical Center–North Iowa, Mason City, IA, p. A234

LUEDERS, Kathy, R.N. Director of Nursing–Acute Care, Saint Elizabeth's Medical Center, Wabasha, MN, p. A353

LUEHRS, Bill, Chief Human Resources Officer, NorthShore University Health System, Evanston, IL, p. A189

LUEHRS, Paul R., Chief Operating Officer, Mercy San Juan Medical Center, Carmichael, CA, p. A59

LUFKIN, Kirk, M.D. VPMA, McLaren Northern Michigan, Petoskey, MI, p. A332

LUGER, Gerald, M.D. President Medical Staff, Gottlieb Memorial Hospital, Melrose Park, IL, p. A196

LUGO, Cesar, Director Human Resources, Victor Valley Global Medical Center, Victorville, CA, p. A99

LUGO–ZENNER, Diana, R.N. Chief Nursing Officer, Citrus Valley Medical Center–Inter Community Campus, Covina, CA, p. A61

LUHRS, Jason J., Vice President Fiscal Services, Westfields Hospital, New Richmond, WI, p. A712

LUKENS, Harry
  Senior Vice President and Chief Information Officer, Lehigh Valley Hospital, Allentown, PA, p. A532
  Senior Vice President and Chief Information Officer, Lehigh Valley Hospital–Muhlenberg, Bethlehem, PA, p. A533

LUKENS, Tammy, Director Information, Kosciusko Community Hospital, Warsaw, IN, p. A224

LUKER, Patricia A., Chief Executive Officer, OSF Holy Family Medical Center, Monmouth, IL, p. A196

LUKHARD, Kenneth W., President, Advocate Christ Medical Center, Oak Lawn, IL, p. A198

LUKISH, Kris, Human Resources Officer, CJW Medical Center, Richmond, VA, p. A677

LULICH, Diane, Director Human Resources, Memorial Medical Center – Ashland, Ashland, WI, p. A701

LULL, Todd, Director Information Technology, Southwest Health Center, Platteville, WI, p. A713

LULOFF, Lynn, Chief Financial Officer, Winneshiek Medical Center, Decorah, IA, p. A229

LUMBARDO, Lanette, MS Chief Nursing Officer, West Branch Regional Medical Center, West Branch, MI, p. A337

LUMIA, Kim, President and Chief Executive Officer, Sharon Hospital, Sharon, CT, p. A117

LUMPKINS, Deborah, MSN Chief Nursing Officer, Maury Regional Hospital, Columbia, TN, p. A581

LUMPP, Karen, Senior Vice President and Chief Financial Officer, Trinitas Regional Medical Center, Elizabeth, NJ, p. A415

LUMSDEN, Chris A., Chief Executive Officer, Halifax Regional Health System, South Boston, VA, p. A678

LUNA, Raul D., Chief Nurse Executive, El Paso Psychiatric Center, El Paso, TX, p. A615

LUNA, Richard, President and Chief Executive Officer, Newport Specialty Hospital, Tustin, CA, p. A98

LUNA, Tony, M.D. Chief of Staff, Minneola District Hospital, Minneola, KS, p. A250

LUND, Alicia, Director Human Resources, Westchester General Hospital, Miami, FL, p. A138

LUND, Elizabeth, M.D. Chief of Staff, Volunteer Community Hospital, Martin, TN, p. A587

LUND, Maggie, Divisional Senior Vice President Human Resources, Mercy Health – Fairfield Hospital, Fairfield, OH, p. A493

LUNDAL, David, Senior Vice President Information Systems and Chief Information Officer, Presence Holy Family Medical Center, Des Plaines, IL, p. A188

LUNDBERG, Lanetta, Vice President Culture and People, PeaceHealth Ketchikan Medical Center, Ketchikan, AK, p. A29

LUNDBERG, Ralph L., Director Human Resources, Yakima Regional Medical and Cardiac Center, Yakima, WA, p. A692

LUNDE, Susan, R.N. Director of Nursing, Fallon Medical Complex, Baker, MT, p. A385

LUNDVALL, Mark, Controller, Van Matre HEALTHSOUTH Rehabilitation Hospital, Rockford, IL, p. A202

LUNDY–PAINE, Robert, Director Information Systems, Alameda Hospital, Alameda, CA, p. A55

LUNN, Eric, M.D. Chief Medical Executive, Altru Health System, Grand Forks, ND, p. A478

LUNN, Stephen, Chief Executive Officer, Porter Regional Hospital, Valparaiso, IN, p. A223

LUNN, William, M.D. Chief Operating Officer, CHRISTUS Highland Medical Center, Shreveport, LA, p. A288

LUNN, William, M.D., Chief Executive Officer, Tulane Medical Center, New Orleans, LA, p. A286

LUNNEBORG, Brandi, Vice President Operations, Mercy Hospital, Coon Rapids, MN, p. A342

LUNSFORD, Cindy, Executive Vice President and Chief Operating Officer, Peninsula Regional Medical Center, Salisbury, MD, p. A303

LUNSFORD, Geralyn, R.N. Administration and Vice President Patient Services, Bethesda Hospital East, Boynton Beach, FL, p. A124

LUNT, Kimberly, Controller, HEALTHSOUTH Rehabilitation Hospital of Spring Hill, Brooksville, FL, p. A125

LUPINACCI, Michael, M.D. Medical Director, HEALTHSOUTH Rehabilitation Hospital of Mechanicsburg, Mechanicsburg, PA, p. A544

LUSKIN, Sue, Director Information Services, Spectrum Health Ludington Hospital, Ludington, MI, p. A329

LUSKIN–HAWK, Roberta, M.D.,
  Chief Executive Officer, Presence Saint Francis Hospital, Evanston, IL, p. A190
  President and Chief Executive Officer, Presence Saint Joseph Hospital, Chicago, IL, p. A185

LUSTERIO, Efren, Director of Nursing, Behavioral Center of Michigan, Warren, MI, p. A336

LUTES, Michael, President, Carolinas Medical Center–Union, Monroe, NC, p. A469

LUTHER, Lori, Chief Operating Officer and Chief Financial Officer, Indiana University Health Ball Memorial Hospital, Muncie, IN, p. A219

LUTHER, Tracie, Vice President Human Resources, Lake Shore Health Care Center, Irving, NY, p. A439

LUTTON, Lorraine, President, St. Joseph's Hospital, Tampa, FL, p. A148

LUTZ, Denise, Chief Human Resources Officer, St. Joseph's Hospital and Health Center, Dickinson, ND, p. A477

LUTZ, Don, Chief Information Officer, Bayonne Medical Center, Bayonne, NJ, p. A413

LUTZ, Rich, Director Human Resources, Fairview Southdale Hospital, Edina, MN, p. A343

LUTZ, Terry, Chief Financial Officer, Scheurer Hospital, Pigeon, MI, p. A332

LUX, Teri, R.N
  Vice President Patient Care Services and Chief Nursing Officer, Community Memorial Hospital, Menomonee Falls, WI, p. A709
  Vice President Patient Care Services and Chief Nursing Officer, St. Joseph's Hospital, West Bend, WI, p. A718
LUZINSKI, Craig, MSN Chief Human Resources Officer, Cheyenne Regional Medical Center, Cheyenne, WY, p. A720
LYDE, Shawna Martin, Director Human Resources, Fairfield Memorial Hospital, Winnsboro, SC, p. A571
LYDEN, Matthew M., Chief Executive Officer, Twin Rivers Regional Medical Center, Kennett, MO, p. A375
LYDICK, Bryan, Chief Executive Officer, Redwood Area Hospital, Redwood Falls, MN, p. A350
LYKINS, Jamey, Interim Chief Executive Officer, Physicians' Hospital in Anadarko, Anadarko, OK, p. A507
LYLE, Janet, Chief Human Resources and Allied Health Services, Springfield Hospital, Springfield, VT, p. A666
LYMAN, Jeremy, Chief Executive Officer, Blue Mountain Hospital, Blanding, UT, p. A659
LYNCE, Danialle, Manager Human Resources, University Hospitals Geauga Medical Center, Chardon, OH, p. A485
LYNCH, Becky, Manager Business Entity Management and Information Systems, OSF St. Mary Medical Center, Galesburg, IL, p. A190
LYNCH, Cecelia, R.N. Vice President Patient Care Services and Chief Nursing Officer, Lowell General Hospital, Lowell, MA, p. A311
LYNCH, Danile, Chief Operating Officer, Saint Luke Institute, Silver Spring, MD, p. A303
LYNCH, David
  Regional Director Information Systems, Summa Barberton Citizens Hospital, Barberton, OH, p. A483
  Regional Director Information Services, Summa Wadsworth–Rittman Hospital, Wadsworth, OH, p. A504
LYNCH, Elizabeth A., Vice President Human Resources, The Hospital of Central Connecticut, New Britain, CT, p. A115
LYNCH III, Ernest C., Chief Executive Officer, Medical Center of McKinney, McKinney, TX, p. A637
LYNCH, G. Michael, M.D. Chief Medical Officer, Inova Fair Oaks Hospital, Fairfax, VA, p. A670
LYNCH, Heather, M.D. Chief of Staff, Purcell Municipal Hospital, Purcell, OK, p. A518
LYNCH, Jim, Chief Financial Officer, Fairbanks Memorial Hospital, Fairbanks, AK, p. A29
LYNCH, John, M.D. Vice President and Chief Medical Officer, Barnes–Jewish Hospital, Saint Louis, MO, p. A380
LYNCH, John, Vice President Chief Information Officer, Catskill Regional Medical Center, Harris, NY, p. A438
LYNCH, Marc, D.O. Chief of Staff, Kindred Hospital–Ontario, Ontario, CA, p. A81
LYNCH, Timothy, Vice President Operations, Spaulding Hospital for Continuing Medical Care Cambridge, Cambridge, MA, p. A309
LYNCH, Torie A., Manager Human Resources, Central Montana Medical Center, Lewistown, MT, p. A389
LYNCH, William, Executive Vice President and Chief Operating Officer, Jamaica Hospital Medical Center,, NY, p. A444
LYNCH–KILIC, Cathy, Vice President Human Resources, St. Mary's Hospital, Passaic, NJ, p. A420
LYND, Samuel, Administrator and Chief Executive Officer, Baptist Memorial Hospital–Tipton, Covington, TN, p. A582
LYNN, Jason, Director Finance, St. Vincent's St. Clair, Pell City, AL, p. A24
LYNN, Teresa, D.O. Chief of Staff, Arbuckle Memorial Hospital, Sulphur, OK, p. A519
LYNSKEY, Jeanne, Vice President and Chief Financial Officer, Milford Regional Medical Center, Milford, MA, p. A312
LYON, Beverly, R.N. Vice President Nursing, Milford Hospital, Milford, CT, p. A115
LYON, David, M.D. Chief Medical Officer, Easton Hospital, Easton, PA, p. A538
LYON, Robert J., Chief Executive Officer, PHS Santa Fe Indian Hospital, Santa Fe, NM, p. A430
LYON, Tami, Director Human Resources, Community Memorial Hospital, Burke, SD, p. A572
LYONS, Althea C., Vice President Human Resources and Development, Beverly Hospital, Beverly, MA, p. A305
LYONS, Jan, Regional Director Health Improvement Management, Ringgold County Hospital, Mount Ayr, IA, p. A234
LYONS, Jim, Chief Operating Officer, Hutchinson Health, Hutchinson, MN, p. A345
LYONS, Lenny
  Administrator, Delta Community Medical Center, Delta, UT, p. A659
  Administrator, Fillmore Community Medical Center, Fillmore, UT, p. A659

LYSAGHT, Marcia C., R.N. Associate Director Patient Care Services, Miami Veterans Affairs Healthcare System, Miami, FL, p. A137
LYSAGHT, William, Chief Financial Officer, Kindred Hospital Las Vegas–Sahara, Las Vegas, NV, p. A406
LYTLE, John, M.D. Chief of Staff, Jefferson Regional Medical Center, Pine Bluff, AR, p. A52
LYTOLLIS, William, M.D. Chief of Staff, Barrow Regional Medical Center, Winder, GA, p. A169

M

MAAS, Vernon, M.D. Vice President, Medical Affairs, St. Mary's Medical Center of Evansville, Evansville, IN, p. A210
MABRY, Bradley, Chief Operating Officer, Clinton Memorial Hospital, Wilmington, OH, p. A505
MABRY, Jerry D., FACHE, Chief Executive Officer, National Park Medical Center, Hot Springs, AR, p. A47
MACAFEE, Francis M., Vice President Finance and Chief Financial Officer, Corning Hospital, Corning, NY, p. A436
MACALEER, Cara, Chief Executive Officer/Managing Director, Two Rivers Behavioral Health System, Kansas City, MO, p. A375
MACARONAS, Thomas, Chief Financial Officer, Labette Health, Parsons, KS, p. A252
MACATOL, Matthew, M.D. President Medical Staff, Marietta Memorial Hospital, Marietta, OH, p. A497
MACDONALD, Laurie, Vice President Finance, Elk Regional Health Center, Saint Marys, PA, p. A554
MACDONALD, Neil, Vice President Operations, MedStar Union Memorial Hospital, Baltimore, MD, p. A297
MACDONALD, Warren, M.D. President Medical Staff, Mayo Regional Hospital, Dover–Foxcroft, ME, p. A293
MACDONALD GALLAGHER, Shelley A., R.N. Senior Vice President for Patient Care Services, Memorial Hospital of Rhode Island, Pawtucket, RI, p. A560
MACDOUGALL, David, Chief Financial Officer, United Health Services Hospitals–Binghamton, Binghamton, NY, p. A434
MACE, Rick, Chief Executive Officer, Adventist Bolingbrook Hospital, Bolingbrook, IL, p. A182
MACE, Robert, M.D. Chief of Staff, Webster County Memorial Hospital, Webster Springs, WV, p. A700
MACEK, Paul E., President and Chief Executive Officer, Proctor Hospital, Peoria, IL, p. A200
MACGREGOR, Nancy, Chief Financial Officer, Salt Lake Behavioral Health, Salt Lake City, UT, p. A663
MACHADO, James, Chief Executive Officer, Clearview Regional Medical Center, Monroe, GA, p. A164
MACHADO, Maria T., Administrator, Hospital Hermanos Melendez, Bayamon, PR, p. A725
MACIEL, Maureen, M.D. Chief of Staff, Shriners Hospitals for Children–Tampa, Tampa, FL, p. A148
MACIOCE, Gary, President and Chief Executive Officer, Clearfield Hospital, Clearfield, PA, p. A536
MACK, Charles, Vice President Finance and Chief Financial Officer, Natchez Regional Medical Center, Natchez, MS, p. A363
MACK, Edward, M.D. Chief of Staff, Northport Veterans Affairs Medical Center, Northport, NY, p. A449
MACK, Russell, M.D. Chief Medical Officer, Lincoln Health, Damariscotta, ME, p. A293
MACKENZIE, Julie, Manager Human Resources, Espanola Hospital, Espanola, NM, p. A428
MACKENZIE, Thomas, M.D. Medical Director, Chief of Clinical Operations, Denver Health, Denver, CO, p. A104
MACKETT, Charles, M.D. Senior Vice President and Chief Medical Officer, Indian River Medical Center, Vero Beach, FL, p. A149
MACKEY Jr.,, Bruce J., President and Chief Executive Officer, Five Star Quality Care, Newton, MA, p. B59
MACKINNON, Paul, MS Senior Vice President Patient Care Services and Chief Nursing Officer, HealthAlliance Hospitals, Leominster, MA, p. A311
MACKSOOD, Dan
  Regional Senior Vice President and Chief Financial Officer, Good Samaritan Hospital Medical Center, West Islip, NY, p. A458
  Regional Vice President and Chief Financial Officer, St. Catherine of Siena Medical Center, Smithtown, NY, p. A454
MACLAUCHLAN, Steven, President and CEO, Saint Vincent Hospital, Worcester, MA, p. A317
MACLAUGHLIN, Jeremy, Director Human Resources, Citizens Memorial Hospital, Bolivar, MO, p. A367
MACLAUGHLIN, Mary Jo, Director Information Systems, Maine Coast Memorial Hospital, Ellsworth, ME, p. A293
MACLEOD, Deborah, MS Vice President Nursing and Patient Care Services, Mid Coast Hospital, Brunswick, ME, p. A292

MACLEOD, John L., President and Chief Executive Officer, Mercy Hospital Cadillac, Cadillac, MI, p. A320
MACLEOD, Robert J., Chief Executive Officer, New Hampshire Hospital, Concord, NH, p. A409
MACLEOD, Susan, Chief Executive Officer, Lakeway Regional Medical Center, Lakeway, TX, p. A632
MACNEILL, Bruce, Chief Financial Officer, Vibra Hospital of Sacramento, Folsom, CA, p. A63
MACPHEE, Alan, Chief Executive Officer, John C. Fremont Healthcare District, Mariposa, CA, p. A76
MACPHERSON, Bonne S., Director Human Resources, Florida Hospital Fish Memorial, Orange City, FL, p. A140
MACPHERSON, David S., M.P.H., Acting Director, Veterans Affairs Pittsburgh Healthcare System, Pittsburgh, PA, p. A552
MACRI, Fredrick, Executive Vice President, Rhode Island Hospital, Providence, RI, p. A561
MACRI, William P., Chief Executive Officer, Kindred Hospital–Nashville, Nashville, TN, p. A590
MACUGA, Paul, Chief Human Resources Officer, Fletcher Allen Health Care, Burlington, VT, p. A665
MACY, Tom, FACHE, Chief Executive Officer, Nebraska Orthopaedic Hospital, Omaha, NE, p. A400
MADDEN, R. Craig, Director Employee Relations, Reynolds Memorial Hospital, Glen Dale, WV, p. A695
MADDOCK, Dan S., President, Taylor Regional Hospital, Hawkinsville, GA, p. A160
MADDOX, Dale, Chief Financial Officer, Medical Center of South Arkansas, El Dorado, AR, p. A45
MADDOX, Truett, M.D. Chief of Staff, Lea Regional Medical Center, Hobbs, NM, p. A428
MADER, Elaine, M.D. Chief of Staff, Integris Baptist Regional Health Center, Miami, OK, p. A513
MADER, Frank, Director Information Services, East Liverpool City Hospital, East Liverpool, OH, p. A493
MADER, Vikki, Director Health Information Services, Pratt Regional Medical Center, Pratt, KS, p. A253
MADISON, Jeffrey, Chief Executive Officer, Little River Healthcare, Rockdale, TX, p. A644
MADKINS, Catrina, Controller and Chief Financial Officer, HEALTHSOUTH Plano Rehabilitation Hospital, Plano, TX, p. A642
MADRID, Melissa, R.N. Chief Nursing Officer, Harper County Community Hospital, Buffalo, OK, p. A508
MADRID, Stephanie, Chief Executive Officer, Kindred Hospital Dallas Central, Dallas, TX, p. A610
MADSEN, Greg T., Chief Executive Officer, Spotsylvania Regional Medical Center, Fredericksburg, VA, p. A671
MAEKAWA, Steve, Chief Financial Officer, Garfield Medical Center, Monterey Park, CA, p. A78
MAENIUS, Linda, Chief Financial Officer, Laurel Ridge Treatment Center, San Antonio, TX, p. A646
MAERTENS, Mary B., FACHE, President and Chief Executive Officer, Avera Marshall Regional Medical Center, Marshall, MN, p. A346
MAES, Jillian, Director Marketing and Public Relations, St. Thomas More Hospital, Canon City, CO, p. A103
MAES, Stephen, Director Information Systems, Franciscan St. James Hospital and Health Centers, Olympia Fields, IL, p. A199
MAESE, John, M.D. Chief Medical Officer, Coney Island Hospital,, NY, p. A443
MAESTRE, Jaime, Chief Executive Officer, Dr. Ramon E. Betances Hospital–Mayaguez Medical Center Branch, Mayaguez, PR, p. A726
MAGALLANES, Diana Zamora, Chief Executive Officer, Arise Austin Medical Center, Austin, TX, p. A598
MAGANA, Shirley P., MSN, President and Chief Operating Officer, Corning Hospital, Corning, NY, p. A436
MAGDANGAL, Connie, Executive Vice President and Chief Financial Officer, Bergen Regional Medical Center, Paramus, NJ, p. A420
MAGEE, Becky, Chief Information Officer, Washington Regional Medical Center, Fayetteville, AR, p. A46
MAGEE, James L., Executive Director, Piggott Community Hospital, Piggott, AR, p. A51
MAGEE, Kyle, M.D., Chief Executive Officer, Riverside Medical Center, Franklinton, LA, p. A277
MAGEE, William F., Chief Financial Officer, Alliance HealthCare System, Holly Springs, MS, p. A359
MAGERS, Gregg, Interim Chief Executive Officer, Tri Valley Health System, Cambridge, NE, p. A394
MAGERS, Raymond M., Chief Executive Officer, Ellett Memorial Hospital, Appleton City, MO, p. A367
MAGESKI, Denise, MSN Chief Nurse Executive, Northwestern Lake Forest Hospital, Lake Forest, IL, p. A194
MAGHAZEHE, Al, FACHE, Chief Executive Officer, Capital Health, Trenton, NJ, p. B27

MAGHAZEHE, Al, FACHE,
Chief Executive Officer, Capital Health Medical Center–Hopewell, Pennington, NJ, p. A421
Chief Executive Officer, Capital Health Regional Medical Center, Trenton, NJ, p. A423

MAGID, Philip, Director Fiscal Services, Shriners Hospitals for Children–Chicago, Chicago, IL, p. A186

MAGILL, Marc, Acting Director, Veterans Affairs St. Louis Health Care System, Saint Louis, MO, p. A382

MAGNER, Johanna, Interim Chief Nursing Officer, Saint Michael's Medical Center, Newark, NJ, p. A420

MAGNISON, Jerry, Chief Financial Officer, Ridgeview Institute, Smyrna, GA, p. A167

MAGNUSON, Johna, Director Nursing, Hillsboro Community Hospital, Hillsboro, KS, p. A245

MAGNUSON, Robert, Business Operations Flight Chief, U. S. Air Force Clinic, Mountain Home AFB, ID, p. A177

MAGOON, Patrick M., President and Chief Executive Officer, Ann & Robert H. Lurie Children's Hospital of Chicago, Chicago, IL, p. A183

MAGRO, Michael, M.D. Chief Medical Officer, Mercy Suburban Hospital, Norristown, PA, p. A546

MAGRUDER, Joan, President, St. Louis Children's Hospital, Saint Louis, MO, p. A382

MAGUIRE, David L., M.D. Vice President Medical Affairs, Wing Memorial Hospital, Palmer, MA, p. A313

MAGUIRE, Edward, Administrator, St. John Vianney Hospital, Downingtown, PA, p. A537

MAGUIRE, Kimberly, R.N
Chief Nursing Officer, Mercy Health, Hackley Campus, Muskegon, MI, p. A331
Chief Nursing Officer, Mercy Health, Mercy Campus, Muskegon, MI, p. A331

MAGUTA, Sam, Coordinator Information Systems, Devereux Georgia Treatment Network, Kennesaw, GA, p. A161

MAHAJAN, Naman, Chief Operating Officer, Select Specialty Hospital–Houston Heights, Houston, TX, p. A626

MAHAJAN, Surnit, M.D. Chief Medical Staff, Hi–Desert Medical Center, Joshua Tree, CA, p. A67

MAHAN, Michael, M.D. Chief Medical Staff, Granville Health System, Oxford, NC, p. A470

MAHAN, Michelle K., Senior Vice President and Chief Financial Officer, Frederick Memorial Hospital, Frederick, MD, p. A301

MAHAN, Vic
Chief Information Officer, Chino Valley Medical Center, Chino, CA, p. A59
Director Information Technology, La Palma Intercommunity Hospital, La Palma, CA, p. A68
Director Information Technology, West Anaheim Medical Center, Anaheim, CA, p. A55

MAHAR, Priscilla, Chief Clinical Officer, Spectrum Health United Hospital, Greenville, MI, p. A326

MAHBOOB, Neeraj, M.D. Chief Medical Officer, Manchester Memorial Hospital, Manchester, KY, p. A267

MAHER, Donna, R.N. Chief Operating Officer, Morton Hospital and Medical Center, Taunton, MA, p. A315

MAHER, James M., Senior Vice President and Chief Financial Officer, Robert Wood Johnson University Hospital at Hamilton, Hamilton, NJ, p. A416

MAHER, John P., Executive Vice President and Chief Financial Officer, Nassau University Medical Center, East Meadow, NY, p. A437

MAHER, Sean, Director Human Resources, Devereux Children's Behavioral Health Center, Malvern, PA, p. A544

MAHER, Thomas, Chief Executive Officer and Administrator, Boulder City Hospital, Boulder City, NV, p. A404

MAHERA, Tina, M.D. Chief Medical Officer, Garfield Park Hospital, Chicago, IL, p. A183

MAHEUX, Diane, Vice President Finance, Memorial Hospital, North Conway, NH, p. A412

MAHL, Morgan G., Director Human Resources, St. Luke's Hospital – Warren Campus, Phillipsburg, NJ, p. A421

MAHMOOD, Ahsan, M.D. Chief Medical Officer, Hamilton Center, Terre Haute, IN, p. A223

MAHMOOD, K. Alec, Chief Financial Officer, Children's Hospitals and Clinics of Minnesota, Minneapolis, MN, p. A347

MAHMOOD, Tariq
Chief Executive Officer, Central Texas Hospital, Cameron, TX, p. A605
Chief Executive Officer, Lake Whitney Medical Center, Whitney, TX, p. A657

MAHONE, William, President and Chief Executive Officer, Halifax Regional Medical Center, Roanoke Rapids, NC, p. A471

MAHONEY, James, Chief Information Officer, Memorial Hospital, York, PA, p. A559

MAHONEY, Marie, M.D. Chief Medical Officer, AMG Specialty Hospital–Slidell, Slidell, LA, p. A288

MAHONEY, Mark, Manager Information Systems, Meadville Medical Center, Meadville, PA, p. A544

MAHONEY, Nicole, Chief Financial Officer, Pioneer Memorial Hospital, Heppner, OR, p. A525

MAHONEY, Theresa, Director Human Resources, Fairmount Behavioral Health System, Philadelphia, PA, p. A548

MAHONEY, William K., President and Chief Executive Officer, Cox Medical Center Branson, Branson, MO, p. A368

MAHR–CHAN, Lydia, Director Human Resources, Chinese Hospital, San Francisco, CA, p. A90

MAHUGH, Marilyn, Vice President Clinical Services, Bakersfield Heart Hospital, Bakersfield, CA, p. A56

MAIDEN, Phillip, M.D. Medical Director, Belmont Pines Hospital, Youngstown, OH, p. A506

MAIDLOW, Spencer, President and Chief Executive Officer, Covenant Medical Center, Saginaw, MI, p. A333

MAIETTA, Carol
Vice President and Talent Resource Officer Human Resources and Learning, St. Vincent's Blount, Oneonta, AL, p. A24
Vice President Human Resources and Chief Learning Officer, St. Vincent's East, Birmingham, AL, p. A17

MAIJALA, Jussi, Vice President, Human Resources, Phelps Memorial Hospital Center, Sleepy Hollow, NY, p. A454

MAIN, Matthew B., M.D. Medical Staff President, Indiana University Health Paoli Hospital, Paoli, IN, p. A221

MAINARDI, Carlo, M.D. Vice President Medical Affairs and Chief Medical Officer, Park Ridge Health, Hendersonville, NC, p. A466

MAINE MSN, RN–B, Cathy Loving, Interim Chief Executive Officer, Smyth County Community Hospital, Marion, VA, p. A673

MAINIERI, John J., Chief Executive Officer, Memorial Hospital of Tampa, Tampa, FL, p. A148

MAINIERI, Kathy, Human Resource Specialist, Sister Emmanuel Hospital, Miami, FL, p. A137

MAISH, Elizabeth, R.N. Vice President and Chief Nursing Officer, TMC Healthcare, Tucson, AZ, p. A41

MAISSEL, Gerda, M.D. Chief Medical Officer, Baystate Franklin Medical Center, Greenfield, MA, p. A310

MAIZE, Makyla, Director Information Services, Washington County Hospital and Clinics, Washington, IA, p. A238

MAJCHRZAK, John, Chief Financial Officer, Touchette Regional Hospitals, Centreville, IL, p. A183

MAJDALANI, Elias, Director Management Information Systems, Mildred Mitchell–Bateman Hospital, Huntington, WV, p. A696

MAJETICH, Stephen D., CPA Chief Financial Officer, Southwestern Vermont Medical Center, Bennington, VT, p. A665

MAJEWSKI, Laura, Director Human Resources, Community Memorial Hospital, Oconto Falls, WI, p. A712

MAJHAIL, Ruby, Chief Financial Officer, St. Luke's Behavioral Health Center, Phoenix, AZ, p. A37

MAJKA, Andrew, Chief Financial Officer and Chief Strategy Officer, Springfield Hospital, Springfield, VT, p. A666

MAJOR, Aprille, Director Human Resources, Newport Specialty Hospital, Tustin, CA, p. A98

MAJOR, Kerry, R.N. Chief Nursing Officer, Cleveland Clinic Florida, Weston, FL, p. A150

MAJOR, Pattie, Chief Financial Officer, Paul B. Hall Regional Medical Center, Paintsville, KY, p. A269

MAJORS, Valerie, Director Information Services, Western State Hospital, Hopkinsville, KY, p. A263

MAJURE, Thomas K., Administrator, Our Community Hospital, Scotland Neck, NC, p. A472

MAKAROFF, Jason, Chief Operating Officer and Associate Vice President, Adventist Rehabilitation Hospital of Maryland, Rockville, MD, p. A303

MAKELA, Taylor, Director Information Technology, Baraga County Memorial Hospital, L'Anse, MI, p. A328

MAKEPEACE, Anne, Director Human Resources, New Ulm Medical Center, New Ulm, MN, p. A348

MAKI, Jacquelyn, Chief Nursing Officer, Oakleaf Surgical Hospital, Eau Claire, WI, p. A704

MAKI, Richard, R.N. Vice President Nursing and Chief Nursing Officer, Anna Jaques Hospital, Newburyport, MA, p. A312

MAKIEVSKY, Inna, FACHE Chief Nursing Officer, St. Cloud Regional Medical Center, Saint Cloud, FL, p. A144

MAKORO, Leslie, Director Information management Systems, Natchez Regional Medical Center, Natchez, MS, p. A363

MAKSOUD, Jane, R.N
Senior Vice President Human Resources and Labor Relations, Mount Sinai Health System, Mount Sinai Beth Israel, New York, NY, p. A446
Senior Vice President Human Resources and Labor Relations, Mount Sinai Hospital, New York, NY, p. A446
Senior Vice President Human Resources and Labor Relations, Mount Sinai Health System, Mount Sinai St. Luke's, New York, NY, p. A446
Senior Vice President Human Resources and Labor Relations, Mount Sinai Health System, New York Eye and Ear Infirmary of Mount Sinai, New York, NY, p. A447

MAKSYMOW, Michael, Vice President Information Systems, Beebe Healthcare, Lewes, DE, p. A119

MAKUNDA, Beejadi, M.D. Chief Medical Officer, Heatherhill Care Communities, Chardon, OH, p. A485

MALAER, Gary, Chief Operating Officer, South Bay Hospital, Sun City Center, FL, p. A146

MALAKOFF, Stacey, Executive Vice President and Chief Financial Officer, Hospital for Special Surgery, New York, NY, p. A444

MALAMED, Michael, M.D. Chief of Staff, Sherman Oaks Hospital,, CA, p. A74

MALAN, Glen, Vice President Information Technology and Chief Information Officer, Northwest Community Hospital, Arlington Heights, IL, p. A180

MALANEY, Scott C., President and Chief Executive Officer, Blanchard Valley Health System, Findlay, OH, p. B24

MALANEY, Scott C., President and Chief Executive Officer, Blanchard Valley Hospital, Findlay, OH, p. A494

MALANOWSKI, John S., Chief Human Resources Officer, Dartmouth–Hitchcock Medical Center, Lebanon, NH, p. A411

MALATEK, Jennifer, Chief Executive Officer, New Braunfels Regional Rehabilitation Hospital, New Braunfels, TX, p. A639

MALBROUGH, Christie, Director of Nursing, Pioneer Community Hospital of Newton, Newton, MS, p. A363

MALCOLMSON, James F., M.D. Chief of Staff, Sierra Vista Hospital, Truth or Consequences, NM, p. A431

MALDONADO, Diraida, Chief Executive Officer, Hospital de la Universidad de Puerto Rico/Dr. Federico Trilla, Carolina, PR, p. A725

MALDONADO, Ramon Lopez, Executive Director, San Juan City Hospital, San Juan, PR, p. A729

MALEK, Frank
Chief Financial Officer, Nacogdoches Medical Center, Nacogdoches, TX, p. A639
Chief Financial Officer, Northern Louisiana Medical Center, Ruston, LA, p. A287

MALENSEK, Frank, M.D. Chief Medical Officer, St. Vincent's East, Birmingham, AL, p. A17

MALEY, Shelley, Director Human Resources, St. Luke's Hospital – Quakertown Campus, Quakertown, PA, p. A553

MALIK, Amir, M.D. Cardiologist, Plaza Medical Center of Fort Worth, Fort Worth, TX, p. A619

MALIK, Azfar, M.D., Chief Executive Officer and Chief Medical Officer, CenterPointe Hospital, Saint Charles, MO, p. A379

MALIK, Azfar, M.D. Chief Executive Officer and Chief Medical Officer, CenterPointe Hospital, Saint Charles, MO, p. A379

MALIK, Azfar, M.D., Chief Executive Officer, Signature Psychiatric Hospital, Kansas City, MO, p. A374

MALIK, Chuck, Director Information Systems, Advocate Good Shepherd Hospital, Barrington, IL, p. A181

MALIK, Tariq F., CP
Acting Chief Financial Officer, CenterPointe Hospital, Saint Charles, MO, p. A379
Chief Financial Officer, Signature Psychiatric Hospital, Kansas City, MO, p. A374

MALIN, Seth, M.D. President Medical and Dental Staff, Delaware County Memorial Hospital, Drexel Hill, PA, p. A537

MALINA, Joanne J., M.D. Chief of Staff, Veterans Affairs Hudson Valley Health Care System–F.D. Roosevelt Hospital, Montrose, NY, p. A441

MALINDZAK, Edward, Chief Human Resources Officer, Oconomowoc Memorial Hospital, Oconomowoc, WI, p. A712

MALISH, Richard, M.D. Deputy Commander Clinical Services, Winn Army Community Hospital, Hinesville, GA, p. A161

MALJOVEC, John, M.D. Medical Director, Warren General Hospital, Warren, PA, p. A557

MALLEK, Brent J., Chief Human Resources Officer, Conemaugh Memorial Medical Center, Johnstown, PA, p. A541

MALLERY, Edwina, Assistant Vice President Information Systems, Lafayette General Medical Center, Lafayette, LA, p. A281

MALLETT, Belinda, R.N
Vice President Patient Care and Clinical Services, Greene Memorial Hospital, Xenia, OH, p. A506
Vice President, Patient Care and Clinical Services, Soin Medical Center, Beavercreek, OH, p. A483

MALLETT, Teresa, Chief Financial Officer, Madison Community Hospital, Madison, SD, p. A574

MALLING, Timothy, M.D. Chief of Staff, CentraCare Health–Paynesville, Paynesville, MN, p. A349

MALLON, Lisa, Chief Executive Officer, J. C. Blair Memorial Hospital, Huntingdon, PA, p. A541

MALLONEE, Teresa, Director Human Resources, Angel Medical Center, Franklin, NC, p. A464

MALLOONEE, Teresa, Director Human Resources, Highlands–Cashiers Hospital, Highlands, NC, p. A466

MALLORY, Brenda, M.D. Medical Director, Penn State Hershey Rehabilitation Hospital, Hummelstown, PA, p. A541

MALLOY, Peter, Chief Information Officer, Cheshire Medical Center, Keene, NH, p. A410

MALM, Brad, Director Human Resources and Education, Lindsborg Community Hospital, Lindsborg, KS, p. A249

MALMSTROM, Ron, Information Research Specialist, Parsons State Hospital and Training Center, Parsons, KS, p. A252

MALONE, Donald, M.D., President, Lutheran Hospital, Cleveland, OH, p. A488

MALONE, MSN, RN–, Ginger, Chief Nursing Officer, St. Mary's Hospital, Madison, WI, p. A708

MALONE, Maureen A., Chief Operating Officer, Arrowhead Regional Medical Center, Colton, CA, p. A60

MALONE, Meredith, Chief Financial Officer, Dyersburg Regional Medical Center, Dyersburg, TN, p. A582

MALONE, Michael, Vice President and Chief Human Resources Officer, Virginia Hospital Center – Arlington, Arlington, VA, p. A668

MALONE, Patty, M.D. Chief Medical Officer, Ocean Beach Hospital, Ilwaco, WA, p. A684

MALONEY, Jay, M.D. Chief of Staff, Cabinet Peaks Medical Center, Libby, MT, p. A389

MALONEY, Patrick
Chief Executive Officer, West Suburban Medical Center, Oak Park, IL, p. A198

Chief Executive Officer, Westlake Hospital, Melrose Park, IL, p. A196

MALONEY, Paul V., Vice President Finance, Behavioral Health Network, Natchaug Hospital, Mansfield Center, CT, p. A115

MALOTT, Deanna, Director Human Resources, Henry County Hospital, New Castle, IN, p. A220

MALOTT, Gregg, Chief Financial Officer, Pulaski Memorial Hospital, Winamac, IN, p. A224

MALOTTE, Rebecca, Executive Director and Chief Nursing Officer, The Heart Hospital at Deaconess Gateway, Newburgh, IN, p. A220

MALSED, Brad, Area Chief Financial Officer, Kaiser Permanente Los Angeles Medical Center, Los Angeles, CA, p. A72

MALTE, Robert H., Chief Executive Officer, EvergreenHealth, Kirkland, WA, p. A684

MAMAMGAKIS, John P., Senior Vice President, Montefiore New Rochelle, New Rochelle, NY, p. A442

MAMARY, Glenn, Chief Information Officer, Hunterdon Medical Center, Flemington, NJ, p. A416

MAMBOURG, Rolland, M.D. Vice President Medical Affairs, Mercy Health Saint Mary's, Grand Rapids, MI, p. A325

MANAS, Julie, President and Chief Executive Officer, Sacred Heart Hospital, Eau Claire, WI, p. A704

MANCHER, Terry, R.N. Chief Nurse Executive, Coney Island Hospital, NY, p. A443

MANCHESTER, George A., M.D. Executive Vice President and Chief Medical Officer, Muncy Valley Hospital, Muncy, PA, p. A546

MANCHUR, Fred M., Chief Executive Officer, Kettering Health Network, Dayton, OH, p. B79

MANDAL, Konoy, M.D. Medical Director, Centennial Peaks Hospital, Louisville, CO, p. A109

MANDALE, Asa, Interim Director Information Systems and Telecommunications, San Ramon Regional Medical Center, San Ramon, CA, p. A93

MANDANAS, Renato, M.D. Chief Medical Officer, Oswego Hospital, Oswego, NY, p. A451

MANDEL, David, M.D. Chief of Staff, East Texas Medical Center Trinity, Trinity, TX, p. A653

MANDERINO, Michelle, Chief Human Resources, Malcom Randall Veterans Affairs Medical Center, Gainesville, FL, p. A129

MANDHAN, Narain, M.D. President Medical Staff, Kirby Medical Center, Monticello, IL, p. A196

MANDI, Deepak, M.D. Chief of Staff, West Palm Beach Veterans Affairs Medical Center, West Palm Beach, FL, p. A150

MANDRACCHIA, Vincent, DPM Chief Medical Officer, Broadlawns Medical Center, Des Moines, IA, p. A229

MANESS, Judith A., FACHE, President and Chief Executive Officer, Mount St. Mary's Hospital and Health Center, Lewiston, NY, p. A440

MANESTRINA, Robert, Vice President Human Resources, Inspira Medical Center–Woodbury, Woodbury, NJ, p. A425

MANFREDI, Susan, R.N. Vice President and Chief Nursing Officer, UW Medicine/Northwest Hospital & Medical Center, Seattle, WA, p. A689

MANFULL, Debra, Interim Chief Executive Officer, State Hospital North, Orofino, ID, p. A177

MANGANELLO, Christy, M.D. Chief of Staff, Lucas County Health Center, Chariton, IA, p. A227

MANGANO, Richard, Administrator and Chief Executive Officer, Malvern Institute, Malvern, PA, p. A544

MANGIN, Paul, Vice President Finance, Mercy Medical Center–Clinton, Clinton, IA, p. A227

MANGIONE, Ellen, M.D. Chief of Staff, Veterans Affairs Eastern Colorado Health Care System, Denver, CO, p. A105

MANGONA, John, Vice President, Chief Information Officer and Compliance Officer, Saratoga Hospital, Saratoga Springs, NY, p. A454

MANGRUM, Charlita, M.D. Chief of Staff, Sandhills Regional Medical Center, Hamlet, NC, p. A466

MANGUM, Rozanne, Administrative Assistant and Director Human Resources, Grover C. Dils Medical Center, Caliente, NV, p. A404

MANHEIMER, Dean, Senior Vice President Human Resources, Northwestern Memorial Hospital, Chicago, IL, p. A185

MANIS, Scott, Chief Executive Officer, Union County General Hospital, Clayton, NM, p. A427

MANKER, Marcia, Chief Executive Officer, Orange Coast Memorial Medical Center, Fountain Valley, CA, p. A63

MANKINS, Mark L., M.D. Chief of Staff, Hamilton Hospital, Olney, TX, p. A640

MANKOSKI, Susan, Vice President Human Resources, St. Marys Health Center, Jefferson City, MO, p. A372

MANLAGNIT, Maybelle, Senior Accounting Officer, Metropolitan State Hospital, Norwalk, CA, p. A80

MANLEY, John, Director Information Systems, Jackson General Hospital, Ripley, WV, p. A699

MANN, Brian, Chief Executive Officer, Select Specialty Hospital–Danville, Danville, PA, p. A537

MANN, Christopher, M.D. Medical Director, Cook Children's Northeast Hospital, Hurst, TX, p. A629

MANN, Lindsay K., Chief Executive Officer, Kaweah Delta Medical Center, Visalia, CA, p. A99

MANN, Rhonda
Chief Nursing Officer, Franklin Woods Community Hospital, Johnson City, TN, p. A585

Vice President and Chief Nursing Officer, Johnson City Medical Center, Johnson City, TN, p. A585

MANN, Todd, Senior Vice President and Chief Executive Officer, Valley Baptist Medical Center–Harlingen, Harlingen, TX, p. A623

MANNICH, Andy, Regional Administrator, Georgia Regional Hospital at Savannah, Savannah, GA, p. A166

MANNING, Angela, Director Health Information Services, HEALTHSOUTH Sunrise Rehabilitation Hospital, Sunrise, FL, p. A146

MANNING, Bain, Director Human Resources, Leonard J. Chabert Medical Center, Houma, LA, p. A279

MANNING, Donald, M.D. Clinical Director, Georgia Regional Hospital at Savannah, Savannah, GA, p. A166

MANNING, James, Administrator, Pathway Rehabilitation Hospital, Bossier City, LA, p. A274

MANNING, JoAnn, Chief Financial Officer, Emory Johns Creek Hospital, Johns Creek, GA, p. A161

MANNING, Kimberly, Chief Nursing Officer, Washington County Hospital, Plymouth, NC, p. A470

MANNING, Laura, Administrative Director, Corning Hospital, Corning, NY, p. A436

MANNING, Lori, Administrator Human Resources, Western State Hospital, Tacoma, WA, p. A691

MANNION, Stephen, Assistant Vice President Information Systems Customer Service, MedStar Franklin Square Medical Center, Baltimore, MD, p. A297

MANNIX, Mary N., FACHE, President and Chief Executive Officer, Augusta Health, Fishersville, VA, p. A670

MANNS, Bill, President, Mercy Health Saint Mary's, Grand Rapids, MI, p. A325

MANNY, Martin, Director, I.S., Providence St. Mary Medical Center, Walla Walla, WA, p. A692

MANOHARA, Anand, Associate Administrator, Good Samaritan Hospital, Bakersfield, CA, p. A57

MANSEAU, Jani, Vice President Operations and Chief Nursing Officer, Freedom Pain Hospital, Scottsdale, AZ, p. A38

MANSFIELD, Al, Chief Financial Officer, Saint Vincent Health Center, Erie, PA, p. A539

MANSFIELD, David, M.D. Chief of Staff, El Paso Specialty Hospital, El Paso, TX, p. A615

MANSFIELD, Deena, Director Human Resources, Ashley Regional Medical Center, Vernal, UT, p. A664

MANSFIELD, Jean, Director Human Resources, McLean Hospital, Belmont, MA, p. A305

MANSFIELD, Robert, Chief Executive Officer, Mesilla Valley Hospital, Las Cruces, NM, p. A429

MANSFIELD, Stephen L., FACHE, President and Chief Executive Officer, Methodist Health System, Dallas, TX, p. B94

MANSKE, Lou Ann, Director Human Resources, Madonna Rehabilitation Hospital, Lincoln, NE, p. A398

MANSON, David, Manager Human Resources, Santa Clara Valley Medical Center, San Jose, CA, p. A92

MANSON, Kelly, Chief Financial Officer, Veterans Affairs Sierra Nevada Health Care System, Reno, NV, p. A408

MANSON, III, William T., President, AnMed Health Medical Center, Anderson, SC, p. A562

MANSOOR, Ureej, M.D. Chief of Staff, Southeast Health Center of Ripley County, Doniphan, MO, p. A370

MANSUE, Amy B., President and Chief Executive Officer, Children's Specialized Hospital–PSE&G, New Brunswick, NJ, p. A419

MANSUKHANI, Martin, Chief Financial Officer, Desert Valley Hospital, Victorville, CA, p. A99

MANSURE, John F., FACHE, President, Greer Memorial Hospital, Greer, SC, p. A567

MANTELL, Amy, Vice President Human Resources, Mercy Hospital of Folsom, Folsom, CA, p. A63

MANTERNACH, Paul, M.D. Senior Vice President Physician Integration, Mercy Medical Center–North Iowa, Mason City, IA, p. A234

MANTZ, David, Chief Executive Officer, Chicot Memorial Medical Center, Lake Village, AR, p. A48

MANUBENS, Claudio, M.D. Chief of Staff, Heart of Florida Regional Medical Center, Davenport, FL, p. A127

MANUEL, Shasta, Executive Director Finance, St. Anthony Hospital, Oklahoma City, OK, p. A516

MANUEL, Wendy, Chief Financial Officer, Rehabilitation Hospital of the Pacific, Honolulu, HI, p. A171

MANZ, Louis, Director Information and Communication Services, Chatham Hospital, Siler City, NC, p. A472

MANZER, Andrew R., President and Chief Executive Officer, Schuyler Hospital, Montour Falls, NY, p. A441

MANZO, Arnold D., Vice President Human Resources, Saint Barnabas Medical Center, Livingston, NJ, p. A417

MANZO–LUNA, Hilda, Chief Nursing Officer, La Palma Intercommunity Hospital, La Palma, CA, p. A68

MANZOOR, Amir, M.D. Medical Director, Select Specialty Hospital–Panama City, Panama City, FL, p. A142

MAO, Chi C., M.D. Medical Director, Select Specialty Hospital–Houston Heights, Houston, TX, p. A626

MAPES, Kevin, Director Kansas Division System and Technology Service Center, St. Francis Health Center, Topeka, KS, p. A255

MAPLES, Rickie, Interim Chief Financial Officer, Southeast Health Center of Ripley County, Doniphan, MO, p. A370

MAPPIN, F Gregory, M.D. Vice President Medical Affairs and Chief Medical Officer, Self Regional Healthcare, Greenwood, SC, p. A567

MARAS, Greg, Vice President Human Resources, Meadville Medical Center, Meadville, PA, p. A544

MARBAN, Anita L., R.N. Chief Nursing Officer, HEALTHSOUTH Rehabilitation Hospital, Humble, TX, p. A628

MARBLE, Kevin, Director Information Technology, Oklahoma Forensic Center, Vinita, OK, p. A521

MARCANO, Norma, Chief Operating Officer, San Juan City Hospital, San Juan, PR, p. A729

MARCANTANO, Mark R., President and Chief Operating Officer, Women & Infants Hospital of Rhode Island, Providence, RI, p. A561

MARCANTEL, Bill, Chief Information Systems, Allen Parish Hospital, Kinder, LA, p. A280

MARCELLINO, David, Corporate Executive Vice President and Chief Administrative Officer, Botsford Hospital, Farmington Hills, MI, p. A323

MARCH, Riley, Manager Information Technology, Southeast Health Center of Ripley County, Doniphan, MO, p. A370

MARCHAND, Gary G., President and Chief Executive Officer, Memorial Hospital at Gulfport, Gulfport, MS, p. A358

MARCHANT, Joseph, Administrator, Bibb Medical Center, Centreville, AL, p. A18

MARCHETTI, Mark E., Chief Executive Officer, Mt. Graham Regional Medical Center, Safford, AZ, p. A38

MARCOTTE, Melissa, Chief Financial Officer, Rainy Lake Medical Center, International Falls, MN, p. A345

MARCOVICI, Mia, M.D. Chief Medical Officer, Norristown State Hospital, Norristown, PA, p. A546

MARCRUM, Jennifer, Chief Financial Officer, Sumner County Hospital District One, Caldwell, KS, p. A242

MARCRUM, William, M.D. Chief of Staff, Perry County Memorial Hospital, Tell City, IN, p. A222

MARCUCCI, John, M.D. Vice President Medical Affairs, Baylor Regional Medical Center at Plano, Plano, TX, p. A642

MARCUM, Derrick, Director Information Systems, Missouri Baptist Medical Center, Saint Louis, MO, p. A381

MARCUS, Stuart G., FACS, President and Chief Executive Officer, St. Vincent's Medical Center, Bridgeport, CT, p. A113

MARCZAK, Stanley, Chief Financial Officer, Mayo Clinic Health System in Mankato, Mankato, MN, p. A346

MARCZEWSKI, Les, M.D. Chief Medical Officer, Loring Hospital, Sac City, IA, p. A237

MARDY, Paul, Chief Information Technology Officer, Tennessee Valley Healthcare System, Nashville, TN, p. A591

MAREK, Kyle, Manager Information Services, Carteret General Hospital, Morehead City, NC, p. A469

MAREK, Rick, Vice President Medical Information Systems, Post Acute/Warm Springs Rehabilitation Hospital of San Antonio, San Antonio, TX, p. A647

MARGENAU, Randall, Chief Information Officer, William S. Middleton Memorial Veterans Hospital, Madison, WI, p. A708

MARGER, Brian, Chief Operating Officer, Tristar Centennial Medical Center at Ashland City, Ashland City, TN, p. A579

MARGO, John G., Vice President Human Resources, Oneida Healthcare, Oneida, NY, p. A450

MARGOLIS, Marilyn, Interim Chief Executive Officer, Emory Johns Creek Hospital, Johns Creek, GA, p. A161

MARGOLIS, Ron, Chief Information Officer, University of New Mexico Hospitals, Albuquerque, NM, p. A427

MARGOT, Skip, Vice President Patient Care Services and Chief Nurse Executive, Shady Grove Adventist Hospital, Rockville, MD, p. A303

MARGULIS, Richard T., President and Chief Executive Officer, Brookhaven Memorial Hospital Medical Center, Patchogue, NY, p. A451

MARIANI, Julia, Vice President Business Operations, Northern Montana Hospital, Havre, MT, p. A388

MARIANI, Marilyn, R.N. Chief Nursing Officer, Lakeview Hospital, Bountiful, UT, p. A659

MARICN, Tanya, Interim Vice President Human Resources, Mercy Hospital Springfield, Springfield, MO, p. A383

MARIETTA, John, M.D
  Chief Medical Officer, St. David's Medical Center, Austin, TX, p. A600
  Chief Medical Officer, St. David's Rehabilitation Center, Austin, TX, p. A600

MARIETTA, Megan, Chief Operating Officer, Kingwood Medical Center, Kingwood, TX, p. A631

MARIETTA, Richard, M.D. Medical Director, Clear Lake Regional Medical Center, Webster, TX, p. A656

MARIGOMEN, Nancy Ann, R.N. Director of Nursing, Milwaukee County Behavioral Health Division, Milwaukee, WI, p. A710

MARIN, Loyman, Chief Human Resources, Miami Veterans Affairs Healthcare System, Miami, FL, p. A137

MARINELLO, Anthony, Chief Executive Officer, Mountain Vista Medical Center, Mesa, AZ, p. A34

MARINI, Frank, Vice President and Chief Information Officer, TMC Healthcare, Tucson, AZ, p. A41

MARINICH, Patsy, Chief Nursing Officer, Cumberland River Hospital, Celina, TN, p. A580

MARINO, A. Michael, M.D. Senior Vice President Medical Administration, Greenwich Hospital, Greenwich, CT, p. A114

MARINO, Christopher, M.D. Chief of Staff, Memphis Veterans Affairs Medical Center, Memphis, TN, p. A589

MARINO, Marchita H., Vice President Human Resources, Wuesthoff Medical Center – Rockledge, Rockledge, FL, p. A144

MARINOFF, Peter, President, Paul Oliver Memorial Hospital, Frankfort, MI, p. A324

MARION, Ben, Chief Executive Officer and Managing Director, Turning Point Hospital, Moultrie, GA, p. A164

MARION, Kristie, Chief Nurse Executive, Memorial Hospital Los Banos, Los Banos, CA, p. A76

MARION, Sue, Manager Business Office, Knox County Hospital, Knox City, TX, p. A632

MARIOTTI, Denise
  Chief Human Resource Officer, Hospital of the University of Pennsylvania, Philadelphia, PA, p. A548
  Chief Human Resources Officer, Pennsylvania Hospital, Philadelphia, PA, p. A549

MARIOTTI, Nadine A., R.N. Chief Nursing Officer, East Los Angeles Doctors Hospital, Los Angeles, CA, p. A71

MARK, Curtis, M.D. Chief Medical Officer, Pioneer Memorial Hospital and Health Services, Viborg, SD, p. A577

MARKENSON, David, M.D. Chief Medical Officer, Sky Ridge Medical Center, Lone Tree, CO, p. A109

MARKER, Jason, M.D. Chief Medical Officer, Community Hospital of Bremen, Bremen, IN, p. A207

MARKER, John, Chief Nursing Officer, Regional Medical Center of Acadiana, Lafayette, LA, p. A282

MARKESINO, Patricia A., FACHE Chief Nurse Executive and Chief Operating Officer, Providence Willamette Falls Medical Center, Oregon City, OR, p. A527

MARKETTI, Dean M., Vice President Finance, Morris Hospital & Healthcare Centers, Morris, IL, p. A196

MARKEY, Bernie, Chief Information Officer, Virginia Gay Hospital, Vinton, IA, p. A238

MARKGRAF, Janelle K., Director Human Resources, Langlade Hospital, Antigo, WI, p. A701

MARKHAM, Barbara, Chief Financial Officer, Glendive Medical Center, Glendive, MT, p. A387

MARKHAM, Kevin, Chief Financial Officer, EastPointe Hospital, Daphne, AL, p. A18

MARKHAM, Scott, D.O. Chief of Staff, Myrtue Medical Center, Harlan, IA, p. A232

MARKOS, Dennis R., Chief Executive Officer, Ed Fraser Memorial Hospital and Baker Community Health Center, MacClenny, FL, p. A135

MARKOVICH, Stephen, M.D., President, OhioHealth Riverside Methodist Hospital, Columbus, OH, p. A490

MARKOWITZ, Bruce J., President and Chief Executive Officer, Palisades Medical Center, North Bergen, NJ, p. A420

MARKOWITZ, Stuart, M.D., President, Hartford Hospital, Hartford, CT, p. A114

MARKOWSKI, Stan, Chief Financial Officer, Palmetto Lowcountry Behavioral Health, Charleston, SC, p. A563

MARKS, Craig J., FACHE, President, Mark Twain Medical Center, San Andreas, CA, p. A88

MARKS, Jerry, Vice President Finance, Decatur County Memorial Hospital, Greensburg, IN, p. A212

MARKS, Kimberly W., Interim Chief Executive Officer, Southampton Memorial Hospital, Franklin, VA, p. A671

MARKS, Marie, Chief Nursing Officer, Lake Norman Regional Medical Center, Mooresville, NC, p. A469

MARKS, Michael, M.D. Chief of Staff, Norwalk Hospital, Norwalk, CT, p. A116

MARKS, Stanley, M.D
  Chief Medical Officer, Memorial Hospital Miramar, Miramar, FL, p. A138
  Chief Medical Officer, Memorial Hospital Pembroke, Pembroke Pines, FL, p. A142
  Chief Medical Officer, Memorial Regional Hospital,, FL, p. A130

MARKSTROM, Susan, M.D. Chief of Staff, St. Cloud Veterans Affairs Health Care System, Saint Cloud, MN, p. A351

MARLATT, Pam, Business Systems Director, Essentia Health St. Joseph's Medical Center, Brainerd, MN, p. A340

MARLER, Ruth, Chief Operating Officer Johnston Health Smithfield, Johnston UNC Health Care, Smithfield, NC, p. A473

MARLER, Steven R.
  Assistant Administrator, Parkland Health Center, Farmington, MO, p. A371
  Administrator, Parkland Health Center–Bonne Terre, Bonne Terre, MO, p. A367

MARLEY, Charles, D.O. Vice President Medical Affairs, Gettysburg Hospital, Gettysburg, PA, p. A539

MARLEY, Lee
  VP/Information Services Chief Application Officer, Presbyterian Hospital, Albuquerque, NM, p. A426
  VP/Information Services Chief Application Officer, Presbyterian Kaseman Hospital, Albuquerque, NM, p. A427

MARLEY, Mark E., FACHE, President and Chief Executive Officer, Opelousas General Health System, Opelousas, LA, p. A287

MARLEY, Michael, Chief Information Officer, VA Central Western Massachusetts Healthcare System, Leeds, MA, p. A311

MARLIN, Chris, Director Human Resources, Orange Park Medical Center, Orange Park, FL, p. A140

MARLOW, Gary P., Chief Financial Officer, Beverly Hospital, Beverly, MA, p. A305

MARMANDE, Susanne, Administrator, Infirmary Long Term Acute Care Hospital, Mobile, AL, p. A22

MARNELL, George, Director, Veterans Affairs Medical Center, Albuquerque, NM, p. A427

MARNEY, Terri A., R.N. Director of Nursing, Plains Regional Medical Center, Clovis, NM, p. A427

MAROC, Genice, FACHE, President, Cox Monett, Monett, MO, p. A377

MARON, Michael, President and Chief Executive Officer, Holy Name Medical Center, Teaneck, NJ, p. A423

MARONEY, Gerry, Chief Information Officer and Security Officer, Gaylord Hospital, Wallingford, CT, p. A117

MAROSTICA, Tony, Director Human Resources, Spanish Peaks Regional Health Center, Walsenburg, CO, p. A112

MAROTTA, Diane, Vice President Human Resources, John T. Mather Memorial Hospital, Port Jefferson, NY, p. A452

MAROUN, Christiane, M.D. Chief of Staff, Childrens Care Hospital and School, Sioux Falls, SD, p. A576

MARPLE, Richard, M.D. Chief Medical Officer, Baptist Medical Center, San Antonio, TX, p. A646

MARQUARDT, Robert C., FACHE, Chief Executive Officer, Select Specialty Hospital–Fort Wayne, Fort Wayne, IN, p. A211

MARQUES, John
  Vice President Chief Human Resources Officer, University of Arizona Medical Center – South Campus, Tucson, AZ, p. A41
  Vice President Human Resources, University of Arizona Medical Center – University Campus, Tucson, AZ, p. A41

MARQUES, Tony, Director Information Systems, Grace Cottage Hospital, Townshend, VT, p. A666

MARQUSEE, Joanne, President and Chief Executive Officer, Cooley Dickinson Hospital, Northampton, MA, p. A313

MARR, Debbie, Administrative Assistant and Director Human Resources, Fredonia Regional Hospital, Fredonia, KS, p. A244

MARRA, Mary Anne, R.N. Vice President/Chief Nursing Officer, East Orange General Hospital, East Orange, NJ, p. A415

MARRERO, Jamie L., M.D. Medical Director, HEALTHSOUTH Hospital of Manati, Manati, PR, p. A726

MARRERO, Jose, Director Finance, San Jorge Children's Hospital, San Juan, PR, p. A728

MARRERO, Norma, Executive Administrator, Doctors' Center Hospital San Juan, San Juan, PR, p. A728

MARRERO, Waleska, Administrator, Metropolitano De La Montana, Utuado, PR, p. A729

MARRONI, Denise
  Chief Financial Officer, Providence Centralia Hospital, Centralia, WA, p. A682
  Chief Financial Officer, Providence St. Peter Hospital, Olympia, WA, p. A686

MARRUFO, Gabriel, Chief Financial Officer, Methodist Stone Oak Hospital, San Antonio, TX, p. A647

MARSEE, DeWayne, Director Information Systems and Chief Information Officer, Mercer Health, Coldwater, OH, p. A489

MARSH, Daniel L., Director, Oklahoma City Veterans Affairs Medical Center, Oklahoma City, OK, p. A516

MARSH, J. Michael, President and Chief Executive Officer, Overlake Medical Center, Bellevue, WA, p. A681

MARSH, Leslie, Chief Executive Officer, Lexington Regional Health Center, Lexington, NE, p. A397

MARSH, Linda, Vice President Financial Services and Chief Financial Officer, Alhambra Hospital Medical Center, Alhambra, CA, p. A55

MARSH, Mark A., Chief Executive Officer, Gateway Medical Center, Clarksville, TN, p. A581

MARSH, Mitch, Interim Executive Director, Terence Cardinal Cooke Health Care Center, New York, NY, p. A449

MARSH, Rob
  Chief Executive Officer, Cedar Crest Hospital and Residential Treatment Center, Belton, TX, p. A602
  Chief Executive Officer, Red River Hospital, Wichita Falls, TX, p. A657

MARSHAK, Glenn, M.D. Chief of Staff, Mission Community Hospital,, CA, p. A73

MARSHALL, David R., JD Chief Nursing and Patient Care Services Officer, University of Texas Medical Branch Hospitals, Galveston, TX, p. A620

MARSHALL, Deborah K., Vice President Public Relations, Good Samaritan Hospital, Suffern, NY, p. A455

MARSHALL, Glen, Chief Executive Officer, Trios Health, Kennewick, WA, p. A684

MARSHALL, James L., President and Chief Executive Officer, Uintah Basin Medical Center, Roosevelt, UT, p. A662

MARSHALL, Jerry, Director Information Systems, United Regional Health Care System, Wichita Falls, TX, p. A658

MARSHALL, John A., Chief Executive Officer, TriStar Horizon Medical Center, Dickson, TN, p. A582

MARSHALL, Julie, Chief Nursing Officer, Alice Hyde Medical Center, Malone, NY, p. A440

MARSHALL, Ken, M.D. Chief Medical Officer, Indiana University Health Bloomington Hospital, Bloomington, IN, p. A207

MARSHALL, Kenneth P., President, University of Louisville Hospital, Louisville, KY, p. A266

MARSHALL, Michael, Vice President Finance and Chief Financial Officer, Anderson Hospital, Maryville, IL, p. A195

MARSHALL, Michael D., Administrator and Chief Executive Officer, Bryan W. Whitfield Memorial Hospital, Demopolis, AL, p. A19

MARSHALL, Patricia, Assistant Administrator Human Resources, Southwest Regional Medical Center, Waynesburg, PA, p. A557

MARSHALL, Penny, Chief Nursing Officer, Bear River Valley Hospital, Tremonton, UT, p. A664

MARSHALL Jr., Robert L., FACHE, Chief Executive Officer, River Parishes Hospital, La Place, LA, p. A280

MARSHALL, Thomas, Chief Financial Officer, Lakeway Regional Medical Center, Lakeway, TX, p. A632

MARSILIO, Lisa, Executive Director, Good Shepherd Penn Partners Specialty Hospital at Rittenhouse, Philadelphia, PA, p. A548

MARSO, Paul, Vice President Human Resources, Avera St. Mary's Hospital, Pierre, SD, p. A575

MARSTELLER, Brent A., President and Chief Executive Officer, Cabell Huntington Hospital, Huntington, WV, p. A695

MARSTON, Shawn, Director Human Resources, Keystone Newport News, Newport News, VA, p. A674

MARTANIUK, Jean, Director Human Resources, Mt. Ascutney Hospital and Health Center, Windsor, VT, p. A667

MARTENS, Angela, Chief Financial Officer, Cumberland Memorial Hospital, Cumberland, WI, p. A703

MARTENS, Troy, Chief Operating Officer, UnityPoint Health – Trinity Regional Medical Center, Fort Dodge, IA, p. A230

MARTHONE, Frances, R.N. Chief Nursing Officer, Henry Medical Center, Stockbridge, GA, p. A167

MARTI, Maria L., Director Fiscal Services, Auxilio Mutuo Hospital, San Juan, PR, p. A727

MARTIN, Adam, Chief Financial Officer, Terre Haute Regional Hospital, Terre Haute, IN, p. A223

MARTIN, Amanda, Manager Human Resources, Ohio Valley Surgical Hospital, Springfield, OH, p. A502

MARTIN, Angelia, M.D. Chief of Staff, Northwest Medical Center, Albany, MO, p. A367

MARTIN, Barbara, Chief Nursing Officer, Mercy St. Vincent Medical Center, Toledo, OH, p. A503

MARTIN, Barbara J., R.N.,
President and Chief Executive Officer, Vista Medical Center East, Waukegan, IL, p. A205
President and Chief Executive Officer, Vista Medical Center West, Waukegan, IL, p. A205

MARTIN, Brent, Administrator, LifeCare Specialty Hospital of North Louisiana, Ruston, LA, p. A287

MARTIN, Bruce A., Vice President Human Resources, CarolinaEast Health System, New Bern, NC, p. A470

MARTIN, C. Gregory, M.D. Chief Medical Officer, Emerson Hospital, Concord, MA, p. A309

MARTIN, Carmen, Associate Administrator, Auxilio Mutuo Hospital, San Juan, PR, p. A727

MARTIN, Cary, Chief Executive Officer, Houston Healthcare System, Warner Robins, GA, p. B74

MARTIN, Cary, Chief Executive Officer, Houston Medical Center, Warner Robins, GA, p. A169

MARTIN, Cherie, FACHE, Chief Executive Officer, Banner Behavioral Health Hospital – Scottsdale, Scottsdale, AZ, p. A38

MARTIN, Cheryl
Manager Human Resources, Columbia Memorial Hospital, Astoria, OR, p. A523
Chief Information Officer, Tuomey Healthcare System, Sumter, SC, p. A570

MARTIN, Christine M.
Vice President and Chief Financial Officer, Cleveland Regional Medical Center, Shelby, NC, p. A472
Chief Financial Officer, St. Luke's Hospital, Columbus, NC, p. A462

MARTIN, Colette C., Chief Operating Officer, Memorial Hospital, Colorado Springs, CO, p. A103

MARTIN, Connie
Vice President and Chief Support Officer, Methodist Medical Center of Oak Ridge, Oak Ridge, TN, p. A591
Chief Executive Officer and Administrator, Physicians Medical Center, Houma, LA, p. A279

MARTIN, Corey, M.D. Director Medical Affairs, Buffalo Hospital, Buffalo, MN, p. A341

MARTIN, Cyndie, Director, Coal County General Hospital, Coalgate, OK, p. A509

MARTIN, David, Assistant Administrator, Valley Hospital, Spokane Valley, WA, p. A690

MARTIN, David T., President, UPMC Passavant, Pittsburgh, PA, p. A552

MARTIN, Deborah, Assistant Administrator Human Resources, Skagit Valley Hospital, Mount Vernon, WA, p. A685

MARTIN, Debra, Director of Nursing, Hamilton General Hospital, Hamilton, TX, p. A622

MARTIN, Drew, Chief Executive Officer, Behavioral Hospital of Bellaire, Houston, TX, p. A623

MARTIN, Emily Howard, Administrator, Commonwealth Regional Specialty Hospital, Bowling Green, KY, p. A258

MARTIN, Garland, M.D. Chief of Staff, Appling Healthcare System, Baxley, GA, p. A154

MARTIN, Garry, Chief Fiscal, Veterans Affairs North Texas Health Care System, Dallas, TX, p. A612

MARTIN, Gregg
Manager Management Information Systems, Arnot Ogden Medical Center, Elmira, NY, p. A437
Chief Information Officer, Ira Davenport Memorial Hospital, Bath, NY, p. A433
Chief Information Officer, St. Joseph's Hospital, Elmira, NY, p. A437

MARTIN, Harvey C., M.D. Medical Director, Red River Hospital, Wichita Falls, TX, p. A657

MARTIN, Holly, Human Resources Leader, Iowa Specialty Hospital–Clarion, Clarion, IA, p. A227

MARTIN, James C., M.D. Vice President and Chief Medical Officer, CHRISTUS Santa Rosa Health System, San Antonio, TX, p. A646

MARTIN, James D.
Chief Financial Officer, Hawthorn Children Psychiatric Hospital, Saint Louis, MO, p. A380
Chief Financial Officer, Metropolitan St. Louis Psychiatric Center, Saint Louis, MO, p. A381
Chief Financial Officer, St. Louis Psychiatric Rehabilitation Center, Saint Louis, MO, p. A382

MARTIN, Janice S., R.N. Chief Nursing Officer, Davis Regional Medical Center, Statesville, NC, p. A473

MARTIN, Jeanene R., M.P.H
Senior Vice President Human Resources, WakeMed Cary Hospital, Cary, NC, p. A461
Senior Vice President Human Resources, WakeMed Raleigh Campus, Raleigh, NC, p. A471

MARTIN, Jeffrey H., M.D. Chief of Staff, Murphy Medical Center, Murphy, NC, p. A470

MARTIN, Jeffrey L., President, Ministry Saint Michael's Hospital, Stevens Point, WI, p. A716

MARTIN, Jessica, Director Human Resources, Logan Regional Medical Center, Logan, WV, p. A696

MARTIN, Karen, R.N. Chief Nursing Officer, Marshall Medical Center, Lewisburg, TN, p. A587

MARTIN, Kathy, Vice President Patient Care, Baptist Health Medical Center – North Little Rock, North Little Rock, AR, p. A51

MARTIN, Kelly, Chief Financial Officer, Fairchild Medical Center, Yreka, CA, p. A101

MARTIN, Kelly K., Human Resource Officer, Texas Health Presbyterian Hospital Plano, Plano, TX, p. A643

MARTIN, Kenneth A., M.D. Chief of Staff, Arkansas Surgical Hospital, North Little Rock, AR, p. A51

MARTIN, Kevin, R.N., Administrator, Shriners Hospitals for Children–Salt Lake City, Salt Lake City, UT, p. A663

MARTIN, Kevin P., M.D. Chief Medical Officer, Four Winds Hospital, Saratoga Springs, NY, p. A454

MARTIN, Konnie, Chief Executive Officer, San Luis Valley Health, Alamosa, CO, p. A102

MARTIN, Konnie, Chief Executive Officer, San Luis Valley Health, Alamosa, CO, p. B117

MARTIN, Kory Lann, M.D. Chief of Staff, Seymour Hospital, Seymour, TX, p. A648

MARTIN, Leslee, Manager Information Technology, St. Elizabeth's Hospital, Belleville, IL, p. A181

MARTIN, Mary, MSN Chief Nursing Officer, St. Nicholas Hospital, Sheboygan, WI, p. A715

MARTIN, Matthew, Director Resource Management, Naval Hospital Oak Harbor, Oak Harbor, WA, p. A686

MARTIN, Nick, Chief Information Officer, Minidoka Memorial Hospital, Rupert, ID, p. A178

MARTIN, Nikki, Chief Financial Officer, CHRISTUS Jasper Memorial Hospital, Jasper, TX, p. A630

MARTIN, Patrick, Director Information Systems, Calvary Hospital,, NY, p. A443

MARTIN, Patrick, M.D. Medical Director, Wilmington Treatment Center, Wilmington, NC, p. A474

MARTIN, Patsy, Manager Human Resources, Select Rehabilitation Hospital of Denton, Denton, TX, p. A613

MARTIN, Paul J., Director Human Resources, Kaiser Permanente Los Angeles Medical Center, Los Angeles, CA, p. A72

MARTIN, Ric, Information Specialist, Madison State Hospital, Madison, IN, p. A218

MARTIN, Richard A., MSN Senior Vice President and Chief Nursing Officer, Hoag Memorial Hospital Presbyterian, Newport Beach, CA, p. A80

MARTIN, Sabrina, Chief Operating Officer, Rehabilitation Hospital of Southern New Mexico, Las Cruces, NM, p. A429

MARTIN, Sharon E., M.D. President Medical Staff, Fulton County Medical Center, Mc Connellsburg, PA, p. A544

MARTIN, Sherri, M.D. President Medical Staff, Shawnee Mission Medical Center, Shawnee Mission, KS, p. A254

MARTIN, Stacy L., Director Human Resources, Grant Regional Health Center, Lancaster, WI, p. A708

MARTIN, Susan, Vice President Finance, Middlesex Hospital, Middletown, CT, p. A115

MARTIN, Thomas J., Administrator, Lincoln Hospital, Davenport, WA, p. A683

MARTIN, Tom, Vice President and Chief Information Officer, EvergreenHealth, Kirkland, WA, p. A684

MARTIN, Tracie, M.D. Chief Medical Officer, Oakland Mercy Hospital, Oakland, NE, p. A399

MARTIN, Val, Director Financial Management Services Center, Veterans Affairs Salt Lake City Health Care System, Salt Lake City, UT, p. A664

MARTIN, Valene J., Administrative Director Human Resources, Community Hospital of Long Beach, Long Beach, CA, p. A70

MARTIN, Veronica, MSN Vice President Inpatient Services, WellStar Cobb Hospital, Austell, GA, p. A154

MARTIN, W. Carl, Chief Operating Officer, Providence Hospital, Columbia, SC, p. A564

MARTIN–FORMAN, Marty Ann, Chief Operating Officer, Fulton State Hospital, Fulton, MO, p. A372

MARTIN–PRATT, Diane, Director Information Systems, Niagara Falls Memorial Medical Center, Niagara Falls, NY, p. A449

MARTINEAU, Loraine, Chief Financial Officer, Prairie Ridge Hospital and Health Services, Elbow Lake, MN, p. A343

MARTINEK, Jacquelyn, R.N. Chief Nursing Officer, Brookwood Medical Center, Birmingham, AL, p. A16

MARTINEZ, Albino
Director Budget and Finance, Miners' Colfax Medical Center, Raton, NM, p. A429
Director Finance and Budget, New Mexico Behavioral Health Institute at Las Vegas, Las Vegas, NM, p. A429

MARTINEZ, Beverly, Director of Nursing, Rio Grande Hospital, Del Norte, CO, p. A104

MARTINEZ, Carlos J., Director Resource Management, Naval Medical Center, Portsmouth, VA, p. A676

MARTINEZ, Edward, Chief Information Officer, Miami Children's Hospital, Miami, FL, p. A137

MARTINEZ, Eleanor, Chief Nursing Officer, Alhambra Hospital Medical Center, Alhambra, CA, p. A55

MARTINEZ, Fernando
Vice President and Chief Information Officer, Jackson Health System, Miami, FL, p. A137
Senior Vice President and Chief Information Officer, Parkland Health & Hospital System, Dallas, TX, p. A611

MARTINEZ, Frank
Senior Vice President Human Resources, East Jefferson General Hospital, Metairie, LA, p. A284
Vice President Human Resources, West Jefferson Medical Center, Marrero, LA, p. A284

MARTINEZ Jr., Fred, Chief Executive Officer, St. Charles Parish Hospital, Luling, LA, p. A283

MARTINEZ, Jason, Director Information Technology, West Valley Medical Center, Caldwell, ID, p. A175

MARTINEZ, Jorge I., Executive Director, Hospital Perea, Mayaguez, PR, p. A727

MARTINEZ, Jose, M.D. Chief Medical Officer, Northwest Medical Center, Margate, FL, p. A135

MARTINEZ, Josue, Coordinator Information Systems, University Hospital, San Juan, PR, p. A729

MARTINEZ, Katherine, Chief Nursing Officer, North Central Surgical Center, Dallas, TX, p. A611

MARTINEZ, Lee, Chief Information Officer, Cooley Dickinson Hospital, Northampton, MA, p. A313

MARTINEZ, Louisa, Director of Nursing, Frio Regional Hospital, Pearsall, TX, p. A641

MARTINEZ, Michelle, Chief Executive Officer, U. S. Public Health Service Indian Hospital–Whiteriver, Whiteriver, AZ, p. A41

MARTINEZ, Regina M., Director Human Resources, La Paz Regional Hospital, Parker, AZ, p. A35

MARTINEZ, Roberto, Chief Human Resources Officer, Banner Lassen Medical Center, Susanville, CA, p. A96

MARTINEZ, Steve, Executive Director and Administrator, New Mexico Behavioral Health Institute at Las Vegas, Las Vegas, NM, p. A429

MARTINEZ, Suzanne, Director Human Resources, Centennial Peaks Hospital, Louisville, CO, p. A109

MARTINEZ, Terri, Chief Financial Officer, Plains Memorial Hospital, Dimmitt, TX, p. A614

MARTINEZ, Tina, Director Human Resources, J. D. McCarty Center for Children With Developmental Disabilities, Norman, OK, p. A514

MARTINEZ, Virginia, Manager Human Resources, Copper Queen Community Hospital, Bisbee, AZ, p. A31

MARTINEZ, Yolanda, Chief Fiscal Services, Edward Hines, Jr. Veterans Affairs Hospital, Hines, IL, p. A192

MARTINEZ, Yvette, Director Human Resources, Sutter Auburn Faith Hospital, Auburn, CA, p. A56

MARTINEZ–NIETO, Arlene, M.D. Chief Medical Officer, First Hospital Panamericano, Cidra, PR, p. A725

MARTING, Bill, Senior Vice President and Chief Financial Officer, The University of Kansas Hospital, Kansas City, KS, p. A247

MARTINO, Anthony, Chief Executive Officer, Select Specialty Hospital–Scottsdale, Scottsdale, AZ, p. A38

MARTINSON, Erling, M.D. Medical Director, Nelson County Health System, Mcville, ND, p. A479

MARTINSON, Tiffany, Director Human Resources, Norton Sound Regional Hospital, Nome, AK, p. A29

MARTOCCIO, Debora, R.N. Chief Operating Officer, Florida Hospital at Connerton Long Term Acute Care, Land O'Lakes, FL, p. A134

MARTORANO, Ann, Chief Operating Officer, Halifax Health Medical Center of Daytona Beach, Daytona Beach, FL, p. A127

MARTS, Teresa, M.D. Chief Medical Staff, Community Memorial Hospital, Burke, SD, p. A572

MARTUCCI, Kathleen, Chief Operating Officer, Helen Hayes Hospital, West Haverstraw, NY, p. A457

MARX, Edward
Vice President and Chief Information Officer, Texas Health Harris Methodist Hospital Azle, Azle, TX, p. A601
Senior Vice President and Chief Information Officer, Texas Health Presbyterian Hospital Dallas, Dallas, TX, p. A612

MARX, Tomasine
  Chief Financial Officer, St. John Hospital and Medical Center, Detroit, MI, p. A322
  Chief Financial Officer, St. John Macomb–Oakland Hospital, Warren, MI, p. A336
  Chief Financial Officer, St. John River District Hospital, East China, MI, p. A323
MARX, Troy, Director Human Resources, Upland Hills Health, Dodgeville, WI, p. A703
MARX, William, M.D. Chief of Staff, Syracuse Veterans Affairs Medical Center, Syracuse, NY, p. A456
MARZINZIK, John A., Vice President Finance, Frisbie Memorial Hospital, Rochester, NH, p. A412
MARZOLF, Steve, R.N. Chief Nursing Officer, Pennock Hospital, Hastings, MI, p. A326
MASCHER, Troy, Director Information Systems, Via Christi Hospital in Pittsburg, Pittsburg, KS, p. A253
MASE, Kerin, R.N. Chief Operating Officer and Chief Nursing Officer, Marian Regional Medical Center, Santa Maria, CA, p. A94
MASHAK–EKERN, Jane, Fiscal Officer, Tomah Veterans Affairs Medical Center, Tomah, WI, p. A716
MASI, George V., Chief Executive Officer, Harris Health System, Houston, TX, p. A624
MASKELL, Denise, Chief Information Officer, Springfield Hospital Center, Sykesville, MD, p. A303
MASKUS, Jane, Vice President and Chief Information Officer, Lawrence Memorial Hospital, Lawrence, KS, p. A248
MASLYN, Jay T., Chief Financial Officer, Nicholas H. Noyes Memorial Hospital, Dansville, NY, p. A436
MASON, Bill A., Chief Executive Officer, Meadow Wood Behavioral Health System, New Castle, DE, p. A119
MASON, Cheryl S., Chief Financial Officer, Regional Medical Center, Orangeburg, SC, p. A569
MASON, Jill K., MS Chief Nursing Officer, Blessing Hospital, Quincy, IL, p. A201
MASON, Kathy, Chief Operating Officer, Atrium Medical Center of Corinth, Corinth, TX, p. A608
MASON, Kathy, R.N. Chief Nursing Officer, LifeCare Hospitals of Dallas, Dallas, TX, p. A610
MASON, Kay, Chief Financial Officer, Texas Health Heart & Vascular Hospital Arlington, Arlington, TX, p. A598
MASON, Keith, Chief Executive Officer, Bailey Medical Center, Owasso, OK, p. A517
MASON, Philip A., Chief Executive Officer, Bournewood Health Systems, Brookline, MA, p. A308
MASON, Phyllis, M.D. Chief Medical Officer, Natchitoches Regional Medical Center, Natchitoches, LA, p. A285
MASON, Rhonda, Vice President of Patient Care Services, Tri–State Memorial Hospital, Clarkston, WA, p. A682
MASON, Sally, Director Human Resources, Golden Plains Community Hospital, Borger, TX, p. A603
MASON, Sandra, Director Nursing Services and Senior Nurse Executive, Robert E. Bush Naval Hospital, Twentynine Palms, CA, p. A98
MASON, Steve, Assistant Superintendent and Chief Operating Officer, Clifton T. Perkins Hospital Center, Jessup, MD, p. A301
MASON, William R., Chief Operating Officer, Brooke Glen Behavioral Hospital, Fort Washington, PA, p. A539
MASON–JONES, Taryn, Chief Nurse Executive, Norristown State Hospital, Norristown, PA, p. A546
MASON–WILLIAMS, Lois, Director of Human Resources, Northwest Ohio Psychiatric Hospital, Toledo, OH, p. A503
MASOOD, Shahid, M.D. Clinical Director, Mildred Mitchell–Bateman Hospital, Huntington, WV, p. A696
MASSA, Rhonda, Director of Nursing, Clarion Psychiatric Center, Clarion, PA, p. A535
MASSE, Roger A., FACHE, Chief Executive Officer, Ellsworth County Medical Center, Ellsworth, KS, p. A243
MASSELLA, Joan, Administrative Vice President and Chief Nursing Officer, St. Clair Hospital, Pittsburgh, PA, p. A551
MASSENGALE, David, Chief Financial Officer, Taylor Regional Hospital, Campbellsville, KY, p. A259
MASSENGILL, Leigh, Chief Executive Officer, Medical Center of Trinity, Trinity, FL, p. A149
MASSEY, Gina, Vice President Human Resources, Clarity Child Guidance Center, San Antonio, TX, p. A646
MASSEY, Linda, R.N. Nurse Manager, Norman Specialty Hospital, Norman, OK, p. A514
MASSEY, Rocco K., Community Chief Executive Officer, Beckley ARH Hospital, Beckley, WV, p. A693
MASSEY, Steven, President and Chief Executive Officer, Westfields Hospital, New Richmond, WI, p. A712
MASSEY, Terry, Chief Fiscal Services, Beckley Veterans Affairs Medical Center, Beckley, WV, p. A693
MASSIELLO, Martin, Executive Vice President and Chief Operating Officer, Eisenhower Medical Center, Rancho Mirage, CA, p. A84

MASSIET, Jill, R.N. Vice President Patient Care, Baptist Health Medical Center–Little Rock, Little Rock, AR, p. A49
MASSIMILLA, John P., FACHE Vice President Administration and Chief Operating Officer, Chambersburg Hospital, Chambersburg, PA, p. A535
MASSMAN, Patty, Director of Nursing, Granite Falls Municipal Hospital and Manor, Granite Falls, MN, p. A344
MAST, Dave, Chief Financial Officer, Providence Holy Cross Medical Center,, CA, p. A74
MAST, Delvin, R.N. Director of Nursing, Weatherford Regional Hospital, Weatherford, OK, p. A522
MAST, Duane, M.D. Medical Director, Hocking Valley Community Hospital, Logan, OH, p. A496
MAST, Joelle, Ph.D. Chief Medical Officer, Blythedale Children's Hospital, Valhalla, NY, p. A457
MASTALSKI, Richard, Senior Director Operations, Carilion Giles Community Hospital, Pearisburg, VA, p. A676
MASTERS, Andrea, Chief Nursing Officer, Decatur County Hospital, Leon, IA, p. A233
MASTERS, Emily, Director Human Resources and Marketing, Windom Area Hospital, Windom, MN, p. A354
MASTERS, Ken, Director Information Technology, Chambers Memorial Hospital, Danville, AR, p. A44
MASTERS, Kim, M.D. Medical Director, Saint Simons by–the–Sea Hospital, Saint Simons Island, GA, p. A166
MASTERS, Regina, R.N. Director of Nursing, Continuing Care Hospital, Lexington, KY, p. A264
MASTERSON, David J., President, Sentara Williamsburg Regional Medical Center, Williamsburg, VA, p. A680
MASTERSON, Paul, Chief Financial Officer, Genesis HealthCare System, Zanesville, OH, p. A506
MASTERSON, Sammie, Chief Human Resources Officer, Harney District Hospital, Burns, OR, p. A523
MASTERTON, William, Chief Executive Officer, Piedmont Medical Center, Rock Hill, SC, p. A569
MASTIN, Michelle, Chief Clinical Officer, Kindred Hospital Boston–North Shore, Peabody, MA, p. A313
MASTRO, Mary Lou, President and Chief Executive Officer, Elmhurst Memorial Hospital,, IL, p. A189
MASTROIANNI, Tom, Vice President Human Resources, Lawrence Hospital Center, Bronxville, NY, p. A434
MASTROPIETRO, N. A., M.D. Medical Director, Lancaster Regional Medical Center, Lancaster, PA, p. A542
MATA, Maribel, Director Information Services, Doctors Hospital of Laredo, Laredo, TX, p. A632
MATA–GUERRERO, Rita, Nurse Director, Weslaco Rehabilitation Hospital, Weslaco, TX, p. A657
MATAMOROS, Mary L., R.N., Chief Executive Officer, SeaSide Behavioral Center, New Orleans, LA, p. A286
MATEJKA, Cheryl
  Chief Financial Officer, Mercy Hospital St. Louis, Saint Louis, MO, p. A380
  Chief Financial Officer, Mercy Hospital Washington, Washington, MO, p. A384
MATENS, Brett, Chief Operating Officer, St. David's South Austin Medical Center, Austin, TX, p. A600
MATHAI, George, M.D. Chief of Staff, Three Rivers Hospital, Waverly, TN, p. A594
MATHAI, Matt, M.D. Medical Director, Select Specialty Hospital–Milwaukee, Milwaukee, WI, p. A711
MATHEIS, Tracey, Chief Financial Officer, Moberly Regional Medical Center, Moberly, MO, p. A377
MATHER, Charlotte Marie, Chief Nursing Officer, Sheridan Memorial Hospital, Sheridan, WY, p. A722
MATHER, Kelly, Chief Executive Officer, Sonoma Valley Hospital, Sonoma, CA, p. A95
MATHER, Martha S., Chief Operating Officer and Vice President, Our Lady of Peace, Louisville, KY, p. A266
MATHERS, Larry, M.D. Chief of Staff, Tennova Newport Medical Center, Newport, TN, p. A591
MATHEW, Bob, Director Finance, Griffin Memorial Hospital, Norman, OK, p. A514
MATHEW, Finny, Chief Executive Officer, Crossroads Community Hospital, Mount Vernon, IL, p. A197
MATHEW, Jefy, M.D. Chief of Staff, St. Luke's The Woodlands Hospital, The Woodlands, TX, p. A653
MATHEW, Mammen, M.D. Chief Rehabilitation Medicine, Woodrow Wilson Rehabilitation Center, Fishersville, VA, p. A671
MATHEWS, Gary, M.D. Medical Doctor, Beaver County Memorial Hospital, Beaver, OK, p. A508
MATHEWS, Hilary G., MS Administrator, Mayo Clinic Jacksonville, Jacksonville, FL, p. A131
MATHEWS, Nimmy, Acting Director Quality Management, U. S. Public Health Service Indian Hospital, San Carlos, AZ, p. A38
MATHEWS, Paul G., CPA, Administrator, Hardtner Medical Center, Olla, LA, p. A286
MATHEWS, Steve, Vice President and Chief Information Officer, Regional West Medical Center, Scottsbluff, NE, p. A402

MATHEWSON, John, Interim Chief Operating Officer, The HSC Pediatric Center, Washington, DC, p. A122
MATHEWSON, Patricia, Chief Nursing Officer, Tulare Regional Medical Center, Tulare, CA, p. A98
MATHIAS, Matt, Chief Operating Officer, LewisGale Hospital Montgomery, Blacksburg, VA, p. A668
MATHIS, Ashley, Privacy Officer, Columbus Community Hospital, Columbus, TX, p. A607
MATHIS, Jane, Chief Financial Officer, Baylor Surgical Hospital at Fort Worth, Fort Worth, TX, p. A618
MATHIS, Mike, Manager Personnel, North Alabama Regional Hospital, Decatur, AL, p. A18
MATHIS, Rebecca
  Vice President and Chief Financial Officer, Adventist Hinsdale Hospital, Hinsdale, IL, p. A193
  Chief Financial Officer, Adventist La Grange Memorial Hospital, La Grange, IL, p. A194
MATHIS, Susan, R.N
  Chief Operating Officer and Chief Nurse Executive, CenterPointe Hospital, Saint Charles, MO, p. A379
  Chief Operating Officer and Chief Nurse Executive, Signature Psychiatric Hospital, Kansas City, MO, p. A374
MATHURIN, Jr., Emile, M.D. Medical Director, HEALTHSOUTH Rehabilitation Hospital, Humble, TX, p. A628
MATHURIN, Venra, Vice President Human Resources, Interfaith Medical Center,, NY, p. A444
MATLACK, Victoria L.
  Manager and Human Resources Business Partner, OhioHealth Dublin Methodist Hospital, Dublin, OH, p. A493
  Manager and Human Resources Business Partner, OhioHealth Grady Memorial Hospital, Delaware, OH, p. A492
MATNEY, James L., President and Chief Executive Officer, Colquitt Regional Medical Center, Moultrie, GA, p. A164
MATNEY, Patty, Human Resources Consultant, Saint Thomas Hickman Hospital, Centerville, TN, p. A580
MATNEY, Tim, Chief Financial Officer, Logan Regional Medical Center, Logan, WV, p. A696
MATRELLA, Sandra, Manager Finance, Buffalo Hospital, Buffalo, MN, p. A444
MATSIL, Robyn, Human Resources Director, Vista Medical Center West, Waukegan, IL, p. A205
MATSINGER, John, D.O
  Medical Director, Virtua Berlin, Berlin, NJ, p. A413
  Chief Medical Officer, Virtua Marlton, Marlton, NJ, p. A418
MATTERN, Bonnie, Director Human Resources, Mercy Hospital, Devils Lake, ND, p. A477
MATTERN, Joe, M.D. Chief Medical Officer, Jefferson Healthcare, Port Townsend, WA, p. A686
MATTES, Bryan, Associate Administrator, CrossRidge Community Hospital, Wynne, AR, p. A54
MATTES, Dennis, Chief Executive Officer, LifeCare Hospitals of Wisconsin, Pewaukee, WI, p. A713
MATTES, James A., President and Chief Executive Officer, Grande Ronde Hospital, La Grande, OR, p. A526
MATTES, Mark David, R.N. Assistant Administrator/Patient Care Services, Golden Valley Memorial Healthcare, Clinton, MO, p. A369
MATTEUCCI, Dolly, Executive Director, Napa State Hospital, Napa, CA, p. A79
MATTHEW, Mathew, M.D. Chief Medical Officer, Nazareth Hospital, Philadelphia, PA, p. A549
MATTHEWS, Adora, M.D. Medical Director, HEALTHSOUTH Rehabilitation Hospital of Florence, Florence, SC, p. A565
MATTHEWS, Carol, Director Human Resources, Saline Memorial Hospital, Benton, AR, p. A43
MATTHEWS, Clinton, President and Chief Executive Officer, Reading Hospital and Medical Center, West Reading, PA, p. A558
MATTHEWS, Deborah, Administrator, Tanner Medical Center–Carrollton, Carrollton, GA, p. A155
MATTHEWS, Gwen, MSN, Chief Executive Officer, Ukiah Valley Medical Center, Ukiah, CA, p. A98
MATTHEWS, Kenneth, Manager Information Technology, Guadalupe County Hospital, Santa Rosa, NM, p. A430
MATTHEWS, Michael, Vice President Human Resources, Holland Hospital, Holland, MI, p. A326
MATTHEWS, Oliver, M.D. Chief Medical Officer, Eliza Coffee Memorial Hospital, Florence, AL, p. A20
MATTHEWS, Paul, M.D. President of Medical Staff, Palo Alto County Health System, Emmetsburg, IA, p. A230
MATTHEWS, Ted, Chief Executive Officer, Eastland Memorial Hospital, Eastland, TX, p. A614
MATTHEY, Michael, Facility Chief Information Officer, Louis A. Johnson Veterans Affairs Medical Center, Clarksburg, WV, p. A694
MATTHIAS, Mark, M.D. Vice President of Medical Affairs, St. Cloud Hospital, Saint Cloud, MN, p. A350
MATTHIAS, Pam, Vice President of Patient Care Services, J. C. Blair Memorial Hospital, Huntingdon, PA, p. A541

MATTICE, Gloria, R.N. Director Patient Care, George C Grape Community Hospital, Hamburg, IA, p. A231

MATTICE, Thomas, Director, Richard L. Roudebush Veterans Affairs Medical Center, Indianapolis, IN, p. A215

MATTINGLY, Marty, Chief Human Resources Officer, St. Mary's Medical Center of Evansville, Evansville, IN, p. A210

MATTIS, Nancy, Chief Patient Care Services, Catalina Island Medical Center, Avalon, CA, p. A56

MATTIS, Paul, Vice President Finance, Titusville Area Hospital, Titusville, PA, p. A556

MATTISON, Kenneth R., Chief Executive Officer, Florida Hospital–Flagler, Palm Coast, FL, p. A141

MATTKE, Roger, Chief Financial Officer, Lafayette General Medical Center, Lafayette, LA, p. A281

MATTLY, Sheila, Chief Nursing Officer, Wayne County Hospital, Corydon, IA, p. A228

MATTON, Jeffrey A., President, MedStar Good Samaritan Hospital, Baltimore, MD, p. A297

MATTSON, Gayle, R.N., President, North Memorial Medical Center, Robbinsdale, MN, p. A350

MATTSON, Jodi, Director of Nursing, Cedar Springs Hospital, Colorado Springs, CO, p. A103

MATTSON, Wayne, Management Information Systems Specialist, Rogers Memorial Hospital, Oconomowoc, WI, p. A712

MATUS, Jose, M.D. Director Medical, Carrus Rehabilitation Hospital, Sherman, TX, p. A649

MATUSZKIEWICZ, Marcin, M.D. Chief of Staff and Medical Director, Jerold Phelps Community Hospital, Garberville, CA, p. A65

MATZENBACHER, Elaine, Chief Financial Officer, Washington County Hospital, Nashville, IL, p. A197

MATZIGKEIT, Linda, Senior Vice President Human Resources, Children's Healthcare of Atlanta, Atlanta, GA, p. A152

MATZKE, Gerald, M.D. Medical Director, Gothenburg Memorial Hospital, Gothenburg, NE, p. A396

MAUCK, Jan, R.N. Chief Nursing Officer, Sarasota Memorial Health Care System, Sarasota, FL, p. A145

MAUCK, Lynn, R.N. Chief Operating Officer and Chief Nursing Officer, Fishermen's Hospital, Marathon, FL, p. A135

MAUL, Jim, Chief Information Officer and Director Information Services, Southampton Hospital, Southampton, NY, p. A455

MAURER, Gregory L., Administrator, St. Luke's Elmore, Mountain Home, ID, p. A177

MAURER, Jackie, Fiscal Officer, Julian F. Keith Alcohol and Drug Abuse Treatment Center, Black Mountain, NC, p. A460

MAURER, Linda, Vice President Patient Care Services, Wilson Memorial Hospital, Sidney, OH, p. A502

MAURER, Marjorie A., MSN Vice President Operations, Patient Care Services and Chief Nursing Executive, Advocate Good Samaritan Hospital, Downers Grove, IL, p. A188

MAURER, Marsha L., R.N. Chief Nursing Officer Patient Care Services, Beth Israel Deaconess Medical Center, Boston, MA, p. A306

MAURICE, Timothy, Chief Financial Officer, University of California, Davis Medical Center, Sacramento, CA, p. A88

MAURIN, Michael J., Chief Financial Officer, Southern Surgical Hospital, Slidell, LA, p. A289

MAUST, Richard, Chief Information Officer, RMC Jacksonville, Jacksonville, AL, p. A22

MAVROMATIS, Lou, Vice President Data Processing, MedStar Southern Maryland Hospital Center, Clinton, MD, p. A300

MAWYER, David, Chief Financial Officer, Western State Hospital, Staunton, VA, p. A679

MAXEY, Matt, R.N. Director of Nursing, Brookhaven Hospital, Tulsa, OK, p. A520

MAXFIELD, Matt T., FACHE, Chief Executive Officer, Seton Medical Center Harker Heights, Harker Heights, TX, p. A622

MAXIE, Bryan K.
Administrator, Marion General Hospital, Columbia, MS, p. A357
Administrator, Walthall County General Hospital, Tylertown, MS, p. A365

MAXSON, Diana, Director Human Resources, Trinity Hospital of Augusta, Augusta, GA, p. A154

MAXSON, Lorna, R.N. Chief Nursing Officer, Phoenix Baptist Hospital, Phoenix, AZ, p. A36

MAXWELL, Dale
Executive Vice President and Chief Financial Officer, Presbyterian Hospital, Albuquerque, NM, p. A426
Senior VP Chief Financial Officer, Presbyterian Kaseman Hospital, Albuquerque, NM, p. A427

MAXWELL, David, Vice President Operations, St. Vincent Anderson Regional Hospital, Anderson, IN, p. A206

MAXWELL, Jody, Manager Business Office, Smith County Memorial Hospital, Smith Center, KS, p. A254

MAXWELL, John, Chief Operating Officer, Memorial Hospital, Martinsville, VA, p. A674

MAXWELL, Lora, Chief Nursing Officer, Curry General Hospital, Gold Beach, OR, p. A525

MAXWELL, Ronnie, Director Information Systems, Glenwood Regional Medical Center, West Monroe, LA, p. A290

MAY, Brandon, Chief Financial Officer, Sierra Providence East Medical Center, El Paso, TX, p. A616

MAY, Carol, Chief Financial Officer, Vice President Finance and Operations, Sauk Prairie Healthcare, Prairie Du Sac, WI, p. A714

MAY, Frank, Chief Executive Officer, Yampa Valley Medical Center, Steamboat Springs, CO, p. A111

MAY, John, Chief Executive Officer, Sistersville General Hospital, Sistersville, WV, p. A699

MAY, Kevin B.
System Director Finance, Charles A. Cannon Memorial Hospital, Linville, NC, p. A468
Chief Financial Officer, Watauga Medical Center, Boone, NC, p. A460

MAY, Robin, Director Information Systems, Platte County Memorial Hospital, Wheatland, WY, p. A723

MAY, Ronald B., M.D. Vice President Medical Affairs, CarolinaEast Health System, New Bern, NC, p. A470

MAY, Scott, Area Director Technology, Kaiser Permanente Santa Clara Medical Center, Santa Clara, CA, p. A94

MAY, Sonja, Director Human Resources, Morton County Health System, Elkhart, KS, p. A243

MAY, Troy, Chief Information Officer, University of Louisville Hospital, Louisville, KY, p. A266

MAY, Walter E., President and Chief Executive Officer, Pikeville Medical Center, Pikeville, KY, p. A269

MAYBEN, Casey, Chief Nursing Officer, East Texas Medical Center Pittsburg, Pittsburg, TX, p. A642

MAYDEN, Mike, Chief Financial Officer, Methodist McKinney Hospital, McKinney, TX, p. A637

MAYER, Karen, R.N. VP Patient Care Services, Rush Oak Park Hospital, Oak Park, IL, p. A198

MAYER, Peter, Director Information Systems, Bakersfield Heart Hospital, Bakersfield, CA, p. A56

MAYEUX, Michael
Chief Financial Officer, River Parishes Hospital, La Place, LA, p. A280
Chief Financial Officer, Teche Regional Medical Center, Morgan City, LA, p. A284

MAYEUX–HEBERT, Angela, Vice President Medical Affairs, Lafayette General Medical Center, Lafayette, LA, p. A281

MAYEWSKI, Raymond, M.D
Chief Medical Officer, Highland Hospital of Rochester, Rochester, NY, p. A453
Chief Medical Officer, Strong Memorial Hospital of the University of Rochester, Rochester, NY, p. A453

MAYFIELD, Michael Bradley, M.D. Chief of Staff, Chicot Memorial Medical Center, Lake Village, AR, p. A48

MAYFIELD, William, M.D. Chief of Staff, TriStar StoneCrest Medical Center, Smyrna, TN, p. A593

MAYHLE, Douglas, M.D. Medical Director, Nicholas H. Noyes Memorial Hospital, Dansville, NY, p. A436

MAYLE, Connie, Vice President Administrative Services, UPMC Horizon, Greenville, PA, p. A539

MAYNARD, Amy, Acting Chief Finance Service, Central Texas Veterans Healthcare System, Temple, TX, p. A652

MAYNARD, Bob, Chief Information Officer, Fairview Regional Medical Center, Fairview, OK, p. A511

MAYNARD, John, Director Information Systems, OSF Saint Elizabeth Medical Center, Ottawa, IL, p. A199

MAYNARD, Rhonda, Chief Financial Officer, Tennova Physicians Regional Medical Center, Knoxville, TN, p. A586

MAYO, Andrew, M.D., Chief Executive Officer and Managing Director, North Star Behavioral Health System, Anchorage, AK, p. A28

MAYO, Cindy, FACHE, Chief Executive Officer, Providence Medford Medical Center, Medford, OR, p. A527

MAYO, Hal, Chief Financial Officer, Liberty Dayton Regional Medical Center, Liberty, TX, p. A633

MAYO, Jim, M.D. Clinical Director, Cherry Hospital, Goldsboro, NC, p. A465

MAYO, Michael A., FACHE, President, Baptist Medical Center Jacksonville, Jacksonville, FL, p. A131

MAYO, Randy, Director Information Technology, William Newton Hospital, Winfield, KS, p. A257

MAYO, Rob, M.D
Chief Medical Officer, Newark–Wayne Community Hospital, Newark, NY, p. A449
Chief Medical Officer, Rochester General Hospital, Rochester, NY, p. A453

MAYO, Sarah, Vice President Financial and Information Services, Lenoir Memorial Hospital, Kinston, NC, p. A467

MAYORAL, Jorge, M.D. Medical Director, Rehabilitation Hospital of Rhode Island, North Smithfield, RI, p. A560

MAYS, Christine, R.N
Chief Operating Officer and Chief Nurse Executive, Saint Joseph East, Lexington, KY, p. A264
Chief Operating Officer and Chief Nurse Executive, Saint Joseph Hospital, Lexington, KY, p. A264

MAYS, Dawn, Chief Nursing Officer, Scott Memorial Hospital, Scottsburg, IN, p. A222

MAYSILLES, Nancy, R.N. Chief Nursing Officer, Medical Center of Trinity, Trinity, FL, p. A149

MAYSON, Mark J., M.D. Medical Director, Palmetto Health Baptist, Columbia, SC, p. A564

MAZANEC, Lori, Chief Operating Officer, Box Butte General Hospital, Alliance, NE, p. A393

MAZEK, Mariusz, Chief Information Officer, Norwegian American Hospital, Chicago, IL, p. A185

MAZOUR, Linda, M.D. President, Franklin County Memorial Hospital, Franklin, NE, p. A395

MAZUR, Geoff, Director Information Technology, Cole Memorial, Coudersport, PA, p. A536

MAZUR, Robert, Vice President Human Resources, Capital Region Medical Center, Jefferson City, MO, p. A372

MAZZA, Mary, Director Human Resources, HEALTHSOUTH Rehabilitation Hospital of Western Massachusetts, Ludlow, MA, p. A311

MAZZARELLA, Frank, M.D. Chief Medical Officer, Clara Maass Medical Center, Belleville, NJ, p. A413

MAZZARELLI, Anthony J., M.D. Senior VP and Chief Medical Officer, Cooper University Health Care, Camden, NJ, p. A414

MAZZO, Joseph, Chief Operating Officer, River Park Hospital, Mc Minnville, TN, p. A588

MAZZOLA, Joe, D.O. Senior Vice President Medical Affairs and Chief Medical Officer, Blue Ridge Healthcare Hospitals, Morganton, NC, p. A469

MAZZUCA, Darryl, Director Management Information Systems, Little Company of Mary Hospital and Health Care Centers, Evergreen Park, IL, p. A190

MBENGA, Saul, Manager Information Technology, Alliance HealthCare System, Holly Springs, MS, p. A359

MC BRIDE, Brian, Chief Financial Officer, Rice Medical Center, Eagle Lake, TX, p. A614

MC KELLAR, Grey, Chief Operating Officer and Director of Performance Improvement and Risk, Kingwood Pines Hospital, Kingwood, TX, p. A631

MCADAMS, David, Chief Financial Officer, Lindner Center of HOPE, Mason, OH, p. A497

MCAFEE, Thomas J., President, Northwestern Lake Forest Hospital, Lake Forest, IL, p. A194

MCALLISTER, Guy, Vice President and Chief Information Officer, Tift Regional Medical Center, Tifton, GA, p. A168

MCALLISTER, Kimberlie, Administrator Nursing Operations, Oakwood Hospital–Dearborn, Dearborn, MI, p. A321

MCALLISTER, Ric, Chief Executive Officer, Windsor–Laurelwood Center for Behavioral Medicine, Willoughby, OH, p. A505

MCALLISTER, Yvonne C., Senior Director Human Resources, Southern Maine Health Care – Biddeford Medical Center X, Biddeford, ME, p. A292

MCALOON, Richard, Vice President Human Resources, Hartford Hospital, Hartford, CT, p. A114

MCANALLY, Eileen, Senior Vice President Human Resources, Lankenau Medical Center, Wynnewood, PA, p. A559

MCANDREW, Michael, Chief Executive Officer, Hopkins County Memorial Hospital, Sulphur Springs, TX, p. A651

MCANDREWS, Susan, Vice President and Administrator, Riverside Shore Memorial Hospital, Nassawadox, VA, p. A674

MCARTHUR, Ronald L., Chief Executive Officer, Summit Healthcare Regional Medical Center, Show Low, AZ, p. A39

MCARTOR, Dana, R.N. Director of Nursing, Perkins County Health Services, Grant, NE, p. A396

MCAULIFFE, Gregory, M.D
Chief Medical Officer, San Luis Valley Health, Alamosa, CO, p. A102
Chief Medical Officer, San Luis Valley Health Conejos County Hospital, La Jara, CO, p. A108

MCAULIFFE, John, M.D. Medical Director, Sauk Prairie Healthcare, Prairie Du Sac, WI, p. A714

MCBEE, Gala, Administrator, Muscogee Creek Nation Physical Rehabilitation Center, Okmulgee, OK, p. A517

MCBEE, Jeff, Administrator, Presbyterian Rust Medical Center, Rio Rancho, NM, p. A430

MCBEE, Marie, Chief Executive Officer, Warwick Manor Behavioral Health, East New Market, MD, p. A300

MCBREARTY, Michael, M.D. Vice President Medical Affairs, Thomas Hospital, Fairhope, AL, p. A20

MCBRIDE, Anne, Chief Executive Officer, Regional Hospital for Respiratory and Complex Care, Seattle, WA, p. A688

MCBRIDE, Brandon, Operations Officer, Logan Regional Hospital, Logan, UT, p. A660

MCBRIDE, Dina, Chief Operating Officer and Director Human Resources, East Adams Rural Hospital, Ritzville, WA, p. A688

MCBRIDE, Kate, Chief Operating Officer, Poplar Springs Hospital, Petersburg, VA, p. A676

MCBRIDE, Michael J., FACHE, President and Chief Executive Officer, St. Mary's Hospital and Regional Medical Center, Grand Junction, CO, p. A107

MCBRIDE, III, Thomas Y., Executive Vice President and Chief Financial Officer, Gwinnett Hospital System, Lawrenceville, GA, p. A162

MCBROOM, Robert, M.D. Medical Director, Promise Hospital of Wichita Falls, Wichita Falls, TX, p. A657

MCBRYDE, Richard, Senior Vice President and Chief Operating Officer, North Arkansas Regional Medical Center, Harrison, AR, p. A47

MCBRYDE, Robin, Chief Information Officer, Alexandria Veterans Affairs Health Care System, Pineville, LA, p. A287

MCCAA, Karen, R.N. Vice President Patient Care Services and Chief Nursing Officer, Baptist Medical Center South, Montgomery, AL, p. A23

MCCABE, John B., M.D., Chief Executive Officer, Upstate University Hospital, Syracuse, NY, p. A456

MCCABE, John P., Executive Vice President, Shriners Hospitals for Children, Tampa, FL, p. B124

MCCABE, Mary, Chief Financial Officer, North Colorado Medical Center, Greeley, CO, p. A107

MCCABE, Patrick, Senior Vice President Finance and Chief Financial Officer, Bridgeport Hospital, Bridgeport, CT, p. A113

MCCABE Jr., Patrick G., FACHE, President and Chief Executive Officer, Levi Hospital, Hot Springs National Park, AR, p. A47

MCCABE, Rhonda, Chief Financial Officer, Physicians' Specialty Hospital, Fayetteville, AR, p. A45

MCCABE, Steve, Chief Executive Officer, Hill Crest Behavioral Health Services, Birmingham, AL, p. A16

MCCAFFERTY, Michael, Chief Executive Officer, Sheridan Memorial Hospital, Sheridan, WY, p. A722

MCCAHILL, Connie, R.N. Chief Operating Officer, Cameron Memorial Community Hospital, Angola, IN, p. A206

MCCAHILL, Mary, Chief Nursing Officer, Thorek Memorial Hospital, Chicago, IL, p. A187

MCCAIN, Rebecca, Chief Financial Officer and Assistant Administrator, Electra Memorial Hospital, Electra, TX, p. A617

MCCAIN, Robert, M.D. Chief of Staff, TriStar Southern Hills Medical Center, Nashville, TN, p. A591

MCCALL, Brad
President and Chief Executive Officer, Physicians Surgical Hospital – Panhandle Campus, Amarillo, TX, p. A596
President and Chief Executive Officer, Physicians Surgical Hospital – Quail Creek, Amarillo, TX, p. A596

MCCALL, Cynde, R.N. Chief Nursing Officer, Select Specialty Hospital–Omaha, Omaha, NE, p. A400

MCCALL, Debbie, Director Human Resources, WK Bossier Health Center, Bossier City, LA, p. A274

MCCALL, Harlo, Chief Operating Officer, Lehigh Regional Medical Center, Lehigh Acres, FL, p. A134

MCCALL, Lee, Administrator, Winston Medical Center, Louisville, MS, p. A361

MCCALL, Pam, Director Human Resources, Heatherhill Care Communities, Chardon, OH, p. A485

MCCALLISTER, Bob, Director Human Resources, Baptist Memorial Hospital–Golden Triangle, Columbus, MS, p. A357

MCCALLISTER, Darla, Chief Financial Officer, Lakeside Women's Hospital, Oklahoma City, OK, p. A515

MCCALLISTER, Dianne, M.D. Chief Medical Officer, Medical Center of Aurora, Aurora, CO, p. A102

MCCAMPBELL, Kellie, Coordinator Human Resources, Kindred Hospital–Chattanooga, Chattanooga, TN, p. A580

MCCAMPBELL, Marcia, M.D. Chief Medical Officer, Shasta Regional Medical Center, Redding, CA, p. A85

MCCANDLESS, Barbara, Vice President Human Resources, St. Mary's Hospital, Troy, NY, p. A456

MCCANN, Barbara, Director Human Resources, Sunrise Canyon Hospital, Lubbock, TX, p. A635

MCCANN, Joseph, Chief Information Officer, MidHudson Regional Hospital of Westchester Medical Center, Poughkeepsie, NY, p. A452

MCCANN, Kyle, Chief Operating Officer, St. Joseph's Hospital, Savannah, GA, p. A166

MCCANN, Lew, Director Management Information Systems, OSF Holy Family Medical Center, Monmouth, IL, p. A196

MCCANNA, Peter J., Executive Vice President Administration and Chief Financial Officer, Northwestern Memorial Hospital, Chicago, IL, p. A185

MCCARDELL, Tom, Administrator, Physicians Behavioral Hospital, Shreveport, LA, p. A288

MCCARTAN, Mary E., Manager Human Resources, Veterans Affairs Long Beach Healthcare System, Long Beach, CA, p. A70

MCCARTER, Alyssa, Chief Financial Officer, W. J. Mangold Memorial Hospital, Lockney, TX, p. A634

MCCARTER, Scott, Chief Information Officer, Karmanos Cancer Center, Detroit, MI, p. A322

MCCARTER, Jr., Thomas G., M.D. Chief Medical Officer, Lankenau Medical Center, Wynnewood, PA, p. A559

MCCARTHY, Barbara, Chief Executive Officer, Specialty Hospital Jacksonville, Jacksonville, FL, p. A132

MCCARTHY, Brian, Director Information Systems, Memorial Hospital of Salem County, Salem, NJ, p. A422

MCCARTHY, Linda M., R.N. VP/ Chief Nursing Officer, Citrus Memorial Health System, Inverness, FL, p. A131

MCCARTHY, Rick, Chief Information Officer, St. Vincent's Medical Center, Bridgeport, CT, p. A113

MCCARTHY, Robert R., Vice President Finance and Chief Financial Officer, Chenango Memorial Hospital, Norwich, NY, p. A450

MCCARTHY, Sue, Senior Vice President and Chief Financial Officer, Akron General Medical Center, Akron, OH, p. A482

MCCARTHY, Tim, President Puerto Rico Division, First Hospital Panamericano, Cidra, PR, p. A725

MCCARTY, Daniel P., Chief Operating Officer, Orange City Area Health System, Orange City, IA, p. A235

MCCARTY, Maryland, Director Information Systems, Atlanta Medical Center, Atlanta, GA, p. A152

MCCARTY, Melany, R.N. Chief Clinical Officer, Vibra Hospital of Amarillo, Amarillo, TX, p. A596

MCCARTY, Wendy, Director Human Resources, Hillsboro Community Hospital, Hillsboro, KS, p. A245

MCCARY, Steve C., Administrator, Riverside Doctors' Hospital, Williamsburg, VA, p. A680

MCCASLIN, Anna, Chief Financial Officer, Nebraska Orthopaedic Hospital, Omaha, NE, p. A400

MCCAUGHEY, James, Chief Strategy Officer, Lucile Salter Packard Children's Hospital at Stanford, Palo Alto, CA, p. A82

MCCAULEY, Cynthia, Chief Financial Officer, Good Samaritan Medical Center, West Palm Beach, FL, p. A149

MCCAULEY, Dudley, Controller, Lincoln County Medical Center, Ruidoso, NM, p. A430

MCCAULEY, Lauren, Marketing Director, West Boca Medical Center, Boca Raton, FL, p. A124

MCCAULEY, Sue E., Director Finance, Baum Harmon Mercy Hospital, Primghar, IA, p. A236

MCCAULEY, W. Roger, Senior Vice President Administration and Chief Financial Officer, UPMC Northwest, Seneca, PA, p. A554

MCCAWLEY, Thomas J., Vice President Human Resources, Beloit Health System, Beloit, WI, p. A702

MCCHESNEY, Lisa D., R.N. Senior Director Information Systems, UPMC Hamot, Erie, PA, p. A539

MCCLAIN, Barbara, Human Resources, Horton Community Hospital, Horton, KS, p. A246

MCCLAIN, James, Deputy Director, Clement J. Zablocki Veterans Affairs Medical Center, Milwaukee, WI, p. A710

MCCLAIN, Richard, M.D. Chief Medical Officer, Chickasaw Nation Medical Center, Ada, OK, p. A507

MCCLANAHAN, Gary, Chief Information Officer, Sequoyah Memorial Hospital, Sallisaw, OK, p. A518

MCCLARIGAN, Linda, R.N. Chief Nursing Officer, Adirondack Medical Center, Saranac Lake, NY, p. A454

MCCLASKEY, Cynthia, Ph.D., Director, Southwestern Virginia Mental Health Institute, Marion, VA, p. A674

MCCLEESE, Randy, Vice President Information Services and Chief Information Officer, St. Claire Regional Medical Center, Morehead, KY, p. A268

MCCLELLAN, Ashley, Chief Executive Officer, Medical Center of Lewisville, Lewisville, TX, p. A633

MCCLELLAND, Michele
Vice President Human Resources, Kishwaukee Hospital, DeKalb, IL, p. A188
Vice President Human Resources, Valley West Hospital, Sandwich, IL, p. A202

MCCLELLAND, Patricia, Director Human Resources, South Texas Health System, Edinburg, TX, p. A615

MCCLENDON, Pat, MSN Chief Nursing Officer, Palmdale Regional Medical Center, Palmdale, CA, p. A82

MCCLINTIC, James, M.D. Vice President Medical Affairs, St. Anthony's Hospital, Saint Petersburg, FL, p. A145

MCCLINTICK, Cliff, Chief Information Officer, Lindner Center of HOPE, Mason, OH, p. A497

MCCLOSKEY, Louis, Chief Human Resources, Veterans Affairs Medical Center, Wilmington, DE, p. A120

MCCLUNG, David, Chief Financial Officer, Monmouth Medical Center, Long Branch Campus, Long Branch, NJ, p. A418

MCCLUNG, James W., Chief Executive Officer, HEALTHSOUTH Rehabilitation Hospital of Alexandria, Alexandria, LA, p. A272

MCCLUNG, Lyle, M.D. Chief of Staff, Carilion Stonewall Jackson Hospital, Lexington, VA, p. A673

MCCLURE, David K., President and Chief Executive Officer, Camden Clark Medical Center, Parkersburg, WV, p. A698

MCCLURE, Jan, Chief Executive Officer, Hill Regional Hospital, Hillsboro, TX, p. A623

MCCLURE, Joy, Chief Financial Officer, Ashe Memorial Hospital, Jefferson, NC, p. A467

MCCLURE, Kenneth, M.D. Chief of Staff, Longview Regional Medical Center, Longview, TX, p. A634

MCCLURE, Thomas, M.D. Vice President Medical Affairs and Chief Medical Officer, Allegheny Valley Hospital, Natrona Heights, PA, p. A546

MCCLURG, Cathy, Director Human Resources, William Newton Hospital, Winfield, KS, p. A257

MCCLURG, Melissa, Chief Human Resources Officer, St. Francis Hospital and Health Services, Maryville, MO, p. A376

MCCLURKAN, Mac, Chief Information Officer, Bethesda Hospital, Saint Paul, MN, p. A351

MCCLUSKEY, Tabb, M.D. Chief Medical Officer, Hendricks Community Hospital, Hendricks, MN, p. A345

MCCLUSKY, Derek, M.D. Chief of Staff, Northern Louisiana Medical Center, Ruston, LA, p. A287

MCCLYMONT, Troy, Chief Information Technology Officer, Sheridan Memorial Hospital, Plentywood, MT, p. A390

MCCOBB, David, Chief Information Officer, Foothill Presbyterian Hospital, Glendora, CA, p. A66

MCCOIC, Kristie, Clinic Operations Officer and Director Human Resources, Gundersen St. Joseph's Hospital and Clinics, Hillsboro, WI, p. A706

MCCOLE–WICHER, Sharon, R.N. Chief Nursing Officer, San Francisco General Hospital and Trauma Center, San Francisco, CA, p. A91

MCCOLLUM, Kathleen, Chief Operating Officer and Senior Vice President Clinical Integration, University of Maryland Baltimore Washington Medical Center, Glen Burnie, MD, p. A301

MCCOLLUM, Ken, Vice President, Human Resources, NorthBay Medical Center, Fairfield, CA, p. A62

MCCOLLUM, Rodger, Chief Executive Officer, Snoqualmie Valley Hospital, Snoqualmie, WA, p. A689

MCCOLM, Denni, Chief Information Officer, Citizens Memorial Hospital, Bolivar, MO, p. A367

MCCOMB, Canise A., Director Human Resources, Graham Hospital, Canton, IL, p. A182

MCCONNELL, George, Director, Earle E. Morris Alcohol and Drug Treatment Center, Columbia, SC, p. A564

MCCONNELL, John D., M.D., Chief Executive Officer, Wake Forest Baptist Health, Winston–Salem, NC, p. B151

MCCONNELL, John D., M.D., Chief Executive Officer, Wake Forest Baptist Medical Center, Winston–Salem, NC, p. A475

MCCONNELL, Linda M., R.N. Associate Medical Center Director Patient Care Services, James H. Quillen Veterans Affairs Medical Center, Mountain Home, TN, p. A590

MCCONNELL, Patrick G., Chief Financial Officer, West Park Hospital, Cody, WY, p. A721

MCCONNELL, Ron, Chief Operating Officer, UPMC Altoona, Altoona, PA, p. A532

MCCONNELL, Will, Ph.D. Vice President Operations – Outreach Strategy and Centura Health Physicians Group Administrator Southwest, Mercy Regional Medical Center, Durango, CO, p. A105

MCCORD, Sam, Chief Nursing Officer, Willow Springs Center, Reno, NV, p. A408

MCCORMACK, Cynthia, MS, Director, Cheyenne Veterans Affairs Medical Center, Cheyenne, WY, p. A720

MCCORMACK, Jane, R.N. Vice President, Chief Nursing Officer and Nursing and Patient Care Services, Unity Hospital, Rochester, NY, p. A453

MCCORMICK, Brad, Chief Financial Officer, Natchitoches Regional Medical Center, Natchitoches, LA, p. A285

MCCORMICK, Daniel, M.D. Vice President Medical Staff Affairs, Franciscan St. Anthony Health – Crown Point, Crown Point, IN, p. A209

MCCORMICK, Dee Dawn, Director Personnel and Human Resources, Coon Memorial Hospital, Dalhart, TX, p. A609

MCCORMICK, Jason, Vice President Finance and Chief Financial Officer, Family Health West, Fruita, CO, p. A106

MCCORMICK, Jayne, M.D
Chief Medical Officer CDS, Presbyterian Hospital, Albuquerque, NM, p. A426
Chief Medical Officer CDS, Presbyterian Kaseman Hospital, Albuquerque, NM, p. A427

MCCORMICK, John, President and Chief Executive Officer, Oak Valley Hospital District, Oakdale, CA, p. A80

MCCORMICK, Martha, Chief Executive Officer, United Regional Medical Center, Manchester, TN, p. A587

MCCORMICK, Pam, Director Human Resources, Permian Regional Medical Center, Andrews, TX, p. A597

MCCOWN, Fran, Administrator, Haskell Memorial Hospital, Haskell, TX, p. A623

MCCOY, Andrea C., M.D. Chief Medical Officer, Jeanes Hospital, Philadelphia, PA, p. A548

MCCOY, Craig, Chief Executive Officer, Emory Saint Joseph's Hospital of Atlanta, Atlanta, GA, p. A152

MCCOY, Elizabeth, Chief Human Resources Management, Stony Brook University Medical Center, Stony Brook, NY, p. A455

MCCOY, Janice M., MS Chief Clinical Officer, Promise Hospital of Florida at The Villages, Oxford, FL, p. A141

MCCOY, Jessica, Director Human Resources, Cedar Springs Hospital, Colorado Springs, CO, p. A103

MCCOY, Mike, Chief Operating Officer, Saint Mary's Regional Medical Center, Russellville, AR, p. A52

MCCOY, Shawn W., Chief Administrative Officer, Deaconess Hospital, Evansville, IN, p. A210

MCCOY, Stephanie, President and Chief Executive Officer, Jackson General Hospital, Ripley, WV, p. A699

MCCRANIE, Robbie, Director Human Resources, Plano Specialty Hospital, Plano, TX, p. A642

MCCRAW, Elizabeth, Vice President, Human Resources, Caromont Regional Medical Center, Gastonia, NC, p. A465

MCCRAW, Nicki, Assistant Vice President Human Resources, UW Medicine/Harborview Medical Center, Seattle, WA, p. A689

MCCREA, Kim, Chief Human Resources Officer, Ortonville Area Health Services, Ortonville, MN, p. A349

MCCREA, Mary Anne, Chief Nursing Officer, Desert Regional Medical Center, Palm Springs, CA, p. A82

MCCREA, Yvette, Chief Human Resources, Winn Army Community Hospital, Hinesville, GA, p. A161

MCCREARY, Michael, Chief of Services, Mercy Hospital Washington, Washington, MO, p. A384

MCCRIMMON, Scott, Manager Information Technology, Northern Arizona Veterans Affairs Health Care System, Prescott, AZ, p. A37

MCCROSKEY, Mark, Vice President Operations, Northeastern Health System, Tahlequah, OK, p. A519

MCCUE, Cathy, Director Human Resources, St. Anthony's Hospital, Houston, TX, p. A626

MCCUE, Jennifer, Director Patient Care, Summersville Regional Medical Center, Summersville, WV, p. A699

MCCUE, Raymond, M.D. Chief Medical Officer, Bon Secours–DePaul Medical Center, Norfolk, VA, p. A675

MCCUE, Robert N., Vice President Finance, Mid Coast Hospital, Brunswick, ME, p. A292

MCCUE, Steven
Chief Financial Officer, Clinton Hospital, Clinton, MA, p. A309
Chief Financial Officer, UMass Memorial–Marlborough Hospital, Marlborough, MA, p. A312

MCCULLEY, Becky, Chief Operating Officer, University of Texas Southwestern Medical Center, Dallas, TX, p. A612

MCCULLEY, Larry W., President and Chief Executive Officer, Touchette Regional Hospitals, Centreville, IL, p. A183

MCCULLOCH, Greg, CPA Vice President of Finance and Chief Financial Officer, Sonora Regional Medical Center, Sonora, CA, p. A95

MCCULLOCH, Liz, Chief Information Resource Management Systems, Cheyenne Veterans Affairs Medical Center, Cheyenne, WY, p. A720

MCCULLOUGH, Barbara A., Vice President Human Resources, Washington Hospital, Washington, PA, p. A557

MCCULLOUGH, Bobby, Chief Operating Officer, Memorial Hospital Jacksonville, Jacksonville, FL, p. A131

MCCULLOUGH, Mary Kelly, Associate Director Patient Care Services, Veterans Affairs Medical Center–Lexington, Lexington, KY, p. A265

MCCULLOUGH, Patrick, M.D. Chief Medical Services, Summit Behavioral Healthcare, Cincinnati, OH, p. A487

MCCULLOUGH, Paula
VP Patient Care Services, St. Vincent's Blount, Oneonta, AL, p. A24
Chief Nursing Officer, St. Vincent's East, Birmingham, AL, p. A17

MCCULLOUGH, Rose, R.N. Associate Administrator Patient Care and Chief Nursing Officer, Angleton Danbury Medical Center, Angleton, TX, p. A597

MCCULLOUGH, Wadra, Chief Nursing Officer, Spalding Regional Medical Center, Griffin, GA, p. A160

MCCUNE, Anne, Chief Operating Officer, Lucile Salter Packard Children's Hospital at Stanford, Palo Alto, CA, p. A82

MCCUNE, Becky, Director Human Resources, Community Relations and Education, Coffeyville Regional Medical Center, Coffeyville, KS, p. A242

MCCUNE, Connie, Vice President Human Resources, Via Christi Hospital in Pittsburg, Pittsburg, KS, p. A253

MCCURDY, Brent, Director Management Information, St. Croix Regional Medical Center, St. Croix Falls, WI, p. A715

MCCURDY, Judy, R.N. Vice President and Chief Nursing Officer, St. Vincent Medical Center, Los Angeles, CA, p. A75

MCCURRY, Mark, M.D. Chief of Staff, Haskell County Community Hospital, Stigler, OK, p. A519

MCCUSKER, Kevin, M.D. Chief Medical Officer, Quincy Medical Center, Quincy, MA, p. A314

MCCUTCHAN, Matt, Chief Financial Officer, Greater Regional Medical Center, Creston, IA, p. A228

MCCUTCHEON, Edna I.
Chief Executive Officer, Norristown State Hospital, Norristown, PA, p. A546
Chief Executive Officer, Torrance State Hospital, Torrance, PA, p. A556

MCCUTCHEON Jr., Henry, Chief Executive Officer, Lake City Community Hospital, Lake City, SC, p. A568

MCDADE, E., R.N.Walter P. Reuther Psychiatric Hospital, Westland, MI, p. A337

MCDANALD, Matt, M.D. Chief Medical Officer, Baptist Health La Grange, La Grange, KY, p. A263

MCDANEL, Joyce
Vice President Human Resources and Education, UnityPoint Health – Des Moines, Des Moines, IA, p. A229
Vice President Human Resources and Education, UnityPoint Health – Iowa Methodist Medical Center, Des Moines, IA, p. A229

MCDANIEL, Amy, Administrator and Chief Executive Officer, Iowa Specialty Hospital–Belmond, Belmond, IA, p. A225

MCDANIEL, Burton, M.D. Medical Director, Roosevelt Warm Springs Rehabilitation and Specialty Hospitals, Warm Springs, GA, p. A169

MCDANIEL, III, Donald E., Chief Financial Officer, Mineral Area Regional Medical Center, Farmington, MO, p. A371

MCDANIEL, Graciela, Chief Financial Officer, Philadelphia Veterans Affairs Medical Center, Philadelphia, PA, p. A549

MCDANIEL, Kim, Director Human Resources, HEALTHSOUTH Rehabilitation Hospital of Montgomery, Montgomery, AL, p. A23

MCDANIEL, LaDonna, Financial Manager, Prattville Baptist Hospital, Prattville, AL, p. A25

MCDANIEL, Lisa A., Chief Human Resources Officer, Samaritan Healthcare, Moses Lake, WA, p. A685

MCDANIEL, Suzie Q., Chief Human Resource Officer, Bay Area Hospital, Coos Bay, OR, p. A524

MCDANIEL, Jr., W. Burton, M.D. Physician Executive, Roosevelt Warm Springs LTAC Hospital, Warm Springs, GA, p. A169

MCDAVID, Clarence, Vice President Human Resources, Rose Medical Center, Denver, CO, p. A105

MCDEARMONT, Scott, M.D. Chief Medical Staff, Hopkins County Memorial Hospital, Sulphur Springs, TX, p. A651

MCDERMOTT, James, M.D. Chief of Staff, Sedan City Hospital, Sedan, KS, p. A254

MCDERMOTT, Thomas, Vice President Finance, Fayette County Memorial Hospital, Washington Court House, OH, p. A504

MCDERMOTT, Vincent, Vice President, Finance and Real Estate, Brigham and Women's Faulkner Hospital, Boston, MA, p. A306

MCDERMOTT–LORD, Sheila, Chief Executive Officer, Abilene Behavioral Health, Abilene, TX, p. A595

MCDEVITT, Mike, Chief Information Officer, The Children's Hospital of Alabama, Birmingham, AL, p. A17

MCDEVITT, Robert J., M.D. Chief of Staff, Wilson Memorial Hospital, Sidney, OH, p. A502

MCDIVITT, Robert P., FACHE, Director, Veterans Affairs Ann Arbor Healthcare System, Ann Arbor, MI, p. A318

MCDONALD, Andrew, M.D. Chief Medical Officer, Aurora West Allis Medical Center, West Allis, WI, p. A718

MCDONALD, Buck, Chief Financial Officer, St. Helena Hospital Clear Lake, Clearlake, CA, p. A60

MCDONALD, Carl, Regional Director Human Resources, Broward Health Imperial Point, Fort Lauderdale, FL, p. A128

MCDONALD, Connie, Chief Financial Officer, Marion Veterans Affairs Medical Center, Marion, IL, p. A195

MCDONALD, Craig L., M.D. Chief Medical Officer, Angleton Danbury Medical Center, Angleton, TX, p. A597

MCDONALD, Douglas, M.D. Vice President Medical Affairs, University Hospitals Elyria Medical Center, Elyria, OH, p. A493

MCDONALD, Edward A., Chief Financial Officer, St. Helena Hospital–Center for Behavioral Health, Vallejo, CA, p. A99

MCDONALD, Elizabeth, Director Human Resources, Wayne Memorial Hospital, Honesdale, PA, p. A540

MCDONALD, Gary
Associate Administrator Human Resources, Stone County Medical Center, Mountain View, AR, p. A50
Associate Administrator Human Resources, White River Medical Center, Batesville, AR, p. A43

MCDONALD, Gregory, Vice President Finance and Chief Financial Officer, Roswell Park Cancer Institute, Buffalo, NY, p. A434

MCDONALD, Harold E., Deputy Executive Director and Senior Vice President Administration, Nassau University Medical Center, East Meadow, NY, p. A437

MCDONALD, Jeff
Chief Executive Officer, Canyon Ridge Hospital, Chino, CA, p. A59
Information Technology Manager, Florida Hospital Wauchula, Wauchula, FL, p. A149

MCDONALD, John, M.D. Chief Medical Officer, North Hills Hospital, North Richland Hills, TX, p. A640

MCDONALD, Joseph D., President and Chief Executive Officer, Catholic Health System, Buffalo, NY, p. B33

MCDONALD, Larry, Director Human Resources, Miami Jewish Home and Hospital for Aged, Miami, FL, p. A175

MCDONALD, Mark, M.D., President and Chief Executive Officer, Institute for Orthopaedic Surgery, Lima, OH, p. A496

MCDONALD, Michael, Chief Executive Officer, Holly Hill Hospital, Raleigh, NC, p. A471

MCDONALD, Rick, Chief Financial Officer, Anson General Hospital, Anson, TX, p. A597

MCDONALD, Rosalind S., MSN Vice President Nursing Services, Lenoir Memorial Hospital, Kinston, NC, p. A467

MCDONALD, Shelly, Chief Human Resources Officer, Ness County Hospital, Ness City, KS, p. A250

MCDONALD, Stanton B., M.D. Medical Director, Heber Valley Medical Center, Heber City, UT, p. A660

MCDONALD, Stuart, M.D. President Medical Staff, Kindred Hospital–Fort Worth, Fort Worth, TX, p. A618

MCDONALD, Susan, M.D. Vice President, St. Joseph's Medical Center, Stockton, CA, p. A96

MCDONALD, Tedd, M.D. Chief Medical Officer, Banner Churchill Community Hospital, Fallon, NV, p. A404

MCDONALD, William A., President and Chief Executive Officer, St. Joseph's Regional Medical Center, Paterson, NJ, p. A420

MCDONALD–UPTON, Ann, Chief Nursing Officer, St. Joseph Mercy Oakland, Pontiac, MI, p. A332

MCDONNELL, M. Therese, M.D. Interim Vice President Patient Safety, Quality and Medical Affairs, Sibley Memorial Hospital, Washington, DC, p. A122

MCDONNELL, Michael, M.D. Chief Medical Officer, Mercy Hospital and Medical Center, Chicago, IL, p. A185

MCDONNELL, Nancy, Manager Information Systems, Illinois Valley Community Hospital, Peru, IL, p. A200

MCDONOUGH, Jeffrey, Vice President Human Resources, Vassar Brothers Medical Center, Poughkeepsie, NY, p. A452

MCDONOUGH, Sharon, Chief Executive Officer, First Street Hospital, Bellaire, TX, p. A602

MCDOUGLE, Mark, Executive Vice President and Chief Operating Officer, Maimonides Medical Center,, NY, p. A445

MCDOWELL, III, Arthur V., M.D. Vice President Clinical Affairs, Middlesex Hospital, Middletown, CT, p. A115

MCDOWELL, Jane, FACHE, Administrator, Jefferson County Hospital, Waurika, OK, p. A522

MCDOWELL, Jean, Chief Financial Officer, Kindred Hospital–Dallas, Dallas, TX, p. A610

MCDOWELL, Paul L., Vice President Finance and Chief Financial Officer, King's Daughters Medical Center, Ashland, KY, p. A258

MCDOWELL, Richard, Chief Financial Officer, Ridge Behavioral Health System, Lexington, KY, p. A264

MCDRURY, Martha M., R.N. Chief Operating Officer and Chief Nursing Officer, Holy Family Hospital and Medical Center, Methuen, MA, p. A312

MCEACHERN, John, Controller, Sebastian River Medical Center, Sebastian, FL, p. A145

MCEACHERN, Michael L., Chief Executive Officer, Bowie Memorial Hospital, Bowie, TX, p. A603

MCELDOWNEY, Erin, Manager Human Resources, Haven Senior Horizons, Phoenix, AZ, p. A35

MCELLIGOTT, Daniel P., FACHE, President, CHI Health Saint Francis, Grand Island, NE, p. A396

MCELMURRAY, Dodie, Chief Operating Officer, Greenwood Leflore Hospital, Greenwood, MS, p. A358

MCELRATH, Matthew
Chief Human Resources Officer, Keck Hospital of USC, Los Angeles, CA, p. A72
Chief Human Resources Officer, University of Southern California–Norris Cancer Hospital, Los Angeles, CA, p. A75

MCELROY, Sherry, Director Health Information Management, Osceola Community Hospital, Sibley, IA, p. A237

MCELROY, Wayne, Administrator, Pickens County Medical Center, Carrollton, AL, p. A18

MCENTEE, Chris, Network Specialist, Van Buren County Hospital, Keosauqua, IA, p. A233

MCEUEN, Jacqueline, Coordinator Human Resources, Bellville St. Joseph Health Center, Bellville, TX, p. A602

MCEVILLY, Kerrie, Director Finance and Information Systems, Stevens Community Medical Center, Morris, MN, p. A348

MCEWEN, David S., Vice President Operations, Port Huron Hospital, Port Huron, MI, p. A332

MCEWEN, Mary Louise, Superintendent, Riverview Psychiatric Center, Augusta, ME, p. A291

MCEWEN, Michelle, President and Chief Executive Officer, Speare Memorial Hospital, Plymouth, NH, p. A412

MCFADDEN, Mary T., MSN Chief Nurse Executive, Providence Portland Medical Center, Portland, OR, p. A528

MCFALL, Cathy, Human Resources Manager, Kiowa County Memorial Hospital, Greensburg, KS, p. A244

MCFALL, Michael, Chief Financial Officer, Kindred Rehabilitation Hospital Clear Lake, Webster, TX, p. A656

MCFALL, Vicky, Chief Executive Officer, Monroe County Medical Center, Tompkinsville, KY, p. A270

MCFALL–ROBERTS, Ebuni, Director Human Resources, Anchor Hospital, Atlanta, GA, p. A151

MCFARLAND, Kenneth, President and Chief Executive Officer, Mission Hospital, Mission Viejo, CA, p. A77

MCFARLAND, Nita, Director of Nursing, Kingman Community Hospital, Kingman, KS, p. A247

MCFARLAND, Rhonda
  Director Human Resources, Anson Community Hospital, Wadesboro, NC, p. A474
  Director Human Resources, Carolinas Medical Center–Union, Monroe, NC, p. A469

MCFARLAND, Rodney, M.D. Medical Director, Freeman Neosho Hospital, Neosho, MO, p. A377

MCFARLAND, Scott
  Interim Regional Chief Executive Officer, Kauai Veterans Memorial Hospital, Waimea, HI, p. A173
  Interim Regional Chief Executive Officer, Samuel Mahelona Memorial Hospital, Kapaa, HI, p. A172

MCFARLAND, Tracee, Chief Financial Officer, Claiborne Medical Center, Tazewell, TN, p. A593

MCFAUL, Joan, Senior Vice President and Chief Information Officer, Southcoast Hospitals Group, Fall River, MA, p. A310

MCFERRAN, Virginia
  Chief Information Officer, Ronald Reagan University of California Los Angeles Medical Center, Los Angeles, CA, p. A74
  Chief Information Officer, Santa Monica–UCLA Medical Center and Orthopaedic Hospital, Santa Monica, CA, p. A95

MCGAHEY, Nikki, Information Officer, Jefferson County Hospital, Waurika, OK, p. A522

MCGANN, Robert, M.D. President Medical Staff, Jameson Hospital, New Castle, PA, p. A546

MCGARIGLE, Kristine, R.N
  Vice President Patient Care, Ministry Good Samaritan Health Center, Merrill, WI, p. A710
  Vice President Patient Care, Ministry Saint Clare's Hospital, Weston, WI, p. A718

MCGARVEY, Missy, Chief Information Officer, Twin Valley Behavioral Healthcare, Columbus, OH, p. A491

MCGAUGH, Jamie, Controller, Atoka County Medical Center, Atoka, OK, p. A508

MCGEACHEY, Edward J., President and Chief Executive Officer, Southern Maine Health Care – Biddeford Medical Center X, Biddeford, ME, p. A292

MCGEE, Dana, Chief Financial Officer, Winn Parish Medical Center, Winnfield, LA, p. A290

MCGEE, Genemarie, R.N. Chief Nursing Officer, Sentara Leigh Hospital, Norfolk, VA, p. A675

MCGEE, Jessica
  Chief Financial Officer, AMG Specialty Hospital–Denham Springs, Denham Springs, LA, p. A277
  Chief Financial Officer, AMG Specialty Hospital–Lafayette, Lafayette, LA, p. A281
  Chief Financial Officer, AMG Specialty Hospital–Slidell, Slidell, LA, p. A288

MCGEE, Mark F., M.D. Chief Clinical Officer, Appalachian Behavioral Healthcare, Athens, OH, p. A483

MCGEE, Terry, Chief Operations Officer, Central State Hospital, Milledgeville, GA, p. A163

MCGETTIGAN, Ryan, Chief Information Officer, Coatesville Veterans Affairs Medical Center, Coatesville, PA, p. A536

MCGHEE, Michael, M.D. Medical Director, Behavioral HealthCare Center at Clarksville, Clarksville, TN, p. A581

MCGIBBON, Monica, Chief Nursing Officer, Terence Cardinal Cooke Health Care Center, New York, NY, p. A449

MCGILL, Cindy, Senior Vice President Human Resources, Presbyterian Kaseman Hospital, Albuquerque, NM, p. A427

MCGILL, Martha, Executive Vice President and Chief Operating Officer, Miami Children's Hospital, Miami, FL, p. A137

MCGILL, Rusty, System Director Information Technology, Indiana University Health Arnett Hospital, Lafayette, IN, p. A217

MCGILL, Steve, Chief Financial Officer, Wabash General Hospital, Mount Carmel, IL, p. A197

MCGILL, Timothy W., Chief Executive Officer, River Park Hospital, Mc Minnville, TN, p. A588

MCGILVRAY, Greg, Chief Financial Officer, Medical Center Enterprise, Enterprise, AL, p. A19

MCGIMSEY, Erika, Controller, Jewish Hospital–Shelbyville, Shelbyville, KY, p. A270

MCGINNIS, Christina, Director Information Technology, Menorah Medical Center, Overland Park, KS, p. A252

MCGINNIS, Jeff, M.D. President Medical Staff, Saint Joseph Mount Sterling, Mount Sterling, KY, p. A268

MCGINNIS, Mark J., Executive Vice President and Chief Financial Officer, St. Vincent Infirmary Medical Center, Little Rock, AR, p. A49

MCGIRL, John, Chief Human Resources Officer, NCH Downtown Naples Hospital, Naples, FL, p. A138

MCGLADE, James, Director Human Resources, United Hospital, Saint Paul, MN, p. A351

MCGLEW, Timothy, Chief Executive Officer, Kern Valley Healthcare District, Lake Isabella, CA, p. A69

MCGLON, Tracy, Director Human Resources, Gulf Coast Regional Medical Center, Panama City, FL, p. A141

MCGLORY, Joyce, Vice President Human Resources, Methodist Hospitals, Gary, IN, p. A212

MCGLOTHLIN, Wylie, M.D. Chief Medical Officer, Henry County Hospital, New Castle, IN, p. A220

MCGLYNN, Mia, Director Management Information Systems, Plantation General Hospital, Plantation, FL, p. A143

MCGOLDRICK, Margaret M., Executive Vice President and Chief Operating Officer, Abington Memorial Hospital, Abington, PA, p. A532

MCGONNELL, James, Chief Financial Officer, Memorial Medical Center, Las Cruces, NM, p. A429

MCGOVERN, Julia, Vice President Human Resources, Chilton Medical Center, Pompton Plains, NJ, p. A421

MCGOVERN, Julie, Vice President Human Resources, Anne Arundel Medical Center, Annapolis, MD, p. A296

MCGOVERN, Pam, Director Technology, Huggins Hospital, Wolfeboro, NH, p. A412

MCGOWAN, Donna, Administrator, Lane County Hospital, Dighton, KS, p. A243

MCGOWAN, Gloria, Chief Financial Officer, Wiregrass Medical Center, Geneva, AL, p. A20

MCGOWAN, Marion A., Executive Vice President and Chief Population Health Officer, Lancaster General Health, Lancaster, PA, p. A542

MCGOWEN, Bernard A., M.D. Medical Director, Kindred Hospital Tarrant County–Arlington, Arlington, TX, p. A597

MCGOWIN, III, Norman F., M.D. Chief of Staff, L. V. Stabler Memorial Hospital, Greenville, AL, p. A21

MCGRAIL, David, Vice President Finance, Carney Hospital, Boston, MA, p. A306

MCGRAIL, Robert, Chief Financial Officer, West Branch Regional Medical Center, West Branch, MI, p. A337

MCGRATH, Denise B., Chief Executive Officer, HEALTHSOUTH Sea Pines Rehabilitation Hospital, Melbourne, FL, p. A136

MCGRATH, James, M.D. Chief Medical Officer, Yadkin Valley Community Hospital, Yadkinville, NC, p. A475

MCGRATH, Lynn, M.D. Vice President Medical Affairs, Deborah Heart and Lung Center, Browns Mills, NJ, p. A414

MCGRATH, Michael
  Manager Finance, University Hospitals Conneaut Medical Center, Conneaut, OH, p. A491
  Manager Finance, University Hospitals Geneva Medical Center, Geneva, OH, p. A494

MCGRAW, Belinda
  Director Human Resources, Boulder City Hospital, Boulder City, NV, p. A404
  Director Human Resources, Complex Care Hospital at Tenaya, Las Vegas, NV, p. A405

MCGRAW, Karin L., FACHE, Director, Beckley Veterans Affairs Medical Center, Beckley, WV, p. A693

MCGRAW, Scott, M.D. Medical Director, Irving Coppell Surgical Hospital, Irving, TX, p. A629

MCGREAHAM, David S., M.D. Vice President Medical Affairs, Munson Medical Center, Traverse City, MI, p. A336

MCGREEVY, John, Chief Executive Officer, Mother Frances Hospital – Tyler, Tyler, TX, p. A654

MCGREGOR, Julie
  Vice President and Chief People Officer, Jewish Hospital, Louisville, KY, p. A265
  Director Human Resources, Sts. Mary & Elizabeth Hospital, Louisville, KY, p. A266

MCGREGOR, Robert, M.D. Chief Medical Officer, Akron Children's Hospital, Akron, OH, p. A482

MCGREW, David S., Chief Financial Officer, San Mateo Medical Center, San Mateo, CA, p. A93

MCGREW, Deb, Chief Operating Officer, University of Texas Medical Branch Hospitals, Galveston, TX, p. A620

MCGREW, Diane, Chief Nurse Executive, Montgomery County Memorial Hospital, Red Oak, IA, p. A236

MCGRIFF, Marchelle M., Chief Nursing Executive, Sutter Medical Center, Sacramento, Sacramento, CA, p. A88

MCGUCKEN, Holly, R.N. Chief Nursing Officer, Fort Walton Beach Medical Center, Fort Walton Beach, FL, p. A129

MCGUE, Lisa, Controller, HEALTHSOUTH Northern Kentucky Rehabilitation Hospital, Edgewood, KY, p. A260

MCGUE, Thomas E., M.D. Vice President Medical Affairs and Chief Medical Officer, Newport Hospital, Newport, RI, p. A560

MCGUFFIN, Patty, R.N. Chief Nursing Officer, Allen County Regional Hospital, Iola, KS, p. A246

MCGUIGAN, Kevin, M.D. Medical Director, St. Lawrence Rehabilitation Center, Lawrenceville, NJ, p. A417

MCGUILL, Gail, R.N. Chief Nursing Officer and Administrative Director of Patient Care Services, Shriners Hospitals for Children–Salt Lake City, Salt Lake City, UT, p. A663

MCGUINNESS, Luke, President and CEO, Health Quest Systems, Inc., LaGrangeville, NY, p. B68

MCGUINNESS, Patrick, Chief Information Management, Keller Army Community Hospital, West Point, NY, p. A458

MCGUIRE, Ann M., Vice President Human Resources, Indiana University Health Ball Memorial Hospital, Muncie, IN, p. A219

MCGUIRE, Cynthia, Chief Executive Officer, Monadnock Community Hospital, Peterborough, NH, p. A412

MCGUIRE, Karen, Chief Financial Officer, Audubon County Memorial Hospital, Audubon, IA, p. A225

MCGUIRE, Lee, Chief Nurse Executive, Kerrville State Hospital, Kerrville, TX, p. A631

MCGUIRE, Matthew, President and Chief Executive Officer, Western Regional Medical Center, Goodyear, AZ, p. A33

MCGUIRE, Shane, Chief Operations Officer and Information Technology Director, Columbia County Health System, Dayton, WA, p. A683

MCGUIRK, Christina, Chief Nursing Officer, Health Central Hospital, Ocoee, FL, p. A140

MCGUIRL, Mary, Director Information Systems, Oneida Healthcare, Oneida, NY, p. A450

MCGURK, Kevin, Controller, Bellin Psychiatric Center, Green Bay, WI, p. A706

MCHANEY, Tracy, Director Human Resources, Cedar Crest Hospital and Residential Treatment Center, Belton, TX, p. A602

MCHARDY, Bryson, M.D. President Medical Staff, Hannibal Regional Hospital, Hannibal, MO, p. A372

MCHUGH, Matthew, Director Information Services, Vaughan Regional Medical Center, Selma, AL, p. A25

MCHUGH, Michael J., M.D., Medical Director, Cleveland Clinic Children's Hospital for Rehabilitation, Cleveland, OH, p. A488

MCHUGH, William, M.D. Medical Director and Chief Medical Officer, Trinitas Regional Medical Center, Elizabeth, NJ, p. A415

MCILROY, Gail, Director Medical Records, Promise Hospital of Wichita Falls, Wichita Falls, TX, p. A657

MCILWAIN, T. Pinckney, M.D
  Vice President Medical Affairs and Chief Medical Officer, CAMC Teays Valley Hospital, Hurricane, WV, p. A696
  Vice President and Chief Medical Officer, Charleston Area Medical Center, Charleston, WV, p. A694

MCINERNEY, Terry, Director of Nursing, Inpatient, Navos, Seattle, WA, p. A688

MCINTOSH, Craig, Chief Information Officer, Northwest Specialty Hospital, Post Falls, ID, p. A178

MCINTOSH, Ernasha, Interim Director of Nursing, Sage Memorial Hospital, Ganado, AZ, p. A32

MCINTOSH, Joe, Director Management Information Systems, Logansport State Hospital, Logansport, IN, p. A218

MCINTOSH, Sean, M.D. Chief of Staff, Progress West Hospital, O'Fallon, MO, p. A378

MCINTOSH, Tyler, Chief Financial Officer, Creek Nation Community Hospital, Okemah, OK, p. A514

MCINTYRE, Cindy, R.N. Administrative Director Clinical Services, Magee General Hospital, Magee, MS, p. A361

MCINTYRE, Daniel J., President and Chief Executive Officer, The Charlotte Hungerford Hospital, Torrington, CT, p. A117

MCINTYRE, Kathleen, Province Leader, American Province of Little Company of Mary Sisters, Evergreen Park, IL, p. B10

MCIWAIN, John, Director Human Resources, Wayne Memorial Hospital, Jesup, GA, p. A161

MCKALE, Brigitte, MSN Vice President and Chief Nurse Executive, Pali Momi Medical Center, Aiea, HI, p. A170

MCKAY, Amy, Chief Nursing Officer, Mid–America Rehabilitation Hospital, Shawnee Mission, KS, p. A254

MCKAY, Daniel E.
  Chief Executive Officer, Sparks Regional Medical Center, Fort Smith, AR, p. A46
  Chief Executive Officer, Summit Medical Center, Van Buren, AR, p. A53

MCKAY, Danny H., Administrator, Noxubee General Hospital, Macon, MS, p. A361

MCKAY, Michael, Manager Information Systems, Wickenburg Community Hospital, Wickenburg, AZ, p. A41

MCKAY, Ronda, MSN Vice President Patient Care Services, Chief Nursing Officer, Community Hospital, Munster, IN, p. A219

MCKEAN, Kathy, M.P.H. Vice President, Chief Nursing Executive, Riverview Medical Center, Red Bank, NJ, p. A422

MCKEE, Debra, R.N. Chief Nursing Officer, Joint Township District Memorial Hospital, Saint Marys, OH, p. A501

MCKEE, Jed, M.D. Medical Director, Select Specialty Hospital–Topeka, Topeka, KS, p. A255

MCKEE, Judy, FACHE, Director, William S. Middleton Memorial Veterans Hospital, Madison, WI, p. A708

MCKEE, Michele, Vice President and Chief Financial Officer, St. Louis Children's Hospital, Saint Louis, MO, p. A382

MCKEE, Robert J., Vice President Human Resources, DuBois Regional Medical Center, Du Bois, PA, p. A537

MCKEE, Jr., Willis P., M.D. Chief Medical Officer, Frankfort Regional Medical Center, Frankfort, KY, p. A261

MCKEEBY, Jon W., Chief Information Officer, National Institutes of Health Clinical Center, Bethesda, MD, p. A299

MCKEEN, Marcia, Director Human Resources, Twin Valley Behavioral Healthcare, Columbus, OH, p. A491

MCKELDIN, Pat, Human Resource Business Partner, Kaiser Permanente Manteca Medical Center, Manteca, CA, p. A76

MCKENNA, Bertine C., Ph.D. Executive Vice President and Chief Operating Officer, Bassett Medical Center, Cooperstown, NY, p. A436

MCKENNA, Dennis, M.D. Interim Vice President Medical Affairs, Albany Medical Center, Albany, NY, p. A432

MCKENNA, Donald, President and Chief Executive Officer, St. Mary's Health Care System, Athens, GA, p. A151

MCKENNA, John F., Chief Executive Officer and Managing Director, Rockford Center, Newark, DE, p. A119

MCKENNA, Kathleen, Public Affairs Leader, Kaiser Permanente South Sacramento Medical Center, Sacramento, CA, p. A87

MCKENNA, Quinn, Chief Operating Officer, University of Utah Health Care – Hospital and Clinics, Salt Lake City, UT, p. A663

MCKENNEY, Jennifer, M.D. Chief Medical Officer, Fredonia Regional Hospital, Fredonia, KS, p. A244

MCKENZIE, Christine, Director Human Resources, Davis Regional Medical Center, Statesville, NC, p. A473

MCKENZIE, Jackie, Director Administrative Services, Beacham Memorial Hospital, Magnolia, MS, p. A361

MCKENZIE, Janice, R.N. Chief Clinical Officer, Habersham Medical Center, Demorest, GA, p. A158

MCKENZIE, Kimberly, R.N. Chief Nursing Officer and Chief Operations Officer, Harbor–UCLA Medical Center, Torrance, CA, p. A97

MCKENZIE, Sandra D., Executive Vice President and Chief Operating Officer, Hamilton Medical Center, Dalton, GA, p. A158

MCKENZIE, Susan, Director, Providence Veterans Affairs Medical Center, Providence, RI, p. A561

MCKENZIE, William G., Interim Administrator, Evergreen Medical Center, Evergreen, AL, p. A19

MCKENZIE, William G., President, Chief Executive Officer and Chairman, Gilliard Health Services, Montgomery, AL, p. B61

MCKEON, John, Vice President Human Resources, Kingsbrook Jewish Medical Center,, NY, p. A445

MCKEON, Sean, Director, Information Technology, Franciscan Hospital for Children, Boston, MA, p. A306

MCKEOWN, Colleen
Senior Vice President, Kaiser Permanente Antioch Medical Center, Antioch, CA, p. A55
Senior Vice President and Area Manager, Kaiser Permanente Walnut Creek Medical Center, Walnut Creek, CA, p. A100

MCKERNAN, James E., Chief Operating Officer, Bronson Battle Creek, Battle Creek, MI, p. A319

MCKERNAN, Kathleen S., Director Information Systems, Pioneers Memorial Healthcare District, Brawley, CA, p. A58

MCKERNAN, Stephen W., Chief Executive Officer, University of New Mexico Hospitals, Albuquerque, NM, p. A427

MCKERNAN, Stephen W., Chief Executive Officer, University of New Mexico Hospitals, Albuquerque, NM, p. B146

MCKEVETT, Timothy M., President and Chief Executive Officer, Beloit Health System, Beloit, WI, p. A702

MCKIBBEN, Leeanna, R.N. Vice President Patient Services and Chief Nursing Officer, UPMC McKeesport, McKeesport, PA, p. A544

MCKIBBEN, Sean, President and Chief Operating Officer, Mount Carmel, Columbus, OH, p. A490

MCKIDDY, Paul, Director Information Technology, Monroe County Medical Center, Tompkinsville, KY, p. A270

MCKIE, Kathy, Director Human Resources, Montrose Memorial Hospital, Montrose, CO, p. A110

MCKILLIP, Ed, Director of Finance, Riddle Hospital, Media, PA, p. A545

MCKIMMY, Doyle L., FACHE, Chief Executive Officer, Jewell County Hospital, Mankato, KS, p. A249

MCKINLEY, Bryan, Chief Financial Officer, St. Mark's Hospital, Salt Lake City, UT, p. A663

MCKINLEY, Ernie, Chief Information Officer, University Medical Center, Las Vegas, NV, p. A407

MCKINLEY, Ivy
Director Human Resources, Presence Holy Family Medical Center, Des Plaines, IL, p. A188
Regional Human Resources Officer, Presence Our Lady of the Resurrection Medical Center, Chicago, IL, p. A185

MCKINLEY, Katie, Assistant Administrator/Nursing, Southwest Mississippi Regional Medical Center, McComb, MS, p. A362

MCKINLEY, Mike, Information Security Officer, West Texas Veterans Affairs Health Care System, Big Spring, TX, p. A603

MCKINLEY, Ronald, Ph.D. Vice President Human Resources and Employee Services, University of Texas Medical Branch Hospitals, Galveston, TX, p. A620

MCKINLEY, Jr., Rudolph, Vice President Operations and Chief Operating Officer, East Tennessee Children's Hospital, Knoxville, TN, p. A585

MCKINNEY, Brenda, Chief Financial Officer, Reeves County Hospital, Pecos, TX, p. A641

MCKINNEY, Dan, Administrator, Hermann Area District Hospital, Hermann, MO, p. A372

MCKINNEY, Dana, Chief Nursing Officer, Select Specialty Hospital–Madison, Madison, WI, p. A708

MCKINNEY, Diane, R.N. Vice President Patient Care Service, Decatur County Memorial Hospital, Greensburg, IN, p. A212

MCKINNEY, Paul, Administrator, Martin County Hospital District, Stanton, TX, p. A650

MCKINNON, Mark, M.D. Chief of Staff, North Runnels Hospital, Winters, TX, p. A658

MCKINNON, Scott, President and Chief Executive Officer, Memorial Hospital, North Conway, NH, p. A412

MCKINNON, Shauna, Chief Executive Officer, Bayfront Health Dade City, Dade City, FL, p. A126

MCKNIGHT, Craig L., Senior Vice President and Chief Financial Officer, Phoenix Children's Hospital, Phoenix, AZ, p. A36

MCKNIGHT, Richard B., Senior Vice President and Chief Information Officer, Novant Health Huntersville Medical Center, Huntersville, NC, p. A467

MCKOY, Lori, Business Partner, Pender Memorial Hospital, Burgaw, NC, p. A460

MCKULA, Tim, Vice President Information Systems and Chief Information Officer, Rehabilitation Institute of Chicago, Chicago, IL, p. A186

MCKUNE, Jeff, Director Information Technology, Phelps County Regional Medical Center, Rolla, MO, p. A379

MCLAIN, Allen, M.D. Chief of Staff, Grisell Memorial Hospital District One, Ransom, KS, p. A253

MCLAIN, Cindy, Chief Executive Officer, Select Specialty Hospital–Fort Smith, Fort Smith, AR, p. A46

MCLAIN, Jerry, M.D. Chief of Staff, Chadron Community Hospital and Health Services, Chadron, NE, p. A394

MCLAIN, Kathy, Chief Financial Officer, Childress Regional Medical Center, Childress, TX, p. A606

MCLAIN, Terri L., FACHE, President, Mercy Hospital Washington, Washington, MO, p. A384

MCLANE, Jerry T., M.D. President Medical Staff, Medical West, Bessemer, AL, p. A16

MCLARIN, Benita, Chief Operating Officer, Santa Clara Valley Medical Center, San Jose, CA, p. A92

MCLARTY, Walter L.
Chief Human Resources Officer, Bethesda North Hospital, Cincinnati, OH, p. A486
Chief Human Resources Officer, Good Samaritan Hospital, Cincinnati, OH, p. A487

MCLAUGHLIN, Christine, Vice President Finance, Millinocket Regional Hospital, Millinocket, ME, p. A294

MCLAUGHLIN, Dan C., Vice President Professional Services, Good Samaritan Hospital, Los Angeles, CA, p. A72

MCLAUGHLIN, Gary, Executive Vice President Finance and Chief Financial Officer, Overlake Medical Center, Bellevue, WA, p. A681

MCLAUGHLIN, Kathryn, Vice President and Chief Nursing Officer, Pacific Hospital of Long Beach, Long Beach, CA, p. A70

MCLAUGHLIN, Kevin, Manager Information Systems, Saint Catherine Regional Hospital, Charlestown, IN, p. A208

MCLAUGHLIN, Maribeth, R.N. Vice President Patient Care Services, Magee–Womens Hospital of UPMC, Pittsburgh, PA, p. A551

MCLAUGHLIN, Neil R., R.N.,
President, Hampshire Memorial Hospital, Romney, WV, p. A699
President, War Memorial Hospital, Berkeley Springs, WV, p. A693

MCLAUGHLIN, Pamela, Chief Financial Officer, HEALTHSOUTH Rehabilitation Hospital of Austin, Austin, TX, p. A599

MCLAUGHLIN, Sherry, Director Human Resources, Forrest City Medical Center, Forrest City, AR, p. A46

MCLAUGHLIN, William J., Administrator, Thomas Hospital, Fairhope, AL, p. A20

MCLAURIN, Monty E., President and Chief Executive Officer, Indian Path Medical Center, Kingsport, TN, p. A585

MCLAURIN, Rod, Director Information Systems, Marlboro Park Hospital, Bennettsville, SC, p. A562

MCLAWS, Douglas, D.O. Chief Medical Officer, Manning Regional Healthcare Center, Manning, IA, p. A234

MCLEAN, Anthony, President, St. Francis Hospital, Federal Way, WA, p. A683

MCLEAN, Chris J., Chief Financial Officer, Methodist Healthcare Memphis Hospitals, Memphis, TN, p. A589

MCLEAN, Georgia, Director Human Resources, Mount Sinai Medical Center, Miami Beach, FL, p. A138

MCLENDON, Carla
Director Human Resources, Appling Healthcare System, Baxley, GA, p. A154
Director Information Resource Management Services, Charles George Veterans Affairs Medical Center, Asheville, NC, p. A459

MCLENDON, Connie, Director Human Resources, Piedmont Mountainside Hospital, Jasper, GA, p. A161

MCLENDON, John, Senior Vice President and Chief Information Officer, Adventist Bolingbrook Hospital, Bolingbrook, IL, p. A182

MCLENNAN, Marlene, Controller, Monroe County Hospital, Forsyth, GA, p. A160

MCLEOD, Les, Director of Nursing Services, Blue Mountain Hospital, John Day, OR, p. A526

MCLEOD, Sheldon, Chief Operating Officer, North Central Bronx Hospital,, NY, p. A447

MCLIN, Robert D., President and Chief Executive Officer, Good Samaritan Hospital, Vincennes, IN, p. A223

MCLISTER, Charles, Chief Executive Officer, Fairmount Behavioral Health System, Philadelphia, PA, p. A548

MCLOONE, J. Mark, FACHE, Chief Executive Officer, Pottstown Memorial Medical Center, Pottstown, PA, p. A552

MCLOONE, Paul, M.D
Chief Medical Officer, UnityPoint Health – Trinity Bettendorf, Bettendorf, IA, p. A225
Chief Medical Officer, UnityPoint Health – Trinity Rock Island, Rock Island, IL, p. A201

MCMAHAN, Mike, Chief Executive Officer, St. Francis Regional Medical Center, Shakopee, MN, p. A352

MCMAHON, Alisha, Director Human Resources, Mountrail County Medical Center, Stanley, ND, p. A480

MCMAHON, Andrew, Chief Fiscal Officer, VA Central Western Massachusetts Healthcare System, Leeds, MA, p. A311

MCMAHON, Chris, Chief Operating Officer, The Medical Center of Southeast Texas, Port Arthur, TX, p. A643

MCMAHON, Denise, Director People Services, St. Joseph's Hospital, Chippewa Falls, WI, p. A703

MCMAHON, Elaine, Administrator, Kwajalein Hospital, Kwajalein Island, MH, p. A724

MCMAHON, John, Chief Financial Officer, Jennersville Regional Hospital, West Grove, PA, p. A558

MCMAHON, Leigh, MS Senior Vice President Patient Care Services and Chief Nursing Officer, White Plains Hospital Center, White Plains, NY, p. A458

MCMAHON, Nancy, Vice President Human Resources, Miriam Hospital, Providence, RI, p. A560

MCMANMON, Kristin, Chief Operating Officer, St. Mary's Hospital, Madison, WI, p. A708

MCMANUS, Doug, Chief Medical Officer, Aurora Medical Center Grafton, Grafton, WI, p. A705

MCMANUS, Michael T., Chief Operating Officer, Memorial Hospital, Belleville, IL, p. A181

MCMANUS, Ronald, Senior Vice President Clinical Services and Business Entities, Peconic Bay Medical Center, Riverhead, NY, p. A452

MCMANUS, Tim, President and Chief Executive Officer, CJW Medical Center, Richmond, VA, p. A677

MCMASTER, Melanie, Director Operations, Greenville Health System – Laurens County Memorial Hospital, Clinton, SC, p. A564

MCMASTER, Sandra
Regional Chief Information Officer, Kauai Veterans Memorial Hospital, Waimea, HI, p. A173
Regional Chief Information Officer, Samuel Mahelona Memorial Hospital, Kapaa, HI, p. A172

MCMATH, Mark W., Chief Information Officer, Indiana University Health Bloomington Hospital, Bloomington, IN, p. A207

MCMENAMIN, Anneliese, Vice President Human Resources, Kennedy Health System, Cherry Hill, NJ, p. A414

MCMICHEN, Diane, Director Human Resources, DeKalb Regional Medical Center, Fort Payne, AL, p. A20

MCMILLAN, Deborah, Director Human Resources, Glenn Medical Center, Willows, CA, p. A101

MCMILLAN, Don
Chief Information Officer, PeaceHealth Sacred Heart Medical Center, University District, Eugene, OR, p. A524
Chief Information Officer, PeaceHealth Southwest Medical Center, Vancouver, WA, p. A692

MCMILLAN, Douglas A., Administrator and Chief Executive Officer, West Park Hospital, Cody, WY, p. A721

MCMILLAN, Jon R., Chief Financial Officer, Banner Lassen Medical Center, Susanville, CA, p. A96

MCMILLAN, Sheila, Chief Financial Officer, Park Nicollet Methodist Hospital, Minneapolis, MN, p. A347

MCMILLEN, Eric, Chief Executive Officer, Ochsner Medical Center–Baton Rouge, Baton Rouge, LA, p. A273

MCMINN, Ken, Director Information Technology, Scotland County Hospital, Memphis, MO, p. A376

MCMINN, Melvin, Director Human Resources, Wernersville State Hospital, Wernersville, PA, p. A557

MCMORROUGH, Jerry L., Vice President Human Resources, Medical Center of Arlington, Arlington, TX, p. A598

MCMULLAN, Heidi, R.N. Chief Nursing Officer, Philhaven, Mount Gretna, PA, p. A545

MCMULLEN, Doug, Senior Technical Analyst, Vidant Chowan Hospital, Edenton, NC, p. A464

MCMULLEN, Ronald B., President, Christian Hospital, Saint Louis, MO, p. A380

MCMULLEN, Thomas A., Chief Financial Officer, Kindred Hospital–Philadelphia, Philadelphia, PA, p. A549

MCMURRAY, Sean S., FACHE, Vice President and Chief Executive Officer, Johnston Memorial Hospital, Abingdon, VA, p. A668

MCMURREY, Jean Ann, R.N. Chief Nursing Officer, RMC Jacksonville, Jacksonville, AL, p. A22

MCMURRY, Timothy, Director, Wm. Jennings Bryan Dorn Veterans Affairs Medical Center, Columbia, SC, p. A565

MCNABB, Dana, Human Resources Manager, Field Memorial Community Hospital, Centreville, MS, p. A356

MCNABB, Teresita, R.N. Vice President Nursing Services, Terrebonne General Medical Center, Houma, LA, p. A279

MCNAIR, Lisa, CP
Senior Vice President and Chief Financial Officer, Burleson St. Joseph Health Center, Caldwell, TX, p. A605
Senior Vice President and Chief Financial Officer, St. Joseph Regional Health Center, Bryan, TX, p. A604

MCNAIR, Michael H., Chief Executive Officer, Sandhills Regional Medical Center, Hamlet, NC, p. A466

MCNALLY, John, Chief Executive Officer, Pinnacle Pointe Hospital, Little Rock, AR, p. A49

MCNALLY, Joseph, M.D. Medical Director, Streamwood Behavioral Health Center, Streamwood, IL, p. A204

MCNALLY, Kathy, Chief Nursing Officer, HEALTHSOUTH Rehabilitation Hospital at Drake, Cincinnati, OH, p. A487

MCNALLY, Lou–Ann, Director Human Resources, Claxton–Hepburn Medical Center, Ogdensburg, NY, p. A450

MCNALLY, Michael, Vice President Human Resources, United Health Services Hospitals–Binghamton, Binghamton, NY, p. A434

MCNAMARA, John, M.D. Chief Medical Officer, Torrance Memorial Medical Center, Torrance, CA, p. A97

MCNAMARA, Marilyn, M.D. Vice President Medical Affairs, Southwest General Health Center, Middieburg Heights, OH, p. A498

MCNAMARA, Mike, Chief Information Officer, Mee Memorial Hospital, King City, CA, p. A68

MCNAMARA, Steve, Chief Financial Officer, Orange Coast Memorial Medical Center, Fountain Valley, CA, p. A63

MCNAMARA, Thomas, D.O. Vice President Medical Affairs, WellStar Cobb Hospital, Austell, GA, p. A154

MCNAMARA, Timothy M.
Senior Vice President Human Resources, Bradford Regional Medical Center, Bradford, PA, p. A534
Senior Vice President Human Resources, Olean General Hospital, Olean, NY, p. A450

MCNAMEE, Hugar, D.O. Chief Medical Officer, Florida Hospital Zephyrhills, Zephyrhills, FL, p. A150

MCNATT, James, Chief Financial Officer, Baylor Medical Center at Carrollton, Carrollton, TX, p. A605

MCNAUGHTON, Richard, Chief Information Management Service, Maine Veterans Affairs Medical Center, Augusta, ME, p. A291

MCNEA, Melvin, Interim Chief Executive Officer, Great Plains Health, North Platte, NE, p. A398

MCNEAR, Michael, M.D. Chief Medical Officer, Jersey Community Hospital, Jerseyville, IL, p. A193

MCNEECE, Steve, Chief Executive Officer, Community Hospital of Anaconda, Anaconda, MT, p. A385

MCNEEL, Jacob, D.O. Chief of Staff, Plateau Medical Center, Oak Hill, WV, p. A698

MCNEEL, Wakelin, M.D. Medical Director, BHC Alhambra Hospital, Rosemead, CA, p. A86

MCNEICE, Keith, Vice President and Chief Information Officer, Carolinas Medical Center–NorthEast, Concord, NC, p. A462

MCNEIL, Ane, Vice President Human Resources, St. Joseph Mercy Oakland, Pontiac, MI, p. A332

MCNEIL, Greg R., Chief Executive Officer, Crittenden County Hospital, Marion, KY, p. A267

MCNEIL, John, President and Chief Executive Officer, Eastern Regional Medical Center, Philadelphia, PA, p. A548

MCNEIL, Karen
Chief Nursing Officer, University Hospitals Conneaut Medical Center, Conneaut, OH, p. A491
Chief Nursing Officer, University Hospitals Geneva Medical Center, Geneva, OH, p. A494

MCNEILL, Michael, Chief Financial Management, Veterans Affairs Medical Center, Albuquerque, NM, p. A427

MCNELIS, John, M.D. Acting Medical Director, Jacobi Medical Center,, NY, p. A444

MCNEY, Jim, Senior Vice President Finance and Chief Financial Officer, North Kansas City Hospital, North Kansas City, MO, p. A378

MCNULTY III,, Joseph S., President and Chief Executive Officer, Pioneer Health Services, Magee, MS, p. B106

MCNULTY, Stephanie, Chief Operating Officer, St. Petersburg General Hospital, Saint Petersburg, FL, p. A145

MCNULTY, Timothy, Director Human Resources, Spring Harbor Hospital, Westbrook, ME, p. A295

MCNUTT, Mike, Assistant Administrator, Covenant Hospital Plainview, Plainview, TX, p. A642

MCNUTT, Pamela
Vice President Information Systems, Methodist Charlton Medical Center, Dallas, TX, p. A611
Senior Vice President and Chief Information Officer, Methodist Dallas Medical Center, Dallas, TX, p. A611
Senior Vice President and Chief Information Officer, Methodist Mansfield Medical Center, Mansfield, TX, p. A636

MCPEAK, Sara, Chief Nursing Officer, Carlinville Area Hospital, Carlinville, IL, p. A182

MCPHERSON, Brian, Chief Information Officer, Botsford Hospital, Farmington Hills, MI, p. A323

MCPHERSON, Lon, M.D. Senior Vice President Medical Affairs and Chief Quality Officer, Munroe Regional Medical Center, Ocala, FL, p. A139

MCPHERSON, Rhonda, Vice President Human Resources, Fayette Regional Health System, Connersville, IN, p. A208

MCPHERSON, Stephen B., President, Masonicare Health Center, Wallingford, CT, p. A117

MCQUAID, Bill, Assistant Vice President and Chief Information Officer, Parkview Adventist Medical Center, Brunswick, ME, p. A292

MCQUAID, David P., FACHE, President, Thomas Jefferson University Hospital, Philadelphia, PA, p. A550

MCQUAIDE, Teresa A., Chief Executive Officer, Trenton Psychiatric Hospital, Trenton, NJ, p. A424

MCQUEEN, Elbert T., President and Chief Executive Officer, Rehabilitation Hospital, Navicent Health, Macon, GA, p. A163

MCQUILLAN, Kent, Chief Information Officer, Summit Healthcare Regional Medical Center, Show Low, AZ, p. A39

MCQUISTAN, Bob, Vice President Finance, York General Hospital, York, NE, p. A403

MCQUISTON, Mike, Administrative Director Human Resources, Wise Regional Health System, Decatur, TX, p. A612

MCRAE, Colin, Chief Executive Officer, Tennova Healthcare–Jefferson Memorial Hospital, Jefferson City, TN, p. A584

MCROBERTS, Kevin, Senior Vice President of Operations, Lake Regional Health System, Osage Beach, MO, p. A378

MCROBERTS, Susan, R.N. Vice President and Chief Nursing Officer, Franciscan St. Francis Health – Indianapolis, Indianapolis, IN, p. A214

MCSHANE, Brian, IT Manager, Lakes Regional Healthcare, Spirit Lake, IA, p. A238

MCSWAIN, Marilyn, MSN, Administrator, Lake Charles Memorial Hospital for Women, Lake Charles, LA, p. A282

MCTAGGART, Jac, Chief Executive Officer, Sanford Hillsboro Medical Center, Hillsboro, ND, p. A478

MCTAGUE, Jerome, JD, Administrator and Chief Executive Officer, Physician's Choice Hospital – Fremont, Fremont, OH, p. A494

MCTIGRIT, Chris, Manager Information Technology, Delta Memorial Hospital, Dumas, AR, p. A45

MCTIGUE, Mary, Vice President Patient Care Services and Chief Nursing Officer, Trinitas Regional Medical Center, Elizabeth, NJ, p. A415

MCTIGUE, Michael
Chief Information Officer, Clara Maass Medical Center, Belleville, NJ, p. A413
Chief Information Officer, Saint Barnabas Medical Center, Livingston, NJ, p. A417

MCVAY, Randy, Chief Executive Officer, Ocala Regional Medical Center, Ocala, FL, p. A139

MCVEIGH, Kevin
Interim Chief Human Resources Officer, Banner Behavioral Health Hospital – Scottsdale, Scottsdale, AZ, p. A38
Chief Human Resources Officer, Banner Desert Medical Center, Mesa, AZ, p. A34

MCVEY, Eric A., M.D. Vice President and Chief Medical Officer, Mississippi Baptist Medical Center, Jackson, MS, p. A360

MCVEY, Lynn, Chief Operating Officer, Meadowlands Hospital Medical Center, Secaucus, NJ, p. A422

MCVEY, Marian, Chief Nursing Officer, North Greenville Hospital, Travelers Rest, SC, p. A570

MCVEY, Timothy J., Chief Financial Officer, Mission Regional Medical Center, Mission, TX, p. A638

MCVICKER, Sandra I., MSN, President, University Hospital McDuffie, Thomson, GA, p. A168

MCWATTERS, Pearl, Director Information Services, Highland Hospital, Charleston, WV, p. A694

MCWAY, Jacob, Senior Vice President and Chief Financial Officer, Cox Medical Centers, Springfield, MO, p. A383

MCWEY, Russ, M.D. Vice President and Chief Information Officer, Virginia Hospital Center – Arlington, Arlington, VA, p. A668

MCWHERTER, Joe, Chief Financial Officer, Baptist Memorial Hospital–Desoto, Southaven, MS, p. A365

MCWHORTER III, John B., President, Baylor University Medical Center, Dallas, TX, p. A610

MCWHORTER, Sharon, Director Information Systems, Ephraim McDowell Fort Logan Hospital, Stanford, KY, p. A270

MCWILLIAMS, Jill, Chief Nursing Officer, Sierra Nevada Memorial Hospital, Grass Valley, CA, p. A66

MEACHAM, Sherry, Coordinator Human Resources, Select Specialty Hospital–Winston–Salem, Winston–Salem, NC, p. A475

MEACHAM, Steve, Vice President Finance, King's Daughters' Health, Madison, IN, p. A218

MEACHAM, Verna Stroman, President and Chief Executive Officer, Fort Washington Medical Center, Fort Washington, MD, p. A301

MEACHEM, Michelle, Director Human Resources, Elizabethtown Community Hospital, Elizabethtown, NY, p. A437

MEAD, Barbara, Vice President Behavioral Health and Physician Clinics, Lourdes Counseling Center, Richland, WA, p. A687

MEAD, Linda, Director Human Resources, Margaretville Hospital, Margaretville, NY, p. A441

MEAD, Richard, Senior Director Human Resources, Saint Francis Memorial Hospital, San Francisco, CA, p. A91

MEAD, Rick, Human Resources Leader, Kaiser Permanente Oakland Medical Center, Oakland, CA, p. A80

MEADE, Robert C., Chief Executive Officer, Doctors Hospital of Sarasota, Sarasota, FL, p. A145

MEADE, Stephanie, MSN Chief Nursing Officer, Mercy Health – West Hospital, Cincinnati, OH, p. A487

MEADE, Teresa, R.N. Chief Nursing Officer, Boone Memorial Hospital, Madison, WV, p. A697

MEADOWS, Barbara, Chief Financial Manager, Captain James A. Lovell Federal Health Care Center, North Chicago, IL, p. A198

MEADOWS, Bethany, Director Human Resources, St. Cloud Regional Medical Center, Saint Cloud, FL, p. A144

MEADOWS, Danny, M.D. Medical Director, Logansport State Hospital, Logansport, IN, p. A218

MEADOWS, Hal, M.D. Chief Medical Officer, Banner Lassen Medical Center, Susanville, CA, p. A96

MEADOWS, Julia, Chief Financial Officer, Virginia Gay Hospital, Vinton, IA, p. A238

MEADOWS, Mark, Chief Executive Officer, Lone Peak Hospital, Draper, UT, p. A659

MEADOWS, Nancy, Chief Financial Officer, Methodist Hospital, San Antonio, TX, p. A646

MEADOWS, Peri, Director Human Resources, Rhea Medical Center, Dayton, TN, p. A582

MEADOWS, Theresa, Chief Information Officer, Cook Children's Medical Center, Fort Worth, TX, p. A618

MEANS, Dennis, M.D. Vice President Medical Affairs, Carilion New River Valley Medical Center, Christiansburg, VA, p. A669

MEANS, Jr., William H., Administrator, Sterlington Rehabilitation Hospital, Bastrop, LA, p. A273

MEARNS, Stephanie, Vice President Patient Care Services and Chief Nurse Executive, Seton Medical Center, Daly City, CA, p. A61

MEARS, Terry, Director Information Systems, Duke Regional Hospital, Durham, NC, p. A463

MECHAM, Cindy, Health Information Director, Mountain View Hospital, Payson, UT, p. A662

MECOM, Deborah, R.N., Administrator, CHRISTUS Jasper Memorial Hospital, Jasper, TX, p. A630

MEDAGLIA, Guy A., President and Chief Executive Officer, Saint Anthony Hospital, Chicago, IL, p. A186

MEDCIROS, Ron, Director Applied Information Technology, Worcester Recovery Center and Hospital, Worcester, MA, p. A317

MEDEIROS, Katherine A., President and Chief Executive Officer, Sierra Nevada Memorial Hospital, Grass Valley, CA, p. A66

MEDEROS, Ana J., Chief Executive Officer, Palmetto General Hospital, Hialeah, FL, p. A130

MEDINA, Alberto, Information Technology Senior Consultant, Hospital Manati Medical Center, Manati, PR, p. A726

MEDINA, Betsmari, Director Human Resources, Dr. Ramon E. Betances Hospital–Mayaguez Medical Center Branch, Mayaguez, PR, p. A726

MEDINA, Ed, M.D. Medical Director, Phillips County Hospital, Malta, MT, p. A389

MEDINA, Eleanor, M.D. Chief Medical Officer, Behavioral Center of Michigan, Warren, MI, p. A336

MEDINA, Luz D., Controller, Hospital Hermanos Melendez, Bayamon, PR, p. A725

MEDINA, Marco, Chief Information Officer, Stanton County Hospital, Johnson, KS, p. A246

© 2014 AHA Guide

MEDINA, Obdulia, MSN Associate Director for Administrative Support, Clinical Management and Ambulatory Care, Ashford Presbyterian Community Hospital, San Juan, PR, p. A727

MEDINA, Patricia, Service Unit Director, U. S. Public Health Service Indian Hospital, Winnebago, NE, p. A403

MEDINA, Shelby, Chief Administrative Officer, Buchanan County Health Center, Independence, IA, p. A232

MEDLAND, Jacqueline, MS Regional Chief Nursing Officer, Presence St. Mary's Hospital, Kankakee, IL, p. A194

MEDLEY, Adron, M.D. Chief Medical Staff, Northern Rockies Medical Center, Cut Bank, MT, p. A386

MEDLEY, Barry, Director Information Systems, Cook Medical Center–A Campus of Tift Regional Medical Center, Adel, GA, p. A151

MEDLEY, Dennis, Administrator, Physicians' Medical Center, New Albany, IN, p. A220

MEDLEY, Wathen, M.D. Chief Medical Officer, Owensboro Health Regional Hospital, Owensboro, KY, p. A268

MEDLIN, John, Chief Nursing Officer, North Carolina Specialty Hospital, Durham, NC, p. A463

MEDLIN, Marsha, Senior Vice President of Clinical and Operations, Post Acute Northshore Specialty Hospital, Covington, LA, p. A276

MEDLOCK, Beth, Manager Information Technology, Jackson Hospital, Marianna, FL, p. A135

MEDLOCK, Darci, Manager Human Resources, St. Vincent Dunn Hospital, Bedford, IN, p. A207

MEDOVICH, Lisa, Chief Financial Officer, Val Verde Regional Medical Center, Del Rio, TX, p. A613

MEDUNA, Leo L., M.D. Chief Medical Officer, Saunders Medical Center, Wahoo, NE, p. A402

MEE, Thomas, R.N
  Chief Operating Officer, McLaren Greater Lansing, Lansing, MI, p. A328
  Vice President Operations, McLaren Lapeer Region, Lapeer, MI, p. A329

MEEHAN, Kenneth L., Interim Chief Operating Officer, Saint John's Health Center, Santa Monica, CA, p. A94

MEEHAN, Neil S., D.O. Chief Medical Officer and Chief Medical Information Officer, Lawrence General Hospital, Lawrence, MA, p. A311

MEEK, Julie, Vice President Finance, Kadlec Regional Medical Center, Richland, WA, p. A687

MEEKER, Brian, D.O. President Medical Staff, Virginia Gay Hospital, Vinton, IA, p. A238

MEEKER, Chris, M.D. Chief Medical Officer, Sanford Bismarck, Bismarck, ND, p. A476

MEEKER, Larry, Chief Executive Officer, Howard A. Rusk Rehabilitation Center, Columbia, MO, p. A370

MEEKER, Mark, D.O. Medical Staff President, OSF St. Mary Medical Center, Galesburg, IL, p. A190

MEEKINS, Lance, Administrator, Nocona General Hospital, Nocona, TX, p. A640

MEEKINS, Michelle, Manager Human Resources, Sentara Virginia Beach General Hospital, Virginia Beach, VA, p. A679

MEEKS, Barbara, MSN Chief Nurse Executive, Nemours Children's Hospital, Orlando, FL, p. A140

MEEKS, Deborah, Chief Nursing Officer, Harlingen Medical Center, Harlingen, TX, p. A622

MEEKS, Derek, D.O. Chief of Staff, Boulder City Hospital, Boulder City, NV, p. A404

MEEKS, Janet, Chief Operating Officer, Mount Carmel St. Ann's, Westerville, OH, p. A505

MEEKS, Julia M., Chief Operating Officer, Specialty Hospital of Lorain, Amherst, OH, p. A482

MEEKS, Shane, Manager Technology Information Systems, Spectrum Health Gerber Memorial, Fremont, MI, p. A324

MEEKS, Teresa, Chief Nursing Officer, East Texas Medical Center–Quitman, Quitman, TX, p. A643

MEENK, Susan
  Vice President Service Area, Providence Centralia Hospital, Centralia, WA, p. A682
  Vice President Human Resources, Providence St. Peter Hospital, Olympia, WA, p. A686

MEERT, Tiffany, Chief Operating Officer, Northern Nevada Medical Center, Sparks, NV, p. A408

MEESE, Larry, Chief Executive Officer, Jackson Hospital, Marianna, FL, p. A135

MEESIG, Deborah, M.D. Chief of Staff, Chillicothe Veterans Affairs Medical Center, Chillicothe, OH, p. A486

MEGEHEE, Mark, Vice President and Chief Information Officer, Decatur Morgan Hospital, Decatur, AL, p. A18

MEGGARS, Marla, R.N. Chief Nursing Officer, Gilbert Hospital, Gilbert, AZ, p. A32

MEGILL, Douglas, Manager Information Systems, Warren General Hospital, Warren, PA, p. A557

MEGLI, Cami, Controller, Morrison Community Hospital, Morrison, IL, p. A197

MEGLIOLA, Donna M., Assistant Vice President, Johnson Memorial Hospital, Stafford Springs, CT, p. A117

MEGOW, Kimberly, M.D. Chief Medical Officer, South Georgia Medical Center, Valdosta, GA, p. A168

MEGUIAR, Ramon V., M.D. Chief Medical Officer, Memorial Health, Savannah, GA, p. A166

MEHAFFEY, M. Beth, Vice President Human Resources, Baptist Medical Center Jacksonville, Jacksonville, FL, p. A131

MEHARG, John, Director Health Information Technology, Norman Regional Health System, Norman, OK, p. A514

MEHINDRU, Vinay, M.D
  Vice President/Chief Medical Officer, Florida Hospital Waterman, Tavares, FL, p. A148
  Medical Director, Wuesthoff Medical Center – Rockledge, Rockledge, FL, p. A144

MEHTA, Kalpana, Chief Fiscal Services, Jesse Brown Veterans Affairs Medical Center, Chicago, IL, p. A184

MEHTA, Sonia, M.D., Chief Executive Officer and Chief Medical Officer, Loretto Hospital, Chicago, IL, p. A184

MEHTA, Steven, M.D. Chief Medical Officer, Sierra Vista Regional Health Center, Sierra Vista, AZ, p. A39

MEIAR, Cindy, Human Resources and Payroll Coordinator, Trego County–Lemke Memorial Hospital, Wakeeney, KS, p. A256

MEIDINGER, Duane, Vice President Finance, Walla Walla General Hospital, Walla Walla, WA, p. A692

MEIDINGER, Sue, Manager Business Office, Linton Hospital, Linton, ND, p. A479

MEIDL, M. Mikela, Chief Executive Officer, Saint Anthony's Health Center, Alton, IL, p. A180

MEIER, Suzanne S., System Director, Compensation and Human Resources Technology, Memorial Hermann Memorial City Medical Center, Houston, TX, p. A625

MEIERGERD, Jean, Chief Information Officer, St. Francis Memorial Hospital, West Point, NE, p. A402

MEIERS, Dawn, Coordinator Medical Staff and Personnel Services, Southeast Michigan Surgical Hospital, Warren, MI, p. A336

MEIGS, Jeffrey L., Chief Financial Officer, Louis A. Weiss Memorial Hospital, Chicago, IL, p. A184

MEIGS, Jr., John, M.D. Chief of Staff, Bibb Medical Center, Centreville, AL, p. A18

MEINDEL, Nympha, R.N. Chief Information Officer, North Shore University Hospital, Manhasset, NY, p. A440

MEINHART, Richard, Manager Information Systems, Daviess Community Hospital, Washington, IN, p. A224

MEINKE, Kenneth, Senior Vice President Administrative Services, Finance and Chief Financial Officer, Spartanburg Regional Medical Center, Spartanburg, SC, p. A570

MEINKE, Victor E., Chief Financial Officer, Jewish Home of San Francisco, San Francisco, CA, p. A90

MEINKOTH, Jennifer, Chief Information Officer, Memorial Hospital, Belleville, IL, p. A181

MEIS, Fred J., Chief Executive Officer, Kearney County Health Services, Minden, NE, p. A398

MEISNER, Anne, MSN, President and Chief Executive Officer, Southeastern Regional Medical Center, Newnan, GA, p. A164

MEISSNER, Shari, Chief Financial Officer, Liberty Medical Center, Chester, MT, p. A386

MEITZ, Mary
  Senior Vice President and Chief Financial Officer, Bronson Battle Creek, Battle Creek, MI, p. A319
  Vice President Finance, Bronson Methodist Hospital, Kalamazoo, MI, p. A328

MEJIA, Larry, Vice President and Chief Operating Officer, Seton Smithville Regional Hospital, Smithville, TX, p. A649

MEKHAEL, Hani, M.D. Chief Staff, Havenwyck Hospital, Auburn Hills, MI, p. A318

MELAHN, Will L., M.D. Vice President Medical Affairs and Chief Medical Officer, St. Claire Regional Medical Center, Morehead, KY, p. A268

MELANCON, Eric, Chief of Staff, Teche Regional Medical Center, Morgan City, LA, p. A284

MELANCON, Mary, Chief Financial Officer, Abrom Kaplan Memorial Hospital, Kaplan, LA, p. A280

MELAND, Jeff, M.D. Vice President, Chief Medical Officer, Northfield Hospital, Northfield, MN, p. A348

MELARAGNO, Robert, Vice President Finance, O'Bleness Memorial Hospital, Athens, OH, p. A483

MELBOURNE, John, M.D. Medical Director, Conifer Park, Glenville, NY, p. A438

MELBY, Gina, Chief Executive Officer, JFK Medical Center, Atlantis, FL, p. A123

MELBY, Larry, Chief Executive Officer, Select Specialty Hospital–Palm Beach, Lake Worth, FL, p. A133

MELBY, Rachel, Controller, Crawford County Memorial Hospital, Denison, IA, p. A229

MELCHER, Nancy, Chief Nursing Officer, North Fulton Regional Hospital, Roswell, GA, p. A165

MELCHIODE, Joseph D., Chief Executive Officer, University Hospital and Medical Center, Tamarac, FL, p. A147

MELCHIOR, Eric L., Executive Vice President and Chief Financial Officer, Greater Baltimore Medical Center, Baltimore, MD, p. A296

MELENDEZ, Alma, Controller, Dimmit Regional Hospital, Carrizo Springs, TX, p. A605

MELENDEZ, Pedro
  Chief Executive Officer, Centro De Salud Conductual Menonita–CIMA, Aibonito, PR, p. A724
  Chief Executive Director, Hospital Menonita De Cayey, Cayey, PR, p. A725
  Chief Executive Officer, Mennonite General Hospital, Aibonito, PR, p. A724

MELINE, Brenda, Manager Human Resources, Patients' Hospital of Redding, Redding, CA, p. A85

MELL, Kevin, Vice President Operations, MedStar Montgomery Medical Center, Olney, MD, p. A302

MELL, Vicki, Vice President Human Resources and Support Services, Ohio Valley General Hospital, McKees Rocks, PA, p. A544

MELLETT, David, Chief Financial Officer, Harrison Memorial Hospital, Cynthiana, KY, p. A260

MELLO, Brett, Chief Information Officer, Cayuga Medical Center at Ithaca, Ithaca, NY, p. A439

MELLO, Paul, Manager Data Processing, Metropolitan State Hospital, Norwalk, CA, p. A80

MELLON, Monte, M.D. Chief of Staff, Catalina Island Medical Center, Avalon, CA, p. A56

MELLON, Stacy, Manager Human Resource, Hillsdale Community Health Center, Hillsdale, MI, p. A326

MELLOR, W. Kimball, M.D. Chief Medical Officer, Whitman Hospital and Medical Center, Colfax, WA, p. A682

MELNIKOFF, Jean, Vice President Human Resources, Kaiser Permanente Medical Center, Honolulu, HI, p. A170

MELSON, Benjamin B., CPA Executive Vice President and Chief Financial Officer, Texas Children's Hospital, Houston, TX, p. A627

MELTON, Anne, Chief Nursing Officer, Sumner Regional Medical Center, Gallatin, TN, p. A583

MELTON, Chad, Chief Executive Officer, Hackensack University Medical Center at Pascack Valley, Westwood, NJ, p. A424

MELTON, Linda Dickey, Vice President Human Resources, North Arkansas Regional Medical Center, Harrison, AR, p. A47

MELTON, Samuel Hughes, M.D. Vice President Chief Medical Officer, Virginia Operations Medical Staff Services, Russell County Medical Center, Lebanon, VA, p. A672

MELTVEDT, Jr., Robert, M.D. Vice President Medical Affairs, Warren Memorial Hospital, Front Royal, VA, p. A671

MELTZER, David B., Chief Financial Officer, Texas Health Presbyterian Hospital Denton, Denton, TX, p. A613

MELTZER, Neil M., President and Chief Executive Officer, LifeBridge Health, Baltimore, MD, p. B84

MELVILLE, Carol, Director Human Resources, West Houston Medical Center, Houston, TX, p. A628

MELVIN, Susan, D.O. Chief Medical Officer, Long Beach Memorial Medical Center, Long Beach, CA, p. A70

MENCHINI, August F., Director Human Resources, Eastern Long Island Hospital, Greenport, NY, p. A438

MENDELOWITZ, Susan, Executive Vice President and Chief Operating Officer, Bergen Regional Medical Center, Paramus, NJ, p. A420

MENDEZ, Alex A., Executive Vice President of Operations and Chief Financial Officer, Mount Sinai Medical Center, Miami Beach, FL, p. A138

MENDEZ, James, Chief Executive Officer, Kindred Hospital–Dallas, Dallas, TX, p. A610

MENDEZ, Kim K., Ed.D. Vice President and Chief Nursing Officer, Brookhaven Memorial Hospital Medical Center, Patchogue, NY, p. A451

MENDEZ, Lincoln S., Chief Executive Officer, Baptist Health South Florida, South Miami Hospital, Miami, FL, p. A136

MENDEZ, Samantha, Human Resources, Freedom Pain Hospital, Scottsdale, AZ, p. A38

MENDIOLA–BALDERAS, Rosie L., Director Information Systems, South Texas Health System, Edinburg, TX, p. A615

MENDOZA, Aniceta, R.N. Chief Nursing Officer, Valley Baptist Medical Center–Brownsville, Brownsville, TX, p. A604

MENDOZA, Dana, Chief Information Officer, Maui Memorial Medical Center, Wailuku, HI, p. A172

MENDOZA, Joseph
  Chief Financial Officer, Hillcrest Hospital Cushing, Cushing, OK, p. A509
  Chief Financial Officer, Hillcrest Hospital Henryetta, Henryetta, OK, p. A511

MENDOZA, Joseph, M.D. Medical Director, Porterville Developmental Center, Porterville, CA, p. A84

MENDOZA, Yolanda, Director Human Resources, Rehabilitation Hospital of Southern New Mexico, Las Cruces, NM, p. A429

MENGE, Penny A., MSN Chief Nursing Officer and Vice President Patient Care Services, Touro Infirmary, New Orleans, LA, p. A286

MENGLE, Scott, Vice President Human Resources, St. Joseph Medical Center, Reading, PA, p. A553

MENNINGA, Cathy, R.N. Chief Nursing Officer, Ellett Memorial Hospital, Appleton City, MO, p. A367

MENNONNA, Guy, Senior Vice President Human Resources, Bergen Regional Medical Center, Paramus, NJ, p. A420

MENON, Rema, M.D. Clinical Director, Parsons State Hospital and Training Center, Parsons, KS, p. A252

MENOR, Peter, Vice President Operations, Chandler Regional Medical Center, Chandler, AZ, p. A31

MENSCH, Alan, M.D. Senior Vice President Medical Affairs, Plainview Hospital, Plainview, NY, p. A451

MENSEN, Amy, Chief Administrative Officer, Regional Medical Center, Manchester, IA, p. A234

MENTGEN, John, President and Chief Executive Officer, Regional West Medical Center, Scottsbluff, NE, p. A402

MENTHCOAST, Lynn, Chief Fiscal Service, Tennessee Valley Healthcare System, Nashville, TN, p. A591

MENTINK, Terri, Chief Financial Officer, Oakland Mercy Hospital, Oakland, NE, p. A399

MENTZER, Larry, Chief Human Resources Officer, Veterans Affairs Roseburg Healthcare System, Roseburg, OR, p. A529

MENZIE, Sue, R.N. Director Patient Care, Sierra Tucson, Tucson, AZ, p. A40

MERCADO, Gloria, Director of Nursing, Mennonite General Hospital, Aibonito, PR, p. A724

MERCADO, Leda Marta R, Chief Operating Officer, Hospital Menonita De Cayey, Cayey, PR, p. A725

MERCER, David, Coordinator Information Systems, Baptist Memorial Hospital–Union City, Union City, TN, p. A594

MERCER, Shawna, Director Human Resources, Kansas Neurological Institute, Topeka, KS, p. A255

MERCER, William, M.D. Director, Peterson Rehabilitation Hospital, Wheeling, WV, p. A700

MERCHANT, Deven, M.D. Chief Medical Executive, Sutter Davis Hospital, Davis, CA, p. A61

MERCIECA, Rita, R.N., Executive Director, Forest Hills Hospital,, NY, p. A443

MERCURI, Ralph, Vice President and Chief Financial Officer, Major Hospital, Shelbyville, IN, p. A222

MEREDITH, James, M.D. Chief of Staff, Forrest City Medical Center, Forrest City, AR, p. A46

MEREDITH, Katie, Chief Nursing Officer, Select Specialty Hospital–Lexington, Lexington, KY, p. A264

MEREDITH, Keith, Chief Operating Officer, Salem Regional Medical Center, Salem, OH, p. A501

MEREDITH, Linda, MSN Chief Operating Officer, Scott & White Hospital – Llano, Llano, TX, p. A633

MEREDITH, Stephen L., Interim Chief Executive Officer, Muhlenberg Community Hospital, Greenville, KY, p. A262

MEREK, Gloria, Director of Nursing, Springfield Hospital Center, Sykesville, MD, p. A303

MERGEN, Lynn M., Chief Executive Officer, Mineral Area Regional Medical Center, Farmington, MO, p. A371

MERIDA, Andy, Director Management Information Systems, Fayette Regional Health System, Connersville, IN, p. A208

MERILL, Doug, M.D. Chief Medical Officer, UC Irvine Medical Center, Orange, CA, p. A81

MERILLO, Myra, Supervisor Health Information Management, HEALTHSOUTH Rehabilitation Hospital of Spring Hill, Brooksville, FL, p. A125

MERIWETHER, Wayne, Chief Executive Officer, Twin Lakes Regional Medical Center, Leitchfield, KY, p. A264

MERK, Richard, Executive Vice President, Allegiance Behavioral Health Center of Plainview, Plainview, TX, p. A642

MERKEL, Earl, M.D. Chief of Staff, Russell Regional Hospital, Russell, KS, p. A253

MERKLE, Greg, Director Information Systems, Sheppard Pratt Health System, Baltimore, MD, p. A297

MERKLE, John, Deputy Director, Louis Stokes Cleveland Veterans Affairs Medical Center, Cleveland, OH, p. A488

MERKLE, Scott, Chief Financial Officer, Fishermen's Hospital, Marathon, FL, p. A135

MERKLEY, Jason R., Chief Executive Officer, Brookings Health System, Brookings, SD, p. A572

MERLI, Geno, M.D. Chief Medical Officer, Thomas Jefferson University Hospital, Philadelphia, PA, p. A550

MERLIS, Laurence M., President and Chief Executive Officer, Abington Health, Abington, PA, p. B4

MERLIS, Laurence M., President and Chief Executive Officer, Abington Memorial Hospital, Abington, PA, p. A532

MERRED, Mehdi, Chief Executive Officer, Quincy Valley Medical Center, Quincy, WA, p. A687

MERRELL, Angie K., R.N. Chief Nursing Officer, Navarro Regional Hospital, Corsicana, TX, p. A608

MERRELL, Bruce, FACHE, President, St. Mary's Hospital, Centralia, IL, p. A182

MERRENS, Edward J., M.D. Medical Director, Dartmouth–Hitchcock Medical Center, Lebanon, NH, p. A411

MERRIGAN, Mary C., Manager Public Relations, Sanford Vermillion Medical Center, Vermillion, SD, p. A577

MERRILL, Chuck, M.D. Vice President Medical Affairs, Marian Regional Medical Center, Santa Maria, CA, p. A94

MERRILL, Mark H., President and Chief Executive Officer, Valley Health System, Winchester, VA, p. B148

MERRILL, Mark H., President, Winchester Medical Center, Winchester, VA, p. A680

MERRILL, Michael, M.D. Interim Vice President Medical Affairs, United Memorial Medical Center, Batavia, NY, p. A433

MERRILL, Rick W., President and Chief Executive Officer, Cook Children's Medical Center, Fort Worth, TX, p. A618

MERRILL, Stacie, Chief Nursing Officer, Baylor Surgical Hospital at Fort Worth, Fort Worth, TX, p. A618

MERRILL, Stephanie, Chief Financial Officer, University Medical Center, Las Vegas, NV, p. A407

MERRITT, Becky A., Director Human Resources, Houston Methodist St. John Hospital, Nassau Bay, TX, p. A639

MERRITT, Belinda, M.D. Medical Director, HEALTHSOUTH Cane Creek Rehabilitation Hospital, Martin, TN, p. A587

MERRITT, Bradley, M.D. Medical Director, Trinity Mother Frances Rehabilitation Hospital, Tyler, TX, p. A654

MERRITT, Janet, Chief Financial Officer, St. Vincent Williamsport Hospital, Williamsport, IN, p. A224

MERRITT, Trevor, Director Human Resources, Star Valley Medical Center, Afton, WY, p. A720

MERRY, Duane, Chief Information Officer, Little Falls Hospital, Little Falls, NY, p. A440

MERRYMAN, Mary, Regional Director Information Management, CHRISTUS Highland Medical Center, Shreveport, LA, p. A288

MERRYMAN, Scott
Chief Financial Officer, CHRISTUS Coushatta Health Care Center, Coushatta, LA, p. A275
Chief Financial Officer, CHRISTUS Highland Medical Center, Shreveport, LA, p. A288

MERRYWELL, Paul, Chief Information Officer, Sycamore Shoals Hospital, Elizabethton, TN, p. A582

MERSON, Wendy, Chief Executive Officer, Windmoor Healthcare of Clearwater, Clearwater, FL, p. A125

MERTZ, John, Chief Information Officer, South Nassau Communities Hospital, Oceanside, NY, p. A450

MERWIN, Robert W., Chief Executive Officer, Mills–Peninsula Health Services, Burlingame, CA, p. A58

MESA, Gustavo, Chief Information Officer, San Juan City Hospital, San Juan, PR, p. A729

MESIC, John, M.D. Chief Medical Officer, Sutter Auburn Faith Hospital, Auburn, CA, p. A56

MESKAN, Paula, Director of Nursing, River's Edge Hospital and Clinic, Saint Peter, MN, p. A352

MESORAS, Amber, Chief Human Resources Officer, Veterans Affairs Pittsburgh Healthcare System, Pittsburgh, PA, p. A552

MESSELT, Mary Jo
Senior Human Resources Manager, Mercy Hospital Logan County, Guthrie, OK, p. A511
Manager Human Resources, Mercy Hospital Watonga, Watonga, OK, p. A522

MESSER, Kelly, Director Administrative Services, Devereux Hospital and Children's Center of Florida, Melbourne, FL, p. A135

MESSERSMITH, Darrell, Director Information Systems, Platte Valley Medical Center, Brighton, CO, p. A103

MESSERSMITH, Scott E., Director Human Resources, Columbus Community Hospital, Columbus, NE, p. A395

MESSINA, Arlene, R.N. Director of Nursing, Riverside Doctors' Hospital, Williamsburg, VA, p. A680

MESSINA, Daniel J., FACHE, President and Chief Executive Officer, Richmond University Medical Center,, NY, p. A448

MESTAS, Lisa, Chief Nursing Officer and Assistant Administrator Clinical Services, University of South Alabama Medical Center, Mobile, AL, p. A23

MESTER, Sulynn, R.N. Chief Nursing Officer, Childress Regional Medical Center, Childress, TX, p. A606

MESZLER, Lori A., Chief Financial Officer, Helen Hayes Hospital, West Haverstraw, NY, p. A457

METCALF, Angie L., Vice President and Chief Human Resource Officer, Martin Health System, Stuart, FL, p. A146

METCALF, Chris, Director of Nursing, Utah State Hospital, Provo, UT, p. A662

METCALF, Emma, R.N., Director, Veterans Affairs Medical Center–Lexington, Lexington, KY, p. A265

METCALF, Kathleen, Chief Information Officer, Samaritan Regional Health System, Ashland, OH, p. A482

METCALF, Peter, M.D. President Medical Staff, Genesis Medical Center, Illini Campus, Silvis, IL, p. A202

METCALFE, Kevan, Chief Executive Officer, San Dimas Community Hospital, San Dimas, CA, p. A90

METHE, Joan, Chief Information Officer, Mercy Medical Center, Springfield, MA, p. A315

METHVEN, Jeffrey M., Vice President Ambulatory Services and Chief Human Resources Officer, Saratoga Hospital, Saratoga Springs, NY, p. A454

METHVIN, Jeff, Manager Information Technology, St. Luke Hospital and Living Center, Marion, KS, p. A249

METIKO, Olushola, M.D. Medical Director, Central Prison Hospital, Raleigh, NC, p. A470

METIVIER, Roberta, Vice President Human Resources and Administrator, Western Main Nursing Home, Stephens Memorial Hospital, Norway, ME, p. A294

METRO, Michelle, Vice President Nursing, Cloud County Health Center, Concordia, KS, p. A242

METTEAUER, Ken, Chief Financial Officer, Redmond Regional Medical Center, Rome, GA, p. A165

METZ, Amy, Chief Executive Officer, Regency Hospital of Florence, Florence, SC, p. A566

METZ, Bruce, Ph.D. Senior Vice President and Chief Information Officer, Lahey Hospital & Medical Center, Burlington, Burlington, MA, p. A308

METZ, Carl, Vice President Human Resources, Ephraim McDowell Regional Medical Center, Danville, KY, p. A260

METZ, Karen, Chief Executive Officer, Tennova Physicians Regional Medical Center, Knoxville, TN, p. A586

METZGER, Alysha, Director Human Resources, Hill Country Memorial Hospital, Fredericksburg, TX, p. A619

METZGER, Cynthia, Chief Nursing and Operations Officer, Little River Memorial Hospital, Ashdown, AR, p. A43

METZGER, Jane, Ph.D. Chief Nursing Officer, Morton Hospital and Medical Center, Taunton, MA, p. A315

METZGER, John, Controller, NorthKey Community Care, Covington, KY, p. A260

METZING, Michael J., Vice President Corporate Services, Bayhealth Medical Center, Dover, DE, p. A119

MEUER, Lynn, Interim Chief Nursing Officer, Sibley Memorial Hospital, Washington, DC, p. A122

MEURER, Bryan, Director Information Systems, Mat–Su Regional Medical Center, Palmer, AK, p. A30

MEWHIRTER, Michael, Chief Financial Officer, Florida Hospital North Pinellas, Tarpon Springs, FL, p. A148

MEYER, Anthony, M.D. Medical Director, Aurora Psychiatric Hospital, Wauwatosa, WI, p. A718

MEYER, Cameron, Chief Financial Officer, Thayer County Health Services, Hebron, NE, p. A396

MEYER, Cheryl, MSN Director of Nursing, Haven Behavioral Senior Care of Dayton, Dayton, OH, p. A492

MEYER, Cheryl, Director Human Resources, Palmer Lutheran Health Center, West Union, IA, p. A239

MEYER, Cynthia A., Chief Executive Officer, Dominion Hospital, Falls Church, VA, p. A670

MEYER, Daniel T., President, Aurora BayCare Medical Center, Green Bay, WI, p. A705

MEYER, Eugene W., President and Chief Executive Officer, Lawrence Memorial Hospital, Lawrence, KS, p. A248

MEYER, Francis, Vice President Information Systems Technology, KALEIDA Health, Buffalo, NY, p. A434

MEYER, Gary, M.D. Chief of Staff, Grand River Hospital District, Rifle, CO, p. A111

MEYER, Gary A., President and Chief Executive Officer, Schneck Medical Center, Seymour, IN, p. A222

MEYER, Gerrie, Director Human Resources, Great Bend Regional Hospital, Great Bend, KS, p. A244

MEYER, Gordon, Director Human Resources, Oakland Regional Hospital, Southfield, MI, p. A335

MEYER, Joe S., Chief Financial Officer, Scott County Hospital, Scott City, KS, p. A254

MEYER, June, MSN Vice President Chief Nursing Officer, Laurel Regional Hospital, Laurel, MD, p. A302

MEYER, Karen, Vice President Finance and Chief Financial Officer, Rush Memorial Hospital, Rushville, IN, p. A222

MEYER, Kris, R.N. Director of Nursing, Pawnee County Memorial Hospital and Rural Health Clinic, Pawnee City, NE, p. A401

MEYER, Kurt A.
Chief Human Resource Officer, Saint Joseph Regional Medical Center, Mishawaka, IN, p. A219
Chief Human Resources Officer, Saint Joseph Regional Medical Center–Plymouth Campus, Plymouth, IN, p. A221

MEYER, Lori, Interim Chief Financial Officer, South Peninsula Hospital, Homer, AK, p. A29

MEYER, Mark, Chief Financial Officer, Grady Memorial Hospital, Atlanta, GA, p. A152

MEYER, Nate, Director Finance, Douglas County Hospital, Alexandria, MN, p. A339

MEYER, Philip A., Vice President, Finance, Dearborn County Hospital, Lawrenceburg, IN, p. A217

MEYER, Richard A., Chief Financial Officer, Mary Black Memorial Hospital, Spartanburg, SC, p. A570

MEYER, Robert L., President and Chief Executive Officer, Phoenix Chiidren's Hospital, Phoenix, AZ, p. A36

MEYER, Roger, M.D. Chief of Staff, Warren Memorial Hospital, Friend, NE, p. A395

MEYER, Timothy, M.D. Chief of Staff, Memorial Medical Center – Neillsville, Neillsville, WI, p. A712

MEYER, Traci, Director Human Resources and Public Relations Officer, Sierra Vista Regional Health Center, Sierra Vista, AZ, p. A39

MEYER, Wessel, M.D., Acting Director, Veterans Affairs Central California Health Care System, Fresno, CA, p. A64

MEYERHOEFER, Todd, M.D. Vice President Medical Affairs, Union Hospital, Dover, OH, p. A493

MEYERS, Ann M., Hospital Administrator, Mayo Clinic Hospital, Phoenix, AZ, p. A36

MEYERS, Audrey, FACHE, President and Chief Executive Officer, Valley Hospital, Ridgewood, NJ, p. A422

MEYERS, Betty, Chief Financial Officer, Crook County Medical Services District, Sundance, WY, p. A723

MEYERS, Larry, Chief Information Officer, Wilson Memorial Hospital, Sidney, OH, p. A502

MEYERS, Mark S., M.D. Chief of Staff, Battle Mountain General Hospital, Battle Mountain, NV, p. A404

MEYERS, Russell, President and Chief Executive Officer, Midland Memorial Hospital, Midland, TX, p. A638

MEYERS, Steve, Interim Chief Executive Officer, New York Community Hospital,, NY, p. A447

MEYERS, William, Chief Information Officer, St. Luke's Hospital, Chesterfield, MO, p. A369

MEZA, Eduardo, M.D. Medical Director, Prairie St. John's, Fargo, ND, p. A477

MEZA, Lourdes, Coordinator Human Resources, Doctors Hospital of West Covina, West Covina, CA, p. A100

MEZOFF, Adam, M.D. Vice President and Chief Medical Officer, Children's Medical Center, Dayton, OH, p. A491

MEZOFF, John, M.D. Chief Medical Officer, Rehoboth McKinley Christian Health Care Services, Gallup, NM, p. A428

MEZZA, Nicholas, Director of Finance, LifeCare Hospitals of Mechanicsburg, Mechanicsburg, PA, p. A545

MHERABI, Nader, Senior Vice President and Vice Dean, Chief Information Officer, NYU Langone Medical Center, New York, NY, p. A448

MIANO, Christena, Human Resources Director, Medical Center of Trinity, Trinity, FL, p. A149

MIAO, Winjie Tang, President, Texas Health Harris Methodist Hospital Alliance, Fort Worth, TX, p. A619

MICCOLI, Vinny, Executive Director, Manhattan Psychiatric Center–Ward's Island, New York, NY, p. A445

MICELI, Charlie, Interim Chief Executive Officer, Moses Ludington Hospital, Ticonderoga, NY, p. A456

MICHAEL, Amy J., Chief Operating Officer, Sullivan County Memorial Hospital, Milan, MO, p. A377

MICHAEL, Don, Chief Financial Officer, Jay County Hospital, Portland, IN, p. A221

MICHAEL, Elizabeth, R.N. Vice President Patient Care Services and Chief Nursing Officer, Stillwater Medical Center, Stillwater, OK, p. A519

MICHAEL, Lois, Vice President Human Resources, Torrance Memorial Medical Center, Torrance, CA, p. A97

MICHAELS, Bonnie, R.N. Vice President and Chief Nursing Officer, Hackensack University Medical Center Mountainside, Montclair, NJ, p. A418

MICHAELSON, Linda, Director Human Resources, Lake District Hospital, Lakeview, OR, p. A526

MICHALEK, Debra, Chief Financial Officer, Fayette Regional Health System, Connersville, IN, p. A208

MICHALSKI, Carrie, President and Chief Executive Officer, RiverView Health, Crookston, MN, p. A342

MICHALSKI, Gene, President and Chief Executive Officer, Beaumont Health System, Royal Oak, MI, p. B23

MICHALSKI, Gene, Executive Vice President and Chief Operating Officer, Beaumont Hospital – Royal Oak, Royal Oak, MI, p. A333

MICHAUD, Thomas A., Chief Executive Officer, Foundation Surgical Hospital Affiliates, Oklahoma City, OK, p. B59

MICHEL, Diane, Vice President Nursing, Children's Hospital, New Orleans, LA, p. A285

MICHEL, George J., Chief Operating Officer, Larkin Community Hospital, South Miami, FL, p. A146

MICHEL, Linda, Administrator, North Valley Hospital, Tonasket, WA, p. A691

MICHEL, Randall, M.D. Chief of Staff, Lompoc Valley Medical Center, Lompoc, CA, p. A70

MICHEL–OGBORN, Deborah, Chief Information Resource Management, Malcom Randall Veterans Affairs Medical Center, Gainesville, FL, p. A129

MICHELE, Margorie, Chief Human Resources Officer, Penn Presbyterian Medical Center, Philadelphia, PA, p. A549

MICHELEN, Jeannith
Associate Executive Director, Elmhurst Hospital Center,, NY, p. A443
Senior Associate Executive Director, Lincoln Medical and Mental Health Center,, NY, p. A445
Senior Associate Executive Director, Queens Hospital Center,, NY, p. A448

MICHELETTI, Denise D., R.N., Director, Central Virginia Training Center, Madison Heights, VA, p. A673

MICHELETTI, Susan C., Chief Executive Officer, Emanuel Medical Center, Turlock, CA, p. A98

MICHELL, Pamela W., R.N. Vice President, Chief Nursing Officer, Munroe Regional Medical Center, Ocala, FL, p. A139

MICHL, Michelle, Director Human Resources, Mercy Medical Center Mount Shasta, Mount Shasta, CA, p. A79

MICINSKI, Bob, Chief Executive Officer, Middle Tennessee Mental Health Institute, Nashville, TN, p. A590

MICKENS, Walt, FACHE, President and Chief Executive Officer, Queen of the Valley Medical Center, Napa, CA, p. A79

MICKEY, Lauren Jane, M.D. Chief of Staff, P & S Surgical Hospital, Monroe, LA, p. A284

MICKIEWICZ, Nanette, M.D., President, Dominican Hospital, Santa Cruz, CA, p. A94

MIDDENDORF, Bruce, M.D. Chief Medical Officer, St. Mary's Health Care System, Athens, GA, p. A151

MIDDLEBROOKS, Mark, M.D. Medical Director, Noland Hospital Birmingham, Birmingham, AL, p. A16

MIDDLETON, Frank, M.D. Interim Chief Medical Officer, Phoebe Putney Memorial Hospital, Albany, GA, p. A151

MIDDLETON, Jackie, Vice President Human Resources, Methodist Dallas Medical Center, Dallas, TX, p. A611

MIDKIFF, Rodney, Chief Executive Officer, AMG Specialty Hospital – Muncie, Muncie, IN, p. A219

MIDKIFF, Stephen L., Chief Executive Officer, Lake Norman Regional Medical Center, Mooresville, NC, p. A469

MIEDLER, Michael, M.D. Chief Medical Officer, Continuing Care Hospital, Lexington, KY, p. A264

MIER, David, Chief Financial Officer, El Paso Children's Hospital, El Paso, TX, p. A615

MIESNER, Gail, Chief Financial Officer, Memorial Hospital, Chester, IL, p. A183

MIGOYA, Carlos A., President and Chief Executive Officer, Jackson Health System, Miami, FL, p. A137

MIHAL, Denise B., R.N., Chief Executive Officer, Novant Health Forsyth Medical Center, Winston–Salem, NC, p. A475

MIHALAKAKOS, Paul, M.D. Chief of Staff, Aurora Medical Center – Manitowoc County, Two Rivers, WI, p. A716

MIKELL, Jeffrey, M.D. Chief Medical Officer, Select Specialty Hospital – Northeast Atlanta, Atlanta, GA, p. A153

MIKES, James, Administrator, Heartland Long Term Acute Care Hospital, Saint Joseph, MO, p. A379

MIKHAIL, Ashraf, M.D. Medical Director, Brynn Marr Hospital, Jacksonville, NC, p. A467

MIKI, Nobuyuki, M.D. Vice President Medical Services and Chief Medical Officer, Kuakini Medical Center, Honolulu, HI, p. A170

MIKITARIAN Jr., George, Chief Executive Officer, Parrish Medical Center, Titusville, FL, p. A149

MIKITKA, Joseph, Vice President Human Resources, Sacred Heart Hospital, Allentown, PA, p. A532

MIKKELSON, Tom, M.D. Interim Chief Operating Officer, Touchette Regional Hospitals, Centreville, IL, p. A183

MIKLAVIC, Kirk
Director Human Resources, Bridgton Hospital, Bridgton, ME, p. A292
Director, Human Resources, Central Maine Medical Center, Lewiston, ME, p. A293

MIKLOS, Maggie, Director Human Resources, Northside Hospital, Saint Petersburg, FL, p. A144

MIKULIC, Jeannie, Director Human Resources, Providence Portland Medical Center, Portland, OR, p. A528

MIKUTOWSKI, Melody, Chief Human Resources Management, Portland Veterans Affairs Medical Center, Portland, OR, p. A528

MILAM, Wendy, Chief Nursing Officer, HEALTHSOUTH Rehabilitation Hospital of Ocala, Ocala, FL, p. A139

MILAN, Isabel, R.N. Chief Nursing Officer, LAC/University of Southern California Medical Center, Los Angeles, CA, p. A73

MILAND, Shelly, Vice President Finance and Chief Financial Officer, Texas Health Harris Methodist Hospital Hurst–Euless–Bedford, Bedford, TX, p. A602

MILANES, Carlos, Chief Executive Officer and Managing Director, Aiken Regional Medical Centers, Aiken, SC, p. A562

MILANO, Arthur D., Vice President Human Resources, Berkshire Medical Center, Pittsfield, MA, p. A313

MILATOVICH, Natasha, Association Vice President Human Resources, White Memorial Medical Center, Los Angeles, CA, p. A75

MILAZZO, John, Chief Financial Officer, River Region Medical Center, Vicksburg, MS, p. A366

MILBRANDT, David, M.D. Vice President Medical Affairs, Fairview Lakes Health Services, Wyoming, MN, p. A354

MILBRIDGE, Daniel, Administrator and Chief Operating Officer, Essentia Health–Virginia, Virginia, MN, p. A353

MILBURN, Sandra, Director Human Resources, HEALTHSOUTH Rehabilitation Hospital of Memphis, Memphis, TN, p. A588

MILBURN, Sharon, Chief Nursing Officer, Summers County ARH Hospital, Hinton, WV, p. A695

MILES, Ben, Chief Operating Officer, Parkview Regional Medical Center, Fort Wayne, IN, p. A211

MILES, David K., President and Chief Executive Officer, The Children's Institute of Pittsburgh, Pittsburgh, PA, p. A551

MILES, John, Chief Financial Officer, Piedmont Newnan Hospital, Newnan, GA, p. A164

MILES, Kerry
Site Director, Providence Centralia Hospital, Centralia, WA, p. A682
Chief Information Officer, Providence St. Peter Hospital, Olympia, WA, p. A686

MILES, Paul V.
Interim Community Chief Executive Officer, Harlan ARH Hospital, Harlan, KY, p. A262
Chief Operating Officer, Morgan County ARH Hospital, West Liberty, KY, p. A271
Vice President Administration, Whitesburg ARH Hospital, Whitesburg, KY, p. A271

MILES, Senta, Director Human Resources, Medical Center of McKinney, McKinney, TX, p. A637

MILETO, Dottie, Chief Nursing Officer, Heart of Florida Regional Medical Center, Davenport, FL, p. A127

MILEY, Dennis C., Administrator, CentraCare Health–Paynesville, Paynesville, MN, p. A349

MILIAN, Tony, Chief Financial Officer, Palm Springs General Hospital, Hialeah, FL, p. A130

MILICEVIC, Heather, Director Human Resources, Summa Western Reserve Hospital, Cuyahoga Falls, OH, p. A491

MILIUS, Hank A., Chief Executive Officer, Meridian Health Services, Muncie, IN, p. A219

MILLAN, Wilfredo Rabelo, Chief Operating Officer, Cardiovascular Center of Puerto Rico and the Caribbean, San Juan, PR, p. A728

MILLARD, James M., President and Chief Executive Officer, Kenmore Mercy Hospital, Kenmore, NY, p. A439

MILLEN, Peter S., Chief Medical Officer MHSATS, Community Behavioral Health Hospital – Rochester, Rochester, MN, p. A350

MILLER, Alan B., Chairman and Chief Executive Officer, Universal Health Services, Inc., King of Prussia, PA, p. B140

MILLER, Alicia, Director Human Resources, Aspen Valley Hospital District, Aspen, CO, p. A102

MILLER, Andy, Chief Financial Officer, Memorial Hospital Jacksonville, Jacksonville, FL, p. A131

MILLER, Barbara, Manager Business Office, Regional General Hospital, Williston, FL, p. A150

MILLER, Blaine K., Administrator, Republic County Hospital, Belleville, KS, p. A241

MILLER, Brent R., Manager Human Resources, Brown County Community Treatment Center, Green Bay, WI, p. A706

MILLER, Carol R., R.N. Chief Nursing Officer, Reynolds Memorial Hospital, Glen Dale, WV, p. A695

MILLER, Carrie, Director Human Resources, ProMedica Defiance Regional Hospital, Defiance, OH, p. A492

MILLER, Chad, Chief Financial Officer, Bolivar Medical Center, Cleveland, MS, p. A357

MILLER, Charles F., Chief Executive Officer, Regional Hospital of Jackson, Jackson, TN, p. A584

MILLER, Christine
Vice President Human Resources, Hanover Hospital, Hanover, PA, p. A540
Chief Human Resources Management Services, Maine Veterans Affairs Medical Center, Augusta, ME, p. A291

MILLER, Connie, Vice President Human Resources, Overland Park Regional Medical Center, Overland Park, KS, p. A252

MILLER, Daniel
Chief Operating Officer, Swedish Medical Center, Englewood, CO, p. A106
Vice President Human Resources, University Hospitals Elyria Medical Center, Elyria, OH, p. A493
Vice President Human Resources, University Hospitals Parma Medical Center, Parma, OH, p. A500

MILLER, David, Chief Financial Officer, Sturgis Hospital, Sturgis, MI, p. A335

MILLER, David L., Chief Information Officer, UAMS Medical Center, Little Rock, AR, p. A49

MILLER, David R., President, River Falls Area Hospital, River Falls, WI, p. A714

MILLER, David T., Vice President and Chief Financial Officer, Children's Medical Center, Dayton, OH, p. A491

MILLER, Debra, Administrator, Crosbyton Clinic Hospital, Crosbyton, TX, p. A609

MILLER, Denise K., M.D. Chief Medical Officer, Menorah Medical Center, Overland Park, KS, p. A252

MILLER, Derek, Senior Vice President and Chief Financial Officer, Southeast Alabama Medical Center, Dothan, AL, p. A19

MILLER, Dionne, Chief Operating Officer, Sutter Roseville Medical Center, Roseville, CA, p. A87

MILLER, Duane
Chief Financial Officer, Integris Bass Baptist Health Center, Enid, OK, p. A510
Chief Financial Officer, Integris Bass Pavilion, Enid, OK, p. A510

MILLER, Eileen, Director Human Resources, Northern Dutchess Hospital, Rhinebeck, NY, p. A452

MILLER, Elaine G., Director of Nursing, Oaklawn Psychiatric Center, Goshen, IN, p. A212

MILLER, Elizabeth, CPA Chief Financial Officer, Stamford Memorial Hospital, Stamford, TX, p. A650

MILLER, Gary L.
Senior Director Information Systems, Saint Joseph Regional Medical Center, Mishawaka, IN, p. A219
Regional Director Information Systems, Saint Joseph Regional Medical Center–Plymouth Campus, Plymouth, IN, p. A221

MILLER, Gary P., President and Chief Executive Officer, St. Alexius Medical Center, Bismarck, ND, p. A476

MILLER, Gene, Chief Executive Officer, Northeastern Nevada Regional Hospital, Elko, NV, p. A404

MILLER, Greg, Senior Vice President Operations, UF Health Jacksonville, Jacksonville, FL, p. A132

MILLER, Harvey, Director, G. Werber Bryan Psychiatric Hospital, Columbia, SC, p. A564

MILLER, Heidi, Chief Executive Officer, Kindred Hospital Arizona–Phoenix, Phoenix, AZ, p. A36

MILLER, J. D., M.D
Chief Medical Officer, Hazard ARH Regional Medical Center, Hazard, KY, p. A262
Vice President Medical Affairs, Morgan County ARH Hospital, West Liberty, KY, p. A271
Vice President Medical Affairs, Williamson ARH Hospital, South Williamson, KY, p. A270

MILLER, J. Todd, Vice President and Chief Operating Officer, Alice Peck Day Memorial Hospital, Lebanon, NH, p. A410

MILLER, James, Interim Chief Executive Officer, Alliance Health Center, Meridian, MS, p. A362

MILLER, James, CPA Chief Financial Officer, Regional Medical Center of Acadiana, Lafayette, LA, p. A282

MILLER, James L., D.O. Chief of Staff, Bates County Memorial Hospital, Butler, MO, p. A368

MILLER, James L., Chief Financial Officer, King's Daughters Hospital, Yazoo City, MS, p. A366

MILLER, Jane E., Human Resources Officer, Avera Sacred Heart Hospital, Yankton, SD, p. A578

MILLER, Jason, Interim Chief Executive Officer, The BridgeWay, North Little Rock, AR, p. A51

MILLER, Jeff, Chief Operating Officer, Citizens Memorial Hospital, Bolivar, MO, p. A367

MILLER, Jeff, M.D. Chief of Staff, Wabash County Hospital, Wabash, IN, p. A224

MILLER, Jeri, M.D. President Medical Staff, Fairview Park Hospital, Dublin, GA, p. A159

MILLER, John, Director Human Resources, Day Kimball Hospital, Putnam, CT, p. A116

MILLER Jr., John A., FACHE, Chief Executive Officer, AnMed Health Medical Center, Anderson, SC, p. A562

MILLER Jr.,, John A., FACHE, Chief Executive Officer, AnMed Health, Anderson, SC, p. B10

MILLER, Jon, Director Accounting and Information Services, Hancock Regional Hospital, Greenfield, IN, p. A212

MILLER, Joshua, Director Information Systems, Joint Township District Memorial Hospital, Saint Marys, OH, p. A501

MILLER, Joy, Chief Nursing Officer, Cornerstone Hospital of North Little Rock, Jacksonville, AR, p. A48

MILLER, Judy, Director Human Resources, Tampa Community Hospital, Tampa, FL, p. A148

MILLER, Julie, Chief Operating Officer, Williamson Medical Center, Franklin, TN, p. A583

MILLER, Kay A., MS Chief Nursing Officer, St. Anthony Hospital, Lakewood, CO, p. A108

MILLER, Ken, Chief Financial Officer, Memorial Medical Center – Livingston, Livingston, TX, p. A633

MILLER, Kevin J., FACHE, President and Chief Executive Officer, Hutchinson Regional Medical Center, Hutchinson, KS, p. A246

MILLER, Kimberly J., FACHE, Chief Executive Officer, Beaver Dam Community Hospitals, Beaver Dam, WI, p. A702

MILLER, Kris, Senior Human Resources Business Partner, Spectrum Health Reed City Hospital, Reed City, MI, p. A333

MILLER, Laura L., MSN Chief Nursing Officer, Lakeway Regional Medical Center, Lakeway, TX, p. A632

MILLER, Leanne R., Director Human Resources, Community Hospital, McCook, NE, p. A398

MILLER, Lisa, Director Human Resources, Hendry Regional Medical Center, Clewiston, FL, p. A126

MILLER, Lisa, R.N. Director of Nursing, North Sunflower Medical Center, Ruleville, MS, p. A365

MILLER, Mark, Chief Financial Officer, Freeman Regional Health Services, Freeman, SD, p. A574

MILLER, Mark, FACHE Chief Operating Officer, Largo Medical Center, Largo, FL, p. A134

MILLER, Mark, Director Information Systems, Perry County Memorial Hospital, Tell City, IN, p. A222

MILLER, Mark A., FACHE, Chief Executive Officer, Memorial Health System, Abilene, KS, p. A241

MILLER, Marty, Vice President and Chief Information Officer, Children's Hospital Los Angeles, Los Angeles, CA, p. A71

MILLER, Mary, Vice President Finance and Business Development, Mt. Washington Pediatric Hospital, Baltimore, MD, p. A297

MILLER, Mary Beth, M.D. Chief of Staff, Cheyenne County Hospital, Saint Francis, KS, p. A253

MILLER, Mathew, M.D. Vice President and Chief Medical Officer, St. Joseph Hospital, Eureka, CA, p. A62

MILLER, Matthew, M.D. Vice President Medical Affairs, Danbury Hospital, Danbury, CT, p. A113

MILLER, Melissa, Director Human Resources, St. Elizabeth Hospital, Gonzales, LA, p. A278

MILLER, Michael J., Director Human Resources, Progress West Hospital, O'Fallon, MO, p. A378

MILLER, Michele A., R.N. Vice President, Acute and Nursing Services, University Hospital, Piscataway, NJ, p. A421

MILLER, Mike, Director Human Resources, Barnes–Jewish St. Peters Hospital, Saint Peters, MO, p. A382

MILLER, Nancy, Prioress, Benedictine Sisters of the Annunciation, Bismarck, ND, p. B23

MILLER, Nancy, R.N. Chief Nursing Officer, Van Matre HEALTHSOUTH Rehabilitation Hospital, Rockford, IL, p. A202

MILLER, Nicole, Director Human Resources, Riverside Shore Memorial Hospital, Nassawadox, VA, p. A674

MILLER, Patrick, Technology Coordinator, San Bernardino Mountains Community Hospital District, Lake Arrowhead, CA, p. A69

MILLER, Paul, Director of Operations, Sanford Chamberlain Medical Center, Chamberlain, SD, p. A572

MILLER, Phil, Chief Financial Officer, Shelby Memorial Hospital, Shelbyville, IL, p. A202

MILLER, Redonda G., M.D. Vice President Medical Affairs, Johns Hopkins Hospital, Baltimore, MD, p. A296

MILLER, Richard
Administrator Finance, Banner Thunderbird Medical Center, Glendale, AZ, p. A33
Administrator and Chief Executive Officer, Norton County Hospital, Norton, KS, p. A251

MILLER, Richard P., Chief Executive Officer, Virtua Health, Marlton, NJ, p. B150

MILLER, Rick
Chief Financial Officer, District One Hospital, Faribault, MN, p. A343
President and Chief Operating Officer, Nationwide Children's Hospital, Columbus, OH, p. A490

MILLER, Rip, Chief Executive Officer, The Hospital at Westlake Medical Center, Austin, TX, p. A600

MILLER, Robert, Chief Executive Officer, Coshocton County Memorial Hospital, Coshocton, OH, p. A491

MILLER, II, Robert R., Chief Operating Officer, Kings County Hospital Center,, NY, p. A444

MILLER, Rod, Chief Information Technology, Community Hospital, Torrington, WY, p. A723

MILLER, Ronald, M.D. Chief Medical Officer, North Valley Hospital, Whitefish, MT, p. A392

MILLER, Sam, Chief Operating Officer, North Sunflower Medical Center, Ruleville, MS, p. A365

MILLER, Scott, Director Information Services, Forrest City Medical Center, Forrest City, AR, p. A46

MILLER, Shane
Chief Information Officer, St. Mary's Hospital Medical Center, Green Bay, WI, p. A706
Chief Information Officer, St. Nicholas Hospital, Sheboygan, WI, p. A715
Chief Information Officer, St. Vincent Hospital, Green Bay, WI, p. A706

MILLER, Stephen R., Chief Executive Officer, Kosciusko Community Hospital, Warsaw, IN, p. A224

MILLER, Steve
Director Information Systems, Baptist Medical Center South, Montgomery, AL, p. A23
Chief Financial Officer, East Texas Medical Center Pittsburg, Pittsburg, TX, p. A642
Chief Information Officer, Oklahoma Heart Hospital, Oklahoma City, OK, p. A516

MILLER, Steven, Chief Financial Officer, Takoma Regional Hospital, Greeneville, TN, p. A583

MILLER, Susan, Financial Administrator, Faulkton Area Medical Center, Faulkton, SD, p. A573

MILLER, Suzanne, R.N. Senior Director Patient Care Services and Nursing, St. Luke's Wood River Medical Center, Ketchum, ID, p. A176

MILLER, Tamara, R.N., Administrator, Madison Community Hospital, Madison, SD, p. A574

MILLER, Ted, Chief Financial Officer, Floyd Memorial Hospital and Health Services, New Albany, IN, p. A220

MILLER, Thomas, M.D
Chief Medical Officer, Cameron Memorial Community Hospital, Angola, IN, p. A206
Medical Director, University of Utah Health Care – Hospital and Clinics, Salt Lake City, UT, p. A663

MILLER, Tim C., M.D. Vice President, Chief Medical Officer and Director Academy Affairs, OSF Saint Francis Medical Center, Peoria, IL, p. A200

MILLER, Tish, Chief Financial Officer, Colusa Regional Medical Center, Colusa, CA, p. A60

MILLER, Trey, Chief Executive Officer, Cambridge Hospital in Houston, Houston, TX, p. A623

MILLER, Valerie L., MSN Director of Nursing, Major Hospital, Shelbyville, IN, p. A222

MILLER, Wanda, R.N. Director of Clinical Services, Asheville Specialty Hospital, Asheville, NC, p. A459

MILLER, William, Coordinator Management Information Systems, Livengrin Foundation, Bensalem, PA, p. A533

MILLER, DNP, Linda, R.N. Senior Vice President Operations and Chief Nursing Officer, Our Lady of Lourdes Memorial Hospital, Inc., Binghamton, NY, p. A433

MILLER–BALFOUR, Pam, Director Human Resources, Socorro General Hospital, Socorro, NM, p. A431

MILLER–CAMPBELL, Michele, Chief Financial Officer, Community Memorial Hospital, Oconto Falls, WI, p. A712

MILLER–COLLETTE, Melody M., Director Human Resources, North Okaloosa Medical Center, Crestview, FL, p. A126

MILLER–PHIPPS, Julie K., Senior Vice President and Executive Director, Kaiser Permanente Orange County Anaheim Medical Center, Anaheim, CA, p. A55

MILLERMAIER, Ed, M.D
Chief Medical Officer, Bellin Memorial Hospital, Green Bay, WI, p. A705
Chief Medical Officer, Bellin Psychiatric Center, Green Bay, WI, p. A706

MILLIGAN, Jan, Chief Executive Officer, Cook Children's Northeast Hospital, Hurst, TX, p. A629

MILLIGAN, Jeffrey, Director, Veterans Affairs North Texas Health Care System, Dallas, TX, p. A612

MILLIS, David, M.D. Clinical Director, Thomas B. Finan Center, Cumberland, MD, p. A300

MILLS, Bryan A., President and Chief Executive Officer, Community Health Network, Indianapolis, IN, p. B36

MILLS, Craig
Chief Financial Officer, Heber Valley Medical Center, Heber City, UT, p. A660
Senior Financial Advisor, Park City Medical Center, Park City, UT, p. A662
Regional Vice President Culture and People, PeaceHealth Sacred Heart Medical Center at RiverBend, Springfield, OR, p. A530
Vice President Human Resources, PeaceHealth Sacred Heart Medical Center, University District, Eugene, OR, p. A524

MILLS, Dennis, Director Human Resources, San Ramon Regional Medical Center, San Ramon, CA, p. A93

MILLS, Gene, Director Information Technology, Scenic Mountain Medical Center, Big Spring, TX, p. A603

MILLS, Jim, Regional Director Information Technology, Sutter Medical Center, Sacramento, Sacramento, CA, p. A88

MILLS, John C., Senior Vice President Operations, Fairview Hospital, Cleveland, OH, p. A488

MILLS, John E.H., President and Chief Executive Officer, United Medical Healthwest–New Orleans, Gretna, LA, p. A278

MILLS, John E.H., President & Chief Executive Officer, United Medical Rehabilitation Hospitals, Gretna, LA, p. B139

MILLS, Marianne, R.N. Chairperson, Stanton County Hospital, Johnson, KS, p. A246

MILLS, Nikki, Director Human Resources and Operations, Buffalo Hospital, Buffalo, MN, p. A341

MILLS, Scott, M.D. Vice President Medical Staff Administration and Chief Medical Officer, Mid Coast Hospital, Brunswick, ME, p. A292

MILLS, Sean, Chief Financial Officer, Samaritan Medical Center, Watertown, NY, p. A457

MILLS, Stephen S., President and Chief Executive Officer, New York Hospital Queens,, NY, p. A447

MILLS, Toni, Interim Chief Executive Officer, Dubuis Health System, Houston, TX, p. B54

MILLS, Vicki L., Chief Financial Officer, Anderson County Hospital, Garnett, KS, p. A244

MILLS, William, M.D
Senior Vice President Quality and Professional Affairs, Bradford Regional Medical Center, Bradford, PA, p. A534
Senior Vice President Quality and Professional Affairs, Olean General Hospital, Olean, NY, p. A450

MILLS, William H., Director, James E. Van Zandt Veterans Affairs Medical Center, Altoona, PA, p. A532

MILLS–MATHEWS, Marcy, Director Human Resources, Palms West Hospital, Loxahatchee, FL, p. A134

MILLSAPS, Janet
Chief Human Resources Officer, Harris Regional Hospital, Sylva, NC, p. A473
Vice President Human Resources, Haywood Regional Medical Center, Clyde, NC, p. A462

MILLSTEAD, Bart, Administrator, Memorial Hospital of Carbondale, Carbondale, IL, p. A182

MILLWOOD, Barbara, Chief Executive Officer, Victory Medical Center Mid–Cities, Hurst, TX, p. A629

MILNE, C. Dean, D.O. Medical Director, Complex Care Hospital at Tenaya, Las Vegas, NV, p. A405

MILNER, Charles, Chief Financial Officer, Dundy County Hospital, Benkelman, NE, p. A394

MILNER, Eve, R.N. Assistant Vice President, Clinical Services, East Alabama Medical Center–Lanier, Valley, AL, p. A26

MILNER, Rene, Chief Medical Officer, Osceola Medical Center, Osceola, WI, p. A712

MILONE, Sheri, Chief Executive Officer and Administrator, Lovelace Women's Hospital, Albuquerque, NM, p. A426

MILOVICH, David, Vice President Human Resources, Saint Mary's Regional Medical Center, Reno, NV, p. A408

MILSTIEN, Kim S., President and Chief Executive Officer, Simi Valley Hospital and Health Care Services, Simi Valley, CA, p. A95

MILTON, Kerry K., R.N. Chief Nursing Officer, St. Tammany Parish Hospital, Covington, LA, p. A276

MILTON, Paul A., Executive Vice President and Chief Operating Officer, Ellis Hospital, Schenectady, NY, p. A454

MILUS, Lori, R.N. Director of Nursing, Aurora Phoenix Hospital, Glendale, AZ, p. A33

MILVET, Jr., Robert W., Chief Financial Officer, Preston Memorial Hospital, Kingwood, WV, p. A696

MIMOSO, Michael, FACHE, President and Chief Executive Officer, Monmouth Medical Center, Southern Campus, Lakewood, NJ, p. A417

MIMS, Staci, Chief Nursing Officer, Dorminy Medical Center, Fitzgerald, GA, p. A159

MIMS, Tammy, Chief Operating Officer, Effingham Hospital, Springfield, GA, p. A167

MINCY, Lowney, Director Information Services, Southside Hospital, Bay Shore, NY, p. A433

MINDEN, Philip, Chief Executive Officer, Bartow Regional Medical Center, Bartow, FL, p. A123

MINDER, Cindy, Coordinator Information Systems, Wagner Community Memorial Hospital Avera, Wagner, SD, p. A578

MINDER, George, Chief Executive Officer, Big Horn County Memorial Hospital, Hardin, MT, p. A388

MINEAR, Michael N., Chief Information Officer, University of California, Davis Medical Center, Sacramento, CA, p. A88

MINER, Edwina A., R.N. Chief Nursing Officer, Ennis Regional Medical Center, Ennis, TX, p. A617

MINER, Greg, Administrator, Siouxland Surgery Center, Dakota Dunes, SD, p. A573

MINER, John, Chief Financial Officer, Kindred Hospital Central Tampa, Tampa, FL, p. A148

MINGLE, Regina, Senior Vice President and Chief Leadership Officer, Lancaster General Health, Lancaster, PA, p. A542

MINGS, William, M.D. Medical Director, Carl Albert Community Mental Health Center, McAlester, OK, p. A513

MINGUS, Linda, Director Human Resources, Aurora Medical Center of Oshkosh, Oshkosh, WI, p. A712

MINICK, Mark J., President and Chief Executive Officer, Van Wert County Hospital, Van Wert, OH, p. A504

MINIER, Mary, Vice President Operations, Indiana University Health White Memorial Hospital, Monticello, IN, p. A219

MINIOR, Devin, M.D. Interim Chief Medical Officer, Banner Goldfield Medical Center, Apache Junction, AZ, p. A31

MINISSALE, Joseph, President, Methodist McKinney Hospital, McKinney, TX, p. A637

MINKS, Mike, Chief Information Officer, Seton Edgar B. Davis Hospital, Luling, TX, p. A636

MINNICK, Peggy, R.N., Chief Executive Officer, BHC Alhambra Hospital, Rosemead, CA, p. A86

MINNIS, Rosanne, Business Officer, Rochester Psychiatric Center, Rochester, NY, p. A453

MINON, Maria, M.D
Vice President Medical Affairs and Chief Medical Officer, Children's Hospital at Mission, Mission Viejo, CA, p. A77
Vice President Medical Affairs and Chief Medical Officer, Children's Hospital of Orange County, Orange, CA, p. A81

MINOR, Amy, Chief Nursing Officer, Troy Regional Medical Center, Troy, AL, p. A26

MINOR, Athena, Chief Nursing Officer, Ohio County Hospital, Hartford, KY, p. A262

MINOR, Beverly, Chief Human Resources, Schleicher County Medical Center, Eldorado, TX, p. A617

MINOR, Blaine, M.D. Chief of Staff, Murray Medical Center, Chatsworth, GA, p. A155

MINOR, Denise, R.N. Chief Nursing Officer, Lutheran Hospital, Cleveland, OH, p. A488

MINSINGER, Linda, Vice President Hospital Division, Gifford Medical Center, Randolph, VT, p. A666

MINTON, Tamra, R.N. Vice President Patient Care Services and Chief Nursing Officer, UPMC East, Monroeville, PA, p. A545

MINTONYE, Traci, Chief Financial Officer, River Hospital, Alexandria Bay, NY, p. A432

MINTZ, Michael, M.D. Chief Medical Officer, South Texas Surgical Hospital, Corpus Christi, TX, p. A608

MIR, Sidney, M.D. Vice President Medical Affairs and Chief Medical Officer, Bon Secours Baltimore Health System, Baltimore, MD, p. A296

MIRABELLA, Ilene, Director Human Resources, New Bedford Rehabilitation Hospital, New Bedford, MA, p. A312

MIRANDA, A. Greg, D.O. President Medical Staff, St. Joseph's Hospital, Highland, IL, p. A192

MIRANDA, Ada S., M.D. Medical Director, Hospital Metropolitano Dr. Susoni, Arecibo, PR, p. A724

MIRANDA, Juliet, Chief Nursing Officer, Tri–City Regional Medical Center, Hawaiian Gardens, CA, p. A66

MIRANDA, Kimberly, Regional Vice President Finance and Chief Financial Officer, Mercy Medical Center Redding, Redding, CA, p. A85

MIRANDA, Michael, Chief of Staff, Booneville Community Hospital, Booneville, AR, p. A44

MIRANDA, Vicki, Vice President Human Resources, Dominican Hospital, Santa Cruz, CA, p. A94

MIRANDA, Victor Hernandez, M.D. Chief of Staff, Mennonite General Hospital, Aibonito, PR, p. A724

MIRDITA, Anthony, Chief Financial Officer, Putnam Hospital Center, Carmel, NY, p. A435

MIRE, Nona, Director Information Systems, Our Lady of Lourdes Regional Medical Center, Lafayette, LA, p. A281

MIRISOLA, Virginia, Fiscal Director, Spaulding Hospital for Continuing Medical Care North Shore, Salem, MA, p. A314

MIRZA, Irfan, Chief Financial Officer, Plantation General Hospital, Plantation, FL, p. A143

MIRZABEGIAN, Edward, Corporate Chief Executive Officer, Avanti Hospitals, El Segundo, CA, p. B17

MISERENDINO, Carole, MS
Chief Nursing Officer, Presence Holy Family Medical Center, Des Plaines, IL, p. A188
Vice President Patient Care Services and Chief Nursing Officer, Presence Our Lady of the Resurrection Medical Center, Chicago, IL, p. A185
Vice President Patient Care Services and Chief Nursing Officer, Presence Resurrection Medical Center, Chicago, IL, p. A185

MISHKIND, Steven, M.D. Chief of Staff, DeSoto Memorial Hospital, Arcadia, FL, p. A123

MISHRA, Sanjeeb, M.D. Chief of Staff, University of Maryland Charles Regional Medical Center, La Plata, MD, p. A302

MISITANO, Anthony F., President and Chief Executive Officer, Post Acute Medical, LLC, Enola, PA, p. B107

MISITI, Joseph, M.D. President Medical Staff, Medina Memorial Hospital, Medina, NY, p. A441

MISKIMEN, Theresa, M.D. Vice President Medical Services, University Hospital, Piscataway, NJ, p. A421

MISKO, Michael, M.D. Medical Officer, Citizens Memorial Hospital, Bolivar, MO, p. A367

MISLAN, Tim, MS Vice President and Chief Nurse Executive, Missouri Baptist Medical Center, Saint Louis, MO, p. A381

MISSERITTI, Colomba, Director Human Resources, Rochester Psychiatric Center, Rochester, NY, p. A453

MISSI, Pamela, R.N. Vice President and Chief Nursing Officer, Columbus Regional Hospital, Columbus, IN, p. A208

MISTRETTA, Mike, Vice President and Chief Information Officer, Kaweah Delta Medical Center, Visalia, CA, p. A99

MITCHAM, Debbie, Chief Financial Officer, Northside Hospital, Atlanta, GA, p. A152

MITCHEL, David M., Chief Executive Officer, Avoyelles Hospital, Marksville, LA, p. A283

MITCHELL, Adonna, Director Fiscal Services, North Mississippi Medical Center–Eupora, Eupora, MS, p. A357

MITCHELL, Andrew J., President and Chief Executive Officer, Peconic Bay Medical Center, Riverhead, NY, p. A452

MITCHELL, Barbara, Senior Vice President Marketing and Human Resources, UW Medicine/Valley Medical Center, Renton, WA, p. A687

MITCHELL, Bill, Administrator, Noland Hospital Anniston, Anniston, AL, p. A15

MITCHELL, Bryan, Director Information Systems, Fairfield Memorial Hospital, Fairfield, IL, p. A190

MITCHELL, Clifton, Manager Human Resources, Southwestern State Hospital, Thomasville, GA, p. A168

MITCHELL, Daniel, President and Chief Executive Officer, Radius Specialty Hospital Boston, Boston, MA, p. A307

MITCHELL, Debbie, Director Human Resources, Woodrow Wilson Rehabilitation Center, Fishersville, VA, p. A671

MITCHELL, Elizabeth C., Vice President and Administrator, Specialty Hospital of Meridian, Meridian, MS, p. A363

MITCHELL, Errol
Chief Financial Officer, INTEGRIS Canadian Valley Hospital, Yukon, OK, p. A522
Vice President, Integris Southwest Medical Center, Oklahoma City, OK, p. A515

MITCHELL, Heath, Chief Operating Officer, Memorial Hospital, Seminole, TX, p. A648

MITCHELL, Ivan, Chief Executive Officer, Towner County Medical Center, Cando, ND, p. A476

MITCHELL III, J. Stuart
Interim Chief Executive Officer, Health First Cape Canaveral Hospital, Cocoa Beach, FL, p. A126
Interim President, Health First Palm Bay Hospital, Melbourne, FL, p. A136
Interim President, Health First Viera Hospital, Melbourne, FL, p. A136

MITCHELL, Jack C., FACHE, Chief Executive Officer, HEALTHSOUTH Rehabilitation Hospital, Fayetteville, AR, p. A45

MITCHELL, Jodie, Facility Financial Director, Sturgis Regional Hospital, Sturgis, SD, p. A577

MITCHELL, John, Assistant Vice President Operations, St. Elizabeth Grant, Williamstown, KY, p. A271

MITCHELL, Joni K., Vice President Nursing, Lakes Regional Healthcare, Spirit Lake, IA, p. A238

MITCHELL, Joseph J., President, Trinity Hospital Twin City, Dennison, OH, p. A493

MITCHELL, Judi, Vice President Administrative Services, Navos, Seattle, WA, p. A688

MITCHELL, Kathy, R.N. Chief Nursing Officer, Doctors Hospital of Sarasota, Sarasota, FL, p. A145

MITCHELL, Kathy
Director Human Resources, Lakeview Medical Center, Rice Lake, WI, p. A714
Chief Nursing Officer, Muhlenberg Community Hospital, Greenville, KY, p. A262

MITCHELL, Kenneth W., M.D. Medical Director, St. David's North Austin Medical Center, Austin, TX, p. A600

MITCHELL, Kent, Chief Financial Officer, Hamilton Memorial Hospital District, McLeansboro, IL, p. A196

MITCHELL, Larry, M.D. Chief of Staff, Clinch Valley Medical Center, Richlands, VA, p. A677

MITCHELL, Lee, Chief Financial Officer, Red River Hospital, Wichita Falls, TX, p. A657

MITCHELL, Lori J., Chief Financial Officer, University of Washington Medical Center, Seattle, WA, p. A689

MITCHELL, Marsha, Director Human Resources, Fleming County Hospital, Flemingsburg, KY, p. A260

MITCHELL, Mary S., Chief Resource Management Services, Birmingham Veterans Affairs Medical Center, Birmingham, AL, p. A16

MITCHELL, Morris, Director Human Resources, Poplar Springs Hospital, Petersburg, VA, p. A676

MITCHELL, Naomi, Director Human Resources, Kentucky River Medical Center, Jackson, KY, p. A263

MITCHELL, Perry, M.D. Chief of Staff, Little Colorado Medical Center, Winslow, AZ, p. A41

MITCHELL, Rebekah, Chief Financial Officer, Madison County Health Care System, Winterset, IA, p. A240

MITCHELL, Richard R., Director Information Technology, Eagleville Hospital, Eagleville, PA, p. A537

MITCHELL, Sarah, Director Finance, Mary S Harper Geriatric Psychiatry Center, Tuscaloosa, AL, p. A26

MITCHELL, Steve, Chief Operating Officer, Memorial Medical Center, Modesto, CA, p. A78

MITCHELL, Susan
System Executive Vice President Human Resources, Edward Hospital, Naperville, IL, p. A197
Senior Vice President Human Resources, Elmhurst Memorial Hospital,, IL, p. A189
Vice President Patient Care Services, Vidant Roanoke–Chowan Hospital, Ahoskie, NC, p. A459

MITCHELL, Timothy, R.N. Chief Nursing Officer, Complex Care Hospital at Ridgelake, Sarasota, FL, p. A145

MITCHELL, Vernadine, R.N. Chief Nursing Officer, De Soto Regional Health System, Mansfield, LA, p. A283

MITCHELL III, Walton F., Director, Catawba Hospital, Catawba, VA, p. A669

MITHUN, Robert, M.D. Physician in Chief, Kaiser Permanente San Francisco Medical Center, San Francisco, CA, p. A91

MITRICK, Joseph M., FACHE, President, Baptist Medical Center Beaches, Jacksonville Beach, FL, p. A132

MITRY, Norman F., President and Chief Executive Officer, Heritage Valley Health System, Beaver, PA, p. B73

MITRY, Norman F.
President and Chief Executive Officer, Heritage Valley Health System, Beaver, PA, p. A533
President and Chief Executive Officer, Sewickley Valley Hospital, (A Division of Valley Medical Facilities), Sewickley, PA, p. A555

MITTAL, Vikrant, M.D. Chief Medical Officer, Danville State Hospital, Danville, PA, p. A536

MITTELSTAEDT, Doug, Vice President Human Resources, Children's Hospital, New Orleans, LA, p. A285

MITZNER, Jennifer C., Senior Vice President Finance and Chief Financial Officer, Hoag Memorial Hospital Presbyterian, Newport Beach, CA, p. A80

MIYAMOTO, Faye, Vice President Human Resources, Rehabilitation Hospital of the Pacific, Honolulu, HI, p. A171

MIYASAWA, Patricia, CPA Director Fiscal Service, Shriners Hospitals for Children–Honolulu, Honolulu, HI, p. A171

MIYAUCHI, Kimberly, R.N. Chief Nursing Officer, Kingman Regional Medical Center, Kingman, AZ, p. A33

MIZE, William D., Chief Operating Officer, Trousdale Medical Center, Hartsville, TN, p. A583

MIZELL, Philip L., M.D. Medical Director, The BridgeWay, North Little Rock, AR, p. A51

MIZER, Alison, Chief Financial Officer, St. Anthony North Hospital, Westminster, CO, p. A112

MIZIA, Robert, Director Information Systems and Chief Information Officer, Inspira Medical Center–Woodbury, Woodbury, NJ, p. A425

MIZONO, Gary, M.D. Physician–in–Chief, Kaiser Permanente San Rafael Medical Center, San Rafael, CA, p. A93

MIZRACH, Kenneth H., Director, Veterans Affairs New Jersey Health Care System, East Orange, NJ, p. A415

MLADY, Celine M., Chief Executive Officer, Osmond General Hospital, Osmond, NE, p. A401

MLAWSKY, Karen, Chief Executive Officer, University of Arizona Medical Center – University Campus, Tucson, AZ, p. A41

MMEJE, Ike, Chief Operating Officer, Sierra Vista Regional Medical Center, San Luis Obispo, CA, p. A93

MOAD, Harold, Chief Operating Officer, Elkview General Hospital, Hobart, OK, p. A512

MOAK, Huey, M.D. Chief of Staff, Riverland Medical Center, Ferriday, LA, p. A277

MOAK, Jennifer, Business Office Manager, Lawrence County Hospital, Monticello, MS, p. A363

MOAK, Mike, Chief Information Officer, Southwest Mississippi Regional Medical Center, McComb, MS, p. A362

MOAKLER, Thomas J., Chief Executive Officer, Houlton Regional Hospital, Houlton, ME, p. A293

MOALLEMIAN, Patrick, Chief Executive Officer and Managing Director, Arbour H. R. I. Hospital, Brookline, MA, p. A308

MOATS, Susan, R.N. Vice President of Patient Care Services and Chief Nursing Officer, The Heart Hospital Baylor Plano, Plano, TX, p. A643

MOBLEY, Barbara, Chief Executive Officer, Select Specialty Hospital–Dallas, Carrollton, TX, p. A605

MOBLEY, Cheryl, FACHE, President, Texas Health Specialty Hospital, Fort Worth, TX, p. A619

MOBLEY, Dana, Chief Information Officer, Our Community Hospital, Scotland Neck, NC, p. A472

MOBURG, Steven T., Chief Executive Officer, Madison Hospital, Madison, MN, p. A346

MOCK, Presley, M.D. Chief of Staff, Texas Institute for Surgery at Texas Health Presbyterian Dallas, Dallas, TX, p. A612

MOCK, Sara, Director Administrative Services, Kansas Neurological Institute, Topeka, KS, p. A255

MOCKLIN, Kevin, M.D. Director Medical Staff, Lake Charles Memorial Hospital, Lake Charles, LA, p. A282

MOCKUS, Tom, R.N. Interim Chief Nursing Officer, Mount Desert Island Hospital, Bar Harbor, ME, p. A291

MODLIN, Stacy, Chief Executive Officer, HEALTHSOUTH Sunrise Rehabilitation Hospital, Sunrise, FL, p. A146

MOE, Aldean J., Chief Operating Officer, Alpena Regional Medical Center, Alpena, MI, p. A318

MOE, Jonathan, Chief Executive Officer, Landmann–Jungman Memorial Hospital Avera, Scotland, SD, p. A576

MOEEN, Farida, M.D., Interim Administrator, Doctor's Hospital – Tidwell, Houston, TX, p. A624

MOELLER, Debbie A., R.N. Chief Operating Officer, Lake Pointe Medical Center, Rowlett, TX, p. A645

MOELLER, Jerry G., FACHE, President and Chief Executive Officer, Stillwater Medical Center, Stillwater, OK, p. A519

MOEN, Belinda, Interim Director of Nursing, Mountrail County Medical Center, Stanley, ND, p. A480

MOEN, Daniel P., President and Chief Executive Officer, Mercy Medical Center, Springfield, MA, p. A315

MOEN, Larry, Chief Financial Officer, Coteau des Prairies Hospital, Sisseton, SD, p. A577

MOEN, Nellie, Coordinator Human Resources, Kindred Hospital–Bay Area, Pasadena, TX, p. A641

MOFFAT, Jeanne, Manager Information Technology, Keefe Memorial Hospital, Cheyenne Wells, CO, p. A103

MOFFAT, Jennifer, Staff Accountant, Garden County Health Services, Oshkosh, NE, p. A401

MOFFATT, Dan, Chief Information Officer, Sanford Bemidji Medical Center, Bemidji, MN, p. A340

MOFFATT, Tracey, Chief Operating Officer, Wellmont Hancock County Hospital, Sneedville, TN, p. A593

MOFFET, Chris, Director Information Services, Bob Wilson Memorial Grant County Hospital, Ulysses, KS, p. A255

MOFFITT, Mark, Chief Information Officer, Adena Medical Center, Chillicothe, OH, p. A486

MOFFITT, Scott, Director Information Systems, Sanford Sheldon Medical Center, Sheldon, IA, p. A237

MOGG, Cassie, Chief Financial Officer, Covenant Hospital Plainview, Plainview, TX, p. A642

MOHAMED, Antonia, Acting Chief Information Officer, Birmingham Veterans Affairs Medical Center, Birmingham, AL, p. A16

MOHAMMED, Ehtaisham, M.D. Chief Medical Officer, Sibley Medical Center, Arlington, MN, p. A339

MOHAMMED, Larry, Director Information Systems, Tampa Community Hospital, Tampa, FL, p. A148

MOHAN, Amit, Executive Director, Shore Rehabilitation Institute, Brick, NJ, p. A413

MOHLER, Brittany, Director Human Resources, Essentia Health–Deer River, Deer River, MN, p. A342

MOHNKERN, Pearl, Vice President and Director Human Resources, Christus St. Vincent Regional Medical Center, Santa Fe, NM, p. A430

MOHR, Amy, Coordinator Human Resources, Forest Health Medical Center, Ypsilanti, MI, p. A337

MOHR, Angela, R.N. Vice President Nursing and Chief Operating Officer, St. Anthony Shawnee Hospital, Shawnee, OK, p. A519

MOHR, Jill, Manager Human Resources, Sanford Aberdeen Medical Center, Aberdeen, SD, p. A572

MOHR, Steve
Senior Vice President Finance and Chief Financial Officer, Loma Linda University Behavioral Medicine Center, Redlands, CA, p. A85
Senior Vice President Finance and Chief Financial Officer, Loma Linda University Medical Center, Loma Linda, CA, p. A69

MOISAN, Terrence, M.D., Interim Chief Executive Officer, Palos Community Hospital, Palos Heights, IL, p. A199

MOK, Michelle, Chief Financial Officer, Saint John's Health Center, Santa Monica, CA, p. A94

MOKFI, Shaya, M.D. Medical Director and President Medical Staff, Kindred Hospital of Northern Indiana, Mishawaka, IN, p. A218

MOLACEK, Shane, Chief Information Officer, Valley County Health System, Ord, NE, p. A400

MOLELUS, Elena, Manager Human Resources, Santa Barbara County Psychiatric Health Facility, Santa Barbara, CA, p. A94

MOLINA, Isabel, M.D. Chief Medical Officer, Lamb Healthcare Center, Littlefield, TX, p. A633

MOLINA, John, JD, Chief Executive Officer, U. S. Public Health Service Phoenix Indian Medical Center, Phoenix, AZ, p. A37

MOLINA, Luis
Vice President Finance and Chief Financial Officer, Community Hospital, Munster, IN, p. A219
Chief Financial Officer, St. Catherine Hospital, East Chicago, IN, p. A209

MOLINARI, Michael, M.D. Chief of Staff, Corona Regional Medical Center, Corona, CA, p. A60

MOLINARO, Frank L., Chief Executive Officer, Arrowhead Hospital, Glendale, AZ, p. A33

MOLITOR, Margie, R.N., Chief Executive Officer, Washakie Medical Center, Worland, WY, p. A723

MOLL, Ben, Assistant Chief Financial Officer, Nashoba Valley Medical Center, Ayer, MA, p. A305

MOLL, Eric, Chief Executive Officer, Mason General Hospital, Shelton, WA, p. A689

MOLL, Gudrun, R.N. Chief Nursing Officer, St. John's Regional Medical Center, Oxnard, CA, p. A82

MOLL, Jeffrey, M.D. Medical Director, Clarion Psychiatric Center, Clarion, PA, p. A535

MOLLER, Dan, M.D. Chief Medical Officer, Willis–Knighton Medical Center, Shreveport, LA, p. A288

MOLLER, Lynn, Chief Financial Officer, Weston County Health Services, Newcastle, WY, p. A722

MOLLOHAN, Joan, Vice President Human Resources, Ochsner Medical Center, New Orleans, LA, p. A286

MOLLOY, Kevin
Senior Vice President and Chief Operating Officer, Mount Sinai Beth Israel, New York, NY, p. A446
Senior Vice President and Chief Operating Officer, Mount Sinai St. Luke's, New York, NY, p. A446

MOLLOY, Reuben D., Chief Information Officer, Governor Juan F. Louis Hospital, Christiansted, VI, p. A729

MOLMEN, David R., Chief Executive Officer, Altru Health System, Grand Forks, ND, p. A478

MOLSBERGER, Shawn, Chief Operating Officer, Gateway Medical Center, Clarksville, TN, p. A581

MOLYNEUX, Phyllis, Associate Administrator Human Resources and Education, Williamson Medical Center, Franklin, TN, p. A583

MOMBOURQUETTE, Arthur, Chief Operating Officer, Cape Cod Hospital, Hyannis, MA, p. A311

MOMEYER, Polly, Manager Human Resources, Millcreek Community Hospital, Erie, PA, p. A538

MON, Kathy, Vice President Operations, The Hospital at Hebrew Health Care, West Hartford, CT, p. A118

MONAHAN, Jane, Vice President Ministry and Human Resources, Monroe Clinic, Monroe, WI, p. A711

MONASTERIO, Eugene A., M.D. Medical Director, Children's Hospital of Richmond at VCU–Brook Road Campus, Richmond, VA, p. A677

MONCHER, Daniel J., Vice President and Chief Financial Officer, Firelands Regional Health System, Sandusky, OH, p. A501

MONCRIEF, William
Director Information Systems, Garden City Hospital, Garden City, MI, p. A324
ORH IT Client Executive, Oakland Regional Hospital, Southfield, MI, p. A335

MONCRIEF–WELLS, Angela, Coordinator Human Resources, Kindred Hospital Detroit, Detroit, MI, p. A322

MONCZEWSKI, Patricia, Chief Operating Officer, Mercy General Hospital, Sacramento, CA, p. A87

MONCZEWSKI, Ted, Vice President Human Resources, St. Vincent Charity Medical Center, Cleveland, OH, p. A489

MONDA, Cam, D.O. Medical Director, Greenwood Regional Rehabilitation Hospital, Greenwood, SC, p. A567

MONETTE, Steven, Chief Financial Officer, Valley Regional Hospital, Claremont, NH, p. A409

MONEY, Lourene, R.N., Interim Chief Executive Officer, Kindred Hospital South Bay, Gardena, CA, p. A65

MONGE, Catherine, Senior Vice President Operations, MedStar Washington Hospital Center, Washington, DC, p. A121

MONGE, Peter W., President, MedStar Montgomery Medical Center, Olney, MD, p. A302

MONGELL, Mitchell P., FACHE, Chief Executive Officer, Fort Walton Beach Medical Center, Fort Walton Beach, FL, p. A129

MONGER, Lloyd, Administrator, Jackson Parish Hospital, Jonesboro, LA, p. A280

MONGER, Shelton, Director Information Technology, Wayne Hospital, Greenville, OH, p. A495

MONIACI, Cathy, Chief Operating Officer, Shriners Hospitals for Children–Houston, Houston, TX, p. A626

MONICAL, Robert, President and Chief Executive Officer, McPherson Hospital, McPherson, KS, p. A250

MONJE, Mary Anne, Chief Financial Officer and Chief Operating Officer, Whittier Hospital Medical Center, Whittier, CA, p. A100

MONKRES, Paula, Administrative Assistant and Director Human Resources, Nocona General Hospital, Nocona, TX, p. A640

MONROE, Ame, Director Human Resources, Rolling Plains Memorial Hospital, Sweetwater, TX, p. A651

MONROE, Janet J., R.N., Chief Executive Officer, Greystone Park Psychiatric Hospital, Morris Plains, NJ, p. A418

MONROE, Lori, Director of Nursing, Winnebago Mental Health Institute, Winnebago, WI, p. A719

MONROIG, Domingo, Executive Director, Castaner General Hospital, Castaner, PR, p. A725

MONROY–MILLER, Cherry, M.D. Acting Medical Director, Greystone Park Psychiatric Hospital, Morris Plains, NJ, p. A418

MONSANTO, Monte, Chief Information Systems, Russell County Hospital, Russell Springs, KY, p. A270

MONSERRATE, Humberto M., Chief Executive Officer, Hospital Universitario Dr. Ramon Ruiz Arnau, Bayamon, PR, p. A725

MONSON, Mark G., President and Chief Executive Officer, Fairbanks, Indianapolis, IN, p. A214

MONSRUD, Michele, Director Human Resources, Clearview Regional Medical Center, Monroe, GA, p. A164

MONTAG, Kathy, Administrator Health Care, State Correctional Institution at Camp Hill, Camp Hill, PA, p. A535

MONTAGNESE, Robert A., President and Chief Executive Officer, Licking Memorial Hospital, Newark, OH, p. A499

MONTALBO, Tripp, Chief Operating Officer, Conroe Regional Medical Center, Conroe, TX, p. A607

MONTALVO, Cary L., Chief Executive Officer, Solara Hospital Harlingen, Harlingen, TX, p. A622

MONTALVO, Eladio, Chief Operating Officer, Doctors Hospital of Laredo, Laredo, TX, p. A632

MONTALVO, Jose, M.D. Medical Director, Hospital Del Maestro, San Juan, PR, p. A728

MONTANA-RHODES, Lou, Vice President of Patient Care Services, Vidant Beaufort Hospital, Washington, NC, p. A474

MONTANEZ, Edwin, R.N. Chief Nursing Officer, HEALTHSOUTH Rehabilitation Hospital of Spring Hill, Brooksville, FL, p. A125

MONTANO, Mayra, Director Information Systems, Hospital Metropolitano Dr. Susoni, Arecibo, PR, p. A724

MONTANTE, Carl, Director Information Systems and Information Technology, Shriners Hospitals for Children-Portland, Portland, OR, p. A529

MONTANYE-IRELAND, Cherelle, Chief Executive Officer, Hansen Family Hospital, Iowa Falls, IA, p. A233

MONTEL, Janet, Chief Financial Officer, Paris Regional Medical Center, Paris, TX, p. A641

MONTELLA, Alan J., Assistant Administrator Finance, Sullivan County Community Hospital, Sullivan, IN, p. A222

MONTENEGRO, Diana, Director Human Resources, Baptist Health South Florida, South Miami Hospital, Miami, FL, p. A136

MONTENEGRO, Robert, M.D. Chief of Staff, Glacial Ridge Health System, Glenwood, MN, p. A344

MONTES, Lisa K., Chief Executive Officer, Del Amo Hospital, Torrance, CA, p. A97

MONTGOMERY, Charles, M.D. Medical Director, Logansport Memorial Hospital, Logansport, IN, p. A218

MONTGOMERY, James T., FACHE, President, Touro Infirmary, New Orleans, LA, p. A286

MONTGOMERY, Jennifer, FACHE Vice President, Nursing, Port Huron Hospital, Port Huron, MI, p. A332

MONTGOMERY, Jennifer
 Chief Nursing Officer, Rochelle Community Hospital, Rochelle, IL, p. A201
 Chief Financial Officer, Washakie Medical Center, Worland, WY, p. A723

MONTGOMERY, Lee Anne, R.N. Chief Nursing Officer, HEALTHSOUTH Rehabilitation Hospital of Montgomery, Montgomery, AL, p. A23

MONTGOMERY, Margaret, Chief Nursing Officer, HEALTHSOUTH Reading Rehabilitation Hospital, Reading, PA, p. A553

MONTGOMERY, Mark, M.D. Chief Medical Officer, Texas Health Harris Methodist Hospital Southwest Fort Worth, Fort Worth, TX, p. A619

MONTGOMERY, Mary Jim, R.N. Chief Operating Officer, Crisp Regional Hospital, Cordele, GA, p. A157

MONTGOMERY, Michael J., President and Chief Executive Officer, Cleo Wallace Centers Hospital, Westminster, CO, p. A112

MONTGOMERY, Peggy, Director Medical Records, Arrowhead Behavioral Health Hospital, Maumee, OH, p. A498

MONTGOMERY II, Raymond W., FACHE, President and Chief Executive Officer, White County Medical Center, Searcy, AR, p. A52

MONTGOMERY, Robert, Chief Financial Officer, Shriners Hospitals for Children-Lexington, Lexington, KY, p. A264

MONTGOMERY, Susan, Chief Nursing Officer, Asante Ashland Community Hospital, Ashland, OR, p. A523

MONTGOMERY, Tina, Chief Financial Officer, Sidney Health Center, Sidney, MT, p. A391

MONTGOMERY, Vicki, Director and Chief Executive Officer, Central State Hospital, Petersburg, VA, p. A676

MONTOIS, John D., Chief Financial Officer, Brownwood Regional Medical Center, Brownwood, TX, p. A604

MONTOUR, Vina, Director Information Technology, U. S. Public Health Service Phoenix Indian Medical Center, Phoenix, AZ, p. A37

MONTOWSKI, Deborah, M.D. Chief Medical Officer, Providence Mount Carmel Hospital, Colville, WA, p. A682

MONTOYA, Brooke, Director Human Resources, Lake Granbury Medical Center, Granbury, TX, p. A621

MONVESKY, Kimberly, Chief Financial Officer, Pikes Peak Regional Hospital, Woodland Park, CO, p. A112

MONZINGO, Ashley, Human Resources, Accounts Payable and Payroll, TOPS Surgical Specialty Hospital, Houston, TX, p. A627

MOODY, David, Vice President Human Resources, Salina Regional Health Center, Salina, KS, p. A254

MOODY, Heather, Chief Human Resource Management, Hunter Holmes McGuire Veterans Affairs Medical Center, Richmond, VA, p. A678

MOODY, James, Chief Financial Officer, Donalsonville Hospital, Donalsonville, GA, p. A158

MOODY, Michael
 Senior Vice President and Chief Financial Officer, John Muir Behavioral Health Center, Concord, CA, p. A60
 Chief Financial Officer, John Muir Medical Center, Concord, Concord, CA, p. A60
 Senior Vice President and Chief Financial Officer, John Muir Medical Center, Walnut Creek, Walnut Creek, CA, p. A100

MOODY, Vicky, Director Human Resources, Houlton Regional Hospital, Houlton, ME, p. A293

MOOERS, Margaret, R.N. Chief Operating Officer and Chief Nursing Officer, OSS Orthopaedic Specialty Hospital, York, PA, p. A559

MOOG, Darlene, Director Human Resources, HEALTHSOUTH Deaconess Rehabilitation Hospital, Evansville, IN, p. A210

MOON, Bob, Chief Financial Officer, Christus St. Vincent Regional Medical Center, Santa Fe, NM, p. A430

MOON, Jr., David, Director Information Systems, Lake City Community Hospital, Lake City, SC, p. A568

MOON, James, Chief Financial Officer, Pana Community Hospital, Pana, IL, p. A199

MOON, John, Associate Director, Veterans Affairs Eastern Kansas Health Care System, Topeka, KS, p. A255

MOON, Lori, R.N. Vice President Clinical Operations/Business Development, McDonough District Hospital, Macomb, IL, p. A195

MOON, Robert, Chief Financial Officer, Mercy St. Anne Hospital, Toledo, OH, p. A503

MOONEY, Robert W., M.D. Medical Director, Willingway Hospital, Statesboro, GA, p. A167

MOONEY, Susan E., MS, President and Chief Executive Officer, Alice Peck Day Memorial Hospital, Lebanon, NH, p. A410

MOONEY, Thomas, M.D. President Executive Committee Medical Staff, Naval Medical Center, Portsmouth, VA, p. A676

MOORE, Alison, Chief Financial Officer, Methodist Extended Care Hospital, Memphis, TN, p. A589

MOORE, Amy, Human Resources, Hamilton Hospital, Olney, TX, p. A640

MOORE III, Ben, President and Chief Executive Officer, River Hospital, Alexandria Bay, NY, p. A432

MOORE, Betty, Business Manager, North Mississippi Medical Center-Iuka, Iuka, MS, p. A359

MOORE, Bill, Chief Human Resources, El Centro Regional Medical Center, El Centro, CA, p. A62

MOORE, Bob, FACHE, Chief Executive Officer, Lancaster Regional Medical Center, Lancaster, PA, p. A542

MOORE, Brandon, Administrator and Chief Executive Officer, Park Place Surgical Hospital, Lafayette, LA, p. A281

MOORE, Brett, CPA Assistant Administrator Finance, Sutter Amador Hospital, Jackson, CA, p. A67

MOORE, Brian, President and Chief Executive Officer, St. Mary-Corwin Medical Center, Pueblo, CO, p. A110

MOORE, C. Thomas, Chief Financial Officer, Delta Regional Medical Center, Greenville, MS, p. A358

MOORE, Carrie, Director Human Resources, Meadowbrook Rehabilitation Hospital, Gardner, KS, p. A244

MOORE, Cecelia B., CPA Associate Vice Chancellor Finance, Vanderbilt Hospital and Clinics, Nashville, TN, p. A591

MOORE, Christie, Director Human Resources, Reliant Rehabilitation Hospital Mid-Cities, Bedford, TX, p. A602

MOORE, Dana
 Senior Vice President Information Services, St. Anthony Hospital, Lakewood, CO, p. A108
 Senior Vice President Information Services, St. Anthony North Hospital, Westminster, CO, p. A112

MOORE, Darrell W., Chief Executive Officer, Parkridge Medical Center, Chattanooga, TN, p. A580

MOORE, Deborah, Director Human Resources, Walter P. Reuther Psychiatric Hospital, Westland, MI, p. A337

MOORE, Debra, Chief Executive Officer, Parkside Hospital, Tulsa, OK, p. A520

MOORE, Diane, Chief Financial Officer, Memorial Medical Center, Port Lavaca, TX, p. A643

MOORE, Dylan, Controller, Rogers City Rehabilitation Hospital, Rogers City, MI, p. A333

MOORE, Edward H., President and Chief Executive Officer, Harrington Memorial Hospital, Southbridge, MA, p. A314

MOORE, Elizabeth, Chief Operating Officer, Silver Hill Hospital, New Canaan, CT, p. A116

MOORE, Emily, Director Human Resources and Information Technology, Haskell Memorial Hospital, Haskell, TX, p. A623

MOORE, Ethel L., M.D. Director of Medical Affairs, Fort Belknap U. S. Public Health Service Indian Hospital, Harlem, MT, p. A388

MOORE, Gary, Chief Executive Officer, Shoshone Medical Center, Kellogg, ID, p. A176

MOORE, Harold, Chief Information Technology Officer, Spartanburg Regional Medical Center, Spartanburg, SC, p. A570

MOORE, James D., FACHE, President, Integris Southwest Medical Center, Oklahoma City, OK, p. A515

MOORE, Jane, Director, Fiscal Services, Quitman County Hospital, Marks, MS, p. A362

MOORE, Jason H., Vice President and Chief Operating Officer, Tallahassee Memorial HealthCare, Tallahassee, FL, p. A147

MOORE, Jeffrey Steve, Chief Financial Officer, Fort Walton Beach Medical Center, Fort Walton Beach, FL, p. A129

MOORE, Jennifer, Interim Chief Information Officer, Carroll Hospital Center, Westminster, MD, p. A304

MOORE, Jody Dewen, District Director Human Resources, Kindred Hospital-San Diego, San Diego, CA, p. A89

MOORE, John, M.D. Medical Director, Granite County Medical Center, Philipsburg, MT, p. A390

MOORE, John
 Administrator, Hiawatha Community Hospital, Hiawatha, KS, p. A245
 President, South Lake Hospital, Clermont, FL, p. A125

MOORE, John, M.D. Vice President Medical Affairs, SSM DePaul Health Center, Bridgeton, MO, p. A368

MOORE, John G.
 Chief Financial Officer, Anson Community Hospital, Wadesboro, NC, p. A474
 Vice President and Chief Financial Officer, Carolinas Medical Center-Union, Monroe, NC, p. A469

MOORE, Kadie, Director Human Resources, Vidant Edgecombe Hospital, Tarboro, NC, p. A473

MOORE, Kandi, Administrator, Specialists Hospital – Shreveport, Shreveport, LA, p. A288

MOORE, Karen, Vice President Information Technology and Chief Information Officer, Southern Regional Medical Center, Riverdale, GA, p. A165

MOORE, Kathy D., Chief Executive Officer, St. Luke's Regional Medical Center, Boise, ID, p. A175

MOORE, Keri, Vice President Human Resources and Support Services, Presbyterian-St. Luke's Medical Center, Denver, CO, p. A105

MOORE, Kermit, R.N. Chief Operating Officer and Chief Nursing Officer, Nemaha County Hospital, Auburn, NE, p. A393

MOORE, Kerry, M.D. Chief of Staff, Carilion Tazewell Community Hospital, Tazewell, VA, p. A679

MOORE, Kim S., President, CHI Health St Elizabeth, Lincoln, NE, p. A397

MOORE, Kyna, R.N. Director of Nursing, Bath Community Hospital, Hot Springs, VA, p. A672

MOORE, Larry E., Executive Vice President and Chief Operating Officer and Chief Financial Officer, Cumberland Medical Center, Crossville, TN, p. A582

MOORE, Lauralinda, Manager Finance, CHRISTUS Spohn Hospital Kleberg, Kingsville, TX, p. A631

MOORE, Leigh, Administrative Assistant Human Resources, H. C. Watkins Memorial Hospital, Quitman, MS, p. A364

MOORE, Linda, Manager Human Resources, Seymour Hospital, Seymour, TX, p. A648

MOORE, Margaret, Manager Business Office, Sabine County Hospital, Hemphill, TX, p. A623

MOORE, Mark E., President and Chief Executive Officer, Indiana University Health Bloomington Hospital, Bloomington, IN, p. A207

MOORE, Mary Ann, Director of Nursing, KidsPeace Children's Hospital, Orefield, PA, p. A547

MOORE, Matthew, Executive Vice President and Chief Integration Officer, St. Francis Hospital, Columbus, GA, p. A156

MOORE, Mayzelle, Director Human Resources, Methodist Extended Care Hospital, Memphis, TN, p. A589

MOORE, Melinda, Director Human Resources, Deaconess Hospital, Spokane, WA, p. A690

MOORE, Mike, Chief Financial Officer, Jane Phillips Medical Center, Bartlesville, OK, p. A508

MOORE, Mindy S., Chief Executive Officer, Landmark Hospital of Columbia, Columbia, MO, p. A370

MOORE, Neil J., President and Chief Executive Officer, Dimensions Healthcare System, Cheverly, MD, p. B53

MOORE, Nelda, Director Data Processing, Memorial Hospital and Manor, Bainbridge, GA, p. A154

MOORE, Nickie, Chief Financial Officer, North Sunflower Medical Center, Ruleville, MS, p. A365

MOORE, Patricia J., Director Human Resource, Valley Behavioral Health System, Barling, AR, p. A43

MOORE, Paul, Chief Information Officer, Connecticut Mental Health Center, New Haven, CT, p. A116

MOORE, Paula, Chief Clinical Officer, Hugh Chatham Memorial Hospital, Elkin, NC, p. A464

MOORE, Phyllis, Director Information Systems and Data Center, Doctors Medical Center, San Pablo, CA, p. A93

MOORE, Rick
 Chief Information Officer, Bethesda North Hospital, Cincinnati, OH, p. A486
 Chief Information Officer, Good Samaritan Hospital, Cincinnati, OH, p. A487

MOORE, Robin A., Vice President Human Resources, Concord Hospital, Concord, NH, p. A409

MOORE, Ronald E., R.N. Vice President Professional Practice and Chief Nursing Officer, Charleston Area Medical Center, Charleston, WV, p. A694

MOORE, Sandee, Chief Operating Officer, Eastern Idaho Regional Medical Center, Idaho Falls, ID, p. A176

MOORE, Saunya, Chief Financial Officer, Parkside Hospital, Tulsa, OK, p. A520

MOORE, Steve, Chief Financial Officer, Southern Tennessee Regional Health System–Winchester, Winchester, TN, p. A594

MOORE, Susan L., R.N. Director of Nursing, Thayer County Health Services, Hebron, NE, p. A396

MOORE, Sylvia, Vice President and Chief Operating Officer, Southeast Hospital, Cape Girardeau, MO, p. A369

MOORE, Tim, Chief Accounting Officer and Vice President Ancillary Services and Finance, Blessing Hospital, Quincy, IL, p. A201

MOORE, Tim, R.N. Senior Vice President and Chief Information Officer, Hoag Memorial Hospital Presbyterian, Newport Beach, CA, p. A80

MOORE, Vernon, Senior Vice President Chief Business and Finance, University of Texas Health Science Center at Tyler, Tyler, TX, p. A654

MOORE, Warren E., Executive Vice President and Chief Operating Officer, Children's Specialized Hospital–PSE&G, New Brunswick, NJ, p. A419

MOORE, William, Chief Information Officer, Parrish Medical Center, Titusville, FL, p. A149

MOORE–CONNELLY, Marci, M.D. Vice President Chief Medical Officer, Memorial Hospital of Carbondale, Carbondale, IL, p. A182

MOORE–HARDY, Cynthia, FACHE, President and Chief Executive Officer, Lake Health, Concord Township, OH, p. A491

MOOREHOUSE, Brett, FACHE Vice President and Chief Operating Officer, Ranken Jordan Pediatric Bridge Hospital, Maryland Heights, MO, p. A376

MOORER, Thad, Chief Information Officer, Eastside Psychiatric Hospital, Tallahassee, FL, p. A146

MOORHEAD, David, M.D. Chief Medical Officer, Florida Hospital, Orlando, FL, p. A140

MOORMAN, Gary L., D.O. Chief Medical Officer and Senior Vice President Medical Affairs, Mercy Memorial Hospital System, Monroe, MI, p. A330

MOOTS, Eric, Vice President and Chief Financial Officer, Adventist GlenOaks Hospital, Glendale Heights, IL, p. A191

MORACA, Lynn, Director Human Resources, Lodi Community Hospital, Lodi, OH, p. A496

MORAHAN, John, Vice President Finance, St. Joseph Hospital, Bethpage, NY, p. A433

MORAHAN, John R., FACHE, President and Chief Executive Officer, St. Joseph Medical Center, Reading, PA, p. A553

MORALES, Anthony, M.D. Medical Director, Louisiana Heart Hospital, Lacombe, LA, p. A280

MORALES, Autumn, Chief Medical Staff Officer, Clarinda Regional Health Center, Clarinda, IA, p. A227

MORALES, Carmela, M.D. Chief of Staff, University Medical Center of El Paso, El Paso, TX, p. A616

MORALES, Daniza
Chief Information Officer, Hospital Menonita De Cayey, Cayey, PR, p. A725
Manager Information System, Mennonite General Hospital, Aibonito, PR, p. A724

MORALES, Elsie, Chief Financial Officer, Hospital Universitario Dr. Ramon Ruiz Arnau, Bayamon, PR, p. A725

MORALES, Joel, Chief Financial Officer, Fort Duncan Regional Medical Center, Eagle Pass, TX, p. A614

MORALES, John R., Chief Financial Officer, John H. Stroger Jr. Hospital of Cook County, Chicago, IL, p. A184

MORALES, Juan A., MSN, Health System Director, Tennessee Valley Healthcare System, Nashville, TN, p. A591

MORALES, Steve, Director Human Resources, Sutter Medical Center of Santa Rosa, Chanate Campus, Santa Rosa, CA, p. A95

MORALES, Trish, Director Human Resources, Lakewood Ranch Medical Center, Bradenton, FL, p. A124

MORAN, Alina, Chief Financial Officer, Elmhurst Hospital Center,, NY, p. A443

MORAN, Colleen M., Director Human Resources, Spaulding Hospital for Continuing Medical Care North Shore, Salem, MA, p. A314

MORAN, Debbie
Executive Director, Carl Albert Community Mental Health Center, McAlester, OK, p. A513
Executive Director, Jim Taliaferro Community Mental Health, Lawton, OK, p. A512

MORAN, Timothy M., Chief Executive Officer, Tri-City Medical Center, Oceanside, CA, p. A81

MORANDEIRA, Ana, Director Marketing, San Juan Capestrano Hospital, San Juan, PR, p. A728

MORASKO, Jerome, President and Chief Executive Officer, Avita Health System, Galion, OH, p. B18

MORASKO, Jerome
Chief Executive Officer, Bucyrus Community Hospital, Bucyrus, OH, p. A484
President and Chief Executive Officer, Galion Community Hospital, Galion, OH, p. A494

MORASKO, Robert A., Chief Executive Officer, Heart of the Rockies Regional Medical Center, Salida, CO, p. A111

MORAVICK, Donna, MSN, Executive Director, Southside Hospital, Bay Shore, NY, p. A433

MORDACH, John P., Senior Vice President and Chief Financial Officer, Rush University Medical Center, Chicago, IL, p. A186

MORDECAI, Steve, Director Human Resources, Griffin Hospital, Derby, CT, p. A114

MOREAU, Steven C., President and Chief Executive Officer, St. Joseph Hospital, Orange, CA, p. A81

MOREFIELD, Terri, Deputy Chief Human Resources Division, Bassett Army Community Hospital, Fort Wainwright, AK, p. A29

MOREH, Swenda, Chief Executive Officer, Kindred Hospital–Baldwin Park, Baldwin Park, CA, p. A57

MOREIN, Sandy, Chief Operating Officer, Mercy Regional Medical Center, Ville Platte, LA, p. A290

MORELAND, John, M.D. Chief Medical Officer, Marcus Daly Memorial Hospital, Hamilton, MT, p. A388

MORELAND, Tresha
Regional Vice President Human Resources, Dameron Hospital, Stockton, CA, p. A96
Vice President Human Resources, Fremont–Rideout Health Group, Marysville, CA, p. A77

MORELL, Ixel, Director Business Development, Sierra Vista Hospital, Sacramento, CA, p. A87

MORELLI, Gerald, Director Human Resources, Philadelphia Veterans Affairs Medical Center, Philadelphia, PA, p. A549

MORELLO, Salvatore, Vice President Finance, Mount Sinai Queens,, NY, p. A446

MORENO, Debbie, Chief Nursing Officer, Lodi Memorial Hospital, Lodi, CA, p. A69

MORENO, Jorge, Director Information Technology Operations, Sierra Vista Regional Health Center, Sierra Vista, AZ, p. A39

MORENO–COOK, Shannon, Chief Nursing Officer, St. Vincent Rehabilitation Hospital, Sherwood, AR, p. A52

MORESI, Randy, Chief Executive Officer, North Hills Hospital, North Richland Hills, TX, p. A640

MORETTE, Joseph M., Executive Vice President, Methodist Rehabilitation Center, Jackson, MS, p. A360

MOREY, Scott, Chief Nursing Officer, Maryvale Hospital Medical Center, Phoenix, AZ, p. A36

MORGAN, Bradley, Vice President of Operations, The Heart Hospital Baylor Denton, Denton, TX, p. A613

MORGAN, Charlene, Chief Nursing Officer, Henderson County Community Hospital, Lexington, TN, p. A587

MORGAN, Christian, M.D. Chief of Staff, Star Valley Medical Center, Afton, WY, p. A720

MORGAN, Christopher, M.D. Chief of Staff, Baptist Health Medical Center–Stuttgart, Stuttgart, AR, p. A53

MORGAN, David, Vice President and Chief Financial Officer, Bristol Bay Area Health Corporation, Dillingham, AK, p. A28

MORGAN, Dennis P., Chief of Staff, Baptist Memorial Hospital–North Mississippi, Oxford, MS, p. A364

MORGAN, Dirk, Vice President, Murray–Calloway County Hospital, Murray, KY, p. A268

MORGAN, Jeff, Director Information Systems, Northeastern Nevada Regional Hospital, Elko, NV, p. A404

MORGAN, Jon, M.D. Chief Medical Officer, Regional West Medical Center, Scottsbluff, NE, p. A402

MORGAN, Kelly C., President and Chief Executive Officer, Mercy Medical Center, Roseburg, OR, p. A529

MORGAN, Lisa, R.N. Vice President Patient Services, King's Daughters' Health, Madison, IN, p. A218

MORGAN, Lois, MSN Vice President and Chief Nursing Officer, Methodist Hospital, Henderson, KY, p. A262

MORGAN, Lori, M.D., Chief Administrative Officer, Legacy Emanuel Hospital and Health Center, Portland, OR, p. A528

MORGAN, Mace, Director Information Systems, Minden Medical Center, Minden, LA, p. A284

MORGAN, Matthew, Associate Administrator, Hillcrest Hospital – South, Tulsa, OK, p. A520

MORGAN, Michael, Interim Chief Executive Officer, Northeast Alabama Regional Medical Center, Anniston, AL, p. A15

MORGAN, Norma J., Chief Executive Officer, Effingham Hospital, Springfield, GA, p. A167

MORGAN, Nyle, Chief Information Officer, Sheridan Memorial Hospital, Sheridan, WY, p. A722

MORGAN, Rose, R.N. Vice President Patient Care Services, Princeton Community Hospital, Princeton, WV, p. A698

MORGAN, Sandra, Chief Executive Officer, Kindred Hospital Bay Area–Tampa, Tampa, FL, p. A147

MORGAN, Shawn, Acting Finance Officer, Northern Navajo Medical Center, Shiprock, NM, p. A431

MORGAN, Suzanne M., Chief Clinical Officer, Kindred Hospital of Northern Indiana, Mishawaka, IN, p. A218

MORGAN, Teresa
Chief Financial Officer, McGehee–Desha County Hospital, McGehee, AR, p. A50
Assistant Vice President Human Resources, Shannon Medical Center, San Angelo, TX, p. A645

MORGAN, W. Hugh, M.D. Chief Medical Staff, Edgefield County Hospital, Edgefield, SC, p. A565

MORGAN, William, Director Management Information Systems, CHRISTUS Spohn Hospital Alice, Alice, TX, p. A595

MORGAN–FINE, Richard, IT Director, Clarinda Regional Health Center, Clarinda, IA, p. A227

MORGESE, Vincent, M.D. Executive Vice President, Chief Operating Officer and Chief Medical Officer, Queen of the Valley Medical Center, Napa, CA, p. A79

MORIARTY, Sharon J., Chief Operating Officer, St. Mary's Hospital, Cottonwood, ID, p. A175

MORIMOTO, Scott, Director Clinical Informatics, Rehabilitation Hospital of the Pacific, Honolulu, HI, p. A171

MORIN, Linda, Director of Nursing, Copper Queen Community Hospital, Bisbee, AZ, p. A31

MORIN–SCRIBNER, Nicole, Director Human Resources, St. Mary's Regional Medical Center, Lewiston, ME, p. A294

MORISCO, Antonietta, M.D. Medical Director, Chairman Anesthesiology, Jamaica Hospital Medical Center,, NY, p. A444

MORISSETTE, Philip
Chief Financial Officer, Bridgton Hospital, Bridgton, ME, p. A292
Chief Financial Officer, Central Maine Medical Center, Lewiston, ME, p. A293

MORITZ, Mary, Administrator Human Resources, Humboldt County Memorial Hospital, Humboldt, IA, p. A232

MORJI, Nagy, Chief of Staff, TriStar Greenview Regional Hospital, Bowling Green, KY, p. A259

MORK Jr., David L., FACHE,
Chief Executive Officer, Roosevelt Warm Springs LTAC Hospital, Warm Springs, GA, p. A169
Chief Executive Officer, Roosevelt Warm Springs Rehabilitation and Specialty Hospitals, Warm Springs, GA, p. A169

MORKEL, Derek, Chief Executive Officer, HealthTech Management Services, Brentwood, TN, p. B72

MORLEY, Denise M., Director Human Resources, Wyoming County Community Hospital, Warsaw, NY, p. A457

MORLEY, Michael, M.D. Chief of Staff, Arkansas Valley Regional Medical Center, La Junta, CO, p. A108

MORLOCK, David, Chief Executive Officer, The University of Toledo Medical Center, Toledo, OH, p. A503

MORLOCK, Paul, Vice President Human Resources, Stanly Regional Medical Center, Albemarle, NC, p. A459

MORON, David, M.D. Clinical Director, Rio Grande State Center/South Texas Health Care System, Harlingen, TX, p. A622

MORONY, David, Chief Financial Officer, Casa Colina Hospital for Rehabilitative Medicine, Pomona, CA, p. A84

MORQUECHO, Adam
Director Information Systems, Garden Grove Hospital and Medical Center, Garden Grove, CA, p. A65
Director Information Technology, Huntington Beach Hospital, Huntington Beach, CA, p. A67

MORREALE, Daniel
Vice President and Chief Information Officer, Kingsbrook Jewish Medical Center,, NY, p. A445
Chief Information Officer, St. John's Riverside Hospital, Yonkers, NY, p. A458

MORREALE, Gene, President and Chief Executive Officer, Oneida Healthcare, Oneida, NY, p. A450

MORRELL, Dan, Manager Information Systems, Sierra Vista Hospital, Truth or Consequences, NM, p. A431

MORRELL, Jeffrey F., Chief Executive Officer, Intermountain Hospital, Boise, ID, p. A174

MORRICAL, Michael G., Chief Executive Officer, McKenzie Regional Hospital, McKenzie, TN, p. A588

MORRIS, Alexander, Corporate Director Human Resources, Fort Washington Medical Center, Fort Washington, MD, p. A301

MORRIS, Barbara, R.N. Chief Nursing Officer, HEALTHSOUTH Rehabilitation Hospital of Beaumont, Beaumont, TX, p. A602

MORRIS, Beverly
Vice President Human Resources, Kettering Medical Center, Kettering, OH, p. A495
Vice President Human Resources, Sycamore Medical Center, Miamisburg, OH, p. A498

MORRIS, Christi, Director of Nursing, Chambers County Public Hospital District 1, Anahuac, TX, p. A597

MORRIS, Christopher
  Director Human Resources, Wheaton Franciscan Healthcare –
    Elmbrook Memorial, Brookfield, WI, p. A703
  Vice President Human Resources, Wheaton Franciscan
    Healthcare – St. Joseph's, Milwaukee, WI, p. A711
  Director Human Resources, Wheaton Franciscan Healthcare –
    The Wisconsin Heart Hospital, Wauwatosa, WI, p. A718
MORRIS, Darrel, Chief Executive Officer, Drumright Regional
  Hospital, Drumright, OK, p. A509
MORRIS, David W., Chief Executive Officer, University Behavioral
  Health of El Paso, El Paso, TX, p. A616
MORRIS, Debbie M., Director Human Resources, Marcus Daly
  Memorial Hospital, Hamilton, MT, p. A388
MORRIS, Dennis, Area Finance Officer, Kaiser Permanente
  Oakland Medical Center, Oakland, CA, p. A80
MORRIS, Donald, System Vice President Human Resources,
  Memorial Medical Center – Livingston, Livingston, TX,
  p. A633
MORRIS, Douglas
  Chief Financial Officer, St. Francis Health Care Centre, Green
    Springs, OH, p. A495
  Chief Financial Officer, Vibra Hospital of Northwestern Indiana,
    Crown Point, IN, p. A209
  Chief Financial Officer, Vibra Hospital of Southeastern
    Michigan, Lincoln Park, MI, p. A329
MORRIS, Gerry, Administrator, Magnolia Behavioral Healthcare,
  Lacombe, LA, p. A280
MORRIS, Janet, Director Human Resources, HEALTHSOUTH
  Lakeview Rehabilitation Hospital, Elizabethtown, KY, p. A260
MORRIS, Janice, Accountant, CrossRidge Community Hospital,
  Wynne, AR, p. A54
MORRIS, Jarrett, Vice President Finance, Carolinas Medical
  Center–Lincoln, Lincolnton, NC, p. A468
MORRIS, Jeffrey, M.D
  Medical Director, Summa Barberton Citizens Hospital,
    Barberton, OH, p. A483
  Vice President Medical Affairs, Summa Wadsworth–Rittman
    Hospital, Wadsworth, OH, p. A504
MORRIS, Jim
  Vice President Finance, Baptist Health La Grange, La Grange,
    KY, p. A263
  Vice President Finance, Baptist Health Louisville, Louisville,
    KY, p. A265
MORRIS, Jody, President and Chief Operating Officer, Novant
  Health Franklin Medical Center, Louisburg, NC, p. A468
MORRIS, Jonathan B., M.D
  Senior Vice President and Chief Information Officer, WellStar
    Cobb Hospital, Austell, GA, p. A154
  Senior Vice President and Chief Information Officer, WellStar
    Kennestone Hospital, Marietta, GA, p. A163
MORRIS, Lisa, Vice President Human Resources, Swedish
  Medical Center, Englewood, CO, p. A106
MORRIS, Luke P.
  Regional Director Human Resources, American Fork Hospital,
    American Fork, UT, p. A659
  Regional Director Human Resources, Utah Valley Regional
    Medical Center, Provo, UT, p. A662
MORRIS, Marsha, Manager Information Services, Fairview Park
  Hospital, Dublin, GA, p. A159
MORRIS, R. Randall, Administrator, West Carroll Memorial
  Hospital, Oak Grove, LA, p. A286
MORRIS, Rosanna D., R.N. Chief Operating Officer, Nebraska
  Medical Center, Omaha, NE, p. A400
MORRIS, Shawna, Senior Vice President Operations and Chief
  Operating Officer, Menninger Clinic, Houston, TX, p. A626
MORRIS, Terri, Director Information Systems, Methodist
  Richardson Medical Center, Richardson, TX, p. A644
MORRIS, Tony, Business Manager, Mental Health Institute,
  Cherokee, IA, p. A227
MORRIS, Will, Director Information Technology, Tri–Lakes
  Medical Center, Batesville, MS, p. A355
MORRISON, Christopher, Deputy Chief Executive Officer,
  Trenton Psychiatric Hospital, Trenton, NJ, p. A424
MORRISON, Deane, Chief Information Officer, Concord Hospital,
  Concord, NH, p. A409
MORRISON, Devin, Director Administration, Naval Hospital
  Pensacola, Pensacola, FL, p. A142
MORRISON, Dianne, Director Human Resources, Mizell Memorial
  Hospital, Opp, AL, p. A24
MORRISON, Gary, Chief Operating Officer, Karmanos Cancer
  Center, Detroit, MI, p. A322
MORRISON, Greg, M.D. Vice President Medical Affairs,
  OhioHealth Grant Medical Center, Columbus, OH, p. A490
MORRISON, J. E., M.D. Chief Medical Officer, Hillcrest Baptist
  Medical Center, Waco, TX, p. A655
MORRISON, Kathy E., Executive Director Human Resources, St.
  Catherine Hospital, Garden City, KS, p. A244
MORRISON, Kevin, Chief Financial Officer, Dickenson Community
  Hospital, Clintwood, VA, p. A669

MORRISON, Maureen, Vice President Financial Services,
  Advocate Trinity Hospital, Chicago, IL, p. A183
MORRISON, Michael, Chief Financial Officer, TriStar
  Hendersonville Medical Center, Hendersonville, TN, p. A584
MORRISON, Ron, Chief Human Resources Officer, Lakeway
  Regional Medical Center, Lakeway, TX, p. A632
MORRISON, Sarah, Vice President Clinical Services, Shepherd
  Center, Atlanta, GA, p. A153
MORRISON, Teresa J., Chief Financial Officer, Bell Hospital,
  Ishpeming, MI, p. A327
MORRISSETT, Barbara, Vice President Human Resources, St.
  Mary's Medical Center, San Francisco, CA, p. A91
MORRISSETTE, Daniel, Chief Financial Officer, Stanford Hospital
  and Clinics, Palo Alto, CA, p. A82
MORRISSEY, Dawn, Chief Operating Officer, Northern Colorado
  Long Term Acute Hospital, Johnstown, CO, p. A107
MORRISSEY, Moira, Chief Operating Officer and General
  Counsel, Four Winds Hospital, Katonah, NY, p. A439
MORRISSEY, Una E., R.N. Senior Vice President, Chief Nursing
  Officer and Chief Operating Officer, New York Community
  Hospital,, NY, p. A447
MORROW, Charles, M.D. Chief Medical Officer, Spartanburg
  Regional Medical Center, Spartanburg, SC, p. A570
MORROW, Ginger
  Executive Vice President Human Resources, Good Shepherd
    Medical Center, Longview, TX, p. A634
  Executive Vice President Human Resources, Good Shepherd
    Medical Center–Marshall, Marshall, TX, p. A636
MORROW, Jeffrey, Chief Executive Officer, Doctor's Hospital of
  Deer Creek, Leesville, LA, p. A283
MORROW, Jennifer, Director Human Resources, San Joaquin
  Valley Rehabilitation Hospital, Fresno, CA, p. A64
MORROW, Pat, Director Human Resources, Walker Baptist
  Medical Center, Jasper, AL, p. A22
MORROW, Shawn, Administrator, Heber Valley Medical Center,
  Heber City, UT, p. A660
MORROW, Susan, R.N. Chief Nursing Officer, Garfield County
  Public Hospital District, Pomeroy, WA, p. A686
MORROW, W. Robert, M.D. Executive Vice President and Chief
  Medical Officer, Children's Medical Center of Dallas, Dallas,
  TX, p. A610
MORSCHAUSER, Roberta, Administrator, Brown County
  Community Treatment Center, Green Bay, WI, p. A706
MORSE, Brad S., Chief Executive Officer, Pampa Regional
  Medical Center, Pampa, TX, p. A641
MORSE, Craig, Chief Financial Officer, Carlsbad Medical Center,
  Carlsbad, NM, p. A427
MORSE, Jason, Director Information Technology, Cumberland
  Memorial Hospital, Cumberland, WI, p. A703
MORSE, Larry, Chief Executive Officer and Administrator,
  Johnson Regional Medical Center, Clarksville, AR, p. A44
MORSE, Patrick, M.D. President Medical Staff, West Branch
  Regional Medical Center, West Branch, MI, p. A337
MORSTAD, Joan, Director Information Systems, Coliseum
  Medical Centers, Macon, GA, p. A162
MORTENSEN, Lorrie, R.N. Chief Patient Services, Murray County
  Medical Center, Slayton, MN, p. A352
MORTENSEN, Shane
  Chief Financial Officer, San Luis Valley Health, Alamosa, CO,
    p. A102
  Chief Financial Officer, San Luis Valley Health Conejos County
    Hospital, La Jara, CO, p. A108
MORTENSSON, Marcie, Chief Human Resources Officer, Tahoe
  Forest Hospital District, Truckee, CA, p. A97
MORTINSEN, Roy, M.D. Chief of Staff, Sanford Vermillion
  Medical Center, Vermillion, SD, p. A577
MORTON, David, M.D. Chief Medical Officer, St. Anthony's
  Medical Center, Saint Louis, MO, p. A381
MORTON, Lauren, Chief Operating Officer, Sierra Providence
  East Medical Center, El Paso, TX, p. A616
MORTON, Leslie, Manager Human Resources, Riverview
  Regional Medical Center, Gadsden, AL, p. A20
MORTON, Robert, M.D. Medical Director, Rolling Hills Hospital,
  Ada, OK, p. A507
MORTON, Stan C., FACHE, President, Texas Health
  Presbyterian Hospital Denton, Denton, TX, p. A613
MORTON, Stephanie, Chief Information Officer, Providence
  Alaska Medical Center, Anchorage, AK, p. A28
MORTOZA, Angela, Administrator, Adair County Memorial
  Hospital, Greenfield, IA, p. A231
MORVANT, Stephanie, Chief Executive Officer, Post Acute
  Northshore Specialty Hospital, Covington, LA, p. A276
MOSBY, Charmaine T., Area Director Health Information
  Management, Promise Hospital Baton Rouge – Main Campus,
  Baton Rouge, LA, p. A273
MOSBY HENRY, Nita, Vice President Human Resources,
  Children's Hospital Colorado, Aurora, CO, p. A102
MOSCATO, Mary K., President, Hebrew Rehabilitation Center,
  Boston, MA, p. A307

MOSCHITTA, Philip C., Director, Northport Veterans Affairs
  Medical Center, Northport, NY, p. A449
MOSCHKAU, Don, Senior Director Human Resources, University
  of Minnesota Medical Center, Fairview, Minneapolis, MN,
  p. A348
MOSCOSO, Ricardo, M.D. Medical Director, University Hospital,
  San Juan, PR, p. A729
MOSEBAR, Anjanette, Director Human Resources, Poudre Valley
  Hospital, Fort Collins, CO, p. A106
MOSELY, Chisty, Director Information Management, Saint
  Simons by–the–Sea Hospital, Saint Simons Island, GA,
  p. A166
MOSER, Brenda, Vice President Finance, Regional Health
  Services of Howard County, Cresco, IA, p. A228
MOSER, Cindy, Director Human Resources, Allegheny Valley
  Hospital, Natrona Heights, PA, p. A546
MOSER, Neal, M.D. Medical Director, HEALTHSOUTH Northern
  Kentucky Rehabilitation Hospital, Edgewood, KY, p. A260
MOSER, Stan, Vice President Information Systems, Community
  Medical Center, Missoula, MT, p. A389
MOSER, Tracy, Director Human Resources, Upper Valley
  Medical Center, Troy, OH, p. A503
MOSES, James, Director Human Resources, St. Charles Parish
  Hospital, Luling, LA, p. A283
MOSESIAN, Robert, Controller, HEALTHSOUTH Bakersfield
  Rehabilitation Hospital, Bakersfield, CA, p. A57
MOSHIER, John, Director Human Resources, Clara Barton
  Hospital, Hoisington, KS, p. A245
MOSHIRPUR, Jasmin, M.D
  Dean and Medical Director, Elmhurst Hospital Center,, NY,
    p. A443
  Chief Medical Officer, Queens Hospital Center,, NY, p. A448
MOSHOFSKY, Bill, M.D. Chief of Staff, PeaceHealth Sacred
  Heart Medical Center, University District, Eugene, OR,
  p. A524
MOSIER, Dawn, Director Human Resources, HEALTHSOUTH
  Rehabilitation Institute of Tucson, Tucson, AZ, p. A40
MOSIER, John, D.O. Chief of Staff, Herington Municipal Hospital,
  Herington, KS, p. A245
MOSKOWITZ, Samuel E., President, MedStar Franklin Square
  Medical Center, Baltimore, MD, p. A297
MOSLEY, Christopher J., Chief Operating Officer, Orange Park
  Medical Center, Orange Park, FL, p. A140
MOSLEY, Christopher R., FACHE Chief Operating Officer, Grady
  Memorial Hospital, Atlanta, GA, p. A152
MOSLEY, Tonja, Chief Financial Officer, Heart of Florida Regional
  Medical Center, Davenport, FL, p. A127
MOSMEYER, Kathleen C., Director Human Resources, Citizens
  Medical Center, Victoria, TX, p. A655
MOSS, Austin, Vice President Human Resources, Jennie Stuart
  Medical Center, Hopkinsville, KY, p. A263
MOSS, Barry, Assistant Chief Executive Officer, Flowers
  Hospital, Dothan, AL, p. A19
MOSS, Bradley, Administrator, Behavioral Healthcare Center at
  Huntsville, Huntsville, AL, p. A21
MOSS, C. Renee, M.D. Chief Medical Officer, Riverside
  Rehabilitation Institute, Newport News, VA, p. A675
MOSS, Jennifer, Chief Clinical Officer, Kirby Medical Center,
  Monticello, IL, p. A196
MOSS, Misty, Director Business Administration, Logansport
  State Hospital, Logansport, IN, p. A218
MOSS, Stuart, Chief Financial Officer, Marlton Rehabilitation
  Hospital, Marlton, NJ, p. A418
MOSSER, Kevin H., M.D., President and Chief Executive
  Officer, WellSpan Health, York, PA, p. B151
MOSSOFF, Alan, Chief Financial Officer, Northern Dutchess
  Hospital, Rhinebeck, NY, p. A452
MOSSOP, Karen, Director Human Resources, Montgomery
  County Emergency Service, Norristown, PA, p. A546
MOST, Kevin, D.O. Vice President Medical Affairs, Central
  DuPage Hospital, Winfield, IL, p. A205
MOSTOFI, Ann R., MSN Vice President Patient Care and Chief
  Nursing Officer, Eisenhower Medical Center, Rancho Mirage,
  CA, p. A84
MOTAKEF, Shahin, Chief Executive Officer, Scott & White
  Memorial Hospital, Temple, TX, p. A652
MOTEJZIK, Thomas, Director Information Systems, Carlsbad
  Medical Center, Carlsbad, NM, p. A427
MOTONAGA, Gregg, M.D. Chief of Staff, Central Peninsula
  General Hospital, Soldotna, AK, p. A30
MOTTE, Michael J., Chief Executive Officer, St. Alexius Hospital
  – Broadway Campus, Saint Louis, MO, p. A381
MOUGHAN, Jennifer L., Chief Human Resources Officer, Our
  Lady of Lourdes Medical Center, Camden, NJ, p. A414
MOUISSET, Rena B., Director Human Resources and Contract
  Compliance, St. Martin Hospital, Breaux Bridge, LA, p. A275
MOULTON, Susan, Interim Director Health Information
  Management, Spring Harbor Hospital, Westbrook, ME,
  p. A295

MOUNIE, Mike, Director Finance, Sentara Obici Hospital, Suffolk, VA, p. A679

MOUNTAIN, J. Michael, Chief Financial Officer, RiverValley Behavioral Health Hospital, Owensboro, KY, p. A268

MOUSA. Ayman, Ph.D., Chief Executive Officer, Pacifica Hospital of the Valley,, CA, p. A74

MOUSA, Barry L., Chief Executive Officer, Rehoboth McKinley Christian Health Care Services, Gallup, NM, p. A428

MOUSTAKAKIS, John, Senior Vice President Information Systems and Chief Information Officer, Westchester Medical Center, Valhalla, NY, p. A457

MOVSESIAN, Gregory, M.D. Acting Chief of Staff, Aleda E. Lutz Veterans Affairs Medical Center, Saginaw, MI, p. A333

MOWAN, Chris, Chief Executive Officer, MountainView Hospital, Las Vegas, NV, p. A406

MOWDER, Kristan, Director Administration and Patient Care Services, Eastern State Hospital, Lexington, KY, p. A264

MOYA, Linda, Director Human Resources, Mesilla Valley Hospital, Las Cruces, NM, p. A429

MOYER, Dale, Vice President Information Systems, Evangelical Community Hospital, Lewisburg, PA, p. A543

MOYER, Douglas J., Chief Executive Officer, Southside Regional Medical Center, Petersburg, VA, p. A676

MOYER, Ed, Chief Operating Officer, Emory–Adventist Hospital, Smyrna, GA, p. A166

MOYER, Mark, Vice President and Chief Financial Officer, Novant Health Presbyterian Medical Center, Charlotte, NC, p. A462

MOYER, Patricia M., Chief Financial Officer, Herington Municipal Hospital, Herington, KS, p. A245

MOYER, William E., President, St. Luke's Hospital – Miners Campus, Coaldale, PA, p. A536

MRAMOR, Joann, Director Human Resources, Seven Rivers Regional Medical Center, Crystal River, FL, p. A126

MUCCILLI, Pamela M., Regional Director Management Information Systems, The William W. Backus Hospital, Norwich, CT, p. A116

MUCK, Erin, Chief Nursing Officer, Grand River Hospital District, Rifle, CO, p. A111

MUDEN, Todd, Section Head Information Management, Mayo Clinic Health System – Northland in Barron, Barron, WI, p. A702

MUDRY, Janel, Chief Operating Officer, Southwest Regional Medical Center, Waynesburg, PA, p. A557

MUELLER, Arthur, Director Management Information Systems, Cuero Community Hospital, Cuero, TX, p. A609

MUELLER, Charles, M.D. Chief of Staff, Texas County Memorial Hospital, Houston, MO, p. A372

MUELLER, Eric, Chief Executive Officer, Reliant Rehabilitation Hospital Central Texas, Round Rock, TX, p. A644

MUELLER, Jeff T., M.D. Chief Medical Officer, Medical Director, Mayo Clinic Hospital, Phoenix, AZ, p. A36

MUELLER, Michael E., Chief Financial Officer, Health Central Hospital, Ocoee, FL, p. A140

MUELLER, Michelle, Manager Human Resources, Genoa Community Hospital, Genoa, NE, p. A396

MUELLER, Paul, Chief Financial Officer, Sparta Community Hospital, Sparta, IL, p. A202

MUELLER, Paul A., Chief Executive Officer, Rogers Memorial Hospital, Oconomowoc, WI, p. A712

MUELLER, Scarlott, Chief Nursing Officer, North Florida Regional Medical Center, Gainesville, FL, p. A129

MUGAN, James, Senior Vice President for Clinical Services and Chief Operating Officer, Agnesian HealthCare, Fond Du Lac, WI, p. A704

MUHAMMAD, Mark, Manager Human Resources, Michael E. DeBakey Veterans Affairs Medical Center, Houston, TX, p. A626

MUHS, David, Chief Financial Officer, Henry County Health Center, Mount Pleasant, IA, p. A234

MUILENBURG, Jeff, Chief of Staff, Memorial Community Health, Aurora, NE, p. A393

MUIR, Brian, Chief of Staff, Minidoka Memorial Hospital, Rupert, ID, p. A178

MULDER, Dale R., Chief Executive Officer, Kindred Rehabilitation Hospital Clear Lake, Webster, TX, p. A656

MULDER, Doris, Vice President Nursing, Beloit Health System, Beloit, WI, p. A702

MULDER, Steven, M.D., President and Chief Executive Officer, Hutchinson Health, Hutchinson, MN, p. A345

MULDERIG, Marsha L., R.N. Chief Nursing Officer, Crisp Regional Hospital, Cordele, GA, p. A157

MULDOON, Patrick L., FACHE, President and CEO, UMass Memorial Medical Center, Worcester, MA, p. A317

MULDOON, Sean R., M.D. Senior Vice President and Chief Medical Officer–Kindred Healthcare, Hospital Division, Kindred Hospital Northland, Kansas City, MO, p. A373

MULIS, Becky, Director of Health Information Management Systems, Four County Counseling Center, Logansport, IN, p. A217

MULKERRIN, Maureen, Vice President Technology Risk Management, Corporate Compliance and Chief Information Officer, New England Baptist Hospital, Boston, MA, p. A307

MULKEY, Peter, Chief Executive Officer, Clinch Valley Medical Center, Richlands, VA, p. A677

MULLANEY, Ruth, Personnel Officer, Dorothea Dix Psychiatric Center, Bangor, ME, p. A291

MULLANEY, Susan, Chief Executive Officer, Kaiser Foundation Hospital Westside Medical Center, Hillsboro, OR, p. A525

MULLEN, Ron, Superintendent, Mental Health Institute, Mount Pleasant, IA, p. A235

MULLEN, Thomas R., President and Chief Executive Officer, Mercy Medical Center, Baltimore, MD, p. A297

MULLENAX, Paul, Business Manager, Wyoming State Hospital, Evanston, WY, p. A721

MULLENS, Allen, M.D. Chief Medical Staff, Norton Community Hospital, Norton, VA, p. A676

MULLER, Lynn, Chief Financial Officer, North Metro Medical Center, Jacksonville, AR, p. A48

MULLER, Oz, Director Human Resources, Porter Adventist Hospital, Denver, CO, p. A105

MULLER, Ralph W., President and Chief Executive Officer, University of Pennsylvania Health System, Philadelphia, PA, p. B146

MULLER, William, M.D. Vice President Medical Affairs, Milford Regional Medical Center, Milford, MA, p. A312

MULLIGAN, Marie, R.N. Vice President Nursing, John T. Mather Memorial Hospital, Port Jefferson, NY, p. A452

MULLIGAN, Michael, M.D. President Medical Staff, Anderson Hospital, Maryville, IL, p. A195

MULLIGAN, Regina, Vice President Nursing, Nathan Littauer Hospital and Nursing Home, Gloversville, NY, p. A438

MULLIN, Tom, Chief Executive Officer, Select Specialty Hospital–Central Pennsylvania, Camp Hill, PA, p. A535

MULLINGS, Donna, Director of Nursing, Assumption Community Hospital, Napoleonville, LA, p. A285

MULLINGS, Paul, Chief Operating Officer, Howard University Hospital, Washington, DC, p. A121

MULLINS, Bandy, M.D. Chief of Staff, Summersville Regional Medical Center, Summersville, WV, p. A699

MULLINS, Brad, Director Information Technology, Gove County Medical Center, Quinter, KS, p. A253

MULLINS, Cindy, Director Information Technology, Saint Mary's Regional Medical Center, Reno, NV, p. A408

MULLINS, Dustin, Chief Resource Management, Bayne–Jones Army Community Hospital, Fort Polk, LA, p. A277

MULLINS, Erin, D.O. Chief Medical Staff, Dickenson Community Hospital, Clintwood, VA, p. A669

MULLINS Jr., John David, Administrator, Clinton County Hospital, Albany, KY, p. A258

MULLINS, Kem, FACHE, Senior Vice President and Hospital President, WellStar Cobb Hospital, Austell, GA, p. A154

MULLINS, Larry, Chief Executive Officer, W. J. Mangold Memorial Hospital, Lockney, TX, p. A634

MULLINS, Larry A., FACHE, Chief Executive Officer, Good Samaritan Regional Medical Center, Corvallis, OR, p. A524

MULLINS, Larry A., FACHE, President and Chief Executive Officer, Samaritan Health Services, Corvallis, OR, p. B117

MULLINS, Mary Beth, Associate Administrator and Chief Nursing Officer, CAMC Teays Valley Hospital, Hurricane, WV, p. A696

MULLINS, Tommy H., Administrator, Boone Memorial Hospital, Madison, WV, p. A697

MULROONEY, JoAnn M., R.N. Chief Operating Officer, Trinity Health System, Steubenville, OH, p. A502

MULVIHILL, Jody, Vice President Finance, The Children's Institute of Pittsburgh, Pittsburgh, PA, p. A551

MUMMA, Barbara, Vice President Human Resources, Ephrata Community Hospital, Ephrata, PA, p. A538

MUMOLIE, Gina, Senior Vice President and Chief Nurse Executive, Inspira Medical Center–Woodbury, Woodbury, NJ, p. A425

MUNCHEL, Bryan, Senior Vice President and Chief Information Officer, Post Acute Northshore Specialty Hospital, Covington, LA, p. A276

MUNDY, Mark J., President and Chief Executive Officer, New York Methodist Hospital,, NY, p. A447

MUNDY, Stephens M., President and Chief Executive Officer, Champlain Valley Physicians Hospital Medical Center, Plattsburgh, NY, p. A451

MUNFORD, Thedosia, Senior Vice President and Chief Nursing Officer, Providence Hospital, Washington, DC, p. A121

MUNGER, Richard, Administrator, Mount Grant General Hospital, Hawthorne, NV, p. A405

MUNGOVAN, Sandy, Chief Information Officer, Harbor–UCLA Medical Center, Torrance, CA, p. A97

MUNHOLLAND, Cleta
Administrator, Louisiana Extended Care Hospital West Monroe, West Monroe, LA, p. A290
Administrator, Specialty Extended Care Hospital of Monroe, Monroe, LA, p. A284

MUNIR, Amjad, M.D. Medical Director, HEALTHSOUTH Chattanooga Rehabilitation Hospital, Chattanooga, TN, p. A580

MUNOZ, Astro, Executive Director, First Hospital Panamericano, Cidra, PR, p. A725

MUNOZ, Thalia H., MS, Hospital Administrator, Starr County Memorial Hospital, Rio Grande City, TX, p. A644

MUNSON, Bill, Vice President and Chief Financial Officer, Boulder Community Hospital, Boulder, CO, p. A102

MUNSON, Jennifer, Chief Financial Officer, Three Rivers Hospital, Brewster, WA, p. A682

MUNSON, Joan, Manager Information Systems, Fairchild Medical Center, Yreka, CA, p. A101

MUNSON, John, Vice President and Chief Financial Officer, St. Anthony Regional Hospital, Carroll, IA, p. A226

MUNSON, Kris, Director Human Resources, Arbour H. R. I. Hospital, Brookline, MA, p. A308

MUNTEFERING, Denise, Vice President Patient Care Services, Avera St. Benedict Health Center, Parkston, SD, p. A575

MUNTZ, Dana M., Chief Executive Officer, St. Vincent Salem Hospital, Salem, IN, p. A222

MUNTZ, Tim, President and Chief Executive Officer, St. Margaret's Hospital, Spring Valley, IL, p. A203

MUNYAN, Lori, Director, Human Resources, HEALTHSOUTH Rehabilitation Hospital of Toms River, Toms River, NJ, p. A423

MURANSKY, Ed, Owner, Surgical Hospital at Southwoods, Youngstown, OH, p. A506

MURCHISON, Sandra, Director Medical Records, Coosa Valley Medical Center, Sylacauga, AL, p. A25

MURDOCH, William, M.D. Medical Director, Loma Linda University Behavioral Medicine Center, Redlands, CA, p. A85

MURDOCK, Guy, Vice President Human Resources, Healthbridge Children's Hospital of Houston, Houston, TX, p. A624

MURDOCK, Holly, Human Resources Coordinator, Kindred Hospital Rome, Rome, GA, p. A165

MURDOCK, Mark, Associate Director, Dayton Veterans Affairs Medical Center, Dayton, OH, p. A492

MURDOCK–LANGAN, Patricia, Chief Medical Officer, CHI Health Lakeside, Omaha, NE, p. A399

MURDY, James B., Chief Financial Officer, Belmont Community Hospital, Bellaire, OH, p. A483

MURFEE, Patrick, Chief Operating Officer, Hemphill County Hospital, Canadian, TX, p. A605

MURIN, William J., Chief Human Resources Officer, UC San Diego Health System, San Diego, CA, p. A90

MURPHY, Bruce, M.D., President and Chief Executive Officer, Arkansas Heart Hospital, Little Rock, AR, p. A48

MURPHY, Charles J., Associate Vice President Human Resources, Strong Memorial Hospital of the University of Rochester, Rochester, NY, p. A453

MURPHY, Christine, MS, Administrator, Liberty Healthcare Systems, Bastrop, LA, p. A272

MURPHY, Colleen, M.D. Chief of Staff, Clay County Hospital, Flora, IL, p. A190

MURPHY, Dennis M., Chief Operating Officer, Indiana University Health University Hospital, Indianapolis, IN, p. A214

MURPHY, Elizabeth A., R.N. Vice President for Patient Care Services, Mercy Health Saint Mary's, Grand Rapids, MI, p. A325

MURPHY, Evelyn, R.N. Chief Nursing Officer, Ty Cobb Regional Medical Center, Lavonia, GA, p. A162

MURPHY, J. Patrick, Chief Financial Officer, North Baldwin Infirmary, Bay Minette, AL, p. A16

MURPHY, James, Chief Executive Officer, South Texas Surgical Hospital, Corpus Christi, TX, p. A608

MURPHY, James M., M.D. Chief Medical Officer Regional Development and Outpatient Services, New London Hospital, New London, NH, p. A411

MURPHY, John B., M.D. Vice President Medical Affairs and Chief Medical Officer, Rhode Island Hospital, Providence, RI, p. A561

MURPHY, John M., M.D., President and Chief Executive Officer, Danbury Hospital, Danbury, CT, p. A113

MURPHY, John M., M.D., President, Western Connecticut Health Network, Danbury, CT, p. B152

MURPHY, Judy, Vice President Human Resources, Southwest General Health Center. Middleburg Heights, OH, p. A498

MURPHY, Julie
Chief Financial Officer, Saint Luke's Cushing Hospital, Leavenworth, KS, p. A248
Chief Financial Officer, Saint Luke's North Hospital – Barry Road, Kansas City, MO, p. A374

MURPHY, Kathryn, Chief Operating Officer and Chief Nursing Officer, Forest Park Medical Center Frisco, Frisco, TX, p. A620

MURPHY, Kathy, Site Manager, Mescalero Public Health Service Indian Hospital, Mescalero, NM, p. A429

MURPHY, Kelly, Director Human Resources, Family Health West, Fruita, CO, p. A106

MURPHY, Kevin, Director, Information Technology Services, Bayfront Health St. Petersburg, Saint Petersburg, FL, p. A144

MURPHY, Kyle, Director Information Technology, Mayhill Hospital, Denton, TX, p. A613

MURPHY, Linda, Chief Financial Officer, Osborne County Memorial Hospital, Osborne, KS, p. A251

MURPHY, Lionel
Chief Executive Officer and Administrator, Bethesda Rehabilitation Hospital, Baton Rouge, LA, p. A273
Chief Executive Officer, Southeast Regional Medical Center, Kentwood, LA, p. A280

MURPHY, Lynda J., Vice President Human Resources, Logansport Memorial Hospital, Logansport, IN, p. A218

MURPHY, Margaret M., Interim Chief Executive Officer, Kindred Hospital–Philadelphia, Philadelphia, PA, p. A549

MURPHY, Mary S., R.N. Regional Chief Nursing Officer, Adventist La Grange Memorial Hospital, La Grange, IL, p. A194

MURPHY, Marybeth, Director Human Resources, Madison St. Joseph Health Center, Madisonville, TX, p. A636

MURPHY, Matthew, Chief Financial Officer, Marengo Memorial Hospital, UnityPoint Health, Marengo, IA, p. A234

MURPHY, Maureen, M.D. Director of Medical Affairs, St. Clare Hospital, Baraboo, WI, p. A702

MURPHY, Michael, M.D. Chief Medical Officer, Sharp Grossmont Hospital, La Mesa, CA, p. A68

MURPHY, Michael, CPA, President & Chief Executive Officer, Sharp HealthCare, San Diego, CA, p. B123

MURPHY, Michael D., Chief Executive Officer, Abilene Regional Medical Center, Abilene, TX, p. A595

MURPHY, Michael J., FACHE, Chief Executive Officer, Veterans Affairs Puget Sound Health Care System, Seattle, WA, p. A689

MURPHY, Mike, Chief Patient Care Officer, Beaver Dam Community Hospitals, Beaver Dam, WI, p. A702

MURPHY, Nancy, Vice President, Human Resources, Franciscan Hospital for Children, Boston, MA, p. A306

MURPHY, Peter J., Senior Vice President and Chief Operating Officer, Franciscan St. Francis Health – Mooresville, Mooresville, IN, p. A219

MURPHY, Richard J., President and Chief Executive Officer, South Nassau Communities Hospital, Oceanside, NY, p. A450

MURPHY, Rita, Director Human Resources, Cobre Valley Regional Medical Center, Globe, AZ, p. A33

MURPHY, Rob, President, Jewish Hospital–Shelbyville, Shelbyville, KY, p. A270

MURPHY, Steve, Director Networks, Good Samaritan Regional Health Center, Mount Vernon, IL, p. A197

MURPHY, Steven, Executive Director, Devereux Hospital and Children's Center of Florida, Melbourne, FL, p. A135

MURPHY, Terry
President and Chief Executive Officer, Bayhealth Medical Center, Dover, DE, p. A119
Director Information Services, Phoenixville Hospital, Phoenixville, PA, p. A550

MURPHY, Timothy, R.N. Chief Nursing Officer, HEALTHSOUTH Desert Canyon Rehabilitation Hospital, Las Vegas, NV, p. A405

MURPHY, Timothy
Vice President Human Resources, Mercy Hospital Fort Scott, Fort Scott, KS, p. A244
Vice President Human Resources, Mercy Hospital Joplin, Joplin, MO, p. A373

MURPHY, Tom, Chief Executive Officer, Weiser Memorial Hospital, Weiser, ID, p. A179

MURPHY–FROBISH, Erin, Vice President Human Resources, Morris Hospital & Healthcare Centers, Morris, IL, p. A196

MURRAY, Alexander, Interim Associate Director, Veterans Affairs Gulf Coast Veterans Health Care System, Biloxi, MS, p. A356

MURRAY, Brian, M.D. Medical Director, Erie County Medical Center, Buffalo, NY, p. A434

MURRAY, Brian, Chief Financial Officer, Gunnison Valley Hospital, Gunnison, UT, p. A660

MURRAY, Cindy, R.N. Chief Nursing Officer and Chief Operating Officer, Baylor Medical Center at Waxahachie, Waxahachie, TX, p. A656

MURRAY, Denise R., Chief Executive Officer, Crawley Memorial Hospital, Shelby, NC, p. A472

MURRAY, Diana, Director Information Systems, Grand River Hospital District, Rifle, CO, p. A111

MURRAY, Geno, President and Chief Executive Officer, Charles A. Dean Memorial Hospital, Greenville, ME, p. A293

MURRAY, Gerald, President, UPMC Altoona, Altoona, PA, p. A532

MURRAY, James Patrick, FACHE, Chief Executive Officer, Peterson Regional Medical Center, Kerrville, TX, p. A631

MURRAY, Judi, Facility Director, Lanterman Developmental Center, Pomona, CA, p. A84

MURRAY, Julie, Chief Executive Officer, Litzenberg Memorial County Hospital, Central City, NE, p. A394

MURRAY, Kent, M.D. Chief of Staff, Robert J. Dole Veterans Affairs Medical Center, Wichita, KS, p. A256

MURRAY, Kevin, M.D. Director Medical Services, Lake Taylor Transitional Care Hospital, Norfolk, VA, p. A675

MURRAY, Kevin J., Senior Vice President, John T. Mather Memorial Hospital, Port Jefferson, NY, p. A452

MURRAY, Patricia M., Information Officer, Southern Inyo Healthcare District, Lone Pine, CA, p. A70

MURRAY, Sherri, Chief Financial Officer, Montgomery General Hospital, Montgomery, WV, p. A697

MURRAY, Susan, Director Information Services, Trident Medical Center, Charleston, SC, p. A563

MURRAY, Wesley E., Chief Executive Officer, Texas County Memorial Hospital, Houston, MO, p. A372

MURRELL, Joseph, Chief Executive Officer, Wayne County Hospital, Monticello, KY, p. A267

MURRILL, Mike, Vice President and Chief Financial Officer, Adventist Bolingbrook Hospital, Bolingbrook, IL, p. A182

MURROW, Carol, Vice President Business Development, Cox Medical Center Branson, Branson, MO, p. A368

MURRY, Jim, Chief Information Officer, Stony Brook University Medical Center, Stony Brook, NY, p. A455

MURT, Mary Lou, R.N. Senior Vice President Nursing, Monongahela Valley Hospital, Monongahela, PA, p. A545

MURTHY, Bangalore, M.D. Director Medical Staff, Jackson Park Hospital and Medical Center, Chicago, IL, p. A184

MUSACK, Scott, Chief Information Officer, Silver Lake Medical Center, Los Angeles, CA, p. A74

MUSOIU, Robert, Director Human Resources, Fairfield Memorial Hospital, Fairfield, IL, p. A190

MUSSI, Natalie, Chief Executive Officer, Los Robles Hospital and Medical Center, Thousand Oaks, CA, p. A97

MUSSMAN, Rebekah, Chief Financial Officer, Kearney County Health Services, Minden, NE, p. A398

MUSSO, Lewis C., Vice President Human Resources, Trinity Health System, Steubenville, OH, p. A502

MUSTARD, Ruth W., R.N. Associate Director Nursing and Patient Services, Wm. Jennings Bryan Dorn Veterans Affairs Medical Center, Columbia, SC, p. A565

MUSTIAN, J. Perry, President, Archbold Medical Center, Thomasville, GA, p. B11

MUSTIAN, J. Perry, President and Chief Executive Officer, John D. Archbold Memorial Hospital, Thomasville, GA, p. A168

MUTARELLI, Richard, Interim Chief Executive Officer, Munroe Regional Medical Center, Ocala, FL, p. A139

MUTZIGER, John, M.D. Chief Medical Officer, Laird Hospital, Union, MS, p. A366

MWANIKI, Mary
Chief Financial Officer, Reliant Rehabilitation Hospital Dallas, Dallas, TX, p. A611
Chief Financial Officer, Reliant Rehabilitation Hospital Mid–Cities, Bedford, TX, p. A602

MWEBE, David, M.D. Chief of Staff, Osmond General Hospital, Osmond, NE, p. A401

MYATT, Kevin A., Senior Vice President Human Resources, Yale–New Haven Hospital, New Haven, CT, p. A116

MYBURGH, Ronell, Chief Executive Officer, Healthbridge Children's Hospital of Houston, Houston, TX, p. A624

MYDLER, Todd, M.D. Vice President and Chief Medical Officer, Exempla Good Samaritan Medical Center, Lafayette, CO, p. A108

MYER, Amber, Director Medical Technology, Throckmorton County Memorial Hospital, Throckmorton, TX, p. A653

MYERS, April, Administrator, Kindred Hospital–La Mirada, La Mirada, CA, p. A68

MYERS, Becky, Human Resources Specialist, Illini Community Hospital, Pittsfield, IL, p. A200

MYERS, Carl, M.D. Vice President Medical Affairs and Chief Medical Officer, Yuma Regional Medical Center, Yuma, AZ, p. A42

MYERS, Chrissy, R.N. Director of Nursing, Behavioral HealthCare Center at Clarksville, Clarksville, TN, p. A581

MYERS, Doug, Senior Vice President and Chief Financial Officer, Children's Hospital and Research Center Oakland, Oakland, CA, p. A80

MYERS, Douglas, Executive Vice President and Chief Financial Officer, Children's National Medical Center, Washington, DC, p. A121

MYERS, Edward W., Chief Executive Officer, St. Luke's Medical Center, Phoenix, AZ, p. A37

MYERS, Frederick, M.D. Chief Medical Officer, Takoma Regional Hospital, Greeneville, TN, p. A583

MYERS, Gabby, Human Resources Director, Victory Surgical Hospital East Houston, Houston, TX, p. A628

MYERS, Gary, Chief Executive Officer, Mammoth Hospital, Mammoth Lakes, CA, p. A76

MYERS, Grace, MSN Vice President, Nurse Executive, Sentara Princess Anne Hospital, Virginia Beach, VA, p. A679

MYERS, Jeffrey D., President and Chief Executive Officer, Hamilton Medical Center, Dalton, GA, p. A158

MYERS, Jerry, M.D., Chief Executive Officer, Kell West Regional Hospital, Wichita Falls, TX, p. A657

MYERS, Karen, Vice President Financial Services, Stoughton Hospital Association, Stoughton, WI, p. A716

MYERS, Karen K., MSN Vice President and Chief Nursing Officer, St. Luke's Medical Center, Houston, TX, p. A627

MYERS, Kathy R., MS Chief Nursing Officer, Tennova Healthcare–LaFollette Medical Center, La Follette, TN, p. A586

MYERS, Keith G., Chairman and Chief Executive Officer, LHC Group, Lafayette, LA, p. B84

MYERS, Kevin, Director Information Systems, Lake Granbury Medical Center, Granbury, TX, p. A621

MYERS, Kimberly, Director Human Resources, Guthrie County Hospital, Guthrie Center, IA, p. A231

MYERS, Lisa, Director Human Resources, Heritage Oaks Hospital, Sacramento, CA, p. A87

MYERS, Loretta, MS Director, Patient Care, Floyd Valley Hospital, Le Mars, IA, p. A233

MYERS, Lynn, Controller, Kindred Hospital–Tucson, Tucson, AZ, p. A40

MYERS, Mark, M.D. Chief Medical Officer, AMG Specialty Hospital–Tulsa, Tulsa, OK, p. A520

MYERS, Mary, R.N. Chief Nursing Officer, St. Vincent Indianapolis Hospital, Indianapolis, IN, p. A215

MYERS, Michael D., Chief Executive Officer, Veterans Memorial Hospital, Waukon, IA, p. A239

MYERS, Michelle F., Director Human Resources, Florida Hospital Wauchula, Wauchula, FL, p. A149

MYERS, Paul, M.D. Neonatologist and Chief Medical Officer, Children's Hospital of Wisconsin–Fox Valley, Neenah, WI, p. A711

MYERS, Philip, M.D. Vice President Medical Affairs, Samaritan Regional Health System, Ashland, OH, p. A482

MYERS, Randy, Chief Information Officer, Information Technology, Mitchell County Hospital, Colorado City, TX, p. A607

MYERS, Robert T., President, Parkview LaGrange Hospital, LaGrange, IN, p. A217

MYERS, Russ, Chief Executive Officer, Yakima Valley Memorial Hospital, Yakima, WA, p. A692

MYERS, Shane P., Chief Operating Officer, Iberia Medical Center, New Iberia, LA, p. A285

MYERS, Sheri, Vice President Patient Care Services, McLaren Central Michigan, Mount Pleasant, MI, p. A330

MYERS, Steve, Assistant Administrator, Southeast Health Center of Reynolds County, Ellington, MO, p. A370

MYERS, Tara, Director Human Resources, AnMed Health Rehabilitation Hospital, Anderson, SC, p. A562

MYERS, William, Chief Operating Officer, Montgomery County Emergency Service, Norristown, PA, p. A546

MYHRE, Jane, MS Director Health Information, Chippewa County–Montevideo Hospital, Montevideo, MN, p. A348

MYHRZ, Tracy, Chief Nursing Officer, Tomah Memorial Hospital, Tomah, WI, p. A716

MYLAN, Marci
Director, Veterans Affairs – Western Iowa Healthcare System, Omaha, NE, p. A400
Director, Veterans Affairs Nebraska–Western Iowa Health Care System, Lincoln, NE, p. A398

MYLES, Lee T., President and Chief Executive Officer, St. Mary's Regional Medical Center, Lewiston, ME, p. A294

MYSTER, Jennifer, President, Buffalo Hospital, Buffalo, MN, p. A341

N

NABEL, Elizabeth, M.D., President, Brigham and Women's Hospital, Boston, MA, p. A306

NABORS, Teresa, Director of Nursing, Greenwood Regional Rehabilitation Hospital, Greenwood, SC, p. A567

NACEY, Marley, Director Finance, Sentara Virginia Beach General Hospital, Virginia Beach, VA, p. A679

NACHIMUTHU, Anbu, Chief Financial Officer, Atrium Medical Center of Corinth, Corinth, TX, p. A608

NACHTIGAL, Amy, Chief Financial Officer, Saint Luke's Hospital of Kansas City, Kansas City, MO, p. A374

NACHTRIEB, Han, Vice President Human Resources, Seattle Cancer Care Alliance, Seattle, WA, p. A688

NACION, Glenn, Vice President Human Resources, Trinitas Regional Medical Center, Elizabeth, NJ, p. A415

NADEAU, Barbara, Chief Human Resources Management Service, White River Junction Veterans Affairs Medical Center, White River Junction, VT, p. A666

NADEAU, Colleen, Vice President and Patient Care Operations, Maple Grove Hospital, Maple Grove, MN, p. A346

NADEAU, Steve, Senior Vice President Human Resources, Gwinnett Hospital System, Lawrenceville, GA, p. A162

NADER, Daniel, D.O. Chief of Staff, Southwestern Regional Medical Center, Tulsa, OK, p. A521

NADER, Keoni, Director Human Resources, Louis A. Weiss Memorial Hospital, Chicago, IL, p. A184

NADER, Mary, Director Information Technology, Spectrum Health Special Care Hospital, Grand Rapids, MI, p. A325

NADKARNI, Manasi, M.D. Vice President Medical Affairs, UnityPoint Health – Trinity Muscatine, Muscatine, IA, p. A235

NADLE, Patricia A., R.N. Chief Nursing Officer, St. Joseph Health Services of Rhode Island, North Providence, RI, p. A560

NADOLNY, Stephanie, Vice President Clinical Services, Spaulding Rehabilitation Hospital Cape Cod, East Sandwich, MA, p. A309

NADONE, John, Chief Financial Officer, Southwest Memorial Hospital, Cortez, CO, p. A104

NAEVE, Clayton, Vice President and Chief Information Officer, St. Jude Children's Research Hospital, Memphis, TN, p. A589

NAFZIGER, Laurie N., President and Chief Executive Officer, Oaklawn Psychiatric Center, Goshen, IN, p. A212

NAFZIGER, Steve, M.D. Vice President Medical Affairs, Parkview Medical Center, Pueblo, CO, p. A110

NAGALA, Vani, M.D. Chief Medical Officer, Oakes Community Hospital, Oakes, ND, p. A480

NAGARAJ, Alaka, M.D. Medical Director, Regency Hospital of Minneapolis, Golden Valley, MN, p. A344

NAGEL, Donna, Director Human Resources, AMG Specialty Hospital–Tulsa, Tulsa, OK, p. A520

NAGEL, Melody, Executive Director Operations, Baylor Specialty Hospital, Dallas, TX, p. A609

NAGLE, Jolene, Director Medical Records, Peterson Rehabilitation Hospital, Wheeling, WV, p. A700

NAGLER, Richard, M.D. Chief of Staff, Mayo Clinic Health System – Northland in Barron, Barron, WI, p. A702

NAGLOSKY, Paul, Administrator, Indianhead Medical Center, Shell Lake, WI, p. A715

NAGOWSKI, Michael, President and Chief Executive Officer, Cape Fear Valley Health System, Fayetteville, NC, p. B26

NAGOWSKI, Michael, Chief Executive Officer, Cape Fear Valley Medical Center, Fayetteville, NC, p. A464

NAGY, Jeff, Chief Financial Officer, River Bend Hospital, West Lafayette, IN, p. A224

NAGY, Kimberly, R.N. Executive Vice President, Patient Services and Chief Nursing Officer, Northwest Community Hospital, Arlington Heights, IL, p. A180

NAGY, Linda J., MSN Chief Nursing Officer, Brattleboro Retreat, Brattleboro, VT, p. A665

NAHAPETIAN, Arby, M.D. Vice President Medical Affairs and Quality, Glendale Adventist Medical Center, Glendale, CA, p. A65

NAIBERK, Donald T., Administrator, Butler County Health Care Center, David City, NE, p. A395

NAIR, Chand, M.D. Medical Director, Brooke Glen Behavioral Hospital, Fort Washington, PA, p. A539

NAIR, Vijayachandran, M.D. Chief of Staff, John J. Pershing Veterans Affairs Medical Center, Poplar Bluff, MO, p. A378

NAJIEB, LaDonna, Service Area Director Human Resources, Providence Saint Joseph Medical Center, Burbank, CA, p. A58

NAJJAR, Maher, M.D. Medical Director, Kindred Hospital Chicago–Northlake, Northlake, IL, p. A198

NAJJAR, Milad, Information Technology, Freedom Pain Hospital, Scottsdale, AZ, p. A38

NAKAGAWA, Marc, Vice President and Chief Financial Officer, Transylvania Regional Hospital, Brevard, NC, p. A460

NAKAMOTO, Kenneth, M.D. Vice President Medical Affairs, Pomona Valley Hospital Medical Center, Pomona, CA, p. A84

NAKAMURA, Bridget, Director Information Systems, Simi Valley Hospital and Health Care Services, Simi Valley, CA, p. A95

NAKASUJI, Jody, Chief Financial Officer, Harbor–UCLA Medical Center, Torrance, CA, p. A97

NALDI, Robert, Chief Financial Officer, Maimonides Medical Center,, NY, p. A445

NALEPPA, Margaret, President and Chief Executive Officer, Peninsula Regional Medical Center, Salisbury, MD, p. A303

NALL, Brian, President and Chief Executive Officer, Greenville Regional Hospital, Greenville, IL, p. A191

NALL, Wes, Chief Financial Officer, Monroe County Hospital, Monroeville, AL, p. A23

NALLE, Tambara, Chief Financial Officer, Eastern State Hospital, Lexington, KY, p. A264

NALLEY, Leanna W., Director Human Resources, Texas Health Harris Methodist Hospital Southwest Fort Worth, Fort Worth, TX, p. A619

NANCE, Christi, R.N. Chief Nursing Officer, Northwest Specialty Hospital, Post Falls, ID, p. A178

NANCE, Sally S., Chief Executive Officer, Excelsior Springs Hospital, Excelsior Springs, MO, p. A370

NANIA, James A., System Vice President and Chief Financial Officer, Hallmark Health System, Melrose, MA, p. A312

NANTZ, Mark S., FACHE, Chief Executive Officer, Bon Secours St. Francis Health System, Greenville, SC, p. A566

NAPIER, Lisa, Chief Financial Officer, Atlanta Medical Center, Atlanta, GA, p. A152

NAPIER, Michelle, Director of Nursing, Central State Hospital, Louisville, KY, p. A265

NAPIER, Pamela, R.N. Chief Nursing Officer, Mercy Willard Hospital, Willard, OH, p. A505

NAPIER, Randy L.
President, Frazier Rehab Institute, Louisville, KY, p. A265
President, Southern Indiana Rehabilitation Hospital, New Albany, IN, p. A220

NAPIERALA, Edward A., FACHE, Chief Executive Officer, West Branch Regional Medical Center, West Branch, MI, p. A337

NAPOLITANO, Mary Pat, Director Human Resources, Specialty Hospital of Central Jersey, Lakewood, NJ, p. A417

NAPP, Marc L., M.D. Vice President Medical Affairs, Lenox Hill Hospital, New York, NY, p. A445

NAPPS, Greg, Acting Chief Executive Officer, Culpeper Regional Hospital, Culpeper, VA, p. A670

NAQVI, Al, Chief Financial Officer, Decatur Memorial Hospital, Decatur, IL, p. A188

NARAMORE, G. Harold, M.D. Chief Medical Officer and In house Legal Counsel, Blount Memorial Hospital, Maryville, TN, p. A588

NARANG, Steve, M.D., Chief Executive Officer, Banner Good Samaritan Medical Center, Phoenix, AZ, p. A35

NARANJO, Maria, Director Human Resources, Memorial Hospital West, Pembroke Pines, FL, p. A142

NARBUTAS, Virgis
Chief Executive Officer, Garden Grove Hospital and Medical Center, Garden Grove, CA, p. A65
Chief Executive Officer, Huntington Beach Hospital, Huntington Beach, CA, p. A67
Chief Executive Officer, La Palma Intercommunity Hospital, La Palma, CA, p. A68
Chief Executive Officer, West Anaheim Medical Center, Anaheim, CA, p. A55

NARCIA, Richard, Chief Executive Officer, Huhukam Memorial Hospital, Sacaton, AZ, p. A38

NAREMORE, Bruce, Senior Vice President and Chief Financial Officer, East Jefferson General Hospital, Metairie, LA, p. A284

NARROW, Ann, Director of Nursing, River Hospital, Alexandria Bay, NY, p. A432

NARY, Ed, Director Information Technology and Chief Compliance Officer, Wilbarger General Hospital, Vernon, TX, p. A655

NASET–PAYNE, Janet, R.N. Chief Nursing Officer, Van Diest Medical Center, Webster City, IA, p. A239

NASH, Gayle, R.N. Chief Nursing Officer, New Mexico Rehabilitation Center, Roswell, NM, p. A430

NASH, Jan, Ph.D. Vice President Patient Services and Chief Nursing Officer, Paoli Hospital, Paoli, PA, p. A547

NASH, Jeff, Director Information Technology and Services, Mary Black Memorial Hospital, Spartanburg, SC, p. A570

NASH, Jerry, Chief Executive Officer, Aspire Hospital, Conroe, TX, p. A607

NASH, John D., FACHE, President and Chief Executive Officer, Franciscan Hospital for Children, Boston, MA, p. A306

NASH, Mary G., Ph.D. Chief Nursing Officer, Ohio State University Wexner Medical Center, Columbus, OH, p. A490

NASH, Robert, M.D. Chief of Staff, Richland Memorial Hospital, Olney, IL, p. A198

NASH, Sandra, Chief Fiscal Service, James H. Quillen Veterans Affairs Medical Center, Mountain Home, TN, p. A590

NASH, Tim, M.D. Chief of Staff, Marshall Medical Center, Lewisburg, TN, p. A587

NASHID, Nadia, M.D. Chief of Staff, Windham Hospital, Willimantic, CT, p. A118

NASIR, Iqbal, M.D. Chief of Staff, Oakwood Hospital–Southshore, Trenton, MI, p. A336

NASK, Frank P., President and Chief Executive Officer, Broward Health, Fort Lauderdale, FL, p. B25

NASR, Anthony, M.D. Chief Medical Staff, Feather River Hospital, Paradise, CA, p. A82

NASRALLA, Anthony J., FACHE, President and Chief Executive Officer, Titusville Area Hospital, Titusville, PA, p. A556

NASRALLAH, Naseem, M.D. Chief of Staff, Pender Memorial Hospital, Burgaw, NC, p. A460

NASSIEF, Raymond, Senior Vice President Operations and Clinical Transformation, John Muir Medical Center, Walnut Creek, Walnut Creek, CA, p. A100

NASSTROM, Jeff, D.O. Chief of Staff, Mitchell County Regional Health Center, Osage, IA, p. A236

NATAL, Yesenia, Coordinator Human Resources, Hospital Dr. Cayetano Coll Y Toste, Arecibo, PR, p. A724

NATALONI, Tom, Senior Director Information Technology, Hahnemann University Hospital, Philadelphia, PA, p. A548

NATCHER, Charles
Chief Financial Officer, Kindred Hospital–Los Angeles, Los Angeles, CA, p. A73
Chief Financial Officer, Placentia–Linda Hospital, Placentia, CA, p. A83

NATELSON, Richard, M.D. Chief of Staff, Steele Memorial Medical Center, Salmon, ID, p. A178

NATEMAN, Barry, Manager Human Resources, French Hospital Medical Center, San Luis Obispo, CA, p. A93

NATH, Pravene, Chief Information Officer, Stanford Hospital and Clinics, Palo Alto, CA, p. A82

NATHAN, James R.
President and Chief Executive Officer, Cape Coral Hospital, Cape Coral, FL, p. A125
President and Chief Executive Officer, Gulf Coast Medical Center, Fort Myers, FL, p. A129

NATHAN, James R., President and Chief Executive Officer, Lee Memorial Health System, Fort Myers, FL, p. B83

NATHAN, James R., President and Chief Executive Officer, Lee Memorial Hospital, Fort Myers, FL, p. A129

NATHAN, Matthew L., Surgeon General, Bureau of Medicine and Surgery, Department of the Navy, Washington, DC, p. B25

NATHANSON, Andrea, Director Finance, Baystate Franklin Medical Center, Greenfield, MA, p. A310

NATHEM, Joanne, MSN Chief Clinical and Nursing Officer, Waverly Health Center, Waverly, IA, p. A239

NATOLI, Joseph B., Senior Vice President Business and Finance and Chief Financial Officer, University of Miami Hospital and Clinics, Miami, FL, p. A138

NATRAJAN, Sunil, M.D. Medical Director, Kindred Hospital–Tucson, Tucson, AZ, p. A40

NAU, James, Manager Computer and Applications Support, Delaware Psychiatric Center, New Castle, DE, p. A119

NAUMAN, Brenda, Controller, Keefe Memorial Hospital, Cheyenne Wells, CO, p. A103

NAVA, Madeline, Chief Operating Officer, Palms West Hospital, Loxahatchee, FL, p. A134

NAVARRO, Israel, Chief Executive Officer, Integrity Transitional Hospital, Denton, TX, p. A613

NAVARRO, Ramomita, Director Human Resources, University Hospital, San Juan, PR, p. A729

NAVARRO, Tess, Chief Financial Officer, Laguna Honda Hospital and Rehabilitation Center, San Francisco, CA, p. A91

NAVAS, Manuel, M.D. Medical Director, Hospital San Pablo Del Este, Fajardo, PR, p. A726

NAWROCKI, Bernie
Administrative Director Finance, ProMedica Bixby Hospital, Adrian, MI, p. A318
Administrative Director Finance, ProMedica Herrick Hospital, Tecumseh, MI, p. A336

NAWROCKI, Edward, President, St. Luke's Hospital – Anderson Campus, Easton, PA, p. A538

NAYAK, Raghu, Chief Executive Officer, Hind General Hospital, Hobart, IN, p. A213

NAZ, Haroon, Chief Executive Officer, Pinnacle Hospital, Crown Point, IN, p. A209

NAZARIAN, Alexander, Chief Financial Officer, Kirby Medical Center, Monticello, IL, p. A196

NAZE, Jesse, Chief Financial Officer, Fall River Hospital, Hot Springs, SD, p. A574

NDOW, Emmanuel, Chief Information Officer, Marion General Hospital, Marion, IN, p. A218

NEAL, Bob, Information Technology, Sparrow Ionia Hospital, Ionia, MI, p. A327

NEAL, Greg, President, Wellmont Bristol Regional Medical Center, Bristol, TN, p. A579

NEAL, Robert, Manager Information Technology Services, Newman Memorial Hospital, Shattuck, OK, p. A518

NEAL, Roger, Vice President and Chief Information Officer, Duncan Regional Hospital, Duncan, OK, p. A509

NEAL, Terri, Director Human Resources, Crittenton Children's Center, Kansas City, MO, p. A373

NEALE, Debra, R.N. Chief Nursing Officer, O'Connor Hospital, Delhi, NY, p. A436

NEALON, Matthew, Vice President Financial Services, University of Cincinnati Medical Center, Cincinnati, OH, p. A487

NEAPOLITAN, David, Chief Financial Officer, Emanuel Medical Center, Turlock, CA, p. A98

NEAR, Holly, Chief Administrative Officer, Harsha Behavioral Center, Terre Haute, IN, p. A223

NECAS, Kevin, Chief Financial Officer, University of Missouri Hospitals and Clinics, Columbia, MO, p. A370

NECHANICKY, Jeff, Assistant Director, Richard L. Roudebush Veterans Affairs Medical Center, Indianapolis, IN, p. A215

NEEB, Verette, R.N. Chief Nursing Officer, Baylor Medical Center at Uptown, Dallas, TX, p. A609

NEECE, Patrick, Chief Information Officer, Jefferson Regional Medical Center, Pine Bluff, AR, p. A52

NEEDHAM, Kim
Assistant Chief Executive Officer, Vista Medical Center East, Waukegan, IL, p. A205
Assistant Chief Executive Officer, Vista Medical Center West, Waukegan, IL, p. A205

NEEDLES, Kim, Manager Business Office, Patients' Hospital of Redding, Redding, CA, p. A85

NEEDMAN, Herbert G., President and Chief Executive Officer, Temple Community Hospital, Los Angeles, CA, p. A75

NEELAGARU, Narasimhulu, M.D. Chief of Staff, Northridge Medical Center, Commerce, GA, p. A157

NEELEY, Scott, M.D. Chief Medical Officer, St. Alexius Medical Center, Hoffman Estates, IL, p. A193

NEELY, Cindy, Administrator, Mercy Maude Norton Hospital, Columbus, KS, p. A242

NEELY, Dale, Chief Executive Officer, HEALTHSOUTH Rehabilitation Hospital of Tallahassee, Tallahassee, FL, p. A147

NEELY, Denise, R.N. Vice President and Chief Nursing Officer, Bronson Methodist Hospital, Kalamazoo, MI, p. A328

NEELY, Joseph H., FACHE, Chief Executive Officer, Hillcrest Hospital – South, Tulsa, OK, p. A520

NEELY, Randall, Chief Executive Officer, Simpson General Hospital, Mendenhall, MS, p. A362

NEERGHEEN, Chabilal, M.D. Medical Director, Western Massachusetts Hospital, Westfield, MA, p. A316

NEESEN, Cindy, Director of Information Technology, Butler County Health Care Center, David City, NE, p. A395

NEET, Bradley D., FACHE, Chief Executive Officer, Southwest Healthcare System, Murrieta, CA, p. A79

NEFCY, Christine, M.D. Chief Medical Officer, McKay–Dee Hospital Center, Ogden, UT, p. A661

NEFF, Brenda, MSN Vice President Patient Care Services and Chief Nursing Officer, North Country Hospital and Health Center, Newport, VT, p. A666

NEFF, Mark J., FACHE, President and Chief Executive Officer, St. Claire Regional Medical Center, Morehead, KY, p. A268

NEFF, Mary L., R.N. Chief Operating Officer and Chief Nursing Officer, Mercy Hospital Cadillac, Cadillac, MI, p. A320

NEFF, Mary Beth, Director Human Resources, Sistersville General Hospital, Sistersville, WV, p. A699

NEFF, William, M.D
Chief Medical Officer, Medical Center of the Rockies, Loveland, CO, p. A110
Chief Medical Officer, Poudre Valley Hospital, Fort Collins, CO, p. A106

NEFF, William, M.D., Interim President and Chief Executive Officer, University of Colorado Health, Fort Collins, CO, p. B145

NEGOSHIAN, Carol, MSN Chief Nursing Officer, Putnam Community Medical Center, Palatka, FL, p. A141

NEGRO, Frank, Interim Chief Information Officer, New York Presbyterian Lower Manhattan Hospital, New York, NY, p. A447

NEGRON, Manuel, Chief Information Technology Service, Veterans Affairs Caribbean Healthcare System, San Juan, PR, p. A729

NEIKIRK, Richard, Chief Executive Officer, Cumberland County Hospital, Burkesville, KY, p. A259

NEIL, Eric, Interim Chief Information Officer, UW Medicine/Northwest Hospital & Medical Center, Seattle, WA, p. A689

NEIL, William, Vice President and Chief Information Officer, Indian River Medical Center, Vero Beach, FL, p. A149

NEILSON, Richard, Director of Information Services, Timpanogos Regional Hospital, Orem, UT, p. A661

NEIMAN, Carla, Chief Financial Officer, Clark Fork Valley Hospital, Plains, MT, p. A390

NEISWONGER, Randy, Chief Executive Officer, Select Specialty Hospital–Erie, Erie, PA, p. A539

NEITZEL, Monte, Chief Executive Officer, Greater Regional Medical Center, Creston, IA, p. A228

NELKIN MCCORMICK, Elizabeth, MSN Chief Nursing Officer, Memorial Sloan–Kettering Cancer Center, New York, NY, p. A445

NELL, Rocio, M.D., Chief Executive Officer, Montgomery County Emergency Service, Norristown, PA, p. A546

NELL, Sergio, Director Information Systems, Watsonville Community Hospital, Watsonville, CA, p. A100

NELSON, Allison
Chief Financial Officer, Sanford Canby Medical Center, Canby, MN, p. A341
Chief Financial Officer, Sanford Clear Lake Medical Center, Clear Lake, SD, p. A573

NELSON, Barbara J., Ph.D. Chief Nursing Executive, Sutter Roseville Medical Center, Roseville, CA, p. A87

NELSON, Bill, Chief Executive Officer, Mille Lacs Health System, Onamia, MN, p. A349

NELSON, Brad, Director Information Services, Baptist Health Paducah, Paducah, KY, p. A269

NELSON, Brock D., President and Chief Executive Officer, Regions Hospital, Saint Paul, MN, p. A351

NELSON, Carol, Director Human Resources, Montevista Hospital, Las Vegas, NV, p. A406

NELSON, Christie, Director Human Resources, Hutcheson Medical Center, Fort Oglethorpe, GA, p. A160

NELSON, David, M.D. Medical Director, Barlow Respiratory Hospital, Los Angeles, CA, p. A71

NELSON, David
Chief Financial Officer, Sacred Heart Hospital, Eau Claire, WI, p. A704
Divisional Chief Financial Officer, St. Joseph's Hospital, Chippewa Falls, WI, p. A703

NELSON, David A., President, CHI St. Francis Health, Breckenridge, MN, p. A341

NELSON, Dawn
Director Human Resources, Riverton Memorial Hospital, Riverton, WY, p. A722
Manager Human Resources, SageWest Healthcare–Lander, Lander, WY, p. A721

NELSON, Deana, FACHE Executive Vice President and Chief Operating Officer, Tampa General Hospital, Tampa, FL, p. A148

NELSON, Diana, R.N. Associate Director for Patient Care Services/Nurse Executive, Jonathan M. Wainwright Memorial Veterans Affairs Medical Center, Walla Walla, WA, p. A692

NELSON, Elaine, R.N. Chief Nursing Officer, Texas Health Harris Methodist Hospital Fort Worth, Fort Worth, TX, p. A619

NELSON, Fritz, Administrator, Ochsner Extended Care Hospital of Kenner, Kenner, LA, p. A280

NELSON, Gina, Chief Financial Officer, Renown South Meadows Medical Center, Reno, NV, p. A408

NELSON, Jackie, Director Human Resources, Hansford Hospital, Spearman, TX, p. A650

NELSON, James, MSN Director of Nursing, Saunders Medical Center, Wahoo, NE, p. A402

NELSON, James J., Senior Vice President Finance and Strategic Planning, Fort HealthCare, Fort Atkinson, WI, p. A705

NELSON, Jamie, Vice President and Chief Information Officer, Hospital for Special Surgery, New York, NY, p. A444

NELSON, Jeri, Chief Financial Officer, Eastern Plumas Health Care, Portola, CA, p. A84

NELSON, John, M.D. Chief of Staff, Hutcheson Medical Center, Fort Oglethorpe, GA, p. A160

NELSON, Joseph, M.D. President Medical Staff, Lewis–Gale Medical Center, Salem, VA, p. A678

NELSON, Julia, Director Human Resources, Memorial Hospital of Carbon County, Rawlins, WY, p. A722

NELSON, Katey, Director Human Resources, Sevier Valley Medical Center, Richfield, UT, p. A662

NELSON, Kathleen, R.N. Chief Nursing Officer, Eastern Idaho Regional Medical Center, Idaho Falls, ID, p. A176

NELSON, Kathy
Chief Financial Officer, Marshall Medical Center North, Guntersville, AL, p. A21
Chief Financial Officer, Marshall Medical Center South, Boaz, AL, p. A17

NELSON, Kenneth W., Superintendent, Bridgewater State Hospital, Bridgewater, MA, p. A308

NELSON, Kerri, Chief Financial Officer, Spectrum Health Ludington Hospital, Ludington, MI, p. A329

NELSON, Linda M., R.N. Director of Nursing Services, Chippewa County–Montevideo Hospital, Montevideo, MN, p. A348

NELSON, Lucy, Director Finance, Vice President, Maniilaq Health Center, Kotzebue, AK, p. A29

NELSON, Lynn M., R.N. Chief Operating Officer and Chief Nursing Officer, St. John's Riverside Hospital, Yonkers, NY, p. A458

NELSON, Marlin Pete, Vice President Fiscal Services, Divine Savior Healthcare, Portage, WI, p. A713

NELSON, Martha
Chief Financial Officer, Antelope Memorial Hospital, Neligh, NE, p. A398
Chief Financial Officer, Niobrara Valley Hospital, Lynch, NE, p. A398

NELSON, Melissa, Assistant Administrator, Baptist Memorial Hospital for Women, Memphis, TN, p. A588

NELSON, Meredith, Chief Financial Officer, Willamette Valley Medical Center, McMinnville, OR, p. A526

NELSON, Michael
Chief Financial Officer, Kindred Hospital–Atlanta, Atlanta, GA, p. A152
Executive Vice President and Chief Financial Officer, Pomona Valley Hospital Medical Center, Pomona, CA, p. A84

NELSON, Michael E., Chief Financial Officer, Riveredge Hospital, Forest Park, IL, p. A190

NELSON, Mike, Chief Financial Officer, Saint Anthony's Health Center, Alton, IL, p. A180

NELSON, Nan, Senior Vice President Finance, Aurora St. Luke's Medical Center, Milwaukee, WI, p. A710

NELSON, Nick, Director Support Services, Adams Memorial Hospital, Decatur, IN, p. A209

NELSON, Nicole, Human Resources Coordinator, Select Specialty Hospital–Omaha, Omaha, NE, p. A400

NELSON, Raymond, Acting Chief Information Resource Management, Fargo Veterans Affairs Health Care System, Fargo, ND, p. A477

NELSON, Rhonda, Chief Nursing Officer, Forrest City Medical Center, Forrest City, AR, p. A46

NELSON, Richard, Chief of Human Resources Management Services, Central Arkansas Veterans Healthcare System, Little Rock, AR, p. A49

NELSON, Robin, Chief Financial Officer, Gundersen St. Joseph's Hospital and Clinics, Hillsboro, WI, p. A706

NELSON, Rodney M., Chief Executive Officer, Mackinac Straits Health System, Saint Ignace, MI, p. A334

NELSON, Selena, Chief Financial Officer, Fallon Medical Complex, Baker, MT, p. A385

NELSON, Shelby, Chief Executive Officer, Platte County Memorial Hospital, Wheatland, WY, p. A723

NELSON, Sherry, JD Chief Nursing Officer, Springfield Regional Medical Center, Springfield, OH, p. A502

NELSON, Siri, Chief Administrative Officer, Sutter Lakeside Hospital, Lakeport, CA, p. A69

NELSON, Il, Stacy, Director Human Resources, St. Helena Hospital Napa Valley, Saint Helena, CA, p. A88

NELSON, Stewart R., Chief Financial Officer, Halifax Regional Health System, South Boston, VA, p. A678

NELSON, Tracanne L., MS, Administrator, Community Behavioral Health Hospital – Annandale, Annandale, MN, p. A339

NELSON, Tricia, Chief Financial Officer, RiverWoods Behavioral Health System, Riverdale, GA, p. A165

NELSON, William, M.D. Medical Director, Riverview Psychiatric Center, Augusta, ME, p. A291

NELSON–JONES, Susan, Director Human Resources, Tehachapi Valley Healthcare District, Tehachapi, CA, p. A96

NEMAZIE, Siamack, M.D. Director, Patient Safety Officer, Flushing Hospital Medical Center,, NY, p. A443

NEMETH, James, Chief Nursing Officer, Borgess–Lee Memorial Hospital, Dowagiac, MI, p. A323

NEMETH, Jim, Chief Financial Officer, Monroe Clinic, Monroe, WI, p. A711

NEMI, Neil, Administrator Facility Information Center, Richard H. Hutchings Psychiatric Center, Syracuse, NY, p. A455

NEONAKIS, Stephanie W., Manager Human Resources, UH Regional Hospitals, Cleveland, OH, p. A489

NERO, Theresa R., R.N. Chief Nursing Officer, Kaiser Permanente San Jose Medical Center, San Jose, CA, p. A92

NESBITT, William, M.D. President Medical Staff, Texas Health Heart & Vascular Hospital Arlington, Arlington, TX, p. A598

NESMITH, Nikki, Chief Nursing Officer, Evans Memorial Hospital, Claxton, GA, p. A156

NESPOLI, John L., Chief Executive Officer, Sacred Heart Hospital, Allentown, PA, p. A532

NESS, David L., Vice President Operations, Grinnell Regional Medical Center, Grinnell, IA, p. A231

NESS, Edwin, President and Chief Executive Officer, Munson Healthcare, Traverse City, MI, p. B96

NESS, Jon, Chief Executive Officer, Kootenai Health, Coeur D'Alene, ID, p. A175

NESSEL, Mark
Executive Vice President and Chief Operating Officer, Lourdes Medical Center of Burlington County, Willingboro, NJ, p. A424
Chief Operating Officer, Our Lady of Lourdes Medical Center, Camden, NJ, p. A414

NESSELBUSH, Robert, President, Rochester General Hospital, Rochester, NY, p. A453

NESSELRODT, Derek, Director Information Systems, Grant Memorial Hospital, Petersburg, WV, p. A698

NESTER, Brian, D.O., Interim President and Chief Executive Officer, Lehigh Valley Health Network, Allentown, PA, p. B83

NESTER, Brian, D.O.,
Interim President and Chief Executive Officer, Lehigh Valley Hospital, Allentown, PA, p. A532
Interim President and Chief Executive Officer, Lehigh Valley Hospital–Muhlenberg, Bethlehem, PA, p. A533

NESTER, Darlene
Market Chief Human Resources Officer, Coastal Carolina Hospital, Hardeeville, SC, p. A567
Chief Human Resources Officer, Hilton Head Hospital, Hilton Head Island, SC, p. A567

NESTER, Michael, Administrator, John C. Stennis Memorial Hospital, De Kalb, MS, p. A357

NESTER WOLFE, Cheryl R., R.N. Senior Vice President Operations, Salem Hospital, Salem, OR, p. A530

NETH, Marvin, Chief Executive Officer, Callaway District Hospital, Callaway, NE, p. A394

NETTERVILLE, Chad, Administrator, Field Memorial Community Hospital, Centreville, MS, p. A356

NETTLES, Angela F., Director Human Resources, KershawHealth, Camden, SC, p. A562

NETTLES, Robert, Director Human Resources, MountainView Hospital, Las Vegas, NV, p. A406

NETZER, Craig, M.D. President Medical Staff, Wilcox Memorial Hospital, Lihue, HI, p. A172

NEUBERT, Todd, Nurse Administrator, LDS Hospital, Salt Lake City, UT, p. A663

NEUENDORF, David A., FACHE, President and Chief Executive Officer, Audrain Medical Center, Mexico, MO, p. A376

NEUENDORF, Deborah, Vice President Administration, Hudson Valley Hospital Center, Cortlandt Manor, NY, p. A436

NEUENDORF, Michael, Chief Executive Officer, Wesley Medical Center, Hattiesburg, MS, p. A359

NEUFELDER, Daniel, Interim Chief Executive Officer, St. Elizabeth Hospital, Appleton, WI, p. A701

NEUGENT, Kevin, Chief Information Officer, Hayes Green Beach Memorial Hospital, Charlotte, MI, p. A320

NEUHAUS, Joan E., Senior Vice President Chief Operating Officer, CHI Health Lakeside, Omaha, NE, p. A399

NEUMAN, Keith A.

Chief Information Officer, Dupont Hospital, Fort Wayne, IN, p. A210

Chief Information Officer, Lutheran Hospital of Indiana, Fort Wayne, IN, p. A211

Chief Information Officer, Orthopaedic Hospital of Lutheran Health Network, Fort Wayne, IN, p. A211

Chief Information Officer, Rehabilitation Hospital of Fort Wayne, Fort Wayne, IN, p. A211

NEUMAN, Michael J., Vice President Finance, Kennedy Krieger Institute, Baltimore, MD, p. A296

NEUMAN, Richard, Assistant Administrator and Chief Human Resources Officer, Olympic Medical Center, Port Angeles, WA, p. A686

NEUMANN, Harley, Ph.D. Regional Vice President Human Resources, Sutter Maternity and Surgery Center of Santa Cruz, Santa Cruz, CA, p. A94

NEUMANN, Jamie, Director Human Resources, Iroquois Memorial Hospital and Resident Home, Watseka, IL, p. A204

NEUMEISTER, Daniel P., Administrator, SEARHC MT. Edgecumbe Hospital, Sitka, AK, p. A30

NEUNER, Kathy, R.N. Chief Nursing Officer, Clark Memorial Hospital, Jeffersonville, IN, p. A215

NEUVIRTH, Stephanie, Chief Human Resource and Diversity Officer, City of Hope's Helford Clinical Research Hospital, Duarte, CA, p. A62

NEVILLE, Bette, R.N. Vice President and Chief Nursing Officer, Mercy Hospital of Portland, Portland, ME, p. A294

NEVILLE, Ryan T., FACHE, President and Chief Executive Officer, Memorial Medical Center – Neillsville, Neillsville, WI, p. A712

NEVIN, James, M.D. Vice President Medical Management, Advocate BroMenn Medical Center, Normal, IL, p. A198

NEVIN, Janice E., M.D. Chief Medical Officer, Christiana Care Health System, Newark, DE, p. A119

NEVINS, Michael R.

Chief Financial Officer, St. John Broken Arrow, Broken Arrow, OK, p. A508

Chief Financial Officer, St. John Owasso, Owasso, OK, p. A517

NEVINS, Norm, Manager Human Resources, Kansas Medical Center, Andover, KS, p. A241

NEVINSKI, Lois, Manager Information Services, Buffalo Hospital, Buffalo, MN, p. A341

NEWBERRY–FERGUSON, Linda, Chief Executive Officer, Rehabilitation Hospital of Wisconsin, Waukesha, WI, p. A717

NEWBOLD, Philip A., Chief Executive Officer, Beacon Health System, South Bend, IN, p. B22

NEWBY, Doug, Chief Information Officer, Highlands Medical Center, Scottsboro, AL, p. A25

NEWBY, Nancy M., FACHE, President and Chief Executive Officer, Washington County Hospital, Nashville, IL, p. A197

NEWCOMB, James, M.D. Vice President Medical, Ochsner Medical Center – North Shore, Slidell, LA, p. A289

NEWCOMB, Michael, D.O

Senior Vice President and Chief Operating Officer, Legacy Meridian Park Medical Center, Tualatin, OR, p. A531

Senior Vice President and Chief Operating Officer, Legacy Mount Hood Medical Center, Gresham, OR, p. A525

Senior Vice President and Chief Operating Officer, Legacy Salmon Creek Medical Center, Vancouver, WA, p. A691

NEWCOMER, Jeremy, Director Information Services, Elmira Psychiatric Center, Elmira, NY, p. A437

NEWELL, Dan, Chief Financial Officer, Highlands Medical Center, Scottsboro, AL, p. A25

NEWELL, Janice

Chief Information Officer, Swedish Medical Center–Cherry Hill Campus, Seattle, WA, p. A688

Chief Information Officer, Swedish Medical Center–First Hill, Seattle, WA, p. A688

NEWELL, Rich, Chief Executive Officer, Carlisle Regional Medical Center, Carlisle, PA, p. A535

NEWEY, Mark, D.O. Chief of Staff, Mercy Hospital Healdton, Healdton, OK, p. A511

NEWHOUSE, Paul R., Chief Executive Officer, Wallace Thomson Hospital, Union, SC, p. A570

NEWLAND, Judy, R.N., Chief Nursing Officer, Incline Village Community Hospital, Incline Village, NV, p. A405

NEWMAN, Billy, Department Head, Naval Hospital Lemoore, Lemoore, CA, p. A69

NEWMAN, Cynthia, Manager Human Resources, Petersburg Medical Center, Petersburg, AK, p. A30

NEWMAN, Dan, Interim Chief Executive Officer, Houston Methodist St. John Hospital, Nassau Bay, TX, p. A639

NEWMAN, Diane, Administrator, Johnson County Hospital, Tecumseh, NE, p. A402

NEWMAN, Douglas A., Chief Executive Officer, LaSalle General Hospital, Jena, LA, p. A279

NEWMAN, Edith, Interim Administrator, John J. Madden Mental Health Center, Hines, IL, p. A192

NEWMAN, Karen, Ed.D. Vice President and Chief Nursing Officer, Baptist Health Louisville, Louisville, KY, p. A265

NEWMAN, Kurt, M.D., President and Chief Executive Officer, Children's National Medical Center, Washington, DC, p. A121

NEWMAN, Sonya, R.N. Chief Nursing Officer, Blount Memorial Hospital, Maryville, TN, p. A588

NEWMAN, Thomas M.

Chief Financial Officer, UPMC Passavant, Pittsburgh, PA, p. A552

Vice President Finance, UPMC St. Margaret, Pittsburgh, PA, p. A552

NEWMILLER, Vicki, Chief Operating Officer, Great Falls Clinic Medical Center, Great Falls, MT, p. A388

NEWPOWER, Nicole, Coordinator Human Resources, Kindred Hospital–Fort Worth, Fort Worth, TX, p. A618

NEWQUIST, Dennis, Director Information Systems, Abilene Regional Medical Center, Abilene, TX, p. A595

NEWSOM, Paul, Chief Operating Officer, Kentuckiana Medical Center, Clarksville, IN, p. A208

NEWSOME, Samuel C., M.D. Chief of Staff, Pioneer Community Hospital of Stokes, Danbury, NC, p. A463

NEWSOME, Vickie L., Chief Executive Officer, Cleveland Regional Medical Center, Cleveland, TX, p. A606

NEWTON, Gail, R.N. Vice President Patient Care Services, St. Luke's Hospital – Warren Campus, Phillipsburg, NJ, p. A421

NEWTON, Harold, Chief Operating Officer, California Hospital Medical Center, Los Angeles, CA, p. A71

NEWTON, James R., Facility Director, Northern Virginia Mental Health Institute, Falls Church, VA, p. A670

NEWTON, Jennifer, R.N. Chief Nursing Officer, Neosho Memorial Regional Medical Center, Chanute, KS, p. A242

NEWTON, Keith, Chief Executive Officer, South Baldwin Regional Medical Center, Foley, AL, p. A20

NEWTON, Mark, President and Chief Executive Officer, Swedish Covenant Hospital, Chicago, IL, p. A187

NEWTON, Milissa, Supervisor Human Resources, Good Samaritan Hospital, Bakersfield, CA, p. A57

NEWTON, Steven R., President, Baylor Regional Medical Center at Grapevine, Grapevine, TX, p. A621

NEWTON, Susan, Chief Financial Officer, Broward Health Imperial Point, Fort Lauderdale, FL, p. A128

NEWTON, Terri, Chief Nursing Officer, Lakewood Regional Medical Center, Lakewood, CA, p. A69

NEWTON, Wilma, Executive Vice President and Chief Financial Officer, St. Vincent's Birmingham, Birmingham, AL, p. A17

NEZBETH, Jacqueline, Human Resources Officer, Select Specialty Hospital–Zanesville, Zanesville, OH, p. A506

NG, Anthony, M.D. Vice President and Chief Medical Officer, The Acadia Hospital, Bangor, ME, p. A291

NG, Thomas T., Chief Information Officer, Collingsworth General Hospital, Wellington, TX, p. A656

NG, Vincent

Interim Director, Brockton Veterans Affairs Medical Center, Brockton, MA, p. A308

Director, Veterans Affairs Boston Healthcare System, Boston, MA, p. A307

NGUYEN, Abby, R.N. Chief Nursing Officer, Genesis HealthCare System, Zanesville, OH, p. A506

NGUYEN, Anhtai H., M.D. Vice President Medical Affairs and Chief Medical Officer, Fauquier Hospital, Warrenton, VA, p. A680

NGUYEN, Bach, Chief Information Officer, Northwest Texas Healthcare System, Amarillo, TX, p. A596

NGUYEN, Dat, M.D. Chief of Staff, ValleyCare Medical Center, Pleasanton, CA, p. A83

NGUYEN, Hao, M.D. Medical Director, Lanterman Developmental Center, Pomona, CA, p. A84

NGUYEN, Harry, Medical Director, The Woods at Parkside, Gahanna, OH, p. A494

NGUYEN, Nga, Manager Human Resources and Organizational Development, Glendale Memorial Hospital and Health Center, Glendale, CA, p. A65

NGUYEN, Son, M.D. President of Medical Staff, Integris Southwest Medical Center, Oklahoma City, OK, p. A515

NGUYEN, Vicki, Chief Financial Officer, Good Samaritan Hospital, Bakersfield, CA, p. A57

NIAZI, A., M.D. Chief of Staff, Anson Community Hospital, Wadesboro, NC, p. A474

NIBLOCK, Christine, Chief Financial Officer, Sheridan County Health Complex, Hoxie, KS, p. A246

NICAUD, Kent, Chief Operating Officer, Memorial Hospital at Gulfport, Gulfport, MS, p. A358

NICEWONGER, David, Chief Operating Officer, Multicare Auburn Medical Center, Auburn, WA, p. A681

NICHELSON, Kathleen, Director Human Resources, Horsham Clinic, Ambler, PA, p. A533

NICHOLAS, Connie, Interim Chief Executive Officer, L. V. Stabler Memorial Hospital, Greenville, AL, p. A21

NICHOLS, Amanda, M.D. Chief of Staff, Sistersville General Hospital, Sistersville, WV, p. A699

NICHOLS, Arthur W., President and Chief Executive Officer, Cheshire Medical Center, Keene, NH, p. A410

NICHOLS, Barbara, R.N., President and Chief Executive Officer, Corry Memorial Hospital, Corry, PA, p. A536

NICHOLS, Bryan, Chief Financial Officer, The Heart Hospital Baylor Plano, Plano, TX, p. A643

NICHOLS, Christopher, Chief Executive Officer, Horn Memorial Hospital, Ida Grove, IA, p. A232

NICHOLS, Cynthia, MSN, Chief Executive Officer, Lakeland Community Hospital, Haleyville, AL, p. A21

NICHOLS, Dia, Chief Executive Officer, Northside Hospital, Saint Petersburg, FL, p. A144

NICHOLS, Donna, R.N. Chief Nursing Officer, Goodall–Witcher Hospital Authority, Clifton, TX, p. A606

NICHOLS, Gretchen, R.N., Chief Administrative Officer, Legacy Mount Hood Medical Center, Gresham, OR, p. A525

NICHOLS, Laura L., Director Human Resources, Hancock Regional Hospital, Greenfield, IN, p. A212

NICHOLS, Mark, FACHE, Chief Executive Officer, LewisGale Hospital Pulaski, Pulaski, VA, p. A676

NICHOLS, Mark, R.N. Director of Nurses, Liberty Dayton Regional Medical Center, Liberty, TX, p. A633

NICHOLS, Michael, Chief Information Officer, Masonicare Health Center, Wallingford, CT, p. A117

NICHOLS, Owen, PsyD, President and Chief Executive Officer, NorthKey Community Care, Covington, KY, p. A260

NICHOLS, Randy

Chief Financial Officer, Great River Medical Center, Blytheville, AR, p. A43

Chief Financial Officer, South Mississippi County Regional Medical Center, Osceola, AR, p. A51

NICHOLS, Robert R., M.D. Vice President Medical Affairs, Mercy Hospital Fort Scott, Fort Scott, KS, p. A244

NICHOLS, Robin, Chief Financial Officer, Coshocton County Memorial Hospital, Coshocton, OH, p. A491

NICHOLS, Suzanne, Director Human Resources, Muleshoe Area Medical Center, Muleshoe, TX, p. A639

NICHOLS, Terry, Chief Executive Officer, Iron County Medical Center, Pilot Knob, MO, p. A378

NICHOLSON, Britain, M.D. Chief Medical Officer, Massachusetts General Hospital, Boston, MA, p. A307

NICHOLSON, Chrissy, Director Human Resources, Delta Regional Medical Center, Greenville, MS, p. A358

NICHOLSON, Cindy, Director Human Resources, Shelby Baptist Medical Center, Alabaster, AL, p. A15

NICHOLSON, Debra, Manager Finance, Central Alabama Veterans Health Care System, Montgomery, AL, p. A23

NICHOLSON, Donna, Chief Nursing Officer, Gadsden Regional Medical Center, Gadsden, AL, p. A20

NICHOLSON, Kristin, Coordinator Human Resources, Genesis Medical Center, DeWitt, De Witt, IA, p. A229

NICHOLSON, Molly, R.N

Chief Nurse Executive, Presence Covenant Medical Center, Urbana, IL, p. A204

Vice President of Patient Care/Chief Nurse Executive, Presence United Samaritans Medical Center, Danville, IL, p. A187

NICHOLSON, Tim, Chief Executive Officer, Encore Healthcare, Columbia, MD, p. B56

NICKEL, Kathleen, Director Communications, Mercy Medical Center, Roseburg, OR, p. A529

NICKELL, Jerry, Vice President Human Resource and Mission, Saint Alphonsus Medical Center – Baker City, Baker City, OR, p. A523

NORDAHL, Richard E., Chief Executive Officer, Sanford Sheldon Medical Center, Sheldon, IA, p. A237

NORDBERG, Traci, Chief Human Resources Officer, Vanderbilt Hospital and Clinics, Nashville, TN, p. A591

NORDBY, Shawn A., Chief Financial Officer, Mary Lanning Healthcare, Hastings, NE, p. A396

NORDING, Rodney, Vice President Organizational Support, Mayo Clinic Health System in Austin, Austin, MN, p. A340

NORDLUND, Judy, R.N. Chief Nursing Officer, Trinity Hospital, Weaverville, CA, p. A100

NORDLUND, Sarah, Director of Nursing, Garfield County Health Center, Jordan, MT, p. A388

NORDMARK, Gary, Administrator and Vice President Operations, Bethesda Hospital East, Boynton Beach, FL, p. A124

NORDSTROM, Janice, Director Human Resources, Landmark Hospital of Joplin, Joplin, MO, p. A373

NORDSTROM, Katie, Director Human Resources, Beartooth Billings Clinic, Red Lodge, MT, p. A390

NORDWICK, Thomas, Chief Executive Officer, Uvalde County Hospital Authority, Uvalde, TX, p. A654

NORDYKE, Charles
 Chief Executive Officer, Vibra Hospital of Northwestern Indiana, Crown Point, IN, p. A209
 Chief Executive Officer, Vibra Hospital of Springfield, Springfield, IL, p. A203

NORDYKE, Melissa, Chief Financial Officer, Seton Smithville Regional Hospital, Smithville, TX, p. A649

NOREEN, James, M.D. Chief Medical Officer, Regina Hospital, Hastings, MN, p. A345

NORELDIN, Mohsen, M.D. President Medical Staff, Athol Memorial Hospital, Athol, MA, p. A305

NOREM, Ashley, Chief Information Systems, Indiana University Health Starke Hospital, Knox, IN, p. A216

NOREN, Tom, M.D. Chief Medical Officer, Marquette General Hospital, Marquette, MI, p. A330

NORGAARD, Margaret B.
 Chief Executive Officer, Poplar Community Hospital, Poplar, MT, p. A390
 Chief Executive Officer, Trinity Hospital, Wolf Point, MT, p. A392

NORICK, Laurence, M.D. Clinical Director, U. S. Public Health Service Indian Hospital, Parker, AZ, p. A35

NORIEGA, Donna, Chief Operating Officer, Arizona State Hospital, Phoenix, AZ, p. A35

NORMAN, Daniel, Regional Service Manager, UnityPoint Health – Allen Hospital, Waterloo, IA, p. A239

NORMAN, Debbie, Director Human Resources, Central Louisiana Surgical Hospital, Alexandria, LA, p. A272

NORMAN, Jimmy, Chief Financial Officer, Mountain Lakes Medical Center, Clayton, GA, p. A156

NORMAN, Kasey, Chief Executive Officer, Reliant Rehabilitation Hospital Dallas, Dallas, TX, p. A611

NORMAN, Lori, Chief Financial Officer, HEALTHSOUTH Rehabilitation of Gadsden, Gadsden, AL, p. A20

NORMAN, Mark, Administrator, Pioneer Community Hospital of Newton, Newton, MS, p. A363

NORMAN, Mary, R.N. Chief Nursing Officer, Bear Valley Community Hospital, Big Bear Lake, CA, p. A58

NORMAN, Michael L., Executive Vice President and Chief Operating Officer, Landmark Hospital, Cape Girardeau, MO, p. A368

NORMAN, Robin, Senior Vice President and Chief Financial Officer, Virginia Hospital Center – Arlington, Arlington, VA, p. A668

NORMAN, Rolf, Chief Financial Officer, Kaiser Permanente Sunnyside Medical Center, Clackamas, OR, p. A523

NORMAND, Lorrie, R.N. Chief Nursing Officer, Texas Health Harris Methodist Hospital Cleburne, Cleburne, TX, p. A606

NORMINGTON–SLAY, Jeremy, FACHE, Chief Executive Officer, Moundview Memorial Hospital & Clinics, Friendship, WI, p. A705

NORO, Sharon, Chief Executive Officer, Select Specialty Hospital–Youngstown, Youngstown, OH, p. A506

NORONHA, Augusto A., Vice President Finance and Chief Financial Officer, Missouri Baptist Medical Center, Saint Louis, MO, p. A381

NORQUEST, Cathy, Director Human Resources, York General Hospital, York, NE, p. A403

NORR–MCPHILLIPS, Karina, Associate Executive Director Human Resources, Franklin Hospital, Valley Stream, NY, p. A457

NORRIS, Charles, Chief Executive Officer, Memorial Hospital, Gonzales, TX, p. A621

NORRIS, Doug, Administrator and Chief Operating Officer, Western Medical Center–Santa Ana, Santa Ana, CA, p. A93

NORRIS, John, M.D. Vice President Medical Affairs, Johnson Memorial Hospital, Franklin, IN, p. A212

NORRIS, Kathy, Director Human Resources, Bear Valley Community Hospital, Big Bear Lake, CA, p. A58

NORTH, Scott L., FACHE,
 Senior Vice President and President, Acute Care Hospitals, St. John's Hospital, Saint Paul, MN, p. A351
 Senior Vice President and President, Acute Care Hospitals, St. Joseph's Hospital, Saint Paul, MN, p. A351
 Senior Vice President and President, Acute Care Hospitals, Woodwinds Health Campus, Woodbury, MN, p. A354

NORTHCUTT, Lynn, Chief Information Officer, Carolinas Hospital System, Florence, SC, p. A565

NORTHERN, Gail M., Director Human Resources, Blue Mountain Hospital, Blanding, UT, p. A659

NORTHROP, James, Director, Southern Nevada Adult Mental Health Services, Las Vegas, NV, p. A406

NORTHUP, Carol, R.N. Chief Nursing Officer, J. Arthur Dosher Memorial Hospital, Southport, NC, p. A473

NORTHUP, Jeffrey, D.O. Chief Medical Officer, Summit Healthcare Regional Medical Center, Show Low, AZ, p. A39

NORTON, Andrew J., M.D
 Chief Medical Officer, Bryn Mawr Hospital, Bryn Mawr, PA, p. A534
 Chief Medical Officer, Paoli Hospital, Paoli, PA, p. A547

NORTON, Bruce J., Senior Vice President and Chief Operating Officer, Sierra Vista Regional Health Center, Sierra Vista, AZ, p. A39

NORTON, Debbie, Chief Financial Officer, Medical Center Barbour, Eufaula, AL, p. A19

NORTON, Julie, Chief Financial Officer, Avera McKennan Hospital and University Health Center, Sioux Falls, SD, p. A576

NORTON, Lizette O., Vice President Human Resources, Parkview Community Hospital Medical Center, Riverside, CA, p. A86

NORTON, Meg, Executive Vice President and Chief Administrative Officer, Rady Children's Hospital – San Diego, San Diego, CA, p. A89

NORTON, Robert G., President and Chief Executive Officer, North Shore Medical Center, Salem, MA, p. A314

NORTON, Susan, Vice President Human Resources, Georgia Regents Medical Center, Augusta, GA, p. A153

NORWOOD, Lyle, M.D. Chief of Staff, Northside Medical Center, Columbus, GA, p. A156

NOSACKA, David, Chief Financial Officer, St. Elizabeth's Hospital, Belleville, IL, p. A181

NOSACKA, Mark, Chief Executive Officer, Good Samaritan Medical Center, West Palm Beach, FL, p. A149

NOSBISCH, Don, Director Human Resources, Floyd County Medical Center, Charles City, IA, p. A227

NOSEWORTHY, Ed, President and Chief Executive Officer, Florida Hospital Fish Memorial, Orange City, FL, p. A140

NOSEWORTHY, John, M.D., President and Chief Executive Officer, Mayo Clinic, Rochester, MN, p. B89

NOTARANTONIO, Rosemary, MSN, Chief Executive Officer, Brentwood Meadows, Newburgh, IN, p. A220

NOTEMAN, Laurali, Director Human Resources, Kane County Hospital, Kanab, UT, p. A660

NOTTEBART, Cathy, Acting Superintendent, Austin State Hospital, Austin, TX, p. A599

NOTTINGHAM, Cheryl, Chief Financial Officer, Atlantic General Hospital, Berlin, MD, p. A298

NOUNA, Nabil, M.D. Chief of Staff, Allegan General Hospital, Allegan, MI, p. A318

NOVAK, Christopher, Chief Operating Officer, Alexian Brothers Behavioral Health Hospital, Hoffman Estates, IL, p. A193

NOVAK, Georgene, Director Human Resources, Littleton Regional Hospital, Littleton, NH, p. A411

NOVAK, James, Vice President, Human Resources, St. Francis Medical Center, Monroe, LA, p. A284

NOVAK, Kristen, Manager Human Resources, River Falls Area Hospital, River Falls, WI, p. A714

NOVAK, Michael, Vice President, Operations and Chief Information Officer, Saint Mary's Hospital, Waterbury, CT, p. A118

NOVAK, Sharon, CPA Vice President Finance, Adena Pike Medical Center, Waverly, OH, p. A505

NOVELLO, Regina, R.N. Chief Operating Officer, Healdsburg District Hospital, Healdsburg, CA, p. A66

NOVICK, Peggy, Vice President, Clinical Support and Outpatient Services, Milford Regional Medical Center, Milford, MA, p. A312

NOVOA LOYOLA, Jose E., M.D. Medical Director, Cardiovascular Center of Puerto Rico and the Caribbean, San Juan, PR, p. A728

NOVOTNY, Mark, M.D. Chief Medical Officer, Cooley Dickinson Hospital, Northampton, MA, p. A313

NOWACHEK, Debra S., Director Human Resources, Grinnell Regional Medical Center, Grinnell, IA, p. A231

NOWICKI, Becky, Director Human Resources, Michiana Behavioral Health Center, Plymouth, IN, p. A221

NOWICKI, Michelle, R.N. Chief Nurse Executive, Kaiser Permanente Baldwin Park Medical Center, Baldwin Park, CA, p. A57

NOWICKI, Zigmund, Director Human Resources, Catskill Regional Medical Center, Harris, NY, p. A438

NOWLAND, Bob, M.D. Chief of Staff, Texas Health Harris Methodist Hospital Hurst–Euless–Bedford, Bedford, TX, p. A602

NOWLIN, Angela, R.N. Senior VP, Operations, Magnolia Regional Health Center, Corinth, MS, p. A357

NOWLIN, Jeffrey D., President and Chief Operating Officer, St. John Medical Center, Tulsa, OK, p. A521

NOWLIN, Patricia, Director Accounting, Cooper County Memorial Hospital, Boonville, MO, p. A368

NOWLING, Tara, Director Human Resources, Monroe County Hospital, Monroeville, AL, p. A23

NOYES, Debra, Chief Financial Officer, Putnam Community Medical Center, Palatka, FL, p. A141

NUAKO, Kofi, M.D. President Medical Staff, Baptist Memorial Hospital–Union City, Union City, TN, p. A594

NUDD, Brandon, Chief Operating Officer, Gordon Hospital, Calhoun, GA, p. A155

NUESSLEIN, Cindy, Chief Executive Officer, Interim LSU Public Hospital, New Orleans, LA, p. A285

NUNELLEY, Preston, M.D. Chief Medical Officer, Baptist Health Lexington, Lexington, KY, p. A264

NUNEZ, Michael, Chief Financial Officer, University Medical Center of El Paso, El Paso, TX, p. A616

NUNEZ, Milton, Executive Director, Lincoln Medical and Mental Health Center,, NY, p. A445

NUNEZ, Sheila, Director Human Resources, Eastern New Mexico Medical Center, Roswell, NM, p. A430

NUNLEY, Julie, R.N.,
 Chief Executive Officer, Banner Goldfield Medical Center, Apache Junction, AZ, p. A31
 Chief Executive Officer, Banner Ironwood Medical Center, San Tan Valley, AZ, p. A38

NUNN, Brian, R.N. Chief Nursing Officer, Novant Health Gaffney Medical Center, Gaffney, SC, p. A566

NUNN, Chalmers, M.D. Chief Medical Officer and Senior Vice President, Centra Lynchburg General Hospital, Lynchburg, VA, p. A673

NURICK, Paul E., Chief Executive Officer, Kittitas Valley Healthcare, Ellensburg, WA, p. A683

NURY, Alex, Chief Information Officer, Providence Tarzana Medical Center,, CA, p. A74

NUSBAUM, Neil, M.D. Chief of Staff, VA Central Western Massachusetts Healthcare System, Leeds, MA, p. A311

NUSS, Michelle, M.D. Chief Medical Officer, West Virginia University Hospitals, Morgantown, WV, p. A697

NUSSBAUM, Joseph, M.D. Chief of Staff, California Hospital Medical Center, Los Angeles, CA, p. A71

NUSSBAUM, Mark, Vice President Operations, Marymount Hospital, Garfield Heights, OH, p. A494

NUTTER, Robert, Chief Operating Officer, Vice President of Human Resources and Support Services, Mercy Hospital of Portland, Portland, ME, p. A294

NUTZ, Joseph, M.D. Vice President Medical Staff Services, Carteret General Hospital, Morehead City, NC, p. A469

NWANGBURUKA, Okechukwu, M.D. Medical Director, Sierra Vista Hospital, Sacramento, CA, p. A87

NYAMU, Samuel, M.D. Chief Medical Officer, Sanford Aberdeen Medical Center, Aberdeen, SD, p. A572

NYBERG, Becky T., Chief Financial Officer, Bloomington Meadows Hospital, Bloomington, IN, p. A207

NYIKES, Debra, Director Finance and Chief Financial Officer, Cleveland Clinic Children's Hospital for Rehabilitation, Cleveland, OH, p. A488

NYKAMP, Robert, Vice President and Chief Operating Officer, Pine Rest Christian Mental Health Services, Grand Rapids, MI, p. A325

NYLUND, Barbara, M.D. Chief of Staff, Novato Community Hospital, Novato, CA, p. A80

NYP, Randall G., FACHE,
 Chief Executive Officer, Providence Medical Center, Kansas City, KS, p. A247
 President and Chief Executive Officer, Saint John Hospital, Leavenworth, KS, p. A248

NYSTROM, Dale, M.D. Chief Medical Officer, Physician, Hawarden Regional Healthcare, Hawarden, IA, p. A232

NZERUE, Chike, M.D. Chief Medical Officer, Nashville General Hospital, Nashville, TN, p. A590

O

O'BAR, Dorothy, R.N., Regional Administrator, Mercy Hospital Waldron, Waldron, AR, p. A53

O'BRIEN Jr., Charles M., President and Chief Executive Officer, Weirton Medical Center, Weirton, WV, p. A700

O'BRIEN, David, Chief Nursing Officer, Coral Gables Hospital, Coral Gables, FL, p. A126

O'BRIEN, David, M.D.,
President, Redwood Memorial Hospital, Fortuna, CA, p. A63
President, St. Joseph Hospital, Eureka, CA, p. A62

O'BRIEN, Eileen, Director Human Resources, Broward Health Coral Springs, Coral Springs, FL, p. A126

O'BRIEN, Elizabeth, Chief Financial Officer, Northern Nevada Adult Mental Health Services, Sparks, NV, p. A408

O'BRIEN, Gracie, Chief Information Officer, Sequoia Hospital, Redwood City, CA, p. A86

O'BRIEN, Jane E., M.D. Medical Director, Franciscan Hospital for Children, Boston, MA, p. A306

O'BRIEN, John, Chief Executive Officer, Manning Regional Healthcare Center, Manning, IA, p. A234

O'BRIEN, John A., FACHE, President, Prince George's Hospital Center, Cheverly, MD, p. A299

O'BRIEN, Karen, Director Human Resources, Gerald Champion Regional Medical Center, Alamogordo, NM, p. A426

O'BRIEN, Kelly, Chief Operating Officer, Riverview Medical Center, Red Bank, NJ, p. A422

O'BRIEN, Kevin, Chief Financial Officer, Share Medical Center, Alva, OK, p. A507

O'BRIEN, Laureen, Chief Information Officer, Providence Newberg Medical Center, Newberg, OR, p. A527

O'BRIEN, Maureen, Chief Operating Officer, Kaiser Permanente Redwood City Medical Center, Redwood City, CA, p. A85

O'BRIEN, Renee, Director Human Resources, Greater Binghamton Health Center, Binghamton, NY, p. A433

O'BRIEN, Yvonne M., MS Chief of Nursing, Pella Regional Health Center, Pella, IA, p. A236

O'BRYANT, G. Mark, President and Chief Executive Officer, Tallahassee Memorial HealthCare, Tallahassee, FL, p. A147

O'CONNELL, Brian, Director Information Services, North Star Behavioral Health System, Anchorage, AK, p. A28

O'CONNELL, Kimberly, President, Roger Williams Medical Center, Providence, RI, p. A561

O'CONNELL, Melody M., Director Human Resources, St. Bernard Parish Hospital, Chalmette, LA, p. A275

O'CONNER, Marcia, Chief Executive Officer, Choctaw Memorial Hospital, Hugo, OK, p. A512

O'CONNOR, Colleen, Director Human Resources, Manatee Glens Hospital and Addiction Center, Bradenton, FL, p. A124

O'CONNOR, David, Executive Vice President and Chief Financial Officer, Caromont Regional Medical Center, Gastonia, NC, p. A465

O'CONNOR, Delia, FACHE, President and Chief Executive Officer, Anna Jaques Hospital, Newburyport, MA, p. A312

O'CONNOR, Dennis, M.D. Medical Director, Ira Davenport Memorial Hospital, Bath, NY, p. A433

O'CONNOR, Ellen, Chief Nursing Officer, Jacobi Medical Center,, NY, p. A444

O'CONNOR, J. T., M.D. Medical Director, Mercy Health Love County, Marietta, OK, p. A513

O'CONNOR, James, Executive Vice President and Chief Administrative Officer, St. Charles Hospital, Port Jefferson, NY, p. A452

O'CONNOR, Kathy
Vice President Finance, St. Joseph Mercy Hospital Ann Arbor, Ypsilanti, MI, p. A338
Vice President Finance and Controller, St. Joseph Mercy Livingston Hospital, Howell, MI, p. A327

O'CONNOR, Kevin, D.O. President Medical Staff, Spectrum Health United Hospital, Greenville, MI, p. A326

O'CONNOR, Michael F., Senior Vice President Finance, York Hospital, York, PA, p. A559

O'CONNOR, Nicholas, Vice President and Chief Information Officer, Plainview Hospital, Plainview, NY, p. A451

O'CONNOR, Patrick, Chief Operating Officer, Morris Hospital & Healthcare Centers, Morris, IL, p. A196

O'CONNOR, Steve, Manager Human Resources, Kern Medical Center, Bakersfield, CA, p. A57

O'CONNOR, Thomas, President, United Hospital, Saint Paul, MN, p. A351

O'CONNOR, Tim, Area Finance Officer, Kaiser Permanente Redwood City Medical Center, Redwood City, CA, p. A85

O'CONNOR, Timothy P., Executive Vice President and Chief Financial Officer, Lahey Hospital & Medical Center, Burlington, Burlington, MA, p. A308

O'DAY, Ken, Supervisor Information Systems, Corry Memorial Hospital, Corry, PA, p. A536

O'DEA, Edward
Vice President and Chief Financial Officer, Lehigh Valley Hospital, Allentown, PA, p. A532
Chief Financial Officer, Lehigh Valley Hospital–Muhlenberg, Bethlehem, PA, p. A533

O'DELL, Darrell, Director Information Services, Good Samaritan Hospital, San Jose, CA, p. A92

O'DONNELL, James, Physician in Chief, Kaiser Permanente Redwood City Medical Center, Redwood City, CA, p. A85

O'DONNELL, Jan, Chief Nursing Officer, South Texas Surgical Hospital, Corpus Christi, TX, p. A608

O'DONNELL, Michael, Chief Financial Officer, Peconic Bay Medical Center, Riverhead, NY, p. A452

O'DONNELL, Patrick W., CPA, President and Chief Executive Officer, Chambersburg Hospital, Chambersburg, PA, p. A535

O'DONNELL, Patrick W., CPA, President and Chief Executive Officer, Summit Health, Chambersburg, PA, p. B130

O'DONNELL, Randall L., Ph.D.,
President and Chief Executive Officer, Children's Mercy Hospitals and Clinics, Kansas City, MO, p. A373
President and Chief Executive Officer, Children's Mercy South, Overland Park, KS, p. A252

O'FLANAGAN, Jayne, Director Human Resources, Incline Village Community Hospital, Incline Village, NV, p. A405

O'GORMAN, Jr., Thomas, Chief Financial Officer, East Texas Medical Center–Gilmer, Gilmer, TX, p. A621

O'HALLA, Mark S., President and Chief Executive Officer, McLaren Macomb, Mount Clemens, MI, p. A330

O'HARA, Denise, Vice President Human Resources, Wilson Medical Center, Wilson, NC, p. A475

O'HARA, Kathleen, Vice President Human Resources, Erie County Medical Center, Buffalo, NY, p. A434

O'HARA, Michael
Senior Executive Director Human Resources, Houston Medical Center, Warner Robins, GA, p. A169
Senior Executive Director, Perry Hospital, Perry, GA, p. A164

O'HARE, Rose Ann, R.N. Senior Vice President Patient Services, Lawrence Hospital Center, Bronxville, NY, p. A434

O'HEARN, Brian, Vice President Patient Care Services and Chief Nursing Officer, Samaritan Medical Center, Watertown, NY, p. A457

O'HOLLAREN, Janet, Chief Operating Officer, Kaiser Foundation Hospital Westside Medical Center, Hillsboro, OR, p. A525

O'KEEFE, Charles, Director Health Information Services, HEALTHSOUTH Rehabilitation Hospital of Tallahassee, Tallahassee, FL, p. A147

O'KEEFE, James, Chief Financial Officer, Westerly Hospital, Westerly, RI, p. A561

O'KEEFE, James M., President and Chief Executive Officer, Mile Bluff Medical Center, Mauston, WI, p. A709

O'KEEFE, John, Chief Executive Officer, Select Specialty Hospital–Gulf Coast, Gulfport, MS, p. A359

O'KEEFE, Kathy
Executive Director, Pilgrim Psychiatric Center, Brentwood, NY, p. A434
Interim Executive Director, Sagamore Children's Psychiatric Center, Dix Hills, NY, p. A436

O'KEEFE, Kelly, Interim Chief Executive Officer, Natividad Medical Center, Salinas, CA, p. A88

O'KEEFE, Michael N., President and Chief Executive Officer, Evangelical Community Hospital, Lewisburg, PA, p. A543

O'KEEFE, Sharon L., R.N., President, University of Chicago Medical Center, Chicago, IL, p. A187

O'KEEFE, Trish, R.N. Chief Nursing Officer and Chief Experience Officer, Morristown Medical Center, Morristown, NJ, p. A418

O'KEEFFE, Maureen, Vice President and Chief Human Resource Officer, St. Luke's Regional Medical Center, Boise, ID, p. A175

O'LAIRE, Beth, Manager Human Resources, Calumet Medical Center, Chilton, WI, p. A703

O'LEARY, Bill, Chief Executive Officer, Pondera Medical Center, Conrad, MT, p. A386

O'LEARY, Daniel H., M.D. Chief Medical Officer, HealthAlliance Hospitals, Leominster, MA, p. A311

O'LEARY, Kevin J., Senior Vice President and Chief Financial Officer, Exeter Hospital, Exeter, NH, p. A410

O'LEARY, Megan A., Vice President Human Resources and Rehabilitation Services, McKenzie–Willamette Medical Center, Springfield, OR, p. A530

O'LEARY, Rand, Senior Vice President and Chief Operating Officer, Henry Ford Wyandotte Hospital, Wyandotte, MI, p. A337

O'LOUGHLIN, James F., President and Chief Executive Officer, Memorial Hospital Jacksonville, Jacksonville, FL, p. A131

O'MALLEY, Constance, Chief Nursing Officer, St. John Macomb–Oakland Hospital, Warren, MI, p. A336

O'MALLEY, John F., FACHE, Chief Executive Officer, Select Specialty Hospital–Ann Arbor, Ypsilanti, MI, p. A338

O'MALLEY, Jon P., Chief Executive Officer, Select Specialty Hospital–Macomb County, Mount Clemens, MI, p. A330

O'MALLEY, Mary Jo, R.N. Vice President Diagnostics and Support Services, Oconomowoc Memorial Hospital, Oconomowoc, WI, p. A712

O'MALLEY, Terry, Vice President Human Resources, Frederick Memorial Hospital, Frederick, MD, p. A301

O'MALLEY, Trevor, Site Manager, Presence Saint Joseph Hospital, Elgin, IL, p. A189

O'NEAL, Becky, R.N. Interim Chief Nursing Officer, Lincoln County Medical Center, Troy, MO, p. A384

O'NEAL, Charlotte, Vice President Human Resources, Research Medical Center, Kansas City, MO, p. A374

O'NEAL, Michael, Administrator and Chief Executive Officer, George C Grape Community Hospital, Hamburg, IA, p. A231

O'NEAL, Stephen, R.N. Chief Clinical Officer, Manchester Memorial Hospital, Manchester, KY, p. A267

O'NEIL, Alan, Chief Executive Officer, Unity Medical Center, Grafton, ND, p. A478

O'NEIL, Jeremy, Manager Finance, Providence Valdez Medical Center, Valdez, AK, p. A30

O'NEIL, Linda B., R.N., Chief Executive Officer, Hospital for Extended Recovery, Norfolk, VA, p. A675

O'NEIL Jr., Mark T., President and Chief Executive Officer, Hilton Head Hospital, Hilton Head Island, SC, p. A567

O'NEIL, Terry, Chief Information Technology, Nazareth Hospital, Philadelphia, PA, p. A549

O'NEILL, Beth, Chief Nursing Officer, Morgan Memorial Hospital, Madison, GA, p. A163

O'NEILL, Bonnie, Vice President Employee Services, Northern Montana Hospital, Havre, MT, p. A388

O'NEILL, Colene, Associate Director Patient Nursing Services, Syracuse Veterans Affairs Medical Center, Syracuse, NY, p. A456

O'NEILL, Jennifer A., R.N. Vice President Patient Care Services, Saint Barnabas Medical Center, Livingston, NJ, p. A417

O'NEILL, Joseph J., M.D. Vice President Medical Affairs, South County Hospital, Wakefield, RI, p. A561

O'NEILL, Lynn, R.N. Chief Nursing Officer, Medical Center of Lewisville, Lewisville, TX, p. A633

O'NEILL, Melissa, Vice President Human Resources, Advocate Sherman Hospital, Elgin, IL, p. A189

O'NEILL, Michael, M.D. Chief Medical Officer, Eastside Medical Center, Snellville, GA, p. A167

O'NEILL, Stephan, Vice President Information Services, Hartford Hospital, Hartford, CT, p. A114

O'PREY, Mary, Chief Nursing Officer, Martin General Hospital, Williamston, NC, p. A474

O'REAR, Caleb F., Chief Executive Officer, Denton Regional Medical Center, Denton, TX, p. A613

O'ROURKE, Jane, R.N. Chief Nursing Officer, Vice President Operations, St. Peter's Hospital, Albany, NY, p. A432

O'ROURKE, Michael, Regional Human Resources Lead, Presence Saint Joseph Hospital, Elgin, IL, p. A189

O'SHEA, James E.
Administrator, Springbrook Hospital, Brooksville, FL, p. A125
Administrator, Willough Healthcare System, Naples, FL, p. A139

O'SHEA, Kristen, R.N. Vice President Patient Care Services, Gettysburg Hospital, Gettysburg, PA, p. A539

O'SHIELDS, Hugh, M.D. President Medical Staff, Trinity Medical Center, Birmingham, AL, p. A17

O'STEEN, Neil, Director Information Technology, Bacon County Hospital and Health System, Alma, GA, p. A151

O'SULLIVAN, Barbara, M.D. Medical Director, Rockefeller University Hospital, New York, NY, p. A448

O'SULLIVAN, Colin
Acting Chief Executive Officer, Complex Care Hospital at Tenaya, Las Vegas, NV, p. A405
Administrator, Tahoe Pacific Hospitals, Reno, NV, p. A408

O'SULLIVAN, Peggy, Director Patient Services, Spearfish Regional Surgery Center, Spearfish, SD, p. A577

OAKES, Julie P., R.N. Manager Risk and Quality, Ocean Beach Hospital, Ilwaco, WA, p. A684

OAKES FERRUCCI, Susan, Vice President Patient Services and Chief Nursing Officer, Cobleskill Regional Hospital, Cobleskill, NY, p. A436

OAKLEY, Lisa, Chief Financial Officer, Harper County Community Hospital, Buffalo, OK, p. A508

OAKS, Dana, Chief Executive Officer, West Palm Hospital, West Palm Beach, FL, p. A150

OATES, John
Director Information Systems, Geneva General Hospital, Geneva, NY, p. A437
Director Information Systems, Soldiers and Sailors Memorial Hospital of Yates County, Penn Yan, NY, p. A451

OATES, Susie, Assistant Superintendent for Administration, Southwestern State Hospital, Thomasville, GA, p. A168

OAXACA, Norma, Director Human Resources, Peak Behavioral Health Services, Santa Teresa, NM, p. A430

OBER, Tammy L., Chief Executive Officer, Lancaster Rehabilitation Hospital, Lancaster, PA, p. A542

OBERHEU, Todd, Chief Executive Officer, Spanish Peaks Regional Health Center, Walsenburg, CO, p. A112

OBERMIER, Jenny, VP, Director of Nursing, York General Hospital, York, NE, p. A403

OBERRIEDER, Marsha, Vice President Operations, Northwestern Lake Forest Hospital, Lake Forest, IL, p. A194

OBERST, Larry, Vice President Finance, Spectrum Health Special Care Hospital, Grand Rapids, MI, p. A325

OBEY, Bianca A., Chief Financial Officer, Alexandria Veterans Affairs Health Care System, Pineville, LA, p. A287

OCASIO, J. Manuel, Vice President Human Resources, Holy Cross Hospital, Silver Spring, MD, p. A303

OCHOA, Mark S., M.D. Deputy Commander, Clinical Services, Irwin Army Community Hospital, Junction City, KS, p. A247

OCHOA, Nikki, Interim Chief Financial Officer, St. Joseph's Medical Center, Stockton, CA, p. A96

OCHS, David T., President and Chief Executive Officer, OSF Saint James – John W. Albrecht Medical Center, Pontiac, IL, p. A200

OCHS, Kristine, R.N., Administrator, Grisell Memorial Hospital District One, Ransom, KS, p. A253

OCHSENDORF, Derrick, Manager Information Technology and Systems, Johnson Memorial Health Services, Dawson, MN, p. A342

OCKER, Danielle, R.N., Acting Director, White River Junction Veterans Affairs Medical Center, White River Junction, VT, p. A666

ODATO, David, Chief Administrative and Chief Human Resources Officer, UCSF Medical Center, San Francisco, CA, p. A91

ODDIS, Joseph M., Chief Executive Officer, Bon Secours Maryview Medical Center, Portsmouth, VA, p. A676

ODEGAARD, Daniel, FACHE, Chief Executive Officer, Rainy Lake Medical Center, International Falls, MN, p. A345

ODELL, Cheryl, R.N. Chief Nursing Officer, Sharp Mesa Vista Hospital, San Diego, CA, p. A90

ODELL, JoAnn, Chief People Resource Officer, Banner Estrella Medical Center, Phoenix, AZ, p. A35

ODETOYINBO, Adedapo, M.D. Chief Medical Office, Emory Johns Creek Hospital, Johns Creek, GA, p. A161

ODOM, Jennifer, Interim Director Human Resources, Flowers Hospital, Dothan, AL, p. A19

ODOM, Lee Ann, Division President, Oakwood Hospital–Taylor, Taylor, MI, p. A335

ODOM, Mark, Chief Information Officer, St. Bernards Medical Center, Jonesboro, AR, p. A48

ODOM, Robbin, R.N. Chief Nursing Officer, Lake Area Medical Center, Lake Charles, LA, p. A282

ODUWOLE, Adedapo, M.D. Medical Director, Lighthouse Care Center of Conway, Conway, SC, p. A565

OEHLERS, Randi, Site Director Management Information Systems, Mercy Hospital Cadillac, Cadillac, MI, p. A320

OEHLKE, Tammy, Director Human Resources, St. Mark's Medical Center, La Grange, TX, p. A632

OEHM, Janice, Manager Business Office, Johnson County Hospital, Tecumseh, NE, p. A402

OERTLI, Stuart, Executive Director, Covenant Specialty Hospital, Lubbock, TX, p. A634

OESTREICH, Alyssa, Chief Operating Officer, Odessa Memorial Healthcare Center, Odessa, WA, p. A686

OESTREICH, Pearl, Director Human Resources, Scott & White Hospital – Llano, Llano, TX, p. A633

OETTING, Phyllis, Director Human Resources, Mitchell County Hospital Health Systems, Beloit, KS, p. A242

OETZEL, Gerald P., Chief Financial Officer, Temple University Hospital, Philadelphia, PA, p. A550

OFFUTT, Dan, Manager Finance, Knox County Hospital, Knox City, TX, p. A632

OFNER, Lori, Vice President Human Resources, Easton Hospital, Easton, PA, p. A538

OFSTEDAL, Jeff, Director Information Technology, St. Andrew's Health Center, Bottineau, ND, p. A476

OGASAWARA, Keith, M.D. Associate Medical Director and Professional Chief of Staff, Kaiser Permanente Medical Center, Honolulu, HI, p. A170

OGAWA, Quin, Vice President Finance and Chief Financial Officer, Kuakini Medical Center, Honolulu, HI, p. A170

OGBURN, J. Anthony, M.D. Chief Medical Officer, UNM Sandoval Regional Medical Center, Rio Rancho, NM, p. A430

OGDEN, Judy, Director Information Technology, Franklin Medical Center, Winnsboro, LA, p. A290

OGDEN, Lesley, M.D. Chief Operating Officer, Samaritan North Lincoln Hospital, Lincoln City, OR, p. A526

OGDEN, Michael L., President and Chief Executive Officer, Little Falls Hospital, Little Falls, NY, p. A440

OGG, Tom, Vice President Information Services and Chief Information Officer, Akron Children's Hospital, Akron, OH, p. A482

OGILVIE, Richard, Chief Information Officer, Southwestern Vermont Medical Center, Bennington, VT, p. A665

OGLESBY, Darrell M., Administrator, Putnam General Hospital, Eatonton, GA, p. A159

OGLESBY, Michele D., Manager Human Resources, Eastern Oklahoma Medical Center, Poteau, OK, p. A517

OGORZALEK, Ed, Chief Financial Officer, Rutland Regional Medical Center, Rutland, VT, p. A666

OGRINC, Mary L., R.N. Chief Nursing Officer, Senior Vice President Patient Care Services, Lake Health, Concord Township, OH, p. A491

OGROD, Eugene, M.D. Chief Medical Officer, Kingwood Medical Center, Kingwood, TX, p. A631

OHASHI, Curtis, Chief Executive Officer, Select Specialty Hospital–Cincinnati, Cincinnati, OH, p. A487

OHE, Gregory P., President, Health Central Hospital, Ocoee, FL, p. A140

OHL, Connie, Acting Chief Human Resources, Veterans Affairs Illiana Health Care System, Danville, IL, p. A187

OHLER, Kevin, Director of Finance, Promise Hospital of San Diego, San Diego, CA, p. A89

OHLSON, Susan, Ph.D. Director of Nursing–Acute, Wahiawa General Hospital, Wahiawa, HI, p. A172

OHM, Barbara, Administrator, The Orthopedic Specialty Hospital, Murray, UT, p. A661

OHMAN, Jordan, Chief Financial Officer, St. Cloud Regional Medical Center, Saint Cloud, FL, p. A144

OHMART, Dean, Assistant Administrator and Chief Financial Officer, Ransom Memorial Hospital, Ottawa, KS, p. A251

OHNOUTKA, Debra
 Chief Nursing Officer, St. Joseph Medical Center, Kansas City, MO, p. A374
 Chief Nursing Officer, St. Mary's Medical Center, Blue Springs, MO, p. A367

OHRT, James M., M.D. Director Medical Staff, Henderson Health Care Services, Henderson, NE, p. A396

OISHI, Gregg, Senior Vice President and Chief Administrative Officer, Kuakini Medical Center, Honolulu, HI, p. A170

OJOMO, Karanita, M.D. Chief of Staff, LewisGale Hospital Pulaski, Pulaski, VA, p. A676

OKABE, David
 Senior Vice President, Chief Financial Officer and Treasurer, Kapiolani Medical Center for Women & Children, Honolulu, HI, p. A170
 Executive Vice President, Chief Financial Officer and Treasurer, Pali Momi Medical Center, Aiea, HI, p. A170
 Executive Vice President, Chief Financial Officer and Treasurer, Straub Clinic & Hospital, Honolulu, HI, p. A171
 Executive Vice President, Chief Financial Officer and Treasurer, Wilcox Memorial Hospital, Lihue, HI, p. A172

OKASHIMA, Mark, Area Finance Officer, Kaiser Permanente South San Francisco, South San Francisco, CA, p. A96

OKECHUKWU, Vitalis C., M.D. President Medical Staff, Post Acute Medical Specialty Hospital of Lafayette, Lafayette, LA, p. A282

OKERSON, Tara, Director Human Resources, Presentation Medical Center, Rolla, ND, p. A480

OKESON, Keith, President and Chief Executive Officer, LifeCare Medical Center, Roseau, MN, p. A350

OKEY, Suzi, Director of Nursing, Southwest Health Center, Platteville, WI, p. A713

OKONIEWSKI, Susan, M.D. Chief of Staff, St. Gabriel's Hospital, Little Falls, MN, p. A346

OKSENDAHL, Elaine, Director Human Resources and Risk Management, Schick Shadel Hospital, Seattle, WA, p. A688

OKUHARA, Mary, Director Human Resources, Lakewood Regional Medical Center, Lakewood, CA, p. A69

OLAND, Charisse S., FACHE, Chief Executive Officer, Rusk County Memorial Hospital, Ladysmith, WI, p. A707

OLD ELK, Clayton, Service Unit Director, Crow/Northern Cheyenne Hospital, Crow Agency, MT, p. A386

OLDEN, R. Don, Chief Executive Officer, Wahiawa General Hospital, Wahiawa, HI, p. A172

OLDER, Michael, M.D. President Medical Staff, Nashoba Valley Medical Center, Ayer, MA, p. A305

OLDHAM, Jennie, Director Human Resources, Goodall–Witcher Hospital Authority, Clifton, TX, p. A606

OLDHAM, John M., M.D. Senior Vice President and Chief of Staff, Menninger Clinic, Houston, TX, p. A626

OLDHAM, Lawrence, Chief Financial Officer, Arise Austin Medical Center, Austin, TX, p. A598

OLDHAM, Marriner, M.D. Chief Medical Officer, U. S. Air Force Regional Hospital, Elmendorf AFB, AK, p. A28

OLDS, Debbie D., R.N. Director of Nursing, Willis–Knighton Medical Center, Shreveport, LA, p. A288

OLEJNICZAK, David R.
 Interim President and Chief Executive Officer, St. Francis Hospital, Litchfield, IL, p. A195
 Chief Operating Officer, St. John's Hospital, Springfield, IL, p. A203

OLEKSYK, Mike, M.D. Vice President and Chief Medical Officer, Baptist Hospital, Pensacola, FL, p. A142

OLESON, Chuck, Chief Information Officer, Butler Health System, Butler, PA, p. A534

OLESZAK, Randy, Director Fiscal Services, Milwaukee County Behavioral Health Division, Milwaukee, WI, p. A710

OLEY, Edwin M., President and Chief Executive Officer, Mercy Regional Medical Center, Lorain, OH, p. A497

OLINDE, Chad E., CPA, Administrator and Chief Executive Officer, Pointe Coupee General Hospital, New Roads, LA, p. A286

OLINGER, Richard P., Chief Financial Officer, Millcreek Community Hospital, Erie, PA, p. A538

OLINGER, Terry, System Chief Human Resources Officer, Benefis Hospitals, Great Falls, MT, p. A388

OLINSKI, Janis, R.N. Vice President Clinical Services, Harrison Community Hospital, Cadiz, OH, p. A484

OLIPHANT, Gerald P., Executive Vice President and Chief Operating Officer, Good Samaritan Hospital, Cincinnati, OH, p. A487

OLIPHANT, Jenny, Executive Vice President and Chief Operating Officer, Bethesda North Hospital, Cincinnati, OH, p. A486

OLIPHANT, Phillip, Chief Information Officer, U. S. Air Force Regional Hospital, Elmendorf AFB, AK, p. A28

OLIVA, George, Associate Information Systems Analyst, Lanterman Developmental Center, Pomona, CA, p. A84

OLIVARES, Rafael, Controller, Starr County Memorial Hospital, Rio Grande City, TX, p. A644

OLIVAS, Ray, Chief Fiscal Service, West Texas Veterans Affairs Health Care System, Big Spring, TX, p. A603

OLIVE, Alan C., Chief Executive Officer, Northern Nevada Medical Center, Sparks, NV, p. A408

OLIVEIRA, Edgar, M.D. Chief of Staff, Wishek Community Hospital and Clinics, Wishek, ND, p. A481

OLIVENCIA, Humberto, M.D. Medical Director, Hospital Perea, Mayaguez, PR, p. A727

OLIVER, Athan, Administrator and Chief Executive Officer, Iberia Rehabilitation Hospital, New Iberia, LA, p. A285

OLIVER, David, Director Information Systems, King's Daughters Medical Center, Ashland, KY, p. A258

OLIVER, Diane, R.N. Chief Nursing Officer, Parkwest Medical Center, Knoxville, TN, p. A586

OLIVER, Doug, Chief Financial Officer, Windhaven Psychiatric Hospital, Prescott Valley, AZ, p. A37

OLIVER, Julie, Chief Human Resources Officer, Mayo Clinic Health System in Mankato, Mankato, MN, p. A346

OLIVER, Kelley, R.N. Chief Nursing Officer, Physicians' Specialty Hospital, Fayetteville, AR, p. A45

OLIVER, Rick, Information Technology, Hamilton Hospital, Olney, TX, p. A640

OLIVER, Rosalie
 Chief Financial Officer, Florida Hospital Heartland Medical Center, Sebring, FL, p. A145
 Senior Vice President and Chief Financial Officer, Florida Hospital Wauchula, Wauchula, FL, p. A149

OLIVER, Terri, Interim Executive Director Information Systems, Santa Rosa Memorial Hospital, Santa Rosa, CA, p. A95

OLIVER, Vincent, Administrator, Island Hospital, Anacortes, WA, p. A681

OLIVERA, Faith, R.N. Interim Director of Nursing, Hale Ho'ola Hamakua, Honokaa, HI, p. A170

OLIVERA, Sue, Vice President, Aultman Hospital, Canton, OH, p. A485

OLIVERIO, John D., President and Chief Executive Officer, Wheaton Franciscan Healthcare, Wheaton, IL, p. B152

OLIVIER, Edward
 Chief Financial Officer, Charles A. Dean Memorial Hospital, Greenville, ME, p. A293
 Chief Financial Officer, Martha's Vineyard Hospital, Oak Bluffs, MA, p. A313

OLIVIER, Jennifer, Chief Clinical Officer, Advanced Specialty Hospital of Toledo, Toledo, OH, p. A503

OLLI, Cindy, R.N. Chief Nursing Officer, Schoolcraft Memorial Hospital, Manistique, MI, p. A329

OLLIE, Edwin J., Executive Vice President and Chief Financial Officer, New Hanover Regional Medical Center, Wilmington, NC, p. A474

OLLIS, Linda Neu, FACHE Chief Operating Officer, Monongalia General Hospital, Morgantown, WV, p. A697

OLLSON, Joanne, Vice President Human Resources, Noble Hospital, Westfield, MA, p. A316

OLM, Brad, Director Human Resources, Edgerton Hospital and Health Services, Edgerton, WI, p. A704

OLMSTEAD, David, Associate Administrator and Director Human Resources, Lake Pointe Medical Center, Rowlett, TX, p. A645

OLMSTEAD, Linda, Director, Human Resources, UW Medicine/Northwest Hospital & Medical Center, Seattle, WA, p. A689

OLS, Timothy A., FACHE, President and Chief Executive Officer, Sarah Bush Lincoln Health Center, Mattoon, IL, p. A195

OLSCAMP, Karen E., President and Chief Executive Officer, University of Maryland Baltimore Washington Medical Center, Glen Burnie, MD, p. A301

OLSEN, Debbie, Human Resource Partner, Sparrow Ionia Hospital, Ionia, MI, p. A327

OLSEN, Ryan, Vice President of Operations, St. Jude Medical Center, Fullerton, CA, p. A65

OLSEN, Sabrina, Chief Financial Officer, Duke University Hospital, Durham, NC, p. A463

OLSON, Cheryl, Chief Human Resources Officer, Othello Community Hospital, Othello, WA, p. A686

OLSON, Connie, R.N. Director of Nursing, Rock County Hospital, Bassett, NE, p. A393

OLSON, Craig, Director Information Technology, Southwestern Regional Medical Center, Tulsa, OK, p. A521

OLSON, Dan, President, Sanford Bemidji Medical Center, Bemidji, MN, p. A340

OLSON, Dave, Director of Nursing, Montana State Hospital, Warm Springs, MT, p. A391

OLSON, Diana, Chief Human Resources Officer, Mercy Willard Hospital, Willard, OH, p. A505

OLSON, Eric, Chief Financial Officer, Providence Portland Medical Center, Portland, OR, p. A528

OLSON, Forrest, M.D. Chief Medical Officer, Enloe Medical Center, Chico, CA, p. A59

OLSON, Gary R., President and Chief Executive Officer, St. Luke's Hospital, Chesterfield, MO, p. A369

OLSON, Gregory A., President and Chief Executive Officer, Aspirus Medford Hospital, Medford, WI, p. A709

OLSON, John L., M.D. Medical Director, Lakeview Medical Center, Rice Lake, WI, p. A714

OLSON, Karl, M.D. Chief of Staff, St. Luke's Elmore, Mountain Home, ID, p. A177

OLSON, Kent, Administrator and Chief Executive Officer, Philip Health Services, Philip, SD, p. A575

OLSON, Kevin, Director Information Systems, St. Anthony Hospital, Oklahoma City, OK, p. A516

OLSON, Lynn R., Director Human Resources, Hendricks Community Hospital, Hendricks, MN, p. A345

OLSON, Lynn W., President and Chief Executive Officer, Hannibal Regional Hospital, Hannibal, MO, p. A372

OLSON, Marcia
Director Finance, Spearfish Regional Hospital, Spearfish, SD, p. A577
Business Office Manager, Webster County Community Hospital, Red Cloud, NE, p. A401

OLSON, MariBeth, R.N. Vice President Patient Care Services, Mercy Hospital, Coon Rapids, MN, p. A342

OLSON, Mark, M.D. Chief of Staff, Lincoln Community Hospital and Nursing Home, Hugo, CO, p. A107

OLSON, Mark, Interim Chief Information Officer, Behavioral Health Network, Natchaug Hospital, Mansfield Center, CT, p. A115

OLSON, Michael R., Administrator, American Fork Hospital, American Fork, UT, p. A659

OLSON, Nate, Chief Executive Officer, St. Peter's Hospital, Helena, MT, p. A388

OLSON, Randall M., Chief Executive Officer, Lane Regional Medical Center, Zachary, LA, p. A290

OLSON, Rick, M.D. Chief of Staff, Kaiser Permanente Sunnyside Medical Center, Clackamas, OR, p. A523

OLSON, Tim
Senior Vice President Finance, Appleton Medical Center, Appleton, WI, p. A701
Senior Vice President Finance, Theda Clark Medical Center, Neenah, WI, p. A711

OLSON, Tracy, Human Resource Officer, Avera St. Luke's Hospital, Aberdeen, SD, p. A572

OLSON, William, Director Finance, Providence St. Vincent Medical Center, Portland, OR, p. A528

OLSSON, Clifford Lee, Chief Financial Officer, Tuba City Regional Health Care Corporation, Tuba City, AZ, p. A40

OLSSON, Dave, Director of Marketing, Aspirus Keweenaw Hospital, Laurium, MI, p. A329

OLSZYK, Mark, M.D. Vice President Medical Affairs and Chief Medical Officer, Carroll Hospital Center, Westminster, MD, p. A304

OMAN, Michelle, D.O
Chief Medical Officer, Essentia Health Northern Pines, Aurora, MN, p. A340
Chief Medical Officer, Essentia Health–Virginia, Virginia, MN, p. A353

OMAR, Sharif, Chief Executive Officer, Northwest Medical Center – Springdale, Springdale, AR, p. A53

OMOLARA, Khar, M.D. Chief Medical Staff, Jefferson County Hospital, Fayette, MS, p. A357

OMONDI, Tom, Interim Chief Executive Officer, Promise Hospital of Houston, Houston, TX, p. A626

OMRAN, Yasser, M.D. President Medical Staff, Pomerene Hospital, Millersburg, OH, p. A499

OMTA, Stephen R., Chief Operating Officer, PeaceHealth St. Joseph Medical Center, Bellingham, WA, p. A681

OMURA, David, Associate Director, Wm. Jennings Bryan Dorn Veterans Affairs Medical Center, Columbia, SC, p. A565

ONG, Richard B., Chief Information Officer, Saint Vincent Health Center, Erie, PA, p. A539

ONI, Buki, M.D. Chief Medical Officer, Kenmare Community Hospital, Kenmare, ND, p. A479

ONIFATHER, Jeff, Chief Financial Officer, Cornerstone of Medical Arts Center Hospital, Fresh Meadows, NY, p. A437

ONO, Craig, M.D. Chief of Staff, Shriners Hospitals for Children–Honolulu, Honolulu, HI, p. A171

ONO, Sidney M., Administrator, Shriners Hospitals for Children–Los Angeles, Los Angeles, CA, p. A74

ONOFRE, Bonnie J., MS Vice President and Chief Nursing Officer, Robert Packer Hospital, Sayre, PA, p. A554

ONTON, Wendy, Chief Nursing Officer, Alleghany Memorial Hospital, Sparta, NC, p. A473

OOSTHUYSEN, Gabriel, Director Human Resources, Prairie du Chien Memorial Hospital, Prairie Du Chien, WI, p. A713

OOSTRA, Randall D., FACHE, President and Chief Executive Officer, ProMedica Health System, Toledo, OH, p. B109

OPBROEK, Steve, Manager Information Technology, Skyline Hospital, White Salmon, WA, p. A692

OPDAHL, Jim, Interim Chief Executive Officer, Orchard Hospital, Gridley, CA, p. A66

OPHEIKENS, Robyn, Assistant Administrator Human Resources, St. Mark's Hospital, Salt Lake City, UT, p. A663

OPPEGARD, Stanley C., Chief Executive Officer, Trinity Hospital, Weaverville, CA, p. A100

OPRANDI, Allison, M.D. Chief Medical Officer, Aultman Hospital, Canton, OH, p. A485

OPRISKO, Judy P.
Vice President, Allied Services Rehabilitation Hospital, Scranton, PA, p. A554
Vice President Human Resources, John Heinz Institute of Rehabilitation Medicine, Wilkes-Barre, PA, p. A558

OPSTEDAHL, DeeAnna, Vice President Patient Care Services, St. Joseph's Hospital and Health Center, Dickinson, ND, p. A477

OPSUT, Jennifer, Interim Chief Operating Officer, West Valley Medical Center, Caldwell, ID, p. A175

ORCUTT, David, Chief Executive Officer, Weatherford Regional Medical Center, Weatherford, TX, p. A656

ORDYNA, Daniel, Chief Executive Officer, Portneuf Medical Center, Pocatello, ID, p. A177

ORE, Ruta, Director Human Resources, Pottstown Memorial Medical Center, Pottstown, PA, p. A552

OREAR, Kathy, Director Human Resources, Newman Regional Health, Emporia, KS, p. A243

OREGEL, Omar, Controller, Kindred Hospital–Ontario, Ontario, CA, p. A81

OREOL, Harry, Acting Chief Executive Officer, Patton State Hospital, Patton, CA, p. A83

OREY, Lon, Vice President Human Resources, Presbyterian Intercommunity Health Hospital, Whittier, CA, p. A100

ORIOL, Albert, Vice President Information Management and Chief Information Officer, Rady Children's Hospital – San Diego, San Diego, CA, p. A89

ORLANDI, Mary, Manager Human Resources, Carney Hospital, Boston, MA, p. A306

ORLANDO, Anthony T., Senior Vice President Finance, Englewood Hospital and Medical Center, Englewood, NJ, p. A416

ORLANDO, Joseph S., President, Bergen Regional Medical Center, Paramus, NJ, p. A420

ORLANDO, Lorraine, Vice President Human Resources, New York Hospital Queens, NY, p. A447

ORMAN Jr., Bernard A., Administrator, Samaritan Memorial Hospital, Macon, MO, p. A376

ORMOND, Evalyn, Chief Executive Officer, Union General Hospital, Farmerville, LA, p. A277

ORMOND, Jack, Chief Financial Officer, Cuba Memorial Hospital, Cuba, NY, p. A436

ORMS, J. Michael, M.D. Chief of Staff, East Texas Medical Center Fairfield, Fairfield, TX, p. A617

ORMSBY, Joan
Vice President, West Suburban Medical Center, Oak Park, IL, p. A198
Chief Operating Officer, Westlake Hospital, Melrose Park, IL, p. A196

ORNELAS, Henry, Chief Operating Officer, LAC/University of Southern California Medical Center, Los Angeles, CA, p. A73

ORONA, Rene, M.D. Chief of Staff, Marshall Medical Center, Placerville, CA, p. A83

OROZCO, Jorge, Chief Executive Officer, Rancho Los Amigos National Rehabilitation Center, Downey, CA, p. A62

ORR, Karen, Chief Nursing Officer, Providence Medical Center, Kansas City, KS, p. A247

ORR, Stephanie, R.N. Chief Nursing Officer, Steele Memorial Medical Center, Salmon, ID, p. A178

ORRELL, Linda, Interim Chief Nursing Officer, Drew Memorial Hospital, Monticello, AR, p. A50

ORRICK, Charles H., Administrator, Donalsonville Hospital, Donalsonville, GA, p. A158

ORSINI, John
Executive Vice President and Chief Financial Officer, Central DuPage Hospital, Winfield, IL, p. A205
Executive Vice President and Chief Financial Officer, Delnor Hospital, Geneva, IL, p. A191

ORSINI, Thomas J., President and Chief Executive Officer, Lake Taylor Transitional Care Hospital, Norfolk, VA, p. A675

ORSKEY, David, Administrator, Physicians Care Surgical Hospital, Royersford, PA, p. A554

ORT, Linda, Chief Financial Officer, Piggott Community Hospital, Piggott, AR, p. A51

ORTEGA, Cesar, M.D. Chief of Staff, Doctor's Hospital – Tidwell, Houston, TX, p. A624

ORTEGA, Debbie, Chief Human Resource Officer and Vice President Administrative Services, Huntington Memorial Hospital, Pasadena, CA, p. A83

ORTEGA, Jose, Chief Operating Officer, Greater El Monte Community Hospital, South El Monte, CA, p. A96

ORTEGO, Ashley, Director Human Resources and Marketing, Springhill Medical Center, Springhill, LA, p. A289

ORTHAUS, Denis, Director Human Resources, Philhaven, Mount Gretna, PA, p. A545

ORTIZ, Bienvenido, Coordinator Information Systems, Hospital De Damas, Ponce, PR, p. A727

ORTIZ, Jr., Blas, Assistant Superintendent and Public Information Officer, Rio Grande State Center/South Texas Health Care System, Harlingen, TX, p. A622

ORTIZ, Edson, Chief Information Officer, Hospital Metropolitano Dr. Tito Mattei, Yauco, PR, p. A729

ORTIZ, Evelyn Padilla
Director Human Resources, Hospital Menonita De Cayey, Cayey, PR, p. A725
Director Human Resources, Mennonite General Hospital, Aibonito, PR, p. A724

ORTIZ, Felix, Administrator, I. Gonzalez Martinez Oncologic Hospital,, PR, p. A728

ORTIZ, Francisco, M.D. Chief of Staff, Jackson County Hospital District, Edna, TX, p. A615

ORTIZ, Hector, Financial Director, Hospital Metropolitano Dr. Susoni, Arecibo, PR, p. A724

ORTIZ, Jose O., Chief Financial Officer, Ryder Memorial Hospital, Humacao, PR, p. A726

ORTIZ, Migdalia, Director Human Resources, Hospital San Carlos Borromeo, Moca, PR, p. A727

ORTIZ, Norma, M.D. Medical Director, Hospital Hermanos Melendez, Bayamon, PR, p. A725

ORTIZ VARGAS, Ruth M., Administrator, Lafayette Hospital, Arroyo, PR, p. A724

ORTIZ–BITNER, Olivia, Acting Chief Financial Officer, Veterans Affairs Greater Los Angeles Healthcare System, Los Angeles, CA, p. A75

ORTO, Victoria K., R.N. Chief Nursing and Patient Care Services Officer, Duke Regional Hospital, Durham, NC, p. A463

ORTOLANI, Philip A., Vice President Operations, Mid Coast Hospital, Brunswick, ME, p. A292

OSANTOSKI, Tina, Director Human Resources, Harbor Beach Community Hospital, Harbor Beach, MI, p. A326

OSARIO, Cesar, Specialist Information Technology, Cedar Crest Hospital and Residential Treatment Center, Belton, TX, p. A602

OSBAHR, Leah, Administrator, Washington County Memorial Hospital, Potosi, MO, p. A379

OSBERG, Art, M.D. Chief Medical Officer, Ocala Regional Medical Center, Ocala, FL, p. A139

OSBORN, Mary Ann, R.N. Senior Vice President and Chief Care Coordinator Officer, UnityPoint Health – St. Luke's Hospital, Cedar Rapids, IA, p. A226

OSBORN, Melodie
Chief Nursing Officer, Renown Rehabilitation Hospital, Reno, NV, p. A408
Chief Nursing Officer, Renown South Meadows Medical Center, Reno, NV, p. A408

OSBORN, Tom, D.O. Chief Medical Staff, Holdenville General Hospital, Holdenville, OK, p. A512

OSBORNE, Anna, Chief Human Resources Management Service, West Texas Veterans Affairs Health Care System, Big Spring, TX, p. A603

OSBORNE, Jay, M.D. Senior Vice President Medical Affairs, Northside Medical Center, Youngstown, OH, p. A506

OSBORNE, Phil, Director Information Technology, Bourbon Community Hospital, Paris, KY, p. A269

OSBURN, Jerry, Chief Executive Officer, Yoakum County Hospital, Denver City, TX, p. A614

OSCADAL, Martin
Vice President Human Resources, St. Elizabeth Edgewood, Edgewood, KY, p. A260
Senior Vice President Human Resources, St. Elizabeth Florence, Florence, KY, p. A261
Senior Vice President Human Resources, St. Elizabeth Fort Thomas, Fort Thomas, KY, p. A261

OSEGARD, Jeff, Chief Information Officer, Cass County Memorial Hospital, Atlantic, IA, p. A225

OSEHOBO, Philip, M.D. Chief Medical Officer, Spalding Regional Medical Center, Griffin, GA, p. A160

OSER, William F., M.D. Senior Vice President and Chief Medical Officer, JFK Medical Center, Edison, NJ, p. A415

OSGOOD, John, Interim Chief Operating Officer, Hackensack University Medical Center at Pascack Valley, Westwood, NJ, p. A424

OSINOWO, Thomas, M.D. Chief Clinical Officer, Northwest Ohio Psychiatric Hospital, Toledo, OH, p. A503

OSINSKI, Kathleen, Chief Human Resources Service, John D. Dingell Veterans Affairs Medical Center, Detroit, MI, p. A322

OSLIN, Dave, M.D. Chief of Staff, Philadelphia Veterans Affairs Medical Center, Philadelphia, PA, p. A549

OSMUS, Richard D., Chief Executive Officer, Abbeville Area Medical Center, Abbeville, SC, p. A562

OSSE, John M., Interim Chief Executive Officer, Murray County Medical Center, Slayton, MN, p. A352

OSSELLO, Susan, Chief Financial Officer, Granite County Medical Center, Philipsburg, MT, p. A390

OSTASZEWSKI, Patricia, MS, Chief Executive Officer, HEALTHSOUTH Rehabilitation Hospital of Toms River, Toms River, NJ, p. A423

OSTBERG, Melissa, Chief Financial Officer, Marias Medical Center, Shelby, MT, p. A391

OSTBLOOM, Jan, Human Resources Consultant, Our Lady of Peace, Louisville, KY, p. A266

OSTEEN, Tom J., Director Area Technology, Kaiser Permanente Manteca Medical Center, Manteca, CA, p. A76

OSTENDORF, Todd, Chief Financial Officer, North Memorial Medical Center, Robbinsdale, MN, p. A350

OSTENSON, Scott, Chief Financial Officer, Jacobson Memorial Hospital Care Center, Elgin, ND, p. A477

OSTER, Kurt, Human Resources Officer, Carl Vinson Veterans Affairs Medical Center, Dublin, GA, p. A159

OSTERBERG, Valerie, Chief Financial Officer, Sanford Vermillion Medical Center, Vermillion, SD, p. A577

OSTERHOLM, Tim, Senior Vice President and Chief People Officer, St. Vincent Infirmary Medical Center, Little Rock, AR, p. A49

OSTERHOUT, David, Assistant Superintendent and Chief Financial Officer, El Paso Psychiatric Center, El Paso, TX, p. A615

OSTERLY, Eric, Chief Financial Officer, Florida Hospital Fish Memorial, Orange City, FL, p. A140

OSTLIG, Jane, Chief Medical Officer, Sanford Mayville Medical Center, Mayville, ND, p. A479

OSTRANDER, Maria DC, R.N. Chief Nurse Executive, San Antonio State Hospital, San Antonio, TX, p. A647

OSTRANDER, Mark, Vice President Financial Services, Community Medical Center, Toms River, NJ, p. A423

OSTRANDER, Michael, Chief Financial Officer, Nathan Littauer Hospital and Nursing Home, Gloversville, NY, p. A438

OSTROWSKY, Barry, President and Chief Executive Officer, Barnabas Health, West Orange, NJ, p. B21

OSWALD, Kathy, Senior Vice President and Chief Human Resources Officer, Henry Ford Hospital, Detroit, MI, p. A322

OSWALD, Traci L., Vice President Human Resources, Galion Community Hospital, Galion, OH, p. A494

OSWALT, Charles, Vice President, Chief Financial Officer and Compliance Officer, Levi Hospital, Hot Springs National Park, AR, p. A47

OTERO, Jorge Torres, Executive Director, Hospital Del Maestro, San Juan, PR, p. A728

OTERO, Victoria, Director Human Resources, HEALTHSOUTH Rehabilitation Hospital, Albuquerque, NM, p. A426

OTHOLE, Jean, Chief Executive Officer, U. S. Public Health Service Indian Hospital, Zuni, NM, p. A431

OTREMBIAK, Robert J., Director Human Resources, St. Joseph's Hospital, Breese, IL, p. A182

OTT, Christopher, M.D. Chief Medical Officer, St. Anthony Hospital, Lakewood, CO, p. A108

OTT, Darin, D.O. Chief of Staff, Kane County Hospital, Kanab, UT, p. A660

OTT, Kathryn Lynne, MSN Vice President Patient Care Services and Chief Nursing Officer, Fitzgibbon Hospital, Marshall, MO, p. A376

OTT, Laurie, Vice President Human Resources and President University Health Care Foundation, University Hospital, Augusta, GA, p. A154

OTT, Pamela, Vice President Finance, Aurora Sheboygan Memorial Medical Center, Sheboygan, WI, p. A715

OTT, Ronald A., Chief Executive Officer, Fitzgibbon Hospital, Marshall, MO, p. A376

OTT, Ronald H.
President, Excela Frick Hospital, Mount Pleasant, PA, p. A546
President, Excela Health Westmoreland Hospital, Greensburg, PA, p. A539

OTTATI, David, Chief Executive Officer, Florida Hospital Waterman, Tavares, FL, p. A148

OTTE, Elaine, Chief Operating Officer, Clarinda Regional Health Center, Clarinda, IA, p. A227

OTTENBACHER, John, Chief of Staff, Bowdle Hospital, Bowdle, SD, p. A572

OTTENS, Mark, Chief Nursing Officer, Baptist Memorial Hospital–North Mississippi, Oxford, MS, p. A364

OTTERSBACH, Virginia, Chief Nursing Officer, Saint Catherine Regional Hospital, Charlestown, IN, p. A208

OTTMAR, Kellie, Manager Information Services, East Adams Rural Hospital, Ritzville, WA, p. A688

OTTO, Sara, Director Human Resources, North Canyon Medical Center, Gooding, ID, p. A176

OTTO, Steve
Chief Executive Officer, TriStar Skyline Madison Campus, Madison, TN, p. A587
Chief Executive Officer, TriStar Skyline Medical Center, Nashville, TN, p. A591

OUELETTE, Lisa, Director Human Resources, Beaumont Hospital – Troy, Troy, MI, p. A336

OUELLETTE, Demetra, Chief Operating Officer, Rehabilitation Hospital of Rhode Island, North Smithfield, RI, p. A560

OUIMET, Mary Elizabeth, MSN Senior Vice President and Chief Nursing Officer, Wheaton Franciscan Healthcare – All Saints, Racine, WI, p. A714

OUNGST, Laurie, Vice President and Chief Operating Officer, Ministry Saint Mary's Hospitals, Rhinelander, WI, p. A714

OURS, Matt, Chief Executive Officer, Kempsville Center for Behavioral Health, Norfolk, VA, p. A675

OUSEY, Tracy, Director Human Resources, Washington County Hospital and Clinics, Washington, IA, p. A238

OUTHIER, Amy, Director Health Information Management, Weatherford Regional Hospital, Weatherford, OK, p. A522

OUTLAW, Debbie, R.N. Director Patient Care Services, Riverside Rehabilitation Institute, Newport News, VA, p. A675

OVANDO, Benjamin, Chief Operations Officer, Rancho Los Amigos National Rehabilitation Center, Downey, CA, p. A62

OVERBEY, William J., Chief Executive Officer, Kansas Rehabilitation Hospital, Topeka, KS, p. A255

OVERBY, Roger, Executive Director Information Systems, Greene County Medical Center, Jefferson, IA, p. A233

OVERCASH, Jenny, Director Human Resources, HEALTHSOUTH Huntington Rehabilitation Hospital, Huntington, WV, p. A696

OVEREEM, Mark, Chief Financial Officer, USC Verdugo Hills Hospital, Glendale, CA, p. A65

OVERMAN, David S., President and Chief Operating Officer, Children's Hospitals and Clinics of Minnesota, Minneapolis, MN, p. A347

OVERSTREET, Alyson, Chief Financial Officer, Washington County Hospital and Nursing Home, Chatom, AL, p. A18

OVERSTREET, Amy, Director Human Resources, Trousdale Medical Center, Hartsville, TN, p. A583

OVERSTREET, Dain, Manager Information Technology, Jefferson Hospital, Louisville, GA, p. A162

OVERTON, Deana, Director Human Resources, Mitchell County Hospital, Colorado City, TX, p. A607

OVWIGHO, Godfrey, Vice President Information Technology and Chief Information Officer, The University of Toledo Medical Center, Toledo, OH, p. A503

OWEN, Carey M., Chief Executive Officer, East Alabama Medical Center–Lanier, Valley, AL, p. A26

OWEN, Joanne, Interim Vice President Operations, PeaceHealth Southwest Medical Center, Vancouver, WA, p. A692

OWEN, Ronald S., FACHE, Chief Executive Officer, Southeast Alabama Medical Center, Dothan, AL, p. A19

OWEN, Sabrina, Human Resources Officer, Veterans Affairs Central Iowa Health Care System, Des Moines, IA, p. A230

OWEN, Sandra, Director Fiscal and Accounting, Harper Hospital District Five, Harper, KS, p. A245

OWEN–PLIETZ, Carrie, Chief Executive Officer, Sutter Medical Center, Sacramento, Sacramento, CA, p. A88

OWENS, Beverly, Controller, Rehabilitation Hospital, Navicent Health, Macon, GA, p. A163

OWENS, Brian, Chief Operating Officer, Lindner Center of HOPE, Mason, OH, p. A497

OWENS, Craig A., President, WellStar Douglas Hospital, Douglasville, GA, p. A158

OWENS, Diane, Administrator, St. David's Rehabilitation Center, Austin, TX, p. A600

OWENS, Johnathan, Chief Executive Officer, Decatur Health Systems, Oberlin, KS, p. A251

OWENS, Leon, Director, Caswell Center, Kinston, NC, p. A467

OWENS, Loma, Data Manager, Southwestern State Hospital, Thomasville, GA, p. A168

OWENS, Mark, M.D. Vice President Medical Affairs, Mercy San Juan Medical Center, Carmichael, CA, p. A59

OWENS, Pamela, Director Health Information Management, Hanover Hospital, Hanover, PA, p. A540

OWENS, Rick, Chief Financial Officer, D. W. McMillan Memorial Hospital, Brewton, AL, p. A17

OWENS, Stephanie, Manager Human Resources, McDowell ARH Hospital, McDowell, KY, p. A267

OWENS, RN, Steven Vance, Chief Nursing Officer, Southwestern Medical Center, Lawton, OK, p. A512

OWENSBY, Karen, R.N. Chief Clinical Officer, Florida Hospital North Pinellas, Tarpon Springs, FL, p. A148

OWREY, Donald R., President, UPMC Horizon, Greenville, PA, p. A539

OWSLEY, Lindsay, Manager Human Resources, Ellinwood District Hospital, Ellinwood, KS, p. A243

OWUSU, Frederick K., Chief Human Resources Officer, Desert Regional Medical Center, Palm Springs, CA, p. A82

OXENDALE, Roger A., Chief Executive Officer, Nemours Children's Hospital, Orlando, FL, p. A140

OXENDALE, Sharon, Chief Operating Officer, Northwest Texas Healthcare System, Amarillo, TX, p. A596

OXFORD, Tammy, Director Human Resources, Bob Wilson Memorial Grant County Hospital, Ulysses, KS, p. A255

OXLER, Karen, Vice President Nursing, Lancaster General Health, Lancaster, PA, p. A542

OXLEY, Dawn, R.N., Acting Director, Iowa City Veterans Affairs Health Care System, Iowa City, IA, p. A232

OXLEY, James, D.O. Vice President Medical Affairs, Orange Regional Medical Center, Middletown, NY, p. A441

OXLEY, Stephen, M.D. Chief Medical Officer, Central Regional Hospital, Butner, NC, p. A461

OXTON, Alice, Director Information Technology, Sentara Obici Hospital, Suffolk, VA, p. A679

OZBURN, Thomas H., Chief Executive Officer, TriStar Southern Hills Medical Center, Nashville, TN, p. A591

OZEL, A. Deniz, M.D. Medical Director, New England Rehabilitation Hospital, Woburn, MA, p. A316

OZMENT, Mary, Chief Nursing Officer, Integris Mayes County Medical Center, Pryor, OK, p. A518

P

PAARLBERG, Ted, Chief Executive Officer, Kindred Hospital Peoria, Peoria, IL, p. A199

PAASCH, Michael, Regional Vice President and Chief Information Officer, SSM Cardinal Glennon Children's Medical Center, Saint Louis, MO, p. A381

PABLO, Gary M., M.D. Chief Medical Officer, Sacred Heart Hospital on the Emerald Coast, Miramar Beach, FL, p. A138

PABON, Jose O., Director Operations, Wilma N. Vazquez Medical Center, Vega Baja, PR, p. A729

PABON–RAMIREZ, Felix, Chief Information Officer, St. Charles Hospital, Port Jefferson, NY, p. A452

PACCAPANICCIA, Dominic, Chief Operating Officer, Indiana Regional Medical Center, Indiana, PA, p. A541

PACE, Debbie, Chief Operating Officer, Vaughan Regional Medical Center, Selma, AL, p. A25

PACE, Dewane, Executive Director Ancillary Departments, Valley View Hospital, Glenwood Springs, CO, p. A106

PACE, Kathleen, MS
Chief Nursing Officer, Englewood Community Hospital, Englewood, FL, p. A128
Vice President and Chief Nursing Officer, Fawcett Memorial Hospital, Port Charlotte, FL, p. A143

PACE, Matt, Information Technology Director, Lakeway Regional Medical Center, Lakeway, TX, p. A632

PACEK, Thomas
Vice President Information Systems and Chief Information Officer, Inspira Medical Center–Elmer, Elmer, NJ, p. A416
Vice President Information Systems and Chief Information Officer, Inspira Medical Center–Vineland, Vineland, NJ, p. A424

PACEY, Amy, Vice President Human Resources, Exempla Good Samaritan Medical Center, Lafayette, CO, p. A108

PACHECO, Robert W., Vice President Finance, Women & Infants Hospital of Rhode Island, Providence, RI, p. A561

PACHUCKI, Jr., James J., Chief Financial Officer, Sunbury Community Hospital and Outpatient Center, Sunbury, PA, p. A555

PACINI, Jenna, Human Resources Specialist, Belmont Center for Comprehensive Treatment, Philadelphia, PA, p. A547

PACK, Kathy, Manager Human Resources, Copper Basin Medical Center, Copperhill, TN, p. A581

PACK, Natalie, Chief Financial Officer, St. David's North Austin Medical Center, Austin, TX, p. A600

PACK, William
Chief Financial Officer, Memorial Hermann – Texas Medical Center, Houston, TX, p. A625
Chief Financial Officer, TIRR Memorial Hermann, Houston, TX, p. A627

PACK–HOOKFIN, Sherre, Administrator, Lallie Kemp Medical Center, Independence, LA, p. A279

PACKER, Eric, Administrator, Bear River Valley Hospital, Tremonton, UT, p. A664

PARET, Jason, Chief Executive Officer, Bath Community Hospital, Hot Springs, VA, p. A672

PARETI, Donna, Business Unit Chief Financial Officer, Presence Holy Family Medical Center, Des Plaines, IL, p. A188

PARHAM, Eva, R.N. Chief Nurse Executive, Central State Hospital, Petersburg, VA, p. A676

PARHAM, Tracy, MSNUniversity of North Carolina Hospitals, Chapel Hill, NC, p. A461

PARIELLE, Susan
Director Human Resources, Blue Ridge Regional Hospital, Spruce Pine, NC, p. A473
Director Human Resources Affiliate Mission Health System, McDowell Hospital, Marion, NC, p. A468

PARIGI, II, John S., Interim Chief Financial Officer, Healdsburg District Hospital, Healdsburg, CA, p. A66

PARIS, Cindy, R.N. President, Texas Health Presbyterian Hospital of Rockwall, Rockwall, TX, p. A644

PARIS, David, Chief Executive Officer, Perry County General Hospital, Richton, MS, p. A365

PARIS, John, M.D. Chief Medical Officer, Riverview Hospital, Noblesville, IN, p. A220

PARIS, Karen, Controller, Crittenden County Hospital, Marion, KY, p. A267

PARIS, Richard, M.D. Chief Medical Officer, Robert Wood Johnson University Hospital Somerset, Somerville, NJ, p. A422

PARIS, Trevor, M.D. Medical Director, Brooks Rehabilitation Hospital, Jacksonville, FL, p. A131

PARK, Bockhi
Chief Executive Officer, Encino Hospital Medical Center,, CA, p. A71
Chief Executive Officer, Sherman Oaks Hospital,, CA, p. A74

PARK, David B., Chief Operating Officer and General Counsel, Methodist Hospital, Henderson, KY, p. A262

PARK, Denten, Chief Executive Officer, MountainView Regional Medical Center, Las Cruces, NM, p. A429

PARK, Gary L., President, University of North Carolina Hospitals, Chapel Hill, NC, p. A461

PARK, Jessica, Director Accounting, Penn Highlands Brookville, Brookville, PA, p. A534

PARKER, Audrey, Budget Analyst, U. S. Public Health Service Indian Hospital, Winnebago, NE, p. A403

PARKER, Brandon, Vice President Finance and Chief Financial Officer, Frank R. Howard Memorial Hospital, Willits, CA, p. A100

PARKER, Calvin, M.D. Chief of Staff, Baptist Orange Hospital, Orange, TX, p. A640

PARKER, Christopher J., R.N
Senior Vice President Patient Care Services and Chief Nursing Officer, University of Maryland Shore Medical Center at Chestertown, Chestertown, MD, p. A299
Chief Nursing Officer, University of Maryland Shore Medical Center at Easton, Easton, MD, p. A300

PARKER, Cindy, Chief Financial Officer and Director Human Resources, Throckmorton County Memorial Hospital, Throckmorton, TX, p. A653

PARKER, Cythia, Fiscal Director, Washington County Regional Medical Center, Sandersville, GA, p. A166

PARKER, Dan, M.D. Chief of Staff, Winona Health, Winona, MN, p. A354

PARKER, David, VP Information Technology, Magnolia Regional Health Center, Corinth, MS, p. A357

PARKER, Diana, Chief Executive Officer, Advanced Care Hospital of Montana, Billings, MT, p. A385

PARKER, Donald J., President and Chief Executive Officer, Carrier Clinic, Belle Mead, NJ, p. A413

PARKER, Grace E., R.N. Chief Nursing Officer, University of Washington Medical Center, Seattle, WA, p. A689

PARKER, Janie, Chief Financial Officer, Hardin County General Hospital, Rosiclare, IL, p. A202

PARKER, Jennifer, Interim Director Information Systems, Delta Regional Medical Center, Greenville, MS, p. A358

PARKER, Jon–Michael, R.N. Chief Nursing Officer, Lillian M. Hudspeth Memorial Hospital, Sonora, TX, p. A649

PARKER, Judy Goforth, Ph.D., Secretary of Health, Chickasaw Nation Medical Center, Ada, OK, p. A507

PARKER, Michael, M.D. Chief of Staff, Sharon Hospital, Sharon, CT, p. A117

PARKER, Robert, Chief Executive Officer, Meadowview Regional Medical Center, Maysville, KY, p. A267

PARKER, Rodney, Senior Associate Executive Director, Coney Island Hospital,, NY, p. A443

PARKER, Sandra K., M.D. Chief Medical Officer, EastPointe Hospital, Daphne, AL, p. A18

PARKER, Thomas, Chief Executive Officer, Upper Valley Medical Center, Troy, OH, p. A503

PARKER, Tina, Director Human Resources, HEALTHSOUTH Rehabilitation Hospital Midland–Odessa, Midland, TX, p. A638

PARKER, Valerie, M.D. Clinical Director, U. S. Public Health Service Indian Hospital, Rosebud, SD, p. A576

PARKEY, Kasey, Coordinator Payroll and Benefits, Post Acute Medical Specialty Hospital of Corpus Christi, Corpus Christi, TX, p. A608

PARKHILL, Cherie, Chief Financial Officer, Crosbyton Clinic Hospital, Crosbyton, TX, p. A609

PARKHURST, James E., President and Chief Executive Officer, Newport Bay Hospital, Newport Beach, CA, p. A80

PARKINSON, Justin, M.D. President Medical Staff, Pioneer Valley Hospital, West Valley City, UT, p. A664

PARKINSON, Michelle A., Director Human Resources, Prairie St. John's, Fargo, ND, p. A477

PARKS, Audrey, Senior Administrative Director Information Technology, Salinas Valley Memorial Healthcare System, Salinas, CA, p. A88

PARKS, Cary, Chief Information Resource Management, Hampton Veterans Affairs Medical Center, Hampton, VA, p. A672

PARKS, Dave, Chief Information Officer, Three Rivers Health, Three Rivers, MI, p. A336

PARKS, Ginger, Director Human Resources, Cape Fear Valley – Bladen County Hospital, Elizabethtown, NC, p. A464

PARKS, Jody, Administrator, Ottawa County Health Center, Minneapolis, KS, p. A250

PARKS, Kathi, Director of Nursing, South Lincoln Medical Center, Kemmerer, WY, p. A721

PARKS, Kyle, Chief of Staff, Evans Memorial Hospital, Claxton, GA, p. A156

PARKS, Michelle, Administrator, RiverValley Behavioral Health Hospital, Owensboro, KY, p. A268

PARKS, Richard H., FACHE, President and Chief Executive Officer, Covenant Health System, Lubbock, TX, p. B45

PARKS, Vicki, Chief Financial Officer, Jackson Purchase Medical Center, Mayfield, KY, p. A267

PARMER, David N., Chief Executive Officer, Baptist Hospitals of Southeast Texas, Beaumont, TX, p. A601

PARMER, Dennis, M.D. Chief Medical Staff, Community Hospital of Long Beach, Long Beach, CA, p. A70

PARNEL, George, Chief Financial Officer, Clifton T. Perkins Hospital Center, Jessup, MD, p. A301

PARNELL, Brenda, Chief Executive Officer, Benewah Community Hospital, Saint Maries, ID, p. A178

PAROBY, Carmen, Administrator, West Florida Community Care Center, Milton, FL, p. A138

PAROD, Daniel A., Senior Vice President Hospital and Administrative Affairs, Rockford Memorial Hospital, Rockford, IL, p. A201

PAROSKI, Margaret, M.D. Executive Vice President and Chief Medical Officer, KALEIDA Health, Buffalo, NY, p. A434

PARR, Lynnette, Chief Financial Officer, Down East Community Hospital, Machias, ME, p. A294

PARRA, Kristin, Chief Nursing Officer, Yuma Rehabilitation Hospital, Yuma, AZ, p. A42

PARRA, Michelle, Director Human Resources, Kindred Hospital South Bay, Gardena, CA, p. A65

PARRINELLO, Kathleen M., Ph.D. Chief Operating Officer, Strong Memorial Hospital of the University of Rochester, Rochester, NY, p. A453

PARRISH, Becky, Director Human Resources, Southern Virginia Regional Medical Center, Emporia, VA, p. A670

PARRISH, Carl, Chief Fiscal Service, James E. Van Zandt Veterans Affairs Medical Center, Altoona, PA, p. A532

PARRISH, James G., FACHE, Chief Executive Officer, Humboldt General Hospital, Winnemucca, NV, p. A408

PARRISH, Jerry A., Vice President, AnMed Health Medical Center, Anderson, SC, p. A562

PARRISH, Pamela, Director Information Systems, Novant Health Brunswick Medical Center, Bolivia, NC, p. A460

PARRISH, Suann, Chief Financial Officer, Yoakum County Hospital, Denver City, TX, p. A614

PARROTT, Keith, FACHE, President and Chief Executive Officer, Baptist Health System, Birmingham, AL, p. B20

PARRY, Timothy, R.N. Vice President Nursing, Highland District Hospital, Hillsboro, OH, p. A495

PARSON, Charlynne, Nurse Executive, Moccasin Bend Mental Health Institute, Chattanooga, TN, p. A580

PARSONS, Beth, R.N., Administrator, Dubuis Hospital of Alexandria, Alexandria, LA, p. A272

PARSONS, Brad, FACHE, Administrator and Chief Executive Officer, NEA Baptist Memorial Hospital, Jonesboro, AR, p. A48

PARSONS, Debra, Chief Nursing Officer, Pikeville Medical Center, Pikeville, KY, p. A269

PARSONS, Jamie, Human Resources Director, Johnson City Medical Center, Johnson City, TN, p. A585

PARSONS, John, R.N. Chief Nursing Officer, TrustPoint Hospital, Lubbock, TX, p. A635

PARSONS, Lauren, M.D. Clinical Director, North Texas State Hospital, Wichita Falls Campus, Wichita Falls, TX, p. A657

PARSONS, Lisa, M.D. Chief Medical Officer, Windhaven Psychiatric Hospital, Prescott Valley, AZ, p. A37

PARSONS, Terri L., Administrator, Advanced Care Hospital of White County, Searcy, AR, p. A52

PARTAMIAN, Gregory A., Chief Operating Officer, Crittenton Hospital Medical Center, Rochester, MI, p. A333

PARTEE, Paris I., Associate Administrator and Director Human Resources, John H. Stroger Jr. Hospital of Cook County, Chicago, IL, p. A184

PARTENZA, John, Vice President and Treasurer, Northern Westchester Hospital, Mount Kisco, NY, p. A442

PARTHEMORE, Warrenette, Director Human Resources, Memorial Hospital, Fremont, OH, p. A494

PARTON, Scott, Director Human Resources, Oconee Regional Medical Center, Milledgeville, GA, p. A163

PARTRIDGE, Susan, Director Human Resources, Nantucket Cottage Hospital, Nantucket, MA, p. A312

PARUCH, Randy J., Director, Information Systems, Holland Hospital, Holland, MI, p. A326

PARUNGAO, Amy, Director of Nursing, Rehabilitation Hospital of the Pacific, Honolulu, HI, p. A171

PASCASIO, Robert A., FACHE, Chief Executive Officer, Lillian M. Hudspeth Memorial Hospital, Sonora, TX, p. A649

PASCH, Deborah, Chief Nurse Executive, University of Missouri Hospitals and Clinics, Columbia, MO, p. A370

PASCHALL, Francine, R.N. Chief Nursing Officer, Riverside Community Hospital, Riverside, CA, p. A86

PASCO, Teri, Director Human Resources, East Liverpool City Hospital, East Liverpool, OH, p. A493

PASCOE, John, M.D. Executive Medical Director, Timberlawn Mental Health System, Dallas, TX, p. A612

PASCUZZI, Robert, Chief Financial Officer, Mercy San Juan Medical Center, Carmichael, CA, p. A59

PASKERT, James, M.D. Vice President Chief Medical and Quality Officer, Kaweah Delta Medical Center, Visalia, CA, p. A99

PASLEY, Debra L., Chief Nursing Officer, OU Medical Center, Oklahoma City, OK, p. A516

PASSANNANTE, Jr., Anthony, M.D. Vice President, Chief Medical Officer and Co–Chief Quality Officer, Saint Peter's University Hospital, New Brunswick, NJ, p. A419

PASSARELLI, Theresa, Human Resources Generalist, Warm Springs Medical Center, Warm Springs, GA, p. A169

PASSMANN, Frederic K., M.D. Chief of Staff, Stonewall Memorial Hospital, Aspermont, TX, p. A598

PASSMORE, Gary, Chief Information Officer, Endless Mountain Health Systems, Montrose, PA, p. A545

PASTERNAK, L. Reuven, M.P.H., Vice President for Health System and Chief Executive Officer, Stony Brook University Medical Center, Stony Brook, NY, p. A455

PASTIAN, Andre, R.N. Chief Nursing Officer, Boulder City Hospital, Boulder City, NV, p. A404

PASTORE, Raymond, M.D. Chief Medical Officer, St. John's Episcopal Hospital–South Shore,, NY, p. A448

PASTRANA, Guillermo, Executive Director, Hospital Pavia–Hato Rey, San Juan, PR, p. A728

PASZTOR, Barbara J., R.N
Vice President Patient Care Services and Chief Nursing Officer, Blanchard Valley Hospital, Findlay, OH, p. A494
Vice President Nursing and Patient Care Services, Bluffton Hospital, Bluffton, OH, p. A484

PATAK, David, President and Chief Executive Officer, Our Lady of Lourdes Memorial Hospital, Inc., Binghamton, NY, p. A433

PATASHNICK, Melvyn, President and Chief Executive Officer, Copley Hospital, Morrisville, VT, p. A665

PATCHELL, Lee, Lead Human Resources Business Partner, Presbyterian Hospital, Albuquerque, NM, p. A426

PATCHIN, J. Craig, Administrator, Shriners Hospitals for Children–Portland, Portland, OR, p. A529

PATE, Danny, M.D. Chief Medical Staff, Vidant Duplin Hospital, Kenansville, NC, p. A467

PATE, David C., JD, President and Chief Executive Officer, St. Luke's Health System, Boise, ID, p. B128

PATE, John, M.D. Chief Medical Officer, Tri–County Hospital, Wadena, MN, p. A353

PATE, Lois, R.N. Chief Nursing Officer, Island Hospital, Anacortes, WA, p. A681

PATEL, Amita, M.D. Medical Director, Haven Behavioral Senior Care of Dayton, Dayton, OH, p. A492

PATEL, C. N., M.D. Chief of Staff, Belmont Community Hospital, Bellaire, OH, p. A483

PATEL, Deepak, M.D. Medical Director, Cumberland Hall Hospital, Hopkinsville, KY, p. A263

PATEL, Dilip, M.D. Chief of Staff, Greater El Monte Community Hospital, South El Monte, CA, p. A96

PATEL, Fatma, M.D. Vice President Medical Affairs, Niagara Falls Memorial Medical Center, Niagara Falls, NY, p. A449

PATEL, Govind, M.D. Medical Director, HEALTHSOUTH MountainView Regional Rehabilitation Hospital, Morgantown, WV, p. A697

PATEL, Hema, Director Medical Records, RiverWoods Behavioral Health System, Riverdale, GA, p. A165

PATEL, Ketul J., Executive Vice President and Chief Operations and Strategy Officer, Hackensack University Medical Center, Hackensack, NJ, p. A416

PATEL, Malini, M.D. Medical Director, Elgin Mental Health Center, Elgin, IL, p. A189

PATEL, Natu M., M.D. Chief of Staff, Phoebe Worth Medical Center, Sylvester, GA, p. A167

PATEL, Nayan, Director Information Systems, The Heart Hospital Baylor Plano, Plano, TX, p. A643

PATEL, Nirav, M.D. Interim Chief Medical Officer, Saint Louis University Hospital, Saint Louis, MO, p. A381

PATEL, Paryus, M.D. Chief Medical Officer, Centinela Hospital Medical Center, Inglewood, CA, p. A67

PATEL, Prakash Chandra, M.D. Chief of Staff, Kindred Hospital–La Mirada, La Mirada, CA, p. A68

PATEL, Pravin, M.D. Acting President and Chief Executive Officer, Southern Virginia Mental Health Institute, Danville, VA, p. A670

PATEL, Pravinchandra, M.D. Chief Medical Officer, Barnes–Kasson County Hospital, Susquehanna, PA, p. A555

PATEL, Rajesh, M.D. Chief of Staff, Lock Haven Hospital, Lock Haven, PA, p. A543

PATEL, Rakesh, D.O. Medical Director, HEALTHSOUTH Rehabilitation Hospital of Altoona, Altoona, PA, p. A532

PATEL, Shailesh, M.D. Medical Director, Anchor Hospital, Atlanta, GA, p. A151

PATEL, Shalin, M.D. Chief Medical Officer, Memorial Hermann Rehabilitation Hospital – Katy, Katy, TX, p. A630

PATEL, Sharad, M.D. Medical Director, Florida Hospital at Connerton Long Term Acute Care, Land O'Lakes, FL, p. A134

PATEL, Suresh, M.D. Chief Medical Officer, Cavalier County Memorial Hospital, Langdon, ND, p. A479

PATEL, Viraj, M.D. Chief Medical Officer, Unity Medical & Surgical Hospital, Mishawaka, IN, p. A219

PATER, Tom
Vice President Finance and Chief Financial Officer, RML Specialty Hospital, Chicago, IL, p. A186
Chief Financial Officer, RML Specialty Hospital, Hinsdale, IL, p. A193

PATHI, Janna, M.D. Chief Medical Officer, Ohio County Hospital, Hartford, KY, p. A262

PATIL, Steve, Chief Financial Officer, W. G. (Bill) Heffner Veterans Affairs Medical Center, Salisbury, NC, p. A472

PATILLO, Laura, Manager Human Resources, Fresno Surgical Hospital, Fresno, CA, p. A64

PATINO, Beth, Chief Information Officer, DeKalb Medical at North Decatur, Decatur, GA, p. A158

PATLA, Rich
Director Information Technology, California Hospital Medical Center, Los Angeles, CA, p. A71
Site Director, St. Mary Medical Center, Long Beach, CA, p. A70

PATONAI, Steven D., Chief Executive Officer, Frye Regional Medical Center, Hickory, NC, p. A466

PATRICK, Ann M., Vice President Human Resources, Northwest Community Hospital, Arlington Heights, IL, p. A180

PATRICK, Barbara, Director Human Resources, Chestatee Regional Hospital, Dahlonega, GA, p. A157

PATRICK, II, Calvin, Director Information Services, Bert Fish Medical Center, New Smyrna Beach, FL, p. A139

PATRICK, Chad, President and Chief Executive Officer, Orange Park Medical Center, Orange Park, FL, p. A140

PATRICK, Christian C., M.D. Chief Medical Officer, Baptist Memorial Hospital – Memphis, Memphis, TN, p. A588

PATRICK, Deborah A.
Senior Vice President Human Resources, Lehigh Valley Hospital, Allentown, PA, p. A532
Vice President Human Resources, Lehigh Valley Hospital–Muhlenberg, Bethlehem, PA, p. A533

PATRICK, Devin, Manager Human Resources, Utah State Hospital, Provo, UT, p. A662

PATRICK, Lisa, Chief Operating Officer, Caldwell Memorial Hospital, Columbia, LA, p. A275

PATRICK, Ronald, Chief Financial Officer, Northwest Medical Center, Tucson, AZ, p. A40

PATRICK, Sandra, Chief Financial Officer, Three Rivers Hospital, Waverly, TN, p. A594

PATRICK, Sean, Director Information Systems, Gifford Medical Center, Randolph, VT, p. A666

PATRICK, Wade, Senior Vice President Information Services, Indiana Regional Medical Center, Indiana, PA, p. A541

PATTEN Jr., Bill D., Chief Executive Officer, Powell Valley Healthcare, Powell, WY, p. A722

PATTEN, Sally, MS Chief Nursing Officer, New London Hospital, New London, NH, p. A411

PATTERSON, Anthony, Senior Vice President Inpatient Services, University of Alabama Hospital, Birmingham, AL, p. A17

PATTERSON, Barbara, Chief Financial Officer, Provident Hospital of Cook County, Chicago, IL, p. A186

PATTERSON, Benjamin, Chief Executive Officer, Fairway Medical Center, Covington, LA, p. A276

PATTERSON, Camie, Chief Operating Officer and Chief Financial Officer, Indiana University Health La Porte Hospital, La Porte, IN, p. A216

PATTERSON, Christina, Chief Financial Officer, River Park Hospital, Mc Minnville, TN, p. A588

PATTERSON, Dave, Information Systems Manager, Memorial Hospital of Converse County, Douglas, WY, p. A721

PATTERSON, David, Director Human Resources, Parkside Hospital, Tulsa, OK, p. A520

PATTERSON, Debbie, Director Health Information Management, Wesley Rehabilitation Hospital, Wichita, KS, p. A257

PATTERSON, Donna, Director of Nursing, Samuel Simmonds Memorial Hospital, Barrow, AK, p. A28

PATTERSON, Elmore, Chief Executive Officer, Greene County Health System, Eutaw, AL, p. A19

PATTERSON, Jan, Chief Nursing Officer, Avera St. Luke's Hospital, Aberdeen, SD, p. A572

PATTERSON, Jeffrey, Chief Operating Officer, Desert Regional Medical Center, Palm Springs, CA, p. A82

PATTERSON, Jerrie, Chief Nursing Officer, Brazosport Regional Health System, Lake Jackson, TX, p. A632

PATTERSON, Karen, Deputy Director Operations, Elmira Psychiatric Center, Elmira, NY, p. A437

PATTERSON, Larry R., Deputy Commander Administration, Bayne–Jones Army Community Hospital, Fort Polk, LA, p. A277

PATTERSON, Lisa, Director Human Resources, Pointe Coupee General Hospital, New Roads, LA, p. A286

PATTERSON, Marcia, Chief Financial Officer, Valley Regional Medical Center, Brownsville, TX, p. A604

PATTERSON, Maria, Manager Health Information Management, Canyon Ridge Hospital, Chino, CA, p. A59

PATTERSON, Mark, M.D. Chief Medical Officer, Laughlin Memorial Hospital, Greeneville, TN, p. A583

PATTERSON, Melanie, R.N
Vice President Patient Care Services and Chief Nursing Officer, Children's Hospital at Mission, Mission Viejo, CA, p. A77
Vice President Patient Care Services and Chief Nursing Officer, Children's Hospital of Orange County, Orange, CA, p. A81

PATTERSON, Melody, Chief Nurse Executive, Hawthorn Children Psychiatric Hospital, Saint Louis, MO, p. A380

PATTERSON, Michael C., Chief Executive Officer, Southwest Regional Medical Center, Georgetown, OH, p. A494

PATTERSON, Michael N., Chief Executive Officer, Colorado Plains Medical Center, Fort Morgan, CO, p. A106

PATTERSON, Mike, Director of Operations, Northside Hospital–Cherokee, Canton, GA, p. A155

PATTERSON, Philip A., President and Chief Executive Officer, Owensboro Health Regional Hospital, Owensboro, KY, p. A268

PATTERSON, Renee A., Vice President Employment and Training Services, Rogers Memorial Hospital, Oconomowoc, WI, p. A712

PATTERSON, Richard, Chief Financial Officer, TriStar Greenview Regional Hospital, Bowling Green, KY, p. A259

PATTERSON, Robert, Vice President Human Resources and Rehabilitation Services, Central Vermont Medical Center, Berlin, VT, p. A665

PATTERSON, Russ, Director Information Technology, St. Rose Dominican Hospitals – Siena Campus, Henderson, NV, p. A405

PATTERSON, Sam, Chief Financial Officer, Bay Area Hospital, Coos Bay, OR, p. A524

PATTERSON, Sarah, Executive Vice President and Chief Operating Officer, Virginia Mason Medical Center, Seattle, WA, p. A689

PATTERSON, Steve, Chief Executive Officer, Cornerstone Hospital of North Little Rock, Jacksonville, AR, p. A48

PATTERSON, Stuart, M.D. Chief of Staff, Bartow Regional Medical Center, Bartow, FL, p. A123

PATTERSON, Tony, Chief Executive Officer, James B. Haggin Memorial Hospital, Harrodsburg, KY, p. A262

PATTERSON, William, Chief Executive Officer, Delta Medical Center, Memphis, TN, p. A588

PATTI, Rosa, Chief Financial Officer, Cameron Regional Medical Center, Cameron, MO, p. A368

PATTON, Beth, Director Human Resources, OSS Orthopaedic Specialty Hospital, York, PA, p. A559

PATTON, Christina, Chief Financial Officer, Colorado Plains Medical Center, Fort Morgan, CO, p. A106

PATTON, Daniel, Director Information Systems, Henrico Doctors' Hospital, Richmond, VA, p. A677

PATTON, David J.
Vice President Operations, UPMC Northwest, Seneca, PA, p. A554
President, UPMC St. Margaret, Pittsburgh, PA, p. A552

PATTON, Joy, Chief Information Services, Pampa Regional Medical Center, Pampa, TX, p. A641

PATTON, Kevin, Chief Executive Officer, Old Vineyard Behavioral Health Services, Winston–Salem, NC, p. A475

PATTON, Meghan, Vice President Human Resources, Abington Memorial Hospital, Abington, PA, p. A532

PAUGH, J. William, FACHE, President and Chief Executive Officer, Wayne Memorial Hospital, Goldsboro, NC, p. A465

PAUL, Adam, Chief Financial Officer, Prairie Lakes Healthcare System, Watertown, SD, p. A578

PAUL, Donn
Chief Human Resources, Lackey Memorial Hospital, Forest, MS, p. A358
Vice President Human Resources, Pioneer Community Hospital of Patrick County, Stuart, VA, p. A679

PAUL, John W., President and Chief Executive Officer, Allegheny Health Network, Pittsburgh, PA, p. B8

PAUL, Joseph, Chief Financial Officer, Wellington Regional Medical Center, West Palm Beach, FL, p. A150

PAUL, Mary
Chief Information Officer, Columbia St. Mary's Hospital Milwaukee, Milwaukee, WI, p. A710
Chief Information Officer, Columbia St. Mary's Ozaukee Hospital, Mequon, WI, p. A709
Vice President and Chief Information Officer, Sacred Heart Rehabilitation Institute, Milwaukee, WI, p. A711

PAULDINE, Donna M., Deputy Commissioner, Summit Park Hospital and Nursing Care Center, Pomona, NY, p. A451

PAULEY, Clarence, Vice President Human Resources, University of Cincinnati Medical Center, Cincinnati, OH, p. A487

PAULK, Nikki, Chief Executive Officer, Bleckley Memorial Hospital, Cochran, GA, p. A156

PAULL, Judy C., R.N. Market Chief Nursing Executive, Physicians Regional – Pine Ridge, Naples, FL, p. A139

PAULOSKY, David, Chief Financial Officer, Phoenixville Hospital, Phoenixville, PA, p. A550

PAULS, Scott, Manager Information Systems, Gundersen Boscobel Area Hospital and Clinics, Boscobel, WI, p. A702

PAULSEN, Susan, Director Human Resources, Northridge Hospital Medical Center,, CA, p. A73

PAULSON, Adam, Director Finance, CentraCare Health–Melrose, Melrose, MN, p. A346

PAULSON, Erik, Director of Finance, J. D. McCarty Center for Children With Developmental Disabilities, Norman, OK, p. A514

PAULSON, Gordon, Manager Personnel, Glacial Ridge Health System, Glenwood, MN, p. A344

PAULSON, Mark E., Chief Executive Officer, Chippewa County–Montevideo Hospital, Montevideo, MN, p. A348

PAULSON, Sherry, Executive Assistant, Edgerton Hospital and Health Services, Edgerton, WI, p. A704

PAULSON, Sybil K., R.N. Administrator, North Oaks Rehabilitation Hospital, Hammond, LA, p. A278

PAULUS, Ken, President and Chief Executive Officer, Allina Health, Minneapolis, MN, p. B9

PAULUS, Ronald A., M.D., President and Chief Executive Officer, Mission Health System, Asheville, NC, p. B95

PAULUS, Ronald A., M.D., President and Chief Executive Officer, Mission Hospital, Asheville, NC, p. A460

PAULUS, Terri
Chief Nursing Officer, Banner Goldfield Medical Center, Apache Junction, AZ, p. A31
Chief Nursing Officer, Banner Ironwood Medical Center, San Tan Valley, AZ, p. A38

PAUTLER, Stephen, FACHE Chief Operating Officer, Peterson Regional Medical Center, Kerrville, TX, p. A631

PAVEY, Joyal, Executive Director, Rogers City Rehabilitation Hospital, Rogers City, MI, p. A333

PAVIA, Antoine, M.D. Medical Director, Hospital Dr. Cayetano Coll Y Toste, Arecibo, PR, p. A724

PAVIK, Sarah, Director Human Resources and Guest Services, Inova Loudoun Hospital, Leesburg, VA, p. A673

PAVILANIS, Charlotte J., R.N. Director of Patient Care Services, Sturgis Hospital, Sturgis, MI, p. A335

PAVLATOS, Thales, Medical Director, Ohio Valley Surgical Hospital, Springfield, OH, p. A502

PAWAR, Ganesh, M.D. Chief of Staff, Rusk County Memorial Hospital, Ladysmith, WI, p. A707

PAWLAK, Paul, President and Chief Executive Officer, Silver Cross Hospital, New Lenox, IL, p. A198

PAWLOWICZ, James E., Director Human Resources, Shriners Hospitals for Children–Chicago, Chicago, IL, p. A186

PAWLOWSKI, Phil, Chief Financial Officer, Glenbeigh Hospital and Outpatient Centers, Rock Creek, OH, p. A501

PAWOLA, Ken
Chief Operating Officer, RML Specialty Hospital, Chicago, IL, p. A186
Chief Operating Officer, RML Specialty Hospital, Hinsdale, IL, p. A193

PAXSON, Gary
  Associate Administrator Information Systems, Stone County Medical Center, Mountain View, AR, p. A50
  Chief Information Officer, White River Medical Center, Batesville, AR, p. A43
PAYNE, Angel, Clinical Director, Director of Nursing, Sonora Behavioral Health Hospital, Tucson, AZ, p. A40
PAYNE, Candyce, Administrator, Prairie Community Hospital, Terry, MT, p. A391
PAYNE, Gary, Chief Executive Officer, Cardinal Hill Rehabilitation Hospital, Lexington, KY, p. A264
PAYNE, James, Director Information Systems, Southern Tennessee Regional Health System–Winchester, Winchester, TN, p. A594
PAYNE, Janet S.
  Vice President Human Resources, Presence Covenant Medical Center, Urbana, IL, p. A204
  Vice President Human Resources, Presence United Samaritans Medical Center, Danville, IL, p. A187
PAYNE, Judy, R.N. Chief Operating Officer, Turning Point Hospital, Moultrie, GA, p. A164
PAYNE, Kenneth G., Chief Financial Officer, Holzer Medical Center, Gallipolis, OH, p. A494
PAYNE, Michael, M.D. Chief of Staff, Dallas County Medical Center, Fordyce, AR, p. A46
PAYNE, Michael E., Administrator, Girard Medical Center, Girard, KS, p. A244
PAYNE, Rick, Director Information Systems, Santa Rosa Medical Center, Milton, FL, p. A138
PAYNE, Steven, Chief Financial Officer, Pioneer Valley Hospital, West Valley City, UT, p. A664
PAYTON, Becky J., Vice President Human Resources, Mercy Hospital Oklahoma City, Oklahoma City, OK, p. A515
PAYTON, J. Ronald, Director Human Resources, Gateway Regional Medical Center, Granite City, IL, p. A191
PAYTON, Melissa, Manager Human Resources, Baptist Health La Grange, La Grange, KY, p. A263
PAZDERNIK, Mary, Chief Financial Officer, Mahnomen Health Center, Mahnomen, MN, p. A346
PEA, Gary, Chief Financial Officer, Glenn Medical Center, Willows, CA, p. A101
PEA, Richard, Director Human Resources, Memorial Hospital and Health Care Center, Jasper, IN, p. A215
PEABODY, Kim, Chief Operating Officer, The Brook Hospital – KMI, Louisville, KY, p. A266
PEABODY, Paul
  Vice President Information Technology and Chief Information Officer, Bronson Battle Creek, Battle Creek, MI, p. A319
  Vice President Information Technology Chief Information Officer, Bronson LakeView Hospital, Paw Paw, MI, p. A332
  Vice President Information Technology and Chief Information Officer, Bronson Methodist Hospital, Kalamazoo, MI, p. A328
PEACE, James, M.D. Chief of Staff, Olympia Medical Center, Los Angeles, CA, p. A73
PEACE III, Lother E., President and Chief Executive Officer, Russell Medical Center, Alexander City, AL, p. A15
PEACH, Larry, Chief Financial Officer, Jefferson County Health Center, Fairfield, IA, p. A230
PEACH, Susan M., R.N., Chief Executive Officer, Sumner Regional Medical Center, Gallatin, TN, p. A583
PEACOCK, Steve, Assistant Vice President, Plaza Specialty Hospital, Houston, TX, p. A626
PEAL, Chip, Chief Executive Officer, Frankfort Regional Medical Center, Frankfort, KY, p. A261
PEARCE, Charles T.
  Chief Financial and Information Officer, Kalispell Regional Medical Center, Kalispell, MT, p. A389
  Chief Financial and Information Officer, The HealthCenter, Kalispell, MT, p. A389
PEARCE, Darren, Executive Director, Rehabilitation Hospital, Navicent Health, Macon, GA, p. A163
PEARCE, Deedra, Director Information Technology, Green Clinic Surgical Hospital, Ruston, LA, p. A287
PEARCE, Edward, M.D. Chief of Staff, Caldwell Memorial Hospital, Lenoir, NC, p. A468
PEARCE, Margaret, R.N. Chief Nursing Officer, University of Utah Health Care – Hospital and Clinics, Salt Lake City, UT, p. A663
PEARCH, William, Chief Information Officer, Yukon–Kuskokwim Delta Regional Hospital, Bethel, AK, p. A28
PEARCY, Joetta J., Director, Human Resources, Glendive Medical Center, Glendive, MT, p. A387
PEARCY, Steve
  Director Human Resources, Community Heart and Vascular Hospital, Indianapolis, IN, p. A213
  Director Human Resources, Community Hospital North, Indianapolis, IN, p. A213
PEARLMAN, Helen, Nurse Executive, Minneapolis Veterans Affairs Health Care System, Minneapolis, MN, p. A347

PEARSALL, Cynthia, Chief Nursing Officer, Fairfield Medical Center, Lancaster, OH, p. A496
PEARSON, David, Chief Information Officer, St. Luke's Hospital, Columbus, NC, p. A462
PEARSON, Dawn, Director Human Resources, HEALTHSOUTH Rehabilitation Hospital of Vineland, Vineland, NJ, p. A424
PEARSON, Debra, Chief Financial Officer, Jonathan M. Wainwright Memorial Veterans Affairs Medical Center, Walla Walla, WA, p. A692
PEARSON, Fenorris
  Chief Human Resources Officer, Seton Medical Center Austin, Austin, TX, p. A599
  Chief Human Resources Officer, University Medical Center at Brackenridge, Austin, TX, p. A600
PEARSON, Gregory, Chief Executive Officer, River Region Medical Center, Vicksburg, MS, p. A366
PEARSON, Jeff
  Chief Information Officer, Mother Frances Hospital – Jacksonville, Jacksonville, TX, p. A630
  Vice President and Chief Information Officer, Mother Frances Hospital – Tyler, Tyler, TX, p. A654
PEARSON, Kellie T., Director Human Resources, Lower Bucks Hospital, Bristol, PA, p. A534
PEARSON, Linnie, Coordinator Human Resources and Benefits, Montfort Jones Memorial Hospital, Kosciusko, MS, p. A361
PEARSON, Madelyn, R.N. Sr. Vice President Patient Care Services, Englewood Hospital and Medical Center, Englewood, NJ, p. A416
PEARSON, Marshall, Director Management Information Systems, St. David's North Austin Medical Center, Austin, TX, p. A600
PEARSON, Matthew Paul, Chief Executive Officer, Select Specialty Hospital – Northeast Atlanta, Atlanta, GA, p. A153
PEART, Carol, Chief Financial Officer, Aurora Chicago Lakeshore Hospital, Chicago, IL, p. A183
PEBURN, Eric, Chief Financial Officer, Halifax Health Medical Center of Daytona Beach, Daytona Beach, FL, p. A127
PECHOUS, Bryan, M.D. Vice President Medical Affairs, UnityPoint Health – Finley Hospital, Dubuque, IA, p. A230
PECK, Bob, Chief Financial Officer, Wesley Rehabilitation Hospital, Wichita, KS, p. A257
PECK, Darin, M.D. Chief of Staff, Charles A. Dean Memorial Hospital, Greenville, ME, p. A293
PECK, Gary V., Interim Chief Executive Officer, Whitman Hospital and Medical Center, Colfax, WA, p. A682
PECK, Kay E., Ph.D., Chief Executive Officer, Vibra Hospital of Amarillo, Amarillo, TX, p. A596
PECK, Kay E., Ph.D. Chief Executive Officer, Vibra Hospital of Amarillo, Amarillo, TX, p. A596
PECK, Kay E., Ph.D., Chief Executive Officer, Vibra Rehabilitation Hospital of Amarillo, Amarillo, TX, p. A597
PECK, Lori, Vice President Finance, Aspirus Medford Hospital, Medford, WI, p. A709
PECK, Michael D., Assistant Administrator, Caribou Memorial Hospital and Living Center, Soda Springs, ID, p. A178
PECK, Robert C., M.D. Chief Medical Officer, Mayo Clinic Health System in Eau Claire, Eau Claire, WI, p. A704
PEDERSEN, Alan, Vice President Human Resources, Cayuga Medical Center at Ithaca, Ithaca, NY, p. A439
PEDERSEN, Darren, Coordinator Information Technology, Weisman Children's Rehabilitation Hospital, Marlton, NJ, p. A418
PEDERSEN, Paul E., M.D. Vice President and Chief Medical Officer, OSF St. Joseph Medical Center, Bloomington, IL, p. A181
PEDERSON, Bryan, Human Resources Manager, Tri–County Hospital, Wadena, MN, p. A353
PEDERSON, Karn, Manager Health Information Management, McKenzie County Healthcare System, Watford City, ND, p. A480
PEDERSON, Randall K., Chief Executive Officer, Tioga Medical Center, Tioga, ND, p. A480
PEDLEY, Joe, CPA Vice President and Chief Financial Officer, Lawrence Memorial Hospital, Lawrence, KS, p. A248
PEDLOW, Bernadette R., Senior Vice President Business and Chief Operating Officer, Albany Medical Center, Albany, NY, p. A432
PEDROZA, Fernando, Vice President Information Technology, Poudre Valley Hospital, Fort Collins, CO, p. A106
PEEBLES, Wanda V., Chief Nursing Officer, JPS Health Network, Fort Worth, TX, p. A618
PEED, Nancy, Administrator and Chief Executive Officer, Medical Center of Peach County, Navicent Health, Fort Valley, GA, p. A160
PEEK, Michael Scott, Chief Executive Officer, Chambers Memorial Hospital, Danville, AR, p. A44
PEEK, Scott, FACHE, President, Baylor Medical Center at McKinney, McKinney, TX, p. A637
PEELER, Cindy K., R.N. Chief Nursing Officer, Adair County Memorial Hospital, Greenfield, IA, p. A231

PEELGREN, Jim, Chief Information Officer, Tulare Regional Medical Center, Tulare, CA, p. A98
PEEPLES, John, Senior Vice President Human Resources, Laurel Regional Hospital, Laurel, MD, p. A302
PEER, Julie, President, Penn Highlands Brookville, Brookville, PA, p. A534
PEERY, Lori, Chief Human Resource Management Services, Veterans Affairs Palo Alto Health Care System, Palo Alto, CA, p. A82
PEET, Carole, MSN, President and Chief Executive Officer, St. Anthony North Hospital, Westminster, CO, p. A112
PEETERS, Marie, Director Human Resources, Mercy Iowa City, Iowa City, IA, p. A232
PEGE, Diane, M.D. Vice President Medical Affairs, Sutter Lakeside Hospital, Lakeport, CA, p. A69
PEGHEE, Donald, M.D. President, Saint Luke's Cushing Hospital, Leavenworth, KS, p. A248
PEHRSON, Felicia, M.D., Commanding Officer, Keller Army Community Hospital, West Point, NY, p. A458
PEHRSON, Timothy T., Chief Executive Officer, McKay–Dee Hospital Center, Ogden, UT, p. A661
PEIFFER, Paul, Chief Financial Officer and Vice President, Jackson Hospital and Clinic, Montgomery, AL, p. A24
PEIL, Michael, M.D. Chief Medical Director, Kindred Hospital Peoria, Peoria, IL, p. A199
PEKOFSKE, Robert, Vice President Finance, Advocate Christ Medical Center, Oak Lawn, IL, p. A198
PELACCIA, Joseph, President and Chief Executive Officer, Milford Hospital, Milford, CT, p. A115
PELFREY, Joy S., R.N. Vice President and Chief Nursing Officer, Cabell Huntington Hospital, Huntington, WV, p. A695
PELKOWSKI, Margaret, R.N. Vice President Patient Care Services, Calvary Hospital,, NY, p. A443
PELLE, Fred L., FACHE,
  President, Mountain View Regional Medical Center, Norton, VA, p. A676
  Interim Chief Executive Officer, Wellmont Hancock County Hospital, Sneedville, TN, p. A593
  Interim Chief Executive Officer, Wellmont Hawkins County Memorial Hospital, Rogersville, TN, p. A592
  Interim President and Chief Executive Officer, Wellmont Lonesome Pine Hospital, Big Stone Gap, VA, p. A668
PELLEGRINO, Cynthia Miller, Chief Executive Officer, Western Maryland Regional Medical Center, Hagerstown, MD, p. A301
PELLERIN, Yvonne, Chief Nursing Officer, St. Elizabeth Hospital, Gonzales, LA, p. A278
PELLETIER, Stephen, Leader Guest Services, York Hospital, York, ME, p. A295
PELLICONE, John T., M.D. Medical Director, Helen Hayes Hospital, West Haverstraw, NY, p. A457
PELOT, Jeff, Interim Chief Information Officer, Denver Health, Denver, CO, p. A104
PELSMAN, Mara, Chief Executive Officer, Gateways Hospital and Mental Health Center, Los Angeles, CA, p. A72
PELTIER, Glenn, Chief Financial Officer, Mother Frances Hospital – Winnsboro, Winnsboro, TX, p. A658
PELTIER, Robert, M.D. Senior Vice President and Chief Medical Officer, North Oaks Medical Center, Hammond, LA, p. A278
PELTOLA, Gene, President and Chief Executive Officer, Yukon–Kuskokwim Delta Regional Hospital, Bethel, AK, p. A28
PELTON, Deborah, R.N. Chief Nursing Officer, Texas Spine & Joint Hospital, Tyler, TX, p. A654
PELZER, Amber, Director, Information Services, Skiff Medical Center, Newton, IA, p. A235
PEMBERTON, John S., Director Human Resources, Tuba City Regional Health Care Corporation, Tuba City, AZ, p. A40
PENA, Deshire, Assistant Director Administrator, Larkin Community Hospital, South Miami, FL, p. A146
PENA, Julie, Director Finance, Community Howard Specialty Hospital, Kokomo, IN, p. A216
PENA, Terry, Chief Operating Officer and Chief Nursing Officer, San Bernardino Mountains Community Hospital District, Lake Arrowhead, CA, p. A69
PENCE, Carla, M.D. President Medical Staff, Iredell Memorial Hospital, Statesville, NC, p. A473
PENCO, Kris, Director Information Systems, Coffeyville Regional Medical Center, Coffeyville, KS, p. A242
PENDER, Carol, Assistant Vice President Human Resources, Walden Psychiatric Care, Waltham, MA, p. A316
PENDER, Debra, R.N. Vice President of Nursing, Mercy Hospital Ardmore, Ardmore, OK, p. A507
PENDERGAST, Debra, Senior Vice President Patient Care Services and Chief Nursing Officer, John Muir Medical Center, Walnut Creek, Walnut Creek, CA, p. A100
PENDERGAST, Jim, Administrator Human Resources, University of New Mexico Hospitals, Albuquerque, NM, p. A427
PENDERGRAFT, Tina, Chief Nursing Officer, Satanta District Hospital, Satanta, KS, p. A254
PENDLETON, Debbie, Human Resources Specialist, Weslaco Rehabilitation Hospital, Weslaco, TX, p. A657

PENDLETON, Gretchen, Chief Human Resources Officer, Mercy Suburban Hospital, Norristown, PA, p. A546

PENDLETON, Timothy, M.D. President Medical Staff, Penn Highlands Brookville, Brookville, PA, p. A534

PENICK, Lisa, R.N. Chief Nursing Officer, Carroll County Memorial Hospital, Carrollton, KY, p. A259

PENLAND, Jennifer
Controller, Kindred Hospital Tarrant County–Arlington, Arlington, TX, p. A597
Controller, Kindred Hospital–White Rock, Dallas, TX, p. A610
Controller, Kindred Rehabilitation Hospital Arlington, Arlington, TX, p. A597

PENLEY, Douglas, Chief Operating Officer, Community Westview Hospital, Indianapolis, IN, p. A213

PENNACCHIO, Suzanne, Senior Vice President Patient Care Services, Brookdale Hospital Medical Center,, NY, p. A443

PENNER, Jerome, Chief Executive Officer, Murray–Calloway County Hospital, Murray, KY, p. A268

PENNEY, Cindy L., R.N. Vice President Nursing, Mercy Iowa City, Iowa City, IA, p. A232

PENNEY, Jan, R.N. Vice President and Chief Nursing Officer, MidMichigan Medical Center–Midland, Midland, MI, p. A330

PENNINGTON, Keith, President and Chief Executive Officer, Medical West, Bessemer, AL, p. A16

PENNINGTON, Stephen G., Chief Executive Officer, Gadsden Regional Medical Center, Gadsden, AL, p. A20

PENNINO, Jackie, Director Human Resources, Old Vineyard Behavioral Health Services, Winston–Salem, NC, p. A475

PENNISSON, Jay M., Chief Financial Officer, Piedmont Medical Center, Rock Hill, SC, p. A569

PENOVICH, Carrie L., Chief Clinical Services Officer, Aurora Medical Center – Manitowoc County, Two Rivers, WI, p. A716

PENQUE, Sue, R.N. Senior Vice President and Chief Nursing Officer, South Nassau Communities Hospital, Oceanside, NY, p. A450

PENROD, Kirt, Chief Financial Officer, Shadow Mountain Behavioral Health System, Tulsa, OK, p. A521

PENROD, Pat, Controller, HEALTHSOUTH Rehabilitation Hospital of Colorado Springs, Colorado Springs, CO, p. A103

PENROSE, Lee, President and Chief Executive Officer, St. Jude Medical Center, Fullerton, CA, p. A65

PENTON, Kelly, Chief Financial Officer, Vaughan Regional Medical Center, Selma, AL, p. A25

PENTON, Lance
Director, Information Services, Memorial Hospital Jacksonville, Jacksonville, FL, p. A131
Director, Information Services, Specialty Hospital Jacksonville, Jacksonville, FL, p. A132

PENUEL, Jennifer, Director Human Resources, Madison Medical Center, Fredericktown, MO, p. A371

PEOPLES, Diane, Director Human Resources, Two Rivers Behavioral Health System, Kansas City, MO, p. A375

PEOPLES, Kathleen K., R.N. Vice President and Nursing, St. Joseph Hospital & Health Center, Kokomo, IN, p. A216

PEOPLES, Kyle, Director Technology Management Services, Springfield Hospital, Springfield, VT, p. A666

PEOPLES, Lynn, Interim Chief Nursing Officer, Person Memorial Hospital, Roxboro, NC, p. A472

PEOPLES, Phyllis L., R.N., President and Chief Executive Officer, Terrebonne General Medical Center, Houma, LA, p. A279

PEPE, Joseph, M.D., President and Chief Executive Officer, Catholic Medical Center, Manchester, NH, p. A411

PEPE, Michael, Ph.D. Chief Human Resources Officer, Virtua Berlin, Berlin, NJ, p. A413

PEPPEL, David, Director Operations, Richard H. Hutchings Psychiatric Center, Syracuse, NY, p. A455

PEPPLER, Lisa, Financial Manager, Parkview Whitley Hospital, Columbia City, IN, p. A208

PERAL, Sherry, Manager Information Systems, Oak Valley Hospital District, Oakdale, CA, p. A80

PERALTA, Nora, Chief Nursing Officer, St. Anthony's Hospital, Houston, TX, p. A626

PERALTA, Pennie, R.N. VP, Nursing & Chief Nursing Officer, Bon Secours St. Francis Xavier Hospital, Charleston, SC, p. A563

PERAZA, Faye, Director Human Resources, Venice Regional Bayfront Health, Venice, FL, p. A149

PERCIVAL, Steve, Director Human Resources, Washington Regional Medical Center, Fayetteville, AR, p. A46

PERDUE, Eric, Chief Human Resource Officer, Adena Medical Center, Chillicothe, OH, p. A486

PERDUE, Melina Dee, R.N., Executive Vice President, Carilion New River Valley Medical Center, Christiansburg, VA, p. A669

PEREACE, Vicki, Manager Human Resources, William Bee Ririe Hospital, Ely, NV, p. A404

PERECKO, Gary L., President, Riddle Hospital, Media, PA, p. A545

PEREIRA, Raul Ramos, M.D. Medical Director, Ryder Memorial Hospital, Humacao, PR, p. A726

PEREL, Michael
Regional Chief Financial Officer, Kauai Veterans Memorial Hospital, Waimea, HI, p. A173
Regional Chief Financial Officer, Samuel Mahelona Memorial Hospital, Kapaa, HI, p. A172

PEREZ, Brenda, R.N. Chief Clinical Officer, Kindred Hospital–White Rock, Dallas, TX, p. A610

PEREZ, Carmen, Director Human Resources, Doctors' Center Hospital San Juan, San Juan, PR, p. A728

PEREZ, David, Vice President and Chief Information Officer, Eisenhower Medical Center, Rancho Mirage, CA, p. A84

PEREZ, Francisco, Manager Management Information Systems, Hospital de la Universidad de Puerto Rico/Dr. Federico Trilla, Carolina, PR, p. A725

PEREZ, Homar, Chief Executive Officer and Vice President Administration, Hospital Dr. Cayetano Coll Y Toste, Arecibo, PR, p. A724

PEREZ, Julie, Chief Financial Officer, St. David's Medical Center, Austin, TX, p. A600

PEREZ, Lisa, R.N. Director Nursing, Meadowbrook Rehabilitation Hospital, Gardner, KS, p. A244

PEREZ, Miguel, Director Information Systems, Driscoll Children's Hospital, Corpus Christi, TX, p. A608

PEREZ, Nina, R.N. Chief Nursing Officer, North Okaloosa Medical Center, Crestview, FL, p. A126

PEREZ, Rosalyn, Director Human Resources, Wahiawa General Hospital, Wahiawa, HI, p. A172

PEREZ, Tony, M.D. President Medical Staff, Jewish Hospital–Shelbyville, Shelbyville, KY, p. A270

PERILLI, Ernest N., Administrator, Shriners Hospitals for Children–Philadelphia, Philadelphia, PA, p. A550

PERILLI, John, M.D., Health Services Director, Ossining Correctional Facilities Hospital, Ossining, NY, p. A451

PERIMENIS, Vasilia, Vice President Human Resources, Novant Health Medical Park Hospital, Winston–Salem, NC, p. A475

PERJON, Cindy, Associate Director, Southwest Connecticut Mental Health System, Bridgeport, CT, p. A113

PERKERSON, Robyn, R.N., Administrator, LifeCare Hospitals of North Carolina, Rocky Mount, NC, p. A471

PERKES, Neil C., Operations Officer, Logan Regional Hospital, Logan, UT, p. A660

PERKET, William, Vice President Human Resources, North Country Hospital and Health Center, Newport, VT, p. A666

PERKINS, A. William, Administrator, Atmore Community Hospital, Atmore, AL, p. A16

PERKINS, Brett, M.D. Chief Medical Staff, Madison County Memorial Hospital, Madison, FL, p. A135

PERKINS, Chris, Director Information Services, Clinch Valley Medical Center, Richlands, VA, p. A677

PERKINS, Dan
Corporate Director Human Resources, Cornerstone Hospital–West Monroe, West Monroe, LA, p. A290
Vice President of Human Resources, Solara Hospital Harlingen, Harlingen, TX, p. A622

PERKINS, Gary A., FACHE, President and Chief Executive Officer, Children's Hospital and Medical Center, Omaha, NE, p. A400

PERKINS, Jeanne, Vice President Nursing and Interim Manager Human Resources, Bucyrus Community Hospital, Bucyrus, OH, p. A484

PERKINS, Kathryn, M.D
Chief Medical Officer, Banner Boswell Medical Center, Sun City, AZ, p. A39
Chief Medical Officer, Banner Thunderbird Medical Center, Glendale, AZ, p. A33

PERKINS, Kelly, Director Human Resources, New Horizons Health Systems, Owenton, KY, p. A268

PERKINS, Mike, Vice President and Administrator, Baptist Health Extended Care Hospital, Little Rock, AR, p. A49

PERKINS, Richard, Chief Financial Officer, Hillcrest Baptist Medical Center, Waco, TX, p. A655

PERKINS, Sherry, Ph.D. Chief Operating Officer and Chief Nursing Officer, Anne Arundel Medical Center, Annapolis, MD, p. A296

PERKINS, Steven J., Chief Executive Officer, South Central Kansas Medical Center, Arkansas City, KS, p. A241

PERKINS, Tom, Chief Information Officer, Shannon Medical Center, San Angelo, TX, p. A645

PERKINS–PEPPERS, Andrea, Manager Information Services, Forks Community Hospital, Forks, WA, p. A684

PERKINSON, B. Leonard, M.D. Chief of Staff, Humboldt General Hospital, Winnemucca, NV, p. A408

PERKO, Tina, Vice President Operations, Adena Pike Medical Center, Waverly, OH, p. A505

PERLA, Salvatore, President, Nashoba Valley Medical Center, Ayer, MA, p. A305

PERLICH, Gwynn, Vice President of Patient Services and Chief Nursing Officer, St. Vincent Carmel Hospital, Carmel, IN, p. A208

PERLIN, Mitch, Chief Information Officer, Interim LSU Public Hospital, New Orleans, LA, p. A285

PERLMAN, Barry, M.D. Medical Director and Director Psychiatry, St. Joseph's Medical Center, Yonkers, NY, p. A458

PERLMAN, Joel A., Executive Vice President Finance, Montefiore Medical Center,, NY, p. A446

PERMANN, Darcy, Manager Business Office, Landmann–Jungman Memorial Hospital Avera, Scotland, SD, p. A576

PERNICE, Paul, Vice President Finance, Beebe Healthcare, Lewes, DE, p. A119

PERONA, Lorene, Market Chief Executive Officer, Kindred Hospital Sugar Land, Sugar Land, TX, p. A650

PERRA, Scott H.
President and Chief Executive Officer, Faxton–St. Luke's Healthcare, Utica, NY, p. A456
Chief Executive Officer, St. Elizabeth Medical Center, Utica, NY, p. A456

PERRATTO, Bonnie I., MSN Senior Vice President, Chief Nurse Executive, Bayhealth Medical Center, Dover, DE, p. A119

PERRIGOT, Keri, Director Human Resources, Cassia Regional Medical Center, Burley, ID, p. A175

PERRIN, Mary R., President and Chief Executive Officer, Children's Hospital, New Orleans, LA, p. A285

PERRINE, Vicki, FACHE Chief Operating Officer, Claxton–Hepburn Medical Center, Ogdensburg, NY, p. A450

PERRITT, Daniel, Chief Financial Officer, Sunrise Hospital and Medical Center, Las Vegas, NV, p. A407

PERRONG, Elizabeth, Vice President Human Resources, KidsPeace Children's Hospital, Orefield, PA, p. A547

PERROTTE, Kenneth, Director Operations, Rockland Children's Psychiatric Center, Orangeburg, NY, p. A451

PERROTTI, Paul R., CPA Chief Financial Officer, West Georgia Health, La Grange, GA, p. A162

PERRY, Amy, President, Sinai Hospital of Baltimore, Baltimore, MD, p. A298

PERRY, Bill, Director Information Systems, Mercy Hospital Hot Springs, Hot Springs National Park, AR, p. A48

PERRY, Carol, R.N. Vice President and Chief Nursing Officer, Stormont–Vail HealthCare, Topeka, KS, p. A255

PERRY, Cheryl
Chief Financial Officer, New Bedford Rehabilitation Hospital, New Bedford, MA, p. A312
Director Human Resources, Paris Regional Medical Center, Paris, TX, p. A641

PERRY, Cynthia, M.D. Chief of Staff, Stephens Memorial Hospital, Breckenridge, TX, p. A603

PERRY, Doug, M.D. Chief of Staff, Baptist Medical Center Leake, Carthage, MS, p. A356

PERRY, Faye, Chief Nursing Officer, Gateway Medical Center, Clarksville, TN, p. A581

PERRY, George H., Ph.D., Chief Executive Officer, Belmont Pines Hospital, Youngstown, OH, p. A506

PERRY, James, Chief Executive Officer, Mental Health Services for Clark and Madison Counties, Springfield, OH, p. A502

PERRY, Jan, R.N. Vice President Patient Care Services, Community Medical Center, Missoula, MT, p. A389

PERRY, Jeff
Director Information Technology, St. John's Pleasant Valley Hospital, Camarillo, CA, p. A58
Director Information Technology, St. John's Regional Medical Center, Oxnard, CA, p. A82

PERRY, John, M.D. Chief of Staff, Wagoner Community Hospital, Wagoner, OK, p. A522

PERRY, Karen, Chief Information Resource Management Services, James H. Quillen Veterans Affairs Medical Center, Mountain Home, TN, p. A590

PERRY, Kathleen, Senior Vice President and Chief Information Officer, Mercy Medical Center, Baltimore, MD, p. A297

PERRY, Marcia F., Chief Operating Officer, Hawthorn Children Psychiatric Hospital, Saint Louis, MO, p. A380

PERRY, Matthew, Director Information Systems, Andalusia Regional Hospital, Andalusia, AL, p. A15

PERRY, Matthew J., President and Chief Executive Officer, Genesis HealthCare System, Zanesville, OH, p. A506

PERRY, Michael R., M.D., President and Chief Executive Officer, FHN Memorial Hospital, Freeport, IL, p. A190

PERRY, Rhonda, Chief Financial Officer, Medical Center, Navicent Health, Macon, GA, p. A163

PERRY, Shaun, Chief Information Officer, McGehee–Desha County Hospital, McGehee, AR, p. A50

PERRY, Solette, Regional Director Human Resources, Kauai Veterans Memorial Hospital, Waimea, HI, p. A173

PERRY, Stacey, Director of Nursing, Beaver County Memorial Hospital, Beaver, OK, p. A508

PERRY, Tim, Executive Director Human Services, Baptist Health Corbin, Corbin, KY, p. A260

PERRY, V. Mark, Chief Financial Officer, Adventist Medical Center–Portland, Portland, OR, p. A528

PERRYMAN, Daniel L., Chief Executive Officer, St. Mary's Hospital, Decatur, IL, p. A188

PERRYMAN, Mike, Chief Financial Officer, Baptist Memorial Hospital–Union City, Union City, TN, p. A594

PERSE, David, M.D., President and Chief Executive Officer, St. Vincent Charity Medical Center, Cleveland, OH, p. A489

PERSILY, Cynthia A., R.N., President and Chief Executive Officer, Highland Hospital, Charleston, WV, p. A694

PERSINGER, Keith D.
Senior Vice President Finance and Chief Financial Officer, University of Maryland Medical Center, Baltimore, MD, p. A298
Chief Financial Officer, University of Maryland Medical Center Midtown Campus, Baltimore, MD, p. A298

PERSON, Lisa, MSN Vice President and Chief Nursing Officer, Mercy Hospital Springfield, Springfield, MO, p. A383

PERSON, Peter E., M.D., Chief Executive Officer, Essentia Health, Duluth, MN, p. B57

PERSONS, Linda, Executive Director, Atascadero State Hospital, Atascadero, CA, p. A56

PERT, Robert M., Vice President Finance and Chief Financial Officer, United Regional Health Care System, Wichita Falls, TX, p. A658

PESCHEL, Colleen, Director Human Resources, Sutter Medical Center, Sacramento, Sacramento, CA, p. A88

PESKIN, Ted, M.D. Acute Care Medical Director, Hilo Medical Center, Hilo, HI, p. A170

PESSAGNO, Paul, Chief Financial Officer, Richard L. Roudebush Veterans Affairs Medical Center, Indianapolis, IN, p. A215

PESTLE, Janet K., R.N. Vice President Nursing and Chief Nursing Officer, SSM St. Joseph Hospital West, Lake Saint Louis, MO, p. A375

PETER, David, M.D
Senior Vice President Medical Affairs and Chief Medical Director, Akron General Medical Center, Akron, OH, p. A482
Senior Vice President Medical Affairs and Chief Medical Officer, Lodi Community Hospital, Lodi, OH, p. A496

PETER, Douglas G., M.D. Chief Medical Officer, Gallup Indian Medical Center, Gallup, NM, p. A428

PETER, Jan D., Vice President Fiscal Services and Chief Financial Officer, Good Shepherd Health Care System, Hermiston, OR, p. A525

PETER, John, M.D. Vice President Medical Affairs, SSM Cardinal Glennon Children's Medical Center, Saint Louis, MO, p. A381

PETERMAN, John, Vice President and Administrator, Riverside Tappahannock Hospital, Tappahannock, VA, p. A679

PETERMAN, Tammy, R.N. Executive Vice President, Chief Operating Officer and Chief Nursing Officer, The University of Kansas Hospital, Kansas City, KS, p. A247

PETERMEIER, Jill, Senior Executive Human Resources, Marshalltown Medical & Surgical Center, Marshalltown, IA, p. A234

PETERS, Amy, R.N. Interim Chief Operating Officer, Truman Medical Center–Lakewood, Kansas City, MO, p. A374

PETERS, Brian, Chief Information Officer, St. Vincent Indianapolis Hospital, Indianapolis, IN, p. A215

PETERS, Bruce, Vice President and Chief Operating Officer, Bakersfield Memorial Hospital, Bakersfield, CA, p. A57

PETERS, Cindy, Chief Information Officer, Oak Hill Hospital, Brooksville, FL, p. A125

PETERS, Connie, R.N., President, CHI Health Schuyler, Schuyler, NE, p. A401

PETERS, Dave, Chief Human Resources Officer, Veterans Affairs Nebraska–Western Iowa Health Care System, Lincoln, NE, p. A398

PETERS, Gerald, Vice President Information Technologies and Chief Information Officer, Lake Health, Concord Township, OH, p. A491

PETERS, Jan, Vice President Human Resources, Saint Vincent Hospital, Worcester, MA, p. A317

PETERS, John, Chief Financial Officer, St. Joseph's Hospital and Medical Center, Phoenix, AZ, p. A37

PETERS, Mark J., M.D., President and Chief Executive Officer, East Jefferson General Hospital, Metairie, LA, p. A284

PETERS, Patrick, Chief Executive Officer, Guthrie County Hospital, Guthrie Center, IA, p. A231

PETERS, Sue, Vice President Human Resources, Munson Medical Center, Traverse City, MI, p. A336

PETERS, Vanessa, Chief Nursing Officer, River Parishes Hospital, La Place, LA, p. A280

PETERS, Violeta, R.N., Chief Executive Officer, Specialty Hospital of Central New Jersey, Lakewood, NJ, p. A417

PETERS, Wayne, Administrator, Southern Virginia Mental Health Institute, Danville, VA, p. A670

PETERS–LEWIS, Angelleen, R.N. Chief Nurse and Senior Vice President Patient Care, Women & Infants Hospital of Rhode Island, Providence, RI, p. A561

PETERSEN, Brenda, Human Resources, Sanford Wheaton Medical Center, Wheaton, MN, p. A354

PETERSEN, Debbie, R.N. Chief Operating Officer and Chief Nursing Officer, Spalding Rehabilitation Hospital, Aurora, CO, p. A102

PETERSEN, Gary, Administrator, Kaiser Permanente Sunnyside Medical Center, Clackamas, OR, p. A523

PETERSEN, Julie, Chief Executive Officer, PMH Medical Center, Prosser, WA, p. A687

PETERSEN, Richard W., President and Chief Executive Officer, Maine Medical Center, Portland, ME, p. A294

PETERSON, Alison, Vice President Medical Affairs, United Hospital, Saint Paul, MN, p. A351

PETERSON, Anne, Vice President Human Resources and Support Services, Licking Memorial Hospital, Newark, OH, p. A499

PETERSON, Bill, Director Human Resources, EASTAR Health System, Muskogee, OK, p. A514

PETERSON, Bonnie, Chief Executive Officer, Richard P. Stadter Psychiatric Center, Grand Forks, ND, p. A478

PETERSON, Brent A., Administrator, Cherry County Hospital, Valentine, NE, p. A402

PETERSON, Brett, Director of Information Services, Florida Hospital North Pinellas, Tarpon Springs, FL, p. A148

PETERSON, Bruce, Chief Information Officer, Rome Memorial Hospital, Rome, NY, p. A453

PETERSON, Chad, Chief Information Officer, Northwood Deaconess Health Center, Northwood, ND, p. A479

PETERSON, Cheryl, Business Office Manager, Surgical Institute of Reading, Wyomissing, PA, p. A559

PETERSON, Cindy, Vice President and Chief Information Officer, Henry Mayo Newhall Memorial Hospital, Valencia, CA, p. A98

PETERSON, Dane C., Chief Operating Officer, Emory University Hospital Midtown, Atlanta, GA, p. A152

PETERSON, David, Chief Information Officer, Laurel Regional Hospital, Laurel, MD, p. A302

PETERSON, Dennis, Chief Information Officer, George E. Weems Memorial Hospital, Apalachicola, FL, p. A123

PETERSON, Douglas R., President and Chief Executive Officer, Chippewa Valley Hospital and Oakview Care Center, Durand, WI, p. A704

PETERSON, Eric
Director Information Technology, Lakeview Hospital, Bountiful, UT, p. A659
Director, Ogden Regional Medical Center, Ogden, UT, p. A661

PETERSON, Erica, Chief Executive Officer and Chief Financial Officer, Sanford Chamberlain Medical Center, Chamberlain, SD, p. A572

PETERSON, Gary, M.D. Vice President Medical Affairs and Medical Director, St. Luke's Hospital, Duluth, MN, p. A343

PETERSON, Jeff, M.D. Chief of Staff, Essentia Health Ada, Ada, MN, p. A339

PETERSON, Jeffrey, M.D. Medical Director, Cooperstown Medical Center, Cooperstown, ND, p. A477

PETERSON, Josilyn, Chief Financial Officer, Ballinger Memorial Hospital, Ballinger, TX, p. A601

PETERSON, Judy, R.N. Chief Nursing Officer, East Texas Medical Center Carthage, Carthage, TX, p. A605

PETERSON, Julie, Chief Financial Officer, Sutter Delta Medical Center, Antioch, CA, p. A56

PETERSON, Kathy, Director Information Services, OSF Saint Anthony Medical Center, Rockford, IL, p. A201

PETERSON, Katie, R.N. Director of Nursing, Pender Community Hospital, Pender, NE, p. A401

PETERSON, Larry, Chief Financial Officer, Allen County Regional Hospital, Iola, KS, p. A246

PETERSON, Linda, M.D. Vice President Medical Affairs, McLaren Greater Lansing, Lansing, MI, p. A328

PETERSON, Mackenzie, M.D. Chief of Staff, Anderson County Hospital, Garnett, KS, p. A244

PETERSON, Margaret R., R.N., President, California Hospital Medical Center, Los Angeles, CA, p. A71

PETERSON, Mercy, Interim Chief Executive Officer, Nye Regional Medical Center, Tonopah, NV, p. A408

PETERSON, Michael, M.D. Chief of Staff, Pineville Community Hospital Association, Pineville, KY, p. A269

PETERSON, Michael, Chief Operating Officer, Sebasticook Valley Health, Pittsfield, ME, p. A294

PETERSON, Natalie
Director of Human Resources, Jenkins County Hospital, Millen, GA, p. A163
Human Resources Director, Screven County Hospital, Sylvania, GA, p. A167

PETERSON, Polly, Information Technology Director, Winona Health, Winona, MN, p. A354

PETERSON, Randall, President and Chief Executive Officer, Stormont-Vail HealthCare, Topeka, KS, p. A255

PETERSON, Robert
Chief Financial Officer, Hackettstown Regional Medical Center, Hackettstown, NJ, p. A416
Chief Executive Officer, Millinocket Regional Hospital, Millinocket, ME, p. A294

PETERSON, Ron, FACHE, President and Chief Executive Officer, Baxter Regional Medical Center, Mountain Home, AR, p. A50

PETERSON, Ron, Chief Information Officer, Pottstown Memorial Medical Center, Pottstown, PA, p. A552

PETERSON, Ronald R., President, Johns Hopkins Health System, Baltimore, MD, p. B78

PETERSON, Ronald R., President, Johns Hopkins Hospital, Baltimore, MD, p. A296

PETERSON, Scott, M.D. President Medical Staff, Avera Flandreau Hospital, Flandreau, SD, p. A573

PETERSON, Scott, Vice President of People and Organizational Development, Peninsula Regional Medical Center, Salisbury, MD, p. A303

PETERSON, Seth, Director Information Services, Coshocton County Memorial Hospital, Coshocton, OH, p. A491

PETERSON, Shelley, R.N. Vice President Patient Services and Chief Nursing Officer, St. Mary's Hospital and Regional Medical Center, Grand Junction, CO, p. A107

PETERSON, Stephen, Vice President Chief Information Officer, Garrett County Memorial Hospital, Oakland, MD, p. A302

PETERSON, Thomas, M.D. President, Richard P. Stadter Psychiatric Center, Grand Forks, ND, p. A478

PETERSON, Tim, M.D. Chief of Staff, Meeker Memorial Hospital, Litchfield, MN, p. A345

PETERSON, Todd, Director Information Systems, St. Helena Hospital Napa Valley, Saint Helena, CA, p. A88

PETERSON, Tracie, R.N. Chief Nursing Officer, Great Lakes Specialty Hospital–Grand Rapids Campus, Grand Rapids, MI, p. A325

PETIK, Jason, Chief Executive Officer, Sidney Regional Medical Center, Sidney, NE, p. A402

PETITT, Michael
Director of Finance, Wheaton Franciscan Healthcare – Elmbrook Memorial, Brookfield, WI, p. A703
Director of Finance, Wheaton Franciscan Healthcare – St. Joseph's, Milwaukee, WI, p. A711
Director of Finance, Wheaton Franciscan Healthcare – The Wisconsin Heart Hospital, Wauwatosa, WI, p. A718

PETRE, Patrick A., Chief Executive Officer, AHMC Anaheim Regional Medical Center, Anaheim, CA, p. A55

PETRIK, Jennifer, Interim Chief Nursing Officer, Deaconess Hospital, Spokane, WA, p. A690

PETRILLO, Mary Ann, R.N. Acting Associate Director, Nursing, Bedford Veterans Affairs Medical Center, Edith Nourse Rogers Memorial Veterans Hospital, Bedford, MA, p. A305

PETRILLO, Nancy, Director Human Resources, Matheny Medical and Educational Center, Peapack, NJ, p. A420

PETRINA, Robert, Chief Financial Officer, Alta Bates Summit Medical Center, Berkeley, CA, p. A58

PETRINO, Robert, M.D. Chief of Staff, Northwest Medical Center – Springdale, Springdale, AR, p. A53

PETRITZ, Jennifer J., Director Human Resources, University of Washington Medical Center, Seattle, WA, p. A689

PETROVICH, Lawrence, M.D. Chief Medical Officer, York Hospital, York, ME, p. A295

PETRY, Gary, M.D. Chief of Staff, St. Vincent General Hospital District, Leadville, CO, p. A108

PETTEY, Robbie, Chief Financial Officer, National Park Medical Center, Hot Springs, AR, p. A47

PETTIGREW, Dennis, Chief Operating Officer, Saint Michael's Medical Center, Newark, NJ, p. A420

PETTIGREW, Rob, Director Information Technology, Wyoming Medical Center, Casper, WY, p. A720

PETTIJOHN, Trent, M.D. Chief Medical Officer, The Heart Hospital Baylor Plano, Plano, TX, p. A643

PETTINATO, Jim, Director Patient Care Services, Wayne Memorial Hospital, Honesdale, PA, p. A540

PETTIT, Donny, Chief Financial Officer, Coon Memorial Hospital, Dalhart, TX, p. A609

PETTITE, Shirley F., Chief Human Resources Officer, Tennessee Valley Healthcare System, Nashville, TN, p. A591

PETTREY, Lisa J., R.N., Chief Executive Officer, Regency Hospital of Columbus, Columbus, OH, p. A490

PETTY, Jane, Director Human Resources, Southern Tennessee Regional Health System–Pulaski, Pulaski, TN, p. A592

PETTY, Russ, M.D. Chief of Staff, Towner County Medical Center, Cando, ND, p. A476

PETULA, Ron
Vice President Finance, Good Shepherd Penn Partners Specialty Hospital at Rittenhouse, Philadelphia, PA, p. A548
Chief Financial Officer, Good Shepherd Rehabilitation Hospital, Allentown, PA, p. A532

PETZEL, Robert A., M.D., Under Secretary for Health, Department of Veterans Affairs, Washington, DC, p. B48

PFAFF, Joni, Chief Nursing Officer, Grisell Memorial Hospital District One, Ransom, KS, p. A253

PFAFF, Tony, Chief Executive Officer, Deer Lodge Medical Center, Deer Lodge, MT, p. A386

PFALTZGRAFF, George, Chief Medical Officer, Hansen Family Hospital, Iowa Falls, IA, p. A233

PFAU, Ben, Chief Facility and Information Officer, Bay Area Hospital, Coos Bay, OR, p. A524

PFAU, Beth, M.D. Chief Medical Officer, Larue D. Carter Memorial Hospital, Indianapolis, IN, p. A214

PFEFFER, Daniel William, Nurse Executive, Weisman Children's Rehabilitation Hospital, Marlton, NJ, p. A418

PFEFFER, Stacey, Senior Vice President Human Resources, Winthrop–University Hospital, Mineola, NY, p. A441

PFEIFER, Mark P., M.D. Senior Vice President and Chief Medical Officer, University of Louisville Hospital, Louisville, KY, p. A266

PFEIFFER, James A., FACHE, President and Chief Executive Officer, Self Regional Healthcare, Greenwood, SC, p. A567

PFEIFFER, Margaret, R.N. Vice President Patient Care Services, Good Samaritan Hospital, Los Angeles, CA, p. A72

PFISTER, Joann M.
Director Human Resources, Providence Milwaukie Hospital, Milwaukie, OR, p. A527
Director Human Resources, Providence Willamette Falls Medical Center, Oregon City, OR, p. A527

PFISTER, Pam, Chief Executive Officer, Morrison Community Hospital, Morrison, IL, p. A197

PFRANK, Kym
Senior Vice President and Chief Operating Officer, Union Hospital, Terre Haute, IN, p. A223
Vice President Information Systems, Union Hospital Clinton, Clinton, IN, p. A208

PHAM, Bong, Chief Medical Officer, Kit Carson County Health Service District, Burlington, CO, p. A103

PHAM, K., M.D. Chief of Staff, Winkler County Memorial Hospital, Kermit, TX, p. A631

PHELAN, Cynthia, Vice President Human Resources, Lawrence General Hospital, Lawrence, MA, p. A311

PHELPS, Britton, Chief Executive Officer, HEALTHSOUTH Rehabilitation Hospital of Rock Hill, Rock Hill, SC, p. A569

PHELPS, David E., President and Chief Executive Officer, Berkshire Health Systems, Inc., Pittsfield, MA, p. B23

PHELPS, David E., President and Chief Executive Officer, Berkshire Medical Center, Pittsfield, MA, p. A313

PHELPS, Joel, Chief Operating Officer, Salina Regional Health Center, Salina, KS, p. A254

PHELPS, Kathleen, Director Human Resources, Treasure Valley Hospital, Boise, ID, p. A175

PHELPS, Rick, M.D. President and Chief Operating Officer, Elliot Hospital, Manchester, NH, p. A411

PHETTEPLACE, Danial, Director Information Technology, Gundersen St. Joseph's Hospital and Clinics, Hillsboro, WI, p. A706

PHILIPS, III, Grady W., Senior Vice President and Chief Operating Officer, Winchester Medical Center, Winchester, VA, p. A680

PHILIPS, J. Michael, Chief Strategy Officer, San Juan Regional Medical Center, Farmington, NM, p. A428

PHILLIPE, James R., President, Holzer Medical Center, Gallipolis, OH, p. A494

PHILLIPPE II, James R., President, Holzer Medical Center – Jackson, Jackson, OH, p. A495

PHILLIPS, Alan M., Controller, HEALTHSOUTH Nittany Valley Rehabilitation Hospital, Pleasant Gap, PA, p. A552

PHILLIPS, Annette S., President and Chief Executive Officer, Mercy Memorial Hospital System, Monroe, MI, p. A330

PHILLIPS, Barry, Executive Director Human Resources, Camden General Hospital, Camden, TN, p. A579

PHILLIPS, Bill, Vice President Information Services, University Health System, San Antonio, TX, p. A648

PHILLIPS, Bobby, Chief Nursing Officer, Medical Center Enterprise, Enterprise, AL, p. A19

PHILLIPS, Chance, Chief Financial Officer, Oak Hill Hospital, Brooksville, FL, p. A125

PHILLIPS, Courtney, Chief Executive Officer, South Sunflower County Hospital, Indianola, MS, p. A359

PHILLIPS, David D., Chief Executive Officer and Administrator, Barnesville Hospital, Barnesville, OH, p. A483

PHILLIPS, David L.
Chief Executive Officer, St. John Broken Arrow, Broken Arrow, OK, p. A508
President and Chief Executive Officer, St. John Owasso, Owasso, OK, p. A517
Chief Executive Officer, St. John Sapulpa, Sapulpa, OK, p. A518

PHILLIPS, Donna, President, Bryn Mawr Rehabilitation Hospital, Malvern, PA, p. A543

PHILLIPS, Donna Z., M.D., Chief Executive Officer, HEALTHSOUTH Rehabilitation Hospital of Fredericksburg, Fredericksburg, VA, p. A671

PHILLIPS, Eddie, M.D
Chief Medical Affairs, Baptist Health Medical Center – North Little Rock, North Little Rock, AR, p. A51
Chief Medical Officer, Baptist Health Medical Center–Arkadelphia, Arkadelphia, AR, p. A43

PHILLIPS, Frank, M.D. Chief of Staff, Novant Health Gaffney Medical Center, Gaffney, SC, p. A566

PHILLIPS, Glenn, Director Information Systems, Gadsden Regional Medical Center, Gadsden, AL, p. A20

PHILLIPS, Heath, Administrator and Chief Executive Officer, HEALTHSOUTH Lakeshore Rehabilitation Hospital, Birmingham, AL, p. A16

PHILLIPS, John
Chief of Staff, Great River Medical Center, West Burlington, IA, p. A239
Vice President Information Services, St. Joseph Regional Health Center, Bryan, TX, p. A604

PHILLIPS, John E., FACHE, President, Methodist Mansfield Medical Center, Mansfield, TX, p. A636

PHILLIPS, Kelly, M.D. Clinical Director and Chief Staff, Spring Grove Hospital Center, Baltimore, MD, p. A298

PHILLIPS, Kimberly A., Chief Financial Officer, The Children's Home of Pittsburgh, Pittsburgh, PA, p. A551

PHILLIPS, Lionel J., Vice President Financial Services, Fauquier Hospital, Warrenton, VA, p. A680

PHILLIPS, Lori, Vice President and Chief Nursing Officer, Gibson General Hospital, Princeton, IN, p. A221

PHILLIPS, Margaret, Director Human Resources, Memorial Hospital, North Conway, NH, p. A412

PHILLIPS, Michael, Chief Executive Officer, Elkhorn Valley Rehabilitation Hospital, Casper, WY, p. A720

PHILLIPS, Pam, Chief Human Resource Officer, Wiregrass Medical Center, Geneva, AL, p. A20

PHILLIPS, Richard, Chief Financial Officer, Desert Regional Medical Center, Palm Springs, CA, p. A82

PHILLIPS, Robert, Administrator, Walker Baptist Medical Center, Jasper, AL, p. A22

PHILLIPS, Rusty, Administrator, Jennings Senior Care Hospital, Jennings, LA, p. A279

PHILLIPS, Sarah, Manager Human Resources, Morgan Memorial Hospital, Madison, GA, p. A163

PHILLIPS, Steve, Information Officer, Greene County General Hospital, Linton, IN, p. A217

PHILLIPS, Todd, M.D. Interim Vice President, Medical Affairs, Monmouth Medical Center, Southern Campus, Lakewood, NJ, p. A417

PHINNEY, Cody, Administrator, Northern Nevada Adult Mental Health Services, Sparks, NV, p. A408

PHIPPS, Bonnie, President and Chief Executive Officer, Saint Agnes Hospital, Baltimore, MD, p. A297

PHIPPS, Jackie G., Director Human Resources, Johnston Memorial Hospital, Abingdon, VA, p. A668

PIANALTO, Eric, President, Mercy Hospital Rogers, Rogers, AR, p. A52

PIATKOWSKI, Shannon, Director Information Technology, Blake Medical Center, Bradenton, FL, p. A124

PIAZZA, Tony, Director Human Resources, Titus Regional Medical Center, Mount Pleasant, TX, p. A638

PICAZA, Jose, M.D. Chief of Staff, Unicoi County Memorial Hospital, Erwin, TN, p. A582

PICCIONE, Jennifer, Chief Nursing and Clinical Services Officer, Madison County Hospital, London, OH, p. A496

PICCONE, Robert, President, Clear Brook Manor, Wilkes–Barre, PA, p. A558

PICKARD, Bert, Chief Financial Officer, Gilmore Memorial Regional Medical Center, Amory, MS, p. A355

PICKEL, Joseph, Director Resource Management, Walter Reed National Military Medical Center, Bethesda, MD, p. A299

PICKENS, Gayle, Chief Nursing Officer, Putnam County Memorial Hospital, Unionville, MO, p. A384

PICKENS, Ramona, Chief Operating Officer, East Cooper Medical Center, Mount Pleasant, SC, p. A568

PICKENS, Troy, Chief Financial Officer, Southern Palmetto Hospital, Barnwell, SC, p. A562

PICKERING, Sheridan
Chief Executive Officer, Muscogee Creek Nation Medical Center, Okmulgee, OK, p. A517
Administrator, Okmulgee Memorial Hospital, Okmulgee, OK, p. A517

PICKETT, Beverly, R.N. Chief Nursing Officer, Oklahoma Surgical Hospital, Tulsa, OK, p. A520

PICKETT, Lisa C., M.D. Chief Medical Officer, Duke University Hospital, Durham, NC, p. A463

PICKLER, Nancy, Director of Human Resources, HEALTHSOUTH East Valley Rehabilitation Hospital, Mesa, AZ, p. A34

PICKUL, David, M.D. Chief Medical Officer, Circle Health, Lowell General Hospital, Lowell, MA, p. A311

PICONE, Anthony, M.D. Medical Director, Roswell Park Cancer Institute, Buffalo, NY, p. A434

PICOU, Timothy, Manager Information Technology, Lower Umpqua Hospital District, Reedsport, OR, p. A529

PIEARSON, Timothy, D.O. Chief Medical Officer, Adair County Memorial Hospital, Greenfield, IA, p. A231

PIEPER, Blaine, Chief Executive Officer, Ohio County Hospital, Hartford, KY, p. A262

PIEPRZYCA, Shaneece, Director Information Technology, Otto Kaiser Memorial Hospital, Kenedy, TX, p. A631

PIERCE, Bonnie, MSN Associate Director for Patient Care Services, Jack C. Montgomery Veterans Affairs Medical Center, Muskogee, OK, p. A514

PIERCE, Eddie, M.D. Chief Medical Staff, Kearney County Health Services, Minden, NE, p. A398

PIERCE, Jeff M.
Manager Human Resources, Marshall Medical Center, Lewisburg, TN, p. A587
Manager Human Resources, Wayne Medical Center, Waynesboro, TN, p. A594

PIERCE, Jennifer, Administrative Director of Finance, St. Anthony Shawnee Hospital, Shawnee, OK, p. A519

PIERCE, Kenneth, Chief Financial Officer, Brookhaven Hospital, Tulsa, OK, p. A520

PIERCE, Laura, Chief Administrative Officer Human Resources, Memorial Medical Center, Las Cruces, NM, p. A429

PIERCE, Margaret H., Executive Director, Kaiser Permanente Baldwin Park Medical Center, Baldwin Park, CA, p. A57

PIERCE, Pamela, Chief Operating Officer, Windhaven Psychiatric Hospital, Prescott Valley, AZ, p. A37

PIERCE, Pat, Director Information Systems, Lakewood Regional Medical Center, Lakewood, CA, p. A69

PIERCE, Trent, R.N.,
Chief Executive Officer, HEALTHSOUTH City View Rehabilitation Hospital, Fort Worth, TX, p. A618
Chief Executive Officer, HEALTHSOUTH Rehabilitation Hospital of Fort Worth, Fort Worth, TX, p. A618

PIERDON, Steven, M.D. Executive Vice President and Chief Medical Officer, Geisinger Wyoming Valley Medical Center, Wilkes Barre, PA, p. A558

PIERESCHI, Giovanni
Vice President Enterprise Information and Chief Information Officer, Hospital HIMA San Pablo Caguas, Caguas, PR, p. A725
Vice President Management Information Systems, Hospital HMA de Humacao, Humacao, PR, p. A726

PIERRE, Andre, Chief Financial Officer, Forest View Psychiatric Hospital, Grand Rapids, MI, p. A325

PIERRE, Letonia, Coordinator Human Resources, Assumption Community Hospital, Napoleonville, LA, p. A285

PIERSON, Jerome, Chief Medical Officer, Mercy Medical Center–Sioux City, Sioux City, IA, p. A238

PIERSON, Kari, Manager, Howard County Medical Center, Saint Paul, NE, p. A401

PIERSON, Kim, R.N. Chief Nursing Officer, Hancock Medical Center, Bay Saint Louis, MS, p. A355

PIERSON, Kyle, Chief Financial Officer, Minnie Hamilton HealthCare Center, Grantsville, WV, p. A695

PIERSON, Lois K., Chief Financial Officer, University of Texas Harris County Psychiatric Center, Houston, TX, p. A627

PIERSON, Marc, M.D. Vice President Clinical Information and Quality, PeaceHealth St. Joseph Medical Center, Bellingham, WA, p. A681

PIETRANGELO, Steve, Director Information Services, War Memorial Hospital, Sault Sainte Marie, MI, p. A334

PIETRO, Daniel, M.D. Medical Director, Sturdy Memorial Hospital, Attleboro, MA, p. A305

PIETSCH, Al, CPA Senior Vice President and Chief Financial Officer, University of Maryland Baltimore Washington Medical Center, Glen Burnie, MD, p. A301

PIETZ, Gerald, Vice President Finance, Mercy Hospital, Coon Rapids, MN, p. A342

PIFER, Eric, M.D. Chief Medical Officer, El Camino Hospital, Mountain View, CA, p. A79

PIFKO, Duane, Interim Director Financial Services, Daniel Drake Center for Post Acute Care, Cincinnati, OH, p. A486

PIGG, Russell, Chief Executive Officer, Eliza Coffee Memorial Hospital, Florence, AL, p. A20

PIGOTT, John, M.D. Chief Medical Officer, Tulane Medical Center, New Orleans, LA, p. A286

PIKE, David, Interim Chief Financial Officer, Memorial Hospital of Carbon County, Rawlins, WY, p. A722

PIKE, Irving, M.D. Chief Medical Officer, John Muir Medical Center, Walnut Creek, Walnut Creek, CA, p. A100

PIKE, Pauline, Chief Operating Officer, Beverly Hospital, Beverly, MA, p. A305

PIKE, Randi, Director of Nursing, Pioneer Medical Center, Big Timber, MT, p. A385

PIKE, Ronald F., M.D. Medical Director, Adcare Hospital of Worcester, Worcester, MA, p. A316

PIKE, Tim, M.D. Chief Medical Officer, Portsmouth Regional Hospital, Portsmouth, NH, p. A412

PIKER, John F., M.D. Medical Director, Villa Feliciana Medical Complex, Jackson, LA, p. A279

PIL, Pieter, M.D. Chief Medical Staff, Martha's Vineyard Hospital, Oak Bluffs, MA, p. A313

PILANT, Jason B., Chief Operating Officer, Roane Medical Center, Harriman, TN, p. A583

PILE, Larry, Director Human Resources, Deaconess Hospital, Evansville, IN, p. A210

PILEGGI, Tim
Interim Chief Financial Officer, Good Shepherd Medical Center, Longview, TX, p. A634
Interim Chief Financial Officer, Good Shepherd Medical Center–Marshall, Marshall, TX, p. A636

PILLION, Scott, Chief Executive Officer, Helen Newberry Joy Hospital, Newberry, MI, p. A331

PILONG, Alfred E., President, Munson Medical Center, Traverse City, MI, p. A336

PILOT, Dave, Chief Financial Officer, Essentia Health St. Joseph's Medical Center, Brainerd, MN, p. A340

PINDERSKI, Christopher, M.D. Medical Director of Emergency Room, Black River Medical Center, Poplar Bluff, MO, p. A378

PINE, Richard M., President and Chief Executive Officer, Livengrin Foundation, Bensalem, PA, p. A533

PINEDA, Omar, R.N. Chief Nursing Officer, Medical Center of Arlington, Arlington, TX, p. A598

PINEIRO, Carlos M., President, Hospital HMA de Humacao, Humacao, PR, p. A726

PINKELMAN, Janet, Director Human Resources, Faith Regional Health Services, Norfolk, NE, p. A398

PINKOSKY, Frank
Senior Vice President, Robert Packer Hospital, Sayre, PA, p. A554
Executive Vice President, Troy Community Hospital, Troy, PA, p. A556

PINO, Elena, Chief Operating Officer and Chief Nursing Officer, Mesa Hills Specialty Hospital, El Paso, TX, p. A616

PINO, Joseph, M.D. Chief Medical Officer, Regional Medical Center Bayonet Point, Hudson, FL, p. A131

PINO, Loretta Ortiz y, M.D. Chief Medical Officer, Holy Cross Hospital, Taos, NM, p. A431

PINON, Richard, Chief Medical Officer, Eastern New Mexico Medical Center, Roswell, NM, p. A430

PINSKY, Karen, M.D. Chief Medical Information Officer, Chester County Hospital, West Chester, PA, p. A558

PINSON, Charles Wright, M.D., Deputy Vice Chancellor for Health Affairs and Chief Executive Officer of Vanderbilt Health System, Vanderbilt Health, Nashville, TN, p. B148

PINTO, Frank, Chief Information Officer, The Hospital of Central Connecticut, New Britain, CT, p. A115

PIPER, Ed, Ph.D., President and Chief Executive Officer, Onslow Memorial Hospital, Jacksonville, NC, p. A467

PIPER, Kevin, Director Information Systems, Florida Hospital DeLand, DeLand, FL, p. A127

PIPER, Vicky, Vice President Human Resources, Loyola University Medical Center, Maywood, IL, p. A195

PIPGRASS, Michele, Chief Fiscal Service, Oklahoma City Veterans Affairs Medical Center, Oklahoma City, OK, p. A516

PIPKINS, David, Controller, HEALTHSOUTH Rehabilitation Hospital of Beaumont, Beaumont, TX, p. A602

PIPPIN, Kim, Chief Nursing Officer, Select Specialty Hospital–Augusta, Augusta, GA, p. A154

PIRKL, Rollie, Chief Financial Officer, Sierra Vista Regional Medical Center, San Luis Obispo, CA, p. A93

PIRO, Michael J., Chief Information Officer, St. John's Episcopal Hospital–South Shore,, NY, p. A448

PIRRI, Christine, Senior Director Human Resources, Cobleskill Regional Hospital, Cobleskill, NY, p. A436

PIRTLE, Kathleen, Director Human Resources, HEALTHSOUTH Rehabilitation Hospital–Wichita Falls, Wichita Falls, TX, p. A657

PIRTLE, Randy B., Chief Financial Officer, King's Daughters Medical Center, Brookhaven, MS, p. A356

PISANO, Thomas, M.D. Chief Professional Services, Connecticut Valley Hospital, Middletown, CT, p. A115

PISCIOTTA, Michael J., Chief Executive Officer, Southern Surgical Hospital, Slidell, LA, p. A289

PISPISA, D. Patricia, Vice President Patient Care Services, Eastern Long Island Hospital, Greenport, NY, p. A438

PISTONE, Maureen
Senior Vice President Talent Development and Human Resources, Appleton Medical Center, Appleton, WI, p. A701
Senior Vice President Human Resources, Theda Clark Medical Center, Neenah, WI, p. A711

PISZCZATOSKI, Thomas J., Director Human Resources, St. Mary's Medical Center, West Palm Beach, FL, p. A150

PITCHER, Ellen, MSN Vice President and Chief Nursing Officer, Baylor All Saints Medical Center at Fort Worth, Fort Worth, TX, p. A618

PITCHER, Karen, Chief Executive Officer, Post Acute/Warm Springs Specialty Hospital of San Antonio, San Antonio, TX, p. A647

PITCHFORD, Edward C., President and Chief Executive Officer, Cole Memorial, Coudersport, PA, p. A536

PITCOCK, Nancy, Vice President Nursing and Chief Nursing Officer, St. Vincent Anderson Regional Hospital, Anderson, IN, p. A206

PITMAN, David R., Vice President Finance, MedStar Harbor Hospital, Baltimore, MD, p. A297

PITOSCIA, Susan, MSN Chief Operating Officer, Touro Infirmary, New Orleans, LA, p. A286

PITTMAN, Cyndi, Chief Financial Officer, Baptist Memorial Hospital – Memphis, Memphis, TN, p. A588

PITTMAN, Jennifer, Chief Financial Officer, Shelby Baptist Medical Center, Alabaster, AL, p. A15

PITTMAN, Jeremy, Chief Financial Officer, Castle Rock Adventist Hospital, Castle Rock, CO, p. A103

PITTMAN, Keisha, Director Human Resources, HEALTHSOUTH Rehabilitation Hospital of Cypress, Houston, TX, p. A624

PITTMAN, Michael
Chief Nursing Officer, Memorial Hospital, Martinsville, VA, p. A674
Chief Operating Officer and Chief Nursing Officer, Scott & White Hospital – Brenham, Brenham, TX, p. A604

PITTMAN, Nancy, MS Vice President, Nursing, Houston Methodist St. John Hospital, Nassau Bay, TX, p. A639

PITTS, Celeste, Chief Financial Officer, Upper Connecticut Valley Hospital, Colebrook, NH, p. A409

PITTS, Clara, Director Human Resources, East Alabama Medical Center–Lanier, Valley, AL, p. A26

PITTS, Lynn, Director Human Resources, Calhoun–Liberty Hospital, Blountstown, FL, p. A123

PITTS, Richard, D.O. Medical Director, Arrowhead Regional Medical Center, Colton, CA, p. A60

PITTS, Robert, Executive Director, Wilmington Treatment Center, Wilmington, NC, p. A474

PITTS, Ron, Chief Financial Officer, Veterans Affairs Loma Linda Healthcare System, Loma Linda, CA, p. A70

PITTS, Sherry J., Chief Executive Officer, Woman's Hospital, Flowood, MS, p. A358

PITTS, Stephen R., Chief Executive Officer, Morehouse General Hospital, Bastrop, LA, p. A273

PITZER, Kevin M., President and Chief Executive Officer, Bozeman Deaconess Hospital, Bozeman, MT, p. A385

PIVONKA, Mary, Director Quality Management, Rockland Children's Psychiatric Center, Orangeburg, NY, p. A451

PIZ, Tom, Director Human Resources, Fremont Hospital, Fremont, CA, p. A64

PIZARRO, Hugo A., Vice President Human Resources, Terence Cardinal Cooke Health Care Center, New York, NY, p. A449

PIZZI, Chris, Chief Operating Officer and Chief Financial Officer, Providence Medford Medical Center, Medford, OR, p. A527

PIZZINO, Mary, Chief Information Officer, Effingham Hospital, Springfield, GA, p. A167

PLACE, Michael, M.D. Deputy Commander Clinical Services, Colonel Florence A. Blanchfield Army Community Hospital, Fort Campbell, KY, p. A247

PLADSON, Terence, M.D., President and Chief Executive Officer, CentraCare Health, Saint Cloud, MN, p. B34

PLAGGEMEYER, Rikki, Director Acute Care Nursing, Sturgis Regional Hospital, Sturgis, SD, p. A577

PLAIA, Kelly C., Manager Human Resources, Greenville Health System – Laurens County Memorial Hospital, Clinton, SC, p. A564

PLAISANCE, Stephen, Chief Financial Officer, Meeker Memorial Hospital, Litchfield, MN, p. A345

PLAMONDON, Richard, Vice President Finance and Chief Financial Officer, St. Joseph Hospital, Nashua, NH, p. A411

PLANO, Crystal, Controller, St. Vincent Dunn Hospital, Bedford, IN, p. A207

PLANT, Steven L., Chief Financial Officer, Cottage Hospital, Woodsville, NH, p. A412

PLASKETT, Darice S., FACHE, Interim Chief Executive Officer, Governor Juan F. Louis Hospital, Christiansted, VI, p. A729

PLASS, Robert, M.D. Chief Medical Officer, Fremont–Rideout Health Group, Marysville, CA, p. A77

PLATE, James, M.D. Chief of Staff, Kimball Health Services, Kimball, NE, p. A397

PLATER, Queenie C., Vice President and Chief Human Resources Officer, Sibley Memorial Hospital, Washington, DC, p. A122

PLATOU, Kenneth E. S., President, Mercy Medical Center Mount Shasta, Mount Shasta, CA, p. A79

PLATT, Anne, Chief Executive Officer, Sutter Amador Hospital, Jackson, CA, p. A67

PLATT, C. James, Chief Executive Officer, Fort Madison Community Hospital, Fort Madison, IA, p. A231

PLATZ, Scott, Director Finance, UH Regional Hospitals, Cleveland, OH, p. A489

PLAUTH, Bill, M.D. Vice President Operations and Chief Medical Officer, Mercy Regional Medical Center, Durango, CO, p. A105

PLAVIAK, David J., Interim Chief Financial Officer, Culpeper Regional Hospital, Culpeper, VA, p. A670

PLAVIN, Joshua, M.D. Medical Director Medicine Division, Gifford Medical Center, Randolph, VT, p. A666

PLAZA, Marta Rivera, Chief Executive Officer and Managing Director, San Juan Capestrano Hospital, San Juan, PR, p. A728

PLEDGER, Michelle, Coordinator Human Resources, Grady General Hospital, Cairo, GA, p. A155

PLEMMONS, Debbie, MSN Chief Nursing Officer, St. Luke's Elmore, Mountain Home, ID, p. A177

PLESKOW, Eric D., President and Chief Executive Officer, BryLin Hospitals, Buffalo, NY, p. A434

PLISKO, Rick, Director information Systems, New York Methodist Hospital,, NY, p. A447

PLOPPER, Michael, M.D. Chief Medical Officer, Sharp Mesa Vista Hospital, San Diego, CA, p. A90

PLOSZEK, Michael, Vice President Physician Strategy and Clinical Operations, Advocate Good Shepherd Hospital, Barrington, IL, p. A181

PLOUCK, Tracy, Director, Ohio Department of Mental Health, Columbus, OH, p. B103

PLOUSHA–MOORE, Debra, Senior Vice President Human Resources, Carolinas Medical Center, Charlotte, NC, p. A461

PLUARD, Dennis, Vice President Operations, Sarah Bush Lincoln Health Center, Mattoon, IL, p. A195

PLUMERI, Thomas R., Chief of Staff, Sheridan County Health Complex, Hoxie, KS, p. A246

PLUMLEE, Steve, Chief Executive Officer, Select Specialty Hospital–North Knoxville, Knoxville, TN, p. A586

PLUMMER, Doug, Chief Operating Officer, Sabine Medical Center, Many, LA, p. A283

PLUMMER, James S., Chief Executive Officer, Aurora San Diego Hospital, San Diego, CA, p. A89

PLUNKETT, Alicia, Director of Nursing, Parkwood Behavioral Health System, Olive Branch, MS, p. A363

PLYMELL, Shane, Chief Financial Officer, Shannon Medical Center, San Angelo, TX, p. A645

POBLETE, Ronald, M.D. President Medical and Dental Staff, St. Mary's Hospital, Passaic, NJ, p. A420

POCKRANDT, Barry R., Commander, Irwin Army Community Hospital, Junction City, KS, p. A247

POCOCK, Donald, M.D
Vice President Medical Affairs, Johnston UNC Health Care, Smithfield, NC, p. A473
Chief Medical Officer, Mease Countryside Hospital, Safety Harbor, FL, p. A144
Chief Medical Officer, Mease Dunedin Hospital, Dunedin, FL, p. A128
Chief Medical Officer, Morton Plant North Bay Hospital, New Port Richey, FL, p. A139

PODESTA, Charles H., Vice President Information Services, Fletcher Allen Health Care, Burlington, VT, p. A665

PODGES, Christopher J., Vice President and Chief Information Officer, Munson Medical Center, Traverse City, MI, p. A336

PODLEY, Sandra C., Administrator, Presbyterian Hospital, Albuquerque, NM, p. A426

PODUSKA, Donna D., MS Chief Nursing Officer, Poudre Valley Hospital, Fort Collins, CO, p. A106

PODZIMEK, Marcia, Chief Human Resources Officer, Wagner Community Memorial Hospital Avera, Wagner, SD, p. A578

POE, Bernard T., Administrator and Chief Executive Officer, New Horizons Health Systems, Owenton, KY, p. A268

POE, Dale
Vice President Hospital Division, Wellmont Bristol Regional Medical Center, Bristol, TN, p. A579
Chief Financial Officer, Wellmont Hawkins County Memorial Hospital, Rogersville, TN, p. A592
Vice President Finance and Operations, Wellmont Holston Valley Medical Center, Kingsport, TN, p. A585

POE, Terri Lyn, Interim Chief Nursing Officer, University of Alabama Hospital, Birmingham, AL, p. A17

POEHLER, Kathy, Vice President Human Resources, University of Maryland Baltimore Washington Medical Center, Glen Burnie, MD, p. A301

POEST, Scott, Chief Information Officer, Lake Regional Health System, Osage Beach, MO, p. A378

POFAHL, Barnetta, Director Human Resources, Wagoner Community Hospital, Wagoner, OK, p. A522

POFF, Heather, Director Human Resources, Princeton Community Hospital, Princeton, WV, p. A698

POFFENBARGER, John, Director Fiscal Services, Northern Virginia Mental Health Institute, Falls Church, VA, p. A670

POGAS, George, CPA Senior Vice President and Chief Financial Officer, Witham Memorial Hospital, Lebanon, IN, p. A217

POGLIANO, Chris, M.D. Chief Medical Staff, Aspirus Grand View Hospital, Ironwood, MI, p. A327

POHAR, Twyla, Manager Computer Systems, James Cancer Hospital and Solove Research Institute, Columbus, OH, p. A489

POHJALA, Eric, Vice President and Chief Financial Officer, Lima Memorial Health System, Lima, OH, p. A496

POHL, David F., M.D. Chief of Staff, Cornerstone Hospital of Austin, Austin, TX, p. A599

POHL, David L., M.D. Chief of Staff, Hillcrest Hospital – South, Tulsa, OK, p. A520

POHREN, Allen E., Administrator, Montgomery County Memorial Hospital, Red Oak, IA, p. A236

POIROT, Diane, Vice President Human Resources, Harris Health System, Houston, TX, p. A624

POISKER, Karen C., MSN Vice President Patient Care Services and Chief Nursing Officer, Peninsula Regional Medical Center, Salisbury, MD, p. A303

POISSON, Keith R., Executive Vice President and Chief Operating Officer, Greater Baltimore Medical Center, Baltimore, MD, p. A296

POLAND, David, Vice President Finance, Grove City Medical Center, Grove City, PA, p. A540

POLHEBER, Richard, Chief Executive Officer, Benson Hospital, Benson, AZ, p. A31

POLHILL, James, M.D. Chief Medical Officer, Jefferson Hospital, Louisville, GA, p. A162

POLIKAITIS, Audrius, Chief Information Officer, University of Illinois Hospital & Health Sciences System, Chicago, IL, p. A187

POLINAK, Elaine, Director Information Management, Ohio Valley General Hospital, McKees Rocks, PA, p. A544

POLING, Rodney, M.D. Medical Director, Behavioral HealthCare Center at Columbia, Columbia, TN, p. A581

POLING, Susan, Director Human Resources, King's Daughters' Health, Madison, IN, p. A218

POLITE, Elmer, Chief Financial Officer, East Georgia Regional Medical Center, Statesboro, GA, p. A167

POLITI, Victor, M.D., President and Chief Executive Officer, Nassau University Medical Center, East Meadow, NY, p. A437

POLITO, Janine
Chief Human Resources Officer, Banner Goldfield Medical Center, Apache Junction, AZ, p. A31
Chief Human Resources Officer, Banner Ironwood Medical Center, San Tan Valley, AZ, p. A38

POLIZZI, Arturo
Chief Human Resources Officer, ProMedica Flower Hospital, Sylvania, OH, p. A502
President, ProMedica Toledo Hospital, Toledo, OH, p. A503
Chief Human Resources Officer, ProMedica Toledo Hospital, Toledo, OH, p. A503

POLK, Brent, M.D. Chair Department of Pediatrics and Vice President Academic Affairs, Children's Hospital Los Angeles, Los Angeles, CA, p. A71

POLLACK, Murray, M.D. Vice President and Chief Medical Officer, Phoenix Children's Hospital, Phoenix, AZ, p. A36

POLLACK, Neil, Senior Administrator, Terence Cardinal Cooke Health Care Center, New York, NY, p. A449

POLLACK, Richard, Chief Executive Information Services, VCU Medical Center, Richmond, VA, p. A678

POLLARD, Amy, R.N., President and Chief Executive Officer, Nicholas H. Noyes Memorial Hospital, Dansville, NY, p. A436

POLLARD, Anthony, D.O. Chief Medical Officer, Progressive Hospital, Las Vegas, NV, p. A406

POLLARD, Dennis, President, Community Memorial Hospital, Menomonee Falls, WI, p. A709

POLLMAN, Brian, Chief Medical Officer, Hutchinson Health, Hutchinson, MN, p. A345

POLLNOW, Dean, M.D. President Medical Staff, Ministry Saint Mary's Hospitals, Rhinelander, WI, p. A714

POLLOCK, Jeffrey, Chief Information Officer, Wentworth–Douglass Hospital, Dover, NH, p. A410

POLLOCK, Jill, Administrator, Loma Linda University Behavioral Medicine Center, Redlands, CA, p. A85

POLLOCK, Maureen King, Chief Executive Officer, Eagleville Hospital, Eagleville, PA, p. A537

POLLOCK, Tina, Chief Executive Officer, Dallas Regional Medical Center, Mesquite, TX, p. A637

POLO, Fabian, Chief Executive Officer, Baylor Institute for Rehabilitation, Dallas, TX, p. A609

POLONSKY, Dana, Vice President of Clinical Services, Craig Hospital, Englewood, CO, p. A106

POLSELLI, Donna, Chief Operating Officer, Franciscan Hospital for Children, Boston, MA, p. A306

POLSTER, Peggy, Manager Personnel and Administrative Assistant, Falls Community Hospital and Clinic, Marlin, TX, p. A636

POLT, Cynthia, Chief Financial Officer, Touro Infirmary, New Orleans, LA, p. A286

POLTRACK, Andrew, M.D. Chief of Staff, Margaret Mary Health, Batesville, IN, p. A206

POLUNAS, David M., Chief Executive Officer, Beckett Springs, West Chester, OH, p. A505

POLZIN, Greg
Chief Financial Officer, Iowa Specialty Hospital–Belmond, Belmond, IA, p. A225
Chief Financial Officer, Iowa Specialty Hospital–Clarion, Clarion, IA, p. A227

POMA, Frank W., President, St. John River District Hospital, East China, MI, p. A323

POMPOS, Jeff, Manager Information Technology, Henry County Hospital, Napoleon, OH, p. A499

PONCE, Agustin, Supervisor Maintenance, Castaner General Hospital, Castaner, PR, p. A725

PONCE, Joseph A., Chief Information Management, Dwight David Eisenhower Army Medical Center, Fort Gordon, GA, p. A160

PONCE, Martha, Director Information Technologies and Telecommunications, Saint John's Health Center, Santa Monica, CA, p. A94

POND–BELL, Michele, R.N. Nurse Administrator, Cassia Regional Medical Center, Burley, ID, p. A175

PONDER, Beverly K., Executive Assistant and Human Resources Coordinator, Covington County Hospital, Collins, MS, p. A357

PONDER, David, Information Technology Officer, Claremore Indian Hospital, Claremore, OK, p. A509

PONETA, Jan, Director Information Services, Mercy Hospital Jefferson, Crystal City, MO, p. A370

PONOZZO, Nancy Lynn, Chief Nursing Officer, NORTHSTAR Health System, Iron River, MI, p. A327

PONT, Allan, M.D. Vice President Medical Affairs, California Pacific Medical Center, San Francisco, CA, p. A90

PONTI, Mary–Anne D., R.N. Chief Operating Officer, McLaren Northern Michigan, Petoskey, MI, p. A332

PONTICELLO, Nat, Vice President Human Resources, Children's Hospital Central California, Madera, CA, p. A76

PONTIOUS, Becky, Human Resources/Accounting, Loring Hospital, Sac City, IA, p. A237

PONTIUS, Carolyn D., R.N. Chief Nurse Executive, Kaiser Permanente Panorama City Medical Center,, CA, p. A72

PONTREMOLI, Del, Director Human Resources, Spaulding Rehabilitation Hospital Cape Cod, East Sandwich, MA, p. A309

POOCH, Fred, Supervisor Information Technology, Johnson County Hospital, Tecumseh, NE, p. A402

POOK, Lots, Chief Information Officer, National Jewish Health, Denver, CO, p. A105

POOLE, Karen, Chief Operating Officer, Boca Raton Regional Hospital, Boca Raton, FL, p. A124

POOLE, Rob, Director, Jane Phillips Medical Center, Bartlesville, OK, p. A508

POOLE–ADAMS, Veronica, R.N. Vice President, Chief Operating Officer and Chief Nursing Executive, Cleveland Regional Medical Center, Shelby, NC, p. A472

POORE, Justin, D.O. Chief Medical Staff, Cloud County Health Center, Concordia, KS, p. A242

POORE, Luke, Administrator, Webster County Community Hospital, Red Cloud, NE, p. A401

POORE, Timothy T., Chief Executive Officer, HEALTHSOUTH Scottsdale Rehabilitation Hospital, Scottsdale, AZ, p. A38

POORTEN, Kevin P., President and Chief Executive Officer, Kish Health System, DeKalb, IL, p. B82

POOS, Joshua, M.D. President Medical Staff, Community Memorial Hospital, Staunton, IL, p. A203

POPARAD, Paul C., R.N. Chief Nursing Officer, Clinton Memorial Hospital, Wilmington, OH, p. A505

POPE, Alan R., M.D
Vice President, Medical Affairs, Lourdes Medical Center of Burlington County, Willingboro, NJ, p. A424
Chief Medical Officer, Our Lady of Lourdes Medical Center, Camden, NJ, p. A414

POPE, Brad W., Vice President Human Resources, Memorial Health Care System, Chattanooga, TN, p. A580

POPE, Eddie
Chief Information Officer, Lackey Memorial Hospital, Forest, MS, p. A358
Director Information Systems, Pioneer Community Hospital of Patrick County, Stuart, VA, p. A679

POPE, J. Larry, Vice President Finance, Baptist Easley Hospital, Easley, SC, p. A565

POPE, James W., FACHE, President and Chief Executive Officer, Sylvania Franciscan Health, Toledo, OH, p. B131

POPE, Jayne E., Chief Executive Officer, Hill Country Memorial Hospital, Fredericksburg, TX, p. A619

POPE, Lona
Director Financial Services, Shriners Hospitals for Children–Galveston Burns Hospital, Galveston, TX, p. A620
Director Fiscal Services, Shriners Hospitals for Children–Houston, Houston, TX, p. A626

POPE, Richard, Vice President Human Resources, Jackson County Memorial Hospital, Altus, OK, p. A507

POPE, Robert, Information Technology Director and Ministry Liaison, St. Vincent Anderson Regional Hospital, Anderson, IN, p. A206

POPHAN, Cameron, Chief Financial Officer, Spalding Regional Medical Center, Griffin, GA, p. A160

POPKIN, Steven, Chief Executive Officer, Parkview Community Hospital Medical Center, Riverside, CA, p. A86

POPLAWSKI, Steven, M.D. Medical Director, Forest Health Medical Center, Ypsilanti, MI, p. A337

POPLI, Anand, Medical Director, Porter–Starke Services, Valparaiso, IN, p. A223

POPOVICH, Cal, Vice President Information Technology, All Children's Hospital Johns Hopkins Medicine, Saint Petersburg, FL, p. A144

POPOVICH, John, M.D., President and Chief Executive Officer, Henry Ford Hospital, Detroit, MI, p. A322

POPP, Adam, Director Information Systems, Avera St. Benedict Health Center, Parkston, SD, p. A575

POPP, Jason, Chief of Medical Staff, Rochelle Community Hospital, Rochelle, IL, p. A201

POPP, Susan, Controller, Kindred Hospital–Fort Worth, Fort Worth, TX, p. A618

POPPEN, Jeffrey, Chief Financial Officer, Sanford Aberdeen Medical Center, Aberdeen, SD, p. A572

POPPEN, Jennifer, Chief Executive Officer, Avera Creighton Hospital, Creighton, NE, p. A395

POQUETTE, Gary R., FACHE, Chief Executive Officer, Niobrara Health and Life Center, Lusk, WY, p. A722

PORADA, John, Chief Financial Officer, TriStar Southern Hills Medical Center, Nashville, TN, p. A591

PORCO, Albert, Director Management Information Systems, Palisades Medical Center, North Bergen, NJ, p. A420

PORRAL, Azucena, M.D. Chief of Staff, Monterey Park Hospital, Monterey Park, CA, p. A78

PORTCHY, Mindy, Manager Human Resources, Summit Pacific Medical Center, Elma, WA, p. A683

PORTER, Carol A., R.N. Chief Nursing Officer, Senior Vice President, Mount Sinai Hospital, New York, NY, p. A446

PORTER, Cedric, M.D. President Medical Staff, Emanuel Medical Center, Swainsboro, GA, p. A167

PORTER, Don, Senior Vice President and Chief Financial Officer, J. Arthur Dosher Memorial Hospital, Southport, NC, p. A473

PORTER, Dorothy L., Director of Compliance/Risk/Quality, Asheville Specialty Hospital, Asheville, NC, p. A459

PORTER, Glen, Vice President Human Resources, Essentia Health St. Mary's Medical Center, Duluth, MN, p. A342

PORTER, Greg, Chief Financial Officer, Rio Grande Hospital, Del Norte, CO, p. A104

PORTER, James, Chief Financial Officer, Brookdale Hospital Medical Center,, NY, p. A443

PORTER, James, M.D. Vice President Medical Affairs, Deaconess Hospital, Evansville, IN, p. A210

PORTER, Jody, R.N. Senior Vice President Patient Care Services and Chief Nursing Officer, Greater Baltimore Medical Center, Baltimore, MD, p. A296

PORTER Jr., John M., President and Chief Executive Officer, Ephrata Community Hospital, Ephrata, PA, p. A538

PORTER, John T., President and Chief Executive Officer, Avera Health, Sioux Falls, SD, p. B17

PORTER, Lance, Chief Executive Officer, Payson Regional Medical Center, Payson, AZ, p. A35

PORTER, Lisa, Director Human Resources, Leadership and Education, Veterans Affairs Salt Lake City Health Care System, Salt Lake City, UT, p. A664

PORTER, Patricia, Chief Financial Officer, South Oaks Hospital, Amityville, NY, p. A432

PORTER, Sharon, Chief Financial Officer, Massachusetts Hospital School, Canton, MA, p. A309

PORTER, Stephen D., President, Sentara Northern Virginia Medical Center, Woodbridge, VA, p. A680

PORTER, T. J., Director Human Resources, Bennett County Hospital and Nursing Home, Martin, SD, p. A574

PORTMAN, Angela, Chief Nursing Officer and Co–Interim Administrator, Breckinridge Memorial Hospital, Hardinsburg, KY, p. A262

PORTNER, Barry, M.D. Chief of Staff, Prowers Medical Center, Lamar, CO, p. A108

PORTNER, Michael, M.D. Chief Medical Staff, Bolivar Medical Center, Cleveland, MS, p. A357

PORWOLL, Amy, Vice President of Information Systems, St. Cloud Hospital, Saint Cloud, MN, p. A350

POSAR, Steven, M.D. Chief of Medicine, Doctors NeuroMedical Hospital, Bremen, IN, p. A208

POSCH, David R., Chief Executive Officer, Vanderbilt Hospital and Clinics, Nashville, TN, p. A591

POSCH, Tim B., Business Manager and Director Personnel, Parsons State Hospital and Training Center, Parsons, KS, p. A252

POSECAI, Scott J., Executive Vice President and Chief Financial Officer, Ochsner Medical Center, New Orleans, LA, p. A286

POSEY, Dawn, Chief Operating Officer, Promise Hospital of Vicksburg, Vicksburg, MS, p. A366

POSEY, M. Kenneth, FACHE, Administrator, Jasper General Hospital, Bay Springs, MS, p. A355

POSEY, Richard B., Director Human Resources, Baptist Easley Hospital, Easley, SC, p. A565

POSMOGA, Paul, Chief Financial Officer, Twin Cities Community Hospital, Templeton, CA, p. A97

POST, Eleanor, R.N. Chief Nursing Officer, Rockdale Medical Center, Conyers, GA, p. A157

POST, John, M.D. Medical Director, Morrill County Community Hospital, Bridgeport, NE, p. A394

POST, Kevin, D.O. Chief Medical Officer, Hegg Memorial Health Center Avera, Rock Valley, IA, p. A237

POST, Kimberly, R.N., Vice President and Administrator, Scottsdale Healthcare Thompson Peak Hospital, Scottsdale, AZ, p. A38

POSTERNACK, Charles, M.D. Vice President, Boca Raton Regional Hospital, Boca Raton, FL, p. A124

POSTLER–SLATTERY, Diane, Ph.D., President and Chief Executive Officer, MidMichigan Health, Midland, MI, p. B94

POSTLETHWAIT, Betsy, President, Princeton Baptist Medical Center, Birmingham, AL, p. A16

POSTON, Anne, Director of Human Resources/Compliance, Lake City Community Hospital, Lake City, SC, p. A568

POSTON, Sharon, President and Chief Executive Officer, Williamsburg Regional Hospital, Kingstree, SC, p. A567

POSTULKA, Carol, Administrative Coordinator, Avera Gregory Hospital, Gregory, SD, p. A574

POTEATE, Kathy, Interim Director Human Resources, Hugh Chatham Memorial Hospital, Elkin, NC, p. A464

POTEETE, Robin
Manager Human Resources, Wellmont Hancock County Hospital, Sneedville, TN, p. A593
Manager Human Resources, Wellmont Hawkins County Memorial Hospital, Rogersville, TN, p. A592

POTHAST, Joyce, Vice President Human and Environmental Services, Van Wert County Hospital, Van Wert, OH, p. A504

POTITADKUL, Wendy, Chief Information Officer, Sunrise Canyon Hospital, Lubbock, TX, p. A635

POTTENGER, Jay, Administrator, Missouri River Medical Center, Fort Benton, MT, p. A387

POTTER, Carolyn
Vice President Human Resources, McLaren Bay Region, Bay City, MI, p. A319
Vice President Human Resources, McLaren Bay Special Care, Bay City, MI, p. A319
Vice President Human Resources, McLaren Central Michigan, Mount Pleasant, MI, p. A330

POTTER, Dianne P., Manager Human Resources, Parkview Whitley Hospital, Columbia City, IN, p. A208

POTTER, Joe, M.D. Chief of Staff, Integris Marshall County Medical Center, Madill, OK, p. A513

POTTER, Rhonda, Director Human Resources, De Soto Regional Health System, Mansfield, LA, p. A283

POTTER, Val, Director Human Resources, St. Vincent Salem Hospital, Salem, IN, p. A222

POTTI, Esther, M.D. Chief Medical Staff, Sanford Bagley Medical Center, Bagley, MN, p. A340

POTTS, Kevin, M.D. Medical Director, Kindred Hospital Detroit, Detroit, MI, p. A322

POTTS, Mary Ann, Director Personnel, Community Hospitals and Wellness Centers, Bryan, OH, p. A484

POUGNAUD, Teresa, Vice President Human Resources, McLeod Loris Seacoast Hospital, Loris, SC, p. A568

POUND, Steve, Vice President Human Resources, St. Joseph's Hospital, Savannah, GA, p. A166

POUND, Terry, Chief Financial Officer, Rice County District Hospital, Lyons, KS, p. A249

POUND, Veronica, R.N., Administrator, Socorro General Hospital, Socorro, NM, p. A431

POVICH, Mark, D.O. Medical Director, OSF St. Francis Hospital and Medical Group, Escanaba, MI, p. A323

POWE, Lee, Director Management Information Systems, Hugh Chatham Memorial Hospital, Elkin, NC, p. A464

POWEL, Linda J., M.D. Medical Director, Odessa Memorial Healthcare Center, Odessa, WA, p. A686

POWELL, Candy, Administrator, Collingsworth General Hospital, Wellington, TX, p. A656

POWELL, Charles, Chief Financial Officer, Arkansas Surgical Hospital, North Little Rock, AR, p. A51

POWELL, Claudia, R.N. Director of Nursing, Melissa Memorial Hospital, Holyoke, CO, p. A107

POWELL, D. Jerome, M.D
Chief Information Officer, Highland Hospital of Rochester, Rochester, NY, p. A453
Chief Information Officer, Strong Memorial Hospital of the University of Rochester, Rochester, NY, p. A453

POWELL, Frank R., Chief Financial Officer, Piedmont Mountainside Hospital, Jasper, GA, p. A161

POWELL, Hannah, Chief Nursing Officer, Mercy Hospital Kingfisher, Kingfisher, OK, p. A512

POWELL, Holly, Administrator, Dubuis Hospital of Texarkana, Texarkana, TX, p. A652

POWELL, Jackie, Director Human Resources, Pemiscot Memorial Health System, Hayti, MO, p. A372

POWELL, Jimmy, Manager Human Resources, Harry S. Truman Memorial Veterans Hospital, Columbia, MO, p. A370

POWELL, Josh, Facility Controller, Cox Monett, Monett, MO, p. A377

POWELL, Kay, Director Human Resources, CHRISTUS Jasper Memorial Hospital, Jasper, TX, p. A630

POWELL, Lorie, Interim Director Human Resources, Regency Hospital of Jackson, Jackson, MS, p. A360

POWELL, Michelle, Chief Executive Officer, Select Rehabilitation Hospital of Denton, Denton, TX, p. A613

POWELL, Mike, Executive Director, Missouri Rehabilitation Center, Mount Vernon, MO, p. A377

POWELL, Parker, Chief Executive Officer, Glendive Medical Center, Glendive, MT, p. A387

POWELL, Robyn L., Chief Financial Officer, Marion General Hospital, Marion, IN, p. A218

POWELL, Roy A., President and Chief Executive Officer, Crittenton Hospital Medical Center, Rochester, MI, p. A333

POWELL, Tammy, M.P.H., President, St. Anthony Hospital, Oklahoma City, OK, p. A516

POWELL, Traci, Director Human Resources, HEALTHSOUTH Emerald Coast Rehabilitation Hospital, Panama City, FL, p. A142

POWELL, Troy, Chief Executive Officer, HEALTHSOUTH Rehabilitation Hospital of Charleston, Charleston, SC, p. A563

POWELL, Virginia, Director Finance, Wilmington Treatment Center, Wilmington, NC, p. A474

POWELL–STAFFORD, Valerie L., Chief Operating Officer, Blake Medical Center, Bradenton, FL, p. A124

POWELSON, Jeffrey A., Chief Executive Officer, Broaddus Hospital, Philippi, WV, p. A698

POWER, Bob, Vice President Information Services, Good Samaritan Regional Medical Center, Corvallis, OR, p. A524

POWER, Robert
Vice President Information Services, Samaritan Lebanon Community Hospital, Lebanon, OR, p. A526
Chief Information Officer, Samaritan Pacific Communities Hospital, Newport, OR, p. A527
Associate Executive Director Finance, Southside Hospital, Bay Shore, NY, p. A433

POWERS, Anthony, Vice President Patient Care Services, Baptist Health Corbin, Corbin, KY, p. A260

POWERS, Barbara, R.N. Chief Nursing Officer, Austin Lakes Hospital, Austin, TX, p. A599

POWERS, Brent, M.D. Vice President/Chief Medical Officer, Lexington Medical Center, West Columbia, SC, p. A571

POWERS, Charles, M.D. Administrative Medical Director, WK Bossier Health Center, Bossier City, LA, p. A274

POWERS, Donald, Chairman, President and Chief Executive Officer, Community Healthcare System, Hammond, IN, p. B43

POWERS, Jamekia, Assistant Director Human Resources, Georgia Regional Hospital at Savannah, Savannah, GA, p. A166

POWERS, Judy, Chief Nursing Officer, Singing River Health System, Pascagoula, MS, p. A364

POWERS, Kelli, Chief Financial Officer, Huntsville Hospital, Huntsville, AL, p. A22

POWERS, Marcia, Vice President Human Resources, Norwegian American Hospital, Chicago, IL, p. A185

POWERS, Mary, MS
Senior Vice President Patient Care Services, Manchester Memorial Hospital, Manchester, CT, p. A114
Senior Vice President Patient Care Services, Rockville General Hospital, Vernon Rockville, CT, p. A117

POWERS, Michael K., FACHE, Chief Executive Officer, Fairbanks Memorial Hospital, Fairbanks, AK, p. A29

POWERS, Ryan J., Vice President Finance, Spectrum Health Zeeland Community Hospital, Zeeland, MI, p. A338

POWERS, Taylor, Administrator, Tanner Medical Center–Villa Rica, Villa Rica, GA, p. A168

POWERS, Tim, Chief Executive Officer, North Canyon Medical Center, Gooding, ID, p. A176

POWRIE, Raymond, M.D. Senior Vice President Quality and Clinical Effectiveness, Women & Infants Hospital of Rhode Island, Providence, RI, p. A561

POYER, Melinda, D.O. President, Medical Staff, Memorial Hospital of Sweetwater County, Rock Springs, WY, p. A722

POYNTER, Carmen, Director Human Resources, Rockcastle Regional Hospital and Respiratory Care Center, Mount Vernon, KY, p. A268

PRABHU, Asha, M.D. Chief Medical Officer, Warren State Hospital, Warren, PA, p. A557

PRACHT, Matthew, Vice President Finance, Scotland Health Care System, Laurinburg, NC, p. A468

PRADA, Janina
Director Information Technology, El Paso Children's Hospital, El Paso, TX, p. A615
Director Information Services, University Medical Center of El Paso, El Paso, TX, p. A616

PRAGER, Jay E., Chief Executive Officer, Reynolds Memorial Hospital, Glen Dale, WV, p. A695

PRAKASH, Amitabh, M.D. Chief Medical Officer, AHMC Anaheim Regional Medical Center, Anaheim, CA, p. A55

PRATER, Jeffrey, Chief Executive Officer, Samuel Simmonds Memorial Hospital, Barrow, AK, p. A28

PRATER, Marita, MS Vice President Patient Care Services, Sturdy Memorial Hospital, Attleboro, MA, p. A305

PRATER, Marsha A., Ph.D. Senior Vice President and Chief Nursing Officer, Memorial Medical Center, Springfield, IL, p. A203

PRATER, Robin, Director Human Resources, Howard A. Rusk Rehabilitation Center, Columbia, MO, p. A370

PRATI, Richard, Chief Executive Officer, Fort Duncan Regional Medical Center, Eagle Pass, TX, p. A614

PRATT, Bailey, Chief Financial Officer, Saint Thomas Hickman Hospital, Centerville, TN, p. A580

PRATT, Debbie, Chief Financial Officer, Washington County Memorial Hospital, Potosi, MO, p. A379

PRATT, Dustin, M.D. Chief of Staff, Childress Regional Medical Center, Childress, TX, p. A606

PRATT, Lisa, Vice President Human Resources, Memorial Hospital of Rhode Island, Pawtucket, RI, p. A560

PRATT, Mary Ellen, FACHE, Chief Executive Officer, St. James Parish Hospital, Lutcher, LA, p. A283

PRATT, Timothy J., M.D. Vice President Medical Affairs and Chief Medical Officer, SSM St. Clare Health Center, Fenton, MO, p. A371

PRATT, Troy, Information Technology Site Director, Covenant Medical Center, Lubbock, TX, p. A634

PRAY, Jan, Coordinator Payroll and Benefits, Kindred Hospital Boston–North Shore, Peabody, MA, p. A313

PRAYWELL, Hunter, Vice President Information Technology and Chief Information Officer, Queen's Medical Center, Honolulu, HI, p. A171

PREAU, William, M.D. Medical Director, Fairway Medical Center, Covington, LA, p. A276

PRECHT, James, Chief Financial Officer, Goodland Regional Medical Center, Goodland, KS, p. A244

PREMO, Mark, Senior Director HC Intelligence, Providence Portland Medical Center, Portland, OR, p. A528

PRENOT, Traci, Chief Financial Officer, Teton Valley Health Care, Driggs, ID, p. A176

PRENTISS, Kristin, Chief Financial Officer, Specialty Hospital of Central Jersey, Lakewood, NJ, p. A417

PRESCOTT, Tina, Vice President, Hospital Services, Jackson–Madison County General Hospital, Jackson, TN, p. A584

PRESS, Robert, M.D. Chief Medical Officer, NYU Langone Medical Center, New York, NY, p. A448

PRESSER, Jonathan, Vice President Finance and Operations, Norton Audubon Hospital, Louisville, KY, p. A266

PRESSMAN, Eric, D.O. Chair Department of Medicine, Englewood Community Hospital, Englewood, FL, p. A128

PREST, Craig, Director Operation Services, Humboldt General Hospital, Winnemucca, NV, p. A408

PRESTON, Tara
Director Human Resources, Bingham Memorial Hospital, Blackfoot, ID, p. A174
Director Human Resources, Mountain River Birthing and Surgery Center, Blackfoot, ID, p. A174

PRESTON, Troy, Director Human Resources, Schuyler Hospital, Montour Falls, NY, p. A441

PRESTRIDGE, Tim, Chief Operating Officer, Terre Haute Regional Hospital, Terre Haute, IN, p. A223

PRETE, Mark, M.D. Vice President Medical Affairs, The Charlotte Hungerford Hospital, Torrington, CT, p. A117

PRETTYMAN, Edgar E., PsyD, Chief Executive Officer, Rock Springs, Georgetown, TX, p. A621

PRETZLAFF, Robert, M.D
Chief Medical Officer, St. Rose Dominican Hospitals – San Martin Campus, Las Vegas, NV, p. A406
Chief Medical Officer, St. Rose Dominican Hospitals – Siena Campus, Henderson, NV, p. A405

PREWITT, Connie F., Chief Financial Officer, Billings Clinic, Billings, MT, p. A385

PREWITT, Margaret Elizabeth, Vice President Patient Services and Chief Nursing Officer, St. Catherine Hospital, Garden City, KS, p. A244

PRIBYL, Stephen J., FACHE, Chief Executive Officer, District One Hospital, Faribault, MN, p. A343

PRICE, Bernard J., Assistant Vice President, Medical Center, Navicent Health, Macon, GA, p. A163

PRICE, Cecil, M.D., Director, Wake Forest University Health Service, Winston–Salem, NC, p. A475

PRICE, Eric, Financial Specialist, Senior, State Hospital South, Blackfoot, ID, p. A174

PRICE, Fred, R.N., President and Chief Executive Officer, DeKalb Health, Auburn, IN, p. A206

PRICE, John D., Chief Financial Officer, FirstHealth Richmond Memorial Hospital, Rockingham, NC, p. A471

PRICE, Julie, Chief Financial Officer, Rooks County Health Center, Plainville, KS, p. A253

PRICE, Kelley, R.N. Chief Nursing Officer, Battle Mountain General Hospital, Battle Mountain, NV, p. A404

PRICE, Kevin A.
Vice President and Chief Operating Officer, Sparrow Clinton Hospital, Saint Johns, MI, p. A334
Vice President and Chief Operating Officer, Sparrow Ionia Hospital, Ionia, MI, p. A327

PRICE, Kim, Chief Executive Officer, Franklin General Hospital, Hampton, IA, p. A231

PRICE, Larry, Chief Executive Officer, Limestone Medical Center, Groesbeck, TX, p. A622

PRICE, Lawrence, M.D., President and Chief Operating Officer, Butler Hospital, Providence, RI, p. A560

PRICE, Lori, President, Gottlieb Memorial Hospital, Melrose Park, IL, p. A196

PRICE, Lorraine B., Associate Director, Hampton Veterans Affairs Medical Center, Hampton, VA, p. A672

PRICE, Manuel, Director Information Systems, Brookwood Medical Center, Birmingham, AL, p. A16

PRICE, Meredith, Vice President Fiscal Services and Chief Financial Officer, St. Joseph's Hospital Health Center, Syracuse, NY, p. A456

PRICE, Norman M., FACHE, Chief Executive Officer and Administrator, Southwest Health Systems, Mccomb, MS, p. B126

PRICE, Norman M., FACHE, Chief Executive Officer, Southwest Mississippi Regional Medical Center, McComb, MS, p. A362

PRICE, Peggy Cain, Vice President and Chief Operating Officer, Lutheran Medical Center, Wheat Ridge, CO, p. A112

PRICE, Sam, Executive Vice President Finance/Chief Financial Officer, East Alabama Medical Center, Opelika, AL, p. A24

PRICE, Shari, Director Information Services, Baptist Health Louisville, Louisville, KY, p. A265

PRICE, Sheila C., R.N. Chief Nursing Officer/Vice President of Nursing, Angel Medical Center, Franklin, NC, p. A464

PRICE, Shelby, Chief Executive Officer, Louisiana State Hospitals, Baton Rouge, LA, p. B87

PRICE, Tonya, Chief Nursing Officer, Texas Health Presbyterian Hospital–WNJ, Sherman, TX, p. A649

PRICE, Walter, Director Information Technology, Newport Hospital and Health Services, Newport, WA, p. A685

PRICE, Wendy, Manager Human Resources, Nicholas County Hospital, Carlisle, KY, p. A259

PRICE–GHARZEDDINE, Karen, R.N. Chief Nursing Officer and Chief Operating Officer, San Gabriel Valley Medical Center, San Gabriel, CA, p. A92

PRICHARD, Barbara, Assistant Administrator, South Sunflower County Hospital, Indianola, MS, p. A359

PRICKEL, Trisha, Director Information Systems, Margaret Mary Health, Batesville, IN, p. A206

PRIDDY, III, Ernest C., Chief Financial Officer, Old Vineyard Behavioral Health Services, Winston–Salem, NC, p. A475

PRIDDY, Steven L., M.D. Vice President Physician Affairs and Chief Medical Officer, St. Vincent Carmel Hospital, Carmel, IN, p. A208

PRIDEAUX, Heather, Chief Financial Officer, Rawlins County Health Center, Atwood, KS, p. A241

PRIDGEN, Kim, Chief Financial Officer, Northcrest Medical Center, Springfield, TN, p. A593

PRIEBE, Cedric T., M.D. Vice President and Chief Information Officer, Butler Hospital, Providence, RI, p. A560

PRIES, Kathleen M., Director Human Resources, Nazareth Hospital, Philadelphia, PA, p. A549

PRIEST, David, Director Information Systems, Charlevoix Area Hospital, Charlevoix, MI, p. A320

PRIEST, Geoff, M.D. Chief Medical Officer, Meriter Hospital, Madison, WI, p. A708

PRIEST, Mike, M.D. Chief of Staff, Pawhuska Hospital, Pawhuska, OK, p. A517

PRIESTLEY, Betty, Manager Business Office, Promise Hospital of Houston, Houston, TX, p. A626

PRIESTLEY, Carlos W., Chief Operating Officer, Providence Little Company of Mary Medical Center San Pedro,, CA, p. A74

PRINCE, Gayle, Director Human Resources, Washington County Regional Medical Center, Sandersville, GA, p. A166

PRINCE, Sue, Director Information Systems, Northern Westchester Hospital, Mount Kisco, NY, p. A442

PRINCE, Thomas A., Vice President Human Resources, Northeast Rehabilitation Hospital, Salem, NH, p. A412

PRINCIPE, Hector Cintron, M.D. Director, Hospital Universitario Dr. Ramon Ruiz Arnau, Bayamon, PR, p. A725

PRINGLE, Robert W., M.D. Vice President Medical Affairs and Chief Medical Officer, Glens Falls Hospital, Glens Falls, NY, p. A438

PRINGLE–MILLER, Letitia, Administrative Director, Tuomey Healthcare System, Sumter, SC, p. A570

PRINTY, Wayne, Chief Financial Officer and Senior Vice President Finance, Lincoln Health, Damariscotta, ME, p. A293

PRIOLA, Pat, Chief Financial Officer, Jerome Golden Center for Behavioral Health, Inc., West Palm Beach, FL, p. A150

PRIORE, Jacqueline, Chief Nursing Officer, Samaritan Hospital, Troy, NY, p. A456

PRISELAC, Thomas M., President and Chief Executive Officer, Cedars–Sinai Medical Center, Los Angeles, CA, p. A71

PRISTER, James R.
President and Chief Executive Officer, RML Specialty Hospital, Chicago, IL, p. A186
President and Chief Executive Officer, RML Specialty Hospital, Hinsdale, IL, p. A193

PRITCHARD, Jason, Chief Financial Officer, Hackensack University Medical Center at Pascack Valley, Westwood, NJ, p. A424

PRITCHARD, Jeff, Chief Executive Officer, SummitRidge Hospital, Lawrenceville, GA, p. A162

PRITCHARD, Joann, Chief Financial Officer, Erie Veterans Affairs Medical Center, Erie, PA, p. A538

PRITCHETT, Greg, Controller, Cuero Community Hospital, Cuero, TX, p. A609

PRITT, Wayne M., Commander, U. S. Air Force Hospital, Hampton, VA, p. A672

PRIVETT, David, Deputy Director, Western New York Children's Psychiatric Center, West Seneca, NY, p. A458

PROBASCO, Brent, Chief Financial Officer, Cass Regional Medical Center, Harrisonville, MO, p. A685

PROBST, Keith, M.D. Chief of Staff, Avera Holy Family Hospital, Estherville, IA, p. A230

PROBST, Nancy, R.N. Chief Nursing Officer, Bigfork Valley Hospital, Bigfork, MN, p. A340

PROCHILO, John F., Chief Executive Officer and Administrator, Northeast Rehabilitation Hospital, Salem, NH, p. A412

PROCHNOW, Bryan, Chief Financial Officer, Matagorda Regional Medical Center, Bay City, TX, p. A601

PROCTOR, Brandy, Director of Nursing, North Star Behavioral Health System, Anchorage, AK, p. A28

PROCTOR, Deborah A., President and Chief Executive Officer, St. Joseph Health, Irvine, CA, p. B128

PROCTOR, George M., Senior Vice President and Executive Director, Woodhull Medical and Mental Health Center,, NY, p. A449

PROCTOR, Kenneth S., MS Director Human Resources, Mayo Regional Hospital, Dover–Foxcroft, ME, p. A293

PROCTOR, Quinn, Director Human Resources, Claremore Indian Hospital, Claremore, OK, p. A509

PROCTOR, Sandra, R.N. Chief Nurse Executive, Memorial Medical Center, Modesto, CA, p. A78

PROCTOR, Scott, Chief Executive Officer, Safe Haven Hospital of Treasure Valley, Boise, ID, p. A174

PROCTOR, Stephen, Director of Human Resources/Risk, Russellville Hospital, Russellville, AL, p. A25

PROCTOR, Steven M., President, Matheny Medical and Educational Center, Peapack, NJ, p. A420

PROFF, Melissa, Director Human Resources, Pondera Medical Center, Conrad, MT, p. A386

PROKOSCH, Brian, M.D. Vice President Medical Affairs, St. Francis Regional Medical Center, Shakopee, MN, p. A352

PRONGER, Derk, Chief Operating Officer, Munson Medical Center, Traverse City, MI, p. A336

PRONI, John, CPA Manager Finance, BayCare Alliant Hospital, Dunedin, FL, p. A127

PROPP, Elizabeth R., Vice President Finance and Chief Financial Officer, Dameron Hospital, Stockton, CA, p. A96

PROSKE, Donna, MS Executive Director, Staten Island University Hospital,, NY, p. A448

PROSKOCIL, Danielle, Director Human Resources, Valley County Health System, Ord, NE, p. A400

PROSPER, Charles
Chief Executive Officer, Alta Bates Summit Medical Center, Berkeley, CA, p. A58
Chief Executive Officer, Alta Bates Summit Medical Center – Summit Campus, Oakland, CA, p. A80

PROSSER, Alita, Chief Financial Officer, Scott & White Memorial Hospital, Temple, TX, p. A652

PROSSER, Edna, Chief Nursing Officer, Ozark Health Medical Center, Clinton, AR, p. A44

PROSSER, Joseph, M.D
Chief Medical Officer, Texas Health Harris Methodist Hospital Fort Worth, Fort Worth, TX, p. A619
Chief Medical Officer, Texas Health Specialty Hospital, Fort Worth, TX, p. A619

PROSTKO, Michael, M.D. Chief of Staff, Rhea Medical Center, Dayton, TN, p. A582

PROUD, James, Vice President Human Resources and Marketing, Uniontown Hospital, Uniontown, PA, p. A556

PROUJANSKY, Roy, M.D., Chief Executive Officer, Alfred I. duPont Hospital for Children, Wilmington, DE, p. A120

PROULX, David R., Assistant Vice President Operations, Valley West Hospital, Sandwich, IL, p. A202

PROVENZANO, Jeff, Vice President and Chief Financial Officer, MidMichigan Medical Center–Gratiot, Alma, MI, p. A318

PROVINCE, Steven, Senior Vice President and Chief Operating Officer, Providence Health Center, Waco, TX, p. A656

PRUESS, Mark, M.D. Chief Medical Staff, Sparta Community Hospital, Sparta, IL, p. A202

PRUETT, Linda, R.N. Vice President Chief Nursing Officer, Kaweah Delta Medical Center, Visalia, CA, p. A99

PRUETT–BAER, Karen, Senior Nurse Executive, Naval Hospital Oak Harbor, Oak Harbor, WA, p. A686

PRUITT, Jeffrey, M.D. Chief of Staff, Mercy Hospital of Defiance, Defiance, OH, p. A492

PRUITT, Michael W., Administrator and Chief Executive Officer, Coleman County Medical Center, Coleman, TX, p. A606

PRUKOP, Jeff, Director Professional Services, Jackson County Hospital District, Edna, TX, p. A615

PRUNCHUNAS, Edward M., Senior Vice President and Chief Financial Officer, Cedars–Sinai Medical Center, Los Angeles, CA, p. A71

PRUNOSKE, Mark, Chief Financial Officer and Senior Vice President Finance, F. F. Thompson Hospital, Canandaigua, NY, p. A435

PRUSATIS, Michael, Vice President Finance, Sinai–Grace Hospital, Detroit, MI, p. A322

PRYBYLO, Mary, President and Chief Executive Officer, St. Joseph Hospital, Bangor, ME, p. A291

PRYOR, David, President, Athens–Limestone Hospital, Athens, AL, p. A16

PRYOR, Dennis P., Administrator, Salem Memorial District Hospital, Salem, MO, p. A382

PRYOR, Jon, M.D., Chief Executive Officer, Hennepin County Medical Center, Minneapolis, MN, p. A347

PRYOR, Vincent, System Executive Vice President and Chief Financial Officer, Edward Hospital, Naperville, IL, p. A197

PRYOR, William B., Senior Vice President, Human Resources, Cape Fear Valley Medical Center, Fayetteville, NC, p. A464

PRZESTRZELSKI, David, Associate Director, Patient Care Services and Chief Nursing Executive, Charles George Veterans Affairs Medical Center, Asheville, NC, p. A459

PRZYBYLSKI, David, Interim Controller, Sparrow Specialty Hospital, Lansing, MI, p. A329

PSAILA, Justin P., M.D. Vice President Medical Affairs, St. Luke's Hospital – Anderson Campus, Easton, PA, p. A538

PSCODNA, Susan, Director Human Resources, Mercy Hospital of Defiance, Defiance, OH, p. A492

PSHEA, Pam, R.N. Chief Nursing Officer, San Ramon Regional Medical Center, San Ramon, CA, p. A93

PU, Steve, D.O. Chief Medical Officer, Poplar Bluff Regional Medical Center, Poplar Bluff, MO, p. A378

PUCKETT, Clay, Assistant Administrator and Chief Information Officer, Blount Memorial Hospital, Maryville, TN, p. A588

PUCKETT, Doug, President and Chief Executive Officer, Indiana University Health Morgan Hospital, Martinsville, IN, p. A218

PUCKETT, Frank, M.D. Chief Medical Officer, Pocahontas Memorial Hospital, Buckeye, WV, p. A693

PUCKETT, Kristi, Director Human Resources, Grande Ronde Hospital, La Grande, OR, p. A526

PUCKETT, Steven, Director Information Technology, Central State Hospital, Louisville, KY, p. A265

PUCLIK, Becky, Division Chief People Officer, St. John's Hospital, Springfield, IL, p. A203

PUENTES, Francisco, Human Resource Officer, San Diego County Psychiatric Hospital, San Diego, CA, p. A89

PUFFENBERGER, James, Vice President and Chief Financial Officer, Mercy Hospital of Defiance, Defiance, OH, p. A492

PUFFENBERGER, Jim, Senior Vice President Northern Region and Chief Financial Officer, Mercy St. Charles Hospital, Oregon, OH, p. A500

PUFFENBERGER, Sheila, Manager Information Technology, Hillsdale Community Health Center, Hillsdale, MI, p. A326

PUGH, Larry, Vice President and Chief Financial Officer, Beverly Hospital, Montebello, CA, p. A78

PUGH, Melodee, Director Human Resources, Navarro Regional Hospital, Corsicana, TX, p. A608

PUGH, William H., Senior Vice President Corporate Finance and Chief Financial Officer, Pinnacle Health System, Harrisburg, PA, p. A540

PUGSLEY, Tim, Chief Information Officer, Nebraska Orthopaedic Hospital, Omaha, NE, p. A400

PUHL, Cathy A., Vice President Human Resources, Chambersburg Hospital, Chambersburg, PA, p. A535

PUHY, Dorothy E., Executive VP and Chief Operating Officer, Dana–Farber Cancer Institute, Boston, MA, p. A306

PUKALA, Shirley, R.N. Assistant Administrator of Operations, St. Lawrence Rehabilitation Center, Lawrenceville, NJ, p. A417

PULASKI, Jason, Controller, HEALTHSOUTH Reading Rehabilitation Hospital, Reading, PA, p. A553

PULCO, Dominic J., Executive Vice President Finance and Chief Financial Officer, VCU Medical Center, Richmond, VA, p. A678

PULEO, Mark, Vice President and Chief Human Resources Officer, Henry Mayo Newhall Memorial Hospital, Valencia, CA, p. A98

PULIDO, Michael, Chief Administrative Officer, Heartland Regional Medical Center, Saint Joseph, MO, p. A379

PULLARKAT, Sajit, Chief Executive Officer and Managing Director, Centennial Hills Hospital Medical Center, Las Vegas, NV, p. A405

PULLIAM, Elizabeth, Chief Financial Officer, Mother Frances Hospital – Jacksonville, Jacksonville, TX, p. A630

PULLIN, Dennis W., FACHE, President, MedStar Harbor Hospital, Baltimore, MD, p. A297

PULLIN, Tadd M., Interim Vice President, Human Resources, Nebraska Medical Center, Omaha, NE, p. A400

PULLMAN, Debbie, Director Finance, Avera Hand County Memorial Hospital, Miller, SD, p. A574

PULLMAN, Jayson, Chief Executive Officer, Hawarden Regional Healthcare, Hawarden, IA, p. A232

PULSIPHER, Gary W., President and Chief Executive Officer, Mercy Hospital Joplin, Joplin, MO, p. A373

PUNG, Margaret, R.N. Chief Nursing Officer, University of Texas Harris County Psychiatric Center, Houston, TX, p. A627

PUNJABI, Rishab
Chief Financial Officer, Kindred Hospital–La Mirada, La Mirada, CA, p. A68
Chief Financial Officer, Kindred Hospital–New Jersey Morris County, Dover, NJ, p. A415

PURCELL, Terrance J.
Vice President Support Services and Ambulatory Care, Gnaden Huetten Memorial Hospital, Lehighton, PA, p. A543
Vice President Ambulatory Care and Support Services, Palmerton Hospital, Palmerton, PA, p. A547

PURCELL, Terry, Director Information Services, Lea Regional Medical Center, Hobbs, NM, p. A428

PURDY, Bruce, M.D. Chief of Staff, Muleshoe Area Medical Center, Muleshoe, TX, p. A639

PURINGTON, Denise, Vice President and Chief Information Officer, Elliot Hospital, Manchester, NH, p. A411

PURINTON, Sandy, Chief Nursing Officer, Trego County–Lemke Memorial Hospital, Wakeeney, KS, p. A256

PUROHIT, Divyesh, M.D. Chief of Staff, Sullivan County Community Hospital, Sullivan, IN, p. A222

PUROHIT, Kumar, Chief Financial Officer, Rockford Center, Newark, DE, p. A119

PUROHIT, Shamb, Chief Financial Officer, Colquitt Regional Medical Center, Moultrie, GA, p. A164

PURRINGTON, Janice, Coordinator Medical Records, Avera Hand County Memorial Hospital, Miller, SD, p. A574

PURSLEY, Roger, Chief Executive Officer, Western Mental Health Institute, Bolivar, TN, p. A579

PURTLE, Mark, M.D
Vice President Medical Affairs, UnityPoint Health – Des Moines, Des Moines, IA, p. A229
Vice President Medical Affairs, UnityPoint Health – Iowa Methodist Medical Center, Des Moines, IA, p. A229

PURTZER, Dan, M.D. Chief of Staff, Mercy Medical Center Mount Shasta, Mount Shasta, CA, p. A79

PURUSHOTHAM, Sanjay, Executive Director Information Systems, Bon Secours Baltimore Health System, Baltimore, MD, p. A296

PURVANCE, Clint, M.D. Chief Medical Officer, Barton Memorial Hospital, South Lake Tahoe, CA, p. A96

PURVES, Stephen A., FACHE, President and Chief Executive Officer, Maricopa Integrated Health System, Phoenix, AZ, p. A36

PURVIS, Jay, Administrator, Wabash General Hospital, Mount Carmel, IL, p. A197

PURVIS, Kevin, Chief Information Officer, Community Howard Regional Health, Kokomo, IN, p. A216

PURVIS, Michael L., Chief Executive Officer, Cook Medical Center–A Campus of Tift Regional Medical Center, Adel, GA, p. A151

PURVIS, Mike, Chief Administrative Officer, Sutter Medical Center of Santa Rosa, Chanate Campus, Santa Rosa, CA, p. A95

PUSTINA, Karl, Vice President Finance, Upland Hills Health, Dodgeville, WI, p. A703

PUSZKARSKA, Lucyna M., M.D. Medical Director, Riveredge Hospital, Forest Park, IL, p. A190

PUTHOFF, Timothy, Chief Executive Officer, Houston Northwest Medical Center, Houston, TX, p. A625

PUTNAM, Larry E., Interim Chief Executive Officer, Mineral Community Hospital, Superior, MT, p. A391

PUTNAM, Mark, M.D. Medical Director, Haven Behavioral Health of Eastern Pennsylvania, Reading, PA, p. A553

PUTNAM, Stewart C., Executive Vice President and Chief Operating Officer, Unity Hospital, Rochester, NY, p. A453

PUTNAM, Timothy L., FACHE, President and Chief Executive Officer, Margaret Mary Health, Batesville, IN, p. A206

PUTT, David G., FACHE,
Chief Executive Officer, Holmes County Hospital and Clinics, Lexington, MS, p. A361
Chief Executive Officer, University of Mississippi Medical Center Grenada, Grenada, MS, p. A358

PUU, Linda, Chief Nursing Executive, Kaiser Permanente Medical Center, Honolulu, HI, p. A170

PUVOGEL, LuAnn, R.N., Administrator, Salina Surgical Hospital, Salina, KS, p. A254

PUYAU, Susan, M.D. Medical Director, Woman's Hospital, Baton Rouge, LA, p. A274

PUZO, Thomas C., President and Chief Operating Officer, Cornerstone of Medical Arts Center Hospital, Fresh Meadows, NY, p. A437

PUZZUTO, David, M.D. Vice President Medical Affairs and Chief Medical Officer, Waterbury Hospital, Waterbury, CT, p. A118

PYE, Irma L.
Chief Human Resource Officer, Valley Baptist Medical Center–Brownsville, Brownsville, TX, p. A604
Senior Vice President and Chief Human Resource Officer, Valley Baptist Medical Center–Harlingen, Harlingen, TX, p. A623

PYGON, Bernard, M.D. Chief Medical Officer, University of Illinois Hospital & Health Sciences System, Chicago, IL, p. A187

PYLE, Diana, Director Human Resources, Cedar County Memorial Hospital, El Dorado Springs, MO, p. A370

PYLE, Julia, R.N. Chief Nursing Officer, Newman Regional Health, Emporia, KS, p. A243

PYLE, Rick, Director Information Systems, Harrisburg Medical Center, Harrisburg, IL, p. A191

PYLE FARRELL, Martha, Vice President Human Resources and General Counsel, Massachusetts Eye and Ear Infirmary, Boston, MA, p. A307

PYNE, Mel
Chief Executive Officer, Dorminy Medical Center, Fitzgerald, GA, p. A159
Chief Executive Officer, Emanuel Medical Center, Swainsboro, GA, p. A167

PYRAH, Scott, Director Information Systems, Elks Rehab Hospital, Boise, ID, p. A174

Q

QUACKENBUSH, Kirk, M.D. Chief of Staff, Platte Valley Medical Center, Brighton, CO, p. A103

QUALIA, Leigh Ann, Director Human Resources, Val Verde Regional Medical Center, Del Rio, TX, p. A613

QUALLS, Brenda, Chief Financial Officer, Oconee Regional Medical Center, Milledgeville, GA, p. A163

QUAM, David, M.D
Area Medical Director, Kaiser Permanente Fontana Medical Center, Fontana, CA, p. A63
Area Medical Director, Kaiser Permanente Ontario Medical Center, Ontario, CA, p. A81

QUANSTROM, Julie, Director Information Systems, Wilson Medical Center, Neodesha, KS, p. A250

QUARLES, Christopher, M.D. Director Medical Services, Naval Hospital Jacksonville, Jacksonville, FL, p. A132

QUATTROCCHI, Robert, President and Chief Executive Officer, Northside Healthcare System, Atlanta, GA, p. B101

QUATTROCCHI, Robert, President and Chief Executive Officer, Northside Hospital, Atlanta, GA, p. A152

QUEBEDEAUX, Jay, Chief Executive Officer, Sabine Medical Center, Many, LA, p. A283

QUEBODEAUX, Bryce, Chief Executive Officer, Abrom Kaplan Memorial Hospital, Kaplan, LA, p. A280

QUEEN, Sharon H., R.N. Chief Nursing Officer, Clearview Regional Medical Center, Monroe, GA, p. A164

QUENAN, James, M.D. Chief Medical Officer, Amery Regional Medical Center, Amery, WI, p. A701

QUESNEL, Brenda, R.N. Vice President of Patient Care and Chief Nursing Officer, West Calcasieu Cameron Hospital, Sulphur, LA, p. A289

QUESNEL, Heather Iorio, Director of Nursing, Waldo County General Hospital, Belfast, ME, p. A292

QUICHOCHO, Vince, Manager Information Systems, Guam Memorial Hospital Authority, Tamuning, GU, p. A724

QUIGLEY, Scott, Director Information Services, Grays Harbor Community Hospital, Aberdeen, WA, p. A681

QUIGLEY, Stephen J., Chief Executive Officer, Southwood Psychiatric Hospital, Pittsburgh, PA, p. A551

QUILLEN, Suzanne, R.N., Chief Executive Officer, Advanced Care Hospital of Southern New Mexico, Las Cruces, NM, p. A428

QUILLIN, Gayla, Administrator, Parmer Medical Center, Friona, TX, p. A620

QUIN, Robert, Vice President Finance and Chief Financial Officer, UnityPoint Health – Methodist, Peoria, IL, p. A200

QUINLAN, Christine, MS Chief Nursing Officer, Alexian Brothers Behavioral Health Hospital, Hoffman Estates, IL, p. A193

QUINLAN, Patrick J., M.D. Chief Executive Officer, Ochsner Medical Center, New Orleans, LA, p. A286

QUINLIVAN, John, Chief Executive Officer, Redmond Regional Medical Center, Rome, GA, p. A165

QUINLIVAN, Kathy, Director Management Information Systems, Avera Sacred Heart Hospital, Yankton, SD, p. A578

QUINN, Brian, D.O. Chief Medical Officer, Ottumwa Regional Health Center, Ottumwa, IA, p. A236

QUINN, Clifton, Chief Executive Officer, Regency Hospital of Meridian, Meridian, MS, p. A362

QUINN, David, M.D. Chief of Staff, Arkansas Methodist Medical Center, Paragould, AR, p. A51

QUINN, Donna, Vice President Operations and Quality, Driscoll Children's Hospital, Corpus Christi, TX, p. A608

QUINN, Edward M., Interim Chief Financial Officer, J. C. Blair Memorial Hospital, Huntingdon, PA, p. A541

QUINN, Jennifer, Quality and Safety Coordinator, Shawano Medical Center, Shawano, WI, p. A715

QUINN, John A.
Chief Executive Officer, Spalding Regional Medical Center, Griffin, GA, p. A160
Chief Executive Officer, Sylvan Grove Hospital, Jackson, GA, p. A161

QUINN, Judith, Vice President Patient Care Services, Cape Cod Hospital, Hyannis, MA, p. A311

QUINN, Mary Anna, Vice President, St. Jude Children's Research Hospital, Memphis, TN, p. A589

QUINN, Paul, Information Systems Manager, Kern Valley Healthcare District, Lake Isabella, CA, p. A69

QUINONES, Kathleen
Interim Vice President Finance, Berkeley Medical Center, Martinsburg, WV, p. A697
Interim Vice President Finance, Jefferson Medical Center, Ranson, WV, p. A699

QUINONES, Yolanda, Director Finance, I. Gonzalez Martinez Oncologic Hospital,, PR, p. A728

QUINONEZ, Yolanda, Chief Financial Officer, Hospital de la Universidad de Puerto Rico/Dr. Federico Trilla, Carolina, PR, p. A725

QUINT–BOUZID, Marjorie, Chief Nursing Officer and Vice President Patient Care Services, Fort Washington Medical Center, Fort Washington, MD, p. A301

QUINTANA, Francisco, Warden, Federal Medical Center, Lexington, KY, p. A264

QUINTANA, Jay, Vice President Operations, Cornerstone Hospital–West Monroe, West Monroe, LA, p. A290

QUINTANA, Sonya, R.N. Chief Nursing Officer, Osceola Regional Medical Center, Kissimmee, FL, p. A133

QUINTO, Mike, Chief Information Officer, Watauga Medical Center, Boone, NC, p. A460

QUINTON, Byron, Chief Executive Officer, Clarion Hospital, Clarion, PA, p. A535

QUINTON, J. Ben, Administrator, William Newton Hospital, Winfield, KS, p. A257

QUINTYNE, Stephen, Chief Executive Officer, The Vines, Ocala, FL, p. A140

QUIRICONI, Stephan F.
Vice President Finance, Bon Secours Memorial Regional Medical Center, Mechanicsville, VA, p. A674
Chief Financial Officer, Bon Secours St. Mary's Hospital, Richmond, VA, p. A677

QUIRIN, Julie L., FACHE, Chief Executive Officer, Saint Luke's Hospital of Kansas City, Kansas City, MO, p. A374

QUIRK, James, M.D. Chief Medical Officer, Radius Specialty Hospital Boston, Boston, MA, p. A307

QUIRKE, David, Vice President Information Services, Frederick Memorial Hospital, Frederick, MD, p. A301

QUIST, Robert, Chief Executive Officer, Mt. San Rafael Hospital, Trinidad, CO, p. A111

QUIST, Ryan, Administrative Assistant, Orchard Hospital, Gridley, CA, p. A66

QUITO, Arturo L., M.D. Chief of Staff, Erlanger Bledsoe Hospital, Pikeville, TN, p. A592

R

RAAB, Daniel J., President and Chief Executive Officer, Taylorville Memorial Hospital, Taylorville, IL, p. A204

RAAB, Matt, Site Executive, McLaren Northern Michigan, Petoskey, MI, p. A332

RAAUM, Elizabeth, Manger Business Office, Roosevelt Medical Center, Culbertson, MT, p. A386

RAB, Shafiq, Chief Information Officer, Orange Regional Medical Center, Middletown, NY, p. A441

RABAGO, Janie, Chief Accountant, San Antonio State Hospital, San Antonio, TX, p. A647

RABBIT, Kera, Assistant Administrator, Finance, UW Medicine/Harborview Medical Center, Seattle, WA, p. A689

RABIDEAU, Ray, M.D. Senior Vice President and Chief Medical Officer, Memorial Hospital, North Conway, NH, p. A412

RABIN, Barry, M.D. Medical Director, Linden Oaks Hospital at Edward, Naperville, IL, p. A197

RABINE, Traci, Vice President Clinic Operations, Prairie Lakes Healthcare System, Watertown, SD, p. A578

RABINOWITZ, Abraham, Assistant Finance Officer, William S. Middleton Memorial Veterans Hospital, Madison, WI, p. A708

RABNER, Barry S., President and Chief Executive Officer, University Medical Center of Princeton at Plainsboro, Plainsboro, NJ, p. A421

RABOIN, Kirk, Chief Administrative Officer, PeaceHealth St. John Medical Center, Longview, WA, p. A685

RABON, Catherine, M.D. Chief Medical Officer, Clarendon Memorial Hospital, Manning, SC, p. A568

RABORN, Janelle, Chief Operating Officer, Lovelace Women's Hospital, Albuquerque, NM, p. A426

RACHAL, I. M., Chief Fiscal Service, South Texas Veterans Health Care System, San Antonio, TX, p. A647

RACHUIG, Sue, Director Information Services, Tulane Medical Center, New Orleans, LA, p. A286

RACKLIFFE, David, Assistant Vice President Information Services, Bristol Hospital, Bristol, CT, p. A113

RACKOVAN, Patricia G., Senior Vice President & Chief Nurse Executive, JFK Medical Center, Edison, NJ, p. A415

RACZEK, James, M.D. Sr. Vice President of Operations and Chief Medical Officer, Eastern Maine Medical Center, Bangor, ME, p. A291

RADANDT, Jeremiah, Chief Financial Officer, Primary Children's Medical Center, Salt Lake City, UT, p. A663

RADBILL, Brian, M.D. Chief Medical Officer, Mount Sinai Queens,, NY, p. A446

RADCLIFF, Joey, Chief Financial Officer, Five Rivers Medical Center, Pocahontas, AR, p. A52

RADCLIFFE, Eric, M.D. Medical Director, United Hospital Center, Bridgeport, WV, p. A693

RADCLIFFE, Kerry, JD Chief Nursing Officer, Central Texas Rehabilitation Hospital, Austin, TX, p. A599

RADEMACHER, Frank
Senior Director Information Systems, St. Joseph Mercy Hospital Ann Arbor, Ypsilanti, MI, p. A338
Director, Information Systems, St. Joseph Mercy Livingston Hospital, Howell, MI, p. A327

RADENHEIMER, Tony, Network Administrator, River Park Hospital, Huntington, WV, p. A696

RADER, Herbert, M.D. Vice President and Medical Director, New York Community Hospital,, NY, p. A447

RADER, Mark, FACHE, Chief Executive Officer, Northwest Medical Center, Margate, FL, p. A135

RADER, Michael E., M.D. Vice President and Medical Director, Nyack Hospital, Nyack, NY, p. A450

RADFORD, Jeffrey, Chief Nursing Officer, Select Specialty Hospital–Tri Cities, Bristol, TN, p. A579

RADFORD, Juanita, Coordinator Team Resource, South Florida Baptist Hospital, Plant City, FL, p. A143

RADKE, Erma, Director of Operations, Oakleaf Surgical Hospital, Eau Claire, WI, p. A704

RADKE, Sam, Vice President of Finance, Estes Park Medical Center, Estes Park, CO, p. A106

RADKE, Shannon, M.D. Chief Medical Staff, Newport Hospital and Health Services, Newport, WA, p. A685

RADNER, Allen, M.D. Chief Medical Officer, Salinas Valley Memorial Healthcare System, Salinas, CA, p. A88

RADOCY, Lesley, R.N. Chief Nursing Officer, Avista Adventist Hospital, Louisville, CO, p. A109

RADOTICH, Maureen, Director Human Resources, Providence Valdez Medical Center, Valdez, AK, p. A30

RADTKE, Lisa
Regional Administrator Human Resources, Mayo Clinic Health System – Franciscan Healthcare in La Crosse, La Crosse, WI, p. A707
Regional Administrator Human Resources, Mayo Clinic Health System – Franciscan Healthcare in Sparta, Sparta, WI, p. A715
Interim Chief Administrative Officer, Winneshiek Medical Center, Decorah, IA, p. A229

RADUNSKY, Daniel, M.D. Medical Staff President, Union County General Hospital, Clayton, NM, p. A427

RADZEVICH, Jason, Vice President Finance, Beth Israel Deaconess Hospital Plymouth, Plymouth, MA, p. A314

RADZIESKI, Shauna, Chief Executive Officer, Roxbury Treatment Center, Shippensburg, PA, p. A555

RAETHEL, Kathryn A., M.P.H., President and Chief Executive Officer, Castle Medical Center, Kailua, HI, p. A171

RAFALA, Paula, Director, Human Resources, Memorial Medical Center, Modesto, CA, p. A78

RAFFERTY, Joyce, Vice President Finance, Champlain Valley Physicians Hospital Medical Center, Plattsburgh, NY, p. A451

RAFFERTY, Patrick W., Executive Vice President and Chief Operating Officer, Community Regional Medical Center, Fresno, CA, p. A64

RAFFETY, Leannette, Administrative Generalist, Stroud Regional Medical Center, Stroud, OK, p. A519

RAFFOUL, John, Senior Vice President Finance, White Memorial Medical Center, Los Angeles, CA, p. A75

RAFUS, Matthew, Chief Information Officer, White River Junction Veterans Affairs Medical Center, White River Junction, VT, p. A666

RAGAIN, Michael, M.D
Chief Medical Officer, Texas Specialty Hospital at Lubbock, Lubbock, TX, p. A635
Chief Medical Officer and Senior Vice President, University Medical Center, Lubbock, TX, p. A635

RAGAR–THOMAS, Twila, Director Health Information Management and Quality Improvement, Timberlawn Mental Health System, Dallas, TX, p. A612

RAGAS, Rene, Chief Operating Officer, Our Lady of the Angels Hospital, Bogalusa, LA, p. A274

RAGEL, Larry, Chief Financial Officer, St. John's Hospital, Springfield, IL, p. A203

RAGER, Claudia, R.N. Vice President Patient Care Services, Conemaugh Memorial Medical Center, Johnstown, PA, p. A541

RAGGIO, James J., Chief Executive Officer, Lompoc Valley Medical Center, Lompoc, CA, p. A70

RAGGIO, Sharon, President and Chief Executive Officer, West Springs Hospital, Grand Junction, CO, p. A107

RAGLE, Bertha, Director Personnel, CrossRidge Community Hospital, Wynne, AR, p. A54

RAGONA, Robert A., Vice President Finance, Eastern Long Island Hospital, Greenport, NY, p. A438

RAGSDALE, Sarah, R.N. Chief Nursing Officer, Smith County Memorial Hospital, Smith Center, KS, p. A254

RAHAMAN, Sheer, M.D. Chief of Medical Staff, Limestone Medical Center, Groesbeck, TX, p. A622

RAHAMAN, Suara, M.D. Chief Medical Staff, Bolivar General Hospital, Bolivar, TN, p. A579

RAHDERT, Richard, M.D. Medical Director, River Bend Hospital, West Lafayette, IN, p. A224

RAHMAN, Syed, M.D. Chief of Staff, Horizon Specialty Hospital, Las Vegas, NV, p. A406

RAHN, Douglas L., President and Chief Executive Officer, Passavant Area Hospital, Jacksonville, IL, p. A193

RAHN, Kevin, President Medical Staff, Orthopaedic Hospital of Lutheran Health Network, Fort Wayne, IN, p. A211

RAI, Amrita, Administrator, Pacific Grove Hospital, Riverside, CA, p. A86

RAICA, Dagmar, R.N. Chief Nursing Officer, Marquette General Hospital, Marquette, MI, p. A330

RAINA, Suresh, M.D. Vice President Medical Staff and Chief Medical Officer, Palisades Medical Center, North Bergen, NJ, p. A420

RAINBOLT, Mike, Chief Financial Officer, Rivendell Behavioral Health Services of Arkansas, Benton, AR, p. A43

RAINDL, Donna, Manager Business Office, Lynn County Hospital District, Tahoka, TX, p. A651

RAINEY, Jackie, Chief Financial Officer, Little River Memorial Hospital, Ashdown, AR, p. A43

RAINEY, Mark J., Director Human Resources, Texas Health Presbyterian Hospital Kaufman, Kaufman, TX, p. A630

RAINS, Celeste, D.O. Chief of Staff, Logan County Hospital, Oakley, KS, p. A251

RAINS, Debbie, Coordinator Health Information Management, Erlanger Bledsoe Hospital, Pikeville, TN, p. A592

RAINS, Gail, R.N. Director Patient Care Services, Shriners Hospitals for Children–Shreveport, Shreveport, LA, p. A288

RAINS, Jeff G., Chief Executive Officer, Baptist Medical Center East, Montgomery, AL, p. A23

RAINS, Jon Michael
Chief Executive Officer, Carrus Rehabilitation Hospital, Sherman, TX, p. A649
Chief Executive Officer, Carrus Specialty Hospital, Sherman, TX, p. A649

RAINS, Paul, MSN, President, St. Joseph's Behavioral Health Center, Stockton, CA, p. A96

RAINS, Steve, Director Information Services, McKee Medical Center, Loveland, CO, p. A109

RAISNER, Gary, Chief Operating Officer, Norristown State Hospital, Norristown, PA, p. A546

RAJATATNAM, Richard, M.D. Area Medical Director, Kaiser Permanente Riverside Medical Center, Riverside, CA, p. A86

RAJPARA, Suresh, M.D. Chief Medical Officer, Jerome Golden Center for Behavioral Health, Inc., West Palm Beach, FL, p. A150

RAJU, Ramanathan, M.D., President, New York City Health and Hospitals Corporation, New York, NY, p. B98

RAK, Roger, Director Human Resources, South Shore Hospital, Chicago, IL, p. A186

RAK, Ronald C., JD, Chief Executive Officer, Saint Peter's University Hospital, New Brunswick, NJ, p. A419

RAKES, Lori, Chief Operating Officer, Cartersville Medical Center, Cartersville, GA, p. A155

RAKES–STEPHENS, Kim, M.D. Chief Medical Staff, Colleton Medical Center, Walterboro, SC, p. A570

RAKOV, Robert, M.D. Chief Medical Officer, Cogdell Memorial Hospital, Snyder, TX, p. A649

RALPH, Chandler M., President and Chief Executive Officer, Adirondack Medical Center, Saranac Lake, NY, p. A454

RALPH, Stephen A., President and Chief Executive Officer, Huntington Memorial Hospital, Pasadena, CA, p. A83

RALSTIN, Char, Director of Nursing, Haven Senior Horizons, Phoenix, AZ, p. A35

RALSTON, Mary Beth, Human Resources Director, North Georgia Medical Center, Ellijay, GA, p. A159

RAMAGE, Debra, Director Human Resources and Payroll, Cornerstone Hospital of SouthEast Arizona, Tucson, AZ, p. A40

RAMAGE, Gary, M.D. Chief Medical Officer, McKenzie County Healthcare System, Watford City, ND, p. A480

RAMAN, Jayashree, Vice President and Chief Information Officer, Reading Hospital and Medical Center, West Reading, PA, p. A558

RAMAN, Reggie, M.D. Medical Director, Peninsula Hospital, Louisville, TN, p. A587

RAMAZANI, Regina, Chief Financial Officer, Garden Park Medical Center, Gulfport, MS, p. A358

RAMER, Gary, Manager Information Management, Jonathan M. Wainwright Memorial Veterans Affairs Medical Center, Walla Walla, WA, p. A692

RAMEY, Rita, Director Information Systems, Buchanan General Hospital, Grundy, VA, p. A671

RAMEY, Robert L., Chief Executive Officer, Russell County Hospital, Russell Springs, KY, p. A270

RAMEY, Steve, Chief Financial Officer, Southampton Memorial Hospital, Franklin, VA, p. A671

RAMIREZ, Arthur L., M.D. Medical Director, University Behavioral Health of El Paso, El Paso, TX, p. A616

RAMIREZ, Corazon, M.D., Chief Executive Officer, Pine Creek Medical Center, Dallas, TX, p. A611

RAMIREZ, Eddy, Assistant Vice President Business Development, Ochsner Medical Center – Kenner, Kenner, LA, p. A280

RAMIREZ, Harvey, Chief Information Officer, Coleman County Medical Center, Coleman, TX, p. A606

RAMIREZ, Jaime, Chief Executive Officer, McCamey County Hospital District, McCamey, TX, p. A637

RAMIREZ, Marcos A., Human Resources Business Partner, Baylor Medical Center at Waxahachie, Waxahachie, TX, p. A656

RAMIREZ, Omar, Chief Executive Officer, Los Angeles Community Hospital at Los Angeles, Los Angeles, CA, p. A73

RAMIREZ, Willie, Manager Labor Relations, Laguna Honda Hospital and Rehabilitation Center, San Francisco, CA, p. A91

RAMLO, Ricki, Chief Operating Officer and Vice President Operations, Jamestown Regional Medical Center, Jamestown, ND, p. A478

RAMMLER, Linda, R.N. Chief Nursing Officer, Bonner General Hospital, Sandpoint, ID, p. A178

RAMOS, Eduardo, M.D. Medical Director, HEALTHSOUTH Rehabilitation Hospital of San Juan, San Juan, PR, p. A728

RAMOS, Eric, M.D. Division Chief Medical Officer, Southern Hills Hospital and Medical Center, Las Vegas, NV, p. A406

RAMOS, Gracie, Human Resource Generalist, East Morgan County Hospital, Brush, CO, p. A103

RAMOS, Holly, R.N. Chief Clinical Officer, Kindred Hospital–Ontario, Ontario, CA, p. A81

RAMOS, Jessie, Manager Human Resources, Skyline Hospital, White Salmon, WA, p. A692

RAMOS, Jet, Head Staff Administration, Naval Hospital Camp Pendleton, Camp Pendleton, CA, p. A59

RAMPAT, Ananda, Chief Financial Officer, Northwest Medical Center, Margate, FL, p. A135

RAMPP, Randal D., M.D. Chief Medical Officer, River Park Hospital, Mc Minnville, TN, p. A588

RAMSAY, Kathy, R.N. Director Communications and Development, Rooks County Health Center, Plainville, KS, p. A253

RAMSEY, Alice, M.D. Chief of Staff, Palo Pinto General Hospital, Mineral Wells, TX, p. A638

RAMSEY, Beryl O., FACHE, Chief Executive Officer, Houston Methodist Willowbrook Hospital, Houston, TX, p. A624

RAMSEY, David L., President and Chief Executive Officer, Charleston Area Medical Center, Charleston, WV, p. A694

RAMSEY, David L., President and Chief Executive Officer, Charleston Area Medical Center Health System, Inc., Charleston, WV, p. B34

RAMSEY, Lisa, Chief Financial Officer, Prairie View, Newton, KS, p. A250

RAMSEY, Lorie N., MSN Chief Nursing Executive, Central Mississippi Medical Center, Jackson, MS, p. A360

RAMSEY, Paul G., Chief Executive Officer, UW Medicine, Seattle, WA, p. B148

RAMSEY, Roy M., Executive Director, Bradford Health Services at Warrior Lodge, Warrior, AL, p. A26

RAMSEY, Thomas, Chief Financial Officer, Hancock Medical Center, Bay Saint Louis, MS, p. A355

RAMTHUN, Jane, Chief Financial Officer, Story County Medical Center, Nevada, IA, p. A235

RAND, Kevin, M.D. Clinical Director, Chinle Comprehensive Health Care Facility, Chinle, AZ, p. A31

RANDALL, Bryan J.
Vice President Finance and Chief Financial Officer, Heritage Valley Health System, Beaver, PA, p. A533
Vice President Finance and Chief Financial Officer, Sewickley Valley Hospital, (A Division of Valley Medical Facilities), Sewickley, PA, p. A555

RANDALL, Cherry, Business Officer, Greater Binghamton Health Center, Binghamton, NY, p. A433

RANDALL, Kenneth W., Chief Executive Officer, Artesia General Hospital, Artesia, NM, p. A427

RANDLE, Emily, Vice President Operations, Orange Coast Memorial Medical Center, Fountain Valley, CA, p. A63

RANDOLPH, Arianne, Director Human Resources, Pikes Peak Regional Hospital, Woodland Park, CO, p. A112

RANDOLPH, Bonnie, M.D. Chief of Staff, Community Hospital, Torrington, WY, p. A723

RANDOLPH, Bruce, Chief Information Technology, Arizona State Hospital, Phoenix, AZ, p. A35

RANDOLPH, Daylashunta
Vice President Human Resources, Advocate South Suburban Hospital, Hazel Crest, IL, p. A192
Senior Vice President Human Resources, Advocate Trinity Hospital, Chicago, IL, p. A183

RANDOLPH, Geoffrey, M.D. Chief Medical Officer, Lutheran Hospital of Indiana, Fort Wayne, IN, p. A211

RANDOLPH, Joseph, M.D. Chairman Medical Executive Committee, Indiana Orthopaedic Hospital, Indianapolis, IN, p. A214

RANDOLPH, Karsten, Executive Vice President and Chief Financial Officer, Shawnee Mission Medical Center, Shawnee Mission, KS, p. A254

RANDOLPH, Jr., Leonard M., M.D. Senior Vice President and Chief Medical Officer, Mercy Health – Anderson Hospital, Cincinnati, OH, p. A487

RANDOLPH, Linda, Director Personnel Services, Washington County Hospital and Nursing Home, Chatom, AL, p. A18

RANEY, Hollie, Director of Nursing, Dallas County Medical Center, Fordyce, AR, p. A46

RANGAVIZ, Rassoul, Chief Financial Officer, Copley Hospital, Morrisville, VT, p. A665

RANGE, Bonny, MSN Chief Nursing Officer, Holy Family Memorial, Manitowoc, WI, p. A708

RANGHELLI, Gloria, Deputy Chief Financial Officer, Henry J. Carter Specialty Hospital and Nursing Facility, New York, NY, p. A444

RANKIN, Beverley A., R.N. Vice President & Chief Nursing Officer, Alice Peck Day Memorial Hospital, Lebanon, NH, p. A410

RANKIN, Cynthia, Chief Nursing Officer, Lovelace Rehabilitation Hospital, Albuquerque, NM, p. A426

RANKIN III, Fred M.
President and Chief Executive Officer, Mary Washington Hospital, Fredericksburg, VA, p. A671
President and Chief Executive Officer, Stafford Hospital, Stafford, VA, p. A679

RANKIN III,, Fred M., President and Chief Executive Officer, Mary Washington Healthcare, Fredericksburg, VA, p. B88

RANKIN, Kim, Chief Nursing Officer, Geisinger HEALTHSOUTH Rehabilitation Hospital, Danville, PA, p. A536

RANNEY, Timothy, M.D. Chief Medical Officer, Banner Estrella Medical Center, Phoenix, AZ, p. A35

RANSOM, Jim, Chief Executive Officer, Reliant Rehabilitation Hospital North Texas, Richardson, TX, p. A644

RANSOM, Natalie, Chief Nursing Officer, MountainView Hospital, Las Vegas, NV, p. A406

RANTZ III,, August J., Founder and Chief Executive Officer, AMG Integrated Healthcare Management, Lafayette, LA, p. B10

RAO, Gutti, M.D. Medical Director, AMG Specialty Hospital–Greenwood, Greenwood, MS, p. A358

RAO, Kalapala, M.D. Medical Director, HEALTHSOUTH Western Hills Rehabilitation Hospital, Parkersburg, WV, p. A698

RAO, Noel, M.D. Medical Director, Marianjoy Rehabilitation Hospital, Wheaton, IL, p. A205

RAO, Raghu, M.D. Chief of Staff, Helen Newberry Joy Hospital, Newberry, MI, p. A331

RAPAPORT, Gary D., Chief Executive Officer, Sutter Delta Medical Center, Antioch, CA, p. A56

RAPENSKE, Jennifer, Manager Financial Services, Mercy Medical Center–New Hampton, New Hampton, IA, p. A235

RAPP, Catherine, R.N. Vice President Nursing, Oconomowoc Memorial Hospital, Oconomowoc, WI, p. A712

RAPP, David, Chief Information Officer, Wheeling Hospital, Wheeling, WV, p. A700

RAPP, Peter F., Vice President and Executive Director, OHSU Hospital, Portland, OR, p. A528

RAPP, Robin, R.N., Chief Executive Officer, Kindred Hospital–Ontario, Ontario, CA, p. A81

RAPP, Ron, Controller, Cole Memorial, Coudersport, PA, p. A536

RAPPACH, Shannon, Chief Fiscal Services, Dayton Veterans Affairs Medical Center, Dayton, OH, p. A492

RASCHKE, Judy, Director Human Resources, Pipestone County Medical Center Avera, Pipestone, MN, p. A349

RASHID, Harun, Chief Information Officer, Magee–Womens Hospital of UPMC, Pittsburgh, PA, p. A551

RASK, Brenda, Vice President Operations, Carrington Health Center, Carrington, ND, p. A476

RASKE, Jamie, Information Technology Lead, Avera St. Mary's Hospital, Pierre, SD, p. A575

RASMUSSEN, Diane, Director Human Resources, Cambridge Medical Center, Cambridge, MN, p. A341

RASMUSSEN, Jeanell, R.N. Senior Vice President and Chief Nursing Officer, Harrison Medical Center, Bremerton, WA, p. A681

RASMUSSEN, Kyle R., Chief Executive Officer, Meeker Memorial Hospital, Litchfield, MN, p. A345

RASMUSSEN, Renee, Senior Vice President and Chief Financial Officer, UnityPoint Health – Allen Hospital, Waterloo, IA, p. A239

RASMUSSEN, Rick, Chief Financial Officer, Northwest Specialty Hospital, Post Falls, ID, p. A178

RASMUSSEN, Scott, Director Human Resources, Lincoln Regional Center, Lincoln, NE, p. A397

RASMUSSEN, Steven, M.D. Medical Director, Butler Hospital, Providence, RI, p. A560

RASMUSSON, Duane, Vice President Human Resources, St. Cloud Hospital, Saint Cloud, MN, p. A350

RASOOL, Chaudri, D.O. Chief of Staff, Palmer Lutheran Health Center, West Union, IA, p. A239

RASOR, Linda, R.N., Chief Executive Officer, Plains Memorial Hospital, Dimmitt, TX, p. A614

RASSIER, Mark, M.D. President Howard Young Medical Center Staff, Howard Young Medical Center, Woodruff, WI, p. A719

RASTER, Robert, M.D. Medical Director, Michiana Behavioral Health Center, Plymouth, IN, p. A221

RATAJ, Marianne, R.N. Chief of Nursing Officer, Mercy Hospital Fort Smith, Fort Smith, AR, p. A46

RATCLIFF, David, M.D. Chief Medical Affairs, Washington Regional Medical Center, Fayetteville, AR, p. A46

RATCLIFF, Paul, Director Information Services, Baylor Medical Center at Carrollton, Carrollton, TX, p. A605

RATCLIFFE, Alma, M.D. Executive Vice President Medical Staff and Business Development, Saint Clare's Health System, Denville, NJ, p. A415

RATCLIFFE, Denise, Executive Vice President and Chief Operating Officer, Christian Health Care Center, Wyckoff, NJ, p. A425

RATHBUN, Lori, Chief Executive Officer, Van Diest Medical Center, Webster City, IA, p. A239

RATLIFF, Ada, Chief Information Officer, Claiborne County Medical Center, Port Gibson, MS, p. A364

RATLIFF, Kim, Director Health Information Management, Southwestern Virginia Mental Health Institute, Marion, VA, p. A674

RATLIFF, Maggie, Vice President Information Systems, Sarah Bush Lincoln Health Center, Mattoon, IL, p. A195

RATLIFF, Steve, Director Information Technology, Guadalupe Regional Medical Center, Seguin, TX, p. A648

RATLIFFE, Kathy, Chief Human Resources Officer, Tuality Healthcare, Hillsboro, OR, p. A525

RATNER, Jeffrey, M.D. Senior Vice President Medical Affairs, Mount Nittany Medical Center, State College, PA, p. A555

RATTRAY, Cindy Stewart, Director Human Resources, Jewish Hospital–Shelbyville, Shelbyville, KY, p. A270

RAU, John, President and Chief Executive Officer, Stevens Community Medical Center, Morris, MN, p. A348

RAU, Robin, Chief Executive Officer, Miller County Hospital, Colquitt, GA, p. A156

RAUCH, Scott C., Vice President Human Resources, Reid Hospital and Health Care Services, Richmond, IN, p. A221

RAUCH, Scott L., M.D., President, McLean Hospital, Belmont, MA, p. A305

RAUH, Cindy, R.N. Vice President and Chief Nursing Officer, Duncan Regional Hospital, Duncan, OK, p. A509

RAUNER, Mary Ellen, R.N. Chief Nursing Officer, Mercy Suburban Hospital, Norristown, PA, p. A546

RAUPERS, Debra, MSN Chief Nursing Officer, Corning Hospital, Corning, NY, p. A436

RAVELING, Lynn, Chief Financial Officer, Pocahontas Community Hospital, Pocahontas, IA, p. A236

RAVLIN, Suzanne M., Director Human Resources, Katherine Shaw Bethea Hospital, Dixon, IL, p. A188

RAWLINGS, Linda, Director Human Resources and Personnel, Three Rivers Hospital, Waverly, TN, p. A594

RAWLINGS, Sheri, Chief Information Officer, San Juan Regional Medical Center, Farmington, NM, p. A428

RAWSON, Richard L., Chief Executive Officer, Loma Linda University Medical Center–Murrieta, Murrieta, CA, p. A79

RAY, Beverly, Director Human Resources, Dyersburg Regional Medical Center, Dyersburg, TN, p. A582

RAY, Brenda, Director Human Resources, Huntsville Memorial Hospital, Huntsville, TX, p. A629

RAY, Denise, President and Chief Executive Officer, Piedmont Mountainside Hospital, Jasper, GA, p. A161

RAY, Donald, Vice President of Operations, University of Maryland Medical Center Midtown Campus, Baltimore, MD, p. A298

RAY, Dwayne, Chief Financial Officer, Medical Center of McKinney, McKinney, TX, p. A637

RAY, Elaine, Administrator, Choate Mental Health Center, Anna, IL, p. A180

RAY, Evan
President, St. Vincent's Blount, Oneonta, AL, p. A24
President, St. Vincent's St. Clair, Pell City, AL, p. A24

RAY, Jerilyn, Manager Human Resources, St. Elizabeth Hospital, Enumclaw, WA, p. A683

RAY, Joel, MSN Vice President and Chief Nursing Officer, Rex Healthcare, Raleigh, NC, p. A471

RAY, Lisa, R.N. Vice President Patient Care Services, Murray–Calloway County Hospital, Murray, KY, p. A268

RAY, Marilyn, MSN Chief Nursing Officer, Upson Regional Medical Center, Thomaston, GA, p. A168

RAY, Nancy L., R.N. Executive Vice President, Chief Nursing Executive, University Health System, San Antonio, TX, p. A648

RAY, Rachel, Chief Financial Officer, Unity Medical Center, Grafton, ND, p. A478

RAY, Roger A., M.D. Executive Vice President and Chief Medical Officer, Carolinas Medical Center, Charlotte, NC, p. A461

RAYE, Charles, M.D. Chief Medical Officer, St. Mary–Corwin Medical Center, Pueblo, CO, p. A110

RAYL, Cheryl, Chief Executive Officer, Behavioral Health Center of the Permian Basin, Midland, TX, p. A638

RAYMER, Chris, R.N
Chief Operating Officer and Chief Nursing Officer, Great River Medical Center, Blytheville, AR, p. A43
Chief Operating Officer and Chief Nursing Officer, South Mississippi County Regional Medical Center, Osceola, AR, p. A51

RAYMOND, Jane, Vice President and Chief Operating Officer, Reston Hospital Center, Reston, VA, p. A677

RAYMOND, Mindy, Vice President Human Resources, Boca Raton Regional Hospital, Boca Raton, FL, p. A124

RAYMOND, Scott, Director Information Systems, Orange Coast Memorial Medical Center, Fountain Valley, CA, p. A63

RAYNER, Evan J., Chief Executive Officer, Madera Community Hospital, Madera, CA, p. A76

RAYNER, Thomas J., Senior Vice President and Chief Operating Officer, Kaweah Delta Medical Center, Visalia, CA, p. A99

RAYNES, Anthony, M.D. Psychiatrist in Chief, Arbour H. R. I. Hospital, Brookline, MA, p. A308

RAYNES, Christy, R.N. Director Clinical Services, Carson Valley Medical Center, Gardnerville, NV, p. A404

RAYNES, Scott
Interim Administrator, Baptist Hospital, Pensacola, FL, p. A142
Senior Vice President, Gulf Breeze Market Segment, Gulf Breeze Hospital, Gulf Breeze, FL, p. A130

RAYNOR, Robert, Human Resources Director, Park Royal Hospital, Fort Myers, FL, p. A129

RAYUDU, Subbu, M.D. Chief of Staff, Alliance HealthCare System, Holly Springs, MS, p. A359

RAZMIC, Tammy, Associate Administrator Finance and Chief Financial Officer, Inova Mount Vernon Hospital, Alexandria, VA, p. A668

RAZO, Virginia, Chief Operating Officer, Incline Village Community Hospital, Incline Village, NV, p. A405

REA, Jerry A., Ph.D.,
Superintendent, Osawatomie State Hospital, Osawatomie, KS, p. A251
Superintendent, Parsons State Hospital and Training Center, Parsons, KS, p. A252
Interim Superintendent, Rainbow Mental Health Facility, Kansas City, KS, p. A247

READ, John, Chief Nursing Officer, Allegiance Specialty Hospital of Greenville, Greenville, MS, p. A358

READ, Paul, R.N. Vice President and Chief Nursing Officer, Springhill Memorial Hospital, Mobile, AL, p. A23

READ, Richard
Chief Financial Officer, Central Florida Regional Hospital, Sanford, FL, p. A145
Chief Financial Officer, Regional Hospital of Jackson, Jackson, TN, p. A584

READER, G. Whitney, M.D. Chief Medical Officer, Kansas Medical Center, Andover, KS, p. A241

REAGAN Jr., James H., Ph.D., Chief Executive Officer, Morris County Hospital, Council Grove, KS, p. A243

REAGAN, Kevin, M.D. Chief Medical Officer, CHI Health Bergan Mercy, Omaha, NE, p. A399

REALE, Kelli, Vice President Human Resources, UPMC McKeesport, McKeesport, PA, p. A544

REAM, Tom, Regional Chief Information Officer, Sutter Auburn Faith Hospital, Auburn, CA, p. A56

REAMER, Roger J., Chief Executive Officer, Memorial Health Care Systems, Seward, NE, p. A402

REAMES, Jim, Director Human Resources, Bayfront Health St. Petersburg, Saint Petersburg, FL, p. A144

REANDEAU, Michael
Chief Information Officer, Mills–Peninsula Health Services, Burlingame, CA, p. A58
Regional Chief Information Officer, Sutter Maternity and Surgery Center of Santa Cruz, Santa Cruz, CA, p. A94

REANO, Paul
Chief Executive Officer, Atoka County Medical Center, Atoka, OK, p. A508
Chief Executive Officer, Pushmataha Hospital & Home Health, Antlers, OK, p. A507

REARDON, Jerry, Director Information Systems, Catawba Valley Medical Center, Hickory, NC, p. A466

REASER, Michelle, R.N. Chief Nursing Executive, Lancaster Regional Medical Center, Lancaster, PA, p. A542

REASONER, Vanessa, Chief Executive Officer, Grace Medical Center, Lubbock, TX, p. A634

REAVIS, Mack, M.D., President and Chief Medical Officer, Lakeland Regional Medical Center, Lakeland, FL, p. A134

REBERRY, Darinda, Chief Nursing Officer, Western Missouri Medical Center, Warrensburg, MO, p. A384

REBLOCK, Kimberly, M.D. Chief Operating Officer, The Children's Home of Pittsburgh, Pittsburgh, PA, p. A551

RECA, Sr., Thomas, Senior Vice President Finance and Chief Financial Officer, Staten Island University Hospital,, NY, p. A448

RECH, Eunice A., MSN Chief Clinical Officer and Administrator of Quality Services, Tuality Healthcare, Hillsboro, OR, p. A525

RECHSTEINER, Hans, M.D. Chief of Staff, Burnett Medical Center, Grantsburg, WI, p. A705

RECKDENWALD, Jeanine, Vice President Human Resources and Support Services, Bristol Hospital, Bristol, CT, p. A113

RECKERT, Sandy, Director Communications and Public Affairs, Johns Hopkins Bayview Medical Center, Baltimore, MD, p. A296

RECTOR, III, Fax, Director Information Technology, Sunbury Community Hospital and Outpatient Center, Sunbury, PA, p. A555

RECTOR, Jeanne, Chief Nursing Officer, Carroll County Memorial Hospital, Carrollton, MO, p. A369

RECUPERO, David, Chief Financial Officer, San Gorgonio Memorial Hospital, Banning, CA, p. A57

RED THUNDER, Charlene, Chief Executive Officer, U. S. Public Health Service Indian Hospital, Eagle Butte, SD, p. A573

REDD, Dakota, R.N. Chief Clinical Officer, Kindred Hospital–St. Louis, Saint Louis, MO, p. A380

REDDEN, Robert, Site Director Information Technology, Community Hospital of San Bernardino, San Bernardino, CA, p. A88

REDDICK, Shawn, Director Information Management, Flint River Community Hospital, Montezuma, GA, p. A164

REDDING, Georgia, Director Human Resources, Forbes Regional Hospital, Monroeville, PA, p. A545

REDDING, Lisa, Manager Human Resources, Morgan County ARH Hospital, West Liberty, KY, p. A271

REDDY, Lex, President and Chief Executive Officer, St. Rose Hospital, Hayward, KY, p. A66

REDDY, Prem, M.D., Interim President and Chief Executive Officer, Prime Healthcare Services, Ontario, CA, p. B108

REDDY, Sunil, Chief Executive Officer, Care Regional Medical Center, Aransas Pass, TX, p. A597

REDFIELD, Gregg, Director Finance, CentraCare Health–Paynesville, Paynesville, MN, p. A349

REDHORSE–CHARLEY, Gloria, Director Human Resources, Northern Navajo Medical Center, Shiprock, NM, p. A431

REDING, Janeen K., Director Human Resources, St. Anthony Hospital, Pendleton, OR, p. A527

REDINGTON, James, M.D. Chief of Staff, Bath Community Hospital, Hot Springs, VA, p. A672

REDMAN, Sharon, Director Patient Care Services, Espanola Hospital, Espanola, NM, p. A428

REDMON, Gary, Chief Financial Officer, South Texas Regional Medical Center, Jourdanton, TX, p. A630

REDMOND, Michael, Senior Vice President and Chief Operating Officer, Crotched Mountain Rehabilitation Center, Greenfield, NH, p. A410

REDMOND, Paula, Controller, HEALTHSOUTH Tustin Rehabilitation Hospital, Tustin, CA, p. A98

REECE, Jeff, MSN,
Chief Executive Officer, Chesterfield General Hospital, Cheraw, SC, p. A563
Chief Executive Officer, Marlboro Park Hospital, Bennettsville, SC, p. A562

REECE, Morris A.
EVP/COO, Laird Hospital, Union, MS, p. A366
President and Chief Executive Officer, Rush Foundation Hospital, Meridian, MS, p. A362
President and Chief Operating Officer, Rush Foundation Hospital, Meridian, MS, p. A362

REECER, Jeff, President, Texas Health Presbyterian Hospital Allen, Allen, TX, p. A596

REED, Cindy, Director Community Relations, Austin State Hospital, Austin, TX, p. A599

REED, Dianne, Director Information Systems, Higgins General Hospital, Bremen, GA, p. A154

REED, Fred, M.D. Chief of Staff, Lincoln Hospital, Davenport, WA, p. A683

REED, Gloria, Leader Human Resources, SSM DePaul Health Center, Bridgeton, MO, p. A368

REED, Helen, Director Health Information, North Mississippi Medical Center–Eupora, Eupora, MS, p. A357

REED, Jan A., CPA, Administrator and Chief Executive Officer, Electra Memorial Hospital, Electra, TX, p. A617

REED, Jason, President and Chief Executive Officer, Oceans Healthcare, Lake Charles, LA, p. B102

REED, John E., M.D. Medical Director, Baptist Memorial Hospital–Golden Triangle, Columbus, MS, p. A357

REED, Karen, R.N
Chief Nursing Officer, St. Charles Medical Center – Bend, Bend, OR, p. A523
Chief Nursing Officer, St. Charles Medical Center – Redmond, Redmond, OR, p. A529

REED, Kathleen, Manager Human Resources, Missouri Baptist Sullivan Hospital, Sullivan, MO, p. A383

REED, Kirby, Director Information Systems, Jasper County Hospital, Rensselaer, IN, p. A221

REED, Laura, Chief Nursing Officer, University of Minnesota Medical Center, Fairview, Minneapolis, MN, p. A348

REED, Leslie, Chief Financial Officer, Wright Memorial Hospital, Trenton, MO, p. A384

REED, Lester, M.D. Vice President Medical Affairs and Acute Care, MultiCare Mary Bridge Children's Hospital and Health Center, Tacoma, WA, p. A691

REED, Linda
Vice President and Chief Information Officer, Morristown Medical Center, Morristown, NJ, p. A418
Vice President Information Systems and Chief Information Officer, Newton Medical Center, Newton, NJ, p. A420
Vice President and Chief Information Officer, Overlook Medical Center, Summit, NJ, p. A423

REED, Margaret M., R.N. Chief Nursing Executive, Altru Health System, Grand Forks, ND, p. A478

REED, Renee
Director Human Resources, Mercy Regional Health Center,, KS, p. A249
Director Human Resources, Wamego Health Center, Wamego, KS, p. A256

REED, Ronald R., President and Chief Executive Officer, Mercy Iowa City, Iowa City, IA, p. A232

REED, Tim, Vice President and Chief Financial Officer, Yakima Valley Memorial Hospital, Yakima, WA, p. A692

REED, Victoria L., FACHE, Chief Executive Officer, James B. Haggin Memorial Hospital, Harrodsburg, KY, p. A262

REEDER, Carol, R.N. Chief Nursing Officer, St. Joseph Hospital, Eureka, CA, p. A62

REEDER, Wendy, R.N. Chief Nursing Officer, Harrison Memorial Hospital, Cynthiana, KY, p. A260

REEDY, Janet, Manager Human Resources, St. Thomas More Hospital, Canon City, CO, p. A103

REEFER, John C., M.D. Director, Butler Health System, Butler, PA, p. A534

REEL, Micah, Director of Bio–Med, Potomac Valley Hospital, Keyser, WV, p. A696

REEL, Stephanie L., Senior Vice President Information Services, Johns Hopkins Hospital, Baltimore, MD, p. A296

REES, Adam, President, Essentia Health St. Joseph's Medical Center, Brainerd, MN, p. A340

REES, Elizabeth, Chief Executive Officer, AMG Specialty Hospital–Albuquerque, Albuquerque, NM, p. A426

REES, Jeff, Director Information Systems, Bacharach Institute for Rehabilitation, Pomona, NJ, p. A421

REES, Matthew, Chief Executive Officer, Mayers Memorial Hospital District, Fall River Mills, CA, p. A63

REESE, Bert
Chief Information Officer, Sentara Leigh Hospital, Norfolk, VA, p. A675
Chief Information Officer, Sentara Norfolk General Hospital, Norfolk, VA, p. A675
Chief Information Officer, Sentara Princess Anne Hospital, Virginia Beach, VA, p. A679

REESE, Kathie, Administrator, Dubuis Hospital of Paris, Paris, TX, p. A641

REESE, Maryann, FACHE, President and Chief Executive Officer, St. Elizabeth's Hospital, Belleville, IL, p. A181

REESE, Mike, Chief Financial Officer, OU Medical Center, Oklahoma City, OK, p. A516

REESE, Sandra, Administrator, Lower Umpqua Hospital District, Reedsport, OR, p. A529

REESE, Todd, Director Human Resources, Castle Medical Center, Kailua, HI, p. A171

REESE, Willis L., Administrator, Falls Community Hospital and Clinic, Marlin, TX, p. A636

REETZ, Brenda, R.N., Chief Executive Officer, Greene County General Hospital, Linton, IN, p. A217

REETZ, Renee, Director Human Resources, St. Mary's of Michigan Standish Hospital, Standish, MI, p. A335

REEVE, Jay A., President and Chief Executive Officer, Eastside Psychiatric Hospital, Tallahassee, FL, p. A146

REEVES, Amy D., Director Human Resources, Cedar Park Regional Medical Center, Cedar Park, TX, p. A605

REEVES, Cory, Chief Financial Officer, Gordon Hospital, Calhoun, GA, p. A155

REEVES, Katy, Vice President Human Resources, Fauquier Hospital, Warrenton, VA, p. A680

REEVES, Kaylene, Director, Tahoe Pacific Hospitals, Reno, NV, p. A408

REEVES, Mary, Controller, Rehabilitation Hospital of Wisconsin, Waukesha, WI, p. A717

REEVES, Mike
Vice President, St. John Medical Center, Tulsa, OK, p. A521
Chief Information Officer, St. John Owasso, Owasso, OK, p. A517

REEVES, Pamela J., M.D., Director, John D. Dingell Veterans Affairs Medical Center, Detroit, MI, p. A322

REEVES, Rachel, Manager Human Resources, Post Acute Medical Specialty Hospital of Victoria, Victoria, TX, p. A655

REEVES, Valerie
Chief Financial Officer, Integris Baptist Regional Health Center, Miami, OK, p. A513
Chief Financial Officer, Integris Grove Hospital, Grove, OK, p. A511

REFNESS, Kristen, Chief Financial Officer, Linden Oaks Hospital at Edward, Naperville, IL, p. A197

REGAL, Wendy, Director Human Resources, Providence Tarzana Medical Center,, CA, p. A74

REGEHR, Stan, President and Chief Executive Officer, Nemaha Valley Community Hospital, Seneca, KS, p. A254

REGEN, Debbie, MS Vice President and Chief Nursing Officer, Saint Clare's Health System, Denville, NJ, p. A415

REGIER, Donald, M.D. Chief Medical Officer, Sedgwick County Health Center, Julesburg, CO, p. A108

REGIER, Marion, Chief Executive Officer, Hillsboro Community Hospital, Hillsboro, KS, p. A245

REGULA, John
Chief Information Officer, Allied Services Rehabilitation Hospital, Scranton, PA, p. A554
Chief Information Officer, John Heinz Institute of Rehabilitation Medicine, Wilkes–Barre, PA, p. A558

REHM, Janice, Manager Human Resources, University of South Alabama Children's and Women's Hospital, Mobile, AL, p. A23

REHM, Micah, Chief Nursing Officer, Forrest General Hospital, Hattiesburg, MS, p. A359

REHMER, Patricia, Commissioner, Connecticut Department of Mental Health and Addiction Services, Hartford, CT, p. B43

REHN, Ronald G.
Chief Operating Officer, Providence Mount Carmel Hospital, Colville, WA, p. A682
Chief Operating Officer, Providence St. Joseph's Hospital, Chewelah, WA, p. A682

REIBER, Gayle, Interim Chief Nursing Officer, Sampson Regional Medical Center, Clinton, NC, p. A462

REICH, David L., M.D., President, Mount Sinai Hospital, New York, NY, p. A446

REICH, Joel R., M.D
  Senior Vice President Medical Affairs, Manchester Memorial Hospital, Manchester, CT, p. A114
  Senior Vice President Medical Affairs, Rockville General Hospital, Vernon Rockville, CT, p. A117

REICHARD, Steve, Manager Information Systems, Brigham City Community Hospital, Brigham City, UT, p. A659

REICHFIELD, Michael L., President, OhioHealth Doctors Hospital, Columbus, OH, p. A490

REICHLE, Paula, Senior Vice President and Chief Operating Officer, Sparrow Hospital, Lansing, MI, p. A328

REICHMAN, Joseph, M.D. Vice President Medical Affairs and Clinical Effectiveness, Riverview Medical Center, Red Bank, NJ, p. A422

REID, Barbara S., Chief Executive Officer, Willingway Hospital, Statesboro, GA, p. A167

REID, Bernadette, Chief Information Officer, Torrance Memorial Medical Center, Torrance, CA, p. A97

REID, Bev, Chief Financial Officer, St. Luke Hospital and Living Center, Marion, KS, p. A249

REID, Deressa, Interim Chief Executive Officer, Hoag Orthopedic Institute, Irvine, CA, p. A67

REID, Jamie, Information Systems Director, Methodist Hospital, Henderson, KY, p. A262

REID, Jim, Vice President and Chief Information Officer, Covenant Children's Hospital, Lubbock, TX, p. A634

REID, Karl, Chief Information Officer, Minneapolis Veterans Affairs Health Care System, Minneapolis, MN, p. A347

REID, Kelly, Human Resources Director, South Mississippi State Hospital, Purvis, MS, p. A364

REID, Kenneth G., President and Chief Executive Officer, Carlinville Area Hospital, Carlinville, IL, p. A182

REID, Patricia, Director of Nursing, Marion General Hospital, Columbia, MS, p. A357

REID, Richard
  Vice President Chief Finance Officer, Carson City Hospital, Carson City, MI, p. A320
  Chief Financial Officer, Sonoma Valley Hospital, Sonoma, CA, p. A95

REID, Stephanie, R.N. Vice President of Quality and Chief Nursing Officer, Carroll Hospital Center, Westminster, MD, p. A304

REID, Timothy, M.D. Chief Medical Staff, Carroll County Memorial Hospital, Carrollton, MO, p. A369

REIDER, Rochelle, Vice President Patient Care, Avera Queen of Peace Hospital, Mitchell, SD, p. A575

REIDER, Stephen, R.N. Director of Nursing, Assistant Vice President Patient Care Services, Walden Psychiatric Care, Waltham, MA, p. A316

REIDY, Margaret, M.D. Vice President Medical Affairs, UPMC Presbyterian Shadyside, Pittsburgh, PA, p. A552

REIFF, Troy T.
  Corporate Director Operations, St. Vincent Seton Specialty Hospital, Indianapolis, IN, p. A215
  Corporate Director Operations, St. Vincent Seton Specialty Hospital, Lafayette, IN, p. A217

REIFSNYDER, Daniel, M.D. President Medical and Dental Staff, Geisinger–Lewistown Hospital, Lewistown, PA, p. A543

REILLY, Brian M., Chief Financial Officer, Robert Wood Johnson University Hospital, New Brunswick, NJ, p. A419

REILLY, Dennis A., President and Chief Executive Officer, Little Company of Mary Hospital and Health Care Centers, Evergreen Park, IL, p. A190

REILLY, Jeff
  Senior Vice President Operations, Bon Secours Community Hospital, Port Jervis, NY, p. A452
  Senior Vice President Operations, St. Anthony Community Hospital, Warwick, NY, p. A457

REILLY, John, M.D. Vice President Medical Affairs and Chief Medical Officer, Mercy Medical Center, Rockville Centre, NY, p. A453

REILLY, Richard, Deputy Executive Director, Syosset Hospital, Syosset, NY, p. A455

REILLY, Robert, Vice President and Chief Financial Officer, Anne Arundel Medical Center, Annapolis, MD, p. A296

REILLY, Theresa, MSN Senior Vice President Patient Services and Chief Nursing Officer, Abington Memorial Hospital, Abington, PA, p. A532

REILLY, Tiffany, Director Human Resources, Childrens Care Hospital and School, Sioux Falls, SD, p. A576

REIMER, Arlo, M.D. Chief of Staff, Kearny County Hospital, Lakin, KS, p. A248

REIMER, Charm, Chief Financial Officer, Western State Hospital, Tacoma, WA, p. A691

REIMER, Randy, Chief Financial Officer, Adventist Behavioral Health Rockville, Rockville, MD, p. A303

REIMER, Ronda, R.N. Chief Nursing Officer and Assistant Administrator, Franklin General Hospital, Hampton, IA, p. A231

REIN, Mitchell S., M.D. Chief Medical Officer, North Shore Medical Center, Salem, MA, p. A314

REINART, Greg, Chief Financial Officer, Hereford Regional Medical Center, Hereford, TX, p. A623

REINBOTH, Thomas, Chief Financial Officer, Roxborough Memorial Hospital, Philadelphia, PA, p. A550

REINER, Scott, President and Chief Executive Officer, Adventist Health, Roseville, CA, p. B5

REINERT, Brenda, Director Human Resources, Tomah Memorial Hospital, Tomah, WI, p. A716

REINERT, Chad, Director Information Technology, Hamilton General Hospital, Hamilton, TX, p. A622

REINHARD, Diane, R.N. Vice President of Patient Care Services, Craig Hospital, Englewood, CO, p. A106

REINHARD, James S., M.D., Commissioner, Virginia Department of Mental Health, Richmond, VA, p. B150

REINHARD, Patrick, R.N. Chief Nursing Officer, Desert Valley Hospital, Victorville, CA, p. A99

REINHARD, Russ, Chief Executive, Providence Willamette Falls Medical Center, Oregon City, OR, p. A527

REINHART, Jeffery, M.D. Chief of Staff, Drew Memorial Hospital, Monticello, AR, p. A50

REINKE, Bradley, M.D. Vice President Medical Affairs and Chief Medical Officer, Dameron Hospital, Stockton, CA, p. A96

REINKE, N. Sue, Vice President Human Resources, Geisinger–Lewistown Hospital, Lewistown, PA, p. A543

REINKE, Ryan, Chief Financial Officer, CHI Health Midlands, Papillion, NE, p. A401

REINKING, Cheryl, R.N. Chief Nursing Officer, El Camino Hospital, Mountain View, CA, p. A79

REISELT, Doug
  Vice President and Chief Information Officer, Baptist Memorial Hospital – Memphis, Memphis, TN, p. A588
  Vice President and Chief Information Officer, Baptist Memorial Hospital–Collierville, Collierville, TN, p. A581

REISMAN, Ernestine O., Vice President Human Resources, Down East Community Hospital, Machias, ME, p. A294

REISMAN, Ronald, M.D
  Chief Medical Director, St. Vincent Seton Specialty Hospital, Indianapolis, IN, p. A215
  rireisma@stvincent.org, St. Vincent Seton Specialty Hospital, Lafayette, IN, p. A217

REISS, Deanna, Hospital Director of Nursing, Devereux Children's Behavioral Health Center, Malvern, PA, p. A544

REISZ, Carol, Chief Financial Officer, North Caddo Medical Center, Vivian, LA, p. A290

REITER, Scott, D.O. Chief of Staff, Scheurer Hospital, Pigeon, MI, p. A332

REITES, Tammy, Vice President Patient Financial Services, Children's Hospital, New Orleans, LA, p. A285

REITZ, Brent, President, Adventist Rehabilitation Hospital of Maryland, Rockville, MD, p. A303

REITZ, Judy A., Sc.D. Executive Vice President and Chief Operating Officer, Johns Hopkins Hospital, Baltimore, MD, p. A296

REITZEL, David, Chief Information Officer, Brookdale Hospital Medical Center,, NY, p. A443

RELPH, Daren, Chief Executive Officer, Wayne County Hospital, Corydon, IA, p. A228

REMALEY, Anne, Vice President Human Resources, ACMH Hospital, Kittanning, PA, p. A542

REMBIS, Michael A., FACHE, Chief Executive Officer, Providence Saint Joseph Medical Center, Burbank, CA, p. A58

REMIGIO, Odalys, Assistant Vice President, Finance, Baptist Health South Florida, West Kendall Baptist Hospital, Miami, FL, p. A136

REMILLARD, Jean D., M.D. Chief Medical Officer/Chief Quality Officer, Lovelace Medical Center, Albuquerque, NM, p. A426

REMILLARD, John R., President, Aurelia Osborn Fox Memorial Hospital, Oneonta, NY, p. A450

REMINGTON, Amanda
  Director Human Resources, Spalding Regional Medical Center, Griffin, GA, p. A160
  Director Human Resources, Sylvan Grove Hospital, Jackson, GA, p. A161

REMPHER, Kenneth, Ph.D. Interim Chief Nursing Officer, University of Iowa Hospitals and Clinics, Iowa City, IA, p. A232

REMSPECHER, Mark, Director Human Resources, Southeast Missouri Mental Health Center, Farmington, MO, p. A371

REMSTEIN, Robert, D.O. Vice President Medical Affairs, Capital Health Medical Center–Hopewell, Pennington, NJ, p. A421

RENC, William, Chief Fiscal Officer, Summit Park Hospital and Nursing Care Center, Pomona, NY, p. A451

RENDER–LEACH, Cynthia, Director Human Resources, Highland Community Hospital, Picayune, MS, p. A364

RENDON, Eloise, Director Human Resources, Twin Cities Community Hospital, Templeton, CA, p. A97

RENEY, Michael, Chief Financial Officer, Brigham and Women's Hospital, Boston, MA, p. A306

RENFREE, Mark, Chief Financial Officer, La Rabida Children's Hospital, Chicago, IL, p. A184

RENIER, Hugh, M.D
  Vice President Medical Affairs, Essentia Health Duluth, Duluth, MN, p. A342
  Vice President Medical Affairs, Essentia Health St. Mary's Medical Center, Duluth, MN, p. A342

RENNEKER, James M., MSN Vice President and Chief Nursing Officer, Loretto Hospital, Chicago, IL, p. A184

RENNER, Dianne, Director Human Resources, Logansport State Hospital, Logansport, IN, p. A218

RENO, Kelly, R.N. Chief Nursing Officer, Menorah Medical Center, Overland Park, KS, p. A252

RENO, Vera, Chief Nursing Officer, Lynn County Hospital District, Tahoka, TX, p. A651

RENO, III, William, M.D. President Medical Staff, Wesley Medical Center, Hattiesburg, MS, p. A359

RENSHAW, Dee, Chief Executive Officer, Hillcrest Hospital Henryetta, Henryetta, OK, p. A511

RENTAS, Margarita, R.N. Nursing Director, Castaner General Hospital, Castaner, PR, p. A725

RENTFRO, Donald, Chief Executive Officer, Natchez Regional Medical Center, Natchez, MS, p. A363

RENTSCH, Richard E., President, Stroud Regional Medical Center, Stroud, OK, p. A519

RENTZ, Norman G., President and Chief Executive Officer, Cannon Memorial Hospital, Pickens, SC, p. A569

REOHR, Sara, Regional Controller, West Gables Rehabilitation Hospital, Miami, FL, p. A138

REPAC, Kimberly S., Senior Vice President and Chief Financial Officer, Western Maryland Regional Medical Center, Cumberland, MD, p. A300

REPASS, Lois, Quality Assurance Specialist and Coordinator Performance Improvement, Northern Nevada Adult Mental Health Services, Sparks, NV, p. A408

REPETTI, Gregory, Interim Chief Executive Officer, Valley Hospital, Spokane Valley, WA, p. A690

REPINO, Thomas, Executive Director Ancillary Services, Connally Memorial Medical Center, Floresville, TX, p. A617

REPKO, Keith D., Associate Medical Center Director, Veterans Affairs St. Louis Health Care System, Saint Louis, MO, p. A382

REPPERT, Joseph A., Executive Vice President and Chief Financial Officer, North Mississippi Medical Center – Tupelo, Tupelo, MS, p. A365

RESENDEZ, James R., Chief Executive Officer, South Texas Regional Medical Center, Jourdanton, TX, p. A630

RESETAR, Gayle L.
  Chief Operating Officer, Georgetown Memorial Hospital, Georgetown, SC, p. A566
  Vice President and Chief Operating Officer, Georgetown Memorial Hospital, Georgetown, SC, p. A566
  Chief Operating Officer, Waccamaw Community Hospital, Murrells Inlet, SC, p. A569

RESLER, Lori, R.N. Chief Nurse, Sullivan County Community Hospital, Sullivan, IN, p. A222

RESSLER, David R., Senior Vice President and Chief Operations Officer, TMC Healthcare, Tucson, AZ, p. A41

RESSLER, Dennis, Chief Financial Officer, St. Joseph Hospital & Health Center, Kokomo, IN, p. A216

RESTREPO, Macarena, Manager Business Office, Sister Emmanuel Hospital, Miami, FL, p. A137

RESTREPO, Nicolas, M.D. Vice President Medical Affairs, Winchester Medical Center, Winchester, VA, p. A680

RESTUCCIA, Michael, Chief Information Officer, Hospital of the University of Pennsylvania, Philadelphia, PA, p. A548

RESTUM, William H., Ph.D., President, Rehabilitation Institute of Michigan, Detroit, MI, p. A322

RETALIC, Tammy B., R.N. Vice President Nursing and Patient and Family Centered Care, Hebrew Rehabilitation Center, Boston, MA, p. A307

RETTGER, Linda, M.D. President Medical Staff, Kane Community Hospital, Kane, PA, p. A541

RETTIG, Linda, Director Financial Services, Washington County Hospital, Washington, KS, p. A256

RETTKE, Matthew, Commander, Ireland Army Community Hospital, Fort Knox, KY, p. A261

RETZLAFF, Nancy, Director Human Resources, OakBend Medical Center, Richmond, TX, p. A644

REULAND, Charlie, Sc.D. Executive Vice President and Chief Operating Officer, Johns Hopkins Bayview Medical Center, Baltimore, MD, p. A296

REUST, Michele, Controller, Memorial Hospital of Texas County, Guymon, OK, p. A511

REVAL, Mary, R.N. Chief Nursing Officer, Gulf Coast Regional Medical Center, Panama City, FL, p. A141

REVELS, Beverly, Director Human Resources, Sutter Amador Hospital, Jackson, CA, p. A67

REVERMAN, Larry, Director Information Systems, Clark Memorial Hospital, Jeffersonville, IN, p. A215

REVIEL, Jackie, Interim Administrator, Allen Parish Hospital, Kinder, LA, p. A280

REWERTS, Karen
 Regional Vice President Finance and Chief Financial Officer, SSM Cardinal Glennon Children's Medical Center, Saint Louis, MO, p. A381
 Vice President Finance and Chief Financial Officer, SSM St. Clare Health Center, Fenton, MO, p. A371
 System Vice President Finance, SSM St. Joseph Health Center, Saint Charles, MO, p. A379

REXFORD, Linda, Director Human Resources, Weeks Medical Center, Lancaster, NH, p. A410

REXROAD, Ann, Director Information Technology, Grafton City Hospital, Grafton, WV, p. A695

REXWINKLE, Lori, Chief Nursing Officer, Coffeyville Regional Medical Center, Coffeyville, KS, p. A242

REYES, Arnold, Administrator, U. S. Penitentiary Infirmary, Lewisburg, PA, p. A543

REYES, Marco, Vice President of Operations, Hospital Metropolitano Dr. Tito Mattei, Yauco, PR, p. A729

REYES, Raul, M.D. Medical Director, San Juan City Hospital, San Juan, PR, p. A729

REYES, Roxanne, Director of Nursing, Cornerstone Regional Hospital, Edinburg, TX, p. A615

REYES BENCITO, ACA–AC,, Norie Lee, R.N. Director of Nursing, Loma Linda University Behavioral Medicine Center, Redlands, CA, p. A85

REYMAN, Reed, President, St. Joseph's Hospital and Health Center, Dickinson, ND, p. A477

REYNOLDS, Angela D., Chief Financial Officer, Lewis–Gale Medical Center, Salem, VA, p. A678

REYNOLDS, Denise, Chief Nursing Officer, Memorial Hospital Miramar, Miramar, FL, p. A138

REYNOLDS, George, M.D. Vice President, Chief Information Officer and Chief Medical Information Officer, Children's Hospital and Medical Center, Omaha, NE, p. A400

REYNOLDS, Hope, Executive Director Human Resources and Support Services, Margaret R. Pardee Memorial Hospital, Hendersonville, NC, p. A466

REYNOLDS, Ian, Chief Medical Officer, Victory Surgical Hospital East Houston, Houston, TX, p. A628

REYNOLDS, James B., M.D. Medical Director, Northwest Missouri Psychiatric Rehabilitation Center, Saint Joseph, MO, p. A380

REYNOLDS, Jay, M.D. Chief Medical Officer and Chief Clinical Officer, The Aroostook Medical Center, Presque Isle, ME, p. A295

REYNOLDS, Katelyn, Manager Human Resources, Greeley County Health Services, Tribune, KS, p. A255

REYNOLDS, Lennetta M., Administrative Supervisor, Community Behavioral Health Hospital – Annandale, Annandale, MN, p. A339

REYNOLDS, Linda K., FACHE, Director, Mann–Grandstaff Veterans Affairs Medical Center, Spokane, WA, p. A690

REYNOLDS, Mike, Chief Financial Officer, Newberry County Memorial Hospital, Newberry, SC, p. A569

REYNOLDS, Paul, M.D. Medical Director, Coleman County Medical Center, Coleman, TX, p. A606

REYNOLDS, Phyllis, R.N. VP, Nursing, Beaumont Hospital Grosse Pointe, Grosse Pointe, MI, p. A326

REYNOLDS, Randee, President, Parkview Adventist Medical Center, Brunswick, ME, p. A292

REYNOLDS, Ray, Chief Executive Officer, Glen Rose Medical Center, Glen Rose, TX, p. A621

REYNOLDS, Robert, Director Information Systems, Mary Rutan Hospital, Bellefontaine, OH, p. A483

REYNOLDS, Ronald J., President, Muncy Valley Hospital, Muncy, PA, p. A546

REYNOLDS, Rose, Director Health Information, Avera Flandreau Hospital, Flandreau, SD, p. A573

REYNOLDS, Scott, Vice President Finance, Mercy Hospital Springfield, Springfield, MO, p. A383

REYNOLDS, Teresa, Chief Operating Officer, Haywood Regional Medical Center, Clyde, NC, p. A462

REYNOLDS, Todd, Chief Information Officer, Memorial Medical Center – Ashland, Ashland, WI, p. A701

REYNOLDS, Vance V., CPA, Chief Executive Officer, Texas Health Presbyterian Hospital–WNJ, Sherman, TX, p. A649

REYNOLDS–GOSSETTE, Youdie, Controller, Wilma N. Vazquez Medical Center, Vega Baja, PR, p. A729

REZAC, Julie A., R.N. Chief Operating Officer, Saunders Medical Center, Wahoo, NE, p. A402

RHEE, Carolyn F., Chief Executive Officer, LAC–Olive View–UCLA Medical Center,, CA, p. A73

RHEINHEIMER, Rick, Chief Clinical Officer, Kindred Hospital–Chattanooga, Chattanooga, TN, p. A580

RHINEHART, Jennie R., Administrator and Chief Executive Officer, Community Hospital, Tallassee, AL, p. A26

RHOADES, Charles E., M.D., Chief Executive Officer, Kansas City Orthopaedic Institute, Leawood, KS, p. A248

RHOADES, Mark, Vice President and Chief Human Resources Officer, Duncan Regional Hospital, Duncan, OK, p. A509

RHOADES, Shelly, Chief Financial Officer, Clarion Psychiatric Center, Clarion, PA, p. A535

RHOADS, Jack, M.D. Medical Director, Landmark Hospital of Joplin, Joplin, MO, p. A373

RHOADS, Pam, Chief Financial Officer, Fairfax Hospital, Kirkland, WA, p. A684

RHODES, David, M.D. Senior Vice President Medical Affairs and Chief Medical Officer, Rapides Regional Medical Center, Alexandria, LA, p. A272

RHODES, Helen, R.N. Associate Director Operations, Veterans Affairs Northern Indiana Health Care System, Fort Wayne, IN, p. A211

RHODES, J. Gary, FACHE,
 Interim President and Chief Executive Officer, Brooks Memorial Hospital, Dunkirk, NY, p. A436
 Chief Executive Officer, Kane Community Hospital, Kane, PA, p. A541

RHODES, Jerome E., Chief Executive Officer, CRC Health Group, Inc., Cupertino, CA, p. B45

RHODES, Lee, Interim Administrator and Chief Executive Officer, Greeley County Health Services, Tribune, KS, p. A255

RHODES, Robert, Director Information Systems, Perry Hospital, Perry, GA, p. A164

RHODES, Roger, Chief Executive Officer, Baylor Surgical Hospital at Fort Worth, Fort Worth, TX, p. A618

RHODES, Tracey, Coordinator Human Resources, Evergreen Medical Center, Evergreen, AL, p. A19

RHONE, Steve, R.N. Vice President Patient Care Services, Beebe Healthcare, Lewes, DE, p. A119

RHUDY, Kenneth D.
 Chief Executive Officer, Brooks County Hospital, Quitman, GA, p. A165
 Administrator, Grady General Hospital, Cairo, GA, p. A155

RHYNE, Catherine A., M.P.H. Chief Nursing Officer, Gerald Champion Regional Medical Center, Alamogordo, NM, p. A426

RHYNE, Craig, M.D. Chief Medical Officer, Covenant Medical Center, Lubbock, TX, p. A634

RHYNE, Dennis, M.D. Acting Medical Director, Fairbanks, Indianapolis, IN, p. A214

RHYNE, Tim, Personnel Officer, Ventura County Medical Center, Ventura, CA, p. A99

RIAL, Joanne, Chief Financial Officer, Cumberland Hospital, New Kent, VA, p. A674

RIALS, Joe, Director Fiscal Services, North Mississippi State Hospital, Tupelo, MS, p. A365

RIALS, Loren, Chief Financial Officer, Carolinas Hospital System, Florence, SC, p. A565

RIANO, Omaira D., Chief Nursing Officer, HEALTHSOUTH Sunrise Rehabilitation Hospital, Sunrise, FL, p. A146

RIAZ, Mohammad, M.D. Chief of Staff, Raulerson Hospital, Okeechobee, FL, p. A140

RIBA, Chris, Director Human Resources, Baldwin Area Medical Center, Baldwin, WI, p. A701

RICARD, Joan M., FACHE, Director, Edward Hines, Jr. Veterans Affairs Hospital, Hines, IL, p. A192

RICARTTI, Rebecca R., Interim Director Human Resources, Garfield Medical Center, Monterey Park, CA, p. A78

RICCI, David A., President and Chief Executive Officer, Saint Michael's Medical Center, Newark, NJ, p. A420

RICCIO, John A., M.D. Chief Medical Officer, Auburn Community Hospital, Auburn, NY, p. A433

RICCIONI, Mich
 Chief Financial Officer, Petaluma Valley Hospital, Petaluma, CA, p. A83
 Vice President and Chief Financial Officer, Northern California Region, Queen of the Valley Medical Center, Napa, CA, p. A79
 Chief Financial Officer, Santa Rosa Memorial Hospital, Santa Rosa, CA, p. A95
 Chief Financial Officer, St. Joseph Hospital, Eureka, CA, p. A62

RICCITELLI, Anthony, Chief Operating Officer, Worcester Recovery Center and Hospital, Worcester, MA, p. A317

RICCITELLI, Vincent, Vice President and Chief Financial Officer, Hoboken University Medical Center, Hoboken, NJ, p. A417

RICE, Amy, Chief Financial Officer, Helena Regional Medical Center, Helena, AR, p. A47

RICE, Ann Madden, Chief Executive Officer, University of California, Davis Medical Center, Sacramento, CA, p. A88

RICE, Carolyn, M.D. Director Medical Services, Naval Hospital Pensacola, Pensacola, FL, p. A142

RICE, Craig, Director Information, Schneck Medical Center, Seymour, IN, p. A222

RICE, Devin, Director Information Systems, Clifton–Fine Hospital, Star Lake, NY, p. A455

RICE, Eric, Vice President Patient Care Services, St. Joseph's Hospital of Buckhannon, Buckhannon, WV, p. A694

RICE, James W., Director, Oscar G. Johnson Veterans Affairs Medical Center, Iron Mountain, MI, p. A327

RICE, Mark, CPA Controller, Jersey Shore Hospital, Jersey Shore, PA, p. A541

RICE, Mark, Administrator, Mid–Jefferson Extended Care Hospital, Nederland, TX, p. A639

RICE, Peter, M.D. Medical Director, PeaceHealth Ketchikan Medical Center, Ketchikan, AK, p. A29

RICE, R. Timothy, Chief Executive Officer, Cone Health, Greensboro, NC, p. B43

RICE, Thomas J., FACHE, President and Chief Executive Officer, Fawcett Memorial Hospital, Port Charlotte, FL, p. A143

RICE, Tim, President and Chief Executive Officer, Lakewood Health System, Staples, MN, p. A352

RICH, Anna, Chief Financial Officer, Complex Care Hospital at Tenaya, Las Vegas, NV, p. A405

RICH, Dan, Director Finance, Texas Health Presbyterian Hospital Allen, Allen, TX, p. A596

RICH, Jeri
 Assistant Administrator and Chief Financial Officer, Hunt Regional Community Hospital, Commerce, TX, p. A607
 Assistant Administrator and Chief Financial Officer, Hunt Regional Medical Center, Greenville, TX, p. A622

RICH, Judy F., President and Chief Executive Officer, TMC Healthcare, Tucson, AZ, p. A41

RICH, Kori, Chief Executive Officer, The Physicians Centre Hospital, Bryan, TX, p. A604

RICH, Mark, Director Information Services, Ashley Regional Medical Center, Vernal, UT, p. A664

RICH, Philip, M.D. Chief Medical Officer, West Hills Hospital, Reno, NV, p. A408

RICH–MCLERRAN, Andrea, Chief Administrative Officer, Cumberland River Hospital, Celina, TN, p. A580

RICHARD, Brent, Administrative Director Information Systems, Southern Ohio Medical Center, Portsmouth, OH, p. A501

RICHARD, Christina, Administrator, Kindred Hospital Tarrant County–Arlington, Arlington, TX, p. A597

RICHARD, Larry, M.D. Chief Medical Staff, Decatur County Hospital, Leon, IA, p. A233

RICHARD, Marilyn, Director Human Resources, Daviess Community Hospital, Washington, IN, p. A224

RICHARD, Mark, Chief Information Officer, Port Huron Hospital, Port Huron, MI, p. A332

RICHARD, Paul, President and Chief Executive Officer, Sanford Medical Center Fargo, Fargo, ND, p. A477

RICHARD, Scott, Vice President Finance and Chief Financial Officer, St. Elizabeth Hospital, Gonzales, LA, p. A278

RICHARD, Thomas, Director Budget and Revenue Cycle, Redwood Area Hospital, Redwood Falls, MN, p. A350

RICHARD, Tim, IT Coordinator, Crawford Memorial Hospital, Robinson, IL, p. A201

RICHARDS, Amy, Accounting, Franklin County Memorial Hospital, Franklin, NE, p. A395

RICHARDS, Craig A., Chief Executive Officer, Mildred Mitchell–Bateman Hospital, Huntington, WV, p. A696

RICHARDS, Frank
 Chief Information Officer, Geisinger Medical Center, Danville, PA, p. A537
 Chief Information Officer, Geisinger Wyoming Valley Medical Center, Wilkes Barre, PA, p. A558

RICHARDS, Jaena, Chief Financial Officer, Deer Lodge Medical Center, Deer Lodge, MT, p. A386

RICHARDS, Joan K., President and Chief Executive Officer, Crozer–Keystone Health System, Springfield, PA, p. B46

RICHARDS, Jon, Chief Financial Officer, Tennova Newport Medical Center, Newport, TN, p. A591

RICHARDS, Jonathan, Chief Financial Officer, David Grant USAF Medical Center, Travis AFB, CA, p. A97

RICHARDS, Judith, Director of Nursing, Adcare Hospital of Worcester, Worcester, MA, p. A316

RICHARDS, Mandy, R.N. Vice President Patient Care, United Hospital, Saint Paul, MN, p. A351

RICHARDS, Nate, Director Information Technology, Mitchell County Hospital Health Systems, Beloit, KS, p. A242

RICHARDS, Robert J., Vice President Finance and Chief Financial Officer, The Good Samaritan Hospital, Lebanon, PA, p. A543

RICHARDS, Sheila K., Human Resources Director, Dallas Medical Center, Dallas, TX, p. A610

RICHARDS, Suzanne, M.P.H.,
 Chief Executive Officer, Victor Valley Global Medical Center, Victorville, CA, p. A99
 Chief Executive Officer, Western Medical Center Anaheim, Anaheim, CA, p. A55

RICHARDS, Thom, Director Information Technology, Knoxville Hospital & Clinics, Knoxville, IA, p. A233

RICHARDSON, Connie, Director of Nursing, Weisbrod Memorial County Hospital, Eads, CO, p. A105

RICHARDSON, David, M.D. Chief of Staff, Delta Medical Center, Memphis, TN, p. A588

RICHARDSON, Denise, R.N. Senior Vice President and Chief Nursing Officer, St. Barnabas Hospital,, NY, p. A448

RICHARDSON, Dwayne, Interim Chief Executive Officer, Placentia–Linda Hospital, Placentia, CA, p. A83

RICHARDSON, Irene, Chief Financial Officer, Memorial Hospital of Sweetwater County, Rock Springs, WY, p. A722

RICHARDSON, Jana
Chief Financial Officer, Stone County Medical Center, Mountain View, AR, p. A50
Chief Financial Officer, White River Medical Center, Batesville, AR, p. A43

RICHARDSON, Janice, Chief Executive Officer and Managing Director, Rivendell Behavioral Health, Bowling Green, KY, p. A259

RICHARDSON, Judy, M.D. President Medical Staff, Mid–Columbia Medical Center, The Dalles, OR, p. A530

RICHARDSON, Karen K., Vice President Finance and Chief Information Officer, Providence Health Center, Waco, TX, p. A656

RICHARDSON, Keith, Chief Financial Officer, Jellico Community Hospital, Jellico, TN, p. A585

RICHARDSON, Kevin, M.D. Chief of Staff, Southwest Mississippi Regional Medical Center, McComb, MS, p. A362

RICHARDSON, Kirk, Chief Operating Officer, Bronson LakeView Hospital, Paw Paw, MI, p. A332

RICHARDSON, Kristy, Director of Nursing, De Queen Medical Center, De Queen, AR, p. A45

RICHARDSON, Mark D., President and Chief Executive Officer, Great River Medical Center, West Burlington, IA, p. A239

RICHARDSON Jr., Nathaniel, President, Decatur Morgan Hospital, Decatur, AL, p. A18

RICHARDSON, Robert, Information Technology Administrator, Porter Regional Hospital, Valparaiso, IN, p. A223

RICHARDSON, Sarah, Director Information Systems, Belton Regional Medical Center, Belton, MO, p. A367

RICHARDSON, Shazetta, Director of Nursing, Cypress Creek Hospital, Houston, TX, p. A624

RICHARDSON, Sonya, Chief Nursing Officer, Chillicothe Hospital District, Chillicothe, TX, p. A606

RICHARDSON, Stanley, Coordinator Human Resources and Payroll Benefits, Kindred Hospital–San Antonio, San Antonio, TX, p. A646

RICHARDSON, Terika, M.P.H. Associate Administrator, Spotsylvania Regional Medical Center, Fredericksburg, VA, p. A671

RICHARDSON, Terrie, Coordinator Human Resources, Select Specialty Hospital–Augusta, Augusta, GA, p. A154

RICHARDSON, Timothy J., M.D. Chief of Staff, Maine Veterans Affairs Medical Center, Augusta, ME, p. A291

RICHARDSON, William T., President and Chief Executive Officer, Tift Regional Health System, Tifton, GA, p. B135

RICHARDSON, William T., President and Chief Executive Officer, Tift Regional Medical Center, Tifton, GA, p. A168

RICHARDT, Claudia, Vice President, Human Resources, Community Relations and Marketing, Dearborn County Hospital, Lawrenceburg, IN, p. A217

RICHARDVILLE, Craig D.
Senior Vice President and Chief Information Officer, Carolinas Medical Center, Charlotte, NC, p. A461
Chief Information Officer, Carolinas Rehabilitation, Charlotte, NC, p. A462
Chief Information Officer, Cleveland Regional Medical Center, Shelby, NC, p. A472

RICHASON, Amie
Vice President Human Resources, Leesburg Regional Medical Center, Leesburg, FL, p. A134
Vice President Human Resources, The Villages Regional Hospital, The Villages, FL, p. A149

RICHBOURG, Gail A., Director Human Resources, Clarendon Memorial Hospital, Manning, SC, p. A568

RICHCREEK, Keith, Manager Technical Services, Lafayette Regional Health Center, Lexington, MO, p. A376

RICHENS, Ken, Chief Information Officer, Central Valley Medical Center, Nephi, UT, p. A661

RICHER, R. David, Chief Executive Officer, Fairlawn Rehabilitation Hospital, Worcester, MA, p. A316

RICHERSON, Kathleen, R.N. Vice President and Chief Nursing Officer, NorthBay Medical Center, Fairfield, CA, p. A62

RICHERT, Ed, M.D. Chief of Staff, Modoc Medical Center, Alturas, CA, p. A55

RICHETTI, Michael, Chief Financial Officer, Chilton Medical Center, Pompton Plains, NJ, p. A421

RICHEY, Mark, Interim Administrator, Tippah County Hospital, Ripley, MS, p. A365

RICHHART, David, Vice President Fiscal Services, Community Medical Center, Missoula, MT, p. A389

RICHMAN, Craig, M.D. Medical Director, Meadows Psychiatric Center, Centre Hall, PA, p. A535

RICHMAN, Jonathan, M.D. Chief of Staff, Chase County Community Hospital, Imperial, NE, p. A397

RICHMAN, Timothy, President, Calumet Medical Center, Chilton, WI, p. A703

RICHMOND, Andy, Director Information Technology, Choctaw Memorial Hospital, Hugo, OK, p. A512

RICHMOND, Craig, Senior Vice President and Chief Financial Officer, MetroHealth Medical Center, Cleveland, OH, p. A489

RICHMOND, Ira, Associate Director Patient Care Services, Veterans Affairs Pittsburgh Healthcare System, Pittsburgh, PA, p. A552

RICHOLSON, Melissa, R.N. Director of Nursing, Brownfield Regional Medical Center, Brownfield, TX, p. A604

RICHOUX, Jacquelyn, Chief Financial Officer, Lady of the Sea General Hospital, Cut Off, LA, p. A276

RICHTER, Daniel, M.D. Chief of Staff, CHI Health Missouri Valley, Missouri Valley, IA, p. A234

RICHTER, Thomas V., Chief Executive Officer, Pioneer Memorial Hospital and Health Services, Viborg, SD, p. A577

RICK, Bob, Vice President Information Technology, USMD Hospital at Arlington, Arlington, TX, p. A598

RICKARD, Sheryl, Chief Financial Officer, Bonner General Hospital, Sandpoint, ID, p. A178

RICKENS, Chris, R.N. Senior Vice President and Chief Nursing Officer, UPMC Altoona, Altoona, PA, p. A532

RICKS, Edward, Vice President and Chief Information Officer, Beaufort Memorial Hospital, Beaufort, SC, p. A562

RICKS, Michael R.
President, Mercy Hospital of Folsom, Folsom, CA, p. A63
Chief Operating Officer, St. Joseph's Medical Center, Stockton, CA, p. A96

RICO, Richard, Vice President and Chief Financial Officer, Sky Lakes Medical Center, Klamath Falls, OR, p. A526

RIDALL, Jackie, Director Human Resources, Berwick Hospital Center, Berwick, PA, p. A533

RIDDER, Terri, Director Human Resources, St. Francis Memorial Hospital, West Point, NE, p. A402

RIDDLE, Kent, Chief Executive Officer, Mary Free Bed Rehabilitation Hospital, Grand Rapids, MI, p. A325

RIDDLES, Lawrence, M.D. Executive Vice President Medical Affairs and Quality, St. Dominic–Jackson Memorial Hospital, Jackson, MS, p. A360

RIDGE, Carolyn, Chief Financial Officer, Lakeview Regional Medical Center, Covington, LA, p. A276

RIDGE, Frederick R., Chief of Staff, Greene County General Hospital, Linton, IN, p. A217

RIDGEWAY, Kerrie, R.N. Chief Nursing Officer, Pocahontas Memorial Hospital, Buckeye, WV, p. A693

RIDLEY, Pam, Director Information Systems, Henry County Medical Center, Paris, TN, p. A592

RIDLEY, Zena, Director Human Resources, Harbor Oaks Hospital, New Baltimore, MI, p. A331

RIDNER, Sheila, R.N. Director of Nursing, Behavioral HealthCare Center at Columbia, Columbia, TN, p. A581

RIEBEL, William, M.D. Vice President Medical Operations, Lakewood Hospital, Lakewood, OH, p. A496

RIEBER, Dan, Interim Chief Financial Officer, Memorial Hospital, Colorado Springs, CO, p. A103

RIEBER, Jim, Director Information Systems, Perham Health, Perham, MN, p. A349

RIECHERS, Thomas, M.D. Chief Medical Staff, Mercy Hospital Washington, Washington, MO, p. A384

RIEDEL, Jennifer, Chief Operating Officer, Fairmount Behavioral Health System, Philadelphia, PA, p. A548

RIEDLINGER, Joann, Vice President Nursing and Manager Information Systems, Bucyrus Community Hospital, Bucyrus, OH, p. A484

RIEG, Kevin, M.D. President Medical Staff, Via Christi Rehabilitation Hospital, Wichita, KS, p. A257

RIEGE, Michael J., Chief Executive Officer, Virginia Gay Hospital, Vinton, IA, p. A238

RIEGER, Bill, Chief Information Officer, Flagler Hospital, Saint Augustine, FL, p. A144

RIEGERT, Patricia, Director Fiscal Services, Danville State Hospital, Danville, PA, p. A536

RIEGLE, Tina, R.N. Chief Clinical Officer, AMG Specialty Hospital – Muncie, Muncie, IN, p. A219

RIEKE, Diane, Director Patient Care Services, Patients' Hospital of Redding, Redding, CA, p. A85

RIEKS, Katie, Chief Nursing Officer, Hansen Family Hospital, Iowa Falls, IA, p. A233

RIEMER–MATUZAK, Stephanie J., Chief Executive Officer, Mercy Hospital Grayling, Grayling, MI, p. A325

RIER, Kirk, Chief Operating Officer, Iowa Specialty Hospital–Clarion, Clarion, IA, p. A227

RIESEBERG, Eric F., President, Specialty Hospitals of America, LLC, Portsmouth, NH, p. B126

RIESER, Michael, M.D. Medical Director, Ridge Behavioral Health System, Lexington, KY, p. A264

RIESTER, Debby, Manager Human Resources, Coastal Communities Hospital, Santa Ana, CA, p. A93

RIETSEMA, Wouter, M.D. Chief Quality and Information Officer, Champlain Valley Physicians Hospital Medical Center, Plattsburgh, NY, p. A451

RIEVES, S. Kathleen, M.D. Chief Medical Officer, Rangely District Hospital, Rangely, CO, p. A110

RIFFLE, Virginia, Vice President Patient Care Services, Samaritan North Lincoln Hospital, Lincoln City, OR, p. A526

RIGAS, Warren Alston, Executive Vice President and Chief Operating Officer, Floyd Medical Center, Rome, GA, p. A165

RIGDON, Edward, M.D. Chief Medical Officer, Crossgates River Oaks Hospital, Brandon, MS, p. A356

RIGDON, Pam, Director Nursing, Laird Hospital, Union, MS, p. A366

RIGG, Darla, Interim Director, Information Systems, Madera Community Hospital, Madera, CA, p. A76

RIGGINS, Mark, Administrator, Bellville St. Joseph Health Center, Bellville, TX, p. A602

RIGGLE, Vikki, Director Human Resources, Eastern Louisiana Mental Health System, Jackson, LA, p. A279

RIGGS, Jon, Chief Financial Officer, Medical Center Health System, Odessa, TX, p. A640

RIGNEY, Alice, Chief Human Resources Officer, Abbeville Area Medical Center, Abbeville, SC, p. A562

RIGSBEE CARROLL, Cristina, Chief Operating Officer, Granville Health System, Oxford, NC, p. A470

RIGSBY, Brent, Chief Financial Officer, Southwest Georgia Regional Medical Center, Cuthbert, GA, p. A157

RIGSBY, Diane, Chief Information Officer, Capital Hospice, Arlington, VA, p. A668

RIGSBY, Jimmy, Chief Executive Officer, Campbellton Graceville Hospital, Graceville, FL, p. A130

RIKER, Sharon, Administrator Hospital Applications, Okmulgee Memorial Hospital, Okmulgee, OK, p. A517

RILEY, Colleen, M.D. Medical Director, Laguna Honda Hospital and Rehabilitation Center, San Francisco, CA, p. A91

RILEY, Doug, Director Information Services, Skagit Valley Hospital, Mount Vernon, WA, p. A685

RILEY, Edward E., Chief Executive Officer and Administrator, Kingman Community Hospital, Kingman, KS, p. A247

RILEY, Jennifer, Chief Organizational Excellence, Memorial Hospital at Craig, Craig, CO, p. A104

RILEY, Jim, Director Information Technology, Wagoner Community Hospital, Wagoner, OK, p. A522

RILEY, Joe B., President and Chief Executive Officer, Jackson Hospital and Clinic, Montgomery, AL, p. A24

RILEY, John, Chief Financial Officer, Harrisburg Medical Center, Harrisburg, IL, p. A191

RILEY, Kenneth, Director Information Systems, Wing Memorial Hospital, Palmer, MA, p. A313

RILEY, Linzie, Interim Human Resource Manager, LifeCare Hospitals of Dallas, Dallas, TX, p. A610

RILEY, Mike, Senior Vice President and Chief Operating Officer, Novant Health Charlotte Orthopaedic Hospital, Charlotte, NC, p. A462

RILEY, Randy
Chief Financial Officer, Center for Behavioral Medicine, Kansas City, MO, p. A373
Fiscal and Administrative Manager, Northwest Missouri Psychiatric Rehabilitation Center, Saint Joseph, MO, p. A380

RILEY, Susan, Director Human Resources, HEALTHSOUTH Rehabilitation Hospital of Miami, Cutler Bay, FL, p. A126

RILEY, Jr., William, M.D. Chief of Staff, Memorial Hermann Sugar Land Hospital, Sugar Land, TX, p. A651

RIMA, Pat, Health Care Manager, State Penitentiary Hospital, Walla Walla, WA, p. A692

RIMAR, Stephen, M.D. Senior Vice President Medical Affairs, New York Hospital Queens,, NY, p. A447

RIMEL, Jeff, Chief Financial Officer, Cibola General Hospital, Grants, NM, p. A428

RINALDI, Anthony, Executive Vice President, Fairview Hospital, Great Barrington, MA, p. A310

RINALDI, Blythe, Vice President, Mayo Clinic Health System – Northland in Barron, Barron, WI, p. A702

RINALDI, Daniel, Chief Financial Officer, Ellis Hospital, Schenectady, NY, p. A454

RINAUDO, Helen, Vice President Human Resources, MidHudson Regional Hospital of Westchester Medical Center, Poughkeepsie, NY, p. A452

RINDELS, Doris, Vice President Operations, Grinnell Regional Medical Center, Grinnell, IA, p. A231

RINDFLEISCH, Jody, Manager Human Resources, Redwood Area Hospital, Redwood Falls, MN, p. A350

RINDLISBACHER, Diane, Manager Information Systems, Orem Community Hospital, Orem, UT, p. A661

RINEHARDT, Mark, Chief Executive Officer, Wishek Community Hospital and Clinics, Wishek, ND, p. A481

RINEHART, Linda, Director Human Resources, HEALTHSOUTH Treasure Coast Rehabilitation Hospital, Vero Beach, FL, p. A149

RINEHART, Rick, Chief Information Officer, Carle Foundation Hospital, Urbana, IL, p. A204

RINEY, Jeremy, Chief Executive Officer, San Angelo Community Medical Center, San Angelo, TX, p. A645

RING, Brian K., Chief Operating Officer, Henry County Hospital, New Castle, IN, p. A220

RING, Cynthia, Vice President Human Resources and Patient Experience, HealthAlliance Hospitals, Leominster, MA, p. A311

RING, Melissa, M.D., Chief Executive Officer, Alaska Psychiatric Institute, Anchorage, AK, p. A28

RINGE, Kathy, Director Human Resources, Sage Rehabilitation Hospital, Baton Rouge, LA, p. A274

RINGER, Dave, M.D. Chief of Staff, St. Mary's Good Samaritan Hospital, Greensboro, GA, p. A160

RINGLER, Judith A., Chief Information Resources Management, San Franciso Veterans Affairs Medical Center, San Francisco, CA, p. A91

RINKENBERGER, Sean, Chief Financial Officer, St. Andrew's Health Center, Bottineau, ND, p. A476

RINTOUL, Alexander M., Chief Executive Officer, The Medical Center at Elizabeth Place, Dayton, OH, p. A492

RION, Trey, Chief Information Officer, West Calcasieu Cameron Hospital, Sulphur, LA, p. A289

RIORDAN, Michael C., President and Chief Executive Officer, Greenville Health System, Greenville, SC, p. B62

RIOS, Cindy, Chief Financial Officer, Medical Center of Southeastern Oklahoma, Durant, OK, p. A510

RIOS, Jose C., Director Information Services, Murray Medical Center, Chatsworth, GA, p. A155

RIOS, Margot, R.N. Chief Nursing Officer, CHRISTUS Spohn Hospital Alice, Alice, TX, p. A595

RIPPE, Diana, Chief Financial Officer, Tri Valley Health System, Cambridge, NE, p. A394

RIPPERGER, Ted, Administrative Director Human Resources, Atrium Medical Center, Middletown, OH, p. A498

RIPPEY, Wesley E., M.D. Chief Medical Officer, Adventist Medical Center–Portland, Portland, OR, p. A528

RIPSCH, Sue, R.N. Vice President and Chief Nursing Officer, Mercy Hospital and Trauma Center, Janesville, WI, p. A707

RISBY, Emile, M.D. Clinical Director, Georgia Regional Hospital at Atlanta, Decatur, GA, p. A158

RISER, Donna, Administrator, Lackey Memorial Hospital, Forest, MS, p. A358

RISHA, Holly, Administrative Director Human Resources, College Hospital Cerritos, Cerritos, CA, p. A59

RISINGER, Jeff, Director Human Resources, UAMS Medical Center, Little Rock, AR, p. A49

RISK II, Carl W., Administrator, St. Vincent Jennings Hospital, North Vernon, IN, p. A220

RISKA, Marilouise, Chief Executive Officer, Select Specialty Hospital–Northwest Detroit, Detroit, MI, p. A322

RISLOW, Deb, Chief Information Officer, Gundersen Health System, La Crosse, WI, p. A707

RISSE, Thomas, Chief Financial Officer and Vice President Business Services, Kaiser Permanente Medical Center, Honolulu, HI, p. A170

RISSI, Daniel, M.D. Vice President, Chief Medical and Clinical Operations Officer, Lawrence + Memorial Hospital, New London, CT, p. A116

RITCHEY, Jim, Director Human Resources, Sky Ridge Medical Center, Lone Tree, CO, p. A109

RITCHIE, Ann, Director Human Resources, Ochsner St. Anne General Hospital, Raceland, LA, p. A287

RITCHIE, Bruce, Vice President of Finance and Chief Financial Officer, Peninsula Regional Medical Center, Salisbury, MD, p. A303

RITCHIE, Jim, Director Management Information Systems, South Shore Hospital, Chicago, IL, p. A186

RITCHIE, Shannan, Interim President, Lakewood Hospital, Lakewood, OH, p. A496

RITON, John, Director Information Services, Memorial Hospital of Tampa, Tampa, FL, p. A148

RITTENOUR, Melanie, Director Human Resources, Paulding County Hospital, Paulding, OH, p. A500

RITTER, Jane, R.N. Chief Nursing Officer, Lovelace Women's Hospital, Albuquerque, NM, p. A426

RITTER, Robert G., Associate Director, Harry S. Truman Memorial Veterans Hospital, Columbia, MO, p. A370

RITTMAN, Todd, Director of Nursing, Larue D. Carter Memorial Hospital, Indianapolis, IN, p. A214

RITZ, Robert P., FACHE,
President, Mercy Medical Center – West Lakes, West Des Moines, IA, p. A239
President, Mercy Medical Center–Des Moines, Des Moines, IA, p. A229

RIVARD, Betty, Vice President Human Resources, Gillette Children's Specialty Healthcare, Saint Paul, MN, p. A351

RIVAS, Eloy, Director of Information Systems, Venice Regional Bayfront Health, Venice, FL, p. A149

RIVAS, Jessica, R.N. Vice President and Chief Nursing Officer, John C. Lincoln Deer Valley Hospital, Phoenix, AZ, p. A36

RIVAS, Jose, M.D. Chief of Staff, Community Hospital of Huntington Park, Huntington Park, CA, p. A67

RIVAS, Ramon Rodriguez, M.D. Medical Director, Hospital San Cristobal, Coto Laurel, PR, p. A725

RIVERA, Anita, Director Human Resources, Peninsula Hospital, Louisville, TN, p. A587

RIVERA, Anthony, Director Human Resources, Hartgrove Hospital, Chicago, IL, p. A184

RIVERA, Christina, Director Human Resources, Southwest General Hospital, San Antonio, TX, p. A647

RIVERA, Cristina, Chief Executive Officer, Rio Grande Regional Hospital, McAllen, TX, p. A637

RIVERA, Enrique, Chief Financial Officer, Bella Vista Hospital, Mayaguez, PR, p. A726

RIVERA, Ivonne, Director Finance, Hospital Oriente, Humacao, PR, p. A726

RIVERA, Jamie, Chief Financial Officer, Hospital Dr. Cayetano Coll Y Toste, Arecibo, PR, p. A724

RIVERA, Joe, Chief Information Technology Officer, Laredo Medical Center, Laredo, TX, p. A633

RIVERA, Jose Garcia, Director Human Resources, Hospital Buen Samaritano, Aguadilla, PR, p. A724

RIVERA, Luis, Director Human Resources, San Juan Capestrano Hospital, San Juan, PR, p. A728

RIVERA, Maria, Director Human Resources, Westside Regional Medical Center, Plantation, FL, p. A143

RIVERA, Zamarys, R.N. Chief Nursing Officer, HEALTHSOUTH Rehabilitation Hospital of San Juan, San Juan, PR, p. A728

RIVERA–POL, Noriselle, Vice President Finance, Hospital Manati Medical Center, Manati, PR, p. A726

RIVERS, Guy, Chief Financial Officer, Columbia Memorial Hospital, Astoria, OR, p. A523

RIVERS, Jan, Director Human Resources, Ochsner Medical Center–Baton Rouge, Baton Rouge, LA, p. A273

RIVERS, Kenneth I., President and Chief Executive Officer, Hollywood Presbyterian Medical Center, Los Angeles, CA, p. A72

RIVES, Patricia, R.N. Chief Nursing Officer, Western Medical Center–Santa Ana, Santa Ana, CA, p. A93

RIVEST, Jeffrey A., FACHE,
President and Chief Executive Officer, University of Maryland Medical Center, Baltimore, MD, p. A298
President and Chief Executive Officer, University of Maryland Medical Center Midtown Campus, Baltimore, MD, p. A298

RIVOIRE, John, Administrator, Louisiana Extended Care Hospital of Natchitoches, Natchitoches, LA, p. A285

RIZK, Magdy, M.D. Chief of Staff, West Houston Medical Center, Houston, TX, p. A628

RIZK, Norman, M.D. Chief Medical Officer, Stanford Hospital and Clinics, Palo Alto, CA, p. A82

RIZK, Rob, Director Information Technology, Good Shepherd Health Care System, Hermiston, OR, p. A525

RIZKALLA, Nasseem, M.D. Chief Medical Officer, NORTHSTAR Health System, Iron River, MI, p. A327

RIZZO, Frank, Chief Financial Officer, Central Region, North Shore University Hospital, Manhasset, NY, p. A440

ROACH, Crystal, Chief Financial Officer, TrustPoint Hospital, Lubbock, TX, p. A635

ROACH, David, Vice President Information Systems, Kadlec Regional Medical Center, Richland, WA, p. A687

ROACH, Dee A., M.D. Chief of Staff, Mitchell County Hospital, Coiorado City, TX, p. A607

ROACH, Donna, Chief Information Officer, Borgess Medical Center, Kalamazoo, MI, p. A328

ROACH, Geoff, Director Human Resources, Barrett Hospital & HealthCare, Dillon, MT, p. A387

ROACH, Joseph, Chief Executive Officer, Holy Family Hospital and Medical Center, Methuen, MA, p. A312

ROACH, Maureen, Senior Chief Financial Officer, Kindred Hospital–St. Louis, Saint Louis, MO, p. A380

ROACH, Patricia A., R.N. Senior Vice President and Chief Nursing Officer, Faxton–St. Luke's Healthcare, Utica, NY, p. A456

ROACH, Steven P., FACHE, President and Chief Executive Officer, UMass Memorial–Marlborough Hospital, Marlborough, MA, p. A312

ROADER, Charles, Vice President Finance, Edgerton Hospital and Health Services, Edgerton, WI, p. A704

ROANHORSE, Anslem, Chief Executive Officer, U. S. Public Health Service Indian Hospital, Crownpoint, NM, p. A428

ROARK, Chris, Chief Information Officer, Stillwater Medical Center, Stillwater, OK, p. A519

ROARK, Robert, Director Human Resources, Laughlin Memorial Hospital, Greeneville, TN, p. A583

ROARTY, Maureen, Executive Vice President Human Resources, Nassau University Medical Center, East Meadow, NY, p. A437

ROAT, David, D.O. Medical Director, Ancora Psychiatric Hospital, Hammonton, NJ, p. A416

ROATH, Lee, System Chief Information Officer, Benefis Hospitals, Great Falls, MT, p. A388

ROB, Lee, Director Human Resources, Pioneer Community Hospital of Aberdeen, Aberdeen, MS, p. A355

ROBB, Joy, Vice President Human Resources, Prairie View, Newton, KS, p. A250

ROBBINS, Dan, Information Technology and Account Executive, St. Vincent Medical Center, Los Angeles, CA, p. A75

ROBBINS, Danielle A., Vice President Human Resources, St. Catherine of Siena Medical Center, Smithtown, NY, p. A454

ROBBINS, Jr., Donald, M.D. Chief Staff, Hills & Dales General Hospital, Cass City, MI, p. A320

ROBBINS, Jan, M.D. Chief of Staff, Tennova Healthcare–LaFollette Medical Center, La Follette, TN, p. A586

ROBBINS, Joe, M.D. Vice President Medical Affairs, Sentara Williamsburg Regional Medical Center, Williamsburg, VA, p. A680

ROBBINS, Juanita D., Chief Operating and Development Officer, University of Maryland Rehabilitation and Orthopaedic Institute, Baltimore, MD, p. A298

ROBBINS, Shannon, Chief Operating Officer, Ohio Hospital for Psychiatry, Columbus, OH, p. A490

ROBEANO, Karen, R.N. Chief Nursing Officer and Vice President Patient Care Services, FirstHealth Moore Regional Hospital, Pinehurst, NC, p. A470

ROBERGE, Jeremy
Director Reimbursement, Androscoggin Valley Hospital, Berlin, NH, p. A409
Chief Financial Officer, Huggins Hospital, Wolfeboro, NH, p. A412

ROBERSON, Ed, Director Information Systems, Houston Northwest Medical Center, Houston, TX, p. A625

ROBERSON, Joe, Chief Executive Officer, Reliant Rehabilitation Hospital Abilene, Abilene, TX, p. A595

ROBERSON, Lynda, Senior Program Director, Rusk State Hospital, Rusk, TX, p. A645

ROBERSON, Madeleine, Chief Executive Officer, Presbyterian–St. Luke's Medical Center, Denver, CO, p. A105

ROBERSON, Meika, M.D. Chief Medical Officer, Hoboken University Medical Center, Hoboken, NJ, p. A417

ROBERT, Thomas W., Senior Vice President of Finance and Chief Financial Officer, Mercy Medical Center, Springfield, MA, p. A315

ROBERTS, Alden, M.D. Chief Medical Officer, PeaceHealth Southwest Medical Center, Vancouver, WA, p. A692

ROBERTS, Allyson, CPA Chief Financial Officer, Nor–Lea General Hospital, Lovington, NM, p. A429

ROBERTS, Andrew, Interim Chief Human Resources Officer, Veterans Affairs Gulf Coast Veterans Health Care System, Biloxi, MS, p. A356

ROBERTS, Barbara, Chief Financial Officer, Robley Rex Veterans Affairs Medical Center, Louisville, KY, p. A266

ROBERTS, Bert, Controller, Miracle Mile Medical Center, Los Angeles, CA, p. A73

ROBERTS, Brad, Network Administrator, Swisher Memorial Hospital District, Tulia, TX, p. A653

ROBERTS, Cathy, Vice President Mission Integration Human Resources, Mercy Regional Medical Center, Durango, CO, p. A105

ROBERTS, Charles, M.D
Executive Vice President and Executive Medical Director, Children's Mercy Hospitals and Clinics, Kansas City, MO, p. A373
Medical Director, Children's Mercy South, Overland Park, KS, p. A252

ROBERTS, Cheryl, Chief Nursing Officer, McCamey County Hospital District, McCamey, TX, p. A637

ROBERTS, Curtis L., Chief Executive Officer, Select Specialty Hospital–Augusta, Augusta, GA, p. A154

ROBERTS, Cyndi, Director Human Resources, Plaza Medical Center of Fort Worth, Fort Worth, TX, p. A619

ROBERTS, Deborah, R.N. Chief Nursing Officer, The Surgical Hospital of Phoenix, Phoenix, AZ, p. A37

ROBERTS, Debra, Director of Human Resources, St. Luke's Lakeside Hospital, The Woodlands, TX, p. A653

ROBERTS, Floyd, M.D. Chief Medical Officer, Baton Rouge General Medical Center, Baton Rouge, LA, p. A273

ROBERTS, Greg, Superintendent, Oregon State Hospital, Salem, OR, p. A529

ROBERTS, Jack, Director Information Systems, Twin County Regional Hospital, Galax, VA, p. A671

ROBERTS, Jeff, Director Information Technology, Pinckneyville Community Hospital, Pinckneyville, IL, p. A200

ROBERTS, Joanne, M.D. Chief Medical Officer, Providence Regional Medical Center Everett, Everett, WA, p. A683

ROBERTS, Jonelle A., Chief Financial Officer, Cleo Wallace Centers Hospital, Westminster, CO, p. A112

ROBERTS, Kathryn, Director Human Resources, Mercy Medical Center–Dubuque, Dubuque, IA, p. A230

ROBERTS, Kenneth D., President, John T. Mather Memorial Hospital, Port Jefferson, NY, p. A452

ROBERTS, Kevin A., FACHE, President and Chief Executive Officer, Glendale Adventist Medical Center, Glendale, CA, p. A65

ROBERTS, Krista, Chief Operating Officer, St. Mary's Regional Medical Center, Enid, OK, p. A510

ROBERTS, Lisa, Chief Operating Officer, Purcell Municipal Hospital, Purcell, OK, p. A518

ROBERTS, Matthew S., Chief Executive Officer, Glenwood Regional Medical Center, West Monroe, LA, p. A290

ROBERTS, Michael, Chief Information Officer, Highlands Regional Medical Center, Prestonsburg, KY, p. A269

ROBERTS, Michele, Hospital Recruiter, Kindred Hospital–Greensboro, Greensboro, NC, p. A465

ROBERTS, Pamela W., Chief Executive Officer, McNairy Regional Hospital, Selmer, TN, p. A592

ROBERTS, Phillip, Vice President Finance and Chief Financial Officer, Columbus Community Hospital, Columbus, WI, p. A703

ROBERTS, Rob, Director Information Technology, Benson Hospital, Benson, AZ, p. A31

ROBERTS, Robert C.
Vice President, Baptist Health Extended Care Hospital, Little Rock, AR, p. A49
Senior Vice President Financial Services, Baptist Health Medical Center – North Little Rock, North Little Rock, AR, p. A51
Vice President and Chief Financial Officer, Baptist Health Medical Center–Arkadelphia, Arkadelphia, AR, p. A43
Senior Vice President Financial Services, Baptist Health Medical Center–Little Rock, Little Rock, AR, p. A49
Senior Vice President, Baptist Health Rehabilitation Institute, Little Rock, AR, p. A49

ROBERTS, Roslyn, Manager, Northside Hospital–Cherokee, Canton, GA, p. A155

ROBERTS, Stacie
Coordinator Human Resources, Baylor Specialty Hospital, Dallas, TX, p. A609
Coordinator Human Resources, Our Children's House at Baylor, Dallas, TX, p. A611

ROBERTS, Teresa, Chief Financial Officer, Ringgold County Hospital, Mount Ayr, IA, p. A234

ROBERTS, Todd, Manager Business Operations, Peninsula Hospital, Louisville, TN, p. A587

ROBERTSHAW, Hazel, R.N. Chief Nursing Officer, Vice President Patient Services, F. F. Thompson Hospital, Canandaigua, NY, p. A435

ROBERTSON, Bradley, Chief Financial Officer, Saint Francis Hospital, Memphis, TN, p. A589

ROBERTSON, Carla, Chief Operating Officer and Chief Financial Officer, Saline Memorial Hospital, Benton, AR, p. A43

ROBERTSON, Casey, Chief Executive Officer, Woodland Heights Medical Center, Lufkin, TX, p. A636

ROBERTSON, Darcy, Chief Financial Officer, Page Hospital, Page, AZ, p. A35

ROBERTSON, Gary W., Chief Executive Officer, Ferry County Memorial Hospital, Republic, WA, p. A687

ROBERTSON, James, Chief Executive Officer, White Mountain Regional Medical Center, Springerville, AZ, p. A39

ROBERTSON, Jr., James A., Chief Financial Officer, Bothwell Regional Health Center, Sedalia, MO, p. A382

ROBERTSON, Jean, M.D. Chief Information Officer, Fairfield Medical Center, Lancaster, OH, p. A496

ROBERTSON, John L., Administrator, West Central Georgia Regional Hospital, Columbus, GA, p. A156

ROBERTSON, Larry, President, Texas Health Center for Diagnostic & Surgery, Plano, TX, p. A642

ROBERTSON, Laura, R.N.,
Chief Executive Officer, Banner Baywood Medical Center, Mesa, AZ, p. A34
Chief Executive Officer, Banner Heart Hospital, Mesa, AZ, p. A34

ROBERTSON, Michael
Chief Executive Officer, Piedmont Fayette Hospital, Fayetteville, GA, p. A159
Chief Executive Officer, Piedmont Newnan Hospital, Newnan, GA, p. A164

ROBERTSON, Michelle, R.N.,
President and Chief Executive Officer, Seton Highland Lakes, Burnet, TX, p. A605
President and Chief Executive Officer, Seton Medical Center Williamson, Round Rock, TX, p. A645
President and Chief Executive Officer, Seton Northwest Hospital, Austin, TX, p. A599

ROBERTSON, Patricia Dianne, Chief Financial Officer, Mercy Hospital Watonga, Watonga, OK, p. A522

ROBERTSON, Patricia L., Executive Vice President, Mary Immaculate Hospital, Newport News, VA, p. A675

ROBERTSON, Steve
Vice President, Kapiolani Medical Center for Women & Children, Honolulu, HI, p. A170
Senior Vice President, Pali Momi Medical Center, Aiea, HI, p. A170
Executive Vice President and Chief Information Officer, Straub Clinic & Hospital, Honolulu, HI, p. A171
Executive Vice President Revenue Cycle Management and Chief Information Officer, Wilcox Memorial Hospital, Lihue, HI, p. A172

ROBERTSON, Tana, Chief Operating Officer, McCamey County Hospital District, McCamey, TX, p. A637

ROBERTSON, William G., President and Chief Executive Officer, MultiCare Health System, Tacoma, WA, p. B96

ROBERTSON, William G., President and Chief Executive Officer, MultiCare Tacoma General Hospital, Tacoma, WA, p. A691

ROBERTSON–KECK, Karen, Vice President Human Resources, MedStar Franklin Square Medical Center, Baltimore, MD, p. A297

ROBERTSTAD, John R., FACHE,
President, Oconomowoc Memorial Hospital, Oconomowoc, WI, p. A712
President, Waukesha Memorial Hospital, Waukesha, WI, p. A717

ROBESON, Gail, Vice President Patient Services, Huron Regional Medical Center, Huron, SD, p. A574

ROBESON, Ricky, Chief Executive Officer, AMG Specialty Hospital–Houma, Houma, LA, p. A278

ROBICHAUX, Matthew, Chief Financial Officer, John C. Fremont Healthcare District, Mariposa, CA, p. A76

ROBICHEAUX, James Warren
Senior Administrator, East Texas Medical Center Pittsburg, Pittsburg, TX, p. A642
Administrator, East Texas Medical Center–Gilmer, Gilmer, TX, p. A621
Interim Administrator, East Texas Medical Center–Quitman, Quitman, TX, p. A643

ROBINS, David, D.O. Chief of Staff, Starr Regional Medical Center–Etowah, Etowah, TN, p. A582

ROBINS, Scott, M.D. Chief Medical Officer, Covenant Children's Hospital, Lubbock, TX, p. A634

ROBINSON, Alan, Chief Financial Officer, Logan Regional Hospital, Logan, UT, p. A660

ROBINSON, Bradley, Chief Financial Officer, Evans U. S. Army Community Hospital, Fort Carson, CO, p. A106

ROBINSON, Carol, R.N. Chief Patient Care Services Officer, University of California, Davis Medical Center, Sacramento, CA, p. A88

ROBINSON, Cliff, M.D. Chief of Staff, Central Alabama Veterans Health Care System, Montgomery, AL, p. A23

ROBINSON, David, D.O. Medical Director, St. Joseph's Behavioral Health Center, Stockton, CA, p. A96

ROBINSON, Elena, Chief Human Resources Officer, Hospital HIMA San Pablo Caguas, Caguas, PR, p. A725

ROBINSON, Eric, Chief Executive Officer, Natchez Community Hospital, Natchez, MS, p. A363

ROBINSON, Girard, M.D. Senior Vice President Medical and Clinical Affairs, Spring Harbor Hospital, Westbrook, ME, p. A295

ROBINSON, Glenn A., Chief Executive Officer, Hillcrest Baptist Medical Center, Waco, TX, p. A655

ROBINSON, Jack, Chief Financial Officer, St. Joseph's Regional Medical Center, Paterson, NJ, p. A420

ROBINSON, James, Chief Financial Officer, George E. Weems Memorial Hospital, Apalachicola, FL, p. A123

ROBINSON, Jeanne, Director Human Resources, Inova Fair Oaks Hospital, Fairfax, VA, p. A670

ROBINSON, Jennifer, Administrator, Behavioral HealthCare Center at Clarksville, Clarksville, TN, p. A581

ROBINSON, John, M.D. Clinical Director, U.S. Public Health Service Indian Hospital, Redlake, MN, p. A350

ROBINSON, Lance, Associate Director, Amarillo Veterans Affairs Health Care System, Amarillo, TX, p. A596

ROBINSON, Mark, Associate Administrator and Chief Financial Officer, Hazel Hawkins Memorial Hospital, Hollister, CA, p. A67

ROBINSON, Mark, FACHE, Chief Executive Officer, Lake City Medical Center, Lake City, FL, p. A133

ROBINSON, Mary, Chief Nursing Officer and Vice President Patient Care Services, Texas Health Harris Methodist Hospital Southwest Fort Worth, Fort Worth, TX, p. A619

ROBINSON, Michael
Chief Executive Officer, Bon Secours Memorial Regional Medical Center, Mechanicsville, VA, p. A674
Executive Vice President and Administrator, Bon Secours–Richmond Community Hospital, Richmond, VA, p. A677

ROBINSON, Paul H., M.D. Medical Director, American Fork Hospital, American Fork, UT, p. A659

ROBINSON, Phil, Chief Financial Officer, Saint Agnes Medical Center, Fresno, CA, p. A64

ROBINSON, Phillip D., President, Lankenau Medical Center, Wynnewood, PA, p. A559

ROBINSON, Stephen, Chief Executive Officer, Ochsner Medical Center – Kenner, Kenner, LA, p. A280

ROBINSON, Susan Beth, Vice President Human Resources, St. Mary's Medical Center, Huntington, WV, p. A696

ROBINSON, Tim, Executive Vice President, Chief Financial and Administrative Officer and Treasurer, Nationwide Children's Hospital, Columbus, OH, p. A490

ROBINSON, Vance, Chief Information Officer, Iberia Medical Center, New Iberia, LA, p. A285

ROBINSON, William, Director Human Resources, HEALTHSOUTH Rehabilitation Hospital of Erie, Erie, PA, p. A538

ROBINSON, William J., Senior Vice President and Treasurer, UF Health Shands Hospital, Gainesville, FL, p. A130

ROBISCH, Christine, Senior Vice President and Area Manager, Kaiser Permanente San Francisco Medical Center, San Francisco, CA, p. A91

ROBINSON, Bruce, Vice President and Chief Information Officer, Cox Medical Centers, Springfield, MO, p. A383

ROBISON, Donna Gail, Interim Chief Executive Officer, Sayre Memorial Hospital, Sayre, OK, p. A518

ROBISON, Keith, Chief Information Officer, Woman's Christian Association Hospital, Jamestown, NY, p. A439

ROBISON, Neely, Director Human Resources, The BridgeWay, North Little Rock, AR, p. A51

ROBISON, Rob, Director Information Technology, Medical Center of South Arkansas, El Dorado, AR, p. A45

ROBISON, Ryan, Chief Nursing Officer, Sanpete Valley Hospital, Mount Pleasant, UT, p. A660

ROBISON, Wendell, M.D. Chief of Staff, Sheridan Veterans Affairs Medical Center, Sheridan, WY, p. A722

ROBITAILLE, Mark E., President and Chief Executive Officer, Martin Health System, Stuart, FL, p. A146

ROBSON, Marcia, R.N. Chief Nursing Officer, Ozarks Medical Center, West Plains, MO, p. A384

ROBSON, Melissa, President, Novant Health Prince William Medical Center, Manassas, VA, p. A673

ROCA, Robert, M.D. Vice President Medical Affairs, Sheppard Pratt Health System, Baltimore, MD, p. A297

ROCCO, Carmen, M.D. Chief Medical Officer, Presence United Samaritans Medical Center, Danville, IL, p. A187

ROCHA, Israel, Chief Executive Officer, Doctor's Hospital at Renaissance, Edinburg, TX, p. A615

ROCHA, Julie, Vice President Human Resources, Mercy Medical Center Merced, Merced, CA, p. A77

ROCHE, Kathleen M., R.N. Executive Vice President and Chief Operating Officer, Saint Francis Hospital and Medical Center, Hartford, CT, p. A114

ROCHE, Rick, Director Human Resources and Information Systems, Lakeside Medical Center, Belle Glade, FL, p. A123

ROCHE, Robert, M.D. Interim Chief Medical Officer, Brookhaven Memorial Hospital Medical Center, Patchogue, NY, p. A451

ROCHE, Sarah, Director Human Resources, Lakes Regional Healthcare, Spirit Lake, IA, p. A238

ROCHELEAU, John, Vice President Business Support and Information Technology, Bellin Memorial Hospital, Green Bay, WI, p. A705

ROCHESTER, Charmaine, Vice President Finance, Bon Secours–DePaul Medical Center, Norfolk, VA, p. A675

ROCK, Betty Ann, Vice President Nursing and Chief Nursing Officer, Uniontown Hospital, Uniontown, PA, p. A556

ROCK, David, Executive Vice President and Chief Operating Officer, Wyckoff Heights Medical Center,, NY, p. A449

ROCKSMITH, Eugenio, M.D. Medical Director, HEALTHSOUTH Rehabilitation Hospital of Vineland, Vineland, NJ, p. A424

ROCKWELL, Jane, Director Support Services, North Metro Medical Center, Jacksonville, AR, p. A48

ROCKWELL, Karla, Director of Nursing, Doctors Memorial Hospital, Bonifay, FL, p. A124

ROCKWOOD, John D., President, MedStar National Rehabilitation Hospital, Washington, DC, p. A121

RODDEN, Celeste, Chief Information Officer, Hillcrest Hospital Claremore, Claremore, OK, p. A509

RODDY, Thomas, Chief Operating Officer, Riverview Regional Medical Center, Gadsden, AL, p. A20

RODDY, Tim, M.D. Vice President Medical Affairs, Swedish/Edmonds, Edmonds, WA, p. A683

RODDY–STURM, Yvonne, R.N. Chief Nurse Executive, Kaiser Permanente Ontario Medical Center, Ontario, CA, p. A81

RODEN, George
Vice President Human Resources, Mercy Hospital Aurora, Aurora, MO, p. A367
Vice President Human Resources, Mercy Hospital Cassville, Cassville, MO, p. A369

RODENBAUGH, Cathy, Director Human Resources, Holy Rosary Healthcare, Miles City, MT, p. A389

RODERMAN, Nicki, Chief Nursing Officer, Denton Regional Medical Center, Denton, TX, p. A613

RODGE, Mark, Director Information Systems, Eaton Rapids Medical Center, Eaton Rapids, MI, p. A323

RODGERS, April, Vice President, Human Resources, Holy Name Medical Center, Teaneck, NJ, p. A423

RODGERS, Dondie, Interim Chief Nursing Officer, Memorial Hospital of Texas County, Guymon, OK, p. A511

RODGERS, Jamie, Interim Chief Executive Officer, Choctaw County Hospital, Ackerman, MS, p. A355

RODGERS, Kliff, Chief Financial Officer, Crawley Memorial Hospital, Shelby, NC, p. A472

RODGERS, Larry, Chief Executive Officer, Scenic Mountain Medical Center, Big Spring, TX, p. A603

RODIER, James Barton, M.D. Chief Quality Officer, Health Central Hospital, Ocoee, FL, p. A140

RODOWICZ, Darlene, Chief Financial Officer, Berkshire Medical Center, Pittsfield, MA, p. A313

RODRIGUES, Pablo, M.D. Medical Director, Vibra Hospital of Amarillo, Amarillo, TX, p. A596

RODRIGUEZ, Alex
Vice President and Chief Information Officer, St. Elizabeth Edgewood, Edgewood, KY, p. A260
Vice President and Chief Information Officer, St. Elizabeth Florence, Florence, KY, p. A261
Vice President and Chief Information Officer, St. Elizabeth Fort Thomas, Fort Thomas, KY, p. A261

RODRIGUEZ, Angie, Human Resources Business Partner, Carson Tahoe Continuing Care Hospital, Carson City, NV, p. A404

RODRIGUEZ, Ben A., Chief Executive Officer, Hialeah Hospital, Hialeah, FL, p. A130

RODRIGUEZ, Candie, Director Human Resources, Hospital San Cristobal, Coto Laurel, PR, p. A725

RODRIGUEZ, Edgardo, Director Management Information Systems, Auxilio Mutuo Hospital, San Juan, PR, p. A727

RODRIGUEZ, Enrique, M.D. Medical Director, Ilano Specialty Hospital of Lubbock, Lubbock, TX, p. A635

RODRIGUEZ, Heather, Chief Nursing Officer, Fresno Heart and Surgical Hospital, Fresno, CA, p. A64

RODRIGUEZ, Jaime, Chief Financial Officer, San Juan City Hospital, San Juan, PR, p. A729

RODRIGUEZ, Jose, Director Information Technology, Rehoboth McKinley Christian Health Care Services, Gallup, NM, p. A428

RODRIGUEZ, Jose Luis, Chief Executive Officer, Hospital Pavia–Santurce, San Juan, PR, p. A728

RODRIGUEZ, Jose O., M.D. Medical Director, Castaner General Hospital, Castaner, PR, p. A725

RODRIGUEZ, Joseph R., Chief Executive Officer, Acadia Vermilion Hospital, Lafayette, LA, p. A281

RODRIGUEZ, Laura, Director Medical Records, Hospital Del Maestro, San Juan, PR, p. A728

RODRIGUEZ, Lea, Chief Nursing Officer, Clara Maass Medical Center, Belleville, NJ, p. A413

RODRIGUEZ, Leticia, Controller, Ward Memorial Hospital, Monahans, TX, p. A638

RODRIGUEZ, Lizzette, Director Finance, Hospital San Francisco, San Juan, PR, p. A728

RODRIGUEZ, Mario, Chief Executive Officer, Laredo Specialty Hospital, Laredo, TX, p. A633

RODRIGUEZ, Maritza, Chief Financial Officer, Hospital Metropolitan, San Juan, PR, p. A728

RODRIGUEZ, Miguel, Medical Director, Caribbean Medical Center, Fajardo, PR, p. A725

RODRIGUEZ, Oscar, Chief Fiscal Officer, Veterans Affairs Caribbean Healthcare System, San Juan, PR, p. A729

RODRIGUEZ, Patricia M., Senior Vice President and Area Manager, Kaiser Permanente South Sacramento Medical Center, Sacramento, CA, p. A87

RODRIGUEZ, Ramon J., President and Chief Executive Officer, Wyckoff Heights Medical Center,, NY, p. A449

RODRIGUEZ, Rufus, M.D. Medical Director, Mayo Clinic Health System in Fairmont, Fairmont, MN, p. A343

RODRIGUEZ, Sara
Chief Financial Officer, Kindred Hospital Sugar Land, Sugar Land, TX, p. A650
Human Resources, Seton Smithville Regional Hospital, Smithville, TX, p. A649

RODRIGUEZ, Tammy, Vice President of Patient Care Services, Rollins–Brook Community Hospital, Lampasas, TX, p. A632

RODRIGUEZ, Tomas, Chief Information Technology Officer, First Hospital Panamericano, Cidra, PR, p. A725

RODRIGUEZ, Tony, Director Human Resources, South Texas Rehabilitation Hospital, Brownsville, TX, p. A604

RODRIGUEZ, Vilma, Director Human Resources, Hospital San Pablo Del Este, Fajardo, PR, p. A726

RODRIGUEZ, Wilfredo, M.D. Chief of Staff, Battle Creek Veterans Affairs Medical Center, Battle Creek, MI, p. A319

RODRIGUEZ SCHMIDT, Myriam T., Director Human Resources, Cardiovascular Center of Puerto Rico and the Caribbean, San Juan, PR, p. A728

RODRIQUEZ, Daisy, Director Human Resources, Fort Duncan Regional Medical Center, Eagle Pass, TX, p. A614

ROE, Carolyn J., R.N. Chief Nursing Officer, Copley Hospital, Morrisville, VT, p. A665

ROE, Timothy, Chief Information Officer, Hillside Rehabilitation Hospital, Warren, OH, p. A504

ROE, Timothy J., M.D., President and Chief Executive Officer, Rehabilitation Hospital of the Pacific, Honolulu, HI, p. A171

ROEBKEN, Curtis, M.D. Chief Medical Staff, Kentfield Rehabilitation and Specialty Hospital, Kentfield, CA, p. A68

ROEBUCK, Amanda, Director Patient Care Services, Genoa Community Hospital, Genoa, NE, p. A396

ROEDER, Donna, Chief Financial Officer, Jackson County Regional Health Center, Maquoketa, IA, p. A234

ROEDER, Werner, M.D. Vice President Medical Affairs, Lawrence Hospital Center, Bronxville, NY, p. A434

ROEDERER, Chris, Senior Vice President Human Resources, Tampa General Hospital, Tampa, FL, p. A148

ROEHRICH, Jeff, Chief Financial Officer, Spearfish Regional Surgery Center, Spearfish, SD, p. A577

ROEHRLE, Andreas, Director Finance, Sentara Williamsburg Regional Medical Center, Williamsburg, VA, p. A680

ROEMER, Dennis, Executive Vice President and Chief Financial Officer, Lancaster General Health, Lancaster, PA, p. A542

ROERICK, Diane, Interim Chief Nursing Executive, Albany Area Hospital and Medical Center, Albany, MN, p. A339

ROESER, William, President and Chief Executive Officer, Sparrow Ionia Hospital, Ionia, MI, p. A327

ROESLER, Bruce E., FACHE, President and Chief Executive Officer, Mercy Medical Center–New Hampton, New Hampton, IA, p. A235

ROETMAN, James D., President and Chief Executive Officer, Pocahontas Community Hospital, Pocahontas, IA, p. A236

ROEVER, Judy, MSN Chief Nursing Officer, Scenic Mountain Medical Center, Big Spring, TX, p. A603

ROFF, Lynette A., Director, Veterans Affairs Eastern Colorado Health Care System, Denver, CO, p. A105

ROGALSKI, Robert, Chief Executive Officer, Excela Health, Greensburg, PA, p. B58

ROGALSKI, Ted, Administrator, Genesis Medical Center–Aledo, Aledo, IL, p. A180

ROGAN, Edie, Manager Human Resources, Eastern State Hospital, Williamsburg, VA, p. A680

ROGENESS, Graham, M.D. Medical Director, Clarity Child Guidance Center, San Antonio, TX, p. A646

ROGERS, Aaron, Chief Executive Officer, Mountainview Medical Center, White Sulphur Springs, MT, p. A391

ROGERS, Bard, M.D. Chief of Staff, Golden Plains Community Hospital, Borger, TX, p. A603

ROGERS, Cindy, Chief Nursing Officer, Horton Community Hospital, Horton, KS, p. A246

ROGERS, David, Chief Executive Officer, Sanford Webster Medical Center, Webster, SD, p. A578

ROGERS, Doris, Vice President Human Resources, Saint Luke's Hospital of Kansas City, Kansas City, MO, p. A374

ROGERS, Emily, Director Human Resources, Community Westview Hospital, Indianapolis, IN, p. A213

ROGERS, Gregory H., President, MidMichigan Medical Center–Midland, Midland, MI, p. A330

ROGERS, Gus, Chief Financial Officer, Coffey County Hospital, Burlington, KS, p. A242

ROGERS, James H., FACHE, Chief Executive Officer, Select Specialty Hospital–Savannah, Savannah, GA, p. A166

ROGERS, Jared, M.D.,
Interim Regional President and Chief Executive Officer, Presence Covenant Medical Center, Urbana, IL, p. A204
Interim Regional President and Chief Executive Officer, Presence United Samaritans Medical Center, Danville, IL, p. A187

ROGERS, Joel, Chief Operating Officer, Minidoka Memorial Hospital, Rupert, ID, p. A178

ROGERS, Joseph E.C., M.D. Chief of Staff, John C. Fremont Healthcare District, Mariposa, CA, p. A76

ROGERS, Joseph J., Vice President and Chief Operating Officer, Redwood Memorial Hospital, Fortuna, CA, p. A63

ROGERS, Judith, Ph.D., President and Chief Executive Officer, Holy Cross Hospital, Silver Spring, MD, p. A303

ROGERS, Kathy, Vice President Marketing, San Luis Valley Health Conejos County Hospital, La Jara, CO, p. A108

ROGERS, Keith
Interim Administrator, Advance Care Hospital of Fort Smith, Fort Smith, AR, p. A46
Administrator, Advance Care Hospital of Hot Springs, Hot Springs National Park, AR, p. A47

ROGERS, LaDonna, Director Human Resources, T. J. Samson Community Hospital, Glasgow, KY, p. A262

ROGERS, Lucy, Chief Information Resource Management Systems, Veterans Affairs North Texas Health Care System, Dallas, TX, p. A612

ROGERS, Mark G.
Interim Vice President Finance and Chief Financial Officer, Genesis Medical Center, Illini Campus, Silvis, IL, p. A202
Chief Financial Officer, Genesis Medical Center–Aledo, Aledo, IL, p. A180
Interim Vice President Finance and Chief Financial Officer, Genesis Medical Center–Davenport, Davenport, IA, p. A228

ROGERS, Matt, Chief Financial Officer, Philhaven, Mount Gretna, PA, p. A545

ROGERS, Michael, Vice President Fiscal Services, Brattleboro Memorial Hospital, Brattleboro, VT, p. A665

ROGERS, Patricia, Director of Nursing, Dahl Memorial Healthcare Association, Ekalaka, MT, p. A387

ROGERS, Ralph, M.D. Vice President Medical Affairs and Chief Medical Officer, Spectrum Health – Butterworth Hospital, Grand Rapids, MI, p. A325

ROGERS, Randy, FACHE Chief Financial Officer, Rapides Regional Medical Center, Alexandria, LA, p. A272

ROGERS, Rhonda, Chief Financial Officer, Des Peres Hospital, Saint Louis, MO, p. A380

ROGERS, Richard K., FACHE Vice President Human Resources, Wayne Memorial Hospital, Goldsboro, NC, p. A465

ROGERS, Robert, Interim President, Mercy St. Francis Hospital, Mountain View, MO, p. A377

ROGERS, II, Robert T., M.D. Medical Director, Canton–Potsdam Hospital, Potsdam, NY, p. A452

ROGERS, Scott, Chief Operating Officer, Bear Valley Community Hospital, Big Bear Lake, CA, p. A58

ROGERS, Sherry L., MS Chief Nursing Officer, Redington–Fairview General Hospital, Skowhegan, ME, p. A295

ROGERS, Tammy, Director Human Resources, Mt. San Rafael Hospital, Trinidad, CO, p. A111

ROGERS, Valerie J., Director of Nursing, Cherokee Nation W.W. Hastings Indian Hospital, Tahlequah, OK, p. A519

ROGERS, William, Chief Medical Officer, Gilmore Memorial Regional Medical Center, Amory, MS, p. A355

ROGNESS, Robin, Vice President and Chief Financial Officer, Mercy Hospital of Folsom, Folsom, CA, p. A63

ROGOLS, Kevin L., FACHE, Administrator, Kalkaska Memorial Health Center, Kalkaska, MI, p. A328

ROGOZ, Brian, Vice President Finance and Treasurer, The Hospital of Central Connecticut, New Britain, CT, p. A115

ROHAN, Colleen, Director Human Resources, Little Company of Mary Hospital and Health Care Centers, Evergreen Park, IL, p. A190

ROHAN, Heather J.
Chief Executive Officer, Tristar Centennial Medical Center, Nashville, TN, p. A591
Chief Executive Officer, Tristar Centennial Medical Center at Ashland City, Ashland City, TN, p. A579

ROHLEDER, Scott, Chief Information Officer, Hays Medical Center, Hays, KS, p. A245

ROHMAN, Cindy, R.N. Vice President/Chief Nursing Officer, Lexington Medical Center, West Columbia, SC, p. A571

ROHN, Stephen G., M.D. VP and Chief Medical Officer, Hamilton Medical Center, Dalton, GA, p. A158

ROHRBACH, Dan D., President and Chief Executive Officer, Southwest Health Center, Platteville, WI, p. A713

ROHRBACH, William K., Chief Operating Officer, Memorial Hospital, Towanda, PA, p. A556

ROHRER, Harry
Chief Financial Officer, Bascom Palmer Eye Institute–Anne Bates Leach Eye Hospital, Miami, FL, p. A136
Chief Financial Officer, University of Miami Hospital, Miami, FL, p. A137
Chief Financial Officer, University of Miami Hospital and Clinics, Miami, FL, p. A138

ROHRER, Mark, M.D. Chief Medical Officer, Kindred Hospital–Boston, Brighton, MA, p. A308

ROHRICH, George A., FACHE, Chief Executive Officer, River's Edge Hospital and Clinic, Saint Peter, MN, p. A352

ROIG, Emilio, M.D. Network Medical Director, Devereux Hospital and Children's Center of Florida, Melbourne, FL, p. A135

ROIZ, PHR, JoAnn, Director Human Resources, HEALTHSOUTH Tustin Rehabilitation Hospital, Tustin, CA, p. A98

ROKAVEC, Kathleen, M.D. Medical Director, Kona Community Hospital, Kealakekua, HI, p. A172

ROKOSZ, Gregory, D.O. Senior Vice President Medical and Academic Affairs, Saint Barnabas Medical Center, Livingston, NJ, p. A417

ROKSVAAG, George, M.D. Chief Medical Officer, Hunterdon Medical Center, Flemington, NJ, p. A416

ROLAND, Brian, Chief Executive Officer, Hamilton General Hospital, Hamilton, TX, p. A622

ROLEK, Jim, Vice President Human Resources, Clara Maass Medical Center, Belleville, NJ, p. A413

ROLERSON, Jana, Chief Nursing Officer, Shands Live Oak Regional Medical Center, Live Oak, FL, p. A134

ROLEY, Margaret, Chief Nursing Officer, South Baldwin Regional Medical Center, Foley, AL, p. A20

ROLFE, David, Chief Information Officer, Madonna Rehabilitation Hospital, Lincoln, NE, p. A398

ROLFF, Christi, Director Business Development, San Joaquin Valley Rehabilitation Hospital, Fresno, CA, p. A64

ROLING, Robin, Chief Executive Officer, Hot Springs County Memorial Hospital, Thermopolis, WY, p. A723

ROLLI, Molli Martha, M.D. Medical Director, Mendota Mental Health Institute, Madison, WI, p. A708

ROLLING, Andy, Director of Finance, Regina Hospital, Hastings, MN, p. A345

ROLLINS, David, Chief Resource Management Division, Reynolds Army Community Hospital, Fort Sill, OK, p. A511

ROLLINS, David W., Chief Financial Officer, Mt. San Rafael Hospital, Trinidad, CO, p. A111

ROLLINS, James
  Chief Financial Officer, Arbour H. R. I. Hospital, Brookline, MA, p. A308
  Chief Financial Officer, Arbour–Fuller Hospital, Attleboro, MA, p. A305

ROLLINS, Larry, Supervisor Information Technology, McCamey County Hospital District, McCamey, TX, p. A637

ROLOFF, Maria, Vice President Human Resources, Mission Hospital, Asheville, NC, p. A460

ROLON, Waleska, Manager, Hospital Santa Rosa, Guayama, PR, p. A726

ROMACK, Lenae, Manager Human Resources, GLOBALREHAB Hospital – Fort Worth, Fort Worth, TX, p. A618

ROMAN, Eloy, M.D. Chief of Staff, Palmetto General Hospital, Hialeah, FL, p. A130

ROMAN, Linda K., Administrator, Coast Plaza Hospital, Norwalk, CA, p. A80

ROMAN, Marina, M.D. Medical Director, Hospital de la Universidad de Puerto Rico/Dr. Federico Trilla, Carolina, PR, p. A725

ROMAN, Tracy, Chief Financial Officer, Doctors Hospital of Manteca, Manteca, CA, p. A76

ROMANIA, Matt, Director of Nursing, Soldiers and Sailors Memorial Hospital, Wellsboro, PA, p. A557

ROMANICK, Odile, Chief information Officer, Day Kimball Hospital, Putnam, CT, p. A116

ROMANIELLO, Guy, Director Fiscal Services, Belmont Center for Comprehensive Treatment, Philadelphia, PA, p. A547

ROMANO, C. James, M.D. President Medical Staff, St. Francis Medical Center, Trenton, NJ, p. A423

ROMANO, Corinne, R.N. Chief Nursing Officer, HEALTHSOUTH Sea Pines Rehabilitation Hospital, Melbourne, FL, p. A136

ROMANO, Jana, Manager Human Resources, Good Shepherd Penn Partners Specialty Hospital at Rittenhouse, Philadelphia, PA, p. A548

ROMANO, Michael A., M.D. Vice President Medical Affairs, Methodist Jennie Edmundson Hospital, Council Bluffs, IA, p. A228

ROMANO, Sara, R.N. Vice President, Mountain View Hospital, Gadsden, AL, p. A20

ROMANOWSKI, Ellen, Chief Nursing Officer, HEALTHSOUTH Rehabilitation Hospital of Miami, Cutler Bay, FL, p. A126

ROMANS, Alan, Director Information Technology, Ashland Health Center, Ashland, KS, p. A241

ROMARY, Paul, Chief Executive Officer, Lemuel Shattuck Hospital, Jamaica Plain, MA, p. A311

ROMBERGER, Randall R., Administrator, Shriners Hospitals for Children–Greenville, Greenville, SC, p. A566

ROMEO, John, Chief Information Officer, Mercy Hospital and Medical Center, Chicago, IL, p. A185

ROMERO, Brenda, Administrator, Espanola Hospital, Espanola, NM, p. A428

ROMERO, Ed, Chief Financial Officer, Laredo Medical Center, Laredo, TX, p. A633

ROMERO, Frank, M.D
  Chief Medical Officer, Cox Medical Centers, Springfield, MO, p. A383
  Vice President Medical Affairs and Chief Medical Officer, Cox Monett, Monett, MO, p. A377

ROMIG, Glenn, Chief Financial Officer, Osceola Regional Medical Center, Kissimmee, FL, p. A133

ROMINE, Andy, Chief Nursing Officer, Trinity Medical Center, Birmingham, AL, p. A17

ROMINE, Donnie, Chief Operating Officer, St. Vincent's Medical Center Riverside, Jacksonville, FL, p. A132

ROMITO, Edmund J., Chief Information Officer, Genesis HealthCare System, Zanesville, OH, p. A506

ROMITO, John A., M.D. Chief Medical Officer, Overland Park Regional Medical Center, Overland Park, KS, p. A252

ROMO, Jose, Vice President Operations, Asante Rogue Regional Medical Center, Medford, OR, p. A527

ROMOFF, Jeffrey A., President and Chief Executive Officer, UPMC, Pittsburgh, PA, p. B147

RONAN, Barry P., President and Chief Executive Officer, Western Maryland Regional Medical Center, Cumberland, MD, p. A300

RONAN, John, President and Chief Executive Officer, Blue Hill Memorial Hospital, Blue Hill, ME, p. A292

RONCA, Cyndi, Director Human Resources, Twin Cities Hospital, Niceville, FL, p. A139

RONDE, Christa, Assistant Chief Financial Officer, Palo Verde Hospital, Blythe, CA, p. A58

RONE, Tom, Chief Clinical Officer, Kindred Hospital–Nashville, Nashville, TN, p. A590

RONKE, Lisa, Director Finance, St. Michael's Hospital Avera, Tyndall, SD, p. A577

RONUM, Josh, Chief of Staff, West River Regional Medical Center, Hettinger, ND, p. A478

ROODMAN, Richard D., Chief Executive Officer, UW Medicine/Valley Medical Center, Renton, WA, p. A687

ROOF, Marie, Executive Vice President Information Systems, Vibra Specialty Hospital of Portland, Portland, OR, p. A529

ROOKER, Mark, Director Information Systems, Susan B. Allen Memorial Hospital, El Dorado, KS, p. A243

ROONEY, Al, Director Information Systems, St. Vincent Healthcare, Billings, MT, p. A385

ROONEY, Jeffrey, Chief Financial Officer, University of Illinois Hospital & Health Sciences System, Chicago, IL, p. A187

ROONEY, Michael T., M.D., Interim President and Chief Executive Officer, St. Joseph Regional Medical Center, Lewiston, ID, p. A176

ROONEY, Ronald K., FACHE, Interim Chief Executive Officer, Drew Memorial Hospital, Monticello, AR, p. A50

ROONEY, Thomas, Chief Information Resource Management, Veterans Affairs Hudson Valley Health Care System–F.D. Roosevelt Hospital, Montrose, NY, p. A441

ROOP, Terri, Director Patient Care Services, Dickenson Community Hospital, Clintwood, VA, p. A669

ROOSA, Carol, Vice President Information Services and Chief Information Officer, Athol Memorial Hospital, Athol, MA, p. A305

ROOT, Jim, Vice President Human Resources, Saint Elizabeth's Medical Center, Wabasha, MN, p. A353

ROOT, Mary Ann, Supervisor Personnel, Essex County Hospital Center, Cedar Grove, NJ, p. A414

ROOT, Rodney Mark, D.O. Vice President Medical Affairs, Bakersfield Memorial Hospital, Bakersfield, CA, p. A57

ROPER, Embra, Chief Medical Officer, Regional Hospital for Respiratory and Complex Care, Seattle, WA, p. A688

ROPER, Sandra, Chief Human Resources, General Leonard Wood Army Community Hospital, Fort Leonard Wood, MO, p. A371

ROPER, William L., M.P.H., Chief Executive Officer, UNC Health Care, Chapel Hill, NC, p. B138

ROSA–TOLEDO, Luis R., M.D. Medical Director, Hospital Manati Medical Center, Manati, PR, p. A726

ROSAAEN, Nancy, Chief Executive Officer, McCone County Health Center, Circle, MT, p. A386

ROSADO, Jose, Chief Executive Officer, Hospital Metropolitan, San Juan, PR, p. A728

ROSALES, Teresa, M.D. Clinical Director, Mental Health Institute, Clarinda, IA, p. A227

ROSATI, Rosemarie, Chief Operating Officer, University Hospital, Piscataway, NJ, p. A421

ROSATO, Ricardo, M.D. President Medical Staff, Shands Lake Shore Regional Medical Center, Lake City, FL, p. A133

ROSBOROUGH, Brian S., M.D. Chief Medical Officer, OSF Saint Elizabeth Medical Center, Ottawa, IL, p. A199

ROSBURG, Deb, Chief Financial Officer, Sanford Sheldon Medical Center, Sheldon, IA, p. A237

ROSCOE, Joan
  Chief Information Officer, Shenandoah Memorial Hospital, Woodstock, VA, p. A680
  Chief Information Officer, Winchester Medical Center, Winchester, VA, p. A680

ROSE, Cheryi, Human Resources Director, Fulton County Medical Center, Mc Connellsburg, PA, p. A544

ROSE, Hugh, Vice President Fiscal Management, Palos Community Hospital, Palos Heights, IL, p. A199

ROSE, J. Anthony, President and Chief Executive Officer, Catawba Valley Medical Center, Hickory, NC, p. A466

ROSE, Kenneth, M.D. Chief Medical Staff, Wallowa Memorial Hospital, Enterprise, OR, p. A524

ROSE, Kim, Director Information Technology, Crouse Hospital, Syracuse, NY, p. A455

ROSE, Mary R., R.N. Chief Clinical Officer, Community Health Center of Branch County, Coldwater, MI, p. A321

ROSE, May, Director Human Resources, Memorial Hospital, Chester, IL, p. A183

ROSE, Michael S., Senior Vice President Finance and Chief Financial Officer, Southern New Hampshire Medical Center, Nashua, NH, p. A411

ROSE, Regina P., R.N. Vice President Nursing Services, Mid–Columbia Medical Center, The Dalles, OR, p. A530

ROSE, Richard T., Associate Director, Manchester Veterans Affairs Medical Center, Manchester, NH, p. A411

ROSE, Robert, R.N. Senior Vice President and System Chief Nursing Officer, Mother Frances Hospital – Tyler, Tyler, TX, p. A654

ROSE, Robin, R.N. Chief Nursing Officer, Gibson Area Hospital and Health Services, Gibson City, IL, p. A191

ROSE, Silvia B., R.N. Director of Patient Care Services, Vidant Bertie Hospital, Windsor, NC, p. A475

ROSE, Steven P., Chief Financial Officer, Conway Regional Medical Center, Conway, AR, p. A44

ROSE, Steven A., R.N., President and Chief Executive Officer, Nanticoke Memorial Hospital, Seaford, DE, p. A119

ROSECRANS, Brenda, Executive Director Human Resources, Sentara Albemarle Medical Center, Elizabeth City, NC, p. A464

ROSEMORE, Michael, M.D. Medical Director, HEALTHSOUTH Lakeshore Rehabilitation Hospital, Birmingham, AL, p. A16

ROSEN, Barry, M.D. Vice President Medical Management, Advocate Good Shepherd Hospital, Barrington, IL, p. A181

ROSEN, Michael, M.D. Chief Medical Officer, Havasu Regional Medical Center, Lake Havasu City, AZ, p. A34

ROSEN, Raymond, FACHE Vice President Operations, York Hospital, York, PA, p. A559

ROSENA, Robens, Director Information Systems, Delray Medical Center, Delray Beach, FL, p. A127

ROSENBALM, Jennifer, Manager Business Office, Veterans Affairs – Western Iowa Healthcare System, Omaha, NE, p. A400

ROSENBAUM, Victor, Chief Operating Officer, Alaska Regional Hospital, Anchorage, AK, p. A28

ROSENBERG, Steven
  Chief Financial Officer, Danbury Hospital, Danbury, CT, p. A113
  Senior Vice President, Chief Financial Officer and Treasurer, New Milford Hospital, New Milford, CT, p. A116

ROSENBERG, Stuart E., President and Chief Executive Officer, Johnson Memorial Hospital, Stafford Springs, CT, p. A117

ROSENBERGER–SLAMPACK, Janie
  Market Chief Executive Officer, Kindred Hospital Pittsburgh–North Shore, Pittsburgh, PA, p. A551
  Market Chief Executive Officer, Kindred Hospital–Heritage Valley, Beaver, PA, p. A533
  Market Chief Executive Officer, Kindred Hospital–Pittsburgh, Oakdale, PA, p. A547

ROSENBLATT, Michael, M.D. Medical Director, Kindred Rehabilitation Hospital Clear Lake, Webster, TX, p. A656

ROSENBURG, Deborah L., Vice President Human Resources, Chesapeake Regional Medical Center, Chesapeake, VA, p. A669

ROSENCRANCE, Daris, Chief Financial Officer, Monongalia General Hospital, Morgantown, WV, p. A697

ROSENCRANCE, Michael, Vice President Information Services, Spectrum Health – Butterworth Hospital, Grand Rapids, MI, p. A325

ROSENDAHL, Lisa, Director Human Resources, St. Cloud Veterans Affairs Health Care System, Saint Cloud, MN, p. A351

ROSENDORFF, Clive, M.D. Chief Medical Program, James J. Peters Veterans Affairs Medical Center,, NY, p. A444

ROSENFELD, Merryll, Vice President, Human Resources, Catholic Medical Center, Manchester, NH, p. A411

ROSENSTEIN, Gaynor, Vice President Operations, Bon Secours Community Hospital, Port Jervis, NY, p. A452

ROSENTHAL, J. Thomas, M.D. Chief Medical Officer, Ronald Reagan University of California Los Angeles Medical Center, Los Angeles, CA, p. A74

ROSENTHAL, Raul, M.D. Interim Chief of Staff, Cleveland Clinic Florida, Weston, FL, p. A150

ROSETTA, Kathy, Chief Nursing Officer, Laurel Ridge Treatment Center, San Antonio, TX, p. A646

ROSETTI, Sharon, R.N., Chief Executive Officer, Select Specialty Hospital–Wilmington, Wilmington, DE, p. A120

ROSHAN, Payman, Chief Operating Officer, Kaiser Permanente Baldwin Park Medical Center, Baldwin Park, CA, p. A57

ROSIAK, Michael, Chief Operating Officer, Weisman Children's Rehabilitation Hospital, Marlton, NJ, p. A418

ROSILES, Nancy, Director Human Resources, HEALTHSOUTH Rehabilitation Hospital of Arlington, Arlington, TX, p. A597

ROSKE, Jeff, D.O. Chief Medical Staff, Community Memorial Hospital, Sumner, IA, p. A238

ROSKOVSKI, Stephanie, Chief Operating Officer, Butler Health System, Butler, PA, p. A534

ROSLER, Andrea P., Vice President Human Resources, Huntsville Hospital, Huntsville, AL, p. A22

ROSMAN, Joseph, M.D. Chief Medical Director, RML Specialty Hospital, Chicago, IL, p. A186

ROSNER, Neil, Area Director Human Resources, Kindred Hospital–New Jersey Morris County, Dover, NJ, p. A415

ROSS, Aletha, Vice President Human Resources, Ingalls Memorial Hospital, Harvey, IL, p. A192

ROSS, Candace, Coordinator Human Resources, HEALTHSOUTH Western Hills Rehabilitation Hospital, Parkersburg, WV, p. A698

ROSS, Carmella, Manager Human Resources, The Hospital at Hebrew Health Care, West Hartford, CT, p. A118

ROSS, Charles, M.D. Vice President Medical Affairs, Chilton Medical Center, Pompton Plains, NJ, p. A421

ROSS, Chris, Chief Information Technology Officer, Mayo Clinic Hospital – Rochester, Rochester, MN, p. A350

ROSS, Harvey, Chief Executive Officer, Kindred Hospital–Denver, Denver, CO, p. A104

ROSS, Hoyt, Chief Executive Officer, Promise Hospital of Florida at The Villages, Oxford, FL, p. A141

ROSS, Jacqueline, Chief Human Resources Officer, Mann–Grandstaff Veterans Affairs Medical Center, Spokane, WA, p. A690

ROSS, James E.
Chief Operating Officer, Camden General Hospital, Camden, TN, p. A579
Vice President and Chief Operating Officer, Jackson–Madison County General Hospital, Jackson, TN, p. A584

ROSS, Jay, Chief Financial Officer, CHI St. Joseph's Health, Park Rapids, MN, p. A349

ROSS, Jeffrey, M.D
Medical Director, AMG Specialty Hospital–Albuquerque, Albuquerque, NM, p. A426
Chief of Staff, King's Daughters Medical Center, Brookhaven, MS, p. A356

ROSS, Jim
Interim Senior Vice President and Chief Operating Officer, University of Maryland Shore Medical Center at Dorchester, Cambridge, MD, p. A299
Interim Senior Vice President and Chief Operating Officer, University of Maryland Shore Medical Center at Easton, Easton, MD, p. A300

ROSS, John
Vice President, Franciscan St. Francis Health – Mooresville, Mooresville, IN, p. A219
Chief Financial Officer, I–70 Community Hospital, Sweet Springs, MO, p. A383

ROSS, Johnny Shane, Executive Medical Director, HEALTHSOUTH Rehabilitation Hospital of Austin, Austin, TX, p. A599

ROSS, Joseph, Chief Financial Officer, Livingston Regional Hospital, Livingston, TN, p. A587

ROSS, Joseph P., President and Chief Executive Officer, Meritus Medical Center, Hagerstown, MD, p. A301

ROSS, Kathy
Chief Information Officer, Providence Hospital, Mobile, AL, p. A22
Chief Information Officer, Sacred Heart Hospital of Pensacola, Pensacola, FL, p. A142

ROSS, Laurie, Chief Nursing Officer, Southampton Memorial Hospital, Franklin, VA, p. A671

ROSS, Lisa, Human Resources Officer, Greater Regional Medical Center, Creston, IA, p. A228

ROSS, Phil, Chief Executive Officer, Surgical Hospital of Oklahoma, Oklahoma City, OK, p. A516

ROSS, Randall W.
Chief Executive Officer, Renown Rehabilitation Hospital, Reno, NV, p. A408
Chief Executive Officer, Renown South Meadows Medical Center, Reno, NV, p. A408

ROSS, Robert, President and Chief Executive Officer, St. Luke's Cornwall Hospital, Newburgh, NY, p. A449

ROSS, Samuel Lee, MS, Chief Executive Officer, Bon Secours Baltimore Health System, Baltimore, MD, p. A296

ROSS Jr., Semmes, Administrator, Lawrence County Hospital, Monticello, MS, p. A363

ROSS, Shana, Vice President Human Resources, Bayhealth Medical Center, Dover, DE, p. A119

ROSS, Zeff, FACHE, Senior Vice President and Chief Executive Officer, Memorial Regional Hospital,, FL, p. A130

ROSS–COLE, Melissa, Director Human Resources, Regency Hospital of Northwest Arkansas, Fayetteville, AR, p. A45

ROSS–SPANG, Carol, Senior Vice President, Methodist Healthcare Memphis Hospitals, Memphis, TN, p. A589

ROSSDALE, Robert, Deputy Executive Director, Queens Hospital Center, Queens, NY, p. A448

ROSSER, Mary, Director Human Resources, Cadillac, MI, p. A320

ROSSETTI, Stephen J., Ph.D., President and Chief Executive Officer, Saint Luke Institute, Silver Spring, MD, p. A303

ROSSFELD, John, Interim Chief Executive Officer, Memorial Hospital at Craig, Craig, CO, p. A104

ROSSI, Alfred N., M.D., Chief Executive Officer, Hopedale Medical Complex, Hopedale, IL, p. A193

ROSSI, Coleen, Director Quality Services, HEALTHSOUTH Rehabilitation Hospital of Toms River, Toms River, NJ, p. A423

ROSSI, Lawrence, M.D. Clinical Director, Trenton Psychiatric Hospital, Trenton, NJ, p. A424

ROSSI, Mark F., Chief Operating Officer and General Counsel, Hopedale Medical Complex, Hopedale, IL, p. A193

ROSSITTO, Erica, R.N. Chief Nursing Officer, North Suburban Medical Center, Thornton, CO, p. A111

ROSSMAN, Greg, Chief Human Resource Officer, Denver Health, Denver, CO, p. A104

ROSSMANN, Barbara, R.N., President and Chief Executive Officer, Henry Ford Macomb Hospitals, Clinton Township, MI, p. A321

ROSSOW, Scott, D.O. Chief of Staff, Atchison Hospital, Atchison, KS, p. A241

ROSVOLD, Robert, Director Finance, Virtua Voorhees, Voorhees, NJ, p. A424

ROTELLA, William, Vice President Human Resources, University of North Carolina Hospitals, Chapel Hill, NC, p. A461

ROTENBERRY–BAGGETT, Katie, Administrative Assistant and Human Resources, Yalobusha General Hospital, Water Valley, MS, p. A366

ROTERT, Angela Lynne, Chief Clinical Officer, Kindred Hospital–Indianapolis, Indianapolis, IN, p. A214

ROTGER, Lindsey, Chief Nursing Officer, HEALTHSOUTH Cane Creek Rehabilitation Hospital, Martin, TN, p. A587

ROTH, Anna M., M.P.H., Chief Executive Officer, Contra Costa Regional Medical Center, Martinez, CA, p. A77

ROTH, Diane, Chief Financial Officer, Rockdale Medical Center, Conyers, GA, p. A157

ROTH III, Edward J., President and Chief Executive Officer, Aultman Hospital, Canton, OH, p. A485

ROTH III,, Edward J., President and Chief Executive Officer, Aultman Health Foundation, Canton, OH, p. B16

ROTH, Eugene, Vice President Information Services, Mercy Hospital St. Louis, Saint Louis, MO, p. A380

ROTH, Norman G., Executive Vice President and Chief Operating Officer, Bridgeport Hospital, Bridgeport, CT, p. A113

ROTH, Randy, Interim Chief Medical Officer, Singing River Health System, Pascagoula, MS, p. A364

ROTH, Steven, Vice President Informatics and Chief Information Officer, Pinnacle Health System, Harrisburg, PA, p. A540

ROTHBERGER, Richard, Corporate Executive Vice President and Chief Financial Officer, Scripps Green Hospital, La Jolla, CA, p. A68

ROTHE, Brian, Site Director Information Systems, Castle Medical Center, Kailua, HI, p. A171

ROTHERMICH, Michael, M.D. Chief of Staff, Hermann Area District Hospital, Hermann, MO, p. A372

ROTHMAN, Marc, M.D. Medical Director, Friends Hospital, Philadelphia, PA, p. A548

ROTHSCHILD, Marylee, M.D., Interim Director, Robley Rex Veterans Affairs Medical Center, Louisville, KY, p. A266

ROTHSTEIN, Fred C., M.D., President, University Hospitals Case Medical Center, Cleveland, OH, p. A489

ROTHSTEIN, Robert, M.D. Vice President Medical Affairs, Suburban Hospital, Bethesda, MD, p. A299

ROTY, Chris, President, Baptist Health La Grange, La Grange, KY, p. A263

ROUBIDEAUX, Yvette, M.P.H., Director, U. S. Indian Health Service, Rockville, MD, p. B136

ROULEAU, Greg, Vice President Nursing, Mercy Medical Center Merced, Merced, CA, p. A77

ROUND, Laurie, R.N. Chief Nurse Executive, Advocate BroMenn Medical Center, Normal, IL, p. A198

ROUNDS, Jason, Chief Operating Officer and Administrator, CHRISTUS St. Michael Health System, Texarkana, TX, p. A652

ROUNDY, Ann, Vice President Employee Services, Columbus Community Hospital, Columbus, WI, p. A703

ROUNSLEY, Karen, Controller, HEALTHSOUTH Chesapeake Rehabilitation Hospital, Salisbury, MD, p. A303

ROUSH, Sharon L., Chief Executive Officer, South Bay Hospital, Sun City Center, FL, p. A146

ROUSSEAU, Mickie, Director Human Resources, Terrebonne General Medical Center, Houma, LA, p. A279

ROUSSEL, Steve
Chief Financial Officer, Baylor Medical Center at McKinney, McKinney, TX, p. A637
Vice President Finance, Baylor Medical Center at Waxahachie, Waxahachie, TX, p. A656

ROUSSOS, Michael, Chief Operating Officer, Corpus Christi Medical Center, Corpus Christi, TX, p. A608

ROUTH, Lori, R.N
Nurse Administrator, Mayo Clinic Health System in Albert Lea, Albert Lea, MN, p. A339
Nurse Administrator, Mayo Clinic Health System in Austin, Austin, MN, p. A340

ROUX, Roger, Chief Financial Officer, Rady Children's Hospital – San Diego, San Diego, CA, p. A89

ROUZER, Cindy, Director Human Resources, Spooner Health System, Spooner, WI, p. A715

ROVITO, Kevin, Chief Financial Officer, Jackson Hospital, Marianna, FL, p. A135

ROW, Tyler, Director Information Technology, Fredonia Regional Hospital, Fredonia, KS, p. A244

ROWAN, Brian, Chief of Staff, North Georgia Medical Center, Ellijay, GA, p. A159

ROWAN, Cary, Chief Financial Officer, Sunnyside Community Hospital and Clinics, Sunnyside, WA, p. A690

ROWAN, R. C., Director Human Resources, Neosho Memorial Regional Medical Center, Chanute, KS, p. A242

ROWE, Aaron, Chief Financial Officer, Green Oaks Hospital, Dallas, TX, p. A610

ROWE, Chad D., Regional Director Human Resources, Aspirus Keweenaw Hospital, Laurium, MI, p. A329

ROWE, David B., Chief Executive Officer, Great Falls Clinic Medical Center, Great Falls, MT, p. A388

ROWE, Jeanne M., M.D. Chief Medical Officer, Shore Medical Center, Somers Point, NJ, p. A422

ROWE, Mike, M.D. Chief of Staff, Fayette Regional Health System, Connersville, IN, p. A208

ROWE, Paul W., Director Information Technology, St. Francis Hospital, Wilmington, DE, p. A120

ROWE, Richard, PharmD, Chief Executive Officer, Coast Plaza Hospital, Norwalk, CA, p. A80

ROWE, Scott, Chief Executive Officer, HEALTHSOUTH Chattanooga Rehabilitation Hospital, Chattanooga, TN, p. A580

ROWELL, Julie, R.N. Chief Nursing Officer, Thomas Hospital, Fairhope, AL, p. A20

ROWEN, Lisa, R.N. Senior Vice President and Chief Nursing Officer, University of Maryland Medical Center, Baltimore, MD, p. A298

ROWLAND, Claire, Director Human Resources, Acadia Vermilion Hospital, Lafayette, LA, p. A281

ROWLAND, Michael, M.D. Vice President Medical Affairs, Franklin Memorial Hospital, Farmington, ME, p. A293

ROWLAND, Nick, Chief Operating Officer, Pushmataha Hospital & Home Health, Antlers, OK, p. A507

ROWLAND, Robert, M.D. Medical Director, HEALTHSOUTH Rehabilitation Hospital of Tallahassee, Tallahassee, FL, p. A147

ROWLANDS, Dewey R., Vice President and Chief Financial Officer, Rome Memorial Hospital, Rome, NY, p. A453

ROWLEY, Charla, Chief Financial Officer, Southwest Mississippi Regional Medical Center, McComb, MS, p. A362

ROWLEY, Daniel, M.D. Chief of Medical Staff, Knoxville Hospital & Clinics, Knoxville, IA, p. A233

ROWLEY, Mike, Chief Executive Officer, Springbrook Behavioral Health System, Travelers Rest, SC, p. A570

ROY, Joel, Manager Information Systems, The Brook Hospital – KMI, Louisville, KY, p. A266

ROY, Merri, Director Information Services, Weatherford Regional Medical Center, Weatherford, TX, p. A656

ROY, Rock, Professional Services Director, Power County Hospital District, American Falls, ID, p. A174

ROY, Schindelheim, M.D. Chief of Staff, Mee Memorial Hospital, King City, CA, p. A68

ROYAL, Keli, Director Human Resources, Shenandoah Medical Center, Shenandoah, IA, p. A237

ROYAL, Ty, Executive Director of Support Services and Human Resources, Gibson Area Hospital and Health Services, Gibson City, IL, p. A191

ROYNE, Sharon
Interim Senior Vice President Human Resources, St. Francis Hospital, Federal Way, WA, p. A683
Interim Senior Vice President Human Resources, St. Joseph Medical Center, Tacoma, WA, p. A691

ROZELL, Becky, Chief Human Resources Officer, Madison County Hospital, London, OH, p. A496

ROZENBOOM, Steve, Chief Financial Officer, Holy Cross Hospital, Taos, NM, p. A431

ROZMUS, Mike, Director Information Systems, Sentara RMH Medical Center, Harrisonburg, VA, p. A672

ROZNOVSKY, Karen, Director Human Resources, Yoakum Community Hospital, Yoakum, TX, p. A658

RUBANO, Kathleen A., MSN Chief Nursing Officer, Corpus Christi Medical Center, Corpus Christi, TX, p. A608

RUBAR, Jackie, Administrative Assistant and Director Human Resources, Leesville Rehabilitation Hospital, Leesville, LA, p. A283

RUBE, David M., M.D. Clinical Director, New York City Children's Center,, NY, p. A446

RUBENS, Deborah, Director Human Resources, Shriners Hospitals for Children–Northern California, Sacramento, CA, p. A87

RUBERG, Greg, Administrator, Lake View Memorial Hospital, Two Harbors, MN, p. A353

RUBERTE, Henry, Administrator, Hospital San Gerardo, San Juan, PR, p. A728

RUBERTI, Charlene, Director Information Technology Development, Ancora Psychiatric Hospital, Hammonton, NJ, p. A416

RUBIN, Amir Dan, President and Chief Executive Officer, Stanford Health Care, Palo Alto, CA, p. B129

RUBIN, Amir Dan, President and Chief Executive Officer, Stanford Hospital and Clinics, Palo Alto, CA, p. A82

RUBIN, Nancy, Vice President Human Resources, Motion Picture and Television Fund Hospital and Residential Services,, CA, p. A73

RUBIN, Vincent, Chief Financial Officer, Southern California Hospital at Culver City, Culver City, CA, p. A61

RUBINATE, Donna, R.N. Chief Operating Officer, Good Samaritan Medical Center, Brockton, MA, p. A308

RUBINATE, Donna, R.N., Interim President, Quincy Medical Center, Quincy, MA, p. A314

RUBINO, Mark, M.D. Chief Medical Officer, Forbes Regional Hospital, Monroeville, PA, p. A545

RUBINSTEIN, Mitchell, M.D. Vice President Medical Affairs, Valley Hospital, Ridgewood, NJ, p. A422

RUBIO, Felipe, M.D. Medical Director, Kindred Hospital–Dayton, Dayton, OH, p. A492

RUBLE, Charalene, Chief Nursing Officer, Ilano Specialty Hospital of Lubbock, Lubbock, TX, p. A635

RUBLE, Chris, Executive Director, The Pavilion at Williamsburg Place, Williamsburg, VA, p. A680

RUCHTI, Kevin, Coordinator Information Systems, Grant Regional Health Center, Lancaster, WI, p. A708

RUCHTI, Robert D., Chief Executive Officer, Buchanan General Hospital, Grundy, VA, p. A671

RUCKER, Alisa, Vice President Finance and Chief Financial Officer, Washington Hospital, Washington, PA, p. A557

RUCKER, Genesia L., MSN Chief Nursing Officer, Vaughan Regional Medical Center, Selma, AL, p. A25

RUCKER, Marty, Chief Operating Officer, Carroll County Memorial Hospital, Carrollton, MO, p. A369

RUCKER, Sheryl, Chief Information Officer, Edgerton Hospital and Health Services, Edgerton, WI, p. A704

RUCKER, William H., Administrator, Riverland Medical Center, Ferriday, LA, p. A277

RUDBERG, Susan, M.D. Chief Medical Officer, Range Regional Health Services, Hibbing, MN, p. A345

RUDD, Barry, Chief Information Officer, Mayo Clinic Health System in Waycross, Waycross, GA, p. A169

RUDD, John, President and Chief Executive Officer, Cayuga Medical Center at Ithaca, Ithaca, NY, p. A439

RUDDEN, Elizabeth, Vice President Human Resources, Connecticut Children's Medical Center, Hartford, CT, p. A114

RUDEK, Charles M., Chief Information Officer, UPMC St. Margaret, Pittsburgh, PA, p. A552

RUDIN, Joel, Chief Executive Officer, New England Rehabilitation Hospital, Woburn, MA, p. A316

RUDIS, Lorrie, Vice President, Human Resources, Crotched Mountain Rehabilitation Center, Greenfield, NH, p. A410

RUDITZ, Bettiann S., Chief Nursing Officer, Broward Health North, Deerfield Beach, FL, p. A127

RUDNICK, Jim, Vice President Information Technology, Navos, Seattle, WA, p. A688

RUDOLF, Steven, Vice President Human Resources, Baptist Health Louisville, Louisville, KY, p. A265

RUDZIK, Donna, Director Human Resources, Hopkins County Memorial Hospital, Sulphur Springs, TX, p. A651

RUE, Loring, M.D. Senior Vice President, Quality Patient Safety and Clinical Effectiveness, University of Alabama Hospital, Birmingham, AL, p. A17

RUECKERT, Sebastian, M.D
Vice President and Chief Medical Officer, Alton Memorial Hospital, Alton, IL, p. A180
Chief Medical Officer, Christian Hospital, Saint Louis, MO, p. A380

RUEDISUELI, Amy, Chief Financial Officer, McKenzie Health System, Sandusky, MI, p. A334

RUELLO, Rocky, Vice President Human Resources, Mercy Hospital St. Louis, Saint Louis, MO, p. A380

RUETSCH, Rebecca, Human Resource Partner, CHI Health Creighton University Medical Center, Omaha, NE, p. A399

RUFAT, Berta, Controller, Baptist Health South Florida, South Miami Hospital, Miami, FL, p. A136

RUFF, Victoria, M.D. Medical Director, Select Specialty Hospital–Columbus, Columbus, OH, p. A491

RUFFOLO, Joseph A., President and Chief Executive Officer, Niagara Falls Memorial Medical Center, Niagara Falls, NY, p. A449

RUGE, Randy, Chief Executive Officer, Paulding County Hospital, Paulding, OH, p. A500

RUGGERO, Robert, Senior Vice President Operations, Lourdes Medical Center of Burlington County, Willingboro, NJ, p. A424

RUGGIERO, Taren, R.N. Vice President and Chief Nursing Officer, Holy Cross Hospital, Fort Lauderdale, FL, p. A128

RUGGLES, Kevin, M.D. Chief Medical Officer, Rockford Memorial Hospital, Rockford, IL, p. A201

RUIZ, Javier, M.D
Medical Director, Intracare North Hospital, Houston, TX, p. A625
Medical Director, Kingwood Pines Hospital, Kingwood, TX, p. A631

RUIZ, Jesus, Chief Executive Officer, Mesa Hills Specialty Hospital, El Paso, TX, p. A616

RUIZ, Kathleen, M.D. Associate Director Patient Care Services, Veterans Affairs Caribbean Healthcare System, San Juan, PR, p. A729

RUIZ, Mary, Chief Executive Officer, Manatee Glens Hospital and Addiction Center, Bradenton, FL, p. A124

RUIZ, Tony, Chief Operating Officer, Medical Center Health System, Odessa, TX, p. A640

RUKSTAD, Julie, Chief Financial Officer, Olympic Medical Center, Port Angeles, WA, p. A686

RUMBAUT, Michelle, Chief Strategy Officer, Guadalupe Regional Medical Center, Seguin, TX, p. A648

RUMFORD, Darren K., Chief Financial Officer, Geary Community Hospital, Junction City, KS, p. A246

RUMMEL, Jennifer
Director Human Resources, East Texas Medical Center Athens, Athens, TX, p. A598
Director Human Resources, East Texas Medical Center Fairfield, Fairfield, TX, p. A617

RUNGE, Andrew, Chief Operating Officer, Mercy Hospital Hot Springs, Hot Springs National Park, AR, p. A48

RUNNELS, Clay, Vice President Chief Medical Officer Washington County, Johnson City Medical Center, Johnson City, TN, p. A585

RUNT, David, Chief Information Officer, Banner Del E. Webb Medical Center, Sun City West, AZ, p. A39

RUNYAN, Mark
Director Information Systems, Pioneer Valley Hospital, West Valley City, UT, p. A664
Director Information Services, Salt Lake Regional Medical Center, Salt Lake City, UT, p. A663

RUPA, Maitra, M.D. Acting Medical Director, Chester Mental Health Center, Chester, IL, p. A183

RUPERT, Duke, President and Chief Executive Officer, West Penn Hospital, Pittsburgh, PA, p. A552

RUPERT, James M., Chief Fiscal Services, Battle Creek Veterans Affairs Medical Center, Battle Creek, MI, p. A319

RUPERT, Michael J., Chief Financial Officer, Veterans Affairs Long Beach Healthcare System, Long Beach, CA, p. A70

RUPP, Kathy, R.N. Chief Nursing Officer, HEALTHSOUTH Valley of the Sun Rehabilitation Hospital, Glendale, AZ, p. A33

RUPP, Robert, Chief Executive Officer, Harris Hospital, Newport, AR, p. A51

RUPP, William C., M.D., Chief Executive Officer, Mayo Clinic Jacksonville, Jacksonville, FL, p. A131

RUPPERT, Jennifer, Chief Financial Officer, Iowa City Veterans Affairs Health Care System, Iowa City, IA, p. A232

RUPPERT SCHILLER, Kerri
Senior Vice President and Chief Financial Officer, Children's Hospital at Mission, Mission Viejo, CA, p. A77
Senior Vice President and Chief Financial Officer, Children's Hospital of Orange County, Orange, CA, p. A81

RUSCITTO, Kathryn H., President, St. Joseph's Hospital Health Center, Syracuse, NY, p. A456

RUSH, Andy, Senior Vice President and Chief Operating Officer, Somerset Hospital, Somerset, PA, p. A555

RUSH, Ann Marie, Chief Financial Officer, Penobscot Valley Hospital, Lincoln, ME, p. A294

RUSH, Cindy, Director Human Resources, Clay County Medical Center, Clay Center, KS, p. A242

RUSH, Donald J., Chief Executive Officer, Providence Kodiak Island Medical Center, Kodiak, AK, p. A29

RUSH, Ed, President and Chief Executive Officer, Iredell Memorial Hospital, Statesville, NC, p. A473

RUSH, Jeff, Chief Financial Officer, Rutherford Regional Health System, Rutherfordton, NC, p. A472

RUSH, Jeff W., Chief Financial Officer, Wallace Thomson Hospital, Union, SC, p. A570

RUSH, Matthew, President and Chief Executive Officer, Hayes Green Beach Memorial Hospital, Charlotte, MI, p. A320

RUSHIN, Denise, Director Human Resources, Poplar Bluff Regional Medical Center, Poplar Bluff, MO, p. A378

RUSHING, Heath, Chief Operating Officer, Memorial Hermann Northeast, Humble, TX, p. A628

RUSHING, R. Lynn, Chief Executive Officer, Brook Lane Health Services, Hagerstown, MD, p. A301

RUSHING, Robyn, Administrator, Lakeview Specialty Hospital and Rehabilitation Center, Waterford, WI, p. A717

RUSHLOW, David, Vice President Medical Affairs, Mayo Clinic Health System – Franciscan Healthcare in La Crosse, La Crosse, WI, p. A707

RUSINKO, Steve, Chief Financial Officer, Eastern Regional Medical Center, Philadelphia, PA, p. A548

RUSK, Scott, M.D. Vice President Medical Administration, Mercy Hospital of Portland, Portland, ME, p. A294

RUSKOWSKI, David, President, Franciscan St. Anthony Health – Crown Point, Crown Point, IN, p. A209

RUSNACZYK, John, Senior Vice President and Chief Financial Officer, St. Vincent Charity Medical Center, Cleveland, OH, p. A489

RUSS, Nicole L., Vice President Colleague Relations, Alliance Community Hospital, Alliance, OH, p. A482

RUSSEL, Kimberly A., FACHE, President and Chief Executive Officer, Bryan Health, Lincoln, NE, p. B25

RUSSELL, Bill, Senior Chief Information Officer, Mission Hospital, Mission Viejo, CA, p. A77

RUSSELL, Dardanella, Chief Human Resources Management Service, Veterans Affairs Hudson Valley Health Care System–F.D. Roosevelt Hospital, Montrose, NY, p. A441

RUSSELL, Donald
Vice President, Adventist GlenOaks Hospital, Glendale Heights, IL, p. A191
Regional Vice President Human Resources, Adventist Hinsdale Hospital, Hinsdale, IL, p. A193

RUSSELL, Erin, Controller, Kindred Hospital–San Antonio, San Antonio, TX, p. A646

RUSSELL, Freda, R.N., Chief Executive Officer and Chief Nursing Officer, Three Rivers Hospital, Waverly, TN, p. A594

RUSSELL, Georgette, Vice President of Talent & Organizational Effectiveness, Carson City Hospital, Carson City, MI, p. A320

RUSSELL, James G., Chief Operating Officer, Medical Center of Lewisville, Lewisville, TX, p. A633

RUSSELL, John D., President and Chief Executive Officer, Columbus Community Hospital, Columbus, WI, p. A703

RUSSELL, Jon
Vice President Information Systems, Kettering Medical Center, Kettering, OH, p. A495
Chief Information Officer, Sycamore Medical Center, Miamisburg, OH, p. A498

RUSSELL, Judy, Director of Nurses, Ochiltree General Hospital, Perryton, TX, p. A642

RUSSELL, Karen, Director Human Resources, Perry Memorial Hospital, Princeton, IL, p. A200

RUSSELL, Kathy, R.N. Chief Nursing Officer, Bluegrass Community Hospital, Versailles, KY, p. A271

RUSSELL, Kim, M.D. Chief of Staff, Scott & White Hospital – Llano, Llano, TX, p. A633

RUSSELL, Linda, Vice President and Chief Nursing Officer, Self Regional Healthcare, Greenwood, SC, p. A567

RUSSELL, Linda B., Chief Executive Officer, Woman's Hospital of Texas, Houston, TX, p. A628

RUSSELL, Michelle L., Administrator, Community Howard Specialty Hospital, Kokomo, IN, p. A216

RUSSELL, Nancy, Chief Financial Officer, Clifton–Fine Hospital, Star Lake, NY, p. A455

RUSSELL, Patti, Vice President Nursing, Masonicare Health Center, Wallingford, CT, p. A117

RUSSELL, Randall, Vice President and Chief Financial Officer, Memorial Hospital and Health Care Center, Jasper, IN, p. A215

RUSSELL, Robert, Chief Operating Officer, Atlanta Medical Center, Atlanta, GA, p. A152

RUSSELL, Robert J., Associate Executive Director Operations, Penn Presbyterian Medical Center, Philadelphia, PA, p. A549

RUSSELL, Shelia, Director Human Resources, Jamestown Regional Medical Center, Jamestown, TN, p. A584

RUSSELL, Shelly, Chief Executive Officer, Mitchell County Regional Health Center, Osage, IA, p. A236

RUSSELL, Sherrie
Vice President and Chief Information Officer, Alexian Brothers Behavioral Health Hospital, Hoffman Estates, IL, p. A193
Chief Information Officer, St. Alexius Medical Center, Hoffman Estates, IL, p. A193

RUSSELL, Susan, Chief Financial Officer, OCH Regional Medical Center, Starkville, MS, p. A365

RUSSELL, Thomas, President and Chief Executive Officer, Adventist Medical Center–Portland, Portland, OR, p. A528

RUSSELL, Tim, Administrator, Stillwater Community Hospital, Columbus, MT, p. A386

RUSSELL, William B., Chief Executive Officer, Three Rivers Health, Three Rivers, MI, p. A336

RUSSELL–COOK, Donna, FACHE, President, St. Elizabeth Hospital, Enumclaw, WA, p. A683

RUSSO, Arthur, M.D. Director Medical Affairs, Harrington Memorial Hospital, Southbridge, MA, p. A314

RUSSO, Kimberly, Chief Operating Officer, George Washington University Hospital, Washington, DC, p. A121

RUSSO, Mary Jo, R.N. Chief Nursing Officer, North Vista Hospital, North Las Vegas, NV, p. A407

RUSSO, Mike, Vice President Information Systems, Grimes St. Joseph Health Center, Navasota, TX, p. A639

RUSSO, Paul M., FACHE, Director, Miami Veterans Affairs Healthcare System, Miami, FL, p. A137

RUST, Jeff, Information Technology Systems Site Manager, Mercy Medical Center, Williston, ND, p. A480

RUSTIN, Wayne, Vice President, Chief Human Resources Officer, St. Vincent's Medical Center, Bridgeport, CT, p. A113

RUTH, Daniel R., President and Chief Executive Officer, Jewish Home of San Francisco, San Francisco, CA, p. A90

RUTH, Joseph, Executive Vice President and Chief Operating Officer, Sparrow Hospital, Lansing, MI, p. A328

RUTHER, Randy, Vice President Finance and Chief Financial Officer, Little Company of Mary Hospital and Health Care Centers, Evergreen Park, IL, p. A190

RUTHERFORD, C. Michael, Vice President Financial Services and Chief Financial Officer, Wake Forest Baptist Medical Center, Winston–Salem, NC, p. A475

RUTHERFORD, Cynthia, Manager Business Office, Hood Memorial Hospital, Amite, LA, p. A272

RUTHERFORD, Dennis E., CPA Chief Financial Officer, Gilbert Hospital, Gilbert, AZ, p. A32

RUTHERFORD, Jeremiah, Chief Medical Officer, Solara Hospital of Muskogee, Muskogee, OK, p. A514

RUTHERFORD, Peter, M.D.,
    Chief Executive Officer, Central Washington Hospital, Wenatchee, WA, p. A692
    Chief Executive Officer, Wenatchee Valley Medical Center, Wenatchee, WA, p. A692

RUTHERFORD, Ronald, Chief Information Officer, Beth Israel Deaconess Hospital Plymouth, Plymouth, MA, p. A314

RUTHERFORD, Theresa, FACHE, President and Chief Executive Officer, St. Anthony's Memorial Hospital, Effingham, IL, p. A188

RUTHS, Steve, M.D. Medical Director, Aurora Vista Del Mar Hospital, Ventura, CA, p. A99

RUTKOWSKI, James C., Chief Financial Officer, Southwest Regional Medical Center, Waynesburg, PA, p. A557

RUTKOWSKI, Jennifer, R.N. Vice President Professional Services, Grant Regional Health Center, Lancaster, WI, p. A708

RUTTER, James, M.D. Chief of Staff, Integris Grove Hospital, Grove, OK, p. A511

RUWOLDT, Steven T., Chief Operating Officer, Memorial Medical Center, Las Cruces, NM, p. A429

RUYTER, Mary J., Chief Executive Officer, Sanford Jackson Medical Center, Jackson, MN, p. A345

RYALS, Billie, Director Human Resources, Sullivan County Memorial Hospital, Milan, MO, p. A377

RYAN, Charleen, Vice President Nursing Services, Down East Community Hospital, Machias, ME, p. A294

RYAN, Chris, Chief Information Officer, Auburn Community Hospital, Auburn, NY, p. A433

RYAN, Christie, Chief Nursing Officer, HEALTHSOUTH Rehabilitation Hospital, Sewickley, PA, p. A555

RYAN, Christina M., R.N., Chief Executive Officer, The Women's Hospital, Newburgh, IN, p. A220

RYAN, Colleen
    Director Management Information Systems, Landmark Medical Center, Woonsocket, RI, p. A561
    Chief Information Officer and Vice President Professional Services, Rehabilitation Hospital of Rhode Island, North Smithfield, RI, p. A560

RYAN, Connie, Chief Nursing Officer, Select Specialty Hospital–Tulsa Midtown, Tulsa, OK, p. A521

RYAN, Cory, M.D. Chief of Staff, Wayne County Hospital, Monticello, KY, p. A267

RYAN, David P., Vice President Human Resources, Hallmark Health System, Melrose, MA, p. A312

RYAN, Debora, R.N. Vice President Patient Care, St. Francis Regional Medical Center, Shakopee, MN, p. A352

RYAN, Dennis, Senior Vice President and Chief Financial Officer, Children's Hospital of The King's Daughters, Norfolk, VA, p. A675

RYAN, Frank, Chief Financial Officer, Manchester Veterans Affairs Medical Center, Manchester, NH, p. A411

RYAN, Jacqueline, Director Human Resources, Mayo Clinic Health System in Lake City, Lake City, MN, p. A345

RYAN, Kimberly, Chief Executive Officer, Eastside Medical Center, Snellville, GA, p. A167

RYAN, Lisa M., Coordinator Human Resources, Hampstead Hospital, Hampstead, NH, p. A410

RYAN, Maria, Ph.D., Chief Executive Officer, Cottage Hospital, Woodsville, NH, p. A412

RYAN, Michael J., Chief Executive Officer, Herington Municipal Hospital, Herington, KS, p. A245

RYAN, Mike, Director of Information Services, Gunnison Valley Hospital, Gunnison, UT, p. A660

RYAN, Patrice
    Vice President Human Resources, Goleta Valley Cottage Hospital, Santa Barbara, CA, p. A94
    Vice President Human Resources, Santa Barbara Cottage Hospital, Santa Barbara, CA, p. A94
    Vice President Human Resources, Santa Ynez Valley Cottage Hospital, Solvang, CA, p. A95

RYAN, Patrick, Chief Financial Officer, Christ Hospital, Jersey City, NJ, p. A417

RYAN, Patrick G., Chief Executive Officer, Promise Hospital Baton Rouge – Main Campus, Baton Rouge, LA, p. A273

RYAN, Patrick J., Chief Human Resources Officer, Helen Hayes Hospital, West Haverstraw, NY, p. A457

RYAN, Rebecca, Interim Director Human Resources and Employee Health, Ukiah Valley Medical Center, Ukiah, CA, p. A98

RYAN, Robert, M.D. Chief Medical Officer, Guadalupe Regional Medical Center, Seguin, TX, p. A648

RYAN, Sharon, Regional Controller, Select Specialty Hospital–Macomb County, Mount Clemens, MI, p. A330

RYAN, Stacy, Corporate Director Human Resources, Warren General Hospital, Warren, PA, p. A557

RYAN, Tim, Director Finance, Centennial Peaks Hospital, Louisville, CO, p. A109

RYBA, Janice L., JD, Chief Executive Officer, St. Mary Medical Center, Hobart, IN, p. A213

RYBA, Thomas L., Chief Executive Officer, Lighthouse Care Center of Conway, Conway, SC, p. A565

RYBA, Tomi S., President and Chief Executive Officer, El Camino Hospital, Mountain View, CA, p. A79

RYBAK, Paul, Director Human Resources, Flambeau Hospital, Park Falls, WI, p. A713

RYBICKI, Catherine, Vice President Physician Services and Chief Operating Officer, Spectrum Health Big Rapids Hospital, Big Rapids, MI, p. A319

RYBICKI, Cathy, Chief Operating Officer, Spectrum Health Reed City Hospital, Reed City, MI, p. A333

RYBOLT, Andrew, Vice President and Chief Financial Officer, Redwood Memorial Hospital, Fortuna, CA, p. A63

RYCKMAN, George, D.O. Chief of Staff, Paul Oliver Memorial Hospital, Frankfort, MI, p. A324

RYDER, Jeff, Director Information Systems, Saint Joseph Mount Sterling, Mount Sterling, KY, p. A268

RYDER, John E.
    Chief Operating Officer, Borgess–Lee Memorial Hospital, Dowagiac, MI, p. A323
    Chief Operating Officer, Borgess–Lee Memorial Hospital, Dowagiac, MI, p. A323
    Administrator and Chief Operating Officer, Borgess–Pipp Hospital, Plainwell, MI, p. A332

RYDER, Ronald, D.O. President of the Medical Staff, Robert Wood Johnson University Hospital at Hamilton, Hamilton, NJ, p. A416

RYDER, Troy, Director of Nursing, Aspire Hospital, Conroe, TX, p. A607

RYERSON, Michelle, Chief Nursing Officer, University Medical Center at Brackenridge, Austin, TX, p. A600

RYKERT, Lauren P., Senior Vice President, Houston Methodist Hospital, Houston, TX, p. A624

RYLAND, Jennifer M., R.N. Chief Administrative Officer, Jackson Medical Center, Jackson, AL, p. A22

RYLE, Barry W., Chief Information Officer, Oswego Hospital, Oswego, NY, p. A451

RYLE, Deborah L., Administrator and Chief Executive Officer, St. David's Round Rock Medical Center, Round Rock, TX, p. A645

RYMER, Brandy, Coordinator Human Resources, Murray Medical Center, Chatsworth, GA, p. A155

RZENDZIAN, Michael, Chief Financial Officer, Baylor Emergency Medical Center at Aubrey, Aubrey, TX, p. A598

RZOMP, Kimberly
    Vice President and Chief Financial Officer, Chambersburg Hospital, Chambersburg, PA, p. A535
    Vice President Finance, Waynesboro Hospital, Waynesboro, PA, p. A557

S

SAADAT, Annette, Human Resources Business Partner, Saint Joseph Mount Sterling, Mount Sterling, KY, p. A268

SAAL, A. Kim, M.D. President Medical Staff, Mount Auburn Hospital, Cambridge, MA, p. A309

SAALFELD, Thomas, Senior Vice President and Chief Operating Officer, St. Elizabeth Fort Thomas, Fort Thomas, KY, p. A261

SAARI, Heidi L., Director, Human Resources, Upper Connecticut Valley Hospital, Colebrook, NH, p. A409

SAAVEDRA, JayLynn, Chief Information Officer, U. S. Public Health Service Indian Hospital, Parker, AZ, p. A35

SABA, Francis M., Chief Executive Officer, Milford Regional Medical Center, Milford, MA, p. A312

SABAHI, Hugh, M.D. President Professional Staff, Columbia Memorial Hospital, Astoria, OR, p. A523

SABANDIT, Elizabeth, Director Human Resources, Alhambra Hospital Medical Center, Alhambra, CA, p. A55

SABHARRWAL, Parajeet, Administrator, Minimally Invasive Surgery Center, Lenexa, KS, p. A248

SABIA, John, M.D. Vice President Medical Affairs, Northern Dutchess Hospital, Rhinebeck, NY, p. A452

SABIN, Bridget, Director Human Resources, Madison Hospital, Madison, MN, p. A346

SABIN, Margaret D., President and Chief Executive Officer, Penrose–St. Francis Health Services, Colorado Springs, CO, p. A104

SABLE, Kenneth N., M.D. Executive Vice President and Chief Operating Officer, Saint Peter's University Hospital, New Brunswick, NJ, p. A419

SABOTTA, John, Director Information Systems, St. Margaret's Hospital, Spring Valley, IL, p. A203

SABUS, Matthew, Director Information Systems, Boone County Hospital, Boone, IA, p. A226

SACCO, Frank V., FACHE, President and Chief Executive Officer, Memorial Healthcare System,, FL, p. B91

SACCOIO, Saria, M.D. Chief Medical Officer, Bon Secours St. Francis Health System, Greenville, SC, p. A566

SACHDEV, Aruna, M.D. Medical Director, Massachusetts Hospital School, Canton, MA, p. A309

SACHEDINA, Azeem, M.D. Chief of Staff, Broward Health Coral Springs, Coral Springs, FL, p. A126

SACHS, III, Henry T., M.D. Medical Director, Emma Pendleton Bradley Hospital, East Providence, RI, p. A560

SACHTLEBEN, Michael, Chief Operating Officer, MedStar Georgetown University Hospital, Washington, DC, p. A121

SACK, Michael V., FACHE, President and Chief Executive Officer, Hallmark Health System, Melrose, MA, p. A312

SACKETT, John, Chief Executive Officer, Shady Grove Adventist Hospital, Rockville, MD, p. A303

SACKETT, Walter, President, Sycamore Medical Center, Miamisburg, OH, p. A498

SACKRISON, Jeffrey N., FACHE,
    President, Vidant Bertie Hospital, Windsor, NC, p. A475
    President, Vidant Chowan Hospital, Edenton, NC, p. A464

SACKSTEDER, James L., M.D., Medical Director and Chief Executive Officer, Austen Riggs Center, Stockbridge, MA, p. A315

SADA, Judy, Chief Financial Officer, Memorial Hospital Miramar, Miramar, FL, p. A138

SADAU, Ernie W., President and Chief Executive Officer, CHRISTUS Health, Irving, TX, p. B35

SADLER, Donna, Director Human Resources, Arkansas State Hospital, Little Rock, AR, p. A49

SADLER, Joy, Director Human Resources, Bear River Valley Hospital, Tremonton, UT, p. A664

SADR, Farrokh, M.D. Chief Medical Officer, Sacred Heart Hospital, Allentown, PA, p. A532

SADRO, Cheryl A., Vice President and Chief Financial Officer, Memorial Health Care System, Chattanooga, TN, p. A580

SADVARY, Thomas J., FACHE, President and Chief Executive Officer, Scottsdale Healthcare, Scottsdale, AZ, p. B119

SAENZ, Luis J Rodriquez, M.D. Medical Director, Hospital Menonita De Cayey, Cayey, PR, p. A725

SAFDIE, Ezra R., Associate Director, San Franciso Veterans Affairs Medical Center, San Francisco, CA, p. A91

SAFF, Eric, Senior Vice President and Chief Information Officer, John Muir Behavioral Health Center, Concord, CA, p. A60

SAFFA, Steve, Director Human Resources, St. Francis Health Center, Topeka, KS, p. A255

SAFIAN, Keith F., President and Chief Executive Officer, Phelps Memorial Hospital Center, Sleepy Hollow, NY, p. A454

SAFLEY, Thomas, Chief Financial Officer, St. Joseph Regional Medical Center, Lewiston, ID, p. A176

SAFYER, Steven M., M.D., President and CEO, Montefiore Health System,, NY, p. B95

SAFYER, Steven M., M.D., President and Chief Executive Officer, Montefiore Medical Center,, NY, p. A446

SAGMIT, Rodney, Chief Information Management, Veterans Affairs Long Beach Healthcare System, Long Beach, CA, p. A70

SAHA, Sanjay K., Chief Operating Officer, Sibley Memorial Hospital, Washington, DC, p. A122

SAHAI, Subhosh, M.D. Chief of Staff, Van Diest Medical Center, Webster City, IA, p. A239

SAHLOLBEI, Hossain, M.D. Chief of Staff, Palo Verde Hospital, Blythe, CA, p. A58

SAHLSTROM, Christopher, M.D. Chief of Staff, Mat–Su Regional Medical Center, Palmer, AK, p. A30

SAHMAUNT, Sarabeth, Supervisory Accountant, Lawton Indian Hospital, Lawton, OK, p. A512

SAIA, Carrie L., R.N., Chief Executive Officer, Holton Community Hospital, Holton, KS, p. A245

SAINBERT, Wilmino, Chief Human Resources Management Service, Northport Veterans Affairs Medical Center, Northport, NY, p. A449

SAINTZ, Jeffrey, Vice President Human Resources, Titusville Area Hospital, Titusville, PA, p. A556

SAIYED, Ashfaq, M.D. Medical Director, Irwin County Hospital, Ocilla, GA, p. A164

SAJID, Muhammad W., M.D. Medical Director, Lincoln Trail Behavioral Health System, Radcliff, KY, p. A269

SALADO, Martha, Interim Director Human Resources, Whittier Hospital Medical Center, Whittier, CA, p. A100

SALAMA, Mustafa, M.D. Chief of Staff, Val Verde Regional Medical Center, Del Rio, TX, p. A613

SALAMANCA, Mary, Director Human Resources, HEALTHSOUTH Rehabilitation Hospital of Spring Hill, Brooksville, FL, p. A125

SALANGER, Matthew J., President and Chief Executive Officer, United Health Services, Binghamton, NY, p. B138

SALANGER, Matthew J., President and Chief Executive Officer, United Health Services Hospitals–Binghamton, Binghamton, NY, p. A434

SALAS, Dawn, Controller, HEALTHSOUTH Rehabilitation Hospital at Martin Health, Stuart, FL, p. A146

SALAS, Victor, M.D. President Medical Staff, UnityPoint Health – Jones Regional Medical Center, Anamosa, IA, p. A225

SALAWAY, Tarek, Chief Operating Officer, University of Southern California–Norris Cancer Hospital, Los Angeles, CA, p. A75

SALAZAR, Juan, Director Human Resources, St. Luke's Episcopal Hospital, Ponce, PR, p. A727

SALAZAR, Leanne, Chief Nursing Officer, Oak Hill Hospital, Brooksville, FL, p. A125

SALAZAR, Linda C., Information Technology Leader, Kaiser Permanente Baldwin Park Medical Center, Baldwin Park, CA, p. A57

SALAZAR, Pamela, M.D. Chief of Staff, HEALTHSOUTH Walton Rehabilitation Hospital, Augusta, GA, p. A153

SALCEDO, Nydimar, Chief Human Resources Officer, Castaner General Hospital, Castaner, PR, p. A725

SALDIVAR, Duke, FACHE, Chief Executive Officer, Mercy Rehabilitation Hospital Springfield, Springfield, MO, p. A383

SALEEBY, Manhal, M.D. Associate Chief of Staff, Geriatrics and Extended Care, VCU Community Memorial Hospital, South Hill, VA, p. A678

SALEEM, David, Director Information Technology, Greystone Park Psychiatric Hospital, Morris Plains, NJ, p. A418

SALEM, Gary, M.D. Vice President Medical Affairs, McLaren Lapeer Region, Lapeer, MI, p. A329

SALEM, Michael, M.D., President and Chief Executive Officer, National Jewish Health, Denver, CO, p. A105

SALERNO, Thomas A., President and Chief Executive Officer, St. Mary Medical Center, Long Beach, CA, p. A70

SALGADO, Joe, M.D. Chief of Staff, Artesia General Hospital, Artesia, NM, p. A427

SALGADO, Laura, Administrator, Baptist Emergency Hospital, San Antonio, TX, p. A645

SALIBA, K. Michael, M.D. Medical Director, Shadow Mountain Behavioral Health System, Tulsa, OK, p. A521

SALIMAN, Al, M.D. Chief Medical Officer, Valley View Hospital, Glenwood Springs, CO, p. A106

SALINAS, Amaro, Assistant Administrator and Human Resource Officer, Starr County Memorial Hospital, Rio Grande City, TX, p. A644

SALINAS, Daniel, M.D. Senior Vice President and Chief Medical Officer, Children's Healthcare of Atlanta, Atlanta, GA, p. A152

SALISBURY, Dennis, M.D. Vice President for Medical Affairs, St. James Healthcare, Butte, MT, p. A386

SALISBURY, Evelyn, M.D. Chief of Staff, Caverna Memorial Hospital, Horse Cave, KY, p. A263

SALISBURY, Renee A., Director Human Resources, OSF Saint Luke Medical Center, Kewanee, IL, p. A194

SALISBURY, Tracy
Regional Manager Human Resources, Central State Hospital, Petersburg, VA, p. A676
Director Human Resources, Hiram W. Davis Medical Center, Petersburg, VA, p. A676

SALLER, William, Chief Financial Officer, Rio Grande Regional Hospital, McAllen, TX, p. A637

SALLEY, Wanda, Vice President Human Resources, West Florida Hospital, Pensacola, FL, p. A142

SALLIS, Tom, Director Information Systems, Sparks Regional Medical Center, Fort Smith, AR, p. A46

SALLOUM, Fadi, M.D. Medical Director, Select Specialty Hospital–Pontiac, Pontiac, MI, p. A332

SALMAN, Wael, M.D. Vice President Medical Affairs, Memorial Healthcare, Owosso, MI, p. A331

SALNAS, Todd
President, Petaluma Valley Hospital, Petaluma, CA, p. A83
President, Santa Rosa Memorial Hospital, Santa Rosa, CA, p. A95

SALO, Saliba, President, Northridge Hospital Medical Center,, CA, p. A73

SALOME, Jenny, Chief Financial Officer and Assistant Administrator, Northwest Hills Surgical Hospital, Austin, TX, p. A599

SALOMON, Kathryn, Director Human Resources, Kona Community Hospital, Kealakekua, HI, p. A172

SALTAFORMAGGIO, Cheri, Chief Executive Officer, St. Charles Surgical Hospital, New Orleans, LA, p. A286

SALTER, Cherry B., Director of Nursing, Hardtner Medical Center, Olla, LA, p. A286

SALTONSTALL, Christine, Chief Financial Officer, Kindred Hospital–Baldwin Park, Baldwin Park, CA, p. A57

SALTZ, Catherine, Chief Financial Officer, Baptist Rehabilitation–Germantown, Germantown, TN, p. A583

SALVADOR, Ed, Chief Financial Officer, St. Jude Medical Center, Fullerton, CA, p. A65

SALVATI, Mario, Director Fiscal Services, Shriners Hospitals for Children–Philadelphia, Philadelphia, PA, p. A550

SALVINO, Sonia, Vice President Finance, University Hospitals Case Medical Center, Cleveland, OH, p. A489

SALVITTI, Alfred P., Chief Financial Officer, Eagleville Hospital, Eagleville, PA, p. A537

SALVO, Stephen, Vice President Human Resources, Anna Jaques Hospital, Newburyport, MA, p. A312

SALVO, Thomas, Associate Executive Director Human Resources, Glen Cove Hospital, Glen Cove, NY, p. A438

SALY, David, Director, Information Services, Largo Medical Center, Largo, FL, p. A134

SALYER, Steven, Senior Vice President and Chief Operating Officer, Indian River Medical Center, Vero Beach, FL, p. A149

SALZMAN, Shona, Chief Operating Officer, William Newton Hospital, Winfield, KS, p. A257

SAMBASIVAN, Venkataraman, M.D. Chief Medical Officer, Lourdes Medical Center, Pasco, WA, p. A686

SAMESS, Ronald, M.D. Chief of Staff, Fishermen's Hospital, Marathon, FL, p. A135

SAMET, Kenneth A., President and Chief Executive Officer, MedStar Health, Columbia, MD, p. B90

SAMILO, Nick, Vice President Fiscal Services and Chief Financial Officer, Stanly Regional Medical Center, Albemarle, NC, p. A459

SAMMARCO, Michael, M.D. Chief Financial Officer, Erie County Medical Center, Buffalo, NY, p. A434

SAMMONS, Craig, Chief Financial Officer, Sky Ridge Medical Center, Lone Tree, CO, p. A109

SAMMS, Caswell, Network Chief Financial Officer, Lincoln Medical and Mental Health Center,, NY, p. A445

SAMORA, Martha, R.N., Chief Executive Officer, HEALTHSOUTH Bakersfield Rehabilitation Hospital, Bakersfield, CA, p. A57

SAMPAGA, Arthur, Assistant Director Nursing, Hilo Medical Center, Hilo, HI, p. A170

SAMPSON, Arthur J., FACHE,
President, Miriam Hospital, Providence, RI, p. A560
Interim President, Newport Hospital, Newport, RI, p. A560

SAMPSON, Bob, Vice President Human Resources, Redwood Memorial Hospital, Fortuna, CA, p. A63

SAMPSON, Cherie L., Director Human Resources, Kaiser Permanente San Diego Medical Center, San Diego, CA, p. A89

SAMPSON, Jill, Director Human Resources, Lemuel Shattuck Hospital, Jamaica Plain, MA, p. A311

SAMS, Tricia, M.D. Medical Director, Memorial Health Care Systems, Seward, NE, p. A402

SAMSON, Ley, Director Management Information Systems, Clear Lake Regional Medical Center, Webster, TX, p. A656

SAMUDRALA, Siresha, M.D. Medical Director, Mercy Rehabilitation Hospital, Chesterfield, MO, p. A369

SAMUEL, Guy, Director Human Resources, St. Petersburg General Hospital, Saint Petersburg, FL, p. A145

SAMUELS, Steven, M.D. Medical Director, Kindred Hospital Indianapolis South, Greenwood, IN, p. A212

SAMUELS, Tammy, Director Human Resources, Union County Hospital, Anna, IL, p. A180

SAMUELSON, Melissa A., R.N. Chief Nurse Executive, Poplar Bluff Regional Medical Center, Poplar Bluff, MO, p. A378

SAMYN, Mike, Vice President, Finance and Chief Financial Officer, St. Mary Mercy Hospital, Livonia, MI, p. A329

SAMZ, Jeff, Chief Operating Officer, Huntsville Hospital, Huntsville, AL, p. A22

SAN FILIPPO, Bruce, M.D. Chief Medical Officer, Memorial Medical Center, Las Cruces, NM, p. A429

SANBORN, Michael, FACHE, President, Baylor Medical Center at Carrollton, Carrollton, TX, p. A605

SANBORN, Randall, Director Information Technology, HealthSource Saginaw, Saginaw, MI, p. A334

SANCHEZ, Antonio, M.D. Chief of Staff, Veterans Affairs Caribbean Healthcare System, San Juan, PR, p. A729

SANCHEZ, Arnaldo Rodriguez, M.D. Chief Operating Officer, Hospital Episcopal San Lucas Guayama, Guayama, PR, p. A726

SANCHEZ, Emalie, Director Human Resources, Baylor Medical Center at Uptown, Dallas, TX, p. A609

SANCHEZ, Esperanza, Chief Clinical Officer, Kindred Hospital–La Mirada, La Mirada, CA, p. A68

SANCHEZ, Freddie, Director Information Systems, Fountain Valley Regional Hospital and Medical Center, Fountain Valley, CA, p. A63

SANCHEZ, John, Vice President Human Resources, White Plains Hospital Center, White Plains, NY, p. A458

SANCHEZ, Jose R., President and Chief Executive Officer, Norwegian American Hospital, Chicago, IL, p. A185

SANCHEZ, Nancy, Senior Vice President and Vice Dean Human Resources, NYU Langone Medical Center, New York, NY, p. A448

SANCHEZ, Rachel, Director Information Systems, Providence Little Company of Mary Medical Center San Pedro,, CA, p. A74

SANCHEZ, Rebecca, R.N. Director of Nursing, Texas Center for Infectious Disease, San Antonio, TX, p. A648

SANCHEZ–BICKLEY, Michelle
Vice President Human Resources, Renown Regional Medical Center, Reno, NV, p. A407
Vice President Human Resources, Renown Rehabilitation Hospital, Reno, NV, p. A408
Vice President Human Resources, Renown South Meadows Medical Center, Reno, NV, p. A408

SANCHEZ–JIMENEZ, Aida, M.D. Chief Medical Officer, Osceola Regional Medical Center, Kissimmee, FL, p. A133

SANCHEZ–RICO, Gloria, Chief Nursing Officer and Vice President, Huntington Memorial Hospital, Pasadena, CA, p. A83

SAND, Michelle, R.N. Assistant Administrator Patient Care, Cascade Valley Hospital and Clinics, Arlington, WA, p. A681

SANDAGER, Brian, Chief Information Officer, Lowell General Hospital, Lowell, MA, p. A311

SANDBERG, Susan, R.N
Chief Operating Officer, Community Heart and Vascular Hospital, Indianapolis, IN, p. A213
Chief Operating Officer, Community Hospital North, Indianapolis, IN, p. A213

SANDBERG, Todd, Chief Executive Officer and Administrator, Sibley Medical Center, Arlington, MN, p. A339

SANDBULTE, Nyla H., R.N. Chief Nursing Officer, Sanford Luverne Medical Center, Luverne, MN, p. A346

SANDEFUR, Gwen L., Executive Vice President and Chief Operating Officer, St. Mary's Medical Center of Evansville, Evansville, IN, p. A210

SANDER, Cindy, Coordinator Human Resources, Kindred Hospital–St. Louis, Saint Louis, MO, p. A380

SANDER, Wendy, Director Human Resources, Kaiser Permanente Riverside Medical Center, Riverside, CA, p. A86

SANDERLIN, Lisa, Chief Information Officer, University Hospital McDuffie, Thomson, GA, p. A168

SANDERS, Amy, Chief Human Resources, Captain James A. Lovell Federal Health Care Center, North Chicago, IL, p. A198

SANDERS, David, Chief Financial Officer, Jackson Parish Hospital, Jonesboro, LA, p. A280

SANDERS, David S., Chief Executive Officer, Fannin Regional Hospital, Blue Ridge, GA, p. A154

SANDERS, Diane M., Chief Nursing Officer, Trios Health, Kennewick, WA, p. A684

SANDERS, Gale H., Director, Gadsden Regional Medical Center, Gadsden, AL, p. A20

SANDERS, Harv, Chief Financial Officer, Rhea Medical Center, Dayton, TN, p. A582

SANDERS, Jeff, Chief Operating Officer, Maine Medical Center, Portland, ME, p. A294

SAUTER, Michael, M.D. Chief Medical Officer, St. Charles Hospital, Port Jefferson, NY, p. A452

SAVAGE, Heather, Director Human Resources, The Rehabilitation Institute of St. Louis, Saint Louis, MO, p. A382

SAVAGE, Josh, Chief Financial Officer, Brownfield Regional Medical Center, Brownfield, TX, p. A604

SAVAGE, Steve, Chief Executive Officer, Stonecrest Center, Detroit, MI, p. A322

SAVAGE-TRACY, Elizabeth, Vice President and Human Resources Officer, Winchester Medical Center, Winchester, VA, p. A680

SAVINO, Linda A., MS, Chief Executive Officer, Rehabilitation Hospital of Tinton Falls, Tinton Falls, NJ, p. A423

SAVITSKY, Marian, R.N. Chief Nursing Officer, Sky Ridge Medical Center, Lone Tree, CO, p. A109

SAVOY III, F. Peter, Chief Executive Officer, Acadia–St. Landry Hospital, Church Point, LA, p. A275

SAVOY, Greg, M.D. Chief Medical Officer, Savoy Medical Center, Mamou, LA, p. A283

SAVOY, Remi, Administrator, Oceans Behavioral Hospital of Opelousas, Opelousas, LA, p. A286

SAWA, Kendall, R.N., Chief Executive Officer, Ocean Beach Hospital, Ilwaco, WA, p. A684

SAWDEY, Don, M.D. Medical Director, Daniels Memorial Healthcare Center, Scobey, MT, p. A391

SAWICKI, Mitzi, Director of Nursing, Havenwyck Hospital, Auburn Hills, MI, p. A318

SAWTELLE, Bradley, M.D. President Medical Staff, Memorial Community Hospital and Health System, Blair, NE, p. A394

SAWYER, Anne, Chief Financial Officer, Wayne County Hospital, Monticello, KY, p. A267

SAWYER, Colleen A., MSN,
Executive Director, Mohawk Valley Psychiatric Center, Utica, NY, p. A456
Executive Director, Richard H. Hutchings Psychiatric Center, Syracuse, NY, p. A455

SAWYER, Dorothy, Chief Executive Officer, Eastern State Hospital, Medical Lake, WA, p. A685

SAWYER, Robert, Senior Project Specialist, Spaulding Hospital for Continuing Medical Care North Shore, Salem, MA, p. A314

SAWYER, Scott, Chief Financial Officer, Community Medical Center, Falls City, NE, p. A395

SAWYER, Stephen, Chief Financial Officer, Norton Community Hospital, Norton, VA, p. A676

SAXON, Kathy, R.N. Vice President Patient Care Services, Tillamook Regional Medical Center, Tillamook, OR, p. A530

SAXTON, Beth, R.N. Vice President Patient Care Services, Yuma District Hospital, Yuma, CO, p. A112

SAYAH, Assaad, M.D. Chief Medical Officer, Cambridge Health Alliance, Cambridge, MA, p. A309

SAYLER, Elizabeth, M.D. Chief of Staff, Lead–Deadwood Regional Hospital, Deadwood, SD, p. A573

SAYLER, Roger, Finance Officer, Fargo Veterans Affairs Health Care System, Fargo, ND, p. A477

SAYLER, Timothy, Chief Operating Officer, Essentia Health Fargo, Fargo, ND, p. A477

SAYLES, Debbie A., R.N. Vice President and Chief Nursing Officer, Texas Scottish Rite Hospital for Children, Dallas, TX, p. A612

SAYLOR, Craig M., Interim CEO, Somerset Hospital, Somerset, PA, p. A555

SAYLOR, Richard F., M.D. Chief Medical Officer, Pottstown Memorial Medical Center, Pottstown, PA, p. A552

SAYLORS, Julie, Controller, AnMed Health Rehabilitation Hospital, Anderson, SC, p. A562

SAYRE, Amy, Director Human Resources, General John J. Pershing Memorial Hospital, Brookfield, MO, p. A368

SAYRE, Michelle, R.N. Chief Nursing Officer, Arrowhead Regional Medical Center, Colton, CA, p. A60

SBARDELLA, Steven, M.D. Chief Medical Officer, Hallmark Health System, Melrose, MA, p. A312

SCAFIDDI, Darlene, R.N. Vice President Nursing and Patient Care Services, Pomona Valley Hospital Medical Center, Pomona, CA, p. A84

SCAFIDI, Frank
Vice President and Chief Information Officer, Georgetown Memorial Hospital, Georgetown, SC, p. A566
Chief Information Officer, Waccamaw Community Hospital, Murrells Inlet, SC, p. A569

SCALES, Melisa, Director of Nursing, Parkview Hospital, Wheeler, TX, p. A657

SCALISE, Jayne, R.N. Chief Nursing Executive, Lompoc Valley Medical Center, Lompoc, CA, p. A70

SCALISE, Paul, M.D. Chief Pulmonary Medicine and Internal Medicine, Hospital for Special Care, New Britain, CT, p. A115

SCALLION, Jessika, Administrator, Beacon Behavioral Hospital – New Orleans, New Orleans, LA, p. A285

SCALLON, Jean, Chief Executive Officer, Bloomington Meadows Hospital, Bloomington, IN, p. A207

SCAMARDO, II, Luke P., M.D. Chief of Staff, Grimes St. Joseph Health Center, Navasota, TX, p. A639

SCANLON, Donald
Chief Corporate Services, Mount Sinai Health System, Mount Sinai Beth Israel, New York, NY, p. A446
Chief Financial Officer, Mount Sinai Hospital, New York, NY, p. A446
Chief Corporate Services, Mount Sinai Health System, Mount Sinai St. Luke's, New York, NY, p. A446
Chief Corporate Services, Mount Sinai Health System, New York Eye and Ear Infirmary of Mount Sinai, New York, NY, p. A447

SCANLON, Jill, Director Human Resources, Northern Colorado Rehabilitation Hospital, Johnstown, CO, p. A108

SCANLON, John, DPM Chief Medical Officer, Chestnut Hill Hospital, Philadelphia, PA, p. A547

SCANLON, Kerri, MSN Chief Nursing Officer, North Shore University Hospital, Manhasset, NY, p. A440

SCANLON, Sharon, Chief Nursing Officer, Epic Medical Center, Eufaula, OK, p. A510

SCANNELL, Stephen J.
Chief Financial Officer, McLaren Bay Region, Bay City, MI, p. A319
Chief Financial Officer, McLaren Bay Special Care, Bay City, MI, p. A319

SCANZERA, Christopher A., Vice President and Chief Information Officer, AtlantiCare Regional Medical Center, Atlantic City, NJ, p. A413

SCARANO, Jenaro, M.D. Medical Director, St. Luke's Episcopal Hospital, Ponce, PR, p. A727

SCARBORO, Parrish, Chief Operating Officer, John F. Kennedy Memorial Hospital, Indio, CA, p. A67

SCARBROUGH, Keith, Chief Information Officer, Saint Francis Hospital, Memphis, TN, p. A589

SCARLATTI, Shirley K., Associate Chief Nursing Officer, Parkridge West Hospital, Jasper, TN, p. A584

SCARLETT, Kamesha, Chief Information Resource Management, Veterans Affairs New Jersey Health Care System, East Orange, NJ, p. A415

SCARMATO, Victor, M.D. Acting Medical Director, Nassau University Medical Center, East Meadow, NY, p. A437

SCARPINO, David
President and Chief Executive Officer, Health Alliance Hospital – Broadway Campus, Kingston, NY, p. A440
President and Chief Executive Officer, Health Alliance Hospital – Mary's Avenue Campus, Kingston, NY, p. A440

SCARPINO, David, President and Chief Executive Officer, HealthAlliance of the Hudson Valley, Kingston, NY, p. B68

SCENNA, Maria, Chief Operating Officer, St. Christopher's Hospital for Children, Philadelphia, PA, p. A550

SCEPANSKI, Theresa, Vice President People and Organizational Development, University Health System, San Antonio, TX, p. A648

SCERCY, Charles, Chief Executive Officer, Snowden at Fredericksburg, Fredericksburg, VA, p. A671

SCHAAB, Ben, VP Fiscal Services/ Chief Financial Officer, CGH Medical Center, Sterling, IL, p. A203

SCHAACK, Gregory J., CP
Vice President and Chief Financial Officer, Candler Hospital, Savannah, GA, p. A166
Vice President and Chief Financial Officer, St. Joseph's Hospital, Savannah, GA, p. A166

SCHAAF, Jerry, M.D. Chief Medical Officer, Shenandoah Medical Center, Shenandoah, IA, p. A237

SCHAAF, Kay, Chief Nursing Officer, Prairie Community Hospital, Terry, MT, p. A391

SCHABERG, Dennis, M.D. Chief Medicine, Veterans Affairs Greater Los Angeles Healthcare System, Los Angeles, CA, p. A75

SCHACHTNER, Janet, R.N. Senior Vice President, Patient Care Services, Mount Nittany Medical Center, State College, PA, p. A555

SCHADE, Sue, Chief Information Officer, University of Michigan Hospitals and Health Centers, Ann Arbor, MI, p. A318

SCHAEF, Toby, Director Information Technology, Memorial Hospital of Carbon County, Rawlins, WY, p. A722

SCHAEFER, Becky, Chief Financial Officer, University of Utah Neuropsychiatric Institute, Salt Lake City, UT, p. A663

SCHAEFER, Jamie, Vice President Finance, Avera Sacred Heart Hospital, Yankton, SD, p. A578

SCHAEFER, Kevin, Manager Information Services, River's Edge Hospital and Clinic, Saint Peter, MN, p. A352

SCHAEFER, Michael J., Executive Vice President and Chief Financial Officer, Methodist Charlton Medical Center, Dallas, TX, p. A611

SCHAEFER, Michele, Interim President, Mercy Hospital Lebanon, Lebanon, MO, p. A375

SCHAEFER, Michelle, Chief Financial Officer, Lillian M. Hudspeth Memorial Hospital, Sonora, TX, p. A649

SCHAEFER, Stephen, Chief Executive Officer, HEALTHSOUTH Rehabilitation Hospital of Colorado Springs, Colorado Springs, CO, p. A103

SCHAEFFER, Andre, M.D. Chief of Staff, Union General Hospital, Blairsville, GA, p. A154

SCHAEFFER, Darlene, Chief Nursing Officer, Garden County Health Services, Oshkosh, NE, p. A401

SCHAEFFER, Richard, Vice President Information Systems and Chief Information Officer, St. Clair Hospital, Pittsburgh, PA, p. A551

SCHAETTI, Susan, Administrator, Kindred Hospital–Mansfield, Mansfield, TX, p. A636

SCHAFER, Laurie, Interim Chief Executive Officer, San Juan Hospital, Monticello, UT, p. A660

SCHAFER, Michael, Chief Executive Officer and Administrator, Spooner Health System, Spooner, WI, p. A715

SCHAFER, Mona, Regional Manager Human Resources, Milbank Area Hospital Avera, Milbank, SD, p. A574

SCHAFF, Vicki, Chief Operating Officer, Epic Medical Center, Eufaula, OK, p. A510

SCHAFFER, Megan, Administrative Assistant, Surgical Institute of Reading, Wyomissing, PA, p. A559

SCHAFFER, Renee, Coordinator Human Resources, Select Specialty Hospital–Wichita, Wichita, KS, p. A256

SCHAFFER, Todd, M.D. Chief Medical Officer, Carrington Health Center, Carrington, ND, p. A476

SCHAFFMEYER, MaryJeanne
Chief Operating Officer, Appleton Medical Center, Appleton, WI, p. A701
Chief Operating Officer, Theda Clark Medical Center, Neenah, WI, p. A711

SCHAFFNER, Leroy, Chief Executive Officer, Coon Memorial Hospital, Dalhart, TX, p. A609

SCHAFFNER, Marilyn J., Ph.D. Administrator Clinical Services and Chief Nursing Officer, MUSC Medical Center of Medical University of South Carolina, Charleston, SC, p. A563

SCHAFFNER, Randall, M.D. Chief of Staff and Medical Director, Wilbarger General Hospital, Vernon, TX, p. A655

SCHAFFNER, Richard, Senior Vice President and Chief Operating Officer, Holy Spirit Hospital, Camp Hill, PA, p. A535

SCHAFFT, Jonathan
Director Information Systems, Hunt Regional Community Hospital, Commerce, TX, p. A607
Director Information Systems, Hunt Regional Medical Center, Greenville, TX, p. A622

SCHAKELAAR, Christie, Chief Financial Officer, Fairview Regional Medical Center, Fairview, OK, p. A511

SCHALES, Marion, Chief Financial Officer, Alameda County Medical Center, Oakland, CA, p. A80

SCHALL, Dee, Chief Nursing Officer, Baptist Health Medical Center–Hot Spring County, Malvern, AR, p. A50

SCHALSKI, Paula
Director Human Resources, Atoka County Medical Center, Atoka, OK, p. A508
Director Human Resources, Pushmataha Hospital & Home Health, Antlers, OK, p. A507

SCHAMP, Cindy K., President, Baylor Medical Center at Irving, Irving, TX, p. A629

SCHANDLER, Jon B., Chief Executive Officer, White Plains Hospital Center, White Plains, NY, p. A458

SCHANWALD, Pamela R., Chief Executive Officer, The Children's Home of Pittsburgh, Pittsburgh, PA, p. A551

SCHAPP, Susan, Vice President Finance and Treasurer, The Charlotte Hungerford Hospital, Torrington, CT, p. A117

SCHAPPER, Robert A., Chief Executive Officer, Tahoe Forest Health System, Truckee, CA, p. B131

SCHAPPER, Robert A., Chief Executive Officer, Tahoe Forest Hospital District, Truckee, CA, p. A97

SCHARBER, Laurel, Administrative Assistant and Coordinator Human Resources, Kindred Hospital–Ontario, Ontario, CA, p. A81

SCHARDIN, Janice, MS, Administrator and Chief Executive Officer, Avera De Smet Memorial Hospital, De Smet, SD, p. A573

SCHARENBROCK, Chris, M.D. Chief Medical Staff, David Grant USAF Medical Center, Travis AFB, CA, p. A97

SCHARFF, Tom, Director Information Services, University Hospital and Medical Center, Tamarac, FL, p. A147

SCHARLES, Susan L., Director Human Resources, Valley View Medical Center, Fort Mohave, AZ, p. A32

SCHARNBERG, Cathi Rae, R.N. Vice President Patient Services, Avera Holy Family Hospital, Estherville, IA, p. A230

SCHARNHORST, Alicia, Human Resources and Business Office Manager, Garfield County Public Hospital District, Pomeroy, WA, p. A686

SCHAUF, Jeffrey, Director Information Systems, Wesley Medical Center, Wichita, KS, p. A257

SCHAUF, Victoria, M.D. Chief of Staff, Ridgecrest Regional Hospital, Ridgecrest, CA, p. A86

SCHAY, Maria, Chief Information Officer, Veterans Administration New York Harbor Healthcare System,, NY, p. A449

SCHEAFFEL, Margaret, R.N. Chief Nursing Officer, Presbyterian–St. Luke's Medical Center, Denver, CO, p. A105

SCHEER, Michael, M.D. President Medical Staff, Vista Medical Center East, Waukegan, IL, p. A205

SCHEERER, Dan, M.D. Chief Medical Officer, Genesis HealthCare System, Zanesville, OH, p. A506

SCHEETS, Frank, Senior Vice President, Lutheran Medical Center,, NY, p. A445

SCHEETZ, Allison, M.D. Medical Director, Rehabilitation Hospital, Navicent Health, Macon, GA, p. A163

SCHEFFLER, Robert, Chief Executive Officer, Clarion Psychiatric Center, Clarion, PA, p. A535

SCHEFFLER, Tom, Chief Fiscal Officer, Veterans Affairs Maryland Health Care System–Baltimore Division, Baltimore, MD, p. A298

SCHEIB, Garry L., Executive Director, Hospital of the University of Pennsylvania, Philadelphia, PA, p. A548

SCHEINBERG, Paul, M.D. Chief of Staff, Emory Saint Joseph's Hospital of Atlanta, Atlanta, GA, p. A152

SCHEINBLUM, Richard, Chief Financial Officer, Monadnock Community Hospital, Peterborough, NH, p. A412

SCHEK, Larry, M.D. Senior Vice President Chief Medical Director and Vice President Cardiology, St. Vincent's Medical Center, Bridgeport, CT, p. A113

SCHELBAR, E. Joe, M.D. Medical Director, Select Specialty Hospital–Tulsa Midtown, Tulsa, OK, p. A521

SCHELL, James, M.D. Vice President Medical Affairs, Saint Francis Medical Center, Cape Girardeau, MO, p. A368

SCHELL, Nicole, Director Human Resources, Perham Health, Perham, MN, p. A349

SCHELLPFEFFER, Donald A., M.D., Chief Executive Officer, Sioux Falls Specialty Hospital, Sioux Falls, SD, p. A576

SCHEMER, Tonia, Interim Chief Human Resources, St. Joseph Mercy Livingston Hospital, Howell, MI, p. A327

SCHENCK, Debbie, Administrator, Omega Hospital, Metairie, LA, p. A284

SCHEPMANN, Jane, Vice President and Chief Nursing Officer, Clara Barton Hospital, Hoisington, KS, p. A245

SCHER, Kathleen, R.N. Vice President Nursing, Mount Sinai Queens,, NY, p. A446

SCHERAMIC, Mychail, M.D., Chief Executive Officer, Northwest Ohio Psychiatric Hospital, Toledo, OH, p. A503

SCHERLER, Jay, Director Information Systems and Vice President Business Services, Providence Health Center, Waco, TX, p. A656

SCHERNECK, Michael D.
Executive Vice President and Chief Financial Officer, Southeast Georgia Health System Brunswick Campus, Brunswick, GA, p. A155

Executive Vice President, Southeast Georgia Health System Camden Campus, Saint Marys, GA, p. A166

SCHIEFELBEIN, Shelia, Coordinator Human Resources, Northwest Florida Community Hospital, Chipley, FL, p. A125

SCHIERECK, Stacie, Director Management Services, Mendota Mental Health Institute, Madison, WI, p. A708

SCHIESL, Troy, Director Information Services, Bellin Psychiatric Center, Green Bay, WI, p. A706

SCHIFFER, Christopher, Administrator, Community Behavioral Health Hospital – St. Peter, Saint Peter, MN, p. A352

SCHILLER, Ann Mattia, Vice President Human Resources, Pacific Hospital of Long Beach, Long Beach, CA, p. A70

SCHILLING, Helen, M.D. Medical Director, Kindred Rehabilitation Hospital Northeast Houston, Humble, TX, p. A628

SCHILLING, Thomas, Chief Financial Officer and Senior Vice President Finance, Mercy Memorial Hospital System, Monroe, MI, p. A330

SCHIMEROWSKI, Deborah
Vice President Finance and Chief Financial Officer, Presence Covenant Medical Center, Urbana, IL, p. A204

Chief Financial Officer, Presence United Samaritans Medical Center, Danville, IL, p. A187

SCHIPPER, Brad J., Chief Operating Officer, Sanford USD Medical Center, Sioux Falls, SD, p. A576

SCHIRALLI, Rocco, President/Chief Executive Officer, Porter–Starke Services, Valparaiso, IN, p. A223

SCHIROS, Judith, Chief Executive Officer, Restora Hospital of Mesa, Mesa, AZ, p. A34

SCHLABACH, Michael, M.D. Chief Medical Officer, Scott & White Hospital – Brenham, Brenham, TX, p. A604

SCHLAGER, Robert, M.D. Chief Medical Officer, Sebasticook Valley Health, Pittsfield, ME, p. A294

SCHLATTER, Christina, Chief Financial Officer, Oswego Community Hospital, Oswego, KS, p. A251

SCHLECHTER, Sandy, Chief Executive Officer, Bowdle Hospital, Bowdle, SD, p. A572

SCHLEETER, Larry C., Chief Human Resources Officer, Memorial Hospital of Union County, Marysville, OH, p. A497

SCHLEGEL, Patricia, Executive Director Finance, Minnesota Valley Health Center, Le Sueur, MN, p. A345

SCHLEGELMILCH, John, M.D. Chief Medical Officer, Monadnock Community Hospital, Peterborough, NH, p. A412

SCHLEICHER, Larry, Manager Information Services, Dr. John Warner Hospital, Clinton, IL, p. A187

SCHLEIF, John V., Senior Vice President and Chief Operating Officer, Henry Mayo Newhall Memorial Hospital, Valencia, CA, p. A98

SCHLEMMER, Tom, Chief Financial Officer, St. Mary's Medical Center, West Palm Beach, FL, p. A150

SCHLENKER, Jim, Vice President and Chief Financial Officer, St. Anthony Hospital, Pendleton, OR, p. A527

SCHLESENBERG, Avery, Chief Financial Officer, Sutter Medical Center of Santa Rosa, Chanate Campus, Santa Rosa, CA, p. A95

SCHLESINGER, J. Tuerk, Chief Executive Officer, AltaPointe Health Systems, Mobile, AL, p. B10

SCHLESINGER, James, Interim Chief Information Officer, MetroHealth Medical Center, Cleveland, OH, p. A489

SCHLESKE, Brenda, Interim Administrator, Community Behavioral Health Hospital – Fergus Falls, Fergus Falls, MN, p. A343

SCHLESSMAN, Alissa, Administrator, Beaver County Memorial Hospital, Beaver, OK, p. A508

SCHLEY, Kurt, President, St. Anthony Hospital, Gig Harbor, WA, p. A684

SCHLICHTING, Nancy M., Chief Executive Officer, Henry Ford Health System, Detroit, MI, p. B73

SCHLOSS, William, Senior Vice President and Administrator, Laureate Psychiatric Clinic and Hospital, Tulsa, OK, p. A520

SCHLUTER, Robin M., Chief Executive Officer, Regional Health Services of Howard County, Cresco, IA, p. A228

SCHMELZEL, Mark, M.D. Vice President and Medical Director, CGH Medical Center, Sterling, IL, p. A203

SCHMID, Nancy, Chief Executive Officer, Healdsburg District Hospital, Healdsburg, CA, p. A66

SCHMID, Nancy A., R.N. Associate Director Patient Care Services, Coatesville Veterans Affairs Medical Center, Coatesville, PA, p. A536

SCHMIDT, Allen J., M.D. President, Medical Staff, Decatur Morgan Hospital, Decatur, AL, p. A18

SCHMIDT, Barbara, Chief Executive Officer, Mesa Springs, Fort Worth, TX, p. A618

SCHMIDT, Bobbi, Chief Nursing Officer, Select Specialty Hospital–Cincinnati, Cincinnati, OH, p. A487

SCHMIDT, Constance, R.N. Chief Nursing Officer, Cheyenne Regional Medical Center, Cheyenne, WY, p. A720

SCHMIDT, David, R.N. Chief Nursing Officer, Jennersville Regional Hospital, West Grove, PA, p. A558

SCHMIDT, Holly, Chief Information Officer, Hill Country Memorial Hospital, Fredericksburg, TX, p. A619

SCHMIDT, Joan E., Director Human Resources, St. Francis Health Care Centre, Green Springs, OH, p. A495

SCHMIDT, Jodi A., President and Chief Executive Officer, Labette Health, Parsons, KS, p. A252

SCHMIDT, Julie, Director Human Resources, Grand Itasca Clinic and Hospital, Grand Rapids, MN, p. A344

SCHMIDT, Loretta, President, Saint Joseph Regional Medical Center–Plymouth Campus, Plymouth, IN, p. A221

SCHMIDT, Mark, President and Chief Executive Officer, Avera Gettysburg Hospital, Gettysburg, SD, p. A574

SCHMIDT Jr., Richard O.
President and Chief Executive Officer, United Health System–Kenosha Campus, Kenosha, WI, p. A707

President and Chief Executive Officer, United Hospital System, St. Catherine's Medical Center Campus, Pleasant Prairie, WI, p. A713

SCHMIDT, Robert F., Director Human Resources, Hocking Valley Community Hospital, Logan, OH, p. A496

SCHMIDT, Rosanne, R.N. Chief Nursing Officer, St. Alexius Medical Center, Bismarck, ND, p. A476

SCHMIDT, Steve, Director Information Services, Evans Memorial Hospital, Claxton, GA, p. A156

SCHMIDT, Timothy E., Chief Executive Officer, Laredo Medical Center, Laredo, TX, p. A633

SCHMIDT, Tressa, Administrator, Albany Area Hospital and Medical Center, Albany, MN, p. A339

SCHMIDT, Veronica, Chief Executive Officer, Custer Regional Hospital, Custer, SD, p. A573

SCHMIDT, William, President and Chief Executive Officer, New London Family Medical Center, New London, WI, p. A712

SCHMIDTBERGER, Sheryl, Chief Financial Officer, Integris Blackwell Regional Hospital, Blackwell, OK, p. A508

SCHMIEGE, Ardis, Chief Financial Officer, Cascade Valley Hospital and Clinics, Arlington, WA, p. A681

SCHMIER, Joe, Director Human Resources, Payroll & Employee Health, Community Medical Center, Missoula, MT, p. A389

SCHMIESING, Karee, Director of Nursing, Sleepy Eye Medical Center, Sleepy Eye, MN, p. A352

SCHMITS, Peggy, Director, Nursing Operations, New Braunfels Regional Rehabilitation Hospital, New Braunfels, TX, p. A639

SCHMITT, John, Senior Vice President and Chief Financial Officer, Kingsbrook Jewish Medical Center,, NY, p. A445

SCHMITT, Joseph, Chief Information Officer, St. Elizabeth's Medical Center, Brighton, MA, p. A308

SCHMITT, III, Joseph, Senior Vice President Finance and Chief Financial Officer, Henry Ford Hospital, Detroit, MI, p. A322

SCHMITT, Karl, M.D. Chief of Staff, St. Elizabeth Edgewood, Edgewood, KY, p. A260

SCHMITT, Michael, M.D., Chief Executive Officer, Kindred Hospital–Atlanta, Atlanta, GA, p. A152

SCHMITT, Peggy, President and Chief Executive Officer, North Kansas City Hospital, North Kansas City, MO, p. A378

SCHMITT II, Robert C., Chief Executive Officer, Gibson Area Hospital and Health Services, Gibson City, IL, p. A191

SCHMITT, Thomas M., Chief Executive Officer, Kansas Spine and Specialty Hospital, Wichita, KS, p. A256

SCHMITZ, Bonnie
Vice President and Chief Financial Officer, Agnesian HealthCare, Fond Du Lac, WI, p. A704

Chief Financial Officer, Ripon Medical Center, Ripon, WI, p. A714

Chief Financial Officer, Waupun Memorial Hospital, Waupun, WI, p. A717

SCHMITZ, Christopher, Director Human Resources, Stoughton Hospital Association, Stoughton, WI, p. A716

SCHMITZ, Joseph, Chief Financial Officer, St. Cloud Veterans Affairs Health Care System, Saint Cloud, MN, p. A351

SCHMITZ, Vince, Senior Vice President and Chief Financial Officer, MultiCare Mary Bridge Children's Hospital and Health Center, Tacoma, WA, p. A691

SCHMOTZER, Dave, Chief Financial Officer, Bryn Mawr Rehabilitation Hospital, Malvern, PA, p. A543

SCHMUS, Angie, Chief Information Technology, Aleda E. Lutz Veterans Affairs Medical Center, Saginaw, MI, p. A333

SCHNACK, Tim H.
Vice President Financial Services, CHI Health Bergan Mercy, Omaha, NE, p. A399

Chief Financial Officer, CHI Health Creighton University Medical Center, Omaha, NE, p. A399

Chief Financial Officer, CHI Health Immanuel, Omaha, NE, p. A399

Chief Financial Officer, CHI Health Lakeside, Omaha, NE, p. A399

Chief Financial Officer, CHI Health Schuyler, Schuyler, NE, p. A401

Vice President Operations Finance, CHI Health St. Mary's, Nebraska City, NE, p. A398

SCHNACKEL, Donald, Chief Financial Officer, Carthage Area Hospital, Carthage, NY, p. A435

SCHNEDLER, Lisa W., FACHE, President and Chief Executive Officer, Upland Hills Health, Dodgeville, WI, p. A703

SCHNEE, Lee, M.D. Chief Medical Staff, Holton Community Hospital, Holton, KS, p. A245

SCHNEIDER, Andrew, M.D. Chief of Staff, Davis Regional Medical Center, Statesville, NC, p. A473

SCHNEIDER, Barbara, R.N., Chief Executive Officer, Southern California Hospital at Culver City, Culver City, CA, p. A61

SCHNEIDER, Barry S., Interim Chief Executive Officer, College Station Medical Center, College Station, TX, p. A607

SCHNEIDER, Brenda, Chief Financial Officer, Skyline Hospital, White Salmon, WA, p. A692

SCHNEIDER, Brian, Chief Financial Officer, Dupont Hospital, Fort Wayne, IN, p. A210

SCHNEIDER, Carol L., President and Chief Executive Officer, Mercy Hospital and Medical Center, Chicago, IL, p. A185

SCHNEIDER, Catherine, M.D. Chief Medical Officer, Mt. Ascutney Hospital and Health Center, Windsor, VT, p. A667

SCHNEIDER, David R., Executive Director, Langlade Hospital, Antigo, WI, p. A701

SCHNEIDER, Doug, Director Information Systems, Raulerson Hospital, Okeechobee, FL, p. A140

SCHNEIDER, Gina, Director Human Resources, Northwest Specialty Hospital, Post Falls, ID, p. A178

SCHNEIDER, H. Frank, Chief Executive Officer, Kindred Hospital Northland, Kansas City, MO, p. A373

SCHNEIDER, Jessie, Director Human Resources, Community Memorial Healthcare, Marysville, KS, p. A249

SCHNEIDER, John, M.D. Medical Director, Milwaukee County Behavioral Health Division, Milwaukee, WI, p. A710

SCHNEIDER, John, Human Resources Director, Putnam Community Medical Center, Palatka, FL, p. A141

SCHNEIDER, Ken, Chair Human Resources, Mayo Clinic Hospital – Rochester, Rochester, MN, p. A350

SCHNEIDER, Kevin, Chief Executive Officer, Sterling Surgical Hospital, Slidell, LA, p. A289

SCHNEIDER, Maureen, MSN Senior Vice President Clinical Program Development and Chief Operating Officer, Robert

Wood Johnson University Hospital Somerset, Somerville, NJ, p. A422

SCHNEIDER, Shanon, Chief Information Officer, Greeley County Health Services, Tribune, KS, p. A255

SCHNEIDER, Stacie A.
Director Human Resources, Aurora Medical Center – Manitowoc County, Two Rivers, WI, p. A716
Director Human Resources, Aurora Sheboygan Memorial Medical Center, Sheboygan, WI, p. A715

SCHNEIDER, Stephen, Manager Information Services, Alaska Psychiatric Institute, Anchorage, AK, p. A28

SCHNEIDER, Steve, Director of Operations, New Ulm Medical Center, New Ulm, MN, p. A348

SCHNEIDER, Steven E., M.D. Chief Medical Officer, Saint Mary's Hospital, Waterbury, CT, p. A118

SCHNEIDER, Thomas D., D.O. Chief of Staff, Jack C. Montgomery Veterans Affairs Medical Center, Muskogee, OK, p. A514

SCHNEIDER, Valerie, Director Human Resources, Gove County Medical Center, Quinter, KS, p. A253

SCHNEIDERMAN, Henry, M.D. Vice President Medical Services and Physician in Chief, The Hospital at Hebrew Health Care, West Hartford, CT, p. A118

SCHNELL, Dawn, Chief Nursing Officer, Sanford Jackson Medical Center, Jackson, MN, p. A345

SCHNELL, Mary, R.N. Chief Nursing Officer, Howard A. Rusk Rehabilitation Center, Columbia, MO, p. A370

SCHNEPP, Dennis, Chief Executive Officer, Lafayette Regional Rehabilitation Hospital, Lafayette, IN, p. A217

SCHNIEDERS, Michael H., FACHE, President, CHI Health Good Samaritan, Kearney, NE, p. A397

SCHNIER, Martin, D.O. Chief of Staff, West Texas Veterans Affairs Health Care System, Big Spring, TX, p. A603

SCHNOOR, Jeff
Director Information Technology and Systems, North Suburban Medical Center, Thornton, CO, p. A111
Director Information Systems, Swedish Medical Center, Englewood, CO, p. A106

SCHOELKOPF, Lawrence, M.D. Chief Medical Officer, East Morgan County Hospital, Brush, CO, p. A103

SCHOELL, Mark C., Chief Executive Officer, United Memorial Medical Center, Batavia, NY, p. A433

SCHOELLER, Betsy V., Director Human Resources and Education, Mary Greeley Medical Center, Ames, IA, p. A225

SCHOEN, Greg, M.D. Regional Medical Director, Fairview Northland Medical Center, Princeton, MN, p. A349

SCHOEN, Lynn, Chief Executive Officer, Kindred Hospital–Dayton, Dayton, OH, p. A492

SCHOENDIENST, Gerald A., Chief Executive Officer, Jeff Davis Hospital, Hazlehurst, GA, p. A160

SCHOENECKER, Perry L., M.D. Chief of Staff, Shriners Hospitals for Children–St. Louis, Saint Louis, MO, p. A381

SCHOENER, Timothy E.
Senior Vice President and Chief Information Officer, Soldiers and Sailors Memorial Hospital, Wellsboro, PA, p. A557
Senior Vice President and Chief Information Officer, Williamsport Regional Medical Center, Williamsport, PA, p. A559

SCHOENIG, Thomas
Regional Chief Information Officer, Adventist GlenOaks Hospital, Glendale Heights, IL, p. A191
Chief Information Officer, Adventist Hinsdale Hospital, Hinsdale, IL, p. A193
Chief Information Officer, Adventist La Grange Memorial Hospital, La Grange, IL, p. A194

SCHOENIG, Tom
System Director Information Services, Desert Springs Hospital Medical Center, Las Vegas, NV, p. A405
Regional Director Information Services, Valley Hospital Medical Center, Las Vegas, NV, p. A407

SCHOENOW, David, M.D. Chief Medical Officer, Schoolcraft Memorial Hospital, Manistique, MI, p. A329

SCHOEPLEIN, Kevin D., Chief Executive Officer, OSF Healthcare System, Peoria, IL, p. B104

SCHOETTLE, Steve, M.D. Chief Medical Staff, Ozark Health Medical Center, Clinton, AR, p. A44

SCHOFIELD, John, Chief Information Officer, Flagstaff Medical Center, Flagstaff, AZ, p. A32

SCHOFIELD, Sherry, Director Human Resources, Memorial Hospital, Martinsville, VA, p. A674

SCHOLEFIELD, Robert, Chief Operating Officer, St. Elizabeth Medical Center, Utica, NY, p. A456

SCHOLER, Duane, Chief Executive Officer, Arizona Orthopedic Surgical Hospital, Chandler, AZ, p. A31

SCHOLTEN, Ted, Chief Operating Officer, Rehabilitation Hospital of Fort Wayne, Fort Wayne, IN, p. A211

SCHOLZ, Suzanne, Director Medical Records, Horsham Clinic, Ambler, PA, p. A533

SCHON, John, Administrator and Chief Executive Officer, Dickinson County Healthcare System, Iron Mountain, MI, p. A327

SCHONEBERY, Jeremy, Director Information Technology, Heart of America Medical Center, Rugby, ND, p. A480

SCHONLAU, Dan
Chief Financial Officer and Vice President of Finance, CHI Health Nebraska Heart, Lincoln, NE, p. A397
Chief Financial Officer and Vice President of Finance, CHI Health St Elizabeth, Lincoln, NE, p. A397

SCHONS, Jeri, R.N. Chief Nursing Officer, Sanford Tracy Medical Center, Tracy, MN, p. A353

SCHOOLER, Nevelyn, Health Information Manager, Garfield County Public Hospital District, Pomeroy, WA, p. A686

SCHOOLER, Richard D., M.D. Executive Vice President and Chief Operating Officer, Freeman Hospital West, Joplin, MO, p. A373

SCHOOLER, Rick, Vice President and Chief Information Officer, Orlando Regional Medical Center, Orlando, FL, p. A141

SCHOOMAKER, Eric B., Surgeon General, Department of the Army, Office of the Surgeon General, Falls Church, VA, p. B47

SCHOPP, Mary Ellen, Senior Vice President Human Resources, Rush University Medical Center, Chicago, IL, p. A186

SCHOR, Mark, Chief Executive Officer, First Hospital Wyoming Valley, Kingston, PA, p. A541

SCHORER, Emily
Senior Vice President Human Resources, Cape Cod Hospital, Hyannis, MA, p. A311
Vice President, Human Resources, Falmouth Hospital, Falmouth, MA, p. A310

SCHORI, Melissa, M.D. Medical Director, Lincoln Medical and Mental Health Center,, NY, p. A445

SCHOTT, Lynn, Director Information Technology, Mobridge Regional Hospital, Mobridge, SD, p. A575

SCHOTTEL, Roxanne, Chief Executive Officer, Washington County Hospital, Washington, KS, p. A256

SCHOTTLAND, Edward M., Acting President, Memorial Hospital of Rhode Island, Pawtucket, RI, p. A560

SCHOULTIES, Daniel L., M.D. Vice President Medical Affairs, Good Samaritan Hospital, Dayton, OH, p. A492

SCHOWENGERDT, Daniel, M.D. Chief of Staff, Comanche County Hospital, Coldwater, KS, p. A242

SCHRADER, Guillermo, M.D. Acting Medical Director, Eastern State Hospital, Williamsburg, VA, p. A680

SCHRAEDER, David, Director Information Systems, Russell Regional Hospital, Russell, KS, p. A253

SCHRAMM, Michael, Chief Executive Officer, Rice Memorial Hospital, Willmar, MN, p. A354

SCHRAMM, Steven R., Chief Financial Officer, Mountain View Hospital, Payson, UT, p. A662

SCHREEG, Timothy M., President and Chief Executive Officer, Jasper County Hospital, Rensselaer, IN, p. A221

SCHREFFLER, Mary Jane, Director Human Resources, Meadows Psychiatric Center, Centre Hall, PA, p. A535

SCHREIBER, Anne, Manager Human Resources, Fairfax Hospital, Kirkland, WA, p. A684

SCHREIBER, Elizabeth, R.N. Director Patient Care Services, Flambeau Hospital, Park Falls, WI, p. A713

SCHREIBER, John, M.D. President and Chief Physician Executive, Baystate Medical Center, Springfield, MA, p. A314

SCHREIBER, Mary Jo, R.N. Vice President Patient Services, Winter Haven Hospital, Winter Haven, FL, p. A150

SCHREIER, Susan, R.N. Chief Nursing Executive, Rockford Memorial Hospital, Rockford, IL, p. A201

SCHREINER, David L., FACHE, President and Chief Executive Officer, Katherine Shaw Bethea Hospital, Dixon, IL, p. A188

SCHRODER, Loren D., Chief Financial Officer, Phelps Memorial Health Center, Holdrege, NE, p. A396

SCHROEDER, Brian D., M.D. Senior Vice President and Chief Medical Officer, Sparrow Hospital, Lansing, MI, p. A328

SCHROEDER, Cygnet, D.O. Medical Director, HEALTHSOUTH Rehabilitation Hospital of Fort Smith, Fort Smith, AR, p. A46

SCHROEDER, Heather, R.N. Chief Nurse Executive and Vice President of Nursing, Aurora BayCare Medical Center, Green Bay, WI, p. A705

SCHROEDER, Larry, Chief Executive Officer, Sauk Prairie Healthcare, Prairie Du Sac, WI, p. A714

SCHROEDER, Rick, Chief Executive Officer, North Big Horn Hospital District, Lovell, WY, p. A722

SCHROEDER, Russell, Chief Nursing Officer, Saint Louis University Medical Center, Saint Louis, MO, p. A381

SCHROEDER, Steve, M.D. Chief of Staff, Avera Hand County Memorial Hospital, Miller, SD, p. A574

SCHROEDL, Greg, M.D. Vice President, Medical and Chief Medical Officer, UW Medicine/Northwest Hospital & Medical Center, Seattle, WA, p. A689

SCHROEPPEL, Stacie, Director Human Resources, Lakeside Behavioral Health System, Memphis, TN, p. A588

SCHROYER, Mike, Chief Operating Officer, St. Vincent Heart Center, Indianapolis, IN, p. A215

SCHROYER, Renee, Chief Executive Officer, Sutter Surgical Hospital – North Valley, Yuba City, CA, p. A101

SCHRUMPF, Jason, President, Missouri Delta Medical Center, Sikeston, MO, p. A382

SCHUBERTH, Michael, Director, Fiscal Services and Plant Operations, Connecticut Valley Hospital, Middletown, CT, p. A115

SCHUCK, Jennifer, Associate Administrator, Emory Wesley Woods Geriatric Hospital, Atlanta, GA, p. A152

SCHUCKMAN, Tim, Chief Financial Officer, Jennie M. Melham Memorial Medical Center, Broken Bow, NE, p. A394

SCHUE, Janine
Senior Vice President People Resources, Newark–Wayne Community Hospital, Newark, NY, p. A449
Senior Vice President Human Resources, Rochester General Hospital, Rochester, NY, p. A453

SCHUELER, Joe, Chief Financial Officer, Morrow County Hospital, Mount Gilead, OH, p. A499

SCHUERCH, Timothy, President and Chief Executive Officer, Maniilaq Health Center, Kotzebue, AK, p. A29

SCHUESSLER, Donald, M.D. Medical Director, Gouverneur Hospital, Gouverneur, NY, p. A438

SCHUESSLER, Dwight, Chief Information Officer, Iowa City Veterans Affairs Health Care System, Iowa City, IA, p. A232

SCHUETT, Susan M., Chief Information Officer, Olmsted Medical Center, Rochester, MN, p. A350

SCHUETZ, Jill, Director Human Resources, LifeCare Hospitals of Wisconsin, Pewaukee, WI, p. A713

SCHUH, Jason, M.D. Chief of Staff, Wise Regional Health System, Decatur, TX, p. A612

SCHUITEMAN, Jackson, Chief Financial Officer, Sioux Center Health, Sioux Center, IA, p. A237

SCHULER, Allison, R.N. Chief Nursing Officer, Montfort Jones Memorial Hospital, Kosciusko, MS, p. A361

SCHULER, Kathy, R.N. Vice President of Patient Care Services, Winchester Hospital, Winchester, MA, p. A316

SCHULTE, Mark, FACHE, Chief Executive Officer, Sturgis Regional Hospital, Sturgis, SD, p. A577

SCHULTEIS, Chris, Vice President/Chief Financial Officer, Southampton Hospital, Southampton, NY, p. A455

SCHULTES, Donna, Director Information Technology, Aurelia Osborn Fox Memorial Hospital, Oneonta, NY, p. A450

SCHULTHEIS, Hal, Director Information Systems, TriStar Hendersonville Medical Center, Hendersonville, TN, p. A584

SCHULTZ, Bradley
Chief Financial Officer, TriStar Skyline Madison Campus, Madison, TN, p. A587
Chief Financial Officer, TriStar Skyline Medical Center, Nashville, TN, p. A591

SCHULTZ, David W., FACHE Executive Vice President and Chief Operating Officer, Overlake Medical Center, Bellevue, WA, p. A681

SCHULTZ, Diana, Chief Executive Officer, Kindred Hospital El Paso, El Paso, TX, p. A616

SCHULTZ, Jacky, R.N. Executive Vice President and Chief Operating Officer, Suburban Hospital, Bethesda, MD, p. A299

SCHULTZ, Josh, Manager Corporate Services, Southwest Regional Rehabilitation Center, Battle Creek, MI, p. A319

SCHULTZ, Kim, Senior Application Analyst, Connally Memorial Medical Center, Floresville, TX, p. A617

SCHULTZ, Kurt
Group Chief Financial Officer, Cornerstone Hospital of SouthEast Arizona, Tucson, AZ, p. A40
Chief Financial Officer, Cornerstone Hospital–West Monroe, West Monroe, LA, p. A290
Chief Financial Officer, Solara Hospital Harlingen, Harlingen, TX, p. A622

SCHULTZ, Mary Kay, Director Human Resources, Sturgis Hospital, Sturgis, MI, p. A335

SCHULTZ, Merrilee, Chief Finance, Sanford USD Medical Center, Sioux Falls, SD, p. A576

SCHULTZ, Rachelle H., President and Chief Executive Officer, Winona Health, Winona, MN, p. A354

SCHULTZ, Sharon A., MSN Chief Nurse Executive and Vice President, Tri–City Medical Center, Oceanside, CA, p. A81

SCHULTZ, Teresa L., R.N. Vice President of Patient Care, Rogers Memorial Hospital, Oconomowoc, WI, p. A712

SCHULTZ, Vince, M.D. Chief Medical Officer, Mercy Hospital Grayling, Grayling, MI, p. A325

SCHULZ, Charles K., Chief Executive Officer, York General Hospital, York, NE, p. A403

SCHULZ, Ken, Chief Operating Officer, North Dakota State Hospital, Jamestown, ND, p. A479

SCHULZ, Larry A., Chief Executive Officer, Lake Region Healthcare, Fergus Falls, MN, p. A343

SCHULZ, Leah, Director of Nursing, North Dakota State Hospital, Jamestown, ND, p. A479

SCRIVO, Jr., Joseph A., Director Human Resources, Mercy Hospital, Buffalo, NY, p. A434

SCRUGGS, Sherry, Administrator, Milan General Hospital, Milan, TN, p. A589

SCUDDER, Angela, R.N. Vice President Patient Care Services, Dearborn County Hospital, Lawrenceburg, IN, p. A217

SCULL, Stephen W., Vice President Ethics and Compliance officer, Rapides Regional Medical Center, Alexandria, LA, p. A272

SCULLY, Charles
 Chief Information Officer, Renown Regional Medical Center, Reno, NV, p. A407
 Chief Information Officer, Renown Rehabilitation Hospital, Reno, NV, p. A408
 Chief Information Officer, Renown South Meadows Medical Center, Reno, NV, p. A408

SCULLY, Kem, Chief Executive Officer, Purcell Municipal Hospital, Purcell, OK, p. A518

SCULLY, Trish
 Manager Employment Services, Massachusetts Hospital School, Canton, MA, p. A309
 Director Human Resources, Taunton State Hospital, Taunton, MA, p. A315

SCZYGELSKI, Sidney C., Senior Vice President Finance and Chief Financial Officer, Aspirus Wausau Hospital, Wausau, WI, p. A717

SEAGER, Jerry, Assistant Vice President and Chief Financial Officer, Inova Fair Oaks Hospital, Fairfax, VA, p. A670

SEAGO, Terri, Chief Financial Officer, Baptist Memorial Hospital–Collierville, Collierville, TN, p. A581

SEAGROVES, Matthew, Chief Financial Officer, Bayfront Health Brooksville, Brooksville, FL, p. A125

SEAHORN, Martha, R.N. Chief Nurse Office, Shelby Baptist Medical Center, Alabaster, AL, p. A15

SEAL, John, Director Human Resources, Riverside Medical Center, Franklinton, LA, p. A277

SEAL, Ronald T., Chief Executive Officer, Texoma Medical Center, Denison, TX, p. A613

SEALE, Corey A., Administrator, Kaiser Permanente Moreno Valley Medical Center, Moreno Valley, CA, p. A78

SEALE, Edward, Chief Information Officer, New Horizons Health Systems, Owenton, KY, p. A268

SEALE, Jonathan, Chief Information Officer, Erie Veterans Affairs Medical Center, Erie, PA, p. A538

SEALE, Paul E., FACHE Chief Operating Officer, Upstate University Hospital, Syracuse, NY, p. A456

SEALS, Molly, Senior Vice President Human Resources and Learning, St. Joseph Health Center, Warren, OH, p. A504

SEALS, Robert, D.O. Medical Director, Carson City Hospital, Carson City, MI, p. A320

SEAMON, Robert L., Chief Executive Officer, Clifton–Fine Hospital, Star Lake, NY, p. A455

SEARBY, Tonya L., Chief Human Resources, Marion Veterans Affairs Medical Center, Marion, IL, p. A195

SEARLE, Anne, Chief Information Officer, University Medical Center of Princeton at Plainsboro, Plainsboro, NJ, p. A421

SEARLE, Reynolds, Director Information Systems, Fairfield Memorial Hospital, Winnsboro, SC, p. A571

SEARLS, Barbara, Chief Financial Officer, SEARHC MT. Edgecumbe Hospital, Sitka, AK, p. A30

SEARLS, Gary, Chief Financial Officer, Northside Hospital, Saint Petersburg, FL, p. A144

SEARS, Christopher, M.D. President Medical Staff, Mercy Tiffin Hospital, Tiffin, OH, p. A503

SEARS, Erin Clare, Associate Director of Operations, Providence Veterans Affairs Medical Center, Providence, RI, p. A561

SEARS, Marilyn, President and Chief Executive Officer, Shelby Memorial Hospital, Shelbyville, IL, p. A202

SEARS, Michelle, Director Information Systems, Helen Newberry Joy Hospital, Newberry, MI, p. A331

SEASE, Peggy
 Vice President Human Resources, DCH Regional Medical Center, Tuscaloosa, AL, p. A26
 Vice President Human Resources, Northport Medical Center, Northport, AL, p. A24

SEATON, Tracy, Director of Nursing, Taylorville Memorial Hospital, Taylorville, IL, p. A204

SEAVER, Roger E., President and Chief Executive Officer, Henry Mayo Newhall Memorial Hospital, Valencia, CA, p. A98

SEBASTIAN, Peggy A., R.N., President and Chief Executive Officer, St. Joseph's Hospital, Highland, IL, p. A192

SEBEK, Brenda Jean, R.N. Vice President Patient Care Services, CHI Health St. Mary's, Nebraska City, NE, p. A398

SECKINGER, Mark R., Administrator and Chief Executive Officer, OhioHealth Hardin Memorial Hospital, Kenton, OH, p. A495

SECOR, Diane K., Director Human Resources, Lawrence Medical Center, Moulton, AL, p. A24

SECREST, Jack, M.D. Chief Medical Officer, St. Mary's Hospital, Cottonwood, ID, p. A175

SECREST, Stephanie R., Group Director Human Resources and Acute Care Services, Woodwinds Health Campus, Woodbury, MN, p. A354

SECURRO, Matthew J., Vice President Human Resources, Conway Medical Center, Conway, SC, p. A565

SEDA, Jolene R., Administrative Director, Yakima Valley Memorial Hospital, Yakima, WA, p. A692

SEDGLEY, Don, President, Novant Health Haymarket Medical Center, Haymarket, VA, p. A672

SEDGWICK, Sally, Manager Public Relations and Marketing, Bigfork Valley Hospital, Bigfork, MN, p. A340

SEDIGHI, Hooman, M.D., President and Chief Executive Officer, GLOBALREHAB, Dallas, TX, p. B61

SEDMINIK, Vince, Chief Executive Officer, Springhill Medical Center, Springhill, LA, p. A289

SEDORE, Ann, Ph.D. Chief Nursing Officer, Crouse Hospital, Syracuse, NY, p. A455

SEEDER, Rachael, Controller, Santiam Memorial Hospital, Stayton, OR, p. A530

SEEGERS, Robert, M.D. Vice President Medical Affairs, St. Francis Medical Center, Monroe, LA, p. A284

SEEKINS, DeAnne, Director, Durham Veterans Affairs Medical Center, Durham, NC, p. A463

SEELEY, Kevin, Chief Information Officer, Mike O'Callaghan Federal Hospital, Nellis AFB, NV, p. A407

SEELEY, Pam, Chief Nursing Officer, Elmira Psychiatric Center, Elmira, NY, p. A437

SEELMAN, Michael, Chief Operating Officer, Northside Medical Center, Youngstown, OH, p. A506

SEELY, Paula, Manager Human Resources, Kossuth Regional Health Center, Algona, IA, p. A225

SEEMS, Steven, Director of Information Technology, Phillips County Hospital, Phillipsburg, KS, p. A252

SEESE, Rebecca, Chief Operating Officer, U. S. Air Force Regional Hospital, Elmendorf AFB, AK, p. A28

SEEVER, Jennifer, Regional Chief Financial Officer, Sedan City Hospital, Sedan, KS, p. A254

SEGAL, Jonathan, Chief Financial Officer, New York State Psychiatric Institute, New York, NY, p. A447

SEGAL, Rebecca, Chief Operating Officer, Lake Cumberland Regional Hospital, Somerset, KY, p. A270

SEGAL, Stanton, M.D. Chief Medical Officer, Aria Health, Philadelphia, PA, p. A547

SEGAR–MILLER, Cindy, MS, Interim Chief Executive Officer, Williamson Memorial Hospital, Williamson, WV, p. A700

SEGELEON, Kurt, Director Health Information Management, Kindred Hospital–Pittsburgh, Oakdale, PA, p. A547

SEGER, LaDonna, Director Information Services, Saint Luke's North Hospital – Barry Road, Kansas City, MO, p. A374

SEGIN, Robert
 Chief Financial Officer, Virtua Berlin, Berlin, NJ, p. A413
 Executive Vice President & Chief Financial Officer, Virtua Marlton, Marlton, NJ, p. A418
 Chief Financial Officer, Virtua Memorial, Mount Holly, NJ, p. A419

SEGLER, Randall K., FACHE, Chief Executive Officer, Comanche County Memorial Hospital, Lawton, OK, p. A512

SEGRAVES, Steven, M.D. Medical Director, Research Psychiatric Center, Kansas City, MO, p. A374

SEGURA, Mario, Director of Nursing, Starr County Memorial Hospital, Rio Grande City, TX, p. A644

SEHRT, Lori, Chief Financial Officer, McKee Medical Center, Loveland, CO, p. A109

SEIBERT, Nancy, Director Human Resources, Franklin Hospital District, Benton, IL, p. A181

SEID, Lynette, Area Chief Financial Officer, Kaiser Permanente San Diego Medical Center, San Diego, CA, p. A89

SEIDE, Rob, Manager Marketing and Communications, St. Luke's Hospital, San Francisco, CA, p. A91

SEIDL, Doris A., Vice President Human Resources, Port Huron Hospital, Port Huron, MI, p. A332

SEIDLER, Richard A., FACHE,
 President and Chief Executive Officer, UnityPoint Health – Trinity Bettendorf, Bettendorf, IA, p. A225
 President and Chief Executive Officer, UnityPoint Health – Trinity Rock Island, Rock Island, IL, p. A201

SEIDMAN, Robert
 Chief Operating Officer, Health Alliance Hospital – Broadway Campus, Kingston, NY, p. A440
 Chief Operating Officer, Health Alliance Hospital – Mary's Avenue Campus, Kingston, NY, p. A440

SEIFER, Jill, Vice President Human Resources, Oaklawn Psychiatric Center, Goshen, IN, p. A212

SEIGLER, Leslie G., Executive Assistant and Coordinator Human Resources, Edgefield County Hospital, Edgefield, SC, p. A565

SEIM, Lori, R.N. Director Nursing Services, First Care Health Center, Park River, ND, p. A480

SEINER, Ralph, Chief Executive Officer, Kindred Hospital Central Tampa, Tampa, FL, p. A148

SEIRER, Jeff, Interim Chief Financial Officer, Via Christi Hospital on St. Francis, Wichita, KS, p. A257

SEITZ, Stewart R., Chief Executive Officer, Gladys Spellman Specialty Hospital and Nursing Center, Cheverly, MD, p. A299

SELBOVITZ, Leslie, M.D. Senior Vice President Medical Affairs, Newton–Wellesley Hospital, Newton Lower Falls, MA, p. A313

SELBY, Eric, R.N. Chief Nursing Officer, Chicot Memorial Medical Center, Lake Village, AR, p. A48

SELDEN, Thomas A., FACHE, President and Chief Executive Officer, Southwest General Health Center, Middleburg Heights, OH, p. A498

SELEY, Jim, Chief Information Officer, Clay County Medical Center, Clay Center, KS, p. A242

SELF, Debbie, Chief Financial Officer, North Georgia Medical Center, Ellijay, GA, p. A159

SELF, Joshua, Chief Operating Officer, Biloxi Regional Medical Center, Biloxi, MS, p. A355

SELFRIDGE, Tara, Manager Human Resources, Purcell Municipal Hospital, Purcell, OK, p. A518

SELHORST, Sonya, R.N., Administrator, Mercy Hospital of Defiance, Defiance, OH, p. A492

SELIGA, Patricia, R.N. Chief Nursing Officer, Moses Taylor Hospital, Scranton, PA, p. A554

SELIGMAN, Joel, President and Chief Executive Officer, Northern Westchester Hospital, Mount Kisco, NY, p. A442

SELIGMAN, Morris H., M.D. Chief Medical Officer and Chief Medical Information Officer, Sycamore Shoals Hospital, Elizabethton, TN, p. A582

SELL, Paula, Director Human Resources, Allen County Regional Hospital, Iola, KS, p. A246

SELLARDS, Michael G., Chief Executive Officer, Pallottine Health Services, Huntington, WV, p. B104

SELLARDS, Michael G., President and Chief Executive Officer, St. Mary's Medical Center, Huntington, WV, p. A696

SELLE, Ginger, Vice President Patient Care Services, St. Clare Hospital, Baraboo, WI, p. A702

SELLE, Justin, Chief Operating Officer, Pike County Memorial Hospital, Louisiana, MO, p. A376

SELLERS, Dan, Chief Financial Officer, Eskenazi Health, Indianapolis, IN, p. A214

SELLERS, Laura, Director Information Systems, Youth Villages Inner Harbour Campus, Douglasville, GA, p. A158

SELLERS, Liz, MSN, Interim Chief Executive Officer, Southwest Memorial Hospital, Cortez, CO, p. A104

SELLERS, Regena, Chief Nursing Officer, Three Rivers Behavioral Health, West Columbia, SC, p. A571

SELLERS, Robert R.
 Administrator, Jenkins County Hospital, Millen, GA, p. A163
 Administrator, Screven County Hospital, Sylvania, GA, p. A167

SELLHEIM, Kevin, Chief Executive Officer, Sleepy Eye Medical Center, Sleepy Eye, MN, p. A352

SELLS, Matt, CPA Chief Financial Officer, Shenandoah Medical Center, Shenandoah, IA, p. A237

SELMAN, J. Peter, Chief Executive Officer, Baptist Medical Center South, Montgomery, AL, p. A23

SELMON, Patricia, Director Public Relations and Chief Human Resources, Jefferson County Hospital, Fayette, MS, p. A357

SELPH, Wendy, Director Human Resources, Dodge County Hospital, Eastman, GA, p. A159

SELSOR, Doug, Director Finance, Select Rehabilitation Hospital of Denton, Denton, TX, p. A613

SELTZER, Paul, M.D. Chief of Staff, West Palm Hospital, West Palm Beach, FL, p. A150

SELVAGGI, Richard, M.D. Chief of Staff, Hunt Regional Community Hospital, Commerce, TX, p. A607

SELVAM, A. Panneer, M.D. Chief of Staff, Northern Arizona Veterans Affairs Health Care System, Prescott, AZ, p. A37

SELVIDGE, Sandra, Chief Fiscal Service, Cincinnati Veterans Affairs Medical Center, Cincinnati, OH, p. A486

SELZ, Timothy P., Vice President, Orange Regional Medical Center, Middletown, NY, p. A441

SEMAR, Dale, Controller, Medina Regional Hospital, Hondo, TX, p. A623

SEMELSBERGER, Kimberly, Vice President Financial Operations, Conemaugh Miners Medical Center, Hastings, PA, p. A540

SEMERDJIAN, Nancy, R.N. Chief Nursing Officer, NorthShore University Health System, Evanston, IL, p. A189

SEMINARO, Anthony, Chief Financial Officer, Trumbull Memorial Hospital, Warren, OH, p. A504

SEMINGSON, John H., Chief Executive Officer, Ruby Valley Hospital, Sheridan, MT, p. A391

SEMRAU, Clint, Chief of Staff, Baldwin Area Medical Center, Baldwin, WI, p. A701

SENDAYDIEGO, Fe, Director Information Systems, Sonoma Valley Hospital, Sonoma, CA, p. A95

SENELICK, Richard, M.D. Medical Director, HEALTHSOUTH Rehabilitation Institute of San Antonio, San Antonio, TX, p. A646

SENGER, Richard, Chief Financial Officer, Portsmouth Regional Hospital, Portsmouth, NH, p. A412

SENGER, Tricia, Chief Financial Officer, St. Luke's Elmore, Mountain Home, ID, p. A177

SENKER, Margaret, Chief Information Officer, Veterans Affairs Western New York Healthcare System–Buffalo Division, Buffalo, NY, p. A435

SENNEFF, Robert G., FACHE, President and Chief Executive Officer, Graham Hospital, Canton, IL, p. A182

SENNETT, Paul, Chief Financial Officer, Centinela Hospital Medical Center, Inglewood, CA, p. A67

SENNISH, James, Vice President Human Resources, Firelands Regional Health System, Sandusky, OH, p. A501

SEPP Jr., Howard W., FACHE, Vice President and Administrator, Southeast Georgia Health System Camden Campus, Saint Marys, GA, p. A166

SERAFIN, Deborah J., Vice President Human Resources, Mount St. Mary's Hospital and Health Center, Lewiston, NY, p. A440

SERAPHINE, Jeffrey G., FACHE, Division President, Duke LifePoint Healthcare, Brentwood, TN, p. B54

SERENO, Joe, Chief Financial Officer, Southwest General Hospital, San Antonio, TX, p. A647

SERENO, Joseph, Chief Financial Officer, Lovelace Women's Hospital, Albuquerque, NM, p. A426

SERFLING, G. Aubrey, President and Chief Executive Officer, Eisenhower Medical Center, Rancho Mirage, CA, p. A84

SERKETICH, Steve, Manager Information Services, Aurora Sheboygan Memorial Medical Center, Sheboygan, WI, p. A715

SERLE, John, FACHE, President and Chief Executive Officer, Lourdes Medical Center, Pasco, WA, p. A686

SERNYAK, Michael, M.D., Director, Connecticut Mental Health Center, New Haven, CT, p. A116

SERRANO, Jorge L. Matta, Administrator, Auxilio Mutuo Hospital, San Juan, PR, p. A727

SERRATORE, Deborah, Chief Human Resources Officer, Kansas City Veterans Affairs Medical Center, Kansas City, MO, p. A373

SERRATT, Jim, Chief Executive Officer, Willow Springs Center, Reno, NV, p. A408

SESSIONS, Jerry W., M.D. Chief Medical Staff, Springhill Medical Center, Springhill, LA, p. A289

SESSIONS, Tracey, Administrator, State Hospital South, Blackfoot, ID, p. A174

SESSLER, Connie, Director Human Resources, ProMedica St. Luke's Hospital, Maumee, OH, p. A498

SESTERHENN, Steven, Vice President, UnityPoint Health – Allen Hospital, Waterloo, IA, p. A239

SETCHEL, David P., Chief Operating Officer, St. Francis Health Center, Topeka, KS, p. A255

SETHI, Sanjiv, M.D. Medical Director, Fulton State Hospital, Fulton, MO, p. A372

SETTELMEYER, Camille, Assistant Administrator Clinical Services, Mercy Hospital, Valley City, ND, p. A480

SETTLE, Andrea, Director Human Resources, Taylor Regional Hospital, Campbellsville, KY, p. A259

SETTLES, April, Chief Financial Officer, Greene County General Hospital, Linton, IN, p. A217

SETTLES, Laura, Director Human Resources, Baylor Medical Center at Garland, Garland, TX, p. A620

SETZER, Jeffery, Administrator Information Systems, J. D. McCarty Center for Children With Developmental Disabilities, Norman, OK, p. A514

SETZKORN–MEYER, Marsha, Director Public Relations and Marketing, Hillsboro Community Hospital, Hillsboro, KS, p. A245

SEVCO, Mark
President, UPMC East, Monroeville, PA, p. A545
President, UPMC McKeesport, McKeesport, PA, p. A544

SEVERA, Jeff, D.O. Chief of Staff, Vidant Roanoke–Chowan Hospital, Ahoskie, NC, p. A459

SEVERANCE, Matthew J., FACHE, Chief Executive Officer, Roper Hospital, Charleston, SC, p. A563

SEVILLIAN, Clarence, President and Chief Executive Officer, McLaren Oakland, Pontiac, MI, p. A332

SEWATSKY, Mary, M.D. Chief Medical Officer, Moses Taylor Hospital, Scranton, PA, p. A554

SEWELL, Lance, Chief Financial Officer, South Lake Hospital, Clermont, FL, p. A125

SEWELL, Sue, Chief Nursing Officer, Wise Regional Health System, Decatur, TX, p. A612

SEXTON, Cheryl, Director Nursing Operations, South Texas Rehabilitation Hospital, Brownsville, TX, p. A604

SEXTON, Cindy, Chief Financial Officer, St. David's Round Rock Medical Center, Round Rock, TX, p. A645

SEXTON, Kevin, Director Information Systems, Raleigh General Hospital, Beckley, WV, p. A693

SEXTON, Paul, Chief Executive Officer, Highlands Behavioral Health System, Littleton, CO, p. A109

SEXTON, William J., Administrator, Wyoming State Hospital, Evanston, WY, p. A721

SEXTON, William P., Chief Executive Officer, Prairie du Chien Memorial Hospital, Prairie Du Chien, WI, p. A713

SEY, Mark, Vice President and Chief Administrative Officer, Lodi Memorial Hospital, Lodi, CA, p. A69

SEYBOLD, Henry, Senior Vice President and Chief Financial Officer, Rockford Memorial Hospital, Rockford, IL, p. A201

SEYMOUR, Claudette, Director Personnel, Memphis Mental Health Institute, Memphis, TN, p. A589

SEYMOUR, Galen, M.D. Chief of Staff, Horton Community Hospital, Horton, KS, p. A246

SEYMOUR, Jose, Chief Information Resource Management, James A. Haley Veterans' Hospital, Tampa, FL, p. A147

SEYMOUR, Russell, Chief Information Management Division, Reynolds Army Community Hospital, Fort Sill, OK, p. A511

SHACKELFORD, Denice, R.N. Interim Chief Nurse Executive, Pender Memorial Hospital, Burgaw, NC, p. A460

SHACKELFORD, Gerald, Staff Support Specialist, Texas Center for Infectious Disease, San Antonio, TX, p. A648

SHACKELFORD, Paul, M.D. Chief Medical Officer, Vidant Medical Center, Greenville, NC, p. A465

SHADENSACK, Don, Vice President Clinical Services, OSF St. Mary Medical Center, Galesburg, IL, p. A190

SHADOWEN, Michael, M.D. Chief of Staff, T. J. Samson Community Hospital, Glasgow, KY, p. A262

SHADWICK, Shirley A., Administrator Human Resources, Desert Springs Hospital Medical Center, Las Vegas, NV, p. A405

SHAFER, Robert
Vice President Finance, Mercy Medical Center–Dubuque, Dubuque, IA, p. A230
Vice President Finance, Mercy Medical Center–Dyersville, Dyersville, IA, p. A230

SHAFER, Timothy, M.D. Medical Director, Grace Cottage Hospital, Townshend, VT, p. A666

SHAFFER, Diana, Director Human Resources, CHI Health Saint Francis, Grand Island, NE, p. A396

SHAFICI, Khaled, M.D. President Medical Staff, Cornerstone Hospital–West Monroe, West Monroe, LA, p. A290

SHAFIE, Taghi, M.D. Interim Medical Director, Cedar Crest Hospital and Residential Treatment Center, Belton, TX, p. A602

SHAH, Aman Ali, M.D. Chief Medical Staff, Lake Whitney Medical Center, Whitney, TX, p. A657

SHAH, Avani D., M.D. Chief of Medical Staff, MedStar St. Mary's Hospital, Leonardtown, MD, p. A302

SHAH, Beemal A., Chief Executive Officer, Person Memorial Hospital, Roxboro, NC, p. A472

SHAH, Girishkumar, M.D. Clinical Director, Northlake Behavioral Hospital, Mandeville, LA, p. A283

SHAH, Jay, M.D. President Medical Staff, San Antonio Community Hospital, Upland, CA, p. A98

SHAH, Jayendra H., M.D. Chief Medical Officer, Southern Arizona Veterans Affairs Health Care System, Tucson, AZ, p. A41

SHAH, Paresh, Director Information Systems, Reston Hospital Center, Reston, VA, p. A677

SHAH, Shalin, Chief Operating Officer, Regional Medical Center Bayonet Point, Hudson, FL, p. A131

SHAH, Vital, M.D., Director, Central State Hospital, Louisville, KY, p. A265

SHAHAN, Mary Jo, Vice President and Chief Financial Officer, West Virginia University Hospitals, Morgantown, WV, p. A697

SHAHEEN, Jim, President, Strategic Behavioral Health, LLC, Memphis, TN, p. B129

SHAHRIARI, Sia, M.D. Chief of Staff, Great River Medical Center, Blytheville, AR, p. A43

SHAHRYAR, Syed, M.D. Medical Director, Promise Hospital of Phoenix, Mesa, AZ, p. A34

SHAHSAVARI, Mehan, M.D. Chief of Staff, Norman Specialty Hospital, Norman, OK, p. A514

SHAHZADA, Kamran, M.D. Chief Medical Staff, South Central Kansas Medical Center, Arkansas City, KS, p. A241

SHAKER, Mark S., President and Chief Executive Officer, Miami Valley Hospital, Dayton, OH, p. A492

SHALLASH, Anthony J., M.D. Interim Medical Director, Franklin Hospital, Valley Stream, NY, p. A457

SHALLOCK, James R., Chief Financial Officer, Memorial Hermann Northwest Hospital, Houston, TX, p. A625

SHAMBLES, Terry W., Chief Financial Officer, Evanston Regional Hospital, Evanston, WY, p. A721

SHAMBURG, Steffen, M.D. Chief of Staff, Hiawatha Community Hospital, Hiawatha, KS, p. A245

SHAMIYEH, Souhail, M.D. Chief of Staff, Mountain View Regional Medical Center, Norton, VA, p. A676

SHANAHAN, Thomas, Chief Financial Officer and Senior Vice President, Raritan Bay Medical Center, Perth Amboy, NJ, p. A421

SHAND, Natalie, M.D. Vice President Integrative Medicine and Chief Medical Officer, Freedom Pain Hospital, Scottsdale, AZ, p. A38

SHANLEY, Diane, Deputy Service Unit Director, U. S. Public Health Service Indian Hospital–Sells, Sells, AZ, p. A39

SHANLEY, Linda, Vice President and Chief Information Officer, Saint Francis Hospital and Medical Center, Hartford, CT, p. A114

SHANNON, David A., President and Chief Executive Officer, Jersey Shore Hospital, Jersey Shore, PA, p. A541

SHANNON, Greg, Director Human Resources, Ozarks Medical Center, West Plains, MO, p. A384

SHANNON, John Jay, M.D., Chief Executive Officer, Cook County Health and Hospitals System, Chicago, IL, p. B44

SHANNON, Richard, M.D. Chief of Staff, Montrose Memorial Hospital, Montrose, CO, p. A110

SHANNON, Scott, Director Finance, Socorro General Hospital, Socorro, NM, p. A431

SHAPE, Amy, Information Technology, North Dakota State Hospital, Jamestown, ND, p. A479

SHAPIRO, David, M.D
Vice President Medical Affairs and Chief Medical Officer, Columbia St. Mary's Hospital Milwaukee, Milwaukee, WI, p. A710
Vice President Medical Affairs and Chief Medical Officer, Columbia St. Mary's Ozaukee Hospital, Mequon, WI, p. A709
Vice President Medical Affairs and Chief Medical Officer, Sacred Heart Rehabilitation Institute, Milwaukee, WI, p. A711

SHAPIRO, Ira, M.D. Chief Medical Officer, St. Mary's Regional Medical Center, Lewiston, ME, p. A294

SHAPIRO, Louis A., President and Chief Executive Officer, Hospital for Special Surgery, New York, NY, p. A444

SHAPIRO, Marc, M.D. Chief Medical Officer, St. Helena Hospital Clear Lake, Clearlake, CA, p. A60

SHAPIRO, Robert S., Senior Vice President and Chief Financial Officer, Forest Hills Hospital,, NY, p. A443

SHAPIRO, Steven D., M.D
Chief Medical Officer, Bon Secours St. Francis Xavier Hospital, Charleston, SC, p. A563
Chief Medical Officer, Mount Pleasant Hospital, Mount Pleasant, SC, p. A568
Vice President Medical Affairs, Roper Hospital, Charleston, SC, p. A563

SHARANGPANI, Rojesh, M.D. Chief of Staff, Capital Medical Center, Olympia, WA, p. A686

SHARBER–HOWELL, Sheryl, Administrator, Creek Nation Community Hospital, Okemah, OK, p. A514

SHARFSTEIN, Steven S., M.D., President and Chief Executive Officer, Sheppard Pratt Health System, Baltimore, MD, p. A297

SHARKEY, Linda, R.N. Vice President Patient Care Services and Chief Nurse Executive, Fauquier Hospital, Warrenton, VA, p. A680

SHARLOW, Joseph, M.D. Chief of Staff, Ste. Genevieve County Memorial Hospital, Ste. Genevieve, MO, p. A383

SHARMA, Aika, M.D. President Medical Staff, Alameda Hospital, Alameda, CA, p. A55

SHARMA, Chandra, M.D. Chief of Staff, Welch Community Hospital, Welch, WV, p. A700

SHARMA, Roger, Chief Financial Officer, Citrus Valley Medical Center–Inter Community Campus, Covina, CA, p. A61

SHARMA, Satish C., M.D. Chief of Staff, Providence Veterans Affairs Medical Center, Providence, RI, p. A561

SHARON, Joesph P., Associate Director, Wilkes–Barre Veterans Affairs Medical Center, Wilkes–Barre, PA, p. A558

SHARP, Cindy, M.D. Chief Medical Officer, Madison Valley Medical Center, Ennis, MT, p. A387

SHARP, Gina, FACHE, President, Linden Oaks Hospital at Edward, Naperville, IL, p. A197

SHARP, Janet, Interim Chief Executive Officer, Choctaw Nation Health Care Center, Talihina, OK, p. A519

SHARP, John K., Chief Financial Officer, Seton Medical Center Harker Heights, Harker Heights, TX, p. A622

SHARP, Julie, Supervisor Human Resources, Chase County Community Hospital, Imperial, NE, p. A397

SHARP, Patrick, Senior Vice President and Chief Operating Officer, Range Regional Health Services, Hibbing, MN, p. A345

SHARP, Rebecca, Chief Financial Officer, Wagoner Community Hospital, Wagoner, OK, p. A522

SHARP, Richard, M.D. Medical Director, CHRISTUS St. Michael Rehabilitation Hospital, Texarkana, TX, p. A652

SHARP, Tanya, Chief Financial Officer, Litzenberg Memorial County Hospital, Central City, NE, p. A394

SHARP, Tony, Supervisor Information System, Sweetwater Hospital, Sweetwater, TN, p. A593

SHARPTON, Debra, Director of Nursing, Devereux Georgia Treatment Network, Kennesaw, GA, p. A161

SHARRER, Steven, Vice President Human Resources, Saint John's Health Center, Santa Monica, CA, p. A94

SHARTLE, William, Senior Vice President Human Resources, Holy Spirit Hospital, Camp Hill, PA, p. A535

SHARUM, Gary, Administrator, Mercy Hospital Tishomingo, Tishomingo, OK, p. A520

SHARUM, Melinda
Director of Human Resources, Mercy Hospital Ardmore, Ardmore, OK, p. A507
Director Human Resources, Mercy Hospital Healdton, Healdton, OK, p. A511

SHARY, Dave, Administrator Human Resources, Ridgecrest Regional Hospital, Ridgecrest, CA, p. A86

SHATRAW, Thomas, Director Human Resources, Samaritan Medical Center, Watertown, NY, p. A457

SHATTO, Leslie, Director Human Resources, Carlisle Regional Medical Center, Carlisle, PA, p. A535

SHAUGHNESSY, John, Chief Financial Officer, Clarendon Memorial Hospital, Manning, SC, p. A568

SHAUGHNESSY, Mary
Vice President Finance, Spaulding Hospital for Continuing Medical Care Cambridge, Cambridge, MA, p. A309
Vice President Finance, Spaulding Rehabilitation Hospital, Charlestown, MA, p. A309
Vice President Finance, Spaulding Rehabilitation Hospital Cape Cod, East Sandwich, MA, p. A309

SHAULL, Ty, Chief Operating Officer, Wyandot Memorial Hospital, Upper Sandusky, OH, p. A503

SHAVER, Chris
Vice President Human Resources, Covenant Medical Center, Lubbock, TX, p. A634
Vice President Human Resources, Covenant Specialty Hospital, Lubbock, TX, p. A634

SHAVER, Jennifer, Director of Nursing, Lewis County General Hospital, Lowville, NY, p. A440

SHAVER, John, Chief Financial Officer, Noble Hospital, Westfield, MA, p. A316

SHAVER, Robert D., M.D. Vice President Medical Affairs, The Good Samaritan Hospital, Lebanon, PA, p. A543

SHAW, Barbara, Chief Nursing Officer, Brighton Center for Recovery, Brighton, MI, p. A320

SHAW, David
Vice President Information Systems, Eskenazi Health, Indianapolis, IN, p. A214
Vice President and Chief Operating Officer, Susan B. Allen Memorial Hospital, El Dorado, KS, p. A243

SHAW, David B., Chief Executive Officer and Administrator, Nor–Lea General Hospital, Lovington, NM, p. A429

SHAW, Douglas A., Chief Executive Officer, Mad River Community Hospital, Arcata, CA, p. A56

SHAW, Gary, President, Cambridge Medical Center, Cambridge, MN, p. A341

SHAW, Gene, Chief Information Officer, Yuma Regional Medical Center, Yuma, AZ, p. A42

SHAW, Greg, Chief Financial Officer, Nevada Regional Medical Center, Nevada, MO, p. A377

SHAW, Jan, Director Personnel, River Bend Hospital, West Lafayette, IN, p. A224

SHAW, John C., M.D. Medical Director, Southern Indiana Rehabilitation Hospital, New Albany, IN, p. A220

SHAW, Kathy, Chief Executive Officer, Haven Senior Horizons, Phoenix, AZ, p. A35

SHAW, Kendra, Chief Information Officer, Baldwin Area Medical Center, Baldwin, WI, p. A701

SHAW, Kimberly, Vice President Patient Care and Chief Nursing Executive, Mercy Medical Center Redding, Redding, CA, p. A85

SHAW, Mandy, M.D. Chief of Staff, Sidney Regional Medical Center, Sidney, NE, p. A402

SHAW, Patrick, Chief Executive Officer, Grafton City Hospital, Grafton, WV, p. A695

SHAW, Shane, M.D. Chief of Staff, Memorial Medical Center – Livingston, Livingston, TX, p. A633

SHAW, Violet, R.N. Director of Nursing, Grafton City Hospital, Grafton, WV, p. A695

SHAWAN, Christy, Chief Executive Officer, Black River Medical Center, Poplar Bluff, MO, p. A378

SHAWGO, Darla, Director Human Resources, Sparta Community Hospital, Sparta, IL, p. A202

SHEA, Daniel, Administrator, Compass Behavioral Center of Houma, Houma, LA, p. A278

SHEA, Drew, Chief Financial Officer, Doctors Hospital at White Rock Lake, Dallas, TX, p. A610

SHEA, Kevin, M.D. Chief of Staff, Carolinas Hospital System, Florence, SC, p. A565

SHEA, Natalie, Chief Nursing Officer, Central Community Hospital, Elkader, IA, p. A230

SHEA, Peggy, Human Resources Lead, Mad River Community Hospital, Arcata, CA, p. A56

SHEAFF, Charles, M.D. President Medical Staff, Passavant Area Hospital, Jacksonville, IL, p. A193

SHEAGREN, Craig, Vice President Finance, Sarah Bush Lincoln Health Center, Mattoon, IL, p. A195

SHEALY, Keith, M.D. Chief of Staff, Springs Memorial Hospital, Lancaster, SC, p. A568

SHEAR, Larry, Administrative Assistant, Norwood Health Center, Marshfield, WI, p. A709

SHEARER, Christopher, M.D. Chief Medical Officer, John C. Lincoln North Mountain Hospital, Phoenix, AZ, p. A36

SHEARER, Laura, R.N. Senior Vice President and Chief Nursing Officer, Phoebe Putney Memorial Hospital, Albany, GA, p. A151

SHEARER, Ron, M.D. Regional Medical Director, PeaceHealth Peace Harbor Medical Center, Florence, OR, p. A524

SHEEHAN, Karen, Vice President and Chief Information Officer, Swedish Covenant Hospital, Chicago, IL, p. A187

SHEEHAN, Terrence P., M.D. Medical Director, Adventist Rehabilitation Hospital of Maryland, Rockville, MD, p. A303

SHEEHY, Earl N., Administrator, Ray County Memorial Hospital, Richmond, MO, p. A379

SHEEHY, Joseph, Chief Executive Officer and Managing Director, The Pavilion, Champaign, IL, p. A183

SHEEKS, Margaret, R.N. Vice President Patient Services, Sauk Prairie Healthcare, Prairie Du Sac, WI, p. A714

SHEERIN, Cathy, R.N. Director Patient Care Services, Glen Cove Hospital, Glen Cove, NY, p. A438

SHEERIN, Rick
Vice President Fiscal Services, Floyd Medical Center, Rome, GA, p. A165
Chief Financial Officer, Polk Medical Center, Cedartown, GA, p. A155

SHEETS, Cindy, Vice President Information Systems and Chief Information Officer, OhioHealth MedCentral Mansfield Hospital, Mansfield, OH, p. A497

SHEETS, Jim, Chief Executive Officer and Administrator, LDS Hospital, Salt Lake City, UT, p. A663

SHEFFIELD, Aubrey, Administrative Assistant Human Resources and Public Relations, Grove Hill Memorial Hospital, Grove Hill, AL, p. A21

SHEFTE, David H., Chief Executive Officer, HEALTHSOUTH Rehabilitation Hospital of Denver, Littleton, CO, p. A109

SHEGOLEV, Igor
Interim Director, Carondelet Holy Cross Hospital, Nogales, AZ, p. A34
Vice President Human Resources, Carondelet St. Joseph's Hospital, Tucson, AZ, p. A40

SHEHAN, Mary, R.N. Senior Vice President and Chief Nursing Officer, Swedish Covenant Hospital, Chicago, IL, p. A187

SHEHATA, Adel R., M.D. Medical Director, Desert Springs Hospital Medical Center, Las Vegas, NV, p. A405

SHEHATA, Nady, M.D. Vice President Medical Affairs, Sisters of Charity Hospital of Buffalo, Buffalo, NY, p. A435

SHEHI, G. Michael, M.D., Interim Chief Executive Officer, Mountain View Hospital, Gadsden, AL, p. A20

SHELAK, Matt, Chief Operating Officer, Lower Bucks Hospital, Bristol, PA, p. A534

SHELBURNE, John D., M.D. Chief of Staff, Durham Veterans Affairs Medical Center, Durham, NC, p. A463

SHELBY, Dennis R., Chief Executive Officer, Wilson Medical Center, Neodesha, KS, p. A250

SHELBY, Joyce, Manager Human Resources, Hardin County General Hospital, Rosiclare, IL, p. A202

SHELDEN, Diana, Chief Nursing Officer, Stone County Medical Center, Mountain View, AR, p. A50

SHELDON, Donald S., M.D., President and Chief Executive Officer, University Hospitals Elyria Medical Center, Elyria, OH, p. A493

SHELDON, Lyle Ernest, FACHE,
President and Chief Executive Officer, Harford Memorial Hospital, Havre De Grace, MD, p. A301
President and Chief Executive Officer, Upper Chesapeake Medical Center, Bel Air, MD, p. A298

SHELDON, Mo P., Administrator, Odessa Memorial Healthcare Center, Odessa, WA, p. A686

SHELDON, Richard, M.D. Vice President Medical Affairs, San Gorgonio Memorial Hospital, Banning, CA, p. A57

SHELFORD, Dave, Assistant Superintendent, Richmond State Hospital, Richmond, IN, p. A222

SHELT, Elizabeth, Civilian Personnel Officer, Dwight David Eisenhower Army Medical Center, Fort Gordon, GA, p. A160

SHELTON, Carol, Director Human Resources, Lovelace Women's Hospital, Albuquerque, NM, p. A426

SHELTON, Darlene, Coordinator Team Resources, BayCare Alliant Hospital, Dunedin, FL, p. A127

SHELTON, Jeffrey D., Chief Executive Officer, Newman Memorial Hospital, Shattuck, OK, p. A518

SHELTON, John
President and Chief Executive Officer, DeKalb Medical at Downtown Decatur, Decatur, GA, p. A158
Executive Vice President and Chief Operating Officer, DeKalb Medical at Downtown Decatur, Decatur, GA, p. A158
President and Chief Executive Officer, DeKalb Medical at Hillandale, Lithonia, GA, p. A162
Chief Operating Officer, DeKalb Medical at Hillandale, Lithonia, GA, p. A162
President and Chief Executive Officer, DeKalb Medical at North Decatur, Decatur, GA, p. A158

SHELTON, John, President and Chief Executive Officer, DeKalb Regional Health System, Decatur, GA, p. B46

SHELTON, Kathy
Director Human Resources, East Texas Medical Center Clarksville, Clarksville, TX, p. A606
Director Human Resources, East Texas Medical Center Pittsburg, Pittsburg, TX, p. A642
Director Human Resources, East Texas Medical Center–Mount Vernon, Mount Vernon, TX, p. A638

SHELTON, Scott, Chief Financial Officer, Atrium Medical Center, Middletown, OH, p. A498

SHELTON, Tom, Coordinator of Nursing Services, Porterville Developmental Center, Porterville, CA, p. A84

SHELVOCK, Kathy, R.N. Assistant Administrator Patient Care Services, Fairchild Medical Center, Yreka, CA, p. A101

SHENDELL–FALIK, Nancy, R.N. Senior Vice President, Chief Operating Officer and Chief Nursing Officer, Baystate Medical Center, Springfield, MA, p. A314

SHENEFIELD, Jason, Chief Operating Officer, Cheyenne Regional Medical Center, Cheyenne, WY, p. A720

SHENGLE, Lori, Director Information Technology, Morrill County Community Hospital, Bridgeport, NE, p. A394

SHEPARD, Bridget, Director Human Resources, Wabash General Hospital, Mount Carmel, IL, p. A197

SHEPARD, Karen
Senior Vice President and Chief Financial Officer, Pioneer Memorial Hospital, Prineville, OR, p. A529
Executive Vice President Finance and Chief Financial Officer, St. Charles Medical Center – Bend, Bend, OR, p. A523
Senior Vice President Finance and Chief Financial Officer, St. Charles Medical Center – Redmond, Redmond, OR, p. A529

SHEPARD, Megan, Director Clinical Services, Odessa Memorial Healthcare Center, Odessa, WA, p. A686

SHEPARD, Sheila, Controller, HEALTHSOUTH Rehabilitation Hospital, Humble, TX, p. A628

SHEPARDSON, Dean, Chief Financial Officer, Banner Estrella Medical Center, Phoenix, AZ, p. A35

SHEPARDSON, Heather, Vice President Human Resources, Carilion Roanoke Memorial Hospital, Roanoke, VA, p. A678

SHEPHARD, Bryan, Chief Financial Officer, TriStar Summit Medical Center, Hermitage, TN, p. A584

SHEPHARD, Russ, Senior Systems Analyst, Dyersburg Regional Medical Center, Dyersburg, TN, p. A582

SHEPHERD, RN, BSN,, Linda M., Chief Nursing Officer, LewisGale Hospital Pulaski, Pulaski, VA, p. A676

SHEPHERD, Stephen C., Chief Executive Officer, Candler County Hospital, Metter, GA, p. A163

SHEPHERD, Thomas, Executive Vice President and Chief Operating Officer, Gwinnett Hospital System, Lawrenceville, GA, p. A162

SHEPLER, Mary, R.N. Vice President and Chief Nursing Officer, Exempla Saint Joseph Hospital, Denver, CO, p. A104

SHEPPARD, Sandy, Vice President Patient Services, Wilkes Regional Medical Center, North Wilkesboro, NC, p. A470

SHEPPARD, Sharon, Manager Human Resources, Sycamore Shoals Hospital, Elizabethton, TN, p. A582

SHEPPARD, Varinya, R.N. Chief Nursing Officer, St. Elizabeth Medical Center, Utica, NY, p. A456

SHERBELL, Stanley, M.D. Executive Vice President Medical Affairs, New York Methodist Hospital,, NY, p. A447

SHERBONDY, Lori, Director Human Resources, Battle Mountain General Hospital, Battle Mountain, NV, p. A404

SHERBUN, Michael, Ph.D., Chief Executive Officer, Cedar Hills Hospital, Portland, OR, p. A528

SHERER, Janet L., Chief of Patient Care Services, Springfield Hospital, Springfield, VT, p. A666

SHERER, Ryan, M.D. President Medical Staff, Memorial Hospital and Health Care Center, Jasper, IN, p. A215

SHERER, Susan, Chief Information Resource Management, Dayton Veterans Affairs Medical Center, Dayton, OH, p. A492

SHERIDAN, Bridget, Chief Human Resources Officer, Beaver Dam Community Hospitals, Beaver Dam, WI, p. A702

SHERIDAN, Cheryl, R.N
Senior Vice President and Chief Nursing Officer, Newark–Wayne Community Hospital, Newark, NY, p. A449
Senior Vice President Patient Care Services, Rochester General Hospital, Rochester, NY, p. A453

SHERIDAN, Elizabeth
  Chief Operating Officer and Chief Nursing Executive, Inspira Medical Center–Elmer, Elmer, NJ, p. A416
  Chief Operating Officer and Chief Nursing Executive, Inspira Medical Center–Vineland, Vineland, NJ, p. A424
SHERIDAN, Tristen, Administrator, Weisbrod Memorial County Hospital, Eads, CO, p. A105
SHERMAN, Angelina, R.N. Chief Nursing Officer, The Rehabilitation Institute of St. Louis, Saint Louis, MO, p. A382
SHERMAN, Frederick C., M.D. Chief Medical Officer, The Children's Home of Pittsburgh, Pittsburgh, PA, p. A551
SHERMAN, James, President and Chief Executive Officer, Tri-City Regional Medical Center, Hawaiian Gardens, CA, p. A66
SHERMAN, Linda, Chief Executive Officer, Select Specialty Hospital–Topeka, Topeka, KS, p. A255
SHERMAN, Sheila, Vice President Patient Care Services, Vail Valley Medical Center, Vail, CO, p. A111
SHERMAN, Stephanie, Chief Human Resources Officer, West Boca Medical Center, Boca Raton, FL, p. A124
SHERON, William E., Chief Executive Officer, Wooster Community Hospital, Wooster, OH, p. A505
SHERRETT, John, Chief Financial Officer and Chief Operating Officer, Forks Community Hospital, Forks, WA, p. A684
SHERRILL, Angela
  Chief Information Officer, Laird Hospital, Union, MS, p. A366
  Corporate Director Information System, Rush Foundation Hospital, Meridian, MS, p. A362
  Corporate Director Information System, Specialty Hospital of Meridian, Meridian, MS, p. A363
SHERROD, Michael, Chief Executive Officer, TriStar Greenview Regional Hospital, Bowling Green, KY, p. A259
SHERROD, Rhonda Kay, MSN,
  Administrator, Shands Lake Shore Regional Medical Center, Lake City, FL, p. A133
  Interim Chief Executive Officer, Shands Live Oak Regional Medical Center, Live Oak, FL, p. A134
  Interim Chief Executive Officer, Shands Starke Regional Medical Center, Starke, FL, p. A146
SHERRON, Tammy M., Vice President Finance, CarolinaEast Health System, New Bern, NC, p. A470
SHERRY, Bernard
  President and CEO, Saint Thomas Midtown Hospital, Nashville, TN, p. A590
  President and CEO, Saint Thomas West Hospital, Nashville, TN, p. A590
SHERRY, Mark A., Director Human Resources, Scott & White Hospital at Round Rock, Round Rock, TX, p. A644
SHERWOOD, Jennifer L., Chief Human Resources Officer, Platte County Memorial Hospital, Wheatland, WY, p. A723
SHERWOOD, Matthew M., Chief Financial Officer, Unity Medical & Surgical Hospital, Mishawaka, IN, p. A219
SHETLER, Charles L., CPA Chief Financial Officer, Indiana University Health Bedford Hospital, Bedford, IN, p. A206
SHETTLESWORTH, Amanda, Director Human Resources, Bloomington Meadows Hospital, Bloomington, IN, p. A207
SHEW, Angel, Director Area Technology, Kaiser Permanente South San Francisco, South San Francisco, CA, p. A96
SHEWBRIDGE, Rick, M.D. Vice President Medical Operations, Medina Hospital, Medina, OH, p. A498
SHEYKA, Patricia, Chief Nursing Officer, Gila Regional Medical Center, Silver City, NM, p. A431
SHICKOLOVICH, William, Chief Information Officer, Tufts Medical Center, Boston, MA, p. A307
SHIELDS, Charlie
  President and Chief Executive Officer, Truman Medical Center–Hospital Hill, Kansas City, MO, p. A374
  President and Chief Executive Officer, Truman Medical Center–Lakewood, Kansas City, MO, p. A374
SHIELDS, Charlie, President and Chief Executive Officer, Truman Medical Centers, Kansas City, MO, p. B136
SHIELDS, Diane, Chief Human Resources Officer, Alpena Regional Medical Center, Alpena, MI, p. A318
SHIFF, Mary Treacy, Chief Financial Officer, Kindred Chicago–Central Hospital, Chicago, IL, p. A184
SHIFFERMILLER, William, M.D. Vice President Medical Affairs, Nebraska Methodist Hospital, Omaha, NE, p. A400
SHIHADY, Sharon, Director Human Resources, HEALTHSOUTH Cane Creek Rehabilitation Hospital, Martin, TN, p. A587
SHILKAITIS, Mary, Vice President Patient Care and Chief Nursing Officer, Rush–Copley Medical Center, Aurora, IL, p. A181
SHILLING, Stacy, Controller, St. Vincent Rehabilitation Hospital, Sherwood, AR, p. A52
SHIM, Eunmee, Vice President Operations, Shady Grove Adventist Hospital, Rockville, MD, p. A303
SHIMP, David, Chief Operating Officer, St. David's Medical Center, Austin, TX, p. A600
SHINER, Cindy, Manager Human Resources, Lebanon Veterans Affairs Medical Center, Lebanon, PA, p. A542

SHINGLETON, Kathy J., Ed.D. Vice President, Human Resources, Virginia Mason Medical Center, Seattle, WA, p. A689
SHINICK, Mary K., Vice President Human Resources, Nyack Hospital, Nyack, NY, p. A450
SHININGER, Kimberly R., Director Human Resources, Wabash County Hospital, Wabash, IN, p. A224
SHIPIERSKI, Sally, Controller, Geisinger HEALTHSOUTH Rehabilitation Hospital, Danville, PA, p. A536
SHIPLEY, Carolyn, Chief Nursing Officer, Roane Medical Center, Harriman, TN, p. A583
SHIPLEY, Janice, M.D. Chief Medical Officer, Cibola General Hospital, Grants, NM, p. A428
SHIPLEY, Kurt, Chief Financial Officer, Jordan Valley Medical Center, West Jordan, UT, p. A664
SHIPLEY, Sheila, Human Resources Educator, Signature Psychiatric Hospital, Kansas City, MO, p. A374
SHIPP, Geraldine H., Director of Risk Management, Sampson Regional Medical Center, Clinton, NC, p. A462
SHIRAH, Anita, Director Human Resources, University of South Alabama Medical Center, Mobile, AL, p. A23
SHIRLEY, Christian, Director Human Resources, Geisinger HEALTHSOUTH Rehabilitation Hospital, Danville, PA, p. A536
SHIRLEY, Steve, Chief Information Officer, Parkview Medical Center, Pueblo, CO, p. A110
SHISLER, Catherine, Director Information Services, Baylor Medical Center at Irving, Irving, TX, p. A629
SHIVELY, Lori
  Vice President of Finance, Mercy Hospital Cadillac, Cadillac, MI, p. A320
  Vice President of Finance, Mercy Hospital Grayling, Grayling, MI, p. A325
SHIVERY, Toni M.
  Vice President Human Resources, Harford Memorial Hospital, Havre De Grace, MD, p. A301
  Vice President Human Resources, Upper Chesapeake Medical Center, Bel Air, MD, p. A298
SHMERLING, James E., Chief Executive Officer, Children's Hospital Colorado, Aurora, CO, p. A102
SHOBE, Franklin, Administrator and Chief Executive Officer, Black Hills Surgery Center, Rapid City, SD, p. A575
SHOBE, Susan, Director Administration and Support Services, Alton Mental Health Center, Alton, IL, p. A180
SHOCKEY, Kathryn L., Director Human Resources, Lead–Deadwood Regional Hospital, Deadwood, SD, p. A573
SHOCKLEY, Mary, Director Human Resources, Russell Medical Center, Alexander City, AL, p. A15
SHOCKNEY, Brian T., FACHE Chief Operating Officer, Indiana University Health Arnett Hospital, Lafayette, IN, p. A217
SHOEMAKER, Larry D., M.D. Chief Operating Officer, Singing River Health System, Pascagoula, MS, p. A364
SHOEMAKER, Lorie K., MSN, Interim Chief Administrative Officer, Palomar Medical Center, Escondido, CA, p. A62
SHOEMAKER, Matt, D.O. Vice President and Chief Medical Officer, Southeast Hospital, Cape Girardeau, MO, p. A369
SHOEMAKER, Robert, M.D. Chief of Staff Community Heart and Vascular, Community Heart and Vascular Hospital, Indianapolis, IN, p. A213
SHOEN, Timothy, M.D. Vice President Medical Staff Services, St. Mary's Healthcare, Amsterdam, NY, p. A432
SHOENER, Carl, Information Officer, Lehigh Valley Hospital – Hazleton, Hazleton, PA, p. A540
SHOFNER, Connie, Chief Nursing Officer, Carlsbad Medical Center, Carlsbad, NM, p. A427
SHOLLER, Peter, M.D. Medical Director, Spectrum Health Special Care Hospital, Grand Rapids, MI, p. A325
SHOMAKER, Susan, Director Information Management Systems, J. Arthur Dosher Memorial Hospital, Southport, NC, p. A473
SHONNARD, John, M.D. Medical Director, UPMC Northwest, Seneca, PA, p. A554
SHOOK, Susan, Interim Chief Executive Officer, Murray Medical Center, Chatsworth, GA, p. A155
SHOR, Joel, M.D. Chief of Staff, Bluefield Regional Medical Center, Bluefield, WV, p. A693
SHORB, Gary S., President and Chief Executive Officer, Methodist Le Bonheur Healthcare, Memphis, TN, p. B94
SHORES, Larry, M.D. Executive Medical Director, Cedar Springs Hospital, Colorado Springs, CO, p. A103
SHORT, Jo, Director of Nursing, Fulton County Health Center, Wauseon, OH, p. A504
SHORT, Kathy, D.O. Family Practice, Carroll County Memorial Hospital, Carrollton, KY, p. A259
SHORT, M. Andrew, Vice President Information Services, Samaritan Medical Center, Watertown, NY, p. A457
SHORT, Margaret W., Coordinator Information Technology, Webster County Memorial Hospital, Webster Springs, WV, p. A700
SHORT, Penny, R.N. Chief Operating Officer, Nanticoke Memorial Hospital, Seaford, DE, p. A119

SHORT, Peter H., M.D. Senior Vice President Medical Affairs, Beverly Hospital, Beverly, MA, p. A305
SHORT, Steve, Executive Vice President Finance and Administration and Chief Financial Officer, Tampa General Hospital, Tampa, FL, p. A148
SHORT, Ted, Chief Financial Officer, Fairview Park Hospital, Dublin, GA, p. A159
SHORT, W. L., M.D. Chief Medical Officer, Memorial Health System, Abilene, KS, p. A241
SHORTT, Sheila, R.N. Human Resources Consultant, SSM St. Joseph Hospital West, Lake Saint Louis, MO, p. A375
SHOUKAIR, Sami, M.D. Chief Medical Officer, La Palma Intercommunity Hospital, La Palma, CA, p. A68
SHOUP, Chris, President, Methodist Hospital for Surgery, Addison, TX, p. A595
SHOUP, Emily, Director Nursing Services, Roundup Memorial Healthcare, Roundup, MT, p. A390
SHOUSE, Shellie, Chief Financial Officer, Bluegrass Community Hospital, Versailles, KY, p. A271
SHOWALTER, Will
  Senior Vice President Information Technology, Wellmont Bristol Regional Medical Center, Bristol, TN, p. A579
  Senior Vice President Information Technology, Wellmont Hancock County Hospital, Sneedville, TN, p. A593
  Senior Vice President Information Technology, Wellmont Holston Valley Medical Center, Kingsport, TN, p. A585
SHOWS, Carla
  Payroll Clerk, George Regional Hospital, Lucedale, MS, p. A361
  Payroll Clerk, Greene County Hospital, Leakesville, MS, p. A361
SHREEVE, Susan
  Chief Financial Officer, Belton Regional Medical Center, Belton, MO, p. A367
  Chief Financial Officer, Research Medical Center, Kansas City, MO, p. A374
  Chief Financial Officer, Research Psychiatric Center, Kansas City, MO, p. A374
SHREVE, Susan, Executive Director Information Technology, Boone Memorial Hospital, Madison, WV, p. A697
SHREVES, Melissa, Director Human Resources, Monongalia General Hospital, Morgantown, WV, p. A697
SHREWSBURY, Kim, Vice President and Chief Financial Officer, Decatur Morgan Hospital, Decatur, AL, p. A18
SHRIVER, Debra, R.N. Chief Nurse Executive, UnityPoint Health – Trinity Regional Medical Center, Fort Dodge, IA, p. A230
SHROADES, David W., Vice President Technology Services, Alliance Community Hospital, Alliance, OH, p. A482
SHRODER, Robert W.
  President and Chief Executive Officer, St. Elizabeth Health Center, Youngstown, OH, p. A506
  President and Chief Executive Officer, St. Joseph Health Center, Warren, OH, p. A504
SHROFF, Divya, Chief Medical Officer, Tristar Centennial Medical Center at Ashland City, Ashland City, TN, p. A579
SHROFF, Rajendra, M.D. Administrative Medical Director, St. Mary's Hospital, Centralia, IL, p. A182
SHROYER, Linda K., Administrator, Potomac Valley Hospital, Keyser, WV, p. A696
SHUBIN, Allan, Chief Financial Officer, Pacific Alliance Medical Center, Los Angeles, CA, p. A74
SHUEY, Keith, M.D. Chief Medical Staff, Johnson County Hospital, Tecumseh, NE, p. A402
SHUFFIELD, Sean, Regional Chief Information Officer, University of Maryland St. Joseph Medical Center, Towson, MD, p. A304
SHUFFLEBARGER, Tom, Chief Operating Officer, The Children's Hospital of Alabama, Birmingham, AL, p. A17
SHUFORD, Little, Manager Medical Information, Kindred Hospital–Greensboro, Greensboro, NC, p. A465
SHUGARMAN, Mark D., President and Chief Executive Officer, Floyd Memorial Hospital and Health Services, New Albany, IN, p. A220
SHUGHART, Deborah A., Vice President and Chief Financial Officer, Fulton County Medical Center, Mc Connellsburg, PA, p. A544
SHUGRUE, Dianne, President and Chief Executive Officer, Glens Falls Hospital, Glens Falls, NY, p. A438
SHULER, Conrad K., M.D. Chief Medical Officer, Oconee Medical Center, Seneca, SC, p. A569
SHULIK, David, Vice President and Chief Financial Officer, UPMC Horizon, Greenville, PA, p. A539
SHULKIN, David J., M.D., President, Morristown Medical Center, Morristown, NJ, p. A418
SHULL, Jennifer, R.N. Chief Nursing Officer, Florida Hospital Fish Memorial, Orange City, FL, p. A140
SHULL, Kenneth A., FACHE, Chief Executive Officer, St. Luke's Hospital, Columbus, NC, p. A462
SHULMAN, Lawrence N., M.D. Senior Vice President Medical Affairs and Chief Medical Officer, Dana–Farber Cancer Institute, Boston, MA, p. A306

SHULTS, Randi L., Chief Executive Officer, North Carolina Specialty Hospital, Durham, NC, p. A463

SHUMAN, Betty, Director Human Resources, Wesley Rehabilitation Hospital, Wichita, KS, p. A257

SHUMAN, Daniel, D.O. Chief Medical Officer, Ashland Health Center, Ashland, KS, p. A241

SHUMATE, Karen J., R.N. Chief Operating Officer, Lawrence Memorial Hospital, Lawrence, KS, p. A248

SHUMATE, Kim, Human Resources Officer, Ohio State University Wexner Medical Center, Columbus, OH, p. A490

SHUMWAY, Barbara, Director Human Resources, North Big Horn Hospital District, Lovell, WY, p. A722

SHUMWAY, Donald L., Chief Executive Officer, Crotched Mountain Rehabilitation Center, Greenfield, NH, p. A410

SHUPERT, Charlene
  Director Staff Services, Carrus Rehabilitation Hospital, Sherman, TX, p. A649
  Director Staff Services, Carrus Specialty Hospital, Sherman, TX, p. A649

SHUPP, Susan, Director Human Resources, Nemaha County Hospital, Auburn, NE, p. A393

SHUTE, Keith M., M.D. Senior Vice President Medical Affairs and Clinical Services, Androscoggin Valley Hospital, Berlin, NH, p. A409

SHUTE, Leonard J., Chief Financial Officer, Strong Memorial Hospital of the University of Rochester, Rochester, NY, p. A453

SHUTER, Mark H., President and Chief Executive Officer, Adena Health System, Chillicothe, OH, p. B5

SHUTER, Mark H., President and Chief Executive Officer, Adena Medical Center, Chillicothe, OH, p. A486

SIBBITT, Stephen, M.D. Chief Medical Officer, Scott & White Memorial Hospital, Temple, TX, p. A652

SIBLEY, Beth, Director of Nursing, Sage Rehabilitation Hospital, Baton Rouge, LA, p. A274

SIBLEY, Cherie, R.N., Chief Executive Officer, Clark Regional Medical Center, Winchester, KY, p. A271

SIBLEY, Jeri, Director Revenue Cycle, Riverside Tappahannock Hospital, Tappahannock, VA, p. A679

SICA, Vincent A., President and Chief Executive Officer, DeSoto Memorial Hospital, Arcadia, FL, p. A123

SICHTS, Pam, Director Human Resources, Sycamore Springs Hospital, Lafayette, IN, p. A217

SICILIA, Bruce, M.D. Medical Director, HEALTHSOUTH Rehabilitation Hospital of York, York, PA, p. A559

SIDDIQI, Ather, M.D
  Medical Director, Nexus Specialty Hospital, Shenandoah, TX, p. A649
  Medical Director, Nexus Specialty Hospital The Woodlands, Spring, TX, p. A650

SIDDIQI, Syed, M.D. President Medical Staff, Raleigh General Hospital, Beckley, WV, p. A693

SIDDIQUI, Hugh, Senior Applications Analyst, Linden Oaks Hospital at Edward, Naperville, IL, p. A197

SIDDIQUI, Joseph, Vice President Human Resources, The Aroostook Medical Center, Presque Isle, ME, p. A295

SIDES, Tim, Chief Financial Officer, Valle Vista Hospital, Greenwood, IN, p. A212

SIDMAN, Robert, M.D. Medical Director, The William W. Backus Hospital, Norwich, CT, p. A116

SIEBENALER, Christopher, Chief Executive Officer, Houston Methodist Sugar Land Hospital, Sugar Land, TX, p. A650

SIEBERT, Kristy, Manager Finance, John J. Pershing Veterans Affairs Medical Center, Poplar Bluff, MO, p. A378

SIEBERT, Matt, Assistant Administrator Ancillary Services, Hermann Area District Hospital, Hermann, MO, p. A372

SIEBRECHT, Kaylee, Director Human Resources, Story County Medical Center, Nevada, IA, p. A235

SIEDLECKI, Cathy, Director Human Resources, Carthage Area Hospital, Carthage, NY, p. A435

SIEGEL, Fredric, M.D. Chief of Staff, Desert View Hospital, Pahrump, NV, p. A407

SIEGEL, Lesley, M.D. Medical Director, Albert J. Solnit Psychiatric Center – South Campus, Middletown, CT, p. A115

SIEGELMAN, Gary M., M.D. Senior Vice President and Chief Medical Officer, Bayhealth Medical Center, Dover, DE, p. A119

SIEGFRIED, Carole A., MSN Campus Nurse Executive, Palmetto Health Richland, Columbia, SC, p. A564

SIEGLEN, Linda, M.D. Chief Medical Officer, Mission Hospital, Mission Viejo, CA, p. A77

SIEGMAN, Ira, M.D. Chief Medical Officer, Northside Hospital, Saint Petersburg, FL, p. A144

SIEK, Terry, MSN Chief Nursing Officer, Hays Medical Center, Hays, KS, p. A245

SIELEMAN, Sharron, R.N. VP, Nursing, Central Maine Medical Center, Lewiston, ME, p. A293

SIEMERS, Thomas R., Chief Executive Officer, J. Arthur Dosher Memorial Hospital, Southport, NC, p. A473

SIEWERT, Charles
  Director Human Resources, Buffalo Psychiatric Center, Buffalo, NY, p. A434
  Director Human Resources, Western New York Children's Psychiatric Center, West Seneca, NY, p. A458

SIFERS, Carl, Director Information Technology and System Services, Centerpoint Medical Center, Independence, MO, p. A372

SIFRI, Christi, Chief Nursing Executive, Regional Hospital for Respiratory and Complex Care, Seattle, WA, p. A688

SIGEL, Jay, M.D. Chief Medical Staff, Crane Memorial Hospital, Crane, TX, p. A608

SIGLAR, Harold L., Interim Chief Executive Officer, Southern Tennessee Regional Health System–Pulaski, Pulaski, TN, p. A592

SIGLER, Wes, Administrator, Quitman County Hospital, Marks, MS, p. A362

SIGNOR, Kristin, Director Finance, Sunnyview Rehabilitation Hospital, Schenectady, NY, p. A454

SIGREST, Marion, M.D. Chief of Staff, King's Daughters Hospital, Yazoo City, MS, p. A366

SILARD, Kathleen A., R.N. Executive Vice President Operations and Chief Operating Officer, Stamford Hospital, Stamford, CT, p. A117

SILBERSCHLAG, Kelly, Chief Executive Officer, Scottsdale Healthcare Rehabilitation Hospital, Scottsdale, AZ, p. A38

SILKWORTH, Jim, Chief Human Resources Officer, Our Lady of Lourdes Memorial Hospital, Inc., Binghamton, NY, p. A433

SILLS, John M., Chief Information Officer, Health Central Hospital, Ocoee, FL, p. A140

SILSBEE, Dave, Chief Information Officer, Cary Medical Center, Caribou, ME, p. A292

SILSBY, Harry, M.D. Medical Director, Intermountain Hospital, Boise, ID, p. A174

SILVA, Carmen, R.N. Chief Operating Officer, Doctors Hospital of Manteca, Manteca, CA, p. A76

SILVA, Lorena, MSN Vice President Patient Care Services, Chief Nursing Officer, Quincy Medical Center, Quincy, MA, p. A314

SILVA, Shawn, Chief Executive Officer, Heritage Oaks Hospital, Sacramento, CA, p. A87

SILVA, Tracy, Chief Financial Officer, The Heart Hospital at Deaconess Gateway, Newburgh, IN, p. A220

SILVA–STEELE, Jamie A., R.N., Interim Chief Executive Officer, UNM Sandoval Regional Medical Center, Rio Rancho, NM, p. A430

SILVER, Jonathan, Chief Financial Officer, Ballard Rehabilitation Hospital, San Bernardino, CA, p. A88

SILVER, Michael R., M.D. Vice President Medical Affairs, Rush Oak Park Hospital, Oak Park, IL, p. A198

SILVER, Timothy, M.D. Medical Director, Sheltering Arms Hospital South, Midlothian, VA, p. A674

SILVERMAN, Daniel C., M.D
  Chief Medical Officer, Acute Care Troy, Samaritan Hospital, Troy, NY, p. A456
  Vice President and Chief Medical Officer, Sinai Hospital of Baltimore, Baltimore, MD, p. A298
  Chief Medical Officer, St. Mary's Hospital, Troy, NY, p. A456

SILVERMAN, Glen, Chief Executive Officer, Crossgates River Oaks Hospital, Brandon, MS, p. A356

SILVERSTEIN, Douglas M., President, NorthShore University Health System, Evanston, IL, p. A189

SILVERSTEIN, Joel, M.D. Chief Medical Officer, Copley Hospital, Morrisville, VT, p. A665

SILVERTHORNE, Samuel, Chief Information Officer, U. S. Air Force Medical Center Keesler, Keesler AFB, MS, p. A360

SILVEUS, Patrick, M.D. Medical Director, Kosciusko Community Hospital, Warsaw, IN, p. A224

SILVIA, Charles B., M.D. Chief Medical Officer and Vice President Medical Affairs, Peninsula Regional Medical Center, Salisbury, MD, p. A303

SIM, Carol, President and Chief Executive Officer, Siskin Hospital for Physical Rehabilitation, Chattanooga, TN, p. A580

SIMCHUK, Cathy J., Chief Operating Officer, Providence Holy Family Hospital, Spokane, WA, p. A690

SIMIA, Greg
  Chief Financial Officer, St. Mary's Hospital Medical Center, Green Bay, WI, p. A706
  Chief Financial Officer, St. Nicholas Hospital, Sheboygan, WI, p. A715

SIMKINS, Palma, Chief Human Resources Management Services, Battle Creek Veterans Affairs Medical Center, Battle Creek, MI, p. A319

SIMMER, Edward D., USN, Commanding Officer, General and Forensic Psychiatrist, Naval Hospital Oak Harbor, Oak Harbor, WA, p. A686

SIMMONS, Angela L., Chief Executive Officer, HEALTHSOUTH Rehabilitation Hospital, Humble, TX, p. A628

SIMMONS, Brad, Chief Operating Officer, Saint Luke's Hospital of Kansas City, Kansas City, MO, p. A374

SIMMONS, Daniel F., Senior Vice President and Treasurer, Monongahela Valley Hospital, Monongahela, PA, p. A545

SIMMONS, Dorlynn, Chief Executive Officer, Mescalero Public Health Service Indian Hospital, Mescalero, NM, p. A429

SIMMONS, Eileen
  Chief Financial Officer, Magee–Womens Hospital of UPMC, Pittsburgh, PA, p. A551
  Chief Financial Officer, UPMC Presbyterian Shadyside, Pittsburgh, PA, p. A552

SIMMONS, Jeanette, Chief Operating Officer, Center for Behavioral Medicine, Kansas City, MO, p. A373

SIMMONS, Leslie, FACHE, President and Chief Executive Officer, Carroll Hospital Center, Westminster, MD, p. A304

SIMMONS, Linda V., President and Chief Executive Officer, Decatur County Memorial Hospital, Greensburg, IN, p. A212

SIMMONS, Nancy B., Executive Vice President and Chief Administrative Officer, Good Samaritan Hospital Medical Center, West Islip, NY, p. A458

SIMMONS, Preston M., FACHE, Chief Executive Officer, Providence Regional Medical Center Everett, Everett, WA, p. A683

SIMMONS, Randy, Interim Chief Executive Officer, Summersville Regional Medical Center, Summersville, WV, p. A699

SIMMONS, Sherry, Vice President Patient Care Services and Chief Nursing Officer, Camden Clark Medical Center, Parkersburg, WV, p. A698

SIMMONS, Steven, Chief Human Resources Officer, Hahnemann University Hospital, Philadelphia, PA, p. A548

SIMMONS, Terry E., Chief Nursing Officer, Madison County Health Care System, Winterset, IA, p. A240

SIMMONS, Tim C., Chief Executive Officer, Westbury Community Hospital, Houston, TX, p. A628

SIMMONS, William, Chief Executive Officer, St. Luke's Patients Medical Center, Pasadena, TX, p. A641

SIMMS, Sr., Michael S., Vice President Human Resources, Northeast Alabama Regional Medical Center, Anniston, AL, p. A15

SIMON, Anha, Director Human Resources, Winnie Community Hospital, Winnie, TX, p. A658

SIMON, Ashley, Chief Financial Officer, Kansas Surgery and Recovery Center, Wichita, KS, p. A256

SIMON, Deborah R., R.N., President and Chief Executive Officer, UnityPoint Health – Methodist, Peoria, IL, p. A200

SIMON, Joan M., R.N. Chief Nursing Officer, Kootenai Health, Coeur D'Alene, ID, p. A175

SIMON, Kenneth B., M.D. Chief of Staff, Veterans Affairs Gulf Coast Veterans Health Care System, Biloxi, MS, p. A356

SIMON, Lisa M.
  Senior Vice President Chief Financial Officer, East Ohio Regional Hospital, Martins Ferry, OH, p. A497
  Senior Vice President and Chief Financial Officer, Ohio Valley Medical Center, Wheeling, WV, p. A700

SIMON, Lloyd, M.D. Medical Director, Eastern Long Island Hospital, Greenport, NY, p. A438

SIMON, Patricia, Manager Information Systems, Canandaigua Veterans Affairs Medical Center, Canandaigua, NY, p. A435

SIMON, Richard, M.D. Chief of Staff, University of Connecticut Health Center, John Dempsey Hospital, Farmington, CT, p. A114

SIMON, Stuart, M.D. Medical Director, North Central Surgical Center, Dallas, TX, p. A611

SIMON, Teresa, Director Information Systems, Nacogdoches Medical Center, Nacogdoches, TX, p. A639

SIMON, Thresa, M.D. Medical Director, Poplar Springs Hospital, Petersburg, VA, p. A676

SIMONDS, Brock, Interim Chief Financial Officer, Chatham Hospital, Siler City, NC, p. A472

SIMONIN, Steven J., Chief Executive Officer, Iowa Specialty Hospital–Clarion, Clarion, IA, p. A227

SIMONIN, Steven J., Chief Executive Officer, Iowa Specialty Hospitals, Clarion, IA, p. B77

SIMONS, Janice, FACHE, Chief Executive Officer, Medina Regional Hospital, Hondo, TX, p. A623

SIMONSON, Paul, Vice President, Trinity Health, Minot, ND, p. A479

SIMPATICO, Thomas, M.D., Facility Director and Network System Manager, Chicago–Read Mental Health Center, Chicago, IL, p. A183

SIMPSON, Brenda, R.N. Chief Nursing Officer, Largo Medical Center, Largo, FL, p. A134

SIMPSON, Chris, Chief Executive Officer, Cornerstone Hospital–West Monroe, West Monroe, LA, p. A290

SIMPSON, John, Director Information Systems, Central Mississippi Medical Center, Jackson, MS, p. A360

SIMPSON, Keith J., Chief Operating Officer, Jennings American Legion Hospital, Jennings, LA, p. A279

SIMPSON, Jr., Lee A., Chief Executive Officer, Post Acute Medical Specialty Hospital of Tulsa, Tulsa, OK, p. A520

SIMPSON, Linda, Vice President Human Resources, OhioHealth Grant Medical Center, Columbus, OH, p. A490

SIMPSON, Mark, Director of Nursing, Welch Community Hospital, Welch, WV, p. A700

SIMPSON, Pamela, Director Human Resources, Select Specialty Hospital–Houston Heights, Houston, TX, p. A626

SIMPSON, Reagan, Chief Executive Officer, Kindred Rehabilitation Hospital Northeast Houston, Humble, TX, p. A628

SIMPSON, Robert, Vice President Operations, Methodist Richardson Medical Center, Richardson, TX, p. A644

SIMPSON Jr., Robert E., M.P.H., President and Chief Executive Officer, Brattleboro Retreat, Brattleboro, VT, p. A665

SIMPSON, Shannon, Director Information Services, St. Elizabeth Hospital, Gonzales, LA, p. A278

SIMPSON, Sheila, Vice President Human Resources, Palmetto Lowcountry Behavioral Health, Charleston, SC, p. A563

SIMPSON, Tanya, Chief Nursing Officer, Regional Medical Center Bayonet Point, Hudson, FL, p. A131

SIMPSON–TUGGLE, Deloris, Vice President Human Resources and Organizational Development and Chief Human Resources Officer, Greater Baltimore Medical Center, Baltimore, MD, p. A296

SIMS, Abraham, Chief Executive Officer, Reliant Rehabilitation Hospital North Houston, Shenandoah, TX, p. A649

SIMS, Anthony, M.D. Chief of Staff, DeKalb Regional Medical Center, Fort Payne, AL, p. A20

SIMS, B. Wayne, President and Chief Executive Officer, KVC Prairie Ridge Psychiatric Hospital, Kansas City, KS, p. A247

SIMS, Brian, Director Administrative Services, Knoxville Hospital & Clinics, Knoxville, IA, p. A233

SIMS, Jason, M.D. Chief Medical Officer, Cleveland Area Hospital, Cleveland, OK, p. A509

SIMS, Jason, Facility Information Security Officer, North Hills Hospital, North Richland Hills, TX, p. A640

SIMS, Jeffrey, Chief Executive Officer, Heartland Behavioral Healthcare, Massillon, OH, p. A498

SIMS, Kristin, MSN Chief Nursing Officer, Oaklawn Hospital, Marshall, MI, p. A330

SIMS, Mark E., Chief Executive Officer, Grand Strand Regional Medical Center, Myrtle Beach, SC, p. A569

SIMS, Robyn, Director of Nursing, Vantage Point of Northwest Arkansas, Fayetteville, AR, p. A46

SIMS, W. Larry, Chief Operating Officer, Colquitt Regional Medical Center, Moultrie, GA, p. A164

SINACORE–JABERG, Janie, FACHE, Chief Executive Officer, Haywood Regional Medical Center, Clyde, NC, p. A462

SINCICH, Robert
Vice President Human Resources, Ashtabula County Medical Center, Ashtabula, OH, p. A482
Vice President Human Resources, Trumbull Memorial Hospital, Warren, OH, p. A504

SINCLAIR, Brad, Chief Financial Officer, River Oaks Hospital, Flowood, MS, p. A357

SINCLAIR, Elyria, Director Human Resources, Crestwood Medical Center, Huntsville, AL, p. A21

SINCLAIR, Jan, Chief Personnel Officer, Oaklawn Hospital, Marshall, MI, p. A330

SINCLAIR, Kathy, Vice President Human Resources, Spartanburg Regional Medical Center, Spartanburg, SC, p. A570

SINCLAIR, Laura, Director Human Resources, Kansas City Orthopaedic Institute, Leawood, KS, p. A248

SINCLAIR, Michael, Chief Executive Officer, Rooks County Health Center, Plainville, KS, p. A253

SINCLAIR, Nicole, Chief Financial Officer, Sierra Vista Hospital, Sacramento, CA, p. A87

SINCLAIR–CHUNG, Opal, R.N. Chief Nursing Officer, Deputy Executive Director, Kings County Hospital Center,, NY, p. A444

SINCOCK, Gregory M., Information Technology Leader, Kaiser Permanente West Los Angeles Medical Center, Los Angeles, CA, p. A72

SINDELAR, David, Chairman of the Board, St. Anthony's Medical Center, Saint Louis, MO, p. A381

SINDELAR, Michael, Vice President and Chief Financial Officer, Fremont Health, Fremont, NE, p. A395

SINDLINGER, Julie A., Director of Human Resources, Weston County Health Services, Newcastle, WY, p. A722

SINGAL, Manisha, M.D. Medical Director, Specialty Hospital of Washington, Washington, DC, p. A122

SINGH, Brij, Medical Staff Director, Kindred Hospital Rome, Rome, GA, p. A165

SINGH, Himanshu, M.D. Associate Director, Veterans Affairs Ann Arbor Healthcare System, Ann Arbor, MI, p. A318

SINGH, Inderjit, M.D. Clinical Director, Pilgrim Psychiatric Center, Brentwood, NY, p. A434

SINGH, Jagdeep, M.D. Chief Medical Officer, Henry Medical Center, Stockbridge, GA, p. A167

SINGH, Sabi, Co–Chief Operating Officer, University of Iowa Hospitals and Clinics, Iowa City, IA, p. A232

SINGH, Sandip, Acting Chief Executive Officer, Brunswick Psych Center, Amityville, NY, p. A432

SINGLES, James L., Chief Financial Officer, Marlette Regional Hospital, Marlette, MI, p. A330

SINGLETARY, Robert G., Chief Executive Officer, Maria Parham Medical Center, Henderson, NC, p. A466

SINGLETON, Al, M.D. Chief Psychiatry and Chief Medical Staff, Colorado Mental Health Institute at Pueblo, Pueblo, CO, p. A110

SINGLETON, J. Knox, President and Chief Executive Officer, Inova Health System, Falls Church, VA, p. B76

SINGLETON, Roy, Director Computer Information Systems, Palmdale Regional Medical Center, Palmdale, CA, p. A82

SINHA, Sunil K., M.D. Chief Medical Officer, Bon Secours Memorial Regional Medical Center, Mechanicsville, VA, p. A674

SINICKAS, Robert, Director Information Services, Marianjoy Rehabilitation Hospital, Wheaton, IL, p. A205

SINICROPE, Jr., Frank J., Vice President Financial Services, Princeton Community Hospital, Princeton, WV, p. A698

SINISI, Albert, Director Information Systems, Doctors' Hospital of Michigan, Pontiac, MI, p. A332

SINISI, Linda, Entity Information Officer, Pennsylvania Hospital, Philadelphia, PA, p. A549

SINNER, Laurie K., Chief Human Resource Officer, Ogallala Community Hospital, Ogallala, NE, p. A399

SINNOTT, James, M.D. Chief Medical Staff, Coquille Valley Hospital, Coquille, OR, p. A524

SINNOTT, Lisa M., Director Human Resources, Lourdes Specialty Hospital of Southern New Jersey, Willingboro, NJ, p. A425

SINOTTE, Brian, Chief Executive Officer, MetroSouth Medical Center, Blue Island, IL, p. A182

SINTICH, Maureen, R.N. Vice President and Chief Nursing Officer, Wake Forest Baptist Medical Center, Winston–Salem, NC, p. A475

SIOSON, Stephanie
Director Human Resources, Garden Grove Hospital and Medical Center, Garden Grove, CA, p. A65
Director Human Resources, Huntington Beach Hospital, Huntington Beach, CA, p. A67
Director Human Resources, La Palma Intercommunity Hospital, La Palma, CA, p. A68
Director Human Resources, West Anaheim Medical Center, Anaheim, CA, p. A55

SIPEK, John, Supervisor Client Services, Aurora Medical Center in Washington County, Hartford, WI, p. A706

SIREK, David, Chief Information Officer, Myrtue Medical Center, Harlan, IA, p. A232

SIRIO, Carl, M.D. Professor, Vice President Medical Affairs, Associate Dean for Clinical Affairs, Chief Medical Information Officer, The University of Toledo Medical Center, Toledo, OH, p. A503

SIRK, David R., Chief Executive Officer, Vaughan Regional Medical Center, Selma, AL, p. A25

SIRK, Donald, Director Information Systems, MedStar St. Mary's Hospital, Leonardtown, MD, p. A302

SIRMAN, Gary, Chief Human Resource Officer, North Hawaii Community Hospital, Kamuela, HI, p. A171

SIROIS, Peter, Chief Executive Officer, Northern Maine Medical Center, Fort Kent, ME, p. A293

SIROTTA, Ted D., Chief Financial Officer, Northwestern Medical Center, Saint Albans, VT, p. A666

SISARCICK, Barbara, Administrator, Peterson Rehabilitation Hospital, Wheeling, WV, p. A700

SISILLO, Sabato, M.D
Chief Medical Officer, Providence Medical Center, Kansas City, KS, p. A247
Chief Medical Officer, Saint John Hospital, Leavenworth, KS, p. A248

SISK, Bryan W., Associate Director Patient and Nursing Services, Central Texas Veterans Healthcare System, Temple, TX, p. A652

SISK, Glenn C., President, Coosa Valley Medical Center, Sylacauga, AL, p. A25

SISK, Jack, Chief Financial Officer, Punxsutawney Area Hospital, Punxsutawney, PA, p. A553

SISK, Lori, R.N.,
Chief Executive Officer, Sanford Canby Medical Center, Canby, MN, p. A341
Chief Executive Officer, Sanford Clear Lake Medical Center, Clear Lake, SD, p. A573

SISK, Rodney, Chief Financial Officer, Fannin Regional Hospital, Blue Ridge, GA, p. A154

SISK, Susan, Chief Financial Officer, St. Alexius Medical Center, Bismarck, ND, p. A476

SISLER, Debbie, Director Human Resources, Vidant Roanoke–Chowan Hospital, Ahoskie, NC, p. A459

SISON, Joseph, M.D. Medical Director, Heritage Oaks Hospital, Sacramento, CA, p. A87

SISSON, Travis, Interim Chief Executive Officer, Tri–Lakes Medical Center, Batesville, MS, p. A355

SISSON, William G., President, Baptist Health Lexington, Lexington, KY, p. A264

SISTO, Steven A., Senior Vice President and Chief Operating Officer, Methodist Hospital of Southern California, Arcadia, CA, p. A56

SISTRUNK, Heather, R.N. Chief Operating Officer, River Oaks Hospital, Flowood, MS, p. A357

SITLINGER, James, Chief Human Resources Management, Charles George Veterans Affairs Medical Center, Asheville, NC, p. A459

SITTIG, Kevin, M.D. Senior Associate Dean and Chief Medical Officer, University Health Shreveport, Shreveport, LA, p. A288

SITTLOW, Jo, Vice President Patient Care and Chief Nursing Officer, Lakeview Hospital, Stillwater, MN, p. A352

SIVAK, Steven, M.D. Chair, Department of Medicine, Einstein Medical Center Philadelphia, Philadelphia, PA, p. A548

SIVESS, Chuck, Vice President Human Resources, Providence Health Center, Waco, TX, p. A656

SIVLEY, Susanna S., Chief Personnel Officer, Highlands Medical Center, Scottsboro, AL, p. A25

SIX, Deborah, Coordinator Data Processing, Wayne Memorial Hospital, Jesup, GA, p. A161

SJOBERG, Rochelle, Director Human Resources, Ely–Bloomenson Community Hospital, Ely, MN, p. A343

SKABELUND, Hoyt, Chief Executive Officer, Banner Churchill Community Hospital, Fallon, NV, p. A404

SKAGGS, Lynda, Chief Nursing Officer, Fleming County Hospital, Flemingsburg, KY, p. A260

SKALA, Pat
Chief Information Officer, Laguna Honda Hospital and Rehabilitation Center, San Francisco, CA, p. A91
Chief Information Officer, San Francisco General Hospital and Trauma Center, San Francisco, CA, p. A91

SKARKA, Kathy, MSN Executive Vice President Patient Care Services, Nassau University Medical Center, East Meadow, NY, p. A437

SKARULIS, Patricia, Vice President Information Systems, Memorial Sloan–Kettering Cancer Center, New York, NY, p. A445

SKARZYNSKI, Joseph, M.D. Medical Director, North Central Bronx Hospital,, NY, p. A447

SKEANS, John L., Chief Financial Officer, Chesapeake Regional Medical Center, Chesapeake, VA, p. A669

SKEEN, Steven, R.N. Chief Nursing Officer, Mizell Memorial Hospital, Opp, AL, p. A24

SKEHAN, Michael, M.D. Senior Vice President and Chief Medical Officer, Martin Health System, Stuart, FL, p. A146

SKELDON, Timothy K., Senior Vice President and Chief Financial Officer, Parrish Medical Center, Titusville, FL, p. A149

SKELTON, Jenny, System Integration Manager, The Women's Hospital, Newburgh, IN, p. A220

SKELTON, John, Director Finance, Temple Community Hospital, Los Angeles, CA, p. A75

SKELTON, Katie, MSN Vice President Nursing and Chief Nursing Officer, St. Joseph Hospital, Orange, CA, p. A81

SKIDMORE, Jocelyn, Director Finance, St. Francis Hospital and Health Services, Maryville, MO, p. A376

SKIDMORE, Kim, Administrator, Community Medical Center of Izard County, Calico Rock, AR, p. A44

SKIEM, Paul
Senior Vice President Human Resources, Presence Resurrection Medical Center, Chicago, IL, p. A185
Senior Vice President Human Resources, Presence Saint Francis Hospital, Evanston, IL, p. A190

SKILLINGS, Charles E., President and Chief Executive Officer, St. Anthony Shawnee Hospital, Shawnee, OK, p. A519

SKILLINGS, Lois N., MSN, President and Chief Executive Officer, Mid Coast Hospital, Brunswick, ME, p. A292

SKILLMAN, Sally, Director Human Resources, Shriners Hospitals for Children–Cincinnati Burns Hospital, Cincinnati, OH, p. A487

SKINNER, Eileen F., FACHE, President and Chief Executive Officer, Mercy Hospital of Portland, Portland, ME, p. A294

SKINNER, Gary, Director Information Technology, Rehabilitation Hospital of Indiana, Indianapolis, IN, p. A214

SKINNER, Gwendolyn, Executive Director, Devereux Georgia Treatment Network, Kennesaw, GA, p. A161

SKINNER, Jeannette, FACHE, Administrator, Shriners Hospitals for Children–Tampa, Tampa, FL, p. A148

SKINNER, Kellcie, Controller, Newman Memorial Hospital, Shattuck, OK, p. A518

SKINNER, Marjorie, Director Finance, Pershing General Hospital, Lovelock, NV, p. A407

SKINNER, Richard, Chief Information Technology Officer, University of Virginia Medical Center, Charlottesville, VA, p. A669

SKINNER, Sue, Vice President of Patient Care Services, Grand Itasca Clinic and Hospital, Grand Rapids, MN, p. A344

SKIPPER, Kymberli, Manager Human Resources, Prattville Baptist Hospital, Prattville, AL, p. A25

SKJOLDEN, Jessica, M.D. Chief of Staff, St. Andrew's Health Center, Bottineau, ND, p. A476

SKLAMBERG, Todd, President, Sunrise Hospital and Medical Center, Las Vegas, NV, p. A407

SKLAR, Joel, M.D. Chief Medical Officer, Marin General Hospital, Greenbrae, CA, p. A66

SKOCH, Michael, M.D. Chief Medical Officer, Mary Lanning Healthcare, Hastings, NE, p. A396

SKOGSBERGH, Jim H., President and Chief Executive Officer, Advocate Health Care, Downers Grove, IL, p. B7

SKORA, Lori, Chief Executive Officer, Kindred Hospital of Northern Indiana, Mishawaka, IN, p. A218

SKOW, Glenn, M.D. Chief of Staff, Fayette County Hospital, Vandalia, IL, p. A204

SKRINDE, Tracie, Director Human Resources, PeaceHealth United General Hospital, Sedro-Woolley, WA, p. A689

SKRIPPS, Michele M., R.N., Chief Executive Officer, AnMed Health Rehabilitation Hospital, Anderson, SC, p. A562

SKULA, Erika, President and Chief Executive Officer, Manchester Memorial Hospital, Manchester, KY, p. A267

SKUPIEN, Mary Beth, Director, Battle Creek Veterans Affairs Medical Center, Battle Creek, MI, p. A319

SKVARENINA, Michael, Assistant Vice President Information Systems, Holy Name Medical Center, Teaneck, NJ, p. A423

SKYLES, Jill, R.N
Vice President and Chief Nursing Officer, Barnes-Jewish St. Peters Hospital, Saint Peters, MO, p. A382
Vice President and Chief Nurse Executive, Progress West Hospital, O'Fallon, MO, p. A378

SLABA, Bryan, Chief Executive Officer, Wagner Community Memorial Hospital Avera, Wagner, SD, p. A578

SLABIK, Shauna, Chief Financial Officer, Sanford Mayville Medical Center, Mayville, ND, p. A479

SLACK, Randy, Interim Chief Executive Officer, Memorial Medical Center – Livingston, Livingston, TX, p. A633

SLADKY, Todd J., Chief Financial Officer, Great River Medical Center, West Burlington, IA, p. A239

SLAGLE, Julie A., R.N. Vice President Patient Care Services, Sidney Regional Medical Center, Sidney, NE, p. A402

SLATE, Sonny, Chief Operating Officer, Georgia Regional Hospital at Atlanta, Decatur, GA, p. A158

SLATER, Craig M., M.D
Chief Medical Officer, Carolinas Medical Center–Union, Monroe, NC, p. A469
Chief Medical Officer, Columbus Regional Healthcare System, Whiteville, NC, p. A474

SLATER, Mark, Director Information Systems, Lake Pointe Medical Center, Rowlett, TX, p. A645

SLATER-NESUOLD, Stephanie, Director of Nursing, Landmark Hospital of Joplin, Joplin, MO, p. A373

SLATON, Brenda, Administrator, Rusk State Hospital, Rusk, TX, p. A645

SLATTERY, Greg, Vice President Information, Community Hospitals and Wellness Centers, Bryan, OH, p. A484

SLATTERY, Susan L., Director Human Resources, UnityPoint Health – St. Luke's Hospital, Cedar Rapids, IA, p. A226

SLATTMAN, Robin, Chief Nursing Officer, Memorial Hospital of Union County, Marysville, OH, p. A497

SLAVIN, Kevin J., FACHE, President and Chief Executive Officer, East Orange General Hospital, East Orange, NJ, p. A415

SLAVIN, Peter L., M.D., President, Massachusetts General Hospital, Boston, MA, p. A307

SLAWITSKY, Bruce, Vice President Human Resources, Hospital for Special Surgery, New York, NY, p. A444

SLAWKOWSKI, Ken, Interim Director Information Systems, Holy Cross Hospital, Chicago, IL, p. A184

SLAYDON, Cindy, Chief Nursing Executive, Sparks Regional Medical Center, Fort Smith, AR, p. A46

SLAYTON, Val, M.D. Vice President Medical Affairs, Sts. Mary & Elizabeth Hospital, Louisville, KY, p. A266

SLBERS, Craig, Vice President Patient Care and Chief Nursing Officer, Mercy St. Charles Hospital, Oregon, OH, p. A500

SLEDGE, Cynthia Moore, M.D. Medical Director, Bryce Hospital, Tuscaloosa, AL, p. A26

SLEDGE, Tasha, Director Human Resources, Texas Health Harris Methodist Hospital Southlake, Southlake, TX, p. A650

SLEEPER, Justin, Vice President Clinical Operations, Behavioral Health Network, Natchaug Hospital, Mansfield Center, CT, p. A115

SLENSZAK, David, Director, Information Services, Williamsburg Regional Hospital, Kingstree, SC, p. A567

SLESSOR, Steve Robert, Chief Executive Officer, Buchanan County Health Center, Independence, IA, p. A232

SLICK, Lois, Director Human Resources, LakeWood Health Center, Baudette, MN, p. A340

SLIDER, Carol, Chief Nursing Officer, Titus Regional Medical Center, Mount Pleasant, TX, p. A638

SLIETER Jr., Richard G., Administrator, Community Behavioral Health Hospital – Baxter, Baxter, MN, p. A340

SLIGER, Susan, Director Human Resources, War Memorial Hospital, Sault Sainte Marie, MI, p. A334

SLINGERLAND, Micki J., Chief Operating Officer, Tristar Centennial Medical Center, Nashville, TN, p. A591

SLITER, Elizabeth, M.D. Chairman Medical Staff, Decatur Health Systems, Oberlin, KS, p. A251

SLIWA, James, M.D. Chief Medical Officer, Rehabilitation Institute of Chicago, Chicago, IL, p. A186

SLIWINSKI, Jeff, Chief Financial Officer, Clear Lake Regional Medical Center, Webster, TX, p. A656

SLIWINSKI, Ron, Chief Operations Officer, University of Wisconsin Hospital and Clinics, Madison, WI, p. A708

SLOAN, Gary, Chief Executive Officer, San Ramon Regional Medical Center, San Ramon, CA, p. A93

SLOAN, Mona, Chief Nursing Officer, Comanche County Medical Center, Comanche, TX, p. A607

SLOAN, Patrick, Chief Financial Officer, Sandhills Regional Medical Center, Hamlet, NC, p. A466

SLOAN, Prudence, Coordinator Human Resources, Select Specialty Hospital–Pittsburgh/UPMC, Pittsburgh, PA, p. A551

SLOAN, Ronald A., FACHE, President, The Outer Banks Hospital, Nags Head, NC, p. A470

SLOAN, Steve, Chief Financial Officer, Lake Cumberland Regional Hospital, Somerset, KY, p. A270

SLOANE, Dean, Vice President Finance, Harrison Community Hospital, Cadiz, OH, p. A484

SLOCUM, Brandon H., Senior Vice President and Chief Financial Officer, Medical West, Bessemer, AL, p. A16

SLOCUM, Gregg Y., Chief Financial Officer, Valley Forge Medical Center and Hospital, Norristown, PA, p. A546

SLONIM, Anthony D., Dr.PH, President and Chief Executive Officer, Renown Health, Reno, NV, p. B114

SLONIM, Sheryl A., Executive Vice President and Chief Nursing Officer, Holy Name Medical Center, Teaneck, NJ, p. A423

SLONINA, Marrianne, Director Human Resources, Georgetown Community Hospital, Georgetown, KY, p. A262

SLOPER, Carol, Manager Information Technology, Cheyenne County Hospital, Saint Francis, KS, p. A253

SLOUGH, Sharlet, D.O. Chief of Staff, East Texas Medical Center Jacksonville, Jacksonville, TX, p. A630

SLUBOWSKI, Michael A., FACHE, Chief Executive Officer, SCL Health System, Denver, CO, p. B119

SLUCK, Jeana, R.N. Executive Director Nursing Clinical Inpatient Departments, Allied Services Rehabilitation Hospital, Scranton, PA, p. A554

SLUSHER, Carlene, Director Finance, Seneca Healthcare District, Chester, CA, p. A59

SLUSHER, Michael, Community Chief Executive Officer, Middlesboro ARH Hospital, Middlesboro, KY, p. A267

SLYTER, Mark F., FACHE, Chief Executive Officer, Baton Rouge General Medical Center, Baton Rouge, LA, p. A273

SMAJSTRLA, Julie, Director Nursing, Seymour Hospital, Seymour, TX, p. A648

SMALE, Cindy, Director Human Resources, Indiana University Health Paoli Hospital, Paoli, IN, p. A221

SMALL, Becky, Chief Human Resources Officer, Kindred Hospital–Aurora, Aurora, CO, p. A102

SMALL, Brenda, Chief Clinical Officer, AMG Specialty Hospital–Greenwood, Greenwood, MS, p. A358

SMALL, David, M.D
Chief Medical Officer, Greene Memorial Hospital, Xenia, OH, p. A506
Chief Medical Officer, Soin Medical Center, Beavercreek, OH, p. A483

SMALL, David R., FACHE, Chief Executive Officer, United Medical Center, Washington, DC, p. A122

SMALL, Deborah C., R.N. Vice President Patient Care Services and Chief Nursing Officer, Fairview Hospital, Cleveland, OH, p. A488

SMALL, Donna, R.N. Chief Nursing Officer, St. Mary's Medical Center, West Palm Beach, FL, p. A150

SMALL, Jonathan
Chief Operations Information and Technology, John D. Dingell Veterans Affairs Medical Center, Detroit, MI, p. A322
Vice President, Human Resources, Memorial Health, Savannah, GA, p. A166

SMALL, Terry L., Assistant Chief Executive Officer, William R. Sharpe, Jr. Hospital, Weston, WV, p. A700

SMALLEY, Diana, Acting Interim Chief Executive Officer, Mercy Hospital Ada, Ada, OK, p. A507

SMALLWOOD, Ravae, IS Coordinator, CHI Health Missouri Valley, Missouri Valley, IA, p. A234

SMANIK, Robert E., FACHE, President and Chief Executive Officer, Day Kimball Hospital, Putnam, CT, p. A116

SMARR, Susan, M.D. Physician-in-Chief, Kaiser Permanente Santa Clara Medical Center, Santa Clara, CA, p. A94

SMART, Dan, Chief Information Management Officer, Permian Regional Medical Center, Andrews, TX, p. A597

SMART, George J., VP Finance & IT, Alpena Regional Medical Center, Alpena, MI, p. A318

SMART, Joanne F., M.D. Director of Medical Affairs, Indiana University Health Bedford Hospital, Bedford, IN, p. A206

SMART, Melissa, Communication ad Public Relations Specialist, Texas Health Presbyterian Hospital Denton, Denton, TX, p. A613

SMART, Paul, CPA Chief Financial Officer, Franklin County Medical Center, Preston, ID, p. A178

SMART, Robert M., Chief Executive Officer, Reliant Rehabilitation Hospital Mid–Cities, Bedford, TX, p. A602

SMEEKS, Frank C., M.D. Chief Medical Officer, Frye Regional Medical Center, Hickory, NC, p. A466

SMELSER, Scott, M.D. Chief of Staff, French Hospital Medical Center, San Luis Obispo, CA, p. A93

SMELTZER, Sharon, Chief Executive Officer, Mercy Rehabilitation Hospital Oklahoma City, Oklahoma City, OK, p. A515

SMENDIK, Douglas, M.D. Chief Medical Officer, Pennock Hospital, Hastings, MI, p. A326

SMIDT, Jessica, R.N. Director of Nursing, Pipestone County Medical Center Avera, Pipestone, MN, p. A349

SMIGA, Lance, Chief Financial Officer, Jackson County Hospital District, Edna, TX, p. A615

SMILEY, Christy, Director Human Resources, Audrain Medical Center, Mexico, MO, p. A376

SMILEY, Jon D., Interim Chief Executive Officer, Columbia County Health System, Dayton, WA, p. A683

SMITH, Agnes A., R.N. Chief Nursing Officer, Twin County Regional Hospital, Galax, VA, p. A671

SMITH, Alan H.
Chief Financial Officer, Garden Grove Hospital and Medical Center, Garden Grove, CA, p. A65
Chief Financial Officer, Huntington Beach Hospital, Huntington Beach, CA, p. A67
Chief Financial Officer, La Palma Intercommunity Hospital, La Palma, CA, p. A68
Chief Financial Officer, West Anaheim Medical Center, Anaheim, CA, p. A55

SMITH, Andrew
Chief Information Management, Madigan Healthcare System, Tacoma, WA, p. A690
CFO, St. Petersburg General Hospital, Saint Petersburg, FL, p. A145

SMITH, Barbara H., Senior Vice President & Chief Operating Officer, Robert Wood Johnson University Hospital at Hamilton, Hamilton, NJ, p. A416

SMITH, Bennie, Chief Information Officer, Lady of the Sea General Hospital, Cut Off, LA, p. A276

SMITH, Bernie, Chief Financial Officer, Troy Community Hospital, Troy, PA, p. A556

SMITH, Beth, Controller, Mercy Hospital, Valley City, ND, p. A480

SMITH, Bethany, Controller, HEALTHSOUTH Cane Creek Rehabilitation Hospital, Martin, TN, p. A587

SMITH, Beverly Bzdek, Chief Nursing Officer, Southside Regional Medical Center, Petersburg, VA, p. A676

SMITH, Bill, M.D. Chief of Staff, Cullman Regional Medical Center, Cullman, AL, p. A18

SMITH, Blythe, Administrative Assistant, Faulkton Area Medical Center, Faulkton, SD, p. A573

SMITH, Bobby, Vice President Physician Services and Quality, Illinois Valley Community Hospital, Peru, IL, p. A200

SMITH, Brad, M.D. Chief Medical Staff, Lane Regional Medical Center, Zachary, LA, p. A290

SMITH, Bradley, President and Chief Executive Officer, Rush Memorial Hospital, Rushville, IN, p. A222

SMITH, Brenda, Director Financial Services, Alliance Health Center, Meridian, MS, p. A362

SMITH, Brent, Chief Financial Officer, Comanche County Memorial Hospital, Lawton, OK, p. A512

SMITH, Brent, M.D. Chief Medical Officer and Vice President Clinical Integration, Edward Hospital, Naperville, IL, p. A197

SMITH, Brian
Executive Vice President and Chief Operating Officer, St. Rita's Medical Center, Lima, OH, p. A496
Director Risk Management, Quality and Safety, Wamego Health Center, Wamego, KS, p. A256

SMITH, Buddy, M.D. Director Medical Staff, Clay County Hospital, Ashland, AL, p. A15

SMITH, Carl, Director Information Systems, King's Daughters Medical Center, Brookhaven, MS, p. A356

SMITH, Carol, R.N. Vice President Patient Care and Chief Nursing Officer, Tift Regional Medical Center, Tifton, GA, p. A168

SMITH, Cheryl, Manager Human Resources, New Braunfels Regional Rehabilitation Hospital, New Braunfels, TX, p. A639

SMITH, Chris, Chief Information Officer, Falls Community Hospital and Clinic, Marlin, TX, p. A636

SMITH, Chuck, Interim Chief Executive Officer, Promise Hospital of San Diego, San Diego, CA, p. A89

SMITH, Cindy, Chief Executive Officer, Kindred Hospital–Sycamore, Sycamore, IL, p. A204

SMITH, Connie, President and Chief Executive Officer, Commonwealth Health Corporation, Bowling Green, KY, p. B36

SMITH, Connie, Chief Executive Officer, Medical Center at Bowling Green, Bowling Green, KY, p. A259

SMITH, Dale, Director Human Resources, Texas Health Harris Methodist Hospital Hurst–Euless–Bedford, Bedford, TX, p. A602

SMITH, Dan
Director Human Resources, Austin Lakes Hospital, Austin, TX, p. A599
Director Human Resources, Memorial Hospital, Carthage, IL, p. A182

SMITH, Daniel
Interim Chief Executive Officer, Sugar Land Surgical Hospital, Sugar Land, TX, p. A651
Interim Chief Executive Officer, TOPS Surgical Specialty Hospital, Houston, TX, p. A627

SMITH, Daniel B.
Vice President Finance, Good Samaritan Regional Medical Center, Corvallis, OR, p. A524
Vice President Finance, Samaritan Albany General Hospital, Albany, OR, p. A523
Vice President Finance, Samaritan Lebanon Community Hospital, Lebanon, OR, p. A526
Chief Financial Officer, Samaritan Pacific Communities Hospital, Newport, OR, p. A527

SMITH, Danny, Director Human Resources, Bryan W. Whitfield Memorial Hospital, Demopolis, AL, p. A19

SMITH, Darrin, Vice President Human Resources, Parkview Medical Center, Pueblo, CO, p. A110

SMITH, Darwin K., Vice President Human Resources, Union Hospital, Dover, OH, p. A493

SMITH, David, President and Chief Operating Officer, Cornerstone Healthcare Group, Dallas, TX, p. B44

SMITH, David
Chief Executive Officer, Cornerstone Hospital of Southwest Louisiana, Sulphur, LA, p. A289
Chief Executive Officer, GLOBALREHAB Hospital – Dallas, Dallas, TX, p. A610
Chief Financial Officer, Memorial Regional Hospital,, FL, p. A130
Manager Data Center, Texas Health Huguley Hospital Fort Worth South, Fort Worth, TX, p. A619

SMITH, Deborah S., R.N. Vice President, Chief Nursing Officer, OSF St. Joseph Medical Center, Bloomington, IL, p. A181

SMITH, Debra, Chief Executive Officer, Gundersen St. Joseph's Hospital and Clinics, Hillsboro, WI, p. A706

SMITH, Denise
Director Financial Services, Florida State Hospital, Chattahoochee, FL, p. A125
Director Health Information, HEALTHSOUTH Chattanooga Rehabilitation Hospital, Chattanooga, TN, p. A580

SMITH, Dennis H., Director, Veterans Affairs Maryland Health Care System–Baltimore Division, Baltimore, MD, p. A298

SMITH, Dennis J., Chief Operating Officer, James Cancer Hospital and Solove Research Institute, Columbus, OH, p. A489

SMITH, Denny R., Administrator, Camden General Hospital, Camden, TN, p. A579

SMITH, Diana B., Chief Financial Officer, Promise Hospital of Dallas, Dallas, TX, p. A611

SMITH, Diane, Chief Nursing Officer, Baptist Health Extended Care Hospital, Little Rock, AR, p. A49

SMITH, Dianne, Director Personnel and Human Resources, Potomac Valley Hospital, Keyser, WV, p. A696

SMITH, Dick, Director Human Resources, West Park Hospital, Cody, WY, p. A721

SMITH, Donna M., Chief Nursing Officer, Barstow Community Hospital, Barstow, CA, p. A58

SMITH, Donna P., R.N. Vice President Patient Care Services and Chief Nursing Officer, Clifton Springs Hospital and Clinic, Clifton Springs, NY, p. A435

SMITH, Donnie
Chief Human Resources Officer, Laird Hospital, Union, MS, p. A366
Director Human Resources, Rush Foundation Hospital, Meridian, MS, p. A362
Director of Human Resources, Specialty Hospital of Meridian, Meridian, MS, p. A363

SMITH, Doug, Chief Financial Officer, McKay–Dee Hospital Center, Ogden, UT, p. A661

SMITH, Drew, Director Human Resources, Baylor Medical Center at Carrollton, Carrollton, TX, p. A605

SMITH Jr., Edward H., President and Chief Executive Officer, St. Anthony Regional Hospital, Carroll, IA, p. A226

SMITH, Elizabeth A., Director of Nursing, John J. Pershing Veterans Affairs Medical Center, Poplar Bluff, MO, p. A378

SMITH, Ellen, Administrator, LCMH Specialty Hospital, Lake Charles, LA, p. A282

SMITH, Eric, Chief Financial Officer, Bayfront Health St. Petersburg, Saint Petersburg, FL, p. A144

SMITH, Ericka, Chief Operating Officer, Monterey Park Hospital, Monterey Park, CA, p. A78

SMITH, Eugene, Chief Information Officer, Maniilaq Health Center, Kotzebue, AK, p. A29

SMITH, Jr., Forrest Bud H., Chief Financial Officer, Fulton State Hospital, Fulton, MO, p. A372

SMITH, G. Todd, President, St. Elizabeth Community Hospital, Red Bluff, CA, p. A85

SMITH, Gene
Senior Vice President Operations, AMG Specialty Hospital–Slidell, Slidell, LA, p. A288
Interim Vice President and Chief Financial Officer, Ottumwa Regional Health Center, Ottumwa, IA, p. A236
Interim Chief Financial Officer, West Suburban Medical Center, Oak Park, IL, p. A198
Interim Chief Financial Officer, Westlake Hospital, Melrose Park, IL, p. A196

SMITH, Geoffrey, Chief Financial Officer, Lebanon Veterans Affairs Medical Center, Lebanon, PA, p. A542

SMITH, Gia, Chief Executive Officer, Central Valley Specialty Hospital, Modesto, CA, p. A77

SMITH, Ginger S., Chief Nursing Officer, Homer Memorial Hospital, Homer, LA, p. A278

SMITH, Gregory
Chief Information Officer, Covenant Medical Center, Waterloo, IA, p. A239
Senior Vice President and Chief Information Officer, Midwest Orthopedic Specialty Hospital, Franklin, WI, p. A705
Senior Vice President and Chief Information Officer, Wheaton Franciscan Healthcare – Franklin, Franklin, WI, p. A705
Senior Vice President and Chief Information Officer, Wheaton Franciscan Healthcare – St. Francis, Milwaukee, WI, p. A711
Senior Vice President and Chief Information Officer, Wheaton Franciscan Healthcare – The Wisconsin Heart Hospital, Wauwatosa, WI, p. A718

SMITH, Gretchen, Vice President Nursing and Compliance and Risk, Rush Memorial Hospital, Rushville, IN, p. A222

SMITH, Hal, M.D. Chief of Staff, South Peninsula Hospital, Homer, AK, p. A29

SMITH, Harley, Chief Executive Officer, Pioneer Community Hospital of Aberdeen, Aberdeen, MS, p. A355

SMITH Jr., Harry L., President, Novant Health Presbyterian Medical Center, Charlotte, NC, p. A462

SMITH, Heather
Director Finance, Conemaugh Meyersdale Medical Center, Meyersdale, PA, p. A545
Chief Operating Officer, Welch Community Hospital, Welch, WV, p. A700

SMITH, Jack, Acting Chief Information Resources Management Service, Veterans Affairs Sierra Nevada Health Care System, Reno, NV, p. A408

SMITH, Jackie, R.N. Chief Nursing Officer, Holdenville General Hospital, Holdenville, OK, p. A512

SMITH, James, Chief Financial Officer, Massena Memorial Hospital, Massena, NY, p. A441

SMITH, James E.
Superintendent, North Texas State Hospital, Vernon, TX, p. A655
Superintendent, North Texas State Hospital, Wichita Falls Campus, Wichita Falls, TX, p. A657

SMITH, James M., M.D. Medical Director, Sterlington Rehabilitation Hospital, Bastrop, LA, p. A273

SMITH, Jamie, Supervisor Health Information Management Systems, HEALTHSOUTH Rehabilitation Hospital, Sewickley, PA, p. A555

SMITH, Janet, Chief Financial Officer, Troy Regional Medical Center, Troy, AL, p. A26

SMITH, Jason, M.D. Chief of Staff, Mitchell County Hospital, Camilla, GA, p. A155

SMITH, Jason, Chief Nursing Officer, Piedmont Newnan Hospital, Newnan, GA, p. A164

SMITH, Jay, Director Information Systems, Brownwood Regional Medical Center, Brownwood, TX, p. A604

SMITH, Jeanna, Administrative Assistant and Human Resources Officer, Polk Medical Center, Cedartown, GA, p. A155

SMITH, Jeff, Chief Information Officer, Holy Cross Hospital, Fort Lauderdale, FL, p. A128

SMITH, Jeffrey A., M.D. Senior Vice President and Chief Medical Officer, Aurora St. Luke's Medical Center, Milwaukee, WI, p. A710

SMITH, Jeremy, Manager Human Resources, Okmulgee Memorial Hospital, Okmulgee, OK, p. A517

SMITH, Jill, Administrative Coordinator, J. Paul Jones Hospital, Camden, AL, p. A18

SMITH, Jim, Director Information Systems, Washington County Memorial Hospital, Potosi, MO, p. A379

SMITH, Jo Beth, Chief Support Services and Human Resources, Decatur County Hospital, Leon, IA, p. A233

SMITH, Joanne C., M.D., President and Chief Executive Officer, Rehabilitation Institute of Chicago, Chicago, IL, p. A186

SMITH, JoBeth, Chief Operating Officer and Director of Human Resources, Medical Arts Hospital, Lamesa, TX, p. A632

SMITH, Jodi, Administrative Assistant Human Resources, Eureka Springs Hospital, Eureka Springs, AR, p. A45

SMITH, Jon
Chief Financial Officer, Caribou Memorial Hospital and Living Center, Soda Springs, ID, p. A178
Chief Financial Officer, Lost Rivers Medical Center, Arco, ID, p. A174

SMITH, Jonathan, Assistant Administrator and Chief Financial Officer, Blount Memorial Hospital, Maryville, TN, p. A588

SMITH, Joseph B., Vice President Finance, MedStar Union Memorial Hospital, Baltimore, MD, p. A297

SMITH, Joseph S., Chief Executive Officer, Boone County Hospital, Boone, IA, p. A226

SMITH, Julia
Chief Financial Officer, Kindred Hospital Rome, Rome, GA, p. A165
Chief Financial Officer, Kindred Hospital–Chattanooga, Chattanooga, TN, p. A580
Chief Financial Officer, Vibra Hospital of Charleston, Mt. Pleasant, SC, p. A568

SMITH, Julie, Director Human Resources, HEALTHSOUTH Lakeshore Rehabilitation Hospital, Birmingham, AL, p. A16

SMITH, Julie, R.N. Director of Nursing, Jersey Community Hospital, Jerseyville, IL, p. A193

SMITH, Karen S., Director Information Services, Chilton Medical Center, Pompton Plains, NJ, p. A421

SMITH, Karyl, Director Human Resources, Harbor–UCLA Medical Center, Torrance, CA, p. A97

SMITH, Kathy A., MSN Nurse Executive, Summit Behavioral Healthcare, Cincinnati, OH, p. A487

SMITH, Kelli, M.D. Chief of Staff, Magee General Hospital, Magee, MS, p. A361

SMITH, Kelly C., Division President, Oakwood Hospital–Dearborn, Dearborn, MI, p. A321

SMITH, Ken, Chief Financial Officer, Brown County Hospital, Ainsworth, NE, p. A393

SMITH, Kevin, Vice President Finance and Support Services, Rehabilitation Institute of Michigan, Detroit, MI, p. A322

SMITH, Kevin E., Chief Operating Officer, Scott & White Hospital at Round Rock, Round Rock, TX, p. A644

SMITH, Kevin F., President and Chief Executive Officer, Winchester Hospital, Winchester, MA, p. A316

SMITH, Kim, Director Business Office, Doctor's Hospital of Deer Creek, Leesville, LA, p. A283

SMITH, Kris, Controller, Madison St. Joseph Health Center, Madisonville, TX, p. A636

SMITH, Kyle, Director Information Systems, Iredell Memorial Hospital, Statesville, NC, p. A473

SMITH, Larry, Senior Vice President and Chief Financial Officer, UW Medicine/Valley Medical Center, Renton, WA, p. A687

SMITH, LaVonne, Director Health Information Technology, Tomah Memorial Hospital, Tomah, WI, p. A716

SMITH, Lawrence, M.D. Senior Vice President and Chief Medical Officer, Forest Hills Hospital,, NY, p. A443

SMITH, Leighton, M.D. Chief Medical Officer, Florida Hospital Fish Memorial, Orange City, FL, p. A140

SMITH, Leora, Information System and Health Information Management Team Leader, Phelps Memorial Health Center, Holdrege, NE, p. A396

SMITH, Leslie, Director Human Resources, Howard County Medical Center, Saint Paul, NE, p. A401

SMITH, Lex, Chief Executive Officer, Mee Memorial Hospital, King City, CA, p. A68

SMITH, Linda C., M.D. Medical Director, HEALTHSOUTH Rehabilitation Hospital of Beaumont, Beaumont, TX, p. A602

SMITH, Linda D., FACHE, Director, Cincinnati Veterans Affairs Medical Center, Cincinnati, OH, p. A486

SMITH, Linda T., Director Human Resources, Clay County Hospital, Ashland, AL, p. A15

SMITH, Linda V., Vice President Human Resources, Central Florida Regional Hospital, Sanford, FL, p. A145

SMITH, Lori, Chief Financial Officer, North Big Horn Hospital District, Lovell, WY, p. A722

SMITH, Lorie, Director Human Resources, Nason Hospital, Roaring Spring, PA, p. A553

SMITH, Lorraine, Supervisory Human Resource Specialist, Chinle Comprehensive Health Care Facility, Chinle, AZ, p. A31

SMITH Jr., Louis G., Chief Executive Officer, Memorial Hermann Northeast, Humble, TX, p. A628

SMITH, Marisa, Director, Tomball Regional Medical Center, Tomball, TX, p. A653

SMITH, Mark, M.D. Chief Medical Officer, Methodist Richardson Medical Center, Richardson, TX, p. A644

SMITH, Mark T., CPA, President, Fort Hamilton Hospital, Hamilton, OH, p. A495

SMITH, Marsh, Manager Health Information, University Behavioral Health of Denton, Denton, TX, p. A613

SMITH, Martha, Chief Executive Officer, Kapiolani Medical Center for Women & Children, Honolulu, HI, p. A170

SMITH, Martha M., R.N. Chief Nursing Officer, Park Plaza Hospital, Houston, TX, p. A626

SMITH, Mary Clare, M.D. Medical Director, Western State Hospital, Staunton, VA, p. A679

SMITH, Mary Jo, Assistant Vice President Human Resources, University of Illinois Hospital & Health Sciences System, Chicago, IL, p. A187

SMITH, Marybeth
Director Human Resources, Saint Francis Hospital, Charleston, WV, p. A694
Director Human Resources, Thomas Memorial Hospital, South Charleston, WV, p. A699

SMITH, Matthew, M.D. Vice President Medical Affairs and Chief Medical Officer, Baylor Medical Center at Carrollton, Carrollton, TX, p. A605

SMITH, Melinda, Chief Information Systems, H. C. Watkins Memorial Hospital, Quitman, MS, p. A364

SMITH, Melissa, Controller, Select Specialty Hospital–Jackson, Jackson, MS, p. A360

SMITH, Michael, Director Support Services and Information Technology, Medina Regional Hospital, Hondo, TX, p. A623

SMITH, Michael, M.D. Vice President Medical Affairs, St. Joseph Mercy Oakland, Pontiac, MI, p. A332

SMITH, Michael K., D.O. Vice President Medical Affairs, McLaren Macomb, Mount Clemens, MI, p. A330

SMITH, Michelle, Coordinator Human Resources, Baton Rouge Rehabilitation Hospital, Baton Rouge, LA, p. A273

SMITH, Michelle, R.N. Chief Clinical Officer, Memorial Hospital, Colorado Springs, CO, p. A103

SMITH, Michelle T., R.N. Chief Nursing Officer, Greenville Memorial Hospital, Greenville, SC, p. A566

SMITH, Mickey, Chief Executive Officer, Oak Hill Hospital, Brooksville, FL, p. A125

SMITH, Mike
Chief Information Officer, Cape Coral Hospital, Cape Coral, FL, p. A125
Chief Information Officer, Gulf Coast Medical Center, Fort Myers, FL, p. A129
Chief Information Officer, Lee Memorial Hospital, Fort Myers, FL, p. A129

SMITH, Missy, Coordinator Human Resources, Scotland County Hospital, Memphis, MO, p. A376

SMITH, Nadine, Director Human Resources, Reeves County Hospital, Pecos, TX, p. A641

SMITH, Natalie R., R.N. Vice President Patient Care Services and Chief Nursing Officer, Portneuf Medical Center, Pocatello, ID, p. A177

SMITH, Neil, D.O., President, Fairview Hospital, Cleveland, OH, p. A488

SMITH, Nekisha, Director Medical Records, Riverland Medical Center, Ferriday, LA, p. A277

SMITH, Nicholas T., Chief Executive Officer, Palm Springs General Hospital, Hialeah, FL, p. A130

SMITH, Norine, Chief Executive Officer, U. S. Public Health Service Indian Hospital, Cass Lake, MN, p. A341

SMITH, Oliver, President and Chief Executive Officer, Paris Community Hospital, Paris, IL, p. A199

SMITH, Pam
Senior Director Human Resources, Harrison Community Hospital, Cadiz, OH, p. A484
Chief Nursing Officer, Reliant Rehabilitation Hospital North Texas, Richardson, TX, p. A644

SMITH, Pat J., Vice President Nursing, Oconee Medical Center, Seneca, SC, p. A569

SMITH, Patrick, M.D. Chief Medical Officer, Arrowhead Hospital, Glendale, AZ, p. A33

SMITH, Paula
Leader Information Services and Chief Information Officer, Oakwood Hospital–Dearborn, Dearborn, MI, p. A321
Vice President Information Services and Chief Information Officer, Oakwood Hospital–Southshore, Trenton, MI, p. A336
Chief Information Officer, Oakwood Hospital–Taylor, Taylor, MI, p. A335
Senior Vice President Chief Information Officer, Oakwood Hospital–Wayne, Wayne, MI, p. A337

SMITH, Peg, Vice President and Chief Nursing Officer, Chandler Regional Medical Center, Chandler, AZ, p. A31

SMITH, Peyton A., Chief Executive Officer, Appling Healthcare System, Baxley, GA, p. A154

SMITH, Phyllis, Vice President Human Resources, Northeastern Health System, Tahlequah, OK, p. A519

SMITH, Phyllis J., Associate Director, Birmingham Veterans Affairs Medical Center, Birmingham, AL, p. A16

SMITH, Randall, Executive Vice President, Jackson Park Hospital and Medical Center, Chicago, IL, p. A184

SMITH, Rebecca, Chief Operating Officer and Vice President, Caldwell Memorial Hospital, Lenoir, NC, p. A468

SMITH, Rebekah, R.N., President and Chief Executive Officer, St. Joseph Mercy Port Huron, Port Huron, MI, p. A333

SMITH, Renee, M.D. Chief Medical Staff, Langlade Hospital, Antigo, WI, p. A701

SMITH, Rhonda, Director Human Resources, Shriners Hospitals for Children–Portland, Portland, OR, p. A529

SMITH, Rhonda E., R.N
Vice President Patient Care Services and Chief Nursing Officer, Union Hospital, Terre Haute, IN, p. A223
Chief Nursing Officer, Union Hospital Clinton, Clinton, IN, p. A208

SMITH, Rich, Vice President Human Resources, Kaiser Permanente Sunnyside Medical Center, Clackamas, OR, p. A523

SMITH, Richard C.
Senior Vice President and Chief Financial Officer, JFK Medical Center, Edison, NJ, p. A415
Senior Vice President Finance, Shore Rehabilitation Institute, Brick, NJ, p. A413

SMITH, Rick
Director Information Services, Cibola General Hospital, Grants, NM, p. A428
Chief Operating Officer, Health Central Hospital, Ocoee, FL, p. A140
Director Information Systems, Jamestown Regional Medical Center, Jamestown, TN, p. A584
Senior Vice President Human Resources and Chief Administrative Officer, Vail Valley Medical Center, Vail, CO, p. A111

SMITH, Robert M., M.D. Chief of Staff, Veterans Affairs San Diego Healthcare System, San Diego, CA, p. A90

SMITH, Robin S., Chief Nursing Officer, Indiana University Health White Memorial Hospital, Monticello, IN, p. A219

SMITH, Rodney, Chief Executive Officer, Harrisburg Medical Center, Harrisburg, IL, p. A191

SMITH, Ron, Chief Financial Officer, Wickenburg Community Hospital, Wickenburg, AZ, p. A41

SMITH, Roy, Chief Financial Officer, Onslow Memorial Hospital, Jacksonville, NC, p. A467

SMITH, Ryan J., Administrator, Mayo Clinic Health System in Saint James, Saint James, MN, p. A351

SMITH, Ryan K., Chief Executive Officer, Memorial Hospital of Converse County, Douglas, WY, p. A721

SMITH, Scott M., Chief Executive Officer, Mercy Regional Medical Center, Ville Platte, LA, p. A290

SMITH, Sherry, Manager Human Resources, Dallas County Hospital, Perry, IA, p. A236

SMITH, Sherry Bea, R.N., Chief Executive Officer, Lead–Deadwood Regional Hospital, Deadwood, SD, p. A573

SMITH, Shirley M., Chief Financial Officer, Andalusia Regional Hospital, Andalusia, AL, p. A15

SMITH, Sid, Director Information Resources, Larned State Hospital, Larned, KS, p. A248

SMITH, Skip, Vice President Finance, Iredell Memorial Hospital, Statesville, NC, p. A473

SMITH, Stacy, R.N., Interim Chief Executive Officer, Valir Rehabilitation Hospital, Oklahoma City, OK, p. A516

SMITH, Stephen, President, Selby General Hospital, Marietta, OH, p. A497

SMITH, Steve
Chief Financial Officer, Albany Area Hospital and Medical Center, Albany, MN, p. A339
Chief Financial Officer, Kansas Heart Hospital, Wichita, KS, p. A256

SMITH, Steve, M.D. Chief of Staff, Providence Kodiak Island Medical Center, Kodiak, AK, p. A29

SMITH, Steve, Assistant Vice President Finance, St. Gabriel's Hospital, Little Falls, MN, p. A346

SMITH, Steven
Chief Financial Officer, Lea Regional Medical Center, Hobbs, NM, p. A428
Chief Information Officer, NorthShore University Health System, Evanston, IL, p. A189
Chief Information Officer, Presence Saints Mary & Elizabeth Medical Center, Chicago, IL, p. A186

SMITH, Steven L., Chief Executive Officer, Matagorda Regional Medical Center, Bay City, TX, p. A601

SMITH, Suzanne E., R.N. Chief Nursing Officer, San Juan Regional Medical Center, Farmington, NM, p. A428

SMITH, Tammy, Director Human Resources, St. Vincent Morrilton, Morrilton, AR, p. A50

SMITH, Teresa, Chief Financial Officer, Memorial Hospital, Carthage, IL, p. A182

SMITH, Terrance, M.D. Chairman Medical Staff, Sanford Clear Lake Medical Center, Clear Lake, SD, p. A573

SMITH, Thomas, M.D. Vice President Medical Affairs, Hutchinson Regional Medical Center, Hutchinson, KS, p. A246

SMITH III, Thomas C., FACHE, Director, Birmingham Veterans Affairs Medical Center, Birmingham, AL, p. A16

SMITH, Thomas G., Administrator and Chief Executive Officer, Audubon County Memorial Hospital, Audubon, IA, p. A225

SMITH, Tiffany, Director Human Resources, Wellstone Regional Hospital, Jeffersonville, IN, p. A215

SMITH, Tim
Director Information Systems, Iroquois Memorial Hospital and Resident Home, Watseka, IL, p. A204
Senior Vice President and Chief Executive Officer, Sharp Memorial Hospital, San Diego, CA, p. A90

SMITH, Todd A., Chief Executive Officer, Aurora Charter Oak Hospital, Covina, CA, p. A61

SMITH, Tommy, Chief Executive Officer, Stroud Regional Medical Center, Stroud, OK, p. A519

SMITH, Tracy, Director Human Resources, Mercy St. Francis Hospital, Mountain View, MO, p. A377

SMITH, Trevor, Chief Management Information Services, Gunnison Valley Hospital, Gunnison, CO, p. A107

SMITH, Tripp, Chief Executive Officer, HEALTHSOUTH Rehabilitation Hospital, Largo, FL, p. A134

SMITH, Trisha, Interim Chief Financial Officer, Mimbres Memorial Hospital, Deming, NM, p. A428

SMITH, Trueman, M.D. Chief Medical Officer, Livingston Regional Hospital, Livingston, TN, p. A587

SMITH, Tyson, M.D. Chief Medical Officer, Haywood Regional Medical Center, Clyde, NC, p. A462

SMITH, Vincent
Chief Information Officer, Elmhurst Hospital Center,, NY, p. A443
Chief Information Officer, Queens Hospital Center,, NY, p. A448

SMITH, Wayne, President and Chief Executive Officer, Southeast Hospital, Cape Girardeau, MO, p. A369

SMITH, Wayne, President and Chief Executive Officer, SoutheastHEALTH, Cape Girardeau, MO, p. B125

SMITH, Wayne T., Chairman, President and Chief Executive Officer, Community Health Systems, Inc., Franklin, TN, p. B37

SMITH, Wendell, Chief Operating Officer, St. James Behavioral Health Hospital, Gonzales, LA, p. A278

SMITH, SPHR, Kevin M., Director Human Resources, Indian Path Medical Center, Kingsport, TN, p. A585

SMITH–HILL, Janet
Senior Vice President Human Resources, Novant Health Forsyth Medical Center, Winston–Salem, NC, p. A475
Senior Vice President Human Resources, Novant Health Presbyterian Medical Center, Charlotte, NC, p. A462

SMITH–ZUBA, Lorraina, R.N. Chief Nursing Officer, Porter Medical Center, Middlebury, VT, p. A665

SMITHERS, John, Network Specialist, River Hospital, Alexandria Bay, NY, p. A432

SMITHERS, Sandy, Director of Nursing, Wellstone Regional Hospital, Jeffersonville, IN, p. A215

SMITHHART, Paula, Director Human Resources, Coryell Memorial Hospital, Gatesville, TX, p. A621

SMITHHISLER, John E., President, Saint Joseph Hospital, Lexington, KY, p. A264

SMITHSON, Tracey, Chief Nursing Officer, North Hills Hospital, North Richland Hills, TX, p. A640

SMOCK, Tait, Manager Information Systems, Pella Regional Health Center, Pella, IA, p. A236

SMOCYNSKI, Nancy, Director Payroll, Personnel and Human Resources, Kindred Hospital–Pittsburgh, Oakdale, PA, p. A547

SMOKER, Bret, M.D. Clinical Director, PHS Santa Fe Indian Hospital, Santa Fe, NM, p. A430

SMOOT, Steve, Administrator, Utah Valley Regional Medical Center, Provo, UT, p. A662

SMOTHERS, Carol, M.D. Chief of Staff, Pointe Coupee General Hospital, New Roads, LA, p. A286

SMOTHERS, Margaret Shawn, Administrator, Kenmare Community Hospital, Kenmare, ND, p. A479

SMOTHERS, Stephen, Director Information Systems, Medical Center Enterprise, Enterprise, AL, p. A19

SMOTHESS, Kevin, M.D. Vice President Chief Medical Officer, Shady Grove Adventist Hospital, Rockville, MD, p. A303

SNAPP, Jeremy, Director Information Systems, Lindsborg Community Hospital, Lindsborg, KS, p. A249

SNAPP, Richard, Chief Financial Officer, Caverna Memorial Hospital, Horse Cave, KY, p. A263

SNAPP, III, William R.
Vice President and Chief Financial Officer, Ephraim McDowell Fort Logan Hospital, Stanford, KY, p. A270
Vice President Finance and Chief Financial Officer, Ephraim McDowell Regional Medical Center, Danville, KY, p. A260

SNAVELY, Gretchen, Director Human Resources, Holton Community Hospital, Holton, KS, p. A245

SNEAD, Jr., Raymond A., FACHE Interim Chief Financial Officer, South Georgia Medical Center, Valdosta, GA, p. A168

SNEATH, Roger, Chief Financial Officer, Memorial Medical Center – Neillsville, Neillsville, WI, p. A712

SNEDEGAR, Michael, Chief Financial Officer, Bourbon Community Hospital, Paris, KY, p. A269

SNEED, Farron, FACHE, Chief Executive Officer, Lovelace Westside Hospital, Albuquerque, NM, p. A426

SNEED, Jim, Chief Financial Officer, Lauderdale Community Hospital, Ripley, TN, p. A592

SNEEN, Tina, Interim Hospital Administrator, Anoka–Metropolitan Regional Treatment Center, Anoka, MN, p. A339

SNELGROVE, Steven C., President, Howard County General Hospital, Columbia, MD, p. A300

SNELL, Peggy, Chief Finance Officer, Cherry County Hospital, Valentine, NE, p. A402

SNENK, Don, Chief Financial Officer, Mercy Fitzgerald Hospital, Darby, PA, p. A537

SNIDER, Charles, Vice President Human Resources, Oak Hill Hospital, Brooksville, FL, p. A125

SNIDER, Cheryl, Director Human Resources, St. Vincent General Hospital District, Leadville, CO, p. A108

SNIDER, Glenn R., M.D. Chief of Staff, Louis A. Johnson Veterans Affairs Medical Center, Clarksburg, WV, p. A694

SNIDER, Tim, Senior Vice President and Chief Financial Officer, Upper Valley Medical Center, Troy, OH, p. A503

SNIDER, Timothy, Manager Information Systems, Fannin Regional Hospital, Blue Ridge, GA, p. A154

SNIDERMAN, Howard, Chief Operating Officer, Fairfield Medical Center, Lancaster, OH, p. A496

SNIPES, Rob
Chief Information Officer, Jenkins County Hospital, Millen, GA, p. A163
Chief Information Officer, Screven County Hospital, Sylvania, GA, p. A167

SNODGRASS, Liz, Chief Financial Officer, Trigg County Hospital, Cadiz, KY, p. A259

SNOOK, Joel, Chief Financial Officer, Westchester General Hospital, Miami, FL, p. A138

SNOW, David, Area Information Officer, Kaiser Permanente Woodland Hills Medical Center,, CA, p. A72

SNOW, Dorothy, M.D. Chief of Staff, Veterans Affairs Maryland Health Care System–Baltimore Division, Baltimore, MD, p. A298

SNOW, Jason T., Director People Services, St. Elizabeth's Hospital, Belleville, IL, p. A181

SNOW, John, Vice President Ancillary and Support Services, Iredell Memorial Hospital, Statesville, NC, p. A473

SNOW, Ryan, Interim Director Human Resources, Habersham Medical Center, Demorest, GA, p. A158

SNOWDEN, Raymond W., President and Chief Executive Officer, Memorial Hospital and Health Care Center, Jasper, IN, p. A215

SNOWDON, Susan, Director Information Technology, Four Winds Hospital, Saratoga Springs, NY, p. A454

SNYDER, Alice, Vice President, Chief Nursing Officer, OSF St. Mary Medical Center, Galesburg, IL, p. A190

SNYDER, Bobby, Chief Executive Officer, Specialty Hospital of Midwest City, Midwest City, OK, p. A513

SNYDER, David, M.D. Chief of Staff, DeKalb Medical at Downtown Decatur, Decatur, GA, p. A158

SNYDER, David, Chief Information Officer and Vice President Information Technology, Ellis Hospital, Schenectady, NY, p. A454

SNYDER, Fred, Vice President Information Technology, Promise Hospital of East Los Angeles, Suburban Medical Center Campus, Paramount, CA, p. A82

SNYDER, Jeffrey, Chief Executive Officer, Pocono Medical Center, East Stroudsburg, PA, p. A538

SNYDER, John, Executive Vice President and Chief Operating Officer, Carle Foundation Hospital, Urbana, IL, p. A204

SNYDER, Judy, Director Human Resources, Olympia Medical Center, Los Angeles, CA, p. A73

SNYDER, Kristi, Vice President Human Resources, Charleston Area Medical Center, Charleston, WV, p. A694

SNYDER, Kristy, Director Human Resources, Fulton County Health Center, Wauseon, OH, p. A504

SNYDER, Leah, Director Health Information Services, Loring Hospital, Sac City, IA, p. A237

SNYDER, Marilyn, Chief Information Officer, Liberty Medical Center, Chester, MT, p. A386

SNYDER, Marjorie, M.D. Clinical Director, Dorothea Dix Psychiatric Center, Bangor, ME, p. A291

SNYDER, Mary E., Interim Chief Executive Officer, Montrose Memorial Hospital, Montrose, CO, p. A110

SNYDER, Norman, M.D. Medical Director, Vantage Point of Northwest Arkansas, Fayetteville, AR, p. A46

SNYDER, Phyllis, Chief Nursing Officer, AHMC Anaheim Regional Medical Center, Anaheim, CA, p. A55

SNYDER, R. Brad, Chief Operating Officer, Torrance State Hospital, Torrance, PA, p. A556

SNYDER, Renae, Chief Financial Officer, Sakakawea Medical Center, Hazen, ND, p. A478

SNYDER, Ron, Chief Financial Officer, OhioHealth Hardin Memorial Hospital, Kenton, OH, p. A495

SNYDER, Steve, Chief Financial Officer, Ohio Hospital for Psychiatry, Columbus, OH, p. A490

SNYDER, Tony, Administrator and Chief Executive Officer, Pomerene Hospital, Millersburg, OH, p. A499

SNYDER, Vicky, Chief Operating Officer and Chief Financial Officer, Medina Hospital, Medina, OH, p. A498

SOARES, Denise C., R.N., Executive Director, Harlem Hospital Center, New York, NY, p. A444

SOARES, Jair C., M.D., Executive Director, University of Texas Harris County Psychiatric Center, Houston, TX, p. A627

SOBECK, Brenda, Director of Human Resources, Jones Memorial Hospital, Wellsville, NY, p. A457

SOBIECK, Bridget, Director of Nursing, Cook County North Shore Hospital, Grand Marais, MN, p. A344

SOCHA, Jake, Chief Executive Officer, Vibra Hospital of Western Massachusetts, Springfield, MA, p. A315

SOD, Rhonda, Chief Nursing Officer, First Hospital Wyoming Valley, Kingston, PA, p. A541

SODERHOLM, Jon, President, Avera Heart Hospital of South Dakota, Sioux Falls, SD, p. A576

SODERLING, Marcia, R.N. Hospital Nurse Executive, Legacy Mount Hood Medical Center, Gresham, OR, p. A525

SOEKEN, Charles
Director Information Technology, Providence Medical Center, Kansas City, KS, p. A247
Director Information Technology, Saint John Hospital, Leavenworth, KS, p. A248

SOEKORO, Julie, Chief Financial Officer, Trinity Medical Center, Birmingham, AL, p. A17

SOGARD, Matt, Chief Executive Officer, Lee's Summit Medical Center, Lee's Summit, MO, p. A375

SOHN, Steven, M.D. President Medical Staff, Dallas County Hospital, Perry, IA, p. A236

SOK, James E., FACHE,
President and Chief Executive Officer, Sheltering Arms Hospital South, Midlothian, VA, p. A674
President and Chief Executive Officer, Sheltering Arms Rehabilitation Hospital, Mechanicsville, VA, p. A674

SOKOLA, Thomas P., Chief Administrative Officer, Geisinger Medical Center, Danville, PA, p. A537

SOKOLOW, Norman J., Chairman and Chief Executive Officer, Cornerstone of Medical Arts Center Hospital, Fresh Meadows, NY, p. A437

SOKOLOWSKI, Magdalena, R.N. Director of Nursing, St. Lawrence Rehabilitation Center, Lawrenceville, NJ, p. A417

SOLAIMAN, Shereen, Vice President Human Resources, OhioHealth Riverside Methodist Hospital, Columbus, OH, p. A490

SOLARE, Frank A., Chief Executive Officer, Kindred Hospital Northwest Indiana, Hammond, IN, p. A213

SOLAZZO, Mark J.
Senior Vice President and Chief Operating Officer, Forest Hills Hospital,, NY, p. A443
Executive Vice President and Chief Operating Officer, Franklin Hospital, Valley Stream, NY, p. A457
Regional Chief Operating Officer, Syosset Hospital, Syosset, NY, p. A455

SOLBERG, Bradley, FACHE, Chief Executive Officer, Hammond–Henry Hospital, Geneseo, IL, p. A190

SOLBERG, Don, M.D. Chief Medical Officer, Kittitas Valley Healthcare, Ellensburg, WA, p. A683

SOLCHER, Barry, M.D. Chief of Staff, The Physicians Centre Hospital, Bryan, TX, p. A604

SOLDO, Stephen, M.D. Chief Medical Officer, Saint Agnes Medical Center, Fresno, CA, p. A64

SOLER, Eddie, Chief Financial Officer, Florida Hospital, Orlando, FL, p. A140

SOLES, Jason, Manager Information Systems, St. James Mercy Health System, Hornell, NY, p. A439

SOLHEIM, John H., Chief Executive Officer, Cuyuna Regional Medical Center, Crosby, MN, p. A342

SOLIE, Carol M., M.D. Chief Medical Officer, Wyoming Medical Center, Casper, WY, p. A720

SOLIMAN, Russell
System Manager Client Services and Management Information Services, Presence Saint Joseph Medical Center, Joliet, IL, p. A194
Director Information Services, Presence St. Mary's Hospital, Kankakee, IL, p. A194

SOLIMAN, Shawn, Manager Information Services, Mendota Community Hospital, Mendota, IL, p. A196

SOLIN, Andrea, Chief Financial Officer, Lovelace Rehabilitation Hospital, Albuquerque, NM, p. A426

SOLINSKI, Ruth
Vice President Organizational Development, Bell Hospital, Ishpeming, MI, p. A327
Senior Director Human Resources, Marquette General Hospital, Marquette, MI, p. A330

SOLIS, Gloria, R.N. Chief Operating Officer and Chief Nursing Officer, Saint Luke's East Hospital, Lee's Summit, MO, p. A375

SOLIVAN, Jose E.
Chief Financial Officer, Hospital Menonita De Cayey, Cayey, PR, p. A725
Chief Financial Officer, Mennonite General Hospital, Aibonito, PR, p. A724

SOLIZ, Mindy, Director Human Resources, CHRISTUS Spohn Hospital Alice, Alice, TX, p. A595

SOLLENBERGER, Donna K., Executive Vice President and Chief Executive Officer, University of Texas Medical Branch Hospitals, Galveston, TX, p. A620

SOLOM, Mike, Director Information Technology, Signature Psychiatric Hospital, Kansas City, MO, p. A374

SOLOMITA, Joy B., R.N. Vice President and Chief Nursing Officer, Florida Hospital Tampa, Tampa, FL, p. A147

SOLOMON, Elizabeth, R.N. Regional Quality/Risk Director and Interim Chief Nursing Officer, HEALTHSOUTH Rehabilitation Hospital–Las Vegas, Las Vegas, NV, p. A405

SOLOMON, John, M.D., Director, South Carolina Department of Corrections Hospital, Columbia, SC, p. A564

SOLOMON, Steven, Vice President Human Resources, Garden City Hospital, Garden City, MI, p. A324

SOLOMON, Tina, Executive Director Finance, Winter Haven Hospital, Winter Haven, FL, p. A150

SOLOMON–OWENS, Felicia, Director Human Resources, Fayette Medical Center, Fayette, AL, p. A20

SOLORZANO, Rosa, Interim Director Human Resources, Toppenish Community Hospital, Toppenish, WA, p. A691

SOLOW, Jodie Sartor, Director Human Resources, Chatham Hospital, Siler City, NC, p. A472

SOLVERSON, Paul, Chief Information Officer, St. Luke's Lakeside Hospital, The Woodlands, TX, p. A653

SOMERVILLE, Jacqueline G., R.N. Senior Vice President for Patient Care Services and Chief Nursing Officer, Brigham and Women's Hospital, Boston, MA, p. A306

SOMERVILLE, Susan, R.N., President, Mount Sinai Beth Israel, New York, NY, p. A446

SOMMERS, Belinda, Chief Information Officer, Lake Charles Memorial Hospital, Lake Charles, LA, p. A282

SOMMERS, Dorene M., Associate Director Patient Care Services, Erie Veterans Affairs Medical Center, Erie, PA, p. A538

SOMMERS, Thomas W., FACHE, President and Chief Executive Officer, Beatrice Community Hospital and Health Center, Beatrice, NE, p. A394

SOMMERS, Vickie, Director Business Office, Wellstone Regional Hospital, Jeffersonville, IN, p. A215

SONATORE, Carol, D.O. Medical Director, HEALTHSOUTH Rehabilitation Hospital of Toms River, Toms River, NJ, p. A423

SONDAG, Timothy, Senior Nursing Officer, Hopedale Medical Complex, Hopedale, IL, p. A193

SONDERMAN, Betty, Manager Human Resources, Ridgeview Institute, Smyrna, GA, p. A167

SONDERMAN, Thomas, M.D. Vice President and Chief Medical Officer, Columbus Regional Hospital, Columbus, IN, p. A208

SONEL, Ali, M.D. Chief of Staff, Veterans Affairs Pittsburgh Healthcare System, Pittsburgh, PA, p. A552

SONENREICH, Steven D., President and Chief Executive Officer, Mount Sinai Medical Center, Miami Beach, FL, p. A138

SONG, Daniel, Chief Financial Officer, Monterey Park Hospital, Monterey Park, CA, p. A78

SONGER, Lucille, Chief Nursing Officer, Athol Memorial Hospital, Athol, MA, p. A305

SONNENBERG, Martha, M.D. Chief of Staff, Southern California Hospital at Culver City, Culver City, CA, p. A61

SONNENBERG, Stephanie
Director Information Technology, ProMedica Bixby Hospital, Adrian, MI, p. A318
Director Information Technology, ProMedica Herrick Hospital, Tecumseh, MI, p. A336

SONNENBERG, William, M.D. President Medical Staff, Titusville Area Hospital, Titusville, PA, p. A556

SONNENSCHEIN, Silvia, M.D. Chief of Staff, Kohala Hospital, Kohala, HI, p. A172

SONS, Regina K., Administrative Director Human Resources and Volunteer Services Associate Ethics and Compliance Officer, Mineral Area Regional Medical Center, Farmington, MO, p. A371

SONTZ, Jennifer
  Director Human Resources, Evansville Psychiatric Children
    Center, Evansville, IN, p. A210
  Director Human Resources, Evansville State Hospital,
    Evansville, IN, p. A210
SOOHOO, Richard, Chief Financial Officer, Sutter Medical
  Center, Sacramento, Sacramento, CA, p. A88
SOPER, Brent, Chief Financial Officer, San Joaquin Community
  Hospital, Bakersfield, CA, p. A57
SOPIARZ, Ed, Chief Financial Officer, University Behavioral
  Health of Denton, Denton, TX, p. A613
SOPKO, Joseph, M.D. Chief Medical Officer, St. Vincent Charity
  Medical Center, Cleveland, OH, p. A489
SOPT, Michael, M.D. Chief of Staff, Brooks County Hospital,
  Quitman, GA, p. A165
SORA, Alin, M.D. Chief of Staff, Baraga County Memorial
  Hospital, L'Anse, MI, p. A328
SORAN, Andrei, MSN, President, DMC Huron Valley–Sinai
  Hospital, Commerce Township, MI, p. A321
SORBELLO, Bud, Director Management Information Systems,
  Hudson Valley Hospital Center, Cortlandt Manor, NY, p. A436
SORENSEN, Bonny
  Chief Financial Officer, Wadley Regional Medical Center,
    Texarkana, TX, p. A653
  Chief Financial Officer, Wadley Regional Medical Center at
    Hope, Hope, AR, p. A47
SORENSEN, Shannon, Chief Executive Officer, Brown County
  Hospital, Ainsworth, NE, p. A393
SORENSON Jr.,, Charles W., M.D., President and Chief
  Executive Officer, Intermountain Healthcare, Inc., Salt Lake
  City, UT, p. B77
SORENSON, Chris
  Chief Information Officer, Sheltering Arms Hospital South,
    Midlothian, VA, p. A674
  Chief Information Officer, Sheltering Arms Rehabilitation
    Hospital, Mechanicsville, VA, p. A674
SORENSON, Dennis, Supervisor Information Technology, South
  Haven Health System, South Haven, MI, p. A335
SORENSON, Ed, Vice President Finance and Chief Financial
  Officer, Community Hospital of San Bernardino, San
  Bernardino, CA, p. A88
SORENSON, Eric C., Chief Fiscal Office, Martinsburg Veterans
  Affairs Medical Center, Martinsburg, WV, p. A697
SORENSON, Euretta, R.N. Chief Nursing Officer, CentraCare
  Health–Monticello, Monticello, MN, p. A348
SORENSON, Tawnya, Director of Nursing, Kittson Memorial
  Healthcare Center, Hallock, MN, p. A344
SOREY, Sharon D., R.N., Regional Administrator, Mercy
  Hospital Paris, Paris, AR, p. A51
SORG, Jamie, Director Information Services and Information
  Security Officer, Blanchard Valley Hospital, Findlay, OH,
  p. A494
SOROKO, Theresa, M.D. Chief Medical Officer, Hackensack
  University Medical Center Mountainside, Montclair, NJ,
  p. A418
SORRELL, Rachel, Chief Financial Officer, Tsehootsooi Medical
  Center, Fort Defiance, AZ, p. A32
SORRELL, Sr., Ralph W., Chief Financial Officer, Adena
  Greenfield Medical Center, Greenfield, OH, p. A495
SOSA, Phillip, Chief Financial Officer, University Behavioral
  Health of El Paso, El Paso, TX, p. A616
SOSA–GUERRERO, Sandra, Chief Executive Officer, Larkin
  Community Hospital, South Miami, FL, p. A146
SOSTMAN, Dirk, M.D. Executive Vice President, Chief Medical
  Officer and Chief Academic Officer, Houston Methodist
  Hospital, Houston, TX, p. A624
SOTERAKIS, Jack, M.D. Executive Vice President Medical
  Affairs, St. Francis Hospital, Roslyn, NY, p. A454
SOTO, Ciria, Director Human Resources, Sonora Behavioral
  Health Hospital, Tucson, AZ, p. A40
SOTO, Itza, MSN Nursing Executive, Ashford Presbyterian
  Community Hospital, San Juan, PR, p. A727
SOTO, Juan Carlos, Director Information Systems, Hospital San
  Carlos Borromeo, Moca, PR, p. A727
SOTO, Manuel Ramirez, M.D. Medical Director, Hospital
  Metropolitano Dr. Tito Mattei, Yauco, PR, p. A729
SOTOMAYOR, Eduardo, Executive Director, Caribbean Medical
  Center, Fajardo, PR, p. A725
SOTOS, Steven, M.D. President Medical Staff, LifeCare
  Hospitals of Pittsburgh, Pittsburgh, PA, p. A551
SOTTILE, Frank, M.D. Chief Medical Officer, Crittenton Hospital
  Medical Center, Rochester, MI, p. A333
SOUDERS, Stuart, Coordinator Human Resources, William S.
  Middleton Memorial Veterans Hospital, Madison, WI, p. A708
SOUKUP, Paul, Chief Financial Officer, St. Luke Community
  Healthcare, Ronan, MT, p. A390
SOURBEER, Jay C., Commanding Officer, Robert E. Bush Naval
  Hospital, Twentynine Palms, CA, p. A98
SOUTHARD, Suzanne, Director Finance, Community
  Hospital–Fairfax, Fairfax, MO, p. A371

SOUTHERS, Nancy J., Vice President and Chief Financial Officer,
  The HSC Pediatric Center, Washington, DC, p. A122
SOUTHWICK, Bill, R.N. Chief Nursing Officer, Mountain Vista
  Medical Center, Mesa, AZ, p. A34
SOUTHWORTH, Scott, M.D. Medical Director, South Davis
  Community Hospital, Bountiful, UT, p. A659
SOUZA, Darlene, Vice President, St. Joseph Health Services of
  Rhode Island, North Providence, RI, p. A560
SOUZA, Greg, Vice President Human Resources, Lucile Salter
  Packard Children's Hospital at Stanford, Palo Alto, CA, p. A82
SOUZA, Liz, Coordinator Nursing Services, Atascadero State
  Hospital, Atascadero, CA, p. A56
SOVETSKHY, Ed, Director Information Services, Portsmouth
  Regional Hospital, Portsmouth, NH, p. A412
SOWA, Phillip E., Chief Executive Officer, Saint Louis University
  Hospital, Saint Louis, MO, p. A381
SOWDERS, Dale, President and Chief Executive Officer, Holland
  Hospital, Holland, MI, p. A326
SOWELL, Ronald G.
  Executive Vice President, Commonwealth Regional Specialty
    Hospital, Bowling Green, KY, p. A258
  Executive Vice President, Medical Center at Bowling Green,
    Bowling Green, KY, p. A259
  Executive Vice President, Medical Center at Franklin, Franklin,
    KY, p. A261
  Chief Financial Officer, Medical Center at Scottsville,
    Scottsville, KY, p. A270
SOWELL, Vincent, Chief Nursing Officer, Otto Kaiser Memorial
  Hospital, Kenedy, TX, p. A631
SOWERS, Chuck, Vice President Finance and Chief Financial
  Officer, Mercy Gilbert Medical Center, Gilbert, AZ, p. A33
SOWERS, Kevin W., MSN, President, Duke University Hospital,
  Durham, NC, p. A463
SPACK, Paula, R.N. Vice President Nursing, Punxsutawney Area
  Hospital, Punxsutawney, PA, p. A553
SPACKMAN, Jared, Chief Financial Officer, Davis Hospital and
  Medical Center, Layton, UT, p. A660
SPACONE, Alan, M.D. Chief Medical Officer, Tuba City Regional
  Health Care Corporation, Tuba City, AZ, p. A40
SPACONE, Celia, M.D. Director Operations, Buffalo Psychiatric
  Center, Buffalo, NY, p. A434
SPADE, Ann M., Chief Nursing Executive, Carlisle Regional
  Medical Center, Carlisle, PA, p. A535
SPAHR, Kristen, Director of Marketing, DeSoto Memorial
  Hospital, Arcadia, FL, p. A123
SPAIN, Blake, M.D. Chief Medical Officer, Crawley Memorial
  Hospital, Shelby, NC, p. A472
SPAIN, Jeanine R., R.N. Vice President Patient and Support
  Services and Chief Nursing Officer, UnityPoint Health –
  Methodist, Peoria, IL, p. A200
SPAIN, Steve, Chief Operating Officer, Larned State Hospital,
  Larned, KS, p. A248
SPAIN–REMY, Claire, M.D. Senior Vice President, MultiCare
  Medical Associates, MultiCare Tacoma General Hospital,
  Tacoma, WA, p. A691
SPANBAUER, Lisa, Financial Program Supervisor, Winnebago
  Mental Health Institute, Winnebago, WI, p. A719
SPANGLER, Wendell J., M.D. Chief of Staff, Paulding County
  Hospital, Paulding, OH, p. A500
SPANN, Debbie, Director Human Resources, Morehouse General
  Hospital, Bastrop, LA, p. A273
SPANN, Lori, Director Human Resources, Iberia Medical Center,
  New Iberia, LA, p. A285
SPANO, Dennis, M.D. Medical Director, Mayo Clinic Health
  System in Lake City, Lake City, MN, p. A345
SPANO, Jason, Manager Information Technology, Prowers
  Medical Center, Lamar, CO, p. A108
SPARACINO, Michael, M.D. Chief Medical Staff, River's Edge
  Hospital and Clinic, Saint Peter, MN, p. A352
SPARBY, Francine M., MS Chief Nursing Officer, CHI Health
  Creighton University Medical Center, Omaha, NE, p. A399
SPARE, John, Accountant, Parsons State Hospital and Training
  Center, Parsons, KS, p. A252
SPARGER, Kathy, R.N. Chief Nursing Officer, Baptist Health
  South Florida, South Miami Hospital, Miami, FL, p. A136
SPARKMAN, Dena C., FACHE, Community Chief Executive
  Officer, Whitesburg ARH Hospital, Whitesburg, KY, p. A271
SPARKMAN, Jill, Director Human Resources, Odessa Regional
  Medical Center, Odessa, TX, p. A640
SPARKS, Dennis, Vice President Human Resources, Saint
  Michael's Medical Center, Newark, NJ, p. A420
SPARKS, Gary R., Administrator, CrossRidge Community
  Hospital, Wynne, AR, p. A54
SPARKS, Jason, Director, Human Resources, HEALTHSOUTH
  Rehabilitation Hospital at Drake, Cincinnati, OH, p. A487
SPARKS, Jennifer, Human Resources Generalist, Complex Care
  Hospital at Ridgelake, Sarasota, FL, p. A145
SPARKS, Richard G., President and Chief Executive Officer,
  Appalachian Regional Healthcare System, Boone, NC, p. B11

SPARKS, Richard G., Chief Executive Officer, Watauga Medical
  Center, Boone, NC, p. A460
SPARKS, Rodney, M.D. Chief Medical Staff, Down East Community
  Hospital, Machias, ME, p. A294
SPARKS, Wendy, Chief Operating Officer, North Colorado
  Medical Center, Greeley, CO, p. A107
SPARLING, Nicki, Manager Human Resources, Major Hospital,
  Shelbyville, IN, p. A222
SPARPANA, Eileen, Director Finance, Dickinson County
  Healthcare System, Iron Mountain, MI, p. A327
SPARROW, Francis D., M.D. Medical Director, Philhaven, Mount
  Gretna, PA, p. A545
SPARTZ, Dale A., Chief Human Resources Officer, University of
  Utah Health Care – Hospital and Clinics, Salt Lake City, UT,
  p. A663
SPARZO, John, M.D. Vice President Medical Affairs, Hendricks
  Regional Health, Danville, IN, p. A209
SPATH, Deborah, R.N. Associate Director Patient and Nurses
  Services, Albany Stratton Veterans Affairs Medical Center,
  Albany, NY, p. A432
SPAUDE, Paul A., FACHE, President and Chief Executive
  Officer, Borgess Medical Center, Kalamazoo, MI, p. A328
SPEARE, Mark
  Senior Associate Director Human Resources, Ronald Reagan
    University of California Los Angeles Medical Center, Los
    Angeles, CA, p. A74
  Senior Associate Director Patient Relations and Human
    Resources, Santa Monica–UCLA Medical Center and
    Orthopaedic Hospital, Santa Monica, CA, p. A95
SPEARMAN, John, President and Chief Operating Officer, Laurel
  Regional Hospital, Laurel, MD, p. A302
SPEARS, David, D.O. Chief of Staff, Selby General Hospital,
  Marietta, OH, p. A497
SPEARS, Kevin, Chief Executive Officer, HEALTHSOUTH
  Rehabilitation Hospital of Memphis, Memphis, TN, p. A588
SPEARS, LaLana, Supervisor Accounting, Claremore Indian
  Hospital, Claremore, OK, p. A509
SPEARS, Michael, Human Resource Leader, St. Anthony
  Shawnee Hospital, Shawnee, OK, p. A519
SPEAS, Ryan, Director Finance, Livingston Memorial Hospital,
  Livingston, MT, p. A389
SPEASE, Dorothy, Manager Business Office, Douglas County
  Memorial Hospital, Armour, SD, p. A572
SPECK, Michelle A.
  Vice President Human Resources, UPMC Altoona, Altoona,
    PA, p. A532
  Vice President Human Resources, UPMC Bedford Memorial,
    Everett, PA, p. A539
SPEECH, Thomas, Ph.D., Director, Winnebago Mental Health
  Institute, Winnebago, WI, p. A719
SPEEDLING, Edward, Chief Executive Officer and Managing
  Director, Arrowhead Behavioral Health Hospital, Maumee, OH,
  p. A498
SPEELMAN, Steven, Director Information Systems, Culpeper
  Regional Hospital, Culpeper, VA, p. A670
SPEER, Kevin, Chief Executive Officer, Hendricks Regional
  Health, Danville, IN, p. A209
SPEER–SMITH, Carol, R.N. Chief Nursing Officer, Oroville
  Hospital, Oroville, CA, p. A82
SPEES, M. Shane, President and Chief Executive Officer, North
  Mississippi Health Services, Inc., Tupelo, MS, p. B100
SPEES, M. Shane, President and Chief Executive Officer, North
  Mississippi Medical Center – Tupelo, Tupelo, MS, p. A365
SPEICHER, Larry, Chief Executive Officer, Kearney Regional
  Medical Center, Kearney, NE, p. A397
SPEIER, Ryan, Vice President Administration, KVC Prairie Ridge
  Psychiatric Hospital, Kansas City, KS, p. A247
SPEIGHT, Becky, Chief Financial Officer, Lake Pointe Medical
  Center, Rowlett, TX, p. A645
SPEIGHT, Marianne, Vice President Information System and
  Chief Information Officer, Cincinnati Children's Hospital
  Medical Center, Cincinnati, OH, p. A486
SPEIGHTS, Rosetta, R.N. Chief Nursing Officer, Vista Medical
  Center West, Waukegan, IL, p. A205
SPEIGHTS, Shane, M.D. Vice President Medical Affairs, St.
  Bernards Medical Center, Jonesboro, AR, p. A48
SPEKTOR, Mark, M.D., President and Chief Executive Officer,
  Bayonne Medical Center, Bayonne, NJ, p. A413
SPELL, Kenneth R., Vice President Operations, Baptist Health
  South Florida, Homestead Hospital, Homestead, FL, p. A131
SPELLACY, Tara, Director Human Resources, Braintree
  Rehabilitation Hospital, Braintree, MA, p. A308
SPELLMAN, Warren K., Chief Executive Officer, Grady Memorial
  Hospital, Chickasha, OK, p. A509
SPELLS, Debbie, Chief Nursing Officer, Chesterfield General
  Hospital, Cheraw, SC, p. A563
SPENCE, Karie, Director Human Resources, Miller County
  Hospital, Colquitt, GA, p. A156
SPENCE, Karla, Director of Nursing, St. Andrew's Health Center,
  Bottineau, ND, p. A476

SPENCE, Monte, Chief Operating Officer, Rehabilitation Hospital of Indiana, Indianapolis, IN, p. A214

SPENCE, Sheldon, Director of Revenue Cycle, IT, Memorial Hospital of Texas County, Guymon, OK, p. A511

SPENCE, Terri
Chief Information Officer, Bon Secours Maryview Medical Center, Portsmouth, VA, p. A676
Chief Information Officer, Bon Secours St. Mary's Hospital, Richmond, VA, p. A677
Vice President Information Services, Mary Immaculate Hospital, Newport News, VA, p. A675

SPENCE, William, Director, Roseland Community Hospital, Chicago, IL, p. A186

SPENCER, Jill, Chief Human Resources, Memorial Hospital at Craig, Craig, CO, p. A104

SPENCER, Jim, Director Information System, Chesterfield General Hospital, Cheraw, SC, p. A563

SPENCER, Marianne, R.N. Vice President Operations and Chief Operating Officer, Edward Hospital, Naperville, IL, p. A197

SPENCER, Marie, Chief Nursing Officer and Senior Administrator, Burke Rehabilitation Hospital, White Plains, NY, p. A458

SPENCER, Mark, D.O. Chief of Staff, North Canyon Medical Center, Gooding, ID, p. A176

SPENCER, Mike, Chief Information Officer, Henry County Hospital, New Castle, IN, p. A220

SPENCER, Misti, Director Inpatient Services, Selby General Hospital, Marietta, OH, p. A497

SPENCER, Scott, Chief Financial Officer, South Shore Hospital, Chicago, IL, p. A186

SPENCER, Susan, Chief Financial Officer, Samaritan Memorial Hospital, Macon, MO, p. A376

SPENCER, Todd, M.D. Chief Medical Staff, Adventist Medical Center–Reedley, Reedley, CA, p. A86

SPENNER, Marilyn, R.N. Vice President Patient Care Services, Wheaton Franciscan Healthcare – St. Francis, Milwaukee, WI, p. A711

SPENST, Brett, Chief Executive Officer, Littleton Adventist Hospital, Littleton, CO, p. A109

SPERBER–WEISS, Doreen, Ph.D. Chief Nursing Officer, Greystone Park Psychiatric Hospital, Morris Plains, NJ, p. A418

SPERLING, Louis J., Vice President Human Resources, Rhode Island Hospital, Providence, RI, p. A561

SPERLING, Walter, M.D. Medical Director, Ellenville Regional Hospital, Ellenville, NY, p. A437

SPERRING, Kim
Administrator, LifeCare Hospitals of Pittsburgh, Pittsburgh, PA, p. A551
Administrator, LifeCare Hospitals of Pittsburgh – Monroeville, Monroeville, PA, p. A545

SPEZIA, Anthony, President and Chief Executive Officer, Covenant Health, Knoxville, TN, p. B44

SPICER, Charles, President and Chief Executive Officer, OU Medical Center, Oklahoma City, OK, p. A516

SPICER, Joan G., R.N. Chief Nursing Officer, San Mateo Medical Center, San Mateo, CA, p. A93

SPICER, Michael J., President and Chief Executive Officer, St. Joseph's Medical Center, Yonkers, NY, p. A458

SPICER, Sam, M.D. Vice President Medical Affairs, New Hanover Regional Medical Center, Wilmington, NC, p. A474

SPIDLE, Tara, Chief Financial Officer, Decatur County Hospital, Leon, IA, p. A233

SPIEGEL, Kevin M., FACHE, President and Chief Executive Officer, Erlanger Health System, Chattanooga, TN, p. B56

SPIEGEL, Kevin M., FACHE, Chief Executive Officer, Erlanger Medical Center, Chattanooga, TN, p. A580

SPIER, Deborah, Administrator, Oceans Behavioral Hospital of Greater New Orleans, Kenner, LA, p. A280

SPIER, Scott A., M.D. Senior Vice President Medical Affairs, Mercy Medical Center, Baltimore, MD, p. A297

SPIGEL, Michael, Executive Vice President & Chief Operating Officer, Brooks Rehabilitation Hospital, Jacksonville, FL, p. A131

SPIGNER, Jason
Vice President Human Resources, Advocate Condell Medical Center, Libertyville, IL, p. A194
Vice President Human Resources, Advocate Good Shepherd Hospital, Barrington, IL, p. A181

SPIKE, Jennifer, Director Human Resources, St. James Mercy Health System, Hornell, NY, p. A439

SPILLERS, David S., Chief Executive Officer, Huntsville Hospital, Huntsville, AL, p. A22

SPILLERS, David S., Chief Executive Officer, Huntsville Hospital Health System, Huntsville, AL, p. B74

SPINA, Lori, Vice President Human Resources, Good Samaritan Hospital Medical Center, West Islip, NY, p. A458

SPINA, Patricia, R.N. Director of Nursing, Runnells Specialized Hospital of Union County, Berkeley Heights, NJ, p. A413

SPINALE, Joseph W., D.O. Senior Vice President and Chief Medical Officer, Kent County Memorial Hospital, Warwick, RI, p. A561

SPINHARNEY, Sarah, Senior Vice President, Baptist Medical Center, San Antonio, TX, p. A646

SPISSO, Johnese, Interim Executive Director, UW Medicine/Harborview Medical Center, Seattle, WA, p. A689

SPITSER, Christy
Vice President Finance and Business Development, Saint Joseph – London, London, KY, p. A265
Vice President Finance, Saint Joseph Berea, Berea, KY, p. A258

SPIVAK, Natalie, Director Information Services, Oaklawn Hospital, Marshall, MI, p. A330

SPIVEY, David A., President and Chief Executive Officer, St. Mary Mercy Hospital, Livonia, MI, p. A329

SPIVEY, Sue, Administrator, Irwin County Hospital, Ocilla, GA, p. A164

SPOELMA, Susan G., MSN Chief Nursing Officer, Healdsburg District Hospital, Healdsburg, CA, p. A66

SPONG, Bernadette, Chief Financial Officer, Rex Healthcare, Raleigh, NC, p. A471

SPONSLER, Betsy A., Chief Financial Officer, Valley Hospital Medical Center, Las Vegas, NV, p. A407

SPOON, Barry, M.D. Chief of Staff, Mercy St. Francis Hospital, Mountain View, MO, p. A377

SPOONER, Allan M., President, Sacred Heart Rehabilitation Institute, Milwaukee, WI, p. A711

SPOONER, Christopher, M.D. Chief of Staff, Southeast Arizona Medical Center, Douglas, AZ, p. A32

SPOONER, Jennifer, Controller, HEALTHSOUTH Rehabilitation Hospital of Tallahassee, Tallahassee, FL, p. A147

SPORE, Larry, Chief Financial Officer, Lawrence County Memorial Hospital, Lawrenceville, IL, p. A194

SPRADLIN, John, Information Systems Director, Franklin Foundation Hospital, Franklin, LA, p. A277

SPRAGGINS, Tommy, Director Information Services, Russell Medical Center, Alexander City, AL, p. A15

SPRAGUE, Debbie, R.N. Chief Nursing Officer, Davis Hospital and Medical Center, Layton, UT, p. A660

SPRAGUE, F. Remington, M.D
Chief Medical Officer, Mercy Health, Hackley Campus, Muskegon, MI, p. A331
Chief Medical Officer, Mercy Health, Mercy Campus, Muskegon, MI, p. A331

SPRAGUE, Sharon, Superintendent, Dorothea Dix Psychiatric Center, Bangor, ME, p. A291

SPRAKER, Larissa, Vice President Business Development and Chief Strategy Officer, Mercy Gilbert Medical Center, Gilbert, AZ, p. A33

SPRATLIN, Larry, Chief Financial Officer, Saint Thomas Rutherford Hospital, Murfreesboro, TN, p. A590

SPRATLING, Larry, M.D. Chief Medical Officer, Banner Baywood Medical Center, Mesa, AZ, p. A34

SPRAY, William R., Chief Executive Officer, Harton Regional Medical Center, Tullahoma, TN, p. A593

SPRIGGS, Larry, Controller, HEALTHSOUTH Rehabilitation Institute of San Antonio, San Antonio, TX, p. A646

SPRING, Jason A., FACHE, Chief Executive Officer, North Valley Hospital, Whitefish, MT, p. A392

SPRING, Joni, R.N. Vice President Patient Care Services and Chief Nursing Officer, Elliot Hospital, Manchester, NH, p. A411

SPRINGATE, Brian, Interim Chief Operating Officer, Logan Regional Medical Center, Logan, WV, p. A696

SPRINGER, Amy, Medical Director, Webster County Community Hospital, Red Cloud, NE, p. A401

SPRINGER, Carrie, Interim Chief Financial Officer and Vice President Finance, Indiana University Health Tipton Hospital, Tipton, IN, p. A223

SPRINGER, David, M.D. President Medical Staff, Sanford Hospital Rock Rapids, Rock Rapids, IA, p. A237

SPRINGER, Diane L., MS Chief Nursing Officer, Lutheran Hospital of Indiana, Fort Wayne, IN, p. A211

SPRINGER, Madge, Director Human Resources, Florida Hospital Waterman, Tavares, FL, p. A148

SPRINGER, Theresa, Chief Financial Officer, OSF Holy Family Medical Center, Monmouth, IL, p. A196

SPRINGFIELD, Rick, Vice President Human Resources, Piedmont Hospital, Atlanta, GA, p. A153

SPRINGMAN, Kathleen, Chief Nursing Officer, Berwick Hospital Center, Berwick, PA, p. A533

SPRINGMANN, Tressa
Vice President and Chief Information Officer, Levindale Hebrew Geriatric Center and Hospital, Baltimore, MD, p. A296
Vice President and Chief Information Officer, Northwest Hospital, Randallstown, MD, p. A302

SPRINKEL, George, Chief Financial Officer, Gateway Medical Center, Clarksville, TN, p. A581

SPROUT, Merry, R.N. Chief Nursing Officer, Antelope Memorial Hospital, Neligh, NE, p. A398

SPROWL, Chris, M.D. Vice President, PeaceHealth St. Joseph Medical Center, Bellingham, WA, p. A681

SPRUYT, James, Chief Executive Officer, Cumberland Hall Hospital, Hopkinsville, KY, p. A263

SPUHLER, Richard, Chief Executive Officer, Brigham City Community Hospital, Brigham City, UT, p. A659

SPURGEON, Sharon A., Chief Executive Officer, Coalinga Regional Medical Center, Coalinga, CA, p. A60

SPURGIN, Gregory, M.D. Chief of Staff, Indiana University Health West Hospital, Avon, IN, p. A206

SPURLOCK, Shirley, Director Human Resources, Millwood Hospital, Arlington, TX, p. A598

SQUIRES, Danny
Chief Financial Officer, Wake Forest Baptist Health–Davie Hospital, Mocksville, NC, p. A469
Vice President and Chief Financial Officer, Wake Forest Baptist Health–Lexington Medical Center, Lexington, NC, p. A468

SQUIRES, Paula C., Senior Vice President Human Resources, Baystate Medical Center, Springfield, MA, p. A314

SQUIRES, Teresa, R.N. Chief Nursing Officer, Lake District Hospital, Lakeview, OR, p. A526

SREBINSKI, Ron, Chief Financial Officer, Caro Community Hospital, Caro, MI, p. A320

SREERAMA, Ravi K., M.D. Chief of Staff, East Texas Medical Center Clarksville, Clarksville, TX, p. A606

SRIBNICK, Wayne, M.D. Senior Vice President and Chief Medical Officer, Providence Hospital, Columbia, SC, p. A564

SRIPADA, Subra
Senior Vice President and Chief Information Officer, Beaumont Hospital – Royal Oak, Royal Oak, MI, p. A333
Senior Vice President and Chief Information Officer, Beaumont Hospital – Troy, Troy, MI, p. A336
Senior Vice President and Chief Information Officer, Beaumont Hospital Grosse Pointe, Grosse Pointe, MI, p. A326

SRIVASTAVA, Mohit, M.D. Chief of Staff, Bunkie General Hospital, Bunkie, LA, p. A275

ST CLAIR, Jeffery M., President and Chief Executive Officer, Springhill Memorial Hospital, Mobile, AL, p. A23

ST PIERRE, Jay, Chief Financial Officer, North Florida Regional Medical Center, Gainesville, FL, p. A129

ST. AUBYN, Lisa, Chief Executive Officer, Research Psychiatric Center, Kansas City, MO, p. A374

ST. CLAIR, Jeffery M., President and Chief Executive Officer, Springhill Memorial Hospital, Mobile, AL, p. A23

ST. LEGER, John, Chief Executive Officer, Select Specialty Hospital–Pittsburgh/UPMC, Pittsburgh, PA, p. A551

ST. MARTIN, Andrew, M.D. Chief of Staff, River Parishes Hospital, La Place, LA, p. A280

ST. ONGE, Donald, Chief Operating Officer, Day Kimball Hospital, Putnam, CT, p. A116

ST. PETER, Colette, Senior Manager Human Resources, Mercy Hospital Carthage, Carthage, MO, p. A369

STAATS, Annie, R.N. Director Nursing, Gove County Medical Center, Quinter, KS, p. A253

STABRYLA, Della, Director of Nursing, Ellwood City Hospital, Ellwood City, PA, p. A538

STACEY, Brian, Chief Financial Officer, Queens Hospital Center,, NY, p. A448

STACEY, Rulon F., FACHE, President and Chief Executive Officer, Fairview Health Services, Minneapolis, MN, p. B58

STACHOVSKY, Jeanne M., Director Human Resources, Slidell Memorial Hospital, Slidell, LA, p. A289

STACIE, Beverly, Director Human Resources, Clifton T. Perkins Hospital Center, Jessup, MD, p. A301

STACKER, Loreather, R.N. Chief Nursing Executive, Northwest Mississippi Regional Medical Center, Clarksdale, MS, p. A356

STACKHOUSE, Jenni, Chief Financial Officer, River Point Behavioral Health, Jacksonville, FL, p. A132

STACKHOUSE, Sharon, Assistant Administrator and Director Risk Management, Peachford Behavioral Health System, Atlanta, GA, p. A153

STACY, Doug, Director Information Technology, Marquette General Hospital, Marquette, MI, p. A330

STADHEIM, Barbara, Chief Nursing Officer, West River Regional Medical Center, Hettinger, ND, p. A478

STADLER, James J., M.D. Associate Administrator Medical Services, Guam Memorial Hospital Authority, Tamuning, GU, p. A724

STADLER, Thomas, M.D. Vice President Medical Affairs and Chief Medical Officer, Madonna Rehabilitation Hospital, Lincoln, NE, p. A398

STADNYK, Sheldon, M.D. Chief Medical Officer, North Colorado Medical Center, Greeley, CO, p. A107

STAFFORD, Cindy, Chief Executive Officer, North Metro Medical Center, Jacksonville, AR, p. A48

STAFFORD, Tom, Chief Information Officer, Halifax Health Medical Center of Daytona Beach, Daytona Beach, FL, p. A127

STAFFORD, Walt, Director Information Technology, Chatuge Regional Hospital and Nursing Home, Hiawassee, GA, p. A161

STAGG, Kevin, Executive Vice President Finance and Chief Financial Officer, Christian Health Care Center, Wyckoff, NJ, p. A425

STAGGS, Nathan, Chief Executive Officer, Ochiltree General Hospital, Perryton, TX, p. A642

STAHL, Anthony, Vice President, Florida Hospital Heartland Medical Center, Sebring, FL, p. A145

STAHL, Daniel, M.D. Medical Director, Mayo Clinic Health System in Waseca, Waseca, MN, p. A353

STAHL, Daniel, D.O. Chief of Staff, Rush Memorial Hospital, Rushville, IN, p. A222

STAHL, Marlin G., M.D. Chief Medical Officer, Bellevue Medical Center, Bellevue, NE, p. A394

STAHL, Ronald, M.D. Chief Medical Officer, Crouse Hospital, Syracuse, NY, p. A455

STAHL, Sherri, R.N. Senior Vice President for Hospital Services, Chambersburg Hospital, Chambersburg, PA, p. A535

STAHL, Steven J., Director Human Resources, Columbia County Health System, Dayton, WA, p. A683

STAHL, William D., Chief Operating Officer, Rooks County Health Center, Plainville, KS, p. A253

STAHLKUPPE, Robert F., M.D. Chief of Staff, Chatuge Regional Hospital and Nursing Home, Hiawassee, GA, p. A161

STAIGER, Tom, M.D. Medical Director, University of Washington Medical Center, Seattle, WA, p. A689

STALBAUM, Angela, R.N. Chief Nursing Officer, Seton Medical Center Austin, Austin, TX, p. A599

STALCUP, Connie, Manager Information Systems, Murphy Medical Center, Murphy, NC, p. A470

STALCUP, Linda, Chief Executive Officer, Stevens County Hospital, Hugoton, KS, p. A246

STALEY, Gerald, Director Human Resources, Adventist Bolingbrook Hospital, Bolingbrook, IL, p. A182

STALKER, Neil, M.D. Chief of Staff, Dukes Memorial Hospital, Peru, IN, p. A221

STALL, Kristi, Chief Human Resources Officer, Mahnomen Health Center, Mahnomen, MN, p. A346

STALLINGS, Jennifer, Chief Clinical Officer, Kindred Hospital Indianapolis South, Greenwood, IN, p. A212

STALLINGS, Terry, M.D. Chief Medical Officer, West Florida Hospital, Pensacola, FL, p. A142

STALLWORTH, David, M.D. Chief of Staff, Monroe County Hospital, Monroeville, AL, p. A23

STALLWORTH, Monica, M.D. Chief of Staff, Western Maryland Hospital Center, Hagerstown, MD, p. A301

STALLWORTH, Rebecca, Chief Operating Officer, Presbyterian–St. Luke's Medical Center, Denver, CO, p. A105

STALLWORTH, Terresa, M.D. Clinical Director, San Antonio State Hospital, San Antonio, TX, p. A647

STALNAKER, Avah, Chief Executive Officer, Stonewall Jackson Memorial Hospital, Weston, WV, p. A700

STALNAKER, Jeffrey, M.D. Vice President, Medical Affairs, Health First Cape Canaveral Hospital, Cocoa Beach, FL, p. A126

STALNAKER, Kevin P., CPA Chief Operating Officer, Stonewall Jackson Memorial Hospital, Weston, WV, p. A700

STAMAS, Peter, M.D. Vice President Medical Affairs, Ministry Saint Joseph's Hospital, Marshfield, WI, p. A709

STAMBAUGH, Lynn E., R.N., Chief Executive Officer, Sarah D. Culbertson Memorial Hospital, Rushville, IL, p. A202

STAMM, Pam, Chief Nursing Officer, Throckmorton County Memorial Hospital, Throckmorton, TX, p. A653

STAMP, John, Director Information Services, Ellett Memorial Hospital, Appleton City, MO, p. A367

STAMPOHAR, Jeffry, Chief Executive Officer, Essentia Health–Deer River, Deer River, MN, p. A342

STANCILL, Linda, Vice President and Chief Financial Officer, St. Joseph Health System, Tawas City, MI, p. A335

STANDEFFER, Luke, Administrator, Northport Medical Center, Northport, AL, p. A24

STANDER, Paul, M.D. Chief Medical Officer, Banner Good Samaritan Medical Center, Phoenix, AZ, p. A35

STANDIFORD, Steven B., M.D. Chief of Staff, Eastern Regional Medical Center, Philadelphia, PA, p. A548

STANDRIDGE, Debra K.
President, Wheaton Franciscan Healthcare – Elmbrook Memorial, Brookfield, WI, p. A703
President, Wheaton Franciscan Healthcare – St. Joseph's, Milwaukee, WI, p. A711
President, Wheaton Franciscan Healthcare – The Wisconsin Heart Hospital, Wauwatosa, WI, p. A718

STANDRIDGE, Sonya, Chief Nursing Officer, Copper Basin Medical Center, Copperhill, TN, p. A581

STANEK, Janet, Executive Vice President, Stormont–Vail HealthCare, Topeka, KS, p. A255

STANFORD, Brion, Director Human Resources, Biloxi Regional Medical Center, Biloxi, MS, p. A355

STANFORD, Tracy, Director Human Resources, Baylor All Saints Medical Center at Fort Worth, Fort Worth, TX, p. A618

STANGE, Della G., Executive Director, People Services, Loma Linda University Medical Center, Loma Linda, CA, p. A69

STANGE KOLO, Tracey, Vice President Human Resources, UPMC St. Margaret, Pittsburgh, PA, p. A552

STANGL, Abbey, Chief Financial Officer, Manning Regional Healthcare Center, Manning, IA, p. A234

STANHILL, Keith, Chief Human Resources Officer, Saint Francis Hospital, Memphis, TN, p. A589

STANIC, Steve M.
Vice President and Chief Information Officer, Mississippi Baptist Medical Center, Jackson, MS, p. A360
Vice President and Chief Information Officer, Mississippi Hospital for Restorative Care, Jackson, MS, p. A360

STANKO, Shelley, M.D. Chief Medical Officer, Saint Joseph – London, London, KY, p. A265

STANLEY, Cassandra, Director Personnel, Eastern Shore Hospital Center, Cambridge, MD, p. A299

STANLEY, Ed
Director Information Systems, Barrow Regional Medical Center, Winder, GA, p. A169
Director Information Systems, Clearview Regional Medical Center, Monroe, GA, p. A164

STANLEY, Jennifer, M.D. Chief Medical Officer, St. Vincent Jennings Hospital, North Vernon, IN, p. A220

STANLEY, John T.
Vice President Planning and Information Systems, Riverside Regional Medical Center, Newport News, VA, p. A675
Vice President Planning and Information Systems, Riverside Rehabilitation Institute, Newport News, VA, p. A675

STANLEY, Mark, Director Fiscal Services, Middle Tennessee Mental Health Institute, Nashville, TN, p. A590

STANLEY, Robert
Chief Financial Officer, Ilano Specialty Hospital of Lubbock, Lubbock, TX, p. A635
Chief Financial Officer, Texas Specialty Hospital at Lubbock, Lubbock, TX, p. A635

STANSEL, Robert
Director Human Resources, Avista Adventist Hospital, Louisville, CO, p. A109
Vice President of Human Resources, Estes Park Medical Center, Estes Park, CO, p. A106

STANSKI, Vickie, Financial Manager, Parkview LaGrange Hospital, LaGrange, IN, p. A217

STANTON, Lowell, Chief Financial Officer, Houston Methodist Sugar Land Hospital, Sugar Land, TX, p. A650

STANTON, Melanie, R.N. Chief Nursing Officer, Sycamore Shoals Hospital, Elizabethton, TN, p. A582

STANTON, Mike, D.O. Medical Director, Baylor Medical Center at Trophy Club, Trophy Club, TX, p. A653

STANUSH, Chris, Director Information Management, San Antonio State Hospital, San Antonio, TX, p. A647

STAPLES, Deborah L., Chief Operating Officer, Pennsylvania Hospital, Philadelphia, PA, p. A549

STAPLES, Janet, Vice President Human Resources, South Central Regional Medical Center, Laurel, MS, p. A361

STAPLETON, Carla J., Director Human Resources, Paul B. Hall Regional Medical Center, Paintsville, KY, p. A269

STAPLETON, Matt, Chief Operating Officer, Clearview Regional Medical Center, Monroe, GA, p. A164

STAPLETON, Michael, President and Chief Executive Officer, F. F. Thompson Hospital, Canandaigua, NY, p. A435

STAPLETON, Robert, Director Administration, Richard H. Hutchings Psychiatric Center, Syracuse, NY, p. A455

STARA, Jeanne, R.N. Chief Nursing Officer, Ponca City Medical Center, Ponca City, OK, p. A517

STARESINIC, Barbara, Director Human Resources, Hi-Desert Medical Center, Joshua Tree, CA, p. A67

STARK, David, Chief Financial Officer, Lancaster Rehabilitation Hospital, Lancaster, PA, p. A542

STARK, Donna
Director Human Resources, Baylor Medical Center at Irving, Irving, TX, p. A629
Director Human Resources, Baylor Regional Medical Center at Grapevine, Grapevine, TX, p. A621

STARK, Jared, Chief Executive Officer, University Hospital and Clinics, Lafayette, LA, p. A282

STARK, Patricia Ann, R.N. CNO, Florida Hospital DeLand, DeLand, FL, p. A127

STARK, Sharon, R.N. Manager Clinical Information Systems, Methodist McKinney Hospital, McKinney, TX, p. A637

STARK, Steve, Chief Executive Officer, Palmer Lutheran Health Center, West Union, IA, p. A239

STARKEBAUM, Gordon, M.D. Chief of Staff, Veterans Affairs Puget Sound Health Care System, Seattle, WA, p. A689

STARKES, Henry, M.D. Medical Director, Orchard Hospital, Gridley, CA, p. A66

STARKEY, Gary, M.D. Medical Director, Riverside Behavioral Health Center, Hampton, VA, p. A672

STARKEY, Shelly, Human Resources Coordinator, Cook County North Shore Hospital, Grand Marais, MN, p. A344

STARKEY, Thomas, M.D. Deputy Commander FDR Clinical Services, Bayne–Jones Army Community Hospital, Fort Polk, LA, p. A277

STARLING, Barbara, Chief Financial Officer, Gulf Coast Medical Center, Wharton, TX, p. A657

STARLING, James F., M.D. Chief Medical Officer, Danville Regional Medical Center, Danville, VA, p. A670

STARLING, Mark, M.D. Chief Medical Officer, Banner Heart Hospital, Mesa, AZ, p. A34

STARLING, Susan, President and Chief Executive Officer, Marcum and Wallace Memorial Hospital, Irvine, KY, p. A263

STARMANN–HARRISON, Mary, FACHE, President and Chief Executive Officer, Hospital Sisters Health System, Springfield, IL, p. B73

STARNES, Gregory D., Chief Executive Officer, Fayette County Hospital, Vandalia, IL, p. A204

STARON, Willard, Chief Financial Officer, Crittenton Children's Center, Kansas City, MO, p. A373

STARR, Candie, Chief Operating Officer and Ethics and Compliance Officer, Methodist Stone Oak Hospital, San Antonio, TX, p. A647

STARR, Kay, Manager Human Resources, Vernon Memorial Healthcare, Viroqua, WI, p. A717

STASI, Joseph P., Chief Financial Officer, Saint Luke's East Hospital, Lee's Summit, MO, p. A375

STASIK, Randall, President and Chief Executive Officer, Spectrum Health Gerber Memorial, Fremont, MI, p. A324

STASKIN, David, Director Human Resources, HEALTHSOUTH Rehabilitation Hospital of Mechanicsburg, Mechanicsburg, PA, p. A544

STASTNY, Mark
Vice President Information Technology, Laureate Psychiatric Clinic and Hospital, Tulsa, OK, p. A520
Vice President Information Technology, Saint Francis Hospital, Tulsa, OK, p. A521
Vice President Information Technology, Saint Francis Hospital South, Tulsa, OK, p. A521

STATEN, Gary L., Chief Executive Officer, Trace Regional Hospital, Houston, MS, p. A359

STATEN, James, Senior Vice President Finance, Yale–New Haven Hospital, New Haven, CT, p. A116

STATES, Chuck, Director Information Systems, Punxsutawney Area Hospital, Punxsutawney, PA, p. A553

STATON, Donna, Chief Information Officer, Fauquier Hospital, Warrenton, VA, p. A680

STATON, John, Senior Vice President Operations, Olathe Medical Center, Olathe, KS, p. A251

STATON, Paul
Chief Financial Officer, Ronald Reagan University of California Los Angeles Medical Center, Los Angeles, CA, p. A74
Chief Financial Officer, Santa Monica–UCLA Medical Center and Orthopaedic Hospital, Santa Monica, CA, p. A95

STATUTO, Richard, President and Chief Executive Officer, Bon Secours Health System, Inc., Marriottsville, MD, p. B24

STATZ, Chris, Chief Financial Officer, Lincoln Prairie Behavioral Health Center, Springfield, IL, p. A203

STATZ, Lila, M.D. Chief of Staff, Haxtun Hospital District, Haxtun, CO, p. A107

STATZ, Linda Taplin, System Vice President Human Resources, St. Mary's Hospital, Madison, WI, p. A708

STAUB, David, M.D. Chief of Staff, Coteau des Prairies Hospital, Sisseton, SD, p. A577

STAUBACH, Virginia, R.N. Chief Nursing Officer and Senior Director of Nursing Services, Gaylord Hospital, Wallingford, CT, p. A117

STAUFFER, Karla, Executive Director People Resources, Billings Clinic, Billings, MT, p. A385

STAUFFER, Keith, Regional Chief Information Officer, Carrington Health Center, Carrington, ND, p. A476

STAUSS, Laura, Director of Human Resources, Huggins Hospital, Wolfeboro, NH, p. A412

STAWNIAK, Laura, R.N. Chief Nursing Executive, Memorial Community Hospital and Health System, Blair, NE, p. A394

STEAD, Linda, Chief Nursing Officer, Piedmont Mountainside Hospital, Jasper, GA, p. A161

STEAD, William, Associate Vice Chancellor Health Affairs, Director Informatics Center and Chief Strategy and Information Officer, Vanderbilt Hospital and Clinics, Nashville, TN, p. A591

STEADHAM, Emily, Administrator, Grove Hill Memorial Hospital, Grove Hill, AL, p. A21

STEADHAM, Mark B., President and Chief Executive Officer, Morris Hospital & Healthcare Centers, Morris, IL, p. A196

STEARNS, Mark, Administrator, Pinnacle Specialty Hospital, Tulsa, OK, p. A520

STEBBINS, Deborah E., FACHE, Chief Executive Officer, Alameda Hospital, Alameda, CA, p. A55

STEBBINS, Michael, Director Organization and Talent Effectiveness, Mercy Hospital Cadillac, Cadillac, MI, p. A320

STECKEL, Cindy, Vice President Chief Nurse and Operations Executive, Scripps Memorial Hospital–La Jolla, La Jolla, CA, p. A68

STECKER, Tim, Chief Financial Officer, Kindred Hospital–Denver, Denver, CO, p. A104

STECKLER, Michael J., President and Chief Executive Officer, Jennie M. Melham Memorial Medical Center, Broken Bow, NE, p. A394

STEED, Robert A., Director Information Systems, Capital Regional Medical Center, Tallahassee, FL, p. A146

STEELE, Anthony, M.D. Chief Medical Officer, Witham Memorial Hospital, Lebanon, IN, p. A217

STEELE, Chrys, Director Information Systems, Springs Memorial Hospital, Lancaster, SC, p. A568

STEELE, Daren, Director of Information, Decatur County Hospital, Leon, IA, p. A233

STEELE, David, Vice President Information Technology, Leesburg Regional Medical Center, Leesburg, FL, p. A134

STEELE, Erik N., D.O. Senior Vice President and Chief Medical Officer, Summa Akron City Hospital, Akron, OH, p. A482

STEELE Jr.,, Glenn, Ph.D., President and Chief Executive Officer, Geisinger Health System, Danville, PA, p. B60

STEELE, Mark, M.D
Chief Medical Officer, Truman Medical Center–Hospital Hill, Kansas City, MO, p. A374
Chief Medical Officer, Truman Medical Center–Lakewood, Kansas City, MO, p. A374

STEELE, Michael, M.D. Chief of Staff, Perry County Memorial Hospital, Perryville, MO, p. A378

STEELE, Sherri, Chief Nursing Officer, Providence Medford Medical Center, Medford, OR, p. A527

STEELE, Terry L., Vice President Finance and Chief Financial Officer, Holland Hospital, Holland, MI, p. A326

STEELE, Tina, Chief Executive Officer and Chief Financial Officer, Fairfax Community Hospital, Fairfax, OK, p. A511

STEELE, Wes, M.D. Chief of Staff, Fairmont General Hospital, Fairmont, WV, p. A695

STEELMAN, Jeffrey, Director Information Systems, LewisGale Hospital Alleghany, Low Moor, VA, p. A673

STEEN, Jon, Director Human Resources, Davis Memorial Hospital, Elkins, WV, p. A694

STEENPORT, John, Director Information Technology, Portage Health, Hancock, MI, p. A326

STEEVENS, Alan, Director Information Management, St. Clare Hospital, Baraboo, WI, p. A702

STEFANEK, Allen, Chief Operating Officer, Hollywood Presbyterian Medical Center, Los Angeles, CA, p. A72

STEFANOWICZ, Alex, Vice President Human Resources, USMD Hospital at Fort Worth, Fort Worth, TX, p. A619

STEFFEN, Elizabeth, Director Information Technology, Seneca Healthcare District, Chester, CA, p. A59

STEFFEN, Elly, Chief Executive Officer and Administrator, Continuing Care Hospital at St. Luke's, Cedar Rapids, IA, p. A226

STEFFEN, Keith E., President and Chief Executive Officer, OSF Saint Francis Medical Center, Peoria, IL, p. A200

STEFFENS, Aaron, Chief Operating Officer, Mercy Hospital Oklahoma City, Oklahoma City, OK, p. A515

STEFFIN, Renee, Chief Nursing Officer, Cuyuna Regional Medical Center, Crosby, MN, p. A342

STEFL, William
Director Information Systems, Mercy Health, Hackley Campus, Muskegon, MI, p. A331
Director Information Systems, Mercy Health, Mercy Campus, Muskegon, MI, p. A331

STEFO, Andrew, Senior Vice President Finance and Chief Financial Officer, Ingalls Memorial Hospital, Harvey, IL, p. A192

STEGALL, Christopher A., Regional Chief Financial Officer and Chief Operating Officer, Promise Hospital of Vicksburg, Vicksburg, MS, p. A366

STEGALL, Paula, R.N. Chief Nurse Executive, Anson Community Hospital, Wadesboro, NC, p. A474

STEGGE, Sherri, Director Human Resources, Kaiser Permanente Vallejo Medical Center, Vallejo, CA, p. A99

STEICHEN, Barry L.
Executive Vice President, Chief Administrative Officer and Chief Financial Officer, Laureate Psychiatric Clinic and Hospital, Tulsa, OK, p. A520
Executive Vice President and Chief Financial Officer, Saint Francis Hospital, Tulsa, OK, p. A521
Executive Vice President, Saint Francis Hospital South, Tulsa, OK, p. A521

STEICHEN, Elizabeth, Human Resources, Lewis and Clark Specialty Hospital, Yankton, SD, p. A578

STEIDLE, Ernie, Chief Operating Officer, Woodrow Wilson Rehabilitation Center, Fishersville, VA, p. A671

STEIGER, Nancy, FACHE, Chief Executive Officer and Chief Mission Officer, Northwest Network, PeaceHealth St. Joseph Medical Center, Bellingham, WA, p. A681

STEIGMAN, Don S., Chief Operating Officer, Jackson Health System, Miami, FL, p. A137

STEIGMEYER, Robert P., President and Chief Executive Officer, Concord Hospital, Concord, NH, p. A409

STEIMEL, Ronald, Vice President Administration and Chief Operating Officer, Mercy Medical Center, Rockville Centre, NY, p. A453

STEIN, Cathy, Chief Inpatient Services, Sagamore Children's Psychiatric Center, Dix Hills, NY, p. A436

STEIN, Eric H., FACHE, President and Chief Executive Officer, Cobleskill Regional Hospital, Cobleskill, NY, p. A436

STEIN, Keith L., M.D
Chief Medical Officer, Baptist Medical Center Beaches, Jacksonville Beach, FL, p. A132
Senior Vice President Medical Affairs and Chief Medical Officer, Baptist Medical Center Jacksonville, Jacksonville, FL, p. A131

STEIN, Patrick, M.D. Clinical Director, Western New York Children's Psychiatric Center, West Seneca, NY, p. A458

STEIN, Paul, Chief Operating Officer, MaineGeneral Medical Center, Augusta, ME, p. A291

STEIN, Richard, M.D. Chief Medical Officer, Bay Area Medical Center, Marinette, WI, p. A708

STEIN, Robert, M.D. Vice President Medical Management, Advocate Christ Medical Center, Oak Lawn, IL, p. A198

STEIN, Robert
Chief Executive Officer, Kindred Hospital Midtown, Houston, TX, p. A625
Chief Executive Officer, Kindred Hospital–Houston, Houston, TX, p. A625

STEIN, Sandra, Chief Human Resources Management, Veterans Affairs Central California Health Care System, Fresno, CA, p. A64

STEIN, Sheldon J., President and Chief Executive Officer, Mt. Washington Pediatric Hospital, Baltimore, MD, p. A297

STEINBERG, James P., M.D. Chief Medical Officer, Emory University Hospital Midtown, Atlanta, GA, p. A152

STEINBLOCK, Matthew, Systems Administrator, Community Memorial Hospital, Syracuse, NE, p. A402

STEINER, Dana, R.N. Executive Director of Nursing Services, Lexington Regional Health Center, Lexington, NE, p. A397

STEINER, J. Scott, Chief Executive Officer, MacNeal Hospital, Berwyn, IL, p. A181

STEINER, Jeffrey T., Vice President Finance, Memorial Hospital at Gulfport, Gulfport, MS, p. A358

STEINER, Thomas K., Chief Executive Officer, Hancock Medical Center, Bay Saint Louis, MS, p. A355

STEINES, Jeanne, D.O. Medical Director, Connecticut Mental Health Center, New Haven, CT, p. A116

STEINGALL, Patricia, R.N. Vice President, Patient Care Services, Hunterdon Medical Center, Flemington, NJ, p. A416

STEINHART, Curt, M.D. Chief Medical Officer, OU Medical Center, Oklahoma City, OK, p. A516

STEINKE, Paul, D.O., President and Chief Executive Officer, CGH Medical Center, Sterling, IL, p. A203

STEINKRUGER, Roger W., Interim Chief Executive Officer, Community Hospital–Fairfax, Fairfax, MO, p. A371

STEINKUHLER, Diane, Administrative Assistant Human Resources, I–70 Community Hospital, Sweet Springs, MO, p. A383

STEINMANN, David, President, Mercy Hospital Independence, Independence, KS, p. A246

STEINMANN, Robin, Administrative Director Human Resources, Anderson Hospital, Maryville, IL, p. A195

STEINSICK, Bill, M.D. Chief Medical Staff, Asante Ashland Community Hospital, Ashland, OR, p. A523

STEITZ, David P., Chief Executive Officer, Berwick Hospital Center, Berwick, PA, p. A533

STELL, G. Max, M.D. Medical Director, Minden Medical Center, Minden, LA, p. A284

STELLER, Wayne, Vice President Chief Nursing Officer, The Acadia Hospital, Bangor, ME, p. A291

STELLING, Jonathan, M.D. Vice President Medical Affairs, CHI Health St. Mary's, Nebraska City, NE, p. A398

STELTENPOHL, Robert
Vice President and Chief Financial Officer, Frazier Rehab Institute, Louisville, KY, p. A265
Vice President, Southern Indiana Rehabilitation Hospital, New Albany, IN, p. A220

STELTER, Carolyn, M.D. Chief of Staff, Minnesota Valley Health Center, Le Sueur, MN, p. A345

STELZER, Jason, Director Human Resources, St. Clare Hospital, Baraboo, WI, p. A702

STEMMERMAN, Jill, R.N. Vice President Nursing, Saint Anthony Hospital, Chicago, IL, p. A186

STENDEL–FREELS, Robin, Coordinator Human Resources, AMG Specialty Hospital–Albuquerque, Albuquerque, NM, p. A426

STENERSON, David, Vice President and Chief Financial Officer, OSF Saint Anthony Medical Center, Rockford, IL, p. A201

STENGER, John D., Acting Associate Director, Charlie Norwood Veterans Affairs Medical Center, Augusta, GA, p. A153

STENGER, Sandra, Acting Chief Human Resources, Cincinnati Veterans Affairs Medical Center, Cincinnati, OH, p. A486

STENNETT, Kevin T., M.D. Chief of Staff, W. J. Mangold Memorial Hospital, Lockney, TX, p. A634

STENSRUD, Kirk A., Chief Executive Officer, Glacial Ridge Health System, Glenwood, MN, p. A344

STEPANSKY, David, M.D. Chief Medical Officer, Phoenixville Hospital, Phoenixville, PA, p. A550

STEPHANY, Mark
Executive Director, Elmira Psychiatric Center, Elmira, NY, p. A437
Executive Director, Greater Binghamton Health Center, Binghamton, NY, p. A433

STEPHENS, Brian, Chief Financial Officer, Ministry Door County Medical Center, Sturgeon Bay, WI, p. A716

STEPHENS, Carrie, Director of Information Technology and Support Services, Saunders Medical Center, Wahoo, NE, p. A402

STEPHENS, Eddy, Vice President Information Technology, Mobile Infirmary Medical Center, Mobile, AL, p. A22

STEPHENS, Ellen, Vice President Information Services, Mercy Hospital Oklahoma City, Oklahoma City, OK, p. A515

STEPHENS, Jeremy, Vice President and Chief Human Resources Officer, Chelsea Community Hospital, Chelsea, MI, p. A320

STEPHENS, Kathy, Chief Financial Officer, Carl Vinson Veterans Affairs Medical Center, Dublin, GA, p. A159

STEPHENS, Larry
Chief Financial Officer, Collingsworth General Hospital, Wellington, TX, p. A656
Chief Financial Officer, Kimble Hospital, Junction, TX, p. A630
Chief Financial Officer, Schleicher County Medical Center, Eldorado, TX, p. A617

STEPHENS, Linda, R.N. Chief Nursing Officer, Memorial Hermann Northeast, Humble, TX, p. A628

STEPHENS, Michael R., Market Leader and President, Mercy Health – West Hospital, Cincinnati, OH, p. A487

STEPHENS, Mike, Chief Financial Officer, NCH Downtown Naples Hospital, Naples, FL, p. A138

STEPHENS, Norman F., Chief Executive Officer, St. Luke's Hospital – The Vintage Hospital, Houston, TX, p. A627

STEPHENS, Peggy, M.D., Superintendent and Medical Director, Madison State Hospital, Madison, IN, p. A218

STEPHENS, Ronald, Commander, Womack Army Medical Center, Fort Bragg, NC, p. A464

STEPHENS, Royce, Chief Financial Officer, Riverton Hospital, Riverton, UT, p. A662

STEPHENS, Ruth M., MSN Chief Nursing Officer, Crete Area Medical Center, Crete, NE, p. A395

STEPHENS, Terry A., Chief Executive Officer, River Park Hospital, Huntington, WV, p. A696

STEPHENS, PHR, Maria, Director Human Resources, Education and Occupational Health and Wellness, VCU Community Memorial Hospital, South Hill, VA, p. A678

STEPHENSON, Ben, M.D. Chief of Staff, Phillips County Hospital, Phillipsburg, KS, p. A252

STEPHENSON, Christy, Interim Chief Executive Officer, St. Francis Medical Center, Trenton, NJ, p. A423

STEPHENSON, Darlene, Vice President Operations, Mary Immaculate Hospital, Newport News, VA, p. A675

STEPHENSON, Melinda, Chief Executive Officer, Kingwood Medical Center, Kingwood, TX, p. A631

STEPHENSON, Penny, Chief Financial Officer, Ellinwood District Hospital, Ellinwood, KS, p. A243

STEPHENSON, Ron, Chief Operating Officer, Brookhaven Memorial Hospital Medical Center, Patchogue, NY, p. A451

STEPHENSON, Steve R., M.D. Executive Vice President and Chief Operating Officer, UnityPoint Health – Iowa Methodist Medical Center, Des Moines, IA, p. A229

STEPP, Dana, Human Resources Officer, Marcum and Wallace Memorial Hospital, Irvine, KY, p. A263

STERBACH, Maureen, Vice President Human Resources, St. Joseph's Hospital and Medical Center, Phoenix, AZ, p. A37

STERLING, Julie, Manager Information System, South Sunflower County Hospital, Indianola, MS, p. A359

STERLING, Terrie, R.N. Chief Operating Officer, Our Lady of the Lake Regional Medical Center, Baton Rouge, LA, p. A273

STERLING, Tyson, Chief Executive Officer, Wichita County Health Center, Leoti, KS, p. A248

STERN, Richard, M.D. President Medical Staff, Doctors Medical Center, San Pablo, CA, p. A93

STERN, Robert, M.D. Medical Director, Essex County Hospital Center, Cedar Grove, NJ, p. A414

STERNBERG, Paul, M.D. Professor and Chairman, Vanderbilt Hospital and Clinics, Nashville, TN, p. A591

STERNS, Brian, Director Information Systems Services, Mercy St. Charles Hospital, Oregon, OH, p. A500

STESNEY–RIDENOUR, Chris, Vice President Operations, Beaumont Hospital Grosse Pointe, Grosse Pointe, MI, p. A326

STETTHEIMER, Timothy
Vice President and Chief Information Officer, St. Vincent's Birmingham, Birmingham, AL, p. A17
Regional Chief Information Officer, St. Vincent's Blount, Oneonta, AL, p. A24

STEUTER, Krista, Director Human Resources, Catalina Island Medical Center, Avalon, CA, p. A56

STEVEN, Eva, Chief Financial Officer, Roosevelt General Hospital, Portales, NM, p. A429

STEVENS, Belinda, Chief Executive Officer, Access Hospital Dayton, Dayton, OH, p. A491

STEVENS, Ben, Chief Financial Officer, Buchanan County Health Center, Independence, IA, p. A232

STEVENS, Bryan N., Chief Financial Officer, Field Memorial Community Hospital, Centreville, MS, p. A356

STEVENS, Chris E., Chief Information Officer, Billings Clinic, Billings, MT, p. A385

STEVENS, Dori, Chief Nursing Officer, Sutter Delta Medical Center, Antioch, CA, p. A56

STEVENS, Emily, Chief Nursing Officer, Mat–Su Regional Medical Center, Palmer, AK, p. A30

STEVENS, Eric, Chief Executive Officer, Florida Hospital Heartland Medical Center, Sebring, FL, p. A145

STEVENS, Janis, Director Human Resources, Raulerson Hospital, Okeechobee, FL, p. A140

STEVENS, Kelly, Manager Human Resources, St. Joseph Memorial Hospital, Murphysboro, IL, p. A197

STEVENS, Lisa, Chief Clinical Officer and Chief Operating Officer, Vibra Hospital of Northern California, Redding, CA, p. A85

STEVENS, Maeanne, R.N. Chief Nursing Officer, OSF Saint Elizabeth Medical Center, Ottawa, IL, p. A199

STEVENS, Mark, M.D. Chief Medical Staff, Marion General Hospital, Columbia, MS, p. A357

STEVENS, Mark
Director Human Resources, St. Luke's Jerome, Jerome, ID, p. A176
Senior Director Human Resources, St. Luke's Magic Valley Medical Center, Twin Falls, ID, p. A178

STEVENS, Rick, Chief Administrative Officer, St. Luke's Hospital, San Francisco, CA, p. A91

STEVENS, Robert, President and Chief Executive Officer, Ridgeview Medical Center, Waconia, MN, p. A353

STEVENS, Saundra J., Chief Executive Officer, Adams County Regional Medical Center, Seaman, OH, p. A501

STEVENS, Shelbourn, President, Novant Health Brunswick Medical Center, Bolivia, NC, p. A460

STEVENS, Susan
Information Technology Specialist, Fallon Medical Complex, Baker, MT, p. A385
Director Human Resources, The HealthCenter, Kalispell, MT, p. A389

STEVENS, Tammy, Chief Operating Officer, Madison County Memorial Hospital, Madison, FL, p. A135

STEVENS, Tom, Director Personnel, Morehead Memorial Hospital, Eden, NC, p. A463

STEVENS, Velinda, President, Kalispell Regional Medical Center, Kalispell, MT, p. A389

STEVENS, Vicki, Human Resources Executive, Northfield Hospital, Northfield, MN, p. A348

STEVENSON, Angelia, Manager Finance, Tuscaloosa Veterans Affairs Medical Center, Tuscaloosa, AL, p. A26

STEVENSON, Brett, Controller, Kindred Hospital Kansas City, Kansas City, MO, p. A373

STEVENSON, John, M.D. Senior Vice President and Chief Medical Officer, South Shore Hospital, South Weymouth, MA, p. A314

STEVENSON, Michael, Chief Executive Officer, Murphy Medical Center, Murphy, NC, p. A470

STEVERSON, Denise, Director Human Resources, Dorminy Medical Center, Fitzgerald, GA, p. A159

STEVES, Sonja
Senior Vice President Human Resources and Marketing, Legacy Emanuel Hospital and Health Center, Portland, OR, p. A528
Vice President Marketing, Legacy Good Samaritan Hospital and Medical Center, Portland, OR, p. A528
Vice President Human Resources and Marketing, Legacy Meridian Park Medical Center, Tualatin, OR, p. A531
Senior Vice President Human Resources, Legacy Mount Hood Medical Center, Gresham, OR, p. A525
Senior Vice President Human Resources, Legacy Salmon Creek Medical Center, Vancouver, WA, p. A691

STEWARD, Rachel, Director Human Resources, Hillcrest Hospital – South, Tulsa, OK, p. A520

STEWARD, Todd E., Chief Executive Officer, St. David's South Austin Medical Center, Austin, TX, p. A600

STEWART, Charles R., Vice President Business, Finance and Corporate Compliance, MedStar Southern Maryland Hospital Center, Clinton, MD, p. A300

STEWART, Christine R., FACHE, Chief Executive Officer, Russellville Hospital, Russellville, AL, p. A25

STEWART, Clint
Chief Financial Officer, Blue Ridge Regional Hospital, Spruce Pine, NC, p. A473
Vice President Finance/Business Operations, McDowell Hospital, Marion, NC, p. A468

STEWART, Craig, Chief Financial Officer, Gila Regional Medical Center, Silver City, NM, p. A431

STEWART, Daniel, M.D. Vice President Medical Affairs, Bronson Battle Creek, Battle Creek, MI, p. A319

STEWART, Daphne, Director Human Resources, Northlake Behavioral Hospital, Mandeville, LA, p. A283

STEWART, David K., Chief Financial Officer, Mercy Medical Center, Canton, OH, p. A485

STEWART, Debbie, Human Resources Officer, Herington Municipal Hospital, Herington, KS, p. A245

STEWART, Dianne, Controller, Burke Medical Center, Waynesboro, GA, p. A169

STEWART, Evelyn G., Chief Executive Officer, El Paso LTAC Hospital, El Paso, TX, p. A615

STEWART, Greg, Chief Executive Officer, Wellstone Regional Hospital, Jeffersonville, IN, p. A215

STEWART, Hedda, Director Human Resources, Neshoba County General Hospital, Philadelphia, MS, p. A364

STEWART, Inez, Vice President, Boston Children's Hospital, Boston, MA, p. A306

STEWART, Jane, Director Information Services, JFK Medical Center, Atlantis, FL, p. A123

STEWART, John, Director Finance, Burke Rehabilitation Hospital, White Plains, NY, p. A458

STEWART, Kelly, Director of Human Resources, Community Mental Health Center, Lawrenceburg, IN, p. A217

STEWART, Kendall, M.D. Medical Director, Southern Ohio Medical Center, Portsmouth, OH, p. A501

STEWART, Marc, M.D. Vice President and Medical Director, Seattle Cancer Care Alliance, Seattle, WA, p. A688

STEWART, Marty, Director Information Services, AnMed Health Medical Center, Anderson, SC, p. A562

STEWART, Matthew A., Vice President Finance and Chief Financial Officer, Aultman Orrville Hospital, Orrville, OH, p. A500

STEWART, Michael K., Chief Executive Officer, Navarro Regional Hospital, Corsicana, TX, p. A608

STEWART, Michele, R.N. Chief Operating Officer, Mercy Hospital Joplin, Joplin, MO, p. A373

STEWART, Nova
Chief Information Officer, Western Medical Center Anaheim, Anaheim, CA, p. A55
Chief Information Officer, Western Medical Center–Santa Ana, Santa Ana, CA, p. A93

STEWART, Patty, Chief Financial Officer, Memorial Hospital, Gonzales, TX, p. A621

STEWART, Paul, M.D. Medical Director, Kindred Hospital Las Vegas–Sahara, Las Vegas, NV, p. A406

STEWART, Paul R., President and Chief Executive Officer, Sky Lakes Medical Center, Klamath Falls, OR, p. A526

STEWART, Russell L., M.D. Chief Medical Officer, Braxton County Memorial Hospital, Gassaway, WV, p. A695

STEWART, Scott, M.D. Vice President Medical Management, Good Samaritan Medical Center, Brockton, MA, p. A308

STEWART, Scott, Manager Information Services, Rochelle Community Hospital, Rochelle, IL, p. A201

STEWART, Stephen, M.D. Vice President Medical Affairs, St. Marys Health Center, Jefferson City, MO, p. A372

STEWART, Steve
Director Information Technology, Henry County Health Center, Mount Pleasant, IA, p. A234
Chief Financial Officer, La Paz Regional Hospital, Parker, AZ, p. A35

STEWART, Terri L., R.N. Chief Nursing Officer, Saint Francis Hospital, Memphis, TN, p. A589

STEWART, Terry, Director Information Systems, Dauterive Hospital, New Iberia, LA, p. A285

STEWART, Tim, Chief Information Officer, Abbeville Area Medical Center, Abbeville, SC, p. A562

STEWART, SPHR, Ronnelle, Chief Human Resources Officer, Brookwood Medical Center, Birmingham, AL, p. A16

STIEB, Pamela, Chief Financial Officer, Sterling Regional MedCenter, Sterling, CO, p. A111

STIEGMANN, Greg, M.D. Vice President Clinical Affairs, University of Colorado Hospital, Aurora, CO, p. A102

STIEKES, Robert
Chief Financial Officer, Special Care Hospital, Nanticoke, PA, p. A546
Chief Financial Officer, Tyler Memorial Hospital, Tunkhannock, PA, p. A556

STIENE, Susan M., MS, Interim Chief Administrative Officer, Mayo Clinic Health System in Lake City, Lake City, MN, p. A345

STIFF, Patrick, Coordinator Information Technology, Madison County Memorial Hospital, Madison, FL, p. A135

STIKELEATHER, Janie, Director Marketing and Community Relations, Davis Regional Medical Center, Statesville, NC, p. A473

STILES, Geoffrey, M.D. Chief Medical Officer, Sharp Memorial Hospital, San Diego, CA, p. A90

STILES, Susan M., President and Chief Executive Officer, Western Missouri Medical Center, Warrensburg, MO, p. A384

STILGENBAUER, Mike, Director Finance, Marymount Hospital, Garfield Heights, OH, p. A494

STILLER, Brian G.
Director Medical Center, Veterans Affairs Western New York Healthcare System–Batavia Division, Batavia, NY, p. A433
Director Medical Center, Veterans Affairs Western New York Healthcare System–Buffalo Division, Buffalo, NY, p. A435

STILLMAN, Elizabeth M., Acting Director, Colorado Mental Health Institute at Fort Logan, Denver, CO, p. A104

STILLMAN, Michelle, Director of Care Management, Asheville Specialty Hospital, Asheville, NC, p. A459

STILLWORD, Joseph, Chief of Staff, Putnam Community Medical Center, Palatka, FL, p. A141

STILTNER, Wanda, Director Human Resources, Buchanan General Hospital, Grundy, VA, p. A671

STIMSON–RUSIN, Judi, Chief Financial Officer, Palm Beach Gardens Medical Center, Palm Beach Gardens, FL, p. A141

STINSON, Katy, Director Information Services, Medical Center of Southeastern Oklahoma, Durant, OK, p. A510

STINSON, Martha, Director of Information Technology, Palms West Hospital, Loxahatchee, FL, p. A134

STIPE, Christopher R., FACHE, Chief Executive Officer, Clarinda Regional Health Center, Clarinda, IA, p. A227

STIRE, David R., President and Chief Executive Officer, Jane Phillips Medical Center, Bartlesville, OK, p. A508

STITH, Melanie
Vice President Human Resources, Mount Pleasant Hospital, Mount Pleasant, SC, p. A568
Vice President Human Resources, Roper Hospital, Charleston, SC, p. A563

STITT, Bobby, R.N., Administrator, Mercy Hospital Watonga, Watonga, OK, p. A522

STITZER, Philip, D.O. Chief Medical Officer, Moberly Regional Medical Center, Moberly, MO, p. A377

STOB, David, Chief Financial Officer, Kindred Hospital Seattle–Northgate, Seattle, WA, p. A688

STOBER, Karick
Chief Financial Officer, Post Acute Medical Specialty Hospital of Lafayette, Lafayette, LA, p. A282
Chief Financial Officer, Post Acute Northshore Specialty Hospital, Covington, LA, p. A276

STOBO, John D., M.D., Senior Vice President Health Sciences and Services, University of California–Systemwide Administration, Oakland, CA, p. B145

STOCK, Greg K., Chief Executive Officer, Thibodaux Regional Medical Center, Thibodaux, LA, p. A289

STOCK, Lesa, R.N. Chief Clinical Officer, Citizens Memorial Hospital, Bolivar, MO, p. A367

STOCK, Neil, Director Technology and Facilities, Mercy Regional Medical Center, Durango, CO, p. A105

STOCKARD, Herbert, M.D. Chief Medical Officer, Mercy St. Anne Hospital, Toledo, OH, p. A503

STOCKER, Trena, Chief Nursing Executive, Marcum and Wallace Memorial Hospital, Irvine, KY, p. A263

STOCKHAUSEN, Christopher, Chief Financial Officer, UPMC McKeesport, McKeesport, PA, p. A544

STOCKLEY, Selena, Chief Executive Officer, Rolling Hills Hospital, Ada, OK, p. A507

STOCKMAN, Troy P., Chief Executive Officer, Nebraska Spine Hospital, Omaha, NE, p. A400

STOCKORT, Norbert, M.D. Chief of Staff, Mercy St. Charles Hospital, Oregon, OH, p. A500

STOCKS, Gregory, M.D. Chief of Staff, Texas Orthopedic Hospital, Houston, TX, p. A627

STOCKSTILL, Mark, R.N., Administrator, Highland Community Hospital, Picayune, MS, p. A364

STOCKTON, Kevin, Chief Executive Officer, Northwest Medical Center, Tucson, AZ, p. A40

STOCKTON, Linda, Chief Financial Officer, Bayfront Health Dade City, Dade City, FL, p. A126

STOCKTON, Rick, Chief Executive Officer, Promise Hospital of Louisiana – Shreveport Campus, Shreveport, LA, p. A288

STODDARD, Mark R., President, Central Valley Medical Center, Nephi, UT, p. A661

STODDARD, Mark R., President and Chairman, Rural Health Group, Nephi, UT, p. B116

STOECKMAN, Bill, Chief Information Officer, Spearfish Regional Surgery Center, Spearfish, SD, p. A577

STOGSDILL, Vicki, R.N. Chief Nursing Officer, Owensboro Health Regional Hospital, Owensboro, KY, p. A268

STOJAKOVICH, Edward R.
Chief Financial Officer, Dominion Hospital, Falls Church, VA, p. A670
Chief Financial Officer, Reston Hospital Center, Reston, VA, p. A677

STOKER, Rick, Director Management Information Systems, TriStar Horizon Medical Center, Dickson, TN, p. A582

STOKER, Vicki, Chief Nursing Officer, University Behavioral Health of Denton, Denton, TX, p. A613

STOKES, Elia, Chief Financial Officer, Plaza Medical Center of Fort Worth, Fort Worth, TX, p. A619

STOKES, Gary L., Chief Executive Officer, Nacogdoches Medical Center, Nacogdoches, TX, p. A639

STOKES, Keith, Chief Medical Officer, Holmes County Hospital and Clinics, Lexington, MS, p. A361

STOKES, Laura
Director Financial Services, Roosevelt Warm Springs LTAC Hospital, Warm Springs, GA, p. A169
Director Financial Services, Roosevelt Warm Springs Rehabilitation and Specialty Hospitals, Warm Springs, GA, p. A169

STOKES, Letha, Chief Executive Officer, Medical Arts Hospital, Lamesa, TX, p. A632

STOKES, Lisa, R.N. Vice President Patient Care Services, Shenandoah Memorial Hospital, Woodstock, VA, p. A680

STOKES, Priscilla, MS Vice President Patient Care and Hospital Operations, UnityPoint Health – St. Luke's, Sioux City, IA, p. A238

STOKES, Randell G., Chief Executive Officer, LifeCare Hospitals of San Antonio, San Antonio, TX, p. A646

STOKES, Richard, CPA, Chief Executive Officer, Clarendon Memorial Hospital, Manning, SC, p. A568

STOKES, Tina, Manager Human Resources, Regency Hospital of Florence, Florence, SC, p. A566

STOLBA, Robert J., Chief Financial Officer, Mason District Hospital, Havana, IL, p. A192

STOLDT, Garrick J., Vice President and Chief Financial Officer, Saint Peter's University Hospital, New Brunswick, NJ, p. A419

STOLL, Carol, Vice President Patient Services and Chief Nursing Officer, Covenant Medical Center, Saginaw, MI, p. A333

STOLLER, Theo, Chief Executive Officer, Jacobson Memorial Hospital Care Center, Elgin, ND, p. A477

STOLTZ, Kyla, Vice President Human Resources, Centerpoint Medical Center, Independence, MO, p. A372

STOLTZ, Lori, Chief Financial Officer, Benewah Community Hospital, Saint Maries, ID, p. A178

STOLYAR, Edward B., D.O. Director Management Information Systems, New York Community Hospital,, NY, p. A447

STOMBERG, LeAnn, Chief Financial Officer, Minneapolis Veterans Affairs Health Care System, Minneapolis, MN, p. A347

STONE, Bill, Chief Human Resources Officer, Saint Francis Hospital–Bartlett, Bartlett, TN, p. A579

STONE, Bud, Director Information Systems, Eastern State Hospital, Lexington, KY, p. A264

STONE, Connie, R.N. Chief Nursing Officer, MedStar Montgomery Medical Center, Olney, MD, p. A302

STONE, Darlene, Vice President Human Resources, Baptist Hospital, Pensacola, FL, p. A142

STONE, Duncan, D.D.S. Chief Medical Staff, Mississippi State Hospital, Whitfield, MS, p. A366

STONE, Janice, Vice President Clinical Integration, Spectrum Health Gerber Memorial, Fremont, MI, p. A324

STONE, Jeanette, Vice President Operations, Baptist Health South Florida, South Miami Hospital, Miami, FL, p. A136

STONE, Jeff, Director Human Resources, Marshall Medical Center North, Guntersville, AL, p. A21

STONE, Jill, Manager Human Resources, Lynn County Hospital District, Tahoka, TX, p. A651

STONE, Joanna, Chief Nursing Officer, Livingston Hospital and Healthcare Services, Salem, KY, p. A270

STONE, Levi, R.N. Chief Nursing Officer, Odessa Regional Medical Center, Odessa, TX, p. A640

STONE, Patricia, R.N. Chief Nursing Officer, California Hospital Medical Center, Los Angeles, CA, p. A71

STONE, Richard, M.D. Medical Director, Metropolitan Hospital Center, New York, NY, p. A446

STONE, Robert, President and Chief Executive Officer, City of Hope's Helford Clinical Research Hospital, Duarte, CA, p. A62

STONE, Ronald W., Regional Chief Human Resource Officer, Long Island Jewish Medical Center,, NY, p. A445

STONE, Susan, Director Human Resources, Claiborne Medical Center, Tazewell, TN, p. A593

STONE, Susan, Ph.D., Senior Vice President and Chief Executive Officer, Sharp Coronado Hospital and Healthcare Center, Coronado, CA, p. A60

STONE, Terry, Chief Financial Officer and Chief Information Officer, Willapa Harbor Hospital, South Bend, WA, p. A690

STONE Jr., Timothy D., Executive Vice President and Administrator, Decatur Memorial Hospital, Decatur, IL, p. A188

STONE, Wesley, D.O. Chief of Staff, Allen County Regional Hospital, Iola, KS, p. A246

STONEHOUSE, Sarah, R.N. Director of Nursing, Timberlawn Mental Health System, Dallas, TX, p. A612

STONER, Donald, M.D. Chief Medical Officer, Halifax Health Medical Center of Daytona Beach, Daytona Beach, FL, p. A127

STONER, James, Chief Financial Officer, Lake Norman Regional Medical Center, Mooresville, NC, p. A469

STONER, Steve, Chief Information Officer, Richard L. Roudebush Veterans Affairs Medical Center, Indianapolis, IN, p. A215

STOOPS, Stephens, M.D
Chief Medical Officer, St. Joseph Medical Center, Kansas City, MO, p. A374
Chief Medical Officer, St. Mary's Medical Center, Blue Springs, MO, p. A367

STOPPER, Jim, CPA Interim Chief Financial Officer, Evangelical Community Hospital, Lewisburg, PA, p. A543

STORER, William, M.D. Medical Director, St. Vincent Heart Center, Indianapolis, IN, p. A215

STOREY, Kam, Director Human Resources, Sebastian River Medical Center, Sebastian, FL, p. A145

STOREY, Kevin, Chief Executive Officer, Golden Plains Community Hospital, Borger, TX, p. A603

STOREY, Paul, Chief Operating Officer, Helen Keller Hospital, Sheffield, AL, p. A25

STORFJELL, Judith, Ph.D. Senior Vice President and Chief Nursing Officer, Loma Linda University Medical Center, Loma Linda, CA, p. A69

STORM, Dave, Director Business Support, St. Anthony's Memorial Hospital, Effingham, IL, p. A188

STORR, Katie, Director of Human Resources, Mississippi State Hospital, Whitfield, MS, p. A366

STORTO, David E., President, Spaulding Rehabilitation Hospital, Charlestown, MA, p. A309

STORTZUM, Christopher, M.D. President Medical Staff, McDonough District Hospital, Macomb, IL, p. A195

STORY, Cathy N., Chief Executive Officer, North Vista Hospital, North Las Vegas, NV, p. A407

STOTLER, Sherry, R.N. Chief Nursing Officer, Maricopa Integrated Health System, Phoenix, AZ, p. A36

STOTTLEMYRE, Georgan L., Director Human Resources, Northern Inyo Hospital, Bishop, CA, p. A58

STOTTS, Vicki, Coordinator Human Resources, Flint River Community Hospital, Montezuma, GA, p. A164

STOUGH, Robin
Chief Financial Officer, Belmont Pines Hospital, Youngstown, OH, p. A506
Chief Financial Officer, Windsor–Laurelwood Center for Behavioral Medicine, Willoughby, OH, p. A505

STOUT, Bess, Director Human Resources, Tennova Healthcare–LaFollette Medical Center, La Follette, TN, p. A586

STOUT, Deana
Vice President Financial Services, MedStar Good Samaritan Hospital, Baltimore, MD, p. A297
Interim Chief Financial Officer, MedStar Washington Hospital Center, Washington, DC, p. A121

STOUT, Don, Administrator, Fond Du Lac County Mental Health Center, Fond Du Lac, WI, p. A705

STOUT, Patsy, Director Personnel, Richland Parish Hospital, Delhi, LA, p. A276

STOUT–TORRES, Sherri, R.N. Chief Nursing Executive, Sutter Maternity and Surgery Center of Santa Cruz, Santa Cruz, CA, p. A94

STOVALL, Henry, President, Sacred Heart Hospital of Pensacola, Pensacola, FL, p. A142

STOVALL, Richard G., Senior Vice President Fiscal Services and Chief Financial Officer, Southern Regional Medical Center, Riverdale, GA, p. A165

STOVER, Benny, Vice President Finance, Mercy Hospital Rogers, Rogers, AR, p. A52

STOVER, George M., Chief Executive Officer, Rice County District Hospital, Lyons, KS, p. A249

STOVER, Nick, Director Information Systems, Plateau Medical Center, Oak Hill, WV, p. A698

STOVER, Patricia A., Administrator Nursing, Doylestown Hospital, Doylestown, PA, p. A537

STOVER, Raymond
President and Chief Executive Officer, MidMichigan Medical Center–Clare, Clare, MI, p. A321
President and Chief Executive Officer, MidMichigan Medical Center–Gladwin, Gladwin, MI, p. A324

STOVER, Ryan, Chief Financial Officer, Norton County Hospital, Norton, KS, p. A251

STOVER, Thomas L., M.D., President and Chief Executive Officer, Akron General Health System, Akron, OH, p. B8

STOVERINK, Mike, Chief Financial Officer, Richland Memorial Hospital, Olney, IL, p. A198

STOWE, Mary, R.N. Senior Vice President and Chief Nursing Officer, Children's Medical Center of Dallas, Dallas, TX, p. A610

STOWELL, Dana A., Chief Information Officer, McCurtain Memorial Hospital, Idabel, OK, p. A512

STOWMAN, Amber, Controller, Lisbon Area Health Services, Lisbon, ND, p. A479

STOY, Gale, Manager Information Systems, Mid Coast Hospital, Brunswick, ME, p. A292

STOYANOFF, Pamela
Executive Vice President and Chief Operating Officer, Methodist Charlton Medical Center, Dallas, TX, p. A611
Executive Vice President and Chief Operating Officer, Methodist Dallas Medical Center, Dallas, TX, p. A611

STRABEL, Elizabeth, M.D. Chief Medical Staff, Divine Savior Healthcare, Portage, WI, p. A713

STRACHAN, Eileen, Coordinator Human Resources, Kindred Hospital–Sycamore, Sycamore, IL, p. A204

STRACHAN, Ronald
Chief Information Officer, McLaren Bay Region, Bay City, MI, p. A319
Chief Information Officer, McLaren Flint, Flint, MI, p. A323

STRACK, Kirk, Vice President and Chief Financial Officer, Clark Memorial Hospital, Jeffersonville, IN, p. A215

STRADER, Lynn, Chief Financial Officer, CJW Medical Center, Richmond, VA, p. A677

STRADER, Yvonne M., Chief Nursing Officer, Providence St. Mary Medical Center, Walla Walla, WA, p. A692

STRADI, Silvia, Chief Nursing Officer, Palms West Hospital, Loxahatchee, FL, p. A134

STRAHAN, Greg, Chief Operating Officer, Owensboro Health Regional Hospital, Owensboro, KY, p. A268

STRAIN, Donna, Director Human Resources, Ray County Memorial Hospital, Richmond, MO, p. A379

STRAIN, Lynn, R.N. Chief Nursing Officer, Slidell Memorial Hospital, Slidell, LA, p. A289

STRAMOWSKI, Mallary, Chief Human Resources Officer, Select Specialty Hospital–Madison, Madison, WI, p. A708

STRANATHAN, Sidney, D.O. Chief of Staff, Anthony Medical Center, Anthony, KS, p. A241

STRAND, Eric, Director Information Services, North Florida Regional Medical Center, Gainesville, FL, p. A129

STRAND, Joy A., Chief Executive Officer, McCready Foundation, Crisfield, MD, p. A300

STRANGE, John, President and Chief Executive Officer, St. Luke's Hospital, Duluth, MN, p. A343

STRANGE, Roger, Chief Information Officer, St. Vincent Heart Center, Indianapolis, IN, p. A215

STRASSER, Michael, Vice President and Chief Financial Officer, Mercy Medical Center Merced, Merced, CA, p. A77

STRASSNER III, Lawrence F., Ph.D. Senior Vice President Operations and Chief Nursing Officer, MedStar Franklin Square Medical Center, Baltimore, MD, p. A297

STRATTON, James
Regional Vice President Finance, Audrain Medical Center, Mexico, MO, p. A376
Vice President Finance, St. Marys Health Center, Jefferson City, MO, p. A372

STRATTON, Joseph, FACHE, Chief Executive Officer, Geary Community Hospital, Junction City, KS, p. A246

STRATTON, Mary, Director Human Resources, River Park Hospital, Huntington, WV, p. A696

STRATTON, Tracie, Chief Nursing Officer, Los Alamos Medical Center, Los Alamos, NM, p. A429

STRAUCH, Drew, Chief Financial Officer, Edward White Hospital, Saint Petersburg, FL, p. A144

STRAUGHAN, John, Director Information Technology, Wallowa Memorial Hospital, Enterprise, OR, p. A524

STRAUMAN, Karen S., R.N. Vice President Patient Care Services, Regina Hospital, Hastings, MN, p. A345

STRAUMANIS, John P., M.D. Vice President Medical Affairs and Chief Medical Officer, University of Maryland Rehabilitation and Orthopaedic Institute, Baltimore, MD, p. A298

STRAUSBAUGH, Andy, Vice President Finance and Operations, Norton Brownsboro Hospital, Louisville, KY, p. A266

STRAUSBAUGH, Teresa, Controller, OSS Orthopaedic Specialty Hospital, York, PA, p. A559

STRAUSS, Alan
  Chief Financial Officer, Carondelet Holy Cross Hospital, Nogales, AZ, p. A34
  Chief Financial Officer, Carondelet St. Joseph's Hospital, Tucson, AZ, p. A40
STRAUSS, Thomas J., President and Chief Executive Officer, Summa Akron City Hospital, Akron, OH, p. A482
STRAUSS, Thomas J., President and Chief Executive Officer, Summa Health System, Akron, OH, p. B129
STRAWN, Jill, Chief Executive Officer, HEALTHSOUTH Rehabilitation Hospital of Florence, Florence, SC, p. A565
STRAWN, Keith A., Vice President Human Resources, New Hanover Regional Medical Center, Wilmington, NC, p. A474
STRAWSER, Debbie A., Director Human Resources, Lindner Center of HOPE, Mason, OH, p. A497
STRAYER, Lorna, Interim President and Chief Executive Officer, Fisher–Titus Medical Center, Norwalk, OH, p. A500
STRAYHORN, Shelly, R.N
  Chief Nursing Officer, Wadley Regional Medical Center, Texarkana, TX, p. A653
  Chief Nursing Officer, Wadley Regional Medical Center at Hope, Hope, AR, p. A47
STRBICH, Steve, D.O. Chief of Staff, Spectrum Health Ludington Hospital, Ludington, MI, p. A329
STREATER, Vivian, Co–Acting Chief Executive Officer, Broughton Hospital, Morganton, NC, p. A469
STRECKER, Dede, Chief Nursing Officer, White River Medical Center, Batesville, AR, p. A43
STRECKER, Kevin, President, Via Christi Hospital on St. Teresa, Wichita, KS, p. A257
STRECKER, Robert, M.D. Chief of Staff, Colorado River Medical Center, Needles, CA, p. A79
STREDNEY, Thomas, Chief Human Resources Management Service, Aleda E. Lutz Veterans Affairs Medical Center, Saginaw, MI, p. A333
STREET, Rex, Senior Vice President and Chief Financial Officer, Alamance Regional Medical Center, Burlington, NC, p. A461
STREET, Scott, Chief Executive Officer, Nacogdoches Memorial Hospital, Nacogdoches, TX, p. A639
STREETER, Alan W., Chief Financial Officer, Beatrice Community Hospital and Health Center, Beatrice, NE, p. A394
STREETER, Matthew, Chief Financial Officer, Southwest Health Center, Platteville, WI, p. A713
STREETER, Robert, M.D. Vice President Medical Affairs, Mercy Medical Center Merced, Merced, CA, p. A77
STREICH, Rebecca, Manager Human Resources and Education Manager, Hutchinson Health, Hutchinson, MN, p. A345
STREJC, Irene, Vice President, Nursing, Methodist Richardson Medical Center, Richardson, TX, p. A644
STRICKER, Sean, Chief Executive Officer, Select Specialty Hospital–San Antonio, San Antonio, TX, p. A647
STRICKER, Steven, M.D. Physician in Chief, Kaiser Permanente Vallejo Medical Center, Vallejo, CA, p. A99
STRICKLAND, Barrie, Chief Financial Officer, UCSF Medical Center, San Francisco, CA, p. A91
STRICKLAND, Connie, Chief Executive Officer, Select Specialty Hospital–Oklahoma City, Oklahoma City, OK, p. A516
STRICKLAND, David, Area Information Officer, Kaiser Permanente Los Angeles Medical Center, Los Angeles, CA, p. A72
STRICKLAND, Lee, Regional Director Information Technology, Park Ridge Health, Hendersonville, NC, p. A466
STRICKLAND, Morris S., Chief Financial Officer, Helen Keller Hospital, Sheffield, AL, p. A25
STRICKLAND, Samuel A., Chief Financial Officer, Red Bay Hospital, Red Bay, AL, p. A25
STRICKLAND, Wallace, President and Chief Executive Officer, Rush Health Systems, Meridian, MS, p. B116
STRICKLING, Keith
  Chief Financial Officer, Atmore Community Hospital, Atmore, AL, p. A16
  Chief Accountant, Jay Hospital, Jay, FL, p. A132
STRIEBY, John F., Chief Executive Officer, Nix Health Care System, San Antonio, TX, p. A647
STRIKE, Helen J., R.N., President, Unity Hospital, Fridley, MN, p. A344
STRINDEN, William, M.D. Chief of Staff, Woodland Heights Medical Center, Lufkin, TX, p. A636
STRING, Sherrie
  Senior Vice President Human Resources, Bayshore Community Hospital, Holmdel, NJ, p. A417
  Senior Vice President Human Resources, Ocean Medical Center, Brick Township, NJ, p. A414
  Senior Vice President Human Resources, Riverview Medical Center, Red Bank, NJ, p. A422
STRINGFELLOW, Grace, M.D. Chief of Staff, Veterans Affairs – Western Iowa Healthcare System, Omaha, NE, p. A400
STRITTMATTER, Brenda M., Patient Services Officer, Berger Health System, Circleville, OH, p. A488

STRITTMATTER, Julie, Director Human Resources, Baylor University Medical Center, Dallas, TX, p. A610
STROBEL, Jane, Vice President and Chief Financial Officer, Mercy Regional Medical Center, Durango, CO, p. A105
STROBEL, Rand
  Regional Chief Information Officer, Information Technology Services, Harrison Medical Center, Bremerton, WA, p. A681
  Regional Chief Information Officer, St. Francis Hospital, Federal Way, WA, p. A683
  Vice President Information Technology and Compliance, St. Joseph Medical Center, Tacoma, WA, p. A691
STROEMEL, Douglas M.
  President, Mercy Hospital Aurora, Aurora, MO, p. A367
  President, Mercy Hospital Cassville, Cassville, MO, p. A369
STROH, Rhonda, Chief Human Resources Officer, Community Memorial Hospital, Redfield, SD, p. A576
STROHECKER, Sharon, R.N. Vice President Clinical Operations and Chief Nursing Officer, St. Joseph Medical Center, Reading, PA, p. A553
STROHMYER, Jeffrey, M.D. Chief Medical Officer, CHI Health Midlands, Papillion, NE, p. A401
STROM, Lisa, R.N. Chief Operating Officer, MultiCare Tacoma General Hospital, Tacoma, WA, p. A691
STROM, Lisa, Director Information Systems, North Big Horn Hospital District, Lovell, WY, p. A722
STROMBERG, Audrey, Administrator, Roosevelt Medical Center, Culbertson, MT, p. A386
STROMSTAD, Darlene, FACHE, President and Chief Executive Officer, Waterbury Hospital, Waterbury, CT, p. A118
STRONG, Dana, Chief Financial Officer, Wrangell Medical Center, Wrangell, AK, p. A30
STRONG, David, Chief Financial Officer/Vice President Finance, Cox Medical Center Branson, Branson, MO, p. A368
STRONG, David W., President, Rex Healthcare, Raleigh, NC, p. A471
STRONG, Tanya, Manager Information Technology, Harney District Hospital, Burns, OR, p. A523
STRONG, Tricia, Chief Financial Officer, Cumberland River Hospital, Celina, TN, p. A580
STROPE, Jennifer, Manager Human Resources, Hillcrest Hospital Cushing, Cushing, OK, p. A509
STROSNIDER, Preston, M.D. Vice President Medical Affairs, Conway Medical Center, Conway, SC, p. A565
STROSS, Daniel, Chief Information Officer, Genesys Regional Medical Center, Grand Blanc, MI, p. A324
STROTHER, Brad, Director Information Technology, Clay County Hospital, Ashland, AL, p. A15
STROTHKAMP, Brad, Chief Information Systems, Lakeland Behavioral Health System, Springfield, MO, p. A383
STROUCKEN, Christian, Chief Operating Officer, Carney Hospital, Boston, MA, p. A306
STROUD, Justin, Chief Financial Officer, Northwest Mississippi Regional Medical Center, Clarksdale, MS, p. A356
STROUD, Teresa, Chief Financial Officer, Salem Township Hospital, Salem, IL, p. A202
STROUD, William, M.D. Chief Medical Officer, East Cooper Medical Center, Mount Pleasant, SC, p. A568
STRUB, Lisa, Director Clinical Services, Centennial Peaks Hospital, Louisville, CO, p. A109
STRUMWASSER, Todd, M.D.,
  Chief Executive, Swedish Medical Center–Cherry Hill Campus, Seattle, WA, p. A688
  Chief Executive, Swedish Medical Center–First Hill, Seattle, WA, p A688
STRUTTON, Jill, Director Personnel Systems, University of Texas Harris County Psychiatric Center, Houston, TX, p. A627
STRUYK, Douglas A., CPA, President and Chief Executive Officer, Christian Health Care Center, Wyckoff, NJ, p. A425
STRZELECKI, Sarah, Ed.D. Chief Nursing Officer, Phoenixville Hospital, Phoenixville, PA, p. A550
STRZEMPKO, Stanley, M.D. Vice President Medical Affairs and Chief Medical Officer, Noble Hospital, Westfield, MA, p. A316
STUART, Conan, Director Information Services, East Georgia Regional Medical Center, Statesboro, GA, p. A167
STUART, Danna, M.D. Chief Medical Officer, Newman Memorial Hospital, Shattuck, OK, p. A518
STUART, Jimmy D., Chief Executive Officer, Integris Seminole Medical Center, Seminole, OK, p. A518
STUART, Leslie, Chief Financial Officer, Cypress Creek Hospital, Houston, TX, p. A624
STUART, Philip J., Administrator and Chief Executive Officer, Tomah Memorial Hospital, Tomah, WI, p. A716
STUART, Robin, Chief Executive Officer, Morrill County Community Hospital, Bridgeport, NE, p. A394
STUART, Wendy, Chief Nursing Officer, Kendall Regional Medical Center, Miami, FL, p. A137
STUART, Wilma P., Ph.D. Chief Nursing Officer, Shannon Medical Center, San Angelo, TX, p. A645

STUBBS, Don, Vice President Human Resources, Candler Hospital, Savannah, GA, p. A166
STUBBS, Kay, Chief Nursing Officer, Northwest Medical Center, Tucson, AZ, p. A40
STUBBS, Richard, M.D. Vice President Medical Affairs, Banner Casa Grande Medical Center, Casa Grande, AZ, p. A31
STUBER, Joseph A., President and Chief Executive Officer, Perry County Memorial Hospital, Tell City, IN, p. A222
STUCK, Julie, R.N., Interim Chief Executive Officer, Hocking Valley Community Hospital, Logan, OH, p. A496
STUCKY, Nancy, Director Human Resources and Public Relations, Kingman Community Hospital, Kingman, KS, p. A247
STUCZYNSKI, Joseph, Assistant Administrator Finance and Support, Memorial Hospital Pembroke, Pembroke Pines, FL, p. A142
STUDEBAKER, Shelly, Director Management Information Systems, Clinch Memorial Hospital, Homerville, GA, p. A161
STUDER, Tim, President Medical Staff, Perham Health, Perham, MN, p. A349
STUDER, Vince, Director Finance, Gundersen Tri–County Hospital and Clinics, Whitehall, WI, p. A718
STUDLEY, Jason, Chief Executive Officer, Trinity Hospital of Augusta, Augusta, GA, p. A154
STUENKEL, Kurt, FACHE, President and Chief Executive Officer, Floyd Medical Center, Rome, GA, p. A165
STUERMAN, Jason, M.D. Chief of Staff, Middle Park Medical Center–Kremmling, Kremmling, CO, p. A108
STUERSEL, Marie, Director Human Resources, Seneca Healthcare District, Chester, CA, p. A59
STUEVE, Jo W., Executive Vice President and Co–Chief Operating Officer, Children's Mercy Hospitals and Clinics, Kansas City, MO, p. A373
STUHLMILLER, Michael, Chief Financial Officer, Mann–Grandstaff Veterans Affairs Medical Center, Spokane, WA, p. A690
STULTS, Cynthia S., Executive Assistant and Human Resources Director, Rangely District Hospital, Rangely, CO, p. A110
STULTS, Kim, Director, Information Systems, Bellevue Hospital, Bellevue, OH, p. A484
STUMBAUGH, Terri, R.N. Director Patient Care Services, Johnson Regional Medical Center, Clarksville, AR, p. A44
STUMBO, Kathy, President, Saint Joseph – Martin, Martin, KY, p. A267
STUMME, Sarah, Director Human Resources, Owatonna Hospital, Owatonna, MN, p. A349
STUMP, Jerry, Chief Financial Officer, Good Samaritan Hospital, Vincennes, IN, p. A223
STUMP, Veronica, Chief Nursing Officer, Carilion Giles Community Hospital, Pearisburg, VA, p. A676
STUMPO, Barbara J., R.N. Vice President Patient Care Services, Griffin Hospital, Derby, CT, p. A114
STURGEON, Jim, Area Director Human Resources, Kindred Hospital Las Vegas–Sahara, Las Vegas, NV, p. A406
STURGILL, Lori
  Vice President Business Partnership, Mercy Hospital Fort Scott, Fort Scott, KS, p. A244
  Vice President Business Partnership, Mercy Hospital Springfield, Springfield, MO, p. A383
STURGIS, Gayle
  Vice President Nursing, Glencoe Regional Health Services, Glencoe, MN, p. A344
  Nurse Administrator, Heber Valley Medical Center, Heber City, UT, p. A660
STURGIS, James D., Associate Administrator, Texas Scottish Rite Hospital for Children, Dallas, TX, p. A612
STURGIS, Jonathan, Chief Financial Officer, Houston Methodist San Jacinto Hospital, Baytown, TX, p. A601
STURGIS, Paul, Vice President and Chief Human Resources Officer, Sparrow Hospital, Lansing, MI, p. A328
STURLER, Kelly, Chief Nursing Officer, McKee Medical Center, Loveland, CO, p. A109
STURM, Brenda L., MSN Vice President, Patient Care Services, Northern Montana Hospital, Havre, MT, p. A388
STURSA, Robin, Chief Information Officer, St. Vincent Charity Medical Center, Cleveland, OH, p. A489
STUWE, Shannon, Director of Nursing, Faulkton Area Medical Center, Faulkton, SD, p. A573
STYER, Brent
  Chief Information Officer, Summers County ARH Hospital, Hinton, WV, p. A695
  Director Information Technology, Whitesburg ARH Hospital, Whitesburg, KY, p. A271
STYLES, Kelly R., Vice President and Chief Information Officer, Connecticut Children's Medical Center, Hartford, CT, p. A114
STYRON, Stacie, Chief Nursing Officer, Lamb Healthcare Center, Littlefield, TX, p. A633
SUAREZ, Irma, Network Deputy Executive Director, Woodhull Medical and Mental Health Center,, NY, p. A449
SUAREZ, Orlando, Manager Information Technology, Larkin Community Hospital, South Miami, FL, p. A146

SUBLER, Jeffrey R., Vice President Support Services, Wayne Hospital, Greenville, OH, p. A495

SUBLETTE, Elizabeth
Chief Financial Officer, Providence Milwaukie Hospital, Milwaukie, OR, p. A527
Director Finance, Providence Willamette Falls Medical Center, Oregon City, OR, p. A527

SUBRAMANIAN, Aarti, Vice President and Chief Financial Officer, Psychiatric Institute of Washington, Washington, DC, p. A122

SUCATO, Daniel J., M.D. Chief of Staff, Texas Scottish Rite Hospital for Children, Dallas, TX, p. A612

SUCHER, Therese O., Senior Vice President Operations, Southern Regional Medical Center, Riverdale, GA, p. A165

SUCKOW, Scott, Commander, U. S. Air Force Regional Hospital, Elmendorf AFB, AK, p. A28

SUDA, Shirley, M.D. Area Medical Director, Kaiser Permanente Woodland Hills Medical Center,, CA, p. A72

SUDDUTH, Tony, Chief Financial Officer, Trios Health, Kennewick, WA, p. A684

SUDICKY, Mary, Chief Financial Officer, St. Mary Medical Center, Hobart, IN, p. A213

SUDOLCAN, Joseph, M.D. Medical Director, Reagan Memorial Hospital, Big Lake, TX, p. A602

SUEHS, JoAnne, Manager Human Resources, Chapman Medical Center, Orange, CA, p. A81

SUEIRO, Edwin, Administrator, Hospital De Damas, Ponce, PR, p. A727

SUGAR, Bev, Associate Administrator and Director Human Resources, Inova Mount Vernon Hospital, Alexandria, VA, p. A668

SUGDEN, Elizabeth, M.D. Chief Medical Officer, St. Luke's Jerome, Jerome, ID, p. A176

SUGG, Amy, Director Human Resources, Scott Regional Hospital, Morton, MS, p. A363

SUGG, William T., President and Chief Executive Officer, Valley County Health System, Ord, NE, p. A400

SUGHRUE, Timothy H., Chief Executive Officer, Rapid City Regional Hospital, Rapid City, SD, p. A576

SUGIYAMA, Deborah, President, NorthBay Medical Center, Fairfield, CA, p. A62

SUHR, Nancy, Manager Human Resources, Pender Community Hospital, Pender, NE, p. A401

SUHRE, Elizabeth, Executive Director, Rochester Psychiatric Center, Rochester, NY, p. A453

SUIRE, Bridget, Acting Administrator, MMO Rehabilitation and Wellness Center, Plaquemine, LA, p. A287

SUITTER, Marie, Chief Financial Officer, The Acadia Hospital, Bangor, ME, p. A291

SUKENIK, Richard, CPA Vice President Finance and Chief Financial Officer, Windber Medical Center, Windber, PA, p. A559

SUKIN, Debra F.
Chief Executive Officer, St. Luke's Lakeside Hospital, The Woodlands, TX, p. A653
Chief Executive Officer, St. Luke's The Woodlands Hospital, The Woodlands, TX, p. A653

SUKSI, Eugene, Interim Chief Executive Officer, Tehachapi Valley Healthcare District, Tehachapi, CA, p. A96

SULEIMAN, Ali, M.D. Chief of Staff, Beckley ARH Hospital, Beckley, WV, p. A693

SULIK, Sandra, M.D. Vice President Medical Affairs, St. Joseph's Hospital Health Center, Syracuse, NY, p. A456

SULIT, Maria Teresa, Director Human Resources, Holly Hill Hospital, Raleigh, NC, p. A471

SULLINS, Jacqueline C., R.N. Chief Nursing Officer, Crossgates River Oaks Hospital, Brandon, MS, p. A356

SULLIVAN, Christopher, M.D. Chief Medical Officer, Centerpoint Medical Center, Independence, MO, p. A372

SULLIVAN, Daniel, D.O. Chief Medical Officer, Vice President Medical Administration, Elmhurst Memorial Hospital,, IL, p. A189

SULLIVAN, Danita S., R.N. Chief Nursing Officer, Tulane Medical Center, New Orleans, LA, p. A286

SULLIVAN, David, Director Human Resources, OhioHealth Doctors Hospital, Columbus, OH, p. A490

SULLIVAN, Denis, Chief Human Resources Management, Veterans Affairs Black Hills Health Care System, Fort Meade, SD, p. A574

SULLIVAN, Denise, MSN Vice President Nursing and Chief Nursing Officer, Newport Hospital, Newport, RI, p. A560

SULLIVAN, Donald, M.D. Medical Director, HEALTHSOUTH Rehabilitation Hospital Memphis–North, Memphis, TN, p. A588

SULLIVAN, Gregory, Manager Human Resources, Girard Medical Center, Girard, KS, p. A244

SULLIVAN, Jennie, Director Finance, Wray Community District Hospital, Wray, CO, p. A112

SULLIVAN, Jennifer, President and Chief Executive Officer, St. James Mercy Health System, Hornell, NY, p. A439

SULLIVAN, John
President, MedStar Washington Hospital Center, Washington, DC, p. A121
Chief Executive Officer, Mount Pleasant Hospital, Mount Pleasant, SC, p. A568

SULLIVAN, Keith, Associate Director, Chillicothe Veterans Affairs Medical Center, Chillicothe, OH, p. A486

SULLIVAN, Lowery, M.D. Chief Medical Officer, Northwestern Medical Center, Saint Albans, VT, p. A666

SULLIVAN, Martha, Chief Information Officer, Harrison Memorial Hospital, Cynthiana, KY, p. A260

SULLIVAN, Mary Patricia, R.N. Chief Nursing Officer, Overlook Medical Center, Summit, NJ, p. A423

SULLIVAN, Maurita, Vice President, Mayo Clinic Health System – Northland in Barron, Barron, WI, p. A702

SULLIVAN, Michael, M.D. Chief Medical Officer, Northern Maine Medical Center, Fort Kent, ME, p. A314

SULLIVAN, Michael Dean, M.D. Chief of Staff, Mercy Hospital El Reno, El Reno, OK, p. A510

SULLIVAN, Patrick, Interim President and Chief Executive Officer, Interfaith Medical Center,, NY, p. A444

SULLIVAN, Patrick L., FACHE, Director, Captain James A. Lovell Federal Health Care Center, North Chicago, IL, p. A198

SULLIVAN, Patrick L., Chief Operating Officer, St. John's Episcopal Hospital–South Shore,, NY, p. A448

SULLIVAN, Tammy, R.N. Chief Nursing Officer, Baptist Health Richmond, Richmond, KY, p. A270

SULLIVAN, Theresa, Director Human Resources, Summit Park Hospital and Nursing Care Center, Pomona, NY, p. A451

SULLIVAN, Thomas, Vice President Fiscal Services, Harrington Memorial Hospital, Southbridge, MA, p. A314

SULLIVAN, Thomas, M.D. Chief of Staff, Mena Regional Health System, Mena, AR, p. A50

SULLIVAN, William, Chief Financial Officer, Mount Auburn Hospital, Cambridge, MA, p. A309

SULLIVAN SMITH, Mary, R.N. Vice President Clinical Operations and Chief Nursing Officer, New England Baptist Hospital, Boston, MA, p. A307

SULOG, Amy, Comptroller, Robert E. Bush Naval Hospital, Twentynine Palms, CA, p. A98

SULSER, Jamey, Director Human Resources, South Davis Community Hospital, Bountiful, UT, p. A659

SULU, Dorothy, Budget Analyst, Hopi Health Care Center, Keams Canyon, AZ, p. A33

SUMMER, Jay, M.D. Vice President Corporate Medical Affairs, McLaren Bay Region, Bay City, MI, p. A319

SUMMERLIN, Craig, Chief Human Resources Officer, Singing River Health System, Pascagoula, MS, p. A364

SUMMERLIN, Valerie, R.N. Chief Nursing Officer, Adventist Rehabilitation Hospital of Maryland, Rockville, MD, p. A303

SUMMERS, Andrew, Chief Financial Officer, USMD Hospital at Arlington, Arlington, TX, p. A598

SUMMERS, Barbara L., Ph.D. Vice President Nursing Practice and Chief Nursing Officer, University of Texas M.D. Anderson Cancer Center, Houston, TX, p. A628

SUMMERS, Curtis, Chief Executive Officer, Summit Medical Center, Edmond, OK, p. A510

SUMMERS, David A.
Chief Financial Officer, Tristar Centennial Medical Center, Nashville, TN, p. A591
Chief Financial Officer, Tristar Centennial Medical Center at Ashland City, Ashland City, TN, p. A579

SUMMERS, Debra, Chief Nursing Officer, Calhoun–Liberty Hospital, Blountstown, FL, p. A123

SUMMERS, Jeff, M.D. Medical Director, Select Specialty Hospital–North Knoxville, Knoxville, TN, p. A586

SUMMERS, Kelly, Chief Information Officer, Maricopa Integrated Health System, Phoenix, AZ, p. A36

SUMMERS, Linda, Chief Operating Officer, Canton–Potsdam Hospital, Potsdam, NY, p. A452

SUMMERS, Paul, Interim President and Chief Executive Officer, Delaware Valley Hospital, Walton, NY, p. A457

SUMMERS, Stephen M., FACHE, Chief Executive Officer, Wise Regional Health System, Decatur, TX, p. A612

SUMMERSETT III, James A., FACHE, Interim Chief Executive Officer, Monroe Hospital, Bloomington, IN, p. A207

SUMMERVILLE, Wendell, Chief Financial Officer, Bryce Hospital, Tuscaloosa, AL, p. A26

SUMNER, Donna, Vice President Human Resources and Organizational Development, St. Joseph Medical Center, Kansas City, MO, p. A374

SUMNER, J. Andrew, M.D. Vice President Medical Affairs, MedStar Southern Maryland Hospital Center, Clinton, MD, p. A300

SUMNER, Jack R., Assistant Administrator Finance, Providence Newberg Medical Center, Newberg, OR, p. A527

SUMPTER, Nikki, Senior Vice President Human Resources, JPS Health Network, Fort Worth, TX, p. A618

SUMRA, K. S., M.D. Chief of Staff, Pembina County Memorial Hospital and Wedgewood Manor, Cavalier, ND, p. A476

SUMRALL, Mary Ellen, Chief Nursing Officer, Baptist Memorial Hospital–Golden Triangle, Columbus, MS, p. A357

SUMTER, Rob, Executive Vice President and Chief Operating Officer, Regional One Health, Memphis, TN, p. A589

SUND, Lynn A., R.N. Senior Vice President, Administrator and Chief Nursing Executive, Laureate Psychiatric Clinic and Hospital, Tulsa, OK, p. A520

SUND, Lynn A., MS, Senior Vice President, Administrator and Chief Nurse Executive, Saint Francis Hospital, Tulsa, OK, p. A521

SUND, Lynn A., R.N. Senior Vice President, Administrator and Chief Nurse Executive, Saint Francis Hospital, Tulsa, OK, p. A521

SUNDBERG, Nita, Director Human Resources, Three Rivers Behavioral Health, West Columbia, SC, p. A571

SUNDBLOM, Karin, Chief Nursing Officer, Saint Luke's Cushing Hospital, Leavenworth, KS, p. A248

SUNDERLIN, Tammy, Director of Nursing, Auburn Community Hospital, Auburn, NY, p. A433

SUNDERRAJAN, E. V., M.D. Chief of Staff, Fountain Valley Regional Hospital and Medical Center, Fountain Valley, CA, p. A63

SUNDIN, Jon, M.D. Medical Director, The Orthopedic Specialty Hospital, Murray, UT, p. A661

SUNDQUIST, Joanne, Chief Information Officer, St. John's Hospital, Saint Paul, MN, p. A351

SUNDRUD, Diane
Director Human Resources, Essentia Health Fosston, Fosston, MN, p. A343
Human Resource Service Partner, Essentia Health St. Mary's – Detroit Lakes, Detroit Lakes, MN, p. A342

SUNGA, Marcos N., M.D. Chief of Staff, Hardin County General Hospital, Rosiclare, IL, p. A202

SUNKAVALLE, Krishna, M.D. Chief Medical Officer, Hamlin Memorial Hospital, Hamlin, TX, p. A622

SUNQUIST, Joanne, Chief Information Officer, Woodwinds Health Campus, Woodbury, MN, p. A354

SUNTHA, Mohan, M.D., President and Chief Executive Officer, University of Maryland St. Joseph Medical Center, Towson, MD, p. A304

SUNTRAPAK, Todd, President and Chief Executive Officer, Children's Hospital Central California, Madera, CA, p. A76

SUPPAN, Marchelle, DPM, President and Chief Executive Officer, Aultman Orrville Hospital, Orrville, OH, p. A500

SUPPLEE, Linda, Chief Executive Officer, Select Specialty Hospital–Zanesville, Zanesville, OH, p. A506

SURANI, Salim, M.D. Chief of Staff, Care Regional Medical Center, Aransas Pass, TX, p. A597

SURBER, Randy, Chief Executive Officer, Florida Hospital Zephyrhills, Zephyrhills, FL, p. A150

SURL, Deepak, Chief Information Officer, Eastern New Mexico Medical Center, Roswell, NM, p. A430

SURO, Marta R Mercado, Chief Operating Officer, Mennonite General Hospital, Aibonito, PR, p. A724

SUROWITZ, Dale, Chief Executive, Providence Tarzana Medical Center,, CA, p. A74

SURRATT, Shawn, M.D. Chief of Staff, Memorial Hospital and Manor, Bainbridge, GA, p. A154

SURROCK, Lester
Chief Financial Officer, Nix Community General Hospital, Dilley, TX, p. A614
Chief Financial Officer, Nix Health Care System, San Antonio, TX, p. A647

SUSI, Jeffrey L., President and Chief Executive Officer, Indian River Medical Center, Vero Beach, FL, p. A149

SUSICK, Nancy, MSN, President, Beaumont Hospital – Troy, Troy, MI, p. A336

SUSIE–LATTNER, Debra, M.D. Vice President, Medical Management, Advocate Condell Medical Center, Libertyville, IL, p. A194

SUSSMAN, Andrew, M.D. Chief Operating Officer, UMass Memorial Medical Center, Worcester, MA, p. A317

SUSSMAN, Howard, M.D. Chief Medical Officer, St. Joseph Hospital, Bethpage, NY, p. A433

SUSTERICH, Tim, Chief Financial Officer, Metro Health Hospital, Wyoming, MI, p. A337

SUTER, Brian, Chief Financial Officer, Mayo Clinic Health System in Fairmont, Fairmont, MN, p. A343

SUTER, Mia, Chief Administration Officer, Owensboro Health Regional Hospital, Owensboro, KY, p. A268

SUTHERLAND, Shea, Chief Financial Officer, Midwest Regional Medical Center, Midwest City, OK, p. A513

SUTHERLIN, Shara, R.N. Director Patient Care Services, South Peninsula Hospital, Homer, AK, p. A29

SUTIKA, John, President, DuBois Regional Medical Center, Du Bois, PA, p. A537

SUTTON, Andrew, Chief Human Resources Officer, Coatesville Veterans Affairs Medical Center, Coatesville, PA, p. A536

SUTTON, Bob, President and Chief Executive Officer, Avera St. Mary's Hospital, Pierre, SD, p. A575

TAFUR, Mario, M.D. Chief of Staff, St. Luke's Behavioral Health Center, Phoenix, AZ, p. A37

TAGGART, Travis, Director Information Technology, RiverValley Behavioral Health Hospital, Owensboro, KY, p. A268

TAGGE, Gordon, M.D. President Medical Staff, Three Rivers Hospital, Brewster, WA, p. A682

TAHBO, Robin, Financial Management Officer, U. S. Public Health Service Indian Hospital, Parker, AZ, p. A35

TAKACS, Susan, Market Chief Operating Officer, Physicians Regional – Pine Ridge, Naples, FL, p. A139

TAKES, Kay, R.N. Vice President Patient Care Services and Chief Nursing Officer, Mercy Medical Center–Dubuque, Dubuque, IA, p. A230

TAKEUCHI, Susi, Chief Human Resources Officer, UC Irvine Medical Center, Orange, CA, p. A81

TALAREK, Diane P., R.N. Chief Nursing Officer, Christiana Care Health System, Newark, DE, p. A119

TALBERT, Bradley S., FACHE, Chief Executive Officer, Coastal Carolina Hospital, Hardeeville, SC, p. A567

TALBOT, Angela, Manager Human Resources, Hamilton County Hospital, Syracuse, KS, p. A255

TALBOT, Lisa, Director Human Resources, St. David's South Austin Medical Center, Austin, TX, p. A600

TALBOT, Tom, Chief Executive Officer, Community Mental Health Center, Lawrenceburg, IN, p. A217

TALBOTT, Drew, Vice President Operations, Via Christi Hospital in Pittsburg, Pittsburg, KS, p. A253

TALBOTT, Ellen E., R.N. Vice President Patient Care Services, McLaren Bay Region, Bay City, MI, p. A319

TALBOTT, Sarah, Chief Nursing Officer, Sanford Chamberlain Medical Center, Chamberlain, SD, p. A572

TALENTO, Rick, Senior Vice President and Chief Financial Officer, Providence Hospital, Washington, DC, p. A121

TALLANT–BALL, Mary Jo, Director Health Information Systems, Dallas Medical Center, Dallas, TX, p. A610

TALLARICO, Dominica, President, Advocate Condell Medical Center, Libertyville, IL, p. A194

TALLEY, Cyndi, Director Information Systems, TriStar Greenview Regional Hospital, Bowling Green, KY, p. A259

TALLEY, Linda, MS Vice President and Chief Nursing Officer, Children's National Medical Center, Washington, DC, p. A121

TALLEY, Stephanie S.
Director Human Resources, Centennial Medical Center, Frisco, TX, p. A620
Interim Chief Human Resource Officer, Providence Memorial Hospital, El Paso, TX, p. A616
Interim Chief Human Resource Officer, Sierra Medical Center, El Paso, TX, p. A616

TALLEY, Stu, Chief Nursing Officer, Carson Tahoe Continuing Care Hospital, Carson City, NV, p. A404

TALLMAN, Derrick, Chief Executive Officer, Western Massachusetts Hospital, Westfield, MA, p. A316

TALLON, Joe, Vice President Finance, Salina Regional Health Center, Salina, KS, p. A254

TALLON, Richard, Chief Financial Officer, Jefferson County Hospital, Waurika, OK, p. A522

TALTON, James R., FACHE, Director, Central Alabama Veterans Health Care System, Montgomery, AL, p. A23

TALTY, Stephen, M.D. President Medical Staff, Presence Resurrection Medical Center, Chicago, IL, p. A185

TAM, David A., FACHE, Chief Administrative Officer, Pomerado Hospital, Poway, CA, p. A84

TAMANAHA, Nona, Vice President Human Resources, Queen's Medical Center, Honolulu, HI, p. A171

TAMAR, Earl J., Chief Executive Officer, Galesburg Cottage Hospital, Galesburg, IL, p. A190

TAMBURELLO, Leonardo, Divisional Chief Financial Officer, New York Community Hospital,, NY, p. A447

TAMMINEN, John, M.D. President Medical Staff, Carilion Giles Community Hospital, Pearisburg, VA, p. A676

TAN, Bradford, M.D. Chief Medical Officer, Midwestern Regional Medical Center, Zion, IL, p. A205

TANAKA, Steven, Chief Information Officer, Pomerado Hospital, Poway, CA, p. A84

TANDON, Satwant, M.D. Director of Clinical Services, Oklahoma Forensic Center, Vinita, OK, p. A521

TANDY, Gary R., Chief Financial Officer, General John J. Pershing Memorial Hospital, Brookfield, MO, p. A368

TANEBAUM, Cynthia, Director Information Services, MedStar Harbor Hospital, Baltimore, MD, p. A297

TANG, Francis, Chief Information Officer, Rancho Los Amigos National Rehabilitation Center, Downey, CA, p. A62

TANG, Shirley, R.N. Vice President Nursing Officer, Garfield Medical Center, Monterey Park, CA, p. A78

TANGEDAL, Kathy, Chief Nursing Officer, Sheridan Memorial Hospital, Plentywood, MT, p. A390

TANGEMAN, Todd, Vice President Human Resources, Newton Medical Center, Newton, KS, p. A250

TANGUAY, Denis, Chief Information Officer, Central Maine Medical Center, Lewiston, ME, p. A293

TANJUAKIO, Robert, Chief Information Resources Management, Edward Hines, Jr. Veterans Affairs Hospital, Hines, IL, p. A192

TANKEL, Nancy, R.N. Chief Nurse Executive, Kaiser Permanente Woodland Hills Medical Center,, CA, p. A72

TANNENBAUM, Scott, M.D. Medical Director, HEALTHSOUTH Sunrise Rehabilitation Hospital, Sunrise, FL, p. A146

TANNER, Douglas, Chief Executive Officer, Washington County Hospital and Nursing Home, Chatom, AL, p. A18

TANNER, Kaylee, Human Resources Business Partner, Abraham Lincoln Memorial Hospital, Lincoln, IL, p. A195

TANNER, Laureen K., FACHE, President and Chief Executive Officer, Ranken Jordan Pediatric Bridge Hospital, Maryland Heights, MO, p. A376

TANNOS, Paul, Chief Financial Officer, The Physicians Centre Hospital, Bryan, TX, p. A604

TANTHOREY, Geoff, Director Information Systems, Granville Health System, Oxford, NC, p. A470

TAPLETT, Dean, Controller, Quincy Valley Medical Center, Quincy, WA, p. A687

TAPLEY, Jahni, JD, Interim Chief Executive Officer, McCurtain Memorial Hospital, Idabel, OK, p. A512

TAPP, Gina
Director Human Resources, Samaritan North Lincoln Hospital, Lincoln City, OR, p. A526
Director Human Resources, Samaritan Pacific Communities Hospital, Newport, OR, p. A527

TAPPAN, Hugh L., President and Chief Executive Officer, Wesley Medical Center, Wichita, KS, p. A257

TAPPER, Shane, Director Management Information Systems, Fort Madison Community Hospital, Fort Madison, IA, p. A231

TARAMASCO, Chris, R.N. Chief Nursing Officer, Brandon Regional Hospital, Brandon, FL, p. A124

TARANTINO, David, M.D. Vice President Medical Affairs, Cape Regional Medical Center, Cape May Court House, NJ, p. A414

TARANTINO, Kathryn, Vice President Administration, Robert Wood Johnson University Hospital Rahway, Rahway, NJ, p. A422

TARAR, Ahmad, M.D. Medical Director, Heartland Behavioral Health Services, Nevada, MO, p. A377

TARASOVICH, James
Chief Financial Officer, Mayo Clinic Health System in Saint James, Saint James, MN, p. A351
Chief Financial Officer, Mayo Clinic Health System in Springfield, Springfield, MN, p. A352

TARBAY, Amy, Director Nursing Services, Naval Hospital Pensacola, Pensacola, FL, p. A142

TARBELL, Tim, Assistant Administrator Support Services, Scott & White Hospital – Taylor, Taylor, TX, p. A652

TARBET, Joyce, M.D. Chief Medical Officer, Murray County Medical Center, Slayton, MN, p. A352

TARBET, Michele T., Chief Executive Officer, Sharp Grossmont Hospital, La Mesa, CA, p. A68

TARLOW, Eli
Chief Information Officer, Bellevue Hospital Center, New York, NY, p. A442
Chief Information Officer, Metropolitan Hospital Center, New York, NY, p. A446

TARRANT, Maureen, Chief Executive Officer, Sky Ridge Medical Center, Lone Tree, CO, p. A109

TARTAGLIA, Judith C., President and Chief Executive Officer, Central Vermont Medical Center, Berlin, VT, p. A665

TARULLI, Pamela, Senior Vice President Human Resources, Good Samaritan Hospital, Suffern, NY, p. A455

TARVES, Paul E., R.N. Vice President Nursing Services, Evangelical Community Hospital, Lewisburg, PA, p. A543

TARWATER, Michael C., Chief Executive Officer, Carolinas HealthCare System, Charlotte, NC, p. B27

TASSEY, Karen, MS Chief Operating Officer, Columbia Memorial Hospital, Hudson, NY, p. A439

TASSIN, Bruce J., President and Chief Executive Officer, Christus St. Vincent Regional Medical Center, Santa Fe, NM, p. A430

TASSO, Tina, Manager Human Resources, The Orthopedic Specialty Hospital, Murray, UT, p. A661

TATE, Charlene, M.D. Chief Medical Staff and Clinical Services, Eleanor Slater Hospital, Cranston, RI, p. A560

TATE, Charles, Director Information Technology, Lallie Kemp Medical Center, Independence, LA, p. A279

TATE, James, M.D. Chief of Staff, Patients' Hospital of Redding, Redding, CA, p. A85

TATE, Jean, Manager Human Resources, RiverView Health, Crookston, MN, p. A342

TATE, Jodie, Director Human Resources, Westerly Hospital, Westerly, RI, p. A561

TATELBAUM, Ronald, M.D
Interim Vice President Medical Affairs, Putnam Hospital Center, Carmel, NY, p. A435
Chief Medical Officer – Health Quest, Vassar Brothers Medical Center, Poughkeepsie, NY, p. A452

TATRO, Chad, Supervisor Information Systems, Northeast Regional Medical Center, Kirksville, MO, p. A375

TATUM, Amber, Controller, Kindred Hospital Boston–North Shore, Peabody, MA, p. A313

TATUM, Jesi, Administrator, Pawhuska Hospital, Pawhuska, OK, p. A517

TATUM, Martha F., Chief Executive Officer, Evans Memorial Hospital, Claxton, GA, p. A156

TATUM, Robert, M.D. Chief of Staff, Madison River Oaks Medical Center, Canton, MS, p. A356

TATUM, Stanley D., FACHE, Chief Executive Officer, St. Mary's Regional Medical Center, Enid, OK, p. A510

TAUL, Kelly, Business Manager, Meadowbrook Rehabilitation Hospital, Gardner, KS, p. A244

TAUNER, Gary, Chief Operating Officer, St. John's Medical Center and Living Center, Jackson, WY, p. A721

TAUNTON, David, M.D. Chief of Staff, Texas Health Harris Methodist Hospital Southlake, Southlake, TX, p. A650

TAVARY, James, Chief Executive Officer, Wickenburg Community Hospital, Wickenburg, AZ, p. A41

TAVELLA, Christopher, Executive Director, Rockland Psychiatric Center, Orangeburg, NY, p. A451

TAWNEY, Michael W., D.O. Vice President Medical Affairs, Port Huron Hospital, Port Huron, MI, p. A332

TAYLOR, Adam, Manager Information Technology, Northern Inyo Hospital, Bishop, CA, p. A58

TAYLOR, Alfred P., President and Chief Executive Officer, Stanly Regional Medical Center, Albemarle, NC, p. A459

TAYLOR, Alice, MSN, Chief Executive Officer, Broward Health Imperial Point, Fort Lauderdale, FL, p. A128

TAYLOR, Alvin, Chief Human Resources Officer, Five Rivers Medical Center, Pocahontas, AR, p. A52

TAYLOR, Amy, Chief Financial Officer, Oklahoma Center for Orthopedic and Multi–Specialty Surgery, Oklahoma City, OK, p. A516

TAYLOR, Anthony, Manager Information Technology, Cherokee Indian Hospital, Cherokee, NC, p. A462

TAYLOR, Beth, Vice President, Human Resources, Newton–Wellesley Hospital, Newton Lower Falls, MA, p. A313

TAYLOR, Brenda, Director Information Systems, Texas Health Harris Methodist Hospital Cleburne, Cleburne, TX, p. A606

TAYLOR, Brett, M.D. Manager Information, Van Wert County Hospital, Van Wert, OH, p. A504

TAYLOR, Cecilia, Chief Financial Officer, Midwestern Regional Medical Center, Zion, IL, p. A205

TAYLOR, Cherie, Chief Executive Officer, Northern Rockies Medical Center, Cut Bank, MT, p. A386

TAYLOR, Cheryl, R.N. Director of Nursing, Henry Ford Kingswood Hospital, Ferndale, MI, p. A323

TAYLOR, Christina, Director Human Resources, The Brook Hospital – KMI, Louisville, KY, p. A266

TAYLOR, Clay, Chief Executive Officer, Covenant Hospital Plainview, Plainview, TX, p. A642

TAYLOR, Dana Shantel, Director Organizational Development, Fairfield Memorial Hospital, Fairfield, IL, p. A190

TAYLOR, David, Vice President Information Systems and Chief Information Officer, Stamford Hospital, Stamford, CT, p. A117

TAYLOR, Debra, Chief Nursing Officer, Paris Regional Medical Center, Paris, TX, p. A641

TAYLOR, Diana, Administrator, Sabine County Hospital, Hemphill, TX, p. A623

TAYLOR, Dwayne, Chief Executive Officer, Sycamore Shoals Hospital, Elizabethton, TN, p. A582

TAYLOR, Ernest Lee, M.D. Vice President Medical Affairs, St. Mary's Medical Center, Huntington, WV, p. A696

TAYLOR, Faye M., R.N. Director of Nursing, Stephens County Hospital, Toccoa, GA, p. A168

TAYLOR, Gregory, Chief Financial Officer, Continue Care Hospital at Hendrick Medical Center, Abilene, TX, p. A595

TAYLOR, Gregory W., M.D. Vice President and Chief Operating Officer, High Point Regional Health System, High Point, NC, p. A466

TAYLOR, Iris, R.N., President, Detroit Receiving Hospital/University Health Center, Detroit, MI, p. A321

TAYLOR, Janey, Chief Information and Technology, Overton Brooks Veterans Affairs Medical Center, Shreveport, LA, p. A288

TAYLOR, Jay, M.D. Chief of Staff, Pondera Medical Center, Conrad, MT, p. A386

TAYLOR, Jeff
Senior Vice President Finance, Magnolia Regional Health Center, Corinth, MS, p. A357
Vice President Finance, St. Luke's Regional Medical Center, Boise, ID, p. A175

TAYLOR, Jeremy, Director Information Services, Saint Francis Hospital, Charleston, WV, p. A694

TAYLOR, Jim, Chief Business Office, Malcom Randall Veterans Affairs Medical Center, Gainesville, FL, p. A129

TAYLOR, Joel, Administrator, Citizens Baptist Medical Center, Talladega, AL, p. A25

TAYLOR, Judd, Chief Financial Officer, Ogden Regional Medical Center, Ogden, UT, p. A661

TAYLOR, Julia, Area Director Human Resources, Vibra Hospital of Charleston, Mt. Pleasant, SC, p. A568

TAYLOR, Julie, FACHE, Chief Executive Officer, Alaska Regional Hospital, Anchorage, AK, p. A28

TAYLOR, Kendra, Director Outpatient Nursing, Salem Township Hospital, Salem, IL, p. A202

TAYLOR, Kent, Director Human Resources, Riverside Walter Reed Hospital, Gloucester, VA, p. A671

TAYLOR, Konnie, Chief Financial Officer, Carl Albert Community Mental Health Center, McAlester, OK, p. A513

TAYLOR, Kristie, Chief Financial Officer, Southern Tennessee Regional Health System–Lawrenceburg, Lawrenceburg, TN, p. A586

TAYLOR, Linda, Chief Human Resources Officer, Goodland Regional Medical Center, Goodland, KS, p. A244

TAYLOR, Lisa, Director of Nursing, Mountain View Hospital, Payson, UT, p. A662

TAYLOR, Loren L., Chief Executive Officer, North Memorial Health Care, Robbinsdale, MN, p. B100

TAYLOR, Marc, IS Director, Mountain West Medical Center, Tooele, UT, p. A664

TAYLOR, Marcia, Chief Executive Officer, HEALTHSOUTH Rehabilitation Hospital Memphis–North, Memphis, TN, p. A588

TAYLOR, Meredith, Comptroller, South Sunflower County Hospital, Indianola, MS, p. A359

TAYLOR, Merle, Vice President Operations, UPMC St. Margaret, Pittsburgh, PA, p. A552

TAYLOR, Michael
  Chief Information Officer, Bon Secours St. Francis Xavier Hospital, Charleston, SC, p. A563
  Vice President Finance, Northridge Hospital Medical Center,, CA, p. A73
  Vice President Financial Services and Chief Financial Officer, St. Rose Hospital, Hayward, CA, p. A66

TAYLOR, Michael V.
  Senior Vice President Human Resources, Sentara Leigh Hospital, Norfolk, VA, p. A675
  Vice President Human Resources, Sentara Princess Anne Hospital, Virginia Beach, VA, p. A679

TAYLOR, Mimi
  Corporate Vice President Information Technology, Baptist Health South Florida, Baptist Hospital of Miami, Miami, FL, p. A136
  Corporate Vice President Information Technology, Baptist Health South Florida, Homestead Hospital, Homestead, FL, p. A131
  Vice President Information Technology, Baptist Health South Florida, Mariners Hospital, Tavernier, FL, p. A148
  Vice President Information Technology, Baptist Health South Florida, South Miami Hospital, Miami, FL, p. A136

TAYLOR, Nathan, Director of Nursing, Heartland Behavioral Health Services, Nevada, MO, p. A377

TAYLOR, Norman, Director of Nursing, Brynn Marr Hospital, Jacksonville, NC, p. A467

TAYLOR, Patrick, M.D., President and Chief Executive Officer, Holy Cross Hospital, Fort Lauderdale, FL, p. A128

TAYLOR, Paul
  Administrator, Ozarks Community Hospital, Gravette, AR, p. A47
  Chief Executive Officer, Ozarks Community Hospital, Springfield, MO, p. A383

TAYLOR, Randy, Chief Information Technology Officer, Perry Memorial Hospital, Perry, OK, p. A517

TAYLOR, Renae, Chief Nursing Officer, Southeastern Health, Lumberton, NC, p. A468

TAYLOR, Richard, Chief Financial Officer, Western Mental Health Institute, Bolivar, TN, p. A579

TAYLOR, Richard S., M.D. Chief Medical Officer, Cape Fear Valley Medical Center, Fayetteville, NC, p. A464

TAYLOR, Robbie, Director Human Resources, North Sunflower Medical Center, Ruleville, MS, p. A365

TAYLOR, Robert, Director Information Services, St. Christopher's Hospital for Children, Philadelphia, PA, p. A550

TAYLOR, Ross, M.D. Clinical Director, Austin State Hospital, Austin, TX, p. A599

TAYLOR, Sarah, Chief Human Resources, National Jewish Health, Denver, CO, p. A105

TAYLOR, Scott J., President and Chief Executive Officer, St. Catherine Hospital, Garden City, KS, p. A244

TAYLOR, Scotty, Information Technology Director, East Mississippi State Hospital, Meridian, MS, p. A362

TAYLOR, Sharon, Human Resources Director, Allegiance Specialty Hospital of Greenville, Greenville, MS, p. A358

TAYLOR, Shawnia, Chief Financial Officer, Richardson Medical Center, Rayville, LA, p. A287

TAYLOR, Shelia, Director, Taylor Hardin Secure Medical Facility, Tuscaloosa, AL, p. A26

TAYLOR, Stacy, Chief Financial Officer, Nemaha County Hospital, Auburn, NE, p. A393

TAYLOR, Steve, Chief Information Officer, Anderson Regional Medical Center–South Campus, Meridian, MS, p. A362

TAYLOR, Steve, M.D. Chief Medical Officer, Sarasota Memorial Health Care System, Sarasota, FL, p. A145

TAYLOR, Steven L., Chief Executive Officer, Harrison County Hospital, Corydon, IN, p. A209

TAYLOR, Sue O., Vice President Nursing, Vidant Duplin Hospital, Kenansville, NC, p. A467

TAYLOR, Susan L., Chief Executive Officer, College Hospital Costa Mesa, Costa Mesa, CA, p. A60

TAYLOR, Todd, Chief Executive Officer, Stafford County Hospital, Stafford, KS, p. A254

TAYLOR, Tyrone, Chief Financial Officer, Veterans Affairs New Jersey Health Care System, East Orange, NJ, p. A415

TAYLOR, Venus, Director Human Resources, BHC Alhambra Hospital, Rosemead, CA, p. A86

TAYLOR–WHITEHEAD, Cheryl, Commander, Weed Army Community Hospital, Fort Irwin, CA, p. A63

TEAFORD, Carrie, Vice President Finance, Saint Thomas Midtown Hospital, Nashville, TN, p. A590

TEAGUE, Dean, Chief Operating Officer, Calvert Memorial Hospital, Prince Frederick, MD, p. A302

TEAHL, Bradley, Director Human Resources, HEALTHSOUTH Rehabilitation Hospital of York, York, PA, p. A559

TEAL, Barbara, R.N. Associate Director Patient Care Services and Nurse Executive, Sioux Falls Veterans Affairs Health Care System, Sioux Falls, SD, p. A577

TEAL, Cydney, M.D. Vice President Medical Affairs, Union Hospital, Elkton, MD, p. A300

TEAL, Dianne P., MSN Vice President Clinical Operations, CHRISTUS St. Patrick Hospital of Lake Charles, Lake Charles, LA, p. A282

TEAS, Gregory, M.D. Chief Medical Officer, Alexian Brothers Behavioral Health Hospital, Hoffman Estates, IL, p. A193

TEASDALE, Peggy, Director Human Resources, Southeast Health Center of Ripley County, Doniphan, MO, p. A370

TEATER, Phyllis, Chief Information Officer, Ohio State University Wexner Medical Center, Columbus, OH, p. A490

TEBBE, James, M.D. Vice President Medical Affairs, Ochsner Medical Center – Kenner, Kenner, LA, p. A280

TEDDER, Cookie, Human Resources Manager, Texas Health Center for Diagnostic & Surgery, Plano, TX, p. A642

TEDESCHI, Anthony, M.P.H., Chief Executive Officer and Chief Medical Officer, Louis A. Weiss Memorial Hospital, Chicago, IL, p. A184

TEDESCO, Art, Interim Chief Financial Officer, Gaylord Hospital, Wallingford, CT, p. A117

TEETER, Richard, Chief Financial Officer, Muenster Memorial Hospital, Muenster, TX, p. A639

TEEUWEN, Pat, Director Team Resources, St. Joseph's Hospital, Tampa, FL, p. A148

TEFERA, Tad, Vice President Finance, Ohio Valley General Hospital, McKees Rocks, PA, p. A544

TEFFETELLER, Scott L., President and Chief Executive Officer, Union Hospital Clinton, Clinton, IN, p. A208

TEISSONNIERE, Maria T., Director Public Relations, Hospital Oncologico Andres Grillasca, Ponce, PR, p. A727

TEITELBAUM, Karen
  President and Chief Executive Officer, Mount Sinai Hospital, Chicago, IL, p. A185
  Executive Vice President and Chief Operating Officer, Schwab Rehabilitation Hospital, Chicago, IL, p. A186

TEITELBAUM, Karen, President and Chief Executive Officer, Sinai Health System, Chicago, IL, p. B124

TEIXEIRA, Fred, M.D. Chief of Staff, Vidant Beaufort Hospital, Washington, NC, p. A474

TEJADA, Vanessa, Director Human Resources, HEALTHSOUTH Rehabilitation Institute of San Antonio, San Antonio, TX, p. A646

TEJEDA, Nicholas R., FACHE, Chief Executive Officer, Doctors Hospital of Manteca, Manteca, CA, p. A76

TELITZ, Rita, Chief Administrative Officer, Rusk County Memorial Hospital, Ladysmith, WI, p. A707

TELL, Marjorie, Vice President Information Technology, Riverview Hospital Association, Wisconsin Rapids, WI, p. A719

TELLER, Michele, Director Human Resources, Fishermen's Hospital, Marathon, FL, p. A135

TELLOR, Tammy, Acting Director Human Resources, Choate Mental Health Center, Anna, IL, p. A180

TELTHORSTER, Marcia M., Vice President Human Resources, University Medical Center of Princeton at Plainsboro, Plainsboro, NJ, p. A421

TEMPELMEYER, Zak, M.D. Chief Medical Staff, Community Memorial Hospital, Syracuse, NE, p. A402

TEMPEST, Wendy, Director Human Resources, Vibra Hospital of Northern California, Redding, CA, p. A85

TEMPLE, Amber L., Director Human Resources, Morrison Community Hospital, Morrison, IL, p. A197

TEMPLE, Gina, Chief Nurse Executive, Sutter Auburn Faith Hospital, Auburn, CA, p. A56

TEMPLE, Tracy, Chief Nursing Officer, Central Carolina Hospital, Sanford, NC, p. A472

TEMPLETON, Carrie E., FACHE, Chief Executive Officer, Lafayette General Surgical Hospital, Lafayette, LA, p. A281

TEMPLETON, Gary, M.D. Medical Director, Regency Hospital of Northwest Arkansas, Fayetteville, AR, p. A45

TEMPLETON, Parker A., FACHE, Chief Executive Officer, Iberia Medical Center, New Iberia, LA, p. A285

TEMPLETON, Sheryl, Chief Financial Officer, Scotland County Hospital, Memphis, MO, p. A376

TEMPLETON, III, William, M.D. Medical Director, Clark Memorial Hospital, Jeffersonville, IN, p. A215

TEMPLIN, Nancy, Vice President Finance and Chief Financial Officer, All Children's Hospital Johns Hopkins Medicine, Saint Petersburg, FL, p. A144

TENEWITZ, Edward, M.D. Chief of Staff, Healthmark Regional Medical Center, DeFuniak Springs, FL, p. A127

TENHOUSE, Steven, FACHE, Chief Executive Officer, Kirby Medical Center, Monticello, IL, p. A196

TENNARO, Sonja, Ed.D. Senior Vice President Clinical Operations, New York Eye and Ear Infirmary of Mount Sinai, New York, NY, p. A447

TENNYSON, Ruby, Director Administration, Naval Hospital Jacksonville, Jacksonville, FL, p. A132

TEODO, Paul M., Chief Operating Officer, Holy Cross Hospital, Chicago, IL, p. A184

TEPEDINO, Miguel, M.D. Chief Medicine, Lake City Medical Center, Lake City, FL, p. A133

TEPPER, Gil, M.D., Chief Executive Officer, Miracle Mile Medical Center, Los Angeles, CA, p. A73

TER HORST, Thomas C., Vice President Human Resources, Aurora St. Luke's Medical Center, Milwaukee, WI, p. A710

TERBUSH, Jennifer, Director of Nursing, Hills & Dales General Hospital, Cass City, MI, p. A320

TERI, Anthony, Director Information Technology, Hackensack University Medical Center at Pascack Valley, Westwood, NJ, p. A424

TERNES, Howard, Chief Executive Officer, San Gabriel Valley Medical Center, San Gabriel, CA, p. A92

TERPENING, Ken, Chief Nursing Officer, Mad River Community Hospital, Arcata, CA, p. A56

TERPSTRA, Kelli, R.N
  Chief Nursing Officer, Baylor Specialty Hospital, Dallas, TX, p. A609
  Chief Nursing Officer, Our Children's House at Baylor, Dallas, TX, p. A611

TERRELL, Greg, Senior Vice President and Chief Operating Officer, Norman Regional Health System, Norman, OK, p. A514

TERRELL, Jay, Manager Management Information Systems, Riverview Regional Medical Center, Gadsden, AL, p. A20

TERRELL, Michael T., Chief Financial Officer, Brandon Regional Hospital, Brandon, FL, p. A124

TERRESON, Gregg, Chief Financial Officer, Cascade Behavioral Hospital, Tukwila, WA, p. A691

TERRINONI, Gary G., Chief Financial Officer and Executive Vice President Administration, Kennedy Health System, Cherry Hill, NJ, p. A414

TERRY, Sr., Darrell K., Senior Vice President Operations, Newark Beth Israel Medical Center, Newark, NJ, p. A419

TERRY, Micheal, President and Chief Executive Officer, Salina Regional Health Center, Salina, KS, p. A254

TERRY, Richard, Vice President & Chief Information Officer, Carson City Hospital, Carson City, MI, p. A320

TERRYBERRY, Daniel S., M.D. Vice President of Medical Affairs, Sentara Albemarle Medical Center, Elizabeth City, NC, p. A464

TERTEL, Jenifer K., Director Human Resources, Medical City Dallas Hospital, Dallas, TX, p. A611

TERWILLIGER, Michael, Chief Financial Officer, Friends Hospital, Philadelphia, PA, p. A548

TERZANO, Valerie, MS Chief Nursing Officer, Senior Vice President Nursing, Winthrop–University Hospital, Mineola, NY, p. A441

TESKE, Mark, Chief Financial Officer, Hill Crest Behavioral Health Services, Birmingham, AL, p. A16

TESKE, Tim, D.O. Chief of Staff, St. Mary's Regional Medical Center, Enid, OK, p. A510

TESSARZIK, Connie, Business Manager, Albert J. Solnit Psychiatric Center – South Campus, Middletown, CT, p. A115

TESSMAN, Lisa, Manager Information Technology, Fayette County Hospital, Vandalia, IL, p. A204

TESTA, Nick, M.D. Chief Medical Officer, Providence Saint Joseph Medical Center, Burbank, CA, p. A58

TETRAULT, Jeffrey E., Director Facilities and Construction, Crouse Hospital, Syracuse, NY, p. A455

TETTEH, Walter
Director Human Resources, Children's Hospital of Michigan, Detroit, MI, p. A321
Director Human Resources, Rehabilitation Institute of Michigan, Detroit, MI, p. A322

TETZ, Warren, Senior Vice President and Chief Operating Officer, Glendale Adventist Medical Center, Glendale, CA, p. A65

TETZLAFF, Sue, Vice President of Nursing, War Memorial Hospital, Sault Sainte Marie, MI, p. A334

TEUBNER, Sandra, Chief Financial Officer, St. Aloisius Medical Center, Harvey, ND, p. A478

TEUFEL, George, Vice President Finance, Advocate Good Shepherd Hospital, Barrington, IL, p. A181

TEUMER, Chris, Vice President and Chief Information Officer, Newark-Wayne Community Hospital, Newark, NY, p. A449

TEVES, Alicia, Coordinator Human Resources, Molokai General Hospital, Kaunakakai, HI, p. A172

TEW, Brian, Vice President and Chief Information Officer, Catholic Medical Center, Manchester, NH, p. A411

TEW, David, Interim Chief Executive Officer, Oklahoma State University Medical Center, Tulsa, OK, p. A520

TEWKSBURY, Randy E., Vice President Finance, Geisinger-Lewistown Hospital, Lewistown, PA, p. A543

TEZANOS, Francis, Director Information Technology and Services, Kendall Regional Medical Center, Miami, FL, p. A137

THACKER, Roland, Chief Financial Officer, Northside Medical Center, Columbus, GA, p. A156

THAKOR, Pratapji, M.D. Chief of Staff, South Mississippi County Regional Medical Center, Osceola, AR, p. A51

THAMA, Todd, Chief Operating Officer, Fairfax Hospital, Kirkland, WA, p. A684

THAMES, Lisa, Director of Nursing, Mesa Springs, Fort Worth, TX, p. A618

THAMES, Robert P., Chief Operating Officer, Parkview Medical Center, Pueblo, CO, p. A110

THAMES, Stephen, Chief Executive Officer, Citizens Medical Center, Victoria, TX, p. A655

THAMES, Thomas B., M.D., President, Sentara Princess Anne Hospital, Virginia Beach, VA, p. A679

THARASRI, Luke, Chief Executive Officer, Coastal Communities Hospital, Santa Ana, CA, p. A93

THARP, Beth S., R.N., President and Chief Executive Officer, Community Hospital of Anderson and Madison County, Anderson, IN, p. A206

THARP, John Gary, M.D. Medical Director, Riverview Behavioral Health, Texarkana, AR, p. A53

THARP, Stephen, M.D. Medical Director, St. Vincent Frankfort Hospital, Frankfort, IN, p. A211

THAW, James G., President and Chief Executive Officer, Athens Regional Medical Center, Athens, GA, p. A151

THAYER, Gilbert M., M.D. Chief Medical Staff, Hardin Medical Center, Savannah, TN, p. A592

THAYER, Kendra, Vice President Clinical and Support Services and Chief Nursing Officer, Garrett County Memorial Hospital, Oakland, MD, p. A302

THEBARGE, Steven, Chief Operating Officer and Chief Financial Officer, Dorothea Dix Psychiatric Center, Bangor, ME, p. A291

THEILER, Brian, President and Chief Executive Officer, Gundersen Tri-County Hospital and Clinics, Whitehall, WI, p. A718

THEIRING, James, Chief Executive Officer, Mission Community Hospital,, CA, p. A73

THEISEN, Janet
Chief Information Officer, Sanford Tracy Medical Center, Tracy, MN, p. A353
Chief Information Officer, Sanford Westbrook Medical Center, Westbrook, MN, p. A354

THELEN, Raymond Scott, Vice President and Chief Financial Officer, Masonicare Health Center, Wallingford, CT, p. A117

THEMELIS, Carol, Vice President Human Resources, Frisbie Memorial Hospital, Rochester, NH, p. A412

THEOBALD, Terry, Chief Information Officer, Ventura County Medical Center, Ventura, CA, p. A99

THEODOROU, Andreas, Chief Medical Officer, University of Arizona Medical Center - University Campus, Tucson, AZ, p. A41

THERIAC, Gary, Director Information Technology, Lawrence County Memorial Hospital, Lawrenceville, IL, p. A194

THERIOT, Lyle, Director Human Resources, Lakeview Regional Medical Center, Covington, LA, p. A276

THERIOT, Paul, Chief Operating Officer, Gadsden Regional Medical Center, Gadsden, AL, p. A20

THEROULT, Thomas N., Chief Executive Officer, Select Specialty Hospital-Omaha, Omaha, NE, p. A400

THERRIEN, Charles D., Chief Executive Officer, Maine Coast Memorial Hospital, Ellsworth, ME, p. A293

THERRIEN, Tinna, Chief Information Officer and Director Clinical Infomatics, Gothenburg Memorial Hospital, Gothenburg, NE, p. A394

THETFORD, Carol, Chief Nursing Officer, Baptist Memorial Hospital for Women, Memphis, TN, p. A588

THEUS, Thomas L., M.D. Chief of Medicine, Doctors Specialty Hospital, Columbus, GA, p. A156

THEUS, Will, M.D. Chief of Staff, Gordon Hospital, Calhoun, GA, p. A155

THIBEDEAU, Beatrice, R.N. Senior Vice President Patient Care Services and Chief Nursing Officer, North Shore Medical Center, Salem, MA, p. A314

THIBODEAU, Bernie, Interim Chief Financial Officer, Sharp Memorial Hospital, San Diego, CA, p. A90

THIBODEAU, Helene, R.N. Vice President Patient Care Services, Northeast Rehabilitation Hospital, Salem, NH, p. A412

THIBODEAU, Jan, Director Human Resources, HEALTHSOUTH Southern Hills Rehabilitation Hospital, Princeton, WV, p. A698

THIBODEAUX, Anita, Chief Nursing Officer, Beauregard Memorial Hospital, De Ridder, LA, p. A276

THIBODEAUX, Annette, Director Human Resources, Savoy Medical Center, Mamou, LA, p. A283

THIBODEAUX, Douglas, M.D. Chief Medical Officer, OakBend Medical Center, Richmond, TX, p. A644

THIBODEAUX, Troy, Chief Executive Officer, Covenant Medical Center, Lubbock, TX, p. A634

THIEL, Stefanie
Senior Human Resources Business Partner, Saint Alphonsus Medical Center - Nampa, Nampa, ID, p. A177
Senior Human Resources Business Partner, Saint Alphonsus Medical Center - Ontario, Ontario, OR, p. A527

THIELE, Rosemary, Chief Executive Officer, Progressive Hospital, Las Vegas, NV, p. A406

THIELEMIER, Kevin, Director Human Resources, Arkansas Methodist Medical Center, Paragould, AR, p. A51

THIELEN, Kurt, Manager Business Office, Minneapolis Veterans Affairs Health Care System, Minneapolis, MN, p. A347

THIELKE, Jayne, Chief Financial Officer, Swift County-Benson Hospital, Benson, MN, p. A340

THIEME, Ron, Ph.D
Chief Knowledge and Information Officer, Community Heart and Vascular Hospital, Indianapolis, IN, p. A213
Chief Knowledge and Information Officer, Community Hospital North, Indianapolis, IN, p. A213

THIESFELD, Rebecca A., Executive Director Human Resources, Cuyuna Regional Medical Center, Crosby, MN, p. A342

THIESSEN, David, Associate Director Support Services, Missouri Rehabilitation Center, Mount Vernon, MO, p. A377

THIGPEN, Kevin, Vice President Human Resources, Athens Regional Medical Center, Athens, GA, p. A151

THILGES, Charles, Chief Financial Officer, Veterans Affairs Pittsburgh Healthcare System, Pittsburgh, PA, p. A552

THILGES, Michael, Chief Financial Officer, Clarke County Hospital, Osceola, IA, p. A236

THILL, Jennifer, Chief of Staff, Mid-Valley Hospital, Omak, WA, p. A686

THIMIS, Nicholas, Chief Information Officer, West Jefferson Medical Center, Marrero, LA, p. A284

THOELE, Theresa, Director Human Resources, Coffey County Hospital, Burlington, KS, p. A242

THOENDEL, Victor, M.D. Chief Medical Officer, Butler County Health Care Center, David City, NE, p. A395

THOMAN, Dawn, Vice President Human Resources, Cloud County Health Center, Concordia, KS, p. A242

THOMAN, Michele, R.N. Chief Nursing Officer, NCH Downtown Naples Hospital, Naples, FL, p. A138

THOMAS, Amy, Vice President Finance, Memorial Hospital, Belleville, IL, p. A181

THOMAS, Andrew, M.D. Chief Medical Officer, Ohio State University Wexner Medical Center, Columbus, OH, p. A490

THOMAS, Brian E., Administrator, Alton Mental Health Center, Alton, IL, p. A180

THOMAS, Brian N., Senior Vice President and Chief Operating Officer, Jefferson Regional Medical Center, Pine Bluff, AR, p. A52

THOMAS, Brook, Chief Financial Officer, West Boca Medical Center, Boca Raton, FL, p. A124

THOMAS, IV, Calvin, Chief Operating Officer, St. Lucie Medical Center, Port St. Lucie, FL, p. A143

THOMAS, Charmaine, R.N. Chief Nursing Officer, Polk Medical Center, Cedartown, GA, p. A155

THOMAS, Chris, FACHE, President and Chief Executive Officer, Community Hospital, Grand Junction, CO, p. A107

THOMAS, Cristina, Vice President and Chief Information Officer, Mercy Medical Center-Des Moines, Des Moines, IA, p. A229

THOMAS, Curt, Administrator, Ness County Hospital, Ness City, KS, p. A250

THOMAS, Debbie, Director Human Resources, Central Regional Hospital, Butner, NC, p. A461

THOMAS, Debora, Chief Financial Officer, Florida Hospital Memorial Medical Center, Daytona Beach, FL, p. A127

THOMAS, Debra A., Director Patient Care Services and Chief Nursing Officer, Penn Highlands Brookville, Brookville, PA, p. A534

THOMAS, Denise, Chief Financial Officer, Spring View Hospital, Lebanon, KY, p. A263

THOMAS, Dennis, Chief Nursing Officer, Hardeman County Memorial Hospital, Quanah, TX, p. A643

THOMAS, Dianna F., Director Human Resources, Brentwood Hospital, Shreveport, LA, p. A288

THOMAS, Drake, Chief Information Officer, CarePartners Health Services, Asheville, NC, p. A459

THOMAS, Gene, Vice President, Information Systems, Chief Information Officer, Memorial Hospital at Gulfport, Gulfport, MS, p. A358

THOMAS, Jayne, Chief Nursing Officer, Deaconess Hospital, Oklahoma City, OK, p. A515

THOMAS, Jennifer, Chief Operating Officer and Director of Public Relations, Lake Butler Hospital Hand Surgery Center, Lake Butler, FL, p. A133

THOMAS, Jill, Director of Nursing, Western State Hospital, Hopkinsville, KY, p. A263

THOMAS, Joan, Chief Financial Officer, Novant Health Brunswick Medical Center, Bolivia, NC, p. A460

THOMAS, John, Chief Operating Officer, San Mateo Medical Center, San Mateo, CA, p. A93

THOMAS, John A., M.D. Chief Medical Staff, Culberson Hospital, Van Horn, TX, p. A655

THOMAS, Karen A.
Vice President and Chief Information Officer, Bryn Mawr Hospital, Bryn Mawr, PA, p. A534
Chief Information Officer, Bryn Mawr Rehabilitation Hospital, Malvern, PA, p. A543
Acting Vice President and Chief Information Officer, Lankenau Medical Center, Wynnewood, PA, p. A559
Vice President and Chief Information Officer, Paoli Hospital, Paoli, PA, p. A547

THOMAS, Keith, M.D. Chief of Staff, Blue Mountain Hospital, John Day, OR, p. A526

THOMAS, Kirk E., Vice President Operations, Geisinger-Lewistown Hospital, Lewistown, PA, p. A543

THOMAS, Lizbeth, M.D. Vice President Medical Affairs, Fairview Ridges Hospital, Burnsville, MN, p. A341

THOMAS, Maggie, Vice President Human Resources and Practice Management, South County Hospital, Wakefield, RI, p. A561

THOMAS, Michael, Associate Administrator, Wayne County Hospital, Corydon, IA, p. A228

THOMAS, Michael P., Administrator, Meade District Hospital, Meade, KS, p. A250

THOMAS, Michael S., President and Chief Administrative Officer, John Muir Medical Center, Concord, Concord, CA, p. A60

THOMAS, Michelle, Vice President Human Resources, Berkeley Medical Center, Martinsburg, WV, p. A697

THOMAS, Mitchell T., Chief Financial Officer, Presbyterian Intercommunity Health Hospital, Whittier, CA, p. A100

THOMAS, Nathan, M.D. President Medical Staff, Conemaugh Meyersdale Medical Center, Meyersdale, PA, p. A545

THOMAS, Nicky, Director Human Resources, Baptist Memorial Hospital-Union City, Union City, TN, p. A594

THOMAS, Patric, Corporate Vice President Information Services, Scripps Green Hospital, La Jolla, CA, p. A68

THOMAS, Patricia F., Chief Nursing Officer, Halifax Regional Health System, South Boston, VA, p. A678

THOMAS, Paula, R.N. Vice President Patient Services, UPMC Bedford Memorial, Everett, PA, p. A539

THOMAS, Robert, Chief Executive Officer and Administrator, Columbus Community Hospital, Columbus, TX, p. A607

THOMAS, Russell, M.D. Chief of Staff, Rice Medical Center, Eagle Lake, TX, p. A614

THOMAS, Ruth, Chief Operating Officer, Mercy Fitzgerald Hospital, Darby, PA, p. A537

THOMAS, Sarah, Director of Human Resources, HEALTHSOUTH Rehabilitation Hospital of Denver, Littleton, CO, p. A109

THOMAS, Scott, Administrative Director Human Resources/Communication, Granville Health System, Oxford, NC, p. A470

THOMAS, Sharon, Vice President and Chief Nursing Officer, University Hospitals Parma Medical Center, Parma, OH, p. A500

THOMAS, Shawn M., Director Human Resources, Payson Regional Medical Center, Payson, AZ, p. A35

THOMAS, Spencer, Chief Executive Officer, Tennova Newport Medical Center, Newport, TN, p. A591

THOMAS, Stephanie, Chief Operating Officer, Denver Health, Denver, CO, p. A104

THOMAS, Sue, Manager Human Resources, Beckley ARH Hospital, Beckley, WV, p. A693

THOMAS, Sylvia, Chief Nursing Officer, Jack Hughston Memorial Hospital, Phenix City, AL, p. A25

THOMAS, Warner L., FACHE, President and Chief Executive Officer, Ochsner Health System, New Orleans, LA, p. B102

THOMAS, Jr., William, M.D. Medical Director Clinical and Internal Affairs, Molokai General Hospital, Kaunakakai, HI, p. A172

THOMAS–BOYD, Sharon L., Chief Support and Ancillary Services Officer, Oaklawn Hospital, Marshall, MI, p. A330

THOMAS–FOLDS, Lana, System Director Human Resources, Jack Hughston Memorial Hospital, Phenix City, AL, p. A25

THOMAS–WILLIAMS, Jovita, Associate Vice President Human Resources, The University of Toledo Medical Center, Toledo, OH, p. A503

THOMASON, Blake, Director Information Systems, Troy Regional Medical Center, Troy, AL, p. A26

THOMASON, Joe D., Chief Executive Officer, Centennial Medical Center, Frisco, TX, p. A620

THOMASON, Scott, Director of Nursing, Cumberland Hall Hospital, Hopkinsville, KY, p. A263

THOMBLEY, Stephen, M.D. Chief of Staff, Dorminy Medical Center, Fitzgerald, GA, p. A159

THOMMAN, Connie, Director of Nursing, Covenant Hospital–Levelland, Levelland, TX, p. A633

THOMPSON, Alan, M.D. President Medical Staff, Warm Springs Medical Center, Warm Springs, GA, p. A169

THOMPSON, Angela S., Vice President Human Resources and Support Services, Indiana University Health North Hospital, Carmel, IN, p. A208

THOMPSON, Becki, President, Oakes Community Hospital, Oakes, ND, p. A480

THOMPSON, Becky, Chief Financial Officer, CHI St. Francis Health, Breckenridge, MN, p. A341

THOMPSON, Belinda, Coordinator Human Resources, HEALTHSOUTH Chesapeake Rehabilitation Hospital, Salisbury, MD, p. A303

THOMPSON, Bobby, Director Information Technology, Stephens Memorial Hospital, Breckenridge, TX, p. A603

THOMPSON, Bonnie, Chief Operating Officer and Chief Nursing Officer, Providence Seaside Hospital, Seaside, OR, p. A530

THOMPSON, Bruce, M.D. Chief of Staff, Perry Memorial Hospital, Perry, OK, p. A517

THOMPSON, Chad, Chief Financial Officer, Lallie Kemp Medical Center, Independence, LA, p. A279

THOMPSON, Charles, M.D. Chief Medical Officer, Nacogdoches Medical Center, Nacogdoches, TX, p. A639

THOMPSON, Charolette, Chief Financial Officer, Reeves Memorial Medical Center, Bernice, LA, p. A274

THOMPSON, Cheryl
Facility Director Human Resources, Connecticut Valley Hospital, Middletown, CT, p. A115

Chief Nursing Officer, Garden Park Medical Center, Gulfport, MS, p. A358

THOMPSON, Chris
Chief Financial Officer, Delta Community Medical Center, Delta, UT, p. A659

Chief Financial Officer, Fillmore Community Medical Center, Fillmore, UT, p. A659

Chief Financial Officer, Sanpete Valley Hospital, Mount Pleasant, UT, p. A660

Chief Financial Officer, Sevier Valley Medical Center, Richfield, UT, p. A662

THOMPSON, Cindy, Chief Financial Officer, Northwest Surgical Hospital, Oklahoma City, OK, p. A515

THOMPSON, Craig B., M.D., President and Chief Executive Officer, Memorial Sloan–Kettering Cancer Center, New York, NY, p. A445

THOMPSON, Dale
Chief Financial Officer, McLaren Greater Lansing, Lansing, MI, p. A328

Chief Operating Officer, Western State Hospital, Tacoma, WA, p. A691

THOMPSON, David, M.D. Chief of Staff, Richardson Medical Center, Rayville, LA, p. A287

THOMPSON, David
Chief Financial Officer, St. Anthony Hospital, Lakewood, CO, p. A108

Chief Financial Officer, St. Anthony Summit Medical Center, Frisco, CO, p. A106

THOMPSON, David M., Chief Executive Officer, Sutter Tracy Community Hospital, Tracy, CA, p. A97

THOMPSON, Debbie, Chief Financial Officer, Sweetwater Hospital, Sweetwater, TN, p. A593

THOMPSON, Debbra, Manager Human Resources, McKenzie County Healthcare System, Watford City, ND, p. A480

THOMPSON, Donna K., Chief Executive Officer, Allegiance Health Center of Ruston, Ruston, LA, p. A287

THOMPSON, Douglas, Chief Information Officer, Upson Regional Medical Center, Thomaston, GA, p. A168

THOMPSON, Dwight, Chief Financial Officer, Altru Health System, Grand Forks, ND, p. A478

THOMPSON, Ethan, Chief Financial Officer, St. Theresa Specialty Hospital, Kenner, LA, p. A280

THOMPSON, Frederick G., Ph.D., President, Anson Community Hospital, Wadesboro, NC, p. A474

THOMPSON, Greg, Chief Medical Officer, Gundersen Health System, La Crosse, WI, p. A707

THOMPSON, Helen, Interim Director, Indian Health Service Hospital, Rapid City, SD, p. A575

THOMPSON, James H., FACHE, Owner and Chief Executive Officer, Healthmark Regional Medical Center, DeFuniak Springs, FL, p. A127

THOMPSON, Jeffrey D., Chief Executive Officer, GLOBALREHAB Hospital – Fort Worth, Fort Worth, TX, p. A618

THOMPSON, Jeffrey E., M.D., Chief Executive Officer, Gundersen Health System, La Crosse, WI, p. A707

THOMPSON, John W., M.D. Chief of Staff, Eastern Louisiana Mental Health System, Jackson, LA, p. A279

THOMPSON, Julie
Chief Nursing Officer, Bluffton Regional Medical Center, Bluffton, IN, p. A207

Manager Personnel and Payroll, Mayers Memorial Hospital District, Fall River Mills, CA, p. A63

THOMPSON, Kevin, Chief Financial Officer, Sharp Mesa Vista Hospital, San Diego, CA, p. A90

THOMPSON, Kim, Vice President and Chief Financial Officer, Ozarks Medical Center, West Plains, MO, p. A384

THOMPSON, Linda
Chief Operating Officer, Fairfax Community Hospital, Fairfax, OK, p. A511

Vice President Human Resources, New England Baptist Hospital, Boston, MA, p. A307

THOMPSON, Lisa, MSN Director of Nursing, Hiawatha Community Hospital, Hiawatha, KS, p. A245

THOMPSON, Lisa D., Director Human Resources, Lea Regional Medical Center, Hobbs, NM, p. A428

THOMPSON, Lori L., Manager Human Resources, Nebraska Orthopaedic Hospital, Omaha, NE, p. A400

THOMPSON, Marion A., FACHE, Chief Executive Officer, Goodland Regional Medical Center, Goodland, KS, p. A244

THOMPSON, Mark, Vice President Finance and Chief Financial Officer, Lourdes Hospital, Paducah, KY, p. A269

THOMPSON, Mark, M.D. Chief Medical Officer, Monroe Clinic, Monroe, WI, p. A711

THOMPSON, Mark, Vice President Financial Services, Rapid City Regional Hospital, Rapid City, SD, p. A576

THOMPSON, Matthew J., Chief Executive Officer, Carson City Hospital, Carson City, MI, p. A320

THOMPSON, Michael S., Chief Executive Officer, Frio Regional Hospital, Pearsall, TX, p. A641

THOMPSON, Michele T., Deputy Chief Operating Officer, Provident Hospital of Cook County, Chicago, IL, p. A186

THOMPSON, Ormand P., Administrator, North Baldwin Infirmary, Bay Minette, AL, p. A16

THOMPSON, Pamela, Chief Operations Officer, Huhukam Memorial Hospital, Sacaton, AZ, p. A38

THOMPSON, Patti, Chief Operating Officer, San Luis Valley Health, Alamosa, CO, p. A102

THOMPSON, Ranae M., R.N. Director Patient Care Services, Shriners Hospitals for Children–Greenville, Greenville, SC, p. A566

THOMPSON, Randell, Chief Nursing Officer, Plateau Medical Center, Oak Hill, WV, p. A698

THOMPSON, Sarah, Director Health Information Management, Hardtner Medical Center, Olla, LA, p. A286

THOMPSON, Scott, Market Management Information System Director, Shands Live Oak Regional Medical Center, Live Oak, FL, p. A134

THOMPSON, Selva, R.N. Chief Nurse Executive, Gallup Indian Medical Center, Gallup, NM, p. A428

THOMPSON, Sherene, Director Human Resources, Houston Methodist Willowbrook Hospital, Houston, TX, p. A624

THOMPSON, Sheri, Director Information Technology, Crete Area Medical Center, Crete, NE, p. A395

THOMPSON, Stephen, D.O. Chief of Staff, Grant Memorial Hospital, Petersburg, WV, p. A698

THOMPSON, Stuart, Vice President Human Resources, Memorial Hospital Jacksonville, Jacksonville, FL, p. A131

THOMPSON, Susan K., President and Chief Executive Officer, UnityPoint Health – Trinity Regional Medical Center, Fort Dodge, IA, p. A230

THOMPSON, Thomas R., Chief Executive Officer, Samaritan Healthcare, Moses Lake, WA, p. A685

THOMPSON, Tim, Vice President Information Services, St. Anthony's Hospital, Saint Petersburg, FL, p. A145

THOMPSON, Sr., Timothy L., Senior Vice President and Chief Information Officer, Houston Methodist Hospital, Houston, TX, p. A624

THOMPSON, Tina H., Coordinator Human Resources, FirstHealth Montgomery Memorial Hospital, Troy, NC, p. A474

THOMPSON, Trinise, Director Human Resources, St. Luke's Medical Center, Phoenix, AZ, p. A37

THOMPSON, Vera, Director Human Resources, Kingsboro Psychiatric Center,, NY, p. A444

THOMPSON, Wayne, Senior Vice President and Chief Information Officer, Mount Nittany Medical Center, State College, PA, p. A555

THOMPSON, Wayne D., Interim Chief Executive Officer, Dauterive Hospital, New Iberia, LA, p. A285

THOMPSON, Wesley, M.D. President Medical Staff, Fairfield Memorial Hospital, Fairfield, IL, p. A190

THOMPSON, William, M.D. Chief Medical Officer, Saint Thomas Midtown Hospital, Nashville, TN, p. A590

THOMPSON, William P., President and Chief Executive Officer, SSM Health, Saint Louis, MO, p. B127

THOMPSON–COOK, Timothy, Chief Operating Officer, Contra Costa Regional Medical Center, Martinez, CA, p. A77

THOMSEN, Eric, M.D. Chief of Staff, Beatrice Community Hospital and Health Center, Beatrice, NE, p. A394

THOMSEN, Sue
Chief Financial Officer, New Braunfels Regional Rehabilitation Hospital, New Braunfels, TX, p. A639

Chief Financial Officer, South Texas Rehabilitation Hospital, Brownsville, TX, p. A604

THOMSEN, Vicki
Director Human Resources, Aurora Phoenix Hospital, Glendale, AZ, p. A33

Director Human Resources, Aurora Tempe Hospital, Tempe, AZ, p. A39

THOMSON, Doug, M.D. Chief Medical Officer, Commonwealth Regional Specialty Hospital, Bowling Green, KY, p. A258

THOMSON, Ken, M.D. Medical Director, Sugar Land Surgical Hospital, Sugar Land, TX, p. A651

THOMSON, Nicole, Chief Financial Officer, Saint Louise Regional Hospital, Gilroy, CA, p. A65

THOMSON, Sean, CPA Chief Financial Officer, Spotsylvania Regional Medical Center, Fredericksburg, VA, p. A671

THOMSON, Steven, M.D. Medical Director, Heartland Behavioral Healthcare, Massillon, OH, p. A498

THONE, Tammy, M.D. Chief Medical Staff, Alleghany Memorial Hospital, Sparta, NC, p. A473

THORDARSON, G. Thor, President and Chief Executive Officer, Indiana University Health La Porte Hospital, La Porte, IN, p. A216

THORE, Joe, Chief Operating Officer, Ashe Memorial Hospital, Jefferson, NC, p. A467

THOREEN, Peter W., FACHE,
Interim Chief Executive Officer, Meriter Hospital, Madison, WI, p. A708

President and Chief Executive Officer, UnityPoint Health – St. Luke's, Sioux City, IA, p. A238

THORESON, Scott D., FACHE, Administrator, Mayo Clinic Health System in Springfield, Springfield, MN, p. A352

THORMODSON, Cyndee
Chief Financial Officer, Carrington Health Center, Carrington, ND, p. A476

Assistant Vice President Finance, Mercy Hospital, Devils Lake, ND, p. A477

THORN, III, Eugene A., Vice President Finance and Chief Financial Officer, Union Hospital, Dover, OH, p. A493

THORN, Mark, FACHE Chief Financial Officer, Lincoln County Medical Center, Troy, MO, p. A384

THORNBRUGH, Mitchell, Administrative Officer, Cherokee Nation W.W. Hastings Indian Hospital, Tahlequah, OK, p. A519

THORNE, Dana, Administrator Human Resources, Valley Hospital Medical Center, Las Vegas, NV, p. A407

THORNE, Rob, Director Human Resources, Heritage Medical Center, Shelbyville, TN, p. A593

THORNE Jr., William, Chief Executive Officer, Acoma–Canoncito–Laguna Hospital, Acoma, NM, p. A426

THORNELL, Timothy, FACHE, Chief Executive Officer, Lea Regional Medical Center, Hobbs, NM, p. A428

THORNSBERRY, Michael, M.D. Chief Medical Officer, Coliseum Medical Centers, Macon, GA, p. A162

THORNTON, Carol, Director Human Resources, Cherry Hospital, Goldsboro, NC, p. A465

THORNTON, Cayetano, Chief Information Officer, Walter Reed National Military Medical Center, Bethesda, MD, p. A299

THORNTON, Daryl W., Chief Operating Officer, Kansas Medical Center, Andover, KS, p. A241

THORNTON, Jillisa, Director of Nursing, Coastal Harbor Treatment Center, Savannah, GA, p. A166

THORNTON, Laird, Director Information Systems, Alta Vista Regional Hospital, Las Vegas, NM, p. A429

THORNTON Jr.,, Robert M., Chief Executive Officer, Sunlink Health Systems, Atlanta, GA, p. B130

THORNTON, Timothy J., Chief Financial Officer, Russell Medical Center, Alexander City, AL, p. A15

THORPE, Linda, Chief Executive Officer, East Morgan County Hospital, Brush, CO, p. A103

THORPE, Wendy, Area Director Information Systems, St. Joseph Hospital, Eureka, CA, p. A62

THORSEN, Erik, Chief Executive Officer, Columbia Memorial Hospital, Astoria, OR, p. A523

THORWALD, Robert, Chief Information Officer, Washington Hospital Healthcare System, Fremont, CA, p. A64

THOTAKURA, Raj, M.D. Medical Director, Old Vineyard Behavioral Health Services, Winston-Salem, NC, p. A475

THRASHER, Amanda, Director Nursing, Ellsworth County Medical Center, Ellsworth, KS, p. A243

THRASHER, Barton, M.D. Chief of Staff, Methodist Healthcare–Fayette Hospital, Somerville, TN, p. A593

THRASHER, Charlotte, Vice President and Chief Operating Officer, Seton Medical Center Austin, Austin, TX, p. A599

THRASHER, Kimberly, Controller, HEALTHSOUTH Lakeshore Rehabilitation Hospital, Birmingham, AL, p. A16

THRASHER, Sherri, JD Director Human Resources, Pennock Hospital, Hastings, MI, p. A326

THREEWITS, Sheree, Director Human Resources, Manatee Memorial Hospital, Bradenton, FL, p. A124

THRESHER, A. Jean, M.D. Chief Medical Officer, Mercer Health, Coldwater, OH, p. A489

THULI, Karen, Coordinator Information Systems, Upland Hills Health, Dodgeville, WI, p. A703

THUN, Todd, Director Human Resources, Montana State Hospital, Warm Springs, MT, p. A391

THUNELL, Adam, Chief Operating Officer and Vice President Operations, Community Memorial Health System, Ventura, CA, p. A99

THURBER, Joe, Director Information Technology, Central Regional Hospital, Butner, NC, p. A461

THURMER, DeAnn, Chief Operating Officer, Waupun Memorial Hospital, Waupun, WI, p. A717

THURMOND, Jeff, Vice President Information Systems, Baptist Health Corbin, Corbin, KY, p. A260

THURSTON, Thomas, M.D. Medical Director, J. D. McCarty Center for Children With Developmental Disabilities, Norman, OK, p. A514

THYGESON, Cindy, M.D. Director Medical Affairs, Sutter Center for Psychiatry, Sacramento, CA, p. A87

TIBBETT, Cheryl, Chief Financial Officer, Bayfront Health Port Charlotte, Port Charlotte, FL, p. A143

TIBBITS, Dick, Vice President and Chief Operating Officer, Florida Hospital Tampa, Tampa, FL, p. A147

TIBBITS, Richard M., Vice President and Chief Operating Officer, Loma Linda University Medical Center–Murrieta, Murrieta, CA, p. A79

TIBBS, E. W., President and Chief Executive Officer, Centra Health, Inc., Lynchburg, VA, p. B34

TIBBS, E. W., President and Chief Executive Officer, Centra Lynchburg General Hospital, Lynchburg, VA, p. A673

TICE, Darlette, Chief Nursing Officer, Manatee Memorial Hospital, Bradenton, FL, p. A124

TICE, Evan, Director Information Technology and Systems, Sky Ridge Medical Center, Lone Tree, CO, p. A109

TICE, Heidi, Chief Financial Officer, Cheyenne County Hospital, Saint Francis, KS, p. A253

TICE, Kirk C., President and Chief Executive Officer, Robert Wood Johnson University Hospital Rahway, Rahway, NJ, p. A422

TICE, Linda, Director Information Systems, Riverton Memorial Hospital, Riverton, WY, p. A722

TICHENOR, Florence, Director Information Technology, Copper Basin Medical Center, Copperhill, TN, p. A581

TICHENOR, John, Chief Financial Officer, Ohio County Hospital, Hartford, KY, p. A262

TIDWELL, Joseph, Administrator, Phoenix Behavioral Hospital, Rayne, LA, p. A287

TIDWELL, Wesley, Chief Operating Officer, Memorial Hermann Northwest Hospital, Houston, TX, p. A625

TIEDT, Jerry, Director Information Systems, Waverly Health Center, Waverly, IA, p. A239

TIEFENTHALER, Brenda Marie, R.N. Vice President Patient Care and Informatics, Spencer Hospital, Spencer, IA, p. A238

TIEMENS, Linda, Chief Executive Officer, Select Specialty Hospital–Tulsa Midtown, Tulsa, OK, p. A521

TIERNAN, Kelley, Chief Financial Officer, Claxton–Hepburn Medical Center, Ogdensburg, NY, p. A450

TIERNEY, Mark A., Chief Financial Officer, Manatee Memorial Hospital, Bradenton, FL, p. A124

TIGGELAAR, Tom
 Vice President Finance, Mayo Clinic Health System – Franciscan Healthcare in La Crosse, La Crosse, WI, p. A707
 Vice President Finance ad Chief Financial Officer, Mayo Clinic Health System – Franciscan Healthcare in Sparta, Sparta, WI, p. A715

TILGHMAN, Bradley, Controller, HEALTHSOUTH Emerald Coast Rehabilitation Hospital, Panama City, FL, p. A142

TILLER, Debra, Director Personnel and Administrative Secretary, Healthmark Regional Medical Center, DeFuniak Springs, FL, p. A127

TILLER, Joni R., R.N. Chief Nursing Officer, Integris Baptist Medical Center, Oklahoma City, OK, p. A515

TILLIRSON, Mike, D.O. Executive Vice President and Chief Medical Officer, AnMed Health Medical Center, Anderson, SC, p. A562

TILLMAN, Jill, Assistant Chief Executive Officer, Brandywine Hospital, Coatesville, PA, p. A536

TILLMAN, Kanner, Chief Financial Officer, Encino Hospital Medical Center,, CA, p. A71

TILLMAN, Michael, Vice President Patient Services and Chief Operating Officer, United Hospital Center, Bridgeport, WV, p. A693

TILLMAN, Pamela P., R.N., Chief Executive Officer, Pioneer Community Hospital of Stokes, Danbury, NC, p. A463

TILLMAN, Randy, M.D. Chief Medical Staff, Promise Hospital of Miss Lou, Vidalia, LA, p. A289

TILLMAN–TAYLOR, Susan, Manager Human Resources, Southern Ocean Medical Center, Manahawkin, NJ, p. A418

TILSON, Natalie, Controller, HEALTHSOUTH Rehabilitation Hospital, Kingsport, TN, p. A585

TILTON, David P., President and Chief Executive Officer, AtlantiCare, Egg Harbor Township, NJ, p. B15

TILUS, Sheryl, R.N. Chief Nursing Officer, Skiff Medical Center, Newton, IA, p. A235

TIMANUS, Anthony, Chief Executive Officer, Avera Gregory Hospital, Gregory, SD, p. A574

TIMBERS, Christopher T.
 Chief Information Officer, Sibley Memorial Hospital, Washington, DC, p. A122
 Vice President and Chief Information Officer, Suburban Hospital, Bethesda, MD, p. A299

TIMLIN, Marie, R.N. Chief Nursing Officer, Yampa Valley Medical Center, Steamboat Springs, CO, p. A111

TIMM, Karen, R.N. Vice President Patient Services, St. Anthony Regional Hospital, Carroll, IA, p. A226

TIMM, Mark
 Director Human Resources, Yavapai Regional Medical Center – East, Prescott Valley, AZ, p. A37
 Director Human Resources, Yavapai Regional Medical Center, Prescott, AZ, p. A37

TIMM, Matt, M.D. Medical Director, Pender Community Hospital, Pender, NE, p. A401

TIMMER, Kari, Chief Financial Officer, Hegg Memorial Health Center Avera, Rock Valley, IA, p. A237

TIMMERMAN, Candace, Director Human Resources, Avera Creighton Hospital, Creighton, NE, p. A395

TIMMERMAN, Jo, Manager Accounting, Norwood Health Center, Marshfield, WI, p. A709

TIMMONS, Bret, D.O. Chief Medical Staff, Power County Hospital District, American Falls, ID, p. A174

TIMMONS, William, Chief Executive Officer, Los Ninos Hospital, Phoenix, AZ, p. A36

TIMPE, David A., Interim President and Chief Executive Officer, Childrens Care Hospital and School, Sioux Falls, SD, p. A576

TIMPE, Ronald, Chief Financial Officer, Floyd County Medical Center, Charles City, IA, p. A227

TINCH, Paula, Interim Chief Financial Officer, Newark–Wayne Community Hospital, Newark, NY, p. A449

TINCHER, Pat, Director Finance, Langlade Hospital, Antigo, WI, p. A701

TINDALL, Patricia, Chief Executive Officer, Lyndon B. Johnson Tropical Medical Center, Pago Pago, AS, p. A724

TINDLE, Jeff A., Chief Executive Officer, Carroll County Memorial Hospital, Carrollton, MO, p. A369

TINDLE, Tim, Chief Information Officer, Harris Health System, Houston, TX, p. A624

TINGLE, Billy, Director Information Systems and Respiratory Therapy, Avoyelles Hospital, Marksville, LA, p. A283

TINGSTAD, Jonathan, Vice President and Chief Financial Officer, Seattle Cancer Care Alliance, Seattle, WA, p. A688

TINKER, Peter, Chief Human Resources Officer, James J. Peters Veterans Affairs Medical Center,, NY, p. A444

TINNERELLO, Jeremy, R.N. Chief Nursing Officer, Glenwood Regional Medical Center, West Monroe, LA, p. A290

TINNEY, Sean, FACHE Chief Operating Officer, Medical West, Bessemer, AL, p. A16

TINSA, Udom, M.D. Medical Director, Ashley Medical Center, Ashley, ND, p. A476

TINSLEY, Cassie, Director, Human Resources, Powell Valley Healthcare, Powell, WY, p. A722

TINSLEY III, Edward D., Chief Executive Officer, McLeod Loris Seacoast Hospital, Loris, SC, p. A568

TINSLEY, Kay
 Vice President Fiscal Services, Good Samaritan Regional Health Center, Mount Vernon, IL, p. A197
 Vice President Finance, St. Mary's Hospital, Centralia, IL, p. A182

TINSLEY, Nancy, President and Chief Executive Officer, University Hospitals Parma Medical Center, Parma, OH, p. A500

TINTLE, Keith D., Chief Executive Officer, Timpanogos Regional Hospital, Orem, UT, p. A661

TIPPIN, Russell, Chief Executive Officer and Administrator, Permian Regional Medical Center, Andrews, TX, p. A597

TIPPS, Linda, Director Human Resources, Southern Tennessee Regional Health System–Winchester, Winchester, TN, p. A594

TIPTON, Peggy, Chief Operating Officer and Chief Nursing Officer, Oklahoma Heart Hospital, Oklahoma City, OK, p. A516

TIPTON, Teri, MSN Chief Nursing Officer and Vice President Patient Care Services, Nebraska Methodist Hospital, Omaha, NE, p. A400

TIRA, Cheryl, Director Information Systems, Columbus Community Hospital, Columbus, NE, p. A395

TIRMAN, Kerry, President and Chief Operating Officer, Mercy St. Vincent Medical Center, Toledo, OH, p. A503

TIRMAN, Kerry R., FACHE, President, Mississippi Baptist Medical Center, Jackson, MS, p. A360

TISDALE, Willis E., Director Human Resources, Shriners Hospitals for Children–Greenville, Greenville, SC, p. A566

TISDALL, Renae, Chief Financial Officer, Mobridge Regional Hospital, Mobridge, SD, p. A575

TISSIER, Becky, Chief Fiscal Service, Veterans Affairs Illiana Health Care System, Danville, IL, p. A187

TITSWORTH, Sue, Director Human Resources, Coleman County Medical Center, Coleman, TX, p. A606

TITTLE, G. Keith, Director Information Technology, Unicoi County Memorial Hospital, Erwin, TN, p. A582

TITTLE, JoDee, Director Community and Human Resources, St. Charles Madras, Madras, OR, p. A526

TITUS, Monica, President and Chief Executive Officer, Acuity Specialty Hospital of New Jersey, Atlantic City, NJ, p. A413

TKACIK, Eileen, Vice President Information Technology and Patient Accounts, KidsPeace Children's Hospital, Orefield, PA, p. A547

TOADVINE, Stephen, M.D. Chief Medical Officer, Hardin Memorial Hospital, Elizabethtown, KY, p. A260

TOALSON, Jason
 Chief Executive Officer, Mayhill Hospital, Denton, TX, p. A613
 Chief Executive Officer, University Behavioral Health of Denton, Denton, TX, p. A613

TOBEY, Shelley R., R.N. Chief Operating Officer and Chief Nursing Officer, Texas Health Presbyterian Hospital Flower Mound, Flower Mound, TX, p. A617

TOBIN, Hugh, Chief Financial Officer, DeKalb Regional Medical Center, Fort Payne, AL, p. A20

TOBIN, Karen A., R.N. Chief Operating Officer, Sanford Medical Center Fargo, Fargo, ND, p. A477

TOBIN, Ryan, Chief Operating Officer, Rose Medical Center, Denver, CO, p. A105

TOBLER, Randy, M.D., Interim Chief Executive Officer, Scotland County Hospital, Memphis, MO, p. A376

TOBON–STEVENS, Paula, Associate Administrator, Angleton Danbury Medical Center, Angleton, TX, p. A597

TODD, Bob, Director Information Systems, Mount Auburn Hospital, Cambridge, MA, p. A309

TODD, David, M.D. President Medical Staff, Memorial Specialty Hospital, Lufkin, TX, p. A635

TODD, Fred O., Senior Vice President Finance, McLeod Loris Seacoast Hospital, Loris, SC, p. A568

TODD, James, Chief Financial Officer, River Oaks Hospital, New Orleans, LA, p. A286

TODD, Nate, Chief Financial Officer, Central Arkansas Veterans Healthcare System, Little Rock, AR, p. A49

TODD, Robbie, Director Information Technology, Horn Memorial Hospital, Ida Grove, IA, p. A232

TODD, Steve J., Chief Executive Officer, St. Luke Community Healthcare, Ronan, MT, p. A390

TODD–ATKINSON, Sandra, Chief Operating Officer and Chief Nursing Officer, Broward Health Imperial Point, Fort Lauderdale, FL, p. A128

TODOROW, Thomas, Chief Financial Officer and Executive Vice President, Children's Hospital of Philadelphia, Philadelphia, PA, p. A547

TOEDT, Michael E., M.D. Director Clinical Services, Cherokee Indian Hospital, Cherokee, NC, p. A462

TOFANI, Gerald, Chief Financial Officer, Monmouth Medical Center, Southern Campus, Lakewood, NJ, p. A417

TOL, Daryl, Chief Executive Officer, Florida Hospital Memorial Medical Center, Daytona Beach, FL, p. A127

TOLBERT, Catherine L., R.N. Senior Vice President Nursing and Clinical Services and Chief Nurse Executive, St. Elizabeth Health Center, Youngstown, OH, p. A506

TOLBERT, James, Director Information Systems, EASTAR Health System, Muskogee, OK, p. A514

TOLEDO, Iris, Chief Nursing Officer, Hospital Dr. Cayetano Coll Y Toste, Arecibo, PR, p. A724

TOLINE, Tyler, Interim Chief Executive Officer, Saunders Medical Center, Wahoo, NE, p. A402

TOLLEFSON, Sue, Coordinator Payroll Personnel, Granite Falls Municipal Hospital and Manor, Granite Falls, MN, p. A344

TOLOSKY, Mark R., FACHE, President and Chief Executive Officer, Baystate Medical Center, Springfield, MA, p. A314

TOLSON, Rick, Chief Administrative Officer and Chief Human Resources Officer, Christ Hospital, Cincinnati, OH, p. A486

TOMAS, George, Director Information Services, Griffin Hospital, Derby, CT, p. A114

TOMASINO, Tom, Administrator and Chief Executive Officer, Whidbey General Hospital, Coupeville, WA, p. A682

TOMASO, Nancy, Vice President, Patient Care Services, Milford Regional Medical Center, Milford, MA, p. A312

TOMBERLIN, Terri, Director Human Resources, Curry General Hospital, Gold Beach, OR, p. A525

TOME, Julie, M.D. Vice President North Central Region Medical Affairs, OhioHealth Marion General Hospital, Marion, OH, p. A497

TOME, Michael, M.D. Medical Director, Kaiser Permanente Los Angeles Medical Center, Los Angeles, CA, p. A72

TOMLIN, Kerry W., Associate Administrator, Clay County Hospital, Ashland, AL, p. A15

TOMLINSON, Charles M., M.D. Chief Medical Officer, Cleveland Regional Medical Center, Shelby, NC, p. A472

TOMLINSON, Daniel, Chair Human Resources, Mayo Clinic Jacksonville, Jacksonville, FL, p. A131

TOMLINSON, David
  Executive Vice President Chief Financial Officer and Chief Information Officer, Centegra Hospital – McHenry, McHenry, IL, p. A196
  Executive Vice President Chief Financial Officer and Chief Information Officer, Centegra Hospital – Woodstock, Woodstock, IL, p. A205

TOMLINSON, Sallie, Manager Human Resources, Arbuckle Memorial Hospital, Sulphur, OK, p. A519

TOMORY, Gerald, M.D
  Regional Medical Director, Kauai Veterans Memorial Hospital, Waimea, HI, p. A173
  Regional Medical Director, Samuel Mahelona Memorial Hospital, Kapaa, HI, p. A172

TOMPKINS, Charles, M.D. Chief of Staff, Crenshaw Community Hospital, Luverne, AL, p. A22

TOMPKINS, Kim, Director Information Services, DeTar Healthcare System, Victoria, TX, p. A655

TOMSU, Karen, R.N. Chief Nursing Officer, Conroe Regional Medical Center, Conroe, TX, p. A607

TONER, Tina, Director of Nursing, North Big Horn Hospital District, Lovell, WY, p. A722

TONEY, Mark, President and Chief Executive Officer, Brookdale Hospital Medical Center,, NY, p. A443

TONEY, Patty, R.N. Chief Nurse Executive, CHRISTUS Santa Rosa Health System, San Antonio, TX, p. A646

TONG, Cheryl, Corporate Chief Financial Officer, Community Hospital of Huntington Park, Huntington Park, CA, p. A67

TONGATE, Scott, Chief Executive Officer, Lauderdale Community Hospital, Ripley, TN, p. A592

TONGES, Mary Crabtree, Ph.D. Senior Vice President and Chief Nursing Officer, University of North Carolina Hospitals, Chapel Hill, NC, p. A461

TONJES, Ken, Interim Chief Administrative Officer, PeaceHealth Ketchikan Medical Center, Ketchikan, AK, p. A29

TONKINSON, Robert
  Chief Operating Officer and Chief Financial Officer, Mercy Allen Hospital, Oberlin, OH, p. A500
  Chief Operating Officer and Chief Financial Officer, Mercy Regional Medical Center, Lorain, OH, p. A497

TONN, Deb L., Vice President Patient Care, Campbell County Memorial Hospital, Gillette, WY, p. A721

TONNU, Lannie, Senior Vice President and Chief Financial Officer, Children's Hospital Los Angeles, Los Angeles, CA, p. A71

TOOKE, Landon, Chief Executive Officer, Reeves Memorial Medical Center, Bernice, LA, p. A274

TOOKE, Ryan, Chief Executive Officer, Rosebud Health Care Center, Forsyth, MT, p. A387

TOOKER, Deby, Director Human Resources, The Surgical Hospital of Phoenix, Phoenix, AZ, p. A37

TOOLE, LaDon
  Administrator, Grady General Hospital, Cairo, GA, p. A155
  Administrator, Mitchell County Hospital, Camilla, GA, p. A155
  Vice President Network Operations, Mitchell County Hospital, Camilla, GA, p. A155

TOOLE, Patricia, Vice President Human Resources, East Mountain Hospital, Belle Mead, NJ, p. A413

TOOLE, Trish, Vice President Administrative Services, Carrier Clinic, Belle Mead, NJ, p. A413

TOOMEY, Richard Kirk, FACHE, President and Chief Executive Officer, Beaufort Memorial Hospital, Beaufort, SC, p. A562

TOON, William
  Chief Information Officer, Baptist Hospitals of Southeast Texas, Beaumont, TX, p. A601
  Director, Baptist Orange Hospital, Orange, TX, p. A640

TOOT, Gregory P., Vice President, Post–Acute Care and Professional Services, Hebrew Rehabilitation Center, Boston, MA, p. A307

TOPMILLER, Darrell, Director Finance, Fulton County Health Center, Wauseon, OH, p. A504

TOPOLEWSKI, Ted, Chief Executive Officer, Madison Parish Hospital, Tallulah, LA, p. A289

TOPPEN, Jacki, Director of Nursing, Prairie St. John's, Fargo, ND, p. A477

TOPPER, David, Chief Executive Officer, Alta Healthcare System, Los Angeles, CA, p. B10

TORBETT, Russell B., Director Human Resources, Creek Nation Community Hospital, Okemah, OK, p. A514

TORCHIA, Joseph, M.D. Senior Vice President Medical Affairs and Chief Medical Officer, Holy Spirit Hospital, Camp Hill, PA, p. A535

TORCHIA, Jude, Chief Executive Officer, OrthoColorado Hospital, Lakewood, CO, p. A108

TORDESILLAS, Victor, Director Human Resources, Arrowhead Regional Medical Center, Colton, CA, p. A60

TORGE, Andrew, Director Human Resources, Shasta Regional Medical Center, Redding, CA, p. A85

TORGERSON, Paul, Senior Vice President Chief Administrative Officer and General Counsel, St. John's Hospital, Saint Paul, MN, p. A351

TORMANEN, John, Director Mission and Human Resources, CHI St. Joseph's Health, Park Rapids, MN, p. A349

TORN, Michael, Chief Executive Officer, Edgewood Surgical Hospital, Transfer, PA, p. A556

TOROSSIAN, Lynn M., President and Chief Executive Officer, Henry Ford West Bloomfield Hospital, West Bloomfield, MI, p. A337

TORRES, Chris, Assistant Administrator Chief Financial Officer and Controller, Tyler County Hospital, Woodville, TX, p. A658

TORRES, Diane, Interim President and Chief Executive Officer, Portage Health, Hancock, MI, p. A326

TORRES, Harvey, Chief Financial Officer, Valley Baptist Medical Center–Brownsville, Brownsville, TX, p. A604

TORRES, Maribel, Executive Vice President Patient Care Services and Chief Nursing Officer, United Medical Center, Washington, DC, p. A122

TORRES, Mayra, Chief Financial Officer, Ashford Presbyterian Community Hospital, San Juan, PR, p. A727

TORRES, Victor, Information Technology Specialist Administrator, University Behavioral Health of El Paso, El Paso, TX, p. A616

TORRES AYALA, Eugenio, Director Information Systems, Cardiovascular Center of Puerto Rico and the Caribbean, San Juan, PR, p. A728

TORRICO, Pat, R.N. Chief Nursing Officer, Saint Mary's Regional Medical Center, Russellville, AR, p. A52

TORSCH, Peter, Chief Financial Officer, St. Charles Parish Hospital, Luling, LA, p. A283

TORTELLA, Anthony, Chief Financial Officer, Fairmount Behavioral Health System, Philadelphia, PA, p. A548

TOSI, Stephen E., M.D. Chief Medical Officer, UMass Memorial Medical Center, Worcester, MA, p. A317

TOSTENSON, Brad, Chief Information Officer, Essentia Health–Holy Trinity Hospital, Graceville, MN, p. A344

TOSTI, Debra, Chief Executive Officer, Tewksbury Hospital, Tewksbury, MA, p. A315

TOTH, Jackie, Administrator, Acute Care Specialty Hospital of Aultman, Canton, OH, p. A485

TOUMBIS, C., M.D. Chief of Staff, Citrus Memorial Health System, Inverness, FL, p. A131

TOUPS, Sharon A., Senior Vice President and Chief Operating Officer, St. Tammany Parish Hospital, Covington, LA, p. A276

TOURIGNY, Barry, Vice President Human Resources and Organizational Development, Cabell Huntington Hospital, Huntington, WV, p. A695

TOUSIGNANT, Grace, R.N
  Chief Nursing Officer, Aspirus Grand View Hospital, Ironwood, MI, p. A327
  Chief Nursing Officer, Aspirus Keweenaw Hospital, Laurium, MI, p. A329

TOUVELLE, Cynthia, R.N. Senior Director Care Management and Chief Nursing Officer, Barnesville Hospital, Barnesville, OH, p. A483

TOVAR, Richard, M.D. Chief of Staff, Beaver Dam Community Hospitals, Beaver Dam, WI, p. A702

TOWERS, Darleen, Director Human Resources, Lake Whitney Medical Center, Whitney, TX, p. A657

TOWLE, Sonya, Director Human Resources, Mercy Hospital, Moose Lake, MN, p. A348

TOWN, Alex, Vice President Finance, Tri–State Memorial Hospital, Clarkston, WA, p. A682

TOWNDROW, Geraldine, R.N. Vice President and Chief Nursing Officer, Lutheran Medical Center, Wheat Ridge, CO, p. A112

TOWNE, Jana, Nurse Executive, U. S. Public Health Service Indian Hospital–Whiteriver, Whiteriver, AZ, p. A41

TOWNER, Chad, Chief Executive Officer, Dupont Hospital, Fort Wayne, IN, p. A210

TOWNER, Paul, Chief of Staff, Washington County Hospital and Clinics, Washington, IA, p. A238

TOWNES, Tim, Director Information Systems, Trinity Medical Center, Birmingham, AL, p. A17

TOWNLEY, Nancy, R.N. Senior Vice President Operations, United Regional Health Care System, Wichita Falls, TX, p. A658

TOWNS, Tracy, Chief Human Resources Officer, Rehoboth McKinley Christian Health Care Services, Gallup, NM, p. A428

TOWNSEND, Cathy, Chief Nursing Officer, Banner Boswell Medical Center, Sun City, AZ, p. A39

TOWNSEND, Dona E., Chief Nursing Officer, Northeastern Nevada Regional Hospital, Elko, NV, p. A404

TOWNSEND, Gary, Chief Information Officer, Hurley Medical Center, Flint, MI, p. A323

TOWNSEND, Roxane A., M.D., Chief Executive Officer, UAMS Medical Center, Little Rock, AR, p. A49

TOWNSEND, Stanley, Chief Executive Officer, Stone County Medical Center, Mountain View, AR, p. A50

TOWNSEND, Tanya, Chief Information Officer, Greater Baltimore Medical Center, Baltimore, MD, p. A296

TOWNSEND, Theodore E., FACHE, President and Chief Executive Officer, UnityPoint Health – St. Luke's Hospital, Cedar Rapids, IA, p. A226

TOWNSLEY, Malcolm, M.D. Chief of Staff, St. Anthony Hospital, Pendleton, OR, p. A527

TOY, Linda, Director Information Systems, Havasu Regional Medical Center, Lake Havasu City, AZ, p. A34

TOY Jr., Stanley, M.D., Chief Executive Officer, Greater El Monte Community Hospital, South El Monte, CA, p. A96

TOYE, Lawrence J., Chief Financial Officer, Kindred Hospital–Boston, Brighton, MA, p. A308

TOZER, Chuck, Administrator, Spectrum Health Special Care Hospital, Grand Rapids, MI, p. A325

TRACEY, Karen, Chief Human Resources, Select Specialty Hospital–Greensboro, Greensboro, NC, p. A465

TRACY, Allen R., Senior Vice President and Chief Financial Officer, St. John Medical Center, Westlake, OH, p. A505

TRACY Jr., Larry A., FACHE,
  President, Barnes–Jewish St. Peters Hospital, Saint Peters, MO, p. A382
  President, Progress West Hospital, O'Fallon, MO, p. A378

TRACY, Pat, Administrator, Ridgeview Behavioral Hospital, Middle Point, OH, p. A498

TRACY, Timothy J., Chief Executive Officer, Sanford Vermillion Medical Center, Vermillion, SD, p. A577

TRAHAN, Jennifer Lynch, Assistant Vice President Human Resources, Our Lady of Lourdes Regional Medical Center, Lafayette, LA, p. A281

TRAHERN, Sheri, FACHE, Chief Executive Officer, St. Thomas More Hospital, Canon City, CO, p. A103

TRAHEY, Thomas F., M.D. Vice President Medical Affairs, Novant Health Rowan Medical Center, Salisbury, NC, p. A472

TRAIL, Alan, Director Information Systems, Muhlenberg Community Hospital, Greenville, KY, p. A262

TRAINER, Michael, Chief Financial Officer, Akron Children's Hospital, Akron, OH, p. A482

TRAINOR, Karyn, Director Human Resources, St. Patrick Hospital, Missoula, MT, p. A390

TRAISTER, Lynne, Controller, Rehabilitation Hospital of Tinton Falls, Tinton Falls, NJ, p. A423

TRAMMELL, Patrick, Chief Operating Officer, Redmond Regional Medical Center, Rome, GA, p. A165

TRAMP, Francis G., President, Burgess Health Center, Onawa, IA, p. A235

TRAN, Ann, Chief Financial Officer, Pike County Memorial Hospital, Louisiana, MO, p. A376

TRAN, Kha H., M.D. Vice President Medical Affairs, Lima Memorial Health System, Lima, OH, p. A496

TRAN, Khiem, M.D. Acting Chief of Staff, Veterans Affairs Illiana Health Care System, Danville, IL, p. A187

TRAN, Lac, Senior Vice President Information Services, Rush University Medical Center, Chicago, IL, p. A186

TRAN, Thanh, Chief Operating Officer, North Central Surgical Center, Dallas, TX, p. A611

TRANQUILLA, Nadine, Chief Nursing Officer, Cascade Behavioral Hospital, Tukwila, WA, p. A691

TRANQUILLO, Stephen, Chief Information Officer, Thomas Jefferson University Hospital, Philadelphia, PA, p. A550

TRANSIER, Rhonda, Financial Officer, Rusk State Hospital, Rusk, TX, p. A645

TRANTALIS, Cary, R.N
Regional Vice President Operations, The William W. Backus Hospital, Norwich, CT, p. A116
Chief Operating Officer, East Region, Windham Hospital, Willimantic, CT, p. A118

TRANTHAM, Susan, Director Human Resources, HEALTHSOUTH Rehabilitation Hospital of Florence, Florence, SC, p. A565

TRAPANI, Joseph, Chief Executive Officer, Poplar Springs Hospital, Petersburg, VA, p. A676

TRAPNELL, Kerry A., Chief Executive Officer, Greenwood Regional Rehabilitation Hospital, Greenwood, SC, p. A567

TRAPP, Kathleen, M.D. Medical Director, Broadwater Health Center, Townsend, MT, p. A391

TRAUB, Bruce, Chief Financial Officer, University Medical Center of Princeton at Plainsboro, Plainsboro, NJ, p. A421

TRAUTMAN, Bob, Chief Executive Officer, Saline Memorial Hospital, Benton, AR, p. A43

TRAVIS, Calee, R.N. Chief Nursing Officer, Centennial Medical Center, Frisco, TX, p. A620

TRAVIS, David A.
Chief Financial Officer, East Texas Medical Center Athens, Athens, TX, p. A598
Chief Financial Officer, East Texas Medical Center Fairfield, Fairfield, TX, p. A617

TRAVIS, Dee Dee, Director Community Relations, Calais Regional Hospital, Calais, ME, p. A292

TRAXLER, Martin J., Director, Alexandria Veterans Affairs Health Care System, Pineville, LA, p. A287

TRAYLOR, Desiree, Chief Information Officer, Chickasaw Nation Medical Center, Ada, OK, p. A507

TRAYLOR, Jerri Sue, Director Human Resources and Community and Employee Wellness, The Women's Hospital, Newburgh, IN, p. A220

TRAYNOR, Karen, Chief Financial Officer, Richland Hospital, Richland Center, WI, p. A714

TRCZINSKI, Judi, Vice President and Chief Human Resources Officer, Hospital for Special Care, New Britain, CT, p. A115

TREACY, Nancy, Director Finance, Cambridge Medical Center, Cambridge, MN, p. A341

TREACY–SHIFF, Mary, Vice President Finance, Advocate Good Samaritan Hospital, Downers Grove, IL, p. A188

TREADWAY, Michael G.
Interim Chief Executive Officer, HEALTHSOUTH Rehabilitation Hospital of Texarkana, Texarkana, TX, p. A652
Controller, Trinity Mother Frances Rehabilitation Hospital, Tyler, TX, p. A654

TREADWELL, Karen, Director Human Resources, Lake Martin Community Hospital, Dadeville, AL, p. A18

TREASE, Kevin, Chief Information Officer, Antelope Memorial Hospital, Neligh, NE, p. A398

TREASURE, Martin
Director Human Resources, Schuylkill Medical Center – East Norwegian Street, Pottsville, PA, p. A553
Director Human Resources, Schuylkill Medical Center – South Jackson Street, Pottsville, PA, p. A553

TREECE, Amy, M.D. Medical Director, North Greenville Hospital, Travelers Rest, SC, p. A570

TREGLOWN, Brad, Director Information Systems, Redmond Regional Medical Center, Rome, GA, p. A165

TREHAN, Rajeev, M.D. Chief of Staff, Veterans Affairs Eastern Kansas Health Care System, Topeka, KS, p. A255

TREITLER, Scot, Chief Financial Officer and Chief Operating Officer, Cypress Pointe Surgical Hospital, Hammond, LA, p. A278

TREMAINE, Lisa, Manager Human Resources, Carson Valley Medical Center, Gardnerville, NV, p. A404

TREMBLAY, Marilyn, Chief Information Officer and Vice President. Regional Medical Center, Orangeburg, SC, p. A569

TREMBLE, John, Chief Financial Officer, St. Croix Regional Medical Center, St. Croix Falls, WI, p. A715

TREMBULAK, Frank J., Executive Vice President and Chief Operating Officer, Geisinger Medical Center, Danville, PA, p. A537

TREMONTI, Carl
Chief Financial Officer, Mease Countryside Hospital, Safety Harbor, FL, p. A144
Chief Financial Officer, Mease Dunedin Hospital, Dunedin, FL, p. A128
Chief Financial Officer, Morton Plant Hospital, Clearwater, FL, p. A125
Chief Financial Officer, Morton Plant North Bay Hospital, New Port Richey, FL, p. A139
Chief Financial Officer, St. Anthony's Hospital, Saint Petersburg, FL, p. A145

TREMONTI, Yvette, Vice President Human Resources, H. Lee Moffitt Cancer Center and Research Institute, Tampa, FL, p. A147

TRENARY, Thomas J., President, Baylor Medical Center at Garland, Garland, TX, p. A620

TRENDE, Gary D., FACHE Associate Director, Tuscaloosa Veterans Affairs Medical Center, Tuscaloosa, AL, p. A26

TRENKLE, Kevan, Chief Executive Officer, Citizens Medical Center, Colby, KS, p. A242

TRENT, Cindy, Manager Personnel, Fall River Hospital, Hot Springs, SD, p. A574

TREPAGNIER, Katherine, Director Human Resources, River Parishes Hospital, La Place, LA, p. A280

TREPANIER, Dennis, Interim Chief Operating Officer, Cortland Regional Medical Center, Cortland, NY, p. A436

TRESSA, John, MSN, Chief Executive Officer, Park Plaza Hospital, Houston, TX, p. A626

TRETINA, Mike, Senior Vice President and Chief Financial Officer, Bayhealth Medical Center, Dover, DE, p. A119

TREUTLEIN, Scott, M.D. Medical Director, Wyoming County Community Hospital, Warsaw, NY, p. A457

TREVATHAN, Dave, Director Information Systems, Rose Medical Center, Denver, CO, p. A105

TREVINO, Carlos, Chief Operating Officer, Mission Regional Medical Center, Mission, TX, p. A638

TREVINO, Chris, M.D. Chief Medical Officer, St. Elizabeth Hospital, Gonzales, LA, p. A278

TREVINO, Malissa, Director Human Resources, Pecos County Memorial Hospital, Fort Stockton, TX, p. A618

TREVINO, Paul, Chief Executive Officer, CHRISTUS Hospital–St. Elizabeth, Beaumont, TX, p. A601

TREVISANI, Michael F., M.D. Senior Vice President and Chief Medical Officer, Faxton–St. Luke's Healthcare, Utica, NY, p. A456

TREXLER, Don D., Chief Executive Officer, Cypress Pointe Surgical Hospital, Hammond, LA, p. A278

TRICE, Richard
Director Operations, University Hospitals Conneaut Medical Center, Conneaut, OH, p. A491
Director Operations, University Hospitals Geneva Medical Center, Geneva, OH, p. A494

TRICKEY, Donna, R.N. Chief Nursing Officer, Fairview Park Hospital, Dublin, GA, p. A159

TRIEBES, David G., Chief Executive Officer, Samaritan Albany General Hospital, Albany, OR, p. A523

TRIGG, Terry, Director Human Resources, Wesley Medical Center, Hattiesburg, MS, p. A359

TRIGIANI, Charles, D.O. Medical Director, Hampton Behavioral Health Center, Westampton, NJ, p. A424

TRILIVAS, Judy, Vice President and Chief Operating Officer, Mount Sinai Queens,, NY, p. A446

TRIMBLE, Charley O., Chief Executive Officer, Lubbock Heart Hospital, Lubbock, TX, p. A635

TRIMBLE, Deborah, R.N., Chief Executive Officer, Paul B. Hall Regional Medical Center, Paintsville, KY, p. A269

TRIMBLE, Donald, CPA Chief Financial Officer, Vibra Specialty Hospital at DeSoto, Desoto, TX, p. A614

TRIMBLE, Kevin T., FACHE, President and Chief Executive Officer, Saint Luke's North Hospital – Barry Road, Kansas City, MO, p. A374

TRIMMER, Mary R., Interim Chief Operating Officer, Mount Carmel, Columbus, OH, p. A490

TRIMMER, Matthew, Director Information Services, Holy Cross Hospital, Silver Spring, MD, p. A303

TRINCHETTO, Thomas, M.D. Chief Medical Officer, Doctors Hospital of Sarasota, Sarasota, FL, p. A145

TRINH, Khiet, M.D. Chief Medical Officer, Bon Secours St. Mary's Hospital, Richmond, VA, p. A677

TRINIDAD, Terry, Director Management Information Systems, Clearfield Hospital, Clearfield, PA, p. A536

TRIPLETT, Dan, Acting Chief Operating Officer, Springfield Hospital Center, Sykesville, MD, p. A303

TRIPLETT, John, D.O. President Medical Staff, Saint Joseph – Martin, Martin, KY, p. A267

TRIPLETT, Robin, Chief Financial Officer, Southern Coos Hospital and Health Center, Bandon, OR, p. A523

TRIPP, Gina, Director Information Systems, TIRR Memorial Hermann, Houston, TX, p. A627

TRIPPEL, Donald E., Chief Financial Officer, Hugh Chatham Memorial Hospital, Elkin, NC, p. A464

TRITTIN, Kim, Manager Human Resources, Mayo Clinic Health System in Red Wing, Red Wing, MN, p. A350

TRIVETTE, Chastity, Interim Chief Executive Officer, Johnson County Community Hospital, Mountain City, TN, p. A590

TROCINO, Mark, Chief Information Officer, DeKalb Medical at Hillandale, Lithonia, GA, p. A162

TROGMAN, Richard, FACHE Chief Operating Officer, Kaiser Permanente Woodland Hills Medical Center,, CA, p. A72

TROLLOPE, Grant, Chief Financial Officer, Northeastern Nevada Regional Hospital, Elko, NV, p. A404

TROMBLEY, Barb, Director Financial Services, Munising Memorial Hospital, Munising, MI, p. A331

TROMPETER, Dawn, Vice President Finance, OSF Saint Elizabeth Medical Center, Ottawa, IL, p. A199

TRONCONE, Michael T., Chief Human Resources Officer, Calvary Hospital,, NY, p. A443

TROSCLAIR, Andree, Vice President Human Resources, Arkansas Children's Hospital, Little Rock, AR, p. A48

TROSIN, Jill A., R.N. Chief Nursing Officer, Memorial Hospital, Fremont, OH, p. A494

TROTTER, Kristin, Chief Nursing Officer, Lovelace Regional Hospital – Roswell, Roswell, NM, p. A430

TROTTER, Wally, Director Human Resources, Mountain View Hospital, Payson, UT, p. A662

TROTTIER, Timothy R., Chief Executive Officer, Spring View Hospital, Lebanon, KY, p. A263

TROUBLEFIELD, David, Chief Communications Officer, Hemphill County Hospital, Canadian, TX, p. A605

TROUP, Matthew, Chief Operating Officer, Hillcrest Medical Center, Tulsa, OK, p. A520

TROUP, William, M.D. Chief of Staff, Stanton County Hospital, Johnson, KS, p. A246

TROUT, Gene, Chief Financial Officer, Canonsburg General Hospital, Canonsburg, PA, p. A535

TROUTMAN, Debra, Chief Nursing Officer, Unicoi County Memorial Hospital, Erwin, TN, p. A582

TROUTMAN, Gary, CP
Chief Financial Officer, Baptist Hospitals of Southeast Texas, Beaumont, TX, p. A601
Chief Financial Officer, Baptist Orange Hospital, Orange, TX, p. A640

TROWER, Brad, Administrator, Optim Medical Center – Tattnall, Reidsville, GA, p. A165

TROWHILL, Jan, Director Health Information Management Systems, HEALTHSOUTH Cane Creek Rehabilitation Hospital, Martin, TN, p. A587

TROY, Patrick J., R.N. Associate Director Patient Care Services, Veterans Affairs New Jersey Health Care System, East Orange, NJ, p. A415

TROY, Peggy N., President and Chief Executive Officer, Children's Hospital and Health System, Milwaukee, WI, p. B34

TROY, Peggy N.
President and Chief Executive Officer, Children's Hospital of Wisconsin, Milwaukee, WI, p. A710
President and Chief Executive Officer, Children's Hospital of Wisconsin–Fox Valley, Neenah, WI, p. A711

TROYER, David, Chief Information Officer, Veterans Affairs Northern Indiana Health Care System, Fort Wayne, IN, p. A211

TROYER, Devin, M.D. Medical Director, HEALTHSOUTH Rehabilitation Hospital of Columbia, Columbia, SC, p. A564

TROYO, Glynda, Chief Executive Officer, St. Theresa Specialty Hospital, Kenner, LA, p. A280

TRUAX, Christopher, Chief Executive Officer, Morrow County Hospital, Mount Gilead, OH, p. A499

TRUE, Terry, M.D. Chief of Staff, Shoals Hospital, Muscle Shoals, AL, p. A24

TRUEBLOOD, Susan, Chief Executive Officer, Georgia Regional Hospital at Atlanta, Decatur, GA, p. A158

TRUELOCK, Kerri, M.D. Chief of Staff, Peterson Regional Medical Center, Kerrville, TX, p. A631

TRUESDALE, Jr., Fred A., Administrator, North Mississippi Medical Center–Iuka, Iuka, MS, p. A359

TRUITT, Louise, Vice President Human Resources, Capital Regional Medical Center, Tallahassee, FL, p. A146

TRUJILLO, Jesse, Chief Information Officer, St. Mark's Hospital, Salt Lake City, UT, p. A663

TRUMAN, Julia, Vice President Human Resources, Fort Walton Beach Medical Center, Fort Walton Beach, FL, p. A129

TRUMAN, Mark, Vice President of Operations, Floyd Memorial Hospital and Health Services, New Albany, IN, p. A220

TRUMAN, Michael A., Chief Executive Officer, Riverview Behavioral Health, Texarkana, AR, p. A53

TRUMBULL, Kathryn E., R.N. Chief Nursing Officer and Vice President Patient Care Services, Samaritan Healthcare, Moses Lake, WA, p. A685

TRUMP, Donald L., M.D., President and Chief Executive Officer, Roswell Park Cancer Institute, Buffalo, NY, p. A434

TRUNFIO, Joseph A., Ph.D., President and Chief Executive Officer, Atlantic Health System, Morristown, NJ, p. B15

TRUSSELL, Robert, Chief Executive Officer, Foundation Surgical Hospital of San Antonio, San Antonio, TX, p. A646

TRYON, Ellen, R.N. Chief Nursing Officer, Adventist Medical Center–Portland, Portland, OR, p. A528

TSAI, James, M.D., President, New York Eye and Ear Infirmary of Mount Sinai, New York, NY, p. A447

TSALATE, Cynthia, Human Resource Specialist, U. S. Public Health Service Indian Hospital, Zuni, NM, p. A431

TSAMBIRAS, Petros, M.D. Chief of Staff, Bayfront Health Dade City, Dade City, FL, p. A126

TSANG, To, Interim Area Information Officer, Kaiser Permanente Antioch Medical Center, Antioch, CA, p. A55

TSAO, Sean, Director Information Technology, Blue Mountain Hospital, John Day, OR, p. A526

TSCHABRUN, Dawn M., R.N., Chief Executive Officer, Lovelace Regional Hospital – Roswell, Roswell, NM, p. A430

TSENG, Allen, Chief Operations Officer, Memorial Hermann Memorial City Medical Center, Houston, TX, p. A625

TSO, Ronald, Chief Executive Officer, Chinle Comprehensive Health Care Facility, Chinle, AZ, p. A31

TUAZON, Nelson, Chief Nursing Officer, Baptist Medical Center, San Antonio, TX, p. A646

TUBBS, John, M.D
Chief of Staff, Rock County Hospital, Bassett, NE, p. A393
Chief of Staff, West Holt Memorial Hospital, Atkinson, NE, p. A393

TUBBS, Mary Beth, Chief Nursing Officer, Sunnyside Community Hospital and Clinics, Sunnyside, WA, p. A690

TUBERVILLE, Abby, Human Resource Generalist, Fillmore County Hospital, Geneva, NE, p. A396

TUCK, Greg, Area Information Officer, Kaiser Permanente San Jose Medical Center, San Jose, CA, p. A92

TUCKER, Albert, Chief Financial Officer, Miami Veterans Affairs Healthcare System, Miami, FL, p. A137

TUCKER, Andy, Chief Financial Officer, South Mississippi State Hospital, Purvis, MS, p. A364

TUCKER, Cathy, Director Human Resources, Iraan General Hospital, Iraan, TX, p. A629

TUCKER, Gary, Senior Vice President Operations and Chief Operating Officer, Mount St. Mary's Hospital and Health Center, Lewiston, NY, p. A440

TUCKER, Ian, M.D. Vice President Medical Affairs, Johnson Memorial Hospital, Stafford Springs, CT, p. A117

TUCKER, John, Chief Nursing Executive, Center for Behavioral Medicine, Kansas City, MO, p. A373

TUCKER, John R., FACHE, Administrator and Chief Executive Officer, Dallas County Medical Center, Fordyce, AR, p. A46

TUCKER, Joseph B., Senior Vice President and Chief Financial Officer, Fort Washington Medical Center, Fort Washington, MD, p. A301

TUCKER, Joshua, Administrator, Mercy Hospital Logan County, Guthrie, OK, p. A511

TUCKER, Keith, R.N. Chief Nursing Officer, Val Verde Regional Medical Center, Del Rio, TX, p. A613

TUCKER, Mona, Director Human Resources, Seton Medical Center Harker Heights, Harker Heights, TX, p. A622

TUCKER, Rebecca, Chief Financial Officer, Memorial Hermann Northeast, Humble, TX, p. A628

TUCKER, Ron, Business Office Manager, Kiowa County Memorial Hospital, Greensburg, KS, p. A244

TUCKER, Sidney, Chief Executive Officer, North Runnels Hospital, Winters, TX, p. A658

TUCKER, Steven E., President, Conemaugh Memorial Medical Center, Johnstown, PA, p. A541

TUCKER, Theresa, Human Resources Officer, Sioux Center Health, Sioux Center, IA, p. A237

TUDOR, Nathan, Vice President and Chief Executive Officer, CHRISTUS Spohn Hospital Beeville, Beeville, TX, p. A602

TUELL, William J., MSN, Facility Director, Commonwealth Center for Children and Adolescents, Staunton, VA, p. A679

TUFT, Paul R., President, Southwest Healthcare System, Scottsdale, AZ, p. B126

TULISIAK, Thomas, M.D., President, Medina Hospital, Medina, OH, p. A498

TULLIS, Bea, Chief Financial Officer and Budget Officer, Broughton Hospital, Morganton, NC, p. A469

TULLMAN, Stephen M., Chief Executive Officer, Phoenixville Hospital, Phoenixville, PA, p. A550

TUMA, Bonnie, Human Resources Team Lead, National Institutes of Health Clinical Center, Bethesda, MD, p. A299

TUMLIN, Richard, Chief Operating Officer, TriStar Southern Hills Medical Center, Nashville, TN, p. A591

TUMMURU, Ramireddy K., M.D. Chief Medical Officer, Porter Regional Hospital, Valparaiso, IN, p. A223

TUNGATE, Rex A.
Administrator, Casey County Hospital, Liberty, KY, p. A265
Administrator, Jane Todd Crawford Hospital, Greensburg, KY, p. A262

TUNNELL, Richard, Director Information Systems Technology and Health Management Information Systems, University Hospital, Newark, NJ, p. A420

TUNNEY, Niona, Director Human Resources, Cochran Memorial Hospital, Morton, TX, p. A638

TUNSON, Lynn, Manager Medical Records, Complex Care Hospital at Tenaya, Las Vegas, NV, p. A405

TUPPER, Dave, Chief Executive Officer, Vibra Specialty Hospital of Portland, Portland, OR, p. A529

TUPPONCE, David, M.D., Interim Chief Executive Officer, Paradise Valley Hospital, Phoenix, AZ, p. A36

TURBAK, Shelly, R.N. Chief Nursing Officer, Prairie Lakes Healthcare System, Watertown, SD, p. A578

TURCO, Joseph, Director Human Resources, St. Mary Medical Center, Apple Valley, CA, p. A56

TUREK, Beth, Site Manager Information Systems, Advocate South Suburban Hospital, Hazel Crest, IL, p. A192

TURGEON, Jim, Vice President Finance, Allegiance Behavioral Health Center of Plainview, Plainview, TX, p. A642

TURK, Edward, Vice President Finance, Scripps Mercy Hospital, San Diego, CA, p. A89

TURK, Jan, Chief Executive Officer, Kindred Hospital–New Orleans, New Orleans, LA, p. A285

TURKAL, Nick, M.D., President and Chief Executive Officer, Aurora Health Care, Milwaukee, WI, p. B16

TURKAL–BARRETT, Kari, Flight Commander Resource Management Officer, Mike O'Callaghan Federal Hospital, Nellis AFB, NV, p. A407

TURKEL, Brooks, Chief Executive Officer, Regional Hospital of Scranton, Scranton, PA, p. A554

TURLEY, Mary Ann, D.O. Medical Director, John C. Lincoln Deer Valley Hospital, Phoenix, AZ, p. A36

TURLEY, Matt, Interim Director Information Systems, Greenbrier Valley Medical Center, Ronceverte, WV, p. A699

TURLEY, Susan S., Chief Financial Officer, Doctor's Hospital at Renaissance, Edinburg, TX, p. A615

TURMAN, Anna, Chief Information Officer, Chadron Community Hospital and Health Services, Chadron, NE, p. A394

TURMAN, Tracy Penn, Chief Executive Officer, HEALTHSOUTH Rehabilitation Hospital of Petersburg, Petersburg, VA, p. A676

TURNA, Tarlochan, M.D. Medical Director, Mayo Clinic Health System in Cannon Falls, Cannon Falls, MN, p. A341

TURNBULL, James, Chief Information Officer, University of Utah Health Care – Hospital and Clinics, Salt Lake City, UT, p. A663

TURNBULL, Rosie, Director Human Resources, St. Lawrence Psychiatric Center, Ogdensburg, NY, p. A450

TURNER, Amy, Director Human Resources, Bethesda Butler Hospital, Hamilton, OH, p. A495

TURNER, Bill, Vice President Human Resources, Valir Rehabilitation Hospital, Oklahoma City, OK, p. A516

TURNER, Brenda C.
Chief Human Resources Officer, Palomar Medical Center, Escondido, CA, p. A62
Chief Human Resources Officer, Pomerado Hospital, Poway, CA, p. A84

TURNER, Carol, President and Chief Executive Officer, Atrium Medical Center, Middletown, OH, p. A498

TURNER, Chad, Chief Financial Officer, Star Valley Medical Center, Afton, WY, p. A720

TURNER, Cindy R., Chief Executive Officer, Bacon County Hospital and Health System, Alma, GA, p. A151

TURNER, Dale, Chief Operating Officer, Reedsburg Area Medical Center, Reedsburg, WI, p. A714

TURNER, Dave, Chief Financial Officer, Royal Oaks Hospital, Windsor, MO, p. A384

TURNER, Eileen, Director of Nursing, Post Acute Medical Specialty Hospital of Lafayette, Lafayette, LA, p. A282

TURNER, Glenda, Director Personnel, Oakwood Correctional Facility, Lima, OH, p. A496

TURNER, Howard D., Chief Executive Officer, Perry Memorial Hospital, Perry, OK, p. A517

TURNER, Jeff, FACHE, Chief Executive Officer, Moore County Hospital District, Dumas, TX, p. A614

TURNER, Kathy, Director Human Resources, East Texas Medical Center Trinity, Trinity, TX, p. A653

TURNER, Kelly, Senior Vice President Finance and Chief Financial Officer, Glendale Adventist Medical Center, Glendale, CA, p. A65

TURNER, Kimberly, Chief of Staff, Clearview Regional Medical Center, Monroe, GA, p. A164

TURNER, Laurie
Chief Nursing Officer, TriStar Skyline Madison Campus, Madison, TN, p. A587
Chief Nursing Officer, TriStar Skyline Medical Center, Nashville, TN, p. A591

TURNER, Lucas, Chief Financial Officer, Bowdle Hospital, Bowdle, SD, p. A572

TURNER, Mark, Director Information Systems, Beverly Hospital, Montebello, CA, p. A78

TURNER, Mark J., President and Chief Executive Officer, Memorial Hospital, Belleville, IL, p. A181

TURNER, Mark S., Chief Executive Officer, San Gorgonio Memorial Hospital, Banning, CA, p. A57

TURNER, Marquita, Chief Nursing Officer, Atrium Medical Center, Middletown, OH, p. A498

TURNER, Maurita, Team Leader Health Information Systems Services, Madison St. Joseph Health Center, Madisonville, TX, p. A636

TURNER, Melissa, Senior Vice President Human Resources, Bridgeport Hospital, Bridgeport, CT, p. A113

TURNER, Michael, M.D. Chief of Staff, Abbeville Area Medical Center, Abbeville, SC, p. A562

TURNER, Michael L., Director Human Resources, Carlsbad Medical Center, Carlsbad, NM, p. A427

TURNER, Nancy, Director Communications, Sutter Roseville Medical Center, Roseville, CA, p. A87

TURNER, Pamela, Executive Director, Bronx Psychiatric Center,, NY, p. A442

TURNER, Peggy, Assistant Vice President and Director of Nursing, White County Medical Center, Searcy, AR, p. A52

TURNER, Randy, Chief Human Resource Management Services, Boise Veterans Affairs Medical Center, Boise, ID, p. A174

TURNER, Robert L., Ph.D., Chief Executive Officer, Seven Hills Behavioral Institute, Henderson, NV, p. A405

TURNER, Sara, Director Human Resources, Alvarado Hospital Medical Center, San Diego, CA, p. A89

TURNER, Saundra G., Director Human Resources, Mercy Hospital Jefferson, Crystal City, MO, p. A370

TURNER, Shelly, Chief Clinical Services Officer, Medical Center of Manchester, Manchester, TN, p. A587

TURNER, Sherrilyn, Director Human Resources, Southeast Colorado Hospital District, Springfield, CO, p. A111

TURNER, Spencer, Chief Executive Officer, Texas Health Presbyterian Hospital Flower Mound, Flower Mound, TX, p. A617

TURNER, Steve, Director Information Technology, Salem Township Hospital, Salem, IL, p. A202

TURNEY, Brian, Chief Executive Officer, Kingman Regional Medical Center, Kingman, AZ, p. A33

TURNEY, Larry, Administrator, Cochran Memorial Hospital, Morton, TX, p. A638

TURNQUIST, Carrie, Director Human Resources, Buena Vista Regional Medical Center, Storm Lake, IA, p. A238

TURPIN, Debra, R.N. Vice President Patient Care Services and Chief Nursing Officer, Alton Memorial Hospital, Alton, IL, p. A180

TURQUESA, Sandra
Senior Human Resources Business Partner, Saint Joseph – London, London, KY, p. A265
Human Resources Business Partner, Saint Joseph Berea, Berea, KY, p. A258

TURSKY, Martin, President and Chief Executive Officer, Firelands Regional Health System, Sandusky, OH, p. A501

TURSO, Janet, Controller, HEALTHSOUTH Rehabilitation Hospital of Toms River, Toms River, NJ, p. A423

TURTON, Jonathan, FACHE, Interim President, Baptist Medical Center, San Antonio, TX, p. A646

TUSA, Edward A., Chief Financial Officer, Mayo Clinic Health System in Cannon Falls, Cannon Falls, MN, p. A341

TUSCANY, Joanne E.
Director Human Resources, St. John Hospital and Medical Center, Detroit, MI, p. A322
Director Worklife Services, St. John Macomb–Oakland Hospital, Warren, MI, p. A336

TUSTEN, Jay, Chief Executive Officer, Stanton County Hospital, Johnson, KS, p. A246

TUTT, Michael, M.D. Chief Medical Officer, Tsehootsooi Medical Center, Fort Defiance, AZ, p. A32

TUTTLE, Kathryn, R.N. Director of Nursing, Memorial Medical Center – Ashland, Ashland, WI, p. A701

TUZZOLINO, Donna, Director Administrative Services, Lanterman Developmental Center, Pomona, CA, p. A84

TVEIT, Charles B., Chief Executive Officer, Lake District Hospital, Lakeview, OR, p. A526

TWARDY, Cindi, Manager Human Resources, Meeker Memorial Hospital, Litchfield, MN, p. A345

TWIDALE, Margaret, Manager Information Systems, Kane Community Hospital, Kane, PA, p. A541

TWIDWELL, Lisa, Administrator, Madison Medical Center, Fredericktown, MO, p. A371

TWO HAWK, Sophie M., Chief Executive Officer, U. S. Public Health Service Indian Hospital, Rosebud, SD, p. A576

TYE, Angie, Director Human Resources, Waverly Health Center, Waverly, IA, p. A239

TYK, Robert C., Chief Executive Officer, Hi–Desert Medical Center, Joshua Tree, CA, p. A67

TYLER, Holley, R.N. Chief Nursing Officer, Valley Regional Medical Center, Brownsville, TX, p. A604

TYLER, Philene, Chief Finance Officer, Chinle Comprehensive Health Care Facility, Chinle, AZ, p. A31

TYLER, Richard, Corporate Director Human Resources, Conway Regional Medical Center, Conway, AR, p. A44

TYLER, Rick, M.D. Vice President Medical Affairs, CHRISTUS Hospital–St. Elizabeth, Beaumont, TX, p. A601

TYLER, Rob, Chief Financial Officer, West Oaks Hospital, Houston, TX, p. A628

TYLER, Rosamond M., Administrator, Tyler Holmes Memorial Hospital, Winona, MS, p. A366

TYLER, Tanya
Vice President Human Resources, Memorial Medical Center – Lufkin, Lufkin, TX, p. A635
Vice President Human Resources, Memorial Specialty Hospital, Lufkin, TX, p. A635

TYLKOWSKI, Chester, M.D. Chief of Staff, Shriners Hospitals for Children–Lexington, Lexington, KY, p. A264

TYNAN, Robert M., Chief Information Officer, Memorial Health, Savannah, GA, p. A166

TYNER, Marilou Patalinjug, M.D. Medical Director, Highland–Clarksburg Hospital, Clarksburg, WV, p. A694

TYNER, W. Russell, President and Chief Executive Officer, Baptist Health, Montgomery, AL, p. B19

TYNES, Jr., L. Lee, M.D. Medical Director, Central Louisiana State Hospital, Pineville, LA, p. A287

TYO, Joanne, Chief Financial Officer, Carolinas Specialty Hospital, Charlotte, NC, p. A462

TYRA, Diana, Director Health Information, Kentucky River Medical Center, Jackson, KY, p. A263

TYRA, J. Allen, Chief Executive, Gilmore Memorial Regional Medical Center, Amory, MS, p. A355

TYRER, Andrew, Chief Operating Officer, TriStar StoneCrest Medical Center, Smyrna, TN, p. A593

TYRRELL, Shawn O., R.N. VP/Chief Nursing Officer, Adventist Hinsdale Hospital, Hinsdale, IL, p. A193

TYRRELL, RN, Wade Alan, Chief Nursing Officer, Sterling Regional MedCenter, Sterling, CO, p. A111

TYSON, Bernard J., Chairman and Chief Executive Officer, Kaiser Foundation Hospitals, Oakland, CA, p. B78

TYSON, Charlotte C.
Chief Executive Officer, Lewis–Gale Medical Center, Salem, VA, p. A678
Chief Executive Officer, LewisGale Hospital Alleghany, Low Moor, VA, p. A673

TYSON, Peggy, Director Human Resources, Research Psychiatric Center, Kansas City, MO, p. A374

TYSON, Rhoda, Chief Information Officer, Central Alabama Veterans Health Care System, Montgomery, AL, p. A23

U

UBER, Charlotte M., Chief Executive Officer, Warren State Hospital, Warren, PA, p. A557

UDALL, Ben, M.D. Chief of Staff, Kimble Hospital, Junction, TX, p. A630

UDALL, Jared, Chief Financial Officer, Rehabilitation Hospital of Southern New Mexico, Las Cruces, NM, p. A429

UDOVICH, Christopher, M.D. Chief of Staff, Silver Cross Hospital, New Lenox, IL, p. A198

UGHOUWA, Ejiro, M.D. Chief of Staff, Allen Parish Hospital, Kinder, LA, p. A280

UGWUEKE, Michael O., President and Chief Executive Officer, Methodist Healthcare Memphis Hospitals, Memphis, TN, p. A589

UHARRIET, Bart, Director Information Services, Mississippi State Hospital, Whitfield, MS, p. A366

UHL, Jason, Chief Information Officer, Floyd Valley Hospital, Le Mars, IA, p. A233

UHLIK, Allen, M.D. Chief of Staff, Copper Basin Medical Center, Copperhill, TN, p. A581

UHLIR, Tricia, Chief Executive Officer, Fall River Hospital, Hot Springs, SD, p. A574

ULBRICHT, John E., Chief Operating Officer, Laredo Medical Center, Laredo, TX, p. A633

ULBRICHT, William G., President, St. Anthony's Hospital, Saint Petersburg, FL, p. A145

ULFERTS, Wendy, R.N. Chief Nursing Officer, Rice Memorial Hospital, Willmar, MN, p. A354

ULI, James, Chief Financial Officer, Loma Linda University Medical Center–Murrieta, Murrieta, CA, p. A79

ULICNY, Gary R., Ph.D., President and Chief Executive Officer, Shepherd Center, Atlanta, GA, p. A153

ULMER, Becky, R.N. Director of Nursing, Jasper General Hospital, Bay Springs, MS, p. A355

ULMER, Carlton, Chief Executive Officer, Gulf Coast Regional Medical Center, Panama City, FL, p. A141

ULMER, Carol, Chief Executive Officer, Select Specialty Hospital–Sioux Falls, Sioux Falls, SD, p. A576

ULREICH, Shawn, R.N. Vice President Clinical Operations and Chief Nursing Executive, Spectrum Health – Butterworth Hospital, Grand Rapids, MI, p. A325

ULREY, Chris, Director Management Information Systems, St. Luke's Behavioral Health Center, Phoenix, AZ, p. A37

ULRICH, Alan, Chief Financial Officer, Guam Memorial Hospital Authority, Tamuning, GU, p. A724

ULRICH Jr., James P., President and Chief Executive Officer, Community Hospital, McCook, NE, p. A398

ULSETH, Randy, Chief Executive Officer, FirstLight Health System, Mora, MN, p. A348

UMHAU, John, M.D. Clinical Director, U. S. Public Health Service Indian Hospital–Whiteriver, Whiteriver, AZ, p. A41

UNDERDAHL, Steve, Chief Executive Officer, Northfield Hospital, Northfield, MN, p. A348

UNDERHILL, Robert, Director of Business Services, Central State Hospital, Louisville, KY, p. A265

UNDERWOOD, Ashley, Administrator and Director of Nursing, Rollins–Brook Community Hospital, Lampasas, TX, p. A632

UNDERWOOD, Debbie, Manager Human Resources, Plains Memorial Hospital, Dimmitt, TX, p. A614

UNDERWOOD, Jerri C., R.N. Chief Nursing Officer, Parkridge Medical Center, Chattanooga, TN, p. A580

UNDERWOOD, Ken, Chief Executive Officer, Hazel Hawkins Memorial Hospital, Hollister, CA, p. A67

UNDERWOOD, Martha, Chief Human Resources Officer, Saint Thomas Midtown Hospital, Nashville, TN, p. A590

UNDERWOOD, Patricia A., Chief Financial Officer, Magee Rehabilitation Hospital, Philadelphia, PA, p. A549

UNDERWOOD, Vickie, Director Human Resources, Wyandot Memorial Hospital, Upper Sandusky, OH, p. A503

UNDLIN, Cassie, Chief Administrative Officer, Navos, Seattle, WA, p. A688

UNELL, Deonna, Chief Executive Officer, Irving Coppell Surgical Hospital, Irving, TX, p. A629

UNGER, Kevin L., FACHE,
President and Chief Executive Officer, Medical Center of the Rockies, Loveland, CO, p. A110
President and Chief Executive Officer, Poudre Valley Hospital, Fort Collins, CO, p. A106

UNRUH, Greg, Chief Executive Officer, Community HealthCare System, Onaga, KS, p. A251

UNTCH, Matt, Controller, Research Psychiatric Center, Kansas City, MO, p. A374

UNZEN, John, Chief Financial Officer, Mille Lacs Health System, Onamia, MN, p. A349

UPCHURCH, Jim, M.D. Chief Medical Officer, Crow/Northern Cheyenne Hospital, Crow Agency, MT, p. A386

UPCRAFT, Jeffrey, Director Information Services, Southwest Healthcare System, Murrieta, CA, p. A79

UPFIELD, Jaclyn, Chief Operating Officer, G. Werber Bryan Psychiatric Hospital, Columbia, SC, p. A564

UPHAM, Kevin, Chief Human Resources Officer, Minneapolis Veterans Affairs Health Care System, Minneapolis, MN, p. A347

UPSHAW, Joy, Chief Nursing Officer, Oklahoma State University Medical Center, Tulsa, OK, p. A520

UPTON, Carol, Regional Area Practice Manager, Gilmore Memorial Regional Medical Center, Amory, MS, p. A355

UPTON, Daniel, Vice President and Chief Financial Officer, Doylestown Hospital, Doylestown, PA, p. A537

UPTON, Kerry L., Administrative Director Human Resources, Care Regional Medical Center, Aransas Pass, TX, p. A597

UPTON, Scott, Administrator, Jane Phillips Nowata Health Center, Nowata, OK, p. A514

URADNIK, Michael, Chief Executive Officer, Cascade Behavioral Hospital, Tukwila, WA, p. A691

URAIZEE, Rizwan A., Chief Financial Officer, Kedren Community Mental Health Center, Los Angeles, CA, p. A73

URBAN, Dan, Vice President of Finance, Monroe Hospital, Bloomington, IN, p. A207

URBAN, Frank
Chief Financial Officer, River Crest Hospital, San Angelo, TX, p. A645
Chief Financial Officer, Southwood Psychiatric Hospital, Pittsburgh, PA, p. A551

URBAN, Louise, R.N., President and Chief Executive Officer, Jefferson Hospital, Jefferson Hills, PA, p. A541

URBAN, Thomas S., Market Leader and President, Mercy Health – Fairfield Hospital, Fairfield, OH, p. A493

URBAN, Tom, Director Human Resources, Wills Memorial Hospital, Washington, GA, p. A169

URBANCSIK, Don
Director Finance, Euclid Hospital, Euclid, OH, p. A493
Director Finance, Lutheran Hospital, Cleveland, OH, p. A488

URBANIAK, Cindy, Chief Executive Officer, Kittson Memorial Healthcare Center, Hallock, MN, p. A344

URBANSKI, Joanne, President and Chief Executive Officer, South Haven Health System, South Haven, MI, p. A335

URBANSKI, Pamela A., R.N. Chief Nursing Officer, Senior Vice President, Patient Care Services, Mercy Memorial Hospital System, Monroe, MI, p. A330

URBISTONDO, Lisa, Chief Financial Officer, Medical Center of Peach County, Navicent Health, Fort Valley, GA, p. A160

URDANETA, Alfonso, M.D. President Medical Staff, Washington County Hospital, Nashville, IL, p. A197

URLAUB, Charles J., President and Chief Executive Officer, Mercy Hospital, Buffalo, NY, p. A434

URQUHART, Mary, R.N. Vice President Patient Care, Brattleboro Memorial Hospital, Brattleboro, VT, p. A665

URQUHART, Mary Beth, Vice President Patient Care Services and Director of Quality, New England Sinai Hospital and Rehabilitation Center, Stoughton, MA, p. A315

URQUHART, Teresa C., Chief Operating Officer, North Fulton Regional Hospital, Roswell, GA, p. A165

URVAND, Leslie O., Administrator, St. Luke's Hospital, Crosby, ND, p. A477

USELMAN, Krista, Chief Executive Officer, HEALTHSOUTH Rehabilitation Hospital The Woodlands, Conroe, TX, p. A607

USELMAN, Melissa, Director Finance, Gundersen Boscobel Area Hospital and Clinics, Boscobel, WI, p. A702

USHER, David, Chief Financial Officer, Kimball Health Services, Kimball, NE, p. A397

USHER, Paul L., President and Chief Executive Officer, Marion General Hospital, Marion, IN, p. A218

USHIJIMA, Arthur A., FACHE, President and Chief Executive Officer, Queen's Health Systems, Honolulu, HI, p. B113

USHIJIMA, Arthur A., FACHE, President, Queen's Medical Center, Honolulu, HI, p. A171

UTECHT, Tom, M.D
Senior Vice President and Chief Quality Officer, Community Behavioral Health Center, Fresno, CA, p. A64
Chief Quality Officer, Community Regional Medical Center, Fresno, CA, p. A64
Corporate Chief Quality Officer, Fresno Heart and Surgical Hospital, Fresno, CA, p. A64

UTEMARK, Paul, Chief Executive Officer, Fillmore County Hospital, Geneva, NE, p. A396

UTLEY, Donna, Vice President Human Resources, Mercy San Juan Medical Center, Carmichael, CA, p. A59

UTLEY, Renee, Acting Chief Financial Officer, Hamilton Center, Terre Haute, IN, p. A223

UTTENDORFSKY, Rob, Director Information Management, Lewis County General Hospital, Lowville, NY, p. A440

UTTER, Camille, R.N. Chief Nursing Officer, Scotland Health Care System, Laurinburg, NC, p. A468

UTTER, Mark, Chief Executive Officer, Corona Regional Medical Center, Corona, CA, p. A60

UTTERBACK, Julie
Vice President and Chief Financial Officer, Methodist Medical Center of Oak Ridge, Oak Ridge, TN, p. A591
Chief Financial Officer, Roane Medical Center, Harriman, TN, p. A583

UYEMURA, Monte, M.D. Chief of Staff, Wray Community District Hospital, Wray, CO, p. A112

V

VAAGENES, Carl P., Chief Executive Officer, Douglas County Hospital, Alexandria, MN, p. A339

VAALER, Mark, M.D
Chief Medical Officer, South Florida Baptist Hospital, Plant City, FL, p. A143
Vice President Medical Staff Affairs, St. Joseph's Hospital, Tampa, FL, p. A148

VACCARO, Stacey, Chief Operating Officer, The Children's Institute of Pittsburgh, Pittsburgh, PA, p. A551

VACCO, Michael, M.D. Chief Medical Officer, Wellmont Lonesome Pine Hospital, Big Stone Gap, VA, p. A668

VACHON, Scott, Director Information Technology, Littleton Regional Hospital, Littleton, NH, p. A411

VADEN, Jim, Director Information Systems, Lauderdale Community Hospital, Ripley, TN, p. A592

VAGUE, Jeff, Regional Manager Information Systems, Mercy Hospitals of Bakersfield, Bakersfield, CA, p. A57

VAHLBERG, Susan, Director Employee and Community Relations, Walter Knox Memorial Hospital, Emmett, ID, p. A176

VAIL, B. J., Director Information Systems, Morehouse General Hospital, Bastrop, LA, p. A273

VAIL, Bryan, Chief Information Officer, Clement J. Zablocki Veterans Affairs Medical Center, Milwaukee, WI, p. A710

VAIL, Lisa M., R.N. Chief Nursing Officer and Vice President of Patient Care Services, Bryan Medical Center, Lincoln, NE, p. A397

VAIL, Ronald, M.D. Chief of Staff, Lower Umpqua Hospital District, Reedsport, OR, p. A529

VAIL, Terrence, Acting Chief Human Resources Management Services, San Francisco Veterans Affairs Medical Center, San Francisco, CA, p. A91

VAILLANCOURT, Alex, Chief Information Officer, Christ Hospital, Cincinnati, OH, p. A486

VAILLANCOURT, Stacy, Vice President Marketing, Communications, Advocacy and Human Resources, Saint Agnes Medical Center, Fresno, CA, p. A64

VANSANT, Scott, M.D. Chief Medical Officer, Central State Hospital, Milledgeville, GA, p. A163

VANWICHEN, Ward C., Chief Executive Officer, Phillips County Hospital, Malta, MT, p. A389

VANWYHE, Brenda, Senior Vice President Finance and Chief Financial Officer, Rush–Copley Medical Center, Aurora, IL, p. A181

VARA Jr.,, Raymond P., President and Chief Executive Officer, Hawaii Pacific Health, Honolulu, HI, p. B63

VARELA, Alberto M., M.D., President, INSPIRA Ponce, Ponce, PR, p. A727

VARELA, Nancy, Director Human Resources, Patton State Hospital, Patton, CA, p. A83

VARGA, Patrick, Chief Operating Officer, Mercy Medical Center Redding, Redding, CA, p. A85

VARGAS, Jose L., M.D. Medical Director, West Gables Rehabilitation Hospital, Miami, FL, p. A138

VARGAS, Marisol, Director Finance, Hospital Del Maestro, San Juan, PR, p. A728

VARGAS, Monica, Chief Operating Officer, Providence Memorial Hospital, El Paso, TX, p. A616

VARGAS, Nancy
 Director Human Resources, Mark Twain Medical Center, San Andreas, CA, p. A88
 Chief Human Resources, St. Joseph's Behavioral Health Center, Stockton, CA, p. A96
 Vice President Human Resources, St. Joseph's Medical Center, Stockton, CA, p. A96

VARGHESE, Roy, M.D. Chief of Staff, Mary Breckinridge ARH Hospital, Hyden, KY, p. A263

VARGHESE, Shibu, Vice President Human Resources, University of Texas M.D. Anderson Cancer Center, Houston, TX, p. A628

VARIALE, Vincenzo, Chief Financial Officer, Mission Community Hospital,, CA, p. A73

VARIAN, Grant, M.D. Medical Director, Mary Rutan Hospital, Bellefontaine, OH, p. A483

VARK, Lawrence, M.D
 Chief Medical Officer, Creek Nation Community Hospital, Okemah, OK, p. A514
 Acting Chief Medical Officer, Okmulgee Memorial Hospital, Okmulgee, OK, p. A517

VARLAND, Drew, Chief Nursing Officer and Chief Operating Officer, Pioneers Medical Center, Meeker, CO, p. A110

VARLEY, Kevin
 Chief Financial Officer, Kindred Hospital South Philadelphia, Philadelphia, PA, p. A549
 Chief Financial Officer, Kindred Hospital–Heritage Valley, Beaver, PA, p. A533
 Chief Financial Officer, Kindred Hospital–Pittsburgh, Oakdale, PA, p. A547

VARNADO, Anjanette, M.D. Chief Medical Officer, St. Helena Parish Hospital, Greensburg, LA, p. A278

VARNADO, Darryl, Executive Vice President and Chief People Officer, Children's National Medical Center, Washington, DC, p. A121

VARNADO, Krystyna, Director Human Resources, Garden Park Medical Center, Gulfport, MS, p. A358

VARNADOE, Milo, Director Information Systems, Warm Springs Medical Center, Warm Springs, GA, p. A169

VARNADOE, Tiffany G., Director Finance, Cordova Community Medical Center, Cordova, AK, p. A28

VARNER, Terry, Administrator, Yalobusha General Hospital, Water Valley, MS, p. A366

VARNEY, Tim, R.N. Chief Nursing Officer, Select Specialty Hospital–Ann Arbor, Ypsilanti, MI, p. A338

VARNUM, Daniel, President and Chief Executive Officer, Mercy Medical Center–North Iowa, Mason City, IA, p. A234

VARTELAS, Helene M., Chief Executive Officer, Connecticut Valley Hospital, Middletown, CT, p. A115

VASBINDER, Marie, Chief Nursing Officer, University of Maryland Medical Center Midtown Campus, Baltimore, MD, p. A298

VASEK, Barbara, Director Information Technology, Yoakum Community Hospital, Yoakum, TX, p. A658

VASHISHTA, Ashok, M.D. Vice President Medical Affairs, McLaren Central Michigan, Mount Pleasant, MI, p. A330

VASIL, Kathleen, Vice President Finance, St. Charles Hospital, Port Jefferson, NY, p. A452

VASKELIS, Glenna L., President and Senior Vice President Operations Dignity Health Bay Area Service Area, Sequoia Hospital, Redwood City, CA, p. A86

VASQUEZ, Alberto, Administrator, Garfield Memorial Hospital and Clinics, Panguitch, UT, p. A661

VASQUEZ, Christann, Executive Vice President and Chief Operating Officer, University Health System, San Antonio, TX, p. A648

VASQUEZ, George
 Chief Technology Officer, Clovis Community Medical Center, Clovis, CA, p. A60
 Vice President Information Services, Community Behavioral Health Center, Fresno, CA, p. A64
 Corporate Chief Information Officer, Fresno Heart and Surgical Hospital, Fresno, CA, p. A64

VASQUEZ, J.C., M.D. Chief Medical Staff, Moab Regional Hospital, Moab, UT, p. A660

VASQUEZ, Jill, Manager Human Resources, Spectrum Health Ludington Hospital, Ludington, MI, p. A329

VASQUEZ, Kenneth, Associate Director, West Palm Hospital, West Palm Beach, FL, p. A150

VASQUEZ, Miguel, Chief Financial Officer, Sister Emmanuel Hospital, Miami, FL, p. A137

VASQUEZ, Nelson, Vice President Finance, Jackson Park Hospital and Medical Center, Chicago, IL, p. A184

VASS, Paula, Vice President Clinical Operations, Walden Psychiatric Care, Waltham, MA, p. A316

VASSALL, John, M.D
 Chief Medical Officer, Swedish Medical Center–Cherry Hill Campus, Seattle, WA, p. A688
 Chief Medical Officer, Swedish Medical Center–First Hill, Seattle, WA, p. A688

VASUNAGA, Amy, Chief Nurse Executive, Leahi Hospital, Honolulu, HI, p. A170

VATH, Richard, M.D. Vice President Medical Affairs, Our Lady of the Lake Regional Medical Center, Baton Rouge, LA, p. A273

VATSAVAI, Sundararama R., M.D. Medical Director, Baton Rouge Rehabilitation Hospital, Baton Rouge, LA, p. A273

VAUGHAN, Aaron, Coordinator Information Systems, Pocahontas Memorial Hospital, Buckeye, WV, p. A693

VAUGHAN, Alan, IT Director, Share Medical Center, Alva, OK, p. A507

VAUGHAN, Amanda, Chief Financial Officer, St. Catherine Hospital, Garden City, KS, p. A244

VAUGHAN, Brandon, Chief Financial Officer and Vice President Finance, Jamestown Regional Medical Center, Jamestown, ND, p. A478

VAUGHAN, Hollie, Interim Chief Nursing Officer, Bayfront Health Port Charlotte, Port Charlotte, FL, p. A143

VAUGHAN, Page H., Chief Executive Officer, Chester Regional Medical Center, Chester, SC, p. A564

VAUGHAN, Peggy, M.D
 Senior Vice President Medical Affairs, Harford Memorial Hospital, Havre De Grace, MD, p. A301
 Senior Vice President Medical Affairs, Upper Chesapeake Medical Center, Bel Air, MD, p. A298

VAUGHAN, Rob, Chief Financial Officer, Carilion New River Valley Medical Center, Christiansburg, VA, p. A669

VAUGHAN, Steve, Chief Executive Officer, Pearl River County Hospital, Poplarville, MS, p. A364

VAUGHN, Anita, Administrator and Chief Executive Officer, Baptist Memorial Hospital for Women, Memphis, TN, p. A588

VAUGHN, Barbara, Chief Nursing Officer, Baylor Medical Center at Carrollton, Carrollton, TX, p. A605

VAUGHN, Kerry, Chief Information Officer, St. Mary's Health Care System, Athens, GA, p. A151

VAUGHN, Kevin P., Chief Financial Officer, Kansas Spine and Specialty Hospital, Wichita, KS, p. A256

VAUGHN, Sandy
 Director Information Services, Baylor All Saints Medical Center at Fort Worth, Fort Worth, TX, p. A618
 Director Information Systems, Baylor Regional Medical Center at Grapevine, Grapevine, TX, p. A621

VAUGHN, Sharma, Chief Nursing Officer, Rangely District Hospital, Rangely, CO, p. A110

VAUGHN, Ted W., Director Human Resources, UnityPoint Health – Trinity Regional Medical Center, Fort Dodge, IA, p. A230

VAUGHN, Vickie, Chief Nursing Officer, Heritage Medical Center, Shelbyville, TN, p. A593

VAVARUTSOS, Tony, Director Information Systems, Thorek Memorial Hospital, Chicago, IL, p. A187

VAZIRI, H. Kevin, President, Woodland Healthcare, Woodland, CA, p. A101

VAZQUEZ, Alfonso, Executive Director, Hospital Manati Medical Center, Manati, PR, p. A726

VAZQUEZ, Brunilda, Medical Director, Hospital de Psiquiatria, San Juan, PR, p. A728

VAZQUEZ, Emilio, M.D. Chief Medical Officer, DeKalb Health, Auburn, IN, p. A206

VAZQUEZ, Francisco, Director, Robert J. Dole Veterans Affairs Medical Center, Wichita, KS, p. A256

VAZQUEZ, Manuel J., Executive Administrator, Hospital Oncologico Andres Grillasca, Ponce, PR, p. A727

VEACH, Jamie, Chief Operating Officer, Clay County Hospital, Flora, IL, p. A190

VEACH, Shae, Interim Administrator, Pawnee Valley Community Hospital, Larned, KS, p. A248

VEDRAL–BARON, Jennifer, Commander, Fort Belvoir Community Hospital, Fort Belvoir, VA, p. A671

VEDROS, Allyson Dill, R.N. Chief Nursing Officer, Ochsner St. Anne General Hospital, Raceland, LA, p. A287

VEENSTRA, Henry A., President, Spectrum Health Zeeland Community Hospital, Zeeland, MI, p. A338

VEERAMACHANENI, Harish, M.D. Chief of Staff, Wayne Medical Center, Waynesboro, TN, p. A594

VEESER, Tom, R.N. Chief Nursing Officer, Calumet Medical Center, Chilton, WI, p. A703

VEGA, James, Director Information Systems, Palm Beach Gardens Medical Center, Palm Beach Gardens, FL, p. A141

VEGA, Maria, Director Human Resources, Auxilio Mutuo Hospital, San Juan, PR, p. A727

VEGA, Mary, R.N. Vice President Nursing, St. Margaret's Hospital, Spring Valley, IL, p. A203

VEILLETTE, David, President, Bakersfield Heart Hospital, Bakersfield, CA, p. A56

VEILLETTE, Michael D.
 Senior Vice President and Chief Financial Officer, Manchester Memorial Hospital, Manchester, CT, p. A114
 Senior Vice President and Chief Financial Officer, Rockville General Hospital, Vernon Rockville, CT, p. A117

VEILLEUX, Jeffrey
 Senior Vice President and Chief Financial Officer, Swedish Medical Center–Cherry Hill Campus, Seattle, WA, p. A688
 Executive Vice President and Chief Financial Officer, Swedish Medical Center–First Hill, Seattle, WA, p. A688

VEILLON, Paul, CP
 Chief Financial Officer, Advance Care Hospital of Fort Smith, Fort Smith, AR, p. A46
 Chief Financial Officer, Advance Care Hospital of Hot Springs, Hot Springs National Park, AR, p. A47
 Chief Financial Officer, Kindred Hospital–St. Louis at Mercy, Saint Louis, MO, p. A380

VEITZ, Larry W., Chief Executive Officer, Spearfish Regional Hospital, Spearfish, SD, p. A577

VELA, Javier, Director Information Technology, Baylor Medical Center at Uptown, Dallas, TX, p. A609

VELASCO, Paul, IT Manager, Kit Carson County Health Service District, Burlington, CO, p. A103

VELASQUEZ, Alfred T., Area Information Officer, Kaiser Permanente Riverside Medical Center, Riverside, CA, p. A86

VELASQUEZ, Carol Nunley, R.N. Chief Nursing Officer, Lake Chelan Community Hospital, Chelan, WA, p. A682

VELASQUEZ, Carolina, Director Information Services, Uvalde County Hospital Authority, Uvalde, TX, p. A654

VELASQUEZ, Lin, Vice President Human Resources, Saint Louise Regional Hospital, Gilroy, CA, p. A65

VELASQUEZ, Roberto, M.D. Medical Director, Hospital Oncologico Andres Grillasca, Ponce, PR, p. A727

VELETSOS, Alex, Chief Information Officer, St. Mary's of Michigan, Saginaw, MI, p. A334

VELEZ, Luz M., Director–Administration of Nursing Services, Hospital San Carlos Borromeo, Moca, PR, p. A727

VELEZ, Pablo, Chief Executive Officer, Sharp Chula Vista Medical Center, Chula Vista, CA, p. A59

VELEZ, Raul, Director Information Systems, Huntsville Memorial Hospital, Huntsville, TX, p. A629

VELTRI, Gregory M.
 Vice President, Information Services and Chief Information Officer, CAMC Teays Valley Hospital, Hurricane, WV, p. A696
 Vice President Information Services and Chief Information Officer, Charleston Area Medical Center, Charleston, WV, p. A694

VELTRI, Sam, Vice President Human Resources, Edward White Hospital, Saint Petersburg, FL, p. A144

VELUSWAMY, Ragupathy, M.D. Vice President Medical Affairs, Wilkes–Barre General Hospital, Wilkes-Barre, PA, p. A558

VENABLE, Mark, Interim Director Human Resources, Shriners Hospitals for Children–St. Louis, Saint Louis, MO, p. A381

VENABLE, Robert, M.D. Chief Medical Staff, Washington County Hospital, Plymouth, NC, p. A470

VENDETTI, Marilouise, M.D. Chief Medical Officer, AtlantiCare Regional Medical Center, Atlantic City, NJ, p. A413

VENGCO, Joel L., M
 Vice President and Chief Information Officer, Baystate Health, Baystate Mary Lane Hospital, Ware, MA, p. A316
 Vice President, Chief Information Officer, Baystate Medical Center, Springfield, MA, p. A314

VENHUIZEN, Pamela, Chief Human Resources Officer, Cooperstown Medical Center, Cooperstown, ND, p. A477

VENOIT, Jon-Paul, Chief Operating Officer, Masonicare Health Center, Wallingford, CT, p. A117

VENTAMEGLIA, Tom, Director Information Systems, Crittenton Hospital Medical Center, Rochester, MI, p. A333

VENTRESS, William L., Chief Executive Officer, Moccasin Bend Mental Health Institute, Chattanooga, TN, p. A580

VENTURELLA, James, Chief Information Officer, UPMC Presbyterian Shadyside, Pittsburgh, PA, p. A552

VENUTO, Kenneth, Chief Financial Officer, St. Anthony's Medical Center, Saint Louis, MO, p. A381

VENZANT, Shamada, Manager Health Information, Specialty Hospital of Winnfield, Winnfield, LA, p. A290

VERA, Luis F., M.D. Medical Director, Kensington Hospital, Philadelphia, PA, p. A549

VERAGIWALA, Jignesh, Chief of Staff, Mercy Hospital Logan County, Guthrie, OK, p. A511

VERBEKE, Lori, Chief Financial Officer, Timberlawn Mental Health System, Dallas, TX, p. A612

VERBUS, John R., Senior Vice President and Chief Operating Officer, Frederick Memorial Hospital, Frederick, MD, p. A301

VERCHOTA, Robert P., Vice President Support Services, Regina Hospital, Hastings, MN, p. A345

VERCRUYSSE, Craig, Chief Information Officer, California Pacific Medical Center, San Francisco, CA, p. A90

VERDEJA, Juan–Carlos, M.D. President of Medical Staff, Baptist Health South Florida, West Kendall Baptist Hospital, Miami, FL, p. A136

VERDON, Chris, Director Finance, Phillips Eye Institute, Minneapolis, MN, p. A347

VERFURTH, Larry, D.O
 Chief Medical Officer and Senior Vice President, Good Shepherd Medical Center, Longview, TX, p. A634
 Executive Vice President and Chief Medical Officer, Good Shepherd Medical Center–Marshall, Marshall, TX, p. A636

VERGA, Joseph P., FACHE, Chief Executive Officer, Guam Memorial Hospital Authority, Tamuning, GU, p. A724

VERGNE, Roger T., Chief Fiscal Service, Hunter Holmes McGuire Veterans Affairs Medical Center, Richmond, VA, p. A678

VERGONIO, Merlinda, Chief Information Management and Technology, U. S. Air Force Hospital, Hampton, VA, p. A672

VERGOS, Katherine, Chief Operating Officer, Ripon Medical Center, Ripon, WI, p. A714

VERHASSELT, Helen, Chief Financial Officer, North Valley Hospital, Tonasket, WA, p. A691

VERINDER, David, Interim Chief Executive Officer, Sarasota Memorial Health Care System, Sarasota, FL, p. A145

VERMA, Ashish, M.D. President Medical Staff, Sturgis Hospital, Sturgis, MI, p. A335

VERMILLION, Kerry, Senior Vice President Finance and Chief Financial Officer, Gulf Breeze Hospital, Gulf Breeze, FL, p. A130

VERMULEN, Peter, Director Information Technology, Schick Shadel Hospital, Seattle, WA, p. A688

VERNON, Janice, Supervisory Information Technology Specialist, John J. Pershing Veterans Affairs Medical Center, Poplar Bluff, MO, p. A378

VERNON–YOUNG, Karen, Vice President Human Resources and Communications, CarePartners Health Services, Asheville, NC, p. A459

VERRET, Dean, Vice President Financial Services, Terrebonne General Medical Center, Houma, LA, p. A279

VERRET, Deborah, J
 Chief Human Resources Officer, Baptist Hospitals of Southeast Texas, Beaumont, TX, p. A601
 Chief Human Resources Officer and Risk Manager, Baptist Orange Hospital, Orange, TX, p. A640

VERRETTE, Paul, M.D. Chief Medical Officer, St. Bernard Parish Hospital, Chalmette, LA, p. A275

VERRETTE, Paula, M.D. Vice President Quality and Performance Improvement and Chief Medical Officer, Huntington Memorial Hospital, Pasadena, CA, p. A83

VERRILL, Alan, M.D. President Medical Staff, Bridgton Hospital, Bridgton, ME, p. A292

VERSCHEURE, Teresa, Executive Director Human Resources, Sparrow Specialty Hospital, Lansing, MI, p. A329

VERSECKES, Mike, Financial Officer, Terrell State Hospital, Terrell, TX, p. A652

VERSTEEG, Linda, Director of Nursing, Hegg Memorial Health Center Avera, Rock Valley, IA, p. A237

VERZI, Dennis, Executive Vice President and Chief Administrative Officer, St. Catherine of Siena Medical Center, Smithtown, NY, p. A454

VETTER, Rich, M.D. Associate Chief, Essentia Health St. Mary's – Detroit Lakes, Detroit Lakes, MN, p. A342

VIALL, John, M.D. Vice President Medical Affairs, Holzer Medical Center, Gallipolis, OH, p. A494

VIALL, Sandra E., MSN Chief Nursing Officer, Hendry Regional Medical Center, Clewiston, FL, p. A126

VIATOR, Kathy A., R.N., Chief Executive Officer, Regency Hospital of Hattiesburg, Hattiesburg, MS, p. A359

VIBBARD, Cheryl
 Manager Health Information Services, University Hospitals Conneaut Medical Center, Conneaut, OH, p. A491
 Manager Health Information Systems, University Hospitals Geneva Medical Center, Geneva, OH, p. A494

VIBETO, Brett, M.D. Chief of Staff, Mercy Medical Center, Williston, ND, p. A480

VICCELLIO, Cathrine, Chief Nursing Officer, Select Long Term Care Hospital – Colorado Springs, Colorado Springs, CO, p. A104

VICE, Jeff, Chief Operating Officer, St. Joseph Hospital, Fort Wayne, IN, p. A211

VICENS–RIVERA Jr., Enrique A., JD, Chief Executive Officer, HEALTHSOUTH Hospital of Manati, Manati, PR, p. A726

VICENTE, Oscar, Chief Financial Officer, Palmetto General Hospital, Hialeah, FL, p. A130

VICENTI, Darren, M.D. Clinical Director, Hopi Health Care Center, Keams Canyon, AZ, p. A33

VICK, Dan J., M.D. Vice President of Medical Affairs and Chief Medical Officer, Oneida Healthcare, Oneida, NY, p. A450

VICKERS, Cynthia, R.N. Assistant Administrator for Nursing Services, Memorial Hospital and Manor, Bainbridge, GA, p. A154

VICKERS, Dave, Chief Financial Officer, Los Alamitos Medical Center, Los Alamitos, CA, p. A71

VICKERS, Don, Chief Executive Officer, Doctors Diagnostic Hospital, Cleveland, TX, p. A606

VICKERY, Ian, Director Information Technology, D. W. McMillan Memorial Hospital, Brewton, AL, p. A17

VICKERY, Tim, Chief Information Officer, Ty Cobb Regional Medical Center, Lavonia, GA, p. A162

VICKROY, Joseph, M.D. Medical Director, HEALTHSOUTH Rehabilitation Hospital of Utah, Sandy, UT, p. A664

VICTORIA, Mario, M.D. Vice President, Medical Affairs, Samaritan Medical Center, Watertown, NY, p. A457

VIDONI–CLARK, Clotilde, R.N. Chief Nurse Executive, St. Elizabeths Hospital, Washington, DC, p. A122

VIEIRA, Terri, President and Chief Executive Officer, Sebasticook Valley Health, Pittsfield, ME, p. A294

VIELKIND, James, Chief Financial Officer, Little Falls Hospital, Little Falls, NY, p. A440

VIENNEAU, Marie E., FACHE, President and Chief Executive Officer, Mayo Regional Hospital, Dover–Foxcroft, ME, p. A293

VIERKANT, Matthew, M.D. President Medical Staff, Mother Frances Hospital – Jacksonville, Jacksonville, TX, p. A630

VIERLING, Taryn, Chief Nursing Officer, Select Specialty Hospital–Zanesville, Zanesville, OH, p. A506

VIETH, Amy, Chief Executive Officer, HEALTHSOUTH Cane Creek Rehabilitation Hospital, Martin, TN, p. A587

VIGGERS, Andreas, Director Human Resources, Providence Little Company of Mary Medical Center San Pedro,, CA, p. A74

VIGIL, Kevin, Director Information Systems, Los Alamos Medical Center, Los Alamos, NM, p. A429

VILANOVA, Lynda, Director Patient Care Services, Shriners Hospitals for Children–Spokane, Spokane, WA, p. A690

VILAR, Ramon J., Administrator, Wilma N. Vazquez Medical Center, Vega Baja, PR, p. A729

VILHAUER, Beverly, Chief Operating Officer and Chief Financial Officer, Linton Hospital, Linton, ND, p. A479

VILLA, Alex, Chief Executive Officer, Western Arizona Regional Medical Center, Bullhead City, AZ, p. A31

VILLAFLOR, Osias, M.D. Chief Medical Staff, Nicholas County Hospital, Carlisle, KY, p. A259

VILLALOBOS, Max, Senior Vice President, Kaiser Permanente Vacaville Medical Center, Vacaville, CA, p. A98

VILLANO, Jeremi, M.D. Chief of Staff, Crook County Medical Services District, Sundance, WY, p. A723

VILLANUEVA, Alice A.
 Senior Vice President Human Resources, John Muir Behavioral Health Center, Concord, CA, p. A60
 Senior Vice President Human Resources, John Muir Medical Center, Walnut Creek, Walnut Creek, CA, p. A100

VILLANUEVA, Andrew, M.D. Interim Chief Medical Officer, Lahey Hospital & Medical Center, Burlington, Burlington, MA, p. A308

VILLARAZA, II, Christopher, M.D. Chief Medical Staff, Grafton City Hospital, Grafton, WV, p. A695

VILLAREAL, Xavier, Chief Operating Officer, CHRISTUS Spohn Hospital Corpus Christi Memorial, Corpus Christi, TX, p. A608

VILLARREAL, Troy, President and Chief Executive Officer, Medical City Dallas Hospital, Dallas, TX, p. A611

VILLARREAL, Xavier, Chief Executive Officer, CHRISTUS Spohn Hospital Corpus Christi Memorial, Corpus Christi, TX, p. A608

VILLARRUZ, Alex, Chief Operating Officer, Barlow Respiratory Hospital, Los Angeles, CA, p. A71

VILLEGAS, Lorraine, Manager Human Resources, Paradise Valley Hospital, National City, CA, p. A79

VILORIA, Bonnie, Chief Nursing Officer, La Paz Regional Hospital, Parker, AZ, p. A35

VINAS, Elmo, Director Human Resources, Franklin Foundation Hospital, Franklin, LA, p. A277

VINCENT, Ben, FACHE, Chief Executive Officer, Braxton County Memorial Hospital, Gassaway, WV, p. A695

VINCENT, Cynthia, Vice President Finance, St. Francis Regional Medical Center, Shakopee, MN, p. A352

VINCENT, David, Director Information Systems, Canonsburg General Hospital, Canonsburg, PA, p. A535

VINCENT, Hugh, M.D., Interim Chief Executive Officer, Saint Francis Memorial Hospital, San Francisco, CA, p. A91

VINCENT, Larry, Director Human Resources, Delta County Memorial Hospital, Delta, CO, p. A104

VINCENT, Laurence Marie, Chief Nursing Officer, University Hospital and Clinics, Lafayette, LA, p. A282

VINCENT, Mitch, Vice President Organizational Support, Range Regional Health Services, Hibbing, MN, p. A345

VINCENT, Sherril, Vice President Finance/CFO, Alexian Brothers Acute Care Ministries, St. Alexius Medical Center, Hoffman Estates, IL, p. A193

VINCENZ, Felix T., Ph.D. Chief Operating Officer, St. Louis Psychiatric Rehabilitation Center, Saint Louis, MO, p. A382

VINNAKOTA, Radha, M.D. President Medical Staff, Robert Wood Johnson University Hospital Rahway, Rahway, NJ, p. A422

VINYARD, Roy G., FACHE, President and Chief Executive Officer, Asante Health System, Medford, OR, p. B12

VIOLETTE, Brenda, M.D. Director Medical Staff, Firelands Regional Health System, Sandusky, OH, p. A501

VIOLI, Ronald L., Chief Executive Officer, Wheeling Hospital, Wheeling, WV, p. A700

VIPOND, Kathleen, Assistant Administrator and Director, Abraham Lincoln Memorial Hospital, Lincoln, IL, p. A195

VIPPERMAN, Mark, President, Spectrum Health Ludington Hospital, Ludington, MI, p. A329

VIRAMOUTES, Allison, Chief Financial Officer, Sutter Davis Hospital, Davis, CA, p. A61

VIRDEN, Larkin, Chief Executive Officer, Kindred Hospital–Houston Northwest, Houston, TX, p. A625

VIRGEN, Tomas, R.N., Interim Administrator and Chief Executive Officer, El Centro Regional Medical Center, El Centro, CA, p. A62

VIRGIL, Cindy L., MSN Senior Vice President Patient Care Services, Indiana Regional Medical Center, Indiana, PA, p. A541

VIRGIL–BELDING, Kathy H., Chief Nursing Officer, Banner Lassen Medical Center, Susanville, CA, p. A96

VIRKLER, Joe, Chief Information Officer, Carthage Area Hospital, Carthage, NY, p. A435

VISAGGIO, Stella, Chief Operating Officer, Hackettstown Regional Medical Center, Hackettstown, NJ, p. A416

VISCONI, Deborah, Director, Hospital Operations, Morristown Medical Center, Morristown, NJ, p. A418

VISH, Nancy, Ph.D., President, Baylor Jack and Jane Hamilton Heart and Vascular Hospital, Dallas, TX, p. A609

VITAL, Dale, Chief Nursing Officer, Orange Coast Memorial Medical Center, Fountain Valley, CA, p. A63

VITALE, Lisa, Director Human Resources, Van Matre HEALTHSOUTH Rehabilitation Hospital, Rockford, IL, p. A202

VITALE, Nickolas A.
 Executive Vice President and Chief Financial Officer, Beaumont Hospital – Royal Oak, Royal Oak, MI, p. A333
 Senior Vice President and Chief Financial Officer, Beaumont Hospital Grosse Pointe, Grosse Pointe, MI, p. A326

VITALE–NOLEN, Roberta A., Administrator, Patient Care Services, New Hampshire Hospital, Concord, NH, p. A409

VITALI, Joe, Director Information Technology, Parkside Hospital, Tulsa, OK, p. A520

VITALIS, Lee Ann, Executive Director Human Resources, St. Croix Regional Medical Center, St. Croix Falls, WI, p. A715

VITIELLO, Jon, Chief Financial Officer, Mercy Hospital Oklahoma City, Oklahoma City, OK, p. A515

VITOLAS, Victor, Acting Chief Information Technology Services, Central Texas Veterans Healthcare System, Temple, TX, p. A652

VIVIANO, Paul S., Chief Executive Officer, UC San Diego Health System, San Diego, CA, p. A90

VIVIT, Romeo, Chief Surgeon, U. S. Public Health Service Indian Hospital, Rosebud, SD, p. A576

VIVODA, Michael, Chief Executive Officer, Cadence Health, Winfield, IL, p. B26

VLAHAVAS, Beth, Vice President Patient Care Services and Chief Nursing Officer, Mercy Medical Center, Rockville Centre, NY, p. A453

VLARS, Scott, Chief Information Technology Services, Veterans Affairs Medical Center, Wilmington, DE, p. A120

VLODARCHYK, Coreen, R.N. Vice President, Patient Care Services and Chief Nursing Officer, Barnes–Jewish Hospital, Saint Louis, MO, p. A380

VLOSICH, Wade, Director, Harry S. Truman Memorial Veterans Hospital, Columbia, MO, p. A370

VOCCA, Lori A., Vice President Human Resources, Providence Regional Medical Center Everett, Everett, WA, p. A683

VOECKS, Barbara, Chief Information Officer, Ortonville Area Health Services, Ortonville, MN, p. A349

VOELKEL, Jonathon, Chief Executive Officer, Wilbarger General Hospital, Vernon, TX, p. A655

VOELKER, Dolph, Director Information Services, Indiana University Health Goshen Hospital, Goshen, IN, p. A212

VOELKER, Justin, Chief Financial Officer, Valley Hospital, Spokane Valley, WA, p. A690

VOGELSANG, Mark, Director Information Services, Providence Holy Family Hospital, Spokane, WA, p. A690

VOGENTIZ, William, M.D. Medical Director, AnMed Health Rehabilitation Hospital, Anderson, SC, p. A562

VOGT, Allen J., Chief Executive Officer, Cook Hospital and Convalescent Nursing Care Unit, Cook, MN, p. A341

VOGT, Dennis, Director Information Technology, Madison County Hospital, London, OH, p. A496

VOHS, Lester, Manager Information Systems, Cass Regional Medical Center, Harrisonville, MO, p. A372

VOISARD, Victor, Director Human Resources, San Gabriel Valley Medical Center, San Gabriel, CA, p. A92

VOISELLE, Dana, Director Human Resources, Baptist Medical Center Beaches, Jacksonville Beach, FL, p. A132

VOKOUN, Cory, Chief Nursing Officer, Nevada Regional Medical Center, Nevada, MO, p. A377

VOLANTO, John, Vice President and Chief Information Officer, Nyack Hospital, Nyack, NY, p. A450

VOLGER, Helen, Director of Information Services, Aspirus Medford Hospital, Medford, WI, p. A709

VOLINSKI, Douglas R., Vice President and Chief Financial Officer, Duncan Regional Hospital, Duncan, OK, p. A509

VOLK, Charles T., M.D. Regional Chief Medical Officer, CHRISTUS Spohn Hospital Corpus Christi Memorial, Corpus Christi, TX, p. A608

VOLKERDING, Elizabeth, Director Workforce Excellence, San Juan Regional Medical Center, Farmington, NM, p. A428

VOLKERT, Brent, Director Information Technology, Ferrell Hospital, Eldorado, IL, p. A188

VOLLER, Kristi, Director of Nursing, Mobridge Regional Hospital, Mobridge, SD, p. A575

VOLLMER, Cyndy, Director Human Resources, Southern Coos Hospital and Health Center, Bandon, OR, p. A523

VOLOCH, Bill, Chief Operating Officer, Wesley Medical Center, Wichita, KS, p. A257

VOLPE, Buddy, Director Human Resources, Peterson Regional Medical Center, Kerrville, TX, p. A631

VOLPE, Michele M., Executive Director and Chief Executive Officer, Penn Presbyterian Medical Center, Philadelphia, PA, p. A549

VOLTAIRE, Adler, Chief Administrative Officer, Interim LSU Public Hospital, New Orleans, LA, p. A285

VON BEHREN, Rachel, Director Financial Services, UnityPoint Health – Jones Regional Medical Center, Anamosa, IA, p. A225

VONDERAU, Mary, Vice President Strategy and Operations, Presence Mercy Medical Center, Aurora, IL, p. A180

VONNIDA, Ashley Marie, Chief Nursing Officer, Coastal Carolina Hospital, Hardeeville, SC, p. A567

VOORHEES, Michael, MS, Executive Director, East Mountain Hospital, Belle Mead, NJ, p. A413

VOSBURGH, Mary M., R.N
  Vice President Nursing and Chief Nursing Officer, Arnot Ogden Medical Center, Elmira, NY, p. A437
  Vice President Nursing and Chief Nursing Officer, St. Joseph's Hospital, Elmira, NY, p. A437

VOSHELL, Shane, Director Human Resources, Adventist Medical Center–Portland, Portland, OR, p. A528

VOSS, Daryle, FACHE, President, Mercy Hospital Ardmore, Ardmore, OK, p. A507

VOSS, Kathy, Director Human Resources, CentraCare Health–Monticello, Monticello, MN, p. A348

VOSS, Robert, Chief Financial Officer, Laredo Specialty Hospital, Laredo, TX, p. A633

VOSS, Wayne M., Chief Executive Officer, Houston Methodist West Hospital, Houston, TX, p. A624

VOSSBERG, Brad, M.D. Chief Rehabilitation, Community Howard Specialty Hospital, Kokomo, IN, p. A216

VOSSLER, Jeffrey W., Chief Financial Officer, Joint Township District Memorial Hospital, Saint Marys, OH, p. A501

VOTTO, John J., D.O., President and Chief Executive Officer, Hospital for Special Care, New Britain, CT, p. A115

VOWELL, Christy, D.O. Chief of Staff, North Mississippi Medical Center–Eupora, Eupora, MS, p. A357

VOZOS, Frank J., FACS, President and Chief Executive Officer, Monmouth Medical Center, Long Branch Campus, Long Branch, NJ, p. A418

VRABEL, Amy Z., Chief Information Officer, Mayo Clinic Hospital, Phoenix, AZ, p. A36

VRANA, Daniel A.
  Controller, HEALTHSOUTH Harmarville Rehabilitation Hospital, Pittsburgh, PA, p. A551
  Area Controller, HEALTHSOUTH Rehabilitation Hospital, Sewickley, PA, p. A555

VRBA, Frank, Chief Information Officer, Annie Jeffrey Memorial County Health Center, Osceola, NE, p. A400

VREELAND, Matthew, M.D. Chief Medical Officer, FirstHealth Richmond Memorial Hospital, Rockingham, NC, p. A471

VROTSOS, Darlene, R.N. Vice President and Chief Nursing Officer, Virginia Hospital Center – Arlington, Arlington, VA, p. A668

VRZAK, Staci, Vice President Patient Care Services, Regional Health Services of Howard County, Cresco, IA, p. A228

VUCHAK, Jerry
  Vice President Information Systems, Barnes–Jewish Hospital, Saint Louis, MO, p. A380
  Vice President Information Systems, Barnes–Jewish West County Hospital, Saint Louis, MO, p. A380

VUKICH, David, M.D. Senior Vice President, Chief Medical Officer and Chief Quality Officer, UF Health Jacksonville, Jacksonville, FL, p. A132

VUKSTA, Jeanne, Chief Financial Officer, Bacharach Institute for Rehabilitation, Pomona, NJ, p. A421

VUTRANO, Frank A., Chief Financial Officer, Wyckoff Heights Medical Center,, NY, p. A449

W

WAARALA, Kirsten, D.O. Vice President Medical Services, Garden City Hospital, Garden City, MI, p. A324

WABLE, Chad W., President and Chief Executive Officer, Saint Mary's Hospital, Waterbury, CT, p. A118

WACHOWIAK, Darrell, Associate Vice President Operations, ProMedica Bay Park Hospital, Oregon, OH, p. A500

WACHTEL, Andrew, Chief Executive Officer, Integris Blackwell Regional Hospital, Blackwell, OK, p. A508

WACHTEL, R. Andrew, FACHE, Chief Executive Officer, Ponca City Medical Center, Ponca City, OK, p. A517

WACK, Mark, Chief Financial Officer, Biloxi Regional Medical Center, Biloxi, MS, p. A355

WADA, Takashi, Interim Director, Santa Barbara County Psychiatric Health Facility, Santa Barbara, CA, p. A94

WADDELL, Lesa, Director Human Resources, Marengo Memorial Hospital, UnityPoint Health, Marengo, IA, p. A234

WADE, Donald, Chief Executive Officer, Kit Carson County Health Service District, Burlington, CO, p. A103

WADE, Donna, Senior Director Human Resources, Comanche County Memorial Hospital, Lawton, OK, p. A512

WADE, Glenn, Director Information Systems, Highlands Medical Center, Sparta, TN, p. A593

WADE, Hong, Chief Financial Officer, Sweeny Community Hospital, Sweeny, TX, p. A651

WADE, Jonathan O., Administrator and Chief Executive Officer, Jersey Community Hospital, Jerseyville, IL, p. A193

WADE, Karen, Chief Information Officer, U. S. Public Health Service Indian Hospital–Sells, Sells, AZ, p. A39

WADE, Linda, Chief Executive Officer, HEALTHSOUTH Rehabilitation Hospital of Montgomery, Montgomery, AL, p. A23

WADE, Susan, Assistant Vice President, Hendrick Health System, Abilene, TX, p. A595

WADEWITZ, Martin, Chief Operations Officer/ Vice President, Operations, Angel Medical Center, Franklin, NC, p. A464

WADLE, Don, Vice President Clinical and Support Services, Portneuf Medical Center, Pocatello, ID, p. A177

WADMAN, Timothy, Chief Executive Officer, SSM Select Rehabilitation Hospital, Richmond Heights, MO, p. A379

WADSWORTH, Barbara A., MSN Chief Nursing Officer, Bryn Mawr Hospital, Bryn Mawr, PA, p. A543

WAFFORD, Marty, Executive Officer of Support and Programs, Chickasaw Nation Medical Center, Ada, OK, p. A507

WAGENAAR, Jen, Chief Nursing Officer, Sanford Aberdeen Medical Center, Aberdeen, SD, p. A572

WAGERS, Rick, Senior Executive Vice President and Chief Financial Officer, Regional One Health, Memphis, TN, p. A589

WAGGENER, Yvonne, Chief Financial Officer, San Bernardino Mountains Community Hospital District, Lake Arrowhead, CA, p. A69

WAGGONER, Jeff, M.D. Chief of Staff, Weisbrod Memorial County Hospital, Eads, CO, p. A105

WAGGONER, Michelle, Chief Executive Officer, Community Memorial Hospital, Hicksville, OH, p. A495

WAGMEISTER, Lee, M.D. President Medical Staff, The Heart Hospital at Deaconess Gateway, Newburgh, IN, p. A220

WAGNER, Alan, Chief Operating Officer, Coulee Medical Center, Grand Coulee, WA, p. A684

WAGNER, Arthur, Senior Vice President and Executive Director, Coney Island Hospital,, NY, p. A443

WAGNER, Dale, Chief Financial Officer, Kindred Hospital–Westminster, Westminster, CA, p. A100

WAGNER, David D., Chief Information Management Service, Veterans Affairs Gulf Coast Veterans Health Care System, Biloxi, MS, p. A356

WAGNER, Elaina, Director Human Resources, Sunnyside Community Hospital and Clinics, Sunnyside, WA, p. A690

WAGNER, Fred, Chief Financial Officer, OSF St. Francis Hospital and Medical Group, Escanaba, MI, p. A323

WAGNER, Gwendolyn Dianne, R.N. Chief Nursing Officer, Mission Community Hospital,, CA, p. A73

WAGNER, Janet, R.N., Chief Executive Officer, Sutter Davis Hospital, Davis, CA, p. A61

WAGNER, Jeffrey, Supervisor Information Systems, Bell Hospital, Ishpeming, MI, p. A327

WAGNER, Linda, Chief Financial Officer, Sanford Worthington Medical Center, Worthington, MN, p. A354

WAGNER, Linda S., FACHE, Chief Executive Officer, Seneca Healthcare District, Chester, CA, p. A59

WAGNER, Lynne, R.N. Chief Nursing Officer, Rose Medical Center, Denver, CO, p. A105

WAGNER, Michael, M.D., President and Chief Executive Officer, Tufts Medical Center, Boston, MA, p. A307

WAGNER, Randall J., Chief Operating Officer, Mercy Health Saint Mary's, Grand Rapids, MI, p. A325

WAGNER, Russell R., Executive Vice President and Chief Financial Officer, Holy Redeemer Hospital, Meadowbrook, PA, p. A544

WAGNER, Sarah, Human Resources Officer, Memorial Hospital of Texas County, Guymon, OK, p. A511

WAGNER, Sherry, Director Human Resources, Oklahoma Center for Orthopedic and Multi–Specialty Surgery, Oklahoma City, OK, p. A516

WAGNER, Suzie, Director Human Resources, HEALTHSOUTH Rehabilitation Hospital of Alexandria, Alexandria, LA, p. A272

WAGNER, Terry, R.N. Chief Operating Officer, Pocahontas Memorial Hospital, Buckeye, WV, p. A693

WAGNER, Terry, Chief Information Officer, Upstate University Hospital, Syracuse, NY, p. A456

WAGNER, Timothy, M.D. Chief Medical Staff, Yoakum Community Hospital, Yoakum, TX, p. A658

WAGNER, Tom, Interim Vice President Finance, Avera St. Mary's Hospital, Pierre, SD, p. A575

WAGNER, Vanessa, Chief Financial Officer, Lawrence Memorial Hospital, Walnut Ridge, AR, p. A53

WAGNON, LaNell, Director Medical Records, Comanche County Hospital, Coldwater, KS, p. A242

WAGNON, William, Chief Executive Officer, Henrico Doctors' Hospital, Richmond, VA, p. A677

WAGONER, Craig, Chief Operating Officer, Community Behavioral Health Center, Fresno, CA, p. A64

WAGONER, Dean, Director Human Resources, Good Samaritan Hospital, Vincennes, IN, p. A223

WAHL, Carol R., R.N. Vice President Patient Care Services, CHI Health Good Samaritan, Kearney, NE, p. A397

WAHL, Josephine Sclafani, R.N. VP, Patient Care Services & CNO, Henry Ford Wyandotte Hospital, Wyandotte, MI, p. A337

WAHL, Tony, Chief Executive Officer, Texas Spine & Joint Hospital, Tyler, TX, p. A654

WAHLERS, Brenda, M.D. Chief of Staff, Cole Memorial, Coudersport, PA, p. A536

WAHLMEIER, James E., Chief Executive Officer, Sheridan County Health Complex, Hoxie, KS, p. A246

WAHLUND, Keith, Vice President Human Resources, Essentia Health Fargo, Fargo, ND, p. A477

WAIBEL, David, M.D. Medical Director, Clarks Summit State Hospital, Clarks Summit, PA, p. A535

WAIDE, Mary Beth, JD, Chief Executive Officer, Deer's Head Hospital Center, Salisbury, MD, p. A303

WAIN, Matthew, Chief Operating Officer, MUSC Medical Center of Medical University of South Carolina, Charleston, SC, p. A563

WAIND, Mark, Administrative Director Information Services, Altru Health System, Grand Forks, ND, p. A478

WAITE, Douglas, M.D. Chief Medical Officer, Saint Vincent Hospital, Worcester, MA, p. A317

WAITE, Douglas D.
  Senior Vice President and Chief Financial Officer, Seton Highland Lakes, Burnet, TX, p. A605
  Chief Financial Officer, Seton Medical Center Austin, Austin, TX, p. A599
  Senior Vice President and Chief Financial Officer, Seton Medical Center Williamson, Round Rock, TX, p. A645
  Chief Financial Officer, Seton Northwest Hospital, Austin, TX, p. A599
  Chief Financial Officer, Seton Shoal Creek Hospital, Austin, TX, p. A600
  Chief Financial Officer, University Medical Center at Brackenridge, Austin, TX, p. A600

WAITES, Alan, Chief Financial Officer, Gove County Medical Center, Quinter, KS, p. A253

WAITES, Cherri, Chief Financial Officer, Palacios Community Medical Center, Palacios, TX, p. A640

WAJDA, David
Chief Financial Officer, Mercy Suburban Hospital, Norristown, PA, p. A546
Chief Financial Officer, Nazareth Hospital, Philadelphia, PA, p. A549

WAKEFIELD, Brett
Vice President Human Resources, Gottlieb Memorial Hospital, Melrose Park, IL, p. A196
Director Human Resources, Thorek Memorial Hospital, Chicago, IL, p. A187

WAKEFIELD, Mamie
Vice President Finance and Chief Financial Officer, Emma Pendleton Bradley Hospital, East Providence, RI, p. A560
Chief Financial Officer, Miriam Hospital, Providence, RI, p. A560
Senior Vice President and Chief Financial Officer, Rhode Island Hospital, Providence, RI, p. A561

WAKEMAN, Daniel L., President, ProMedica St. Luke's Hospital, Maumee, OH, p. A498

WAKIM, Tina, Vice President Information, Northside Hospital, Atlanta, GA, p. A152

WAKULCHIK, Grace, R.N. Chief Operating Officer, Akron Children's Hospital, Akron, OH, p. A482

WALAS, Steven, Chief Executive Officer, HEALTHSOUTH Chesapeake Rehabilitation Hospital, Salisbury, MD, p. A303

WALCEK, Peter, Vice President Finance, Wentworth–Douglass Hospital, Dover, NH, p. A410

WALCH, Tina, M.D. Medical Director, South Oaks Hospital, Amityville, NY, p. A432

WALCZAK, Charles, FACHE, Regional Administrator, Shriners Hospitals for Children–Springfield, Springfield, MA, p. A315

WALD, Barry, Chief Financial Officer, Wilkes Regional Medical Center, North Wilkesboro, NC, p. A470

WALDBART, Andy, Department Manager, Heart of the Rockies Regional Medical Center, Salida, CO, p. A111

WALDBILLIG, Karla, Director Human Resources, UnityPoint Health – Finley Hospital, Dubuque, IA, p. A230

WALDEN, Anita, Vice President and Chief Nursing Officer, Decatur Morgan Hospital, Decatur, AL, p. A18

WALDEN, Christopher, Vice President and Chief Information Officer, HealthAlliance Hospitals, Leominster, MA, p. A311

WALDEN, Kristy, R.N., Chief Executive Officer, Kindred Hospital–Indianapolis, Indianapolis, IN, p. A214

WALDERA, John, Director Information Technology, Gundersen Tri–County Hospital and Clinics, Whitehall, WI, p. A718

WALDO, Bruce
Chief Executive Officer, Aurora Phoenix Hospital, Glendale, AZ, p. A33
Chief Executive Officer, Aurora Tempe Hospital, Tempe, AZ, p. A39

WALDO, Gail, Director Information Technology, Rockdale Medical Center, Conyers, GA, p. A157

WALDOW, Dee, Chief Financial Officer, Palo Pinto General Hospital, Mineral Wells, TX, p. A638

WALDRON, Michele, Senior Vice President and Chief Financial Officer, Children's Hospital Central California, Madera, CA, p. A76

WALDRON, Ray, Director Information Technology, Gordon Memorial Hospital, Gordon, NE, p. A396

WALDROP, Cathy
Director, Hospital Nursing Services, North Mississippi Medical Center–Pontotoc, Pontotoc, MS, p. A364
Administrator, Sterlington Rehabilitation Hospital, Bastrop, LA, p. A273

WALI, Jyotika, M.D. Chief of Staff, Kindred Hospital–Brea, Brea, CA, p. A58

WALIGURA, R. Curtis, D.O. Vice President Medical Affairs, Chief Medical Officer, UPMC McKeesport, McKeesport, PA, p. A544

WALKENHORST, Debbie G.
Network Vice President, SSM Cardinal Glennon Children's Medical Center, Saint Louis, MO, p. A381
System Vice President Talent Management, SSM St. Joseph Health Center, Saint Charles, MO, p. A379

WALKER, Alene, Director Human Resources, Quincy Valley Medical Center, Quincy, WA, p. A687

WALKER, Alexander J., Senior Vice President Operations and Strategic Development, Catholic Medical Center, Manchester, NH, p. A411

WALKER, Amy, Chief Nursing Officer, Delta Regional Medical Center, Greenville, MS, p. A358

WALKER, Angela, Manager Human Resources, Aspire Hospital, Conroe, TX, p. A607

WALKER, Angela, M.D. Medical Director, HEALTHSOUTH Rehabilitation Hospital, Albuquerque, NM, p. A426

WALKER, Annette, Associate Director, John D. Dingell Veterans Affairs Medical Center, Detroit, MI, p. A322

WALKER, Austin, Accounting Manager, Kindred Hospital Northland, Kansas City, MO, p. A373

WALKER, Beth, R.N., President, FirstHealth Montgomery Memorial Hospital, Troy, NC, p. A474

WALKER, C. O., M.D. Chief of Staff, Donalsonville Hospital, Donalsonville, GA, p. A158

WALKER, Candace, Chief Financial Officer, East Central Regional Hospital, Augusta, GA, p. A153

WALKER, Carol, Chief Financial Officer, Oklahoma Heart Hospital, Oklahoma City, OK, p. A516

WALKER, Cass
Senior Director Administrative Services, Franklin Regional Hospital, Franklin, NH, p. A410
Senior Director, Administrative Services, Lakes Region General Hospital, Laconia, NH, p. A410

WALKER, Charity, Controller and Regional Business Officer Manager, Greenwood Regional Rehabilitation Hospital, Greenwood, SC, p. A567

WALKER, Charles, Director Information Technology, Kimball Health Services, Kimball, NE, p. A397

WALKER, Cheri, R.N. Chief Nursing Officer, King's Daughters Medical Center, Brookhaven, MS, p. A356

WALKER, Codie, Chief Financial Officer, Salem Veterans Affairs Medical Center, Salem, VA, p. A678

WALKER, Daniel T., Vice President Finance and Chief Financial Officer, Manchester Memorial Hospital, Manchester, KY, p. A267

WALKER, Donna, Chief Nurse Executive, Weeks Medical Center, Lancaster, NH, p. A410

WALKER, Durwin, M.D. Chief Medical Officer, AMG Specialty Hospital–Denham Springs, Denham Springs, LA, p. A277

WALKER, Gale N., President and Chief Executive Officer, Avera St. Benedict Health Center, Parkston, SD, p. A575

WALKER, Gregory J., Chief Executive Officer, Wentworth–Douglass Hospital, Dover, NH, p. A410

WALKER, Jan
Director Human Resources, Centra Lynchburg General Hospital, Lynchburg, VA, p. A673
Director Human Resources, Glenwood Regional Medical Center, West Monroe, LA, p. A290

WALKER, Janice L., R.N
Chief Operating Officer, Baylor All Saints Medical Center at Fort Worth, Fort Worth, TX, p. A618
Chief Nursing Officer and Chief Operating Officer, Baylor Medical Center at Garland, Garland, TX, p. A620

WALKER, Jeremy Tyler, Vice President and Chief Financial Officer, Hendrick Health System, Abilene, TX, p. A595

WALKER, Kathy, Chief Financial Officer, Trinity Hospital, Weaverville, CA, p. A100

WALKER, Kevin, Vice President Operations, Research Psychiatric Center, Kansas City, MO, p. A374

WALKER, Kristie, Director Human Resources, LewisGale Hospital Montgomery, Blacksburg, VA, p. A668

WALKER, Larry D., Chief Operating Officer, Glenwood Regional Medical Center, West Monroe, LA, p. A290

WALKER, Lawrence, M.D. Chief of Staff, San Bernardino Mountains Community Hospital District, Lake Arrowhead, CA, p. A69

WALKER, LeRoy, Vice President Human Resources, DeKalb Medical at North Decatur, Decatur, GA, p. A158

WALKER, Lynette, R.N. Vice President Human Resources, Baptist Health Lexington, Lexington, KY, p. A264

WALKER, Mary, Manager Information Technology, HEALTHSOUTH Rehabilitation Hospital–Wichita Falls, Wichita Falls, TX, p. A657

WALKER, Melissa
Senior Vice President and Chief Financial Officer, McAlester Regional Health Center, McAlester, OK, p. A513
Chief Financial Officer, St. Rose Dominican Hospitals – San Martin Campus, Las Vegas, NV, p. A406

WALKER, Michael, D.O. Chief of Staff, East Texas Medical Center–Mount Vernon, Mount Vernon, TX, p. A638

WALKER, Randy
Chief Nursing Officer, Hillcrest Hospital Claremore, Claremore, OK, p. A509
Vice President, Methodist Dallas Medical Center, Dallas, TX, p. A611
Director Nursing Services, State Hospital South, Blackfoot, ID, p. A174

WALKER, Renee, Director Human Resources, Sterlington Rehabilitation Hospital, Bastrop, LA, p. A273

WALKER, Rick, Network, Chief Financial Officer, Woodhull Medical and Mental Health Center,, NY, p. A449

WALKER, Robert, M.D. Medical Director, HEALTHSOUTH Southern Hills Rehabilitation Hospital, Princeton, WV, p. A698

WALKER, Robert L., President and Chief Executive Officer, Texas Scottish Rite Hospital for Children, Dallas, TX, p. A612

WALKER, Robin, Chief Nursing Officer, Field Memorial Community Hospital, Centreville, MS, p. A356

WALKER, Scott, Chief Financial Officer, Southeastern Regional Medical Center, Newnan, GA, p. A164

WALKER, Scott, M.D. Chief Medical Staff, Weatherford Regional Medical Center, Weatherford, TX, p. A656

WALKER, Tim, Manager Information Services, PeaceHealth Ketchikan Medical Center, Ketchikan, AK, p. A29

WALKER, Troy, Director Finance, St. Clare Hospital, Baraboo, WI, p. A702

WALKER, Tyree, Chief Human Resources Officer, Vidant Medical Center, Greenville, NC, p. A465

WALKER, Virginia, Vice President Nursing Services and Chief Nursing Officer, Kuakini Medical Center, Honolulu, HI, p. A170

WALKER Jr., William J., Chief Executive Officer, Memorial Hospital and Manor, Bainbridge, GA, p. A154

WALKUP, Jessica, Controller, HEALTHSOUTH Western Hills Rehabilitation Hospital, Parkersburg, WV, p. A698

WALL, Daniel J., President and Chief Executive Officer, Emma Pendleton Bradley Hospital, East Providence, RI, p. A560

WALL, Doug, M.D. Vice President Medical Affairs, Novant Health Prince William Medical Center, Manassas, VA, p. A673

WALL, J. C., M.D. Chief of Staff, Stones River Hospital, Woodbury, TN, p. A594

WALL, Kathryn S.
Executive Vice President Human Resources and Organizational Development, Mary Washington Hospital, Fredericksburg, VA, p. A671
Executive Vice President Human Resources and Organizational Development, Stafford Hospital, Stafford, VA, p. A679

WALLACE, Arthur, Chief Financial Officer, Broward Health Coral Springs, Coral Springs, FL, p. A126

WALLACE, Bernadine L., MSN Chief Nursing Officer and Chief Operating Officer, Marion General Hospital, Marion, IN, p. A218

WALLACE, Brenda, R.N. Chief Nursing Officer, Ouachita Community Hospital, West Monroe, LA, p. A290

WALLACE, Carolyn, Director Human Resources, Connecticut Mental Health Center, New Haven, CT, p. A116

WALLACE, Cynthia, M.D. Medical Director, Vibra Specialty Hospital of Portland, Portland, OR, p. A529

WALLACE, David, Chief Executive Officer, Woodward Regional Hospital, Woodward, OK, p. A522

WALLACE, Debra, M.D. Chief of Staff, Methodist Hospital Union County, Morganfield, KY, p. A268

WALLACE, Dianne, County Information Manager, Douglas County Community Mental Health Center, Omaha, NE, p. A400

WALLACE, Donna Geiken, Chief Operating Officer and Chief Financial Officer, Hopkins County Memorial Hospital, Sulphur Springs, TX, p. A651

WALLACE, Glenn, Chief Operating Officer, Medical Center of Plano, Plano, TX, p. A642

WALLACE, Jennifer, Chief Executive Officer, AMG Specialty Hospital–Greenwood, Greenwood, MS, p. A358

WALLACE, Jo Lynn, Vice President Nursing, Asante Rogue Regional Medical Center, Medford, OR, p. A527

WALLACE, Kelly, Senior Vice President and Chief Financial Officer, Seattle Children's Hospital, Seattle, WA, p. A688

WALLACE, Kent H., Chief Executive Officer, RegionalCare Hospital Partners, Brentwood, TN, p. B114

WALLACE, Kristina, R.N. Chief Operating Officer, OU Medical Center, Oklahoma City, OK, p. A516

WALLACE, Lisa, R.N. Chief Nursing Officer, Redmond Regional Medical Center, Rome, GA, p. A165

WALLACE, Mark A., President and Chief Executive Officer, Texas Children's Hospital, Houston, TX, p. A627

WALLACE, Mark T., Director Human Resources, Lodi Memorial Hospital, Lodi, CA, p. A69

WALLACE, Martha, Administrator, California Mens Colony Hospital, San Luis Obispo, CA, p. A92

WALLACE, Melanie, Manager Human Resources, Sutter Tracy Community Hospital, Tracy, CA, p. A97

WALLACE, Michael S., President and Chief Executive Officer, Fort HealthCare, Fort Atkinson, WI, p. A705

WALLACE, Nancy
Vice President Human Resources, CHI Health Bergan Mercy, Omaha, NE, p. A399
Vice President Human Resources, CHI Health Immanuel, Omaha, NE, p. A399
Vice President Human Resources, CHI Health Lakeside, Omaha, NE, p. A399
Senior Vice President Human Resources, CHI Health Mercy Council Bluffs, Council Bluffs, IA, p. A228
Interim Senior Vice President Human Resources, CHI Health Midlands, Papillion, NE, p. A401
Vice President Human Resources, CHI Health Schuyler, Schuyler, NE, p. A401

WALLACE, Patrick L., Administrator, East Texas Medical Center Athens, Athens, TX, p. A598

WALLACE, Penny, Chief Financial Officer, Guadalupe Regional Medical Center, Seguin, TX, p. A648

WALLACE, Rick D., FACHE, President and Chief Executive Officer, San Juan Regional Medical Center, Farmington, NM, p. A428

WALLACE, Tabatha, Director Human Resources, Bayfront Health Dade City, Dade City, FL, p. A126

WALLACE–MOORE, Patrice, Chief Executive Officer and Executive Director, Arms Acres, Carmel, NY, p. A435

WALLEN, Carla, Manager Human Resources, Cass Regional Medical Center, Harrisonville, MO, p. A372

WALLENHAUPT, Stephen, M.D. Executive Vice President Medical Affairs, Novant Health Presbyterian Medical Center, Charlotte, NC, p. A462

WALLER, Ernie, Director Information Technology, Ed Fraser Memorial Hospital and Baker Community Health Center, MacClenny, FL, p. A135

WALLER, Kenneth, Fiscal Administrator, Deer's Head Hospital Center, Salisbury, MD, p. A303

WALLER, Patricia A., R.N. Assistant Administrator Patient Care Services, Newton Medical Center, Covington, GA, p. A157

WALLER, Raymond, Director, Brighton Center for Recovery, Brighton, MI, p. A320

WALLER, Yoemy, Director Information Technology Systems, Lake District Hospital, Lakeview, OR, p. A526

WALLINE, Linda K., R.N. Vice President Nursing, Columbus Community Hospital, Columbus, NE, p. A395

WALLING, John R., President, River Bend Hospital, West Lafayette, IN, p. A224

WALLING, Vernon, M.D. Executive Medical Director, West Oaks Hospital, Houston, TX, p. A628

WALLINGA, Joel, Chief Financial Officer, Veterans Affairs Ann Arbor Healthcare System, Ann Arbor, MI, p. A318

WALLINGA, Melvin, M.D. Medical Director, St. Michael's Hospital Avera, Tyndall, SD, p. A577

WALLIS, Carla, Director Human Resources, North Ottawa Community Hospital, Grand Haven, MI, p. A324

WALLIS, Eric, R.N. Vice President Patient Care and Chief Nursing Officer, OhioHealth Marion General Hospital, Marion, OH, p. A497

WALLIS, MSN, RN–, Pam B., MSN Vice President Nursing Services, Magnolia Regional Health Center, Corinth, MS, p. A357

WALLMAN, Gerald H., Administrator, Doctors Hospital of West Covina, West Covina, CA, p. A100

WALLS, Martha Delaney, R.N. Chief Nursing Officer, Crestwood Medical Center, Huntsville, AL, p. A21

WALLS, Randy, Manager Information Services, Fairbanks, Indianapolis, IN, p. A214

WALLSCHLAEGER, Erich, Chief Financial Officer, Cedar Park Regional Medical Center, Cedar Park, TX, p. A605

WALMSLEY III, George J., CPA,
President and Chief Executive Officer, Girard Medical Center, Philadelphia, PA, p. A548
President and Chief Executive Officer, North Philadelphia Health System, Philadelphia, PA, p. A549

WALMUS, Adam C., Director, Michael E. DeBakey Veterans Affairs Medical Center, Houston, TX, p. A626

WALRATH, Andrea, Chief Operating Officer, Forest Health Medical Center, Ypsilanti, MI, p. A337

WALSER, Bill, Coordinator Technology, Cameron Regional Medical Center, Cameron, MO, p. A368

WALSH, Brad, M.D. Chief of Staff, Ashley County Medical Center, Crossett, AR, p. A44

WALSH, Catherine
Interim Chief Nursing Officer, Mercy Allen Hospital, Oberlin, OH, p. A500
Interim Nursing Executive, Mercy Regional Medical Center, Lorain, OH, p. A497

WALSH, Dan, Interim Chief Information Officer, Aria Health, Philadelphia, PA, p. A547

WALSH, Debbie, MSN, Chief Executive Officer, USC Verdugo Hills Hospital, Glendale, CA, p. A65

WALSH, John, M.D. Chief Medical Officer, Florida Hospital–Flagler, Palm Coast, FL, p. A141

WALSH, John
Chief Executive Officer, Trumbull Memorial Hospital, Warren, OH, p. A504
Chief Fiscal Services, Veterans Affairs Hudson Valley Health Care System–F.D. Roosevelt Hospital, Montrose, NY, p. A441

WALSH, Kate, President and Chief Executive Officer, Boston Medical Center, Boston, MA, p. A306

WALSH, Ken, Chief Financial Officer, St. Luke's Medical Center, Phoenix, AZ, p. A37

WALSH, Kim, Chief Nursing Officer, Signature Healthcare Brockton Hospital, Brockton, MA, p. A308

WALSH, Len, Executive Vice President and Chief Operating Officer, St. Barnabas Hospital,, NY, p. A448

WALSH, Leon, Chief Financial Officer, Petersburg Medical Center, Petersburg, AK, p. A30

WALSH, Linda, R.N. Vice President Chief Nursing Executive, Bayshore Community Hospital, Holmdel, NJ, p. A417

WALSH, Marcia S., M.P.H. Chief Operating Officer, Community HealthCare System, Onaga, KS, p. A251

WALSH, Marilyn J., Vice President Human Resources, Kent County Memorial Hospital, Warwick, RI, p. A561

WALSH, Mary, R.N
Vice President Patient Care Services and Chief Nursing Officer, Mount Sinai Beth Israel, New York, NY, p. A446
Vice President Patient Care Services and Chief Nursing Officer, Mount Sinai St. Luke's, New York, NY, p. A446

WALSH, Mary Beth, M.D., Chief Executive Officer, Burke Rehabilitation Hospital, White Plains, NY, p. A458

WALSH, Michael, Senior Vice President Finance and Chief Financial Officer, Abington Memorial Hospital, Abington, PA, p. A532

WALSH, Richard J., Ph.D. Chief Human Resources Officer, Duke Regional Hospital, Durham, NC, p. A463

WALSH, Ryan, M.D. Chief Medical Information Officer, UnityPoint Health – Methodist, Peoria, IL, p. A200

WALSH, Shawn, Chief Operating Officer, Rockford Center, Newark, DE, p. A119

WALSH, Timothy J., Chief Executive Officer, Martha's Vineyard Hospital, Oak Bluffs, MA, p. A313

WALSH, William P.
Senior Vice President and Executive Director, Jacobi Medical Center,, NY, p. A444
Executive Director, North Central Bronx Hospital,, NY, p. A447

WALSTON, John, Chief Information Officer, Southern Arizona Veterans Affairs Health Care System, Tucson, AZ, p. A41

WALTER, Gayle, Director of Nursing, Thomas B. Finan Center, Cumberland, MD, p. A300

WALTER, Marcia Michelle, Chief Nursing Officer, Cameron Memorial Community Hospital, Angola, IN, p. A206

WALTER, Melissa, Chief Financial Officer, Clarinda Regional Health Center, Clarinda, IA, p. A227

WALTER, Mitch, Director Information Technology, Morton General Hospital, Morton, WA, p. A685

WALTER, Stephen
Senior Vice President and Chief Financial Officer, Community Behavioral Health Center, Fresno, CA, p. A64
Senior Vice President and Chief Financial Officer, Community Regional Medical Center, Fresno, CA, p. A64

WALTERS, David, D.O. Vice President and Chief Clinical Officer, Botsford Hospital, Farmington Hills, MI, p. A323

WALTERS, Jane, Director of Nursing, Mendota Mental Health Institute, Madison, WI, p. A708

WALTERS, Julie, Chief Nursing Officer, Hillsdale Community Health Center, Hillsdale, MI, p. A326

WALTERS, Kevin
Chief Financial Officer, St. Rose Dominican Hospitals – Rose de Lima Campus, Henderson, NV, p. A405
Chief Financial Officer, St. Rose Dominican Hospitals – Siena Campus, Henderson, NV, p. A405

WALTERS, Leslie, R.N. Chief Nursing Officer, Clarion Hospital, Clarion, PA, p. A535

WALTERS, Lisa, R.N. Director of Nursing, Bellevue Medical Center, Bellevue, NE, p. A394

WALTERS, Patrick, Chief Executive Officer, Inova Loudoun Hospital, Leesburg, VA, p. A673

WALTERS, Todd, Director of UHC Information Technology Services, University Health Conway, Monroe, LA, p. A284

WALTERS, Wayne, Chief Executive Officer, North Sunflower Medical Center, Ruleville, MS, p. A365

WALTHALL, Wayne, Vice President and Chief Financial Officer, St. John Medical Center, Tulsa, OK, p. A521

WALTON, Brian, Vice President and Chief Financial Officer, Baptist St. Anthony Health System, Amarillo, TX, p. A596

WALTON, Carlyle L. E., FACHE, Chief Executive Officer, Metroplex Adventist Hospital, Killeen, TX, p. A631

WALTON, Dawn, Chief Financial Officer, The Children's Hospital of Alabama, Birmingham, AL, p. A17

WALTON, Gary, M.D. Chief Medical Officer, Hill Hospital of Sumter County, York, AL, p. A27

WALTON, Georgian, Director Human Resources, Elbert Memorial Hospital, Elberton, GA, p. A159

WALTON, Greg, Chief Information Officer, El Camino Hospital, Mountain View, CA, p. A79

WALTON, Harold, M.D. Chief of Staff, Bayshore Medical Center, Pasadena, TX, p. A641

WALTON, Linda, R.N. Chief Nursing Officer, South Lake Hospital, Clermont, FL, p. A125

WALTZ, Brenda M., FACHE, Chief Executive Officer, Garden Park Medical Center, Gulfport, MS, p. A358

WALTZ, Dan, Vice President and Chief Information Officer, MidMichigan Medical Center–Gladwin, Gladwin, MI, p. A324

WALZ, Pat, President and Chief Executive Officer, Yuma Regional Medical Center, Yuma, AZ, p. A42

WALZ, Rachel A., Director Patient Care, CentraCare Health–Paynesville, Paynesville, MN, p. A349

WAMPLER, Beth A., R.N. Chief Nursing Officer, Fayette Regional Health System, Connersville, IN, p. A208

WAMPLER, Janice, Chief Information Technology Officer, Monroe Hospital, Bloomington, IN, p. A207

WAMPLER, Tamara, Chief Nursing Executive, Claremore Indian Hospital, Claremore, OK, p. A509

WAMSLEY, Marie, Chief Financial Officer, Memorial Hospital of Lafayette County, Darlington, WI, p. A703

WANG, Ted, Chief Financial Officer, Providence Tarzana Medical Center,, CA, p. A74

WANGSMO, Gary L., Chief Financial Officer, Mee Memorial Hospital, King City, CA, p. A68

WANGSNESS, Erik, Interim President and Chief Executive Officer, Adventist HealthCare, Gaithersburg, MD, p. B7

WANGSNESS, Erik
Chief Executive Officer, Jellico Community Hospital, Jellico, TN, p. A585
President, Washington Adventist Hospital, Takoma Park, MD, p. A303

WANNA, Fady, M.D. Chief Clinical Officer and Chief Medical Officer, Medical Center, Navicent Health, Macon, GA, p. A163

WANNER, David
Director Information Technology, Kenmare Community Hospital, Kenmare, ND, p. A479
Chief Information Officer, Trinity Health, Minot, ND, p. A479

WANNER, Joe, Chief Financial Officer, Wallowa Memorial Hospital, Enterprise, OR, p. A524

WANTLAND, Margaret, Chief Financial Officer, Kindred Hospital–Albuquerque, Albuquerque, NM, p. A426

WAPPELHORST, Andrea, Chief Nursing Officer, TOPS Surgical Specialty Hospital, Houston, TX, p. A627

WARBURTON, Kerry, Chief Financial Officer, Cheyenne Regional Medical Center, Cheyenne, WY, p. A720

WARD, Brook, Executive Vice President, Washington Hospital, Washington, PA, p. A557

WARD, Celia F., Controller and Chief Financial Officer, Doctors Memorial Hospital, Bonifay, FL, p. A124

WARD, Charlotte, Entity Financial Officer, Texas Health Harris Methodist Hospital Southwest Fort Worth, Fort Worth, TX, p. A619

WARD, Chris
Director Management Information Systems, Dorminy Medical Center, Fitzgerald, GA, p. A159
Interim Chief Nursing Officer, Mercy Hospital Grayling, Grayling, MI, p. A325

WARD, David M., Senior Vice President and Chief Financial Officer, Cabell Huntington Hospital, Huntington, WV, p. A695

WARD, Debra, Chief Operating Officer, Laurel Ridge Treatment Center, San Antonio, TX, p. A646

WARD, Elizabeth S., Chief Financial Officer, University of Texas Southwestern Medical Center, Dallas, TX, p. A612

WARD, Greg, Vice President Operations, Copley Hospital, Morrisville, VT, p. A665

WARD, Jeanne L., R.N., President and Chief Executive Officer, Oconee Medical Center, Seneca, SC, p. A569

WARD, Julie
Vice President Finance, Northeastern Health System, Tahlequah, OK, p. A519
Chief Nursing Officer, St. Joseph's Hospital and Medical Center, Phoenix, AZ, p. A37

WARD, Julie R., MSN Vice President Patient Care Services, Hutchinson Regional Medical Center, Hutchinson, KS, p. A246

WARD, Kevin, Chief Operating Officer, Jewish Home of San Francisco, San Francisco, CA, p. A90

WARD, Kevin J., Vice President and Chief Financial Officer, New York Hospital Queens,, NY, p. A447

WARD, Lesli, Vice President Human Resources, UF Health Jacksonville, Jacksonville, FL, p. A132

WARD, Lisa, Director Management Information Systems, Columbus Regional Healthcare System, Whiteville, NC, p. A474

WARD, Louise, Vice President Financial and Support Services, Roane General Hospital, Spencer, WV, p. A699

WARD, Mark, M.D. Chief of Staff, Roundup Memorial Healthcare, Roundup, MT, p. A390

WARD, Michael
Director Information Services, Anderson Hospital, Maryville, IL, p. A195
Chief Executive Officer, HEALTHSOUTH Rehabilitation Hospital–Las Vegas, Las Vegas, NV, p. A405

WARD, Mike
Senior Vice President and Chief Information Officer, Methodist Medical Center of Oak Ridge, Oak Ridge, TN, p. A591
Chief Information Officer, Morristown–Hamblen Healthcare System, Morristown, TN, p. A590
Senior Vice President Chief Information Officer, Roane Medical Center, Harriman, TN, p. A583

WARD, Rhonda, R.N. Chief Nursing Officer, Littleton Adventist Hospital, Littleton, CO, p. A109

WARD, Robert, Chief Executive Officer, Select Rehabilitation Hospital of San Antonio, San Antonio, TX, p. A647

WARD, Rory, Chief Financial Officer, Pushmataha Hospital & Home Health, Antlers, OK, p. A507

WARD, Sandy, Administrator, Johnson County Healthcare Center, Buffalo, WY, p. A720

WARD, Silva, Director Human Resources, Center for Behavioral Medicine, Kansas City, MO, p. A373

WARD, Stormy, Chief Nurse Executive, Big Spring State Hospital, Big Spring, TX, p. A603

WARD, Vaughn, Chief Executive Officer, Northwest Specialty Hospital, Post Falls, ID, p. A178

WARD, Virginia, Human Resources Officer, Robert E. Bush Naval Hospital, Twentynine Palms, CA, p. A98

WARD, Wendy, Director Human Resources, Mercy Hospital El Reno, El Reno, OK, p. A510

WARDA, Paul, Chief Financial Officer, MedStar Georgetown University Hospital, Washington, DC, p. A121

WARDELL, Patrick R., Chief Executive Officer, Cambridge Health Alliance, Cambridge, MA, p. A309

WARDEN, Michael S.
  Senior Vice President Information Technology, Banner Good Samaritan Medical Center, Phoenix, AZ, p. A35
  Senior Vice President and Chief Information Officer, East Morgan County Hospital, Brush, CO, p. A103

WARDWELL, Robert D.
  Chief Financial Officer, St. John's Pleasant Valley Hospital, Camarillo, CA, p. A58
  Chief Financial Officer, St. John's Regional Medical Center, Oxnard, CA, p. A82

WARE, Bobbie K., R.N. Vice President/Patient Care/Chief Nursing Officer, Mississippi Baptist Medical Center, Jackson, MS, p. A360

WARE, Bobbie K., FACHE, Chief Executive Officer and Chief Nursing Officer, Mississippi Hospital for Restorative Care, Jackson, MS, p. A360

WARE, Dana, M.D. Chief of Staff, Seneca Healthcare District, Chester, CA, p. A59

WARE, John D., Human Resources Director, Highlands Regional Medical Center, Sebring, FL, p. A146

WARE, Judy, Director Human Resources, Johnson Memorial Hospital, Franklin, IN, p. A212

WARE, Karen, Director Human Resources, Integris Blackwell Regional Hospital, Blackwell, OK, p. A508

WARE, Kathy, Director of Nursing, Daniels Memorial Healthcare Center, Scobey, MT, p. A391

WAREING, Colleen, Vice President Patient Care Services, Atlantic General Hospital, Berlin, MD, p. A298

WARFIELD, William, Chief Human Resources Management, Veterans Affairs Boston Healthcare System, Boston, MA, p. A307

WARING, Lance, Director Human Resources, Texas Health Harris Methodist Hospital Azle, Azle, TX, p. A601

WARLITNER, Todd, Vice President Business Operations, The Outer Banks Hospital, Nags Head, NC, p. A470

WARM, Ira, Senior Vice President Human Resources, Brooklyn Hospital Center,, NY, p. A443

WARMAN, Debbie, Vice President Human Resources, MetroHealth Medical Center, Cleveland, OH, p. A489

WARMAN Jr., Harold C., FACHE, President and Chief Executive Officer, Highlands Regional Medical Center, Prestonsburg, KY, p. A269

WARMBOLD, Steve, Director Information Management Service Line, Veterans Affairs St. Louis Health Care System, Saint Louis, MO, p. A382

WARMERDAM, David, Chief Financial Officer, Brynn Marr Hospital, Jacksonville, NC, p. A467

WARNER, Grady, Director of Information Technology, Burgess Health Center, Onawa, IA, p. A235

WARNER, John, M.D., Chief Executive Officer, University of Texas Southwestern Medical Center, Dallas, TX, p. A612

WARNER, Norma, Area Director Health Information Management, Kindred Hospital–Fort Worth, Fort Worth, TX, p. A618

WARNER–PACHECO, Paula, Chief Human Resources, Rio Grande Hospital, Del Norte, CO, p. A104

WARNOCK, Dawn, Director Medical Records, Taylor Regional Hospital, Hawkinsville, GA, p. A160

WARREN, Charlene, R.N. Chief Nursing Officer, Greenbrier Valley Medical Center, Ronceverte, WV, p. A699

WARREN, Danny, Chief Financial Officer, Lake Wales Medical Center, Lake Wales, FL, p. A133

WARREN, Gidgett, Director of Nursing, Westlake Regional Hospital, Columbia, KY, p. A259

WARREN, Jennifer, Chief Financial Officer, Purcell Municipal Hospital, Purcell, OK, p. A518

WARREN, Karen, Fiscal Officer, Porterville Developmental Center, Porterville, CA, p. A84

WARREN, Linda, Director Human Resources, Cogdell Memorial Hospital, Snyder, TX, p. A649

WARREN, Michael D., President, Good Samaritan Regional Health Center, Mount Vernon, IL, p. A197

WARREN, Richard
  Vice President Health Information Systems, Allegiance Health, Jackson, MI, p. A327
  Chief Information Officer, Hillcrest Baptist Medical Center, Waco, TX, p. A655

WARREN, Roger D., M.D., Administrator, Hanover Hospital, Hanover, KS, p. A245

WARREN, Sarah, Coordinator Human Resources, Hickory Trail Hospital, Desoto, TX, p. A614

WARREN, Shanna, Director Human Resources, Medical Center of Plano, Plano, TX, p. A642

WARREN Jr., Wm. Michael, Chief Executive Officer, The Children's Hospital of Alabama, Birmingham, AL, p. A17

WARRENER, Gerald, M.D. Chief Medical Officer, Parkview Noble Hospital, Kendallville, IN, p. A216

WARRINER, Ken, Market Chief Financial Officer, Physicians Regional – Pine Ridge, Naples, FL, p. A139

WARRINGTON, Sr., James E., M.D. Chief of Staff, Quitman County Hospital, Marks, MS, p. A362

WARSHAW, Leah, Coordinator Human Resources, Select Specialty Hospital–Ann Arbor, Ypsilanti, MI, p. A338

WARSING, Tracy, M.D. Site Leader Chief of Staff, Mayo Clinic Health System – Franciscan Healthcare in Sparta, Sparta, WI, p. A715

WARTENBERG, Daniel, M.P.H., Chief Executive Officer, Southwest Connecticut Mental Health System, Bridgeport, CT, p. A113

WAS, Gregory J., CPA Chief Financial Officer, Melissa Memorial Hospital, Holyoke, CO, p. A107

WASDEN, Mitchell L., Ed.D., Chief Executive Officer and Chief Operating Officer, University of Missouri Health Care, Columbia, MO, p. B146

WASDEN, Mitchell L., Ed.D., Chief Executive Officer and Chief Operating Officer, University of Missouri Hospitals and Clinics, Columbia, MO, p. A370

WASEK, Arthur A.
  Director Human Resources, Northwest Mississippi Regional Medical Center, Clarksdale, MS, p. A356
  Director Human Resources, Tri–Lakes Medical Center, Batesville, MS, p. A355

WASHAM, Mark, Chief Information Officer, Shriners Hospitals for Children-Cincinnati Burns Hospital, Cincinnati, OH, p. A487

WASHBURN, Geoffrey A., Vice President, Regional Medical Center Bayonet Point, Hudson, FL, p. A131

WASHBURN, Kimberly D., Director Human Resources, Snoqualmie Valley Hospital, Snoqualmie, WA, p. A689

WASHBURN, Sheryl M., MSN Chief Nursing Officer, Gritman Medical Center, Moscow, ID, p. A177

WASHBURN, Tonya, M.D. Medical Director, Valir Rehabilitation Hospital, Oklahoma City, OK, p. A516

WASHECKA, James, Chief Financial Officer, Hillcrest Hospital – South, Tulsa, OK, p. A520

WASHINGTON, Carolyn, Director of Human Resources, Doctor's Hospital – Tidwell, Houston, TX, p. A624

WASHINGTON, Glen A., Chief Executive Officer, Pleasant Valley Hospital, Point Pleasant, WV, p. A698

WASHINGTON, Lorraine, Vice President Human Resources, St. Dominic–Jackson Memorial Hospital, Jackson, MS, p. A360

WASHINGTON, Reginald, M.D. Chief Medical Officer, Presbyterian–St. Luke's Medical Center, Denver, CO, p. A105

WASHINGTON, Stephanie, Director Community Relations and Human Resources, King's Daughters Hospital, Yazoo City, MS, p. A366

WASHINGTON, Vindell, M.D. Vice President Performance Excellence and Technology, Our Lady of the Lake Regional Medical Center, Baton Rouge, LA, p. A273

WASSILAK, Leighton, Manager Information Systems and Telecommunications, SSM St. Clare Health Center, Fenton, MO, p. A371

WATERBURY, Brad, Director Human Resources, Bonner General Hospital, Sandpoint, ID, p. A178

WATERCUTTER, William, Director Management Information System, Upper Valley Medical Center, Troy, OH, p. A503

WATERS, Danny
  Director, Information Services, Palms of Pasadena Hospital, Saint Petersburg, FL, p. A144
  Director Information Technology and Systems, South Bay Hospital, Sun City Center, FL, p. A146

WATERS, Eric, Vice President Operations, Pen Bay Medical Center, Rockport, ME, p. A295

WATERS, Gina, Director Human Resources, Evans Memorial Hospital, Claxton, GA, p. A156

WATERS, Glenn S., FACHE, President, Morton Plant Mease Health Care, Clearwater, FL, p. B95

WATERS, Jerod, Chief Nursing Officer, Chickasaw Nation Medical Center, Ada, OK, p. A507

WATERS, Karen, Chief Nursing Officer, St. Mary's Warrick Hospital, Boonville, IN, p. A207

WATERS, Mickey, Director Information Technology, Conway Medical Center, Conway, SC, p. A565

WATERS, Nancy, Interim Chief Information Officer, High Point Regional Health System, High Point, NC, p. A466

WATERS, Patrick, Director Information Technology, Marshall County Hospital, Benton, KY, p. A258

WATERS, Scott, Director Information Technology, Carson Tahoe Continuing Care Hospital, Carson City, NV, p. A404

WATERS, Stephen F., M.D. Medical Director, Atlantic General Hospital, Berlin, MD, p. A298

WATERS, Victor, M.D. Chief of Staff, Sioux Falls Veterans Affairs Health Care System, Sioux Falls, SD, p. A577

WATERSTON, Judith C., MS, President and Chief Executive Officer, New England Sinai Hospital and Rehabilitation Center, Stoughton, MA, p. A315

WATHEN, Cheryl A., Interim Chief Financial Officer, Deaconess Hospital, Evansville, IN, p. A210

WATHEN, Susan R., Vice President Human Resources, Hannibal Regional Hospital, Hannibal, MO, p. A372

WATKINS, Chris, Director of Information Technology, Craig Hospital, Englewood, CO, p. A106

WATKINS, Christi, R.N. Chief Operating Officer, Palestine Regional Medical Center, Palestine, TX, p. A640

WATKINS, James, M.D. President Medical Staff, Providence Willamette Falls Medical Center, Oregon City, OR, p. A527

WATKINS, Lynnette, M.D. Chief Medical Officer, Phoenix Baptist Hospital, Phoenix, AZ, p. A36

WATKINS, Pamela, Chief Financial Officer, Atlanta Veterans Affairs Medical Center, Decatur, GA, p. A158

WATKINS, Paul, Chief Administrative Officer, Santa Monica–UCLA Medical Center and Orthopaedic Hospital, Santa Monica, CA, p. A95

WATKINS, Rolanda, Chief Human Resources Management Service, Dayton Veterans Affairs Medical Center, Dayton, OH, p. A492

WATKINS, Terri, R.N. Chief Nursing Officer, Castleview Hospital, Price, UT, p. A662

WATRY, Margaret, Director of Patient Care Services and Nurse Executive, Phillips Eye Institute, Minneapolis, MN, p. A347

WATSON, B. Keith, M.D. Chief Medical Staff, North Mississippi Medical Center–West Point, West Point, MS, p. A366

WATSON, Betty A., Chief Financial Officer, Syringa Hospital and Clinics, Grangeville, ID, p. A176

WATSON, Brent, M.D. Chief Medical Staff, Roane General Hospital, Spencer, WV, p. A699

WATSON, Danine, R.N. Interim Vice President Nursing and Chief Nursing Officer, Memorial Health Care System, Chattanooga, TN, p. A580

WATSON, Dean, M.D. Chief Medical Officer, Tallahassee Memorial HealthCare, Tallahassee, FL, p. A147

WATSON, Deborah, Senior Vice President and Chief Operating Officer, Bayhealth Medical Center, Dover, DE, p. A119

WATSON, Deborah, R.N
  Senior Director of Nursing and Vice President, Patient Care Services, Providence Mount Carmel Hospital, Colville, WA, p. A682
  Chief Nursing Officer, Providence St. Joseph's Hospital, Chewelah, WA, p. A682

WATSON, Dolores, Director Health Information Management, Arms Acres, Carmel, NY, p. A435

WATSON, H. Alan, FACHE, Chief Executive Officer, Maury Regional Health System, Columbia, TN, p. B89

WATSON, H. Alan, FACHE, Chief Executive Officer, Maury Regional Hospital, Columbia, TN, p. A581

WATSON, Heath
  Controller, HEALTHSOUTH Rehabilitation Hospital, Dothan, AL, p. A19
  Controller, HEALTHSOUTH Rehabilitation Hospital of Montgomery, Montgomery, AL, p. A23

WATSON, James, Chief Financial Officer, University of Chicago Medical Center, Chicago, IL, p. A187

WATSON, James B., President and Chief Operating Officer, Ira Davenport Memorial Hospital, Bath, NY, p. A433

WATSON, Kathy, R.N., Administrator and Chief Nursing Officer, Saint Thomas Hospital for Spinal Surgery, Nashville, TN, p. A590

WATSON, Kerry, President, Newton–Wellesley Hospital, Newton Lower Falls, MA, p. A313

WATSON, Lisa, Chief Executive Officer, St. Vincent Rehabilitation Hospital, Sherwood, AR, p. A52

WATSON, Luke, M.D. Chief of Staff, Pacific Hospital of Long Beach, Long Beach, CA, p. A70

WATSON, Mary Lou, MS Vice President Nursing, MedStar St. Mary's Hospital, Leonardtown, MD, p. A302

WATSON, Michael, M.D. Chief of Staff, Memorial Hospital, Seminole, TX, p. A648

WATSON, Michelle, Chief Operating Officer and Chief Nursing Officer, Livingston Regional Hospital, Livingston, TN, p. A587

WATSON, Nancy, Director Human Resources, Mercy Hospital, Coon Rapids, MN, p. A342

WATSON, Jr., Nathan, M.D. Chief of Staff, Carrus Specialty Hospital, Sherman, TX, p. A649

WATSON, Rob, M.D. Chief Medical Officer, Scott & White Hospital at Round Rock, Round Rock, TX, p. A644

WATSON, Shane, Chief Executive Officer, Red Bud Regional Hospital, Red Bud, IL, p. A201

WATSON, Susan, MSN Vice President, Bronson Battle Creek, Battle Creek, MI, p. A319

WATSON, Teresa C., Vice President Administration, Carolinas Medical Center–Lincoln, Lincolnton, NC, p. A468

WATSON, Thelma Ruth, M.D. Medical Director, Schneider Regional Medical Center, Saint Thomas, VI, p. A729

WATSON, Trey, Network Administrator, Sumner County Hospital District One, Caldwell, KS, p. A242

WATSON, Vicki, Manager Human Resources, Select Specialty Hospital–Jackson, Jackson, MS, p. A360

WATSON, Virgil, Administrator, Sumner County Hospital District One, Caldwell, KS, p. A242

WATT, Andrew, M.D. Vice President, Chief Information Officer and Chief Medical Information Officer, Southern New Hampshire Medical Center, Nashua, NH, p. A411

WATT, Ella, Chief Financial Officer, University of New Mexico Hospitals, Albuquerque, NM, p. A427

WATT, Tracy, Director Information Systems, Jackson Purchase Medical Center, Mayfield, KY, p. A267

WATTENBARGER, Mike, Chief Information Officer, LifeCare Hospitals of San Antonio, San Antonio, TX, p. A646

WATTERS, Greg, Chief Financial Officer, El Paso Specialty Hospital, El Paso, TX, p. A615

WATTOO, Dost, M.D. Chief of Staff, Valley Hospital Medical Center, Las Vegas, NV, p. A407

WATTS, Dawn, Chief Executive Officer, HEALTHSOUTH Rehabilitation Hospital of Fort Smith, Fort Smith, AR, p. A46

WATTS, Hugh, M.D. Chief of Staff, Shriners Hospitals for Children–Los Angeles, Los Angeles, CA, p. A74

WATTS, Karen, MSN Vice President of Patient Care and Chief Nursing Officer, Northeast Georgia Medical Center, Gainesville, GA, p. A160

WATTS, Larry, Chief Medical Officer, Hays Medical Center, Hays, KS, p. A245

WATTS, Lynda, R.N. Vice President Patient Care Services, University Hospital, Augusta, GA, p. A154

WATTS–JOHNSON, Christine M., Assistant Vice President, Madera Community Hospital, Madera, CA, p. A76

WAUN, Cynthia, Chief Operating Officer and Risk Manager, Brynn Marr Hospital, Jacksonville, NC, p. A467

WAUTERS, Ron, Chief Financial Officer, Pella Regional Health Center, Pella, IA, p. A236

WAY, Dee, Director Human Resources, Jerold Phelps Community Hospital, Garberville, CA, p. A65

WAY, Harold, Chief Financial Officer, St. Mary Medical Center, Long Beach, CA, p. A70

WAYNE, Ann, Director of Nursing, Meadows Psychiatric Center, Centre Hall, PA, p. A535

WAYNE, Denise, Chief Executive Officer, Vibra Hospital of Southeastern Michigan, Lincoln Park, MI, p. A329

WAYTULA, Elizabeth, Chief Executive Officer, Solara Hospital of Shawnee, Shawnee, OK, p. A518

WEADICK, James F., Administrator and Chief Executive Officer, Newton Medical Center, Covington, GA, p. A157

WEAR, Sondra, Director Financial Services, Eureka Springs Hospital, Eureka Springs, AR, p. A45

WEATHERFORD, Dennis, Chief Executive Officer, Putnam County Hospital, Greencastle, IN, p. A212

WEATHERFORD, Ted, Chief Financial Officer, Howard A. Rusk Rehabilitation Center, Columbia, MO, p. A370

WEATHERLY, Dan, On Site Administrator, Cape Fear Valley – Bladen County Hospital, Elizabethtown, NC, p. A464

WEATHERSBY, Mae C., R.N. Chief Clinical Officer, Vibra Specialty Hospital at DeSoto, Desoto, TX, p. A614

WEATHERWAX, Marlene, Vice President and Chief Financial Officer, Columbus Regional Hospital, Columbus, IN, p. A208

WEAVER, Angie L., Director Human Resources, Gilmore Memorial Regional Medical Center, Amory, MS, p. A355

WEAVER, Daryl W., Interim Chief Executive Officer, Baptist Medical Center Leake, Carthage, MS, p. A356

WEAVER, Douglas K., FACHE, President, Integris Mayes County Medical Center, Pryor, OK, p. A518

WEAVER, Harry, M.D. Chief of Staff, Covenant Hospital–Levelland, Levelland, TX, p. A633

WEAVER, Jason, Director Information Systems, Southern Tennessee Regional Health System–Lawrenceburg, Lawrenceburg, TN, p. A586

WEAVER, Jeff, Chief Financial Officer, Medical Arts Hospital, Lamesa, TX, p. A632

WEAVER, Joe
  Chief Operating Officer and Vice President Operations, Northeast Alabama Regional Medical Center, Anniston, AL, p. A15
  Vice President Operations, RMC Jacksonville, Jacksonville, AL, p. A22

WEAVER, Judy K., MS, Chief Executive Officer, Acuity Specialty Hospitals Ohio Valley, Steubenville, OH, p. A502

WEAVER, Kim, CPA Chief Financial Officer, Sumner Regional Medical Center, Wellington, KS, p. A256

WEAVER, Kimberli, Chief Nursing Officer, L. V. Stabler Memorial Hospital, Greenville, AL, p. A21

WEAVER, Lisa, Nurse Executive, Lakeside Behavioral Health System, Memphis, TN, p. A588

WEAVER, Nancy, Vice President of Nursing, Chief Nursing Officer, Carson City Hospital, Carson City, MI, p. A320

WEAVER, Rudolph D., Vice President Human Resources, Southwestern Vermont Medical Center, Bennington, VT, p. A665

WEAVER, William, Chief Executive Officer, Brentwood Hospital, Shreveport, LA, p. A288

WEBB, Amy, Chief Operating Officer, Cascade Medical Center, Leavenworth, WA, p. A685

WEBB Jr., Charles L., Chief Executive Officer, Lincoln Trail Behavioral Health System, Radcliff, KY, p. A269

WEBB, David, Chief Financial Officer, Baptist Memorial Hospital–Golden Triangle, Columbus, MS, p. A357

WEBB, Dee, Vice President Human Resources, St. Bernardine Medical Center, San Bernardino, CA, p. A88

WEBB, Donald, Chief Executive Officer, Williamson Medical Center, Franklin, TN, p. A583

WEBB, Glenn T., M.D. Medical Director, Ten Broeck Tennessee Treatment Facility, Cookeville, TN, p. A581

WEBB, Herbert, M.D. Chief Medical Officer, Providence Little Company of Mary Medical Center San Pedro,, CA, p. A74

WEBB, Jeffrey D., CPA Chief Financial Officer, Jasper County Hospital, Rensselaer, IN, p. A221

WEBB, Karen, M.D. Chief Medical Officer, Des Peres Hospital, Saint Louis, MO, p. A380

WEBB, Kimberly, Chief Financial Officer, Kootenai Health, Coeur D'Alene, ID, p. A175

WEBB, Linda, R.N. Chief Nursing Executive, Pulaski Memorial Hospital, Winamac, IN, p. A224

WEBB, Lisa
  Vice President for Operational Finance, CHI Health Good Samaritan, Kearney, NE, p. A397
  Vice President Finance, CHI Health Saint Francis, Grand Island, NE, p. A396

WEBB, Melanie R.
  Director Human Resources, Houston Northwest Medical Center, Houston, TX, p. A625
  Chief Human Resources Officer, Park Plaza Hospital, Houston, TX, p. A626

WEBB, Paula, Chief Financial Officer and Compliance Officer, Lake Butler Hospital Hand Surgery Center, Lake Butler, FL, p. A133

WEBB, Renick, M.D. Chief Medical Director, Central Louisiana Surgical Hospital, Alexandria, LA, p. A272

WEBB, W. Larry, Senior Vice President and Chief Financial Officer, Athens Regional Medical Center, Athens, GA, p. A151

WEBB, William, Assistant Superintendent, Eastern Shore Hospital Center, Cambridge, MD, p. A299

WEBBER, Cathy, Chief Information Officer, Franklin County Memorial Hospital, Franklin, NE, p. A395

WEBBER, Chelsea, Director Human Resources, LifeCare Hospitals of Pittsburgh – Monroeville, Monroeville, PA, p. A545

WEBBER, Deborah G., Chief Operating Officer, AHMC Anaheim Regional Medical Center, Anaheim, CA, p. A55

WEBBER, Joyce, Chief Financial Officer, Spalding Rehabilitation Hospital, Aurora, CO, p. A102

WEBDALE, Ralph, Vice President Finance, Brooks Memorial Hospital, Dunkirk, NY, p. A436

WEBER, Ann, M.D. Chief Medical Officer, North Florida Regional Medical Center, Gainesville, FL, p. A129

WEBER, Ayanna, Director Human Resources, DMC Huron Valley–Sinai Hospital, Commerce Township, MI, p. A321

WEBER, Barbara, Chief Operating Officer, Advocate Lutheran General Hospital, Park Ridge, IL, p. A199

WEBER, Carmen, Administrator, Eureka Community Health Services Avera, Eureka, SD, p. A573

WEBER, Jr., Ernest P., Interim Chief Information Officer, SUNY Downstate Medical Center University Hospital,, NY, p. A448

WEBER, Frank, Chief Executive Officer, Select Specialty Hospital–Charleston, Charleston, WV, p. A694

WEBER, Gordon, Chief Operating Officer, Clarks Summit State Hospital, Clarks Summit, PA, p. A535

WEBER, James, D.O. Chief of Staff, Washington County Memorial Hospital, Potosi, MO, p. A379

WEBER, Jan, Chief Human Resources Officer, Hamilton Center, Terre Haute, IN, p. A223

WEBER, Lauren, Administrator, Oceans Behavioral Hospital Longview, Longview, TX, p. A634

WEBER, Pete M., President and Chief Executive Officer, Gordon Hospital, Calhoun, GA, p. A155

WEBER, Rebecca
  Senior Vice President and Chief Information Officer, Bayshore Community Hospital, Holmdel, NJ, p. A417
  Senior Vice President and Chief Information Officer, Jersey Shore University Medical Center, Neptune, NJ, p. A419
  Senior Vice President and Chief Information Officer, Ocean Medical Center, Brick Township, NJ, p. A414
  Senior Vice President Information Technology, Riverview Medical Center, Red Bank, NJ, p. A422
  Senior Vice President and Chief Information Officer, Southern Ocean Medical Center, Manahawkin, NJ, p. A418

WEBER, Robert, M.D. Chief Medical Staff, Watsonville Community Hospital, Watsonville, CA, p. A100

WEBER, Stephen, M.D. Chief Medical Officer, University of Chicago Medical Center, Chicago, IL, p. A187

WEBER, Tiffany, Chief Financial Officer, Perkins County Health Services, Grant, NE, p. A396

WEBER, Trish, Vice President Operations and Chief Nursing Officer, Franciscan St. Anthony Health – Michigan City, Michigan City, IN, p. A218

WEBSTER, Cindy, Vice President Financial Services, Licking Memorial Hospital, Newark, OH, p. A499

WEBSTER, Gwen, M.D. President Medical Staff, Texas Health Presbyterian Hospital Plano, Plano, TX, p. A643

WEBSTER, Janice, Director Human Resources, West Oaks Hospital, Houston, TX, p. A628

WEBSTER, Kathleen, R.N. Vice President Patient Services, Hudson Valley Hospital Center, Cortlandt Manor, NY, p. A436

WEBSTER, Mark
  President and CEO, Cortland Regional Medical Center, Cortland, NY, p. A436
  Vice President Finance, Hudson Valley Hospital Center, Cortlandt Manor, NY, p. A436

WEBSTER, William W., FACHE, Chief Executive Officer, Medical Center Health System, Odessa, TX, p. A640

WECKENBORG, Janet, FACHE Vice President Operations, Capital Region Medical Center, Jefferson City, MO, p. A372

WECKESSER, Kim, Director Human Resources, West Shore Medical Center, Manistee, MI, p. A329

WEDEL, Sandy, Director Human Resources, Ellsworth County Medical Center, Ellsworth, KS, p. A243

WEDGEWORTH, Joyce, Financial Clerk, Hill Hospital of Sumter County, York, AL, p. A27

WEDO, Aaron, Manager, Human Resources, Grundy County Memorial Hospital, Grundy Center, IA, p. A231

WEE, Donald, Chief Executive Officer, Tri–State Memorial Hospital, Clarkston, WA, p. A682

WEED, III, John, M.D. Medical Director, Little River Healthcare, Rockdale, TX, p. A644

WEED, Warren
  Director Human Resources, River Oaks Hospital, Flowood, MS, p. A357
  Director Associate Relations, Woman's Hospital, Flowood, MS, p. A358

WEEKS, Ed, Manager Information Services, Paris Community Hospital, Paris, IL, p. A199

WEEKS, James
  Interim Chief Information Officer, Manchester Memorial Hospital, Manchester, CT, p. A114
  Interim Chief Information Officer, Rockville General Hospital, Vernon Rockville, CT, p. A117

WEEKS, Rolaine, R.N. Director of Nursing, Dublin Springs, Dublin, OH, p. A493

WEELDREYER, Jim, Manager Information Technology, Pershing General Hospital, Lovelock, NV, p. A407

WEEMS, Taylor, Director Information Systems, Midland Memorial Hospital, Midland, TX, p. A638

WEG, Jennifer, R.N. Chief Nursing Officer, Sanford Worthington Medical Center, Worthington, MN, p. A354

WEGG, Daniel, M.D. Medical Director, St. Vincent Randolph Hospital, Winchester, IN, p. A224

WEGHORST, George, M.D. Chief Medical Officer, Providence Newberg Medical Center, Newberg, OR, p. A527

WEGLARZ, Ron, Chief Executive Officer and Managing Director, Streamwood Behavioral Health Center, Streamwood, IL, p. A204

WEGLEITNER, Theodore, President, Lakeview Hospital, Stillwater, MN, p. A352

WEGNER, Michael, Senior Vice President and Chief Financial Officer, Mercy Medical Center–Des Moines, Des Moines, IA, p. A229

WEHE, Brad, Chief Operating Officer, Altru Health System, Grand Forks, ND, p. A478

WEHLING, Robert D., Interim Chief Financial Officer, Saint Alphonsus Medical Center – Baker City, Baker City, OR, p. A523

WEHNER, Jill, Vice President Financial Services, Harbor Beach Community Hospital, Harbor Beach, MI, p. A326

WEHRMEISTER, Erica, Chief Operating Officer, Lutheran Hospital of Indiana, Fort Wayne, IN, p. A211

WEIDEMANN, Donald, Chief Executive Officer, Cibola General Hospital, Grants, NM, p. A428

WEIDER, Will
Chief Information Officer, Calumet Medical Center, Chilton, WI, p. A703
Chief Information Officer, Mercy Medical Center, Oshkosh, WI, p. A713
Chief Information Officer, Ministry Saint Joseph's Hospital, Marshfield, WI, p. A709
Chief Information Officer, Ministry Saint Michael's Hospital, Stevens Point, WI, p. A716
Chief Information Officer, St. Elizabeth Hospital, Appleton, WI, p. A701

WEIDNER, Deborah, M.D. Medical Director, Natchaug Hospital, Mansfield Center, CT, p. A115

WEIGEL, Cherry, Director Health Information Management, RC Hospital and Clinics, Olivia, MN, p. A349

WEIGEL, Christine H., R.N. Clinical Operating Officer, McBride Clinic Orthopedic Hospital, Oklahoma City, OK, p. A515

WEIL, David S., Senior Vice President and Administrator, Saint Francis Hospital South, Tulsa, OK, p. A521

WEILAND, David, M.D. Chief Medical Officer, Largo Medical Center, Largo, FL, p. A134

WEILENMAN, Shelly L., R.N. Administrator and Chief Nursing Executive, Summit Medical Center, Van Buren, AR, p. A53

WEIMER, Theresa, Director Personnel, Fallon Medical Complex, Baker, MT, p. A385

WEINBAUM, Frederic, M.D. Executive Vice President Operations and Chief Medical Officer, Southampton Hospital, Southampton, NY, p. A455

WEINBERG, Assa, M.D. Chief of Staff, Temple Community Hospital, Los Angeles, CA, p. A75

WEINBERG, Meryl, Executive Director, Metropolitan Hospital Center, New York, NY, p. A446

WEINBERG, Mitch, M.D. Chief of Staff, EvergreenHealth, Kirkland, WA, p. A684

WEINER, Gary
Vice President Information Technology, Chief Information Officer, Community Hospital, Munster, IN, p. A219
Chief Information Officer, St. Catherine Hospital, East Chicago, IN, p. A209
Vice President Information Technology and Chief Information Officer, St. Mary Medical Center, Hobart, IN, p. A213

WEINER, Howard, Senior Vice President Administrative Services, LifeStream Behavioral Center, Leesburg, FL, p. A134

WEINER, Jack, President and Chief Executive Officer, St. Joseph Mercy Oakland, Pontiac, MI, p. A332

WEINER, Jerome, M.D. Senior Vice President Medical Affairs, Good Samaritan Hospital Medical Center, West Islip, NY, p. A458

WEINER, Martin E., M.D. Chief of Staff, Seton Edgar B. Davis Hospital, Luling, TX, p. A636

WEINER, Roger, Chief of Staff, Northwest Mississippi Regional Medical Center, Clarksdale, MS, p. A356

WEINER, Ronald, Vice President Finance and Chief Financial Officer, Magruder Memorial Hospital, Port Clinton, OH, p. A500

WEINGARTNER, Ronald, Vice President Administration, St. Charles Hospital, Port Jefferson, NY, p. A452

WEINHOLD, Chantal, Executive Director, Long Island Jewish Medical Center,, NY, p. A445

WEINHOLD, Robert, Chief Executive Officer, Foundations Behavioral Health, Doylestown, PA, p. A537

WEINKRANTZ, Alan, Chief Financial Officer, Finance, University Hospital, Piscataway, NJ, p. A421

WEINMANN, Shannon, Director Human Resources, Community Medical Center, Falls City, NE, p. A395

WEINMEISTER, Kurt, Chief Operating Officer, St. Francis Medical Center, Lynwood, CA, p. A76

WEINREIS, Brian, Vice President Operations and Finance, Abbott Northwestern Hospital, Minneapolis, MN, p. A347

WEINSTEIN, Barry S., Chief Financial Officer, Four Winds Hospital, Katonah, NY, p. A439

WEINSTEIN, Brian, M.D. Chief of Staff, Westside Regional Medical Center, Plantation, FL, p. A143

WEINSTEIN, Freddie, M.D. Chief Medical Officer, Dominican Hospital, Santa Cruz, CA, p. A94

WEINSTEIN, Gary B., President and Chief Executive Officer, Washington Hospital, Washington, PA, p. A557

WEINSTEIN, James, President and Chief Executive Officer, Dartmouth–Hitchcock Medical Center, Lebanon, NH, p. A411

WEINSTEIN, James, Chief Financial Officer, Lourdes Specialty Hospital of Southern New Jersey, Willingboro, NJ, p. A425

WEIS, Charles
Chief Financial Officer, Mount Sinai Hospital, Chicago, IL, p. A185
Chief Financial Officer, Schwab Rehabilitation Hospital, Chicago, IL, p. A186

WEIS, Maurine
Vice President Nursing and Chief Nursing Officer, ProMedica Flower Hospital, Sylvania, OH, p. A502
Chief Nursing Officer, ProMedica St. Luke's Hospital, Maumee, OH, p. A498

WEIS, Robert
Director Information Systems, Bingham Memorial Hospital, Blackfoot, ID, p. A174
Director Information Technology, Mountain River Birthing and Surgery Center, Blackfoot, ID, p. A174

WEIS, Shirley, Chief Administrative Officer, Mayo Clinic Hospital – Rochester, Rochester, MN, p. A350

WEIS, Wade, Senior Director Finance, Grande Ronde Hospital, La Grande, OR, p. A526

WEISENBERGER, Scott, Administrator, Kirkbride Center, Philadelphia, PA, p. A549

WEISENFREUND, Jochanan, M.D. Senior Vice President Academic and Medical Affairs, Interfaith Medical Center,, NY, p. A444

WEISER, Marcus, D.O. Chief of Staff, Community HealthCare System, Onaga, KS, p. A251

WEISFIELD, Phyllis, Chief Executive Officer and Managing Director, Horsham Clinic, Ambler, PA, p. A533

WEISHAPL, Natasha, Manager Business Office and Human Resources, Decatur Health Systems, Oberlin, KS, p. A251

WEISNER, Brad, Executive Vice President and Chief Operating Officer, Nash Health Care Systems, Rocky Mount, NC, p. A471

WEISS, Allen S., M.D., President and Chief Executive Officer, NCH Downtown Naples Hospital, Naples, FL, p. A138

WEISS, Anthony, M.D. Medical Director, Upstate University Hospital, Syracuse, NY, p. A456

WEISS, Barry J., Chairman of the Board, College Health Enterprises, Santa Fe Springs, CA, p. B36

WEISS, David, Vice President Information System, Alton Memorial Hospital, Alton, IL, p. A180

WEISS, Gary, Chief Financial Officer, NorthShore University Health System, Evanston, IL, p. A189

WEISS, Linda W., FACHE, Director, Albany Stratton Veterans Affairs Medical Center, Albany, NY, p. A432

WEISS, Mark
Executive Director Enterprise Technology Services, Bellevue Medical Center, Bellevue, NE, p. A394
Executive Director, Enterprise Technical Services, Nebraska Medical Center, Omaha, NE, p. A400

WEISS, Phyllis, Director Human Resources, Alameda Hospital, Alameda, CA, p. A55

WEISS, Terri, Chief Financial Officer, Reliant Rehabilitation Hospital North Houston, Shenandoah, TX, p. A649

WEISSENBERGER, Ralf, Director Information Systems, White Memorial Medical Center, Los Angeles, CA, p. A75

WEISSER, Lisa, Supervisor Finance, Wagner Community Memorial Hospital Avera, Wagner, SD, p. A578

WEISSLER, Jonathan, M.D. Chief Medical Officer, LifeCare Hospitals of Dallas, Dallas, TX, p. A610

WEISTREICH, Tracy, Ph.D. Associate Director Patient Care Services/Nurse Executive, Veterans Affairs Roseburg Healthcare System, Roseburg, OR, p. A529

WEISUL, Jonathan, M.D. Vice President Medical Affairs and Chief Medical Officer, CHRISTUS Coushatta Health Care Center, Coushatta, LA, p. A275

WEITZELL, Kristine, Superintendent, Mental Health Institute, Clarinda, IA, p. A227

WELCH, Abbey, Director Human Resources, Harmon Memorial Hospital, Hollis, OK, p. A512

WELCH, Adam M., Interim Director, West Texas Veterans Affairs Health Care System, Big Spring, TX, p. A603

WELCH, Andrew, Director, Amarillo Veterans Affairs Health Care System, Amarillo, TX, p. A596

WELCH, Bryant, Chief Human Resources, Washington Hospital Healthcare System, Fremont, CA, p. A64

WELCH, Charlotte, Chief Nursing Officer, Haskell Memorial Hospital, Haskell, TX, p. A623

WELCH, David, M.D. Medical Director, Clifton–Fine Hospital, Star Lake, NY, p. A455

WELCH, David, Director Information Technology, Simpson General Hospital, Mendenhall, MS, p. A362

WELCH, Donald E., Chief Operating Officer, Florida Hospital Zephyrhills, Zephyrhills, FL, p. A150

WELCH, Douglas, Chief Executive Officer, Doctors Hospital, Augusta, GA, p. A153

WELCH, Gary A., Assistant to the Chief Executive Officer and Administrative Director Support Systems, Bon Secours Memorial Regional Medical Center, Mechanicsville, VA, p. A674

WELCH, Jeffrey M., Chief Executive Officer, Coral Gables Hospital, Coral Gables, FL, p. A126

WELCH, Jennifer, Director Human Resources, Marlboro Park Hospital, Bennettsville, SC, p. A562

WELCH, Maryrose, Chief Compliance Officer, Riverland Medical Center, Ferriday, LA, p. A277

WELCH, Matthew, Chief Clinical Information Officer and Director of Pharmacy, NORTHSTAR Health System, Iron River, MI, p. A327

WELCH, Melissa, Director Health Information Management, Oakdale Community Hospital, Oakdale, LA, p. A286

WELCH, Rosemary C., R.N. Vice President and Chief Nursing Officer, MedStar National Rehabilitation Hospital, Washington, DC, p. A121

WELCH, Shelly, R.N. Senior Vice President and Chief Nursing Officer, North Oaks Medical Center, Hammond, LA, p. A278

WELCH, Sherri, R.N. Chief Nursing Officer, College Station Medical Center, College Station, TX, p. A607

WELCH, Thomas, M.D. Chief Medical Officer, Mercy St. Vincent Medical Center, Toledo, OH, p. A503

WELCH, Tony
Vice President, Human Resources, Englewood Community Hospital, Englewood, FL, p. A128
Vice President Human Resources, Fawcett Memorial Hospital, Port Charlotte, FL, p. A143

WELDAY, Doug, Vice President Finance, Spectrum Health – Butterworth Hospital, Grand Rapids, MI, p. A325

WELDING, Theodore L., Administrator, Kindred Hospital South Florida–Fort Lauderdale, Fort Lauderdale, FL, p. A128

WELDON, Jim, Chief Information Officer, St. Anthony's Medical Center, Saint Louis, MO, p. A381

WELDON, Marie L., FACHE, Director, South Texas Veterans Health Care System, San Antonio, TX, p. A647

WELDON, William W., Ph.D., Interim Chief Executive Officer, Cogdell Memorial Hospital, Snyder, TX, p. A649

WELDY, Alan, Vice President Human Resources, Compliance and Legal Services, Indiana University Health Goshen Hospital, Goshen, IN, p. A212

WELKER, Suzanne, Chief Human Resources Officer and Vice President Marketing Strategy, Berger Health System, Circleville, OH, p. A488

WELKIE, Katy, R.N., Chief Executive Officer, Primary Children's Medical Center, Salt Lake City, UT, p. A663

WELLBROCK, Jenna, Chief Nursing Officer, Gateway Rehabilitation Hospital, Florence, KY, p. A261

WELLENDORF, Sharon A., Chief Nursing Officer, Horn Memorial Hospital, Ida Grove, IA, p. A232

WELLER, Deidre, Vice President, Finance, Spectrum Health Gerber Memorial, Fremont, MI, p. A324

WELLING, Lynn, M.D. Chief Medical Officer, Sharp Chula Vista Medical Center, Chula Vista, CA, p. A59

WELLING, Michele, M.D. Chief of Staff, Bluegrass Community Hospital, Versailles, KY, p. A271

WELLMAN, James, Senior Director Information Services, Comanche County Memorial Hospital, Lawton, OK, p. A512

WELLMANN, Jane, Chief Financial Officer, Scott & White Hospital – Brenham, Brenham, TX, p. A604

WELLS, A. Shane, Chief Financial Officer, Cornerstone Hospital of Houston at Clearlake, Webster, TX, p. A649

WELLS, Benjamin, Chief Financial Officer, Red Bud Regional Hospital, Red Bud, IL, p. A201

WELLS, Carol, R.N. Chief Nursing Officer, Central Louisiana Surgical Hospital, Alexandria, LA, p. A272

WELLS, Craig, Chief Information Officer, George C Grape Community Hospital, Hamburg, IA, p. A231

WELLS, Dale, Chief Financial and Operating Officer, Alliance Community Hospital, Alliance, OH, p. A482

WELLS, Dennis, Chief Information Officer, Syracuse Veterans Affairs Medical Center, Syracuse, NY, p. A456

WELLS, Jason, Chief Human Resources Management Service, Fargo Veterans Affairs Health Care System, Fargo, ND, p. A477

WELLS, Jonathan, Supervisor Information Technology, Kansas Surgery and Recovery Center, Wichita, KS, p. A256

WELLS, Mary S., R.N., Chief Executive Officer, Community Memorial Hospital, Sumner, IA, p. A238

WELLS, Mary Ellen, FACHE, Administrator, CentraCare Health–Monticello, Monticello, MN, p. A348

WELLS, Pamela, R.N. Chief Nursing Officer, Sharp Memorial Hospital, San Diego, CA, p. A90

WELLS, Robert, M.D. Chief Medical Officer, Providence Portland Medical Center, Portland, OR, p. A528

WELLS, Scott E., MSN Chief Nursing Officer, St. Francis Health Center, Topeka, KS, p. A255

WELLS, Troy R., Chief Executive Officer, Baptist Health, Little Rock, AR, p. B20

WELLS, Valerie, Manager Human Resources, HEALTHSOUTH Rehabilitation Hospital The Woodlands, Conroe, TX, p. A607

WELSH Jr., J. Luckey, Chief Executive Officer, Cherry Hospital, Goldsboro, NC, p. A465

WHEELER, Don, Director Information Systems, Twin Cities Community Hospital, Templeton, CA, p. A97

WHEELER, James A., Vice President Human Relations and Community Development, Androscoggin Valley Hospital, Berlin, NH, p. A409

WHEELER, Kevin, Information Technology Leader, Kaiser Permanente Walnut Creek Medical Center, Walnut Creek, CA, p. A100

WHEELER, Kim, R.N. Director of Nursing, Kingwood Pines Hospital, Kingwood, TX, p. A631

WHEELER, Lynette, MS
Chief Nursing Officer, Truman Medical Center–Hospital Hill, Kansas City, MO, p. A374
Chief Nursing Officer, Truman Medical Center–Lakewood, Kansas City, MO, p. A374

WHEELER, Newman, Chief Financial Officer and Chief Operating Officer, Covenant Hospital–Levelland, Levelland, TX, p. A633

WHEELER, Pamela R., Manager Human Resources, Scott County Hospital, Scott City, KS, p. A254

WHEELER, Penny Ann, M.D. President and Chief Medical Officer, Abbott Northwestern Hospital, Minneapolis, MN, p. A347

WHEELER, Philip, Director Finance, Mercy Health – Clermont Hospital, Batavia, OH, p. A483

WHEELER, Rebecca, Director Finance, Kaiser Permanente Baldwin Park Medical Center, Baldwin Park, CA, p. A57

WHEELER, Robert
Controller, HEALTHSOUTH Rehabilitation Hospital of Florence, Florence, SC, p. A565
Vice President Human Resources, South Shore Hospital, South Weymouth, MA, p. A314

WHEELER, Terry J., Chief Executive Officer, Cypress Fairbanks Medical Center, Houston, TX, p. A624

WHEELER, Tina, R.N. Director Nursing, William Newton Hospital, Winfield, KS, p. A257

WHEELER, Zach, Senior Vice President Human Resources, John D. Archbold Memorial Hospital, Thomasville, GA, p. A168

WHEELER-MOORE, Juanita, Director Financial Services, Four Winds Hospital, Saratoga Springs, NY, p. A454

WHEELES, Locke, Information Technology Manager, Field Memorial Community Hospital, Centreville, MS, p. A356

WHEELUS, Matthew, Chief Operating Officer, Spring Valley Hospital Medical Center, Las Vegas, NV, p. A406

WHELAN, Doris, Chief Information Officer, Moberly Regional Medical Center, Moberly, MO, p. A377

WHELAN, Laurie A., Senior Vice President Finance and Chief Financial Officer, Hospital for Special Care, New Britain, CT, p. A115

WHELAN, Thomas
President, Edwin Shaw Rehab, Cuyahoga Falls, OH, p. A491
President, Lodi Community Hospital, Lodi, OH, p. A496

WHERRY, Richard, M.D. Chief of Staff, Chestatee Regional Hospital, Dahlonega, GA, p. A157

WHERRY, Robin, Risk Manager and Director Quality Assurance and Health Information Management, HEALTHSOUTH MountainView Regional Rehabilitation Hospital, Morgantown, WV, p. A697

WHETTON, Matthew, Chief Business Administration, Veterans Affairs Central California Health Care System, Fresno, CA, p. A64

WHICHARD, Forrest, Chief Financial Officer, Ochsner Medical Center – North Shore, Slidell, LA, p. A289

WHIDDON, William, Chief Financial Officer, Woodland Heights Medical Center, Lufkin, TX, p. A636

WHILDEN, Sean
Chief Financial Officer, Houston Medical Center, Warner Robins, GA, p. A169
Chief Financial Officer, Perry Hospital, Perry, GA, p. A164

WHILLOCK, Mary C., R.N. Associate Nursing Officer and Chief Operating Officer, Florida Hospital Carrollwood, Tampa, FL, p. A147

WHIPKEY, Jared, Chief Financial Officer, Santa Rosa Medical Center, Milton, FL, p. A138

WHIPPLE, C. Cynthia, Administrative Director and Director of Nursing, Muncy Valley Hospital, Muncy, PA, p. A546

WHIPPLE, James, Chief Executive Officer, Marshall Medical Center, Placerville, CA, p. A83

WHIPPLE, Jennifer, Director Nursing, Lane County Hospital, Dighton, KS, p. A243

WHITACRE, James, Chief Operating Officer, Select Specialty Hospital–Orlando, Orlando, FL, p. A141

WHITAKER, Bert, Interim Chief Executive Officer, Northern Hospital of Surry County, Mount Airy, NC, p. A469

WHITAKER, Catherine, R.N. Vice President and Chief Nursing Officer, University of Maryland Baltimore Washington Medical Center, Glen Burnie, MD, p. A301

WHITAKER, Charles, Director Information Technology, Madison Parish Hospital, Tallulah, LA, p. A289

WHITAKER, David D., FACHE, President and Chief Executive Officer, Norman Regional Health System, Norman, OK, p. A514

WHITAKER, Dedra, R.N. Chief Nursing Officer, Morristown–Hamblen Healthcare System, Morristown, TN, p. A590

WHITAKER, Doris, Vice President and Manager, Booneville Community Hospital, Booneville, AR, p. A44

WHITAKER, James B., President, Circles of Care, Melbourne, FL, p. A135

WHITAKER, Jimmy, Director Information Systems, Central Carolina Hospital, Sanford, NC, p. A472

WHITAKER, Neil, M.D. Chief Medical Director, Orem Community Hospital, Orem, UT, p. A661

WHITE, Al, CPA Senior Vice President Business Services, Broadlawns Medical Center, Des Moines, IA, p. A229

WHITE, Alexander, Vice President Medical Affairs, Carney Hospital, Boston, MA, p. A306

WHITE, Andrea, Chief Executive Officer, Select Specialty Hospital–Birmingham, Birmingham, AL, p. A16

WHITE, Barbara, Director Human Resources, Cascade Valley Hospital and Clinics, Arlington, WA, p. A681

WHITE, Beverly, MS, Facility Director, Mary S Harper Geriatric Psychiatry Center, Tuscaloosa, AL, p. A26

WHITE, Brian M., President, Northwest Hospital, Randallstown, MD, p. A302

WHITE, Bruce, Administrator, Covenant Hospital–Levelland, Levelland, TX, p. A633

WHITE, Bruce D., Chief Executive Officer, Knox Community Hospital, Mount Vernon, OH, p. A499

WHITE, Catherine, Chief Financial Officer, Harney District Hospital, Burns, OR, p. A523

WHITE, Chris L., Administrator, Grover M. Herman Hospital, Callicoon, NY, p. A435

WHITE, Cindy, CPA Vice President of Operations, INTEGRIS Canadian Valley Hospital, Yukon, OK, p. A522

WHITE, Clifford, M.D. Chief of Staff, Uvalde County Hospital Authority, Uvalde, TX, p. A654

WHITE, Darrell, R.N. Administrator and Chief Nursing Officer, Tristar Centennial Medical Center at Ashland City, Ashland City, TN, p. A579

WHITE, Debbie, Chief Financial Officer, CHRISTUS St. Frances Cabrini Hospital, Alexandria, LA, p. A272

WHITE, Debra, Chief Nursing Officer, Saint Luke's Hospital of Kansas City, Kansas City, MO, p. A374

WHITE, Denise, MSN Chief Nurse Executive, Carolinas Medical Center–Union, Monroe, NC, p. A469

WHITE, Diane B., Director Human Resources, Jerome Golden Center for Behavioral Health, Inc., West Palm Beach, FL, p. A150

WHITE, Diane K., MSN Chief Clinical Officer, Kindred Hospital South Philadelphia, Philadelphia, PA, p. A549

WHITE, Donna, Director Human Resources, HEALTHSOUTH Rehabilitation Hospital of Charleston, Charleston, SC, p. A563

WHITE, Dudley R., Administrator and Chief Executive Officer, Concho County Hospital, Eden, TX, p. A614

WHITE, Gary B., M.D. Chief Medical Staff, Uintah Basin Medical Center, Roosevelt, UT, p. A662

WHITE, Harold, Vice Chancellor, University Health Shreveport, Shreveport, LA, p. A288

WHITE, J. B., Director Information Systems, River Region Medical Center, Vicksburg, MS, p. A366

WHITE, James P., M.D. Chief Medical Officer, Integris Baptist Medical Center, Oklahoma City, OK, p. A515

WHITE, Jason, M.D. Vice President of Medical Affairs, McLaren Flint, Flint, MI, p. A323

WHITE, Jean, Vice President Finance, Avera Heart Hospital of South Dakota, Sioux Falls, SD, p. A576

WHITE, Jeffrey L., Senior Vice President and Chief Financial Officer, Beaufort Memorial Hospital, Beaufort, SC, p. A562

WHITE, Jim, Chief Information Officer, Lompoc Valley Medical Center, Lompoc, CA, p. A70

WHITE, Joanne, Chief Information Officer, Wood County Hospital, Bowling Green, OH, p. A484

WHITE, Joe
Chief Financial Officer, Central Texas Hospital, Cameron, TX, p. A605
Chief Financial Officer, Lake Whitney Medical Center, Whitney, TX, p. A657

WHITE, John D., Chief Financial Officer, Wythe County Community Hospital, Wytheville, VA, p. A680

WHITE, John R., Administrator, Shriners Hospitals for Children–Honolulu, Honolulu, HI, p. A171

WHITE, Kathy, R.N. Interim Chief Operating Officer, Doctors Medical Center, San Pablo, CA, p. A93

WHITE, Kay, Director Human Resources and Diversity, Carolinas Hospital System Marion, Mullins, SC, p. A568

WHITE, Kelli, Manager Human Resources, CenterPointe Hospital, Saint Charles, MO, p. A379

WHITE, Kevin A., Administrator, Medicine Lodge Memorial Hospital, Medicine Lodge, KS, p. A250

WHITE, Kimberly, R.N. Chief of Nursing, Memorial Hospital at Craig, Craig, CO, p. A104

WHITE, Knicole S., Director Human Resources, Kendall Regional Medical Center, Miami, FL, p. A137

WHITE, Linda E., President and Chief Executive Officer, Deaconess Health System, Evansville, IN, p. B46

WHITE, Lindy P., Chief Executive Officer, Franklin Woods Community Hospital, Johnson City, TN, p. A585

WHITE, Mary M., Chief Executive Officer, Swedish Medical Center, Englewood, CO, p. A106

WHITE, Mary–Louise, M.D., Chief Executive Officer, Dr. Solomon Carter Fuller Mental Health Center, Boston, MA, p. A306

WHITE, Mike, Chief Financial Officer, Hansen Family Hospital, Iowa Falls, IA, p. A233

WHITE, Padraic, Administrator, Chief Executive Officer and Chief Financial Officer, Ward Memorial Hospital, Monahans, TX, p. A638

WHITE, Pamela K., R.N. Chief Nursing Officer, Mayo Clinic Health System in Eau Claire, Eau Claire, WI, p. A704

WHITE, Patricia, Vice President Human Resources, Seton Medical Center, Daly City, CA, p. A61

WHITE, Patty, MS, President, St. Joseph's Hospital and Medical Center, Phoenix, AZ, p. A37

WHITE, Randall, Chief Executive Officer, Fayette Regional Health System, Connersville, IN, p. A208

WHITE, Randy, Chief Nursing Officer, Baptist Memorial Hospital–Union County, New Albany, MS, p. A363

WHITE, Robert, Director Information Technology, Helena Regional Medical Center, Helena, AR, p. A47

WHITE, Sabrina, Coordinator Human Resources, Select Specialty Hospital–Charleston, Charleston, WV, p. A694

WHITE, Sam R., Chief Nursing Officer, Crossroads Community Hospital, Mount Vernon, IL, p. A197

WHITE, Shelia, Director Human Resources, Bon Secours–Richmond Community Hospital, Richmond, VA, p. A677

WHITE, Shirley, Director Human Resources, Ashley County Medical Center, Crossett, AR, p. A44

WHITE, Terri, Commissioner, Oklahoma Department of Mental Health and Substance Abuse Services, Oklahoma City, OK, p. B104

WHITE, Wendy
Vice President Human Resources, CHRISTUS Highland Medical Center, Shreveport, LA, p. A288
Regional Vice President Human Resources, CHRISTUS St. Frances Cabrini Hospital, Alexandria, LA, p. A272
Assistant Administrator Human Resources, CHRISTUS St. Patrick Hospital of Lake Charles, Lake Charles, LA, p. A282

WHITE, Wesley D., Chief Financial Officer, North Valley Hospital, Whitefish, MT, p. A392

WHITE, Willie, M.D. Director Medical Staff, J. Paul Jones Hospital, Camden, AL, p. A18

WHITE, Woody, Chief Executive Officer, Covington County Hospital, Collins, MS, p. A357

WHITE HOUSE, Judy, Vice President Human Resources, St. Mary's Hospital and Regional Medical Center, Grand Junction, CO, p. A107

WHITE–JACOBS, Mary Beth, FACHE, President and Chief Executive Officer, Black River Memorial Hospital, Black River Falls, WI, p. A702

WHITE–TREVINO, Karen, Chief Nursing Officer, West Florida Hospital, Pensacola, FL, p. A142

WHITED, Brian, M.D. Medical Director, Mayo Clinic Health System in Mankato, Mankato, MN, p. A346

WHITED, Steve, Chief Executive Officer, Minnie Hamilton HealthCare Center, Grantsville, WV, p. A695

WHITEHEAD, Alva W., M.D. Vice President Medical Services, McLeod Regional Medical Center, Florence, SC, p. A566

WHITEHEAD, David A.
President and CEO, The William W. Backus Hospital, Norwich, CT, p. A116
President and CEO, Windham Hospital, Willimantic, CT, p. A118

WHITEHEAD, Pamela, Chief Financial Officer, Anchor Hospital, Atlanta, GA, p. A151

WHITEHORN, Jeffrey T., Chief Executive Officer, TriStar Summit Medical Center, Hermitage, TN, p. A584

WHITEHURST, Rob, Chief, Office of Information and Technology, Veterans Affairs Ann Arbor Healthcare System, Ann Arbor, MI, p. A318

WHITELEY, Earl S., FACHE, Chief Executive Officer, North Georgia Medical Center, Ellijay, GA, p. A159

WHITESEL, Carol, Vice President Patient Care Services and Chief Nursing Officer, Community Hospital of Anderson and Madison County, Anderson, IN, p. A206

WHITESELL, Jr., Thomas C., MSC Chief of Staff, Southeast Georgia Health System Camden Campus, Saint Marys, GA, p. A166

WHITESIDE, Anne, Vice President Nursing, Winchester Medical Center, Winchester, VA, p. A680

WHITESIDE, Patrick, Manager Information Services, Spectrum Health Big Rapids Hospital, Big Rapids, MI, p. A319

WHITETHORNE, Priscilla, Chief Executive Officer, U. S. Public Health Service Indian Hospital–Sells, Sells, AZ, p. A39

WHITFIELD, Bruce, CPA, Chief Executive Officer and Chief Financial Officer, Cabinet Peaks Medical Center, Libby, MT, p. A389

WHITFIELD Jr., Charles H., President and Chief Executive Officer, Laughlin Memorial Hospital, Greeneville, TN, p. A583

WHITFIELD, Jay, Chief Financial Officer, Baylor University Medical Center, Dallas, TX, p. A610

WHITFIELD, Jo Ann, Business Officer, Walter B. Jones Alcohol and Drug Abuse Treatment Center, Greenville, NC, p. A465

WHITFIELD, Teresa L., R.N. Chief Nursing Officer, Seneca Healthcare District, Chester, CA, p. A59

WHITING, Barbara, Director Health Information Management, Promise Hospital of Vicksburg, Vicksburg, MS, p. A366

WHITING, Joseph K., FACHE, Interim Chief Executive Officer, Keokuk Area Hospital, Keokuk, IA, p. A233

WHITIS, Matt, Chief Medical Officer, Mahaska Health Partnership, Oskaloosa, IA, p. A236

WHITLATCH, Kristine, President and Chief Executive Officer, King's Daughters Medical Center, Ashland, KY, p. A258

WHITLEY, Darla, Manager Health Information Technology, Syringa Hospital and Clinics, Grangeville, ID, p. A176

WHITLEY, Myra, Human Resources Director, Columbus Specialty Hospital, Columbus, GA, p. A156

WHITLEY, Pam, R.N. Chief Operating Officer and Chief Nursing Officer, Green Oaks Hospital, Dallas, TX, p. A610

WHITLOCK, Jr., James A., M.D. Medical Director, Northeast Rehabilitation Hospital, Salem, NH, p. A412

WHITMAN, Bill, Chief Operating Officer, JPS Health Network, Fort Worth, TX, p. A618

WHITMER, Carl, President and Chief Executive Officer, IASIS Healthcare, Franklin, TN, p. B74

WHITMER, Seth, Administrator, Morton General Hospital, Morton, WA, p. A685

WHITMORE, Ray B., Chief Financial Officer, McCurtain Memorial Hospital, Idabel, OK, p. A512

WHITMORE, W. Patrick, Chief Financial Officer, Medical Center of Plano, Plano, TX, p. A642

WHITNEY, Donald, Director Human Resources, Kindred Hospital–Albuquerque, Albuquerque, NM, p. A426

WHITNUM, Rhonda, Director Health Improvement Management, Prague Community Hospital, Prague, OK, p. A518

WHITSON, Charles P., CPA Senior Vice President Finance, Lake Charles Memorial Hospital, Lake Charles, LA, p. A282

WHITT, Alicia, R.N. Chief Nursing Officer, Stephens Memorial Hospital, Breckenridge, TX, p. A603

WHITT, Charles Christopher, Chief Nursing Officer, River Park Hospital, Huntington, WV, p. A696

WHITT, Stevan, M.D. Chief Medical Officer, University of Missouri Hospitals and Clinics, Columbia, MO, p. A370

WHITTAKER, Kelly, Vice President Nursing, Caro Community Hospital, Caro, MI, p. A320

WHITTAKER, Shawn, Chief Nursing Officer, Miller County Hospital, Colquitt, GA, p. A156

WHITTAKER, Sheena, M.D. President Medical Staff, Maine Coast Memorial Hospital, Ellsworth, ME, p. A293

WHITTEMORE, Marjorie, Director Human Resources, Rio Grande Regional Hospital, McAllen, TX, p. A637

WHITTEMORE, Scott, Chief Financial Officer, Central Mississippi Medical Center, Jackson, MS, p. A360

WHITTEN, Jacquelyn, R.N. Chief Nurse Executive and Vice President Nursing, Advocate Trinity Hospital, Chicago, IL, p. A183

WHITTINGTON, Bruce
Vice President Human Resources, Hays Medical Center, Hays, KS, p. A245
Vice President Human Resources, Pawnee Valley Community Hospital, Larned, KS, p. A248

WHITTINGTON, Carol, Chief Human Resources Officer, Sacred Heart Hospital of Pensacola, Pensacola, FL, p. A142

WHITTINGTON, Dorothy, Chief Financial Officer, University Health Conway, Monroe, LA, p. A284

WHITTINGTON, Hilary, Chief Financial Officer, Jefferson Healthcare, Port Townsend, WA, p. A686

WHITTINGTON, Laurie A., Chief Operating Officer, Memorial Hospital of Union County, Marysville, OH, p. A497

WHITTINGTON, Shane, Chief Financial Officer, Caldwell Medical Center, Princeton, KY, p. A269

WHITTON, Beth, Director Human Resources, Ocean Beach Hospital, Ilwaco, WA, p. A684

WHOLLEY, Diane, Director Fiscal Services, Bridgewater State Hospital, Bridgewater, MA, p. A308

WHORLEY, Chris, Chief Information Officer, Nashville General Hospital, Nashville, TN, p. A590

WHYBROW, Peter, M.D., Chief Executive Officer, Stewart & Lynda Resnick Neuropsychiatric Hospital at UCLA, Los Angeles, CA, p. A75

WIBBENMEYER, Christopher, Director Human Resources, Perry County Memorial Hospital, Perryville, MO, p. A378

WIBBENS, Cheryl, M.D. Vice President Medical Staff Affairs, Memorial Hospital of South Bend, South Bend, IN, p. A222

WIBBLESMAN, Christopher, M.D. Chief of Staff, Family Health West, Fruita, CO, p. A106

WIBORG, Shelley, MS Director of Nursing, OSF Holy Family Medical Center, Monmouth, IL, p. A196

WICKE, III, Julius, Vice President Finance and Hospital Financial Officer, Baylor Jack and Jane Hamilton Heart and Vascular Hospital, Dallas, TX, p. A609

WICKE, Regina, Chief Financial Officer, Columbus Community Hospital, Columbus, TX, p. A607

WICKE, Trey, Vice President, Baylor Specialty Hospital, Dallas, TX, p. A609

WICKENS, Amy Lynn, Executive Director Human Resources, Decatur County Memorial Hospital, Greensburg, IN, p. A212

WICKENS, Jeanne, Senior Vice President Finance and Chief Financial Officer, Allegiance Health, Jackson, MI, p. A327

WICKER, Kenneth R., Chief Executive Officer, Bayfront Health Brooksville, Brooksville, FL, p. A125

WICKERSHAM, Jason, M.D. Chief of Staff, Avera St. Benedict Health Center, Parkston, SD, p. A575

WICKIZER, Jr., Boyd, M.D. Chief Medical Officer, Southside Regional Medical Center, Petersburg, VA, p. A676

WICKLINE, Melissa, Director Marketing, Greenbrier Valley Medical Center, Ronceverte, WV, p. A699

WICKLUND, Grant, President and Chief Executive Officer, Lutheran Medical Center, Wheat Ridge, CO, p. A112

WIDEMAN, Jeff, Director Information Systems, Gilmore Memorial Regional Medical Center, Amory, MS, p. A355

WIDENER, Michael, Chief Financial Officer, Twin County Regional Hospital, Galax, VA, p. A671

WIDENER, William, Administrator and Chief Executive Officer, Harper Hospital District Five, Harper, KS, p. A245

WIDGER, Judy, M.D. Chief of Staff, Healdsburg District Hospital, Healdsburg, CA, p. A66

WIDICK, Brent, Interim Superintendent, Kansas Neurological Institute, Topeka, KS, p. A255

WIDNER, Eric W., Division President, Oakwood Hospital–Wayne, Wayne, MI, p. A337

WIDRA, Linda S., R.N., Interim Chief Executive Officer, Lakewood Ranch Medical Center, Bradenton, FL, p. A124

WIEBE, Robert, M.D. Chief Medical Officer, Mercy General Hospital, Sacramento, CA, p. A87

WIECHART, Michael, President and Chief Executive Officer, Capella Healthcare, Franklin, TN, p. B26

WIECK, Jennifer, Director Financial Services, Genoa Community Hospital, Genoa, NE, p. A396

WIECZOREK, Pawel, Director Information Technology, BryLin Hospitals, Buffalo, NY, p. A434

WIEGENSTEIN, Adrianne, Director Human Resources, Cascade Medical Center, Leavenworth, WA, p. A685

WIEGENSTEIN, Robert, Chief Financial Officer, Lake Chelan Community Hospital, Chelan, WA, p. A682

WIEMANN, Michael, M.D., President, Providence Hospital, Southfield, MI, p. A335

WIENS, Ron, Chief Financial Officer, Shodair Children's Hospital, Helena, MT, p. A388

WIENTJES, Keri, Director Human Resources, Mobridge Regional Hospital, Mobridge, SD, p. A575

WIERZBICKI, Barb, Manager Human Resources, Select Specialty Hospital–Downriver, Wyandotte, MI, p. A337

WIEWORA, Ron, M.D. Chief Medical Officer, Lakeside Medical Center, Belle Glade, FL, p. A123

WIGGINS, Carla, Director Human Resources, Livingston Hospital and Healthcare Services, Salem, KY, p. A270

WIGGINS, John, Chief Financial Officer, Evans Memorial Hospital, Claxton, GA, p. A156

WIGGINS, Josh
Vice President Controller, MidMichigan Medical Center–Clare, Clare, MI, p. A321
Vice President and Controller, MidMichigan Medical Center–Gladwin, Gladwin, MI, p. A324

WIGGINS, Leslie, Director, Atlanta Veterans Affairs Medical Center, Decatur, GA, p. A158

WIGHTMAN, Lori, R.N. Chief Nursing Officer, Saint Agnes Medical Center, Fresno, CA, p. A64

WIGINGTON, James, M.D. Chief of Staff, Heart of the Rockies Regional Medical Center, Salida, CO, p. A111

WIGINGTON, Yvonne, Vice President, Chief Financial Officer, Wyoming Medical Center, Casper, WY, p. A720

WIGNALL, Terry A.
Director Human Resources, St. Vincent Seton Specialty Hospital, Indianapolis, IN, p. A215
Director Human Resources, St. Vincent Seton Specialty Hospital, Lafayette, IN, p. A217

WIIK, Jennifer, Chief Nursing Officer, Ortonville Area Health Services, Ortonville, MN, p. A349

WIJAYA, Joanne, Chief Operating Officer, Hampton Behavioral Health Center, Westampton, NJ, p. A424

WIJEWARDANE, Chamath, Director Information Technology, OCH Regional Medical Center, Starkville, MS, p. A365

WILBANKS, John F., FACH
Chief Operating Officer, Baptist Medical Center Beaches, Jacksonville Beach, FL, p. A132
Chief Operating Officer, Baptist Medical Center Jacksonville, Jacksonville, FL, p. A131

WILBERDING, Deborah, Controller, Rush Oak Park Hospital, Oak Park, IL, p. A198

WILBUR, Bruce, M.D. Chief Medical Officer, Good Samaritan Hospital, San Jose, CA, p. A92

WILBUR, Thomas W., Chief Executive Officer and Superintendent, Newport Hospital and Health Services, Newport, WA, p. A685

WILBURN, Sue, Vice President Human Resources and Organizational Development, East Tennessee Children's Hospital, Knoxville, TN, p. A585

WILCHER, Greta
Senior Vice President and Chief Financial Officer, Mercy Hospital Fort Smith, Fort Smith, AR, p. A46
Senior Vice President and Chief Financial Officer, Mercy Hospital Waldron, Waldron, AR, p. A53

WILCHER, Kelly, Chief Executive Officer, Carson Tahoe Continuing Care Hospital, Carson City, NV, p. A404

WILCOX, Bill, Chief Information Technology Officer, Bristol Bay Area Health Corporation, Dillingham, AK, p. A28

WILCOX, Jack, Chief Financial Officer, Ennis Regional Medical Center, Ennis, TX, p. A617

WILCOX, James, Chief Executive Officer, El Paso Specialty Hospital, El Paso, TX, p. A615

WILCOX, John, Interim Chief Information Officer, United Medical Center, Washington, DC, p. A122

WILCOX, Kyle M., Assistant Vice President Finance, Grinnell Regional Medical Center, Grinnell, IA, p. A231

WILCOX, William H., President and Chief Executive Officer, United Surgical Partners International, Addison, TX, p. B139

WILCZEK, Joseph, Chief Executive Officer, St. Elizabeth Hospital, Enumclaw, WA, p. A683

WILCZEK, Vincent Scot, Vice President and Chief Financial Officer, Pratt Regional Medical Center, Pratt, KS, p. A253

WILD, James, M.D. Medical Director, Lake Shore Health Care Center, Irving, NY, p. A439

WILD, Mary Lou, Vice President Patient Care Continuum and Chief Nursing Officer, Sarah Bush Lincoln Health Center, Mattoon, IL, p. A195

WILDE, Gary, President and Chief Executive Officer, Community Memorial Health System, Ventura, CA, p. A99

WILDE, Kathy R., R.N. Chief Nursing Officer, Hennepin County Medical Center, Minneapolis, MN, p. A347

WILDE, Stacy, Chief Executive Officer, AMG Specialty Hospital–Tulsa, Tulsa, OK, p. A520

WILDER, Claudia, R.N. Chief Nursing Officer, Baylor University Medical Center, Dallas, TX, p. A610

WILDER, Janet, Director Human Resources, Knox County Hospital, Barbourville, KY, p. A258

WILDER, John, Director Information Systems, Spaulding Hospital for Continuing Medical Care Cambridge, Cambridge, MA, p. A309

WILDER, Kathy, R.N. Chief Clinical Officer, Medical Center Barbour, Eufaula, AL, p. A19

WILEY, Chuck, Manager Information Systems, Harrison County Hospital, Corydon, IN, p. A209

WILEY, Donald J., President and Chief Executive Officer, St. Joseph's Medical Center, Stockton, CA, p. A96

WILEY, George, Chief Financial Officer, North Vista Hospital, North Las Vegas, NV, p. A407

WILEY, Mark, Manager Information Systems Development, UPMC Bedford Memorial, Everett, PA, p. A539

WILFORD, Linda, CPA Senior Vice President and Chief Financial Officer, Holy Cross Hospital, Fort Lauderdale, FL, p. A128

WILHELM, Christine, Vice President Operations, Charlevoix Area Hospital, Charlevoix, MI, p. A320

WILHELM, Connie, Chief Financial Officer, Swisher Memorial Hospital District, Tulia, TX, p. A653

WILHELM, Jr., John O., Senior Vice President and Chief Financial Officer, Emerson Hospital, Concord, MA, p. A309

WILHELM, Paul, M.D. Chief of Staff, Kiowa District Hospital and Manor, Kiowa, KS, p. A247

WILHELMSEN Jr., Thomas E., President and Chief Executive Officer, Southern New Hampshire Medical Center, Nashua, NH, p. A411

WILHITE, James, Director Systems Information, North Mississippi State Hospital, Tupelo, MS, p. A365

WILHITE, Jerald, Administrator Human Resources, Heartland Behavioral Healthcare, Massillon, OH, p. A498

WILHITE, Mark C., Commander, Bayne–Jones Army Community Hospital, Fort Polk, LA, p. A277

WILHOITE, David, CPA Senior Vice President Finance and Chief Financial Officer, Trousdale Medical Center, Hartsville, TN, p. A583

WILK, Leonard, President and Chief Executive Officer, St. Alexius Medical Center, Hoffman Estates, IL, p. A193

WILK, Michael, Senior President Financial Services and Chief Financial Officer, Pocono Medical Center, East Stroudsburg, PA, p. A538

WILKE, Julie, Vice President, Monroe Clinic, Monroe, WI, p. A711

WILKE, Kris, Manager Health Information, Granite Falls Municipal Hospital and Manor, Granite Falls, MN, p. A344

WILKEN, Thomas
Senior Vice President and Chief Human Resources Officer, Mother Frances Hospital – Tyler, Tyler, TX, p. A654
Vice President Human Resources, Seton Medical Center Williamson, Round Rock, TX, p. A645
Vice President Human Resources, Seton Shoal Creek Hospital, Austin, TX, p. A600

WILKENS, Gregory, M.D. Chief of Staff, Jellico Community Hospital, Jellico, TN, p. A585

WILKER, Johnathan, Vice President Finance and Chief Financial Officer, Faith Regional Health Services, Norfolk, NE, p. A398

WILKERSON, Donald H., Chief Executive Officer, St. David's Medical Center, Austin, TX, p. A600

WILKERSON, Jacquelyn, R.N. Chief Nursing Officer, Conway Regional Medical Center, Conway, AR, p. A44

WILKERSON–UDDYBACK, Patricia, M.D. Chief Medical Officer, DMC Harper University Hospital, Detroit, MI, p. A322

WILKES, Chris, MS Director Human Resources, Blount Memorial Hospital, Maryville, TN, p. A588

WILKES, Wendell, Chief Financial Officer, Byrd Regional Hospital, Leesville, LA, p. A282

WILKIE, Chance, Information Technology Specialist, Public Health Service Indian Hospital – Quentin N. Burdick Memorial Health Facility, Belcourt, ND, p. A476

WILKIE, Paula, Chief Financial Officer, Presentation Medical Center, Rolla, ND, p. A480

WILKINS, Michael, Chief Operating Officer, Advocate Christ Medical Center, Oak Lawn, IL, p. A198

WILKINS, Monica, Chief Executive Officer, Lincoln Community Hospital and Nursing Home, Hugo, CO, p. A107

WILKINSON, Kyle, Chief Financial Officer, Morgan Memorial Hospital, Madison, GA, p. A163

WILKINSON, Paul G., Chief Operating Officer, Providence St. Peter Hospital, Olympia, WA, p. A686

WILKINSON, Steven D., President and Chief Executive Officer, Menorah Medical Center, Overland Park, KS, p. A252

WILL, Charles, Chief Financial Officer, Ferrell Hospital, Eldorado, IL, p. A188

WILL, DeDe, Director Finance, Douglas County Community Mental Health Center, Omaha, NE, p. A400

WILL–MOWERY, Nicki L., Ph.D., Chief Executive Officer, Lower Keys Medical Center, Key West, FL, p. A133

WILLAMS, Brandon, Chief Financial Officer, East Cooper Medical Center, Mount Pleasant, SC, p. A568

WILLAMS, Kyle, Director Information Technology, Kirby Medical Center, Monticello, IL, p. A196

WILLAMS, Mike, Chief Information Officer, FHN Memorial Hospital, Freeport, IL, p. A190

WILLARD, Cheri, R.N. Chief Nursing Officer, Evanston Regional Hospital, Evanston, WY, p. A721

WILLARD, Craig, Director Information Technology and Systems, Frankfort Regional Medical Center, Frankfort, KY, p. A261

WILLARD, Ruth, Chief Nursing Officer, TriStar StoneCrest Medical Center, Smyrna, TN, p. A593

WILLARS, Susan, Vice President Human Resources, Mission Regional Medical Center, Mission, TX, p. A638

WILLE, Lesley A., Administrator and Executive Director, Kaiser Permanente South Bay Medical Center,, CA, p. A72

WILLE, Matt, Chief Executive Officer, Dallas County Hospital, Perry, IA, p. A236

WILLEKE, Louis R., Administrator, Refugio County Memorial Hospital, Refugio, TX, p. A643

WILLEMSEN, Jane, Chief Administrative Officer, John Muir Medical Center, Walnut Creek, Walnut Creek, CA, p. A100

WILLERT, Todd, Chief Executive Officer, Monroe County Hospital and Clinics, Albia, IA, p. A225

WILLET, Terry, Chief Financial Officer, Allen Parish Hospital, Kinder, LA, p. A280

WILLETT, Charles, Administrator and Chief Executive Officer, Fulton County Hospital, Salem, AR, p. A52

WILLETT, Richard, Chief Executive Officer, Redington–Fairview General Hospital, Skowhegan, ME, p. A295

WILLETT, Simon, Director Administrative Operations, South Texas Veterans Health Care System, San Antonio, TX, p. A647

WILLETT, Vita M., Administrator and Executive Director, Kaiser Permanente Riverside Medical Center, Riverside, CA, p. A86

WILLEY, Randy, Business Manager, Lincoln Regional Center, Lincoln, NE, p. A397

WILLHITE, Jean, Director Human Resources, Sutter Solano Medical Center, Vallejo, CA, p. A99

WILLIAMS, Adrian, Chief Executive Officer, Serenity Springs Specialty Hospital, Farmerville, LA, p. A277

WILLIAMS, Amy, M.D. Chief Medical Officer, Mayo Clinic Hospital – Rochester, Rochester, MN, p. A350

WILLIAMS, Andrea K., Manager, Employee Relations, Winter Haven Hospital, Winter Haven, FL, p. A150

WILLIAMS, Andrew, Chief Executive Officer, Methodist Ambulatory Surgery Hospital – Northwest, San Antonio, TX, p. A646

WILLIAMS, Antoinette, Chief Nursing Officer, John H. Stroger Jr. Hospital of Cook County, Chicago, IL, p. A184

WILLIAMS, Arthur, M.D. Medical Director, Braintree Rehabilitation Hospital, Braintree, MA, p. A308

WILLIAMS, Ashley, Manager Human Resources, Southern Inyo Healthcare District, Lone Pine, CA, p. A70

WILLIAMS, Avilla, MS, President, INTEGRIS Health Edmond, Edmond, OK, p. A510

WILLIAMS, Beverly, R.N. Chief Nursing Officer, Washington County Memorial Hospital, Potosi, MO, p. A379

WILLIAMS, Beverly, Chief Nursing Officer, Washington Regional Medical Center, Fayetteville, AR, p. A46

WILLIAMS, Bob
President and Chief Executive Officer, Baptist St. Anthony Health System, Amarillo, TX, p. A596
Director of Nursing, Centennial Peaks Hospital, Louisville, CO, p. A109

WILLIAMS, Brian, Service Leader Corporate Information Systems, St. Joseph's Hospital of Buckhannon, Buckhannon, WV, p. A694

WILLIAMS, Brit, M.D. President Medical Staff, Dr. John Warner Hospital, Clinton, IL, p. A187

WILLIAMS, Cara, Director Human Resources, Scripps Memorial Hospital–Encinitas, Encinitas, CA, p. A62

WILLIAMS, CarolAnn, Chief Financial Officer, Massachusetts Eye and Ear Infirmary, Boston, MA, p. A307

WILLIAMS, Carrie, R.N. Chief Nursing Officer, Henry County Hospital, New Castle, IN, p. A220

WILLIAMS, Catherine, M.D. Medical Director, Lewis County General Hospital, Lowville, NY, p. A440

WILLIAMS, Cecille, Assistant Administrator, Shamrock General Hospital, Shamrock, TX, p. A648

WILLIAMS, Christopher, M.D. Chief of Staff, Keefe Memorial Hospital, Cheyenne Wells, CO, p. A103

WILLIAMS, Dan, Vice President Finance and Support, Liberty Hospital, Liberty, MO, p. A376

WILLIAMS, Dana, Chief Financial Officer, Baptist Memorial Hospital–North Mississippi, Oxford, MS, p. A364

WILLIAMS, Dana D., Chief Executive Officer, Jennings American Legion Hospital, Jennings, LA, p. A279

WILLIAMS, Darek, Director Human Resources, Elgin Mental Health Center, Elgin, IL, p. A189

WILLIAMS, Darlene, R.N., Administrator, Memorial Medical Center – San Augustine, San Augustine, TX, p. A648

WILLIAMS, David, Director Information Technology, Franklin Hospital District, Benton, IL, p. A181

WILLIAMS, David C., D.O., President and Chief Executive Officer, Community Westview Hospital, Indianapolis, IN, p. A213

WILLIAMS, David L., M.D. Chief Medical Officer, St. Joseph Hospital & Health Center, Kokomo, IN, p. A216

WILLIAMS, David R., Chief Executive Officer, Centerpoint Medical Center, Independence, MO, p. A372

WILLIAMS, Denise R., Interim Chief Executive Officer, Nashville General Hospital, Nashville, TN, p. A590

WILLIAMS, Dionne, Director Human Resources, Vaughan Regional Medical Center, Selma, AL, p. A25

WILLIAMS, Frank L., Executive Vice President/ Medical Director, Kedren Community Mental Health Center, Los Angeles, CA, p. A73

WILLIAMS, Gary, Administrator, Houston Hospital for Specialized Surgery, Houston, TX, p. A624

WILLIAMS, Ginger, M.D., President and Chief Executive Officer, Oaklawn Hospital, Marshall, MI, p. A330

WILLIAMS, Jackie, Director Human Resources, Madison River Oaks Medical Center, Canton, MS, p. A356

WILLIAMS, James, M.D. Chief of Staff, Riverside Medical Center, Waupaca, WI, p. A717

WILLIAMS, Jeremy, Chief Financial Officer, Banner Boswell Medical Center, Sun City, AZ, p. A39

WILLIAMS, Jeremy, M.D. President Medical Staff, Stonewall Jackson Memorial Hospital, Weston, WV, p. A700

WILLIAMS, Jim, Chief Financial Officer, Minden Medical Center, Minden, LA, p. A284

WILLIAMS, Joan, Administrative Assistant/Human Resources, Lamb Healthcare Center, Littlefield, TX, p. A633

WILLIAMS, John
Chief Information Officer, Bay Pines Veterans Affairs Medical Center, Bay Pines, FL, p. A123
Administrator and Chief Executive Officer, Oneida County Hospital, Malad City, ID, p. A176
Chief Financial Officer, Upson Regional Medical Center, Thomaston, GA, p. A168

WILLIAMS, Jr., John D., Chief Financial Officer, Veterans Affairs Gulf Coast Veterans Health Care System, Biloxi, MS, p. A356

WILLIAMS Jr., John F., M.P.H., President, SUNY Downstate Medical Center University Hospital,, NY, p. A448

WILLIAMS, John G., President and Chief Executive Officer, Barton Memorial Hospital, South Lake Tahoe, CA, p. A96

WILLIAMS, Joyce, Consultant Human Resources and Organizational Development, Memorial Hermann Rehabilitation Hospital – Katy, Katy, TX, p. A630

WILLIAMS, Julie, Chief Financial Officer, Smith County Memorial Hospital, Smith Center, KS, p. A254

WILLIAMS, Karen, Chief Financial Officer, Streamwood Behavioral Health Center, Streamwood, IL, p. A204

WILLIAMS, Kate, M.D. President, Medical Staff, Carlinville Area Hospital, Carlinville, IL, p. A182

WILLIAMS, Kathy, Chief Nursing Officer, Eastern New Mexico Medical Center, Roswell, NM, p. A430

WILLIAMS, Kenneth, Chief Information Officer, Fayetteville Veterans Affairs Medical Center, Fayetteville, NC, p. A464

WILLIAMS, Kim, R.N
Director of Nursing, Mercy Hospital Logan County, Guthrie, OK, p. A511
Chief Operating Officer, Providence Regional Medical Center Everett, Everett, WA, p. A683

WILLIAMS, L. Dale, M.D. Vice President and Chief Medical Director, High Point Regional Health System, High Point, NC, p. A466

WILLIAMS, Lana R., Chief Nursing Officer, Arkansas Methodist Medical Center, Paragould, AR, p. A51

WILLIAMS, Lauren, R.N. Vice President of Professional Services and Chief Nursing Officer, Lawrence + Memorial Hospital, New London, CT, p. A116

WILLIAMS, Linda, Director of Nursing, Villa Feliciana Medical Complex, Jackson, LA, p. A279

WILLIAMS, Lorie, R.N. Vice President Nursing, Samaritan Pacific Communities Hospital, Newport, OR, p. A527

WILLIAMS, Lynn
Vice President, Commonwealth Regional Specialty Hospital, Bowling Green, KY, p. A258
Vice President Human Resources, Medical Center at Bowling Green, Bowling Green, KY, p. A259
Vice President Human Resources, Medical Center at Scottsville, Scottsville, KY, p. A270

WILLIAMS, Margaret, Chief Financial Officer, Baptist Memorial Hospital for Women, Memphis, TN, p. A588

WILLIAMS, Margo L., R.N. Chief Nursing Officer, Anderson County Hospital, Garnett, KS, p. A244

WILLIAMS, Mark, Chief Financial Officer, Citrus Memorial Health System, Inverness, FL, p. A131

WILLIAMS, Mark, M.D. Vice President and Chief Medical Officer, Miami Valley Hospital, Dayton, OH, p. A492

WILLIAMS, Mary, Director Human Resources, Medina Memorial Hospital, Medina, NY, p. A441

WILLIAMS, Matthew, R.N. Chief Financial Officer, Olympia Medical Center, Los Angeles, CA, p. A73

WILLIAMS, Michael, FACHE, Administrator, Fairfield Memorial Hospital, Winnsboro, SC, p. A571

WILLIAMS, Michael D., President and Chief Executive Officer, Community Hospital Corporation, Plano, TX, p. B43

WILLIAMS, Michael L., FACHE Vice President Human Resources, Community Howard Regional Health, Kokomo, IN, p. A216

WILLIAMS, Michelle, Administrator, Sedan City Hospital, Sedan, KS, p. A254

WILLIAMS, Mickey, Manager Information Technology, Moccasin Bend Mental Health Institute, Chattanooga, TN, p. A580

WILLIAMS, Mike, Accountant, Limestone Medical Center, Groesbeck, TX, p. A622

WILLIAMS, Pam, Chief Executive Officer, Minnesota Valley Health Center, Le Sueur, MN, p. A345

WILLIAMS, Pamela G., Director Human Resources, White County Medical Center, Searcy, AR, p. A52

WILLIAMS, Patricia, Regional VP for Behavioral Medicine and Population Health, St. Helena Hospital–Center for Behavioral Health, Vallejo, CA, p. A99

WILLIAMS Sr., Perry E., Administrator and Chief Executive Officer, Alliance HealthCare System, Holly Springs, MS, p. A359

WILLIAMS, R. D., Chief Executive Officer, Hendry Regional Medical Center, Clewiston, FL, p. A126

WILLIAMS, Randy, Director Management Information Systems, Maria Parham Medical Center, Henderson, NC, p. A466

WILLIAMS, Rich, Director Human Resources, Upson Regional Medical Center, Thomaston, GA, p. A168

WILLIAMS, Richard, Chief Operating Officer, Southwest Mississippi Regional Medical Center, McComb, MS, p. A362

WILLIAMS, Robert, Chief Executive Officer, HEALTHSOUTH Southern Hills Rehabilitation Hospital, Princeton, WV, p. A698

WILLIAMS, Robert D., Chief Executive Officer, Special Care Hospital, Nanticoke, PA, p. A546

WILLIAMS, Robert J., M.D. Chief Medical Staff, Wills Memorial Hospital, Washington, GA, p. A169

WILLIAMS, Roberta A., Director of Nursing, U. S. Public Health Service Indian Hospital, Cass Lake, MN, p. A341

WILLIAMS, Roby D., Administrator, Hardin County General Hospital, Rosiclare, IL, p. A202

WILLIAMS, Rod, Manager Information Systems, Citizens Medical Center, Colby, KS, p. A242

WILLIAMS, Roderick L., M.P.H., President, University Health Shreveport, Shreveport, LA, p. A288

WILLIAMS, Rodney W., M.D. Vice President Medical Affairs, Good Samaritan Hospital, Suffern, NY, p. A455

WILLIAMS, Ronald G., Administrator, Central Louisiana State Hospital, Pineville, LA, p. A287

WILLIAMS, Ryan, Human Resources Director, Sumner Regional Medical Center, Gallatin, TN, p. A583

WILLIAMS, Sandra
Chief Financial Officer, Cape Fear Valley – Bladen County Hospital, Elizabethtown, NC, p. A464
Chief Financial Officer, Cape Fear Valley Medical Center, Fayetteville, NC, p. A464

WILLIAMS, Scott
Chief Operating Officer, Cookeville Regional Medical Center, Cookeville, TN, p. A581
Chief Executive Officer, Regency Hospital Cleveland East, Warrensville Heights, OH, p. A504

WILLIAMS, Sean J., President and Chief Executive Officer, Mercy Medical Center–Clinton, Clinton, IA, p. A227

WILLIAMS, Shane, Director Information Systems, Davis Hospital and Medical Center, Layton, UT, p. A660

WILLIAMS, Sharon, Vice President Finance and Information Technology, Avera Marshall Regional Medical Center, Marshall, MN, p. A346

WILLIAMS, Sheila, Vice President and Administrator, Baptist Health Medical Center–Hot Spring County, Malvern, AR, p. A50

WILLIAMS, Stephanie
Coordinator Human Resources, Kindred Rehabilitation Hospital Northeast Houston, Humble, TX, p. A628
Market Director Human Resources, Lake Norman Regional Medical Center, Mooresville, NC, p. A469

WILLIAMS, Stephanie, R.N. Chief Nursing Officer, Washington Hospital Healthcare System, Fremont, CA, p. A64

WILLIAMS, Stephen, Chief Executive Officer, Norton Healthcare, Louisville, KY, p. B101

WILLIAMS, Steve, Chief Executive Officer, Victory Medical Center Plano, Plano, TX, p. A643

WILLIAMS, Susan, R.N. Chief Nursing Officer, Baptist Health Medical Center–Stuttgart, Stuttgart, AR, p. A53

WILLIAMS, Tammy J., R.N. Chief Nursing Officer and Senior Vice President, University Medical Center, Lubbock, TX, p. A635

WILLIAMS, Teresa, R.N., Interim Administrator, Mercy Hospital Ozark, Ozark, AR, p. A51

WILLIAMS, Thaddeus, Controller, HEALTHSOUTH Rehabilitation Hospital Memphis–North, Memphis, TN, p. A588

WILLIAMS, Thomas, D.O. Chief of Staff, Sullivan County Memorial Hospital, Milan, MO, p. A377

WILLIAMS, Tina, Chief Financial Officer, Alaska Psychiatric Institute, Anchorage, AK, p. A28

WILLIAMS, Todd, M.D. President Medical Staff, Eastern Idaho Regional Medical Center, Idaho Falls, ID, p. A176

WILLIAMS, Tom, Vice President Human Resources, Lake Regional Health System, Osage Beach, MO, p. A378

WILLIAMS, Tonja, R.N., President, Continuing Care Hospital, Lexington, KY, p. A264

WILLIAMS, Jr., Wendell H., M.D. Medical Director, Specialty Hospital Jacksonville, Jacksonville, FL, p. A132

WILLIAMSON, Alan, M.D. Chief Medical Officer, Eisenhower Medical Center, Rancho Mirage, CA, p. A84

WILLIAMSON, Barry, President Medical Staff, Southeastern Health, Lumberton, NC, p. A468

WILLIAMSON, John, Human Resources Site Manager, Baptist Health South Florida, Mariners Hospital, Tavernier, FL, p. A148

WILLIAMSON, Johnny, M.D. Chief Medical Officer, Hartgrove Hospital, Chicago, IL, p. A184

WILLIAMSON, Judy, R.N. Chief Nursing Officer, Riverton Hospital, Riverton, UT, p. A662

WILLIAMSON, Marilyn, Chief Human Resources Officer, Rainbow Mentai Health Facility, Kansas City, KS, p. A247

WILLIAMSON, Sara H., MSN Chief Nursing Officer, Yakima Regional Medical and Cardiac Center, Yakima, WA, p. A692

WILLIAMSON, Sharon, Chief Information Technology, Robert J. Dole Veterans Affairs Medical Center, Wichita, KS, p. A256

WILLIE, David, Chief Financial Officer, Yuma Regional Medical Center, Yuma, AZ, p. A42

WILLIE, Pat, R.N. Chief Nursing Officer, Edward White Hospital, Saint Petersburg, FL, p. A144

WILLIFORD, Sandy, Chief Health Information Management and Revenue Administration, Charlie Norwood Veterans Affairs Medical Center, Augusta, GA, p. A153

WILLINGHAM, Alex, M.D. Medical Director, Post Acute/Warm Springs Rehabilitation Hospital of San Antonio, San Antonio, TX, p. A647

WILLINGHAM, John, Chief Executive Officer and Managing Director, Carolina Center for Behavioral Health, Greer, SC, p. A567

WILLIS, Bill, Director Information Technology, River Point Behavioral Health, Jacksonville, FL, p. A132

WILLIS, Brenda, Director of Nursing, Doctor's Hospital of Deer Creek, Leesville, LA, p. A283

WILLIS, Darrell, M.D. Chief of Staff, Dr. Dan C. Trigg Memorial Hospital, Tucumcari, NM, p. A431

WILLIS, Jonathon, Director Information Services, Heritage Medical Center, Shelbyville, TN, p. A593

WILLIS, Joy, Acting Chief Fiscal Service, G.V. (Sonny) Montgomery Veterans Affairs Medical Center, Jackson, MS, p. A360

WILLIS, Kathleen, R.N. Chief Nursing Officer, Hillcrest Medical Center, Tulsa, OK, p. A520

WILLIS, Kathy, M.D. Medical Director, Lallie Kemp Medical Center, Independence, LA, p. A279

WILLIS, Mona M.
Director Human Resources, Landmark Medical Center, Woonsocket, RI, p. A561
Director Human Resources, Rehabilitation Hospital of Rhode Island, North Smithfield, RI, p. A560

WILLIS, Raymond, IT Manager, Choctaw Health Center, Philadelphia, MS, p. A364

WILLIS, Sandra, Manager Human Resources, Citizens Baptist Medical Center, Talladega, AL, p. A25

WILLIS, Toni, M.D. Medical Director, Reliant Rehabilitation Hospital Mid–Cities, Bedford, TX, p. A602

WILLIS, Wendy L., Assistant Vice President Human Resources, Ochsner Medical Center – Kenner, Kenner, LA, p. A280

WILLMANN, Adam, President and Chief Executive Officer, Goodall–Witcher Hospital Authority, Clifton, TX, p. A606

WILLMON, Brian, M.D. Medical Director, Plains Regional Medical Center, Clovis, NM, p. A427

WILLMORE, Lois, Supervisor Health Information Management, Cedar County Memorial Hospital, El Dorado Springs, MO, p. A370

WILLMS, Frederick, M.D. Vice President Medical Affairs, Piedmont Fayette Hospital, Fayetteville, GA, p. A159

WILLS, Andrea, R.N. Chief Nursing Executive, Munising Memorial Hospital, Munising, MI, p. A331

WILLS, Andy, Medical Director, Colquitt Regional Medical Center, Moultrie, GA, p. A164

WILLS, Kim, Chief Operating Officer, Cook Medical Center–A Campus of Tift Regional Medical Center, Adel, GA, p. A151

WILLS, Laura S.
Administrator, Noland Hospital Birmingham, Birmingham, AL, p. A16
Administrator, Noland Hospital Shelby, Alabaster, AL, p. A15

WILLS, Michele, Registered Health Information Administrator, Caro Center, Caro, MI, p. A320

WILLS, Robert, M.D. Chief Medical Officer, Arise Austin Medical Center, Austin, TX, p. A598

WILLS, Shannon, Director Human Resources, Delray Medical Center, Delray Beach, FL, p. A127

WILLSHER, Jay
Chief Operating Officer, UnityPoint Health – Trinity Bettendorf, Bettendorf, IA, p. A225
Chief Operating Officer, UnityPoint Health – Trinity Rock Island, Rock Island, IL, p. A201

WILLSIE, Brett, Vice President Human Resources, Sentara Northern Virginia Medical Center, Woodbridge, VA, p. A680

WILLWERTH, Deborah J., MSN, Administrator, Heart of Lancaster Regional Medical Center, Lititz, PA, p. A543

WILMOT, Joan, Chief Finance Officer, White River Junction Veterans Affairs Medical Center, White River Junction, VT, p. A666

WILMOTH, Donna, Vice President Patient Care Services and Chief Nursing Officer, Sentara Williamsburg Regional Medical Center, Williamsburg, VA, p. A680

WILMS, Mike, Director Information Systems, Regional Medical Center Bayonet Point, Hudson, FL, p. A131

WILSON, Ada, R.N., Interim Administrator, Jefferson County Hospital, Fayette, MS, p. A357

WILSON, Alice, FACHE Vice President Administration, St. Luke's Hospital – Warren Campus, Phillipsburg, NJ, p. A421

WILSON, Amy, M.D. Medical Director, Baylor Institute for Rehabilitation, Dallas, TX, p. A609

WILSON, Amy, Vice President and Chief Nursing Officer, Sacred Heart Hospital of Pensacola, Pensacola, FL, p. A142

WILSON, Becky, Manager Human Resources, Allegiance Specialty Hospital of Kilgore, Kilgore, TX, p. A631

WILSON, Bill, Chief Financial Officer, North Carolina Specialty Hospital, Durham, NC, p. A463

WILSON, Bobbie, Director Human Resources, Crete Area Medical Center, Crete, NE, p. A395

WILSON, Carolyn, R.N., President, University of Minnesota Medical Center, Fairview, Minneapolis, MN, p. A348

WILSON, Charlene J., Vice President Human Resources, St. Francis Hospital, Wilmington, DE, p. A120

WILSON, Christopher, M.D. Inpatient Medical Director, South Texas Rehabilitation Hospital, Brownsville, TX, p. A604

WILSON, Christy, Chief Financial Officer, Crossgates River Oaks Hospital, Brandon, MS, p. A356

WILSON, Craig, Chief Medical Officer, St. Vincent Fishers Hospital, Fishers, IN, p. A210

WILSON, David C., President and Chief Executive Officer, Shelby Baptist Medical Center, Alabaster, AL, p. A15

WILSON, David R., M.D. Chief of Staff, St. Vincent's Blount, Oneonta, AL, p. A24

WILSON, Deanna, VP Patient Care Services/Site Manager, Aspirus Ontonagon Hospital, Ontonagon, MI, p. A331

WILSON, Deb, Director Human Resources, Kalispell Regional Medical Center, Kalispell, MT, p. A389

WILSON, Deborah J., Senior Vice President and Chief Financial Officer, Lawrence General Hospital, Lawrence, MA, p. A311

WILSON, Dottie, Director Human Resources, Pickens County Medical Center, Carrollton, AL, p. A18

WILSON, Eleanor, R.N. Vice President and Chief Operating Officer, Doylestown Hospital, Doylestown, PA, p. A537

WILSON, Elizabeth M., Coordinator Human Resources, Select Specialty Hospital – Cincinnati North, Cincinnati, OH, p. A487

WILSON, Hamlin J.
Senior Vice President Human Resources, Wellmont Bristol Regional Medical Center, Bristol, TN, p. A579
Senior Vice President Human Resources, Wellmont Holston Valley Medical Center, Kingsport, TN, p. A585

WILSON, Jason, Administrator, Valley View Medical Center, Cedar City, UT, p. A659

WILSON, Jim
Chief Operating Officer, Mary Free Bed Rehabilitation Hospital, Grand Rapids, MI, p. A325
Vice President Information Technology, Promise Hospital of San Diego, San Diego, CA, p. A89

WILSON, Jodi, President and Chief Operating Officer, Diley Ridge Medicai Center, Canal Winchester, OH, p. A485

WILSON, John P., Chief Financial Officer, Heartland Regional Medical Center, Saint Joseph, MO, p. A379

WILSON, John R., Vice President, Human Resources, Murray–Calloway County Hospital, Murray, KY, p. A268

WILSON, Kari, R.N. Vice President Clinical Services, Chief Operating Officer and Chief Nursing Officer, Audrain Medical Center, Mexico, MO, p. A376

WILSON, Kim A., R.N
Chief Operating Officer, St. John's Pleasant Valley Hospital, Camarillo, CA, p. A58
Chief Operating Officer, St. John's Regional Medical Center, Oxnard, CA, p. A82

WILSON, Kimberly P., Director Human Resources, University of Kentucky Albert B. Chandler Hospital, Lexington, KY, p. A265

WILSON, Lerae, R.N. Vice President Patient Services and Chief Nursing Officer, St. Claire Regional Medical Center, Morehead, KY, p. A268

WILSON, Lindsay, Leader Human Resources, SSM St. Clare Health Center, Fenton, MO, p. A371

WILSON, Lois, Controller, Roger Mills Memorial Hospital, Cheyenne, OK, p. A508

WILSON, Loretta, Administrator, Hill Hospital of Sumter County, York, AL, p. A27

WILSON, Mallory, Administrative Assistant and Human Resources Coordinator, Select Specialty Hospital–North Knoxville, Knoxville, TN, p. A586

WILSON, Mary L., M.D. Area Medical Director, Kaiser Permanente Panorama City Medical Center,, CA, p. A72

WILSON, Monte, Chief Operating Officer, WellStar Kennestone Hospital, Marietta, GA, p. A163

WILSON, Nancy, Senior Vice President and Chief Financial Officer, St. Francis Medical Center, Lynwood, CA, p. A76

WILSON, Nicole, Manager Human Resources, St. Theresa Specialty Hospital, Kenner, LA, p. A280

WILSON, Regina, R.N. Director of Nursing, Share Medical Center, Alva, OK, p. A507

WILSON, Robert, D.O. Director Medical Services, Eagleville Hospital, Eagleville, PA, p. A537

WILSON, Robert E.
Vice President and Chief Information Officer, Crozer–Chester Medical Center, Upland, PA, p. A556
Vice President and Chief Information Officer, Delaware County Memorial Hospital, Drexel Hill, PA, p. A537

WILSON, Roy, M.D
Medical Director, Metropolitan St. Louis Psychiatric Center, Saint Louis, MO, p. A381
Medical Director, St. Louis Psychiatric Rehabilitation Center, Saint Louis, MO, p. A382

WILSON, Sara, Director Human Resources, Cheyenne County Hospital, Saint Francis, KS, p. A253

WILSON, Sherry, R.N. Chief Nursing Officer, Mayers Memorial Hospital District, Fall River Mills, CA, p. A63

WILSON, Sondra, R.N. Chief Nursing Officer, Tyler County Hospital, Woodville, TX, p. A658

WILSON, Stephan A., Chief Financial Officer, Montrose Memorial Hospital, Montrose, CO, p. A110

WILSON, Terrance E.
President and CEO, Franciscan St. Elizabeth Health – Crawfordsville, Crawfordsville, IN, p. A209
President and CEO, Franciscan St. Elizabeth Health – Lafayette Central, Lafayette, IN, p. A216
President and CEO, Franciscan St. Elizabeth Health – Lafayette East, Lafayette, IN, p. A216

WILSON, Vicki, Human Resources Director, Dixie Regional Medical Center, Saint George, UT, p. A662

WILSON, Yolande, Chief Executive Officer, Kindred Hospital Boston–North Shore, Peabody, MA, p. A313

WILSON–NEIL, Carla, FACHE Chief Operating Officer, Pennock Hospital, Hastings, MI, p. A326

WILTERMOOD, Michael C., President and Chief Executive Officer, Enloe Medical Center, Chico, CA, p. A59

WILTROUT, Kristy, R.N. Chief Operating Officer, Vernon Memorial Healthcare, Viroqua, WI, p. A717

WIMMER, Keri, R.N. Patient Care Director, CentraCare Health–Melrose, Melrose, MN, p. A346

WIMSATT, Michael, Director Human Resources, Piedmont Geriatric Hospital, Burkeville, VA, p. A669

WINBERY, Ben, Chief Financial Officer, Vantage Point of Northwest Arkansas, Fayetteville, AR, p. A46

WINDHAM, Joel R., Director Human Resources, Trinity Medical Center, Birmingham, AL, p. A17

WINDHAM, Vann, Chief Financial Officer, L. V. Stabler Memorial Hospital, Greenville, AL, p. A21

WINDLAND, J. Michael, M.D. Chief of Staff, Southern Tennessee Regional Health System–Pulaski, Pulaski, TN, p. A592

WINDLE, Jane, R.N. Director of Nurses, North Mississippi Medical Center–West Point, West Point, MS, p. A366

WINDROW, Matthew, M.D. Chief of Staff, Medina Regional Hospital, Hondo, TX, p. A623

WINDSOR, Bonnie, Senior Vice President Human Resources, Johns Hopkins Hospital, Baltimore, MD, p. A296

WINEGARNER, Rodney, Chief Financial Officer, Mercy Hospitals of Bakersfield, Bakersfield, CA, p. A57

WINEGEART, Steve, Chief Financial Officer, Hillcrest Medical Center, Tulsa, OK, p. A520

WINENGER, John, FACHE, Interim Chief Executive Officer, Dr. John Warner Hospital, Clinton, IL, p. A187

WINFREE, Kersey, M.D. Chief Medical Officer, St. Anthony Hospital, Oklahoma City, OK, p. A516

WING, Lilly, Chief Nursing Officer, Novant Health Franklin Medical Center, Louisburg, NC, p. A468

WING, Susan M., R.N., Interim Chief Operating Officer, Falmouth Hospital, Falmouth, MA, p. A310

WING, Yakesun, Business Strategy and Finance Leader, Kaiser Permanente Walnut Creek Medical Center, Walnut Creek, CA, p. A100

WINGATE, Phyllis A., FACHE, President, Carolinas Medical Center–NorthEast, Concord, NC, p. A462

WINGET, Mary, Director Human Resources, Minden Medical Center, Minden, LA, p. A284

WINGFIELD, Gena, Senior Vice President and Chief Financial Officer, Arkansas Children's Hospital, Little Rock, AR, p. A48

WINKLE, Derek, Director Human Resources, LeConte Medical Center, Sevierville, TN, p. A592

WINKLER, Gordon W., Administrator and Chief Executive Officer, Ringgold County Hospital, Mount Ayr, IA, p. A234

WINN, Ann, M.D. Chief Nursing Officer, Methodist Stone Oak Hospital, San Antonio, TX, p. A647

WINN, George, Chief Executive Officer, Evanston Regional Hospital, Evanston, WY, p. A721

WINN, Holly, Vice President Human Resources and Ancillary Services, Black River Memorial Hospital, Black River Falls, WI, p. A702

WINN, Michael R., Director, Central Arkansas Veterans Healthcare System, Little Rock, AR, p. A49

WINN, Roger P., President, UPMC Bedford Memorial, Everett, PA, p. A539

WINNENBERG, William
Chief Information Officer, St. Charles Medical Center – Bend, Bend, OR, p. A523
Chief Information Officer, St. Charles Medical Center – Redmond, Redmond, OR, p. A529

WINNER, Douglas, Chief Financial Officer, Providence Hospital, Southfield, MI, p. A335

WINNETT, Steve, Chief Executive Officer, Victory Surgical Hospital East Houston, Houston, TX, p. A628

WINRIGHT, Donna, Director Human Resources and Senior Services, Kearny County Hospital, Lakin, KS, p. A248

WINSETT, Gracia, Chief Financial Officer, Wellstone Regional Hospital, Jeffersonville, IN, p. A215

WINSLOW, Grover C., M.D. Chief of Staff, Sabine County Hospital, Hemphill, TX, p. A623

WINSTON, Bob, M.D. Medical Director, Acadia Vermilion Hospital, Lafayette, LA, p. A281

WINT, Jesse, Director of Nursing, Hardin Medical Center, Savannah, TN, p. A592

WINTER, Jan, Chief Executive Officer, Bristow Medical Center, Bristow, OK, p. A508

WINTER, Jon R., D.O. Chief of Staff, Camden General Hospital, Camden, TN, p. A579

WINTER, Melissa, R.N. Chief Operating Officer and Chief Nursing Officer, Baylor Medical Center at McKinney, McKinney, TX, p. A637

WINTERS, Gene, Chief Financial Officer, Northwest Texas Healthcare System, Amarillo, TX, p. A596

WINTERS, Heidi, Director of Human Resources, Thayer County Health Services, Hebron, NE, p. A396

WINTERS, Janice, Controller, Pickens County Medical Center, Carrollton, AL, p. A18

WINTERS, Rob, Controller, HEALTHSOUTH Deaconess Rehabilitation Hospital, Evansville, IN, p. A210

WINTHER, Mark, M.D. Medical Director, Little Falls Hospital, Little Falls, NY, p. A440

WINTHROP, Michael, President, Bellevue Hospital, Bellevue, OH, p. A484

WIRTHGEN, Doug
Facility Chief Information Officer, Veterans Affairs Loma Linda Healthcare System, Loma Linda, CA, p. A70
Chief Information Officer, Veterans Affairs Palo Alto Health Care System, Palo Alto, CA, p. A82

WIRTZ, David
Supervisor Information Technology, Evansville Psychiatric Children Center, Evansville, IN, p. A210
Senior LAN Administrator, Evansville State Hospital, Evansville, IN, p. A210

WISCHKAEMPER, Jo Nell, Administrator and Chief Executive Officer, Lamb Healthcare Center, Littlefield, TX, p. A633

WISE, Dan, Manager Information Technology, Sarah D. Culbertson Memorial Hospital, Rushville, IL, p. A202

WISE, Elizabeth, R.N. Chief Nursing Officer and Vice President, Patient Care Services, Saint Peter's University Hospital, New Brunswick, NJ, p. A419

WISE, Gregory, M.D
Vice President Medical Affairs, Kettering Medical Center, Kettering, OH, p. A495
Vice President Medical Affairs, Sycamore Medical Center, Miamisburg, OH, p. A498

WISE, Jennifer, Chief Nursing Officer, Franklin Foundation Hospital, Franklin, LA, p. A277

WISE, Jerry, Controller, Mercy Rehabilitation Hospital, Chesterfield, MO, p. A369

WISE, Jerry R., Chief Executive Officer, Habersham Medical Center, Demorest, GA, p. A158

WISE, Kim, Director Human Resources, South Haven Health System, South Haven, MI, p. A335

WISE, Lori, Chief Nursing Officer and Director of Clinical Services, St. Vincent Jennings Hospital, North Vernon, IN, p. A220

WISE, Melissa, Chief Nursing Officer, Highland Community Hospital, Picayune, MS, p. A364

WISE, Robert P., FACHE, President and Chief Executive Officer, Hunterdon Medical Center, Flemington, NJ, p. A416

WISE, Toby, Chief Nursing Officer, Winn Parish Medical Center, Winnfield, LA, p. A290

WISEMANN, Jacob, Chief Financial Officer, Parkland Medical Center, Derry, NH, p. A409

WISEMORE, Donna S., Chief Nursing Officer Vice President, Patient Care Services, DeKalb Health, Auburn, IN, p. A206

WISLER, Tam, Director Human Resources, Dublin Springs, Dublin, OH, p. A493

WISMER, Doug, Chief Financial Officer, Putnam County Memorial Hospital, Unionville, MO, p. A384

WISNER, Donna, Chief Financial Officer, Dr. John Warner Hospital, Clinton, IL, p. A187

WISNIESKI, Thomas, FACHE,
Director, Lake City Veterans Affairs Medical Center, Lake City, FL, p. A133
Director, Malcom Randall Veterans Affairs Medical Center, Gainesville, FL, p. A129

WISNIEWSKI, Cass, Interim Chief Financial Officer, Hurley Medical Center, Flint, MI, p. A323

WISNIEWSKI, Richard, Senior Vice President Finance and Chief Financial Officer, Mount Nittany Medical Center, State College, PA, p. A555

WISNOSKI, Joseph, Vice President Finance and Chief Financial Officer, John T. Mather Memorial Hospital, Port Jefferson, NY, p. A452

WISSEL, Andrew
Director Human Resources, Mount Sinai Hospital, Chicago, IL, p. A185
Director Human Resources, Schwab Rehabilitation Hospital, Chicago, IL, p. A186

WISSLER, James, President and Chief Executive Officer, Hanover Hospital, Hanover, PA, p. A540

WISWELL, Ashleigh, Director Human Resources, Moore County Hospital District, Dumas, TX, p. A614

WITCHER–BOATENG, Bernetta, Director Quality Improvement Services and Compliance, Southwest Connecticut Mental Health System, Bridgeport, CT, p. A113

WITENSKE, James, Chief Information Officer, Jefferson Hospital, Jefferson Hills, PA, p. A541

WITHERRITE, Troy, M.D. Chief Medical Officer, Skyline Hospital, White Salmon, WA, p. A692

WITHERSPOON, Lynn, Vice President and Chief Information Officer, Ochsner Medical Center, New Orleans, LA, p. A286

WITHIAM, Cathy, Director Human Resources, McBride Clinic Orthopedic Hospital, Oklahoma City, OK, p. A515

WITHINGTON, Amber, R.N. Chief Nursing Officer, Rawlins County Health Center, Atwood, KS, p. A241

WITKOWICZ, Victor J., Senior Vice President and Chief Financial Officer, Madonna Rehabilitation Hospital, Lincoln, NE, p. A398

WITMER, Bruce, M.D. Medical Director, Fresno Surgical Hospital, Fresno, CA, p. A64

WITT, David A., Vice President Finances, Houston Methodist St. John Hospital, Nassau Bay, TX, p. A639

WITT, James, Interim Chief Executive Officer, Westside Surgical Hospital, Houston, TX, p. A628

WITT, Jana, Chief Executive Officer, Cedar County Memorial Hospital, El Dorado Springs, MO, p. A370

WITT, Laura, Administrator Human Resources, Banner Thunderbird Medical Center, Glendale, AZ, p. A33

WITT, Lori, Site Finance Director, Marcum and Wallace Memorial Hospital, Irvine, KY, p. A263

WITT, Michelle, Administrator, CCC at PineView Hospital, Lakeside, AZ, p. A34

WITT, Sarah, Director Human Resources, Richmond State Hospital, Richmond, IN, p. A222

WITT, Stephen, President and Chief Executive Officer, College Hospital Cerritos, Cerritos, CA, p. A59

WITT, Thomas J., M.D.,
President and Chief Executive Officer, Mayo Clinic Health System in Cannon Falls, Cannon Falls, MN, p. A341
President and Chief Executive Officer, Mayo Clinic Health System in Red Wing, Red Wing, MN, p. A350

WITTE, Kari, Director Patient Care, Windom Area Hospital, Windom, MN, p. A354

WITTERSTAETER, Ellen, FACHE, Chief Executive Officer, HEALTHSOUTH Rehabilitation Hospital of Ocala, Ocala, FL, p. A139

WITTHAUS, Patricia, Director Information Services, Valley Regional Hospital, Claremont, NH, p. A409

WITTMAN, Thomas, Chief Information Officer, Jewish Hospital, Louisville, KY, p. A265

WITTON, David, Manager Information Systems, St. John's Medical Center and Living Center, Jackson, WY, p. A721

WITTROCK, Edward A., Vice President Regional System, Mayo Clinic Health System – Chippewa Valley in Bloomer, Bloomer, WI, p. A702

WITTWER, Julie, Chief Financial Officer, South Texas Surgical Hospital, Corpus Christi, TX, p. A608

WODARZ, Christopher A., Chief, Resource Management Division, Tripler Army Medical Center, Honolulu, HI, p. A171

WODICKA, Mary Jo, Vice President Human Resources, Wheaton Franciscan Healthcare – All Saints, Racine, WI, p. A714

WOELKERS, Joe, Executive Vice President and Chief Staff, University of Texas Health Science Center at Tyler, Tyler, TX, p. A654

WOELTJEN, Bill, Chief Financial Officer, Sarasota Memorial Health Care System, Sarasota, FL, p. A145

WOEN, Linda, Director Human Resources, Yuma Rehabilitation Hospital, Yuma, AZ, p. A42

WOERNER, Steve, President and Chief Executive Officer, Driscoll Children's Hospital, Corpus Christi, TX, p. A608

WOHLFARDT, Diana, Director Human Resources, Nashville General Hospital, Nashville, TN, p. A590

WOHLFORD, Steve, Chief Operating Officer, Johnson Memorial Hospital, Franklin, IN, p. A212

WOHLMAN, John, Manager Information Systems, Shoshone Medical Center, Kellogg, ID, p. A176

WOIRHAYE, Ted, R.N. Director of Nursing, Ruby Valley Hospital, Sheridan, MT, p. A391

WOISKE, Edward, M.D. Chief Medical Officer, Avera Marshall Regional Medical Center, Marshall, MN, p. A346

WOJNO, Kathy, Vice President Nursing Services and Chief Nursing Officer, Beverly Hospital, Montebello, CA, p. A78

WOJTALEWICZ, Jeanette, Chief Financial Officer, CHI Health Mercy Council Bluffs, Council Bluffs, IA, p. A228

WOLAK, Robert, Chief Information Resource Management Service, G.V. (Sonny) Montgomery Veterans Affairs Medical Center, Jackson, MS, p. A360

WOLBERS, Chad, Chief Operating Officer, UnityPoint Health – Finley Hospital, Dubuque, IA, p. A230

WOLCOTT, Daniel, President, Takoma Regional Hospital, Greeneville, TN, p. A583

WOLD, Lynn, Chief Operation Officer, UnityPoint Health – St. Luke's, Sioux City, IA, p. A238

WOLF, Brenda J., President and Chief Executive Officer, La Rabida Children's Hospital, Chicago, IL, p. A184

WOLF, Bryan, M.D. Senior Vice President and Chief Information Officer, Children's Hospital of Philadelphia, Philadelphia, PA, p. A547

WOLF, Edward H., President and Chief Executive Officer, Lakeview Medical Center, Rice Lake, WI, p. A714

WOLF, Gregory A., Director Information Systems, Shriners Hospitals for Children–Honolulu, Honolulu, HI, p. A171

WOLF, Jack, Vice President Information Systems, Montefiore Medical Center,, NY, p. A446

WOLF, Laura J., President, Franciscan Sisters of Christian Charity Sponsored Ministries, Inc., Manitowoc, WI, p. B60

WOLF, Manuela, R.N., Chief Executive Officer, Harlan County Health System, Alma, NE, p. A393

WOLF, Marc, Assistant Vice President Human Resources, St. Barnabas Hospital,, NY, p. A448

WOLF, R. Chris, Chief Executive Officer, Alta Vista Regional Hospital, Las Vegas, NM, p. A429

WOLF, Randall, Vice President Finance, Perry County Memorial Hospital, Perryville, MO, p. A378

WOLF, Robin, Chief Nursing Officer, Complex Care Hospital at Tenaya, Las Vegas, NV, p. A405

WOLF, Scott A., D.O. Senior Vice President, Medical Affairs, Chief Medical Officer and Chief Operating Officer, Mercy Medical Center, Springfield, MA, p. A315

WOLF, Stephanne, Chief Nursing Officer, Morris County Hospital, Council Grove, KS, p. A243

WOLF, Tricia, Director Information Technology, OSS Orthopaedic Specialty Hospital, York, PA, p. A559

WOLF-ROSENBLUM, Stephanie, M.D. Chief Medical Officer, Southern New Hampshire Medical Center, Nashua, NH, p. A411

WOLFE, Cathy Allyson, Chief Nursing Officer, Wabash County Hospital, Wabash, IN, p. A224

WOLFE, John, Chief Financial Officer, Saint Elizabeth's Medical Center, Wabasha, MN, p. A353

WOLFE, Judy, Chief Executive Officer, Christus Dubuis Hospital of Bryan, Bryan, TX, p. A604

WOLFE, Kari, M.D. Medical Director, Seton Shoal Creek Hospital, Austin, TX, p. A600

WOLFE, Lois, Director Human Resources, Geisinger–Community Medical Center, Scranton, PA, p. A554

WOLFE, Mitchell, M.D. Chief of Staff, Clay County Memorial Hospital, Henrietta, TX, p. A623

WOLFE, Philip R., President and Chief Executive Officer, Gwinnett Hospital System, Lawrenceville, GA, p. A162

WOLFE, Phillip R., Administrator, Kindred Hospital–Los Angeles, Los Angeles, CA, p. A73

WOLFE, Scott R., CPA, President, St. Luke's Hospital – Warren Campus, Phillipsburg, NJ, p. A421

WOLFE, Stephen A., President and Chief Executive Officer, Indiana Regional Medical Center, Indiana, PA, p. A541

WOLFE, Teresa E., Manager Human Resources, Kansas Heart Hospital, Wichita, KS, p. A256

WOLFENBARGER, Carol C., R.N. Chief Nursing Officer, Tennova Healthcare–Jefferson Memorial Hospital, Jefferson City, TN, p. A584

WOLFF, Barbara Jo, Chief Financial Officer, Bakersfield Heart Hospital, Bakersfield, CA, p. A56

WOLFF, Cathy, Vice President Financial Services and Chief Financial Officer, Yuma District Hospital, Yuma, CO, p. A112

WOLFF, David, Director Information Technology, Newberry County Memorial Hospital, Newberry, SC, p. A569

WOLFF, Ellen, R.N
Chief Nursing Officer and Senior Vice President Patient Care Services, Franklin Regional Hospital, Franklin, NH, p. A410
Chief Nursing Officer/Senior VP/Patient Care Services, Lakes Region General Hospital, Laconia, NH, p. A410

WOLFF, Patrice P.
Director Management Information Systems, Amery Regional Medical Center, Amery, WI, p. A701
Director Information Services, Westfields Hospital, New Richmond, WI, p. A712

WOLFGANG, Tony, Chief Financial Officer, Coatesville Veterans Affairs Medical Center, Coatesville, PA, p. A536

WOLFMAN, Barry A., Chief Executive Officer and Managing Director, George Washington University Hospital, Washington, DC, p. A121

WOLFORD, Dennis A., FACHE, Chief Executive Officer, Macon County General Hospital, Lafayette, TN, p. A586

WOLIN, Harry, Administrator and Chief Executive Officer, Mason District Hospital, Havana, IL, p. A192

WOLKART, Kristin, Chief Operating Officer, St. Francis Medical Center, Monroe, LA, p. A284

WOLLEN, Allison, Vice President Human Resources, Rutland Regional Medical Center, Rutland, VT, p. A666

WOLOSZYN, Daniel B., Chief Executive Officer, Rehabilitation Hospital of Indiana, Indianapolis, IN, p. A214

WOLTEMATH, Kelli, D.O. Chief Medical Staff, George C Grape Community Hospital, Hamburg, IA, p. A231

WOLTER, Nicholas, M.D., Chief Executive Officer, Billings Clinic, Billings, MT, p. A385

WOLTERMAN, Daniel J., President and Chief Executive Officer, Memorial Hermann Healthcare System, Houston, TX, p. B91

WOLTERMAN, Robert K., Chief Executive Officer, Ochsner Medical Center, New Orleans, LA, p. A286

WOLTHER, Eunice, Public Information Officer, Colorado Mental Health Institute at Pueblo, Pueblo, CO, p. A110

WOLTHUIZEN, Dianne, Director Human Resources, Sanford Sheldon Medical Center, Sheldon, IA, p. A237

WOLZ, John, M.D. Chief Medical Staff, Yuma District Hospital, Yuma, CO, p. A112

WOMEODU, Robin, M.D. Chief Medical Officer, Methodist Healthcare Memphis Hospitals, Memphis, TN, p. A589

WONG, Art, Chief Financial Officer, Heritage Oaks Hospital, Sacramento, CA, p. A87

WONG, Bryan, M.D. Medical Director, Ventura County Medical Center, Ventura, CA, p. A99

WONG, Davies, M.D. Medical Director, Kindred Hospital–San Diego, San Diego, CA, p. A89

WONG, Dionne, Vice President and Chief Human Resources Officer, Broward Health Medical Center, Fort Lauderdale, FL, p. A128

WONG, Howard, Chief of Staff, North Hawaii Community Hospital, Kamuela, HI, p. A171

WONG, Karen, Chief Human Resources Officer, Mee Memorial Hospital, King City, CA, p. A68

WONG, Wesley, M.D. Acting Vice President Medical and Academic Affairs, Community Hospital North, Indianapolis, IN, p. A213

WONSER, Matt, Director, Information Services, Providence Regional Medical Center Everett, Everett, WA, p. A683

WOOD, Aaron, Administrator, Sanpete Valley Hospital, Mount Pleasant, UT, p. A660

WOOD, Brian, Director Human Resources, Southern Hills Hospital and Medical Center, Las Vegas, NV, p. A406

WOOD, Bud, Chief Human Resources Officer, Saint Thomas West Hospital, Nashville, TN, p. A590

WOOD, Cathy, Vice President, Human Resources, Memorial Hospital at Gulfport, Gulfport, MS, p. A358

WOOD, Clyde, Chief Executive Officer, Lakeway Regional Hospital, Morristown, TN, p. A590

WOOD, David, M.D. Executive Vice President and Chief Medical Officer, Beaumont Hospital – Royal Oak, Royal Oak, MI, p. A333

WOOD, David P., FACHE, Director, Boise Veterans Affairs Medical Center, Boise, ID, p. A174

WOOD, Debbie, Vice President Human Resources, Kaweah Delta Medical Center, Visalia, CA, p. A99

WOOD, Drew, Director Information Technology, Eureka Springs Hospital, Eureka Springs, AR, p. A45

WOOD, Erik, Chief Executive Officer, Pioneer Medical Center, Big Timber, MT, p. A385

WOOD, Gerry, Information Technologist, Kalamazoo Psychiatric Hospital, Kalamazoo, MI, p. A328

WOOD, Gregory C., President and Chief Executive Officer, Scotland Health Care System, Laurinburg, NC, p. A468

WOOD, Jim
Chief Human Resources Officer, Central Washington Hospital, Wenatchee, WA, p. A692
Chief Human Resources Officer, Wenatchee Valley Medical Center, Wenatchee, WA, p. A692

WOOD, Joann, M.D. Chief Medical Officer, Baptist Memorial Hospital–Desoto, Southaven, MS, p. A365

WOOD, John
Chief Executive Officer, Baylor Emergency Medical Center at Aubrey, Aubrey, TX, p. A598
Administrator, Scott & White Emergency Hospital– Cedar Park, Cedar Park, TX, p. A606

WOOD, Joyce, Vice President Organizational Improvement and Chief Nursing Officer, Riverview Hospital, Noblesville, IN, p. A220

WOOD, Kenneth W., Interim President, Sentara Albemarle Medical Center, Elizabeth City, NC, p. A464

WOOD, Kevin, Interim Chief Clinical Officer, Promise Hospital of San Diego, San Diego, CA, p. A89

WOOD, Lawrence, M.D. Chief Medical Officer, Littleton Adventist Hospital, Littleton, CO, p. A109

WOOD, Michael K., M.D. Chief Medical Officer, Mills–Peninsula Health Services, Burlingame, CA, p. A58

WOOD, Jr., Phillip C., Chief Information Officer, Cape Fear Valley Medical Center, Fayetteville, NC, p. A464

WOOD, Rachel, Chief Nursing Officer, Crawley Memorial Hospital, Shelby, NC, p. A472

WOOD, Richard, Chief Financial Officer, Seton Medical Center, Daly City, CA, p. A61

WOOD, Sandy, Chief Clinical Officer, OhioHealth Doctors Hospital Nelsonville, Nelsonville, OH, p. A499

WOOD, Thomas, M.D. Chief Medical Officer, Page Hospital, Page, AZ, p. A35

WOOD, Tina, Chief Financial Officer, DMC Harper University Hospital, Detroit, MI, p. A322

WOOD, William, M.D. Vice President Medical Affairs, St. Joseph Hospital, Bangor, ME, p. A291

WOOD, William E., M.D. Chief of Staff, Sequoyah Memorial Hospital, Sallisaw, OK, p. A518

WOOD–ALLEN, Diane, MS Chief Nursing Officer, Concord Hospital, Concord, NH, p. A409

WOODALL, Jay, Chief Executive Officer, Corpus Christi Medical Center, Corpus Christi, TX, p. A608

WOODALL, Lois, Director Human Resources, Lighthouse Care Center of Conway, Conway, SC, p. A565

WOODARD, Andy, Chief Financial Officer, Forrest General Hospital, Hattiesburg, MS, p. A359

WOODARD, Cathy, R.N. Chief Clinical Officer, Victory Medical Center Craig Ranch, McKinney, TX, p. A637

WOODARD, Victor, Manager Information Technology, Dodge County Hospital, Eastman, GA, p. A159

WOODBECK, Terry L., Administrator, Tulsa Spine and Specialty Hospital, Tulsa, OK, p. A521

WOODBY, Karla, R.N. Director of Nursing, Siskin Hospital for Physical Rehabilitation, Chattanooga, TN, p. A580

WOODDELL, Mike, Director Information Services, Fairmont General Hospital, Fairmont, WV, p. A695

WOODHOUSE, Janice, Director of Nursing, Missouri River Medical Center, Fort Benton, MT, p. A387

WOODIN, Joseph L., President and Chief Executive Officer, Gifford Medical Center, Randolph, VT, p. A666

WOODLIFF, Brian K., President and Chief Executive Officer Northeastern Health System, Northeastern Health System, Tahlequah, OK, p. A519

WOODLOCK, Kristin M., R.N., Acting Commissioner, New York State Office of Mental Health, Albany, NY, p. B99

WOODRICH, John T., President and Chief Operating Officer, Bryan Medical Center, Lincoln, NE, p. A397

WOODRUFF, Kathy, R.N. Chief Nursing Officer, Marshall Medical Center North, Guntersville, AL, p. A21

WOODRUFF, Stephen, M.D. Chief Medical Officer, NEA Baptist Memorial Hospital, Jonesboro, AR, p. A48

WOODS, Bob, Chief Information Officer, ValleyCare Medical Center, Pleasanton, CA, p. A83

WOODS, Brian, Director Human Resources, Stones River Hospital, Woodbury, TN, p. A594

WOODS, Cheryl, Chief Nursing Officer, Ochsner Medical Center – North Shore, Slidell, LA, p. A289

WOODS, Dan, President, WellStar Kennestone Hospital, Marietta, GA, p. A163

WOODS, Jr., Duane L., Chief Financial Officer, Fisher–Titus Medical Center, Norwalk, OH, p. A500

WOODS, Fred, Chief Financial Officer, The BridgeWay, North Little Rock, AR, p. A51

WOODS, Jeffrey, Chief Executive Officer, TrustPoint Hospital, Murfreesboro, TN, p. A590

WOODS, Jennifer, R.N. Chief Nursing Officer, McLaren Northern Michigan, Petoskey, MI, p. A332

WOODS, Josh, Director Information Systems, Camden Clark Medical Center, Parkersburg, WV, p. A698

WOODS, Julia, R.N. Vice President and Chief Nursing Officer, Saint Luke's South Hospital, Overland Park, KS, p. A252

WOODS, Matthew, Executive Vice President Finance and Chief Financial Officer, Winchester Hospital, Winchester, MA, p. A316

WURM, Scott, M.D. Chief Medical Officer, St. Cloud Regional Medical Center, Saint Cloud, FL, p. A144

WURTZEL, Leann, Director Human Resources, Mayo Clinic Health System – Red Cedar in Menomonie, Menomonie, WI, p. A709

WURZBURGER, Kristen, M.D. Chief of Staff, Genesis Medical Center–Aledo, Aledo, IL, p. A180

WYACO, Melissa, Chief Nurse Executive, Hopi Health Care Center, Kearns Canyon, AZ, p. A33

WYATT, Basil, Chief Financial Officer, AMG Specialty Hospital–Tulsa, Tulsa, OK, p. A520

WYATT, Charles, M.D. Medical Director, Regional Medical Center of Acadiana, Lafayette, LA, p. A282

WYATT, Jana, Chief Executive Officer, Mizell Memorial Hospital, Opp, AL, p. A24

WYATT, Leslie G., Senior Vice President Children's Services and Executive Director, Children's Hospital of Richmond at VCU–Brook Road Campus, Richmond, VA, p. A677

WYATT, Robert, M.D. Chief Medical Officer, Forest Park Medical Center Frisco, Frisco, TX, p. A620

WYDICK, Sue, Director Human Resources, Ohio County Hospital, Hartford, KY, p. A262

WYDRA, Lana, Vice President Human Resources, Nathan Littauer Hospital and Nursing Home, Gloversville, NY, p. A438

WYERS, Michael, Chief Financial Officer, Medical Center of Trinity, Trinity, FL, p. A149

WYLES, Rick, Chief Financial Officer, McLaren Flint, Flint, MI, p. A323

WYLIE, Eugene, Chief Human Resources Officer, Veterans Affairs Loma Linda Healthcare System, Loma Linda, CA, p. A70

WYLIE, Jamie–Crystal, Chief Executive Officer, East Texas Medical Center–Mount Vernon, Mount Vernon, TX, p. A638

WYLIE, Matthew, Administrator, East Texas Medical Center Clarksville, Clarksville, TX, p. A606

WYLIE, Patrick, Director Information Systems, Petaluma Valley Hospital, Petaluma, CA, p. A83

WYMAN, Alan, Chief Information Officer, Providence Hospital, Washington, DC, p. A121

WYMER, Melanie, Director Human Resources, Highland District Hospital, Hillsboro, OH, p. A495

WYNES, Jim Bob, Director Human Resources, Southwest Memorial Hospital, Cortez, CO, p. A104

WYNN, Katherine, Director Human Resource, Oklahoma Heart Hospital, Oklahoma City, OK, p. A516

WYNN, Paige, Chief Financial Officer, Dorminy Medical Center, Fitzgerald, GA, p. A159

WYSE, LaMar L., Chief Operating Officer, OhioHealth Doctors Hospital Nelsonville, Nelsonville, OH, p. A499

WYSOCKI, Greg, Chief Financial Officer, Austin Lakes Hospital, Austin, TX, p. A599

WYSONG–HARDER, Alyson, Chief Executive Officer, Heartland Behavioral Health Services, Nevada, MO, p. A377

X

XAOCHAY, Billy, Manager Information Technology, Blue Mountain Hospital, Blanding, UT, p. A659

XINIS, James J., President and Chief Executive Officer, Calvert Memorial Hospital, Prince Frederick, MD, p. A302

Y

YABLONKA, Eric, Vice President and Chief Information Officer, University of Chicago Medical Center, Chicago, IL, p. A187

YABUT, Eduardo, M.D. Medical Director, North Dakota State Hospital, Jamestown, ND, p. A479

YAEGER, Eric, M.D
  Chief Medical Officer, Kindred Hospital–Aurora, Aurora, CO, p. A102
  Medical Director, Kindred Hospital–Denver, Denver, CO, p. A104

YAHNER, Michael, Chief Financial Officer, Torrance State Hospital, Torrance, PA, p. A556

YAHYA, Zuhair, M.D. Chief Medical Officer, San Dimas Community Hospital, San Dimas, CA, p. A90

YAKLIN, Shelleye, President and Chief Executive Officer, North Ottawa Community Hospital, Grand Haven, MI, p. A324

YAMADA, Brian, Interim Area Finance Officer, Kaiser Permanente Antioch Medical Center, Antioch, CA, p. A55

YAMADA, Chrissy, CPA Senior Vice President Finance, EvergreenHealth, Kirkland, WA, p. A684

YAMADA, Jeff, Vice President, Yakima Valley Memorial Hospital, Yakima, WA, p. A692

YAMAKAWA, Mark, Chief Operating Officer, Queen's Medical Center, Honolulu, HI, p. A171

YANAI, Christopher, Warden and Chief Executive Officer, Oakwood Correctional Facility, Lima, OH, p. A496

YANCY, Daniel, Administrator and Chief Executive Officer, Winnie Community Hospital, Winnie, TX, p. A658

YANDOW, Suzanne, M.D. Chief of Staff, Shriners Hospitals for Children–Salt Lake City, Salt Lake City, UT, p. A663

YANES, John C., Chief Executive Officer, Select Specialty Hospital–Columbus, Columbus, OH, p. A491

YANEZ, Maria J., Chief Financial Officer, Baptist Health South Florida, Doctors Hospital, Coral Gables, FL, p. A126

YANNI, Anthony, M.D. Vice President Medical Affairs, Regional Hospital of Scranton, Scranton, PA, p. A554

YANNI, Jason, Senior Financial Analyst, Novant Health Huntersville Medical Center, Huntersville, NC, p. A467

YAP, Eric, Chief Executive Officer, OhioHealth Rehabilitation Hospital, Columbus, OH, p. A490

YARBOROUGH, Dianne, Director of Information Technology, Centennial Medical Center, Frisco, TX, p. A620

YARBOROUGH, James, FACHE, Chief Executive Officer, Elbert Memorial Hospital, Elberton, GA, p. A159

YARBROUGH, Lance, M.D. Chief of Medical Staff, Atoka County Medical Center, Atoka, OK, p. A508

YARLING, John, M.D. Medical Director, Four County Counseling Center, Logansport, IN, p. A217

YARMEL, Jeffrey N., Chief Operating Officer, St. Mary Medical Center, Langhorne, PA, p. A542

YARN, Jayce, Director Information Technology, Marias Medical Center, Shelby, MT, p. A391

YAROCH, Julie, D.O., President and Chief Executive Officer, ProMedica Defiance Regional Hospital, Defiance, OH, p. A492

YAROCH, Julie, D.O. Vice President Medical Affairs, ProMedica Herrick Hospital, Tecumseh, MI, p. A336

YARRAMSETTI, Sri, Chief Information Officer, Chapman Medical Center, Orange, CA, p. A81

YASKO, Joyce M., Ph.D. Chief Operating Officer, Roswell Park Cancer Institute, Buffalo, NY, p. A434

YATES, Ann C., R.N. Director Patient Care and Clinical Services, St. Vincent Mercy Hospital, Elwood, IN, p. A210

YATES, Brian, Administrator, Novant Health Gaffney Medical Center, Gaffney, SC, p. A566

YATES, Jackie, R.N. Nurse Executive, Mississippi State Hospital, Whitfield, MS, p. A366

YATES, Randy, M.D. Chief Medical Officer, Straub Clinic & Hospital, Honolulu, HI, p. A171

YATSATTIE, Clyde, Administrative Officer, U. S. Public Health Service Indian Hospital, Zuni, NM, p. A431

YAWN, Julia K., MSN Chief Nursing Officer and Vice President for Patient Care and Services, Regional Medical Center, Orangeburg, SC, p. A569

YAWORSKY, Jason
  Chief Information Officer, Bradford Regional Medical Center, Bradford, PA, p. A534
  Senior Vice President Information Systems and Chief Information Officer, Olean General Hospital, Olean, NY, p. A450

YAZAWA, Albert, M.D. Regional Medical Director, Leahi Hospital, Honolulu, HI, p. A170

YBARRA, Farra, R.N. Chief Nursing Officer, Coal County General Hospital, Coalgate, OK, p. A509

YEAGER, Angela, Director Information Technology, Palacios Community Medical Center, Palacios, TX, p. A640

YEAGER, David, Vice President Finance, Aurora Medical Center, Kenosha, WI, p. A707

YEAGER, Dianne, Chief Executive Officer, Crane Memorial Hospital, Crane, TX, p. A608

YEAGER, Kevin, Vice President Fiscal Services, Holzer Medical Center – Jackson, Jackson, OH, p. A495

YEARWOOD, Janice, Director Human Resources, W. J. Mangold Memorial Hospital, Lockney, TX, p. A634

YEASTED, G. Alan, M.D. Senior Vice President and Chief Medical Officer, St. Clair Hospital, Pittsburgh, PA, p. A551

YEATES, Alan H., Vice President Fiscal Services, Wyandot Memorial Hospital, Upper Sandusky, OH, p. A503

YEATES, Diane, Chief Operating Officer, Terrebonne General Medical Center, Houma, LA, p. A279

YEATS, Melanie, M.D. Vice President Medical Affairs, San Juan Regional Medical Center, Farmington, NM, p. A428

YEBOAH, Ben, Chief Clinical Officer, Vibra Hospital of Springfield, Springfield, IL, p. A203

YECNY, Rick, Chief Executive Officer and Chief Mission Officer, PeaceHealth Peace Harbor Medical Center, Florence, OR, p. A524

YEE, Brenda, MSN, Chief Executive Officer, Chinese Hospital, San Francisco, CA, p. A90

YEE, Jr., Hal F., M.D. Interim Chief Medical Officer, LAC/University of Southern California Medical Center, Los Angeles, CA, p. A73

YEE, Martin, M.D. Medical Director, HEALTHSOUTH East Valley Rehabilitation Hospital, Mesa, AZ, p. A34

YEH, Ada, R.N. Chief Operating Officer and Chief Nursing Officer, Chapman Medical Center, Orange, CA, p. A81

YEHL, Warren, Chief Operating Officer, Eastern New Mexico Medical Center, Roswell, NM, p. A430

YEHLEN, Lorraine, R.N
  Vice President Patient Care Services, DCH Regional Medical Center, Tuscaloosa, AL, p. A26
  Chief Nursing Officer, Northport Medical Center, Northport, AL, p. A24

YELTON, Gene, Director Support Services, Keystone Newport News, Newport News, VA, p. A674

YETMAN, Robert, M.D. Medical Director, Healthbridge Children's Hospital of Houston, Houston, TX, p. A624

YETTER, Tad A., M.D. President Medical Staff, Mason District Hospital, Havana, IL, p. A192

YEUNG, Christopher A., M.D. Chief of Staff, The Surgical Hospital of Phoenix, Phoenix, AZ, p. A37

YEUNG, Diem, M.D. Medical Director, HEALTHSOUTH Rehabilitation of Gadsden, Gadsden, AL, p. A20

YHLEN, David, Chief Operating Officer, Inspira Medical Center–Elmer, Elmer, NJ, p. A416

YI, Brenda, Director Medical Resource Management and Chief Financial Officer, U. S. Air Force Medical Center Keesler, Keesler AFB, MS, p. A360

YIM, Janet, Director Information Services, St. Mary Mercy Hospital, Livonia, MI, p. A329

YINGLING, Barbara, R.N. Vice President Patient Care Services and Chief Nursing Officer, Mercy Medical Center, Canton, OH, p. A485

YINGLING, Regina, Supervisor, Sandhills Regional Medical Center, Hamlet, NC, p. A466

YITTA, Prasad, M.D. Medical Director, River Hospital, Alexandria Bay, NY, p. A432

YOAKUM, Jerrie, Director Human Resources, Ilano Specialty Hospital of Lubbock, Lubbock, TX, p. A635

YOCHELSON, Michael R., M.D. Vice President and Medical Director, MedStar National Rehabilitation Hospital, Washington, DC, p. A121

YOCHUM, Richard E., President and Chief Executive Officer, Pomona Valley Hospital Medical Center, Pomona, CA, p. A84

YODER, Cathy
  Chief Financial Officer, South Florida Baptist Hospital, Plant City, FL, p. A143
  Chief Financial Officer, St. Joseph's Hospital, Tampa, FL, p. A148

YON, Robin, Site Finance Director, Mercy Health – Fairfield Hospital, Fairfield, OH, p. A493

YOO, George, M.D. Chief Medical Officer, Karmanos Cancer Center, Detroit, MI, p. A322

YOON, Chris, M.D. Medical Director, HEALTHSOUTH Bakersfield Rehabilitation Hospital, Bakersfield, CA, p. A57

YORDY, Alan R., President and Chief Mission Officer, PeaceHealth, Vancouver, WA, p. B105

YORK, Ana, Coordinator Human Resources and Benefits, Harlan County Health System, Alma, NE, p. A393

YORK, Christopher, FACHE, President, Baylor Medical Center at Waxahachie, Waxahachie, TX, p. A656

YORK, Don, Vice President Human Resources, Sky Lakes Medical Center, Klamath Falls, OR, p. A526

YORK, Jack
  Chief Information Officer, Pioneer Community Hospital of Newton, Newton, MS, p. A363
  Chief Information Officer, Pioneer Community Hospital of Stokes, Danbury, NC, p. A463

YORK, Linda, Manager Human Resources, Memorial Hospital of Converse County, Douglas, WY, p. A721

YORK, Russell W.
  Chief Financial Officer, Mississippi Baptist Medical Center, Jackson, MS, p. A360
  Vice President and Chief Financial Officer, Mississippi Hospital for Restorative Care, Jackson, MS, p. A360

YOSHII, Brian, Vice President Information Technology, Kaiser Permanente Medical Center, Honolulu, HI, p. A170

YOSKO, Kathleen C., President and Chief Executive Officer, Marianjoy Rehabilitation Hospital, Wheaton, IL, p. A205

YOST, Carla J., R.N. Administrator Operations, Mercy Regional Health Center,, KS, p. A249

YOUMANS, Kevin, Interim President, Genesis Medical Center, Illini Campus, Silvis, IL, p. A202

YOUNG, Aaron, Director Information Technology Services, Mary Lanning Healthcare, Hastings, NE, p. A396

YOUNG, Abby, Chief Nursing Officer, Iowa Specialty Hospital–Clarion, Clarion, IA, p. A227

YOUNG, Angela, Human Resources Officer, Chillicothe Veterans Affairs Medical Center, Chillicothe, OH, p. A486

Z

ZEITLER, Irvin, D.O. Vice President Medical Affairs, Shannon Medical Center, San Angelo, TX, p. A645

ZEITLER, Jenny, Network Administrator, North Okaloosa Medical Center, Crestview, FL, p. A126

ZELENKA, Anthony, President and Chief Operating Officer, Berkeley Medical Center, Martinsburg, WV, p. A697

ZELIN, Mira, D.O. Medical Director, HEALTHSOUTH Rehabilitation Hospital of Spring Hill, Brooksville, FL, p. A125

ZELINSKI, Barbara C., Chief Operating Officer, Kaiser Permanente Panorama City Medical Center,, CA, p. A72

ZELL, John R., Chief Financial Officer, OSF St. Joseph Medical Center, Bloomington, IL, p. A181

ZELLER, April, Director Nursing, Holton Community Hospital, Holton, KS, p. A245

ZELLER, Brad, Vice President Operations, Hayward Area Memorial Hospital and Nursing Home, Hayward, WI, p. A706

ZELLER, Clifford, M.D. Chief Medical Officer, Banner Behavioral Health Hospital – Scottsdale, Scottsdale, AZ, p. A38

ZELLER, Paul, Vice President Human Resources, MedStar Southern Maryland Hospital Center, Clinton, MD, p. A300

ZELLER, Sonya, R.N. Vice President, Chief Operating Officer and Chief Nursing Officer, Indiana University Health Paoli Hospital, Paoli, IN, p. A221

ZEMAN, Brian, Chief Human Resources, Salem Veterans Affairs Medical Center, Salem, VA, p. A678

ZENDER, Dale, Regional Vice President Finance and Chief Financial Officer, PeaceHealth St. Joseph Medical Center, Bellingham, WA, p. A681

ZENGOTITA, Jamie, M.D. Chief Medical Staff, Mercy Hospital Cassville, Cassville, MO, p. A369

ZENK, Ann, Vice President Patient Care Services, Ministry Saint Mary's Hospitals, Rhinelander, WI, p. A714

ZENTY III,, Thomas F., President and Chief Executive Officer, University Hospitals, Cleveland, OH, p. B144

ZEOLI, Diane, Chief Executive Officer, Kindred Hospital–Brea, Brea, CA, p. A58

ZEPHIER, Michelle, Human Resource Specialist, U. S. Public Health Service Indian Hospital, Rosebud, SD, p. A576

ZEPS, Joseph, Vice President Finance, Tomah Memorial Hospital, Tomah, WI, p. A716

ZERINGUE, Christopher, Chief Operating Officer, Starr Regional Medical Center–Etowah, Etowah, TN, p. A582

ZERINGUE, Rhonda, Chief Nursing Officer, St. James Parish Hospital, Lutcher, LA, p. A283

ZEROSKE, Joanne, President, Marymount Hospital, Garfield Heights, OH, p. A494

ZERRER, Lana, M.D. Chief of Staff, Harry S. Truman Memorial Veterans Hospital, Columbia, MO, p. A370

ZETTER, David, M.D. Chief of Staff, Jackson Purchase Medical Center, Mayfield, KY, p. A267

ZEVENBERGEN, Glenn, Chief Executive Officer, Hegg Memorial Health Center Avera, Rock Valley, IA, p. A237

ZEWE, Jeff S., R.N
  Senior Vice President Patient Care and Chief Nursing Officer, Bradford Regional Medical Center, Bradford, PA, p. A534
  Vice President Patient Care Services and Chief Nursing Officer, Olean General Hospital, Olean, NY, p. A450

ZHIRKIN, Georgii, Chief Financial Officer, Community Mental Health Center, Lawrenceburg, IN, p. A217

ZIA, Michael, M.D. Vice President Quality Systems and Medical Affairs, Decatur Memorial Hospital, Decatur, IL, p. A188

ZICHAL, Frances J., Chief Executive Officer, Central Community Hospital, Elkader, IA, p. A230

ZIDANSEK, John A., President and Chief Executive Officer, Easton Hospital, Easton, PA, p. A538

ZIEGLER, Derick, Administrator and Chief Executive Officer, Baptist Memorial Hospital – Memphis, Memphis, TN, p. A588

ZIEGLER, John C., FACHE Vice President Human Resources, Memorial Hospital, Belleville, IL, p. A181

ZIEGLER, Peter, M.D. Acting Chief Medical Officer, U. S. Public Health Service Indian Hospital–Sells, Sells, AZ, p. A39

ZIELAZINSKI, Mark, Chief Information and Technology Integration Officer, Marin General Hospital, Greenbrae, CA, p. A66

ZIELINSKI, Dennis G., Chief Executive Officer and Administrator, Coquille Valley Hospital, Coquille, OR, p. A524

ZIELINSKI, Sharon
  Manager Health Information, HEALTHSOUTH Rehabilitation Hospital of Erie, Erie, PA, p. A538
  Chief Information Resource Officer, Veterans Affairs Maryland Health Care System–Baltimore Division, Baltimore, MD, p. A298

ZIEMBA, Mike, Information Technology Project Lead, Northlake Behavioral Hospital, Mandeville, LA, p. A283

ZIEMER, Patrick C., Chief Executive Officer, Alvarado Parkway Institute Behavioral Health System, La Mesa, CA, p. A68

ZIEMIANSKI, Karen, R.N. Senior Vice President Nursing, Erie County Medical Center, Buffalo, NY, p. A434

ZIENIEWICZ, Stephen P., FACHE, Executive Director, University of Washington Medical Center, Seattle, WA, p. A689

ZIEROLD, Bob, Senior Vice President Human Resources, Christian Health Care Center, Wyckoff, NJ, p. A425

ZIESMER, Bill, Chief Financial Officer, Skyridge Medical Center, Cleveland, TN, p. A581

ZIESMER, Valerie, Chief Financial Officer, Florida Hospital–Flagler, Palm Coast, FL, p. A141

ZIGLOR, Danyale, Assistant Director Human Resources, WellStar Douglas Hospital, Douglasville, GA, p. A158

ZILE, Ron, M.D. Chief of Staff, Highland District Hospital, Hillsboro, OH, p. A495

ZILKOW, Jon, Chief Financial Officer, Southwest Healthcare System, Murrieta, CA, p. A79

ZILLER, Andrew, M.D. Chief Medical Officer, Rose Medical Center, Denver, CO, p. A105

ZIMA, Cheryl F.
  Vice President Human Resources Ministry Health Care, Ministry Saint Joseph's Hospital, Marshfield, WI, p. A709
  Vice President Human Resources, Ministry Saint Michael's Hospital, Stevens Point, WI, p. A716

ZIMMEL, Robert, Senior Vice President Human Resources, St. Luke's University Hospital – Bethlehem Campus, Bethlehem, PA, p. A534

ZIMMER, Jan, R.N. Chief Nursing Officer, Regional Hospital of Jackson, Jackson, TN, p. A584

ZIMMERLY, Kara, Manager Human Resources, ProMedica Bay Park Hospital, Oregon, OH, p. A500

ZIMMERMAN, Aimee, R.N. Chief Operations Officer, Logan County Hospital, Oakley, KS, p. A251

ZIMMERMAN, Coleen, Chief Executive Officer, Regency Hospital of Northwest Indiana, East Chicago, IN, p. A209

ZIMMERMAN, David, M.D. Chief of Staff, Swain County Hospital, Bryson City, NC, p. A460

ZIMMERMAN, Deborah, R.N. Chief Nursing Officer and Vice President Patient Care Services, VCU Medical Center, Richmond, VA, p. A678

ZIMMERMAN, Don, Director Human Resources, Morris County Hospital, Council Grove, KS, p. A243

ZIMMERMAN, Joanna, Chief Financial Officer, Carlisle Regional Medical Center, Carlisle, PA, p. A535

ZIMMERMAN, Maria, R.N. Chief Nursing Officer, Sheridan County Health Complex, Hoxie, KS, p. A246

ZIMMERMAN, Mark, Regional Vice President Human Resources, Sentara RMH Medical Center, Harrisonburg, VA, p. A672

ZIMMERMAN, Michael P., Chief Executive Officer, Sierra Vista Hospital, Truth or Consequences, NM, p. A431

ZIMMERMAN, Nancy, R.N., Administrator, Comanche County Hospital, Coldwater, KS, p. A242

ZIMMERMAN, Robert, Vice President Financial Services, Charlevoix Area Hospital, Charlevoix, MI, p. A320

ZIMMERMAN, Wayne, Chief Operating Officer, Elmhurst Hospital Center,, NY, p. A443

ZINK, Jayne, Director of Nursing, Ohio Hospital for Psychiatry, Columbus, OH, p. A490

ZINKER, Dena, MSN Vice President Patient Services, Colquitt Regional Medical Center, Moultrie, GA, p. A164

ZINKULA, Lisa, Chief Financial Officer, Grundy County Memorial Hospital, Grundy Center, IA, p. A231

ZINN, David, M.D. Vice President Medical Affairs, Northeast Alabama Regional Medical Center, Anniston, AL, p. A15

ZINNER, Barbara, Chief Nursing Officer, Marymount Hospital, Garfield Heights, OH, p. A494

ZIOLKOWSKI, David
  Chief Operating Officer, Petaluma Valley Hospital, Petaluma, CA, p. A83
  Chief Operating Officer, Santa Rosa Memorial Hospital, Santa Rosa, CA, p. A84

ZIPPARO, Maureen, Chief Operating Officer, Putnam Hospital Center, Carmel, NY, p. A435

ZIRKELBACH, Mark, Chief Information Officer, Loma Linda University Medical Center, Loma Linda, CA, p. A69

ZIRKELBACK, Mark, Chief Information Officer, Loma Linda University Behavioral Medicine Center, Redlands, CA, p. A85

ZIRKLE, William, Manager Information Systems, Halifax Regional Health System, South Boston, VA, p. A678

ZISK, Sherry L., Chief Nursing Officer, Weirton Medical Center, Weirton, WV, p. A700

ZISKIN, Robert, Chief Information Officer, Northport Veterans Affairs Medical Center, Northport, NY, p. A449

ZOCH, Jeremy, Executive Vice President and Chief Operating Officer, St. Joseph Hospital, Orange, CA, p. A81

ZOGELMAN, Sharon, Director Human Resources, St. Luke Hospital and Living Center, Marion, KS, p. A249

ZOLKIWSKY, Walter R., M.D. Chief Medical Officer, Reston Hospital Center, Reston, VA, p. A677

ZOOK, Danette, Chief Financial Officer, Mercy Medical Center–North Iowa, Mason City, IA, p. A234

ZOPH, Timothy R., Senior Vice President and Chief Information Officer, Northwestern Memorial Hospital, Chicago, IL, p. A185

ZORZA, Elizabeth, Assistant Administrator, OSF St. Francis Hospital and Medical Group, Escanaba, MI, p. A323

ZOUCHA, Larry, Chief Information Officer, Boone County Health Center, Albion, NE, p. A393

ZUANICH, Elizabeth
  Chief Financial Officer, Providence Little Company of Mary Medical Center – Torrance, Torrance, CA, p. A97
  Chief Financial Officer, Providence Little Company of Mary Medical Center San Pedro,, CA, p. A74

ZUBKO, Elizabeth, Deputy Executive Director and Chief Financial Officer, Franklin Hospital, Valley Stream, NY, p. A457

ZUBRICKI, Thomas, Vice President Finance, Chief Financial Officer, Crotched Mountain Rehabilitation Center, Greenfield, NH, p. A410

ZUCCARO, Vickie, R.N. Director of Nursing, Riverland Medical Center, Ferriday, LA, p. A277

ZUEL, Sally
  Vice President Human Resources, Union Hospital, Terre Haute, IN, p. A223
  Vice President Human Resources, Union Hospital Clinton, Clinton, IN, p. A208

ZUHD, Dajani, M.D. President Medical Staff, Punxsutawney Area Hospital, Punxsutawney, PA, p. A553

ZUINO, Matthew, Vice President, Virtua Memorial, Mount Holly, NJ, p. A419

ZULIANI, Michael E., Chief Executive Officer, HEALTHSOUTH Huntington Rehabilitation Hospital, Huntington, WV, p. A696

ZULTANKY, Lynne, Director Corporate Communications and Media Relations, Bon Secours–DePaul Medical Center, Norfolk, VA, p. A675

ZUMPANO, Anthony, Chief Financial Officer, Penn Presbyterian Medical Center, Philadelphia, PA, p. A549

ZUMWALT, Philip, M.D. Chief of Staff, Iroquois Memorial Hospital and Resident Home, Watseka, IL, p. A204

ZUNNO, Gerard, R.N. Vice President Patient Care Services, Peconic Bay Medical Center, Riverhead, NY, p. A452

ZWANZIGER, Marcia, Vice President Finance, Huron Regional Medical Center, Huron, SD, p. A574

ZWEIFEL, Mary A.
  Chief Operating Officer, Sheltering Arms Hospital South, Midlothian, VA, p. A674
  Chief Operating Officer, Sheltering Arms Rehabilitation Hospital, Mechanicsville, VA, p. A674

ZWENG, Thomas, M.D. Senior Vice President Medical Affairs, Novant Health Matthews Medical Center, Matthews, NC, p. A469

ZWICKER, Mike, Chief Executive Officer, Wheatland Memorial Healthcare, Harlowton, MT, p. A388

ZWICKEY, Tim E., Chief Executive Officer, Baraga County Memorial Hospital, L'Anse, MI, p. A328

ZWIEFEL, Laura, Chief Nursing Officer and Assistant Administration, Hancock County Health System, Britt, IA, p. A226

ZWIEG, Faye, Vice President and Chief Nursing Officer, Aurora St. Luke's Medical Center, Milwaukee, WI, p. A710

ZWINGER, Glenn, Manager Information Systems Services, Veterans Affairs Puget Sound Health Care System, Seattle, WA, p. A689

ZWINGMAN–BAGLEY, Cheryl, R.N. Chief Nursing Officer, Calais Regional Hospital, Calais, ME, p. A292

ZWIRCHITZ, Faith, Director Nursing and Professional Practice, Maple Grove Hospital, Maple Grove, MN, p. A346

ZYCH, Anita, Director of Nursing, Arrowhead Behavioral Health Hospital, Maumee, OH, p. A498

ZYLA, Jeffrey, Chief Financial Officer, Paradise Valley Hospital, Phoenix, AZ, p. A36

AHA Membership Categories

The American Hospital Association is primarily an organization of hospitals and related institutions. Its object, according to its bylaws, is ''to promote high–quality health care and health services for all the people through leadership in the development of public policy, leadership in the representation and advocacy of hospital and health care organization interests, and leadership in the provision of services to assist hospitals and health care organizations in meeting the health care needs of their communities.''

Institutional Members

Hospitals or health services organizations or systems which provide a continuum of integrated, community health resources and which include at least one licensed hospital that is owned, leased, managed or religiously sponsored.

Institutional members include hospitals, health care systems, integrated delivery systems, and physician hospital organizations (PHOs) and health maintenance organizations (HMOs) wholly or partially owned by or owning a member hospital or system. An Institutional member hospital, health care system or integrated delivery system may, at its discretion and upon approval of a membership application by the Association chief executive officer, extend membership to the health care provider organizations, other than a hospital that it owns, leases, or fully controls.

Freestanding Health Care Provider Organizations

These are health provider organizations, other than registered hospitals, that provide patient care services, including, but not limited to, ambulatory, preventive, rehabilitative, specialty, post–acute and continuing care, as well as physician groups, health insurance services, and staff and group model health maintenance organizations without a hospital component. Freestanding Health Care Provider Organizations members are not owned or controlled by an Institutional member hospital, health care system or integrated delivery system member. They may, however, be part of an organization eligible for, but not holding, Institutional membership.

Other Organizations

This category includes organizations interested in the objectives of the American Hospital Association, but not eligible for Institutional or Freestanding Health Care Provider Organization Membership. Organizations eligible for Other membership shall include, but not be limited to, associations, societies, foundations, corporations, educational and academic institutions, companies, government agencies, international health providers, and organizations having an interest in and a desire to support the objectives of the Association.

Provisional Members

Hospitals that are in the planning or construction stage and that, on completion, will be eligible for institutional membership. Provisional membership may also be granted to applicant institutions that cannot, at present, meet the requirements of Institutional or Freestanding Health Care Provider Organization membership.

Government Institution Group Members

Groups of government hospitals operated by the same unit of government may obtain institutional membership under a group plan. Membership dues are based on a special schedule set forth in the bylaws of the AHA.

Other Institutional Members

U.S. hospitals and hospitals in areas associated with the U.S. that are Institutional members of the American Hospital Association are included in the list of hospitals in section A. Canadian Institutional members of the American Hospital Association are listed below.

Canada

ALBERTA

Lamont: LAMONT HEALTH CARE CENTRE, P.O. Bag 10, Zip T0B 2R0; tel. 780/895–2211; Harold James, Executive Director

MANITOBA

Winnipeg: RIVERVIEW HEALTH CENTRE, 1 Morley Avenue East, Zip R3L 2P4; tel. 204/452–3411; Norman R. Kasian, President and Chief Executive Officer

ONTARIO

Renfrew: RENFREW VICTORIA HOSPITAL, 499 Raglan Street North, Zip K7V 1P6; tel. 613/432–4851; Randy V. Penney, Executive Director
Thornhill: SHOULDICE HOSPITAL, 7750 Bayview Avenue, Zip L3T 4A3; tel. 905/889–1125; John Hughes, Chief Administrative Officer

QUEBEC

Montreal: MOUNT SINAI HOSPITAL CENTER, 5690 Cavendish Cote St–Luc', Zip H4W 1S7; tel. 514/369–2222; Michel Amar, Executive Director

Associated University Programs in Health Administration

CALIFORNIA

San Diego: CALIFORNIA COLLEGE SAN DIEGO, 6602 Convoy Court # 100, Zip 92111–1009; tel. 619/680–4430; Barbara Thomas, Chief Operations Officer

San Francisco: GOLDEN GATE UNIVERSITY, 536 Mission Street, Univ Library, Zip 94105–2968; tel. 415/442–7242; Steven Dunlap, Head Technical Services

IOWA

Iowa City: DEPARTMENT OF HEALTH MANAGEMENT AND POLICY, UNIVERSITY OF IOWA, 105 River Street, N232A CPHB, Zip 52246; tel. 319/384–3830; Keith Mueller, Ph.D., Professor and Head

MISSOURI

Columbia: UNIVERSITY OF MISSOURI, HEALTH MANAGEMENT AND INFORMATICS, CE707 Clinical Support and Education Building, DC 00600, One Hospital Drive, Zip 65212; tel. 573/882–6179; Lanis Hicks, Ph.D., Professor and Associate Chair

PENNSYLVANIA

University Park: PENNSYLVANIA STATE UNIVERSITY, 604 Ford Building, Zip 16802; tel. 814/863–2859; Dennis Shea, Department Head

TEXAS

San Antonio: ARMY–BAYLOR UNIVERSITY PROGRAM IN HEALTH CARE ADMINISTRATION, 3151 Scott Road, Building 2841, Zip 78234–6135; tel. 210/221–6443; Lieutenant Colonel M. Nicholas Coppola, Program Director

TRINITY UNIVERSITY, One Trinity Place, #58, Zip 78212–7200; tel. 210/736–8107; Mary E. Stefl, Ph.D., Chairman

Sheppard AFB: U. S. AIR FORCE SCHOOL OF HEALTH CARE SCIENCES, Building 1900, MST/114, Academic Library, Zip 76311; tel. 817/851–2511

PUERTO RICO

San Juan: SCHOOL OF PUBLIC HEALTH, P.O. Box 5067, Zip 00936; tel. 809/767–9626; Orlando Nieves, Dean

Hospital Schools
of Nursing

NEW YORK

Elmira: ARNOT–OGDEN MEMORIAL HOSPITAL School
of Nursing

PENNSYLVANIA

New Castle: JAMESON HOSPITAL School of Nursing

Nonhospital Preacute and Postacute Care Facilities

ALABAMA

Fort Rucker: LYSTER ARMY HEALTH CLINIC, Andrews Lane, Building 301, Zip 36362–5000; tel. 334/255–7359; Colonel Patrick N. Denman, Commander

Maxwell Afb: MAXWELL CLINIC, 300 Twining Street, Zip 36112–6027; tel. 334/953–7801; Colonel Bart O. Iddins, Commander

ALASKA

Anchorage: ALASKA VETERANS AFFAIRS HEALTHCARE SYSTEM, 1201 North Muldoon Road, Zip 99504–6104; tel. 907/257–6930; Alex Spector, Director

ARIZONA

Davis–Monthan AFB: U. S. AIR FORCE CLINIC, 4175 South Alamo Avenue, Zip 85707–4405; tel. 520/228–2930

Fort Huachuca: RAYMOND W. BLISS ARMY HEALTH CENTER, 45001 Winrow Avenue, Zip 85613–7040; tel. 520/533–2350; Colonel Thomas W. Smith, M.D., MSC, Commander

Glendale: U. S. AIR FORCE HOSPITAL LUKE, Luke AFB, 7219 North Litchfield Road, Zip 85309–1525; tel. 623/856–7502; Colonel Schuyler K. Geller, Commander

ARKANSAS

Jacksonville: U. S. AIR FORCE CLINIC LITTLE ROCK, Little Rock AFB, Zip 72099–5057; tel. 501/987–7411; Colonel Rebecca A. Russell, USAF, Commander

CALIFORNIA

Beale AFB: U. S. AIR FORCE HOSPITAL, 15301 Warren Shingle Road, Zip 95903–1907; tel. 530/634–4838; Lieutenant Colonel Robert G. Quinn, MSC, USAF, FACHE, Administrator

Edwards AFB: U. S. AIR FORCE CLINIC, 10 Hospital Road, Building 5500, Zip 93524–1730; tel. 661/277–2010; Colonel Sally Petty, Commander

Los Angeles: VETERANS AFFAIRS OUTPATIENT CLINIC LOS ANGELES, 351 East Temple Street, Zip 90012; tel. 213/253–5000; Jules Morevac, Ph.D., Director

Martinez: VETERANS AFFAIRS NORTHERN CALIFORNIA HEALTH SYSTEM, 150 Muir Road, Zip 94553; tel. 925/372–2000; Brian J. O'Neill, M.D., Director

Port Hueneme: NAVAL AMBULATORY CARE CENTER, Zip 93043; tel. 805/982–6301; Major Frederick White, Officer–in–Charge

San Francisco: VETERANS AFFAIRS OUTPATIENT CLINIC, 4150 Clement Street, Zip 94121; tel. 415/221–4810; Lawrence C. Stewart, Director

Sepulveda: VETERANS AFFAIRS MEDICAL CENTER, 16111 Plummer Street, Zip 91343; tel. 818/891–7711; Charles M. Doorman, Acting Director

Vandenberg AFB: U. S. AIR FORCE HOSPITAL, 338 South Dakota Street, Zip 93437–6307; tel. 805/606–1110; Commander Janice Wallace, Commander

Winterhaven: U. S. PUBLIC HEALTH SERVICE INDIAN HOSPITAL, P.O. Box 1368, Zip 85366–1368; tel. 760/572–0217; Geniel Harrison, M.D., Clinic Director

COLORADO

Las Animas: SOUTHERN COLORADO HEALTHCARE SYSTEM, P.O. Box 390, Zip 81054–0390; tel. 719/456–1260; Stuart C. Collyer, Director

USAF Academy: U. S. AIR FORCE ACADEMY CLINIC, 4102 Pinion Drive, Zip 80840–4000; tel. 719/333–5102; Colonel Alan B. Berg, Commander

CONNECTICUT

Groton: NAVAL HOSPITAL, 1 Wahoo Drive, Box 600, Zip 06349–5600; tel. 860/694–3261

Newington: VETERANS AFFAIRS MEDICAL CENTER–NEWINGTON CAMPUS, 555 Willard Avenue, Zip 06111–2600; tel. 860/666–6951; Roger L. Johnson, Director

DELAWARE

Dover: U. S. AIR FORCE HOSPITAL DOVER, 300 Tuskegee Boulevard, Zip 19902–7307; tel. 302/677–2525; Colonel Genanne Hansen–Bayless, Administrator

Newark: HEALTH CARE CENTER AT CHRISTIANA, 200 Hygeia Drive, Zip 19714

FLORIDA

Jacksonville: NEMOURS CHILDREN'S CLINIC, 807 Children's Way, Zip 32207; tel. 904/390–3600; William A. Cover, Administrator

Key West: NAVAL REGIONAL MEDICAL CLINIC, 1500 Douglas Circle, Zip 33040; tel. 305/293–4613; Lieutenant Commander Michael Grande, Officer–in–Charge

MacDill AFB: U. S. AIR FORCE HOSPITAL, 8415 Bayshore Boulevard, Zip 33621–1607; tel. 813/827–9521

Patrick AFB: U. S. AIR FORCE CLINIC, 1381 South Patrick Drive, Zip 32925–3606; tel. 407/494–8102; Colonel William Swindling, Commanding Officer

Tyndall AFB: U. S. AIR FORCE CLINIC, 340 Magnolia Avenue, Zip 32403–5612; tel. 850/283–7515; Colonel Michael J. Murphy, Commander

GEORGIA

Calhoun: ALLIANT HEALTH PLANS, INC., 401 South Wall Street, Suite 201, Zip 30701; tel. 706/629–8848; Judy Pair, Chief Executive Officer

GEORGIA HEALTH PLUS, 401 South Wall Street, Suite 201, Zip 30701; tel. 706/629–1833

Moody AFB: U. S. AIR FORCE HOSPITAL MOODY, 3278 Mitchell Boulevard, Zip 31699–1500; tel. 229/257–3772

Robins AFB: U. S. AIR FORCE CLINIC, 655 Seventh Street, Zip 31098–2227; tel. 912/327–7996; Colonel John A. Lee, USAF, MSC, Commander

Rome: CENTREX, 420 East Second Avenue, Zip 30161; tel. 706/235–1006; Dee B. Russell, M.D., Chief Executive Officer

COMMUNITY HOSPICECARE, P.O. Box 233, Zip 30162–0233; tel. 706/232–0807; Kurt Stuenkel, FACHE, President and Chief Executive Officer

FLOYD HOME HEALTH AGENCY, P.O. Box 6248, Zip 30162–6248; tel. 706/802–4600; Kurt Stuenkel, FACHE, President and Chief Executive Officer

FLOYD MEDICAL OUTPATIENT SURGERY, P.O. Box 233, Zip 30162–0233; tel. 706/802–2070; Kurt Stuenkel, FACHE, President and Chief Executive Officer

FLOYD REHABILITATION CENTER, P.O. Box 233, Zip 30162–0233; tel. 706/802–2091; Kurt Stuenkel, FACHE, President and Chief Executive Officer

HAWAII

Honolulu: MALUHIA HOSPITAL, 1027 Hala Drive, Zip 96817; tel. 808/832–5874; Sally T. Ishikawa, Administrator

VETERANS AFFAIRS PACIFIC ISLANDS HEALTHCARE SYSTEM, 459 Patterson Road, Zip 96819; tel. 808/433–0600; James E. Hastings, M.D., Director

Pearl Harbor: NAVAL HEALTH CLINIC HAWAII, Box 121, Building 1750, Zip 96860–5080; tel. 808/471–3025; Lieutenant Commander David Lang, Director Administration

ILLINOIS

North Chicago: CAPTAIN JAMES A. LOVELL FEDERAL HEALTH CENTER, 3001 Green Bay Road, Zip 60064–3048; tel. 847/688–1900; Commander Christian Wallis, Assistant Director Facility Support

Oak Forest: OAK FOREST HEALTH CENTER OF COOK COUNTY, 15900 South Cicero Avenue, Zip 60452–4006; tel. 708/687–7200

Scott AFB: SCOTT MEDICAL CENTER, 310 West Losey Street, Zip 62225–5252; tel. 618/256–7456; Colonel Bret D. Burton, Commander

KANSAS

Fort Leavenworth: MUNSON ARMY HEALTH CENTER, 550 Pope Avenue, Zip 66027–2332; tel. 913/684–6420; Colonel David Bitterman, Commander

Wichita: U. S. AIR FORCE HOSPITAL, 59570 Leavenworth Street, Suite 6E4, Zip 67221–5300; tel. 316/759–5421

LOUISIANA

Barksdale AFB: U. S. AIR FORCE CLINIC, 243 Curtiss Road, Suite 100, Zip 71110–5300; tel. 318/456–6004; Colonel James M. Benge, Commander

New Orleans: NAVAL MEDICAL CLINIC, 1 Sanctuary Drive, Zip 70142–5300; tel. 504/678–2400; Lieutenant Commander Edward Brinston, Officer–in–Charge

SOUTHEAST LOUISIANA VETERANS HEALTH CARE SYSTEM, 1601 Perdido Street, Zip 70112–1262; tel. 504/412–3700; Julie A. Catellier, Director

MAINE

Damariscotta: COVE'S EDGE, 26 Schooner Street, Zip 04543; tel. 207/563–4645; Judy McGuire, Administrator

MILES MEDICAL GROUP, INC., 35 Miles Street, Zip 04543; tel. 207/563–1234; Stacey Miller–Friant, Director

Kennebunk: SOUTHERN MAINE HEALTH AND HOME SERVICES, P.O. Box 739, Zip 04043; tel. 207/985–4767; Elaine Brady, R.N., Executive Director

MARYLAND

Andrews AFB: MALCOLM GROW MEDICAL CLINIC, 1050 West Perimeter, Suite B5–10, Zip 20762–6600; tel. 240/857–3001; Colonel Rudolph Cachuela, Commanding Officer

Annapolis: NAVAL HEALTH CLINIC ANNAPOLIS, 250 Wood Road, Zip 21402–1257; tel. 410/293–1330; Lieutenant Commander Matthew Holcomb, Director Administration

Baltimore: ST. AGNES HEALTH SERVICES, 900 Caton Avenue, Zip 21229; tel. 410/368–2945; Peter Clay, Senior Vice President Managed Care

ST. AGNES HOME CARE AND HOSPICE, 3421 Benson Avenue, Suite G100, Zip 21227; tel. 410/368–2825; Robin Dowell, Director

Ellicott City: ST. AGNES NURSING AND REHABILITATION CENTER, 3000 North Ridge Road, Zip 21043; tel. 410/461–7577; Barbara A. Gustke, R.N., Administrator Extended Care Facility

Fort George G Meade: KIMBROUGH ARMY HEALTH CENTER, 2480 Llewellyn Avenue, Zip 20755; tel. 301/677–4171; Colonel Billie J. Mielcarek, Commanding Officer

Fort Howard: VETERANS AFFAIRS MARYLAND HEALTH CARE SYSTEM–FORT HOWARD DIVISION, 9600 North Point Road, Zip 21052–9989; tel. 410/477–1800; Patricia Vicari, Director

Patuxent River: NAVAL HEALTH CLINIC PATUXENT RIVER, 47149 Buse Road, Zip 20670–5370; tel. 301/342–1418; Commander Romeo Tizon, Director Administration

MASSACHUSETTS

Boston: JOSLIN DIABETES CENTER, One Joslin Place, Zip 02215; tel. 617/732–2400; John L. Brooks, III., President and Chief Executive Officer

Springfield: BAY STATE VISITING NURSE ASSOCIATION AND HOSPICE, 50 Maple Street, Zip 01105; tel. 413/781–5070; Ruth Odgren, President

MICHIGAN

Big Rapids: MECOSTA HEALTH SERVICES, 650 Linden Street, Zip 49307; tel. 231/796–3200; Gail Bullard, R.N., Director

Sault Sainte Marie: SAULT SAINTE MARIE TRIBAL HEALTH AND HUMAN SERVICES CENTER, 2864 Ashmun Street, Zip 49783; tel. 906/495–5651; Russell Vizina, Division Director Health

MISSISSIPPI

Columbus: U. S. AIR FORCE CLINIC, 201 Independence, Suite 101, Zip 39701–5300; tel. 662/434–2297; Colonel Dave Armstrong, Commander

MISSOURI

Independence: SURGI–CARE CENTER OF INDEPENDENCE, 2311 Redwood Avenue, Zip 64057; tel. 816/373–7995

Whiteman AFB: U. S. AIR FORCE CLINIC WHITEMAN, 331 Sijan Avenue, Zip 65305–5001; tel. 660/687–1194; Lieutenant Colonel David Wilmot, USAF, MSC, Administrator

MONTANA

Malmstrom AFB: U. S. AIR FORCE CLINIC, Zip 59402–5300; tel. 406/731–3863; Colonel David L. Doty, Administrator

Miles City: VETERANS AFFAIRS MEDICAL CENTER, 210 South Winchester Avenue, Zip 59301–4742; tel. 406/232–3060

NEBRASKA

Grand Island: GRAND ISLAND DIVISION, 2211 North Broadwell Avenue, Zip 68803–2196; tel. 308/382–3660; Gary N. Nugent, Chief Executive Officer

North Platte: GREAT PLAINS PHO, INC., P.O. Box 1167, Zip 69103; tel. 308/535–7496; Todd Hlavaty, M.D., Chairman

Offutt AFB: EHRLING BERGQUIST HOSPITAL, 2501 Capehart Road, Zip 68113–2160; tel. 402/294–7312; Colonel Howard Googins, Deputy Commander

NEW HAMPSHIRE

Portsmouth: NAVAL MEDICAL CLINIC, Building H–1, Zip 03801; tel. 207/439–1000; Commander Kendra Nowak, Officer–in–Charge

NEW JERSEY

Fort Monmouth: PATTERSON ARMY HEALTH CLINIC, Stephenson Avenue, Building 1075, Zip 07703–5504; tel. 908/532–1266; Colonel Don Speers, Commander

Jersey City: ST. FRANCIS HOSPITAL, 25 McWilliams Place, Zip 07302–1698; tel. 201/418–1000

Millburn: ATLANTIC HOME CARE AND HOSPICE, 33 Bleeker Street, Zip 07041; tel. 973/379–8400; Susan Quinn, Administrator

Morristown: ALLIANCE IMAGING CENTER, 65 Maple Street, Zip 07960; tel. 973/267–5700; Barbara Picorale, Administrator

Succasunna: DIALYSIS CENTER OF NORTHWEST NEW JERSEY, 170 Righter Road, Zip 07876; tel. 973/584–1117; Carol Cahill, Administrator

NEW MEXICO

Albuquerque: ALBUQUERQUE IHS HEALTH CENTER, 801 Vassar Drive N.E., Zip 87106–2799; tel. 505/248–4000; Maria Rickert, Chief Executive Officer

Cannon AFB: U. S. AIR FORCE CLINIC, 208 West Casablanca Avenue, Zip 88103–5300; tel. 505/784–6318; Lieutenant Colonel Michelle Pufall, Administrator

Holloman AFB: U. S. AIR FORCE CLINIC, 280 First Street, Zip 88330–8273; tel. 505/572–5587

Kirtland AFB: U. S. AIR FORCE CLINIC–KIRTLAND, 2050 A Second Street S.E., Zip 87117–5559; tel. 505/846–3547; Colonel Regina Aune, Commander

NEW YORK

Bronx: MORRISANIA DIAGNOSTIC AND TREATMENT CENTER, 1225 Gerard Avenue, Zip 10452; tel. 718/960–2777; Victor Hernandez, Administrator

SEGUNDO RUIZ BELVIS DIAGNOSTIC AND TREATMENT CENTER, 545 East 142nd Street, Zip 10454; tel. 718/579–4000; Victor Hernandez, Administrator

Brooklyn: CUMBERLAND DIAGNOSTIC AND TREATMENT CENTER, 100 North Portland Avenue, Zip 11205; tel. 718/260–7500; Candis Best, Administrator

DR. SUSAN SMITH NURSING REHABILITATION CENTER, 594 Albany Avenue, Zip 11203; tel. 718/245–7000; Peola Small, Chief Operating Officer

EAST NEW YORK DIAGNOSTIC AND TREATMENT CENTER, 2094 Pitkin Avenue, Zip 11207; tel. 718/240–0400; Yvette Isaac, Administrator

Fort Drum: U. S. ARMY MEDICAL DEPARTMENT ACTIVITY, 11050 Mount Belvedere Boulevard, Zip 13602–5004; tel. 315/772–4024; Colonel Mark W. Thompson, MC, Commander

New York: GOUVERNEUR HOSPITAL, 227 Madison Street, Zip 10002; tel. 212/238–7000; Gregory M. Kaladjian, Executive Director

RENAISSANCE DIAGNOSTIC AND TREATMENT CENTER, 215 West 125 Street, Zip 10027; tel. 212/932–6500; Rose Garcia, Administrator

Staten Island: SEA VIEW HOSPITAL REHABILITATION CENTER AND HOME, 460 Brielle Avenue, Zip 10314; tel. 212/390–8181; Jane M. Lyons, Executive Director

Tuckahoe: HOME NURSING ASSOCIATION OF WESTCHESTER, 69 Main Street, Zip 10707; tel. 919/961–2818; Mary Wehrberger, Director

NORTH CAROLINA

Cherry Point: NAVAL HEALTH CLINIC CHERRY POINT, PSC Box 8023, Zip 28533–0023; tel. 252/466–0266; Lieutenant Commander Tim Barnes, Director Administration

Jefferson: AMH SEGRAVES CARE CENTER, 200 Hospital Avenue, Zip 28640; tel. 336/246–7101

Seymour Johnson AFB: U. S. AIR FORCE HOSPITAL SEYMOUR JOHNSON, 1050 Curtis Avenue, Zip 27531–5300; tel. 919/722–1812; Colonel Eleanor Nazar–Smith, Commanding Officer

Wilson: WILMED NURSING CARE CENTER, 1705 Tarboro Street S.W., Zip 27893–3428; tel. 252/399–8998; Gene Fulcher, Administrator

NORTH DAKOTA

Grand Forks AFB: U. S. AIR FORCE HOSPITAL, 220 G Street, Zip 58205–6332; tel. 701/747–5391

Minot: U. S. AIR FORCE REGIONAL HOSPITAL, 10 Missile Avenue, Zip 58705–5024; tel. 701/723–5103

OHIO

Cleveland: METROHEALTH CENTER FOR SKILLED NURSING CARE, 4229 Pearl Road, Zip 44109; tel. 216/957–3675; Yvette Bozman, Administrator

Columbus: CHALMERS WYLIE VETERANS AFFAIRS AMBULATORY CARE CENTER, 420 North James Road, Zip 43219–1834; tel. 614/257–5200; Lillian T. Thone, Chief Executive Officer

OKLAHOMA

Altus: U. S. AIR FORCE CLINIC ALTUS, 301 North First Street, Zip 73523–5005; tel. 580/481–5204; Colonel Charles W. Cotta, USAF, Commander

Clinton: U. S. PUBLIC HEALTH SERVICE INDIAN HOSPITAL, Route 1, Box 3060, Zip 73601–9303; tel. 580/323–2884

Enid: U. S. AIR FORCE CLINIC, Vance AFB, Building 810, Zip 73705–5000; tel. 405/249–7494; Lieutenant Colonel Andrew F. Love, MSC, USAF, Commander Medical Group

Eufaula: EUFALA INDIAN HEALTH CENTER, 800 Forest Avenue, Zip 74432; tel. 918/689–2547; Shelly Crow, Health System Administrator

Okmulgee: OKMULGEE INDIAN HEALTH SYSTEM, 1313 East 20th, Zip 74447; tel. 918/758–1926; Jo Ann Skaggs, Administrator

Sapulpa: SAPULPA INDIAN HEALTH CENTER, 1125 East Clevelend, Zip 74066; tel. 918/224–9310

Tinker AFB: U. S. AIR FORCE HOSPITAL TINKER, 5700 Arnold Street, Zip 73145; tel. 405/736–2084; Colonel Lloyd A. Reinke, Commander

OREGON

White City: VETERANS AFFAIRS DOMICILIARY, Zip 97503; tel. 503/826–2111; Frank A. Drake, Director

PENNSYLVANIA

Warminster: ABINGTON MEMORIAL HEALTH CENTER – WARMINSTER CAMPUS, 225 Newtown Road, Zip 18974–5221; tel. 215/441–6600; Katie Farrell, Chief Executive Officer

RHODE ISLAND

Newport: NAVAL HEALTH CLINIC NEW ENGLAND, 43 Smith Road, Zip 02841–1006; tel. 401/841–3771; Lieutenant Commander Jason Lewis

SOUTH CAROLINA

North Charleston: NAVAL HEALTH CLINIC – CHARLESTON, 3600 Rivers Avenue, Zip 29405; tel. 843/794–6621; Commander Amy Smith, Director Administration

Shaw AFB: U. S. AIR FORCE HOSPITAL SHAW, 431 Meadowlark Street, Zip 29152–5019; tel. 803/895–6324; Colonel Troy Molnar, Commander

SOUTH DAKOTA

Ellsworth AFB: U. S. AIR FORCE CLINIC, 2900 Doolittle Drive, Zip 57706–4821; tel. 605/385–3201; Colonel Chris Gray, Commanding Officer

TEXAS

Abilene: U. S. AIR FORCE CLINIC, 697 Hospital Road, Zip 79607–1367; tel. 915/696–5429; Major John G. Wiseman, Administrator

Corpus Christi: NAVAL HEALTH CLINIC CORPUS CHRISTI, 10651 E Street, Zip 78419–5131; tel. 361/961–2688; Captain Jimy Bradley, Officer–in–Charge

Dallas: NAVAL HOSPITAL BRANCH MEDICAL CLINIC, Naval Air Station, Zip 75211–9516; tel. 214/266–6281; Lieutenant Commander Jayson Huber

SURGICARE OF TRAVIS CENTER, INC., 13355 Noel Road, Suite 650, Zip 75240–6694; tel. 713/520–1782

El Paso: EL PASO VETERANS AFFAIRS HEALTH CARE SYSTEM, 5001 North Piedras Street, Zip 79930–4211; tel. 915/564–6100; John A. Mendoza, Director

Houston: GRAMERCY OUTPATIENT SURGERY CENTER. LTD., 2727 Gramercy, Zip 77025; tel. 713/660–6900; Hamel Patel, Administrator

WEST HOUSTON SURGICARE, 970 Campbell Road, Zip 77024; tel. 713/461–3547

Laughlin AFB: U. S. AIR FORCE HOSPITAL, 590 Mitchell Boulevard, Zip 78843–5200; tel. 210/298–6311

San Antonio: U. S. AIR FORCE CLINIC BROOKS, Building 615, Zip 78235–5300; tel. 210/536–2087; Lieutenant Colonel Donald Sampson, Commanding Officer

WILFORD HALL AMBULATORY SURGICAL CENTER, 2200 Bergquist Drive, Suite 1, Zip 78236–9908; tel. 210/292–7412; Brigadier General Thomas Travis, Commanding Officer

Sheppard AFB: U. S. AIR FORCE REGIONAL HOSPITAL–SHEPPARD, 149 Hart Street, Suite 1, Zip 76311–3478; tel. 940/676–5874; Lieutenant Colonel Lance Rogers, Administrator

Universal City: U. S. AIR FORCE CLINIC RANDOLPH, 221 3rd Street West, Zip 78150–4801; tel. 210/652–5701; Lieutenant Colonel Dennis E. Franks, Administrator

Webster: BAY AREA SURGICARE CENTER, 502 Medical Center Boulevard, Zip 77598; tel. 281/332–2433; Carol Simons, Administrator

VIRGINIA

Fort Eustis: MCDONALD ARMY HEALTH CENTER, Jefferson Avenue, Zip 23604–5548; tel. 757/314–7501; Colonel Cass Scott, Administrator

Fort Lee: KENNER ARMY HEALTH CENTER, 700 24th Street, Zip 23801–1716; tel. 804/734–9256; Colonel Vivian T. Hutson, Commander

Quantico: NAVAL HEALTH CLINIC, QUANTICO, 3259 Catlin Avenue, Zip 22134; tel. 703/784–1699; Lieutenant Commander Dawn Freeman, Director Administration

WASHINGTON

Fairchild AFB: U. S. AIR FORCE CLINIC, 701 Hospital Loop, Suite 102, Zip 99011–8701; tel. 509/247–5217; Colonel Barbara Jefts, R.N., MS, Commanding Officer

WISCONSIN

Green Bay: UNITY HOSPICE, P.O. Box 28345, Zip 54324–8345; tel. 920/494–0225; Donald Seibel, Executive Director

WYOMING

Cheyenne: U. S. AIR FORCE HOSPITAL, 6900 Alden Drive, Zip 82005–3913; tel. 307/773–2045; Major Brenda Bullard, Administrator

Provisional Hospitals

This listing includes organizations that, as of September 16, 2014, were in the planning or construction stage and that, on completion, will be eligible for Institutional membership. Some hospitals are granted provisional membership for reasons related to other Association requirements. Hospitals classified as provisional members for reasons other than being under construction are indicated by a bullet (•).

LOUSIANA:

New Orleans: UNIVERSITY MEDICAL CENTER – NEW ORLEANS, 2000 Canal Street, Zip 70112; tel. 504/588–3000; Cindy Nuesslein, Interim Chief Executive Officer

TEXAS

College Station: SCOTT & WHITE HOSPITAL – COLLEGE STATION, 700 Scott & White Drive, Zip 77845; tel. 979/207–0100; Jason Jennings, Chief Executive Officer

Marble Falls: WAYNE & EILEEN HURD REGIONAL MEDICAL CENTER – SCOTT & WHITE, 800 West Highway 71, Zip 78654; tel. 830/598–1204; Eric N. Looper, Chief Executive Officer

GUAM

Dededo: GUAM REGIONAL MEDICAL CITY, P.O. Box 3830, Zip 96932; tel. 671/649–4764; Gloria Long, Chief Operating Officer

Associate Members

Ambulatory Centers and Home Care Agencies

United States

NEW HAMPSHIRE

DARTMOUTH COLLEGE HEALTH SERVICE, 7 Rope Ferry Road, Hanover, Zip 03755–1421; tel. 603/650–1400; John H. Turco, M.D., Director

NEW YORK

MIDTOWN SURGERY CENTER, 305 East 47th Street, New York, Zip 10017–2303; tel. 212/751–2100; Julia Ferguson, Director, Operations

PENNSYLVANIA

WILLS EYE HOSPITAL, 840 Walnut Street, Philadelphia, Zip 19107–5109; tel. 215/928–3000; Joseph P. Bilson, Executive Director

Blue Cross Plans

United States

ARIZONA

BLUE CROSS AND BLUE SHIELD OF ARIZONA, Box 13466, Phoenix, Zip 85002–3466; tel. 602/864–4541; Vishu Jhaveri, M.D., Senior Vice President and Chief Medical Officer

The members listed in **bold** *are Associate Advantage members.* © 2014 AHA Guide

Other Members

UNITED STATES

Architecture:

DEVENNEY GROUP ARCHITECTS, 201 West Indian School Road, Phoenix, Arizona Zip 85013–3203; tel. 602/943–8950; Julie Barkenbush, Chief Executive Officer; www.devenneygroup.com

EARL SWENSSON ASSOCIATES, INC., 2100 West End Avenue, Suite 1200, Nashville, Tennessee Zip 37203; tel. 615/329–9445; Richard L. Miller, President; www.esarch.com

HDR ARCHITECTURE, INC., 8404 Indian Hills Drive, Omaha, Nebraska Zip 68114; tel. 402/399–1000; Doug Wignall, Executive Vice President; www.hdrinc.com

MATTHEI AND COLIN ASSOCIATES, 332 South Michigan Avenue, Suite 614, Chicago, Illinois Zip 60604; tel. 312/939–4002; Ronald G. Kobold, Managing Partner

MESSER CONSTRUCTION COMPANY, 5158 Fishwick Drive, Cincinnati, Ohio Zip 45216; tel. 513/242–1541; Tiffany Witham, Director Marketing; www.messer.com

PERKINS+WILL, INC., 617 West Seventh Street, Suite 1200, Los Angeles, California Zip 90017–3830; tel. 213/270–8400; Timothy Pettigrew, Associate, Healthcare Knowledge Coordinator; www.perkinswill.com

Bank:

BANK OF AMERICA, 101 South Tryon Street, Charlotte, North Carolina Zip 28255–0001; tel. 704/388–2255; Gayle Higaki, Senior Vice President; www.bankofamerica.com

Communication Systems Org:

AT & T, 1010 Wilshire Boulevard, Room 1240, Los Angeles, California Zip 90017; tel. 805/648–2463; Deborah Sunday, Director Product Marketing Management

AVAILITY, LLC, 740 East Campbell Road, Suite 1000, Richardson, Texas Zip 75081–1886; tel. 972/383–6326; Andrea Overman, Director, Marketing; www.availity.com

COOPER SIGNAGE & GRAPHICS, INC., 2405 Lance Court, Loganville, Georgia Zip 30052–4613; tel. 800/297–2324; Randy R. Cooper, President; www.sinsystems.org

Consulting Firm:

ACUSTAF SOFTWARE, 7601 France Avenue, Suite 575, Edina, Minnesota Zip 55435–5968; tel. 952/831–4122; Terry Suby, President; www.acustafsoftware.com

AON HEWITT, 901 Marquette Avenue, Suite 2200, Minneapolis, Minnesota Zip 55402–3721; tel. 612/337–1193; James Craig Nelson, Senior Vice President; www.stratford360.com

ARAMARK, 1101 Market Street, Philadelphia, Pennsylvania Zip 19107–2988; tel. 856/858–3822; Denise Spillane, Vice President Marketing and Communications

BENEFIT RECOVERY ANALYSTS, INC., 403 West Fisher Avenue, Greensboro, North Carolina Zip 27401; tel. 336/273–0737; Judy Tisdale, Accounting Manager; www.benefitrecoveryanalysts.com

BEST DOCTORS, INC., 100 Federal Street, 21st Floor, Boston, Massachusetts Zip 02110–1802; tel. 617/426–3666; Ryan Schoenecker, Vice President Business Development; www.bestdoctors.com

BMGI, 1200 17th Street, Suite 180, Denver, Colorado Zip 80202–5815; tel. 303/827–0010; Scott McAllister, Senior Performance Excellence Consultant; www.bmgi.com/default.aspx

BOXWOOD TECHNOLOGY, INC, 11350 McCormick Road, Suite 101, Hunt Valley, Maryland Zip 21031; tel. 888/491–8833; John Bell, Chairman; www.boxwoodtech.com

BURWOOD GROUP, INC., 125 South Wacker Drive, Suite 2950, Chicago, Illinois Zip 60602; tel. 312/327–4600; Mark Theoharous, President; www.burwood.com

CARE TECH SOLUTIONS, 901 Wilshire Drive, Suite 100, Troy, Michigan Zip 48084; tel. 248/823–0950; Jody Meehan, Vice President, Marketing, Communications, and Government Affairs; www.caretech.com/

COMMUNITY INFUSION SOLUTIONS, 316 South Goliad Street, Suite 215, Rockwall, Texas Zip 75087–3760; tel. 817/798–8013; Sean Kirby, Vice President for Operations; www.communityiv.com

COMPDATA CONSULTING, 1713 East 123rd Street, Olathe, Kansas Zip 66061–5983; tel. 800/300–9570; Jessica Wahaus, Marketing Manager; www.compdataconsulting.com

CONIFER HEALTH SOLUTIONS, 2401 Internet Boulevard, Suite 201, Frisco, Texas Zip 75034–5977; tel. 972/335–6120; Vanessa Harris, Senior Market Research Specialist; www.coniferhealth.com

COPYRIGHT CLEARANCE CENTER, 222 Rosewood Drive, Danvers, Massachusetts Zip 01923–4520; tel. 978/646–2633; Stephanie Fox, Alliances Director; www.copyright.com

DEVELOPMENT DIMENSIONS INTERNATIONAL, 1225 Washington Pike, Bridgeville, Pennsylvania Zip 15017–2838; tel. 412/257–3623; Colby Fazio, Marketing Consultant; www.ddiworld.com

DRAEGER, 3135 Quarry Road, Telford, Pennsylvania Zip 18969–1042; tel. 215/660–2310; Susan Thornton, Senior Marketing Manager, Information Technology Solutions; www.draeger.com

ECLIPSYS, 76 Batterson Park Road, Farmington, Connecticut Zip 06032; tel. 860/246–3000; Marvin S. Goldwasser, Vice President Product Marketing, Patient Flow and Performance Management; www.eclipsys.com

EIDE BAILLY, LLP, 800 Nicollet Mall, Suite 1300, Minneapolis, Minnesota Zip 55402–7033; tel. 612/253–6582; Jen Dreis, Marketing Manager; www.eidebailly.com/healthcare

ELSEVIER, INC., 3251 Riverport Lane, Maryland Heights, Missouri Zip 63043–4816; tel. 314/447–8434; Scott Iverson, Marketing Director; www.clinicaldecisionsupport.com

ERDMAN, P.O. Box 44975, Madison, Wisconsin Zip 53744–4975; tel. 608/410–8000; Molly Hamm, Research Librarian; www.erdman.com

ERNST & YOUNG, 41 South High Street, Columbus, Ohio Zip 43215–6101; tel. 949/437–0220; Jonathan G. Weaver, Partner

ERNST & YOUNG, 5 Times Square, 14th Floor, New York, New York Zip 10036–6530; tel. 212/773–3000; Frank Bresz, Senior Manager; www.ey.com/global/content.nsf/us/home

EXECUTIVE HEALTH RESOURCES, INC., 15 Campus Boulevard, Suite 200, Newtown Square, Pennsylvania Zip 19073; tel. 610/446–6100; Michele Bowman, Vice President, Marketing and Communications; www.ehrdocs.com

FIDELITY INVESTMENTS, 100 Magellan Way, Mail Zone KW23, Covington, Kentucky Zip 41015–1987; tel. 859/386–3117; John Campbell, Manager; www.fmr.com

GETWELLNETWORK, INC., 7920 Norfolk Avenue, 11th Floor, Bethesda, Maryland Zip 20814–2500; tel. 240/482–3200; Michael B. O'Neil, Jr., President and Chief Executive Officer; www.getwellnetwork.com

GLOBAL HEALTHCARE EXCHANGE, LLC, 1315 West Century Drive, Louisville, Colorado Zip 80027–9560; tel. 720/887–7000; Karen Conway, Executive Director, Industry Relations; www.ghx.com

GOLDMAN, SACHS AND COMPANY, 200 West Street, New York, New York Zip 10282–2198; Cynthia Rivera, Public Sector and Infrastructure Banking

H. R. S. INTERNATIONAL, 25 East Washington, 6th Floor, Chicago, Illinois Zip 60602; tel. 312/236–7770; Carrie Parks, Marketing Specialist; www.hrsolutions.com

HEALTHCARE CHAPLAINCY NETWORK, INC., 65 Broadway, 12th Floor, New York, New York Zip 10010; tel. 212/644–1111; Father Eric J. Hall, President and Chief Executive Officer; www.healthcarechaplaincy.org

HEALTHCARE STRATEGY GROUP, LLC, 9900 Corporate Campus Drive Suite 2000, Louisville, Kentucky Zip 40223–4062; tel. 502/814–1180; Donna Russell, Marketing Director; www.healthcarestrategygroup.com

HEALTHCARESOURCE, 100 Sylvan Road, Suite 100, Woburn, Massachusetts Zip 01801–1851; tel. 800/691–3737; Sean Parlin, Strategic Alliances Manager; www.healthcaresource.com

HEALTHEQUITY, INC., 15 West Scenic Pointe Drive, Suite 100, Draper, Utah Zip 84020–6120; tel. 801/727–1000; Stephen Neeleman, Founder and Vice Chairman; www.healthequity.com

HEALTHPORT, 925 North Point Parkway, Alpharetta, Georgia Zip 30005–5210; tel. 770/360–1700; Catherine Valyi, Vice President Marketing; www.healthport.com

INTEGRATED HEALTHCARE STRATEGIES, 901 Marquette Avenue South, Suite 2100, Minneapolis, Minnesota Zip 55402–3713; tel. 612/339–0919; Julie McCauley, Senior Vice President, Corporate; www.ihstrategies.com

INTERWOVEN, 160 East Tasman Drive, San Jose, California Zip 95134; tel. 408/774–2000; Joe Cowan, Chief Executive Officer and Director; www.interwoven.com

KAUFMAN HALL, 5202 Old Orchard Road, Suite N700, Skokie, Illinois Zip 60077; tel. 847/441–8780; Jason H. Sussman, Partner; www.kaufmanhall.com

KROLL ONTRACK, INC., 18350 Mount Langley Street, Suite 110, Fountain Valley, California Zip 92708; tel. 800/872–2599; Stacey May, Manager; www.krollontrack.com

KURT SALMON ASSOCIATES, 1355 Peachtree Street N.E., Suite 900, Atlanta, Georgia Zip 30309–0900; tel. 404/892–0321; Nancy Snell, Senior Research Analyst; www.kurtsalmon.com

LATHAM AND WATKINS, LLP, 633 West 5th Street, Suite 4000, Los Angeles, California Zip 90071; tel. 213/485–1234; Daniel K. Settelmayer, Partner; www.lw.com

LEXISNEXIS, 1000 Alderman Drive, Alpharetta, Georgia Zip 30005; tel. 404/577–1779; Sarah J. Stansberry, Senior Director, Marketing; www.lexisnexis.com

LIVEPROCESS, 271 Grove Avenue, Building D., Verona, New Jersey Zip 07044; tel. 973/571–2500; Nathaniel Weiss, Chief Executive Officer; www.liveprocess.com

MARITZ, INC., 1375 North Highway Drive, Fenton, Missouri Zip 63099; tel. 636/827–4000; Amy Kramer, Healthcare Section Strategist; www.maritz.com

MCDONALD HOPKINS, LLC, 600 Superior Avenue East, Suite 2100, Cleveland, Ohio Zip 44114–2690; tel. 216/348–5400; Richard S. Cooper, Member; www.mcdonaldhopkins.com

MCG HEALTH, LLC, 901 5th Avenue, Suite 2000, Seattle, Washington Zip 98164–2076; tel. 206/389–5300; Mara Osman, Director Government Relations; www.careguidelines.com

MCKESSON CORPORATION, 1 Post Street, 33rd Floor, San Francisco, California Zip 94104–5203; tel. 404/338–3519; Barbara Swan, Manager, Library and Information Services

MEDASSETS, 100 North Pointe Center East, Suite 200, Alpharetta, Georgia Zip 30022–1506; tel. 678/248–8154; Ron DeCarlo, Senior Vice President; www.medassets.com

MEDICAL SIMULATION CORPORATION, 4643 South Ulster Street, Suite 650, Denver, Colorado Zip 80237–2964; tel. 888/889–5882; www.medsimulation.com

NAVEX GLOBAL, 6000 Meadows Road, Suite 200, Lake Oswego, Oregon Zip 97035–3172; tel. 503/924–1640; Stephen J. Molen, Vice President Strategic Solutions; www.navexglobal. com

NORTH AMERICAN PARTNERS IN ANESTHESIA, 68 South Service Road, Suite 350, Melville, New York Zip 11747–2358; tel. 516/945–3000; Jill Aaronson, Marketing Coordinator; www.napaanesthesia.com

NUANCE, 3715 Northside Parkway, 100 Northcreek, Suite 200, Atlanta, Georgia Zip 30327; tel. 770/438–8537; Melissa Dickinson, Coordinator Marketing; www. jathomas.com

NVOQ, 1715 38th Street, Boulder, Colorado Zip 80301–2603; tel. 720/562–4500; Charles Corfield, Chief Executive Officer; www.mvoq.com

OPPENHEIMER MULTIFAMILY HOUSING AND HEALTHCARE FINANCE, 1180 Welsh Road, Suite 210, North Wales, Pennsylvania Zip 19454–2057; tel. 215/631–9151; Thomas P. Cassidy, Associate Vice President; www. opcomortgagefinance.com

PACKETMOTION, INC., 260 Santa Ana Court, Sunnyvale, California Zip 94085–4512; tel. 408/449–4300; Ravi Khatod, Senior Vice President, Sales and Business Development; www. packetmotion.com

PEER CONSULTING, 2856 80Th Avenue S.E., Suite 200, Mercer Island, Washington Zip 98040–2984; tel. 206/236–1300; Rick Nunn, Senior Managing Partner; www.peerconsulting.net

PHYSICIAN WELLNESS SERVICES, 5000 West 36th Street, Suite 230, Minneapolis, Minnesota Zip 55416–2771; tel. 877/731–3949; Lori Brostrom, Vice President Marketing; www.physicianwellnessservices.com

PREMIERE GLOBAL SERVICES, 3280 Peachtree Road N.W., Suite 1000, Atlanta, Georgia Zip 30305–2422; tel. 404/543–9449; Mark H. Horne, Vice President Marketing, Notifications and Reminders; www.premiereglobal.com

PRESS GANEY ASSOCIATES, INC., 404 Columbia Place, South Bend, Indiana Zip 46601–2315; tel. 800/232–8032; Kathryn Ryan, Marketing Director; www.pressganey.com

PROFESSIONAL RESEARCH CONSULTANTS, INC., 11326 P. Street, Omaha, Nebraska Zip 68137–2316; tel. 800/428–7455; Janna Binder, Director Marketing and Public Relations; www.prconline.com

PUBLIC FINANCIAL MANAGEMENT, INC., 99 Summer Street, Suite 1020, Boston, Massachusetts Zip 02110–1200; tel. 617/330–6914; Christine Doyle, Managing Director; www.pfm.com

QUAMMEN HEALTH CARE CONSULTANTS, 522B Brandies Circle, Suite 4, Murfreesboro, Tennessee Zip 37128–4873; tel. 407/539–2015; Robecca Quammen, President; www.quammengroup.com

RYCAN, P.O. Box 306, Marshall, Minnesota Zip 56258–0306; tel. 800/201–3324; Marg Louwagie, Administrative Assistant; www.rycan.com

SAMUELI INSTITUTE, 1737 King Street, Suite 600, Alexandria, Virginia Zip 22314–2764; tel. 703/299–4800; Bonnie R. Sakallaris, Vice President Optimal Healing Environments; www.siib.org

SEERHEALTH, LLC, 1600 Parkwood Circle S.E., Suite 600, Atlanta, Georgia Zip 30339; tel. 770/767–3879; Anthony Begando, Chief Executive Officer; www. seerhealth.com

SERVICE MANAGEMENT SYSTEMS, 7135 Charlotte Pike, Nashville, Tennessee Zip 37209–5015; tel. 615/399–1839; Ned Van Allan, Director of Business Development; www.smsclean.com

SHERIDAN HEALTHCARE, INC., 1613 North Harrison Parkway, Suite 200, Sunrise, Florida Zip 33323–2853; tel. 954/838–2749; Terri Burgess, Director Operations, Business Development; www.sheridanhealthcare.com

SIEMENS HEALTHCARE, 51 Valley Stream Parkway, Malvern, Pennsylvania Zip 19355; tel. 610/448–4500; Barbara Sivek, Senior Director Industry Relations; www.medical.siemens. com

SODEXO HEALTH CARE, 86 Hopmeadow Street, Simsbury, Connecticut Zip 06089; tel. 860/325–1220; Shirley Palmieri, Director Creative Services; www.sodexo.com

SOYRING CONSULTING, 880 21st Avenue North, Saint Petersburg, Florida Zip 33704; tel. 727/822–8774; Adam Higman, Vice President; www.soyringconsulting. com

SPECIALTYCARE, 3100 West End Avenue, Suite 800, Nashville, Tennessee Zip 37203; tel. 615/345–5400; Nancy R. Becker, Senior Vice President Marketing and Client Relations; www.specialtycare.net

STOCKAMP AND ASSOCIATES, INC., 6000 S.W. Meadows Road, Suite 300, Lake Oswego, Oregon Zip 97035; tel. 503/303–1200; Karen Andrews, Senior Marketing Manager; www.stockamp.com

STROUDWATER ASSOCIATES, 50 Sewall Street, Suite 102, Portland, Maine Zip 04102–2646; tel. 207/221–8255; Marc Voyvodich, Chief Executive Officer

SULLIVAN, COTTER AND ASSOCIATES, INC., 1100 Peachtree Street, Suite 620, Atlanta, Georgia Zip 30309; tel. 678/551–7190; Maureen Cotter, Director Research and Information; www.sullivancotter. com

SUNRISE DETOX CENTERS, 2328 10th Avenue N, Suite 302, Lake Worth, Florida Zip 33461–6612; tel. 561/533–0074; Joseph Horrocks, Business Officer Manager

SURGICAL CARE AFFILIATES, 3000 Galleria Boulevard, Suite 500, Birmingham, Alabama Zip 35244; tel. 205/545–2759; Julie Dunn, Vice President; www. scasurgery.com

SURGICAL INFORMATION SYSTEMS, 555 North Point Center East, Suite 700, Alpharetta, Georgia Zip 30022–8268; tel. 800/930–0895; Katie Allen, Director, Marketing; www.sisfirst.com

SYSCOM SERVICES, INC, 1010 Wayne Avenue, Suite 320, Silver Spring, Maryland Zip 20910; tel. 301/768–0118; Lee Weinstein, President; www.syscomservices.com

THE CHARTIS GROUP, 220 West Kinzie Street, 5th Floor, Chicago, Illinois Zip 60654–4912; tel. 877/667–4700; Katy Pinter, Principal; www.chartis.com

THE HSM GROUP, LTD, 8777 East Via de Ventura #188, Scottsdale, Arizona Zip 85258; tel. 480/947–8078; Sheryl Bronkesh, President; www.hsmgroup.com

THE STUDER GROUP, 8222 Douglas Avenue, Suite 780, Dallas, Texas Zip 75225–5923; tel. 972/860–0551; B. G. Porter, Chief Executive Officer and President; www.studergroup.com

TIAA CREF, 8500 Andrew Carnegie Boulevard, B208, Charlotte, North Carolina Zip 28262–8500; tel. 704/988–8064; Kevin S. Nazworth, Vice President Healthcare Market; www.tiaa–cref.org

VECNA TECHNOLOGIES, INC., 36 Cambridgepark Drive, Cambridge, Massachusetts Zip 02140; tel. 617/864–0636; Amanda Baldi, Director, Marketing and Communications; www.vecna.com

VENDOR CREDENTIALING SERVICE, INC., 616 Cypress Creek Parkway, Suite 800, Houston, Texas Zip 77090–3029; tel. 281/863–9500; Troy Kyle, President and Chief Executive Officer; www. vcsdatabase.com

VERITY, INC, 5758 West Las Positas Boulevard, Suite 100, Pleasanton, California Zip 94588; tel. 925/598–3003; Michael Pliner, President; www.verity.com

VERRAS HEALTHCARE INTERNATIONAL, tel. 888/791–5556; Robert T. Langston, Partner

WASTE MANAGEMENT, 1001 Fannin St. Suite 4000, Houston, Texas Zip 77002–6711; tel. 713/265–1352; Bill Turpin, Director Strategic Development

WESTERN HEALTHCARE ALLIANCE, 715 Horizon Drive, Suite 401, Grand Junction, Colorado Zip 81506–8731; tel. 970/683–5223; Carolyn S. Bruce, Chief Executive Officer; www.wha1.org

XANITOS, INC., 3809 West Chester Pike, Suite 210, Newtown Square, Pennsylvania Zip 19073–2304; tel. 484/654–2300; Graeme A. Crothall, Chairman and Chief Executive Officer; www.xanitos.com

Educational Services:

NATIONAL RURAL HEALTH RESOURCE CENTER, 600 East Superior Street, Suite 404, Duluth, Minnesota Zip 55802; tel. 218/727–9390; Sally Buck, Chief Executive Officer; www.ruralcenter.org

RAYTHEON PROFESSIONAL SERVICES, 870 Winter Street, Waltham, Massachusetts Zip 02451–1449; tel. 781/522–3000; Dave Letts, Vice President and General Manager; www.raytheon.com

Information Systems:

3M HEALTH INFORMATION SYSTEMS, 575 West Murray Boulevard, Murray, Utah Zip 84123–4611; tel. 801/265–4390; Ann Chenoweth, Senior Director, Industry Relations; www.mmm.com

CERNER CORPORATION, 2800 Rockcreek Parkway, Kansas City, Missouri Zip 64117; tel. 816/221–1024; Laurel Vine, Program Manager, Industry Events; www.cerner. com

DESIGN CLINICALS, 5200 Southcenter Boulevard, Suite 250, Seattle, Washington Zip 98188–7911; tel. 888/633–7320; Dewey Howell, Chief Executive Officer; www.designclinicals.com

HEALTHLAND, 1600 Utica Avenue South, Suite 300, Minneapolis, Minnesota Zip 55416–1468; tel. 612/787–3120; Tracey Schroeder, Vice President Marketing

IMPRIVATA, INC., 10 Maguire Road Building 4, Lexington, Massachusetts Zip 02421–3110; tel. 781/674–2700; Ed Gaudel, Chief Marketing Officer; www.imprivata.com

KPMG LLP, 200 East Randolph Street, Suite 5500, Chicago, Illinois Zip 60601–6607; tel. 312/665–2073; Edward J. Giniat, National Line of Business Leader, Healthcare and Pharmaceuticals Practice

MEDHOST, 6100 West Plano Parkway, Suite 3100, Plano, Texas Zip 75093–8342; tel. 888/218–4678; Leslie LaFon, Departmental Segment Manager; www.medhost.com

MPOWR, A SUPPLYCORE SOLUTION, 303 North Main Street, Suite 800, Rockford, Illinois Zip 61101–1018; tel. 815/964–7940; Bryan Davis, Director; www. mpowr.com

SCC SOFT COMPUTER, 5400 Tech Data Drive, Clearwater, Florida Zip 33760–3116; tel. 727/789–0100; Gilbert Hakim, Chief Executive Officer; www.softcomputer.com

SHIFTWISE, 1800 S.W. 1st Avenue, Suite 510, Portland, Oregon Zip 97201–5322; tel. 503/548–2030; Nick Haselwander, Marketing Manager; www.shiftwise.com

VALENCE HEALTH, 600 West Jackson Boulevard, Chicago, Illinois Zip 60661–5636; tel. 312/273–6623; Kevin Weinstein, Chief Marketing Officer; www.valencehealth.com

Insurance Broker:

AMERICAN FIDELITY ASSURANCE COMPANY, 2000 North Classen Boulevard, Oklahoma City, Oklahoma Zip 73106; tel. 877/967–5748; Brian Mauck, National Sales Director; www.af–group. com

BOSTON MUTUAL LIFE INSURANCE COMPANY, 120 Royall Street, Canton, Massachusetts Zip 02021; tel. 781/828–7000; Peter Tillson, Vice President; www.bostonmutual.com

CHUBB INSURANCE, 82 Hopmeadow Street, Simsbury, Connecticut Zip 06070; tel. 860/408–2017; Kimberly Holmes, Assistant Vice President Healthcare; www.chubb.com

DYE & ESKIN, 1324 Vincent Place, Mc Lean, Virginia Zip 22101; tel. 703/556–0744; Rick Eskin, President

G. E. FINANCIAL, GE Appliance Park Building, Suite 100, Louisville, Kentucky Zip 40225; tel. 502/254–1756; Greg Miller, Director Business Development; www.ge.com

ING EMPLOYEE BENEFITS, 20 Washington Avenue South, Minneapolis, Minnesota Zip 55401; tel. 612/372–1122; Steve Pitzer, Vice President

ISR CONSULTING GROUP, 695 Trade Center Boulevard, Suite 110, Chesterfield, Missouri Zip 63005–1276; tel. 636/530–4606; Jeffrey A. Combs, Executive Vice President; www.isricg.com

LOYAL INSURANCE, 423 Westport Road, Suite 201, Kansas City, Missouri Zip 64111; tel. 816/841–3597; Michael Reidy, Vice President

MESIROW FINANCIAL, 353 North Clark Street, Chicago, Illinois Zip 60654–4704; tel. 312/595–7183; Sheila Kelly, Senior Managing Director; www.mesirowfinancial.com

NEBCO, 1264 Knollwood Drive West, West Chester, Pennsylvania Zip 19380; tel. 877/739–3330; James M. Mattison, Vice President; www.nebenefit. com

THE ALLEN J. FLOOD COMPANIES, INC., 2 Madison Avenue, Larchmont, New York Zip 10538; tel. 914/834–9326; Allen J. Flood, President; www.ajfusa.com

UNITED CONCORDIA COMPANY, INC., 4401 Deer Path Road, Harrisburg, Pennsylvania Zip 17110; tel. 717/260–6800; Brett Altland, Product Development Analyst; www.ucci.com

*The members listed in **bold** are Associate Advantage members.* © 2014 AHA Guide

VALIC, 2929 Allen Parkway (L6–40), Houston, Texas Zip 77019–2111; tel. 713/831–6128; Nicole Mott, Associate Director Marketing; www.valic.com

ZURICH INSURANCE GROUP, tel. 312/496–9418; Daniel R. Nash, National Healthcare Practice Leader; www.zurichna.com/healthcare

Managed Care/Utilization:

CENTENE CORPORATION, 111 East Capitol Street, Suite 500, Jackson, Mississippi Zip 39201; tel. 601/863–0835; K. Michael Bailey, Vice President; www.centene.com

Manufacturer/Supplier:

AMERISOURCE BERGEN, 1300 Morris Drive, Chesterbrook, Pennsylvania Zip 19087–5559; tel. 610/727–2441; Elisa Moxley, Director, Health Systems Market Development; www.amerisourcebergen.com

BAXTER HEALTHCARE CORPORATION, Route 120 and Wilson Road, Round Lake, Illinois Zip 60073; tel. 224/948–2000; Tom Progar, Vice President Marketing Strategy and Operations; www.baxter.com

BOEHRINGER INGELHEIM PHARMACEUTICALS, INC., 800 Ridgebury Road, Mail Stop 2D 113F, Ridgebury, Connecticut Zip 06877; tel. 203/798–9988; Michelle Jenkins–Woodman, Senior Manager, Managed Markets Marketing; www.us.boehringer-ingelheim.com

CARDINAL HEALTH, 2215 Citygate Drive, Columbus, Ohio Zip 43219–3589; tel. 614/757–5000; Seham Yennes, Vice President, Marketing Acute; www. cardinal.com

CARDINAL HEALTH MEDICAL DEVICE DIVISION, 7000 Cardinal Place, Dublin, Ohio Zip 43017–1091; tel. 614/553–4526; Lisa Ashby, President, Medical Devices and Diagnostics; www.cardinalhealth.com

CARDIONET, 227 Washington Street, Second Floor, Conshohocken, Pennsylvania Zip 19428–2086; tel. 610/729–0433; Michael Geldart, Senior Vice President, Corporate Strategy and Business Development; www.https://www.cardionet.com

CAREFUSION CORPORATION, 3750 Torrey View Court, San Diego, California Zip 92130–2622; tel. 858/617–2000; Jocelyn Ochinang, Market Research Manager; www.carefusion.com

CORNING INC., 13221 Woodland Park Road, Suite 400, Herndon, Virginia Zip 20171–5505; tel. 202/230–3306; Grace Alcivar, Director Vertical Programs, Healthcare; www.corning.com

EXTENSION, INC, 6435 West Jefferson Boulevard, Suite 201, Fort Wayne, Indiana Zip 46804–6203; tel. 877/207–3753; Whitney St. Pierre, Director Marketing; www.opentheredbox.com

GE HEALTHCARE, 9900 West Innovation Drive, RP–2177, Wauwatosa, Wisconsin Zip 53226–4856; tel. 262/548–2088; Michael Becker, Director of Marketing

HILL–ROM, 1069 State Route 46 East, Batesville, Indiana Zip 47006–9167; tel. 812/934–7958; Thomas J. Jeffers, Director Government Relations; www.hill–rom.com

JOHNSON & JOHNSON, 829 Williamsburg Boulevard, Downingtown, Pennsylvania Zip 19335–4124; tel. 610/518–7295; Larry Westfall, Director Healthcare Quality Alliances

LILLY USA, LLC, Lilly Corporate Center–DC 5021, Indianapolis, Indiana Zip 46285–4113; tel. 317/277–8173; John H. Poulin, Advisor Professional Relations; www.lilly.com

OTSUKA AMERICA PHARMACEUTICAL, INC., 2440 Research Boulevard, Rockville, Maryland Zip 20850; tel. 301/990–0030; Jennifer Greaney, Director; www.otsuka.com

SWISSLOG HEALTHCARE SOLUTIONS, 10825 East 47th Avenue, Denver, Colorado Zip 80239–2913; tel. 800/764–0300; Marion M. Robinson, Vice President Marketing; www.swisslog.com

UMF CORPORATION, 4709 Golf Road, Suite 300A, Skokie, Illinois Zip 60076–1231; tel. 847/920–0370; Red Degala, Director Finance; www.perfectclean.com

XEROX BUSINESS SERVICES, LLC, 2828 North Haskell Avenue, Dallas, Texas Zip 75204–2909; tel. 214/584–5964; Kirsten LeMaster, VP, Marketing and Communication, Healthcare Provider Solutions; www.services.xerox.com/healthcare–solutions/enus.html

Metro Hospital Assn:

HOSPITAL ASSOCIATION OF SOUTHERN CALIFORNIA, 515 South Figueroa Street, Suite 1300, Los Angeles, California Zip 90071–3300; tel. 213/538–0700; James D. Barber, President; www.hasc.org

National Health Care Prof Assn:

AMERICAN DENTAL ASSOCIATION, 211 East Chicago Avenue, Chicago, Illinois Zip 60611–2678; tel. 312/440–2500; Jane Grover, Director, Council on Access, Prevention and Interprofessional Relations; www.ada.org

NATIONAL ASSOCIATION FOR HEALTHCARE QUALITY, 8735 West Higgins Road, Suite 300, Chicago, Illinois Zip 60631–2738; tel. 847/375–4867; Stephanie Mercado, Executive Director

Other:

21ST CENTURY ONCOLOGY, 2270 Colonial Boulevard, Fort Myers, Florida Zip 33907; tel. 239/461–8584; Gheorghe Pusta, Vice President; www.21stcenturyoncology.com

3N, 505 North Brand Boulevard, Suite 700, Glendale, California Zip 91203; tel. 818/230–9728; Steve Kirchmeier, Vice President Healthcare; www. 3nonline.com

AEROSCOUT, 1300 Island Drive, Suite 202, Redwood City, California Zip 94065; tel. 650/596–2994; Gabi Daniely, Vice President Marketing and Product Strategy; www.aeroscout.com

AGILITY RECOVERY SOLUTIONS, 11030 Circle Point Road, Suite 450, Westminster, Colorado Zip 80020–2791; tel. 877/495–9615; Jenny Boyd, Director Marketing Account; www.agilityrecovery. com

AIR METHODS CORPORATION, 7301 South Peoria Street, Englewood, Colorado Zip 80112–4133; tel. 303/792–7565; Ryan Frazier, Senior Advisor to the Chief Executive Officer Strategic Relations; www.airmethods.com

AMERICA'S BLOOD CENTERS, 725 15th Street N.W., Suite 700, Washington, District of Columbia Zip 20005; tel. 202/393–5725; William M. Coenen, Interim Chief Executive Officer

AMERICAN ACADEMY OF PHYSICIAN ASSISTANTS, 2318 Mill Road, Suite 1300, Alexandria, Virginia Zip 22314–6833; tel. 703/836–2272; Michael L. Powe, Vice President Reimbursement and Professional Advocacy; www.aapa.org

AMERICAN ASSOCIATION FOR WOUND CARE MANAGEMENT, 4109 Glenrose Street, Kensington, Maryland Zip 20895–3718; tel. 301/933–2200; Jule Crider, Executive Director; www.aawcm.org

AMERICAN ASSOCIATION OF NURSE ANESTHETISTS, 222 South Prospect Avenue, Park Ridge, Illinois Zip 60068–4001; tel. 847/655–1100; Wanda O. Wilson, Executive Director and Chief Executive Officer; www.aana.com

AMERICAN BOARD OF MEDICAL SPECIALTIES, 353 North Clark Street, Suite 1400, Chicago, Illinois Zip 60654–3454; tel. 312/436–2626; Lois Margaret Nora, President and Chief Executive Officer; www.abms.org

AMERICAN COLLEGE OF HEALTHCARE EXECUTIVES, One North Franklin, Suite 1700, Chicago, Illinois Zip 60606–4425; tel. 312/424–2800; Deborah Bowen, President and Chief Executive Officer; www.ache.org

AMERICAN DENTAL EDUCATION ASSOCIATION, 1400 K Street N.W., Suite 1100, Washington, District of Columbia Zip 20005; tel. 202/289–7201; Richard Valachovic, Executive Director; www.adea.org

AMERICAN HEALTH INFORMATION MANAGEMENT ASSOCIATION, 233 North Michigan Avenue, Suite 2150, Chicago, Illinois Zip 60601–5806; tel. 312/233–1100; David A. Sweet, Director Library Services

AMERICAN SOCIETY OF ANESTHESIOLOGISTS, 1061 American Lane, Schaumburg, Illinois Zip 60173; tel. 847/268–9160; Paul Pomerantz, Chief Executive Officer; www.asahq.org

AMERINET, INC., 500 Commonwealth Drive, Warrendale, Pennsylvania Zip 15086–7516; tel. 877/711–5700; Laurie McGrath, Vice President Marketing; www.amerinet-gpo.com

AMN HEALTHCARE, INC., 12400 High Bluff Drive, Suite 100, San Diego, California Zip 92130–3581; tel. 866/871–8519; Steve Wehn, Senior Vice President of Corporate Development

AMS STORE AND SHRED, LLC, 13 Prosper Court, Lake In The Hills, Illinois Zip 60156–9603; tel. 800/262–2344; Denise Hammer, Manager, Marketing Business Development

APOGEE PHYSICIANS, 2525 East Camelback Road, Suite 1100, Phoenix, Arizona Zip 85016–4282; tel. 602/778–3600; Michael Gregory, Chairman; www.apogeephysicians.com

ARC GROUP ASSOCIATES, 330 South Warminster Road, Suite 345, Hatboro, Pennsylvania Zip 19040; tel. 215/881–9500; Eric Malakoff, Vice President Sales and Marketing; www. arcgroup.net

ARMED FORCES INSTITUTE OF PATHOLOGY, 6825 16th Street N.W., Building 54, Washington, District of Columbia Zip 20306–6000; tel. 202/782–2100; Colonel Renata Greenspan, Director; www.afip.osd.mil

ASSOCIATION OF PERIOPERATIVE REGISTERED NURSES, 2170 South Parker Road, Suite 400, Denver, Colorado Zip 80231; tel. 303/755–6304; Linda Kay Groah, Executive Director and Chief Executive Officer; www.aorn.org

AVATAR SOLUTIONS, 25 East Washington Street, Suite 600, Chicago, Illinois Zip 60602; tel. 312/236–7170; Jeffrey Brady, Chief Executive Officer; www.hrsolutionsinc.com

BACTES, 8344 Clairemont Mesa Boulevard, Suite 201, San Diego, California Zip 92111–1327; tel. 858/244–1811; Jim Bailey, President; www.bactes.com

BERNARD HODES GROUP, 220 East 42nd Street, 14th Floor, New York, New York Zip 10017; tel. 888/438–9911; Karen Hart, Senior Vice President Healthcare Division; www.hodes.com

BEST UPON REQUEST, 8170 Corporate Park Drive, Suite 300, Cincinnati, Ohio Zip 45242; tel. 513/605–7800; Kirsten Lecky, Vice President Business Development; www.bestuponrequest.com

BKD, LLP, P.O. Box 1190, Springfield, Missouri Zip 65801–1900; tel. 417/831–7283; Shelbey Stockton, Marketing and Business Development; www.bkd.com

BLUE CROSS AND BLUE SHIELD ASSOCIATION, 225 North Michigan Avenue, Chicago, Illinois Zip 60601–7680; tel. 312/297–6000; Scott P. Serota, President and Chief Executive Officer; www.bcbs.com

BOHAN ADVERTISING AND MARKETING, 124 12th Avenue S., Nashville, Tennessee Zip 37203–3146; tel. 615/327–1189; Jeremi Griggs, Group Account Director; www.bohanideas.com

CANON SOLUTIONS AMERICA, INC., 300 Commerce Square Boulevard, Burlington, New Jersey Zip 08016–1270; tel. 847/706–3411; Paul T. Murphy, Director Strategic Contract Support; www.solutions.canon.com

CAP SITE INC., 85 South Prospect Street, Burlington, Vermont Zip 05401–3444; tel. 802/383–0675; Gino Johnson, Senior Vice President; www.capsite. com

CARETECH SOLUTIONS, INC., tel. 248/823–0800; Paula Gwyn, Senior Manager Business Development; www.caretechsolutions.com

CCM ADVISORS, LLC, 190 South La Salle Street, Suite 2800, Chicago, Illinois Zip 60603; tel. 312/444–6200; Michael Randall, Director Sales and Marketing; www.ahafunds.org

CERTIPHI SCREENING, INC., 1105 Industrial Highway, Southampton, Pennsylvania Zip 18966; tel. 888/260–1370; Tony D'Orazio, President; www.certiphi.com

CHAMBERLIN EDMONDS, 14 Piedmont Center N.E., Atlanta, Georgia Zip 30305–1543; tel. 404/279–5000; Kim Williams, Chief Financial Officer; www.chamberlinedmonds.com

CHAN HEALTHCARE AUDITORS, 231 South Bemiston Avenue, Suite 300, Saint Louis, Missouri Zip 63105; tel. 314/802–2008; Dan Clayton, Director, Knowledge Management; www.chanllc.com

CISCO SYSTEMS, 165 Needletree Lane, Glastonbury, Connecticut Zip 06033; tel. 860/657–8127; Michael Haymaker, Director Healthcare Industry Marketing; www.cisco.com

CLAIMS EVAL INC., 6905 Mystery Creek Lane, Granite Bay, California Zip 95746–7353; tel. 916/797–9997; Michael Hamby, Executive Director; www.claimseval.com

CLAREDI CORPORATION, 2525 Lake Park Boulevard, Salt Lake City, Utah Zip 84120; tel. 801/982–3001; Kepa Zubeldia, Senior Vice President; www.claredi.com

COMPREHENSIVE PHARMACY SERVICES, 6409 North Quail Hollow Road, Memphis, Tennessee Zip 38120–1414; tel. 901/748–0470; Walker Upshaw, Chief Development Officer; www.cpspharm.com

COMPUTER ASSOCIATES, One Computer Associates Plaza, Islandia, New York Zip 11749; tel. 800/225–5224; Michael McDermand, Vice President Healthcare; www.ca.com

CONCUITY, INCORPORATED, 200 North Fairway Drive Suite 182, Vernon Hills, Illinois Zip 60061–1861; tel. 847/465–6003; James Farrar, Vice President Sales; www.concuity.com

CONTINUUM HEALTH ALLIANCE, LLC, 402 Lippincott Drive, Marlton, New Jersey Zip 08053–4112; tel. 856/782–3300; Sean Porrini, Chief Operating Officer; www.challc.net

COVENANT HOSPICE, 5041 North 12th Avenue, Pensacola, Florida Zip 32504; tel. 850/433–2155; Dale O. Knee, President and Chief Executive Officer; www.covenanthospice.org

CRANEWARE, INC., 3340 Peachtree Road N.E. Suite 850, Atlanta, Georgia Zip 30326–1072; tel. 404/364–2037; Ann Marie Brown, Executive Vice President Marketing; www.craneware.com

CYRACOM, 5780 North Swan Road, Tucson, Arizona Zip 85718–4527; tel. 800/713–4950; Jeremy Woan, President and Chief Executive Officer; www.cyracom.com

DELPHI TECHNOLOGY, INC., tel. 617/259–1200; Bonnie Clark, Vice President Marketing; www.delphi-tech.com

DEPARTMENT OF AIR FORCE MEDICAL SERVICE, HQ USAF/SG, Bolling AFB, District of Columbia Zip 20332–6188; tel. 202/545–6700

DEPARTMENT OF THE ARMY, OFFICE OF THE SURGEON GENERAL, 5109 Leesburg Pike, Falls Church, Virginia Zip 22041–3258; tel. 202/690–6467

DILIGENT, A DIVISION OF ARJO, 2349 West Lake Street, Suite 250, Addison, Illinois Zip 60101–6183; tel. 800/323–1245; Andrew Hepburn, Vice President; www.arjohuntleigh.com

DISH, 9601 South Meridian Boulevard, Englewood, Colorado Zip 80112–5905; tel. 720/514–6019; Steven Wilson, Manager; www.dish.com

DNV HEALTHCARE, INC., 400 Techne Center Drive, Suite 100, Milford, Ohio Zip 45150–2792; tel. 513/388–4863; Shannon Walker, Team Operator and Planner; www.dnvhealthcareinc.com

EKTRON, 542 Amherst Street, Nashua, New Hampshire Zip 03063–1016; tel. 603/594–0249; Deb Symons, Director, Field Marketing and Programs; www.ektron.com

FIRST AMERICAN EQUIPMENT FINANCE, 255 Woodcliff Drive, Fairport, New York Zip 14450–4219; tel. 585/643–3266; Mike Wiedemer, Senior Vice President, Sales; www.faef.com

FTI HEALTHCARE, 5310 Maryland Way, Suite 250, Brentwood, Tennessee Zip 37027–5370; tel. 615/324–8500; Ashley Frericks, Operations Associate; www.ftihealthcare.com

HEALTHCARE BUSINESS ASSOCIATES, P.O. Box 1188, Rancho Mirage, California Zip 92270–1188; tel. 888/292–6929; Jack C. Nixon, President

HEALTHWAYS, INC, 701 Cool Springs Boulevard, Franklin, Tennessee Zip 37067–2697; tel. 800/327–3822; Karen Meyer, Principal; www.healthways.com

HIRERIGHT, 3349 Michelson Drive, Suite 150, Irvine, California Zip 92612–0653; tel. 800/400–2761; Bob Sparanese, Manager Product Marketing; www.hireright.com

HMS, 355 Quartermaster Court, Jeffersonville, Indiana Zip 47130–3670; tel. 812/704–5747; Rich Flaherty, Vice President Sales and Marketing; www.hms.com

HOOPER, LUNDY & BOOKMAN, INC., 1875 Century Park East, Suite 1600, Los Angeles, California Zip 90067; tel. 310/551–8111; Lloyd Bookman, Partner; www.health-law.com

HQ ACC/SGMS, 162 Dodd, Suite 100, Langley AFB, Virginia Zip 23665–1995

HQ AETC/SGAL, 63 Main Circle, Suite 3, Randolph AFB, Texas Zip 78150–4549

HQ AFMC/SGAR, 4225 Logistics Avenue, N–209, Dayton, Ohio Zip 45433–5761; tel. 937/656–3655; Alice Rohrbach

HQ AFSPC/SGAL, 150 Vandenberg Street, Suite 1105, Petterson AFB, Colorado Zip 80914–4550

HQ AMC/SGSL, 203 West Losey Street, Room 1180, Scott AFB, Illinois Zip 62225–5219

HQ PACAF/SGAL, 25 East Street, Suite D1, Hickam AFB, Hawaii Zip 96853–5418

HQ USAFA/SGAL, Pinion Drive, Building 4102, Suite 3, USAF Academy, Colorado Zip 80840

HYLAND SOFTWARE, INC., 28500 Clemens Road, Westlake, Ohio Zip 44145; tel. 440/788–5814; Michael Kortan, Director Health Care Solutions; www.onbase.com

ID EXPERTS, 10300 S.W. Greenburg Road, Suite 570, Portland, Oregon Zip 97223–5410; tel. 866/726–4271; Sally Gray, Manager Sales Support; www.idexpertscorp.com

IDENTITY FORCE, 1257 Worcester Road, Suite 308, Framingham, Massachusetts Zip 01701; tel. 508/788–6660; Mike Lawson, Vice President; www.identityforce.com

INNOVATIVE CAPITAL LLC, 1489 Baltimore Pike, Building 400, Springfield, Pennsylvania Zip 19064–3958; tel. 610/543–2490; Alan P. Richman, President and Chief Executive Officer; www.innovativecapital.com

INTELLICENTRICS, INC., 1420 Lakeside Parkway, Suite 110, Flowermound, Texas Zip 75028; tel. 972/316–6524; Greg Goyne, Vice President of Marketing; www.intellicentrics.com

INTERACTIVE HEALTH SOLUTIONS, 3800 North Wilke Road, Suite 155, Arlington Heights, Illinois Zip 60004–1278; tel. 847/754–2698; Joseph O'Brien, President; www.interactivesolutions.com

INTERNATIONAL ASSOCIATION FOR HEALTHCARE SECURITY AND SAFETY, P.O. Box 5038, Glendale Heights, Illinois Zip 60139; tel. 630/529–3913; Nancy Felesena, Executive Assistant; www.iahss.org

IRONPORT, 950 Elm Avenue, San Bruno, California Zip 94066; tel. 650/989–6500; Jeff Williams, Vice President Sales; www.ironport.com

JANI–KING, 16885 Dallas Parkway, Addison, Texas Zip 75001; tel. 972/991–0900; Bob Carabajal, Director Healthcare Services; www.janiking.com

JEWISH GUILD HEALTHCARE, 15 West 65th Street, New York, New York Zip 10023; tel. 212/769–6200; Alan R. Morse, President and Chief Executive Officer; www.jgb.org

LIFE LINE SCREENING, 6150 Oak Tree Boulevard, Suite 200, Independence, Ohio Zip 44131–2569; tel. 800/897–9177; Kellie D. Privette, Senior Vice President; www.lifelinescreening.com

LITTLER MENDELSON, P.C., 1100 Superior Avenue, 20th Floor, Cleveland, Ohio Zip 44114–2530; tel. 216/623–6104; Angela Lupardus, Manager, Regional Business Development and Marketing; www.littler.com

MAGELLAN HEALTH SERVICES, 6950 Columbia Gateway Drive, Columbia, Maryland Zip 21046; tel. 314/387–4000; Rick Lee, President Employer Solutions; www.magellanhealth.com

MEDICAL INFORMATION TECHNOLOGY, INC., tel. 781/821–3000; Lynn Robblee, Supervisor of Event Coordination and Memberships; www.meditech.com

MEDIMPACT HEALTHCARE SYSTEMS, INC, 10680 Treena Street, San Diego, California Zip 92128; tel. 858/566–2727; Dana Felthouse, Vice President Marketing; www.medimpact.com

MEDSOLUTIONS, 730 Cool Springs Boulevard, Suite 800, Franklin, Tennessee Zip 37067–7289; tel. 615/468–4116; Yvonne Daugherty, Vice President Marketing; www.medsolutions.com

METLIFE RESOURCES, 300 Davidson Avenue, Somerset, New Jersey Zip 08873–4162; tel. 732/652–1268; Anthony Agentowicz, Divisional Marketing Director; www.metlife.com

MODERN HEALTHCARE, 360 North Michigan Avenue, Chicago, Illinois Zip 60601–3806; tel. 312/649–5491; Fawn Lopez, Publisher; www.modernhealthcare.com

NOBLIS, 3150 Fairview Park South, Falls Church, Virginia Zip 22042; tel. 703/610–2255; Alan Dowling, Executive Director; www.mitretek.org

PERKINELMER GENETICS, INC., P.O. Box 219, Bridgeville, Pennsylvania Zip 15017; tel. 412/220–2300; Joseph M. Quashnock, Laboratory Director; www.perkinelmergenetics.com

PILAT, 460 U.S. Highway 22 West Suite 408, Whitehouse Station, New Jersey Zip 08889–3447; tel. 908/823–9417; Travis Lupo, Director Business Development; www.pilat-nai.com

PINSTRIPE, 200 South Executive Drive, Suite 400, Brookfield, Wisconsin Zip 53005–4216; tel. 262/754–5061; Jill Schwieters, Executive Vice President; www.pinstripetalent.com

PLUM HEALTHCARE GROUP, 100 East San Marcos Boulevard, Suite 200, San Marcos, California Zip 92069–2987; tel. 760/471–0388; Nanci Wilson, Vice President Research and Development; www.plumh.com

RF TECHNOLOGIES, 3125 North 126th Street, Brookfield, Wisconsin Zip 53005; tel. 800/669–9946; Glenn Jonas, President and Chief Executive Officer; www.rft.com

RISESMART, INC., 2055 Gateway Place, Suite 150, San Jose, California Zip 95110–1015; tel. 877/384–0004; Komal Patel, Marketing Manager; www.risesmart.com

ROSARIO INCORPORATED, 501 Burwood Drive, Winston Salem, North Carolina Zip 27127; tel. 866/279–8485; Sandra R. Rosario, Director/Owner; www.rosarioinc.com

SEVEN BAR AVIATION, 2101 Cedar Springs Road, Suite 1875, Dallas, Texas Zip 75201–2152; tel. 214/468–8229; Steve Johnson, Senior Vice President Marketing; www.7bar.com

SHIPMAN & GOODWIN LLP, One Constitution Plaza, Hartford, Connecticut Zip 06103–1919; tel. 860/251–5056; Joan W. Feldman, Partner

SIMPLEE, 480 South California Avenue, Suite 301, Palo Alto, California Zip 94306–1609; tel. 800/464–5125; Tim Holthaus, Engagement Marketing Manager; www.simplee.com

SIMPLEX GRINNELL, 50 Technology Drive, Westminster, Massachusetts Zip 01441; tel. 978/731–8486; Suzanne Rahall, Marketing Manager, Healthcare Communications; www.simplexgrinnell.com

STRAND GENOMICS, INC., 548 Market Street, Suite 82804, San Francisco, California Zip 94104–5401; tel. 540/239–0465; Harsha K. Rajasimha, Senior Director; www.strandgenomics.com

SUBWAY, 325 Bic Drive, Milford, Connecticut Zip 06461; tel. 800/888–4848; Joanne Kilgore, Global Account Manager; www.subway.com

TANDBERG, 29 Norfolk Avenue, Peabody, Massachusetts Zip 01960; tel. 978/531–1516; Luke Leininger, Senior Product Manager, Healthcare TelePresence; www.tandberg.com

THE ADVISORY BOARD COMPANY, 2445 M Street N.W., Washington, District of Columbia Zip 20037–2403; tel. 202/266–5600; Christina Brady, Associate Director, Information Resource Center; www.advisory.com

THE AMERICAN COLLEGE OF OBSTETRICIANS AND GYNECOLOGISTS, 409 12th Street, S.W., Washington, District of Columbia Zip 20024–2188; tel. 202/638–5577; Hal Lawrence, Executive Vice President; www.acog.org

THE BERYL INSTITUTE, 3600 Harwood Road, Suite A., Bedford, Texas Zip 76021–4011; tel. 800/833–2000; Stacy Palmer, Vice President Strategy and Member Experience; www.theberylinstitute.org

THE WALKER COMPANY, 31090 S.W. Boones Bend Road, Wilsonville, Oregon Zip 97070–6412; tel. 503/694–8539; Larry W. Walker, Principal; www.walkercompany.com

THERMO USCS, 120 Bishop's Way, Brookfield, Wisconsin Zip 53008; tel. 262/784–5600; Christine Miller, Executive Vice President Healthcare Group; www.thermo.com

TRANSAMERICA RETIREMENT SOLUTIONS, 4 Manhattanville Road, Purchase, New York Zip 10577; tel. 914/697–8952; Peter Kunkel, President and Chief Executive Officer; www.https://www.trsretire.com

TRANSUNION, LLC, 445 Hutchinson Avenue, Suite 800, Columbus, Ohio Zip 43235; tel. 614/785–6411; Martin Callahan, Vice President Business Development; www.transunion.com

TRAVELERS INSURANCE COMPANY, One Tower Square, 6th Floor, Hartford, Connecticut Zip 06183–1134; tel. 860/277–9830; John Truhan, Operations Manager; www.travelers.com

U. S. ARMY MEDICAL COMMAND, 2050 Worth Road, Suite 10, San Antonio, Texas Zip 78234–6010; tel. 210/221–2212; Ann Russell Potter

UNIFORM DATA SYSTEM FOR MEDICAL REHABILITATION, 270 Northpointe Parkway, Suite 300, Amherst, New York Zip 14228; tel. 716/817–7800; Beth Demakos, Associate Product Manager; www.udsmr.org

VERGE SOLUTIONS, LLC, 710 Johnnie Dodds Boulevard, Suite 202, Mount Pleasant, South Carolina Zip 29464–3045; tel. 843/628–4168; Katie Layman, Marketing Manager; www.verge-solutions.com

*The members listed in **bold** are Associate Advantage members.*   © 2014 AHA Guide

VERISYS CORPORATION, 1001 North Fairfax Avenue, Suite 640, Alexandria, Virginia Zip 22314–1798; tel. 703/535–1471; John Benson, Chief Operating Officer; www.verisys.com/

VERSUS TECHNOLOGY, INC., 2600 Miller Creek Road, Traverse City, Michigan Zip 49684; tel. 231/946–5868; Stephanie Bertschy, Director Marketing; www.versustech.com

VERTICAL CLAIMS MANAGEMENT, L.L.C., 12300 Perry Highway, Suite 300, Wexford, Pennsylvania Zip 15090–8380; tel. 800/501–6248; Clare Bello, President; www.vcm–llc.com

VOCERA COMMUNICATIONS, 525 Race Street, Suite 150, San Jose, California Zip 95126–3495; tel. 408/882–5100; Diana Cropley, Marketing Program Specialist; www.vocera.com

WALGREENS HEALTH SERVICES, 1411 Lake Cook Road, MS L414, Deerfield, Illinois Zip 60015; tel. 847/374–2640; Mariana Boggiana, Director, Payor Marketing Strategy; www.walgreens.com

WESTERN LITIGATION, INC, 9821 Katy Freeway, Suite 600, Houston, Texas Zip 77024–1206; tel. 800/588–0619; Robert B. Blasio, President and Chief Executive Officer; www.westernliitigation.com

WIGGIN AND DANA, LLP, P.O. Box 1832, New Haven, Connecticut Zip 06508–1832; tel. 203/498–4400; Maureen Weaver, Partner

ZCO CORPORATION, 58 Technology Way, Suite 2W 10, Nashua, New Hampshire Zip 03060–3245; tel. 603/881–9200; Kathryn Bisson, Marketing Specialist; www.zco.com

Recruitment Services:

B. E. SMITH, 8801 Renner Avenue, Lenexa, Kansas Zip 66219–9746; tel. 855/296–6318; Allison Murphy, Marketing Manager; www.besmith.com

DOCCAFE.COM, tel. 715/302–8881; Laura Fitzsimmons, Managing Member; www.doccafe.com

FURST GROUP, 2902 McFarland Road, Rockford, Illinois Zip 61107–6801; tel. 800/642–9940; Patrick Kampert, Director of Communications; www.furstgroup.com

UNITED ANESTHESIA, P.O. Box 1847, Kernersville, North Carolina Zip 27285–1847; tel. 800/334–8320; Tracy Strother–Mayer, Chief Operating Officer; www.unitedanesthesia.com

Other:

COMMONWEALTH HEALTH CENTER, P.O. Box 500409, Saipan, Northern Mariana Islands Zip 96950; tel. 670/234–8950; Esther L. Muna, Chief Executive Officer; www.chcc.gov.mp

CANADA

Consulting Firm:

IMPARK, 601 West Cordova Street, Suite 300, Vancouver, British Columbia Zip V6B 1G1; tel. 215/678–5040; Eric Vasterling, Director of Business Development – Healthcare; www.impark.com

RL SOLUTIONS, INC., 1 Yonge Street, Suite 2300, Toronto, Ontario Zip M5E 1E5; tel. 416/410–8456; Sanjay Malaviya, President and CEO; www.rl–solutions.com

Other:

HALOGEN SOFTWARE CORPORATION, 495 March Road, Suite 500, Ottawa, Ontario Zip K2K 3G1; tel. 613/270–1011; Lorna Daly, Channel Manager Healthcare; www.halogensoftware.com

INTERNATIONAL MEDICAL INTERPRETERS ASSOCIATION, 80 Corporatate Drive, Suite 305, Toronto, Zip M1H 3G5; tel. 416/296–0842; Izabel Arocha, Executive Director; www.imiaweb.org

Provincial Hospital Assn:

ONTARIO HOSPITAL ASSOCIATION, 200 Front Street West, Suite 2800, Toronto, Ontario Zip M5V 3L1; tel. 416/205–1300; Warren DiClemente, Vice President Educational Services and Operations; www.oha.com

FOREIGN

BAHAMAS

Other:

PRINCESS MARGARET HOSPITAL, P.O. Box N–8200, Nassau, tel. 242/322–2861; Coralie Adderley, Chief Hospital Administrator; www.phabahamas.org

BAHRAIN

Other:

INTERNATIONAL HOSPITAL OF BAHRAIN, P.O. Box 1084, Manama, tel. 011/759–8222; F. S. Zeerah, President; www.ihb.net/

BANGLADESH

Consulting Firm:

U. S. BANGLADESH FOUNDATION, House 32, Road 10, Block D., Banani, Dhaka, Zip 1213; tel. 880/881–3070; Mohammad Zahurul Haque, Chief Executive Officer; www.banglasoy.com/usbdf.htm

BRAZIL

Other:

HOSPITAL SAMARITANO, Rua Conselheiro Brotero, 1486, Sao Paulo, Zip 01232–010; tel. 551/821–5300; Jose Antonio de Lima, General Superintendent; www.samaritano.com.br

CHINA

Consulting Firm:

ASSOCIATED INTERNATIONAL HOSPITAL CORPORATION CENTER, No. 1 South Street, Beijing, Gao Xingyan, Manager

COLOMBIA

Other:

ASOCIACION COLOMBIANA DE HOSPITALES Y CLINICAS, Carrera 4, No 73–15, Bogota, Juan Carlos Giraldo Valencia, Director General; www.achc.org.co

ECUADOR

Other:

JUNTA DE BENEFICENCIA DE GUAYAQUIL, P.O. Box 09–01–789, Guayaquil, tel. 011/432–0760; Lautaro Aspiazu Wright, Director; www.jbg.org.ec

GEORGIA

Other:

ARCHANGEL ST. MICHAEL MULTIPROFILE CLINICAL HOSPITAL, 21 Lubliana Street, Tbilisi, Zip 0159; tel. 995/295–1100; Anna Rekhviashvili, Professor and Cardiologist

MARITIME HOSPITAL JSC, Melikishrin 102B, Batumi, Zip 60100; Tamari Kachlishvili, Medical Director; www.mh.com.ge

MEDI CLUB GEORGIA, 22A, Tashkenti Street, Tbilisi, Zip 0160; tel. 995/225–1991; Nugzar Abramishvili, General Director; www.mediclubgeorgia.ge

GERMANY

Other:

HQ USAFE/SGPXL, Unit 3050, Box 130, Ramstein AB, Armed Forces Africa, Canada, E Zip 09094–5001

GREECE

Other:

DIAGNOSTIC AND THERAPEUTIC CENTRE OF ATHENS HYGEIA, S A, 4 Erythrou Stavrou & Kifissiap, Athens, tel. 302/686–7000; Andreas Kartapanis, General Manager; www.hygeia.gr/default.aspx

INDIA

Other:

SAMAST PATIDAR AAROGYA TRUST, Kirti Patel, Chief Executive Officer

ISRAEL

Other:

HADASSAH MEDICAL ORGANIZATION, Box 12000, Jerusalem, Zip 91120; tel. 972/677–7111; Avigdor Kaplan, Director General; www.hadassah.org.il

JAPAN

Other:

KAMEDA MEDICAL CENTER AND CLINICS, 929 Higashi–Cho, Kamogawa City, Zip 296–8602; tel. 814/092–2211; John C. Wocher, Executive Vice President; www.kameda.com

ST. LUKE'S INTERNATIONAL HOSPITAL, 10–1 Akashi–Cho, Chuo–Ku, Tokyo 104, tel. 910/550–7091; Shigeaki Hinohara, Honorary President; www.luke.or.jp/eng/index.html

JORDAN

Other:

SPECIALTY HOSPITAL, P.O. Box 930186, Amman, Zip 11193; tel. 962/592–3960; Fawzi Al–Hammouri, General Manager; www.specialty–hospital.com

LEBANON

Other:

SAINT GEORGE HOSPITAL UNIVERSITY MEDICAL CENTER, P.O. Box 166378, Beirut, Zip 1100–2807; tel. 961/158–5700; Ziad Kamel, Administrative Director; www.stgeorgehospital.org

MEXICO

Other:

SHRINERS HOSPITAL FOR CHILDREN, Av Del Iman 257, Col Pedregal de Santa Ursula, Delegacion Coyoacan, Mexico City, Zip 04600; Araceli Nagore, Administrator

MYANMAR

Other:

ASIA ROYAL GENERAL HOSPITAL, 14 Baho Street, Sanchaung Township, Yangon, Zip 11162; tel. 951/153–8055; Myat Thu, Managing Director; www.asiaroyalmedical.com

NETHERLANDS ANTILLES

Other:

SINT MAARTEN MEDICAL CENTER FOUNDATION, Welgelegen Road 30 Ut 1 Cay Hill, Sint Maarten, tel. 599/543–1111; George Scot, General Director

PANAMA

Other:

CLINICA HOSPITAL SAN FERNANDO, S. A., Dept PTY 1663, P.O. Box 25207, Miami, Florida Zip 33102–5207; tel. 507/305–6399; Edgardo Fernandez, Medical Director; www.hospitalsanfernando.com

PERU

Hospital:

SANNA HEALTHCARE NETWORK, Av. Aurelio Miro Quesada 1030, San Isidro, Lima, tel. 950/922–2555; Santiago Rivera, Chief Executive Officer; www.sanna.pe

Other:

BRITISH AMERICAN HOSPITAL, Avenue Alfredo Salazar 3 Era, Lima 27, tel. 511/712–3000; Gonzalo Garrido–Lecca, Director; www.angloamericana.com.pe

PHILIPPINES

Ambulatory Care Center:

DEPARTMENT OF VETERANS AFFAIRS, OUTPATIENT CLINIC, Pasay City, APO, Zip 96440; tel. 632/833–4566; Artemio Arugay, Commander; www.va.gov

SAUDI ARABIA

Other:

ABDUL RAHMAN AL MISHARI GENERAL HOSPITAL, Olaya, P.O. Box 56929, Riyadh, Zip 11564; tel. 011/465–7700; Abdul Rahman Al Mishari, President; www.drabdulrahmanalmishari.com.sa/

MUHAMMAD SALEH BASHARAHIL HOSPITAL, P.O. Box 10505, Madinah Road, Omora Gadida, Makkah, tel. 009/520–4444; Turki M. Basharahil, General Manager; www.msbasharahil.com/

SIERRA LEONE

Other:

HANDS OF CHARITY RURAL HOME BASE HOSPITAL, 52th Freetown Road, Babdorie Lumley, Freetown, tel. 002/912–3424; Kingibomeh Nyandoeboh, Director and Founder

TURKEY

Other:

ANADOLU MEDICAL CENTER, Cumhuriyet Mahallesi 2255 Sokak Gebze, Kocaeli, Zip 41400; tel. 011/678–5400; Robert Gerard Kiely, President and Chief Executive Officer; www.anadolusaglik.org

MEDICANA INTERNATIONAL ANKARA HOSPITAL, Sogutozu Caddesi 2165 Sokak No. 6, Ankara, Zip 06520; tel. 905/749–0384; Oguz Engiz, Chief Executive Officer; www.medicana.com

UNITED ARAB EMIRATES

Other:

AMERICAN HOSPITAL–DUBAI, Oud Metha Road, P.O. Box 5566, Dubai, tel. 011/336–7777; Saeed M. Almulla, Chairman; www.ahdubai.com/main/index.aspx

UNITED KINGDOM

Other:

MOOR PARK CAPITAL PARTNERS, GLOBAL HEALTHCARE CAPITAL, 14850 North Scottsdale Road, Suite 375, Scottsdale, Arizona Zip 85254–2885; tel. 480/922–3760; Dan J. Rice, Founder and Executive Chairman; www.moorparkcapital.com

Notes

Notes

Notes

Notes

Health Care Systems

B

Health Care Systems, Networks and Alliances

Section B

Introduction

This section includes listings for networks, health care systems and alliances.

Health Care Systems

To reflect the diversity that exists among health care organizations, this publication uses the term health care system to identify both multihospital and diversified single hospital systems.

Multihospital Systems

A multihospital health care system is two or more hospitals owned, leased, sponsored, or contract managed by a central organization.

Single Hospital Systems

Single, freestanding member hospitals may be categorized as health care systems by bringing into membership three or more, and at least 25 percent, of their owned or leased non–hospital preacute and postacute health care organizations. (For purposes of definition, health care delivery is the availability of professional healthcare staff during all hours of the organization's operations). Organizations provide, or provide and finance, diagnostic, therapeutic, and/or consultative patient or client services that normally precede or follow acute, inpatient, hospitalization; or that serve to prevent or substitute for such hospitalization. These services are provided in either a freestanding facility not eligible for licensure as a hospital under state statue or through one that is a subsidiary of a hospital.

The first part of this section is an alphabetical list of health care systems which are listed under the system by state. Data for this section were compiled from the 2013 *Annual Survey* and the membership information base as published in section A of the *AHA Guide.*

One of the following codes appears after the name of each system listed to indicate the type of organizational control reported by that system:

CC	Catholic (Roman) church–related system, not–for–profit
CO	Other church–related system, not–for–profit
NP	Other not–for–profit system, including nonfederal, governmental systems
IO	Investor–owned, for profit system
FG	Federal Government

One of the following codes appears after the name of each hospital to indicate how that hospital is related to the system:

O	Owned
L	Leased
S	Sponsored
CM	Contract–managed

Health System Classification System

An identification system for Health Systems was developed jointly by the American Hospital Association's Health Research and Education Trust and Health Forum, and the University of California-Berkeley.[1] A health system is assigned to one of five categories based on how much they differentiate and centralized their hospital services, physician arrangements, and provider-based insurance products. Differentiation refers to the number of different products or services that the organization offers. Centralization refers to whether decision-making and service delivery emanate from the system level more so than individual hospitals.

Categories:

Centralized Health System: A delivery system in which the system centrally organizes individual hospital service delivery, physician arrangements, and insurance product development. The number of different products/services that are offered across the system is moderate.

Centralized Physician/Insurance Health System: A delivery system with highly centralized physician arrangements and insurance product development. Within this group, hospital services are relatively decentralized with individual hospitals having discretion over the array of services they offer. The number of different products/services that are offered across the system is moderate.

Moderately Centralized Health System: A delivery system that is distinguished by the presence of both centralized and decentralized activity for hospital services, physician arrangements, and insurance product development. For example, a system within this group may have centralized care of expensive, high technology services, such as open heart surgery, but allows individual hospitals to provide an array of other health services based on local needs. The number of different products/services that are offered across the system is moderate.

Decentralized Health System: A delivery system with a high degree of decentralized of hospital services, physician arrangements, and insurance product development. Within this group, systems may lack an overarching structure for coordination. Service and product differentiation is high, which may explain why centralization is hard to achieve. In this group, the system may simply service a role in sharing information and providing administrative support to highly developed local delivery systems centered around hospitals.

Independent Hospital System: A delivery system with limited differentiation in hospital services, physician arrangements, and insurance product development. These systems are largely horizontal affiliations of autonomous hospitals.

No Assignment: For some systems sufficient data from the Annual Survey were not available to determine a cluster assignment.

The second part of this section lists health care systems indexed geographically by state and city. Every effort has been made to be as inclusive and accurate as possible. However, as in all efforts of this type, there may be omissions. For further information, write to the Section for Health Care Systems, American Hospital Association, 155 N. Wacker Drive, Chicago, IL 60606.

Networks

The *AHA Guide* shows listings of networks. A network is defined as a group of hospitals, physicians, other providers, insurers and/or community agencies that work together to coordinate and deliver a broad spectrum of services to their community. Organizations listed represent the lead or hub of the network activity. Networks are listed by state, then alphabetically by name including participating partners.

The network identification process has purposely been designed to capture networks of varying organization type. Sources include but are not limited to the following: *AHA Annual Survey,* national, state and metropolitan associations, national news and periodical searches, and the networks and their health care providers themselves. Therefore, networks are included regardless of whether a hospital or healthcare system is the network lead. When an individual hospital does appear in the listing, it is indicative of the role the hospital plays as the network lead. In addition, the network listing is **not** mutually exclusive of the hospital, health care system or alliance listings within this publication.

Networks are very fluid in their composition as goals evolve and partners change. Therefore, some of the networks included in this listing may have dissolved, reformed, or simply been renamed as this section was being produced for publication.

The network identification process is an ongoing and responsive initiative. As more information is collected and validated, it will be made available in other venues, in addition to the *AHA Guide.* For more information concerning the network identification process, please contact The American Hospital Association Resource Center at 312/422–2050.

Alliances

An alliance is a formal organization, usually owned by shareholders/members, that works on behalf of its individual members in the provision of services and products and in the promotion of activities and ventures. The organization functions under a set of bylaws or other written rules to which each member agrees to abide.

Alliances are listed alphabetically by name. Its members are listed alphabetically by state, city, and then by member name.

---

[1] Bazzoli, CJ; Shortell, SM; Dubbs, N; Chan, C; and Kralovec, P; ''A Taxonomy of Health networks and Systems: Bringing Order Out of Chaos'' *Health Services Research*, February; 1999

Statistics for Health Care Systems and their Hospitals

The following tables describing health care systems refers to information in section B of the 2015 *AHA Guide*.

Table 1 shows the number of health care systems by type of control. Table 2 provides a breakdown of the number of systems that own, lease, sponsor or contract manage hospitals within each control category. Table 3 gives the number of hospitals and beds in each control category as well as total hospitals and beds. Finally, shows the percentage of hospitals and beds in each control category.

For more information on health care systems, please write to the Section for Health Care Systems, 155 N. Wacker Drive, Chicago, Illinois 60606 or call 312/422–3000.

Table 1. Multihospital Health Care Systems, by Type of Organizaton Control

Type of Control	Code	Number of Systems
Catholic (Roman) church–related	CC	34
Other church–related	CO	7
Subtotal, church–related		41
Other not-for-profit	NP	307
Subtotal, not-for-profit		348
Investor Owned	IO	83
Federal Government	FG	5
Total		436

Table 2. Multihospital Health Care Systems, by Type of Ownership and Control

Type of Ownership	Catholic Church–Related (CC)	Other Church–Related (CO)	Total Church–Related (CC + CO)	Other Not-for-Profit (NP)	Total Not-for-Profit (CC, CO, + NP)	Investor–Owned (IO)	Federal Government (FG)	All Systems
Systems that only own, lease or sponsor	25	5	30	274	304	74	5	383
Systems that only contract–manage	0	0	0	2	2	3	0	5
Systems that manage, own, lease, or sponsor	9	2	11	31	42	6	0	48
Total	34	7	41	307	348	83	5	436

Table 3. Hospitals and Beds in Multihospital Health Care Systems, by Type of Ownership and Control

Type of Ownership	Catholic Church–Related (CC)		Other Church–Related (CO)		Total Church–Related (CC + CO)		Other Not-for-Profit (NP)		Total Not-for-Profit (CC, CO, + NP)		Investor–Owned (IO)		Federal Government (FG)		All Systems	
	H	B	H	B	H	B	H	B	H	B	H	B	H	B	H	B
Owned, leased or sponsored	567	103,514	75	16,260	642	119,774	1,507	326,740	2,149	446,514	1,362	160,389	212	39,658	3,723	646,561
Contract–managed	40	1,918	4	585	44	2,503	94	7,939	138	10,442	111	6,525	0	0	249	16,967
Total	607	105,432	79	16,845	686	122,277	1,601	334,679	2,287	456,956	1,473	166,914	212	39,658	3,972	663,528

H = hospitals; **B** = beds.

Table 4. Hospitals and Beds in Multihospital Health Care Systems, by Type of Ownership and Control as a Percentage of All Systems

Type of Ownership	Catholic Church–Related (CC)		Other Church–Related (CO)		Total Church–Related (CC + CO)		Other Not-for-Profit (NP)		Total Not-for-Profit (CC, CO, + NP)		Investor–Owned (IO)		Federal Government (FG)		All Systems	
	H	B	H	B	H	B	H	B	H	B	H	B	H	B	H	B
Owned, leased or sponsored	15.2	16.0	2.0	2.5	17.2	18.5	40.5	50.5	57.7	69.1	36.6	24.8	5.7	6.1	100.0	100.0
Contract–managed	16.1	11.3	1.6	3.4	17.7	14.8	37.8	46.8	55.4	61.5	44.6	38.5	0.0	0.0	100.0	100.0
Total	15.3	15.9	2.0	2.5	17.3	18.4	40.3	50.4	57.6	68.9	37.1	25.2	5.3	6.0	100.0	100.0

H = hospitals; **B** = beds.
*Please note that figures may not always equal the provided subtotal or total percentages due to rounding.

Health Care Systems and Their Hospitals

★**2375: ABINGTON HEALTH** (NP)
1200 Old York Road, Abington, PA Zip 19001; tel. 215/481–2000; Laurence M. Merlis, President and Chief Executive Officer
(Moderately Centralized Health System)

PENNSYLVANIA: ABINGTON HEALTH LANSDALE HOSPITAL (O, 127 beds) 100 Medical Campus Drive, Lansdale, PA Zip 19446–1200; tel. 215/368–2100; Gary R. Candia, Ph.D., FACHE, Chief Executive Officer
Web address: www.amh.org/lansdale/index.aspx

ABINGTON MEMORIAL HOSPITAL (O, 621 beds) 1200 Old York Road, Abington, PA Zip 19001–3720; tel. 215/481–2000; Laurence M. Merlis, President and Chief Executive Officer
Web address: www.abingtonhealth.org

Owned, leased, sponsored:	2 hospitals	748 beds
Contract–managed:	0 hospitals	0 beds
Totals:	2 hospitals	748 beds

0091: ACADIA HEALTHCARE COMPANY, INC. (IO)
830 Crescent Centre Drive, Suite 610, Franklin, TN Zip 37067–7323; tel. 615/861–6000; Joey Jacobs, Chairman and Chief Executive Officer
(Independent Hospital System)

ARIZONA: SONORA BEHAVIORAL HEALTH HOSPITAL (O, 72 beds) 6050 North Corona Road, #3, Tucson, AZ Zip 85704–1096; tel. 520/469–8700; Edeli Kinsala, Chief Executive Officer

ARKANSAS: RIVERVIEW BEHAVIORAL HEALTH (O, 62 beds) 701 Arkansas Boulevard, Texarkana, AR Zip 71854–2105; tel. 870/772–5028; Michael A. Truman, Chief Executive Officer
Web address: www.riverviewbehavioralhealth.com

VALLEY BEHAVIORAL HEALTH SYSTEM (O, 75 beds) 10301 Mayo Drive, Barling, AR Zip 72923–1660; tel. 479/494–5700; Holli Baker, Chief Executive Officer
Web address: www.valleybehavioral.com

VANTAGE POINT OF NORTHWEST ARKANSAS (O, 92 beds) 4253 North Crossover Road, Fayetteville, AR Zip 72703–4596; tel. 479/521–5731; Connie Borengasser, Chief Executive Officer
Web address: www.vantagepointnwa.com

CALIFORNIA: PACIFIC GROVE HOSPITAL (O, 50 beds) 5900 Brockton Avenue, Riverside, CA Zip 92506–1862; tel. 951/275–8400; Amrita Rai, Administrator
Web address: www.pacificgrovehospital.com

DELAWARE: MEADOW WOOD BEHAVIORAL HEALTH SYSTEM (O, 53 beds) 575 South Dupont Highway, New Castle, DE Zip 19720–4606; tel. 302/328–3330; Bill A. Mason, Chief Executive Officer
Web address: www.meadowwoodhospital.com

FLORIDA: PARK ROYAL HOSPITAL (O, 103 beds) 9241 Park Royal Drive, Fort Myers, FL Zip 33908–9204; tel. 239/985–2700; Michael K. Evans, Chief Executive Officer
Web address: www.ParkRoyalHospital.com

GEORGIA: GREENLEAF CENTER (O, 50 beds) 2209 Pineview Drive, Valdosta, GA Zip 31602–7316; tel. 229/247–4357; Mike Ham, Chief Executive Officer
Web address: www.greenleafcounseling.net

RIVERWOODS BEHAVIORAL HEALTH SYSTEM (O, 75 beds) 233 Medical Center Drive, Riverdale, GA Zip 30274–2640; tel. 770/991–8500; Kirk Kureska, Chief Executive Officer
Web address: www.riverwoodsbehavioral.com

INDIANA: OPTIONS BEHAVIORAL HEALTH SYSTEM (O, 42 beds) 5602 Caito Drive, Indianapolis, IN Zip 46226–1346; tel. 317/544–4340; Rick Bangert, Chief Executive Officer
Web address: www.optionsbehavioralhealthsystem.com/

LOUISIANA: ACADIA OPTIMA HOSPITAL (O, 24 beds) 1131 Rue De Belier, Lafayette, LA Zip 70506–6532; tel. 337/991–0571; Michael E. Geissler, Chief Executive Officer
Web address: www.optimaspecialtyhospital.com/

ACADIA VERMILION HOSPITAL (O, 44 beds) 2520 North University Avenue, Lafayette, LA Zip 70507–5306; tel. 337/234–5614; Joseph R. Rodriguez, Chief Executive Officer
Web address: www.acadiavermilion.com

LONGLEAF HOSPITAL (O, 70 beds) 110 John Eskew Drive, Alexandria, LA Zip 71303; tel. 318/445–5111; Eric Kennedy, Chief Executive Officer
Web address: www.crossroadshospital.com

MICHIGAN: HARBOR OAKS HOSPITAL (O, 45 beds) 35031 23 Mile Road, New Baltimore, MI Zip 48047–3649; tel. 586/725–5777; Sari Abromovich, Chief Executive Officer
Web address: www.harboroaks.com

STONECREST CENTER (O, 81 beds) 15000 Gratiot Avenue, Detroit, MI Zip 48205–1973; tel. 313/245–0600; Steve Savage, Chief Executive Officer
Web address: www.bcastonecrestcenter.com

MISSOURI: LAKELAND BEHAVIORAL HEALTH SYSTEM (O, 122 beds) 440 South Market Street, Springfield, MO Zip 65806–2026; tel. 417/865–5581; Nathan Duncan, Chief Executive Officer
Web address: www.lakeland–hospital.com

NEVADA: SEVEN HILLS BEHAVIORAL INSTITUTE (O, 58 beds) 3021 West Horizon Ridge Parkway, Henderson, NV Zip 89052–3990; tel. 702/646–5000; Robert L. Turner, Ph.D., Chief Executive Officer
Web address: www.sevenhillsbi.com

OHIO: OHIO HOSPITAL FOR PSYCHIATRY (O, 90 beds) 880 Greenlawn Avenue, Columbus, OH Zip 43223–2616; tel. 614/449–9664; Roxanne Jividen, Chief Executive Officer
Web address: www.ohiohospitalforpsychiatry.com/

TEN LAKES CENTER (O, 16 beds) 819 North First Street, 3rd Floor, Dennison, OH Zip 44621–1003; tel. 740/922–7499; Debra C. Gardner, R.N., MSN, Administrator
Web address: www.tenlakescenter.com/

OKLAHOMA: ROLLING HILLS HOSPITAL (O, 44 beds) 1000 Rolling Hills Lane, Ada, OK Zip 74820–9415; tel. 580/436–3600; Selena Stockley, Chief Executive Officer
Web address: www.rollinghillshospital.com

PENNSYLVANIA: SOUTHWOOD PSYCHIATRIC HOSPITAL (O, 156 beds) 2575 Boyce Plaza Road, Pittsburgh, PA Zip 15241–3925; tel. 412/257–2290; Stephen J. Quigley, Chief Executive Officer
Web address: www.southwoodhospital.com

TENNESSEE: DELTA MEDICAL CENTER (O, 173 beds) 3000 Getwell Road, Memphis, TN Zip 38118–2299; tel. 901/369–8100; William Patterson, Chief Executive Officer
Web address: www.deltamedcenter.com

TEXAS: ABILENE BEHAVIORAL HEALTH (O, 92 beds) 4225 Woods Place, Abilene, TX Zip 79602–7991, Mailing Address: P.O. Box 5559, Zip 79608–5559; tel. 325/698–6600; Sheila McDermott–Lord, Chief Executive Officer
Web address: www.abilenebehavioralhealth.com/

CEDAR CREST HOSPITAL AND RESIDENTIAL TREATMENT CENTER (O, 70 beds) 3500 I-35 South, Belton, TX Zip 76513; tel. 254/939–2100; Rob Marsh, Chief Executive Officer
Web address: www.cedarcresthospital.com

RED RIVER HOSPITAL (O, 74 beds) 1505 Eighth Street, Wichita Falls, TX Zip 76301–3106; tel. 940/322–3171; Rob Marsh, Chief Executive Officer
Web address: www.redriverhospital.com

VIRGINIA: MOUNT REGIS CENTER (O, 25 beds) 405 Kimball Avenue, Salem, VA Zip 24153–6299; tel. 540/389–4761; Gail S. Basham, Chief Executive Officer

For explanation of codes following names, see page B2.
★ Indicates Type III membership in the American Hospital Association.

WASHINGTON: CASCADE BEHAVIORAL HOSPITAL (O, 63 beds) 12844 Military Road South, Tukwila, WA Zip 98168–3045; tel. 206/244–0180; Michael Uradnik, Chief Executive Officer
Web address: www.cascadebh.com

Owned, leased, sponsored:	27 hospitals	1921 beds
Contract–managed:	0 hospitals	0 beds
Totals:	27 hospitals	1921 beds

★**0640:   ACUITYHEALTHCARE, LP** (IO)
10200 Mallard Creek Road, Suite 300, Charlotte, NC Zip 28262–9705; tel. 704/887–7280; Edwin H. Cooper, Jr., MS, President and Chief Executive Officer
(Independent Hospital System)

NEW JERSEY: ACUITY SPECIALTY HOSPITAL OF NEW JERSEY (O, 30 beds) 1925 Pacific Avenue, 7th Floor, Atlantic City, NJ Zip 08401–6713; tel. 609/441–2122; Monica Titus, President and Chief Executive Officer
Web address: www.acuityhealthcare.net

LOURDES SPECIALTY HOSPITAL OF SOUTHERN NEW JERSEY (O, 69 beds) 218 Sunset Road, Willingboro, NJ Zip 08046–1110; tel. 609/835–3650; Cheri Cowperthwait, R.N., Chief Executive Officer
Web address: www.acuityhealthcarenj.com

NORTH CAROLINA: CAROLINAS SPECIALTY HOSPITAL (C, 38 beds) 10648 Park Road, Charlotte, NC Zip 28210; tel. 704/667–8060; Daniel C. Dunmyer, Chief Executive Officer
Web address: www.cshnc.com

OHIO: ACUITY SPECIALTY HOSPITALS OHIO VALLEY (O, 61 beds) 380 Summit Avenue, 3rd Floor, Steubenville, OH Zip 43952–2667; tel. 740/283–7600; Judy K. Weaver, MS, Chief Executive Officer
Web address: www.acuityhealthcare.net

TEXAS: ACUITY HOSPITAL OF SOUTH TEXAS (O, 30 beds) 718 Lexington Avenue, San Antonio, TX Zip 78212–4768; tel. 210/572–4600; Kris Karns, Ph.D., FACHE, Chief Executive Officer
Web address: www.acuitysouthtexas.com

ICON HOSPITAL (C, 32 beds) 19211 McKay Boulevard, Humble, TX Zip 77338–5502; tel. 281/883–5500; Hilda Long, Chief Executive Officer
Web address: www.acuityhealthcare.net

Owned, leased, sponsored:	4 hospitals	190 beds
Contract–managed:	2 hospitals	70 beds
Totals:	6 hospitals	260 beds

0895:   ADENA HEALTH SYSTEM (NP)
272 Hospital Road, Chillicothe, OH Zip 45601–9031; tel. 740/779–7500; Mark H. Shuter, President and Chief Executive Officer
(Independent Hospital System)

OHIO: ADENA GREENFIELD MEDICAL CENTER (O, 25 beds) 550 Mirabeau Street, Greenfield, OH Zip 45123–1617; tel. 937/981–9400; Kathy Dye, Interim Administrator
Web address: www.adena.org

ADENA MEDICAL CENTER (O, 279 beds) 272 Hospital Road, Chillicothe, OH Zip 45601–9031; tel. 740/779–7500; Mark H. Shuter, President and Chief Executive Officer
Web address: www.adena.org

ADENA PIKE MEDICAL CENTER (O, 25 beds) 100 Dawn Lane, Waverly, OH Zip 45690–9138; tel. 740/947–2186; David M. Zanni, Associate Administrator
Web address: www.pikecommunityhospital.org

Owned, leased, sponsored:	3 hospitals	329 beds
Contract–managed:	0 hospitals	0 beds
Totals:	3 hospitals	329 beds

★**0235:   ADVENTIST HEALTH** (CO)
2100 Douglas Boulevard, Roseville, CA Zip 95661–3898, Mailing Address: P.O. Box 619002, Zip 95661–9002; tel. 916/781–2000; Scott Reiner, President and Chief Executive Officer
(Moderately Centralized Health System)

CALIFORNIA: ADVENTIST MEDICAL CENTER – HANFORD (O, 199 beds) 115 Mall Drive, Hanford, CA Zip 93230–3513; tel. 559/582–9000; Wayne Ferch, President and Chief Executive Officer
Web address: www.adventisthealthcv.com/hospital_newhanfordhospital.aspx

ADVENTIST MEDICAL CENTER–REEDLEY (L, 49 beds) 372 West Cypress Avenue, Reedley, CA Zip 93654–2199; tel. 559/638–8155; Wayne Ferch, President and Chief Executive Officer
Web address: www.skdh.org

CENTRAL VALLEY GENERAL HOSPITAL (O, 49 beds) 1025 North Douty Street, Hanford, CA Zip 93230–3722, Mailing Address: P.O. Box 480, Zip 93232–2113; tel. 559/583–2100; Wayne Ferch, President and Chief Executive Officer
Web address: www.hanfordhealth.com

FEATHER RIVER HOSPITAL (O, 54 beds) 5974 Pentz Road, Paradise, CA Zip 95969–5593; tel. 530/877–9361; Kevin R. Erich, President and Chief Executive Officer
Web address: www.frhosp.org

FRANK R. HOWARD MEMORIAL HOSPITAL (L, 25 beds) One Madrone Street, Willits, CA Zip 95490–4298; tel. 707/459–6801; Rick Bockmann, Chief Executive Officer
Web address: www.howardhospital.com

GLENDALE ADVENTIST MEDICAL CENTER (O, 462 beds) 1509 Wilson Terrace, Glendale, CA Zip 91206–4098; tel. 818/409–8000; Kevin A. Roberts, FACHE, President and Chief Executive Officer
Web address: www.glendaleadventist.com

SAN JOAQUIN COMMUNITY HOSPITAL (O, 255 beds) 2615 Chester Avenue, Bakersfield, CA Zip 93301–2014, Mailing Address: P.O. Box 2615, Zip 93303–2615; tel. 661/395–3000; Douglas Duffield, President and Chief Executive Officer
Web address: www.sanjoaquinhospital.org

SIMI VALLEY HOSPITAL AND HEALTH CARE SERVICES (O, 144 beds) 2975 North Sycamore Drive, Simi Valley, CA Zip 93065–1277; tel. 805/955–6000; Kim S. Milstien, President and Chief Executive Officer
Web address: www.simivalleyhospital.com

SONORA REGIONAL MEDICAL CENTER (O, 152 beds) 1000 Greenley Road, Sonora, CA Zip 95370–4819; tel. 209/536–5000; Andrew Jahn, President and Chief Executive Officer
Web address: www.sonoramedicalcenter.org/

ST. HELENA HOSPITAL CLEAR LAKE (O, 25 beds) 15630 18th Avenue, Clearlake, CA Zip 95422–9336, Mailing Address: P.O. Box 6710, Zip 95422; tel. 707/994–6486; David Santos, President and Chief Executive Officer
Web address: www.adventisthealth.org

ST. HELENA HOSPITAL NAPA VALLEY (O, 116 beds) 10 Woodland Road, Saint Helena, CA Zip 94574–9554; tel. 707/963–3611; Steven Herber, M.D., FACS, President and Chief Executive Officer
Web address: www.sthelenahospital.org

ST. HELENA HOSPITAL–CENTER FOR BEHAVIORAL HEALTH (O, 61 beds) 525 Oregon Street, Vallejo, CA Zip 94590–3201; tel. 707/648–2200; Patricia Williams, Regional VP for Behavioral Medicine and Population Health
Web address: www.sthelenahospitals.org/location/center-for-behavioral-health

UKIAH VALLEY MEDICAL CENTER (O, 48 beds) 275 Hospital Drive, Ukiah, CA Zip 95482–4531; tel. 707/462–3111; Gwen Matthews, R.N., MSN, Chief Executive Officer
Web address: www.adventisthealth.org

WHITE MEMORIAL MEDICAL CENTER (O, 353 beds) 1720 Cesar Chavez Avenue, Los Angeles, CA Zip 90033–2414; tel. 323/268–5000; Beth D. Zachary, FACHE, President and Chief Executive Officer
Web address: www.whitememorial.com

HAWAII: CASTLE MEDICAL CENTER (O, 160 beds) 640 Ulukahiki Street, Kailua, HI Zip 96734–4454; tel. 808/263–5500; Kathryn A. Raethel, R.N., M.P.H., President and Chief Executive Officer
Web address: www.castlemed.org

OREGON: ADVENTIST MEDICAL CENTER–PORTLAND (O, 248 beds) 10123 S.E. Market Street, Portland, OR Zip 97216–2599; tel. 503/257–2500; Thomas Russell, President and Chief Executive Officer
Web address: www.adventisthealthnw.com

TILLAMOOK REGIONAL MEDICAL CENTER (L, 25 beds) 1000 Third Street, Tillamook, OR Zip 97141–3430; tel. 503/842–4444; David Butler, President and Chief Executive Officer
Web address: www.tillamookregionalmc.com

For explanation of codes following names, see page B2.
★ Indicates Type III membership in the American Hospital Association.

WASHINGTON: WALLA WALLA GENERAL HOSPITAL (O, 37 beds) 1025 South Second Avenue, Walla Walla, WA Zip 99362–4116, Mailing Address: P.O. Box 1398, Zip 99362–0309; tel. 509/525–0480; Monty E. Knittel, President and Chief Executive Officer
Web address: www.wwgh.com

Owned, leased, sponsored:	18 hospitals	2462 beds
Contract–managed:	0 hospitals	0 beds
Totals:	18 hospitals	2462 beds

★**4165: ADVENTIST HEALTH SYSTEM SUNBELT HEALTH CARE CORPORATION** (CO)
900 Hope Way, Altamonte Springs, FL Zip 32714–1502; tel. 407/357–1000; Donald L. Jernigan, Ph.D., President and Chief Executive Officer
(Decentralized Health System)

COLORADO: AVISTA ADVENTIST HOSPITAL (O, 114 beds) 100 Health Park Drive, Louisville, CO Zip 80027–9583; tel. 303/673–1000; Dennis Barts, Chief Executive Officer
Web address: www.avistahospital.org

CASTLE ROCK ADVENTIST HOSPITAL (O, 50 beds) 2350 Meadows Boulevard, Castle Rock, CO Zip 80109–8405; tel. 720/455–5000; Todd Folkenberg, Chief Executive Officer
Web address: www.castlerockhospital.org

LITTLETON ADVENTIST HOSPITAL (O, 201 beds) 7700 South Broadway Street, Littleton, CO Zip 80122–2628; tel. 303/730–8900; Brett Spenst, Chief Executive Officer
Web address: www.centura.org

PARKER ADVENTIST HOSPITAL (O, 143 beds) 9395 Crown Crest Boulevard, Parker, CO Zip 80138–8573; tel. 303/269–4000; Morre Dean, Chief Executive Officer
Web address: www.parkerhospital.org

PORTER ADVENTIST HOSPITAL (O, 250 beds) 2525 South Downing Street, Denver, CO Zip 80210–5876; tel. 303/778–1955; Randall L. Haffner, Ph.D., Chief Executive Officer
Web address: www.centura.org

FLORIDA: FLORIDA HOSPITAL (O, 2396 beds) 601 East Rollins Street, Orlando, FL Zip 32803–1248; tel. 407/303–6611; Lars D. Houmann, President
Web address: www.flhosp.org

FLORIDA HOSPITAL AT CONNERTON LONG TERM ACUTE CARE (O, 50 beds) 9441 Health Center Drive, Land O'Lakes, FL Zip 34637–5837; tel. 813/903–3701; Brian Adams, President and Chief Executive Officer
Web address: www.elevatinghealthcare.org

FLORIDA HOSPITAL CARROLLWOOD (O, 90 beds) 7171 North Dale Mabry Highway, Tampa, FL Zip 33614–2665; tel. 813/932–2222; Joe Johnson, Chief Executive Officer
Web address: www.elevatinghealthcare.org/locations/carrollwood

FLORIDA HOSPITAL DELAND (O, 156 beds) 701 West Plymouth Avenue, DeLand, FL Zip 32720–3236; tel. 386/943–4522; Timothy W. Cook, President and CEO
Web address: www.fhdeland.org

FLORIDA HOSPITAL FISH MEMORIAL (O, 175 beds) 1055 Saxon Boulevard, Orange City, FL Zip 32763–8468; tel. 386/917–5000; Ed Noseworthy, President and Chief Executive Officer
Web address: www.fhfishmemorial.org

FLORIDA HOSPITAL HEARTLAND MEDICAL CENTER (O, 214 beds) 4200 Sun'n Lake Boulevard, Sebring, FL Zip 33872–1986, Mailing Address: P.O. Box 9400, Zip 33871–9400; tel. 863/314–4466; Eric Stevens, Chief Executive Officer
Web address: www.fhheartland.org/

FLORIDA HOSPITAL MEMORIAL MEDICAL CENTER (O, 211 beds) 301 Memorial Medical Parkway, Daytona Beach, FL Zip 32117–5167; tel. 386/676–6000; Daryl Tol, Chief Executive Officer
Web address: www.floridahospitalmemorial.org

FLORIDA HOSPITAL NORTH PINELLAS (O, 168 beds) 1395 South Pinellas Avenue, Tarpon Springs, FL Zip 34689–3790; tel. 727/942–5000; Bruce Bergherm, Chief Executive Officer
Web address: www.fhnorthpinellas.com/

FLORIDA HOSPITAL TAMPA (O, 369 beds) 3100 East Fletcher Avenue, Tampa, FL Zip 33613–4688; tel. 813/971–6000; Brian Adams, President and CEO
Web address: www.floridahospital.com/tampa

FLORIDA HOSPITAL WATERMAN (O, 269 beds) 1000 Waterman Way, Tavares, FL Zip 32778–5266; tel. 352/253–3333; David Ottati, Chief Executive Officer
Web address: www.fhwat.org

FLORIDA HOSPITAL WAUCHULA (O, 25 beds) 533 West Carlton Street, Wauchula, FL Zip 33873–3407; tel. 863/773–3101; Denise Grimsley, Administrator
Web address: www.fh.floridahospital.com/heartland/home.aspx

FLORIDA HOSPITAL WESLEY CHAPEL (O, 83 beds) 2600 Bruce B. Downs Bouelvard, Wesley Chapel, FL Zip 33544–9207; tel. 813/929–5000; Denyse Bales–Chubb, Chief Executive Officer
Web address: www.https://www.floridahospital.com/wesley–chapel

FLORIDA HOSPITAL ZEPHYRHILLS (O, 139 beds) 7050 Gall Boulevard, Zephyrhills, FL Zip 33541–1399; tel. 813/788–0411; Randy Surber, Chief Executive Officer
Web address: www.fhzeph.org

FLORIDA HOSPITAL–FLAGLER (O, 99 beds) 60 Memorial Medical Parkway, Palm Coast, FL Zip 32164–5980; tel. 386/586–2000; Kenneth R. Mattison, Chief Executive Officer
Web address: www.floridahospitalflagler.com/

GEORGIA: EMORY–ADVENTIST HOSPITAL (O, 54 beds) 3949 South Cobb Drive S.E., Smyrna, GA Zip 30080–6300; tel. 770/434–0710; Dennis Kiley, President
Web address: www.emoryadventist.org

GORDON HOSPITAL (O, 85 beds) 1035 Red Bud Road, Calhoun, GA Zip 30701–2082, Mailing Address: P.O. Box 12938, Zip 30703–7013; tel. 706/629–2895; Pete M. Weber, President and Chief Executive Officer
Web address: www.gordonhospital.com

ILLINOIS: ADVENTIST BOLINGBROOK HOSPITAL (O, 148 beds) 500 Remington Boulevard, Bolingbrook, IL Zip 60440–4906; tel. 630/312–5000; Rick Mace, Chief Executive Officer
Web address: www.keepingyouwell.com/abh/

ADVENTIST GLENOAKS HOSPITAL (O, 140 beds) 701 Winthrop Avenue, Glendale Heights, IL Zip 60139–1403; tel. 630/545–8000; Bruce C. Christian, Chief Executive Officer
Web address: www.adventistglenoaks.com

ADVENTIST HINSDALE HOSPITAL (O, 281 beds) 120 North Oak Street, Hinsdale, IL Zip 60521–3890; tel. 630/856–9000; Michael Goebel, Executive Officer
Web address: www.keepingyouwell.com

ADVENTIST LA GRANGE MEMORIAL HOSPITAL (O, 187 beds) 5101 South Willow Spring Road, La Grange, IL Zip 60525–2600; tel. 708/245–9000; Michael Goebel, Chief Executive Officer
Web address: www.keepingyouwell.com

KANSAS: SHAWNEE MISSION MEDICAL CENTER (O, 393 beds) 9100 West 74th Street, Shawnee Mission, KS Zip 66204–4004, Mailing Address: Box 2923, Zip 66201–1323; tel. 913/676–2000; Ken J. Bacon, President and Chief Executive Officer
Web address: www.shawneemission.org

KENTUCKY: MANCHESTER MEMORIAL HOSPITAL (O, 63 beds) 210 Marie Langdon Drive, Manchester, KY Zip 40962–6388; tel. 606/598–5104; Erika Skula, President and Chief Executive Officer
Web address: www.manchestermemorial.org

NORTH CAROLINA: PARK RIDGE HEALTH (O, 98 beds) 100 Hospital Drive, Hendersonville, NC Zip 28792–5272; tel. 828/684–8501; Jimm Bunch, President and Chief Executive Officer
Web address: www.parkridgehealth.org

TENNESSEE: JELLICO COMMUNITY HOSPITAL (L, 31 beds) 188 Hospital Lane, Jellico, TN Zip 37762–4400; tel. 423/784–7252; Erik Wangsness, Chief Executive Officer
Web address: www.jellicohospital.com

TAKOMA REGIONAL HOSPITAL (C, 100 beds) 401 Takoma Avenue, Greeneville, TN Zip 37743–4647; tel. 423/639–3151; Daniel Wolcott, President
Web address: www.takoma.org

For explanation of codes following names, see page B2.
★ Indicates Type III membership in the American Hospital Association.

TEXAS: CENTRAL TEXAS MEDICAL CENTER (O, 140 beds) 1301 Wonder World Drive, San Marcos, TX Zip 78666–7544; tel. 512/353–8979; Sam Huenergardt, President and Chief Executive Officer
Web address: www.ctmc.org

METROPLEX ADVENTIST HOSPITAL (O, 177 beds) 2201 South Clear Creek Road, Killeen, TX Zip 76549–4110; tel. 254/526–7523; Carlyle L. E. Walton, FACHE, Chief Executive Officer
Web address: www.mplex.org

ROLLINS–BROOK COMMUNITY HOSPITAL (O, 35 beds) 608 North Key Avenue, Lampasas, TX Zip 76550–1106, Mailing Address: P.O. Box 589, Zip 76550–0032; tel. 512/556–3682; Ashley Underwood, Administrator and Director of Nursing
Web address: www.mplex.org

TEXAS HEALTH HUGULEY HOSPITAL FORT WORTH SOUTH (C, 192 beds) 11801 South Freeway, Fort Worth, TX Zip 76028–7021, Mailing Address: P.O. Box 6337, Zip 76115–0337; tel. 817/293–9110; Kenneth A. Finch, President and Chief Executive Officer
Web address: www.huguley.org

WISCONSIN: CHIPPEWA VALLEY HOSPITAL AND OAKVIEW CARE CENTER (O, 75 beds) 1220 Third Avenue West, Durand, WI Zip 54736–1600, Mailing Address: P.O. Box 224, Zip 54736–0224; tel. 715/672–4211; Douglas R. Peterson, President and Chief Executive Officer
Web address: www.chippewavalleyhospital.com/

Owned, leased, sponsored:	33 hospitals	7109 beds
Contract–managed:	2 hospitals	292 beds
Totals:	35 hospitals	7401 beds

0214: ADVENTIST HEALTHCARE (NP)
820 West Diamond Avenue, Suite 600, Gaithersburg, MD Zip 20878–1419; tel. 301/315–3141; Erik Wangsness, Interim President and Chief Executive Officer
(Independent Hospital System)

MARYLAND: ADVENTIST BEHAVIORAL HEALTH ROCKVILLE (O, 283 beds) 14901 Broschart Road, Rockville, MD Zip 20850–3318; tel. 301/251–4500; Kevin Young, FACHE, President
Web address: www.adventistbehavioralhealth.com

ADVENTIST REHABILITATION HOSPITAL OF MARYLAND (O, 77 beds) 9909 Medical Center Drive, Rockville, MD Zip 20850–6361; tel. 240/864–6000; Brent Reitz, President
Web address: www.adventistrehab.com

SHADY GROVE ADVENTIST HOSPITAL (O, 331 beds) 9901 Medical Center Drive, Rockville, MD Zip 20850–3395; tel. 240/826–6000; John Sackett, Chief Executive Officer
Web address: www.adventisthealthcare.com

WASHINGTON ADVENTIST HOSPITAL (O, 252 beds) 7600 Carroll Avenue, Takoma Park, MD Zip 20912–6392; tel. 301/891–7600; Erik Wangsness, President
Web address: www.adventisthealthcare.com

NEW JERSEY: HACKETTSTOWN REGIONAL MEDICAL CENTER (O, 111 beds) 651 Willow Grove Street, Hackettstown, NJ Zip 07840–1799; tel. 908/852–5100; Jason C. Coe, President and Chief Executive Officer
Web address: www.hrmcnj.org

Owned, leased, sponsored:	5 hospitals	1054 beds
Contract–managed:	0 hospitals	0 beds
Totals:	5 hospitals	1054 beds

★0064: ADVOCATE HEALTH CARE (NP)
3075 Highland Parkway, Suite 600, Downers Grove, IL Zip 60515–1206; tel. 630/929–8700; Jim H. Skogsbergh, President and Chief Executive Officer
(Moderately Centralized Health System)

ILLINOIS: ADVOCATE BROMENN MEDICAL CENTER (O, 199 beds) 1304 Franklin Avenue, Normal, IL Zip 61761–3558, Mailing Address: P.O. Box 2850, Bloomington, Zip 61702–2850; tel. 309/454–1400; Colleen Kannaday, FACHE, President
Web address: www.bromenn.org

ADVOCATE CHRIST MEDICAL CENTER (O, 684 beds) 4440 West 95th Street, Oak Lawn, IL Zip 60453–2699; tel. 708/684–8000; Kenneth W. Lukhard, President
Web address: www.advocatehealth.com/christ

ADVOCATE CONDELL MEDICAL CENTER (O, 277 beds) 801 South Milwaukee Avenue, Libertyville, IL Zip 60048–3199; tel. 847/362–2900; Dominica Tallarico, President
Web address: www.advocatehealth.com/condell/

ADVOCATE EUREKA HOSPITAL (O, 18 beds) 101 South Major Street, Eureka, IL Zip 61530–1246; tel. 309/467–2371; Colleen Kannaday, FACHE, President
Web address: www.advocatehealth.com/eureka/

ADVOCATE GOOD SAMARITAN HOSPITAL (O, 319 beds) 3815 Highland Avenue, Downers Grove, IL Zip 60515–1590; tel. 630/275–5900; David Fox, President
Web address: www.advocatehealth.com/gsam

ADVOCATE GOOD SHEPHERD HOSPITAL (O, 169 beds) 450 West Highway 22, Barrington, IL Zip 60010–1919; tel. 847/381–0123; Karen A. Lambert, President
Web address: www.advocatehealth.com/gshp/

ADVOCATE ILLINOIS MASONIC MEDICAL CENTER (O, 328 beds) 836 West Wellington Avenue, Chicago, IL Zip 60657–5147; tel. 773/975–1600; Susan Nordstrom Lopez, President
Web address: www.advocatehealth.com/masonic

ADVOCATE LUTHERAN GENERAL HOSPITAL (O, 625 beds) 1775 Dempster Street, Park Ridge, IL Zip 60068–1174; tel. 847/723–2210; Richard B. Floyd, President
Web address: www.advocatehealth.com/luth/

ADVOCATE SHERMAN HOSPITAL (O, 255 beds) 1425 North Randall Road, Elgin, IL Zip 60123–2300; tel. 847/742–9800; Linda Deering, MSN, R.N., President
Web address: www.advocatehealth.com/sherman

ADVOCATE SOUTH SUBURBAN HOSPITAL (O, 250 beds) 17800 South Kedzie Avenue, Hazel Crest, IL Zip 60429–0989; tel. 708/799–8000; Richard Heim, President
Web address: www.advocatehealth.com/ssub/

ADVOCATE TRINITY HOSPITAL (O, 188 beds) 2320 East 93rd Street, Chicago, IL Zip 60617–3983; tel. 773/967–2000; Michelle Gaskill, R.N., President
Web address: www.advocatehealth.com/trinity

Owned, leased, sponsored:	11 hospitals	3312 beds
Contract–managed:	0 hospitals	0 beds
Totals:	11 hospitals	3312 beds

0312: AHMC & HEALTHCARE, INC. (IO)
55 South Raymond Avenue, Suite 105, Alhambra, CA Zip 91801–7101; tel. 626/457–9600; Jonathan Wu, M.D., President and Chairman
(Independent Hospital System)

CALIFORNIA: AHMC ANAHEIM REGIONAL MEDICAL CENTER (O, 223 beds) 1111 West La Palma Avenue, Anaheim, CA Zip 92801–2881; tel. 714/774–1450; Patrick A. Petre, Chief Executive Officer
Web address: www.anaheimregionalmc.com

ALHAMBRA HOSPITAL MEDICAL CENTER (O, 144 beds) 100 South Raymond Avenue, Alhambra, CA Zip 91801–3199, Mailing Address: P.O. Box 510, Zip 91802–2510; tel. 626/570–1606; Iris Lai, Chief Executive Officer
Web address: www.alhambrahospital.com

GARFIELD MEDICAL CENTER (O, 210 beds) 525 North Garfield Avenue, Monterey Park, CA Zip 91754–1205; tel. 626/573–2222; David J. Batista, Chief Executive Officer
Web address: www.garfieldmedicalcenter.com

GREATER EL MONTE COMMUNITY HOSPITAL (O, 117 beds) 1701 Santa Anita Avenue, South El Monte, CA Zip 91733–3411; tel. 626/579–7777; Stanley Toy, Jr., M.D., Chief Executive Officer
Web address: www.greaterelmonte.com

MONTEREY PARK HOSPITAL (O, 101 beds) 900 South Atlantic Boulevard, Monterey Park, CA Zip 91754–4780; tel. 626/570–9000; Philip A. Cohen, Chief Executive Officer
Web address: www.montereyparkhosp.com

For explanation of codes following names, see page B2.
★ Indicates Type III membership in the American Hospital Association.

SAN GABRIEL VALLEY MEDICAL CENTER (O, 273 beds) 438 West Las Tunas Drive, San Gabriel, CA Zip 91776–1216, Mailing Address: P.O. Box 1507, Zip 91778–1507; tel. 626/289–5454; Howard Ternes, Chief Executive Officer
Web address: www.sgvmc.org

WHITTIER HOSPITAL MEDICAL CENTER (O, 81 beds) 9080 Colima Road, Whittier, CA Zip 90605–1600; tel. 562/945–3561; Richard Castro, Chief Executive Officer
Web address: www.whittierhospital.com

Owned, leased, sponsored:	7 hospitals	1149 beds
Contract–managed:	0 hospitals	0 beds
Totals:	7 hospitals	1149 beds

★0247: AKRON GENERAL HEALTH SYSTEM (NP)
1 Akron General Avenue, Akron, OH Zip 44307–2433; tel. 330/344–6000; Thomas L. Stover, M.D., President and Chief Executive Officer
(Moderately Centralized Health System)

OHIO: AKRON GENERAL MEDICAL CENTER (O, 442 beds) 1 Akron General Avenue, Akron, OH Zip 44307–2433; tel. 330/344–6000; Alan Papa, President
Web address: www.akrongeneral.org

EDWIN SHAW REHAB (O, 38 beds) 330 Broadway Street East, Cuyahoga Falls, OH Zip 44221–3312; tel. 330/436–0910; Thomas Whelan, President
Web address: www.edwinshaw.com

LODI COMMUNITY HOSPITAL (O, 25 beds) 225 Elyria Street, Lodi, OH Zip 44254–1096; tel. 330/948–1222; Thomas Whelan, President
Web address: www.lodihospital.org

Owned, leased, sponsored:	3 hospitals	505 beds
Contract–managed:	0 hospitals	0 beds
Totals:	3 hospitals	505 beds

0225: ALAMEDA HEALTH SYSTEM (NP)
15400 Foothill Boulevard, San Leandro, CA Zip 94578–1009; tel. 510/677–7920; Wright L. Lassiter, III, Chief Executive Officer

CALIFORNIA: ALAMEDA COUNTY MEDICAL CENTER (O, 384 beds) 1411 East 31st Street, Oakland, CA Zip 94602–1018; tel. 510/437–4800; Wright L. Lassiter, III, Chief Executive Officer
Web address: www.alamedahealthsystem.org

SAN LEANDRO HOSPITAL (O, 80 beds) 13855 East 14th Street, San Leandro, CA Zip 94578–2600; tel. 510/357–6500; James E. T. Jackson, M.P.H., Chief Administrative Officer
Web address: www.sanleandrohospital.org

Owned, leased, sponsored:	2 hospitals	464 beds
Contract–managed:	0 hospitals	0 beds
Totals:	2 hospitals	464 beds

★0199: ALLEGHENY HEALTH NETWORK (NP)
30 Isabella Street, Suite 300, Pittsburgh, PA Zip 15212–5862; tel. 412/330–2403; John W. Paul, President and Chief Executive Officer
(Decentralized Health System)

NEW YORK: WESTFIELD MEMORIAL HOSPITAL (O, 4 beds) 189 East Main Street, Westfield, NY Zip 14787–1195; tel. 716/326–4921; Scott Whalen, Ph.D., FACHE, President and Chief Executive Officer
Web address: www.wmhinc.org

PENNSYLVANIA: ALLEGHENY GENERAL HOSPITAL (O, 385 beds) 320 East North Avenue, Pittsburgh, PA Zip 15212–4756; tel. 412/359–3131; Michael Harlovic, R.N., President and Chief Executive Officer
Web address: www.wpahs.org/locations/allegheny–general–hospital

ALLEGHENY VALLEY HOSPITAL (O, 228 beds) 1301 Carlisle Street, Natrona Heights, PA Zip 15065–1152; tel. 724/224–5100; David Goldberg, President & Interim Chief Executive Officer
Web address: www.wpahs.org

CANONSBURG GENERAL HOSPITAL (O, 104 beds) 100 Medical Boulevard, Canonsburg, PA Zip 15317–9762; tel. 724/745–6100; Jane B. Sarra, President and Chief Executive Officer
Web address: www.wpahs.org

FORBES REGIONAL HOSPITAL (O, 349 beds) 2570 Haymaker Road, Monroeville, PA Zip 15146–3513; tel. 412/858–2000; Reese Jackson, President and Chief Executive Officer
Web address: www.ahn.org

JEFFERSON HOSPITAL (O, 373 beds) 565 Coal Valley Road, Jefferson Hills, PA Zip 15025–3703, Mailing Address: Box 18119, Pittsburgh, Zip 15236–0119; tel. 412/469–5000; Louise Urban, R.N., President and Chief Executive Officer
Web address: www.jeffersonregional.com

SAINT VINCENT HEALTH CENTER (O, 407 beds) 232 West 25th Street, Erie, PA Zip 16544–0002; tel. 814/452–5000; Scott Whalen, Ph.D., FACHE, President and Chief Executive Officer
Web address: www.svhs.org

WEST PENN HOSPITAL (O, 308 beds) 4800 Friendship Avenue, Pittsburgh, PA Zip 15224–1722; tel. 412/578–5000; Duke Rupert, President and Chief Executive Officer
Web address: www.wpahs.org

Owned, leased, sponsored:	8 hospitals	2158 beds
Contract–managed:	0 hospitals	0 beds
Totals:	8 hospitals	2158 beds

0413: ALLEGIANCE HEALTH MANAGEMENT (IO)
504 Texas Street, Suite 200, Shreveport, LA Zip 71101–3526; tel. 318/226–8202; Rock Bordelon, President and Chief Executive Officer
(Independent Hospital System)

ARKANSAS: EUREKA SPRINGS HOSPITAL (O, 15 beds) 24 Norris Street, Eureka Springs, AR Zip 72632–3541; tel. 479/253–7400; Christopher L. Bariola, Chief Executive Officer
Web address: www.eurekaspringshospital.com

NORTH METRO MEDICAL CENTER (O, 73 beds) 1400 West Braden Street, Jacksonville, AR Zip 72076–3788; tel. 501/985–7000; Cindy Stafford, Chief Executive Officer
Web address: www.northmetromed.com

RIVER VALLEY MEDICAL CENTER (O, 35 beds) 200 North Third Street, Dardanelle, AR Zip 72834–3802, Mailing Address: P.O. Box 578, Zip 72834–0578; tel. 479/229–4677; Christopher L. Bariola, Chief Executive Officer

LOUISIANA: ALLEGIANCE HEALTH CENTER OF RUSTON (O, 14 beds) 1401 Ezell Street, Ruston, LA Zip 71270–7218; tel. 318/255–8085; Donna K. Thompson, Chief Executive Officer
Web address: www.ahmgt.com

BIENVILLE MEDICAL CENTER (O, 21 beds) 1175 Pine Street, Suite 200, Arcadia, LA Zip 71001–3122; tel. 318/263–4700; Kirk Lemoine, Chief Operating Officer

SABINE MEDICAL CENTER (O, 44 beds) 240 Highland Drive, Many, LA Zip 71449–3718; tel. 318/256–5691; Jay Quebedeaux, Chief Executive Officer
Web address: www.sabinemedicalcenter.net

MISSISSIPPI: ALLEGIANCE SPECIALTY HOSPITAL OF GREENVILLE (O, 39 beds) 300 South Washington Avenue, 3rd Floor, Greenville, MS Zip 38701–4719; tel. 662/332–7344; Vernail Herzog, Chief Executive Officer
Web address: www.ahmgt.com

TEXAS: ALLEGIANCE BEHAVIORAL HEALTH CENTER OF PLAINVIEW (O, 20 beds) 2601 Dimmit Road, 4th Floor, Plainview, TX Zip 79072–1833; tel. 806/296–9191; Angie Alexander, Chief Executive Officer
Web address: www.ahmgt.com

ALLEGIANCE SPECIALTY HOSPITAL OF KILGORE (O, 60 beds) 1612 South Henderson Boulevard, Kilgore, TX Zip 75662–3594; tel. 903/984–3505; Sherry Bustin, Chief Executive Officer
Web address: www.ahmgt.com

BEHAVIORAL HEALTH CENTER OF THE PERMIAN BASIN (O, 48 beds) 3300 South FM 1788, Midland, TX Zip 79706–2601; tel. 432/561–5915; Cheryl Rayl, Chief Executive Officer
Web address: www.ahmgt.com

For explanation of codes following names, see page B2.
★ Indicates Type III membership in the American Hospital Association.

Owned, leased, sponsored:	10 hospitals	369 beds
Contract–managed:	0 hospitals	0 beds
Totals:	10 hospitals	369 beds

0317: ALLIANT MANAGEMENT SERVICES (IO)
2650 Eastpoint Parkway, Suite 300, Louisville, KY Zip 40223–5164; tel. 502/992–3525; Timothy L. Jarm, President and Chief Executive Officer
(Decentralized Health System)

FLORIDA: NORTHWEST FLORIDA COMMUNITY HOSPITAL (C, 59 beds) 1360 Brickyard Road, Chipley, FL Zip 32428–6303, Mailing Address: P.O. Box 889, Zip 32428–0889; tel. 850/638–1610; Mark E. Bush, Chief Executive Officer
Web address: www.nfch.org

ILLINOIS: FAIRFIELD MEMORIAL HOSPITAL (C, 55 beds) 303 N.W. 11th Street, Fairfield, IL Zip 62837–1203; tel. 618/842–2611; Katherine Bunting, Chief Executive Officer
Web address: www.fairfieldmemorial.org

FAYETTE COUNTY HOSPITAL (O, 110 beds) 650 West Taylor Street, Vandalia, IL Zip 62471–1296; tel. 618/283–1231; Gregory D. Starnes, Chief Executive Officer
Web address: www.fayettecountyhospital.org

GIBSON AREA HOSPITAL AND HEALTH SERVICES (C, 67 beds) 1120 North Melvin Street, Gibson City, IL Zip 60936–1477, Mailing Address: P.O. Box 429, Zip 60936–0429; tel. 217/784–4251; Robert C. Schmitt, II, Chief Executive Officer
Web address: www.gibsonhospital.org

PARIS COMMUNITY HOSPITAL (C, 25 beds) 721 East Court Street, Paris, IL Zip 61944–2460; tel. 217/465–4141; Oliver Smith, President and Chief Executive Officer
Web address: www.pariscommunityhospital.com

WABASH GENERAL HOSPITAL (C, 25 beds) 1418 College Drive, Mount Carmel, IL Zip 62863–2638; tel. 618/262–8621; Jay Purvis, Administrator
Web address: www.wabashgeneral.com

INDIANA: GIBSON GENERAL HOSPITAL (C, 70 beds) 1808 Sherman Drive, Princeton, IN Zip 47670–1043; tel. 812/385–3401; Emmett C. Schuster, President and Chief Executive Officer
Web address: www.gibsongeneral.com

PERRY COUNTY MEMORIAL HOSPITAL (C, 25 beds) 1 Hospital Road, Tell City, IN Zip 47586–2750; tel. 812/547–7011; Joseph A. Stuber, President and Chief Executive Officer
Web address: www.pchospital.org

WABASH COUNTY HOSPITAL (C, 25 beds) 710 North East Street, Wabash, IN Zip 46992–1924, Mailing Address: P.O. Box 548, Zip 46992–0548; tel. 260/563–3131; Marilyn J. Custer-Mitchell, President and Chief Executive Officer
Web address: www.wchospital.com

KENTUCKY: BRECKINRIDGE MEMORIAL HOSPITAL (C, 43 beds) 1011 Old Highway 60, Hardinsburg, KY Zip 40143–2597; tel. 270/756–7000; Jeffrey L. Buckley, Interim Chief Executive Officer
Web address: www.breckinridgehealth.org/

CARROLL COUNTY MEMORIAL HOSPITAL (C, 25 beds) 309 11th Street, Carrollton, KY Zip 41008–1400; tel. 502/732–4321; Michael A. Kozar, Chief Executive Officer
Web address: www.ccmhosp.com

CAVERNA MEMORIAL HOSPITAL (C, 25 beds) 1501 South Dixie Street, Horse Cave, KY Zip 42749–1477; tel. 270/786–2191; Alan B. Alexander, Chief Executive Officer
Web address: www.cavernahospital.com

JAMES B. HAGGIN MEMORIAL HOSPITAL (C, 25 beds) 464 Linden Avenue, Harrodsburg, KY Zip 40330–1862; tel. 859/734–5441; Victoria L. Reed, R.N., FACHE, Chief Executive Officer
Web address: www.hagginhosp.org

LIVINGSTON HOSPITAL AND HEALTHCARE SERVICES (C, 25 beds) 131 Hospital Drive, Salem, KY Zip 42078–8043; tel. 270/988–2299; Mark A. Edwards, Chief Executive Officer
Web address: www.lhhs.org

MUHLENBERG COMMUNITY HOSPITAL (C, 90 beds) 440 Hopkinsville Street, Greenville, KY Zip 42345–1172, Mailing Address: P.O. Box 387, Zip 42345–0387; tel. 270/338–8000; Stephen L. Meredith, Interim Chief Executive Officer
Web address: www.mchky.org

TWIN LAKES REGIONAL MEDICAL CENTER (C, 75 beds) 910 Wallace Avenue, Leitchfield, KY Zip 42754–2414; tel. 270/259–9400; Wayne Meriwether, Chief Executive Officer
Web address: www.tlrmc.com

NORTH CAROLINA: ALLEGHANY MEMORIAL HOSPITAL (C, 25 beds) 233 Doctors Street, Sparta, NC Zip 28675–9247; tel. 336/372–5511; Brent R. Lammers, Chief Executive Officer
Web address: www.amhsparta.org

HUGH CHATHAM MEMORIAL HOSPITAL (C, 208 beds) 180 Parkwood Drive, Elkin, NC Zip 28621–2430, Mailing Address: P.O. Box 560, Zip 28621–0560; tel. 336/527–7000; Paul Hammes, Chief Executive Officer
Web address: www.hughchatham.org

Owned, leased, sponsored:	1 hospital	110 beds
Contract–managed:	17 hospitals	892 beds
Totals:	18 hospitals	1002 beds

★0041: ALLINA HEALTH (NP)
2925 Chicago Avenue, Minneapolis, MN Zip 55407–1321, Mailing Address: P.O. Box 43, Zip 55440–0043; tel. 612/262–5000; Ken Paulus, President and Chief Executive Officer
(Moderately Centralized Health System)

MINNESOTA: ABBOTT NORTHWESTERN HOSPITAL (O, 670 beds) 800 East 28th Street, Minneapolis, MN Zip 55407–3799; tel. 612/863–4000; Ben Bache–Wiig, M.D., President
Web address: www.abbottnorthwestern.com

BUFFALO HOSPITAL (O, 44 beds) 303 Catlin Street, Buffalo, MN Zip 55313–1947; tel. 763/682–1212; Jennifer Myster, President
Web address: www.buffalohospital.org

CAMBRIDGE MEDICAL CENTER (O, 78 beds) 701 South Dellwood Street, Cambridge, MN Zip 55008–1920; tel. 763/689–7700; Gary Shaw, President
Web address: www.allina.com/ahs/cambridge.nsf

HUTCHINSON HEALTH (C, 57 beds) 1095 Highway 15 South, Hutchinson, MN Zip 55350–3182; tel. 320/234–5000; Steven Mulder, M.D., President and Chief Executive Officer
Web address: www.hutchhealth.com

MERCY HOSPITAL (O, 254 beds) 4050 Coon Rapids Boulevard, Coon Rapids, MN Zip 55433–2586; tel. 763/236–6000; Sara J. Criger, President
Web address: www.allinamercy.org

NEW ULM MEDICAL CENTER (O, 45 beds) 1324 Fifth Street North, New Ulm, MN Zip 56073–1553; tel. 507/217–5000; Toby Freier, President
Web address: www.newulmmedicalcenter.com

OWATONNA HOSPITAL (O, 43 beds) 2250 N.W. 26th Street, Owatonna, MN Zip 55060–5503; tel. 507/451–3850; David L. Albrecht, President
Web address: www.owatonnahospital.com

PHILLIPS EYE INSTITUTE (O, 8 beds) 2215 Park Avenue, Minneapolis, MN Zip 55404–3756; tel. 612/775–8800; Daniel S. Conrad, M.D., Chief Executive Officer
Web address: www.allinahealth.org/ahs/pei.nsf/

REGINA HOSPITAL (O, 50 beds) 1175 Nininger Road, Hastings, MN Zip 55033–1098; tel. 651/480–4100; Ty W. Erickson, President
Web address: www.reginamedical.org

ST. FRANCIS REGIONAL MEDICAL CENTER (O, 86 beds) 1455 St. Francis Avenue, Shakopee, MN Zip 55379–3380; tel. 952/428–3000; Mike McMahan, Chief Executive Officer
Web address: www.stfrancis–shakopee.com

UNITED HOSPITAL (O, 392 beds) 333 North Smith Avenue, Saint Paul, MN Zip 55102–2389; tel. 651/241–8000; Thomas O'Connor, President
Web address: www.allina.com

UNITY HOSPITAL (O, 220 beds) 550 Osborne Road N.E., Fridley, MN Zip 55432–2799; tel. 763/236–5000; Helen J. Strike, R.N., President
Web address: www.allina.com

Section B

For explanation of codes following names, see page B2.
★ Indicates Type III membership in the American Hospital Association.

WISCONSIN: RIVER FALLS AREA HOSPITAL (O, 8 beds) 1629 East Division Street, River Falls, WI Zip 54022–1571; tel. 715/425–6155; David R. Miller, President
Web address: www.allina.com

Owned, leased, sponsored:	12 hospitals	1898 beds
Contract–managed:	1 hospital	57 beds
Totals:	13 hospitals	1955 beds

0187: ALTA HEALTHCARE SYSTEM (IO)
10780 Santa Monica Boulevard, Suite 400, Los Angeles, CA Zip 90025–7616; tel. 310/943–4500; David Topper, Chief Executive Officer

CALIFORNIA: LOS ANGELES COMMUNITY HOSPITAL AT LOS ANGELES (O, 180 beds) 4081 East Olympic Boulevard, Los Angeles, CA Zip 90023–3330; tel. 323/267–0477; Omar Ramirez, Chief Executive Officer

SOUTHERN CALIFORNIA HOSPITAL AT HOLLYWOOD (O, 45 beds) 6245 De Longpre Avenue, Los Angeles, CA Zip 90028–9001; tel. 323/462–2271; Bruce P. Grimshaw, Chief Executive Officer
Web address: www.hollywoodcommunityhospital.org/

Owned, leased, sponsored:	2 hospitals	225 beds
Contract–managed:	0 hospitals	0 beds
Totals:	2 hospitals	225 beds

0877: ALTAPOINTE HEALTH SYSTEMS (IO)
5750–A Southland Drive, Mobile, AL Zip 36693–3316; tel. 251/473–4423; J. Tuerk Schlesinger, Chief Executive Officer

ALABAMA: BAYPOINTE BEHAVIORAL HEALTH (O, 60 beds) 5800 Southland Drive, Mobile, AL Zip 36693–3313; tel. 251/661–0153; Heather Joseph, Administrator
Web address: www.altapointe.org

EASTPOINTE HOSPITAL (O, 66 beds) 7400 Roper Lane, Daphne, AL Zip 36526–5274; tel. 251/378–6500; Jarett Crum, Administrator
Web address: www.altapointe.org/eastpointe.php

Owned, leased, sponsored:	2 hospitals	126 beds
Contract–managed:	0 hospitals	0 beds
Totals:	2 hospitals	126 beds

2295: AMERICAN PROVINCE OF LITTLE COMPANY OF MARY SISTERS (CC)
9350 South California Avenue, Evergreen Park, IL Zip 60805–2595; tel. 708/229–5491; Sister Kathleen McIntyre, Province Leader
(Moderately Centralized Health System)

ILLINOIS: LITTLE COMPANY OF MARY HOSPITAL AND HEALTH CARE CENTERS (O, 254 beds) 2800 West 95th Street, Evergreen Park, IL Zip 60805–2795; tel. 708/422–6200; Dennis A. Reilly, President and Chief Executive Officer
Web address: www.lcmh.org

INDIANA: MEMORIAL HOSPITAL AND HEALTH CARE CENTER (O, 143 beds) 800 West Ninth Street, Jasper, IN Zip 47546–2516; tel. 812/996–2345; Raymond W. Snowden, President and Chief Executive Officer
Web address: www.mhhcc.org

Owned, leased, sponsored:	2 hospitals	397 beds
Contract–managed:	0 hospitals	0 beds
Totals:	2 hospitals	397 beds

0644: AMG INTEGRATED HEALTHCARE MANAGEMENT (IO)
101 La Rue France, Suite 500, Lafayette, LA Zip 70508–3144; tel. 337/269–9828; August J. Rantz, III, Founder and Chief Executive Officer
(Independent Hospital System)

KANSAS: AMG SPECIALTY HOSPITAL–WICHITA (O, 26 beds) 8080 East Pawnee Street, Wichita, KS Zip 67207–5475; tel. 316/682–0004; Robert A. Loepp, Jr., FACHE, Chief Executive Officer
Web address: www.amgwichita.com/

LOUISIANA: AMG SPECIALTY HOSPITAL–DENHAM SPRINGS (O, 117 beds) 8375 Florida Boulevard, Denham Springs, LA Zip 70726–7806; tel. 225/665–2664; Karen Crayton, Administrator
Web address: www.amgdenham.com/

AMG SPECIALTY HOSPITAL–FELICIANA (O, 16 beds) 9725 Grace Lane, Clinton, LA Zip 70722–4925; tel. 225/683–1600; Keith Carruth, Chief Executive Officer
Web address: www.amgfeliciana.com/

AMG SPECIALTY HOSPITAL–HOUMA (O, 40 beds) 629 Dunn Street, Houma, LA Zip 70360–4707; tel. 985/274–0001; Ricky Robeson, Chief Executive Officer

AMG SPECIALTY HOSPITAL–LAFAYETTE (O, 58 beds) 310 Youngsville Highway, Lafayette, LA Zip 70508–4524; tel. 337/839–9880; Jason Branson, Chief Executive Officer
Web address: www.amglafayette.com

AMG SPECIALTY HOSPITAL–SLIDELL (O, 40 beds) 1400 Lindberg Drive, Slidell, LA Zip 70458–8056; tel. 985/326–0440; Richard Daughdrill, R.N., Chief Executive Officer
Web address: www.amgslidell.com/

LAFAYETTE PHYSICAL REHABILITATION HOSPITAL (O, 32 beds) 307 Polly Lane, Lafayette, LA Zip 70508–4960; tel. 337/314–1111; Jonathan Landreth, Chief Executive Officer

THE NEUROMEDICAL CENTER REHABILITATION HOSPITAL (O, 23 beds) 10101 Park Rowe Avenue, Suite 500, Baton Rouge, LA Zip 70810–1685; tel. 225/906–2999; Jay Ivy, R.N., Chief Executive Officer
Web address: www.theneuromedicalcenter.com

MISSISSIPPI: AMG SPECIALTY HOSPITAL–GREENWOOD (O, 40 beds) 1401 River Road Floor 2, Greenwood, MS Zip 38930–4030; tel. 662/459–2681; Jennifer Wallace, Chief Executive Officer
Web address: www.amggreenwood.com/

NEW MEXICO: AMG SPECIALTY HOSPITAL–ALBUQUERQUE (O, 24 beds) 235 Elm Street N.E., Albuquerque, NM Zip 87102–3672; tel. 505/842–5550; Elizabeth Rees, Chief Executive Officer
Web address: www.amgalbuquerque.com/

OKLAHOMA: AMG SPECIALTY HOSPITAL–EDMOND (O, 37 beds) 1100 East Ninth Street, Edmond, OK Zip 73034–5755; tel. 405/341–8150; Ginger Creech, Chief Executive Officer
Web address: www.amgedmond.com/

AMG SPECIALTY HOSPITAL–TULSA (O, 46 beds) 1923 South Utica Avenue, 4 South, Tulsa, OK Zip 74104–6510; tel. 918/744–3047; Stacy Wilde, Chief Executive Officer
Web address: www.amgihm.com

Owned, leased, sponsored:	12 hospitals	499 beds
Contract–managed:	0 hospitals	0 beds
Totals:	12 hospitals	499 beds

● **0389: ANMED HEALTH** (NP)
800 North Fant Street, Anderson, SC Zip 29621–5793; tel. 864/512–1000; John A. Miller, Jr., FACHE, Chief Executive Officer
(Moderately Centralized Health System)

SOUTH CAROLINA: ANMED HEALTH MEDICAL CENTER (O, 414 beds) 800 North Fant Street, Anderson, SC Zip 29621–5793; tel. 864/512–1000; John A. Miller, Jr., FACHE, Chief Executive Officer
Web address: www.anmedhealth.org

Owned, leased, sponsored:	1 hospital	414 beds
Contract–managed:	0 hospitals	0 beds
Totals:	1 hospital	414 beds

For explanation of codes following names, see page B2.
★ Indicates Type III membership in the American Hospital Association.
● Single hospital health care system

★0866: APPALACHIAN REGIONAL HEALTHCARE SYSTEM
(NP)
336 Deerfield Road, Boone, NC Zip 28607–5008, Mailing Address:
P.O. Box 2600, Zip 28607–2600; tel. 828/262–4100; Richard G.
Sparks, President and Chief Executive Officer
(Centralized Health System)

NORTH CAROLINA: BLOWING ROCK REHABILITATION & DAVANT EXTENDED
CARE CENTER (C, 72 beds) 418 Chestnut Street, Blowing Rock, NC
Zip 28605–0148, Mailing Address: P.O. Box 148, Zip 28605–0148;
tel. 828/295–3136; Elizabeth Hayes, R.N., Interim Administrator

CHARLES A. CANNON MEMORIAL HOSPITAL (C, 35 beds) 434 Hospital Drive,
Linville, NC Zip 28646, Mailing Address: P.O. Box 767, Zip 28646–0767;
tel. 828/737–7000; Carmen Lacey, MSN, R.N., President
Web address: www.https://apprhs.org/locations/cannon–memorial–hospital

WATAUGA MEDICAL CENTER (C, 99 beds) 336 Deerfield Road, Boone, NC
Zip 28607–5008, Mailing Address: P.O. Box 2600, Zip 28607–2600;
tel. 828/262–4100; Richard G. Sparks, Chief Executive Officer
Web address: www.https://apprhs.org/contact–us

Owned, leased, sponsored:	0 hospitals	0 beds
Contract–managed:	3 hospitals	206 beds
Totals:	3 hospitals	206 beds

0145: APPALACHIAN REGIONAL HEALTHCARE, INC. (NP)
2285 Executive Drive, Suite 400, Lexington, KY Zip 40505–4810,
Mailing Address: P.O. Box 8086, Zip 40533–8086;
tel. 859/226–2440; Jerry Haynes, President and Chief Executive
Officer
(Decentralized Health System)

KENTUCKY: HARLAN ARH HOSPITAL (O, 137 beds) 81 Ball Park Road,
Harlan, KY Zip 40831–1792; tel. 606/573–8100; Paul V. Miles, Interim
Community Chief Executive Officer
Web address: www.arh.org

HAZARD ARH REGIONAL MEDICAL CENTER (O, 308 beds) 100 Medical Center
Drive, Hazard, KY Zip 41701–9421; tel. 606/439–6600; Donald R. Fields,
Senior Community Chief Executive Officer
Web address: www.arh.org

MARY BRECKINRIDGE ARH HOSPITAL (O, 25 beds) 130 Kate Ireland Drive,
Hyden, KY Zip 41749–9071, Mailing Address: P.O. Box 447–A,
Zip 41749–0717; tel. 606/672–2901; Mallie S. Noble, Administrator
Web address: www.frontiernursing.org

MCDOWELL ARH HOSPITAL (O, 25 beds) Route 122, McDowell, KY
Zip 41647, Mailing Address: P.O. Box 247, Zip 41647–0247;
tel. 606/377–3400; Russell Barker, Community Chief Executive Officer
Web address: www.arh.org

MIDDLESBORO ARH HOSPITAL (O, 96 beds) 3600 West Cumberland Avenue,
Middlesboro, KY Zip 40965–2614, Mailing Address: P.O. Box 340,
Zip 40965–0340; tel. 606/242–1100; Michael Slusher, Community Chief
Executive Officer
Web address: www.arh.org/middlesboro

MORGAN COUNTY ARH HOSPITAL (L, 25 beds) 476 Liberty Road, West
Liberty, KY Zip 41472–2049, Mailing Address: P.O. Box 579,
Zip 41472–0579; tel. 606/743–3186; Stephen M. Gavalchik, FACHE,
Community Chief Executive Officer
Web address: www.arh.org

WHITESBURG ARH HOSPITAL (O, 87 beds) 240 Hospital Road, Whitesburg,
KY Zip 41858–7627; tel. 606/633–3600; Dena C. Sparkman, FACHE,
Community Chief Executive Officer
Web address: www.arh.org/whitesburg

WILLIAMSON ARH HOSPITAL (O, 126 beds) 260 Hospital Drive, South
Williamson, KY Zip 41503–4072; tel. 606/237–1710; Timothy A. Hatfield,
Community Chief Executive Officer
Web address: www.arh.org

WEST VIRGINIA: BECKLEY ARH HOSPITAL (O, 170 beds) 306 Stanaford
Road, Beckley, WV Zip 25801–3142; tel. 304/255–3000; Rocco K.
Massey, Community Chief Executive Officer
Web address: www.arh.org

SUMMERS COUNTY ARH HOSPITAL (L, 25 beds) Terrace Street, Hinton, WV
Zip 25951–2407, Mailing Address: Drawer 940, Zip 25951–0940;
tel. 304/466–1000; Wesley Dangerfield, Community Chief Executive Officer
Web address: www.arh.org

Owned, leased, sponsored:	10 hospitals	1024 beds
Contract–managed:	0 hospitals	0 beds
Totals:	10 hospitals	1024 beds

★0104: ARCHBOLD MEDICAL CENTER (NP)
910 South Broad Street, Thomasville, GA Zip 31792–6113;
tel. 229/228–2739; J. Perry Mustian, President
(Moderately Centralized Health System)

GEORGIA: BROOKS COUNTY HOSPITAL (L, 25 beds) 903 North Court Street,
Quitman, GA Zip 31643–1315, Mailing Address: P.O. Box 5000,
Zip 31643–5000; tel. 229/263–4171; Kenneth D. Rhudy, Chief Executive
Officer
Web address: www.archbold.org

GRADY GENERAL HOSPITAL (L, 48 beds) 1155 Fifth Street S.E., Cairo, GA
Zip 39828–3142, Mailing Address: P.O. Box 360, Zip 39828–0360;
tel. 229/377–1150; Kenneth D. Rhudy, Administrator
Web address: www.archbold.org

JOHN D. ARCHBOLD MEMORIAL HOSPITAL (O, 328 beds) 915 Gordon
Avenue, Thomasville, GA Zip 31792–6614, Mailing Address: P.O. Box 1018,
Zip 31799–1018; tel. 229/228–2000; J. Perry Mustian, President and Chief
Executive Officer
Web address: www.archbold.org

MITCHELL COUNTY HOSPITAL (L, 181 beds) 90 East Stephens Street,
Camilla, GA Zip 31730–1836, Mailing Address: P.O. Box 639,
Zip 31730–0639; tel. 229/336–5284; LaDon Toole, Administrator
Web address: www.archbold.org

Owned, leased, sponsored:	4 hospitals	582 beds
Contract–managed:	0 hospitals	0 beds
Totals:	4 hospitals	582 beds

★0069: ARDENT HEALTH SERVICES (IO)
1 Burton Hills Boulevard, Suite 250, Nashville, TN Zip 37215–6195;
tel. 615/296–3000; David T. Vandewater, President and Chief
Executive Officer
(Centralized Physician/Insurance Health System)

NEW MEXICO: LOVELACE MEDICAL CENTER (O, 263 beds) 601 Martin
Luther King Avenue N.E., Albuquerque, NM Zip 87102–3619;
tel. 505/727–8000; Troy Greer, Chief Executive Officer
Web address: www.lovelace.
com/albuquerque–hospital/lovelace–medical–center#.UDZ1laDhf48

LOVELACE REGIONAL HOSPITAL – ROSWELL (O, 26 beds) 117 East 19th
Street, Roswell, NM Zip 88201–5151; tel. 575/627–7000; Dawn M.
Tschabrun, R.N., Chief Executive Officer
Web address: www.lovelace.com

LOVELACE REHABILITATION HOSPITAL (O, 52 beds) 505 Elm Street N.E.,
Albuquerque, NM Zip 87102–2500; tel. 505/727–4700; Derrick Jones, Chief
Executive Officer
Web address: www.lovelace.com

LOVELACE WESTSIDE HOSPITAL (O, 80 beds) 10501 Golf Course Road N.W.,
Albuquerque, NM Zip 87114–5000, Mailing Address: P.O. Box 25555,
Zip 87125–0555; tel. 505/727–2000; Farron Sneed, FACHE, Chief Executive
Officer
Web address: www.lovelace.
com/albuquerque–hospital/lovelace–westside–hospital#.UDZ1t6Dhf48

LOVELACE WOMEN'S HOSPITAL (O, 78 beds) 4701 Montgomery Boulevard
N.E., Albuquerque, NM Zip 87109–1251, Mailing Address: P.O. Box 25555,
Zip 87125–0555; tel. 505/727–7800; Sheri Milone, Chief Executive Officer
and Administrator
Web address: www.lovelace.
com/albuquerque–hospital/lovelace–womens–hospital#.UDZ17KDhf48

OKLAHOMA: BAILEY MEDICAL CENTER (O, 37 beds) 10502 North 110th
East Avenue, Owasso, OK Zip 74055–6655; tel. 918/376–8000; Keith
Mason, Chief Executive Officer
Web address: www.baileymedicalcenter.com

HILLCREST HOSPITAL – SOUTH (O, 160 beds) 8801 South 101st East
Avenue, Tulsa, OK Zip 74133–5716; tel. 918/294–4000; Joseph H. Neely,
FACHE, Chief Executive Officer
Web address: www.southcresthospital.com

For explanation of codes following names, see page B2.
★ Indicates Type III membership in the American Hospital Association.

HILLCREST HOSPITAL CLAREMORE (O, 55 beds) 1202 North Muskogee Place, Claremore, OK Zip 74017–3036; tel. 918/341–2556; David Chaussard, Chief Executive Officer
Web address: www.hillcrestclaremore.com

HILLCREST HOSPITAL CUSHING (O, 95 beds) 1027 East Cherry Street, Cushing, OK Zip 74023–4101, Mailing Address: P.O. Box 1409, Zip 74023–1409; tel. 918/225–2915; Kevin Hawk, Chief Executive Officer
Web address: www.hillcrestcushing.com/

HILLCREST HOSPITAL HENRYETTA (O, 41 beds) Dewey Bartlett & Main Streets, Henryetta, OK Zip 74437–6820, Mailing Address: P.O. Box 1269, Zip 74437–1269; tel. 918/650–1100; Dee Renshaw, Chief Executive Officer
Web address: www.hillcresthenryetta.com/

HILLCREST MEDICAL CENTER (O, 532 beds) 1120 South Utica, Tulsa, OK Zip 74104–4090; tel. 918/579–1000; Kevin J. Gross, Interim Chief Executive Officer
Web address: www.hillcrest.com/home

Owned, leased, sponsored:	11 hospitals	1419 beds
Contract–managed:	0 hospitals	0 beds
Totals:	11 hospitals	1419 beds

★**0809: ARNOT HEALTH** (NP)
600 Roe Avenue, Elmira, NY Zip 14905–1629; tel. 607/737–4100; Robert K. Lambert, M.D., FACHE, President and Chief Executive Officer
(Independent Hospital System)

NEW YORK: ARNOT OGDEN MEDICAL CENTER (O, 216 beds) 600 Roe Avenue, Elmira, NY Zip 14905–1629; tel. 607/737–4100; H. Fred Farley, R.N., Ph.D., FACHE, President and Chief Operating Officer
Web address: www.aomc.org

IRA DAVENPORT MEMORIAL HOSPITAL (O, 184 beds) 7571 State Route 54, Bath, NY Zip 14810–9590; tel. 607/776–8500; James B. Watson, President and Chief Operating Officer
Web address: www.arnothealth.org

ST. JOSEPH'S HOSPITAL (O, 250 beds) 555 St. Joseph's Boulevard, Elmira, NY Zip 14901–3223; tel. 607/733–6541; H. Fred Farley, R.N., Ph.D., FACHE, President and Chief Operating Officer
Web address: www.stjosephs.org

Owned, leased, sponsored:	3 hospitals	650 beds
Contract–managed:	0 hospitals	0 beds
Totals:	3 hospitals	650 beds

★**0094: ASANTE HEALTH SYSTEM** (NP)
2650 Siskiyou Boulevard, Suite 200, Medford, OR Zip 97504–8170; tel. 541/789–4100; Roy G. Vinyard, FACHE, President and Chief Executive Officer
(Moderately Centralized Health System)

OREGON: ASANTE ASHLAND COMMUNITY HOSPITAL (O, 36 beds) 280 Maple Street, Ashland, OR Zip 97520–1593; tel. 541/201–4000; Sheila Clough, Chief Executive Officer
Web address: www.ashlandhospital.org

ASANTE ROGUE REGIONAL MEDICAL CENTER (O, 320 beds) 2825 East Barnett Road, Medford, OR Zip 97504–8332; tel. 541/789–7000; Scott A. Kelly, Chief Executive Officer
Web address: www.asante.org

ASANTE THREE RIVERS MEDICAL CENTER (O, 111 beds) 500 S.W. Ramsey Avenue, Grants Pass, OR Zip 97527–5554; tel. 541/472–7000; Win Howard, Chief Executive Officer
Web address: www.asante.org/trmc/

Owned, leased, sponsored:	3 hospitals	467 beds
Contract–managed:	0 hospitals	0 beds
Totals:	3 hospitals	467 beds

★**0198: ASCENSION HEALTH** (CC)
101 South Hanley Road, Suite 450, Saint Louis, MO Zip 63105–3406; tel. 314/733–8000; Robert J. Henkel, FACHE, President and Chief Executive Officer
(Decentralized Health System)

ALABAMA: PROVIDENCE HOSPITAL (S, 349 beds) 6801 Airport Boulevard, Mobile, AL Zip 36608–3785, Mailing Address: P.O. Box 850429, Zip 36685–0429; tel. 251/633–1000; Clark P. Christianson, President and Chief Executive Officer
Web address: www.providencehospital.org

ST. VINCENT'S BIRMINGHAM (S, 409 beds) 810 St. Vincent's Drive, Birmingham, AL Zip 35205–1695, Mailing Address: P.O. Box 12407, Zip 35202–2407; tel. 205/939–7000; Andy Davis, President
Web address: www.stvhs.com

ST. VINCENT'S BLOUNT (S, 40 beds) 150 Gilbreath, Oneonta, AL Zip 35121–2827, Mailing Address: P.O. Box 1000, Zip 35121–0013; tel. 205/274–3000; Evan Ray, President
Web address: www.stvhs.com

ST. VINCENT'S EAST (S, 328 beds) 50 Medical Park East Drive, Birmingham, AL Zip 35235–9987; tel. 205/838–3000; Michael Korpiel, President and Chief Operating Officer
Web address: www.stvhs.com

ST. VINCENT'S ST. CLAIR (S, 40 beds) 7063 Veterans Parkway, Pell City, AL Zip 35125–1499; tel. 205/814–2105; Evan Ray, President
Web address: www.stvhs.com

ARIZONA: CARONDELET HOLY CROSS HOSPITAL (S, 25 beds) 1171 West Target Range Road, Nogales, AZ Zip 85621–2415; tel. 520/285–3000; Debbie Knapheide, MSN, Site Administrator, Chief Nursing Officer and Chief Operating Officer
Web address: www.carondelet.org

CARONDELET ST. JOSEPH'S HOSPITAL (S, 486 beds) 350 North Wilmot Road, Tucson, AZ Zip 85711–2678; tel. 520/873–3000; Tony Fonze, President and Chief Executive Officer
Web address: www.carondelet.org

CARONDELET ST. MARY'S HOSPITAL (S, 262 beds) 1601 West St. Mary's Road, Tucson, AZ Zip 85745–2682; tel. 520/872–3000; Amy Beiter, M.D., President and Chief Executive Officer
Web address: www.carondelet.org

CONNECTICUT: ST. VINCENT'S MEDICAL CENTER (S, 416 beds) 2800 Main Street, Bridgeport, CT Zip 06606–4292; tel. 203/576–5454; Stuart G. Marcus, M.D., FACS, President and Chief Executive Officer
Web address: www.stvincents.org

DISTRICT OF COLUMBIA: PROVIDENCE HOSPITAL (S, 541 beds) 1150 Varnum Street N.E., Washington, DC Zip 20017–2104; tel. 202/269–7000; Amy E. Freeman, President and Chief Executive Officer
Web address: www.provhosp.org

FLORIDA: SACRED HEART HOSPITAL OF PENSACOLA (S, 560 beds) 5151 North Ninth Avenue, Pensacola, FL Zip 32504–8795, Mailing Address: P.O. Box 2700, Zip 32513–2700; tel. 850/416–7000; Henry Stovall, President
Web address: www.sacred–heart.org

SACRED HEART HOSPITAL ON THE EMERALD COAST (S, 58 beds) 7800 Highway 98 West, Miramar Beach, FL Zip 32550; tel. 850/278–3000; Roger L. Hall, President
Web address: www.sacredheartemerald.org

SACRED HEART HOSPITAL ON THE GULF (S, 19 beds) 3801 East Highway 98, Port St. Joe, FL Zip 32456–5318; tel. 850/229–5600; Roger L. Hall, President
Web address: www.sacred–heart.org/gulf/

ST. VINCENT'S MEDICAL CENTER RIVERSIDE (S, 528 beds) 1 Shircliff Way, Jacksonville, FL Zip 32204–4748, Mailing Address: P.O. Box 2982, Zip 32203–2982; tel. 904/308–7300; Moody L. Chisholm, President & Chief Executive Officer
Web address: www.jaxhealth.com

ST. VINCENT'S MEDICAL CENTER SOUTHSIDE (S, 288 beds) 4201 Belfort Road, Jacksonville, FL Zip 32216–1431; tel. 904/296–3700; Moody L. Chisholm, President and Chief Executive Officer
Web address: www.jaxhealth.com

For explanation of codes following names, see page B2.
★ Indicates Type III membership in the American Hospital Association.

IDAHO: ST. JOSEPH REGIONAL MEDICAL CENTER (S, 119 beds) 415 Sixth Street, Lewiston, ID Zip 83501–2431; tel. 208/743–2511; Michael T. Rooney, M.D., Interim President and Chief Executive Officer
Web address: www.sjrmc.org

ILLINOIS: ALEXIAN BROTHERS BEHAVIORAL HEALTH HOSPITAL (O, 141 beds) 1650 Moon Lake Boulevard, Hoffman Estates, IL Zip 60169–1010; tel. 847/882–1600; Clayton Ciha, President and Chief Executive Officer
Web address: www.abbhh.org

ALEXIAN BROTHERS MEDICAL CENTER (O, 375 beds) 800 Biesterfield Road, Elk Grove Village, IL Zip 60007–3397; tel. 847/437–5500; John P. Werrbach, Chief Executive Officer
Web address: www.alexian.org

ST. ALEXIUS MEDICAL CENTER (O, 261 beds) 1555 Barrington Road, Hoffman Estates, IL Zip 60169–1019; tel. 847/843–2000; Leonard Wilk, President and Chief Executive Officer
Web address: www.stalexius.org

INDIANA: ST. JOSEPH HOSPITAL & HEALTH CENTER (S, 137 beds) 1907 West Sycamore Street, Kokomo, IN Zip 46901–4197; tel. 765/452–5611; Kathlene A. Young, MS, FACHE, President and Chief Executive Officer
Web address: www.stvincent.org/stjoseph

ST. MARY'S WARRICK HOSPITAL (S, 35 beds) 1116 Millis Avenue, Boonville, IN Zip 47601–2204; tel. 812/897–4800; Kathy J. Hall, Administrator
Web address: www.stmarys.org/warrick

ST. MARY'S MEDICAL CENTER OF EVANSVILLE (S, 436 beds) 3700 Washington Avenue, Evansville, IN Zip 47714–0541; tel. 812/485–4000; Keith Jewell, President
Web address: www.stmarys.org

ST. VINCENT ANDERSON REGIONAL HOSPITAL (S, 185 beds) 2015 Jackson Street, Anderson, IN Zip 46016–4339; tel. 765/649–2511; Thomas J. VanOsdol, President
Web address: www.stvincent.org/Saint–Johns/Default.aspx

ST. VINCENT CARMEL HOSPITAL (S, 104 beds) 13500 North Meridian Street, Carmel, IN Zip 46032–1456; tel. 317/582–7000; Michael D. Chittenden, President
Web address: www.stvincent.org

ST. VINCENT CLAY HOSPITAL (S, 25 beds) 1206 East National Avenue, Brazil, IN Zip 47834–2797, Mailing Address: P.O. Box 489, Zip 47834–0489; tel. 812/442–2500; Jerry Laue, Administrator
Web address: www.stvincent.org

ST. VINCENT DUNN HOSPITAL (S, 25 beds) 1600 23rd Street, Bedford, IN Zip 47421–4704; tel. 812/275–3331; Matt Balla, Chief Executive Officer
Web address: www.stvincent.org/St–Vincent–Dunn/Default.aspx

ST. VINCENT FISHERS HOSPITAL (S, 46 beds) 13861 Olio Road, Fishers, IN Zip 46037–3487; tel. 317/415–9000; Gary Fammartino, Administrator
Web address: www.stvincent.org

ST. VINCENT FRANKFORT HOSPITAL (S, 25 beds) 1300 South Jackson Street, Frankfort, IN Zip 46041–3394, Mailing Address: P.O. Box 669, Zip 46041–0669; tel. 765/656–3000; Thomas Crawford, Administrator
Web address: www.stvincent.org

ST. VINCENT HEART CENTER (S, 107 beds) 10580 North Meridian Street, Indianapolis, IN Zip 46290–1028; tel. 317/583–5000; Blake A. Dye, President
Web address: www.bestheartcare.com/

ST. VINCENT INDIANAPOLIS HOSPITAL (S, 921 beds) 2001 West 86th Street, Indianapolis, IN Zip 46260–1991, Mailing Address: P.O. Box 40970, Zip 46240–0970; tel. 317/338–2345; Kyle De Fur, FACHE, President
Web address: www.stvincent.org

ST. VINCENT JENNINGS HOSPITAL (S, 25 beds) 301 Henry Street, North Vernon, IN Zip 47265–1097; tel. 812/352–4200; Carl W. Risk, II, Administrator
Web address: www.stvincent.org

ST. VINCENT MERCY HOSPITAL (S, 25 beds) 1331 South A Street, Elwood, IN Zip 46036–1942; tel. 765/552–4600; Francis G. Albarano, Administrator
Web address: www.stvincent.org

ST. VINCENT RANDOLPH HOSPITAL (S, 16 beds) 473 Greenville Avenue, Winchester, IN Zip 47394–9436, Mailing Address: P.O. Box 407, Zip 47394–0407; tel. 765/584–0004; Francis G. Albarano, Administrator
Web address: www.stvincent.org

ST. VINCENT SALEM HOSPITAL (S, 25 beds) 911 North Shelby Street, Salem, IN Zip 47167–1694; tel. 812/883–5881; Dana M. Muntz, Chief Executive Officer
Web address: www.stvincent.org/St–Vincent–Salem/Default.aspx

ST. VINCENT SETON SPECIALTY HOSPITAL (S, 30 beds) 1501 Hartford Street, Lafayette, IN Zip 47904–2134; tel. 765/236–8900; Peter H. Alexander, Administrator
Web address: www.stvincent.org

ST. VINCENT SETON SPECIALTY HOSPITAL (S, 74 beds) 8050 Township Line Road, Indianapolis, IN Zip 46260–2478; tel. 317/415–8353; Peter H. Alexander, Administrator
Web address: www.stvincent.org/

ST. VINCENT WILLIAMSPORT HOSPITAL (S, 16 beds) 412 North Monroe Street, Williamsport, IN Zip 47993–1049; tel. 765/762–4000; Jane Craigin, Chief Executive Officer
Web address: www.stvincent.org

KANSAS: MERCY REGIONAL HEALTH CENTER (O, 96 beds) 1823 College Avenue, Manhattan, KS Zip 66502–3346; tel. 785/776–3322; John R. Broberg, FACHE, Senior Administrator
Web address: www.mercyregional.org

VIA CHRISTI HOSPITAL IN PITTSBURG (O, 111 beds) 1 Mt. Carmel Way, Pittsburg, KS Zip 66762–7587; tel. 620/232–0109; Randall R. Cason, FACHE, President and Chief Executive Officer
Web address: www.viachristi.org

VIA CHRISTI HOSPITAL ON ST. FRANCIS (O, 719 beds) 929 North St. Francis Street, Wichita, KS Zip 67214–3882; tel. 316/268–5000; Sherry Hausmann, Senior Administrator
Web address: www.via–christi.org

VIA CHRISTI HOSPITAL ON ST. TERESA (O, 70 beds) 14800 West St. Teresa, Wichita, KS Zip 67235–9602; tel. 316/796–7000; Kevin Strecker, President
Web address: www.via–christi.org/st–teresa

VIA CHRISTI REHABILITATION HOSPITAL (O, 58 beds) 1151 North Rock Road, Wichita, KS Zip 67206–1262; tel. 316/634–3400; Cindy LaFleur, Senior Administrator
Web address: www.via–christi.org

MARYLAND: SAINT AGNES HOSPITAL (S, 339 beds) 900 Caton Avenue, Baltimore, MD Zip 21229–5201; tel. 410/368–6000; Bonnie Phipps, President and Chief Executive Officer
Web address: www.stagnes.org

MICHIGAN: BORGESS MEDICAL CENTER (S, 387 beds) 1521 Gull Road, Kalamazoo, MI Zip 49048–1640; tel. 269/226–7000; Paul A. Spaude, FACHE, President and Chief Executive Officer
Web address: www.borgess.com

BORGESS–LEE MEMORIAL HOSPITAL (S, 25 beds) 420 West High Street, Dowagiac, MI Zip 49047–1943; tel. 269/782–8681; John E. Ryder, Chief Operating Officer
Web address: www.borgess.com

BORGESS–PIPP HOSPITAL (S, 43 beds) 411 Naomi Street, Plainwell, MI Zip 49080–1222; tel. 269/685–6811; John E. Ryder, Administrator and Chief Operating Officer
Web address: www.borgess.com

BRIGHTON CENTER FOR RECOVERY (S, 99 beds) 12851 Grand River Road, Brighton, MI Zip 48116–8506; tel. 810/227–1211; Raymond Waller, Director
Web address: www.brightonrecovery.org

GENESYS REGIONAL MEDICAL CENTER (S, 410 beds) One Genesys Parkway, Grand Blanc, MI Zip 48439–8066; tel. 810/606–5000; Elizabeth Aderholdt, President and Chief Executive Officer
Web address: www.genesys.org

PROVIDENCE HOSPITAL (S, 626 beds) 16001 West Nine Mile Road, Southfield, MI Zip 48075–4818, Mailing Address: P.O. Box 2043, Zip 48037–2043; tel. 248/424–3000; Michael Wiemann, M.D., President
Web address: www.providence–stjohnhealth.org

ST. JOHN HOSPITAL AND MEDICAL CENTER (S, 673 beds) 22101 Moross Road, Detroit, MI Zip 48236–2148; tel. 313/343–4000; David Brooks, President
Web address: www.stjohn.org

ST. JOHN MACOMB–OAKLAND HOSPITAL (S, 524 beds) 11800 East 12 Mile Road, Warren, MI Zip 48093–3472; tel. 586/573–5000; Terry Hamilton, President
Web address: www.stjohnprovidence.org/macomb

For explanation of codes following names, see page B2.
★ Indicates Type III membership in the American Hospital Association.

Section B

ST. JOHN RIVER DISTRICT HOSPITAL (S, 68 beds) 4100 River Road, East China, MI Zip 48054–2909; tel. 810/329–7111; Frank W. Poma, President
Web address: www.stjohn.org

ST. JOSEPH HEALTH SYSTEM (S, 20 beds) 200 Hemlock Street, Tawas City, MI Zip 48763–9237, Mailing Address: P.O. Box 659, Zip 48764–0659; tel. 989/362–3411; Ann M. Balfour, R.N., President
Web address: www.sjhsys.org

ST. MARY'S OF MICHIGAN (S, 236 beds) 800 South Washington Avenue, Saginaw, MI Zip 48601–2594; tel. 989/907–8000; John R. Graham, President and Chief Executive Officer
Web address: www.stmarysofmichigan.org

ST. MARY'S OF MICHIGAN STANDISH HOSPITAL (S, 68 beds) 805 West Cedar Street, Standish, MI Zip 48658–9526; tel. 989/846–4521; John R. Graham, President and Chief Executive Officer
Web address: www.stmarysofmichigan.org/standish

MINNESOTA: SAINT ELIZABETH'S MEDICAL CENTER (O, 166 beds) 1200 Grant Boulevard West, Wabasha, MN Zip 55981–1042; tel. 651/565–4531; Thomas Crowley, President and Chief Executive Officer
Web address: www.stelizabethswabasha.org

MISSOURI: ST. JOSEPH MEDICAL CENTER (S, 190 beds) 1000 Carondelet Drive, Kansas City, MO Zip 64114–4673; tel. 816/942–4400; Michael A. Dorsey, FACHE, Chief Executive Officer
Web address: www.carondelethealth.org

ST. MARY'S MEDICAL CENTER (S, 146 beds) 201 West R. D. Mize Road, Blue Springs, MO Zip 64014–2518; tel. 816/228–5900; Michael A. Dorsey, FACHE, Chief Executive Officer
Web address: www.carondelethealth.org

NEW YORK: MOUNT ST. MARY'S HOSPITAL AND HEALTH CENTER (S, 377 beds) 5300 Military Road, Lewiston, NY Zip 14092–1903; tel. 716/297–4800; Judith A. Maness, FACHE, President and Chief Executive Officer
Web address: www.msmh.org

OUR LADY OF LOURDES MEMORIAL HOSPITAL, INC. (S, 154 beds) 169 Riverside Drive, Binghamton, NY Zip 13905–4246; tel. 607/798–5111; David Patak, President and Chief Executive Officer
Web address: www.lourdes.com

ST. MARY'S HEALTHCARE (S, 153 beds) 427 Guy Park Avenue, Amsterdam, NY Zip 12010–1054; tel. 518/842–1900; Victor Giulianelli, FACHE, President and Chief Executive Officer
Web address: www.smha.org

OKLAHOMA: JANE PHILLIPS MEDICAL CENTER (O, 119 beds) 3500 East Frank Phillips Boulevard, Bartlesville, OK Zip 74006–2411; tel. 918/333–7200; David R. Stire, President and Chief Executive Officer
Web address: www.jpmc.org

JANE PHILLIPS NOWATA HEALTH CENTER (O, 13 beds) 237 South Locust Street, Nowata, OK Zip 74048–3660, Mailing Address: P.O. Box 426, Zip 74048–0426; tel. 918/273–3102; Scott Upton, Administrator
Web address: www.jpmc.org

ST. JOHN BROKEN ARROW (O, 44 beds) 1000 West Boise Circle, Broken Arrow, OK Zip 74012–4900; tel. 918/994–8100; David L. Phillips, Chief Executive Officer
Web address: www.stjohnbrokenarrow.com

ST. JOHN MEDICAL CENTER (O, 547 beds) 1923 South Utica Avenue, Tulsa, OK Zip 74104–6502; tel. 918/744–2345; Jeffrey D. Nowlin, President and Chief Operating Officer
Web address: www.sjmc.org

ST. JOHN OWASSO (O, 45 beds) 12451 East 100th Street North, Owasso, OK Zip 74055–4600; tel. 918/274–5000; David L. Phillips, President and Chief Executive Officer
Web address: www.stjohnowasso.com

ST. JOHN SAPULPA (O, 25 beds) 519 South Division Street, Sapulpa, OK Zip 74066–4501, Mailing Address: P.O. Box 1368, Zip 74067–1368; tel. 918/224–4280; David L. Phillips, Chief Executive Officer
Web address: www.sjmc.org

TENNESSEE: SAINT THOMAS HICKMAN HOSPITAL (S, 65 beds) 135 East Swan Street, Centerville, TN Zip 37033–1417; tel. 931/729–4271; Jack M. Keller, Chief Executive Officer
Web address: www.hickmanhospital.com

SAINT THOMAS HOSPITAL FOR SPINAL SURGERY (S, 23 beds) 2011 Murphy Avenue, Suite 400, Nashville, TN Zip 37203–2065; tel. 615/341–7500; Kathy Watson, R.N., Administrator and Chief Nursing Officer
Web address: www.hospitalforspinalsurgery.com

SAINT THOMAS MIDTOWN HOSPITAL (S, 425 beds) 2000 Church Street, Nashville, TN Zip 37236–0002; tel. 615/284–5555; Bernard Sherry, President and CEO
Web address: www.sths.com

SAINT THOMAS RUTHERFORD HOSPITAL (S, 286 beds) 1700 Medical Center Parkway, Murfreesboro, TN Zip 37129–2245; tel. 615/396–4100; Gordon B. Ferguson, President and Chief Executive Officer
Web address: www.mtmc.org

SAINT THOMAS WEST HOSPITAL (S, 395 beds) 4220 Harding Road, Nashville, TN Zip 37205–2095, Mailing Address: P.O. Box 380, Zip 37202–0380; tel. 615/222–2111; Bernard Sherry, President and CEO
Web address: www.stthomas.org

TEXAS: DELL CHILDREN'S MEDICAL CENTER OF CENTRAL TEXAS (S, 248 beds) 4900 Mueller Boulevard, Austin, TX Zip 78723–3079; tel. 512/324–0000; Robert I. Bonar, Jr., Chief Executive Officer
Web address: www.dellchildrens.net

PROVIDENCE HEALTH CENTER (S, 620 beds) 6901 Medical Parkway, Waco, TX Zip 76712–7998, Mailing Address: P.O. Box 2589, Zip 76702–2589; tel. 254/751–4000; Brett A. Esrock, President and Chief Executive Officer
Web address: www.providence.net

SETON EDGAR B. DAVIS HOSPITAL (S, 25 beds) 130 Hays Street, Luling, TX Zip 78648–3207; tel. 830/875–7000; Apryl Haynes, R.N., Vice President, Chief Operating Officer, Chief Nursing Officer and Administrator
Web address: www.seton.net/locations/edgar_davis/

SETON HIGHLAND LAKES (S, 23 beds) 3201 South Water Street, Burnet, TX Zip 78611–4510, Mailing Address: P.O. Box 1219, Zip 78611–7219; tel. 512/715–3000; Michelle Robertson, R.N., President and Chief Executive Officer
Web address: www.seton.net

SETON MEDICAL CENTER AUSTIN (S, 426 beds) 1201 West 38th Street, Austin, TX Zip 78705–1006; tel. 512/324–1000; Katherine Henderson, Chief Executive Officer
Web address: www.seton.net

SETON MEDICAL CENTER HAYS (O, 96 beds) 6001 Kyle Parkway, Kyle, TX Zip 78640–6112, Mailing Address: 6001 Kyle Prkway, Zip 78640–6112; tel. 512/504–5000; Christopher L. Hartle, President
Web address: www.seton.net/locations/seton_medical_center_hays/

SETON MEDICAL CENTER WILLIAMSON (S, 143 beds) 201 Seton Parkway, Round Rock, TX Zip 78665–8000; tel. 512/324–4000; Michelle Robertson, R.N., President and Chief Executive Officer
Web address: www.seton.net/williamson

SETON NORTHWEST HOSPITAL (S, 64 beds) 11113 Research Boulevard, Austin, TX Zip 78759–5236; tel. 512/324–6000; Michelle Robertson, R.N., President and Chief Executive Officer
Web address: www.seton.net

SETON SHOAL CREEK HOSPITAL (S, 92 beds) 3501 Mills Avenue, Austin, TX Zip 78731–6391; tel. 512/324–2000; Alan Isaacson, Vice President and Chief Operating Officer
Web address: www.seton.net

SETON SMITHVILLE REGIONAL HOSPITAL (O, 10 beds) 800 East Highway 71, Smithville, TX Zip 78957–1730; tel. 512/237–3214; Larry Mejia, Vice President and Chief Operating Officer
Web address: www.seton.org

SETON SOUTHWEST HOSPITAL (S, 33 beds) 7900 F. M. 1826, Austin, TX Zip 78737–1407; tel. 512/324–9000; Mary Faria, FACHE, Administrator
Web address: www.seton.net

UNIVERSITY MEDICAL CENTER AT BRACKENRIDGE (S, 244 beds) 601 East 15th Street, Austin, TX Zip 78701–1996; tel. 512/324–7000; Katherine Henderson, Chief Executive Officer
Web address: www.seton.net

WASHINGTON: LOURDES COUNSELING CENTER (S, 32 beds) 1175 Carondelet Drive, Richland, WA Zip 99354–3300; tel. 509/943–9104; Barbara Mead, Vice President Behavioral Health and Physician Clinics
Web address: www.lourdeshealth.net

LOURDES MEDICAL CENTER (S, 53 beds) 520 North Fourth Avenue, Pasco, WA Zip 99301–5257, Mailing Address: P.O. Box 2568, Zip 99302–2568; tel. 509/547–7704; John Serle, FACHE, President and Chief Executive Officer
Web address: www.lourdeshealth.net

For explanation of codes following names, see page B2.
★ Indicates Type III membership in the American Hospital Association.

WISCONSIN: CALUMET MEDICAL CENTER (O, 15 beds) 614 Memorial Drive, Chilton, WI Zip 53014–1597; tel. 920/849–2386; Timothy Richman, President
Web address: www.affinityhealth.org

COLUMBIA ST. MARY'S HOSPITAL MILWAUKEE (S, 266 beds) 2301 North Lake Drive, Milwaukee, WI Zip 53211–4508; tel. 414/291–1000; Travis Andersen, President and Chief Executive Officer
Web address: www.columbia–stmarys.org

COLUMBIA ST. MARY'S OZAUKEE HOSPITAL (S, 102 beds) 13111 North Port Washington Road, Mequon, WI Zip 53097–2416; tel. 262/243–7300; Travis Andersen, President and Chief Executive Officer
Web address: www.columbia–stmarys.org

FLAMBEAU HOSPITAL (O, 25 beds) 98 Sherry Avenue, Park Falls, WI Zip 54552–1467, Mailing Address: P.O. Box 310, Zip 54552–0310; tel. 715/762–2484; David A. Grundstrom, Chief Administrative Officer
Web address: www.flambeauhospital.org

HOWARD YOUNG MEDICAL CENTER (O, 53 beds) 240 Maple Street, Woodruff, WI Zip 54568–9190, Mailing Address: P.O. Box 470, Zip 54568–0470; tel. 715/356–8000; Monica Hilt, President
Web address: www.ministryhealth.org

MERCY MEDICAL CENTER (O, 122 beds) 500 South Oakwood Road, Oshkosh, WI Zip 54904–7944; tel. 920/223–2000; William Calhoun, President
Web address: www.affinityhealth.org

MINISTRY DOOR COUNTY MEDICAL CENTER (O, 55 beds) 323 South 18th Avenue, Sturgeon Bay, WI Zip 54235–1495; tel. 920/743–5566; Gerald M. Worrick, President and Chief Executive Officer
Web address: www.ministryhealth.org

MINISTRY EAGLE RIVER MEMORIAL HOSPITAL (O, 7 beds) 201 Hospital Road, Eagle River, WI Zip 54521–8835; tel. 715/479–7411; Monica Hilt, President
Web address: www.ministryhealth.org

MINISTRY GOOD SAMARITAN HEALTH CENTER (O, 10 beds) 601 South Center Avenue, Merrill, WI Zip 54452–3404; tel. 715/536–5511; Mary T. Krueger, President
Web address: www.ministryhealth.org

MINISTRY OUR LADY OF VICTORY HOSPITAL (O, 12 beds) 1120 Pine Street, Stanley, WI Zip 54768–1297; tel. 715/644–5571; Vanessa Freitag, President
Web address: www.ministryhealth.org

MINISTRY SACRED HEART HOSPITAL (O, 6 beds) 401 West Mohawk Drive, Tomahawk, WI Zip 54487–2274; tel. 715/453–7700; Monica Hilt, President
Web address: www.ministryhealth.org

MINISTRY SAINT CLARE'S HOSPITAL (O, 77 beds) 3400 Ministry Parkway, Weston, WI Zip 54476–5220; tel. 715/393–3000; Mary T. Krueger, President
Web address: www.ministryhealth.org

MINISTRY SAINT JOSEPH'S HOSPITAL (O, 319 beds) 611 St. Joseph Avenue, Marshfield, WI Zip 54449–1898; tel. 715/387–1713; Brian Kief, Regional Vice President Ministry Health Care and President Ministry Saint Joseph's Hospital
Web address: www.stjosephs–marshfield.org

MINISTRY SAINT MARY'S HOSPITALS (O, 51 beds) 2251 North Shore Drive, Rhinelander, WI Zip 54501–6710; tel. 715/361–2000; Monica Hilt, President
Web address: www.ministryhealth.org

MINISTRY SAINT MICHAEL'S HOSPITAL (O, 50 beds) 900 Illinois Avenue, Stevens Point, WI Zip 54481–3196; tel. 715/346–5000; Jeffrey L. Martin, President
Web address: www.ministryhealth.org/SMH/home.nws

SACRED HEART REHABILITATION INSTITUTE (S, 31 beds) 2323 North Lake Drive, Milwaukee, WI Zip 53211–4508; tel. 414/298–6750; Allan M. Spooner, President
Web address: www.columbia–stmarys.org/SHRI

ST. ELIZABETH HOSPITAL (O, 211 beds) 1506 South Oneida Street, Appleton, WI Zip 54915–1305; tel. 920/738–2000; Daniel Neufelder, Interim Chief Executive Officer
Web address: www.affinityhealth.org

Owned, leased, sponsored:	103 hospitals	18768 beds
Contract–managed:	0 hospitals	0 beds
Totals:	103 hospitals	18768 beds

★**0519: ASPIRUS, INC.** (NP)
425 Pine Ridge Boulevard, Wausau, WI Zip 54401–4123; tel. 715/847–2118; Matthew Heywood, Chief Executive Officer
(Moderately Centralized Health System)

MICHIGAN: ASPIRUS GRAND VIEW HOSPITAL (O, 25 beds) N10561 Grand View Lane, Ironwood, MI Zip 49938–9622; tel. 906/932–2525; Paula L. Chermside, Chief Operating Officer
Web address: www.aspirusgrandview.org

ASPIRUS KEWEENAW HOSPITAL (O, 25 beds) 205 Osceola Street, Laurium, MI Zip 49913–2134; tel. 906/337–6500; Michael Hauswirth, Chief Operating Officer
Web address: www.aspiruskeweenaw.org

ASPIRUS ONTONAGON HOSPITAL (O, 18 beds) 601 South Seventh Street, Ontonagon, MI Zip 49953–1459; tel. 906/884–8000; Michael Hauswirth, Chief Operating Officer
Web address: www.aspirus–ontonagon.org

WISCONSIN: ASPIRUS MEDFORD HOSPITAL (O, 124 beds) 135 South Gibson Street, Medford, WI Zip 54451–1696; tel. 715/748–8100; Gregory A. Olson, President and Chief Executive Officer
Web address: www.memhc.com

ASPIRUS WAUSAU HOSPITAL (O, 257 beds) 333 Pine Ridge Boulevard, Wausau, WI Zip 54401–4187; tel. 715/847–2121; Darrell Lentz, Interim President
Web address: www.aspirus.org

Owned, leased, sponsored:	5 hospitals	449 beds
Contract–managed:	0 hospitals	0 beds
Totals:	5 hospitals	449 beds

★**0865: ATLANTIC HEALTH SYSTEM** (NP)
475 South Street, Morristown, NJ Zip 07962, Mailing Address: P.O. Box 1905, Zip 07962–1905; tel. 973/660–3270; Joseph A. Trunfio, Ph.D., President and Chief Executive Officer
(Centralized Physician/Insurance Health System)

NEW JERSEY: CHILTON MEDICAL CENTER (O, 260 beds) 97 West Parkway, Pompton Plains, NJ Zip 07444–1696; tel. 973/831–5000; Deborah Zastocki, R.N., FACHE, FACHE, President and Chief Executive Officer
Web address: www.chiltonmemorial.org

MORRISTOWN MEDICAL CENTER (O, 662 beds) 100 Madison Avenue, Morristown, NJ Zip 07960–6136; tel. 973/971–5000; David J. Shulkin, M.D., President
Web address: www.atlantichealth.org/Morristown/

NEWTON MEDICAL CENTER (O, 148 beds) 175 High Street, Newton, NJ Zip 07860–1004; tel. 973/383–2121; Joseph DiPaolo, President
Web address: www.atlantichealth.org/newton/

OVERLOOK MEDICAL CENTER (O, 461 beds) 99 Beauvoir Avenue, Summit, NJ Zip 07901–3533; tel. 908/522–2000; Alan R. Lieber, President
Web address: www.atlantichealth.org/Overlook

Owned, leased, sponsored:	4 hospitals	1531 beds
Contract–managed:	0 hospitals	0 beds
Totals:	4 hospitals	1531 beds

● ★**0293: ATLANTICARE** (NP)
2500 English Creek Avenue, Building 500, Suite 501, Egg Harbor Township, NJ Zip 08234; tel. 609/407–2309; David P. Tilton, President and Chief Executive Officer
(Centralized Health System)

ATLANTICARE REGIONAL MEDICAL CENTER (O, 534 beds) 1925 Pacific Avenue, Atlantic City, NJ Zip 08401–6713; tel. 609/441–8994; Lori Herndon, R.N., President and Chief Executive Officer
Web address: www.atlanticare.org

Owned, leased, sponsored:	1 hospital	534 beds
Contract–managed:	0 hospitals	0 beds
Totals:	1 hospital	534 beds

For explanation of codes following names, see page B2.
★ Indicates Type III membership in the American Hospital Association.
● Single hospital health care system

0894: AUDUBON BEHAVIORAL HEALTHCARE (IO)
100 West Hawkins, Suite D., Longview, TX Zip 75605;
tel. 903/212–2930; William V. Brown, Chief Executive Officer

TEXAS: OCEANS BEHAVIORAL HOSPITAL LONGVIEW (O, 24 beds) 615 Clinic
Drive, Longview, TX Zip 75605–5172; tel. 903/212–3105; Lauren Weber,
Administrator
Web address: www.oceanslongview.com/

OCEANS BEHAVIORAL HOSPITAL LUFKIN (O, 24 beds) 302 Gobblers Knob,
Lufkin, TX Zip 75904–5419; tel. 936/632–2276; Ronald E. Hand,
Administrator
Web address: www.oceanslufkin.com/

Owned, leased, sponsored:	2 hospitals	48 beds
Contract–managed:	0 hospitals	0 beds
Totals:	2 hospitals	48 beds

0859: AULTMAN HEALTH FOUNDATION (NP)
2600 Sixth Street S.W., Canton, OH Zip 44710–1702;
tel. 330/363–6192; Edward J. Roth, III, President and Chief
Executive Officer
(Moderately Centralized Health System)

OHIO: AULTMAN HOSPITAL (O, 545 beds) 2600 Sixth Street S.W., Canton,
OH Zip 44710–1702; tel. 330/452–9911; Edward J. Roth, III, President
and Chief Executive Officer
Web address: www.aultman.com

AULTMAN ORRVILLE HOSPITAL (O, 25 beds) 832 South Main Street, Orrville,
OH Zip 44667–2208; tel. 330/682–3010; Marchelle Suppan, DPM, President
and Chief Executive Officer
Web address: www.aultmanorrville.org

Owned, leased, sponsored:	2 hospitals	570 beds
Contract–managed:	0 hospitals	0 beds
Totals:	2 hospitals	570 beds

0360: AURORA BEHAVIORAL HEALTH CARE (IO)
4238 Green River Road, Corona, CA Zip 92880–1669;
tel. 951/549–8032; Soon K. Kim, M.D., President and Chief
Executive Officer
(Independent Hospital System)

ARIZONA: AURORA PHOENIX HOSPITAL (O, 90 beds) 6015 West Peoria
Avenue, Glendale, AZ Zip 85302–1213; tel. 623/344–4400; Bruce Waldo,
Chief Executive Officer
Web address: www.aurorabehavioral.com

AURORA TEMPE HOSPITAL (O, 70 beds) 6350 South Maple Street, Tempe,
AZ Zip 85283–2857; tel. 480/345–5400; Bruce Waldo, Chief Executive
Officer
Web address: www.auroraarizona.com

CALIFORNIA: AURORA CHARTER OAK HOSPITAL (O, 95 beds) 1161 East
Covina Boulevard, Covina, CA Zip 91724–1599; tel. 626/966–1632;
Todd A. Smith, Chief Executive Officer
Web address: www.aurorabehavioral.com

AURORA LAS ENCINAS HOSPITAL (O, 138 beds) 2900 East Del Mar
Boulevard, Pasadena, CA Zip 91107–4399; tel. 626/795–9901; Gerard
Conway, Chief Executive Officer
Web address: www.lasencinashospital.com

AURORA SAN DIEGO HOSPITAL (O, 80 beds) 11878 Avenue of Industry, San
Diego, CA Zip 92128–3490; tel. 858/487–3200; James S. Plummer, Chief
Executive Officer
Web address: www.sandiego.aurorabehavioral.com/

AURORA VISTA DEL MAR HOSPITAL (O, 87 beds) 801 Seneca Street,
Ventura, CA Zip 93001–1411; tel. 805/653–6434; Mayla Krebsbach, Chief
Executive Officer
Web address: www.vistadelmarhospital.com

ILLINOIS: AURORA CHICAGO LAKESHORE HOSPITAL (O, 108 beds) 4840
North Marine Drive, Chicago, IL Zip 60640–4296; tel. 773/878–9700; C.
Alan Eaks, Chief Executive Officer
Web address: www.chicagolakeshorehospital.com

Owned, leased, sponsored:	7 hospitals	668 beds
Contract–managed:	0 hospitals	0 beds
Totals:	7 hospitals	668 beds

★2215: AURORA HEALTH CARE (NP)
3000 West Montana, Milwaukee, WI Zip 53215–3628, Mailing
Address: P.O. Box 341880, Zip 53234–1880; tel. 414/647–3000;
Nick Turkal, M.D., President and Chief Executive Officer
(Decentralized Health System)

WISCONSIN: AURORA BAYCARE MEDICAL CENTER (O, 167 beds) 2845
Greenbrier Road, Green Bay, WI Zip 54311–6519, Mailing Address: P.O.
Box 8900, Zip 54308–8900; tel. 920/288–8000; Daniel T. Meyer,
President
Web address: www.aurorabaycare.com

AURORA LAKELAND MEDICAL CENTER (O, 67 beds) W3985 County Road NN,
Elkhorn, WI Zip 53121–4389; tel. 262/741–2000; Lisa Just, President
Web address: www.aurorahealthcare.org

AURORA MEDICAL CENTER (O, 74 beds) 10400 South 75th Street, Kenosha,
WI Zip 53142–7884; tel. 262/948–5600; Doug Koch, Market President
Web address: www.aurorahealthcare.org

AURORA MEDICAL CENTER – MANITOWOC COUNTY (O, 63 beds) 5000
Memorial Drive, Two Rivers, WI Zip 54241–3900; tel. 920/794–5000; Cathie
A. Kocourek, President
Web address: www.aurorahealthcare.org

AURORA MEDICAL CENTER GRAFTON (O, 101 beds) 975 Port Washington
Road, Grafton, WI Zip 53024–9201; tel. 262/329–1000; Carrie Killoran,
Interim President
Web address: www.aurorahealthcare.org

AURORA MEDICAL CENTER IN WASHINGTON COUNTY (O, 34 beds) 1032
East Sumner Street, Hartford, WI Zip 53027–1698; tel. 262/673–2300;
Carrie Killoran, Interim President
Web address: www.aurorahealthcare.org

AURORA MEDICAL CENTER OF OSHKOSH (O, 61 beds) 855 North Westhaven
Drive, Oshkosh, WI Zip 54904–7668; tel. 920/456–6000; Jeffrey Bard,
President
Web address: www.aurorahealthcare.com

AURORA MEDICAL CENTER SUMMIT (O, 85 beds) 36500 Aurora Drive,
Summit, WI Zip 53066–4899; tel. 262/434–1000; Michael Bergmann,
President
Web address: www.aurorahealthcare.org

AURORA MEMORIAL HOSPITAL OF BURLINGTON (O, 55 beds) 252 McHenry
Street, Burlington, WI Zip 53105–1828; tel. 262/767–6000; Lisa Just,
President
Web address: www.aurorahealthcare.org

AURORA PSYCHIATRIC HOSPITAL (O, 80 beds) 1220 Dewey Avenue,
Wauwatosa, WI Zip 53213–2598; tel. 414/454–6600; Peter Carlson,
Administrator
Web address: www.aurorahealthcare.org

AURORA SHEBOYGAN MEMORIAL MEDICAL CENTER (O, 136 beds) 2629
North Seventh Street, Sheboygan, WI Zip 53083–4998; tel. 920/451–5000;
David Graebner, President
Web address: www.aurorahealthcare.org

AURORA SINAI MEDICAL CENTER (O, 189 beds) 945 North 12th Street,
Milwaukee, WI Zip 53233–1337, Mailing Address: P.O. Box 342,
Zip 53201–0342; tel. 414/219–2000; Carolynn Glocka, R.N., President
Web address: www.aurorahealthcare.org

AURORA ST. LUKE'S MEDICAL CENTER (O, 709 beds) 2900 West Oklahoma
Avenue, Milwaukee, WI Zip 53215–4330, Mailing Address: P.O. Box 2901,
Zip 53201–2901; tel. 414/649–6000; Marie Golanowski, R.N., MS, President
Web address: www.aurorahealthcare.org

AURORA WEST ALLIS MEDICAL CENTER (O, 220 beds) 8901 West Lincoln
Avenue, West Allis, WI Zip 53227–2409, Mailing Address: P.O. Box 27901,
Zip 53227–0901; tel. 414/328–6000; Richard A. Kellar, President
Web address: www.aurorahealthcare.org

Owned, leased, sponsored:	14 hospitals	2041 beds
Contract–managed:	0 hospitals	0 beds
Totals:	14 hospitals	2041 beds

For explanation of codes following names, see page B2.
★ Indicates Type III membership in the American Hospital Association.

0869: AVANTI HOSPITALS (IO)
222 North Sepulveda Boulevard, Suite 950, El Segundo, CA Zip 90245–5614; tel. 310/356–0550; Edward Mirzabegian, Corporate Chief Executive Officer
(Independent Hospital System)

CALIFORNIA: COAST PLAZA HOSPITAL (O, 123 beds) 13100 Studebaker Road, Norwalk, CA Zip 90650–2500; tel. 562/868–3751; Richard Rowe, PharmD, Chief Executive Officer
Web address: www.coastplaza.com

COMMUNITY HOSPITAL OF HUNTINGTON PARK (O, 81 beds) 2623 East Slauson Avenue, Huntington Park, CA Zip 90255–2926; tel. 323/583–1931; Hector Hernandez, M.D., Chief Executive Officer
Web address: www.chhplax.com

EAST LOS ANGELES DOCTORS HOSPITAL (O, 127 beds) 4060 Whittier Boulevard, Los Angeles, CA Zip 90023–2526; tel. 323/268–5514; Araceli Lonergan, Chief Executive Officer
Web address: www.elalax.com

MEMORIAL HOSPITAL OF GARDENA (O, 172 beds) 1145 West Redondo Beach Boulevard, Gardena, CA Zip 90247–3528; tel. 310/532–4200; Araceli Lonergan, Chief Executive Officer
Web address: www.mhglax.com/

Owned, leased, sponsored:	4 hospitals	503 beds
Contract–managed:	0 hospitals	0 beds
Totals:	4 hospitals	503 beds

★5255: AVERA HEALTH (CC)
3900 West Avera Drive, Suite 301, Sioux Falls, SD Zip 57108–5721; tel. 605/322–4700; John T. Porter, President and Chief Executive Officer
(Decentralized Health System)

IOWA: AVERA HOLY FAMILY HOSPITAL (O, 25 beds) 826 North Eighth Street, Estherville, IA Zip 51334–1598; tel. 712/362–2631; Dale Hustedt, Administrator
Web address: www.avera–holyfamily.org

FLOYD VALLEY HOSPITAL (C, 25 beds) 714 Lincoln Street N.E., Le Mars, IA Zip 51031–3314; tel. 712/546–7871; Michael T. Donlin, FACHE, Administrator
Web address: www.floydvalleyhospital.org

HEGG MEMORIAL HEALTH CENTER AVERA (C, 85 beds) 1202 21st Avenue, Rock Valley, IA Zip 51247–1497; tel. 712/476–8000; Glenn Zevenbergen, Chief Executive Officer
Web address: www.hegghc.org

LAKES REGIONAL HEALTHCARE (C, 30 beds) 2301 Highway 71 South, Spirit Lake, IA Zip 51360–6810, Mailing Address: P.O. Box AB, Zip 51360–0159; tel. 712/336–1230; Jason Harrington, President and Chief Executive Officer
Web address: www.lakeshealth.org

OSCEOLA COMMUNITY HOSPITAL (C, 25 beds) 600 Ninth Avenue North, Sibley, IA Zip 51249–1012, Mailing Address: P.O. Box 258, Zip 51249–0258; tel. 712/754–2574; Janet H. Dykstra, Chief Executive Officer
Web address: www.osceolacommunityhospital.org

SIOUX CENTER HEALTH (C, 90 beds) 1101 9th Street, S.E., Sioux Center, IA Zip 51250–1398; tel. 712/722–8107; Kayleen R. Lee, Chief Executive Officer
Web address: www.schospital.org

MINNESOTA: AVERA MARSHALL REGIONAL MEDICAL CENTER (O, 25 beds) 300 South Bruce Street, Marshall, MN Zip 56258–3900; tel. 507/532–9661; Mary B. Maertens, FACHE, President and Chief Executive Officer
Web address: www.averamarshall.org

PIPESTONE COUNTY MEDICAL CENTER AVERA (C, 25 beds) 916 4th Avenue S.W., Pipestone, MN Zip 56164–1890; tel. 507/825–5811; Bradley D. Burris, Chief Executive Officer
Web address: www.pcmchealth.org

TYLER HEALTHCARE CENTER AVERA (C, 25 beds) 240 Willow Street, Tyler, MN Zip 56178–1166; tel. 507/247–5521; Dale K. Kruger, Chief Executive Officer and Chief Financial Officer
Web address: www.www1.avera.org/amck/regionalfacilities/tyler/index.aspx

NEBRASKA: AVERA CREIGHTON HOSPITAL (O, 70 beds) 1503 Main Street, Creighton, NE Zip 68729–3007, Mailing Address: P.O. Box 186, Zip 68729–0186; tel. 402/358–5700; Jennifer Poppen, Chief Executive Officer
Web address: www.avera.org/creighton/

AVERA ST. ANTHONY'S HOSPITAL (O, 25 beds) 300 North Second Street, O'Neill, NE Zip 68763–1514, Mailing Address: P.O. Box 270, Oneill, Zip 68763–0270; tel. 402/336–2611; Ronald J. Cork, President and Chief Executive Officer
Web address: www.avera.org/st-anthonys

SOUTH DAKOTA: AVERA DE SMET MEMORIAL HOSPITAL (L, 14 beds) 306 Prairie Avenue S.W., De Smet, SD Zip 57231–2285, Mailing Address: P.O. Box 160, Zip 57231–0160; tel. 605/854–3329; Janice Schardin, R.N., MS, Administrator and Chief Executive Officer
Web address: www.desmetmemorial.org

AVERA DELLS AREA HOSPITAL (L, 23 beds) 909 North Iowa Avenue, Dell Rapids, SD Zip 57022–1231; tel. 605/428–5431; Lindsay Flannery, R.N., Administrator and Chief Executive Officer
Web address: www.www1.avera.org/amck/regionalfacilities/dellsareahealth/index.aspx

AVERA FLANDREAU HOSPITAL (L, 18 beds) 214 North Prairie Street, Flandreau, SD Zip 57028–1243; tel. 605/997–2433; Lindsay Flannery, R.N., Administrator and Chief Executive Officer
Web address: www.avera.org/flandreau–medical/

AVERA GETTYSBURG HOSPITAL (O, 60 beds) 606 East Garfield Avenue, Gettysburg, SD Zip 57442–1398; tel. 605/765–2480; Mark Schmidt, President and Chief Executive Officer
Web address: www.st-marys.com

AVERA GREGORY HOSPITAL (O, 67 beds) 400 Park Avenue, Gregory, SD Zip 57533–1302, Mailing Address: P.O. Box 408, Zip 57533–0408; tel. 605/835–8394; Anthony Timanus, Chief Executive Officer
Web address: www.gregoryhealthcare.org

AVERA HAND COUNTY MEMORIAL HOSPITAL (L, 9 beds) 300 West Fifth Street, Miller, SD Zip 57362–1238; tel. 605/853–2421; Bryan Breitling, Administrator
Web address: www.avera.org

AVERA HEART HOSPITAL OF SOUTH DAKOTA (O, 53 beds) 4500 West 69th Street, Sioux Falls, SD Zip 57108–8148; tel. 605/977–7000; Jon Soderholm, President
Web address: www.avera.org/heart–hospital

AVERA MCKENNAN HOSPITAL AND UNIVERSITY HEALTH CENTER (O, 400 beds) 1325 South Cliff Avenue, Sioux Falls, SD Zip 57105–1007, Mailing Address: P.O. Box 5045, Zip 57117–5045; tel. 605/322–8000; David Kapaska, D.O., Regional President and Chief Executive Officer
Web address: www.averamckennan.org

AVERA QUEEN OF PEACE HOSPITAL (O, 194 beds) 525 North Foster, Mitchell, SD Zip 57301–2999; tel. 605/995–2000; Thomas A. Clark, Regional President and Chief Executive Officer
Web address: www.averaqueenofpeace.org

AVERA SACRED HEART HOSPITAL (O, 293 beds) 501 Summit Avenue, Yankton, SD Zip 57078–3855; tel. 605/668–8000; Douglas R. Ekeren, Interim Chief Executive Officer
Web address: www.averasacredheart.com

AVERA ST. BENEDICT HEALTH CENTER (O, 100 beds) 401 West Glynn Drive, Parkston, SD Zip 57366–9605; tel. 605/928–3311; Gale N. Walker, President and Chief Executive Officer
Web address: www.averastbenedict.org

AVERA ST. LUKE'S HOSPITAL (O, 270 beds) 305 South State Street, Aberdeen, SD Zip 57401–4527; tel. 605/622–5000; Todd Forkel, President and Chief Executive Officer
Web address: www.avera.org/st–lukes–hospital/

AVERA ST. MARY'S HOSPITAL (O, 164 beds) 801 East Sioux Avenue, Pierre, SD Zip 57501–3323; tel. 605/224–3100; Bob Sutton, President and Chief Executive Officer
Web address: www.avera.org/st–marys–pierre/

AVERA WESKOTA MEMORIAL HOSPITAL (L, 23 beds) 604 First Street N.E., Wessington Springs, SD Zip 57382–2166; tel. 605/539–1201; Gaea Blue, R.N., Administrator and Chief Executive Officer
Web address: www.averaweskota.org

Section B

For explanation of codes following names, see page B2.
★ Indicates Type III membership in the American Hospital Association.

EUREKA COMMUNITY HEALTH SERVICES AVERA (C, 6 beds) 410 Ninth Street, Eureka, SD Zip 57437–2182, Mailing Address: P.O. Box 517, Zip 57437–0517; tel. 605/284–2661; Carmen Weber, Administrator
Web address: www.avera.org

LANDMANN–JUNGMAN MEMORIAL HOSPITAL AVERA (C, 19 beds) 600 Billars Street, Scotland, SD Zip 57059–2026; tel. 605/583–2226; Jonathan Moe, Chief Executive Officer
Web address: www.ljmh.org

MARSHALL COUNTY HEALTHCARE CENTER AVERA (C, 18 beds) 413 Ninth Street, Britton, SD Zip 57430–2274; tel. 605/448–2253; Nick Fosness, Chief Executive Officer
Web address: www.avera.org

MILBANK AREA HOSPITAL AVERA (L, 25 beds) 901 East Virgil Avenue, Milbank, SD Zip 57252–2124; tel. 605/432–4538; Natalie Gauer, Administrator
Web address: www.averamilbank.org

PLATTE HEALTH CENTER AVERA (C, 65 beds) 601 East Seventh, Platte, SD Zip 57369–2123, Mailing Address: P.O. Box 200, Zip 57369–0200; tel. 605/337–3364; Mark Burket, Chief Executive Officer
Web address: www.phcavera.org

ST. MICHAEL'S HOSPITAL AVERA (C, 25 beds) 410 West 16th Avenue, Tyndall, SD Zip 57066–2318; tel. 605/589–3341; Carol Deurmier, Chief Executive Officer
Web address: www.stmichaels–bhfp.org

WAGNER COMMUNITY MEMORIAL HOSPITAL AVERA (C, 20 beds) 513 Third Street S.W., Wagner, SD Zip 57380–9675, Mailing Address: P.O. Box 280, Zip 57380–0280; tel. 605/384–3611; Bryan Slaba, Chief Executive Officer
Web address: www.avera.org/wagnerhospital

Owned, leased, sponsored:	19 hospitals	1858 beds
Contract–managed:	13 hospitals	458 beds
Totals:	32 hospitals	2316 beds

★**0633:   AVITA HEALTH SYSTEM** (NP)
269 Portland Way South, Galion, OH Zip 44833–2399; tel. 419/468–4841; Jerome Morasko, President and Chief Executive Officer
(Independent Hospital System)

OHIO: BUCYRUS COMMUNITY HOSPITAL (O, 25 beds) 629 North Sandusky Avenue, Bucyrus, OH Zip 44820–1821; tel. 419/562–4677; Jerome Morasko, Chief Executive Officer
Web address: www.bchonline.org

GALION COMMUNITY HOSPITAL (O, 35 beds) 269 Portland Way South, Galion, OH Zip 44833–2399; tel. 419/468–4841; Jerome Morasko, President and Chief Executive Officer
Web address: www.galionhospital.org

Owned, leased, sponsored:	2 hospitals	60 beds
Contract–managed:	0 hospitals	0 beds
Totals:	2 hospitals	60 beds

★**0194:   BANNER HEALTH** (NP)
1441 North 12th Street, Phoenix, AZ Zip 85006–2837, Mailing Address: P.O. Box 25489, Zip 85002–5489; tel. 602/747–4000; Peter S. Fine, FACHE, President and Chief Executive Officer
(Decentralized Health System)

ALASKA: FAIRBANKS MEMORIAL HOSPITAL (L, 217 beds) 1650 Cowles Street, Fairbanks, AK Zip 99701–5998; tel. 907/452–8181; Michael K. Powers, FACHE, Chief Executive Officer
Web address: www.bannerhealth.com/locations/alaska/fairbanks+memorial+Hospital

ARIZONA: BANNER BAYWOOD MEDICAL CENTER (O, 388 beds) 6644 East Baywood Avenue, Mesa, AZ Zip 85206–1797; tel. 480/321–2000; Laura Robertson, R.N., Chief Executive Officer
Web address: www.bannerhealth.com/locations/Arizona/banner+baywood+medical+center

BANNER BEHAVIORAL HEALTH HOSPITAL – SCOTTSDALE (O, 95 beds) 7575 East Earll Drive, Scottsdale, AZ Zip 85251–6915; tel. 480/941–7500; Cherie Martin, R.N., MSN, FACHE, Chief Executive Officer
Web address: www.bannerhealth.com/Locations/Arizona/Banner+Behavioral+Health

BANNER BOSWELL MEDICAL CENTER (O, 441 beds) 10401 West Thunderbird Boulevard, Sun City, AZ Zip 85351–3004, Mailing Address: P.O. Box 1690, Zip 85372–1690; tel. 623/832–4000; David Cheney, Chief Executive Officer
Web address: www.bannerhealth.com/Locations/Arizona/Banner+Boswell+Medical+Center

BANNER DEL E. WEBB MEDICAL CENTER (O, 373 beds) 14502 West Meeker Boulevard, Sun City West, AZ Zip 85375–5299, Mailing Address: P.O. Box 5169, Zip 85376–5169; tel. 623/214–4000; Debbie Flores, Chief Executive Officer
Web address: www.bannerhealth.com/Locations/Arizona/Banner+Del+Webb+Medical+Center/

BANNER DESERT MEDICAL CENTER (O, 549 beds) 1400 South Dobson Road, Mesa, AZ Zip 85202–4707; tel. 480/412–3000; Robert Gould, Chief Executive Officer
Web address: www.bannerhealth.com/Locations/Arizona/Banner+Desert+Medical+Center

BANNER ESTRELLA MEDICAL CENTER (O, 213 beds) 9201 West Thomas Road, Phoenix, AZ Zip 85037–3332; tel. 623/327–4000; Debra J. Krmpotic, R.N., Chief Executive Officer
Web address: www.bannerhealth.com/Locations/Arizona/Banner+Estrella+Medical+Center/

BANNER GATEWAY MEDICAL CENTER (O, 177 beds) 1900 North Higley Road, Gilbert, AZ Zip 85234–1604; tel. 480/543–2000; Todd S. Werner, Chief Executive Officer
Web address: www.bannerhealth.com/Locations/Arizona/Banner+Gateway+Medical+Center/

BANNER GOLDFIELD MEDICAL CENTER (O, 30 beds) 2050 West Southern Avenue, Apache Junction, AZ Zip 85120–7305; tel. 480/733–3300; Julie Nunley, R.N., Chief Executive Officer
Web address: www.bannerhealth.com/Locations/Arizona/Banner+Goldfield+Medical+Center/_Welcome+to+Banner+Goldfield.htm

BANNER GOOD SAMARITAN MEDICAL CENTER (O, 685 beds) 1111 East McDowell Road, Phoenix, AZ Zip 85006–2666, Mailing Address: P.O. Box 2989, Zip 85062–2989; tel. 602/239–2000; Steve Narang, M.D., Chief Executive Officer
Web address: www.bannerhealth.com/Locations/Arizona/Banner+Good+Samaritan+Medical+Center

BANNER HEART HOSPITAL (O, 111 beds) 6750 East Baywood Avenue, Mesa, AZ Zip 85206–1749; tel. 480/854–5000; Laura Robertson, R.N., Chief Executive Officer
Web address: www.bannerhealth.com/Locations/Arizona/Banner+Heart+Hospital/

BANNER IRONWOOD MEDICAL CENTER (O, 53 beds) 37000 North Gantzel Road, San Tan Valley, AZ Zip 85140–7303; tel. 480/394–4000; Julie Nunley, R.N., Chief Executive Officer
Web address: www.bannerhealth.com/Locations/Arizona/Banner+Ironwood/

BANNER THUNDERBIRD MEDICAL CENTER (O, 476 beds) 5555 West Thunderbird Road, Glendale, AZ Zip 85306–4696; tel. 602/865–5555; Thomas C. Dickson, Chief Executive Officer
Web address: www.bannerhealth.com/Locations/Arizona/Banner+Thunderbird+Medical+Center/

PAGE HOSPITAL (C, 25 beds) 501 North Navajo Drive, Page, AZ Zip 86040, Mailing Address: P.O. Box 1447, Zip 86040–1447; tel. 928/645–2424; Sandy Haryasz, R.N., Chief Executive Officer
Web address: www.bannerhealth.com/Locations/Arizona/Page+Hospital

CALIFORNIA: BANNER LASSEN MEDICAL CENTER (O, 25 beds) 1800 Spring Ridge Drive, Susanville, CA Zip 96130–6100; tel. 530/252–2000; Catherine S. Harshbarger, R.N., Chief Executive Officer
Web address: www.bannerhealth.com/Locations/California/Banner+Lassen+Medical+Center

COLORADO: EAST MORGAN COUNTY HOSPITAL (L, 17 beds) 2400 West Edison Street, Brush, CO Zip 80723–1640; tel. 970/842–6200; Linda Thorpe, Chief Executive Officer
Web address: www.emchbrush.com

For explanation of codes following names, see page B2.
★ Indicates Type III membership in the American Hospital Association.

MCKEE MEDICAL CENTER (O, 105 beds) 2000 Boise Avenue, Loveland, CO Zip 80538–4281; tel. 970/669–4640; Michelle L. Joy, Chief Operating Officer
Web address: www.mckeeloveland.com

NORTH COLORADO MEDICAL CENTER (L, 238 beds) 1801 16th Street, Greeley, CO Zip 80631–5154; tel. 970/352–4121; Richard O. Sutton, Chief Executive Officer
Web address: www.ncmcgreeley.com

STERLING REGIONAL MEDCENTER (O, 25 beds) 615 Fairhurst Street, Sterling, CO Zip 80751–4523; tel. 970/522–0122; Julie Klein, Chief Executive Officer
Web address: www.bannerhealth.com/Locations/Colorado/Sterling+Regional+MedCenter

NEBRASKA: OGALLALA COMMUNITY HOSPITAL (L, 18 beds) 2601 North Spruce Street, Ogallala, NE Zip 69153–2465; tel. 308/284–4011; Sharon Lind, MSN, Chief Executive Officer
Web address: www.bannerhealth.com/Locations/Nebraska/Ogallala+Community+Hospital

NEVADA: BANNER CHURCHILL COMMUNITY HOSPITAL (O, 40 beds) 801 East Williams Avenue, Fallon, NV Zip 89406–3052; tel. 775/867–7000; Hoyt Skabelund, Chief Executive Officer
Web address: www.bannerhealth.com/Locations/Nevada/Banner+Churchill+Community+Hospital

WYOMING: COMMUNITY HOSPITAL (O, 25 beds) 2000 Campbell Drive, Torrington, WY Zip 82240–1597; tel. 307/532–4181; Vincent B. DiFranco, Chief Executive Officer
Web address: www.bannerhealth.com/Locations/Wyoming/Community+Hospital/

PLATTE COUNTY MEMORIAL HOSPITAL (L, 25 beds) 201 14th Street, Wheatland, WY Zip 82201–3201, Mailing Address: P.O. Box 848, Zip 82201–0848; tel. 307/322–3636; Shelby Nelson, Chief Executive Officer
Web address: www.bannerhealth.com/Locations/Wyoming/Platte+County+Memorial+Hospital

WASHAKIE MEDICAL CENTER (L, 25 beds) 400 South 15th Street, Worland, WY Zip 82401–3531, Mailing Address: P.O. Box 700, Zip 82401–0700; tel. 307/347–3221; Margie Molitor, R.N., Chief Executive Officer
Web address: www.washakiemedicalcenter.com

Owned, leased, sponsored:	23 hospitals	4351 beds
Contract–managed:	1 hospital	25 beds
Totals:	24 hospitals	4376 beds

★0005: BAPTIST HEALTH (NP)
841 Prudential Drive, Suite 1601, Jacksonville, FL Zip 32207–8202; tel. 904/202–4011; Hugh Greene, President and Chief Executive Officer
(Moderately Centralized Health System)

FLORIDA: BAPTIST MEDICAL CENTER BEACHES (O, 136 beds) 1350 13th Avenue South, Jacksonville Beach, FL Zip 32250–3205; tel. 904/627–2900; Joseph M. Mitrick, FACHE, President
Web address: www.community.e–baptisthealth.com/bmc/beaches/index.html

BAPTIST MEDICAL CENTER JACKSONVILLE (O, 878 beds) 800 Prudential Drive, Jacksonville, FL Zip 32207–8202; tel. 904/202–2000; Michael A. Mayo, FACHE, President
Web address: www.e–baptisthealth.com

BAPTIST MEDICAL CENTER NASSAU (O, 52 beds) 1250 South 18th Street, Fernandina Beach, FL Zip 32034–3098; tel. 904/321–3500; Stephen Lee, FACHE, President
Web address: www.baptistjax.com/locations/baptist–medical–center–nassau

Owned, leased, sponsored:	3 hospitals	1066 beds
Contract–managed:	0 hospitals	0 beds
Totals:	3 hospitals	1066 beds

0150: BAPTIST HEALTH (NP)
301 Brown Springs Road, Montgomery, AL Zip 36117–7005; tel. 334/273–4400; W. Russell Tyner, President and Chief Executive Officer
(Independent Hospital System)

ALABAMA: BAPTIST MEDICAL CENTER EAST (O, 183 beds) 400 Taylor Road, Montgomery, AL Zip 36117–3512, Mailing Address: P.O. Box 241267, Zip 36124–1267; tel. 334/277–8330; Jeff G. Rains, Chief Executive Officer
Web address: www.baptistfirst.org

BAPTIST MEDICAL CENTER SOUTH (O, 387 beds) 2105 East South Boulevard, Montgomery, AL Zip 36116–2409, Mailing Address: Box 11010, Zip 36111–0010; tel. 334/288–2100; J. Peter Selman, Chief Executive Officer
Web address: www.baptistfirst.org

PRATTVILLE BAPTIST HOSPITAL (O, 50 beds) 124 South Memorial Drive, Prattville, AL Zip 36067–3619, Mailing Address: P.O. Box 681630, Zip 36068–1638; tel. 334/365–0651; Ginger Henry, Chief Executive Officer
Web address: www.baptistfirst.org/facilities/prattville–baptist–hospital/default.aspx

Owned, leased, sponsored:	3 hospitals	620 beds
Contract–managed:	0 hospitals	0 beds
Totals:	3 hospitals	620 beds

★0315: BAPTIST HEALTH (CO)
2701 Eastpoint Parkway, Louisville, KY Zip 40223; tel. 502/896–5000; Stephen C. Hanson, Chief Executive Officer
(Moderately Centralized Health System)

KENTUCKY: BAPTIST HEALTH CORBIN (O, 268 beds) 1 Trillium Way, Corbin, KY Zip 40701–8420; tel. 606/528–1212; Larry Gray, President
Web address: www.baptistregional.com

BAPTIST HEALTH LA GRANGE (O, 108 beds) 1025 New Moody Lane, La Grange, KY Zip 40031–9154; tel. 502/222–5388; Chris Roty, President
Web address: www.baptisthealthlagrange.com

BAPTIST HEALTH LEXINGTON (O, 344 beds) 1740 Nicholasville Road, Lexington, KY Zip 40503–1499; tel. 859/260–6100; William G. Sisson, President
Web address: www.centralbap.com

BAPTIST HEALTH LOUISVILLE (O, 519 beds) 4000 Kresge Way, Louisville, KY Zip 40207–4676; tel. 502/897–8100; David L. Gray, FACHE, President
Web address: www.baptisteast.com

BAPTIST HEALTH MADISONVILLE (O, 197 beds) 900 Hospital Drive, Madisonville, KY Zip 42431–1694; tel. 270/825–5100; Michael A. Baumgartner, President
Web address: www.baptisthealthmadisonville.com

BAPTIST HEALTH PADUCAH (O, 271 beds) 2501 Kentucky Avenue, Paducah, KY Zip 42003–3200; tel. 270/575–2100; William A. Brown, FACHE, President and CEO
Web address: www.westernbaptist.com

BAPTIST HEALTH RICHMOND (O, 66 beds) 801 Eastern Bypass, Richmond, KY Zip 40475–2405, Mailing Address: P.O. Box 1600, Zip 40476–2603; tel. 859/623–3131; Todd Jones, President
Web address: www.baptisthealthrichmond.com

HARDIN MEMORIAL HOSPITAL (C, 268 beds) 913 North Dixie Avenue, Elizabethtown, KY Zip 42701–2503; tel. 270/737–1212; Dennis B. Johnson, President & CEO
Web address: www.hmh.net

RUSSELL COUNTY HOSPITAL (C, 25 beds) 153 Dowell Road, Russell Springs, KY Zip 42642–4579, Mailing Address: P.O. Box 1610, Zip 42642–1610; tel. 270/866–4141; Robert L. Ramey, Chief Executive Officer
Web address: www.russellcohospital.org

Owned, leased, sponsored:	7 hospitals	1773 beds
Contract–managed:	2 hospitals	293 beds
Totals:	9 hospitals	2066 beds

For explanation of codes following names, see page B2.
★ Indicates Type III membership in the American Hospital Association.

Section B

★**0355: BAPTIST HEALTH** (NP)
9601 Interstate 630, Exit 7, Little Rock, AR Zip 72205–7299;
tel. 501/202–2000; Troy R. Wells, Chief Executive Officer
(Centralized Health System)

ARKANSAS: BAPTIST HEALTH EXTENDED CARE HOSPITAL (O, 37 beds)
9601 Interstate 630, Exit 7, 10th Floor, Little Rock, AR Zip 72205–7202;
tel. 501/202–1070; Mike Perkins, Vice President and Administrator
Web address: www.baptist–health.com/maps–directions/bh_extended_care/default.aspx

BAPTIST HEALTH MEDICAL CENTER – NORTH LITTLE ROCK (O, 225 beds)
3333 Springhill Drive, North Little Rock, AR Zip 72117–2922;
tel. 501/202–3000; Harrison M. Dean, FACHE, Senior Vice President and Administrator
Web address: www.baptist–health.com/locations/accesspoint.aspx?accessPointID=190

BAPTIST HEALTH MEDICAL CENTER–ARKADELPHIA (L, 25 beds) 3050 Twin Rivers Drive, Arkadelphia, AR Zip 71923–4299; tel. 870/245–2622; John Bowen, Assistant Vice President and Administrator
Web address: www.baptist–health.com/locations/accesspoint.aspx?accessPointID=187

BAPTIST HEALTH MEDICAL CENTER–HEBER SPRINGS (O, 25 beds) 1800 Bypass Road, Heber Springs, AR Zip 72543–9135; tel. 501/887–3000; Edward L. Lacy, FACHE, Vice President and Administrator
Web address: www.baptist–health.com/maps–directions/bhmc–heber–springs

BAPTIST HEALTH MEDICAL CENTER–HOT SPRING COUNTY (L, 72 beds) 1001 Schneider Drive, Malvern, AR Zip 72104–4811; tel. 501/332–1000; Sheila Williams, Vice President and Administrator
Web address: www.https://www.baptist–health.org

BAPTIST HEALTH MEDICAL CENTER–LITTLE ROCK (O, 688 beds) 9601 Interstate 630, Exit 7, Little Rock, AR Zip 72205–7299; tel. 501/202–2000; Greg Crain, FACHE, Vice President and Administrator
Web address: www.baptist–health.org/maps–directions/bhmc–lr

BAPTIST HEALTH MEDICAL CENTER–STUTTGART (L, 49 beds) North Buerkle Road, Stuttgart, AR Zip 72160–3420, Mailing Address: P.O. Box 1905, Zip 72160–1905; tel. 870/673–3511; Terry L. Amstutz, FACHE, Vice President and Administrator
Web address: www.baptist–health.org/maps–directions/bhmc–stuttgart/default.aspx

BAPTIST HEALTH REHABILITATION INSTITUTE (O, 100 beds) 9601 Interstate 630, Exit 7, Little Rock, AR Zip 72205–7202; tel. 501/202–7000; Lee Gentry, FACHE, Vice President and Administrator
Web address: www.baptist–health.com/locations/accesspoint.aspx?accessPointID=202

Owned, leased, sponsored:	8 hospitals	1221 beds
Contract–managed:	0 hospitals	0 beds
Totals:	8 hospitals	1221 beds

★**0185: BAPTIST HEALTH CARE CORPORATION** (NP)
1717 North E Street Suite 320, Pensacola, FL Zip 32501–6377,
Mailing Address: P.O. Box 17500, Zip 32522–7500;
tel. 850/434–4011; Mark T. Faulkner, President
(Moderately Centralized Health System)

ALABAMA: ATMORE COMMUNITY HOSPITAL (L, 33 beds) 401 Medical Park Drive, Atmore, AL Zip 36502–3091; tel. 251/368–2500; A. William Perkins, Administrator
Web address: www.ebaptisthealthcare.org/AtmoreCommunityHospital/

FLORIDA: BAPTIST HOSPITAL (O, 339 beds) 1000 West Moreno, Pensacola, FL Zip 32501–2316, Mailing Address: P.O. Box 17500, Zip 32522–7500; tel. 850/434–4011; Scott Raynes, Interim Administrator
Web address: www.ebaptisthealthcare.org

GULF BREEZE HOSPITAL (O, 77 beds) 1110 Gulf Breeze Parkway, Gulf Breeze, FL Zip 32561–4884; tel. 850/934–2000; Scott Raynes, Senior Vice President, Gulf Breeze Market Segment
Web address: www.ebaptisthealthcare.org/GulfBreezeHospital/

JAY HOSPITAL (L, 49 beds) 14114 South Alabama Street, Jay, FL Zip 32565–1219; tel. 850/675–8000; Michael T. Hutchins, Administrator
Web address: www.bhcpns.org/jayhospital/

Owned, leased, sponsored:	4 hospitals	498 beds
Contract–managed:	0 hospitals	0 beds
Totals:	4 hospitals	498 beds

★**0122: BAPTIST HEALTH SOUTH FLORIDA** (NP)
6855 Red Road, Suite 600, Coral Gables, FL Zip 33143–3632;
tel. 786/662–7111; Brian E. Keeley, President and Chief Executive Officer
(Centralized Health System)

BAPTIST HEALTH SOUTH FLORIDA, BAPTIST HOSPITAL OF MIAMI (O, 672 beds) 8900 North Kendall Drive, Miami, FL Zip 33176–2197; tel. 786/596–1960; Albert Boulenger, Chief Executive Officer
Web address: www.baptisthealth.net

BAPTIST HEALTH SOUTH FLORIDA, DOCTORS HOSPITAL (O, 146 beds) 5000 University Drive, Coral Gables, FL Zip 33146–2094; tel. 786/308–3000; Nelson Lazo, Chief Executive Officer
Web address: www.baptisthealth.net

BAPTIST HEALTH SOUTH FLORIDA, HOMESTEAD HOSPITAL (O, 142 beds) 975 Baptist Way, Homestead, FL Zip 33033–7600; tel. 786/243–8000; William M. Duquette, Chief Executive Officer
Web address: www.baptisthealth.net

BAPTIST HEALTH SOUTH FLORIDA, MARINERS HOSPITAL (O, 25 beds) 91500 Overseas Highway, Tavernier, FL Zip 33070–2547; tel. 305/434–3000; Rick Freeburg, Chief Executive Officer
Web address: www.baptisthealth.net/en/facilities/mariners–hospital/Pages/default.aspx

BAPTIST HEALTH SOUTH FLORIDA, SOUTH MIAMI HOSPITAL (O, 364 beds) 6200 S.W. 73rd Street, Miami, FL Zip 33143–4679; tel. 786/662–4000; Lincoln S. Mendez, Chief Executive Officer
Web address: www.baptisthealth.net

BAPTIST HEALTH SOUTH FLORIDA, WEST KENDALL BAPTIST HOSPITAL (O, 133 beds) 9555 S.W. 162nd Avenue, Miami, FL Zip 33196–6408; tel. 786/467–2000; Javier Hernandez–Lichtl, Chief Executive Officer
Web address: www.baptisthealth.net/en/facilities/West–Kendall–Baptist–Hospital/Pages/default.aspx

Owned, leased, sponsored:	6 hospitals	1482 beds
Contract–managed:	0 hospitals	0 beds
Totals:	6 hospitals	1482 beds

0345: BAPTIST HEALTH SYSTEM (CO)
3201 Fourth Avenue South, Birmingham, AL Zip 35222–1723,
Mailing Address: P.O. Box 830605, Zip 35283–0605;
tel. 205/715–5319; Keith Parrott, FACHE, President and Chief Executive Officer
(Centralized Physician/Insurance Health System)

ALABAMA: CITIZENS BAPTIST MEDICAL CENTER (O, 116 beds) 604 Stone Avenue, Talladega, AL Zip 35160–2217, Mailing Address: P.O. Box 978, Zip 35161–0978; tel. 256/362–8111; Joel Taylor, Administrator
Web address: www.bhsala.com/home_citizens.cfm?id=38

PRINCETON BAPTIST MEDICAL CENTER (O, 297 beds) 701 Princeton Avenue S.W., Birmingham, AL Zip 35211–1303; tel. 205/783–3000; Betsy Postlethwait, President
Web address: www.bhsala.com

SHELBY BAPTIST MEDICAL CENTER (O, 247 beds) 1000 First Street North, Alabaster, AL Zip 35007–8703; tel. 205/620–8100; David C. Wilson, President and Chief Executive Officer
Web address: www.bhsala.com/shelby/Home.aspx

WALKER BAPTIST MEDICAL CENTER (O, 236 beds) 3400 Highway 78 East, Jasper, AL Zip 35501–8907, Mailing Address: P.O. Box 3547, Zip 35502–3547; tel. 205/387–4000; Robert Phillips, Administrator
Web address: www.bhsala.com/home_walker.cfm?id=41

Owned, leased, sponsored:	4 hospitals	896 beds
Contract–managed:	0 hospitals	0 beds
Totals:	4 hospitals	896 beds

For explanation of codes following names, see page B2.
★ Indicates Type III membership in the American Hospital Association.

★1625: BAPTIST MEMORIAL HEALTH CARE CORPORATION (NP)

350 North Humphreys Boulevard, Memphis, TN Zip 38120–2177;
tel. 901/227–5117; Janice Hill, President and Chief Executive Officer
(Decentralized Health System)

ARKANSAS: NEA BAPTIST MEMORIAL HOSPITAL (O, 100 beds) 4800 East
Johnson Avenue, Jonesboro, AR Zip 72401–8413; tel. 870/936–1000;
Brad Parsons, FACHE, Administrator and Chief Executive Officer
Web address: www.neabaptist.com

MISSISSIPPI: BAPTIST MEMORIAL HOSPITAL–BOONEVILLE (L, 66 beds) 100
Hospital Street, Booneville, MS Zip 38829–3359; tel. 662/720–5000;
James Grantham, Administrator and Chief Executive Officer
Web address: www.bmhcc.org/booneville

BAPTIST MEMORIAL HOSPITAL–DESOTO (O, 250 beds) 7601 Southcrest
Parkway, Southaven, MS Zip 38671–4742; tel. 662/772–4000; James
Huffman, Chief Executive Officer and Administrator
Web address: www.baptistonline.org/desoto/

BAPTIST MEMORIAL HOSPITAL–GOLDEN TRIANGLE (O, 236 beds) 2520 Fifth
Street North, Columbus, MS Zip 39705–2095, Mailing Address: P.O. Box
1307, Zip 39703–1307; tel. 662/244–1000; Paul Cade, Administrator and
Chief Executive Officer
Web address: www.baptistonline.org/golden–triangle/

BAPTIST MEMORIAL HOSPITAL–NORTH MISSISSIPPI (O, 217 beds) 2301
South Lamar Boulevard, Oxford, MS Zip 38655–5373, Mailing Address: P.O.
Box 946, Zip 38655–6002; tel. 662/232–8100; William C. Henning,
Administrator and Chief Executive Officer
Web address: www.baptistonline.org/north–mississippi/

BAPTIST MEMORIAL HOSPITAL–UNION COUNTY (L, 153 beds) 200 Highway
30 West, New Albany, MS Zip 38652–3112; tel. 662/538–7631; Walter
Grace, Chief Executive Officer and Administrator
Web address: www.baptistonline.org/union–county/

TENNESSEE: BAPTIST MEMORIAL HOSPITAL – MEMPHIS (O, 605 beds) 6019
Walnut Grove Road, Memphis, TN Zip 38120–2173; tel. 901/226–5000;
Derick Ziegler, Administrator and Chief Executive Officer
Web address: www.baptistonline.org/memphis/

BAPTIST MEMORIAL HOSPITAL FOR WOMEN (O, 140 beds) 6225 Humphreys
Boulevard, Memphis, TN Zip 38120–2373; tel. 901/227–9000; Anita
Vaughn, Administrator and Chief Executive Officer
Web address: www.baptistonline.org/womens/

BAPTIST MEMORIAL HOSPITAL–COLLIERVILLE (O, 61 beds) 1500 West Poplar
Avenue, Collierville, TN Zip 38017–0601; tel. 901/861–9400; Kyle E.
Armstrong, Administrator and Chief Executive Officer
Web address: www.baptistonline.org/collierville/

BAPTIST MEMORIAL HOSPITAL–HUNTINGDON (O, 33 beds) 631 R.B. Wilson
Drive, Huntingdon, TN Zip 38344–1727; tel. 731/986–4461; Susan M.
Breeden, Administrator and Chief Executive Officer
Web address: www.baptistonline.org/huntingdon/

BAPTIST MEMORIAL HOSPITAL–TIPTON (O, 44 beds) 1995 Highway 51
South, Covington, TN Zip 38019–3635; tel. 901/476–2621; Samuel Lynd,
Administrator and Chief Executive Officer
Web address: www.baptistonline.org/tipton/

BAPTIST MEMORIAL HOSPITAL–UNION CITY (O, 85 beds) 1201 Bishop Street,
Union City, TN Zip 38261–5403, Mailing Address: P.O. Box 310,
Zip 38281–0310; tel. 731/885–2410; Barry Bondurant, Administrator and
Chief Executive Officer
Web address: www.baptistonline.org/union–city/

BAPTIST MEMORIAL RESTORATIVE CARE HOSPITAL (O, 30 beds) 6019
Walnut Grove Road, Memphis, TN Zip 38120–2113; tel. 901/226–1400;
Janice Hill, R.N., Administrator
Web address: www.baptistonline.org/restorative–care/

BAPTIST REHABILITATION–GERMANTOWN (O, 68 beds) 2100 Exeter Road,
Germantown, TN Zip 38138–3978; tel. 901/757–1350; Janice Hill, Chief
Executive Officer and Administrator
Web address: www.baptistonline.org/germantown/

Owned, leased, sponsored:	14 hospitals	2088 beds
Contract–managed:	0 hospitals	0 beds
Totals:	14 hospitals	2088 beds

★0118: BARNABAS HEALTH (NP)

95 Old Short Hills Road, West Orange, NJ Zip 07052–1008;
tel. 973/322–4000; Barry Ostrowsky, President and Chief Executive
Officer
(Moderately Centralized Health System)

NEW JERSEY: BARNABAS HEALTH BEHAVIORAL HEALTH CENTER (O, 40
beds) 1691 Highway 9, Toms River, NJ Zip 08755–1245;
tel. 732/914–1688; Joe Hicks, President and Chief Executive Officer
Web address: www.barnabashealth.org/hospitals/psychiatric/index.html

CLARA MAASS MEDICAL CENTER (O, 429 beds) One Clara Maass Drive,
Belleville, NJ Zip 07109–3557; tel. 973/450–2000; Mary Ellen Clyne, Ph.D.,
President and Chief Executive Officer
Web address: www.barnabashealth.org/hospitals/clara_maass/index.html

COMMUNITY MEDICAL CENTER (O, 523 beds) 99 Route 37 West, Toms
River, NJ Zip 08755–6423; tel. 732/557–8051; Stephanie L. Bloom, FACHE,
President and Chief Executive Officer
Web address: www.barnabashealth.org/hospitals/community_medical/index.
html

JERSEY CITY MEDICAL CENTER (O, 316 beds) 355 Grand Street, Jersey City,
NJ Zip 07302–4321; tel. 201/915–2000; Joseph F. Scott, FACHE, President
and Chief Executive Officer
Web address: www.barnabashealth.org/Jersey–City–Medical–Center.aspx

MONMOUTH MEDICAL CENTER, LONG BRANCH CAMPUS (O, 294 beds) 300
Second Avenue, Long Branch, NJ Zip 07740–6303; tel. 732/222–5200;
Frank J. Vozos, M.D., FACS, President and Chief Executive Officer
Web address: www.barnabashealth.org/hospitals/monmouth_medical/index.
html

MONMOUTH MEDICAL CENTER, SOUTHERN CAMPUS (O, 240 beds) 600
River Avenue, Lakewood, NJ Zip 08701–5237; tel. 732/363–1900; Michael
Mimoso, FACHE, President and Chief Executive Officer
Web address: www.barnabashealth.
org/hospitals/monmouth–medical–center–southern–campus.aspx

NEWARK BETH ISRAEL MEDICAL CENTER (O, 362 beds) 201 Lyons Avenue,
Newark, NJ Zip 07112–2027; tel. 973/926–7000; John A. Brennan, M.D.,
M.P.H., President and Chief Executive Officer
Web address: www.barnabashealth.org/hospitals/newark_beth_israel/index.
html

SAINT BARNABAS MEDICAL CENTER (O, 545 beds) 94 Old Short Hills Road,
Livingston, NJ Zip 07039–5672; tel. 973/322–5000; John F. Bonamo, M.D.,
MS, President and Chief Executive Officer
Web address: www.barnabashealth.org/hospitals/saint_barnabas/index.html

Owned, leased, sponsored:	8 hospitals	2749 beds
Contract–managed:	0 hospitals	0 beds
Totals:	8 hospitals	2749 beds

★0528: BASSETT HEALTHCARE NETWORK (NP)

1 Atwell Road, Cooperstown, NY Zip 13326–1301;
tel. 607/547–3456; Vance Brown, M.D., President and Chief
Executive Officer
(Independent Hospital System)

NEW YORK: AURELIA OSBORN FOX MEMORIAL HOSPITAL (O, 205 beds) 1
Norton Avenue, Oneonta, NY Zip 13820–2629; tel. 607/432–2000; John
R. Remillard, President
Web address: www.bassett.org/ao–fox–hospital/

BASSETT MEDICAL CENTER (O, 164 beds) One Atwell Road, Cooperstown,
NY Zip 13326–1394; tel. 607/547–3100; Vance Brown, M.D., President and
Chief Executive Officer
Web address: www.bassett.org

COBLESKILL REGIONAL HOSPITAL (O, 40 beds) 178 Grandview Drive,
Cobleskill, NY Zip 12043–5144; tel. 518/254–3456; Eric H. Stein, FACHE,
President and Chief Executive Officer
Web address: www.cobleskillhospital.org

LITTLE FALLS HOSPITAL (O, 59 beds) 140 Burwell Street, Little Falls, NY
Zip 13365–1725; tel. 315/823–1000; Michael L. Ogden, President and Chief
Executive Officer
Web address: www.lfhny.org

Section B

For explanation of codes following names, see page B2.
★ Indicates Type III membership in the American Hospital Association.

O'CONNOR HOSPITAL (O, 16 beds) 460 Andes Road, State Route 28, Delhi, NY Zip 13753–7407; tel. 607/746–0300; Daniel M. Ayres, Chief Executive Officer
Web address: www.bassett.org

Owned, leased, sponsored:	5 hospitals	484 beds
Contract–managed:	0 hospitals	0 beds
Totals:	5 hospitals	484 beds

★**0918: BAYLOR SCOTT & WHITE HEALTH** (NP)
4005 Crutcher Street, Suite 310, Dallas, TX Zip 75246–1779; tel. 214/820–0111; Joel T. Allison, Chief Executive Officer

TEXAS: BAYLOR ALL SAINTS MEDICAL CENTER AT FORT WORTH (O, 449 beds) 1400 Eighth Avenue, Fort Worth, TX Zip 76104–4192; tel. 817/926–2544; David G. Klein, M.D., President
Web address: www.baylorhealth. com/PhysiciansLocations/AllSaints/Pages/Default.aspx

BAYLOR INSTITUTE FOR REHABILITATION (O, 89 beds) 909 North Washington Avenue, Dallas, TX Zip 75246–1520; tel. 214/820–9300; Fabian Polo, Chief Executive Officer
Web address: www.baylorhealth. com/PhysiciansLocations/BIR/Pages/Default.aspx

BAYLOR MEDICAL CENTER AT GARLAND (O, 220 beds) 2300 Marie Curie Drive, Garland, TX Zip 75042–5706; tel. 972/487–5000; Thomas J. Trenary, President
Web address: www.baylorhealth. com/PhysiciansLocations/Garland/Pages/Default.aspx

BAYLOR MEDICAL CENTER AT IRVING (L, 242 beds) 1901 North MacArthur Boulevard, Irving, TX Zip 75061–2220; tel. 972/579–8100; Cindy K. Schamp, President
Web address: www.baylorhealth. com/PhysiciansLocations/Irving/Pages/Default.aspx

BAYLOR MEDICAL CENTER AT MCKINNEY (O, 91 beds) 5252 West University Drive, McKinney, TX Zip 75071–7822; tel. 469/764–1000; Scott Peek, FACHE, President
Web address: www.baylorhealth. com/PhysiciansLocations/McKinney/Pages/Default.aspx

BAYLOR MEDICAL CENTER AT WAXAHACHIE (O, 54 beds) 1405 West Jefferson Street, Waxahachie, TX Zip 75165–2275; tel. 972/923–7000; Christopher York, FACHE, President
Web address: www.baylorhealth. com/PhysiciansLocations/Waxahachie/Pages/Default.aspx

BAYLOR REGIONAL MEDICAL CENTER AT GRAPEVINE (O, 284 beds) 1650 West College Street, Grapevine, TX Zip 76051–3565; tel. 817/481–1588; Steven R. Newton, President
Web address: www.https://www.baylorhealth. com/PhysiciansLocations/Grapevine/Pages/Default.aspx

BAYLOR REGIONAL MEDICAL CENTER AT PLANO (O, 108 beds) 4700 Alliance Boulevard, Plano, TX Zip 75093–5323; tel. 469/814–2000; Jerri Garison, R.N., President
Web address: www.baylorhealth. com/PhysiciansLocations/Plano/Pages/Default.aspx

BAYLOR SPECIALTY HOSPITAL (O, 61 beds) 3504 Swiss Avenue, Dallas, TX Zip 75204–6224; tel. 214/820–9700; Elizabeth Youngblood, President
Web address: www.baylorhealth. com/PhysiciansLocations/BSH/Pages/Default.aspx

BAYLOR UNIVERSITY MEDICAL CENTER (O, 874 beds) 3500 Gaston Avenue, Dallas, TX Zip 75246–2088; tel. 214/820–0111; John B. McWhorter, III, President
Web address: www.baylorhealth. com/PhysiciansLocations/Dallas/Pages/Default.aspx

HILLCREST BAPTIST MEDICAL CENTER (C, 263 beds) 100 Hillcrest Medical Boulevard, Waco, TX Zip 76712–8897, Mailing Address: P.O. Box 21146, Zip 76702–1146; tel. 254/202–2000; Glenn A. Robinson, Chief Executive Officer
Web address: www.hillcrest.net

OUR CHILDREN'S HOUSE AT BAYLOR (O, 54 beds) 1208 North Hall Street, Dallas, TX Zip 75204; tel. 214/820–9838; Elizabeth Youngblood, President
Web address: www.baylorhealth. com/PhysiciansLocations/OCH/Pages/Default.aspx

SCOTT & WHITE EMERGENCY HOSPITAL– CEDAR PARK (O, 8 beds) 900 East Whitestone Boulevard, Cedar Park, TX Zip 78613–9093; tel. 512/684–4911; John Wood, Administrator
Web address: www.sweh.org

SCOTT & WHITE HOSPITAL – BRENHAM (O, 60 beds) 700 Medical Parkway, Brenham, TX Zip 77833–5498; tel. 979/337–5000; Michael Pittman, Chief Operating Officer and Chief Nursing Officer
Web address: www.swbrenham.org

SCOTT & WHITE HOSPITAL – LLANO (O, 22 beds) 200 West Ollie Street, Llano, TX Zip 78643–2628; tel. 325/247–5040; Eric N. Looper, Chief Executive Officer
Web address: www.llanomemorial.org

SCOTT & WHITE HOSPITAL – TAYLOR (O, 25 beds) 305 Mallard Lane, Taylor, TX Zip 76574–1208; tel. 512/352–7611; Jay Fox, Chief Executive Officer, Round Rock Region
Web address: www.swtaylor.org

SCOTT & WHITE HOSPITAL AT ROUND ROCK (O, 101 beds) 300 University Boulevard, Round Rock, TX Zip 78665–1032; tel. 512/509–0100; Jay Fox, Chief Executive Officer
Web address: www.sw.org

SCOTT & WHITE MEMORIAL HOSPITAL (O, 638 beds) 2401 South 31st Street, Temple, TX Zip 76508–0002; tel. 254/724–2111; Shahin Motakef, Chief Executive Officer
Web address: www.sw.org/location/temple–hospital

SCOTT AND WHITE CONTINUING CARE HOSPITAL (O, 50 beds) 546 North Kegley Road, Temple, TX Zip 76502–4069; tel. 254/215–0900; Kimberly K. Langston, R.N., Chief Executive Officer
Web address: www.sw.org/location/temple–cch

Owned, leased, sponsored:	18 hospitals	3430 beds
Contract–managed:	1 hospital	263 beds
Totals:	19 hospitals	3693 beds

★**1095: BAYSTATE HEALTH, INC.** (NP)
759 Chestnut Street, Springfield, MA Zip 01199–0001; tel. 413/794–0000; Mark A. Keroack, M.D., President and Chief Executive Officer
(Centralized Physician/Insurance Health System)

MASSACHUSETTS: BAYSTATE FRANKLIN MEDICAL CENTER (O, 90 beds) 164 High Street, Greenfield, MA Zip 01301–2613; tel. 413/773–0211; Steven F. Bradley, President, Baystate Northern Region
Web address: www.baystatehealth.com/fmc

BAYSTATE MARY LANE HOSPITAL (O, 25 beds) 85 South Street, Ware, MA Zip 01082–1697; tel. 413/967–6211; Mohammed Shafeeq Ahmed, M.D., Interim President
Web address: www.baystatehealth.com

BAYSTATE MEDICAL CENTER (O, 715 beds) 759 Chestnut Street, Springfield, MA Zip 01199–0001; tel. 413/794–0000; Mark R. Tolosky, JD, FACHE, President and Chief Executive Officer
Web address: www.baystatehealth.org/bmc

WING MEMORIAL HOSPITAL (O, 74 beds) 40 Wright Street, Palmer, MA Zip 01069–1138; tel. 413/283–7651; Charles E. Cavagnaro, III, M.D., President and Chief Executive Officer
Web address: www.winghealth.org

Owned, leased, sponsored:	4 hospitals	904 beds
Contract–managed:	0 hospitals	0 beds
Totals:	4 hospitals	904 beds

0940: BEACON HEALTH SYSTEM (NP)
615 North Michigan Street, South Bend, IN Zip 46601–1033; tel. 574/647–1000; Philip A. Newbold, Chief Executive Officer

INDIANA: ELKHART GENERAL HEALTHCARE SYSTEM (O, 260 beds) 600 East Boulevard, Elkhart, IN Zip 46514–2499, Mailing Address: P.O. Box 1329, Zip 46515–1329; tel. 574/294–2621; Greg Losasso, President
Web address: www.egh.org

For explanation of codes following names, see page B2.
★ Indicates Type III membership in the American Hospital Association.

MEMORIAL HOSPITAL OF SOUTH BEND (O, 445 beds) 615 North Michigan Street, South Bend, IN Zip 46601–1033; tel. 574/647–1000; Kreg Gruber, President
Web address: www.qualityoflife.org

Owned, leased, sponsored:	2 hospitals	705 beds
Contract–managed:	0 hospitals	0 beds
Totals:	2 hospitals	705 beds

★9575: BEAUMONT HEALTH SYSTEM (NP)
3711 West 13 Mile Road, Royal Oak, MI Zip 48073–6767; tel. 248/898–5000; Gene Michalski, President and Chief Executive Officer
(Centralized Health System)

MICHIGAN: BEAUMONT HOSPITAL – ROYAL OAK (O, 1070 beds) 3601 West Thirteen Mile Road, Royal Oak, MI Zip 48073–6712; tel. 248/898–5000; Shane Cerone, President
Web address: www.beaumont.edu/royal–oak–hospital–campus

BEAUMONT HOSPITAL – TROY (O, 458 beds) 44201 Dequindre Road, Troy, MI Zip 48085–1117; tel. 248/964–5000; Nancy Susick, MSN, President
Web address: www.beaumont.edu/troy–hospital–campus

BEAUMONT HOSPITAL GROSSE POINTE (O, 250 beds) 468 Cadieux Road, Grosse Pointe, MI Zip 48230–1507; tel. 313/473–1000; Richard P. Swaine, President
Web address: www.beaumont.edu/grosse–pointe–hospital–campus

Owned, leased, sponsored:	3 hospitals	1778 beds
Contract–managed:	0 hospitals	0 beds
Totals:	3 hospitals	1778 beds

0545: BENEDICTINE SISTERS OF THE ANNUNCIATION (CC)
7520 University Drive, Bismarck, ND Zip 58504–9653; tel. 701/255–1520; Sister Nancy Miller, Prioress
(Moderately Centralized Health System)

NORTH DAKOTA: GARRISON MEMORIAL HOSPITAL (S, 50 beds) 407 Third Avenue S.E., Garrison, ND Zip 58540–7235; tel. 701/463–2275; Tod Graeber, Administrator
Web address: www.garrisonmh.com

ST. ALEXIUS MEDICAL CENTER (S, 271 beds) 900 East Broadway, Bismarck, ND Zip 58501–4586, Mailing Address: P.O. Box 5510, Zip 58506–5510; tel. 701/530–7000; Gary P. Miller, President and Chief Executive Officer
Web address: www.st.alexius.org

Owned, leased, sponsored:	2 hospitals	321 beds
Contract–managed:	0 hospitals	0 beds
Totals:	2 hospitals	321 beds

0538: BENEFIS HEALTH SYSTEM (NP)
1101 26th Street South, Great Falls, MT Zip 59405–5161; tel. 406/455–5000; John H. Goodnow, Chief Executive Officer
(Moderately Centralized Health System)

MONTANA: BENEFIS HOSPITALS (O, 434 beds) 1101 26th Street South, Great Falls, MT Zip 59405–5104; tel. 406/455–5000; John H. Goodnow, Chief Executive Officer
Web address: www.benefis.org

MISSOURI RIVER MEDICAL CENTER (C, 52 beds) 1501 St. Charles Street, Fort Benton, MT Zip 59442–0249, Mailing Address: P.O. Box 249, Zip 59442–0249; tel. 406/622–3331; Jay Pottenger, Administrator
Web address: www.mrmcfb.org

Owned, leased, sponsored:	1 hospital	434 beds
Contract–managed:	1 hospital	52 beds
Totals:	2 hospitals	486 beds

★2435: BERKSHIRE HEALTH SYSTEMS, INC. (NP)
725 North Street, Pittsfield, MA Zip 01201–4124; tel. 413/447–2750; David E. Phelps, President and Chief Executive Officer
(Independent Hospital System)

MASSACHUSETTS: BERKSHIRE MEDICAL CENTER (O, 270 beds) 725 North Street, Pittsfield, MA Zip 01201–4124; tel. 413/447–2000; David E. Phelps, President and Chief Executive Officer
Web address: www.bhs1.org/body_bmc.cfm?id=43

FAIRVIEW HOSPITAL (O, 24 beds) 29 Lewis Avenue, Great Barrington, MA Zip 01230–1713; tel. 413/528–0790; Eugene A. Dellea, President
Web address: www.bhs1.org/body_fh.cfm?id=39

Owned, leased, sponsored:	2 hospitals	294 beds
Contract–managed:	0 hospitals	0 beds
Totals:	2 hospitals	294 beds

★0051: BJC HEALTHCARE (NP)
4901 Forest Park Avenue, Suite 1200, Saint Louis, MO Zip 63108–1402; tel. 314/747–9322; Steven H. Lipstein, President and Chief Executive Officer
(Centralized Health System)

ILLINOIS: ALTON MEMORIAL HOSPITAL (O, 253 beds) One Memorial Drive, Alton, IL Zip 62002–6722; tel. 618/463–7311; David A. Braasch, President
Web address: www.altonmemorialhospital.org

MISSOURI: BARNES–JEWISH HOSPITAL (O, 1322 beds) 1 Barnes–Jewish Hospital Plaza, Saint Louis, MO Zip 63110–1003; tel. 314/747–3000; Richard J. Liekweg, President
Web address: www.barnesjewish.org

BARNES–JEWISH ST. PETERS HOSPITAL (O, 113 beds) 10 Hospital Drive, Saint Peters, MO Zip 63376–1659; tel. 636/916–9000; Larry A. Tracy, Jr., FACHE, President
Web address: www.bjsph.org/

BARNES–JEWISH WEST COUNTY HOSPITAL (O, 77 beds) 12634 Olive Boulevard, Saint Louis, MO Zip 63141–6337; tel. 314/996–8000; Doug Black, President
Web address: www.barnesjewishwestcounty.org

CHRISTIAN HOSPITAL (O, 258 beds) 11133 Dunn Road, Saint Louis, MO Zip 63136–6119; tel. 314/653–5000; Ronald B. McMullen, President
Web address: www.christianhospital.org

MISSOURI BAPTIST MEDICAL CENTER (O, 463 beds) 3015 North Ballas Road, Saint Louis, MO Zip 63131–2329; tel. 314/996–5000; John Antes, President
Web address: www.missouribaptist.org

MISSOURI BAPTIST SULLIVAN HOSPITAL (O, 35 beds) 751 Sappington Bridge Road, Sullivan, MO Zip 63080–2354; tel. 573/468–4186; Tony Schwarm, President
Web address: www.missouribaptistsullivan.org

PARKLAND HEALTH CENTER (O, 98 beds) 1101 West Liberty Street, Farmington, MO Zip 63640–1921; tel. 573/756–6451; Thomas P. Karl, President
Web address: www.parklandhealthcenter.org

PARKLAND HEALTH CENTER–BONNE TERRE (O, 3 beds) 7245 Raider Road, Bonne Terre, MO Zip 63628–3767; tel. 573/358–1400; Steven R. Marler, Administrator
Web address: www.parklandhealthcenter.org

PROGRESS WEST HOSPITAL (O, 42 beds) Two Progress Point, O'Fallon, MO Zip 63368–2208; tel. 636/344–1000; Larry A. Tracy, Jr., FACHE, President
Web address: www.progresswesthealthcare.org

ST. LOUIS CHILDREN'S HOSPITAL (O, 264 beds) One Children's Place, Saint Louis, MO Zip 63110–1002; tel. 314/454–6000; Joan Magruder, President
Web address: www.stlouischildrens.org

Owned, leased, sponsored:	11 hospitals	2928 beds
Contract–managed:	0 hospitals	0 beds
Totals:	11 hospitals	2928 beds

For explanation of codes following names, see page B2.
★ Indicates Type III membership in the American Hospital Association.

Section B

★**0852: BLANCHARD VALLEY HEALTH SYSTEM** (NP)
1900 South Main Street, Findlay, OH Zip 45840–1214;
tel. 419/423–4500; Scott C. Malaney, President and Chief Executive Officer
(Centralized Physician/Insurance Health System)

OHIO: BLANCHARD VALLEY HOSPITAL (O, 159 beds) 1900 South Main Street, Findlay, OH Zip 45840–1214; tel. 419/423–4500; Scott C. Malaney, President and Chief Executive Officer
Web address: www.bvhealthsystem.org/?id=204&sid=1

BLUFFTON HOSPITAL (O, 25 beds) 139 Garau Street, Bluffton, OH Zip 45817–1027; tel. 419/358–9010; Christine Keller, Chief Administrative Officer
Web address: www.bvhealthsystem.org/?id=203&sid=1

Owned, leased, sponsored:	2 hospitals	184 beds
Contract–managed:	0 hospitals	0 beds
Totals:	2 hospitals	184 beds

0300: BLUE MOUNTAIN HEALTH SYSTEM (NP)
211 North 12th Street, Lehighton, PA Zip 18235–1138;
tel. 610/377–1300; Andrew E. Harris, President and Chief Executive Officer
(Independent Hospital System)

PENNSYLVANIA: GNADEN HUETTEN MEMORIAL HOSPITAL (O, 181 beds) 211 North 12th Street, Lehighton, PA Zip 18235–1138; tel. 610/377–1300; Andrew E. Harris, Chief Executive Officer
Web address: www.blmtn.org/?id=112&sid=1

PALMERTON HOSPITAL (O, 60 beds) 135 Lafayette Avenue, Palmerton, PA Zip 18071–1596; tel. 610/826–3141; Andrew E. Harris, Chief Executive Officer
Web address: www.ghmh.org/content/palmertoncampus.htm

Owned, leased, sponsored:	2 hospitals	241 beds
Contract–managed:	0 hospitals	0 beds
Totals:	2 hospitals	241 beds

★**0053: BLUE WATER HEALTH SERVICES CORPORATION** (NP)
1221 Pine Grove Avenue, Port Huron, MI Zip 48060–3511;
tel. 810/989–3717; Thomas D. DeFauw, FACHE, President and Chief Executive Officer
(Independent Hospital System)

MICHIGAN: MARWOOD MANOR NURSING HOME (O, 106 beds) 1300 Beard Street, Port Huron, MI Zip 48060; tel. 818/982–2594; Brian Oberly, Administrator

PORT HURON HOSPITAL (O, 186 beds) 1221 Pine Grove Avenue, Port Huron, MI Zip 48060–3511; tel. 810/987–5000; Thomas D. DeFauw, FACHE, President and Chief Executive Officer
Web address: www.porthuronhospital.org

Owned, leased, sponsored:	2 hospitals	292 beds
Contract–managed:	0 hospitals	0 beds
Totals:	2 hospitals	292 beds

★**5085: BON SECOURS HEALTH SYSTEM, INC.** (CC)
1505 Marriottsville Road, Marriottsville, MD Zip 21104–1399;
tel. 410/442–5511; Richard Statuto, President and Chief Executive Officer
(Moderately Centralized Health System)

KENTUCKY: OUR LADY OF BELLEFONTE HOSPITAL (O, 151 beds) St. Christopher Drive, Ashland, KY Zip 41101, Mailing Address: P.O. Box 789, Zip 41105–0789; tel. 606/833–3333; Kevin Halter, Chief Executive Officer
Web address: www.olbh.com

MARYLAND: BON SECOURS BALTIMORE HEALTH SYSTEM (O, 93 beds) 2000 West Baltimore Street, Baltimore, MD Zip 21223–1558; tel. 410/362–3000; Samuel Lee Ross, M.D., MS, Chief Executive Officer
Web address: www.bonsecoursbaltimore.com

NEW YORK: BON SECOURS COMMUNITY HOSPITAL (O, 187 beds) 160 East Main Street, Port Jervis, NY Zip 12771–2245, Mailing Address: P.O. Box 1014, Zip 12771–0268; tel. 845/858–7000; Jeff Reilly, Senior Vice President Operations
Web address: www.bonsecourscommunityhosp.org

GOOD SAMARITAN HOSPITAL (O, 308 beds) 255 Lafayette Avenue, Suffern, NY Zip 10901–4869; tel. 845/368–5000; Mary Leahy, M.D., Chief Executive Officer
Web address: www.goodsamhosp.org

ST. ANTHONY COMMUNITY HOSPITAL (O, 73 beds) 15 Maple Avenue, Warwick, NY Zip 10990–1028; tel. 845/986–2276; Jeff Reilly, Senior Vice President Operations
Web address: www.stanthonycommunityhosp.org

SOUTH CAROLINA: BON SECOURS ST. FRANCIS HEALTH SYSTEM (O, 331 beds) One St. Francis Drive, Greenville, SC Zip 29601–3207; tel. 864/255–1000; Mark S. Nantz, FACHE, Chief Executive Officer
Web address: www.stfrancishealth.org

VIRGINIA: BON SECOURS MARYVIEW MEDICAL CENTER (O, 473 beds) 3636 High Street, Portsmouth, VA Zip 23707–3270; tel. 757/398–2200; Joseph M. Oddis, Chief Executive Officer
Web address: www.bonsecourshamptonroads.com

BON SECOURS MEMORIAL REGIONAL MEDICAL CENTER (O, 225 beds) 8260 Atlee Road, Mechanicsville, VA Zip 23116–1844; tel. 804/764–6000; Michael Robinson, Chief Executive Officer
Web address: www.bonsecours.com

BON SECOURS ST. FRANCIS MEDICAL CENTER (O, 130 beds) 13710 St. Francis Boulevard, Midlothian, VA Zip 23114–3267; tel. 804/594–7300; Mark M. Gordon, Chief Executive Officer
Web address: www.bonsecours.com/sfmc/default.asp

BON SECOURS ST. MARY'S HOSPITAL (O, 391 beds) 5801 Bremo Road, Richmond, VA Zip 23226–1907; tel. 804/285–2011; Toni R. Ardabell, R.N., Chief Executive Officer
Web address: www.bonsecours.com

BON SECOURS–DEPAUL MEDICAL CENTER (O, 204 beds) 150 Kingsley Lane, Norfolk, VA Zip 23505–4650; tel. 757/889–5000; John E. Barrett, III, Chief Executive Officer
Web address: www.bonsecourshamptonroads.com

BON SECOURS–RICHMOND COMMUNITY HOSPITAL (O, 101 beds) 1500 North 28th Street, Richmond, VA Zip 23223–5396, Mailing Address: P.O. Box 27184, Zip 23261–7184; tel. 804/225–1700; Michael Robinson, Executive Vice President and Administrator
Web address: www.bonsecours.com

MARY IMMACULATE HOSPITAL (O, 232 beds) 2 Bernardine Drive, Newport News, VA Zip 23602–4499; tel. 757/886–6000; Patricia L. Robertson, Executive Vice President
Web address: www.bonsecourshamptonroads.com

Owned, leased, sponsored:	13 hospitals	2899 beds
Contract–managed:	0 hospitals	0 beds
Totals:	13 hospitals	2899 beds

2455: BRADFORD HEALTH SERVICES (IO)
2101 Magnolia Avenue South, Suite 518, Birmingham, AL Zip 35205–2853; tel. 205/251–7753; Jerry W. Crowder, President and Chief Executive Officer

ALABAMA: BRADFORD HEALTH SERVICES AT HUNTSVILLE (O, 84 beds) 1600 Browns Ferry Road, Madison, AL Zip 35758–9601, Mailing Address: P.O. Box 1488, Zip 35758–0176; tel. 256/461–7272; Bob Hinds, Executive Director
Web address: www.bradfordhealth.com

BRADFORD HEALTH SERVICES AT WARRIOR LODGE (O, 100 beds) 1189 Allbritt Road, Warrior, AL Zip 35180, Mailing Address: P.O. Box 129, Zip 35180–0129; tel. 205/647–1945; Roy M. Ramsey, Executive Director
Web address: www.bradfordhealth.com

Owned, leased, sponsored:	2 hospitals	184 beds
Contract–managed:	0 hospitals	0 beds
Totals:	2 hospitals	184 beds

For explanation of codes following names, see page B2.
★ Indicates Type III membership in the American Hospital Association.

Section B

★0595: BRONSON HEALTHCARE GROUP, INC. (NP)

301 John Street, Kalamazoo, MI Zip 49007–5295;
tel. 269/341–6000; Frank J. Sardone, President and Chief Executive Officer

(Centralized Health System)

MICHIGAN: BRONSON BATTLE CREEK (O, 198 beds) 300 North Avenue, Battle Creek, MI Zip 49017–3307; tel. 269/245–8000; Frank J. Sardone, President and Chief Executive Officer
Web address: www.bronsonhealth.com

BRONSON LAKEVIEW HOSPITAL (O, 35 beds) 408 Hazen Street, Paw Paw, MI Zip 49079–1019, Mailing Address: P.O. Box 209, Zip 49079–0209; tel. 269/657–3141; Kirk Richardson, Chief Operating Officer
Web address: www.bronsonhealth.com/lakeview

BRONSON METHODIST HOSPITAL (O, 405 beds) 601 John Street, Kalamazoo, MI Zip 49007–5346; tel. 269/341–6000; Frank J. Sardone, President and Chief Executive Officer
Web address: www.bronsonhealth.com

Owned, leased, sponsored:	3 hospitals	638 beds
Contract–managed:	0 hospitals	0 beds
Totals:	3 hospitals	638 beds

★3115: BROWARD HEALTH (NP)

303 S.E. 17th Street, Fort Lauderdale, FL Zip 33316–2523;
tel. 954/355–5100; Frank P. Nask, President and Chief Executive Officer

FLORIDA: BROWARD HEALTH CORAL SPRINGS (O, 182 beds) 3000 Coral Hills Drive, Coral Springs, FL Zip 33065–4108; tel. 954/344–3000; Drew Grossman, Chief Executive Officer
Web address: www.browardhealth.org

BROWARD HEALTH IMPERIAL POINT (O, 180 beds) 6401 North Federal Highway, Fort Lauderdale, FL Zip 33308–1495; tel. 954/776–8500; Alice Taylor, R.N., MSN, Chief Executive Officer
Web address: www.browardhealth.org

BROWARD HEALTH MEDICAL CENTER (O, 625 beds) 1600 South Andrews Avenue, Fort Lauderdale, FL Zip 33316–2510; tel. 954/355–4400; Calvin E. Glidewell, Jr., Chief Executive Officer
Web address: www.browardhealth.org

BROWARD HEALTH NORTH (O, 334 beds) 201 East Sample Road, Deerfield Beach, FL Zip 33064–3502; tel. 954/941–8300; Pauline Grant, FACHE, Chief Executive Officer
Web address: www.browardhealth.org

Owned, leased, sponsored:	4 hospitals	1321 beds
Contract–managed:	0 hospitals	0 beds
Totals:	4 hospitals	1321 beds

★0400: BRYAN HEALTH (NP)

1600 South 48th Street, Lincoln, NE Zip 68506–1283;
tel. 402/481–1111; Kimberly A. Russel, FACHE, President and Chief Executive Officer

(Centralized Physician/Insurance Health System)

NEBRASKA: BRYAN MEDICAL CENTER (O, 351 beds) 1600 South 48th Street, Lincoln, NE Zip 68506–1299; tel. 402/489–0200; John T. Woodrich, President and Chief Operating Officer
Web address: www.bryanhealth.com

CRETE AREA MEDICAL CENTER (O, 24 beds) 2910 Betten Drive, Crete, NE Zip 68333–3084, Mailing Address: P.O. Box 220, Zip 68333–0220; tel. 402/826–2102; Tad M. Hunt, MS, President and Chief Executive Officer
Web address: www.creteareamedicalcenter.com

Owned, leased, sponsored:	2 hospitals	375 beds
Contract–managed:	0 hospitals	0 beds
Totals:	2 hospitals	375 beds

9655: BUREAU OF MEDICINE AND SURGERY, DEPARTMENT OF THE NAVY (FG)

2300 East Street N.W., Washington, DC Zip 20372–5300;
tel. 202/762–3701; Vice Admiral Matthew L. Nathan, Surgeon General

(Independent Hospital System)

CALIFORNIA: NAVAL HOSPITAL CAMP PENDLETON (O, 72 beds) Santa Margarita Road, Building H100, Camp Pendleton, CA Zip 92055–5191, Mailing Address: P.O. Box 555191, Zip 92055–5191; tel. 760/725–1304; Captain Mark A. Kobelja, MC, USN, Commanding Officer
Web address: www.cpen.med.navy.mil/

NAVAL HOSPITAL LEMOORE (O, 16 beds) 937 Franklin Avenue, Lemoore, CA Zip 93246–0001; tel. 559/998–4481; Captain Cynthia J. Gantt, Commanding Officer
Web address: www.med.navy.mil/sites/nhlem/Pages/index.aspx

NAVAL MEDICAL CENTER SAN DIEGO (O, 285 beds) 34800 Bob Wilson Drive, San Diego, CA Zip 92134–5000; tel. 619/532–6400; Rear Admiral Bruce Gillingham, Commander
Web address: www.med.navy.mil/sites/nmcsd/Pages/default.aspx

ROBERT E. BUSH NAVAL HOSPITAL (O, 29 beds) 1145 Sturgis Road, Twentynine Palms, CA Zip 92278, Mailing Address: Box 788250, MCAGCC, Zip 92278–8250; tel. 760/830–2190; Captain Jay C. Sourbeer, Commanding Officer
Web address: www.med.navy.mil/sites/nhtp/Pages/default.aspx

FLORIDA: NAVAL HOSPITAL JACKSONVILLE (O, 64 beds) 2080 Child Street, Jacksonville, FL Zip 32214–5000; tel. 904/542–7300; Commander Darryl Green, Director Administration
Web address: www.med.navy.mil/SITES/NAVALHOSPITALJAX/Pages/default.aspx

NAVAL HOSPITAL PENSACOLA (O, 28 beds) 6000 West Highway 98, Pensacola, FL Zip 32512–0003; tel. 850/505–6413; Commander Devin Morrison, Director Administration
Web address: www.med.navy.mil/sites/pcola/Pages/default.aspx

GUAM: U. S. NAVAL HOSPITAL GUAM (O, 55 beds) Agana, GU Zip 96910; FPO, tel. 671/344–9340; Lieutenant Commander Rona Green,
Web address: www.med.navy.mil/sites/usnhguam/Pages/default.aspx

MARYLAND: WALTER REED NATIONAL MILITARY MEDICAL CENTER (O, 240 beds) 8901 Wisconsin Avenue, Bethesda, MD Zip 20889–5600; tel. 301/295–4611; Colonel John M. Gaal, Deputy Commander Administration
Web address: www.wrnmmc.capmed.mil/SitePages/home.aspx

NORTH CAROLINA: NAVAL HOSPITAL CAMP LEJEUNE (O, 117 beds) 100 Brewster Boulevard, Camp Lejeune, NC Zip 28547–2538, Mailing Address: P.O. Box 10100, Zip 28547–0100; tel. 910/450–4300; Commander Matthew Case, Director Administration
Web address: www.med.navy.mil/sites/nhcl/Pages/default.aspx

SOUTH CAROLINA: NAVAL HOSPITAL BEAUFORT (O, 20 beds) 1 Pinckney Boulevard, Beaufort, SC Zip 29902–6122; tel. 843/228–5301; Lieutenant Commander Willie Brown, Director Administration
Web address: www.med.navy.mil/sites/nhbeaufort/Pages/Welcome_Page.aspx

VIRGINIA: NAVAL MEDICAL CENTER (O, 274 beds) 620 John Paul Jones Circle, Portsmouth, VA Zip 23708–2197; tel. 757/953–0700; Captain David Collins, Director Administration
Web address: www.nmcphc.med.navy.mil/

WASHINGTON: NAVAL HOSPITAL BREMERTON (O, 40 beds) One Boone Road, Bremerton, WA Zip 98312–1898; tel. 360/475–4000; Commander Jeffrey Klinger, Director for Administration
Web address: www.med.navy.mil/sites/nhbrem/Pages/default.aspx

NAVAL HOSPITAL OAK HARBOR (O, 29 beds) 3475 North Saratoga Street, Oak Harbor, WA Zip 98278–8800; tel. 360/257–9500; Captain Edward D. Simmer, MC, USN, Commanding Officer, General and Forensic Psychiatrist
Web address: www.med.navy.mil/sites/nhoh/Pages/default.aspx

Owned, leased, sponsored:	13 hospitals	1269 beds
Contract–managed:	0 hospitals	0 beds
Totals:	13 hospitals	1269 beds

Section B

For explanation of codes following names, see page B2.
★ Indicates Type III membership in the American Hospital Association.

★**0813: CADENCE HEALTH** (NP)
  25 North Winfield Road, Winfield, IL Zip 60190; tel. 630/933–1600;
  Michael Vivoda, Chief Executive Officer
  (Centralized Health System)

ILLINOIS: CENTRAL DUPAGE HOSPITAL (O, 364 beds) 25 North Winfield
  Road, Winfield, IL Zip 60190; tel. 630/933–1600; Brian J. Lemon,
  President
  Web address: www.cdh.org

  DELNOR HOSPITAL (O, 159 beds) 300 Randall Road, Geneva, IL
  Zip 60134–4200; tel. 630/208–3000; Maureen A. Bryant, FACHE, President
  Web address: www.cadencehealth.org

Owned, leased, sponsored:	2 hospitals	523 beds
Contract–managed:	0 hospitals	0 beds
Totals:	2 hospitals	523 beds

0113: CANCER TREATMENT CENTERS OF AMERICA (IO)
  1336 Basswood Road, Schaumburg, IL Zip 60173–4544;
  tel. 847/342–7400; Gerard van Grinsven, President and Chief
  Executive Officer

ARIZONA: WESTERN REGIONAL MEDICAL CENTER (O, 24 beds) 14200 West
  Celebrate Life way, Goodyear, AZ Zip 85338–3005; tel. 623/207–3000;
  Matthew McGuire, President and Chief Executive Officer
  Web address: www.cancercenter.com/western–hospital.cfm

GEORGIA: SOUTHEASTERN REGIONAL MEDICAL CENTER (O, 25 beds) 600
  Parkway North, Newnan, GA Zip 30265–8000; tel. 770/400–6000; Anne
  Meisner, MSN, President and Chief Executive Officer
  Web address: www.cancercenter.com/southeastern–hospital.cfm

ILLINOIS: MIDWESTERN REGIONAL MEDICAL CENTER (O, 73 beds) 2520
  Elisha Avenue, Zion, IL Zip 60099–2587; tel. 847/872–4561; Scott
  Jones, Chief Executive Officer
  Web address: www.cancercenter.com

OKLAHOMA: SOUTHWESTERN REGIONAL MEDICAL CENTER (O, 40 beds)
  10109 East 79th Street, Tulsa, OK Zip 74133–4564;
  tel. 918/286–5000; Richard Haldeman, President and Chief Executive
  Officer
  Web address: www.cancercenter.com

PENNSYLVANIA: EASTERN REGIONAL MEDICAL CENTER (O, 22 beds) 1331
  East Wyoming Avenue, Philadelphia, PA Zip 19124–3808;
  tel. 800/615–3055; John McNeil, President and Chief Executive Officer
  Web address: www.cancercenter.com

Owned, leased, sponsored:	5 hospitals	184 beds
Contract–managed:	0 hospitals	0 beds
Totals:	5 hospitals	184 beds

★**0124: CAPE COD HEALTHCARE, INC.** (NP)
  27 Park Street, Hyannis, MA Zip 02601–5230; tel. 508/862–5121;
  Michael K. Lauf, President and Chief Executive Officer
  (Centralized Health System)

MASSACHUSETTS: CAPE COD HOSPITAL (O, 259 beds) 27 Park Street,
  Hyannis, MA Zip 02601–5230; tel. 508/771–1800; Michael K. Lauf,
  President and Chief Executive Officer
  Web address: www.capecodhealth.org

  FALMOUTH HOSPITAL (O, 95 beds) 100 Ter Heun Drive, Falmouth, MA
  Zip 02540–2599; tel. 508/548–5300; Susan M. Wing, R.N., Interim Chief
  Operating Officer
  Web address: www.capecodhealth.org

Owned, leased, sponsored:	2 hospitals	354 beds
Contract–managed:	0 hospitals	0 beds
Totals:	2 hospitals	354 beds

0835: CAPE FEAR VALLEY HEALTH SYSTEM (NP)
  1638 Owen Drive, Fayetteville, NC Zip 28304–3424, Mailing
  Address: P.O. Box 2000, Zip 28302–2000; tel. 910/615–4000;
  Michael Nagowski, President and Chief Executive Officer
  (Independent Hospital System)

NORTH CAROLINA: CAPE FEAR VALLEY – BLADEN COUNTY HOSPITAL (O,
  25 beds) 501 South Poplar Street, Elizabethtown, NC Zip 28337–9375,
  Mailing Address: P.O. Box 398, Zip 28337–0398; tel. 910/862–5100;
  Dan Weatherly, On Site Administrator
  Web address: www.bchn.org

  CAPE FEAR VALLEY MEDICAL CENTER (O, 660 beds) 1638 Owen Drive,
  Fayetteville, NC Zip 28304–3431, Mailing Address: P.O. Box 2000,
  Zip 28302–2000; tel. 910/615–4000; Michael Nagowski, Chief Executive
  Officer
  Web address: www.capefearvalley.com

  HIGHSMITH–RAINEY SPECIALTY HOSPITAL (O, 66 beds) 150 Robeson Street,
  Fayetteville, NC Zip 28301–5570; tel. 910/615–1000; Kevin Jackson, On
  Site Administrator
  Web address: www.capefearvalley.com

Owned, leased, sponsored:	3 hospitals	751 beds
Contract–managed:	0 hospitals	0 beds
Totals:	3 hospitals	751 beds

0337: CAPELLA HEALTHCARE (IO)
  501 Corporate Centre Drive, Suite 200, Franklin, TN
  Zip 37067–2662; tel. 615/764–3000; Michael Wiechart, President
  and Chief Executive Officer
  (Moderately Centralized Health System)

ARKANSAS: NATIONAL PARK MEDICAL CENTER (O, 193 beds) 1910 Malvern
  Avenue, Hot Springs, AR Zip 71901–7799; tel. 501/321–1000; Jerry D.
  Mabry, FACHE, Chief Executive Officer
  Web address: www.nationalparkmedical.com

  SAINT MARY'S REGIONAL MEDICAL CENTER (O, 151 beds) 1808 West Main
  Street, Russellville, AR Zip 72801–2724; tel. 479/968–2841; Donald J.
  Frederic, FACHE, Chief Executive Officer
  Web address: www.saintmarysregional.com

MISSOURI: MINERAL AREA REGIONAL MEDICAL CENTER (O, 127 beds) 1212
  Weber Road, Farmington, MO Zip 63640–3325; tel. 573/756–4581; Lynn
  M. Mergen, Chief Executive Officer
  Web address: www.mineralarearegional.com

OKLAHOMA: EASTAR HEALTH SYSTEM (L, 206 beds) 300 Rockefeller Drive,
  Muskogee, OK Zip 74401–5081; tel. 918/682–5501; Anthony R. Young,
  Chief Executive Officer
  Web address: www.eastarhealth.com

  SOUTHWESTERN MEDICAL CENTER (O, 178 beds) 5602 S.W. Lee Boulevard,
  Lawton, OK Zip 73505–9635; tel. 580/531–4700; Stephen O. Hyde, FACHE,
  Chief Executive Officer
  Web address: www.swmconline.com

OREGON: WILLAMETTE VALLEY MEDICAL CENTER (O, 88 beds) 2700 S.E.
  Stratus Avenue, McMinnville, OR Zip 97128–6255; tel. 503/472–6131;
  Peter A. Hofstetter, Chief Executive Officer
  Web address: www.wvmcweb.com

TENNESSEE: DEKALB COMMUNITY HOSPITAL (O, 52 beds) 520 West Main
  Street, Smithville, TN Zip 37166–1138, Mailing Address: P.O. Box 640,
  Zip 37166–0640; tel. 615/215–5000; Susan Conley, Chief Executive
  Officer
  Web address: www.dekalbcommunityhospital.com

  HIGHLANDS MEDICAL CENTER (O, 44 beds) 401 Sewell Road, Sparta, TN
  Zip 38583–1299; tel. 931/738–9211; William Little, Chief Executive Officer
  Web address: www.whitecountyhospital.com

  RIVER PARK HOSPITAL (O, 85 beds) 1559 Sparta Street, Mc Minnville, TN
  Zip 37110–1316; tel. 931/815–4000; Timothy W. McGill, Chief Executive
  Officer
  Web address: www.riverparkhospital.com

  STONES RIVER HOSPITAL (O, 60 beds) 324 Doolittle Road, Woodbury, TN
  Zip 37190–1139; tel. 615/563–4001; Susan Conley, Chief Executive Officer
  Web address: www.stonesriverhospital.com

WASHINGTON: CAPITAL MEDICAL CENTER (O, 110 beds) 3900 Capital Mall
  Drive S.W., Olympia, WA Zip 98502–5026, Mailing Address: P.O. Box
  19002, Zip 98507–0013; tel. 360/754–5858; Jim Geist, Chief Executive
  Officer
  Web address: www.capitalmedical.com

For explanation of codes following names, see page B2.
★ Indicates Type III membership in the American Hospital Association.

Owned, leased, sponsored:	11 hospitals	1294 beds
Contract–managed:	0 hospitals	0 beds
Totals:	11 hospitals	1294 beds

★0297: CAPITAL HEALTH (NP)
750 Brunswick Avenue, Trenton, NJ Zip 08638–4143;
tel. 609/394–6000; Al Maghazehe, Ph.D., FACHE, Chief Executive Officer
(Independent Hospital System)

NEW JERSEY: CAPITAL HEALTH MEDICAL CENTER–HOPEWELL (O, 223 beds) 1 Capital Way, Pennington, NJ Zip 08534–2520;
tel. 609/303–4000; Al Maghazehe, Ph.D., FACHE, Chief Executive Officer
Web address: www.capitalhealth.org

CAPITAL HEALTH REGIONAL MEDICAL CENTER (O, 271 beds) 750 Brunswick Avenue, Trenton, NJ Zip 08638–4143; tel. 609/394–6000; Al Maghazehe, Ph.D., FACHE, Chief Executive Officer
Web address: www.capitalhealth.org

Owned, leased, sponsored:	2 hospitals	494 beds
Contract–managed:	0 hospitals	0 beds
Totals:	2 hospitals	494 beds

★0099: CARE NEW ENGLAND HEALTH SYSTEM (NP)
45 Willard Avenue, Providence, RI Zip 02905–3218;
tel. 401/453–7900; Dennis D. Keefe, President and Chief Executive Officer
(Centralized Health System)

RHODE ISLAND: BUTLER HOSPITAL (O, 143 beds) 345 Blackstone Boulevard, Providence, RI Zip 02906–4829; tel. 401/455–6200; Lawrence Price, M.D., President and Chief Operating Officer
Web address: www.butler.org

KENT COUNTY MEMORIAL HOSPITAL (O, 306 beds) 455 Tollgate Road, Warwick, RI Zip 02886–2770; tel. 401/737–7000; Michael J. Dacey, M.D., MS, President and Chief Operating Officer
Web address: www.kentri.org

MEMORIAL HOSPITAL OF RHODE ISLAND (O, 150 beds) 111 Brewster Street, Pawtucket, RI Zip 02860–4499; tel. 401/729–2000; Edward M. Schottland, Acting President
Web address: www.mhri.org

WOMEN & INFANTS HOSPITAL OF RHODE ISLAND (O, 247 beds) 101 Dudley Street, Providence, RI Zip 02905–2499; tel. 401/274–1100; Mark R. Marcantano, President and Chief Operating Officer
Web address: www.womenandinfants.org

Owned, leased, sponsored:	4 hospitals	846 beds
Contract–managed:	0 hospitals	0 beds
Totals:	4 hospitals	846 beds

0931: CAREPOINT HEALTH (IO)
176 Palisade Avenue, Jersey City, NJ Zip 07306–1121;
tel. 877/791–7000; Daniel A. Kane, Board Chairman

NEW JERSEY: BAYONNE MEDICAL CENTER (O, 170 beds) 29th Street & Avenue E., Bayonne, NJ Zip 07002–4699; tel. 201/858–5000; Mark Spektor, M.D., President and Chief Executive Officer
Web address: www.bayonnemedicalcenter.org

CHRIST HOSPITAL (O, 381 beds) 176 Palisade Avenue, Jersey City, NJ Zip 07306–1196, Mailing Address: 176 Palisades Avenue, Zip 07306–1196; tel. 201/795–8200; Nizar Kifaieh, M.D., President and Chief Medical Officer
Web address: www.christhospital.org

HOBOKEN UNIVERSITY MEDICAL CENTER (O, 364 beds) 308 Willow Avenue, Hoboken, NJ Zip 07030–3889; tel. 201/418–1000; Ann Logan, Chief Operating Officer and Chief Nursing Officer
Web address: www.hobokenumc.com

Owned, leased, sponsored:	3 hospitals	915 beds
Contract–managed:	0 hospitals	0 beds
Totals:	3 hospitals	915 beds

★0070: CARILION CLINIC (NP)
1906 Belleview Avenue S.E., Roanoke, VA Zip 24014–1838, Mailing Address: P.O. Box 13367, Zip 24033–3367; tel. 540/981–7000; Nancy Howell Agee, President and Chief Executive Officer
(Moderately Centralized Health System)

VIRGINIA: CARILION FRANKLIN MEMORIAL HOSPITAL (O, 15 beds) 180 Floyd Avenue, Rocky Mount, VA Zip 24151–1389; tel. 540/483–5277; William D. Jacobsen, Vice President and Administrator
Web address: www.carilionclinic.org/Carilion/Franklin+Memorial+Hospital

CARILION GILES COMMUNITY HOSPITAL (O, 17 beds) 159 Hartley Way, Pearisburg, VA Zip 24134–2471; tel. 540/921–6000; Richard Mastalski, Senior Director Operations
Web address: www.carilionclinic.org/Carilion/cgch

CARILION NEW RIVER VALLEY MEDICAL CENTER (O, 94 beds) 2900 Lamb Circle, Christiansburg, VA Zip 24073–6344, Mailing Address: P.O. Box 5, Radford, Zip 24143–0005; tel. 540/731–2000; Melina Dee Perdue, R.N., Executive Vice President
Web address: www.carilionclinic.org/Carilion/cnrv

CARILION ROANOKE MEMORIAL HOSPITAL (O, 646 beds) Belleview at Jefferson Street, Roanoke, VA Zip 24014, Mailing Address: P.O. Box 13367, Zip 24033–3367; tel. 540/981–7000; Steven C. Arner, President
Web address: www.carilionclinic.org

CARILION STONEWALL JACKSON HOSPITAL (O, 14 beds) 1 Health Circle, Lexington, VA Zip 24450–2492; tel. 540/458–3300; Charles E. Carr, Vice President, Regional Hospital
Web address: www.carilionclinic.org/Carilion/csjh

CARILION TAZEWELL COMMUNITY HOSPITAL (O, 7 beds) 141 Ben Bolt Avenue, Tazewell, VA Zip 24651–9700; tel. 276/988–8700; Kathren Dowdy, MSN, Regional Hospital Senior Director
Web address: www.carilionclinic.org/Carilion/Carilion+Tazewell+Community+Hospital

Owned, leased, sponsored:	6 hospitals	793 beds
Contract–managed:	0 hospitals	0 beds
Totals:	6 hospitals	793 beds

★2575: CARLE FOUNDATION (NP)
611 West Park Street, Urbana, IL Zip 61801–2595;
tel. 217/383–3311; James C. Leonard, M.D., President and Chief Executive Officer

ILLINOIS: CARLE FOUNDATION HOSPITAL (O, 345 beds) 611 West Park Street, Urbana, IL Zip 61801–2595; tel. 217/383–3311; James C. Leonard, M.D., President and Chief Executive Officer
Web address: www.carle.org

CARLE HOOPESTON REGIONAL HEALTH CENTER (O, 13 beds) 701 East Orange Street, Hoopeston, IL Zip 60942–1801; tel. 217/283–5531; Harry Brockus, Chief Executive Officer
Web address: www.carle.org

Owned, leased, sponsored:	2 hospitals	358 beds
Contract–managed:	0 hospitals	0 beds
Totals:	2 hospitals	358 beds

★0705: CAROLINAS HEALTHCARE SYSTEM (NP)
1000 Blythe Boulevard, Charlotte, NC Zip 28203–5871, Mailing Address: P.O. Box 32861, Zip 28232–2861; tel. 704/355–2000; Michael C. Tarwater, Chief Executive Officer
(Moderately Centralized Health System)

NORTH CAROLINA: ANSON COMMUNITY HOSPITAL (O, 125 beds) 500 Morven Road, Wadesboro, NC Zip 28170–2745; tel. 704/694–5131; Frederick G. Thompson, Ph.D., President
Web address: www.carolinashealthcare.org/anson–community–hospital

BLUE RIDGE HEALTHCARE HOSPITALS (C, 175 beds) 2201 South Sterling Street, Morganton, NC Zip 28655–4058; tel. 828/580–5000; Kathy C. Bailey, Ph.D., FACHE, President and Chief Executive Officer

CAROLINAS MEDICAL CENTER (O, 1066 beds) 1000 Blythe Boulevard, Charlotte, NC Zip 28203–5871, Mailing Address: P.O. Box 32861, Zip 28232–2861; tel. 704/355–2000; Spencer Lilly, President
Web address: www.carolinasmedicalcenter.org

Section B

For explanation of codes following names, see page B2.
★ Indicates Type III membership in the American Hospital Association.

CAROLINAS MEDICAL CENTER–LINCOLN (O, 101 beds) 433 McAlister Road, Lincolnton, NC Zip 28092–4147; tel. 980/212–2000; Peter W. Acker, President
Web address: www.carolinashealthcare.org/body.cfm?id=7626

CAROLINAS MEDICAL CENTER–NORTHEAST (O, 455 beds) 920 Church Street North, Concord, NC Zip 28025–2983; tel. 704/403–3000; Phyllis A. Wingate, FACHE, President
Web address: www.carolinashealthcare.org

CAROLINAS MEDICAL CENTER–PINEVILLE (O, 215 beds) 10628 Park Road, Charlotte, NC Zip 28210; tel. 704/543–2000; Christopher R. Hummer, President
Web address: www.carolinashealthcare.org/cmc–pineville

CAROLINAS MEDICAL CENTER–UNION (L, 227 beds) 600 Hospital Drive, Monroe, NC Zip 28112–6000, Mailing Address: P.O. Box 5003, Zip 28111–5003; tel. 704/993–3100; Michael Lutes, President
Web address: www.carolinashealthcare.org/cmc–union

CAROLINAS MEDICAL CENTER–UNIVERSITY (O, 94 beds) 8800 North Tryon Street, Charlotte, NC Zip 28262–3300, Mailing Address: P.O. Box 560727, Zip 28256–0727; tel. 704/863–6000; William H. Leonard, President
Web address: www.carolinashealthcare.org/cmc–university

CAROLINAS REHABILITATION (O, 147 beds) 1100 Blythe Boulevard, Charlotte, NC Zip 28203–5864; tel. 704/355–4300; Robert G. Larrison, Jr., President
Web address: www.carolinashealthcare.org/carolinas–rehab

CLEVELAND REGIONAL MEDICAL CENTER (L, 364 beds) 201 East Grover Street, Shelby, NC Zip 28150–3917; tel. 980/487–3000; Brian Gwyn, President and Chief Executive Officer
Web address: www.clevelandregional.org

COLUMBUS REGIONAL HEALTHCARE SYSTEM (C, 103 beds) 500 Jefferson Street, Whiteville, NC Zip 28472–3634; tel. 910/642–8011; Duane L. Erwin, Interim Chief Executive Officer
Web address: www.crhealthcare.org

CRAWLEY MEMORIAL HOSPITAL (L, 41 beds) 706 West King Street, Shelby, NC Zip 28086, Mailing Address: P.O. Box 159, Boiling Springs, Zip 28086; tel. 980/487–1300; Denise R. Murray, Chief Executive Officer
Web address: www.clevelandcountyhealthcaresystem. com/crawley–memorial.html

KINGS MOUNTAIN HOSPITAL (O, 67 beds) 706 West King Street, Kings Mountain, NC Zip 28086–2708; tel. 980/487–5000; Brian Gwyn, President and Chief Executive Officer
Web address: www.clevelandregional.org/kings–mountain–hospital.html

MOSES H. CONE MEMORIAL HOSPITAL (C, 1004 beds) 1200 North Elm Street, Greensboro, NC Zip 27401–1020; tel. 336/832–7000; Mickey Foster, President
Web address: www.conehealth.com/locations/moses–cone–hospital/

MURPHY MEDICAL CENTER (C, 191 beds) 3990 U.S. Highway 64 East Alt, Murphy, NC Zip 28906–7917; tel. 828/837–8161; Michael Stevenson, Chief Executive Officer
Web address: www.murphymedical.org

SCOTLAND HEALTH CARE SYSTEM (C, 102 beds) 500 Lauchwood Drive, Laurinburg, NC Zip 28352–5599; tel. 910/291–7000; Gregory C. Wood, President and Chief Executive Officer
Web address: www.scotlandhealth.org

ST. LUKE'S HOSPITAL (C, 35 beds) 101 Hospital Drive, Columbus, NC Zip 28722–6418; tel. 828/894–3311; Kenneth A. Shull, FACHE, Chief Executive Officer
Web address: www.saintlukeshospital.com

STANLY REGIONAL MEDICAL CENTER (C, 104 beds) 301 Yadkin Street, Albemarle, NC Zip 28001–3441, Mailing Address: P.O. Box 1489, Zip 28002–1489; tel. 704/984–4000; Alfred P. Taylor, President and Chief Executive Officer
Web address: www.stanly.org

WILKES REGIONAL MEDICAL CENTER (C, 107 beds) 1370 West D Street, North Wilkesboro, NC Zip 28659–3506, Mailing Address: P.O. Box 609, Zip 28659–0609; tel. 336/651–8100; J. Gene Faile, Chief Executive Officer and President
Web address: www.wilkesregional.com/

SOUTH CAROLINA: BON SECOURS ST. FRANCIS XAVIER HOSPITAL (C, 170 beds) 2095 Henry Tecklenburg Drive, Charleston, SC Zip 29414–5733; tel. 843/402–1000; Allen P. Carroll, Senior Vice President and Chief Executive Officer
Web address: www.ropersaintfrancis.com

CANNON MEMORIAL HOSPITAL (C, 38 beds) 123 West G. Acker Drive, Pickens, SC Zip 29671–2739, Mailing Address: P.O. Box 188, Zip 29671–0188; tel. 864/878–4791; Norman G. Rentz, President and Chief Executive Officer
Web address: www.cannonhospital.org

MOUNT PLEASANT HOSPITAL (C, 50 beds) 3500 Highway 17 North, Mount Pleasant, SC Zip 29466–9123, Mailing Address: 3500 North Highway 17, Zip 29466–9123; tel. 843/606–7000; John Sullivan, Chief Executive Officer
Web address: www.mymountpleasanthospital.com

ROPER HOSPITAL (C, 308 beds) 316 Calhoun Street, Charleston, SC Zip 29401–1125; tel. 843/724–2000; Matthew J. Severance, FACHE, Chief Executive Officer
Web address: www.ropersaintfrancis.com

Owned, leased, sponsored:	11 hospitals	2902 beds
Contract–managed:	12 hospitals	2387 beds
Totals:	23 hospitals	5289 beds

0656: CARRUS HOSPITALS (IO)
1810 West U.S. Highway 82, Sherman, TX Zip 75092–7069; tel. 903/870–2600; Ronald E. Dorris, Chief Executive Officer
(Independent Hospital System)

TEXAS: CARRUS REHABILITATION HOSPITAL (O, 24 beds) 1810 West U.S. Highway 82, Suite 100, Sherman, TX Zip 75092–7069; tel. 903/870–2600; Jon Michael Rains, Chief Executive Officer
Web address: www.carrushospital.com

CARRUS SPECIALTY HOSPITAL (O, 16 beds) 1810 West U.S. Highway 82, Sherman, TX Zip 75092–7069; tel. 903/870–2600; Jon Michael Rains, Chief Executive Officer
Web address: www.carrushospital.com

Owned, leased, sponsored:	2 hospitals	40 beds
Contract–managed:	0 hospitals	0 beds
Totals:	2 hospitals	40 beds

★0906: CATHOLIC HEALTH EAST / TRINITY HEALTH (CC)
20555 Victor Parkway, Livonia, MI Zip 48152–7031; tel. 734/343–1000; Richard J. Gilfillan, M.D., President and Chief Executive Officer

CALIFORNIA: SAINT AGNES MEDICAL CENTER (O, 436 beds) 1303 East Herndon Avenue, Fresno, CA Zip 93720–3397; tel. 559/450–3000; Nancy Hollingsworth, R.N., MSN, President and Chief Executive Officer
Web address: www.samc.com

DELAWARE: ST. FRANCIS HOSPITAL (O, 214 beds) Seventh and Clayton Streets, Wilmington, DE Zip 19805–0500, Mailing Address: P.O. Box 2500, Zip 19805–0500; tel. 302/421–4100; Brian E. Dietz, FACHE, Interim President and Chief Executive officer
Web address: www.stfrancishealthcare.org

FLORIDA: HOLY CROSS HOSPITAL (O, 559 beds) 4725 North Federal Highway, Fort Lauderdale, FL Zip 33308–4668, Mailing Address: P.O. Box 23460, Zip 33307–3460; tel. 954/771–8000; Patrick Taylor, M.D., President and Chief Executive Officer
Web address: www.holy–cross.com

SOUTH FLORIDA BAPTIST HOSPITAL (S, 125 beds) 301 North Alexander Street, Plant City, FL Zip 33563–4303, Mailing Address: Drawer H, Zip 33564–9058; tel. 813/757–1200; Karen Kerr, R.N., Interim President and Chief Executive Officer
Web address: www.sjbhealth.org

ST. ANTHONY'S HOSPITAL (S, 344 beds) 1200 Seventh Avenue North, Saint Petersburg, FL Zip 33705–1388, Mailing Address: P.O. Box 12588, Zip 33733–2588; tel. 727/825–1100; William G. Ulbricht, President
Web address: www.stanthonys.com/

ST. JOSEPH'S HOSPITAL (S, 1006 beds) 3001 West Martin Luther King Jr. Boulevard, Tampa, FL Zip 33607–6387, Mailing Address: P.O. Box 4227, Zip 33677–4227; tel. 813/870–4000; Lorraine Lutton, President
Web address: www.sjbhealth.org

GEORGIA: ST. MARY'S GOOD SAMARITAN HOSPITAL (O, 25 beds) 5401 Lake Oconee Parkway, Greensboro, GA Zip 30642–4232; tel. 706/453–7331; D. Montez Carter, President
Web address: www.stmarysgoodsam.org

For explanation of codes following names, see page B2.
★ Indicates Type III membership in the American Hospital Association.

ST. MARY'S HEALTH CARE SYSTEM (O, 165 beds) 1230 Baxter Street, Athens, GA Zip 30606–3791; tel. 706/389–3000; Donald McKenna, President and Chief Executive Officer
Web address: www.stmarysathens.com

IDAHO: SAINT ALPHONSUS MEDICAL CENTER – NAMPA (O, 142 beds) 1512 12th Avenue Road, Nampa, ID Zip 83686–6008; tel. 208/463–5000; Karl Keeler, Chief Executive Officer
Web address: www.mercynampa.org

ILLINOIS: GOTTLIEB MEMORIAL HOSPITAL (O, 255 beds) 701 West North Avenue, Melrose Park, IL Zip 60160–1612; tel. 708/681–3200; Lori Price, President
Web address: www.gottliebhospital.org

LOYOLA UNIVERSITY MEDICAL CENTER (O, 520 beds) 2160 South First Avenue, Maywood, IL Zip 60153–3328; tel. 708/216–9000; Larry M. Goldberg, President and Chief Executive Officer
Web address: www.loyolamedicine.org/Medical_Services/index.cfm

MERCY HOSPITAL AND MEDICAL CENTER (O, 189 beds) 2525 South Michigan Avenue, Chicago, IL Zip 60616–2333; tel. 312/567–2000; Carol L. Schneider, President and Chief Executive Officer
Web address: www.mercy–chicago.org

INDIANA: SAINT JOSEPH REGIONAL MEDICAL CENTER (O, 267 beds) 5215 Holy Cross Parkway, Mishawaka, IN Zip 46545–1469; tel. 574/335–5000; Albert Gutierrez, FACHE, President and Chief Executive Officer
Web address: www.sjmed.com

SAINT JOSEPH REGIONAL MEDICAL CENTER–PLYMOUTH CAMPUS (O, 45 beds) 1915 Lake Avenue, Plymouth, IN Zip 46563–9366, Mailing Address: P.O. Box 670, Zip 46563–0670; tel. 574/948–4000; Loretta Schmidt, President
Web address: www.sjmed.com

IOWA: BAUM HARMON MERCY HOSPITAL (O, 12 beds) 255 North Welch Avenue, Primghar, IA Zip 51245–7765, Mailing Address: P.O. Box 528, Zip 51245–0528; tel. 712/957–2300; Roger W. Lenz, Interim Chief Executive Officer
Web address: www.baumharmon.org

CENTRAL COMMUNITY HOSPITAL (C, 15 beds) 901 Davidson Street N.W., Elkader, IA Zip 52043–9015; tel. 563/245–7000; Frances J. Zichal, Chief Executive Officer
Web address: www.centralcommunityhospital.com

FRANKLIN GENERAL HOSPITAL (C, 77 beds) 1720 Central Avenue East, Suite A., Hampton, IA Zip 50441–1867; tel. 641/456–5000; Kim Price, Chief Executive Officer
Web address: www.franklingeneral.com

HANCOCK COUNTY HEALTH SYSTEM (C, 25 beds) 532 First Street N.W., Britt, IA Zip 50423–1227; tel. 641/843–5000; Vance Jackson, FACHE, Administrator and Chief Executive Officer
Web address: www.trusthchs.com/hancock–county–health–system

HANSEN FAMILY HOSPITAL (C, 23 beds) 920 South Oak, Iowa Falls, IA Zip 50126–9506; tel. 641/648–4631; Cherelle Montanye–Ireland, Chief Executive Officer
Web address: www.hansenfamilyhospital.com

HAWARDEN REGIONAL HEALTHCARE (C, 18 beds) 1111 11th Street, Hawarden, IA Zip 51023–1999; tel. 712/551–3100; Jayson Pullman, Chief Executive Officer
Web address: www.hawardenregionalhealthcare.com/

KOSSUTH REGIONAL HEALTH CENTER (C, 23 beds) 1515 South Phillips Street, Algona, IA Zip 50511–3649; tel. 515/295–2451; Scott A. Curtis, Administrator and Chief Executive Officer
Web address: www.krhc.com

MERCY MEDICAL CENTER–CLINTON (O, 307 beds) 1410 North Fourth Street, Clinton, IA Zip 52732–2940; tel. 563/244–5555; Sean J. Williams, President and Chief Executive Officer
Web address: www.mercyclinton.com

MERCY MEDICAL CENTER–DUBUQUE (O, 272 beds) 250 Mercy Drive, Dubuque, IA Zip 52001–7360; tel. 563/589–8000; Russell M. Knight, President and Chief Executive Officer
Web address: www.mercydubuque.com

MERCY MEDICAL CENTER–DYERSVILLE (O, 25 beds) 1111 Third Street S.W., Dyersville, IA Zip 52040–1725; tel. 563/875–7101; Russell M. Knight, President and Chief Executive Officer
Web address: www.mercydubuque.com/mercy–dyersville

MERCY MEDICAL CENTER–NEW HAMPTON (O, 18 beds) 308 North Maple Avenue, New Hampton, IA Zip 50659–1142; tel. 641/394–4121; Bruce E. Roesler, FACHE, President and Chief Executive Officer
Web address: www.mercynewhampton.com

MERCY MEDICAL CENTER–NORTH IOWA (O, 237 beds) 1000 Fourth Street S.W., Mason City, IA Zip 50401–2800; tel. 641/428–7000; Daniel Varnum, President and Chief Executive Officer
Web address: www.mercynorthiowa.com

MERCY MEDICAL CENTER–SIOUX CITY (O, 238 beds) 801 Fifth Street, Sioux City, IA Zip 51101–1326, Mailing Address: P.O. Box 3168, Zip 51102–3168; tel. 712/279–2010; James G. Fitzpatrick, President
Web address: www.mercysiouxcity.com

MITCHELL COUNTY REGIONAL HEALTH CENTER (C, 25 beds) 616 North Eighth Street, Osage, IA Zip 50461–1498; tel. 641/732–6000; Shelly Russell, Chief Executive Officer
Web address: www.mitchellcohospital–clinics.com

PALO ALTO COUNTY HEALTH SYSTEM (C, 47 beds) 3201 First Street, Emmetsburg, IA Zip 50536–2516; tel. 712/852–5500; Desiree Einsweiler, Chief Executive Officer
Web address: www.pachs.org

REGIONAL HEALTH SERVICES OF HOWARD COUNTY (C, 20 beds) 235 Eighth Avenue West, Cresco, IA Zip 52136–1098; tel. 563/547–2101; Robin M. Schluter, Chief Executive Officer
Web address: www.rhshc.com

MARYLAND: HOLY CROSS HOSPITAL (O, 425 beds) 1500 Forest Glen Road, Silver Spring, MD Zip 20910–1487; tel. 301/754–7000; Judith Rogers, R.N., Ph.D., President and Chief Executive Officer
Web address: www.holycrosshealth.org

MASSACHUSETTS: FARREN CARE CENTER (O, 72 beds) 340 Montague City Road, Turners Falls, MA Zip 01376–9983; tel. 413/774–3111; James Clifford, Administrator

MERCY MEDICAL CENTER (O, 301 beds) 271 Carew Street, Springfield, MA Zip 01104–2398, Mailing Address: P.O. Box 9012, Zip 01102–9012; tel. 413/748–9000; Daniel P. Moen, President and Chief Executive Officer
Web address: www.mercycares.com

MICHIGAN: CHELSEA COMMUNITY HOSPITAL (O, 96 beds) 775 South Main Street, Chelsea, MI Zip 48118–1383; tel. 734/593–6000; Nancy Kay Graebner, President and Chief Executive Officer
Web address: www.cch.org

MERCY HEALTH PARTNERS, LAKESHORE CAMPUS (O, 24 beds) 72 South State Street, Shelby, MI Zip 49455–1299; tel. 231/861–2156; Jay Bryan, President and Chief Executive Officer
Web address: www.mercyhealthmuskegon.com

MERCY HEALTH SAINT MARY'S (O, 364 beds) 200 Jefferson Avenue S.E., Grand Rapids, MI Zip 49503–4598; tel. 616/685–5000; Bill Manns, President
Web address: www.mercyhealthsaintmarys.org

MERCY HEALTH, HACKLEY CAMPUS (O, 213 beds) 1700 Clinton Street, Muskegon, MI Zip 49442–5502, Mailing Address: P.O. Box 3302, Zip 49443–3302; tel. 231/726–3511; Greg Loomis, President
Web address: www.mercyhealthmuskegon.com

MERCY HEALTH, MERCY CAMPUS (O, 188 beds) 1500 East Sherman Boulevard, Muskegon, MI Zip 49444–1849; tel. 231/672–2000; Greg Loomis, President
Web address: www.mercyhealth.com

MERCY HOSPITAL CADILLAC (O, 65 beds) 400 Hobart Street, Cadillac, MI Zip 49601–2389; tel. 231/876–7200; John L. MacLeod, President and Chief Executive Officer
Web address: www.munsonhealthcare.org

MERCY HOSPITAL GRAYLING (O, 94 beds) 1100 East Michigan Avenue, Grayling, MI Zip 49738–1312; tel. 989/348–5461; Stephanie J. Riemer–Matuzak, Chief Executive Officer
Web address: www.mercygrayling.munsonhealthcare.org/

ST. JOSEPH MERCY HOSPITAL ANN ARBOR (O, 537 beds) 5301 Mcauley Drive, Ypsilanti, MI Zip 48197–1051, Mailing Address: P.O. Box 995, Ann Arbor, Zip 48106–0995; tel. 734/712–3456; Robert F. Casalou, President and Chief Executive Officer
Web address: www.sjmercyhealth.org

ST. JOSEPH MERCY LIVINGSTON HOSPITAL (O, 36 beds) 620 Byron Road, Howell, MI Zip 48843–1093; tel. 517/545–6000; Robert F. Casalou, President and Chief Executive Officer
Web address: www.stjoeslivingston.org/livingston

Section B

ST. JOSEPH MERCY OAKLAND (O, 409 beds) 44405 Woodward Avenue, Pontiac, MI Zip 48341–5023; tel. 248/858–3000; Jack Weiner, President and Chief Executive Officer
Web address: www.stjoesoakland.com

ST. JOSEPH MERCY PORT HURON (O, 119 beds) 2601 Electric Avenue, Port Huron, MI Zip 48060–6518; tel. 810/985–1500; Rebekah Smith, R.N., President and Chief Executive Officer
Web address: www.mymercy.us

ST. JOSEPH MERCY SALINE (O, 0 beds) 400 West Russell Street, Saline, MI Zip 48176–1183; tel. 734/429–1500; Barbara Fielder, Operations Director

ST. MARY MERCY HOSPITAL (O, 285 beds) 36475 Five Mile Road, Livonia, MI Zip 48154–1988; tel. 734/655–4800; David A. Spivey, President and Chief Executive Officer
Web address: www.stmarymercy.org

NEBRASKA: OAKLAND MERCY HOSPITAL (O, 18 beds) 601 East Second Street, Oakland, NE Zip 68045–1499; tel. 402/685–5601; John W. Werner, Chief Executive Officer
Web address: www.oaklandhospital.org

PENDER COMMUNITY HOSPITAL (C, 67 beds) 100 Hospital Drive, Pender, NE Zip 68047–0100, Mailing Address: P.O. Box 100, Zip 68047–0100; tel. 402/385–3083; Melissa Kelly, Administrator
Web address: www.pendercommunityhospital.com

NEW JERSEY: LOURDES MEDICAL CENTER OF BURLINGTON COUNTY (O, 125 beds) 218–A Sunset Road, Willingboro, NJ Zip 08046–1162; tel. 609/835–2900; Mark Nessel, Executive Vice President and Chief Operating Officer
Web address: www.lourdesnet.org

OUR LADY OF LOURDES MEDICAL CENTER (O, 350 beds) 1600 Haddon Avenue, Camden, NJ Zip 08103–3117; tel. 856/757–3500; Alexander J. Hatala, FACHE, President and Chief Executive Officer
Web address: www.lourdesnet.org

SAINT MICHAEL'S MEDICAL CENTER (O, 147 beds) 111 Central Avenue, Newark, NJ Zip 07102–1909; tel. 973/877–5350; David A. Ricci, President and Chief Executive Officer
Web address: www.smmcnj.org

ST. FRANCIS MEDICAL CENTER (O, 163 beds) 601 Hamilton Avenue, Trenton, NJ Zip 08629–1986; tel. 609/599–5000; Christy Stephenson, Interim Chief Executive Officer
Web address: www.stfrancismedical.com

NEW YORK: ALBANY MEMORIAL HOSPITAL (O, 73 beds) 600 Northern Boulevard, Albany, NY Zip 12204–1083; tel. 518/471–3221; Ann Errichetti, M.D., Chief Executive Officer
Web address: www.nehealth.com

SAMARITAN HOSPITAL (O, 238 beds) 2215 Burdett Avenue, Troy, NY Zip 12180–2475; tel. 518/271–3300; Norman E. Dascher, Jr., Chief Executive Officer
Web address: www.nehealth.com

ST. JAMES MERCY HEALTH SYSTEM (O, 102 beds) 411 Canisteo Street, Hornell, NY Zip 14843–2197; tel. 607/324–8000; Jennifer Sullivan, President and Chief Executive Officer
Web address: www.stjamesmercy.org

ST. MARY'S HOSPITAL (O, 196 beds) 1300 Massachusetts Avenue, Troy, NY Zip 12180–1695; tel. 518/268–5000; Norman E. Dascher, Jr., Chief Executive Officer
Web address: www.setonhealth.org

ST. PETER'S HOSPITAL (O, 442 beds) 315 South Manning Boulevard, Albany, NY Zip 12208–1789; tel. 518/525–1550; Ann Errichetti, M.D., Chief Executive Officer
Web address: www.sphcs.org

SUNNYVIEW REHABILITATION HOSPITAL (O, 115 beds) 1270 Belmont Avenue, Schenectady, NY Zip 12308–2104; tel. 518/382–4500; Edward Eisenman, Chief Executive Officer
Web address: www.sunnyview.org

NORTH CAROLINA: ST. JOSEPH OF THE PINES HOSPITAL (O, 204 beds) 590 Central Drive, Southern Pines, NC Zip 28387; tel. 910/246–1000; Ken Cormier, President and Chief Executive Officer

OHIO: FAYETTE COUNTY MEMORIAL HOSPITAL (C, 25 beds) 1430 Columbus Avenue, Washington Court House, OH Zip 43160–1791; tel. 740/335–1210; Lyndon J. Christman, President and Chief Executive Officer
Web address: www.fcmh.org

MOUNT CARMEL (O, 728 beds) 793 West State Street, Columbus, OH Zip 43222–1551; tel. 614/234–5000; Sean McKibben, President and Chief Operating Officer
Web address: www.mountcarmelhealth.com

MOUNT CARMEL NEW ALBANY SURGICAL HOSPITAL (O, 60 beds) 7333 Smith's Mill Road, New Albany, OH Zip 43054–9291; tel. 614/775–6600; Richard D'Enbeau, Chief Operating Officer
Web address: www.mountcarmelhealth.com

MOUNT CARMEL ST. ANN'S (O, 242 beds) 500 South Cleveland Avenue, Westerville, OH Zip 43081–8998; tel. 614/898–4000; Janet Meeks, Chief Operating Officer
Web address: www.mountcarmelhealth.com

OREGON: SAINT ALPHONSUS MEDICAL CENTER – BAKER CITY (S, 55 beds) 3325 Pocahontas Road, Baker City, OR Zip 97814–1464; tel. 541/523–6461; H. Ray Gibbons, FACHE, Chief Executive Officer
Web address: www.saintalphonsus.org/bakercity

SAINT ALPHONSUS MEDICAL CENTER – ONTARIO (S, 49 beds) 351 S.W. Ninth Street, Ontario, OR Zip 97914–2693; tel. 541/881–7000; Karl Keeler, Chief Executive Officer
Web address: www.saintalphonsus.org/ontario

PENNSYLVANIA: MERCY FITZGERALD HOSPITAL (O, 382 beds) 1500 Lansdowe Avenue, Darby, PA Zip 19023–1200; tel. 610/237–4000; Kathryn Conallen, Chief Executive Officer
Web address: www.mercyhealth.org

MERCY SUBURBAN HOSPITAL (O, 126 beds) 2701 DeKalb Pike, Norristown, PA Zip 19401–1820; tel. 610/278–2000; Kathryn Conallen, Interim Chief Executive Officer
Web address: www.mercyhealth.org

NAZARETH HOSPITAL (O, 231 beds) 2601 Holme Avenue, Philadelphia, PA Zip 19152–2096; tel. 215/335–6000; Nancy Cherone, Executive Director and Administrator
Web address: www.nazarethhospital.org

ST. MARY MEDICAL CENTER (O, 323 beds) 1201 Langhorne–Newtown Road, Langhorne, PA Zip 19047–1201; tel. 215/710–2000; Gregory T. Wozniak, President and Chief Executive Officer
Web address: www.stmaryhealthcare.org

Owned, leased, sponsored:	58 hospitals	12998 beds
Contract–managed:	11 hospitals	365 beds
Totals:	69 hospitals	13363 beds

★0092: CATHOLIC HEALTH INITIATIVES (CC)
198 Inverness Drive West, Suite 800, Englewood, CO Zip 80112–5202; tel. 303/298–9100; Kevin E. Lofton, FACHE, President and Chief Executive Officer
(Decentralized Health System)

ARKANSAS: ST. VINCENT INFIRMARY MEDICAL CENTER (S, 447 beds) Two St. Vincent Circle, Little Rock, AR Zip 72205–5499; tel. 501/552–3000; Chad S. Aduddell, President
Web address: www.chistvincent.com/

ST. VINCENT MEDICAL CENTER–NORTH (S, 58 beds) 2215 Wildwood Avenue, Sherwood, AR Zip 72120–5089; tel. 501/552–7100; David R. Fox, Administrator and Chief Executive Officer
Web address: www.stvincenthealth.com

ST. VINCENT MORRILTON (S, 25 beds) 4 Hospital Drive, Morrilton, AR Zip 72110–4510; tel. 501/977–2300; Leslie Arnold, Chief Executive Officer and Administrator
Web address: www.stanthonysmorrilton.com/

COLORADO: MERCY REGIONAL MEDICAL CENTER (S, 82 beds) 1010 Three Springs Boulevard, Durango, CO Zip 81301–8296; tel. 970/247–4311; Thomas Gessel, FACHE, President and Chief Executive Officer
Web address: www.mercydurango.org

PENROSE–ST. FRANCIS HEALTH SERVICES (S, 371 beds) 2222 North Nevada Avenue, Colorado Springs, CO Zip 80907–6799, Mailing Address: P.O. Box 7021, Zip 80933–7021; tel. 719/776–5000; Margaret D. Sabin, President and Chief Executive Officer
Web address: www.penrosestfrancis.org

ST. ANTHONY HOSPITAL (S, 224 beds) 11600 West Second Place, Lakewood, CO Zip 80228–1527; tel. 720/321–0000; Jeffrey Brickman, FACHE, President and Chief Executive Officer
Web address: www.stanthonyhosp.org

For explanation of codes following names, see page B2.
★ Indicates Type III membership in the American Hospital Association.

ST. ANTHONY NORTH HOSPITAL (S, 122 beds) 2551 West 84th Avenue, Westminster, CO Zip 80031–3807; tel. 303/426–2151; Carole Peet, R.N., MSN, President and Chief Executive Officer
Web address: www.stanthonynorth.org

ST. ANTHONY SUMMIT MEDICAL CENTER (S, 34 beds) 340 Peak One Drive, Frisco, CO Zip 80443, Mailing Address: P.O. Box 738, Zip 80443–0738; tel. 970/668–3300; Paul J. Chodkowski, Chief Executive Officer
Web address: www.summitmedicalcenter.org

ST. MARY–CORWIN MEDICAL CENTER (S, 153 beds) 1008 Minnequa Avenue, Pueblo, CO Zip 81004–3798; tel. 719/557–4000; Brian Moore, President and Chief Executive Officer
Web address: www.centura.org

ST. THOMAS MORE HOSPITAL (S, 55 beds) 1338 Phay Avenue, Canon City, CO Zip 81212–2302; tel. 719/285–2000; Sheri Trahern, CPA, FACHE, Chief Executive Officer
Web address: www.stmhospital.org

INDIANA: SOUTHERN INDIANA REHABILITATION HOSPITAL (O, 84 beds) 3104 Blackiston Boulevard, New Albany, IN Zip 47150–9579; tel. 812/941–8300; Randy L. Napier, President
Web address: www.sirh.org

IOWA: CHI HEALTH MERCY CORNING (S, 22 beds) 603 Rosary Drive, Corning, IA Zip 50841–1683; tel. 641/322–3121; Debra Goldsmith, Regional Administrator
Web address: www.alegent.com

CHI HEALTH MERCY COUNCIL BLUFFS (S, 163 beds) 800 Mercy Drive, Council Bluffs, IA Zip 51503–3128, Mailing Address: P.O. Box 1C, Zip 51502–3001; tel. 712/328–5000; Marie E. Knedler, R.N., FACHE, President
Web address: www.alegent.com/mercy

CHI HEALTH MISSOURI VALLEY (S, 16 beds) 631 North Eighth Street, Missouri Valley, IA Zip 51555–1102; tel. 712/642–2784; Robert A. Valentine, President
Web address: www.alegentcreighton.com/community–memorial

MERCY MEDICAL CENTER – WEST LAKES (O, 74 beds) 1755 59th Place, West Des Moines, IA Zip 50266–7737; tel. 515/358–8000; Robert P. Ritz, FACHE, President
Web address: www.mercywestlakes.org/

MERCY MEDICAL CENTER–CENTERVILLE (S, 45 beds) 1 St. Joseph's Drive, Centerville, IA Zip 52544–8055; tel. 641/437–4111; Clinton J. Christianson, FACHE, President
Web address: www.mercycenterville.org

MERCY MEDICAL CENTER–DES MOINES (S, 583 beds) 1111 6th Avenue, Des Moines, IA Zip 50314–2611; tel. 515/247–3121; Robert P. Ritz, FACHE, President
Web address: www.mercydesmoines.org

KANSAS: ST. CATHERINE HOSPITAL (S, 110 beds) 401 East Spruce Street, Garden City, KS Zip 67846–5679; tel. 620/272–2561; Scott J. Taylor, President and Chief Executive Officer
Web address: www.StCatherineHosp.org

ST. ROSE FAMILY MEDICINE AND URGENT CARE (S, 0 beds) 3515 Broadway Street, Great Bend, KS Zip 67530–3633; tel. 620/792–2511; Leanne M. Irsik, R.N., Senior Vice President and Administrator

KENTUCKY: CONTINUING CARE HOSPITAL (S, 45 beds) 150 North Eagle Creek Drive, 5th Floor, Lexington, KY Zip 40509–1805; tel. 859/967–5744; Tonja Williams, MSN, R.N., President

FLAGET MEMORIAL HOSPITAL (S, 40 beds) 4305 New Shepherdsville Road, Bardstown, KY Zip 40004–9019; tel. 502/350–5000; Beverly Sue Downs, R.N., MSN, FACHE, President
Web address: www.flaget.com

FRAZIER REHAB INSTITUTE (O, 79 beds) 220 Abraham Flexner Way, Louisville, KY Zip 40202–1887; tel. 502/582–7400; Randy L. Napier, President
Web address: www.frazierrehab.org

JEWISH HOSPITAL (O, 342 beds) 200 Abraham Flexner Way, Louisville, KY Zip 40202–1886; tel. 502/587–4011; Joseph Gilene, President
Web address: www.jewishhospital.org

JEWISH HOSPITAL–SHELBYVILLE (O, 32 beds) 727 Hospital Drive, Shelbyville, KY Zip 40065–1699; tel. 502/647–4000; Rob Murphy, President
Web address: www.jhsmh.org

OUR LADY OF PEACE (O, 261 beds) 2020 Newburg Road, Louisville, KY Zip 40205–1879; tel. 502/479–4500; Jennifer Nolan, President
Web address: www.hopehasaplace.org

SAINT JOSEPH – LONDON (S, 114 beds) 1001 Saint Joseph Lane, London, KY Zip 40741–8345; tel. 606/330–6000; Greg D. Gerard, President
Web address: www.saintjosephhealthsystem.org

SAINT JOSEPH – MARTIN (S, 25 beds) 11203 Main Street, Martin, KY Zip 41649; tel. 606/285–6400; Kathy Stumbo, President
Web address: www.saintjosephmartin.org

SAINT JOSEPH BEREA (S, 25 beds) 305 Estill Street, Berea, KY Zip 40403–1909; tel. 859/986–3151; Eric Gilliam, Chief Executive Officer
Web address: www.kentuckyonehealth.org/berea

SAINT JOSEPH EAST (S, 144 beds) 150 North Eagle Creek Drive, Lexington, KY Zip 40509–1805; tel. 859/967–5000; Eric Gilliam, President
Web address: www.sjhlex.org

SAINT JOSEPH HOSPITAL (S, 291 beds) One St. Joseph Drive, Lexington, KY Zip 40504–3754; tel. 859/278–3436; John E. Smithhisler, President
Web address: www.sjhlex.org

SAINT JOSEPH MOUNT STERLING (S, 40 beds) 225 Falcon Drive, Mount Sterling, KY Zip 40353–1158, Mailing Address: P.O. Box 7, Zip 40353–0007; tel. 859/497–5000; Benny Nolen, President
Web address: www.sjhlex.org

STS. MARY & ELIZABETH HOSPITAL (O, 163 beds) 1850 Bluegrass Avenue, Louisville, KY Zip 40215–1199; tel. 502/361–6000; Jennifer Nolan, President
Web address: www.jhsmh.org

TAYLOR REGIONAL HOSPITAL (C, 90 beds) 1700 Old Lebanon Road, Campbellsville, KY Zip 42718–9600; tel. 270/465–3561; Jane Wheatley, Chief Executive Officer
Web address: www.trhosp.org

UNIVERSITY OF LOUISVILLE HOSPITAL (C, 301 beds) 530 South Jackson Street, Louisville, KY Zip 40202–3611; tel. 502/562–3000; Kenneth P. Marshall, President
Web address: www.ulh.org

MINNESOTA: ALBANY AREA HOSPITAL AND MEDICAL CENTER (S, 17 beds) 300 Third Avenue, Albany, MN Zip 56307–9363; tel. 320/845–2121; Tressa Schmidt, Administrator
Web address: www.albanyareahospital.com

CHI ST. FRANCIS HEALTH (S, 145 beds) 2400 St. Francis Drive, Breckenridge, MN Zip 56520–1025; tel. 218/643–3000; David A. Nelson, President
Web address: www.sfcare.org

CHI ST. JOSEPH'S HEALTH (S, 25 beds) 600 Pleasant Avenue, Park Rapids, MN Zip 56470–1431; tel. 218/732–3311; Benjamin Koppelman, President
Web address: www.sjahs.org

LAKEWOOD HEALTH CENTER (S, 59 beds) 600 Main Avenue South, Baudette, MN Zip 56623–2855; tel. 218/634–2120; Jason Breuer, President
Web address: www.lakewoodhealthcenter.org

ST. GABRIEL'S HOSPITAL (S, 25 beds) 815 Second Street S.E., Little Falls, MN Zip 56345–3596; tel. 320/632–5441; Lee Boyles, President
Web address: www.stgabriels.com

NEBRASKA: CHI HEALTH BERGAN MERCY (S, 336 beds) 7500 Mercy Road, Omaha, NE Zip 68124–2319; tel. 402/398–6060; Marie E. Knedler, R.N., FACHE, President
Web address: www.alegent.com/bergan

CHI HEALTH CREIGHTON UNIVERSITY MEDICAL CENTER (S, 214 beds) 601 North 30th Street, Omaha, NE Zip 68131–2197; tel. 402/449–4000; Kevin J. Nokels, FACHE, President
Web address: www.alegentcreighton.com

CHI HEALTH GOOD SAMARITAN (S, 233 beds) 10 East 31st Street, Kearney, NE Zip 68847–2926, Mailing Address: P.O. Box 1990, Zip 68848–1990; tel. 308/865–7100; Michael H. Schnieders, FACHE, President
Web address: www.gshs.org

CHI HEALTH IMMANUEL (S, 285 beds) 6901 North 72nd Street, Omaha, NE Zip 68122–1799; tel. 402/572–2121; Ann Schumacher, R.N., MSN, President
Web address: www.alegent.com/immanuel

CHI HEALTH LAKESIDE (S, 137 beds) 16901 Lakeside Hills Court, Omaha, NE Zip 68130–2318; tel. 402/717–8000; Cindy Alloway, President
Web address: www.alegent.org

Section B

For explanation of codes following names, see page B2.
★ Indicates Type III membership in the American Hospital Association.

CHI HEALTH MIDLANDS (S, 61 beds) 11111 South 84th Street, Papillion, NE Zip 68046–4122; tel. 402/593–3000; Cindy Alloway, President
Web address: www.alegent.org/midlands

CHI HEALTH NEBRASKA HEART (S, 52 beds) 7500 South 91st Street, Lincoln, NE Zip 68526–9437; tel. 402/327–2700; Deepak Gangahar, President
Web address: www.neheart.com

CHI HEALTH PLAINVIEW (S, 8 beds) 704 North Third Street, Plainview, NE Zip 68769–2047, Mailing Address: P.O. Box 489, Zip 68769–0489; tel. 402/582–4245; Richard B. Gamel, Operations Leader
Web address: www.alegentcreighton.com/plainview–hospital

CHI HEALTH SAINT FRANCIS (S, 215 beds) 2620 West Faidley Avenue, Grand Island, NE Zip 68803–4297, Mailing Address: P.O. Box 9804, Zip 68802–9804; tel. 308/384–4600; Daniel P. McElligott, FACHE, President
Web address: www.saintfrancisgi.org

CHI HEALTH SCHUYLER (S, 25 beds) 104 West 17th Street, Schuyler, NE Zip 68661–1304; tel. 402/352–2441; Connie Peters, R.N., President
Web address: www.alegent.org

CHI HEALTH ST ELIZABETH (S, 260 beds) 555 South 70th Street, Lincoln, NE Zip 68510–2494; tel. 402/219–8000; Kim S. Moore, President
Web address: www.saintelizabethonline.com

CHI HEALTH ST. MARY'S (S, 18 beds) 1314 Third Avenue, Nebraska City, NE Zip 68410–1930; tel. 402/873–3321; Daniel J. Kelly, President
Web address: www.stmaryshospitalnecity.org

NEBRASKA SPINE HOSPiTAL (O, 34 beds) 6901 North 72nd Street, Suite 20300, Omaha, NE Zip 68122–1755, Mailing Address: 6901 North 72nd Street, Zip 68122–1709; tel. 402/572–3000; Troy P. Stockman, Chief Executive Officer
Web address: www.nebraskaspinehospital.com

NEW JERSEY: SAINT CLARE'S HEALTH SYSTEM (S, 412 beds) 25 Pocono Road, Denville, NJ Zip 07834–2954; tel. 973/625–6000; Leslie D. Hirsch, FACHE, President and Chief Executive Officer
Web address: www.saintclares.org

NORTH DAKOTA: CARRINGTON HEALTH CENTER (S, 49 beds) 800 North Fourth Street, Carrington, ND Zip 58421–1217, Mailing Address: P.O. Box 461, Zip 58421–0461; tel. 701/652–3141; Mariann Doeling, R.N., President
Web address: www.carringtonhealthcenter.org

LISBON AREA HEALTH SERVICES (S, 25 beds) 905 Main Street, Lisbon, ND Zip 58054–4334, Mailing Address: P.O. Box 353, Zip 58054–0353; tel. 701/683–5241; Peggy Larson, R.N., Administrator
Web address: www.lisbonhospital.com

MERCY HOSPITAL (S, 25 beds) 1031 Seventh Street N.E., Devils Lake, ND Zip 58301–2798; tel. 701/662–2131; ,
Web address: www.mercyhospitaldl.com

MERCY HOSPITAL (S, 19 beds) 570 Chautauqua Boulevard, Valley City, ND Zip 58072–3199; tel. 701/845–6400; Keith E. Heuser, President
Web address: www.mercyhospitalvalleycity.org

MERCY MEDICAL CENTER (S, 25 beds) 1301 15th Avenue West, Williston, ND Zip 58801–3896; tel. 701/774–7400; Matthew Grimshaw, President
Web address: www.mercy–williston.org

OAKES COMMUNITY HOSPITAL (S, 20 beds) 1200 North Seventh Street, Oakes, ND Zip 58474–2502; tel. 701/742–3291; Becki Thompson, President
Web address: www.oakeshospital.com

ST. JOSEPH'S HOSPITAL AND HEALTH CENTER (S, 25 beds) 30 Seventh Street West, Dickinson, ND Zip 58601–4399; tel. 701/456–4000; Reed Reyman, President
Web address: www.stjoeshospital.org

OHIO: GOOD SAMARITAN HOSPITAL (S, 484 beds) 375 Dixmyth Avenue, Cincinnati, OH Zip 45220–2489; tel. 513/862–1400; Jamie Easterling, Executive Director, Operations
Web address: www.trihealth.com

GOOD SAMARITAN HOSPITAL (S, 467 beds) 2222 Philadelphia Drive, Dayton, OH Zip 45406–1813; tel. 937/734–2612; Eloise Broner, President and Chief Executive Officer
Web address: www.goodsamdayton.com

OREGON: MERCY MEDICAL CENTER (S, 141 beds) 2700 Stewart Parkway, Roseburg, OR Zip 97471–1281; tel. 541/673–0611; Kelly C. Morgan, President and Chief Executive Officer
Web address: www.mercyrose.org

ST. ANTHONY HOSPITAL (S, 25 beds) 1601 S.E. Court Avenue, Pendleton, OR Zip 97801–3217; tel. 541/276–5121; Harold S. Geller, Chief Executive Officer
Web address: www.sahpendleton.org

PENNSYLVANIA: ST. JOSEPH MEDICAL CENTER (S, 180 beds) 2500 Bernville Road, Reading, PA Zip 19605–9453, Mailing Address: P.O. Box 316, Zip 19603–0316; tel. 610/378–2000; John R. Morahan, FACHE, President and Chief Executive Officer
Web address: www.thefutureofhealthcare.org

TENNESSEE: MEMORIAL HEALTH CARE SYSTEM (S, 336 beds) 2525 De Sales Avenue, Chattanooga, TN Zip 37404–1161; tel. 423/495–2525; James M. Hobson, Chief Executive Officer
Web address: www.memorial.org

TEXAS: ST. LUKE'S HOSPITAL – THE VINTAGE HOSPITAL (O, 78 beds) 20171 Chasewood Park Drive, Houston, TX Zip 77070–1437; tel. 832/534–5000; Norman F. Stephens, Chief Executive Officer
Web address: www.stlukesvintage.com/

ST. LUKE'S LAKESIDE HOSPITAL (O, 30 beds) 17400 St. Luke's Way, The Woodlands, TX Zip 77384–8036; tel. 936/266–9000; Debra F. Sukin, Chief Executive Officer
Web address: www.stlukeslakeside.com/

ST. LUKE'S MEDICAL CENTER (O, 690 beds) 6720 Bertner Avenue, Houston, TX Zip 77030–2697, Mailing Address: P.O. Box 20269, Zip 77225–0269; tel. 832/355–1000; Wayne Keathley, M.P.H., President
Web address: www.stlukestexas.com

ST. LUKE'S PATIENTS MEDICAL CENTER (O, 61 beds) 4600 East Sam Houston Parkway South, Pasadena, TX Zip 77505–3948; tel. 713/948–7000; William Simmons, Chief Executive Officer
Web address: www.stlukestexas.com

ST. LUKE'S SUGAR LAND HOSPITAL (O, 58 beds) 1317 Lake Pointe Parkway, Sugar Land, TX Zip 77478–3997; tel. 281/637–7000; Robert A. Heifner, Chief Executive Officer
Web address: www.stlukessugarland.com

ST. LUKE'S THE WOODLANDS HOSPITAL (O, 184 beds) 17200 St. Luke's Way, The Woodlands, TX Zip 77384–8007; tel. 936/266–2000; Debra F. Sukin, Chief Executive Officer
Web address: www.stlukeswoodlands.com

WASHINGTON: ST. ANTHONY HOSPITAL (O, 80 beds) 11567 Canterwood Boulevard N.W., Gig Harbor, WA Zip 98332–5812; tel. 253/530–2000; Kurt Schley, President
Web address: www.fhshealth.org/

ST. CLARE HOSPITAL (S, 106 beds) 11315 Bridgeport Way S.W., Lakewood, WA Zip 98499–3004; tel. 253/985–1711; Kathy Bressler, R.N., President
Web address: www.fhshealth.org

ST. ELIZABETH HOSPITAL (S, 38 beds) 1455 Battersby Avenue, Enumclaw, WA Zip 98022–3634, Mailing Address: P.O. Box 218, Zip 98022–0218; tel. 360/284–4171; Donna Russell–Cook, FACHE, President
Web address: www.fhshealth.org

ST. FRANCIS HOSPITAL (S, 124 beds) 34515 Ninth Avenue South, Federal Way, WA Zip 98003–6799; tel. 253/944–8100; Anthony McLean, President
Web address: www.fhshealth.org

ST. JOSEPH MEDICAL CENTER (S, 366 beds) 1717 South J Street, Tacoma, WA Zip 98405–3004, Mailing Address: P.O. Box 2197, Zip 98401–2197; tel. 253/426–4101; Syd Bersante, R.N., President
Web address: www.fhshealth.org

Owned, leased, sponsored:	75 hospitals	10466 beds
Contract–managed:	2 hospitals	391 beds
Totals:	77 hospitals	10857 beds

0903: CATHOLIC HEALTH SERVICES (CC)
4790 North State Road 7, Lauderdale Lakes, FL Zip 33319–5860; tel. 954/484–1515; Joseph M. Catania, President and Chief Executive Officer

FLORIDA: ST. ANTHONY'S REHABILITATION HOSPITAL (S, 26 beds) 3485 N.W. 30th Street, Lauderdale Lakes, FL Zip 33311–1890; tel. 954/739–6233; Joseph M. Catania, Chief Executive Officer
Web address: www.catholichealthservices.org

For explanation of codes following names, see page B2.
★ Indicates Type III membership in the American Hospital Association.

Section B

ST. CATHERINE'S REHABILITATION HOSPITAL (S, 60 beds) 1050 N.E. 125th Street, North Miami, FL Zip 33161–5881; tel. 305/357–1735; Jaime Gonzalez, Administrator
Web address: www.catholichealthservices.org

Owned, leased, sponsored:	2 hospitals	86 beds
Contract–managed:	0 hospitals	0 beds
Totals:	2 hospitals	86 beds

0233: CATHOLIC HEALTH SERVICES OF LONG ISLAND (CC) 992 North Village Avenue, 1st Floor, Rockville Centre, NY Zip 11570–1002; tel. 516/705–3700; Alan D. Guerci, M.D., President and Chief Executive Officer
(Moderately Centralized Health System)

NEW YORK: GOOD SAMARITAN HOSPITAL MEDICAL CENTER (O, 531 beds) 1000 Montauk Highway, West Islip, NY Zip 11795–4927; tel. 631/376–3000; Nancy B. Simmons, Executive Vice President and Chief Administrative Officer
Web address: www.good–samaritan–hospital.org

MERCY MEDICAL CENTER (O, 219 beds) 1000 North Village Avenue, Rockville Centre, NY Zip 11570–1000; tel. 516/705–2525; Aaron Glatt, M.D., Executive Vice President and Chief Administrative Officer
Web address: www.mercymedicalcenter.chsli.org

ST. CATHERINE OF SIENA MEDICAL CENTER (O, 503 beds) 50 Route 25–A, Smithtown, NY Zip 11787–1348; tel. 631/862–3000; Dennis Verzi, Executive Vice President and Chief Administrative Officer
Web address: www.stcatherinemedicalcenter.org

ST. CHARLES HOSPITAL (O, 289 beds) 200 Belle Terre Road, Port Jefferson, NY Zip 11777–1928; tel. 631/474–6000; James O'Connor, Executive Vice President and Chief Administrative Officer
Web address: www.stcharleshospital.chsli.org

ST. FRANCIS HOSPITAL (O, 306 beds) 100 Port Washington Boulevard, Roslyn, NY Zip 11576–1353; tel. 516/562–6000; Ruth Hennessey, Executive Vice President and Chief Administrative Officer
Web address: www.stfrancisheartcenter.com/index.html

ST. JOSEPH HOSPITAL (S, 140 beds) 4295 Hempstead Turnpike, Bethpage, NY Zip 11714–5769; tel. 516/579–6000; Drew Pallas, Executive Vice President and Chief Administrative Officer
Web address: www.stjosephhospitalny.org

Owned, leased, sponsored:	6 hospitals	1988 beds
Contract–managed:	0 hospitals	0 beds
Totals:	6 hospitals	1988 beds

★0234: CATHOLIC HEALTH SYSTEM (CC) 2121 Main Street, Suite 300, Buffalo, NY Zip 14214–2673; tel. 716/862–2410; Joseph D. McDonald, President and Chief Executive Officer
(Moderately Centralized Health System)

FATHER BAKER MANOR (O, 160 beds) 6400 Powers Road, Orchard Park, NY Zip 14127; tel. 716/667–0001; Christine Kluckhohn, President, Continuing Care

KENMORE MERCY HOSPITAL (O, 315 beds) 2950 Elmwood Avenue, Kenmore, NY Zip 14217–1390; tel. 716/447–6100; James M. Millard, President and Chief Executive Officer
Web address: www.chsbuffalo.org

MCAULEY RESIDENCE (O, 160 beds) 1503 Military Road, Kenmore, NY Zip 14217; tel. 716/447–6600; Christine Kluckhohn, President, Continuing Care

MERCY HOSPITAL (O, 438 beds) 565 Abbott Road, Buffalo, NY Zip 14220–2095; tel. 716/826–7000; Charles J. Urlaub, President and Chief Executive Officer
Web address: www.chsbuffalo.org

MERCY NURSING FACILITY (O, 74 beds) 565 Abbott Road, Buffalo, NY Zip 14220; tel. 716/828–2301; Christine Kluckhohn, President, Continuing Care

NAZARETH HOME (O, 125 beds) 291 West North Street, Buffalo, NY Zip 14201; tel. 716/881–2323; Christine Kluckhohn, President, Continuing Care

SISTERS OF CHARITY HOSPITAL OF BUFFALO (O, 467 beds) 2157 Main Street, Buffalo, NY Zip 14214–2692; tel. 716/862–1000; Peter U. Bergmann, President and Chief Executive Officer
Web address: www.chsbuffalo.org

ST. CATHERINE LABOURE (O, 80 beds) 2157 Main Street, Buffalo, NY Zip 14214; tel. 716/862–1451; Christine Kluckhohn, President, Continuing Care

ST. ELIZABETH'S HOME (O, 117 beds) 5539 Broadway, Lancaster, NY Zip 14086; tel. 716/683–5150; Christine Kluckhohn, President, Continuing Care

ST. FRANCIS OF BUFFALO (O, 120 beds) 34 Benwood Avenue, Buffalo, NY Zip 14214; tel. 716/862–2500; Christine Kluckhohn, President, Continuing Care

ST. FRANCIS OF WILLIAMSVILLE (O, 142 beds) 147 Reist Street, Williamsville, NY Zip 14221; tel. 716/633–5400; Christine Kluckhohn, President, Continuing Care

ST. JOSEPH MANOR (O, 22 beds) 2211 West State Street, Olean, NY Zip 14760; tel. 716/372–7810; Christine Kluckhohn, President, Continuing Care

Owned, leased, sponsored:	12 hospitals	2220 beds
Contract–managed:	0 hospitals	0 beds
Totals:	12 hospitals	2220 beds

★0298: CENTEGRA HEALTH SYSTEM (NP) 385 Millennium Drive, Crystal Lake, IL Zip 60012–3761; tel. 815/788–5800; Michael S. Eesley, Chief Executive Officer
(Independent Hospital System)

ILLINOIS: CENTEGRA HOSPITAL – MCHENRY (O, 173 beds) 4201 Medical Center Drive, McHenry, IL Zip 60050–8409; tel. 815/344–5000; Michael S. Eesley, Chief Executive Officer
Web address: www.centegra.org

CENTEGRA HOSPITAL – WOODSTOCK (O, 135 beds) 3701 Doty Road, Woodstock, IL Zip 60098–7509, Mailing Address: P.O. Box 1990, Zip 60098–1990; tel. 815/338–2500; Michael S. Eesley, Chief Executive Officer
Web address: www.centegra.org

Owned, leased, sponsored:	2 hospitals	308 beds
Contract–managed:	0 hospitals	0 beds
Totals:	2 hospitals	308 beds

0634: CENTERRE HEALTHCARE (IO) 5250 Virginia Way, Suite 240, Brentwood, TN Zip 37027–7576; tel. 615/846–9508; Patrick A. Foster, President and Chief Executive Officer

MISSOURI: MERCY REHABILITATION HOSPITAL (O, 90 beds) 14561 North Outer Forty Road, Chesterfield, MO Zip 63017; tel. 314/881–4000; Donna M. Flannery, Chief Executive Officer
Web address: www.stjohnsmercyrehab.com

MERCY REHABILITION HOSPITAL SPRINGFIELD (O, 60 beds) 5904 South Southwood Road, Springfield, MO Zip 65804–5234; tel. 417/227–9000; Duke Saldivar, FACHE, Chief Executive Officer
Web address: www.mercy.net

OKLAHOMA: MERCY REHABILITATION HOSPITAL OKLAHOMA CITY (O, 50 beds) 5401 West Memorial Road, Oklahoma City, OK Zip 73142–2026; tel. 405/752–3935; Sharon Smeltzer, Chief Executive Officer

PENNSYLVANIA: LANCASTER REHABILITATION HOSPITAL (O, 10 beds) 675 Good Drive, Lancaster, PA Zip 17601–2426; tel. 717/406–3000; Tammy L. Ober, Chief Executive Officer
Web address: www.lancastergeneral.org

TEXAS: TEXAS REHABILITATION HOSPITAL OF FORT WORTH (O, 66 beds) 425 Alabama Avenue, Fort Worth, TX Zip 76104–1022; tel. 817/820–3400; Russell Bailey, Chief Executive Officer
Web address: www.texasrehabhospital.com/

Section B

For explanation of codes following names, see page B2.
★ Indicates Type III membership in the American Hospital Association.

© 2014 AHA Guide · Health Care Systems, Networks and Alliances · B33

WISCONSIN: REHABILITATION HOSPITAL OF WISCONSIN (O, 40 beds) 1625 Coldwater Creek Drive, Waukesha, WI Zip 53188–8028; tel. 262/521–8800; Linda Newberry–Ferguson, Chief Executive Officer
Web address: www.rehabhospitalwi.com

Owned, leased, sponsored:	6 hospitals	316 beds
Contract–managed:	0 hospitals	0 beds
Totals:	6 hospitals	316 beds

2265: CENTRA HEALTH, INC. (NP)
1920 Atherholt Road, Lynchburg, VA Zip 24501–1104; tel. 434/200–3000; E. W. Tibbs, President and Chief Executive Officer
(Moderately Centralized Health System)

VIRGINIA: CENTRA LYNCHBURG GENERAL HOSPITAL (O, 1061 beds) 1920 Atherholt Road, Lynchburg, VA Zip 24501–1104; tel. 434/200–4700; E. W. Tibbs, President and Chief Executive Officer
Web address: www.centrahealth.com

CENTRA SOUTHSIDE COMMUNITY HOSPITAL (O, 86 beds) 800 Oak Street, Farmville, VA Zip 23901–1199; tel. 434/392–8811; William L. Bass, Jr., Vice President and Chief Executive Officer
Web address: www.sch.centrahealth.com/

Owned, leased, sponsored:	2 hospitals	1147 beds
Contract–managed:	0 hospitals	0 beds
Totals:	2 hospitals	1147 beds

★0184: CENTRACARE HEALTH (NP)
1406 Sixth Avenue North, Saint Cloud, MN Zip 56303–1900; tel. 320/251–2700; Terence Pladson, M.D., President and Chief Executive Officer
(Moderately Centralized Health System)

MINNESOTA: CENTRACARE HEALTH–LONG PRAIRIE (O, 20 beds) 20 Ninth Street S.E., Long Prairie, MN Zip 56347–1404; tel. 320/732–2141; Daniel J. Swenson, FACHE, Administrator and Chief Executive Officer
Web address: www.centracare.com

CENTRACARE HEALTH–MELROSE (O, 93 beds) 525 Main Street West, Melrose, MN Zip 56352–1043; tel. 320/256–4231; Gerry Gilbertson, FACHE, Administrator
Web address: www.centracare.com

CENTRACARE HEALTH–MONTICELLO (O, 110 beds) 1013 Hart Boulevard, Monticello, MN Zip 55362–8230; tel. 763/295–2945; Mary Ellen Wells, FACHE, Administrator
Web address: www.newrivermedical.com

CENTRACARE HEALTH–PAYNESVILLE (O, 77 beds) 200 West 1st Street, Paynesville, MN Zip 56362–1496; tel. 320/243–3767; Dennis C. Miley, Administrator
Web address: www.centracare.com

CENTRACARE HEALTH–SAUK CENTRE (O, 85 beds) 425 North Elm Street, Sauk Centre, MN Zip 56378–1010; tel. 320/352–2221; Delano Christianson, Administrator
Web address: www.centracare.com/hospitals/sauk_centre/index.html

ST. CLOUD HOSPITAL (O, 474 beds) 1406 Sixth Avenue North, Saint Cloud, MN Zip 56303–1901; tel. 320/251–2700; Craig J. Broman, FACHE, President
Web address: www.centracare.com

Owned, leased, sponsored:	6 hospitals	859 beds
Contract–managed:	0 hospitals	0 beds
Totals:	6 hospitals	859 beds

0856: CENTRAL FLORIDA HEALTH ALLIANCE (NP)
600 East Dixie Avenue, Leesburg, FL Zip 34748–5925; tel. 352/323–5762; Donald G. Henderson, FACHE, Chief Executive Officer

FLORIDA: LEESBURG REGIONAL MEDICAL CENTER (O, 316 beds) 600 East Dixie Avenue, Leesburg, FL Zip 34748–5999; tel. 352/323–5762; Donald G. Henderson, FACHE, President and Chief Executive Officer
Web address: www.cfhalliance.org

THE VILLAGES REGIONAL HOSPITAL (O, 223 beds) 1451 El Camino Real, The Villages, FL Zip 32159–0041; tel. 352/751–8000; Donald G. Henderson, FACHE, President and Chief Executive Officer
Web address: www.cfhalliance.org

Owned, leased, sponsored:	2 hospitals	539 beds
Contract–managed:	0 hospitals	0 beds
Totals:	2 hospitals	539 beds

★0955: CHARLESTON AREA MEDICAL CENTER HEALTH SYSTEM, INC. (NP)
501 Morris Street, Charleston, WV Zip 25301–1300, Mailing Address: P.O. Box 1547, Zip 25326–1547; tel. 304/388–5432; David L. Ramsey, President and Chief Executive Officer
(Independent Hospital System)

WEST VIRGINIA: CAMC TEAYS VALLEY HOSPITAL (O, 70 beds) 1400 Hospital Drive, Hurricane, WV Zip 25526–9202; tel. 304/757–1700; Randall H. Hodges, FACHE, President and Chief Executive Officer
Web address: www.camc.org

CHARLESTON AREA MEDICAL CENTER (O, 795 beds) 501 Morris Street, Charleston, WV Zip 25301–1300, Mailing Address: P.O. Box 1547, Zip 25326–1547; tel. 304/388–5432; David L. Ramsey, President and Chief Executive Officer
Web address: www.camc.org

Owned, leased, sponsored:	2 hospitals	865 beds
Contract–managed:	0 hospitals	0 beds
Totals:	2 hospitals	865 beds

0934: CHARTERCARE HEALTH PARTNERS (NP)
825 Chalkstone Avenue, Providence, RI Zip 02908–4728; tel. 410/456–2001; Kenneth H. Belcher, Chief Executive Officer

RHODE ISLAND: ROGER WILLIAMS MEDICAL CENTER (O, 86 beds) 825 Chalkstone Avenue, Providence, RI Zip 02908–4735; tel. 401/456–2000; Kimberly O'Connell, President
Web address: www.rwmc.com

ST. JOSEPH HEALTH SERVICES OF RHODE ISLAND (O, 125 beds) 200 High Service Avenue, North Providence, RI Zip 02904–5199; tel. 401/456–3000; Thomas Hughes, President
Web address: www.saintjosephri.com

Owned, leased, sponsored:	2 hospitals	211 beds
Contract–managed:	0 hospitals	0 beds
Totals:	2 hospitals	211 beds

0407: CHILDREN'S HOSPITAL AND HEALTH SYSTEM (NP)
9000 West Wisconsin Avenue, Milwaukee, WI Zip 53226–4810, Mailing Address: P.O. Box 1997, Zip 53201–1997; tel. 414/226–2000; Peggy N. Troy, President and Chief Executive Officer
(Independent Hospital System)

WISCONSIN: CHILDREN'S HOSPITAL OF WISCONSIN (O, 296 beds) 9000 West Wisconsin Avenue, Milwaukee, WI Zip 53226–4810, Mailing Address: P.O. Box 1997, Zip 53201–1997; tel. 414/266–2000; Peggy N. Troy, President and Chief Executive Officer
Web address: www.chw.org

CHILDREN'S HOSPITAL OF WISCONSIN KENOSHA CLINIC (O, 0 beds) 8500 75th Street, Suite 101, Kenosha, WI Zip 53142; tel. 262/653–2260; Peggy N. Troy, President and Chief Executive Officer

CHILDREN'S HOSPITAL OF WISCONSIN–FOX VALLEY (O, 42 beds) 130 Second Avenue, 3rd Floor South, Neenah, WI Zip 54956–2883; tel. 920/969–7900; Peggy N. Troy, President and Chief Executive Officer
Web address: www.chw.org

Owned, leased, sponsored:	3 hospitals	338 beds
Contract–managed:	0 hospitals	0 beds
Totals:	3 hospitals	338 beds

For explanation of codes following names, see page B2.
★ Indicates Type III membership in the American Hospital Association.

●★**0131: CHRISTIANA CARE HEALTH SYSTEM** (NP)
501 West 14th Street, Wilmington, DE Zip 19801–1013, Mailing Address: P.O. Box 1668, Zip 19899–1668; tel. 302/733–1000; Robert J. Laskowski, M.D., President and Chief Executive Officer **(Moderately Centralized Health System)**

DELAWARE: CHRISTIANA CARE HEALTH SYSTEM (O, 1011 beds) 4755 Ogletown–Stanton Road, Newark, DE Zip 19718–0002, Mailing Address: P.O. Box 6001, Zip 19714–6001; tel. 302/733–1000; Robert J. Laskowski, M.D., President and Chief Executive Officer
Web address: www.christianacare.org

Owned, leased, sponsored:	1 hospital	1011 beds
Contract–managed:	0 hospitals	0 beds
Totals:	1 hospital	1011 beds

★**0192: CHRISTUS HEALTH** (CC)
919 Hidden Ridge Drive, Irving, TX Zip 75038; tel. 469/282–2000; Ernie W. Sadau, President and Chief Executive Officer **(Moderately Centralized Health System)**

LOUISIANA: CHRISTUS COUSHATTA HEALTH CARE CENTER (O, 25 beds) 1635 Marvel Street, Coushatta, LA Zip 71019–9022, Mailing Address: P.O. Box 589, Zip 71019–0589; tel. 318/932–2000; Michael Harrington, Chief Executive Officer
Web address: www.christuscoushatta.org

CHRISTUS HIGHLAND MEDICAL CENTER (O, 302 beds) One St. Mary Place, Shreveport, LA Zip 71101–4399; tel. 318/681–4500; Stephen F. Wright, President and Chief Executive Officer
Web address: www.christusschumpert.org

CHRISTUS ST. FRANCES CABRINI HOSPITAL (O, 281 beds) 3330 Masonic Drive, Alexandria, LA Zip 71301–3899; tel. 318/487–1122; Stephen F. Wright, President and Chief Executive Officer
Web address: www.cabrini.org/

CHRISTUS ST. PATRICK HOSPITAL OF LAKE CHARLES (O, 160 beds) 524 Dr. Michael Debakey Drive, Lake Charles, LA Zip 70601–5799, Mailing Address: P.O. Box 3401, Zip 70602–3401; tel. 337/436–2511; Donald H. Lloyd, II, Administrator
Web address: www.stpatrickhospital.org

NATCHITOCHES REGIONAL MEDICAL CENTER (C, 208 beds) 501 Keyser Avenue, Natchitoches, LA Zip 71457–6036, Mailing Address: P.O. Box 2009, Zip 71457–2009; tel. 318/214–4200; Brad McCormick, Chief Financial Officer
Web address: www.natchitocheshospital.org

NEW MEXICO: CHRISTUS ST. VINCENT REGIONAL MEDICAL CENTER (O, 268 beds) 455 St. Michael's Drive, Santa Fe, NM Zip 87505–7663, Mailing Address: P.O. Box 2107, Zip 87504–2107; tel. 505/983–3361; Bruce J. Tassin, President and Chief Executive Officer
Web address: www.stvin.org

TEXAS: CHRISTUS HOSPITAL–ST. ELIZABETH (O, 430 beds) 2830 Calder Avenue, Beaumont, TX Zip 77702–1809, Mailing Address: P.O. Box 5405, Zip 77726–5405; tel. 409/892–7171; Paul Trevino, Chief Executive Officer
Web address: www.christushospital.org

CHRISTUS JASPER MEMORIAL HOSPITAL (L, 50 beds) 1275 Marvin Hancock Drive, Jasper, TX Zip 75951–4995; tel. 409/384–5461; Deborah Mecom, R.N., Administrator
Web address: www.christusjasper.org

CHRISTUS SANTA ROSA HEALTH SYSTEM (O, 560 beds) 333 North Santa Rosa Street, San Antonio, TX Zip 78207–3108; tel. 210/704–4184; Patrick Brian Carrier, President and Chief Executive Officer
Web address: www.christussantarosa.org

CHRISTUS SPOHN HOSPITAL ALICE (O, 91 beds) 2500 East Main Street, Alice, TX Zip 78332–4169; tel. 361/661–8000; Steven G. Daniel, Senior Vice President and Chief Operating Officer
Web address: www.christusspohn.org/locations_alice.htm

CHRISTUS SPOHN HOSPITAL BEEVILLE (L, 49 beds) 1500 East Houston Street, Beeville, TX Zip 78102–5312; tel. 361/354–2000; Nathan Tudor, Vice President and Chief Executive Officer
Web address: www.christusspohn.org

CHRISTUS SPOHN HOSPITAL CORPUS CHRISTI MEMORIAL (O, 774 beds) 2606 Hospital Boulevard, Corpus Christi, TX Zip 78405–1804, Mailing Address: P.O. Box 5280, Zip 78465–5280; tel. 361/902–4000; Xavier Villarreal, Chief Executive Officer
Web address: www.christusspohn.org

CHRISTUS SPOHN HOSPITAL KLEBERG (O, 79 beds) 1311 General Cavazos Boulevard, Kingsville, TX Zip 78363–7130; tel. 361/595–1661; David LeMonte, Vice President and Chief Operating Officer
Web address: www.christusspohn.org

CHRISTUS ST. MICHAEL HEALTH SYSTEM (O, 376 beds) 2600 St. Michael Drive, Texarkana, TX Zip 75503–5220; tel. 903/614–1000; Chris Karam, President and Chief Executive Officer
Web address: www.christusstmichael.org

CHRISTUS ST. MICHAEL REHABILITATION HOSPITAL (O, 50 beds) 2400 St. Michael Drive, Texarkana, TX Zip 75503–2374; tel. 903/614–4000; Aloma Gender, R.N., MSN, Administrator and Chief Nursing Officer
Web address: www.christusstmichael.org/rehab

Owned, leased, sponsored:	14 hospitals	3495 beds
Contract–managed:	1 hospital	208 beds
Totals:	15 hospitals	3703 beds

★**0101: CITRUS VALLEY HEALTH PARTNERS** (NP)
210 West San Bernardino Road, Covina, CA Zip 91723–1515; tel. 626/331–7331; Robert H. Curry, President and Chief Executive Officer

CALIFORNIA: CITRUS VALLEY MEDICAL CENTER–INTER COMMUNITY CAMPUS (O, 326 beds) 210 West San Bernadino Road, Covina, CA Zip 91723–1515, Mailing Address: P.O. Box 6108, Zip 91722–5108; tel. 626/331–7331; Robert H. Curry, President and Chief Executive Officer
Web address: www.cvhp.org

FOOTHILL PRESBYTERIAN HOSPITAL (O, 75 beds) 250 South Grand Avenue, Glendora, CA Zip 91741–4218; tel. 626/963–8411; Robert H. Curry, President and Chief Executive Officer
Web address: www.cvhp.org/Our_Facilities/Foothill_Presbyterian.aspx

Owned, leased, sponsored:	2 hospitals	401 beds
Contract–managed:	0 hospitals	0 beds
Totals:	2 hospitals	401 beds

★**0212: CLEVELAND CLINIC HEALTH SYSTEM** (NP)
9500 Euclid, Cleveland, OH Zip 44195–5108; tel. 216/444–2200; Delos Cosgrove, M.D., President and Chief Executive Officer **(Centralized Health System)**

FLORIDA: CLEVELAND CLINIC FLORIDA (O, 155 beds) 2950 Cleveland Clinic Boulevard, Weston, FL Zip 33331–3602; tel. 954/659–5000; Wael Barsoum, Interim Chief Executive Officer
Web address: www.clevelandclinic.org/florida

OHIO: CLEVELAND CLINIC (O, 1279 beds) 9500 Euclid Avenue, Cleveland, OH Zip 44195–5108; tel. 216/444–2200; Delos Cosgrove, M.D., President and Chief Executive Officer
Web address: www.clevelandclinic.org

CLEVELAND CLINIC CHILDREN'S HOSPITAL FOR REHABILITATION (O, 25 beds) 2801 Martin Luther King Jr. Drive, Cleveland, OH Zip 44104–3865; tel. 216/448–6400; Michael J. McHugh, M.D., Medical Director
Web address: www.my.clevelandclinic.org/childrens–hospital/default.aspx

EUCLID HOSPITAL (O, 231 beds) 18901 Lake Shore Boulevard, Euclid, OH Zip 44119–1090; tel. 216/531–9000; Mark Froimson, M.D., President
Web address: www.euclidhospital.org

FAIRVIEW HOSPITAL (O, 413 beds) 18101 Lorain Avenue, Cleveland, OH Zip 44111–5656; tel. 216/476–7000; Neil Smith, D.O., President
Web address: www.fairviewhospital.org

HILLCREST HOSPITAL (O, 413 beds) 6780 Mayfield Road, Cleveland, OH Zip 44124–2203; tel. 440/312–4500; Brian J. Harte, M.D., President
Web address: www.hillcresthospital.org

LAKEWOOD HOSPITAL (O, 250 beds) 14519 Detroit Avenue, Lakewood, OH Zip 44107–4383; tel. 216/521–4200; Shannan Ritchie, Interim President
Web address: www.lakewoodhospital.org

For explanation of codes following names, see page B2.
★ Indicates Type III membership in the American Hospital Association.
● Single hospital health care system

LUTHERAN HOSPITAL (O, 198 beds) 1730 West 25th Street, Cleveland, OH Zip 44113–3170; tel. 216/696–4300; Donald Malone, M.D., President
Web address: www.lutheranhospital.org

MARYMOUNT HOSPITAL (O, 284 beds) 12300 McCracken Road, Garfield Heights, OH Zip 44125–2975; tel. 216/581–0500; Joanne Zeroske, President
Web address: www.marymount.org

MEDINA HOSPITAL (O, 136 beds) 1000 East Washington Street, Medina, OH Zip 44256–2170; tel. 330/725–1000; Thomas Tulisiak, M.D., President
Web address: www.medinahospital.org

SOUTH POINTE HOSPITAL (O, 155 beds) 20000 Harvard Road, Warrensville Heights, OH Zip 44122–6805; tel. 216/491–6000; Robert S. Juhasz, D.O., President
Web address: www.southpointehospital.org

Owned, leased, sponsored:	11 hospitals	3539 beds
Contract–managed:	0 hospitals	0 beds
Totals:	11 hospitals	3539 beds

0076: COLLEGE HEALTH ENTERPRISES (IO)
11627 Telegraph Road, Suite 200, Santa Fe Springs, CA Zip 90670–6814; tel. 562/923–9449; Barry J. Weiss, Chairman of the Board

CALIFORNIA: COLLEGE HOSPITAL CERRITOS (O, 157 beds) 10802 College Place, Cerritos, CA Zip 90703–1579; tel. 562/924–9581; Stephen Witt, President and Chief Executive Officer
Web address: www.collegehospitals.com

COLLEGE HOSPITAL COSTA MESA (O, 122 beds) 301 Victoria Street, Costa Mesa, CA Zip 92627–7131; tel. 949/642–2734; Susan L. Taylor, Chief Executive Officer
Web address: www.collegehospitals.com/cosHome

Owned, leased, sponsored:	2 hospitals	279 beds
Contract–managed:	0 hospitals	0 beds
Totals:	2 hospitals	279 beds

★**0161: COLUMBUS REGIONAL HEALTHCARE SYSTEM** (NP)
707 Center Street, Suite 400, Columbus, GA Zip 31901–1575; tel. 706/660–6100; Scott Hill, Interim Chief Executive Officer
(Independent Hospital System)

GEORGIA: AZALEA TRACE (O, 110 beds) 910 Talbotton Road, Columbus, GA Zip 31901; tel. 706/323–9513; Todd West, Administrator

DOCTORS SPECIALTY HOSPITAL (O, 171 beds) 616 19th Street, Columbus, GA Zip 31901–1528, Mailing Address: P.O. Box 2188, Zip 31902–2188; tel. 706/494–4262; Tamara L. Jackson, R.N., MSN, FACHE, Chief Executive Officer
Web address: www.columbusregional.com

HAMILTON HOUSE NURSING CENTER/ADULT LIVING CENTER (O, 128 beds) 1911 Hamilton Road, Columbus, GA Zip 31901; tel. 706/571–1850; John Sims, Administrator

MARION MEMORIAL NURSING HOME (O, 70 beds) Highway 41, Buena Vista, GA Zip 31803, Mailing Address: P.O. Box 197, Zip 31803; tel. 229/649–7100; Barbara Mitchell, Administrator

NORTHSIDE MEDICAL CENTER (O, 100 beds) 100 Frist Court, Columbus, GA Zip 31909–3578, Mailing Address: P.O. Box 7188, Zip 31908–7188; tel. 706/494–2100; Tamara L. Jackson, R.N., MSN, FACHE, Chief Executive Officer
Web address: www.columbusregional.com

THE MEDICAL CENTER (O, 497 beds) 710 Center Street, Columbus, GA Zip 31901–1527, Mailing Address: P.O. Box 951, Zip 31902–0951; tel. 706/571–1000; Ryan Chandler, President and Chief Executive Officer
Web address: www.columbusregional.com

Owned, leased, sponsored:	6 hospitals	1076 beds
Contract–managed:	0 hospitals	0 beds
Totals:	6 hospitals	1076 beds

0520: COMMONWEALTH HEALTH CORPORATION (NP)
800 Park Street, Bowling Green, KY Zip 42101–2356; tel. 270/745–1500; Connie Smith, President and Chief Executive Officer
(Centralized Physician/Insurance Health System)

KENTUCKY: COMMONWEALTH REGIONAL SPECIALTY HOSPITAL (O, 24 beds) 250 Park Drive, 6th Floor, Bowling Green, KY Zip 42101–1760, Mailing Address: P.O. Box 90010, Zip 42102–9010; tel. 270/796–6200; Emily Howard Martin, Administrator
Web address: www.commonwealthregionalspecialtyhospital.org

MEDICAL CENTER AT BOWLING GREEN (O, 337 beds) 250 Park Street, Bowling Green, KY Zip 42101–1795, Mailing Address: P.O. Box 90010, Zip 42102–9010; tel. 270/745–1000; Connie Smith, Chief Executive Officer
Web address: www.themedicalcenter.org

MEDICAL CENTER AT FRANKLIN (O, 25 beds) 1100 Brookhaven Road, Franklin, KY Zip 42134–2746; tel. 270/598–4800; Eric Hagan, R.N., Vice President/Administrator
Web address: www.themedicalcenterfranklin.org

MEDICAL CENTER AT SCOTTSVILLE (O, 135 beds) 456 Burnley Road, Scottsville, KY Zip 42164–6355; tel. 270/622–2800; Eric Hagan, R.N., Vice President/Administrator
Web address: www.themedicalcenterscottsville.org/

Owned, leased, sponsored:	4 hospitals	521 beds
Contract–managed:	0 hospitals	0 beds
Totals:	4 hospitals	521 beds

0401: COMMUNITY HEALTH NETWORK (NP)
7330 Shadeland Station, Indianapolis, IN Zip 46256–3957; tel. 317/355–1411; Bryan A. Mills, President and Chief Executive Officer
(Moderately Centralized Health System)

INDIANA: COMMUNITY HEART AND VASCULAR HOSPITAL (O, 56 beds) 8075 North Shadeland Avenue, Indianapolis, IN Zip 46250–2693; tel. 317/621–8000; Jason Fahrlander, FACHE, President
Web address: www.ecommunity.com/heart

COMMUNITY HOSPITAL EAST (O, 243 beds) 1500 North Ritter Avenue, Indianapolis, IN Zip 46219–3095; tel. 317/355–1411; Robin Ledyard, M.D., M.P.H., President
Web address: www.ecommunity.com/east/

COMMUNITY HOSPITAL NORTH (O, 363 beds) 7150 Clearvista Drive, Indianapolis, IN Zip 46256–1695; tel. 317/621–6262; Jason Fahrlander, FACHE, President
Web address: www.ecommunity.com/north

COMMUNITY HOSPITAL OF ANDERSON AND MADISON COUNTY (O, 127 beds) 1515 North Madison Avenue, Anderson, IN Zip 46011–3453; tel. 765/298–4242; Beth S. Tharp, R.N., President and Chief Executive Officer
Web address: www.communityanderson.com

COMMUNITY HOSPITAL SOUTH (O, 158 beds) 1402 East County Line Road South, Indianapolis, IN Zip 46227–0963; tel. 317/887–7000; Anthony B. Lennen, President
Web address: www.ecommunity.com

COMMUNITY HOWARD REGIONAL HEALTH (O, 168 beds) 3500 South Lafountain Street, Kokomo, IN Zip 46902–3803, Mailing Address: P.O. Box 9011, Zip 46904–9011; tel. 765/453–0702; Ron Lewis, President and Chief Executive Officer
Web address: www.howardregional.org

COMMUNITY HOWARD SPECIALTY HOSPITAL (O, 30 beds) 829 North Dixon Road, Kokomo, IN Zip 46901–7709; tel. 765/452–6700; Michelle L. Russell, Administrator
Web address: www.communityhoward.org

COMMUNITY WESTVIEW HOSPITAL (O, 57 beds) 3630 Guion Road, Indianapolis, IN Zip 46222–1699; tel. 317/924–6661; David C. Williams, D.O., President and Chief Executive Officer
Web address: www.westviewhospital.org

Owned, leased, sponsored:	8 hospitals	1202 beds
Contract–managed:	0 hospitals	0 beds
Totals:	8 hospitals	1202 beds

For explanation of codes following names, see page B2.
★ Indicates Type III membership in the American Hospital Association.

★**0080: COMMUNITY HEALTH SYSTEMS, INC.** (IO)
4000 Meridian Boulevard, Franklin, TN Zip 37067–6325, Mailing
Address: P.O. Box 689020, Zip 37068–9020; tel. 615/465–7000;
Wayne T. Smith, Chairman, President and Chief Executive Officer
(Decentralized Health System)

ALABAMA: CHEROKEE MEDICAL CENTER (O, 45 beds) 400 Northwood Drive,
Centre, AL Zip 35960–1023; tel. 256/927–5531; Terry Long, Interim
Chief Executive Officer
Web address: www.cherokeemedicalcenter.com

CRESTWOOD MEDICAL CENTER (O, 150 beds) One Hospital Drive, Huntsville,
AL Zip 35801–3403; tel. 256/429–4000; Pamela Hudson, M.D., Chief
Executive Officer
Web address: www.crestwoodmedcenter.com

DEKALB REGIONAL MEDICAL CENTER (O, 115 beds) 200 Medical Center
Drive, Fort Payne, AL Zip 35968–3458, Mailing Address: P.O. Box 680778,
Zip 35968–1608; tel. 256/845–3150; Corey Ewing, Chief Executive Officer
Web address: www.dekalbregional.com

FLOWERS HOSPITAL (O, 139 beds) 4370 West Main Street, Dothan, AL
Zip 36305–4000, Mailing Address: P.O. Box 6907, Zip 36302–6907;
tel. 334/793–5000; Suzanne Woods, President and Chief Executive Officer
Web address: www.flowershospital.com

GADSDEN REGIONAL MEDICAL CENTER (O, 286 beds) 1007 Goodyear
Avenue, Gadsden, AL Zip 35903–1195; tel. 256/494–4000; Stephen G.
Pennington, Chief Executive Officer
Web address: www.gadsdenregional.com

L. V. STABLER MEMORIAL HOSPITAL (O, 61 beds) 29 L. V. Stabler Drive,
Greenville, AL Zip 36037–3800; tel. 334/382–2671; Connie Nicholas, Interim
Chief Executive Officer
Web address: www.lvstabler.com

MEDICAL CENTER ENTERPRISE (O, 117 beds) 400 North Edwards Street,
Enterprise, AL Zip 36330–2510; tel. 334/347–0584; Richard Ellis, Chief
Executive Officer
Web address: www.mcehospital.com

RIVERVIEW REGIONAL MEDICAL CENTER (O, 250 beds) 600 South Third
Street, Gadsden, AL Zip 35901–5399; tel. 256/543–5200; James H.
Edmondson, Chief Executive Officer
Web address: www.riverviewregional.com

SOUTH BALDWIN REGIONAL MEDICAL CENTER (L, 112 beds) 1613 North
McKenzie Street, Foley, AL Zip 36535–2299; tel. 251/949–3400; Keith
Newton, Chief Executive Officer
Web address: www.southbaldwinrmc.com

STRINGFELLOW MEMORIAL HOSPITAL (O, 75 beds) 301 East 18th Street,
Anniston, AL Zip 36207–3952; tel. 256/235–8900; Jay Hinesley, Chief
Executive Officer
Web address: www.stringfellowhealth.com

TRINITY MEDICAL CENTER (O, 379 beds) 800 Montclair Road, Birmingham,
AL Zip 35213–1984; tel. 205/592–1000; Keith Granger, President and Chief
Executive Officer
Web address: www.bhsala.com

ALASKA: MAT–SU REGIONAL MEDICAL CENTER (O, 74 beds) 2500 South
Woodworth Loop, Palmer, AK Zip 99645–8984, Mailing Address: P.O. Box
1687, Zip 99645–1687; tel. 907/861–6000; John R. Lee, Chief
Executive Officer
Web address: www.matsuregional.com

ARIZONA: NORTHWEST MEDICAL CENTER (O, 270 beds) 6200 North La
Cholla Boulevard, Tucson, AZ Zip 85741–3599; tel. 520/742–9000;
Kevin Stockton, Chief Executive Officer
Web address: www.northwestmedicalcenter.com

ORO VALLEY HOSPITAL (O, 144 beds) 1551 East Tangerine Road, Oro Valley,
AZ Zip 85755–6213; tel. 520/901–3500; Jae Dale, Chief Executive Officer
Web address: www.nmcorovalley.com

PAYSON REGIONAL MEDICAL CENTER (L, 39 beds) 807 South Ponderosa
Street, Payson, AZ Zip 85541–5599; tel. 928/474–3222; Lance Porter,
Chief Executive Officer
Web address: www.paysonhospital.com

WESTERN ARIZONA REGIONAL MEDICAL CENTER (O, 139 beds) 2735 Silver
Creek Road, Bullhead City, AZ Zip 86442–8303; tel. 928/763–2273; Alex
Villa, Chief Executive Officer
Web address: www.warmc.com

ARKANSAS: FORREST CITY MEDICAL CENTER (L, 39 beds) 1601 Newcastle
Road, Forrest City, AR Zip 72335–2218; tel. 870/261–0000; Kevin
Decker, Chief Executive Officer
Web address: www.forrestcitymedicalcenter.com

HARRIS HOSPITAL (O, 104 beds) 1205 McLain Street, Newport, AR
Zip 72112–3533; tel. 870/523–8911; Robert Rupp, Chief Executive Officer
Web address: www.harrishospital.com

HELENA REGIONAL MEDICAL CENTER (L, 105 beds) 1801 Martin Luther King
Drive, Helena, AR Zip 72342, Mailing Address: P.O. Box 788,
Zip 72342–0788; tel. 870/338–5800; Buddy Daniels, Chief Executive Officer
Web address: www.helenarmc.com

MEDICAL CENTER OF SOUTH ARKANSAS (L, 120 beds) 700 West Grove
Street, El Dorado, AR Zip 71730–4416; tel. 870/863–2000; Kyle Swift, Chief
Executive Officer
Web address: www.themedcenter.net

NORTHWEST MEDICAL CENTER – SPRINGDALE (O, 346 beds) 609 West
Maple Avenue, Springdale, AR Zip 72764–5394, Mailing Address: P.O. Box
47, Zip 72765–0047; tel. 479/751–5711; Sharif Omar, Chief Executive
Officer
Web address: www.northwesthealth.com

SILOAM SPRINGS REGIONAL HOSPITAL (O, 54 beds) 603 North Progress
Avenue, Siloam Springs, AR Zip 72761–4352; tel. 479/524–4141; Kevin J.
Clement, Chief Executive Officer
Web address: www.ssrh.net/Pages/home.aspx

SPARKS REGIONAL MEDICAL CENTER (O, 303 beds) 100 Towson Avenue,
Fort Smith, AR Zip 72901–2632, Mailing Address: P.O. Box 2406,
Zip 72917–7006; tel. 479/441–4000; Daniel E. McKay, Chief Executive
Officer
Web address: www.sparks.org

SUMMIT MEDICAL CENTER (L, 103 beds) East Main and South 20th Streets,
Van Buren, AR Zip 72956–5715, Mailing Address: P.O. Box 409,
Zip 72957–0409; tel. 479/474–3401; Daniel E. McKay, Chief Executive
Officer
Web address: www.summitmedicalcenter.net

CALIFORNIA: BARSTOW COMMUNITY HOSPITAL (L, 30 beds) 820 East
Mountain View Street, Barstow, CA Zip 92311–3004; tel. 760/256–1761;
Steven Foster, Chief Executive Officer
Web address: www.barstowhospital.com

FALLBROOK HOSPITAL (L, 86 beds) 624 East Elder Street, Fallbrook, CA
Zip 92028–3099; tel. 760/728–1191; Kirkpatrick Conley, Chief Executive
Officer
Web address: www.fallbrookhospital.com

WATSONVILLE COMMUNITY HOSPITAL (O, 106 beds) 75 Nielson Street,
Watsonville, CA Zip 95076–2468; tel. 831/724–4741; Audra Earle, FACHE,
Chief Executive Officer
Web address: www.watsonvillehospital.com

FLORIDA: BARTOW REGIONAL MEDICAL CENTER (O, 72 beds) 2200 Osprey
Boulevard, Bartow, FL Zip 33830–3308, Mailing Address: P.O. Box 1050,
Zip 33831–1050; tel. 863/533–8111; Philip Minden, Chief Executive
Officer
Web address: www.bartowregional.com

BAYFRONT HEALTH BROOKSVILLE (L, 91 beds) 17240 Cortez Boulevard,
Brooksville, FL Zip 34601–8921, Mailing Address: P.O. Box 37,
Zip 34605–0037; tel. 352/796–5111; Kenneth R. Wicker, Chief Executive
Officer
Web address: www.brooksvilleregionalhospital.org

BAYFRONT HEALTH DADE CITY (O, 120 beds) 13100 Fort King Road, Dade
City, FL Zip 33525–5294; tel. 352/521–1100; Shauna McKinnon, Chief
Executive Officer
Web address: www.pascoregionalmc.com

BAYFRONT HEALTH PORT CHARLOTTE (O, 296 beds) 2500 Harbor
Boulevard, Port Charlotte, FL Zip 33952–5000; tel. 941/766–4122; Richard
H. Satcher, Market Chief Executive Officer
Web address: www.bayfrontcharlotte.com

BAYFRONT HEALTH PUNTA GORDA (O, 208 beds) 809 East Marion Avenue,
Punta Gorda, FL Zip 33950–3819, Mailing Address: P.O. Box 51–1328,
Zip 33951–1328; tel. 941/639–3131; Brandon Downey, Chief Executive
Officer
Web address: www.charlotteregional.com

Section B

For explanation of codes following names, see page B2.
★ Indicates Type III membership in the American Hospital Association.

BAYFRONT HEALTH ST. PETERSBURG (O, 382 beds) 701 Sixth Street South, Saint Petersburg, FL Zip 33701–4891; tel. 727/823–1234; Kathryn Gillette, President and Chief Executive Officer
Web address: www.bayfrontstpete.com

HEART OF FLORIDA REGIONAL MEDICAL CENTER (O, 194 beds) 40100 Highway 27, Davenport, FL Zip 33837–5906; tel. 863/422–4971; Ann Barnhart, Chief Executive Officer
Web address: www.heartofflorida.com

HIGHLANDS REGIONAL MEDICAL CENTER (L, 116 beds) 3600 South Highlands Avenue, Sebring, FL Zip 33870–5495, Mailing Address: Drawer 2066, Zip 33871–2066; tel. 863/471–5800; Joseph Bernard, Chief Executive Officer
Web address: www.highlandsregional.com

LAKE WALES MEDICAL CENTER (O, 131 beds) 410 South 11th Street, Lake Wales, FL Zip 33853–4256; tel. 863/676–1433; Andrew Howard, Interim Chief Executive Officer
Web address: www.lakewalesmedicalcenter.com

LEHIGH REGIONAL MEDICAL CENTER (O, 88 beds) 1500 Lee Boulevard, Lehigh Acres, FL Zip 33936–4835; tel. 239/369–2101; Joanie Jeannette, MSN, Chief Executive Officer
Web address: www.lehighregional.com

LOWER KEYS MEDICAL CENTER (L, 90 beds) 5900 College Road, Key West, FL Zip 33040–4396, Mailing Address: P.O. Box 9107, Zip 33041–9107; tel. 305/294–5531; Nicki L. Will–Mowery, Ph.D., Chief Executive Officer
Web address: www.lkmc.com

NORTH OKALOOSA MEDICAL CENTER (O, 110 beds) 151 Redstone Avenue S.E., Crestview, FL Zip 32539–6026; tel. 850/689–8100; David W. Fuller, Chief Executive Officer
Web address: www.northokaloosa.com

PHYSICIANS REGIONAL – PINE RIDGE (O, 70 beds) 6101 Pine Ridge Road, Naples, FL Zip 34119–3900; tel. 239/348–4000; C. Scott Campbell, Market Chief Executive Officer
Web address: www.physiciansregional.com

SANTA ROSA MEDICAL CENTER (L, 68 beds) 6002 Berryhill Road, Milton, FL Zip 32570–5062; tel. 850/626–7762; Phillip L. Wright, FACHE, Chief Executive Officer
Web address: www.santarosamedicalcenter.org

SEBASTIAN RIVER MEDICAL CENTER (O, 140 beds) 13695 North U.S. Highway 1, Sebastian, FL Zip 32958–3230, Mailing Address: Box 780838, Zip 32978–0838; tel. 772/589–3186; Kelly Enriquez, Chief Executive Officer
Web address: www.sebastianrivermedical.com

SEVEN RIVERS REGIONAL MEDICAL CENTER (O, 128 beds) 6201 North Suncoast Boulevard, Crystal River, FL Zip 34428–6712; tel. 352/795–6560; Joyce A. Brancato, Chief Executive Officer
Web address: www.srrmc.com

SHANDS LAKE SHORE REGIONAL MEDICAL CENTER (O, 85 beds) 368 N.E. Franklin Street, Lake City, FL Zip 32055–3047; tel. 386/292–8000; Rhonda Kay Sherrod, R.N., MSN, Administrator
Web address: www.shandslakeshore.com

SHANDS LIVE OAK REGIONAL MEDICAL CENTER (O, 25 beds) 1100 S.W. 11th Street, Live Oak, FL Zip 32064–3608; tel. 386/362–0800; Rhonda Kay Sherrod, R.N., MSN, Interim Chief Executive Officer
Web address: www.shandsliveoak.com/

SHANDS STARKE REGIONAL MEDICAL CENTER (O, 25 beds) 922 East Call Street, Starke, FL Zip 32091–3699; tel. 904/368–2300; Rhonda Kay Sherrod, R.N., MSN, Interim Chief Executive Officer
Web address: www.shands.org

ST. CLOUD REGIONAL MEDICAL CENTER (O, 84 beds) 2906 17th Street, Saint Cloud, FL Zip 34769–6099; tel. 407/892–2135; Brent Burish, Chief Executive Officer
Web address: www.stcloudregional.com

VENICE REGIONAL BAYFRONT HEALTH (O, 312 beds) 540 The Rialto, Venice, FL Zip 34285–2900; tel. 941/485–7711; Peter Wozniak, MS, R.N., Chief Executive Officer
Web address: www.veniceregional.com

WUESTHOFF MEDICAL CENTER – MELBOURNE (O, 119 beds) 250 North Wickham Road, Melbourne, FL Zip 32935–8625; tel. 321/752–1200; Richard Frank, Chief Executive Officer
Web address: www.wuesthoff.com/locations/wuesthoff–medical–center–melbourne

WUESTHOFF MEDICAL CENTER – ROCKLEDGE (O, 298 beds) 110 Longwood Avenue, Rockledge, FL Zip 32955–2887, Mailing Address: P.O. Box 565002, Mail Stop 1, Zip 32956–5002; tel. 321/636–2211; Timothy J. Cerullo, Chief Executive Officer
Web address: www.wuesthoff.org

GEORGIA: BARROW REGIONAL MEDICAL CENTER (O, 56 beds) 316 North Broad Street, Winder, GA Zip 30680–2150, Mailing Address: P.O. Box 688, Zip 30680–0688; tel. 770/867–3400; Chad Hatfield, Chief Executive Officer
Web address: www.barrowregional.com

CLEARVIEW REGIONAL MEDICAL CENTER (O, 77 beds) 2151 West Spring Street, Monroe, GA Zip 30655–3115; tel. 770/267–8461; James Machado, Chief Executive Officer

EAST GEORGIA REGIONAL MEDICAL CENTER (O, 149 beds) 1499 Fair Road, Statesboro, GA Zip 30458–1683, Mailing Address: P.O. Box 1048, Zip 30459–1048; tel. 912/486–1000; Robert F. Bigley, President and Chief Executive Officer
Web address: www.eastgeorgiaregional.com

FANNIN REGIONAL HOSPITAL (O, 50 beds) 2855 Old Highway 5, Blue Ridge, GA Zip 30513–6248; tel. 706/632–3711; David S. Sanders, Chief Executive Officer
Web address: www.fanninregionalhospital.com

TRINITY HOSPITAL OF AUGUSTA (O, 105 beds) 2260 Wrightsboro Road, Augusta, GA Zip 30904–4726; tel. 706/481–7000; Jason Studley, Chief Executive Officer
Web address: www.trinityofaugusta.com

ILLINOIS: CROSSROADS COMMUNITY HOSPITAL (O, 47 beds) 8 Doctors Park Road, Mount Vernon, IL Zip 62864–6224; tel. 618/244–5500; Finny Mathew, Chief Executive Officer
Web address: www.crossroadscommunityhospital.com

GALESBURG COTTAGE HOSPITAL (O, 119 beds) 695 North Kellogg Street, Galesburg, IL Zip 61401–2885; tel. 309/343–8131; Earl J. Tamar, Chief Executive Officer
Web address: www.cottagehospital.com

GATEWAY REGIONAL MEDICAL CENTER (O, 147 beds) 2100 Madison Avenue, Granite City, IL Zip 62040–4799; tel. 618/798–3000; M. Edward Cunningham, Chief Executive Officer
Web address: www.gatewayregional.net

HEARTLAND REGIONAL MEDICAL CENTER (O, 92 beds) 3333 West DeYoung, Marion, IL Zip 62959–5884; tel. 618/998–7000; James Flynn, Chief Executive Officer
Web address: www.heartlandregional.com

METROSOUTH MEDICAL CENTER (O, 285 beds) 12935 South Gregory Street, Blue Island, IL Zip 60406–2470; tel. 708/597–2000; Brian Sinotte, Chief Executive Officer
Web address: www.metrosouthmedicalcenter.com

RED BUD REGIONAL HOSPITAL (O, 25 beds) 325 Spring Street, Red Bud, IL Zip 62278–1105; tel. 618/282–3831; Shane Watson, Chief Executive Officer
Web address: www.redbudregional.com

UNION COUNTY HOSPITAL (L, 47 beds) 517 North Main Street, Anna, IL Zip 62906–1696; tel. 618/833–4511; James R. Farris, FACHE, Chief Executive Officer
Web address: www.unioncountyhospital.com

VISTA MEDICAL CENTER EAST (O, 190 beds) 1324 North Sheridan Road, Waukegan, IL Zip 60085–2161; tel. 847/360–3000; Barbara J. Martin, R.N., President and Chief Executive Officer
Web address: www.vistahealth.com

VISTA MEDICAL CENTER WEST (O, 67 beds) 2615 Washington Street, Waukegan, IL Zip 60085–4988; tel. 847/249–3900; Barbara J. Martin, R.N., President and Chief Executive Officer
Web address: www.vistahealth.com

INDIANA: BLUFFTON REGIONAL MEDICAL CENTER (O, 79 beds) 303 South Main Street, Bluffton, IN Zip 46714–2503; tel. 260/824–3210; Aaron Garofola, Chief Executive Officer
Web address: www.blufftonregional.com

DUKES MEMORIAL HOSPITAL (O, 25 beds) 275 West 12th Street, Peru, IN Zip 46970–1638; tel. 765/472–8000; Debra Close, Chief Executive Officer
Web address: www.dukesmemorialhosp.com

DUPONT HOSPITAL (O, 131 beds) 2520 East Dupont Road, Fort Wayne, IN Zip 46825–1675; tel. 260/416–3000; Chad Towner, Chief Executive Officer
Web address: www.thedupontdifference.com

For explanation of codes following names, see page B2.
★ Indicates Type III membership in the American Hospital Association.

KOSCIUSKO COMMUNITY HOSPITAL (O, 72 beds) 2101 East Dubois Drive, Warsaw, IN Zip 46580–3288; tel. 574/267–3200; Stephen R. Miller, Chief Executive Officer
Web address: www.kch.com

LUTHERAN HOSPITAL OF INDIANA (O, 396 beds) 7950 West Jefferson Boulevard, Fort Wayne, IN Zip 46804–4140; tel. 260/435–7001; Brian Bauer, Chief Executive Officer
Web address: www.lutheranhospital.com

ORTHOPAEDIC HOSPITAL OF LUTHERAN HEALTH NETWORK (O, 44 beds) 7952 West Jefferson Boulevard, Fort Wayne, IN Zip 46804–4140; tel. 260/435–2999; Kenneth Jones, Chief Executive Officer
Web address: www.theorthohospital.com

PORTER REGIONAL HOSPITAL (O, 276 beds) 85 East U.S. Highway 6, Valparaiso, IN Zip 46383–8947; tel. 219/983–8300; Stephen Lunn, Chief Executive Officer
Web address: www.porterhealth.com

REHABILITATION HOSPITAL OF FORT WAYNE (O, 36 beds) 7970 West Jefferson Boulevard, Fort Wayne, IN Zip 46804–4140; tel. 260/435–6100; Ted Scholten, Chief Operating Officer
Web address: www.rehabhospital.com

ST. JOSEPH HOSPITAL (O, 182 beds) 700 Broadway, Fort Wayne, IN Zip 46802–1493; tel. 260/425–3000; Kenneth Jones, Chief Executive Officer
Web address: www.stjoehospital.com

KENTUCKY: KENTUCKY RIVER MEDICAL CENTER (L, 54 beds) 540 Jett Drive, Jackson, KY Zip 41339–9622; tel. 606/666–6000; ,
Web address: www.kentuckyrivermc.com

PARKWAY REGIONAL HOSPITAL (O, 70 beds) 2000 Holiday Lane, Fulton, KY Zip 42041–8468; tel. 270/472–2522; John Ballard, Ph.D., Chief Executive Officer
Web address: www.parkwayregionalhospital.com

PAUL B. HALL REGIONAL MEDICAL CENTER (O, 72 beds) 625 James S. Trimble Boulevard, Paintsville, KY Zip 41240–0000; tel. 606/789–3511; Deborah Trimble, R.N., Chief Executive Officer
Web address: www.pbhrmc.com

THREE RIVERS MEDICAL CENTER (O, 80 beds) 2485 Highway 644, Louisa, KY Zip 41230–9242, Mailing Address: P.O. Box 769, Zip 41230–0769; tel. 606/638–9451; Greg Kiser, Chief Executive Officer
Web address: www.threeriversmedicalcenter.com

LOUISIANA: BYRD REGIONAL HOSPITAL (O, 60 beds) 1020 West Fertitta Boulevard, Leesville, LA Zip 71446–4645; tel. 337/239–9041; Roger C. LeDoux, Chief Executive Officer
Web address: www.byrdregional.com

LAKE AREA MEDICAL CENTER (O, 88 beds) 4200 Nelson Road, Lake Charles, LA Zip 70605–4118; tel. 337/474–6370; Bryan S. Bateman, Chief Executive Officer
Web address: www.women–childrens.com

NORTHERN LOUISIANA MEDICAL CENTER (O, 91 beds) 401 East Vaughn Avenue, Ruston, LA Zip 71270–5950; tel. 318/254–2100; Brady Dubois, Chief Executive Officer
Web address: www.northernlouisianamedicalcenter.com

MISSISSIPPI: BILOXI REGIONAL MEDICAL CENTER (L, 198 beds) 150 Reynoir Street, Biloxi, MS Zip 39530–4199, Mailing Address: P.O. Box 128, Zip 39533–0128; tel. 228/432–1571; Monte J. Bostwick, Chief Executive Officer
Web address: www.biloxiregional.net

CENTRAL MISSISSIPPI MEDICAL CENTER (L, 217 beds) 1850 Chadwick Drive, Jackson, MS Zip 39204–3479, Mailing Address: P.O. Box 59001, Zip 39284–9001; tel. 601/376–1000; Charlotte W. Dupre', Chief Executive Officer
Web address: www.centralmississippimedicalcenter.com

CROSSGATES RIVER OAKS HOSPITAL (L, 149 beds) 350 Crossgates Boulevard, Brandon, MS Zip 39042–2698; tel. 601/825–2811; Glen Silverman, Chief Executive Officer
Web address: www.crossgatesriveroaks.com

GILMORE MEMORIAL REGIONAL MEDICAL CENTER (O, 95 beds) 1105 Earl Frye Boulevard, Amory, MS Zip 38821–5500, Mailing Address: P.O. Box 459, Zip 38821–0459; tel. 662/256–7111; J. Allen Tyra, Chief Executive
Web address: www.gilmorehealth.com

MADISON RIVER OAKS MEDICAL CENTER (L, 44 beds) Highway 16 East, Canton, MS Zip 39046–8823, Mailing Address: P.O. Box 1607, Zip 39046–1607; tel. 601/859–1331; Bryan Bogle, Chief Executive Officer
Web address: www.madisonriveroaks.com

NATCHEZ COMMUNITY HOSPITAL (O, 101 beds) 129 Jefferson Davis Boulevard, Natchez, MS Zip 39120–5100, Mailing Address: P.O. Box 1203, Zip 39121–1203; tel. 601/445–6200; Eric Robinson, Chief Executive Officer
Web address: www.natchezcommunityhospital.com/default.aspx

NORTHWEST MISSISSIPPI REGIONAL MEDICAL CENTER (L, 181 beds) 1970 Hospital Drive, Clarksdale, MS Zip 38614–7202, Mailing Address: P.O. Box 1218, Zip 38614–1218; tel. 662/627–3211; William G. Buck, Chief Executive Officer
Web address: www.northwestregional.org

RIVER OAKS HOSPITAL (O, 158 beds) 1030 River Oaks Drive, Flowood, MS Zip 39232–9553, Mailing Address: P.O. Box 5100, Jackson, Zip 39296–5100; tel. 601/932–1030; L. Dwayne Blaylock, Chief Executive Officer
Web address: www.riveroakshosp.com

RIVER REGION MEDICAL CENTER (O, 297 beds) 2100 Highway 61 North, Vicksburg, MS Zip 39183–8211, Mailing Address: P.O. Box 590, Zip 39181–0590; tel. 601/883–5000; Gregory Pearson, Chief Executive Officer
Web address: www.riverregion.com

TRI–LAKES MEDICAL CENTER (O, 112 beds) 303 Medical Center Drive, Batesville, MS Zip 38606–8608; tel. 662/563–5611; Travis Sisson, Interim Chief Executive Officer
Web address: www.trilakesmc.com

WESLEY MEDICAL CENTER (O, 211 beds) 5001 Hardy Street, Hattiesburg, MS Zip 39402–1308, Mailing Address: P.O. Box 16509, Zip 39404–6509; tel. 601/268–8000; Michael Neuendorf, Chief Executive Officer
Web address: www.wesley.com

WOMAN'S HOSPITAL (O, 60 beds) 1026 North Flowood Drive, Flowood, MS Zip 39232–9532, Mailing Address: P.O. Box 4546, Jackson, Zip 39296–4546; tel. 601/932–1000; Sherry J. Pitts, Chief Executive Officer
Web address: www.womanshospitalms.com

MISSOURI: MOBERLY REGIONAL MEDICAL CENTER (O, 94 beds) 1515 Union Avenue, Moberly, MO Zip 65270–9449; tel. 660/263–8400; Christian Jones, Chief Executive Officer
Web address: www.moberlyhospital.com

NORTHEAST REGIONAL MEDICAL CENTER (L, 115 beds) 315 South Osteopathy, Kirksville, MO Zip 63501–6401, Mailing Address: P.O. Box C8502, Zip 63501–8599; tel. 660/785–1000; Ranee C. Brayton, R.N., MSN, Chief Executive Officer
Web address: www.nermc.com

POPLAR BLUFF REGIONAL MEDICAL CENTER (O, 241 beds) 3100 Oak Grove Road, Poplar Bluff, MO Zip 63901, Mailing Address: P.O. Box 88, Zip 63902–0088; tel. 573/776–2000; Kenneth James, Chief Executive Officer
Web address: www.poplarbluffregional.com

TWIN RIVERS REGIONAL MEDICAL CENTER (O, 116 beds) 1301 First Street, Kennett, MO Zip 63857–2508, Mailing Address: P.O. Box 728, Zip 63857–0728; tel. 573/888–4522; Matthew M. Lyden, Chief Executive Officer
Web address: www.twinriversregional.com

NEVADA: MESA VIEW REGIONAL HOSPITAL (O, 25 beds) 1299 Bertha Howe Avenue, Mesquite, NV Zip 89027–7500; tel. 702/346–8040; Patricia Holden, Chief Executive Officer
Web address: www.mesaviewhospital.com

NEW JERSEY: MEMORIAL HOSPITAL OF SALEM COUNTY (O, 110 beds) 310 Woodstown Road, Salem, NJ Zip 08079–2080; tel. 856/935–1000; Ryan Jensen, Chief Executive Officer
Web address: www.salemhospitalnj.org

NEW MEXICO: ALTA VISTA REGIONAL HOSPITAL (O, 52 beds) 104 Legion Drive, Las Vegas, NM Zip 87701–4804; tel. 505/426–3500; R. Chris Wolf, Chief Executive Officer
Web address: www.altavistaregionalhospital.com

CARLSBAD MEDICAL CENTER (O, 127 beds) 2430 West Pierce Street, Carlsbad, NM Zip 88220–3597; tel. 575/887–4100; Elmer Hyde, Chief Executive Officer
Web address: www.carlsbadmedicalcenter.com

For explanation of codes following names, see page B2.
★ Indicates Type III membership in the American Hospital Association.

Section B

EASTERN NEW MEXICO MEDICAL CENTER (O, 149 beds) 405 West Country Club Road, Roswell, NM Zip 88201–5209; tel. 575/622–8170; Maridel Acosta–Cruz, Chief Executive Officer
Web address: www.enmmc.com

LEA REGIONAL MEDICAL CENTER (O, 195 beds) 5419 North Lovington Highway, Hobbs, NM Zip 88240–9125, Mailing Address: P.O. Box 3000, Zip 88241–9501; tel. 575/492–5000; Timothy Thornell, FACHE, Chief Executive Officer
Web address: www.learegionalmedical.com

MIMBRES MEMORIAL HOSPITAL (O, 99 beds) 900 West Ash Street, Deming, NM Zip 88030–4098, Mailing Address: P.O. Box 710, Zip 88031–0710; tel. 575/546–2761; Steve Westenhofer, Chief Executive Officer
Web address: www.mimbresmemorial.com

MOUNTAINVIEW REGIONAL MEDICAL CENTER (O, 142 beds) 4311 East Lohman Avenue, Las Cruces, NM Zip 88011–8255; tel. 575/556–7600; Denten Park, Chief Executive Officer
Web address: www.mountainviewregional.com

NORTH CAROLINA: DAVIS REGIONAL MEDICAL CENTER (O, 130 beds) 218 Old Mocksville Road, Statesville, NC Zip 28625–1930, Mailing Address: P.O. Box 1823, Zip 28687–1823; tel. 704/873–0281; William Chad French, Chief Executive Officer
Web address: www.davisregional.com

LAKE NORMAN REGIONAL MEDICAL CENTER (O, 123 beds) 171 Fairview Road, Mooresville, NC Zip 28117–9500, Mailing Address: P.O. Box 3250, Zip 28117–3250; tel. 704/660–4010; Stephen L. Midkiff, Chief Executive Officer
Web address: www.lnrmc.com

MARTIN GENERAL HOSPITAL (L, 49 beds) 310 South McCaskey Road, Williamston, NC Zip 27892–2150, Mailing Address: P.O. Box 1128, Zip 27892–1128; tel. 252/809–6179; Craig R. Fichter, Interim Chief Executive Officer
Web address: www.martingeneral.com

SANDHILLS REGIONAL MEDICAL CENTER (O, 64 beds) 1000 West Hamlet Avenue, Hamlet, NC Zip 28345–4522, Mailing Address: P.O. Box 1109, Zip 28345–1109; tel. 910/205–8000; Michael H. McNair, Chief Executive Officer
Web address: www.sandhillsregional.com

OHIO: AFFINITY MEDICAL CENTER (O, 112 beds) 875 Eighth Street N.E., Massillon, OH Zip 44646–8503, Mailing Address: P.O. Box 805, Zip 44648–0805; tel. 330/832–8761; Ronald L. Bierman, Chief Executive Officer
Web address: www.affinitymedicalcenter.com

HILLSIDE REHABILITATION HOSPITAL (O, 65 beds) 8747 Squires Lane N.E., Warren, OH Zip 44484–1649; tel. 330/841–3700; Ian Cooper, Chief Executive Officer
Web address: www.valleycarehealth.net

NORTHSIDE MEDICAL CENTER (O, 373 beds) 500 Gypsy Lane, Youngstown, OH Zip 44504–1315; tel. 330/884–1000; W. Trent Crable, Chief Executive Officer
Web address: www.northsidemedicalcenter.net

TRUMBULL MEMORIAL HOSPITAL (O, 292 beds) 1350 East Market Street, Warren, OH Zip 44483–6628; tel. 330/841–9011; John Walsh, Chief Executive Officer
Web address: www.vchs.net

OKLAHOMA: DEACONESS HOSPITAL (O, 273 beds) 5501 North Portland Avenue, Oklahoma City, OK Zip 73112–2099; tel. 405/604–6000; Cathryn A. Hibbs, FACHE, Chief Executive Officer
Web address: www.deaconessokc.com

INTEGRIS BLACKWELL REGIONAL MEDICAL CENTER (O, 49 beds) 710 South 13th Street, Blackwell, OK Zip 74631–3700; tel. 580/363–2311; Andrew Wachtel, Chief Executive Officer
Web address: www.integris–health.com

INTEGRIS CLINTON REGIONAL HOSPITAL (O, 49 beds) 100 North 30th Street, Clinton, OK Zip 73601–3117, Mailing Address: P.O. Box 1569, Zip 73601–1569; tel. 580/323–2363; Robin E. Lake, Chief Executive Officer
Web address: www.integris–health.com

INTEGRIS MARSHALL COUNTY MEDICAL CENTER (O, 21 beds) 1 Hospital Drive, Madill, OK Zip 73446, Mailing Address: P.O. Box 827, Zip 73446–0827; tel. 580/795–3384; Gregory Holder, Administrator and Chief Nursing Executive
Web address: www.integrismarshallcounty.com

INTEGRIS MAYES COUNTY MEDICAL CENTER (O, 24 beds) 111 North Bailey Street, Pryor, OK Zip 74361–4201, Mailing Address: P.O. Box 278, Zip 74362–0278; tel. 918/825–1600; Douglas K. Weaver, FACHE, President
Web address: www.integrismayescounty.com

INTEGRIS SEMINOLE MEDICAL CENTER (O, 32 beds) 2401 Wrangler Boulevard, Seminole, OK Zip 74868–1917; tel. 405/303–4000; Jimmy D. Stuart, Chief Executive Officer
Web address: www.hma.com

MEDICAL CENTER OF SOUTHEASTERN OKLAHOMA (O, 148 beds) 1800 University Boulevard, Durant, OK Zip 74701–3006, Mailing Address: P.O. Box 1207, Zip 74702–1207; tel. 580/924–3080; Patricia Dorris, Executive Director
Web address: www.mymcso.com

MIDWEST REGIONAL MEDICAL CENTER (L, 255 beds) 2825 Parklawn Drive, Midwest City, OK Zip 73110–4258; tel. 405/610–4411; Damon Brown, Chief Executive Officer
Web address: www.midwestregional.com

PONCA CITY MEDICAL CENTER (O, 72 beds) 1900 North 14th Street, Ponca City, OK Zip 74601–2099; tel. 580/765–3321; R. Andrew Wachtel, FACHE, Chief Executive Officer
Web address: www.poncamedcenter.com

WOODWARD REGIONAL HOSPITAL (L, 40 beds) 900 17th Street, Woodward, OK Zip 73801–2448; tel. 580/256–5511; David Wallace, Chief Executive Officer
Web address: www.woodwardhospital.com

OREGON: MCKENZIE–WILLAMETTE MEDICAL CENTER (O, 113 beds) 1460 G Street, Springfield, OR Zip 97477–4197; tel. 541/726–4400; Chad Campbell, Chief Executive Officer
Web address: www.mckweb.com

PENNSYLVANIA: BERWICK HOSPITAL CENTER (O, 341 beds) 701 East 16th Street, Berwick, PA Zip 18603–2397; tel. 570/759–5000; David P. Steitz, Chief Executive Officer
Web address: www.berwick–hospital.com

BRANDYWINE HOSPITAL (O, 140 beds) 201 Reeceville Road, Coatesville, PA Zip 19320–1536; tel. 610/383–8000; Bryan Burklow, Chief Executive Officer
Web address: www.brandywinehospital.com

CARLISLE REGIONAL MEDICAL CENTER (O, 165 beds) 361 Alexander Spring Road, Carlisle, PA Zip 17015–6940; tel. 717/249–1212; Rich Newell, Chief Executive Officer
Web address: www.carlislermc.com/default.aspx

CHESTNUT HILL HOSPITAL (O, 212 beds) 8835 Germantown Avenue, Philadelphia, PA Zip 19118–2718; tel. 215/248–8200; John D. Cacciamani, M.D., Chief Executive Officer
Web address: www.chhealthsystem.com

EASTON HOSPITAL (O, 224 beds) 250 South 21st Street, Easton, PA Zip 18042–3892; tel. 610/250–4000; John A. Zidansek, President and Chief Executive Officer
Web address: www.easton–hospital.com

FIRST HOSPITAL WYOMING VALLEY (O, 127 beds) 562 Wyoming Avenue, Kingston, PA Zip 18704–3721; tel. 570/552–3900; Mark Schor, Chief Executive Officer
Web address: www.firsthospital.net/Pages/home.aspx

HEART OF LANCASTER REGIONAL MEDICAL CENTER (O, 148 beds) 1500 Highlands Drive, Lititz, PA Zip 17543–7694; tel. 717/625–5000; Deborah J. Willwerth, R.N., MSN, Administrator
Web address: www.heartoflancaster.com

JENNERSVILLE REGIONAL HOSPITAL (O, 63 beds) 1015 West Baltimore Pike, West Grove, PA Zip 19390–9459; tel. 610/869–1000; Mathew Gooch, Chief Executive Officer
Web address: www.jennersville.com

LANCASTER REGIONAL MEDICAL CENTER (O, 150 beds) 250 College Avenue, Lancaster, PA Zip 17603–3363, Mailing Address: P.O. Box 3434, Zip 17604–3434; tel. 717/291–8211; Bob Moore, FACHE, Chief Executive Officer
Web address: www.lancasterregional.com

LOCK HAVEN HOSPITAL (O, 110 beds) 24 Cree Drive, Lock Haven, PA Zip 17745–2699; tel. 570/893–5000; Steven T. Davis, Chief Executive Officer
Web address: www.lockhavenhospital.com

For explanation of codes following names, see page B2.
★ Indicates Type III membership in the American Hospital Association.

MEMORIAL HOSPITAL (O, 100 beds) 325 South Belmont Street, York, PA Zip 17403–2609, Mailing Address: P.O. Box 15118, Zip 17405–7118; tel. 717/843–8623; Sally J. Dixon, Chief Executive Officer
Web address: www.mhyork.org

MOSES TAYLOR HOSPITAL (O, 217 beds) 700 Quincy Avenue, Scranton, PA Zip 18510–1724; tel. 570/770–5000; Justin Davis, Chief Executive Officer
Web address: www.mth.org

PHOENIXVILLE HOSPITAL (O, 113 beds) 140 Nutt Road, Phoenixville, PA Zip 19460–3900, Mailing Address: P.O. Box 3001, Zip 19460–0916; tel. 610/983–1000; Stephen M. Tullman, Chief Executive Officer
Web address: www.phoenixvillehospital.com

POTTSTOWN MEMORIAL MEDICAL CENTER (O, 224 beds) 1600 East High Street, Pottstown, PA Zip 19464–5093; tel. 610/327–7000; J. Mark McLoone, FACHE, Chief Executive Officer
Web address: www.pottstownmemorial.com

REGIONAL HOSPITAL OF SCRANTON (O, 192 beds) 746 Jefferson Avenue, Scranton, PA Zip 18510–1624; tel. 570/348–7100; Brooks Turkel, Chief Executive Officer
Web address: www.regionalhospitalofscranton.net

SHARON REGIONAL HEALTH SYSTEM (O, 256 beds) 740 East State Street, Sharon, PA Zip 16146–3395; tel. 724/983–3911; John R. Janoso, President and Chief Executive Officer
Web address: www.sharonregional.com

SPECIAL CARE HOSPITAL (O, 64 beds) 128 West Washington Street, Nanticoke, PA Zip 18634–3113; tel. 570/735–5000; Robert D. Williams, Chief Executive Officer
Web address: www.specialcarehospital.net

SUNBURY COMMUNITY HOSPITAL AND OUTPATIENT CENTER (O, 76 beds) 350 North Eleventh Street, Sunbury, PA Zip 17801–1611; tel. 570/286–3333; Jeff Hunt, Chief Executive Officer
Web address: www.sunburyhospital.com

TYLER MEMORIAL HOSPITAL (O, 48 beds) 5950 State Route 6, Tunkhannock, PA Zip 18657–7905; tel. 570/836–2161; Diane Ljungquist, R.N., MS, Chief Executive Officer
Web address: www.tylermemorialhospital.net

WILKES–BARRE GENERAL HOSPITAL (O, 374 beds) 575 North River Street, Wilkes–Barre, PA Zip 18764–0001; tel. 570/829–8111; Cornelio R. Catena, President and Chief Executive Officer
Web address: www.wvhc.org

SOUTH CAROLINA: CAROLINA PINES REGIONAL MEDICAL CENTER (O, 120 beds) 1304 West Bobo Newsom Highway, Hartsville, SC Zip 29550–4710; tel. 843/339–2100; J. Timothy Browne, FACHE, Chief Executive Officer
Web address: www.cprmc.com

CAROLINAS HOSPITAL SYSTEM (O, 429 beds) 805 Pamplico Highway, Florence, SC Zip 29505–6050, Mailing Address: P.O. Box 100550, Zip 29502–0550; tel. 843/674–5000; Darcy Craven, Chief Executive Officer
Web address: www.carolinashospital.com

CAROLINAS HOSPITAL SYSTEM MARION (O, 216 beds) 2829 East Highway 76, Mullins, SC Zip 29574–6035, Mailing Address: P.O. Drawer 1150, Marion, Zip 29571–1150; tel. 843/431–2000; Ronnie Daves, Chief Executive Officer
Web address: www.carolinashospitalmarion.com/Pages/Home.aspx

CHESTER REGIONAL MEDICAL CENTER (L, 36 beds) 1 Medical Park Drive, Chester, SC Zip 29706–9769; tel. 803/581–3151; Page H. Vaughan, Chief Executive Officer
Web address: www.chesterregional.com

CHESTERFIELD GENERAL HOSPITAL (L, 59 beds) 711 Chesterfield Highway, Cheraw, SC Zip 29520–7002; tel. 843/537–7881; Jeff Reece, R.N., MSN, Chief Executive Officer
Web address: www.chesterfieldgeneral.com

MARLBORO PARK HOSPITAL (L, 102 beds) 1138 Cheraw Highway, Bennettsville, SC Zip 29512–2466; tel. 843/479–2881; Jeff Reece, R.N., MSN, Chief Executive Officer
Web address: www.marlboroparkhospital.com

MARY BLACK MEMORIAL HOSPITAL (O, 181 beds) 1700 Skylyn Drive, Spartanburg, SC Zip 29307–1061, Mailing Address: P.O. Box 3217, Zip 29304–3217; tel. 864/573–3000; Sean T. Dardeau, Chief Executive Officer
Web address: www.maryblackhealthsystem.com

SPRINGS MEMORIAL HOSPITAL (O, 186 beds) 800 West Meeting Street, Lancaster, SC Zip 29720–2298; tel. 803/286–1214; Janice Dabney, Chief Executive Officer
Web address: www.springsmemorial.com

TENNESSEE: DYERSBURG REGIONAL MEDICAL CENTER (O, 105 beds) 400 East Tickle Street, Dyersburg, TN Zip 38024–3120; tel. 731/285–2410; Ben Youree, Chief Executive Officer
Web address: www.dyersburgregionalmc.com

GATEWAY MEDICAL CENTER (O, 247 beds) 651 Dunlop Lane, Clarksville, TN Zip 37040–5015, Mailing Address: P.O. Box 31629, Zip 37040–0028; tel. 931/502–1000; Mark A. Marsh, Chief Executive Officer
Web address: www.ghsystem.com

HARTON REGIONAL MEDICAL CENTER (O, 104 beds) 1801 North Jackson Street, Tullahoma, TN Zip 37388–8259; tel. 931/393–3000; William R. Spray, Chief Executive Officer
Web address: www.hartonmedicalcenter.com

HENDERSON COUNTY COMMUNITY HOSPITAL (O, 45 beds) 200 West Church Street, Lexington, TN Zip 38351–2038; tel. 731/968–3646; Dale Humphrey, Chief Executive Officer
Web address: www.hendersoncchospital.com

HERITAGE MEDICAL CENTER (O, 70 beds) 2835 Highway 231 North, Shelbyville, TN Zip 37160–7327; tel. 931/685–5433; David V. Bunch, Chief Executive Officer
Web address: www.heritagemedicalcenter.com

JAMESTOWN REGIONAL MEDICAL CENTER (O, 85 beds) 436 Central Avenue West, Jamestown, TN Zip 38556–3031, Mailing Address: P.O. Box 1500, Zip 38556–1500; tel. 931/879–8171; Larry R. Jeter, Chief Executive Officer
Web address: www.jamestownregional.org

LAKEWAY REGIONAL HOSPITAL (O, 135 beds) 726 McFarland Street, Morristown, TN Zip 37814–3990; tel. 423/586–2302; Clyde Wood, Chief Executive Officer
Web address: www.lakewayregionalhospital.com

MCKENZIE REGIONAL HOSPITAL (O, 35 beds) 161 Hospital Drive, McKenzie, TN Zip 38201–1636; tel. 731/352–5344; Michael G. Morrical, Chief Executive Officer
Web address: www.mckenzieregionalhospital.com

MCNAIRY REGIONAL HOSPITAL (O, 45 beds) 705 East Poplar Avenue, Selmer, TN Zip 38375–1828; tel. 731/645–3221; Pamela W. Roberts, Chief Executive Officer
Web address: www.mcnairyregionalhospital.com

REGIONAL HOSPITAL OF JACKSON (O, 134 beds) 367 Hospital Boulevard, Jackson, TN Zip 38305–2080; tel. 731/661–2000; Charles F. Miller, Chief Executive Officer
Web address: www.regionalhospitaljackson.com/Pages/Home.aspx

SKYRIDGE MEDICAL CENTER (O, 186 beds) 2305 Chambliss Avenue N.W., Cleveland, TN Zip 37311–3847, Mailing Address: P.O. Box 3060, Zip 37320–3060; tel. 423/559–6000; R. Coleman Foss, Chief Executive Officer
Web address: www.skyridgemedicalcenter.net

TENNOVA HEALTHCARE–JEFFERSON MEMORIAL HOSPITAL (L, 54 beds) 110 Hospital Drive, Jefferson City, TN Zip 37760–5281; tel. 865/471–2500; Colin McRae, Chief Executive Officer
Web address: www.tennova.com/

TENNOVA HEALTHCARE–LAFOLLETTE MEDICAL CENTER (O, 164 beds) 923 East Central Avenue, La Follette, TN Zip 37766–2768, Mailing Address: P.O. Box 1301, Zip 37766–1301; tel. 423/907–1200; Mark Cain, Chief Executive Officer
Web address: www.tennova.com

TENNOVA NEWPORT MEDICAL CENTER (O, 47 beds) 435 Second Street, Newport, TN Zip 37821–3799; tel. 423/625–2200; Spencer Thomas, Chief Executive Officer
Web address: www.tennova.com

TENNOVA PHYSICIANS REGIONAL MEDICAL CENTER (O, 223 beds) 900 East Oak Hill Avenue, Knoxville, TN Zip 37917–4556; tel. 865/545–8000; Karen Metz, Chief Executive Officer
Web address: www.hma.com/content/physicians–regional–medical–center

UNIVERSITY MEDICAL CENTER (O, 245 beds) 1411 Baddour Parkway, Lebanon, TN Zip 37087–2513; tel. 615/444–8262; Matthew T. Caldwell, Chief Executive Officer
Web address: www.universitymedicalcenter.com

For explanation of codes following names, see page B2.
★ Indicates Type III membership in the American Hospital Association.

VOLUNTEER COMMUNITY HOSPITAL (O, 65 beds) 161 Mount Pelia Road, Martin, TN Zip 38237–3811; tel. 731/587–4261; Darrell Blaylock, Chief Executive Officer
Web address: www.volunteercommunityhospital.com

TEXAS: ABILENE REGIONAL MEDICAL CENTER (O, 205 beds) 6250 U.S. Highway 83, Abilene, TX Zip 79606–5299; tel. 325/428–1000; Michael D. Murphy, Chief Executive Officer
Web address: www.abileneregional.com

BIG BEND REGIONAL MEDICAL CENTER (O, 25 beds) 2600 Highway 118 North, Alpine, TX Zip 79830–2002; tel. 432/837–3447; Michael J. Ellis, Chief Executive Officer
Web address: www.bigbendhealthcare.com

BROWNWOOD REGIONAL MEDICAL CENTER (O, 168 beds) 1501 Burnet Drive, Brownwood, TX Zip 76801–8520, Mailing Address: P.O. Box 760, Zip 76804–0760; tel. 325/646–8541; Claude E. Camp, III, Chief Executive Officer
Web address: www.brmc–cares.com

CEDAR PARK REGIONAL MEDICAL CENTER (O, 85 beds) 1401 Medical Parkway, Cedar Park, TX Zip 78613–7763; tel. 512/528–7000; Brad D. Holland, Chief Executive Officer
Web address: www.cedarparkregional.com

COLLEGE STATION MEDICAL CENTER (O, 85 beds) 1604 Rock Prairie Road, College Station, TX Zip 77845–8345, Mailing Address: P.O. Box 10000, Zip 77842–3500; tel. 979/764–5100; Barry S. Schneider, Interim Chief Executive Officer
Web address: www.csmedcenter.com

DALLAS REGIONAL MEDICAL CENTER (O, 85 beds) 1011 North Galloway Avenue, Mesquite, TX Zip 75149–2433; tel. 214/320–7000; Tina Pollock, Chief Executive Officer
Web address: www.dallasregionalmedicalcenter.com

DETAR HEALTHCARE SYSTEM (O, 245 beds) 506 East San Antonio Street, Victoria, TX Zip 77901–6060, Mailing Address: P.O. Box 2089, Zip 77902–2089; tel. 361/575–7441; William R. Blanchard, Chief Executive Officer
Web address: www.detar.com

HILL REGIONAL HOSPITAL (O, 66 beds) 101 Circle Drive, Hillsboro, TX Zip 76645–2670; tel. 254/580–8500; Jan McClure, Chief Executive Officer
Web address: www.chs.net

LAKE GRANBURY MEDICAL CENTER (L, 83 beds) 1310 Paluxy Road, Granbury, TX Zip 76048–5655; tel. 817/573–2273; Derrick Cuenca, Chief Executive Officer
Web address: www.lakegranburymedicalcenter.com

LAREDO MEDICAL CENTER (O, 326 beds) 1700 East Saunders Avenue, Laredo, TX Zip 78041–5474, Mailing Address: P.O. Box 2068, Zip 78044–2068; tel. 956/796–5000; Timothy E. Schmidt, Chief Executive Officer
Web address: www.laredomedical.com

LONGVIEW REGIONAL MEDICAL CENTER (O, 189 beds) 2901 North Fourth Street, Longview, TX Zip 75605–5191, Mailing Address: P.O. Box 14000, Zip 75607–4000; tel. 903/758–1818; Jim R. Kendrick, Chief Executive Officer
Web address: www.longviewregional.com

NAVARRO REGIONAL HOSPITAL (O, 148 beds) 3201 West State Highway 22, Corsicana, TX Zip 75110–2469; tel. 903/654–6800; Michael K. Stewart, Chief Executive Officer
Web address: www.navarrohospital.com

SAN ANGELO COMMUNITY MEDICAL CENTER (O, 131 beds) 3501 Knickerbocker Road, San Angelo, TX Zip 76904–7698; tel. 325/949–9511; Jeremy Riney, Chief Executive Officer
Web address: www.sacmc.com

SCENIC MOUNTAIN MEDICAL CENTER (O, 75 beds) 1601 West 11th Place, Big Spring, TX Zip 79720–4198; tel. 432/263–1211; Larry Rodgers, Chief Executive Officer
Web address: www.smmccares.com

SOUTH TEXAS REGIONAL MEDICAL CENTER (O, 67 beds) 1905 Highway 97 East, Jourdanton, TX Zip 78026–1504; tel. 830/769–3515; James R. Resendez, Chief Executive Officer
Web address: www.strmc.com

TOMBALL REGIONAL MEDICAL CENTER (O, 200 beds) 605 Holderrieth Street, Tomball, TX Zip 77375–6445; tel. 281/401–7500; Thomas W. Jackson, Chief Executive Officer
Web address: www.tomballregionalmedicalcenter.com

WEATHERFORD REGIONAL MEDICAL CENTER (O, 86 beds) 713 East Anderson Street, Weatherford, TX Zip 76086–5705; tel. 817/596–8751; David Orcutt, Chief Executive Officer
Web address: www.weatherfordregional.com

WOODLAND HEIGHTS MEDICAL CENTER (O, 115 beds) 505 South John Redditt Drive, Lufkin, TX Zip 75904–3157, Mailing Address: P.O. Box 150610, Zip 75904; tel. 936/634–8311; Casey Robertson, Chief Executive Officer
Web address: www.woodlandheights.net

UTAH: MOUNTAIN WEST MEDICAL CENTER (O, 44 beds) 2055 North Main Street, Tooele, UT Zip 84074–9819; tel. 435/843–3600; Philip Eaton, Interim Chief Executive Officer
Web address: www.mountainwestmc.com

VIRGINIA: SOUTHAMPTON MEMORIAL HOSPITAL (O, 72 beds) 100 Fairview Drive, Franklin, VA Zip 23851–1238, Mailing Address: P.O. Box 817, Zip 23851–0817; tel. 757/569–6100; Kimberly W. Marks, Interim Chief Executive Officer
Web address: www.smhfranklin.com

SOUTHERN VIRGINIA REGIONAL MEDICAL CENTER (O, 80 beds) 727 North Main Street, Emporia, VA Zip 23847–1274; tel. 434/348–4400; Linda Burnette, R.N., Interim Chief Executive Officer
Web address: www.svrmc.com

SOUTHSIDE REGIONAL MEDICAL CENTER (O, 300 beds) 200 Medical Park Boulevard, Petersburg, VA Zip 23805–9274; tel. 804/765–5000; Douglas J. Moyer, Chief Executive Officer
Web address: www.srmconline.com

WASHINGTON: DEACONESS HOSPITAL (O, 388 beds) 800 West Fifth Avenue, Spokane, WA Zip 99204–2803, Mailing Address: P.O. Box 248, Zip 99210–0248; tel. 509/458–5800; Maurine Cate, Chief Executive Officer
Web address: www.deaconessspokane.com/Deaconess–Hospital/home. aspx

TOPPENISH COMMUNITY HOSPITAL (O, 63 beds) 502 West Fourth Avenue, Toppenish, WA Zip 98948–1616, Mailing Address: P.O. Box 672, Zip 98948–0672; tel. 509/865–3105; Perry Gay, Chief Executive Officer
Web address: www.toppenishhospital.com

VALLEY HOSPITAL (O, 123 beds) 12606 East Mission Avenue, Spokane Valley, WA Zip 99216–1090; tel. 509/924–6650; Gregory Repetti, Interim Chief Executive Officer
Web address: www.valleyhospital.org

YAKIMA REGIONAL MEDICAL AND CARDIAC CENTER (O, 214 beds) 110 South Ninth Avenue, Yakima, WA Zip 98902–3315; tel. 509/575–5000; Veronica Knudson, Chief Executive Officer
Web address: www.yakimaregional.net

WEST VIRGINIA: BLUEFIELD REGIONAL MEDICAL CENTER (O, 240 beds) 500 Cherry Street, Bluefield, WV Zip 24701–3390; tel. 304/327–1100; David Henry, Chief Executive Officer
Web address: www.bluefield.org

GREENBRIER VALLEY MEDICAL CENTER (O, 113 beds) 202 Maplewood Avenue, Ronceverte, WV Zip 24970–1334, Mailing Address: P.O. Box 497, Zip 24970–0497; tel. 304/647–4411; Robert Calhoun, Chief Executive Officer
Web address: www.gvmc.com

PLATEAU MEDICAL CENTER (O, 25 beds) 430 Main Street, Oak Hill, WV Zip 25901–3455; tel. 304/469–8600; Derek W. Cimala, Interim Chief Executive Officer
Web address: www.plateaumedicalcenter.com

WILLIAMSON MEMORIAL HOSPITAL (O, 76 beds) 859 Alderson Street, Williamson, WV Zip 25661–3215, Mailing Address: P.O. Box 1980, Zip 25661–1980; tel. 304/235–2500; Cindy Segar–Miller, R.N., MS, Interim Chief Executive Officer
Web address: www.williamsonmemorial.net

WYOMING: EVANSTON REGIONAL HOSPITAL (O, 42 beds) 190 Arrowhead Drive, Evanston, WY Zip 82930–9266; tel. 307/789–3636; George Winn, Chief Executive Officer
Web address: www.evanstonregionalhospital.com

Owned, leased, sponsored:	199 hospitals	26653 beds
Contract–managed:	0 hospitals	0 beds
Totals:	199 hospitals	26653 beds

For explanation of codes following names, see page B2.
★ Indicates Type III membership in the American Hospital Association.

0249: COMMUNITY HEALTHCARE SYSTEM (NP)
901 MacArthur Boulevard, Hammond, IN Zip 46321–2959;
tel. 219/836–1600; Donald Powers, Chairman, President and Chief
Executive Officer
(Independent Hospital System)

INDIANA: COMMUNITY HOSPITAL (O, 457 beds) 901 Macarthur Boulevard,
Munster, IN Zip 46321–2959; tel. 219/836–1600; Donald P. Fesko, Chief
Executive Officer and Administrator
Web address: www.comhs.org

ST. CATHERINE HOSPITAL (O, 189 beds) 4321 Fir Street, East Chicago, IN
Zip 46312–3097; tel. 219/392–1700; JoAnn Birdzell, Chief Executive Officer
and Administrator
Web address: www.stcatherinehospital.org

ST. MARY MEDICAL CENTER (O, 195 beds) 1500 South Lake Park Avenue,
Hobart, IN Zip 46342–6699; tel. 219/942–0551; Janice L. Ryba, JD, Chief
Executive Officer
Web address: www.comhs.org

Owned, leased, sponsored:	3 hospitals	841 beds
Contract–managed:	0 hospitals	0 beds
Totals:	3 hospitals	841 beds

★0384: COMMUNITY HOSPITAL CORPORATION (NP)
7800 North Dallas Parkway, Suite 200, Plano, TX Zip 75024–6116;
tel. 972/943–6400; Michael D. Williams, President and Chief
Executive Officer
(Independent Hospital System)

NEW MEXICO: ARTESIA GENERAL HOSPITAL (L, 30 beds) 702 North 13th
Street, Artesia, NM Zip 88210–1199; tel. 575/748–3333; Kenneth W.
Randall, Chief Executive Officer
Web address: www.artesiageneral.com

TEXAS: BAPTIST HOSPITALS OF SOUTHEAST TEXAS (O, 394 beds) 3080
College Street, Beaumont, TX Zip 77701–4689, Mailing Address: P.O.
Box 1591, Zip 77704–1591; tel. 409/212–5000; David N. Parmer, Chief
Executive Officer
Web address: www.bhset.net

BAPTIST ORANGE HOSPITAL (O, 40 beds) 608 Strickland Drive, Orange, TX
Zip 77630–4717; tel. 409/883–9361; Jarren Garrett, Chief Administrative
Officer
Web address: www.bhset.net

ST. MARK'S MEDICAL CENTER (O, 44 beds) One St. Mark's Place, La Grange,
TX Zip 78945; tel. 979/242–2200; Shane Kernell, Chief Executive Officer
Web address: www.smmctx.org

YOAKUM COMMUNITY HOSPITAL (L, 25 beds) 1200 Carl Ramert Drive,
Yoakum, TX Zip 77995–4868; tel. 361/293–2321; Karen Barber, R.N., Chief
Executive Officer
Web address: www.yoakumhospital.org

Owned, leased, sponsored:	5 hospitals	533 beds
Contract–managed:	0 hospitals	0 beds
Totals:	5 hospitals	533 beds

1085: COMMUNITY MEDICAL CENTERS (NP)
Fresno and Maddy Drive, Fresno, CA Zip 93721, Mailing Address:
P.O. Box 1232, Zip 93715–1232; tel. 559/459–6000; Tim A. Joslin,
President and Chief Executive Officer
(Moderately Centralized Health System)

CALIFORNIA: CLOVIS COMMUNITY MEDICAL CENTER (O, 109 beds) 2755
Herndon Avenue, Clovis, CA Zip 93611–6801; tel. 559/324–4000; Craig
Castro, Chief Executive Officer
Web address: www.communitymedical.org

COMMUNITY BEHAVIORAL HEALTH CENTER (O, 61 beds) 7171 North Cedar
Avenue, Fresno, CA Zip 93720–3311; tel. 559/449–8000; Jack Chubb, Chief
Executive Officer
Web address: www.communitymedical.org

COMMUNITY REGIONAL MEDICAL CENTER (O, 808 beds) 2823 Fresno
Street, Fresno, CA Zip 93721–1324, Mailing Address: P.O. Box 1232,
Zip 93715–1232; tel. 559/459–6000; John M. Chubb, Chief Executive
Officer
Web address: www.communitymedical.org

FRESNO HEART AND SURGICAL HOSPITAL (O, 60 beds) 15 East Audubon
Drive, Fresno, CA Zip 93720–1542; tel. 559/433–8000; Wanda Holderman,
R.N., Chief Executive Officer
Web address: www.fresnoheartandsurgical.org

Owned, leased, sponsored:	4 hospitals	1038 beds
Contract–managed:	0 hospitals	0 beds
Totals:	4 hospitals	1038 beds

0909: COMPASS HEALTH (NP)
426 North Avenue G., Crowley, LA Zip 70526–2434;
tel. 337/788–3330; Mark J. Cullen, Chief Executive Officer
(Independent Hospital System)

LOUISIANA: COMPASS BEHAVIORAL CENTER OF ALEXANDRIA (O, 16 beds)
6410 Masonic Drve, Alexandria, LA Zip 71301–2319;
tel. 318/473–0035; Angie Hudson, Administrator
Web address: www.compasshealthcare.com/site191.php

COMPASS BEHAVIORAL CENTER OF CROWLEY (O, 34 beds) 1526 North
Avenue I., Crowley, LA Zip 70526–2434; tel. 337/788–3380; Allison Kidder,
Administrator
Web address: www.compasshealthcare.com

COMPASS BEHAVIORAL CENTER OF HOUMA (O, 20 beds) 4701 West Park
Avenue, Houma, LA Zip 70364–4426; tel. 985/876–1715; Daniel Shea,
Administrator
Web address: www.compasshealthcare.com/site83.php

Owned, leased, sponsored:	3 hospitals	70 beds
Contract–managed:	0 hospitals	0 beds
Totals:	3 hospitals	70 beds

0950: CONE HEALTH (NP)
1200 North Elm Street, Greensboro, NC Zip 27401–1004;
tel. 336/832–7000; R. Timothy Rice, Chief Executive Officer

NORTH CAROLINA: ALAMANCE REGIONAL MEDICAL CENTER (O, 218 beds)
1240 Huffman Mill Road, Burlington, NC Zip 27215–8700, Mailing
Address: P.O. Box 202, Zip 27216–0202; tel. 336/538–7000; Preston
W. Hammock, President and Chief Executive Officer
Web address: www.armc.com

MOSES H. CONE MEMORIAL HOSPITAL (C, 1004 beds) 1200 North Elm
Street, Greensboro, NC Zip 27401–1020; tel. 336/832–7000; Mickey
Foster, President
Web address: www.conehealth.com/locations/moses–cone–hospital/

Owned, leased, sponsored:	1 hospital	218 beds
Contract–managed:	1 hospital	1004 beds
Totals:	2 hospitals	1222 beds

**0014: CONNECTICUT DEPARTMENT OF MENTAL HEALTH
AND ADDICTION SERVICES** (NP)
410 Capitol Avenue, Hartford, CT Zip 06106–1367, Mailing Address:
P.O. Box 341431, Zip 06134–1431; tel. 860/418–7000; Patricia
Rehmer, Commissioner
(Independent Hospital System)

CONNECTICUT: CONNECTICUT MENTAL HEALTH CENTER (O, 32 beds) 34
Park Street, New Haven, CT Zip 06519–1109, Mailing Address: P.O. Box
1842, Zip 06508–1842; tel. 203/974–7144; Michael Sernyak, M.D.,
Director
Web address: www.ct.gov/dmhas/cwp/view.asp?a=2906&q=334596

CONNECTICUT VALLEY HOSPITAL (O, 596 beds) Eastern Drive, Middletown,
CT Zip 06457–3947, Mailing Address: P.O. Box 351, Zip 06457–3947;
tel. 860/262–5000; Helene M. Vartelas, Chief Executive Officer
Web address: www.ct.gov/dmhas/cwp/view.asp?a=3519&q=416778

For explanation of codes following names, see page B2.
★ Indicates Type III membership in the American Hospital Association.

Section B

SOUTHWEST CONNECTICUT MENTAL HEALTH SYSTEM (O, 62 beds) 1635 Central Avenue, Bridgeport, CT Zip 06610–2717; tel. 203/551–7400; Daniel Wartenberg, PsyD, M.P.H., Chief Executive Officer
Web address: www.ct.gov/dmhas/cwp/view.asp?a=2946&q=378936

Owned, leased, sponsored:	3 hospitals	690 beds
Contract–managed:	0 hospitals	0 beds
Totals:	3 hospitals	690 beds

0016: COOK COUNTY HEALTH AND HOSPITALS SYSTEM
(NP)
1900 West Polk Street, Suite 220, Chicago, IL Zip 60612–3723; tel. 312/864–6820; John Jay Shannon, M.D., Chief Executive Officer
(Independent Hospital System)

ILLINOIS: JOHN H. STROGER JR. HOSPITAL OF COOK COUNTY (O, 460 beds) 1969 West Ogden Avenue, Chicago, IL Zip 60612–3714; tel. 312/864–6000; W. Peter Daniels, Chief Operating Officer
Web address: www.cookcountyhealth.net

OAK FOREST HEALTH CENTER OF COOK COUNTY (O, 95 beds) 15900 South Cicero Avenue, Oak Forest, IL Zip 60452–4006; tel. 708/687–7200;

PROVIDENT HOSPITAL OF COOK COUNTY (O, 25 beds) 500 East 51st Street, Chicago, IL Zip 60615–2494; tel. 312/572–2000; Thomas J. Dohm, Interim Chief Operating Officer
Web address: www.ccbhs.org/pages/ProvidentHospitalofCookCounty.htm

Owned, leased, sponsored:	3 hospitals	580 beds
Contract–managed:	0 hospitals	0 beds
Totals:	3 hospitals	580 beds

0905: CORNERSTONE HEALTHCARE GROUP (IO)
2200 Ross Avenue, Suite 5400, Dallas, TX Zip 75201–7984; tel. 469/621–6700; David Smith, President and Chief Operating Officer
(Independent Hospital System)

ARIZONA: CORNERSTONE HOSPITAL OF SOUTHEAST ARIZONA (O, 34 beds) 7220 East Rosewood Drive, Tucson, AZ Zip 85710–1350; tel. 520/546–4595; Louise Cassidy, Chief Executive Officer
Web address: www.chghospitals.com

ARKANSAS: CORNERSTONE HOSPITAL OF NORTH LITTLE ROCK (O, 40 beds) 1400 Braden Street, Jacksonville, AR Zip 72076–3721; tel. 501/985–7026; Steve Patterson, Chief Executive Officer
Web address: www.chghospitals.com/littlerock/

LOUISIANA: CORNERSTONE HOSPITAL OF BOSSIER CITY (O, 54 beds) 4900 Medical Drive, Bossier City, LA Zip 71112–4521; tel. 318/747–9500; Sheri Burnette, R.N., Chief Executive Officer and Administrator
Web address: www.chghospitals.com/

CORNERSTONE HOSPITAL OF SOUTHWEST LOUISIANA (O, 30 beds) 703 Cypress Street, Sulphur, LA Zip 70663–5053; tel. 337/310–6000; David Smith, Chief Executive Officer
Web address: www.chghospitals.com/sulphur/

CORNERSTONE HOSPITAL–WEST MONROE (O, 40 beds) 6198 Cypress Street, West Monroe, LA Zip 71291–9010; tel. 318/396–5600; Chris Simpson, Chief Executive Officer
Web address: www.chghospitals.com/chwm.html

OKLAHOMA: SOLARA HOSPITAL OF MUSKOGEE (O, 41 beds) 351 South 40th Street, Muskogee, OK Zip 74401–4916; tel. 918/682–6161; Craig Koele, Chief Executive Officer
Web address: www.chghospitals.com/muskogee/

SOLARA HOSPITAL OF SHAWNEE (O, 34 beds) 1900 Gordon Cooper Drive, 2nd Floor, Shawnee, OK Zip 74801–8603, Mailing Address: PO BOX 1245, Zip 74802–1245; tel. 405/395–5800; Elizabeth Waytula, Chief Executive Officer
Web address: www.chghospitals.com/shawnee/

TEXAS: CORNERSTONE HOSPITAL OF AUSTIN (O, 157 beds) 4207 Burnet Road, Austin, TX Zip 78756–3396; tel. 512/706–1900; Scott Galliardt, Chief Executive Officer
Web address: www.chghospitals.com/austin/

CORNERSTONE HOSPITAL OF HOUSTON AT CLEARLAKE (O, 134 beds) 709 Medical Center Boulevard, Webster, TX Zip 77598; tel. 281/332–3322; James Camp, R.N., Regional Chief Executive Officer, Houston Market
Web address: www.cornerstonehealthcaregroup.com

CORNERSTONE HOSPITAL OF ROUND ROCK (O, 54 beds) 4681 College Park Drive, Round Rock, TX Zip 78655; tel. 512/533–2525; Edward L. Dyer, Chief Executive Officer
Web address: www.chghospitals.com/roundrock

CORNERSTONE HOSPITAL–MEDICAL CENTER OF HOUSTON (O, 35 beds) 2001 Hermann Drive, Houston, TX Zip 77004; tel. 832/649–6200; Michael Higginbotham, Chief Executive Officer
Web address: www.chghospitals.com

SOLARA HOSPITAL CONROE (O, 41 beds) 1500 Grand Lake Drive, Conroe, TX Zip 77304–2891; tel. 936/523–1800; Suzanne Kretschmer, Interim Hospital Administrator
Web address: www.chghospitals.com/conroe/

SOLARA HOSPITAL HARLINGEN (O, 82 beds) 508 Victoria Lane, Harlingen, TX Zip 78550–3225; tel. 956/425–9600; Cary L. Montalvo, Chief Executive Officer
Web address: www.chghospitals.com/harlingen/

SOLARA HOSPITAL MCALLEN (O, 78 beds) 301 West Expressway 83, McAllen, TX Zip 78503–3045; tel. 956/632–4880; Chris Chizek, Chief Executive Officer
Web address: www.chghospitals.com/mcallen/

WEST VIRGINIA: CORNERSTONE HOSPITAL OF HUNTINGTON (O, 28 beds) 2900 First Avenue, Two East, Huntington, WV Zip 25702–1241; tel. 304/399–2600; Cynthia Isaacs, Chief Executive Officer
Web address: www.chghospitals.com

Owned, leased, sponsored:	15 hospitals	882 beds
Contract–managed:	0 hospitals	0 beds
Totals:	15 hospitals	882 beds

★0103: COTTAGE HEALTH SYSTEM (NP)
400 West Pueblo Street, Santa Barbara, CA Zip 93105–4353, Mailing Address: P.O. Box 689, Zip 93102–0689; tel. 805/569–7290; Ronald C. Werft, President and Chief Executive Officer
(Independent Hospital System)

CALIFORNIA: GOLETA VALLEY COTTAGE HOSPITAL (O, 80 beds) 351 South Patterson Avenue, Santa Barbara, CA Zip 93111–2496, Mailing Address: Box 6306, Zip 93160–6306; tel. 805/967–3411; Ronald C. Werft, President and Chief Executive Officer
Web address: www.sbch.org

SANTA BARBARA COTTAGE HOSPITAL (O, 351 beds) 400 West Pueblo Street, Santa Barbara, CA Zip 93105–4390, Mailing Address: P.O. Box 689, Zip 93102–0689; tel. 805/682–7111; Ronald C. Werft, President and Chief Executive Officer
Web address: www.cottagehealthsystem.org

SANTA YNEZ VALLEY COTTAGE HOSPITAL (O, 11 beds) 2050 Viborg Road, Solvang, CA Zip 93463–2295; tel. 805/688–6431; Ronald C. Werft, President and Chief Executive Officer
Web address: www.cottagehealthsystem.org

Owned, leased, sponsored:	3 hospitals	442 beds
Contract–managed:	0 hospitals	0 beds
Totals:	3 hospitals	442 beds

★0123: COVENANT HEALTH (NP)
100 Fort Sanders West Boulevard, Knoxville, TN Zip 37922–3353; tel. 865/531–5555; Anthony Spezia, President and Chief Executive Officer
(Centralized Health System)

TENNESSEE: CLAIBORNE MEDICAL CENTER (L, 62 beds) 1850 Old Knoxville Road, Tazewell, TN Zip 37879–3625; tel. 423/626–4211; Tim S. Brown, Chief Executive Officer
Web address: www.claibornehospital.org

For explanation of codes following names, see page B2.
★ Indicates Type III membership in the American Hospital Association.

CUMBERLAND MEDICAL CENTER (O, 122 beds) 421 South Main Street, Crossville, TN Zip 38555–5031; tel. 931/484–9511; Jeremy Biggs, President and Chief Administrative Officer
Web address: www.cmchealthcare.org

FORT LOUDOUN MEDICAL CENTER (L, 40 beds) 550 Fort Loudoun Medical Center Drive, Lenoir City, TN Zip 37772–5673; tel. 865/271–6000; Jeffrey Feike, President and Chief Administrative Officer
Web address: www.covenanthealth.com

FORT SANDERS REGIONAL MEDICAL CENTER (O, 386 beds) 1901 West Clinch Avenue, Knoxville, TN Zip 37916–2307; tel. 865/541–1111; Keith Altshuler, President and Chief Administrative Officer
Web address: www.covenanthealth.com

LECONTE MEDICAL CENTER (O, 123 beds) 742 Middle Creek Road, Sevierville, TN Zip 37862–5019, Mailing Address: P.O. Box 8005, Zip 37864–8005; tel. 865/446–7000; Jennifer Hanson, MS, R.N., President and Chief Administrative Officer
Web address: www.lecontemedicalcenter.com

METHODIST MEDICAL CENTER OF OAK RIDGE (O, 210 beds) 990 Oak Ridge Turnpike, Oak Ridge, TN Zip 37830–6976, Mailing Address: P.O. Box 2529, Zip 37831–2529; tel. 865/835–1000; Michael Belbeck, President and Chief Administrative Officer
Web address: www.mmcoakridge.com

MORRISTOWN–HAMBLEN HEALTHCARE SYSTEM (O, 159 beds) 908 West Fourth North Street, Morristown, TN Zip 37814–3894, Mailing Address: P.O. Box 1178, Zip 37816–1178; tel. 423/492–9000; Gordon Lintz, Chief Administrative Officer
Web address: www.mhhs1.org

PARKWEST MEDICAL CENTER (O, 297 beds) 9352 Park West Boulevard, Knoxville, TN Zip 37923–4325, Mailing Address: P.O. Box 22993, Zip 37933–0993; tel. 865/373–1000; Rick Lassiter, President and Chief Administrative Officer
Web address: www.yesparkwest.com

ROANE MEDICAL CENTER (O, 54 beds) 8045 Roane Medical Center Drive, Harriman, TN Zip 37748–8333; tel. 865/316–1000; Gaye Jolly, FACHE, President/Chief Administrative Officer
Web address: www.roanemedical.com

Owned, leased, sponsored:	9 hospitals	1453 beds
Contract–managed:	0 hospitals	0 beds
Totals:	9 hospitals	1453 beds

★**0036: COVENANT HEALTH SYSTEM** (NP)
3615 19th Street, Lubbock, TX Zip 79410–1203; tel. 806/725–0447; Richard H. Parks, FACHE, President and Chief Executive Officer
(Centralized Health System)

TEXAS: COVENANT CHILDREN'S HOSPITAL (O, 73 beds) 4015 22nd Place, Lubbock, TX Zip 79410; tel. 806/725–1011; Christopher J. Dougherty, Chief Executive Officer
Web address: www.covenanthealth.org/About–Us/Facilities/Childrens–Hospital.aspx

COVENANT HOSPITAL PLAINVIEW (L, 68 beds) 2601 Dimmitt Road, Plainview, TX Zip 79072–1833; tel. 806/296–5531; Clay Taylor, Chief Executive Officer
Web address: www.covenantplainview.org

COVENANT HOSPITAL–LEVELLAND (L, 22 beds) 1900 South College Avenue, Levelland, TX Zip 79336–6508; tel. 806/894–4963; Bruce White, Administrator
Web address: www.covenanthospitallevelland.com/

COVENANT MEDICAL CENTER (O, 605 beds) 3615 19th Street, Lubbock, TX Zip 79410–1203, Mailing Address: P.O. Box 1201, Zip 79408–1201; tel. 806/725–0000; Troy Thibodeaux, Chief Executive Officer
Web address: www.covenanthealth.org

COVENANT SPECIALTY HOSPITAL (O, 56 beds) 3815 20th Street, Lubbock, TX Zip 79410–1235; tel. 806/725–9200; Stuart Oertli, Executive Director
Web address: www.covenanthealth.org/view/Facilities/Specialty_Hospital

Owned, leased, sponsored:	5 hospitals	824 beds
Contract–managed:	0 hospitals	0 beds
Totals:	5 hospitals	824 beds

★**5885: COVENANT HEALTH SYSTEMS, INC.** (CC)
100 Ames Pond Drive, Suite 102, Tewksbury, MA Zip 01876–1240; tel. 978/654–6363; David R. Lincoln, FACHE, President and Chief Executive Officer
(Moderately Centralized Health System)

MAINE: ST. JOSEPH HOSPITAL (O, 84 beds) 360 Broadway, Bangor, ME Zip 04401–3979, Mailing Address: P.O. Box 403, Zip 04402–0403; tel. 207/262–1000; Mary Prybylo, President and Chief Executive Officer
Web address: www.sjhhealth.com

ST. MARY'S REGIONAL MEDICAL CENTER (O, 171 beds) 318 Sabattus Street, Lewiston, ME Zip 04240–5553, Mailing Address: P.O. Box 291, Zip 04243–0291; tel. 207/777–8100; Lee T. Myles, President and Chief Executive Officer
Web address: www.stmarysmaine.com

NEW HAMPSHIRE: ST. JOSEPH HOSPITAL (O, 126 beds) 172 Kinsley Street, Nashua, NH Zip 03060–3648; tel. 603/882–3000; Richard Boehler, M.D., President and Chief Executive Officer
Web address: www.stjosephhospital.com

Owned, leased, sponsored:	3 hospitals	381 beds
Contract–managed:	0 hospitals	0 beds
Totals:	3 hospitals	381 beds

0179: COXHEALTH (NP)
1423 North Jefferson Avenue, Springfield, MO Zip 65802–1988; tel. 417/269–3108; Steven D. Edwards, President and Chief Executive Officer
(Moderately Centralized Health System)

MISSOURI: COX MEDICAL CENTER BRANSON (O, 124 beds) 251 Skaggs Road, Branson, MO Zip 65616–2031, Mailing Address: P.O. Box 650, Zip 65615–0650; tel. 417/335–7000; William K. Mahoney, President and Chief Executive Officer
Web address: www.skaggs.net

COX MEDICAL CENTERS (O, 659 beds) 1423 North Jefferson Street, Springfield, MO Zip 65802–1988; tel. 417/269–3000; Steven D. Edwards, President and Chief Executive Officer
Web address: www.coxhealth.com

COX MONETT (O, 25 beds) 801 North Lincoln Avenue, Monett, MO Zip 65708–1641; tel. 417/235–3144; Genice Maroc, FACHE, President
Web address: www.coxhealth.com

Owned, leased, sponsored:	3 hospitals	808 beds
Contract–managed:	0 hospitals	0 beds
Totals:	3 hospitals	808 beds

0930: CRC HEALTH GROUP, INC. (IO)
20400 Stevens Creek Boulevard, Suite 600, Cupertino, CA Zip 95014–2217; tel. 866/540–5240; Jerome E. Rhodes, Chief Executive Officer

ARIZONA: SIERRA TUCSON (O, 139 beds) 39580 South Lago Del Oro Parkway, Tucson, AZ Zip 85739–9637; tel. 520/624–4000; Stephen P. Fahey, Executive Director
Web address: www.sierratucson.com

NORTH CAROLINA: WILMINGTON TREATMENT CENTER (O, 44 beds) 2520 Troy Drive, Wilmington, NC Zip 28401–7643; tel. 910/762–2727; Robert Pitts, Executive Director
Web address: www.wilmtreatment.com

Owned, leased, sponsored:	2 hospitals	183 beds
Contract–managed:	0 hospitals	0 beds
Totals:	2 hospitals	183 beds

Section B

For explanation of codes following names, see page B2.
★ Indicates Type III membership in the American Hospital Association.

★0008:   CROZER–KEYSTONE HEALTH SYSTEM (NP)
100 West Sproul Road, Springfield, PA Zip 19064–2033;
tel. 610/338–8205; Joan K. Richards, President and Chief Executive
Officer
(Moderately Centralized Health System)

PENNSYLVANIA: CROZER–CHESTER MEDICAL CENTER (O, 428 beds) One
Medical Center Boulevard, Upland, PA Zip 19013–3995;
tel. 610/447–2000; Patrick J. Gavin, President
Web address: www.crozer.org

DELAWARE COUNTY MEMORIAL HOSPITAL (O, 195 beds) 501 North
Lansdowne Avenue, Drexel Hill, PA Zip 19026–1114; tel. 610/284–8100;
Robert Haffey, R.N., President
Web address: www.crozer.org

Owned, leased, sponsored:	2 hospitals	623 beds
Contract–managed:	0 hospitals	0 beds
Totals:	2 hospitals	623 beds

★1075:   DAUGHTERS OF CHARITY HEALTH SYSTEM (CC)
26000 Altamont Road, Los Altos Hills, CA Zip 94022–4317;
tel. 650/917–4500; Robert Issai, President and Chief Executive
Officer
(Independent Hospital System)

CALIFORNIA: O'CONNOR HOSPITAL (O, 202 beds) 2105 Forest Avenue, San
Jose, CA Zip 95128–1471; tel. 408/947–2500; James F. Dover, FACHE,
President and CEO
Web address: www.oconnorhospital.org

SAINT LOUISE REGIONAL HOSPITAL (O, 93 beds) 9400 No Name Uno, Gilroy,
CA Zip 95020–3528; tel. 408/848–2000; James F. Dover, FACHE, President
and CEO
Web address: www.dochs.org

SETON MEDICAL CENTER (O, 423 beds) 1900 Sullivan Avenue, Daly City, CA
Zip 94015–2229; tel. 650/992–4000; Joanne E. Allen, President and Chief
Executive Officer
Web address: www.setonmedicalcenter.org

SETON MEDICAL CENTER COASTSIDE (O, 116 beds) 600 Marine Boulevard,
Moss Beach, CA Zip 94038–9641; tel. 650/563–7100; James P.
Schuessler, Interim President and Chief Executive Officer

ST. FRANCIS MEDICAL CENTER (O, 323 beds) 3630 East Imperial Highway,
Lynwood, CA Zip 90262–2636; tel. 310/900–8900; Gerald T. Kozai,
President and Chief Executive Officer
Web address: www.dochs.org

ST. VINCENT MEDICAL CENTER (O, 271 beds) 2131 West Third Street, Los
Angeles, CA Zip 90057–1901, Mailing Address: P.O. Box 57992,
Zip 90057–0992; tel. 213/484–7111; Catherine Fickes, R.N., President and
Chief Executive Officer
Web address: www.stvincentmedicalcenter.com

Owned, leased, sponsored:	6 hospitals	1428 beds
Contract–managed:	0 hospitals	0 beds
Totals:	6 hospitals	1428 beds

★0864:   DAVIS HEALTH SYSTEM (NP)
Reed Street and Gorman Avenue, Elkins, WV Zip 26241, Mailing
Address: P.O. Box 1697, Zip 26241–1697; tel. 304/636–3300;
Mark Doak, President and Chief Executive Officer
(Independent Hospital System)

WEST VIRGINIA: BROADDUS HOSPITAL (O, 72 beds) 1 Healthcare Drive,
Philippi, WV Zip 26416–9405, Mailing Address: P.O. Box 930,
Zip 26416–0930; tel. 304/457–1760; Jeffrey A. Powelson, Chief
Executive Officer
Web address: www.davishealthsystem.org/

DAVIS MEMORIAL HOSPITAL (O, 90 beds) Gorman Avenue and Reed Street,
Elkins, WV Zip 26241, Mailing Address: P.O. Box 1484, Zip 26241–1484;
tel. 304/636–3300; Mark Doak, Chief Executive Officer
Web address: www.davishealthsystem.com

Owned, leased, sponsored:	2 hospitals	162 beds
Contract–managed:	0 hospitals	0 beds
Totals:	2 hospitals	162 beds

1825:   DCH HEALTH SYSTEM (NP)
809 University Boulevard East, Tuscaloosa, AL Zip 35401–2029;
tel. 205/759–7111; Bryan N. Kindred, FACHE, President and Chief
Executive Officer
(Moderately Centralized Health System)

ALABAMA: DCH REGIONAL MEDICAL CENTER (O, 684 beds) 809 University
Boulevard East, Tuscaloosa, AL Zip 35401–2029; tel. 205/759–7111;
William H. Cassels, Administrator
Web address: www.dchsystem.com

FAYETTE MEDICAL CENTER (L, 167 beds) 1653 Temple Avenue North,
Fayette, AL Zip 35555–1314, Mailing Address: P.O. Drawer 710,
Zip 35555–0710; tel. 205/932–5966; Donald J. Jones, FACHE,
Administrator
Web address: www.dchsystem.com

NORTHPORT MEDICAL CENTER (O, 196 beds) 2700 Hospital Drive,
Northport, AL Zip 35476–3360; tel. 205/333–4500; Luke Standeffer,
Administrator
Web address: www.dchsystem.com

Owned, leased, sponsored:	3 hospitals	1047 beds
Contract–managed:	0 hospitals	0 beds
Totals:	3 hospitals	1047 beds

★0313:   DEACONESS HEALTH SYSTEM (NP)
600 Mary Street, Evansville, IN Zip 47710–1658;
tel. 812/450–5000; Linda E. White, President and Chief Executive
Officer
(Centralized Health System)

INDIANA: DEACONESS HOSPITAL (O, 489 beds) 600 Mary Street, Evansville,
IN Zip 47710–1658; tel. 812/450–5000; Shawn W. McCoy, Chief
Administrative Officer
Web address: www.deaconess.com

THE HEART HOSPITAL AT DEACONESS GATEWAY (O, 24 beds) 4007
Gateway Boulevard, Newburgh, IN Zip 47630–8947; tel. 812/842–4784;
Rebecca Malotte, Executive Director and Chief Nursing Officer
Web address: www.deaconess.com/

THE WOMEN'S HOSPITAL (O, 74 beds) 4199 Gateway Boulevard, Newburgh,
IN Zip 47630–8940; tel. 812/842–4200; Christina M. Ryan, R.N., Chief
Executive Officer
Web address: www.deaconess.com

Owned, leased, sponsored:	3 hospitals	587 beds
Contract–managed:	0 hospitals	0 beds
Totals:	3 hospitals	587 beds

0330:   DEKALB REGIONAL HEALTH SYSTEM (NP)
2701 North Decatur Road, Decatur, GA Zip 30033–5918;
tel. 404/501–1000; John Shelton, President and Chief Executive
Officer
(Independent Hospital System)

GEORGIA: DEKALB MEDICAL AT DOWNTOWN DECATUR (O, 44 beds) 450
North Candler Street, Decatur, GA Zip 30030–2671; tel. 404/501–6700;
John Shelton, President and Chief Executive Officer
Web address: www.dekalbmedicalcenter.org

DEKALB MEDICAL AT HILLANDALE (O, 100 beds) 2801 DeKalb Medical
Parkway, Lithonia, GA Zip 30058–4996; tel. 404/501–8700; John Shelton,
President and Chief Executive Officer
Web address: www.dekalbmedical.org

DEKALB MEDICAL AT NORTH DECATUR (O, 417 beds) 2701 North Decatur
Road, Decatur, GA Zip 30033–5995; tel. 404/501–1000; John Shelton,
President and Chief Executive Officer
Web address: www.dekalbmedical.org

For explanation of codes following names, see page B2.
★ Indicates Type III membership in the American Hospital Association.

Section B

Owned, leased, sponsored:	3 hospitals	561 beds
Contract–managed:	0 hospitals	0 beds
Totals:	3 hospitals	561 beds

9495: DEPARTMENT OF THE AIR FORCE (FG)
1420 Pentagon, Room 4E1084, Washington, DC Zip 20330–1420; tel. 202/767–4765; Lieutenant General Charles B. Green, M.D., Surgeon General
(Independent Hospital System)

ALASKA: U. S. AIR FORCE REGIONAL HOSPITAL (O, 64 beds) 5955 Zeamer Avenue, Elmendorf AFB, AK Zip 99506–3702; tel. 907/580–3006; Colonel Scott Suckow, Commander
Web address: www.elmendorf.af.mil/

CALIFORNIA: DAVID GRANT USAF MEDICAL CENTER (O, 110 beds) 101 Bodin Circle, Travis AFB, CA Zip 94535–1809; tel. 707/423–7300; Colonel Brian T. Hayes, Commander
Web address: www.travis.af.mil/units/dgmc/index.asp

FLORIDA: U. S. AIR FORCE REGIONAL HOSPITAL (O, 57 beds) 307 Boatner Road, Suite 114, Eglin AFB, FL Zip 32542–1282; tel. 850/883–8221; Colonel Gianna Zeh, Commander
Web address: www.eglin.af.mil

IDAHO: U. S. AIR FORCE CLINIC (O, 10 beds) 90 Hope Drive, Building 600, Mountain Home AFB, ID Zip 83648–1057; tel. 208/828–7610; Lieutenant Colonel Gregory W. Carson, Administrator

ILLINOIS: SCOTT MEDICAL CENTER (O, 18 beds) 310 West Losey Street, Scott AFB, IL Zip 62225–5252; tel. 618/256–7456; Colonel Bret D. Burton, Commander

MISSISSIPPI: U. S. AIR FORCE MEDICAL CENTER KEESLER (O, 56 beds) 301 Fisher Street, Room 1A132, Keesler AFB, MS Zip 39534–2519; tel. 228/376–2550; Colonel Thomas Harrell, M.D., Commander
Web address: www.keesler.af.mil

NEVADA: MIKE O'CALLAGHAN FEDERAL HOSPITAL (O, 46 beds) 4700 Las Vegas Boulevard North, Suite 2419, Nellis AFB, NV Zip 89191–6600; tel. 702/653–2000; Colonel Christian Benjamin, USAF, MC, Commander
Web address: www.lasvegas.va.gov/

OHIO: WRIGHT PATTERSON MEDICAL CENTER (O, 62 beds) 4881 Sugar Maple Drive, Wright–Patterson AFB, OH Zip 45433–5529; tel. 937/257–9144; Brent Erickson, Administrator
Web address: www.wpafb.af.mil/units/wpmc/

VIRGINIA: U. S. AIR FORCE HOSPITAL (O, 65 beds) 77 Nealy Avenue, Hampton, VA Zip 23665–2040; tel. 757/764–6969; Colonel Wayne M. Pritt, Commander
Web address: www.jble.af.mil

Owned, leased, sponsored:	9 hospitals	488 beds
Contract–managed:	0 hospitals	0 beds
Totals:	9 hospitals	488 beds

9395: DEPARTMENT OF THE ARMY, OFFICE OF THE SURGEON GENERAL (FG)
5109 Leesburg Pike, Falls Church, VA Zip 22041–3215; tel. 703/681–3000; Lieutenant General Eric B. Schoomaker, Surgeon General
(Moderately Centralized Health System)

ALASKA: BASSETT ARMY COMMUNITY HOSPITAL (O, 24 beds) 1060 Gaffney Road, Box 7400, Fort Wainwright, AK Zip 99703–5001, Mailing Address: 1060 Gaffney Road, Box 7440, Zip 99703–5001; tel. 907/361–4000; Timothy Bergeron, Deputy Commander, Administration
Web address: www.alaska.amedd.army.mil

CALIFORNIA: WEED ARMY COMMUNITY HOSPITAL (O, 27 beds) Inner Loop Road and 4th Street, Building 166, Fort Irwin, CA Zip 92310–5065, Mailing Address: P.O. Box 105109, Zip 92310–5109; tel. 760/380–3108; Colonel Cheryl Taylor–Whitehead, Commander
Web address: www.irwin.amedd.army.mil

COLORADO: EVANS U. S. ARMY COMMUNITY HOSPITAL (O, 57 beds) 1650 Cochrane Circle, Building 7500, Fort Carson, CO Zip 80913–4613; tel. 719/526–7200; Colonel Dennis P. LeMaster, Commander
Web address: www.evans.amedd.army.mil

GEORGIA: DWIGHT DAVID EISENHOWER ARMY MEDICAL CENTER (O, 115 beds) 300 West Hospital Road, Fort Gordon, GA Zip 30905–5741; tel. 706/787–5811; Colonel John P. Lamoureux, Commander
Web address: www.ddeamc.amedd.army.mil

MARTIN ARMY COMMUNITY HOSPITAL (O, 57 beds) 7950 Martin Loop, Fort Benning, GA Zip 31905–5648, Mailing Address: 7950 Martin Loop, B9200, Room 010, Zip 31905–5648; tel. 706/544–2516; Colonel Scott B. Avery, Commander
Web address: www.martin.amedd.army.mil

WINN ARMY COMMUNITY HOSPITAL (O, 37 beds) 1061 Harmon Avenue, Hinesville, GA Zip 31314–5641, Mailing Address: 1061 Harmon Avenue, Suite 2311B, Zip 31314–5641; tel. 912/435–6965; Colonel Kirk W. Eggleston, Commanding Officer
Web address: www.winn.amedd.army.mil/

HAWAII: TRIPLER ARMY MEDICAL CENTER (O, 194 beds) 1 Jarret White Road, Honolulu, HI Zip 96859–5001; tel. 808/433–6661; Brigadier General Dennis D. Doyle, Commanding Officer
Web address: www.tamc.amedd.army.mil

KANSAS: IRWIN ARMY COMMUNITY HOSPITAL (O, 44 beds) 600 Caisson Hill Road, Junction City, KS Zip 66442–7037; tel. 785/239–7000; Colonel Barry R. Pockrandt, Commander
Web address: www.iach.amedd.army.mil

KENTUCKY: COLONEL FLORENCE A. BLANCHFIELD ARMY COMMUNITY HOSPITAL (O, 66 beds) 650 Joel Drive, Fort Campbell, KY Zip 42223–5318; tel. 270/798–8040; Colonel Paul Cordts, Commander
Web address: www.campbell.amedd.army.mil/

IRELAND ARMY COMMUNITY HOSPITAL (O, 33 beds) 289 Ireland Avenue, Fort Knox, KY Zip 40121–5111; tel. 502/624–9333; Colonel Matthew Rettke, Commander
Web address: www.iach.knox.amedd.army.mil/

LOUISIANA: BAYNE–JONES ARMY COMMUNITY HOSPITAL (O, 22 beds) 1585 3rd Street, Fort Polk, LA Zip 71459–5102; tel. 337/531–3928; Colonel Mark C. Wilhite, Commander
Web address: www.polk.amedd.army.mil

MARSHALL ISLANDS: KWAJALEIN HOSPITAL (O, 14 beds) U.S. Army Kwajalein Atoll, Kwajalein Island, MH Zip 96960, Mailing Address: Box 1702, APO, UNITZip 96555–5000; tel. 805/355–2225; Elaine McMahon, Administrator

MISSOURI: GENERAL LEONARD WOOD ARMY COMMUNITY HOSPITAL (O, 42 beds) 126 Missouri Avenue, Fort Leonard Wood, MO Zip 65473–8952; tel. 573/596–0414; Colonel Peter Nielsen, M.D., Commander
Web address: www.glwach.amedd.army.mil/

NEW YORK: KELLER ARMY COMMUNITY HOSPITAL (O, 18 beds) 900 Washington Road, West Point, NY Zip 10996–1197, Mailing Address: U.S. Military Academy, Building 900, Zip 10996–1197; tel. 845/938–5169; Colonel Felicia Pehrson, M.D., Commanding Officer
Web address: www.kach.amedd.army.mil/

NORTH CAROLINA: WOMACK ARMY MEDICAL CENTER (O, 156 beds) Normandy Drive, Fort Bragg, NC Zip 28307–5000; tel. 910/907–6000; Colonel Ronald Stephens, Commander
Web address: www.wamc.amedd.army.mil/

OKLAHOMA: REYNOLDS ARMY COMMUNITY HOSPITAL (O, 24 beds) 4301 Wilson Street, Fort Sill, OK Zip 73503–4472; tel. 580/558–3000; Colonel Noel J. Cardenas, FACHE, Commander and Chief Executive Officer
Web address: www.rach.sill.amedd.army.mil

SOUTH CAROLINA: MONCRIEF ARMY COMMUNITY HOSPITAL (O, 60 beds) 4500 Stuart Street, Fort Jackson, SC Zip 29207–5700; tel. 803/751–2160; Colonel Mark L. Higdon, Commander
Web address: www.moncrief.amedd.army.mil

TEXAS: CARL R. DARNALL ARMY MEDICAL CENTER (O, 109 beds) 36000 Darnall Loop, Fort Hood, TX Zip 76544–5095; tel. 254/288–8000; Colonel Patricia Darnauer, Medical Center Commander
Web address: www.crdamc.amedd.army.mil

For explanation of codes following names, see page B2.
★ Indicates Type III membership in the American Hospital Association.

Section B

SAN ANTONIO MILITARY MEDICAL CENTER (O, 226 beds) 3851 Roger Brookes Drive, Fort Sam Houston, TX Zip 78234–4501; tel. 210/916–4141; Colonel Kyle D. Campbell, Commander
Web address: www.bamc.amedd.army.mil

WILLIAM BEAUMONT ARMY MEDICAL CENTER (O, 209 beds) 5005 North Piedras Street, El Paso, TX Zip 79920–5001; tel. 915/742–2121; Colonel Michael S. Heimall, Commander
Web address: www.wbamc.amedd.army.mil

VIRGINIA: FORT BELVOIR COMMUNITY HOSPITAL (O, 46 beds) 9300 Dewitt Loop, Fort Belvoir, VA Zip 22060–5285; tel. 571/231–3224; Captain Jennifer Vedral–Baron, Commander
Web address: www.fbch.capmed.mil/SitePages/Home.aspx

WASHINGTON: MADIGAN HEALTHCARE SYSTEM (O, 207 beds) Fitzsimmons Drive, Building 9040, Tacoma, WA Zip 98431–1100; tel. 253/968–1110; Colonel Dallas Homas, Commander
Web address: www.mamc.amedd.army.mil

Owned, leased, sponsored:	22 hospitals	1787 beds
Contract–managed:	0 hospitals	0 beds
Totals:	22 hospitals	1787 beds

9295: DEPARTMENT OF VETERANS AFFAIRS (FG)
810 Vermont Avenue N.W., Washington, DC Zip 20420–0001; tel. 202/273–5781; Robert A. Petzel, M.D., Under Secretary for Health
(Decentralized Health System)

ALABAMA: BIRMINGHAM VETERANS AFFAIRS MEDICAL CENTER (O, 313 beds) 700 South 19th Street, Birmingham, AL Zip 35233–1927; tel. 205/933–8101; Thomas C. Smith, III, FACHE, Director
Web address: www.birmingham.va.gov/

CENTRAL ALABAMA VETERANS HEALTH CARE SYSTEM (O, 245 beds) 215 Perry Hill Road, Montgomery, AL Zip 36109–3798; tel. 334/272–4670; James R. Talton, MS, FACHE, Director
Web address: www.centralalabama.va.gov/

TUSCALOOSA VETERANS AFFAIRS MEDICAL CENTER (O, 381 beds) 3701 Loop Road East, Tuscaloosa, AL Zip 35404–5015; tel. 205/554–2000; Maria Andrews, MS, Director
Web address: www.tuscaloosa.va.gov

ARIZONA: NORTHERN ARIZONA VETERANS AFFAIRS HEALTH CARE SYSTEM (O, 151 beds) 500 Highway 89 North, Prescott, AZ Zip 86313–5000; tel. 928/445–4860; Donna K. Jacobs, FACHE, Director
Web address: www.prescott.va.gov/

PHOENIX VETERANS AFFAIRS HEALTH CARE SYSTEM (O, 197 beds) 650 East Indian School Road, Phoenix, AZ Zip 85012–1892; tel. 602/277–5551; Steven W. Young, Interim Director
Web address: www.phoenix.va.gov/

SOUTHERN ARIZONA VETERANS AFFAIRS HEALTH CARE SYSTEM (O, 285 beds) 3601 South 6th Avenue, Tucson, AZ Zip 85723–0002; tel. 520/792–1450; Jonathan H. Gardner, FACHE, Director
Web address: www.tucson.va.gov

ARKANSAS: CENTRAL ARKANSAS VETERANS HEALTHCARE SYSTEM (O, 386 beds) 4300 West Seventh Street, Little Rock, AR Zip 72205–5446; tel. 501/257–1000; Michael R. Winn, Director
Web address: www.littlerock.va.gov/

VETERANS HEALTH CARE SYSTEM OF THE OZARKS (O, 72 beds) 1100 North College Avenue, Fayetteville, AR Zip 72703–1944; tel. 479/443–4301; Mark A. Enderele, M.D., Director
Web address: www.fayettevillear.va.gov

CALIFORNIA: SAN FRANCISO VETERANS AFFAIRS MEDICAL CENTER (O, 244 beds) 4150 Clement Street, San Francisco, CA Zip 94121–1545; tel. 415/221–4810; Bonnie S. Graham, Director
Web address: www.sanfrancisco.va.gov/

VETERANS AFFAIRS CENTRAL CALIFORNIA HEALTH CARE SYSTEM (O, 54 beds) 2615 East Clinton Avenue, Fresno, CA Zip 93703–2223; tel. 559/225–6100; Wessel Meyer, M.D., Acting Director
Web address: www.fresno.va.gov/

VETERANS AFFAIRS GREATER LOS ANGELES HEALTHCARE SYSTEM (O, 1087 beds) 11301 Wilshire Boulevard, Los Angeles, CA Zip 90073–1003; tel. 310/478–3711; Donna M. Beiter, R.N., MSN, Director
Web address: www.losangeles.va.gov/

VETERANS AFFAIRS LOMA LINDA HEALTHCARE SYSTEM (O, 268 beds) 11201 Benton Street, Loma Linda, CA Zip 92357–1000; tel. 909/825–7084; Barbara Fallen, FACHE, Director
Web address: www.lomalinda.va.gov

VETERANS AFFAIRS LONG BEACH HEALTHCARE SYSTEM (O, 237 beds) 5901 East 7th Street, Long Beach, CA Zip 90822–5201; tel. 562/826–8000; Michael W. Fisher, Executive Director
Web address: www.longbeach.va.gov/

VETERANS AFFAIRS PALO ALTO HEALTH CARE SYSTEM (O, 473 beds) 3801 Miranda Avenue, Palo Alto, CA Zip 94304–1207; tel. 650/493–5000; Elizabeth Joyce Freeman, FACHE, Director
Web address: www.paloalto.va.gov/

VETERANS AFFAIRS SAN DIEGO HEALTHCARE SYSTEM (O, 216 beds) 3350 LaJolla Village Drive, San Diego, CA Zip 92161–0002; tel. 858/552–8585; Jeffrey T. Gering, FACHE, Director
Web address: www.sandiego.va.gov

COLORADO: GRAND JUNCTION VETERANS AFFAIRS MEDICAL CENTER (O, 23 beds) 2121 North Avenue, Grand Junction, CO Zip 81501–6428; tel. 970/242–0731; Terry S. Atienza, Director
Web address: www.grandjunction.va.gov/

SOUTHERN COLORADO HEALTHCARE SYSTEM (O, 299 beds) Las Animas, CO Zip 81054–0390; tel. 719/456–1260; Stuart C. Collyer, Director

VETERANS AFFAIRS EASTERN COLORADO HEALTH CARE SYSTEM (O, 271 beds) 1055 Clermont Street, Denver, CO Zip 80220–3877; tel. 303/399–8020; Lynette A. Roff, Director
Web address: www.denver.va.gov/

CONNECTICUT: VETERANS AFFAIRS CONNECTICUT HEALTHCARE SYSTEM (O, 160 beds) 950 Campbell Avenue, West Haven, CT Zip 06516–2770; tel. 203/932–5711; Gerald F. Culliton, Medical Center Director
Web address: www.connecticut.va.gov

DELAWARE: VETERANS AFFAIRS MEDICAL CENTER (O, 60 beds) 1601 Kirkwood Highway, Wilmington, DE Zip 19805–4989; tel. 302/994–2511; Robin C. Aube–Warren, Director
Web address: www.va.gov/wilmington

DISTRICT OF COLUMBIA: WASHINGTON DC VETERANS AFFAIRS MEDICAL CENTER (O, 291 beds) 50 Irving Street N.W., Washington, DC Zip 20422–0002; tel. 202/745–8000; Brian A. Hawkins, Director
Web address: www.washingtondc.va.gov/

FLORIDA: BAY PINES VETERANS AFFAIRS MEDICAL CENTER (O, 396 beds) 10000 Bay Pines Boulevard, Bay Pines, FL Zip 33744–8200, Mailing Address: P.O. Box 5005, Zip 33744–5005; tel. 727/398–6661; Suzanne M. Klinker, Director
Web address: www.baypines.va.gov/

JAMES A. HALEY VETERANS' HOSPITAL (O, 566 beds) 13000 Bruce B. Downs Boulevard, Tampa, FL Zip 33612–4745; tel. 813/972–2000; Kathleen R. Fogarty, Director
Web address: www.tampa.va.gov/

LAKE CITY VETERANS AFFAIRS MEDICAL CENTER (O, 180 beds) 619 South Marion Avenue, Lake City, FL Zip 32025–5898; tel. 386/755–3016; Thomas Wisnieski, FACHE, Director
Web address: www.northflorida.va.gov/

MALCOM RANDALL VETERANS AFFAIRS MEDICAL CENTER (O, 222 beds) 1601 S.W. Archer Road, Gainesville, FL Zip 32608–1197; tel. 352/376–1611; Thomas Wisnieski, FACHE, Director
Web address: www.northflorida.va.gov/

MIAMI VETERANS AFFAIRS HEALTHCARE SYSTEM (O, 401 beds) 1201 N.W. 16th Street, Miami, FL Zip 33125–1624; tel. 305/575–7000; Paul M. Russo, FACHE, Director
Web address: www.miami.va.gov/

WEST PALM BEACH VETERANS AFFAIRS MEDICAL CENTER (O, 297 beds) 7305 North Military Trail, West Palm Beach, FL Zip 33410–6400; tel. 561/422–8262; Charleen R. Szabo, FACHE, Director
Web address: www.westpalmbeach.va.gov/

GEORGIA: ATLANTA VETERANS AFFAIRS MEDICAL CENTER (O, 239 beds) 1670 Clairmont Road, Decatur, GA Zip 30033–4004; tel. 404/321–6111; Leslie Wiggins, Director
Web address: www.atlanta.va.gov/

CARL VINSON VETERANS AFFAIRS MEDICAL CENTER (O, 178 beds) 1826 Veterans Boulevard, Dublin, GA Zip 31021–3620; tel. 478/272–1210; John S. Goldman, Director
Web address: www.dublin.va.gov/

For explanation of codes following names, see page B2.
★ Indicates Type III membership in the American Hospital Association.

CHARLIE NORWOOD VETERANS AFFAIRS MEDICAL CENTER (O, 338 beds) 1 Freedom Way, Augusta, GA Zip 30904–6285; tel. 706/733–0188; Robert U. Hamilton, Director
Web address: www.augusta.va.gov/

IDAHO: BOISE VETERANS AFFAIRS MEDICAL CENTER (O, 85 beds) 500 West Fort Street, Boise, ID Zip 83702–4598; tel. 208/422–1000; David P. Wood, FACHE, Director
Web address: www.boise.va.gov/

ILLINOIS: CAPTAIN JAMES A. LOVELL FEDERAL HEALTH CARE CENTER (O, 103 beds) 3001 Green Bay Road, North Chicago, IL Zip 60064–3049; tel. 847/688–1900; Patrick L. Sullivan, FACHE, Director
Web address: www.lovell.fhcc.va.gov

EDWARD HINES, JR. VETERANS AFFAIRS HOSPITAL (O, 450 beds) 5000 South Fifth Avenue, Hines, IL Zip 60141–3030, Mailing Address: P.O. Box 5000, Zip 60141–5000; tel. 708/202–8387; Joan M. Ricard, R.N., FACHE, Director
Web address: www.hines.va.gov/

JESSE BROWN VETERANS AFFAIRS MEDICAL CENTER (O, 198 beds) 820 South Damen, Chicago, IL Zip 60612–3776; tel. 312/569–8387; Ann R. Brown, FACHE, Director
Web address: www.chicago.va.gov/

MARION VETERANS AFFAIRS MEDICAL CENTER (O, 225 beds) 2401 West Main Street, Marion, IL Zip 62959–1188; tel. 618/997–5311; Donald Hutson, Director
Web address: www.marion.va.gov

VETERANS AFFAIRS ILLIANA HEALTH CARE SYSTEM (O, 81 beds) 1900 East Main Street, Danville, IL Zip 61832–5198; tel. 217/554–3000; Russell E. Lloyd, Acting Director
Web address: www.danville.va.gov/

INDIANA: RICHARD L. ROUDEBUSH VETERANS AFFAIRS MEDICAL CENTER (O, 209 beds) 1481 West Tenth Street, Indianapolis, IN Zip 46202–2884; tel. 317/554–0000; Thomas Mattice, Director
Web address: www.indianapolis.va.gov

VETERANS AFFAIRS NORTHERN INDIANA HEALTH CARE SYSTEM (O, 26 beds) 2121 Lake Avenue, Fort Wayne, IN Zip 46805–5100; tel. 260/426–5431; Denise M. Deitzen, Director
Web address: www.northernindiana.va.gov/

IOWA: IOWA CITY VETERANS AFFAIRS HEALTH CARE SYSTEM (O, 68 beds) 601 Highway 6 West, Iowa City, IA Zip 52246–2208; tel. 319/338–0581; Dawn Oxley, R.N., Acting Director
Web address: www.iowacity.va.gov/

VETERANS AFFAIRS CENTRAL IOWA HEALTH CARE SYSTEM (O, 255 beds) 3600 30th Street, Des Moines, IA Zip 50310–5753; tel. 515/699–5999; Judith Johnson–Mekota, Director
Web address: www.centraliowa.va.gov/

KANSAS: ROBERT J. DOLE VETERANS AFFAIRS MEDICAL CENTER (O, 41 beds) 5500 East Kellogg, Wichita, KS Zip 67218–1607; tel. 316/685–2221; Francisco Vazquez, Director
Web address: www.wichita.va.gov

VETERANS AFFAIRS EASTERN KANSAS HEALTH CARE SYSTEM (O, 213 beds) 2200 Gage Boulevard, Topeka, KS Zip 66622–0002; tel. 785/350–3111; Anthony Rudy Klopfer, FACHE, Director
Web address: www.topeka.va.gov/

KENTUCKY: ROBLEY REX VETERANS AFFAIRS MEDICAL CENTER (O, 116 beds) 800 Zorn Avenue, Louisville, KY Zip 40206–1499; tel. 502/287–4000; Marylee Rothschild, M.D., Interim Director
Web address: www.louisville.va.gov

VETERANS AFFAIRS MEDICAL CENTER–LEXINGTON (O, 199 beds) 1101 Veterans Drive, Lexington, KY Zip 40502–2235; tel. 859/281–4901; Emma Metcalf, MSN, R.N., Director
Web address: www.lexington.va.gov/

LOUISIANA: ALEXANDRIA VETERANS AFFAIRS HEALTH CARE SYSTEM (O, 143 beds) 2495 Shreveport Highway, 71 N., Pineville, LA Zip 71360–4044, Mailing Address: P.O. Box 69004, Alexandria, Zip 71306–9004; tel. 318/473–0010; Martin J. Traxler, Director
Web address: www.alexandria.va.gov/

OVERTON BROOKS VETERANS AFFAIRS MEDICAL CENTER (O, 100 beds) 510 East Stoner Avenue, Shreveport, LA Zip 71101–4295; tel. 318/221–8411; Shirley Bealer, Medical Center Director
Web address: www.shreveport.va.gov/

MAINE: MAINE VETERANS AFFAIRS MEDICAL CENTER (O, 157 beds) 1 VA Center, Augusta, ME Zip 04330–6719; tel. 207/623–8411; Ryan S. Lilly, Acting Director
Web address: www.maine.va.gov/

MARYLAND: VETERANS AFFAIRS MARYLAND HEALTH CARE SYSTEM–BALTIMORE DIVISION (O, 727 beds) 10 North Greene Street, Baltimore, MD Zip 21201–1524; tel. 410/605–7001; Dennis H. Smith, Director
Web address: www.maryland.va.gov/

MASSACHUSETTS: BEDFORD VETERANS AFFAIRS MEDICAL CENTER, EDITH NOURSE ROGERS MEMORIAL VETERANS HOSPITAL (O, 316 beds) 200 Springs Road, Bedford, MA Zip 01730–1198; tel. 781/687–2000; Christine Croteau, Director
Web address: www.bedford.va.gov/guide/

BROCKTON VETERANS AFFAIRS MEDICAL CENTER (O, 375 beds) 940 Belmont Street, Brockton, MA Zip 02301–5596; tel. 508/583–4500; Vincent Ng, Interim Director
Web address: www.boston.va.gov/

VA CENTRAL WESTERN MASSACHUSETTS HEALTHCARE SYSTEM (O, 117 beds) 421 North Main Street, Leeds, MA Zip 01053–9764; tel. 413/582–3000; Roger L. Johnson, Director
Web address: www.centralwesternmass.va.gov/

VETERANS AFFAIRS BOSTON HEALTHCARE SYSTEM (O, 361 beds) 1400 VFW Parkway, Boston, MA Zip 02132–4927; tel. 617/323–7700; Vincent Ng, Director
Web address: www.boston.va.gov/

MICHIGAN: ALEDA E. LUTZ VETERANS AFFAIRS MEDICAL CENTER (O, 100 beds) 1500 Weiss Street, Saginaw, MI Zip 48602–5298; tel. 989/497–2500; Peggy W. Kearns, MS, FACHE, Medical Center Director
Web address: www.saginaw.va.gov/

BATTLE CREEK VETERANS AFFAIRS MEDICAL CENTER (O, 188 beds) 5500 Armstrong Road, Battle Creek, MI Zip 49037–7314; tel. 269/966–5600; Mary Beth Skupien, Director
Web address: www.battlecreek.va.gov/

JOHN D. DINGELL VETERANS AFFAIRS MEDICAL CENTER (O, 188 beds) 4646 John R Street, Detroit, MI Zip 48201–1932; tel. 313/576–1000; Pamela J. Reeves, M.D., Director
Web address: www.detroit.va.gov/

OSCAR G. JOHNSON VETERANS AFFAIRS MEDICAL CENTER (O, 17 beds) 325 East H Street, Iron Mountain, MI Zip 49801–4792; tel. 906/774–3300; James W. Rice, Director
Web address: www.ironmountain.va.gov/

VETERANS AFFAIRS ANN ARBOR HEALTHCARE SYSTEM (O, 145 beds) 2215 Fuller Road, Ann Arbor, MI Zip 48105–2399; tel. 734/769–7100; Robert P. McDivitt, FACHE, Director
Web address: www.annarbor.va.gov

MINNESOTA: MINNEAPOLIS VETERANS AFFAIRS HEALTH CARE SYSTEM (O, 279 beds) One Veterans Drive, Minneapolis, MN Zip 55417–2399; tel. 612/725–2000; Patrick J. Kelly, FACHE, Director
Web address: www.minneapolis.va.gov

ST. CLOUD VETERANS AFFAIRS HEALTH CARE SYSTEM (O, 388 beds) 4801 Veterans Drive, Saint Cloud, MN Zip 56303–2099; tel. 320/252–1670; Barry I. Bahl, Director
Web address: www.stcloud.va.gov

MISSISSIPPI: G.V. (SONNY) MONTGOMERY VETERANS AFFAIRS MEDICAL CENTER (O, 323 beds) 1500 East Woodrow Wilson Drive, Jackson, MS Zip 39216–5199; tel. 601/362–4471; Joe Battle, Director
Web address: www.jackson.va.gov/

VETERANS AFFAIRS GULF COAST VETERANS HEALTH CARE SYSTEM (O, 392 beds) 400 Veterans Avenue, Biloxi, MS Zip 39531–2410; tel. 228/523–5000; Anthony L. Dawson, FACHE, Director
Web address: www.biloxi.va.gov/

MISSOURI: HARRY S. TRUMAN MEMORIAL VETERANS HOSPITAL (O, 126 beds) 800 Hospital Drive, Columbia, MO Zip 65201–5275; tel. 573/814–6000; Wade Vlosich, Director
Web address: www.columbiamo.va.gov

JOHN J. PERSHING VETERANS AFFAIRS MEDICAL CENTER (O, 58 beds) 1500 North Westwood Boulevard, Poplar Bluff, MO Zip 63901–3318; tel. 573/686–4151; Marjorie Hedstrom, Director
Web address: www.poplarbluff.va.gov

Section B

For explanation of codes following names, see page B2.
★ Indicates Type III membership in the American Hospital Association.

KANSAS CITY VETERANS AFFAIRS MEDICAL CENTER (O, 157 beds) 4801 East Linwood Boulevard, Kansas City, MO Zip 64128–2226; tel. 816/861–4700; Kent D. Hill, Director
Web address: www.kansascity.va.gov/

VETERANS AFFAIRS ST. LOUIS HEALTH CARE SYSTEM (O, 344 beds) 915 North Grand, Saint Louis, MO Zip 63106–1621; tel. 314/652–4100; Marc Magill, Acting Director
Web address: www.stlouis.va.gov/

MONTANA: VETERANS AFFAIRS MONTANA HEALTH CARE SYSTEM (O, 100 beds) 3687 Veterans Drive, Fort Harrison, MT Zip 59636–9703, Mailing Address: P.O. Box 1500, Zip 59636–1500; tel. 406/442–6410; Christine Gregory, R.N., Director
Web address: www.montana.va.gov/

NEBRASKA: VETERANS AFFAIRS – WESTERN IOWA HEALTHCARE SYSTEM (O, 126 beds) 4101 Woolworth Avenue, Omaha, NE Zip 68105–1873; tel. 402/346–8800; Marci Mylan, Director
Web address: www.nebraska.va.gov/

VETERANS AFFAIRS NEBRASKA–WESTERN IOWA HEALTH CARE SYSTEM (O, 132 beds) 600 South 70th Street, Lincoln, NE Zip 68510–2493; tel. 402/489–3802; Marci Mylan, Director
Web address: www.nebraska.va.gov/

NEVADA: VETERANS AFFAIRS SIERRA NEVADA HEALTH CARE SYSTEM (O, 124 beds) 975 Kirman Avenue, Reno, NV Zip 89502–0993; tel. 775/786–7200; Lisa M. Howard, Acting Director
Web address: www.reno.va.gov/

VETERANS AFFAIRS SOUTHERN NEVADA HEALTHCARE SYSTEM (O, 57 beds) 6900 North Pecos Road, North Las Vegas, NV tel. 702/791–9000; Isabel Duff, MS, Director
Web address: www.lasvegas.va.gov/

NEW HAMPSHIRE: MANCHESTER VETERANS AFFAIRS MEDICAL CENTER (O, 90 beds) 718 Smyth Road, Manchester, NH Zip 03104–4098; tel. 603/624–4366; Tammy A. Krueger, Acting Director
Web address: www.manchester.va.gov/

NEW JERSEY: VETERANS AFFAIRS NEW JERSEY HEALTH CARE SYSTEM (O, 439 beds) 385 Tremont Avenue, East Orange, NJ Zip 07018–1095; tel. 973/676–1000; Kenneth H. Mizrach, Director
Web address: www.newjersey.va.gov/

NEW MEXICO: VETERANS AFFAIRS MEDICAL CENTER (O, 281 beds) 1501 San Pedro S.E., Albuquerque, NM Zip 87108–5153; tel. 505/265–1711; George Marnell, Director
Web address: www.southwest.va.gov/albuquerque/

NEW YORK: ALBANY STRATTON VETERANS AFFAIRS MEDICAL CENTER (O, 150 beds) 113 Holland Avenue, Albany, NY Zip 12208–3473; tel. 518/626–5000; Linda W. Weiss, MS, FACHE, Director
Web address: www.albany.va.gov/

BATH VETERANS AFFAIRS MEDICAL CENTER (O, 371 beds) 76 Veterans Avenue, Bath, NY Zip 14810–0842; tel. 607/664–4000; Michael J. Swartz, FACHE, Medical Center Director
Web address: www.bath.va.gov

CANANDAIGUA VETERANS AFFAIRS MEDICAL CENTER (O, 80 beds) 400 Fort Hill Avenue, Canandaigua, NY Zip 14424–1159; tel. 585/394–2000; Craig Howard, Director
Web address: www.canandaigua.va.gov/

JAMES J. PETERS VETERANS AFFAIRS MEDICAL CENTER (O, 325 beds) 130 West Kingsbridge Road, Bronx, NY Zip 10468–3904; tel. 718/584–9000; Erik Langhoff, M.D., Ph.D., Director
Web address: www.bronx.va.gov/

NORTHPORT VETERANS AFFAIRS MEDICAL CENTER (O, 502 beds) 79 Middleville Road, Northport, NY Zip 11768–2200; tel. 631/261–4400; Philip C. Moschitta, Director
Web address: www.northport.va.gov/index.asp

SYRACUSE VETERANS AFFAIRS MEDICAL CENTER (O, 161 beds) 800 Irving Avenue, Syracuse, NY Zip 13210–2716; tel. 315/425–4400; James Cody, Director
Web address: www.syracuse.va.gov/

VETERANS ADMINISTRATION NEW YORK HARBOR HEALTHCARE SYSTEM (O, 476 beds) 800 Poly Place, Brooklyn, NY Zip 11209–7104; tel. 718/630–3500; Martina A. Parauda, Director
Web address: www.nyharbor.va.gov

VETERANS AFFAIRS HUDSON VALLEY HEALTH CARE SYSTEM–F.D. ROOSEVELT HOSPITAL (O, 403 beds) 2094 Albany Post Road, Montrose, NY Zip 10548–1454, Mailing Address: P.O. Box 100, Zip 10548–0100; tel. 914/737–4400; Margaret B. Caplan, Director
Web address: www.hudsonvalley.va.gov/

VETERANS AFFAIRS WESTERN NEW YORK HEALTHCARE SYSTEM–BATAVIA DIVISION (O, 128 beds) 222 Richmond Avenue, Batavia, NY Zip 14020–1288; tel. 585/297–1000; Brian G. Stiller, Director Medical Center
Web address: www.buffalo.va.gov/batavia.asp

VETERANS AFFAIRS WESTERN NEW YORK HEALTHCARE SYSTEM–BUFFALO DIVISION (O, 113 beds) 3495 Bailey Avenue, Buffalo, NY Zip 14215–1129; tel. 716/834–9200; Brian G. Stiller, Director Medical Center
Web address: www.buffalo.va.gov/index.asp

NORTH CAROLINA: CHARLES GEORGE VETERANS AFFAIRS MEDICAL CENTER (O, 257 beds) 1100 Tunnel Road, Asheville, NC Zip 28805–2087; tel. 828/298–7911; Cynthia Breyfogle, FACHE, Director
Web address: www.asheville.va.gov/

DURHAM VETERANS AFFAIRS MEDICAL CENTER (O, 154 beds) 508 Fulton Street, Durham, NC Zip 27705–3897; tel. 919/286–0411; DeAnne Seekins, Director
Web address: www.durham.va.gov/

FAYETTEVILLE VETERANS AFFAIRS MEDICAL CENTER (O, 58 beds) 2300 Ramsey Street, Fayetteville, NC Zip 28301–3899; tel. 910/488–2120; Elizabeth Goolsby, Director
Web address: www.fayettevillenc.va.gov

W. G. (BILL) HEFFNER VETERANS AFFAIRS MEDICAL CENTER (O, 171 beds) 1601 Brenner Avenue, Salisbury, NC Zip 28144–2559; tel. 704/638–9000; Kaye Green, FACHE, Director
Web address: www.salisbury.va.gov

NORTH DAKOTA: FARGO VETERANS AFFAIRS HEALTH CARE SYSTEM (O, 42 beds) 2101 Elm Street North, Fargo, ND Zip 58102–2498; tel. 701/232–3241; Lavonne Liversage, Director
Web address: www.fargo.va.gov/

OHIO: CHILLICOTHE VETERANS AFFAIRS MEDICAL CENTER (O, 297 beds) 17273 State Route 104, Chillicothe, OH Zip 45601–9718; tel. 740/773–1141; Wendy J. Hepker, FACHE, Director
Web address: www.chillicothe.va.gov/

CINCINNATI VETERANS AFFAIRS MEDICAL CENTER (O, 268 beds) 3200 Vine Street, Cincinnati, OH Zip 45220–2288; tel. 513/475–6300; Linda D. Smith, FACHE, Director
Web address: www.cincinnati.va.gov/

DAYTON VETERANS AFFAIRS MEDICAL CENTER (O, 471 beds) 4100 West Third Street, Dayton, OH Zip 45428–9000; tel. 937/268–6511; Glenn A. Costie, FACHE, Director
Web address: www.dayton.va.gov/

LOUIS STOKES CLEVELAND VETERANS AFFAIRS MEDICAL CENTER (O, 585 beds) 10701 East Boulevard, Cleveland, OH Zip 44106–1702; tel. 216/791–3800; Susan Fuehrer, Director
Web address: www.cleveland.va.gov/

OKLAHOMA: JACK C. MONTGOMERY VETERANS AFFAIRS MEDICAL CENTER (O, 99 beds) 1011 Honor Heights Drive, Muskogee, OK Zip 74401–1318; tel. 918/577–3000; James R. Floyd, Director
Web address: www.muskogee.va.gov

OKLAHOMA CITY VETERANS AFFAIRS MEDICAL CENTER (O, 192 beds) 921 N.E. 13th Street, Oklahoma City, OK Zip 73104–5028; tel. 405/456–1000; Daniel L. Marsh, Director
Web address: www.oklahoma.va.gov

OREGON: PORTLAND VETERANS AFFAIRS MEDICAL CENTER (O, 303 beds) 3710 S.W. U.S. Veterans Hospital Road, Portland, OR Zip 97239–2964, Mailing Address: P.O. Box 1034, Zip 97207–1034; tel. 503/220–8262; Joanne Krumberger, R.N., FACHE, Director
Web address: www.portland.va.gov/

VETERANS AFFAIRS DOMICILIARY (O, 1075 beds) White City, OR Zip 97503; tel. 503/826–2111; Frank A. Drake, Director

VETERANS AFFAIRS ROSEBURG HEALTHCARE SYSTEM (O, 88 beds) 913 N.W. Garden Valley Boulevard, Roseburg, OR Zip 97471–6513; tel. 541/440–1000; Carol Bogedain, FACHE, Director
Web address: www.roseburg.va.gov/

For explanation of codes following names, see page B2.
★ Indicates Type III membership in the American Hospital Association.

PENNSYLVANIA: COATESVILLE VETERANS AFFAIRS MEDICAL CENTER (O, 118 beds) 1400 Black Horse Hill Road, Coatesville, PA Zip 19320–2040; tel. 610/384–7711; Gary W. Devansky, Director
Web address: www.coatesville.va.gov/

ERIE VETERANS AFFAIRS MEDICAL CENTER (O, 26 beds) 135 East 38th Street, Erie, PA Zip 16504–1559; tel. 814/860–2576; Michael Adelman, M.D., Director
Web address: www.erie.va.gov/

JAMES E. VAN ZANDT VETERANS AFFAIRS MEDICAL CENTER (O, 68 beds) 2907 Pleasant Valley Boulevard, Altoona, PA Zip 16602–4305; tel. 877/626–2500; William H. Mills, Director
Web address: www.altoona.va.gov/

LEBANON VETERANS AFFAIRS MEDICAL CENTER (O, 213 beds) 1700 South Lincoln Avenue, Lebanon, PA Zip 17042–7529; tel. 717/272–6621; Robert W. Callahan, Jr., Director
Web address: www.lebanon.va.gov

PHILADELPHIA VETERANS AFFAIRS MEDICAL CENTER (O, 280 beds) 3900 Woodland Avenue, Philadelphia, PA Zip 19104–4594; tel. 215/823–5800; Daniel Hendee, Director
Web address: www.philadelphia.va.gov/

VETERANS AFFAIRS BUTLER HEALTHCARE (O, 126 beds) 325 New Castle Road, Butler, PA Zip 16001–2480; tel. 724/287–4781; John Gennaro, FACHE, Director
Web address: www.butler.va.gov

VETERANS AFFAIRS PITTSBURGH HEALTHCARE SYSTEM (O, 582 beds) University Drive, Pittsburgh, PA Zip 15240–1001; tel. 412/688–6000; David S. Macpherson, M.D., M.P.H., Acting Director
Web address: www.pittsburgh.va.gov/

WILKES–BARRE VETERANS AFFAIRS MEDICAL CENTER (O, 158 beds) 1111 East End Boulevard, Wilkes–Barre, PA Zip 18711–0030; tel. 570/824–3521; Jeffrey Beiler, Interim Director
Web address: www.va.gov/vamcwb

PUERTO RICO: VETERANS AFFAIRS CARIBBEAN HEALTHCARE SYSTEM (O, 330 beds) 10 Casia Street, San Juan, PR Zip 00921–3201; tel. 787/641–7582; DeWayne Hamlin, Director
Web address: www.caribbean.va.gov/

RHODE ISLAND: PROVIDENCE VETERANS AFFAIRS MEDICAL CENTER (O, 73 beds) 830 Chalkstone Avenue, Providence, RI Zip 02908–4799; tel. 401/273–7100; Susan McKenzie, Director
Web address: www.providence.va.gov/

SOUTH CAROLINA: RALPH H. JOHNSON VETERANS AFFAIRS MEDICAL CENTER (O, 98 beds) 109 Bee Street, Charleston, SC Zip 29401–5799; tel. 843/577–5011; Scott R. Isaacks, Interim Director
Web address: www.charleston.va.gov/

WM. JENNINGS BRYAN DORN VETERANS AFFAIRS MEDICAL CENTER (O, 216 beds) 6439 Garners Ferry Road, Columbia, SC Zip 29209–1639; tel. 803/776–4000; Timothy McMurry, Director
Web address: www.columbiasc.va.gov/

SOUTH DAKOTA: SIOUX FALLS VETERANS AFFAIRS HEALTH CARE SYSTEM (O, 98 beds) 2501 West 22nd Street, Sioux Falls, SD Zip 57105–1305, Mailing Address: P.O. Box 5046, Zip 57117–5046; tel. 605/336–3230; Darwin Goodspeed, Director
Web address: www.siouxfalls.va.gov

VETERANS AFFAIRS BLACK HILLS HEALTH CARE SYSTEM (O, 308 beds) 113 Comanche Road, Fort Meade, SD Zip 57741–1099; tel. 605/347–2511; Stephen R. DiStasio, Director
Web address: www.blackhills.va.gov/

TENNESSEE: JAMES H. QUILLEN VETERANS AFFAIRS MEDICAL CENTER (O, 483 beds) Corner of Lamont & Veterans Way, Mountain Home, TN Zip 37684, Mailing Address: P.O. Box 4000, Zip 37684–4000; tel. 423/926–1171; Charlene S. Ehret, FACHE, Director
Web address: www.mountainhome.va.gov/

MEMPHIS VETERANS AFFAIRS MEDICAL CENTER (O, 244 beds) 1030 Jefferson Avenue, Memphis, TN Zip 38104–2193; tel. 901/523–8990; C. Diane Knight, M.D., Director and Chief Executive Officer
Web address: www.memphis.va.gov

TENNESSEE VALLEY HEALTHCARE SYSTEM (O, 546 beds) 1310 24th Avenue South, Nashville, TN Zip 37212–2637; tel. 615/327–4751; Juan A. Morales, R.N., MSN, Health System Director
Web address: www.tennesseevalley.va.gov

TEXAS: AMARILLO VETERANS AFFAIRS HEALTH CARE SYSTEM (O, 55 beds) 6010 West Amarillo Boulevard, Amarillo, TX Zip 79106–1992; tel. 806/355–9703; Andrew Welch, Director
Web address: www.amarillo.va.gov/

CENTRAL TEXAS VETERANS HEALTHCARE SYSTEM (O, 1532 beds) 1901 Veterans Memorial Drive, Temple, TX Zip 76504–7493; tel. 254/778–4811; Sallie Houser–Hanfelder, FACHE, Director
Web address: www.centraltexas.va.gov/

MICHAEL E. DEBAKEY VETERANS AFFAIRS MEDICAL CENTER (O, 479 beds) 2002 Holcombe Boulevard, Houston, TX Zip 77030–4298; tel. 713/791–1414; Adam C. Walmus, Director
Web address: www.houston.va.gov

SOUTH TEXAS VETERANS HEALTH CARE SYSTEM (O, 838 beds) 7400 Merton Minter Boulevard, San Antonio, TX Zip 78229–4404; tel. 210/617–5300; Marie L. Weldon, FACHE, Director
Web address: www.southtexas.va.gov/

VETERANS AFFAIRS NORTH TEXAS HEALTH CARE SYSTEM (O, 875 beds) 4500 South Lancaster Road, Dallas, TX Zip 75216–7167; tel. 214/742–8387; Jeffrey Milligan, Director
Web address: www.northtexas.va.gov/

WEST TEXAS VETERANS AFFAIRS HEALTH CARE SYSTEM (O, 149 beds) 300 Veterans Boulevard, Big Spring, TX Zip 79720–5500; Big Springs, tel. 432/263–7361; Adam M. Welch, Interim Director
Web address: www.bigspring.va.gov/about/

UTAH: VETERANS AFFAIRS SALT LAKE CITY HEALTH CARE SYSTEM (O, 121 beds) 500 Foothill Drive, Salt Lake City, UT Zip 84148–0002; tel. 801/582–1565; Steven W. Young, Director
Web address: www.saltlakecity.va.gov/

VERMONT: WHITE RIVER JUNCTION VETERANS AFFAIRS MEDICAL CENTER (O, 60 beds) 215 North Main Street, White River Junction, VT Zip 05009–0001; tel. 802/295–9363; Danielle Ocker, R.N., Acting Director
Web address: www.whiteriver.va.gov/

VIRGINIA: HAMPTON VETERANS AFFAIRS MEDICAL CENTER (O, 468 beds) 100 Emancipation Drive, Hampton, VA Zip 23667–0001; tel. 757/722–9961; Michael H. Dunfee, Director
Web address: www.hampton.va.gov/

HUNTER HOLMES MCGUIRE VETERANS AFFAIRS MEDICAL CENTER (O, 387 beds) 1201 Broad Rock Boulevard, Richmond, VA Zip 23249–0002; tel. 804/675–5000; John A. Brandecker, Director
Web address: www.richmond.va.gov/

SALEM VETERANS AFFAIRS MEDICAL CENTER (O, 298 beds) 1970 Roanoke Boulevard, Salem, VA Zip 24153–6478; tel. 540/982–2463; Miguel H. LaPuz, M.D., Director
Web address: www.salem.va.gov

WASHINGTON: JONATHAN M. WAINWRIGHT MEMORIAL VETERANS AFFAIRS MEDICAL CENTER (O, 14 beds) 77 Wainwright Drive, Walla Walla, WA Zip 99362–3994; tel. 509/525–5200; Brian W. Westfield, MSN, Director
Web address: www.wallawalla.va.gov

MANN–GRANDSTAFF VETERANS AFFAIRS MEDICAL CENTER (O, 70 beds) 4815 North Assembly Street, Spokane, WA Zip 99205–6197; tel. 509/434–7000; Linda K. Reynolds, FACHE, Director
Web address: www.spokane.va.gov

VETERANS AFFAIRS PUGET SOUND HEALTH CARE SYSTEM (O, 358 beds) 1660 South Columbian Way, Seattle, WA Zip 98108–1597; tel. 206/762–1010; Michael J. Murphy, FACHE, Chief Executive Officer
Web address: www.pugetsound.va.gov/

WEST VIRGINIA: BECKLEY VETERANS AFFAIRS MEDICAL CENTER (O, 40 beds) 200 Veterans Avenue, Beckley, WV Zip 25801–6499; tel. 304/255–2121; Karin L. McGraw, MSN, FACHE, Director
Web address: www.beckley.va.gov/

HUNTINGTON VETERANS AFFAIRS MEDICAL CENTER (O, 80 beds) 1540 Spring Valley Drive, Huntington, WV Zip 25704–9300; tel. 304/429–6741; Brian Nimmo, Director
Web address: www.huntington.va.gov/

LOUIS A. JOHNSON VETERANS AFFAIRS MEDICAL CENTER (O, 71 beds) 1 Medical Center Drive, Clarksburg, WV Zip 26301–4199; tel. 304/623–3461; Beth Brown, Medical Center Director
Web address: www.clarksburg.va.gov

For explanation of codes following names, see page B2.
★ Indicates Type III membership in the American Hospital Association.

MARTINSBURG VETERANS AFFAIRS MEDICAL CENTER (O, 192 beds) 510 Butler Avenue, Martinsburg, WV Zip 25405–9990; tel. 304/263–0811; Timothy J. Cooke, Medical Center Director and Chief Executive Officer
Web address: www.martinsburg.va.gov/

WISCONSIN: CLEMENT J. ZABLOCKI VETERANS AFFAIRS MEDICAL CENTER (O, 637 beds) 5000 West National Avenue, Milwaukee, WI Zip 53295–0001; tel. 414/384–2000; Robert H. Beller, FACHE, Director
Web address: www.milwaukee.va.gov/

TOMAH VETERANS AFFAIRS MEDICAL CENTER (O, 71 beds) 500 East Veterans Street, Tomah, WI Zip 54660–3105; tel. 608/372–3971; Mario DeSanctis, FACHE, Director
Web address: www.tomah.va.gov

WILLIAM S. MIDDLETON MEMORIAL VETERANS HOSPITAL (O, 87 beds) 2500 Overlook Terrace, Madison, WI Zip 53705–2286; tel. 608/256–1901; Judy McKee, FACHE, Director
Web address: www.madison.va.gov

WYOMING: CHEYENNE VETERANS AFFAIRS MEDICAL CENTER (O, 61 beds) 2360 East Pershing Boulevard, Cheyenne, WY Zip 82001–5392; tel. 307/778–7550; Cynthia McCormack, MS, Director
Web address: www.cheyenne.va.gov/

SHERIDAN VETERANS AFFAIRS MEDICAL CENTER (O, 208 beds) 1898 Fort Road, Sheridan, WY Zip 82801–8320; tel. 307/672–3473; Debra L. Hirschman, R.N., MSN, Director
Web address: www.sheridan.va.gov/

Owned, leased, sponsored:	137 hospitals	35036 beds
Contract–managed:	0 hospitals	0 beds
Totals:	137 hospitals	35036 beds

0845: DEVEREUX (NP)
444 Devereux Drive, Villanova, PA Zip 19085–1932, Mailing Address: P.O. Box 638, Zip 19085–0638; tel. 610/520–3000; Robert Q. Kreider, President and Chief Executive Officer
(Independent Hospital System)

FLORIDA: DEVEREUX HOSPITAL AND CHILDREN'S CENTER OF FLORIDA (O, 100 beds) 8000 Devereux Drive, Melbourne, FL Zip 32940–7907; tel. 321/242–9100; Steven Murphy, Executive Director
Web address: www.devereux.org

GEORGIA: DEVEREUX GEORGIA TREATMENT NETWORK (O, 100 beds) 1291 Stanley Road N.W., Kennesaw, GA Zip 30152–4359; tel. 770/427–0147; Gwendolyn Skinner, Executive Director
Web address: www.devereuxga.org

PENNSYLVANIA: DEVEREUX CHILDREN'S BEHAVIORAL HEALTH CENTER (O, 49 beds) 655 Sugartown Road, Malvern, PA Zip 19355–3303, Mailing Address: 655 Sugartown Road, Zip 19355–3303; tel. 800/345–1292; David E. Woodward, Executive Director
Web address: www.devereux.org

TEXAS: DEVEREUX TEXAS TREATMENT NETWORK (O, 39 beds) 1150 Devereux Drive, League City, TX Zip 77573–2043; tel. 281/335–1000; Pamela E. Helm, Executive Director
Web address: www.devereux.org

Owned, leased, sponsored:	4 hospitals	288 beds
Contract–managed:	0 hospitals	0 beds
Totals:	4 hospitals	288 beds

★5205: DIGNITY HEALTH (CC)
185 Berry Street, Suite 300, San Francisco, CA Zip 94107–1773; tel. 415/438–5500; Lloyd H. Dean, President and Chief Executive Officer
(Decentralized Health System)

ARIZONA: CHANDLER REGIONAL MEDICAL CENTER (O, 243 beds) 1955 West Frye Road, Chandler, AZ Zip 85224–6282; tel. 480/728–3000; Tim Bricker, President and Chief Executive Officer
Web address: www.chandlerregional.com

MERCY GILBERT MEDICAL CENTER (S, 212 beds) 3555 South Val Vista Road, Gilbert, AZ Zip 85297–7323; tel. 480/728–8000; Tim Bricker, President and Chief Executive Officer
Web address: www.mercygilbert.org

ST. JOSEPH'S HOSPITAL AND MEDICAL CENTER (S, 586 beds) 350 West Thomas Road, Phoenix, AZ Zip 85013–4496, Mailing Address: P.O. Box 2071, Zip 85001–2071; tel. 602/406–3000; Patty White, R.N., MS, President
Web address: www.stjosephs–phx.org

CALIFORNIA: ARROYO GRANDE COMMUNITY HOSPITAL (O, 67 beds) 345 South Halcyon Road, Arroyo Grande, CA Zip 93420–3899; tel. 805/489–4261; Kenneth Dalebout, Administrator and Chief Executive Officer
Web address: www.arroyograndehospital.org

BAKERSFIELD MEMORIAL HOSPITAL (O, 255 beds) 420 34th Street, Bakersfield, CA Zip 93301–2237; tel. 661/327–1792; Jon Van Boening, President and Chief Executive Officer and Senior Vice President Operations Dignity Health Central Valley Service Area
Web address: www.bakersfieldmemorial.org

CALIFORNIA HOSPITAL MEDICAL CENTER (O, 318 beds) 1401 South Grand Avenue, Los Angeles, CA Zip 90015–3010; tel. 213/748–2411; Margaret R. Peterson, Ph.D., R.N., President
Web address: www.chmcla.org

COMMUNITY HOSPITAL OF SAN BERNARDINO (O, 364 beds) 1805 Medical Center Drive, San Bernardino, CA Zip 92411–1214; tel. 909/887–6333; June Collison, President
Web address: www.chsb.org

DOMINICAN HOSPITAL (S, 275 beds) 1555 Soquel Drive, Santa Cruz, CA Zip 95065–1794; tel. 831/462–7700; Nanette Mickiewicz, M.D., President
Web address: www.dominicanhospital.org

FRENCH HOSPITAL MEDICAL CENTER (O, 112 beds) 1911 Johnson Avenue, San Luis Obispo, CA Zip 93401–4197; tel. 805/543–5353; Alan Iftiniuk, Chief Executive Officer
Web address: www.frenchmedicalcenter.org

GLENDALE MEMORIAL HOSPITAL AND HEALTH CENTER (O, 334 beds) 1420 South Central Avenue, Glendale, CA Zip 91204–2594; tel. 818/502–1900; Jack Ivie, President
Web address: www.glendalememorial.com

MARIAN REGIONAL MEDICAL CENTER (S, 286 beds) 1400 East Church Street, Santa Maria, CA Zip 93454–5906; tel. 805/739–3000; Charles J. Cova, President and Chief Executive Officer
Web address: www.marianmedicalcenter.org

MARK TWAIN MEDICAL CENTER (O, 25 beds) 768 Mountain Ranch Road, San Andreas, CA Zip 95249–9998; tel. 209/754–3521; Craig J. Marks, FACHE, President
Web address: www.marktwainhospital.com

MERCY GENERAL HOSPITAL (S, 286 beds) 4001 J Street, Sacramento, CA Zip 95819–3600; tel. 916/453–4545; Edmundo Castaneda, President
Web address: www.mercygeneral.org

MERCY HOSPITAL OF FOLSOM (S, 106 beds) 1650 Creekside Drive, Folsom, CA Zip 95630–3400; tel. 916/983–7400; Michael R. Ricks, President
Web address: www.mercyfolsom.org

MERCY HOSPITALS OF BAKERSFIELD (S, 222 beds) 2215 Truxtun Avenue, Bakersfield, CA Zip 93301–3698, Mailing Address: P.O. Box 119, Zip 93302–0119; tel. 661/632–5000; Jon Van Boening, Interim President and Chief Executive Officer
Web address: www.mercybakersfield.org

MERCY MEDICAL CENTER MERCED (S, 186 beds) 333 Mercy Avenue, Merced, CA Zip 95340–8319; tel. 209/564–5000; David S. Dunham, President
Web address: www.mercymercedcares.org

MERCY MEDICAL CENTER MOUNT SHASTA (S, 33 beds) 914 Pine Street, Mount Shasta, CA Zip 96067–2143; tel. 530/926–6111; Kenneth E. S. Platou, President
Web address: www.mercymtshasta.org

MERCY MEDICAL CENTER REDDING (S, 267 beds) 2175 Rosaline Avenue, Redding, CA Zip 96001–2549, Mailing Address: P.O. Box 496009, Zip 96049–6009; tel. 530/225–6000; Mark Korth, President
Web address: www.mercy.org

MERCY SAN JUAN MEDICAL CENTER (S, 359 beds) 6501 Coyle Avenue, Carmichael, CA Zip 95608–0306, Mailing Address: P.O. Box 479, Zip 95609–0479; tel. 916/537–5000; Brian K. Ivie, President
Web address: www.mercysanjuan.org

For explanation of codes following names, see page B2.
★ Indicates Type III membership in the American Hospital Association.

Section B

METHODIST HOSPITAL OF SACRAMENTO (O, 325 beds) 7500 Hospital Drive, Sacramento, CA Zip 95823–5477; tel. 916/423–3000; Eugene Bassett, President and Chief Executive Officer
Web address: www.methodistsacramento.org

NORTHRIDGE HOSPITAL MEDICAL CENTER (O, 371 beds) 18300 Roscoe Boulevard, Northridge, CA Zip 91328–4167; tel. 818/885–8500; Saliba Salo, President
Web address: www.northridgehospital.org

SAINT FRANCIS MEMORIAL HOSPITAL (O, 239 beds) 900 Hyde Street, San Francisco, CA Zip 94109–4899, Mailing Address: P.O. Box 7726, Zip 94120–7726; tel. 415/353–6000; Hugh Vincent, M.D., Interim Chief Executive Officer
Web address: www.saintfrancismemorial.org

SEQUOIA HOSPITAL (O, 128 beds) 170 Alameda De Las Pulgas, Redwood City, CA Zip 94062–2799; tel. 650/369–5811; Glenna L. Vaskelis, President and Senior Vice President Operations Dignity Health Bay Area Service Area
Web address: www.sequoiahospital.org

SIERRA NEVADA MEMORIAL HOSPITAL (O, 121 beds) 155 Glasson Way, Grass Valley, CA Zip 95945–5723, Mailing Address: P.O. Box 1029, Zip 95945–1029; tel. 530/274–6000; Katherine A. Medeiros, President and Chief Executive Officer
Web address: www.snmh.org

ST. BERNARDINE MEDICAL CENTER (S, 250 beds) 2101 North Waterman Avenue, San Bernardino, CA Zip 92404–4855; tel. 909/883–8711; Steven R. Barron, President
Web address: www.stbernardinemedicalcenter.com

ST. ELIZABETH COMMUNITY HOSPITAL (S, 65 beds) 2550 Sister Mary Columba Drive, Red Bluff, CA Zip 96080–4397; tel. 530/529–8000; G. Todd Smith, President
Web address: www.mercy.org

ST. JOHN'S PLEASANT VALLEY HOSPITAL (S, 127 beds) 2309 Antonio Avenue, Camarillo, CA Zip 93010–1414; tel. 805/389–5800; Charles Cova, Interim Chief Executive Officer
Web address: www.stjohnshealth.org

ST. JOHN'S REGIONAL MEDICAL CENTER (S, 139 beds) 1600 North Rose Avenue, Oxnard, CA Zip 93030–3723; tel. 805/988–2500; Charles Cova, Interim Chief Executive Officer
Web address: www.stjohnshealth.org

ST. JOSEPH'S BEHAVIORAL HEALTH CENTER (S, 35 beds) 2510 North California Street, Stockton, CA Zip 95204–5568; tel. 209/461–2000; Paul Rains, R.N., MSN, President
Web address: www.stjosephscanhelp.org

ST. JOSEPH'S MEDICAL CENTER (S, 273 beds) 1800 North California Street, Stockton, CA Zip 95204–6019, Mailing Address: P.O. Box 213008, Zip 95213–9008; tel. 209/943–2000; Donald J. Wiley, President and Chief Executive Officer
Web address: www.stjosephsCARES.org

ST. MARY MEDICAL CENTER (S, 131 beds) 1050 Linden Avenue, Long Beach, CA Zip 90813–3321, Mailing Address: P.O. Box 887, Zip 90801–0887; tel. 562/491–9000; Thomas A. Salerno, President and Chief Executive Officer
Web address: www.stmarymedicalcenter.org

ST. MARY'S MEDICAL CENTER (S, 232 beds) 450 Stanyan Street, San Francisco, CA Zip 94117–1079; tel. 415/668–1000; Anna Cheung, President
Web address: www.stmarysmedicalcenter.com

WOODLAND HEALTHCARE (O, 111 beds) 1325 Cottonwood Street, Woodland, CA Zip 95695–5199; tel. 530/662–3961; H. Kevin Vaziri, President
Web address: www.woodlandhealthcare.org

NEVADA: ST. ROSE DOMINICAN HOSPITALS – ROSE DE LIMA CAMPUS (S, 109 beds) 102 East Lake Mead Parkway, Henderson, NV Zip 89015–5524; tel. 702/616–5000; Teressa Conley, Interim President and Chief Executive Officer
Web address: www.strosehospitals.org

ST. ROSE DOMINICAN HOSPITALS – SAN MARTIN CAMPUS (O, 147 beds) 8280 West Warm Springs Road, Las Vegas, NV Zip 89113–3612; tel. 702/492–8000; Victoria J. VanMeetren, President
Web address: www.strosehospitals.org

ST. ROSE DOMINICAN HOSPITALS – SIENA CAMPUS (S, 219 beds) 3001 St. Rose Parkway, Henderson, NV Zip 89052; tel. 702/616–5000; Brian G. Brannman, President and Chief Executive Officer
Web address: www.strosehospitals.com

Owned, leased, sponsored:	36 hospitals	7558 beds
Contract–managed:	0 hospitals	0 beds
Totals:	36 hospitals	7558 beds

0029: DIMENSIONS HEALTHCARE SYSTEM (NP)
3001 Hospital Drive, 3rd Floor, Cheverly, MD Zip 20785–1189; tel. 301/583–4000; Neil J. Moore, President and Chief Executive Officer
(Moderately Centralized Health System)

MARYLAND: LAUREL REGIONAL HOSPITAL (O, 160 beds) 7300 Van Dusen Road, Laurel, MD Zip 20707–9463; tel. 301/725–4300; John Spearman, President and Chief Operating Officer
Web address: www.laurelregionalhospital.org

PRINCE GEORGE'S HOSPITAL CENTER (O, 284 beds) 3001 Hospital Drive, Cheverly, MD Zip 20785–1189; tel. 301/618–2000; John A. O'Brien, FACHE, President
Web address: www.princegeorgeshospital.org

Owned, leased, sponsored:	2 hospitals	444 beds
Contract–managed:	0 hospitals	0 beds
Totals:	2 hospitals	444 beds

0010: DIVISION OF MENTAL HEALTH AND ADDICTION SERVICES, DEPARTMENT OF HUMAN SERVICES, STATE OF NEW JERSEY (NP)
222 South Warren Street, Trenton, NJ Zip 08608–2306, Mailing Address: P.O. Box 700, Zip 08625–0700; tel. 609/777–0702; Lynn Kovich, Assistant Commissioner
(Independent Hospital System)

NEW JERSEY: ANCORA PSYCHIATRIC HOSPITAL (O, 500 beds) 301 Spring Garden Road, Hammonton, NJ Zip 08037–9699; tel. 609/561–1700; John Lubitsky, Chief Executive Officer
Web address: www.state.nj.us/humanservices/dmhs/oshm/aph/

ARTHUR BRISBANE CHILDREN TREATMENT CENTER (O, 92 beds) County Road 524, Farmingdale, NJ Zip 07727, Mailing Address: P.O. Box 625, Zip 07727; Vincent Giampeitro, Chief Executive Officer

GREYSTONE PARK PSYCHIATRIC HOSPITAL (O, 557 beds) 59 Koch Avenue, Morris Plains, NJ Zip 07950–4400; tel. 973/538–1800; Janet J. Monroe, R.N., Chief Executive Officer
Web address: www.state.nj.us/humanservices/dmhs/oshm/gpph/

TRENTON PSYCHIATRIC HOSPITAL (O, 431 beds) Route 29 and Sullivan Way, Trenton, NJ Zip 08628–3425, Mailing Address: P.O. Box 7500, West Trenton, Zip 08628–0500; tel. 609/633–1500; Teresa A. McQuaide, Chief Executive Officer
Web address: www.state.nj.us/humanservices/dmhs/oshm/tph/

Owned, leased, sponsored:	4 hospitals	1580 beds
Contract–managed:	0 hospitals	0 beds
Totals:	4 hospitals	1580 beds

0536: DIVISION OF MENTAL HEALTH, DEPARTMENT OF HUMAN SERVICES (NP)
319 East Madison Street, S–3B, Springfield, IL Zip 62701–1035; tel. 217/785–6023; Lorrie Rickman Jones, Ph.D., Director
(Independent Hospital System)

ILLINOIS: ALTON MENTAL HEALTH CENTER (O, 165 beds) 4500 College Avenue, Alton, IL Zip 62002–5099; tel. 618/474–3800; Brian E. Thomas, Administrator

ANDREW MCFARLAND MENTAL HEALTH CENTER (O, 118 beds) 901 East Southwind Road, Springfield, IL Zip 62703–5125; tel. 217/786–6994; Karen Schweighart, R.N., MS, Administrator

CHESTER MENTAL HEALTH CENTER (O, 245 beds) Chester Road, Chester, IL Zip 62233–0031, Mailing Address: Box 31, Zip 62233–0031; tel. 618/826–4571; Leah Hammel, Acting Administrator

CHICAGO–READ MENTAL HEALTH CENTER (O, 200 beds) 4200 North Oak Park Avenue, Chicago, IL Zip 60634–1457; tel. 773/794–4000; Thomas Simpatico, M.D., Facility Director and Network System Manager

Section B

CHOATE MENTAL HEALTH CENTER (O, 79 beds) 1000 North Main Street, Anna, IL Zip 62906–1699; tel. 618/833–5161; Elaine Ray, Administrator

ELGIN MENTAL HEALTH CENTER (O, 500 beds) 750 South State Street, Elgin, IL Zip 60123–7692; tel. 847/742–1040; Amparo Lopez, Region Executive Director
Web address: www.dhs.state.il.us

JOHN J. MADDEN MENTAL HEALTH CENTER (O, 150 beds) 1200 South First Avenue, Hines, IL Zip 60141–0800; tel. 708/338–7202; Edith Newman, Interim Administrator

Owned, leased, sponsored:	7 hospitals	1457 beds
Contract–managed:	0 hospitals	0 beds
Totals:	7 hospitals	1457 beds

★0226: DUBUIS HEALTH SYSTEM (CC)
1700 West Loop South, Suite 1100A, Houston, TX Zip 77027–3007; tel. 713/277–2300; Toni Mills, Interim Chief Executive Officer
(Independent Hospital System)

ARKANSAS: ADVANCE CARE HOSPITAL OF FORT SMITH (C, 25 beds) 7301 Rogers Avenue, 4th Floor, Fort Smith, AR Zip 72903–4100; tel. 479/314–4900; Keith Rogers, Interim Administrator
Web address: www.dubuis.org/AdvanceCareHospitalofFortSmith

ADVANCE CARE HOSPITAL OF HOT SPRINGS (C, 26 beds) 300 Werner Street, 3rd Floor East, Hot Springs National Park, AR Zip 71913–6406; tel. 501/609–4300; Keith Rogers, Administrator
Web address: www.dubuis.org/AdvanceCareHospitalofHotSprings

GEORGIA: SOUTHERN CRESCENT HOSPITAL FOR SPECIALTY CARE (C, 30 beds) 11 Upper Riverdale Road S.W., 6th Floor, Riverdale, GA Zip 30274–2615; tel. 770/897–7600; Jeff Denney, Administrator
Web address: www.christusdubuis. org/SouthernCrescentHospitalforSpecialtyCare

IOWA: CONTINUING CARE HOSPITAL AT ST. LUKE'S (C, 16 beds) 1026 A Avenue N.E., 6th Floor, Cedar Rapids, IA Zip 52402–5036; tel. 319/369–8142; Elly Steffen, Chief Executive Officer and Administrator
Web address: www.unitypoint. org/cedarrapids/services–continuing–care–hospital.aspx

LOUISIANA: DUBUIS HOSPITAL OF ALEXANDRIA (O, 25 beds) 3330 Masonic Drive, 4th Floor, Alexandria, LA Zip 71301–3841; tel. 318/448–4938; Beth Parsons, R.N., Administrator
Web address: www.christusdubuis. org/CHRISTUSDubuisHospitalofAlexandriaLA

TEXAS: CHRISTUS DUBUIS HOSPITAL OF BRYAN (O, 30 beds) 1600 Joseph Drive, 2nd Floor, Bryan, TX Zip 77802–1502; tel. 979/821–5000; Judy Wolfe, Chief Executive Officer
Web address: www.dubuis.org/CHRISTUSDubuisHospitalofBryan

CHRISTUS DUBUIS HOSPITAL OF PORT ARTHUR (O, 15 beds) 3600 Gates Boulevard, Port Arthur, TX Zip 77642–3858; tel. 409/989–5300; Jeffrey Livingston, Administrator
Web address: www.dubuis.org/CHRISTUSDubuisHospitalofPortArthur

DUBUIS HOSPITAL OF BEAUMONT (O, 51 beds) 2830 Calder Avenue, 4th Floor, Beaumont, TX Zip 77702–1809; tel. 409/899–8154; Jeffrey Livingston, Administrator
Web address: www.dubuis. org/BeaumontandPortArthurSystem–CHRISTUSDubuisHospitalofBeaumont

DUBUIS HOSPITAL OF CORPUS CHRISTI (O, 22 beds) 600 Elizabeth Street, 3rd Floor, Corpus Christi, TX Zip 78404–2235; tel. 361/881–3223; Diane Kaiser, Administrator
Web address: www.dubuis.org/DubuisHospitalofCorpusChristi

DUBUIS HOSPITAL OF PARIS (O, 25 beds) 865 Deshong Drive, 5th Floor, Paris, TX Zip 75460–9313; tel. 903/782–2961; Kathie Reese, Administrator
Web address: www.dubuis.org/CHRISTUSDubuisHospitalofParis

DUBUIS HOSPITAL OF TEXARKANA (O, 49 beds) 2400 St. Michael Drive, 2nd Floor, Texarkana, TX Zip 75503–2372; tel. 903/614–7600; Holly Powell, Administrator
Web address: www.dubuis.org/DubuisHospitalofTexarkanaSystem

Owned, leased, sponsored:	7 hospitals	217 beds
Contract–managed:	4 hospitals	97 beds
Totals:	11 hospitals	314 beds

0861: DUKE LIFEPOINT HEALTHCARE (IO)
103 Powell Court, Brentwood, TN Zip 37027–5079; tel. 615/372–8540; Jeffrey G. Seraphine, FACHE, Division President
(Moderately Centralized Health System)

MICHIGAN: MARQUETTE GENERAL HOSPITAL (O, 268 beds) 580 West College Avenue, Marquette, MI Zip 49855–2736; tel. 906/228–9440; Edward D. Banos, Chief Executive Officer
Web address: www.mgh.org

NORTH CAROLINA: HARRIS REGIONAL HOSPITAL (O, 86 beds) 68 Hospital Road, Sylva, NC Zip 28779–2722; tel. 828/586–7000; Steve Heatherly, Chief Executive Officer
Web address: www.westcare.org

HAYWOOD REGIONAL MEDICAL CENTER (O, 146 beds) 262 Leroy George Drive, Clyde, NC Zip 28721–7430; tel. 828/456–7311; Janie Sinacore–Jaberg, R.N., MS, FACHE, Chief Executive Officer
Web address: www.haymed.org

MARIA PARHAM MEDICAL CENTER (O, 102 beds) 566 Ruin Creek Road, Henderson, NC Zip 27536–2927; tel. 252/438–4143; Robert G. Singletary, Chief Executive Officer
Web address: www.mariaparham.com

PERSON MEMORIAL HOSPITAL (O, 106 beds) 615 Ridge Road, Roxboro, NC Zip 27573–4629; tel. 336/599–2121; Beemal A. Shah, Chief Executive Officer
Web address: www.personhospital.com

RUTHERFORD REGIONAL HEALTH SYSTEM (O, 121 beds) 288 South Ridgecrest Avenue, Rutherfordton, NC Zip 28139–2838; tel. 828/286–5000; Cindy D. Buck, Chief Executive Officer
Web address: www.rutherfordhosp.org

SWAIN COUNTY HOSPITAL (O, 25 beds) 45 Plateau Street, Bryson City, NC Zip 28713–4200; tel. 828/488–2155; Steve Heatherly, Chief Executive Officer
Web address: www.westcare.org

WILSON MEDICAL CENTER (O, 206 beds) 1705 Tarboro Street, S.W., Wilson, NC Zip 27893–3428; tel. 252/399–8040; William E. Caldwell, Jr., Chief Executive Officer
Web address: www.wilmed.org

PENNSYLVANIA: CONEMAUGH MEMORIAL MEDICAL CENTER (O, 555 beds) 1086 Franklin Street, Johnstown, PA Zip 15905–4398; tel. 814/534–9000; Steven E. Tucker, President
Web address: www.conemaugh.org

CONEMAUGH MEYERSDALE MEDICAL CENTER (O, 20 beds) 200 Hospital Drive, Meyersdale, PA Zip 15552–1249; tel. 814/634–5911; Mary L. Libengood, President
Web address: www.conemaugh.org

CONEMAUGH MINERS MEDICAL CENTER (O, 30 beds) 290 Haida Avenue, Hastings, PA Zip 16646–5610, Mailing Address: P.O. Box 689, Zip 16646–0689; tel. 814/247–3100; William R. Crowe, President
Web address: www.minersmedicalcenter.org

VIRGINIA: TWIN COUNTY REGIONAL HOSPITAL (O, 86 beds) 200 Hospital Drive, Galax, VA Zip 24333–2227; tel. 276/236–8181; Jon D. Applebaum, Chief Executive Officer
Web address: www.tcrh.org

Owned, leased, sponsored:	12 hospitals	1751 beds
Contract–managed:	0 hospitals	0 beds
Totals:	12 hospitals	1751 beds

★0190: DUKE UNIVERSITY HEALTH SYSTEM (NP)
201 Trent Drive, Durham, NC Zip 27710–3037, Mailing Address: P.O. Box 3701, Zip 27710–3701; tel. 919/684–2255; William J. Fulkerson, M.D., Interim President and Chief Executive Officer
(Centralized Health System)

NORTH CAROLINA: DUKE RALEIGH HOSPITAL (O, 148 beds) 3400 Wake Forest Road, Raleigh, NC Zip 27609–7373, Mailing Address: P.O. Box 28280, Zip 27611–8280; tel. 919/954–3000; David Zaas, Chief Executive Officer
Web address: www.dukehealthraleigh.org

For explanation of codes following names, see page B2.
★ Indicates Type III membership in the American Hospital Association.

DUKE REGIONAL HOSPITAL (L, 204 beds) 3643 North Roxboro Road, Durham, NC Zip 27704–2763; tel. 919/470–4000; Kathleen B. Galbraith, President
Web address: www.durhamregional.org

DUKE UNIVERSITY HOSPITAL (O, 820 beds) 2301 Erwin Road, Durham, NC Zip 27705–4699, Mailing Address: P.O. Box 3708, Zip 27710–3708; tel. 919/684–8111; Kevin W. Sowers, R.N., MSN, President
Web address: www.dukehealth.org

Owned, leased, sponsored:	3 hospitals	1172 beds
Contract–managed:	0 hospitals	0 beds
Totals:	3 hospitals	1172 beds

★1895: EAST TEXAS MEDICAL CENTER REGIONAL HEALTHCARE SYSTEM (NP)
1000 South Beckham Street, Tyler, TX Zip 75701–1908, Mailing Address: P.O. Box 6400, Zip 75711–6400; tel. 903/535–6211; Elmer G. Ellis, FACHE, President and Chief Executive Officer
(Independent Hospital System)

TEXAS: EAST TEXAS MEDICAL CENTER ATHENS (L, 127 beds) 2000 South Palestine Street, Athens, TX Zip 75751–5610; tel. 903/676–1000; Patrick L. Wallace, Administrator
Web address: www.etmc.org

EAST TEXAS MEDICAL CENTER CARTHAGE (L, 25 beds) 409 Cottage Road, Carthage, TX Zip 75633–1466, Mailing Address: P.O. Box 549, Zip 75633–0549; tel. 903/693–3841; Gary Mikeal Hudson, Administrator
Web address: www.etmc.org

EAST TEXAS MEDICAL CENTER CLARKSVILLE (L, 30 beds) 3000 West Main Street, Clarksville, TX Zip 75426–3371, Mailing Address: P.O. Box 1270, Zip 75426–1270; tel. 903/427–6400; Matthew Wylie, Administrator
Web address: www.etmc.org

EAST TEXAS MEDICAL CENTER CROCKETT (L, 46 beds) 1100 Loop 304 East, Crockett, TX Zip 75835–1810; tel. 936/546–3862; Terry Cutler, Administrator and Chief Executive Officer
Web address: www.etmc.org

EAST TEXAS MEDICAL CENTER FAIRFIELD (L, 44 beds) 125 Newman Street, Fairfield, TX Zip 75840–1499; tel. 903/389–2121; Ruth Cook, Administrator
Web address: www.etmc.org

EAST TEXAS MEDICAL CENTER HENDERSON (O, 41 beds) 300 Wilson Street, Henderson, TX Zip 75652–5956; tel. 903/655–3616; Mark Leitner, Chief Executive Officer
Web address: www.etmc.org/etmchenderson/

EAST TEXAS MEDICAL CENTER JACKSONVILLE (O, 38 beds) 501 South Ragsdale Street, Jacksonville, TX Zip 75766–2413; tel. 903/541–5000; Jack R. Endres, JD, FACHE, Administrator
Web address: www.etmc.org

EAST TEXAS MEDICAL CENTER PITTSBURG (L, 25 beds) 2701 Highway 271 North, Pittsburg, TX Zip 75686–1032; tel. 903/946–5000; James Warren Robicheaux, Senior Administrator
Web address: www.etmc.org/newpittsburg.htm

EAST TEXAS MEDICAL CENTER REHABILITATION HOSPITAL (O, 49 beds) 701 Olympic Plaza Circle, Tyler, TX Zip 75701–1950, Mailing Address: P.O. Box 7530, Zip 75711–7530; tel. 903/596–3000; Eddie L. Howard, Vice President and Chief Operating Officer
Web address: www.etmc.org

EAST TEXAS MEDICAL CENTER SPECIALTY HOSPITAL (O, 36 beds) 1000 South Beckham, 5th Floor, Tyler, TX Zip 75701–1908, Mailing Address: P.O. Box 7018, Zip 75711–7018; tel. 903/596–3600; Eddie L. Howard, Vice President and Chief Operating Officer
Web address: www.etmc.org

EAST TEXAS MEDICAL CENTER TRINITY (L, 22 beds) 317 Prospect Drive, Trinity, TX Zip 75862–6202, Mailing Address: P.O. Box 3169, Zip 75862–3169; tel. 936/744–1100; Terry Cutler, Interim Chief Executive Officer
Web address: www.etmc.org

EAST TEXAS MEDICAL CENTER TYLER (O, 437 beds) 1000 South Beckham Street, Tyler, TX Zip 75701–1908, Mailing Address: Box 6400, Zip 75711–6400; tel. 903/597–0351; Robert B. Evans, Administrator and Chief Executive Officer
Web address: www.etmc.org

EAST TEXAS MEDICAL CENTER–GILMER (O, 35 beds) 712 North Wood Street, Gilmer, TX Zip 75644–1751; tel. 903/841–7100; James Warren Robicheaux, Administrator
Web address: www.etmc.org

EAST TEXAS MEDICAL CENTER–MOUNT VERNON (L, 30 beds) 500 Highway 37 South, Mount Vernon, TX Zip 75457–6550, Mailing Address: P.O. Box 477, Zip 75457–0477; tel. 903/537–8000; Jamie–Crystal Wylie, Chief Executive Officer
Web address: www.etmc.org/etmcmountvernon/

EAST TEXAS MEDICAL CENTER–QUITMAN (L, 25 beds) 117 Winnsboro Street, Quitman, TX Zip 75783–2144, Mailing Address: P.O. Box 1000, Zip 75783–1000; tel. 903/763–6300; James Warren Robicheaux, Interim Administrator
Web address: www.etmc.org/etmcquitman/

Owned, leased, sponsored:	15 hospitals	1010 beds
Contract–managed:	0 hospitals	0 beds
Totals:	15 hospitals	1010 beds

★0270: EASTERN CONNECTICUT HEALTH NETWORK (NP)
71 Haynes Street, Manchester, CT Zip 06040–4131; tel. 860/533–3400; Peter J. Karl, President and Chief Executive Officer
(Centralized Physician/Insurance Health System)

CONNECTICUT: MANCHESTER MEMORIAL HOSPITAL (O, 156 beds) 71 Haynes Street, Manchester, CT Zip 06040–4188; tel. 860/646–1222; Peter J. Karl, President and Chief Executive Officer
Web address: www.echn.org

ROCKVILLE GENERAL HOSPITAL (O, 47 beds) 31 Union Street, Vernon Rockville, CT Zip 06066–3160; tel. 860/872–0501; Peter J. Karl, President and Chief Executive Officer
Web address: www.echn.org

Owned, leased, sponsored:	2 hospitals	203 beds
Contract–managed:	0 hospitals	0 beds
Totals:	2 hospitals	203 beds

★0555: EASTERN MAINE HEALTHCARE SYSTEMS (NP)
43 Whiting Hill Road, Brewer, ME Zip 04412–1005; tel. 207/973–7045; M. Michelle Hood, FACHE, President and Chief Executive Officer
(Centralized Health System)

MAINE: BLUE HILL MEMORIAL HOSPITAL (O, 25 beds) 57 Water Street, Blue Hill, ME Zip 04614–5231; tel. 207/374–3400; John Ronan, President and Chief Executive Officer
Web address: www.bhmh.org

CHARLES A. DEAN MEMORIAL HOSPITAL (O, 36 beds) 364 Pritham Avenue, Greenville, ME Zip 04441–1395, Mailing Address: P.O. Box 1129, Zip 04441–1129; tel. 207/695–5200; Geno Murray, President and Chief Executive Officer
Web address: www.cadean.org

EASTERN MAINE MEDICAL CENTER (O, 364 beds) 489 State Street, Bangor, ME Zip 04401–6674, Mailing Address: P.O. Box 404, Zip 04402–0404; tel. 207/973–7000; Deborah Carey Johnson, R.N., President and Chief Executive Officer
Web address: www.emh.org

INLAND HOSPITAL (O, 26 beds) 200 Kennedy Memorial Drive, Waterville, ME Zip 04901–4595; tel. 207/861–3000; John Dalton, President and Chief Executive Officer
Web address: www.inlandhospital.org

MERCY HOSPITAL OF PORTLAND (O, 148 beds) 144 State Street, Portland, ME Zip 04101–3795; tel. 207/879–3000; Eileen F. Skinner, FACHE, President and Chief Executive Officer
Web address: www.mercyhospital.org

SEBASTICOOK VALLEY HEALTH (O, 25 beds) 447 North Main Street, Pittsfield, ME Zip 04967–3707; tel. 207/487–4000; Terri Vieira, President and Chief Executive Officer
Web address: www.sebasticookvalleyhealth.org

Section B

For explanation of codes following names, see page B2.
★ Indicates Type III membership in the American Hospital Association.

THE ACADIA HOSPITAL (O, 68 beds) 268 Stillwater Avenue, Bangor, ME Zip 04401–3945, Mailing Address: P.O. Box 422, Zip 04402–0422; tel. 207/973–6100; Daniel B. Coffey, President and Chief Executive Officer
Web address: www.acadiahospital.org

THE AROOSTOOK MEDICAL CENTER (O, 122 beds) 140 Academy Street, Presque Isle, ME Zip 04769–3171, Mailing Address: P.O. Box 151, Zip 04769–0151; tel. 207/768–4000; Sylvia Getman, President and Chief Executive Officer
Web address: www.tamc.org

Owned, leased, sponsored:	8 hospitals	814 beds
Contract–managed:	0 hospitals	0 beds
Totals:	8 hospitals	814 beds

★0926: EDWARD–ELMHURST HEALTHCARE (NP)
801 South Washington Street, Naperville, IL Zip 60540–7430; tel. 630/527–3000; Pamela M. Davis, System President and Chief Executive Officer

ILLINOIS: EDWARD HOSPITAL (O, 311 beds) 801 South Washington Street, Naperville, IL Zip 60540–7499; tel. 630/527–3000; Pamela M. Davis, System President and Chief Executive Officer
Web address: www.edward.org

ELMHURST MEMORIAL HOSPITAL (O, 259 beds) 155 East Brush Hill Road, Elmhurst, IL Zip 60126–5658; tel. 331/221–1000; Mary Lou Mastro, President and Chief Executive Officer
Web address: www.emhc.org

LINDEN OAKS HOSPITAL AT EDWARD (O, 108 beds) 852 West Street, Naperville, IL Zip 60540–6400; tel. 630/305–5500; Gina Sharp, FACHE, President
Web address: www.edward.org

Owned, leased, sponsored:	3 hospitals	678 beds
Contract–managed:	0 hospitals	0 beds
Totals:	3 hospitals	678 beds

1685: EINSTEIN HEALTHCARE NETWORK (NP)
5501 Old York Road, Philadelphia, PA Zip 19141–3098; tel. 215/456–7890; Barry R. Freedman, President and Chief Executive Officer

PENNSYLVANIA: BELMONT CENTER FOR COMPREHENSIVE TREATMENT (O, 147 beds) 4200 Monument Road, Philadelphia, PA Zip 19131–1625; tel. 215/877–2000; Sharon A. Bergen, Chief Operating Officer
Web address: www.einstein.edu/locations/belmont–behavioral–health/

EINSTEIN MEDICAL CENTER MONTGOMERY (O, 146 beds) 559 West Germantown Pike, East Norriton, PA Zip 19403–4250; tel. 484/622–1000; Beth Duffy, Chief Operating Officer

EINSTEIN MEDICAL CENTER PHILADELPHIA (O, 505 beds) 5501 Old York Road, Philadelphia, PA Zip 19141–3098; tel. 215/456–7890; Barry R. Freedman, President and Chief Executive Officer
Web address: www.einstein.edu

Owned, leased, sponsored:	3 hospitals	798 beds
Contract–managed:	0 hospitals	0 beds
Totals:	3 hospitals	798 beds

0879: EMERUS (IO)
10077 Grogan's Mill, Suite 100, The Woodlands, TX Zip 77380–1022; tel. 281/292–2450; Toby Hamilton, Chief Executive Officer

TEXAS: BAYLOR EMERGENCY MEDICAL CENTER AT AUBREY (O, 16 beds) 26791 Highway 380, Aubrey, TX Zip 76227; tel. 972/347–2525; John Wood, Chief Executive Officer
Web address: www.bemcataubrey.com

EMERUS (O, 7 beds) 16000 Southwest Freeway, Suite 100, Sugar Land, TX Zip 77479–2674; tel. 281/277–0911; Mike Kohler, Chief Executive Officer
Web address: www.emerus.com

Owned, leased, sponsored:	2 hospitals	23 beds
Contract–managed:	0 hospitals	0 beds
Totals:	2 hospitals	23 beds

★0256: EMORY HEALTHCARE (NP)
1440 Clifton Road N.E., Suite 145, Atlanta, GA Zip 30322–1102; tel. 404/778–5000; John T. Fox, Chief Executive Officer
(Centralized Health System)

GEORGIA: EMORY JOHNS CREEK HOSPITAL (O, 86 beds) 6325 Hospital Parkway, Johns Creek, GA Zip 30097–5775; tel. 678/474–7000; Marilyn Margolis, Interim Chief Executive Officer
Web address: www.emoryjohnscreek.com

EMORY SAINT JOSEPH'S HOSPITAL OF ATLANTA (O, 240 beds) 5665 Peachtree Dunwoody Road N.E., Atlanta, GA Zip 30342–1701; tel. 678/843–7001; Craig McCoy, Chief Executive Officer
Web address: www.stjosephsatlanta.org

EMORY UNIVERSITY HOSPITAL (O, 579 beds) 1364 Clifton Road N.E., Atlanta, GA Zip 30322–1102; tel. 404/712–2000; Robert J. Bachman, Chief Executive Officer
Web address: www.emoryhealthcare.org

EMORY UNIVERSITY HOSPITAL MIDTOWN (O, 431 beds) 550 Peachtree Street N.E., Atlanta, GA Zip 30308–2247; tel. 404/686–4411; Dane C. Peterson, Chief Operating Officer
Web address: www.emoryhealthcare.org

EMORY WESLEY WOODS GERIATRIC HOSPITAL (O, 327 beds) 1821 Clifton Road N.E., Atlanta, GA Zip 30329–4021; tel. 404/728–6200; Jennifer Schuck, Associate Administrator
Web address: www.emoryhealthcare.org

Owned, leased, sponsored:	5 hospitals	1663 beds
Contract–managed:	0 hospitals	0 beds
Totals:	5 hospitals	1663 beds

0647: ENCORE HEALTHCARE (IO)
7150 Columbia Gateway Drive, Suite J., Columbia, MD Zip 21046–2974; tel. 443/539–2350; Tim Nicholson, Chief Executive Officer
(Independent Hospital System)

OKLAHOMA: SPECIALTY HOSPITAL OF MIDWEST CITY (O, 31 beds) 8210 National Avenue, Midwest City, OK Zip 73110–8518; tel. 405/739–0800; Bobby Snyder, Chief Executive Officer

TEXAS: MESA HILLS SPECIALTY HOSPITAL (O, 32 beds) 2311 North Oregon Street, El Paso, TX Zip 79902–3216; tel. 915/545–1823; Jesus Ruiz, Chief Executive Officer
Web address: www.mesahillsspecialtyhospital.com/mesa_hills/index.aspx

PLANO SPECIALTY HOSPITAL (O, 43 beds) 1621 Coit Road, Plano, TX Zip 75075–6141; tel. 972/758–5200; Jay Lindsey, Chief Executive Officer
Web address: www.specialtyhospital–plano.com

PLUM CREEK SPECIALTY HOSPITAL (O, 47 beds) 5601 Plum Creek Drive, Amarillo, TX Zip 79124–1801; tel. 806/351–1000; Billy Blasingame, Chief Executive Officer
Web address: www.specialtyhospital–plumcreek.net

Owned, leased, sponsored:	4 hospitals	153 beds
Contract–managed:	0 hospitals	0 beds
Totals:	4 hospitals	153 beds

0525: ERLANGER HEALTH SYSTEM (NP)
975 East Third Street, Chattanooga, TN Zip 37403–2147; tel. 423/778–7000; Kevin M. Spiegel, FACHE, President and Chief Executive Officer
(Independent Hospital System)

GEORGIA: HUTCHESON MEDICAL CENTER (C, 185 beds) 100 Gross Crescent Circle, Fort Oglethorpe, GA Zip 30742–3669; tel. 706/858–2000; Farrell Hayes, Interim Chief Executive Officer
Web address: www.hutcheson.org

For explanation of codes following names, see page B2.
★ Indicates Type III membership in the American Hospital Association.

Section B

TENNESSEE: ERLANGER BLEDSOE HOSPITAL (C, 25 beds) 71 Wheeler Avenue, Pikeville, TN Zip 37367, Mailing Address: P.O. Box 699, Zip 37367–0699; tel. 423/447–2112; Stephanie Boynton, Administrator
Web address: www.erlanger.org

ERLANGER MEDICAL CENTER (O, 540 beds) 975 East Third Street, Chattanooga, TN Zip 37403–2147; tel. 423/778–7000; Kevin M. Spiegel, FACHE, Chief Executive Officer
Web address: www.erlanger.org

Owned, leased, sponsored:	1 hospital	540 beds
Contract–managed:	2 hospitals	210 beds
Totals:	3 hospitals	750 beds

0382: ERNEST HEALTH, INC. (IO)
7770 Jefferson Street N.E., Suite 320, Albuquerque, NM Zip 87109–4386; tel. 505/856–5300; Darby Brockette, Chief Executive Officer
(Independent Hospital System)

ARIZONA: MOUNTAIN VALLEY REGIONAL REHABILITATION HOSPITAL (O, 16 beds) 3700 North Windsong Drive, Prescott Valley, AZ Zip 86314–1253; tel. 928/759–8800; Judy Baum, Chief Executive Officer
Web address: www.mvrrh.ernesthealth.com

COLORADO: NORTHERN COLORADO LONG TERM ACUTE HOSPITAL (O, 40 beds) 4401 Union Street, Johnstown, CO Zip 80534; tel. 970/619–3663; Dawn Morrissey, Chief Operating Officer
Web address: www.ncltah.ernesthealth.com/

NORTHERN COLORADO REHABILITATION HOSPITAL (O, 40 beds) 4401 Union Street, Johnstown, CO Zip 80534–2800; tel. 970/619–3400; Elizabeth Bullard, Chief Operating Officer
Web address: www.ncrh.ernesthealth.com

IDAHO: NORTHERN IDAHO ADVANCED CARE HOSPITAL (O, 40 beds) 600 North Cecil Road, Post Falls, ID Zip 83854–6200; tel. 208/262–2800; Maria Godley, R.N., Chief Executive Officer
Web address: www.niach.ernesthealth.com

SOUTHWEST IDAHO ADVANCED CARE HOSPITAL (O, 40 beds) 6651 West Franklin Road, Boise, ID Zip 83709–0914; tel. 208/376–5700; Nolan Hoffer, Chief Executive Officer
Web address: www.siach.ernesthealth.com/

INDIANA: LAFAYETTE REGIONAL REHABILITATION HOSPITAL (O, 40 beds) 950 Park East Boulevard, Lafayette, IN Zip 47905–0792; tel. 765/447–4040; Dennis Schnepp, Chief Executive Officer
Web address: www.lrrh.ernesthealth.com

MONTANA: ADVANCED CARE HOSPITAL OF MONTANA (O, 40 beds) 3528 Gabel Road, Billings, MT Zip 59102–7307; tel. 406/373–8000; Diana Parker, Chief Executive Officer
Web address: www.achm.ernesthealth.com

NEW MEXICO: ADVANCED CARE HOSPITAL OF SOUTHERN NEW MEXICO (O, 40 beds) 4451 East Lohman Avenue, Las Cruces, NM Zip 88011–8267; tel. 575/521–6600; Suzanne Quillen, R.N., Chief Executive Officer
Web address: www.achsnm.ernesthealth.com

REHABILITATION HOSPITAL OF SOUTHERN NEW MEXICO (O, 40 beds) 4441 East Lohman Avenue, Las Cruces, NM Zip 88011–8267; tel. 575/521–6400; Sabrina Martin, Chief Operating Officer
Web address: www.rhsnm.ernesthealth.com

SOUTH CAROLINA: GREENWOOD REGIONAL REHABILITATION HOSPITAL (O, 54 beds) 1530 Parkway, Greenwood, SC Zip 29646–4027; tel. 864/330–9070; Kerry A. Trapnell, Chief Executive Officer
Web address: www.grrh.ernesthealth.com

TEXAS: LAREDO SPECIALTY HOSPITAL (O, 60 beds) 2005 Bustamante Street, Laredo, TX Zip 78041–5470; tel. 956/753–5353; Mario Rodriguez, Chief Executive Officer
Web address: www.lsh.ernesthealth.com

MESQUITE REHABILITATION INSTITUTE (O, 20 beds) 1023 North Belt Line Road, Mesquite, TX Zip 75149–1788; tel. 972/216–2400; Brian Abraham, Chief Operating Officer
Web address: www.mesquiterehab.ernesthealth.com/

MESQUITE SPECIALTY HOSPITAL (O, 40 beds) 1024 North Galloway Avenue, Mesquite, TX Zip 75149–2434; tel. 972/216–2300; Louis Bradley, Chief Executive Officer
Web address: www.msh.ernesthealth.com

NEW BRAUNFELS REGIONAL REHABILITATION HOSPITAL (O, 40 beds) 2041 Sundance Parkway, New Braunfels, TX Zip 78130–2779; tel. 830/625–6700; Jennifer Malatek, Chief Executive Officer
Web address: www.nbrrh.ernesthealth.com

SOUTH TEXAS REHABILITATION HOSPITAL (O, 40 beds) 425 East Alton Gloor Boulevard, Brownsville, TX Zip 78526–3361; tel. 956/554–6000; Jessie Eason Smedley, Chief Executive Officer
Web address: www.strh.ernesthealth.com

UTAH: UTAH VALLEY SPECIALTY HOSPITAL (O, 40 beds) 306 River Bend Lane, Provo, UT Zip 84604–5625; tel. 801/226–8880; Ginger Fisher, Interim Chief Executive Officer
Web address: www.uvsh.ernesthealth.com

WYOMING: ELKHORN VALLEY REHABILITATION HOSPITAL (O, 40 beds) 5715 East 2nd Street, Casper, WY Zip 82609–4322; tel. 307/265–0005; Michael Phillips, Chief Executive Officer
Web address: www.evrh.ernesthealth.com/

Owned, leased, sponsored:	17 hospitals	670 beds
Contract–managed:	0 hospitals	0 beds
Totals:	17 hospitals	670 beds

0396: ESSENTIA HEALTH (NP)
502 East Second Street, Duluth, MN Zip 55805–1913; tel. 218/786–8376; Peter E. Person, M.D., Chief Executive Officer
(Moderately Centralized Health System)

IDAHO: CLEARWATER VALLEY HOSPITAL AND CLINICS (O, 23 beds) 301 Cedar, Orofino, ID Zip 83544–9029; tel. 208/476–4555; Patrick J. Branco, President
Web address: www.smh–cvhc.org

ST. MARY'S HOSPITAL (O, 28 beds) Lewiston and North Streets, Cottonwood, ID Zip 83522–9750, Mailing Address: P.O. Box 137, Zip 83522–0137; tel. 208/962–3251; Patrick J. Branco, President
Web address: www.smh–cvhc.org/getpage.php?name=index

MINNESOTA: ESSENTIA HEALTH ADA (O, 14 beds) 201 9th Street West, Ada, MN Zip 56510–1279; tel. 218/784–5000; Ryan Hill, Chief Executive Officer
Web address: www.essentiahealth.org

ESSENTIA HEALTH DULUTH (O, 154 beds) 502 East Second Street, Duluth, MN Zip 55805–1982; tel. 218/727–8762; Barb Wessberg, Administrator
Web address: www.smdcmedicalcenter.org

ESSENTIA HEALTH FOSSTON (O, 75 beds) 900 Hilligoss Boulevard S.E., Fosston, MN Zip 56542–1599; tel. 218/435–1133; Kevin Gish, Administrator and Vice President
Web address: www.essentiahealth.org

ESSENTIA HEALTH NORTHERN PINES (O, 58 beds) 5211 Highway 110, Aurora, MN Zip 55705–1599; tel. 218/229–2211; Laura Ackman, Chief Operating Officer and Administrator
Web address: www.essentiahealth. org/NorthernPines/FindaClinic/Essentia–HealthNorthern–Pines–36.aspx

ESSENTIA HEALTH SANDSTONE (O, 70 beds) 109 Court Avenue South, Sandstone, MN Zip 55072–5120; tel. 320/245–2212; Michael D. Hedrix, Interim Chief Executive Officer
Web address: www.pinemedicalcenter.org

ESSENTIA HEALTH ST. JOSEPH'S MEDICAL CENTER (O, 162 beds) 523 North Third Street, Brainerd, MN Zip 56401–3098; tel. 218/829–2861; Adam Rees, President
Web address: www.essentiahealth.org

ESSENTIA HEALTH ST. MARY'S – DETROIT LAKES (O, 131 beds) 1027 Washington Avenue, Detroit Lakes, MN Zip 56501–3409; tel. 218/847–5611; Peter Jacobson, President
Web address: www.essentiahealth.org

ESSENTIA HEALTH ST. MARY'S MEDICAL CENTER (O, 310 beds) 407 East Third Street, Duluth, MN Zip 55805–1984; tel. 218/786–4000; James Garvey, Executive Vice President, Operations and Administrator
Web address: www.essentiahealth. org/StMarysMedicalCenter/FindaClinic/Essentia–HealthSt–Marys–Medical–Center–46. aspx

Section B

For explanation of codes following names, see page B2.
★ Indicates Type III membership in the American Hospital Association.

© 2014 AHA Guide   Health Care Systems, Networks and Alliances   **B57**

ESSENTIA HEALTH–HOLY TRINITY HOSPITAL (O, 60 beds) 115 West Second Street, Graceville, MN Zip 56240–4845, Mailing Address: P.O. Box 157, Zip 56240–0157; tel. 320/748–7223; John Campion, Administrator **Web address:** www.essentiahealth. org/HolyTrinityHospital/FindaClinic/Essentia–HealthHoly–Trinity–Hospital–96. aspx

MINNESOTA VALLEY HEALTH CENTER (O, 64 beds) 621 South Fourth Street, Le Sueur, MN Zip 56058–2298; tel. 507/665–3375; Pam Williams, Chief Executive Officer **Web address:** www.mvhc.org

NORTH DAKOTA: ESSENTIA HEALTH FARGO (O, 94 beds) 3000 32nd Avenue South, Fargo, ND Zip 58103–6132; tel. 701/364–8000; Timothy Sayler, Chief Operating Officer **Web address:** www.essentiahealth.com

WISCONSIN: ESSENTIA HEALTH ST. MARY'S HOSPITAL OF SUPERIOR (O, 25 beds) 3500 Tower Avenue, Superior, WI Zip 54880–5395; tel. 715/817–7000; Terry Jacobson, Administrator and Chief Executive Officer **Web address:** www.essentiahealth. org/EssentiaHealthStMarysHospitalofSuperiorFoundation/overview.aspx

Owned, leased, sponsored:	14 hospitals	1268 beds
Contract–managed:	0 hospitals	0 beds
Totals:	14 hospitals	1268 beds

2395: EXCELA HEALTH (NP)
134 Industrial Park Road, Greensburg, PA Zip 15601–7328; tel. 724/832–5050; Robert Rogalski, Chief Executive Officer **(Centralized Health System)**

PENNSYLVANIA: EXCELA FRICK HOSPITAL (O, 63 beds) 508 South Church Street, Mount Pleasant, PA Zip 15666–1790; tel. 724/547–1500; Ronald H. Ott, President **Web address:** www.excelahealth. org/PatientsandVisitors/HospitalsFacilities/Hospitals/Frick.aspx

EXCELA HEALTH WESTMORELAND HOSPITAL (O, 359 beds) 532 West Pittsburgh Street, Greensburg, PA Zip 15601–2282; tel. 724/832–4000; Ronald H. Ott, President **Web address:** www.excelahealth.org

EXCELA LATROBE AREA HOSPITAL (O, 121 beds) One Mellon Way, Latrobe, PA Zip 15650–1096; tel. 724/537–1000; Michael D. Busch, Executive Vice President and Chief Operating Officer **Web address:** www.excelahealth.org

Owned, leased, sponsored:	3 hospitals	543 beds
Contract–managed:	0 hospitals	0 beds
Totals:	3 hospitals	543 beds

★1325: FAIRVIEW HEALTH SERVICES (NP)
2450 Riverside Avenue, Minneapolis, MN Zip 55454–1400; tel. 612/672–6141; Rulon F. Stacey, Ph.D., FACHE, President and Chief Executive Officer **(Centralized Physician/Insurance Health System)**

MINNESOTA: FAIRVIEW LAKES HEALTH SERVICES (O, 47 beds) 5200 Fairview Boulevard, Wyoming, MN Zip 55092–8013; tel. 651/982–7000; John W. Herman, Chief Executive Officer **Web address:** www.fairview.org/

FAIRVIEW NORTHLAND MEDICAL CENTER (O, 31 beds) 911 Northland Drive, Princeton, MN Zip 55371–2173; tel. 763/389–1313; John W. Herman, Chief Executive Officer **Web address:** www.northland.fairview.org

FAIRVIEW RIDGES HOSPITAL (O, 171 beds) 201 East Nicollet Boulevard, Burnsville, MN Zip 55337–5799; tel. 952/892–2000; Beth Krehbiel, R.N., FACHE, President and Chief Executive Officer **Web address:** www.fairview.org

FAIRVIEW SOUTHDALE HOSPITAL (O, 326 beds) 6401 France Avenue South, Edina, MN Zip 55435–2199; tel. 952/924–5000; Bradley Beard, President **Web address:** www.fairview.org

RANGE REGIONAL HEALTH SERVICES (O, 85 beds) 750 East 34th Street, Hibbing, MN Zip 55746–4600; tel. 218/262–4881; Debra K. Boardman, FACHE, President and Chief Executive Officer **Web address:** www.range.fairview.org

UNIVERSITY OF MINNESOTA MEDICAL CENTER, FAIRVIEW (O, 844 beds) 2450 Riverside Avenue, Minneapolis, MN Zip 55454–1400; tel. 612/672–6000; Carolyn Wilson, R.N., President **Web address:** www.fairview.org

Owned, leased, sponsored:	6 hospitals	1504 beds
Contract–managed:	0 hospitals	0 beds
Totals:	6 hospitals	1504 beds

0814: FAITH REGIONAL HEALTH SERVICES (NP)
2700 West Norfolk Avenue, Norfolk, NE Zip 68701–4438, Mailing Address: P.O. Box 869, Zip 68702–0869; tel. 402/644–7201; Mark D. Klosterman, FACHE, President and Chief Executive Officer **(Independent Hospital System)**

NEBRASKA: FAITH REGIONAL HEALTH SERVICES (O, 245 beds) 2700 West Norfolk Avenue, Norfolk, NE Zip 68701–4438, Mailing Address: P.O. Box 869, Zip 68702–0869; tel. 402/644–7201; Mark D. Klosterman, FACHE, President and Chief Executive Officer **Web address:** www.frhs.org

NIOBRARA VALLEY HOSPITAL (C, 20 beds) 401 South Fifth Street, Lynch, NE Zip 68746–0118, Mailing Address: P.O. Box 118, Zip 68746–0118; tel. 402/569–2451; Kelly Kalkowski, Chief Executive Officer **Web address:** www.nvhcares.org

WEST HOLT MEMORIAL HOSPITAL (C, 17 beds) 406 West Neely Street, Atkinson, NE Zip 68713–4801; tel. 402/925–2811; Michael F. Coyle, Chief Executive Officer **Web address:** www.westholtmed.org

Owned, leased, sponsored:	1 hospital	245 beds
Contract–managed:	2 hospitals	37 beds
Totals:	3 hospitals	282 beds

0397: FINGER LAKES HEALTH (NP)
196 North Street, Geneva, NY Zip 14456–1651; tel. 315/787–4000; Jose Acevedo, M.D., President and Chief Executive Officer **(Independent Hospital System)**

NEW YORK: GENEVA GENERAL HOSPITAL (O, 132 beds) 196 North Street, Geneva, NY Zip 14456–1694; tel. 315/787–4000; Jose Acevedo, M.D., President and Chief Executive Officer **Web address:** www.flhealth.org

SOLDIERS AND SAILORS MEMORIAL HOSPITAL OF YATES COUNTY (O, 186 beds) 418 North Main Street, Penn Yan, NY Zip 14527–1085; tel. 315/531–2000; Jose Acevedo, M.D., President and Chief Executive Officer **Web address:** www.flhealth.org

Owned, leased, sponsored:	2 hospitals	318 beds
Contract–managed:	0 hospitals	0 beds
Totals:	2 hospitals	318 beds

★0243: FIRSTHEALTH OF THE CAROLINAS (NP)
155 Memorial Drive, Pinehurst, NC Zip 28374–8710, Mailing Address: P.O. Box 3000, Zip 28374–3000; tel. 910/715–1000; David J. Kilarski, Chief Executive Officer **(Centralized Physician/Insurance Health System)**

NORTH CAROLINA: FIRSTHEALTH MONTGOMERY MEMORIAL HOSPITAL (O, 25 beds) 520 Allen Street, Troy, NC Zip 27371–2802, Mailing Address: P.O. Box 486, Zip 27371–0486; tel. 910/571–5000; Beth Walker, R.N., President **Web address:** www.firsthealth.org

For explanation of codes following names, see page B2.
★ Indicates Type III membership in the American Hospital Association.

FIRSTHEALTH MOORE REGIONAL HOSPITAL (O, 371 beds) 155 Memorial Drive, Pinehurst, NC Zip 28374–8710, Mailing Address: P.O. Box 3000, Zip 28374–3000; tel. 910/715–1000; David J. Kilarski, Chief Executive Officer
Web address: www.firsthealth.org

FIRSTHEALTH RICHMOND MEMORIAL HOSPITAL (O, 91 beds) 925 Long Drive, Rockingham, NC Zip 28379–4835; tel. 910/417–3000; John J. Jackson, President
Web address: www.firsthealth.org

Owned, leased, sponsored:	3 hospitals	487 beds
Contract–managed:	0 hospitals	0 beds
Totals:	3 hospitals	487 beds

0378: FIVE STAR QUALITY CARE (IO)
400 Centre Street, Newton, MA Zip 02458–2094; tel. 617/796–8387; Bruce J. Mackey, Jr., President and Chief Executive Officer
(Independent Hospital System)

MASSACHUSETTS: BRAINTREE REHABILITATION HOSPITAL (O, 187 beds) 250 Pond Street, Braintree, MA Zip 02184–5351; tel. 781/348–2500; Randy Doherty, CPA, Chief Executive Officer
Web address: www.braintreerehabhospital.com

NEW ENGLAND REHABILITATION HOSPITAL (O, 210 beds) Two Rehabilitation Way, Woburn, MA Zip 01801–6098; tel. 781/935–5050; Joel Rudin, Chief Executive Officer
Web address: www.newenglandrehab.com

Owned, leased, sponsored:	2 hospitals	397 beds
Contract–managed:	0 hospitals	0 beds
Totals:	2 hospitals	397 beds

0900: FOUNDATION SURGICAL HOSPITAL AFFILIATES (IO)
14000 North Portland Avenue, Suite 204, Oklahoma City, OK Zip 73134–4002; tel. 405/608–1700; Thomas A. Michaud, Chief Executive Officer
(Independent Hospital System)

TEXAS: FOUNDATION SURGICAL HOSPITAL OF EL PASO (O, 20 beds) 1416 George Dieter Drive, El Paso, TX Zip 79936–7601; tel. 915/598–4240; Kane Dawson, Chief Executive Officer
Web address: www.physiciansmedcenter.com

FOUNDATION SURGICAL HOSPITAL OF SAN ANTONIO (O, 20 beds) 9522 Huebner Road, San Antonio, TX Zip 78240–1548; tel. 210/478–5400; Robert Trussell, Chief Executive Officer
Web address: www.fshsanantonio.com/bariatric–foundation–surgical.html

HERITAGE PARK SURGICAL HOSPITAL (O, 10 beds) 3601 North Calais Street, Sherman, TX Zip 75090–1785; tel. 903/870–0999; Raymond Ford, Chief Executive Officer
Web address: www.heritageparksurgicalhospital.com

HOUSTON ORTHOPEDIC AND SPINE HOSPITAL (O, 64 beds) 5410 West Loop South, Bellaire, TX Zip 77401–2103; tel. 713/314–4500; Andrew Knizley, Chief Executive Officer
Web address: www.foundationsurgicalhospital.com

Owned, leased, sponsored:	4 hospitals	114 beds
Contract–managed:	0 hospitals	0 beds
Totals:	4 hospitals	114 beds

5345: FRANCISCAN ALLIANCE (CC)
1515 Dragoon Trail, Mishawaka, IN Zip 46544–4710, Mailing Address: P.O. Box 1290, Zip 46546–1290; tel. 574/256–3935; Kevin D. Leahy, President and Chief Executive Officer
(Independent Hospital System)

ILLINOIS: FRANCISCAN ST. JAMES HOSPITAL AND HEALTH CENTERS (O, 329 beds) 20201 South Crawford Avenue, Olympia Fields, IL Zip 60461–1010; tel. 708/747–4000; Arnold Kimmel, Chief Executive Officer
Web address: www.stjameshhc.org

INDIANA: FRANCISCAN HEALTHCARE – MUNSTER (O, 32 beds) 701 Superior Avenue, Munster, IN Zip 46321–4037; tel. 219/924–1300; Barbara M. Greene, President
Web address: www.franciscanphysicianshospital.org

FRANCISCAN ST. ANTHONY HEALTH – CROWN POINT (O, 254 beds) 1201 South Main Street, Crown Point, IN Zip 46307–8483; tel. 219/738–2100; David Ruskowski, President
Web address: www.franciscanalliance.org

FRANCISCAN ST. ANTHONY HEALTH – MICHIGAN CITY (O, 171 beds) 301 West Homer Street, Michigan City, IN Zip 46360–4358; tel. 219/879–8511; James Callaghan, III, M.D., President
Web address: www.saintanthonymemorial.org

FRANCISCAN ST. ELIZABETH HEALTH – CRAWFORDSVILLE (O, 42 beds) 1710 Lafayette Road, Crawfordsville, IN Zip 47933–1099; tel. 765/362–2800; Terrance E. Wilson, President and CEO
Web address: www.stclaremedical.org

FRANCISCAN ST. ELIZABETH HEALTH – LAFAYETTE CENTRAL (O, 65 beds) 1501 Hartford Street, Lafayette, IN Zip 47904–2134; tel. 765/423–6011; Terrance E. Wilson, President and CEO
Web address: www.ste.org

FRANCISCAN ST. ELIZABETH HEALTH – LAFAYETTE EAST (O, 182 beds) 1701 South Creasy Lane, Lafayette, IN Zip 47905–4972; tel. 765/502–4000; Terrance E. Wilson, President and CEO
Web address: www.ste.org

FRANCISCAN ST. FRANCIS HEALTH – INDIANAPOLIS (O, 455 beds) 8111 South Emerson Avenue, Indianapolis, IN Zip 46237–8601; tel. 317/528–5000; Robert J. Brody, President and Chief Executive Officer
Web address: www.stfrancishospitals.org

FRANCISCAN ST. FRANCIS HEALTH – MOORESVILLE (O, 115 beds) 1201 Hadley Road, Mooresville, IN Zip 46158–1789; tel. 317/831–1160; Peter J. Murphy, Senior Vice President and Chief Operating Officer
Web address: www.franciscanalliance.org/hospitals/mooresville/Pages/default.aspx

FRANCISCAN ST. FRANCIS HEALTH–CARMEL (O, 6 beds) 12188B North Meridian Street, Carmel, IN Zip 46032–4840; tel. 317/705–4500; Stephen Wheatley, Chief Executive Officer
Web address: www.franciscanalliance.org/hospitals/carmel/Pages/default.aspx

FRANCISCAN ST. MARGARET HEALTH – HAMMOND (O, 500 beds) 5454 Hohman Avenue, Hammond, IN Zip 46320–1999; tel. 219/933–2074; Thomas J. Gryzbek, President
Web address: www.smmhc.com

SURGICAL HOSPITAL OF MUNSTER (O, 9 beds) 7847 Calumet Avenue, Munster, IN Zip 46321; tel. 219/836–5102; Paul Skowron, Chief Executive Officer

Owned, leased, sponsored:	12 hospitals	2160 beds
Contract–managed:	0 hospitals	0 beds
Totals:	12 hospitals	2160 beds

★1475: FRANCISCAN MISSIONARIES OF OUR LADY HEALTH SYSTEM, INC. (CC)
4200 Essen Lane, Baton Rouge, LA Zip 70809–2158; tel. 225/923–2701; John J. Finan, Jr., FACHE, President and Chief Executive Officer
(Moderately Centralized Health System)

LOUISIANA: ASSUMPTION COMMUNITY HOSPITAL (O, 6 beds) 135 Highway 402, Napoleonville, LA Zip 70390–2217; tel. 985/369–3600; Wayne M. Arboneaux, Chief Executive Officer
Web address: www.ololrmc.com

OUR LADY OF LOURDES REGIONAL MEDICAL CENTER (O, 186 beds) 4801 Ambassador Caffery Parkway, Lafayette, LA Zip 70508–6917; tel. 337/470–2000; William F. Barrow, II, President and Chief Executive Officer
Web address: www.lourdesrmc.com

OUR LADY OF THE ANGELS HOSPITAL (O, 74 beds) 433 Plaza Street, Bogalusa, LA Zip 70427–3793; tel. 985/730–6700; Rene Ragas, Chief Operating Officer
Web address: www.oloah.org

For explanation of codes following names, see page B2.
★ Indicates Type III membership in the American Hospital Association.

OUR LADY OF THE LAKE REGIONAL MEDICAL CENTER (O, 1087 beds) 5000 Hennessy Boulevard, Baton Rouge, LA Zip 70808–4375; tel. 225/765–6565; K. Scott Wester, FACHE, President and Chief Executive Officer
Web address: www.ololrmc.com

ST. ELIZABETH HOSPITAL (O, 38 beds) 1125 West Highway 30, Gonzales, LA Zip 70737–5004; tel. 225/647–5000; Robert L. Burgess, President and Chief Executive Officer
Web address: www.steh.com

ST. FRANCIS MEDICAL CENTER (O, 343 beds) 309 Jackson Street, Monroe, LA Zip 71201–7407, Mailing Address: P.O. Box 1901, Zip 71210–1901; tel. 318/966–4000; Louis H. Bremer, Jr., President and Chief Executive Officer
Web address: www.stfran.com

Owned, leased, sponsored:	6 hospitals	1734 beds
Contract–managed:	0 hospitals	0 beds
Totals:	6 hospitals	1734 beds

★1455: FRANCISCAN SISTERS OF CHRISTIAN CHARITY SPONSORED MINISTRIES, INC. (CC)
1415 South Rapids Road, Manitowoc, WI 54220–9302; tel. 920/684–7071; Sister Laura J. Wolf, President
(Moderately Centralized Health System)

NEBRASKA: ST. FRANCIS MEMORIAL HOSPITAL (O, 92 beds) 430 North Monitor Street, West Point, NE Zip 68788–1555; tel. 402/372–2404; Ronald O. Briggs, FACHE, President and Chief Executive Officer
Web address: www.fcswp.org

OHIO: GENESIS HEALTHCARE SYSTEM (O, 312 beds) 2951 Maple Avenue, Zanesville, OH Zip 43701–1406; tel. 740/454–5000; Matthew J. Perry, President and Chief Executive Officer
Web address: www.genesishcs.org

WISCONSIN: HOLY FAMILY MEMORIAL (O, 62 beds) 2300 Western Avenue, Manitowoc, WI Zip 54220–3712, Mailing Address: P.O. Box 1450, Zip 54221–1450; tel. 920/320–2011; Mark P. Herzog, President and Chief Executive Officer
Web address: www.hfmhealth.org

Owned, leased, sponsored:	3 hospitals	466 beds
Contract–managed:	0 hospitals	0 beds
Totals:	3 hospitals	466 beds

★0271: FREEMAN HEALTH SYSTEM (NP)
1102 West 32nd Street, Joplin, MO Zip 64804–3503; tel. 417/347–1111; Paula F. Baker, President and Chief Executive Officer
(Centralized Health System)

MISSOURI: FREEMAN HOSPITAL WEST (O, 408 beds) 1102 West 32nd Street, Joplin, MO Zip 64804–3503; tel. 417/347–1111; Paula F. Baker, President and Chief Executive Officer
Web address: www.freemanhealth.com

FREEMAN NEOSHO HOSPITAL (O, 25 beds) 113 West Hickory Street, Neosho, MO Zip 64850–1705; tel. 417/455–4352; Paula F. Baker, President and Chief Executive Officer
Web address: www.freemanhealth.com

Owned, leased, sponsored:	2 hospitals	433 beds
Contract–managed:	0 hospitals	0 beds
Totals:	2 hospitals	433 beds

0182: FUNDAMENTAL LONG TERM CARE HOLDINGS, LLC (IO)
930 Ridgebrook Road, Sparks Glencoe, MD Zip 21152–9390; tel. 410/773–1000; W. Bradley Bennett, President and Chief Executive Officer
(Independent Hospital System)

NEVADA: HARMON MEDICAL AND REHABILITATION HOSPITAL (O, 118 beds) 2170 East Harmon Avenue, Las Vegas, NV Zip 89119–7840; tel. 702/794–0100; Bonnie Essex Hillegass, Chief Executive Officer

HORIZON SPECIALTY HOSPITAL (O, 25 beds) 640 Desert Lane, Las Vegas, NV Zip 89106–4207; tel. 702/382–3155; William Fox, Chief Executive Officer and Administrator
Web address: www.horizonspecialtyhosp.com/

SOUTHERN NEVADA MEDICAL AND REHABILITATION CENTER (O, 100 beds) 2945 Casa Vegas, Las Vegas, NV Zip 89169–2248; tel. 702/735–7179; Maureen Davis, Administrator

TEXAS: LLANO SPECIALTY HOSPITAL OF LUBBOCK (O, 15 beds) 1409 9th Street, Lubbock, TX Zip 79401–2601; tel. 806/767–9133; Dennis Fleenor, R.N., Chief Executive Officer
Web address: www.fundltc.com/Healthcare%20Facility%20Locator/facility_page.aspx?locationID=190

TEXAS SPECIALTY HOSPITAL AT LUBBOCK (O, 35 beds) 4302 Princeton Street, Lubbock, TX Zip 79415–1304; tel. 806/723–8700; Deanna Graves, Chief Executive Officer

Owned, leased, sponsored:	5 hospitals	293 beds
Contract–managed:	0 hospitals	0 beds
Totals:	5 hospitals	293 beds

★5570: GEISINGER HEALTH SYSTEM (NP)
100 North Academy Avenue, Danville, PA Zip 17822–9800; tel. 570/271–6211; Glenn Steele, Jr., M.D., Ph.D., President and Chief Executive Officer
(Centralized Physician/Insurance Health System)

PENNSYLVANIA: GEISINGER MEDICAL CENTER (O, 402 beds) 100 North Academy Avenue, Danville, PA Zip 17822–2201; tel. 570/271–6211; Thomas P. Sokola, Chief Administrative Officer
Web address: www.geisinger.org

GEISINGER WYOMING VALLEY MEDICAL CENTER (O, 178 beds) 1000 East Mountain Boulevard, Wilkes Barre, PA Zip 18711–0027; tel. 570/808–7300; Ronald R. Beer, FACHE, Vice President, Clinical Operations
Web address: www.geisinger.org

GEISINGER–BLOOMSBURG HOSPITAL (O, 72 beds) 549 Fair Street, Bloomsburg, PA Zip 17815–1419; tel. 570/387–2100; Lissa Bryan–Smith, Chief Administrative Officer
Web address: www.bloomhealth.net

GEISINGER–COMMUNITY MEDICAL CENTER (O, 248 beds) 1800 Mulberry Street, Scranton, PA Zip 18510–2369; tel. 570/703–8000; Anthony Aquilina, D.O., Interim Chief Executive Officer
Web address: www.cmccare.org/

Owned, leased, sponsored:	4 hospitals	900 beds
Contract–managed:	0 hospitals	0 beds
Totals:	4 hospitals	900 beds

★0311: GENESIS HEALTH SYSTEM (NP)
1227 East Rusholme Street, Davenport, IA Zip 52803–2498; tel. 563/421–1000; Douglas P. Cropper, President and Chief Executive Officer
(Centralized Physician/Insurance Health System)

ILLINOIS: GENESIS MEDICAL CENTER, ILLINI CAMPUS (O, 101 beds) 801 Illini Drive, Silvis, IL Zip 61282–1893; tel. 309/281–4000; Kevin Youmans, Interim President
Web address: www.genesishealth.com

GENESIS MEDICAL CENTER–ALEDO (O, 22 beds) 409 N.W. Ninth Avenue, Aledo, IL Zip 61231–1296; tel. 309/582–9100; Ted Rogalski, Administrator
Web address: www.genesishealth.com

IOWA: GENESIS MEDICAL CENTER, DEWITT (O, 86 beds) 1118 11th Street, De Witt, IA Zip 52742–1296; tel. 563/659–4200; Curt Coleman, FACHE, Administrator
Web address: www.genesishealth.com

GENESIS MEDICAL CENTER–DAVENPORT (O, 338 beds) 1227 East Rusholme Street, Davenport, IA Zip 52803–2498; tel. 563/421–1000; Wayne A. Diewald, President
Web address: www.genesishealth.com

JACKSON COUNTY REGIONAL HEALTH CENTER (C, 25 beds) 700 West Grove Street, Maquoketa, IA Zip 52060–2163; tel. 563/652–2474; Curt Coleman, FACHE, Administrator
Web address: www.jcrhc.org

For explanation of codes following names, see page B2.
★ Indicates Type III membership in the American Hospital Association.

Owned, leased, sponsored:	4 hospitals	547 beds
Contract–managed:	1 hospital	25 beds
Totals:	5 hospitals	572 beds

★0812: GEORGETOWN HOSPITAL SYSTEM (NP)
606 Black River Road, Georgetown, SC Zip 29440–3304, Mailing Address: P.O. Box 421718, Zip 29442–4203; tel. 843/527–7000; Bruce P. Bailey, President and Chief Executive Officer
(Independent Hospital System)

SOUTH CAROLINA: GEORGETOWN MEMORIAL HOSPITAL (O, 136 beds) 606 Black River Road, Georgetown, SC Zip 29440–3368, Mailing Address: Drawer 421718, Zip 29442–4203; tel. 843/527–7000; Gayle L. Resetar, Chief Operating Officer
Web address: www.georgetownhospitalsystem.org

WACCAMAW COMMUNITY HOSPITAL (O, 169 beds) 4070 Highway 17 Bypass, Murrells Inlet, SC Zip 29576–5033, Mailing Address: P.O. Drawer 3350, Zip 29576–2673; tel. 843/652–1000; Gayle L. Resetar, Chief Operating Officer
Web address: www.gmhsc.com

Owned, leased, sponsored:	2 hospitals	305 beds
Contract–managed:	0 hospitals	0 beds
Totals:	2 hospitals	305 beds

0283: GILLIARD HEALTH SERVICES (IO)
3091 Carter Hill Road, Montgomery, AL Zip 36111–1801; tel. 334/265–5009; William G. McKenzie, President, Chief Executive Officer and Chairman

ALABAMA: EVERGREEN MEDICAL CENTER (O, 39 beds) 101 Crestview Avenue, Evergreen, AL Zip 36401–3333, Mailing Address: P.O. Box 706, Zip 36401–0706; tel. 251/578–2480; William G. McKenzie, Interim Administrator
Web address: www.evergreenmedical.org

JACKSON MEDICAL CENTER (O, 26 beds) 220 Hospital Drive, Jackson, AL Zip 36545–2459, Mailing Address: P.O. Box 428, Zip 36545–0428; tel. 251/246–9021; Amy Gibson, Chief Executive Officer
Web address: www.jacksonmedicalcenter.org

Owned, leased, sponsored:	2 hospitals	65 beds
Contract–managed:	0 hospitals	0 beds
Totals:	2 hospitals	65 beds

0654: GLOBALREHAB (IO)
1420 West Mockingbird Lane, Suite 100, Dallas, TX Zip 75247–4932, Mailing Address: 1340 Empire Central Drive, Zip 75247–4022; tel. 214/879–7500; Hooman Sedighi, M.D., President and Chief Executive Officer
(Independent Hospital System)

TEXAS: GLOBALREHAB HOSPITAL – DALLAS (O, 42 beds) 1340 Empire Central Drive, Dallas, TX Zip 75247–4022; tel. 214/879–7300; David Smith, Chief Executive Officer
Web address: www.baylorhealth.com/bir

GLOBALREHAB HOSPITAL – FORT WORTH (O, 42 beds) 6601 Harris Parkway, Fort Worth, TX Zip 76132–6108; tel. 817/433–9600; Jeffrey D. Thompson, Chief Executive Officer
Web address: www.globalrehabhospitals.com

SELECT REHABILITATION HOSPITAL OF SAN ANTONIO (O, 42 beds) 19126 Stonehue Road, San Antonio, TX Zip 78258–3490; tel. 210/482–3400; Robert Ward, Chief Executive Officer
Web address: www.globalrehabhospitals.com

Owned, leased, sponsored:	3 hospitals	126 beds
Contract–managed:	0 hospitals	0 beds
Totals:	3 hospitals	126 beds

0522: GOOD SHEPHERD HEALTH SYSTEM (NP)
700 East Marshall Avenue, Longview, TX Zip 75601–5580; tel. 903/315–2000; Steve Altmiller, President and Chief Executive Officer
(Independent Hospital System)

GOOD SHEPHERD MEDICAL CENTER (O, 399 beds) 700 East Marshall Avenue, Longview, TX Zip 75601–5580; tel. 903/315–2000; Steve Altmiller, President and Chief Executive Officer
Web address: www.gsmc.org

GOOD SHEPHERD MEDICAL CENTER-MARSHALL (O, 140 beds) 811 South Washington Avenue, Marshall, TX Zip 75670–5336, Mailing Address: P.O. Box 1599, Zip 75671–1599; tel. 903/927–6000; Russell J. Collier, FACHE, President and Chief Executive Officer
Web address: www.gsmcmarshall.org

Owned, leased, sponsored:	2 hospitals	539 beds
Contract–managed:	0 hospitals	0 beds
Totals:	2 hospitals	539 beds

0648: GOOD SHEPHERD REHABILITATION NETWORK (IO)
850 South Fifth Street, Allentown, PA Zip 18103–3308; tel. 610/776–3100; John Kristel, President and Chief Executive Officer
(Independent Hospital System)

PENNSYLVANIA: GOOD SHEPHERD REHABILITATION HOSPITAL (O, 106 beds) 850 South 5th Street, Allentown, PA Zip 18103–3308; tel. 610/776–3299; John Kristel, President and Chief Executive Officer
Web address: www.goodshepherdrehab.org

GOOD SHEPHERD SPECIALTY HOSPITAL (O, 32 beds) 2545 Schoenersville Road, 3rd Floor, Bethlehem, PA Zip 18017–7300; tel. 484/884–5051; Greg Wuchter, Administrator
Web address: www.goodshepherdrehab.org

Owned, leased, sponsored:	2 hospitals	138 beds
Contract–managed:	0 hospitals	0 beds
Totals:	2 hospitals	138 beds

★1535: GREAT PLAINS HEALTH ALLIANCE, INC. (NP)
250 North Rock Road, Suite 160, Wichita, KS Zip 67206–2241; tel. 316/685–1523; Dave Dellasega, President and Chief Executive Officer
(Decentralized Health System)

KANSAS: ASHLAND HEALTH CENTER (C, 45 beds) 709 Oak Street, Ashland, KS Zip 67831–0188, Mailing Address: P.O. Box 188, Zip 67831–0188; tel. 620/635–2241; Roger Barnhart, Chief Executive Officer
Web address: www.ashlandhc.org

CHEYENNE COUNTY HOSPITAL (L, 16 beds) 210 West First Street, Saint Francis, KS Zip 67756–3540, Mailing Address: P.O. Box 547, Zip 67756–0547; tel. 785/332–2104; Scott Jenkins, Administrator
Web address: www.cheyennecountyhospital.com

COMANCHE COUNTY HOSPITAL (C, 12 beds) 202 South Frisco Street, Coldwater, KS Zip 67029–9101, Mailing Address: HC 65, Box 8A, Zip 67029–9500; tel. 620/582–2144; Nancy Zimmerman, R.N., Administrator
Web address: www.gpha.com

ELLINWOOD DISTRICT HOSPITAL (L, 25 beds) 605 North Main Street, Ellinwood, KS Zip 67526–1440; tel. 620/564–2548; John Hughes, Administrator
Web address: www.ellinwooddistricthospital.org

FREDONIA REGIONAL HOSPITAL (C, 34 beds) 1527 Madison Street, Fredonia, KS Zip 66736–1751, Mailing Address: P.O. Box 579, Zip 66736–0579; tel. 620/378–2121; John Hart, Chief Executive Officer
Web address: www.fredoniaregionalhospital.org

GRISELL MEMORIAL HOSPITAL DISTRICT ONE (C, 46 beds) 210 South Vermont Avenue, Ransom, KS Zip 67572–9525; tel. 785/731–2231; Kristine Ochs, R.N., Administrator
Web address: www.grisellmemorialhospital.org

Section B

For explanation of codes following names, see page B2.
★ Indicates Type III membership in the American Hospital Association.

KIOWA COUNTY MEMORIAL HOSPITAL (L, 15 beds) 721 West Kansas Avenue, Greensburg, KS Zip 67054–1633; tel. 620/723–3341; Mary Sweet, Administrator
Web address: www.kcmh.net

LANE COUNTY HOSPITAL (C, 31 beds) 235 West Vine, Dighton, KS Zip 67839–0969, Mailing Address: P.O. Box 969, Zip 67839–0969; tel. 620/397–5321; Donna McGowan, Administrator
Web address: www.lchospital.com

MEDICINE LODGE MEMORIAL HOSPITAL (C, 25 beds) 710 North Walnut Street, Medicine Lodge, KS Zip 67104–1019; tel. 620/886–3771; Kevin A. White, Administrator
Web address: www.mlmh.net/

MINNEOLA DISTRICT HOSPITAL (C, 54 beds) 212 Main Street, Minneola, KS Zip 67865–8511, Mailing Address: P.O. Box 127, Zip 67865–0127; tel. 620/885–4264; Deborah Bruner, Chief Executive Officer and Administrator
Web address: www.minneolahealthcare.com

OSBORNE COUNTY MEMORIAL HOSPITAL (C, 25 beds) 424 West New Hampshire Street, Osborne, KS Zip 67473–2314, Mailing Address: P.O. Box 70, Zip 67473–0070; tel. 785/346–2121; Kiley Floyd, Administrator
Web address: www.ocmh.us

OTTAWA COUNTY HEALTH CENTER (L, 42 beds) 215 East Eighth, Minneapolis, KS Zip 67467–1902, Mailing Address: P.O. Box 290, Zip 67467–0290; tel. 785/392–2122; Jody Parks, Administrator
Web address: www.ottawacountyhealthcenter.com

PHILLIPS COUNTY HOSPITAL (L, 25 beds) 1150 State Street, Phillipsburg, KS Zip 67661–1743, Mailing Address: P.O. Box 607, Zip 67661–0607; tel. 785/543–5226; David Engel, Chief Executive Officer
Web address: www.phillipshospital.org

RAWLINS COUNTY HEALTH CENTER (C, 24 beds) 707 Grant Street, Atwood, KS Zip 67730–1526, Mailing Address: P.O. Box 47, Zip 67730–0047; tel. 785/626–3211; Sharon K. Cox, FACHE, Chief Executive Officer
Web address: www.rchc.us

REPUBLIC COUNTY HOSPITAL (L, 63 beds) 2420 G Street, Belleville, KS Zip 66935–2400; tel. 785/527–2254; Blaine K. Miller, Administrator
Web address: www.rphospital.org

SABETHA COMMUNITY HOSPITAL (L, 25 beds) 14th and Oregon Streets, Sabetha, KS Zip 66534–0229, Mailing Address: P.O. Box 229, Zip 66534–0229; tel. 785/284–2121; Lora Key, Chief Executive Officer
Web address: www.sabethahospital.com

SATANTA DISTRICT HOSPITAL (C, 57 beds) 401 South Cheyenne Street, Satanta, KS Zip 67870–0159, Mailing Address: P.O. Box 159, Zip 67870–0159; tel. 620/649–2761; Jeremy Clingenpeel, Administrator
Web address: www.satantahospital.org

SMITH COUNTY MEMORIAL HOSPITAL (L, 53 beds) 614 South Main Street, Smith Center, KS Zip 66967–3001; tel. 785/282–6845; Allen Van Driel, FACHE, Administrator
Web address: www.gpha.com

TREGO COUNTY–LEMKE MEMORIAL HOSPITAL (C, 62 beds) 320 North 13th Street, Wakeeney, KS Zip 67672–2099; tel. 785/743–2182; David Augustine, Interim Chief Executive Officer
Web address: www.tclmh.org

NEBRASKA: HARLAN COUNTY HEALTH SYSTEM (C, 19 beds) 717 North Brown Street, Alma, NE Zip 68920–2132, Mailing Address: P.O. Box 836, Zip 68920–0836; tel. 308/928–2151; Manuela Wolf, R.N., Chief Executive Officer
Web address: www.harlancountyhealth.com

Owned, leased, sponsored:	8 hospitals	264 beds
Contract–managed:	12 hospitals	434 beds
Totals:	20 hospitals	698 beds

0144: GREATER HUDSON VALLEY HEALTH SYSTEM (NP)
60 Prospect Avenue, Middletown, NY Zip 10940–4133; tel. 845/568–6050; Scott Batulis, President and Chief Executive Officer
(Moderately Centralized Health System)

NEW YORK: CATSKILL REGIONAL MEDICAL CENTER (O, 196 beds) 68 Harris Bushville Road, Harris, NY Zip 12742–5030, Mailing Address: P.O. Box 800, Zip 12742–0800; tel. 845/794–3300; Gerard Galarneau, M.D., Chief Executive Officer and Chief Medical Officer
Web address: www.crmcny.org

GROVER M. HERMAN HOSPITAL (O, 25 beds) 8881 Route 97, Callicoon, NY Zip 12723; tel. 845/887–5530; Chris L. White, Administrator
Web address: www.crmcny.org

ORANGE REGIONAL MEDICAL CENTER (O, 301 beds) 707 East Main Street, Middletown, NY Zip 10940–2650; tel. 845/333–1000; Scott Batulis, President and Chief Executive Officer
Web address: www.ormc.org

Owned, leased, sponsored:	3 hospitals	522 beds
Contract–managed:	0 hospitals	0 beds
Totals:	3 hospitals	522 beds

★1555: GREENVILLE HEALTH SYSTEM (NP)
701 Grove Road, Greenville, SC Zip 29605–5611; tel. 864/455–7000; Michael C. Riordan, President and Chief Executive Officer
(Centralized Health System)

SOUTH CAROLINA: GREENVILLE HEALTH SYSTEM – LAURENS COUNTY MEMORIAL HOSPITAL (L, 70 beds) Highway 76 East, Clinton, SC Zip 29325–2331, Mailing Address: P.O. Drawer 976, Zip 29325–0976; tel. 864/833–9100; Richard E. D'Alberto, FACHE, Campus President
Web address: www.ghs.org/laurens

GREENVILLE MEMORIAL HOSPITAL (O, 792 beds) 701 Grove Road, Greenville, SC Zip 29605–4295; tel. 864/455–7000; Paul F. Johnson, President
Web address: www.ghs.org

GREER MEMORIAL HOSPITAL (O, 70 beds) 830 South Buncombe Road, Greer, SC Zip 29650–2400; tel. 864/797–8000; John F. Mansure, FACHE, President
Web address: www.ghs.org

HILLCREST MEMORIAL HOSPITAL (O, 36 beds) 729 S.E. Main Street, Simpsonville, SC Zip 29681–3280; tel. 864/454–6100; Eric Bour, M.D., President
Web address: www.ghs.org

PATEWOOD MEMORIAL HOSPITAL (O, 36 beds) 175 Patewood Drive, Greenville, SC Zip 29615–3570; tel. 864/797–1000; Beverly J. Haines, R.N., President
Web address: www.ghs.org/patewood

Owned, leased, sponsored:	5 hospitals	1004 beds
Contract–managed:	0 hospitals	0 beds
Totals:	5 hospitals	1004 beds

★0675: GUTHRIE HEALTHCARE SYSTEM (NP)
Guthrie Square, Sayre, PA Zip 18840; tel. 570/887–4312; Joseph A. Scopelliti, M.D., President and Chief Executive Officer
(Moderately Centralized Health System)

NEW YORK: CORNING HOSPITAL (O, 82 beds) 176 Denison Parkway East, Corning, NY Zip 14830–2899; tel. 607/937–7200; Shirley P. Magana, R.N., MSN, President and Chief Operating Officer
Web address: www.corninghospital.com

PENNSYLVANIA: ROBERT PACKER HOSPITAL (O, 253 beds) 1 Guthrie Square, Sayre, PA Zip 18840–1698; tel. 570/888–6666; Marie T. Droege, President
Web address: www.guthrie.org

TROY COMMUNITY HOSPITAL (O, 25 beds) 275 Guthrie Drive, Troy, PA Zip 16947; tel. 570/297–2121; Staci Covey, R.N., MS, President
Web address: www.guthrie.org

Owned, leased, sponsored:	3 hospitals	360 beds
Contract–managed:	0 hospitals	0 beds
Totals:	3 hospitals	360 beds

For explanation of codes following names, see page B2.
★ Indicates Type III membership in the American Hospital Association.

Section B

● ★**0908: HACKENSACK UNIVERSITY HEALTH NETWORK**
(NP)
30 Prospect Avenue, Hackensack, NJ Zip 07601–1914;
tel. 201/996–2000; Robert C. Garrett, FACHE, President and Chief
Executive Officer

NEW JERSEY: HACKENSACK UNIVERSITY MEDICAL CENTER (O, 685 beds)
30 Prospect Avenue, Hackensack, NJ Zip 07601–1914;
tel. 201/996–2000; Robert C. Garrett, FACHE, President and Chief
Executive Officer
Web address: www.hackensackumc.org

Owned, leased, sponsored:	1 hospital	685 beds
Contract–managed:	0 hospitals	0 beds
Totals:	1 hospital	685 beds

★**0541: HARTFORD HEALTHCARE** (NP)
One State Street, 19th Floor, Hartford, CT Zip 06103;
tel. 860/263–4100; Elliot T. Joseph, President and Chief Executive
Officer
(Moderately Centralized Health System)

CONNECTICUT: HARTFORD HOSPITAL (O, 817 beds) 80 Seymour Street,
Hartford, CT Zip 06102–8000, Mailing Address: P.O. Box 5037,
Zip 06102–5037; tel. 860/545–5000; Stuart Markowitz, M.D., President
Web address: www.harthosp.org

MIDSTATE MEDICAL CENTER (O, 129 beds) 435 Lewis Avenue, Meriden, CT
Zip 06451–2101; tel. 203/694–8200; Lucille A. Janatka, President and CEO
Web address: www.midstatemedical.org

NATCHAUG HOSPITAL (O, 57 beds) 189 Storrs Road, Mansfield Center, CT
Zip 06250–1683; tel. 860/456–1311; Stephen W. Larcen, Ph.D., President
and CEO
Web address: www.natchaug.org

THE HOSPITAL OF CENTRAL CONNECTICUT (O, 184 beds) 100 Grand Street,
New Britain, CT Zip 06052–2017, Mailing Address: P.O. Box 100,
Zip 06052–2017; tel. 860/224–5011; Lucille A. Janatka, President and CEO
Web address: www.thocc.org

THE WILLIAM W. BACKUS HOSPITAL (O, 184 beds) 326 Washington Street,
Norwich, CT Zip 06360–2740; tel. 860/889–8331; David A. Whitehead,
President and CEO
Web address: www.backushospital.org

WINDHAM HOSPITAL (O, 79 beds) 112 Mansfield Avenue, Willimantic, CT
Zip 06226–2040; tel. 860/456–9116; David A. Whitehead, President and
CEO
Web address: www.windhamhospital.org

Owned, leased, sponsored:	6 hospitals	1450 beds
Contract–managed:	0 hospitals	0 beds
Totals:	6 hospitals	1450 beds

0637: HAVEN BEHAVIORAL HEALTHCARE (IO)
652 West Iris Drive, Nashville, TN Zip 37204–3191;
tel. 615/250–9500; Michael Lindley, Chief Executive Officer

ARIZONA: HAVEN SENIOR HORIZONS (O, 30 beds) 1201 South 7th Avenue,
Suite 200, Phoenix, AZ Zip 85007–4076; tel. 623/236–2000; Kathy
Shaw, Chief Executive Officer
Web address: www.havenbehavioral.com

COLORADO: HAVEN BEHAVIORAL WAR HEROES HOSPITAL (O, 20 beds)
1008 Minnequa Avenue, Suite 6100, Pueblo, CO Zip 81004–3733;
tel. 719/546–6000; Carrin Harper, M.D., Chief Executive Officer

OHIO: HAVEN BEHAVIORAL SENIOR CARE OF DAYTON (O, 32 beds) One
Elizabeth Place, 4th Floor Southwest Tower, Dayton, OH Zip 45417–3445;
tel. 937/234–0100; Keith Kuhn, Chief Executive Officer
Web address: www.havenbehavioraldayton.com/

PENNSYLVANIA: HAVEN BEHAVIORAL HEALTH OF EASTERN PENNSYLVANIA
(O, 48 beds) 145 North 6th Street, 3rd Floor, Reading, PA
Zip 19601–3096; tel. 610/406–4340; John Baker, Interim Chief
Executive Officer
Web address: www.havenbehavioralhospital.com

Owned, leased, sponsored:	4 hospitals	130 beds
Contract–managed:	0 hospitals	0 beds
Totals:	4 hospitals	130 beds

★**3555: HAWAII HEALTH SYSTEMS CORPORATION** (NP)
3675 Kilauea Avenue, Honolulu, HI Zip 96816–2333;
tel. 808/733–4151; Alice Hall, Acting President and Chief Executive
Officer
(Independent Hospital System)

HAWAII: HALE HO'OLA HAMAKUA (O, 52 beds) 45–547 Plumeria Street,
Honokaa, HI Zip 96727–6902; tel. 808/932–4100; Teana
Kahoohanohano, Interim Administrator
Web address: www.hhh.hhsc.org/

HILO MEDICAL CENTER (O, 276 beds) 1190 Waianuenue Avenue, Hilo, HI
Zip 96720–2089; tel. 808/932–3000; Dan Brinkman, R.N., Interim Chief
Executive Officer
Web address: www.hmc.hhsc.org

KAU HOSPITAL (O, 21 beds) 1 Kamani Street, Pahala, HI Zip 96777, Mailing
Address: P.O. Box 40, Zip 96777–0040; tel. 808/928–2050; Merilyn Harris,
Administrator
Web address: www.hhsc.org

KAUAI VETERANS MEMORIAL HOSPITAL (O, 45 beds) Waimea Canyon Road,
Waimea, HI Zip 96796, Mailing Address: P.O. Box 337, Zip 96796–0337;
tel. 808/338–9431; Scott McFarland, Interim Regional Chief Executive Officer
Web address: www.kvmh.hhsc.org

KOHALA HOSPITAL (O, 26 beds) 54–383 Hospital Road, Kohala, HI
Zip 96755, Mailing Address: P.O. Box 10, Kapaau, Zip 96755–0010;
tel. 808/889–6211; Eugene Amar, Jr., Administrator
Web address: www.koh.hhsc.org

KONA COMMUNITY HOSPITAL (O, 54 beds) 79–1019 Haukapila Street,
Kealakekua, HI Zip 96750–7920; tel. 808/322–9311; Jay E. Kreuzer,
FACHE, Chief Executive Officer
Web address: www.kch.hhsc.org

KULA HOSPITAL (O, 6 beds) 100 Keokea Place, Kula, HI Zip 96790–7450;
tel. 808/878–1221; Nick Hughey, Administrator
Web address: www.hhsc.org

LANAI COMMUNITY HOSPITAL (O, 14 beds) 628 Seventh Street, Lanai City, HI
Zip 96763–0650, Mailing Address: P.O. Box 630650, Zip 96763–0650;
tel. 808/565–8450; Nick Hughey, Administrator
Web address: www.lch.hhsc.org

LEAHI HOSPITAL (O, 188 beds) 3675 Kilauea Avenue, Honolulu, HI
Zip 96816–2398; tel. 808/733–8000; Reid Kondo, Interim Chief Executive
Officer
Web address: www.hhsc.org

MALUHIA HOSPITAL (O, 146 beds) 1027 Hala Drive, Honolulu, HI Zip 96817;
tel. 808/832–5874; Sally T. Ishikawa, Administrator

MAUI MEMORIAL MEDICAL CENTER (O, 213 beds) 221 Mahalani Street,
Wailuku, HI Zip 96793–2581; tel. 808/244–9056; Wesley Lo, Regional Chief
Executive Officer
Web address: www.mmmc.hhsc.org

SAMUEL MAHELONA MEMORIAL HOSPITAL (O, 80 beds) 4800 Kawaihau
Road, Kapaa, HI Zip 96746–1971; tel. 808/822–4961; Scott McFarland,
Interim Regional Chief Executive Officer
Web address: www.smmh.hhsc.org

Owned, leased, sponsored:	12 hospitals	1121 beds
Contract–managed:	0 hospitals	0 beds
Totals:	12 hospitals	1121 beds

0266: HAWAII PACIFIC HEALTH (NP)
55 Merchant Street, Honolulu, HI Zip 96813–4306;
tel. 808/949–9355; Raymond P. Vara, Jr., President and Chief
Executive Officer
(Independent Hospital System)

KAPIOLANI MEDICAL CENTER FOR WOMEN & CHILDREN (O, 225 beds) 1319
Punahou Street, Honolulu, HI Zip 96826–1001; tel. 808/983–6000; Martha
Smith, Chief Executive Officer
Web address: www.kapiolani.org

For explanation of codes following names, see page B2.
★ Indicates Type III membership in the American Hospital Association.
● Single hospital health care system

Section·B

PALI MOMI MEDICAL CENTER (O, 128 beds) 98–1079 Moanalua Road, Aiea, HI Zip 96701–4713; tel. 808/486–6000; Jen Chahanovich, Chief Executive Officer
Web address: www.palimomi.org

STRAUB CLINIC & HOSPITAL (O, 119 beds) 888 South King Street, Honolulu, HI Zip 96813–3097; tel. 808/522–4000; Art Gladstone, R.N., Chief Executive Officer
Web address: www.straubhealth.org

WILCOX MEMORIAL HOSPITAL (O, 65 beds) 3–3420 Kuhio Highway, Lihue, HI Zip 96766–1099; tel. 808/245–1100; Kathy Clark, R.N., President and Chief Executive Officer
Web address: www.wilcoxhealth.org

Owned, leased, sponsored:	4 hospitals	537 beds
Contract–managed:	0 hospitals	0 beds
Totals:	4 hospitals	537 beds

★0048: HCA (IO)
One Park Plaza, Nashville, TN Zip 37203–1548; tel. 615/344–9551; R. Milton Johnson, President and Chief Executive Officer
(Decentralized Health System)

ALASKA: ALASKA REGIONAL HOSPITAL (O, 132 beds) 2801 Debarr Road, Anchorage, AK Zip 99508–2997, Mailing Address: P.O. Box 143889, Zip 99514–3889; tel. 907/264–1754; Julie Taylor, FACHE, Chief Executive Officer
Web address: www.alaskaregional.com

CALIFORNIA: GOOD SAMARITAN HOSPITAL (O, 376 beds) 2425 Samaritan Drive, San Jose, CA Zip 95124–3997, Mailing Address: P.O. Box 240002, Zip 95154–2402; tel. 408/559–2011; Paul Beaupre, M.D., Chief Executive Officer
Web address: www.goodsamsanjose.com

LOS ROBLES HOSPITAL AND MEDICAL CENTER (O, 334 beds) 215 West Janss Road, Thousand Oaks, CA Zip 91360–1899; tel. 805/497–2727; Natalie Mussi, Chief Executive Officer
Web address: www.losrobleshospital.com

REGIONAL MEDICAL CENTER OF SAN JOSE (O, 193 beds) 225 North Jackson Avenue, San Jose, CA Zip 95116–1603; tel. 408/259–5000; Michael T. Johnson, Chief Executive Officer
Web address: www.regionalmedicalsanjose.com

RIVERSIDE COMMUNITY HOSPITAL (O, 373 beds) 4445 Magnolia Avenue, Riverside, CA Zip 92501–4199, Mailing Address: P.O. Box 1669, Zip 92502–1669; tel. 951/788–3000; Patrick D. Brilliant, President and Chief Executive Officer
Web address: www.riversidecommunityhospital.com

WEST HILLS HOSPITAL AND MEDICAL CENTER (O, 225 beds) 7300 Medical Center Drive, West Hills, CA Zip 91307–1900; tel. 818/676–4000; Douglas Long, President and Chief Executive Officer
Web address: www.westhillshospital.com

COLORADO: MEDICAL CENTER OF AURORA (O, 303 beds) 1501 South Potomac Street, Aurora, CO Zip 80012–5411; tel. 303/695–2600; Richard A. Hammett, Chief Executive Officer
Web address: www.auroramed.com

NORTH SUBURBAN MEDICAL CENTER (O, 115 beds) 9191 Grant Street, Thornton, CO Zip 80229–4341; tel. 303/451–7800; Jennifer Alderfer, Chief Executive Officer
Web address: www.northsuburban.com

PRESBYTERIAN–ST. LUKE'S MEDICAL CENTER (O, 399 beds) 1719 East 19th Avenue, Denver, CO Zip 80218–1281; tel. 303/839–6000; Madeleine Roberson, Chief Executive Officer
Web address: www.pslmc.com

ROSE MEDICAL CENTER (O, 262 beds) 4567 East Ninth Avenue, Denver, CO Zip 80220–3941; tel. 303/320–2121; Kenneth H. Feiler, Chief Executive Officer
Web address: www.rosebabies.com

SKY RIDGE MEDICAL CENTER (O, 177 beds) 10101 Ridge Gate Parkway, Lone Tree, CO Zip 80124–5522; tel. 720/225–1000; Maureen Tarrant, Chief Executive Officer
Web address: www.skyridgemedcenter.com

SPALDING REHABILITATION HOSPITAL (O, 40 beds) 900 Potomac Steet, Aurora, CO Zip 80011–6716; tel. 303/367–1166; Kristen DeHart, Interim Administrator
Web address: www.spaldingrehab.com

SWEDISH MEDICAL CENTER (O, 354 beds) 501 East Hampden Avenue, Englewood, CO Zip 80113–2702; tel. 303/788–5000; Mary M. White, Chief Executive Officer
Web address: www.swedishhospital.com

FLORIDA: AVENTURA HOSPITAL AND MEDICAL CENTER (O, 359 beds) 20900 Biscayne Boulevard, Aventura, FL Zip 33180–1407; tel. 305/682–7000; Dianne Goldenberg, Chief Executive Officer
Web address: www.aventurahospital.com

BLAKE MEDICAL CENTER (O, 294 beds) 2020 59th Street West, Bradenton, FL Zip 34209–4669; tel. 941/792–6611; Daniel J. Friedrich, III, Chief Executive Officer
Web address: www.blakemedicalcenter.com

BRANDON REGIONAL HOSPITAL (O, 407 beds) 119 Oakfield Drive, Brandon, FL Zip 33511–5779; tel. 813/681–5551; Bland Eng, Chief Executive Officer
Web address: www.brandonhospital.com

CAPITAL REGIONAL MEDICAL CENTER (O, 198 beds) 2626 Capital Medical Boulevard, Tallahassee, FL Zip 32308–4499; tel. 850/325–5000; Brian Cook, FACHE, Chief Executive Officer
Web address: www.capitalregionalmedicalcenter.com

CENTRAL FLORIDA REGIONAL HOSPITAL (O, 226 beds) 1401 West Seminole Boulevard, Sanford, FL Zip 32771–6764; tel. 407/321–4500; Wendy H. Brandon, Chief Executive Officer
Web address: www.centralfloridaregional.com

DOCTORS HOSPITAL OF SARASOTA (O, 168 beds) 5731 Bee Ridge Road, Sarasota, FL Zip 34233–5056; tel. 941/342–1100; Robert C. Meade, Chief Executive Officer
Web address: www.doctorsofsarasota.com

EDWARD WHITE HOSPITAL (O, 110 beds) 2323 Ninth Avenue North, Saint Petersburg, FL Zip 33713–6898, Mailing Address: P.O. Box 12018, Zip 33733–2018; tel. 727/323–1111; Sharon Hayes, Chief Executive Officer
Web address: www.edwardwhitehospital.com

ENGLEWOOD COMMUNITY HOSPITAL (O, 100 beds) 700 Medical Boulevard, Englewood, FL Zip 34223–3978; tel. 941/475–6571; Dale Alward, Chief Executive Officer
Web address: www.englewoodcommunityhospital.com

FAWCETT MEMORIAL HOSPITAL (O, 238 beds) 21298 Olean Boulevard, Port Charlotte, FL Zip 33952–6765; tel. 941/629–1181; Thomas J. Rice, FACHE, President and Chief Executive Officer
Web address: www.fawcetthospital.com

FORT WALTON BEACH MEDICAL CENTER (O, 257 beds) 1000 Mar–Walt Drive, Fort Walton Beach, FL Zip 32547–6795; tel. 850/862–1111; Mitchell P. Mongell, FACHE, Chief Executive Officer
Web address: www.fwbmc.com

GULF COAST REGIONAL MEDICAL CENTER (O, 176 beds) 449 West 23rd Street, Panama City, FL Zip 32405–4593, Mailing Address: P.O. Box 15309, Zip 32406–5309; tel. 850/769–8341; Carlton Ulmer, Chief Executive Officer
Web address: www.egulfcoastmedical.com

JFK MEDICAL CENTER (O, 424 beds) 5301 South Congress Avenue, Atlantis, FL Zip 33462–1197; tel. 561/965–7300; Gina Melby, Chief Executive Officer
Web address: www.jfkmc.com

KENDALL REGIONAL MEDICAL CENTER (O, 300 beds) 11750 Bird Road, Miami, FL Zip 33175–3530; tel. 305/223–3000; Scott A. Cihak, Chief Executive Officer
Web address: www.kendallmed.com

LAKE CITY MEDICAL CENTER (O, 67 beds) 340 N.W. Commerce Drive, Lake City, FL Zip 32055–4709; tel. 386/719–9000; Mark Robinson, FACHE, Chief Executive Officer
Web address: www.lakecitymedical.com

LARGO MEDICAL CENTER (O, 243 beds) 201 14th Street S.W., Largo, FL Zip 33770–3133, Mailing Address: P.O. Box 2905, Zip 33779–2905; tel. 727/588–5200; Anthony M. Degina, President and Chief Executive Officer
Web address: www.largomedical.com

LAWNWOOD REGIONAL MEDICAL CENTER & HEART INSTITUTE (O, 331 beds) 1700 South 23rd Street, Fort Pierce, FL Zip 34950–4803; tel. 772/461–4000; Greg Lowe, Chief Executive Officer
Web address: www.lawnwoodmed.com

For explanation of codes following names, see page B2.
★ Indicates Type III membership in the American Hospital Association.

MEDICAL CENTER OF TRINITY (O, 282 beds) 9330 State Road 54, Trinity, FL Zip 34655–1808; tel. 727/834–4900; Leigh Massengill, Chief Executive Officer
Web address: www.medicalcentertrinity.com

MEMORIAL HOSPITAL JACKSONVILLE (O, 418 beds) 3625 University Boulevard South, Jacksonville, FL Zip 32216–4207, Mailing Address: P.O. Box 16325, Zip 32245–6325; tel. 904/399–6111; James F. O'Loughlin, President and Chief Executive Officer
Web address: www.memorialhospitaljax.com

MEMORIAL HOSPITAL OF TAMPA (O, 139 beds) 2901 Swann Avenue, Tampa, FL Zip 33609–4057; tel. 813/873–6400; John J. Mainieri, Chief Executive Officer
Web address: www.memorialhospitaltampa.com

MUNROE REGIONAL MEDICAL CENTER (L, 370 beds) 1500 S.W. 1st Avenue, Ocala, FL Zip 34471–6504, Mailing Address: P.O. Box 6000, Zip 34478–6000; tel. 352/351–7200; Richard Mutarelli, Interim Chief Executive Officer
Web address: www.munroeregional.com

NORTH FLORIDA REGIONAL MEDICAL CENTER (O, 445 beds) 6500 Newberry Road, Gainesville, FL Zip 32605–4392, Mailing Address: P.O. Box 147006, Zip 32614–7006; tel. 352/333–4000; Ward Boston, III, Chief Executive Officer
Web address: www.nfrmc.com

NORTHSIDE HOSPITAL (O, 227 beds) 6000 49th Street North, Saint Petersburg, FL Zip 33709–2145; tel. 727/521–4411; Dia Nichols, Chief Executive Officer
Web address: www.northsidehospital.com

NORTHWEST MEDICAL CENTER (O, 223 beds) 2801 North State Road 7, Margate, FL Zip 33063–5727; tel. 954/974–0400; Mark Rader, FACHE, Chief Executive Officer
Web address: www.northwestmed.com

OAK HILL HOSPITAL (O, 262 beds) 11375 Cortez Boulevard, Brooksville, FL Zip 34613–5409; tel. 352/596–6632; Mickey Smith, Chief Executive Officer
Web address: www.oakhillhospital.com

OCALA REGIONAL MEDICAL CENTER (O, 270 beds) 1431 S.W. First Avenue, Ocala, FL Zip 34471–6500, Mailing Address: P.O. Box 2200, Zip 34478–2200; tel. 352/401–1000; Randy McVay, Chief Executive Officer
Web address: www.ocalaregional.com

ORANGE PARK MEDICAL CENTER (O, 297 beds) 2001 Kingsley Avenue, Orange Park, FL Zip 32073–5156; tel. 904/639–8500; Chad Patrick, President and Chief Executive Officer
Web address: www.opmedical.com

OSCEOLA REGIONAL MEDICAL CENTER (O, 235 beds) 700 West Oak Street, Kissimmee, FL Zip 34741–4996; tel. 407/846–2266; Robert M. Krieger, Chief Executive Officer
Web address: www.osceolaregional.com

PALMS OF PASADENA HOSPITAL (O, 307 beds) 1501 Pasadena Avenue South, Saint Petersburg, FL Zip 33707–3798; tel. 727/381–1000; Sharon Hayes, Interim Chief Executive Officer
Web address: www.palmspasadena.com

PALMS WEST HOSPITAL (O, 204 beds) 13001 Southern Boulevard, Loxahatchee, FL Zip 33470–9203; tel. 561/798–3300; Eric Goldman, Chief Executive Officer
Web address: www.palmswesthospital.com

PLANTATION GENERAL HOSPITAL (O, 264 beds) 401 N.W. 42nd Avenue, Plantation, FL Zip 33317–2882; tel. 954/587–5010; Randy Gross, Chief Executive Officer
Web address: www.plantationgeneral.com

POINCIANA MEDICAL CENTER (O, 24 beds) 325 Cypress Parkway, Kissimmee, FL Zip 34758; tel. 407/530–2000; Joanna J. Conley, FACHE, Chief Executive Officer
Web address: www.poincianamedicalcenter.com

RAULERSON HOSPITAL (O, 100 beds) 1796 Highway 441 North, Okeechobee, FL Zip 34972–1918, Mailing Address: P.O. Box 1307, Zip 34973–1307; tel. 863/763–2151; Robert H. Lee, President
Web address: www.raulersonhospital.com

REGIONAL MEDICAL CENTER BAYONET POINT (O, 290 beds) 14000 Fivay Road, Hudson, FL Zip 34667–7199; tel. 727/869–5400; Shayne George, Chief Executive Officer
Web address: www.rmchealth.com

SOUTH BAY HOSPITAL (O, 112 beds) 4016 Sun City Center Boulevard, Sun City Center, FL Zip 33573–5298; tel. 813/634–3301; Sharon L. Roush, Chief Executive Officer
Web address: www.southbayhospital.com

SPECIALTY HOSPITAL JACKSONVILLE (O, 62 beds) 4901 Richard Street, Jacksonville, FL Zip 32207–7328; tel. 904/737–3120; Barbara McCarthy, Chief Executive Officer
Web address: www.specialtyhospitaljax.com

ST. LUCIE MEDICAL CENTER (O, 194 beds) 1800 S.E. Tiffany Avenue, Port St. Lucie, FL Zip 34952–7521; tel. 772/335–4000; Jay Finnegan, Chief Executive Officer
Web address: www.stluciemed.com

ST. PETERSBURG GENERAL HOSPITAL (O, 219 beds) 6500 38th Avenue North, Saint Petersburg, FL Zip 33710–1629; tel. 727/384–1414; Robert B. Conroy, Jr., Chief Executive Officer
Web address: www.stpetegeneral.com

TAMPA COMMUNITY HOSPITAL (O, 197 beds) 6001 Webb Road, Tampa, FL Zip 33615–3291; tel. 813/888–7060; Jacob Fisher, Chief Executive Officer
Web address: www.tampacommunityhospital.com/

TWIN CITIES HOSPITAL (O, 38 beds) 2190 Highway 85 North, Niceville, FL Zip 32578–1045; tel. 850/678–4131; David Whalen, Chief Executive Officer
Web address: www.tchealthcare.com

UNIVERSITY HOSPITAL AND MEDICAL CENTER (O, 317 beds) 7201 North University Drive, Tamarac, FL Zip 33321–2996; tel. 954/721–2200; Joseph D. Melchiode, Chief Executive Officer
Web address: www.uhmchealth.com

WEST FLORIDA HOSPITAL (O, 339 beds) 8383 North Davis Highway, Pensacola, FL Zip 32514–6088; tel. 850/494–4000; Brian Baumgardner, Chief Executive Officer
Web address: www.westfloridahospital.com

WEST PALM HOSPITAL (O, 245 beds) 2201 45th Street, West Palm Beach, FL Zip 33407–2047; tel. 561/842–6141; Dana Oaks, Chief Executive Officer
Web address: www.westpalmhospital.com

WESTSIDE REGIONAL MEDICAL CENTER (O, 215 beds) 8201 West Broward Boulevard, Plantation, FL Zip 33324–2701; tel. 954/473–6600; Lee B. Chaykin, Chief Executive Officer
Web address: www.westsideregional.com

GEORGIA: CARTERSVILLE MEDICAL CENTER (O, 80 beds) 960 Joe Frank Harris Parkway, Cartersville, GA Zip 30120–2129; tel. 770/382–1530; Keith Sandlin, Chief Executive Officer
Web address: www.cartersvillemedical.com

COLISEUM CENTER FOR BEHAVIORAL HEALTH (O, 43 beds) 340 Hospital Drive, Macon, GA Zip 31217–3838; tel. 478/741–1355; James W. Eyler, FACHE, Chief Executive Officer
Web address: www.coliseumhealthsystem.com

COLISEUM MEDICAL CENTERS (O, 227 beds) 350 Hospital Drive, Macon, GA Zip 31217–3871; tel. 478/765–7000; Charles G. Briscoe, FACHE, Chief Executive Officer
Web address: www.coliseumhealthsystem.com

COLISEUM NORTHSIDE HOSPITAL (O, 103 beds) 400 Charter Boulevard, Macon, GA Zip 31210–4853, Mailing Address: P.O. Box 4627, Zip 31208–4627; tel. 478/757–8200; Stephen J. Daugherty, Chief Executive Officer
Web address: www.coliseumhealthsystem.com

DOCTORS HOSPITAL (O, 242 beds) 3651 Wheeler Road, Augusta, GA Zip 30909–6426; tel. 706/651–3232; Douglas Welch, Chief Executive Officer
Web address: www.doctors–hospital.net

EASTSIDE MEDICAL CENTER (O, 294 beds) 1700 Medical Way, Snellville, GA Zip 30078–2195; tel. 770/979–0200; Kimberly Ryan, Chief Executive Officer
Web address: www.eastsidemedical.com

FAIRVIEW PARK HOSPITAL (O, 168 beds) 200 Industrial Boulevard, Dublin, GA Zip 31021–2997, Mailing Address: P.O. Box 1408, Zip 31040–1408; tel. 478/275–2000; Donald R. Avery, FACHE, President and Chief Executive Officer
Web address: www.fairviewparkhospital.com

REDMOND REGIONAL MEDICAL CENTER (O, 230 beds) 501 Redmond Road, Rome, GA Zip 30165–1415, Mailing Address: P.O. Box 107001, Zip 30165–7001; tel. 706/291–0291; John Quinlivan, Chief Executive Officer
Web address: www.redmondregional.com

For explanation of codes following names, see page B2.
★ Indicates Type III membership in the American Hospital Association.

IDAHO: EASTERN IDAHO REGIONAL MEDICAL CENTER (O, 309 beds) 3100 Channing Way, Idaho Falls, ID Zip 83404–7533, Mailing Address: P.O. Box 2077, Zip 83403–2077; tel. 208/529–6111; Douglas Crabtree, Chief Executive Officer
Web address: www.eirmc.com

WEST VALLEY MEDICAL CENTER (O, 122 beds) 1717 Arlington, Caldwell, ID Zip 83605–4802; tel. 208/459–4641; Elizabeth Hunsicker, Chief Executive Officer
Web address: www.westvalleymedctr.com

INDIANA: TERRE HAUTE REGIONAL HOSPITAL (O, 208 beds) 3901 South Seventh Street, Terre Haute, IN Zip 47802–5709; tel. 812/232–0021; Mary Ann Conroy, Chief Executive Officer
Web address: www.regionalhospital.com

KANSAS: ALLEN COUNTY REGIONAL HOSPITAL (O, 25 beds) 3066 N. Kentucky Street, Iola, KS Zip 66749–1951, Mailing Address: P.O. Box 540, Zip 66749–0540; tel. 620/365–1000; Ron Baker, Chief Executive Officer
Web address: www.allencountyhospital.com

MENORAH MEDICAL CENTER (O, 158 beds) 5721 West 119th Street, Overland Park, KS Zip 66209–3722; tel. 913/498–6000; Steven D. Wilkinson, President and Chief Executive Officer
Web address: www.menorahmedicalcenter.com

OVERLAND PARK REGIONAL MEDICAL CENTER (O, 276 beds) 10500 Quivira Road, Overland Park, KS Zip 66215–2306, Mailing Address: P.O. Box 15959, Zip 66215–5959; tel. 913/541–5000; Kevin J. Hicks, President and CEO
Web address: www.oprmc.com

WESLEY MEDICAL CENTER (O, 584 beds) 550 North Hillside, Wichita, KS Zip 67214–4976; tel. 316/962–2000; Hugh C. Tappan, President and Chief Executive Officer
Web address: www.wesleymc.com

KENTUCKY: FRANKFORT REGIONAL MEDICAL CENTER (O, 134 beds) 299 King's Daughters Drive, Frankfort, KY Zip 40601–4186; tel. 502/875–5240; Chip Peal, Chief Executive Officer
Web address: www.frankfortregional.com

TRISTAR GREENVIEW REGIONAL HOSPITAL (O, 167 beds) 1801 Ashley Circle, Bowling Green, KY Zip 42104–3362; tel. 270/793–1000; Michael Sherrod, Chief Executive Officer
Web address: www.greenviewhospital.com

LOUISIANA: DAUTERIVE HOSPITAL (O, 103 beds) 600 North Lewis Street, New Iberia, LA Zip 70563–2043; tel. 337/365–7311; Wayne D. Thompson, Interim Chief Executive Officer
Web address: www.dauterivehospital.com

LAKEVIEW REGIONAL MEDICAL CENTER (O, 172 beds) 95 Judge Tanner Boulevard, Covington, LA Zip 70433–7507; tel. 985/867–3800; Bret G. Kolman, CPA, FACHE, Chief Executive Officer
Web address: www.lakeviewregional.com

RAPIDES REGIONAL MEDICAL CENTER (O, 357 beds) 211 Fourth Street, Alexandria, LA Zip 71301–8421; tel. 318/473–3000; Jason E. Cobb, FACHE, Chief Executive Officer
Web address: www.rapidesregional.com

REGIONAL MEDICAL CENTER OF ACADIANA (O, 292 beds) 2810 Ambassador Caffery Parkway, Lafayette, LA Zip 70506–5906; tel. 337/981–2949; Kathy J. Bobbs, FACHE, President Chief Executive Officer
Web address: www.medicalcenterofacadiana.com

TULANE MEDICAL CENTER (O, 327 beds) 1415 Tulane Avenue, New Orleans, LA Zip 70112–2600; tel. 504/988–5263; William Lunn, M.D., Chief Executive Officer
Web address: www.tuhc.com

MISSISSIPPI: GARDEN PARK MEDICAL CENTER (O, 130 beds) 15200 Community Road, Gulfport, MS Zip 39503–3085, Mailing Address: P.O. Box 1240, Zip 39502–1240; tel. 228/575–7000; Brenda M. Waltz, FACHE, Chief Executive Officer
Web address: www.gpmedical.com

MISSOURI: BELTON REGIONAL MEDICAL CENTER (O, 46 beds) 17065 South 71 Highway, Belton, MO Zip 64012–4631; tel. 816/348–1200; Todd Krass, Chief Executive Officer
Web address: www.beltonregionalmedicalcenter.com

CENTERPOINT MEDICAL CENTER (O, 221 beds) 19600 East 39th Street, Independence, MO Zip 64057–2301; tel. 816/698–7000; David R. Williams, Chief Executive Officer
Web address: www.centerpointmedical.com

LAFAYETTE REGIONAL HEALTH CENTER (O, 25 beds) 1500 State Street, Lexington, MO Zip 64067–1107; tel. 660/259–2203; Darrel Box, Chief Executive Officer
Web address: www.lafayetteregionalhealthcenter.com

LEE'S SUMMIT MEDICAL CENTER (O, 64 beds) 2100 S.E. Blue Parkway, Lee's Summit, MO Zip 64063–1007; tel. 816/282–5000; Matt Sogard, Chief Executive Officer
Web address: www.leessummitmedicalcenter.com

RESEARCH MEDICAL CENTER (O, 361 beds) 2316 East Meyer Boulevard, Kansas City, MO Zip 64132–1136; tel. 816/276–4000; Jacqueline DeSouza, Chief Executive Officer
Web address: www.researchmedicalcenter.com

RESEARCH PSYCHIATRIC CENTER (O, 100 beds) 2323 East 63rd Street, Kansas City, MO Zip 64130–3462; tel. 816/444–8161; Lisa St. Aubyn, Chief Executive Officer
Web address: www.researchpsychiatriccenter.com

NEVADA: MOUNTAINVIEW HOSPITAL (O, 340 beds) 3100 North Tenaya Way, Las Vegas, NV Zip 89128–0436; tel. 702/255–5000; Chris Mowan, Chief Executive Officer
Web address: www.mountainview–hospital.com

SOUTHERN HILLS HOSPITAL AND MEDICAL CENTER (O, 134 beds) 9300 West Sunset Road, Las Vegas, NV Zip 89148–4844; tel. 702/880–2100; Kimball Anderson, FACHE, Chief Executive Officer
Web address: www.southernhillshospital.com

SUNRISE HOSPITAL AND MEDICAL CENTER (O, 664 beds) 3186 Maryland Parkway, Las Vegas, NV Zip 89109–2306, Mailing Address: P.O. Box 98530, Zip 89193; tel. 702/731–8000; Todd Sklamberg, President
Web address: www.sunrisehospital.com

NEW HAMPSHIRE: PARKLAND MEDICAL CENTER (O, 82 beds) One Parkland Drive, Derry, NH Zip 03038–2750; tel. 603/432–1500; Chris Accashian, Chief Executive Officer
Web address: www.parklandmedicalcenter.com

PORTSMOUTH REGIONAL HOSPITAL (O, 165 beds) 333 Borthwick Avenue, Portsmouth, NH Zip 03801–7128; tel. 603/436–5110; Anne Jamieson, FACHE, Chief Executive Officer
Web address: www.portsmouthhospital.com

OKLAHOMA: OU MEDICAL CENTER (O, 677 beds) 1200 Everett Drive, Oklahoma City, OK Zip 73104–5047, Mailing Address: P.O. Box 26307, Zip 73126–0307; tel. 405/271–3636; Charles Spicer, President and Chief Executive Officer
Web address: www.oumedicine.com/oumedicalcenter

SOUTH CAROLINA: COLLETON MEDICAL CENTER (O, 131 beds) 501 Robertson Boulevard, Walterboro, SC Zip 29488–5714; tel. 843/782–2000; Brad Griffin, Chief Executive Officer
Web address: www.colletonmedical.com

GRAND STRAND REGIONAL MEDICAL CENTER (O, 271 beds) 809 82nd Parkway, Myrtle Beach, SC Zip 29572–4607; tel. 843/692–1000; Mark E. Sims, Chief Executive Officer
Web address: www.grandstrandmed.com

TRIDENT MEDICAL CENTER (O, 404 beds) 9330 Medical Plaza Drive, Charleston, SC Zip 29406–9195; tel. 843/797–7000; Todd Gallati, FACHE, President and Chief Executive Officer
Web address: www.tridenthealthsystem.com

TENNESSEE: PARKRIDGE MEDICAL CENTER (O, 464 beds) 2333 McCallie Avenue, Chattanooga, TN Zip 37404–3258; tel. 423/698–6061; Darrell W. Moore, Chief Executive Officer
Web address: www.parkridgemedicalcenter.com

PARKRIDGE WEST HOSPITAL (O, 68 beds) 1000 Highway 28, Jasper, TN Zip 37347–3638; tel. 423/837–9500; Shirley K. Scarlatti, Associate Chief Nursing Officer
Web address: www.parkridgewesthospital.com/

TRISTAR CENTENNIAL MEDICAL CENTER (O, 583 beds) 2300 Patterson Street, Nashville, TN Zip 37203–1528; tel. 615/342–1000; Heather J. Rohan, Chief Executive Officer
Web address: www.tristarcentennial.com

TRISTAR CENTENNIAL MEDICAL CENTER AT ASHLAND CITY (O, 8 beds) 313 North Main Street, Ashland City, TN Zip 37015–1347; tel. 615/792–3030; Heather J. Rohan, Chief Executive Officer
Web address: www.tristarashlandcity.com/

For explanation of codes following names, see page B2.
★ Indicates Type III membership in the American Hospital Association.

TRISTAR HENDERSONVILLE MEDICAL CENTER (O, 96 beds) 355 New Shackle Island Road, Hendersonville, TN Zip 37075–2479; tel. 615/338–1000; Regina Bartlett, Chief Executive Officer
Web address: www.hendersonvillemedicalcenter.com

TRISTAR HORIZON MEDICAL CENTER (O, 130 beds) 111 Highway 70 East, Dickson, TN Zip 37055–2080; tel. 615/446–0446; John A. Marshall, Chief Executive Officer
Web address: www.horizonmedicalcenter.com

TRISTAR SKYLINE MADISON CAMPUS (O, 284 beds) 500 Hospital Drive, Madison, TN Zip 37115–5032; tel. 615/769–5000; Steve Otto, Chief Executive Officer
Web address: www.skylinemadison.com

TRISTAR SKYLINE MEDICAL CENTER (O, 295 beds) 3441 Dickerson Pike, Nashville, TN Zip 37207–2539; tel. 615/769–2000; Steve Otto, Chief Executive Officer
Web address: www.skylinemedicalcenter.com

TRISTAR SOUTHERN HILLS MEDICAL CENTER (O, 87 beds) 391 Wallace Road, Nashville, TN Zip 37211–4859; tel. 615/781–4000; Thomas H. Ozburn, Chief Executive Officer
Web address: www.southernhills.com

TRISTAR STONECREST MEDICAL CENTER (O, 101 beds) 200 StoneCrest Boulevard, Smyrna, TN Zip 37167–6810; tel. 615/768–2000; Louis Caputo, Chief Executive Officer
Web address: www.stonecrestmedical.com

TRISTAR SUMMIT MEDICAL CENTER (O, 188 beds) 5655 Frist Boulevard, Hermitage, TN Zip 37076–2053; tel. 615/316–3000; Jeffrey T. Whitehorn, Chief Executive Officer
Web address: www.summitmedctr.com

TEXAS: BAYSHORE MEDICAL CENTER (O, 481 beds) 4000 Spencer Highway, Pasadena, TX Zip 77504–1202; tel. 713/359–2000; Jeanna Barnard, Chief Executive Officer
Web address: www.bayshoremedical.com

CLEAR LAKE REGIONAL MEDICAL CENTER (O, 699 beds) 500 Medical Center Boulevard, Webster, TX Zip 77598–4220; tel. 281/332–2511; Stephen K. Jones, Jr., FACHE, Chief Executive Officer
Web address: www.clearlakermc.com

CONROE REGIONAL MEDICAL CENTER (O, 312 beds) 504 Medical Boulevard, Conroe, TX Zip 77304, Mailing Address: P.O. Box 1538, Zip 77305–1538; tel. 936/539–1111; Matt Davis, Chief Executive Officer
Web address: www.conroeregional.com/

CORPUS CHRISTI MEDICAL CENTER (O, 415 beds) 3315 South Alameda Street, Corpus Christi, TX Zip 78411–1883, Mailing Address: P.O. Box 8991, Zip 78468–8991; tel. 361/761–1400; Jay Woodall, Chief Executive Officer
Web address: www.ccmedicalcenter.com

DENTON REGIONAL MEDICAL CENTER (O, 208 beds) 3535 South 1–35 East, Denton, TX Zip 76210; tel. 940/384–3535; Caleb F. O'Rear, Chief Executive Officer
Web address: www.dentonregional.com

GREEN OAKS HOSPITAL (O, 124 beds) 7808 Clodus Fields Drive, Dallas, TX Zip 75251–2206; tel. 972/991–9504; Thomas M. Collins, President, Chairman and Chief Executive Officer
Web address: www.greenoakspsych.com

KINGWOOD MEDICAL CENTER (O, 262 beds) 22999 U.S. Highway 59 North, Kingwood, TX Zip 77339; tel. 281/348–8000; Melinda Stephenson, Chief Executive Officer
Web address: www.kingwoodmedical.com

LAS COLINAS MEDICAL CENTER (O, 90 beds) 6800 North MacArthur Boulevard, Irving, TX Zip 75039–2422; tel. 972/969–2000; Daniela Decell, Chief Executive Officer
Web address: www.lascolinasmedical.com

LAS PALMAS MEDICAL CENTER (O, 570 beds) 1801 North Oregon Street, El Paso, TX Zip 79902–3591; tel. 915/521–1200; Hank Hernandez, Chief Executive Officer
Web address: www.laspalmashealth.com

MEDICAL CENTER OF ARLINGTON (O, 284 beds) 3301 Matlock Road, Arlington, TX Zip 76015–2998; tel. 817/465–3241; Winston Borland, FACHE, President and Chief Executive Officer
Web address: www.medicalcenterarlington.com

MEDICAL CENTER OF LEWISVILLE (O, 166 beds) 500 West Main, Lewisville, TX Zip 75057–3699; tel. 972/420–1000; Ashley McClellan, Chief Executive Officer
Web address: www.lewisvillemedical.com

MEDICAL CENTER OF MCKINNEY (O, 217 beds) 4500 Medical Center Drive, McKinney, TX Zip 75069–1650; tel. 972/547–8000; Ernest C. Lynch, III, Chief Executive Officer
Web address: www.medicalcenterofmckinney.com

MEDICAL CENTER OF PLANO (O, 312 beds) 3901 West 15th Street, Plano, TX Zip 75075–7738; tel. 972/596–6800; Charles Gressle, Chief Executive Officer
Web address: www.medicalcenterplano.com

MEDICAL CITY DALLAS HOSPITAL (O, 544 beds) 7777 Forest Lane, Dallas, TX Zip 75230–2598; tel. 972/566–7000; Troy Villarreal, President and Chief Executive Officer
Web address: www.medicalcityhospital.com

METHODIST AMBULATORY SURGERY HOSPITAL – NORTHWEST (O, 23 beds) 9150 Huebner Road, Suite 100, San Antonio, TX Zip 78240–1545; tel. 210/575–5000; Elaine F. Morris, Chief Executive Officer
Web address: www.sahealth.com

METHODIST HOSPITAL (O, 1589 beds) 7700 Floyd Curl Drive, San Antonio, TX Zip 78229–3993; tel. 210/575–4000; Gay Nord, Chief Executive Officer
Web address: www.sahealth.com

METHODIST STONE OAK HOSPITAL (O, 140 beds) 1139 East Sonterra Boulevard, San Antonio, TX Zip 78258–4347; tel. 210/638–2100; Dominic J. Dominguez, Interim Chief Executive Officer
Web address: www.stoneoakhealth.com

NORTH HILLS HOSPITAL (O, 176 beds) 4401 Booth Calloway Road, North Richland Hills, TX Zip 76180–7399; tel. 817/255–1000; Randy Moresi, Chief Executive Officer
Web address: www.northhillshospital.com

PLAZA MEDICAL CENTER OF FORT WORTH (O, 212 beds) 900 Eighth Avenue, Fort Worth, TX Zip 76104–3902; tel. 817/336–2100; Clay Franklin, Chief Executive Officer
Web address: www.plazamedicalcenter.com

RIO GRANDE REGIONAL HOSPITAL (O, 320 beds) 101 East Ridge Road, McAllen, TX Zip 78503–1299; tel. 956/632–6000; Cristina Rivera, Chief Executive Officer
Web address: www.riohealth.com

ST. DAVID'S MEDICAL CENTER (O, 544 beds) 919 East 32nd Street, Austin, TX Zip 78705–2709, Mailing Address: P.O. Box 4039, Zip 78765–4039; tel. 512/476–7111; Donald H. Wilkerson, Chief Executive Officer
Web address: www.stdavids.com

ST. DAVID'S NORTH AUSTIN MEDICAL CENTER (O, 332 beds) 12221 North MoPac Expressway, Austin, TX Zip 78758–2496; tel. 512/901–1000; Allen Harrison, Chief Executive Officer
Web address: www.northaustin.com

ST. DAVID'S REHABILITATION CENTER (O, 62 beds) 1005 East 32nd Street, Austin, TX Zip 78705–2713, Mailing Address: P.O. Box 4270, Zip 78765–4270; tel. 512/544–5100; Diane Owens, Administrator
Web address: www.stdavidsrehab.com/home.aspx

ST. DAVID'S ROUND ROCK MEDICAL CENTER (O, 159 beds) 2400 Round Rock Avenue, Round Rock, TX Zip 78681–4097; tel. 512/341–1000; Deborah L. Ryle, Administrator and Chief Executive Officer
Web address: www.stdavids.com

ST. DAVID'S SOUTH AUSTIN MEDICAL CENTER (O, 242 beds) 901 West Ben White Boulevard, Austin, TX Zip 78704–6903; tel. 512/447–2211; Todd E. Steward, Chief Executive Officer
Web address: www.southaustinmc.com

TEXAS ORTHOPEDIC HOSPITAL (O, 49 beds) 7401 South Main Street, Houston, TX Zip 77030–4509; tel. 713/799–8600; Trent Lind, Chief Executive Officer
Web address: www.texasorthopedic.com

VALLEY REGIONAL MEDICAL CENTER (O, 214 beds) 100A Alton Gloor Boulevard, Brownsville, TX Zip 78526–3354, Mailing Address: P.O. Box 3710, Zip 78523–3710; tel. 956/350–7101; Susan Andrews, Chief Executive Officer
Web address: www.valleyregionalmedicalcenter.com

WEST HOUSTON MEDICAL CENTER (O, 238 beds) 12141 Richmond Avenue, Houston, TX Zip 77082–2499; tel. 281/558–3444; Todd Caliva, Chief Executive Officer
Web address: www.westhoustonmedical.com

WOMAN'S HOSPITAL OF TEXAS (O, 367 beds) 7600 Fannin Street, Houston, TX Zip 77054–1906; tel. 713/790–1234; Linda B. Russell, Chief Executive Officer
Web address: www.womanshospital.com

For explanation of codes following names, see page B2.
★ Indicates Type III membership in the American Hospital Association.

UTAH: BRIGHAM CITY COMMUNITY HOSPITAL (O, 39 beds) 950 South Medical Drive, Brigham City, UT Zip 84302–4724; tel. 435/734–9471; Richard Spuhler, Chief Executive Officer
Web address: www.brighamcityhospital.com

LAKEVIEW HOSPITAL (O, 119 beds) 630 East Medical Drive, Bountiful, UT Zip 84010–4908; tel. 801/299–2200; Rand Kerr, Chief Executive Officer
Web address: www.lakeviewhospital.com

LONE PEAK HOSPITAL (O, 30 beds) 1925 South State Street, Draper, UT Zip 84020; tel. 801/545–8000; Mark Meadows, Chief Executive Officer
Web address: www.lonepeakhospital.com

MOUNTAIN VIEW HOSPITAL (O, 114 beds) 1000 East 100 North, Payson, UT Zip 84651–1600; tel. 801/465–7000; Kevin Johnson, Chief Executive Officer
Web address: www.mvhpayson.com

OGDEN REGIONAL MEDICAL CENTER (O, 167 beds) 5475 South 500 East, Ogden, UT Zip 84405–6905; tel. 801/479–2111; Mark B. Adams, Chief Executive Officer
Web address: www.ogdenregional.com

ST. MARK'S HOSPITAL (O, 317 beds) 1200 East 3900 South, Salt Lake City, UT Zip 84124–1390; tel. 801/268–7111; Steven B. Bateman, Chief Executive Officer
Web address: www.stmarkshospital.com

TIMPANOGOS REGIONAL HOSPITAL (O, 105 beds) 750 West 800 North, Orem, UT Zip 84057–3660; tel. 801/714–6000; Keith D. Tintle, Chief Executive Officer
Web address: www.timpanogosregionalhospital.com

VIRGINIA: CJW MEDICAL CENTER (O, 741 beds) 7101 Jahnke Road, Richmond, VA Zip 23225–4044; tel. 804/320–3911; Tim McManus, President and Chief Executive Officer
Web address: www.cjwmedical.com

DOMINION HOSPITAL (O, 100 beds) 2960 Sleepy Hollow Road, Falls Church, VA Zip 22044–2030; tel. 703/536–2000; Cynthia A. Meyer, Chief Executive Officer
Web address: www.dominionhospital.com

HENRICO DOCTORS' HOSPITAL (O, 571 beds) 1602 Skipwith Road, Richmond, VA Zip 23229–5205; tel. 804/289–4500; William Wagnon, Chief Executive Officer
Web address: www.henricodoctorshospital.com

JOHN RANDOLPH MEDICAL CENTER (O, 118 beds) 411 West Randolph Road, Hopewell, VA Zip 23860–2938; tel. 804/541–1600; Suzanne B. Jackson, FACHE, Chief Executive Officer
Web address: www.johnrandolphmed.com

LEWIS–GALE MEDICAL CENTER (O, 521 beds) 1900 Electric Road, Salem, VA Zip 24153–7494; tel. 540/776–4000; Charlotte C. Tyson, Chief Executive Officer
Web address: www.lewis-gale.com

LEWISGALE HOSPITAL ALLEGHANY (O, 146 beds) One ARH Lane, Low Moor, VA Zip 24457, Mailing Address: P.O. Box 7, Zip 24457–0007; tel. 540/862–6011; Charlotte C. Tyson, Chief Executive Officer
Web address: www.alleghanyregional.com

LEWISGALE HOSPITAL MONTGOMERY (O, 89 beds) 3700 South Main Street, Blacksburg, VA Zip 24060–7081, Mailing Address: P.O. Box 90004, Zip 24062–9004; tel. 540/951–1111; Alan J. Fabian, Chief Executive Officer
Web address: www.lewisgale.com

LEWISGALE HOSPITAL PULASKI (O, 54 beds) 2400 Lee Highway, Pulaski, VA Zip 24301–2326, Mailing Address: P.O. Box 759, Zip 24301–0759; tel. 540/994–8100; Mark Nichols, FACHE, Chief Executive Officer
Web address: www.lewisgale.com/

RESTON HOSPITAL CENTER (O, 199 beds) 1850 Town Center Parkway, Reston, VA Zip 20190–3219; tel. 703/689–9000; John A. Deardorff, Chief Executive Officer
Web address: www.restonhospital.com

SPOTSYLVANIA REGIONAL MEDICAL CENTER (O, 100 beds) 4600 Spotsylvania Parkway, Fredericksburg, VA Zip 22408–7762; tel. 540/834–1500; Greg T. Madsen, Chief Executive Officer
Web address: www.spotsrmc.com

Owned, leased, sponsored:	151 hospitals	37097 beds
Contract–managed:	0 hospitals	0 beds
Totals:	151 hospitals	37097 beds

0328: HEALTH FIRST, INC. (NP)
6450 U.S. Highway 1, Rockledge, FL Zip 32955–5747; tel. 321/434–7000; Steven P. Johnson, Ph.D., President and Chief Executive Officer
(Centralized Physician/Insurance Health System)

FLORIDA: HEALTH FIRST CAPE CANAVERAL HOSPITAL (O, 145 beds) 701 West Cocoa Beach Causeway, Cocoa Beach, FL Zip 32931–5595, Mailing Address: P.O. Box 320069, Zip 32932–0069; tel. 321/799–7111; J. Stuart Mitchell, III, Interim Chief Executive Officer
Web address: www.health–first.org

HEALTH FIRST HOLMES REGIONAL MEDICAL CENTER (O, 514 beds) 1350 South Hickory Street, Melbourne, FL Zip 32901–3224; tel. 321/434–7000; Sean Gregory, President
Web address: www.health–first.org

HEALTH FIRST PALM BAY HOSPITAL (O, 119 beds) 1425 Malabar Road N.E., Melbourne, FL Zip 32907–2506; tel. 321/434–8000; J. Stuart Mitchell, III, Interim President
Web address: www.health–first.org/hospitals_services/pbch/index.cfm

HEALTH FIRST VIERA HOSPITAL (O, 84 beds) 8745 North Wickham Road, Melbourne, FL Zip 32940–5997; tel. 321/434–9164; J. Stuart Mitchell, III, Interim President
Web address: www.vierahospital.org

Owned, leased, sponsored:	4 hospitals	862 beds
Contract–managed:	0 hospitals	0 beds
Totals:	4 hospitals	862 beds

★0307: HEALTH QUEST SYSTEMS, INC. (NP)
1351 Route 55, LaGrangeville, NY Zip 12540–5108; tel. 845/475–9500; Luke McGuinness, President and CEO
(Moderately Centralized Health System)

NEW YORK: NORTHERN DUTCHESS HOSPITAL (O, 168 beds) 6511 Springbrook Avenue, Rhinebeck, NY Zip 12572–3709, Mailing Address: P.O. Box 5002, Zip 12572–5002; tel. 845/876–3001; Denise George, R.N., President
Web address: www.health–quest.org/home_nd.cfm?id=9

PUTNAM HOSPITAL CENTER (O, 164 beds) 670 Stoneleigh Avenue, Carmel, NY Zip 10512–3997; tel. 845/279–5711; James Caldas, President
Web address: www.health–quest.org

VASSAR BROTHERS MEDICAL CENTER (O, 365 beds) 45 Reade Place, Poughkeepsie, NY Zip 12601–3947; tel. 845/454–8500; Robert Friedberg, President
Web address: www.health–quest.org

Owned, leased, sponsored:	3 hospitals	697 beds
Contract–managed:	0 hospitals	0 beds
Totals:	3 hospitals	697 beds

0534: HEALTHALLIANCE OF THE HUDSON VALLEY (NP)
396 Broadway, Kingston, NY Zip 12401–4626; tel. 845/331–3131; David Scarpino, President and Chief Executive Officer
(Independent Hospital System)

HEALTH ALLIANCE HOSPITAL – BROADWAY CAMPUS (O, 150 beds) 396 Broadway, Kingston, NY Zip 12401–4692; tel. 845/331–3131; David Scarpino, President and Chief Executive Officer
Web address: www.hahv.org

HEALTH ALLIANCE HOSPITAL – MARY'S AVENUE CAMPUS (O, 120 beds) 105 Marys Avenue, Kingston, NY Zip 12401–5894; tel. 845/338–2500; David Scarpino, President and Chief Executive Officer
Web address: www.hahv.org

MARGARETVILLE HOSPITAL (O, 15 beds) 42084 State Highway 28, Margaretville, NY Zip 12455–2820; tel. 845/586–2631; Sandra A. Horan, Executive Director
Web address: www.margaretvillehospital.org

Owned, leased, sponsored:	3 hospitals	285 beds
Contract–managed:	0 hospitals	0 beds
Totals:	3 hospitals	285 beds

For explanation of codes following names, see page B2.
★ Indicates Type III membership in the American Hospital Association.

B68 Health Care Systems, Networks and Alliances © 2014 AHA Guide

Section B

★2185: HEALTHEAST CARE SYSTEM (NP)
559 Capitol Boulevard, 6–South, Saint Paul, MN Zip 55103–0000; tel. 651/232–2300; Kathryn G. Correia, President and Chief Executive Officer
(Centralized Physician/Insurance Health System)

MINNESOTA: BETHESDA HOSPITAL (O, 126 beds) 559 Capitol Boulevard, Saint Paul, MN Zip 55103–2101; tel. 651/232–2000; Catherine Barr, Senior Vice President and President, Bethesda Hospital
Web address: www.healtheast.org

ST. JOHN'S HOSPITAL (O, 192 beds) 1575 Beam Avenue, Saint Paul, MN Zip 55109–1126; tel. 651/232–7000; Scott L. North, FACHE, Senior Vice President and President, Acute Care Hospitals
Web address: www.stjohnshospital–mn.org

ST. JOSEPH'S HOSPITAL (O, 234 beds) 45 West 10th Street, Saint Paul, MN Zip 55102–1053; tel. 651/232–3000; Scott L. North, FACHE, Senior Vice President and President, Acute Care Hospitals
Web address: www.healtheast.org

WOODWINDS HEALTH CAMPUS (O, 86 beds) 1925 Woodwinds Drive, Woodbury, MN Zip 55125–4445; tel. 651/232–0228; Scott L. North, FACHE, Senior Vice President and President, Acute Care Hospitals
Web address: www.woodwinds.org

Owned, leased, sponsored:	4 hospitals	638 beds
Contract–managed:	0 hospitals	0 beds
Totals:	4 hospitals	638 beds

0342: HEALTHPARTNERS (NP)
8170 33rd Avenue South, Bloomington, MN Zip 55425–4516; tel. 952/883–7600; Mary K. Brainerd, President and Chief Executive Officer
(Moderately Centralized Health System)

GLENCOE REGIONAL HEALTH SERVICES (C, 135 beds) 1805 Hennepin Avenue North, Glencoe, MN Zip 55336–1416; tel. 320/864–3121; Jon D. Braband, FACHE, President and Chief Executive Officer
Web address: www.grhsonline.org

LAKEVIEW HOSPITAL (O, 54 beds) 927 Churchill Street West, Stillwater, MN Zip 55082–6605; tel. 651/439–5330; Theodore Wegleitner, President
Web address: www.lakeview.org

PARK NICOLLET METHODIST HOSPITAL (O, 393 beds) 6500 Excelsior Boulevard, Saint Louis Park, MN Zip 55426–4702; Minneapolis, tel. 952/993–5000; David Abelson, M.D., President and Chief Executive Officer
Web address: www.parknicollet.com

REGIONS HOSPITAL (O, 446 beds) 640 Jackson Street, Saint Paul, MN Zip 55101–2595; tel. 651/254–3456; Brock D. Nelson, President and Chief Executive Officer
Web address: www.regionshospital.com

WISCONSIN: WESTFIELDS HOSPITAL (O, 25 beds) 535 Hospital Road, New Richmond, WI Zip 54017–1449; tel. 715/243–2600; Steven Massey, President and Chief Executive Officer
Web address: www.westfieldshospital.com

Owned, leased, sponsored:	4 hospitals	918 beds
Contract–managed:	1 hospital	135 beds
Totals:	5 hospitals	1053 beds

★0023: HEALTHSOUTH CORPORATION (IO)
3660 Grandview Parkway, Suite 200, Birmingham, AL Zip 35243–3332; tel. 205/967–7116; Jay F. Grinney, President and Chief Executive Officer
(Independent Hospital System)

ALABAMA: HEALTHSOUTH LAKESHORE REHABILITATION HOSPITAL (O, 100 beds) 3800 Ridgeway Drive, Birmingham, AL Zip 35209–5599; tel. 205/868–2000; Heath Phillips, Administrator and Chief Executive Officer
Web address: www.healthsouthlakeshorerehab.com

HEALTHSOUTH REHABILITATION HOSPITAL (O, 43 beds) 1736 East Main Street, Dothan, AL Zip 36301–3040, Mailing Address: P.O. Box 6708, Zip 36302–6708; tel. 334/712–6333; Margaret A. Futch, Chief Executive Officer
Web address: www.healthsouthdothan.com

HEALTHSOUTH REHABILITATION HOSPITAL OF MONTGOMERY (O, 70 beds) 4465 Narrow Lane Road, Montgomery, AL Zip 36116–2900; tel. 334/284–7700; Linda Wade, Chief Executive Officer
Web address: www.healthsouthmontgomery.com

HEALTHSOUTH REHABILITATION HOSPITAL OF NORTH ALABAMA (O, 70 beds) 107 Governors Drive S.W., Huntsville, AL Zip 35801–4326; tel. 256/535–2300; Douglas H. Beverly, Chief Executive Officer
Web address: www.healthsouthhuntsville.com

HEALTHSOUTH REHABILITATION OF GADSDEN (O, 44 beds) 801 Goodyear Avenue, Gadsden, AL Zip 35903–1133; tel. 256/439–5000; Kayla Feazell, Chief Executive Officer
Web address: www.healthsouthgadsden.com

REGIONAL REHABILITATION HOSPITAL (O, 48 beds) 3715 Highway 280/431 North, Phenix City, AL Zip 36867; tel. 334/732–2200; Jill Jordan, Chief Executive Officer
Web address: www.regionalrehabhospital.com

ARIZONA: HEALTHSOUTH EAST VALLEY REHABILITATION HOSPITAL (O, 60 beds) 5652 East Baseline Road, Mesa, AZ Zip 85206–4713; tel. 480/567–0350; Larry Niemann, Chief Executive Officer
Web address: www.healthsoutheastvalley.com

HEALTHSOUTH REHABILITATION HOSPITAL OF SOUTHERN ARIZONA (O, 60 beds) 1921 West Hospital Drive, Tucson, AZ Zip 85704–7806; tel. 520/742–2800; Robert C. Honeycutt, FACHE, Chief Executive Officer
Web address: www.healthsouthsouthernarizona.com

HEALTHSOUTH REHABILITATION INSTITUTE OF TUCSON (O, 80 beds) 2650 North Wyatt Drive, Tucson, AZ Zip 85712–6108; tel. 520/325–1300; Jeffrey Christensen, Chief Executive Officer
Web address: www.rehabinstituteoftucson.com

HEALTHSOUTH SCOTTSDALE REHABILITATION HOSPITAL (O, 60 beds) 9630 East Shea Boulevard, Scottsdale, AZ Zip 85260–6267; tel. 480/551–5400; Timothy T. Poore, Chief Executive Officer
Web address: www.healthsouthscottsdale.com

HEALTHSOUTH VALLEY OF THE SUN REHABILITATION HOSPITAL (O, 75 beds) 13460 North 67th Avenue, Glendale, AZ Zip 85304–1042; tel. 623/878–8800; Beth Bacher, Chief Executive Officer
Web address: www.healthsouthvalleyofthesun.com

YUMA REHABILITATION HOSPITAL (O, 41 beds) 901 West 24th Street, Yuma, AZ Zip 85364–6384; tel. 928/726–5000; Joshua Bowie, Chief Executive Officer
Web address: www.yumarehabhospital.com

ARKANSAS: HEALTHSOUTH REHABILITATION HOSPITAL (O, 60 beds) 153 East Monte Painter Drive, Fayetteville, AR Zip 72703–4002; tel. 479/444–2200; Jack C. Mitchell, FACHE, Chief Executive Officer
Web address: www.healthsouthfayetteville.com

HEALTHSOUTH REHABILITATION HOSPITAL OF FORT SMITH (O, 60 beds) 1401 South J Street, Fort Smith, AR Zip 72901–5155; tel. 479/785–3300; Dawn Watts, Chief Executive Officer
Web address: www.healthsouthfortsmith.com

HEALTHSOUTH REHABILITATION HOSPITAL OF JONESBORO (O, 67 beds) 1201 Fleming Avenue, Jonesboro, AR Zip 72401–4311, Mailing Address: P.O. Box 1680, Zip 72403–1680; tel. 870/932–0440; Donna Harris, Chief Executive Officer
Web address: www.healthsouthjonesboro.com

ST. VINCENT REHABILITATION HOSPITAL (O, 60 beds) 2201 Wildwood Avenue, Sherwood, AR Zip 72120–5074, Mailing Address: P.O. Box 6930, Zip 72124–6930; tel. 501/834–1800; Lisa Watson, Chief Executive Officer
Web address: www.stvincenthealth.com/svrehabhospital/index.html

CALIFORNIA: HEALTHSOUTH BAKERSFIELD REHABILITATION HOSPITAL (O, 66 beds) 5001 Commerce Drive, Bakersfield, CA Zip 93309–0689; tel. 661/323–5500; Martha Samora, R.N., Chief Executive Officer
Web address: www.healthsouthbakersfield.com

HEALTHSOUTH TUSTIN REHABILITATION HOSPITAL (O, 48 beds) 14851 Yorba Street, Tustin, CA Zip 92780–2925; tel. 714/832–9200; Diana C. Hanyak, Chief Executive Officer
Web address: www.tustinrehab.com

For explanation of codes following names, see page B2.
★ Indicates Type III membership in the American Hospital Association.

COLORADO: HEALTHSOUTH REHABILITATION HOSPITAL OF COLORADO SPRINGS (O, 56 beds) 325 Parkside Drive, Colorado Springs, CO Zip 80910–3134; tel. 719/630–8000; Stephen Schaefer, Chief Executive Officer
Web address: www.healthsouthcoloradosprings.com

HEALTHSOUTH REHABILITATION HOSPITAL OF DENVER (O, 28 beds) 1001 West Mineral Avenue, Littleton, CO Zip 80120–4507; tel. 303/334–1100; David H. Shefte, Chief Executive Officer
Web address: www.healthsouthdenver.com

FLORIDA: HEALTHSOUTH EMERALD COAST REHABILITATION HOSPITAL (O, 75 beds) 1847 Florida Avenue, Panama City, FL Zip 32405–4640; tel. 850/914–8600; Tony N. Bennett, Chief Executive Officer
Web address: www.healthsouthpanamacity.com

HEALTHSOUTH REHABILITATION HOSPITAL (O, 70 beds) 901 North Clearwater–Largo Road, Largo, FL Zip 33770–4126; tel. 727/586–2999; Tripp Smith, Chief Executive Officer
Web address: www.healthsouthlargo.com

HEALTHSOUTH REHABILITATION HOSPITAL AT MARTIN HEALTH (O, 34 beds) 5850 S.E. Community Drive, Stuart, FL Zip 34997–6420; tel. 772/324–3500; Kevin R. Conn, Interim Chief Executive Officer
Web address: www.healthsouthmartin.com

HEALTHSOUTH REHABILITATION HOSPITAL OF MIAMI (O, 60 beds) 20601 Old Cutler Road, Cutler Bay, FL Zip 33189–2400; tel. 305/251–3800; Elizabeth L. Izquierdo, CPA, Chief Executive Officer
Web address: www.healthsouthmiami.com

HEALTHSOUTH REHABILITATION HOSPITAL OF OCALA (O, 40 beds) 2275 S.W. 22nd Lane, Ocala, FL Zip 34471–7710; tel. 352/282–4000; Ellen Witterstaeter, FACHE, Chief Executive Officer
Web address: www.healthsouthocala.com

HEALTHSOUTH REHABILITATION HOSPITAL OF SARASOTA (O, 86 beds) 6400 Edgelake Drive, Sarasota, FL Zip 34240–8813; tel. 941/921–8600; Marcus Braz, Chief Executive Officer
Web address: www.healthsouthsarasota.com

HEALTHSOUTH REHABILITATION HOSPITAL OF SPRING HILL (O, 80 beds) 12440 Cortez Boulevard, Brooksville, FL Zip 34613–2628; tel. 352/592–4250; Lori Bedard, Chief Executive Officer
Web address: www.healthsouthspringhill.com

HEALTHSOUTH REHABILITATION HOSPITAL OF TALLAHASSEE (O, 76 beds) 1675 Riggins Road, Tallahassee, FL Zip 32308–5315; tel. 850/656–4800; Dale Neely, Chief Executive Officer
Web address: www.healthsouthtallahassee.com

HEALTHSOUTH SEA PiNES REHABILITATION HOSPITAL (O, 90 beds) 101 East Florida Avenue, Melbourne, FL Zip 32901–8301; tel. 321/984–4600; Denise B. McGrath, Chief Executive Officer
Web address: www.healthsouthseapines.com

HEALTHSOUTH SUNRISE REHABILITATION HOSPITAL (O, 126 beds) 4399 North Nob Hill Road, Sunrise, FL Zip 33351–5899; tel. 954/749–0300; Stacy Modlin, Chief Executive Officer
Web address: www.healthsouthsunrise.com

HEALTHSOUTH TREASURE COAST REHABILITATION HOSPITAL (O, 80 beds) 1600 37th Street, Vero Beach, FL Zip 32960–4863; tel. 772/778–2100; Michael Kissner, Chief Executive Officer
Web address: www.healthsouthtreasurecoast.com

GEORGIA: HEALTHSOUTH WALTON REHABILITATION HOSPITAL (O, 58 beds) 1355 Independence Drive, Augusta, GA Zip 30901–1037; tel. 706/724–7746; Deborah S. Guthrie, Chief Executive Officer
Web address: www.healthsouthwalton.com/

ILLINOIS: VAN MATRE HEALTHSOUTH REHABILITATION HOSPITAL (O, 53 beds) 950 South Mulford Road, Rockford, IL Zip 61108–4274; tel. 815/381–8500; Ken Bowman, Chief Executive Officer
Web address: www.healthsouth.com

INDIANA: HEALTHSOUTH DEACONESS REHABILITATION HOSPITAL (O, 80 beds) 4100 Covert Avenue, Evansville, IN Zip 47714–5567, Mailing Address: P.O. Box 5349, Zip 47716–5349; tel. 812/476–9983; Barbara Butler, Chief Executive Officer
Web address: www.healthsouthdeaconess.com

KANSAS: KANSAS REHABILITATION HOSPITAL (O, 59 beds) 1504 S.W. Eighth Avenue, Topeka, KS Zip 66606–1632; tel. 785/235–6600; William J. Overbey, Chief Executive Officer
Web address: www.kansasrehabhospital.com

MID–AMERICA REHABILITATION HOSPITAL (O, 98 beds) 5701 West 110th Street, Shawnee Mission, KS Zip 66211–2503; tel. 913/491–2400; Troy DeDecker, Chief Executive Officer
Web address: www.midamericarehabhospital.com

WESLEY REHABILITATION HOSPITAL (O, 65 beds) 8338 West 13th Street North, Wichita, KS Zip 67212–2984; tel. 316/729–9999; James F. Grocholski, FACHE, Chief Executive Officer
Web address: www.wesleyrehabhospital.com

KENTUCKY: HEALTHSOUTH LAKEVIEW REHABILITATION HOSPITAL (O, 40 beds) 134 Heartland Drive, Elizabethtown, KY Zip 42701–2778; tel. 270/769–3100; Lori Jarboe, Chief Executive Officer
Web address: www.healthsouthlakeview.com

HEALTHSOUTH NORTHERN KENTUCKY REHABILITATION HOSPITAL (O, 40 beds) 201 Medical Village Drive, Edgewood, KY Zip 41017–3407; tel. 859/341–2044; Richard R. Evens, Chief Executive Officer
Web address: www.healthsouthkentucky.com

LOUISIANA: HEALTHSOUTH REHABILITATION HOSPITAL OF ALEXANDRIA (O, 47 beds) 104 North Third Street, Alexandria, LA Zip 71301–8581; tel. 318/449–1370; James W. McClung, Chief Executive Officer
Web address: www.healthsouthalexandria.com

MAINE: NEW ENGLAND REHABILITATION HOSPITAL OF PORTLAND (O, 90 beds) 335 Brighton Avenue, Portland, ME Zip 04102–2363; tel. 207/775–4000; Jeanine Chesley, Chief Executive Officer
Web address: www.nerhp.org

MARYLAND: HEALTHSOUTH CHESAPEAKE REHABILITATION HOSPITAL (O, 54 beds) 220 Tilghman Road, Salisbury, MD Zip 21804–1921; tel. 410/546–4600; Steven Walas, Chief Executive Officer
Web address: www.healthsouthchesapeake.com

MASSACHUSETTS: FAIRLAWN REHABILITATION HOSPITAL (O, 110 beds) 189 May Street, Worcester, MA Zip 01602–4339; tel. 508/791–6351; R. David Richer, Chief Executive Officer
Web address: www.fairlawnrehab.org

HEALTHSOUTH REHABILITATION HOSPITAL OF WESTERN MASSACHUSETTS (O, 53 beds) 14 Chestnut Place, Ludlow, MA Zip 01056–3476; tel. 413/589–7581; Victoria Healy, Chief Executive Officer
Web address: www.healthsouthrehab.org

MISSOURI: HOWARD A. RUSK REHABILITATION CENTER (O, 60 beds) 315 Business Loop 70 West, Columbia, MO Zip 65203–3248; tel. 573/817–2703; Larry Meeker, Chief Executive Officer
Web address: www.ruskrehab.com

THE REHABILITATION INSTITUTE OF ST. LOUIS (O, 96 beds) 4455 Duncan Avenue, Saint Louis, MO Zip 63110–1111; tel. 314/658–3800; Tara Diebling, Chief Executive Officer
Web address: www.rehabinstitutestl.com

NEVADA: HEALTHSOUTH DESERT CANYON REHABILITATION HOSPITAL (O, 50 beds) 9175 West Oquendo Road, Las Vegas, NV Zip 89148–1234; tel. 702/252–7342; Andrea Davis, Chief Executive Officer
Web address: www.healthsouthdesertcanyon.com

HEALTHSOUTH REHABILITATION HOSPITAL – HENDERSON (O, 70 beds) 10301 Jeffreys Street, Henderson, NV Zip 89052–3922; tel. 702/939–9400; Nina Beck, Interim Chief Executive Officer
Web address: www.hendersonrehabhospital.com

HEALTHSOUTH REHABILITATION HOSPITAL–LAS VEGAS (O, 79 beds) 1250 South Valley View Boulevard, Las Vegas, NV Zip 89102–1861; tel. 702/877–8898; Michael Ward, Chief Executive Officer
Web address: www.healthsouthlasvegas.com

NEW HAMPSHIRE: HEALTHSOUTH REHABILITATION HOSPITAL (O, 50 beds) 254 Pleasant Street, Concord, NH Zip 03301–2508; tel. 603/226–9800; Catherine Devaney, Chief Executive Officer
Web address: www.healthsouthrehabconcordnh.com

NEW JERSEY: HEALTHSOUTH REHABILITATION HOSPITAL OF TOMS RIVER (O, 129 beds) 14 Hospital Drive, Toms River, NJ Zip 08755–6470; tel. 732/244–3100; Patricia Ostaszewski, MS, Chief Executive Officer
Web address: www.rehabnjtomsriver.com/

HEALTHSOUTH REHABILITATION HOSPITAL OF VINELAND (O, 41 beds) 1237 West Sherman Avenue, Vineland, NJ Zip 08360–6920; tel. 856/696–7100; Tammy Feuer, Chief Executive Officer
Web address: www.healthsouthvineland.com

For explanation of codes following names, see page B2.
★ Indicates Type III membership in the American Hospital Association.

REHABILITATION HOSPITAL OF TINTON FALLS (O, 60 beds) 2 Centre Plaza, Tinton Falls, NJ Zip 07724–9744; tel. 732/460–5320; Linda A. Savino, MS, Chief Executive Officer
Web address: www.rehabnj.com

NEW MEXICO: HEALTHSOUTH REHABILITATION HOSPITAL (O, 87 beds) 7000 Jefferson Street N.E., Albuquerque, NM Zip 87109–4313; tel. 505/344–9478; Sylvia K. Kelly, Chief Executive Officer
Web address: www.healthsouthnewmexico.com

OHIO: HEALTHSOUTH REHABILITATION HOSPITAL AT DRAKE (O, 60 beds) 151 West Galbraith Road, Cincinnati, OH Zip 45216–1015; tel. 513/418–5600; Brad Kennedy, Chief Executive Officer
Web address: www.healthsouthatdrake.com

PENNSYLVANIA: GEISINGER HEALTHSOUTH REHABILITATION HOSPITAL (O, 42 beds) 2 Rehab Lane, Danville, PA Zip 17821–8498; tel. 570/271–6733; Lorie Dillon, Chief Executive Officer
Web address: www.geisingerhealthsouth.com

HEALTHSOUTH HARMARVILLE REHABILITATION HOSPITAL (O, 202 beds) Guys Run Road, Pittsburgh, PA Zip 15238–0460, Mailing Address: P.O. Box 11460, Zip 15238–0460; tel. 412/828–1300; Kenneth J. Anthony, Chief Executive Officer
Web address: www.healthsouthharmarville.com

HEALTHSOUTH NITTANY VALLEY REHABILITATION HOSPITAL (O, 73 beds) 550 West College Avenue, Pleasant Gap, PA Zip 16823–7401; tel. 814/359–3421; Susan Hartman, Chief Executive Officer
Web address: www.nittanyvalleyrehab.com

HEALTHSOUTH READING REHABILITATION HOSPITAL (O, 60 beds) 1623 Morgantown Road, Reading, PA Zip 19607–9455; tel. 610/796–6000; Richard Kruczek, Chief Executive Officer
Web address: www.healthsouthreading.com

HEALTHSOUTH REHABILITATION HOSPITAL (O, 44 beds) 303 Camp Meeting Road, Sewickley, PA Zip 15143–8322; tel. 412/741–9500; Leah Laffey, R.N., Chief Executive Officer
Web address: www.healthsouthsewickley.com

HEALTHSOUTH REHABILITATION HOSPITAL OF ALTOONA (O, 80 beds) 2005 Valley View Boulevard, Altoona, PA Zip 16602–4598; tel. 814/944–3535; Scott Filler, Chief Executive Officer
Web address: www.healthsouthaltoona.com

HEALTHSOUTH REHABILITATION HOSPITAL OF ERIE (O, 100 beds) 143 East Second Street, Erie, PA Zip 16507–1501; tel. 814/878–1200; Lucretia Atti, Chief Executive Officer
Web address: www.healthsoutherie.com

HEALTHSOUTH REHABILITATION HOSPITAL OF MECHANICSBURG (O, 75 beds) 175 Lancaster Boulevard, Mechanicsburg, PA Zip 17055–3562; tel. 717/691–3700; Mark Freeburn, Chief Executive Officer
Web address: www.healthsouthpa.com

HEALTHSOUTH REHABILITATION HOSPITAL OF YORK (O, 90 beds) 1850 Normandie Drive, York, PA Zip 17408–1534; tel. 717/767–6941; Steven Alwine, Chief Executive Officer
Web address: www.healthsouthyork.com

PUERTO RICO: HEALTHSOUTH HOSPITAL OF MANATI (O, 40 beds) Carretera 2, Kilometro 47 7, Manati, PR Zip 00674; tel. 787/621–3800; Enrique A. Vicens–Rivera, Jr., JD, Chief Executive Officer
Web address: www.healthsouth.com

HEALTHSOUTH REHABILITATION HOSPITAL OF SAN JUAN (O, 32 beds) University Hospital, 3rd Floor, San Juan, PR Zip 00923, Mailing Address: P.O. Box 70344, Zip 00923; tel. 787/274–5100; Daniel Del Castillo, Chief Executive Officer
Web address: www.healthsouthsanjuan.com

SOUTH CAROLINA: ANMED HEALTH REHABILITATION HOSPITAL (O, 55 beds) 1 Spring Back Way, Anderson, SC Zip 29621–2676; tel. 864/716–2600; Michele M. Skripps, R.N., Chief Executive Officer
Web address: www.anmedrehab.com

HEALTHSOUTH REHABILITATION HOSPITAL OF CHARLESTON (O, 49 beds) 9181 Medcom Street, Charleston, SC Zip 29406–9168; tel. 843/820–7777; Troy Powell, Chief Executive Officer
Web address: www.healthsouthcharleston.com

HEALTHSOUTH REHABILITATION HOSPITAL OF COLUMBIA (O, 96 beds) 2935 Colonial Drive, Columbia, SC Zip 29203–6811; tel. 803/254–7777; W. Anthony Jackson, Chief Executive Officer
Web address: www.healthsouthcolumbia.com

HEALTHSOUTH REHABILITATION HOSPITAL OF FLORENCE (O, 88 beds) 900 East Cheves Street, Florence, SC Zip 29506–2704; tel. 843/679–9000; Jill Strawn, Chief Executive Officer
Web address: www.healthsouthflorence.com

HEALTHSOUTH REHABILITATION HOSPITAL OF ROCK HILL (O, 50 beds) 1795 Dr. Frank Gaston Boulevard, Rock Hill, SC Zip 29732–1190; tel. 803/326–3500; Britton Phelps, Chief Executive Officer
Web address: www.healthsouthrockhill.com

TENNESSEE: HEALTHSOUTH CANE CREEK REHABILITATION HOSPITAL (O, 40 beds) 180 Mount Pelia Road, Martin, TN Zip 38237–3812; tel. 731/587–4231; Amy Vieth, Chief Executive Officer
Web address: www.healthsouthcanecreek.com

HEALTHSOUTH CHATTANOOGA REHABILITATION HOSPITAL (O, 50 beds) 2412 McCallie Avenue, Chattanooga, TN Zip 37404–3398; tel. 423/698–0221; Scott Rowe, Chief Executive Officer
Web address: www.healthsouthchattanooga.com

HEALTHSOUTH REHABILITATION HOSPITAL (O, 50 beds) 113 Cassel Drive, Kingsport, TN Zip 37660–3775; tel. 423/246–7240; Susan Glenn, Chief Executive Officer
Web address: www.healthsouthkingsport.com

HEALTHSOUTH REHABILITATION HOSPITAL MEMPHIS–NORTH (O, 40 beds) 4100 Austin Peay Highway, Memphis, TN Zip 38128–2502; tel. 901/213–5400; Marcia Taylor, Chief Executive Officer
Web address: www.healthsouthnorthmemphis.com

HEALTHSOUTH REHABILITATION HOSPITAL OF MEMPHIS (O, 72 beds) 1282 Union Avenue, Memphis, TN Zip 38104–3414; tel. 901/722–2000; Kevin Spears, Chief Executive Officer
Web address: www.healthsouthmemphis.com

VANDERBILT STALLWORTH REHABILITATION HOSPITAL (O, 80 beds) 2201 Childrens Way, Nashville, TN Zip 37212–3165; tel. 615/320–7600; Susan Heath, Chief Executive Officer
Web address: www.vanderbiltstallworthrehab.com

TEXAS: HEALTHSOUTH CITY VIEW REHABILITATION HOSPITAL (O, 62 beds) 6701 Oakmont Boulevard, Fort Worth, TX Zip 76132–2957; tel. 817/370–4700; Trent Pierce, R.N., Chief Executive Officer
Web address: www.healthsouthcityview.com

HEALTHSOUTH PLANO REHABILITATION HOSPITAL (O, 83 beds) 2800 West 15th Street, Plano, TX Zip 75075–7526; tel. 972/612–9000; Jennifer Lynn Brewer, Chief Executive Officer
Web address: www.healthsouthplano.com

HEALTHSOUTH REHABILITATION HOSPITAL (O, 60 beds) 19002 McKay Drive, Humble, TX Zip 77338–5701; tel. 281/446–6148; Angela L. Simmons, Chief Executive Officer
Web address: www.healthsouthhumble.com

HEALTHSOUTH REHABILITATION HOSPITAL MIDLAND–ODESSA (O, 60 beds) 1800 Heritage Boulevard, Midland, TX Zip 79707–9750; tel. 432/520–1600; Christopher Wortham, Chief Executive Officer
Web address: www.healthsouthmidland.com

HEALTHSOUTH REHABILITATION HOSPITAL OF ARLINGTON (O, 85 beds) 3200 Matlock Road, Arlington, TX Zip 76015–2911; tel. 817/468–4000; Mark S. Deno, Chief Executive Officer
Web address: www.healthsoutharlington.com

HEALTHSOUTH REHABILITATION HOSPITAL OF AUSTIN (O, 40 beds) 1215 Red River Street, Austin, TX Zip 78701–1921; tel. 512/474–5700; Sandra Hegland, Chief Executive Officer
Web address: www.healthsouthaustin.com

HEALTHSOUTH REHABILITATION HOSPITAL OF BEAUMONT (O, 61 beds) 3340 Plaza 10 Boulevard, Beaumont, TX Zip 77707–2551; tel. 409/835–0835; H. J. Gaspard, Chief Executive Officer
Web address: www.healthsouthbeaumont.com

HEALTHSOUTH REHABILITATION HOSPITAL OF CYPRESS (O, 40 beds) 13031 Wortham Center Drive, Houston, TX Zip 77065–5662; tel. 832/280–2500; Sheila A. Bollier, Chief Executive Officer
Web address: www.healthsouthcypress.com

HEALTHSOUTH REHABILITATION HOSPITAL OF FORT WORTH (O, 60 beds) 1212 West Lancaster Avenue, Fort Worth, TX Zip 76102–4510; tel. 817/870–2336; Trent Pierce, R.N., Chief Executive Officer
Web address: www.healthsouthfortworth.com

HEALTHSOUTH REHABILITATION HOSPITAL OF TEXARKANA (O, 60 beds) 515 West 12th Street, Texarkana, TX Zip 75501–4416; tel. 903/735–5000; Michael G. Treadway, Interim Chief Executive Officer
Web address: www.healthsouthtexarkana.com

Section B

For explanation of codes following names, see page B2.
★ Indicates Type III membership in the American Hospital Association.

HEALTHSOUTH REHABILITATION HOSPITAL THE WOODLANDS (O, 84 beds) 18550 'IH' 45 South, Conroe, TX Zip 77384; tel. 281/364–2000; Krista Uselman, Chief Executive Officer
Web address: www.healthsouththewoodlands.com

HEALTHSOUTH REHABILITATION HOSPITAL–WICHITA FALLS (O, 63 beds) 3901 Armory Road, Wichita Falls, TX Zip 76302–2204; tel. 940/720–5700; Michael L. Bullitt, Chief Executive Officer
Web address: www.healthsouthwichitafalls.com

HEALTHSOUTH REHABILITATION INSTITUTE OF SAN ANTONIO (O, 96 beds) 9119 Cinnamon Hill, San Antonio, TX Zip 78240–5401; tel. 210/691–0737; Scott Butcher, Chief Executive Officer
Web address: www.hsriosa.com

HEALTHSOUTH SUGAR LAND REHABILITATION HOSPITAL (O, 50 beds) 1325 Highway 6, Sugar Land, TX Zip 77478–4906; tel. 281/276–7574; Nicholas Hardin, Chief Executive Officer
Web address: www.healthsouthsugarland.com

TRINITY MOTHER FRANCES REHABILITATION HOSPITAL (O, 74 beds) 3131 Troup Highway, Tyler, TX Zip 75701–8352; tel. 903/510–7000; Sharla Anderson, Chief Executive Officer
Web address: www.tmfrehabhospital.com

UTAH: HEALTHSOUTH REHABILITATION HOSPITAL OF UTAH (O, 105 beds) 8074 South 1300 East, Sandy, UT Zip 84094–0743; tel. 801/561–3400; Jeff Frandsen, Chief Executive Officer
Web address: www.healthsouthutah.com

VIRGINIA: HEALTHSOUTH REHABILITATION HOSPITAL OF FREDERICKSBURG (O, 40 beds) 300 Park Hill Drive, Fredericksburg, VA Zip 22401–3387; tel. 540/368–7300; Donna Z. Phillips, M.D., Chief Executive Officer
Web address: www.fredericksburgrehabhospital.com

HEALTHSOUTH REHABILITATION HOSPITAL OF NORTHERN VIRGINIA (O, 40 beds) 24430 Millstream Drive, Aldie, VA Zip 20105–3098; tel. 703/957–2000; Gary J. Herbek, Chief Executive Officer
Web address: www.healthsouthnorthernvirginia.com

HEALTHSOUTH REHABILITATION HOSPITAL OF PETERSBURG (O, 64 beds) 95 Pinehill Boulevard, Petersburg, VA Zip 23805–9233; tel. 804/504–8100; Tracy Penn Turman, Chief Executive Officer
Web address: www.healthsouthpetersburg.com

HEALTHSOUTH REHABILITATION HOSPITAL OF VIRGINIA (O, 40 beds) 5700 Fitzhugh Avenue, Richmond, VA Zip 23226–1800; tel. 804/288–5700; David Cashwell, Chief Executive Officer
Web address: www.healthsouthrichmond.com

REHABILITATION HOSPITAL OF SOUTHWEST VIRGINIA (O, 25 beds) 103 North Street, Bristol, VA Zip 24201–3201; tel. 276/642–7900; Georgeanne Cole, Chief Executive Officer
Web address: www.rehabilitationhospitalswvirginia.com

UVA–HEALTHSOUTH REHABILITATION HOSPITAL (O, 50 beds) 515 Ray C. Hunt Drive, Charlottesville, VA Zip 22903–2981; tel. 434/244–2000; Thomas J. Cook, Chief Executive Officer
Web address: www.uvahealthsouth.com

WEST VIRGINIA: HEALTHSOUTH HUNTINGTON REHABILITATION HOSPITAL (O, 52 beds) 6900 West Country Club Drive, Huntington, WV Zip 25705–2000; tel. 304/733–1060; Michael E. Zuliani, Chief Executive Officer
Web address: www.healthsouthhuntington.com

HEALTHSOUTH MOUNTAINVIEW REGIONAL REHABILITATION HOSPITAL (O, 96 beds) 1160 Van Voorhis Road, Morgantown, WV Zip 26505–3437; tel. 304/598–1100; Vickie Demers, Chief Executive Officer
Web address: www.healthsouthmountainview.com

HEALTHSOUTH SOUTHERN HILLS REHABILITATION HOSPITAL (O, 45 beds) 120 Twelfth Street, Princeton, WV Zip 24740–2352; tel. 304/487–8000; Robert Williams, Chief Executive Officer
Web address: www.healthsouthsouthernhills.com

HEALTHSOUTH WESTERN HILLS REHABILITATION HOSPITAL (O, 40 beds) 3 Western Hills Drive, Parkersburg, WV Zip 26105–8122; tel. 304/420–1300; Alvin R. Lawson, JD, FACHE, Chief Executive Officer
Web address: www.healthsouthwesternhills.com

Owned, leased, sponsored:	103 hospitals	6725 beds
Contract–managed:	0 hospitals	0 beds
Totals:	103 hospitals	6725 beds

★0585: HEALTHTECH MANAGEMENT SERVICES (IO) 5110 Maryland Way Suite 200, Brentwood, TN Zip 37027–2307; tel. 615/309–6053; Derek Morkel, Chief Executive Officer
(Moderately Centralized Health System)

ARIZONA: COBRE VALLEY REGIONAL MEDICAL CENTER (C, 25 beds) 5880 South Hospital Drive, Globe, AZ Zip 85501–9454; tel. 928/425–3261; Neal Jensen, Chief Executive Officer
Web address: www.cvrmc.org

GEORGIA: UPSON REGIONAL MEDICAL CENTER (C, 74 beds) 801 West Gordon Street, Thomaston, GA Zip 30286–3426, Mailing Address: P.O. Box 1059, Zip 30286–0027; tel. 706/647–8111; David L. Castleberry, FACHE, Chief Executive Officer
Web address: www.urmc.org

ILLINOIS: CARLINVILLE AREA HOSPITAL (C, 25 beds) 20733 North Broad Street, Carlinville, IL Zip 62626–1499; tel. 217/854–3141; Kenneth G. Reid, President and Chief Executive Officer
Web address: www.cahcare.com

HAMMOND–HENRY HOSPITAL (C, 61 beds) 600 North College Avenue, Geneseo, IL Zip 61254–1099; tel. 309/944–4625; Bradley Solberg, FACHE, Chief Executive Officer
Web address: www.hammondhenry.com

HILLSBORO AREA HOSPITAL (C, 25 beds) 1200 East Tremont Street, Hillsboro, IL Zip 62049–1900; tel. 217/532–6111; Rex H. Brown, Chief Executive Officer
Web address: www.hillsborohealth.org

LOUISIANA: IBERIA MEDICAL CENTER (C, 84 beds) 2315 East Main Street, New Iberia, LA Zip 70560–4031, Mailing Address: P.O. Box 13338, Zip 70562–3338; tel. 337/364–0441; Parker A. Templeton, FACHE, Chief Executive Officer
Web address: www.iberiamedicalcenter.com

MONTANA: BARRETT HOSPITAL & HEALTHCARE (C, 25 beds) 600 Highway 91 South, Dillon, MT Zip 59725–7379; tel. 406/683–3000; Ken Westman, Chief Executive Officer
Web address: www.barretthospital.org

NEBRASKA: TRI VALLEY HEALTH SYSTEM (C, 51 beds) 1305 West Highway 6 and 34, Cambridge, NE Zip 69022–0488, Mailing Address: P.O. Box 488, Zip 69022–0488; tel. 308/697–3329; Gregg Magers, Interim Chief Executive Officer
Web address: www.trivalleyhealth.com

NEW MEXICO: UNION COUNTY GENERAL HOSPITAL (C, 21 beds) 300 Wilson Street, Clayton, NM Zip 88415–3304, Mailing Address: P.O. Box 489, Zip 88415–0489; tel. 575/374–2585; Scott Manis, Chief Executive Officer
Web address: www.unioncountygeneral.com/

NEW YORK: ADIRONDACK MEDICAL CENTER (C, 271 beds) 2233 State Route 86, Saranac Lake, NY Zip 12983–5644, Mailing Address: P.O. Box 471, Zip 12983–0471; tel. 518/891–4141; Chandler M. Ralph, President and Chief Executive Officer
Web address: www.adirondackhealth.org

MEDINA MEMORIAL HOSPITAL (C, 101 beds) 200 Ohio Street, Medina, NY Zip 14103–1095; tel. 585/798–2000; Dolores A. Horvath, Chief Executive Officer
Web address: www.medinamemorial.org

OREGON: BLUE MOUNTAIN HOSPITAL (C, 64 beds) 170 Ford Road, John Day, OR Zip 97845–2009; tel. 541/575–1311; Robert Houser, FACHE, Chief Executive Officer
Web address: www.bluemountainhospital.org

WASHINGTON: SUNNYSIDE COMMUNITY HOSPITAL AND CLINICS (C, 25 beds) 1016 Tacoma Avenue, Sunnyside, WA Zip 98944–2263, Mailing Address: P.O. Box 719, Zip 98944–0719; tel. 509/837–1500; John Gallagher, Chief Executive Officer
Web address: www.sunnysidehospital.com

WISCONSIN: GRANT REGIONAL HEALTH CENTER (C, 4 beds) 507 South Monroe Street, Lancaster, WI Zip 53813–2054; tel. 608/723–2143; Nicole Clapp, R.N., MSN, FACHE, President and Chief Executive Officer
Web address: www.grantregional.com

SPOONER HEALTH SYSTEM (C, 25 beds) 819 Ash Street, Spooner, WI Zip 54801–1299; tel. 715/635–2111; Michael Schafer, Chief Executive Officer and Administrator
Web address: www.spoonerhealthsystem.com

For explanation of codes following names, see page B2.
★ Indicates Type III membership in the American Hospital Association.

TOMAH MEMORIAL HOSPITAL (C, 25 beds) 321 Butts Avenue, Tomah, WI Zip 54660-1412; tel. 608/372-2181; Philip J. Stuart, Administrator and Chief Executive Officer
Web address: www.tomahhospital.org

WYOMING: HOT SPRINGS COUNTY MEMORIAL HOSPITAL (C, 25 beds) 150 East Arapahoe Street, Thermopolis, WY Zip 82443-2498; tel. 307/864-3121; Robin Roling, Chief Executive Officer
Web address: www.hscmh.org

POWELL VALLEY HEALTHCARE (C, 125 beds) 777 Avenue H, Powell, WY Zip 82435-2296; tel. 307/754-2267; Bill D. Patten, Jr., Chief Executive Officer
Web address: www.pvhc.org

Owned, leased, sponsored:	0 hospitals	0 beds
Contract–managed:	18 hospitals	1056 beds
Totals:	18 hospitals	1056 beds

★**9505: HENRY FORD HEALTH SYSTEM** (NP)
One Ford Place, Detroit, MI Zip 48202-3450; tel. 313/876-8708; Nancy M. Schlichting, Chief Executive Officer
(Centralized Health System)

MICHIGAN: HENRY FORD HOSPITAL (O, 673 beds) 2799 West Grand Boulevard, Detroit, MI Zip 48202-2608; tel. 313/916-2600; John Popovich, M.D., President and Chief Executive Officer
Web address: www.henryfordhealth.org

HENRY FORD KINGSWOOD HOSPITAL (O, 100 beds) 10300 West Eight Mile Road, Ferndale, MI Zip 48220-2100; tel. 248/398-3200; C. Edward Coffey, M.D., Chief Executive Officer and Director Behavioral Health Services
Web address: www.henryford.org

HENRY FORD MACOMB HOSPITAL–WARREN CAMPUS (O, 0 beds) 13355 East Ten Mile Road, Warren, MI Zip 48089-2048; tel. 586/759-7300; Barbara Rossmann, R.N., President and Chief Executive Officer

HENRY FORD MACOMB HOSPITALS (O, 433 beds) 15855 19 Mile Road, Clinton Township, MI Zip 48038-6324; tel. 586/263-2300; Barbara Rossmann, R.N., President and Chief Executive Officer
Web address: www.henryfordmacomb.com

HENRY FORD WEST BLOOMFIELD HOSPITAL (O, 191 beds) 6777 West Maple Road, West Bloomfield, MI Zip 48322-3013; tel. 248/661-4100; Lynn M. Torossian, President and Chief Executive Officer
Web address: www.henryford.com

HENRY FORD WYANDOTTE HOSPITAL (O, 355 beds) 2333 Biddle Avenue, Wyandotte, MI Zip 48192-4668; tel. 734/246-6000; Denise Brooks–Williams, President and Chief Executive Officer
Web address: www.henryfordhealth.org

Owned, leased, sponsored:	6 hospitals	1752 beds
Contract–managed:	0 hospitals	0 beds
Totals:	6 hospitals	1752 beds

0309: HERITAGE VALLEY HEALTH SYSTEM (NP)
1000 Dutch Ridge Road, Beaver, PA Zip 15009-9727; tel. 724/773-2024; Norman F. Mitry, President and Chief Executive Officer
(Independent Hospital System)

PENNSYLVANIA: HERITAGE VALLEY HEALTH SYSTEM (O, 273 beds) 1000 Dutch Ridge Road, Beaver, PA Zip 15009-9727; tel. 724/728-7000; Norman F. Mitry, President and Chief Executive Officer
Web address: www.heritagevalley.org

SEWICKLEY VALLEY HOSPITAL, (A DIVISION OF VALLEY MEDICAL FACILITIES) (O, 179 beds) 720 Blackburn Road, Sewickley, PA Zip 15143-1459; tel. 412/741-6600; Norman F. Mitry, President and Chief Executive Officer
Web address: www.heritagevalley.org

Owned, leased, sponsored:	2 hospitals	452 beds
Contract–managed:	0 hospitals	0 beds
Totals:	2 hospitals	452 beds

★**5355: HOSPITAL SISTERS HEALTH SYSTEM** (CC)
4936 LaVerna Road, Springfield, IL Zip 62707-9797, Mailing Address: P.O. Box 19456, Zip 62794-9456; tel. 217/523-4747; Mary Starmann–Harrison, FACHE, President and Chief Executive Officer
(Decentralized Health System)

ILLINOIS: ST. ANTHONY'S MEMORIAL HOSPITAL (O, 146 beds) 503 North Maple Street, Effingham, IL Zip 62401-2099; tel. 217/342-2121; Theresa Rutherford, R.N., MS, FACHE, President and Chief Executive Officer
Web address: www.stanthonyshospital.org

ST. ELIZABETH'S HOSPITAL (O, 260 beds) 211 South Third Street, Belleville, IL Zip 62220-1998; tel. 618/234-2120; Maryann Reese, R.N., FACHE, President and Chief Executive Officer
Web address: www.steliz.org

ST. FRANCIS HOSPITAL (O, 25 beds) 1215 Franciscan Drive, Litchfield, IL Zip 62056-1799, Mailing Address: P.O. Box 1215, Zip 62056-0999; tel. 217/324-2191; David R. Olejniczak, Interim President and Chief Executive Officer
Web address: www.stfrancis–litchfield.org

ST. JOHN'S HOSPITAL (O, 430 beds) 800 East Carpenter Street, Springfield, IL Zip 62769-0002; tel. 217/544-6464; Charles Lucore, M.D., President and Chief Executive Officer
Web address: www.st–johns.org

ST. JOSEPH'S HOSPITAL (O, 60 beds) 9515 Holy Cross Lane, Breese, IL Zip 62230-3618; tel. 618/526-4511; Paulette Evans, R.N., MSN, Interim President and Chief Executive Officer
Web address: www.stjoebreese.com

ST. JOSEPH'S HOSPITAL (O, 25 beds) 1515 Main Street, Highland, IL Zip 62249-1656; tel. 618/654-7421; Peggy A. Sebastian, MSN, R.N., President and Chief Executive Officer
Web address: www.stjosephshighland.com

ST. MARY'S HOSPITAL (O, 232 beds) 1800 East Lake Shore Drive, Decatur, IL Zip 62521-3883; tel. 217/464-2966; Daniel L. Perryman, Chief Executive Officer
Web address: www.stmarysdecatur.com

ST. MARY'S HOSPITAL (O, 68 beds) 111 Spring Street, Streator, IL Zip 61364-3399; tel. 815/673-2311; John T. Flanders, MS, R.N., President and Chief Executive Officer
Web address: www.stmaryshospital.org

WISCONSIN: SACRED HEART HOSPITAL (O, 206 beds) 900 West Clairemont Avenue, Eau Claire, WI Zip 54701-6122; tel. 715/717-4121; Julie Manas, President and Chief Executive Officer
Web address: www.sacredhearteauclaire.org

ST. JOSEPH'S HOSPITAL (O, 102 beds) 2661 County Highway I, Chippewa Falls, WI Zip 54729-1498; tel. 715/723-1811; Joan Coffman, President and Chief Executive Officer
Web address: www.stjoeschipfalls.com

ST. MARY'S HOSPITAL MEDICAL CENTER (O, 83 beds) 1726 Shawano Avenue, Green Bay, WI Zip 54303-3282; tel. 920/498-4200; Therese B. Pandl, President and Chief Executive Officer
Web address: www.stmgb.org

ST. NICHOLAS HOSPITAL (O, 53 beds) 3100 Superior Avenue, Sheboygan, WI Zip 53081-1948; tel. 920/459-8300; Andrew Bagnall, President and Chief Executive Officer
Web address: www.stnicholashospital.org

ST. VINCENT HOSPITAL (O, 255 beds) 835 South Van Buren Street, Green Bay, WI Zip 54301-3526, Mailing Address: P.O. Box 13508, Zip 54307-3508; tel. 920/433-0111; Therese B. Pandl, President and Chief Executive Officer
Web address: www.stvincenthospital.org

Owned, leased, sponsored:	13 hospitals	1945 beds
Contract–managed:	0 hospitals	0 beds
Totals:	13 hospitals	1945 beds

Section B

★0642: HOUSTON HEALTHCARE SYSTEM (NP)

1601 Watson Boulevard, Warner Robins, GA Zip 31093–3431,
Mailing Address: P.O. Box 2886, Zip 31099–2886;
tel. 478/922–4281; Cary Martin, Chief Executive Officer
(Independent Hospital System)

GEORGIA: HOUSTON MEDICAL CENTER (O, 237 beds) 1601 Watson
Boulevard, Warner Robins, GA Zip 31093–3431, Mailing Address: P.O.
Box 2886, Zip 31099–2886; tel. 478/922–4281; Cary Martin, Chief
Executive Officer
Web address: www.hhc.org

PERRY HOSPITAL (O, 39 beds) 1120 Morningside Drive, Perry, GA
Zip 31069–2906; tel. 478/987–3600; David Campbell, Administrator
Web address: www.hhc.org

Owned, leased, sponsored:	2 hospitals	276 beds
Contract–managed:	0 hospitals	0 beds
Totals:	2 hospitals	276 beds

★7235: HOUSTON METHODIST (CO)

6565 Fannin Street, D–200, Houston, TX Zip 77030–2707;
tel. 713/441–2221; Marc L. Boom, M.D., Chief Executive Officer
(Centralized Health System)

TEXAS: HOUSTON METHODIST HOSPITAL (O, 849 beds) 6565 Fannin Street,
Houston, TX Zip 77030–2707; tel. 713/790–3311; Roberta Schwartz,
Executive Vice President
Web address: www.methodisthealth.com

HOUSTON METHODIST SAN JACINTO HOSPITAL (O, 275 beds) 4401 Garth
Road, Baytown, TX Zip 77521–2122; tel. 281/420–8600; Donna Gares,
R.N., FACHE, MSN, President and Chief Executive Officer
Web address: www.houstonmethodist.org

HOUSTON METHODIST ST. CATHERINE HOSPITAL (O, 102 beds) 701 Fry
Road, Katy, TX Zip 77450–2255; tel. 281/599–5700; Gary L. Kempf,
Administrator
Web address: www.houstonmethodist.org/katy–st–catherine–hospital

HOUSTON METHODIST ST. JOHN HOSPITAL (O, 137 beds) 18300 St. John
Drive, Nassau Bay, TX Zip 77058–6302; tel. 281/333–5503; Dan Newman,
Interim Chief Executive Officer
Web address: www.houstonmethodist.org/st–john–clear–lake

HOUSTON METHODIST SUGAR LAND HOSPITAL (O, 235 beds) 16655 S.W.
Freeway, Sugar Land, TX Zip 77479–2329; tel. 281/274–7000; Christopher
Siebenaler, Chief Executive Officer
Web address: www.methodisthealth.com

HOUSTON METHODIST WEST HOSPITAL (O, 146 beds) 18500 Katy Freeway,
Houston, TX Zip 77094–1110; tel. 832/522–1000; Wayne M. Voss, Chief
Executive Officer
Web address: www.methodisthealth.com

HOUSTON METHODIST WILLOWBROOK HOSPITAL (O, 241 beds) 18220
Tomball Parkway, Houston, TX Zip 77070–4347; tel. 281/477–1000; Beryl
O. Ramsey, FACHE, Chief Executive Officer
Web address: www.methodisthealth.com

Owned, leased, sponsored:	7 hospitals	1985 beds
Contract–managed:	0 hospitals	0 beds
Totals:	7 hospitals	1985 beds

0907: HUNT REGIONAL HEALTHCARE (NP)

4215 Joe Ramsey Boulevard, Greenville, TX Zip 75401–7852,
Mailing Address: P.O. Box 1059, Zip 75403–1059;
tel. 903/408–5000; Richard Carter, Chief Executive Officer
(Independent Hospital System)

HUNT REGIONAL COMMUNITY HOSPITAL (O, 15 beds) 2900 Sterling Hart
Drive, Commerce, TX Zip 75428–3912; tel. 903/886–3161; Michael R.
Klepin, Administrator
Web address: www.huntregional.org

HUNT REGIONAL MEDICAL CENTER (O, 266 beds) 4215 Joe Ramsey
Boulevard, Greenville, TX Zip 75401–7899, Mailing Address: P.O. Box 1059,
Zip 75403–1059; tel. 903/408–5000; Richard Carter, District Chief
Executive Officer
Web address: www.huntregional.org

Owned, leased, sponsored:	2 hospitals	281 beds
Contract–managed:	0 hospitals	0 beds
Totals:	2 hospitals	281 beds

0117: HUNTSVILLE HOSPITAL HEALTH SYSTEM (NP)

101 Sivley Road S.W., Huntsville, AL Zip 35801–4421;
tel. 265/256–1000; David S. Spillers, Chief Executive Officer
(Moderately Centralized Health System)

ALABAMA: ATHENS–LIMESTONE HOSPITAL (C, 101 beds) 700 West Market
Street, Athens, AL Zip 35611–2457, Mailing Address: P.O. Box 999,
Zip 35612–0999; tel. 256/233–9292; David Pryor, President
Web address: www.athenslimestonehospital.com

DECATUR MORGAN HOSPITAL (O, 147 beds) 1201 Seventh Street S.E.,
Decatur, AL Zip 35601–3303, Mailing Address: P.O. Box 2239,
Zip 35609–2239; tel. 256/341–2000; Nathaniel Richardson, Jr., President
Web address: www.decaturgeneral.org

HELEN KELLER HOSPITAL (C, 159 beds) 1300 South Montgomery Avenue,
Sheffield, AL Zip 35660–6334, Mailing Address: P.O. Box 610,
Zip 35660–0610; tel. 256/386–4196; W. Douglas Arnold, President and
Chief Executive Officer
Web address: www.helenkeller.com

HUNTSVILLE HOSPITAL (O, 876 beds) 101 Sivley Road S.W., Huntsville, AL
Zip 35801–4470; tel. 256/265–1000; David S. Spillers, Chief Executive
Officer
Web address: www.huntsvillehospital.org

LAWRENCE MEDICAL CENTER (C, 43 beds) 202 Hospital Street, Moulton, AL
Zip 35650–1218, Mailing Address: P.O. Box 39, Zip 35650–0039;
tel. 256/974–2200; Kyle Buchanan, Chief Executive Officer
Web address: www.lawrencemedicalcenter.com

RED BAY HOSPITAL (C, 25 beds) 211 Hospital Road, Red Bay, AL
Zip 35582–3858, Mailing Address: P.O. Box 490, Zip 35582–0490;
tel. 256/356–9532; Glen M. Jones, Administrator
Web address: www.redbayhospital.com

Owned, leased, sponsored:	2 hospitals	1023 beds
Contract–managed:	4 hospitals	328 beds
Totals:	6 hospitals	1351 beds

0201: IASIS HEALTHCARE (IO)

117 Seaboard Lane, Building E., Franklin, TN Zip 37067–2855;
tel. 615/844–2747; Carl Whitmer, President and Chief Executive
Officer
(Moderately Centralized Health System)

ARIZONA: MOUNTAIN VISTA MEDICAL CENTER (O, 172 beds) 1301 South
Crismon Road, Mesa, AZ Zip 85209–3767; tel. 480/358–6100; Anthony
Marinello, Chief Executive Officer
Web address: www.mvmedicalcenter.com

ST. LUKE'S BEHAVIORAL HEALTH CENTER (O, 85 beds) 1800 East Van
Buren, Phoenix, AZ Zip 85006–3742; tel. 602/251–8546; Gregory L. Jahn,
R.N., Chief Executive Officer
Web address: www.iasishealthcare.com

ST. LUKE'S MEDICAL CENTER (O, 225 beds) 1800 East Van Buren Street,
Phoenix, AZ Zip 85006–3742; tel. 602/251–8100; Edward W. Myers, Chief
Executive Officer
Web address: www.stlukesmedcenter.com

ARKANSAS: WADLEY REGIONAL MEDICAL CENTER AT HOPE (O, 79 beds)
2001 South Main Street, Hope, AR Zip 71801–8194; tel. 870/722–3800;
Thomas D. Gilbert, FACHE, Chief Executive Officer
Web address: www.wadleyhealthathope.com

COLORADO: PIKES PEAK REGIONAL HOSPITAL (O, 15 beds) 16420 West
Highway 24, Woodland Park, CO Zip 80863; tel. 719/687–9999; Terry
Buckner, Chief Executive Officer
Web address: www.pprmc.org

LOUISIANA: GLENWOOD REGIONAL MEDICAL CENTER (O, 268 beds) 503
McMillan Road, West Monroe, LA Zip 71291–5327; tel. 318/329–4200;
Matthew S. Roberts, Chief Executive Officer
Web address: www.grmc.com

For explanation of codes following names, see page B2.
★ Indicates Type III membership in the American Hospital Association.

NEVADA: NORTH VISTA HOSPITAL (O, 198 beds) 1409 East Lake Mead Boulevard, North Las Vegas, NV Zip 89030–7197; tel. 702/649–7711; Cathy N. Story, Chief Executive Officer
Web address: www.northvistahospital.com

TEXAS: ODESSA REGIONAL MEDICAL CENTER (O, 213 beds) 520 East Sixth Street, Odessa, TX Zip 79761–4565, Mailing Address: P.O. Box 4859, Zip 79760–4859; tel. 432/582–8000; Stacey L. Gerig, Chief Executive Officer
Web address: www.odessaregionalmedicalcenter.com

SOUTHWEST GENERAL HOSPITAL (O, 265 beds) 7400 Barlite Boulevard, San Antonio, TX Zip 78224–1399; tel. 210/921–2000; P. Craig Desmond, Chief Executive Officer
Web address: www.swgeneralhospital.com

ST. JOSEPH MEDICAL CENTER (O, 374 beds) 1401 St. Joseph Parkway, Houston, TX Zip 77002–8301; tel. 713/757–1000; Mark L. Bernard, Chief Executive Officer
Web address: www.sjmctx.com

THE MEDICAL CENTER OF SOUTHEAST TEXAS (O, 185 beds) 2555 Jimmy Johnson Boulevard, Port Arthur, TX Zip 77640–2007; tel. 409/724–7389; Richard Gonzalez, Interim Chief Executive Officer
Web address: www.medicalcentersetexas.com

WADLEY REGIONAL MEDICAL CENTER (O, 179 beds) 1000 Pine Street, Texarkana, TX Zip 75501–5170; tel. 903/798–8000; Thomas D. Gilbert, FACHE, Chief Executive Officer
Web address: www.wadleyhealth.com

UTAH: DAVIS HOSPITAL AND MEDICAL CENTER (O, 200 beds) 1600 West Antelope Drive, Layton, UT Zip 84041–1142; tel. 801/807–1000; Michael E. Jensen, Chief Executive Officer
Web address: www.davishospital.com

JORDAN VALLEY MEDICAL CENTER (O, 284 beds) 3580 West 9000 South, West Jordan, UT Zip 84088–8812; tel. 801/561–8888; Steven Anderson, Chief Executive Officer
Web address: www.jordanvalleymc.com

PIONEER VALLEY HOSPITAL (O, 101 beds) 3460 South Pioneer Parkway, West Valley City, UT Zip 84120–2049; tel. 801/561–8888; Steven Anderson, Chief Executive Officer
Web address: www.pioneervalleyhospital.com

SALT LAKE REGIONAL MEDICAL CENTER (O, 132 beds) 1050 East South Temple, Salt Lake City, UT Zip 84102–1507; tel. 801/350–4111; Dale Johns, Chief Executive Officer
Web address: www.saltlakeregional.com

Owned, leased, sponsored:	16 hospitals	2975 beds
Contract–managed:	0 hospitals	0 beds
Totals:	16 hospitals	2975 beds

★0231: INDIANA UNIVERSITY HEALTH (NP)
340 West 10th Street, Suite 6100, Indianapolis, IN Zip 46202–3082, Mailing Address: P.O. Box 1367, Zip 46206–1367; tel. 317/962–5900; Daniel F. Evans, Jr., JD, President and Chief Executive Officer
(Decentralized Health System)

INDIANA: INDIANA UNIVERSITY HEALTH ARNETT HOSPITAL (O, 201 beds) 5165 McCarty Lane, Lafayette, IN Zip 47905–8764, Mailing Address: P.O. Box 5545, Zip 47903–5545; tel. 765/448–8000; Alfonso W. Gatmaitan, Chief Executive Officer
Web address: www.iuhealth.org

INDIANA UNIVERSITY HEALTH BALL MEMORIAL HOSPITAL (O, 344 beds) 2401 University Avenue, Muncie, IN Zip 47303–3499; tel. 765/747–3111; Michael E. Haley, President and Chief Executive Officer
Web address: www.iuhealth.org

INDIANA UNIVERSITY HEALTH BEDFORD HOSPITAL (O, 25 beds) 2900 West 16th Street, Bedford, IN Zip 47421–3583; tel. 812/275–1200; Bradford W. Dykes, President and Chief Executive Officer
Web address: www.iuhealth.com

INDIANA UNIVERSITY HEALTH BLACKFORD HOSPITAL (O, 15 beds) 410 Pilgrim Boulevard, Hartford City, IN Zip 47348–1897; tel. 765/348–0300; Steven J. West, Chief Executive Officer
Web address: www.iuhealth.org

INDIANA UNIVERSITY HEALTH BLOOMINGTON HOSPITAL (O, 292 beds) 601 West Second Street, Bloomington, IN Zip 47403–2317, Mailing Address: P.O. Box 1149, Zip 47402–-1149; tel. 812/336–6821; Mark E. Moore, President and Chief Executive Officer
Web address: www.iuhealth.org

INDIANA UNIVERSITY HEALTH GOSHEN HOSPITAL (O, 122 beds) 200 High Park Avenue, Goshen, IN Zip 46526–4899, Mailing Address: P.O. Box 139, Zip 46527–0139; tel. 574/533–2141; Randal Christophel, President and Chief Executive Officer
Web address: www.iuhealth.org

INDIANA UNIVERSITY HEALTH LA PORTE HOSPITAL (O, 204 beds) 1007 Lincolnway, La Porte, IN Zip 46350–3201, Mailing Address: P.O. Box 250, Zip 46352–0250; tel. 219/326–1234; G. Thor Thordarson, President and Chief Executive Officer
Web address: www.iuhealth.org

INDIANA UNIVERSITY HEALTH MORGAN HOSPITAL (O, 56 beds) 2209 John R. Wooden Drive, Martinsville, IN Zip 46151–1840, Mailing Address: P.O. Box 1717, Zip 46151–0717; tel. 765/342–8441; Doug Puckett, President and Chief Executive Officer
Web address: www.iuhealth.org/morgan/

INDIANA UNIVERSITY HEALTH NORTH HOSPITAL (O, 161 beds) 11700 North Meridian Avenue, Carmel, IN Zip 46032–4656; tel. 317/688–2000; Jonathan R. Goble, FACHE, President and Chief Executive Officer
Web address: www.iuhealth.org

INDIANA UNIVERSITY HEALTH PAOLI HOSPITAL (O, 24 beds) 642 West Hospital Road, Paoli, IN Zip 47454–9672, Mailing Address: P.O. Box 499, Zip 47454–0499; tel. 812/723–2811; Larry Bailey, Chief Executive Officer
Web address: www.iuhealth.org/paoli

INDIANA UNIVERSITY HEALTH STARKE HOSPITAL (O, 15 beds) 102 East Culver Road, Knox, IN Zip 46534–2216, Mailing Address: P.O. Box 339, Zip 46534–0339; tel. 574/772–6231; Craig Felty, President
Web address: www.iuhealth.org/starke/

INDIANA UNIVERSITY HEALTH TIPTON HOSPITAL (O, 25 beds) 1000 South Main Street, Tipton, IN Zip 46072–9799; tel. 765/675–8500; Michael Harlowe, President and Chief Executive Officer
Web address: www.iuhealth.org

INDIANA UNIVERSITY HEALTH UNIVERSITY HOSPITAL (O, 1266 beds) 550 University Boulevard, Indianapolis, IN Zip 46202–5149, Mailing Address: P.O. Box 1367, Zip 46206–1367; tel. 317/944–5000; Herbert Buchanan, President
Web address: www.iuhealth.org

INDIANA UNIVERSITY HEALTH WEST HOSPITAL (O, 127 beds) 1111 North Ronald Reagan Parkway, Avon, IN Zip 46123–7085; tel. 317/217–3000; Matthew D. Bailey, FACHE, President and Chief Executive Officer
Web address: www.iuhealth.org

INDIANA UNIVERSITY HEALTH WHITE MEMORIAL HOSPITAL (O, 25 beds) 720 South Sixth Street, Monticello, IN Zip 47960–8182; tel. 574/583–7111; Stephanie Long, Chief Executive Officer
Web address: www.iuhealth.org/white–memorial

JAY COUNTY HOSPITAL (C, 35 beds) 500 West Votaw Street, Portland, IN Zip 47371–1322; tel. 260/726–7131; David W. Hyatt, Chief Executive Officer
Web address: www.jaycountyhospital.com

REHABILITATION HOSPITAL OF INDIANA (O, 91 beds) 4141 Shore Drive, Indianapolis, IN Zip 46254–2607; tel. 317/329–2000; Daniel B. Woloszyn, Chief Executive Officer
Web address: www.rhin.com

Owned, leased, sponsored:	16 hospitals	2993 beds
Contract–managed:	1 hospital	35 beds
Totals:	17 hospitals	3028 beds

2025: INFIRMARY HEALTH SYSTEM (NP)
5 Mobile Infirmary Circle, Mobile, AL Zip 36607–3513; tel. 251/435–5500; D. Mark Nix, President and Chief Executive Officer

ALABAMA: INFIRMARY LONG TERM ACUTE CARE HOSPITAL (L, 38 beds) 5 Mobile Infirmary Circle, Mobile, AL Zip 36607–3513, Mailing Address: P.O. Box 2226, Zip 36652–2226; tel. 251/660–5239; Susanne Marmande, Administrator
Web address: www.theinfirmary.com/

For explanation of codes following names, see page B2.
★ Indicates Type III membership in the American Hospital Association.

Section B

MOBILE INFIRMARY MEDICAL CENTER (O, 510 beds) 5 Mobile Infirmary Drive North, Mobile, AL Zip 36607–3513, Mailing Address: P.O. Box 2144, Zip 36652–2144; tel. 251/435–2400; Kenneth C. Brewington, M.D., Administrator
Web address: www.mobileinfirmary.org

NORTH BALDWIN INFIRMARY (L, 50 beds) 1815 Hand Avenue, Bay Minette, AL Zip 36507–4110, Mailing Address: P.O. Box 1409, Zip 36507–1409; tel. 251/937–5521; Ormand P. Thompson, Administrator
Web address: www.mobileinfirmary.org

THOMAS HOSPITAL (L, 136 beds) 750 Morphy Avenue, Fairhope, AL Zip 36532–1812, Mailing Address: P.O. Box 929, Zip 36533–0929; tel. 251/928–2375; William J. McLaughlin, Administrator
Web address: www.thomashospital.com

Owned, leased, sponsored:	4 hospitals	734 beds
Contract–managed:	0 hospitals	0 beds
Totals:	4 hospitals	734 beds

★1305: INOVA HEALTH SYSTEM (NP)
8110 Gatehouse Road, Suite 200 East, Falls Church, VA Zip 22042–1252; tel. 703/289–2069; J. Knox Singleton, President and Chief Executive Officer
(Centralized Health System)

VIRGINIA: INOVA ALEXANDRIA HOSPITAL (O, 334 beds) 4320 Seminary Road, Alexandria, VA Zip 22304–1535; tel. 703/504–3167; Christine Candio, Chief Executive Officer
Web address: www.inova.org

INOVA FAIR OAKS HOSPITAL (O, 196 beds) 3600 Joseph Siewick Drive, Fairfax, VA Zip 22033–1798; tel. 703/391–3600; John L. Fitzgerald, Chief Executive Officer
Web address: www.inova.org

INOVA FAIRFAX HOSPITAL (O, 926 beds) 3300 Gallows Road, Falls Church, VA Zip 22042–3300; tel. 703/776–4001; Patrick Christiansen, Ph.D., Chief Executive Officer
Web address: www.inova.org

INOVA LOUDOUN HOSPITAL (O, 286 beds) 44045 Riverside Parkway, Leesburg, VA Zip 20176–5101, Mailing Address: P.O. Box 6000, Zip 20177–0600; tel. 703/858–6000; Patrick Walters, Chief Executive Officer
Web address: www.inova.org

INOVA MOUNT VERNON HOSPITAL (O, 237 beds) 2501 Parker's Lane, Alexandria, VA Zip 22306–3209; tel. 703/664–7000; Donald Brideau, M.D., Interim Chief Executive Officer
Web address: www.inova.org

Owned, leased, sponsored:	5 hospitals	1979 beds
Contract–managed:	0 hospitals	0 beds
Totals:	5 hospitals	1979 beds

★0151: INSPIRA HEALTH NETWORK (NP)
165 Bridgeton Pike, Mullica Hill, NJ Zip 08062; tel. 856/641–8000; John A. DiAngelo, President and Chief Executive Officer
(Moderately Centralized Health System)

NEW JERSEY: INSPIRA MEDICAL CENTER–ELMER (O, 88 beds) 501 West Front Street, Elmer, NJ Zip 08318–2101; tel. 856/363–1000; John A. DiAngelo, President and Chief Executive Officer
Web address: www.inspirahealthnetwork.org/?id=5281&sid=1

INSPIRA MEDICAL CENTER–VINELAND (O, 335 beds) 1505 West Sherman Avenue, Vineland, NJ Zip 08360–6912; tel. 856/641–8000; John A. DiAngelo, President and Chief Executive Officer
Web address: www.inspirahealthnetwork.org/?id=5280&sid=1

INSPIRA MEDICAL CENTER–WOODBURY (O, 240 beds) 509 North Broad Street, Woodbury, NJ Zip 08096–1697; tel. 856/845–0100; Eileen K. Cardile, R.N., MS, Executive Vice President, Inspira Health Network and President, Inspira Medical Center–Woodbury
Web address: www.inspirahealthnetwork.org/?id=5282&sid=1

Owned, leased, sponsored:	3 hospitals	663 beds
Contract–managed:	0 hospitals	0 beds
Totals:	3 hospitals	663 beds

0333: INTEGRATED HEALTHCARE (IO)
1301 North Tustin Avenue, Santa Ana, CA Zip 92705–8619; tel. 714/953–3652; Kenneth K. Westbrook, President and Chief Executive Officer
(Independent Hospital System)

CALIFORNIA: CHAPMAN MEDICAL CENTER (O, 100 beds) 2601 East Chapman Avenue, Orange, CA Zip 92869–3296; tel. 714/633–0011; Don Kreitz, Chief Executive Officer
Web address: www.chapmanmedicalcenter.com

COASTAL COMMUNITIES HOSPITAL (O, 178 beds) 2701 South Bristol Street, Santa Ana, CA Zip 92704–6278; tel. 714/754–5454; Luke Tharasri, Chief Executive Officer
Web address: www.coastalcommhospital.com

WESTERN MEDICAL CENTER ANAHEIM (O, 188 beds) 1025 South Anaheim Boulevard, Anaheim, CA Zip 92805–5806; tel. 714/533–6220; Suzanne Richards, R.N., M.P.H., Chief Executive Officer
Web address: www.westernmedanaheim.com

WESTERN MEDICAL CENTER–SANTA ANA (O, 282 beds) 1001 North Tustin Avenue, Santa Ana, CA Zip 92705–3577; tel. 714/835–3555; Daniel Brothman, Chief Executive Officer
Web address: www.westernmedicalcenter.com

Owned, leased, sponsored:	4 hospitals	748 beds
Contract–managed:	0 hospitals	0 beds
Totals:	4 hospitals	748 beds

★0305: INTEGRIS HEALTH (NP)
3366 N.W. Expressway, Suite 800, Oklahoma City, OK Zip 73112–9756; tel. 405/949–6066; Bruce Lawrence, President and Chief Executive Officer
(Moderately Centralized Health System)

OKLAHOMA: INTEGRIS BAPTIST MEDICAL CENTER (O, 525 beds) 3300 N.W. Expressway, Oklahoma City, OK Zip 73112–4418; tel. 405/949–3011; Timothy J. Johnsen, MS, President
Web address: www.integrisok.com

INTEGRIS BAPTIST REGIONAL HEALTH CENTER (O, 84 beds) 200 Second Street S.W., Miami, OK Zip 74354–6830, Mailing Address: P.O. Box 1207, Zip 74355–1207; tel. 918/542–6611; Jordan Cash, President
Web address: www.integris-health.com

INTEGRIS BASS BAPTIST HEALTH CENTER (O, 167 beds) 600 South Monroe Street, Enid, OK Zip 73701–7211, Mailing Address: P.O. Box 3168, Zip 73702–3168; tel. 580/233–2300; Edward Herrman, FACHE, R.N., President
Web address: www.integris-health.com

INTEGRIS CANADIAN VALLEY HOSPITAL (O, 75 beds) 1201 Health Center Parkway, Yukon, OK Zip 73099–6381; tel. 405/717–6800; Rex Van Meter, President
Web address: www.integris-health.com

INTEGRIS GROVE HOSPITAL (O, 58 beds) 1001 East 18th Street, Grove, OK Zip 74344–2907; tel. 918/786–2243; Chris Hammes, FACHE, Interim President
Web address: www.integris-health.com

INTEGRIS HEALTH EDMOND (O, 40 beds) 4801 Integris Parkway, Edmond, OK Zip 73034–8864; tel. 405/657–3000; Avilla Williams, MS, President
Web address: www.integrisok.com/edmond

INTEGRIS SOUTHWEST MEDICAL CENTER (O, 327 beds) 4401 South Western, Oklahoma City, OK Zip 73109–3413; tel. 405/636–7000; James D. Moore, FACHE, President
Web address: www.integris-health.com

LAKESIDE WOMEN'S HOSPITAL (O, 23 beds) 11200 North Portland Avenue, Oklahoma City, OK Zip 73120–5045; tel. 405/936–1500; Kelley Brewer, R.N., MSN, President
Web address: www.lakeside-wh.net

For explanation of codes following names, see page B2.
★ Indicates Type III membership in the American Hospital Association.

Owned, leased, sponsored:	8 hospitals	1299 beds
Contract–managed:	0 hospitals	0 beds
Totals:	8 hospitals	1299 beds

★1815: **INTERMOUNTAIN HEALTHCARE, INC.** (NP)
36 South State Street, 22nd Floor, Salt Lake City, UT
Zip 84111–1453; tel. 801/442–2000; Charles W. Sorenson, Jr.,
M.D., President and Chief Executive Officer
(Moderately Centralized Health System)

IDAHO: CASSIA REGIONAL MEDICAL CENTER (O, 25 beds) 1501 Hiland
Avenue, Burley, ID Zip 83318–2688; tel. 208/678–4444; Rod Barton,
Administrator
Web address: www.cassiaregional.org

UTAH: ALTA VIEW HOSPITAL (O, 69 beds) 9660 South 1300 East, Sandy, UT
Zip 84094–3793; tel. 801/501–2600; Bryan L. Johnson, Administrator
Web address: www.intermountainhealthcare.org

AMERICAN FORK HOSPITAL (O, 90 beds) 170 North 1100 East, American
Fork, UT Zip 84003–2096; tel. 801/855–3300; Michael R. Olson,
Administrator
Web address: www.intermountainhealthcare.org

BEAR RIVER VALLEY HOSPITAL (O, 14 beds) 905 North 1000 West,
Tremonton, UT Zip 84337–2497; tel. 435/207–4500; Eric Packer,
Administrator
Web address: www.intermountainhealthcare.org/hospitals/bearriver

DELTA COMMUNITY MEDICAL CENTER (O, 18 beds) 126 South White Sage
Avenue, Delta, UT Zip 84624–8937; tel. 435/864–5591; Lenny Lyons,
Administrator
Web address: www.ihc.com

DIXIE REGIONAL MEDICAL CENTER (O, 261 beds) 1380 East Medical Center
Drive, Saint George, UT Zip 84790–2123; tel. 435/251–1000; Terri Kane,
Chief Executive Officer
Web address: www.intermountainhealthcare.org

FILLMORE COMMUNITY MEDICAL CENTER (O, 19 beds) 674 South Highway
99, Fillmore, UT Zip 84631–5013; tel. 435/743–5591; Lenny Lyons,
Administrator
Web address: www.ihc.com

GARFIELD MEMORIAL HOSPITAL AND CLINICS (C, 41 beds) 200 North 400
East, Panguitch, UT Zip 84759, Mailing Address: P.O. Box 389,
Zip 84759–0389; tel. 435/676–8811; Alberto Vasquez, Administrator
Web address: www.ihc.com/hospitals/garfield

HEBER VALLEY MEDICAL CENTER (O, 19 beds) 1485 South Highway 40,
Heber City, UT Zip 84032–3522; tel. 435/654–2500; Shawn Morrow,
Administrator
Web address: www.intermountainhealthcare.org

INTERMOUNTAIN MEDICAL CENTER (O, 464 beds) 5121 South Cottonwood
Street, Murray, UT Zip 84107–5701; tel. 801/507–7000; David Grauer,
Chief Executive Officer and Administrator
Web address: www.intermountainhealthcare.org

LDS HOSPITAL (O, 253 beds) Eighth Avenue and C Street, Salt Lake City, UT
Zip 84143–0001; tel. 801/408–1100; Jim Sheets, Chief Executive Officer
and Administrator
Web address: www.intermountainhealthcare.org

LOGAN REGIONAL HOSPITAL (O, 135 beds) 1400 North 500 East, Logan, UT
Zip 84341–2455; tel. 435/716–1000; Michael A. Clark, Administrator and
Chief Executive Officer
Web address: www.loganregionalhospital.org

MCKAY–DEE HOSPITAL CENTER (O, 294 beds) 4401 Harrison Boulevard,
Ogden, UT Zip 84403–3195; tel. 801/387–2800; Timothy T. Pehrson, Chief
Executive Officer
Web address: www.mckay–dee.org

OREM COMMUNITY HOSPITAL (O, 18 beds) 331 North 400 West, Orem, UT
Zip 84057–1999; tel. 801/224–4080; Steven Badger, R.N., FACHE,
Administrator
Web address: www.intermountainhealthcare.org

PARK CITY MEDICAL CENTER (O, 26 beds) 900 Round Valley Drive, Park City,
UT Zip 84060–7552; tel. 435/658–7000; Robert W. Allen, FACHE, Chief
Executive Officer
Web address: www.intermountainhealthcare.org

PRIMARY CHILDREN'S MEDICAL CENTER (O, 289 beds) 100 North Mario
Capecchi Drive, Salt Lake City, UT Zip 84113–1100; tel. 801/662–1000;
Katy Welkie, R.N., Chief Executive Officer
Web address: www.intermountainhealthcare.org

RIVERTON HOSPITAL (O, 88 beds) 3741 West 12600 South, Riverton, UT
Zip 84065–7215; tel. 801/285–4000; Blair Kent, Administrator
Web address: www.intermountainhealthcare.org/

SANPETE VALLEY HOSPITAL (O, 15 beds) 1100 South Medical Drive, Mount
Pleasant, UT Zip 84647–2222; tel. 435/462–2441; Aaron Wood,
Administrator
Web address: www.intermountainhealthcare.com

SEVIER VALLEY MEDICAL CENTER (O, 27 beds) 1000 North Main Street,
Richfield, UT Zip 84701–1857; tel. 435/893–4100; Gary E. Beck,
Administrator
Web address: www.sevierhospital.org

THE ORTHOPEDIC SPECIALTY HOSPITAL (O, 40 beds) 5848 South 300 East,
Murray, UT Zip 84107–6121; tel. 801/314–4100; Barbara Ohm,
Administrator
Web address: www.intermountainhealthcare.org

UTAH VALLEY REGIONAL MEDICAL CENTER (O, 373 beds) 1034 North 500
West, Provo, UT Zip 84604–3337; tel. 801/357–7850; Steve Smoot,
Administrator
Web address: www.utahvalleyregional.org

VALLEY VIEW MEDICAL CENTER (O, 48 beds) 1303 North Main Street, Cedar
City, UT Zip 84721–9746; tel. 435/868–5000; Jason Wilson, Administrator
Web address: www.ihc.com

Owned, leased, sponsored:	21 hospitals	2585 beds
Contract–managed:	1 hospital	41 beds
Totals:	22 hospitals	2626 beds

★0902: **IOWA SPECIALTY HOSPITALS** (NP)
1316 South Main Street, Clarion, IA Zip 50525–2019;
tel. 515/532–2811; Steven J. Simonin, Chief Executive Officer
(Independent Hospital System)

IOWA: IOWA SPECIALTY HOSPITAL–BELMOND (C, 22 beds) 403 First Street
S.E., Belmond, IA Zip 50421–1201; tel. 641/444–3223; Amy McDaniel,
Administrator and Chief Executive Officer
Web address: www.iowaspecialtyhospital.com

IOWA SPECIALTY HOSPITAL–CLARION (C, 25 beds) 1316 South Main Street,
Clarion, IA Zip 50525–2019; tel. 515/532–2811; Steven J. Simonin, Chief
Executive Officer
Web address: www.iowaspecialtyhospital.com

Owned, leased, sponsored:	0 hospitals	0 beds
Contract–managed:	2 hospitals	47 beds
Totals:	2 hospitals	47 beds

★7775: **JEFFERSON HEALTH SYSTEM** (NP)
259 Radnor–Chester Road, Suite 290, Radnor, PA Zip 19087–5288;
tel. 610/225–6200; Kirk E. Gorman, Interim President and Chief
Executive Officer
(Centralized Health System)

PENNSYLVANIA: BRYN MAWR HOSPITAL (O, 319 beds) 130 South Bryn
Mawr Avenue, Bryn Mawr, PA Zip 19010–3160; tel. 484/337–3000;
Andrea F. Gilbert, FACHE, President
Web address: www.brynmawrhospital.org

BRYN MAWR REHABILITATION HOSPITAL (O, 148 beds) 414 Paoli Pike,
Malvern, PA Zip 19355–3300, Mailing Address: P.O. Box 3007,
Zip 19355–0707; tel. 484/596–5400; Donna Phillips, President
Web address: www.brynmawrrehab.org

LANKENAU MEDICAL CENTER (O, 339 beds) 100 Lancaster Avenue West,
Wynnewood, PA Zip 19096–3411; tel. 484/476–2000; Phillip D. Robinson,
President
Web address: www.mainlinehealth.org

MAGEE REHABILITATION HOSPITAL (O, 96 beds) 1513 Race Street,
Philadelphia, PA Zip 19102–1177; tel. 215/587–3000; Jack A. Carroll, Ph.D.,
President and Chief Executive Officer
Web address: www.mageerehab.org

Section B

For explanation of codes following names, see page B2.
★ Indicates Type III membership in the American Hospital Association.

PAOLI HOSPITAL (O, 231 beds) 255 West Lancaster Avenue, Paoli, PA Zip 19301–1763; tel. 484/565–1000; James Paradis, President
Web address: www.mainlinehealth.org

RIDDLE HOSPITAL (O, 204 beds) 1068 West Baltimore Pike, Media, PA Zip 19063–5177; tel. 484/227–9400; Gary L. Perecko, President
Web address: www.riddlehospital.org

Owned, leased, sponsored:	6 hospitals	1337 beds
Contract–managed:	0 hospitals	0 beds
Totals:	6 hospitals	1337 beds

★8855: **JFK HEALTH SYSTEM** (NP)
80 James Street, 2nd Floor, Edison, NJ Zip 08820–3938; tel. 732/632–1503; Raymond F. Fredericks, President and Chief Executive Officer

NEW JERSEY: JFK JOHNSON REHABILITATION INSTITUTE (O, 90 beds) 65 James Street, Edison, NJ Zip 08820–3947; tel. 732/321–7050; Anthony Cuzzola, Vice President Rehabilitation Services
Web address: www.njrehab.org

JFK MEDICAL CENTER (O, 441 beds) 65 James Street, Edison, NJ Zip 08820–3947; tel. 732/321–7000; Raymond F. Fredericks, President and CEO
Web address: www.jfkmc.org

Owned, leased, sponsored:	2 hospitals	531 beds
Contract–managed:	0 hospitals	0 beds
Totals:	2 hospitals	531 beds

★0218: **JOHN C. LINCOLN HEALTH NETWORK** (NP)
2500 West Utopia Road, Suite 100, Phoenix, AZ Zip 85027–4172; tel. 623/434–6230; Rhonda Forsyth, President and Chief Executive Officer
(Independent Hospital System)

ARIZONA: JOHN C. LINCOLN DEER VALLEY HOSPITAL (O, 204 beds) 19829 North 27th Avenue, Phoenix, AZ Zip 85027–4002; tel. 623/879–6100; John L. Harrington, Jr., FACHE, Chief Executive Officer
Web address: www.jcl.com

JOHN C. LINCOLN NORTH MOUNTAIN HOSPITAL (O, 262 beds) 250 East Dunlap Avenue, Phoenix, AZ Zip 85020–2825; tel. 602/943–2381; Margaret Elizabeth Griffin, Chief Executive Officer
Web address: www.jcl.com

Owned, leased, sponsored:	2 hospitals	466 beds
Contract–managed:	0 hospitals	0 beds
Totals:	2 hospitals	466 beds

★0324: **JOHN MUIR HEALTH** (NP)
1400 Treat Boulevard, Walnut Creek, CA Zip 94597–2142; tel. 925/941–2100; Calvin K. Knight, President and Chief Executive Officer
(Moderately Centralized Health System)

CALIFORNIA: JOHN MUIR BEHAVIORAL HEALTH CENTER (O, 73 beds) 2740 Grant Street, Concord, CA Zip 94520–2265; tel. 925/674–4100; Cindy Bolter, Chief Nursing and Operations Officer
Web address: www.johnmuirhealth.com

JOHN MUIR MEDICAL CENTER, CONCORD (O, 183 beds) 2540 East Street, Concord, CA Zip 94520–1906; tel. 925/682–8200; Michael S. Thomas, President and Chief Administrative Officer
Web address: www.johnmuirhealth.com

JOHN MUIR MEDICAL CENTER, WALNUT CREEK (O, 367 beds) 1601 Ygnacio Valley Road, Walnut Creek, CA Zip 94598–3194; tel. 925/939–3000; Jane Willemsen, Chief Administrative Officer
Web address: www.jmmdhs.com/index.php/jmmdhs_jmmc.html

Owned, leased, sponsored:	3 hospitals	623 beds
Contract–managed:	0 hospitals	0 beds
Totals:	3 hospitals	623 beds

★1015: **JOHNS HOPKINS HEALTH SYSTEM** (NP)
733 North Broadway, BRB 104, Baltimore, MD Zip 21205–1832; tel. 410/955–5000; Ronald R. Peterson, President
(Centralized Health System)

DISTRICT OF COLUMBIA: SIBLEY MEMORIAL HOSPITAL (O, 246 beds) 5255 Loughboro Road N.W., Washington, DC Zip 20016–2633; tel. 202/537–4000; Richard O. Davis, Ph.D., President
Web address: www.sibley.org

FLORIDA: ALL CHILDREN'S HOSPITAL JOHNS HOPKINS MEDICINE (O, 259 beds) 501 6th Avenue South, Saint Petersburg, FL Zip 33701–4634; tel. 727/898–7451; Jonathan M. Ellen, M.D., President
Web address: www.allkids.org

MARYLAND: HOWARD COUNTY GENERAL HOSPITAL (O, 267 beds) 5755 Cedar Lane, Columbia, MD Zip 21044–2999; tel. 410/740–7890; Steven C. Snelgrove, President
Web address: www.hcgh.org

JOHNS HOPKINS BAYVIEW MEDICAL CENTER (O, 504 beds) 4940 Eastern Avenue, Baltimore, MD Zip 21224–2780; tel. 410/550–0100; Richard G. Bennett, M.D., President
Web address: www.hopkinsbayview.org

JOHNS HOPKINS HOSPITAL (O, 986 beds) 600 North Wolfe Street, Baltimore, MD Zip 21287–2182; tel. 410/955–5000; Ronald R. Peterson, President
Web address: www.hopkinsmedicine.org

SUBURBAN HOSPITAL (O, 233 beds) 8600 Old Georgetown Road, Bethesda, MD Zip 20814–1497; tel. 301/896–3100; Gene E. Green, M.D., President
Web address: www.suburbanhospital.org

Owned, leased, sponsored:	6 hospitals	2495 beds
Contract–managed:	0 hospitals	0 beds
Totals:	6 hospitals	2495 beds

★2105: **KAISER FOUNDATION HOSPITALS** (NP)
One Kaiser Plaza, Oakland, CA Zip 94612–3600; tel. 510/271–5910; Bernard J. Tyson, Chairman and Chief Executive Officer
(Decentralized Health System)

CALIFORNIA: KAISER PERMANENTE ANTIOCH MEDICAL CENTER (O, 150 beds) 4501 Sand Creek Road, Antioch, CA Zip 94531–8687; tel. 925/813–6500; Colleen McKeown, Senior Vice President
Web address: www.https://health.kaiserpermanente.org/wps/portal/facility/100382

KAISER PERMANENTE BALDWIN PARK MEDICAL CENTER (O, 254 beds) 1011 Baldwin Park Boulevard, Baldwin Park, CA Zip 91706–5806; tel. 626/851–1011; Margaret H. Pierce, Executive Director
Web address: www.kp.org

KAISER PERMANENTE DOWNEY MEDICAL CENTER (O, 342 beds) 9333 Imperial Highway, Downey, CA Zip 90242–2812; tel. 562/657–9000; James Branchick, R.N., MS, Executive Director
Web address: www.kaiserpermanente.org

KAISER PERMANENTE FONTANA MEDICAL CENTER (O, 334 beds) 9961 Sierra Avenue, Fontana, CA Zip 92335–6794; tel. 909/427–5000; Greg Christian, Executive Director
Web address: www.kaiserpermanente.org

KAISER PERMANENTE FRESNO MEDICAL CENTER (O, 169 beds) 7300 North Fresno Street, Fresno, CA Zip 93720–2942; tel. 559/448–4500; Jeffrey A. Collins, M.D., Senior Vice President and Area Manager
Web address: www.kaiserpermanente.org

KAISER PERMANENTE HAYWARD MEDICAL CENTER (O, 208 beds) 27400 Hesperian Boulevard, Hayward, CA Zip 94545–4299; tel. 510/784–4000; Thomas S. Hanenburg, Senior Vice President
Web address: www.kaiserpermanente.org

KAISER PERMANENTE LOS ANGELES MEDICAL CENTER (O, 464 beds) 4867 Sunset Boulevard, Los Angeles, CA Zip 90027–5961; tel. 323/783–4011; Mark E. Costa, Executive Director
Web address: www.kaiserpermanente.org

KAISER PERMANENTE MANTECA MEDICAL CENTER (O, 239 beds) 1777 West Yosemite Avenue, Manteca, CA Zip 95337–5187; tel. 209/825–3500; Corwin N. Harper, Senior Vice President and Area Manager
Web address: www.kaiserpermanente.org

For explanation of codes following names, see page B2.
★ Indicates Type III membership in the American Hospital Association.

Section B

KAISER PERMANENTE MORENO VALLEY MEDICAL CENTER (O, 71 beds) 27300 Iris Avenue, Moreno Valley, CA Zip 92555–4800; tel. 951/243–0811; Corey A. Seale, Administrator

KAISER PERMANENTE OAKLAND MEDICAL CENTER (O, 267 beds) 3600 Broadway, Oakland, CA Zip 94611–5693; tel. 510/752–1000; Odette Bolano, R.N., Senior Vice President and Area Manager
Web address: www.kaiserpermanente.org

KAISER PERMANENTE ONTARIO MEDICAL CENTER (O, 176 beds) 2295 South Vineyard Avenue, Ontario, CA Zip 91761–7925; tel. 909/724–5000; Greg Christian, Executive Director
Web address: www.kp.org

KAISER PERMANENTE ORANGE COUNTY ANAHEIM MEDICAL CENTER (O, 436 beds) 3430 East La Palma Avenue, Anaheim, CA Zip 92806–2020; tel. 714/644–2000; Julie K. Miller-Phipps, Senior Vice President and Executive Director
Web address: www.kp.org

KAISER PERMANENTE PANORAMA CITY MEDICAL CENTER (O, 194 beds) 13652 Cantara Street, Panorama City, CA Zip 91402–5497; tel. 818/375–2000; Dennis C. Benton, Executive Director
Web address: www.kaiserpermanente.org

KAISER PERMANENTE REDWOOD CITY MEDICAL CENTER (O, 213 beds) 1150 Veterans Boulevard, Redwood City, CA Zip 94063–2087; tel. 650/299–2000; Frank T. Beirne, FACHE, Senior Vice President and Area Manager
Web address: www.kaiserpermanente.org

KAISER PERMANENTE RIVERSIDE MEDICAL CENTER (O, 226 beds) 10800 Magnolia Avenue, Riverside, CA Zip 92505–3000; tel. 951/353–2000; Vita M. Willett, Administrator and Executive Director
Web address: www.kaiserpermanente.org

KAISER PERMANENTE ROSEVILLE MEDICAL CENTER (O, 340 beds) 1600 Eureka Road, Roseville, CA Zip 95661–3027; tel. 916/784–4000; Edward S. Glavis, Senior Vice President and Area Manager
Web address: www.kp.org

KAISER PERMANENTE SACRAMENTO MEDICAL CENTER (O, 287 beds) 2025 Morse Avenue, Sacramento, CA Zip 95825–2100; tel. 916/973–5000; Ronald Groepper, Senior Vice President and Area Manager
Web address: www.kp.org

KAISER PERMANENTE SAN DIEGO MEDICAL CENTER (O, 414 beds) 4647 Zion Avenue, San Diego, CA Zip 92120–2507; tel. 619/528–5000; E. Jane Finley, Senior Vice President and Executive Director
Web address: www.kaiserpermanente.org

KAISER PERMANENTE SAN FRANCISCO MEDICAL CENTER (O, 215 beds) 2425 Geary Boulevard, San Francisco, CA Zip 94115–3358; tel. 415/833–2000; Christine Robisch, Senior Vice President and Area Manager
Web address: www.kaiserpermanente.org

KAISER PERMANENTE SAN JOSE MEDICAL CENTER (O, 217 beds) 250 Hospital Parkway, San Jose, CA Zip 95119–1199; tel. 408/972–7000; Irene Chavez, Senior Vice President and Area Manager
Web address: www.kaiserpermanente.org

KAISER PERMANENTE SAN RAFAEL MEDICAL CENTER (O, 116 beds) 99 Montecillo Road, San Rafael, CA Zip 94903–3397; tel. 415/444–2000; Judy Coffey, Senior Vice President and Area Manager
Web address: www.kaiserpermanente.org

KAISER PERMANENTE SANTA CLARA MEDICAL CENTER (O, 327 beds) 700 Lawrence Expressway, Santa Clara, CA Zip 95051–5173; tel. 408/851–1000; Christopher L. Boyd, Senior Vice President and Area Manager
Web address: www.kaiserpermanente.org

KAISER PERMANENTE SANTA ROSA MEDICAL CENTER (O, 117 beds) 401 Bicentennial Way, Santa Rosa, CA Zip 95403–2192; tel. 707/571–4000; Judy Coffey, Senior Vice President and Area Manager
Web address: www.kaiserpermanente.org

KAISER PERMANENTE SOUTH BAY MEDICAL CENTER (O, 229 beds) 25825 Vermont Avenue, Harbor City, CA Zip 90710–3599; tel. 310/325–5111; Lesley A. Wille, Administrator and Executive Director

KAISER PERMANENTE SOUTH SACRAMENTO MEDICAL CENTER (O, 181 beds) 6600 Bruceville Road, Sacramento, CA Zip 95823–4691; tel. 916/688–2430; Patricia M. Rodriguez, Senior Vice President and Area Manager
Web address: www.kp.org

KAISER PERMANENTE SOUTH SAN FRANCISCO (O, 120 beds) 1200 El Camino Real, South San Francisco, CA Zip 94080–3208; tel. 650/742–2000; Frank T. Beirne, FACHE, Senior Vice President and Area Manager
Web address: www.kaiserpermanente.org

KAISER PERMANENTE VACAVILLE MEDICAL CENTER (O, 140 beds) 1 Quality Drive, Vacaville, CA Zip 95688–9494; tel. 707/624–4000; Max Villalobos, Senior Vice President
Web address: www.kp.org

KAISER PERMANENTE VALLEJO MEDICAL CENTER (O, 248 beds) 975 Sereno Drive, Vallejo, CA Zip 94589–2441; tel. 707/651–1000; Corwin N. Harper, Senior Vice President and Area Manager
Web address: www.kaiserpermanente.org

KAISER PERMANENTE WALNUT CREEK MEDICAL CENTER (O, 233 beds) 1425 South Main Street, Walnut Creek, CA Zip 94596–5300; tel. 925/295–4000; Colleen McKeown, Senior Vice President and Area Manager
Web address: www.kaiserpermanente.org

KAISER PERMANENTE WEST LOS ANGELES MEDICAL CENTER (O, 199 beds) 6041 Cadillac Avenue, Los Angeles, CA Zip 90034–1700; tel. 323/857–2201; Georgina R. Garcia, R.N., Executive Director
Web address: www.kaiserpermanente.org

KAISER PERMANENTE WOODLAND HILLS MEDICAL CENTER (O, 175 beds) 5601 DeSoto Avenue, Woodland Hills, CA Zip 91367–6798; tel. 818/719–2000; Michael C. Carter, Executive Director
Web address: www.kaiserpermanente.org

HAWAII: KAISER PERMANENTE MEDICAL CENTER (O, 235 beds) 3288 Moanalua Road, Honolulu, HI Zip 96819–1469; tel. 808/432–0000; Leanne M. Hunstock, R.N., Interim Administrator
Web address: www.kaiserpermanente.org

OREGON: KAISER FOUNDATION HOSPITAL WESTSIDE MEDICAL CENTER (O, 122 beds) 2875 N.W. Stucki Avenue, Hillsboro, OR Zip 97124–5806; tel. 971/310–1000; Susan Mullaney, Chief Executive Officer

KAISER PERMANENTE SUNNYSIDE MEDICAL CENTER (O, 283 beds) 10180 S.E. Sunnyside Road, Clackamas, OR Zip 97015–8970; tel. 503/652–2880; Gary Petersen, Administrator
Web address: www.kaiserpermanente.org

Owned, leased, sponsored:	34 hospitals	7941 beds
Contract–managed:	0 hospitals	0 beds
Totals:	34 hospitals	7941 beds

★0258: KETTERING HEALTH NETWORK (NP)
3965 Southern Boulevard, Dayton, OH Zip 45429–1229; tel. 937/395–8150; Fred M. Manchur, Chief Executive Officer
(Centralized Health System)

OHIO: FORT HAMILTON HOSPITAL (O, 166 beds) 630 Eaton Avenue, Hamilton, OH Zip 45013–2770; tel. 513/867–2000; Mark T. Smith, JD, CPA, President
Web address: www.khnetwork.org/fort_hamilton

GRANDVIEW MEDICAL CENTER (O, 280 beds) 405 Grand Avenue, Dayton, OH Zip 45405–4796; tel. 937/226–3200; Russell Wetherell, President
Web address: www.ketteringhealth.org/grandview/

GREENE MEMORIAL HOSPITAL (O, 52 beds) 1141 North Monroe Drive, Xenia, OH Zip 45385–1600; tel. 937/352–2000; Terry M. Burns, President
Web address: www.greenehealth.org

KETTERING MEDICAL CENTER (O, 390 beds) 3535 Southern Boulevard, Kettering, OH Zip 45429–1221; tel. 937/298–4331; Roy G. Chew, Ph.D., President
Web address: www.kmcnetwork.org

SOIN MEDICAL CENTER (O, 85 beds) 3535 Pentagon Boulevard, Beavercreek, OH Zip 45431–1705; tel. 937/702–4000; Terry M. Burns, President
Web address: www.khnetwork.org/soin

For explanation of codes following names, see page B2.
★ Indicates Type III membership in the American Hospital Association.

SYCAMORE MEDICAL CENTER (O, 171 beds) 4000 Miamisburg–Centerville Road, Miamisburg, OH Zip 45342–7615; tel. 937/866–0551; Walter Sackett, President
Web address: www.khnetwork.org

Owned, leased, sponsored:	6 hospitals	1144 beds
Contract–managed:	0 hospitals	0 beds
Totals:	6 hospitals	1144 beds

★**0026: KINDRED HEALTHCARE** (IO)
680 South Fourth Street, Louisville, KY Zip 40202–2412; tel. 502/596–7300; Paul J. Diaz, President and Chief Executive Officer
(Independent Hospital System)

ARIZONA: KINDRED HOSPITAL ARIZONA–PHOENIX (O, 58 beds) 40 East Indianola Avenue, Phoenix, AZ Zip 85012–2059; tel. 602/280–7000; Heidi Miller, Chief Executive Officer
Web address: www.khphoenix.com/

KINDRED HOSPITAL–TUCSON (O, 51 beds) 355 North Wilmot Road, Tucson, AZ Zip 85711–2601; tel. 520/584–4500; Marc Lemon, Chief Executive Officer
Web address: www.khtucson.com

CALIFORNIA: KINDRED HOSPITAL RANCHO (O, 55 beds) 10841 White Oak Avenue, Rancho Cucamonga, CA Zip 91730–3811; tel. 909/581–6400; Jody Knox, Administrator
Web address: www.khrancho.com

KINDRED HOSPITAL RIVERSIDE (O, 40 beds) 2224 Medical Center Drive, Perris, CA Zip 92571–2638; tel. 951/436–3535; James Linhares, Chief Executive Officer
Web address: www.khriverside.com

KINDRED HOSPITAL SOUTH BAY (O, 84 beds) 1246 West 155th Street, Gardena, CA Zip 90247–4062; tel. 310/323–5330; Lourene Money, R.N., Interim Chief Executive Officer
Web address: www.khsouthbay.com/

KINDRED HOSPITAL–BALDWIN PARK (C, 91 beds) 14148 Francisquito Avenue, Baldwin Park, CA Zip 91706–6120; tel. 626/388–2700; Swenda Moreh, Chief Executive Officer
Web address: www.khbaldwinpark.com

KINDRED HOSPITAL–BREA (O, 48 beds) 875 North Brea Boulevard, Brea, CA Zip 92821–2699; tel. 714/529–6842; Diane Zeoli, Chief Executive Officer
Web address: www.kindredhospitalbrea.com/

KINDRED HOSPITAL–LA MIRADA (O, 216 beds) 14900 East Imperial Highway, La Mirada, CA Zip 90638–2172; tel. 562/944–1900; April Myers, Administrator
Web address: www.kindredlamirada.com/

KINDRED HOSPITAL–LOS ANGELES (O, 81 beds) 5525 West Slauson Avenue, Los Angeles, CA Zip 90056–1067; tel. 310/642–0325; Phillip R. Wolfe, Administrator
Web address: www.kindredhospitalla.com/

KINDRED HOSPITAL–ONTARIO (O, 91 beds) 550 North Monterey Avenue, Ontario, CA Zip 91764–3399; tel. 909/391–0333; Robin Rapp, MS, R.N., Chief Executive Officer
Web address: www.khontario.com/

KINDRED HOSPITAL–SAN DIEGO (O, 70 beds) 1940 El Cajon Boulevard, San Diego, CA Zip 92104–1096; tel. 619/543–4500; Cathryn Branch, R.N., Chief Executive Officer
Web address: www.kindredsandiego.com

KINDRED HOSPITAL–SAN FRANCISCO BAY AREA (O, 99 beds) 2800 Benedict Drive, San Leandro, CA Zip 94577–6840; tel. 510/357–8300; Ed Kelly, Chief Executive Officer
Web address: www.kindredhospitalsfba.com

KINDRED HOSPITAL–WESTMINSTER (O, 109 beds) 200 Hospital Circle, Westminster, CA Zip 92683–3910; tel. 714/893–4541; Brooke Saunders, Administrator
Web address: www.khwestminster.com/

COLORADO: KINDRED HOSPITAL–AURORA (O, 37 beds) 700 Potomac Street 2nd Floor, Aurora, CO Zip 80011–6844; tel. 720/857–8333; David Kowalski, Chief Executive Officer
Web address: www.khaurora.com

KINDRED HOSPITAL–DENVER (O, 68 beds) 1920 High Street, Denver, CO Zip 80218–1213; tel. 303/320–5871; Harvey Ross, Chief Executive Officer
Web address: www.kh–denver.com

FLORIDA: KINDRED HOSPITAL BAY AREA–TAMPA (O, 73 beds) 4555 South Manhattan Avenue, Tampa, FL Zip 33611–2397; tel. 813/839–6341; Sandra Morgan, Chief Executive Officer
Web address: www.khtampa.com/

KINDRED HOSPITAL CENTRAL TAMPA (O, 102 beds) 4801 North Howard Avenue, Tampa, FL Zip 33603–1411; tel. 813/874–7575; Ralph Seiner, Chief Executive Officer
Web address: www.kindredcentraltampa.com/

KINDRED HOSPITAL MELBOURNE (O, 60 beds) 765 West Nasa Boulevard, Melbourne, FL Zip 32901–1815; tel. 321/733–5725; Joyce Baldrica, Chief Executive Officer
Web address: www.khmelbourne.com

KINDRED HOSPITAL NORTH FLORIDA (O, 80 beds) 801 Oak Street, Green Cove Springs, FL Zip 32043–4317; tel. 904/284–9230; Susan Drago, Chief Executive Officer
Web address: www.khnorthflorida.com

KINDRED HOSPITAL OCALA (O, 31 beds) 1500 S.W. 1st Avenue, Ocala, FL Zip 34471–6504; tel. 352/369–0513; Merlene Bhoorasingh, Administrator
Web address: www.kindredocala.com/

KINDRED HOSPITAL SOUTH FLORIDA–FORT LAUDERDALE (O, 123 beds) 1516 East Las Olas Boulevard, Fort Lauderdale, FL Zip 33301–2399; tel. 954/764–8900; Theodore L. Welding, Administrator
Web address: www.khfortlauderdale.com/

KINDRED HOSPITAL THE PALM BEACHES (O, 70 beds) 5555 West Blue Heron Boulevard, Riviera Beach, FL Zip 33418–7813; tel. 561/840–0754; Timothy Page, Chief Executive Officer
Web address: www.khthepalmbeaches.com/

GEORGIA: KINDRED HOSPITAL ROME (O, 45 beds) 304 Turner McCall Boulevard, Rome, GA Zip 30165–5621; tel. 706/378–6800; Chad Lovett, Chief Executive Officer
Web address: www.kindredrome.com

KINDRED HOSPITAL–ATLANTA (O, 70 beds) 705 Juniper Street N.E., Atlanta, GA Zip 30308–1307; tel. 404/873–2871; Michael Schmitt, M.D., Chief Executive Officer
Web address: www.kindredatlanta.com/

ILLINOIS: KINDRED CHICAGO–CENTRAL HOSPITAL (O, 187 beds) 4058 West Melrose Street, Chicago, IL Zip 60641–4797; tel. 773/736–7000; Bruce Carey, Chief Executive Officer
Web address: www.khchicagocentral.com

KINDRED HOSPITAL CHICAGO–NORTHLAKE (O, 94 beds) 365 East North Avenue, Northlake, IL Zip 60164–2628; tel. 708/345–8100; Beverly Foster, Chief Executive Officer
Web address: www.kindrednorthlake.com/

KINDRED HOSPITAL PEORIA (O, 50 beds) 500 West Romeo B. Garrett Avenue, Peoria, IL Zip 61605–2301; tel. 309/680–1500; Ted Paarlberg, Chief Executive Officer
Web address: www.khpeoria.com/

KINDRED HOSPITAL–SYCAMORE (O, 69 beds) 225 Edward Street, Sycamore, IL Zip 60178–2137; tel. 815/895–2144; Cindy Smith, Chief Executive Officer
Web address: www.kindredhospitalsyc.com/

INDIANA: KINDRED HOSPITAL INDIANAPOLIS SOUTH (O, 60 beds) 607 Greenwood Springs Drive, Greenwood, IN Zip 46143–6377; tel. 317/888–8155; Matthew Keppler, Market Chief Executive Officer
Web address: www.khindysouth.com/

KINDRED HOSPITAL NORTHWEST INDIANA (O, 70 beds) 5454 Hohman Avenue, 5th Floor, Hammond, IN Zip 46320–1931; tel. 219/937–9900; Frank A. Solare, Chief Executive Officer
Web address: www.khnwindiana.com

KINDRED HOSPITAL OF NORTHERN INDIANA (O, 32 beds) 215 West Fourth Street, Suite 200, Mishawaka, IN Zip 46544–1917; tel. 574/252–2000; Lori Skora, Chief Executive Officer
Web address: www.khnorthernindiana.com

KINDRED HOSPITAL–INDIANAPOLIS (O, 59 beds) 1700 West 10th Street, Indianapolis, IN Zip 46222–3802; tel. 317/636–4400; Kristy Walden, R.N., Chief Executive Officer
Web address: www.kindredhospitalindy.com/

For explanation of codes following names, see page B2.
★ Indicates Type III membership in the American Hospital Association.

KENTUCKY: KINDRED HOSPITAL–LOUISVILLE (O, 197 beds) 1313 Saint Anthony Place, Louisville, KY Zip 40204–1740; tel. 502/587–7001; Wayne Blanchard, Market Chief Executive Officer
Web address: www.kindredlouisville.com/

LOUISIANA: KINDRED HOSPITAL–NEW ORLEANS (O, 75 beds) 3601 Coliseum Street, New Orleans, LA Zip 70115–3606; tel. 504/899–1555; Jan Turk, Chief Executive Officer
Web address: www.kindredhospitalnola.com

MASSACHUSETTS: KINDRED HOSPITAL BOSTON–NORTH SHORE (O, 50 beds) 15 King Street, Peabody, MA Zip 01960–4379; tel. 978/531–2900; Yolande Wilson, Chief Executive Officer
Web address: www.kindredbns.com

KINDRED HOSPITAL NORTHEAST–STOUGHTON (O, 170 beds) 909 Sumner Street, 1st Floor, Stoughton, MA Zip 02072–3396; tel. 781/297–8200; Robert A. Gundersen, Market Chief Executive Officer
Web address: www.khstoughton.com

KINDRED HOSPITAL–BOSTON (O, 59 beds) 1515 Commonwealth Avenue, Brighton, MA Zip 02135–3617; tel. 617/254–1100; Susan Downey, R.N., MS, Chief Executive Officer
Web address: www.kindredbos.com/

MICHIGAN: KINDRED HOSPITAL DETROIT (O, 77 beds) 4777 East Outer Drive, Detroit, MI Zip 48234–3241; tel. 313/369–5800; Reginald Lee, Chief Executive Officer
Web address: www.kindreddetroit.com/

MISSOURI: KINDRED HOSPITAL KANSAS CITY (O, 130 beds) 8701 Troost Avenue, Kansas City, MO Zip 64131–2767; tel. 816/995–2000; Alexander Gill, Chief Executive Officer
Web address: www.kindredhospitalkc.com

KINDRED HOSPITAL NORTHLAND (O, 35 beds) 500 Northwest 68th Street, Kansas City, MO Zip 64118–2455; tel. 816/420–6300; H. Frank Schneider, Chief Executive Officer
Web address: www.khnorthland.com

KINDRED HOSPITAL–ST. LOUIS (O, 98 beds) 4930 Lindell Boulevard, Saint Louis, MO Zip 63108–1510; tel. 314/361–8700; Stephanie Bridges, Chief Executive Officer
Web address: www.kindredstlouis.com/

KINDRED HOSPITAL–ST. LOUIS AT MERCY (O, 54 beds) 615 South New Ballas Road, 7th Floor, Saint Louis, MO Zip 63141–8221; tel. 314/567–4326; George Einhorn, Interim Chief Executive Officer
Web address: www.kindredstlouismercy.com

ST. LUKE'S REHABILITATION HOSPITAL (O, 35 beds) 14709 Olive Boulevard, Chesterfield, MO Zip 63017–2221; tel. 314/317–5700; Elizabeth A. Cooley, R.N., Chief Executive Officer
Web address: www.khrehabstluke.com

NEVADA: KINDRED HOSPITAL LAS VEGAS–SAHARA (O, 238 beds) 5110 West Sahara Avenue, Las Vegas, NV Zip 89146–3406; tel. 702/871–1418; Elaine Glaser, Chief Executive Officer
Web address: www.kindredhospitallvs.com/

NEW JERSEY: KINDRED HOSPITAL–NEW JERSEY MORRIS COUNTY (O, 117 beds) 400 West Blackwell Street, Dover, NJ Zip 07801–2525; tel. 973/537–3818; Barbara Callaghan, Chief Executive Officer
Web address: www.khmorriscounty.com/

NEW MEXICO: KINDRED HOSPITAL–ALBUQUERQUE (O, 61 beds) 700 High Street N.E., Albuquerque, NM Zip 87102–2565; tel. 505/242–4444; Dianne Chartier, R.N., Interim Chief Executive Officer
Web address: www.kindredalbuquerque.com/

NORTH CAROLINA: KINDRED HOSPITAL–GREENSBORO (O, 124 beds) 2401 Southside Boulevard, Greensboro, NC Zip 27406–3311; tel. 336/271–2800; Christopher Haynes, Chief Executive Officer
Web address: www.khgreensboro.com

OHIO: KINDRED HOSPITAL CLEVELAND–GATEWAY (O, 51 beds) 2351 East 22nd Street, 7th Floor, Cleveland, OH Zip 44115–3111; tel. 216/363–2671; Prentice Lipsey, Chief Executive Officer
Web address: www.kindredgateway.com

KINDRED HOSPITAL LIMA (O, 26 beds) 730 West Market Street, 6th Floor, Lima, OH Zip 45801–4602; tel. 419/224–1888; Susan Krinke, Chief Executive Officer
Web address: www.khlima.com

KINDRED HOSPITAL OF CENTRAL OHIO (O, 33 beds) 335 Glessner Avenue, 5th Floor, Mansfield, OH Zip 44903–2269; tel. 419/526–0777; Pamela A. Edson, Chief Executive Officer
Web address: www.khcentralohio.com/

KINDRED HOSPITAL–DAYTON (O, 67 beds) 1 Elizabeth Place, 5th Floor, Dayton, OH Zip 45417–3445; tel. 937/222–5963; Lynn Schoen, Chief Executive Officer
Web address: www.khdayton.com

OKLAHOMA: KINDRED HOSPITAL– OKLAHOMA CITY (O, 93 beds) 1407 North Robinson Avenue, Oklahoma City, OK Zip 73103–4823; tel. 405/232–8000; Robert C. Gladney, Interim Chief Executive Officer
Web address: www.kindredoklahoma.com

PENNSYLVANIA: KINDRED HOSPITAL PITTSBURGH–NORTH SHORE (O, 111 beds) 1004 Arch Street, Pittsburgh, PA Zip 15212–5235; tel. 412/323–5800; Janie Rosenberger–Slampack, Market Chief Executive Officer
Web address: www.kindrednorthshore.com/

KINDRED HOSPITAL SOUTH PHILADELPHIA (O, 58 beds) 1930 South Broad Street, Philadelphia, PA Zip 19145–2328; tel. 267/570–5200; Deborah Karn, Chief Executive Officer
Web address: www.khsouthphilly.com

KINDRED HOSPITAL–HERITAGE VALLEY (O, 35 beds) 1000 Dutch Ridge Road, Beaver, PA Zip 15009–9727; tel. 724/773–8480; Janie Rosenberger–Slampack, Market Chief Executive Officer
Web address: www.kindredhospitalhv.com/

KINDRED HOSPITAL–PHILADELPHIA (O, 52 beds) 6129 Palmetto Street, Philadelphia, PA Zip 19111–5729; tel. 215/722–8555; Margaret M. Murphy, Interim Chief Executive Officer
Web address: www.kindredphila.com/

KINDRED HOSPITAL–PITTSBURGH (O, 63 beds) 7777 Steubenville Pike, Oakdale, PA Zip 15071–3409; tel. 412/494–5500; Janie Rosenberger–Slampack, Market Chief Executive Officer
Web address: www.kindredhospitalpittsburgh.com/

TENNESSEE: KINDRED HOSPITAL–CHATTANOOGA (O, 44 beds) 709 Walnut Street, Chattanooga, TN Zip 37402–1916; tel. 423/266–7721; William J. Bryant, Chief Executive Officer
Web address: www.kindredchattanooga.com/

KINDRED HOSPITAL–NASHVILLE (O, 58 beds) 1412 County Hospital Road, Nashville, TN Zip 37218–3007; tel. 615/687–2600; William P. Macri, Chief Executive Officer
Web address: www.khnashville.com/

TEXAS: CENTRAL TEXAS REHABILITATION HOSPITAL (O, 50 beds) 700 West 45th Street, Austin, TX Zip 78751–2800; tel. 512/407–2111; Peggy Barrett, R.N., Chief Executive Officer
Web address: www.khrehabcentraltexas.com/

KINDRED HOSPITAL DALLAS CENTRAL (O, 60 beds) 8050 Meadows Road, Dallas, TX Zip 75231–3406; tel. 469/232–6500; Stephanie Madrid, Chief Executive Officer
Web address: www.khdallascentral.com/

KINDRED HOSPITAL EAST HOUSTON (O, 230 beds) 15101 East Freeway, Channelview, TX Zip 77530–4104; tel. 832/200–5500; Angel Gradney, Chief Executive Officer
Web address: www.kheasthouston.com

KINDRED HOSPITAL EL PASO (O, 62 beds) 1740 Curie Drive, El Paso, TX Zip 79902–2901; tel. 915/351–9044; Diana Schultz, Chief Executive Officer
Web address: www.khelpaso.com

KINDRED HOSPITAL MIDTOWN (O, 40 beds) 105 Drew Avenue, Houston, TX Zip 77006–1527; tel. 713/529–8922; Robert Stein, Chief Executive Officer
Web address: www.khmidtown.com

KINDRED HOSPITAL SUGAR LAND (O, 171 beds) 1550 First Colony Boulevard, Sugar Land, TX Zip 77479–4000; tel. 281/275–6000; Lorene Perona, Market Chief Executive Officer
Web address: www.khsugarland.com

KINDRED HOSPITAL TARRANT COUNTY–ARLINGTON (O, 55 beds) 1000 North Cooper Street, Arlington, TX Zip 76011–5540; tel. 817/548–3400; Christina Richard, Administrator
Web address: www.kindredhospitalarl.com/

KINDRED HOSPITAL TOMBALL (O, 74 beds) 505 Graham Drive, Tomball, TX Zip 77375–3368; tel. 281/255–5600; Eric Cantrell, Chief Executive Officer
Web address: www.khtomball.com/

For explanation of codes following names, see page B2.
★ Indicates Type III membership in the American Hospital Association.

KINDRED HOSPITAL–BAY AREA (O, 74 beds) 4801 East Sam Houston Parkway South, Pasadena, TX Zip 77505–3955; tel. 281/991–5463; Laura Cedillo–Rodriguez, Chief Executive Officer
Web address: www.khbayareahouston.com/

KINDRED HOSPITAL–DALLAS (O, 50 beds) 9525 Greenville Avenue, Dallas, TX Zip 75243–4116; tel. 214/355–2600; James Mendez, Chief Executive Officer
Web address: www.khdallas.com

KINDRED HOSPITAL–FORT WORTH (O, 54 beds) 815 Eighth Avenue, Fort Worth, TX Zip 76104–2609; tel. 817/332–4812; Angela Harris, Chief Executive Officer
Web address: www.kindredfortworth.com/

KINDRED HOSPITAL–HOUSTON (O, 105 beds) 6441 Main Street, Houston, TX Zip 77030–1596; tel. 713/790–0500; Robert Stein, Chief Executive Officer
Web address: www.khhouston.com/

KINDRED HOSPITAL–HOUSTON NORTHWEST (O, 84 beds) 11297 Fallbrook Drive, Houston, TX Zip 77065–4292; tel. 281/897–8114; Larkin Virden, Chief Executive Officer
Web address: www.khhoustonnw.com/

KINDRED HOSPITAL–MANSFIELD (O, 55 beds) 1802 Highway 157 North, Mansfield, TX Zip 76063–3923; tel. 817/473–6101; Susan Schaetti, Administrator
Web address: www.kindredmansfield.com

KINDRED HOSPITAL–SAN ANTONIO (O, 59 beds) 3636 Medical Drive, San Antonio, TX Zip 78229–2183; tel. 210/616–0616; Katherine Eskew, Chief Executive Officer
Web address: www.khsanantonio.com/

KINDRED HOSPITAL–WHITE ROCK (O, 25 beds) 9440 Poppy Drive, 5th Floor, Dallas, TX Zip 75218–3652; tel. 214/324–6562; Kelly Bailey, Administrator
Web address: www.khwhiterock.com

KINDRED REHABILITATION HOSPITAL ARLINGTON (O, 24 beds) 2601 West Randol Mill Road, Arlington, TX Zip 76012–4289; tel. 817/804–4400; Amy Hoffner, Administrator
Web address: www.khrehabarlington.com

KINDRED REHABILITATION HOSPITAL CLEAR LAKE (O, 60 beds) 655 East Medical Center Boulevard, Webster, TX Zip 77598–4328; tel. 281/286–1500; Dale R. Mulder, Chief Executive Officer
Web address: www.khrehabclearlake.com/

KINDRED REHABILITATION HOSPITAL NORTHEAST HOUSTON (O, 46 beds) 18839 McKay Road, Humble, TX Zip 77338–5721; tel. 281/964–6600; Reagan Simpson, Chief Executive Officer
Web address: www.khrehabnortheasthouston.com

WASHINGTON: KINDRED HOSPITAL SEATTLE–NORTHGATE (O, 42 beds) 10631 8th Avenue N.E., Seattle, WA Zip 98125–7213; tel. 206/364–2050; Jean Clark, Administrator
Web address: www.kindredhospitalseattle.com/

Owned, leased, sponsored:	78 hospitals	6013 beds
Contract–managed:	1 hospital	91 beds
Totals:	79 hospitals	6104 beds

★0149: KISH HEALTH SYSTEM (NP)
1 Kish Hospital Drive, DeKalb, IL Zip 60115–9602, Mailing Address: P.O. Box 707, Zip 60115–0707; tel. 815/756–1521; Kevin P. Poorten, President and Chief Executive Officer
(Independent Hospital System)

ILLINOIS: KISHWAUKEE HOSPITAL (O, 98 beds) 1 Kish Hospital Drive, DeKalb, IL Zip 60115–9602, Mailing Address: P.O. Box 707, Zip 60115–0707; tel. 815/756–1521; Brad Copple, President
Web address: www.kishhospital.org

VALLEY WEST HOSPITAL (O, 25 beds) 1302 North Main Street, Sandwich, IL Zip 60548–2587; tel. 815/786–8484; Brad Copple, President
Web address: www.kishhealth.org

Owned, leased, sponsored:	2 hospitals	123 beds
Contract–managed:	0 hospitals	0 beds
Totals:	2 hospitals	123 beds

★0904: L+M HEALTHCARE (NP)
365 Montauk Avenue, New London, CT Zip 06320–4700; tel. 860/442–0711; Bruce D. Cummings, President and Chief Executive Officer
(Moderately Centralized Health System)

CONNECTICUT: LAWRENCE + MEMORIAL HOSPITAL (O, 252 beds) 365 Montauk Avenue, New London, CT Zip 06320–4769; tel. 860/442–0711; Bruce D. Cummings, President and Chief Executive Officer
Web address: www.lmhospital.org

RHODE ISLAND: WESTERLY HOSPITAL (O, 100 beds) 25 Wells Street, Westerly, RI Zip 02891–2934; tel. 401/596–6000; Bruce D. Cummings, President and Chief Executive Officer
Web address: www.westerlyhospital.org

Owned, leased, sponsored:	2 hospitals	352 beds
Contract–managed:	0 hospitals	0 beds
Totals:	2 hospitals	352 beds

0911: LAFAYETTE GENERAL HEALTH (NP)
1214 Coolidge Boulevard, Lafayette, LA Zip 70503–2621; tel. 337/289–7991; David L. Callecod, FACHE, President and CEO
(Independent Hospital System)

LOUISIANA: ABROM KAPLAN MEMORIAL HOSPITAL (C, 35 beds) 1310 West Seventh Street, Kaplan, LA Zip 70548–2910; tel. 337/643–8300; Bryce Quebodeaux, Chief Executive Officer
Web address: www.lafayettegeneral.com

LAFAYETTE GENERAL MEDICAL CENTER (O, 377 beds) 1214 Coolidge Avenue, Lafayette, LA Zip 70503–2696, Mailing Address: P.O. Box 52009 OCS, Zip 70505–2009; tel. 337/289–7991; Patrick W. Gandy, CPA, Executive Vice President and Chief Executive Officer
Web address: www.lafayettegeneral.org

LAFAYETTE GENERAL SURGICAL HOSPITAL (C, 10 beds) 1000 West Pinhook Road, Lafayette, LA Zip 70503–2460; tel. 337/289–8088; Carrie E. Templeton, FACHE, Chief Executive Officer
Web address: www.lgsh.us

ST. MARTIN HOSPITAL (C, 25 beds) 210 Champagne Boulevard, Breaux Bridge, LA Zip 70517–3700, Mailing Address: P.O. Box 357, Zip 70517–0357; tel. 337/332–2178; Katherine D. Hebert, Chief Executive Officer
Web address: www.stmartinhospital.org

UNIVERSITY HOSPITAL AND CLINICS (L, 105 beds) 2390 West Congress Street, Lafayette, LA Zip 70506–4298; tel. 337/261–6000; Jared Stark, Chief Executive Officer
Web address: www.lafayettegeneral.com

Owned, leased, sponsored:	2 hospitals	482 beds
Contract–managed:	3 hospitals	70 beds
Totals:	5 hospitals	552 beds

0891: LAHEY HEALTH (NP)
41 Mall Road, Burlington, MA Zip 01805–0001; tel. 781/744–7100; Howard R. Grant, JD, M.D., President and Chief Executive Officer
(Centralized Health System)

MASSACHUSETTS: BEVERLY HOSPITAL (O, 404 beds) 85 Herrick Street, Beverly, MA Zip 01915–1777; tel. 978/922–3000; Denis S. Conroy, President
Web address: www.beverlyhospital.org

LAHEY HOSPITAL & MEDICAL CENTER, BURLINGTON (O, 341 beds) 41 Mall Road, Burlington, MA Zip 01805–0001; tel. 781/744–5100; Joanne Conroy, M.D., Chief Executive Officer
Web address: www.lahey.org

Owned, leased, sponsored:	2 hospitals	745 beds
Contract–managed:	0 hospitals	0 beds
Totals:	2 hospitals	745 beds

For explanation of codes following names, see page B2.
★ Indicates Type III membership in the American Hospital Association.

© 2014 AHA Guide

0056: LAKELAND HEALTHCARE (NP)
1234 Napier Avenue, Saint Joseph, MI Zip 49085–2158;
tel. 269/983–8300; Loren Hamel, M.D., President and Chief
Executive Officer
(Independent Hospital System)

MICHIGAN: LAKELAND COMMUNITY HOSPITAL WATERVLIET (O, 38 beds)
400 Medical Park Drive, Watervliet, MI Zip 49098–9225;
tel. 269/463–3111; Ray Cruse, Chief Executive Officer

LAKELAND REGIONAL MEDICAL CENTER–ST. JOSEPH (O, 250 beds) 1234
Napier Avenue, Saint Joseph, MI Zip 49085–2158; tel. 269/983–8300;
Loren Hamel, M.D., President and Chief Executive Officer
Web address: www.lakelandhealth.org

LAKELAND SPECIALTY HOSPITAL–BERRIEN CENTER (O, 26 beds) 6418
Deans Hill Road, Berrien Center, MI Zip 49102–9750; tel. 269/473–3003;
Loren Hamel, M.D., President and Chief Executive Officer
Web address: www.lakelandhealth.org

Owned, leased, sponsored:	3 hospitals	314 beds
Contract–managed:	0 hospitals	0 beds
Totals:	3 hospitals	314 beds

0393: LANDMARK HOSPITALS (IO)
3255 Independence Street, Cape Girardeau, MO Zip 63701–4914;
tel. 573/335–1091; William K. Kapp, III, M.D., President and Chief
Executive Officer
(Independent Hospital System)

GEORGIA: LANDMARK HOSPITAL OF ATHENS (O, 42 beds) 775 Sunset Drive,
Athens, GA Zip 30606–2211; tel. 706/425–1500; Tommy Jackson, Chief
Executive Officer
Web address: www.landmarkhospitals.com

MISSOURI: LANDMARK HOSPITAL (O, 30 beds) 3255 Independence Street,
Cape Girardeau, MO Zip 63701–4914; tel. 573/335–1091; Rodney
Brown, Chief Executive Officer
Web address: www.landmarkhospitals.com

LANDMARK HOSPITAL OF COLUMBIA (O, 10 beds) 604 Old 63 North,
Columbia, MO Zip 65201–6308; tel. 573/499–6600; Mindy S. Moore, Chief
Executive Officer
Web address: www.landmarkhospitals.com

LANDMARK HOSPITAL OF JOPLIN (O, 30 beds) 2040 West 32nd Street,
Joplin, MO Zip 64804–3512; tel. 417/627–1300; Kenneth D'Amico, Chief
Executive Officer
Web address: www.landmarkhospitals.com

Owned, leased, sponsored:	4 hospitals	112 beds
Contract–managed:	0 hospitals	0 beds
Totals:	4 hospitals	112 beds

0932: LCMC HEALTH (NP)
200 Henry Clay Avenue, New Orleans, LA Zip 70118–5720;
tel. 504/899–9511; Greg Feirn, CPA, President and Chief Executive
Officer

LOUISIANA: CHILDREN'S HOSPITAL (O, 200 beds) 200 Henry Clay Avenue,
New Orleans, LA Zip 70118–5720; tel. 504/899–9511; Mary R. Perrin,
President and Chief Executive Officer
Web address: www.chnola.org

INTERIM LSU PUBLIC HOSPITAL (O, 201 beds) 2021 Perdido Street, New
Orleans, LA Zip 70112–1396; tel. 504/903–3000; Cindy Nuesslein, Chief
Executive Officer
Web address: www.umcno.org

TOURO INFIRMARY (O, 411 beds) 1401 Foucher Street, New Orleans, LA
Zip 70115–1396; tel. 504/897–7011; James T. Montgomery, FACHE,
President
Web address: www.touro.com

UNIVERSITY MEDICAL CENTER (O, 242 beds) 2000 Canal Street, New
Orleans, LA Zip 70112–1396; tel. 504/588–3000; Cindy Nuesslein, Interim
Chief Executive Officer

Owned, leased, sponsored:	4 hospitals	1054 beds
Contract–managed:	0 hospitals	0 beds
Totals:	4 hospitals	1054 beds

★0369: LEE MEMORIAL HEALTH SYSTEM (NP)
2776 Cleveland Avenue, Fort Myers, FL Zip 33901–5856, Mailing
Address: P.O. Box 2218, Zip 33902–2218; tel. 239/343–2000;
James R. Nathan, President and Chief Executive Officer
(Centralized Health System)

FLORIDA: CAPE CORAL HOSPITAL (O, 291 beds) 636 Del Prado Boulevard,
Cape Coral, FL Zip 33990–2695; tel. 239/424–2000; James R. Nathan,
President and Chief Executive Officer
Web address: www.leememorial.org

GULF COAST MEDICAL CENTER (O, 349 beds) 13681 Doctor's Way, Fort
Myers, FL Zip 33912–4300; tel. 239/343–1000; James R. Nathan, President
and Chief Executive Officer
Web address: www.leememorial.org

LEE MEMORIAL HOSPITAL (O, 835 beds) 2776 Cleveland Avenue, Fort Myers,
FL Zip 33901–5855, Mailing Address: P.O. Box 2218, Zip 33902–2218;
tel. 239/332–1111; James R. Nathan, President and Chief Executive Officer
Web address: www.leememorial.org

Owned, leased, sponsored:	3 hospitals	1475 beds
Contract–managed:	0 hospitals	0 beds
Totals:	3 hospitals	1475 beds

★2755: LEGACY HEALTH (NP)
1919 N.W. Lovejoy Street, Portland, OR Zip 97209–1503;
tel. 503/415–5600; George J. Brown, M.D., President and Chief
Executive Officer
(Centralized Health System)

OREGON: LEGACY EMANUEL HOSPITAL AND HEALTH CENTER (O, 427 beds)
2801 North Gantenbein Avenue, Portland, OR Zip 97227–1674;
tel. 503/413–2200; Lori Morgan, M.D., Chief Administrative Officer
Web address: www.legacyhealth.org

LEGACY GOOD SAMARITAN HOSPITAL AND MEDICAL CENTER (O, 247 beds)
1015 N.W. 22nd Avenue, Portland, OR Zip 97210–3099;
tel. 503/413–7711; Jonathan Avery, Chief Administrative Officer
Web address: www.legacyhealth.org

LEGACY MERIDIAN PARK MEDICAL CENTER (O, 130 beds) 19300 S.W. 65th
Avenue, Tualatin, OR Zip 97062–9741; tel. 503/692–1212; Allyson
Anderson, Chief Administrative Officer
Web address: www.legacyhealth.org

LEGACY MOUNT HOOD MEDICAL CENTER (O, 91 beds) 24800 S.E. Stark,
Gresham, OR Zip 97030–3378; tel. 503/667–1122; Gretchen Nichols, R.N.,
Chief Administrative Officer
Web address: www.legacyhealth.org

WASHINGTON: LEGACY SALMON CREEK MEDICAL CENTER (O, 198 beds)
2211 N.E. 139th Street, Vancouver, WA Zip 98686–2742;
tel. 360/487–1000; Bryce R. Helgerson, Chief Executive Officer
Web address: www.legacyhealth.org

Owned, leased, sponsored:	5 hospitals	1093 beds
Contract–managed:	0 hospitals	0 beds
Totals:	5 hospitals	1093 beds

★0370: LEHIGH VALLEY HEALTH NETWORK (NP)
1200 South Cedar Crest Boulevard, Allentown, PA Zip 18103–6202,
Mailing Address: P.O. Box 689, Zip 18105–1556;
tel. 610/402–8000; Brian Nester, D.O., Interim President and Chief
Executive Officer
(Centralized Health System)

PENNSYLVANIA: LEHIGH VALLEY HOSPITAL (O, 812 beds) 1200 South
Cedar Crest Boulevard, Allentown, PA Zip 18103–6248, Mailing Address:
P.O. Box 689, Zip 18105–1556; tel. 610/402–8000; Brian Nester, D.O.,
Interim President and Chief Executive Officer
Web address: www.lvhhn.org

Section B

For explanation of codes following names, see page B2.
★ Indicates Type III membership in the American Hospital Association.

LEHIGH VALLEY HOSPITAL – HAZLETON (O, 116 beds) 700 East Broad Street, Hazleton, PA Zip 18201–6897; tel. 570/501–4000; John R. Fletcher, President
Web address: www.lvhn.org/hazleton/

LEHIGH VALLEY HOSPITAL-MUHLENBERG (O, 186 beds) 2545 Schoenersville Road, Bethlehem, PA Zip 18017–7300; tel. 484/884–2201; Brian Nester, D.O., Interim President and Chief Executive Officer
Web address: www.lvhhn.org

Owned, leased, sponsored:	3 hospitals	1114 beds
Contract–managed:	0 hospitals	0 beds
Totals:	3 hospitals	1114 beds

0632: LHC GROUP (IO)
420 West Pinhook Road, Lafayette, LA Zip 70503–2131; tel. 337/223–1307; Keith G. Myers, Chairman and Chief Executive Officer

LOUISIANA: LOUISIANA EXTENDED CARE HOSPITAL OF LAFAYETTE (O, 42 beds) 1214 Coolidge Boulevard, 8th Floor, Lafayette, LA Zip 70503–2621; tel. 337/289–8180; Kevin Frank, Administrator
Web address: www.lhcgroup.com

LOUISIANA EXTENDED CARE HOSPITAL OF NATCHITOCHES (O, 21 beds) 501 Keyser Avenue, Natchitoches, LA Zip 71457–6018; tel. 318/354–2044; John Rivoire, Administrator
Web address: www.lhcgroup.com

LOUISIANA EXTENDED CARE HOSPITAL WEST MONROE (O, 18 beds) 503 McMillan Road, 3rd Floor, West Monroe, LA Zip 71291–5327; tel. 318/329–4300; Cleta Munholland, Administrator

OCHSNER EXTENDED CARE HOSPITAL OF KENNER (O, 34 beds) 180 West Esplanade Avenue, 5th Floor, Kenner, LA Zip 70065–2467; tel. 504/464–8590; Fritz Nelson, Administrator
Web address: www.lhcgroup.com/

Owned, leased, sponsored:	4 hospitals	115 beds
Contract–managed:	0 hospitals	0 beds
Totals:	4 hospitals	115 beds

★0394: LHP HOSPITAL GROUP (IO)
2400 North Dallas Parkway, Suite 450, Plano, TX Zip 75093–5994; tel. 866/465–9222; John F. Holland, Chief Executive Officer
(Independent Hospital System)

FLORIDA: BAY MEDICAL CENTER SACRED HEART (L, 362 beds) 615 North Bonita Avenue, Panama City, FL Zip 32401–3600, Mailing Address: P.O. Box 59515, Zip 32412–0515; tel. 850/769–1511; Barry L. Keel, Chief Executive Officer
Web address: www.baymedical.org

IDAHO: PORTNEUF MEDICAL CENTER (O, 175 beds) 777 Hospital Way, Pocatello, ID Zip 83201–5175; tel. 208/239–1000; Daniel Ordyna, Chief Executive Officer
Web address: www.portmed.org

NEW JERSEY: HACKENSACK UNIVERSITY MEDICAL CENTER AT PASCACK VALLEY (O, 128 beds) 250 Old Hook Road, Westwood, NJ Zip 07675–3123; tel. 201/880–2700; Chad Melton, Chief Executive Officer
Web address: www.hackensackumcpv.com/

HACKENSACK UNIVERSITY MEDICAL CENTER MOUNTAINSIDE (O, 228 beds) 1 Bay Avenue, Montclair, NJ Zip 07042–4898; tel. 973/429–6000; John A. Fromhold, Chief Executive Officer
Web address: www.mountainsidenow.com

TEXAS: SETON MEDICAL CENTER HARKER HEIGHTS (O, 58 beds) 850 West Central Texas Expressway, Harker Heights, TX Zip 76548–1890; tel. 254/690–0900; Matt T. Maxfield, FACHE, Chief Executive Officer
Web address: www.setonharkerheights.net

TEXAS HEALTH PRESBYTERIAN HOSPITAL-WNJ (O, 235 beds) 500 North Highland Avenue, Sherman, TX Zip 75092–7354; tel. 903/870–4611; Vance V. Reynolds, FACHE, CPA, Chief Executive Officer
Web address: www.wnj.org

Owned, leased, sponsored:	6 hospitals	1186 beds
Contract–managed:	0 hospitals	0 beds
Totals:	6 hospitals	1186 beds

★0158: LIFEBRIDGE HEALTH (NP)
2401 West Belvedere Avenue, Baltimore, MD Zip 21215–5216; tel. 410/601–5134; Neil M. Meltzer, President and Chief Executive Officer
(Centralized Health System)

MARYLAND: LEVINDALE HEBREW GERIATRIC CENTER AND HOSPITAL (O, 490 beds) 2434 West Belvedere Avenue, Baltimore, MD Zip 21215–5267; tel. 410/601–2400; Barry Eisenberg, FACHE, Chief Operating Officer and Executive Director
Web address: www.sinai–balt.com

NORTHWEST HOSPITAL (O, 253 beds) 5401 Old Court Road, Randallstown, MD Zip 21133–5185; tel. 410/521–2200; Brian M. White, President
Web address: www.lifebridgehealth.org

SINAI HOSPITAL OF BALTIMORE (O, 434 beds) 2401 West Belvedere Avenue, Baltimore, MD Zip 21215–5271; tel. 410/601–9000; Amy Perry, President
Web address: www.lifebridgehealth.org

Owned, leased, sponsored:	3 hospitals	1177 beds
Contract–managed:	0 hospitals	0 beds
Totals:	3 hospitals	1177 beds

★0191: LIFECARE MANAGEMENT SERVICES (IO)
5340 Legacy Drive, Suite 150, Plano, TX Zip 75024–3131; tel. 469/241–2100; Phillip B. Douglas, Chairman and Chief Executive Officer
(Independent Hospital System)

COLORADO: COLORADO ACUTE LONG TERM HOSPITAL (O, 63 beds) 1690 North Meade Street, Denver, CO Zip 80204–1552; tel. 303/264–6900; Craig Bailey, MS, Administrator
Web address: www.lifecare–hospitals.com/hospital/colorado

FLORIDA: COMPLEX CARE HOSPITAL AT RIDGELAKE (O, 40 beds) 6150 Edgelake Drive, Sarasota, FL Zip 34240–8803; tel. 941/342–3000; Danny R. Edwards, Administrator
Web address: www.lifecare–hospitals.com/hospital.php?id=23

LOUISIANA: LIFECARE HOSPITALS OF SHREVEPORT (O, 119 beds) 9320 Linwood Avenue, Shreveport, LA Zip 71106–7003; tel. 318/688–8504; Keith Cox, Administrator
Web address: www.lifecare–hospitals.com

LIFECARE SPECIALTY HOSPITAL OF NORTH LOUISIANA (O, 55 beds) 1401 Ezell Street, Ruston, LA Zip 71270–7218; tel. 318/251–3126; Brent Martin, Administrator
Web address: www.lifecare–hospitals.com/hospital.php?id=19

NEVADA: COMPLEX CARE HOSPITAL AT TENAYA (O, 70 beds) 2500 North Tenaya, Las Vegas, NV Zip 89128–0482; tel. 702/562–2021; Colin O'Sullivan, Acting Chief Executive Officer
Web address: www.lifecare–hospitals.com

TAHOE PACIFIC HOSPITALS (O, 60 beds) 201 West Liberty Street, Suite 310, Reno, NV Zip 89501–2017; tel. 775/355–5970; Colin O'Sullivan, Administrator
Web address: www.lifecare–hospitals.com

NORTH CAROLINA: LIFECARE HOSPITALS OF NORTH CAROLINA (O, 41 beds) 1051 Noell Lane, Rocky Mount, NC Zip 27804–1761; tel. 252/451–2300; Robyn Perkerson, R.N., Administrator
Web address: www.lifecare–hospitals.com

OHIO: LIFECARE HOSPITAL OF DAYTON (O, 44 beds) 4000 Miamisburg–Centerville Road, Miamisburg, OH Zip 45342–7615; tel. 937/384–8300; Russell Dean, Administrator
Web address: www.lifecare–hospitals.com

PENNSYLVANIA: LIFECARE HOSPITALS OF CHESTER COUNTY (O, 39 beds) 400 East Marshall Street, West Chester, PA Zip 19380–5412; tel. 484/826–0400; Garrett Arneson, Chief Executive Officer
Web address: www.lifecare–hospitals.com

For explanation of codes following names, see page B2.
★ Indicates Type III membership in the American Hospital Association.

LIFECARE HOSPITALS OF MECHANICSBURG (O, 68 beds) 4950 Wilson Lane, Mechanicsburg, PA Zip 17055–4442; tel. 717/697–7706; Garrett Arneson, Chief Executive Officer
Web address: www.lifecare–hospitals.com/hospital.php?id=20

LIFECARE HOSPITALS OF PITTSBURGH (O, 236 beds) 225 Penn Avenue, Pittsburgh, PA Zip 15221–2148; tel. 412/247–2424; Kim Sperring, Administrator
Web address: www.lifecare–hospitals.com

LIFECARE HOSPITALS OF PITTSBURGH – MONROEVILLE (O, 87 beds) 2380 McGinley Road, Monroeville, PA Zip 15146–4400; tel. 412/856–2400; Kim Sperring, Administrator
Web address: www.lifecare–hospitals.com/hospital.php?id=8

TEXAS: LIFECARE HOSPITALS OF DALLAS (O, 206 beds) 1950 Record Crossing Road, Dallas, TX Zip 75235–6223; tel. 214/640–9600; Kevin S. Cooper, R.N., Chief Executive Officer
Web address: www.lifecare–hospitals.com/hospital/dallas

LIFECARE HOSPITALS OF SAN ANTONIO (O, 62 beds) 8902 Floyd Curl Drive, San Antonio, TX Zip 78240–1681; tel. 210/690–7000; Randell G. Stokes, Chief Executive Officer
Web address: www.lifecare–hospitals.com

LIFECARE HOSPITALS OF SOUTH TEXAS–NORTH MCALLEN (O, 84 beds) 5101 North Jackson, McAllen, TX Zip 78504–6343; tel. 956/926–7000; Michelle Lozano, Chief Executive Officer
Web address: www.lifecare–hospitals.com/hospital/southtexas

WISCONSIN: LIFECARE HOSPITALS OF WISCONSIN (O, 26 beds) 2400 Golf Road, Pewaukee, WI Zip 53072–5590; tel. 262/524–2600; Dennis Mattes, Chief Executive Officer
Web address: www.lifecare–hospitals.com

Owned, leased, sponsored:	16 hospitals	1300 beds
Contract–managed:	0 hospitals	0 beds
Totals:	16 hospitals	1300 beds

★0180: LIFEPOINT HOSPITALS, INC. (IO)
330 Seven Springs Way, Brentwood, TN Zip 37027–4536; tel. 615/920–7000; William F. Carpenter, III, Chairman and Chief Executive Officer
(Moderately Centralized Health System)

ALABAMA: ANDALUSIA REGIONAL HOSPITAL (O, 87 beds) 849 South Three Notch Street, Andalusia, AL Zip 36420–5325, Mailing Address: P.O. Box 760, Zip 36420–1214; tel. 334/222–8466; Rebecca Brewer, FACHE, Interim Chief Executive Officer
Web address: www.andalusiaregionalhospital.com

LAKELAND COMMUNITY HOSPITAL (O, 56 beds) Highway 195 East, Haleyville, AL Zip 35565–9536, Mailing Address: P.O. Box 780, Zip 35565–0780; tel. 205/486–5213; Cynthia Nichols, R.N., MSN, Chief Executive Officer
Web address: www.lakelandcommunityhospital.com/

NORTHWEST MEDICAL CENTER (O, 66 beds) 1530 U.S. Highway 43, Winfield, AL Zip 35594–5056; tel. 205/487–7000; Robert Henger, Interim Chief Executive Officer
Web address: www.northwestmedcenter.com

RUSSELLVILLE HOSPITAL (O, 92 beds) 15155 Highway 43, Russellville, AL Zip 35653–1975, Mailing Address: P.O. Box 1089, Zip 35653–1089; tel. 256/332–1611; Christine R. Stewart, FACHE, Chief Executive Officer
Web address: www.russellvillehospital.com

VAUGHAN REGIONAL MEDICAL CENTER (O, 149 beds) 1015 Medical Center Parkway, Selma, AL Zip 36701–6352; tel. 334/418–4100; David R. Sirk, Chief Executive Officer
Web address: www.vaughanregional.com

ARIZONA: HAVASU REGIONAL MEDICAL CENTER (O, 138 beds) 101 Civic Center Lane, Lake Havasu City, AZ Zip 86403–5683; tel. 928/855–8185; F. Dana Ellerbe, Chief Executive Officer
Web address: www.havasuregional.com

VALLEY VIEW MEDICAL CENTER (O, 66 beds) 5330 South Highway 95, Fort Mohave, AZ Zip 86426–9225; tel. 928/788–2273; Richard G. Carter, Chief Executive Officer
Web address: www.valleyviewmedicalcenter.net

COLORADO: COLORADO PLAINS MEDICAL CENTER (L, 50 beds) 1000 Lincoln Street, Fort Morgan, CO Zip 80701–3298; tel. 970/867–3391; Michael N. Patterson, Chief Executive Officer
Web address: www.coloradoplainsmedicalcenter.com

FLORIDA: PUTNAM COMMUNITY MEDICAL CENTER (O, 99 beds) Highway 20 West, Palatka, FL Zip 32177–8118, Mailing Address: P.O. Box 778, Zip 32178–0778; tel. 386/328–5711; Michael Clark, Interim Chief Executive Officer
Web address: www.pcmcfl.com

GEORGIA: ROCKDALE MEDICAL CENTER (O, 157 beds) 1412 Milstead Avenue N.E., Conyers, GA Zip 30012–3877; tel. 770/918–3000; Deborah Armstrong, Chief Executive Officer
Web address: www.rockdalemedicalcenter.org

INDIANA: SCOTT MEMORIAL HOSPITAL (O, 25 beds) 1415 North Gardner Street, Scottsburg, IN Zip 47170, Mailing Address: Box 430, Zip 47170–0430; tel. 812/752–3456; Michael Everett, Chief Executive Officer
Web address: www.scottmemorial.com

KANSAS: WESTERN PLAINS MEDICAL COMPLEX (O, 89 beds) 3001 Avenue A, Dodge City, KS Zip 67801–6508, Mailing Address: P.O. Box 1478, Zip 67801–1478; tel. 620/225–8400; Michael R. Burroughs, FACHE, Chief Executive Officer
Web address: www.westernplainsmc.com

KENTUCKY: BLUEGRASS COMMUNITY HOSPITAL (O, 16 beds) 360 Amsden Avenue, Versailles, KY Zip 40383–1286; tel. 859/873–3111; Tommy Haggard, Chief Executive Officer
Web address: www.bluegrasscommunityhospital.com

BOURBON COMMUNITY HOSPITAL (O, 58 beds) 9 Linville Drive, Paris, KY Zip 40361–2196; tel. 859/987–3600; Joseph G. Koch, Chief Executive Officer
Web address: www.bourbonhospital.com

CLARK REGIONAL MEDICAL CENTER (O, 100 beds) 175 Hospital Drive, Winchester, KY Zip 40391–9591; tel. 859/745–3500; Cherie Sibley, R.N., Chief Executive Officer
Web address: www.clarkregional.org

GEORGETOWN COMMUNITY HOSPITAL (O, 58 beds) 1140 Lexington Road, Georgetown, KY Zip 40324–9362; tel. 502/868–1100; William Haugh, Administrator
Web address: www.georgetowncommunityhospital.com

JACKSON PURCHASE MEDICAL CENTER (O, 106 beds) 1099 Medical Center Circle, Mayfield, KY Zip 42066–1159; tel. 270/251–4100; David Anderson, Chief Executive Officer
Web address: www.jacksonpurchase.com

LAKE CUMBERLAND REGIONAL HOSPITAL (O, 295 beds) 305 Langdon Street, Somerset, KY Zip 42503–2750, Mailing Address: P.O. Box 620, Zip 42502–0620; tel. 606/679–7441; Timothy A. Bess, Chief Executive Officer
Web address: www.lakecumberlandhospital.com

LOGAN MEMORIAL HOSPITAL (O, 53 beds) 1625 South Nashville Road, Russellville, KY Zip 42276–8834, Mailing Address: P.O. Box 10, Zip 42276–0010; tel. 270/726–4011; James Bills, Chief Executive Officer
Web address: www.loganmemorial.com

MEADOWVIEW REGIONAL MEDICAL CENTER (O, 101 beds) 989 Medical Park Drive, Maysville, KY Zip 41056–8750; tel. 606/759–5311; Robert Parker, Chief Executive Officer
Web address: www.meadowviewregional.com

SPRING VIEW HOSPITAL (O, 60 beds) 320 Loretto Road, Lebanon, KY Zip 40033–1300; tel. 270/692–3161; Timothy R. Trottier, Chief Executive Officer
Web address: www.springviewhospital.com

LOUISIANA: MERCY REGIONAL MEDICAL CENTER (O, 60 beds) 800 East Main Street, Ville Platte, LA Zip 70586–4618, Mailing Address: P.O. Box 349, Zip 70586–0349; tel. 337/363–5684; Scott M. Smith, Chief Executive Officer
Web address: www.mercyregionalmedicalcenter.com

MINDEN MEDICAL CENTER (O, 161 beds) 1 Medical Plaza, Minden, LA Zip 71055–3330, Mailing Address: P.O. Box 5003, Zip 71058–5003; tel. 318/377–2321; George E. French, III, FACHE, Chief Executive Officer
Web address: www.mindenmedicalcenter.com

For explanation of codes following names, see page B2.
★ Indicates Type III membership in the American Hospital Association.

Section B

RIVER PARISHES HOSPITAL (O, 106 beds) 500 Rue De Sante, La Place, LA Zip 70068–5418; tel. 985/652–7000; Robert L. Marshall, Jr., FACHE, Chief Executive Officer
Web address: www.riverparisheshospital.com

TECHE REGIONAL MEDICAL CENTER (L, 165 beds) 1125 Marguerite Street, Morgan City, LA Zip 70380–1855, Mailing Address: P.O. Box 2308, Zip 70381–2308; tel. 985/384–2200; James P. Frazier, III, Chief Executive Officer
Web address: www.techeregional.com

MICHIGAN: MARQUETTE GENERAL HOSPITAL (O, 268 beds) 580 West College Avenue, Marquette, MI Zip 49855–2736; tel. 906/228–9440; Edward D. Banos, Chief Executive Officer
Web address: www.rngh.org

MISSISSIPPI: BOLIVAR MEDICAL CENTER (L, 127 beds) 901 East Sunflower Road, Cleveland, MS Zip 38732–2833, Mailing Address: P.O. Box 1380, Zip 38732–1380; tel. 662/846–0061; James Atkins, Interim Chief Executive Officer
Web address: www.bolivarmedical.com

NEVADA: NORTHEASTERN NEVADA REGIONAL HOSPITAL (O, 75 beds) 2001 Errecart Boulevard, Elko, NV Zip 89801–8333; tel. 775/738–5151; Gene Miller, Chief Executive Officer
Web address: www.nnrhospital.com

NEW MEXICO: LOS ALAMOS MEDICAL CENTER (O, 36 beds) 3917 West Road, Los Alamos, NM Zip 87544–2293; tel. 505/661–9500; Feliciano Jiron, Chief Executive Officer
Web address: www.losalamosmedicalcenter.com

MEMORIAL MEDICAL CENTER (L, 224 beds) 2450 South Telshor Boulevard, Las Cruces, NM Zip 88011–5076; tel. 575/522–8641; John Harris, Chief Executive Officer
Web address: www.mmclc.org

NORTH CAROLINA: HARRIS REGIONAL HOSPITAL (O, 86 beds) 68 Hospital Road, Sylva, NC Zip 28779–2722; tel. 828/586–7000; Steve Heatherly, Chief Executive Officer
Web address: www.westcare.org

HAYWOOD REGIONAL MEDICAL CENTER (O, 146 beds) 262 Leroy George Drive, Clyde, NC Zip 28721–7430; tel. 828/456–7311; Janie Sinacore–Jaberg, R.N., MS, FACHE, Chief Executive Officer
Web address: www.haymed.org

MARIA PARHAM MEDICAL CENTER (O, 102 beds) 566 Ruin Creek Road, Henderson, NC Zip 27536–2927; tel. 252/438–4143; Robert G. Singletary, Chief Executive Officer
Web address: www.mariaparham.com

PERSON MEMORIAL HOSPITAL (O, 106 beds) 615 Ridge Road, Roxboro, NC Zip 27573–4629; tel. 336/599–2121; Beemal A. Shah, Chief Executive Officer
Web address: www.personhospital.com

RUTHERFORD REGIONAL HEALTH SYSTEM (O, 121 beds) 288 South Ridgecrest Avenue, Rutherfordton, NC Zip 28139–2838; tel. 828/286–5000; Cindy D. Buck, Chief Executive Officer
Web address: www.rutherfordhosp.org

SWAIN COUNTY HOSPITAL (O, 25 beds) 45 Plateau Street, Bryson City, NC Zip 28713–4200; tel. 828/488–2155; Steve Heatherly, Chief Executive Officer
Web address: www.westcare.org

WILSON MEDICAL CENTER (O, 206 beds) 1705 Tarboro Street, S.W., Wilson, NC Zip 27893–3428; tel. 252/399–8040; William E. Caldwell, Jr., Chief Executive Officer
Web address: www.wilmed.org

PENNSYLVANIA: CONEMAUGH MEMORIAL MEDICAL CENTER (O, 555 beds) 1086 Franklin Street, Johnstown, PA Zip 15905–4398; tel. 814/534–9000; Steven E. Tucker, President
Web address: www.conemaugh.org

CONEMAUGH MEYERSDALE MEDICAL CENTER (O, 20 beds) 200 Hospital Drive, Meyersdale, PA Zip 15552–1249; tel. 814/634–5911; Mary L. Libengood, President
Web address: www.conemaugh.org

CONEMAUGH MINERS MEDICAL CENTER (O, 30 beds) 290 Haida Avenue, Hastings, PA Zip 16646–5610, Mailing Address: P.O. Box 689, Zip 16646–0689; tel. 814/247–3100; William R. Crowe, President
Web address: www.minersmedicalcenter.org

TENNESSEE: LIVINGSTON REGIONAL HOSPITAL (O, 82 beds) 315 Oak Street, Livingston, TN Zip 38570–1728, Mailing Address: P.O. Box 550, Zip 38570–0550; tel. 931/823–5611; Joanne Fenton, MSN, FACHE, Chief Executive Officer
Web address: www.livingstonregionalhospital.com

RIVERVIEW REGIONAL MEDICAL CENTER (O, 25 beds) 158 Hospital Drive, Carthage, TN Zip 37030–1096; tel. 615/735–1560; Rod Harkleroad, R.N., Administrator
Web address: www.myriverviewmedical.com/

SOUTHERN TENNESSEE REGIONAL HEALTH SYSTEM–LAWRENCEBURG (O, 90 beds) 1607 South Locust Avenue, Lawrenceburg, TN Zip 38464–4011, Mailing Address: P.O. Box 847, Zip 38464–0847; tel. 931/762–6571; Jeff Noblin, FACHE, Chief Executive Officer
Web address: www.crocketthospital.com

SOUTHERN TENNESSEE REGIONAL HEALTH SYSTEM–PULASKI (O, 50 beds) 1265 East College Street, Pulaski, TN Zip 38478–4541; tel. 931/363–7531; Harold L. Siglar, Interim Chief Executive Officer
Web address: www.hillsidehospital.com

SOUTHERN TENNESSEE REGIONAL HEALTH SYSTEM–WINCHESTER (O, 188 beds) 185 Hospital Road, Winchester, TN Zip 37398–2404; tel. 931/967–8200; J. Phillip Young, FACHE, Chief Executive Officer
Web address: www.southerntennessee.com

STARR REGIONAL MEDICAL CENTER (O, 63 beds) 1114 West Madison Avenue, Athens, TN Zip 37303–4150, Mailing Address: P.O. Box 250, Zip 37371–0250; tel. 423/745–1411; Richard Grogan, Interim Chief Executive Officer
Web address: www.starrregional.com

STARR REGIONAL MEDICAL CENTER–ETOWAH (O, 140 beds) 886 Highway 411 North, Etowah, TN Zip 37331–1912; tel. 423/263–3600; Richard Grogan, Interim Chief Executive Officer
Web address: www.starrregional.com

SUMNER REGIONAL MEDICAL CENTER (O, 145 beds) 555 Hartsville Pike, Gallatin, TN Zip 37066–2400, Mailing Address: P.O. Box 1558, Zip 37066–1558; tel. 615/452–4210; Susan M. Peach, R.N., Chief Executive Officer
Web address: www.mysumnermedical.com

TROUSDALE MEDICAL CENTER (O, 25 beds) 500 Church Street, Hartsville, TN Zip 37074–1744; tel. 615/374–2221; Rod Harkleroad, R.N., Chief Executive Officer
Web address: www.mytrousdalemedical.com

TEXAS: ENNIS REGIONAL MEDICAL CENTER (L, 58 beds) 2201 West Lampasas Street, Ennis, TX Zip 75119–5644; tel. 972/875–0900; Kevin Zachary, Chief Executive Officer
Web address: www.ennisregional.com

PALESTINE REGIONAL MEDICAL CENTER (O, 12 beds) 2900 South Loop 256, Palestine, TX Zip 75801–6958; tel. 903/731–1000; Alan E. George, Chief Executive Officer
Web address: www.palestineregional.com

PALESTINE REGIONAL MEDICAL CENTER–EAST (O, 139 beds) 2900 South Loop 256, Palestine, TX Zip 75801–6958; tel. 903/731–1000; Alan E. George, Chief Executive Officer
Web address: www.palestineregional.com

PARKVIEW REGIONAL HOSPITAL (L, 58 beds) 600 South Bonham, Mexia, TX Zip 76667–3603; tel. 254/562–5332; Kevin Zachary, Chief Executive Officer
Web address: www.parkviewregional.com

UTAH: ASHLEY REGIONAL MEDICAL CENTER (O, 39 beds) 150 West 100 North, Vernal, UT Zip 84078–2036; tel. 435/789–3342; Ben Cluff, Chief Executive Officer
Web address: www.ashleyregional.com

CASTLEVIEW HOSPITAL (O, 49 beds) 300 North Hospital Drive, Price, UT Zip 84501–4200; tel. 435/637–4800; Mark Holyoak, Chief Executive Officer
Web address: www.castleviewhospital.net

VIRGINIA: CLINCH VALLEY MEDICAL CENTER (O, 111 beds) 6801 Governor G. C. Peery Highway, Richlands, VA Zip 24641–2194; tel. 276/596–6000; Peter Mulkey, Chief Executive Officer
Web address: www.clinchvalleymedicalcenter.com

DANVILLE REGIONAL MEDICAL CENTER (O, 151 beds) 142 South Main Street, Danville, VA Zip 24541–2922; tel. 434/799–2100; Eric Deaton, Chief Executive Officer
Web address: www.danvilleregional.org

For explanation of codes following names, see page B2.
★ Indicates Type III membership in the American Hospital Association.

MEMORIAL HOSPITAL (O, 220 beds) 320 Hospital Drive, Martinsville, VA Zip 24112–1981, Mailing Address: P.O. Box 4788, Zip 24115–4788; tel. 276/666–7200; Eric Deaton, Interim Chief Executive Officer
Web address: www.martinsvillehospital.com

TWIN COUNTY REGIONAL HOSPITAL (O, 86 beds) 200 Hospital Drive, Galax, VA Zip 24333–2227; tel. 276/236–8181; Jon D. Applebaum, Chief Executive Officer
Web address: www.tcrh.org

WYTHE COUNTY COMMUNITY HOSPITAL (L, 90 beds) 600 West Ridge Road, Wytheville, VA Zip 24382–1099; tel. 276/228–0200; Timothy A. Bess, Chief Executive Officer
Web address: www.wcchcares.com

WEST VIRGINIA: LOGAN REGIONAL MEDICAL CENTER (O, 129 beds) 20 Hospital Drive, Logan, WV Zip 25601–3452; tel. 304/831–1101; Gerald C. Dooley, Interim Chief Executive Officer
Web address: www.loganregionalmedicalcenter.com

RALEIGH GENERAL HOSPITAL (O, 229 beds) 1710 Harper Road, Beckley, WV Zip 25801–3397; tel. 304/256–4100; David B. Darden, Chief Executive Officer
Web address: www.raleighgeneral.com

WYOMING: RIVERTON MEMORIAL HOSPITAL (O, 37 beds) 2100 West Sunset Drive, Riverton, WY Zip 82501–2274; tel. 307/856–4161; Stephen M. Erixon, Interim Chief Executive Officer
Web address: www.riverton–hospital.com

SAGEWEST HEALTHCARE–LANDER (O, 89 beds) 1320 Bishop Randall Drive, Lander, WY Zip 82520–3996; tel. 307/332–4420; Stephen M. Erixon, Chief Executive Officer
Web address: www.sagewesthealthcare.com

Owned, leased, sponsored:	64 hospitals	6845 beds
Contract–managed:	0 hospitals	0 beds
Totals:	64 hospitals	6845 beds

0060: LIFESPAN CORPORATION (NP)
167 Point Street, Providence, RI Zip 02903–4771; tel. 401/444–3500; Timothy J. Babineau, M.D., President and Chief Executive Officer
(Moderately Centralized Health System)

RHODE ISLAND: EMMA PENDLETON BRADLEY HOSPITAL (O, 60 beds) 1011 Veterans Memorial Parkway, East Providence, RI Zip 02915–5099; tel. 401/432–1000; Daniel J. Wall, President and Chief Executive Officer
Web address: www.lifespan.org

MIRIAM HOSPITAL (O, 247 beds) 164 Summit Avenue, Providence, RI Zip 02906–2853; tel. 401/793–2500; Arthur J. Sampson, FACHE, President
Web address: www.lifespan.org

NEWPORT HOSPITAL (O, 119 beds) 11 Friendship Street, Newport, RI Zip 02840–2299; tel. 401/846–6400; Arthur J. Sampson, FACHE, Interim President
Web address: www.newporthospital.org

RHODE ISLAND HOSPITAL (O, 645 beds) 593 Eddy Street, Providence, RI Zip 02903–4900; tel. 401/444–4000; Timothy J. Babineau, M.D., President and Chief Executive Officer
Web address: www.rhodeislandhospital.org/

Owned, leased, sponsored:	4 hospitals	1071 beds
Contract–managed:	0 hospitals	0 beds
Totals:	4 hospitals	1071 beds

2175: LOMA LINDA UNIVERSITY ADVENTIST HEALTH SCIENCES CENTER (NP)
11175 Campus Street, Loma Linda, CA Zip 92350–1700; tel. 909/558–7572; Richard H. Hart, M.D., President and Chief Executive Officer
(Moderately Centralized Health System)

CALIFORNIA: LOMA LINDA UNIVERSITY BEHAVIORAL MEDICINE CENTER (O, 89 beds) 1710 Barton Road, Redlands, CA Zip 92373–5304; tel. 909/558–9200; Jill Pollock, Administrator
Web address: www.llu.edu

LOMA LINDA UNIVERSITY MEDICAL CENTER (O, 829 beds) 11234 Anderson Street, Loma Linda, CA Zip 92354–2804, Mailing Address: P.O. Box 2000, Zip 92354–0200; tel. 909/558–4000; Kerry Heinrich, Interim Chief Executive Officer
Web address: www.llumc.edu

LOMA LINDA UNIVERSITY MEDICAL CENTER–MURRIETA (O, 106 beds) 28062 Baxter Road, Murrieta, CA Zip 92563–1401; tel. 951/290–4000; Richard L. Rawson, Chief Executive Officer
Web address: www.llumcmurrieta.org

Owned, leased, sponsored:	3 hospitals	1024 beds
Contract–managed:	0 hospitals	0 beds
Totals:	3 hospitals	1024 beds

5755: LOS ANGELES COUNTY–DEPARTMENT OF HEALTH SERVICES (NP)
313 North Figueroa Street, Room 912, Los Angeles, CA Zip 90012–2691; tel. 213/240–8101; Mitchell H. Katz, M.D., Director
(Independent Hospital System)

HARBOR–UCLA MEDICAL CENTER (O, 389 beds) 1000 West Carson Street, Torrance, CA Zip 90502–2059; tel. 310/222–2345; Delvecchio Finley, Chief Executive Officer
Web address: www.humc.edu

LAC–OLIVE VIEW–UCLA MEDICAL CENTER (O, 238 beds) 14445 Olive View Drive, Sylmar, CA Zip 91342–1438; tel. 818/364–1555; Carolyn F. Rhee, Chief Executive Officer
Web address: www.ladhs.org

LAC/UNIVERSITY OF SOUTHERN CALIFORNIA MEDICAL CENTER (O, 664 beds) 1200 North State Street, Los Angeles, CA Zip 90033–1029; tel. 323/226–2622; Dan Castillo, Chief Executive Officer
Web address: www.lacusc.org

RANCHO LOS AMIGOS NATIONAL REHABILITATION CENTER (O, 207 beds) 7601 East Imperial Highway, Downey, CA Zip 90242–3496; tel. 562/401–7111; Jorge Orozco, Chief Executive Officer
Web address: www.rancho.org

Owned, leased, sponsored:	4 hospitals	1498 beds
Contract–managed:	0 hospitals	0 beds
Totals:	4 hospitals	1498 beds

0047: LOUISIANA STATE HOSPITALS (NP)
628 North 4th Street, Baton Rouge, LA Zip 70802–5342, Mailing Address: P.O. Box 629, Zip 70821–0628; tel. 225/342–9500; Shelby Price, Chief Executive Officer
(Independent Hospital System)

LOUISIANA: CENTRAL LOUISIANA STATE HOSPITAL (O, 128 beds) 242 West Shamrock Avenue, Pineville, LA Zip 71360–6439, Mailing Address: P.O. Box 5031, Zip 71361–5031; tel. 318/484–6200; Ronald G. Williams, Administrator
Web address: www.dhh.louisiana.gov/index.cfm/directory/detail/217

EASTERN LOUISIANA MENTAL HEALTH SYSTEM (O, 473 beds) 4502 Highway 951, Jackson, LA Zip 70748–5842, Mailing Address: P.O. Box 498, Zip 70748–0498; tel. 225/634–0100; Hampton P. S. Lea, Acting Chief Executive Officer
Web address: www.wwwprd.doa.louisiana. gov/laservices/publicpages/ServiceDetail.cfm?service_id=2445

Owned, leased, sponsored:	2 hospitals	601 beds
Contract–managed:	0 hospitals	0 beds
Totals:	2 hospitals	601 beds

Section B

For explanation of codes following names, see page B2.
★ Indicates Type III membership in the American Hospital Association.

★0320: **LRGHEALTHCARE** (NP)
80 Highland Street, Laconia, NH Zip 03246–3298;
tel. 603/524–3211; Charles K. Van Sluyter, Interim President and
CEO
(Independent Hospital System)

NEW HAMPSHIRE: FRANKLIN REGIONAL HOSPITAL (O, 25 beds) 15 Aiken
Avenue, Franklin, NH Zip 03235–1299; tel. 603/934–2060; Charles K.
Van Sluyter, Interim Chief Executive Officer
Web address: www.lrgh.org

LAKES REGION GENERAL HOSPITAL (O, 88 beds) 80 Highland Street,
Laconia, NH Zip 03246–3298; tel. 603/524–3211; Charles K. Van Sluyter,
Interim Chief Executive Officer
Web address: www.lrgh.org

Owned, leased, sponsored:	2 hospitals	113 beds
Contract–managed:	0 hospitals	0 beds
Totals:	2 hospitals	113 beds

0614: **MAINEHEALTH** (NP)
110 Free Street, Portland, ME Zip 04101–3537; William L. Caron,
Jr., President
(Moderately Centralized Health System)

MAINE: LINCOLN HEALTH (O, 111 beds) 35 Miles Street, Damariscotta, ME
Zip 04543–4047; tel. 207/563–1234; James W. Donovan, President and
Chief Executive Officer
Web address: www.lchcare.org

MAINE MEDICAL CENTER (O, 637 beds) 22 Bramhall Street, Portland, ME
Zip 04102–3175; tel. 207/662–0111; Richard W. Petersen, President and
Chief Executive Officer
Web address: www.mmc.org

PEN BAY MEDICAL CENTER (O, 165 beds) 6 Glen Cove Drive, Rockport, ME
Zip 04856–4240; tel. 207/596–8000; Mark A. Biscone, Interim Chief
Executive Officer
Web address: www.penbayhealthcare.org

SPRING HARBOR HOSPITAL (O, 88 beds) 123 Andover Road, Westbrook, ME
Zip 04092–3850; tel. 207/761–2200; Dennis P. King, Chief Executive Officer
Web address: www.springharbor.org

STEPHENS MEMORIAL HOSPITAL (O, 25 beds) 181 Main Street, Norway, ME
Zip 04268–5664; tel. 207/743–5933; Timothy A. Churchill, President
Web address: www.wmhcc.com

WALDO COUNTY GENERAL HOSPITAL (O, 25 beds) 118 Northport Avenue,
Belfast, ME Zip 04915–6072, Mailing Address: P.O. Box 287,
Zip 04915–0287; tel. 207/338–2500; Mark A. Biscone, Executive Director
Web address: www.wcgh.org

NEW HAMPSHIRE: MEMORIAL HOSPITAL (O, 70 beds) 3073 White Mountain
Highway, North Conway, NH Zip 03860–7101; tel. 603/356–5461; Scott
McKinnon, President and Chief Executive Officer
Web address: www.memorialhospitalnh.org

Owned, leased, sponsored:	7 hospitals	1121 beds
Contract–managed:	0 hospitals	0 beds
Totals:	7 hospitals	1121 beds

1975: **MARSHALL HEALTH SYSTEM** (NP)
227 Britany Road, Guntersville, AL Zip 35976–5766;
tel. 256/894–6615; Gary R. Gore, Chief Executive Officer
(Independent Hospital System)

ALABAMA: MARSHALL MEDICAL CENTER NORTH (O, 90 beds) 8000 Alabama
Highway 69, Guntersville, AL Zip 35976; tel. 256/753–8000; Cheryl M.
Hays, FACHE, Administrator
Web address: www.mmcenters.com

MARSHALL MEDICAL CENTER SOUTH (O, 114 beds) U.S. Highway 431 North,
Boaz, AL Zip 35957–0999, Mailing Address: P.O. Box 758,
Zip 35957–0758; tel. 256/593–8310; John D. Anderson, FACHE,
Administrator
Web address: www.mmcenters.com//index.php/facilities/marshall_south

Owned, leased, sponsored:	2 hospitals	204 beds
Contract–managed:	0 hospitals	0 beds
Totals:	2 hospitals	204 beds

★0523: **MARY WASHINGTON HEALTHCARE** (NP)
2300 Fall Hill Avenue, Suite 308, Fredericksburg, VA
Zip 22401–3343; tel. 540/741–3100; Fred M. Rankin, III, President
and Chief Executive Officer
(Independent Hospital System)

VIRGINIA: MARY WASHINGTON HOSPITAL (O, 437 beds) 1001 Sam Perry
Boulevard, Fredericksburg, VA Zip 22401–3354; tel. 540/741–1100;
Fred M. Rankin, III, President and Chief Executive Officer
Web address: www.marywashingtonhealthcare.
com/locations/mary–washington–hospital

STAFFORD HOSPITAL (O, 100 beds) 101 Hospital Center Boulevard, Stafford,
VA Zip 22554–6200; tel. 540/741–9000; Fred M. Rankin, III, President and
Chief Executive Officer
Web address: www.mwhc.com

Owned, leased, sponsored:	2 hospitals	537 beds
Contract–managed:	0 hospitals	0 beds
Totals:	2 hospitals	537 beds

0013: **MASSACHUSETTS DEPARTMENT OF MENTAL HEALTH**
(NP)
25 Staniford Street, Boston, MA Zip 02114–2575;
tel. 617/626–8123; Marcia Fowler, Commissioner

MASSACHUSETTS: DR. J. CORRIGAN MENTAL HEALTH CENTER (O, 16 beds)
49 Hillside Street, Fall River, MA Zip 02720–5266; tel. 508/235–7200;
Roberta H. Guez, Director

TAUNTON STATE HOSPITAL (O, 45 beds) 60 Hodges Avenue Extension,
Taunton, MA Zip 02780–3034, Mailing Address: PO Box 4007,
Zip 02780–0997; tel. 508/977–3000; Kathleen Duke, Chief Executive Officer

WORCESTER RECOVERY CENTER AND HOSPITAL (O, 126 beds) 305 Belmont
Street, Worcester, MA Zip 01604–1695; tel. 508/368–3300; Anthony
Riccitelli, Chief Operating Officer

Owned, leased, sponsored:	3 hospitals	187 beds
Contract–managed:	0 hospitals	0 beds
Totals:	3 hospitals	187 beds

0280: **MASSACHUSETTS DEPARTMENT OF PUBLIC HEALTH**
(NP)
250 Washington Street, Boston, MA Zip 02108–4619;
tel. 617/624–6000; Sandra Akers, Bureau Director, Public Health
Hospitals
(Independent Hospital System)

LEMUEL SHATTUCK HOSPITAL (O, 260 beds) 170 Morton Street, Jamaica
Plain, MA Zip 02130–3735; tel. 617/522–8110; Paul Romary, Chief
Executive Officer
Web address: www.mass.gov/shattuckhospital

MASSACHUSETTS HOSPITAL SCHOOL (O, 80 beds) 3 Randolph Street,
Canton, MA Zip 02021–2351; tel. 781/828–2440; Brian V. Devin, Chief
Executive Officer
Web address: www.mhsf.us/

TEWKSBURY HOSPITAL (O, 720 beds) 365 East Street, Tewksbury, MA
Zip 01876–1998; tel. 978/851–7321; Debra Tosti, Chief Executive Officer
Web address: www.mass.gov

WESTERN MASSACHUSETTS HOSPITAL (O, 70 beds) 91 East Mountain Road,
Westfield, MA Zip 01085–1801; tel. 413/562–4131; Derrick Tallman, Chief
Executive Officer
Web address: www.mass.
gov/eohhs/gov/departments/dph/programs/western–massachusetts–hospital.
html

For explanation of codes following names, see page B2.
★ Indicates Type III membership in the American Hospital Association.

Owned, leased, sponsored:	4 hospitals	1130 beds
Contract-managed:	0 hospitals	0 beds
Totals:	4 hospitals	1130 beds

★0882: MAURY REGIONAL HEALTH SYSTEM (NP)

1224 Trotwood Avenue, Columbia, TN Zip 38401–4802;
tel. 931/381–1111; H. Alan Watson, FACHE, Chief Executive Officer
(Independent Hospital System)

TENNESSEE: MARSHALL MEDICAL CENTER (O, 12 beds) 1080 North Ellington Parkway, Lewisburg, TN Zip 37091–2227, Mailing Address: P.O. Box 1609, Zip 37091–1609; tel. 931/359–6241; Phyllis Brown, Chief Executive Officer
Web address: www.mauryregional.com

MAURY REGIONAL HOSPITAL (O, 232 beds) 1224 Trotwood Avenue, Columbia, TN Zip 38401–4802; tel. 931/381–1111; H. Alan Watson, FACHE, Chief Executive Officer
Web address: www.mauryregional.com

WAYNE MEDICAL CENTER (L, 78 beds) 103 J. V. Mangubat Drive, Waynesboro, TN Zip 38485–2440, Mailing Address: P.O. Box 580, Zip 38485–0580; tel. 931/722–5411; Paul Betz, FACHE, Interim Chief Executive Officer
Web address: www.mauryregional.com

Owned, leased, sponsored:	3 hospitals	322 beds
Contract-managed:	0 hospitals	0 beds
Totals:	3 hospitals	322 beds

★1875: MAYO CLINIC (NP)

200 First Street S.W., Rochester, MN Zip 55905–0002;
tel. 507/284–2511; John Noseworthy, M.D., President and Chief Executive Officer
(Decentralized Health System)

ARIZONA: MAYO CLINIC HOSPITAL (O, 268 beds) 5777 East Mayo Boulevard, Phoenix, AZ Zip 85054–4502; tel. 480/515–6296; Ann M. Meyers, Hospital Administrator
Web address: www.mayoclinic.org/arizona/

FLORIDA: MAYO CLINIC JACKSONVILLE (O, 249 beds) 4500 San Pablo Road South, Jacksonville, FL Zip 32224–1865; tel. 904/953–2000; William C. Rupp, M.D., Chief Executive Officer
Web address: www.mayoclinic.org/jacksonville/

GEORGIA: MAYO CLINIC HEALTH SYSTEM IN WAYCROSS (O, 198 beds) 410 Darling Avenue, Waycross, GA Zip 31501–6357, Mailing Address: P.O. Box 139, Zip 31502–0139; tel. 912/283–3030; Kenneth Calamia, Chair and Chief Executive Officer
Web address: www.mayoclinichealthsystem.org

IOWA: FLOYD COUNTY MEDICAL CENTER (C, 25 beds) 800 Eleventh Street, Charles City, IA Zip 50616–3499; tel. 641/228–6830; Bill D. Faust, Administrator
Web address: www.fcmc.us.com/

WINNESHIEK MEDICAL CENTER (C, 25 beds) 901 Montgomery Street, Decorah, IA Zip 52101–2325; tel. 563/382–2911; Lisa Radtke, Interim Chief Administrative Officer
Web address: www.winmedical.org

MINNESOTA: MAYO CLINIC HEALTH SYSTEM IN ALBERT LEA (O, 129 beds) 404 West Fountain Street, Albert Lea, MN Zip 56007–2473; tel. 507/373–2384; Mark Ciota, M.D., Chief Executive Officer
Web address: www.almedcenter.org

MAYO CLINIC HEALTH SYSTEM IN AUSTIN (O, 82 beds) 1000 First Drive N.W., Austin, MN Zip 55912–2904; tel. 507/433–7351; Mark Ciota, M.D., Chief Executive Officer
Web address: www.austinmedicalcenter.org

MAYO CLINIC HEALTH SYSTEM IN CANNON FALLS (O, 21 beds) 1116 West Mill Street, Cannon Falls, MN Zip 55009–1898; tel. 507/263–4221; Thomas J. Witt, M.D., President and Chief Executive Officer
Web address: www.mayoclinichealthsystem.org/locations/cannon-falls

MAYO CLINIC HEALTH SYSTEM IN FAIRMONT (O, 96 beds) 800 Medical Center Drive, Fairmont, MN Zip 56031–4575; tel. 507/238–8100; Robert Bartingale, Administrator
Web address: www.fairmontmedicalcenter.org

MAYO CLINIC HEALTH SYSTEM IN LAKE CITY (O, 108 beds) 500 West Grant Street, Lake City, MN Zip 55041–1143; tel. 651/345–3321; Susan M. Stiene, R.N., MS, Interim Chief Administrative Officer
Web address: www.lakecitymedicalcenter.org

MAYO CLINIC HEALTH SYSTEM IN MANKATO (O, 166 beds) 1025 Marsh Street, Mankato, MN Zip 56001–4752, Mailing Address: P.O. Box 8673, Zip 56002–8673; tel. 507/625–4031; Gregory Kutcher, M.D., President and Chief Executive Officer
Web address: www.isj-mhs.org

MAYO CLINIC HEALTH SYSTEM IN NEW PRAGUE (O, 25 beds) 301 Second Street N.E., New Prague, MN Zip 56071–1799; tel. 952/758–4431; Mary J. Klimp, FACHE, Administrator
Web address: www.mayoclinichealthsystem.org/locations/new-prague

MAYO CLINIC HEALTH SYSTEM IN RED WING (O, 134 beds) 701 Hewitt Boulevard, Red Wing, MN Zip 55066–2848, Mailing Address: P.O. Box 95, Zip 55066–0095; tel. 651/267–5000; Thomas J. Witt, M.D., President and Chief Executive Officer
Web address: www.mayoclinichealthsystem.org/locations/red-wing

MAYO CLINIC HEALTH SYSTEM IN SAINT JAMES (O, 13 beds) 1101 Moulton and Parsons Drive, Saint James, MN Zip 56081–5550; tel. 507/375–3261; Ryan J. Smith, Administrator
Web address: www.mayoclinichealthsystem.org/locations/st-james

MAYO CLINIC HEALTH SYSTEM IN SPRINGFIELD (O, 24 beds) 625 North Jackson Avenue, Springfield, MN Zip 56087–1714, Mailing Address: P.O. Box 146, Zip 56087–0146; tel. 507/723–6201; Scott D. Thoreson, FACHE, Administrator
Web address: www.smc-mhs.org

MAYO CLINIC HEALTH SYSTEM IN WASECA (O, 25 beds) 501 North State Street, Waseca, MN Zip 56093–2811; tel. 507/835–1210; Jeffrey Carlson, Administrator
Web address: www.mayoclinichealthsystem.org

MAYO CLINIC HOSPITAL – ROCHESTER (O, 1243 beds) 1216 Second Street S.W., Rochester, MN Zip 55902–1906; tel. 507/255–5123; Lynn Frederick, Administrator
Web address: www.mayoclinic.org

WISCONSIN: MAYO CLINIC HEALTH SYSTEM – CHIPPEWA VALLEY IN BLOOMER (O, 49 beds) 1501 Thompson Street, Bloomer, WI Zip 54724–1299; tel. 715/568–2000; Edward A. Wittrock, Vice President Regional System
Web address: www.bloomermedicalcenter.org

MAYO CLINIC HEALTH SYSTEM – FRANCISCAN HEALTHCARE IN LA CROSSE (O, 155 beds) 700 West Avenue South, La Crosse, WI Zip 54601–4783; tel. 608/785–0940; Timothy J. Johnson, President and Chief Executive Officer
Web address: www.franciscanskemp.org

MAYO CLINIC HEALTH SYSTEM – FRANCISCAN HEALTHCARE IN SPARTA (O, 13 beds) 310 West Main Street, Sparta, WI Zip 54656–2171; tel. 608/269–2132; Kimberly Hawthorne, Administrator
Web address: www.mayohealthsystem.com

MAYO CLINIC HEALTH SYSTEM – NORTHLAND IN BARRON (O, 38 beds) 1222 Woodland Avenue, Barron, WI Zip 54812–1798; tel. 715/537–3186; Maurita Sullivan, Vice President
Web address: www.luthermidelfortnorthland.org

MAYO CLINIC HEALTH SYSTEM – OAKRIDGE IN OSSEO (O, 39 beds) 13025 Eighth Street, Osseo, WI Zip 54758–7634, Mailing Address: P.O. Box 70, Zip 54758–0070; tel. 715/597–3121; Dean Eide, Vice President
Web address: www.mayoclinichealthsystem.org/locations/osseo

MAYO CLINIC HEALTH SYSTEM – RED CEDAR IN MENOMONIE (O, 21 beds) 2321 Stout Road, Menomonie, WI Zip 54751–2397; tel. 715/235–5531; Steven Lindberg, Chief Administrative Officer
Web address: www.rcmc-mhs.org

MAYO CLINIC HEALTH SYSTEM IN EAU CLAIRE (O, 204 beds) 1221 Whipple Street, Eau Claire, WI Zip 54703–5270, Mailing Address: P.O. Box 4105, Zip 54702–4105; tel. 715/838–3311; Randall L. Linton, M.D., President and Chief Executive Officer
Web address: www.mhs.mayo.edu

Owned, leased, sponsored:	22 hospitals	3300 beds
Contract-managed:	2 hospitals	50 beds
Totals:	24 hospitals	3350 beds

For explanation of codes following names, see page B2.
★ Indicates Type III membership in the American Hospital Association.

★**0252:** **MCLAREN HEALTH CARE CORPORATION** (NP)
G3235 Beecher Road, Suite B., Flint, MI Zip 48532–3650;
tel. 810/342–1100; Philip A. Incarnati, President and Chief Executive
Officer
(Moderately Centralized Health System)

MICHIGAN: MCLAREN BAY REGION (O, 338 beds) 1900 Columbus Avenue,
Bay City, MI Zip 48708–6831; tel. 989/894–3000; Alice M. Gerard,
President and Chief Executive Officer
Web address: www.bayregional.org

MCLAREN BAY SPECIAL CARE (O, 26 beds) 3250 East Midland Road, Suite 1,
Bay City, MI Zip 48706–2835; tel. 989/667–6802; Cheryl A. Burzynski,
President
Web address: www.bayspecialcare.org

MCLAREN CENTRAL MICHIGAN (O, 78 beds) 1221 South Drive, Mount
Pleasant, MI Zip 48858–3257; tel. 989/772–6700; William P. Lawrence,
President and Chief Executive Officer
Web address: www.cmch.org

MCLAREN FLINT (O, 336 beds) 401 South Ballenger Highway, Flint, MI
Zip 48532–3685; tel. 810/342–2000; Donald C. Kooy, President and Chief
Executive Officer
Web address: www.mclarenregional.org

MCLAREN GREATER LANSING (O, 322 beds) 401 West Greenlawn Avenue,
Lansing, MI Zip 48910–2819; tel. 517/975–6000; Rick Wright, President and
Chief Executive Officer
Web address: www.irmc.org

MCLAREN LAPEER REGION (O, 159 beds) 1375 North Main Street, Lapeer,
MI Zip 48446–1350; tel. 810/667–5500; Barton Buxton, Ed.D., President
and Chief Executive Officer
Web address: www.lapeerregional.org

MCLAREN MACOMB (O, 288 beds) 1000 Harrington Boulevard, Mount
Clemens, MI Zip 48043–2992; tel. 586/493–8000; Mark S. O'Halla,
President and Chief Executive Officer
Web address: www.mclaren.org/macomb/macomb.aspx

MCLAREN NORTHERN MICHIGAN (O, 0 beds) 748 South Main Street,
Cheboygan, MI Zip 49721–2299, Mailing Address: P.O. Box 419,
Zip 49721–0419; tel. 231/627–5601;

MCLAREN NORTHERN MICHIGAN (O, 188 beds) 416 Connable Avenue,
Petoskey, MI Zip 49770–2297; tel. 231/487–4000; David M. Zechman,
FACHE, President and Chief Executive Officer
Web address: www.northernhealth.org

MCLAREN OAKLAND (O, 285 beds) 50 North Perry Street, Pontiac, MI
Zip 48342–2253; tel. 248/338–5000; Clarence Sevillian, President and Chief
Executive Officer
Web address: www.pohmedical.org

Owned, leased, sponsored:	10 hospitals	2020 beds
Contract–managed:	0 hospitals	0 beds
Totals:	10 hospitals	2020 beds

0874: **MCLEOD HEALTH** (NP)
555 East Cheves Street, Florence, SC Zip 29506–2617, Mailing
Address: P.O. Box 100551, Zip 29502–0551; tel. 843/777–2000;
Robert L. Colones, President and Chief Executive Officer
(Centralized Health System)

SOUTH CAROLINA: MCLEOD LORIS SEACOAST HOSPITAL (O, 243 beds)
3655 Mitchell Street, Loris, SC Zip 29569–2827; tel. 843/716–7000;
Edward D. Tinsley, III, Chief Executive Officer
Web address: www.mcleodhealth.org

MCLEOD MEDICAL CENTER DILLON (O, 63 beds) 301 East Jackson Street,
Dillon, SC Zip 29536–2509, Mailing Address: P.O. Box 1327,
Zip 29536–1327; tel. 843/774–4111; Deborah Locklair, FACHE,
Administrator
Web address: www.mcleodhealth.org

MCLEOD MEDICAL CENTER–DARLINGTON (O, 50 beds) 701 Cashua Ferry
Road, Darlington, SC Zip 29532–8488, Mailing Address: P.O. Box 1859,
Zip 29540; tel. 843/395–1100; Pat Godbold, Administrator
Web address: www.mcleodhealth.org

MCLEOD REGIONAL MEDICAL CENTER (O, 488 beds) 555 East Cheves
Street, Florence, SC Zip 29506–2617, Mailing Address: P.O. Box 100551,
Zip 29502–0551; tel. 843/777–2000; Robert L. Colones, President and
Chief Executive Officer
Web address: www.mcleodhealth.org

Owned, leased, sponsored:	4 hospitals	844 beds
Contract–managed:	0 hospitals	0 beds
Totals:	4 hospitals	844 beds

★**0154:** **MEDSTAR HEALTH** (NP)
5565 Sterrett Place, 5th Floor, Columbia, MD Zip 21044–2665;
tel. 410/772–6500; Kenneth A. Samet, President and Chief
Executive Officer
(Centralized Health System)

DISTRICT OF COLUMBIA: MEDSTAR GEORGETOWN UNIVERSITY HOSPITAL
(O, 396 beds) 3800 Reservoir Road N.W., Washington, DC
Zip 20007–2197; tel. 202/444–2000; Richard L. Goldberg, M.D.,
President
Web address: www.georgetownuniversityhospital.org

MEDSTAR NATIONAL REHABILITATION HOSPITAL (O, 137 beds) 102 Irving
Street N.W., Washington, DC Zip 20010–2949; tel. 202/877–1000; John D.
Rockwood, President
Web address: www.medstarnrh.org

MEDSTAR WASHINGTON HOSPITAL CENTER (O, 769 beds) 110 Irving Street
N.W., Washington, DC Zip 20010–3017; tel. 202/877–7000; John Sullivan,
President
Web address: www.whcenter.org

MARYLAND: MEDSTAR FRANKLIN SQUARE MEDICAL CENTER (O, 385 beds)
9000 Franklin Square Drive, Baltimore, MD Zip 21237–3901;
tel. 443/777–7000; Samuel E. Moskowitz, President
Web address: www.medstarfranklin.org

MEDSTAR GOOD SAMARITAN HOSPITAL (O, 308 beds) 5601 Loch Raven
Boulevard, Baltimore, MD Zip 21239–2995; tel. 443/444–8000; Jeffrey A.
Matton, President
Web address: www.goodsam-md.org

MEDSTAR HARBOR HOSPITAL (O, 213 beds) 3001 South Hanover Street,
Baltimore, MD Zip 21225–1290; tel. 410/350–3200; Dennis W. Pullin,
FACHE, President
Web address: www.harborhospital.org

MEDSTAR MONTGOMERY MEDICAL CENTER (O, 150 beds) 18101 Prince
Philip Drive, Olney, MD Zip 20832–1512; tel. 301/774–8882; Peter W.
Monge, President
Web address: www.medstarmontgomery.org

MEDSTAR SOUTHERN MARYLAND HOSPITAL CENTER (O, 287 beds) 7503
Surratts Road, Clinton, MD Zip 20735–3358; tel. 301/868–8000; Christine
R. Wray, President and Chief Executive Officer
Web address: www.smhcealth.org

MEDSTAR ST. MARY'S HOSPITAL (O, 90 beds) 25500 Point Lookout Road,
Leonardtown, MD Zip 20650–2015, Mailing Address: P.O. Box 527,
Zip 20650–0527; tel. 301/475–6001; Christine R. Wray, President
Web address: www.medstarstmarys.org

MEDSTAR UNION MEMORIAL HOSPITAL (O, 246 beds) 201 East University
Parkway, Baltimore, MD Zip 21218–2895; tel. 410/554–2000; Bradley
Chambers, President
Web address: www.medstarunionmemorial.org

Owned, leased, sponsored:	10 hospitals	2981 beds
Contract–managed:	0 hospitals	0 beds
Totals:	10 hospitals	2981 beds

★**0086:** **MEMORIAL HEALTH SYSTEM** (NP)
701 North First Street, Springfield, IL Zip 62781–0001;
tel. 217/788–3000; Edgar J. Curtis, FACHE, President and Chief
Executive Officer
(Centralized Health System)

ILLINOIS: ABRAHAM LINCOLN MEMORIAL HOSPITAL (O, 25 beds) 200
Stahlhut Drive, Lincoln, IL Zip 62656–5066; tel. 217/732–2161; Dolan
Dalpoas, President and Chief Executive Officer
Web address: www.almh.org

For explanation of codes following names, see page B2.
★ Indicates Type III membership in the American Hospital Association.

MEMORIAL MEDICAL CENTER (O, 473 beds) 701 North First Street, Springfield, IL Zip 62781–0001; tel. 217/788–3000; Edgar J. Curtis, FACHE, President and Chief Executive Officer
Web address: www.memorialmedical.com

TAYLORVILLE MEMORIAL HOSPITAL (O, 45 beds) 201 East Pleasant Street, Taylorville, IL Zip 62568–1597; tel. 217/824–3331; Daniel J. Raab, President and Chief Executive Officer
Web address: www.taylorvillememorial.org

Owned, leased, sponsored:	3 hospitals	543 beds
Contract–managed:	0 hospitals	0 beds
Totals:	3 hospitals	543 beds

0176: MEMORIAL HEALTH SYSTEM OF EAST TEXAS (NP)
1201 Frank Avenue, Lufkin, TX Zip 75904–3357; tel. 936/634–8111; Gary N. Looper, President and Chief Executive Officer
(Moderately Centralized Health System)

TEXAS: MEMORIAL MEDICAL CENTER – LIVINGSTON (O, 66 beds) 1717 Highway 59 Bypass, Livingston, TX Zip 77351–1257, Mailing Address: P.O. Box 1257, Zip 77351–0022; tel. 936/329–8700; Randy Slack, Interim Chief Executive Officer
Web address: www.memorialhealth.org

MEMORIAL MEDICAL CENTER – LUFKIN (O, 217 beds) 1201 West Frank Avenue, Lufkin, TX Zip 75904–3357, Mailing Address: P.O. Box 1447, Zip 75902–1447; tel. 936/634–8111; Gary N. Looper, Chief Executive Officer
Web address: www.memorialhealth.us/centers/lufkin

MEMORIAL MEDICAL CENTER – SAN AUGUSTINE (O, 18 beds) 511 East Hospital Street, San Augustine, TX Zip 75972–2121, Mailing Address: P.O. Box 658, Zip 75972–0658; tel. 936/275–3446; Darlene Williams, R.N., Administrator
Web address: www.memorialhealth.org

MEMORIAL SPECIALTY HOSPITAL (O, 26 beds) 1201 West Frank Avenue, Lufkin, TX Zip 75904–3357; tel. 936/639–7975; Leslie Leach, Administrator
Web address: www.memorialhealth.org

Owned, leased, sponsored:	4 hospitals	327 beds
Contract–managed:	0 hospitals	0 beds
Totals:	4 hospitals	327 beds

★0083: MEMORIAL HEALTHCARE SYSTEM (NP)
3501 Johnson Street, Hollywood, FL Zip 33021–5421; tel. 954/265–5805; Frank V. Sacco, FACHE, President and Chief Executive Officer
(Centralized Health System)

FLORIDA: MEMORIAL HOSPITAL MIRAMAR (O, 178 beds) 1901 S.W. 172nd Avenue, Miramar, FL Zip 33029–5592; tel. 954/538–5000; Leah A. Carpenter, Administrator and Chief Executive Officer
Web address: www.mhs.net

MEMORIAL HOSPITAL PEMBROKE (L, 149 beds) 7800 Sheridan Street, Pembroke Pines, FL Zip 33024–2536; tel. 954/883–8482; Keith W. Gallagher, FACHE, Administrator and Chief Executive Officer
Web address: www.memorialpembroke.com/

MEMORIAL HOSPITAL WEST (O, 384 beds) 703 North Flamingo Road, Pembroke Pines, FL Zip 33028–1014; tel. 954/436–5000; C. Kennon Hetlage, FACHE, Administrator and Chief Executive Officer
Web address: www.mhs.net

MEMORIAL REGIONAL HOSPITAL (O, 757 beds) 3501 Johnson Street, Hollywood, FL Zip 33021–5421; tel. 954/987–2000; Zeff Ross, FACHE, Senior Vice President and Chief Executive Officer
Web address: www.mhs.net

MEMORIAL REGIONAL HOSPITAL SOUTH (O, 324 beds) 3600 Washington Street, Hollywood, FL Zip 33021–8216; tel. 954/966–4500; Douglas Zaren, FACHE, Administrator
Web address: www.memorialregionalsouth.com

Owned, leased, sponsored:	5 hospitals	1792 beds
Contract–managed:	0 hospitals	0 beds
Totals:	5 hospitals	1792 beds

★2645: MEMORIAL HERMANN HEALTHCARE SYSTEM (NP)
929 Gessner, Suite 2700, Houston, TX Zip 77024–2593; tel. 713/242–2700; Daniel J. Wolterman, President and Chief Executive Officer
(Centralized Health System)

TEXAS: MEMORIAL HERMANN – TEXAS MEDICAL CENTER (O, 897 beds) 6411 Fannin Street, Houston, TX Zip 77030–1501; tel. 713/704–4000; Craig Cordola, Chief Executive Officer
Web address: www.mhhs.org

MEMORIAL HERMANN KATY HOSPITAL (O, 142 beds) 23900 Katy Freeway, Katy, TX Zip 77494–1323; tel. 281/644–7000; Brian S. Barbe, Chief Executive Officer
Web address: www.memorialhermann.org/locations/katy/

MEMORIAL HERMANN MEMORIAL CITY MEDICAL CENTER (L, 386 beds) 921 Gessner Road, Houston, TX Zip 77024–2501; tel. 713/242–3000; Keith N. Alexander, Chief Executive Officer
Web address: www.memorialhermann.org

MEMORIAL HERMANN NORTHEAST (L, 227 beds) 18951 North Memorial Drive, Humble, TX Zip 77338–4297; tel. 281/540–7700; Louis G. Smith, Jr., Chief Executive Officer
Web address: www.memorialhermann.org

MEMORIAL HERMANN NORTHWEST HOSPITAL (O, 1200 beds) 1635 North Loop West, Houston, TX Zip 77008–1532; tel. 713/867–3380; Susan Jadlowski, MSN, R.N., Chief Executive Officer
Web address: www.mhbh.org

MEMORIAL HERMANN REHABILITATION HOSPITAL – KATY (O, 35 beds) 21720 Kingsland Boulevard, Katy, TX Zip 77450–2550; tel. 281/579–5555; Carl E. Josehart, Chief Executive Officer
Web address: www.memorialhermann.com

MEMORIAL HERMANN SUGAR LAND HOSPITAL (O, 81 beds) 17500 West Grand Parkway South, Sugar Land, TX Zip 77479–2562; tel. 281/725–5000; Gregory Haralson, Chief Executive Officer
Web address: www.memorialhermann.org

TIRR MEMORIAL HERMANN (O, 119 beds) 1333 Moursund Street, Houston, TX Zip 77030–3405; tel. 713/799–5000; Carl E. Josehart, Chief Executive Officer
Web address: www.memorialhermann.org/locations/tirr.html

Owned, leased, sponsored:	8 hospitals	3087 beds
Contract–managed:	0 hospitals	0 beds
Totals:	8 hospitals	3087 beds

0084: MEMORIALCARE (NP)
17360 Brookhurst Street, Fountain Valley, CA Zip 92708–3720, Mailing Address: P.O. Box 1428, Long Beach, Zip 90801–1428; tel. 714/377–2900; Barry S. Arbuckle, Ph.D., President and Chief Executive Officer
(Centralized Health System)

CALIFORNIA: COMMUNITY HOSPITAL OF LONG BEACH (O, 148 beds) 1720 Termino Avenue, Long Beach, CA Zip 90804–2104; tel. 562/498–1000; Diana Hendel, PharmD, Chief Executive Officer
Web address: www.chlb.org

LONG BEACH MEMORIAL MEDICAL CENTER (O, 420 beds) 2801 Atlantic Avenue, Long Beach, CA Zip 90806–1701, Mailing Address: P.O. Box 1428, Zip 90801–1428; tel. 562/933–2000; Diana Hendel, PharmD, Chief Executive Officer
Web address: www.memorialcare.org/LongBeach

MILLER CHILDREN'S HOSPITAL LONG BEACH (O, 373 beds) 2801 Atlantic Avenue, Long Beach, CA Zip 90806–1701; tel. 562/933–5437; Diana Hendel, PharmD, Chief Executive Officer
Web address: www.memorialcare.org

ORANGE COAST MEMORIAL MEDICAL CENTER (O, 218 beds) 9920 Talbert Avenue, Fountain Valley, CA Zip 92708–5115; tel. 714/378–7000; Marcia Manker, Chief Executive Officer
Web address: www.memorialcare.org

Section B

For explanation of codes following names, see page B2.
★ Indicates Type III membership in the American Hospital Association.

SADDLEBACK MEMORIAL MEDICAL CENTER (O, 313 beds) 24451 Health Center Drive, Laguna Hills, CA Zip 92653–3689; tel. 949/837–4500; Steve Geidt, Chief Executive Officer
Web address: www.memorialcare.org

Owned, leased, sponsored:	5 hospitals	1472 beds
Contract–managed:	0 hospitals	0 beds
Totals:	5 hospitals	1472 beds

★**5155: MERCY HEALTH** (CC)
615 Elsinore Place, Cincinnati, OH Zip 45202–1459; tel. 513/639–2800; Michael D. Connelly, President and Chief Executive Officer
(Moderately Centralized Health System)

KENTUCKY: LOURDES HOSPITAL (O, 262 beds) 1530 Lone Oak Road, Paducah, KY Zip 42003–7900, Mailing Address: P.O. Box 7100, Zip 42002–7100; tel. 270/444–2444; Steven Grinnell, President and Chief Executive Officer
Web address: www.lourdes–pad.org

MARCUM AND WALLACE MEMORIAL HOSPITAL (O, 25 beds) 60 Mercy Court, Irvine, KY Zip 40336–1331; tel. 606/723–2115; Susan Starling, President and Chief Executive Officer
Web address: www.marcumandwallace.org

OHIO: INSTITUTE FOR ORTHOPAEDIC SURGERY (O, 3 beds) 801 Medical Drive, Suite B., Lima, OH Zip 45804–4030; tel. 419/224–7586; Mark McDonald, M.D., President and Chief Executive Officer
Web address: www.ioshospital.com

MERCY ALLEN HOSPITAL (O, 25 beds) 200 West Lorain Street, Oberlin, OH Zip 44074–1077; tel. 440/775–1211; Susan Bowers, R.N., President
Web address: www.mercyonline.org/mercy_allen_hospital.aspx

MERCY HEALTH – ANDERSON HOSPITAL (O, 188 beds) 7500 State Road, Cincinnati, OH Zip 45255–2492; tel. 513/624–4500; Jeff Graham, Market Leader and President
Web address: www.e–mercy.com

MERCY HEALTH – CLERMONT HOSPITAL (O, 119 beds) 3000 Hospital Drive, Batavia, OH Zip 45103–1921; tel. 513/732–8200; Jeff Graham, Market Leader and President
Web address: www.e–mercy.com

MERCY HEALTH – FAIRFIELD HOSPITAL (O, 236 beds) 3000 Mack Road, Fairfield, OH Zip 45014–5335; tel. 513/870–7000; Thomas S. Urban, Market Leader and President
Web address: www.e–mercy.com

MERCY HEALTH – WEST HOSPITAL (O, 250 beds) 3300 Mercy Health Boulevard, Cincinnati, OH Zip 45211; tel. 513/215–5000; Michael R. Stephens, Market Leader and President
Web address: www.e–mercy.com/west–hospital

MERCY HOSPITAL OF DEFIANCE (O, 23 beds) 1404 East Second Street, Defiance, OH Zip 43512–2440; tel. 419/782–8444; Sonya Selhorst, R.N., Administrator
Web address: www.ehealthconnection.com/regions/toledo/

MERCY MEMORIAL HOSPITAL (O, 25 beds) 904 Scioto Street, Urbana, OH Zip 43078–2200; tel. 937/653–5231; Karen S. Gorby, R.N., MSN, FACHE, Administrator and Chief Nursing Officer
Web address: www.health–partners.org

MERCY REGIONAL MEDICAL CENTER (O, 259 beds) 3700 Kolbe Road, Lorain, OH Zip 44053–1697; tel. 440/960–4000; Edwin M. Oley, President and Chief Executive Officer
Web address: www.community–health–partners.com

MERCY ST. ANNE HOSPITAL (O, 96 beds) 3404 West Sylvania Avenue, Toledo, OH Zip 43623–4467; tel. 419/407–2663; Bradley J. Bertke, President and Chief Executive Officer
Web address: www.mercyweb.org

MERCY ST. CHARLES HOSPITAL (O, 264 beds) 2600 Navarre Avenue, Oregon, OH Zip 43616–3297; tel. 419/696–7200; Jeffrey Dempsey, President and Chief Executive Officer
Web address: www.mercyweb.org

MERCY ST. VINCENT MEDICAL CENTER (O, 431 beds) 2213 Cherry Street, Toledo, OH Zip 43608–2691; tel. 419/251–3232; Kerry Tirman, President and Chief Operating Officer
Web address: www.mercyweb.org

MERCY TIFFIN HOSPITAL (O, 51 beds) 45 St. Lawrence Drive, Tiffin, OH Zip 44883–8310; tel. 419/455–7000; B. Lynn Detterman, President and Chief Executive Officer
Web address: www.mercyweb.org

MERCY WILLARD HOSPITAL (O, 20 beds) 1100 Neal Zick Road, Willard, OH Zip 44890–9287; tel. 419/964–5000; B. Lynn Detterman, President and Chief Executive Officer
Web address: www.mercyweb.org

SPRINGFIELD REGIONAL MEDICAL CENTER (O, 254 beds) 100 Medical Center Drive, Springfield, OH Zip 55504–2687; tel. 937/523–1000; Paul C. Hiltz, FACHE, Market President and Chief Executive Officer
Web address: www.community–mercy.org

ST. ELIZABETH BOARDMAN HEALTH CENTER (O, 128 beds) 8401 Market Street, Boardman, OH Zip 44512–6777; tel. 330/729–2929; Eugenia Aubel, President
Web address: www.ehealthconnection.com/regions/youngstown/content/show_facility.asp?facility_id=190

ST. ELIZABETH HEALTH CENTER (O, 405 beds) 1044 Belmont Avenue, Youngstown, OH Zip 44504–1096, Mailing Address: P.O. Box 1790, Zip 44501–1790; tel. 330/746–7211; Robert W. Shroder, President and Chief Executive Officer
Web address: www.hmpartners.org

ST. JOSEPH HEALTH CENTER (O, 141 beds) 667 Eastland Avenue S.E., Warren, OH Zip 44484–4531; tel. 330/841–4000; Kathy Cook, R.N., MSN, President
Web address: www.hmpartners.org

ST. RITA'S MEDICAL CENTER (O, 415 beds) 730 West Market Street, Lima, OH Zip 45801–4602; tel. 419/227–3361; Robert O. Baxter, President and Chief Executive Officer
Web address: www.stritas.org

THE JEWISH HOSPITAL – MERCY HEALTH (O, 209 beds) 4777 East Galbraith Road, Cincinnati, OH Zip 45236–2725; tel. 513/686–3000; Patricia Davis–Hagens, R.N., Chief Executive Officer
Web address: www.jewishhospitalcincinnati.com/

Owned, leased, sponsored:	22 hospitals	3829 beds
Contract–managed:	0 hospitals	0 beds
Totals:	22 hospitals	3829 beds

★**5185: MERCY HEALTH** (CC)
14528 South Outer 40, Suite 100, Chesterfield, MO Zip 63017–5743; tel. 314/579–6100; Lynn Britton, President and Chief Executive Officer
(Decentralized Health System)

ARKANSAS: MERCY HOSPITAL BERRYVILLE (O, 25 beds) 214 Carter Street, Berryville, AR Zip 72616–4303; tel. 870/423–3355; Kristy Estrem, FACHE, President
Web address: www.mercy.net/berryvillear

MERCY HOSPITAL FORT SMITH (O, 374 beds) 7301 Rogers Avenue, Fort Smith, AR Zip 72903–4189, Mailing Address: P.O. Box 17000, Zip 72917–7000; tel. 479/314–6000; Ryan Gehrig, President
Web address: www.mercy.net/fortsmithar

MERCY HOSPITAL HOT SPRINGS (O, 282 beds) 300 Werner Street, Hot Springs National Park, AR Zip 71913–6406, Mailing Address: P.O. Box 29001, Zip 71903–9001; tel. 501/622–1000; Kim Day, Interim President
Web address: www.saintjosephs.com

MERCY HOSPITAL OZARK (O, 25 beds) 801 West River Street, Ozark, AR Zip 72949–3023; tel. 479/667–4138; Teresa Williams, R.N., Interim Administrator
Web address: www.mercy.net/northwestarar/practice/mercy–hospital–ozark

MERCY HOSPITAL PARIS (O, 16 beds) 500 East Academy, Paris, AR Zip 72855–4040; tel. 479/963–6101; Sharon D. Sorey, R.N., Regional Administrator
Web address: www.mercy.net/fortsmithar

MERCY HOSPITAL ROGERS (O, 147 beds) 2710 Rife Medical Lane, Rogers, AR Zip 72758–1452; tel. 479/338–8000; Eric Pianalto, President
Web address: www.mercyhealthnwa.smhs.com

MERCY HOSPITAL WALDRON (O, 24 beds) 1341 West 6th Street, Waldron, AR Zip 72958–7642; tel. 479/637–4135; Dorothy O'Bar, R.N., Regional Administrator
Web address: www.stedwardmercy.com

For explanation of codes following names, see page B2.
★ Indicates Type III membership in the American Hospital Association.

KANSAS: MERCY HOSPITAL FORT SCOTT (O, 61 beds) 401 Woodland Hills Boulevard, Fort Scott, KS Zip 66701–8797; tel. 620/223–2200; Reta K. Baker, President
Web address: www.mercykansas.com

MERCY HOSPITAL INDEPENDENCE (O, 40 beds) 800 West Myrtle Street, Independence, KS Zip 67301–3240, Mailing Address: P.O. Box 388, Zip 67301–0388; tel. 620/331–2200; David Steinmann, President
Web address: www.mercy.net/independenceks

MERCY MAUDE NORTON HOSPITAL (O, 18 beds) 220 North Pennsylvania Avenue, Columbus, KS Zip 66725–1110; tel. 620/429–2545; Cindy Neely, Administrator
Web address: www.mercy.
net/newsroom–mercy–maude–norton–hospital–quick–facts

MISSOURI: MERCY HOSPITAL AURORA (O, 25 beds) 500 Porter Street, Aurora, MO Zip 65605–2365; tel. 417/678–2122; Douglas M. Stroemel, President
Web address: www.stjohns.com/aboutus/aurora.aspx

MERCY HOSPITAL CARTHAGE (L, 49 beds) 3125 Drive Russell Smith Way, Carthage, MO Zip 64836–7402; tel. 417/358–8121; Robert Y. Copeland, Jr., FACHE, Chief Executive Officer
Web address: www.mercy.net

MERCY HOSPITAL CASSVILLE (O, 18 beds) 94 Main Street, Cassville, MO Zip 65625–1610; tel. 417/847–6000; Douglas M. Stroemel, President
Web address: www.mercy.
net/northwestarar/practice/mercy–hospital–cassville

MERCY HOSPITAL JEFFERSON (O, 215 beds) Highway 61 South, Crystal City, MO Zip 63019, Mailing Address: P.O. Box 350, Zip 63019–0350; tel. 636/933–1000; Eric Ammons, President
Web address: www.mercy.net/crystalcitymo

MERCY HOSPITAL JOPLIN (O, 179 beds) 2817 South St. John's Boulevard, Joplin, MO Zip 64804–1626; tel. 417/781–2727; Gary W. Pulsipher, President and Chief Executive Officer
Web address: www.mercy.net/joplinmo

MERCY HOSPITAL LEBANON (O, 58 beds) 100 Hospital Drive, Lebanon, MO Zip 65536–9210; tel. 417/533–6100; Michele Schaefer, Interim President
Web address: www.stjohnslebanon.com

MERCY HOSPITAL SPRINGFIELD (O, 660 beds) 1235 East Cherokee Street, Springfield, MO Zip 65804–2263; tel. 417/820–2000; Jon D. Swope, Interim President
Web address: www.mercy.net/springfieldmo

MERCY HOSPITAL ST. LOUIS (O, 979 beds) 615 South New Ballas Road, Saint Louis, MO Zip 63141–8277; tel. 314/569–6000; Jeffrey A. Johnston, President
Web address: www.mercy.net/stlouismo

MERCY HOSPITAL WASHINGTON (O, 187 beds) 901 East Fifth Street, Washington, MO Zip 63090–3127; tel. 636/239–8000; Terri L. McLain, FACHE, President
Web address: www.mercy.net

MERCY ST. FRANCIS HOSPITAL (O, 20 beds) 100 West Highway 60, Mountain View, MO Zip 65548–7125; tel. 417/934–7000; Robert Rogers, Interim President
Web address: www.stjohns.com/aboutus/stfrancis.aspx

OKLAHOMA: ARBUCKLE MEMORIAL HOSPITAL (C, 13 beds) 2011 West Broadway Street, Sulphur, OK Zip 73086–4221; tel. 580/622–2161; Darin Farrell, Chief Executive Officer
Web address: www.arbucklehospital.com/

MERCY HEALTH LOVE COUNTY (C, 25 beds) 300 Wanda Street, Marietta, OK Zip 73448–1200; tel. 580/276–3347; Richard Barker, Administrator
Web address: www.mercyhealthlovecounty.com

MERCY HOSPITAL ADA (C, 156 beds) 430 North Monte Vista, Ada, OK Zip 74820–4610; tel. 580/332–2323; Diana Smalley, Acting Interim Chief Executive Officer
Web address: www.mercy.net/ada

MERCY HOSPITAL ARDMORE (O, 190 beds) 1011 14th Avenue N.W., Ardmore, OK Zip 73401–1828; tel. 580/223–5400; Daryle Voss, FACHE, President
Web address: www.mercyok.net

MERCY HOSPITAL EL RENO (L, 48 beds) 2115 Parkview Drive, El Reno, OK Zip 73036–2199, Mailing Address: P.O. Box 129, Zip 73036–0129; tel. 405/262–2640; Doug Danker, Administrator
Web address: www.mercyok.net

MERCY HOSPITAL HEALDTON (L, 22 beds) 918 South 8th Street, Healdton, OK Zip 73438–0928, Mailing Address: P.O. Box 928, Zip 73438–0928; tel. 580/229–0701; Jeremy A. Jones, Administrator
Web address: www.mercyok.com

MERCY HOSPITAL KINGFISHER (C, 25 beds) 1000 Kingfisher Regional Hospital Drive, Kingfisher, OK Zip 73750–3528, Mailing Address: P.O. Box 59, Zip 73750–0059; tel. 405/375–3141; Brian Denton, Administrator
Web address: www.kingfisherhospital.com

MERCY HOSPITAL LOGAN COUNTY (O, 25 beds) 200 South Academy Road, Guthrie, OK Zip 73044–8727, Mailing Address: P.O. Box 1017, Zip 73044–1017; tel. 405/282–6700; Joshua Tucker, Administrator
Web address: www.mercy.net

MERCY HOSPITAL OKLAHOMA CITY (O, 369 beds) 4300 West Memorial Road, Oklahoma City, OK Zip 73120–8362; tel. 405/755–1515; Jim Gebhart, Jr., FACHE, President
Web address: www.mercyok.net

MERCY HOSPITAL TISHOMINGO (L, 25 beds) 1000 South Byrd Street, Tishomingo, OK Zip 73460–3299; tel. 580/371–2327; Gary Sharum, Administrator
Web address: www.mercy.net/

MERCY HOSPITAL WATONGA (L, 17 beds) 500 North Clarence Nash Boulevard, Watonga, OK Zip 73772–2845, Mailing Address: P.O. Box 370, Zip 73772–0370; tel. 580/623–7211; Bobby Stitt, R.N., Administrator
Web address: www.mercy.net/watongaok/practice/mercy–hospital–watonga

Owned, leased, sponsored:	27 hospitals	4098 beds
Contract–managed:	4 hospitals	219 beds
Totals:	31 hospitals	4317 beds

0649: MERCY HEALTH SYSTEM (NP)
1000 Mineral Point Avenue, Janesville, WI Zip 53548–2940, Mailing Address: P.O. Box 5003, Zip 53547–5003; tel. 608/756–6000; Javon R. Bea, President and Chief Executive Officer
(Centralized Physician/Insurance Health System)

ILLINOIS: MERCY HARVARD HOSPITAL (O, 45 beds) 901 Grant Street, Harvard, IL Zip 60033–1898, Mailing Address: P.O. Box 850, Zip 60033–0850; tel. 815/943–5431; Jennifer Hallatt, Chief Operating Officer
Web address: www.mercyhealthsystem.org

WISCONSIN: MERCY HOSPITAL AND TRAUMA CENTER (O, 124 beds) 1000 Mineral Point Avenue, Janesville, WI Zip 53548–2982, Mailing Address: P.O. Box 5003, Zip 53547–5003; tel. 608/756–6000; Javon R. Bea, President and Chief Executive Officer
Web address: www.mercyhealthsystem.org

MERCY WALWORTH HOSPITAL AND MEDICAL CENTER (O, 15 beds) N2950 State Road 67, Lake Geneva, WI Zip 53147–2655; tel. 262/245–0535; Jennifer Hallatt, Chief Operating Officer
Web address: www.mercyhealthsystem.org

Owned, leased, sponsored:	3 hospitals	184 beds
Contract–managed:	0 hospitals	0 beds
Totals:	3 hospitals	184 beds

★0257: MERIDIAN HEALTH (NP)
1350 Campus Parkway, Neptune, NJ Zip 07753–6821; tel. 732/751–7510; John K. Lloyd, President and Chief Executive Officer
(Centralized Health System)

NEW JERSEY: BAYSHORE COMMUNITY HOSPITAL (O, 153 beds) 727 North Beers Street, Holmdel, NJ Zip 07733–1598; tel. 732/739–5900; Timothy J. Hogan, FACHE, Regional President
Web address: www.bchs.com

JERSEY SHORE UNIVERSITY MEDICAL CENTER (O, 519 beds) 1945 Route 33, Neptune, NJ Zip 07754–0397; tel. 732/775–5500; Steven G. Littleson, FACHE, President
Web address: www.meridianhealth.com

OCEAN MEDICAL CENTER (O, 265 beds) 425 Jack Martin Boulevard, Brick Township, NJ Zip 08724–7732; tel. 732/840–2200; Dean Q. Lin, FACHE, President
Web address: www.meridianhealth.com

For explanation of codes following names, see page B2.
★ Indicates Type III membership in the American Hospital Association.

Section B

RIVERVIEW MEDICAL CENTER (O, 275 beds) 1 Riverview Plaza, Red Bank, NJ Zip 07701–1864; tel. 732/741–2700; Timothy J. Hogan, FACHE, Regional President
Web address: www.riverviewmedicalcenter.com

SOUTHERN OCEAN MEDICAL CENTER (O, 135 beds) 1140 Route 72 West, Manahawkin, NJ 08050–2499; tel. 609/597–6011; Joseph P. Coyle, President
Web address: www.soch.com

Owned, leased, sponsored:	5 hospitals	1347 beds
Contract–managed:	0 hospitals	0 beds
Totals:	5 hospitals	1347 beds

★2735: METHODIST HEALTH SYSTEM (NP)
1441 North Beckley Avenue, Dallas, TX Zip 75203–1201, Mailing Address: P.O. Box 655999, Zip 75265–5999; tel. 214/947–8181; Stephen L. Mansfield, Ph.D., FACHE, President and Chief Executive Officer
(Moderately Centralized Health System)

TEXAS: METHODIST CHARLTON MEDICAL CENTER (O, 293 beds) 3500 West Wheatland Road, Dallas, TX Zip 75237–3460, Mailing Address: P.O. Box 225357, Zip 75222–5357; tel. 214/947–7777; Jonathan S. Davis, FACHE, President
Web address: www.methodisthealthsystem.org/charlton

METHODIST DALLAS MEDICAL CENTER (O, 408 beds) 1441 North Beckley Avenue, Dallas, TX Zip 75203–1201, Mailing Address: P.O. Box 655999, Zip 75265–5999; tel. 214/947–8181; David D. Clark, President
Web address: www.methodisthealthsystem.org/Dallas

METHODIST MANSFIELD MEDICAL CENTER (O, 175 beds) 2700 East Broad Street, Mansfield, TX Zip 76063–5899; tel. 682/622–2000; John E. Phillips, FACHE, President
Web address: www.methodisthealthsystem.org/mansfield

METHODIST RICHARDSON MEDICAL CENTER (O, 145 beds) 2831 East President George Bush Highway, Richardson, TX Zip 75082–3561; tel. 469/204–1000; E. Kenneth Hutchenrider, President
Web address: www.methodisthealthsystem.org/richardson

Owned, leased, sponsored:	4 hospitals	1021 beds
Contract–managed:	0 hospitals	0 beds
Totals:	4 hospitals	1021 beds

9345: METHODIST LE BONHEUR HEALTHCARE (CO)
1211 Union Avenue, Suite 700, Memphis, TN Zip 38104–6600; tel. 901/516–0791; Gary S. Shorb, President and Chief Executive Officer
(Centralized Health System)

MISSISSIPPI: METHODIST OLIVE BRANCH HOSPITAL (O, 44 beds) 4250 Bethel Road, Olive Branch, MS Zip 38654–8737; tel. 662/932–9000; David G. Baytos, Chief Executive Officer
Web address: www.methodisthealth.org/olivebranch

TENNESSEE: METHODIST EXTENDED CARE HOSPITAL (O, 36 beds) 225 South Claybrook Street, Memphis, TN Zip 38104–3537; tel. 901/516–2595; Sandra Bailey–DeLeeuw, Chief Executive Officer
Web address: www.methodisthealth.org

METHODIST HEALTHCARE MEMPHIS HOSPITALS (O, 1437 beds) 1265 Union Avenue, Memphis, TN Zip 38104–3415; tel. 901/516–7000; Michael O. Ugwueke, President and Chief Executive Officer
Web address: www.methodisthealth.org

METHODIST HEALTHCARE–FAYETTE HOSPITAL (O, 10 beds) 214 Lakeview Drive, Somerville, TN Zip 38068–9737; tel. 901/516–4000; William A. Kenley, Chief Executive Officer
Web address: www.methodisthealth.org

Owned, leased, sponsored:	4 hospitals	1527 beds
Contract–managed:	0 hospitals	0 beds
Totals:	4 hospitals	1527 beds

★0001: MIDMICHIGAN HEALTH (NP)
4000 Wellness Drive, Midland, MI Zip 48670–0001; tel. 989/839–3000; Diane Postler–Slattery, Ph.D., President and Chief Executive Officer
(Centralized Health System)

MICHIGAN: MIDMICHIGAN MEDICAL CENTER–CLARE (O, 55 beds) 703 North McEwan Street, Clare, MI Zip 48617–1440; tel. 989/802–5000; Raymond Stover, President and Chief Executive Officer
Web address: www.midmichigan.org

MIDMICHIGAN MEDICAL CENTER–GLADWIN (O, 25 beds) 515 Quarter Street, Gladwin, MI Zip 48624–1959; tel. 989/426–9286; Raymond Stover, President and Chief Executive Officer
Web address: www.midmichigan.org

MIDMICHIGAN MEDICAL CENTER–GRATIOT (O, 100 beds) 300 East Warwick Drive, Alma, MI Zip 48801–1014; tel. 989/463–1101; Mark A. Santamaria, President
Web address: www.midmichigan.org/gratiot

MIDMICHIGAN MEDICAL CENTER–MIDLAND (O, 246 beds) 4000 Wellness Drive, Midland, MI Zip 48670–2000; tel. 989/839–3000; Gregory H. Rogers, President
Web address: www.midmichigan.org

Owned, leased, sponsored:	4 hospitals	426 beds
Contract–managed:	0 hospitals	0 beds
Totals:	4 hospitals	426 beds

0368: MINNESOTA DEPARTMENT OF HUMAN SERVICES (NP)
540 Cedar Street, Saint Paul, MN Zip 55101–2208, Mailing Address: P.O. Box 64998, Zip 55164–0998; tel. 651/431–3212; Anne Barry, Deputy Commissioner
(Independent Hospital System)

MINNESOTA: ANOKA–METROPOLITAN REGIONAL TREATMENT CENTER (O, 200 beds) 3301 Seventh Avenue, Anoka, MN Zip 55303–4516; tel. 651/431–5000; Tina Sneen, Interim Hospital Administrator
Web address: www.health.state.mn.us

COMMUNITY BEHAVIORAL HEALTH HOSPITAL – ALEXANDRIA (O, 16 beds) 1610 8th Avenue East, Alexandria, MN Zip 56308–2472; tel. 320/335–6201; Jennifer Westrum, Administrator
Web address: www.health.state.mn.us

COMMUNITY BEHAVIORAL HEALTH HOSPITAL – ANNANDALE (O, 16 beds) 400 Annandale Boulevard, Annandale, MN Zip 55302–3141; tel. 651/259–3850; Tracanne L. Nelson, MS, Administrator
Web address: www.health.state.mn.us

COMMUNITY BEHAVIORAL HEALTH HOSPITAL – BAXTER (O, 16 beds) 14241 Grand Oaks Drive, Baxter, MN Zip 56425–8749; tel. 218/316–3101; Richard G. Slieter, Jr., Administrator

COMMUNITY BEHAVIORAL HEALTH HOSPITAL – BEMIDJI (O, 16 beds) 800 Bemidji Avenue North, Bemidji, MN Zip 56601–3054; tel. 218/308–2400; Larry A. Laudon, Administrator

COMMUNITY BEHAVIORAL HEALTH HOSPITAL – FERGUS FALLS (O, 16 beds) 1801 West Alcott Avenue, Fergus Falls, MN Zip 56537–2661, Mailing Address: P.O. Box 478, Zip 56538–0478; tel. 218/332–5001; Brenda Schleske, Interim Administrator

COMMUNITY BEHAVIORAL HEALTH HOSPITAL – ROCHESTER (O, 16 beds) 251 Wood Lake Drive S.E., Rochester, MN Zip 55904–5530; tel. 507/206–2561; Douglas Panser, Interim Administrator
Web address: www.health.state.mn.us

COMMUNITY BEHAVIORAL HEALTH HOSPITAL – ST. PETER (O, 16 beds) 2000 Klein Street, Saint Peter, MN Zip 56082–5800; tel. 507/933–5001; Christopher Schiffer, Administrator
Web address: www.health.state.mn.us

COMMUNITY BEHAVIORAL HEALTH HOSPITAL – WADENA (O, 16 beds) 240 Shady Lane Drive, Wadena, MN Zip 56482, Mailing Address: P.O. Box 430, Zip 56482–0430; tel. 218/319–6001; Richard G. Slieter, Jr., Administrator

Owned, leased, sponsored:	9 hospitals	328 beds
Contract–managed:	0 hospitals	0 beds
Totals:	9 hospitals	328 beds

For explanation of codes following names, see page B2.
★ Indicates Type III membership in the American Hospital Association.

★0143: MISSION HEALTH SYSTEM (NP)
509 Biltmore Avenue, Asheville, NC Zip 28801–4601; tel. 828/213–1111; Ronald A. Paulus, M.D., President and Chief Executive Officer
(Independent Hospital System)

NORTH CAROLINA: ANGEL MEDICAL CENTER (O, 25 beds) 120 Riverview Street, Franklin, NC Zip 28734–2612, Mailing Address: P.O. Box 1209, Zip 28744–0569; tel. 828/524–8411; James B. Bross, President and Chief Executive Officer
Web address: www.angelmed.org

ASHEVILLE SPECIALTY HOSPITAL (O, 32 beds) 428 Biltmore Avenue, 4th Floor, Asheville, NC Zip 28801–4502; tel. 828/213–5400; Robert C. Desotelle, President and Chief Executive Officer
Web address: www.missionhospitals.org/acute–care

BLUE RIDGE REGIONAL HOSPITAL (O, 42 beds) 125 Hospital Drive, Spruce Pine, NC Zip 28777–3035, Mailing Address: P.O. Drawer 9, Zip 28777–0009; tel. 828/765–4201; Lynn Ingram Boggs, President and Chief Executive Officer
Web address: www.spchospital.org

MCDOWELL HOSPITAL (O, 49 beds) 430 Rankin Drive, Marion, NC Zip 28752–6568, Mailing Address: P.O. Box 730, Zip 28752–0730; tel. 828/659–5000; Lynn Ingram Boggs, President
Web address: www.mcdhospital.org

MISSION HOSPITAL (O, 763 beds) 509 Biltmore Avenue, Asheville, NC Zip 28801–4690; tel. 828/213–1111; Ronald A. Paulus, M.D., President and Chief Executive Officer
Web address: www.missionhospitals.org

TRANSYLVANIA REGIONAL HOSPITAL (O, 52 beds) 260 Hospital Drive, Brevard, NC Zip 28712–3378; tel. 828/884–9111; Catherine Landis, R.N., MS, President and Chief Nursing Officer
Web address: www.trhospital.org

Owned, leased, sponsored:	6 hospitals	963 beds
Contract–managed:	0 hospitals	0 beds
Totals:	6 hospitals	963 beds

★0336: MISSISSIPPI BAPTIST HEALTH SYSTEM (NP)
1225 North State Street, Jackson, MS Zip 39202–2064; tel. 601/968–1000; Chris Anderson, Chief Executive Officer
(Moderately Centralized Health System)

MISSISSIPPI: BAPTIST MEDICAL CENTER LEAKE (O, 69 beds) 310 Ellis Street, Carthage, MS Zip 39051–3809, Mailing Address: P.O. Box 909, Zip 39051–0909; tel. 601/267–1100; Daryl W. Weaver, Interim Chief Executive Officer
Web address: www.mbhs.com/locations/baptist–medical–center–leake/

MISSISSIPPI BAPTIST MEDICAL CENTER (O, 638 beds) 1225 North State Street, Jackson, MS Zip 39202–2064; tel. 601/968–1000; Kerry R. Tirman, JD, FACHE, President
Web address: www.mbhs.org

MISSISSIPPI HOSPITAL FOR RESTORATIVE CARE (O, 25 beds) 1225 North State Street, Jackson, MS Zip 39202–2097, Mailing Address: P.O. Box 23695, Zip 39225–3695; tel. 601/968–1000; Bobbie K. Ware, R.N., FACHE, Chief Executive Officer and Chief Nursing Officer
Web address: www.mbhs.org

Owned, leased, sponsored:	3 hospitals	732 beds
Contract–managed:	0 hospitals	0 beds
Totals:	3 hospitals	732 beds

2475: MISSISSIPPI COUNTY HOSPITAL SYSTEM (NP)
1520 North Division Street, Blytheville, AR Zip 72315–1448, Mailing Address: P.O. Box 108, Zip 72316–0108; tel. 870/838–7300; Ralph E. Beaty, Chief Executive Officer
(Independent Hospital System)

ARKANSAS: GREAT RIVER MEDICAL CENTER (O, 73 beds) 1520 North Division Street, Blytheville, AR Zip 72315–1448, Mailing Address: P.O. Box 108, Zip 72316–0108; tel. 870/838–7300; Ralph E. Beaty, Chief Executive Officer
Web address: www.mchsys.org

SOUTH MISSISSIPPI COUNTY REGIONAL MEDICAL CENTER (O, 25 beds) 611 West Lee Avenue, Osceola, AR Zip 72370–3001, Mailing Address: P.O. Box 108, Zip 72370; tel. 870/563–7000; Ralph E. Beaty, Chief Executive Officer
Web address: www.mchsys.com

Owned, leased, sponsored:	2 hospitals	98 beds
Contract–managed:	0 hospitals	0 beds
Totals:	2 hospitals	98 beds

0017: MISSISSIPPI STATE DEPARTMENT OF MENTAL HEALTH (NP)
1101 Robert East Lee Building, 239 North Lamar Street, Jackson, MS Zip 39201–1101; tel. 601/359–1288; Edwin C. LeGrand, III, Executive Director
(Independent Hospital System)

MISSISSIPPI: EAST MISSISSIPPI STATE HOSPITAL (O, 201 beds) 1818 College Drive, Meridian, MS Zip 39307, Mailing Address: Box 4128, West Station, Zip 39304–4128; tel. 601/482–6186; Charles Carlisle, Director
Web address: www.emsh.state.ms.us

MISSISSIPPI STATE HOSPITAL (O, 899 beds) 3550 Highway 468 West, Whitfield, MS Zip 39193–5529, Mailing Address: P.O. Box 157–A, Zip 39193–0157; tel. 601/351–8000; James G. Chastain, FACHE, Director
Web address: www.msh.state.ms.us

NORTH MISSISSIPPI STATE HOSPITAL (O, 50 beds) 1937 Briar Ridge Road, Tupelo, MS Zip 38804–5963; tel. 662/690–4200; Paul A. Callens, Ph.D., Director
Web address: www.nmsh.state.ms.us

SOUTH MISSISSIPPI STATE HOSPITAL (O, 50 beds) 823 Highway 589, Purvis, MS Zip 39475–4194; tel. 601/794–0100; Clint Ashley, Director
Web address: www.smsh.state.ms.us

Owned, leased, sponsored:	4 hospitals	1200 beds
Contract–managed:	0 hospitals	0 beds
Totals:	4 hospitals	1200 beds

0343: MONTEFIORE HEALTH SYSTEM (NP)
111 East 210th Street, Bronx, NY Zip 10467–2490; tel. 718/920–4321; Steven M. Safyer, M.D., President and CEO

NEW YORK: MONTEFIORE MEDICAL CENTER (O, 1516 beds) 111 East 210th Street, Bronx, NY Zip 10467–2401; tel. 718/920–4321; Steven M. Safyer, M.D., President and Chief Executive Officer
Web address: www.montefiore.org

MONTEFIORE MOUNT VERNON (O, 80 beds) 12 North Seventh Avenue, Mount Vernon, NY Zip 10550–2098; tel. 914/664–8000; Susan Green–Lorenzen, SVP, Operations
Web address: www.sshsw.org

MONTEFIORE NEW ROCHELLE (O, 267 beds) 16 Guion Place, New Rochelle, NY Zip 10801–5502; tel. 914/632–5000; Anthony J. Alfano, President and Chief Executive Officer
Web address: www.montefiorehealthsystem.org

Owned, leased, sponsored:	3 hospitals	1863 beds
Contract–managed:	0 hospitals	0 beds
Totals:	3 hospitals	1863 beds

1335: MORTON PLANT MEASE HEALTH CARE (NP)
300 Pinellas Street, Clearwater, FL Zip 33756–3804, Mailing Address: P.O. Box 210, Zip 33757–0210; tel. 727/462–7000; Glenn D. Waters, FACHE, President

FLORIDA: MEASE COUNTRYSIDE HOSPITAL (O, 293 beds) 3231 McMullen–Booth Road, Safety Harbor, FL Zip 34695–6607, Mailing Address: P.O. Box 1098, Zip 34695–1098; tel. 727/725–6222; Lou Galdieri, R.N., President
Web address: www.mpmhealth.com

MEASE DUNEDIN HOSPITAL (O, 124 beds) 601 Main Street, Dunedin, FL Zip 34698–5891, Mailing Address: P.O. Box 760, Zip 34697–0760; tel. 727/733–1111; Lou Galdieri, R.N., President
Web address: www.mpmhealth.com

For explanation of codes following names, see page B2.
★ Indicates Type III membership in the American Hospital Association.

Section B

MORTON PLANT HOSPITAL (O, 662 beds) 300 Pinellas Street, Clearwater, FL Zip 33756–3804, Mailing Address: P.O. Box 210, Zip 33757–0210; tel. 727/462–7000; N. Kristopher Hoce, President
Web address: www.mortonplant.com

MORTON PLANT NORTH BAY HOSPITAL (O, 226 beds) 6600 Madison Street, New Port Richey, FL Zip 34652–1900; tel. 727/754–9222; Michael Yungmann, President
Web address: www.mpmhealth.com

MORTON PLANT REHABILITATION CENTER (O, 126 beds) 400 Corbett Street, Belleair, FL Zip 34640; tel. 813/462–7600; Linda A. Kirk, Administrator

Owned, leased, sponsored:	5 hospitals	1431 beds
Contract–managed:	0 hospitals	0 beds
Totals:	5 hospitals	1431 beds

0917: MOUNT SINAI HEALTH SYSTEM (NP)
One Gustave L. Levy Place, New York, NY Zip 10029; Kenneth L. Davis, M.D., President and Chief Executive

NEW YORK: MOUNT SINAI BETH ISRAEL (O, 1037 beds) First Avenue and 16th Street, New York, NY Zip 10003–3803; tel. 212/420–2000; Susan Somerville, R.N., President
Web address: www.bethisraelny.org

MOUNT SINAI HOSPITAL (O, 1037 beds) One Gustave L. Levy Place, New York, NY Zip 10029–6574; tel. 212/241–6500; David L. Reich, M.D., President
Web address: www.mountsinai.org

MOUNT SINAI QUEENS (O, 182 beds) 25–10 30th Avenue, Long Island City, NY Zip 11102–2448; tel. 718/932–1000; Caryn A. Schwab, Executive Director
Web address: www.mshq.org

MOUNT SINAI ST. LUKE'S (O, 683 beds) 1111 Amsterdam Avenue, New York, NY Zip 10025–1716; tel. 212/523–4000; Arthur A. Gianelli, M.P.H., President
Web address: www.stlukeshospitalnyc.org

NEW YORK EYE AND EAR INFIRMARY OF MOUNT SINAI (O, 32 beds) 310 East 14th Street, New York, NY Zip 10003–4201; tel. 212/979–4000; James Tsai, M.D., President
Web address: www.nyee.edu

Owned, leased, sponsored:	5 hospitals	2971 beds
Contract–managed:	0 hospitals	0 beds
Totals:	5 hospitals	2971 beds

0167: MOUNTAIN STATES HEALTH ALLIANCE (NP)
400 North State of Franklin Road, Johnson City, TN Zip 37604–6035; tel. 423/302–3423; Alan M. Levine, President and Chief Executive Officer
(Centralized Health System)

TENNESSEE: FRANKLIN WOODS COMMUNITY HOSPITAL (O, 80 beds) 300 MedTech Parkway, Johnson City, TN Zip 37604–2277; tel. 423/302–1000; Lindy P. White, Chief Executive Officer
Web address: www.msha.com

INDIAN PATH MEDICAL CENTER (O, 261 beds) 2000 Brookside Drive, Kingsport, TN Zip 37660–4627; tel. 423/857–7000; Monty E. McLaurin, President and Chief Executive Officer
Web address: www.msha.com

JOHNSON CITY MEDICAL CENTER (O, 611 beds) 400 North State of Franklin Road, Johnson City, TN Zip 37604–6094; tel. 423/431–6111; Tony Benton, Interim Chief Executive Officer Washington County Hospitals
Web address: www.msha.com

JOHNSON COUNTY COMMUNITY HOSPITAL (O, 2 beds) 1901 South Shady Street, Mountain City, TN Zip 37683–2271; tel. 423/727–1100; Chastity Trivette, Interim Chief Executive Officer
Web address: www.msha.com

SYCAMORE SHOALS HOSPITAL (O, 74 beds) 1501 West Elk Avenue, Elizabethton, TN Zip 37643–2874; tel. 423/542–1300; Dwayne Taylor, Chief Executive Officer
Web address: www.msha.com

VIRGINIA: DICKENSON COMMUNITY HOSPITAL (O, 25 beds) 312 Hospital Drive, Clintwood, VA Zip 24228, Mailing Address: P.O. Box 1440, Zip 24228–1440; tel. 276/926–0300; Mark T. Leonard, Chief Executive Officer
Web address: www.msha.com/dch

JOHNSTON MEMORIAL HOSPITAL (O, 116 beds) 16000 Johnston Memorial Drive, Abingdon, VA Zip 24211–7659; tel. 276/676–7000; Sean S. McMurray, FACHE, Vice President and Chief Executive Officer
Web address: www.jmh.org

NORTON COMMUNITY HOSPITAL (O, 50 beds) 100 15th Street N.W., Norton, VA Zip 24273–1616; tel. 276/679–9600; Mark T. Leonard, Chief Executive Officer
Web address: www.msha.com/nch

RUSSELL COUNTY MEDICAL CENTER (O, 78 beds) 58 Carroll Street, Lebanon, VA Zip 24266, Mailing Address: P.O. Box 3600, Zip 24266–0200; tel. 276/883–8000; Stephen K. Givens, Assistant Vice President and Administrator
Web address: www.msha.com/rcmc

SMYTH COUNTY COMMUNITY HOSPITAL (O, 153 beds) 245 Medical Park Drive, Marion, VA Zip 24354, Mailing Address: P.O. Box 880, Zip 24354–0880; tel. 276/378–1000; Cathy Loving Maine, MSN, RN–B, Interim Chief Executive Officer
Web address: www.msha.com/scch

Owned, leased, sponsored:	10 hospitals	1450 beds
Contract–managed:	0 hospitals	0 beds
Totals:	10 hospitals	1450 beds

6555: MULTICARE HEALTH SYSTEM (NP)
315 Martin Luther King Jr. Way, Tacoma, WA Zip 98405–4234, Mailing Address: P.O. Box 5299, Zip 98415–0299; tel. 253/403–1000; William G. Robertson, President and Chief Executive Officer
(Centralized Physician/Insurance Health System)

WASHINGTON: MULTICARE AUBURN MEDICAL CENTER (O, 195 beds) 202 North Division, Plaza One, Auburn, WA Zip 98001–4908; tel. 253/833–7711; David Nicewonger, Chief Operating Officer
Web address: www.auburnregional.com

MULTICARE GOOD SAMARITAN HOSPITAL (O, 265 beds) 401 15th Avenue S.E., Puyallup, WA Zip 98372–3770, Mailing Address: P.O. Box 1247, Zip 98371–0192; tel. 253/697–4000; Glenn Kasman, President, East Pierce Region
Web address: www.goodsamhealth.org

MULTICARE MARY BRIDGE CHILDREN'S HOSPITAL AND HEALTH CENTER (O, 72 beds) 317 Martin Luther King Jr. Way, Tacoma, WA Zip 98405–4234, Mailing Address: P.O. Box 5299, Zip 98415–0299; tel. 253/403–1400; Robert Lenza, Chief Operating Officer and Administrator
Web address: www.multicare.org/marybridge

MULTICARE TACOMA GENERAL HOSPITAL (O, 385 beds) 315 Martin Luther King Jr. Way, Tacoma, WA Zip 98405–4234, Mailing Address: P.O. Box 5299, Zip 98415–0299; tel. 253/403–1000; William G. Robertson, President and Chief Executive Officer
Web address: www.multicare.org

Owned, leased, sponsored:	4 hospitals	917 beds
Contract–managed:	0 hospitals	0 beds
Totals:	4 hospitals	917 beds

★1465: MUNSON HEALTHCARE (NP)
1105 Sixth Street, Traverse City, MI Zip 49684–2386; tel. 231/935–6703; Edwin Ness, President and Chief Executive Officer
(Centralized Physician/Insurance Health System)

MICHIGAN: KALKASKA MEMORIAL HEALTH CENTER (O, 96 beds) 419 South Coral Street, Kalkaska, MI Zip 49646–2503; tel. 231/258–7500; Kevin L. Rogols, FACHE, Administrator
Web address: www.munsonhealthcare.org

MUNSON MEDICAL CENTER (O, 391 beds) 1105 Sixth Street, Traverse City, MI Zip 49684–2386; tel. 231/935–5000; Alfred E. Pilong, President
Web address: www.munsonhealthcare.org

For explanation of codes following names, see page B2.
★ Indicates Type III membership in the American Hospital Association.

© 2014 AHA Guide

PAUL OLIVER MEMORIAL HOSPITAL (O, 47 beds) 224 Park Avenue, Frankfort, MI Zip 49635–9658; tel. 231/352–2200; Peter Marinoff, President
Web address: www.munsonhealthcare.org

Owned, leased, sponsored:	3 hospitals	534 beds
Contract–managed:	0 hospitals	0 beds
Totals:	3 hospitals	534 beds

0261: NATIONAL SURGICAL HOSPITALS (IO)
250 South Wacker Drive, Suite 500, Chicago, IL Zip 60606–5897; tel. 312/627–8400; David Crane, Chief Executive Officer
(Independent Hospital System)

ARIZONA: ARIZONA SPINE AND JOINT HOSPITAL (O, 23 beds) 4620 East Baseline Road, Mesa, AZ Zip 85206–4624; tel. 480/832–4770; Chris Hill, Chief Executive Officer
Web address: www.azspineandjoint.com

IDAHO: NORTHWEST SPECIALTY HOSPITAL (O, 34 beds) 1593 East Polston Avenue, Post Falls, ID Zip 83854–5326; tel. 208/262–2300; Vaughn Ward, Chief Executive Officer
Web address: www.northwestspecialtyhospital.com

LOUISIANA: LAFAYETTE SURGICAL SPECIALTY HOSPITAL (O, 20 beds) 1101 Kaliste Saloom Road, Lafayette, LA Zip 70508–5705; tel. 337/769–4100; Buffy Domingue, Chief Executive Officer
Web address: www.lafayettesurgical.com

MICHIGAN: SOUTHEAST MICHIGAN SURGICAL HOSPITAL (O, 13 beds) 21230 Dequindre, Warren, MI Zip 48091–2287; tel. 586/427–1000; Yvonne Kughn, Chief Executive Officer
Web address: www.nshinc.com

NORTH CAROLINA: NORTH CAROLINA SPECIALTY HOSPITAL (O, 18 beds) 3916 Ben Franklin Boulevard, Durham, NC Zip 27704–2383; tel. 919/956–9300; Randi L. Shults, Chief Executive Officer
Web address: www.ncspecialty.com

TEXAS: EL PASO SPECIALTY HOSPITAL (O, 27 beds) 1755 Curie Drive, El Paso, TX Zip 79902–2919; tel. 915/544–3636; James Wilcox, Chief Executive Officer
Web address: www.elpasospecialtyhospital.com

SOUTH TEXAS SPINE AND SURGICAL HOSPITAL (O, 30 beds) 18600 Hardy Oak Boulevard, San Antonio, TX Zip 78258–4206; tel. 210/507–4090; Debbie Kelly, Chief Executive Officer
Web address: www.southtexassurgical.com

SOUTH TEXAS SURGICAL HOSPITAL (O, 20 beds) 6130 Parkway Drive, Corpus Christi, TX Zip 78414–2455; tel. 361/993–2000; James Murphy, Chief Executive Officer
Web address: www.nshinc.com

UTAH: CACHE VALLEY HOSPITAL (O, 22 beds) 2380 North 400 East, North Logan, UT Zip 84341–6000; tel. 435/713–9700; John C. Worley, III, Chief Executive Officer
Web address: www.cvsh.com

WISCONSIN: OAKLEAF SURGICAL HOSPITAL (O, 13 beds) 3802 West Oakwood Mall Drive, Eau Claire, WI Zip 54701–3016; tel. 715/831–8130; Anne Hargrave–Thomas, Chief Executive Officer
Web address: www.oakleafmedical.com

WYOMING: MOUNTAIN VIEW REGIONAL HOSPITAL (O, 23 beds) 6550 East Second Street, Casper, WY Zip 82609–4321, Mailing Address: P.O. Box 51888, Zip 82605–1888; tel. 307/995–8100; Jeff Van Horn, Chief Executive Officer
Web address: www.mountainviewregionalhospital.com

Owned, leased, sponsored:	11 hospitals	243 beds
Contract–managed:	0 hospitals	0 beds
Totals:	11 hospitals	243 beds

0923: NAVICENT HEALTH (NP)
777 Hemlock Street, Macon, GA Zip 31201–2155; tel. 478/633–1000; Ninfa Saunders, Chief Executive Officer

GEORGIA: MEDICAL CENTER OF PEACH COUNTY, NAVICENT HEALTH (O, 25 beds) 601 Blue Bird Boulevard, Fort Valley, GA Zip 31030–4599, Mailing Address: P.O. Box 1799, Zip 31030–1799; tel. 478/825–8691; Nancy Peed, Administrator and Chief Executive Officer
Web address: www.peachregional.org

MEDICAL CENTER, NAVICENT HEALTH (O, 659 beds) 777 Hemlock Street, Macon, GA Zip 31201–2155; tel. 478/633–1000; Ninfa Saunders, Chief Executive Officer
Web address: www.mccg.org

REHABILITATION HOSPITAL, NAVICENT HEALTH (O, 58 beds) 3351 Northside Drive, Macon, GA Zip 31210–2587; tel. 478/201–6500; Elbert T. McQueen, President and Chief Executive Officer
Web address: www.centralgarehab.com

Owned, leased, sponsored:	3 hospitals	742 beds
Contract–managed:	0 hospitals	0 beds
Totals:	3 hospitals	742 beds

★9265: NEBRASKA METHODIST HEALTH SYSTEM, INC. (CO)
8511 West Dodge Road, Omaha, NE Zip 68114–3403; tel. 402/354–5411; John M. Fraser, President and Chief Executive Officer
(Centralized Physician/Insurance Health System)

IOWA: METHODIST JENNIE EDMUNDSON HOSPITAL (O, 114 beds) 933 East Pierce Street, Council Bluffs, IA Zip 51503–4652, Mailing Address: P.O. Box 2C, Zip 51502–3002; tel. 712/396–6000; Steven P. Baumert, President and Chief Executive Officer
Web address: www.bestcare.org

NEBRASKA: NEBRASKA METHODIST HOSPITAL (O, 394 beds) 8303 Dodge Street, Omaha, NE Zip 68114–4199; tel. 402/354–4000; Stephen L. Goeser, FACHE, President and Chief Executive Officer
Web address: www.bestcare.org

Owned, leased, sponsored:	2 hospitals	508 beds
Contract–managed:	0 hospitals	0 beds
Totals:	2 hospitals	508 beds

0892: NEMOURS (NP)
10140 Centurion Parkway North, Jacksonville, FL Zip 32256–0532; tel. 904/697–4100; David J. Bailey, M.D., President and Chief Executive Officer
(Independent Hospital System)

DELAWARE: ALFRED I. DUPONT HOSPITAL FOR CHILDREN (O, 195 beds) 1600 Rockland Road, Wilmington, DE Zip 19803–3616, Mailing Address: Box 269, Zip 19899–0269; tel. 302/651–4000; Roy Proujansky, M.D., Chief Executive Officer
Web address: www.nemours.org

FLORIDA: NEMOURS CHILDREN'S HOSPITAL (O, 100 beds) 13535 Nemours Parkway, Orlando, FL Zip 32827–7402; tel. 407/567–4000; Roger A. Oxendale, Chief Executive Officer
Web address: www.nemours.org

Owned, leased, sponsored:	2 hospitals	295 beds
Contract–managed:	0 hospitals	0 beds
Totals:	2 hospitals	295 beds

0620: NEUROPSYCHIATRIC HOSPITALS (IO)
1625 East Jefferson Boulevard, Mishawaka, IN Zip 46545–7103; tel. 574/255–1400; Cameron R. Gilbert, Ph.D., President and Chief Executive Officer
(Independent Hospital System)

INDIANA: DOCTORS NEUROMEDICAL HOSPITAL (O, 20 beds) 411 South Whitlock Street, Bremen, IN Zip 46506–1626, Mailing Address: P.O. Box 36, Zip 46506–0036; tel. 574/546–3830; DeWayne Long, Chief Executive Officer
Web address: www.physicianshospitalsystem.net

For explanation of codes following names, see page B2.
★ Indicates Type III membership in the American Hospital Association.

Section B

DOCTORS NEUROPSYCHIATRIC HOSPITAL AND RESEARCH INSTITUTE (O, 20 beds) 417 South Whitlock Street, Bremen, IN Zip 46506–1626; tel. 574/546–0330; Cameron R. Gilbert, Ph.D., President and Chief Executive Officer

RIVERCREST SPECIALTY HOSPITAL (O, 30 beds) 1625 East Jefferson Boulevard, Mishawaka, IN Zip 46545–7103; tel. 574/255–1400; Cameron R. Gilbert, Ph.D., President and Chief Executive Officer
Web address: www.physicianshospitalsystem.net/

Owned, leased, sponsored:	3 hospitals	70 beds
Contract–managed:	0 hospitals	0 beds
Totals:	3 hospitals	70 beds

★**0213: NEW HANOVER REGIONAL MEDICAL CENTER** (NP)
2131 South 17th Street, Wilmington, NC Zip 28401–7407; tel. 910/343–7040; John K. Barto, Jr., President and Chief Executive Officer
(Moderately Centralized Health System)

NORTH CAROLINA: NEW HANOVER REGIONAL MEDICAL CENTER (O, 668 beds) 2131 South 17th Street, Wilmington, NC Zip 28401–7483, Mailing Address: P.O. Box 9000, Zip 28402–9000; tel. 910/343–7000; John K. Barto, Jr., President and Chief Executive Officer
Web address: www.nhrmc.org

PENDER MEMORIAL HOSPITAL (C, 68 beds) 507 East Freemont Street, Burgaw, NC Zip 28425–5131; tel. 910/259–5451; Ruth Glaser, President
Web address: www.pendermemorial.org

Owned, leased, sponsored:	1 hospital	668 beds
Contract–managed:	1 hospital	68 beds
Totals:	2 hospitals	736 beds

★**3075: NEW YORK CITY HEALTH AND HOSPITALS CORPORATION** (NP)
125 Worth Street, Room 514, New York, NY Zip 10013–4006; tel. 212/788–3321; Ramanathan Raju, M.D., President
(Decentralized Health System)

NEW YORK: BELLEVUE HOSPITAL CENTER (O, 812 beds) 462 First Avenue, New York, NY Zip 10016–9198; tel. 212/562–4141; Steven Alexander, Executive Director
Web address: www.nyc.gov/bellevue

CONEY ISLAND HOSPITAL (O, 231 beds) 2601 Ocean Parkway, Brooklyn, NY Zip 11235–7795; tel. 718/616–3000; Arthur Wagner, Senior Vice President and Executive Director
Web address: www.nyc.gov/html/hhc/html/facilities/coneyisland.shtml

ELMHURST HOSPITAL CENTER (O, 551 beds) 79–01 Broadway, Elmhurst, NY Zip 11373–1329; tel. 718/334–4000; Chris D. Constantino, Executive Director
Web address: www.nyc.gov/html/hhc/ehc/html/home/home.shtml

GOUVERNEUR HOSPITAL (O, 196 beds) 227 Madison Street, New York, NY Zip 10002; tel. 212/238–7000; Gregory M. Kaladjian, Executive Director

HARLEM HOSPITAL CENTER (O, 273 beds) 506 Lenox Avenue, New York, NY Zip 10037–1802; tel. 212/939–1000; Denise C. Soares, R.N., Executive Director
Web address: www.nyc.gov/html/hhc/harlem

HENRY J. CARTER SPECIALTY HOSPITAL AND NURSING FACILITY (O, 2016 beds) 1752 Park Avenue, New York, NY Zip 10035; tel. 646/686–0000; Robert K. Hughes, Executive Director
Web address: www.coler–goldwater.org

JACOBI MEDICAL CENTER (O, 457 beds) 1400 Pelham Parkway South, Bronx, NY Zip 10461–1197; tel. 718/918–5000; William P. Walsh, Senior Vice President and Executive Director
Web address: www.nyc.gov/html/hhc/jacobi/home.html

KINGS COUNTY HOSPITAL CENTER (O, 599 beds) 451 Clarkson Avenue, Brooklyn, NY Zip 11203–2097; tel. 718/245–3131; Ernest Baptiste, Executive Director
Web address: www.nyc.gov/html/hhc/kchc/html/home/home.shtml

LINCOLN MEDICAL AND MENTAL HEALTH CENTER (O, 338 beds) 234 East 149th Street, Bronx, NY Zip 10451–5504; tel. 718/579–5700; Milton Nunez, Executive Director
Web address: www.nyc.gov/html/hhc/lincoln/

METROPOLITAN HOSPITAL CENTER (O, 317 beds) 1901 First Avenue, New York, NY Zip 10029–7404; tel. 212/423–6262; Meryl Weinberg, Executive Director
Web address: www.nyc.gov/html/hhc/mhc/html/home/home.shtml

NORTH CENTRAL BRONX HOSPITAL (O, 207 beds) 3424 Kossuth Avenue, Bronx, NY Zip 10467–2489; tel. 718/519–3500; William P. Walsh, Executive Director
Web address: www.nyc.gov/html/hhc/ncbh/html/home/home.shtml

QUEENS HOSPITAL CENTER (O, 281 beds) 82–68 164th Street, Jamaica, NY Zip 11432–1104; tel. 718/883–3000; Julius Wool, Executive Director
Web address: www.nyc.gov/html/hhc/qhc/html/home/home.shtml

SEA VIEW HOSPITAL REHABILITATION CENTER AND HOME (O, 304 beds) 460 Brielle Avenue, Staten Island, NY Zip 10314; tel. 212/390–8181; Jane M. Lyons, Executive Director

WOODHULL MEDICAL AND MENTAL HEALTH CENTER (O, 334 beds) 760 Broadway, Brooklyn, NY Zip 11206–5383; tel. 718/963–8000; George M. Proctor, Senior Vice President and Executive Director
Web address: www.nyc.gov/html/hhc

Owned, leased, sponsored:	14 hospitals	6916 beds
Contract–managed:	0 hospitals	0 beds
Totals:	14 hospitals	6916 beds

0142: NEW YORK PRESBYTERIAN HEALTHCARE SYSTEM (NP)
525 East 68th Street, Box 182, New York, NY Zip 10065; tel. 212/746–3745; Steven J. Corwin, M.D., Chief Executive Officer
(Moderately Centralized Health System)

BROOKLYN HOSPITAL CENTER (S, 332 beds) 121 DeKalb Avenue, Brooklyn, NY Zip 11201–5425; tel. 718/250–8000; Richard B. Becker, M.D., President, Chief Executive Officer and Interim Chief Medical Officer
Web address: www.tbh.org

GRACIE SQUARE HOSPITAL (S, 157 beds) 420 East 76th Street, New York, NY Zip 10021–3396; tel. 212/988–4400; Frank Bruno, Chief Executive Officer
Web address: www.nygsh.org

HOSPITAL FOR SPECIAL SURGERY (S, 199 beds) 535 East 70th Street, New York, NY Zip 10021–4898; tel. 212/606–1000; Louis A. Shapiro, President and Chief Executive Officer
Web address: www.hss.edu

NEW YORK COMMUNITY HOSPITAL (S, 127 beds) 2525 Kings Highway, Brooklyn, NY Zip 11229–1705; tel. 718/692–5300; Steve Meyers, Interim Chief Executive Officer
Web address: www.nych.com

NEW YORK HOSPITAL QUEENS (S, 559 beds) 56–45 Main Street, Flushing, NY Zip 11355–5045; tel. 718/670–1231; Stephen S. Mills, President and Chief Executive Officer
Web address: www.nyhq.org

NEW YORK METHODIST HOSPITAL (S, 591 beds) 506 Sixth Street, Brooklyn, NY Zip 11215–3609; tel. 718/780–3000; Mark J. Mundy, President and Chief Executive Officer
Web address: www.nym.org

NEW YORK PRESBYTERIAN LOWER MANHATTAN HOSPITAL (O, 128 beds) 170 William Street, New York, NY Zip 10038–2649; tel. 212/312–5000; Robert E. Kelly, M.D., President
Web address: www.nyp.org/lowermanhattan

NEW YORK–PRESBYTERIAN HOSPITAL (O, 2364 beds) 525 East 68th Street, New York, NY Zip 10065–4870; tel. 212/746–5454; Steven J. Corwin, M.D., Chief Executive Officer
Web address: www.nyp.org

NYACK HOSPITAL (S, 375 beds) 160 North Midland Avenue, Nyack, NY Zip 10960–1998; tel. 845/348–2000; David H. Freed, President and Chief Executive Officer
Web address: www.nyackhospital.org

Owned, leased, sponsored:	9 hospitals	4832 beds
Contract–managed:	0 hospitals	0 beds
Totals:	9 hospitals	4832 beds

For explanation of codes following names, see page B2.
★ Indicates Type III membership in the American Hospital Association.

0009: NEW YORK STATE OFFICE OF MENTAL HEALTH (NP)
44 Holland Avenue, Albany, NY Zip 12208–3411;
tel. 518/474–7056; Kristin M. Woodlock, R.N., Acting Commissioner
(Independent Hospital System)

BRONX PSYCHIATRIC CENTER (O, 450 beds) 1500 Waters Place, Bronx, NY Zip 10461–2796; tel. 718/931–0600; Pamela Turner, Executive Director
Web address: www.omh.ny.gov

BUFFALO PSYCHIATRIC CENTER (O, 240 beds) 400 Forest Avenue, Buffalo, NY Zip 14213–1298; tel. 716/885–2261; Thomas Dodson, Executive Director
Web address: www.omh.ny.gov

CAPITAL DISTRICT PSYCHIATRIC CENTER (O, 200 beds) 75 New Scotland Avenue, Albany, NY Zip 12208–3474; tel. 518/447–9611; William Dickson, Acting Executive Director
Web address: www.omh.ny.gov/omhweb/facilities/cdpc/facility.htm

CENTRAL NEW YORK PSYCHIATRIC CENTER (O, 226 beds) 9005 Old River Road, Marcy, NY Zip 13403–3000; Mailing Address: P.O. Box 300, Zip 13403–0300; tel. 315/765–3600; Maureen Bosco, Executive Director
Web address: www.omh.ny.gov

CREEDMOOR PSYCHIATRIC CENTER (O, 420 beds) 79–25 Winchester Boulevard, Jamaica, NY Zip 11427–2128; tel. 718/264–3600; Ann Marie Barbarotta, Executive Director
Web address: www.omh.ny.gov

ELMIRA PSYCHIATRIC CENTER (O, 100 beds) 100 Washington Street, Elmira, NY Zip 14901–2898; tel. 607/737–4739; Mark Stephany, Executive Director
Web address: www.omh.ny.gov/omhweb/facilities/elpc/facility.htm

GREATER BINGHAMTON HEALTH CENTER (O, 115 beds) 425 Robinson Street, Binghamton, NY Zip 13904–1735; tel. 607/724–1391; Mark Stephany, Executive Director
Web address: www.omh.ny.gov/omhweb/facilities/bipc/facility.htm

KINGSBORO PSYCHIATRIC CENTER (O, 290 beds) 681 Clarkson Avenue, Brooklyn, NY Zip 11203–2125; tel. 718/221–7395; Deborah Parchment, Executive Director
Web address: www.omh.ny.gov/omhweb/facilities/kbpc/facility/htm

MANHATTAN PSYCHIATRIC CENTER–WARD'S ISLAND (O, 745 beds) 600 East 125th Street, New York, NY Zip 10035–6000; tel. 646/672–6767; Vinny Miccoli, Executive Director
Web address: www.omh.ny.gov

MID–HUDSON FORENSIC PSYCHIATRIC CENTER (O, 268 beds) Route 17M, New Hampton, NY Zip 10958, Mailing Address: P.O. Box 158, Zip 10958–0158; tel. 845/374–8700; Peggi Healy, Executive Director
Web address: www.omh.ny.gov

MOHAWK VALLEY PSYCHIATRIC CENTER (O, 614 beds) 1400 Noyes Street, Utica, NY Zip 13502–3854; tel. 315/738–3800; Colleen A. Sawyer, R.N., MSN, Executive Director
Web address: www.omh.ny.gov/omhweb/facilities/mvpc/facility.htm

NEW YORK CITY CHILDREN'S CENTER (O, 84 beds) 74–03 Commonwealth Boulevard, Jamaica, NY Zip 11426–1890; tel. 718/264–4506; Anita Daniels, Acting Executive Director
Web address: www.omh.ny.gov

NEW YORK STATE PSYCHIATRIC INSTITUTE (O, 58 beds) 1051 Riverside Drive, New York, NY Zip 10032–1007; tel. 212/543–5000; Jeffrey A. Lieberman, M.D., Executive Director
Web address: www.nyspi.org

PILGRIM PSYCHIATRIC CENTER (O, 569 beds) 998 Crooked Hill Road, Brentwood, NY Zip 11717–1019; tel. 631/761–3500; Kathy O'Keefe, Executive Director
Web address: www.omh.ny.gov/omhweb/facilities/pgpc/facility.htm

RICHARD H. HUTCHINGS PSYCHIATRIC CENTER (O, 131 beds) 620 Madison Street, Syracuse, NY Zip 13210–2319; tel. 315/426–3632; Colleen A. Sawyer, R.N., MSN, Executive Director
Web address: www.omh.ny.gov

ROCHESTER PSYCHIATRIC CENTER (O, 180 beds) 1111 Elmwood Avenue, Rochester, NY Zip 14620–3005; tel. 585/241–1200; Elizabeth Suhre, Executive Director
Web address: www.omh.ny.gov/omhweb/facilities/ropc/facility.htm

ROCKLAND CHILDREN'S PSYCHIATRIC CENTER (O, 54 beds) 599 Convent Road, Orangeburg, NY Zip 10962–1162; tel. 845/359–7400; Anita Daniels, Executive Director
Web address: www.omh.ny.gov/

ROCKLAND PSYCHIATRIC CENTER (O, 525 beds) 140 Old Orangeburg Road, Orangeburg, NY Zip 10962–1157; tel. 845/359–1000; Christopher Tavella, Executive Director
Web address: www.omh.ny.gov/

SAGAMORE CHILDREN'S PSYCHIATRIC CENTER (O, 69 beds) 197 Half Hollow Road, Dix Hills, NY Zip 11746–5861; tel. 631/370–1700; Kathy O'Keefe, Interim Executive Director
Web address: www.omh.ny.gov

SOUTH BEACH PSYCHIATRIC CENTER (O, 340 beds) 777 Seaview Avenue, Staten Island, NY Zip 10305–3409; tel. 718/667–2300; Rosanne Gaylor, M.D., Acting Executive Director
Web address: www.omh.ny.gov/omhweb/facilities/sbpc/facility.htm

ST. LAWRENCE PSYCHIATRIC CENTER (O, 146 beds) 1 Chimney Point Drive, Ogdensburg, NY Zip 13669–2291; tel. 315/541–2001; Timothy Farrell, Executive Director
Web address: www.omh.ny.gov/omhweb/facilities/slpc/facility.htm

WESTERN NEW YORK CHILDREN'S PSYCHIATRIC CENTER (O, 46 beds) 1010 East and West Road, West Seneca, NY Zip 14224–3602; tel. 716/677–7000; Kathe Hayes, Executive Director
Web address: www.omh.ny.gov

Owned, leased, sponsored:	22 hospitals	5870 beds
Contract–managed:	0 hospitals	0 beds
Totals:	22 hospitals	5870 beds

0353: NEXUS HEALTH SYSTEMS (IO)
One Riverway, Suite 600, Houston, TX Zip 77056–1993; tel. 713/355–6111; John W. Cassidy, M.D., President, Chief Executive Officer and Chief Medical Officer
(Independent Hospital System)

CALIFORNIA: HEALTHBRIDGE CHILDREN'S HOSPITAL (O, 27 beds) 393 South Tustin Street, Orange, CA Zip 92866–2501; tel. 714/289–2400; Brian Cotter, Chief Executive Officer
Web address: www.HealthBridgeOrange.com

TEXAS: HEALTHBRIDGE CHILDREN'S HOSPITAL OF HOUSTON (O, 40 beds) 2929 Woodland Park Drive, Houston, TX Zip 77082–2687; tel. 281/293–7774; Ronell Myburgh, Chief Executive Officer
Web address: www.healthbridgehouston.com/

NEXUS SPECIALTY HOSPITAL (O, 75 beds) 123 Vision Park Boulevard, Shenandoah, TX Zip 77384–3001; tel. 281/364–0317; Judith Butryn, Chief Executive Officer
Web address: www.nexusspecialty.com

Owned, leased, sponsored:	3 hospitals	142 beds
Contract–managed:	0 hospitals	0 beds
Totals:	3 hospitals	142 beds

0349: NOLAND HEALTH SERVICES, INC. (NP)
600 Corporate Parkway, Suite 100, Birmingham, AL Zip 35242–5451; tel. 205/783–8484; Gary M. Glasscock, President and Chief Executive Officer

ALABAMA: NOLAND HOSPITAL ANNISTON (O, 38 beds) 400 East 10th Street, 4th Floor, Anniston, AL Zip 36207–4716; tel. 256/741–6141; Bill Mitchell, Administrator
Web address: www.nolandhealth.com

NOLAND HOSPITAL BIRMINGHAM (O, 45 beds) 50 Medical Park East Drive, 8th Floor, Birmingham, AL Zip 35235; tel. 205/808–5100; Laura S. Wills, Administrator
Web address: www.nolandhealth.com

NOLAND HOSPITAL DOTHAN (O, 35 beds) 1108 Ross Clark Circle, 4th Floor, Dothan, AL Zip 36301–3022; tel. 334/699–4300; Kaye Burke, Administrator
Web address: www.nolandhealth.com

NOLAND HOSPITAL MONTGOMERY (O, 65 beds) 1725 Pine Street, 5 North, Montgomery, AL Zip 36106–1109; tel. 334/240–0532; Susan E. Legg, Interim Administrator
Web address: www.nolandhealth.com

NOLAND HOSPITAL SHELBY (O, 52 beds) 1000 First Street North, 3rd Floor, Alabaster, AL Zip 35007–8703; tel. 205/620–8641; Laura S. Wills, Administrator
Web address: www.nolandhospitals.com

Section B

For explanation of codes following names, see page B2.
★ Indicates Type III membership in the American Hospital Association.

NOLAND HOSPITAL TUSCALOOSA (O, 32 beds) 809 University Boulevard E, 4th Floor, Tuscaloosa, AL Zip 35401–2029; tel. 205/759–7241; Dale Jones, Administrator
Web address: www.nolandhealth.com

Owned, leased, sponsored:	6 hospitals	267 beds
Contract–managed:	0 hospitals	0 beds
Totals:	6 hospitals	267 beds

★**0887: NORTH MEMORIAL HEALTH CARE** (NP)
3300 Oakdale Avenue North, Robbinsdale, MN Zip 55422–2926; tel. 763/520–5200; Loren L. Taylor, Chief Executive Officer
(Centralized Physician/Insurance Health System)

MINNESOTA: MAPLE GROVE HOSPITAL (C, 108 beds) 9875 Hospital Drive, Maple Grove, MN Zip 55369–4648; tel. 763/581–1000; Andrew S. Cochrane, Chief Executive Officer
Web address: www.maplegrovehospital.org

NORTH MEMORIAL MEDICAL CENTER (O, 355 beds) 3300 Oakdale Avenue North, Robbinsdale, MN Zip 55422–2926; tel. 763/520–5200; Gayle Mattson, R.N., President
Web address: www.northmemorial.com

Owned, leased, sponsored:	1 hospital	355 beds
Contract–managed:	1 hospital	108 beds
Totals:	2 hospitals	463 beds

★**0032: NORTH MISSISSIPPI HEALTH SERVICES, INC.** (NP)
830 South Gloster Street, Tupelo, MS Zip 38801–4996; tel. 662/377–3136; M. Shane Spees, President and Chief Executive Officer
(Centralized Physician/Insurance Health System)

ALABAMA: MARION REGIONAL MEDICAL CENTER (O, 36 beds) 1256 Military Street South, Hamilton, AL Zip 35570–5003; tel. 205/921–6200; Tanya Brasher, Administrator
Web address: www.nmhs.net

MISSISSIPPI: CALHOUN HEALTH SERVICES (C, 150 beds) 140 Burke–Calhoun City Road, Calhoun City, MS Zip 38916–9690; tel. 662/628–6611; James P. Franklin, Administrator
Web address: www.nmhs.net/calhoun_city

NORTH MISSISSIPPI MEDICAL CENTER – TUPELO (O, 757 beds) 830 South Gloster Street, Tupelo, MS Zip 38801–4934; tel. 662/377–3000; M. Shane Spees, President and Chief Executive Officer
Web address: www.nmhs.net

NORTH MISSISSIPPI MEDICAL CENTER–EUPORA (O, 73 beds) 70 Medical Plaza, Eupora, MS Zip 39744–4018; tel. 662/258–6221; John R. Jones, Administrator
Web address: www.nmhs.net/eupora

NORTH MISSISSIPPI MEDICAL CENTER–IUKA (O, 48 beds) 1777 Curtis Drive, Iuka, MS Zip 38852–1001, Mailing Address: P.O. Box 860, Zip 38852–0860; tel. 662/423–6051; Fred A. Truesdale, Jr., Administrator
Web address: www.nmhs.net

NORTH MISSISSIPPI MEDICAL CENTER–PONTOTOC (L, 69 beds) 176 South Main Street, Pontotoc, MS Zip 38863–3311, Mailing Address: P.O. Box 790, Zip 38863–0790; tel. 662/488–7640; Fred B. Hood, FACHE, Administrator
Web address: www.nmhs.net

NORTH MISSISSIPPI MEDICAL CENTER–WEST POINT (O, 60 beds) 835 Medical Center Drive, West Point, MS Zip 39773–9320; tel. 662/495–2300; James W. Hahn, Administrator
Web address: www.nmhs.net/westpoint

Owned, leased, sponsored:	6 hospitals	1043 beds
Contract–managed:	1 hospital	150 beds
Totals:	7 hospitals	1193 beds

0867: NORTH OAKS HEALTH SYSTEM (NP)
15790 Paul Vega MD Drive, Hammond, LA Zip 70403–1436, Mailing Address: P.O. Box 2668, Zip 70404–2668; tel. 985/345–2700; James E. Cathey, Jr., Chief Executive Officer
(Independent Hospital System)

LOUISIANA: NORTH OAKS MEDICAL CENTER (O, 344 beds) 15790 Paul Vega, MD, Drive, Hammond, LA Zip 70401–1436, Mailing Address: P.O. Box 2668, Zip 70404–2668; tel. 985/345–2700; Michele K. Sutton, FACHE, Administrator
Web address: www.northoaks.org

NORTH OAKS REHABILITATION HOSPITAL (O, 27 beds) 1900 South Morrison Boulevard, Hammond, LA Zip 70403–5742; tel. 504/230–5700; Sybil K. Paulson, R.N., Administrator
Web address: www.northoaks.org

Owned, leased, sponsored:	2 hospitals	371 beds
Contract–managed:	0 hospitals	0 beds
Totals:	2 hospitals	371 beds

★**0062: NORTH SHORE–LONG ISLAND JEWISH HEALTH SYSTEM** (NP)
145 Community Drive, Great Neck, NY Zip 11021–5502; tel. 516/465–8100; Michael J. Dowling, President and Chief Executive Officer
(Centralized Health System)

NEW YORK: FOREST HILLS HOSPITAL (O, 235 beds) 102–01 66th Road, Forest Hills, NY Zip 11375–2029; tel. 718/830–4000; Rita Mercieca, R.N., Executive Director
Web address: www.northshorelij.com

FRANKLIN HOSPITAL (O, 330 beds) 900 Franklin Avenue, Valley Stream, NY Zip 11580–2190; tel. 516/256–6000; Catherine Hottendorf, R.N., MS, Executive Director
Web address: www.northshorelij.com

GLEN COVE HOSPITAL (O, 235 beds) 101 St. Andrews Lane, Glen Cove, NY Zip 11542–2254; tel. 516/674–7300; Susan Kwiatek, R.N., Executive Director
Web address: www.northshorelij.com

HUNTINGTON HOSPITAL (O, 290 beds) 270 Park Avenue, Huntington, NY Zip 11743–2799; tel. 631/351–2200; Kevin F. Lawlor, President and Chief Executive Officer
Web address: www.hunthosp.org

LENOX HILL HOSPITAL (O, 508 beds) 100 East 77th Street, New York, NY Zip 10075–1850; tel. 212/434–2000; Dennis Connors, Executive Director
Web address: www.lenoxhillhospital.org

LONG ISLAND JEWISH MEDICAL CENTER (O, 885 beds) 270–05 76th Avenue, New York, New Hyde Park, NY Zip 11040–1496; tel. 718/470–7000; Chantal Weinhold, Executive Director
Web address: www.lij.edu

NORTH SHORE UNIVERSITY HOSPITAL (O, 764 beds) 300 Community Drive, Manhasset, NY Zip 11030–3816; tel. 516/562–0100; Alessandro Bellucci, M.D., Executive Director
Web address: www.northshorelij.com

PLAINVIEW HOSPITAL (O, 189 beds) 888 Old Country Road, Plainview, NY Zip 11803–4978; tel. 516/719–3000; Michael Fener, Executive Director
Web address: www.northshorelij.com

SOUTH OAKS HOSPITAL (O, 260 beds) 400 Sunrise Highway, Amityville, NY Zip 11701–2508; tel. 631/264–4000; Robert E. Detor, Chief Executive Officer
Web address: www.longislandhome.org

SOUTHSIDE HOSPITAL (O, 300 beds) 301 East Main Street, Bay Shore, NY Zip 11706–8458; tel. 631/968–3000; Donna Moravick, R.N., MSN, Executive Director
Web address: www.southsidehospital.org

STATEN ISLAND UNIVERSITY HOSPITAL (O, 663 beds) 475 Seaview Avenue, Staten Island, NY Zip 10305–3436; tel. 718/226–9000; Anthony C. Ferreri, President and Chief Executive Officer
Web address: www.siuh.edu

SYOSSET HOSPITAL (O, 72 beds) 221 Jericho Turnpike, Syosset, NY Zip 11791–4515; tel. 516/496–6500; Michael Fener, Executive Director
Web address: www.northshorelij.com

Owned, leased, sponsored:	12 hospitals	4731 beds
Contract–managed:	0 hospitals	0 beds
Totals:	12 hospitals	4731 beds

For explanation of codes following names, see page B2.
★ Indicates Type III membership in the American Hospital Association.

★**0281: NORTHERN ARIZONA HEALTHCARE** (NP)
1200 North Beaver Street, Flagstaff, AZ Zip 86001–3118;
tel. 928/779–3366; William T. Bradel, President and Chief Executive Officer
(Moderately Centralized Health System)

ARIZONA: FLAGSTAFF MEDICAL CENTER (O, 267 beds) 1200 North Beaver Street, Flagstaff, AZ Zip 86001–3118; tel. 928/779–3366; Irwin Bloom, President and Chief Executive Officer
Web address: www.flagstaffmedicalcenter.com

VERDE VALLEY MEDICAL CENTER (O, 110 beds) 269 South Candy Lane, Cottonwood, AZ Zip 86326–4170; tel. 928/639–6000; Barbara Dember, President and Chief Executive Officer
Web address: www.nahealth.com

Owned, leased, sponsored:	2 hospitals	377 beds
Contract–managed:	0 hospitals	0 beds
Totals:	2 hospitals	377 beds

★**0410: NORTHSIDE HEALTHCARE SYSTEM** (NP)
1000 Johnson Ferry Road N.E., Atlanta, GA Zip 30342–1611;
tel. 404/851–8000; Robert Quattrocchi, President and Chief Executive Officer

GEORGIA: NORTHSIDE HOSPITAL (O, 567 beds) 1000 Johnson Ferry Road N.E., Atlanta, GA Zip 30342–1611; tel. 404/851–8000; Robert Quattrocchi, President and Chief Executive Officer
Web address: www.northside.com

NORTHSIDE HOSPITAL–CHEROKEE (O, 88 beds) 201 Hospital Road, Canton, GA Zip 30114–2408, Mailing Address: P.O. Box 906, Zip 30169–0906; tel. 770/720–5100; William M. Hayes, Chief Executive Officer
Web address: www.northside.com

NORTHSIDE HOSPITAL–FORSYTH (O, 228 beds) 1200 Northside Forsyth Drive, Cumming, GA Zip 30041–7659; tel. 770/844–3200; Lynn Jackson, Administrator
Web address: www.northside.com

Owned, leased, sponsored:	3 hospitals	883 beds
Contract–managed:	0 hospitals	0 beds
Totals:	3 hospitals	883 beds

★**0024: NORTHWESTERN MEMORIAL HEALTHCARE** (NP)
251 East Huron Street, Chicago, IL Zip 60611–2908;
tel. 312/926–2000; Dean M. Harrison, President and Chief Executive Officer
(Moderately Centralized Health System)

ILLINOIS: NORTHWESTERN LAKE FOREST HOSPITAL (O, 189 beds) 660 North Westmoreland Road, Lake Forest, IL Zip 60045–1696; tel. 847/234–5600; Thomas J. McAfee, President
Web address: www.lfh.org

NORTHWESTERN MEMORIAL HOSPITAL (O, 885 beds) 251 East Huron Street, Chicago, IL Zip 60611–2908; tel. 312/926–2000; Dean M. Harrison, President and Chief Executive Officer
Web address: www.nmh.org

Owned, leased, sponsored:	2 hospitals	1074 beds
Contract–managed:	0 hospitals	0 beds
Totals:	2 hospitals	1074 beds

★**2285: NORTON HEALTHCARE** (NP)
4967 U.S. Highway 42, Suite 100, Louisville, KY Zip 40222–6363, Mailing Address: P.O. Box 35070, Zip 40232–5070;
tel. 502/629–8000; Stephen Williams, Chief Executive Officer
(Centralized Health System)

KENTUCKY: KOSAIR CHILDREN'S HOSPITAL (O, 260 beds) 231 East Chestnut Street, Louisville, KY Zip 40202–1821; tel. 502/629–6000; Thomas D. Kmetz, President
Web address: www.kosairchildrens.com/

NORTON AUDUBON HOSPITAL (O, 278 beds) One Audubon Plaza Drive, Louisville, KY Zip 40217–1300, Mailing Address: P.O. Box 17550, Zip 40217–0550; tel. 502/636–7111; Jon Cooper, President
Web address: www.nortonhealthcare.com/NortonAudubonHospital

NORTON BROWNSBORO HOSPITAL (O, 117 beds) 4960 Norton Healthcare Boulevard, Louisville, KY Zip 40241–2831; tel. 502/446–8000; John D. Harryman, Chief Administrative Officer
Web address: www.nortonhealthcare.com/nortonbrownsborohospital

NORTON HOSPITAL (O, 348 beds) 200 East Chestnut Street, Louisville, KY Zip 40202–1800, Mailing Address: P.O. Box 35070, Zip 40232–5070; tel. 502/629–8000; Matthew Ayers, Chief Executive Officer
Web address: www.nortonhealthcare.com/nortonhospital

NORTON SUBURBAN HOSPITAL (O, 351 beds) 4001 Dutchmans Lane, Louisville, KY Zip 40207–4799; tel. 502/893–1000; Charlotte Ipsan, President
Web address: www.nortonhealthcare.com/nortonsuburbanhospital

Owned, leased, sponsored:	5 hospitals	1354 beds
Contract–managed:	0 hospitals	0 beds
Totals:	5 hospitals	1354 beds

★**0139: NOVANT HEALTH** (NP)
2085 Frontis Plaza Boulevard, Winston Salem, NC Zip 27103–5614;
tel. 336/718–5600; Carl S. Armato, President and Chief Executive Officer
(Moderately Centralized Health System)

NORTH CAROLINA: ASHE MEMORIAL HOSPITAL (C, 25 beds) 200 Hospital Avenue, Jefferson, NC Zip 28640–9244; tel. 336/846–7101; Laura Lambeth, Chief Executive Officer
Web address: www.ashememorial.org

HALIFAX REGIONAL MEDICAL CENTER (C, 142 beds) 250 Smith Church Road, Roanoke Rapids, NC Zip 27870–4914, Mailing Address: P.O. Box 1089, Zip 27870–1089; tel. 252/535–8011; William Mahone, President and Chief Executive Officer
Web address: www.halifaxmedicalcenter.org

NOVANT HEALTH BRUNSWICK MEDICAL CENTER (O, 66 beds) 240 Hospital Drive N.E., Bolivia, NC Zip 28422–8346; tel. 910/721–1000; Shelbourn Stevens, President
Web address: www.brunswicknovant.org

NOVANT HEALTH CHARLOTTE ORTHOPAEDIC HOSPITAL (O, 80 beds) 1901 Randolph Road, Charlotte, NC Zip 28207–1195; tel. 704/316–2000; Mike Riley, Senior Vice President and Chief Operating Officer
Web address: www.novanthealth.org

NOVANT HEALTH FORSYTH MEDICAL CENTER (O, 660 beds) 3333 Silas Creek Parkway, Winston–Salem, NC Zip 27103–3090; tel. 336/718–5000; Denise B. Mihal, R.N., Chief Executive Officer
Web address: www.forsythmedicalcenter.org

NOVANT HEALTH FRANKLIN MEDICAL CENTER (O, 43 beds) 100 Hospital Drive, Louisburg, NC Zip 27549–2256, Mailing Address: P.O. Box 609, Zip 27549–0609; tel. 919/497–8401; Jody Morris, President and Chief Operating Officer
Web address: www.https://www.novanthealth.org/franklin–medical–center.aspx

NOVANT HEALTH HUNTERSVILLE MEDICAL CENTER (O, 75 beds) 10030 Gilead Road, Huntersville, NC Zip 28078–7545, Mailing Address: P.O. Box 3508, Zip 28070–3508; tel. 704/316–4000; Tanya S. Blackmon, President
Web address: www.novanthealth.org

NOVANT HEALTH MATTHEWS MEDICAL CENTER (O, 137 beds) 1500 Matthews Township Parkway, Matthews, NC Zip 28105–4656, Mailing Address: P.O. Box 3310, Zip 28106–3310; tel. 704/384–6500; Roland R. Bibeau, FACHE, President
Web address: www.presbyterian.org

NOVANT HEALTH MEDICAL PARK HOSPITAL (O, 22 beds) 1950 South Hawthorne Road, Winston–Salem, NC Zip 27103–3993; tel. 336/718–0600; Teresa Carter, Vice President and Chief Operating Officer
Web address: www.novanthealth.org

NOVANT HEALTH PRESBYTERIAN MEDICAL CENTER (O, 588 beds) 200 Hawthorne Lane, Charlotte, NC Zip 28204–2528, Mailing Address: P.O. Box 33549, Zip 28233–3549; tel. 704/384–4000; Harry L. Smith, Jr., President
Web address: www.presbyterian.org

Section B

For explanation of codes following names, see page B2.
★ Indicates Type III membership in the American Hospital Association.

NOVANT HEALTH ROWAN MEDICAL CENTER (O, 145 beds) 612 Mocksville Avenue, Salisbury, NC Zip 28144–2799; tel. 704/210–5000; Dari Caldwell, R.N., Ph.D., FACHE, President
Web address: www.rowan.org

NOVANT HEALTH THOMASVILLE MEDICAL CENTER (O, 66 beds) 207 Old Lexington Road, Thomasville, NC Zip 27360–3428, Mailing Address: P.O. Box 789, Zip 27361–0789; tel. 336/472–2000; Kathie A. Johnson, R.N., MS, Ph.D., Chief Executive Officer
Web address: www.thomasvillemedicalcenter.org

SOUTH CAROLINA: NOVANT HEALTH GAFFNEY MEDICAL CENTER (O, 125 beds) 1530 North Limestone Street, Gaffney, SC Zip 29340–4738; tel. 864/487–4271; Brian Yates, Administrator
Web address: www.upstatecarolina.org

VIRGINIA: NOVANT HEALTH HAYMARKET MEDICAL CENTER (O, 60 beds) 15225 Heathcote Boulevard, Haymarket, VA Zip 20155–4023, Mailing Address: 14535 John Marshall Highway, Gainesville, Zip 20155–4023; tel. 571/284–1000; Don Sedgley, President
Web address: www.novanthealth.org

NOVANT HEALTH PRINCE WILLIAM MEDICAL CENTER (O, 168 beds) 8700 Sudley Road, Manassas, VA Zip 20110–4418, Mailing Address: P.O. Box 2610, Zip 20108–0867; tel. 703/369–8000; Melissa Robson, President
Web address: www.pwhs.org

Owned, leased, sponsored:	13 hospitals	2235 beds
Contract–managed:	2 hospitals	167 beds
Totals:	15 hospitals	2402 beds

★1165: OAKWOOD HEALTHCARE, INC. (NP)
One Parklane Boulevard, Suite 1000E, Dearborn, MI Zip 48126–2400; tel. 313/253–6050; Brian M. Connolly, President and Chief Executive Officer
(Centralized Health System)

MICHIGAN: OAKWOOD HOSPITAL–DEARBORN (O, 524 beds) 18101 Oakwood Boulevard, Dearborn, MI Zip 48124–4089, Mailing Address: P.O. Box 2500, Zip 48123–2500; tel. 313/593–7000; Kelly C. Smith, Division President
Web address: www.oakwood.org

OAKWOOD HOSPITAL–SOUTHSHORE (O, 173 beds) 5450 Fort Street, Trenton, MI Zip 48183–4625; tel. 734/671–3800; Edith M. Hughes, R.N., President
Web address: www.oakwood.org

OAKWOOD HOSPITAL–TAYLOR (O, 133 beds) 10000 Telegraph Road, Taylor, MI Zip 48180–3330; tel. 313/295–5000; Lee Ann Odom, Division President
Web address: www.oakwood.org

OAKWOOD HOSPITAL–WAYNE (O, 204 beds) 33155 Annapolis Street, Wayne, MI Zip 48184–2405; tel. 734/467–4000; Eric W. Widner, Division President
Web address: www.oakwood.org

Owned, leased, sponsored:	4 hospitals	1034 beds
Contract–managed:	0 hospitals	0 beds
Totals:	4 hospitals	1034 beds

0616: OCEANS HEALTHCARE (IO)
2720 Rue de Jardin, Suite 100, Lake Charles, LA Zip 70605–4050; tel. 337/721–1900; Jason Reed, President and Chief Executive Officer

LOUISIANA: OCEANS BEHAVIORAL HOSPITAL OF ALEXANDRIA (O, 24 beds) 2621 North Bolton Avenue, Alexandria, LA Zip 71303–4506; tel. 318/448–8473; Gene Amons, Administrator
Web address: www.obha.info/

OCEANS BEHAVIORAL HOSPITAL OF BATON ROUGE (O, 20 beds) 11135 Florida Boulevard, Baton Rouge, LA Zip 70815–2013; tel. 225/356–7030; Valerie Dalton, R.N., Administrator
Web address: www.obhbr.info/

OCEANS BEHAVIORAL HOSPITAL OF BROUSSARD (O, 38 beds) 418 Albertson Parkway, Broussard, LA Zip 70518–4971; tel. 337/237–6444; Amy Dysart–Credeur, Administrator
Web address: www.obhb.info/

OCEANS BEHAVIORAL HOSPITAL OF DE RIDDER (O, 20 beds) 1420 Blankenship Drive, Deridder, LA Zip 70634–4604; tel. 337/460–9472; Sheila Langston, Administrator
Web address: www.obhd.info/

OCEANS BEHAVIORAL HOSPITAL OF GREATER NEW ORLEANS (O, 18 beds) 716 Village Road, Kenner, LA Zip 70065–2751; tel. 504/464–8895; Deborah Spier, Administrator
Web address: www.obhgno.info/

OCEANS BEHAVIORAL HOSPITAL OF KENTWOOD (O, 18 beds) 921 Avenue G., Kentwood, LA Zip 70444–2636; tel. 985/229–0717; Gina Isbell, Administrator
Web address: www.obhk.info/

OCEANS BEHAVIORAL HOSPITAL OF LAKE CHARLES (O, 20 beds) 302 West Mcneese Street, Lake Charles, LA Zip 70605–5604; tel. 337/474–7581; Christin Bennett, Administrator
Web address: www.obhlc.info/

OCEANS BEHAVIORAL HOSPITAL OF OPELOUSAS (O, 20 beds) 1310 Heather Drive, Opelousas, LA Zip 70570–7714; tel. 337/948–8820; Remi Savoy, Administrator
Web address: www.obho.info/

Owned, leased, sponsored:	8 hospitals	178 beds
Contract–managed:	0 hospitals	0 beds
Totals:	8 hospitals	178 beds

★0359: OCHSNER HEALTH SYSTEM (NP)
1514 Jefferson Highway, New Orleans, LA Zip 70121–2429; tel. 800/874–8984; Warner L. Thomas, FACHE, President and Chief Executive Officer
(Moderately Centralized Health System)

LEONARD J. CHABERT MEDICAL CENTER (L, 74 beds) 1978 Industrial Boulevard, Houma, LA Zip 70363–7094; tel. 985/873–2200; Ritchie Dupre, Chief Executive Officer
Web address: www.ochsner.org/locations/leonard_j_chabert_medical_center/

OCHSNER MEDICAL CENTER (O, 877 beds) 1514 Jefferson Highway, New Orleans, LA Zip 70121–2429; tel. 504/842–3000; Robert K. Wolterman, Chief Executive Officer
Web address: www.ochsner.org

OCHSNER MEDICAL CENTER – KENNER (O, 119 beds) 180 West Esplanade Avenue, Kenner, LA Zip 70065–6001; tel. 504/468–8600; Stephen Robinson, Chief Executive Officer
Web address: www.ochsner.org/locations/ochsner_health_center_kenner_w_esplanade_ave/

OCHSNER MEDICAL CENTER – NORTH SHORE (L, 110 beds) 100 Medical Center Drive, Slidell, LA Zip 70461–5520; tel. 985/646–5000; Polly J. Davenport, R.N., Chief Executive Officer
Web address: www.ochsner.org/locations/northshore

OCHSNER MEDICAL CENTER–BATON ROUGE (O, 159 beds) 17000 Medical Center Drive, Baton Rouge, LA Zip 70816–3224; tel. 225/752–2470; Eric McMillen, Chief Executive Officer
Web address: www.ochsner.org/page.cfm?id=103

OCHSNER ST. ANNE GENERAL HOSPITAL (O, 35 beds) 4608 Highway 1, Raceland, LA Zip 70394–2623; tel. 985/537–6841; Timothy J. Allen, FACHE, Chief Executive Officer
Web address: www.ochsnerstanne.org

MISSISSIPPI: HANCOCK MEDICAL CENTER (C, 86 beds) 149 Drinkwater Boulevard, Bay Saint Louis, MS Zip 39520–1658, Mailing Address: P.O. Box 2790, Zip 39521–2790; tel. 228/467–8600; Thomas K. Steiner, Chief Executive Officer
Web address: www.hmc.org

Owned, leased, sponsored:	6 hospitals	1374 beds
Contract–managed:	1 hospital	86 beds
Totals:	7 hospitals	1460 beds

0388: OCONEE REGIONAL HEALTH SYSTEMS (NP)
821 North Cobb Street, Milledgeville, GA Zip 31061–2343; tel. 478/454–3505; Jean Aycock, President and Chief Executive Officer
(Independent Hospital System)

For explanation of codes following names, see page B2.
★ Indicates Type III membership in the American Hospital Association.

Section B

GEORGIA: JASPER MEMORIAL HOSPITAL (O, 67 beds) 898 College Street, Monticello, GA Zip 31064–1258; tel. 706/468–6411; Jan Gaston, Administrator
Web address: www.jaspermemorialhospital.org

OCONEE REGIONAL MEDICAL CENTER (O, 90 beds) 821 North Cobb Street, Milledgeville, GA Zip 31061–2351, Mailing Address: P.O. Box 690, Zip 31059–0690; tel. 478/454–3505; Jean Aycock, President and Chief Executive Officer
Web address: www.oconeeregional.com

Owned, leased, sponsored:	2 hospitals	157 beds
Contract–managed:	0 hospitals	0 beds
Totals:	2 hospitals	157 beds

0537: OHIO DEPARTMENT OF MENTAL HEALTH (NP)
30 East Broad Street, 8th Floor, Columbus, OH Zip 43215–3430; tel. 614/466–2297; Tracy Plouck, Director
(Independent Hospital System)

OHIO: APPALACHIAN BEHAVIORAL HEALTHCARE (O, 224 beds) 100 Hospital Drive, Athens, OH Zip 45701–2301; tel. 740/594–5000; Jane E. Krason, R.N., Chief Executive Officer
Web address: www.mh.state.oh.us

HEARTLAND BEHAVIORAL HEALTHCARE (O, 130 beds) 3000 Erie Stree South, Massillon, OH Zip 44646–7993, Mailing Address: 3000 Erie Street South, Zip 44646–7976; tel. 330/833–3135; Jeffrey Sims, Chief Executive Officer
Web address: www.mh.state.oh.us/ibhs/bhos/hoh.html

NORTHCOAST BEHAVIORAL HEALTHCARE SYSTEM (O, 260 beds) 1756 Sagamore Road, Northfield, OH Zip 44067–1086; tel. 330/467–7131; Douglas W. Kern, Chief Executive Officer
Web address: www.mha.ohio.gov

NORTHWEST OHIO PSYCHIATRIC HOSPITAL (O, 114 beds) 930 Detroit Avenue, Toledo, OH Zip 43614–2701; tel. 419/381–1881; Mychail Scheramic, M.D., Chief Executive Officer
Web address: www.mh.state.oh.us/

SUMMIT BEHAVIORAL HEALTHCARE (O, 291 beds) 1101 Summit Road, Cincinnati, OH Zip 45237–2652; tel. 513/948–3600; Elizabeth Banks, Chief Executive Officer
Web address: www.mh.state.oh.us/

TWIN VALLEY BEHAVIORAL HEALTHCARE (O, 228 beds) 2200 West Broad Street, Columbus, OH Zip 43223–1297; tel. 614/752–0333; Veronica Lofton, Acting Chief Executive Officer
Web address: www.mh.state.oh.us/ibhs/bhos/tvbh.html

Owned, leased, sponsored:	6 hospitals	1247 beds
Contract–managed:	0 hospitals	0 beds
Totals:	6 hospitals	1247 beds

★0251: OHIO STATE UNIVERSITY HEALTH SYSTEM (NP)
370 West Ninth Avenue, Columbus, OH Zip 43210–1238; tel. 614/247–5555; Peter E. Geier, Chief Executive Officer
(Centralized Health System)

JAMES CANCER HOSPITAL AND SOLOVE RESEARCH INSTITUTE (O, 228 beds) 300 West Tenth Avenue, Columbus, OH Zip 43210–1280; tel. 614/293–3300; Michael Caligiuri, Chief Executive Officer
Web address: www.jamesline.com

OHIO STATE UNIVERSITY WEXNER MEDICAL CENTER (O, 965 beds) 370 West 9th Avenue, Columbus, OH Zip 43210–1238; tel. 614/293–8000; Steven Gabbe, M.D., Chief Executive Officer
Web address: www.medicalcenter.osu.edu

Owned, leased, sponsored:	2 hospitals	1193 beds
Contract–managed:	0 hospitals	0 beds
Totals:	2 hospitals	1193 beds

3315: OHIO VALLEY HEALTH SERVICES AND EDUCATION CORPORATION (NP)
2000 Eoff Street, Wheeling, WV Zip 26003–3823; tel. 304/234–8383; Michael J. Caruso, President and Chief Executive Officer
(Moderately Centralized Health System)

EAST OHIO REGIONAL HOSPITAL (O, 139 beds) 90 North Fourth Street, Martins Ferry, OH Zip 43935–1648; tel. 740/633–1100; Michael J. Caruso, President and Chief Executive Officer
Web address: www.ovmc–eorh.com

WEST VIRGINIA: OHIO VALLEY MEDICAL CENTER (O, 189 beds) 2000 Eoff Street, Wheeling, WV Zip 26003–3870; tel. 304/234–0123; Michael J. Caruso, President and Chief Executive Officer
Web address: www.ovmc–eorh.com

Owned, leased, sponsored:	2 hospitals	328 beds
Contract–managed:	0 hospitals	0 beds
Totals:	2 hospitals	328 beds

★0162: OHIOHEALTH (NP)
180 East Broad Street, Columbus, OH Zip 43215–3707; tel. 614/544–4455; David P. Blom, President and Chief Executive Officer
(Centralized Physician/Insurance Health System)

OHIO: MORROW COUNTY HOSPITAL (C, 23 beds) 651 West Marion Road, Mount Gilead, OH Zip 43338–1027; tel. 419/946–5015; Christopher Truax, Chief Executive Officer
Web address: www.morrowcountyhospital.com

O'BLENESS MEMORIAL HOSPITAL (O, 64 beds) 55 Hospital Drive, Athens, OH Zip 45701–2302; tel. 740/593–5551; Greg Long, Chief Executive Officer
Web address: www.obleness.org

OHIOHEALTH DOCTORS HOSPITAL (O, 243 beds) 5100 West Broad Street, Columbus, OH Zip 43228–1607; tel. 614/544–1000; Michael L. Reichfield, President
Web address: www.ohiohealth.com

OHIOHEALTH DOCTORS HOSPITAL NELSONVILLE (O, 25 beds) 1950 Mount Saint Mary Drive, Nelsonville, OH Zip 45764–1280; tel. 740/753–1931; LaMar L. Wyse, Chief Operating Officer
Web address: www.ohiohealth.com

OHIOHEALTH DUBLIN METHODIST HOSPITAL (O, 100 beds) 7500 Hospital Drive, Dublin, OH Zip 43016–8518; tel. 614/544–8000; Bruce P. Hagen, President
Web address: www.ohiohealth.com

OHIOHEALTH GRADY MEMORIAL HOSPITAL (O, 61 beds) 561 West Central Avenue, Delaware, OH Zip 43015–1410; tel. 740/615–1000; Bruce P. Hagen, Regional Executive and President
Web address: www.ohiohealth.com

OHIOHEALTH GRANT MEDICAL CENTER (O, 427 beds) 111 South Grant Avenue, Columbus, OH Zip 43215–1898; tel. 614/566–9000; Michael Lawson, President and Chief Operating Officer
Web address: www.ohiohealth.com

OHIOHEALTH HARDIN MEMORIAL HOSPITAL (O, 25 beds) 921 East Franklin Street, Kenton, OH Zip 43326–2099; tel. 419/673–0761; Mark R. Seckinger, Administrator and Chief Executive Officer
Web address: www.hardinmemorial.org

OHIOHEALTH MARION GENERAL HOSPITAL (O, 170 beds) 1000 McKinley Park Drive, Marion, OH Zip 43302–6397; tel. 740/383–8400; John W. Sanders, President
Web address: www.ohiohealth.com/mariongeneral

OHIOHEALTH MEDCENTRAL MANSFIELD HOSPITAL (O, 238 beds) 335 Glessner Avenue, Mansfield, OH Zip 44903–2265; tel. 419/526–8000; Jean Halpin, President
Web address: www.medcentral.org

OHIOHEALTH MEDCENTRAL SHELBY HOSPITAL (O, 25 beds) 199 West Main Street, Shelby, OH Zip 44875–1490; tel. 419/342–5015; Jean Halpin, President
Web address: www.medcentral.org/body.cfm?id=153

For explanation of codes following names, see page B2.
★ Indicates Type III membership in the American Hospital Association.

© 2014 AHA Guide

Health Care Systems, Networks and Alliances **B103**

Section B

OHIOHEALTH RIVERSIDE METHODIST HOSPITAL (O, 752 beds) 3535 Olentangy River Road, Columbus, OH Zip 43214–3998; tel. 614/566–5000; Stephen Markovich, M.D., President
Web address: www.ohiohealth.com

Owned, leased, sponsored:	11 hospitals	2130 beds
Contract–managed:	1 hospital	23 beds
Totals:	12 hospitals	2153 beds

0018: OKLAHOMA DEPARTMENT OF MENTAL HEALTH AND SUBSTANCE ABUSE SERVICES (NP)
1200 N.E. 13th Street, Oklahoma City, OK Zip 73117–1022, Mailing Address: P.O. Box 53277, Zip 73152–3277; tel. 405/522–3908; Terri White, Commissioner
(Independent Hospital System)

OKLAHOMA: GRIFFIN MEMORIAL HOSPITAL (O, 120 beds) 900 East Main Street, Norman, OK Zip 73071–5305, Mailing Address: P.O. Box 151, Zip 73070–0151; tel. 405/321–4880; Lawrence Gross, Executive Director
Web address: www.odmhsas.org

NORTHWEST CENTER FOR BEHAVIORAL HEALTH (O, 28 beds) 1 Mi East Highway 270, Fort Supply, OK Zip 73841; tel. 580/766–2311; Trudy Hoffman, Executive Director
Web address: www.ncbhok.org/

OKLAHOMA FORENSIC CENTER (O, 200 beds) 24800 South 4420 Road, Vinita, OK Zip 74301–5544, Mailing Address: P.O. Box 69, Zip 74301–0069; tel. 918/256–7841; Lori Jordan, Chief Executive Officer
Web address: www.odmhsas.org

Owned, leased, sponsored:	3 hospitals	348 beds
Contract–managed:	0 hospitals	0 beds
Totals:	3 hospitals	348 beds

3355: ORLANDO HEALTH (NP)
1414 Kuhl Avenue, Orlando, FL Zip 32806–2093; tel. 321/843–7000; Jamal Hakim, M.D., Interim President and Chief Executive Officer
(Centralized Physician/Insurance Health System)

FLORIDA: HEALTH CENTRAL HOSPITAL (O, 399 beds) 10000 West Colonial Drive, Ocoee, FL Zip 34761–3499; tel. 407/296–1000; Gregory P. Ohe, President
Web address: www.healthcentral.org

ORLANDO REGIONAL MEDICAL CENTER (O, 1168 beds) 1414 Kuhl Avenue, Orlando, FL Zip 32806–2093; tel. 407/841–5111; Mark A. Jones, President
Web address: www.orhs.org

SOUTH LAKE HOSPITAL (O, 122 beds) 1900 Don Wickham Drive, Clermont, FL Zip 34711–1979; tel. 352/394–4071; John Moore, President
Web address: www.southlakehospital.com

Owned, leased, sponsored:	3 hospitals	1689 beds
Contract–managed:	0 hospitals	0 beds
Totals:	3 hospitals	1689 beds

★5335: OSF HEALTHCARE SYSTEM (CC)
800 N.E. Glen Oak Avenue, Peoria, IL Zip 61603–3200; tel. 309/655–2850; Kevin D. Schoeplein, Chief Executive Officer
(Moderately Centralized Health System)

ILLINOIS: OSF HOLY FAMILY MEDICAL CENTER (O, 23 beds) 1000 West Harlem Avenue, Monmouth, IL Zip 61462–1007; tel. 309/734–3141; Patricia A. Luker, Chief Executive Officer
Web address: www.osfholyfamily.org

OSF SAINT ANTHONY MEDICAL CENTER (O, 235 beds) 5666 East State Street, Rockford, IL Zip 61108–2425; tel. 815/226–2000; Paula A. Carynski, MS, R.N., President
Web address: www.osfhealth.com

OSF SAINT ELIZABETH MEDICAL CENTER (O, 90 beds) 1100 East Norris Drive, Ottawa, IL Zip 61350–1687; tel. 815/433–3100; Robert A. Chaffin, President and Chief Executive Officer
Web address: www.osfsaintelizabeth.org

OSF SAINT FRANCIS MEDICAL CENTER (O, 609 beds) 530 N.E. Glen Oak Avenue, Peoria, IL Zip 61637–0001; tel. 309/655–2000; Keith E. Steffen, President and Chief Executive Officer
Web address: www.osfsaintfrancis.org

OSF SAINT JAMES – JOHN W. ALBRECHT MEDICAL CENTER (O, 42 beds) 2500 West Reynolds, Pontiac, IL Zip 61764–9774; tel. 815/842–2828; David T. Ochs, President and Chief Executive Officer
Web address: www.osfsaintjames.org

OSF SAINT LUKE MEDICAL CENTER (O, 25 beds) 1051 West South Street, Kewanee, IL Zip 61443–8354, Mailing Address: P.O. Box 747, Zip 61443–0747; tel. 309/852–7500; Lynn Fulton, President
Web address: www.osfsaintluke.org

OSF ST. JOSEPH MEDICAL CENTER (O, 149 beds) 2200 East Washington Street, Bloomington, IL Zip 61701–4323; tel. 309/662–3311; Chad Boore, President and Chief Executive Officer
Web address: www.osfstjoseph.org

OSF ST. MARY MEDICAL CENTER (O, 90 beds) 3333 North Seminary Street, Galesburg, IL Zip 61401–1299; tel. 309/344–3161; Roxanna Crosser, President
Web address: www.osfstmary.org

SAINT CLARE HOME (O, 0 beds) 5533 North Galena Road, Peoria Heights, IL Zip 61614–4499; tel. 309/682–5428; Candy Conover, Administrator

ST. ANTHONY'S CONTINUING CARE CENTER (O, 179 beds) 767 30th Street, Rock Island, IL Zip 61201; Sister Mary Anthony Mazzaferri, Administrator

MICHIGAN: OSF ST. FRANCIS HOSPITAL AND MEDICAL GROUP (O, 33 beds) 3401 Ludington Street, Escanaba, MI Zip 49829–1377; tel. 906/786–3311; David Lord, President and Chief Executive Officer
Web address: www.osfstfrancis.org

Owned, leased, sponsored:	11 hospitals	1475 beds
Contract–managed:	0 hospitals	0 beds
Totals:	11 hospitals	1475 beds

0367: PACER HEALTH CORPORATION (IO)
14100 Palmetto Frontage Road, Suite 110, Miami Lakes, FL Zip 33016; tel. 305/828–7660; Rainier Gonzalez, Chairman and Chief Executive Officer

KENTUCKY: KNOX COUNTY HOSPITAL (O, 25 beds) 80 Hospital Drive, Barbourville, KY Zip 40906–7363, Mailing Address: P.O. Box 10, Zip 40906–0010; tel. 606/546–4175; Ray B. Canady, Chief Executive Officer and Administrator
Web address: www.knoxcohospital.com

LOUISIANA: CALCASIEU OAKS GERIATRIC PSYCHIATRIC HOSPITAL (O, 24 beds) 2837 Ernest Street, Lake Charles, LA Zip 70601–8785; tel. 337/439–8111; Charles Getwood, Assistant Chief Executive Officer

Owned, leased, sponsored:	2 hospitals	49 beds
Contract–managed:	0 hospitals	0 beds
Totals:	2 hospitals	49 beds

★5235: PALLOTTINE HEALTH SERVICES (CC)
2900 First Avenue, Huntington, WV Zip 25702–1241; tel. 304/526–1234; Michael G. Sellards, Chief Executive Officer
(Independent Hospital System)

WEST VIRGINIA: ST. JOSEPH'S HOSPITAL OF BUCKHANNON (O, 69 beds) 1 Amalia Drive, Buckhannon, WV Zip 26201–2276; tel. 304/473–2000; Sue E. Johnson-Phillippe, FACHE, President and Chief Executive Officer
Web address: www.stj.net

ST. MARY'S MEDICAL CENTER (O, 393 beds) 2900 First Avenue, Huntington, WV Zip 25702–1272; tel. 304/526–1234; Michael G. Sellards, President and Chief Executive Officer
Web address: www.st-marys.org

Owned, leased, sponsored:	2 hospitals	462 beds
Contract–managed:	0 hospitals	0 beds
Totals:	2 hospitals	462 beds

For explanation of codes following names, see page B2.
★ Indicates Type III membership in the American Hospital Association.

★4155: PALMETTO HEALTH (NP)
1301 Taylor Street, Suite 9–A, Columbia, SC Zip 29201–2942,
Mailing Address: P.O. Box 2266, Zip 29202–2266;
tel. 803/296–2100; Charles D. Beaman, Jr., Chief Executive Officer
(Moderately Centralized Health System)

SOUTH CAROLINA: BAPTIST EASLEY HOSPITAL (O, 89 beds) 200 Fleetwood
Drive, Easley, SC Zip 29640–2022, Mailing Address: P.O. Box 2129,
Zip 29641–2129; tel. 864/442–7200; Michael Batchelor, Chief Executive
Officer
Web address: www.baptisteasley.org

PALMETTO HEALTH BAPTIST (O, 400 beds) Taylor at Marion Street,
Columbia, SC Zip 29220–0001; tel. 803/296–5010; Gregory B. Gattman,
Acute Care Executive
Web address: www.palmettohealth.org

PALMETTO HEALTH BAPTIST PARKRIDGE (O, 50 beds) 400 Palmetto Health
Parkway, Columbia, SC Zip 29212–1760, Mailing Address: P.O. BOX 2266,
Zip 29202–2266; tel. 803/907–7000; Sarah Kirby, Acute Care Executive
Web address: www.palmettohealth.org

PALMETTO HEALTH RICHLAND (O, 704 beds) Five Richland Medical Park
Drive, Columbia, SC Zip 29203–6897; tel. 803/434–7000; Jay Hamm, R.N.,
Chief Acute Care Executive
Web address: www.palmettohealth.org

Owned, leased, sponsored:	4 hospitals	1243 beds
Contract–managed:	0 hospitals	0 beds
Totals:	4 hospitals	1243 beds

★7555: PALOMAR HEALTH (NP)
456 East Grand Avenue, Escondido, CA Zip 92025–3319;
tel. 760/740–6393; Robert Hemker, President and Chief Executive
Officer
(Moderately Centralized Health System)

CALIFORNIA: PALOMAR MEDICAL CENTER (O, 345 beds) 2185 West
Citracado Parkway, Escondido, CA Zip 92029–4159; tel. 760/739–3000;
Lorie K. Shoemaker, R.N., MSN, Interim Chief Administrative Officer
Web address: www.palomarhealth.org

POMERADO HOSPITAL (O, 203 beds) 15615 Pomerado Road, Poway, CA
Zip 92064–2460; tel. 858/613–4000; David A. Tam, M.D., FACHE, Chief
Administrative Officer
Web address: www.pph.org

Owned, leased, sponsored:	2 hospitals	548 beds
Contract–managed:	0 hospitals	0 beds
Totals:	2 hospitals	548 beds

★0159: PARKVIEW HEALTH (NP)
10501 Corporate Drive, Fort Wayne, IN Zip 46845–1700;
tel. 260/373–7001; Michael J. Packnett, President and Chief
Executive Officer
(Centralized Physician/Insurance Health System)

INDIANA: PARKVIEW HUNTINGTON HOSPITAL (O, 36 beds) 2001 Stults Road,
Huntington, IN Zip 46750–1291; tel. 260/355–3000; Darlene Garrett,
President
Web address: www.parkview.com

PARKVIEW LAGRANGE HOSPITAL (O, 25 beds) 207 North Townline Road,
LaGrange, IN Zip 46761–1325; tel. 260/463–2143; Robert T. Myers,
President
Web address: www.parkview.com

PARKVIEW NOBLE HOSPITAL (O, 31 beds) 401 Sawyer Road, Kendallville, IN
Zip 46755–2568; tel. 260/347–8700; Gary W. Adkins, Chief Executive
Officer
Web address: www.parkview.com

PARKVIEW REGIONAL MEDICAL CENTER (O, 649 beds) 11109 Parkview Plaza
Drive, Fort Wayne, IN Zip 46845–1701; tel. 260/373–4000; Ben Miles, Chief
Operating Officer
Web address: www.parkview.com

PARKVIEW WHITLEY HOSPITAL (O, 97 beds) 1260 East State Road 205,
Columbia City, IN Zip 46725–9492; tel. 260/248–9000; Scott F. Gabriel,
President
Web address: www.parkview.com

Owned, leased, sponsored:	5 hospitals	838 beds
Contract–managed:	0 hospitals	0 beds
Totals:	5 hospitals	838 beds

★1785: PARTNERS HEALTHCARE SYSTEM, INC. (NP)
800 Boylston Street, Suite 1150, Boston, MA Zip 02199–8123;
tel. 617/278–1004; Gary L. Gottlieb, M.D., President and Chief
Executive Officer
(Moderately Centralized Health System)

MASSACHUSETTS: BRIGHAM AND WOMEN'S FAULKNER HOSPITAL (O, 90
beds) 1153 Centre Street, Boston, MA Zip 02130–3446;
tel. 617/983–7000; Michael Gustafson, M.D., Chief Operating Officer
Web address: www.brighamandwomensfaulkner.org/index.asp

BRIGHAM AND WOMEN'S HOSPITAL (O, 793 beds) 75 Francis Street, Boston,
MA Zip 02115–6110; tel. 617/732–5500; Elizabeth Nabel, M.D., President
Web address: www.brighamandwomens.org

MARTHA'S VINEYARD HOSPITAL (O, 25 beds) One Hospital Road, Oak Bluffs,
MA Zip 02557, Mailing Address: P.O. Box 1477, Zip 02557–1477;
tel. 508/693–0410; Timothy J. Walsh, Chief Executive Officer
Web address: www.marthasvineyardhospital.org

MASSACHUSETTS GENERAL HOSPITAL (O, 999 beds) 55 Fruit Street,
Boston, MA Zip 02114–2696; tel. 617/726–2000; Peter L. Slavin, M.D.,
President
Web address: www.massgeneral.org

MCLEAN HOSPITAL (O, 177 beds) 115 Mill Street, Belmont, MA
Zip 02478–1064; tel. 617/855–2000; Scott L. Rauch, M.D., President
Web address: www.mclean.harvard.edu

NANTUCKET COTTAGE HOSPITAL (O, 19 beds) 57 Prospect Street,
Nantucket, MA Zip 02554–2799; tel. 508/825–8100; Margot Hartmann,
M.D., Ph.D., President and Chief Executive Officer
Web address: www.nantuckethospital.org

NEWTON–WELLESLEY HOSPITAL (O, 240 beds) 2014 Washington Street,
Newton Lower Falls, MA Zip 02462–1699; tel. 617/243–6000; Kerry
Watson, President
Web address: www.nwh.org

NORTH SHORE MEDICAL CENTER (O, 411 beds) 81 Highland Avenue, Salem,
MA Zip 01970–2714; tel. 978/741–1200; Robert G. Norton, President and
Chief Executive Officer
Web address: www.nsmc.partners.org

SPAULDING HOSPITAL FOR CONTINUING MEDICAL CARE NORTH SHORE (O,
160 beds) 1 Dove Avenue, Salem, MA Zip 01970–2999; tel. 978/825–8900;
Maureen Banks, R.N., MS, President
Web address: www.shaughnessy–kaplan.org

SPAULDING HOSPITAL FOR CONTINUING MEDICAL CARE CAMBRIDGE (O, 180
beds) 1575 Cambridge Street, Cambridge, MA Zip 02138–4308;
tel. 617/876–4344; Maureen Banks, R.N., MS, President
Web address: www.spauldingnetwork.org

SPAULDING REHABILITATION HOSPITAL (O, 164 beds) 300 First Avenue,
Charlestown, MA Zip 02129–3109; tel. 617/573–7000; David E. Storto,
President
Web address: www.spauldingrehab.org

SPAULDING REHABILITATION HOSPITAL CAPE COD (O, 60 beds) 311 Service
Road, East Sandwich, MA Zip 02537–1370; tel. 508/833–4000; Maureen
Banks, R.N., MS, President
Web address: www.rhci.org

Owned, leased, sponsored:	12 hospitals	3318 beds
Contract–managed:	0 hospitals	0 beds
Totals:	12 hospitals	3318 beds

★5415: PEACEHEALTH (CC)
1115 S.E. 164th Avenue, Vancouver, WA Zip 98683;
tel. 425/747–1711; Alan R. Yordy, President and Chief Mission
Officer
(Moderately Centralized Health System)

ALASKA: PEACEHEALTH KETCHIKAN MEDICAL CENTER (L, 50 beds) 3100
Tongass Avenue, Ketchikan, AK Zip 99901–5746; tel. 907/225–5171;
Ken Tonjes, Interim Chief Administrative Officer
Web address: www.peacehealth.org

Section B

For explanation of codes following names, see page B2.
★ Indicates Type III membership in the American Hospital Association.

OREGON: PEACEHEALTH COTTAGE GROVE COMMUNITY MEDICAL CENTER (O, 14 beds) 1515 Village Drive, Cottage Grove, OR Zip 97424–9700; tel. 541/942–0511; Chelsea Holland–Bak, Interim Administrator
Web address: www.peacehealth.org

PEACEHEALTH PEACE HARBOR MEDICAL CENTER (O, 21 beds) 400 Ninth Street, Florence, OR Zip 97439–7398; tel. 541/997–8412; Rick Yecny, Chief Executive Officer and Chief Mission Officer
Web address: www.peacehealth.org

PEACEHEALTH SACRED HEART MEDICAL CENTER AT RIVERBEND (O, 379 beds) 3333 Riverbend Drive, Springfield, OR Zip 97477–8800; tel. 541/222–7300; John G. Hill, Chief Executive Officer
Web address: www.peacehealth.org

PEACEHEALTH SACRED HEART MEDICAL CENTER, UNIVERSITY DISTRICT (O, 104 beds) 1255 Hilyard Street, Eugene, OR Zip 97401–3700, Mailing Address: P.O. Box 10905, Zip 97440–2905; tel. 541/686–7300; John G. Hill, Chief Executive Officer
Web address: www.peacehealth.org

WASHINGTON: PEACEHEALTH PEACE ISLAND MEDICAL CENTER (O, 10 beds) 1117 Spring Street, Friday Harbor, WA Zip 98250–9782; tel. 360/378–2141; James R. Barnhart, Chief Administrator Officer
Web address: www.peacehealth.org

PEACEHEALTH SOUTHWEST MEDICAL CENTER (O, 450 beds) 400 N.E. Mother Joseph Place, Vancouver, WA Zip 98664–3200, Mailing Address: P.O. Box 1600, Zip 98668–1600; tel. 360/256–2000; Sy Johnson, Chief Administrative Officer and Chief Operating Officer, PeaceHealth Columbia Network
Web address: www.swmedicalcenter.org

PEACEHEALTH ST. JOHN MEDICAL CENTER (O, 200 beds) 1615 Delaware Street, Longview, WA Zip 98632–2367, Mailing Address: P.O. Box 3002, Zip 98632–0302; tel. 360/414–2000; Kirk Raboin, Chief Administrative Officer
Web address: www.peacehealth.org

PEACEHEALTH ST. JOSEPH MEDICAL CENTER (O, 253 beds) 2901 Squalicum Parkway, Bellingham, WA Zip 98225–1851; tel. 360/734–5400; Nancy Steiger, R.N., FACHE, Chief Executive Officer and Chief Mission Officer, Northwest Network
Web address: www.peacehealth.org

PEACEHEALTH UNITED GENERAL HOSPITAL (C, 25 beds) 2000 Hospital Drive, Sedro–Woolley, WA Zip 98284–4327; tel. 360/856–6021; James R. Barnhart, Chief Administrative Officer
Web address: www.peacehealth.org/united–general/Pages/default.aspx

Owned, leased, sponsored:	9 hospitals	1481 beds
Contract–managed:	1 hospital	25 beds
Totals:	10 hospitals	1506 beds

★0314: PHOEBE PUTNEY HEALTH SYSTEM (NP)
417 Third Avenue, Albany, GA Zip 31701–1943; tel. 229/312–1000; Joel Wernick, President and Chief Executive Officer
(Independent Hospital System)

GEORGIA: PHOEBE SUMTER MEDICAL CENTER (O, 45 beds) 126 Highway 280 West, Americus, GA Zip 31719; tel. 229/924–6011; John Harding, Interim Chief Executive Officer
Web address: www.phoebesumter.org

PHOEBE WORTH MEDICAL CENTER (O, 16 beds) 807 South Isabella Street, Sylvester, GA Zip 31791–7554, Mailing Address: P.O. Box 545, Zip 31791–0545; tel. 229/776–6961; Kim Gilman, Chief Executive Officer
Web address: www.phoebeputney.com

Owned, leased, sponsored:	2 hospitals	61 beds
Contract–managed:	0 hospitals	0 beds
Totals:	2 hospitals	61 beds

0043: PHYSICIANS FOR HEALTHY HOSPITALS (IO)
1117 East Devonshire Avenue, Hemet, CA Zip 92543–3083; tel. 951/652–2811; Joel Bergenfeld, Chief Executive Officer

CALIFORNIA: HEMET VALLEY MEDICAL CENTER (O, 238 beds) 1117 East Devonshire Avenue, Hemet, CA Zip 92543–3083; tel. 951/652–2811; Joel Bergenfeld, Chief Executive Officer
Web address: www.physiciansforhealthyhospitals.com

MENIFEE VALLEY MEDICAL CENTER (O, 74 beds) 28400 McCall Boulevard, Sun City, CA Zip 92585–9537; tel. 951/679–8888; Joel Bergenfeld, Chief Hospital Executive Officer
Web address: www.valleyhealthsystem.com

Owned, leased, sponsored:	2 hospitals	312 beds
Contract–managed:	0 hospitals	0 beds
Totals:	2 hospitals	312 beds

★0310: PIEDMONT HEALTHCARE (NP)
1800 Howell Mill Road N.W., Suite 850, Atlanta, GA Zip 30318–0923; tel. 404/425–1314; Kevin Brown, President and Chief Executive Officer
(Independent Hospital System)

GEORGIA: HENRY MEDICAL CENTER (L, 222 beds) 1133 Eagle's Landing Parkway, Stockbridge, GA Zip 30281–5099; tel. 678/604–1000; Charles F. Scott, President and Chief Executive Officer
Web address: www.henrymedical.com

PIEDMONT FAYETTE HOSPITAL (O, 172 beds) 1255 Highway 54 West, Fayetteville, GA Zip 30214–4526; tel. 770/719–7000; Michael Robertson, Chief Executive Officer
Web address: www.fayettehospital.org

PIEDMONT HOSPITAL (O, 484 beds) 1968 Peachtree Road N.W., Atlanta, GA Zip 30309–1281; tel. 404/605–5000; Leslie A. Donahue, President and Chief Executive Officer
Web address: www.piedmonthospital.org

PIEDMONT MOUNTAINSIDE HOSPITAL (O, 58 beds) 1266 Highway 515 South, Jasper, GA Zip 30143–4872; tel. 706/692–2441; Denise Ray, President and Chief Executive Officer
Web address: www.piedmontmountainsidehospital.org

PIEDMONT NEWNAN HOSPITAL (O, 118 beds) 745 Poplar Road, Newnan, GA Zip 30265–1618; tel. 770/400–1000; Michael Robertson, Chief Executive Officer
Web address: www.piedmontnewnan.org

Owned, leased, sponsored:	5 hospitals	1054 beds
Contract–managed:	0 hospitals	0 beds
Totals:	5 hospitals	1054 beds

★0326: PIONEER HEALTH SERVICES (IO)
110 Pioneer Way, Magee, MS Zip 39111–5501, Mailing Address: P.O. Box 1100, Zip 39111–1100; tel. 601/849–6440; Joseph S. McNulty, III, President and Chief Executive Officer
(Independent Hospital System)

PIONEER COMMUNITY HOSPITAL OF EARLY (L, 151 beds) 11740 Columbia Street, Blakely, GA Zip 39823–2574; tel. 229/723–4241; Allen J. Gamble, Chief Executive Officer
Web address: www.pchearly.com

MISSISSIPPI: LACKEY MEMORIAL HOSPITAL (C, 55 beds) 330 Broad Street, Forest, MS Zip 39074–3508, Mailing Address: P.O. Box 428, Zip 39074–0428; tel. 601/469–4151; Donna Riser, Administrator
Web address: www.lackeymemorialhospital.com

PIONEER COMMUNITY HOSPITAL OF ABERDEEN (L, 35 beds) 400 South Chestnut Street, Aberdeen, MS Zip 39730–3335, Mailing Address: P.O. Box 548, Zip 39730–0548; tel. 662/369–2455; Harley Smith, Chief Executive Officer
Web address: www.pchaberdeen.com

PIONEER COMMUNITY HOSPITAL OF NEWTON (O, 30 beds) 9421 Eastside Drive, Newton, MS Zip 39345–8063; tel. 601/683–2031; Mark Norman, Administrator
Web address: www.pchnewton.com

NORTH CAROLINA: PIONEER COMMUNITY HOSPITAL OF STOKES (L, 65 beds) 1570 Highway 8 and 89 North, Danbury, NC Zip 27016, Mailing Address: P.O. Box 10, Zip 27016–0010; tel. 336/593–2831; Pamela P. Tillman, R.N., Chief Executive Officer
Web address: www.pchstokes.com

VIRGINIA: PIONEER COMMUNITY HOSPITAL OF PATRICK COUNTY (O, 25 beds) 18688 Jeb Stuart Highway, Stuart, VA Zip 24171–1559; tel. 276/694–3151; Jeanette Filpi, Chief Executive Officer
Web address: www.phscorporate.com

For explanation of codes following names, see page B2.
★ Indicates Type III membership in the American Hospital Association.

Owned, leased, sponsored:	5 hospitals	306 beds
Contract–managed:	1 hospital	55 beds
Totals:	6 hospitals	361 beds

0899: POLARIS HOSPITAL COMPANY (IO)
10 Cadillac Drive, Suite 470, Brentwood, TN Zip 37027–1045; tel. 615/577–1111; Kevin D. Lee, Director and Chief Executive Officer
(Independent Hospital System)

TENNESSEE: TRUSTPOINT HOSPITAL (O, 60 beds) 1009 North Thompson Lane, Murfreesboro, TN Zip 37129–4351; tel. 615/867–1111; Jeffrey Woods, Chief Executive Officer
Web address: www.trustpointhospital.com

TEXAS: TRUSTPOINT HOSPITAL (O, 64 beds) 4302 Princeton Street, Lubbock, TX Zip 79415–1304; tel. 806/749–2222; Craig Bragg, Chief Executive Officer
Web address: www.trustpointhospital.com/

Owned, leased, sponsored:	2 hospitals	124 beds
Contract–managed:	0 hospitals	0 beds
Totals:	2 hospitals	124 beds

★0617: POST ACUTE MEDICAL, LLC (IO)
1828 Good Hope Road, Suite 102, Enola, PA Zip 17025–1233; tel. 717/731–9660; Anthony F. Misitano, President and Chief Executive Officer
(Independent Hospital System)

LOUISIANA: POST ACUTE MEDICAL SPECIALTY HOSPITAL OF LAFAYETTE (O, 50 beds) 204 Energy Parkway, Lafayette, LA Zip 70508–3816; tel. 337/232–1905; Brian Holt, Chief Executive Officer
Web address: www.postacutemedical.com

POST ACUTE NORTHSHORE SPECIALTY HOSPITAL (O, 58 beds) 20050 Crestwood Boulevard, Covington, LA Zip 70433–5207; tel. 985/875–7525; Stephanie Morvant, Chief Executive Officer
Web address: www.northshoreltach.com

POST ACUTE SPECIALTY HOSPITAL OF HAMMOND (O, 40 beds) 42074 Veterans Avenue, Hammond, LA Zip 70403–1408; tel. 985/902–8148; Jerry Elenbaas, Administrator
Web address: www.warmsprings.org/locations/hos/h2/

OKLAHOMA: POST ACUTE MEDICAL SPECIALTY HOSPITAL OF TULSA (O, 60 beds) 3219 South 79th East Avenue, Tulsa, OK Zip 74145–1343; tel. 918/663–8183; Lee A. Simpson, Jr., Chief Executive Officer
Web address: www.postacutetulsa.com

TEXAS: POST ACUTE MEDICAL SPECIALTY HOSPITAL OF CORPUS CHRISTI (O, 86 beds) 6226 Saratoga Boulevard, Corpus Christi, TX Zip 78414–3421; tel. 361/986–1600; Jason Carter, Interim Chief Executive Officer
Web address: www.postacutemedical.com

POST ACUTE MEDICAL SPECIALTY HOSPITAL OF VICTORIA (O, 23 beds) 506 East San Antonio Street, 3rd Floor, Victoria, TX Zip 77901–6060; tel. 361/575–1445; Portlyn Brogger, Chief Executive Officer
Web address: www.khvictoria.com

POST ACUTE/WARM SPRINGS REHABILITATION HOSPITAL OF ALLEN (O, 39 beds) 1001 Raintree Circle, Allen, TX Zip 75013–4912; tel. 972/908–2015; Bill Kaupas, Chief Executive Officer
Web address: www.warmsprings.org

POST ACUTE/WARM SPRINGS REHABILITATION HOSPITAL OF SAN ANTONIO (O, 138 beds) 5101 Medical Drive, San Antonio, TX Zip 78229–4801; tel. 210/616–0100; Steve Flaherty, Chief Executive Officer
Web address: www.warmsprings.org

POST ACUTE/WARM SPRINGS SPECIALTY HOSPITAL OF LULING (O, 34 beds) 200 Memorial Drive, Luling, TX Zip 78648–3213; tel. 830/875–8400; Jason Carter, Chief Executive Officer
Web address: www.warmsprings.org

POST ACUTE/WARM SPRINGS SPECIALTY HOSPITAL OF NEW BRAUNFELS (O, 40 beds) 1445 Hanz Drive, New Braunfels, TX Zip 78130–2567; tel. 830/627–7600; Shayne Goode, Administrator
Web address: www.warmsprings.org/locations/hos/h1/

POST ACUTE/WARM SPRINGS SPECIALTY HOSPITAL OF SAN ANTONIO (O, 20 beds) 7400 Barlite Boulevard, 2nd Floor, San Antonio, TX Zip 78224–1308; tel. 210/921–3550; Karen Pitcher, Chief Executive Officer
Web address: www.postacutemedical.com

POST ACUTE/WARM SPRINGS SPECIALTY HOSPITAL OF VICTORIA (O, 26 beds) 102 Medical Drive, Victoria, TX Zip 77904–3101; tel. 361/576–6200; Portlyn Brogger, Chief Executive Officer
Web address: www.warmsprings.org

WISCONSIN: POST ACUTE MEDICAL SPECIALTY HOSPITAL OF MILWAUKEE (O, 56 beds) 5017 South 110Th Street, Greenfield, WI Zip 53228–3131; tel. 414/427–8282; Terry W. Kepler, Chief Executive Officer
Web address: www.khmilwaukee.com/

Owned, leased, sponsored:	13 hospitals	670 beds
Contract–managed:	0 hospitals	0 beds
Totals:	13 hospitals	670 beds

0240: PREFERRED MANAGEMENT CORPORATION (IO)
120 West MacArthur, Suite 121, Shawnee, OK Zip 74804–2005; tel. 405/878–0202; Donald Freeman, President and Chief Executive Officer
(Independent Hospital System)

TEXAS: COLEMAN COUNTY MEDICAL CENTER (L, 25 beds) 310 South Pecos Street, Coleman, TX Zip 76834–4159; tel. 325/625–2135; Michael W. Pruitt, Administrator and Chief Executive Officer
Web address: www.colemantexas.org/hospital.html

COLLINGSWORTH GENERAL HOSPITAL (L, 13 beds) 1013 15th Street, Wellington, TX Zip 79095–3703, Mailing Address: P.O. Box 1112, Zip 79095–1112; tel. 806/447–2521; Candy Powell, Administrator
Web address: www.collingsworthgeneral.net

CULBERSON HOSPITAL (L, 14 beds) Eisenhower–Farm Market Road 2185, Van Horn, TX Zip 79855, Mailing Address: P.O. Box 609, Zip 79855–0609; tel. 432/283–2760; Jared Chanski, Administrator
Web address: www.culbersonhospital.org

KIMBLE HOSPITAL (O, 15 beds) 349 Reid Road, Junction, TX Zip 76849–3049; tel. 325/446–3321; Steve Bowen, Administrator
Web address: www.kimblehospital.org/

PARMER MEDICAL CENTER (C, 15 beds) 1307 Cleveland Avenue, Friona, TX Zip 79035–1121; tel. 806/250–2754; Gayla Quillin, Administrator
Web address: www.parmermedicalcenter.com

SABINE COUNTY HOSPITAL (L, 25 beds) Highway 83 West, Hemphill, TX Zip 75948, Mailing Address: P.O. Box 750, Zip 75948–0750; tel. 409/787–3300; Diana Taylor, Administrator
Web address: www.sabinecountyhospital.com/

SCHLEICHER COUNTY MEDICAL CENTER (L, 14 beds) 400 West Murchison, Eldorado, TX Zip 76936, Mailing Address: P.O. Box V., Zip 76936–1246; tel. 325/853–2507; Paul Burke, Administrator
Web address: www.scmc.us

Owned, leased, sponsored:	6 hospitals	106 beds
Contract–managed:	1 hospital	15 beds
Totals:	7 hospitals	121 beds

★3505: PRESBYTERIAN HEALTHCARE SERVICES (NP)
2501 Buena Vista Drive, S.E., Albuquerque, NM Zip 87106–4260, Mailing Address: P.O. Box 26666, Zip 87125–6666; tel. 505/841–1234; James H. Hinton, President and Chief Executive Officer
(Centralized Physician/Insurance Health System)

NEW MEXICO: DR. DAN C. TRIGG MEMORIAL HOSPITAL (L, 10 beds) 301 East Miel De Luna Avenue, Tucumcari, NM Zip 88401–3810, Mailing Address: P.O. Box 608, Zip 88401–0608; tel. 575/461–7000; Lance C. Labine, Administrator
Web address: www.phs.org

ESPANOLA HOSPITAL (O, 46 beds) 1010 Spruce Street, Espanola, NM Zip 87532–2746; tel. 505/753–7111; Brenda Romero, Administrator
Web address: www.phs.org

Section B

For explanation of codes following names, see page B2.
★ Indicates Type III membership in the American Hospital Association.

LINCOLN COUNTY MEDICAL CENTER (L, 25 beds) 211 Sudderth Drive, Ruidoso, NM Zip 88345–6043, Mailing Address: P.O. Box 8000, Zip 88355–8000; tel. 575/257–8200; Alfred Santos, Administrator
Web address: www.phs.org

PLAINS REGIONAL MEDICAL CENTER (O, 50 beds) 2100 Martin Luther King Boulevard, Clovis, NM Zip 88101–9412, Mailing Address: P.O. Box 1688, Zip 88102–1688; tel. 575/769–2141; Bo Beames, Interim Administrator
Web address: www.phs.org

PRESBYTERIAN HOSPITAL (O, 405 beds) 1100 Central Avenue S.E., Albuquerque, NM Zip 87106–4934, Mailing Address: P.O. Box 26666, Zip 87125–6666; tel. 505/841–1234; Sandra C. Podley, Administrator
Web address: www.phs.org

PRESBYTERIAN KASEMAN HOSPITAL (O, 105 beds) 8300 Constitution Avenue N.E., Albuquerque, NM Zip 87110–7624, Mailing Address: P.O. Box 26666, Zip 87125–6666; tel. 505/291–2000; Doyle Boykin, R.N., MSN, Administrator
Web address: www.phs.org

PRESBYTERIAN RUST MEDICAL CENTER (O, 86 beds) 2400 Unser Boulevard S.E., Rio Rancho, NM Zip 87124–4740; tel. 505/253–7878; Jeff McBee, Administrator
Web address: www.phs.org/phs/riorancho/index.htm

SOCORRO GENERAL HOSPITAL (O, 14 beds) 1202 Highway 60 West, Socorro, NM Zip 87801–3914, Mailing Address: P.O. Box 1009, Zip 87801–1009; tel. 505/835–1140; Veronica Pound, R.N., Administrator
Web address: www.phs.org

Owned, leased, sponsored:	8 hospitals	741 beds
Contract–managed:	0 hospitals	0 beds
Totals:	8 hospitals	741 beds

★0851: PRESENCE HEALTH (CC)
200 South Wacker Drive, Chicago, IL Zip 60606–5829; tel. 312/308–3200; Sandra B. Bruce, FACHE, President and Chief Executive Officer
(Moderately Centralized Health System)

ILLINOIS: OUR LADY OF THE RESURRECTION–LONG TERM CARE (O, 50 beds) 5645 West Addison Street, Chicago, IL Zip 60634;

PRESENCE COVENANT MEDICAL CENTER (O, 194 beds) 1400 West Park Street, Urbana, IL Zip 61801–2396; tel. 217/337–2000; Jared Rogers, M.D., Interim Regional President and Chief Executive Officer
Web address: www.provena.org/covenant

PRESENCE HOLY FAMILY MEDICAL CENTER (O, 118 beds) 100 North River Road, Des Plaines, IL Zip 60016–1255; tel. 847/297–1800; John D. Baird, President and Chief Executive Officer
Web address: www.presencehealth.org

PRESENCE MERCY MEDICAL CENTER (O, 123 beds) 1325 North Highland Avenue, Aurora, IL Zip 60506–1449; tel. 630/859–2222; Michael L. Brown, Regional President and Chief Executive Officer
Web address: www.provena.org/mercy/

PRESENCE OUR LADY OF THE RESURRECTION MEDICAL CENTER (O, 269 beds) 5645 West Addison Street, Chicago, IL Zip 60634–4403; tel. 773/282–7000; John D. Baird, Regional President and Chief Executive Officer
Web address: www.presencehealth.org

PRESENCE RESURRECTION MEDICAL CENTER (O, 402 beds) 7435 West Talcott Avenue, Chicago, IL Zip 60631–3746; tel. 773/774–8000; John D. Baird, Regional President and Chief Executive Officer
Web address: www.presencehealth.org

PRESENCE SAINT FRANCIS HOSPITAL (O, 244 beds) 355 Ridge Avenue, Evanston, IL Zip 60202–3399; tel. 847/316–4000; Roberta Luskin–Hawk, M.D., Chief Executive Officer
Web address: www.reshealth.org

PRESENCE SAINT JOSEPH HOSPITAL (O, 320 beds) 2900 North Lake Shore Drive, Chicago, IL Zip 60657–6274; tel. 773/665–3000; Roberta Luskin–Hawk, M.D., President and Chief Executive Officer
Web address: www.reshealth.org

PRESENCE SAINT JOSEPH HOSPITAL (O, 125 beds) 77 North Airlite Street, Elgin, IL Zip 60123–4912; tel. 847/695–3200; Michael L. Brown, Regional President and Chief Executive Officer
Web address: www.provena.org

PRESENCE SAINT JOSEPH MEDICAL CENTER (O, 457 beds) 333 North Madison Street, Joliet, IL Zip 60435–8200; tel. 815/725–7133; Beth Hughes, President and Chief Executive Officer
Web address: www.provena.org/stjoes

PRESENCE SAINTS MARY & ELIZABETH MEDICAL CENTER (O, 476 beds) 2233 West Division Street, Chicago, IL Zip 60622–3086; tel. 312/770–2000; Martin H. Judd, President and Chief Executive Officer
Web address: www.smemc.reshealth.org

PRESENCE ST. MARY'S HOSPITAL (O, 155 beds) 500 West Court Street, Kankakee, IL Zip 60901–3661; tel. 815/937–2400; Beth Hughes, President and Chief Executive Officer
Web address: www.provena.org/stmarys/

PRESENCE UNITED SAMARITANS MEDICAL CENTER (O, 127 beds) 812 North Logan, Danville, IL Zip 61832–3788; tel. 217/443–5000; Jared Rogers, M.D., Interim Regional President and Chief Executive Officer
Web address: www.provena.org/usmc

RESURRECTION NURSING PAVILION (O, 295 beds) 1001 North Greenwood, Park Ridge, IL Zip 60068; Patricia Tiernan, Administrator

Owned, leased, sponsored:	14 hospitals	3355 beds
Contract–managed:	0 hospitals	0 beds
Totals:	14 hospitals	3355 beds

O357: PRIME HEALTHCARE SERVICES (IO)
3300 East Guasti Road, Ontario, CA Zip 91761–8655; tel. 909/235–4400; Prem Reddy, M.D., Interim President and Chief Executive Officer
(Moderately Centralized Health System)

CALIFORNIA: ALVARADO HOSPITAL MEDICAL CENTER (O, 83 beds) 6655 Alvarado Road, San Diego, CA Zip 92120–5208; tel. 619/287–3270; Robin Gomez, R.N., MSN, Administrator
Web address: www.alvaradohospital.com

CENTINELA HOSPITAL MEDICAL CENTER (O, 353 beds) 555 East Hardy Street, Inglewood, CA Zip 90301–4011, Mailing Address: P.O. Box 720, Zip 90312–6720; tel. 310/673–4660; Linda Bradley, Chief Executive Officer
Web address: www.centinelamed.com

CHINO VALLEY MEDICAL CENTER (O, 112 beds) 5451 Walnut Avenue, Chino, CA Zip 91710–2672; tel. 909/464–8600; James M. Lally, D.O., President and Chief Medical Officer
Web address: www.cvmc.com

DESERT VALLEY HOSPITAL (O, 110 beds) 16850 Bear Valley Road, Victorville, CA Zip 92395–5795; tel. 760/241–8000; Fred Hunter, R.N., Chief Executive Officer
Web address: www.dvmc.com

ENCINO HOSPITAL MEDICAL CENTER (O, 56 beds) 16237 Ventura Boulevard, Encino, CA Zip 91436–2272; tel. 818/995–5000; Bockhi Park, Chief Executive Officer
Web address: www.encinomed.com

GARDEN GROVE HOSPITAL AND MEDICAL CENTER (O, 167 beds) 12601 Garden Grove Boulevard, Garden Grove, CA Zip 92843–1959; tel. 714/537–5160; Virgis Narbutas, Chief Executive Officer
Web address: www.gardengrovehospital.com

HUNTINGTON BEACH HOSPITAL (O, 131 beds) 17772 Beach Boulevard, Huntington Beach, CA Zip 92647–6896; tel. 714/843–5000; Virgis Narbutas, Chief Executive Officer
Web address: www.hbhospital.com

LA PALMA INTERCOMMUNITY HOSPITAL (O, 141 beds) 7901 Walker Street, La Palma, CA Zip 90623–1764; tel. 714/670–7400; Virgis Narbutas, Chief Executive Officer
Web address: www.lapalmaintercommunityhospital.com

MONTCLAIR HOSPITAL MEDICAL CENTER (O, 102 beds) 5000 San Bernardino Street, Montclair, CA Zip 91763–2326; tel. 909/625–5411; Gregory Brentano, Chief Executive Officer
Web address: www.montclair–hospital.com

PARADISE VALLEY HOSPITAL (O, 205 beds) 2400 East Fourth Street, National City, CA Zip 91950–2099; tel. 619/470–4321; Neerav Jadeja, Administrator
Web address: www.paradisevalleyhospital.org

For explanation of codes following names, see page B2.
★ Indicates Type III membership in the American Hospital Association.

SAN DIMAS COMMUNITY HOSPITAL (O, 101 beds) 1350 West Covina Boulevard, San Dimas, CA Zip 91773–3219; tel. 909/599–6811; Kevan Metcalfe, Chief Executive Officer
Web address: www.sandimashospital.com/

SHASTA REGIONAL MEDICAL CENTER (O, 120 beds) 1100 Butte Street, Redding, CA Zip 96001–0853, Mailing Address: P.O. Box 496072, Zip 96049–6072; tel. 530/244–5400; Cynthia Gordon, R.N., Chief Executive Officer
Web address: www.shastaregional.com

SHERMAN OAKS HOSPITAL (O, 77 beds) 4929 Van Nuys Boulevard, Sherman Oaks, CA Zip 91403–1777; tel. 818/981–7111; Bockhi Park, Chief Executive Officer
Web address: www.shermanoakshospital.com

WEST ANAHEIM MEDICAL CENTER (O, 219 beds) 3033 West Orange Avenue, Anaheim, CA Zip 92804–3156; tel. 714/827–3000; Virgis Narbutas, Chief Executive Officer
Web address: www.westanaheimmedctr.com

KANSAS: PROVIDENCE MEDICAL CENTER (O, 140 beds) 8929 Parallel Parkway, Kansas City, KS Zip 66112–1689; tel. 913/596–4000; Randall G. Nyp, FACHE, Chief Executive Officer
Web address: www.providencekc.com

SAINT JOHN HOSPITAL (O, 40 beds) 3500 South Fourth Street, Leavenworth, KS Zip 66048–5043; tel. 913/680–6000; Randall G. Nyp, FACHE, President and Chief Executive Officer
Web address: www.providence–health.org/sjh

NEVADA: SAINT MARY'S REGIONAL MEDICAL CENTER (O, 281 beds) 235 West Sixth Street, Reno, NV Zip 89503–4548; tel. 775/770–3000; Helen Lidholm, Chief Executive Officer
Web address: www.saintmarysreno.org

PENNSYLVANIA: LOWER BUCKS HOSPITAL (O, 150 beds) 501 Bath Road, Bristol, PA Zip 19007–3190; tel. 215/785–9200; Peter J. Adamo, Chief Executive Officer
Web address: www.lowerbuckshosp.com

ROXBOROUGH MEMORIAL HOSPITAL (O, 140 beds) 5800 Ridge Avenue, Philadelphia, PA Zip 19128–1737; tel. 215/483–9900; Peter J. Adamo, Chief Executive Officer
Web address: www.roxboroughmemorial.com

RHODE ISLAND: LANDMARK MEDICAL CENTER (O, 133 beds) 115 Cass Avenue, Woonsocket, RI Zip 02895–4731; tel. 401/769–4100; Richard Charest, President
Web address: www.landmarkmedical.org

REHABILITATION HOSPITAL OF RHODE ISLAND (O, 40 beds) 116 Eddie Dowling Highway, North Smithfield, RI Zip 02896–7327; tel. 401/766–0800; Richard Charest, Chief Executive Officer
Web address: www.rhri.net

TEXAS: DALLAS MEDICAL CENTER (O, 71 beds) Seven Medical Parkway, Dallas, TX Zip 75234–7823, Mailing Address: P.O. Box 819094, Zip 75381–9094; tel. 972/247–1000; Raji Kumar, Chief Executive Officer
Web address: www.dallasmedcenter.com

HARLINGEN MEDICAL CENTER (O, 88 beds) 5501 South Expressway 77, Harlingen, TX Zip 78550–3213; tel. 956/365–1000; Brenda Ivory, Chief Executive Officer
Web address: www.harlingenmedicalcenter.com

KNAPP MEDICAL CENTER (O, 190 beds) 1401 East Eighth Street, Weslaco, TX Zip 78596–6640, Mailing Address: P.O. Box 1110, Zip 78599–1110; tel. 956/968–8567; William D. Adams, Chief Executive Officer
Web address: www.knappmed.org

PAMPA REGIONAL MEDICAL CENTER (O, 50 beds) One Medical Plaza, Pampa, TX Zip 79065; tel. 806/665–3721; Brad S. Morse, Chief Executive Officer
Web address: www.prmctx.com

Owned, leased, sponsored:	25 hospitals	3300 beds
Contract–managed:	0 hospitals	0 beds
Totals:	25 hospitals	3300 beds

★0153: PROHEALTH CARE, INC. (NP)
N17 W24100 Riverwood Drive, Suite 130, Waukesha, WI Zip 53188; tel. 262/928–2242; Susan A. Edwards, President and Chief Executive Officer
(Centralized Health System)

WISCONSIN: OCONOMOWOC MEMORIAL HOSPITAL (O, 58 beds) 791 Summit Avenue, Oconomowoc, WI Zip 53066–3896; tel. 262/569–9400; John R. Robertstad, FACHE, President
Web address: www.prohealthcare.org/locations/locations–v2–detail/?id=1123

WAUKESHA MEMORIAL HOSPITAL (O, 290 beds) 725 American Avenue, Waukesha, WI Zip 53188–5099; tel. 262/928–1000; John R. Robertstad, FACHE, President
Web address: www.prohealthcare.org/locations/locations–v2–detail/?id=1119

Owned, leased, sponsored:	2 hospitals	348 beds
Contract–managed:	0 hospitals	0 beds
Totals:	2 hospitals	348 beds

★0197: PROMEDICA HEALTH SYSTEM (NP)
1801 Richards Road, Toledo, OH Zip 43607–1037; tel. 419/469–3800; Randall D. Oostra, FACHE, President and Chief Executive Officer
(Centralized Physician/Insurance Health System)

MICHIGAN: PROMEDICA BIXBY HOSPITAL (O, 66 beds) 818 Riverside Avenue, Adrian, MI Zip 49221–1446; tel. 517/265–0900; Timothy Jakacki, President
Web address: www.promedica.org

PROMEDICA HERRICK HOSPITAL (O, 60 beds) 500 East Pottawatamie Street, Tecumseh, MI Zip 49286–2018; tel. 517/424–3000; Timothy Jakacki, President
Web address: www.promedica.org

OHIO: PROMEDICA BAY PARK HOSPITAL (O, 72 beds) 2801 Bay Park Drive, Oregon, OH Zip 43616–4920; tel. 419/690–7900; Holly L. Bristoll, President
Web address: www.promedica.org

PROMEDICA DEFIANCE REGIONAL HOSPITAL (O, 35 beds) 1200 Ralston Avenue, Defiance, OH Zip 43512–1396; tel. 419/783–6955; Julie Yaroch, D.O., President and Chief Executive Officer
Web address: www.promedica.org

PROMEDICA FLOWER HOSPITAL (O, 269 beds) 5200 Harroun Road, Sylvania, OH Zip 43560–2196; tel. 419/824–1444; Neeraj Kanwal, M.D., President
Web address: www.promedica.org

PROMEDICA FOSTORIA COMMUNITY HOSPITAL (O, 25 beds) 501 Van Buren Street, Fostoria, OH Zip 44830–1534, Mailing Address: P.O. Box 907, Zip 44830–0907; tel. 419/435–7734; Holly L. Bristoll, President
Web address: www.promedica.org

PROMEDICA ST. LUKE'S HOSPITAL (O, 182 beds) 5901 Monclova Road, Maumee, OH Zip 43537–1899; tel. 419/893–5911; Daniel L. Wakeman, President
Web address: www.stlukeshospital.com

PROMEDICA TOLEDO HOSPITAL (O, 656 beds) 2142 North Cove Boulevard, Toledo, OH Zip 43606–3896; tel. 419/291–4000; Arturo Polizzi, President
Web address: www.promedica.org

Owned, leased, sponsored:	8 hospitals	1365 beds
Contract–managed:	0 hospitals	0 beds
Totals:	8 hospitals	1365 beds

0230: PROMISE HEALTHCARE (IO)
999 Yamato Road, 3rd Floor, Boca Raton, FL Zip 33431–4477; tel. 561/869–3100; Peter R. Baronoff, Chief Executive Officer
(Independent Hospital System)

ARIZONA: PROMISE HOSPITAL OF PHOENIX (L, 40 beds) 433 East 6th Street, Mesa, AZ Zip 85203–7104; tel. 480/427–3000; Scott Floden, Chief Executive Officer
Web address: www.promise–phoenix.com

CALIFORNIA: PROMISE HOSPITAL OF EAST LOS ANGELES (L, 36 beds) 443 South Soto Street, Los Angeles, CA Zip 90033–4398; tel. 323/261–1181; Michael D. Kerr, Chief Executive Officer
Web address: www.promiseeastla.com

For explanation of codes following names, see page B2.
★ Indicates Type III membership in the American Hospital Association.

PROMISE HOSPITAL OF EAST LOS ANGELES, SUBURBAN MEDICAL CENTER CAMPUS (L, 182 beds) 16453 South Colorado Avenue, Paramount, CA Zip 90723–5000; tel. 562/531–3110; Michael D. Kerr, Chief Executive Officer
Web address: www.promiseeastla.com

PROMISE HOSPITAL OF SAN DIEGO (O, 100 beds) 5550 University Avenue, San Diego, CA Zip 92105–2307; tel. 619/582–3800; Chuck Smith, Interim Chief Executive Officer
Web address: www.promisesandiego.com

FLORIDA: PROMISE HOSPITAL OF FLORIDA AT THE VILLAGES (O, 40 beds) 5050 County Road, Oxford, FL Zip 34484; tel. 352/689–6400; Hoyt Ross, Chief Executive Officer
Web address: www.promise–villages.com

KANSAS: PROMISE HOSPITAL OF OVERLAND PARK (O, 104 beds) 6509 West 103rd Street, Overland Park, KS Zip 66212–1728; tel. 913/649–3701; Karen Leverich, Chief Executive Officer
Web address: www.promise–overlandpark.com

LOUISIANA: PROMISE HOSPITAL BATON ROUGE – MAIN CAMPUS (L, 54 beds) 5130 Mancuso Lane, Baton Rouge, LA Zip 70809–3583; tel. 225/490–9600; Patrick G. Ryan, Chief Executive Officer
Web address: www.promise–batonrouge.com

PROMISE HOSPITAL OF BATON ROUGE – MID–CITY CAMPUS (O, 28 beds) 3600 Florida Boulevard, 4th Floor, Baton Rouge, LA Zip 70806–3842; tel. 225/387–7770; Michael R. Sanders, MS, Administrator and Chief Operating Officer
Web address: www.promise–batonrougemidcity.com

PROMISE HOSPITAL OF BATON ROUGE – OCHSNER CAMPUS (O, 29 beds) 17000 Medical Center Drive, 3rd Floor, Baton Rouge, LA Zip 70816–3246; tel. 225/236–5440; Michael R. Sanders, MS, Administrator and Chief Operating Officer
Web address: www.promise–batonrougeochsner.com

PROMISE HOSPITAL OF LOUISIANA – SHREVEPORT CAMPUS (O, 146 beds) 1800 Irving Place, Shreveport, LA Zip 71101–4608; tel. 318/425–4096; Rick Stockton, Chief Executive Officer
Web address: www.promise–shreveport.com

PROMISE HOSPITAL OF MISS LOU (O, 40 beds) 209 Front Street, Vidalia, LA Zip 71373–2837; tel. 318/336–6500; Benny Costello, Chief Executive Officer
Web address: www.promise–misslou.com

MISSISSIPPI: PROMISE HOSPITAL OF VICKSBURG (L, 33 beds) 1111 North Frontage Road, 2nd Floor, Vicksburg, MS Zip 39180–5102; tel. 601/619–3526; Mike Harrell, Chief Executive Officer
Web address: www.promise–vicksburg.com

TEXAS: PROMISE HOSPITAL OF DALLAS (O, 62 beds) 7955 Harry Hines Boulevard, Dallas, TX Zip 75235–3305; tel. 214/637–0000; Mary Alexander, Interim Chief Executive Officer
Web address: www.promise–dallas.com/

PROMISE HOSPITAL OF HOUSTON (O, 25 beds) 6160 South Loop East, Houston, TX Zip 77087–1010; tel. 713/640–2400; Tom Omondi, Interim Chief Executive Officer
Web address: www.promise–houston.com

PROMISE HOSPITAL OF WICHITA FALLS (O, 31 beds) 1103 Grace Street, Wichita Falls, TX Zip 76301–4414; tel. 940/720–6633; Delnita Bray, Administrator
Web address: www.promise–wichitafalls.com

UTAH: PROMISE HOSPITAL OF SALT LAKE (O, 32 beds) 8 Avenue, C. Street, Salt Lake City, UT Zip 84143; tel. 801/408–7110; Wayne Kinsey, Chief Executive Officer
Web address: www.promise–saltlake.com

Owned, leased, sponsored:	16 hospitals	982 beds
Contract–managed:	0 hospitals	0 beds
Totals:	16 hospitals	982 beds

★**0344: PROVIDENCE HEALTH & SERVICES** (CC)
1801 Lind Avenue S.W., 9016, Renton, WA Zip 98057–9016; tel. 425/525–3698; Rodney F. Hochman, M.D., President and Chief Executive Officer
(Decentralized Health System)

ALASKA: PROVIDENCE ALASKA MEDICAL CENTER (O, 368 beds) 3200 Providence Drive, Anchorage, AK Zip 99508–4615, Mailing Address: P.O. Box 196604, Zip 99519–6604; tel. 907/562–2211; Bruce Lamoureux, Vice President and Chief Executive Officer
Web address: www.providence.org/alaska/pamc/default.htm

PROVIDENCE KODIAK ISLAND MEDICAL CENTER (L, 25 beds) 1915 East Rezanof Drive, Kodiak, AK Zip 99615–6602; tel. 907/486–3281; Donald J. Rush, Chief Executive Officer
Web address: www.providence.org

PROVIDENCE SEWARD MEDICAL CENTER (L, 46 beds) 417 First Avenue, Seward, AK Zip 99664, Mailing Address: P.O. Box 365, Zip 99664–0365; tel. 907/224–5205; Joseph Fong, Administrator
Web address: www.providence.org

PROVIDENCE VALDEZ MEDICAL CENTER (C, 21 beds) 911 Meals Avenue, Valdez, AK Zip 99686–0550, Mailing Address: P.O. Box 550, Zip 99686–0550; tel. 907/835–2249; Barbara Bigelow, Administrator
Web address: www.providence.org/alaska

CALIFORNIA: PROVIDENCE HOLY CROSS MEDICAL CENTER (O, 264 beds) 15031 Rinaldi Street, Mission Hills, CA Zip 91345–1207; tel. 818/365–8051; Bernard Klein, M.D., Chief Executive Officer
Web address: www.https://california.providence. org/holy–cross/Pages/default.aspx

PROVIDENCE LITTLE COMPANY OF MARY MEDICAL CENTER – TORRANCE (O, 359 beds) 4101 Torrance Boulevard, Torrance, CA Zip 90503–4664; tel. 310/540–7676; Elizabeth Dunne, Chief Executive
Web address: www.lcmweb.org

PROVIDENCE LITTLE COMPANY OF MARY MEDICAL CENTER SAN PEDRO (O, 327 beds) 1300 West Seventh Street, San Pedro, CA Zip 90732–3505; tel. 310/832–3311; Elizabeth Dunne, Interim Chief Executive Officer
Web address: www.https://california.providence.org/san–pedro

PROVIDENCE SAINT JOSEPH MEDICAL CENTER (O, 488 beds) 501 South Buena Vista Street, Burbank, CA Zip 91505–4866; tel. 818/843–5111; Michael A. Rembis, FACHE, Chief Executive Officer
Web address: www.providence.org

PROVIDENCE TARZANA MEDICAL CENTER (O, 245 beds) 18321 Clark Street, Tarzana, CA Zip 91356–3521; tel. 818/881–0800; Dale Surowitz, Chief Executive
Web address: www.providence.org/tarzana.com

SAINT JOHN'S HEALTH CENTER (O, 234 beds) 2121 Santa Monica Boulevard, Santa Monica, CA Zip 90404–2091; tel. 310/829–5511; Marcel C. Loh, FACHE, Chief Executive Officer
Web address: www.newstjohns.org/home.aspx

MONTANA: COMMUNITY HOSPITAL OF ANACONDA (C, 87 beds) 401 West Pennsylvania Street, Anaconda, MT Zip 59711; tel. 406/563–8500; Steve McNeece, Chief Executive Officer
Web address: www.communityhospitalofanaconda.org

PROVIDENCE ST. JOSEPH MEDICAL CENTER (S, 22 beds) 6 Thirteenth Avenue East, Polson, MT Zip 59860–5315, Mailing Address: P.O. Box 1010, Zip 59860–1010; tel. 406/883–5377; James R. Kiser, II, Chief Executive Officer
Web address: www.saintjoes.org

ST. PATRICK HOSPITAL (S, 193 beds) 500 West Broadway, Missoula, MT Zip 59802–4096, Mailing Address: P.O. Box 4587, Zip 59806–4587; tel. 406/543–7271; Jeff Fee, Chief Executive Officer
Web address: www.saintpatrick.org

OREGON: PROVIDENCE HOOD RIVER MEMORIAL HOSPITAL (O, 25 beds) 810 12th Street, Hood River, OR Zip 97031–1587, Mailing Address: P.O. Box 149, Zip 97031–0055; tel. 541/386–3911; Edward E. Freysinger, Chief Executive Officer
Web address: www.providence.org/hoodriver

PROVIDENCE MEDFORD MEDICAL CENTER (O, 114 beds) 1111 Crater Lake Avenue, Medford, OR Zip 97504–6241; tel. 541/732–5000; Cindy Mayo, R.N., FACHE, Chief Executive Officer
Web address: www.providence.org

PROVIDENCE MILWAUKIE HOSPITAL (O, 51 beds) 10150 S.E. 32nd Avenue, Milwaukie, OR Zip 97222–6516; tel. 503/513–8300; Keith Hyde, Chief Executive Officer
Web address: www.providence.org

PROVIDENCE NEWBERG MEDICAL CENTER (O, 40 beds) 1001 Providence Drive, Newberg, OR Zip 97132–7485; tel. 503/537–1555; Lorinda Van Zanten, MSN, Chief Executive Officer
Web address: www.phsor.org

For explanation of codes following names, see page B2.
★ Indicates Type III membership in the American Hospital Association.

B110 Health Care Systems, Networks and Alliances © 2014 AHA Guide

PROVIDENCE PORTLAND MEDICAL CENTER (O, 403 beds) 4805 N.E. Glisan Street, Portland, OR Zip 97213–2933; tel. 503/215–5526; Paul Gaden, Chief Executive Officer
Web address: www.providence.org

PROVIDENCE SEASIDE HOSPITAL (L, 47 beds) 725 South Wahanna Road, Seaside, OR Zip 97138–7735; tel. 503/717–7000; Michael Blauer, Chief Executive Officer
Web address: www.providence.org

PROVIDENCE ST. VINCENT MEDICAL CENTER (O, 552 beds) 9205 S.W. Barnes Road, Portland, OR Zip 97225–6661; tel. 503/216–1234; Janice Burger, Chief Executive
Web address: www.providence.org/portland/hospitals

PROVIDENCE WILLAMETTE FALLS MEDICAL CENTER (O, 111 beds) 1500 Division Street, Oregon City, OR Zip 97045–1597; tel. 503/656–1631; Russ Reinhard, Chief Executive
Web address: www.providence.org/pwfmc

WASHINGTON: PROVIDENCE CENTRALIA HOSPITAL (O, 97 beds) 914 South Scheuber Road, Centralia, WA Zip 98531–9027; tel. 360/736–2803; Jill Cooper, Site Administrator
Web address: www.providence.org

PROVIDENCE HOLY FAMILY HOSPITAL (S, 189 beds) 5633 North Lidgerwood Street, Spokane, WA Zip 99208–1224; tel. 509/482–0111; Alex Jackson, Chief Executive
Web address: www.providence.org

PROVIDENCE MOUNT CARMEL HOSPITAL (S, 25 beds) 982 East Columbia Avenue, Colville, WA Zip 99114–3352; tel. 509/685–5100; Robert D. Campbell, Jr., Chief Executive
Web address: www.mtcarmelhospital.org

PROVIDENCE REGIONAL MEDICAL CENTER EVERETT (O, 491 beds) 1321 Colby Avenue, Everett, WA Zip 98201–1665, Mailing Address: P.O. Box 1147, Zip 98206–1147; tel. 425/261–2000; Preston M. Simmons, FACHE, Chief Executive Officer
Web address: www.providence.org

PROVIDENCE SACRED HEART MEDICAL CENTER & CHILDREN'S HOSPITAL (S, 642 beds) 101 West Eighth Avenue, Spokane, WA Zip 99204–2364, Mailing Address: P.O. Box 2555, Zip 99220–2555; tel. 509/474–3131; Alex Jackson, Chief Executive
Web address: www.shmc.org

PROVIDENCE ST. JOSEPH'S HOSPITAL (S, 65 beds) 500 East Webster Street, Chewelah, WA Zip 99109–9523; tel. 509/935–8211; Robert D. Campbell, Jr., Chief Executive
Web address: www.sjhospital.org

PROVIDENCE ST. MARY MEDICAL CENTER (S, 79 beds) 401 West Poplar Street, Walla Walla, WA Zip 99362–2846, Mailing Address: P.O. Box 1477, Zip 99362–0312; tel. 509/525–3320; Steven A. Burdick, Chief Executive Officer
Web address: www.washington.providence.org/hospitals/st–mary/

PROVIDENCE ST. PETER HOSPITAL (O, 371 beds) 413 Lilly Road N.E., Olympia, WA Zip 98506–5166; tel. 360/491–9480; Medrice Coluccio, R.N., Chief Executive Officer
Web address: www.providence.org/swsa/facilities/st_peter_hospital

WHITMAN HOSPITAL AND MEDICAL CENTER (C, 25 beds) 1200 West Fairview Street, Colfax, WA Zip 99111–9579; tel. 509/397–3435; Gary V. Peck, Interim Chief Executive Officer
Web address: www.whitmanhospital.com

Owned, leased, sponsored:	27 hospitals	5873 beds
Contract–managed:	3 hospitals	133 beds
Totals:	30 hospitals	6006 beds

★0011: PUERTO RICO DEPARTMENT OF HEALTH (NP)
Building A – Medical Center, San Juan, PR Zip 00936, Mailing Address: Call Box 70184, Zip 00936; tel. 787/765–2929; Francisco M. Joglar, M.D., Secretary of Health
(Independent Hospital System)

PUERTO RICO: CARDIOVASCULAR CENTER OF PUERTO RICO AND THE CARIBBEAN (O, 146 beds) Americo Miranda Centro Medico, San Juan, PR Zip 00936, Mailing Address: P.O. Box 366528, Zip 00936–6528; tel. 787/754–8500; Waleska Crespo, Executive Director
Web address: www.cardiovascular.gobierno.pr

HOSPITAL UNIVERSITARIO DR. RAMON RUIZ ARNAU (O, 101 beds) Avenue Laurel, Santa Juanita, Bayamon, PR Zip 00956; tel. 787/787–5151; Humberto M. Monserrate, Chief Executive Officer

UNIVERSITY HOSPITAL (O, 262 beds) Nineyas 869 Rio Piedras, San Juan, PR Zip 00922, Mailing Address: P.O. Box 2116, Zip 00922; tel. 787/754–0101; Jorge Matta Gonzalez, Executive Director

UNIVERSITY PEDIATRIC HOSPITAL (O, 145 beds) Barrio Monacenno, Carretera 22, Rio Piedras, PR Zip 00935, Mailing Address: P.O. Box 191079, San Juan, Zip 00910–1070; tel. 787/777–3535; Gloria Hernandez, Executive Director
Web address: www.md.rcm.upr.edu/pediatrics/university_pediatric_hospital.php

Owned, leased, sponsored:	4 hospitals	654 beds
Contract–managed:	0 hospitals	0 beds
Totals:	4 hospitals	654 beds

★0002: QHR (IO)
105 Continental Place, Brentwood, TN Zip 37027–1052; tel. 800/233–1470; Mickey Bilbrey, President and Chief Executive Officer
(Decentralized Health System)

COLORADO: ARKANSAS VALLEY REGIONAL MEDICAL CENTER (C, 163 beds) 1100 Carson Avenue, La Junta, CO Zip 81050–2799; tel. 719/383–6000; Lynn Crowell, Chief Executive Officer
Web address: www.avrmc.org

COMMUNITY HOSPITAL (C, 42 beds) 2021 North 12th Street, Grand Junction, CO Zip 81501–2999; tel. 970/242–0920; Chris Thomas, FACHE, President and Chief Executive Officer
Web address: www.yourcommunityhospital.com

MEMORIAL HOSPITAL AT CRAIG (C, 25 beds) 750 Hospital Loop, Craig, CO Zip 81625–8750; tel. 970/824–9411; John Rossfeld, Interim Chief Executive Officer
Web address: www.thememorialhospital.com

MONTROSE MEMORIAL HOSPITAL (C, 69 beds) 800 South Third Street, Montrose, CO Zip 81401–4212; tel. 970/249–2211; Mary E. Snyder, Interim Chief Executive Officer
Web address: www.montrosehospital.com

PIONEERS MEDICAL CENTER (C, 40 beds) 345 Cleveland Street, Meeker, CO Zip 81641–3238; tel. 970/878–5047; Kenneth Harman, Chief Executive Officer
Web address: www.pioneershospital.org

PROWERS MEDICAL CENTER (C, 25 beds) 401 Kendall Drive, Lamar, CO Zip 81052–3993; tel. 719/336–4343; Craig Loveless, Chief Executive Officer
Web address: www.prowersmedical.com

ST. VINCENT GENERAL HOSPITAL DISTRICT (C, 25 beds) 822 West 4th Street, Leadville, CO Zip 80461–3897; tel. 719/486–0230; Joyce Beck, Chief Executive Officer
Web address: www.svghd.org

FLORIDA: FISHERMEN'S HOSPITAL (C, 25 beds) 3301 Overseas Highway, Marathon, FL Zip 33050–2329; tel. 305/743–5533; Hal W. Leftwich, FACHE, Chief Executive Officer
Web address: www.fishermenshospital.org

HENDRY REGIONAL MEDICAL CENTER (C, 25 beds) 524 West Sagamore Avenue, Clewiston, FL Zip 33440–3514; tel. 863/902–3000; R. D. Williams, Chief Executive Officer
Web address: www.hendryregional.org

JACKSON HOSPITAL (C, 68 beds) 4250 Hospital Drive, Marianna, FL Zip 32446–1917, Mailing Address: P.O. Box 1608, Zip 32447–5608; tel. 850/526–2200; Larry Meese, Chief Executive Officer
Web address: www.jacksonhosp.com

IDAHO: GRITMAN MEDICAL CENTER (C, 25 beds) 700 South Main Street, Moscow, ID Zip 83843–3056; tel. 208/882–4511; Kara Besst, President and Chief Executive Officer
Web address: www.gritman.org

STEELE MEMORIAL MEDICAL CENTER (C, 18 beds) 203 South Daisy Street, Salmon, ID Zip 83467–4709; tel. 208/756–5600; Jeff Hill, Chief Executive Officer
Web address: www.steelemh.org

Section B

For explanation of codes following names, see page B2.
★ Indicates Type III membership in the American Hospital Association.

ILLINOIS: CRAWFORD MEMORIAL HOSPITAL (C, 63 beds) 1000 North Allen Street, Robinson, IL Zip 62454–1167; tel. 618/544–3131; Donald E. Annis, Chief Executive Officer
Web address: www.crawfordmh.org

LAWRENCE COUNTY MEMORIAL HOSPITAL (C, 25 beds) 2200 West State Street, Lawrenceville, IL Zip 62439–1852; tel. 618/943–1000; Doug Florkowski, Chief Executive Officer
Web address: www.lcmhosp.org

PEKIN HOSPITAL (C, 107 beds) 600 South 13th Street, Pekin, IL Zip 61554–4936; tel. 309/347–1151; Bob J. Haley, Chief Executive Officer
Web address: www.pekinhospital.org

INDIANA: DAVIESS COMMUNITY HOSPITAL (C, 48 beds) 1314 East Walnut Street, Washington, IN Zip 47501–2860, Mailing Address: P.O. Box 760, Zip 47501–0760; tel. 812/254–2760; David Bixler, Chief Executive Officer
Web address: www.dchosp.org

SULLIVAN COUNTY COMMUNITY HOSPITAL (C, 25 beds) 2200 North Section Street, Sullivan, IN Zip 47882–7523, Mailing Address: P.O. Box 10, Zip 47882–0010; tel. 812/268–4311; Michelle Franklin, Chief Executive Officer
Web address: www.schosp.com

IOWA: BOONE COUNTY HOSPITAL (C, 39 beds) 1015 Union Street, Boone, IA Zip 50036–4821; tel. 515/432–3140; Joseph S. Smith, Chief Executive Officer
Web address: www.boonehospital.com

FORT MADISON COMMUNITY HOSPITAL (C, 50 beds) 5445 Avenue O, Fort Madison, IA Zip 52627–9611, Mailing Address: P.O. Box 174, Zip 52627–0174; tel. 319/372–6530; C. James Platt, Chief Executive Officer
Web address: www.fmchosp.com

KANSAS: GREELEY COUNTY HEALTH SERVICES (C, 50 beds) 506 Third Street, Tribune, KS Zip 67879–9684, Mailing Address: P.O. Box 338, Zip 67879–0338; tel. 620/376–4221; Lee Rhodes, Interim Administrator and Chief Executive Officer
Web address: www.mygchs.com

NEOSHO MEMORIAL REGIONAL MEDICAL CENTER (C, 25 beds) 629 South Plummer, Chanute, KS Zip 66720–1928, Mailing Address: P.O. Box 426, Zip 66720–0426; tel. 620/431–4000; Dennis Franks, FACHE, Chief Executive Officer
Web address: www.nmrmc.com

ST. LUKE HOSPITAL AND LIVING CENTER (C, 37 beds) 535 South Freeborn, Marion, KS Zip 66861–1256; tel. 620/382–2177; Jeremy Ensey, Chief Executive Officer
Web address: www.slhmarion.org

WILSON MEDICAL CENTER (C, 15 beds) 2600 Ottawa Road, Neodesha, KS Zip 66757–1897, Mailing Address: P.O. Box 360, Zip 66757–0360; tel. 620/325–2611; Dennis R. Shelby, Chief Executive Officer
Web address: www.wilsonmedical.org

KENTUCKY: CALDWELL MEDICAL CENTER (C, 25 beds) 100 Medical Center Drive, Princeton, KY Zip 42445–2430, Mailing Address: P.O. Box 410, Zip 42445–0410; tel. 270/365–0300; Charles D. Lovell, Jr., FACHE, President and Chief Executive Officer
Web address: www.caldwellhosp.org

FLEMING COUNTY HOSPITAL (C, 52 beds) 55 Foundation Drive, Flemingsburg, KY Zip 41041–9815, Mailing Address: P.O. Box 388, Zip 41041–0388; tel. 606/849–5000; David M. Faulkner, Chief Executive Officer
Web address: www.flemingcountyhospital.org

JENNIE STUART MEDICAL CENTER (C, 139 beds) 320 West 18th Street, Hopkinsville, KY Zip 42240–1965, Mailing Address: P.O. Box 2400, Zip 42241–2400; tel. 270/887–0100; Eric A. Lee, President and Chief Executive Officer
Web address: www.jsmc.org

MONROE COUNTY MEDICAL CENTER (C, 49 beds) 529 Capp Harlan Road, Tompkinsville, KY Zip 42167–1840; tel. 270/487–9231; Vicky McFall, Chief Executive Officer
Web address: www.mcmccares.com

OHIO COUNTY HOSPITAL (C, 25 beds) 1211 Main Street, Hartford, KY Zip 42347–1619; tel. 270/298–7411; Blaine Pieper, Chief Executive Officer
Web address: www.ohiocountyhospital.com

LOUISIANA: FRANKLIN FOUNDATION HOSPITAL (C, 22 beds) 1097 Northwest Boulevard, Franklin, LA Zip 70538–3407, Mailing Address: P.O. Box 577, Zip 70538–0577; tel. 337/828–0760; Claudia Ann Eisenmann, Chief Executive Officer
Web address: www.franklinfoundation.org

HOMER MEMORIAL HOSPITAL (C, 60 beds) 620 East College Street, Homer, LA Zip 71040–3202; tel. 318/927–2024; Derrick A. Frazier, Chief Executive Officer
Web address: www.homerhospital.com

MAINE: CALAIS REGIONAL HOSPITAL (C, 25 beds) 24 Hospital Lane, Calais, ME Zip 04619–1398; tel. 207/454–7521; Michael K. Lally, Chief Executive Officer
Web address: www.calaishospital.com

CARY MEDICAL CENTER (C, 49 beds) 163 Van Buren Road, Suite 1, Caribou, ME Zip 04736–3567; tel. 207/498–3111; Kris A. Doody, R.N., Chief Executive Officer
Web address: www.carymedicalcenter.org

PENOBSCOT VALLEY HOSPITAL (C, 25 beds) 7 Transalpine Road, Lincoln, ME Zip 04457–4222, Mailing Address: P.O. Box 368, Zip 04457–0368; tel. 207/794–3321; Lynn W. Beasley, FACHE, Interim Chief Executive Officer
Web address: www.pvhme.org

MICHIGAN: ALLEGAN GENERAL HOSPITAL (C, 25 beds) 555 Linn Street, Allegan, MI Zip 49010–1524; tel. 269/673–8424; Gerald J. Barbini, President and Chief Executive Officer
Web address: www.aghosp.org

HAYES GREEN BEACH MEMORIAL HOSPITAL (C, 25 beds) 321 East Harris Street, Charlotte, MI Zip 48813–1629; tel. 517/543–1050; Matthew Rush, President and Chief Executive Officer
Web address: www.hgbhealth.com

STURGIS HOSPITAL (C, 49 beds) 916 Myrtle Street, Sturgis, MI Zip 49091–2326; tel. 269/651–7824; Robert J. LaBarge, Chief Executive Officer
Web address: www.sturgishospital.com

THREE RIVERS HEALTH (C, 35 beds) 701 South Health Parkway, Three Rivers, MI Zip 49093–8352; tel. 269/278–1145; William B. Russell, Chief Executive Officer
Web address: www.threerivershealth.org

MINNESOTA: RAINY LAKE MEDICAL CENTER (C, 25 beds) 1400 Highway 71, International Falls, MN Zip 56649–2189; tel. 218/283–4481; Daniel Odegaard, FACHE, Chief Executive Officer
Web address: www.rainylakemedical.com

MISSISSIPPI: KING'S DAUGHTERS MEDICAL CENTER (C, 122 beds) 427 Highway 51 North, Brookhaven, MS Zip 39601–2350, Mailing Address: P.O. Box 948, Zip 39602–0948; tel. 601/833–6011; Alvin Hoover, FACHE, Chief Executive Officer
Web address: www.kdmc.org

MISSOURI: NEVADA REGIONAL MEDICAL CENTER (C, 71 beds) 800 South Ash Street, Nevada, MO Zip 64772–3223; tel. 417/667–3355; Kevin Leeper, Chief Executive Officer
Web address: www.nrmchealth.com

MONTANA: CENTRAL MONTANA MEDICAL CENTER (C, 90 beds) 408 Wendell Avenue, Lewistown, MT Zip 59457–2261; tel. 406/535–7711; Christopher Noland, Interim Chief Executive Officer
Web address: www.cmmccares.com

NORTH VALLEY HOSPITAL (C, 25 beds) 1600 Hospital Way, Whitefish, MT Zip 59937–7849; tel. 406/863–3500; Jason A. Spring, FACHE, Chief Executive Officer
Web address: www.nvhosp.org

NEBRASKA: PHELPS MEMORIAL HEALTH CENTER (C, 25 beds) 1215 Tibbals Street, Holdrege, NE Zip 68949–1255; tel. 308/995–2211; Mark Harrel, Chief Executive Officer
Web address: www.phelpsmemorial.com

NEW MEXICO: CIBOLA GENERAL HOSPITAL (C, 25 beds) 1016 East Roosevelt Avenue, Grants, NM Zip 87020–2118; tel. 505/287–4446; Donald Weidemann, Chief Executive Officer
Web address: www.cibolahospital.com

HOLY CROSS HOSPITAL (C, 35 beds) 1397 Weimer Road, Taos, NM Zip 87571–6253; tel. 575/758–8883; Phillip W. Lowe, Interim Chief Executive Officer
Web address: www.taoshospital.org

For explanation of codes following names, see page B2.
★ Indicates Type III membership in the American Hospital Association.

NORTH CAROLINA: NORTHERN HOSPITAL OF SURRY COUNTY (C, 108 beds) 830 Rockford Street, Mount Airy, NC Zip 27030–5365, Mailing Address: P.O. Box 1101, Zip 27030–1101; tel. 336/719–7000; Bert Whitaker, Interim Chief Executive Officer
Web address: www.northernhospital.com

OHIO: KNOX COMMUNITY HOSPITAL (C, 49 beds) 1330 Coshocton Road, Mount Vernon, OH Zip 43050–1495; tel. 740/393–9000; Bruce D. White, Chief Executive Officer
Web address: www.knoxcommhosp.org

WOOSTER COMMUNITY HOSPITAL (C, 152 beds) 1761 Beall Avenue, Wooster, OH Zip 44691–2342; tel. 330/263–8100; William E. Sheron, Chief Executive Officer
Web address: www.woosterhospital.org

OKLAHOMA: PERRY MEMORIAL HOSPITAL (C, 26 beds) 501 North 14th Street, Perry, OK Zip 73077–5099; tel. 580/336–3541; Howard D. Turner, Chief Executive Officer
Web address: www.pmh–ok.org

PENNSYLVANIA: CLARION HOSPITAL (C, 77 beds) One Hospital Drive, Clarion, PA Zip 16214–8501; tel. 814/226–9500; Byron Quinton, Chief Executive Officer
Web address: www.clarionhospital.org

JERSEY SHORE HOSPITAL (C, 25 beds) 1020 Thompson Street, Jersey Shore, PA Zip 17740–1794; tel. 570/398–0100; David A. Shannon, President and Chief Executive Officer
Web address: www.jsh.org

MEMORIAL HOSPITAL (C, 203 beds) 91 Hospital Drive, Towanda, PA Zip 18848–9702; tel. 570/265–2191; Gary A. Baker, President
Web address: www.memorialhospital.org

SOUTH CAROLINA: ABBEVILLE AREA MEDICAL CENTER (C, 25 beds) 420 Thomson Circle, Abbeville, SC Zip 29620–5656, Mailing Address: P.O. Box 887, Zip 29620–0887; tel. 864/366–5011; Richard D. Osmus, Chief Executive Officer
Web address: www.abbevilleareamc.com

NEWBERRY COUNTY MEMORIAL HOSPITAL (C, 52 beds) 2669 Kinard Street, Newberry, SC Zip 29108–2911, Mailing Address: P.O. Box 497, Zip 29108–0497; tel. 803/276–7570; Craig R. Cudworth, Interim Chief Executive Officer
Web address: www.newberryhospital.org

REGIONAL MEDICAL CENTER (C, 313 beds) 3000 St. Matthews Road, Orangeburg, SC Zip 29118–1442; tel. 803/395–2200; Thomas C. Dandridge, FACHE, President and Chief Executive Officer
Web address: www.trmchealth.org

SOUTH DAKOTA: HURON REGIONAL MEDICAL CENTER (C, 25 beds) 172 Fourth Street S.E., Huron, SD Zip 57350–2590; tel. 605/353–6200; David Dick, Chief Executive Officer
Web address: www.huronregional.org

TENNESSEE: LINCOLN COUNTY HEALTH SYSTEM (C, 323 beds) 106 Medical Center Boulevard, Fayetteville, TN Zip 37334–2684; tel. 931/438–1100; Jamie W. Guin, Jr., Chief Executive Officer
Web address: www.lchealthsystem.com

MACON COUNTY GENERAL HOSPITAL (C, 25 beds) 204 Medical Drive, Lafayette, TN Zip 37083–1799, Mailing Address: P.O. Box 378, Zip 37083–0378; tel. 615/666–2147; Dennis A. Wolford, FACHE, Chief Executive Officer
Web address: www.mcgh.net

RHEA MEDICAL CENTER (C, 25 beds) 9400 Rhea County Highway, Dayton, TN Zip 37321–7922; tel. 423/775–1121; Kennedy L. Croom, Jr., Administrator and Chief Executive Officer
Web address: www.rheamedical.org

TEXAS: BRAZOSPORT REGIONAL HEALTH SYSTEM (C, 103 beds) 100 Medical Drive, Lake Jackson, TX Zip 77566–5674; tel. 979/297–4411; Al Guevara, FACHE, President and Chief Executive Officer
Web address: www.brhstx.org

MATAGORDA REGIONAL MEDICAL CENTER (C, 58 beds) 104 7th Street, Bay City, TX Zip 77414–4853; tel. 979/245–6383; Steven L. Smith, Chief Executive Officer
Web address: www.matagordaregional.org

MEMORIAL HOSPITAL (C, 33 beds) 1110 Sarah Dewitt Drive, Gonzales, TX Zip 78629–3311, Mailing Address: P.O. Box 587, Zip 78629–0587; tel. 830/672–7581; Charles Norris, Chief Executive Officer
Web address: www.gonzaleshealthcare.com

VERMONT: NORTHWESTERN MEDICAL CENTER (C, 55 beds) 133 Fairfield Street, Saint Albans, VT Zip 05478–1726; tel. 802/524–5911; Jill Berry Bowen, President and Chief Executive Officer
Web address: www.northwesternmedicalcenter.org

WASHINGTON: KADLEC REGIONAL MEDICAL CENTER (C, 251 beds) 888 Swift Boulevard, Richland, WA Zip 99352–3514; tel. 509/946–4611; Rand J. Wortman, Chief Executive Officer
Web address: www.kadlecmed.org

WISCONSIN: AMERY REGIONAL MEDICAL CENTER (C, 11 beds) 265 Griffin Street East, Amery, WI Zip 54001–1439; tel. 715/268–8000; Michael Karuschak, Jr., Chief Executive Officer
Web address: www.amerymedicalcenter.org

WYOMING: MEMORIAL HOSPITAL OF CARBON COUNTY (C, 25 beds) 2221 West Elm Street, Rawlins, WY Zip 82301–5108, Mailing Address: P.O. Box 460, Zip 82301–0460; tel. 307/324–2221; Ned Hill, Chief Executive Officer
Web address: www.imhcc.com

WEST PARK HOSPITAL (C, 140 beds) 707 Sheridan Avenue, Cody, WY Zip 82414–3409; tel. 307/527–7501; Douglas A. McMillan, Administrator and Chief Executive Officer
Web address: www.westparkhospital.org

Owned, leased, sponsored:	0 hospitals	0 beds
Contract–managed:	67 hospitals	4161 beds
Totals:	67 hospitals	4161 beds

★0040: QUEEN'S HEALTH SYSTEMS (NP)
1301 Punchbowl Street, Honolulu, HI Zip 96813–2402; tel. 808/535–5448; Arthur A. Ushijima, FACHE, President and Chief Executive Officer
(Moderately Centralized Health System)

HAWAII: MOLOKAI GENERAL HOSPITAL (O, 15 beds) 280 Home Olu Place, Kaunakakai, HI Zip 96748–0408, Mailing Address: P.O. Box 408, Zip 96748–0408; tel. 808/553–5331; Janice Kalanihuia, President
Web address: www.queens.org

QUEEN'S MEDICAL CENTER (O, 478 beds) 1301 Punchbowl Street, Honolulu, HI Zip 96813–2499; tel. 808/691–5100; Arthur A. Ushijima, FACHE, President
Web address: www.queensmedicalcenter.org

Owned, leased, sponsored:	2 hospitals	493 beds
Contract–managed:	0 hospitals	0 beds
Totals:	2 hospitals	493 beds

★8495: REGIONAL HEALTH (NP)
353 Fairmont Boulevard, Rapid City, SD Zip 57701–7375, Mailing Address: P.O. Box 6000, Zip 57709–6000; tel. 605/719–1000; Charles E. Hart, M.D., MS, President and Chief Executive Officer
(Moderately Centralized Health System)

SOUTH DAKOTA: CUSTER REGIONAL HOSPITAL (L, 87 beds) 1039 Montgomery Street, Custer, SD Zip 57730–1397; tel. 605/673–2229; Veronica Schmidt, Chief Executive Officer
Web address: www.regionalhealth.com

LEAD–DEADWOOD REGIONAL HOSPITAL (O, 18 beds) 61 Charles Street, Deadwood, SD Zip 57732–1303; tel. 605/722–6000; Sherry Bea Smith, R.N., Chief Executive Officer
Web address: www.regionalhealth.com

PHILIP HEALTH SERVICES (C, 48 beds) 503 West Pine Street, Philip, SD Zip 57567–3300, Mailing Address: P.O. Box 790, Zip 57567–0790; tel. 605/859–2511; Kent Olson, Administrator and Chief Executive Officer

RAPID CITY REGIONAL HOSPITAL (O, 408 beds) 353 Fairmont Boulevard, Rapid City, SD Zip 57701–7393, Mailing Address: P.O. Box 6000, Zip 57709–6000; tel. 605/755–1000; Timothy H. Sughrue, Chief Executive Officer
Web address: www.regionalhealth.com

SPEARFISH REGIONAL HOSPITAL (O, 35 beds) 1440 North Main Street, Spearfish, SD Zip 57783–1504; tel. 605/644–4000; Larry W. Veitz, Chief Executive Officer
Web address: www.regionalhealth.com

For explanation of codes following names, see page B2.
★ Indicates Type III membership in the American Hospital Association.

STURGIS REGIONAL HOSPITAL (O, 109 beds) 949 Harmon Street, Sturgis, SD Zip 57785–2452; tel. 605/720–2400; Mark Schulte, FACHE, Chief Executive Officer
Web address: www.regionalhealth.
com/Our–Locations/Regional–Hospitals/Sturgis–Regional–Hospital.aspx

WYOMING: CROOK COUNTY MEDICAL SERVICES DISTRICT (C, 48 beds) 713 Oak Street, Sundance, WY Zip 82729, Mailing Address: P.O. Box 517, Zip 82729–0517; tel. 307/283–3501; Jan VanBeek, Chief Executive Officer
Web address: www.crookcountymedical.com

WESTON COUNTY HEALTH SERVICES (C, 75 beds) 1124 Washington Boulevard, Newcastle, WY Zip 82701–2972; tel. 307/746–4491; Maureen K. Cadwell, Chief Executive Officer
Web address: www.wchs–wy.org

Owned, leased, sponsored:	5 hospitals	657 beds
Contract–managed:	3 hospitals	171 beds
Totals:	8 hospitals	828 beds

0622: REGIONALCARE HOSPITAL PARTNERS (IO)
103 Continental Place, Suite 200, Brentwood, TN Zip 37027–1042; tel. 615/844–9800; Kent H. Wallace, Chief Executive Officer
(Moderately Centralized Health System)

ALABAMA: ELIZA COFFEE MEMORIAL HOSPITAL (O, 278 beds) 205 Marengo Street, Florence, AL Zip 35630–6033, Mailing Address: P.O. Box 818, Zip 35631–0818; tel. 256/768–9191; Russell Pigg, Chief Executive Officer
Web address: www.chgroup.org

SHOALS HOSPITAL (O, 131 beds) 201 Avalon Avenue, Muscle Shoals, AL Zip 35661–2805, Mailing Address: P.O. Box 3359, Zip 35662–3359; tel. 256/386–1600; Jeff Jennings, FACHE, Chief Executive Officer
Web address: www.shoalshospital.com

ARIZONA: SIERRA VISTA REGIONAL HEALTH CENTER (L, 83 beds) 300 El Camino Real, Sierra Vista, AZ Zip 85635–2899; tel. 520/458–4641; Dean French, M.D., Chief Executive Officer
Web address: www.svrhc.org

CONNECTICUT: SHARON HOSPITAL (O, 78 beds) 50 Hospital Hill Road, Sharon, CT Zip 06069–2096, Mailing Address: P.O. Box 789, Zip 06069–0789; tel. 860/364–4000; Kim Lumia, President and Chief Executive Officer
Web address: www.sharonhospital.com

IOWA: OTTUMWA REGIONAL HEALTH CENTER (O, 84 beds) 1001 Pennsylvania Avenue, Ottumwa, IA Zip 52501–2186; tel. 641/684–2300; Philip J. Noel, III, Chief Executive Officer
Web address: www.ottumwaregionalhealth.com

OHIO: CLINTON MEMORIAL HOSPITAL (O, 85 beds) 610 West Main Street, Wilmington, OH Zip 45177–2125; tel. 937/382–6611; Jeff R. Egbert, Interim Chief Executive Officer
Web address: www.cmhregional.com

PENNSYLVANIA: SOUTHWEST REGIONAL MEDICAL CENTER (O, 77 beds) 350 Bonar Avenue, Waynesburg, PA Zip 15370–1608; tel. 724/627–3101; Cynthia Cowie, Chief Executive Officer
Web address: www.sw–rmc.com

TEXAS: PARIS REGIONAL MEDICAL CENTER (O, 192 beds) 820 Clarksville Street, Paris, TX Zip 75460–6027, Mailing Address: P.O. Box 9070, Zip 75461–9070; tel. 903/785–4521; Stephen Grubbs, Chief Executive Officer
Web address: www.parisrmc.com

Owned, leased, sponsored:	8 hospitals	1008 beds
Contract–managed:	0 hospitals	0 beds
Totals:	8 hospitals	1008 beds

0411: RELIANT HEALTHCARE PARTNERS (IO)
1300 East Lookout Drive, Suite 115, Richardson, TX Zip 75082–4114; tel. 469/298–1400; Chester Crouch, Chief Executive Officer
(Independent Hospital System)

OHIO: DAYTON REHABILITATION INSTITUTE (O, 50 beds) One Elizabeth Place, Dayton, OH Zip 45417–3445; tel. 937/424–8200; Randy J. Kitchen, Chief Executive Officer
Web address: www.reliantdayton.com

TEXAS: RELIANT REHABILITATION HOSPITAL ABILENE (O, 30 beds) 6401 Directors Parkway, Abilene, TX Zip 79606–5869; tel. 325/691–1600; Joe Roberson, Chief Executive Officer
Web address: www.reliantabilene.com

RELIANT REHABILITATION HOSPITAL CENTRAL TEXAS (O, 75 beds) 1400 Hester's Crossing, Round Rock, TX Zip 78681–8025; tel. 512/244–4400; Eric Mueller, Chief Executive Officer
Web address: www.reliantcentraltx.com/

RELIANT REHABILITATION HOSPITAL NORTH HOUSTON (O, 60 beds) 117 Vision Park Boulevard, Shenandoah, TX Zip 77384–3001; tel. 936/444–1700; Abraham Sims, Chief Executive Officer
Web address: www.reliantnorthhouston.com/

RELIANT REHABILITATION HOSPITAL NORTH TEXAS (O, 50 beds) 3351 Waterview Parkway, Richardson, TX Zip 75080–1449; tel. 972/398–5700; Jim Ransom, Chief Executive Officer
Web address: www.relianthcp.com

Owned, leased, sponsored:	5 hospitals	265 beds
Contract–managed:	0 hospitals	0 beds
Totals:	5 hospitals	265 beds

★2625: RENOWN HEALTH (NP)
1155 Mill Street, Reno, NV Zip 89502–1576; tel. 775/982–4100; Anthony D. Slonim, M.D., Dr.PH, President and Chief Executive Officer
(Centralized Health System)

NEVADA: RENOWN REGIONAL MEDICAL CENTER (O, 642 beds) 1155 Mill Street, Reno, NV Zip 89502–1576; tel. 775/982–4100; Gregory E. Boyer, Chief Executive Officer
Web address: www.renown.org

RENOWN REHABILITATION HOSPITAL (O, 62 beds) 1495 Mill Street, Reno, NV Zip 89502–1479; tel. 775/982–3500; Randall W. Ross, Chief Executive Officer
Web address: www.renown.org

RENOWN SOUTH MEADOWS MEDICAL CENTER (O, 76 beds) 10101 Double R Boulevard, Reno, NV Zip 89521–5931; tel. 775/982–7000; Randall W. Ross, Chief Executive Officer
Web address: www.renown.org

Owned, leased, sponsored:	3 hospitals	780 beds
Contract–managed:	0 hospitals	0 beds
Totals:	3 hospitals	780 beds

0872: RESTORA HEALTHCARE (IO)
2550 Northwinds Parkway, Suite 160, Alpharetta, GA Zip 30009–2234; tel. 678/736–7780; Rod Laughlin, President and Chief Executive Officer

ARIZONA: RESTORA HOSPITAL OF MESA (O, 120 beds) 215 South Power Road, Mesa, AZ Zip 85206–5235; tel. 480/985–6992; Judith Schiros, Chief Executive Officer
Web address: www.restorahealthcare.com

RESTORA HOSPITAL OF SUN CITY (O, 120 beds) 13818 North Thunderbird Boulevard, Sun City, AZ Zip 85351–2574; tel. 623/977–1325; Gregory Sassman, Interim Chief Executive Officer
Web address: www.restorahealthcare.com

Owned, leased, sponsored:	2 hospitals	240 beds
Contract–managed:	0 hospitals	0 beds
Totals:	2 hospitals	240 beds

4810: RIVERSIDE HEALTH SYSTEM (NP)
701 Town Center Drive, Suite 1000, Newport News, VA Zip 23606–4286; tel. 757/534–7000; William B. Downey, President and Chief Executive Officer
(Centralized Health System)

For explanation of codes following names, see page B2.
★ Indicates Type III membership in the American Hospital Association.

VIRGINIA: HAMPTON ROADS SPECIALTY HOSPITAL (O, 25 beds) 245 Chesapeake Avenue, Newport News, VA Zip 23607–6038; tel. 757/534–5000; Courtney Detwiler, R.N., Administrator
Web address: www.hamptonroadsspecialtyhospital.com

RIVERSIDE BEHAVIORAL HEALTH CENTER (O, 79 beds) 2244 Executive Drive, Hampton, VA Zip 23666–2430; tel. 757/827–1001; Debra Campbell, R.N., Administrator
Web address: www.riversideonline.com

RIVERSIDE DOCTORS' HOSPITAL (O, 12 beds) 1500 Commonwealth Avenue, Williamsburg, VA Zip 23185–5229; tel. 757/585–2200; Steve C. McCary, Administrator
Web address: www.riversideonline.com

RIVERSIDE REGIONAL MEDICAL CENTER (O, 192 beds) 500 J. Clyde Morris Boulevard, Newport News, VA Zip 23601–1929; tel. 757/594–2000; Patrick Parcells, Senior Vice President and Administrator
Web address: www.riverside–online.com

RIVERSIDE REHABILITATION INSTITUTE (O, 25 beds) 245 Chesapeake Avenue, Newport News, VA Zip 23607–6038; tel. 757/928–8000; Edward Heckler, Administrator
Web address: www.riverside–online.com

RIVERSIDE SHORE MEMORIAL HOSPITAL (O, 31 beds) 9507 Hospital Avenue, Nassawadox, VA Zip 23413–1821, Mailing Address: P.O. Box 17, Zip 23413–0017; tel. 757/414–8000; Susan McAndrews, Vice President and Administrator
Web address: www.riversideonline.com

RIVERSIDE TAPPAHANNOCK HOSPITAL (O, 16 beds) 618 Hospital Road, Tappahannock, VA Zip 22560–5000; tel. 804/443–3311; John Peterman, Vice President and Administrator
Web address: www.riverside–online.com

RIVERSIDE WALTER REED HOSPITAL (O, 31 beds) 7519 Hospital Drive, Gloucester, VA Zip 23061–4178, Mailing Address: P.O. Box 1130, Zip 23061–1130; tel. 804/693–8800; Megan Kleckner, Vice President and Administrator
Web address: www.riversideonline.com

Owned, leased, sponsored:	8 hospitals	411 beds
Contract–managed:	0 hospitals	0 beds
Totals:	8 hospitals	411 beds

0268:   ROBERT WOOD JOHNSON HEALTH SYSTEM & NETWORK (NP)
1 Robert Wood Johnson Place, New Brunswick, NJ Zip 08901–1928; tel. 732/828–3000; Stephen K. Jones, President and Chief Executive Officer
(Moderately Centralized Health System)

NEW JERSEY: CHILDREN'S SPECIALIZED HOSPITAL–PSE&G (O, 128 beds) 200 Somerset Street, New Brunswick, NJ Zip 08901–1942; tel. 732/258–7000; Amy B. Mansue, President and Chief Executive Officer
Web address: www.childrens–specialized.org

ROBERT WOOD JOHNSON UNIVERSITY HOSPITAL (O, 610 beds) 1 Robert Wood Johnson Place, New Brunswick, NJ Zip 08901–1928; tel. 732/828–3000; Stephen K. Jones, President and Chief Executive Officer
Web address: www.rwjuh.edu

ROBERT WOOD JOHNSON UNIVERSITY HOSPITAL AT HAMILTON (O, 242 beds) One Hamilton Health Place, Hamilton, NJ Zip 08690–3599; tel. 609/586–7900; Richard Freeman, President and Chief Executive Officer
Web address: www.rwjhamilton.org

ROBERT WOOD JOHNSON UNIVERSITY HOSPITAL RAHWAY (O, 147 beds) 865 Stone Street, Rahway, NJ Zip 07065–2797; tel. 732/381–4200; Kirk C. Tice, President and Chief Executive Officer
Web address: www.rwjuhr.com

ROBERT WOOD JOHNSON UNIVERSITY HOSPITAL SOMERSET (O, 333 beds) 110 Rehill Avenue, Somerville, NJ Zip 08876–2598; tel. 908/685–2200; Vincent D. Joseph, Interim Administrator
Web address: www.smchealthwise.com

Owned, leased, sponsored:	5 hospitals	1460 beds
Contract–managed:	0 hospitals	0 beds
Totals:	5 hospitals	1460 beds

★**0046:   ROCHESTER REGIONAL HEALTH SYSTEM** (NP)
1425 Portland Avenue, 5th Floor, Rochester, NY Zip 14621–3001; tel. 585/922–4000; Mark C. Clement, President and Chief Executive Officer
(Moderately Centralized Health System)

NEW YORK: NEWARK–WAYNE COMMUNITY HOSPITAL (O, 280 beds) 1200 Driving Park Avenue, Newark, NY Zip 14513–1057, Mailing Address: P.O. Box 111, Zip 14513–0111; tel. 315/332–2022; Robert Cercek, Regional President Operations
Web address: www.rochestergeneral.org

ROCHESTER GENERAL HOSPITAL (O, 520 beds) 1425 Portland Avenue, Rochester, NY Zip 14621–3099; tel. 585/922–4000; Robert Nesselbush, President
Web address: www.rochestergeneral.org

UNITY HOSPITAL (O, 451 beds) 1555 Long Pond Road, Rochester, NY Zip 14626–4182; tel. 585/723–7000; Warren Hern, President and Chief Executive Officer
Web address: www.unityhealth.org

Owned, leased, sponsored:	3 hospitals	1251 beds
Contract–managed:	0 hospitals	0 beds
Totals:	3 hospitals	1251 beds

0348:   RURAL COMMUNITY HOSPITALS OF AMERICA (IO)
1100 Main Street, Suite 2350, Kansas City, MO Zip 64105–5186; tel. 816/474–7800; Lawrence J. Arthur, President
(Independent Hospital System)

KANSAS: HILLSBORO COMMUNITY HOSPITAL (O, 10 beds) 701 South Main Street, Hillsboro, KS Zip 67063–1553; tel. 620/947–3114; Marion Regier, Chief Executive Officer
Web address: www.hchks.com

HORTON COMMUNITY HOSPITAL (O, 25 beds) 240 West 18th Street, Horton, KS Zip 66439–1245; tel. 785/486–2642; James Nobie, Chief Executive Officer
Web address: www.horton–hospital.com

OSWEGO COMMUNITY HOSPITAL (O, 12 beds) 800 Barker Drive, Oswego, KS Zip 67356–9014; tel. 620/795–2921; Daniel Hiben, Chief Executive Officer
Web address: www.oswegocommunityhospital.com

MISSOURI: COOPER COUNTY MEMORIAL HOSPITAL (C, 32 beds) 17651 B Highway, Boonville, MO Zip 65233–2839, Mailing Address: P.O. Box 88, Zip 65233–0088; tel. 660/882–7461; Danielle Gearhart, Chief Executive Officer
Web address: www.coopercmh.com

I–70 COMMUNITY HOSPITAL (O, 15 beds) 105 Hospital Drive, Sweet Springs, MO Zip 65351–2229; tel. 660/335–4700; Julie Davenport, Chief Executive Officer
Web address: www.i70medcenter.com

NORTH CAROLINA: WASHINGTON COUNTY HOSPITAL (O, 25 beds) 958 U.S. Highway 64 East, Plymouth, NC Zip 27962–9591; tel. 252/793–4135; Cameron Highsmith, Chief Executive Officer

YADKIN VALLEY COMMUNITY HOSPITAL (O, 22 beds) 624 West Main Street, Yadkinville, NC Zip 27055–7804, Mailing Address: P.O. Box 68, Zip 27055–0068; tel. 336/679–2041; Shawn Bright, Chief Executive Officer
Web address: www.yadkinhospital.com/

OKLAHOMA: DRUMRIGHT REGIONAL HOSPITAL (O, 15 beds) 610 West Bypass, Drumright, OK Zip 74030–5957; tel. 918/382–2300; Darrel Morris, Chief Executive Officer
Web address: www.drumrighthospital.com

FAIRFAX COMMUNITY HOSPITAL (O, 15 beds) Taft Avenue and Highway 18, Fairfax, OK Zip 74637–4028, Mailing Address: P.O. Box 219, Zip 74637–0219; tel. 918/642–3291; Tina Steele, Chief Executive Officer and Chief Financial Officer

HASKELL COUNTY COMMUNITY HOSPITAL (O, 32 beds) 401 Northwest H Street, Stigler, OK Zip 74462–1625; tel. 918/967–4682; Donald E. Buchanan, Interim Chief Executive Officer
Web address: www.haskellhospital.com

Section B

For explanation of codes following names, see page B2.
★ Indicates Type III membership in the American Hospital Association.

PRAGUE COMMUNITY HOSPITAL (O, 15 beds) 1322 Klabzuba Avenue, Prague, OK Zip 74864–9005, Mailing Address: P.O. Box S., Zip 74864–1090; tel. 405/567–4922; William Holland, Chief Executive Officer
Web address: www.praguehospital.com

SEILING COMMUNITY HOSPITAL (O, 18 beds) Highway 60 N.E., Seiling, OK Zip 73663, Mailing Address: P.O. Box 720, Zip 73663–0720; tel. 580/922–7361; Donald E. Buchanan, Interim Chief Executive Officer
Web address: www.seilinghospital.com

TENNESSEE: LAUDERDALE COMMUNITY HOSPITAL (O, 25 beds) 326 Asbury Avenue, Ripley, TN Zip 38063–5577; tel. 731/221–2200; Scott Tongate, Chief Executive Officer
Web address: www.lauderdalehospital.com/

Owned, leased, sponsored:	12 hospitals	229 beds
Contract–managed:	1 hospital	32 beds
Totals:	13 hospitals	261 beds

★0109: RURAL HEALTH GROUP (IO)
48 West 1500 North, Nephi, UT Zip 84648–8900; tel. 435/623–4924; Mark R. Stoddard, President and Chairman
(Independent Hospital System)

NEVADA: DESERT VIEW HOSPITAL (O, 25 beds) 360 South Lola Lane, Pahrump, NV Zip 89048–0884; tel. 775/751–7500; Kelly H. Adams, Chief Executive Officer
Web address: www.desertviewhospital.com

UTAH: CENTRAL VALLEY MEDICAL CENTER (L, 27 beds) 48 West 1500 North, Nephi, UT Zip 84648–8900; tel. 435/623–3000; Mark R. Stoddard, President
Web address: www.cvmed.net

Owned, leased, sponsored:	2 hospitals	52 beds
Contract–managed:	0 hospitals	0 beds
Totals:	2 hospitals	52 beds

★0220: RUSH HEALTH SYSTEMS (NP)
1314 19th Avenue, Meridian, MS Zip 39301–4116; tel. 601/483–0011; Wallace Strickland, President and Chief Executive Officer
(Independent Hospital System)

ALABAMA: CHOCTAW GENERAL HOSPITAL (O, 25 beds) 401 Vanity Fair Avenue, Butler, AL Zip 36904–3032; tel. 205/459–9100; J. W. Cowan, Administrator
Web address: www.choctawgeneral.com/cgh/

MISSISSIPPI: H. C. WATKINS MEMORIAL HOSPITAL (O, 25 beds) 605 South Archusa Avenue, Quitman, MS Zip 39355–2331; tel. 601/776–6925; Clinton Eaves, Administrator
Web address: www.watkinsmemorialhospital.com/hcwmh/

JOHN C. STENNIS MEMORIAL HOSPITAL (O, 25 beds) 14365 Highway 16 West, De Kalb, MS Zip 39328–7974; tel. 769/486–1000; Michael Nester, Administrator
Web address: www.johncstennismemorialhospital.com/jcsmh/

LAIRD HOSPITAL (O, 25 beds) 25117 Highway 15, Union, MS Zip 39365–9099; tel. 601/774–8214; Thomas G. Bartlett, III, Administrator
Web address: www.lairdhospital.com/lh/

RUSH FOUNDATION HOSPITAL (O, 182 beds) 1314 19th Avenue, Meridian, MS Zip 39301–4195; tel. 601/483–0011; Morris A. Reece, President and Chief Executive Officer
Web address: www.rushhealthsystems.org/rfh/

SCOTT REGIONAL HOSPITAL (O, 25 beds) 317 Highway 13 South, Morton, MS Zip 39117–3353, Mailing Address: P.O. Box 259, Zip 39117–0259; tel. 601/732–6301; Michael R. Edwards, Administrator
Web address: www.scottregional.org/srh/

SPECIALTY HOSPITAL OF MERIDIAN (O, 49 beds) 1314 19th Avenue, Meridian, MS Zip 39301–4116; tel. 601/703–4211; Elizabeth C. Mitchell, Vice President and Administrator
Web address: www.specialtyhospitalofmeridian.com/shm/

Owned, leased, sponsored:	7 hospitals	356 beds
Contract–managed:	0 hospitals	0 beds
Totals:	7 hospitals	356 beds

★3855: RUSH UNIVERSITY MEDICAL CENTER (NP)
1653 West Congress Parkway, Chicago, IL Zip 60612–3864; tel. 312/942–5000; Larry J. Goodman, M.D., Chief Executive Officer
(Moderately Centralized Health System)

ILLINOIS: RUSH OAK PARK HOSPITAL (O, 108 beds) 520 South Maple Avenue, Oak Park, IL Zip 60304–1097; tel. 708/383–9300; Bruce M. Elegant, President and Chief Executive Officer
Web address: www.roph.org

RUSH UNIVERSITY MEDICAL CENTER (O, 679 beds) 1653 West Congress Parkway, Chicago, IL Zip 60612–3833; tel. 312/942–5000; Larry J. Goodman, M.D., Chief Executive Officer
Web address: www.rush.edu

RUSH–COPLEY MEDICAL CENTER (O, 210 beds) 2000 Ogden Avenue, Aurora, IL Zip 60504–7222; tel. 630/978–6200; Barry C. Finn, President and Chief Executive Officer
Web address: www.rushcopley.com

Owned, leased, sponsored:	3 hospitals	997 beds
Contract–managed:	0 hospitals	0 beds
Totals:	3 hospitals	997 beds

0912: SAFE HAVEN HEALTH CARE (IO)
2520 South 5th Avenue, Pocatello, ID Zip 83204–1923; tel. 800/261–2443; Scott Burpee, President

IDAHO: SAFE HAVEN HOSPITAL OF POCATELLO (O, 87 beds) 1200 Hospital Way, Pocatello, ID Zip 83201–2708; tel. 208/232–2570; Josiah Dahlstrom, Administrator
Web address: www.safehavenhealthcare.org/safehaven_hospital/index.html

SAFE HAVEN HOSPITAL OF TREASURE VALLEY (O, 22 beds) 8050 Northview Street, Boise, ID Zip 83704–7126; tel. 208/327–0504; Scott Proctor, Chief Executive Officer
Web address: www.boisepsychhospital.com

Owned, leased, sponsored:	2 hospitals	109 beds
Contract–managed:	0 hospitals	0 beds
Totals:	2 hospitals	109 beds

★0318: SAINT FRANCIS CARE, INC. (NP)
114 Woodland Street, Hartford, CT Zip 06105–1208; tel. 860/714–5541; Christopher M. Dadlez, President and Chief Executive Officer
(Independent Hospital System)

CONNECTICUT: MOUNT SINAI REHABILITATION HOSPITAL (O, 30 beds) 490 Blue Hills Avenue, Hartford, CT Zip 06112–1513; tel. 860/714–3500; Christopher M. Dadlez, President and Chief Executive Officer
Web address: www.stfranciscare.org

SAINT FRANCIS HOSPITAL AND MEDICAL CENTER (O, 612 beds) 114 Woodland Street, Hartford, CT Zip 06105–1208; tel. 860/714–4000; Christopher M. Dadlez, President and Chief Executive Officer
Web address: www.saintfranciscare.com

Owned, leased, sponsored:	2 hospitals	642 beds
Contract–managed:	0 hospitals	0 beds
Totals:	2 hospitals	642 beds

★0254: SAINT FRANCIS HEALTH SYSTEM (NP)
6161 South Yale Avenue, Tulsa, OK Zip 74136–1902; tel. 918/494–8454; Jake Henry, Jr., President and Chief Executive Officer
(Centralized Health System)

For explanation of codes following names, see page B2.
★ Indicates Type III membership in the American Hospital Association.

OKLAHOMA: LAUREATE PSYCHIATRIC CLINIC AND HOSPITAL (O, 75 beds)
6655 South Yale Avenue, Tulsa, OK Zip 74136–3329;
tel. 918/481–4000; William Schloss, Senior Vice President and
Administrator
Web address: www.laureate.com

SAINT FRANCIS HOSPITAL (O, 808 beds) 6161 South Yale Avenue, Tulsa, OK
Zip 74136–1902; tel. 918/494–2200; Lynn A. Sund, R.N., MS, Senior Vice
President, Administrator and Chief Nurse Executive
Web address: www.saintfrancis.com

SAINT FRANCIS HOSPITAL SOUTH (O, 78 beds) 10501 East 91St. Streeet,
Tulsa, OK Zip 74133–5790; tel. 918/455–3535; David S. Weil, Senior Vice
President and Administrator
Web address: www.saintfrancis.com/south/

Owned, leased, sponsored:	3 hospitals	961 beds
Contract–managed:	0 hospitals	0 beds
Totals:	3 hospitals	961 beds

★**0120: SAINT LUKE'S HEALTH SYSTEM** (NP)
901 East 104th Street, Mailstop 900N, Kansas City, MO
Zip 64131–4517, Mailing Address: 901 East 104th Street,
Zip 64131–4517; tel. 816/932–2000; Melinda Estes, M.D.,
President and Chief Executive Officer
(Centralized Health System)

KANSAS: ANDERSON COUNTY HOSPITAL (L, 40 beds) 421 South Maple,
Garnett, KS Zip 66032–1334, Mailing Address: P.O. Box 309,
Zip 66032–0309; tel. 785/448–3131; Dennis A. Hachenberg, FACHE,
Chief Executive Officer
Web address: www.saint–lukes.org

SAINT LUKE'S CUSHING HOSPITAL (O, 53 beds) 711 Marshall Street,
Leavenworth, KS Zip 66048–3235; tel. 913/684–1100; Adele Ducharme,
R.N., MSN, Chief Executive Officer
Web address: www.https://www.saintlukeshealthsystem.
org/location/cushing–memorial–hospital

SAINT LUKE'S SOUTH HOSPITAL (O, 110 beds) 12300 Metcalf Avenue,
Overland Park, KS Zip 66213–1324; tel. 913/317–7000; Jani L. Johnson,
President and Chief Executive Officer
Web address: www.saintlukeshealthsystem.org/south

MISSOURI: CRITTENTON CHILDREN'S CENTER (O, 46 beds) 10918 Elm
Avenue, Kansas City, MO Zip 64134–4108; tel. 816/765–6600; Janine
Hron, Chief Executive Officer
Web address: www.crittentonkc.org

HEDRICK MEDICAL CENTER (L, 25 beds) 2799 North Washington Street,
Chillicothe, MO Zip 64601–2902; tel. 660/646–1480; Matthew J. Wenzel,
Chief Executive Officer
Web address: www.saintlukeshealthsystem.org

SAINT LUKE'S EAST HOSPITAL (O, 141 beds) 100 N.E. Saint Luke's
Boulevard, Lee's Summit, MO Zip 64086–6000; tel. 816/347–5000; Ronald
L. Baker, Chief Executive Officer
Web address: www.saint–lukes.org

SAINT LUKE'S HOSPITAL OF KANSAS CITY (O, 447 beds) 4401 Wornall Road,
Kansas City, MO Zip 64111–3220; tel. 816/932–9886; Julie L. Quirin,
FACHE, Chief Executive Officer
Web address: www.saint–lukes.org

SAINT LUKE'S NORTH HOSPITAL – BARRY ROAD (O, 142 beds) 5830 N.W.
Barry Road, Kansas City, MO Zip 64154–2778; tel. 816/891–6000; Kevin T.
Trimble, FACHE, President and Chief Executive Officer
Web address: www.saint–lukes.org

WRIGHT MEMORIAL HOSPITAL (L, 25 beds) 191 Iowa Boulevard, Trenton, MO
Zip 64683–8343; tel. 660/358–5700; Gary W. Jordan, FACHE, Chief
Executive Officer
Web address: www.saintlukeshealthsystem.org

Owned, leased, sponsored:	9 hospitals	1029 beds
Contract–managed:	0 hospitals	0 beds
Totals:	9 hospitals	1029 beds

0403: SALEM HEALTH (NP)
890 Oak Street Building B. POB 14001, Salem, OR
Zip 97309–5014; tel. 503/561–5200; Norman F. Gruber, President
and Chief Executive Officer
(Moderately Centralized Health System)

OREGON: SALEM HOSPITAL (O, 417 beds) 890 Oak Street S.E., Salem, OR
Zip 97301–3959, Mailing Address: P.O. Box 14001, Zip 97309–5014;
tel. 503/561–5200; Norman F. Gruber, President and Chief Executive
Officer
Web address: www.salemhospital.org

WEST VALLEY HOSPITAL (O, 6 beds) 525 S.E. Washington Street, Dallas, OR
Zip 97338–2834, Mailing Address: P.O. Box 378, Zip 97338–0378;
tel. 503/623–8301; Robert C. Brannigan, Administrator
Web address: www.westvalleyhospital.org

Owned, leased, sponsored:	2 hospitals	423 beds
Contract–managed:	0 hospitals	0 beds
Totals:	2 hospitals	423 beds

★**0186: SAMARITAN HEALTH SERVICES** (NP)
3600 N.W. Samaritan Drive, Corvallis, OR Zip 97330–3737, Mailing
Address: P.O. Box 1068, Zip 97339–1068; tel. 541/768–5001;
Larry A. Mullins, FACHE, President and Chief Executive Officer
(Moderately Centralized Health System)

GOOD SAMARITAN REGIONAL MEDICAL CENTER (O, 165 beds) 3600 N.W.
Samaritan Drive, Corvallis, OR Zip 97330–3737, Mailing Address: P.O. Box
1068, Zip 97339–1068; tel. 541/768–5111; Larry A. Mullins, FACHE, Chief
Executive Officer
Web address: www.samhealth.org

SAMARITAN ALBANY GENERAL HOSPITAL (O, 70 beds) 1046 Sixth Avenue,
S.W., Albany, OR Zip 97321–1999; tel. 541/812–4000; David G. Triebes,
Chief Executive Officer
Web address: www.samhealth.org

SAMARITAN LEBANON COMMUNITY HOSPITAL (O, 25 beds) 525 North
Santiam Highway, Lebanon, OR Zip 97355–4363, Mailing Address: P.O. Box
739, Zip 97355–0739; tel. 541/258–2101; Becky A. Pape, R.N., Chief
Executive Officer
Web address: www.samhealth.org

SAMARITAN NORTH LINCOLN HOSPITAL (C, 25 beds) 3043 N.E. 28th Street,
Lincoln City, OR Zip 97367–4518, Mailing Address: P.O. Box 767,
Zip 97367–0767; tel. 541/994–3661; Marty Cahill, Chief Executive Officer
Web address: www.samhealth.org

SAMARITAN PACIFIC COMMUNITIES HOSPITAL (C, 25 beds) 930 S.W. Abbey
Street, Newport, OR Zip 97365–4820, Mailing Address: P.O. Box 945,
Zip 97365–0072; tel. 541/265–2244; David C. Bigelow, PharmD, Chief
Executive Officer
Web address: www.samhealth.org

Owned, leased, sponsored:	3 hospitals	260 beds
Contract–managed:	2 hospitals	50 beds
Totals:	5 hospitals	310 beds

0914: SAN LUIS VALLEY HEALTH (NP)
106 Blanca Avenue, Alamosa, CO Zip 81101–2340;
tel. 719/589–2511; Konnie Martin, Chief Executive Officer

COLORADO: SAN LUIS VALLEY HEALTH (O, 44 beds) 106 Blanca Avenue,
Alamosa, CO Zip 81101–2393; tel. 719/589–2511; Konnie Martin, Chief
Executive Officer
Web address: www.slvrmc.org

SAN LUIS VALLEY HEALTH CONEJOS COUNTY HOSPITAL (O, 17 beds) 19021
U.S. Highway 285, La Jara, CO Zip 81140–0639, Mailing Address: P.O. Box
639, Zip 81140–0639; tel. 719/274–5121; Kelly Gallegos, Administrator
Web address: www.sanluisvalleyhealth.
org/locations/conejos–county–hospital

Owned, leased, sponsored:	2 hospitals	61 beds
Contract–managed:	0 hospitals	0 beds
Totals:	2 hospitals	61 beds

For explanation of codes following names, see page B2.
★ Indicates Type III membership in the American Hospital Association.

★0530: SANFORD HEALTH (NP)
2301 East 60th Street North, Sioux Falls, SD Zip 57104–0569,
Mailing Address: PO Box 5039, Zip 57117–5039;
tel. 605/333–1000; Kelby K. Krabbenhoft, President and Chief
Executive Officer
(Decentralized Health System)

IOWA: ORANGE CITY AREA HEALTH SYSTEM (C, 104 beds) 1000 Lincoln
Circle S.E., Orange City, IA Zip 51041–1862; tel. 712/737–4984; Martin
W. Guthmiller, Chief Executive Officer
Web address: www.ochealthsystem.org

SANFORD HOSPITAL ROCK RAPIDS (L, 14 beds) 801 South Greene Street,
Rock Rapids, IA Zip 51246–1998; tel. 712/472–2591; Tammy Loosbrock,
Chief Executive Officer
Web address: www.sanfordmerrill.org

SANFORD SHELDON MEDICAL CENTER (O, 95 beds) 118 North Seventh
Avenue, Sheldon, IA Zip 51201–1235, Mailing Address: P.O. Box 250,
Zip 51201–0250; tel. 712/324–5041; Richard E. Nordahl, Chief Executive
Officer
Web address: www.sanfordsheldon.org

MINNESOTA: ARNOLD MEMORIAL HEALTH CARE CENTER (L, 50 beds) 601
Louisiana Avenue, Adrian, MN Zip 56110–0279, Mailing Address: P.O. Box
279, Zip 56110–0279; tel. 507/483–2668; Michele Roban, Administrator

MAHNOMEN HEALTH CENTER (C, 18 beds) 414 West Jefferson Avenue,
Mahnomen, MN Zip 56557–4912, Mailing Address: P.O. Box 396,
Zip 56557–0396; tel. 218/935–2511; Susan K. Klassen, Chief Executive
Officer and Administrator
Web address: www.mahnomenhealthcenter.com

MURRAY COUNTY MEDICAL CENTER (C, 18 beds) 2042 Juniper Avenue,
Slayton, MN Zip 56172–1017; tel. 507/836–6111; John M. Osse, Interim
Chief Executive Officer
Web address: www.murraycountymed.org

ORTONVILLE AREA HEALTH SERVICES (C, 81 beds) 450 Eastvold Avenue,
Ortonville, MN Zip 56278–1133; tel. 320/839–2502; Richard M. Ash, Chief
Executive Officer
Web address: www.oahs.us

PERHAM HEALTH (C, 121 beds) 1000 Coney Street West, Perham, MN
Zip 56573–1108; tel. 218/347–4500; Chuck Hofius, Chief Executive Officer
Web address: www.perhamhealth.org

SANFORD BAGLEY MEDICAL CENTER (O, 95 beds) 203 Fourth Street N.W.,
Bagley, MN Zip 56621–8307; tel. 218/694–6501; Kirby Johnson,
Administrator
Web address: www.clearwaterhealthservices.com

SANFORD BEMIDJI MEDICAL CENTER (O, 196 beds) 1300 Anne Street N.W.,
Bemidji, MN Zip 56601–5103; tel. 218/751–5430; Dan Olson, President
Web address: www.nchs.org

SANFORD CANBY MEDICAL CENTER (L, 93 beds) 112 St. Olaf Avenue South,
Canby, MN Zip 56220–1433; tel. 507/223–7277; Lori Sisk, R.N., Chief
Executive Officer
Web address: www.sanfordcanby.org

SANFORD JACKSON MEDICAL CENTER (O, 20 beds) 1430 North Highway,
Jackson, MN Zip 56143–1093; tel. 507/847–2420; Mary J. Ruyter, Chief
Executive Officer
Web address: www.sanfordjackson.org

SANFORD LUVERNE MEDICAL CENTER (O, 25 beds) 1600 North Kniss
Avenue, Luverne, MN Zip 56156–1067; tel. 507/283–2321; Tammy
Loosbrock, Chief Executive Officer
Web address: www.sanfordluverne.org

SANFORD THIEF RIVER FALLS MEDICAL CENTER (O, 35 beds) 120 LaBree
Avenue South, Thief River Falls, MN Zip 56701–2840; tel. 218/681–4240;
Brian J. Carlson, FACHE, Chief Executive Officer
Web address: www.sanfordhealth.org

SANFORD TRACY MEDICAL CENTER (L, 25 beds) 251 Fifth Street East,
Tracy, MN Zip 56175–1536; tel. 507/629–3200; Stacy Barstad, Chief
Executive Officer
Web address: www.sanfordtracy.org

SANFORD WESTBROOK MEDICAL CENTER (L, 6 beds) 920 Bell Avenue,
Westbrook, MN Zip 56183–9669, Mailing Address: P.O. Box 188,
Zip 56183–0188; tel. 507/274–6121; Stacy Barstad, Chief Executive Officer
Web address: www.sanfordwestbrook.org

SANFORD WHEATON MEDICAL CENTER (O, 15 beds) 401 12th Street North,
Wheaton, MN Zip 56296–1099; tel. 320/563–8226; JoAnn M. Foltz, R.N.,
Chief Executive Officer
Web address: www.sanfordhealth.org

SANFORD WORTHINGTON MEDICAL CENTER (O, 48 beds) 1018 Sixth
Avenue, Worthington, MN Zip 56187–2202, Mailing Address: P.O. Box 997,
Zip 56187–0997; tel. 507/372–2941; Michael Hammer, Chief Executive
Officer
Web address: www.sanfordhealth.org

WINDOM AREA HOSPITAL (C, 25 beds) 2150 Hospital Drive, Windom, MN
Zip 56101–1287, Mailing Address: P.O. Box 339, Zip 56101–0339;
tel. 507/831–2400; Geraldine F. Burmeister, FACHE, Chief Executive Officer
Web address: www.windomareahospital.com

NORTH DAKOTA: NORTHWOOD DEACONESS HEALTH CENTER (O, 73 beds)
4 North Park Street, Northwood, ND Zip 58267–4102, Mailing Address:
P.O. Box 190, Zip 58267–0190; tel. 701/587–6060; Pete Antonson,
Chief Executive Officer
Web address: www.ndhc.net

SANFORD BISMARCK (O, 208 beds) 300 North Seventh Street, Bismarck, ND
Zip 58501–4439, Mailing Address: P.O. Box 5525, Zip 58506–5525;
tel. 701/323–6000; Craig Lambrecht, M.D., President
Web address: www.bismarck.sanfordhealth.org/

SANFORD HILLSBORO MEDICAL CENTER (C, 52 beds) 12 Third Street S.E.,
Hillsboro, ND Zip 58045–4840, Mailing Address: P.O. Box 609,
Zip 58045–0609; tel. 701/636–3200; Jac McTaggart, Chief Executive
Officer
Web address: www.hillsboromedicalcenter.com

SANFORD MAYVILLE MEDICAL CENTER (O, 18 beds) 42 Sixth Avenue S.E.,
Mayville, ND Zip 58257–1598; tel. 701/786–3800; Roger Baier, Chief
Executive Officer
Web address: www.unionhospital.com

SANFORD MEDICAL CENTER FARGO (O, 492 beds) 801 Broadway North,
Fargo, ND Zip 58122–3641; tel. 701/234–2000; Paul Richard, President and
Chief Executive Officer
Web address: www.sanfordhealth.org

SOUTH DAKOTA: COMMUNITY MEMORIAL HOSPITAL (C, 16 beds) 809
Jackson Street, Burke, SD Zip 57523–2065, Mailing Address: P.O. Box
319, Zip 57523–0319; tel. 605/775–2621; Jim Frank, Chief Executive
Officer
Web address: www.sanfordhealth.org

PIONEER MEMORIAL HOSPITAL AND HEALTH SERVICES (C, 64 beds) 315
North Washington Street, Viborg, SD Zip 57070–2002, Mailing Address: P.O.
Box 368, Zip 57070–0368; tel. 605/326–5161; Thomas V. Richter, Chief
Executive Officer
Web address: www.pioneermemorial.org

SANFORD ABERDEEN MEDICAL CENTER (O, 16 beds) 2905 3rd Avenue S.E.,
Aberdeen, SD Zip 57401–5420; tel. 605/626–4200; Gordon Larson, Chief
Executive Officer
Web address: www.sanfordaberdeen.org/

SANFORD CANTON–INWOOD MEDICAL CENTER (O, 16 beds) 440 North
Hiawatha Drive, Canton, SD Zip 57013–5800; tel. 605/764–1400; Scott C.
Larson, Chief Executive Officer
Web address: www.sanfordcantoninwood.org

SANFORD CHAMBERLAIN MEDICAL CENTER (O, 69 beds) 300 South Byron
Boulevard, Chamberlain, SD Zip 57325–9741; tel. 605/234–5511; Erica
Peterson, Chief Executive Officer and Chief Financial Officer
Web address: www.sanfordmiddakota.org

SANFORD CLEAR LAKE MEDICAL CENTER (L, 10 beds) 701 Third Avenue
South, Clear Lake, SD Zip 57226–2016; tel. 605/874–2141; Lori Sisk, R.N.,
Chief Executive Officer
Web address: www.sanforddeuelcounty.org

SANFORD USD MEDICAL CENTER (O, 511 beds) 1305 West 18th Street,
Sioux Falls, SD Zip 57105–0496, Mailing Address: P.O. Box 5039,
Zip 57117–5039; tel. 605/333–1000; Paul A. Hanson, FACHE, President
Web address: www.sanfordhealth.org

SANFORD VERMILLION MEDICAL CENTER (L, 114 beds) 20 South Plum
Street, Vermillion, SD Zip 57069–3346; tel. 605/624–2611; Timothy J.
Tracy, Chief Executive Officer
Web address: www.sanfordvermillion.org

For explanation of codes following names, see page B2.
★ Indicates Type III membership in the American Hospital Association.

SANFORD WEBSTER MEDICAL CENTER (L, 20 beds) 1401 West 1st Street, Webster, SD Zip 57274–1054, Mailing Address: P.O. Box 489, Zip 57274–0489; tel. 605/345–3336; David Rogers, Chief Executive Officer
Web address: www.sanfordhealth.org

WINNER REGIONAL HEALTHCARE CENTER (C, 104 beds) 745 East Eighth Street, Winner, SD Zip 57580–2631; tel. 605/842–7100; Kevin Coffey, Chief Executive Officer
Web address: www.winnerregional.org

Owned, leased, sponsored:	24 hospitals	2264 beds
Contract–managed:	10 hospitals	603 beds
Totals:	34 hospitals	2867 beds

0412: SCHUYLKILL HEALTH SYSTEM (NP)
420 South Jackson Street, Pottsville, PA Zip 17901–3625; tel. 570/621–5000; Darnell F. Furer, MS, R.N., Acting Administrator
(Independent Hospital System)

PENNSYLVANIA: SCHUYLKILL MEDICAL CENTER – EAST NORWEGIAN STREET (O, 126 beds) 700 East Norwegian Street, Pottsville, PA Zip 17901–2710; tel. 570/621–4000; Darnell F. Furer, MS, R.N., Acting Administrator
Web address: www.schuylkillhealth.com

SCHUYLKILL MEDICAL CENTER – SOUTH JACKSON STREET (O, 190 beds) 420 South Jackson Street, Pottsville, PA Zip 17901–3625; tel. 570/621–5000; Darnell F. Furer, MS, R.N., Acting Administrator
Web address: www.schuylkillhealth.com

Owned, leased, sponsored:	2 hospitals	316 beds
Contract–managed:	0 hospitals	0 beds
Totals:	2 hospitals	316 beds

★5095: SCL HEALTH SYSTEM (CC)
2420 West 26th Avenue, Suite 100D, Denver, CO Zip 80211–5302; tel. 303/813–5180; Michael A. Slubowski, FACHE, Chief Executive Officer
(Moderately Centralized Health System)

COLORADO: EXEMPLA GOOD SAMARITAN MEDICAL CENTER (S, 192 beds) 200 Exempla Circle, Lafayette, CO Zip 80026–3370; tel. 303/689–4000; David Hamm, President and Chief Executive Officer
Web address: www.exempla.org

EXEMPLA SAINT JOSEPH HOSPITAL (S, 369 beds) 1835 Franklin Street, Denver, CO Zip 80218–1126; tel. 303/837–7111; Bain J. Farris, President and Chief Executive Officer
Web address: www.exempla.org

LUTHERAN MEDICAL CENTER (S, 475 beds) 8300 West 38th Avenue, Wheat Ridge, CO Zip 80033–6005; tel. 303/425–4500; Grant Wicklund, President and Chief Executive Officer
Web address: www.exempla.org

ST. MARY'S HOSPITAL AND REGIONAL MEDICAL CENTER (O, 346 beds) 2635 North 7th Street, Grand Junction, CO Zip 81501–8209, Mailing Address: P.O. Box 1628, Zip 81502–1628; tel. 970/298–2273; Michael J. McBride, FACHE, President and Chief Executive Officer
Web address: www.stmarygj.com

KANSAS: ST. FRANCIS HEALTH CENTER (O, 274 beds) 1700 S.W. 7th Street, Topeka, KS Zip 66606–1690; tel. 785/295–8000; Robert J. Erickson, Chief Executive Officer
Web address: www.stfrancistopeka.org

MONTANA: HOLY ROSARY HEALTHCARE (O, 90 beds) 2600 Wilson Street, Miles City, MT Zip 59301–5094; tel. 406/233–2600; Paul Lewis, Chief Executive Officer
Web address: www.holyrosaryhealthcare.org

ST. JAMES HEALTHCARE (O, 56 beds) 400 South Clark Street, Butte, MT Zip 59701–2328; tel. 406/723–2500; Charles T. Wright, President and Chief Executive Officer
Web address: www.stjameshealthcare.org

ST. VINCENT HEALTHCARE (O, 249 beds) 1233 North 30th Street, Billings, MT Zip 59101–0165, Mailing Address: P.O. Box 35200, Zip 59107–5200; tel. 406/237–7000; Steve Loveless, Acting President and Chief Executive Officer
Web address: www.svh–mt.org

Owned, leased, sponsored:	8 hospitals	2051 beds
Contract–managed:	0 hospitals	0 beds
Totals:	8 hospitals	2051 beds

★0037: SCOTTSDALE HEALTHCARE (NP)
8125 North Hayden Road, Scottsdale, AZ Zip 85258–2463; tel. 480/882–4000; Thomas J. Sadvary, FACHE, President and Chief Executive Officer
(Independent Hospital System)

ARIZONA: SCOTTSDALE HEALTHCARE SHEA MEDICAL CENTER (O, 409 beds) 9003 East Shea Boulevard, Scottsdale, AZ Zip 85260–6771; tel. 480/323–3000; Gary E. Baker, Senior Vice President and Chief Executive Officer
Web address: www.shc.org

SCOTTSDALE HEALTHCARE THOMPSON PEAK HOSPITAL (O, 64 beds) 7400 East Thompson Peak Parkway, Scottsdale, AZ Zip 85255–4109; tel. 480/324–7000; Kimberly Post, R.N., Vice President and Administrator
Web address: www.shc.org

SCOTTSDALE HEALTHCARE–OSBORN MEDICAL CENTER (O, 347 beds) 7400 East Osborn Road, Scottsdale, AZ Zip 85251–6403; tel. 480/882–4000; Gary E. Baker, Senior Vice President and Administrator
Web address: www.shc.org

Owned, leased, sponsored:	3 hospitals	820 beds
Contract–managed:	0 hospitals	0 beds
Totals:	3 hospitals	820 beds

★1505: SCRIPPS HEALTH (NP)
4275 Campus Point Court, San Diego, CA Zip 92121–1513; tel. 858/678–7200; Chris D. Van Gorder, FACHE, President and Chief Executive Officer
(Centralized Health System)

CALIFORNIA: SCRIPPS GREEN HOSPITAL (O, 173 beds) 10666 North Torrey Pines Road, La Jolla, CA Zip 92037–1093; tel. 858/455–9100; Robin Brown, Chief Executive, Senior Vice President
Web address: www.scrippshealth.org

SCRIPPS MEMORIAL HOSPITAL–ENCINITAS (O, 158 beds) 354 Santa Fe Drive, Encinitas, CA Zip 92024–5182, Mailing Address: P.O. Box 230817, Zip 92023–0817; tel. 760/633–6501; Chris D. Van Gorder, FACHE, President and Chief Executive Officer
Web address: www.scripps.org

SCRIPPS MEMORIAL HOSPITAL–LA JOLLA (O, 285 beds) 9888 Genesee Avenue, La Jolla, CA Zip 92037–1200, Mailing Address: P.O. Box 28, Zip 92038–0028; tel. 858/626–4123; Gary G. Fybel, Chief Executive, Senior Vice President
Web address: www.scripps.org/locations/hospitals__ scripps–memorial–hospital–la–jolla

SCRIPPS MERCY HOSPITAL (O, 436 beds) 4077 Fifth Avenue, San Diego, CA Zip 92103–2105; tel. 619/294–8111; Thomas A. Gammiere, Chief Executive, Senior Vice President
Web address: www.scrippshealth.org

Owned, leased, sponsored:	4 hospitals	1052 beds
Contract–managed:	0 hospitals	0 beds
Totals:	4 hospitals	1052 beds

★0181: SELECT MEDICAL CORPORATION (IO)
4714 Gettysburg Road, Mechanicsburg, PA Zip 17055–4325; tel. 717/972–1100; David S. Chernow, President and Chief Executive Officer
(Independent Hospital System)

ALABAMA: SELECT SPECIALTY HOSPITAL–BIRMINGHAM (O, 38 beds) 800 Montclair Road, 9th Floor, Birmingham, AL Zip 35213–1908; tel. 205/599–4600; Andrea White, Chief Executive Officer
Web address: www.selectspecialtyhospitals. com/company/locations/birmingham.aspx

For explanation of codes following names, see page B2.
★ Indicates Type III membership in the American Hospital Association.

Section B

ARIZONA: SCOTTSDALE HEALTHCARE REHABILITATION HOSPITAL (O, 50 beds) 8850 East Pima Center Parkway, Scottsdale, AZ Zip 85258–4619; tel. 480/800–3900; Kelly Silberschlag, Chief Executive Officer
Web address: www.scottsdale–rehab.com/

SELECT SPECIALTY HOSPITAL–PHOENIX (O, 48 beds) 350 West Thomas Road, 3rd Floor Main, Phoenix, AZ Zip 85013–4409; tel. 602/406–6802; Sharon Anthony, Chief Executive Officer
Web address: www.selectspecialtyhospitals. com/company/locations/phoenix.aspx

SELECT SPECIALTY HOSPITAL–SCOTTSDALE (O, 62 beds) 7400 East Osborn Road, 3 West, Scottsdale, AZ Zip 85251–6432; tel. 480/882–4360; Anthony Martino, Chief Executive Officer
Web address: www.selectspecialtyhospitals. com/company/locations/scottsdale.aspx

ARKANSAS: REGENCY HOSPITAL OF NORTHWEST ARKANSAS (O, 50 beds) 1125 North College Avenue, Fayetteville, AR Zip 72703–1908; tel. 479/338–2360; Jerry Alexander, Chief Executive Officer
Web address: www.regencyhospital.com

SELECT SPECIALTY HOSPITAL–FORT SMITH (O, 34 beds) 1001 Towson Avenue, 6 Central, Fort Smith, AR Zip 72901–4921; tel. 479/441–3960; Cindy McLain, Chief Executive Officer
Web address: www.selectspecialtyhospitals. com/company/locations/fortsmith.aspx

COLORADO: SELECT LONG TERM CARE HOSPITAL – COLORADO SPRINGS (O, 30 beds) 6001 East Woodmen Road, 6th Floor, Colorado Springs, CO Zip 80923–2601; tel. 719/571–6000; Kent Helwig, Chief Executive Officer
Web address: www.selectmedical.com

SELECT SPECIALTY HOSPITAL–DENVER (O, 65 beds) 1719 East 19th Avenue, 5B, Denver, CO Zip 80218–1235; tel. 303/563–3700; George Welton, Chief Executive Officer
Web address: www.selectspecialtyhospitals.com/company/locations/denver. aspx

DELAWARE: SELECT SPECIALTY HOSPITAL–WILMINGTON (O, 35 beds) 701 North Clayton Street, 5th Floor, Wilmington, DE Zip 19805–3948; tel. 302/421–4545; Sharon Rosetti, R.N., Chief Executive Officer
Web address: www.selectspecialtyhospitals. com/company/locations/wilmington.aspx

FLORIDA: SELECT SPECIALTY HOSPITAL–GAINESVILLE (O, 44 beds) 2708 S.W. Archer Road, Gainesville, FL Zip 32608–1316; tel. 352/337–3240; Cheryl Hayes, Chief Executive Officer
Web address: www.selectspecialtyhospitals. com/company/locations/gainesville.aspx

SELECT SPECIALTY HOSPITAL–MIAMI (O, 40 beds) 955 N.W. 3rd Street, Miami, FL Zip 33128–1274; tel. 305/416–5700; Dionisio Bencomo, Chief Executive Officer
Web address: www.selectspecialtyhospitals.com/company/locations/miami. aspx

SELECT SPECIALTY HOSPITAL–ORLANDO (O, 75 beds) 2250 Bedford Road, Orlando, FL Zip 32803–1443; tel. 407/303–7869; Nellie Castroman, Chief Executive Officer
Web address: www.selectspecialtyhospitals. com/company/locations/orlando.aspx

SELECT SPECIALTY HOSPITAL–PALM BEACH (O, 60 beds) 3060 Melaleuca Lane, Lake Worth, FL Zip 33461–5174; tel. 561/357–7200; Larry Melby, Chief Executive Officer
Web address: www.selectspecialtyhospitals. com/company/locations/palmbeach.aspx

SELECT SPECIALTY HOSPITAL–PANAMA CITY (O, 30 beds) 615 North Bonita Avenue, 3rd Floor, Panama City, FL Zip 32401–3623; tel. 850/767–3180; Randal S. Hamilton, Chief Executive Officer
Web address: www.selectspecialtyhospitals. com/company/locations/panamacity.aspx

SELECT SPECIALTY HOSPITAL–PENSACOLA (O, 54 beds) 7000 Cobble Creek Drive, Pensacola, FL Zip 32504–8638; tel. 850/473–4800; David Goodson, Chief Executive Officer
Web address: www.selectspecialtyhospitals. com/company/locations/pensacola.aspx

SELECT SPECIALTY HOSPITAL–TALLAHASSEE (O, 29 beds) 1554 Surgeons Drive, Tallahassee, FL Zip 32308–4631; tel. 850/219–6800; Lora Davis, Chief Executive Officer
Web address: www.tallahassee.selectspecialtyhospitals.com/

WEST GABLES REHABILITATION HOSPITAL (O, 60 beds) 2525 S.W. 75th Avenue, Miami, FL Zip 33155–2800; tel. 305/262–6800; Walter Concepcion, Chief Executive Officer
Web address: www.westgablesrehabhospital.com/

GEORGIA: REGENCY HOSPITAL OF CENTRAL GEORGIA (O, 34 beds) 535 Coliseum Drive, Macon, GA Zip 31217–0104; tel. 478/803–7300; Michael S. Boggs, Chief Executive Officer
Web address: www.regencyhospital.com

REGENCY HOSPITAL OF SOUTH ATLANTA (O, 40 beds) 1170 Cleveland Avenue, 4th Floor, East Point, GA Zip 30344–3615; tel. 404/466–6250; Yameeka Jones, Chief Executive Officer
Web address: www.regencyhospital.com

SELECT SPECIALTY HOSPITAL – NORTHEAST ATLANTA (O, 18 beds) 1821 Clifton Road N.E., 2nd Floor, Atlanta, GA Zip 30329–4021; tel. 404/728–6200; Matthew Paul Pearson, Chief Executive Officer
Web address: www.selectspecialtyhospitals.com/

SELECT SPECIALTY HOSPITAL–ATLANTA (O, 30 beds) 550 Peachtree Street N.E., Atlanta, GA Zip 30308–2247; tel. 404/815–0348; Dwayne Hooks, Jr., R.N., Chief Executive Officer
Web address: www.selectspecialtyhospitals.com/company/locations/atlanta. aspx

SELECT SPECIALTY HOSPITAL–AUGUSTA (O, 80 beds) 1537 Walton Way, Augusta, GA Zip 30904–3764; tel. 706/731–1200; Curtis L. Roberts, Chief Executive Officer
Web address: www.augusta.selectspecialtyhospitals.com

SELECT SPECIALTY HOSPITAL–SAVANNAH (O, 36 beds) 5353 Reynolds Street, 4 South, Savannah, GA Zip 31405–6015; tel. 912/819–7972; James H. Rogers, FACHE, Chief Executive Officer
Web address: www.selectspecialtyhospitals. com/company/locations/savannah.aspx

INDIANA: REGENCY HOSPITAL OF NORTHWEST INDIANA (O, 25 beds) 4321 Fir Street, 4th Floor, East Chicago, IN Zip 46312–3049; tel. 219/392–7790; Coleen Zimmerman, Chief Executive Officer
Web address: www.regencyhospital. com/company/locations/indiana–northwest–indiana.aspx

SELECT SPECIALTY HOSPITAL–EVANSVILLE (O, 60 beds) 400 S.E. 4th Street, Evansville, IN Zip 47713–1206; tel. 812/421–2500; Mike Carney, Chief Executive Officer
Web address: www.selectspecialtyhospitals. com/company/locations/evansville.aspx

SELECT SPECIALTY HOSPITAL–FORT WAYNE (O, 32 beds) 700 Broadway, 7th Floor, Fort Wayne, IN Zip 46802–1402; tel. 260/425–3810; Robert C. Marquardt, FACHE, Chief Executive Officer
Web address: www.fortwayne.selectspecialtyhospitals.com

SELECT SPECIALTY HOSPITAL–INDIANAPOLIS (O, 45 beds) 8060 Knue Road, Indianapolis, IN Zip 46250–1976; tel. 317/783–8985; Cheryl G. Gentry, Chief Executive Officer
Web address: www.selectspecialtyhospitals. com/company/locations/indianapolis.aspx

IOWA: SELECT SPECIALTY HOSPITAL–QUAD CITIES (O, 50 beds) 1111 West Kimberly Road, Davenport, IA Zip 52806–5711; tel. 563/468–2000; Austin B. Cleveland, Chief Executive Officer
Web address: www.selectspecialtyhospitals. com/company/locations/quadcities.aspx

KANSAS: SELECT SPECIALTY HOSPITAL–KANSAS CITY (O, 40 beds) 1731 North 90th Street, Kansas City, KS Zip 66112–1515; tel. 913/732–5900; Matthew H. Blevins, Chief Executive Officer
Web address: www.selectspecialtyhospitals.com

SELECT SPECIALTY HOSPITAL–TOPEKA (O, 34 beds) 1700 S.W. Seventh Street, Suite 840, Topeka, KS Zip 66606–1660; tel. 785/295–5551; Linda Sherman, Chief Executive Officer
Web address: www.selectspecialtyhospitals.com/company/locations/topeka. aspx

SELECT SPECIALTY HOSPITAL–WICHITA (O, 58 beds) 929 North St. Francis Street, Wichita, KS Zip 67214–3821; tel. 316/261–8303; Peggy Cliffe, Chief Executive Officer
Web address: www.selectspecialtyhospitals.com/company/locations/wichita. aspx

KENTUCKY: SELECT SPECIALTY HOSPITAL–LEXINGTON (O, 41 beds) 310 South Limestone Street, 3rd Floor, Lexington, KY Zip 40508–3008; tel. 859/226–7096; Mary Lou Guinle, FACHE, Chief Executive Officer
Web address: www.lexington.selectspecialtyhospitals.com/

For explanation of codes following names, see page B2.
★ Indicates Type III membership in the American Hospital Association.

SELECT SPECIALTY HOSPITAL–NORTHERN KENTUCKY (O, 33 beds) 85 North Grand Avenue, Fort Thomas, KY Zip 41075–1793; tel. 859/572–3880; Victor J. Galfano, FACHE, Chief Executive Officer
Web address: www.selectspecialtyhospitals. com/company/locations/northern–kentucky.aspx

LOUISIANA: REGENCY HOSPITAL OF COVINGTON (O, 38 beds) 195 Highland Park Entrance, Covington, LA Zip 70433–7164; tel. 985/867–3977; Kiley P. Cedotal, Chief Executive Officer
Web address: www.regencyhospital.com

MICHIGAN: GREAT LAKES SPECIALTY HOSPITAL–GRAND RAPIDS CAMPUS (O, 20 beds) 200 S.E. Jefferson Avenue, 5th Floor, Grand Rapids, MI Zip 49503–4502; tel. 616/965–8650; Brian Pangle, Chief Executive Officer
Web address: www.selectmedicalcorp.com

GREAT LAKES SPECIALTY HOSPITAL–MUSKEGON (O, 31 beds) 1700 Clinton Street, 3 South, Muskegon, MI Zip 49442–5502; tel. 231/728–5811; Mark Holcomb, Administrator
Web address: www.greatlakesspecialtyhospital.com

SELECT SPECIALTY HOSPITAL–ANN ARBOR (O, 36 beds) 5301 East Huron River Drive, 7th Floor, Ypsilanti, MI Zip 48197–1051; tel. 734/712–0111; John F. O'Malley, FACHE, Chief Executive Officer
Web address: www.selectspecialtyhospitals. com/company/locations/annarbor.aspx

SELECT SPECIALTY HOSPITAL–BATTLE CREEK (O, 25 beds) 300 North Avenue, Battle Creek, MI Zip 49017–3307; tel. 269/245–4675; Salvatore Iweimrin, R.N., Chief Executive Officer
Web address: www.selectspecialtyhospitals. com/company/locations/battlecreek.aspx

SELECT SPECIALTY HOSPITAL–DOWNRIVER (O, 40 beds) 2333 Biddle Avenue, 8th Floor, Wyandotte, MI Zip 48192–4668; tel. 734/246–5500; Miriam Deemer, Interim Chief Executive Officer
Web address: www.downriver.selectspecialtyhospitals.com/

SELECT SPECIALTY HOSPITAL–FLINT (O, 26 beds) 401 South Ballenger Highway, 5th Floor Central, Flint, MI Zip 48532–3638; tel. 810/342–4500; Patricia Adams, Chief Executive Officer
Web address: www.selectspecialtyhospitals.com/company/locations/flint. aspx

SELECT SPECIALTY HOSPITAL–GROSSE POINTE (O, 30 beds) 468 Cadieux Road, 3 North East, Grosse Pointe, MI Zip 48230–1507; tel. 313/473–6131; Miriam Deemer, Chief Executive Officer
Web address: www.grossepointe.selectspecialtyhospitals.com/

SELECT SPECIALTY HOSPITAL–MACOMB COUNTY (O, 36 beds) 215 North Avenue, Mount Clemens, MI Zip 48043–1700; tel. 586/307–9000; Jon P. O'Malley, Chief Executive Officer
Web address: www.macomb.selectspecialtyhospitals.com/

SELECT SPECIALTY HOSPITAL–NORTHWEST DETROIT (O, 36 beds) 6071 West Outer Drive, Detroit, MI Zip 48235–2624; tel. 313/966–4747; Marilouise Riska, Chief Executive Officer
Web address: www.selectspecialtyhospitals. com/company/locations/northwestdetroit.aspx

SELECT SPECIALTY HOSPITAL–PONTIAC (O, 30 beds) 44405 Woodward Avenue, 8th Floor, Pontiac, MI Zip 48341–5023; tel. 248/452–5252; Peggy Kingston, Chief Executive Officer
Web address: www.selectspecialtyhospitals. com/company/locations/pontiac.aspx

SELECT SPECIALTY HOSPITAL–SAGINAW (O, 32 beds) 1447 North Harrison Street, 8th Floor, Saginaw, MI Zip 48602–4785; tel. 989/583–4235; Matthew Cannon, Chief Executive Officer
Web address: www.selectspecialtyhospitals. com/company/locations/saginaw.aspx

MINNESOTA: REGENCY HOSPITAL OF MINNEAPOLIS (O, 64 beds) 1300 Hidden Lakes Parkway, Golden Valley, MN Zip 55422–4286; tel. 763/588–2750; John P. Allen, Chief Executive Officer
Web address: www.regencyhospital.com

MISSISSIPPI: REGENCY HOSPITAL OF HATTIESBURG (O, 33 beds) 6051 U.S. Highway 495, 5th Floor, Hattiesburg, MS Zip 39401–6031; tel. 601/288–8510; Kathy A. Viator, R.N., Chief Executive Officer
Web address: www.regencyhospital.com/hattiesburg

REGENCY HOSPITAL OF JACKSON (O, 36 beds) 969 Lakeland Drive, 6th Floor, Jackson, MS Zip 39216–4643; tel. 601/364–6200; Lorie Powell, Interim Chief Executive Officer
Web address: www.regencyhospital.com

REGENCY HOSPITAL OF MERIDIAN (O, 40 beds) 1102 Constitution Avenue, 2nd Floor, Meridian, MS Zip 39301–4001; tel. 601/484–7900; Clifton Quinn, Chief Executive Officer
Web address: www.regencyhospital.com

SELECT SPECIALTY HOSPITAL–GULF COAST (O, 61 beds) 1520 Broad Avenue, Suite 300, Gulfport, MS Zip 39501–3601; tel. 228/575–7500; John O'Keefe, Chief Executive Officer
Web address: www.selectspecialtyhospitals. com/company/locations/gulfcoast.aspx

SELECT SPECIALTY HOSPITAL–JACKSON (O, 53 beds) 5903 Ridgewood Road, Suite 100, Jackson, MS Zip 39211–3700; tel. 601/899–3800; Chandler Ewing, Chief Executive Officer
Web address: www.selectspecialtyhospitals. com/company/locations/jackson.aspx

MISSOURI: SELECT SPECIALTY HOSPITAL–SPRINGFIELD (O, 44 beds) 1630 East Primrose Street, Springfield, MO Zip 65804–7929; tel. 417/885–4700; Julie De Jean, Chief Executive Officer
Web address: www.selectspecialtyhospitals. com/company/locations/springfield.aspx

SELECT SPECIALTY HOSPITAL–ST. LOUIS (O, 33 beds) 300 First Capitol Drive, Unit 1, Saint Charles, MO Zip 63301–2844; tel. 636/947–5010; Patrice L. Komoroski, Ph.D., R.N., Chief Executive Officer
Web address: www.selectspecialtyhospitals.com/company/locations/stlouis. aspx

SELECT SPECIALTY HOSPITAL–WESTERN MISSOURI (O, 34 beds) 2316 East Meyer Boulevard, 3 West, Kansas City, MO Zip 64132–1136; tel. 816/276–3300; Jeffrey Alexander, Chief Executive Officer
Web address: www.selectspecialtyhospitals. com/company/locations/westernmissouri.aspx

SSM SELECT REHABILITATION HOSPITAL (O, 95 beds) 1027 Bellevue Avenue, 3rd Floor, Richmond Heights, MO Zip 63117–1851, Mailing Address: 1027 Bellevue Avenue, Zip 63117–1851; tel. 314/768–5300; Timothy Wadman, Chief Executive Officer
Web address: www.ssm–select.com

NEBRASKA: SELECT SPECIALTY HOSPITAL–OMAHA (O, 52 beds) 1870 South 75th Street, Omaha, NE Zip 68124–1700; tel. 402/361–5700; Thomas N. Theroult, Chief Executive Officer
Web address: www.selectspecialtyhospitals. com/company/locations/omahacentral.aspx

NEW JERSEY: KESSLER INSTITUTE FOR REHABILITATION (O, 336 beds) 1199 Pleasant Valley Way, West Orange, NJ Zip 07052–1424; tel. 973/731–3600; Robert Brehm, Division President
Web address: www.kessler–rehab.com

SELECT SPECIALTY HOSPITAL–NORTHEAST NEW JERSEY (O, 59 beds) 96 Parkway, Rochelle Park, NJ Zip 07662–4200; tel. 201/221–2358; Barbara E. Hannan, MS, R.N., Chief Executive Officer
Web address: www.selectspecialtyhospitals. com/company/locations/northeastnewjersey.aspx

NORTH CAROLINA: SELECT SPECIALTY HOSPITAL–DURHAM (O, 30 beds) 3643 North Roxboro Road, 6th Floor, Durham, NC Zip 27704–2702; tel. 919/470–9137; Robert F. Jernigan, Jr., Chief Executive Officer
Web address: www.selectspecialtyhospitals. com/company/locations/durham.aspx

SELECT SPECIALTY HOSPITAL–GREENSBORO (O, 30 beds) 1200 North Elm Street, 5th Floor, Greensboro, NC Zip 27401–1004; tel. 336/832–8571; Deana Knight, Chief Executive Officer
Web address: www.selectspecialtyhospitals. com/company/locations/greensboro.aspx

SELECT SPECIALTY HOSPITAL–WINSTON–SALEM (O, 42 beds) 3333 Silas Creek Parkway, 6th Floor, Winston–Salem, NC Zip 27103–3013; tel. 336/718–6300; Leslie Deane, Chief Executive Officer
Web address: www.selectspecialtyhospitals. com/company/locations/winston-salem.aspx

OHIO: OHIOHEALTH REHABILITATION HOSPITAL (O, 144 beds) 1087 Dennison Avenue, 4th Floor, Columbus, OH Zip 43201–3201; tel. 614/484–9700; Eric Yap, Chief Executive Officer
Web address: www.ohiohealth–rehab.com

REGENCY HOSPITAL CLEVELAND EAST (O, 44 beds) 4200 Interchange Corporate Center Road, Warrensville Heights, OH Zip 44128–5631; tel. 216/910–3800; Scott Williams, Chief Executive Officer
Web address: www.regencyhospital.com/

For explanation of codes following names, see page B2.
★ Indicates Type III membership in the American Hospital Association.

REGENCY HOSPITAL OF COLUMBUS (O, 43 beds) 1430 South High Street, Columbus, OH Zip 43207–1045; tel. 614/456–0300; Lisa J. Pettrey, MSN, R.N., Chief Executive Officer
Web address: www.regencyhospital.com/

REGENCY HOSPITAL OF TOLEDO (O, 35 beds) 5220 Alexis Road, Sylvania, OH Zip 43560–2504; tel. 419/318–5700; Diana D. Fisher, Chief Executive Officer
Web address: www.regencyhospital.com

SELECT SPECIALTY HOSPITAL – CINCINNATI NORTH (O, 25 beds) 10500 Montgomery Road, Cincinnati, OH Zip 45242–4402; tel. 513/865–5300; Mark S. Brodeur, FACHE, Chief Executive Officer
Web address: www.cincinnatinorth.selectspecialtyhospitals.com/

SELECT SPECIALTY HOSPITAL–AKRON (O, 60 beds) 200 East Market Street, Akron, OH Zip 44308–2015; tel. 330/761–7500; Sonda Burns, Chief Executive Officer
Web address: www.selectspecialtyhospitals.com/company/locations/akron.aspx

SELECT SPECIALTY HOSPITAL–CANTON (O, 30 beds) 1320 Mercy Drive N.W., 6th Floor, Canton, OH Zip 44708–2614; tel. 330/489–8189; Dawne Wheeler, Chief Executive Officer
Web address: www.selectspecialtyhospitals.com/company/locations/canton.aspx

SELECT SPECIALTY HOSPITAL–CINCINNATI (O, 35 beds) 375 Dixmyth Avenue, 15th Floor, Cincinnati, OH Zip 45220–2475; tel. 513/872–4444; Curtis Ohashi, Chief Executive Officer
Web address: www.selectspecialtyhospitals.com/company/locations/cincinnati.aspx

SELECT SPECIALTY HOSPITAL–COLUMBUS (O, 176 beds) 1087 Dennison Avenue, Columbus, OH Zip 43201–3201; tel. 614/458–9000; John C. Yanes, Chief Executive Officer
Web address: www.selectspecialtyhospitals.com/company/locations/columbus.aspx

SELECT SPECIALTY HOSPITAL–YOUNGSTOWN (O, 51 beds) 1044 Belmont Avenue, Youngstown, OH Zip 44504–1006; tel. 330/480–2349; Sharon Noro, Chief Executive Officer
Web address: www.selectspecialtyhospitals.com/company/locations/youngstown.aspx

SELECT SPECIALTY HOSPITAL–ZANESVILLE (O, 35 beds) 800 Forest Avenue, 6th Floor, Zanesville, OH Zip 43701–2882; tel. 740/588–7888; Linda Supplee, Chief Executive Officer
Web address: www.selectspecialtyhospitals.com/company/locations/zanesville.aspx

OKLAHOMA: SELECT SPECIALTY HOSPITAL–OKLAHOMA CITY (O, 72 beds) 3524 N.W. 56th Street, Oklahoma City, OK Zip 73112–4518; tel. 405/606–6700; Connie Strickland, Chief Executive Officer
Web address: www.selectspecialtyhospitals.com/company/locations/oklahomacity.aspx

SELECT SPECIALTY HOSPITAL–TULSA MIDTOWN (O, 56 beds) 1125 South Trenton Avenue, 3rd Floor, Tulsa, OK Zip 74120–5418; tel. 918/579–7300; Linda Tiemens, Chief Executive Officer
Web address: www.selectmedical.com

PENNSYLVANIA: PENN STATE HERSHEY REHABILITATION HOSPITAL (O, 32 beds) 1135 Old West Chocolate Avenue, Hummelstown, PA Zip 17036; tel. 717/832–2600; Scott Guevin, Chief Executive Officer
Web address: www.psh–rehab.com

SELECT SPECIALTY HOSPITAL–CENTRAL PENNSYLVANIA (O, 54 beds) 503 North 21st Street, 5th Floor, Camp Hill, PA Zip 17011–2204; tel. 717/972–4575; Tom Mullin, Chief Executive Officer
Web address: www.selectspecialtyhospitals.com/company/locations/camphill.aspx

SELECT SPECIALTY HOSPITAL–DANVILLE (O, 30 beds) 100 North Academy Avenue, 3rd Floor, Danville, PA Zip 17822–3050; tel. 570/214–9653; Brian Mann, Chief Executive Officer
Web address: www.selectspecialtyhospitals.com/company/locations/danville.aspx

SELECT SPECIALTY HOSPITAL–ERIE (O, 50 beds) 252 West 11th Street, Erie, PA Zip 16501–1702; tel. 814/874–5300; Randy Neiswonger, Chief Executive Officer
Web address: www.erie.selectspecialtyhospitals.com/

SELECT SPECIALTY HOSPITAL–JOHNSTOWN (O, 39 beds) 320 Main Street, 3rd Floor, Johnstown, PA Zip 15901–1601; tel. 814/534–7300; Kelly Blake, Chief Executive Officer
Web address: www.selectspecialtyhospitals.com/company/locations/johnstown.aspx

SELECT SPECIALTY HOSPITAL–LAUREL HIGHLANDS (O, 40 beds) One Mellon Way, 3rd Floor, Latrobe, PA Zip 15650–1197; tel. 724/539–3230; Laurie Kozorosky, Chief Executive Officer
Web address: www.selectspecialtyhospitals.com/company/locations/laurelhighlands.aspx

SELECT SPECIALTY HOSPITAL–MCKEESPORT (O, 30 beds) 1500 Fifth Avenue, 6th Floor, McKeesport, PA Zip 15132–2422; tel. 412/664–2900; Jeffrey Gorddard, Chief Executive Officer
Web address: www.selectspecialtyhospitals.com/company/locations/mckeesport.aspx

SELECT SPECIALTY HOSPITAL–PITTSBURGH/UPMC (O, 32 beds) 200 Lothrop Street, E824, Pittsburgh, PA Zip 15213–2536; tel. 412/586–9800; John St. Leger, Chief Executive Officer
Web address: www.selectspecialtyhospitals.com/company/locations/pittsburghupmc.aspx

SOUTH CAROLINA: REGENCY HOSPITAL OF FLORENCE (O, 40 beds) 121 East Cedar Street, 4th Floor, Florence, SC Zip 29506–2576; tel. 843/661–3471; Amy Metz, Chief Executive Officer
Web address: www.regencyhospital.com

REGENCY HOSPITAL OF GREENVILLE (O, 32 beds) One St. Francis Drive, 4th Floor, Greenville, SC Zip 29601–3955; tel. 864/255–1438; Stephanie James, Chief Executive Officer
Web address: www.regencyhospital.com

SOUTH DAKOTA: SELECT SPECIALTY HOSPITAL–SIOUX FALLS (O, 21 beds) 1305 West 18th Street, Sioux Falls, SD Zip 57105–0401; tel. 605/322–3500; Carol Ulmer, Chief Executive Officer
Web address: www.selectspecialtyhospitals.com/company/locations/siouxfalls.aspx

TENNESSEE: SELECT SPECIALTY HOSPITAL–KNOXVILLE (O, 35 beds) 1901 Clinch Avenue, 4th Floor North, Knoxville, TN Zip 37916–2307; tel. 865/541–2615; Vanda Scott, M.D., Chief Executive Officer
Web address: www.knoxville.selectspecialtyhospitals.com/

SELECT SPECIALTY HOSPITAL–MEMPHIS (O, 38 beds) 5959 Park Avenue, 12th Floor, Memphis, TN Zip 38119–5200; tel. 901/765–1245; Mark E. Kimball, Chief Executive Officer
Web address: www.selectspecialtyhospitals.com/company/locations/memphis.aspx

SELECT SPECIALTY HOSPITAL–NASHVILLE (O, 47 beds) 2000 Hayes Street, Nashville, TN Zip 37203–2318; tel. 615/284–4599; Jennifer Causey, Chief Executive Officer
Web address: www.selectspecialtyhospitals.com/company/locations/nashville.aspx

SELECT SPECIALTY HOSPITAL–NORTH KNOXVILLE (O, 33 beds) 900 East Oak Hill Avenue, 4th Floor, Knoxville, TN Zip 37917–4505; tel. 865/545–7350; Steve Plumlee, Chief Executive Officer
Web address: www.northknoxville.selectspecialtyhospitals.com/

SELECT SPECIALTY HOSPITAL–TRI CITIES (O, 33 beds) One Medical Park Boulevard, 5th Floor, Bristol, TN Zip 37620–8964; tel. 423/844–5900; Eric Carroll, Chief Executive Officer
Web address: www.selectspecialtyhospitals.com/company/locations/tricities.aspx

TEXAS: BAYLOR INSTITUTE FOR REHABILITATION AT FRISCO (O, 44 beds) 2990 Legacy Drive, Frisco, TX Zip 75034–6066; tel. 469/888–5100; Mark D. Boles, Chief Executive Officer
Web address: www.baylorhealth.com/bir

REGENCY HOSPITAL OF FORT WORTH (O, 44 beds) 6801 Oakmont Boulevard, Fort Worth, TX Zip 76132–3918; tel. 817/840–2500; Natalie D. Lamberton, Chief Executive Officer
Web address: www.regencyhospital.com

SELECT REHABILITATION HOSPITAL OF DENTON (O, 44 beds) 2620 Scripture Street, Denton, TX Zip 76201–4315; tel. 940/297–6500; Michelle Powell, Chief Executive Officer
Web address: www.selectrehab–denton.com/

For explanation of codes following names, see page B2.
★ Indicates Type III membership in the American Hospital Association.

SELECT SPECIALTY HOSPITAL–DALLAS (O, 60 beds) 2329 West Parker Road, Carrollton, TX Zip 75010–4713; tel. 469/892–1400; Barbara Mobley, Chief Executive Officer
Web address: www.selectspecialtyhospitals.com/company/locations/dallas.aspx

SELECT SPECIALTY HOSPITAL–HOUSTON HEIGHTS (O, 182 beds) 1917 Ashland Street, Houston, TX Zip 77008–3994; tel. 713/861–6161; Naman Mahajan, Chief Operating Officer
Web address: www.selectspecialtyhospitals.com/company/locations/houstonheights.aspx

SELECT SPECIALTY HOSPITAL–LONGVIEW (O, 32 beds) 700 East Marshall Avenue, 1st Floor, Longview, TX Zip 75601–5580; tel. 903/315–1100; Dennis Baker, Chief Executive Officer
Web address: www.selectspecialtyhospitals.com/company/locations/longview.aspx

SELECT SPECIALTY HOSPITAL–SAN ANTONIO (O, 44 beds) 111 Dallas Street, 4th Floor, San Antonio, TX Zip 78205–1201; tel. 210/297–7185; Sean Stricker, Chief Executive Officer
Web address: www.selectspecialtyhospitals.com/company/locations/sanantonio.aspx

SELECT SPECIALTY HOSPITAL–SOUTH DALLAS (O, 69 beds) 3500 West Wheatland Road, 4th Floor, Dallas, TX Zip 75237–3460; tel. 972/780–6500; Richard Knowland, Chief Executive Officer
Web address: www.selectspecialtyhospitals.com/company/locations/southdallas.aspx

WEST VIRGINIA: SELECT SPECIALTY HOSPITAL–CHARLESTON (O, 32 beds) 333 Laidley Street, 3rd Floor East, Charleston, WV Zip 25301–1614; tel. 304/720–7234; Frank Weber, Chief Executive Officer
Web address: www.selectspecialtyhospitals.com/company/locations/charleston.aspx

WISCONSIN: SELECT SPECIALTY HOSPITAL–MADISON (O, 58 beds) 801 Braxton Place, 2nd Floor, Madison, WI Zip 53715–1415; tel. 608/260–2700; Raymond F. Carnevale, Chief Executive Officer
Web address: www.madison.selectspecialtyhospitals.com

SELECT SPECIALTY HOSPITAL–MILWAUKEE (O, 34 beds) 8901 West Lincoln Avenue, 2nd Floor, Milwaukee, WI Zip 53227–2409; tel. 414/328–7700; Richard Keddington, Chief Executive Officer
Web address: www.selectspecialtyhospitals.com/company/locations/milwaukee.aspx

Owned, leased, sponsored:	101 hospitals	4917 beds
Contract–managed:	0 hospitals	0 beds
Totals:	101 hospitals	4917 beds

★2565: SENTARA HEALTHCARE (NP)
6015 Poplar Hall Drive, Norfolk, VA Zip 23502–3819; tel. 757/455–7000; David L. Bernd, Chief Executive Officer
(Centralized Health System)

NORTH CAROLINA: SENTARA ALBEMARLE MEDICAL CENTER (L, 89 beds) 1144 North Road Street, Elizabeth City, NC Zip 27909–3473, Mailing Address: P.O. Box 1587, Zip 27906–1587; tel. 252/335–0531; Kenneth W. Wood, Interim President
Web address: www.albemarlehealth.org

VIRGINIA: HALIFAX REGIONAL HEALTH SYSTEM (O, 438 beds) 2204 Wilborn Avenue, South Boston, VA Zip 24592–1638; tel. 434/517–3100; Chris A. Lumsden, Chief Executive Officer
Web address: www.hrhs.org

MARTHA JEFFERSON HOSPITAL (O, 139 beds) 500 Martha Jefferson Drive, Charlottesville, VA Zip 22911–4668; tel. 434/654–7000; James E. Haden, President and Chief Executive Officer
Web address: www.marthajefferson.org

SENTARA CAREPLEX HOSPITAL (O, 136 beds) 3000 Coliseum Drive, Hampton, VA Zip 23666–5963; tel. 757/736–1000; Debra A. Flores, R.N., MS, President and Administrator
Web address: www.sentara.com

SENTARA LEIGH HOSPITAL (O, 238 beds) 830 Kempsville Road, Norfolk, VA Zip 23502–3920; tel. 757/261–6000; Teresa L. Edwards, President and Administrator
Web address: www.sentara.com

SENTARA NORFOLK GENERAL HOSPITAL (O, 495 beds) 600 Gresham Drive, Norfolk, VA Zip 23507–1904; tel. 757/388–3000; Kurt T. Hofelich, President
Web address: www.sentara.com

SENTARA NORTHERN VIRGINIA MEDICAL CENTER (O, 180 beds) 2300 Opitz Boulevard, Woodbridge, VA Zip 22191–3399; tel. 703/523–1000; Stephen D. Porter, President
Web address: www.sentara.com/northernvirginia

SENTARA OBICI HOSPITAL (O, 176 beds) 2800 Godwin Boulevard, Suffolk, VA Zip 23434–8038; tel. 757/934–4000; Steve Julian, M.D., President
Web address: www.sentara.com

SENTARA PRINCESS ANNE HOSPITAL (O, 160 beds) 2025 Glenn Mitchell Drive, Virginia Beach, VA Zip 23456–0178; tel. 757/507–1000; Thomas B. Thames, M.D., President
Web address: www.sentara.com

SENTARA RMH MEDICAL CENTER (O, 244 beds) 2010 Health Campus Drive, Harrisonburg, VA Zip 22801–3293; tel. 540/689–1000; James D. Krauss, President
Web address: www.rmhonline.com

SENTARA VIRGINIA BEACH GENERAL HOSPITAL (O, 259 beds) 1060 First Colonial Road, Virginia Beach, VA Zip 23454–3002; tel. 757/395–8000; Elwood Bernard Boone, III, FACHE, President
Web address: www.sentara.com

SENTARA WILLIAMSBURG REGIONAL MEDICAL CENTER (O, 145 beds) 100 Sentara Circle, Williamsburg, VA Zip 23188–5713; tel. 757/984–6000; David J. Masterson, President
Web address: www.sentara.com

Owned, leased, sponsored:	12 hospitals	2699 beds
Contract–managed:	0 hospitals	0 beds
Totals:	12 hospitals	2699 beds

★2065: SHARP HEALTHCARE (NP)
8695 Spectrum Center Boulevard, San Diego, CA Zip 92123–1489; tel. 858/499–4000; Michael Murphy, CPA, President & Chief Executive Officer
(Centralized Health System)

CALIFORNIA: SHARP CHULA VISTA MEDICAL CENTER (O, 343 beds) 751 Medical Center Court, Chula Vista, CA Zip 91911–6699, Mailing Address: P.O. Box 1297, Zip 91912–1297; tel. 619/502–5800; Pablo Velez, Chief Executive Officer
Web address: www.sharp.com

SHARP CORONADO HOSPITAL AND HEALTHCARE CENTER (L, 181 beds) 250 Prospect Place, Coronado, CA Zip 92118–1999; tel. 619/522–3600; Susan Stone, R.N., Ph.D., Senior Vice President and Chief Executive Officer
Web address: www.sharp.com

SHARP GROSSMONT HOSPITAL (L, 499 beds) 5555 Grossmont Center Drive, La Mesa, CA Zip 91942–3019, Mailing Address: P.O. Box 158, Zip 91944–0158; tel. 619/740–6000; Michele T. Tarbet, Chief Executive Officer
Web address: www.sharp.com

SHARP MEMORIAL HOSPITAL (O, 382 beds) 7901 Frost Street, San Diego, CA Zip 92123–2701; tel. 858/939–3400; Tim Smith, Senior Vice President and Chief Executive Officer
Web address: www.sharp.com

SHARP MESA VISTA HOSPITAL (O, 163 beds) 7850 Vista Hill Avenue, San Diego, CA Zip 92123–2717; tel. 858/278–4110; Kathi Lencioni, Senior Vice President and Chief Executive Officer
Web address: www.sharp.com

Owned, leased, sponsored:	5 hospitals	1568 beds
Contract–managed:	0 hospitals	0 beds
Totals:	5 hospitals	1568 beds

For explanation of codes following names, see page B2.
★ Indicates Type III membership in the American Hospital Association.

Section B

4125: SHRINERS HOSPITALS FOR CHILDREN (NP)
2900 Rocky Point Drive, Tampa, FL Zip 33607–1435, Mailing Address: P.O. Box 31356, Zip 33631–3356; tel. 813/281–0300; John P. McCabe, Executive Vice President
(Independent Hospital System)

SHRINERS HOSPITALS FOR CHILDREN–LOS ANGELES (O, 30 beds) 3160 Geneva Street, Los Angeles, CA Zip 90020–1199; tel. 213/388–3151; Sidney M. Ono, Administrator
Web address: www.shrinershospitalsforchildren.org/Hospitals/Locations/Losangeles.aspx

SHRINERS HOSPITALS FOR CHILDREN–NORTHERN CALIFORNIA (O, 70 beds) 2425 Stockton Boulevard, Sacramento, CA Zip 95817–2215; tel. 916/453–2000; Margaret Bryan, Administrator
Web address: www.shrinershospitalsforchildren.org/Hospitals/Locations/NorthernCalifornia.aspx

FLORIDA: SHRINERS HOSPITALS FOR CHILDREN–TAMPA (O, 25 beds) 12502 USF Pine Drive, Tampa, FL Zip 33612–9499; tel. 813/972–2250; Jeannette Skinner, R.N., FACHE, Administrator
Web address: www.shrinershospitalsforchildren.org/Hospitals/Locations/Tampa.aspx

HAWAII: SHRINERS HOSPITALS FOR CHILDREN–HONOLULU (O, 16 beds) 1310 Punahou Street, Honolulu, HI Zip 96826–1099; tel. 808/941–4466; John R. White, Administrator
Web address: www.shrinershospitalsforchildren.org/Hospitals/Locations/Honolulu.aspx

ILLINOIS: SHRINERS HOSPITALS FOR CHILDREN–CHICAGO (O, 36 beds) 2211 North Oak Park Avenue, Chicago, IL Zip 60707–3392; tel. 773/622–5400; Mark L. Niederpruem, FACHE, Administrator
Web address: www.shrinershospitalsforchildren.org/Hospitals/Locations/Chicago.aspx

KENTUCKY: SHRINERS HOSPITALS FOR CHILDREN–LEXINGTON (O, 50 beds) 1900 Richmond Road, Lexington, KY Zip 40502–1298; tel. 859/266–2101; Tony Lewgood, Administrator
Web address: www.shrinershospitalsforchildren.org/Hospitals/Locations/Lexington.aspx

LOUISIANA: SHRINERS HOSPITALS FOR CHILDREN–SHREVEPORT (O, 45 beds) 3100 Samford Avenue, Shreveport, LA Zip 71103–4289; tel. 318/222–5704; Garry Kim Green, FACHE, Administrator
Web address: www.shrinershospitalsforchildren.org/Hospitals/Locations/Shreveport.aspx

MASSACHUSETTS: SHRINERS HOSPITALS FOR CHILDREN–BOSTON (O, 30 beds) 51 Blossom Street, Boston, MA Zip 02114–2601; tel. 617/722–3000; C. Thomas D'Esmond, FACHE, Administrator
Web address: www.shrinershospitalsforchildren.org/Hospitals/Locations/Boston.aspx

SHRINERS HOSPITALS FOR CHILDREN–SPRINGFIELD (O, 20 beds) 516 Carew Street, Springfield, MA Zip 01104–2396; tel. 413/787–2000; Charles Walczak, FACHE, Regional Administrator
Web address: www.shrinershospitalsforchildren.org/Hospitals/Locations/Springfield.aspx

MINNESOTA: SHRINERS HOSPITALS FOR CHILDREN–TWIN CITIES (O, 40 beds) 2025 East River Parkway, Minneapolis, MN Zip 55414–3696; tel. 612/596–6100; Charles C. Lobeck, Administrator
Web address: www.shrinershospitalsforchildren.org/Hospitals/Locations/twincities.aspx

MISSOURI: SHRINERS HOSPITALS FOR CHILDREN–ST. LOUIS (O, 42 beds) 2001 South Lindbergh Boulevard, Saint Louis, MO Zip 63131–3597; tel. 314/432–3600; John Gloss, FACHE, Administrator
Web address: www.shrinershospitalsforchildren.org/Hospitals/Locations/Stlouis.aspx

OHIO: SHRINERS HOSPITALS FOR CHILDREN–CINCINNATI BURNS HOSPITAL (O, 30 beds) 3229 Burnet Avenue, Cincinnati, OH Zip 45229–3095; tel. 513/872–6000; Tony Lewgood, Interim Administrator
Web address: www.shrinershospitalsforchildren.org/Hospitals/Locations/Cincinnati.aspx

OREGON: SHRINERS HOSPITALS FOR CHILDREN–PORTLAND (O, 8 beds) 3101 S.W. Sam Jackson Park Road, Portland, OR Zip 97239–3009; tel. 503/241–5090; J. Craig Patchin, Administrator
Web address: www.shrinershospitalsforchildren.org/Hospitals/Locations/Portland.aspx

PENNSYLVANIA: SHRINERS HOSPITALS FOR CHILDREN–PHILADELPHIA (O, 39 beds) 3551 North Broad Street, Philadelphia, PA Zip 19140–4160; tel. 215/430–4000; Ernest N. Perilli, Administrator
Web address: www.shrinershospitalsforchildren.org/Hospitals/Locations/Philadelphia.aspx

SOUTH CAROLINA: SHRINERS HOSPITALS FOR CHILDREN–GREENVILLE (O, 15 beds) 950 West Faris Road, Greenville, SC Zip 29605–4277; tel. 864/271–3444; Randall R. Romberger, Administrator
Web address: www.shrinershospitalsforchildren.org/Hospitals/Locations/Greenville.aspx

TEXAS: SHRINERS HOSPITALS FOR CHILDREN–GALVESTON BURNS HOSPITAL (O, 15 beds) 815 Market Street, Galveston, TX Zip 77550–2725; tel. 409/770–6600; Mary Jaco, R.N., MSN, Administrator
Web address: www.shrinershospitalsforchildren.org/Hospitals/Locations/Galveston.aspx

SHRINERS HOSPITALS FOR CHILDREN–HOUSTON (O, 40 beds) 6977 Main Street, Houston, TX Zip 77030–3701; tel. 713/797–1616; David A. Ferrell, Regional Administrator
Web address: www.shrinershospitalsforchildren.org/Hospitals/Locations/Houston.aspx

UTAH: SHRINERS HOSPITALS FOR CHILDREN–SALT LAKE CITY (O, 18 beds) Fairfax Road & Virginia Street, Salt Lake City, UT Zip 84103–4399; tel. 801/536–3500; Kevin Martin, M.P.H., R.N., Administrator
Web address: www.shrinershospitalsforchildren.org/Hospitals/Locations/SaltLakeCity.aspx

WASHINGTON: SHRINERS HOSPITALS FOR CHILDREN–SPOKANE (O, 30 beds) 911 West Fifth Avenue, Spokane, WA Zip 99204–2901, Mailing Address: P.O. Box 2472, Zip 99210–2472; tel. 509/455–7844; Peter G. Brewer, Administrator
Web address: www.shrinershospitalsforchildren.org/Hospitals/Locations/Spokane.aspx

Owned, leased, sponsored:	19 hospitals	599 beds
Contract–managed:	0 hospitals	0 beds
Totals:	19 hospitals	599 beds

★**0284: SINAI HEALTH SYSTEM** (NP)
1500 South California Avenue, Chicago, IL Zip 60608–1729; tel. 773/542–2000; Karen Teitelbaum, President and Chief Executive Officer
(Independent Hospital System)

ILLINOIS: HOLY CROSS HOSPITAL (O, 213 beds) 2701 West 68th Street, Chicago, IL Zip 60629–1882; tel. 773/884–9000; Lori Pacura, R.N., MSN, Senior Vice President
Web address: www.holycrosshospital.org

MOUNT SINAI HOSPITAL (O, 290 beds) California Avenue at 15th Street, Chicago, IL Zip 60608–1729; tel. 773/542–2000; Karen Teitelbaum, President and Chief Executive Officer
Web address: www.sinai.org

SCHWAB REHABILITATION HOSPITAL (O, 101 beds) 1401 South California Avenue, Chicago, IL Zip 60608–1858; tel. 773/522–2010; Alan H. Channing, President and Chief Executive Officer
Web address: www.schwabrehab.org

Owned, leased, sponsored:	3 hospitals	604 beds
Contract–managed:	0 hospitals	0 beds
Totals:	3 hospitals	604 beds

5125: SISTERS OF CHARITY HEALTH SYSTEM (CC)
2475 East 22nd Street, Cleveland, OH Zip 44115–3221; tel. 216/363–2797; Terrence Kessler, Interim President and Chief Executive Officer
(Moderately Centralized Health System)

OHIO: MERCY MEDICAL CENTER (O, 304 beds) 1320 Mercy Drive N.W., Canton, OH Zip 44708–2641; tel. 330/489–1000; Thomas E. Cecconi, President and Chief Executive Officer
Web address: www.cantonmercy.org

For explanation of codes following names, see page B2.
★ Indicates Type III membership in the American Hospital Association.

ST. JOHN MEDICAL CENTER (O, 184 beds) 29000 Center Ridge Road, Westlake, OH Zip 44145–5293; tel. 440/835–8000; William A. Young, Jr., President and Chief Executive Officer
Web address: www.sjws.net

ST. VINCENT CHARITY MEDICAL CENTER (O, 214 beds) 2351 East 22nd Street, Cleveland, OH Zip 44115–3111; tel. 216/861–6200; David Perse, M.D., President and Chief Executive Officer
Web address: www.stvincentcharity.com/

SOUTH CAROLINA: PROVIDENCE HOSPITAL (O, 314 beds) 2435 Forest Drive, Columbia, SC Zip 29204–2098; tel. 803/865–4500; Michael French, Interim Chief Executive Officer
Web address: www.sistersofcharityhealth. org/health–care/providence–hospitals/

Owned, leased, sponsored:	4 hospitals	1016 beds
Contract–managed:	0 hospitals	0 beds
Totals:	4 hospitals	1016 beds

5805: SISTERS OF MARY OF THE PRESENTATION HEALTH SYSTEM (CC)
1202 Page Drive S.W., Fargo, ND Zip 58103–2340, Mailing Address: P.O. Box 10007, Zip 58106–0007; tel. 701/237–9290; Aaron K. Alton, President and Chief Executive Officer
(Independent Hospital System)

ILLINOIS: ST. MARGARET'S HOSPITAL (O, 69 beds) 600 East First Street, Spring Valley, IL Zip 61362–1512; tel. 815/664–5311; Tim Muntz, President and Chief Executive Officer
Web address: www.aboutsmh.org

NORTH DAKOTA: PRESENTATION MEDICAL CENTER (O, 25 beds) 213 Second Avenue N.E., Rolla, ND Zip 58367–7153, Mailing Address: P.O. Box 759, Zip 58367–0759; tel. 701/477–3161; Mark Kerr, Chief Executive Officer
Web address: www.pmc–rolla.com

ST. ALOISIUS MEDICAL CENTER (O, 110 beds) 325 East Brewster Street, Harvey, ND Zip 58341–1653; tel. 701/324–4651; Rockford Zastoupil, President and Chief Executive Officer
Web address: www.staloisius.com

ST. ANDREW'S HEALTH CENTER (O, 25 beds) 316 Ohmer Street, Bottineau, ND Zip 58318–1045; tel. 701/228–9300; Jodi Atkinson, President and Chief Executive Officer
Web address: www.standrewshealth.com

Owned, leased, sponsored:	4 hospitals	229 beds
Contract–managed:	0 hospitals	0 beds
Totals:	4 hospitals	229 beds

5955: SISTERS OF SAINT FRANCIS (CC)
2500 Grant Boulevard, Syracuse, NY Zip 13208–1782; tel. 315/634–7000; Sister Geraldine Ching, Assistant General Minister
(Moderately Centralized Health System)

NEW YORK: ST. ELIZABETH MEDICAL CENTER (S, 181 beds) 2209 Genesee Street, Utica, NY Zip 13501–5999; tel. 315/798–8100; Scott H. Perra, Chief Executive Officer
Web address: www.stemc.org

ST. JOSEPH'S HOSPITAL HEALTH CENTER (S, 431 beds) 301 Prospect Avenue, Syracuse, NY Zip 13203–1807; tel. 315/448–5111; Kathryn H. Ruscitto, President
Web address: www.sjhsyr.org

Owned, leased, sponsored:	2 hospitals	612 beds
Contract–managed:	0 hospitals	0 beds
Totals:	2 hospitals	612 beds

★0253: SOUTHEAST GEORGIA HEALTH SYSTEM (NP)
2415 Parkwood Drive, Brunswick, GA Zip 31520–4722, Mailing Address: P.O. Box 1518, Zip 31521–1518; tel. 912/466–7000; Gary R. Colberg, FACHE, President and Chief Executive Officer

GEORGIA: SOUTHEAST GEORGIA HEALTH SYSTEM BRUNSWICK CAMPUS (O, 494 beds) 2415 Parkwood Drive, Brunswick, GA Zip 31520–4722, Mailing Address: P.O. Box 1518, Zip 31521–1518; tel. 912/466–7000; Gary R. Colberg, FACHE, President and Chief Executive Officer
Web address: www.sghs.org

SOUTHEAST GEORGIA HEALTH SYSTEM CAMDEN CAMPUS (O, 40 beds) 2000 Dan Proctor Drive, Saint Marys, GA Zip 31558–3810; tel. 912/576–6200; Howard W. Sepp, Jr., FACHE, Vice President and Administrator
Web address: www.sghs.org

Owned, leased, sponsored:	2 hospitals	534 beds
Contract–managed:	0 hospitals	0 beds
Totals:	2 hospitals	534 beds

★0628: SOUTHEASTHEALTH (NP)
1701 Lacey Street, Cape Girardeau, MO Zip 63701–5230; tel. 573/334–4822; Wayne Smith, President and Chief Executive Officer
(Independent Hospital System)

MISSOURI: SOUTHEAST HEALTH CENTER OF REYNOLDS COUNTY (L, 8 beds) 100 Highway 21 South, Ellington, MO Zip 63638, Mailing Address: Rural Route 4, Box 4269, Zip 63638–9409; tel. 573/663–2511; Christy Hardin, Chief Executive Officer

SOUTHEAST HEALTH CENTER OF RIPLEY COUNTY (L, 8 beds) 109 Plum Street, Doniphan, MO Zip 63935–1299; tel. 573/996–2141; Christy Hardin, Chief Executive Officer
Web address: www.sehealth. org/southeast–health–center–of–ripley–county/SoutheastHEALTH.aspx?nd=41

SOUTHEAST HEALTH CENTER OF STODDARD COUNTY (L, 16 beds) 1200 North One Mile Road, Dexter, MO Zip 63841–1000; tel. 573/624–5566; Adam Bracks, Chief Executive Officer
Web address: www.sehealth.org

SOUTHEAST HOSPITAL (O, 221 beds) 1701 Lacey Street, Cape Girardeau, MO Zip 63701–5230; tel. 573/334–4822; Wayne Smith, President and Chief Executive Officer
Web address: www.sehealth.org/

Owned, leased, sponsored:	4 hospitals	253 beds
Contract–managed:	0 hospitals	0 beds
Totals:	4 hospitals	253 beds

4175: SOUTHERN ILLINOIS HOSPITAL SERVICES (NP)
1239 East Main Street, Carbondale, IL Zip 62901–3114, Mailing Address: P.O. Box 3988, Zip 62902–3988; tel. 618/457–5200; Rex P. Budde, President and Chief Executive Officer
(Independent Hospital System)

ILLINOIS: HERRIN HOSPITAL (O, 114 beds) 201 South 14th Street, Herrin, IL Zip 62948–3631; tel. 618/942–2171; Terence Farrell, Vice President and Administrator
Web address: www.sih.net

MEMORIAL HOSPITAL OF CARBONDALE (O, 159 beds) 405 West Jackson Street, Carbondale, IL Zip 62901–1467, Mailing Address: P.O. Box 10000, Zip 62902–9000; tel. 618/549–0721; Bart Millstead, Administrator
Web address: www.sih.net

ST. JOSEPH MEMORIAL HOSPITAL (O, 25 beds) 2 South Hospital Drive, Murphysboro, IL Zip 62966–3333; tel. 618/684–3156; John T. Brothers, R.N., MS, Administrator
Web address: www.sih.net

Owned, leased, sponsored:	3 hospitals	298 beds
Contract–managed:	0 hospitals	0 beds
Totals:	3 hospitals	298 beds

For explanation of codes following names, see page B2.
★ Indicates Type III membership in the American Hospital Association.

Section B

0346: SOUTHERN PLAINS MEDICAL GROUP (IO)
4323 N.W. 63rd Street Suite 232, Oklahoma City, OK
Zip 73116–1546; tel. 405/753–6770; Margie Homer, President

OKLAHOMA: PHYSICIANS' HOSPITAL IN ANADARKO (O, 25 beds) 1002
Central Boulevard East, Anadarko, OK Zip 73005–4496;
tel. 405/247–2551; Jamey Lykins, Interim Chief Executive Officer
Web address: www.anadarkohospital.com

STROUD REGIONAL MEDICAL CENTER (O, 25 beds) Highway 66 West,
Stroud, OK Zip 74079, Mailing Address: P.O. Box 530, Zip 74079–0530;
tel. 918/968–3571; Tommy Smith, Chief Executive Officer
Web address: www.stroudhospital.com/

Owned, leased, sponsored:	2 hospitals	50 beds
Contract–managed:	0 hospitals	0 beds
Totals:	2 hospitals	50 beds

0652: SOUTHWEST HEALTH SYSTEMS (NP)
215 Marion Avenue, Mccomb, MS Zip 39648–2705, Mailing Address:
P.O. Box 1307, Zip 39649–1307; tel. 601/249–5500; Norman M.
Price, FACHE, Chief Executive Officer and Administrator
(Independent Hospital System)

MISSISSIPPI: LAWRENCE COUNTY HOSPITAL (O, 25 beds) Highway 84 East,
Monticello, MS Zip 39654–0788, Mailing Address: P.O. Box 788,
Zip 39654–0788; tel. 601/587–4051; Semmes Ross, Jr., Administrator
Web address: www.smrmc.com

SOUTHWEST MISSISSIPPI REGIONAL MEDICAL CENTER (O, 143 beds) 215
Marion Avenue, McComb, MS Zip 39648–2705, Mailing Address: P.O. Box
1307, Zip 39649–1307; tel. 601/249–5500; Norman M. Price, FACHE, Chief
Executive Officer
Web address: www.smrmc.com

Owned, leased, sponsored:	2 hospitals	168 beds
Contract–managed:	0 hospitals	0 beds
Totals:	2 hospitals	168 beds

0164: SOUTHWEST HEALTHCARE SYSTEM (IO)
4400 North Scottsdale Road, Suite 9347, Scottsdale, AZ
Zip 85251–3331; tel. 480/348–9800; Paul R. Tuft, President

OHIO: SOUTHWEST REGIONAL MEDICAL CENTER (O, 40 beds) 425 Home
Street, Georgetown, OH Zip 45121–1407; tel. 937/378–7500; Michael C.
Patterson, Chief Executive Officer
Web address: www.swrmed.org

TEXAS: GULF COAST MEDICAL CENTER (O, 129 beds) 10141 Highway 59,
Wharton, TX Zip 77488–3004; tel. 979/282–6100; Loretta Flynn, Chief
Executive Officer
Web address: www.gulfcoastmedical.com

Owned, leased, sponsored:	2 hospitals	169 beds
Contract–managed:	0 hospitals	0 beds
Totals:	2 hospitals	169 beds

★1245: SPARROW HEALTH SYSTEM (NP)
1215 East Michigan Avenue, Lansing, MI Zip 48912–1811;
tel. 517/364–1000; Dennis A. Swan, JD, FACHE, President and Chief
Executive Officer
(Centralized Health System)

MICHIGAN: SPARROW CLINTON HOSPITAL (O, 25 beds) 805 South Oakland
Street, Saint Johns, MI Zip 48879–2253; tel. 989/227–3400; Edward
Bruun, President and Chief Executive Officer
Web address: www.sparrowclinton.org

SPARROW HOSPITAL (O, 679 beds) 1215 East Michigan Avenue, Lansing, MI
Zip 48912–1811; tel. 517/364–1000; Dennis A. Swan, JD, FACHE, President
and Chief Executive Officer
Web address: www.sparrow.org

SPARROW IONIA HOSPITAL (O, 25 beds) 520 East Washington Street, Ionia,
MI Zip 48846–1870, Mailing Address: Box 1001, Zip 48846–6001;
tel. 616/523–1400; William Roeser, President and Chief Executive Officer
Web address: www.sparrow.org/sparrowionia

SPARROW SPECIALTY HOSPITAL (O, 36 beds) 1210 West Saginaw Street,
Lansing, MI Zip 48915–1927, Mailing Address: P.O. Box 85201,
Zip 48915–1927; tel. 517/364–6800; Kira Carter-Robertson, President and
Chief Executive Officer
Web address: www.sparrowspecialty.org

Owned, leased, sponsored:	4 hospitals	765 beds
Contract–managed:	0 hospitals	0 beds
Totals:	4 hospitals	765 beds

★4195: SPARTANBURG REGIONAL HEALTHCARE SYSTEM
(NP)
101 East Wood Street, Spartanburg, SC Zip 29303–3040;
tel. 864/560–6000; Bruce Holstien, President and Chief Executive
Officer
(Centralized Health System)

SOUTH CAROLINA: SPARTANBURG HOSPITAL FOR RESTORATIVE CARE (O,
116 beds) 389 Serpentine Drive, Spartanburg, SC Zip 29303–3026;
tel. 864/560–3280; Anita M. Butler, Chief Executive Officer
Web address: www.srhs.com

SPARTANBURG REGIONAL MEDICAL CENTER (O, 514 beds) 101 East Wood
Street, Spartanburg, SC Zip 29303–3040; tel. 864/560–6000; Bruce
Holstien, President and Chief Executive Officer
Web address: www.spartanburgregional.com

VILLAGE HOSPITAL (O, 34 beds) 250 Westmoreland Road, Greer, SC
Zip 29651–9013; tel. 864/530–6000; Anthony Kouskolekas, FACHE,
President
Web address: www.villageatpelham.com

Owned, leased, sponsored:	3 hospitals	664 beds
Contract–managed:	0 hospitals	0 beds
Totals:	3 hospitals	664 beds

0352: SPECIALTY HOSPITALS OF AMERICA, LLC (IO)
155 Fleet Street, Portsmouth, NH Zip 03801–4050;
tel. 603/570–4888; Eric F. Rieseberg, President
(Independent Hospital System)

DISTRICT OF COLUMBIA: SPECIALTY HOSPITAL OF WASHINGTON (O, 177
beds) 700 Constitution Avenue N.E., Washington, DC Zip 20002–6058;
tel. 202/546–5700; Susan P. Bailey, R.N., Chief Executive Officer
Web address: www.specialtyhospitalofwashington.com

SPECIALTY HOSPITAL OF WASHINGTON–HADLEY (O, 82 beds) 4601 Martin
Luther King Jr. Avenue, S.W., Washington, DC Zip 20032–1131;
tel. 202/574–5700; Cathy Borris–Hale, Chief Executive Officer

Owned, leased, sponsored:	2 hospitals	259 beds
Contract–managed:	0 hospitals	0 beds
Totals:	2 hospitals	259 beds

★0177: SPECTRUM HEALTH (NP)
100 Michigan Street N.E., Grand Rapids, MI Zip 49503–2551;
tel. 616/391–1774; Richard C. Breon, President and Chief Executive
Officer
(Moderately Centralized Health System)

MICHIGAN: SPECTRUM HEALTH – BUTTERWORTH HOSPITAL (O, 1078 beds)
100 Michigan Street N.E., Grand Rapids, MI Zip 49503–2560;
tel. 616/774–7444; Christina Freese–Decker, President, Spectrum Health
Hospital Group
Web address: www.spectrum–health.org

SPECTRUM HEALTH BIG RAPIDS HOSPITAL (O, 49 beds) 605 Oak Street, Big
Rapids, MI Zip 49307–2099; tel. 231/796–8691; Mary Kay VanDriel,
President
Web address: www.mcmcbr.com

SPECTRUM HEALTH GERBER MEMORIAL (O, 40 beds) 212 South Sullivan
Avenue, Fremont, MI Zip 49412–1548; tel. 231/924–3300; Randall Stasik,
President and Chief Executive Officer
Web address: www.spectrumhealth.org

For explanation of codes following names, see page B2.
★ Indicates Type III membership in the American Hospital Association.

Section B

SPECTRUM HEALTH LUDINGTON HOSPITAL (O, 80 beds) One Atkinson Drive, Ludington, MI Zip 49431–1906; tel. 231/843–2591; Mark Vipperman, President
Web address: www.mmcwm.com

SPECTRUM HEALTH REED CITY HOSPITAL (O, 75 beds) 300 North Patterson Road, Reed City, MI Zip 49677–8041, Mailing Address: P.O. Box 75, Zip 49677–0075; tel. 231/832–3271; Mary Kay VanDriel, President
Web address: www.reedcity.spectrum–health.org

SPECTRUM HEALTH SPECIAL CARE HOSPITAL (O, 36 beds) 750 Fuller Avenue N.E., Grand Rapids, MI Zip 49503–1995; tel. 616/486–3000; Chuck Tozer, Administrator
Web address: www.spectrum–health.org

SPECTRUM HEALTH UNITED HOSPITAL (O, 116 beds) 615 South Bower Street, Greenville, MI Zip 48838–2614; tel. 616/754–4691; Brian Brasser, President
Web address: www.spectrumhealth.org/

SPECTRUM HEALTH ZEELAND COMMUNITY HOSPITAL (O, 50 beds) 8333 Felch Street, Zeeland, MI Zip 49464–2608; tel. 616/772–4644; Henry A. Veenstra, President
Web address: www.spectrumhealth.org/zeeland

Owned, leased, sponsored:	8 hospitals	1524 beds
Contract–managed:	0 hospitals	0 beds
Totals:	8 hospitals	1524 beds

★**5455: SSM HEALTH** (CC)
10101 Woodfield Lane, Saint Louis, MO Zip 63132–2937; tel. 314/994–7800; William P. Thompson, President and Chief Executive Officer
(Decentralized Health System)

ILLINOIS: CLAY COUNTY HOSPITAL (C, 22 beds) 911 Stacy Burk Drive, Flora, IL Zip 62839–3241, Mailing Address: P.O. Box 280, Zip 62839–0280; tel. 618/662–2131; Amanda J. Goostree, President
Web address: www.claycountyhospital.org

GOOD SAMARITAN REGIONAL HEALTH CENTER (O, 134 beds) 605 North 12th Street, Mount Vernon, IL Zip 62864–2899; tel. 618/242–4600; Michael D. Warren, President
Web address: www.smgsi.com

ST. MARY'S HOSPITAL (O, 113 beds) 400 North Pleasant Avenue, Centralia, IL Zip 62801–3056; tel. 618/436–8000; Bruce Merrell, FACHE, President
Web address: www.smgsi.com

MISSOURI: AUDRAIN MEDICAL CENTER (O, 49 beds) 620 East Monroe Street, Mexico, MO Zip 65265–2919; tel. 573/582–5000; David A. Neuendorf, FACHE, President and Chief Executive Officer
Web address: www.audrainmedicalcenter.com

SSM CARDINAL GLENNON CHILDREN'S MEDICAL CENTER (O, 176 beds) 1465 South Grand Boulevard, Saint Louis, MO Zip 63104–1095; tel. 314/577–5600; Kathleen R. Becker, M.P.H., JD, Interim Chief Executive Officer
Web address: www.cardinalglennon.com

SSM DEPAUL HEALTH CENTER (O, 463 beds) 12303 De Paul Drive, Bridgeton, MO Zip 63044–2512; tel. 314/344–6000; Sean Hogan, President
Web address: www.ssmdepaul.com

SSM ST. CLARE HEALTH CENTER (O, 184 beds) 1015 Bowles Avenue, Fenton, MO Zip 63026–2394; tel. 636/496–2000; Ellis Hawkins, President
Web address: www.ssmstclare.com

SSM ST. JOSEPH HEALTH CENTER (O, 331 beds) 300 First Capitol Drive, Saint Charles, MO Zip 63301–2844; tel. 636/947–5000; Michael E. Bowers, President
Web address: www.ssmstjoseph.com

SSM ST. JOSEPH HOSPITAL WEST (O, 126 beds) 100 Medical Plaza, Lake Saint Louis, MO Zip 63367–1366; tel. 636/625–5200; Lisle Wescott, President
Web address: www.ssmstjoseph.com

SSM ST. MARY'S HEALTH CENTER (O, 381 beds) 6420 Clayton Road, Saint Louis, MO Zip 63117–1811; tel. 314/768–8000; Kathleen R. Becker, M.P.H., JD, President
Web address: www.stmarys–stlouis.com

ST. FRANCIS HOSPITAL AND HEALTH SERVICES (O, 57 beds) 2016 South Main Street, Maryville, MO Zip 64468–2655; tel. 660/562–2600; Gray Cox, President
Web address: www.stfrancismaryville.com

ST. MARYS HEALTH CENTER (O, 139 beds) 100 St. Marys Medical Plaza, Jefferson City, MO Zip 65101–1602; tel. 573/761–7000; R. Brent VanConia, President
Web address: www.lethealingbegin.com

OKLAHOMA: ST. ANTHONY HOSPITAL (O, 524 beds) 1000 North Lee Street, Oklahoma City, OK Zip 73102–1080, Mailing Address: P.O. Box 205, Zip 73101–0205; tel. 405/272–7000; Tammy Powell, FACHE, M.P.H., President
Web address: www.saintsok.com

ST. ANTHONY SHAWNEE HOSPITAL (O, 131 beds) 1102 West MacArthur Street, Shawnee, OK Zip 74804–1744; tel. 405/273–2270; Charles E. Skillings, President and Chief Executive Officer
Web address: www.stanthonyshawnee.com

WISCONSIN: ST. CLARE HOSPITAL (O, 60 beds) 707 14th Street, Baraboo, WI Zip 53913–1597; tel. 608/356–1400; Sandra L. Anderson, President
Web address: www.stclare.com

ST. MARY'S HOSPITAL (O, 364 beds) 700 South Park Street, Madison, WI Zip 53715–1830; tel. 608/251–6100; Frank D. Byrne, M.D., President
Web address: www.stmarysmadison.com

ST. MARY'S JANESVILLE HOSPITAL (O, 50 beds) 3400 East Racine Steeet, Janesville, WI Zip 53546–2344; tel. 608/373–8000; Kerry Swanson, President
Web address: www.stmarysjanesville.com

Owned, leased, sponsored:	16 hospitals	3282 beds
Contract–managed:	1 hospital	22 beds
Totals:	17 hospitals	3304 beds

★**0250: ST. CHARLES HEALTH SYSTEM, INC.** (NP)
2500 N.E. Neff Road, Bend, OR Zip 97701–6015; tel. 541/382–4321; James A. Diegel, FACHE, President and Chief Executive Officer
(Moderately Centralized Health System)

OREGON: PIONEER MEMORIAL HOSPITAL (L, 25 beds) 1201 N.E. Elm Street, Prineville, OR Zip 97754–1206; tel. 541/447–6254; Jeanine Gentry, Chief Executive Officer
Web address: www.stcharleshealthcare.org

ST. CHARLES MADRAS (O, 25 beds) 470 N.E. A Street, Madras, OR Zip 97741–1844; tel. 541/475–3882; Jeanine Gentry, Chief Executive Officer
Web address: www.mvhd.org

ST. CHARLES MEDICAL CENTER – BEND (O, 260 beds) 2500 N.E. Neff Road, Bend, OR Zip 97701–6015; tel. 541/382–4321; Robert Gomes, FACHE, Chief Executive Officer
Web address: www.scmc.org

ST. CHARLES MEDICAL CENTER – REDMOND (O, 48 beds) 1253 N.W. Canal Boulevard, Redmond, OR Zip 97756–1395; tel. 541/548–8131; Robert Gomes, FACHE, Chief Executive Officer
Web address: www.stcharleshealthcare.org

Owned, leased, sponsored:	4 hospitals	358 beds
Contract–managed:	0 hospitals	0 beds
Totals:	4 hospitals	358 beds

0618: ST. ELIZABETH HEALTHCARE (NP)
1 Medical Village Drive, Edgewood, KY Zip 41017–3403; tel. 859/301–2000; John S. Dubis, FACHE, President and Chief Executive Officer
(Independent Hospital System)

KENTUCKY: ST. ELIZABETH EDGEWOOD (O, 499 beds) 1 Medical Village Drive, Edgewood, KY Zip 41017–3403; tel. 859/301–2000; John S. Dubis, FACHE, President and Chief Executive Officer
Web address: www.stelizabeth.com

For explanation of codes following names, see page B2.
★ Indicates Type III membership in the American Hospital Association.

Section B

ST. ELIZABETH FLORENCE (O, 169 beds) 4900 Houston Road, Florence, KY Zip 41042–4824; tel. 859/212–5200; Chris Carle, Senior Vice President and Chief Operating Officer
Web address: www.stelizabeth.com

ST. ELIZABETH FORT THOMAS (O, 171 beds) 85 North Grand Avenue, Fort Thomas, KY Zip 41075–1796; tel. 859/572–3100; Thomas Saalfeld, Senior Vice President and Chief Operating Officer
Web address: www.stelizabeth.com

ST. ELIZABETH GRANT (O, 16 beds) 238 Barnes Road, Williamstown, KY Zip 41097–9482; tel. 859/824–8240; John Mitchell, Assistant Vice President Operations
Web address: www.stelizabeth.com

Owned, leased, sponsored:	4 hospitals	855 beds
Contract–managed:	0 hospitals	0 beds
Totals:	4 hospitals	855 beds

★**5425: ST. JOSEPH HEALTH** (CC)
3345 Michelson Drive, Suite 100, Irvine, CA Zip 92612; tel. 949/381–4000; Deborah A. Proctor, President and Chief Executive Officer
(Moderately Centralized Health System)

CALIFORNIA: MISSION HOSPITAL (O, 232 beds) 27700 Medical Center Road, Mission Viejo, CA Zip 92691–6474; tel. 949/364–1400; Kenneth McFarland, President and Chief Executive Officer
Web address: www.mission4health.com

PETALUMA VALLEY HOSPITAL (L, 27 beds) 400 North McDowell Boulevard, Petaluma, CA Zip 94954–2366; tel. 707/778–1111; Todd Salnas, President
Web address: www.stjosephhealth.org/About–Us/Facilities/Petaluma–Valley–Hospital.aspx

QUEEN OF THE VALLEY MEDICAL CENTER (O, 174 beds) 1000 Trancas Street, Napa, CA Zip 94558–2906, Mailing Address: P.O. Box 2340, Zip 94558–0688; tel. 707/252–4411; Walt Mickens, FACHE, President and Chief Executive Officer
Web address: www.thequeen.org

REDWOOD MEMORIAL HOSPITAL (O, 25 beds) 3300 Renner Drive, Fortuna, CA Zip 95540–3198; tel. 707/725–3361; David O'Brien, M.D., President
Web address: www.redwoodmemorial.org/

SANTA ROSA MEMORIAL HOSPITAL (O, 272 beds) 1165 Montgomery Drive, Santa Rosa, CA Zip 95405–4897, Mailing Address: P.O. Box 522, Zip 95402–0522; tel. 707/546–3210; Todd Salnas, President
Web address: www.stjosephhealth.org

ST. JOSEPH HOSPITAL (O, 153 beds) 2700 Dolbeer Street, Eureka, CA Zip 95501–4799; tel. 707/445–8121; David O'Brien, M.D., President
Web address: www.stjosepheureka.org

ST. JOSEPH HOSPITAL (O, 379 beds) 1100 West Stewart Drive, Orange, CA Zip 92868–3849, Mailing Address: P.O. Box 5600, Zip 92863–5600; tel. 714/633–9111; Steven C. Moreau, President and Chief Executive Officer
Web address: www.sjo.org

ST. JUDE MEDICAL CENTER (O, 369 beds) 101 East Valencia Mesa Drive, Fullerton, CA Zip 92835–3875; tel. 714/992–3000; Lee Penrose, President and Chief Executive Officer
Web address: www.stjudemedicalcenter.org

ST. MARY MEDICAL CENTER (O, 208 beds) 18300 Highway 18, Apple Valley, CA Zip 92307–2206, Mailing Address: P.O. Box 7025, Zip 92307–0725; tel. 760/242–2311; Alan H. Garrett, Chief Executive Officer
Web address: www.stmaryapplevalley.com/

Owned, leased, sponsored:	9 hospitals	1839 beds
Contract–managed:	0 hospitals	0 beds
Totals:	9 hospitals	1839 beds

0928: ST. LAWRENCE HEALTH SYSTEM (NP)
50 Leroy Street, Potsdam, NY Zip 13676–1799; tel. 315/265–3300; David B. Acker, FACHE, President and CEO

NEW YORK: CANTON–POTSDAM HOSPITAL (O, 94 beds) 50 Leroy Street, Potsdam, NY Zip 13676–1799; tel. 315/265–3300; David B. Acker, FACHE, President and CEO
Web address: www.cphospital.org

GOUVERNEUR HOSPITAL (O, 65 beds) 77 West Barney Street, Gouverneur, NY Zip 13642–1040; tel. 315/287–1000; Marlinda L. LaValley, Chief Executive Officer
Web address: www.gvnrhospital.org

Owned, leased, sponsored:	2 hospitals	159 beds
Contract–managed:	0 hospitals	0 beds
Totals:	2 hospitals	159 beds

★**0356: ST. LUKE'S HEALTH SYSTEM** (NP)
420 West Idaho Street, Boise, ID Zip 83702–6041; tel. 208/381–4200; David C. Pate, M.D., JD, President and Chief Executive Officer
(Moderately Centralized Health System)

IDAHO: NORTH CANYON MEDICAL CENTER (C, 14 beds) 267 North Canyon Drive, Gooding, ID Zip 83330–5500; tel. 208/934–4433; Tim Powers, Chief Executive Officer
Web address: www.ncm–c.org

ST. LUKE'S ELMORE (O, 57 beds) 895 North Sixth East Street, Mountain Home, ID Zip 83647–2207, Mailing Address: P.O. Box 1270, Zip 83647–1270; tel. 208/587–8401; Gregory L. Maurer, Administrator
Web address: www.elmoremedicalcenter.org

ST. LUKE'S JEROME (O, 25 beds) 709 North Lincoln Street, Jerome, ID Zip 83338–1851, Mailing Address: 709 North Lincoln Avenue, Zip 83338–1851; tel. 208/324–4301; James L. Angle, FACHE, Chief Executive Officer
Web address: www.stlukesonline.org/jerome/

ST. LUKE'S MAGIC VALLEY MEDICAL CENTER (O, 224 beds) 801 Pole Line Road West, Twin Falls, ID Zip 83301–5810, Mailing Address: P.O. Box 409, Zip 83303–0409; tel. 208/814–1000; James L. Angle, FACHE, Regional Chief Executive Officer
Web address: www.stlukesonline.org

ST. LUKE'S MCCALL (O, 15 beds) 1000 State Street, McCall, ID Zip 83638–3704; tel. 208/634–2221; Michael A. Fenello, Chief Executive Officer
Web address: www.mccallhosp.org

ST. LUKE'S REGIONAL MEDICAL CENTER (O, 583 beds) 190 East Bannock Street, Boise, ID Zip 83712–6241; tel. 208/381–2222; Kathy D. Moore, Chief Executive Officer
Web address: www.stlukesonline.org/boise

ST. LUKE'S WOOD RIVER MEDICAL CENTER (O, 25 beds) 100 Hospital Drive, Ketchum, ID Zip 83340, Mailing Address: P.O. Box 100, Zip 83340–0100; tel. 208/727–8800; Cody Langbehn, Chief Executive Officer
Web address: www.slrmc.org

WEISER MEMORIAL HOSPITAL (C, 25 beds) 645 East Fifth Street, Weiser, ID Zip 83672–2202; tel. 208/549–0370; Tom Murphy, Chief Executive Officer
Web address: www.weisermemorialhospital.org

Owned, leased, sponsored:	6 hospitals	929 beds
Contract–managed:	2 hospitals	39 beds
Totals:	8 hospitals	968 beds

0862: ST. LUKE'S UNIVERSITY HEALTH NETWORK (NP)
801 Ostrum Street, Bethlehem, PA Zip 18015–1000; tel. 610/954–4000; Richard A. Anderson, President and Chief Executive Officer
(Moderately Centralized Health System)

NEW JERSEY: ST. LUKE'S HOSPITAL – WARREN CAMPUS (O, 140 beds) 185 Roseberry Street, Phillipsburg, NJ Zip 08865–1690; tel. 908/859–6700; Scott R. Wolfe, CPA, President
Web address: www.slhn.org

PENNSYLVANIA: ST. LUKE'S HOSPITAL – ANDERSON CAMPUS (O, 78 beds) 1872 Riverside Circle, Easton, PA Zip 18045–5669; tel. 484/503–3000; Edward Nawrocki, President
Web address: www.mystlukesonline.org

ST. LUKE'S HOSPITAL – MINERS CAMPUS (O, 92 beds) 360 West Ruddle Street, Coaldale, PA Zip 18218–1027; tel. 570/645–2131; William E. Moyer, President
Web address: www.slhn.org

For explanation of codes following names, see page B2.
★ Indicates Type III membership in the American Hospital Association.

ST. LUKE'S HOSPITAL – QUAKERTOWN CAMPUS (O, 57 beds) 1021 Park Avenue, Quakertown, PA Zip 18951–1573; tel. 215/538–4500; John B. Sylvia, President
Web address: www.slhhn.org

ST. LUKE'S UNIVERSITY HOSPITAL – BETHLEHEM CAMPUS (O, 593 beds) 801 Ostrum Street, Bethlehem, PA Zip 18015–1065; tel. 484/526–4000; Richard A. Anderson, President and Chief Executive Officer
Web address: www.slhn–lehighvalley.org

Owned, leased, sponsored:	5 hospitals	960 beds
Contract–managed:	0 hospitals	0 beds
Totals:	5 hospitals	960 beds

0156: STANFORD HEALTH CARE (NP)
300 Pasteur Drive, Palo Alto, CA Zip 94304–2299; tel. 650/723–4000; Amir Dan Rubin, President and Chief Executive Officer
(Moderately Centralized Health System)

CALIFORNIA: LUCILE SALTER PACKARD CHILDREN'S HOSPITAL AT STANFORD (O, 302 beds) 725 Welch Road, Palo Alto, CA Zip 94304–1614; tel. 650/497–8000; Christopher G. Dawes, President and Chief Executive Officer
Web address: www.stanfordchildrens.org

STANFORD HOSPITAL AND CLINICS (O, 477 beds) 300 Pasteur Drive, Suite H3200, Palo Alto, CA Zip 94304–2203; tel. 650/723–4000; Amir Dan Rubin, President and Chief Executive Officer
Web address: www.stanfordhospital.com/

Owned, leased, sponsored:	2 hospitals	779 beds
Contract–managed:	0 hospitals	0 beds
Totals:	2 hospitals	779 beds

0141: STEWARD HEALTH CARE SYSTEM, LLC (IO)
500 Boylston Street, 5th Floor, Boston, MA Zip 02116–3740; tel. 617/419–4700; Ralph de la Torre, M.D., Chairman and Chief Executive Officer
(Independent Hospital System)

MASSACHUSETTS: CARNEY HOSPITAL (O, 133 beds) 2100 Dorchester Avenue, Boston, MA Zip 02124–5615; tel. 617/296–4000; Andrew Davis, President
Web address: www.carneyhospital.org

GOOD SAMARITAN MEDICAL CENTER (O, 190 beds) 235 North Pearl Street, Brockton, MA Zip 02301–1794; tel. 508/427–3000; John A. Jurczyk, FACHE, Interim President
Web address: www.stewardhealth.org/Good–Samaritan

HOLY FAMILY HOSPITAL AND MEDICAL CENTER (O, 239 beds) 70 East Street, Methuen, MA Zip 01844–4597; tel. 978/687–0151; Joseph Roach, Chief Executive Officer
Web address: www.stewardhealth.org/Holy–Family–Hospital

MERRIMACK VALLEY HOSPITAL (O, 90 beds) 140 Lincoln Avenue, Haverhill, MA Zip 01830–6798; tel. 978/374–2000; Michael F. Collins, Chief Executive Officer
Web address: www.steward.org/merrimack–valley

MORTON HOSPITAL AND MEDICAL CENTER (O, 153 beds) 88 Washington Street, Taunton, MA Zip 02780–2465; tel. 508/828–7000; Kimberly S. Bassett, R.N., President
Web address: www.mortonhospital.org

NASHOBA VALLEY MEDICAL CENTER (O, 48 beds) 200 Groton Road, Ayer, MA Zip 01432–3300; tel. 978/784–9000; Salvatore Perla, President
Web address: www.nashobamed.com

NEW ENGLAND SINAI HOSPITAL AND REHABILITATION CENTER (O, 212 beds) 150 York Street, Stoughton, MA Zip 02072–1881; tel. 781/344–0600; Judith C. Waterston, R.N., MS, President and Chief Executive Officer
Web address: www.newenglandsinai.org

NORWOOD HOSPITAL (O, 205 beds) 800 Washington Street, Norwood, MA Zip 02062–3487; tel. 781/769–4000; Emily L. Holliman, President
Web address: www.stewardhealth.org/Norwood–Hospital

QUINCY MEDICAL CENTER (O, 116 beds) 114 Whitwell Street, Quincy, MA Zip 02169–1899; tel. 617/773–6100; Donna Rubinate, R.N., Interim President
Web address: www.quincymc.org

SAINT ANNE'S HOSPITAL (O, 92 beds) 795 Middle Street, Fall River, MA Zip 02721–1798; tel. 508/674–5741; Craig A. Jesiolowski, FACHE, President
Web address: www.saintanneshospital.org

ST. ELIZABETH'S MEDICAL CENTER (O, 338 beds) 736 Cambridge Street, Brighton, MA Zip 02135–2997; tel. 617/789–3000; Kevin R. Hannifan, President
Web address: www.stewardhealth.org/St_Elizabeths

Owned, leased, sponsored:	11 hospitals	1816 beds
Contract–managed:	0 hospitals	0 beds
Totals:	11 hospitals	1816 beds

0858: STRATEGIC BEHAVIORAL HEALTH, LLC (IO)
8295 Tournament Drive, Suite 201, Memphis, TN Zip 38125–8913; tel. 901/969–3100; Jim Shaheen, President

COLORADO: PEAK VIEW BEHAVIORAL HEALTH (O, 24 beds) 7353 Sisters Grove, Colorado Springs, CO Zip 80923–2615; tel. 719/444–8484; Lana Currance, R.N., MSN, Chief Executive Officer
Web address: www.strategicbh.com/peakview.html

NEVADA: MONTEVISTA HOSPITAL (O, 80 beds) 5900 West Rochelle Avenue, Las Vegas, NV Zip 89103–3327; tel. 702/364–1111; Richard Failla, Chief Executive Officer
Web address: www.montevistahospital.com

RED ROCK BEHAVIORAL HOSPITAL (O, 22 beds) 5975 West Twain Avenue, Las Vegas, NV Zip 89103–1237; tel. 702/214–8099; Toby Davis, Chief Executive Officer
Web address: www.redrockhospital.com

NEW MEXICO: PEAK BEHAVIORAL HEALTH SERVICES (O, 36 beds) 5065 McNutt Road, Santa Teresa, NM Zip 88008–9442; tel. 575/589–3000; Carol Eck, President
Web address: www.peakbehavioral.com/

Owned, leased, sponsored:	4 hospitals	162 beds
Contract–managed:	0 hospitals	0 beds
Totals:	4 hospitals	162 beds

0517: SUCCESS HEALTHCARE (IO)
999 Yamato Road, 3rd Floor, Boca Raton, FL Zip 33431–4477; tel. 561/869–6300; Peter R. Baronoff, President and Chief Executive Officer
(Independent Hospital System)

CALIFORNIA: SILVER LAKE MEDICAL CENTER (O, 150 beds) 1711 West Temple Street, Los Angeles, CA Zip 90026–5421; tel. 213/989–6100; Brent A. Cope, Chief Executive Officer
Web address: www.silverlakemc.com

MISSOURI: ST. ALEXIUS HOSPITAL – BROADWAY CAMPUS (O, 189 beds) 3933 South Broadway, Saint Louis, MO Zip 63118–4601; tel. 314/865–7000; Michael J. Motte, Chief Executive Officer
Web address: www.stalexiushospital.com

Owned, leased, sponsored:	2 hospitals	339 beds
Contract–managed:	0 hospitals	0 beds
Totals:	2 hospitals	339 beds

0399: SUMMA HEALTH SYSTEM (NP)
525 East Market Street, Akron, OH Zip 44304–1619; tel. 330/375–3000; Thomas J. Strauss, President and Chief Executive Officer
(Centralized Health System)

OHIO: ROBINSON MEMORIAL HOSPITAL (O, 141 beds) 6847 North Chestnut Street, Ravenna, OH Zip 44266–3929, Mailing Address: P.O. Box 1204, Zip 44266–1204; tel. 330/297–0811; Stephen Colecchi, President and Chief Executive Officer
Web address: www.robinsonmemorial.org

For explanation of codes following names, see page B2.
★ Indicates Type III membership in the American Hospital Association.

Section B

SUMMA AKRON CITY HOSPITAL (O, 426 beds) 525 East Market Street, Akron, OH Zip 44304–1619; tel. 330/375–3000; Thomas J. Strauss, President and Chief Executive Officer
Web address: www.summahealth.org

SUMMA BARBERTON CITIZENS HOSPITAL (O, 190 beds) 155 Fifth Street N.E., Barberton, OH Zip 44203–3332; tel. 330/615–3000; Jason Niehaus, Senior Vice President Operations and Administrator
Web address: www.summahealth.org/locations/hospitals/barberton

SUMMA REHAB HOSPITAL (O, 60 beds) 29 North Adams Street, Akron, OH Zip 44304–1641; tel. 330/572–7300; Cheryl Henthorn, Chief Executive Officer
Web address: www.summarehabhospital.com/

SUMMA WADSWORTH–RITTMAN HOSPITAL (O, 50 beds) 195 Wadsworth Road, Wadsworth, OH Zip 44281–9505; tel. 330/331–1000; Thomas DeBord, President
Web address: www.wrhhs.org

SUMMA WESTERN RESERVE HOSPITAL (O, 57 beds) 1900 23rd Street, Cuyahoga Falls, OH Zip 44223–1499; tel. 330/971–7000; Robert Kent, D.O., President and Chief Executive Officer
Web address: www.westernreservehospital.org

Owned, leased, sponsored:	6 hospitals	924 beds
Contract–managed:	0 hospitals	0 beds
Totals:	6 hospitals	924 beds

★0189: SUMMIT HEALTH (NP)
112 North Seventh Street, Chambersburg, PA Zip 17201–1720; tel. 717/267–7138; Patrick W. O'Donnell, CPA, President and Chief Executive Officer
(Independent Hospital System)

PENNSYLVANIA: CHAMBERSBURG HOSPITAL (O, 248 beds) 112 North Seventh Street, Chambersburg, PA Zip 17201–1720; tel. 717/267–3000; Patrick W. O'Donnell, CPA, President and Chief Executive Officer
Web address: www.summithealth.org

WAYNESBORO HOSPITAL (O, 64 beds) 501 East Main Street, Waynesboro, PA Zip 17268–2394; tel. 717/765–4000; Melissa Dubrow, Chief Operating Officer
Web address: www.summithealth.org

Owned, leased, sponsored:	2 hospitals	312 beds
Contract–managed:	0 hospitals	0 beds
Totals:	2 hospitals	312 beds

0237: SUNLINK HEALTH SYSTEMS (IO)
900 Circle 75 Parkway, Suite 1120, Atlanta, GA Zip 30339–3005; tel. 770/933–7000; Robert M. Thornton, Jr., Chief Executive Officer
(Independent Hospital System)

GEORGIA: CHESTATEE REGIONAL HOSPITAL (O, 49 beds) 227 Mountain Drive, Dahlonega, GA Zip 30533–1606; tel. 706/864–6136; Jason Cox, Chief Executive Officer
Web address: www.chestateeregionalhospital.com

NORTH GEORGIA MEDICAL CENTER (O, 150 beds) 1362 South Main Street, Ellijay, GA Zip 30540–5410, Mailing Address: P.O. Box 2239, Zip 30540–0025; tel. 706/276–4741; Earl S. Whiteley, FACHE, Chief Executive Officer
Web address: www.northgeorgiamedicalcenter.com

MISSISSIPPI: TRACE REGIONAL HOSPITAL (O, 84 beds) Highway 8 East, Houston, MS Zip 38851–9396, Mailing Address: P.O. Box 626, Zip 38851–0626; tel. 662/456–3700; Gary L. Staten, Chief Executive Officer
Web address: www.traceregional.com

MISSOURI: CALLAWAY COMMUNITY HOSPITAL (O, 37 beds) 10 South Hospital Drive, Fulton, MO Zip 65251–2510; tel. 573/642–3376; Allen D. AufderHeide, Chief Executive Officer
Web address: www.mycallaway.org

Owned, leased, sponsored:	4 hospitals	320 beds
Contract–managed:	0 hospitals	0 beds
Totals:	4 hospitals	320 beds

★0066: SUSQUEHANNA HEALTH SYSTEM (NP)
700 High Street, Williamsport, PA Zip 17701–3100; tel. 570/321–1000; Steven P. Johnson, FACHE, President and Chief Executive Officer
(Centralized Health System)

PENNSYLVANIA: DIVINE PROVIDENCE HOSPITAL (O, 31 beds) 1100 Grampian Boulevard, Williamsport, PA Zip 17701–1995; tel. 570/326–8000; Robert E. Kane, President
Web address: www.susquehannahealth.org

MUNCY VALLEY HOSPITAL (O, 156 beds) 215 East Water Street, Muncy, PA Zip 17756–8700; tel. 570/546–8282; Ronald J. Reynolds, President
Web address: www.susquehannahealth.org

SOLDIERS AND SAILORS MEMORIAL HOSPITAL (O, 83 beds) 32–36 Central Avenue, Wellsboro, PA Zip 16901–1899; tel. 570/724–1631; Janie Hilfiger, President
Web address: www.susquehannahealth.org

WILLIAMSPORT REGIONAL MEDICAL CENTER (O, 205 beds) 700 High Street, Williamsport, PA Zip 17701–3100; tel. 570/321–1000; Jan E. Fisher, President

Owned, leased, sponsored:	4 hospitals	475 beds
Contract–managed:	0 hospitals	0 beds
Totals:	4 hospitals	475 beds

★8795: SUTTER HEALTH (NP)
2200 River Plaza Drive, Sacramento, CA Zip 95833–4134; tel. 916/733–8800; Patrick E. Fry, President and Chief Executive Officer
(Centralized Health System)

CALIFORNIA: ALTA BATES SUMMIT MEDICAL CENTER (O, 441 beds) 2450 Ashby Avenue, Berkeley, CA Zip 94705–2067; tel. 510/204–4444; Charles Prosper, Chief Executive Officer
Web address: www.altabates.com

ALTA BATES SUMMIT MEDICAL CENTER – SUMMIT CAMPUS (O, 382 beds) 350 Hawthorne Avenue, Oakland, CA Zip 94609–3100; tel. 510/655–4000; Charles Prosper, Chief Executive Officer
Web address: www.altabatessummit.com

CALIFORNIA PACIFIC MEDICAL CENTER (O, 724 beds) 2333 Buchanan Street, San Francisco, CA Zip 94115–1925, Mailing Address: P.O. Box 7999, Zip 94120–7999; tel. 415/600–6000; Warren S. Browner, M.D., M.P.H., Chief Executive Officer
Web address: www.cpmc.org

EDEN MEDICAL CENTER (O, 130 beds) 20103 Lake Chabot Road, Castro Valley, CA Zip 94546–5305; tel. 510/537–1234; George Bischalaney, President and Chief Executive Officer
Web address: www.edenmedcenter.org

MEMORIAL HOSPITAL LOS BANOS (O, 46 beds) 520 West I Street, Los Banos, CA Zip 93635–3498; tel. 209/826–0591; Asit Gokli, M.D., Chief Executive Officer
Web address: www.memoriallosbanos.org/

MEMORIAL MEDICAL CENTER (O, 423 beds) 1700 Coffee Road, Modesto, CA Zip 95355–2869, Mailing Address: P.O. Box 942, Zip 95353–0942; tel. 209/526–4500; Daryn J. Kumar, Chief Executive Officer
Web address: www.memorialmedicalcenter.org

MENLO PARK SURGICAL HOSPITAL (O, 12 beds) 570 Willow Road, Menlo Park, CA Zip 94025–2617; tel. 650/324–8500; Kathleen Palange, R.N., Chief Administrative Officer
Web address: www.pamf.org/mpsh

MILLS–PENINSULA HEALTH SERVICES (O, 320 beds) 1501 Trousdale Drive, Burlingame, CA Zip 94010–3282; tel. 650/696–5400; Robert W. Merwin, Chief Executive Officer
Web address: www.mills–peninsula.org

NOVATO COMMUNITY HOSPITAL (O, 40 beds) 180 Rowland Way, Novato, CA Zip 94945–5009, Mailing Address: P.O. Box 1108, Zip 94948–1108; tel. 415/209–1300; Brian Alexander, Chief Administrative Officer
Web address: www.novatocommunity.sutterhealth.org

ST. LUKE'S HOSPITAL (O, 174 beds) 3555 Cesar Chavez Street, San Francisco, CA Zip 94110–4403; tel. 415/600–6000; Warren S. Browner, M.D., M.P.H., Chief Executive Officer
Web address: www.stlukes–sf.org

For explanation of codes following names, see page B2.
★ Indicates Type III membership in the American Hospital Association.

SUTTER AMADOR HOSPITAL (O, 52 beds) 200 Mission Boulevard, Jackson, CA Zip 95642–2564; tel. 209/223–7500; Anne Platt, Chief Executive Officer
Web address: www.sutteramador.org

SUTTER AUBURN FAITH HOSPITAL (O, 72 beds) 11815 Education Street, Auburn, CA Zip 95602–2410; tel. 530/888–4500; Mitchell J. Hanna, Chief Executive Officer
Web address: www.sutterhealth.org

SUTTER CENTER FOR PSYCHIATRY (O, 71 beds) 7700 Folsom Boulevard, Sacramento, CA Zip 95826–2608; tel. 916/386–3000; John W. Boyd, PsyD, Chief Administrative Officer
Web address: www.sutterpsychiatry.org

SUTTER COAST HOSPITAL (O, 49 beds) 800 East Washington Boulevard, Crescent City, CA Zip 95531–8359; tel. 707/464–8511; Mitchell J. Hanna, Interim Chief Executive Officer
Web address: www.sutterhealth.org

SUTTER DAVIS HOSPITAL (O, 48 beds) 2000 Sutter Place, Davis, CA Zip 95616–6201, Mailing Address: P.O. Box 1617, Zip 95617–1617; tel. 530/756–6440; Janet Wagner, R.N., Chief Executive Officer
Web address: www.sutterhealth.org

SUTTER DELTA MEDICAL CENTER (O, 136 beds) 3901 Lone Tree Way, Antioch, CA Zip 94509–6253; tel. 925/779–7200; Gary D. Rapaport, Chief Executive Officer
Web address: www.sutterdelta.org

SUTTER LAKESIDE HOSPITAL (O, 25 beds) 5176 Hill Road East, Lakeport, CA Zip 95453–6300; tel. 707/262–5000; Siri Nelson, Chief Administrative Officer
Web address: www.sutterlakeside.org

SUTTER MATERNITY AND SURGERY CENTER OF SANTA CRUZ (O, 30 beds) 2900 Chanticleer Avenue, Santa Cruz, CA Zip 95065–1816; tel. 831/477–2200; Stephen Gray, Chief Administrative Officer
Web address: www.suttermatsurg.org

SUTTER MEDICAL CENTER OF SANTA ROSA, CHANATE CAMPUS (O, 116 beds) 3325 Chanate Road, Santa Rosa, CA Zip 95404–1707; tel. 707/576–4000; Mike Purvis, Chief Administrative Officer
Web address: www.sutterhealth.org

SUTTER MEDICAL CENTER, SACRAMENTO (O, 620 beds) 5151 F Street, Sacramento, CA Zip 95819–3295; tel. 916/454–3333; Carrie Owen–Plietz, Chief Executive Officer
Web address: www.sutterhealth.org

SUTTER OAKS NURSING CENTER (O, 100 beds) 2600 L. Street, Sacramento, CA Zip 95816–5612; tel. 916/552–2200; John W. Boyd, PsyD, Chief Administrative Officer

SUTTER ROSEVILLE MEDICAL CENTER (O, 328 beds) One Medical Plaza, Roseville, CA Zip 95661–3037; tel. 916/781–1000; Patrick R. Brady, Chief Executive Officer
Web address: www.sutterroseville.org

SUTTER SOLANO MEDICAL CENTER (O, 102 beds) 300 Hospital Drive, Vallejo, CA Zip 94589–2574, Mailing Address: P.O. Box 3189, Zip 94590–0669; tel. 707/554–4444; Theresa Glubka, Chief Executive Officer
Web address: www.suttersolano.org

SUTTER TRACY COMMUNITY HOSPITAL (O, 81 beds) 1420 North Tracy Boulevard, Tracy, CA Zip 95376–3497; tel. 209/835–1500; David M. Thompson, Chief Executive Officer
Web address: www.suttertracy.org

HAWAII: KAHI MOHALA BEHAVIORAL HEALTH (O, 76 beds) 91–2301 Old Fort Weaver Road, Ewa Beach, HI Zip 96706–3602; tel. 808/671–8511; Leonard Licina, Chief Executive Officer
Web address: www.kahimohala.org

Owned, leased, sponsored:	25 hospitals	4598 beds
Contract–managed:	0 hospitals	0 beds
Totals:	25 hospitals	4598 beds

★**0871: SWEDISH HEALTH SERVICES** (NP)
747 Broadway, Seattle, WA Zip 98122–4379; tel. 206/386–6000; Anthony A. Armada, Chief Executive
(Centralized Health System)

WASHINGTON: SWEDISH MEDICAL CENTER–CHERRY HILL CAMPUS (O, 189 beds) 500 17th Avenue, Seattle, WA Zip 98122–5711; tel. 206/320–2000; Todd Strumwasser, M.D., Chief Executive
Web address: www.swedish.org

SWEDISH MEDICAL CENTER–FIRST HILL (O, 631 beds) 747 Broadway, Seattle, WA Zip 98122–4307; tel. 206/386–6000; Todd Strumwasser, M.D., Chief Executive
Web address: www.swedish.org

SWEDISH/EDMONDS (O, 139 beds) 21601 76th Avenue West, Edmonds, WA Zip 98026–7506; tel. 425/640–4000; David E. Jaffe, Chief Executive
Web address: www.swedish.org

SWEDISH/ISSAQUAH (O, 80 beds) 751 N.E. Blakely Drive, Issaquah, WA Zip 98029–6201; tel. 425/313–4000; Rayburn Lewis, M.D., Chief Executive Officer
Web address: www.swedish.org/issaquah

Owned, leased, sponsored:	4 hospitals	1039 beds
Contract–managed:	0 hospitals	0 beds
Totals:	4 hospitals	1039 beds

★**5375: SYLVANIA FRANCISCAN HEALTH** (CC)
3231 Central Park West, Suite 106, Toledo, OH Zip 43617–3009; tel. 419/882–8373; James W. Pope, FACHE, President and Chief Executive Officer
(Independent Hospital System)

OHIO: PROVIDENCE CARE CENTER (S, 138 beds) 2025 Hayes Avenue, Sandusky, OH Zip 44870; Rick G. Ryan, Administrator and Chief Executive Officer

TRINITY HEALTH SYSTEM (S, 312 beds) 380 Summit Avenue, Steubenville, OH Zip 43952–2699; tel. 740/283–7000; Fred B. Brower, President and Chief Executive Officer
Web address: www.trinityhealth.com

TRINITY HOSPITAL TWIN CITY (S, 25 beds) 819 North First Street, Dennison, OH Zip 44621–1098; tel. 740/922–2800; Joseph J. Mitchell, President
Web address: www.trinitytwincity.org

TEXAS: BELLVILLE ST. JOSEPH HEALTH CENTER (S, 23 beds) 44 North Cummings Street, Bellville, TX Zip 77418–1347; tel. 979/413–7400; Mark Riggins, Administrator
Web address: www.st–joseph.org/body.cfm?id=773

BURLESON ST. JOSEPH HEALTH CENTER (S, 25 beds) 1101 Woodson Drive, Caldwell, TX Zip 77836–1052, Mailing Address: P.O. Box 360, Zip 77836–0360; tel. 979/567–3245; John Hughson, Administrator
Web address: www.st–joseph.org/

GRIMES ST. JOSEPH HEALTH CENTER (S, 18 beds) 210 South Judson Street, Navasota, TX Zip 77868–3704; tel. 936/825–6585; Reed Edmundson, Regional Administrator
Web address: www.st–joseph.org

MADISON ST. JOSEPH HEALTH CENTER (S, 25 beds) 100 West Cross Street, Madisonville, TX Zip 77864–2432, Mailing Address: Box 698, Zip 77864–0698; tel. 936/348–2631; Reed Edmundson, Administrator
Web address: www.st–joseph.org

ST. JOSEPH REGIONAL HEALTH CENTER (S, 233 beds) 2801 Franciscan Drive, Bryan, TX Zip 77802–2599; tel. 979/776–3777; Kathleen R. Krusie, FACHE, Chief Executive Officer
Web address: www.st–joseph.org

Owned, leased, sponsored:	8 hospitals	799 beds
Contract–managed:	0 hospitals	0 beds
Totals:	8 hospitals	799 beds

0379: TAHOE FOREST HEALTH SYSTEM (NP)
10121 Pine Avenue, Truckee, CA Zip 96161–4835; tel. 530/587–6011; Robert A. Schapper, Chief Executive Officer

CALIFORNIA: TAHOE FOREST HOSPITAL DISTRICT (O, 25 beds) 10121 Pine Avenue, Truckee, CA Zip 96161–4856, Mailing Address: P.O. Box 759, Zip 96160–0759; tel. 530/587–6011; Robert A. Schapper, Chief Executive Officer
Web address: www.tfhd.com

For explanation of codes following names, see page B2.
★ Indicates Type III membership in the American Hospital Association.

Section B

NEVADA: INCLINE VILLAGE COMMUNITY HOSPITAL (O, 6 beds) 880 Alder Avenue, Incline Village, NV Zip 89451–8335; tel. 775/833–4100; Judy Newland, R.N., Chief Nursing Officer
Web address: www.tfhd.com

Owned, leased, sponsored:	2 hospitals	31 beds
Contract–managed:	0 hospitals	0 beds
Totals:	2 hospitals	31 beds

★**0341: TANNER HEALTH SYSTEM** (NP)
705 Dixie Street, Carrollton, GA Zip 30117–3818; tel. 770/836–9580; Loy M. Howard, President and Chief Executive Officer

GEORGIA: HIGGINS GENERAL HOSPITAL (L, 25 beds) 200 Allen Memorial Drive, Bremen, GA Zip 30110–2012; tel. 770/824–2000; Michael D. Alexander, MS, Administrator
Web address: www.tanner.org/Main/HigginsGeneralHospitalBremen.aspx
TANNER MEDICAL CENTER–CARROLLTON (O, 201 beds) 705 Dixie Street, Carrollton, GA Zip 30117–3818; tel. 770/836–9666; Deborah Matthews, Administrator
Web address: www.tanner.org
TANNER MEDICAL CENTER–VILLA RICA (O, 39 beds) 601 Dallas Road, Villa Rica, GA Zip 30180–1202, Mailing Address: P.O. Box 638, Zip 30180–0638; tel. 770/456–3000; Taylor Powers, Administrator
Web address: www.tanner.org

Owned, leased, sponsored:	3 hospitals	265 beds
Contract–managed:	0 hospitals	0 beds
Totals:	3 hospitals	265 beds

★**0169: TEMPLE UNIVERSITY HEALTH SYSTEM** (NP)
3509 North Broad Street, 9th Floor, Philadelphia, PA Zip 19140–4105; tel. 215/707–0900; Larry Kaiser, M.D., President and Chief Executive Officer
(Moderately Centralized Health System)

PENNSYLVANIA: FOX CHASE CANCER CENTER–AMERICAN ONCOLOGIC HOSPITAL (O, 66 beds) 333 Cottman Avenue, Philadelphia, PA Zip 19111–2434; tel. 215/728–6900; Richard Fisher, President and Chief Executive Officer
Web address: www.fccc.edu
JEANES HOSPITAL (O, 160 beds) 7600 Central Avenue, Philadelphia, PA Zip 19111–2499; tel. 215/728–2000; Linda J. Grass, President and Chief Executive Officer
Web address: www.jeanes.com
TEMPLE UNIVERSITY HOSPITAL (O, 665 beds) 3401 North Broad Street, Philadelphia, PA Zip 19140–5103; tel. 215/707–2000; John N. Kastanis, FACHE, Chief Executive Officer
Web address: www.tuh.templehealth.org/content/default.htm

Owned, leased, sponsored:	3 hospitals	891 beds
Contract–managed:	0 hospitals	0 beds
Totals:	3 hospitals	891 beds

★**0919: TENET HEALTHCARE CORPORATION** (IO)
1445 Ross Avenue, Suite 1400, Dallas, TX Zip 75202–2703, Mailing Address: P.O. Box 1390369, Zip 75313–9036; tel. 469/893–2200; Trevor Fetter, President and Chief Executive Officer

ALABAMA: BROOKWOOD MEDICAL CENTER (O, 631 beds) 2010 Brookwood Medical Center Drive, Birmingham, AL Zip 35209–6875; tel. 205/877–1000; Garry L. Gause, President and Chief Executive Officer
Web address: www.bwmc.com

ARIZONA: ARROWHEAD HOSPITAL (O, 234 beds) 18701 North 67th Avenue, Glendale, AZ Zip 85308–7100; tel. 623/561–1000; Frank L. Molinaro, Chief Executive Officer
Web address: www.arrowheadhospital.com
MARYVALE HOSPITAL MEDICAL CENTER (O, 100 beds) 5102 West Campbell Avenue, Phoenix, AZ Zip 85031–1799; tel. 623/848–5000; Crystal Hamilton, R.N., Chief Executive Officer
Web address: www.maryvalehospital.com

PARADISE VALLEY HOSPITAL (O, 142 beds) 3929 East Bell Road, Phoenix, AZ Zip 85032–2196; tel. 602/923–5000; David Tupponce, M.D., Interim Chief Executive Officer
Web address: www.paradisevalleyhospital.com
PHOENIX BAPTIST HOSPITAL (O, 215 beds) 2000 West Bethany Home Road, Phoenix, AZ Zip 85015–2443; tel. 602/249–0212; Danny L. Jones, Jr., FACHE, Chief Executive Officer
Web address: www.phoenixbaptisthospital.com
WEST VALLEY HOSPITAL (O, 106 beds) 13677 West McDowell Road, Goodyear, AZ Zip 85395–2635; tel. 623/882–1500; Stan V. Holm, FACHE, Chief Executive Officer
Web address: www.wvhospital.com

CALIFORNIA: DESERT REGIONAL MEDICAL CENTER (L, 387 beds) 1150 North Indian Canyon Drive, Palm Springs, CA Zip 92262–4872, Mailing Address: P.O. Box 2739, Zip 92263–2739; tel. 760/323–6511; Carolyn W. Caldwell, Chief Executive Officer
Web address: www.desertmedctr.com
DOCTORS HOSPITAL OF MANTECA (O, 73 beds) 1205 East North Street, Manteca, CA Zip 95336–4900; tel. 209/823–3111; Nicholas R. Tejeda, FACHE, Chief Executive Officer
Web address: www.doctorsmanteca.com
DOCTORS MEDICAL CENTER (O, 455 beds) 1441 Florida Avenue, Modesto, CA Zip 95350–4418, Mailing Address: P.O. Box 4138, Zip 95352–4138; tel. 209/578–1211; Warren J. Kirk, Chief Executive Officer
Web address: www.dmc–modesto.com
FOUNTAIN VALLEY REGIONAL HOSPITAL AND MEDICAL CENTER (O, 242 beds) 17100 Euclid Street, Fountain Valley, CA Zip 92708–4043; tel. 714/966–7200; B. Joseph Badalian, Chief Executive Officer
Web address: www.fountainvalleyhospital.com
JOHN F. KENNEDY MEMORIAL HOSPITAL (O, 109 beds) 47111 Monroe Street, Indio, CA Zip 92201–6799; tel. 760/347–6191; Gary Honts, Interim Chief Executive Officer
Web address: www.jfkmemorialhosp.com
LAKEWOOD REGIONAL MEDICAL CENTER (O, 153 beds) 3700 East South Street, Lakewood, CA Zip 90712–1498, Mailing Address: P.O. Box 6070, Zip 90714–6070; tel. 562/531–2550; Ronald J. Galonsky, Chief Executive Officer
Web address: www.lakewoodregional.com
LOS ALAMITOS MEDICAL CENTER (O, 167 beds) 3751 Katella Avenue, Los Alamitos, CA Zip 90720–3164; tel. 562/598–1311; Kent G. Clayton, Chief Executive Officer
Web address: www.losalamitosmedctr.com
PLACENTIA–LINDA HOSPITAL (O, 114 beds) 1301 North Rose Drive, Placentia, CA Zip 92870–3899; tel. 714/993–2000; Dwayne Richardson, Interim Chief Executive Officer
Web address: www.placentialinda.com
SAN RAMON REGIONAL MEDICAL CENTER (O, 123 beds) 6001 Norris Canyon Road, San Ramon, CA Zip 94583–5400; tel. 925/275–9200; Gary Sloan, Chief Executive Officer
Web address: www.sanramonmedctr.com
SIERRA VISTA REGIONAL MEDICAL CENTER (O, 164 beds) 1010 Murray Avenue, San Luis Obispo, CA Zip 93405–1806, Mailing Address: P.O. Box 1367, Zip 93406–1367; tel. 805/546–7600; Joseph DeSchryver, Chief Executive Officer
Web address: www.sierravistaregional.com
TWIN CITIES COMMUNITY HOSPITAL (O, 122 beds) 1100 Las Tablas Road, Templeton, CA Zip 93465–9796; tel. 805/434–3500; Mark P. Lisa, FACHE, Chief Executive Officer
Web address: www.twincitieshospital.com

FLORIDA: CORAL GABLES HOSPITAL (O, 256 beds) 3100 Douglas Road, Coral Gables, FL Zip 33134–6914; tel. 305/445–8461; Jeffrey M. Welch, Chief Executive Officer
Web address: www.coralgableshospital.com
DELRAY MEDICAL CENTER (O, 493 beds) 5352 Linton Boulevard, Delray Beach, FL Zip 33484–6580; tel. 561/498–4440; Mark Bryan, Chief Executive Officer
Web address: www.delraymedicalctr.com
GOOD SAMARITAN MEDICAL CENTER (O, 174 beds) 1309 North Flagler Drive, West Palm Beach, FL Zip 33401–3499; tel. 561/655–5511; Mark Nosacka, Chief Executive Officer
Web address: www.goodsamaritanmc.com

For explanation of codes following names, see page B2.
★ Indicates Type III membership in the American Hospital Association.

Section B

HIALEAH HOSPITAL (O, 160 beds) 651 East 25th Street, Hialeah, FL Zip 33013–3878; tel. 305/693–6100; Ben A. Rodriguez, Chief Executive Officer
Web address: www.hialeahhosp.com

NORTH SHORE MEDICAL CENTER (O, 357 beds) 1100 N.W. 95th Street, Miami, FL Zip 33150–2098; tel. 305/835–6000; Manuel Linares, Chief Executive Officer
Web address: www.northshoremedical.com

NORTH SHORE MEDICAL CENTER, FLORIDA MEDICAL CENTER CAMPUS (O, 459 beds) 5000 West Oakland Park Boulevard, Fort Lauderdale, FL Zip 33313–1585; tel. 954/735–6000; Gabrielle Finley–Hazle, Chief Executive Officer
Web address: www.fmc–campus.com

PALM BEACH GARDENS MEDICAL CENTER (L, 199 beds) 3360 Burns Road, Palm Beach Gardens, FL Zip 33410–4323; tel. 561/622–1411; Larry Coomes, Chief Executive Officer
Web address: www.pbgmc.com

PALMETTO GENERAL HOSPITAL (O, 360 beds) 2001 West 68th Street, Hialeah, FL Zip 33016–1898; tel. 305/823–5000; Ana J. Mederos, Chief Executive Officer
Web address: www.palmettogeneral.com

ST. MARY'S MEDICAL CENTER (O, 464 beds) 901 45th Street, West Palm Beach, FL Zip 33407–2495; tel. 561/844–6300; Davide M. Carbone, FACHE, Chief Executive Officer
Web address: www.stmarysmc.com

WEST BOCA MEDICAL CENTER (O, 195 beds) 21644 State Road 7, Boca Raton, FL Zip 33428–1899; tel. 561/488–8000; Mitchell S. Feldman, Chief Executive Officer
Web address: www.westbocamedctr.com

GEORGIA: ATLANTA MEDICAL CENTER (O, 536 beds) 303 Parkway Drive N.E., Atlanta, GA Zip 30312–1212; tel. 404/265–4000; Christopher Locke, Interim Chief Executive Officer
Web address: www.atlantamedcenter.com

NORTH FULTON REGIONAL HOSPITAL (L, 196 beds) 3000 Hospital Boulevard, Roswell, GA Zip 30076–3899; tel. 770/751–2500; Deborah C. Keel, Chief Executive Officer
Web address: www.northfultonregional.com

SPALDING REGIONAL MEDICAL CENTER (O, 160 beds) 601 South Eighth Street, Griffin, GA Zip 30224–4294, Mailing Address: P.O. Drawer V, Zip 30224–1168; tel. 770/228–2721; John A. Quinn, Chief Executive Officer
Web address: www.spaldingregional.com

SYLVAN GROVE HOSPITAL (L, 24 beds) 1050 McDonough Road, Jackson, GA Zip 30233–1599; tel. 770/775–7861; John A. Quinn, Chief Executive Officer
Web address: www.sylvangrovehospital.com

ILLINOIS: LOUIS A. WEISS MEMORIAL HOSPITAL (O, 184 beds) 4646 North Marine Drive, Chicago, IL Zip 60640–5759; tel. 773/878–8700; Anthony Tedeschi, M.D., M.P.H., Chief Executive Officer and Chief Medical Officer
Web address: www.weisshospital.com

MACNEAL HOSPITAL (O, 371 beds) 3249 South Oak Park Avenue, Berwyn, IL Zip 60402–0715; tel. 708/783–9100; J. Scott Steiner, Chief Executive Officer
Web address: www.macneal.com

WEST SUBURBAN MEDICAL CENTER (O, 172 beds) 3 Erie Court, Oak Park, IL Zip 60302–2599; tel. 708/383–6200; Patrick Maloney, Chief Executive Officer
Web address: www.westsuburbanmc.com/Home.aspx

WESTLAKE HOSPITAL (O, 181 beds) 1225 Lake Street, Melrose Park, IL Zip 60160–4000; tel. 708/681–3000; Patrick Maloney, Chief Executive Officer
Web address: www.wlhospital.com/Home.aspx

MASSACHUSETTS: METROWEST MEDICAL CENTER (O, 143 beds) 115 Lincoln Street, Framingham, MA Zip 01702–6342; tel. 508/383–1000; Barbara J. Doyle, R.N., MS, Chief Executive Officer
Web address: www.mwmc.com

SAINT VINCENT HOSPITAL (O, 283 beds) 123 Summer Street, Worcester, MA Zip 01608–1216; tel. 508/363–5000; Steven MacLauchlan, President and CEO
Web address: www.stvincenthospital.com

MICHIGAN: CHILDREN'S HOSPITAL OF MICHIGAN (O, 222 beds) 3901 Beaubien Street, Detroit, MI Zip 48201–2119; tel. 313/745–5437; Larry M. Gold, Chief Executive Officer
Web address: www.chmkids.org

DETROIT RECEIVING HOSPITAL/UNIVERSITY HEALTH CENTER (O, 268 beds) 4201 Saint Antoine Street, Detroit, MI Zip 48201–2153; tel. 313/745–3000; Iris Taylor, Ph.D., R.N., President
Web address: www.dmc.org

DMC HARPER UNIVERSITY HOSPITAL (O, 535 beds) 3990 John R Street, Detroit, MI Zip 48201–2018; tel. 313/745–8040; Reginald J. Eadie, M.D., Chief Executive Officer
Web address: www.harperhospital.org

DMC HURON VALLEY–SINAI HOSPITAL (O, 220 beds) 1 William Carls Drive, Commerce Township, MI Zip 48382–2201; tel. 248/937–3300; Andrei Soran, MSN, President
Web address: www.hvsh.org

REHABILITATION INSTITUTE OF MICHIGAN (O, 74 beds) 261 Mack Avenue, Detroit, MI Zip 48201–2495; tel. 313/745–1203; William H. Restum, Ph.D., President
Web address: www.rimrehab.org

SINAI–GRACE HOSPITAL (O, 310 beds) 6071 West Outer Drive, Detroit, MI Zip 48235–2679; tel. 313/966–3300; Reginald J. Eadie, M.D., Interim President
Web address: www.sinaigrace.org

MISSOURI: DES PERES HOSPITAL (O, 143 beds) 2345 Dougherty Ferry Road, Saint Louis, MO Zip 63122–3313; tel. 314/966–9100; John A. Grah, JD, FACHE, Chief Executive Officer
Web address: www.despereshospital.com

SAINT LOUIS UNIVERSITY HOSPITAL (O, 356 beds) 3635 Vista at Grand Boulevard, Saint Louis, MO Zip 63110–0250, Mailing Address: P.O. Box 15250, Zip 63110–0250; tel. 314/577–8000; Phillip E. Sowa, Chief Executive Officer
Web address: www.sluhospital.com

NORTH CAROLINA: CENTRAL CAROLINA HOSPITAL (O, 116 beds) 1135 Carthage Street, Sanford, NC Zip 27330–4162; tel. 919/774–2100; David E. Loving, Chief Executive Officer
Web address: www.centralcarolinahosp.com

FRYE REGIONAL MEDICAL CENTER (L, 306 beds) 420 North Center Street, Hickory, NC Zip 28601–5049; tel. 828/322–6070; Steven D. Patonai, Chief Executive Officer
Web address: www.fryemedctr.com

PENNSYLVANIA: HAHNEMANN UNIVERSITY HOSPITAL (O, 496 beds) Broad and Vine Streets, Philadelphia, PA Zip 19102–1192; tel. 215/762–7000; Michael P. Halter, Chief Executive Officer
Web address: www.hahnemannhospital.com

ST. CHRISTOPHER'S HOSPITAL FOR CHILDREN (O, 189 beds) 3601 A. Street, Philadelphia, PA Zip 19134–1043; tel. 215/427–5000; Carolyn Jackson, Chief Executive Officer
Web address: www.stchristophershospital.com

SOUTH CAROLINA: COASTAL CAROLINA HOSPITAL (O, 41 beds) 1000 Medical Center Drive, Hardeeville, SC Zip 29927–3446; tel. 843/784–8000; Bradley S. Talbert, FACHE, Chief Executive Officer
Web address: www.coastalhospital.com

EAST COOPER MEDICAL CENTER (O, 140 beds) 2000 Hospital Drive, Mount Pleasant, SC Zip 29464–3764; tel. 843/881–0100; Jason P. Alexander, FACHE, Chief Executive Officer
Web address: www.eastcoopermedctr.com

HILTON HEAD HOSPITAL (O, 93 beds) 25 Hospital Center Boulevard, Hilton Head Island, SC Zip 29926–2738; tel. 843/681–6122; Mark T. O'Neil, Jr., President and Chief Executive Officer
Web address: www.hiltonheadregional.com

PIEDMONT MEDICAL CENTER (O, 280 beds) 222 Herlong Avenue, Rock Hill, SC Zip 29732; tel. 803/329–1234; William Masterton, Chief Executive Officer
Web address: www.piedmontmedicalcenter.com

TENNESSEE: SAINT FRANCIS HOSPITAL (O, 511 beds) 5959 Park Avenue, Memphis, TN Zip 38119–5198, Mailing Address: P.O. Box 171808, Zip 38187–1808; tel. 901/765–1000; David L. Archer, Chief Executive Officer
Web address: www.saintfrancishosp.com

For explanation of codes following names, see page B2.
★ Indicates Type III membership in the American Hospital Association.

SAINT FRANCIS HOSPITAL–BARTLETT (O, 100 beds) 2986 Kate Bond Road, Bartlett, TN Zip 38133–4003; tel. 901/820–7000; Jeremy Clark, Chief Executive Officer
Web address: www.saintfrancisbartlett.com

TEXAS: BAPTIST MEDICAL CENTER (O, 1527 beds) 111 Dallas Street, San Antonio, TX Zip 78205–1230; tel. 210/297–7000; Jonathan Turton, FACHE, Interim President
Web address: www.baptisthealthsystem.com

CENTENNIAL MEDICAL CENTER (O, 118 beds) 12505 Lebanon Road, Frisco, TX Zip 75035–8298; tel. 972/963–3333; Joe D. Thomason, Chief Executive Officer
Web address: www.centennialmedcenter.com

CYPRESS FAIRBANKS MEDICAL CENTER (O, 181 beds) 10655 Steepletop Drive, Houston, TX Zip 77065–4297; tel. 281/890–4285; Terry J. Wheeler, Chief Executive Officer
Web address: www.cyfairhospital.com

DOCTORS HOSPITAL AT WHITE ROCK LAKE (O, 151 beds) 9440 Poppy Drive, Dallas, TX Zip 75218–3694; tel. 214/324–6100; Jaikumar Krishnaswamy, Chief Executive Officer
Web address: www.doctorshospitaldallas.com

HOUSTON NORTHWEST MEDICAL CENTER (O, 339 beds) 710 FM 1960 Road West, Houston, TX Zip 77090–3402; tel. 281/440–1000; Timothy Puthoff, Chief Executive Officer
Web address: www.hnmc.com

LAKE POINTE MEDICAL CENTER (O, 112 beds) 6800 Scenic Drive, Rowlett, TX Zip 75088–4552, Mailing Address: P.O. Box 1550, Zip 75030–1550; tel. 972/412–2273; Brett D. Lee, Chief Executive Officer
Web address: www.lakepointemedical.com

NACOGDOCHES MEDICAL CENTER (O, 109 beds) 4920 N.E. Stallings Drive, Nacogdoches, TX Zip 75965–1200; tel. 936/569–9481; Gary L. Stokes, Chief Executive Officer
Web address: www.nacmedicalcenter.com

PARK PLAZA HOSPITAL (O, 157 beds) 1313 Hermann Drive, Houston, TX Zip 77004–7092; tel. 713/527–5000; John Tressa, R.N., MSN, Chief Executive Officer
Web address: www.parkplazahospital.com

PLAZA SPECIALTY HOSPITAL (O, 39 beds) 1300 Binz, Houston, TX Zip 77004–7016; tel. 713/285–1000; Steven Barr, R.N., MSN, Chief Executive Officer
Web address: www.plazaspecialtyhospital.com

PROVIDENCE MEMORIAL HOSPITAL (O, 351 beds) 2001 North Oregon Street, El Paso, TX Zip 79902–3368; tel. 915/577–6625; J. Eric Evans, Chief Executive Officer
Web address: www.sphn.com

SIERRA MEDICAL CENTER (O, 352 beds) 1625 Medical Center Drive, El Paso, TX Zip 79902–5044; tel. 915/747–4000; J. Eric Evans, Chief Executive Officer
Web address: www.sphn.com

SIERRA PROVIDENCE EAST MEDICAL CENTER (O, 110 beds) 3280 Joe Battle Boulevard, El Paso, TX Zip 79938–2622; tel. 915/832–2000; Sally A. Deitch, MSN, R.N., Chief Executive Officer
Web address: www.sphn.com

VALLEY BAPTIST MEDICAL CENTER–BROWNSVILLE (O, 240 beds) 1040 West Jefferson Street, Brownsville, TX Zip 78520–6338, Mailing Address: P.O. Box 3590, Zip 78523–3590; tel. 956/698–5400; Leslie Bingham, Senior Vice President and Chief Executive Officer
Web address: www.valleybaptist.net/brownsville/index.htm

VALLEY BAPTIST MEDICAL CENTER–HARLINGEN (O, 416 beds) 2101 Pease Street, Harlingen, TX Zip 78550–8307, Mailing Address: P.O. Drawer 2588, Zip 78551–2588; tel. 956/389–1100; Todd Mann, Senior Vice President and Chief Executive Officer
Web address: www.valleybaptist.net/harlingen/index.htm

Owned, leased, sponsored:	69 hospitals	17506 beds
Contract–managed:	0 hospitals	0 beds
Totals:	69 hospitals	17506 beds

0876: TENNESSEE HEALTH MANAGEMENT (IO)
52 West Eighth Street, Parsons, TN Zip 38363–4656, Mailing Address: PO Box 10, Zip 38363–0010; tel. 731/847–6343; Dennis Berry, Chief Executive Officer

ALABAMA: BEHAVIORAL HEALTHCARE CENTER AT HUNTSVILLE (O, 20 beds) 5315 Millennium Drive N.W., Huntsville, AL Zip 35806–2458; tel. 256/964–6700; Bradley Moss, Administrator
Web address: www.tnhealthmanagement.com/bhc/huntsville

TENNESSEE: BEHAVIORAL HEALTHCARE CENTER AT CLARKSVILLE (O, 26 beds) 930 Professional Park Drive, Clarksville, TN Zip 37040–5136; tel. 931/538–6420; Jennifer Robinson, Administrator
Web address: www.bhcclarksville.com

BEHAVIORAL HEALTHCARE CENTER AT COLUMBIA (O, 16 beds) 1400 Rosewood Drive, Columbia, TN Zip 38401–4878; tel. 931/388–6573; Paula Chennault, Administrator
Web address: www.bhccolumbia.com

BEHAVIORAL HEALTHCARE CENTER AT MARTIN (O, 16 beds) 458 Hannings Lane, Martin, TN Zip 38237–3308; tel. 731/588–2830; Carrie Brawley, Administrator
Web address: www.tnhealthmanagement.com/BHC/martin/

Owned, leased, sponsored:	4 hospitals	78 beds
Contract–managed:	0 hospitals	0 beds
Totals:	4 hospitals	78 beds

0020: TEXAS DEPARTMENT OF STATE HEALTH SERVICES (NP)
1100 West 49th Street, Austin, TX Zip 78756–3199; tel. 512/458–7111; David L. Lakey, M.D., Commissioner
(Independent Hospital System)

TEXAS: AUSTIN STATE HOSPITAL (O, 314 beds) 4110 Guadalupe Street, Austin, TX Zip 78751–4296; tel. 512/452–0381; Cathy Nottebart, Acting Superintendent
Web address: www.dshs.state.tx.us/mhhospitals/austinsh/default.shtm

BIG SPRING STATE HOSPITAL (O, 200 beds) 1901 North Highway 87, Big Spring, TX Zip 79720–0283; tel. 432/267–8216; Lorie Dunnam, Superintendent
Web address: www.dshs.state.tx.us/mhhospitals/BigSpringSH/default.shtm

EL PASO PSYCHIATRIC CENTER (O, 77 beds) 4615 Alameda Avenue, El Paso, TX Zip 79905–2702; tel. 915/532–2202; Zulema Carrillo, Superintendent
Web address: www.dshs.state.tx.us/mhhospitals/ElPasoPC/default.shtm

KERRVILLE STATE HOSPITAL (O, 202 beds) 721 Thompson Drive, Kerrville, TX Zip 78028–5154; tel. 830/896–2211; Leigh Ann Fitzpatrick, Superintendent
Web address: www.dshs.state.tx.us/mhhospitals/KerrvilleSH/default.shtm

NORTH TEXAS STATE HOSPITAL (O, 640 beds) Highway 70 Northwest, Vernon, TX Zip 76384, Mailing Address: P.O. Box 2231, Zip 76385–2231; tel. 940/552–9901; James E. Smith, Superintendent
Web address: www.dshs.state.tx.us/mhhospitals/NorthTexasSH/default.shtm

RIO GRANDE STATE CENTER/SOUTH TEXAS HEALTH CARE SYSTEM (O, 128 beds) 1401 South Rangerville Road, Harlingen, TX Zip 78552–7638; tel. 956/364–8000; Sonia Hernandez–Keeble, Superintendent
Web address: www.dshs.state.tx.us/mhhospitals/RioGrandeSC/default.shtm

RUSK STATE HOSPITAL (O, 365 beds) 805 North Dickinson, Rusk, TX Zip 75785–2333, Mailing Address: P.O. Box 318, Zip 75785–0318; tel. 903/683–3421; Brenda Slaton, Administrator
Web address: www.dshs.state.tx.us/mhhospitals/RuskSH/default.shtm

SAN ANTONIO STATE HOSPITAL (O, 302 beds) 6711 South New Braunfels, Suite 100, San Antonio, TX Zip 78223–3006; tel. 210/531–7711; Robert C. Arizpe, Superintendent
Web address: www.dshs.state.tx.us/mhhospitals/SanAntonioSH/default.shtm

TERRELL STATE HOSPITAL (O, 288 beds) 1200 East Brin Street, Terrell, TX Zip 75160–2938, Mailing Address: P.O. Box 70, Zip 75160–9000; tel. 972/524–6452; Dorothy Floyd, Ph.D., Superintendent
Web address: www.dshs.state.tx.us/mhhospitals/terrellsh

TEXAS CENTER FOR INFECTIOUS DISEASE (O, 40 beds) 2303 S.E. Military Drive, San Antonio, TX Zip 78223–3597; tel. 210/534–8857; James N. Elkins, FACHE, Superintendent
Web address: www.dshs.state.tx.us/tcid/default.shtm

For explanation of codes following names, see page B2.
★ Indicates Type III membership in the American Hospital Association.

Owned, leased, sponsored:	10 hospitals	2556 beds
Contract–managed:	0 hospitals	0 beds
Totals:	10 hospitals	2556 beds

★**0129: TEXAS HEALTH RESOURCES** (NP)
612 East Lamar Boulevard, Suite 900, Arlington, TX
Zip 76011–4130; tel. 682/236–7900; Barclay E. Berdan, FACHE,
Chief Executive Officer
(Moderately Centralized Health System)

TEXAS HEALTH ARLINGTON MEMORIAL HOSPITAL (O, 299 beds) 800 West
Randol Mill Road, Arlington, TX Zip 76012–2503; tel. 817/548–6100; Kirk
King, FACHE, President
Web address: www.arlingtonmemorial.org

TEXAS HEALTH HARRIS METHODIST HOSPITAL ALLIANCE (O, 58 beds)
10864 Texas Health Trail, Fort Worth, TX Zip 76244–4897;
tel. 682/212–2000; Winjie Tang Miao, President

TEXAS HEALTH HARRIS METHODIST HOSPITAL AZLE (O, 31 beds) 108
Denver Trail, Azle, TX Zip 76020–3614; tel. 817/444–8600; Bob S. Ellzey,
FACHE, President
Web address: www.texashealth.org/Azle

TEXAS HEALTH HARRIS METHODIST HOSPITAL CLEBURNE (O, 85 beds) 201
Walls Drive, Cleburne, TX Zip 76033–4007; tel. 817/641–2551; Blake Kretz,
President
Web address: www.texashealth.org

TEXAS HEALTH HARRIS METHODIST HOSPITAL FORT WORTH (O, 633 beds)
1301 Pennsylvania Avenue, Fort Worth, TX Zip 76104–2122;
tel. 817/250–2000; Lillie Biggins, R.N., President
Web address: www.texashealth.org

TEXAS HEALTH HARRIS METHODIST HOSPITAL HURST–EULESS–BEDFORD
(O, 190 beds) 1600 Hospital Parkway, Bedford, TX Zip 76022–6913, Mailing
Address: P.O. Box 669, Zip 76095–0669; tel. 817/685–4000; Deborah
Paganelli, President
Web address: www.texashealth.org

TEXAS HEALTH HARRIS METHODIST HOSPITAL SOUTHWEST FORT WORTH
(O, 180 beds) 6100 Harris Parkway, Fort Worth, TX Zip 76132–4199;
tel. 817/433–5000; Joseph DeLeon, President
Web address: www.texashealth.org

TEXAS HEALTH HARRIS METHODIST HOSPITAL STEPHENVILLE (O, 54 beds)
411 North Belknap Street, Stephenville, TX Zip 76401–3415;
tel. 254/965–1500; Christopher Leu, President
Web address: www.texashealth.org/landing.cfm?id=108

TEXAS HEALTH PRESBYTERIAN HOSPITAL ALLEN (O, 73 beds) 1105 Central
Expressway North, Allen, TX Zip 75013–6103; tel. 972/747–1000; Jeff
Reecer, President
Web address: www.texashealth.org

TEXAS HEALTH PRESBYTERIAN HOSPITAL DALLAS (O, 621 beds) 8200
Walnut Hill Lane, Dallas, TX Zip 75231–4426; tel. 214/345–6789; James A.
Berg, Interim Chief Executive Officer
Web address: www.texashealth.org

TEXAS HEALTH PRESBYTERIAN HOSPITAL DENTON (O, 208 beds) 3000
North I–35, Denton, TX Zip 76201–5119; tel. 940/898–7000; Stan C.
Morton, FACHE, President
Web address: www.dentonhospital.com

TEXAS HEALTH PRESBYTERIAN HOSPITAL KAUFMAN (O, 68 beds) 850 Ed
Hall Drive, Kaufman, TX Zip 75142–1861, Mailing Address: P.O. Box 1108,
Zip 75142–5401; tel. 972/932–7200; Patsy Youngs, President
Web address: www.texashealth.org/Kaufman

TEXAS HEALTH PRESBYTERIAN HOSPITAL PLANO (O, 338 beds) 6200 West
Parker Road, Plano, TX Zip 75093–8185; tel. 972/981–8000; Mike Evans,
R.N., MS, President
Web address: www.texashealth.org

TEXAS HEALTH SPECIALTY HOSPITAL (O, 10 beds) 1301 Pennsylvania
Avenue, 4th Floor, Fort Worth, TX Zip 76104–2190; tel. 817/250–5500;
Cheryl Mobley, FACHE, President
Web address: www.texashealth.org

Owned, leased, sponsored:	14 hospitals	2848 beds
Contract–managed:	0 hospitals	0 beds
Totals:	14 hospitals	2848 beds

2445: THEDACARE, INC. (NP)
122 East College Avenue, Appleton, WI Zip 54911–5794, Mailing
Address: P.O. Box 8025, Zip 54912–8025; tel. 920/830–5560;
Dean Gruner, M.D., President and Chief Executive Officer
(Moderately Centralized Health System)

WISCONSIN: APPLETON MEDICAL CENTER (O, 149 beds) 1818 North Meade
Street, Appleton, WI Zip 54911–3496; tel. 920/731–4101; Brian
Burmeister, Senior Vice President
Web address: www.thedacare.org

NEW LONDON FAMILY MEDICAL CENTER (O, 25 beds) 1405 Mill Street, New
London, WI Zip 54961–2155, Mailing Address: P.O. Box 307,
Zip 54961–0307; tel. 920/531–2000; William Schmidt, President and Chief
Executive Officer
Web address: www.thedacare.org

RIVERSIDE MEDICAL CENTER (O, 25 beds) 800 Riverside Drive, Waupaca, WI
Zip 54981–1999; tel. 715/258–1000; Craig A. Kantos, Chief Executive
Officer
Web address: www.riversidemedical.org

SHAWANO MEDICAL CENTER (O, 25 beds) 309 North Bartlette Street,
Shawano, WI Zip 54166–2127; tel. 715/526–2111; Dorothy Erdmann, Chief
Executive Officer
Web address: www.shawanomed.org

THEDA CLARK MEDICAL CENTER (O, 151 beds) 130 Second Street, Neenah,
WI Zip 54956–2883, Mailing Address: P.O. Box 2021, Zip 54957–2021;
tel. 920/729–3100; Brian Burmeister, Senior Vice President
Web address: www.thedacare.org

Owned, leased, sponsored:	5 hospitals	375 beds
Contract–managed:	0 hospitals	0 beds
Totals:	5 hospitals	375 beds

★**0643: THOMAS HEALTH SYSTEM, INC.** (NP)
4605 MacCorkle Avenue S.W., South Charleston, WV
Zip 25309–1311; tel. 304/766–3600; Stephen P. Dexter, President
and Chief Executive Officer
(Moderately Centralized Health System)

WEST VIRGINIA: SAINT FRANCIS HOSPITAL (O, 111 beds) 333 Laidley
Street, Charleston, WV Zip 25301–1628, Mailing Address: P.O. Box 471,
Zip 25322–0471; tel. 304/347–6500; Stephen P. Dexter, President and
Chief Executive Officer
Web address: www.stfrancishospital.com

THOMAS MEMORIAL HOSPITAL (O, 215 beds) 4605 MacCorkle Avenue S.W.,
South Charleston, WV Zip 25309–1398; tel. 304/766–3600; Stephen P.
Dexter, President and Chief Executive Officer
Web address: www.thomaswv.org

Owned, leased, sponsored:	2 hospitals	326 beds
Contract–managed:	0 hospitals	0 beds
Totals:	2 hospitals	326 beds

★**0910: TIFT REGIONAL HEALTH SYSTEM** (NP)
901 East 18th Street, Tifton, GA Zip 31794–3648;
tel. 229/353–6100; William T. Richardson, President and Chief
Executive Officer
(Independent Hospital System)

GEORGIA: COOK MEDICAL CENTER–A CAMPUS OF TIFT REGIONAL MEDICAL
CENTER (O, 155 beds) 706 North Parrish Avenue, Adel, GA
Zip 31620–1511; tel. 229/896–8000; Michael L. Purvis, Chief Executive
Officer
Web address: www.cookmedicalcenter.com

TIFT REGIONAL MEDICAL CENTER (O, 191 beds) 901 East 18th Street,
Tifton, GA Zip 31794–3648, Mailing Address: Drawer 747, Zip 31793–0747;
tel. 229/382–7120; William T. Richardson, President and Chief Executive
Officer
Web address: www.tiftregional.com

Owned, leased, sponsored:	2 hospitals	346 beds
Contract–managed:	0 hospitals	0 beds
Totals:	2 hospitals	346 beds

For explanation of codes following names, see page B2.
★ Indicates Type III membership in the American Hospital Association.

Section B

0540: TRINITY MOTHER FRANCES HOSPITALS AND CLINICS (NP)
910 East Houston, Tyler, TX Zip 75702–8369; tel. 903/593–8441; J. Lindsey Bradley, Jr., FACHE, President
(Centralized Physician/Insurance Health System)

TEXAS: MOTHER FRANCES HOSPITAL – JACKSONVILLE (O, 21 beds) 2026 South Jackson, Jacksonville, TX Zip 75766–5822; tel. 903/541–4500; Thomas N. Cammack, Jr., Chief Administrative Officer
Web address: www.tmfhs.org/jacksonville

MOTHER FRANCES HOSPITAL – TYLER (O, 458 beds) 800 East Dawson Street, Tyler, TX Zip 75701–2036; tel. 903/593–8441; John McGreevy, Chief Executive Officer
Web address: www.tmfhs.org

MOTHER FRANCES HOSPITAL – WINNSBORO (O, 23 beds) 719 West Coke Road, Winnsboro, TX Zip 75494–3011, Mailing Address: P.O. Box 628, Zip 75494–0628; tel. 903/342–5227; Janet E. Coates, R.N., President and Chief Executive Officer
Web address: www.tmfhs.org

TYLER CONTINUECARE HOSPITAL AT MOTHER FRANCES (O, 51 beds) 800 East Dawson, 4th Floor, Tyler, TX Zip 75701–2036; tel. 903/531–4080; Stephanie Hyde, Chief Executive Officer
Web address: www.continuecare.org

Owned, leased, sponsored:	4 hospitals	553 beds
Contract–managed:	0 hospitals	0 beds
Totals:	4 hospitals	553 beds

★**9255: TRUMAN MEDICAL CENTERS** (NP)
2301 Holmes Street, Kansas City, MO Zip 64108–2677; tel. 816/404–1000; Charlie Shields, President and Chief Executive Officer
(Independent Hospital System)

MISSOURI: TRUMAN MEDICAL CENTER–HOSPITAL HILL (O, 256 beds) 2301 Holmes Street, Kansas City, MO Zip 64108–2640; tel. 816/404–1000; Charlie Shields, President and Chief Executive Officer
Web address: www.trumed.org

TRUMAN MEDICAL CENTER–LAKEWOOD (O, 296 beds) 7900 Lee's Summit Road, Kansas City, MO Zip 64139–1236; tel. 816/404–7000; Charlie Shields, President and Chief Executive Officer
Web address: www.trumed.org

Owned, leased, sponsored:	2 hospitals	552 beds
Contract–managed:	0 hospitals	0 beds
Totals:	2 hospitals	552 beds

0238: TY COBB HEALTHCARE SYSTEM, INC. (NP)
461 Cook Street, Suite A., Royston, GA Zip 30662–4003; tel. 706/356–7800; Gregory K. Hearn, Chief Executive Officer

GEORGIA: BROWN MEMORIAL CONVALESCENT CENTER (O, 144 beds) 545 Cook Street, Royston, GA Zip 30662–3902, Mailing Address: P.O. Box 589, Zip 30662–0589; tel. 706/245–1900; Bijan Vakili, Administrator

COBB HEALTH CARE CENTER (O, 116 beds) 2430 Paoli Street, Comer, GA Zip 30629–3470, Mailing Address: PO Box 566, Zip 30629; tel. 706/783–5116; Michael Gay, Administrator

HARTWELL HEALTH CARE CENTER (O, 92 beds) 94 Cade Street, Hartwell, GA Zip 30643–1814; tel. 706/856–6992; Marsha Beck, Administrator

TY COBB REGIONAL MEDICAL CENTER (O, 35 beds) 367 Clear Creek Parkway, Lavonia, GA Zip 30553–4173; tel. 706/356–7800; Gregory K. Hearn, Chief Executive Officer
Web address: www.tycobbhealthcare.org

Owned, leased, sponsored:	4 hospitals	387 beds
Contract–managed:	0 hospitals	0 beds
Totals:	4 hospitals	387 beds

9195: U. S. INDIAN HEALTH SERVICE (FG)
801 Thompson Avenue, Rockville, MD Zip 20852–1627; tel. 301/443–1083; Yvette Roubideaux, M.D., M.P.H., Director
(Independent Hospital System)

ARIZONA: CHINLE COMPREHENSIVE HEALTH CARE FACILITY (O, 60 beds) Highway 191, Chinle, AZ Zip 86503, Mailing Address: P.O. Drawer PH, Zip 86503–8000; tel. 928/674–7011; Ronald Tso, Chief Executive Officer
Web address: www.ihs.gov

HOPI HEALTH CARE CENTER (O, 15 beds) Highway 264 Mile Marker 388, Keams Canyon, AZ Zip 86042, Mailing Address: P.O. Box 4000, Polacca, Zip 86042–4000; tel. 928/737–6000; De Alva Honahnie, Chief Executive Officer
Web address: www.ihs.gov/index.asp

TSEHOOTSOOI MEDICAL CENTER (O, 39 beds) Highway 12 & Bonito Drive, Fort Defiance, AZ Zip 86504, Mailing Address: P.O. Box 649, Zip 86504–0649; tel. 928/729–8000; Leland Leonard, Ph.D., Chief Executive Officer
Web address: www.fdihb.org

U. S. PUBLIC HEALTH SERVICE INDIAN HOSPITAL (O, 20 beds) 12033 Agency Road, Parker, AZ Zip 85344–7718; tel. 928/669–2137; Dee Hutchison, Chief Executive Officer
Web address: www.ihs.gov

U. S. PUBLIC HEALTH SERVICE INDIAN HOSPITAL (O, 8 beds) 238 Cibeque Circle, San Carlos, AZ Zip 85550, Mailing Address: P.O. Box 208, Zip 85550–0208; tel. 928/475–2371; Robert Harry, M.D., Chief Executive Officer
Web address: www.ihs.gov

U. S. PUBLIC HEALTH SERVICE INDIAN HOSPITAL–SELLS (O, 12 beds) Highway 86 & Topawa Road, Sells, AZ Zip 85634, Mailing Address: P.O. Box 548, Zip 85634–0548; tel. 520/383–7251; Priscilla Whitethorne, Chief Executive Officer
Web address: www.ihs.gov

U. S. PUBLIC HEALTH SERVICE INDIAN HOSPITAL–WHITERIVER (O, 39 beds) 200 West Hospital Drive, Whiteriver, AZ Zip 85941–0860, Mailing Address: State Route 73, Box 860, Zip 85941–0860; tel. 928/338–4911; Michelle Martinez, Chief Executive Officer
Web address: www.ihs.gov

U. S. PUBLIC HEALTH SERVICE PHOENIX INDIAN MEDICAL CENTER (O, 127 beds) 4212 North 16th Street, Phoenix, AZ Zip 85016–5389; tel. 602/263–1200; John Molina, M.D., JD, Chief Executive Officer
Web address: www.ihs.gov

MARYLAND: NATIONAL INSTITUTES OF HEALTH CLINICAL CENTER (O, 146 beds) 9000 Rockville Pike, Building 10, Room 6–2551, Bethesda, MD Zip 20892–1504; tel. 301/496–4000; John I. Gallin, M.D., Director
Web address: www.clinicalcenter.nih.gov

MINNESOTA: U. S. PUBLIC HEALTH SERVICE INDIAN HOSPITAL (O, 9 beds) 7th Street & Grant Utley Avenue N.W., Cass Lake, MN Zip 56633, Mailing Address: Rural Route 3, Box 211, Zip 56633; tel. 218/335–3200; Norine Smith, Chief Executive Officer
Web address: www.ihs.gov

U.S. PUBLIC HEALTH SERVICE INDIAN HOSPITAL (O, 19 beds) Highway 1, Redlake, MN Zip 56671, Mailing Address: P.O. Box 497, Zip 56671–0497; tel. 218/679–3912; Mark Karzon, Chief Executive Officer
Web address: www.ihs.gov

MONTANA: CROW/NORTHERN CHEYENNE HOSPITAL (O, 24 beds) 10110 South 7650 East, Crow Agency, MT Zip 59022–0009, Mailing Address: P.O. Box 9, Zip 59022–0009; tel. 406/638–2626; Clayton Old Elk, Service Unit Director
Web address: www.ihs.gov/facilitiesservices/areaoffices/billings/crow/index.asp

FORT BELKNAP U. S. PUBLIC HEALTH SERVICE INDIAN HOSPITAL (O, 6 beds) 669 Agency Main Street, Harlem, MT Zip 59526–9455; tel. 406/353–3100; Steve Fox, Chief Executive Officer
Web address: www.ihs.gov

U. S. PUBLIC HEALTH SERVICE BLACKFEET COMMUNITY HOSPITAL (O, 25 beds) 760 New Hospital Circle, Saint Mary, MT Zip 59417–0760, Mailing Address: P.O. Box 760, Browning, Zip 59417–0760; tel. 406/338–6100; Merlin Gilham, Chief Executive Officer
Web address: www.ihs.gov

For explanation of codes following names, see page B2.
★ Indicates Type III membership in the American Hospital Association.

NEBRASKA: U. S. PUBLIC HEALTH SERVICE INDIAN HOSPITAL (O, 30 beds) Highway 7577, Winnebago, NE Zip 68071; tel. 402/878–2231; Patricia Medina, Service Unit Director
Web address: www.ihs.gov

NEW MEXICO: ACOMA–CANONCITO–LAGUNA HOSPITAL (O, 25 beds) 80B Veterans Boulevard, Acoma, NM Zip 87034, Mailing Address: P.O. Box 130, San Fidel, Zip 87049–0130; tel. 505/552–5300; William Thorne, Jr., Chief Executive Officer
Web address: www.ihs.gov/albuquerque/index.cfm?module=dsp_abq_acoma_canoncito_laguna

GALLUP INDIAN MEDICAL CENTER (O, 84 beds) 516 East Nizhoni Boulevard, Gallup, NM Zip 87301–5748, Mailing Address: P.O. Box 1337, Zip 87305–1337; tel. 505/722–1000; Vida J. Khow, Chief Executive Officer
Web address: www.ihs.gov/facilitiesservices/areaoffices/navajo/naihs-hcc-gallup.asp

MESCALERO PUBLIC HEALTH SERVICE INDIAN HOSPITAL (O, 13 beds) 318 Abalone Loop, Mescalero, NM Zip 88340, Mailing Address: Box 210, Zip 88340–0210; tel. 505/671–4441; Dorlynn Simmons, Chief Executive Officer
Web address: www.ihs.gov

NORTHERN NAVAJO MEDICAL CENTER (O, 62 beds) Highway 491 North, Shiprock, NM Zip 87420–0160, Mailing Address: P.O. Box 160, Zip 87420–0160; tel. 505/368–6001; Fannessa Comer, Chief Executive Officer
Web address: www.ihs.gov/

PHS SANTA FE INDIAN HOSPITAL (O, 4 beds) 1700 Cerrillos Road, Santa Fe, NM Zip 87505–3554; tel. 505/988–9821; Robert J. Lyon, Chief Executive Officer

U. S. PUBLIC HEALTH SERVICE INDIAN HOSPITAL (O, 12 beds) Route 9 and State Road 371, Crownpoint, NM Zip 87313, Mailing Address: P.O. Box 358, Zip 87313–0358; tel. 505/786–5291; Anslem Roanhorse, Chief Executive Officer
Web address: www.ihs.gov

U. S. PUBLIC HEALTH SERVICE INDIAN HOSPITAL (O, 32 beds) Route 301 North B. Street, Zuni, NM Zip 87327, Mailing Address: P.O. Box 467, Zip 87327–0467; tel. 505/782–4431; Jean Othole, Chief Executive Officer
Web address: www.ihs.gov

NORTH DAKOTA: PUBLIC HEALTH SERVICE INDIAN HOSPITAL – QUENTIN N. BURDICK MEMORIAL HEALTH FACILITY (O, 27 beds) 1300 Hospital Loop, Belcourt, ND Zip 58316, Mailing Address: P.O. Box 160, Zip 58316–0160; tel. 701/477–6111; Shelly Harris, Chief Executive Officer
Web address: www.ihs.gov

U. S. PUBLIC HEALTH SERVICE INDIAN HOSPITAL (O, 14 beds) N 10 North River Road, Fort Yates, ND Zip 58538, Mailing Address: P.O. Box J, Zip 58538; tel. 701/854–3831; Lisa Guardipee, Director
Web address: www.ihs.gov

OKLAHOMA: CHEROKEE NATION W.W. HASTINGS INDIAN HOSPITAL (O, 58 beds) 100 South Bliss Avenue, Tahlequah, OK Zip 74464–2512; tel. 918/458–3100; Brian Hail, Chief Executive Officer
Web address: www.cherokee.org

CLAREMORE INDIAN HOSPITAL (O, 46 beds) 101 South Moore Avenue, Claremore, OK Zip 74017–5091; tel. 918/342–6200; George Valliere, Chief Executive Officer
Web address: www.ihs.gov

LAWTON INDIAN HOSPITAL (O, 26 beds) 1515 Lawrie Tatum Road, Lawton, OK Zip 73507–3099; tel. 580/353–0350; Greg Ketcher, Administrator
Web address: www.ihs.gov

SOUTH DAKOTA: INDIAN HEALTH SERVICE HOSPITAL (O, 5 beds) 3200 Canyon Lake Drive, Rapid City, SD Zip 57702–8197; tel. 605/355–2280; Helen Thompson, Interim Director
Web address: www.ihs.gov

U. S. PUBLIC HEALTH SERVICE INDIAN HOSPITAL (O, 11 beds) 317 Main Street, Eagle Butte, SD Zip 57625–1012, Mailing Address: P.O. Box 1012, Zip 57625–1012; tel. 605/964–7724; Charlene Red Thunder, Chief Executive Officer
Web address: www.ihs.gov

U. S. PUBLIC HEALTH SERVICE INDIAN HOSPITAL (O, 45 beds) East Highway 18, Pine Ridge, SD Zip 57770, Mailing Address: P.O. Box 1201, Zip 57770–1201; tel. 605/867–5131; Ellen Davis, Service Unit Director
Web address: www.ihs.gov

U. S. PUBLIC HEALTH SERVICE INDIAN HOSPITAL (O, 35 beds) Highway 18, Soldier Creek Road, Rosebud, SD Zip 57570; tel. 605/747–2231; Sophie M. Two Hawk, Chief Executive Officer
Web address: www.ihs.gov

Owned, leased, sponsored:	31 hospitals	1078 beds
Contract–managed:	0 hospitals	0 beds
Totals:	31 hospitals	1078 beds

★**9105:** **UAB HEALTH SYSTEM** (NP)
500 22nd Street South, Suite 408, Birmingham, AL Zip 35233–3110; tel. 205/975–5362; William Ferniany, Ph.D., Chief Executive Officer
(Moderately Centralized Health System)

ALABAMA: MEDICAL WEST (O, 236 beds) 995 Ninth Avenue S.W., Bessemer, AL Zip 35022–4527; tel. 205/481–7000; Keith Pennington, President and Chief Executive Officer
Web address: www.medicalwesthospital.org

UNIVERSITY OF ALABAMA HOSPITAL (O, 1062 beds) 619 19th Street South, Birmingham, AL Zip 35249–1900; tel. 205/934–4011; Anthony Patterson, Senior Vice President Inpatient Services
Web address: www.uabmedicine.org

Owned, leased, sponsored:	2 hospitals	1298 beds
Contract–managed:	0 hospitals	0 beds
Totals:	2 hospitals	1298 beds

★**0082:** **UC HEALTH** (NP)
3200 Burnet Avenue, Cincinnati, OH Zip 45229–3019; tel. 513/585–6000; Richard P. Lofgren, M.D., M.P.H., President and CEO
(Centralized Health System)

OHIO: DANIEL DRAKE CENTER FOR POST ACUTE CARE (O, 217 beds) 151 West Galbraith Road, Cincinnati, OH Zip 45216–1015; tel. 513/418–2500; Debra C. Hampton, Ph.D., Vice President, Administration and Chief Nursing Officer
Web address: www.drakecenter.uchealth.com

UNIVERSITY OF CINCINNATI MEDICAL CENTER (O, 536 beds) 234 Goodman Street, Cincinnati, OH Zip 45219–2316; tel. 513/584–1000; Lee Ann Liska, President and Chief Executive Officer
Web address: www.universityhospital.uchealth.com/

WEST CHESTER HOSPITAL (O, 170 beds) 7700 University Drive, West Chester, OH Zip 45069–2505; tel. 513/298–3000; Kevin Joseph, M.D., Chief Executive Officer
Web address: www.westchesterhospital.uchealth.com

Owned, leased, sponsored:	3 hospitals	923 beds
Contract–managed:	0 hospitals	0 beds
Totals:	3 hospitals	923 beds

★**0111:** **UF HEALTH SHANDS** (NP)
1600 S.W. Archer Road, Gainesville, FL Zip 32610–0326; tel. 352/733–1500; Edward Jimenez, Interim Chief Executive Officer
(Moderately Centralized Health System)

FLORIDA: UF HEALTH JACKSONVILLE (O, 620 beds) 655 West Eighth Street, Jacksonville, FL Zip 32209–6595; tel. 904/244–0411; Russell Armistead, Chief Executive Officer
Web address: www.ufhealthjax.org/

UF HEALTH SHANDS HOSPITAL (O, 952 beds) 1600 S.W. Archer Road, Gainesville, FL Zip 32610–3003, Mailing Address: P.O. Box 100326, Zip 32610–0326; tel. 352/265–0111; Edward Jimenez, Interim Chief Executive Officer
Web address: www.shands.org

Owned, leased, sponsored:	2 hospitals	1572 beds
Contract–managed:	0 hospitals	0 beds
Totals:	2 hospitals	1572 beds

★0224: UMASS MEMORIAL HEALTH CARE, INC. (NP)
1 Biotech Park, Worcester, MA Zip 01605–2982;
tel. 508/334–0100; Eric Dickson, M.D., President and Chief
Executive Officer
(Moderately Centralized Health System)

MASSACHUSETTS: CLINTON HOSPITAL (O, 41 beds) 201 Highland Street,
Clinton, MA Zip 01510–1096; tel. 978/368–3000; Sheila Daly, President
and Chief Executive Officer
Web address: www.clintonhospital.org

HEALTHALLIANCE HOSPITALS (O, 89 beds) 60 Hospital Road, Leominster,
MA Zip 01453–2205; tel. 978/466–2000; Deborah K. Weymouth, President
and Chief Executive Officer
Web address: www.healthalliance.com

UMASS MEMORIAL MEDICAL CENTER (O, 804 beds) 119 Belmont Street,
Worcester, MA Zip 01605–2982; tel. 508/334–1000; Patrick L. Muldoon,
FACHE, President and CEO
Web address: www.umassmemorial.org

UMASS MEMORIAL–MARLBOROUGH HOSPITAL (O, 67 beds) 157 Union
Street, Marlborough, MA Zip 01752–1297; tel. 508/481–5000; Steven P.
Roach, FACHE, President and Chief Executive Officer
Web address: www.marlboroughhospital.org

Owned, leased, sponsored:	4 hospitals	1001 beds
Contract–managed:	0 hospitals	0 beds
Totals:	4 hospitals	1001 beds

★0901: UNC HEALTH CARE (NP)
101 Manning Drive, Chapel Hill, NC Zip 27514–4220;
tel. 919/966–4131; William L. Roper, M.D., M.P.H., Chief Executive
Officer
(Moderately Centralized Health System)

NORTH CAROLINA: CALDWELL MEMORIAL HOSPITAL (O, 76 beds) 321
Mulberry Street S.W., Lenoir, NC Zip 28645–5720, Mailing Address: P.O.
Box 1890, Zip 28645–1890; tel. 828/757–5100; Laura S. Easton, R.N.,
President and Chief Executive Officer
Web address: www.caldwell–mem.org

CHATHAM HOSPITAL (O, 25 beds) 475 Progress Boulevard, Siler City, NC
Zip 27344–6787, Mailing Address: P.O. Box 649, Zip 27344–0649;
tel. 919/799–4000; Robert A. Enders, Jr., President
Web address: www.chathamhospital.org

HIGH POINT REGIONAL HEALTH SYSTEM (O, 335 beds) 601 North Elm
Street, High Point, NC Zip 27262–4398, Mailing Address: P.O. Box HP–5,
Zip 27261–1899; tel. 336/878–6000; Ernest L. Bovio, Jr., Chief Executive
Officer
Web address: www.highpointregional.com

JOHNSTON UNC HEALTH CARE (C, 142 beds) 509 North Bright Leaf
Boulevard, Smithfield, NC Zip 27577–4407, Mailing Address: P.O. Box 1376,
Zip 27577–1376; tel. 919/934–8171; Charles W. Elliott, Jr., Chief Executive
Officer
Web address: www.johnstonhealth.org

MARGARET R. PARDEE MEMORIAL HOSPITAL (C, 138 beds) 800 North
Justice Street, Hendersonville, NC Zip 28791–3410; tel. 828/696–1000;
James M. Kirby, II, President and Chief Executive Officer
Web address: www.pardeehospital.org

REX HEALTHCARE (O, 660 beds) 4420 Lake Boone Trail, Raleigh, NC
Zip 27607–6599; tel. 919/784–3100; David W. Strong, President
Web address: www.rexhealth.com

UNIVERSITY OF NORTH CAROLINA HOSPITALS (O, 818 beds) 101 Manning
Drive, Chapel Hill, NC Zip 27514–4220; tel. 919/966–4131; Gary L. Park,
President
Web address: www.unchealthcare.org

Owned, leased, sponsored:	5 hospitals	1914 beds
Contract–managed:	2 hospitals	280 beds
Totals:	7 hospitals	2194 beds

0922: UNION GENERAL HOSPITAL, INC. (NP)
35 Hospital Road, Blairsville, GA Zip 30512–3139;
tel. 706/745–2111; Mike Gowder, Chief Executive Officer

GEORGIA: CHATUGE REGIONAL HOSPITAL AND NURSING HOME (O, 137
beds) 110 Main Street, Hiawassee, GA Zip 30546–3408, Mailing Address:
P.O. Box 509, Zip 30546–0509; tel. 706/896–2222; R. Lewis Kelley,
Administrator
Web address: www.chatugeregionalhospital.org

UNION GENERAL HOSPITAL (O, 195 beds) 35 Hospital Road, Blairsville, GA
Zip 30512–3139; tel. 706/745–2111; Mike Gowder, Chief Executive Officer
Web address: www.uniongeneralhospital.com

Owned, leased, sponsored:	2 hospitals	332 beds
Contract–managed:	0 hospitals	0 beds
Totals:	2 hospitals	332 beds

0288: UNITED HEALTH SERVICES (NP)
10–42 Mitchell Avenue, Binghamton, NY Zip 13903–1617;
tel. 607/762–2200; Matthew J. Salanger, President and Chief
Executive Officer
(Independent Hospital System)

NEW YORK: CHENANGO MEMORIAL HOSPITAL (O, 138 beds) 179 North
Broad Street, Norwich, NY Zip 13815–1097; tel. 607/337–4111; Drake
M. Lamen, M.D., President and Chief Executive Officer
Web address: www.uhs.net/cmh

DELAWARE VALLEY HOSPITAL (O, 25 beds) 1 Titus Place, Walton, NY
Zip 13856–1498; tel. 607/865–2100; Paul Summers, Interim President and
Chief Executive Officer
Web address: www.uhs.net

UNITED HEALTH SERVICES HOSPITALS–BINGHAMTON (O, 456 beds) 10–42
Mitchell Avenue, Binghamton, NY Zip 13903–1678; tel. 607/763–6000;
Matthew J. Salanger, President and Chief Executive Officer
Web address: www.uhs.net

Owned, leased, sponsored:	3 hospitals	619 beds
Contract–managed:	0 hospitals	0 beds
Totals:	3 hospitals	619 beds

9605: UNITED MEDICAL CORPORATION (IO)
603 Main Street, Windermere, FL Zip 34786–3548, Mailing Address:
P.O. Box 1100, Zip 34786–1100; tel. 407/876–2200; Donald R.
Dizney, Chairman and Chief Executive Officer

PUERTO RICO: HOSPITAL PAVIA–HATO REY (O, 180 beds) 435 Ponce De
Leon Avenue, San Juan, PR Zip 00917–3428; tel. 787/641–2323;
Guillermo Pastrana, Executive Director
Web address: www.paviahealth.com

HOSPITAL PAVIA–SANTURCE (O, 215 beds) 1462 Asia Street, San Juan, PR
Zip 00909–2143, Mailing Address: Box 11137, Santurce Station,
Zip 00910–1137; tel. 787/727–6060; Jose Luis Rodriguez, Chief Executive
Officer
Web address: www.paviahealth.com

HOSPITAL PEREA (O, 103 beds) 15 Basora Street, Mayaguez, PR Zip 00681,
Mailing Address: P.O. Box 170, Zip 00681; tel. 787/834–0101; Jorge I.
Martinez, Executive Director
Web address: www.paviahealth.com/perea_hospital.htm

SAN JORGE CHILDREN'S HOSPITAL (O, 125 beds) 252 San Jorge Street,
Santurce, San Juan, PR Zip 00912–3310; tel. 787/727–1000; Domingo
Cruz, Senior Vice President Operations
Web address: www.sanjorgechildrenshospital.com

TENNESSEE: TEN BROECK TENNESSEE TREATMENT FACILITY (O, 36 beds)
1 Medical Center Boulevard, 5 West, Cookeville, TN Zip 38501;
tel. 931/783–2570; Pamela Lothridge, Chief Executive Officer
Web address: www.tenbroeck.com

Owned, leased, sponsored:	5 hospitals	659 beds
Contract–managed:	0 hospitals	0 beds
Totals:	5 hospitals	659 beds

For explanation of codes following names, see page B2.
★ Indicates Type III membership in the American Hospital Association.

0937: UNITED MEDICAL REHABILITATION HOSPITALS (IO)
3201 Wall Boulevard, Suite B., Gretna, LA Zip 70056–7755;
tel. 504/433–5551; John E.H. Mills, President & Chief Executive
Officer

LOUISIANA: UNITED MEDICAL HEALTHWEST–NEW ORLEANS (O, 15 beds)
3201 Wall Boulevard, Suite B., Gretna, LA Zip 70056–7755;
tel. 504/433–5551; John E.H. Mills, President and Chief Executive Officer
Web address: www.umrhospital.com

UNITED MEDICAL REHABILITATION HOSPITAL (O, 20 beds) 15717 Belle Drive,
Hammond, LA Zip 70403–1439; tel. 985/340–5998; Cyrillia Bonds,
Administrator
Web address: www.umrhospital.com

Owned, leased, sponsored:	2 hospitals	35 beds
Contract–managed:	0 hospitals	0 beds
Totals:	2 hospitals	35 beds

0322: UNITED SURGICAL PARTNERS INTERNATIONAL (IO)
15305 Dallas Parkway, Suite 1600, Addison, TX Zip 75001–6491;
tel. 972/713–3500; William H. Wilcox, President and Chief Executive
Officer
(Independent Hospital System)

ARIZONA: ARIZONA ORTHOPEDIC SURGICAL HOSPITAL (O, 24 beds) 2905
West Warner Road, Chandler, AZ Zip 85224–1674; tel. 480/603–9000;
Duane Scholer, Chief Executive Officer
Web address: www.azosh.com

OKLAHOMA: OKLAHOMA CENTER FOR ORTHOPEDIC AND MULTI–SPECIALTY
SURGERY (O, 10 beds) 8100 South Walker, Suite C., Oklahoma City, OK
Zip 73139–9402, Mailing Address: P.O. Box 890609, Zip 73189–0609;
tel. 405/602–6500; Mike Kimzey, Chief Executive Officer and
Administrator
Web address: www.ocomhospital.com

TEXAS: BAYLOR MEDICAL CENTER AT FRISCO (O, 68 beds) 5601 Warren
Parkway, Frisco, TX Zip 75034–4069; tel. 214/407–5000; William A.
Keaton, Chief Executive Officer
Web address: www.bmcf.com

BAYLOR MEDICAL CENTER AT UPTOWN (O, 24 beds) 2727 East Lemmon
Avenue, Dallas, TX Zip 75204–2895; tel. 214/443–3000; Matt Chance, Chief
Executive Officer
Web address: www.bmcuptown.com

IRVING COPPELL SURGICAL HOSPITAL (O, 12 beds) 400 West Interstate 635,
Irving, TX Zip 75063; tel. 972/868–4000; Deonna Unell, Chief Executive
Officer
Web address: www.ic–sh.com

SUGAR LAND SURGICAL HOSPITAL (O, 6 beds) 16906 Southwest Freeway,
Sugar Land, TX Zip 77479–2350; tel. 281/243–1000; Daniel Smith, Interim
Chief Executive Officer
Web address: www.sugarlandsurgicalhospital.com/

TOPS SURGICAL SPECIALTY HOSPITAL (O, 15 beds) 17080 Red Oak Drive,
Houston, TX Zip 77090–2602; tel. 281/539–2900; Daniel Smith, Interim
Chief Executive Officer
Web address: www.tops–hospital.com

Owned, leased, sponsored:	7 hospitals	159 beds
Contract–managed:	0 hospitals	0 beds
Totals:	7 hospitals	159 beds

★0061: UNITYPOINT HEALTH (NP)
1776 Westlakes Parkway, Suite 400, West Des Moines, IA
Zip 50266–8239; tel. 515/241–6161; William B. Leaver, President
and Chief Executive Officer
(Decentralized Health System)

ILLINOIS: UNITYPOINT HEALTH – METHODIST (O, 282 beds) 221 N.E. Glen
Oak Avenue, Peoria, IL Zip 61636–4310; tel. 309/672–5522; Deborah R.
Simon, R.N., President and Chief Executive Officer
Web address: www.mymethodist.net

UNITYPOINT HEALTH – TRINITY ROCK ISLAND (O, 343 beds) 2701 17th
Street, Rock Island, IL Zip 61201–5393; tel. 309/779–5000; Richard A.
Seidler, FACHE, President and Chief Executive Officer
Web address: www.trinityqc.com

IOWA: BUENA VISTA REGIONAL MEDICAL CENTER (C, 35 beds) 1525 West
Fifth Street, Storm Lake, IA Zip 50588–3027, Mailing Address: P.O. Box
309, Zip 50588–0309; tel. 712/732–4030; Steven Colerick, Chief
Executive Officer
Web address: www.bvrmc.org

CLARKE COUNTY HOSPITAL (C, 25 beds) 800 South Fillmore Street, Osceola,
IA Zip 50213–1619; tel. 641/342–2184; Brian G. Evans, FACHE, Chief
Executive Officer
Web address: www.clarkehosp.org

COMMUNITY MEMORIAL HOSPITAL (C, 16 beds) 909 West First Street,
Sumner, IA Zip 50674–1203, Mailing Address: P.O. Box 148,
Zip 50674–0148; tel. 563/578–3275; Mary S. Wells, R.N., Chief Executive
Officer
Web address: www.cmhsumner.org

GREATER REGIONAL MEDICAL CENTER (C, 25 beds) 1700 West Townline
Street Suite 3, Creston, IA Zip 50801–1099; tel. 641/782–7091; Monte
Neitzel, Chief Executive Officer
Web address: www.greaterregional.org

GREENE COUNTY MEDICAL CENTER (C, 90 beds) 1000 West Lincolnway,
Jefferson, IA Zip 50129–1645; tel. 515/386–2114; Carl P. Behne,
Administrator and Chief Executive Officer
Web address: www.gcmchealth.com

GRUNDY COUNTY MEMORIAL HOSPITAL (C, 80 beds) 201 East J Avenue,
Grundy Center, IA Zip 50638–2096; tel. 319/824–5421; Brian Kellar, Chief
Executive Officer
Web address: www.grundycountyhospital.com

GUTHRIE COUNTY HOSPITAL (C, 25 beds) 710 North 12th Street, Guthrie
Center, IA Zip 50115–1544; tel. 641/332–2201; Patrick Peters, Chief
Executive Officer
Web address: www.guthriecountyhospital.org

GUTTENBERG MUNICIPAL HOSPITAL (C, 20 beds) 200 Main Street,
Guttenberg, IA Zip 52052–9108, Mailing Address: P.O. Box 550,
Zip 52052–0550; tel. 563/252–1121; Kimberley A. Gau, FACHE, Chief
Executive Officer
Web address: www.guttenberghospital.org

HUMBOLDT COUNTY MEMORIAL HOSPITAL (C, 49 beds) 1000 North 15th
Street, Humboldt, IA Zip 50548–1008; tel. 515/332–4200; James Atty, Chief
Executive Officer
Web address: www.humboldthospital.org

LORING HOSPITAL (C, 25 beds) 211 Highland Avenue, Sac City, IA
Zip 50583–2424; tel. 712/662–7105; James Beck, Interim President and
Chief Executive Officer
Web address: www.loringhospital.org

MARENGO MEMORIAL HOSPITAL, UNITYPOINT HEALTH (O, 25 beds) 300
West May Street, Marengo, IA Zip 52301–1261, Mailing Address: P.O. Box
228, Zip 52301–0228; tel. 319/642–5543; Barry Goettsch, Chief Executive
Officer
Web address: www.marengohospital.org

POCAHONTAS COMMUNITY HOSPITAL (C, 20 beds) 606 N.W. Seventh Street,
Pocahontas, IA Zip 50574–1099; tel. 712/335–3501; James D. Roetman,
President and Chief Executive Officer
Web address: www.pocahontashospital.org

STEWART MEMORIAL COMMUNITY HOSPITAL (C, 25 beds) 1301 West Main,
Lake City, IA Zip 51449–1585; tel. 712/464–3171; Heather L. Cain, Chief
Executive Officer
Web address: www.stewartmemorial.org

STORY COUNTY MEDICAL CENTER (C, 77 beds) 640 South 19th Street,
Nevada, IA Zip 50201–2902; tel. 515/382–2111; Timothy Ahlers, Chief
Executive Officer
Web address: www.storymedical.org

UNITYPOINT HEALTH – ALLEN HOSPITAL (O, 201 beds) 1825 Logan Avenue,
Waterloo, IA Zip 50703–1916; tel. 319/235–3941; Pamela K. Delagardelle,
President and Chief Executive Officer
Web address: www.allenhospital.org

UNITYPOINT HEALTH – DES MOINES (O, 187 beds) 700 East University
Avenue, Des Moines, IA Zip 50316–2392; tel. 515/263–5612; Eric T.
Crowell, President and Chief Executive Officer
Web address: www.iowahealth.org

For explanation of codes following names, see page B2.
★ Indicates Type III membership in the American Hospital Association.

UNITYPOINT HEALTH – FINLEY HOSPITAL (O, 109 beds) 350 North Grandview Avenue, Dubuque, IA Zip 52001–6392; tel. 563/582–1881; David R. Brandon, President and Chief Executive Officer
Web address: www.unitypoint.org

UNITYPOINT HEALTH – IOWA METHODIST MEDICAL CENTER (O, 478 beds) 1200 Pleasant Street, Des Moines, IA Zip 50309–1406; tel. 515/241–6212; Eric T. Crowell, President and Chief Executive Officer
Web address: www.iowahealth.org

UNITYPOINT HEALTH – JONES REGIONAL MEDICAL CENTER (O, 22 beds) 1795 Highway 64 East, Anamosa, IA Zip 52205–2112; tel. 319/462–6131; Eric Briesemeister, Chief Executive Officer
Web address: www.jonesregional.org

UNITYPOINT HEALTH – ST. LUKE'S (O, 151 beds) 2720 Stone Park Boulevard, Sioux City, IA Zip 51104–3734; tel. 712/279–3500; Peter W. Thoreen, FACHE, President and Chief Executive Officer
Web address: www.stlukes.org

UNITYPOINT HEALTH – ST. LUKE'S HOSPITAL (O, 347 beds) 1026 A Avenue N.E., Cedar Rapids, IA Zip 52402–3026, Mailing Address: P.O. Box 3026, Zip 52406–3026; tel. 319/369–7211; Theodore E. Townsend, FACHE, President and Chief Executive Officer
Web address: www.unitypoint.org

UNITYPOINT HEALTH – TRINITY BETTENDORF (O, 76 beds) 4500 Utica Ridge Road, Bettendorf, IA Zip 52722–1626; tel. 563/742–5000; Richard A. Seidler, FACHE, President and Chief Executive Officer
Web address: www.trinityqc.com

UNITYPOINT HEALTH – TRINITY MUSCATINE (O, 48 beds) 1518 Mulberry Avenue, Muscatine, IA Zip 52761–3499; tel. 563/264–9100; James M. Hayes, Chief Executive Officer
Web address: www.unitypoint.org/quadcities/trinity-muscatine.aspx

UNITYPOINT HEALTH – TRINITY REGIONAL MEDICAL CENTER (O, 110 beds) 802 Kenyon Road, Fort Dodge, IA Zip 50501–5795; tel. 515/573–3101; Susan K. Thompson, President and Chief Executive Officer
Web address: www.trmc.org

Owned, leased, sponsored:	13 hospitals	2379 beds
Contract–managed:	13 hospitals	512 beds
Totals:	26 hospitals	2891 beds

9555: UNIVERSAL HEALTH SERVICES, INC. (IO)
367 South Gulph Road, King of Prussia, PA Zip 19406–3121, Mailing Address: P.O. Box 61558, Zip 19406–0958; tel. 610/768–3300; Alan B. Miller, Chairman and Chief Executive Officer
(Decentralized Health System)

ALABAMA: HILL CREST BEHAVIORAL HEALTH SERVICES (O, 94 beds) 6869 Fifth Avenue South, Birmingham, AL Zip 35212–1866; tel. 205/833–9000; Steve McCabe, Chief Executive Officer
Web address: www.hillcrestbhs.com

LAUREL OAKS BEHAVIORAL HEALTH CENTER (O, 38 beds) 700 East Cottonwood Road, Dothan, AL Zip 36301–3644; tel. 334/794–7373; Derek Johnson, Chief Executive Officer
Web address: www.laureloaksbhc.com

ALASKA: NORTH STAR BEHAVIORAL HEALTH SYSTEM (O, 200 beds) 2530 DeBarr Circle, Anchorage, AK Zip 99508–2948; tel. 907/258–7575; Andrew Mayo, M.D., Chief Executive Officer and Managing Director
Web address: www.northstarbehavioral.com

ARIZONA: PALO VERDE MENTAL HEALTH SERVICES (O, 48 beds) 2695 North Craycroft, Tucson, AZ Zip 85712–2244, Mailing Address: P.O. Box 40030, Zip 85717–0030; tel. 520/322–2888; P. Jay Frayser, Chief Executive Officer
Web address: www.paloverdebh.com/

VALLEY HOSPITAL PHOENIX (O, 122 beds) 3550 East Pinchot Avenue, Phoenix, AZ Zip 85018–7434; tel. 602/957–4000; Michelle David, Chief Executive Officer
Web address: www.valleyhospital–phoenix.com

ARKANSAS: PINNACLE POINTE HOSPITAL (O, 124 beds) 11501 Financial Center Parkway, Little Rock, AR Zip 72211–3715; tel. 501/223–3322; John McNally, Chief Executive Officer
Web address: www.pinnaclepointehospital.com

RIVENDELL BEHAVIORAL HEALTH SERVICES OF ARKANSAS (O, 77 beds) 100 Rivendell Drive, Benton, AR Zip 72019–9100; tel. 501/316–1255; Dwight A. Lacy, Chief Executive Officer
Web address: www.rivendellofarkansas.com

THE BRIDGEWAY (L, 103 beds) 21 Bridgeway Road, North Little Rock, AR Zip 72113–9516; tel. 501/771–1500; Jason Miller, Interim Chief Executive Officer
Web address: www.thebridgeway.com

CALIFORNIA: BHC ALHAMBRA HOSPITAL (O, 97 beds) 4619 North Rosemead Boulevard, Rosemead, CA Zip 91770–1478, Mailing Address: P.O. Box 369, Zip 91770–0369; tel. 626/286–1191; Peggy Minnick, R.N., Chief Executive Officer
Web address: www.bhcalhambra.com

CANYON RIDGE HOSPITAL (O, 106 beds) 5353 G Street, Chino, CA Zip 91710–5250; tel. 909/590–3700; Jeff McDonald, Chief Executive Officer
Web address: www.canyonridgehospital.com

CORONA REGIONAL MEDICAL CENTER (O, 240 beds) 800 South Main Street, Corona, CA Zip 92882–3400; tel. 951/737–4343; Mark Utter, Chief Executive Officer
Web address: www.coronaregional.com

DEL AMO HOSPITAL (O, 70 beds) 23700 Camino Del Sol, Torrance, CA Zip 90505–5000; tel. 310/530–1151; Lisa K. Montes, Chief Executive Officer
Web address: www.delamohospital.com

FREMONT HOSPITAL (O, 96 beds) 39001 Sundale Drive, Fremont, CA Zip 94538–2005; tel. 510/796–1100; John C. Cooper, Chief Executive Officer
Web address: www.fremonthospital.com

HERITAGE OAKS HOSPITAL (O, 120 beds) 4250 Auburn Boulevard, Sacramento, CA Zip 95841–4164; tel. 916/489–3336; Shawn Silva, Chief Executive Officer
Web address: www.heritageoakshospital.com

PALMDALE REGIONAL MEDICAL CENTER (O, 157 beds) 38600 Medical Center Drive, Palmdale, CA Zip 93551–4483; tel. 661/382–5000; Richard Allen, Chief Executive Officer
Web address: www.palmdaleregional.com

SIERRA VISTA HOSPITAL (O, 120 beds) 8001 Bruceville Road, Sacramento, CA Zip 95823–2329; tel. 916/288–0300; Mike Zauner, Chief Executive Officer
Web address: www.sierravistahospital.com

SOUTHWEST HEALTHCARE SYSTEM (O, 252 beds) 25500 Medical Center Drive, Murrieta, CA Zip 92562–5965; tel. 951/696–6000; Bradley D. Neet, FACHE, Chief Executive Officer
Web address: www.swhealthcaresystem.com/

COLORADO: CEDAR SPRINGS HOSPITAL (O, 110 beds) 2135 Southgate Road, Colorado Springs, CO Zip 80906–2693; tel. 719/633–4114; A. Elaine Crnkovic, Chief Executive Officer
Web address: www.cedarspringsbhs.com

CENTENNIAL PEAKS HOSPITAL (O, 72 beds) 2255 South 88th Street, Louisville, CO Zip 80027–9716; tel. 303/673–9990; Elicia Bunch, Chief Executive Officer
Web address: www.centennialpeaks.com

HIGHLANDS BEHAVIORAL HEALTH SYSTEM (O, 86 beds) 8565 South Poplar Way, Littleton, CO Zip 80130–3602; tel. 720/348–2800; Paul Sexton, Chief Executive Officer
Web address: www.highlandsbhs.com

DELAWARE: DOVER BEHAVIORAL HEALTH SYSTEM (O, 52 beds) 725 Horsepond Road, Dover, DE Zip 19901–7232; tel. 302/741–0140; Jean–Charles Constant, Administrator
Web address: www.doverbehavioral.com

ROCKFORD CENTER (O, 118 beds) 100 Rockford Drive, Newark, DE Zip 19713–2121; tel. 302/996–5480; John F. McKenna, Chief Executive Officer and Managing Director
Web address: www.rockfordcenter.com

DISTRICT OF COLUMBIA: GEORGE WASHINGTON UNIVERSITY HOSPITAL (O, 363 beds) 900 23rd Street N.W., Washington, DC Zip 20037–2342; tel. 202/715–4000; Barry A. Wolfman, Chief Executive Officer and Managing Director
Web address: www.gwhospital.com

For explanation of codes following names, see page B2.
★ Indicates Type III membership in the American Hospital Association.

FLORIDA: ATLANTIC SHORES HOSPITAL (O, 72 beds) 4545 North Federal Highway, Fort Lauderdale, FL Zip 33308–5274; tel. 954/771–2711; Manuel R. Llano, Chief Executive Officer
Web address: www.atlanticshoreshospital.com

CENTRAL FLORIDA BEHAVIORAL HOSPITAL (O, 126 beds) 6601 Central Florida Parkway, Orlando, FL Zip 32821–8064: tel. 407/370–0111; Vickie Lewis, Chief Executive Officer
Web address: www.centralfloridabehavioral.com

EMERALD COAST BEHAVIORAL HOSPITAL (O, 86 beds) 1940 Harrison Avenue, Panama City, FL Zip 32405–4542; tel. 850/763–0017; Tim Bedford, Chief Executive Officer
Web address: www.emeraldcoastbehavioral.com

FORT LAUDERDALE HOSPITAL (L, 100 beds) 1601 East Las Olas Boulevard, Fort Lauderdale, FL Zip 33301–2393; tel. 954/463–4321; Manuel R. Llano, Chief Executive Officer
Web address: www.fortlauderdalehospital.org

LAKEWOOD RANCH MEDICAL CENTER (O, 120 beds) 8330 Lakewood Ranch Boulevard, Bradenton, FL Zip 34202–5174; tel. 941/782–2100; Linda S. Widra, FACHE, Ph.D., R.N., Interim Chief Executive Officer
Web address: www.lakewoodranchmedicalcenter.com

MANATEE MEMORIAL HOSPITAL (O, 319 beds) 206 Second Street East, Bradenton, FL Zip 34208–1000; tel. 941/746–5111; Kevin DiLallo, Chief Executive Officer
Web address: www.manateememorial.com

MANATEE PALMS YOUTH SERVICES (O, 60 beds) 4480 51st Street West, Bradenton, FL Zip 34210–2855; tel. 941/792–2222; Kerry Knott, Chief Executive Officer
Web address: www.mpys.com

RIVER POINT BEHAVIORAL HEALTH (O, 92 beds) 6300 Beach Boulevard, Jacksonville, FL Zip 32216–2782; tel. 904/724–9202; Gayle Eckerd, Chief Executive Officer
Web address: www.riverpointbehavioral.com

SANDYPINES (O, 80 beds) 11301 S.E. Tequesta Terrace, Tequesta, FL Zip 33469–8146; tel. 561/744–0211; John McCarthy, Chief Executive Officer

THE VINES (O, 64 beds) 3130 S.W. 27th Avenue, Ocala, FL Zip 34471–4306; tel. 352/671–3130; Stephen Quintyne, Chief Executive Officer
Web address: www.thevineshospital.com

WEKIVA SPRINGS CENTER FOR WOMEN (O, 60 beds) 3947 Salisbury Road, Jacksonville, FL Zip 32216–6115; tel. 904/296–3533; Gayle Eckerd, Chief Executive Officer
Web address: www.wekivacenter.com

WELLINGTON REGIONAL MEDICAL CENTER (L, 108 beds) 10101 Forest Hill Boulevard, West Palm Beach, FL Zip 33414–6199; tel. 561/798–8500; Robbin Lee, Chief Executive Officer
Web address: www.wellingtonregional.com

WINDMOOR HEALTHCARE OF CLEARWATER (O, 100 beds) 11300 U.S. 19 North, Clearwater, FL Zip 33764; tel. 727/541–2646; Wendy Merson, Chief Executive Officer
Web address: www.windmoor.com

GEORGIA: ANCHOR HOSPITAL (O, 111 beds) 5454 Yorktowne Drive, Atlanta, GA Zip 30349–5317; tel. 770/991–6044; Margaret P. Collier, Chief Executive Officer and Managing Director
Web address: www.anchorhospital.com

COASTAL HARBOR TREATMENT CENTER (O, 182 beds) 1150 Cornell Avenue, Savannah, GA Zip 31406–2702; tel. 912/354–3911; Ray Heckerman, Chief Executive Officer and Managing Director
Web address: www.coastalharbor.com

PEACHFORD BEHAVIORAL HEALTH SYSTEM (O, 224 beds) 2151 Peachford Road, Atlanta, GA Zip 30338–6599; tel. 770/455–3200; Matthew Crouch, Chief Executive Officer and Managing Director
Web address: www.peachfordhospital.com

SAINT SIMONS BY–THE–SEA HOSPITAL (O, 101 beds) 2927 Demere Road, Saint Simons Island, GA Zip 31522–1620; tel. 912/638–1999; Monica Cook, Interim Chief Executive Officer
Web address: www.ssbythesea.com

TURNING POINT HOSPITAL (O, 59 beds) 3015 Veterans Parkway South, Moultrie, GA Zip 31788–6705, Mailing Address: P.O. Box 1177, Zip 31776–1177; tel. 229/985–4815; Ben Marion, Chief Executive Officer and Managing Director
Web address: www.turningpointcare.com

IDAHO: INTERMOUNTAIN HOSPITAL (O, 140 beds) 303 North Allumbaugh Street, Boise, ID Zip 83704–9208; tel. 208/377–8400; Jeffrey F. Morrell, Chief Executive Officer
Web address: www.intermountainhospital.com

ILLINOIS: GARFIELD PARK HOSPITAL (O, 88 beds) 520 North Ridgeway Avenue, Chicago. IL Zip 60624–1232; tel. 773/265–3700; Kathe Dellacecca, Chief Executive Officer
Web address: www.garfieldparkhospital.com

HARTGROVE HOSPITAL (O, 128 beds) 5730 West Roosevelt Road, Chicago, IL Zip 60644–1580; tel. 773/413–1700; Steven Airhart, Chief Executive Officer
Web address: www.hartgrovehospital.com

LINCOLN PRAIRIE BEHAVIORAL HEALTH CENTER (O, 88 beds) 5230 South Sixth Street, Springfield, IL Zip 62703–5128; tel. 217/585–1180; Mark Littrell, Chief Executive Officer
Web address: www.lincolnprairiebhc.com/

RIVEREDGE HOSPITAL (O, 224 beds) 8311 West Roosevelt Road, Forest Park, IL Zip 60130–2500; tel. 708/771–7000; Carey Carlock, Chief Executive Officer
Web address: www.riveredgehospital.com

STREAMWOOD BEHAVIORAL HEALTH CENTER (O, 177 beds) 1400 East Irving Park Road, Streamwood, IL Zip 60107–3203; tel. 630/837–9000; Ron Weglarz, Chief Executive Officer and Managing Director
Web address: www.streamwoodhospital.com

THE PAVILION (O, 46 beds) 809 West Church Street, Champaign, IL Zip 61820–3399; tel. 217/373–1700; Joseph Sheehy, Chief Executive Officer and Managing Director
Web address: www.pavilionhospital.com

INDIANA: BLOOMINGTON MEADOWS HOSPITAL (O, 67 beds) 3600 North Prow Road, Bloomington, IN Zip 47404–1616; tel. 812/331–8000; Jean Scallon, Chief Executive Officer
Web address: www.bloomingtonmeadows.com

MICHIANA BEHAVIORAL HEALTH CENTER (O, 75 beds) 1800 North Oak Drive, Plymouth, IN Zip 46563–3492; tel. 574/936–3784; Bryan W. Lett, Chief Executive Officer
Web address: www.michianabhc.com

VALLE VISTA HOSPITAL (O, 102 beds) 898 East Main Street, Greenwood, IN Zip 46143–1400; tel. 317/887–1348; Sherri R. Jewett, Chief Executive Officer
Web address: www.vallevistahospital.com

WELLSTONE REGIONAL HOSPITAL (O, 100 beds) 2700 Vissing Park Road, Jeffersonville, IN Zip 47130–5989; tel. 812/284–8000; Greg Stewart, Chief Executive Officer
Web address: www.wellstonehospital.com

KENTUCKY: CUMBERLAND HALL HOSPITAL (O, 97 beds) 270 Walton Way, Hopkinsville, KY Zip 42240–6808; tel. 270/886–1919; James Spruyt, Chief Executive Officer
Web address: www.cumberlandhallhospital.com

LINCOLN TRAIL BEHAVIORAL HEALTH SYSTEM (O, 67 beds) 3909 South Wilson Road, Radcliff, KY Zip 40160–8944, Mailing Address: P.O. Box 369, Zip 40159–0369; tel. 270/351–9444; Charles L. Webb, Jr., Chief Executive Officer
Web address: www.lincolnbehavioral.com

RIDGE BEHAVIORAL HEALTH SYSTEM (O, 110 beds) 3050 Rio Dosa Drive, Lexington, KY Zip 40509–1540; tel. 859/269–2325; Nina W. Eisner, Chief Executive Officer and Managing Director
Web address: www.ridgebhs.com

RIVENDELL BEHAVIORAL HEALTH (O, 125 beds) 1035 Porter Pike, Bowling Green, KY Zip 42103–9581; tel. 270/843–1199; Janice Richardson, Chief Executive Officer and Managing Director
Web address: www.rivendellbehavioral.com

THE BROOK AT DUPONT (O, 88 beds) 1405 Browns Lane, Louisville, KY Zip 40207–4608; tel. 502/896–0495; Paul Andrews, Chief Executive Officer
Web address: www.thebrookhospitals.com/

THE BROOK HOSPITAL – KMI (O, 94 beds) 8521 Old LaGrange Road, Louisville, KY Zip 40242–3800; tel. 502/426–6380; Paul Andrews, Chief Executive Officer
Web address: www.thebrookhospitals.com

For explanation of codes following names, see page B2.
★ Indicates Type III membership in the American Hospital Association.

LOUISIANA: BRENTWOOD HOSPITAL (O, 172 beds) 1006 Highland Avenue, Shreveport, LA Zip 71101–4103; tel. 318/678–7500; William Weaver, Chief Executive Officer
Web address: www.brentwoodbehavioral.com

RIVER OAKS HOSPITAL (O, 126 beds) 1525 River Oaks Road West, New Orleans, LA Zip 70123–2162; tel. 504/734–1740; Evelyn Nolting, Chief Executive Officer and Managing Director
Web address: www.riveroakshospital.com

MASSACHUSETTS: ARBOUR H. R. I. HOSPITAL (O, 68 beds) 227 Babcock Street, Brookline, MA Zip 02446–6799; tel. 617/731–3200; Patrick Moallemian, Chief Executive Officer and Managing Director
Web address: www.arbourhealth.com

ARBOUR HOSPITAL (O, 118 beds) 49 Robinwood Avenue, Boston, MA Zip 02130–2156; tel. 617/522–4400; Laura Ames, Chief Executive Officer
Web address: www.arbourhealth.com

ARBOUR–FULLER HOSPITAL (O, 46 beds) 200 May Street, Attleboro, MA Zip 02703–5520; tel. 508/761–8500; Kevin Burchill, Chief Executive Officer
Web address: www.arbourhealth.com

PEMBROKE HOSPITAL (O, 115 beds) 199 Oak Street, Pembroke, MA Zip 02359–1953; tel. 781/829–7000; Thomas P. Hickey, Chief Executive Officer and Managing Director
Web address: www.arbourhealth.com/organizations/pembroke–hospital/

WESTWOOD LODGE HOSPITAL (O, 65 beds) 45 Clapboardtree Street, Westwood, MA Zip 02090–2903; tel. 781/762–7764; Gregory Brownstein, Chief Executive Officer
Web address: www.arbourhealth.com

MICHIGAN: FOREST VIEW PSYCHIATRIC HOSPITAL (O, 82 beds) 1055 Medical Park Drive S.E., Grand Rapids, MI Zip 49546–3607; tel. 616/942–9610; Andrew Hotaling, Chief Executive Officer
Web address: www.forestviewhospital.com

HAVENWYCK HOSPITAL (O, 253 beds) 1525 University Drive, Auburn Hills, MI Zip 48326–2673; tel. 248/373–9200; Diane Henneman, Chief Executive Officer
Web address: www.havenwyckhospital.com

MISSISSIPPI: ALLIANCE HEALTH CENTER (O, 134 beds) 5000 Highway 39 North, Meridian, MS Zip 39301–1021; tel. 601/483–6211; James Miller, Interim Chief Executive Officer
Web address: www.alliancehealthcenter.com

BRENTWOOD BEHAVIORAL HEALTHCARE OF MISSISSIPPI (O, 105 beds) 3531 East Lakeland Drive, Jackson, MS Zip 39232–8839; tel. 601/936–2024; Michael J. Carney, Chief Executive Officer
Web address: www.brentwoodjackson.com

PARKWOOD BEHAVIORAL HEALTH SYSTEM (O, 128 beds) 8135 Goodman Road, Olive Branch, MS Zip 38654–2103; tel. 662/895–4900; Coleby Wright, Chief Executive Officer
Web address: www.parkwoodbhs.com

MISSOURI: HEARTLAND BEHAVIORAL HEALTH SERVICES (O, 69 beds) 1500 West Ashland Street, Nevada, MO Zip 64772–1710; tel. 417/667–2666; Alyson Wysong–Harder, Chief Executive Officer
Web address: www.heartlandbehavioral.com

TWO RIVERS BEHAVIORAL HEALTH SYSTEM (O, 105 beds) 5121 Raytown Road, Kansas City, MO Zip 64133–2141; tel. 816/382–6300; Cara Macaleer, Chief Executive Officer/Managing Director
Web address: www.tworivershospital.com

NEVADA: CENTENNIAL HILLS HOSPITAL MEDICAL CENTER (O, 165 beds) 6900 North Durango Drive, Las Vegas, NV Zip 89149–4409; tel. 702/835–9700; Sajit Pullarkat, Chief Executive Officer and Managing Director
Web address: www.centennialhillshospital.com

DESERT SPRINGS HOSPITAL MEDICAL CENTER (O, 346 beds) 2075 East Flamingo Road, Las Vegas, NV Zip 89119–5121; tel. 702/733–8800; Samuel Kaufman, Chief Executive Officer and Managing Director
Web address: www.desertspringshospital.com

NORTHERN NEVADA MEDICAL CENTER (O, 80 beds) 2375 East Prater Way, Sparks, NV Zip 89434–9641; tel. 775/331–7000; Alan C. Olive, Chief Executive Officer
Web address: www.nnmc.com

SPRING MOUNTAIN SAHARA (O, 30 beds) 5460 West Sahara, Las Vegas, NV Zip 89146–3307; tel. 702/216–8900; Darryl S. Dubroca, Chief Executive Officer and Managing Director
Web address: www.springmountainsahara.com

SPRING MOUNTAIN TREATMENT CENTER (L, 82 beds) 7000 West Spring Mountain Road, Las Vegas, NV Zip 89117–3816; tel. 702/873–2400; Darryl S. Dubroca, Chief Executive Officer and Managing Director
Web address: www.springmountaintreatmentcenter.com/

SPRING VALLEY HOSPITAL MEDICAL CENTER (O, 169 beds) 5400 South Rainbow Boulevard, Las Vegas, NV Zip 89118–1859; tel. 702/853–3000; Leonard Freehof, Chief Executive Officer and Managing Director
Web address: www.springvalleyhospital.com

SUMMERLIN HOSPITAL MEDICAL CENTER (O, 148 beds) 657 Town Center Drive, Las Vegas, NV Zip 89144–6367; tel. 702/233–7000; Robert S. Freymuller, Chief Executive Officer
Web address: www.summerlinhospital.com

VALLEY HOSPITAL MEDICAL CENTER (O, 365 beds) 620 Shadow Lane, Las Vegas, NV Zip 89106–4119; tel. 702/388–4000; Samuel Kaufman, Chief Executive Officer, Managing Director
Web address: www.valleyhospital.net

WEST HILLS HOSPITAL (O, 190 beds) 1240 East Ninth Street, Reno, NV Zip 89512–2964; tel. 775/323–0478; Allison Zednicek, Chief Executive Officer
Web address: www.westhillshospital.net

NEW JERSEY: HAMPTON BEHAVIORAL HEALTH CENTER (O, 110 beds) 650 Rancocas Road, Westampton, NJ Zip 08060–5613; tel. 609/267–7000; Craig Hilton, Chief Executive Officer
Web address: www.hamptonhospital.com

SUMMIT OAKS HOSPITAL (O, 90 beds) 19 Prospect Street, Summit, NJ Zip 07901–2530; tel. 908/522–7000; James P. Gallagher, Chief Executive Officer
Web address: www.summitoakshospital.com/

NEW MEXICO: MESILLA VALLEY HOSPITAL (O, 120 beds) 3751 Del Rey Boulevard, Las Cruces, NM Zip 88012–8526; tel. 575/382–3500; Robert Mansfield, Chief Executive Officer
Web address: www.mesillavalleyhospital.com

NORTH CAROLINA: BRYNN MARR HOSPITAL (O, 87 beds) 192 Village Drive, Jacksonville, NC Zip 28546–7299; tel. 910/577–1400; Jay Kortemeyer, Chief Executive Officer
Web address: www.brynnmarr.org

HOLLY HILL HOSPITAL (O, 168 beds) 3019 Falstaff Road, Raleigh, NC Zip 27610–1812; tel. 919/250–7000; Michael McDonald, Chief Executive Officer
Web address: www.hollyhillhospital.com

OLD VINEYARD BEHAVIORAL HEALTH SERVICES (O, 102 beds) 3637 Old Vineyard Road, Winston–Salem, NC Zip 27104–4842; tel. 336/794–3550; Kevin Patton, Chief Executive Officer
Web address: www.oldvineyardbhs.com

NORTH DAKOTA: PRAIRIE ST. JOHN'S (O, 94 beds) 510 4th Street South, Fargo, ND Zip 58103–1914; tel. 701/476–7200; Gregory LaFrancois, Chief Executive Officer
Web address: www.prairie–stjohns.com

OHIO: ARROWHEAD BEHAVIORAL HEALTH HOSPITAL (O, 42 beds) 1725 Timber Line Road, Maumee, OH Zip 43537–4015; tel. 419/891–9333; Edward Speedling, Chief Executive Officer and Managing Director
Web address: www.arrowheadbehavioral.com

BELMONT PINES HOSPITAL (O, 46 beds) 615 Churchill–Hubbard Road, Youngstown, OH Zip 44505–1379; tel. 330/759–2700; George H. Perry, Ph.D., Chief Executive Officer
Web address: www.belmontpines.com

WINDSOR–LAURELWOOD CENTER FOR BEHAVIORAL MEDICINE (O, 159 beds) 35900 Euclid Avenue, Willoughby, OH Zip 44094–4648; tel. 440/953–3000; Ric McAllister, Chief Executive Officer
Web address: www.windsorlaurelwood.com

OKLAHOMA: CEDAR RIDGE HOSPITAL (O, 36 beds) 6501 N.E. 50th Street, Oklahoma City, OK Zip 73141–9118; tel. 405/605–6111; Robert Jackson, Interim Chief Executive Officer
Web address: www.cedarridgebhs.com

SHADOW MOUNTAIN BEHAVIORAL HEALTH SYSTEM (O, 202 beds) 6262 South Sheridan Road, Tulsa, OK Zip 74133–4055; tel. 918/492–8200; Mike Kistler, Chief Executive Officer
Web address: www.shadowmountainbhs.com

For explanation of codes following names, see page B2.
★ Indicates Type III membership in the American Hospital Association.

ST. MARY'S REGIONAL MEDICAL CENTER (O, 150 beds) 305 South Fifth Street, Enid, OK Zip 73701–5899, Mailing Address: P.O. Box 232, Zip 73702–0232; tel. 580/233–6100; Stanley D. Tatum, FACHE, Chief Executive Officer
Web address: www.stmarysregional.com

OREGON: CEDAR HILLS HOSPITAL (O, 78 beds) 10300 S.W. Eastridge Street, Portland, OR Zip 97225–5004; tel. 503/944–5000; Michael Sherbun, Ph.D., Chief Executive Officer
Web address: www.cedarhillshospital.com

PENNSYLVANIA: BROOKE GLEN BEHAVIORAL HOSPITAL (O, 146 beds) 7170 Lafayette Avenue, Fort Washington, PA Zip 19034–2301; tel. 215/641–5300; Neil Callahan, Chief Executive Officer
Web address: www.brookeglenhospital.com

CLARION PSYCHIATRIC CENTER (O, 74 beds) 2 Hospital Drive, Clarion, PA Zip 16214–8502; tel. 814/226–9545; Robert Scheffler, Chief Executive Officer
Web address: www.clarioncenter.com

FAIRMOUNT BEHAVIORAL HEALTH SYSTEM (O, 239 beds) 561 Fairthorne Avenue, Philadelphia, PA Zip 19128–2499; tel. 215/487–4000; Charles McLister, Chief Executive Officer
Web address: www.fairmountbhs.com

FOUNDATIONS BEHAVIORAL HEALTH (O, 96 beds) 833 East Butler Avenue, Doylestown, PA Zip 18901–2280; tel. 215/345–0444; Robert Weinhold, Chief Executive Officer
Web address: www.fbh.com

FRIENDS HOSPITAL (O, 192 beds) 4641 Roosevelt Boulevard, Philadelphia, PA Zip 19124–2343; tel. 215/831–4600; Geoff Botak, Chief Executive Officer
Web address: www.friendshospital.com

HORSHAM CLINIC (O, 138 beds) 722 East Butler Pike, Ambler, PA Zip 19002–2310; tel. 215/643–7800; Phyllis Weisfield, Chief Executive Officer and Managing Director
Web address: www.horshamclinic.com

MEADOWS PSYCHIATRIC CENTER (O, 107 beds) 132 The Meadows Drive, Centre Hall, PA Zip 16828–9231; tel. 814/364–2161; Jeffrey Herman, Chief Executive Officer
Web address: www.themeadows.net

ROXBURY TREATMENT CENTER (O, 94 beds) 601 Roxbury Road, Shippensburg, PA Zip 17257–9302; tel. 800/648–4673; Shauna Radzieski, Chief Executive Officer
Web address: www.roxburyhospital.com

PUERTO RICO: FIRST HOSPITAL PANAMERICANO (O, 153 beds) State Road 787 KM 1 5, Cidra, PR Zip 00739, Mailing Address: P.O. Box 1400, Zip 00739; tel. 787/739–5555; Astro Munoz, Executive Director
Web address: www.hospitalpanamericano.com

SOUTH CAROLINA: AIKEN REGIONAL MEDICAL CENTERS (O, 271 beds) 302 University Parkway, Aiken, SC Zip 29801–6302; tel. 803/641–5000; Carlos Milanes, Chief Executive Officer and Managing Director
Web address: www.aikenregional.com

CAROLINA CENTER FOR BEHAVIORAL HEALTH (O, 112 beds) 2700 East Phillips Road, Greer, SC Zip 29650–4816; tel. 864/235–2335; John Willingham, Chief Executive Officer and Managing Director
Web address: www.thecarolinacenter.com

LIGHTHOUSE CARE CENTER OF CONWAY (O, 90 beds) 152 Waccamaw Medical Park Drive, Conway, SC Zip 29526–8901; tel. 843/347–8871; Thomas L. Ryba, Chief Executive Officer
Web address: www.lighthousecarecenterofconway.com/

PALMETTO LOWCOUNTRY BEHAVIORAL HEALTH (O, 112 beds) 2777 Speissegger Drive, Charleston, SC Zip 29405–8229; tel. 843/747–5830; Shari Baker, Chief Executive Officer
Web address: www.palmettobehavioralhealth.com

THREE RIVERS BEHAVIORAL HEALTH (O, 118 beds) 2900 Sunset Boulevard, West Columbia, SC Zip 29169–3422; tel. 803/796–9911; Elyssia Lowe, Chief Executive Officer
Web address: www.threeriversbehavioral.org

TENNESSEE: LAKESIDE BEHAVIORAL HEALTH SYSTEM (O, 311 beds) 2911 Brunswick Road, Memphis, TN Zip 38133–4199; tel. 901/377–4700; Joy Golden, Chief Executive Officer
Web address: www.lakesidebhs.com

ROLLING HILLS HOSPITAL (O, 80 beds) 2014 Quail Hollow Circle, Franklin, TN Zip 37067–5967; tel. 615/628–5700; Richard Clark, Chief Executive Officer
Web address: www.rollinghillshospital.org/

TEXAS: AUSTIN LAKES HOSPITAL (O, 58 beds) 1025 East 32nd Street, Austin, TX Zip 78705–2714; tel. 512/544–5253; Rick Buckelew, Chief Executive Officer
Web address: www.austinlakeshospital.com

AUSTIN OAKS HOSPITAL (O, 80 beds) 1407 West Stassney Lane, Austin, TX Zip 78745–2947; tel. 512/440–4800; Ramona Key, Chief Executive Officer
Web address: www.austinoakshospital.com

BEHAVIORAL HOSPITAL OF BELLAIRE (O, 76 beds) 5314 Dashwood Drive, Houston, TX Zip 77081–4603; tel. 713/600–9500; Drew Martin, Chief Executive Officer
Web address: www.bhbhospital.com

CORNERSTONE REGIONAL HOSPITAL (L, 14 beds) 2302 Cornerstone Boulevard, Edinburg, TX Zip 78539–8471; tel. 956/618–4444; Roxanna M. Godinez, Chief Executive Officer
Web address: www.cornerstoneregional.com

CYPRESS CREEK HOSPITAL (O, 96 beds) 17750 Cali Drive, Houston, TX Zip 77090–2700; tel. 281/586–7600; Brian Brooker, Chief Executive Officer
Web address: www.cypresscreekhospital.com

DOCTORS HOSPITAL OF LAREDO (O, 183 beds) 10700 McPherson Road, Laredo, TX Zip 78045–6268; tel. 956/523–2000; Rene Lopez, Chief Executive Officer
Web address: www.doctorshosplaredo.com

FORT DUNCAN REGIONAL MEDICAL CENTER (O, 101 beds) 3333 North Foster Maldonado Boulevard, Eagle Pass, TX Zip 78852–5893; tel. 830/773–5321; Richard Prati, Chief Executive Officer
Web address: www.fortduncanmedicalcenter.com

GLEN OAKS HOSPITAL (O, 54 beds) 301 Division Street, Greenville, TX Zip 75401–4101; tel. 903/454–6000; Joel Klein, Chief Executive Officer and Managing Director
Web address: www.glenoakshospital.com

HICKORY TRAIL HOSPITAL (O, 86 beds) 2000 Old Hickory Trail, Desoto, TX Zip 75115–2242; tel. 972/298–7323; Lance Folske, Chief Executive Officer
Web address: www.hickorytrail.com

KINGWOOD PINES HOSPITAL (O, 116 beds) 2001 Ladbrook Drive, Kingwood, TX Zip 77339–3004; tel. 281/404–1001; James Burroughs, Chief Executive Officer
Web address: www.kingwoodpines.com

LAUREL RIDGE TREATMENT CENTER (O, 208 beds) 17720 Corporate Woods Drive, San Antonio, TX Zip 78259–3500; tel. 210/491–9400; Jacob Cuellar, M.D., Chief Executive Officer
Web address: www.laurelridgetc.com

MAYHILL HOSPITAL (O, 59 beds) 2809 South Mayhill Road, Denton, TX Zip 76208–5910; tel. 940/239–3000; Jason Toalson, Chief Executive Officer
Web address: www.mayhillhospital.com

MILLWOOD HOSPITAL (O, 122 beds) 1011 North Cooper Street, Arlington, TX Zip 76011–5517; tel. 817/261–3121; Rick Paczkowski, Chief Executive Officer
Web address: www.millwoodhospital.com

NORTHWEST TEXAS HEALTHCARE SYSTEM (O, 414 beds) 1501 South Coulter Avenue, Amarillo, TX Zip 79106–1770, Mailing Address: P.O. Box 1110, Zip 79105–1110; tel. 806/354–1000; Mark W. Crawford, Chief Executive Officer
Web address: www.nwtexashealthcare.com

RIVER CREST HOSPITAL (O, 80 beds) 1636 Hunters Glen Road, San Angelo, TX Zip 76901–5016; tel. 325/949–5722; Mandy Westerman, Chief Executive Officer
Web address: www.rivercresthospital.com

SOUTH TEXAS HEALTH SYSTEM (O, 775 beds) 1102 West Trenton Road, Edinburg, TX Zip 78539–9105; tel. 956/388–6000; Jennifer Garza, Chief Executive Officer
Web address: www.southtexashealthsystem.com

TEXAS NEUROREHAB CENTER (O, 47 beds) 1106 West Dittmar, Austin, TX Zip 78745–6328, Mailing Address: P.O. Box 150459, Zip 78715–0459; tel. 512/444–4835; Janet Bitner, Interim Chief Executive Officer
Web address: www.texasneurorehab.com

TEXOMA MEDICAL CENTER (O, 288 beds) 5016 South U.S. Highway 75, Denison, TX Zip 75020–4584, Mailing Address: P.O. Box 890, Zip 75021–0890; tel. 903/416–4000; Ronald T. Seal, Chief Executive Officer
Web address: www.texomamedicalcenter.net

For explanation of codes following names, see page B2.
★ Indicates Type III membership in the American Hospital Association.

TIMBERLAWN MENTAL HEALTH SYSTEM (O, 144 beds) 4600 Samuell Boulevard, Dallas, TX Zip 75228–6800; tel. 214/381–7181; Shelah Adams, Chief Executive Officer
Web address: www.timberlawn.com

UNIVERSITY BEHAVIORAL HEALTH OF DENTON (O, 104 beds) 2026 West University Drive, Denton, TX Zip 76201–0644; tel. 940/320–8100; Jason Toalson, Chief Executive Officer
Web address: www.ubhdenton.com

UNIVERSITY BEHAVIORAL HEALTH OF EL PASO (O, 163 beds) 1900 Denver Avenue, El Paso, TX Zip 79902–3008; tel. 915/544–4000; David W. Morris, Chief Executive Officer
Web address: www.ubhelpaso.com/

WEST OAKS HOSPITAL (O, 144 beds) 6500 Hornwood Drive, Houston, TX Zip 77074–5095; tel. 713/995–0909; Gregory Drummond, Chief Executive Officer
Web address: www.westoakshospital.com

UTAH: PROVO CANYON BEHAVIORAL HOSPITAL (O, 80 beds) 1350 East 750 North, Orem, UT Zip 84097–4345; tel. 801/852–2273; Jeremy Cottle, Ph.D., Chief Executive Officer
Web address: www.pcbh.com

SALT LAKE BEHAVIORAL HEALTH (O, 118 beds) 3802 South 700 East, Salt Lake City, UT Zip 84106–1182; tel. 801/264–6000; Kreg Gillman, Chief Executive Officer
Web address: www.saltlakebehavioralhealth.com

VIRGINIA: CUMBERLAND HOSPITAL (O, 132 beds) 9407 Cumberland Road, New Kent, VA Zip 23124–2029; tel. 804/966–2242; Patrice Gay Brooks, Chief Executive Officer
Web address: www.cumberlandhospital.com

POPLAR SPRINGS HOSPITAL (O, 180 beds) 350 Poplar Drive, Petersburg, VA Zip 23805–9367; tel. 804/733–6874; Joseph Trapani, Chief Executive Officer
Web address: www.poplarsprings.com

VIRGINIA BEACH PSYCHIATRIC CENTER (O, 100 beds) 1100 First Colonial Road, Virginia Beach, VA Zip 23454–2403; tel. 757/496–6000; Frank Gallagher, Chief Executive Officer
Web address: www.absfirst.com

WASHINGTON: FAIRFAX HOSPITAL (O, 103 beds) 10200 N.E. 132nd Street, Kirkland, WA Zip 98034–2899; tel. 425/821–2000; Ron Escarda, Chief Executive Officer
Web address: www.fairfaxhospital.com

WEST VIRGINIA: RIVER PARK HOSPITAL (O, 173 beds) 1230 Sixth Avenue, Huntington, WV Zip 25701–2312, Mailing Address: P.O. Box 1875, Zip 25719–1875; tel. 304/526–9111; Terry A. Stephens, Chief Executive Officer
Web address: www.riverparkhospital.net

WYOMING: WYOMING BEHAVIORAL INSTITUTE (O, 129 beds) 2521 East 15th Street, Casper, WY Zip 82609–4126; tel. 307/237–7444; Joseph Gallagher, Chief Executive Officer
Web address: www.wbihelp.com

Owned, leased, sponsored:	141 hospitals	18150 beds
Contract–managed:	0 hospitals	0 beds
Totals:	141 hospitals	18150 beds

0916: UNIVERSITY GENERAL HEALTH SYSTEM (IO)
7501 Fannin Street, Houston, TX Zip 77054–1938; tel. 713/375–7100; Hassan Chahadeh, M.D., Chief Executive Officer

TEXAS: UNIVERSITY GENERAL HOSPITAL (O, 69 beds) 7501 Fannin Street, Houston, TX Zip 77054–1938; tel. 713/375–7000; David Kreye, Chief Executive Officer
Web address: www.ughospital.com

UNIVERSITY GENERAL HOSPITAL–DALLAS (O, 111 beds) 2929 South Hampton Road, Dallas, TX Zip 75224–3026; tel. 214/623–4400; Susie Edler, Chief Executive Officer
Web address: www.universitygeneralhospital.com

Owned, leased, sponsored:	2 hospitals	180 beds
Contract–managed:	0 hospitals	0 beds
Totals:	2 hospitals	180 beds

★0896: UNIVERSITY HEALTH CARE SYSTEM (NP)
1350 Walton Way, Augusta, GA Zip 30901–2629; tel. 706/722–9011; James R. Davis, President and Chief Executive Officer
(Independent Hospital System)

GEORGIA: UNIVERSITY HOSPITAL (O, 494 beds) 1350 Walton Way, Augusta, GA Zip 30901–2629; tel. 706/722–9011; James R. Davis, Chief Executive Officer
Web address: www.universityhealth.org

UNIVERSITY HOSPITAL MCDUFFIE (O, 25 beds) 521 Hill Street S.W., Thomson, GA Zip 30824–2199; tel. 706/595–1411; Sandra I. McVicker, R.N., MSN, President
Web address: www.uh.org

Owned, leased, sponsored:	2 hospitals	519 beds
Contract–managed:	0 hospitals	0 beds
Totals:	2 hospitals	519 beds

★0112: UNIVERSITY HOSPITALS (NP)
11100 Euclid Avenue, Cleveland, OH Zip 44106–5000; tel. 216/844–1000; Thomas F. Zenty, III, President and Chief Executive Officer
(Centralized Health System)

OHIO: UH REGIONAL HOSPITALS (O, 101 beds) 27100 Chardon Road, Cleveland, OH Zip 44143–1116; tel. 440/585–6500; Robert G. David, President
Web address: www.uhhospitals.org

UNIVERSITY HOSPITALS AHUJA MEDICAL CENTER (O, 144 beds) 3999 Richmond Road, Beachwood, OH Zip 44122–6046; tel. 216/593–5500; Susan V. Juris, President
Web address: www.uhhospitals.org/ahuja/tabid/7051/uhahujamedicalcenter.aspx

UNIVERSITY HOSPITALS CASE MEDICAL CENTER (O, 763 beds) 11100 Euclid Avenue, Cleveland, OH Zip 44106–1716; tel. 216/844–1000; Fred C. Rothstein, M.D., President
Web address: www.UHhospitals.org

UNIVERSITY HOSPITALS CONNEAUT MEDICAL CENTER (O, 25 beds) 158 West Main Road, Conneaut, OH Zip 44030–2039; tel. 440/593–1131; M. Steven Jones, President
Web address: www.uhhospitals.org

UNIVERSITY HOSPITALS ELYRIA MEDICAL CENTER (O, 257 beds) 630 East River Street, Elyria, OH Zip 44035–5902; tel. 440/329–7500; Donald S. Sheldon, M.D., President and Chief Executive Officer
Web address: www.emh–healthcare.org

UNIVERSITY HOSPITALS GEAUGA MEDICAL CENTER (O, 126 beds) 13207 Ravenna Road, Chardon, OH Zip 44024–7032; tel. 440/269–6000; M. Steven Jones, President
Web address: www.uhhospitals.org/geauga/

UNIVERSITY HOSPITALS GENEVA MEDICAL CENTER (O, 25 beds) 870 West Main Street, Geneva, OH Zip 44041–1295; tel. 440/466–1141; M. Steven Jones, President
Web address: www.uhhs.com

UNIVERSITY HOSPITALS PARMA MEDICAL CENTER (O, 271 beds) 7007 Powers Boulevard, Parma, OH Zip 44129–5495; tel. 440/743–3000; Nancy Tinsley, President and Chief Executive Officer
Web address: www.parmahospital.org

Owned, leased, sponsored:	8 hospitals	1712 beds
Contract–managed:	0 hospitals	0 beds
Totals:	8 hospitals	1712 beds

0915: UNIVERSITY HOSPITALS AND HEALTH SYSTEM (NP)
2500 North State Street, Jackson, MS Zip 39216–4500; tel. 601/984–1000; James Keeton, M.D., Vice Chancellor for Health Affairs

MISSISSIPPI: HOLMES COUNTY HOSPITAL AND CLINICS (O, 25 beds) 239 Bowling Green Road, Lexington, MS Zip 39095–5167; tel. 662/834–1321; David G. Putt, FACHE, Chief Executive Officer
Web address: www.ummchealth.com/holmes/

For explanation of codes following names, see page B2.
★ Indicates Type III membership in the American Hospital Association.

Section B

UNIVERSITY HOSPITAL (O, 673 beds) 2500 North State Street, Jackson, MS Zip 39216–4505; tel. 601/984–1000; Kevin S. Cook, Chief Executive Officer
Web address: www.umc.edu

UNIVERSITY OF MISSISSIPPI MEDICAL CENTER GRENADA (C, 132 beds) 960 Avent Drive, Grenada, MS Zip 38901–5230; tel. 662/227–7000; David G. Putt, FACHE, Chief Executive Officer
Web address: www.glmc.net

Owned, leased, sponsored:	2 hospitals	698 beds
Contract–managed:	1 hospital	132 beds
Totals:	3 hospitals	830 beds

★6405: UNIVERSITY OF CALIFORNIA–SYSTEMWIDE ADMINISTRATION (NP)
1111 Franklin Street, 11th Floor, Oakland, CA Zip 94607–5200; tel. 510/987–9071; John D. Stobo, M.D., Senior Vice President Health Sciences and Services
(Moderately Centralized Health System)

CALIFORNIA: RONALD REAGAN UNIVERSITY OF CALIFORNIA LOS ANGELES MEDICAL CENTER (O, 466 beds) 757 Westwood Plaza, Los Angeles, CA Zip 90095–8358; tel. 310/825–9111; David Feinberg, M.D., Chief Executive Officer
Web address: www.uclahealth.org

SANTA MONICA–UCLA MEDICAL CENTER AND ORTHOPAEDIC HOSPITAL (O, 266 beds) 1250 16th Street, Santa Monica, CA Zip 90404–1249; tel. 310/319–4000; Paul Watkins, Chief Administrative Officer
Web address: www.healthcare.ucla.edu

STEWART & LYNDA RESNICK NEUROPSYCHIATRIC HOSPITAL AT UCLA (O, 74 beds) 760 Westwood Plaza, Los Angeles, CA Zip 90095–8353; tel. 310/825–9989; Peter Whybrow, M.D., Chief Executive Officer
Web address: www.semel.ucla.edu/resnick

UC IRVINE MEDICAL CENTER (O, 409 beds) 101 The City Drive South, Orange, CA Zip 92868–3298; tel. 714/456–6011; Terry A. Belmont, Chief Executive Officer
Web address: www.ucihealth.com

UC SAN DIEGO HEALTH SYSTEM (O, 524 beds) 200 West Arbor Drive, San Diego, CA Zip 92103–9000; tel. 619/543–6222; Paul S. Viviano, Chief Executive Officer
Web address: www.health.ucsd.edu

UCSF MEDICAL CENTER (O, 650 beds) 500 Parnassus Avenue, San Francisco, CA Zip 94143–0296, Mailing Address: 500 Parnassus Avenue, Box 0296, Zip 94143–0296; tel. 415/476–1000; Mark R. Laret, Chief Executive Officer
Web address: www.ucsfhealth.org

UNIVERSITY OF CALIFORNIA, DAVIS MEDICAL CENTER (O, 581 beds) 2315 Stockton Boulevard, Sacramento, CA Zip 95817–2282; tel. 916/734–2011; Ann Madden Rice, Chief Executive Officer
Web address: www.ucdmc.ucdavis.edu

Owned, leased, sponsored:	7 hospitals	2970 beds
Contract–managed:	0 hospitals	0 beds
Totals:	7 hospitals	2970 beds

★0381: UNIVERSITY OF COLORADO HEALTH (NP)
2315 East Harmony Road, Suite 200, Fort Collins, CO Zip 80528–8620; tel. 970/237–7001; William Neff, M.D., Interim President and Chief Executive Officer
(Independent Hospital System)

COLORADO: MEDICAL CENTER OF THE ROCKIES (O, 166 beds) 2500 Rocky Mountain Avenue, Loveland, CO Zip 80538–9004; tel. 970/624–2500; Kevin L. Unger, FACHE, President and Chief Executive Officer
Web address: www.medctrrockies.org

MEMORIAL HOSPITAL (L, 448 beds) 1400 East Boulder Street, Colorado Springs, CO Zip 80909–5599; tel. 719/365–9888; George E. Hayes, FACHE, President and Chief Executive Officer
Web address: www.memorialhealthsystem.com

POUDRE VALLEY HOSPITAL (O, 226 beds) 1024 South Lemay Avenue, Fort Collins, CO Zip 80524–3998; tel. 970/495–7000; Kevin L. Unger, FACHE, President and Chief Executive Officer
Web address: www.uchealth.org

Owned, leased, sponsored:	3 hospitals	840 beds
Contract–managed:	0 hospitals	0 beds
Totals:	3 hospitals	840 beds

★0216: UNIVERSITY OF MARYLAND MEDICAL SYSTEM (NP)
250 West Pratt Street, 24th Floor, Baltimore, MD Zip 21201–1595; tel. 410/328–8667; Robert A. Chrencik, President and Chief Executive Officer
(Centralized Health System)

MARYLAND: HARFORD MEMORIAL HOSPITAL (O, 89 beds) 501 South Union Avenue, Havre De Grace, MD Zip 21078–3493; tel. 443/843–5000; Lyle Ernest Sheldon, FACHE, President and Chief Executive Officer
Web address: www.uchs.org

MT. WASHINGTON PEDIATRIC HOSPITAL (O, 70 beds) 1708 West Rogers Avenue, Baltimore, MD Zip 21209–4545; tel. 410/578–8600; Sheldon J. Stein, President and Chief Executive Officer
Web address: www.mwph.org

UNIVERSITY OF MARYLAND BALTIMORE WASHINGTON MEDICAL CENTER (O, 323 beds) 301 Hospital Drive, Glen Burnie, MD Zip 21061–5899; tel. 410/787–4000; Karen E. Olscamp, President and Chief Executive Officer
Web address: www.bwmc.umms.org

UNIVERSITY OF MARYLAND CHARLES REGIONAL MEDICAL CENTER (O, 110 beds) 5 Garrett Avenue, La Plata, MD Zip 20646–5960, Mailing Address: P.O. Box 1070, Zip 20646–1070; tel. 301/609–4000; Noel A. Cervino, President and Chief Executive Officer
Web address: www.charlesregional.org

UNIVERSITY OF MARYLAND MEDICAL CENTER (O, 718 beds) 22 South Greene Street, Baltimore, MD Zip 21201–1595; tel. 410/328–8667; Jeffrey A. Rivest, FACHE, President and Chief Executive Officer
Web address: www.umm.edu

UNIVERSITY OF MARYLAND MEDICAL CENTER MIDTOWN CAMPUS (O, 225 beds) 827 Linden Avenue, Baltimore, MD Zip 21201–4606; tel. 410/225–8000; Jeffrey A. Rivest, FACHE, President and Chief Executive Officer
Web address: www.marylandgeneral.org

UNIVERSITY OF MARYLAND REHABILITATION AND ORTHOPAEDIC INSTITUTE (O, 157 beds) 2200 Kernan Drive, Baltimore, MD Zip 21207–6697; tel. 410/448–2500; Michael Jablonover, M.D., President and Chief Executive Officer
Web address: www.umrehabortho.org

UNIVERSITY OF MARYLAND SHORE MEDICAL CENTER AT CHESTERTOWN (O, 47 beds) 100 Brown Street, Chestertown, MD Zip 21620–1499; tel. 410/778–3300; Kenneth D. Kozel, FACHE, President and Chief Executive Officer
Web address: www.umms.org/hospitals/shore–health–system.htm

UNIVERSITY OF MARYLAND SHORE MEDICAL CENTER AT DORCHESTER (O, 46 beds) 300 Byrn Street, Cambridge, MD Zip 21613–1908; tel. 410/228–5511; Kenneth D. Kozel, FACHE, President and Chief Executive Officer
Web address: www.shorehealth.org

UNIVERSITY OF MARYLAND SHORE MEDICAL CENTER AT EASTON (O, 132 beds) 219 South Washington Street, Easton, MD Zip 21601–2996; tel. 410/822–1000; Kenneth D. Kozel, FACHE, President and Chief Executive Officer
Web address: www.shorehealth.org

UNIVERSITY OF MARYLAND ST. JOSEPH MEDICAL CENTER (O, 320 beds) 7601 Osler Drive, Towson, MD Zip 21204–7582; tel. 410/337–1000; Mohan Suntha, M.D., President and Chief Executive Officer
Web address: www.sjmcmd.org

UPPER CHESAPEAKE MEDICAL CENTER (O, 181 beds) 500 Upper Chesapeake Drive, Bel Air, MD Zip 21014–4324; tel. 443/643–1000; Lyle Ernest Sheldon, FACHE, President and Chief Executive Officer
Web address: www.uchs.org

Owned, leased, sponsored:	12 hospitals	2418 beds
Contract–managed:	0 hospitals	0 beds
Totals:	12 hospitals	2418 beds

Section B

For explanation of codes following names, see page B2.
★ Indicates Type III membership in the American Hospital Association.

0881: UNIVERSITY OF MIAMI HEALTH SYSTEM (NP)
1400 N.W. 12th Avenue, Miami, FL Zip 33136–1003;
tel. 305/243–4000; Pascal J. Goldschmidt, M.D., Chief Executive
Officer
(Centralized Health System)

FLORIDA: BASCOM PALMER EYE INSTITUTE–ANNE BATES LEACH EYE
HOSPITAL (O, 56 beds) 900 N.W. 17th Street, Miami, FL
Zip 33136–1199, Mailing Address: Box 016880, Zip 33101–6880;
tel. 305/326–6000; Michael B. Gittelman, Administrator
Web address: www.bascompalmer.org

UNIVERSITY OF MIAMI HOSPITAL (O, 516 beds) 1400 N.W. 12th Avenue,
Miami, FL Zip 33136–1003; tel. 305/325–5511; David Zambrana, R.N.,
Chief Executive Officer
Web address: www.umiamihospital.com

UNIVERSITY OF MIAMI HOSPITAL AND CLINICS (O, 40 beds) 1475 N.W. 12th
Avenue, Miami, FL Zip 33136–1002; tel. 305/243–4000; Richard R. Ballard,
Chief Executive Officer and Administrator
Web address: www.uhealthsystem.com

Owned, leased, sponsored:	3 hospitals	612 beds
Contract–managed:	0 hospitals	0 beds
Totals:	3 hospitals	612 beds

★0227: UNIVERSITY OF MISSOURI HEALTH CARE (NP)
One Hospital Drive, DC 031, Columbia, MO Zip 65212–0001;
tel. 573/884–8738; Mitchell L. Wasden, Ed.D., Chief Executive
Officer and Chief Operating Officer
(Moderately Centralized Health System)

MISSOURI: CAPITAL REGION MEDICAL CENTER (O, 114 beds) 1125 Madison
Street, Jefferson City, MO Zip 65101–5200, Mailing Address: P.O. Box
1128, Zip 65102–1128; tel. 573/632–5000; Gaspare Calvaruso,
President
Web address: www.crmc.org

MISSOURI REHABILITATION CENTER (O, 63 beds) 600 North Main Street,
Mount Vernon, MO Zip 65712–1004; tel. 417/466–3711; Mike Powell,
Executive Director
Web address: www.muhealth.org/mrcrehab

UNIVERSITY OF MISSOURI HOSPITALS AND CLINICS (O, 472 beds) One
Hospital Drive, Columbia, MO Zip 65212–0001; tel. 573/882–4141; Mitchell
L. Wasden, Ed.D., Chief Executive Officer and Chief Operating Officer
Web address: www.muhealth.org

Owned, leased, sponsored:	3 hospitals	649 beds
Contract–managed:	0 hospitals	0 beds
Totals:	3 hospitals	649 beds

0021: UNIVERSITY OF NEW MEXICO HOSPITALS (NP)
915 Camino De Salud, Albuquerque, NM Zip 87131–0001;
tel. 505/272–5849; Stephen W. McKernan, Chief Executive Officer
(Moderately Centralized Health System)

NEW MEXICO: UNIVERSITY OF NEW MEXICO HOSPITALS (O, 537 beds) 2211
Lomas Boulevard N.E., Albuquerque, NM Zip 87106–2745;
tel. 505/272–2111; Stephen W. McKernan, Chief Executive Officer
Web address: www.unm.edu

UNM SANDOVAL REGIONAL MEDICAL CENTER (O, 72 beds) 3001 Broadmoor
Boulevard N.E., Rio Rancho, NM Zip 87144–2100; tel. 505/994–7000;
Jamie A. Silva-Steele, R.N., Interim Chief Executive Officer
Web address: www.hospitals.unm.edu/

Owned, leased, sponsored:	2 hospitals	609 beds
Contract–managed:	0 hospitals	0 beds
Totals:	2 hospitals	609 beds

★0168: UNIVERSITY OF PENNSYLVANIA HEALTH SYSTEM
(NP)
3400 Civic Center Bouelvard, Philadelphia, PA Zip 19104–5127;
tel. 215/662–2203; Ralph W. Muller, President and Chief Executive
Officer
(Centralized Physician/Insurance Health System)

PENNSYLVANIA: CHESTER COUNTY HOSPITAL (O, 221 beds) 701 East
Marshall Street, West Chester, PA Zip 19380–4412; tel. 610/431–5000;
Michael J. Duncan, System Chief Executive Officer
Web address: www.chestercountyhospital.org

HOSPITAL OF THE UNIVERSITY OF PENNSYLVANIA (O, 789 beds) 3400
Spruce Street, Philadelphia, PA Zip 19104–4206; tel. 215/662–4000; Garry
L. Scheib, Executive Director
Web address: www.pennhealth.com

PENN PRESBYTERIAN MEDICAL CENTER (O, 331 beds) 51 North 39th Street,
Philadelphia, PA Zip 19104–2699; tel. 215/662–8000; Michele M. Volpe,
Executive Director and Chief Executive Officer
Web address: www.pennmedicine.org/pmc/

PENNSYLVANIA HOSPITAL (O, 423 beds) 800 Spruce Street, Philadelphia, PA
Zip 19107–6192; tel. 215/829–3000; R. Michael Buckley, M.D., Executive
Director
Web address: www.pahosp.com

Owned, leased, sponsored:	4 hospitals	1764 beds
Contract–managed:	0 hospitals	0 beds
Totals:	4 hospitals	1764 beds

★0223: UNIVERSITY OF ROCHESTER MEDICAL CENTER (NP)
601 Elmwood Avenue, Rochester, NY Zip 14642–0002;
tel. 585/275–2100; Steven I. Goldstein, General Director and Chief
Executive Officer
(Centralized Health System)

NEW YORK: F. F. THOMPSON HOSPITAL (O, 251 beds) 350 Parrish Street,
Canandaigua, NY Zip 14424–1731; tel. 585/396–6000; Michael
Stapleton, President and Chief Executive Officer
Web address: www.thompsonhealth.com

HIGHLAND HOSPITAL OF ROCHESTER (O, 261 beds) 1000 South Avenue,
Rochester, NY Zip 14620–2733; tel. 585/473–2200; Steven I. Goldstein,
President and Chief Executive Officer
Web address: www.stronghealth.com

STRONG MEMORIAL HOSPITAL OF THE UNIVERSITY OF ROCHESTER (O, 777
beds) 601 Elmwood Avenue, Rochester, NY Zip 14642–0002;
tel. 585/275–2100; Steven I. Goldstein, President and Chief Executive Officer
Web address: www.urmc.rochester.edu

Owned, leased, sponsored:	3 hospitals	1289 beds
Contract–managed:	0 hospitals	0 beds
Totals:	3 hospitals	1289 beds

★0057: UNIVERSITY OF SOUTH ALABAMA HOSPITALS (NP)
2451 Fillingim Street, Mobile, AL Zip 36617–2238;
tel. 251/471–7000; Stanley K. Hammack, Chief Executive Officer
(Independent Hospital System)

ALABAMA: UNIVERSITY OF SOUTH ALABAMA CHILDREN'S AND WOMEN'S
HOSPITAL (O, 198 beds) 1700 Center Street, Mobile, AL
Zip 36604–3301; tel. 251/415–1000; Owen Bailey, Administrator
Web address: www.usahealthsystem.com/usacwh

UNIVERSITY OF SOUTH ALABAMA MEDICAL CENTER (O, 132 beds) 2451
Fillingim Street, Mobile, AL Zip 36617–2293; tel. 251/471–7000; A.
Elizabeth Anderson, Administrator
Web address: www.usahealthsystem.com/usamc

Owned, leased, sponsored:	2 hospitals	330 beds
Contract–managed:	0 hospitals	0 beds
Totals:	2 hospitals	330 beds

For explanation of codes following names, see page B2.
★ Indicates Type III membership in the American Hospital Association.

★0033: UNIVERSITY OF TEXAS SYSTEM (NP)
601 Colorado Street, Suite 205, Austin, TX Zip 78701–2904;
tel. 512/499–4224; Raymond Greenberg, M.D., Executive Vice
Chancellor
(Moderately Centralized Health System)

TEXAS: UNIVERSITY OF TEXAS HARRIS COUNTY PSYCHIATRIC CENTER (O,
204 beds) 2800 South MacGregor Way, Houston, TX Zip 77021–1000,
Mailing Address: P.O. Box 20249, Zip 77225–0249; tel. 713/741–7870;
Jair C. Soares, M.D., Executive Director
Web address: www.hcpc.uth.tmc.edu

UNIVERSITY OF TEXAS HEALTH SCIENCE CENTER AT TYLER (O, 111 beds)
11937 Highway 271, Tyler, TX Zip 75708–3154; tel. 903/877–7777; Kirk A.
Calhoun, M.D., President
Web address: www.uthct.edu

UNIVERSITY OF TEXAS M.D. ANDERSON CANCER CENTER (O, 656 beds)
1515 Holcombe Boulevard, Box 91, Houston, TX Zip 77030–4000;
tel. 713/792–2121; Ronald A. DePinho, M.D., President
Web address: www.mdanderson.org

UNIVERSITY OF TEXAS MEDICAL BRANCH HOSPITALS (O, 397 beds) 301
University Boulevard, Galveston, TX Zip 77555–0128; tel. 409/772–1011;
Donna K. Sollenberger, Executive Vice President and Chief Executive Officer
Web address: www.utmb.edu

Owned, leased, sponsored:	4 hospitals	1368 beds
Contract–managed:	0 hospitals	0 beds
Totals:	4 hospitals	1368 beds

0137: UPMC (NP)
600 Grant Street, U.S. Steel Tower, Suite 6262, Pittsburgh, PA
Zip 15219–2702; tel. 412/647–8762; Jeffrey A. Romoff, President
and Chief Executive Officer
(Centralized Physician/Insurance Health System)

PENNSYLVANIA: CHILDREN'S HOSPITAL OF PITTSBURGH OF UPMC (O, 296
beds) 4401 Penn Avenue, Pittsburgh, PA Zip 15224–1334;
tel. 412/692–5325; Christopher Gessner, President
Web address: www.chp.edu

MAGEE–WOMENS HOSPITAL OF UPMC (O, 363 beds) 300 Halket Street,
Pittsburgh, PA Zip 15213–3108; tel. 412/641–1000; Leslie C. Davis,
President
Web address: www.magee.edu

UPMC ALTOONA (O, 380 beds) 620 Howard Avenue, Altoona, PA
Zip 16601–4804; tel. 814/889–2011; Gerald Murray, President
Web address: www.altoonaregional.org

UPMC BEDFORD MEMORIAL (O, 27 beds) 10455 Lincoln Highway, Everett, PA
Zip 15537–7046; tel. 814/623–6161; Roger P. Winn, President
Web address: www.upmcbedfordmemorial.com

UPMC EAST (O, 115 beds) 2775 Mosside Boulevard, Monroeville, PA
Zip 15146–2760; tel. 412/357–3000; Mark Sevco, President
Web address: www.upmc.com/locations/hospitals/east/Pages/default.aspx

UPMC HAMOT (O, 331 beds) 201 State Street, Erie, PA Zip 16550–0002;
tel. 814/877–6000; V. James Fiorenzo, President
Web address: www.hamot.org

UPMC HORIZON (O, 184 beds) 110 North Main Street, Greenville, PA
Zip 16125–1726; tel. 724/588–2100; Donald R. Owrey, President
Web address: www.horizon.upmc.com

UPMC MCKEESPORT (O, 213 beds) 1500 Fifth Avenue, McKeesport, PA
Zip 15132–2422; tel. 412/664–2000; Mark Sevco, President
Web address: www.mckeesport.upmc.com

UPMC MERCY (O, 488 beds) 1400 Locust Street, Pittsburgh, PA
Zip 15219–5166; tel. 412/232–8111; Will L. Cook, President
Web address: www.upmc.com/HospitalsFacilities/HFHome/Hospitals/Mercy/

UPMC NORTHWEST (O, 180 beds) 100 Fairfield Drive, Seneca, PA
Zip 16346–2130; tel. 814/676–7600; David Gibbons, President
Web address: www.upmc.com/locations/hospitals/northwest/Pages/default.
aspx

UPMC PASSAVANT (O, 424 beds) 9100 Babcock Boulevard, Pittsburgh, PA
Zip 15237–5815; tel. 412/748–6700; David T. Martin, President
Web address: www.upmc.edu/passavant

UPMC PRESBYTERIAN SHADYSIDE (O, 1582 beds) 200 Lothrop Street,
Pittsburgh, PA Zip 15213–2536; tel. 412/647–2345; John Innocenti, Sr.,
President and Chief Executive Officer
Web address: www.upmc.edu

UPMC ST. MARGARET (O, 249 beds) 815 Freeport Road, Pittsburgh, PA
Zip 15215–3301; tel. 412/784–4000; David J. Patton, President
Web address: www.upmc.
com/locations/hospitals/st–margaret/Pages/default.aspx

Owned, leased, sponsored:	13 hospitals	4832 beds
Contract–managed:	0 hospitals	0 beds
Totals:	13 hospitals	4832 beds

0816: UPPER ALLEGHENY HEALTH SYSTEM (NP)
130 South Union Street, Suite 300, Olean, NY Zip 14760–3676;
tel. 716/375–6190; Timothy J. Finan, FACHE, President and Chief
Executive Officer
(Independent Hospital System)

NEW YORK: OLEAN GENERAL HOSPITAL (O, 186 beds) 515 Main Street,
Olean, NY Zip 14760–1513; tel. 716/373–2600; Timothy J. Finan,
FACHE, President and Chief Executive Officer
Web address: www.ogh.org

PENNSYLVANIA: BRADFORD REGIONAL MEDICAL CENTER (O, 182 beds)
116 Interstate Parkway, Bradford, PA Zip 16701–1036;
tel. 814/368–4143; Timothy J. Finan, FACHE, President and Chief
Executive Officer
Web address: www.brmc.com

Owned, leased, sponsored:	2 hospitals	368 beds
Contract–managed:	0 hospitals	0 beds
Totals:	2 hospitals	368 beds

0868: USMD INC. (IO)
6333 North State Highway 161 Suite 200, Irving, TX
Zip 75038–2229; tel. 214/493–4000; Karen A. Fiducia, FACHE,
President, Hospital Division
(Independent Hospital System)

TEXAS: USMD HOSPITAL AT ARLINGTON (O, 34 beds) 801 West Interstate
20, Arlington, TX Zip 76017–5851; tel. 817/472–3400; Marcia Crim,
R.N., MSN, Chief Executive Officer
Web address: www.usmdarlington.com

USMD HOSPITAL AT FORT WORTH (O, 8 beds) 5900 Dirks Road, Fort Worth,
TX Zip 76132–5473; tel. 817/433–9100; Stephanie Atkins–Guidry,
Administrator
Web address: www.usmdfortworth.com/

Owned, leased, sponsored:	2 hospitals	42 beds
Contract–managed:	0 hospitals	0 beds
Totals:	2 hospitals	42 beds

0860: UVA HEALTH SYSTEM (NP)
1215 Lee Street, Charlottesville, VA Zip 22908–0816;
tel. 434/924–0211; R. Edward Howell, Vice President and Chief
Executive Officer
(Centralized Health System)

VIRGINIA: UNIVERSITY OF VIRGINIA MEDICAL CENTER (O, 570 beds) 1215
Lee Street, Charlottesville, VA Zip 22908–0001, Mailing Address: P.O.
Box 800809, Zip 22908–0809; tel. 434/924–0211; Pamela
Sutton–Wallace, Chief Executive Officer
Web address: www.healthsystem.virginia.edu

UVA TRANSITIONAL CARE HOSPITAL (O, 40 beds) 2965 Ivy Road (250 West),
Charlottesville, VA Zip 22903–9330; tel. 434/924–7897; Michelle Hereford,
Chief
Web address: www.uvahealth.com/services/transitional–care–hospital

Owned, leased, sponsored:	2 hospitals	610 beds
Contract–managed:	0 hospitals	0 beds
Totals:	2 hospitals	610 beds

Section B

For explanation of codes following names, see page B2.
★ Indicates Type III membership in the American Hospital Association.

6415: UW MEDICINE (NP)
1959 N.E. Pacific Street, Seattle, WA Zip 98195–0001, Mailing Address: P.O. Box 356350, Zip 98195–6350; tel. 206/543–7718; Paul G. Ramsey, Chief Executive Officer
(Independent Hospital System)

WASHINGTON: UNIVERSITY OF WASHINGTON MEDICAL CENTER (O, 419 beds) 1959 N.E. Pacific Street, Seattle, WA Zip 98195–6151; tel. 206/598–3300; Stephen P. Zieniewicz, FACHE, Executive Director
Web address: www.uwmedicine.
org/Patient–Care/Locations/UWMC/Pages/default.aspx

UW MEDICINE/HARBORVIEW MEDICAL CENTER (O, 413 beds) 325 Ninth Avenue, Seattle, WA Zip 98104–2499, Mailing Address: P.O. Box 359717, Zip 98195–9717; tel. 206/744–3000; Johnese Spisso, Interim Executive Director
Web address: www.uwmedicine.
org/Patient–Care/Locations/HMC/Pages/default.aspx

UW MEDICINE/NORTHWEST HOSPITAL & MEDICAL CENTER (O, 177 beds) 1550 North 115th Street, Seattle, WA Zip 98133–8401; tel. 206/364–0500; Cynthia Hecker, R.N., Executive Director
Web address: www.uwmedicine.
org/Patient–Care/Locations/nwh/Pages/default.aspx

UW MEDICINE/VALLEY MEDICAL CENTER (O, 182 beds) 400 South 43rd Street, Renton, WA Zip 98055–5714, Mailing Address: P.O. Box 50010, Zip 98058–5010; tel. 425/228–3450; Richard D. Roodman, Chief Executive Officer
Web address: www.valleymed.org

Owned, leased, sponsored:	4 hospitals	1191 beds
Contract–managed:	0 hospitals	0 beds
Totals:	4 hospitals	1191 beds

★**0128: VALLEY HEALTH SYSTEM** (NP)
220 Campus Boulevard, Suite 310, Winchester, VA Zip 22601–2889, Mailing Address: P.O. Box 3340, Zip 22604–2540; tel. 540/536–8024; Mark H. Merrill, President and Chief Executive Officer
(Moderately Centralized Health System)

VIRGINIA: PAGE MEMORIAL HOSPITAL (O, 25 beds) 200 Memorial Drive, Luray, VA Zip 22835–1005; tel. 540/743–4561; N. Travis Clark, President
Web address: www.valleyhealthlink.com/page

SHENANDOAH MEMORIAL HOSPITAL (O, 25 beds) 759 South Main Street, Woodstock, VA Zip 22664–1127; tel. 540/459–1100; Floyd Heater, President
Web address: www.valleyhealthlink.com/shenandoah

WARREN MEMORIAL HOSPITAL (O, 166 beds) 1000 North Shenandoah Avenue, Front Royal, VA Zip 22630–3598; tel. 540/636–0300; Patrick B. Nolan, President and Chief Executive Officer
Web address: www.valleyhealthlink.com/WMH

WINCHESTER MEDICAL CENTER (O, 475 beds) 1840 Amherst Street, Winchester, VA Zip 22601–2808, Mailing Address: P.O. Box 3340, Zip 22604–2540; tel. 540/536–8000; Mark H. Merrill, President
Web address: www.valleyhealthlink.com/WMC

WEST VIRGINIA: HAMPSHIRE MEMORIAL HOSPITAL (O, 44 beds) 363 Sunrise Boulevard, Romney, WV Zip 26757–4607; tel. 304/822–4561; Neil R. McLaughlin, R.N., President
Web address: www.valleyhealthlink.com/hampshire

WAR MEMORIAL HOSPITAL (O, 41 beds) One Healthy Way, Berkeley Springs, WV Zip 25411–7463; tel. 304/258–1234; Neil R. McLaughlin, R.N., President
Web address: www.valleyhealthlink.com/war

Owned, leased, sponsored:	6 hospitals	776 beds
Contract–managed:	0 hospitals	0 beds
Totals:	6 hospitals	776 beds

● ★**0387: VANDERBILT HEALTH** (NP)
1211 22nd Avenue South, Nashville, TN Zip 37232; tel. 615/322–5000; Charles Wright Pinson, M.D., Deputy Vice Chancellor for Health Affairs and Chief Executive Officer of Vanderbilt Health System
(Moderately Centralized Health System)

TENNESSEE: VANDERBILT HOSPITAL AND CLINICS (O, 998 beds) 1211 22nd Avenue North, Nashville, TN Zip 37232–2102; tel. 615/322–5000; David R. Posch, Chief Executive Officer
Web address: www.mc.vanderbilt.edu

Owned, leased, sponsored:	1 hospital	998 beds
Contract–managed:	0 hospitals	0 beds
Totals:	1 hospital	998 beds

0939: VCU HEALTH SYSTEM (NP)
1250 East Marshall Street, Richmond, VA Zip 23298–5051, Mailing Address: P.O. Box 980510, Zip 23298–0510; tel. 804/828–9000; John Duval, Chief Executive Officer

VIRGINIA: VCU COMMUNITY MEMORIAL HOSPITAL (O, 178 beds) 125 Buena Vista Circle, South Hill, VA Zip 23970–1431, Mailing Address: P.O. Box 90, Zip 23970–0090; tel. 434/447–3151; W. Scott Burnette, President and Chief Executive Officer
Web address: www.cmh–sh.org

VCU MEDICAL CENTER (O, 758 beds) 1250 East Marshall Street, Richmond, VA Zip 23298–5051, Mailing Address: P.O. Box 980510, Zip 23298–0510; tel. 804/828–9000; John Duval, Chief Executive Officer
Web address: www.vcuhealth.org

Owned, leased, sponsored:	2 hospitals	936 beds
Contract–managed:	0 hospitals	0 beds
Totals:	2 hospitals	936 beds

★**0299: VIBRA HEALTHCARE** (IO)
4550 Lena Drive, Suite 225, Mechanicsburg, PA Zip 17055–4920; tel. 717/591–5700; Brad Hollinger, Chairman and Chief Executive Officer
(Independent Hospital System)

CALIFORNIA: BALLARD REHABILITATION HOSPITAL (O, 45 beds) 1760 West 16th Street, San Bernardino, CA Zip 92411–1160; tel. 909/473–1200; Mary Miles Hunt, Chief Executive Officer
Web address: www.ballardrehab.com

KENTFIELD REHABILITATION AND SPECIALTY HOSPITAL (O, 48 beds) 1125 Sir Francis Drake Boulevard, Kentfield, CA Zip 94904–1455; tel. 415/456–9680; Ann Gors, Chief Executive Officer
Web address: www.kentfieldrehab.com

SAN JOAQUIN VALLEY REHABILITATION HOSPITAL (O, 62 beds) 7173 North Sharon Avenue, Fresno, CA Zip 93720–3329; tel. 559/436–3600; Mary Jo Jacobson, Chief Executive Officer
Web address: www.sanjoaquinrehab.com

VIBRA HOSPITAL OF NORTHERN CALIFORNIA (O, 88 beds) 2801 Eureka Way, Redding, CA Zip 96001–0222; tel. 530/246–9000; Chris Jones, Chief Executive Officer
Web address: www.norcalrehab.com

VIBRA HOSPITAL OF SACRAMENTO (O, 37 beds) 330 Montrose Drive, Folsom, CA Zip 95630–2720; tel. 916/351–9151; Janet Biedron, R.N., Chief Executive Officer
Web address: www.vhsacramento.com

VIBRA HOSPITAL OF SAN DIEGO (O, 57 beds) 555 Washington Street, San Diego, CA Zip 92103–2294; tel. 619/260–8300; Natalie Germuska, R.N., MSN, Chief Executive Officer
Web address: www.vhsandiego.com/

COLORADO: VIBRA HOSPITAL OF DENVER (O, 71 beds) 8451 Pearl Street, Thornton, CO Zip 80229–4804; tel. 303/288–3000; Craig L. Johnson, FACHE, Resource Chief Executive Officer
Web address: www.vhdenver.com

For explanation of codes following names, see page B2.
★ Indicates Type III membership in the American Hospital Association.
● Single hospital health care system

Section B

IDAHO: VIBRA HOSPITAL OF BOISE (O, 60 beds) 2131 South Bonito Way, Meridian, ID Zip 83642–1659; tel. 877/801–2244; Randall J. Evaro, Chief Executive Officer
Web address: www.vhboise.com

ILLINOIS: VIBRA HOSPITAL OF SPRINGFIELD (O, 50 beds) 701 North Walnut Street, Springfield, IL Zip 62702–4931; tel. 217/528–1217; Charles Nordyke, Chief Executive Officer
Web address: www.vibrahealthcare.com

INDIANA: VIBRA HOSPITAL OF FORT WAYNE (O, 50 beds) 2200 Randallia Drive, Fort Wayne, IN Zip 46805–4638; tel. 260/399–2900; Kerry Ashment, Chief Executive Officer
Web address: www.vhfortwayne.com

VIBRA HOSPITAL OF NORTHWESTERN INDIANA (O, 40 beds) 9509 Georgia Street, Crown Point, IN Zip 46307–6518; tel. 219/472–2200; Charles Nordyke, Chief Executive Officer
Web address: www.vhnwindiana.com/

KENTUCKY: SOUTHERN KENTUCKY REHABILITATION HOSPITAL (O, 60 beds) 1300 Campbell Lane, Bowling Green, KY Zip 42104–4162; tel. 270/782–6900; Stuart Locke, Chief Executive Officer
Web address: www.skyrehab.com

MASSACHUSETTS: NEW BEDFORD REHABILITATION HOSPITAL (O, 90 beds) 4499 Acushnet Avenue, New Bedford, MA Zip 02745–4707; tel. 508/995–6900; Edward B. Leary, Chief Executive Officer
Web address: www.newbedfordrehab.com

VIBRA HOSPITAL OF WESTERN MASSACHUSETTS (O, 202 beds) 1400 State Street, Springfield, MA Zip 01109–2550; tel. 413/726–6700; Jake Socha, Chief Executive Officer
Web address: www.vhwmass.com

MICHIGAN: VIBRA HOSPITAL OF SOUTHEASTERN MICHIGAN (O, 140 beds) 26400 West Outer Drive, Lincoln Park, MI Zip 48146–2088; tel. 313/386–2000; Denise Wayne, Chief Executive Officer
Web address: www.vhsemichigan.com/

NEW JERSEY: MARLTON REHABILITATION HOSPITAL (O, 61 beds) 92 Brick Road, Marlton, NJ Zip 08053–2177; tel. 856/988–8778; Michael Long, MS, Chief Executive Officer
Web address: www.marltonrehab.com

NORTH DAKOTA: VIBRA HOSPITAL OF CENTRAL DAKOTAS (O, 41 beds) 1000 18th Street N.W., Mandan, ND Zip 58554–1612; tel. 701/667–2000; Custer Huseby, Interim Chief Executive Officer
Web address: www.vhcentraldakotas.com

VIBRA HOSPITAL OF FARGO (O, 31 beds) 1720 University Drive South, Fargo, ND Zip 58103–4940; tel. 701/241–9099; Custer Huseby, Chief Executive Officer
Web address: www.vhfargo.com

OHIO: VIBRA HOSPITAL OF MAHONING VALLEY (O, 42 beds) 8049 South Avenue, Boardman, OH Zip 44512–6154; tel. 330/726–5000; Mary Lou Sankovich, R.N., MSN, Chief Executive Officer
Web address: www.vhmvalley.com

OREGON: VIBRA SPECIALTY HOSPITAL OF PORTLAND (O, 68 beds) 10300 N.E. Hancock Street, Portland, OR Zip 97220–3831; tel. 503/257–5500; Dave Tupper, Chief Executive Officer
Web address: www.vshportland.com

SOUTH CAROLINA: VIBRA HOSPITAL OF CHARLESTON (O, 94 beds) 1200 Hospital Drive, Mt. Pleasant, SC Zip 29464; tel. 843/375–4000; Darrell Jones, Chief Executive Officer
Web address: www.vhcharleston.com

TEXAS: VIBRA HOSPITAL OF AMARILLO (O, 72 beds) 7501 Wallace Boulevard, Amarillo, TX Zip 79124–2150; tel. 806/467–7000; Kay E. Peck, Ph.D., Chief Executive Officer
Web address: www.vhamarillo.com

VIBRA REHABILITATION HOSPITAL OF AMARILLO (O, 44 beds) 7200 West 9th Avenue, Amarillo, TX Zip 79106–1703; tel. 806/468–2900; Kay E. Peck, Ph.D., Chief Executive Officer
Web address: www.vrhamarillo.com

VIBRA SPECIALTY HOSPITAL AT DESOTO (O, 40 beds) 2700 Walker Way, Desoto, TX Zip 75115–2088; tel. 972/298–1100; Greg Floyd, Chief Executive Officer
Web address: www.vshdesoto.com

VIRGINIA: VIBRA HOSPITAL OF RICHMOND (O, 60 beds) 2220 Edward Holland Drive, Richmond, VA Zip 23230–2519; tel. 804/678–7000; Timothy C. Deaton, Chief Executive Officer
Web address: www.vhrichmond.com

Owned, leased, sponsored:	25 hospitals	1653 beds
Contract–managed:	0 hospitals	0 beds
Totals:	25 hospitals	1653 beds

0920: VIBRANT HEALTHCARE (IO)
12222 North Central Expressway, Suite 440, Dallas, TX Zip 75243–3767; tel. 469/330–6745; Wilton M. Burt, Chief Executive Officer

TEXAS: FOREST PARK MEDICAL CENTER (C, 84 beds) 11990 North Central Expressway, Dallas, TX Zip 75243–3714; tel. 972/234–1900; Cindy Bledsoe, Chief Executive Officer
Web address: www.forestparkmc.com/

FOREST PARK MEDICAL CENTER FRISCO (C, 54 beds) 5500 Frisco Square Boulevard, Frisco, TX Zip 75034–3305; tel. 214/618–0500; Julie A. Camp, R.N., Chief Executive Officer
Web address: www.forestparkfrisco.com/default.aspx

FOREST PARK MEDICAL CENTER–SOUTHLAKE (C, 15 beds) 421 East State Highway 114, Southlake, TX Zip 76092; tel. 817/865–4400; Dawn Beljin, R.N., Chief Operating Officer
Web address: www.forestparksouthlake.com

Owned, leased, sponsored:	0 hospitals	0 beds
Contract–managed:	3 hospitals	153 beds
Totals:	3 hospitals	153 beds

0897: VICTORY HEALTHCARE (IO)
2201 Timberloch Place, Suite 200, The Woodlands, TX Zip 77380; tel. 281/863–2100; Robert N. Helms, Jr., Board Chair, President and Chief Executive Officer
(Independent Hospital System)

VICTORY MEDICAL CENTER – SOUTHCROSS (O, 9 beds) 5330 N. Loop 1604 W., San Antonio, TX Zip 78249; tel. 210/877–8000; Louis O. Garcia, Chief Executive Officer
Web address: www.victory–healthcare.com/san–antonio–location/

VICTORY MEDICAL CENTER BEAUMONT (O, 17 beds) 6025 Metropolitan Drive, Beaumont, TX Zip 77706–2407; tel. 409/617–7700; Becky Ames, Chief Executive Officer
Web address: www.victory–healthcare.com/beaumont

VICTORY MEDICAL CENTER CRAIG RANCH (O, 24 beds) 6045 Alma Road, McKinney, TX Zip 75070–2188; tel. 972/908–1215; Ashley Anson, Chief Executive Officer
Web address: www.victory–healthcare.com/craig–ranch/

VICTORY MEDICAL CENTER HOUSTON (O, 25 beds) 2001 Hermann Drive, Houston, TX Zip 77004–7643; tel. 713/285–5500; Nicholas Crafts, Chief Executive Officer
Web address: www.victory–healthcare.com

VICTORY MEDICAL CENTER LANDMARK (O, 25 beds) 5330 North Loop 1604 West, San Antonio, TX Zip 78249–1371; tel. 210/877–8000; Alex Garcia, Chief Executive Officer
Web address: www.victory–healthcare.com/sanantoniolandmark

VICTORY MEDICAL CENTER MID–CITIES (O, 16 beds) 1612 Hurst Town Center Drive, Hurst, TX Zip 76054–6236; tel. 817/345–4100; Barbara Millwood, Chief Executive Officer
Web address: www.victory–healthcare.com

VICTORY MEDICAL CENTER PLANO (O, 20 beds) 2301 Marsh Lane, Plano, TX Zip 75093–8497; tel. 972/820–2600; Steve Williams, Chief Executive Officer
Web address: www.victory–healthcare.com/plano

For explanation of codes following names, see page B2.
★ Indicates Type III membership in the American Hospital Association.

VICTORY SURGICAL HOSPITAL EAST HOUSTON (O, 42 beds) 12950 East Freeway, Houston, TX Zip 77015–5710; tel. 713/330–3887; Steve Winnett, Chief Executive Officer
Web address: www.victory–healthcare.com/easthouston

Owned, leased, sponsored:	8 hospitals	178 beds
Contract–managed:	0 hospitals	0 beds
Totals:	8 hospitals	178 beds

★**0217: VIDANT HEALTH** (NP)
2100 Stantonsburg Road, Greenville, NC Zip 27834–2818, Mailing Address: P.O. Box 6028, Zip 27835–6028; tel. 252/847–4100; David C. Herman, M.D., President and Chief Executive Officer
(Moderately Centralized Health System)

NORTH CAROLINA: THE OUTER BANKS HOSPITAL (O, 21 beds) 4800 South Croatan Highway, Nags Head, NC Zip 27959–9704; tel. 252/449–4511; Ronald A. Sloan, FACHE, President
Web address: www.theouterbankshospital.com

VIDANT BEAUFORT HOSPITAL (L, 43 beds) 628 East 12th Street, Washington, NC Zip 27889–3409; tel. 252/975–4100; Harvey Case, President
Web address: www.vidanthealth.com

VIDANT BERTIE HOSPITAL (L, 6 beds) 1403 South King Street, Windsor, NC Zip 27983–9666, Mailing Address: P.O. Box 40, Zip 27983–0040; tel. 252/794–6600; Jeffrey N. Sackrison, FACHE, President
Web address: www.vidanthealth.com

VIDANT CHOWAN HOSPITAL (L, 19 beds) 211 Virginia Road, Edenton, NC Zip 27932–9668, Mailing Address: P.O. Box 629, Zip 27932–0629; tel. 252/482–8451; Jeffrey N. Sackrison, FACHE, President
Web address: www.vidanthealth.com

VIDANT DUPLIN HOSPITAL (L, 48 beds) 401 North Main Street, Kenansville, NC Zip 28349–8801, Mailing Address: P.O. Box 278, Zip 28349–0278; tel. 910/296–0941; Jay Briley, President
Web address: www.vidanthealth.com

VIDANT EDGECOMBE HOSPITAL (O, 59 beds) 111 Hospital Drive, Tarboro, NC Zip 27886–2011; tel. 252/641–7700; Wendell H. Baker, Jr., President
Web address: www.https://www.vidanthealth.com/edgecombe/default.aspx

VIDANT MEDICAL CENTER (O, 909 beds) 2100 Stantonsburg Road, Greenville, NC Zip 27834–2818, Mailing Address: P.O. Box 6028, Zip 27835–6028; tel. 252/847–4100; Stephen Lawler, President
Web address: www.https://www.vidanthealth.com/

VIDANT PUNGO HOSPITAL (O, 25 beds) 202 East Water Street, Belhaven, NC Zip 27810–1450; tel. 252/943–2111; Harvey Case, President
Web address: www.vidanthealth.com/vidant/dynamic–detail.aspx?id=11781

VIDANT ROANOKE–CHOWAN HOSPITAL (L, 70 beds) 500 South Academy Street, Ahoskie, NC Zip 27910–3261, Mailing Address: P.O. Box 1385, Zip 27910–1385; tel. 252/209–3000; Susan S. Lassiter, FACHE, President and Chief Executive Officer
Web address: www.vidanthealth.com

Owned, leased, sponsored:	9 hospitals	1200 beds
Contract–managed:	0 hospitals	0 beds
Totals:	9 hospitals	1200 beds

0012: VIRGINIA DEPARTMENT OF MENTAL HEALTH (NP)
1220 Bank Street, Richmond, VA Zip 23219–3645, Mailing Address: P.O. Box 1797, Zip 23218–1797; tel. 804/786–3921; James S. Reinhard, M.D., Commissioner
(Independent Hospital System)

VIRGINIA: CATAWBA HOSPITAL (O, 110 beds) 5525 Catawba Hospital Drive, Catawba, VA Zip 24070–2115, Mailing Address: P.O. Box 200, Zip 24070–0200; tel. 540/375–4200; Walton F. Mitchell, III, Director
Web address: www.catawba.dbhds.virginia.gov

CENTRAL STATE HOSPITAL (O, 277 beds) 26317 West Washington Street, Petersburg, VA Zip 23803–2727, Mailing Address: P.O. Box 4030, Zip 23803–0030; tel. 804/524–7000; Vicki Montgomery, Director and Chief Executive Officer
Web address: www.csh.dbhds.virginia.gov

CENTRAL VIRGINIA TRAINING CENTER (O, 1112 beds) 210 East Colony Road, Madison Heights, VA Zip 24572–2005, Mailing Address: P.O. Box 1098, Lynchburg, Zip 24505–1098; tel. 434/947–6326; Denise D. Micheletti, R.N., Director
Web address: www.cvtc.dmhmrsas.virginia.gov/

COMMONWEALTH CENTER FOR CHILDREN AND ADOLESCENTS (O, 60 beds) 1355 Richmond Road, Staunton, VA Zip 24401–9146, Mailing Address: Box 4000, Zip 24402–4000; tel. 540/332–2100; William J. Tuell, MSN, Facility Director
Web address: www.ccca.dbhds.virginia.gov

EASTERN STATE HOSPITAL (O, 334 beds) 4601 Ironbound Road, Williamsburg, VA Zip 23188–2652; tel. 757/253–5161; John M. Favret, Director
Web address: www.esh.dmhmrsas.virginia.gov/

HIRAM W. DAVIS MEDICAL CENTER (O, 10 beds) 26317 West Washington Street, Petersburg, VA Zip 23803–2727, Mailing Address: P.O. Box 4030, Zip 23803–0030; tel. 804/524–7344; Bill Hawkins, Director

NORTHERN VIRGINIA MENTAL HEALTH INSTITUTE (O, 123 beds) 3302 Gallows Road, Falls Church, VA Zip 22042–3398; tel. 703/207–7110; James R. Newton, Facility Director
Web address: www.nvmhi.dmhmrsas.virginia.gov

PIEDMONT GERIATRIC HOSPITAL (O, 150 beds) 5001 East Patrick Henry Highway, Burkeville, VA Zip 23922–3460, Mailing Address: P.O. Box 427, Zip 23922–0427; tel. 434/767–4401; Stephen M. Herrick, Ph.D., Director
Web address: www.pgh.dmhmrsas.virginia.gov

SOUTHERN VIRGINIA MENTAL HEALTH INSTITUTE (O, 72 beds) 382 Taylor Drive, Danville, VA Zip 24541–4023; tel. 434/799–6220; William Cook, Director
Web address: www.svmhi.dbhds.virginia.gov

SOUTHWESTERN VIRGINIA MENTAL HEALTH INSTITUTE (O, 266 beds) 340 Bagley Circle, Marion, VA Zip 24354–3390; tel. 276/783–1200; Cynthia McClaskey, Ph.D., Director
Web address: www.swmhi.dmhmrsas.virginia.gov/

WESTERN STATE HOSPITAL (O, 260 beds) 1301 Richmond Avenue, Staunton, VA Zip 24401–9146, Mailing Address: P.O. Box 2500, Zip 24402–2500; tel. 540/332–8000; Jack W. Barber, M.D., Director
Web address: www.dbhds.virginia.gov

Owned, leased, sponsored:	11 hospitals	2774 beds
Contract–managed:	0 hospitals	0 beds
Totals:	11 hospitals	2774 beds

★**6725: VIRTUA HEALTH** (NP)
50 Lake Center Executive Drive, Suite 401, Marlton, NJ Zip 08053; tel. 856/355–0010; Richard P. Miller, Chief Executive Officer
(Centralized Health System)

NEW JERSEY: VIRTUA BERLIN (O, 83 beds) 100 Townsend Avenue, Berlin, NJ Zip 08009–9035; tel. 856/322–3000; Gary L. Long, Senior Vice President Population Management
Web address: www.virtua.org

VIRTUA MARLTON (O, 192 beds) 90 Brick Road, Marlton, NJ Zip 08053–2177; tel. 856/355–6000; Gary L. Long, Senior Vice President Population Management
Web address: www.virtua.org

VIRTUA MEMORIAL (O, 333 beds) 175 Madison Avenue, Mount Holly, NJ Zip 08060–2099; tel. 609/267–0700; Matthew Zuino, Vice President
Web address: www.virtua.org

VIRTUA VOORHEES (O, 398 beds) 100 Bowman Drive, Voorhees, NJ Zip 08043–9612; tel. 856/325–3000; Gary L. Long, Senior Vice President Population Management
Web address: www.virtua.org

Owned, leased, sponsored:	4 hospitals	1006 beds
Contract–managed:	0 hospitals	0 beds
Totals:	4 hospitals	1006 beds

For explanation of codes following names, see page B2.
★ Indicates Type III membership in the American Hospital Association.

★0221: **WAKE FOREST BAPTIST HEALTH** (NP)
Medical Center Boulevard, Winston–Salem, NC Zip 27157; tel. 336/716–2011; John D. McConnell, M.D., Chief Executive Officer
(Moderately Centralized Health System)

NORTH CAROLINA: WAKE FOREST BAPTIST HEALTH–DAVIE HOSPITAL (O, 25 beds) 223 Hospital Street, Mocksville, NC Zip 27028–2038, Mailing Address: P.O. Box 1209, Zip 27028–1209; tel. 336/702–5500; Chad J. Brown, M.P.H., President
Web address: www.daviehospital.org

WAKE FOREST BAPTIST HEALTH–LEXINGTON MEDICAL CENTER (O, 77 beds) 250 Hospital Drive, Lexington, NC Zip 27292–6728, Mailing Address: P.O. Box 1817, Zip 27293–1817; tel. 336/248–5161; William B. James, FACHE, Chief Executive Officer
Web address: www.lexingtonmemorial.com

WAKE FOREST BAPTIST MEDICAL CENTER (O, 854 beds) Medical Center Boulevard, Winston–Salem, NC Zip 27157–0001; tel. 336/716–2011; John D. McConnell, M.D., Chief Executive Officer
Web address: www.wakehealth.edu

Owned, leased, sponsored:	3 hospitals	956 beds
Contract–managed:	0 hospitals	0 beds
Totals:	3 hospitals	956 beds

★6705: **WAKEMED HEALTH & HOSPITALS** (NP)
3000 New Bern Avenue, Raleigh, NC Zip 27610–1231; tel. 919/350–8000; Donald R. Gintzig, President and Chief Executive Officer
(Moderately Centralized Health System)

HARNETT HEALTH SYSTEM (C, 76 beds) 800 Tilghman Drive, Dunn, NC Zip 28334–5599, Mailing Address: P.O. Box 1706, Zip 28335–1706; tel. 910/892–1000; Kenneth E. Bryan, FACHE, President and Chief Executive Officer
Web address: www.myharnetthealth.org/

WAKEMED CARY HOSPITAL (O, 192 beds) 1900 Kildaire Farm Road, Cary, NC Zip 27518–6616; tel. 919/350–2300; David C. Coulter, Senior Vice President and Administrator
Web address: www.wakemed.org

WAKEMED RALEIGH CAMPUS (O, 683 beds) 3000 New Bern Avenue, Raleigh, NC Zip 27610–1295; tel. 919/350–8000; Donald R. Gintzig, President and Chief Executive Officer
Web address: www.wakemed.org

Owned, leased, sponsored:	2 hospitals	875 beds
Contract–managed:	1 hospital	76 beds
Totals:	3 hospitals	951 beds

★0188: **WELLMONT HEALTH SYSTEM** (NP)
1905 American Way, Kingsport, TN Zip 37660–5882; tel. 423/230–8200
(Centralized Physician/Insurance Health System)

TENNESSEE: WELLMONT BRISTOL REGIONAL MEDICAL CENTER (O, 312 beds) 1 Medical Park Boulevard, Bristol, TN Zip 37620–7430; tel. 423/844–1121; Greg Neal, President
Web address: www.wellmont.org

WELLMONT HANCOCK COUNTY HOSPITAL (O, 10 beds) 1519 Main Street, Sneedville, TN Zip 37869–3657; tel. 423/733–5000; Fred L. Pelle, FACHE, Interim Chief Executive Officer
Web address: www.wellmont.org/Hospitals/Hancock–County–Hospital.aspx

WELLMONT HAWKINS COUNTY MEMORIAL HOSPITAL (L, 16 beds) 851 Locust Street, Rogersville, TN Zip 37857–2407, Mailing Address: P.O. Box 130, Zip 37857–0130; tel. 423/921–7000; Fred L. Pelle, FACHE, Interim Chief Executive Officer
Web address: www.wellmont.org

WELLMONT HOLSTON VALLEY MEDICAL CENTER (O, 318 beds) 130 West Ravine Street, Kingsport, TN Zip 37660–3837, Mailing Address: P.O. Box 238, Zip 37662–0238; tel. 423/224–4000; Tim Attebery, Chief Executive Officer
Web address: www.wellmont.org

VIRGINIA: MOUNTAIN VIEW REGIONAL MEDICAL CENTER (O, 72 beds) 310 Third Street N.E., Norton, VA Zip 24273–1137; tel. 276/679–9100; Fred L. Pelle, FACHE, President
Web address: www.wellmont.org

WELLMONT LONESOME PINE HOSPITAL (O, 30 beds) 1990 Holton Avenue East, Big Stone Gap, VA Zip 24219–3350; tel. 276/523–3111; Fred L. Pelle, FACHE, Interim President and Chief Executive Officer
Web address: www.wellmont.org

Owned, leased, sponsored:	6 hospitals	758 beds
Contract–managed:	0 hospitals	0 beds
Totals:	6 hospitals	758 beds

★0068: **WELLSPAN HEALTH** (NP)
45 Monument Road, Suite 200, York, PA Zip 17403–5071; tel. 717/851–2121; Kevin H. Mosser, M.D., President and Chief Executive Officer
(Centralized Physician/Insurance Health System)

PENNSYLVANIA: EPHRATA COMMUNITY HOSPITAL (O, 130 beds) 169 Martin Avenue, Ephrata, PA Zip 17522–1724, Mailing Address: P.O. Box 1002, Zip 17522–1002; tel. 717/733–0311; John M. Porter, Jr., President and Chief Executive Officer
Web address: www.ephratahospital.org

GETTYSBURG HOSPITAL (O, 76 beds) 147 Gettys Street, Gettysburg, PA Zip 17325–2534; tel. 717/334–2121; Jane E. Hyde, President
Web address: www.wellspan.org

YORK HOSPITAL (O, 552 beds) 1001 South George Street, York, PA Zip 17403–3645; tel. 717/851–2345; Keith D. Noll, President
Web address: www.wellspan.org

Owned, leased, sponsored:	3 hospitals	758 beds
Contract–managed:	0 hospitals	0 beds
Totals:	3 hospitals	758 beds

★0995: **WELLSTAR HEALTH SYSTEM** (NP)
805 Sandy Plains Road, Marietta, GA Zip 30066–6340; tel. 770/792–5012; Reynold J. Jennings, President and Chief Executive Officer
(Centralized Health System)

GEORGIA: WELLSTAR COBB HOSPITAL (O, 362 beds) 3950 Austell Road, Austell, GA Zip 30106–1121; tel. 770/732–4000; Kem Mullins, FACHE, Senior Vice President and Hospital President
Web address: www.wellstar.org

WELLSTAR DOUGLAS HOSPITAL (O, 102 beds) 8954 Hospital Drive, Douglasville, GA Zip 30134–2282; tel. 770/949–1500; Craig A. Owens, President
Web address: www.wellstar.org

WELLSTAR KENNESTONE HOSPITAL (O, 588 beds) 677 Church Street, Marietta, GA Zip 30060–1148; tel. 770/793–5000; Dan Woods, President
Web address: www.wellstar.org

WELLSTAR PAULDING HOSPITAL (O, 216 beds) 600 West Memorial Drive, Dallas, GA Zip 30132–4117; tel. 770/445–4411; Mark Haney, President
Web address: www.wellstar.org

WELLSTAR WINDY HILL HOSPITAL (O, 55 beds) 2540 Windy Hill Road, Marietta, GA Zip 30067–8632; tel. 770/644–1000; Lou Little, President
Web address: www.wellstar.org

Owned, leased, sponsored:	5 hospitals	1323 beds
Contract–managed:	0 hospitals	0 beds
Totals:	5 hospitals	1323 beds

For explanation of codes following names, see page B2.
★ Indicates Type III membership in the American Hospital Association.

★0004:   WEST TENNESSEE HEALTHCARE (NP)
620 Skyline Drive, Jackson, TN Zip 38301–3923;
tel. 731/541–5000; Bobby Arnold, President and Chief Executive Officer
(Centralized Physician/Insurance Health System)

TENNESSEE: BOLIVAR GENERAL HOSPITAL (O, 21 beds) 650 Nuckolls Road, Bolivar, TN Zip 38008–1532, Mailing Address: P.O. Box 509, Zip 38008–0509; tel. 731/658–3100; Ruby Kirby, Administrator
Web address: www.wth.net

CAMDEN GENERAL HOSPITAL (O, 12 beds) 175 Hospital Drive, Camden, TN Zip 38320–1617; tel. 731/584–6135; Denny R. Smith, Administrator
Web address: www.wth.net

HUMBOLDT MEDICAL CENTER (O, 30 beds) 3525 Chere Carol Road, Humboldt, TN Zip 38343–3638; tel. 731/784–2321;

JACKSON–MADISON COUNTY GENERAL HOSPITAL (O, 633 beds) 620 Skyline Drive, Jackson, TN Zip 38301–3923; tel. 731/541–5000; Bobby Arnold, President and Chief Executive Officer
Web address: www.wth.org

MILAN GENERAL HOSPITAL (O, 28 beds) 4039 Highland Street, Milan, TN Zip 38358–3483; tel. 731/686–1591; Sherry Scruggs, Administrator
Web address: www.wth.org

PATHWAYS OF TENNESSEE (O, 25 beds) 238 Summar Drive, Jackson, TN Zip 38301–3906; tel. 731/541–8200; Pam Henson, Executive Director
Web address: www.wth.net

TRENTON MEDICAL CENTER (O, 32 beds) 200 Hospital Drive, Trenton, TN Zip 38382–3324; tel. 731/855–7900;

Owned, leased, sponsored:	7 hospitals	781 beds
Contract–managed:	0 hospitals	0 beds
Totals:	7 hospitals	781 beds

★0119:   WEST VIRGINIA UNITED HEALTH SYSTEM (NP)
1000 Technology Drive, Suite 2320, Fairmont, WV Zip 26554–8834; tel. 304/368–2700; Christopher Colenda, M.D., M.P.H., President and Chief Executive Officer
(Centralized Physician/Insurance Health System)

WEST VIRGINIA: BERKELEY MEDICAL CENTER (O, 170 beds) 2500 Hospital Drive, Martinsburg, WV Zip 25401–3402; tel. 304/264–1000; Anthony Zelenka, President and Chief Operating Officer
Web address: www.cityhospital.org

CAMDEN CLARK MEDICAL CENTER (O, 255 beds) 800 Garfield Avenue, Parkersburg, WV Zip 26101–5378, Mailing Address: P.O. Box 718, Zip 26102–0718; tel. 304/424–2111; David K. McClure, President and Chief Executive Officer
Web address: www.camdenclark.org

JEFFERSON MEDICAL CENTER (O, 25 beds) 300 South Preston Street, Ranson, WV Zip 25438–1631; tel. 304/728–1600; Christina DeRosa, Ph.D., Chief Administrative Officer
Web address: www.wvuniversityhealthcare.com/locations/Jefferson–Medical–Center.aspx

POTOMAC VALLEY HOSPITAL (O, 25 beds) 100 Pin Oak Lane, Keyser, WV Zip 26726–5908; tel. 304/597–3500; Linda K. Shroyer, Administrator
Web address: www.potomacvalleyhospital.com

UNITED HOSPITAL CENTER (O, 264 beds) 327 Medical Park Drive, Bridgeport, WV Zip 26330–9006; tel. 681/342–1000; Bruce C. Carter, President and Chief Executive Officer
Web address: www.thenewuhc.com

WEST VIRGINIA UNIVERSITY HOSPITALS (O, 514 beds) 1 Medical Center Drive, Morgantown, WV Zip 26506–4749; tel. 304/598–4000; ,
Web address: www.health.wvu.edu

Owned, leased, sponsored:	6 hospitals	1253 beds
Contract–managed:	0 hospitals	0 beds
Totals:	6 hospitals	1253 beds

★0811:   WESTERN CONNECTICUT HEALTH NETWORK (NP)
24 Hospital Avenue, Danbury, CT Zip 06810–6099; tel. 203/739–7066; John M. Murphy, M.D., President
(Moderately Centralized Health System)

CONNECTICUT: DANBURY HOSPITAL (O, 336 beds) 24 Hospital Avenue, Danbury, CT Zip 06810–6099; tel. 203/739–7000; John M. Murphy, M.D., President and Chief Executive Officer
Web address: www.danburyhospital.org

NEW MILFORD HOSPITAL (O, 59 beds) 21 Elm Street, New Milford, CT Zip 06776–2993; tel. 860/355–2611; Thomas Koobatian, M.D., Executive Director and Chief of Staff
Web address: www.newmilfordhospital.org

Owned, leased, sponsored:	2 hospitals	395 beds
Contract–managed:	0 hospitals	0 beds
Totals:	2 hospitals	395 beds

★6745:   WHEATON FRANCISCAN HEALTHCARE (CC)
26W171 Roosevelt Road, Wheaton, IL Zip 60187–6002, Mailing Address: P.O. Box 667, Zip 60187–0667; tel. 630/909–6900; John D. Oliverio, President and Chief Executive Officer
(Moderately Centralized Health System)

ILLINOIS: MARIANJOY REHABILITATION HOSPITAL (O, 128 beds) 26 West 171 Roosevelt Road, Wheaton, IL Zip 60187–0795, Mailing Address: P.O. Box 795, Zip 60187–0795; tel. 630/909–8000; Kathleen C. Yosko, President and Chief Executive Officer
Web address: www.marianjoy.org

IOWA: COVENANT MEDICAL CENTER (O, 220 beds) 3421 West Ninth Street, Waterloo, IA Zip 50702–5401; tel. 319/272–8000; Jack Dusenbery, President and Chief Executive Officer
Web address: www.wheatoniowa.org

MERCY HOSPITAL OF FRANCISCAN SISTERS (O, 64 beds) 201 Eighth Avenue S.E., Oelwein, IA Zip 50662–2447; tel. 319/283–6000; Terri Derflinger, Administrator
Web address: www.covhealth.com

SARTORI MEMORIAL HOSPITAL (O, 50 beds) 515 College Street, Cedar Falls, IA Zip 50613–2500; tel. 319/268–3000; Rose Fowler, MS, Administrator
Web address: www.wheatoniowa.org

WISCONSIN: MIDWEST ORTHOPEDIC SPECIALTY HOSPITAL (O, 16 beds) 10101 South 27th Street, 2nd Floor, Franklin, WI Zip 53132–7209; tel. 414/817–5800; Coreen Dicus–Johnson, President
Web address: www.mymosh.com/

UNITED HOSPITAL SYSTEM, ST. CATHERINE'S MEDICAL CENTER CAMPUS (O, 202 beds) 9555 76th Street, Pleasant Prairie, WI Zip 53158–1984; tel. 262/656–2011; Richard O. Schmidt, Jr., President and Chief Executive Officer
Web address: www.uhsi.org

WHEATON FRANCISCAN HEALTHCARE – ALL SAINTS (O, 405 beds) 3801 Spring Street, Racine, WI Zip 53405–1690; tel. 262/687–4011; Susan Boland, R.N., MSN, President and Chief Executive Officer
Web address: www.allsaintshealth.com

WHEATON FRANCISCAN HEALTHCARE – ELMBROOK MEMORIAL (O, 100 beds) 19333 West North Avenue, Brookfield, WI Zip 53045–4198; tel. 262/785–2000; Debra K. Standridge, President
Web address: www.wfhealthcare.org

WHEATON FRANCISCAN HEALTHCARE – FRANKLIN (O, 32 beds) 10101 South 27th Street, Franklin, WI Zip 53132–7209; tel. 414/325–4700; Coreen Dicus–Johnson, President
Web address: www.mywheaton.org/

WHEATON FRANCISCAN HEALTHCARE – ST. FRANCIS (S, 165 beds) 3237 South 16th Street, Milwaukee, WI Zip 53215–4592; tel. 414/647–5000; Coreen Dicus–Johnson, President
Web address: www.mywheaton.org/stfrancis

WHEATON FRANCISCAN HEALTHCARE – ST. JOSEPH'S (O, 316 beds) 5000 West Chambers Street, Milwaukee, WI Zip 53210–1650; tel. 414/447–2000; Debra K. Standridge, President
Web address: www.mywheaton.org/stjoseph

For explanation of codes following names, see page B2.
★ Indicates Type III membership in the American Hospital Association.

WHEATON FRANCISCAN HEALTHCARE – THE WISCONSIN HEART HOSPITAL (O, 30 beds) 10000 West Bluemound Road, Wauwatosa, WI Zip 53226–4321; tel. 414/778–7800; Debra K. Standridge, President
Web address: www.mywheaton.org/hearthospital

Owned, leased, sponsored:	12 hospitals	1728 beds
Contract–managed:	0 hospitals	0 beds
Totals:	12 hospitals	1728 beds

★0468: WHITE RIVER HEALTH SYSTEM (NP)
1710 Harrison Street, Batesville, AR Zip 72501–7303; tel. 870/262–1200; Gary Bebow, FACHE, Administrator and Chief Executive Officer
(Independent Hospital System)

ARKANSAS: STONE COUNTY MEDICAL CENTER (O, 25 beds) 2106 East Main Street, Mountain View, AR Zip 72560–6439, Mailing Address: P.O. Box 510, Zip 72560–0510; tel. 870/269–4361; Stanley Townsend, Chief Executive Officer
Web address: www.whiteriverhealthsystem.com

WHITE RIVER MEDICAL CENTER (O, 210 beds) 1710 Harrison Street, Batesville, AR Zip 72501–7303, Mailing Address: P.O. Box 2197, Zip 72503–2197; tel. 870/262–1200; Gary Bebow, FACHE, Administrator and Chief Executive Officer
Web address: www.whiteriverhealthsystem.com

Owned, leased, sponsored:	2 hospitals	235 beds
Contract–managed:	0 hospitals	0 beds
Totals:	2 hospitals	235 beds

0646: WHITTIER HEALTH NETWORK (IO)
25 Railroad Square, Haverhill, MA Zip 01832–5721; tel. 978/556–5858; Alfred L. Arcidi, M.D., President
(Independent Hospital System)

MASSACHUSETTS: WHITTIER PAVILION (O, 65 beds) 76 Summer Street, Haverhill, MA Zip 01830–5814; tel. 978/373–8222; Alfred L. Arcidi, M.D., Chief Executive Officer
Web address: www.whittierhealth.com

WHITTIER REHABILITATION HOSPITAL (O, 74 beds) 150 Flanders Road, Westborough, MA Zip 01581–1017; tel. 508/871–2000; Alfred J. Arcidi, M.D., Senior Vice President
Web address: www.whittierhealth.com

WHITTIER REHABILITATION HOSPITAL (O, 60 beds) 145 Ward Hill Avenue, Bradford, MA Zip 01835–6928; tel. 978/372–8000; Alfred J. Arcidi, M.D., Senior Vice President
Web address: www.whittierhealth.com

Owned, leased, sponsored:	3 hospitals	199 beds
Contract–managed:	0 hospitals	0 beds
Totals:	3 hospitals	199 beds

1945: WILLIS–KNIGHTON HEALTH SYSTEM (NP)
2600 Greenwood Road, Shreveport, LA Zip 71103–3908; tel. 318/212–4000; James K. Elrod, FACHE, President and Chief Executive Officer
(Centralized Health System)

LOUISIANA: DE SOTO REGIONAL HEALTH SYSTEM (C, 10 beds) 207 Jefferson Street, Mansfield, LA Zip 71052–2603, Mailing Address: P.O. Box 1636, Zip 71052–1636; tel. 318/871–3100; Todd Eppler, FACHE, Chief Executive Officer
Web address: www.desotoregional.com

SPRINGHILL MEDICAL CENTER (C, 58 beds) 2001 Doctors Drive, Springhill, LA Zip 71075–4526, Mailing Address: P.O. Box 920, Zip 71075–0920; tel. 318/539–1000; Vince Sedminik, Chief Executive Officer
Web address: www.smccare.com

WILLIS–KNIGHTON MEDICAL CENTER (O, 898 beds) 2600 Greenwood Road, Shreveport, LA Zip 71103–3908, Mailing Address: P.O. Box 32600, Zip 71130–2600; tel. 318/212–4600; Jaf Fielder, Vice President and Administrator
Web address: www.wkhs.com

WK BOSSIER HEALTH CENTER (O, 166 beds) 2400 Hospital Drive, Bossier City, LA Zip 71111–2385; tel. 318/212–7000; Clifford M. Broussard, FACHE, Administrator
Web address: www.wkhs.com/wkb/

Owned, leased, sponsored:	2 hospitals	1064 beds
Contract–managed:	2 hospitals	68 beds
Totals:	4 hospitals	1132 beds

★0157: YALE NEW HAVEN HEALTH SYSTEM (NP)
789 Howard Avenue, New Haven, CT Zip 06519–1304; tel. 203/688–4608; Marna P. Borgstrom, President and Chief Executive Officer
(Centralized Physician/Insurance Health System)

CONNECTICUT: BRIDGEPORT HOSPITAL (O, 330 beds) 267 Grant Street, Bridgeport, CT Zip 06610–2805, Mailing Address: P.O. Box 5000, Zip 06610–0120; tel. 203/384–3000; William M. Jennings, President and Chief Executive Officer
Web address: www.bridgeporthospital.org

GREENWICH HOSPITAL (O, 174 beds) 5 Perryridge Road, Greenwich, CT Zip 06830–4697; tel. 203/863–3000; Frank A. Corvino, President and Chief Executive Officer
Web address: www.greenhosp.org

YALE–NEW HAVEN HOSPITAL (O, 1612 beds) 20 York Street, New Haven, CT Zip 06510–3202; tel. 203/688–4242; Marna P. Borgstrom, Chief Executive Officer
Web address: www.ynhh.org

Owned, leased, sponsored:	3 hospitals	2116 beds
Contract–managed:	0 hospitals	0 beds
Totals:	3 hospitals	2116 beds

Section B

For explanation of codes following names, see page B2.
★ Indicates Type III membership in the American Hospital Association.

Headquarters of Health Care Systems

Geographically

United States

ALABAMA

Birmingham: BAPTIST HEALTH SYSTEM 3201 Fourth Avenue South, Zip 35222–1723, Mailing Address: P.O. Box 830605, Zip 35283–0605; tel. 205/715–5319; Keith Parrott, FACHE, President and Chief Executive Officer, p. B20

BRADFORD HEALTH SERVICES 2101 Magnolia Avenue South, Suite 518, Zip 35205–2853; tel. 205/251–7753; Jerry W. Crowder, President and Chief Executive Officer, p. B24

★ HEALTHSOUTH CORPORATION 3660 Grandview Parkway, Suite 200, Zip 35243–3332; tel. 205/967–7116; Jay F. Grinney, President and Chief Executive Officer, p. B69

NOLAND HEALTH SERVICES, INC. 600 Corporate Parkway, Suite 100, Zip 35242–5451; tel. 205/783–8484; Gary M. Glasscock, President and Chief Executive Officer, p. B99

★ UAB HEALTH SYSTEM 500 22nd Street South, Suite 408, Zip 35233–3110; tel. 205/975–5362; William Ferniany, Ph.D., Chief Executive Officer, p. B137

Guntersville: MARSHALL HEALTH SYSTEM 227 Britany Road, Zip 35976–5766; tel. 256/894–6615; Gary R. Gore, Chief Executive Officer, p. B88

Huntsville: HUNTSVILLE HOSPITAL HEALTH SYSTEM 101 Sivley Road S.W., Zip 35801–4421; tel. 265/256–1000; David S. Spillers, Chief Executive Officer, p. B74

Mobile: ALTAPOINTE HEALTH SYSTEMS 5750–A Southland Drive, Zip 36693–3316; tel. 251/473–4423; J. Tuerk Schlesinger, Chief Executive Officer, p. B10

INFIRMARY HEALTH SYSTEM 5 Mobile Infirmary Circle, Zip 36607–3513; tel. 251/435–5500; D. Mark Nix, President and Chief Executive Officer, p. B75

★ UNIVERSITY OF SOUTH ALABAMA HOSPITALS 2451 Fillingim Street, Zip 36617–2238; tel. 251/471–7000; Stanley K. Hammack, Chief Executive Officer, p. B146

Montgomery: BAPTIST HEALTH 301 Brown Springs Road, Zip 36117–7005; tel. 334/273–4400; W. Russell Tyner, President and Chief Executive Officer, p. B19

GILLIARD HEALTH SERVICES 3091 Carter Hill Road, Zip 36111–1801; tel. 334/265–5009; William G. McKenzie, President, Chief Executive Officer and Chairman, p. B61

Tuscaloosa: DCH HEALTH SYSTEM 809 University Boulevard East, Zip 35401–2029; tel. 205/759–7111; Bryan N. Kindred, FACHE, President and Chief Executive Officer, p. B46

ARIZONA

Flagstaff: ★ NORTHERN ARIZONA HEALTHCARE 1200 North Beaver Street, Zip 86001–3118; tel. 928/779–3366; William T. Bradel, President and Chief Executive Officer, p. B101

Phoenix: ★ BANNER HEALTH 1441 North 12th Street, Zip 85006–2837, Mailing Address: P.O. Box 25489, Zip 85002–5489; tel. 602/747–4000; Peter S. Fine, FACHE, President and Chief Executive Officer, p. B18

★ JOHN C. LINCOLN HEALTH NETWORK 2500 West Utopia Road, Suite 100, Zip 85027–4172; tel. 623/434–6230; Rhonda Forsyth, President and Chief Executive Officer, p. B78

Scottsdale: ★ SCOTTSDALE HEALTHCARE 8125 North Hayden Road, Zip 85258–2463; tel. 480/882–4000; Thomas J. Sadvary, FACHE, President and Chief Executive Officer, p. B119

SOUTHWEST HEALTHCARE SYSTEM 4400 North Scottsdale Road, Suite 9347, Zip 85251–3331; tel. 480/348–9800; Paul R. Tuft, President, p. B126

ARKANSAS

Batesville: ★ WHITE RIVER HEALTH SYSTEM 1710 Harrison Street, Zip 72501–7303; tel. 870/262–1200; Gary Bebow, FACHE, Administrator and Chief Executive Officer, p. B153

Blytheville: MISSISSIPPI COUNTY HOSPITAL SYSTEM 1520 North Division Street, Zip 72315–1448, Mailing Address: P.O. Box 108, Zip 72316–0108; tel. 870/838–7300; Ralph E. Beaty, Chief Executive Officer, p. B95

Little Rock: ★ BAPTIST HEALTH 9601 Interstate 630, Exit 7, Zip 72205–7299; tel. 501/202–2000; Troy R. Wells, Chief Executive Officer, p. B20

CALIFORNIA

Alhambra: AHMC & HEALTHCARE, INC. 55 South Raymond Avenue, Suite 105, Zip 91801–7101; tel. 626/457–9600; Jonathan Wu, M.D., President and Chairman, p. B7

Corona: AURORA BEHAVIORAL HEALTH CARE 4238 Green River Road, Zip 92880–1669; tel. 951/549–8032; Soon K. Kim, M.D., President and Chief Executive Officer, p. B16

Covina: ★ CITRUS VALLEY HEALTH PARTNERS 210 West San Bernardino Road, Zip 91723–1515; tel. 626/331–7331; Robert H. Curry, President and Chief Executive Officer, p. B35

Cupertino: CRC HEALTH GROUP, INC. 20400 Stevens Creek Boulevard, Suite 600, Zip 95014–2217; tel. 866/540–5240; Jerome E. Rhodes, Chief Executive Officer, p. B45

El Segundo: AVANTI HOSPITALS 222 North Sepulveda Boulevard, Suite 950, Zip 90245–5614; tel. 310/356–0550; Edward Mirzabegian, Corporate Chief Executive Officer, p. B17

Escondido: ★ PALOMAR HEALTH 456 East Grand Avenue, Zip 92025–3319; tel. 760/740–6393; Robert Hemker, President and Chief Executive Officer, p. B105

Fountain Valley: MEMORIALCARE 17360 Brookhurst Street, Zip 92708–3720, Mailing Address: P.O. Box 1428, Long Beach, Zip 90801–1428; tel. 714/377–2900; Barry S. Arbuckle, Ph.D., President and Chief Executive Officer, p. B91

Fresno: COMMUNITY MEDICAL CENTERS Fresno and Maddy Drive, Zip 93721, Mailing Address: P.O. Box 1232, Zip 93715–1232; tel. 559/459–6000; Tim A. Joslin, President and Chief Executive Officer, p. B43

Hemet: PHYSICIANS FOR HEALTHY HOSPITALS 1117 East Devonshire Avenue, Zip 92543–3083; tel. 951/652–2811; Joel Bergenfeld, Chief Executive Officer, p. B106

Irvine: ★ ST. JOSEPH HEALTH 3345 Michelson Drive, Suite 100, Zip 92612; tel. 949/381–4000; Deborah A. Proctor, President and Chief Executive Officer, p. B128

Loma Linda: LOMA LINDA UNIVERSITY ADVENTIST HEALTH SCIENCES CENTER 11175 Campus Street, Zip 92350–1700; tel. 909/558–7572; Richard H. Hart, M.D., President and Chief Executive Officer, p. B87

Los Altos Hills: ★ DAUGHTERS OF CHARITY HEALTH SYSTEM 26000 Altamont Road, Zip 94022–4317; tel. 650/917–4500; Robert Issai, President and Chief Executive Officer, p. B46

Los Angeles: ALTA HEALTHCARE SYSTEM 10780 Santa Monica Boulevard, Suite 400, Zip 90025–7616; tel. 310/943–4500; David Topper, Chief Executive Officer, p. B10

LOS ANGELES COUNTY–DEPARTMENT OF HEALTH SERVICES 313 North Figueroa Street, Room 912, Zip 90012–2691; tel. 213/240–8101; Mitchell H. Katz, M.D., Director, p. B87

Oakland: ★ KAISER FOUNDATION HOSPITALS One Kaiser Plaza, Zip 94612–3600; tel. 510/271–5910; Bernard J. Tyson, Chairman and Chief Executive Officer, p. B78

★ UNIVERSITY OF CALIFORNIA–SYSTEMWIDE ADMINISTRATION 1111 Franklin Street, 11th Floor, Zip 94607–5200; tel. 510/987–9071; John D. Stobo, M.D., Senior Vice President Health Sciences and Services, p. B145

Ontario: PRIME HEALTHCARE SERVICES 3300 East Guasti Road, Zip 91761–8655; tel. 909/235–4400; Prem Reddy, M.D., Interim President and Chief Executive Officer, p. B108

Palo Alto: STANFORD HEALTH CARE 300 Pasteur Drive, Zip 94304–2299; tel. 650/723–4000; Amir Dan Rubin, President and Chief Executive Officer, p. B129

Roseville: ★ ADVENTIST HEALTH 2100 Douglas Boulevard, Zip 95661–3898, Mailing Address: P.O. Box 619002, Zip 95661–9002; tel. 916/781–2000; Scott Reiner, President and Chief Executive Officer, p. B5

Sacramento: ★ SUTTER HEALTH 2200 River Plaza Drive, Zip 95833–4134; tel. 916/733–8800; Patrick E. Fry, President and Chief Executive Officer, p. B130

San Diego: ★ SCRIPPS HEALTH 4275 Campus Point Court, Zip 92121–1513; tel. 858/678–7200; Chris D. Van Gorder, FACHE, President and Chief Executive Officer, p. B119

★ SHARP HEALTHCARE 8695 Spectrum Center Boulevard, Zip 92123–1489; tel. 858/499–4000; Michael Murphy, CPA, President & Chief Executive Officer, p. B123

San Francisco: ★ DIGNITY HEALTH 185 Berry Street, Suite 300, Zip 94107–1773; tel. 415/438–5500; Lloyd H. Dean, President and Chief Executive Officer, p. B52

San Leandro: ALAMEDA HEALTH SYSTEM 15400 Foothill Boulevard, Zip 94578–1009; tel. 510/677–7920; Wright L. Lassiter, III, Chief Executive Officer, p. B8

Santa Ana: INTEGRATED HEALTHCARE 1301 North Tustin Avenue, Zip 92705–8619; tel. 714/953–3652; Kenneth K. Westbrook, President and Chief Executive Officer, p. B76

Santa Barbara: ★ COTTAGE HEALTH SYSTEM 400 West Pueblo Street, Zip 93105–4353, Mailing Address: P.O. Box 689, Zip 93102–0689; tel. 805/569–7290; Ronald C. Werft, President and Chief Executive Officer, p. B44

Santa Fe Springs: COLLEGE HEALTH ENTERPRISES 11627 Telegraph Road, Suite 200, Zip 90670–6814; tel. 562/923–9449; Barry J. Weiss, Chairman of the Board, p. B36

Truckee: TAHOE FOREST HEALTH SYSTEM 10121 Pine Avenue, Zip 96161–4835; tel. 530/587–6011; Robert A. Schapper, Chief Executive Officer, p. B131

Walnut Creek: ★ JOHN MUIR HEALTH 1400 Treat Boulevard, Zip 94597–2142; tel. 925/941–2100; Calvin K. Knight, President and Chief Executive Officer, p. B78

COLORADO

Alamosa: SAN LUIS VALLEY HEALTH 106 Blanca Avenue, Zip 81101–2340; tel. 719/589–2511; Konnie Martin, Chief Executive Officer, p. B117

Denver: ★ SCL HEALTH SYSTEM 2420 West 26th Avenue, Suite 100D, Zip 80211–5302; tel. 303/813–5180; Michael A. Slubowski, FACHE, Chief Executive Officer, p. B119

Englewood: ★ CATHOLIC HEALTH INITIATIVES 198 Inverness Drive West, Suite 800, Zip 80112–5202; tel. 303/298–9100; Kevin E. Lofton, FACHE, President and Chief Executive Officer, p. B30

Fort Collins: ★ UNIVERSITY OF COLORADO HEALTH 2315 East Harmony Road, Suite 200, Zip 80528–8620; tel. 970/237–7001; William Neff, M.D., Interim President and Chief Executive Officer, p. B145

CONNECTICUT

Danbury: ★ WESTERN CONNECTICUT HEALTH NETWORK 24 Hospital Avenue, Zip 06810–6099; tel. 203/739–7066; John M. Murphy, M.D., President, p. B152

Hartford: CONNECTICUT DEPARTMENT OF MENTAL HEALTH AND ADDICTION SERVICES 410 Capitol Avenue, Zip 06106–1367, Mailing Address: P.O. Box 341431, Zip 06134–1431; tel. 860/418–7000; Patricia Rehmer, Commissioner, p. B43

★ HARTFORD HEALTHCARE One State Street, 19th Floor, Zip 06103; tel. 860/263–4100; Elliot T. Joseph, President and Chief Executive Officer, p. B63

★ SAINT FRANCIS CARE, INC. 114 Woodland Street, Zip 06105–1208; tel. 860/714–5541; Christopher M. Dadlez, President and Chief Executive Officer, p. B116

Manchester: ★ EASTERN CONNECTICUT HEALTH NETWORK 71 Haynes Street, Zip 06040–4131; tel. 860/533–3400; Peter J. Karl, President and Chief Executive Officer, p. B55

New Haven: ★ YALE NEW HAVEN HEALTH SYSTEM 789 Howard Avenue, Zip 06519–1304; tel. 203/688–4608; Marna P. Borgstrom, President and Chief Executive Officer, p. B153

New London: ★ L+M HEALTHCARE 365 Montauk Avenue, Zip 06320–4700; tel. 860/442–0711; Bruce D. Cummings, President and Chief Executive Officer, p. B82

DELAWARE

Wilmington: ★ CHRISTIANA CARE HEALTH SYSTEM 501 West 14th Street, Zip 19801–1013, Mailing Address: P.O. Box 1668, Zip 19899–1668; tel. 302/733–1000; Robert J. Laskowski, M.D., President and Chief Executive Officer, p. B35

DISTRICT OF COLUMBIA

Washington: BUREAU OF MEDICINE AND SURGERY, DEPARTMENT OF THE NAVY 2300 East Street N.W., Zip 20372–5300; tel. 202/762–3701; Vice Admiral Matthew L. Nathan, Surgeon General, p. B25

DEPARTMENT OF THE AIR FORCE 1420 Pentagon, Room 4E1084, Zip 20330–1420; tel. 202/767–4765; Lieutenant General Charles B. Green, M.D., Surgeon General, p. B47

DEPARTMENT OF VETERANS AFFAIRS 810 Vermont Avenue N.W., Zip 20420–0001; tel. 202/273–5781; Robert A. Petzel, M.D., Under Secretary for Health, p. B48

FLORIDA

Altamonte Springs: ★ ADVENTIST HEALTH SYSTEM SUNBELT HEALTH CARE CORPORATION 900 Hope Way, Zip 32714–1502; tel. 407/357–1000; Donald L. Jernigan, Ph.D., President and Chief Executive Officer, p. B6

Boca Raton: PROMISE HEALTHCARE 999 Yamato Road, 3rd Floor, Zip 33431–4477; tel. 561/869–3100; Peter R. Baronoff, Chief Executive Officer, p. B109

SUCCESS HEALTHCARE 999 Yamato Road, 3rd Floor, Zip 33431–4477; tel. 561/869–6300; Peter R. Baronoff, President and Chief Executive Officer, p. B129

Clearwater: MORTON PLANT MEASE HEALTH CARE 300 Pinellas Street, Zip 33756–3804, Mailing Address: P.O. Box 210, Zip 33757–0210; tel. 727/462–7000; Glenn D. Waters, FACHE, President, p. B95

Coral Gables: ★ BAPTIST HEALTH SOUTH FLORIDA 6855 Red Road, Suite 600, Zip 33143–3632; tel. 786/662–7111; Brian E. Keeley, President and Chief Executive Officer, p. B20

Fort Lauderdale: ★ BROWARD HEALTH 303 S.E. 17th Street, Zip 33316–2523; tel. 954/355–5100; Frank P. Nask, President and Chief Executive Officer, p. B25

Fort Myers: ★ LEE MEMORIAL HEALTH SYSTEM 2776 Cleveland Avenue, Zip 33901–5856, Mailing Address: P.O. Box 2218, Zip 33902–2218; tel. 239/343–2000; James R. Nathan, President and Chief Executive Officer, p. B83

Gainesville: ★ UF HEALTH SHANDS 1600 S.W. Archer Road, Zip 32610–0326; tel. 352/733–1500; Edward Jimenez, Interim Chief Executive Officer, p. B137

Hollywood: ★ MEMORIAL HEALTHCARE SYSTEM 3501 Johnson Street, Zip 33021–5421; tel. 954/265–5805; Frank V. Sacco, FACHE, President and Chief Executive Officer, p. B91

Jacksonville: ★ BAPTIST HEALTH 841 Prudential Drive, Suite 1601, Zip 32207–8202; tel. 904/202–4011; Hugh Greene, President and Chief Executive Officer, p. B19

NEMOURS 10140 Centurion Parkway North, Zip 32256–0532; tel. 904/697–4100; David J. Bailey, M.D., President and Chief Executive Officer, p. B97

Lauderdale Lakes: CATHOLIC HEALTH SERVICES 4790 North State Road 7, Zip 33319–5860; tel. 954/484–1515; Joseph M. Catania, President and Chief Executive Officer, p. B32

Leesburg: CENTRAL FLORIDA HEALTH ALLIANCE 600 East Dixie Avenue, Zip 34748–5925; tel. 352/323–5762; Donald G. Henderson, FACHE, Chief Executive Officer, p. B34

Miami: UNIVERSITY OF MIAMI HEALTH SYSTEM 1400 N.W. 12th Avenue, Zip 33136–1003; tel. 305/243–4000; Pascal J. Goldschmidt, M.D., Chief Executive Officer, p. B146

Miami Lakes: PACER HEALTH CORPORATION 14100 Palmetto Frontage Road, Suite 110, Zip 33016; tel. 305/828–7660; Rainier Gonzalez, Chairman and Chief Executive Officer, p. B104

Orlando: ORLANDO HEALTH 1414 Kuhl Avenue, Zip 32806–2093; tel. 321/843–7000; Jamal Hakim, M.D., Interim President and Chief Executive Officer, p. B104

Pensacola: ★ BAPTIST HEALTH CARE CORPORATION 1717 North E Street Suite 320, Zip 32501–6377, Mailing Address: P.O. Box 17500, Zip 32522–7500; tel. 850/434–4011; Mark T. Faulkner, President, p. B20

Rockledge: HEALTH FIRST, INC. 6450 U.S. Highway 1, Zip 32955–5747; tel. 321/434–7000; Steven P. Johnson, Ph.D., President and Chief Executive Officer, p. B68

Tampa: SHRINERS HOSPITALS FOR CHILDREN 2900 Rocky Point Drive, Zip 33607–1435, Mailing Address: P.O. Box 31356, Zip 33631–3356; tel. 813/281–0300; John P. McCabe, Executive Vice President, p. B124

Windermere: UNITED MEDICAL CORPORATION 603 Main Street, Zip 34786–3548, Mailing Address: P.O. Box 1100, Zip 34786–1100; tel. 407/876–2200; Donald R. Dizney, Chairman and Chief Executive Officer, p. B138

GEORGIA

Albany: ★ PHOEBE PUTNEY HEALTH SYSTEM 417 Third Avenue, Zip 31701–1943; tel. 229/312–1000; Joel Wernick, President and Chief Executive Officer, p. B106

Alpharetta: RESTORA HEALTHCARE 2550 Northwinds Parkway, Suite 160, Zip 30009–2234; tel. 678/736–7780; Rod Laughlin, President and Chief Executive Officer, p. B114

Atlanta: ★ EMORY HEALTHCARE 1440 Clifton Road N.E., Suite 145, Zip 30322–1102; tel. 404/778–5000; John T. Fox, Chief Executive Officer, p. B56

★ NORTHSIDE HEALTHCARE SYSTEM 1000 Johnson Ferry Road N.E., Zip 30342–1611; tel. 404/851–8000; Robert Quattrocchi, President and Chief Executive Officer, p. B101

★ PIEDMONT HEALTHCARE 1800 Howell Mill Road N.W., Suite 850, Zip 30318–0923; tel. 404/425–1314; Kevin Brown, President and Chief Executive Officer, p. B106

SUNLINK HEALTH SYSTEMS 900 Circle 75 Parkway, Suite 1120, Zip 30339–3005; tel. 770/933–7000; Robert M. Thornton, Jr., Chief Executive Officer, p. B130

Augusta: ★ UNIVERSITY HEALTH CARE SYSTEM 1350 Walton Way, Zip 30901–2629; tel. 706/722–9011; James R. Davis, President and Chief Executive Officer, p. B144

Blairsville: UNION GENERAL HOSPITAL, INC. 35 Hospital Road, Zip 30512–3139; tel. 706/745–2111; Mike Gowder, Chief Executive Officer, p. B138

Brunswick: ★ SOUTHEAST GEORGIA HEALTH SYSTEM 2415 Parkwood Drive, Zip 31520–4722, Mailing Address: P.O. Box 1518, Zip 31521–1518; tel. 912/466–7000; Gary R. Colberg, FACHE, President and Chief Executive Officer, p. B125

Carrollton: ★ TANNER HEALTH SYSTEM 705 Dixie Street, Zip 30117–3818; tel. 770/836–9580; Loy M. Howard, President and Chief Executive Officer, p. B132

Columbus: ★ COLUMBUS REGIONAL HEALTHCARE SYSTEM 707 Center Street, Suite 400, Zip 31901–1575; tel. 706/660–6100; Scott Hill, Interim Chief Executive Officer, p. B36

Decatur: DEKALB REGIONAL HEALTH SYSTEM 2701 North Decatur Road, Zip 30033–5918; tel. 404/501–1000; John Shelton, President and Chief Executive Officer, p. B46

Macon: NAVICENT HEALTH 777 Hemlock Street, Zip 31201–2155; tel. 478/633–1000; Ninfa Saunders, Chief Executive Officer, p. B97

Marietta: ★ WELLSTAR HEALTH SYSTEM 805 Sandy Plains Road, Zip 30066–6340; tel. 770/792–5012; Reynold J. Jennings, President and Chief Executive Officer, p. B151

Milledgeville: OCONEE REGIONAL HEALTH SYSTEMS 821 North Cobb Street, Zip 31061–2343; tel. 478/454–3505; Jean Aycock, President and Chief Executive Officer, p. B102

Royston: TY COBB HEALTHCARE SYSTEM, INC. 461 Cook Street, Suite A., Zip 30662–4003; tel. 706/356–7800; Gregory K. Hearn, Chief Executive Officer, p. B136

Thomasville: ★ ARCHBOLD MEDICAL CENTER 910 South Broad Street, Zip 31792–6113; tel. 229/228–2739; J. Perry Mustian, President, p. B11

Tifton: ★ TIFT REGIONAL HEALTH SYSTEM 901 East 18th Street, Zip 31794–3648; tel. 229/353–6100; William T. Richardson, President and Chief Executive Officer, p. B135

Warner Robins: ★ HOUSTON HEALTHCARE SYSTEM 1601 Watson Boulevard, Zip 31093–3431, Mailing Address: P.O. Box 2886, Zip 31099–2886; tel. 478/922–4281; Cary Martin, Chief Executive Officer, p. B74

HAWAII

Honolulu: ★ HAWAII HEALTH SYSTEMS CORPORATION 3675 Kilauea Avenue, Zip 96816–2333; tel. 808/733–4151; Alice Hall, Acting President and Chief Executive Officer, p. B63

HAWAII PACIFIC HEALTH 55 Merchant Street, Zip 96813–4306; tel. 808/949–9355; Raymond P. Vara, Jr., President and Chief Executive Officer, p. B63

★ QUEEN'S HEALTH SYSTEMS 1301 Punchbowl Street, Zip 96813–2402; tel. 808/535–5448; Arthur A. Ushijima, FACHE, President and Chief Executive Officer, p. B113

IDAHO

Boise: ★ ST. LUKE'S HEALTH SYSTEM 420 West Idaho Street, Zip 83702–6041; tel. 208/381–4200; David C. Pate, M.D., JD, President and Chief Executive Officer, p. B128

Pocatello: SAFE HAVEN HEALTH CARE 2520 South 5th Avenue, Zip 83204–1923; tel. 800/261–2443; Scott Burpee, President, p. B116

ILLINOIS

Carbondale: SOUTHERN ILLINOIS HOSPITAL SERVICES 1239 East Main Street, Zip 62901–3114, Mailing Address: P.O. Box 3988, Zip 62902–3988; tel. 618/457–5200; Rex P. Budde, President and Chief Executive Officer, p. B125

Chicago: COOK COUNTY HEALTH AND HOSPITALS SYSTEM 1900 West Polk Street, Suite 220, Zip 60612–3723; tel. 312/864–6820; John Jay Shannon, M.D., Chief Executive Officer, p. B44

NATIONAL SURGICAL HOSPITALS 250 South Wacker Drive, Suite 500, Zip 60606–5897; tel. 312/627–8400; David Crane, Chief Executive Officer, p. B97

★ NORTHWESTERN MEMORIAL HEALTHCARE 251 East Huron Street, Zip 60611–2908; tel. 312/926–2000; Dean M. Harrison, President and Chief Executive Officer, p. B101

★ PRESENCE HEALTH 200 South Wacker Drive, Zip 60606–5829; tel. 312/308–3200; Sandra B. Bruce, FACHE, President and Chief Executive Officer, p. B108

★ RUSH UNIVERSITY MEDICAL CENTER 1653 West Congress Parkway, Zip 60612–3864; tel. 312/942–5000; Larry J. Goodman, M.D., Chief Executive Officer, p. B116

★ SINAI HEALTH SYSTEM 1500 South California Avenue, Zip 60608–1729; tel. 773/542–2000; Karen Teitelbaum, President and Chief Executive Officer, p. B124

Crystal Lake: ★ CENTEGRA HEALTH SYSTEM 385 Millennium Drive, Zip 60012–3761; tel. 815/788–5800; Michael S. Eesley, Chief Executive Officer, p. B33

DeKalb: ★ KISH HEALTH SYSTEM 1 Kish Hospital Drive, Zip 60115–9602, Mailing Address: P.O. Box 707, Zip 60115–0707; tel. 815/756–1521; Kevin P. Poorten, President and Chief Executive Officer, p. B82

Downers Grove: ★ ADVOCATE HEALTH CARE 3075 Highland Parkway, Suite 600, Zip 60515–1206; tel. 630/929–8700; Jim H. Skogsbergh, President and Chief Executive Officer, p. B7

Evergreen Park: AMERICAN PROVINCE OF LITTLE COMPANY OF MARY SISTERS 9350 South California Avenue, Zip 60805–2595; tel. 708/229–5491; Sister Kathleen McIntyre, Province Leader, p. B10

Naperville: ★ EDWARD–ELMHURST HEALTHCARE 801 South Washington Street, Zip 60540–7430; tel. 630/527–3000; Pamela M. Davis, System President and Chief Executive Officer, p. B56

Peoria: ★ OSF HEALTHCARE SYSTEM 800 N.E. Glen Oak Avenue, Zip 61603–3200; tel. 309/655–2850; Kevin D. Schoeplein, Chief Executive Officer, p. B104

Schaumburg: CANCER TREATMENT CENTERS OF AMERICA 1336 Basswood Road, Zip 60173–4544; tel. 847/342–7400; Gerard van Grinsven, President and Chief Executive Officer, p. B26

Springfield: DIVISION OF MENTAL HEALTH, DEPARTMENT OF HUMAN SERVICES 319 East Madison Street, S–3B, Zip 62701–1035; tel. 217/785–6023; Lorrie Rickman Jones, Ph.D., Director, p. B53

★ HOSPITAL SISTERS HEALTH SYSTEM 4936 LaVerna Road, Zip 62707–9797, Mailing Address: P.O. Box 19456, Zip 62794–9456; tel. 217/523–4747; Mary Starmann–Harrison, FACHE, President and Chief Executive Officer, p. B73

★ MEMORIAL HEALTH SYSTEM 701 North First Street, Zip 62781–0001; tel. 217/788–3000; Edgar J. Curtis, FACHE, President and Chief Executive Officer, p. B90

Urbana: ★ CARLE FOUNDATION 611 West Park Street, Zip 61801–2595; tel. 217/383–3311; James C. Leonard, M.D., President and Chief Executive Officer, p. B27

Wheaton: ★ WHEATON FRANCISCAN HEALTHCARE 26W171 Roosevelt Road, Zip 60187–6002, Mailing Address: P.O. Box 667, Zip 60187–0667; tel. 630/909–6900; John D. Oliverio, President and Chief Executive Officer, p. B152

Winfield: ★ CADENCE HEALTH 25 North Winfield Road, Zip 60190; tel. 630/933–1600; Michael Vivoda, Chief Executive Officer, p. B26

INDIANA

Evansville: ★ DEACONESS HEALTH SYSTEM 600 Mary Street, Zip 47710–1658; tel. 812/450–5000; Linda E. White, President and Chief Executive Officer, p. B46

Fort Wayne: ★ PARKVIEW HEALTH 10501 Corporate Drive, Zip 46845–1700; tel. 260/373–7001; Michael J. Packnett, President and Chief Executive Officer, p. B105

Hammond: COMMUNITY HEALTHCARE SYSTEM 901 MacArthur Boulevard, Zip 46321–2959; tel. 219/836–1600; Donald Powers, Chairman, President and Chief Executive Officer, p. B43

Indianapolis: COMMUNITY HEALTH NETWORK 7330 Shadeland Station, Zip 46256–3957; tel. 317/355–1411; Bryan A. Mills, President and Chief Executive Officer, p. B36

★ INDIANA UNIVERSITY HEALTH 340 West 10th Street, Suite 6100, Zip 46202–3082, Mailing Address: P.O. Box 1367, Zip 46206–1367; tel. 317/962–5900; Daniel F. Evans, Jr., JD, President and Chief Executive Officer, p. B75

Mishawaka: FRANCISCAN ALLIANCE 1515 Dragoon Trail, Zip 46544–4710, Mailing Address: P.O. Box 1290, Zip 46546–1290; tel. 574/256–3935; Kevin D. Leahy, President and Chief Executive Officer, p. B59

NEUROPSYCHIATRIC HOSPITALS 1625 East Jefferson Boulevard, Zip 46545–7103; tel. 574/255–1400; Cameron R. Gilbert, Ph.D., President and Chief Executive Officer, p. B97

South Bend: BEACON HEALTH SYSTEM 615 North Michigan Street, Zip 46601–1033; tel. 574/647–1000; Philip A. Newbold, Chief Executive Officer, p. B22

IOWA

Clarion: ★ IOWA SPECIALTY HOSPITALS 1316 South Main Street, Zip 50525–2019; tel. 515/532–2811; Steven J. Simonin, Chief Executive Officer, p. B77

Davenport: ★ GENESIS HEALTH SYSTEM 1227 East Rusholme Street, Zip 52803–2498; tel. 563/421–1000; Douglas P. Cropper, President and Chief Executive Officer, p. B60

West Des Moines: ★ UNITYPOINT HEALTH 1776 Westlakes Parkway, Suite 400, Zip 50266–8239; tel. 515/241–6161; William B. Leaver, President and Chief Executive Officer, p. B139

KANSAS

Wichita: ★ GREAT PLAINS HEALTH ALLIANCE, INC. 250 North Rock Road, Suite 160, Zip 67206–2241; tel. 316/685–1523; Dave Dellasega, President and Chief Executive Officer, p. B61

KENTUCKY

Bowling Green: COMMONWEALTH HEALTH CORPORATION 800 Park Street, Zip 42101–2356; tel. 270/745–1500; Connie Smith, President and Chief Executive Officer, p. B36

Edgewood: ST. ELIZABETH HEALTHCARE 1 Medical Village Drive, Zip 41017–3403; tel. 859/301–2000; John S. Dubis, FACHE, President and Chief Executive Officer, p. B127

Lexington: APPALACHIAN REGIONAL HEALTHCARE, INC. 2285 Executive Drive, Suite 400, Zip 40505–4810, Mailing Address: P.O. Box 8086, Zip 40533–8086; tel. 859/226–2440; Jerry Haynes, President and Chief Executive Officer, p. B11

Louisville: ALLIANT MANAGEMENT SERVICES 2650 Eastpoint Parkway, Suite 300, Zip 40223–5164; tel. 502/992–3525; Timothy L. Jarm, President and Chief Executive Officer, p. B9

★ BAPTIST HEALTH 2701 Eastpoint Parkway, Zip 40223; tel. 502/896–5000; Stephen C. Hanson, Chief Executive Officer, p. B19

★ KINDRED HEALTHCARE 680 South Fourth Street, Zip 40202–2412; tel. 502/596–7300; Paul J. Diaz, President and Chief Executive Officer, p. B80

★ NORTON HEALTHCARE 4967 U.S. Highway 42, Suite 100, Zip 40222–6363, Mailing Address: P.O. Box 35070, Zip 40232–5070; tel. 502/629–8000; Stephen Williams, Chief Executive Officer, p. B101

LOUISIANA

Baton Rouge: ★ FRANCISCAN MISSIONARIES OF OUR LADY HEALTH SYSTEM, INC. 4200 Essen Lane, Zip 70809–2158; tel. 225/923–2701; John J. Finan, Jr., FACHE, President and Chief Executive Officer, p. B59

LOUISIANA STATE HOSPITALS 628 North 4th Street, Zip 70802–5342, Mailing Address: P.O. Box 629, Zip 70821–0628; tel. 225/342–9500; Shelby Price, Chief Executive Officer, p. B87

Crowley: COMPASS HEALTH 426 North Avenue G., Zip 70526–2434; tel. 337/788–3330; Mark J. Cullen, Chief Executive Officer, p. B43

Gretna: UNITED MEDICAL REHABILITATION HOSPITALS 3201 Wall Boulevard, Suite B., Zip 70056–7755; tel. 504/433–5551; John E.H. Mills, President & Chief Executive Officer, p. B139

Hammond: NORTH OAKS HEALTH SYSTEM 15790 Paul Vega MD Drive, Zip 70403–1436, Mailing Address: P.O. Box 2668, Zip 70404–2668; tel. 985/345–2700; James E. Cathey, Jr., Chief Executive Officer, p. B100

Lafayette: AMG INTEGRATED HEALTHCARE MANAGEMENT 101 La Rue France, Suite 500, Zip 70508–3144; tel. 337/269–9828; August J. Rantz, III, Founder and Chief Executive Officer, p. B10

LAFAYETTE GENERAL HEALTH 1214 Coolidge Boulevard, Zip 70503–2621; tel. 337/289–7991; David L. Callecod, FACHE, President and CEO, p. B82

LHC GROUP 420 West Pinhook Road, Zip 70503–2131; tel. 337/223–1307; Keith G. Myers, Chairman and Chief Executive Officer, p. B84

Lake Charles: OCEANS HEALTHCARE 2720 Rue de Jardin, Suite 100, Zip 70605–4050; tel. 337/721–1900; Jason Reed, President and Chief Executive Officer, p. B102

New Orleans: LCMC HEALTH 200 Henry Clay Avenue, Zip 70118–5720; tel. 504/899–9511; Greg Feirn, CPA, President and Chief Executive Officer, p. B83

★ OCHSNER HEALTH SYSTEM 1514 Jefferson Highway, Zip 70121–2429; tel. 800/874–8984; Warner L. Thomas, FACHE, President and Chief Executive Officer, p. B102

Shreveport: ALLEGIANCE HEALTH MANAGEMENT 504 Texas Street, Suite 200, Zip 71101–3526; tel. 318/226–8202; Rock Bordelon, President and Chief Executive Officer, p. B8

WILLIS–KNIGHTON HEALTH SYSTEM 2600 Greenwood Road, Zip 71103–3908; tel. 318/212–4000; James K. Elrod, FACHE, President and Chief Executive Officer, p. B153

MAINE

Brewer: ★ EASTERN MAINE HEALTHCARE SYSTEMS 43 Whiting Hill Road, Zip 04412–1005; tel. 207/973–7045; M. Michelle Hood, FACHE, President and Chief Executive Officer, p. B55

Portland: MAINEHEALTH 110 Free Street, Zip 04101–3537; William L. Caron, Jr., President, p. B88

MARYLAND

Baltimore: ★ JOHNS HOPKINS HEALTH SYSTEM 733 North Broadway, BRB 104, Zip 21205–1832; tel. 410/955–5000; Ronald R. Peterson, President, p. B78

★ LIFEBRIDGE HEALTH 2401 West Belvedere Avenue, Zip 21215–5216; tel. 410/601–5134; Neil M. Meltzer, President and Chief Executive Officer, p. B84

★ UNIVERSITY OF MARYLAND MEDICAL SYSTEM 250 West Pratt Street, 24th Floor, Zip 21201–1595; tel. 410/328–8667; Robert A. Chrencik, President and Chief Executive Officer, p. B145

Cheverly: DIMENSIONS HEALTHCARE SYSTEM 3001 Hospital Drive, 3rd Floor, Zip 20785–1189; tel. 301/583–4000; Neil J. Moore, President and Chief Executive Officer, p. B53

Columbia: ENCORE HEALTHCARE 7150 Columbia Gateway Drove, Suite J., Zip 21046–2974; tel. 443/539–2350; Tim Nicholson, Chief Executive Officer, p. B56

★ MEDSTAR HEALTH 5565 Sterrett Place, 5th Floor, Zip 21044–2665; tel. 410/772–6500; Kenneth A. Samet, President and Chief Executive Officer, p. B90

Gaithersburg: ADVENTIST HEALTHCARE 820 West Diamond Avenue, Suite 600, Zip 20878–1419; tel. 301/315–3141; Erik Wangsness, Interim President and Chief Executive Officer, p. B7

Marriottsville: ★ BON SECOURS HEALTH SYSTEM, INC. 1505 Marriottsville Road, Zip 21104–1399; tel. 410/442–5511; Richard Statuto, President and Chief Executive Officer, p. B24

Rockville: U. S. INDIAN HEALTH SERVICE 801 Thompson Avenue, Zip 20852–1627; tel. 301/443–1083; Yvette Roubideaux, M.D., M.P.H., Director, p. B136

Sparks Glencoe: FUNDAMENTAL LONG TERM CARE HOLDINGS, LLC 930 Ridgebrook Road, Zip 21152–9390; tel. 410/773–1000; W. Bradley Bennett, President and Chief Executive Officer, p. B60

MASSACHUSETTS

Boston: MASSACHUSETTS DEPARTMENT OF MENTAL HEALTH 25 Staniford Street, Zip 02114–2575; tel. 617/626–8123; Marcia Fowler, Commissioner, p. B88

MASSACHUSETTS DEPARTMENT OF PUBLIC HEALTH 250 Washington Street, Zip 02108–4619; tel. 617/624–6000; Sandra Akers, Bureau Director, Public Health Hospitals, p. B88

★ PARTNERS HEALTHCARE SYSTEM, INC. 800 Boylston Street, Suite 1150, Zip 02199–8123; tel. 617/278–1004; Gary L. Gottlieb, M.D., President and Chief Executive Officer, p. B105

STEWARD HEALTH CARE SYSTEM, LLC 500 Boylston Street, 5th Floor, Zip 02116–3740; tel. 617/419–4700; Ralph de la Torre, M.D., Chairman and Chief Executive Officer, p. B129

Burlington: LAHEY HEALTH 41 Mall Road, Zip 01805–0001; tel. 781/744–7100; Howard R. Grant, JD, M.D., President and Chief Executive Officer, p. B82

Haverhill: WHITTIER HEALTH NETWORK 25 Railroad Square, Zip 01832–5721; tel. 978/556–5858; Alfred L. Arcidi, M.D., President, p. B153

Hyannis: ★ CAPE COD HEALTHCARE, INC. 27 Park Street, Zip 02601–5230; tel. 508/862–5121; Michael K. Lauf, President and Chief Executive Officer, p. B26

Newton: FIVE STAR QUALITY CARE 400 Centre Street, Zip 02458–2094; tel. 617/796–8387; Bruce J. Mackey, Jr., President and Chief Executive Officer, p. B59

Pittsfield: ★ BERKSHIRE HEALTH SYSTEMS, INC. 725 North Street, Zip 01201–4124; tel. 413/447–2750; David E. Phelps, President and Chief Executive Officer, p. B23

Springfield: ★ BAYSTATE HEALTH, INC. 759 Chestnut Street, Zip 01199–0001; tel. 413/794–0000; Mark A. Keroack, M.D., President and Chief Executive Officer, p. B22

Tewksbury: ★ COVENANT HEALTH SYSTEMS, INC. 100 Ames Pond Drive, Suite 102, Zip 01876–1240; tel. 978/654–6363; David R. Lincoln, FACHE, President and Chief Executive Officer, p. B45

Worcester: ★ UMASS MEMORIAL HEALTH CARE, INC. 1 Biotech Park, Zip 01605–2982; tel. 508/334–0100; Eric Dickson, M.D., President and Chief Executive Officer, p. B138

MICHIGAN

Dearborn: ★ OAKWOOD HEALTHCARE, INC. One Parklane Boulevard, Suite 1000E, Zip 48126–2400; tel. 313/253–6050; Brian M. Connolly, President and Chief Executive Officer, p. B102

Detroit: ★ HENRY FORD HEALTH SYSTEM One Ford Place, Zip 48202–3450; tel. 313/876–8708; Nancy M. Schlichting, Chief Executive Officer, p. B73

Flint: ★ MCLAREN HEALTH CARE CORPORATION G3235 Beecher Road, Suite B., Zip 48532–3650; tel. 810/342–1100; Philip A. Incarnati, President and Chief Executive Officer, p. B90

Grand Rapids: ★ SPECTRUM HEALTH 100 Michigan Street N.E., Zip 49503–2551; tel. 616/391–1774; Richard C. Breon, President and Chief Executive Officer, p. B126

Kalamazoo: ★ BRONSON HEALTHCARE GROUP, INC. 301 John Street, Zip 49007–5295; tel. 269/341–6000; Frank J. Sardone, President and Chief Executive Officer, p. B25

Lansing: ★ SPARROW HEALTH SYSTEM 1215 East Michigan Avenue, Zip 48912–1811; tel. 517/364–1000; Dennis A. Swan, JD, FACHE, President and Chief Executive Officer, p. B126

Livonia: ★ CATHOLIC HEALTH EAST / TRINITY HEALTH 20555 Victor Parkway, Zip 48152–7031; tel. 734/343–1000; Richard J. Gilfillan, M.D., President and Chief Executive Officer, p. B28

Midland: ★ MIDMICHIGAN HEALTH 4000 Wellness Drive, Zip 48670–0001; tel. 989/839–3000; Diane Postler–Slattery, Ph.D., President and Chief Executive Officer, p. B94

Port Huron: ★ BLUE WATER HEALTH SERVICES CORPORATION 1221 Pine Grove Avenue, Zip 48060–3511; tel. 810/989–3717; Thomas D. DeFauw, FACHE, President and Chief Executive Officer, p. B24

Royal Oak: ★ BEAUMONT HEALTH SYSTEM 3711 West 13 Mile Road, Zip 48073–6767; tel. 248/898–5000; Gene Michalski, President and Chief Executive Officer, p. B23

Saint Joseph: LAKELAND HEALTHCARE 1234 Napier Avenue, Zip 49085–2158; tel. 269/983–8300; Loren Hamel, M.D., President and Chief Executive Officer, p. B83

Traverse City: ★ MUNSON HEALTHCARE 1105 Sixth Street, Zip 49684–2386; tel. 231/935–6703; Edwin Ness, President and Chief Executive Officer, p. B96

MINNESOTA

Bloomington: HEALTHPARTNERS 8170 33rd Avenue South, Zip 55425–4516; tel. 952/883–7600; Mary K. Brainerd, President and Chief Executive Officer, p. B69

Duluth: ESSENTIA HEALTH 502 East Second Street, Zip 55805–1913; tel. 218/786–8376; Peter E. Person, M.D., Chief Executive Officer, p. B57

Minneapolis: ★ ALLINA HEALTH 2925 Chicago Avenue, Zip 55407–1321, Mailing Address: P.O. Box 43, Zip 55440–0043; tel. 612/262–5000; Ken Paulus, President and Chief Executive Officer, p. B9

★ FAIRVIEW HEALTH SERVICES 2450 Riverside Avenue, Zip 55454–1400; tel. 612/672–6141; Rulon F. Stacey, Ph.D., FACHE, President and Chief Executive Officer, p. B58

Robbinsdale: ★ NORTH MEMORIAL HEALTH CARE 3300 Oakdale Avenue North, Zip 55422–2926; tel. 763/520–5200; Loren L. Taylor, Chief Executive Officer, p. B100

Rochester: ★ MAYO CLINIC 200 First Street S.W., Zip 55905–0002; tel. 507/284–2511; John Noseworthy, M.D., President and Chief Executive Officer, p. B89

Saint Cloud: ★ CENTRACARE HEALTH 1406 Sixth Avenue North, Zip 56303–1900; tel. 320/251–2700; Terence Pladson, M.D., President and Chief Executive Officer, p. B34

Saint Paul: ★ HEALTHEAST CARE SYSTEM 559 Capitol Boulevard, 6–South, Zip 55103–0000; tel. 651/232–2300; Kathryn G. Correia, President and Chief Executive Officer, p. B69

MINNESOTA DEPARTMENT OF HUMAN SERVICES 540 Cedar Street, Zip 55101–2208, Mailing Address: P.O. Box 64998, Zip 55164–0998; tel. 651/431–3212; Anne Barry, Deputy Commissioner, p. B94

MISSISSIPPI

Jackson: ★ MISSISSIPPI BAPTIST HEALTH SYSTEM 1225 North State Street, Zip 39202–2064; tel. 601/968–1000; Chris Anderson, Chief Executive Officer, p. B95

MISSISSIPPI STATE DEPARTMENT OF MENTAL HEALTH 1101 Robert East Lee Building, 239 North Lamar Street, Zip 39201–1101; tel. 601/359–1288; Edwin C. LeGrand, III, Executive Director, p. B95

UNIVERSITY HOSPITALS AND HEALTH SYSTEM 2500 North State Street, Zip 39216–4500; tel. 601/984–1000; James Keeton, M.D., Vice Chancellor for Health Affairs, p. B144

Magee: ★ PIONEER HEALTH SERVICES 110 Pioneer Way, Zip 39111–5501, Mailing Address: P.O. Box 1100, Zip 39111–1100; tel. 601/849–6440; Joseph S. McNulty, III, President and Chief Executive Officer, p. B106

Mccomb: SOUTHWEST HEALTH SYSTEMS 215 Marion Avenue, Zip 39648–2705, Mailing Address: P.O. Box 1307, Zip 39649–1307; tel. 601/249–5500; Norman M. Price, FACHE, Chief Executive Officer and Administrator, p. B126

Meridian: ★ RUSH HEALTH SYSTEMS 1314 19th Avenue, Zip 39301–4116; tel. 601/483–0011; Wallace Strickland, President and Chief Executive Officer, p. B116

Tupelo: ★ NORTH MISSISSIPPI HEALTH SERVICES, INC. 830 South Gloster Street, Zip 38801–4996; tel. 662/377–3136; M. Shane Spees, President and Chief Executive Officer, p. B100

MISSOURI

Cape Girardeau: LANDMARK HOSPITALS 3255 Independence Street, Zip 63701–4914; tel. 573/335–1091; William K. Kapp, III, M.D., President and Chief Executive Officer, p. B83

★ SOUTHEASTHEALTH 1701 Lacey Street, Zip 63701–5230; tel. 573/334–4822; Wayne Smith, President and Chief Executive Officer, p. B125

Chesterfield: ★ MERCY HEALTH 14528 South Outer 40, Suite 100, Zip 63017–5743; tel. 314/579–6100; Lynn Britton, President and Chief Executive Officer, p. B92

Columbia: ★ UNIVERSITY OF MISSOURI HEALTH CARE One Hospital Drive, DC 031, Zip 65212–0001; tel. 573/884–8738; Mitchell L. Wasden, Ed.D., Chief Executive Officer and Chief Operating Officer, p. B146

Joplin: ★ FREEMAN HEALTH SYSTEM 1102 West 32nd Street, Zip 64804–3503; tel. 417/347–1111; Paula F. Baker, President and Chief Executive Officer, p. B60

Kansas City: RURAL COMMUNITY HOSPITALS OF AMERICA 1100 Main Street, Suite 2350, Zip 64105–5186; tel. 816/474–7800; Lawrence J. Arthur, President, p. B115

★ SAINT LUKE'S HEALTH SYSTEM 901 East 104th Street, Mailstop 900N, Zip 64131–4517, Mailing Address: 901 East 104th Street, Zip 64131–4517; tel. 816/932–2000; Melinda Estes, M.D., President and Chief Executive Officer, p. B117

★ TRUMAN MEDICAL CENTERS 2301 Holmes Street, Zip 64108–2677; tel. 816/404–1000; Charlie Shields, President and Chief Executive Officer, p. B136

Saint Louis: ★ ASCENSION HEALTH 101 South Hanley Road, Suite 450, Zip 63105–3406; tel. 314/733–8000; Robert J. Henkel, FACHE, President and Chief Executive Officer, p. B12

★ BJC HEALTHCARE 4901 Forest Park Avenue, Suite 1200, Zip 63108–1402; tel. 314/747–9322; Steven H. Lipstein, President and Chief Executive Officer, p. B23

★ SSM HEALTH 10101 Woodfield Lane, Zip 63132–2937; tel. 314/994–7800; William P. Thompson, President and Chief Executive Officer, p. B127

Springfield: COXHEALTH 1423 North Jefferson Avenue, Zip 65802–1988; tel. 417/269–3108; Steven D. Edwards, President and Chief Executive Officer, p. B45

MONTANA

Great Falls: BENEFIS HEALTH SYSTEM 1101 26th Street South, Zip 59405–5161; tel. 406/455–5000; John H. Goodnow, Chief Executive Officer, p. B23

NEBRASKA

Lincoln: ★ BRYAN HEALTH 1600 South 48th Street, Zip 68506–1283; tel. 402/481–1111; Kimberly A. Russel, FACHE, President and Chief Executive Officer, p. B25

Norfolk: FAITH REGIONAL HEALTH SERVICES 2700 West Norfolk Avenue, Zip 68701–4438, Mailing Address: P.O. Box 869, Zip 68702–0869; tel. 402/644–7201; Mark D. Klosterman, FACHE, President and Chief Executive Officer, p. B58

Omaha: ★ NEBRASKA METHODIST HEALTH SYSTEM, INC. 8511 West Dodge Road, Zip 68114–3403; tel. 402/354–5411; John M. Fraser, President and Chief Executive Officer, p. B97

NEVADA

Reno: ★ RENOWN HEALTH 1155 Mill Street, Zip 89502–1576; tel. 775/982–4100; Anthony D. Slonim, M.D., Dr.PH, President and Chief Executive Officer, p. B114

NEW HAMPSHIRE

Laconia: ★ LRGHEALTHCARE 80 Highland Street, Zip 03246–3298; tel. 603/524–3211; Charles K. Van Sluyter, Interim President and CEO, p. B88

Portsmouth: SPECIALTY HOSPITALS OF AMERICA, LLC 155 Fleet Street, Zip 03801–4050; tel. 603/570–4888; Eric F. Rieseberg, President, p. B126

NEW JERSEY

Edison: ★ JFK HEALTH SYSTEM 80 James Street, 2nd Floor, Zip 08820–3938; tel. 732/632–1503; Raymond F. Fredericks, President and Chief Executive Officer, p. B78

Egg Harbor Township: ★ ATLANTICARE 2500 English Creek Avenue, Building 500, Suite 501, Zip 08234; tel. 609/407–2309; David P. Tilton, President and Chief Executive Officer, p. B15

Hackensack: ★ HACKENSACK UNIVERSITY HEALTH NETWORK 30 Prospect Avenue, Zip 07601–1914; tel. 201/996–2000; Robert C. Garrett, FACHE, President and Chief Executive Officer, p. B63

Jersey City: CAREPOINT HEALTH 176 Palisade Avenue, Zip 07306–1121; tel. 877/791–7000; Daniel A. Kane, Board Chairman, p. B27

Marlton: ★ VIRTUA HEALTH 50 Lake Center Executive Drive, Suite 401, Zip 08053; tel. 856/355–0010; Richard P. Miller, Chief Executive Officer, p. B150

Morristown: ★ ATLANTIC HEALTH SYSTEM 475 South Street, Zip 07962, Mailing Address: P.O. Box 1905, Zip 07962–1905; tel. 973/660–3270; Joseph A. Trunfio, Ph.D., President and Chief Executive Officer, p. B15

Mullica Hill: ★ INSPIRA HEALTH NETWORK 165 Bridgeton Pike, Zip 08062; tel. 856/641–8000; John A. DiAngelo, President and Chief Executive Officer, p. B76

Neptune: ★ MERIDIAN HEALTH 1350 Campus Parkway, Zip 07753–6821; tel. 732/751–7510; John K. Lloyd, President and Chief Executive Officer, p. B93

New Brunswick: ROBERT WOOD JOHNSON HEALTH SYSTEM & NETWORK 1 Robert Wood Johnson Place, Zip 08901–1928; tel. 732/828–3000; Stephen K. Jones, President and Chief Executive Officer, p. B115

Trenton: ★ CAPITAL HEALTH 750 Brunswick Avenue, Zip 08638–4143; tel. 609/394–6000; Al Maghazehe, Ph.D., FACHE, Chief Executive Officer, p. B27

DIVISION OF MENTAL HEALTH AND ADDICTION SERVICES, DEPARTMENT OF HUMAN SERVICES, STATE OF NEW JERSEY 222 South Warren Street, Zip 08608–2306, Mailing Address: P.O. Box 700, Zip 08625–0700; tel. 609/777–0702; Lynn Kovich, Assistant Commissioner, p. B53

West Orange: ★ BARNABAS HEALTH 95 Old Short Hills Road, Zip 07052–1008; tel. 973/322–4000; Barry Ostrowsky, President and Chief Executive Officer, p. B21

NEW MEXICO

Albuquerque: ERNEST HEALTH, INC. 7770 Jefferson Street N.E., Suite 320, Zip 87109–4386; tel. 505/856–5300; Darby Brockette, Chief Executive Officer, p. B57

★ PRESBYTERIAN HEALTHCARE SERVICES 2501 Buena Vista Drive, S.E., Zip 87106–4260, Mailing Address: P.O. Box 26666, Zip 87125–6666; tel. 505/841–1234; James H. Hinton, President and Chief Executive Officer, p. B107

UNIVERSITY OF NEW MEXICO HOSPITALS 915 Camino De Salud, Zip 87131–0001; tel. 505/272–5849; Stephen W. McKernan, Chief Executive Officer, p. B146

NEW YORK

Albany: NEW YORK STATE OFFICE OF MENTAL HEALTH 44 Holland Avenue, Zip 12208–3411; tel. 518/474–7056; Kristin M. Woodlock, R.N., Acting Commissioner, p. B99

Binghamton: UNITED HEALTH SERVICES 10–42 Mitchell Avenue, Zip 13903–1617; tel. 607/762–2200; Matthew J. Salanger, President and Chief Executive Officer, p. B138

Bronx: MONTEFIORE HEALTH SYSTEM 111 East 210th Street, Zip 10467–2490; tel. 718/920–4321; Steven M. Safyer, M.D., President and CEO, p. B95

Buffalo: ★ CATHOLIC HEALTH SYSTEM 2121 Main Street, Suite 300, Zip 14214–2673; tel. 716/862–2410; Joseph D. McDonald, President and Chief Executive Officer, p. B33

Cooperstown: ★ BASSETT HEALTHCARE NETWORK 1 Atwell Road, Zip 13326–1301; tel. 607/547–3456; Vance Brown, M.D., President and Chief Executive Officer, p. B21

Elmira: ★ ARNOT HEALTH 600 Roe Avenue, Zip 14905–1629; tel. 607/737–4100; Robert K. Lambert, M.D., FACHE, President and Chief Executive Officer, p. B12

Geneva: FINGER LAKES HEALTH 196 North Street, Zip 14456–1651; tel. 315/787–4000; Jose Acevedo, M.D., President and Chief Executive Officer, p. B58

Great Neck: ★ NORTH SHORE–LONG ISLAND JEWISH HEALTH SYSTEM 145 Community Drive, Zip 11021–5502; tel. 516/465–8100; Michael J. Dowling, President and Chief Executive Officer, p. B100

Kingston: HEALTHALLIANCE OF THE HUDSON VALLEY 396 Broadway, Zip 12401–4626; tel. 845/331–3131; David Scarpino, President and Chief Executive Officer, p. B68

LaGrangeville: ★ HEALTH QUEST SYSTEMS, INC. 1351 Route 55, Zip 12540–5108; tel. 845/475–9500; Luke McGuinness, President and CEO, p. B68

Middletown: GREATER HUDSON VALLEY HEALTH SYSTEM 60 Prospect Avenue, Zip 10940–4133; tel. 845/568–6050; Scott Batulis, President and Chief Executive Officer, p. B62

New York: MOUNT SINAI HEALTH SYSTEM One Gustave L. Levy Place, Zip 10029; Kenneth L. Davis, M.D., President and Chief Executive, p. B96

★ NEW YORK CITY HEALTH AND HOSPITALS CORPORATION 125 Worth Street, Room 514, Zip 10013–4006; tel. 212/788–3321; Ramanathan Raju, M.D., President, p. B98

NEW YORK PRESBYTERIAN HEALTHCARE SYSTEM 525 East 68th Street, Box 182, Zip 10065; tel. 212/746–3745; Steven J. Corwin, M.D., Chief Executive Officer, p. B98

Olean: UPPER ALLEGHENY HEALTH SYSTEM 130 South Union Street, Suite 300, Zip 14760–3676; tel. 716/375–6190; Timothy J. Finan, FACHE, President and Chief Executive Officer, p. B147

Potsdam: ST. LAWRENCE HEALTH SYSTEM 50 Leroy Street, Zip 13676–1799; tel. 315/265–3300; David B. Acker, FACHE, President and CEO, p. B128

Rochester: ★ ROCHESTER REGIONAL HEALTH SYSTEM 1425 Portland Avenue, 5th Floor, Zip 14621–3001; tel. 585/922–4000; Mark C. Clement, President and Chief Executive Officer, p. B115

★ UNIVERSITY OF ROCHESTER MEDICAL CENTER 601 Elmwood Avenue, Zip 14642–0002; tel. 585/275–2100; Steven I. Goldstein, General Director and Chief Executive Officer, p. B146

Rockville Centre: CATHOLIC HEALTH SERVICES OF LONG ISLAND 992 North Village Avenue, 1st Floor, Zip 11570–1002; tel. 516/705–3700; Alan D. Guerci, M.D., President and Chief Executive Officer, p. B33

Syracuse: SISTERS OF SAINT FRANCIS 2500 Grant Boulevard, Zip 13208–1782; tel. 315/634–7000; Sister Geraldine Ching, Assistant General Minister, p. B125

NORTH CAROLINA

Asheville: ★ MISSION HEALTH SYSTEM 509 Biltmore Avenue, Zip 28801–4601; tel. 828/213–1111; Ronald A. Paulus, M.D., President and Chief Executive Officer, p. B95

Boone: ★ APPALACHIAN REGIONAL HEALTHCARE SYSTEM 336 Deerfield Road, Zip 28607–5008, Mailing Address: P.O. Box 2600, Zip 28607–2600; tel. 828/262–4100; Richard G. Sparks, President and Chief Executive Officer, p. B11

Chapel Hill: ★ UNC HEALTH CARE 101 Manning Drive, Zip 27514–4220; tel. 919/966–4131; William L. Roper, M.D., M.P.H., Chief Executive Officer, p. B138

Charlotte: ★ ACUITYHEALTHCARE, LP 10200 Mallard Creek Road, Suite 300, Zip 28262–9705; tel. 704/887–7280; Edwin H. Cooper, Jr., MS, President and Chief Executive Officer, p. B5

★ CAROLINAS HEALTHCARE SYSTEM 1000 Blythe Boulevard, Zip 28203–5871, Mailing Address: P.O. Box 32861, Zip 28232–2861; tel. 704/355–2000; Michael C. Tarwater, Chief Executive Officer, p. B27

Durham: ★ DUKE UNIVERSITY HEALTH SYSTEM 201 Trent Drive, Zip 27710–3037, Mailing Address: P.O. Box 3701, Zip 27710–3701; tel. 919/684–2255; William J. Fulkerson, M.D., Interim President and Chief Executive Officer, p. B54

Fayetteville: CAPE FEAR VALLEY HEALTH SYSTEM 1638 Owen Drive, Zip 28304–3424, Mailing Address: P.O. Box 2000, Zip 28302–2000; tel. 910/615–4000; Michael Nagowski, President and Chief Executive Officer, p. B26

Greensboro: CONE HEALTH 1200 North Elm Street, Zip 27401–1004; tel. 336/832–7000; R. Timothy Rice, Chief Executive Officer, p. B43

Greenville: ★ VIDANT HEALTH 2100 Stantonsburg Road, Zip 27834–2818, Mailing Address: P.O. Box 6028, Zip 27835–6028; tel. 252/847–4100; David C. Herman, M.D., President and Chief Executive Officer, p. B150

Pinehurst: ★ FIRSTHEALTH OF THE CAROLINAS 155 Memorial Drive, Zip 28374–8710, Mailing Address: P.O. Box 3000, Zip 28374–3000; tel. 910/715–1000; David J. Kilarski, Chief Executive Officer, p. B58

Raleigh: ★ WAKEMED HEALTH & HOSPITALS 3000 New Bern Avenue, Zip 27610–1231; tel. 919/350–8000; Donald R. Gintzig, President and Chief Executive Officer, p. B151

Wilmington: ★ NEW HANOVER REGIONAL MEDICAL CENTER 2131 South 17th Street, Zip 28401–7407; tel. 910/343–7040; John K. Barto, Jr., President and Chief Executive Officer, p. B98

Winston Salem: ★ NOVANT HEALTH 2085 Frontis Plaza Boulevard, Zip 27103–5614; tel. 336/718–5600; Carl S. Armato, President and Chief Executive Officer, p. B101

Winston–Salem: ★ WAKE FOREST BAPTIST HEALTH Medical Center Boulevard, Zip 27157; tel. 336/716–2011; John D. McConnell, M.D., Chief Executive Officer, p. B151

NORTH DAKOTA

Bismarck: BENEDICTINE SISTERS OF THE ANNUNCIATION 7520 University Drive, Zip 58504–9653; tel. 701/255–1520; Sister Nancy Miller, Prioress, p. B23

Fargo: SISTERS OF MARY OF THE PRESENTATION HEALTH SYSTEM 1202 Page Drive S.W., Zip 58103–2340, Mailing Address: P.O. Box 10007, Zip 58106–0007; tel. 701/237–9290; Aaron K. Alton, President and Chief Executive Officer, p. B125

OHIO

Akron: ★ AKRON GENERAL HEALTH SYSTEM 1 Akron General Avenue, Zip 44307–2433; tel. 330/344–6000; Thomas L. Stover, M.D., President and Chief Executive Officer, p. B8

SUMMA HEALTH SYSTEM 525 East Market Street, Zip 44304–1619; tel. 330/375–3000; Thomas J. Strauss, President and Chief Executive Officer, p. B129

Canton: AULTMAN HEALTH FOUNDATION 2600 Sixth Street S.W., Zip 44710–1702; tel. 330/363–6192; Edward J. Roth, III, President and Chief Executive Officer, p. B16

Chillicothe: ADENA HEALTH SYSTEM 272 Hospital Road, Zip 45601–9031; tel. 740/779–7500; Mark H. Shuter, President and Chief Executive Officer, p. B5

Cincinnati: ★ MERCY HEALTH 615 Elsinore Place, Zip 45202–1459; tel. 513/639–2800; Michael D. Connelly, President and Chief Executive Officer, p. B92

★ UC HEALTH 3200 Burnet Avenue, Zip 45229–3019; tel. 513/585–6000; Richard P. Lofgren, M.D., M.P.H., President and CEO, p. B137

Cleveland: ★ CLEVELAND CLINIC HEALTH SYSTEM 9500 Euclid, Zip 44195–5108; tel. 216/444–2200; Delos Cosgrove, M.D., President and Chief Executive Officer, p. B35

SISTERS OF CHARITY HEALTH SYSTEM 2475 East 22nd Street, Zip 44115–3221; tel. 216/363–2797; Terrence Kessler, Interim President and Chief Executive Officer, p. B124

★ UNIVERSITY HOSPITALS 11100 Euclid Avenue, Zip 44106–5000; tel. 216/844–1000; Thomas F. Zenty, III, President and Chief Executive Officer, p. B144

Columbus: OHIO DEPARTMENT OF MENTAL HEALTH 30 East Broad Street, 8th Floor, Zip 43215–3430; tel. 614/466–2297; Tracy Plouck, Director, p. B103

★ OHIO STATE UNIVERSITY HEALTH SYSTEM 370 West Ninth Avenue, Zip 43210–1238; tel. 614/247–5555; Peter E. Geier, Chief Executive Officer, p. B103

★ OHIOHEALTH 180 East Broad Street, Zip 43215–3707; tel. 614/544–4455; David P. Blom, President and Chief Executive Officer, p. B103

Dayton: ★ KETTERING HEALTH NETWORK 3965 Southern Boulevard, Zip 45429–1229; tel. 937/395–8150; Fred M. Manchur, Chief Executive Officer, p. B79

Findlay: ★ BLANCHARD VALLEY HEALTH SYSTEM 1900 South Main Street, Zip 45840–1214; tel. 419/423–4500; Scott C. Malaney, President and Chief Executive Officer, p. B24

Galion: ★ AVITA HEALTH SYSTEM 269 Portland Way South, Zip 44833–2399; tel. 419/468–4841; Jerome Morasko, President and Chief Executive Officer, p. B18

Toledo: ★ PROMEDICA HEALTH SYSTEM 1801 Richards Road, Zip 43607–1037; tel. 419/469–3800; Randall D. Oostra, FACHE, President and Chief Executive Officer, p. B109

★ SYLVANIA FRANCISCAN HEALTH 3231 Central Park West, Suite 106, Zip 43617–3009; tel. 419/882–8373; James W. Pope, FACHE, President and Chief Executive Officer, p. B131

OKLAHOMA

Oklahoma City: FOUNDATION SURGICAL HOSPITAL AFFILIATES 14000 North Portland Avenue, Suite 204, Zip 73134–4002; tel. 405/608–1700; Thomas A. Michaud, Chief Executive Officer, p. B59

★ INTEGRIS HEALTH 3366 N.W. Expressway, Suite 800, Zip 73112–9756; tel. 405/949–6066; Bruce Lawrence, President and Chief Executive Officer, p. B76

OKLAHOMA DEPARTMENT OF MENTAL HEALTH AND SUBSTANCE ABUSE SERVICES 1200 N.E. 13th Street, Zip 73117–1022, Mailing Address: P.O. Box 53277, Zip 73152–3277; tel. 405/522–3908; Terri White, Commissioner, p. B104

SOUTHERN PLAINS MEDICAL GROUP 4323 N.W. 63rd Street Suite 232, Zip 73116–1546; tel. 405/753–6770; Margie Homer, President, p. B126

Shawnee: PREFERRED MANAGEMENT CORPORATION 120 West MacArthur, Suite 121, Zip 74804–2005; tel. 405/878–0202; Donald Freeman, President and Chief Executive Officer, p. B107

Tulsa: ★ SAINT FRANCIS HEALTH SYSTEM 6161 South Yale Avenue, Zip 74136–1902; tel. 918/494–8454; Jake Henry, Jr., President and Chief Executive Officer, p. B116

OREGON

Bend: ★ ST. CHARLES HEALTH SYSTEM, INC. 2500 N.E. Neff Road, Zip 97701–6015; tel. 541/382–4321; James A. Diegel, FACHE, President and Chief Executive Officer, p. B127

Corvallis: ★ SAMARITAN HEALTH SERVICES 3600 N.W. Samaritan Drive, Zip 97330–3737, Mailing Address: P.O. Box 1068, Zip 97339–1068; tel. 541/768–5001; Larry A. Mullins, FACHE, President and Chief Executive Officer, p. B117

Medford: ★ ASANTE HEALTH SYSTEM 2650 Siskiyou Boulevard, Suite 200, Zip 97504–8170; tel. 541/789–4100; Roy G. Vinyard, FACHE, President and Chief Executive Officer, p. B12

Portland: ★ LEGACY HEALTH 1919 N.W. Lovejoy Street, Zip 97209–1503; tel. 503/415–5600; George J. Brown, M.D., President and Chief Executive Officer, p. B83

Salem: SALEM HEALTH 890 Oak Street Building B. POB 14001, Zip 97309–5014; tel. 503/561–5200; Norman F. Gruber, President and Chief Executive Officer, p. B117

PENNSYLVANIA

Abington: ★ ABINGTON HEALTH 1200 Old York Road, Zip 19001; tel. 215/481–2000; Laurence M. Merlis, President and Chief Executive Officer, p. B4

Allentown: GOOD SHEPHERD REHABILITATION NETWORK 850 South Fifth Street, Zip 18103–3308; tel. 610/776–3100; John Kristel, President and Chief Executive Officer, p. B61

★ LEHIGH VALLEY HEALTH NETWORK 1200 South Cedar Crest Boulevard, Zip 18103–6202, Mailing Address: P.O. Box 689, Zip 18105–1556; tel. 610/402–8000; Brian Nester, D.O., Interim President and Chief Executive Officer, p. B83

Beaver: HERITAGE VALLEY HEALTH SYSTEM 1000 Dutch Ridge Road, Zip 15009–9727; tel. 724/773–2024; Norman F. Mitry, President and Chief Executive Officer, p. B73

Bethlehem: ST. LUKE'S UNIVERSITY HEALTH NETWORK 801 Ostrum Street, Zip 18015–1000; tel. 610/954–4000; Richard A. Anderson, President and Chief Executive Officer, p. B128

Chambersburg: ★ SUMMIT HEALTH 112 North Seventh Street, Zip 17201–1720; tel. 717/267–7138; Patrick W. O'Donnell, CPA, President and Chief Executive Officer, p. B130

Danville: ★ GEISINGER HEALTH SYSTEM 100 North Academy Avenue, Zip 17822–9800; tel. 570/271–6211; Glenn Steele, Jr., M.D., Ph.D., President and Chief Executive Officer, p. B60

Enola: ★ POST ACUTE MEDICAL, LLC 1828 Good Hope Road, Suite 102, Zip 17025–1233; tel. 717/731–9660; Anthony F. Misitano, President and Chief Executive Officer, p. B107

Greensburg: EXCELA HEALTH 134 Industrial Park Road, Zip 15601–7328; tel. 724/832–5050; Robert Rogalski, Chief Executive Officer, p. B58

King of Prussia: UNIVERSAL HEALTH SERVICES, INC. 367 South Gulph Road, Zip 19406–3121, Mailing Address: P.O. Box 61558, Zip 19406–0958; tel. 610/768–3300; Alan B. Miller, Chairman and Chief Executive Officer, p. B140

Lehighton: BLUE MOUNTAIN HEALTH SYSTEM 211 North 12th Street, Zip 18235–1138; tel. 610/377–1300; Andrew E. Harris, President and Chief Executive Officer, p. B24

Mechanicsburg: ★ SELECT MEDICAL CORPORATION 4714 Gettysburg Road, Zip 17055–4325; tel. 717/972–1100; David S. Chernow, President and Chief Executive Officer, p. B119

★ VIBRA HEALTHCARE 4550 Lena Drive, Suite 225, Zip 17055–4920; tel. 717/591–5700; Brad Hollinger, Chairman and Chief Executive Officer, p. B148

Philadelphia: EINSTEIN HEALTHCARE NETWORK 5501 Old York Road, Zip 19141–3098; tel. 215/456–7890; Barry R. Freedman, President and Chief Executive Officer, p. B56

★ TEMPLE UNIVERSITY HEALTH SYSTEM 3509 North Broad Street, 9th Floor, Zip 19140–4105; tel. 215/707–0900; Larry Kaiser, M.D., President and Chief Executive Officer, p. B132

★ UNIVERSITY OF PENNSYLVANIA HEALTH SYSTEM 3400 Civic Center Bouelvard, Zip 19104–5127; tel. 215/662–2203; Ralph W. Muller, President and Chief Executive Officer, p. B146

Pittsburgh: ★ ALLEGHENY HEALTH NETWORK 30 Isabella Street, Suite 300, Zip 15212–5862; tel. 412/330–2403; John W. Paul, President and Chief Executive Officer, p. B8

UPMC 600 Grant Street, U.S. Steel Tower, Suite 6262, Zip 15219–2702; tel. 412/647–8762; Jeffrey A. Romoff, President and Chief Executive Officer, p. B147

Pottsville: SCHUYLKILL HEALTH SYSTEM 420 South Jackson Street, Zip 17901–3625; tel. 570/621–5000; Darnell F. Furer, MS, R.N., Acting Administrator, p. B119

Radnor: ★ JEFFERSON HEALTH SYSTEM 259 Radnor–Chester Road, Suite 290, Zip 19087–5288; tel. 610/225–6200; Kirk E. Gorman, Interim President and Chief Executive Officer, p. B77

Sayre: ★ GUTHRIE HEALTHCARE SYSTEM Guthrie Square, Zip 18840; tel. 570/887–4312; Joseph A. Scopelliti, M.D., President and Chief Executive Officer, p. B62

Springfield: ★ CROZER–KEYSTONE HEALTH SYSTEM 100 West Sproul Road, Zip 19064–2033; tel. 610/338–8205; Joan K. Richards, President and Chief Executive Officer, p. B46

Villanova: DEVEREUX 444 Devereux Drive, Zip 19085–1932, Mailing Address: P.O. Box 638, Zip 19085–0638; tel. 610/520–3000; Robert Q. Kreider, President and Chief Executive Officer, p. B52

Williamsport: ★ SUSQUEHANNA HEALTH SYSTEM 700 High Street, Zip 17701–3100; tel. 570/321–1000; Steven P. Johnson, FACHE, President and Chief Executive Officer, p. B130

York: ★ WELLSPAN HEALTH 45 Monument Road, Suite 200, Zip 17403–5071; tel. 717/851–2121; Kevin H. Mosser, M.D., President and Chief Executive Officer, p. B151

PUERTO RICO

San Juan: ★ PUERTO RICO DEPARTMENT OF HEALTH Building A – Medical Center, Zip 00936, Mailing Address: Call Box 70184, Zip 00936; tel. 787/765–2929; Francisco M. Joglar, M.D., Secretary of Health, p. B111

RHODE ISLAND

Providence: ★ CARE NEW ENGLAND HEALTH SYSTEM 45 Willard Avenue, Zip 02905–3218; tel. 401/453–7900; Dennis D. Keefe, President and Chief Executive Officer, p. B27

CHARTERCARE HEALTH PARTNERS 825 Chalkstone Avenue, Zip 02908–4728; tel. 410/456–2001; Kenneth H. Belcher, Chief Executive Officer, p. B34

LIFESPAN CORPORATION 167 Point Street, Zip 02903–4771; tel. 401/444–3500; Timothy J. Babineau, M.D., President and Chief Executive Officer, p. B87

SOUTH CAROLINA

Anderson: ANMED HEALTH 800 North Fant Street, Zip 29621–5793; tel. 864/512–1000; John A. Miller, Jr., FACHE, Chief Executive Officer, p. B10

Columbia: ★ PALMETTO HEALTH 1301 Taylor Street, Suite 9–A, Zip 29201–2942, Mailing Address: P.O. Box 2266, Zip 29202–2266; tel. 803/296–2100; Charles D. Beaman, Jr., Chief Executive Officer, p. B105

Florence: MCLEOD HEALTH 555 East Cheves Street, Zip 29506–2617, Mailing Address: P.O. Box 100551, Zip 29502–0551; tel. 843/777–2000; Robert L. Colones, President and Chief Executive Officer, p. B90

Georgetown: ★ GEORGETOWN HOSPITAL SYSTEM 606 Black River Road, Zip 29440–3304, Mailing Address: P.O. Box 421718, Zip 29442–4203; tel. 843/527–7000; Bruce P. Bailey, President and Chief Executive Officer, p. B61

Greenville: ★ GREENVILLE HEALTH SYSTEM 701 Grove Road, Zip 29605–5611; tel. 864/455–7000; Michael C. Riordan, President and Chief Executive Officer, p. B62

Spartanburg: ★ SPARTANBURG REGIONAL HEALTHCARE SYSTEM 101 East Wood Street, Zip 29303–3040; tel. 864/560–6000; Bruce Holstien, President and Chief Executive Officer, p. B126

SOUTH DAKOTA

Rapid City: ★ REGIONAL HEALTH 353 Fairmont Boulevard, Zip 57701–7375, Mailing Address: P.O. Box 6000, Zip 57709–6000; tel. 605/719–1000; Charles E. Hart, M.D., MS, President and Chief Executive Officer, p. B113

Sioux Falls: ★ AVERA HEALTH 3900 West Avera Drive, Suite 301, Zip 57108–5721; tel. 605/322–4700; John T. Porter, President and Chief Executive Officer, p. B17

★ SANFORD HEALTH 2301 East 60th Street North, Zip 57104–0569, Mailing Address: PO Box 5039, Zip 57117–5039; tel. 605/333–1000; Kelby K. Krabbenhoft, President and Chief Executive Officer, p. B118

TENNESSEE

Brentwood: CENTERRE HEALTHCARE 5250 Virginia Way, Suite 240, Zip 37027–7576; tel. 615/846–9508; Patrick A. Foster, President and Chief Executive Officer, p. B33

DUKE LIFEPOINT HEALTHCARE 103 Powell Court, Zip 37027–5079; tel. 615/372–8540; Jeffrey G. Seraphine, FACHE, Division President, p. B54

★ HEALTHTECH MANAGEMENT SERVICES 5110 Maryland Way Suite 200, Zip 37027–2307; tel. 615/309–6053; Derek Morkel, Chief Executive Officer, p. B72

★ LIFEPOINT HOSPITALS, INC. 330 Seven Springs Way, Zip 37027–4536; tel. 615/920–7000; William F. Carpenter, III, Chairman and Chief Executive Officer, p. B85

POLARIS HOSPITAL COMPANY 10 Cadillac Drive, Suite 470, Zip 37027–1045; tel. 615/577–1111; Kevin D. Lee, Director and Chief Executive Officer, p. B107

★ QHR 105 Continental Place, Zip 37027–1052; tel. 800/233–1470; Mickey Bilbrey, President and Chief Executive Officer, p. B111

REGIONALCARE HOSPITAL PARTNERS 103 Continental Place, Suite 200, Zip 37027–1042; tel. 615/844–9800; Kent H. Wallace, Chief Executive Officer, p. B114

Chattanooga: ERLANGER HEALTH SYSTEM 975 East Third Street, Zip 37403–2147; tel. 423/778–7000; Kevin M. Spiegel, FACHE, President and Chief Executive Officer, p. B56

Columbia: ★ MAURY REGIONAL HEALTH SYSTEM 1224 Trotwood Avenue, Zip 38401–4802; tel. 931/381–1111; H. Alan Watson, FACHE, Chief Executive Officer, p. B89

Franklin: ACADIA HEALTHCARE COMPANY, INC. 830 Crescent Centre Drive, Suite 610, Zip 37067–7323; tel. 615/861–6000; Joey Jacobs, Chairman and Chief Executive Officer, p. B4

CAPELLA HEALTHCARE 501 Corporate Centre Drive, Suite 200, Zip 37067–2662; tel. 615/764–3000; Michael Wiechart, President and Chief Executive Officer, p. B26

★ COMMUNITY HEALTH SYSTEMS, INC. 4000 Meridian Boulevard, Zip 37067–6325, Mailing Address: P.O. Box 689020, Zip 37068–9020; tel. 615/465–7000; Wayne T. Smith, Chairman, President and Chief Executive Officer, p. B37

IASIS HEALTHCARE 117 Seaboard Lane, Building E., Zip 37067–2855; tel. 615/844–2747; Carl Whitmer, President and Chief Executive Officer, p. B74

Jackson: ★ WEST TENNESSEE HEALTHCARE 620 Skyline Drive, Zip 38301–3923; tel. 731/541–5000; Bobby Arnold, President and Chief Executive Officer, p. B152

Johnson City: MOUNTAIN STATES HEALTH ALLIANCE 400 North State of Franklin Road, Zip 37604–6035; tel. 423/302–3423; Alan M. Levine, President and Chief Executive Officer, p. B96

Kingsport: ★ WELLMONT HEALTH SYSTEM 1905 American Way, Zip 37660–5882; tel. 423/230–8200; , p. B151

Knoxville: ★ COVENANT HEALTH 100 Fort Sanders West Boulevard, Zip 37922–3353; tel. 865/531–5555; Anthony Spezia, President and Chief Executive Officer, p. B44

Memphis: ★ BAPTIST MEMORIAL HEALTH CARE CORPORATION 350 North Humphreys Boulevard, Zip 38120–2177; tel. 901/227–5117; Janice Hill, President and Chief Executive Officer, p. B21

METHODIST LE BONHEUR HEALTHCARE 1211 Union Avenue, Suite 700, Zip 38104–6600; tel. 901/516–0791; Gary S. Shorb, President and Chief Executive Officer, p. B94

STRATEGIC BEHAVIORAL HEALTH, LLC 8295 Tournament Drive, Suite 201, Zip 38125–8913; tel. 901/969–3100; Jim Shaheen, President, p. B129

Nashville: ★ ARDENT HEALTH SERVICES 1 Burton Hills Boulevard, Suite 250, Zip 37215–6195; tel. 615/296–3000; David T. Vandewater, President and Chief Executive Officer, p. B11

HAVEN BEHAVIORAL HEALTHCARE 652 West Iris Drive, Zip 37204–3191; tel. 615/250–9500; Michael Lindley, Chief Executive Officer, p. B63

★ HCA One Park Plaza, Zip 37203–1548; tel. 615/344–9551; R. Milton Johnson, President and Chief Executive Officer, p. B64

★ VANDERBILT HEALTH 1211 22nd Avenue South, Zip 37232; tel. 615/322–5000; Charles Wright Pinson, M.D., Deputy Vice Chancellor for Health Affairs and Chief Executive Officer of Vanderbilt Health System, p. B148

Parsons: TENNESSEE HEALTH MANAGEMENT 52 West Eighth Street, Zip 38363–4656, Mailing Address: PO Box 10, Zip 38363–0010; tel. 731/847–6343; Dennis Berry, Chief Executive Officer, p. B134

TEXAS

Addison: UNITED SURGICAL PARTNERS INTERNATIONAL 15305 Dallas Parkway, Suite 1600, Zip 75001–6491; tel. 972/713–3500; William H. Wilcox, President and Chief Executive Officer, p. B139

Arlington: ★ TEXAS HEALTH RESOURCES 612 East Lamar Boulevard, Suite 900, Zip 76011–4130; tel. 682/236–7900; Barclay E. Berdan, FACHE, Chief Executive Officer, p. B135

Austin: TEXAS DEPARTMENT OF STATE HEALTH SERVICES 1100 West 49th Street, Zip 78756–3199; tel. 512/458–7111; David L. Lakey, M.D., Commissioner, p. B134

★ UNIVERSITY OF TEXAS SYSTEM 601 Colorado Street, Suite 205, Zip 78701–2904; tel. 512/499–4224; Raymond Greenberg, M.D., Executive Vice Chancellor, p. B147

Dallas: ★ BAYLOR SCOTT & WHITE HEALTH 4005 Crutcher Street, Suite 310, Zip 75246–1779; tel. 214/820–0111; Joel T. Allison, Chief Executive Officer, p. B22

CORNERSTONE HEALTHCARE GROUP 2200 Ross Avenue, Suite 5400, Zip 75201–7984; tel. 469/621–6700; David Smith, President and Chief Operating Officer, p. B44

GLOBALREHAB 1420 West Mockingbird Lane, Suite 100, Zip 75247–4932, Mailing Address: 1340 Empire Central Drive, Zip 75247–4022; tel. 214/879–7500; Hooman Sedighi, M.D., President and Chief Executive Officer, p. B61

★ METHODIST HEALTH SYSTEM 1441 North Beckley Avenue, Zip 75203–1201, Mailing Address: P.O. Box 655999, Zip 75265–5999; tel. 214/947–8181; Stephen L. Mansfield, Ph.D., FACHE, President and Chief Executive Officer, p. B94

★ TENET HEALTHCARE CORPORATION 1445 Ross Avenue, Suite 1400, Zip 75202–2703, Mailing Address: P.O. Box 1390369, Zip 75313–9036; tel. 469/893–2200; Trevor Fetter, President and Chief Executive Officer, p. B132

VIBRANT HEALTHCARE 12222 North Central Expressway, Suite 440, Zip 75243–3767; tel. 469/330–6745; Wilton M. Burt, Chief Executive Officer, p. B149

Greenville: HUNT REGIONAL HEALTHCARE 4215 Joe Ramsey Boulevard, Zip 75401–7852, Mailing Address: P.O. Box 1059, Zip 75403–1059; tel. 903/408–5000; Richard Carter, Chief Executive Officer, p. B74

Houston: ★ DUBUIS HEALTH SYSTEM 1700 West Loop South, Suite 1100A, Zip 77027–3007; tel. 713/277–2300; Toni Mills, Interim Chief Executive Officer, p. B54

★ HOUSTON METHODIST 6565 Fannin Street, D–200, Zip 77030–2707; tel. 713/441–2221; Marc L. Boom, M.D., Chief Executive Officer, p. B74

★ MEMORIAL HERMANN HEALTHCARE SYSTEM 929 Gessner, Suite 2700, Zip 77024–2593; tel. 713/242–2700; Daniel J. Wolterman, President and Chief Executive Officer, p. B91

NEXUS HEALTH SYSTEMS One Riverway, Suite 600, Zip 77056–1993; tel. 713/355–6111; John W. Cassidy, M.D., President, Chief Executive Officer and Chief Medical Officer, p. B99

UNIVERSITY GENERAL HEALTH SYSTEM 7501 Fannin Street, Zip 77054–1938; tel. 713/375–7100; Hassan Chahadeh, M.D., Chief Executive Officer, p. B144

Irving: ★ CHRISTUS HEALTH 919 Hidden Ridge Drive, Zip 75038; tel. 469/282–2000; Ernie W. Sadau, President and Chief Executive Officer, p. B35

USMD INC. 6333 North State Highway 161 Suite 200, Zip 75038–2229; tel. 214/493–4000; Karen A. Fiducia, FACHE, President, Hospital Division, p. B147

Longview: AUDUBON BEHAVIORAL HEALTHCARE 100 West Hawkins, Suite D., Zip 75605; tel. 903/212–2930; William V. Brown, Chief Executive Officer, p. B16

GOOD SHEPHERD HEALTH SYSTEM 700 East Marshall Avenue, Zip 75601–5580; tel. 903/315–2000; Steve Altmiller, President and Chief Executive Officer, p. B61

Lubbock: ★ COVENANT HEALTH SYSTEM 3615 19th Street, Zip 79410–1203; tel. 806/725–0447; Richard H. Parks, FACHE, President and Chief Executive Officer, p. B45

Lufkin: MEMORIAL HEALTH SYSTEM OF EAST TEXAS 1201 Frank Avenue, Zip 75904–3357; tel. 936/634–8111; Gary N. Looper, President and Chief Executive Officer, p. B91

Plano: ★ COMMUNITY HOSPITAL CORPORATION 7800 North Dallas Parkway, Suite 200, Zip 75024–6116; tel. 972/943–6400; Michael D. Williams, President and Chief Executive Officer, p. B43

★ LHP HOSPITAL GROUP 2400 North Dallas Parkway, Suite 450, Zip 75093–5994; tel. 866/465–9222; John F. Holland, Chief Executive Officer, p. B84

★ LIFECARE MANAGEMENT SERVICES 5340 Legacy Drive, Suite 150, Zip 75024–3131; tel. 469/241–2100; Phillip B. Douglas, Chairman and Chief Executive Officer, p. B84

Richardson: RELIANT HEALTHCARE PARTNERS 1300 East Lookout Drive, Suite 115, Zip 75082–4114; tel. 469/298–1400; Chester Crouch, Chief Executive Officer, p. B114

Sherman: CARRUS HOSPITALS 1810 West U.S. Highway 82, Zip 75092–7069; tel. 903/870–2600; Ronald E. Dorris, Chief Executive Officer, p. B28

The Woodlands: EMERUS 10077 Grogan's Mill, Suite 100, Zip 77380–1022; tel. 281/292–2450; Toby Hamilton, Chief Executive Officer, p. B56

VICTORY HEALTHCARE 2201 Timberloch Place, Suite 200, Zip 77380; tel. 281/863–2100; Robert N. Helms, Jr., Board Chair, President and Chief Executive Officer, p. B149

Tyler: ★ EAST TEXAS MEDICAL CENTER REGIONAL HEALTHCARE SYSTEM 1000 South Beckham Street, Zip 75701–1908, Mailing Address: P.O. Box 6400, Zip 75711–6400; tel. 903/535–6211; Elmer G. Ellis, FACHE, President and Chief Executive Officer, p. B55

TRINITY MOTHER FRANCES HOSPITALS AND CLINICS 910 East Houston, Zip 75702–8369; tel. 903/593–8441; J. Lindsey Bradley, Jr., FACHE, President, p. B136

UTAH

Nephi: ★ RURAL HEALTH GROUP 48 West 1500 North, Zip 84648–8900; tel. 435/623–4924; Mark R. Stoddard, President and Chairman, p. B116

Salt Lake City: ★ INTERMOUNTAIN HEALTHCARE, INC. 36 South State Street, 22nd Floor, Zip 84111–1453; tel. 801/442–2000; Charles W. Sorenson, Jr., M.D., President and Chief Executive Officer, p. B77

VIRGINIA

Charlottesville: UVA HEALTH SYSTEM 1215 Lee Street, Zip 22908–0816; tel. 434/924–0211; R. Edward Howell, Vice President and Chief Executive Officer, p. B147

Falls Church: DEPARTMENT OF THE ARMY, OFFICE OF THE SURGEON GENERAL 5109 Leesburg Pike, Zip 22041–3215; tel. 703/681–3000; Lieutenant General Eric B. Schoomaker, Surgeon General, p. B47

★ INOVA HEALTH SYSTEM 8110 Gatehouse Road, Suite 200 East, Zip 22042–1252; tel. 703/289–2069; J. Knox Singleton, President and Chief Executive Officer, p. B76

Fredericksburg: ★ MARY WASHINGTON HEALTHCARE 2300 Fall Hill Avenue, Suite 308, Zip 22401–3343; tel. 540/741–3100; Fred M. Rankin, III, President and Chief Executive Officer, p. B88

Lynchburg: CENTRA HEALTH, INC. 1920 Atherholt Road, Zip 24501–1104; tel. 434/200–3000; E. W. Tibbs, President and Chief Executive Officer, p. B34

Newport News: RIVERSIDE HEALTH SYSTEM 701 Town Center Drive, Suite 1000, Zip 23606–4286; tel. 757/534–7000; William B. Downey, President and Chief Executive Officer, p. B114

Norfolk: ★ SENTARA HEALTHCARE 6015 Poplar Hall Drive, Zip 23502–3819; tel. 757/455–7000; David L. Bernd, Chief Executive Officer, p. B123

Richmond: VCU HEALTH SYSTEM 1250 East Marshall Street, Zip 23298–5051, Mailing Address: P.O. Box 980510, Zip 23298–0510; tel. 804/828–9000; John Duval, Chief Executive Officer, p. B148

VIRGINIA DEPARTMENT OF MENTAL HEALTH 1220 Bank Street, Zip 23219–3645, Mailing Address: P.O. Box 1797, Zip 23218–1797; tel. 804/786–3921; James S. Reinhard, M.D., Commissioner, p. B150

Roanoke: ★ CARILION CLINIC 1906 Belleview Avenue S.E., Zip 24014–1838, Mailing Address: P.O. Box 13367, Zip 24033–3367; tel. 540/981–7000; Nancy Howell Agee, President and Chief Executive Officer, p. B27

Winchester: ★ VALLEY HEALTH SYSTEM 220 Campus Boulevard, Suite 310, Zip 22601–2889, Mailing Address: P.O. Box 3340, Zip 22604–2540; tel. 540/536–8024; Mark H. Merrill, President and Chief Executive Officer, p. B148

WASHINGTON

Renton: ★ PROVIDENCE HEALTH & SERVICES 1801 Lind Avenue S.W., 9016, Zip 98057–9016; tel. 425/525–3698; Rodney F. Hochman, M.D., President and Chief Executive Officer, p. B110

Seattle: ★ SWEDISH HEALTH SERVICES 747 Broadway, Zip 98122–4379; tel. 206/386–6000; Anthony A. Armada, Chief Executive, p. B131

UW MEDICINE 1959 N.E. Pacific Street, Zip 98195–0001, Mailing Address: P.O. Box 356350, Zip 98195–6350; tel. 206/543–7718; Paul G. Ramsey, Chief Executive Officer, p. B148

Tacoma: MULTICARE HEALTH SYSTEM 315 Martin Luther King Jr. Way, Zip 98405–4234, Mailing Address: P.O. Box 5299, Zip 98415–0299; tel. 253/403–1000; William G. Robertson, President and Chief Executive Officer, p. B96

Vancouver: ★ PEACEHEALTH 1115 S.E. 164th Avenue, Zip 98683; tel. 425/747–1711; Alan R. Yordy, President and Chief Mission Officer, p. B105

WEST VIRGINIA

Charleston: ★ CHARLESTON AREA MEDICAL CENTER HEALTH SYSTEM, INC. 501 Morris Street, Zip 25301–1300, Mailing Address: P.O. Box 1547, Zip 25326–1547; tel. 304/388–5432; David L. Ramsey, President and Chief Executive Officer, p. B34

Elkins: ★ DAVIS HEALTH SYSTEM Reed Street and Gorman Avenue, Zip 26241, Mailing Address: P.O. Box 1697, Zip 26241–1697; tel. 304/636–3300; Mark Doak, President and Chief Executive Officer, p. B46

Fairmont: ★ WEST VIRGINIA UNITED HEALTH SYSTEM 1000 Technology Drive, Suite 2320, Zip 26554–8834; tel. 304/368–2700; Christopher Colenda, M.D., M.P.H., President and Chief Executive Officer, p. B152

Huntington: ★ PALLOTTINE HEALTH SERVICES 2900 First Avenue, Zip 25702–1241; tel. 304/526–1234; Michael G. Sellards, Chief Executive Officer, p. B104

South Charleston: ★ THOMAS HEALTH SYSTEM, INC. 4605 MacCorkle Avenue S.W., Zip 25309–1311; tel. 304/766–3600; Stephen P. Dexter, President and Chief Executive Officer, p. B135

Wheeling: OHIO VALLEY HEALTH SERVICES AND EDUCATION CORPORATION 2000 Eoff Street, Zip 26003–3823; tel. 304/234–8383; Michael J. Caruso, President and Chief Executive Officer, p. B103

WISCONSIN

Appleton: THEDACARE, INC. 122 East College Avenue, Zip 54911–5794, Mailing Address: P.O. Box 8025, Zip 54912–8025; tel. 920/830–5560; Dean Gruner, M.D., President and Chief Executive Officer, p. B135

Janesville: MERCY HEALTH SYSTEM 1000 Mineral Point Avenue, Zip 53548–2940, Mailing Address: P.O. Box 5003, Zip 53547–5003; tel. 608/756–6000; Javon R. Bea, President and Chief Executive Officer, p. B93

Manitowoc: ★ FRANCISCAN SISTERS OF CHRISTIAN CHARITY SPONSORED MINISTRIES, INC. 1415 South Rapids Road, Zip 54220–9302; tel. 920/684–7071; Sister Laura J. Wolf, President, p. B60

Milwaukee: ★ AURORA HEALTH CARE 3000 West Montana, Zip 53215–3628, Mailing Address: P.O. Box 341880, Zip 53234–1880; tel. 414/647–3000; Nick Turkal, M.D., President and Chief Executive Officer, p. B16

CHILDREN'S HOSPITAL AND HEALTH SYSTEM 9000 West Wisconsin Avenue, Zip 53226–4810, Mailing Address: P.O. Box 1997, Zip 53201–1997; tel. 414/226–2000; Peggy N. Troy, President and Chief Executive Officer, p. B34

Waukesha: ★ PROHEALTH CARE, INC. N17 W24100 Riverwood Drive, Suite 130, Zip 53188; tel. 262/928–2242; Susan A. Edwards, President and Chief Executive Officer, p. B109

Wausau: ★ ASPIRUS, INC. 425 Pine Ridge Boulevard, Zip 54401–4123; tel. 715/847–2118; Matthew Heywood, Chief Executive Officer, p. B15

Health Care Systems Index

Networks and
their Hospitals

ARIZONA

NORTHERN ARIZONA HEALTHCARE
**1200 North Beaver Street, Flagstaff, AZ 86001–3118;
tel. 928/779–3366; William T. Bradel, President and Chief Executive
Officer**

FLAGSTAFF MEDICAL CENTER, 1200 North Beaver Street, Flagstaff, AZ,
   Zip 86001–3118; tel. 928/779–3366; Irwin Bloom, President and Chief
   Executive Officer
VERDE VALLEY MEDICAL CENTER, 269 South Candy Lane, Cottonwood, AZ,
   Zip 86326–4170; tel. 928/639–6000; Barbara Dember, President and Chief
   Executive Officer

SCOTTSDALE LINCOLN HEALTH NETWORK
**8125 North Hayden Road, Scottsdale, AZ 85258–2463;
tel. 480/882–4000; Thomas J. Sadvary, FACHE, Chief Executive Officer**

JOHN C. LINCOLN DEER VALLEY HOSPITAL, 19829 North 27th Avenue, Phoenix,
   AZ, Zip 85027–4002; tel. 623/879–6100; John L. Harrington, Jr., FACHE,
   Chief Executive Officer
JOHN C. LINCOLN NORTH MOUNTAIN HOSPITAL, 250 East Dunlap Avenue,
   Phoenix, AZ, Zip 85020–2825; tel. 602/943–2381; Margaret Elizabeth
   Griffin, Chief Executive Officer
SCOTTSDALE HEALTHCARE REHABILITATION HOSPITAL, 8850 East Pima Center
   Parkway, Scottsdale, AZ, Zip 85258–4619; tel. 480/800–3900; Kelly
   Silberschlag, Chief Executive Officer
SCOTTSDALE HEALTHCARE SHEA MEDICAL CENTER, 9003 East Shea Boulevard,
   Scottsdale, AZ, Zip 85260–6771; tel. 480/323–3000; Gary E. Baker, Senior
   Vice President and Chief Executive Officer
SCOTTSDALE HEALTHCARE THOMPSON PEAK HOSPITAL, 7400 East Thompson
   Peak Parkway, Scottsdale, AZ, Zip 85255–4109; tel. 480/324–7000;
   Kimberly Post, R.N., Vice President and Administrator
SCOTTSDALE HEALTHCARE–OSBORN MEDICAL CENTER, 7400 East Osborn
   Road, Scottsdale, AZ, Zip 85251–6403; tel. 480/882–4000; Gary E. Baker,
   Senior Vice President and Administrator

CALIFORNIA

COVENANT HEALTH NETWORK
**3345 Michelson Drive, Suite 100, Irvine, CA 92612–0693;
tel. 949/381–4019; Richard Afable, M.D., M.P.H., President and Chief
Executive Officer**

COVENANT CHILDREN'S HOSPITAL, 4015 22nd Place, Lubbock, TX, Zip 79410;
   tel. 806/725–1011; Christopher J. Dougherty, Chief Executive Officer
COVENANT HOSPITAL PLAINVIEW, 2601 Dimmitt Road, Plainview, TX,
   Zip 79072–1833; tel. 806/296–5531; Clay Taylor, Chief Executive Officer
COVENANT HOSPITAL–LEVELLAND, 1900 South College Avenue, Levelland, TX,
   Zip 79336–6508; tel. 806/894–4963; Bruce White, Administrator
COVENANT MEDICAL CENTER, 3615 19th Street, Lubbock, TX, Zip 79410–1203,
   Mailing Address: P.O. Box 1201, Zip 79408–1201; tel. 806/725–0000;
   Troy Thibodeaux, Chief Executive Officer
MISSION HOSPITAL, 27700 Medical Center Road, Mission Viejo, CA,
   Zip 92691–6474; tel. 949/364–1400; Kenneth McFarland, President and
   Chief Executive Officer
PETALUMA VALLEY HOSPITAL, 400 North McDowell Boulevard, Petaluma, CA,
   Zip 94954–2366; tel. 707/778–1111; Todd Salnas, President
QUEEN OF THE VALLEY MEDICAL CENTER, 1000 Trancas Street, Napa, CA,
   Zip 94558–2906, Mailing Address: P.O. Box 2340, Zip 94558–0688;
   tel. 707/252–4411; Walt Mickens, FACHE, President and Chief Executive
   Officer
REDWOOD MEMORIAL HOSPITAL, 3300 Renner Drive, Fortuna, CA,
   Zip 95540–3198; tel. 707/725–3361; David O'Brien, M.D., President
SANTA ROSA MEMORIAL HOSPITAL, 1165 Montgomery Drive, Santa Rosa, CA,
   Zip 95405–4897, Mailing Address: P.O. Box 522, Zip 95402–0522;
   tel. 707/546–3210; Todd Salnas, President
ST. JOSEPH HOSPITAL, 2700 Dolbeer Street, Eureka, CA, Zip 95501–4799;
   tel. 707/445–8121; David O'Brien, M.D., President
ST. JOSEPH HOSPITAL, 1100 West Stewart Drive, Orange, CA, Zip 92868–3849,
   Mailing Address: P.O. Box 5600, Zip 92863–5600; tel. 714/633–9111;
   Steven C. Moreau, President and Chief Executive Officer
ST. JUDE MEDICAL CENTER, 101 East Valencia Mesa Drive, Fullerton, CA,
   Zip 92835–3875; tel. 714/992–3000; Lee Penrose, President and Chief
   Executive Officer
ST. MARY MEDICAL CENTER, 18300 Highway 18, Apple Valley, CA,
   Zip 92307–2206, Mailing Address: P.O. Box 7025, Zip 92307–0725;
   tel. 760/242–2311; Alan H. Garrett, Chief Executive Officer

NORTHERN CALIFORNIA NETWORK
**821 South St. Helena Highway Suite 208, St. Helena, CA 95661–3804;
tel. 707/967–7515; Terry Newmyer, President and Chief Executive
Officer**

FRANK R. HOWARD MEMORIAL HOSPITAL, One Madrone Street, Willits, CA,
   Zip 95490–4298; tel. 707/459–6801; Rick Bockmann, Chief Executive
   Officer
ST. HELENA HOSPITAL CLEAR LAKE, 15630 18th Avenue, Clearlake, CA,
   Zip 95422–9336, Mailing Address: P.O. Box 6710, Zip 95422;
   tel. 707/994–6486; David Santos, President and Chief Executive Officer
ST. HELENA HOSPITAL NAPA VALLEY, 10 Woodland Road, Saint Helena, CA,
   Zip 94574–9554; tel. 707/963–3611; Steven Herber, M.D., FACS,
   President and Chief Executive Officer
ST. HELENA HOSPITAL–CENTER FOR BEHAVIORAL HEALTH, 525 Oregon Street,
   Vallejo, CA, Zip 94590–3201; tel. 707/648–2200; Patricia Williams,
   Regional VP for Behavioral Medicine and Population Health
UKIAH VALLEY MEDICAL CENTER, 275 Hospital Drive, Ukiah, CA,
   Zip 95482–4531; tel. 707/462–3111; Gwen Matthews, R.N., MSN, Chief
   Executive Officer

PROVIDENCE HEALTH AND SERVICES – SOUTHERN CALIFORNIA
**501 South Buena Vista Street, Burbank, CA 91505–4809;
tel. 818/843–5111; Michael A. Rembis, FACHE, Chief Executive Officer**

PROVIDENCE HOLY CROSS MEDICAL CENTER, 15031 Rinaldi Street, Mission Hills,
   CA, Zip 91345–1207; tel. 818/365–8051; Bernard Klein, M.D., Chief
   Executive Officer
PROVIDENCE LITTLE COMPANY OF MARY MEDICAL CENTER – TORRANCE, 4101
   Torrance Boulevard, Torrance, CA, Zip 90503–4664; tel. 310/540–7676;
   Elizabeth Dunne, Chief Executive
PROVIDENCE LITTLE COMPANY OF MARY MEDICAL CENTER SAN PEDRO, 1300
   West Seventh Street, San Pedro, CA, Zip 90732–3505; tel. 310/832–3311;
   Elizabeth Dunne, Interim Chief Executive Officer
PROVIDENCE SAINT JOSEPH MEDICAL CENTER, 501 South Buena Vista Street,
   Burbank, CA, Zip 91505–4866; tel. 818/843–5111; Michael A. Rembis,
   FACHE, Chief Executive Officer
PROVIDENCE TARZANA MEDICAL CENTER, 18321 Clark Street, Tarzana, CA,
   Zip 91356–3521; tel. 818/881–0800; Dale Surowitz, Chief Executive

COLORADO

CENTURA HEALTH
**188 Inverness Drive West, Suite 500, Englewood, CO 80112–5204;
tel. 303/290–6500; Gary Campbell, Chief Executive Officer**

AVISTA ADVENTIST HOSPITAL, 100 Health Park Drive, Louisville, CO,
   Zip 80027–9583; tel. 303/673–1000; Dennis Barts, Chief Executive Officer
CASTLE ROCK ADVENTIST HOSPITAL, 2350 Meadows Boulevard, Castle Rock,
   CO, Zip 80109–8405; tel. 720/455–5000; Todd Folkenberg, Chief
   Executive Officer
LITTLETON ADVENTIST HOSPITAL, 7700 South Broadway Street, Littleton, CO,
   Zip 80122–2628; tel. 303/730–8900; Brett Spenst, Chief Executive Officer
PARKER ADVENTIST HOSPITAL, 9395 Crown Crest Boulevard, Parker, CO,
   Zip 80138–8573; tel. 303/269–4000; Morre Dean, Chief Executive Officer
PENROSE–ST. FRANCIS HEALTH SERVICES, 2222 North Nevada Avenue,
   Colorado Springs, CO, Zip 80907–6799, Mailing Address: P.O. Box 7021,
   Zip 80933–7021; tel. 719/776–5000; Margaret D. Sabin, President and
   Chief Executive Officer
PORTER ADVENTIST HOSPITAL, 2525 South Downing Street, Denver, CO,
   Zip 80210–5876; tel. 303/778–1955; Randall L. Haffner, Ph.D., Chief
   Executive Officer
ST. ANTHONY HOSPITAL, 11600 West Second Place, Lakewood, CO,
   Zip 80228–1527; tel. 720/321–0000; Jeffrey Brickman, FACHE, President
   and Chief Executive Officer
ST. ANTHONY NORTH HOSPITAL, 2551 West 84th Avenue, Westminster, CO,
   Zip 80031–3807; tel. 303/426–2151; Carole Peet, R.N., MSN, President
   and Chief Executive Officer
ST. ANTHONY SUMMIT MEDICAL CENTER, 340 Peak One Drive, Frisco, CO,
   Zip 80443, Mailing Address: P.O. Box 738, Zip 80443–0738;
   tel. 970/668–3300; Paul J. Chodkowski, Chief Executive Officer
ST. MARY–CORWIN MEDICAL CENTER, 1008 Minnequa Avenue, Pueblo, CO,
   Zip 81004–3798; tel. 719/557–4000; Brian Moore, President and Chief
   Executive Officer
ST. THOMAS MORE HOSPITAL, 1338 Phay Avenue, Canon City, CO,
   Zip 81212–2302; tel. 719/285–2000; Sheri Trahern, CPA, FACHE, Chief
   Executive Officer

COMMUNITY HEALTH PROVIDERS ORGANIZATION
**2021 North 12th Street, Grand Junction, CO 81501–2980;
tel. 970/256–6200; Chris Thomas, FACHE, President and Chief
Executive Officer**

COMMUNITY HOSPITAL, 2021 North 12th Street, Grand Junction, CO,
   Zip 81501–2999; tel. 970/242–0920; Chris Thomas, FACHE, President and
   Chief Executive Officer

Section B

HCA HEALTHONE, LLC
　　4900 South Monaco Street, Suite 380, Denver, CO 80237–3487; tel. 303/788–2500; Sylvia Young, President

MEDICAL CENTER OF AURORA, 1501 South Potomac Street, Aurora, CO, Zip 80012–5411; tel. 303/695–2600; Richard A. Hammett, Chief Executive Officer

NORTH SUBURBAN MEDICAL CENTER, 9191 Grant Street, Thornton, CO, Zip 80229–4341; tel. 303/451–7800; Jennifer Alderfer, Chief Executive Officer

PRESBYTERIAN–ST. LUKE'S MEDICAL CENTER, 1719 East 19th Avenue, Denver, CO, Zip 80218–1281; tel. 303/839–6000; Madeleine Roberson, Chief Executive Officer

ROSE MEDICAL CENTER, 4567 East Ninth Avenue, Denver, CO, Zip 80220–3941; tel. 303/320–2121; Kenneth H. Feiler, Chief Executive Officer

SKY RIDGE MEDICAL CENTER, 10101 Ridge Gate Parkway, Lone Tree, CO, Zip 80124–5522; tel. 720/225–1000; Maureen Tarrant, Chief Executive Officer

SPALDING REHABILITATION HOSPITAL, 900 Potomac Steet, Aurora, CO, Zip 80011–6716; tel. 303/367–1166; Kristen DeHart, Interim Administrator

SWEDISH MEDICAL CENTER, 501 East Hampden Avenue, Englewood, CO, Zip 80113–2702; tel. 303/788–5000; Mary M. White, Chief Executive Officer

CONNECTICUT

EASTERN CONNECTICUT HEALTH NETWORK
　　71 Haynes Street, Manchester, CT 06040–4131; tel. 860/533–3400; Peter J. Karl, President and Chief Executive Officer

MANCHESTER MEMORIAL HOSPITAL, 71 Haynes Street, Manchester, CT, Zip 06040–4188; tel. 860/646–1222; Peter J. Karl, President and Chief Executive Officer

ROCKVILLE GENERAL HOSPITAL, 31 Union Street, Vernon Rockville, CT, Zip 06066–3160; tel. 860/872–0501; Peter J. Karl, President and Chief Executive Officer

FLORIDA

BAYCARE HEALTH SYSTEM
　　16255 Bay Vista Drive, Clearwater, FL 33760–3127; tel. 877/692–2922; Stephen R. Mason, President and Chief Executive Officer

BAYCARE ALLIANT HOSPITAL, 601 Main Street, Dunedin, FL, Zip 34698–5848; tel. 727/736–9999; Jacqueline Arocho, Administrator

MEASE COUNTRYSIDE HOSPITAL, 3231 McMullen–Booth Road, Safety Harbor, FL, Zip 34695–6607, Mailing Address: P.O. Box 1098, Zip 34695–1098; tel. 727/725–6222; Lou Galdieri, R.N., President

MEASE DUNEDIN HOSPITAL, 601 Main Street, Dunedin, FL, Zip 34698–5891, Mailing Address: P.O. Box 760, Zip 34697–0760; tel. 727/733–1111; Lou Galdieri, R.N., President

MORTON PLANT HOSPITAL, 300 Pinellas Street, Clearwater, FL, Zip 33756–3804, Mailing Address: P.O. Box 210, Zip 33757–0210; tel. 727/462–7000; N. Kristopher Hoce, President

MORTON PLANT NORTH BAY HOSPITAL, 6600 Madison Street, New Port Richey, FL, Zip 34652–1900; tel. 727/754–9222; Michael Yungmann, President

SOUTH FLORIDA BAPTIST HOSPITAL, 301 North Alexander Street, Plant City, FL, Zip 33563–4303, Mailing Address: Drawer H, Zip 33564–9058; tel. 813/757–1200; Karen Kerr, R.N., Interim President and Chief Executive Officer

ST. ANTHONY'S HOSPITAL, 1200 Seventh Avenue North, Saint Petersburg, FL, Zip 33705–1388, Mailing Address: P.O. Box 12588, Zip 33733–2588; tel. 727/825–1100; William G. Ulbricht, President

ST. JOSEPH'S HOSPITAL, 3001 West Martin Luther King Jr. Boulevard, Tampa, FL, Zip 33607–6387, Mailing Address: P.O. Box 4227, Zip 33677–4227; tel. 813/870–4000; Lorraine Lutton, President

WINTER HAVEN HOSPITAL, 200 Avenue F. N.E., Winter Haven, FL, Zip 33881–4193; tel. 863/293–1121; Stephen A. Nierman, President

GEORGIA

ST. JOSEPH'S/CANDLER HEALTH SYSTEM, INC.
　　5353 Reynolds Street, Savannah, GA 31405–6015; tel. 912/819–6000; Paul P. Hinchey, President and Chief Executive Officer

APPLING HEALTHCARE SYSTEM, 163 East Tollison Street, Baxley, GA, Zip 31513–0120; tel. 912/367–9841; Peyton A. Smith, Chief Executive Officer

CANDLER HOSPITAL, 5353 Reynolds Street, Savannah, GA, Zip 31405–6015; tel. 912/819–6000; Paul P. Hinchey, President and Chief Executive Officer

EFFINGHAM HOSPITAL, 459 Highway 119 South, Springfield, GA, Zip 31329–3021, Mailing Address: P.O. Box 386, Zip 31329–0386; tel. 912/754–6451; Norma J. Morgan, Chief Executive Officer

EMORY UNIVERSITY HOSPITAL, 1364 Clifton Road N.E., Atlanta, GA, Zip 30322–1102; tel. 404/712–2000; Robert J. Bachman, Chief Executive Officer

LIBERTY REGIONAL MEDICAL CENTER, 462 Elma G. Miles Parkway, Hinesville, GA, Zip 31313–4000, Mailing Address: P.O. Box 919, Zip 31310–0919; tel. 912/369–9400; H. Scott Kroell, Jr., Chief Executive Officer

MEADOWS REGIONAL MEDICAL CENTER, One Meadows Parkway, Vidalia, GA, Zip 30474–8759, Mailing Address: P.O. Box 1048, Zip 30475–1048; tel. 912/535–5555; Alan Kent, Chief Executive Officer

ST. JOSEPH'S HOSPITAL, 11705 Mercy Boulevard, Savannah, GA, Zip 31419–1791; tel. 912/819–4100; Paul P. Hinchey, President and Chief Executive Officer

WILLINGWAY HOSPITAL, 311 Jones Mill Road, Statesboro, GA, Zip 30458–4765; tel. 912/764–6236; Barbara S. Reid, Chief Executive Officer

IDAHO

NORTH IDAHO HEALTH NETWORK
　　1250 West Ironwood Drive, Suite 201, Coeur D'Alene, ID 83814–2681; tel. 208/666–3212; Richard McMaster, Executive Director

BENEWAH COMMUNITY HOSPITAL, 229 South Seventh Street, Saint Maries, ID, Zip 83861–1803; tel. 208/245–5551; Brenda Parnell, Chief Executive Officer

BONNER GENERAL HOSPITAL, 520 North Third Avenue, Sandpoint, ID, Zip 83864–1507; tel. 208/263–1441; Sheryl Rickard, Chief Executive Officer

BOUNDARY COMMUNITY HOSPITAL, 6640 Kaniksu Street, Bonners Ferry, ID, Zip 83805–7532; tel. 208/267–3141; Craig A. Johnson, Chief Executive Officer

KOOTENAI HEALTH, 2003 Kootenai Health Way, Coeur D'Alene, ID, Zip 83814–2677; tel. 208/625–4000; Jon Ness, Chief Executive Officer

SHOSHONE MEDICAL CENTER, 25 Jacobs Gulch, Kellogg, ID, Zip 83837–2023; tel. 208/784–1221; Gary Moore, Chief Executive Officer

SOUTHWEST IDAHO COMMUNITY HEALTH NETWORK
　　PO Box 607, Boise, ID 83701–0607; tel. 208/473–3006; Stephen R. Stoddard, FACHE, Executive Director

CASCADE MEDICAL CENTER, 402 Lake Cascade Parkway, Cascade, ID, Zip 83611–7702, Mailing Address: P.O. Box 1330, Zip 83611–1330; tel. 208/382–4242; Virgil Boss, Chief Executive Officer

ELKS REHAB HOSPITAL, 600 North Robbins Road, Boise, ID, Zip 83702–4565, Mailing Address: P.O. Box 1100, Zip 83701–1100; tel. 208/489–4444; Joseph P. Caroselli, Chief Executive Officer

NORTH CANYON MEDICAL CENTER, 267 North Canyon Drive, Gooding, ID, Zip 83330–5500; tel. 208/934–4433; Tim Powers, Chief Executive Officer

ST. LUKE'S ELMORE, 895 North Sixth East Street, Mountain Home, ID, Zip 83647–2207, Mailing Address: P.O. Box 1270, Zip 83647–1270; tel. 208/587–8401; Gregory L. Maurer, Administrator

ST. LUKE'S JEROME, 709 North Lincoln Street, Jerome, ID, Zip 83338–1851, Mailing Address: 709 North Lincoln Avenue, Zip 83338–1851; tel. 208/324–4301; James L. Angle, FACHE, Chief Executive Officer

ST. LUKE'S MAGIC VALLEY MEDICAL CENTER, 801 Pole Line Road West, Twin Falls, ID, Zip 83301–5810, Mailing Address: P.O. Box 409, Zip 83303–0409; tel. 208/814–1000; James L. Angle, FACHE, Regional Chief Executive Officer

ST. LUKE'S MCCALL, 1000 State Street, McCall, ID, Zip 83638–3704; tel. 208/634–2221; Michael A. Fenello, Chief Executive Officer

ST. LUKE'S WOOD RIVER MEDICAL CENTER, 100 Hospital Drive, Ketchum, ID, Zip 83340, Mailing Address: P.O. Box 100, Zip 83340–0100; tel. 208/727–8800; Cody Langbehn, Chief Executive Officer

SYRINGA HOSPITAL AND CLINICS, 607 West Main Street, Grangeville, ID, Zip 83530–1396; tel. 208/983–1700; Joseph Cladouhos, Chief Executive Officer

WALTER KNOX MEMORIAL HOSPITAL, 1202 East Locust Street, Emmett, ID, Zip 83617–2715; tel. 208/365–3561; Wade C. Johnson, MS, FACHE, Chief Executive Officer

WEISER MEMORIAL HOSPITAL, 645 East Fifth Street, Weiser, ID, Zip 83672–2202; tel. 208/549–0370; Tom Murphy, Chief Executive Officer

THE HOSPITAL COOPERATIVE
　　500 South 11th Avenue Suite 503, Pocatello, ID 83201–4881; tel. 208/239–1951; Jon Smith, Executive Director

BEAR LAKE MEMORIAL HOSPITAL, 164 South Fifth Street, Montpelier, ID, Zip 83254–1597; tel. 208/847–1630; Rodney D. Jacobson, Administrator

BINGHAM MEMORIAL HOSPITAL, 98 Poplar Street, Blackfoot, ID, Zip 83221–1799; tel. 208/785–4100; Louis D. Kraml, FACHE, Chief Executive Officer

CARIBOU MEMORIAL HOSPITAL AND LIVING CENTER, 300 South Third West, Soda Springs, ID, Zip 83276–1598; tel. 208/547–3341; John L. Hoopes, Chief Executive Officer

EASTERN IDAHO REGIONAL MEDICAL CENTER, 3100 Channing Way, Idaho Falls, ID, Zip 83404–7533, Mailing Address: P.O. Box 2077, Zip 83403–2077; tel. 208/529–6111; Douglas Crabtree, Chief Executive Officer

FRANKLIN COUNTY MEDICAL CENTER, 44 North First East Street, Preston, ID, Zip 83263–1399; tel. 208/852–0137; Michael G. Andrus, Administrator and Chief Executive Officer

LOST RIVERS MEDICAL CENTER, 551 Highland Drive, Arco, ID, Zip 83213–9771, Mailing Address: P.O. Box 145, Zip 83213–0145; tel. 208/527–8206; Brad Huerta, Chief Executive Officer and Administrator

MADISON MEMORIAL HOSPITAL, 450 East Main Street, Rexburg, ID, Zip 83440–2048, Mailing Address: P.O. Box 310, Zip 83440–0310; tel. 208/359–6900; Rachel Ann Gonzales, MSN, R.N., Chief Executive Officer

MINIDOKA MEMORIAL HOSPITAL, 1224 Eighth Street, Rupert, ID, Zip 83350–1599; tel. 208/436–0481; Carl Hanson, Administrator

ONEIDA COUNTY HOSPITAL, 150 North 200 West, Malad City, ID, Zip 83252–1239, Mailing Address: Box 126, Zip 83252–0126; tel. 208/766–2231; John Williams, Administrator and Chief Executive Officer

PORTNEUF MEDICAL CENTER, 777 Hospital Way, Pocatello, ID, Zip 83201–5175; tel. 208/239–1000; Daniel Ordyna, Chief Executive Officer

POWER COUNTY HOSPITAL DISTRICT, 510 Roosevelt Road, American Falls, ID, Zip 83211–1362, Mailing Address: P.O. Box 420, Zip 83211–0420; tel. 208/226–3200; Dallas Clinger, Administrator

STAR VALLEY MEDICAL CENTER, 901 Adams Street, Afton, WY, Zip 83110–9621, Mailing Address: P.O. Box 579, Zip 83110–0579; tel. 307/885–5800; Charlie A. Button, President and Chief Executive Officer

STEELE MEMORIAL MEDICAL CENTER, 203 South Daisy Street, Salmon, ID, Zip 83467–4709; tel. 208/756–5600; Jeff Hill, Chief Executive Officer

TETON VALLEY HEALTH CARE, 120 East Howard Street, Driggs, ID, Zip 83422–5112; tel. 208/354–2383; Keith Gnagey, Chief Executive Officer

ILLINOIS

FELICIAN SERVICES, INC.
3800 West Peterson Avenue, Chicago, IL 60659–3116; tel. 773/463–3806; Sister Mary Clarette Stryzewski, President and Chief Executive Officer

ST. MARY'S HOSPITAL, 400 North Pleasant Avenue, Centralia, IL, Zip 62801–3056; tel. 618/436–8000; Bruce Merrell, FACHE, President

WHEATON FRANCISCAN HEALTHCARE – ST. FRANCIS, 3237 South 16th Street, Milwaukee, WI, Zip 53215–4592; tel. 414/647–5000; Coreen Dicus–Johnson, President

INDIANA

LUTHERAN HEALTH NETWORK
7950 West Jefferson Boulevard, Fort Wayne, IN 46804–4140; tel. 260/435–7001; Brian Bauer, Chief Executive Officer

BLUFFTON REGIONAL MEDICAL CENTER, 303 South Main Street, Bluffton, IN, Zip 46714–2503; tel. 260/824–3210; Aaron Garofola, Chief Executive Officer

DUKES MEMORIAL HOSPITAL, 275 West 12th Street, Peru, IN, Zip 46970–1638; tel. 765/472–8000; Debra Close, Chief Executive Officer

DUPONT HOSPITAL, 2520 East Dupont Road, Fort Wayne, IN, Zip 46825–1675; tel. 260/416–3000; Chad Towner, Chief Executive Officer

KOSCIUSKO COMMUNITY HOSPITAL, 2101 East Dubois Drive, Warsaw, IN, Zip 46580–3288; tel. 574/267–3200; Stephen R. Miller, Chief Executive Officer

LUTHERAN HOSPITAL OF INDIANA, 7950 West Jefferson Boulevard, Fort Wayne, IN, Zip 46804–4140; tel. 260/435–7001; Brian Bauer, Chief Executive Officer

ORTHOPAEDIC HOSPITAL OF LUTHERAN HEALTH NETWORK, 7952 West Jefferson Boulevard, Fort Wayne, IN, Zip 46804–4140; tel. 260/435–2999; Kenneth Jones, Chief Executive Officer

REHABILITATION HOSPITAL OF FORT WAYNE, 7970 West Jefferson Boulevard, Fort Wayne, IN, Zip 46804–4140; tel. 260/435–6100; Ted Scholten, Chief Operating Officer

ST. JOSEPH HOSPITAL, 700 Broadway, Fort Wayne, IN, Zip 46802–1493; tel. 260/425–3000; Kenneth Jones, Chief Executive Officer

ST. VINCENT HEALTH
2001 West 86Th Street, Indianapolis, IN 46260–1902; tel. 317/338–2273; Jonathan Nalli, Chief Executive Officer

ST. JOSEPH HOSPITAL & HEALTH CENTER, 1907 West Sycamore Street, Kokomo, IN, Zip 46901–4197; tel. 765/452–5611; Kathlene A. Young, MS, FACHE, President and Chief Executive Officer

ST. MARY'S WARRICK HOSPITAL, 1116 Millis Avenue, Boonville, IN, Zip 47601–2204; tel. 812/897–4800; Kathy J. Hall, Administrator

ST. VINCENT ANDERSON REGIONAL HOSPITAL, 2015 Jackson Street, Anderson, IN, Zip 46016–4339; tel. 765/649–2511; Thomas J. VanOsdol, President

ST. VINCENT CARMEL HOSPITAL, 13500 North Meridian Street, Carmel, IN, Zip 46032–1456; tel. 317/582–7000; Michael D. Chittenden, President

ST. VINCENT CLAY HOSPITAL, 1206 East National Avenue, Brazil, IN, Zip 47834–2797, Mailing Address: P.O. Box 489, Zip 47834–0489; tel. 812/442–2500; Jerry Laue, Administrator

ST. VINCENT DUNN HOSPITAL, 1600 23rd Street, Bedford, IN, Zip 47421–4704; tel. 812/275–3331; Matt Balla, Chief Executive Officer

ST. VINCENT FISHERS HOSPITAL, 13861 Olio Road, Fishers, IN, Zip 46037–3487; tel. 317/415–9000; Gary Fammartino, Administrator

ST. VINCENT FRANKFORT HOSPITAL, 1300 South Jackson Street, Frankfort, IN, Zip 46041–3394, Mailing Address: P.O. Box 669, Zip 46041–0669; tel. 765/656–3000; Thomas Crawford, Administrator

ST. VINCENT HEART CENTER, 10580 North Meridian Street, Indianapolis, IN, Zip 46290–1028; tel. 317/583–5000; Blake A. Dye, President

ST. VINCENT INDIANAPOLIS HOSPITAL, 2001 West 86th Street, Indianapolis, IN, Zip 46260–1991, Mailing Address: P.O. Box 40970, Zip 46240–0970; tel. 317/338–2345; Kyle De Fur, FACHE, President

ST. VINCENT JENNINGS HOSPITAL, 301 Henry Street, North Vernon, IN, Zip 47265–1097; tel. 812/352–4200; Carl W. Risk, II, Administrator

ST. VINCENT MERCY HOSPITAL, 1331 South A Street, Elwood, IN, Zip 46036–1942; tel. 765/552–4600; Francis G. Albarano, Administrator

ST. VINCENT RANDOLPH HOSPITAL, 473 Greenville Avenue, Winchester, IN, Zip 47394–9436, Mailing Address: P.O. Box 407, Zip 47394–0407; tel. 765/584–0004; Francis G. Albarano, Administrator

ST. VINCENT SETON SPECIALTY HOSPITAL, 1501 Hartford Street, Lafayette, IN, Zip 47904–2134; tel. 765/236–8900; Peter H. Alexander, Administrator

ST. VINCENT WILLIAMSPORT HOSPITAL, 412 North Monroe Street, Williamsport, IN, Zip 47993–1049; tel. 765/762–4000; Jane Craigin, Chief Executive Officer

SUBURBAN HEALTH ORGANIZATION
2780 Waterfront Parkway East Drive, Suite 300, Indianapolis, IN 46214; tel. 317/692–5222; Dave Lippincott, President

COMMUNITY WESTVIEW HOSPITAL, 3630 Guion Road, Indianapolis, IN, Zip 46222–1699; tel. 317/924–6661; David C. Williams, D.O., President and Chief Executive Officer

HANCOCK REGIONAL HOSPITAL, 801 North State Street, Greenfield, IN, Zip 46140–1270, Mailing Address: P.O. Box 827, Zip 46140–0827; tel. 317/462–5544; Steven V. Long, FACHE, President and Chief Executive Officer

HENDRICKS REGIONAL HEALTH, 1000 East Main Street, Danville, IN, Zip 46122–1948, Mailing Address: P.O. Box 409, Zip 46122–0409; tel. 317/745–4451; Kevin Speer, Chief Executive Officer

HENRY COUNTY HOSPITAL, 1000 North 16th Street, New Castle, IN, Zip 47362–4319, Mailing Address: P.O. Box 490, Zip 47362–0490; tel. 765/521–0890; Paul Janssen, President and Chief Executive Officer

JOHNSON MEMORIAL HOSPITAL, 1125 West Jefferson Street, Franklin, IN, Zip 46131–2140, Mailing Address: P.O. Box 549, Zip 46131–0549; tel. 317/736–3300; Larry Heydon, President and Chief Executive Officer

MAJOR HOSPITAL, 150 West Washington Street, Shelbyville, IN, Zip 46176–1236; tel. 317/392–3211; John M. Horner, President and Chief Executive Officer

MARGARET MARY HEALTH, 321 Mitchell Avenue, Batesville, IN, Zip 47006–8909, Mailing Address: P.O. Box 226, Zip 47006–0226; tel. 812/934–6624; Timothy L. Putnam, FACHE, President and Chief Executive Officer

RIVERVIEW HOSPITAL, 395 Westfield Road, Noblesville, IN, Zip 46060–1425, Mailing Address: P.O. Box 220, Zip 46061–0220; tel. 317/773–0760; Patricia K. Fox, President and Chief Executive Officer

RUSH MEMORIAL HOSPITAL, 1300 North Main Street, Rushville, IN, Zip 46173–1198, Mailing Address: P.O. Box 608, Zip 46173–0608; tel. 765/932–4111; Bradley Smith, President and Chief Executive Officer

WITHAM MEMORIAL HOSPITAL, 2605 North Lebanon Street, Lebanon, IN, Zip 46052–1476, Mailing Address: P.O. Box 1200, Zip 46052–3005; tel. 765/485–8000; Raymond V. Ingham, Ph.D., President and Chief Executive Officer

IOWA

GENESIS HEALTH SYSTEM
1227 East Rusholme Street, Davenport, IA 52803–2498; tel. 563/421–1000; Douglas P. Cropper, President and Chief Executive Officer

GENESIS MEDICAL CENTER, DEWITT, 1118 11th Street, De Witt, IA, Zip 52742–1296; tel. 563/659–4200; Curt Coleman, FACHE, Administrator

GENESIS MEDICAL CENTER, ILLINI CAMPUS, 801 Illini Drive, Silvis, IL, Zip 61282–1893; tel. 309/281–4000; Kevin Youmans, Interim President

GENESIS MEDICAL CENTER–DAVENPORT, 1227 East Rusholme Street, Davenport, IA, Zip 52803–2498; tel. 563/421–1000; Wayne A. Diewald, President

MERCY HEALTH NETWORK – CENTRAL IOWA
1111 6th Avenue, Des Moines, IA 50314–2611; tel. 515/358–8023; Jim FitzPatrick, Senior Vice President, Network Development

ADAIR COUNTY MEMORIAL HOSPITAL, 609 S.E. Kent Street, Greenfield, IA, Zip 50849–9454; tel. 641/743–2123; Angela Mortoza, Administrator

AUDUBON COUNTY MEMORIAL HOSPITAL, 515 Pacific Street, Audubon, IA, Zip 50025–1056; tel. 712/563–2611; Thomas G. Smith, Administrator and Chief Executive Officer

BOONE COUNTY HOSPITAL, 1015 Union Street, Boone, IA, Zip 50036–4821; tel. 515/432–3140; Joseph S. Smith, Chief Executive Officer

CLARINDA REGIONAL HEALTH CENTER, 220 Essie Davison Drive, Clarinda, IA, Zip 51632–2915, Mailing Address: P.O. Box 217, Zip 51632–0217; tel. 712/542–2176; Christopher R. Stipe, FACHE, Chief Executive Officer

DALLAS COUNTY HOSPITAL, 610 10th Street, Perry, IA, Zip 50220–2221; tel. 515/465–3547; Matt Wille, Chief Executive Officer

DAVIS COUNTY HOSPITAL, 509 North Madison Street, Bloomfield, IA, Zip 52537–1271; tel. 641/664–2145; Deborah L. Herzberg, R.N., MS, FACHE, Chief Executive Officer

DECATUR COUNTY HOSPITAL, 1405 N.W. Church Street, Leon, IA, Zip 50144–1299; tel. 641/446–4871; Suzanne Cooner, R.N., MSN, Chief Executive Officer

GRINNELL REGIONAL MEDICAL CENTER, 210 Fourth Avenue, Grinnell, IA, Zip 50112–1898; tel. 641/236–2300; Todd C. Linden, President and Chief Executive Officer

KNOXVILLE HOSPITAL & CLINICS, 1002 South Lincoln Street, Knoxville, IA, Zip 50138–3155; tel. 641/842–2151; Kevin Kincaid, Chief Executive Officer

MADISON COUNTY HEALTH CARE SYSTEM, 300 West Hutchings Street, Winterset, IA, Zip 50273–2109; tel. 515/462–2373; Marcia Hendricks, R.N., FACHE, Chief Executive Officer

MANNING REGIONAL HEALTHCARE CENTER, 1550 6th Street, Manning, IA, Zip 51455–1093; tel. 712/655–2072; John O'Brien, Chief Executive Officer

MERCY MEDICAL CENTER–CENTERVILLE, 1 St. Joseph's Drive, Centerville, IA, Zip 52544–8055; tel. 641/437–4111; Clinton J. Christianson, FACHE, President

MERCY MEDICAL CENTER–DES MOINES, 1111 6th Avenue, Des Moines, IA, Zip 50314–2611; tel. 515/247–3121; Robert P. Ritz, FACHE, President

MONROE COUNTY HOSPITAL AND CLINICS, 6580 165th Street, Albia, IA, Zip 52531–8793; tel. 641/932–2134; Todd Willert, Chief Executive Officer

RINGGOLD COUNTY HOSPITAL, 504 North Cleveland Street, Mount Ayr, IA, Zip 50854–2201; tel. 641/464–3226; Gordon W. Winkler, Administrator and Chief Executive Officer

VAN DIEST MEDICAL CENTER, 2350 Hospital Drive, Webster City, IA, Zip 50595–6600; tel. 515/832–9400; Lori Rathbun, Chief Executive Officer

WAYNE COUNTY HOSPITAL, 417 South East Street, Corydon, IA, Zip 50060–1860, Mailing Address: P.O. Box 305, Zip 50060–0305; tel. 641/872–2260; Daren Relph, Chief Executive Officer

MERCY HEALTH NETWORK – NORTH IOWA
1000 4th Street S.W., Mason City, IA 50401–2800; tel. 641/428–7000; Daniel Varnum, Chief Executive Officer

FRANKLIN GENERAL HOSPITAL, 1720 Central Avenue East, Suite A., Hampton, IA, Zip 50441–1867; tel. 641/456–5000; Kim Price, Chief Executive Officer

HANCOCK COUNTY HEALTH SYSTEM, 532 First Street N.W., Britt, IA, Zip 50423–1227; tel. 641/843–5000; Vance Jackson, FACHE, Administrator and Chief Executive Officer

HANSEN FAMILY HOSPITAL, 920 South Oak, Iowa Falls, IA, Zip 50126–9506; tel. 641/648–4631; Cherelle Montanye–Ireland, Chief Executive Officer

KOSSUTH REGIONAL HEALTH CENTER, 1515 South Phillips Street, Algona, IA, Zip 50511–3649; tel. 515/295–2451; Scott A. Curtis, Administrator and Chief Executive Officer

MERCY MEDICAL CENTER–NEW HAMPTON, 308 North Maple Avenue, New Hampton, IA, Zip 50659–1142; tel. 641/394–4121; Bruce E. Roesler, FACHE, President and Chief Executive Officer

MITCHELL COUNTY REGIONAL HEALTH CENTER, 616 North Eighth Street, Osage, IA, Zip 50461–1498; tel. 641/732–6000; Shelly Russell, Chief Executive Officer

PALO ALTO COUNTY HEALTH SYSTEM, 3201 First Street, Emmetsburg, IA, Zip 50536–2516; tel. 712/852–5500; Desiree Einsweiler, Chief Executive Officer

REGIONAL HEALTH SERVICES OF HOWARD COUNTY, 235 Eighth Avenue West, Cresco, IA, Zip 52136–1098; tel. 563/547–2101; Robin M. Schluter, Chief Executive Officer

KANSAS

HAYS MEDICAL CENTER
2220 Canterbury Drive, Hays, KS 67601–2370; tel. 785/623–2300; John H. Jeter, M.D., President and Chief Executive Officer

HEALTH INNOVATIONS NETWORK OF KANSAS
1500 S.W. 10th Avenue, Topeka, KS 66604–1301; tel. 785/354–6137; Kristi Gosser, Network Operations Director

ATCHISON HOSPITAL, 800 Raven Hill Drive, Atchison, KS, Zip 66002–9204; tel. 913/367–2131; John L. Jacobson, Chief Executive Officer

CLAY COUNTY MEDICAL CENTER, 617 Liberty Street, Clay Center, KS, Zip 67432–1564, Mailing Address: P.O. Box 512, Zip 67432–0512; tel. 785/632–2144; Ron Bender, Chief Executive Officer

COFFEY COUNTY HOSPITAL, 801 North Fourth Street, Burlington, KS, Zip 66839–2602; tel. 620/364–2121; Randy L. Lindauer, Ph.D., FACHE, Chief Executive Officer

COMMUNITY HEALTHCARE SYSTEM, 120 West Eighth Street, Onaga, KS, Zip 66521–9574; tel. 785/889–4272; Greg Unruh, Chief Executive Officer

F. W. HUSTON MEDICAL CENTER, 408 Delaware Street, Winchester, KS, Zip 66097–4003; tel. 913/774–4340; LaMont Cook, Administrator

GEARY COMMUNITY HOSPITAL, 1102 St. Mary's Road, Junction City, KS, Zip 66441–4196, Mailing Address: P.O. Box 490, Zip 66441–0490; tel. 785/238–4131; Joseph Stratton, FACHE, Chief Executive Officer

HERINGTON MUNICIPAL HOSPITAL, 100 East Helen Street, Herington, KS, Zip 67449–1606; tel. 785/258–2207; Michael J. Ryan, Chief Executive Officer

HIAWATHA COMMUNITY HOSPITAL, 300 Utah Street, Hiawatha, KS, Zip 66434–2314; tel. 785/742–2131; John Moore, Administrator

HOLTON COMMUNITY HOSPITAL, 1110 Columbine Drive, Holton, KS, Zip 66436–8824; tel. 785/364–2116; Carrie L. Saia, R.N., Chief Executive Officer

HORTON COMMUNITY HOSPITAL, 240 West 18th Street, Horton, KS, Zip 66439–1245; tel. 785/486–2642; James Noble, Chief Executive Officer

IRWIN ARMY COMMUNITY HOSPITAL, 600 Caisson Hill Road, Junction City, KS, Zip 66442–7037; tel. 785/239–7000; Colonel Barry R. Pockrandt, Commander

KANSAS REHABILITATION HOSPITAL, 1504 S.W. Eighth Avenue, Topeka, KS, Zip 66606–1632; tel. 785/235–6600; William J. Overbey, Chief Executive Officer

MERCY REGIONAL HEALTH CENTER, 1823 College Avenue, Manhattan, KS, Zip 66502–3346; tel. 785/776–3322; John R. Broberg, FACHE, Senior Administrator

MORRIS COUNTY HOSPITAL, 600 North Washington Street, Council Grove, KS, Zip 66846–1422; tel. 620/767–6811; James H. Reagan, Jr., Ph.D., Chief Executive Officer

NEMAHA VALLEY COMMUNITY HOSPITAL, 1600 Community Drive, Seneca, KS, Zip 66538–9739; tel. 785/336–6181; Stan Regehr, President and Chief Executive Officer

SABETHA COMMUNITY HOSPITAL, 14th and Oregon Streets, Sabetha, KS, Zip 66534–0229, Mailing Address: P.O. Box 229, Zip 66534–0229; tel. 785/284–2121; Lora Key, Chief Executive Officer

STORMONT–VAIL HEALTHCARE, 1500 S.W. Tenth Avenue, Topeka, KS, Zip 66604–1353; tel. 785/354–6000; Randall Peterson, President and Chief Executive Officer

WAMEGO HEALTH CENTER, 711 Genn Drive, Wamego, KS, Zip 66547–1179; tel. 785/456–2295; Shannan Flach, Chief Executive Officer

WASHINGTON COUNTY HOSPITAL, 304 East Third Street, Washington, KS, Zip 66968–2033; tel. 785/325–2211; Roxanne Schottel, Chief Executive Officer

MED-OP, INC.
205 East 7th Street, Hays, KS 67601–4907; tel. 785/621–4510; David Brittain, Executive Director

CITIZENS MEDICAL CENTER, 100 East College Drive, Colby, KS, Zip 67701–3799; tel. 785/462–7511; Kevan Trenkle, Chief Executive Officer

CLARA BARTON HOSPITAL, 250 West Ninth Street, Hoisington, KS, Zip 67544–1706; tel. 620/653–2114; Curt Colson, President and Chief Executive Officer

GOODLAND REGIONAL MEDICAL CENTER, 220 West Second Street, Goodland, KS, Zip 67735–1602; tel. 785/890–3625; Marion A. Thompson, FACHE, Chief Executive Officer

GOVE COUNTY MEDICAL CENTER, 520 West Fifth Street, Quinter, KS, Zip 67752–9705, Mailing Address: P.O. Box 129, Zip 67752–0129; tel. 785/754–3341; Richard Q. Bergling, Chief Executive Officer

GRAHAM COUNTY HOSPITAL, 304 West Prout Street, Hill City, KS, Zip 67642–1435; tel. 785/421–2121; Melissa Atkins, CPA, Chief Executive Officer

HAYS MEDICAL CENTER, 2220 Canterbury Drive, Hays, KS, Zip 67601–2370, Mailing Address: P.O. Box 8100, Zip 67601–8100; tel. 785/623–5000; John H. Jeter, M.D., President and Chief Executive Officer

LOGAN COUNTY HOSPITAL, 211 Cherry Street, Oakley, KS, Zip 67748–1201; tel. 785/672–3211; Darcy Howard, Interim Chief Executive Officer

MERCY HOSPITAL AND TRAUMA CENTER, 1000 Mineral Point Avenue, Janesville, WI, Zip 53548–2982, Mailing Address: P.O. Box 5003, Zip 53547–5003; tel. 608/756–6000; Javon R. Bea, President and Chief Executive Officer

NESS COUNTY HOSPITAL, 312 Custer Street, Ness City, KS, Zip 67560–1654; tel. 785/798–2291; Curt Thomas, Administrator

NORTON COUNTY HOSPITAL, 102 East Holme, Norton, KS, Zip 67654–1406, Mailing Address: P.O. Box 250, Zip 67654–0250; tel. 785/877–3351; Richard Miller, Administrator and Chief Executive Officer

RICE COUNTY DISTRICT HOSPITAL, 619 South Clark Street, Lyons, KS, Zip 67554–3003, Mailing Address: P.O. Box 828, Zip 67554–0828; tel. 620/257–5173; George M. Stover, Chief Executive Officer

ROOKS COUNTY HEALTH CENTER, 1210 North Washington Street, Plainville, KS, Zip 67663–1632, Mailing Address: P.O. Box 389, Zip 67663–0389; tel. 785/434–4553; Michael Sinclair, Chief Executive Officer

RUSH COUNTY MEMORIAL HOSPITAL, 801 Locust Street, La Crosse, KS, Zip 67548–9673, Mailing Address: P.O. Box 520, Zip 67548–0520; tel. 785/222–2545; Brenda Legleiter, R.N., Chief Executive Officer

RUSSELL REGIONAL HOSPITAL, 200 South Main Street, Russell, KS, Zip 67665–2920; tel. 785/483–3131; Harold Courtois, Chief Executive Officer

SCOTT COUNTY HOSPITAL, 201 East Albert Avenue, Scott City, KS, Zip 67871–1203; tel. 620/872–5811; Mark Burnett, President and Chief Executive Officer

SHERIDAN COUNTY HEALTH COMPLEX, 826 18th Street, Hoxie, KS, Zip 67740–0167, Mailing Address: P.O. Box 167, Zip 67740–0167; tel. 785/675–3281; James E. Wahlmeier, Chief Executive Officer

NEK CENTER FOR HEALTH & WELLNESS
  240 West 18th Street, Horton, KS 66439–1245; tel. 785/486–2642

PIONEER HEALTH NETWORK, INC.
  310 East Walnut Street, Suite 210, Garden City, KS 67846–5565; tel. 620/276–6100; Mary Adam, Executive Director

BOB WILSON MEMORIAL GRANT COUNTY HOSPITAL, 415 North Main Street, Ulysses, KS, Zip 67880–2133; tel. 620/356–1266; Arthur H. Frable, Chief Executive Officer

CITIZENS MEDICAL CENTER, 100 East College Drive, Colby, KS, Zip 67701–3799; tel. 785/462–7511; Kevan Trenkle, Chief Executive Officer

DECATUR HEALTH SYSTEMS, 810 West Columbia Street, Oberlin, KS, Zip 67749–2450, Mailing Address: P.O. Box 268, Zip 67749–0268; tel. 785/475–2208; Johnathan Owens, Chief Executive Officer

EDWARDS COUNTY HOSPITAL AND HEALTHCARE CENTER, 620 West Eighth Street, Kinsley, KS, Zip 67547–2329, Mailing Address: P.O. Box 99, Zip 67547–0099; tel. 620/659–3621; Robert Krickbaum, Chief Executive Officer

GREELEY COUNTY HEALTH SERVICES, 506 Third Street, Tribune, KS, Zip 67879–9684, Mailing Address: P.O. Box 338, Zip 67879–0338; tel. 620/376–4221; Lee Rhodes, Interim Administrator and Chief Executive Officer

HAMILTON COUNTY HOSPITAL, 700 North Huser Street, Syracuse, KS, Zip 67878–0948, Mailing Address: P.O. Box 948, Zip 67878–0948; tel. 620/384–7461; Bryan D. Coffey, Chief Executive Officer

HODGEMAN COUNTY HEALTH CENTER, 809 Bramley Street, Jetmore, KS, Zip 67854–9320, Mailing Address: P.O. Box 310, Zip 67854–0310; tel. 620/357–8361; Teresa L. Deuel, Chief Executive Officer

KEARNY COUNTY HOSPITAL, 500 Thorpe Street, Lakin, KS, Zip 67860–9625; tel. 620/355–7111; Benjamin Anderson, Chief Executive Officer and Administrator

LANE COUNTY HOSPITAL, 235 West Vine, Dighton, KS, Zip 67839–0969, Mailing Address: P.O. Box 969, Zip 67839–0969; tel. 620/397–5321; Donna McGowan, Administrator

MEADE DISTRICT HOSPITAL, 510 East Carthage Street, Meade, KS, Zip 67864–6401, Mailing Address: P.O. Box 820, Zip 67864–0820; tel. 620/873–2141; Michael P. Thomas, Administrator

MINNEOLA DISTRICT HOSPITAL, 212 Main Street, Minneola, KS, Zip 67865–8511, Mailing Address: P.O. Box 127, Zip 67865–0127; tel. 620/885–4264; Deborah Bruner, Chief Executive Officer and Administrator

MORTON COUNTY HEALTH SYSTEM, 445 Hilltop Street, Elkhart, KS, Zip 67950–0937, Mailing Address: P.O. Box 937, Zip 67950–0937; tel. 620/697–2141; Joe Duerr, Chief Executive Officer

SATANTA DISTRICT HOSPITAL, 401 South Cheyenne Street, Satanta, KS, Zip 67870–0159, Mailing Address: P.O. Box 159, Zip 67870–0159; tel. 620/649–2761; Jeremy Clingenpeel, Administrator

SCOTT COUNTY HOSPITAL, 201 East Albert Avenue, Scott City, KS, Zip 67871–1203; tel. 620/872–5811; Mark Burnett, President and Chief Executive Officer

SOUTHWEST MEDICAL CENTER, 315 West 15th Street, Liberal, KS, Zip 67901–2455, Mailing Address: Box 1340, Zip 67905–1340; tel. 620/624–1651; William Ermann, President and Chief Executive Officer

ST. CATHERINE HOSPITAL, 401 East Spruce Street, Garden City, KS, Zip 67846–5679; tel. 620/272–2561; Scott J. Taylor, President and Chief Executive Officer

STANTON COUNTY HOSPITAL, 404 North Chestnut Street, Johnson, KS, Zip 67855–5001, Mailing Address: P.O. Box 779, Zip 67855–0779; tel. 620/492–6250; Jay Tusten, Chief Executive Officer

STEVENS COUNTY HOSPITAL, 1006 South Jackson Street, Hugoton, KS, Zip 67951–2858, Mailing Address: P.O. Box 10, Zip 67951–0010; tel. 620/544–8511; Linda Stalcup, Chief Executive Officer

WICHITA COUNTY HEALTH CENTER, 211 East Earl Street, Leoti, KS, Zip 67861–9620; tel. 620/375–2233; Tyson Sterling, Chief Executive Officer

SUNFLOWER HEALTH NETWORK
  400 South Santa Fe Avenue, Salina, KS 67401–4144; tel. 785/452–6102; Heather Fuller, Executive Director

ANTHONY MEDICAL CENTER, 1101 East Spring Street, Anthony, KS, Zip 67003–2122; tel. 620/842–5111; J. Bryant Anderson, Administrator and Chief Executive Officer

CLAY COUNTY MEDICAL CENTER, 617 Liberty Street, Clay Center, KS, Zip 67432–1564, Mailing Address: P.O. Box 512, Zip 67432–0512; tel. 785/632–2144; Ron Bender, Chief Executive Officer

CLOUD COUNTY HEALTH CENTER, 1100 Highland Drive, Concordia, KS, Zip 66901–3923; tel. 785/243–1234; Don Bates, President and Chief Executive Officer

ELLSWORTH COUNTY MEDICAL CENTER, 1604 Aylward Street, Ellsworth, KS, Zip 67439–2541, Mailing Address: P.O. Box 87, Zip 67439–0087; tel. 785/472–3111; Roger A. Masse, FACHE, Chief Executive Officer

HERINGTON MUNICIPAL HOSPITAL, 100 East Helen Street, Herington, KS, Zip 67449–1606; tel. 785/258–2207; Michael J. Ryan, Chief Executive Officer

HILLSBORO COMMUNITY HOSPITAL, 701 South Main Street, Hillsboro, KS, Zip 67063–1553; tel. 620/947–3114; Marion Regier, Chief Executive Officer

JEWELL COUNTY HOSPITAL, 100 Crestvue Avenue, Mankato, KS, Zip 66956–2407, Mailing Address: P.O. Box 327, Zip 66956–0327; tel. 785/378–3137; Doyle L. McKimmy, FACHE, Chief Executive Officer

LINCOLN COUNTY HOSPITAL, 624 North Second Street, Lincoln, KS, Zip 67455–1738, Mailing Address: P.O. Box 406, Zip 67455–0406; tel. 785/524–4403; Steven L. Granzow, Chief Executive Officer

LINDSBORG COMMUNITY HOSPITAL, 605 West Lincoln Street, Lindsborg, KS, Zip 67456–2328; tel. 785/227–3308; Larry VanDerWege, Administrator

MEMORIAL HEALTH SYSTEM, 511 N.E. Tenth Street, Abilene, KS, Zip 67410–2153; tel. 785/263–2100; Mark A. Miller, FACHE, Chief Executive Officer

MITCHELL COUNTY HOSPITAL HEALTH SYSTEMS, 400 West Eighth, Beloit, KS, Zip 67420–1605, Mailing Address: P.O. Box 399, Zip 67420–0399; tel. 785/738–2266; Jeremy Armstrong, FACHE, Chief Executive Officer

OSBORNE COUNTY MEMORIAL HOSPITAL, 424 West New Hampshire Street, Osborne, KS, Zip 67473–2314, Mailing Address: P.O. Box 70, Zip 67473–0070; tel. 785/346–2121; Kiley Floyd, Administrator

OTTAWA COUNTY HEALTH CENTER, 215 East Eighth, Minneapolis, KS, Zip 67467–1902, Mailing Address: P.O. Box 290, Zip 67467–0290; tel. 785/392–2122; Jody Parks, Administrator

REPUBLIC COUNTY HOSPITAL, 2420 G Street, Belleville, KS, Zip 66935–2400; tel. 785/527–2254; Blaine K. Miller, Administrator

RICE COUNTY DISTRICT HOSPITAL, 619 South Clark Street, Lyons, KS, Zip 67554–3003, Mailing Address: P.O. Box 828, Zip 67554–0828; tel. 620/257–5173; George M. Stover, Chief Executive Officer

SALINA REGIONAL HEALTH CENTER, 400 South Santa Fe Avenue, Salina, KS, Zip 67401–4198, Mailing Address: P.O. Box 5080, Zip 67402–5080; tel. 785/452–7000; Micheal Terry, President and Chief Executive Officer

SMITH COUNTY MEMORIAL HOSPITAL, 614 South Main Street, Smith Center, KS, Zip 66967–3001; tel. 785/282–6845; Allen Van Driel, FACHE, Administrator

KENTUCKY

COMMONWEALTH HEALTH CORPORATION
  800 Park Street, Bowling Green, KY 42101–2356; tel. 270/745–1500; Connie Smith, President and Chief Executive Officer

COMMONWEALTH REGIONAL SPECIALTY HOSPITAL, 250 Park Drive, 6th Floor, Bowling Green, KY, Zip 42101–1760, Mailing Address: P.O. Box 90010, Zip 42102–9010; tel. 270/796–6200; Emily Howard Martin, Administrator

MEDICAL CENTER AT BOWLING GREEN, 250 Park Street, Bowling Green, KY, Zip 42101–1795, Mailing Address: P.O. Box 90010, Zip 42102–9010; tel. 270/745–1000; Connie Smith, Chief Executive Officer

MEDICAL CENTER AT FRANKLIN, 1100 Brookhaven Road, Franklin, KY, Zip 42134–2746; tel. 270/598–4800; Eric Hagan, R.N., Vice President/Administrator

MEDICAL CENTER AT SCOTTSVILLE, 456 Burnley Road, Scottsville, KY, Zip 42164–6355; tel. 270/622–2800; Eric Hagan, R.N., Vice President/Administrator

COMMUNITY CARE NETWORK
  110 A. Second Street, Henderson, KY 42420; tel. 619/278–2273; Roberta Alexander, Director

BAPTIST HEALTH MADISONVILLE, 900 Hospital Drive, Madisonville, KY, Zip 42431–1694; tel. 270/825–5100; Michael A. Baumgartner, President

BAPTIST HEALTH PADUCAH, 2501 Kentucky Avenue, Paducah, KY, Zip 42003–3200; tel. 270/575–2100; William A. Brown, FACHE, President and CEO

CALDWELL MEDICAL CENTER, 100 Medical Center Drive, Princeton, KY, Zip 42445–2430, Mailing Address: P.O. Box 410, Zip 42445–0410; tel. 270/365–0300; Charles D. Lovell, Jr., FACHE, President and Chief Executive Officer

CRITTENDEN COUNTY HOSPITAL, 520 West Gum Street, Marion, KY, Zip 42064–1516, Mailing Address: P.O. Box 386, Zip 42064–0386; tel. 270/965–5281; Greg R. McNeil, Chief Executive Officer

HEALTHSOUTH DEACONESS REHABILITATION HOSPITAL, 4100 Covert Avenue, Evansville, IN, Zip 47714–5567, Mailing Address: P.O. Box 5349, Zip 47716–5349; tel. 812/476–9983; Barbara Butler, Chief Executive Officer

JENNIE STUART MEDICAL CENTER, 320 West 18th Street, Hopkinsville, KY, Zip 42240–1965, Mailing Address: P.O. Box 2400, Zip 42241–2400; tel. 270/887–0100; Eric A. Lee, President and Chief Executive Officer

KOSAIR CHILDREN'S HOSPITAL, 231 East Chestnut Street, Louisville, KY, Zip 40202–1821; tel. 502/629–6000; Thomas D. Kmetz, President

LINCOLN TRAIL BEHAVIORAL HEALTH SYSTEM, 3909 South Wilson Road, Radcliff, KY, Zip 40160–8944, Mailing Address: P.O. Box 369, Zip 40159–0369; tel. 270/351–9444; Charles L. Webb, Jr., Chief Executive Officer

LIVINGSTON HOSPITAL AND HEALTHCARE SERVICES, 131 Hospital Drive, Salem, KY, Zip 42078–8043; tel. 270/988–2299; Mark A. Edwards, Chief Executive Officer

MEDICAL CENTER AT FRANKLIN, 1100 Brookhaven Road, Franklin, KY, Zip 42134–2746; tel. 270/598–4800; Eric Hagan, R.N., Vice President/Administrator

METHODIST HOSPITAL, 1305 North Elm Street, Henderson, KY, Zip 42420–2775, Mailing Address: P.O. Box 48, Zip 42419–0048; tel. 270/827–7700; Bruce D. Begley, Executive Director

METHODIST HOSPITAL UNION COUNTY, 4604 Highway 60 West, Morganfield, KY, Zip 42437–9570; tel. 270/389–5000; Patrick Donahue, Vice President and Administrator

MUHLENBERG COMMUNITY HOSPITAL, 440 Hopkinsville Street, Greenville, KY, Zip 42345–1172, Mailing Address: P.O. Box 387, Zip 42345–0387; tel. 270/338–8000; Stephen L. Meredith, Interim Chief Executive Officer

MURRAY–CALLOWAY COUNTY HOSPITAL, 803 Poplar Street, Murray, KY, Zip 42071–2432; tel. 270/762–1100; Colonel Jerome Penner, Chief Executive Officer

NORTON AUDUBON HOSPITAL, One Audubon Plaza Drive, Louisville, KY, Zip 40217–1300, Mailing Address: P.O. Box 17550, Zip 40217–0550; tel. 502/636–7111; Jon Cooper, President

NORTON HOSPITAL, 200 East Chestnut Street, Louisville, KY, Zip 40202–1800, Mailing Address: P.O. Box 35070, Zip 40232–5070; tel. 502/629–8000; Matthew Ayers, Chief Executive Officer

NORTON SUBURBAN HOSPITAL, 4001 Dutchmans Lane, Louisville, KY, Zip 40207–4799; tel. 502/893–1000; Charlotte Ipsan, President

OHIO COUNTY HOSPITAL, 1211 Main Street, Hartford, KY, Zip 42347–1619; tel. 270/298–7411; Blaine Pieper, Chief Executive Officer

RIVERVALLEY BEHAVIORAL HEALTH HOSPITAL, 1000 Industrial Drive, Owensboro, KY, Zip 42301–8715; tel. 270/689–6500; Gayle DiCesare, President and Chief Executive Officer

SAINT THOMAS WEST HOSPITAL, 4220 Harding Road, Nashville, TN, Zip 37205–2095, Mailing Address: P.O. Box 380, Zip 37202–0380; tel. 615/222–2111; Bernard Sherry, President and CEO

ST. MARY'S MEDICAL CENTER OF EVANSVILLE, 3700 Washington Avenue, Evansville, IN, Zip 47714–0541; tel. 812/485–4000; Keith Jewell, President

STS. MARY & ELIZABETH HOSPITAL, 1850 Bluegrass Avenue, Louisville, KY, Zip 40215–1199; tel. 502/361–6000; Jennifer Nolan, President

TRIGG COUNTY HOSPITAL, 254 Main Street, Cadiz, KY, Zip 42211–9153, Mailing Address: P.O. Box 312, Zip 42211–0312; tel. 270/522–3215; Alisa Coleman, Chief Executive Officer

KENTUCKYONE
  200 Abraham Flexner Way, Louisville, KY 40202–2877; tel. 502/587–4011; Ruth W. Brinkley, R.N., MSN, F, President and Chief Executive Officer

CONTINUING CARE HOSPITAL, 150 North Eagle Creek Drive, 5th Floor, Lexington, KY, Zip 40509–1805; tel. 859/967–5744; Tonja Williams, MSN, R.N., President

FLAGET MEMORIAL HOSPITAL, 4305 New Shepherdsville Road, Bardstown, KY, Zip 40004–9019; tel. 502/350–5000; Beverly Sue Downs, R.N., MSN, FACHE, President

FRAZIER REHAB INSTITUTE, 220 Abraham Flexner Way, Louisville, KY, Zip 40202–1887; tel. 502/582–7400; Randy L. Napier, President

JEWISH HOSPITAL, 200 Abraham Flexner Way, Louisville, KY, Zip 40202–1886; tel. 502/587–4011; Joseph Gilene, President

JEWISH HOSPITAL–SHELBYVILLE, 727 Hospital Drive, Shelbyville, KY, Zip 40065–1699; tel. 502/647–4000; Rob Murphy, President

OUR LADY OF PEACE, 2020 Newburg Road, Louisville, KY, Zip 40205–1879; tel. 502/479–4500; Jennifer Nolan, President

SAINT JOSEPH – LONDON, 1001 Saint Joseph Lane, London, KY, Zip 40741–8345; tel. 606/330–6000; Greg D. Gerard, President

SAINT JOSEPH – MARTIN, 11203 Main Street, Martin, KY, Zip 41649; tel. 606/285–6400; Kathy Stumbo, President

SAINT JOSEPH BEREA, 305 Estill Street, Berea, KY, Zip 40403–1909; tel. 859/986–3151; Eric Gilliam, Chief Executive Officer

SAINT JOSEPH EAST, 150 North Eagle Creek Drive, Lexington, KY, Zip 40509–1805; tel. 859/967–5000; Eric Gilliam, President

SAINT JOSEPH HOSPITAL, One St. Joseph Drive, Lexington, KY, Zip 40504–3754; tel. 859/278–3436; John E. Smithhisler, President

SAINT JOSEPH MOUNT STERLING, 225 Falcon Drive, Mount Sterling, KY, Zip 40353–1158, Mailing Address: P.O. Box 7, Zip 40353–0007; tel. 859/497–5000; Benny Nolen, President

SOUTHERN INDIANA REHABILITATION HOSPITAL, 3104 Blackiston Boulevard, New Albany, IN, Zip 47150–9579; tel. 812/941–8300; Randy L. Napier, President

STS. MARY & ELIZABETH HOSPITAL, 1850 Bluegrass Avenue, Louisville, KY, Zip 40215–1199; tel. 502/361–6000; Jennifer Nolan, President

TAYLOR REGIONAL HOSPITAL, 1700 Old Lebanon Road, Campbellsville, KY, Zip 42718–9600; tel. 270/465–3561; Jane Wheatley, Chief Executive Officer

UNIVERSITY OF LOUISVILLE HOSPITAL, 530 South Jackson Street, Louisville, KY, Zip 40202–3611; tel. 502/562–3000; Kenneth P. Marshall, President

ST. ELIZABETH EDGEWOOD
  1 Medical Village Drive, Edgewood, KY 41017–3403; tel. 859/301–2000; John S. Dubis, FACHE, President and Chief Executive Officer

ST. ELIZABETH GRANT, 238 Barnes Road, Williamstown, KY, Zip 41097–9482; tel. 859/824–8240; John Mitchell, Assistant Vice President Operations

MAINE

MAINE NETWORK FOR HEALTH
  Key Plaza, 23 Water Street, Bangor, ME 04401; tel. 207/942–2844; Stephen A. Ryan, President and Chief Executive Officer

BLUE HILL MEMORIAL HOSPITAL, 57 Water Street, Blue Hill, ME, Zip 04614–5231; tel. 207/374–3400; John Ronan, President and Chief Executive Officer

CHARLES A. DEAN MEMORIAL HOSPITAL, 364 Pritham Avenue, Greenville, ME, Zip 04441–1395, Mailing Address: P.O. Box 1129, Zip 04441–1129; tel. 207/695–5200; Geno Murray, President and Chief Executive Officer

EASTERN MAINE MEDICAL CENTER, 489 State Street, Bangor, ME, Zip 04401–6674, Mailing Address: P.O. Box 404, Zip 04402–0404; tel. 207/973–7000; Deborah Carey Johnson, R.N., President and Chief Executive Officer

HOULTON REGIONAL HOSPITAL, 20 Hartford Street, Houlton, ME, Zip 04730–1891; tel. 207/532–9471; Thomas J. Moakler, Chief Executive Officer

INLAND HOSPITAL, 200 Kennedy Memorial Drive, Waterville, ME, Zip 04901–4595; tel. 207/861–3000; John Dalton, President and Chief Executive Officer

MAYO REGIONAL HOSPITAL, 897 West Main Street, Dover–Foxcroft, ME, Zip 04426–1099; tel. 207/564–8401; Marie E. Vienneau, FACHE, President and Chief Executive Officer

MILLINOCKET REGIONAL HOSPITAL, 200 Somerset Street, Millinocket, ME, Zip 04462–1298; tel. 207/723–5161; Robert Peterson, Chief Executive Officer

MOUNT DESERT ISLAND HOSPITAL, 10 Wayman Lane, Bar Harbor, ME, Zip 04609–1625, Mailing Address: P.O. Box 8, Zip 04609–0008; tel. 207/288–5081; Arthur J. Blank, President and Chief Executive Officer

NORTHERN MAINE MEDICAL CENTER, 194 East Main Street, Fort Kent, ME, Zip 04743–1497; tel. 207/834–3155; Peter Sirois, Chief Executive Officer

SEBASTICOOK VALLEY HEALTH, 447 North Main Street, Pittsfield, ME, Zip 04967–3707; tel. 207/487–4000; Terri Vieira, President and Chief Executive Officer

THE ACADIA HOSPITAL, 268 Stillwater Avenue, Bangor, ME, Zip 04401–3945, Mailing Address: P.O. Box 422, Zip 04402–0422; tel. 207/973–6100; Daniel B. Coffey, President and Chief Executive Officer

THE AROOSTOOK MEDICAL CENTER, 140 Academy Street, Presque Isle, ME, Zip 04769–3171, Mailing Address: P.O. Box 151, Zip 04769–0151; tel. 207/768–4000; Sylvia Getman, President and Chief Executive Officer

MASSACHUSETTS

LAHEY HEALTH
  41 Mall Road, Burlington, MA 01805–0001; tel. 781/744–7100; Howard R. Grant, JD, M.D., President and Chief Executive Officer

BEVERLY HOSPITAL, 85 Herrick Street, Beverly, MA, Zip 01915–1777; tel. 978/922–3000; Denis S. Conroy, President

LAHEY HOSPITAL & MEDICAL CENTER, BURLINGTON, 41 Mall Road, Burlington, MA, Zip 01805–0001; tel. 781/744–5100; Joanne Conroy, M.D., Chief Executive Officer

WINCHESTER HOSPITAL, 41 Highland Avenue, Winchester, MA, Zip 01890–1496; tel. 781/729–9000; Kevin F. Smith, President and Chief Executive Officer

MICHIGAN

GENESYS HEALTH SYSTEM
  1 Genesys Parkway, Grand Blanc, MI 48439–8065; tel. 810/606–5000; Elizabeth Aderholdt, Chief Executive Officer

LAKELAND REGIONAL HEALTH SYSTEM
  1234 Napier Avenue, Saint Joseph, MI 49085–2112; tel. 269/983–8300; Loren Hamel, M.D., President and Chief Executive Officer

LAKELAND COMMUNITY HOSPITAL WATERVLIET, 400 Medical Park Drive, Watervliet, MI, Zip 49098–9225; tel. 269/463–3111; Ray Cruse, Chief Executive Officer

LAKELAND REGIONAL MEDICAL CENTER–ST. JOSEPH, 1234 Napier Avenue, Saint Joseph, MI, Zip 49085–2158; tel. 269/983–8300; Loren Hamel, M.D., President and Chief Executive Officer

LAKELAND SPECIALTY HOSPITAL–BERRIEN CENTER, 6418 Deans Hill Road, Berrien Center, MI, Zip 49102–9750; tel. 269/473–3003; Loren Hamel, M.D., President and Chief Executive Officer

ST. JOHN PROVIDENCE HEALTH SYSTEM
  28000 Dequindre Drive, Warren, MI 48092; tel. 586/753–1259; Jean Meyer, President and Chief Executive Officer

BRIGHTON CENTER FOR RECOVERY, 12851 Grand River Road, Brighton, MI, Zip 48116–8506; tel. 810/227–1211; Raymond Waller, Director

PROVIDENCE HOSPITAL, 16001 West Nine Mile Road, Southfield, MI, Zip 48075-4818, Mailing Address: P.O. Box 2043, Zip 48037-2043; tel. 248/424-3000; Michael Wiemann, M.D., President

ST. JOHN HOSPITAL AND MEDICAL CENTER, 22101 Moross Road, Detroit, MI, Zip 48236-2148; tel. 313/343-4000; David Brooks, President

ST. JOHN MACOMB-OAKLAND HOSPITAL, 11800 East 12 Mile Road, Warren, MI, Zip 48093-3472; tel. 586/573-5000; Terry Hamilton, President

ST. JOHN RIVER DISTRICT HOSPITAL, 4100 River Road, East China, MI, Zip 48054-2909; tel. 810/329-7111; Frank W. Poma, President

UPPER PENINSULA HEALTH CARE NETWORK (UPHCN)
228 West Washington Street, Marquette, MI 49855-4330;
tel. 906/225-3146; Dennis Smith, Chief Executive Officer

ASPIRUS GRAND VIEW HOSPITAL, N10561 Grand View Lane, Ironwood, MI, Zip 49938-9622; tel. 906/932-2525; Paula L. Chermside, Chief Operating Officer

ASPIRUS KEWEENAW HOSPITAL, 205 Osceola Street, Laurium, MI, Zip 49913-2134; tel. 906/337-6500; Michael Hauswirth, Chief Operating Officer

ASPIRUS ONTONAGON HOSPITAL, 601 South Seventh Street, Ontonagon, MI, Zip 49953-1459; tel. 906/884-8000; Michael Hauswirth, Chief Operating Officer

BARAGA COUNTY MEMORIAL HOSPITAL, 18341 U.S. Highway 41, L'Anse, MI, Zip 49946-8024; tel. 906/524-3300; Tim E. Zwickey, Chief Executive Officer

BELL HOSPITAL, 901 Lakeshore Drive, Ishpeming, MI, Zip 49849-1367; tel. 906/486-4431; Mitchell D. Leckelt, Interim Chief Executive Officer

DICKINSON COUNTY HEALTHCARE SYSTEM, 1721 South Stephenson Avenue, Iron Mountain, MI, Zip 49801-3637; tel. 906/774-1313; John Schon, Administrator and Chief Executive Officer

HELEN NEWBERRY JOY HOSPITAL, 502 West Harrie Street, Newberry, MI, Zip 49868-1209; tel. 906/293-9200; Scott Pillion, Chief Executive Officer

MACKINAC STRAITS HEALTH SYSTEM, 1140 North State Street, Saint Ignace, MI, Zip 49781-1048; tel. 906/643-8585; Rodney M. Nelson, Chief Executive Officer

MUNISING MEMORIAL HOSPITAL, 1500 Sand Point Road, Munising, MI, Zip 49862-1406; tel. 906/387-4110; Kevin P. Calhoun, Chief Executive Officer

NORTHSTAR HEALTH SYSTEM, 1400 West Ice Lake Road, Iron River, MI, Zip 49935-9526; tel. 906/265-6121; Connie L. Koutouzos, R.N., MSN, Chief Executive Officer and President

PORTAGE HEALTH, 500 Campus Drive, Hancock, MI, Zip 49930-1569; tel. 906/483-1000; Diane Torres, Interim President and Chief Executive Officer

SCHOOLCRAFT MEMORIAL HOSPITAL, 7870W U.S. Highway 2, Manistique, MI, Zip 49854-8992; tel. 906/341-3200; Tanya Hoar, Chief Executive Officer and Chief Financial Officer

WAR MEMORIAL HOSPITAL, 500 Osborn Boulevard, Sault Sainte Marie, MI, Zip 49783-1884; tel. 906/635-4460; David B. Jahn, President and Chief Executive Officer

MISSOURI

HEALTH NETWORK OF MISSOURI
1600 East Broadway, Columbia, MO 65201-5844; tel. 573/815-8000;
Marty McCormick, Chief Executive Officer

BOTHWELL REGIONAL HEALTH CENTER, 601 East 14th Street, Sedalia, MO, Zip 65301-5972, Mailing Address: P.O. Box 1706, Zip 65302-1706; tel. 660/826-8833; John M. Dawes, FACHE, Chief Executive Officer

CAPITAL REGION MEDICAL CENTER, 1125 Madison Street, Jefferson City, MO, Zip 65101-5200, Mailing Address: P.O. Box 1128, Zip 65102-1128; tel. 573/632-5000; Gaspare Calvaruso, President

LAKE REGIONAL HEALTH SYSTEM, 54 Hospital Drive, Osage Beach, MO, Zip 65065-3050; tel. 573/348-8000; Michael E. Henze, Chief Executive Officer

MERCY HEALTH EAST
615 South New Ballas Road, Saint Louis, MO 63141-8221;
tel. 314/364-3000; Donn Sorensen, President, East Region

MERCY HOSPITAL JEFFERSON, Highway 61 South, Crystal City, MO, Zip 63019, Mailing Address: P.O. Box 350, Zip 63019-0350; tel. 636/933-1000; Eric Ammons, President

MERCY HOSPITAL ST. LOUIS, 615 South New Ballas Road, Saint Louis, MO, Zip 63141-8277; tel. 314/569-6000; Jeffrey A. Johnston, President

MERCY HOSPITAL WASHINGTON, 901 East Fifth Street, Washington, MO, Zip 63090-3127; tel. 636/239-8000; Terri L. McLain, FACHE, President

MONTANA

MONTANA HEALTH NETWORK
11 South 7th Street, Suite 241, Miles City, MT 59301;
tel. 406/234-1420; Janet Bastian, Chief Executive Officer

BEARTOOTH BILLINGS CLINIC, 2525 North Broadway, Red Lodge, MT, Zip 59068-9222, Mailing Address: P.O. Box 590, Zip 59068-0590; tel. 406/446-2345; Kelley Evans, Chief Executive Officer

BILLINGS CLINIC, 2800 10th Avenue North, Billings, MT, Zip 59101-0703, Mailing Address: P.O. Box 37000, Zip 59107-7000; tel. 406/657-4000; Nicholas Wolter, M.D., Chief Executive Officer

CENTRAL MONTANA MEDICAL CENTER, 408 Wendell Avenue, Lewistown, MT, Zip 59457-2261; tel. 406/535-7711; Christopher Noland, Interim Chief Executive Officer

DANIELS MEMORIAL HEALTHCARE CENTER, 105 Fifth Avenue East, Scobey, MT, Zip 59263, Mailing Address: P.O. Box 400, Zip 59263-0400; tel. 406/487-2296; David Hubbard, Chief Executive Officer

FALLON MEDICAL COMPLEX, 202 South 4th Street West, Baker, MT, Zip 59313-9156, Mailing Address: P.O. Box 820, Zip 59313-0820; tel. 406/778-3331; David Espeland, Chief Executive Officer

FRANCES MAHON DEACONESS HOSPITAL, 621 Third Street South, Glasgow, MT, Zip 59230-2699; tel. 406/228-3500; Randall G. Holom, Chief Executive Officer

GLENDIVE MEDICAL CENTER, 202 Prospect Drive, Glendive, MT, Zip 59330-1999; tel. 406/345-3306; Parker Powell, Chief Executive Officer

HOLY ROSARY HEALTHCARE, 2600 Wilson Street, Miles City, MT, Zip 59301-5094; tel. 406/233-2600; Paul Lewis, Chief Executive Officer

MCCONE COUNTY HEALTH CENTER, 605 Sullivan Avenue, Circle, MT, Zip 59215, Mailing Address: P.O. Box 48, Zip 59215-0048; tel. 406/485-3381; Nancy Rosaaen, Chief Executive Officer

PHILLIPS COUNTY HOSPITAL, 417 South Fourth East, Malta, MT, Zip 59538-8825, Mailing Address: P.O. Box 640, Zip 59538-0640; tel. 406/654-1100; Ward C. VanWichen, Chief Executive Officer

ROOSEVELT MEDICAL CENTER, 818 Second Avenue East, Culbertson, MT, Zip 59218, Mailing Address: P.O. Box 419, Zip 59218-0419; tel. 406/787-6401; Audrey Stromberg, Administrator

ROUNDUP MEMORIAL HEALTHCARE, 1202 Third Street West, Roundup, MT, Zip 59072-1816, Mailing Address: P.O. Box 40, Zip 59072-0040; tel. 406/323-2301; Bradley Howell, Chief Executive Officer

SHERIDAN MEMORIAL HOSPITAL, 440 West Laurel Avenue, Plentywood, MT, Zip 59254-1596; tel. 406/765-1420; Sandra Christensen, Chief Executive Officer

SIDNEY HEALTH CENTER, 216 14th Avenue S.W., Sidney, MT, Zip 59270-3586; tel. 406/488-2100; Richard Haraldson, Chief Executive Officer

STILLWATER COMMUNITY HOSPITAL, 44 West Fourth Avenue North, Columbus, MT, Zip 59019-0959, Mailing Address: P.O. Box 959, Zip 59019-0959; tel. 406/322-5316; Tim Russell, Administrator

NEBRASKA

BLUE RIVER VALLEY HEALTH NETWORK
2222 North Lincoln Avenue, York, NE 68467-1030; tel. 402/362-0445;
Charles K. Schulz, President

ANNIE JEFFREY MEMORIAL COUNTY HEALTH CENTER, 531 Beebe Street, Osceola, NE, Zip 68651-5537, Mailing Address: P.O. Box 428, Zip 68651-0428; tel. 402/747-2031; Joseph W. Lohrman, Chief Executive Officer

BOONE COUNTY HEALTH CENTER, 723 West Fairview Street, Albion, NE, Zip 68620-1725, Mailing Address: P.O. Box 151, Zip 68620-0151; tel. 402/395-2191; Victor N. Lee, FACHE, President and Chief Executive Officer

BRODSTONE MEMORIAL HOSPITAL, 520 East Tenth Street, Superior, NE, Zip 68978-1225, Mailing Address: P.O. Box 187, Zip 68978-0187; tel. 402/879-3281; John E. Keelan, Administrator and Chief Executive Officer

BUTLER COUNTY HEALTH CARE CENTER, 372 South Ninth Street, David City, NE, Zip 68632-2116; tel. 402/367-1200; Donald T. Naiberk, Administrator

COMMUNITY MEMORIAL HOSPITAL, 1579 Midland Street, Syracuse, NE, Zip 68446-9732, Mailing Address: P.O. Box N., Zip 68446-0518; tel. 402/269-2011; Michael Harvey, President and Chief Executive Officer

CRETE AREA MEDICAL CENTER, 2910 Betten Drive, Crete, NE, Zip 68333-3084, Mailing Address: P.O. Box 220, Zip 68333-0220; tel. 402/826-2102; Tad M. Hunt, MS, President and Chief Executive Officer

FILLMORE COUNTY HOSPITAL, 1900 F Street, Geneva, NE, Zip 68361-1325, Mailing Address: P.O. Box 193, Zip 68361-0193; tel. 402/759-3167; Paul Utemark, Chief Executive Officer

HENDERSON HEALTH CARE SERVICES, 1621 Front Street, Henderson, NE, Zip 68371-8902; tel. 402/723-4512; Cheryl Brown, Administrator

HOWARD COUNTY MEDICAL CENTER, 1113 Sherman Street, Saint Paul, NE, Zip 68873-1546, Mailing Address: P.O. Box 406, Zip 68873-0406; tel. 308/754-4421; Arlan D. Johnson, Chief Executive Officer

JEFFERSON COMMUNITY HEALTH CENTER, 2200 H Street, Fairbury, NE, Zip 68352-1119, Mailing Address: P.O. Box 277, Zip 68352-0277; tel. 402/729-3351; Chad Jurgens, Chief Executive Officer

JOHNSON COUNTY HOSPITAL, 202 High Street, Tecumseh, NE, Zip 68450-2443, Mailing Address: P.O. Box 599, Zip 68450-0599; tel. 402/335-3361; Diane Newman, Administrator

LITZENBERG MEMORIAL COUNTY HOSPITAL, 1715 26th Street, Central City, NE, Zip 68826-9620; tel. 308/946-3015; Julie Murray, Chief Executive Officer

MEMORIAL COMMUNITY HEALTH, 1423 Seventh Street, Aurora, NE,
Zip 68818–1197; tel. 402/694–3171; Diane R. Keller, Chief Executive
Officer

MEMORIAL HEALTH CARE SYSTEMS, 300 North Columbia Avenue, Seward, NE,
Zip 68434–2228; tel. 402/643–2971; Roger J. Reamer, Chief Executive
Officer

THAYER COUNTY HEALTH SERVICES, 120 Park Avenue, Hebron, NE,
Zip 68370–2019, Mailing Address: P.O. Box 49, Zip 68370–0049;
tel. 402/768–6041; Michael G. Burcham, Sr., Chief Executive Officer

VALLEY COUNTY HEALTH SYSTEM, 2707 L. Street, Ord, NE, Zip 68862–1275;
tel. 308/728–4200; William T. Sugg, President and Chief Executive Officer

WARREN MEMORIAL HOSPITAL, 905 Second Street, Friend, NE,
Zip 68359–1133; tel. 402/947–2541; Christopher R. Bjornberg, Chief
Executive Officer

YORK GENERAL HOSPITAL, 2222 North Lincoln Avenue, York, NE,
Zip 68467–1095; tel. 402/362–6671; Charles K. Schulz, Chief Executive
Officer

CHI HEALTH
**12809 West Dodge Road, Omaha, NE 68154–2155;
tel. 402/343–4000; Cliff Robertson, M.D., President and Chief
Executive Officer**

CHI HEALTH BERGAN MERCY, 7500 Mercy Road, Omaha, NE, Zip 68124–2319;
tel. 402/398–6060; Marie E. Knedler, R.N., FACHE, President

CHI HEALTH CREIGHTON UNIVERSITY MEDICAL CENTER, 601 North 30th Street,
Omaha, NE, Zip 68131–2197; tel. 402/449–4000; Kevin J. Nokels, FACHE,
President

CHI HEALTH IMMANUEL, 6901 North 72nd Street, Omaha, NE, Zip 68122–1799;
tel. 402/572–2121; Ann Schumacher, R.N., MSN, President

CHI HEALTH LAKESIDE, 16901 Lakeside Hills Court, Omaha, NE,
Zip 68130–2318; tel. 402/717–8000; Cindy Alloway, President

CHI HEALTH MERCY CORNING, 603 Rosary Drive, Corning, IA, Zip 50841–1683;
tel. 641/322–3121; Debra Goldsmith, Regional Administrator

CHI HEALTH MERCY COUNCIL BLUFFS, 800 Mercy Drive, Council Bluffs, IA,
Zip 51503–3128, Mailing Address: P.O. Box 1C, Zip 51502–3001;
tel. 712/328–5000; Marie E. Knedler, R.N., FACHE, President

CHI HEALTH MIDLANDS, 11111 South 84th Street, Papillion, NE,
Zip 68046–4122; tel. 402/593–3000; Cindy Alloway, President

CHI HEALTH MISSOURI VALLEY, 631 North Eighth Street, Missouri Valley, IA,
Zip 51555–1102; tel. 712/642–2784; Robert A. Valentine, President

CHI HEALTH PLAINVIEW, 704 North Third Street, Plainview, NE, Zip 68769–2047,
Mailing Address: P.O. Box 489, Zip 68769–0489; tel. 402/582–4245;
Richard B. Gamel, Operations Leader

CHI HEALTH SCHUYLER, 104 West 17th Street, Schuyler, NE, Zip 68661–1304;
tel. 402/352–2441; Connie Peters, R.N., President

NORTHEAST HEALTH SERVICES
**PO Box 186, Creighton, NE 68729–0186; tel. 402/358–5700; Jeff
Lingerfelt, Chief Executive Officer**

AVERA CREIGHTON HOSPITAL, 1503 Main Street, Creighton, NE,
Zip 68729–3007, Mailing Address: P.O. Box 186, Zip 68729–0186;
tel. 402/358–5700; Jennifer Poppen, Chief Executive Officer

CHI HEALTH PLAINVIEW, 704 North Third Street, Plainview, NE, Zip 68769–2047,
Mailing Address: P.O. Box 489, Zip 68769–0489; tel. 402/582–4245;
Richard B. Gamel, Operations Leader

OSMOND GENERAL HOSPITAL, 402 North Maple Street, Osmond, NE,
Zip 68765–5726, Mailing Address: P.O. Box 429, Zip 68765–0429;
tel. 402/748–3393; Celine M. Mlady, Chief Executive Officer

REGIONAL CARE, INC.
**905 West 27th Street, Scottsbluff, NE 69361–1545; tel. 308/635–2260;
Steve Hetzel, President**

NEW HAMPSHIRE

CARING COMMUNITY NETWORK OF THE TWIN RIVERS
**c/o First Health, 841 Central Street, Franklin, NH 03235–2026;
tel. 603/934–0177; Rick Silverberg, Managing Director**

FRANKLIN REGIONAL HOSPITAL, 15 Aiken Avenue, Franklin, NH, Zip 03235–1299;
tel. 603/934–2060; Charles K. Van Sluyter, Interim Chief Executive Officer

NEW JERSEY

HACKENSACK UNIVERSITY HEALTH NETWORK
**30 Prospect Avenue, Hackensack, NJ 07601–1914; tel. 201/996–2000;
Robert C. Garrett, FACHE, President and Chief Executive Officer**

QUALCARE, INC.
**242 Old New Brunswick Road, Piscataway, NJ 08854–3754;
tel. 732/562–2800; Jerry Eisenberg, Network Contact**

CAPITAL HEALTH MEDICAL CENTER–HOPEWELL, 1 Capital Way, Pennington, NJ,
Zip 08534–2520; tel. 609/303–4000; Al Maghazehe, Ph.D., FACHE, Chief
Executive Officer

CHILTON MEDICAL CENTER, 97 West Parkway, Pompton Plains, NJ,
Zip 07444–1696; tel. 973/831–5000; Deborah Zastocki, R.N., FACHE,
FACHE, President and Chief Executive Officer

CHRIST HOSPITAL, 176 Palisade Avenue, Jersey City, NJ, Zip 07306–1196,
Mailing Address: 176 Palisades Avenue, Zip 07306–1196;
tel. 201/795–8200; Nizar Kifaieh, M.D., President and Chief Medical Officer

CLARA MAASS MEDICAL CENTER, One Clara Maass Drive, Belleville, NJ,
Zip 07109–3557; tel. 973/450–2000; Mary Ellen Clyne, Ph.D., President
and Chief Executive Officer

DEBORAH HEART AND LUNG CENTER, 200 Trenton Road, Browns Mills, NJ,
Zip 08015–1705; tel. 609/893–6611; Joseph P. Chirichella, President and
Chief Executive Officer

ENGLEWOOD HOSPITAL AND MEDICAL CENTER, 350 Engle Street, Englewood,
NJ, Zip 07631–1898; tel. 201/894–3000; Warren Geller, President and
Chief Executive Officer

HACKENSACK UNIVERSITY MEDICAL CENTER, 30 Prospect Avenue, Hackensack,
NJ, Zip 07601–1914; tel. 201/996–2000; Robert C. Garrett, FACHE,
President and Chief Executive Officer

HACKETTSTOWN REGIONAL MEDICAL CENTER, 651 Willow Grove Street,
Hackettstown, NJ, Zip 07840–1799; tel. 908/852–5100; Jason C. Coe,
President and Chief Executive Officer

INSPIRA MEDICAL CENTER–VINELAND, 1505 West Sherman Avenue, Vineland, NJ,
Zip 08360–6912; tel. 856/641–8000; John A. DiAngelo, President and Chief
Executive Officer

JFK MEDICAL CENTER, 65 James Street, Edison, NJ, Zip 08820–3947;
tel. 732/321–7000; Raymond F. Fredericks, President and CEO

MEMORIAL HOSPITAL OF SALEM COUNTY, 310 Woodstown Road, Salem, NJ,
Zip 08079–2080; tel. 856/935–1000; Ryan Jensen, Chief Executive Officer

OCEAN MEDICAL CENTER, 425 Jack Martin Boulevard, Brick Township, NJ,
Zip 08724–7732; tel. 732/840–2200; Dean Q. Lin, FACHE, President

PIEDMONT MOUNTAINSIDE HOSPITAL, 1266 Highway 515 South, Jasper, GA,
Zip 30143–4872; tel. 706/692–2441; Denise Ray, President and Chief
Executive Officer

RARITAN BAY MEDICAL CENTER, 530 New Brunswick Avenue, Perth Amboy, NJ,
Zip 08861–3654; tel. 732/442–3700; Michael R. D'Agnes, FACHE,
President and Chief Executive Officer

RIVERVIEW MEDICAL CENTER, 1 Riverview Plaza, Red Bank, NJ, Zip 07701–1864;
tel. 732/741–2700; Timothy J. Hogan, FACHE, Regional President

ROBERT WOOD JOHNSON UNIVERSITY HOSPITAL, 1 Robert Wood Johnson Place,
New Brunswick, NJ, Zip 08901–1928; tel. 732/828–3000; Stephen K.
Jones, President and Chief Executive Officer

SAINT MICHAEL'S MEDICAL CENTER, 111 Central Avenue, Newark, NJ,
Zip 07102–1909; tel. 973/877–5350; David A. Ricci, President and Chief
Executive Officer

ST. MARY'S HOSPITAL, 350 Boulevard, Passaic, NJ, Zip 07055–2840;
tel. 973/365–4300; Edward Condit, President and Chief Executive Officer

UNIVERSITY HOSPITAL, 150 Bergen Street, Newark, NJ, Zip 07103–2496;
tel. 973/972–4300; James R. Gonzalez, President and Chief Executive
Officer

UNIVERSITY MEDICAL CENTER OF PRINCETON AT PLAINSBORO, One Plainsboro
Road, Plainsboro, NJ, Zip 08536–1913; tel. 609/853–7100; Barry S.
Rabner, President and Chief Executive Officer

VIRTUA BERLIN, 100 Townsend Avenue, Berlin, NJ, Zip 08009–9035;
tel. 856/322–3000; Gary L. Long, Senior Vice President Population
Management

VIRTUA MARLTON, 90 Brick Road, Marlton, NJ, Zip 08053–2177;
tel. 856/355–6000; Gary L. Long, Senior Vice President Population
Management

NEW YORK

ALLEGANY WESTERN STEUBEN RURAL HEALTH NETWORK, INC.
**85 North Main Street, Suite 4, Wellsville, NY 14895–1254;
tel. 585/593–5223; Carrie Whitwood, Executive Director**

JONES MEMORIAL HOSPITAL, 191 North Main Street, Wellsville, NY,
Zip 14895–1150, Mailing Address: P.O. Box 72, Zip 14895–0072;
tel. 585/593–1100; Eva Benedict, R.N., President and Chief Executive
Officer

ST. JAMES MERCY HEALTH SYSTEM, 411 Canisteo Street, Hornell, NY,
Zip 14843–2197; tel. 607/324–8000; Jennifer Sullivan, President and Chief
Executive Officer

ARNOT HEALTH
**600 Roe Avenue, Elmira, NY 14905–1629; tel. 607/737–4100; Robert
K. Lambert, M.D., FACHE, President and Chief Executive Officer**

ARNOT OGDEN MEDICAL CENTER, 600 Roe Avenue, Elmira, NY,
Zip 14905–1629; tel. 607/737–4100; H. Fred Farley, R.N., Ph.D., FACHE,
President and Chief Operating Officer

IRA DAVENPORT MEMORIAL HOSPITAL, 7571 State Route 54, Bath, NY,
Zip 14810–9590; tel. 607/776–8500; James B. Watson, President and
Chief Operating Officer

ST. JOSEPH'S HOSPITAL, 555 St. Joseph's Boulevard, Elmira, NY,
Zip 14901–3223; tel. 607/733–6541; H. Fred Farley, R.N., Ph.D., FACHE,
President and Chief Operating Officer

BASSETT HEALTHCARE NETWORK
 1 Atwell Road, Cooperstown, NY 13326–1301; tel. 607/547–3456;
 William F. Streck, M.D., President and Chief Executive Officer

AURELIA OSBORN FOX MEMORIAL HOSPITAL, 1 Norton Avenue, Oneonta, NY,
 Zip 13820–2629; tel. 607/432–2000; John R. Remillard, President

BASSETT MEDICAL CENTER, One Atwell Road, Cooperstown, NY,
 Zip 13326–1394; tel. 607/547–3100; Vance Brown, M.D., President and
 Chief Executive Officer

COBLESKILL REGIONAL HOSPITAL, 178 Grandview Drive, Cobleskill, NY,
 Zip 12043–5144; tel. 518/254–3456; Eric H. Stein, FACHE, President and
 Chief Executive Officer

LITTLE FALLS HOSPITAL, 140 Burwell Street, Little Falls, NY, Zip 13365–1725;
 tel. 315/823–1000; Michael L. Ogden, President and Chief Executive Officer

O'CONNOR HOSPITAL, 460 Andes Road, State Route 28, Delhi, NY,
 Zip 13753–7407; tel. 607/746–0300; Daniel M. Ayres, Chief Executive
 Officer

GREAT LAKES HEALTH SYSTEM OF WESTERN NEW YORK
 726 Exchange Street, Suite 522, Buffalo, NY 14210–1485;
 tel. 716/859–8820; Jody Lomeo, Interim Chief Executive Officer

ERIE COUNTY MEDICAL CENTER, 462 Grider Street, Buffalo, NY,
 Zip 14215–3098; tel. 716/898–3000; Richard C. Cleland, FACHE, President
 and Chief Operating Officer and Interim Chief Executive Officer

KALEIDA HEALTH, 100 High Street, Buffalo, NY, Zip 14203–1154;
 tel. 716/859–5600; Jody Lomeo, Interim CEO

LAKE ERIE REGIONAL HEALTH SYSTEM OF NEW YORK
 529 Central Avenue, Dunkirk, NY 14048–2514; tel. 716/366–1111; J.
 Gary Rhodes, FACHE, Interim Chief Executive Officer

BROOKS MEMORIAL HOSPITAL, 529 Central Avenue, Dunkirk, NY,
 Zip 14048–2599; tel. 716/366–1111; J. Gary Rhodes, FACHE, Interim
 President and Chief Executive Officer

LAKE SHORE HEALTH CARE CENTER, 845 Route 5 and 20, Irving, NY,
 Zip 14081–9716; tel. 716/951–7000; John P. Galati, Interim Chief
 Executive Officer

MOHAWK VALLEY NETWORK, INC.
 1710 Burrstone Road, New Hartford, NY 13413–1002;
 tel. 315/624–6001; Scott H. Perra, President and Chief Executive
 Officer

FAXTON–ST. LUKE'S HEALTHCARE, 1656 Champlin Avenue, Utica, NY,
 Zip 13502–4830, Mailing Address: P.O. Box 479, Zip 13503–0479;
 tel. 315/624–6000; Scott H. Perra, President and Chief Executive Officer

ST. ELIZABETH MEDICAL CENTER, 2209 Genesee Street, Utica, NY,
 Zip 13501–5999; tel. 315/798–8100; Scott H. Perra, Chief Executive
 Officer

MOUNT SINAI NYU HEALTH NETWORK
 One Gustave L. Levy Place, New York, NY 10029; tel. 212/659–8888;
 Arthur A. Klein, M.D., President

ELMHURST HOSPITAL CENTER, 79–01 Broadway, Elmhurst, NY,
 Zip 11373–1329; tel. 718/334–4000; Chris D. Constantino, Executive
 Director

ENGLEWOOD HOSPITAL AND MEDICAL CENTER, 350 Engle Street, Englewood,
 NJ, Zip 07631–1898; tel. 201/894–3000; Warren Geller, President and
 Chief Executive Officer

JAMES J. PETERS VETERANS AFFAIRS MEDICAL CENTER, 130 West Kingsbridge
 Road, Bronx, NY, Zip 10468–3904; tel. 718/584–9000; Erik Langhoff, M.D.,
 Ph.D., Director

JERSEY CITY MEDICAL CENTER, 355 Grand Street, Jersey City, NJ,
 Zip 07302–4321; tel. 201/915–2000; Joseph F. Scott, FACHE, President
 and Chief Executive Officer

LUTHERAN MEDICAL CENTER, 150 55th Street, Brooklyn, NY, Zip 11220–2559;
 tel. 718/630–7000; Wendy Z. Goldstein, President and Chief Executive
 Officer

MEADOWLANDS HOSPITAL MEDICAL CENTER, 55 Meadowlands Parkway,
 Secaucus, NJ, Zip 07094–2977; tel. 201/392–3100; Thomas Considine,
 Chief Executive Officer

MORRISTOWN MEDICAL CENTER, 100 Madison Avenue, Morristown, NJ,
 Zip 07960–6136; tel. 973/971–5000; David J. Shulkin, M.D., President

MOUNT SINAI HOSPITAL, One Gustave L. Levy Place, New York, NY,
 Zip 10029–6574; tel. 212/241–6500; David L. Reich, M.D., President

MOUNT SINAI QUEENS, 25–10 30th Avenue, Long Island City, NY,
 Zip 11102–2448; tel. 718/932–1000; Caryn A. Schwab, Executive Director

OVERLOOK MEDICAL CENTER, 99 Beauvoir Avenue, Summit, NJ,
 Zip 07901–3533; tel. 908/522–2000; Alan R. Lieber, President

PHELPS MEMORIAL HOSPITAL CENTER, 701 North Broadway, Sleepy Hollow, NY,
 Zip 10591–1020; tel. 914/366–3000; Keith F. Safian, President and Chief
 Executive Officer

QUEENS HOSPITAL CENTER, 82–68 164th Street, Jamaica, NY,
 Zip 11432–1104; tel. 718/883–3000; Julius Wool, Executive Director

ST. JOHN'S RIVERSIDE HOSPITAL, 967 North Broadway, Yonkers, NY,
 Zip 10701–1399; tel. 914/964–4444; Ronald Corti, President and Chief
 Executive Officer

ST. JOSEPH'S REGIONAL MEDICAL CENTER, 703 Main Street, Paterson, NJ,
 Zip 07503–2691; tel. 973/754–2000; William A. McDonald, President and
 Chief Executive Officer

ST. LUKE'S CORNWALL HOSPITAL, 70 Dubois Street, Newburgh, NY,
 Zip 12550–4851; tel. 845/561–4400; Robert Ross, President and Chief
 Executive Officer

VASSAR BROTHERS MEDICAL CENTER, 45 Reade Place, Poughkeepsie, NY,
 Zip 12601–3947; tel. 845/454–8500; Robert Friedberg, President

NORTHEAST HEALTH
 2212 Burdett Avenue, Troy, NY 12180–2475; tel. 518/274–3382;
 James K. Reed, M.D., President and Chief Executive Officer

NORTHERN NY RURAL HEALTH CARE ALLIANCE
 800 Starbuck Avenue, Suite A–5, Watertown, NY 13601;
 tel. 315/755–2500

RURAL HEALTH NETWORK OF OSWEGO COUNTY
 10 George Street, Oswego, NY 13126; tel. 315/592–0827; Danielle
 Wert, Coordinator

OSWEGO HOSPITAL, 110 West Sixth Street, Oswego, NY, Zip 13126–2507;
 tel. 315/349–5511; Ann C. Gilpin, President and Chief Executive Officer

STELLARIS HEALTH
 1 North Greenwich Road, Armonk, NY 10504–2311; tel. 914/273–5454

LAWRENCE HOSPITAL CENTER, 55 Palmer Avenue, Bronxville, NY,
 Zip 10708–3403; tel. 914/787–1000; Edward M. Dinan, President and Chief
 Executive Officer

NORTHERN WESTCHESTER HOSPITAL, 400 East Main Street, Mount Kisco, NY,
 Zip 10549–3477; tel. 914/666–1200; Joel Seligman, President and Chief
 Executive Officer

PHELPS MEMORIAL HOSPITAL CENTER, 701 North Broadway, Sleepy Hollow, NY,
 Zip 10591–1020; tel. 914/366–3000; Keith F. Safian, President and Chief
 Executive Officer

WHITE PLAINS HOSPITAL CENTER, 41 East Post Road, White Plains, NY,
 Zip 10601–4699; tel. 914/681–0600; Jon B. Schandler, Chief Executive
 Officer

NORTH CAROLINA

COASTAL CAROLINAS HEALTH ALLIANCE
 5305–M Wrightsville Avenue, Wilmington, NC 28403;
 tel. 910/332–8012; Yvonne Hughes, Executive Director

CAPE FEAR VALLEY – BLADEN COUNTY HOSPITAL, 501 South Poplar Street,
 Elizabethtown, NC, Zip 28337–9375, Mailing Address: P.O. Box 398,
 Zip 28337–0398; tel. 910/862–5100; Dan Weatherly, On Site Administrator

COLUMBUS REGIONAL HEALTHCARE SYSTEM, 500 Jefferson Street, Whiteville,
 NC, Zip 28472–3634; tel. 910/642–8011; Duane L. Erwin, Interim Chief
 Executive Officer

J. ARTHUR DOSHER MEMORIAL HOSPITAL, 924 North Howe Street, Southport,
 NC, Zip 28461–3099; tel. 910/457–3800; Thomas R. Siemers, Chief
 Executive Officer

MCLEOD LORIS SEACOAST HOSPITAL, 3655 Mitchell Street, Loris, SC,
 Zip 29569–2827; tel. 843/716–7000; Edward D. Tinsley, III, Chief Executive
 Officer

MCLEOD REGIONAL MEDICAL CENTER, 555 East Cheves Street, Florence, SC,
 Zip 29506–2617, Mailing Address: P.O. Box 100551, Zip 29502–0551;
 tel. 843/777–2000; Robert L. Colones, President and Chief Executive
 Officer

NEW HANOVER REGIONAL MEDICAL CENTER, 2131 South 17th Street,
 Wilmington, NC, Zip 28401–7483, Mailing Address: P.O. Box 9000,
 Zip 28402–9000; tel. 910/343–7000; John K. Barto, Jr., President and
 Chief Executive Officer

PENDER MEMORIAL HOSPITAL, 507 East Freemont Street, Burgaw, NC,
 Zip 28425–5131; tel. 910/259–5451; Ruth Glaser, President

SAMPSON REGIONAL MEDICAL CENTER, 607 Beaman Street, Clinton, NC,
 Zip 28328–2697, Mailing Address: P.O. Box 260, Zip 28329–0260;
 tel. 910/592–8511; Shawn Howerton, M.D., Chief Executive Officer and
 President, Medical Staff

SCOTLAND HEALTH CARE SYSTEM, 500 Lauchwood Drive, Laurinburg, NC,
 Zip 28352–5599; tel. 910/291–7000; Gregory C. Wood, President and
 Chief Executive Officer

SOUTHEASTERN HEALTH, 300 West 27th Street, Lumberton, NC,
 Zip 28358–3075, Mailing Address: P.O. Box 1408, Zip 28359–1408;
 tel. 910/671–5000; Joann Anderson, President and Chief Executive Officer

VIDANT DUPLIN HOSPITAL, 401 North Main Street, Kenansville, NC,
 Zip 28349–8801, Mailing Address: P.O. Box 278, Zip 28349–0278;
 tel. 910/296–0941; Jay Briley, President

VIDANT MEDICAL CENTER, 2100 Stantonsburg Road, Greenville, NC,
 Zip 27834–2818, Mailing Address: P.O. Box 6028, Zip 27835–6028;
 tel. 252/847–4100; Stephen Lawler, President

MISSION HEALTH SYSTEM
 509 Biltmore Avenue, Asheville, NC 28801–4601; tel. 828/213–1111;
 Ronald A. Paulus, M.D., President and Chief Executive Officer

ANGEL MEDICAL CENTER, 120 Riverview Street, Franklin, NC, Zip 28734–2612, Mailing Address: P.O. Box 1209, Zip 28744–0569; tel. 828/524–8411; James B. Bross, President and Chief Executive Officer

BLUE RIDGE REGIONAL HOSPITAL, 125 Hospital Drive, Spruce Pine, NC, Zip 28777–3035, Mailing Address: P.O. Drawer 9, Zip 28777–0009; tel. 828/765–4201; Lynn Ingram Boggs, President and Chief Executive Officer

HIGHLANDS–CASHIERS HOSPITAL, 190 Hospital Drive, Highlands, NC, Zip 28741–7600, Mailing Address: P.O. Drawer 190, Zip 28741–0190; tel. 828/526–1200; Craig B. James, FACHE, Chief Executive Officer

MCDOWELL HOSPITAL, 430 Rankin Drive, Marion, NC, Zip 28752–6568, Mailing Address: P.O. Box 730, Zip 28752–0730; tel. 828/659–5000; Lynn Ingram Boggs, President

MISSION HOSPITAL, 509 Biltmore Avenue, Asheville, NC, Zip 28801–4690; tel. 828/213–1111; Ronald A. Paulus, M.D., President and Chief Executive Officer

TRANSYLVANIA REGIONAL HOSPITAL, 260 Hospital Drive, Brevard, NC, Zip 28712–3378; tel. 828/884–9111; Catherine Landis, R.N., MS, President and Chief Nursing Officer

WNC HEALTH NETWORK, INC.
1200 Ridgefield Boulevard Suite 200, Asheville, NC 28806–2280; tel. 828/667–8220; Tim Bugg, Interim Executive Director

ANGEL MEDICAL CENTER, 120 Riverview Street, Franklin, NC, Zip 28734–2612, Mailing Address: P.O. Box 1209, Zip 28744–0569; tel. 828/524–8411; James B. Bross, President and Chief Executive Officer

BLUE RIDGE REGIONAL HOSPITAL, 125 Hospital Drive, Spruce Pine, NC, Zip 28777–3035, Mailing Address: P.O. Drawer 9, Zip 28777–0009; tel. 828/765–4201; Lynn Ingram Boggs, President and Chief Executive Officer

CHARLES A. CANNON MEMORIAL HOSPITAL, 434 Hospital Drive, Linville, NC, Zip 28646, Mailing Address: P.O. Box 767, Zip 28646–0767; tel. 828/737–7000; Carmen Lacey, MSN, R.N., President

CHARLES GEORGE VETERANS AFFAIRS MEDICAL CENTER, 1100 Tunnel Road, Asheville, NC, Zip 28805–2087; tel. 828/298–7911; Cynthia Breyfogle, FACHE, Director

CHEROKEE INDIAN HOSPITAL, 1 Hospital Road, Cherokee, NC, Zip 28719; tel. 828/497–9163; Casey Cooper, Chief Executive Officer

HAYWOOD REGIONAL MEDICAL CENTER, 262 Leroy George Drive, Clyde, NC, Zip 28721–7430; tel. 828/456–7311; Janie Sinacore–Jaberg, R.N., MS, FACHE, Chief Executive Officer

HIGHLANDS–CASHIERS HOSPITAL, 190 Hospital Drive, Highlands, NC, Zip 28741–7600, Mailing Address: P.O. Drawer 190, Zip 28741–0190; tel. 828/526–1200; Craig B. James, FACHE, Chief Executive Officer

MARGARET R. PARDEE MEMORIAL HOSPITAL, 800 North Justice Street, Hendersonville, NC, Zip 28791–3410; tel. 828/696–1000; James M. Kirby, II, President and Chief Executive Officer

MCDOWELL HOSPITAL, 430 Rankin Drive, Marion, NC, Zip 28752–6568, Mailing Address: P.O. Box 730, Zip 28752–0730; tel. 828/659–5000; Lynn Ingram Boggs, President

MISSION HOSPITAL, 509 Biltmore Avenue, Asheville, NC, Zip 28801–4690; tel. 828/213–1111; Ronald A. Paulus, M.D., President and Chief Executive Officer

MURPHY MEDICAL CENTER, 3990 U.S. Highway 64 East Alt, Murphy, NC, Zip 28906–7917; tel. 828/837–8161; Michael Stevenson, Chief Executive Officer

PARK RIDGE HEALTH, 100 Hospital Drive, Hendersonville, NC, Zip 28792–5272; tel. 828/684–8501; Jimm Bunch, President and Chief Executive Officer

RUTHERFORD REGIONAL HEALTH SYSTEM, 288 South Ridgecrest Avenue, Rutherfordton, NC, Zip 28139–2838; tel. 828/286–5000; Cindy D. Buck, Chief Executive Officer

ST. LUKE'S HOSPITAL, 101 Hospital Drive, Columbus, NC, Zip 28722–6418; tel. 828/894–3311; Kenneth A. Shull, FACHE, Chief Executive Officer

NORTH DAKOTA

NORTHLAND HEALTHCARE ALLIANCE
3811 Lockport Street Suite 3, Bismarck, ND 58503–5554; tel. 701/250–0709; Timothy Cox, Director

ASHLEY MEDICAL CENTER, 612 North Center Avenue, Ashley, ND, Zip 58413–7013, Mailing Address: P.O. Box 450, Zip 58413–0450; tel. 701/288–3433; Jerry Lepp, Chief Executive Officer

COMMUNITY MEMORIAL HOSPITAL, 220 Fifth Avenue, Turtle Lake, ND, Zip 58575–4005, Mailing Address: P.O. Box 280, Zip 58575–0280; tel. 701/448–2331; Tod Graeber, Administrator

GARRISON MEMORIAL HOSPITAL, 407 Third Avenue S.E., Garrison, ND, Zip 58540–7235; tel. 701/463–2275; Tod Graeber, Administrator

LINTON HOSPITAL, 518 North Broadway, Linton, ND, Zip 58552–7308, Mailing Address: P.O. Box 850, Zip 58552–0850; tel. 701/254–4511; Robert O. Black, Chief Executive Officer

MCKENZIE COUNTY HEALTHCARE SYSTEM, 516 North Main Street, Watford City, ND, Zip 58854–7310; tel. 701/842–3000; Daniel R. Kelly, Chief Executive Officer

MOBRIDGE REGIONAL HOSPITAL, 1401 Tenth Avenue West, Mobridge, SD, Zip 57601–1106, Mailing Address: P.O. Box 580, Zip 57601–0580; tel. 605/845–3692; Angelia K. Svihovec, Chief Executive Officer

PRESENTATION MEDICAL CENTER, 213 Second Avenue N.E., Rolla, ND, Zip 58367–7153, Mailing Address: P.O. Box 759, Zip 58367–0759; tel. 701/477–3161; Mark Kerr, Chief Executive Officer

SAKAKAWEA MEDICAL CENTER, 510 Eighth Avenue N.E., Hazen, ND, Zip 58545–4637; tel. 701/748–2225; Darrold Bertsch, Chief Executive Officer

SOUTHWEST HEALTHCARE SERVICES, 802 2nd Street Northwest, Bowman, ND, Zip 58623–4483, Mailing Address: P.O. Drawer C, Zip 58623; tel. 701/523–5265; Becky Hansen, Chief Executive Officer

ST. ALEXIUS MEDICAL CENTER, 900 East Broadway, Bismarck, ND, Zip 58501–4586, Mailing Address: P.O. Box 5510, Zip 58506–5510; tel. 701/530–7000; Gary P. Miller, President and Chief Executive Officer

ST. ALOISIUS MEDICAL CENTER, 325 East Brewster Street, Harvey, ND, Zip 58341–1653; tel. 701/324–4651; Rockford Zastoupil, President and Chief Executive Officer

ST. ANDREW'S HEALTH CENTER, 316 Ohmer Street, Bottineau, ND, Zip 58318–1045; tel. 701/228–9300; Jodi Atkinson, President and Chief Executive Officer

ST. JOSEPH'S HOSPITAL AND HEALTH CENTER, 30 Seventh Street West, Dickinson, ND, Zip 58601–4399; tel. 701/456–4000; Reed Reyman, President

WEST RIVER REGIONAL MEDICAL CENTER, 1000 Highway 12, Hettinger, ND, Zip 58639–7530; tel. 701/567–4561; James K. Long, CPA, Administrator and Chief Executive Officer

WISHEK COMMUNITY HOSPITAL AND CLINICS, 1007 Fourth Avenue South, Wishek, ND, Zip 58495–7527, Mailing Address: P.O. Box 647, Zip 58495–0647; tel. 701/452–2326; Mark Rinehardt, Chief Executive Officer

OHIO

CLEVELAND HEALTH NETWORK
6000 West Creek Road, Suite 20, Independence, OH 44131–2139; tel. 216/986–1100; Fred M. DeGrandis, President

AKRON CHILDREN'S HOSPITAL, One Perkins Square, Akron, OH, Zip 44308–1062; tel. 330/543–1000; William H. Considine, President

ASHTABULA COUNTY MEDICAL CENTER, 2420 Lake Avenue, Ashtabula, OH, Zip 44004–4954; tel. 440/997–2262; Michael J. Habowski, President and Chief Executive Officer

CLEVELAND CLINIC, 9500 Euclid Avenue, Cleveland, OH, Zip 44195–5108; tel. 216/444–2200; Delos Cosgrove, M.D., President and Chief Executive Officer

CLEVELAND CLINIC CHILDREN'S HOSPITAL FOR REHABILITATION, 2801 Martin Luther King Jr. Drive, Cleveland, OH, Zip 44104–3865; tel. 216/448–6400; Michael J. McHugh, M.D., Medical Director

EUCLID HOSPITAL, 18901 Lake Shore Boulevard, Euclid, OH, Zip 44119–1090; tel. 216/531–9000; Mark Froimson, M.D., President

FAIRVIEW HOSPITAL, 18101 Lorain Avenue, Cleveland, OH, Zip 44111–5656; tel. 216/476–7000; Neil Smith, D.O., President

FIRELANDS REGIONAL HEALTH SYSTEM, 1111 Hayes Avenue, Sandusky, OH, Zip 44870–3323; tel. 419/557–7400; Martin Tursky, President and Chief Executive Officer

FISHER–TITUS MEDICAL CENTER, 272 Benedict Avenue, Norwalk, OH, Zip 44857–2374; tel. 419/668–8101; Lorna Strayer, Interim President and Chief Executive Officer

HILLCREST HOSPITAL, 6780 Mayfield Road, Cleveland, OH, Zip 44124–2203; tel. 440/312–4500; Brian J. Harte, M.D., President

LAKEWOOD HOSPITAL, 14519 Detroit Avenue, Lakewood, OH, Zip 44107–4383; tel. 216/521–4200; Shannan Ritchie, Interim President

LUTHERAN HOSPITAL, 1730 West 25th Street, Cleveland, OH, Zip 44113–3170; tel. 216/696–4300; Donald Malone, M.D., President

MARYMOUNT HOSPITAL, 12300 McCracken Road, Garfield Heights, OH, Zip 44125–2975; tel. 216/581–0500; Joanne Zeroske, President

MEDINA HOSPITAL, 1000 East Washington Street, Medina, OH, Zip 44256–2170; tel. 330/725–1000; Thomas Tulisiak, M.D., President

METROHEALTH MEDICAL CENTER, 2500 MetroHealth Drive, Cleveland, OH, Zip 44109–1998; tel. 216/778–7800; Akram Boutros, M.D., FACHE, President and Chief Executive Officer

SOUTH POINTE HOSPITAL, 20000 Harvard Road, Warrensville Heights, OH, Zip 44122–6805; tel. 216/491–6000; Robert S. Juhasz, D.O., President

SUMMA AKRON CITY HOSPITAL, 525 East Market Street, Akron, OH, Zip 44304–1619; tel. 330/375–3000; Thomas J. Strauss, President and Chief Executive Officer

SUMMA BARBERTON CITIZENS HOSPITAL, 155 Fifth Street N.E., Barberton, OH, Zip 44203–3332; tel. 330/615–3000; Jason Niehaus, Senior Vice President Operations and Administrator

SUMMA WADSWORTH–RITTMAN HOSPITAL, 195 Wadsworth Road, Wadsworth, OH, Zip 44281–9505; tel. 330/331–1000; Thomas DeBord, President

SUMMA WESTERN RESERVE HOSPITAL, 1900 23rd Street, Cuyahoga Falls, OH, Zip 44223–1499; tel. 330/971–7000; Robert Kent, D.O., President and Chief Executive Officer

Section B

UNIVERSITY HOSPITALS ELYRIA MEDICAL CENTER, 630 East River Street, Elyria, OH, Zip 44035–5902; tel. 440/329–7500; Donald S. Sheldon, M.D., President and Chief Executive Officer

UNIVERSITY HOSPITALS PARMA MEDICAL CENTER, 7007 Powers Boulevard, Parma, OH, Zip 44129–5495; tel. 440/743–3000; Nancy Tinsley, President and Chief Executive Officer

COMPREHENSIVE HEALTHCARE OF OHIO, INC.
630 East River Street, Elyria, OH 44035–5902; tel. 440/329–7700; Donald S. Sheldon, M.D., President and Chief Executive Officer

UNIVERSITY HOSPITALS ELYRIA MEDICAL CENTER, 630 East River Street, Elyria, OH, Zip 44035–5902; tel. 440/329–7500; Donald S. Sheldon, M.D., President and Chief Executive Officer

LAKE HEALTH
7590 Auburn Road, Concord Township, OH 44077–9176; tel. 440/375–8100; Cynthia Moore–Hardy, FACHE, President and Chief Executive Officer

MERCY HEALTH – SOUTHWEST OHIO
4600 McAuley Place, Cincinnati, OH 45242; tel. 513/981–6000; James May, President and Chief Executive Officer

MERCY HEALTH – ANDERSON HOSPITAL, 7500 State Road, Cincinnati, OH, Zip 45255–2492; tel. 513/624–4500; Jeff Graham, Market Leader and President

MERCY HEALTH – CLERMONT HOSPITAL, 3000 Hospital Drive, Batavia, OH, Zip 45103–1921; tel. 513/732–8200; Jeff Graham, Market Leader and President

MERCY HEALTH – FAIRFIELD HOSPITAL, 3000 Mack Road, Fairfield, OH, Zip 45014–5335; tel. 513/870–7000; Thomas S. Urban, Market Leader and President

MERCY HEALTH – WEST HOSPITAL, 3300 Mercy Health Boulevard, Cincinnati, OH, Zip 45211; tel. 513/215–5000; Michael R. Stephens, Market Leader and President

THE JEWISH HOSPITAL – MERCY HEALTH, 4777 East Galbraith Road, Cincinnati, OH, Zip 45236–2725; tel. 513/686–3000; Patricia Davis–Hagens, R.N., Chief Executive Officer

OHIO STATE HEALTH NETWORK
660 Ackerman Road, Suite 601F, Columbus, OH 43202–4500; tel. 614/293–3785; Joann Ort, Executive Director

BARNESVILLE HOSPITAL, 639 West Main Street, Barnesville, OH, Zip 43713–1039, Mailing Address: P.O. Box 309, Zip 43713–0309; tel. 740/425–3941; David D. Phillips, Chief Executive Officer and Administrator

MADISON COUNTY HOSPITAL, 210 North Main Street, London, OH, Zip 43140–1115; tel. 740/845–7000; Dana E. Engle, Chief Executive Officer

MARY RUTAN HOSPITAL, 205 Palmer Avenue, Bellefontaine, OH, Zip 43311–2281; tel. 937/592–4015; Mandy C. Goble, President and Chief Executive Officer

MERCER HEALTH, 800 West Main Street, Coldwater, OH, Zip 45828–1698; tel. 419/678–2341; Lisa R. Klenke, R.N., Chief Executive Officer and Chief Nursing Officer

OHIO STATE UNIVERSITY WEXNER MEDICAL CENTER, 370 West 9th Avenue, Columbus, OH, Zip 43210–1238; tel. 614/293–8000; Steven Gabbe, M.D., Chief Executive Officer

OHIO VALLEY MEDICAL CENTER, 2000 Eoff Street, Wheeling, WV, Zip 26003–3870; tel. 304/234–0123; Michael J. Caruso, President and Chief Executive Officer

TRINITY HOSPITAL TWIN CITY, 819 North First Street, Dennison, OH, Zip 44621–1098; tel. 740/922–2800; Joseph J. Mitchell, President

WILSON MEMORIAL HOSPITAL, 915 West Michigan Street, Sidney, OH, Zip 45365–2491; tel. 937/498–2311; Mark J. Dooley, Chief Executive Officer

WYANDOT MEMORIAL HOSPITAL, 885 North Sandusky Avenue, Upper Sandusky, OH, Zip 43351–1098; tel. 419/294–4991; Joseph A. D'Ettorre, Chief Executive Officer

PREMIER HEALTH PARTNERS
110 North Main Street, Suite 390, Dayton, OH 45402–3720; tel. 937/499–9401; James R. Pancoast, President and Chief Executive Officer

ATRIUM MEDICAL CENTER, One Medical Center Drive, Middletown, OH, Zip 45005–1066; tel. 513/424–2111; Carol Turner, President and Chief Executive Officer

GOOD SAMARITAN HOSPITAL, 2222 Philadelphia Drive, Dayton, OH, Zip 45406–1813; tel. 937/734–2612; Eloise Broner, President and Chief Executive Officer

MIAMI VALLEY HOSPITAL, One Wyoming Street, Dayton, OH, Zip 45409–2793; tel. 937/208–8000; Mark S. Shaker, President and Chief Executive Officer

UPPER VALLEY MEDICAL CENTER, 3130 North County Road 25A, Troy, OH, Zip 45373–1309; tel. 937/440–4000; Thomas Parker, Chief Executive Officer

TRIHEALTH
619 Oak Street, Cincinnati, OH 45206; tel. 513/569–6507; John S. Prout, President and Chief Executive Officer

BETHESDA BUTLER HOSPITAL, 3125 Hamilton Mason Road, Hamilton, OH, Zip 45011–5307; tel. 513/894–8888; Chuck Brown, Administrator

BETHESDA NORTH HOSPITAL, 10500 Montgomery Road, Cincinnati, OH, Zip 45242–4402; tel. 513/865–1111; Barb Boyne, Executive Director, Operations

GOOD SAMARITAN HOSPITAL, 375 Dixmyth Avenue, Cincinnati, OH, Zip 45220–2489; tel. 513/862–1400; Jamie Easterling, Executive Director, Operations

TRIHEALTH EVENDALE HOSPITAL, 3155 Glendale Milford Road, Cincinnati, OH, Zip 45241–3134; tel. 513/454–2222; Kelvin Hanger, Chief Executive Officer

OKLAHOMA

MERCY HEALTH SYSTEM OF OKLAHOMA
4300 West Memorial Road, Oklahoma City, OK 73120–8304; tel. 405/752–3756; Diana Smalley, President and Chief Executive Officer

ARBUCKLE MEMORIAL HOSPITAL, 2011 West Broadway Street, Sulphur, OK, Zip 73086–4221; tel. 580/622–2161; Darin Farrell, Chief Executive Officer

MERCY HEALTH LOVE COUNTY, 300 Wanda Street, Marietta, OK, Zip 73448–1200; tel. 580/276–3347; Richard Barker, Administrator

MERCY HOSPITAL ADA, 430 North Monte Vista, Ada, OK, Zip 74820–4610; tel. 580/332–2323; Diana Smalley, Acting Interim Chief Executive Officer

MERCY HOSPITAL ARDMORE, 1011 14th Avenue N.W., Ardmore, OK, Zip 73401–1828; tel. 580/223–5400; Daryle Voss, FACHE, President

MERCY HOSPITAL EL RENO, 2115 Parkview Drive, El Reno, OK, Zip 73036–2199, Mailing Address: P.O. Box 129, Zip 73036–0129; tel. 405/262–2640; Doug Danker, Administrator

MERCY HOSPITAL HEALDTON, 918 South 8th Street, Healdton, OK, Zip 73438–0928, Mailing Address: P.O. Box 928, Zip 73438–0928; tel. 580/229–0701; Jeremy A. Jones, Administrator

MERCY HOSPITAL KINGFISHER, 1000 Kingfisher Regional Hospital Drive, Kingfisher, OK, Zip 73750–3528, Mailing Address: P.O. Box 59, Zip 73750–0059; tel. 405/375–3141; Brian Denton, Administrator

MERCY HOSPITAL LOGAN COUNTY, 200 South Academy Road, Guthrie, OK, Zip 73044–8727, Mailing Address: P.O. Box 1017, Zip 73044–1017; tel. 405/282–6700; Joshua Tucker, Administrator

MERCY HOSPITAL OKLAHOMA CITY, 4300 West Memorial Road, Oklahoma City, OK, Zip 73120–8362; tel. 405/755–1515; Jim Gebhart, Jr., FACHE, President

MERCY HOSPITAL TISHOMINGO, 1000 South Byrd Street, Tishomingo, OK, Zip 73460–3299; tel. 580/371–2327; Gary Sharum, Administrator

MERCY HOSPITAL WATONGA, 500 North Clarence Nash Boulevard, Watonga, OK, Zip 73772–2845, Mailing Address: P.O. Box 370, Zip 73772–0370; tel. 580/623–7211; Bobby Stitt, R.N., Administrator

MERCY REHABILITATION HOSPITAL OKLAHOMA CITY, 5401 West Memorial Road, Oklahoma City, OK, Zip 73142–2026; tel. 405/752–3935; Sharon Smeltzer, Chief Executive Officer

OKLAHOMA HEART HOSPITAL, 4050 West Memorial Road, Oklahoma City, OK, Zip 73120–8382; tel. 405/608–3200; John Harvey, M.D., President and Chief Executive Officer

OKLAHOMA HEART HOSPITAL SOUTH CAMPUS, 5200 East I–240 Service Road, Oklahoma City, OK, Zip 73135; tel. 405/628–6000; John Harvey, M.D., President and Chief Executive Officer

OREGON

HEALTH FUTURE, LLC
916 Town Centre Drive, Medford, OR 97504–6100; tel. 541/772–3062; Chris Chang–Howitz, Chief Executive Officer

ASANTE ASHLAND COMMUNITY HOSPITAL, 280 Maple Street, Ashland, OR, Zip 97520–1593; tel. 541/201–4000; Sheila Clough, Chief Executive Officer

ASANTE ROGUE REGIONAL MEDICAL CENTER, 2825 East Barnett Road, Medford, OR, Zip 97504–8332; tel. 541/789–7000; Scott A. Kelly, Chief Executive Officer

ASANTE THREE RIVERS MEDICAL CENTER, 500 S.W. Ramsey Avenue, Grants Pass, OR, Zip 97527–5554; tel. 541/472–7000; Win Howard, Chief Executive Officer

BAY AREA HOSPITAL, 1775 Thompson Road, Coos Bay, OR, Zip 97420–2198; tel. 541/269–8111; Paul Janke, FACHE, President and Chief Executive Officer

MID–COLUMBIA MEDICAL CENTER, 1700 East 19th Street, The Dalles, OR, Zip 97058–3317; tel. 541/296–1111; Duane Francis, President and Chief Executive Officer

OHSU HOSPITAL, 3181 S.W. Sam Jackson Park Road, Portland, OR, Zip 97239–3098; tel. 503/494–8311; Peter F. Rapp, Vice President and Executive Director

PIONEER MEMORIAL HOSPITAL, 1201 N.E. Elm Street, Prineville, OR, Zip 97754–1206; tel. 541/447–6254; Jeanine Gentry, Chief Executive Officer

SKY LAKES MEDICAL CENTER, 2865 Daggett Avenue, Klamath Falls, OR, Zip 97601–1106; tel. 541/882–6311; Paul R. Stewart, President and Chief Executive Officer

ST. CHARLES MADRAS, 470 N.E. A Street, Madras, OR, Zip 97741–1844; tel. 541/475–3882; Jeanine Gentry, Chief Executive Officer

ST. CHARLES MEDICAL CENTER – BEND, 2500 N.E. Neff Road, Bend, OR, Zip 97701–6015; tel. 541/382–4321; Robert Gomes, FACHE, Chief Executive Officer

ST. CHARLES MEDICAL CENTER – REDMOND, 1253 N.W. Canal Boulevard, Redmond, OR, Zip 97756–1395; tel. 541/548–8131; Robert Gomes, FACHE, Chief Executive Officer

PENNSYLVANIA

ALLEGHENY HEALTH NETWORK
120 Fifth Avenue, Suite 2901, Pittsburgh, PA 15222–3002; tel. 412/544–3075; John W. Paul, President and Chief Executive Officer

ALLEGHENY GENERAL HOSPITAL, 320 East North Avenue, Pittsburgh, PA, Zip 15212–4756; tel. 412/359–3131; Michael Harlovic, R.N., President and Chief Executive Officer

ALLEGHENY VALLEY HOSPITAL, 1301 Carlisle Street, Natrona Heights, PA, Zip 15065–1152; tel. 724/224–5100; David Goldberg, President & Interim Chief Executive Officer

CANONSBURG GENERAL HOSPITAL, 100 Medical Boulevard, Canonsburg, PA, Zip 15317–9762; tel. 724/745–6100; Jane B. Sarra, President and Chief Executive Officer

FORBES REGIONAL HOSPITAL, 2570 Haymaker Road, Monroeville, PA, Zip 15146–3513; tel. 412/858–2000; Reese Jackson, President and Chief Executive Officer

JEFFERSON HOSPITAL, 565 Coal Valley Road, Jefferson Hills, PA, Zip 15025–3703, Mailing Address: Box 18119, Pittsburgh, Zip 15236–0119; tel. 412/469–5000; Louise Urban, R.N., President and Chief Executive Officer

SAINT VINCENT HEALTH CENTER, 232 West 25th Street, Erie, PA, Zip 16544–0002; tel. 814/452–5000; Scott Whalen, Ph.D., FACHE, President and Chief Executive Officer

WEST PENN HOSPITAL, 4800 Friendship Avenue, Pittsburgh, PA, Zip 15224–1722; tel. 412/578–5000; Duke Rupert, President and Chief Executive Officer

COMMONWEALTH HEALTH
575 North River Street, Wilkes Barre, PA 18764–0999; tel. 570/829–8111; Cornelio R. Catena, Chief Executive Officer

BERWICK HOSPITAL CENTER, 701 East 16th Street, Berwick, PA, Zip 18603–2397; tel. 570/759–5000; David P. Steitz, Chief Executive Officer

FIRST HOSPITAL WYOMING VALLEY, 562 Wyoming Avenue, Kingston, PA, Zip 18704–3721; tel. 570/552–3900; Mark Schor, Chief Executive Officer

MOSES TAYLOR HOSPITAL, 700 Quincy Avenue, Scranton, PA, Zip 18510–1724; tel. 570/770–5000; Justin Davis, Chief Executive Officer

REGIONAL HOSPITAL OF SCRANTON, 746 Jefferson Avenue, Scranton, PA, Zip 18510–1624; tel. 570/348–7100; Brooks Turkel, Chief Executive Officer

SPECIAL CARE HOSPITAL, 128 West Washington Street, Nanticoke, PA, Zip 18634–3113; tel. 570/735–5000; Robert D. Williams, Chief Executive Officer

TYLER MEMORIAL HOSPITAL, 5950 State Route 6, Tunkhannock, PA, Zip 18657–7905; tel. 570/836–2161; Diane Ljungquist, R.N., MS, Chief Executive Officer

WILKES–BARRE GENERAL HOSPITAL, 575 North River Street, Wilkes–Barre, PA, Zip 18764–0001; tel. 570/829–8111; Cornelio R. Catena, President and Chief Executive Officer

PENN HIGHLANDS HEALTHCARE
204 Hospital Avenue, Du Bois, PA 15801–1442; tel. 814/371–2200; Raymond A. Graeca, Chief Executive Officer

CLEARFIELD HOSPITAL, 809 Turnpike Avenue, Clearfield, PA, Zip 16830–1232, Mailing Address: P.O. Box 992, Zip 16830–0992; tel. 814/765–5341; Gary Macioce, President and Chief Executive Officer

DUBOIS REGIONAL MEDICAL CENTER, 100 Hospital Avenue, Du Bois, PA, Zip 15801–1440, Mailing Address: P.O. Box 447, Zip 15801–0447; tel. 814/371–2200; John Sutika, President

ELK REGIONAL HEALTH CENTER, 763 Johnsonburg Road, Saint Marys, PA, Zip 15857–3498; tel. 814/788–8000; Rose Campbell, R.N., President

PENN HIGHLANDS BROOKVILLE, 100 Hospital Road, Brookville, PA, Zip 15825–1367; tel. 814/849–2312; Julie Peer, President

VANTAGE HEALTHCARE NETWORK, INC.
18282 Technology Drive, Suite 202, Meadville, PA 16335; tel. 814/337–0000; David Petrarca, Director Retail Operations

BRADFORD REGIONAL MEDICAL CENTER, 116 Interstate Parkway, Bradford, PA, Zip 16701–1036; tel. 814/368–4143; Timothy J. Finan, FACHE, President and Chief Executive Officer

CLARION HOSPITAL, One Hospital Drive, Clarion, PA, Zip 16214–8501; tel. 814/226–9500; Byron Quinton, Chief Executive Officer

ELK REGIONAL HEALTH CENTER, 763 Johnsonburg Road, Saint Marys, PA, Zip 15857–3498; tel. 814/788–8000; Rose Campbell, R.N., President

JAMESON HOSPITAL, 1211 Wilmington Avenue, New Castle, PA, Zip 16105–2516; tel. 724/658–9001; Douglas Danko, President and Chief Executive Officer

KANE COMMUNITY HOSPITAL, 4372 Route 6, Kane, PA, Zip 16735–3060; tel. 814/837–8585; J. Gary Rhodes, FACHE, Chief Executive Officer

MEADVILLE MEDICAL CENTER, 751 Liberty Street, Meadville, PA, Zip 16335–2559; tel. 814/333–5000; Philip Pandolph, Chief Executive Officer

PENN HIGHLANDS BROOKVILLE, 100 Hospital Road, Brookville, PA, Zip 15825–1367; tel. 814/849–2312; Julie Peer, President

PUNXSUTAWNEY AREA HOSPITAL, 81 Hillcrest Drive, Punxsutawney, PA, Zip 15767–2616; tel. 814/938–1800; Daniel D. Blough, Jr., Chief Executive Officer

TITUSVILLE AREA HOSPITAL, 406 West Oak Street, Titusville, PA, Zip 16354–1404; tel. 814/827–1851; Anthony J. Nasralla, FACHE, President and Chief Executive Officer

UPMC BEDFORD MEMORIAL, 10455 Lincoln Highway, Everett, PA, Zip 15537–7046; tel. 814/623–6161; Roger P. Winn, President

UPMC HAMOT, 201 State Street, Erie, PA, Zip 16550–0002; tel. 814/877–6000; V. James Fiorenzo, President

UPMC MCKEESPORT, 1500 Fifth Avenue, McKeesport, PA, Zip 15132–2422; tel. 412/664–2000; Mark Sevco, President

UPMC NORTHWEST, 100 Fairfield Drive, Seneca, PA, Zip 16346–2130; tel. 814/676–7600; David Gibbons, President

UPMC PASSAVANT, 9100 Babcock Boulevard, Pittsburgh, PA, Zip 15237–5815; tel. 412/748–6700; David T. Martin, President

UPMC ST. MARGARET, 815 Freeport Road, Pittsburgh, PA, Zip 15215–3301; tel. 412/784–4000; David J. Patton, President

WARREN GENERAL HOSPITAL, Two Crescent Park West, Warren, PA, Zip 16365–0068, Mailing Address: P.O. Box 68, Zip 16365–0068; tel. 814/723–4973; Randy California, Interim Chief Executive Officer

SOUTH DAKOTA

REGIONAL HEALTH
353 Fairmont Boulevard, Rapid City, SD 57701–7375; tel. 605/719–1000; Charles E. Hart, M.D., MS, President and Chief Executive Officer

REGIONAL HEALTH NETWORK
353 Fairmont Boulevard, Rapid City, SD 57701–7375; tel. 605/719–1000; Timothy H. Sughrue, Chief Executive Officer

CUSTER REGIONAL HOSPITAL, 1039 Montgomery Street, Custer, SD, Zip 57730–1397; tel. 605/673–2229; Veronica Schmidt, Chief Executive Officer

LEAD–DEADWOOD REGIONAL HOSPITAL, 61 Charles Street, Deadwood, SD, Zip 57732–1303; tel. 605/722–6000; Sherry Bea Smith, R.N., Chief Executive Officer

PHILIP HEALTH SERVICES, 503 West Pine Street, Philip, SD, Zip 57567–3300, Mailing Address: P.O. Box 790, Zip 57567–0790; tel. 605/859–2511; Kent Olson, Administrator and Chief Executive Officer

RAPID CITY REGIONAL HOSPITAL, 353 Fairmont Boulevard, Rapid City, SD, Zip 57701–7393, Mailing Address: P.O. Box 6000, Zip 57709–6000; tel. 605/755–1000; Timothy H. Sughrue, Chief Executive Officer

SPEARFISH REGIONAL HOSPITAL, 1440 North Main Street, Spearfish, SD, Zip 57783–1504; tel. 605/644–4000; Larry W. Veitz, Chief Executive Officer

STURGIS REGIONAL HOSPITAL, 949 Harmon Street, Sturgis, SD, Zip 57785–2452; tel. 605/720–2400; Mark Schulte, FACHE, Chief Executive Officer

WESTON COUNTY HEALTH SERVICES, 1124 Washington Boulevard, Newcastle, WY, Zip 82701–2972; tel. 307/746–4491; Maureen K. Cadwell, Chief Executive Officer

TENNESSEE

TRISTAR HEALTH
110 Winners Circle, First Floor, Brentwood, TN 37027–5070; tel. 615/886–4900; Stephen Corbeil, President

CARTERSVILLE MEDICAL CENTER, 960 Joe Frank Harris Parkway, Cartersville, GA, Zip 30120–2129; tel. 770/382–1530; Keith Sandlin, Chief Executive Officer

EASTSIDE MEDICAL CENTER, 1700 Medical Way, Snellville, GA, Zip 30078–2195; tel. 770/979–0200; Kimberly Ryan, Chief Executive Officer

REDMOND REGIONAL MEDICAL CENTER, 501 Redmond Road, Rome, GA, Zip 30165–1415, Mailing Address: P.O. Box 107001, Zip 30165–7001; tel. 706/291–0291; John Quinlivan, Chief Executive Officer

TRISTAR CENTENNIAL MEDICAL CENTER, 2300 Patterson Street, Nashville, TN, Zip 37203–1528; tel. 615/342–1000; Heather J. Rohan, Chief Executive Officer

TRISTAR CENTENNIAL MEDICAL CENTER AT ASHLAND CITY, 313 North Main Street, Ashland City, TN, Zip 37015–1347; tel. 615/792–3030; Heather J. Rohan, Chief Executive Officer

Section B

TRISTAR GREENVIEW REGIONAL HOSPITAL, 1801 Ashley Circle, Bowling Green, KY, Zip 42104–3362; tel. 270/793–1000; Michael Sherrod, Chief Executive Officer

TRISTAR HENDERSONVILLE MEDICAL CENTER, 355 New Shackle Island Road, Hendersonville, TN, Zip 37075–2479; tel. 615/338–1000; Regina Bartlett, Chief Executive Officer

TRISTAR HORIZON MEDICAL CENTER, 111 Highway 70 East, Dickson, TN, Zip 37055–2080; tel. 615/446–0446; John A. Marshall, Chief Executive Officer

TRISTAR SKYLINE MADISON CAMPUS, 500 Hospital Drive, Madison, TN, Zip 37115–5032; tel. 615/769–5000; Steve Otto, Chief Executive Officer

TRISTAR SKYLINE MEDICAL CENTER, 3441 Dickerson Pike, Nashville, TN, Zip 37207–2539; tel. 615/769–2000; Steve Otto, Chief Executive Officer

TRISTAR SOUTHERN HILLS MEDICAL CENTER, 391 Wallace Road, Nashville, TN, Zip 37211–4859; tel. 615/781–4000; Thomas H. Ozburn, Chief Executive Officer

TRISTAR STONECREST MEDICAL CENTER, 200 StoneCrest Boulevard, Smyrna, TN, Zip 37167–6810; tel. 615/768–2000; Louis Caputo, Chief Executive Officer

TRISTAR SUMMIT MEDICAL CENTER, 5655 Frist Boulevard, Hermitage, TN, Zip 37076–2053; tel. 615/316–3000; Jeffrey T. Whitehorn, Chief Executive Officer

TEXAS

METHODIST HEALTHCARE SYSTEM
8109 Fredericksburg Road, San Antonio, TX 78229–3311; tel. 210/575–0355; Andrew Williams, President and Chief Executive Officer

METHODIST AMBULATORY SURGERY HOSPITAL – NORTHWEST, 9150 Huebner Road, Suite 100, San Antonio, TX, Zip 78240–1545; tel. 210/575–5000; Andrew Williams, Chief Executive Officer

METHODIST HOSPITAL, 7700 Floyd Curl Drive, San Antonio, TX, Zip 78229–3993; tel. 210/575–4000; Gay Nord, Chief Executive Officer

METHODIST STONE OAK HOSPITAL, 1139 East Sonterra Boulevard, San Antonio, TX, Zip 78258–4347; tel. 210/638–2100; Dominic J. Dominguez, Interim Chief Executive Officer

REGIONAL HEALTHCARE ALLIANCE
530 South Beckham Avenue, Tyler, TX 75702–8310; tel. 903/531–4449; John Webb, President

ALLEGIANCE SPECIALTY HOSPITAL OF KILGORE, 1612 South Henderson Boulevard, Kilgore, TX, Zip 75662–3594; tel. 903/984–3505; Sherry Bustin, Chief Executive Officer

BAYLOR UNIVERSITY MEDICAL CENTER, 3500 Gaston Avenue, Dallas, TX, Zip 75246–2088; tel. 214/820–0111; John B. McWhorter, III, President

CHILDREN'S MEDICAL CENTER OF DALLAS, 1935 Medical District Drive, Dallas, TX, Zip 75235; tel. 214/456–7000; Christopher J. Durovich, President and Chief Executive Officer

EAST TEXAS MEDICAL CENTER HENDERSON, 300 Wilson Street, Henderson, TX, Zip 75652–5956; tel. 903/655–3616; Mark Leitner, Chief Executive Officer

GOOD SHEPHERD MEDICAL CENTER, 700 East Marshall Avenue, Longview, TX, Zip 75601–5580; tel. 903/315–2000; Steve Altmiller, President and Chief Executive Officer

HOPKINS COUNTY MEMORIAL HOSPITAL, 115 Airport Road, Sulphur Springs, TX, Zip 75482–2105; tel. 903/885–7671; Michael McAndrew, Chief Executive Officer

MOTHER FRANCES HOSPITAL – JACKSONVILLE, 2026 South Jackson, Jacksonville, TX, Zip 75766–5822; tel. 903/541–4500; Thomas N. Cammack, Jr., Chief Administrative Officer

MOTHER FRANCES HOSPITAL – TYLER, 800 East Dawson Street, Tyler, TX, Zip 75701–2036; tel. 903/593–8441; John McGreevy, Chief Executive Officer

NACOGDOCHES MEDICAL CENTER, 4920 N.E. Stallings Drive, Nacogdoches, TX, Zip 75965–1200; tel. 936/569–9481; Gary L. Stokes, Chief Executive Officer

PALESTINE REGIONAL MEDICAL CENTER-EAST, 2900 South Loop 256, Palestine, TX, Zip 75801–6958; tel. 903/731–1000; Alan E. George, Chief Executive Officer

PARIS REGIONAL MEDICAL CENTER, 820 Clarksville Street, Paris, TX, Zip 75460–6027, Mailing Address: P.O. Box 9070, Zip 75461–9070; tel. 903/785–4521; Stephen Grubbs, Chief Executive Officer

TITUS REGIONAL MEDICAL CENTER, 2001 North Jefferson Avenue, Mount Pleasant, TX, Zip 75455–2398; tel. 903/577–6000; Ronald D. Davis, Chief Executive Officer

TRINITY MOTHER FRANCES REHABILITATION HOSPITAL, 3131 Troup Highway, Tyler, TX, Zip 75701–8352; tel. 903/510–7000; Sharla Anderson, Chief Executive Officer

TYLER CONTINUECARE HOSPITAL AT MOTHER FRANCES, 800 East Dawson, 4th Floor, Tyler, TX, Zip 75701–2036; tel. 903/531–4080; Stephanie Hyde, Chief Executive Officer

UNIVERSITY OF TEXAS HEALTH SCIENCE CENTER AT TYLER, 11937 Highway 271, Tyler, TX, Zip 75708–3154; tel. 903/877–7777; Kirk A. Calhoun, M.D., President

ST. DAVID'S HEALTH NETWORK
98 San Jacinto Boulevard, Austin, TX 78701–4082; tel. 512/708–9700; C. David Huffstutler, President and Chief Executive Officer

ST. DAVID'S MEDICAL CENTER, 919 East 32nd Street, Austin, TX, Zip 78705–2709, Mailing Address: P.O. Box 4039, Zip 78765–4039; tel. 512/476–7111; Donald H. Wilkerson, Chief Executive Officer

ST. DAVID'S NORTH AUSTIN MEDICAL CENTER, 12221 North MoPac Expressway, Austin, TX, Zip 78758–2496; tel. 512/901–1000; Allen Harrison, Chief Executive Officer

ST. DAVID'S REHABILITATION CENTER, 1005 East 32nd Street, Austin, TX, Zip 78705–2713, Mailing Address: P.O. Box 4270, Zip 78765–4270; tel. 512/544–5100; Diane Owens, Administrator

ST. DAVID'S ROUND ROCK MEDICAL CENTER, 2400 Round Rock Avenue, Round Rock, TX, Zip 78681–4097; tel. 512/341–1000; Deborah L. Ryle, Administrator and Chief Executive Officer

ST. DAVID'S SOUTH AUSTIN MEDICAL CENTER, 901 West Ben White Boulevard, Austin, TX, Zip 78704–6903; tel. 512/447–2211; Todd E. Steward, Chief Executive Officer

VIRGINIA

CENTRAL VIRGINIA HEALTH NETWORK
2201 West Broad Street, Suite 202, Richmond, VA 23220–2022; tel. 804/359–4500; Michael Matthews, Chief Executive Officer

BON SECOURS MEMORIAL REGIONAL MEDICAL CENTER, 8260 Atlee Road, Mechanicsville, VA, Zip 23116–1844; tel. 804/764–6000; Michael Robinson, Chief Executive Officer

BON SECOURS ST. FRANCIS MEDICAL CENTER, 13710 St. Francis Boulevard, Midlothian, VA, Zip 23114–3267; tel. 804/594–7300; Mark M. Gordon, Chief Executive Officer

BON SECOURS ST. MARY'S HOSPITAL, 5801 Bremo Road, Richmond, VA, Zip 23226–1907; tel. 804/285–2011; Toni R. Ardabell, R.N., Chief Executive Officer

BON SECOURS–RICHMOND COMMUNITY HOSPITAL, 1500 North 28th Street, Richmond, VA, Zip 23223–5396, Mailing Address: P.O. Box 27184, Zip 23261–7184; tel. 804/225–1700; Michael Robinson, Executive Vice President and Administrator

CENTRA SOUTHSIDE COMMUNITY HOSPITAL, 800 Oak Street, Farmville, VA, Zip 23901–1199; tel. 434/392–8811; William L. Bass, Jr., Vice President and Chief Executive Officer

MARY IMMACULATE HOSPITAL, 2 Bernardine Drive, Newport News, VA, Zip 23602–4499; tel. 757/886–6000; Patricia L. Robertson, Executive Vice President

RAPPAHANNOCK GENERAL HOSPITAL, 101 Harris Drive, Kilmarnock, VA, Zip 22482–3880, Mailing Address: P.O. Box 1449, Zip 22482–1449; tel. 804/435–8000; James M. Holmes, Jr., President and Chief Executive Officer

SHELTERING ARMS REHABILITATION HOSPITAL, 8254 Atlee Road, Mechanicsville, VA, Zip 23116–1844; tel. 804/764–1000; James E. Sok, FACHE, President and Chief Executive Officer

UNIVERSITY OF VIRGINIA MEDICAL CENTER, 1215 Lee Street, Charlottesville, VA, Zip 22908–0001, Mailing Address: P.O. Box 800809, Zip 22908–0809; tel. 434/924–0211; Pamela Sutton–Wallace, Chief Executive Officer

VCU COMMUNITY MEMORIAL HOSPITAL, 125 Buena Vista Circle, South Hill, VA, Zip 23970–1431, Mailing Address: P.O. Box 90, Zip 23970–0090; tel. 434/447–3151; W. Scott Burnette, President and Chief Executive Officer

VIRGINIA HEALTH NETWORK
7400 Beaufont Springs Drive, Suite 505, Richmond, VA 23225–5521; tel. 804/320–3837; Michael J. Doucette, President

AUGUSTA HEALTH, 78 Medical Center Drive, Fishersville, VA, Zip 22939–2332, Mailing Address: P.O. Box 1000, Zip 22939–1000; tel. 540/932–4000; Mary N. Mannix, FACHE, President and Chief Executive Officer

BATH COMMUNITY HOSPITAL, 83 Park Drive, Hot Springs, VA, Zip 24445–2788, Mailing Address: P.O. Box Z., Zip 24445–0750; tel. 540/839–7000; Jason Paret, Chief Executive Officer

BEDFORD MEMORIAL HOSPITAL, 1613 Oakwood Street, Bedford, VA, Zip 24523–1213, Mailing Address: P.O. Box 688, Zip 24523–0688; tel. 540/586–2441; Patti Jurkus, Vice President, Regional Hospital

BON SECOURS MARYVIEW MEDICAL CENTER, 3636 High Street, Portsmouth, VA, Zip 23707–3270; tel. 757/398–2200; Joseph M. Oddis, Chief Executive Officer

BON SECOURS MEMORIAL REGIONAL MEDICAL CENTER, 8260 Atlee Road, Mechanicsville, VA, Zip 23116–1844; tel. 804/764–6000; Michael Robinson, Chief Executive Officer

BON SECOURS ST. FRANCIS MEDICAL CENTER, 13710 St. Francis Boulevard, Midlothian, VA, Zip 23114–3267; tel. 804/594–7300; Mark M. Gordon, Chief Executive Officer

BON SECOURS ST. MARY'S HOSPITAL, 5801 Bremo Road, Richmond, VA, Zip 23226–1907; tel. 804/285–2011; Toni R. Ardabell, R.N., Chief Executive Officer

BON SECOURS–DEPAUL MEDICAL CENTER, 150 Kingsley Lane, Norfolk, VA, Zip 23505–4650; tel. 757/889–5000; John E. Barrett, III, Chief Executive Officer

BON SECOURS–RICHMOND COMMUNITY HOSPITAL, 1500 North 28th Street, Richmond, VA, Zip 23223–5396, Mailing Address: P.O. Box 27184, Zip 23261–7184; tel. 804/225–1700; Michael Robinson, Executive Vice President and Administrator

BUCHANAN GENERAL HOSPITAL, 1535 Slate Creek Road, Grundy, VA, Zip 24614–6974; tel. 276/935–1000; Robert D. Ruchti, Chief Executive Officer

CARILION FRANKLIN MEMORIAL HOSPITAL, 180 Floyd Avenue, Rocky Mount, VA, Zip 24151–1389; tel. 540/483–5277; William D. Jacobsen, Vice President and Administrator

CARILION GILES COMMUNITY HOSPITAL, 159 Hartley Way, Pearisburg, VA, Zip 24134–2471; tel. 540/921–6000; Richard Mastalski, Senior Director Operations

CARILION NEW RIVER VALLEY MEDICAL CENTER, 2900 Lamb Circle, Christiansburg, VA, Zip 24073–6344, Mailing Address: P.O. Box 5, Radford, Zip 24143–0005; tel. 540/731–2000; Melina Dee Perdue, R.N., Executive Vice President

CARILION ROANOKE MEMORIAL HOSPITAL, Belleview at Jefferson Street, Roanoke, VA, Zip 24014, Mailing Address: P.O. Box 13367, Zip 24033–3367; tel. 540/981–7000; Steven C. Arner, President

CARILION STONEWALL JACKSON HOSPITAL, 1 Health Circle, Lexington, VA, Zip 24450–2492; tel. 540/458–3300; Charles E. Carr, Vice President, Regional Hospital

CARILION TAZEWELL COMMUNITY HOSPITAL, 141 Ben Bolt Avenue, Tazewell, VA, Zip 24651–9700; tel. 276/988–8700; Kathren Dowdy, MSN, Regional Hospital Senior Director

CENTRA SOUTHSIDE COMMUNITY HOSPITAL, 800 Oak Street, Farmville, VA, Zip 23901–1199; tel. 434/392–8811; William L. Bass, Jr., Vice President and Chief Executive Officer

CHESAPEAKE REGIONAL MEDICAL CENTER, 736 Battlefield Boulevard North, Chesapeake, VA, Zip 23320–4941, Mailing Address: P.O. Box 2028, Zip 23327–2028; tel. 757/312–8121; Peter F. Bastone, Chief Executive Officer

CHILDREN'S HOSPITAL OF RICHMOND AT VCU–BROOK ROAD CAMPUS, 2924 Brook Road, Richmond, VA, Zip 23220–1298; tel. 804/321–7474; Leslie G. Wyatt, Senior Vice President Children's Services and Executive Director

CHILDREN'S HOSPITAL OF THE KING'S DAUGHTERS, 601 Children's Lane, Norfolk, VA, Zip 23507–1910; tel. 757/668–7000; James D. Dahling, President and Chief Executive Officer

CJW MEDICAL CENTER, 7101 Jahnke Road, Richmond, VA, Zip 23225–4044; tel. 804/320–3911; Tim McManus, President and Chief Executive Officer

CLINCH VALLEY MEDICAL CENTER, 6801 Governor G. C. Peery Highway, Richlands, VA, Zip 24641–2194; tel. 276/596–6000; Peter Mulkey, Chief Executive Officer

CULPEPER REGIONAL HOSPITAL, 501 Sunset Lane, Culpeper, VA, Zip 22701–3917, Mailing Address: P.O. Box 592, Zip 22701–0500; tel. 540/829–4100; Greg Napps, Acting Chief Executive Officer

DOMINION HOSPITAL, 2960 Sleepy Hollow Road, Falls Church, VA, Zip 22044–2030; tel. 703/536–2000; Cynthia A. Meyer, Chief Executive Officer

FAUQUIER HOSPITAL, 500 Hospital Drive, Warrenton, VA, Zip 20186–3099; tel. 540/316–5000; Rodger H. Baker, President and Chief Executive Officer

HEALTHSOUTH REHABILITATION HOSPITAL OF VIRGINIA, 5700 Fitzhugh Avenue, Richmond, VA, Zip 23226–1800; tel. 804/288–5700; David Cashwell, Chief Executive Officer

HENRICO DOCTORS' HOSPITAL, 1602 Skipwith Road, Richmond, VA, Zip 23229–5205; tel. 804/289–4500; William Wagnon, Chief Executive Officer

INOVA ALEXANDRIA HOSPITAL, 4320 Seminary Road, Alexandria, VA, Zip 22304–1535; tel. 703/504–3167; Christine Candio, Chief Executive Officer

INOVA FAIR OAKS HOSPITAL, 3600 Joseph Siewick Drive, Fairfax, VA, Zip 22033–1798; tel. 703/391–3600; John L. Fitzgerald, Chief Executive Officer

INOVA FAIRFAX HOSPITAL, 3300 Gallows Road, Falls Church, VA, Zip 22042–3300; tel. 703/776–4001; Patrick Christiansen, Ph.D., Chief Executive Officer

INOVA LOUDOUN HOSPITAL, 44045 Riverside Parkway, Leesburg, VA, Zip 20176–5101, Mailing Address: P.O. Box 6000, Zip 20177–0600; tel. 703/858–6000; Patrick Walters, Chief Executive Officer

INOVA MOUNT VERNON HOSPITAL, 2501 Parker's Lane, Alexandria, VA, Zip 22306–3209; tel. 703/664–7000; Donald Brideau, M.D., Interim Chief Executive Officer

JOHN RANDOLPH MEDICAL CENTER, 411 West Randolph Road, Hopewell, VA, Zip 23860–2938; tel. 804/541–1600; Suzanne B. Jackson, FACHE, Chief Executive Officer

JOHNSTON MEMORIAL HOSPITAL, 16000 Johnston Memorial Drive, Abingdon, VA, Zip 24211–7659; tel. 276/676–7000; Sean S. McMurray, FACHE, Vice President and Chief Executive Officer

LEWISGALE HOSPITAL ALLEGHANY, One ARH Lane, Low Moor, VA, Zip 24457, Mailing Address: P.O. Box 7, Zip 24457–0007; tel. 540/862–6011; Charlotte C. Tyson, Chief Executive Officer

LEWISGALE HOSPITAL PULASKI, 2400 Lee Highway, Pulaski, VA, Zip 24301–2326, Mailing Address: P.O. Box 759, Zip 24301–0759; tel. 540/994–8100; Mark Nichols, FACHE, Chief Executive Officer

MARTHA JEFFERSON HOSPITAL, 500 Martha Jefferson Drive, Charlottesville, VA, Zip 22911–4668; tel. 434/654–7000; James E. Haden, President and Chief Executive Officer

MARY IMMACULATE HOSPITAL, 2 Bernardine Drive, Newport News, VA, Zip 23602–4499; tel. 757/886–6000; Patricia L. Robertson, Executive Vice President

MARY WASHINGTON HOSPITAL, 1001 Sam Perry Boulevard, Fredericksburg, VA, Zip 22401–3354; tel. 540/741–1100; Fred M. Rankin, III, President and Chief Executive Officer

MEMORIAL HOSPITAL, 320 Hospital Drive, Martinsville, VA, Zip 24112–1981, Mailing Address: P.O. Box 4788, Zip 24115–4788; tel. 276/666–7200; Eric Deaton, Interim Chief Executive Officer

MOUNTAIN VIEW REGIONAL MEDICAL CENTER, 310 Third Street N.E., Norton, VA, Zip 24273–1137; tel. 276/679–9100; Fred L. Pelle, FACHE, President

NORTHERN HOSPITAL OF SURRY COUNTY, 830 Rockford Street, Mount Airy, NC, Zip 27030–5365, Mailing Address: P.O. Box 1101, Zip 27030–1101; tel. 336/719–7000; Bert Whitaker, Interim Chief Executive Officer

NOVANT HEALTH PRINCE WILLIAM MEDICAL CENTER, 8700 Sudley Road, Manassas, VA, Zip 20110–4418, Mailing Address: P.O. Box 2610, Zip 20108–0867; tel. 703/369–8000; Melissa Robson, President

PIONEER COMMUNITY HOSPITAL OF PATRICK COUNTY, 18688 Jeb Stuart Highway, Stuart, VA, Zip 24171–1559; tel. 276/694–3151; Jeanette Filpi, Chief Executive Officer

RAPPAHANNOCK GENERAL HOSPITAL, 101 Harris Drive, Kilmarnock, VA, Zip 22482–3380, Mailing Address: P.O. Box 1449, Zip 22482–1449; tel. 804/435–8000; James M. Holmes, Jr., President and Chief Executive Officer

RESTON HOSPITAL CENTER, 1850 Town Center Parkway, Reston, VA, Zip 20190–3219; tel. 703/689–9000; John A. Deardorff, Chief Executive Officer

RIVERSIDE BEHAVIORAL HEALTH CENTER, 2244 Executive Drive, Hampton, VA, Zip 23666–2430; tel. 757/827–1001; Debra Campbell, R.N., Administrator

RIVERSIDE REGIONAL MEDICAL CENTER, 500 J. Clyde Morris Boulevard, Newport News, VA, Zip 23601–1929; tel. 757/594–2000; Michael J. Doucette, Senior Vice President and Administrator

RIVERSIDE REHABILITATION INSTITUTE, 245 Chesapeake Avenue, Newport News, VA, Zip 23607–6038; tel. 757/928–8000; Edward Heckler, Administrator

RIVERSIDE SHORE MEMORIAL HOSPITAL, 9507 Hospital Avenue, Nassawadox, VA, Zip 23413–1821, Mailing Address: P.O. Box 17, Zip 23413–0017; tel. 757/414–8000; Susan McAndrews, Vice President and Administrator

RIVERSIDE TAPPAHANNOCK HOSPITAL, 618 Hospital Road, Tappahannock, VA, Zip 22560–5000; tel. 804/443–3311; John Peterman, Vice President and Administrator

RIVERSIDE WALTER REED HOSPITAL, 7519 Hospital Drive, Gloucester, VA, Zip 23061–4178, Mailing Address: P.O. Box 1130, Zip 23061–1130; tel. 804/693–8800; Megan Kleckner, Vice President and Administrator

RUSSELL COUNTY MEDICAL CENTER, 58 Carroll Street, Lebanon, VA, Zip 24266, Mailing Address: P.O. Box 3600, Zip 24266–0200; tel. 276/883–8000; Stephen K. Givens, Assistant Vice President and Administrator

SENTARA CAREPLEX HOSPITAL, 3000 Coliseum Drive, Hampton, VA, Zip 23666–5963; tel. 757/736–1000; Debra A. Flores, R.N., MS, President and Administrator

SENTARA LEIGH HOSPITAL, 830 Kempsville Road, Norfolk, VA, Zip 23502–3920; tel. 757/261–6000; Teresa L. Edwards, President and Administrator

SENTARA NORFOLK GENERAL HOSPITAL, 600 Gresham Drive, Norfolk, VA, Zip 23507–1904; tel. 757/388–3000; Kurt T. Hofelich, President

SENTARA NORTHERN VIRGINIA MEDICAL CENTER, 2300 Opitz Boulevard, Woodbridge, VA, Zip 22191–3399; tel. 703/523–1000; Stephen D. Porter, President

SENTARA OBICI HOSPITAL, 2800 Godwin Boulevard, Suffolk, VA, Zip 23434–8038; tel. 757/934–4000; Steve Julian, M.D., President

SENTARA PRINCESS ANNE HOSPITAL, 2025 Glenn Mitchell Drive, Virginia Beach, VA, Zip 23456–0178; tel. 757/507–1000; Thomas B. Thames, M.D., President

SENTARA VIRGINIA BEACH GENERAL HOSPITAL, 1060 First Colonial Road, Virginia Beach, VA, Zip 23454–3002; tel. 757/395–8000; Elwood Bernard Boone, III, FACHE, President

SENTARA WILLIAMSBURG REGIONAL MEDICAL CENTER, 100 Sentara Circle, Williamsburg, VA, Zip 23188–5713; tel. 757/984–6000; David J. Masterson, President

SHELTERING ARMS REHABILITATION HOSPITAL, 8254 Atlee Road, Mechanicsville, VA, Zip 23116–1844; tel. 804/764–1000; James E. Sok, FACHE, President and Chief Executive Officer

SMYTH COUNTY COMMUNITY HOSPITAL, 245 Medical Park Drive, Marion, VA, Zip 24354, Mailing Address: P.O. Box 880, Zip 24354–0880; tel. 276/378–1000; Cathy Loving Maine, MSN, RN–B, Interim Chief Executive Officer

SOUTHAMPTON MEMORIAL HOSPITAL, 100 Fairview Drive, Franklin, VA, Zip 23851–1238, Mailing Address: P.O. Box 817, Zip 23851–0817; tel. 757/569–6100; Kimberly W. Marks, Interim Chief Executive Officer

SOUTHERN VIRGINIA REGIONAL MEDICAL CENTER, 727 North Main Street, Emporia, VA, Zip 23847–1274; tel. 434/348–4400; Linda Burnette, R.N., Interim Chief Executive Officer

SOUTHSIDE REGIONAL MEDICAL CENTER, 200 Medical Park Boulevard, Petersburg, VA, Zip 23805–9274; tel. 804/765–5000; Douglas J. Moyer, Chief Executive Officer

TWIN COUNTY REGIONAL HOSPITAL, 200 Hospital Drive, Galax, VA, Zip 24333–2227; tel. 276/236–8181; Jon D. Applebaum, Chief Executive Officer

UNIVERSITY OF VIRGINIA MEDICAL CENTER, 1215 Lee Street, Charlottesville, VA, Zip 22908–0001, Mailing Address: P.O. Box 800809, Zip 22908–0809; tel. 434/924–0211; Pamela Sutton–Wallace, Chief Executive Officer

UVA–HEALTHSOUTH REHABILITATION HOSPITAL, 515 Ray C. Hunt Drive, Charlottesville, VA, Zip 22903–2981; tel. 434/244–2000; Thomas J. Cook, Chief Executive Officer

VCU COMMUNITY MEMORIAL HOSPITAL, 125 Buena Vista Circle, South Hill, VA, Zip 23970–1431, Mailing Address: P.O. Box 90, Zip 23970–0090; tel. 434/447–3151; W. Scott Burnette, President and Chief Executive Officer

VCU MEDICAL CENTER, 1250 East Marshall Street, Richmond, VA, Zip 23298–5051, Mailing Address: P.O. Box 980510, Zip 23298–0510; tel. 804/828–9000; John Duval, Chief Executive Officer

VIRGINIA HOSPITAL CENTER – ARLINGTON, 1701 North George Mason Drive, Arlington, VA, Zip 22205–3698; tel. 703/558–5000; James B. Cole, Chief Executive Officer

WYTHE COUNTY COMMUNITY HOSPITAL, 600 West Ridge Road, Wytheville, VA, Zip 24382–1099; tel. 276/228–0200; Timothy A. Bess, Chief Executive Officer

WASHINGTON

GROUP HEALTH COOPERATIVE
320 Westlake Avenue North, Suite 100, Seattle, WA 98109–5233; tel. 206/448–5083; Scott Armstrong, Chief Executive Officer

CASCADE VALLEY HOSPITAL AND CLINICS, 330 South Stillaguamish Avenue, Arlington, WA, Zip 98223–1642; tel. 360/435–2133; W. Clark Jones, Superintendent and Administrator

COLUMBIA COUNTY HEALTH SYSTEM, 1012 South Third Street, Dayton, WA, Zip 99328–1696; tel. 509/382–2531; Jon D. Smiley, Interim Chief Executive Officer

DEACONESS HOSPITAL, 800 West Fifth Avenue, Spokane, WA, Zip 99204–2803, Mailing Address: P.O. Box 248, Zip 99210–0248; tel. 509/458–5800; Maurine Cate, Chief Executive Officer

GROUP HEALTH COOPERATIVE CENTRAL HOSPITAL, 201 16th Avenue East, Seattle, WA, Zip 98112–5226; tel. 206/326–3000; Jane Hutcheson, Administrator and Director Clinical Operations

HARRISON MEDICAL CENTER, 2520 Cherry Avenue, Bremerton, WA, Zip 98310–4229; tel. 360/744–3911; Joseph M. Kortum, Interim President

ISLAND HOSPITAL, 1211 24th Street, Anacortes, WA, Zip 98221–2562; tel. 360/299–1300; Vincent Oliver, Administrator

KADLEC REGIONAL MEDICAL CENTER, 888 Swift Boulevard, Richland, WA, Zip 99352–3514; tel. 509/946–4611; Rand J. Wortman, Chief Executive Officer

KITTITAS VALLEY HEALTHCARE, 603 South Chestnut Street, Ellensburg, WA, Zip 98926–3875; tel. 509/962–7302; Paul E. Nurick, Chief Executive Officer

KOOTENAI HEALTH, 2003 Kootenai Health Way, Coeur D'Alene, ID, Zip 83814–2677; tel. 208/625–4000; Jon Ness, Chief Executive Officer

LOURDES MEDICAL CENTER, 520 North Fourth Avenue, Pasco, WA, Zip 99301–5257, Mailing Address: P.O. Box 2568, Zip 99302–2568; tel. 509/547–7704; John Serle, FACHE, President and Chief Executive Officer

MULTICARE MARY BRIDGE CHILDREN'S HOSPITAL AND HEALTH CENTER, 317 Martin Luther King Jr. Way, Tacoma, WA, Zip 98405–4234, Mailing Address: P.O. Box 5299, Zip 98415–0299; tel. 253/403–1400; Robert Lenza, Chief Operating Officer and Administrator

NORTHWEST SPECIALTY HOSPITAL, 1593 East Polston Avenue, Post Falls, ID, Zip 83854–5326; tel. 208/262–2300; Vaughn Ward, Chief Executive Officer

OVERLAKE MEDICAL CENTER, 1035 116th Avenue N.E., Bellevue, WA, Zip 98004–4604; tel. 425/688–5000; J. Michael Marsh, President and Chief Executive Officer

PEACEHEALTH ST. JOSEPH MEDICAL CENTER, 2901 Squalicum Parkway, Bellingham, WA, Zip 98225–1851; tel. 360/734–5400; Nancy Steiger, R.N., FACHE, Chief Executive Officer and Chief Mission Officer, Northwest Network

PEACEHEALTH UNITED GENERAL HOSPITAL, 2000 Hospital Drive, Sedro–Woolley, WA, Zip 98284–4327; tel. 360/856–6021; James R. Barnhart, Chief Administrative Officer

PMH MEDICAL CENTER, 723 Memorial Street, Prosser, WA, Zip 99350–1593; tel. 509/786–2222; Julie Petersen, Chief Executive Officer

PROVIDENCE CENTRALIA HOSPITAL, 914 South Scheuber Road, Centralia, WA, Zip 98531–9027; tel. 360/736–2803; Jill Cooper, Site Administrator

PROVIDENCE HOLY FAMILY HOSPITAL, 5633 North Lidgerwood Street, Spokane, WA, Zip 99208–1224; tel. 509/482–0111; Alex Jackson, Chief Executive

PROVIDENCE REGIONAL MEDICAL CENTER EVERETT, 1321 Colby Avenue, Everett, WA, Zip 98201–1665, Mailing Address: P.O. Box 1147, Zip 98206–1147; tel. 425/261–2000; Preston M. Simmons, FACHE, Chief Executive Officer

PROVIDENCE SACRED HEART MEDICAL CENTER & CHILDREN'S HOSPITAL, 101 West Eighth Avenue, Spokane, WA, Zip 99204–2364, Mailing Address: P.O. Box 2555, Zip 99220–2555; tel. 509/474–3131; Alex Jackson, Chief Executive

PROVIDENCE ST. MARY MEDICAL CENTER, 401 West Poplar Street, Walla Walla, WA, Zip 99362–2846, Mailing Address: P.O. Box 1477, Zip 99362–0312; tel. 509/525–3320; Steven A. Burdick, Chief Executive Officer

PULLMAN REGIONAL HOSPITAL, 835 S.E. Bishop Boulevard, Pullman, WA, Zip 99163–5512; tel. 509/332–2541; Scott K. Adams, Chief Executive Officer

SEATTLE CHILDREN'S HOSPITAL, 4800 Sand Point Way N.E., Seattle, WA, Zip 98105–3901, Mailing Address: P.O. Box 5371, Zip 98145–5005; tel. 206/987–2000; Thomas N. Hansen, M.D., Chief Executive Officer

SKAGIT VALLEY HOSPITAL, 1415 East Kincaid Street, Mount Vernon, WA, Zip 98274–4126, Mailing Address: P.O. Box 1376, Zip 98273–1376; tel. 360/424–4111; Gregg A. Davidson, FACHE, Chief Executive Officer

ST. FRANCIS HOSPITAL, 34515 Ninth Avenue South, Federal Way, WA, Zip 98003–6799; tel. 253/944–8100; Anthony McLean, President

ST. JOSEPH MEDICAL CENTER, 1717 South J Street, Tacoma, WA, Zip 98405–3004, Mailing Address: P.O. Box 2197, Zip 98401–2197; tel. 253/426–4101; Syd Bersante, R.N., President

SUNNYSIDE COMMUNITY HOSPITAL AND CLINICS, 1016 Tacoma Avenue, Sunnyside, WA, Zip 98944–2263, Mailing Address: P.O. Box 719, Zip 98944–0719; tel. 509/837–1500; John Gallagher, Chief Executive Officer

TOPPENISH COMMUNITY HOSPITAL, 502 West Fourth Avenue, Toppenish, WA, Zip 98948–1616, Mailing Address: P.O. Box 672, Zip 98948–0672; tel. 509/865–3105; Perry Gay, Chief Executive Officer

TRIOS HEALTH, 900 South Auburn Street, Kennewick, WA, Zip 99336–5621, Mailing Address: P.O. Box 6128, Zip 99336–0128; tel. 509/586–6111; Glen Marshall, Chief Executive Officer

VALLEY HOSPITAL, 12606 East Mission Avenue, Spokane Valley, WA, Zip 99216–1090; tel. 509/924–6650; Gregory Repetti, Interim Chief Executive Officer

VIRGINIA MASON MEDICAL CENTER, 1100 Ninth Avenue, Seattle, WA, Zip 98101–2756, Mailing Address: P.O. Box 900, Zip 98111–0900; tel. 206/223–6600; Gary Kaplan, M.D., FACHE, Chairman and Chief Executive Officer

WALLA WALLA GENERAL HOSPITAL, 1025 South Second Avenue, Walla Walla, WA, Zip 99362–4116, Mailing Address: P.O. Box 1398, Zip 99362–0309; tel. 509/525–0480; Monty E. Knittel, President and Chief Executive Officer

WHIDBEY GENERAL HOSPITAL, 101 North Main Street, Coupeville, WA, Zip 98239–3413; tel. 360/678–5151; Tom Tomasino, Administrator and Chief Executive Officer

WHITMAN HOSPITAL AND MEDICAL CENTER, 1200 West Fairview Street, Colfax, WA, Zip 99111–9579; tel. 509/397–3435; Gary V. Peck, Interim Chief Executive Officer

YAKIMA REGIONAL MEDICAL AND CARDIAC CENTER, 110 South Ninth Avenue, Yakima, WA, Zip 98902–3315; tel. 509/575–5000; Veronica Knudson, Chief Executive Officer

YAKIMA VALLEY MEMORIAL HOSPITAL, 2811 Tieton Drive, Yakima, WA, Zip 98902–3761; tel. 509/575–8000; Russ Myers, Chief Executive Officer

LINCOLN COUNTY HEALTH DEPARTMENT
90 Nichols Street, Davenport, WA 99122–9729; tel. 509/725–1001; Ed Dzedzy, Public Health Administration

LINCOLN HOSPITAL, 10 Nicholls Street, Davenport, WA, Zip 99122–9729; tel. 509/725–7101; Thomas J. Martin, Administrator

ODESSA MEMORIAL HEALTHCARE CENTER, 502 East Amende Drive, Odessa, WA, Zip 99159–7003, Mailing Address: P.O. Box 368, Zip 99159–0368; tel. 509/982–2611; Mo P. Sheldon, Administrator

WEST VIRGINIA

HEALTH PARTNERS NETWORK, INC.
1000 Technology Drive, Suite 2320, Fairmont, WV 26554–8834; tel. 304/368–2740; William G. MacLean, Executive Director

BROADDUS HOSPITAL, 1 Healthcare Drive, Philippi, WV, Zip 26416–9405, Mailing Address: P.O. Box 930, Zip 26416–0930; tel. 304/457–1760; Jeffrey A. Powelson, Chief Executive Officer

CAMDEN CLARK MEDICAL CENTER, 800 Garfield Avenue, Parkersburg, WV, Zip 26101–5378, Mailing Address: P.O. Box 718, Zip 26102–0718; tel. 304/424–2111; David K. McClure, President and Chief Executive Officer

DAVIS MEMORIAL HOSPITAL, Gorman Avenue and Reed Street, Elkins, WV, Zip 26241, Mailing Address: P.O. Box 1484, Zip 26241–1484; tel. 304/636–3300; Mark Doak, Chief Executive Officer

FAIRMONT GENERAL HOSPITAL, 1325 Locust Avenue, Fairmont, WV, Zip 26554–1435; tel. 304/367–7100; Margaret C. Coster, R.N., MSN, President and Chief Executive Officer

GRAFTON CITY HOSPITAL, 1 Hospital Plaza, Grafton, WV, Zip 26354–1283; tel. 304/265–0400; Patrick Shaw, Chief Executive Officer

HEALTHSOUTH MOUNTAINVIEW REGIONAL REHABILITATION HOSPITAL, 1160 Van Voorhis Road, Morgantown, WV, Zip 26505–3437; tel. 304/598–1100; Vickie Demers, Chief Executive Officer

MINNIE HAMILTON HEALTHCARE CENTER, 186 Hospital Drive, Grantsville, WV, Zip 26147–7100; tel. 304/354–9244; Steve Whited, Chief Executive Officer

ST. JOSEPH'S HOSPITAL OF BUCKHANNON, 1 Amalia Drive, Buckhannon, WV, Zip 26201–2276; tel. 304/473–2000; Sue E. Johnson–Phillippe, FACHE, President and Chief Executive Officer

STONEWALL JACKSON MEMORIAL HOSPITAL, 230 Hospital Plaza, Weston, WV, Zip 26452–8558; tel. 304/269–8000; Avah Stalnaker, Chief Executive Officer

UNITED HOSPITAL CENTER, 327 Medical Park Drive, Bridgeport, WV, Zip 26330–9006; tel. 681/342–1000; Bruce C. Carter, President and Chief Executive Officer

WEBSTER COUNTY MEMORIAL HOSPITAL, 324 Miller Mountain Drive, Webster Springs, WV, Zip 26288–1087, Mailing Address: P.O. Box 312, Zip 26288–0312; tel. 304/847–5682; Annette M. Keenan, Chief Executive Officer

WEST VIRGINIA UNIVERSITY HOSPITALS, 1 Medical Center Drive, Morgantown, WV, Zip 26506–4749; tel. 304/598–4000

PARTNERS IN HEALTH NETWORK, INC.
405 Capitol Street, Suite 505, Charleston, WV 25301–1783; tel. 304/388–7385; Robert D. Whitler, Executive Director

BOONE MEMORIAL HOSPITAL, 701 Madison Avenue, Madison, WV, Zip 25130–1699; tel. 304/369–1230; Tommy H. Mullins, Administrator

BRAXTON COUNTY MEMORIAL HOSPITAL, 100 Hoylman Drive, Gassaway, WV, Zip 26624–9318; tel. 304/364–5156; Ben Vincent, FACHE, Chief Executive Officer

CAMC TEAYS VALLEY HOSPITAL, 1400 Hospital Drive, Hurricane, WV, Zip 25526–9202; tel. 304/757–1700; Randall H. Hodges, FACHE, President and Chief Executive Officer

CHARLESTON AREA MEDICAL CENTER, 501 Morris Street, Charleston, WV, Zip 25301–1300, Mailing Address: P.O. Box 1547, Zip 25326–1547; tel. 304/388–5432; David L. Ramsey, President and Chief Executive Officer

EYE AND EAR CLINIC OF CHARLESTON, 1306 Kanawha Boulevard East, Charleston, WV, Zip 25301–3001, Mailing Address: P.O. Box 2271, Zip 25328–2271; tel. 304/343–4371; Christina Arvon, Administrator and Chief Executive Officer

HIGHLAND HOSPITAL, 300 56th Street S.E., Charleston, WV, Zip 25304–2361, Mailing Address: P.O. Box 4107, Zip 25364–4107; tel. 304/926–1600; Cynthia A. Persily, Ph.D., R.N., President and Chief Executive Officer

JACKSON GENERAL HOSPITAL, 122 Pinnell Street, Ripley, WV, Zip 25271–9101, Mailing Address: P.O. Box 720, Zip 25271–0720; tel. 304/372–2731; Stephanie McCoy, President and Chief Executive Officer

MINNIE HAMILTON HEALTHCARE CENTER, 186 Hospital Drive, Grantsville, WV, Zip 26147–7100; tel. 304/354–9244; Steve Whited, Chief Executive Officer

MONTGOMERY GENERAL HOSPITAL, 401 Sixth Avenue, Montgomery, WV, Zip 25136–2116, Mailing Address: P.O. Box 270, Zip 25136–0270; tel. 304/442–5151; Vickie Gay, Chief Executive Officer

POCAHONTAS MEMORIAL HOSPITAL, 150 Duncan Road, Buckeye, WV, Zip 24924, Mailing Address: Rural Route 2, Box 52 W, Zip 24924; tel. 304/799–7400; Barbara Lay, Chief Executive Officer

ROANE GENERAL HOSPITAL, 200 Hospital Drive, Spencer, WV, Zip 25276–1050; tel. 304/927–4444; Douglas E. Bentz, Chief Executive Officer

STONEWALL JACKSON MEMORIAL HOSPITAL, 230 Hospital Plaza, Weston, WV, Zip 26452–8558; tel. 304/269–8000; Avah Stalnaker, Chief Executive Officer

SUMMERSVILLE REGIONAL MEDICAL CENTER, 400 Fairview Heights Road, Summersville, WV, Zip 26651–9308; tel. 304/872–2891; Randy Simmons, Interim Chief Executive Officer

WEBSTER COUNTY MEMORIAL HOSPITAL, 324 Miller Mountain Drive, Webster Springs, WV, Zip 26288–1087, Mailing Address: P.O. Box 312, Zip 26288–0312; tel. 304/847–5682; Annette M. Keenan, Chief Executive Officer

WISCONSIN

AFFINITY HEALTH SYSTEM
1570 Midway Place, Menasha, WI 54952–1165; tel. 920/720–1713; Daniel Neufelder, President and Chief Executive Officer

CALUMET MEDICAL CENTER, 614 Memorial Drive, Chilton, WI, Zip 53014–1597; tel. 920/849–2386; Timothy Richman, President

MERCY MEDICAL CENTER, 500 South Oakwood Road, Oshkosh, WI, Zip 54904–7944; tel. 920/223–2000; William Calhoun, President

ST. ELIZABETH HOSPITAL, 1506 South Oneida Street, Appleton, WI, Zip 54915–1305; tel. 920/738–2000; Daniel Neufelder, Interim Chief Executive Officer

ASPIRUS, INC.
425 Pine Ridge Boulevard, Wausau, WI 54401–4123; tel. 715/847–2118; Matthew Heywood, Chief Executive Officer

ASPIRUS GRAND VIEW HOSPITAL, N10561 Grand View Lane, Ironwood, MI, Zip 49938–9622; tel. 906/932–2525; Paula L. Chermside, Chief Operating Officer

ASPIRUS KEWEENAW HOSPITAL, 205 Osceola Street, Laurium, MI, Zip 49913–2134; tel. 906/337–6500; Michael Hauswirth, Chief Operating Officer

ASPIRUS MEDFORD HOSPITAL, 135 South Gibson Street, Medford, WI, Zip 54451–1696; tel. 715/748–8100; Gregory A. Olson, President and Chief Executive Officer

ASPIRUS ONTONAGON HOSPITAL, 601 South Seventh Street, Ontonagon, MI, Zip 49953–1459; tel. 906/884–8000; Michael Hauswirth, Chief Operating Officer

ASPIRUS WAUSAU HOSPITAL, 333 Pine Ridge Boulevard, Wausau, WI, Zip 54401–4187; tel. 715/847–2121; Darrell Lentz, Interim President

LANGLADE HOSPITAL, 112 East Fifth Avenue, Antigo, WI, Zip 54409–2796; tel. 715/623–2331; David R. Schneider, Executive Director

UNIVERSITY OF WISCONSIN HOSPITAL AND CLINICS, 600 Highland Avenue, Madison, WI, Zip 53792–0002; tel. 608/263–6400; Donna Katen–Bahensky, President and Chief Executive Officer

COLUMBIA ST. MARY'S
2025 East Newport Avenue, Milwaukee, WI 53211–2906; tel. 414/961–3300; Travis Andersen, President and Chief Executive Officer

COLUMBIA ST. MARY'S HOSPITAL MILWAUKEE, 2301 North Lake Drive, Milwaukee, WI, Zip 53211–4508; tel. 414/291–1000; Travis Andersen, President and Chief Executive Officer

COLUMBIA ST. MARY'S OZAUKEE HOSPITAL, 13111 North Port Washington Road, Mequon, WI, Zip 53097–2416; tel. 262/243–7300; Travis Andersen, President and Chief Executive Officer

SACRED HEART REHABILITATION INSTITUTE, 2323 North Lake Drive, Milwaukee, WI, Zip 53211–4508; tel. 414/298–6750; Allan M. Spooner, President

COMMUNITY HEALTH NETWORK, INC.
225 Memorial Drive, Berlin, WI 54923–1243; tel. 920/361–5580; John Feeney, President and Chief Executive Officer

BERLIN MEMORIAL HOSPITAL, 225 Memorial Drive, Berlin, WI, Zip 54923–1295; tel. 920/361–1313; John Feeney, President and Chief Executive Officer

WILD ROSE COMMUNITY MEMORIAL HOSPITAL, 601 Grove Avenue, Wild Rose, WI, Zip 54984–6903, Mailing Address: P.O. Box 243, Zip 54984–0243; tel. 920/622–3257; Donald Caves, President

FROEDTERT HEALTH & THE MEDICAL COLLEGE OF WISCONSIN
9200 West Wisconsin Avenue, Milwaukee, WI 53226–3596; tel. 414/805–3000; Catherine A. Jacobson, President and Chief Executive Officer

COMMUNITY MEMORIAL HOSPITAL, W180 N8085 Town Hall Road, Menomonee Falls, WI, Zip 53051–3518, Mailing Address: P.O. Box 408, Zip 53052–0408; tel. 262/251–1000; Dennis Pollard, President

FROEDTERT MEMORIAL LUTHERAN HOSPITAL, 9200 West Wisconsin Avenue, Milwaukee, WI, Zip 53226–3596, Mailing Address: P.O. Box 26099, Zip 53226–0099; tel. 414/805–3000; Catherine Buck, President

ST. JOSEPH'S HOSPITAL, 3200 Pleasant Valley Road, West Bend, WI, Zip 53095–9274; tel. 262/334–5533; Allen Ericson, President

GUNDERSON HEALTH SYSTEM
1900 South Avenue, La Crosse, WI 54601–5467; tel. 608/782–7300; Jeffrey E. Thompson, M.D., Chief Executive Officer

GUNDERSEN BOSCOBEL AREA HOSPITAL AND CLINICS, 205 Parker Street, Boscobel, WI, Zip 53805–1698; tel. 608/375–4112; David Hartberg, Administrator

GUNDERSEN HEALTH SYSTEM, 1900 South Avenue, La Crosse, WI, Zip 54601–5467; tel. 608/782–7300; Jeffrey E. Thompson, M.D., Chief Executive Officer

GUNDERSEN ST. JOSEPH'S HOSPITAL AND CLINICS, 400 Water Avenue, Hillsboro, WI, Zip 54634–9054, Mailing Address: P.O. Box 527, Zip 54634–0527; tel. 608/489–8000; Debra Smith, Chief Executive Officer

GUNDERSEN TRI–COUNTY HOSPITAL AND CLINICS, 18601 Lincoln Street, Whitehall, WI, Zip 54773–8605; tel. 715/538–4361; Brian Theiler, President and Chief Executive Officer

PALMER LUTHERAN HEALTH CENTER, 112 Jefferson Street, West Union, IA, Zip 52175–1022; tel. 563/422–3811; Steve Stark, Chief Executive Officer

MERCY ALLIANCE, INC.
1000 Mineral Point Avenue, Janesville, WI 53548–2940; tel. 608/756–6000; Javon R. Bea, President and Chief Executive Officer

MERCY HARVARD HOSPITAL, 901 Grant Street, Harvard, IL, Zip 60033–1898, Mailing Address: P.O. Box 850, Zip 60033–0850; tel. 815/943–5431; Jennifer Hallatt, Chief Operating Officer

MERCY HOSPITAL AND TRAUMA CENTER, 1000 Mineral Point Avenue, Janesville, WI, Zip 53548–2982, Mailing Address: P.O. Box 5003, Zip 53547–5003; tel. 608/756–6000; Javon R. Bea, President and Chief Executive Officer

MERCY WALWORTH HOSPITAL AND MEDICAL CENTER, N2950 State Road 67, Lake Geneva, WI, Zip 53147–2655; tel. 262/245–0535; Jennifer Hallatt, Chief Operating Officer

MINISTRY HEALTH CARE
11925 West Lake Park Drive, Milwaukee, WI 53224–3002; tel. 414/359–1060; Nicholas Desien, President and Chief Executive Officer

CALUMET MEDICAL CENTER, 614 Memorial Drive, Chilton, WI, Zip 53014–1597; tel. 920/849–2386; Timothy Richman, President

FLAMBEAU HOSPITAL, 98 Sherry Avenue, Park Falls, WI, Zip 54552–1467, Mailing Address: P.O. Box 310, Zip 54552–0310; tel. 715/762–2484; David A. Grundstrom, Chief Administrative Officer

HOWARD YOUNG MEDICAL CENTER, 240 Maple Street, Woodruff, WI, Zip 54568–9190, Mailing Address: P.O. Box 470, Zip 54568–0470; tel. 715/356–8000; Monica Hilt, President

MERCY MEDICAL CENTER, 500 South Oakwood Road, Oshkosh, WI, Zip 54904–7944; tel. 920/223–2000; William Calhoun, President

MINISTRY DOOR COUNTY MEDICAL CENTER, 323 South 18th Avenue, Sturgeon Bay, WI, Zip 54235–1495; tel. 920/743–5566; Gerald M. Worrick, President and Chief Executive Officer

MINISTRY EAGLE RIVER MEMORIAL HOSPITAL, 201 Hospital Road, Eagle River, WI, Zip 54521–8835; tel. 715/479–7411; Monica Hilt, President

MINISTRY GOOD SAMARITAN HEALTH CENTER, 601 South Center Avenue, Merrill, WI, Zip 54452–3404; tel. 715/536–5511; Mary T. Krueger, President

MINISTRY OUR LADY OF VICTORY HOSPITAL, 1120 Pine Street, Stanley, WI, Zip 54768–1297; tel. 715/644–5571; Vanessa Freitag, President

MINISTRY SACRED HEART HOSPITAL, 401 West Mohawk Drive, Tomahawk, WI, Zip 54487–2274; tel. 715/453–7700; Monica Hilt, President

MINISTRY SAINT CLARE'S HOSPITAL, 3400 Ministry Parkway, Weston, WI, Zip 54476–5220; tel. 715/393–3000; Mary T. Krueger, President

MINISTRY SAINT JOSEPH'S HOSPITAL, 611 St. Joseph Avenue, Marshfield, WI, Zip 54449–1898; tel. 715/387–1713; Brian Kief, Regional Vice President Ministry Health Care and President Ministry Saint Joseph's Hospital

MINISTRY SAINT MARY'S HOSPITALS, 2251 North Shore Drive, Rhinelander, WI, Zip 54501–6710; tel. 715/361–2000; Monica Hilt, President

MINISTRY SAINT MICHAEL'S HOSPITAL, 900 Illinois Avenue, Stevens Point, WI, Zip 54481–3196; tel. 715/346–5000; Jeffrey L. Martin, President

SAINT ELIZABETH'S MEDICAL CENTER, 1200 Grant Boulevard West, Wabasha, MN, Zip 55981–1042; tel. 651/565–4531; Thomas Crowley, President and Chief Executive Officer

ST. ELIZABETH HOSPITAL, 1506 South Oneida Street, Appleton, WI, Zip 54915–1305; tel. 920/738–2000; Daniel Neufelder, Interim Chief Executive Officer

WHEATON FRANCISCAN HEALTHCARE
400 West River Woods Parkway, Glendale, WI 53212–1060; tel. 414/465–3000; John D. Oliverio, President and Chief Executive Officer

MIDWEST ORTHOPEDIC SPECIALTY HOSPITAL, 10101 South 27th Street, 2nd Floor, Franklin, WI, Zip 53132–7209; tel. 414/817–5800; Coreen Dicus–Johnson, President

WHEATON FRANCISCAN HEALTHCARE – ALL SAINTS, 3801 Spring Street, Racine, WI, Zip 53405–1690; tel. 262/687–4011; Susan Boland, R.N., MSN, President and Chief Executive Officer

WHEATON FRANCISCAN HEALTHCARE – ELMBROOK MEMORIAL, 19333 West North Avenue, Brookfield, WI, Zip 53045–4198; tel. 262/785–2000; Debra K. Standridge, President

WHEATON FRANCISCAN HEALTHCARE – FRANKLIN, 10101 South 27th Street, Franklin, WI, Zip 53132–7209; tel. 414/325–4700; Coreen Dicus–Johnson, President

WHEATON FRANCISCAN HEALTHCARE – ST. FRANCIS, 3237 South 16th Street, Milwaukee, WI, Zip 53215–4592; tel. 414/647–5000; Coreen Dicus–Johnson, President

WHEATON FRANCISCAN HEALTHCARE – ST. JOSEPH'S, 5000 West Chambers Street, Milwaukee, WI, Zip 53210–1650; tel. 414/447–2000; Debra K. Standridge, President

WHEATON FRANCISCAN HEALTHCARE – THE WISCONSIN HEART HOSPITAL, 10000 West Bluemound Road, Wauwatosa, WI, Zip 53226–4321; tel. 414/778–7800; Debra K. Standridge, President

Alliances

ALLIANCE OF INDEPENDENT ACADEMIC MEDICAL CENTERS
233 East Erie Street, Ste 306, Chicago, IL Zip 60611; tel. 312/988–7572; Nancie Noie Thompson, Executive Director

ARIZONA
Phoenix
Member
　Maricopa Integrated Health System

Scottsdale
Member
　Scottsdale Healthcare–Osborn Medical Center

CALIFORNIA
Los Angeles
Member
　Cedars–Sinai Medical Center

CONNECTICUT
Danbury
Member
　Danbury Hospital

Hartford
Member
　Saint Francis Hospital and Medical Center

DELAWARE
Newark
Member
　Christiana Care Health System

Wilmington
Member
　Christiana Care Health System

DISTRICT OF COLUMBIA
Washington
Member
　MedStar Georgetown University Hospital
　MedStar National Rehabilitation Hospital
　MedStar Washington Hospital Center

FLORIDA
Orlando
Member
　Florida Hospital
　Orlando Health

ILLINOIS
Chicago
Member
　Advocate Illinois Masonic Medical Center

Downers Grove
Member
　Advocate Health Care

Oak Lawn
Member
　Advocate Christ Medical Center

Park Ridge
Member
　Advocate Lutheran General Hospital

Peoria
Member
　OSF Saint Francis Medical Center

Urbana
Member
　Carle Foundation Hospital

IOWA
Des Moines
Member
　UnityPoint Health – Des Moines
　UnityPoint Health – Iowa Methodist Medical Center

KENTUCKY
Louisville
Member
　Kosair Children's Hospital
　Norton Audubon Hospital
　Norton Brownsboro Hospital
　Norton Healthcare
　Norton Hospital
　Norton Suburban Hospital

LOUISIANA
Baton Rouge
Member
　Our Lady of the Lake Regional Medical Center

New Orleans
Member
　Ochsner Health System

MAINE
Portland
Member
　Maine Medical Center

MARYLAND
Baltimore
Member
　MedStar Franklin Square Medical Center
　MedStar Good Samaritan Hospital
　MedStar Harbor Hospital
　MedStar Union Memorial Hospital
　Sinai Hospital of Baltimore

Columbia
Member
　MedStar Health

MASSACHUSETTS
Burlington
Member
　Lahey Hospital & Medical Center, Burlington

Springfield
Member
　Baystate Health, Inc.

MICHIGAN
Detroit
Member
　Henry Ford Health System

Grand Rapids
Member
　Mercy Health Saint Mary's
　Spectrum Health

Lansing
Member
　Sparrow Hospital

Rochester
Member
　Crittenton Hospital Medical Center

Royal Oak
Member
　Beaumont Hospital – Royal Oak

MINNESOTA
Bloomington
Member
　HealthPartners

NEW JERSEY
Brick Township
Member
　Ocean Medical Center

Holmdel
Member
　Bayshore Community Hospital

Livingston
Member
　Saint Barnabas Medical Center

Long Branch
Member
　Monmouth Medical Center, Long Branch Campus

Manahawkin
Member
　Southern Ocean Medical Center

Morristown
Member
　Morristown Medical Center

Neptune
Member
　Jersey Shore University Medical Center

Newark
Member
　Newark Beth Israel Medical Center

Phillipsburg
Member
　St. Luke's Hospital – Warren Campus

Red Bank
Member
　Riverview Medical Center

Summit
Member
　Overlook Medical Center

NEW YORK
Brooklyn
Member
　Maimonides Medical Center

Cooperstown
Member
　Bassett Medical Center

Mineola
Member
　Winthrop–University Hospital

NORTH CAROLINA
Charlotte
Member
　Carolinas Medical Center

Greensboro
Member
　Moses H. Cone Memorial Hospital

OHIO
Akron
Member
　Akron General Medical Center

Cincinnati
Member
　TriHealth

Columbus
Member
　Mount Carmel
　OhioHealth Grant Medical Center
　OhioHealth Riverside Methodist Hospital

PENNSYLVANIA
Allentown
Member
　Lehigh Valley Health Network

Bethlehem
Member
　St. Luke's University Hospital – Bethlehem Campus

Bryn Mawr
Member
　Bryn Mawr Hospital

Johnstown
Member
　Conemaugh Memorial Medical Center

Philadelphia
Member
　Einstein Medical Center Philadelphia

Sayre
Member
　Robert Packer Hospital

West Reading
Member
　Reading Hospital and Medical Center

Wynnewood
Member
　Lankenau Medical Center

York
Member
　WellSpan Health
　York Hospital

SOUTH DAKOTA
Sioux Falls
Member
　Sanford Health

TEXAS

Dallas
Member
  Baylor University Medical Center
  Parkland Health & Hospital System

Fort Worth
Member
  JPS Health Network

Garland
Member
  Baylor Medical Center at Garland

WASHINGTON

Seattle
Member
  Virginia Mason Medical Center

WISCONSIN

Marshfield
Member
  Ministry Saint Joseph's Hospital

Milwaukee
Member
  Aurora Health Care
  Aurora Sinai Medical Center
  Aurora St. Luke's Medical Center

CAPSTONE HEALTH ALLIANCE

1200 Ridgefield Boulevard, Suite 200,
Asheville, NC Zip 28806;
tel. 828/418–5050; Tim Bugg, President
and Chief Executive Officer

ALABAMA

Dothan
Member
  Southeast Alabama Medical Center

Opelika
Member
  East Alabama Medical Center

Valley
Member
  East Alabama Medical Center–Lanier

GEORGIA

Bremen
Member
  Higgins General Hospital

Carrollton
Member
  Tanner Medical Center–Carrollton

La Grange
Member
  West Georgia Health

Villa Rica
Member
  Tanner Medical Center–Villa Rica

KENTUCKY

Bowling Green
Member
  Commonwealth Regional Specialty Hospital
  Medical Center at Bowling Green

Franklin
Member
  Medical Center at Franklin

Scottsville
Member
  Medical Center at Scottsville

NORTH CAROLINA

Asheboro
Member
  Randolph Hospital

Asheville
Member
  Asheville Specialty Hospital
  CarePartners Health Services
  Mission Hospital

Blowing Rock
Member
  Blowing Rock Rehabilitation & Davant Extended Care
    Center

Boone
Member
  Watauga Medical Center

Brevard
Member
  Transylvania Regional Hospital

Bryson City
Member
  Swain County Hospital

Cherokee
Member
  Cherokee Indian Hospital

Clyde
Member
  Haywood Regional Medical Center

Columbus
Member
  St. Luke's Hospital

Elizabeth City
Member
  Sentara Albemarle Medical Center

Elizabethtown
Member
  Cape Fear Valley – Bladen County Hospital

Fayetteville
Member
  Cape Fear Valley Medical Center
  Highsmith–Rainey Specialty Hospital

Franklin
Member
  Angel Medical Center

Gastonia
Member
  Caromont Regional Medical Center

Goldsboro
Member
  Wayne Memorial Hospital

Hendersonville
Member
  Margaret R. Pardee Memorial Hospital
  Park Ridge Health

Hickory
Member
  Catawba Valley Medical Center

Highlands
Member
  Highlands–Cashiers Hospital

Kinston
Member
  Lenoir Memorial Hospital

Linville
Member
  Charles A. Cannon Memorial Hospital

Lumberton
Member
  Southeastern Health

Marion
Member
  McDowell Hospital

Morehead City
Member
  Carteret General Hospital

Oxford
Member
  Granville Health System

Pinehurst
Member
  FirstHealth Moore Regional Hospital

Roanoke Rapids
Member
  Halifax Regional Medical Center

Rockingham
Member
  FirstHealth Richmond Memorial Hospital

Rutherfordton
Member
  Rutherford Regional Health System

Spruce Pine
Member
  Blue Ridge Regional Hospital

Statesville
Member
  Iredell Memorial Hospital

Sylva
Member
  Harris Regional Hospital

Troy
Member
  FirstHealth Montgomery Memorial Hospital

PENNSYLVANIA

Erie
Member
  Millcreek Community Hospital

Kittanning
Member
  ACMH Hospital

Meadville
Member
  Meadville Medical Center

SOUTH CAROLINA

Barnwell
Member
  Southern Palmetto Hospital

Conway
Member
  Conway Medical Center

Dillon
Member
  McLeod Medical Center Dillon

Florence
Member
  McLeod Regional Medical Center

Greenwood
Member
  Self Regional Healthcare

Loris
Member
  McLeod Loris Seacoast Hospital

Seneca
Member
  Oconee Medical Center

West Columbia
Member
  Lexington Medical Center

Winnsboro
Member
  Fairfield Memorial Hospital

TENNESSEE

Crossville
Member
  Cumberland Medical Center

Elizabethton
Member
  Sycamore Shoals Hospital

Erwin
Member
  Unicoi County Memorial Hospital

Greeneville
Member
  Laughlin Memorial Hospital

Johnson City
Member
  Franklin Woods Community Hospital
  Johnson City Medical Center

Kingsport
Member
  Indian Path Medical Center

Knoxville
Member
  University of Tennessee Medical Center

Maryville
Member
  Blount Memorial Hospital

Mountain City
Member
  Johnson County Community Hospital

VIRGINIA

Abingdon
Member
　Johnston Memorial Hospital

Bedford
Member
　Bedford Memorial Hospital

Chesapeake
Member
　Chesapeake Regional Medical Center

Christiansburg
Member
　Carilion New River Valley Medical Center

Clintwood
Member
　Dickenson Community Hospital

Gloucester
Member
　Riverside Walter Reed Hospital

Grundy
Member
　Buchanan General Hospital

Lebanon
Member
　Russell County Medical Center

Lexington
Member
　Carilion Stonewall Jackson Hospital

Marion
Member
　Smyth County Community Hospital

Nassawadox
Member
　Riverside Shore Memorial Hospital

Newport News
Member
　Riverside Regional Medical Center

Norton
Member
　Norton Community Hospital

Pearisburg
Member
　Carilion Giles Community Hospital

Roanoke
Member
　Carilion Clinic
　Carilion Roanoke Memorial Hospital

Rocky Mount
Member
　Carilion Franklin Memorial Hospital

South Hill
Member
　VCU Community Memorial Hospital

Tappahannock
Member
　Riverside Tappahannock Hospital

Williamsburg
Member
　Riverside Doctors' Hospital

CATHOLIC CEO HEALTHCARE CONNECTION
　3333 Warrenville Rd, Ste 200, Lisle, IL
　Zip 60532; tel. 630/799–8315; Roger N.
　Butler, Executive Director

CALIFORNIA

Irvine
Member
　St. Joseph Health

San Francisco
Member
　Dignity Health

COLORADO

Denver
Member
　SCL Health System

Englewood
Member
　Catholic Health Initiatives

ILLINOIS

Chicago
Member
　Presence Health

Peoria
Member
　OSF Healthcare System

Springfield
Member
　Hospital Sisters Health System

Wheaton
Member
　Wheaton Franciscan Healthcare

LOUISIANA

Baton Rouge
Member
　Franciscan Missionaries of Our Lady Health System,
　Inc.

MARYLAND

Marriottsville
Member
　Bon Secours Health System, Inc.

MASSACHUSETTS

Tewksbury
Member
　Covenant Health Systems, Inc.

MISSOURI

Chesterfield
Member
　Mercy Health

Saint Louis
Member
　Ascension Health
　SSM Health

OHIO

Cincinnati
Member
　Mercy Health

Toledo
Member
　Sylvania Franciscan Health

SOUTH DAKOTA

Sioux Falls
Member
　Avera Health

TEXAS

Irving
Member
　CHRISTUS Health

WASHINGTON

Renton
Member
　Providence Health & Services

Vancouver
Member
　PeaceHealth

WISCONSIN

Manitowoc
Member
　Franciscan Sisters of Christian Charity Sponsored
　　Ministries, Inc.

COMMUNITY HEALTH COLLABORATIVE, LLC
　630 East River Street, Elyria, OH
　Zip 44035–5902; tel. 440/329–7500;
　Frank L. Lordeman, President and Chief
　Executive Officer

OHIO

Elyria
Member
　University Hospitals Elyria Medical Center

Middleburg Heights
Member
　Southwest General Health Center

Parma
Member
　University Hospitals Parma Medical Center

CONFLUENCE HEALTH
　820 North Chelan Avenue, Wenatchee,
　WA Zip 98801–2028;
　tel. 509/663–8711; Peter Rutherford
　M.D., Chief Executive Officer

WASHINGTON

Wenatchee
Member
　Central Washington Hospital
　Wenatchee Valley Medical Center

FLETCHER ALLEN PARTNERS
　111 Colchester Avenue, Burlington, VT
　Zip 05401–1473; tel. 802/847–3983;
　John R. Brumsted M.D., President and
　Chief Executive Officer

NEW YORK

Elizabethtown
Member
　Elizabethtown Community Hospital

Plattsburgh
Member
　Champlain Valley Physicians Hospital Medical Center

VERMONT

Berlin
Member
　Central Vermont Medical Center

Burlington
Member
　Fletcher Allen Health Care

HEALTH ENTERPRISES OF IOWA
　5825 Dry Creek Lane NE, Cedar Rapids,
　IA Zip 52402–1225; tel. 319/368–3619;
　Judy L. Sadler, President and Chief
　Executive Officer

IOWA

Ames
Member
　Mary Greeley Medical Center

Chariton
Member
　Lucas County Health Center

Charles City
Member
　Floyd County Medical Center

Cherokee
Affiliate
　Cherokee Regional Medical Center

Davenport
Member
　Genesis Health System

Denison
Member
　Crawford County Memorial Hospital

Des Moines
Affiliate
　Broadlawns Medical Center

Fairfield
Member
　Jefferson County Health Center

Guthrie Center
Member
　Guthrie County Hospital

Humboldt
Member
　Humboldt County Memorial Hospital

Ida Grove
Affiliate
　Horn Memorial Hospital

Independence
Affiliate
　Buchanan County Health Center

Section B

Iowa City
Member
Mercy Iowa City

Manchester
Member
Regional Medical Center

Maquoketa
Member
Jackson County Regional Health Center

Marshalltown
Member
Marshalltown Medical & Surgical Center

Mount Pleasant
Member
Henry County Health Center

Newton
Member
Skiff Medical Center

Oskaloosa
Member
Mahaska Health Partnership

Pella
Member
Pella Regional Health Center

Pocahontas
Member
Pocahontas Community Hospital

Sac City
Member
Loring Hospital

Waukon
Affiliate
Veterans Memorial Hospital

Waverly
Member
Waverly Health Center

West Burlington
Member
Great River Medical Center

HOSPITAL NETWORK VENTURES, LLC
6212 American Avenue, Portage, MI
Zip 49002; tel. 269/329–3200; Gregory
L. Hedegore, President and Chief
Executive Officer

MICHIGAN
Allegan
Partner
Allegan General Hospital

Charlotte
Partner
Hayes Green Beach Memorial Hospital

Coldwater
Partner
Community Health Center of Branch County

Hastings
Partner
Pennock Hospital

Kalamazoo
Partner
Bronson Healthcare Group, Inc.

Marlette
Partner
Marlette Regional Hospital

Marshall
Partner
Oaklawn Hospital

Owosso
Partner
Memorial Healthcare

Paw Paw
Partner
Bronson LakeView Hospital

Saint Joseph
Partner
Lakeland Healthcare

South Haven
Partner
South Haven Health System

Sturgis
Partner
Sturgis Hospital

Watervliet
Partner
Lakeland Community Hospital Watervliet

HOSPITAL SHARED SERVICES ASSOCIATION
P O Box 19741, Seattle, WA
Zip 98109–6741; tel. 425/899–2753;
Chrissy Yamada CPA, Senior Vice
President, Finance, Evergreen Health

WASHINGTON
Bellevue
Member
Overlake Medical Center

Burien
Member
Highline Medical Center

Chelan
Member
Lake Chelan Community Hospital

Clarkston
Member
Tri–State Memorial Hospital

Davenport
Member
Lincoln Hospital

Edmonds
Member
Swedish/Edmonds

Ephrata
Member
Columbia Basin Hospital

Grand Coulee
Member
Coulee Medical Center

Kirkland
Member
EvergreenHealth

Moses Lake
Member
Samaritan Healthcare

Mount Vernon
Member
Skagit Valley Hospital

Newport
Member
Newport Hospital and Health Services

Odessa
Member
Odessa Memorial Healthcare Center

Othello
Member
Othello Community Hospital

Prosser
Member
PMH Medical Center

Pullman
Member
Pullman Regional Hospital

Quincy
Member
Quincy Valley Medical Center

Republic
Member
Ferry County Memorial Hospital

Ritzville
Member
East Adams Rural Hospital

Tacoma
Member
Western State Hospital

Tonasket
Member
North Valley Hospital

MEDI–SOTA, INC.
1280 Locust Street Suite 16, Dawson,
MN Zip 56232–2375;
tel. 320/769–2269; Deb Ranallo,
Executive Director

MINNESOTA
Appleton
Member
Appleton Area Health Services

Arlington
Member
Sibley Medical Center

Benson
Member
Swift County–Benson Hospital

Canby
Member
Sanford Canby Medical Center

Dawson
Member
Johnson Memorial Health Services

Elbow Lake
Member
Prairie Ridge Hospital and Health Services

Glencoe
Member
Glencoe Regional Health Services

Glenwood
Member
Glacial Ridge Health System

Graceville
Member
Essentia Health–Holy Trinity Hospital

Granite Falls
Member
Granite Falls Municipal Hospital and Manor

Hendricks
Member
Hendricks Community Hospital

Litchfield
Member
Meeker Memorial Hospital

Long Prairie
Member
CentraCare Health–Long Prairie

Madelia
Member
Madelia Community Hospital

Mahnomen
Member
Mahnomen Health Center

Marshall
Member
Avera Marshall Regional Medical Center

Montevideo
Member
Chippewa County–Montevideo Hospital

Olivia
Member
RC Hospital and Clinics

Ortonville
Member
Ortonville Area Health Services

Paynesville
Member
CentraCare Health–Paynesville

Perham
Member
Perham Health

Pipestone
Member
Pipestone County Medical Center Avera

Redwood Falls
Member
Redwood Area Hospital

Saint Peter
Member
River's Edge Hospital and Clinic

Slayton
Member
Murray County Medical Center

Sleepy Eye
Member
Sleepy Eye Medical Center

Staples
Member
Lakewood Health System

Tracy
Member
Sanford Tracy Medical Center

Tyler
Member
Tyler Healthcare Center Avera

NORTH REGION HEALTH ALLIANCE
120 East Bridge Avenue, Warren, MN
Zip 56762; tel. 218/745–5343; Jon E.
Linnell, Chief Executive Officer

MINNESOTA
Ada
Member
Essentia Health Ada

Bagley
Member
Sanford Bagley Medical Center

Baudette
Member
LakeWood Health Center

Crookston
Member
RiverView Health

Fosston
Member
Essentia Health Fosston

Hallock
Member
Kittson Memorial Healthcare Center

Roseau
Member
LifeCare Medical Center

Thief River Falls
Member
Sanford Thief River Falls Medical Center

Warren
Member
North Valley Health Center

NORTH DAKOTA
Cavalier
Member
Pembina County Memorial Hospital and Wedgewood
Manor

Cooperstown
Member
Cooperstown Medical Center

Devils Lake
Member
Mercy Hospital

Grafton
Member
Unity Medical Center

Grand Forks
Member
Altru Health System

Hillsboro
Member
Sanford Hillsboro Medical Center

Langdon
Member
Cavalier County Memorial Hospital

Mayville
Member
Sanford Mayville Medical Center

Mcville
Member
Nelson County Health System

Northwood
Member
Northwood Deaconess Health Center

Park River
Member
First Care Health Center

NORTHWEST KANSAS HEALTH ALLIANCE
2220 Canterbury Drive, Hays, KS
Zip 67601–2370; tel. 785/623–2300;
John H. Jeter M.D., President and Chief
Executive Officer

KANSAS
Ashland
Member
Ashland Health Center

Atwood
Member
Rawlins County Health Center

Beloit
Member
Mitchell County Hospital Health Systems

Colby
Member
Citizens Medical Center

Dighton
Member
Lane County Hospital

Dodge City
Member
Western Plains Medical Complex

Ellsworth
Member
Ellsworth County Medical Center

Garden City
Member
St. Catherine Hospital

Goodland
Member
Goodland Regional Medical Center

Great Bend
Member
Great Bend Regional Hospital

Greensburg
Member
Kiowa County Memorial Hospital

Hill City
Member
Graham County Hospital

Hoisington
Member
Clara Barton Hospital

Hoxie
Member
Sheridan County Health Complex

Hutchinson
Member
Hutchinson Regional Medical Center

Jetmore
Member
Hodgeman County Health Center

Kinsley
Member
Edwards County Hospital and Healthcare Center

La Crosse
Member
Rush County Memorial Hospital

Larned
Member
Pawnee Valley Community Hospital

Lawrence
Member
Lawrence Memorial Hospital

Leoti
Member
Wichita County Health Center

Lincoln
Member
Lincoln County Hospital

Lyons
Member
Rice County District Hospital

Minneola
Member
Minneola District Hospital

Ness City
Member
Ness County Hospital

Norton
Member
Norton County Hospital

Oakley
Member
Logan County Hospital

Oberlin
Member
Decatur Health Systems

Osborne
Member
Osborne County Memorial Hospital

Ottawa
Member
Ransom Memorial Hospital

Phillipsburg
Member
Phillips County Hospital

Plainville
Member
Rooks County Health Center

Quinter
Member
Gove County Medical Center

Ransom
Member
Grisell Memorial Hospital District One

Russell
Member
Russell Regional Hospital

Saint Francis
Member
Cheyenne County Hospital

Salina
Member
Salina Regional Health Center

Satanta
Member
Satanta District Hospital

Scott City
Member
Scott County Hospital

Smith Center
Member
Smith County Memorial Hospital

Stafford
Member
Stafford County Hospital

Tribune
Member
Greeley County Health Services

Wakeeney
Member
Trego County–Lemke Memorial Hospital

PENNANT HEALTH ALLIANCE
2122 Health Drive SW Suite 100,
Wyoming, MI Zip 49519–9698;
tel. 616/252–6800; Michael D. Faas,
Chief Executive Officer

MICHIGAN
Ann Arbor
Member
University of Michigan Hospitals and Health Centers

Cadillac
Member
Mercy Hospital Cadillac

Carson City
Member
Carson City Hospital

Grand Rapids
Member
Mary Free Bed Rehabilitation Hospital
Mercy Health Saint Mary's

Grayling
Member
Mercy Hospital Grayling

Muskegon
Member
Mercy Health, Mercy Campus

Wyoming
Member
Metro Health Hospital

PREMIER, INC.
13034 Ballantyne Corporate Place,
Charlotte, NC Zip 28277–1498;
tel. 704/816–5353; Susan DeVore,
President and Chief Executive Officer

ALABAMA
Dothan
Owner
Southeast Alabama Medical Center

Opelika
Owner
East Alabama Medical Center

ARIZONA
Phoenix
John C. Lincoln Health Network
Owner
Banner Health

ARKANSAS
Batesville
White River Health System

Pine Bluff
Owner
Jefferson Regional Medical Center

CALIFORNIA
Long Beach
St. Mary Medical Center

Los Altos Hills
Daughters of Charity Health System

Mountain View
El Camino Hospital

Oceanside
Tri–City Medical Center

Rancho Mirage
Owner
Eisenhower Medical Center

Roseville
Owner
Adventist Health

San Francisco
Owner
Dignity Health

CONNECTICUT
Hartford
Owner
Saint Francis Hospital and Medical Center

Waterbury
Saint Mary's Hospital

DELAWARE
Dover
Owner
Bayhealth Medical Center

Lewes
Owner
Beebe Healthcare

DISTRICT OF COLUMBIA
Washington
Owner
Sibley Memorial Hospital

FLORIDA
Altamonte Springs
Owner
Adventist Health System Sunbelt Health Care
Corporation

Clearwater
BayCare Health System

Coral Gables
Owner
Baptist Health South Florida

Hollywood
Memorial Healthcare System

Jacksonville
Baptist Health
Nemours

Miami Beach
Owner
Mount Sinai Medical Center

Saint Petersburg
Member
Bayfront Health St. Petersburg

Tampa
Member
H. Lee Moffitt Cancer Center and Research Institute

Vero Beach
Owner
Indian River Medical Center

Winter Haven
Owner
Winter Haven Hospital

GEORGIA
Carrollton
Tanner Medical Center–Carrollton

Columbus
Owner
St. Francis Hospital

La Grange
Owner
West Georgia Health

Savannah
St. Joseph's Hospital
Owner
Memorial Health

HAWAII
Honolulu
Owner
Kuakini Medical Center

ILLINOIS
Chicago
Presence Health
Owner
Mount Sinai Hospital

Harvey
Ingalls Memorial Hospital

Naperville
Edward Hospital

Peoria
UnityPoint Health – Methodist

Urbana
Owner
Carle Foundation Hospital

Winfield
Cadence Health

INDIANA
Gary
Owner
Methodist Hospitals

IOWA
Cedar Rapids
Member
Health Enterprises of Iowa

Davenport
Member
Genesis Medical Center–Davenport

De Witt
Member
Genesis Medical Center, DeWitt

KENTUCKY
Ashland
King's Daughters Medical Center

Bowling Green
Commonwealth Regional Specialty Hospital

Danville
Ephraim McDowell Regional Medical Center

Edgewood
St. Elizabeth Edgewood

Glasgow
Owner
T. J. Samson Community Hospital

Henderson
Owner
Methodist Hospital

Louisville
Baptist Health
Member
University of Louisville Hospital
Owner
Norton Healthcare

Murray
Owner
Murray–Calloway County Hospital

LOUISIANA
Baton Rouge
Baton Rouge General Medical Center
Member
Woman's Hospital

Columbia
Caldwell Memorial Hospital

Hammond
North Oaks Health System

Houma
Owner
Terrebonne General Medical Center

Lafayette
Owner
Lafayette General Medical Center

Marrero
Owner
West Jefferson Medical Center

MAINE
Lewiston
Central Maine Medical Center

MARYLAND
Annapolis
Owner
Anne Arundel Medical Center

Baltimore
Greater Baltimore Medical Center
Member
Mercy Medical Center
Sinai Hospital of Baltimore

Bethesda
Owner
Suburban Hospital

Columbia
Owner
Howard County General Hospital

Elkton
Owner
Union Hospital

Frederick
Owner
Frederick Memorial Hospital

Gaithersburg
Owner
Adventist HealthCare

Hagerstown
Western Maryland Hospital Center
Owner
Meritus Medical Center

Lanham
Owner
Doctors Community Hospital

Marriottsville
Owner
Bon Secours Health System, Inc.

Randallstown
Member
Northwest Hospital

Salisbury
Owner
Peninsula Regional Medical Center

Westminster
Owner
  Carroll Hospital Center

MASSACHUSETTS
Boston
  Tufts Medical Center
Springfield
Owner
  Baystate Health, Inc.

MICHIGAN
Detroit
Owner
  Henry Ford Health System
Flint
  McLaren Health Care Corporation
Jackson
  Allegiance Health
Lansing
Owner
  Sparrow Hospital
Rochester
Member
  Crittenton Hospital Medical Center

MINNESOTA
Minneapolis
Owner
  Fairview Health Services

MISSISSIPPI
Jackson
  Mississippi Baptist Health System
Laurel
Owner
  South Central Regional Medical Center
Meridian
Owner
  Rush Health Systems

MISSOURI
Saint Louis
  St. Anthony's Medical Center
Owner
  SSM Health

MONTANA
Billings
  Billings Clinic

NEW MEXICO
Albuquerque
  Presbyterian Healthcare Services

NEW YORK
Rochester
Owner
  Rochester Regional Health System
  Seagate Alliance

NORTH CAROLINA
Asheboro
Owner
  Randolph Hospital
Asheville
  Mission Health System
Boone
Owner
  Watauga Medical Center
Burlington
Owner
  Alamance Regional Medical Center
Charlotte
  Carolinas HealthCare System
Clyde
Owner
  Haywood Regional Medical Center
Fayetteville
  Cape Fear Valley Medical Center
Gastonia
Owner
  Caromont Regional Medical Center
Goldsboro
Owner
  Wayne Memorial Hospital

Hendersonville
Owner
  Margaret R. Pardee Memorial Hospital
Hickory
Owner
  Catawba Valley Medical Center
Kinston
Owner
  Lenoir Memorial Hospital
Lumberton
Owner
  Southeastern Health
Morehead City
  Carteret General Hospital
Pinehurst
  FirstHealth of the Carolinas
Roanoke Rapids
Owner
  Halifax Regional Medical Center
Statesville
Owner
  Iredell Memorial Hospital
Wilson
Owner
  Wilson Medical Center

OHIO
Akron
Owner
  Summa Akron City Hospital
Cincinnati
Owner
  Bethesda North Hospital
  Mercy Health
Cleveland
  Cleveland Clinic Health System
  University Hospitals
Owner
  Cleveland Clinic
Elyria
Member
  University Hospitals Elyria Medical Center
Kettering
  Kettering Medical Center
Parma
Member
  University Hospitals Parma Medical Center

OKLAHOMA
Tulsa
Owner
  Saint Francis Hospital

OREGON
Salem
Member
  Salem Hospital

PENNSYLVANIA
Beaver
  Heritage Valley Health System
Danville
Member
  Geisinger Health System
Philadelphia
  Einstein Healthcare Network
Radnor
Owner
  Jefferson Health System
Washington
  Washington Hospital

SOUTH CAROLINA
Anderson
Owner
  AnMed Health Medical Center
Conway
Owner
  Conway Medical Center
Florence
Owner
  McLeod Regional Medical Center

Greenwood
Owner
  Self Regional Healthcare
West Columbia
Owner
  Lexington Medical Center

SOUTH DAKOTA
Rapid City
Owner
  Rapid City Regional Hospital
Sioux Falls
Owner
  Avera Health

TENNESSEE
Crossville
  Cumberland Medical Center
Greeneville
  Laughlin Memorial Hospital
Johnson City
Owner
  Mountain States Health Alliance
Knoxville
  University of Tennessee Medical Center
Maryville
Owner
  Blount Memorial Hospital

TEXAS
Arlington
  Texas Health Resources
Dallas
  University of Texas Southwestern Medical Center
Owner
  Methodist Health System
Galveston
  University of Texas Medical Branch Hospitals
Houston
  Harris Health System
Owner
  University of Texas M.D. Anderson Cancer Center
Lubbock
Owner
  University Medical Center
Nacogdoches
Owner
  Nacogdoches Memorial Hospital

VIRGINIA
Abingdon
Owner
  Johnston Memorial Hospital
Chesapeake
Owner
  Chesapeake Regional Medical Center
Marion
Owner
  Smyth County Community Hospital
Newport News
  Riverside Health System
Roanoke
Owner
  Carilion Clinic
South Hill
Owner
  VCU Community Memorial Hospital
Winchester
Member
  Winchester Medical Center

WASHINGTON
Seattle
  Group Health Cooperative Central Hospital
Vancouver
Owner
  PeaceHealth

WEST VIRGINIA
Elkins
Owner
  Davis Memorial Hospital
Fairmont
Owner
  West Virginia United Health System

Section B

Huntington
Cabell Huntington Hospital
Pallottine Health Services

Morgantown
Owner
Monongalia General Hospital

Parkersburg
Owner
Camden Clark Medical Center

Point Pleasant
Owner
Pleasant Valley Hospital

South Charleston
Owner
Thomas Memorial Hospital

Weirton
Owner
Weirton Medical Center

WISCONSIN

Milwaukee
Owner
Aurora Health Care

SEAGATE ALLIANCE
3445 Winton Place, Suite 222, Rochester, NY Zip 14623–2950;
tel. 888/732–4284; Diane H. Ashley, President and Chief Executive Officer

NEW JERSEY

Newark
Member
Columbus Hospital LTACH

NEW YORK

Bath
Member
Bath Veterans Affairs Medical Center
Ira Davenport Memorial Hospital

Buffalo
Member
BryLin Hospitals
Catholic Health System
Erie County Medical Center
Roswell Park Cancer Institute

Canandaigua
Member
F. F. Thompson Hospital

Carthage
Member
Carthage Area Hospital

Clifton Springs
Member
Clifton Springs Hospital and Clinic

Corning
Member
Corning Hospital

Cuba
Member
Cuba Memorial Hospital

Dansville
Member
Nicholas H. Noyes Memorial Hospital

Dunkirk
Member
Brooks Memorial Hospital

Elmira
Member
Arnot Ogden Medical Center
Elmira Psychiatric Center
St. Joseph's Hospital

Geneva
Member
Geneva General Hospital

Hornell
Member
St. James Mercy Health System

Kenmore
Member
Kenmore Mercy Hospital

Lockport
Member
Eastern Niagara Hospital

Montour Falls
Member
Schuyler Hospital

Newark
Member
Newark–Wayne Community Hospital

Olean
Member
Olean General Hospital

Penn Yan
Member
Soldiers and Sailors Memorial Hospital of Yates County

Rochester
Member
Highland Hospital of Rochester
Rochester General Hospital
Rochester Psychiatric Center
Strong Memorial Hospital of the University of Rochester
Unity Hospital

Springville
Member
Bertrand Chaffee Hospital

Syracuse
Member
Upstate University Hospital

Wellsville
Member
Jones Memorial Hospital

PENNSYLVANIA

Bradford
Member
Bradford Regional Medical Center

Coudersport
Member
Cole Memorial

SYNERNET, INC.
110 Free Street, Portland, ME Zip 04101–3908; tel. 207/771–3456; Gerry Vicenzi, President and Chief Executive Officer

MAINE

Augusta
Affiliate
MaineGeneral Medical Center

Bangor
Affiliate
St. Joseph Hospital

Bar Harbor
Affiliate
Mount Desert Island Hospital

Brunswick
Affiliate
Mid Coast Hospital

Damariscotta
Lincoln Health

Farmington
Owner
Franklin Memorial Hospital

Fort Kent
Affiliate
Northern Maine Medical Center

Norway
Owner
Stephens Memorial Hospital

Portland
Member
Mercy Hospital of Portland
Owner
Maine Medical Center
New England Rehabilitation Hospital of Portland

Rockport
Affiliate
Pen Bay Medical Center

Skowhegan
Affiliate
Redington–Fairview General Hospital

Westbrook
Owner
Spring Harbor Hospital

THE NEW JERSEY COUNCIL OF TEACHING HOSPITALS
154 West State Street, Trenton, NJ Zip 08608; tel. 609/656–9600; Deborah S. Briggs, President

NEW JERSEY

Camden
Member
Cooper University Health Care

Hackensack
Member
Hackensack University Medical Center

Marlton
Member
Weisman Children's Rehabilitation Hospital

Montclair
Member
Hackensack University Medical Center Mountainside

Morristown
Member
Atlantic Health System
Morristown Medical Center

Neptune
Member
Meridian Health

New Brunswick
Member
Children's Specialized Hospital–PSE&G

North Bergen
Member
Palisades Medical Center

Paterson
Member
St. Joseph's Regional Medical Center

Summit
Member
Overlook Medical Center

UNIVERSITY HEALTHSYSTEM CONSORTIUM, INC.
155 North Wacker Drive, Chicago, IL Zip 60606–1787; tel. 312/775–4100; Irene M. Thompson, President and Chief Executive Officer

ALABAMA

Alexander City
Member
Russell Medical Center

Bessemer
Member
Medical West

Birmingham
Member
University of Alabama Hospital

Mobile
Member
University of South Alabama Children's and Women's Hospital
University of South Alabama Medical Center

ARIZONA

Phoenix
Member
Maricopa Integrated Health System
Mayo Clinic Hospital

Tucson
Member
University of Arizona Medical Center – South Campus
University of Arizona Medical Center – University Campus

ARKANSAS
Little Rock
Member
 UAMS Medical Center

CALIFORNIA
Bakersfield
Member
 Kern Medical Center

Colton
Member
 Arrowhead Regional Medical Center

Downey
Affiliate
 Rancho Los Amigos National Rehabilitation Center

Duarte
Member
 City of Hope's Helford Clinical Research Hospital

French Camp
Member
 San Joaquin General Hospital

Joshua Tree
Member
 Hi–Desert Medical Center

Los Angeles
Lease
 Stewart & Lynda Resnick Neuropsychiatric Hospital at
  UCLA
Member
 Cedars–Sinai Medical Center
 Keck Hospital of USC
 LAC/University of Southern California Medical Center
 Ronald Reagan University of California Los Angeles
  Medical Center
 Stewart & Lynda Resnick Neuropsychiatric Hospital at
  UCLA

Martinez
Affiliate
 Contra Costa Regional Medical Center

Moreno Valley
Member
 Riverside County Regional Medical Center

Oakland
Member
 Alameda County Medical Center

Orange
Mernber
 UC Irvine Medical Center

Palo Alto
Member
 Lucile Salter Packard Children's Hospital at Stanford
 Stanford Hospital and Clinics

Portola
Member
 Eastern Plumas Health Care

Sacramento
Member
 University of California, Davis Medical Center

San Diego
Member
 UC San Diego Health System

San Francisco
Member
 Laguna Honda Hospital and Rehabilitation Center
 San Francisco General Hospital and Trauma Center
 UCSF Medical Center

San Jose
Affiliate
 Santa Clara Valley Medical Center

Santa Monica
Affiliate
 Santa Monica–UCLA Medical Center and Orthopaedic
  Hospital

Stockton
Member
 Dameron Hospital

Sylmar
Affiliate
 LAC–Olive View–UCLA Medical Center

Torrance
Member
 Harbor–UCLA Medical Center

COLORADO
Aurora
Member
 University of Colorado Hospital

Colorado Springs
Member
 Memorial Hospital

Denver
Affiliate
 National Jewish Health
Member
 Denver Health

Fort Collins
Member
 Poudre Valley Hospital

Loveland
Member
 Medical Center of the Rockies

CONNECTICUT
Bridgeport
Member
 Bridgeport Hospital

Farmington
Member
 University of Connecticut Health Center, John
  Dempsey Hospital

Greenwich
Member
 Greenwich Hospital

New Haven
Member
 Yale–New Haven Hospital

DISTRICT OF COLUMBIA
Washington
Member
 Howard University Hospital
 MedStar Georgetown University Hospital
 MedStar Washington Hospital Center

FLORIDA
Gainesville
Member
 UF Health Shands
 UF Health Shands Hospital

Jacksonville
Member
 Mayo Clinic Jacksonville
 UF Health Jacksonville
Owner
 UF Health Jacksonville

Miami
Member
 Jackson Health System

Miami Beach
Member
 Mount Sinai Medical Center

Tampa
Member
 H. Lee Moffitt Cancer Center and Research Institute
 Tampa General Hospital

Weston
Member
 Cleveland Clinic Florida

GEORGIA
Atlanta
Member
 Emory Healthcare
 Emory Saint Joseph's Hospital of Atlanta
 Emory University Hospital
 Emory University Hospital Midtown
 Grady Memorial Hospital
 Select Specialty Hospital – Northeast Atlanta

Augusta
Member
 Georgia Regents Medical Center

Johns Creek
Member
 Emory Johns Creek Hospital

Waycross
Member
 Mayo Clinic Health System in Waycross

ILLINOIS
Aurora
Member
 Rush–Copley Medical Center

Chicago
Member
 Cook County Health and Hospitals System
 John H. Stroger Jr. Hospital of Cook County
 La Rabida Children's Hospital
 Northwestern Memorial Hospital
 Provident Hospital of Cook County
 Rush University Medical Center
 Sinai Health System
 University of Chicago Medical Center
 University of Illinois Hospital & Health Sciences
  System

Hinsdale
Member
 RML Specialty Hospital

Lake Forest
Member
 Northwestern Lake Forest Hospital

Maywood
Member
 Loyola University Medical Center

Melrose Park
Member
 Gottlieb Memorial Hospital

Oak Forest
Member
 Oak Forest Health Center of Cook County

Oak Park
Member
 Rush Oak Park Hospital

INDIANA
Avon
Member
 Indiana University Health West Hospital

Bedford
Member
 Indiana University Health Bedford Hospital

Bloomington
Member
 Indiana University Health Bloomington Hospital

Carmel
Member
 Indiana University Health North Hospital

Goshen
Member
 Indiana University Health Goshen Hospital

Hartford City
Member
 Indiana University Health Blackford Hospital

Indianapolis
Member
 Eskenazi Health
 Indiana University Health

Knox
Member
 Indiana University Health Starke Hospital

La Porte
Member
 Indiana University Health La Porte Hospital

Lafayette
Member
 Indiana University Health Arnett Hospital

Martinsville
Member
 Indiana University Health Morgan Hospital

Monticello
Member
 Indiana University Health White Memorial Hospital

Muncie
Member
 Indiana University Health Ball Memorial Hospital

Paoli
Member
 Indiana University Health Paoli Hospital

Alliances

Seymour
Member
 Schneck Medical Center

Tipton
Member
 Indiana University Health Tipton Hospital

IOWA
Belmond
Member
 Iowa Specialty Hospital–Belmond

Clarion
Member
 Iowa Specialty Hospital–Clarion

Iowa City
Member
 University of Iowa Hospitals and Clinics

Keosauqua
Member
 Van Buren County Hospital

Marengo
Member
 Marengo Memorial Hospital, UnityPoint Health

Shenandoah
Member
 Shenandoah Medical Center

Sigourney
Member
 Keokuk County Health Center

Waverly
Member
 Waverly Health Center

KANSAS
Kansas City
Member
 The University of Kansas Hospital

Overland Park
Member
 Saint Luke's South Hospital

KENTUCKY
Cynthiana
Member
 Harrison Memorial Hospital

Lexington
Member
 University of Kentucky Albert B. Chandler Hospital

Louisville
Member
 University of Louisville Hospital

Morehead
Member
 St. Claire Regional Medical Center

Mount Vernon
Member
 Rockcastle Regional Hospital and Respiratory Care Center

LOUISIANA
Monroe
Member
 University Health Conway

MAINE
Portland
Member
 Maine Medical Center

MARYLAND
Baltimore
Affiliate
 University of Maryland Rehabilitation and Orthopaedic Institute
Member
 Johns Hopkins Bayview Medical Center
 Johns Hopkins Hospital
 MedStar Franklin Square Medical Center
 MedStar Good Samaritan Hospital
 MedStar Harbor Hospital
 MedStar Union Memorial Hospital
 Mt. Washington Pediatric Hospital
 University of Maryland Medical Center
 University of Maryland Medical Center Midtown Campus
 University of Maryland Rehabilitation and Orthopaedic Institute

Cambridge
Member
 University of Maryland Shore Medical Center at Dorchester

Chestertown
Member
 University of Maryland Shore Medical Center at Chestertown

Easton
Member
 University of Maryland Shore Medical Center at Easton

Glen Burnie
Member
 University of Maryland Baltimore Washington Medical Center

La Plata
Member
 University of Maryland Charles Regional Medical Center

Leonardtown
Member
 MedStar St. Mary's Hospital

Olney
Member
 MedStar Montgomery Medical Center

Towson
Member
 University of Maryland St. Joseph Medical Center

MASSACHUSETTS
Ayer
Member
 Nashoba Valley Medical Center

Boston
 Dana–Farber Cancer Institute
Member
 Beth Israel Deaconess Medical Center
 Boston Medical Center
 Brigham and Women's Faulkner Hospital
 Brigham and Women's Hospital
 Carney Hospital
 Dana–Farber Cancer Institute
 Massachusetts General Hospital
 Partners HealthCare System, Inc.
 Steward Health Care System, LLC
 Tufts Medical Center

Brighton
Member
 St. Elizabeth's Medical Center

Brockton
Member
 Good Samaritan Medical Center

Burlington
Member
 Lahey Hospital & Medical Center, Burlington

Cambridge
Member
 Cambridge Health Alliance

Clinton
Affiliate
 Clinton Hospital

Concord
Member
 Emerson Hospital

Fall River
Member
 Saint Anne's Hospital

Greenfield
Member
 Baystate Franklin Medical Center

Haverhill
Member
 Merrimack Valley Hospital

Holyoke
Member
 Holyoke Medical Center

Leominster
Member
 HealthAlliance Hospitals

Marlborough
Affiliate
 UMass Memorial–Marlborough Hospital

Melrose
Member
 Hallmark Health System

Methuen
Member
 Holy Family Hospital and Medical Center

Newton Lower Falls
Member
 Newton–Wellesley Hospital

Norwood
Member
 Norwood Hospital

Palmer
Member
 Wing Memorial Hospital and Medical Centers

Quincy
Member
 Quincy Medical Center

Salem
Member
 North Shore Medical Center

Springfield
Member
 Baystate Medical Center

Taunton
Member
 Morton Hospital and Medical Center

Ware
Member
 Baystate Mary Lane Hospital

Worcester
Member
 UMass Memorial Medical Center

MICHIGAN
Ann Arbor
Member
 University of Michigan Hospitals and Health Centers

Flint
Member
 Hurley Medical Center

Grosse Pointe
Member
 Beaumont Hospital Grosse Pointe

Royal Oak
Member
 Beaumont Hospital – Royal Oak

Troy
Member
 Beaumont Hospital – Troy

MINNESOTA
Albert Lea
Member
 Mayo Clinic Health System in Albert Lea

Austin
Member
 Mayo Clinic Health System in Austin

Burnsville
Lease
 Fairview Ridges Hospital
Member
 Fairview Ridges Hospital

Edina
Member
 Fairview Southdale Hospital

Fairmont
Member
 Mayo Clinic Health System in Fairmont

Hibbing
Member
 Range Regional Health Services

Mankato
Member
 Mayo Clinic Health System in Mankato

Minneapolis
Member
 Hennepin County Medical Center
 University of Minnesota Medical Center, Fairview

Section B

Princeton
Member
  Fairview Northland Medical Center

Rochester
Member
  Mayo Clinic Hospital – Rochester

Saint Paul
Member
  Regions Hospital

Stillwater
Member
  Lakeview Hospital

Wyoming
Member
  Fairview Lakes Health Services

MISSISSIPPI
Jackson
Member
  University Hospital

Lexington
Member
  Holmes County Hospital and Clinics

MISSOURI
Boonville
Member
  Cooper County Memorial Hospital

Columbia
Member
  University of Missouri Health Care
  University of Missouri Hospitals and Clinics

Jefferson City
Member
  Capital Region Medical Center

Kansas City
Member
  Saint Luke's Hospital of Kansas City
  Saint Luke's North Hospital – Barry Road
  Truman Medical Center–Hospital Hill
  Truman Medical Center–Lakewood

Lee's Summit
Member
  Saint Luke's East Hospital

Milan
Member
  Sullivan County Memorial Hospital

Saint Louis
Member
  Barnes–Jewish Hospital
  Barnes–Jewish West County Hospital

NEBRASKA
Bellevue
Member
  Bellevue Medical Center

O'Neill
Member
  Avera St. Anthony's Hospital

Omaha
Member
  Nebraska Medical Center
  Nebraska Orthopaedic Hospital

NEVADA
Las Vegas
Affiliate
  University Medical Center

NEW HAMPSHIRE
Lebanon
Member
  Dartmouth–Hitchcock Medical Center

NEW JERSEY
Hamilton
Member
  Robert Wood Johnson University Hospital at Hamilton

Morristown
Member
  Atlantic Health System
  Morristown Medical Center

Neptune
Member
  Meridian Health

New Brunswick
Member
  Robert Wood Johnson University Hospital

Newark
Member
  University Hospital

Newton
Member
  Newton Medical Center

Rahway
Member
  Robert Wood Johnson University Hospital Rahway

Summit
Member
  Overlook Medical Center

NEW MEXICO
Albuquerque
Member
  University of New Mexico Hospitals

Rio Rancho
Member
  UNM Sandoval Regional Medical Center

NEW YORK
Albany
Member
  Albany Medical Center

Bay Shore
Member
  Southside Hospital

Bronx
Member
  Jacobi Medical Center
  Lincoln Medical and Mental Health Center
  Montefiore Medical Center
  North Central Bronx Hospital

Brooklyn
Member
  Coney Island Hospital
  SUNY Downstate Medical Center University Hospital
  Woodhull Medical and Mental Health Center

Canandaigua
Member
  F. F. Thompson Hospital

Elmhurst
Member
  Elmhurst Hospital Center

Forest Hills
Member
  Forest Hills Hospital

Glen Cove
Member
  Glen Cove Hospital

Great Neck
Member
  North Shore–Long Island Jewish Health System

Greenport
Member
  Eastern Long Island Hospital

Huntington
Member
  Huntington Hospital

Jamaica
Member
  Queens Hospital Center

Manhasset
Member
  North Shore University Hospital

New Hyde Park
Member
  Long Island Jewish Medical Center

New York
Member
  Henry J. Carter Specialty Hospital and Nursing Facility
  Lenox Hill Hospital
  Mount Sinai Hospital
  New York City Health and Hospitals Corporation
  New York–Presbyterian Hospital
  NYU Langone Medical Center

Plainview
Member
  Plainview Hospital

Riverhead
Member
  Peconic Bay Medical Center

Rochester
Member
  Highland Hospital of Rochester
  Strong Memorial Hospital of the University of Rochester

Staten Island
Member
  Staten Island University Hospital

Stony Brook
Member
  Stony Brook University Medical Center

Syosset
Member
  Syosset Hospital

Syracuse
Member
  Upstate University Hospital

Valley Stream
Member
  Franklin Hospital

NORTH CAROLINA
Ahoskie
Affiliate
  Vidant Roanoke–Chowan Hospital

Chapel Hill
Member
  University of North Carolina Hospitals

Danbury
Member
  Pioneer Community Hospital of Stokes

Durham
Member
  Duke Regional Hospital
  Duke University Hospital

Edenton
Member
  Vidant Chowan Hospital

Greenville
Member
  Vidant Medical Center

Lexington
Member
  Wake Forest Baptist Health–Lexington Medical Center

Mocksville
Member
  Wake Forest Baptist Health–Davie Hospital

Nags Head
Member
  The Outer Banks Hospital

Raleigh
Member
  Duke Raleigh Hospital
  Rex Healthcare

Tarboro
Member
  Vidant Edgecombe Hospital

Windsor
Affiliate
  Vidant Bertie Hospital

Winston–Salem
Member
  Wake Forest Baptist Health
  Wake Forest Baptist Medical Center

OHIO
Ashtabula
Member
  Ashtabula County Medical Center

Barnesville
Member
  Barnesville Hospital

Bellefontaine
Member
  Mary Rutan Hospital

Section B

Bucyrus
Member
Bucyrus Community Hospital

Cadiz
Member
Harrison Community Hospital

Chardon
Affiliate
University Hospitals Geauga Medical Center

Cincinnati
Member
Cincinnati Children's Hospital Medical Center
Daniel Drake Center for Post Acute Care
University of Cincinnati Medical Center

Circleville
Member
Berger Health System

Cleveland
Member
Cleveland Clinic
Fairview Hospital
Hillcrest Hospital
Lutheran Hospital
University Hospitals Case Medical Center

Coldwater
Member
Mercer Health

Columbus
Member
Ohio State University Wexner Medical Center

Conneaut
Affiliate
University Hospitals Conneaut Medical Center

Euclid
Member
Euclid Hospital

Galion
Member
Galion Community Hospital

Garfield Heights
Member
Marymount Hospital

Geneva
Affiliate
University Hospitals Geneva Medical Center

Lakewood
Member
Lakewood Hospital

London
Member
Madison County Hospital

Martins Ferry
Member
East Ohio Regional Hospital

Medina
Member
Medina Hospital

Middleburg Heights
Member
Southwest General Health Center

Sidney
Member
Wilson Memorial Hospital

Springfield
Member
Ohio Valley Surgical Hospital

Toledo
Member
The University of Toledo Medical Center

Upper Sandusky
Member
Wyandot Memorial Hospital

Warrensville Heights
Member
South Pointe Hospital

Washington Court House
Member
Fayette County Memorial Hospital

Westlake
Member
St. John Medical Center

OREGON

Grants Pass
Member
Asante Three Rivers Medical Center

Medford
Member
Asante Health System
Asante Rogue Regional Medical Center

Portland
Member
OHSU Hospital

PENNSYLVANIA

Allentown
Member
Lehigh Valley Hospital

Bryn Mawr
Member
Bryn Mawr Hospital

Hershey
Member
Penn State Milton S. Hershey Medical Center

Media
Member
Riddle Hospital

Paoli
Member
Paoli Hospital

Philadelphia
Affiliate
Penn Presbyterian Medical Center
Thomas Jefferson University Hospital
Member
Children's Hospital of Philadelphia
Fox Chase Cancer Center–American Oncologic
Hospital
Hospital of the University of Pennsylvania
Jeanes Hospital
Pennsylvania Hospital
Temple University Hospital

Pittsburgh
Member
UPMC Presbyterian Shadyside

Wynnewood
Member
Lankenau Medical Center

RHODE ISLAND

Newport
Member
Newport Hospital

Providence
Member
Miriam Hospital
Rhode Island Hospital

Westerly
Member
Westerly Hospital

SOUTH CAROLINA

Camden
Member
KershawHealth

Charleston
Member
MUSC Medical Center of Medical University of South
Carolina

Clinton
Member
Greenville Health System – Laurens County Memorial
Hospital

Columbia
Member
Palmetto Health

Easley
Member
Baptist Easley Hospital

Greenville
Member
Greenville Health System
Patewood Memorial Hospital

Greer
Member
Greer Memorial Hospital

Simpsonville
Member
Hillcrest Memorial Hospital

Travelers Rest
Member
North Greenville Hospital

TENNESSEE

Knoxville
Member
University of Tennessee Medical Center

Nashville
Member
Vanderbilt Hospital and Clinics

TEXAS

Baytown
Member
Houston Methodist San Jacinto Hospital

Dallas
Member
Parkland Health & Hospital System
University of Texas Southwestern Medical Center

Fort Worth
Member
JPS Health Network

Galveston
Member
University of Texas Medical Branch Hospitals

Houston
Member
Harris Health System
Houston Methodist Hospital
Houston Methodist West Hospital
Houston Methodist Willowbrook Hospital
Memorial Hermann – Texas Medical Center
St. Luke's Hospital – The Vintage Hospital
St. Luke's Medical Center
TIRR Memorial Hermann
University of Texas M.D. Anderson Cancer Center

Pasadena
Member
St. Luke's Patients Medical Center

Sugar Land
Member
Houston Methodist Sugar Land Hospital
St. Luke's Sugar Land Hospital

The Woodlands
Member
St. Luke's Lakeside Hospital
St. Luke's The Woodlands Hospital

Tyler
Affiliate
University of Texas Health Science Center at Tyler

UTAH

Gunnison
Member
Gunnison Valley Hospital

Moab
Member
Moab Regional Hospital

Monticello
Member
San Juan Hospital

Salt Lake City
Member
University of Utah Health Care – Hospital and Clinics

VERMONT

Berlin
Member
Central Vermont Medical Center

Brattleboro
Member
Brattleboro Retreat

Burlington
Member
Fletcher Allen Health Care

VIRGINIA

Charlottesville
Member
  University of Virginia Medical Center
  UVA–HEALTHSOUTH Rehabilitation Hospital

Culpeper
Member
  Culpeper Regional Hospital

Norfolk
Member
  Sentara Norfolk General Hospital

Richmond
Member
  VCU Medical Center

WASHINGTON

Renton
Member
  UW Medicine/Valley Medical Center

Seattle
Member
  Seattle Cancer Care Alliance
  University of Washington Medical Center
  UW Medicine/Harborview Medical Center
  UW Medicine/Northwest Hospital & Medical Center

WEST VIRGINIA

Morgantown
Member
  West Virginia University Hospitals

Ranson
Member
  Jefferson Medical Center

WISCONSIN

Chippewa Falls
Member
  St. Joseph's Hospital

Eau Claire
Member
  Mayo Clinic Health System in Eau Claire

Friendship
Member
  Moundview Memorial Hospital & Clinics

Hudson
Member
  Hudson Hospital and Clinic

Madison
Member
  University of Wisconsin Hospital and Clinics

Medford
Affiliate
  Aspirus Medford Hospital

New Richmond
Member
  Westfields Hospital

Oconto Falls
Member
  Community Memorial Hospital

Portage
Member
  Divine Savior Healthcare

Wausau
Affiliate
  Aspirus Wausau Hospital

West Bend
Member
  St. Joseph's Hospital

Wisconsin Rapids
Member
  Riverview Hospital Association

WYOMING

Laramie
Member
  Ivinson Memorial Hospital

UNIVERSITY OF IOWA HEALTH ALLIANCE
1755 59th Place, West Des Moines, IA
Zip 50266–7737; tel. 515/643–4000;
Dan Kueter, Chief Executive Officer

ILLINOIS

Aledo
Member
  Genesis Medical Center–Aledo

Silvis
Member
  Genesis Medical Center, Illini Campus

IOWA

Albia
Member
  Monroe County Hospital and Clinics

Algona
Member
  Kossuth Regional Health Center

Audubon
Member
  Audubon County Memorial Hospital

Belmond
Member
  Iowa Specialty Hospital–Belmond

Bloomfield
Member
  Davis County Hospital

Britt
Member
  Hancock County Health System

Cedar Falls
Member
  Sartori Memorial Hospital

Cedar Rapids
Member
  Mercy Medical Center–Cedar Rapids

Centerville
Member
  Mercy Medical Center–Centerville

Clarinda
Member
  Clarinda Regional Health Center

Clarion
Member
  Iowa Specialty Hospital–Clarion

Clinton
Member
  Mercy Medical Center–Clinton

Corydon
Member
  Wayne County Hospital

Cresco
Member
  Regional Health Services of Howard County

Davenport
Member
  Genesis Medical Center–Davenport

De Witt
Member
  Genesis Medical Center, DeWitt

Des Moines
Member
  Mercy Medical Center–Des Moines

Dubuque
Member
  Mercy Medical Center–Dubuque

Dyersville
Member
  Mercy Medical Center–Dyersville

Elkader
Member
  Central Community Hospital

Emmetsburg
Member
  Palo Alto County Health System

Fairfield
Member
  Jefferson County Health Center

Greenfield
Member
  Adair County Memorial Hospital

Grinnell
Member
  Grinnell Regional Medical Center

Hampton
Member
  Franklin General Hospital

Hawarden
Member
  Hawarden Regional Healthcare

Iowa City
Member
  University of Iowa Hospitals and Clinics

Iowa Falls
Member
  Hansen Family Hospital

Keosauqua
Member
  Van Buren County Hospital

Knoxville
Member
  Knoxville Hospital & Clinics

Leon
Member
  Decatur County Hospital

Manning
Member
  Manning Regional Healthcare Center

Maquoketa
Member
  Jackson County Regional Health Center

Mason City
Member
  Mercy Medical Center–North Iowa

Mount Ayr
Member
  Ringgold County Hospital

Mount Pleasant
Member
  Henry County Health Center

New Hampton
Member
  Mercy Medical Center–New Hampton

Oelwein
Member
  Mercy Hospital of Franciscan Sisters

Osage
Member
  Mitchell County Regional Health Center

Pella
Member
  Pella Regional Health Center

Perry
Member
  Dallas County Hospital

Primghar
Member
  Baum Harmon Mercy Hospital

Sigourney
Member
  Keokuk County Health Center

Sioux City
Member
  Mercy Medical Center–Sioux City

Vinton
Member
  Virginia Gay Hospital

Washington
Member
  Washington County Hospital and Clinics

Waterloo
Member
  Covenant Medical Center

Waverly
Member
  Waverly Health Center

Webster City
Member
  Van Diest Medical Center

West Des Moines
Member
Mercy Medical Center – West Lakes

Winterset
Member
Madison County Health Care System

NEBRASKA

Oakland
Member
Oakland Mercy Hospital

Pender
Member
Pender Community Hospital

VANTAGE HEALTHCARE NETWORK, INC.
18282 Technology Drive, Suite 202,
Meadville, PA Zip 16335;
tel. 814/337–0000; David Petrarca,
Director Retail Operations

VHA, INC.
901 New York Avenue NW, Washington,
DC Zip 20001–4432;
tel. 202/354–2607; Edward Goodman,
Executive Vice President Policy

ALABAMA

Alabaster
Shelby Baptist Medical Center

Anniston
Partner
Northeast Alabama Regional Medical Center

Athens
Partner
Athens–Limestone Hospital

Atmore
Atmore Community Hospital

Birmingham
Princeton Baptist Medical Center
Shareholder
Baptist Health System

Boaz
Marshall Medical Center South

Brewton
D. W. McMillan Memorial Hospital

Carrollton
Pickens County Medical Center

Chatom
Washington County Hospital and Nursing Home

Decatur
Decatur Morgan Hospital

Fairhope
Thomas Hospital

Fayette
Fayette Medical Center

Fort Payne
DeKalb Regional Medical Center

Grove Hill
Grove Hill Memorial Hospital

Guntersville
Marshall Medical Center North
Partner
Marshall Health System

Hamilton
Marion Regional Medical Center

Huntsville
Huntsville Hospital

Jasper
Walker Baptist Medical Center

Montgomery
Baptist Medical Center East
Shareholder
Baptist Medical Center South

Moulton
Lawrence Medical Center

Northport
Northport Medical Center

Opp
Mizell Memorial Hospital

Ozark
Dale Medical Center

Prattville
Prattville Baptist Hospital

Scottsboro
Partner
Highlands Medical Center

Sylacauga
Coosa Valley Medical Center

Talladega
Citizens Baptist Medical Center

Tuscaloosa
DCH Regional Medical Center
Partner
DCH Health System

Union Springs
Bullock County Hospital

ALASKA

Anchorage
Providence Alaska Medical Center

Cordova
Cordova Community Medical Center

Kodiak
Providence Kodiak Island Medical Center

Seward
Providence Seward Medical Center

Valdez
Providence Valdez Medical Center

Wrangell
Wrangell Medical Center

ARIZONA

Bisbee
Copper Queen Community Hospital

Phoenix
Mayo Clinic Hospital

Safford
Mt. Graham Regional Medical Center

Scottsdale
Scottsdale Healthcare Shea Medical Center
Scottsdale Healthcare Thompson Peak Hospital
Unit_of
Scottsdale Healthcare–Osborn Medical Center

Tucson
TMC Healthcare

ARKANSAS

Arkadelphia
Baptist Health Medical Center–Arkadelphia

Booneville
Booneville Community Hospital

Clinton
Ozark Health Medical Center

Conway
Partner
Conway Regional Medical Center

Fayetteville
Partner
Washington Regional Medical Center

Heber Springs
Baptist Health Medical Center–Heber Springs

Jonesboro
NEA Baptist Memorial Hospital
Partner
St. Bernards Medical Center

Little Rock
Baptist Health Medical Center–Little Rock
Shareholder
Baptist Health

North Little Rock
Baptist Health Medical Center – North Little Rock

Paragould
Partner
Arkansas Methodist Medical Center

Piggott
Piggott Community Hospital

Searcy
White County Medical Center

Stuttgart
Baptist Health Medical Center–Stuttgart

Walnut Ridge
Lawrence Memorial Hospital

Wynne
CrossRidge Community Hospital

CALIFORNIA

Alameda
Alameda Hospital

Antioch
Sutter Delta Medical Center

Arcadia
Methodist Hospital of Southern California

Auburn
Sutter Auburn Faith Hospital

Berkeley
Alta Bates Medical Center–Herrick Campus
Alta Bates Summit Medical Center

Burbank
Providence Saint Joseph Medical Center

Burlingame
Mills–Peninsula Health Services

Castro Valley
Eden Medical Center

Clovis
Clovis Community Medical Center

Concord
John Muir Medical Center, Concord

Covina
Citrus Valley Health Partners

Crescent City
Sutter Coast Hospital

Davis
Sutter Davis Hospital

El Centro
El Centro Regional Medical Center

Encinitas
Scripps Memorial Hospital–Encinitas

Escondido
Palomar Health
Palomar Medical Center

Fresno
Community Regional Medical Center
Fresno Heart and Surgical Hospital
Shareholder
Community Medical Centers

Glendora
Foothill Presbyterian Hospital

Greenbrae
Marin General Hospital

Jackson
Sutter Amador Hospital

La Jolla
Scripps Green Hospital
Shareholder
Scripps Memorial Hospital–La Jolla

Lakeport
Sutter Lakeside Hospital

Lancaster
Partner
Antelope Valley Hospital

Los Angeles
Shareholder
Cedars–Sinai Medical Center

Mariposa
John C. Fremont Healthcare District

Menlo Park
Menlo Park Surgical Hospital

Mission Hills
Providence Holy Cross Medical Center

Modesto
Partner
Memorial Medical Center

Monterey
Community Hospital of the Monterey Peninsula

Novato
Novato Community Hospital

Oakland
Alta Bates Summit Medical Center – Summit Campus

Pasadena
Huntington Memorial Hospital

Pleasanton
ValleyCare Medical Center

Pomona
Partner
Pomona Valley Hospital Medical Center

Poway
Pomerado Hospital

Roseville
Sutter Roseville Medical Center

Sacramento
Sutter Medical Center, Sacramento
Shareholder
Sutter Health

San Diego
Scripps Health
Scripps Mercy Hospital

San Francisco
California Pacific Medical Center–Davies Campus
Chinese Hospital
St. Luke's Hospital
Shareholder
California Pacific Medical Center

San Pedro
Providence Little Company of Mary Medical Center
San Pedro

Santa Barbara
Cottage Health System
Goleta Valley Cottage Hospital
Partner
Santa Barbara Cottage Hospital

Santa Cruz
Sutter Maternity and Surgery Center of Santa Cruz

Santa Rosa
Sutter Medical Center of Santa Rosa, Chanate
Campus

Solvang
Santa Ynez Valley Cottage Hospital

Tarzana
Providence Tarzana Medical Center

Torrance
Providence Little Company of Mary Medical Center –
Torrance
Partner
Torrance Memorial Medical Center

Tracy
Sutter Tracy Community Hospital

Turlock
Partner
Emanuel Medical Center

Vallejo
Sutter Solano Medical Center

Walnut Creek
John Muir Health
John Muir Medical Center, Walnut Creek

Whittier
Partner
Presbyterian Intercommunity Health Hospital

COLORADO

Alamosa
Partner
San Luis Valley Health

Aspen
Partner
Aspen Valley Hospital District

Boulder
Partner
Boulder Community Hospital

Colorado Springs
Partner
Memorial Hospital

Denver
Exempla Healthcare, Inc.
Exempla Saint Joseph Hospital

Englewood
Craig Hospital

Estes Park
Estes Park Medical Center

Fort Collins
Poudre Valley Hospital

Gunnison
Partner
Gunnison Valley Hospital

Haxtun
Haxtun Hospital District

Kremmling
Middle Park Medical Center–Kremmling

La Jara
San Luis Valley Health Conejos County Hospital

Lafayette
Exempla Good Samaritan Medical Center

Longmont
Partner
Longmont United Hospital

Loveland
Medical Center of the Rockies

Steamboat Springs
Partner
Yampa Valley Medical Center

Vail
Shareholder
Vail Valley Medical Center

Wheat Ridge
Shareholder
Lutheran Medical Center

Yuma
Yuma District Hospital

CONNECTICUT

Bridgeport
Bridgeport Hospital

Danbury
Partner
Danbury Hospital

Greenwich
Partner
Greenwich Hospital

Hartford
Connecticut Children's Medical Center
Shareholder
Hartford Hospital

Manchester
Eastern Connecticut Health Network
Manchester Memorial Hospital

Meriden
Partner
MidState Medical Center

Middletown
Partner
Middlesex Hospital

New Haven
Yale New Haven Health System
Yale–New Haven Hospital

New Milford
New Milford Hospital

Norwalk
Norwalk Hospital

Putnam
Day Kimball Hospital

Stamford
Partner
Stamford Hospital

Torrington
Partner
The Charlotte Hungerford Hospital

Vernon Rockville
Rockville General Hospital

Wallingford
Gaylord Hospital

Willimantic
Windham Hospital

DISTRICT OF COLUMBIA

Washington
MedStar Georgetown University Hospital
MedStar Washington Hospital Center

FLORIDA

Apalachicola
George E. Weems Memorial Hospital

Boca Raton
Partner
Boca Raton Regional Hospital

Boynton Beach
Partner
Bethesda Hospital East

Cape Coral
Cape Coral Hospital

Clermont
South Lake Hospital

Cocoa Beach
Health First Cape Canaveral Hospital

Daytona Beach
Shareholder
Halifax Health Medical Center of Daytona Beach

Fort Myers
Gulf Coast Medical Center
Partner
Lee Memorial Hospital

Gulf Breeze
Gulf Breeze Hospital

Inverness
Partner
Citrus Memorial Health System

Jacksonville
Mayo Clinic Jacksonville

Jay
Jay Hospital

Lakeland
Shareholder
Lakeland Regional Medical Center

Leesburg
Leesburg Regional Medical Center

Melbourne
Circles of Care
Health First Palm Bay Hospital
Shareholder
Health First Holmes Regional Medical Center

New Smyrna Beach
Bert Fish Medical Center

Ocala
Partner
Munroe Regional Medical Center

Ocoee
Health Central Hospital

Orlando
Orlando Regional Medical Center
Shareholder
Orlando Health

Panama City
Bay Medical Center Sacred Heart

Pensacola
Baptist Hospital
Shareholder
Baptist Health Care Corporation

Rockledge
Health First, Inc.

Stuart
Martin Health System

Tallahassee
Shareholder
Tallahassee Memorial HealthCare

Tampa
Florida Hospital Carrollwood
Partner
Florida Hospital Tampa

Tarpon Springs
Florida Hospital North Pinellas

Titusville
Partner
Parrish Medical Center

GEORGIA

Albany
Phoebe Putney Health System

Americus
Phoebe Sumter Medical Center

Athens
Partner
Athens Regional Medical Center

Atlanta
Partner
Northside Hospital

Augusta
University Hospital

Austell
WellStar Cobb Hospital

Blakely
Pioneer Community Hospital of Early

Brunswick
Southeast Georgia Health System
Southeast Georgia Health System Brunswick Campus

Cairo
Grady General Hospital
Camilla
Mitchell County Hospital
Canton
Northside Hospital–Cherokee
Chatsworth
Murray Medical Center
Cochran
Bleckley Memorial Hospital
Columbus
Columbus Regional Healthcare System
Columbus Specialty Hospital
Doctors Specialty Hospital
Northside Medical Center
Partner
The Medical Center
Cordele
Crisp Regional Hospital
Cumming
Northside Hospital–Forsyth
Cuthbert
Southwest Georgia Regional Medical Center
Dallas
WellStar Paulding Hospital
Dalton
Partner
Hamilton Medical Center
Decatur
DeKalb Medical at Downtown Decatur
Partner
DeKalb Medical at North Decatur
Douglas
Coffee Regional Medical Center
Douglasville
WellStar Douglas Hospital
Fitzgerald
Dorminy Medical Center
Gainesville
Northeast Georgia Medical Center
Hawkinsville
Taylor Regional Hospital
Homerville
Clinch Memorial Hospital
Lakeland
South Georgia Medical Center Lanier Campus
Lawrenceville
Partner
Gwinnett Hospital System
Lithonia
DeKalb Medical at Hillandale
Macon
Partner
Medical Center, Navicent Health
Marietta
WellStar Health System
WellStar Windy Hill Hospital
Partner
WellStar Kennestone Hospital
Moultrie
Colquitt Regional Medical Center
Perry
Perry Hospital
Quitman
Brooks County Hospital
Riverdale
Partner
Southern Regional Medical Center
Rome
Kindred Hospital Rome
Partner
Floyd Medical Center
Saint Marys
Southeast Georgia Health System Camden Campus
Sylvester
Phoebe Worth Medical Center
Thomasville
Partner
Archbold Medical Center
John D. Archbold Memorial Hospital
Tifton
Tift Regional Medical Center

Valdosta
Partner
South Georgia Medical Center
Warner Robins
Houston Medical Center
Waycross
Mayo Clinic Health System in Waycross
HAWAII
Honolulu
Queen's Health Systems
Queen's Medical Center
Kaunakakai
Molokai General Hospital
Wahiawa
Wahiawa General Hospital
IDAHO
American Falls
Power County Hospital District
Arco
Lost Rivers Medical Center
Blackfoot
Bingham Memorial Hospital
Boise
Elks Rehab Hospital
St. Luke's Health System
Shareholder
St. Luke's Regional Medical Center
Bonners Ferry
Boundary Community Hospital
Cascade
Cascade Medical Center
Coeur D'Alene
Partner
Kootenai Health
Emmett
Walter Knox Memorial Hospital
Gooding
North Canyon Medical Center
Grangeville
Syringa Hospital and Clinics
Jerome
St. Luke's Jerome
Ketchum
St. Luke's Wood River Medical Center
Malad City
Oneida County Hospital
McCall
St. Luke's McCall
Montpelier
Bear Lake Memorial Hospital
Mountain Home
St. Luke's Elmore
Orofino
Clearwater Valley Hospital and Clinics
Preston
Franklin County Medical Center
Rupert
Minidoka Memorial Hospital
Sandpoint
Partner
Bonner General Hospital
Twin Falls
Partner
St. Luke's Magic Valley Medical Center
Weiser
Weiser Memorial Hospital
ILLINOIS
Alton
Alton Memorial Hospital
Belleville
Partner
Memorial Hospital
Canton
Graham Hospital
Carbondale
Memorial Hospital of Carbondale
Partner
Southern Illinois Hospital Services
Chester
Memorial Hospital

Chicago
Partner
Swedish Covenant Hospital
Decatur
Decatur Memorial Hospital
DeKalb
Kish Health System
Partner
Kishwaukee Hospital
Elgin
Partner
Advocate Sherman Hospital
Elmhurst
Partner
Elmhurst Memorial Hospital
Eureka
Advocate Eureka Hospital
Evanston
NorthShore University Health System
Evergreen Park
Partner
Little Company of Mary Hospital and Health Care Centers
Flora
Clay County Hospital
Freeport
Partner
FHN Memorial Hospital
Geneseo
Hammond–Henry Hospital
Geneva
Delnor Hospital
Greenville
Greenville Regional Hospital
Herrin
Herrin Hospital
Jacksonville
Partner
Passavant Area Hospital
Jerseyville
Jersey Community Hospital
Lake Forest
Partner
Northwestern Lake Forest Hospital
Lincoln
Abraham Lincoln Memorial Hospital
Macomb
Partner
McDonough District Hospital
Maryville
Partner
Anderson Hospital
Mattoon
Sarah Bush Lincoln Health Center
Mendota
Mendota Community Hospital
Monticello
Kirby Medical Center
Murphysboro
St. Joseph Memorial Hospital
Naperville
Edward Hospital
New Lenox
Partner
Silver Cross Hospital
Normal
Partner
Advocate BroMenn Medical Center
Peoria
Partner
Proctor Hospital
Pittsfield
Illini Community Hospital
Quincy
Partner
Blessing Hospital
Rockford
SwedishAmerican Hospital
Rushville
Sarah D. Culbertson Memorial Hospital

Salem
  Salem Township Hospital
Sandwich
  Valley West Hospital
Shelbyville
  Shelby Memorial Hospital
Springfield
  Memorial Health System
  Shareholder
  Memorial Medical Center
Taylorville
  Taylorville Memorial Hospital
INDIANA
Anderson
  Community Hospital of Anderson and Madison County
Avon
  Indiana University Health West Hospital
Batesville
  Margaret Mary Health
Bedford
  Indiana University Health Bedford Hospital
Bloomington
  Partner
  Indiana University Health Bloomington Hospital
Bremen
  Community Hospital of Bremen
  Doctors NeuroMedical Hospital
Carmel
  Indiana University Health North Hospital
Clinton
  Union Hospital Clinton
Columbia City
  Parkview Whitley Hospital
Columbus
  Partner
  Columbus Regional Hospital
Danville
  Partner
  Hendricks Regional Health
Elkhart
  Partner
  Elkhart General Healthcare System
Evansville
  Deaconess Health System
  Shareholder
  Deaconess Hospital
Fort Wayne
  Parkview Health
Franklin
  Johnson Memorial Hospital
Goshen
  Indiana University Health Goshen Hospital
Greenfield
  Hancock Regional Hospital
Hartford City
  Indiana University Health Blackford Hospital
Huntington
  Parkview Huntington Hospital
Indianapolis
  Community Health Network
  Community Heart and Vascular Hospital
  Community Hospital East
  Community Hospital North
  Community Hospital South
  Community Westview Hospital
  Indiana University Health Methodist Hospital
  Shareholder
  Indiana University Health University Hospital
Kendallville
  Parkview Noble Hospital
Knox
  Indiana University Health Starke Hospital
Kokomo
  Partner
  Community Howard Regional Health
La Porte
  Partner
  Indiana University Health La Porte Hospital
Lafayette
  Franciscan St. Elizabeth Health – Lafayette Central
  Indiana University Health Arnett Hospital

LaGrange
  Parkview LaGrange Hospital
Madison
  Partner
  King's Daughters' Health
Marion
  Partner
  Marion General Hospital
Martinsville
  Indiana University Health Morgan Hospital
Muncie
  Shareholder
  Indiana University Health Ball Memorial Hospital
New Albany
  Partner
  Floyd Memorial Hospital and Health Services
New Castle
  Henry County Hospital
Noblesville
  Partner
  Riverview Hospital
Paoli
  Indiana University Health Paoli Hospital
Portland
  Jay County Hospital
Richmond
  Partner
  Reid Hospital and Health Care Services
Seymour
  Schneck Medical Center
Shelbyville
  Major Hospital
South Bend
  Healthwin Hospital
  Memorial Hospital of South Bend
Terre Haute
  Partner
  Union Hospital
Tipton
  Indiana University Health Tipton Hospital
Vincennes
  Partner
  Good Samaritan Hospital
IOWA
Atlantic
  Shareholder
  Cass County Memorial Hospital
Council Bluffs
  Shareholder
  Methodist Jennie Edmundson Hospital
Decorah
  Winneshiek Medical Center
Hamburg
  George C Grape Community Hospital
Harlan
  Partner
  Myrtue Medical Center
Keokuk
  Shareholder
  Keokuk Area Hospital
Le Mars
  Partner
  Floyd Valley Hospital
Muscatine
  UnityPoint Health – Trinity Muscatine
Onawa
  Partner
  Burgess Health Center
Orange City
  Orange City Area Health System
Red Oak
  Shareholder
  Montgomery County Memorial Hospital
Rock Rapids
  Sanford Hospital Rock Rapids
Sheldon
  Sanford Sheldon Medical Center
Sioux City
  Shareholder
  UnityPoint Health – St. Luke's

West Union
  Palmer Lutheran Health Center
KANSAS
Abilene
  Memorial Health System
Anthony
  Anthony Medical Center
Atchison
  Shareholder
  Atchison Hospital
Atwood
  Rawlins County Health Center
Belleville
  Republic County Hospital
Beloit
  Mitchell County Hospital Health Systems
Clay Center
  Clay County Medical Center
Colby
  Shareholder
  Citizens Medical Center
Coldwater
  Comanche County Hospital
Concordia
  Cloud County Health Center
Dighton
  Lane County Hospital
El Dorado
  Susan B. Allen Memorial Hospital
Ellinwood
  Ellinwood District Hospital
Ellsworth
  Ellsworth County Medical Center
Fredonia
  Fredonia Regional Hospital
Garnett
  Anderson County Hospital
Goodland
  Goodland Regional Medical Center
Greensburg
  Kiowa County Memorial Hospital
Hays
  Shareholder
  Hays Medical Center
Herington
  Herington Municipal Hospital
Hiawatha
  Partner
  Hiawatha Community Hospital
Hill City
  Graham County Hospital
Hoisington
  Clara Barton Hospital
Hoxie
  Sheridan County Health Complex
Junction City
  Geary Community Hospital
La Crosse
  Rush County Memorial Hospital
Lawrence
  Lawrence Memorial Hospital
Leavenworth
  Saint Luke's Cushing Hospital
Leoti
  Wichita County Health Center
Liberal
  Shareholder
  Southwest Medical Center
Lincoln
  Lincoln County Hospital
Lindsborg
  Lindsborg Community Hospital
Lyons
  Rice County District Hospital
Mankato
  Jewell County Hospital
McPherson
  McPherson Hospital
Medicine Lodge
  Medicine Lodge Memorial Hospital

Minneapolis
Ottawa County Health Center
Minneola
Minneola District Hospital
Ness City
Ness County Hospital
Norton
Norton County Hospital
Oakley
Logan County Hospital
Osborne
Osborne County Memorial Hospital
Overland Park
Saint Luke's South Hospital
Parsons
Partner
Labette Health
Phillipsburg
Phillips County Hospital
Plainville
Rooks County Health Center
Pratt
Shareholder
Pratt Regional Medical Center
Quinter
Gove County Medical Center
Ransom
Grisell Memorial Hospital District One
Russell
Russell Regional Hospital
Sabetha
Sabetha Community Hospital
Saint Francis
Cheyenne County Hospital
Salina
Salina Surgical Hospital
Partner
Salina Regional Health Center
Satanta
Satanta District Hospital
Scott City
Scott County Hospital
Smith Center
Smith County Memorial Hospital
Stafford
Stafford County Hospital
Topeka
Shareholder
Stormont–Vail HealthCare
Wakeeney
Trego County–Lemke Memorial Hospital
Wichita
Shareholder
Great Plains Health Alliance, Inc.

KENTUCKY
Pikeville
Pikeville Medical Center

LOUISIANA
Amite
Hood Memorial Hospital
Baton Rouge
Franciscan Missionaries of Our Lady Health System, Inc.
Ochsner Medical Center–Baton Rouge
Member
Our Lady of the Lake Regional Medical Center
Partner
Woman's Hospital
Bossier City
WK Bossier Health Center
Bunkie
Bunkie General Hospital
Church Point
Acadia–St. Landry Hospital
Columbia
Citizens Medical Center
Covington
Partner
St. Tammany Parish Hospital
Crowley
Partner
Acadia General Hospital

De Ridder
Partner
Beauregard Memorial Hospital
Ferriday
Riverland Medical Center
Gonzales
St. Elizabeth Hospital
Greensburg
St. Helena Parish Hospital
Jennings
Jennings American Legion Hospital
Kenner
Ochsner Medical Center – Kenner
Lafayette
Partner
Our Lady of Lourdes Regional Medical Center
Lake Charles
Partner
Lake Charles Memorial Hospital
Mansfield
De Soto Regional Health System
Monroe
Partner
St. Francis Medical Center
Napoleonville
Assumption Community Hospital
Natchitoches
Natchitoches Regional Medical Center
New Iberia
Iberia Medical Center
New Orleans
Shareholder
Ochsner Medical Center
Oak Grove
West Carroll Memorial Hospital
Raceland
Ochsner St. Anne General Hospital
Shreveport
Willis–Knighton Health System
Shareholder
Willis–Knighton Medical Center
Springhill
Springhill Medical Center
Sulphur
Partner
West Calcasieu Cameron Hospital
Vivian
North Caddo Medical Center

MAINE
Augusta
MaineGeneral Medical Center–Augusta Campus
Shareholder
MaineGeneral Medical Center
Bangor
Eastern Maine Medical Center
The Acadia Hospital
Bar Harbor
Mount Desert Island Hospital
Belfast
Waldo County General Hospital
Blue Hill
Blue Hill Memorial Hospital
Brewer
Partner
Eastern Maine Healthcare Systems
Bridgton
Bridgton Hospital
Brunswick
Mid Coast Hospital
Damariscotta
Lincoln Health
Dover–Foxcroft
Mayo Regional Hospital
Ellsworth
Maine Coast Memorial Hospital
Greenville
Charles A. Dean Memorial Hospital
Houlton
Houlton Regional Hospital
Machias
Down East Community Hospital

Millinocket
Unit_of
Millinocket Regional Hospital
Norway
Stephens Memorial Hospital
Pittsfield
Sebasticook Valley Health
Portland
Shareholder
Maine Medical Center
Presque Isle
The Aroostook Medical Center
Rockport
Pen Bay Medical Center
Skowhegan
Redington–Fairview General Hospital
Waterville
Inland Hospital
Westbrook
Spring Harbor Hospital
York
York Hospital

MARYLAND
Baltimore
MedStar Franklin Square Medical Center
MedStar Good Samaritan Hospital
MedStar Harbor Hospital
MedStar Union Memorial Hospital
Bel Air
Upper Chesapeake Medical Center
Partner
Upper Chesapeake Health System
Columbia
MedStar Health
Havre De Grace
Harford Memorial Hospital
Leonardtown
MedStar St. Mary's Hospital
Olney
MedStar Montgomery Medical Center
Prince Frederick
Calvert Memorial Hospital

MASSACHUSETTS
Belmont
McLean Hospital
Beverly
Partner
Beverly Hospital
Boston
Brigham and Women's Faulkner Hospital
Brigham and Women's Hospital
Dana–Farber Cancer Institute
Massachusetts General Hospital
Partner
Massachusetts Eye and Ear Infirmary
Shareholder
Partners HealthCare System, Inc.
Burlington
Partner
Lahey Hospital & Medical Center, Burlington
Cambridge
Spaulding Hospital for Continuing Medical Care Cambridge
Partner
Mount Auburn Hospital
Charlestown
Spaulding Rehabilitation Hospital
Concord
Partner
Emerson Hospital
East Sandwich
Spaulding Rehabilitation Hospital Cape Cod
Falmouth
Falmouth Hospital
Gardner
Partner
Heywood Hospital
Hyannis
Cape Cod Healthcare, Inc.
Partner
Cape Cod Hospital

Lawrence
Owner
   Lawrence General Hospital

Melrose
   Hallmark Health System
Partner
   Melrose–Wakefield Hospital

Nantucket
   Nantucket Cottage Hospital

Newton Lower Falls
   Newton–Wellesley Hospital

Northampton
   Cooley Dickinson Hospital

Oak Bluffs
   Martha's Vineyard Hospital

Salem
   North Shore Medical Center
   Spaulding Hospital for Continuing Medical Care North
    Shore

South Weymouth
Partner
   South Shore Hospital

Southbridge
Partner
   Harrington Memorial Hospital

MICHIGAN

Adrian
   ProMedica Bixby Hospital

Allegan
   Allegan General Hospital

Alpena
   Alpena Regional Medical Center

Bad Axe
   Huron Medical Center

Big Rapids
   Spectrum Health Big Rapids Hospital

Cass City
   Hills & Dales General Hospital

Coldwater
   Community Health Center of Branch County

Dearborn
Member
   Oakwood Healthcare, Inc.
Partner
   Oakwood Hospital–Dearborn

Detroit
Partner
   St. John Hospital and Medical Center

East China
   St. John River District Hospital

Fremont
   Spectrum Health Gerber Memorial

Grand Haven
   North Ottawa Community Hospital

Grand Rapids
   Mary Free Bed Rehabilitation Hospital
   Spectrum Health
   Spectrum Health – Butterworth Hospital

Greenville
   Spectrum Health United Hospital

Hastings
   Pennock Hospital

Holland
Partner
   Holland Hospital

Jackson
   Allegiance Health

Kalamazoo
Partner
   Bronson Healthcare Group, Inc.
   Bronson Methodist Hospital

Laurium
   Aspirus Keweenaw Hospital

Ludington
   Spectrum Health Ludington Hospital

Marquette
   Marquette General Hospital

Marshall
   Oaklawn Hospital

Monroe
Partner
   Mercy Memorial Hospital System

Ontonagon
   Aspirus Ontonagon Hospital

Owosso
Partner
   Memorial Healthcare

Paw Paw
   Bronson LakeView Hospital

Petoskey
   McLaren Northern Michigan

Port Huron
   Port Huron Hospital
Partner
   Blue Water Health Services Corporation

Reed City
   Spectrum Health Reed City Hospital

Royal Oak
Shareholder
   Beaumont Hospital – Royal Oak

Saginaw
   Covenant Medical Center

Saint Ignace
   Mackinac Straits Health System

Saint Joseph
   Lakeland Healthcare
   Lakeland Regional Medical Center–St. Joseph

Shelby
   Mercy Health Partners, Lakeshore Campus

South Haven
   South Haven Health System

Taylor
   Oakwood Hospital–Taylor

Tecumseh
   ProMedica Herrick Hospital

Trenton
   Oakwood Hospital–Southshore

Troy
   Beaumont Hospital – Troy

Vicksburg
   Bronson Vicksburg Hospital

Wayne
   Oakwood Hospital–Wayne

West Branch
Partner
   West Branch Regional Medical Center

Wyoming
   Metro Health Hospital

Zeeland
   Spectrum Health Zeeland Community Hospital

MINNESOTA

Ada
   Essentia Health Ada

Albert Lea
   Mayo Clinic Health System in Albert Lea

Arlington
   Sibley Medical Center

Austin
   Mayo Clinic Health System in Austin

Bemidji
Partner
   Sanford Bemidji Medical Center

Benson
   Swift County–Benson Hospital

Blue Earth
   United Hospital District

Brainerd
   Essentia Health St. Joseph's Medical Center

Buffalo
   Buffalo Hospital

Cambridge
   Cambridge Medical Center

Canby
   Sanford Canby Medical Center

Cannon Falls
   Mayo Clinic Health System in Cannon Falls

Coon Rapids
   Mercy Hospital

Detroit Lakes
   Essentia Health St. Mary's – Detroit Lakes

Duluth
   Essentia Health
   Essentia Health Duluth
   Essentia Health St. Mary's Medical Center
Partner
   St. Luke's Hospital

Fairmont
   Mayo Clinic Health System in Fairmont

Fergus Falls
Partner
   Lake Region Healthcare

Fosston
   Essentia Health Fosston

Fridley
   Unity Hospital

Graceville
   Essentia Health–Holy Trinity Hospital

Grand Rapids
   Grand Itasca Clinic and Hospital

Hallock
   Kittson Memorial Healthcare Center

Hutchinson
   Hutchinson Health

Jackson
   Sanford Jackson Medical Center

Lake City
   Mayo Clinic Health System in Lake City

Le Sueur
   Minnesota Valley Health Center

Long Prairie
   CentraCare Health–Long Prairie

Luverne
   Sanford Luverne Medical Center

Madelia
   Madelia Community Hospital

Mahnomen
   Mahnomen Health Center

Mankato
Partner
   Mayo Clinic Health System in Mankato

Maple Grove
   Maple Grove Hospital

Melrose
   CentraCare Health–Melrose

Minneapolis
   Abbott Northwestern Hospital
Shareholder
   Allina Health

Morris
   Stevens Community Medical Center

New Ulm
   New Ulm Medical Center

Ortonville
   Ortonville Area Health Services

Owatonna
   Owatonna Hospital

Paynesville
   CentraCare Health–Paynesville

Perham
   Perham Health

Redwood Falls
   Redwood Area Hospital

Robbinsdale
   North Memorial Medical Center

Rochester
   Mayo Clinic

Roseau
   LifeCare Medical Center

Saint Cloud
   CentraCare Health
Partner
   St. Cloud Hospital

Saint James
   Mayo Clinic Health System in Saint James

Saint Paul
   Bethesda Hospital
   St. John's Hospital
   St. Joseph's Hospital
   United Hospital
Shareholder
   HealthEast Care System

Saint Peter
River's Edge Hospital and Clinic

Sandstone
Essentia Health Sandstone

Shakopee
St. Francis Regional Medical Center

Slayton
Murray County Medical Center

Springfield
Mayo Clinic Health System in Springfield

Thief River Falls
Sanford Thief River Falls Medical Center

Tracy
Sanford Tracy Medical Center

Waconia
Partner
Ridgeview Medical Center

Warren
North Valley Health Center

Waseca
Mayo Clinic Health System in Waseca

Westbrook
Sanford Westbrook Medical Center

Willmar
Partner
Rice Memorial Hospital

Windom
Windom Area Hospital

Woodbury
Woodwinds Health Campus

Worthington
Sanford Worthington Medical Center

MISSISSIPPI

Booneville
Baptist Memorial Hospital–Booneville

Calhoun City
Calhoun Health Services

Columbus
Baptist Memorial Hospital–Golden Triangle

Corinth
Magnolia Regional Health Center

Eupora
North Mississippi Medical Center–Eupora

Greenville
Delta Regional Medical Center

Greenwood
Partner
Greenwood Leflore Hospital

Gulfport
Partner
Memorial Hospital at Gulfport

Hattiesburg
Partner
Forrest General Hospital

Jackson
Partner
St. Dominic–Jackson Memorial Hospital

McComb
Partner
Southwest Mississippi Regional Medical Center

Meridian
Partner
Anderson Regional Medical Center

Monticello
Lawrence County Hospital

New Albany
Baptist Memorial Hospital–Union County

Oxford
Baptist Memorial Hospital–North Mississippi

Pascagoula
Singing River Health System

Picayune
Highland Community Hospital

Pontotoc
North Mississippi Medical Center–Pontotoc

Southaven
Baptist Memorial Hospital–Desoto

Starkville
OCH Regional Medical Center

Tupelo
North Mississippi Health Services, Inc.
North Mississippi Medical Center – Tupelo

Tylertown
Walthall County General Hospital

West Point
North Mississippi Medical Center–West Point

MISSOURI

Bolivar
Partner
Citizens Memorial Hospital

Bonne Terre
Parkland Health Center–Bonne Terre

Branson
Partner
Cox Medical Center Branson

Brookfield
General John J. Pershing Memorial Hospital

Cameron
Partner
Cameron Regional Medical Center

Cape Girardeau
Landmark Hospital
Partner
Saint Francis Medical Center

Carthage
Partner
Mercy Hospital Carthage

Chillicothe
Hedrick Medical Center

Clinton
Golden Valley Memorial Healthcare

Crystal City
Mercy Hospital Jefferson

Farmington
Parkland Health Center

Joplin
Freeman Health System
Freeman Hospital East

Kansas City
Crittenton Children's Center
Saint Luke's North Hospital – Barry Road
Shareholder
Saint Luke's Health System
Saint Luke's Hospital of Kansas City

Lamar
Barton County Memorial Hospital

Lee's Summit
Saint Luke's East Hospital

Liberty
Partner
Liberty Hospital

Macon
Samaritan Memorial Hospital

Marshall
Fitzgibbon Hospital

Monett
Cox Monett

Neosho
Freeman Neosho Hospital

Potosi
Washington County Memorial Hospital

Saint Louis
Barnes–Jewish Hospital
Barnes–Jewish West County Hospital
Christian Hospital
Missouri Baptist Medical Center
St. Louis Children's Hospital
Shareholder
BJC HealthCare

Saint Peters
Barnes–Jewish St. Peters Hospital

Salem
Salem Memorial District Hospital

Sikeston
Missouri Delta Medical Center

Springfield
Cox Medical Center North
CoxHealth
Shareholder
Cox Medical Centers

Ste Genevieve
Ste. Genevieve County Memorial Hospital

Sullivan
Missouri Baptist Sullivan Hospital

Trenton
Wright Memorial Hospital

Warrensburg
Western Missouri Medical Center

MONTANA

Anaconda
Community Hospital of Anaconda

Big Timber
Pioneer Medical Center

Billings
Partner
Billings Clinic

Bozeman
Partner
Bozeman Deaconess Hospital

Columbus
Unit_of
Stillwater Community Hospital

Fort Benton
Missouri River Medical Center

Glasgow
Frances Mahon Deaconess Hospital

Glendive
Partner
Glendive Medical Center

Great Falls
Benefis Hospitals

Hamilton
Partner
Marcus Daly Memorial Hospital

Helena
Partner
St. Peter's Hospital

Kalispell
The HealthCenter

Livingston
Livingston Memorial Hospital

Missoula
St. Patrick Hospital
Partner
Community Medical Center

Plains
Clark Fork Valley Hospital

Polson
Providence St. Joseph Medical Center

Red Lodge
Beartooth Billings Clinic

Ronan
Partner
St. Luke Community Healthcare

Scobey
Daniels Memorial Healthcare Center

Sidney
Partner
Sidney Health Center

NEBRASKA

Alliance
Box Butte General Hospital

Alma
Harlan County Health System

Atkinson
West Holt Memorial Hospital

Beatrice
Partner
Beatrice Community Hospital and Health Center

Bridgeport
Morrill County Community Hospital

Broken Bow
Jennie M. Melham Memorial Medical Center

Columbus
Partner
Columbus Community Hospital

Crete
Crete Area Medical Center

Falls City
Community Medical Center

Franklin
Franklin County Memorial Hospital
Gordon
Gordon Memorial Hospital
Hastings
Partner
Mary Lanning Healthcare
Lexington
Partner
Lexington Regional Health Center
Lincoln
Bryan Health
Bryan Medical Center
Partner
Madonna Rehabilitation Hospital
Lynch
Niobrara Valley Hospital
McCook
Partner
Community Hospital
Minden
Kearney County Health Services
Neligh
Antelope Memorial Hospital
Norfolk
Partner
Faith Regional Health Services
Omaha
Nebraska Methodist Health System, Inc.
Shareholder
Nebraska Methodist Hospital
Ord
Valley County Health System
Oshkosh
Garden County Health Services
Osmond
Osmond General Hospital
Plainview
CHI Health Plainview
Scottsbluff
Partner
Regional West Medical Center
York
Partner
York General Hospital

NEW HAMPSHIRE
Claremont
Valley Regional Hospital
Colebrook
Upper Connecticut Valley Hospital
Dover
Partner
Wentworth–Douglass Hospital
Keene
Partner
Cheshire Medical Center
Lancaster
Weeks Medical Center
Lebanon
Alice Peck Day Memorial Hospital
Dartmouth–Hitchcock Medical Center
Nashua
Partner
Southern New Hampshire Medical Center
New London
New London Hospital
Peterborough
Monadnock Community Hospital
Rochester
Partner
Frisbie Memorial Hospital
Woodsville
Cottage Hospital

NEW JERSEY
Atlantic City
AtlantiCare Regional Medical Center
Edison
JFK Health System
JFK Medical Center

Egg Harbor Township
AtlantiCare
Elmer
Inspira Medical Center–Elmer
Flemington
Partner
Hunterdon Medical Center
Mullica Hill
Inspira Health Network
Newton
Partner
Newton Medical Center
Pennington
Capital Health Medical Center–Hopewell
Phillipsburg
Partner
St. Luke's Hospital – Warren Campus
Pomona
Bacharach Institute for Rehabilitation
Pompton Plains
Partner
Chilton Medical Center
Ridgewood
Valley Hospital
Somers Point
Partner
Shore Medical Center
Trenton
Capital Health
Capital Health Regional Medical Center
Vineland
Inspira Medical Center–Vineland
Woodbury
Partner
Inspira Medical Center–Woodbury

NEW MEXICO
Artesia
Artesia General Hospital
Farmington
Partner
San Juan Regional Medical Center
Gallup
Partner
Rehoboth McKinley Christian Health Care Services

NEW YORK
Binghamton
Shareholder
United Health Services Hospitals–Binghamton
Bronxville
Lawrence Hospital Center
Brooklyn
New York Community Hospital
New York Methodist Hospital
Wyckoff Heights Medical Center
Buffalo
Erie County Medical Center
Roswell Park Cancer Institute
Cobleskill
Partner
Cobleskill Regional Hospital
Cooperstown
Partner
Bassett Medical Center
Corning
Corning Hospital
Elmira
St. Joseph's Hospital
Flushing
New York Hospital Queens
Geneva
Finger Lakes Health
Partner
Geneva General Hospital
Hamilton
Community Memorial Hospital
Ithaca
Partner
Cayuga Medical Center at Ithaca
Jamestown
Woman's Christian Association Hospital

Little Falls
Little Falls Hospital
Malone
Alice Hyde Medical Center
Mineola
Winthrop–University Hospital
Mount Kisco
Partner
Northern Westchester Hospital
New York
New York–Presbyterian Hospital
Shareholder
New York–Presbyterian/Columbia University Medical Center
Norwich
Chenango Memorial Hospital
Nyack
Nyack Hospital
Ogdensburg
Claxton–Hepburn Medical Center
Penn Yan
Soldiers and Sailors Memorial Hospital of Yates County
Rochester
Strong Memorial Hospital of the University of Rochester
Unity Hospital
University of Rochester Medical Center
Partner
Highland Hospital of Rochester
Sleepy Hollow
Phelps Memorial Hospital Center
Syracuse
Partner
Crouse Hospital
Utica
Faxton–St. Luke's Healthcare
Walton
Delaware Valley Hospital
White Plains
Partner
White Plains Hospital Center

NORTH CAROLINA
Ahoskie
Vidant Roanoke–Chowan Hospital
Bolivia
Novant Health Brunswick Medical Center
Cary
WakeMed Cary Hospital
Charlotte
Carolinas Medical Center
Novant Health Charlotte Orthopaedic Hospital
Novant Health Presbyterian Medical Center
Shareholder
Carolinas HealthCare System
Clinton
Sampson Regional Medical Center
Concord
Shareholder
Carolinas Medical Center–NorthEast
Dunn
Harnett Health System
Edenton
Vidant Chowan Hospital
Greensboro
Moses H. Cone Memorial Hospital
Greenville
Shareholder
Vidant Medical Center
High Point
Shareholder
High Point Regional Health System
Huntersville
Novant Health Huntersville Medical Center
Kenansville
Vidant Duplin Hospital
Lexington
Wake Forest Baptist Health–Lexington Medical Center
Lincolnton
Carolinas Medical Center–Lincoln

Louisburg
Novant Health Franklin Medical Center

Matthews
Novant Health Matthews Medical Center

Monroe
Carolinas Medical Center–Union

Nags Head
The Outer Banks Hospital

Raleigh
WakeMed Health & Hospitals
Partner
WakeMed Raleigh Campus

Rocky Mount
Partner
Nash Health Care Systems

Salisbury
Partner
Novant Health Rowan Medical Center

Tarboro
Vidant Edgecombe Hospital

Thomasville
Partner
Novant Health Thomasville Medical Center

Windsor
Vidant Bertie Hospital

Winston Salem
Novant Health

Winston–Salem
Novant Health Forsyth Medical Center
Novant Health Medical Park Hospital

NORTH DAKOTA

Bismarck
Partner
Sanford Bismarck

Fargo
Essentia Health Fargo
Sanford Medical Center Fargo

Grafton
Unity Medical Center

Grand Forks
Partner
Altru Health System

Hillsboro
Sanford Hillsboro Medical Center

Jamestown
Partner
Jamestown Regional Medical Center

Kenmare
Kenmare Community Hospital

Mayville
Sanford Mayville Medical Center

Mcville
Nelson County Health System

Minot
Trinity Health

OHIO

Akron
Akron General Health System
Shareholder
Akron General Medical Center

Ashland
Samaritan Regional Health System

Athens
O'Bleness Memorial Hospital

Bellaire
Belmont Community Hospital

Bowling Green
Wood County Hospital

Cambridge
Partner
Southeastern Ohio Regional Medical Center

Cincinnati
UC Health
Shareholder
Christ Hospital

Cleveland
University Hospitals Case Medical Center

Columbus
OhioHealth Doctors Hospital
OhioHealth Grant Medical Center
OhioHealth Riverside Methodist Hospital
Member
OhioHealth

Concord Township
Partner
Lake Health

Cuyahoga Falls
Edwin Shaw Rehab

Dayton
Miami Valley Hospital
Partner
Good Samaritan Hospital

Defiance
ProMedica Defiance Regional Hospital

Delaware
OhioHealth Grady Memorial Hospital

Dover
Partner
Union Hospital

Dublin
OhioHealth Dublin Methodist Hospital

Findlay
Blanchard Valley Hospital

Fostoria
ProMedica Fostoria Community Hospital

Fremont
Partner
Memorial Hospital

Galion
Galion Community Hospital

Georgetown
Southwest Regional Medical Center

Greenville
Wayne Hospital

Kenton
OhioHealth Hardin Memorial Hospital

Lima
Partner
Lima Memorial Health System

Lodi
Lodi Community Hospital

Logan
Hocking Valley Community Hospital

Mansfield
OhioHealth MedCentral Mansfield Hospital

Marion
OhioHealth Marion General Hospital

Maumee
Partner
ProMedica St. Luke's Hospital

Middletown
Partner
Atrium Medical Center

Mount Gilead
Morrow County Hospital

Nelsonville
OhioHealth Doctors Hospital Nelsonville

Newark
Partner
Licking Memorial Hospital

Norwalk
Fisher–Titus Medical Center

Oregon
ProMedica Bay Park Hospital

Oxford
McCullough–Hyde Memorial Hospital

Portsmouth
Southern Ohio Medical Center

Shelby
OhioHealth MedCentral Shelby Hospital

Sidney
Wilson Memorial Hospital

Steubenville
Partner
Trinity Health System

Sylvania
ProMedica Flower Hospital

Toledo
ProMedica Health System
Shareholder
ProMedica Toledo Hospital

Troy
Partner
Upper Valley Medical Center

Warren
Hillside Rehabilitation Hospital

Wauseon
Fulton County Health Center

Youngstown
Northside Medical Center

Zanesville
Partner
Genesis HealthCare System

OKLAHOMA

Ada
Partner
Mercy Hospital Ada

Altus
Partner
Jackson County Memorial Hospital

Carnegie
Carnegie Tri–County Municipal Hospital

Chickasha
Partner
Grady Memorial Hospital

Duncan
Partner
Duncan Regional Hospital

Ei Reno
Mercy Hospital El Reno

Elk City
Great Plains Regional Medical Center

Enid
Integris Bass Baptist Health Center
Integris Bass Pavilion

Frederick
Memorial Hospital and Physician Group

Grove
Integris Grove Hospital

Guymon
Partner
Memorial Hospital of Texas County

Hobart
Elkview General Hospital

Lawton
Partner
Comanche County Memorial Hospital

McAlester
Partner
McAlester Regional Health Center

Miami
Integris Baptist Regional Health Center

Norman
Norman Regional Health System

Oklahoma City
Integris Baptist Medical Center
INTEGRIS Health
Integris Southwest Medical Center

Purcell
Purcell Municipal Hospital

Shawnee
St. Anthony Shawnee Hospital

Stillwater
Partner
Stillwater Medical Center

Tahlequah
Northeastern Health System

Waurika
Jefferson County Hospital

Yukon
INTEGRIS Canadian Valley Hospital

OREGON

Hillsboro
Partner
Tuality Healthcare

Hood River
Providence Hood River Memorial Hospital

Medford
Providence Medford Medical Center
Milwaukie
Providence Milwaukie Hospital
Newberg
Providence Newberg Medical Center
Oregon City
Providence Willamette Falls Medical Center
Portland
Providence Portland Medical Center
Providence St. Vincent Medical Center
Seaside
Providence Seaside Hospital
Silverton
Silverton Hospital

PENNSYLVANIA
Abington
Partner
Abington Memorial Hospital
Allentown
Shareholder
Lehigh Valley Hospital
Bethlehem
Lehigh Valley Hospital–Muhlenberg
Brookville
Penn Highlands Brookville
Butler
Partner
Butler Health System
Chambersburg
Chambersburg Hospital
Summit Health
Clearfield
Clearfield Hospital
Coudersport
Cole Memorial
Drexel Hill
Delaware County Memorial Hospital
Du Bois
DuBois Regional Medical Center
East Stroudsburg
Pocono Medical Center
Ephrata
Partner
Ephrata Community Hospital
Erie
Shareholder
UPMC Hamot
Gettysburg
Gettysburg Hospital
Hanover
Hanover Hospital
Harrisburg
Community Hospital
Pinnacle Health System
Hastings
Conemaugh Miners Medical Center
Indiana
Indiana Regional Medical Center
Jefferson Hills
Jefferson Hospital
Johnstown
Conemaugh Memorial Medical Center
Kane
Kane Community Hospital
Kittanning
ACMH Hospital
Lancaster
Partner
Lancaster General Health
Lebanon
The Good Samaritan Hospital
Lehighton
Blue Mountain Health System
Gnaden Huetten Memorial Hospital
Mc Connellsburg
Fulton County Medical Center
Meadowbrook
Holy Redeemer Hospital
Meyersdale
Conemaugh Meyersdale Medical Center

Monongahela
Monongahela Valley Hospital
New Castle
Jameson Hospital
Palmerton
Palmerton Hospital
Philadelphia
Hospital of the University of Pennsylvania
Penn Presbyterian Medical Center
University of Pennsylvania Health System
Shareholder
Pennsylvania Hospital
Pittsburgh
Partner
St. Clair Hospital
Punxsutawney
Punxsutawney Area Hospital
Renovo
Bucktail Medical Center
Roaring Spring
Nason Hospital
Saint Marys
Elk Regional Health Center
Sayre
Robert Packer Hospital
Shareholder
Guthrie Healthcare System
Scranton
Partner
Geisinger–Community Medical Center
Sellersville
Partner
Grand View Hospital
Sharon
Partner
Sharon Regional Health System
Springfield
Crozer–Keystone Health System
State College
Mount Nittany Medical Center
Troy
Troy Community Hospital
Tyrone
Tyrone Hospital
Uniontown
Partner
Uniontown Hospital
Upland
Crozer–Chester Medical Center
Waynesboro
Waynesboro Hospital
Wellsboro
Soldiers and Sailors Memorial Hospital
West Chester
Partner
Chester County Hospital
West Reading
Reading Hospital and Medical Center
Williamsport
Divine Providence Hospital
Partner
Susquehanna Health System
Windber
Windber Medical Center
York
Partner
WellSpan Health
Shareholder
York Hospital

RHODE ISLAND
East Providence
Emma Pendleton Bradley Hospital
Newport
Newport Hospital
Pawtucket
Memorial Hospital of Rhode Island
Providence
Butler Hospital
Care New England Health System
Miriam Hospital
Women & Infants Hospital of Rhode Island
Shareholder
Lifespan Corporation
Rhode Island Hospital

Warwick
Kent County Memorial Hospital
Westerly
Westerly Hospital
SOUTH CAROLINA
Gaffney
Novant Health Gaffney Medical Center
SOUTH DAKOTA
Armour
Douglas County Memorial Hospital
Burke
Community Memorial Hospital
Canton
Sanford Canton–Inwood Medical Center
Chamberlain
Sanford Chamberlain Medical Center
Clear Lake
Sanford Clear Lake Medical Center
Sioux Falls
Sanford Health
Shareholder
Sanford USD Medical Center
Vermillion
Sanford Vermillion Medical Center
Viborg
Pioneer Memorial Hospital and Health Services
Watertown
Prairie Lakes Healthcare System
Webster
Sanford Webster Medical Center
Winner
Winner Regional Healthcare Center

TENNESSEE
Bolivar
Bolivar General Hospital
Camden
Camden General Hospital
Chattanooga
Erlanger Health System
Erlanger North Hospital
Collierville
Baptist Memorial Hospital–Collierville
Columbia
Partner
Maury Regional Hospital
Covington
Baptist Memorial Hospital–Tipton
Franklin
Williamson Medical Center
Harriman
Roane Medical Center
Huntingdon
Baptist Memorial Hospital–Huntingdon
Jackson
Shareholder
Jackson–Madison County General Hospital
Knoxville
Covenant Health
East Tennessee Children's Hospital
Fort Sanders Regional Medical Center
Parkwest Medical Center
Lenoir City
Fort Loudoun Medical Center
Lewisburg
Marshall Medical Center
Louisville
Peninsula Hospital
Memphis
Baptist Memorial Health Care Corporation
Baptist Memorial Hospital for Women

Baptist Memorial Hospital – Memphis
Milan
Milan General Hospital
Oak Ridge
Partner
Methodist Medical Center of Oak Ridge
Paris
Henry County Medical Center
Parsons
Decatur County General Hospital

Pikeville
Erlanger Bledsoe Hospital
Ripley
Lauderdale Community Hospital
Savannah
Hardin Medical Center
Sevierville
LeConte Medical Center
Trenton
Trenton Medical Center
Union City
Baptist Memorial Hospital–Union City
Waynesboro
Wayne Medical Center

TEXAS
Amarillo
Partner
Baptist St. Anthony Health System
Andrews
Permian Regional Medical Center
Beaumont
Baptist Hospitals of Southeast Texas
Bellville
Bellville St. Joseph Health Center
Caldwell
Burleson St. Joseph Health Center
Dallas
Baylor Jack and Jane Hamilton Heart and Vascular
Hospital
Baylor Specialty Hospital
Baylor University Medical Center
Children's Medical Center of Dallas
Methodist Health System
Shareholder
Baylor Scott & White Health
Decatur
Wise Regional Health System
Del Rio
Val Verde Regional Medical Center
Electra
Electra Memorial Hospital
Floresville
Connally Memorial Medical Center
Fort Worth
Shareholder
Baylor All Saints Medical Center at Fort Worth
Garland
Baylor Medical Center at Garland
Gatesville
Coryell Memorial Hospital
Grapevine
Partner
Baylor Regional Medical Center at Grapevine
Houston
Memorial Hermann – Texas Medical Center
Memorial Hermann Healthcare System
Memorial Hermann Northwest Hospital
Humble
Memorial Hermann Northeast
Huntsville
Huntsville Memorial Hospital
Irving
Partner
Baylor Medical Center at Irving
Jacksonville
Mother Frances Hospital – Jacksonville
Katy
Memorial Hermann Katy Hospital
Levelland
Covenant Hospital–Levelland
Longview
Partner
Good Shepherd Medical Center
Lubbock
Covenant Children's Hospital
Covenant Medical Center
Covenant Medical Center–Lakeside
Shareholder
Covenant Health System
Madisonville
Madison St. Joseph Health Center

Marshall
Partner
Good Shepherd Medical Center–Marshall
Midland
Midland Memorial Hospital
Partner
Midland Memorial Hospital
Navasota
Grimes St. Joseph Health Center
Odessa
Medical Center Health System
Orange
Baptist Orange Hospital
Pearsall
Frio Regional Hospital
Plainview
Covenant Hospital Plainview
Plano
Baylor Regional Medical Center at Plano
Community Hospital Corporation
The Heart Hospital Baylor Plano
Port Lavaca
Memorial Medical Center
Richardson
Partner
Methodist Richardson Medical Center
Rockdale
Little River Healthcare
Round Rock
Scott & White Hospital at Round Rock
San Angelo
Shannon Medical Center
Sherman
Partner
Texas Health Presbyterian Hospital–WNJ
Sugar Land
Memorial Hermann Sugar Land Hospital
Sulphur Springs
Hopkins County Memorial Hospital
Sweeny
Sweeny Community Hospital
Temple
Scott & White Memorial Hospital
Tomball
Tomball Regional Medical Center
Tyler
Partner
Mother Frances Hospital – Tyler
Waco
Partner
Hillcrest Baptist Medical Center
Waxahachie
Baylor Medical Center at Waxahachie
Wichita Falls
Partner
United Regional Health Care System
United Regional Health Care System–Eighth Street
Campus
Winnie
Winnie Community Hospital
Yoakum
Yoakum Community Hospital

VERMONT
Bennington
Southwestern Vermont Medical Center
Berlin
Partner
Central Vermont Medical Center
Morrisville
Copley Hospital
Newport
North Country Hospital and Health Center
Rutland
Partner
Rutland Regional Medical Center
Saint Johnsbury
Northeastern Vermont Regional Hospital
Windsor
Mt. Ascutney Hospital and Health Center

VIRGIN ISLANDS
Saint Thomas
Schneider Regional Medical Center

VIRGINIA
Charlottesville
Partner
Martha Jefferson Hospital
Farmville
Centra Southside Community Hospital
Fredericksburg
Mary Washington Hospital
Hampton
Sentara CarePlex Hospital
Harrisonburg
Partner
Sentara RMH Medical Center
Lynchburg
Centra Lynchburg General Hospital
Manassas
Novant Health Prince William Medical Center
Norfolk
Hospital for Extended Recovery
Sentara Leigh Hospital
Sentara Norfolk General Hospital
Shareholder
Sentara Healthcare
Suffolk
Sentara Obici Hospital
Virginia Beach
Sentara Princess Anne Hospital
Sentara Virginia Beach General Hospital
Williamsburg
Sentara Williamsburg Regional Medical Center
Woodbridge
Sentara Northern Virginia Medical Center

WASHINGTON
Aberdeen
Grays Harbor Community Hospital
Centralia
Providence Centralia Hospital
Chewelah
Providence St. Joseph's Hospital
Colfax
Whitman Hospital and Medical Center
Colville
Providence Mount Carmel Hospital
Everett
Providence Regional Medical Center Everett
Morton
Morton General Hospital
Olympia
Providence St. Peter Hospital
Puyallup
MultiCare Good Samaritan Hospital
Renton
Providence Health & Services
Seattle
Swedish Medical Center–Cherry Hill Campus
Spokane
Providence Holy Family Hospital
Tacoma
MultiCare Tacoma General Hospital
Shareholder
MultiCare Health System
Vancouver
PeaceHealth Southwest Medical Center
Walla Walla
Providence St. Mary Medical Center
Wenatchee
Central Washington Hospital
Yakima
Partner
Yakima Valley Memorial Hospital

WEST VIRGINIA
Charleston
Charleston Area Medical Center
Women and Children's Hospital
Shareholder
Charleston Area Medical Center Health System, Inc.
Gassaway
Braxton County Memorial Hospital

Glen Dale
Partner
Reynolds Memorial Hospital

Madison
Boone Memorial Hospital

Montgomery
Montgomery General Hospital

Princeton
Partner
Princeton Community Hospital

Ripley
Jackson General Hospital

Spencer
Roane General Hospital

Wheeling
Partner
Wheeling Hospital

WISCONSIN

Antigo
Langlade Hospital

Appleton
Appleton Medical Center
Shareholder
ThedaCare, Inc.

Barron
Mayo Clinic Health System – Northland in Barron

Beaver Dam
Partner
Beaver Dam Community Hospitals

Beloit
Partner
Beloit Health System

Bloomer
Mayo Clinic Health System – Chippewa Valley in Bloomer

Eau Claire
Partner
Mayo Clinic Health System in Eau Claire

Green Bay
Partner
Bellin Memorial Hospital

La Crosse
Mayo Clinic Health System – Franciscan Healthcare in La Crosse
Shareholder
Gundersen Health System

Madison
Shareholder
Meriter Hospital

Marinette
Bay Area Medical Center

Medford
Aspirus Medford Hospital

Menomonee Falls
Partner
Community Memorial Hospital

Menomonie
Mayo Clinic Health System – Red Cedar in Menomonie

Milwaukee
Partner
Froedtert Memorial Lutheran Hospital

Neenah
Theda Clark Medical Center

Neillsville
Memorial Medical Center – Neillsville

New London
New London Family Medical Center

Oconomowoc
Oconomowoc Memorial Hospital

Oconto
Bellin Health Oconto Hospital

Osseo
Mayo Clinic Health System – Oakridge in Osseo

River Falls
River Falls Area Hospital

Sparta
Mayo Clinic Health System – Franciscan Healthcare in Sparta

Superior
Essentia Health St. Mary's Hospital of Superior

Watertown
Partner
Watertown Regional Medical Center

Waukesha
ProHealth Care, Inc.
Waukesha Memorial Hospital

Waupaca
Riverside Medical Center

Wausau
Aspirus Wausau Hospital

West Bend
Partner
St. Joseph's Hospital

Whitehall
Gundersen Tri–County Hospital and Clinics

Wisconsin Rapids
Riverview Hospital Association

WYOMING

Buffalo
Johnson County Healthcare Center

Casper
Partner
Wyoming Medical Center

Cheyenne
Partner
Cheyenne Regional Medical Center

Douglas
Memorial Hospital of Converse County

Gillette
Campbell County Memorial Hospital

Jackson
St. John's Medical Center and Living Center

Kemmerer
South Lincoln Medical Center

Laramie
Partner
Ivinson Memorial Hospital

Lovell
North Big Horn Hospital District

Lusk
Niobrara Health and Life Center

Rawlins
Memorial Hospital of Carbon County

Sheridan
Sheridan Memorial Hospital

YANKEE ALLIANCE
138 River Road, Andover, MA
Zip 01810–1083; tel. 978/470–2000; R. Paul O'Neill, President

ARIZONA

Scottsdale
Member
Freedom Pain Hospital

CALIFORNIA

Cerritos
Member
College Hospital Cerritos

Oceanside
Member
Tri–City Medical Center

CONNECTICUT

Derby
Member
Griffin Hospital

Hartford
Member
Saint Francis Hospital and Medical Center

New London
Member
Lawrence + Memorial Hospital

Stafford Springs
Member
Johnson Memorial Hospital

FLORIDA

Boca Raton
Member
Promise Healthcare

Coral Gables
Member
Baptist Health South Florida, Doctors Hospital

Hollywood
Member
Memorial Regional Hospital
Memorial Regional Hospital South

Homestead
Lease
Baptist Health South Florida, Homestead Hospital
Member
Baptist Health South Florida, Homestead Hospital

Miami
Member
Baptist Health South Florida, Baptist Hospital of Miami
Baptist Health South Florida, South Miami Hospital
Baptist Health South Florida, West Kendall Baptist Hospital

Miami Beach
Member
Mount Sinai Medical Center

Miramar
Member
Memorial Hospital Miramar

Oxford
Member
Promise Hospital of Florida at The Villages

Pembroke Pines
Member
Memorial Hospital Pembroke
Memorial Hospital West

South Miami
Member
Larkin Community Hospital

Tavernier
Member
Baptist Health South Florida, Mariners Hospital

INDIANA

Greencastle
Member
Putnam County Hospital

Greenfield
Member
Hancock Regional Hospital

Rushville
Member
Rush Memorial Hospital

KANSAS

Manhattan
Member
Manhattan Surgical Center

KENTUCKY

Ashland
Member
King's Daughters Medical Center

Benton
Member
Marshall County Hospital

Corbin
Member
Baptist Health Corbin
Oak Tree Hospital

Elizabethtown
Member
Hardin Memorial Hospital

La Grange
Member
Baptist Health La Grange

Lexington
Member
Baptist Health Lexington

Madisonville
Member
Baptist Health Madisonville

Paducah
Member
Baptist Health Paducah

Prestonsburg
Member
Highlands Regional Medical Center

Richmond
Member
  Baptist Health Richmond

LOUISIANA
Baton Rouge
Member
  Promise Hospital Baton Rouge – Main Campus
  Promise Hospital of Baton Rouge – Mid–City Campus
  Promise Hospital of Baton Rouge – Ochsner Campus

Shreveport
Member
  Promise Hospital of Louisiana – Shreveport Campus

Vidalia
Member
  Promise Hospital of Miss Lou

MAINE
Bangor
Member
  St. Joseph Hospital

Lewiston
Member
  St. Mary's Regional Medical Center

MASSACHUSETTS
Attleboro
Member
  Sturdy Memorial Hospital

Boston
Member
  Boston Medical Center
  Hebrew Rehabilitation Center
  New England Baptist Hospital
  Tufts Medical Center

Brockton
Member
  Signature Healthcare Brockton Hospital

Brookline
Member
  Bournewood Health Systems

Fall River
Member
  Southcoast Hospitals Group

Great Barrington
Member
  Fairview Hospital

Haverhill
Member
  Baldpate Hospital

Lowell
Member
  Lowell General Hospital

Milford
Member
  Milford Regional Medical Center

Newburyport
Member
  Anna Jaques Hospital

Oak Bluffs
Member
  Martha's Vineyard Hospital

Pittsfield
Member
  Berkshire Medical Center

Westfield
Member
  Noble Hospital

Winchester
Member
  Winchester Hospital

MICHIGAN
Alma
Member
  MidMichigan Medical Center–Gratiot

Clare
Member
  MidMichigan Medical Center–Clare

Gladwin
Member
  MidMichigan Medical Center–Gladwin

Midland
Member
  MidMichigan Medical Center–Midland

Ypsilanti
Member
  Forest Health Medical Center

NEVADA
Las Vegas
Member
  Montevista Hospital

NEW HAMPSHIRE
Concord
Member
  Concord Hospital

Exeter
Member
  Exeter Hospital

Franklin
Lease
  Franklin Regional Hospital
Member
  Franklin Regional Hospital

Laconia
Member
  Lakes Region General Hospital

Manchester
Member
  Catholic Medical Center
  Elliot Hospital

Nashua
Member
  Southern New Hampshire Medical Center
  St. Joseph Hospital

North Conway
Member
  Memorial Hospital

Rochester
Member
  Frisbie Memorial Hospital

Salem
Member
  Northeast Rehabilitation Hospital

Wolfeboro
Member
  Huggins Hospital

NEW YORK
Albany
Member
  Albany Memorial Hospital

Batavia
Member
  United Memorial Medical Center

Bath
Member
  Ira Davenport Memorial Hospital

Buffalo
Member
  Buffalo Psychiatric Center

Elizabethtown
Member
  Elizabethtown Community Hospital

Elmira
Member
  Arnot Ogden Medical Center
  St. Joseph's Hospital

Glens Falls
Member
  Glens Falls Hospital

Gloversville
Member
  Nathan Littauer Hospital and Nursing Home

Plattsburgh
Member
  Champlain Valley Physicians Hospital Medical Center

Schenectady
Member
  Sunnyview Rehabilitation Hospital

Troy
Member
  Samaritan Hospital

Warsaw
Member
  Wyoming County Community Hospital

OHIO
Amherst
Member
  Specialty Hospital of Lorain

Bryan
Member
  Community Hospitals and Wellness Centers

Cadiz
Member
  Harrison Community Hospital

Canton
Member
  Mercy Medical Center

Cincinnati
Member
  Bridgewell Hospital of Cincinnati

Cleveland
Member
  Grace Hospital
  Kindred Hospital Cleveland–Gateway
  St. Vincent Charity Medical Center

Columbus
Member
  Select Specialty Hospital–Columbus

East Liverpool
Member
  East Liverpool City Hospital

Greenville
Member
  Wayne Hospital

Logan
Member
  Hocking Valley Community Hospital

Montpelier
Member
  Community Hospitals and Wellness
    Centers–Montpelier

Salem
Member
  Salem Regional Medical Center

Seaman
Member
  Adams County Regional Medical Center

Sidney
Member
  Wilson Memorial Hospital

Steubenville
Member
  Life Line Hospital

OKLAHOMA
Hugo
Member
  Lane Frost Health and Rehabilitation Center

PENNSYLVANIA
Honesdale
Member
  Wayne Memorial Hospital

Langhorne
Member
  Barix Clinics of Pennsylvania

Washington
Member
  Advanced Surgical Hospital

RHODE ISLAND
Pawtucket
Member
  Memorial Hospital of Rhode Island

Providence
Member
  Roger Williams Medical Center

Wakefield
Member
  South County Hospital

Westerly
Member
  Westerly Hospital

SOUTH CAROLINA
Columbia
Member
  Providence Hospital

Fairfax
Member
  Allendale County Hospital

TEXAS
Aransas Pass
Member
  Care Regional Medical Center

Austin
Member
  Arise Austin Medical Center

Dallas
Member
  University General Hospital–Dallas

Houston
Member
  Healthbridge Children's Hospital of Houston
  St. Anthony's Hospital

New Braunfels
Member
  Post Acute/Warm Springs Specialty Hospital of New
    Braunfels

Plainview
Member
  Covenant Hospital Plainview

WEST VIRGINIA
New Martinsville
Member
  Wetzel County Hospital

Section B

†List supplied by The Joint Commission

Description of Lists

This section of AHA Guide provides a directory of information useful to the health care field.

National and International Organizations

The national and international lists include many types of voluntary organizations concerned with matters of interest to the health care field. The organizational information includes address, telephone number, FAX number, and the primary contact. The information was obtained directly from the organizations.

Organizations are searchable by state, then city within state, and "kind of organization."

We present these organization listings simply as a convenient directory. Inclusion or omission of any organization's name indicates neither approval nor disapproval by Health Forum LLC, an American Hospital Association company.

United States Government Agencies

National, state and provincial government agencies concerned with health–related matters are listed by the major department of government under which the different functions fall.

The selected state and provincial government agencies include the state department of health, facility licensure, medical and nursing licensure, and managed care organization licensure.

Organizations and Agencies

The lists of organizations include hospital associations and councils, group purchasing organizations, quality improvement organizations, and health information exchanges.

There are many active local organizations that do not fall within these categories. Contact the hospital association of the state or province for information about such additional groups. The hospital association and councils listed have offices with full-time executives.

Other Health Care Providers

A list of Freestanding Ambulatory Surgery Centers is provided.

Lists of The Joint Commission Accredited Long Term Care Organizations and Joint Commission Accredited Behavioral Health Organizations are provided for your information.

These lists are provided simply as a convenient reference. Inclusion or omission of any organization's name indicates neither approval or disapproval by Health Forum LLC.

National Organizations

A

AARP, 601 E Street, NW, Washington, DC 20049; tel. 202/434–2277; FAX. 888/836–3985; Addison Barry Rand, Chief Executive Officer

Academic Pediatric Association, 6728 Old McLean Village Drive, McLean, VA 22101; tel. 703/556–9222; FAX. 703/556–8729; Connie MacKay, Executive Director

AcademyHealth, 1150 17th Street, NW, Suite 600, Washington, DC 20036; tel. 202/292–6700; FAX. 202/292–6800; Lisa Simpson, MB, BCh, MPH, FAAP, President and Chief Executive Officer

Accreditation Association for Ambulatory Health Care, 5250 Old Orchard Rd., Suite 200, Skokie, IL 60077; tel. 847/853–6060; FAX. 847/853–9028; John E. Burke, Ph. D., President and CEO

Accreditation Council for Graduate Medical Education, ACGME, 515 N. State Street, Suite 2000, Chicago, IL 60654; tel. 312/755–5000; FAX. 312/755–7498; Thomas J. Nasca, MD, MACP, Chief Executive Officer

Accreditation Council for Pharmacy Education, ACPE, 135 S. LaSalle Street, Suite 4100, Chicago, IL 60603–4810; tel. 312/664–3575; FAX. 312/664–4652; Peter H. Vlasses, Pharm. D., BCPS, FCCP, Executive Director

Advanced Medical Technology Association/ AdvaMed, 701 Pennsylvania Avenue, NW, Suite 800, Washington, DC 20004; tel. 202/783–8700; FAX. 202/783–8750; Stephen J. Ubl, President and Chief Executive Officer

Aerospace Medical Association, 320 South Henry Street, Alexandria, VA 22314–3579; tel. 703/739–2240; FAX. 703/739–9652; Jeffrey C. Sventek, MS, CASP, Executive Director

Alcoholics Anonymous World Services, Inc., PO Box 459, New York, NY 10163; tel. 212/870–3400; FAX. 212/870–3003

Alexander Graham Bell Association for the Deaf & Hard of Hearing, 3417 Volta Place, NW, Washington, DC 20007; tel. 202/204–4683; FAX. 202/337–5087; Garrett W. Yates, Acting Development Director

Allergy Associates, 2004 Grand Avenue, Baldwin, NY 11510; tel. 516/223–7656; FAX. 516/223–0583; Joe D' Amore, MD, President

Alliance for Children & Families, 11700 West Lake Park Drive, Milwaukee, WI 53224; tel. 414/359–1040; FAX. 414/359–1074; Susan N. Dreyfus, President and Chief Executive Officer

Alzheimer's Association, (Alzheimer's Disease and Related Disorders Association, Inc.), 225 North Michigan Avenue, Suite 1700, Chicago, IL 60601; tel. 312/335–8700; FAX. 866/699–1246; Cyndy Cordell, Healthcare Professional Services

America's Blood Centers, 725 15th Street, NW, Suite 700, Washington, DC 20005–2109; tel. 202/393–5725; FAX. 202/393–1282; Christine S. Zambricki, Chief Executive Officer

America's Health Insurance Plans, 601 Pennsylvania Ave, NW, South Bldg, Suite 500, Washington, DC 20004; tel. 202/778–3200; FAX. 202/778–8486; Charles W. Stellar, Executive Vice President

American Academy for Cerebral Palsy and Developmental Medicine, 555 E. Wells Street, Suite 1100, Milwaukee, WI 53202; tel. 414/918–3014; FAX. 414/276–2146; Tracy Burr, Executive Director

American Academy of Allergy, Asthma and Immunology, 555 East Wells Street, Suite 1100, Milwaukee, WI 53202; tel. 414/272–6071; FAX. 414/272–6070; Kay Whalen, Executive Director

American Academy of Child and Adolescent Psychiatry, 3615 Wisconsin Avenue, NW, Washington, DC 20016; tel. 202/966–7300; FAX. 202/966–2891; Heidi B. Fordi, Executive Director

American Academy of Dental Practice Administration, 1063 Whippoorwill Lane, Palatine, IL 60067; tel. 847/934–4404; Kathleen Uebel, Executive Director

American Academy of Dermatology, 930 East Woodfield Road, Schaumburg, IL 60173; tel. 847/330–0230; FAX. 847/330–0050; Robert S. Bolan, PhD, Interim Executive Director

American Academy of Family Physicians, 11400 Tomahawk Creek Parkway, Leawood, KS 66211; tel. 913/906–6000; FAX. 913/906–6075; Douglas E. Henley, M.D., FAAFP, Chief Executive Officer

American Academy of Medical Administrators, 701 Lee Street, Suite 600, Des Plaines, IL 60016; tel. 847/759–8601; FAX. 847/759–8602; Renee Schleicher, CAE, President and Chief Executive Officer

American Academy of Neurology, 201 Chicago Avenue, Minneapolis, MN 55415; tel. 612/928–6100; FAX. 612/454–2744; Catherine M. Rydell, CAE, Executive Director

American Academy of Ophthalmology, 655 Beach Street, P.O. Box 7424, San Francisco, CA 94120; tel. 415/561–8500; FAX. 415/561–8533; David W. Parke, II, Executive Vice President and Chief Executive Officer

American Academy of Optometry, 2909 Fairgreen Street, Orlando, FL 32803; tel. 321/710–3937; FAX. 410/893–9890; Lois Schoenbrun, CAE, FAAO Executive Director

American Academy of Oral Medicine, 23607 Highway 99, Suite 2C, Edmonds, WA 98020–9516; tel. 425/778–6162; FAX. 425/771–9588; Nick Senzee, Executive Director

American Academy of Orthopaedic Surgeons, 6300 North River Road, Rosemont, IL 60018–4262; tel. 847/823–7186; FAX. 847/823–8125; Karen L. Hackett, FACHE, CAE, Chief Executive Officer

American Academy of Otolaryngic Allergy, 11130 Sunrise Valley Drive, Suite 100, Reston, VA 20191; tel. 202/955–5010; FAX. 202/955–5016; Jami Lucas, Executive Director and Chief Executive Officer

American Academy of Otolaryngology-Head and Neck Surgery, Inc., 1650 Diagonal Road, Alexandria, VA 22314; tel. 703/836–4444; FAX. 703/683–5100; David R. Nielsen, MD, FACS, Chief Executive Officer and Executive Vice President

American Academy of Pain Management, 975 Morning Star Dr., Suite A, Sonora, CA 95370; tel. 209/533–9744; FAX. 209/533–9750

American Academy of Pediatrics, 141 Northwest Point Boulevard, Elk Grove Village, IL 60007–1098; tel. 847/434–4000; FAX. 847/434–8000; Errol R. Alden MD, FAAP, Executive Director and Chief Executive Officer

American Academy of Physical Medicine and Rehabilitation, 9700 West Bryn Mawr Avenue, Suite 200, Rosemont, IL 60018–5701; tel. 847/737–6000; FAX. 847/737–6001; Thomas E. Stautzenbach, CAE, Executive Director

American Academy of Physician Assistants, 2318 Mill Road, Suite 1300, Alexandria, VA 22314; tel. 703/836–2272; FAX. 703/684–1924; Jennifer L. Dorn, Chief Executive Officer

American Academy of Psychoanalysis And Dynamic Psychiatry, One Regency Drive, PO Box 30, Bloomfield, CT 06002; tel. 888/691–8281; FAX. 860/286–0787; Jacquelyn T. Coleman, CAE, Executive Director

American Aging Association, The Sally Balin Medical Center, 110 Chesley Drive, Media, PA 19063; tel. 610/627–2626; FAX. 610/565–9747; Arthur K. Balin, MD, PhD., FACP

American Ambulance Association, 8400 Westpark Drive, Second Floor, McLean, VA 22102; tel. 703/610–9018; FAX. 703/610–0210; Maria Bianchi, Executive Vice President

American Art Therapy Association, Inc., 11160 - C1 South Lakes Drive, Suite 813, Reston, VA 20191; tel. 703/212–2238; Peg Dunn-Snow, PhD, ATR-BC, President

American Assembly for Men In Nursing, PO Box 130220, Birmingham, AL 35213; tel. 205/956–0146; FAX. 205/956–0149; Byron McCain, Executive Director

American Association for Clinical Chemistry, Inc. (AACC), 1850 K Street, NW, Suite 625, Washington, DC 20006; tel. 202/857–0717; FAX. 202/877–5093; Janet B. Kreizman, Chief Executive Officer

American Association for Dental Research, 1619 Duke Street, Alexandria, VA 22314–3406; tel. 703/548–0066; FAX. 703/548–1883; Christopher Fox, Executive Director

American Association for Health Education, 1900 Association Drive, Reston, VA 20191; tel. 703/476–3400; FAX. 703/476–9527; Malcolm Goldsmith, Executive Director

American Association For Homecare, 1707 L Street NW, Suite 350, Washington, DC 20036; tel. 202/372–0107; FAX. 202/835–8306; Kim Brummett, Vice President

American Association for Laboratory Animal Science, AALAS, 9190 Crestwyn Hills Drive, Memphis, TN 38125; tel. 901/754–8620; FAX. 901/753–0046; Ann T. Turner, PhD, CAE, Executive Director

American Association for Respiratory Care, 9425 N. MacArthur, Suite 100, Irving, TX 75063; tel. 972/243–2272; FAX. 972/484–2720

American Association for the Advancement of Science, 1200 New York Avenue, NW, Washington, DC 20005; tel. 202/326–6640; FAX. 202/371–9526; Alan Leshner, Chief Executive Officer

American Association for the Surgery of Trauma, 633 N. Saint Clair Street, Suite 2600, Chicago, IL 60611; tel. 800/789–4006; FAX. 312/202–5064; Sharon Gautschy, Executive Director

American Association of Ambulatory Surgery Centers, 1012 Cameron Street, Alexandria, VA 22314; tel. 703/836–8808; FAX. 703/549–0976; Kathy Bryant, President

American Association of Anatomists, 9650 Rockville Pike, Bethesda, MD 20814; tel. 301/634–7910; FAX. 301/634–7965; Shawn Boynes, CAE, Executive Director

American Association of Bioanalysts, 906 Olive, Suite 1200, St. Louis, MO 63101–1448; tel. 314/241–1445; FAX. 314/241–1449; Mark S. Birenbaum, PhD, Administrator

American Association of Certified Orthoptists, 3914 Nakoma Road, Madison, WI 53711; tel. 608/233–5383; FAX. 608/263–4247; Marlo Galli, CO

American Association of Colleges of Nursing, One DuPont Circle, NW, Suite 530, Washington, DC 20036; tel. 202/463–6930; FAX. 202/785–8320; Geraldine Bednash, PhD, RN FAAN, Chief Executive Officer and Executive Director

American Association of Colleges of Osteopathic Medicine, 5550 Friendship Boulevard, Suite 310, Chevy Chase, MD 20815–7231; tel. 301/968–4100; FAX. 301/968–4101; Stephen C. Shannon, DO, MPH, President and Chief Executive Officer

American Association of Colleges of Pharmacy, 1727 King Street, Floor 2, Alexandria, VA 22314–2700; tel. 703/739–2330; FAX. 703/836–8982; Lucinda Maine, PhD, Executive Vice President

Section C

American Association of Colleges of Podiatric Medicine, 15850 Crabbs Branch Way, Suite 320, Rockville, MD 20855–2622; tel. 301/948–9760; FAX. 301/948–1928; Moraith G. North, Executive Director

American Association of Critical-Care Nurses, 101 Columbia, Aliso Viejo, CA 92656–1491; tel. 949/362–2000; FAX. 949/362–2020; Dana Woods, Chief Executive Officer

American Association of Dental Consultants, Inc., 10032 Wind Hill Drive, Greenville, IN 47124; tel. 812/923–2600; FAX. 812/923–2900; Judy Salisbury, Executive Director

American Association of Endodontists, 211 East Chicago Avenue, Suite 1100, Chicago, IL 60611–2691; tel. 312/266–7255; FAX. 312/266–9867; Trina Anderson, Executive Assistant to the Executive Director

American Association of Healthcare Administrative Management, 11240 Waples Mill Road, Suite 200, Fairfax, VA 22030; tel. 703/281–4043; FAX. 703/359–7562; Sharon Galler, Executive Director

American Association of Kidney Patients, 2701 North Rocky Point Drive, Suite 150, Tampa, FL 33607; tel. 800/749–2257; FAX. 813/636–8122; Diana Clynes, Director of Programs and Services

American Association of Medical Assistants, 20 North Wacker Drive, Suite 1575, Chicago, IL 60606; tel. 312/899–1500; FAX. 312/899–1259; Donald A. Balasa, JD, MBA, Executive Director, Legal Counsel

American Association of Nurse Anesthetists, 222 South Prospect Avenue, Park Ridge, IL 60068–4001; tel. 847/692–7050; FAX. 847/685–4501; Wanda O. Wilson, CRNA, PhD, Executive Director and Chief Executive Officer

American Association of Occupational Health Nurses, Inc., 7794 Grow Drive, Pensacola, FL 32514; tel. 770/455–7757; FAX. 770/455–7271; Ann R. Cox, CAE, Executive Director

American Association of Oral and Maxillofacial Surgeons, 9700 West Bryn Mawr Avenue, Rosemont, IL 60018–5701; tel. 847/678–6200; FAX. 847/678–6286; Robert C. Rinaldi, PhD, Executive Director

American Association of Orthodontists, 401 North Lindbergh Boulevard, St. Louis, MO 63141–7816; tel. 314/993–1700; FAX. 314/997–1745; Chris P. Vranas, Executive Director

American Association of Pastoral Counselors, 9504A Lee Highway, Fairfax, VA 22031–2303; tel. 703/385–6967; FAX. 703/352–7725; Douglas M. Ronsheim, D.Min, Executive Director

American Association of Physicists in Medicine, One Physics Ellipse, College Park, MD 20740–3846; tel. 301/209–3350; FAX. 301/209–0862; Angela R. Keyser, Executive Director

American Association of Plastic Surgeons, 500 Cummings Center, Suite 4550, Beverly, MA 01915; tel. 978/927–8330; FAX. 978/524–0461; Aurelie Alger, JD, Executive Director

American Association of Poison Control Centers, 515 King Street, Suite 510, Alexandria, VA 22314; tel. 703/894–1858; FAX. 703/683–2812; John L. Fiegel, Interim Executive Director

American Association of Psychiatric Technicians, Inc., A.A.P.T., 1220 S Street, Suite 100, Sacramento, CA 95814–7138; tel. 800/391–7589; FAX. 916/329–9145; Debi Loger, Executive Director

American Association of Public Health Dentistry, 3085 Stevenson Drive, Suite 200, Springfield, IL 62703; tel. 217/529–6941; FAX. 217/529–9120

American Association on Intellectual and Developmental Disabilities (AAIDD), 501 Third Street, NW, Suite 200, Washington, DC 20001–2760; tel. 202/387–1968; FAX. 202/387–2193; Margaret A. Nygren, Executive Director & Chief Executive Officer

American Baptist Homes and Caring Ministries, PO Box 851 (National Ministries), Valley Forge, PA 19482–0851; tel. 610/768–2051; Laura Miraz, Liaison

American Board of Allergy and Immunology, 111 S. Independence Mall East, Suite 701, Philadelphia, PA 19106–3699; tel. 215/592–9466; FAX. 215/592–9411; Stephen I. Wasserman, MD, President

American Board of Cardiovascular Medicine, Inc., PO Box 3219, Spring Hill, FL 34611; tel. 352/293–3131; Jonni Cooper, Chief Executive Officer

American Board of Cardiovascular Perfusion, 2903 Arlington Loop, Hattiesburg, MS 39401; tel. 601/268–2221; FAX. 601/268–2229; Beth A. Richmond, PhD, Stephen Oshrin, PhD, Executive Co-Directors

American Board of Colon and Rectal Surgery, 20600 Eureka Road, Suite 600, Taylor, MI 48180; tel. 734/282–9400; FAX. 734/282–9402; David J. Schoetz, MD, Executive Director

American Board of Dermatology, Inc., Henry Ford Health System, One Ford Place, Detroit, MI 48202–3450; tel. 313/874–1088; FAX. 313/872–3221; Thomas D. Horn, MD, MBA, Executive Director

American Board of Emergency Medicine, 3000 Coolidge Road, East Lansing, MI 48823; tel. 517/332–4800; FAX. 517/332–6371; Earl J. Reisdorff, MD, Executive Director

American Board of Family Medicine, Inc., 1648 McGrathiana Parkway, Suite 550, Lexington, KY 40511–1247; tel. 859/269–5626; FAX. 859/335–7501; James Puffer, MD, President and Chief Executive Officer

American Board of Internal Medicine, 510 Walnut Street, Suite 1700, Philadelphia, PA 19106–3699; tel. 215/446–3500; FAX. 215/446–3473; Christine K. Cassel, MD, President

American Board of Medical Specialties, 353 North Clark Street, Suite 1400, Chicago, IL 60654; tel. 312/436–2600; FAX. 312/436–2700; Rich Waters, Vice President, Marketing and Communications

American Board of Neurological Surgery, 245 Amity Road #208, Woodbridge, CT 06525; tel. 203/397–2267; FAX. 203/392–0400; Mary Louise Spencer, Executive Director

American Board of Nuclear Medicine, 4555 Forest Park Blvd, Suite 119, St. Louis, MO 63108; tel. 314/367–2225; Henry D. Royal, MD, Executive Director

American Board of Ophthalmology, 111 Presidential Boulevard, Suite 241, Bala Cynwyd, PA 19004; tel. 610/664–1175; FAX. 610/664–6503; John G. Clarkson, MD, Executive Director

American Board of Oral and Maxillofacial Surgery, 625 North Michigan Avenue, Suite 1820, Chicago, IL 60611; tel. 312/642–0070; FAX. 312/642–8584; Lance O. Hoxie, Executive Vice President

American Board of Orthopedic Surgery, Inc., 400 Silver Cedar Court, Chapel Hill, NC 27514; tel. 919/929–7103; FAX. 919/942–8988; Shepard R. Hurwitz, MD, Executive Director

American Board of Pathology, One Urban Centre, 4830 West Kennedy Boulevard, Suite 690, Tampa, FL 33622–5915; tel. 813/286–2444; FAX. 813/289–5279; Rebecca L. Johnson, MD, Chief Executive Officer

American Board of Pediatrics, 111 Silver Cedar Court, Chapel Hill, NC 27514; tel. 919/929–0461; FAX. 919/929–9255; David G. Nichols, MD, MBA, President and Chief Executive Officer

American Board of Physical Medicine and Rehabilitation, 3015 Allegro Park Lane SW, Rochester, MN 55902; tel. 507/282–1776; FAX. 507/282–9242; Anthony M. Tarvestad, JD, Executive Director

American Board of Podiatric Surgery, 445 Fillmore Street, San Francisco, CA 94117–3404; tel. 415/553–7800; FAX. 415/553–7801; James A. Lamb, Executive Director

American Board of Preventive Medicine, Inc., 111 West Jackson Boulevard, Suite 1110, Chicago, IL 60604; tel. 312/939–2276; FAX. 312/939–2218; William W. Greaves, MD, MSPH, Executive Director

American Board of Prosthodontics, PO Box 271894, West Hartford, CT 06127–1894; tel. 860/679–2649; FAX. 860/206–1169; Thomas D. Taylor, DDS, MSD, Executive Director

American Board of Psychiatry and Neurology, Inc., 2150 E. Lake Cook Road, Suite 900, Buffalo Grove, IL 60089; tel. 847/229–6500; FAX. 847/229–6600; Larry Faulkner, MD, President and Chief Executive Officer

American Board of Quality Assurance and Utilization Review Physicians, Inc., ABQAURP, 6640 Congress St, New Port Richey, FL 34653; tel. 800/998–6030; FAX. 727/569–0195; Renee Willoughby, Managing Director

American Board of Radiology, 5441 E. Williams Circle, Tucson, AZ 85711; tel. 520/790–2900; FAX. 520/790–3200; Valerie P. Jackson, MD, Executive Director

American Board of Surgery, Inc., 1617 John F. Kennedy Boulevard, Suite 860, Philadelphia, PA 19103; tel. 215/568–4000; FAX. 215/563–5718; Frank R. Lewis, MD, Executive Director

American Board of Thoracic Surgery, 633 N. Street Clair Street, Suite 2320, Chicago, IL 60611; tel. 312/202–5900; FAX. 312/202–5960; William A. Baumgartner, MD, Executive Director

American Broncho-Esophagological Association, Office of the Secretary, Stanford University School of Medicine, Division of Pediatric Otolaryngology, Stanford, CA 94305–5739; tel. 650/725–6500; FAX. 650/725–8502; Peter Koltai, MD, Secretary

American Burn Association, 311 South Wacker Drive, Suite 4150, Chicago, IL 60606; tel. 312/642–9260; FAX. 312/642–9130; John Krichbaum, JD, Executive Director

American Cancer Society, 250 Williams Street, NW, Suite 600, Atlanta, GA 30303; tel. 800/227–2345; Otis Brawley, MD, Chief Medical Officer

American Center for the Alexander Technique, Inc., 39 W. 14th Street, #507, New York, NY 10011; tel. 212/633–2229; FAX. 212/633–2239; Jane Tomkiewicz, Executive Director

American Chiropractic Association, 1701 Clarendon Boulevard, Arlington, VA 22209; tel. 703/276–8800; FAX. 703/243–2593; Janet Ridgely, Acting Executive Vice President

American Cleft Palate-Craniofacial Association, 1504 E. Franklin Street, Suite 102, Chapel Hill, NC 27514; tel. 919/933–9044; FAX. 919/933–9604; Nancy C. Smythe, Executive Director

American College Health Association, 1362 Mellon Road, Suite 180, Hanover, MD 21076; tel. 410/859–1500; FAX. 410/859–1510; Doyle E. Randol, MS, Executive Director

American College of Allergy, Asthma and Immunology, 85 West Algonquin Road, Suite 550, Arlington Heights, IL 60005; tel. 847/427–1200; FAX. 847/427–1294; Rick Slawny, Executive Director

American College of Apothecaries, PO Box 341266, Bartlett, TN 38184; tel. 901/383–8119; FAX. 901/383–8882; D. C. Huffman, Jr., PhD, Executive Vice President

American College of Cardiology, 2400 N Street, NW, Washington, DC 20037; tel. 202/375–6000; FAX. 202/375–6819; Shalom Jacobovitz, Chief Executive Officer

American College of Cardiovascular Nurses, Inc., PO Box 3219, Spring Hill, FL 34611; tel. 813/394–4968; Jonni Cooper, Chief Executive Officer

American College of Chest Physicians, 2595 Patriot Blvd., Glenview, IL 60026; tel. 224/521–9600; FAX. 224/521–9801; Paul A. Markowski, CAE

American College of Dentists, 839J Quince Orchard Boulevard, Gaithersburg, MD 20878–1614; tel. 301/977–3223; FAX. 301/977–3330; Stephen A. Ralls, DDS

American College of Emergency Physicians, PO Box 619911, Dallas, TX 75261–9911; tel. 972/550–0911; FAX. 972/580–2816; Dean Wilkerson, Executive Director

American College of Foot and Ankle Surgeons, 8725 W. Higgins Rd, Suite 555, Chicago, IL 60631; tel. 773/693–9300; FAX. 773/693–9304; J.C. Mahaffey, CAE, Executive Director

American College of Gastroenterology, 6400 Goldsboro Road, Suite 200, Bethesda, MD 20817; tel. 301/263–9000; FAX. 301/263–9025; Bradley C. Stillman, Executive Director

American College of Healthcare Executives, One North Franklin, Suite 1700, Chicago, IL 60606–3491; tel. 312/424–2800; FAX. 312/424–0023; Deborah J. Bowen, FACHE, CAE, President and Chief Executive Officer

American College of Mohs Surgery, 555 E. Wells, Suite 1100, Milwaukee, WI 53202–3823; tel. 414/347–1103; FAX. 414/276–3349; Kim Schardin, MBA, CAE, Executive Director

American College of Nurse-Midwives, Silver Spring Metro Plaza, 8403 Colesville Rd, Suite1550, Silver Spring, MD 20910–6374; tel. 240/485–1800; FAX. 240/485–1818; Lorrie Kline Kaplan, Executive Director

American College of Obstetricians and Gynecologists, 409 12th Street, SW, Washington, DC 20090–6920; tel. 202/638–5577; FAX. 202/484–5107; Hal C. Lawrence III, MD, Executive Vice President

American College of Occupational and Environmental Medicine, (Includes Occupational & Environmental Health Foundation and The Occupational Physicians Scholarship Fund), 25 Northwest Point Blvd, Suite 700, Elk Grove Village, IL 60007; tel. 847/818–1800; FAX. 847/818–9266; Barry S. Eisenberg, CAE., Executive Director

American College of Physician Executives, 400 N. Ashley Drive, Suite 400, Tampa, FL 33602; tel. 813/287–2000; FAX. 813/287–8993; Peter Angood, MD, Chief Executive Officer

American College of Physicians, 190 North Independence Mall West, Philadelphia, PA 19106–1572; tel. 215/351–2800; FAX. 215/351–2829; Steven Weinberger, MD, FACP, Executive Vice President and Chief Executive Officer

American College of Preventive Medicine, 455 Massachusetts Avenue, NW, Suite 200, Washington, DC 20001; tel. 202/466–2044; FAX. 202/466–2662; Michael Barry, Executive Director

American College of Radiology, 1891 Preston White Drive, Reston, VA 20191–4397; tel. 703/648–8900; FAX. 703/648–9176; Harvey L. Neiman, MD, Executive Director

American College of Rheumatology, 2200 Lake Boulevard, NE, Atlanta, GA 30319; tel. 404/633–3777; FAX. 404/633–1870; Helen Anne Richards, Director of Membership

American College of Sports Medicine, PO Box 1440, Indianapolis, IN 46206–1440; tel. 317/637–9200; FAX. 317/634–7817; James R. Whitehead, Executive Vice President

American College of Surgeons, 633 N. Saint Clair Street, Chicago, IL 60611–3211; tel. 312/202–5000; FAX. 312/202–5001; David B. Hoyt, MD, FACS, Executive Director

American Congress of Rehabilitation Medicine, 11654 Plaza America Drive #535, Reston, VA 20190–4700; tel. 317/471–8760; FAX. 866/692–1619; Jon W. Lindberg, MBA, CAE, Chief Executive Officer

American Dental Assistants Association, 35 E. Wacker Driver, Suite 1730, Chicago, IL 60601; tel. 312/541–1550; FAX. 312/541–1496; Lawrence H. Sepin, Executive Director

American Dental Association, 211 East Chicago Avenue, Chicago, IL 60611; tel. 312/440–2500; Kathleen T. O'Loughlin, DMD, MPH, Executive Director

American Dental Education Association, 1400 K. Street, NW, Suite 1100, Washington, DC 20005; tel. 202/289–7201; FAX. 202/289–7204; Richard Valachovic, President and Chief Executive Officer

American Dental Society of Anesthesiology, Inc., 211 East Chicago Avenue, Suite 780, Chicago, IL 60611; tel. 312/664–8270; FAX. 312/224–8624; R. Knight Charlton, Executive Director

American Diabetes Association, Inc., 1701 N. Beauregard Street, Alexandria, VA 22311; tel. 703/549–1500; FAX. 703/836–7439; Larry Hausner, Chief Executive Officer

American Federation for Aging Research, 55 West 39th Street, 16th Floor, New York, NY 10018; tel. 212/703–9977; FAX. 212/997–0330; Stephanie Lederman, Director

American Foundation for the Blind, Inc., 2 Penn Plaza, Suite 1102, New York, NY 10121; tel. 212/502–7600; FAX. 888/545–8331; Carl Augusto, President and Chief Executive Officer

American Group Psychotherapy Association, Inc., 25 East 21st Street, Sixth Floor, New York, NY 10010; tel. 212/477–2677; FAX. 212/979–6627; Marsha S. Block, CAE, Chief Executive Officer

American Head and Neck Society, 11300 W. Olympic Blvd #600, Los Angles, CA 90064; tel. 310/437–0559; FAX. 310/437–0585; Christina Kasendorf, Executive Director

American Headache Society, 19 Mantua Road, Mt. Royal, NJ 08061; tel. 856/423–0043; FAX. 856/423–0082; Linda McGillicuddy, Executive Director

American Health Care Association, 1201 L Street, NW, Washington, DC 20005; tel. 202/842–4444; FAX. 202/842–3860; Mark Parkinson, President and Chief Executive Officer

American Health Information Management Association (AHIMA), 233 North Michigan Avenue, 21st Floor, Chicago, IL 60601–5800; tel. 312/233–1100; FAX. 312/233–1090; Alan F. Dowling PhD, Chief Executive Officer

American Health Lawyers Association, 1620 Eye Street NW, Washington, DC 20006–4010; tel. 202/833–1100; FAX. 202/833–1105; Peter M. Leibold, Esq, Executive Vice President and Chief Executive Officer

American Health Planning Association, 7245 Arlington Boulevard, Suite 300, Falls Church, VA 22042; tel. 703/573–3103; FAX. 703/573–3103; Dean Montgomery, Director

American Healthcare Radiology Administrators, 490 - B Boston, Post Road, Suite 101, Sudbury, MA 01776; tel. 978/443–7591; FAX. 978/443–8046; Mary S. Reitter, Executive Director

American Heart Association, Inc., 7272 Greenville Avenue, Dallas, TX 75231; tel. 214/706–1574; FAX. 214/373–9818; Rose Marie Robertson, MD, FAHA, Chief Science and Medical Officer

American Hospital Association, 800 10th Street, NW, TwoCity Center, Suite 400, Washington, DC 20001–4956; tel. 202/638–1100; Richard Umbdenstock, President and Chief Executive Officer

American Hospital Association, 155 N. Wacker Drive, Suite 400, Chicago, IL 60606; tel. 312/422–3000; Richard Umbdenstock, President and Chief Executive Officer

American International Health Alliance, 1250 Eye Street, NW, Suite 350, Washington, DC 20005; tel. 202/789–1136; FAX. 202/789–1277; James P. Smith, Executive Director

American Laryngological Association, Office of the Secretary, 193-39 Keno Avenue, Holliswood, NY 11423–1214; tel. 212/744–4368; FAX. 212/434–6620; Gady Har-El, MD, Secretary

American Library Association, 50 East Huron Street, Chicago, IL 60611; tel. 312/280–5063; FAX. 312/280–5270; Cynthia Vivian, Director

American Lung Association, 1301 Pennsylvania Avenue, NW, Washington, DC 20004–1725; tel. 202/785–3355; FAX. 202/452–1805; Harold Wimmer, President and Chief Executive Officer

American Lung Association in Ohio, 4050 Executive Park Drive, Suite 405, Cincinnati, OH 45241; tel. 513/985–3990; FAX. 513/985–3995; Gale Steitz, Program Director

American Medical Association, AMA Plaza, 330 N. Wabash Ave., Suite 39300, Chicago, IL 60611–5885; tel. 312/464–5000; James L. Madara, MD, Chief Executive Officer and Executive Vice President

American Medical Association Alliance, 550M Ritchie Hwy, #271, Severna Park, MD 21146; tel. 800/549–4619; FAX. 410/544–4650; Patricia Troy, Executive Director

American Medical Group Association, One Prince Street, Alexandria, VA 22314–3318; tel. 703/838–0033; FAX. 703/548–1890; William B. Baron, Director of Membership Development

American Medical Student Association/Foundation, 45610 Woodland Road, Suite 300, Sterling, VA 20166; tel. 703/620–6600; FAX. 703/620–5873; Meeghan De Cagna, Interim Executive Director

American Medical Technologists, 10700 W. Higgins Road, Suite 150, Rosemont, IL 60018; tel. 847/823–5169; FAX. 847/823–0458; Christopher Damon, Executive Director

American Medical Women's Association, 100 North 20th Street, 4th Floor, Philadelphia, PA 19103; tel. 866/564–2483; FAX. 215/564–2175; Gina Marinilli, Associate Director

American Medical Writers Association, 30 West Gude Drive #525, Rockville, MD 20850; tel. 204/238–0940; FAX. 301/294–9006; Mark Rosal, Member Services Coordinator

American Music Therapy Association, 8455 Colesville Road, Suite 1000, Silver Spring, MD 20910; tel. 301/589–3300; FAX. 301/589–5175; Andrea Farbman, Ed.D., Executive Director

American National Standards Institute, 25 West 43rd Street, Fourth Floor, New York, NY 10036; tel. 212/642–4900; FAX. 212/398–0023; S. Joe Bhatia, President and Chief Executive Officer

American Nephrology Nurses' Association, East Holly Avenue, PO Box 56, Pitman, NJ 08071; tel. 856/256–2320; FAX. 856/589–7463; Mike Cunningham, Executive Director

American Neurological Association, 15000 Commerce Parkway, Suite C, Mt. Laurel, NJ 08054; tel. 856/638–0423; FAX. 856/439–0525; Victoria Elliott, Executive Director

American Occupational Therapy Association, Inc., 4720 Montgomery Lane, P.O. Box 31220, Bethesda, MD 20814–1220; tel. 301/652–2682; FAX. 301/652–7711; Frederick P. Somers, Executive Director

American Ontological Society, Inc., 3096 Riverdale Rd., The Villages, FL 32162; tel. 352/751–0932; FAX. 352/751–0696; Shirley Gossard, Administrator

American Ophthalmological Society, 655 Beach Street, San Francisco, CA 94109; tel. 415/561–8578; FAX. 415/561–8531; Thomas J. Liesegang, MD, Executive Vice President

American Optometric Association, 243 North Lindbergh Boulevard, St. Louis, MO 63141; tel. 314/991–4100; FAX. 314/991–4101; Jon Hymes, Interim Executive Director

American Organization of Nurse Executives (AONE), 325 Seventh Street, NW, Suite 700, Washington, DC 20004; tel. 202/626–2240; FAX. 202/638–5499; Pamela A. Thompson, MS, RN, CENP, FAAN, Chief Executive Officer, and AHA Senior Vice President for Nursing

American Orthopsychiatric Association, Department of Psychology, Box 871104, Tempe, AZ 85287–1104; tel. 480/965–0380; FAX. 480/965–8544; Nicole Bruno, Director

American Orthoptic Council, 3914 Nakoma Road, Madison, WI 53711; tel. 608/233–5383; FAX. 608/263–4247; Leslie France, CO, Administrator

American Osteopathic Association, 142 East Ontario Street, Chicago, IL 60611; tel. 312/202–8003; FAX. 312/202–8303; Adrienne White-Faines, MPA, Executive Director and Chief Executive Officer

American Parkinson Disease Association, Inc., 135 Parkinson Avenue, Parkinson Plaza, Staten Island, NY 10305; tel. 800/223–2732; FAX. 718/981–4399; G. Maestrone, DVM, Scientific and Medical Affairs Director

American Pediatric Society, Inc., 3400 Research Forest Drive, Suite B7, The Woodlands, TX 77381; tel. 281/419–0052; FAX. 281/419–0082; Kathy Cannon, Associate Executive Director

American Pharmacists Association, 2215 Constitution Avenue, NW, Washington, DC 20037; tel. 202/628–4410; FAX. 202/783–2351; Thomas E. Menighan, BSPharm, MBA, ScD(Hon.), Executive Vice President/Chief Executive Officer

American Physical Therapy Association, 1111 North Fairfax Street, Alexandria, VA 22314–1488; tel. 703/684–2782; FAX. 703/684–7343; J. Michael Bowers, Chief Executive Officer

American Physiological Society, 9650 Rockville Pike, Bethesda, MD 20814–3991; tel. 301/634–7118; FAX. 301/634–7241; Martin Frank, PhD, Executive Director

American Podiatric Medical Association, 9312 Old Georgetown Road, Bethesda, MD 20814–1698; tel. 301/571–9200; FAX. 301/530–2752; Glenn B. Gastwirth, DPM, Executive Director

American Psychiatric Association, 1000 Wilson Boulevard, Suite 1825, Arlington, VA 22209; tel. 703/907–8650; FAX. 703/907–1086; Saul Levin, Chief Executive Officer and Medical Director

American Psychoanalytic Association, 309 East 49th Street, New York, NY 10017; tel. 212/752–0450; FAX. 212/593–0571; Dean K. Stein, Executive Director

American Psychological Association, 750 First Street, NE, Washington, DC 20002–4242; tel. 202/336–5800; FAX. 202/336–5797; Katherine Nordal, PhD, Executive Director For Professional Practice

American Psychosomatic Society, 6728 Old McLean Village Drive, McLean, VA 22101–3906; tel. 703/556–9222; FAX. 703/556–8729; George K. Degnon, Executive Director

American Public Health Association, 800 I Street, NW, Washington, DC 20001–3710; tel. 202/777–2742; FAX. 202/777–2534; Georges C. Benjamin, MD, FACP, FACEP(E), Executive Director

American Public Human Services Association, 1133 Nineteenth Street, NW, Suite 400, Washington, DC 20036; tel. 202/682–0100; FAX. 202/289–6555; Amy Plotnick, Publications Manager

American Red Cross, National Headquarters, 2025 E. Street, NW, Washington, DC 20006; tel. 407/894–4141; Peter Giamalva, Senior Vice President, Sales and Hospital Marketing

American Registry of Medical Assistants, 61 Union Street, Suite 5, Westfield, MA 01085–2476; tel. 413/562–7336; FAX. 413/562–9021; Marie Bergeron, RMA, Director

American Registry of Radiologic Technologists, 1255 Northland Drive, St. Paul, MN 55120; tel. 651/687–0048; Jerry B. Reid, PhD, Executive Director

American Rhinologic Society, PO Box 495, Warwick, NY 10990; tel. 845/988–1631; FAX. 845/986–1527; Wendi Perez, Administrator/Executive Director

American Roentgen Ray Society, 44211 Slate Stone Court, Leesburg, VA 20176; tel. 703/729–3353; FAX. 703/729–4839; Susan Brown Cappitelli, Executive Director

American School Health Association, 4340 East West Highway, Suite 403, Bethesda, MD 20814; tel. 301/652–8072; FAX. 301/652–8077; Stephen Conley, Executive Director

American Society for Adolescent Psychiatry, PO Box 570218, Dallas, TX 75357–0218; tel. 972/613–0985; FAX. 972/613–5532; Frances M. Roton Bell, Executive Director

American Society for Biochemistry and Molecular Biology, Inc., 9650 Rockville Pike, Bethesda, MD 20814–3996; tel. 301/634–7145; FAX. 301/634–7126; Charles C. Hancock, Executive Officer

American Society for Clinical Laboratory Science, 1861 International Dr., Suite 200, McLean, VA 22102; tel. 571/748–3770; FAX. 571/354–7570; Elissa Passiment, Executive Vice President

American Society for Clinical Pathology, (Includes Board of Certification), 33 W. Monroe Street, Suite 1600, Chicago, IL 60603; tel. 312/541–4999; FAX. 312/541–4767; E. Blair Holladay, PhD, SCT (ASCP), Executive Vice President

American Society for Clinical Pharmacology and Therapeutics, 528 North Washington Street, Alexandria, VA 22314; tel. 703/836–6981; FAX. 703/836–5223; Sharon J. Swan, CAE, Chief Executive Officer

American Society for Cytotechnology, 1500 Sunday Drive, Suite 102, Raleigh, NC 27607; tel. 800/948–3947; FAX. 919/787–4916; Beth Denny, Executive Director

American Society for Healthcare Engineering (ASHE), 155 N. Wacker Drive, Suite 400, Chicago, IL 60606–1725; tel. 312/422–3800; FAX. 312/422–4571; Dale Woodin, CHFM, FASHE, Executive Director

American Society for Healthcare Human Resources Administration (ASHHRA), 155 N. Wacker Drive, Suite 400, Chicago, IL 60606; tel. 312/422–3720; FAX. 312/422–4577; Stephanie Drake, MBA, Executive Director

American Society for Healthcare Risk Management (ASHRM), 155 N. Wacker Drive, Suite 400, Chicago, IL 60606; tel. 312/422–3980; FAX. 312/422–4580; Kim Hoarle, MBA, CAE, Executive Director

American Society for Investigative Pathology, 9650 Rockville Pike, Bethesda, MD 20814–3993; tel. 301/634–7130; FAX. 301/634–7990; Mark E. Sobel, MD, Ph.D, Executive Director

American Society for Laser Medicine and Surgery, Inc., 2100 Stewart Avenue, Suite 240, Wausau, WI 54401; tel. 715/845–9283; FAX. 715/848–2493; Elizabeth Tanzi, MD, Secretary

American Society for Microbiology, 1752 North Street, NW, Washington, DC 20036; tel. 202/924–9265; FAX. 202/942–9333; Michael I. Goldberg, PhD, Executive Director

American Society for Pharmacology and Experimental Therapeutics, 9650 Rockville Pike, Bethesda, MD 20814–3995; tel. 301/634–7060; FAX. 301/634–7061; Christine K. Carrico, PhD, Executive Officer

American Society for Public Administration, 1301 Pennsylvania Avenue, NW, Suite 840, Washington, DC 20004; tel. 202/393–7878; FAX. 202/638–4952; Antoinette Samuel, CAE

American Society for Radiation Oncology, 8280 Willow Oaks Corporate Drive, Suite 500, Fairfax, VA 22031; tel. 703/502–1550; FAX. 703/502–7852; Laura I. Thevenot, Chief Executive Officer

American Society for Reproductive Medicine, 1209 Montgomery Highway, Birmingham, AL 35216–2809; tel. 205/978–5000; FAX. 205/293–5201; Richard Reindollar, MD, Executive Director

American Society for the Advancement of Anesthesia and Sedation in Dentistry, Six East Union Avenue, PO Box 551, Bound Brook, NJ 08805; tel. 732/469–9050; FAX. 732/271–1985; David Crystal, DDS, Executive Secretary

American Society of Anesthesiologists, 520 North Northwest Highway, Park Ridge, IL 60068; tel. 847/825–5586; FAX. 847/825–2085; Paul Pomerantz, Chief Executive Officer

American Society of Colon and Rectal Surgeons, 85 West Algonquin Road, Suite 550, Arlington Heights, IL 60005; tel. 847/290–9184; FAX. 847/290–9203; James Slawny, Executive Director

American Society of Consultant Pharmacists, 1321 Duke Street, Alexandria, VA 22314–3563; tel. 703/739–1300; FAX. 703/739–1321; Vera Jackson, PhD, Executive Director and Chief Executive Officer

American Society of Cytopathology, 100 West 10th Street, Suite 605, Wilmington, DE 19801; tel. 302/543–6583; FAX. 302/543–6597; Elizabeth A. Jenkins, Executive Director

American Society of Health-System Pharmacists, 7272 Wisconsin Avenue, Bethesda, MD 20814; tel. 301/664–8794; FAX. 301/634–5977; Paul W. Abramowitz, Chief Executive Officer

American Society of Law, Medicine & Ethics, 765 Commonwealth Avenue, Suite 1634, Boston, MA 02215; tel. 617/262–4990; FAX. 617/437–7596; Edward Hutchinson, Executive Director

American Society of Neuroimaging, 5841 Cedar Lake Road, Suite 204, Minneapolis, MN 55416; tel. 952/545–6291; FAX. 952/545–6073; Shannon Wild, Executive Director

American Society of Plastic Surgeons, 444 East Algonquin Road, Arlington Heights, IL 60005; tel. 847/228–9900; FAX. 847/228–9131; Michael D. Costelloe, Executive Vice President

American Society of Radiologic Technologists, 15000 Central Avenue, SE, Albuquerque, NM 87123–3909; tel. 505/298–4500; FAX. 505/298–5063; Ceela McElveny, Chief Communications and Membership Officer

American Speech-Language-Hearing Association, 2200 Research Boulevard, Rockville, MD 20850–3289; tel. 301/296–5700; FAX. 301/296–8580; Arlene A. Pietranton, PhD, Chief Executive Officer

American Surgical Association, 500 Cummings Center, Suite 4550, Beverly, MA 01915; tel. 978/927–8330; FAX. 978/524–8890; Jon Blackstone, Executive Director

American Thoracic Society, 25 Broadway, 18th Floor, New York, NY 10004; tel. 212/315–8600; FAX. 212/315–6498; Stephen C. Crane, PhD, MPH, Executive Director

American Trauma Society, 201 Park Washington Court, Falls Church, VA 22046; tel. 800/556–7890; FAX. 703/241–5603; Ian Weston, Executive Director

American Urological Association, Inc., 1000 Corporate Boulevard, Linthicum, MD 21090; tel. 410/689–3700; Michael Sheppard, Executive Director

amfAR, The Foundation for AIDS Research, 120 Wall Street, 13th Floor, New York, NY 10005–3902; tel. 212/806–1600; FAX. 212/806–1601; Rachel Carr, Assistant Coordinator, Public Information

AORN, Association of periOperative Registered Nurses, 2170 South Parker Road, Suite 400, Denver, CO 80231–5711; tel. 303/755–6300; FAX. 303/750–2927; Linda Groah, RN, MSN, CNOR, NEA-BC, FAAN, Executive Director and Chief Executive Officer

Arthritis Foundation, 1330 West Peachtree Street, Suite 100, Atlanta, GA 30309; tel. 404/872–7100; FAX. 404/965–7712; John H. Klippel, MD, President and Chief Executive Officer

ASET - The Neurodiagnostic Society, 402 East Bannister Road, Suite A, Kansas City, MO 64131; tel. 816/931–1120; FAX. 816/931–1145; Arlen Reimnitz, Executive Director

Association for Applied Psychophysiology and Biofeedback, 10200 West 44th Avenue, Suite 304, Wheat Ridge, CO 80033; tel. 303/422–8436; FAX. 303/422–8894; David Stumph, Executive Director

Association for Clinical Pastoral Education, Inc., 1549 Clairmont Road, Suite 103, Decatur, GA 30033; tel. 404/320–1472; FAX. 404/320–0849; Trace Haythorn, Executive Director

Association for Community Health Improvement (ACHI), 155 N. Wacker Drive, Suite 400, Chicago, IL 60606; tel. 312/422–2193; FAX. 312/422–4522; Stephen A. Martin, Jr., Ph.D., MPH, Executive Director

Association for Healthcare Administrative Professionals (AHCAP), 455 S. Fourth Street, Suite 650, Louisville, KY 40202; tel. 888/320–0808; FAX. 502/589–3602; Monica Harper, Executive Director

Association for Healthcare Foodservice, AHF, 455 S. Fourth Street, Suite 650, Louisville, KY 40202; tel. 888/528–9552; FAX. 502/589–3602; Billye Potts, Executive Vice President

Association for Healthcare Philanthropy, 313 Park Avenue, Suite 400, Falls Church, VA 22046; tel. 703/532–6243; FAX. 703/532–7170; William C. McGinly, Ph.D., CA, President and Chief Executive Officer

Association for Healthcare Resource & Materials Management (AHRMM), 155 N. Wacker Drive, Suite 400, Chicago, IL 60606; tel. 312/422–3840; FAX. 312/422–4573; Deborah L. Sprindzunas, Executive Director

Association for Healthcare Volunteer Resource Professionals (AHVRP), 155 N. Wacker Drive, Suite 400, Chicago, IL 60606; tel. 312/422–3939; FAX. 312/278–0884; Joan M. Miller, MHA, Executive Director

Association for Hospital Medical Education, 109 Brush Creek Road, Irwin, PA 15642; tel. 724/864–7321; FAX. 724/864–6153; Kimball Mohn, MD, Executive Director

Association for Professionals in Infection Control and Epidemiology, 1275 K Street, NW, Suite 1000, Washington, DC 20005; tel. 202/789–1890; FAX. 202/789–1899; Katrina Crist, MBA, Chief Executive Officer

Association for the Advancement of Automotive Medicine (AAAM), PO Box 4176, Barrington, IL 60146; tel. 847/844–3880; FAX. 847/844–3884; Irene Herzau, Executive Director

Association for the Healthcare Environment (AHE), 155 N. Wacker Drive, Suite 400, Chicago, IL 60606; tel. 312/422–3860; FAX. 312/422–4578; Patti Costello, Executive Director

Association of American Medical Colleges, 2450 N Street, NW, Washington, DC 20037–1127; tel. 202/828–0400; FAX. 202/828–1125; Darrell G. Kirch, MD, President and Chief Executive Officer

Association of American Physicians and Surgeons, Inc., 1601 North Tucson Boulevard, Suite Nine, Tucson, AZ 85716; tel. 520/327–4885; FAX. 520/325–4230; Jane M. Orient, MD, Executive Director

Association of American Veterinary Medical Colleges, 1101 Vermont Ave, NW, Suite 301, Washington, DC 20005; tel. 202/371-9195; FAX. 202/842-0773; Dr. Andrew Maccabe, Executive Director

Association of Community Cancer Centers, 11600 Nebel Street, Suite 201, Rockville, MD 20852-2557; tel. 301/984-9496; FAX. 301/770-1949; Christian Downs, JD, MHA, Executive Director

Association of Environmental Health Academic Programs, 4500 9th Ave. NE, Suite 394, Seattle, WA 98105; tel. 206/522-5272; FAX. 206/985-9805; Yalonda Sinde, Executive Director

Association of Healthcare Administrative Professionals, AHCAP, 455 S. Fourth Street, Suite 650, Louisville, KY 40202; tel. 502/574-9040; FAX. 502/589-3602; Monica Harper, Executive Director

Association of Nutrition and Foodservice Professionals, 406 Surrey Woods Drive, St. Charles, IL 60174; tel. 630/587-6336; FAX. 630/587-6308; Joyce Gilbert, President, Chief Executive Officer

Association of Occupational & Environmental Clinics, 1010 Vermont Avenue, NW # 513, Washington, DC 20005; tel. 202/347-4976; Katherine Kirkland, Dr PH, MPH, Executive Director

Association of Professional Chaplains, 1701 East Woodfield Road, Suite 400, Schaumburg, IL 60173; tel. 847/240-1014; FAX. 847/240-1015; Patricia F. Appelhans, JD, Executive Director

Association of Public Health Laboratories, 8515 Georgia Avenue, Suite 700, Silver Spring, MD 20910; tel. 240/485-2745; FAX. 240/485-2700; Scott J. Becker, MS, Executive Director

Association of Schools of Allied Health Professions, 122 C. St. NW, Suite 650, Washington, DC 20001; tel. 202/237-6481; FAX. 202/237-6485; John Colbert, Esq., Executive Director

Association of Schools of Public Health, 1900 M Street, NW, Suite 710, Washington, DC 20036; tel. 202/296-1099; FAX. 202/296-1252; Harrison C. Spencer, MD, MPH, President and Chief Executive Officer

Association of Specialized and Cooperative Library Agencies, 50 East Huron Street, Chicago, IL 60611; tel. 312/280-4398; FAX. 312/280-5273; Susan Hornung, Executive Director

Association of State and Territorial Health Officials, 2231 Crystal Drive, Suite 450, Arlington, VA 22202; tel. 202/371-9090; FAX. 571/527-3189; Paul E. Jarris, MD, MBA, Executive Director

Association of Surgical Technologists, Inc., 6 West Dry Creek Circle, Suite 200, Littleton, CO 80120; tel. 303/694-9130; FAX. 303/694-9169; William J. Teutsch, CAE, Chief Executive Officer

Association of University Programs in Health Administration, 2000 14th Street, N., Suite 780, Arlington, VA 22201; tel. 703/894-0940; FAX. 703/894-0941; Jaime E. Stephens, CMD, Vice President

Asthma and Allergy Foundation of America, 8201 Corporate Drive, Suite 1000, Landover, MD 20785; tel. 800-7-ASTHMA; FAX. 202/466-8940; William McLin, M.Ed., President and Chief Executive Officer

At Large of the AHA, 155 N. Wacker Drive, Suite 400, Chicago, IL 60606; tel. 312/422-3700; FAX. 312/278-0882; Elizabeth Summy, Executive Director

B

Bereavement and Advance Care Planning Services, Gundersen Lutheran Medical Foundation, Inc., 1900 South Avenue-Alex, La Crosse, WI 54601; tel. 608/775-4747; FAX. 608/775-5137; Rana Limbo, Director

Bioethics Research Library, Georgetown University, 102 Healy Hall, 37th and O Streets, NW, Washington, DC 20057; tel. 202/687-3885; FAX. 202/687-6770; Janice Swiatek-Kelley, MLS,PhD, Director

Biological Stain Commission, University of Rochester Medical Center, Department Pathology and Lab Medicine, Rochester, NY 14642-0001; tel. 585/275-2751; FAX. 585/442-8993; Chad Ragan, Laboratory Operations

Birth Defect Research for Children, 976 Lake Baldwin Lane, Suite 104, Orlando, FL 32814; tel. 407/895-0802; Betty Mekdeci, Executive Director

Blinded Veterans Association, 477 H Street, NW, Washington, DC 20001; tel. 202/371-8880; FAX. 202/371-8258; Thomas H. Miller, Executive Director

Blue Cross and Blue Shield Association, 225 N. Michigan Avenue, Chicago, IL 60601-7680; tel. 312/297-6000; Scott P. Serota, President and Chief Executive Officer

Brady Center to Prevent Gun Violence, 840 First Street NE, Suite 400, Washington, DC 20002; tel. 202/370-8100; FAX. 202/370-8102; Dan Gross, President

C

California Distance Learning Health Network, 9245 Sky Park Court, Suite 100, San Diego, CA 92123; tel. 619/594-3364; Violet Macias-Reynolds, MS, M.Ed, Executive Director

CARE Program, EPA, Mail Code 8001A, 1200 Pennsylvania Ave. NW, Washington, DC 20460; tel. 877/227-3909; FAX. 202/343-2395; Dennis O'Connor, Senior Policy Advisor

CARF International, 6951 East Southpoint, Tucson, AZ 85756; tel. 888/281-6531; FAX. 520/318-1129; Dr. Brian J. Boon, President and Chief Executive Officer

Catholic Health Association of the United States, 1875 Eye Street, NW, Suite 1000, Washington, DC 20006; tel. 202/296-3993; FAX. 202/296-3997; Sr. Carol Keehan, DC, President and Chief Executive Officer

Catholic Medical Association, 29 Bala Avenue, Suite 205, Bala Cynwyd, PA 19004; tel. 484/270-8002; FAX. 866/666-2319; John Brehany, PhD, STL, Executive Director

Center for Health Administration Studies, University of Chicago, 969 East 60th Street, Chicago, IL 60637; tel. 773/702-7104; FAX. 773/702-7222; Jeanne Marsh, PhD., Director

Center for Healthcare Governance (CHG), 155 N. Wacker Drive, Suite 400, Chicago, IL 60606; tel. 888/540-6111; FAX. 312/278-0868; John R. Combes, MD, President and Chief Operating Officer

Center for Healthy Aging, c/o National Council on Aging, 1901 L Street, NW, 4th Floor, Washington, DC 20036; tel. 202/479-1200; FAX. 202/479-0735; Richard Birkel, PhD, Senior Vice President and Director

Center to Advance Palliative Care, 55 W. 125th St., Suite 1302, New York, NY 10027; tel. 212/201-2670; FAX. 212/426-1369; Diane E. Meier, MD, FACP, Director

Central Surgical Association, University of Chicago, 5841 S. Maryland m/c 5094, Chicago, IL 60637; tel. 913/402-7102; FAX. 913/273-1116; Nonie Lowry, Meeting Coordinator

Children's Eye Foundation, 1631 Lancaster Drive, #200, Grapevine, TX 76051; tel. 817/301-2641; FAX. 817/329-5532; Sarah Buckmeier, Program Manager

Children's Hospital Association, 401 Wythe Street, Alexandria, VA 22314; tel. 703/684-1355; FAX. 703/684-1589; Mark Wietecha, President and Chief Executive Officer

CHIME—College of Healthcare Information Management Executives, 3300 Washtenaw Avenue, Suite 225, Ann Arbor, MI 48104; tel. 734/665-0000; FAX. 734/665-4922; Russell P. Branzell, FCHIME, CHCIO, President and Chief Executive Officer

Christian Record Services, Inc., 4444 South 52nd Street, Lincoln, NE 68516; tel. 402/488-0981; FAX. 402/488-7582; Shelly Kittleson, Treasurer

College of American Pathologists, 325 Waukegan Road, Northfield, IL 60093-2750; tel. 847/832-7000; FAX. 847/832-8000; Charles Roussel, Chief Executive Officer

Community Anti-Drug Coalitions of America, 625 Slaters Lane, Suite 300, Alexandria, VA 22314; tel. 800/542-2322; FAX. 703/706-0565; Arthur T. Dean, Chairman and Chief Executive Officer

Community Health Accreditation Program, 1275 K Street, NW, Suite 800, Washington, DC 20005; tel. 202/862-3413; FAX. 202/862-3419; Karen Collishaw, President and Chief Executive Officer

Cooley's Anemia Foundation, Inc., 330 Seventh Avenue, Suite 200, New York, NY 10001; tel. 212/279-8090; FAX. 212/279-5999; Gina Cioffi, National Executive Director

Corporate Angel Network, Inc. (CAN), Westchester County Airport, One Loop Road, White Plains, NY 10604; tel. 914/328-1313; FAX. 914/328-3938; Amanda Askew, Office Manager

Council of Medical Specialty Societies, 35 E. Wacker Drive, Suite 850, Chicago, IL 60601; tel. 312/224-2535; FAX. 312/644-8557; Norman B. Kahn, Jr., MD, EVP, and Chief Executive Officer

Council on Education for Public Health, 800 Eye Street, NW, Suite 202, Washington, DC 20001-3710; tel. 202/789-1050; FAX. 202/789-1895; Laura Rasar King, Executive Director

Crohn's & Colitis Foundation of America, Inc., 733 Third Ave., Suite 510, New York, NY 10017; tel. 800/932-2423; FAX. 212/779-4098; Richard J. Geswell, President

Cystic Fibrosis Foundation, 6931 Arlington Road, Bethesda, MD 20814; tel. 301/951-4422; FAX. 301/951-6378; Robert J. Beall, PhD, President and Chief Executive Officer

D

Damien Dutton Society for Leprosy Aid, Inc., 616 Bedford Avenue, Bellmore, NY 11710; tel. 516/221-5829; FAX. 516/221-5909; Elizabeth Campbell, Vice President

Depression and Bipolar Support Alliance, 730 North Franklin Street, Suite 501, Chicago, IL 60654-7225; tel. 800/826-3632; FAX. 312/642-7243; Allen Doederlein, President

Dysautonomia Foundation, Inc., 315 W. 39th Street, Suite 701, New York, NY 10018; tel. 212/279-1066; FAX. 212/279-2066; David Brenner, Executive Director

E

Easter Seals, Inc., 233 South Wacker Drive, Suite 2400, Chicago, IL 60606; tel. 800/221-6827; FAX. 312/726-1494; Rosemary Garza, Information & Referral

ECRI Institute, 5200 Butler Pike, Plymouth Meeting, PA 19462; tel. 610/825-6000; FAX. 610/834-1275; Jeffrey C. Lerner, PhD, President and Chief Executive Officer

Educational Commission for Foreign Medical Graduates, 3624 Market Street, 4th Floor, Philadelphia, PA 19104-2685; tel. 215/823-2101; Emmanuel G. Cassimatis, MD, President and Chief Executive Officer

Ehlers-Danlos National Foundation, 1760 Old Meadow Rd., Suite 500, McLean, VA 22102; tel. 703/506-2892; FAX. 703/506-3266; Shane Robinson, Executive Director

Emergency Nurses Association, 915 Lee Street, Des Plaines, IL 60016; tel. 800/900-9659; FAX. 847/460-4006; Susan Hohenhaus, Executive Director

Epilepsy Foundation, 8301 Professional Place-East, Landover, MD 20785; tel. 301/459-3700; FAX. 301/577-2684; Philip M. Gattone, President and Chief Executive Officer

Epilepsy Foundation of Connecticut, 386 Main Street, Middletown, CT 06457; tel. 860/346–1924; FAX. 860/346–1928; Linda Wallace, Executive Director

F

Federated Ambulatory Surgery Association, 1012 Cameron Street, Alexandria, VA 22314; tel. 703/836–8808; FAX. 703/549–0976; Kathy Bryant, Executive Director

Federation of American Hospitals, 750 9th Street, NW, Suite 600, Washington, DC 20001; tel. 202/624–1500; FAX. 202/737–6462; Chip Kahn, President and Chief Executive Officer

Federation of State Medical Boards of the United States, Inc., 400 Fuller Wiser Rd, Suite 300, Euless, TX 76039; tel. 817/868–4000; FAX. 817/868–4097; Humayun J. Chaudhry, DO, MACP President and Chief Executive Officer

Financial Accounting Standards Board, 401 Merritt 7, P.O. Box 5116, Norwalk, CT 06856–5116; tel. 203/847–0700; FAX. 203/849–9714; Susan M. Cosper, Technical DirectorSusan M. Cosper, Technical Director

Frontline Healthcare Workers Safety Foundation, Ltd., Three Dunwoody Park, Suite 103, Atlanta, GA 30338; tel. 678/781–5241; FAX. 678/781–5242; Jennifer Elin Cole, MSW, Marketing Director

G

Great Plains Health Alliance, Inc., 625 Third Street, Box 366, Phillipsburg, KS 67661; tel. 785/543–2111; FAX. 785/543–5098; Dave Dellasega, President and Chief Executive Officer

Guide Dog Users, Inc., 14311 Astrodome Drive, Silver Spring, MD 20906–2245; tel. 866/799–8436; FAX. 301/871–7591; Jane Sheehan, Office Manager

H

Health Industry Distributors Association, 310 Montgomery Street, Alexandria, VA 22314–1516; tel. 703/549–4432; FAX. 703/549–6495; Matthew J. Rowan, President and Chief Executive Officer

Health Research and Educational Trust (HRET), 155 N. Wacker Drive, Suite 400, Chicago, IL 60606; tel. 312/422–2600; FAX. 312/422–4568; Maulik Joshi, President

Healthcare Financial Management Association, Two Westbrook Corporate Center, Suite 700, Westchester, IL 60154; tel. 708/531–9600; FAX. 708/531–0032; Richard L. Clarke, DHA, FHFMA, President and Chief Executive Officer

Healthcare Information and Management Systems Society (HIMSS), 33 West Monroe Street, Suite 1700, Chicago, IL 60603–5616; tel. 312/664–4467; FAX. 312/664–6143; H. Stephen Lieber, CAE President and Chief Executive Officer

HEAR Center, 301 East Del Mar Boulevard, Pasadena, CA 91101; tel. 626/796–2016; FAX. 626/796–2320; Ellen Simon, Executive Director

Huntington's Disease Society of America, Inc., 505 Eighth Avenue, Suite 902, New York, NY 10018; tel. 800/345–4372; FAX. 212/239–3430; Louise Vetter, National Executive Director and Chief Executive Officer

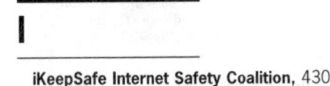

I

iKeepSafe Internet Safety Coalition, 4301 N. Fairfax Drive, Suite 190, Arlington, VA 22203; tel. 703/717–9066; FAX. 202/737–4097; Marsali S. Hancock, President

Infusion Nurses Society, 315 Norwood Park South, Norwood, MA 02062; tel. 781/440–9408; FAX. 781/440–9409; Mary Alexander, Chief Executive Officer

Institute for Diversity in Health Management (IFD), 155 N. Wacker Drive, Suite 400, Chicago, IL 60606; tel. 312/422–2630; FAX. 312/278–0893; Frederick D. Hobby, President and Chief Executive Officer

Institute of Medicine, 500 Fifth Street, NW, Washington, DC 20001; tel. 202/334–2352; FAX. 202/334–1412; Harvey V. Fineberg, MD, PhD, President

Institute of Medicine of The National Academies, 500 Fifth Street, NW, Washington, DC 20001–2721; tel. 202/334–3300; FAX. 202/334–3851; Harvey V. Fineberg, President, Institute of Medicine

Institutes for the Achievement of Human Potential, 8801 Stenton Avenue, Wyndmoor, PA 19038; tel. 215/233–2050; FAX. 215/233–3940; Leland Green, Medical Director

International Childbirth Education Association, Inc., 1500 Sunday Drive, Suite 102, Raleigh, NC 27607; tel. 919/863–9487; FAX. 919/787–4916; Ryan T. Couch, Executive Director

International College of Surgeons/United States Section, 1516 North Lake Shore Drive, Chicago, IL 60610–1694; tel. 312/787–6274; FAX. 312/787–9289; Maggie Kearney, Meeting and Publications Manager

International Council for Health, Physical Education, Recreation, Sport and Dance, 1900 Association Drive, Reston, VA 20191; tel. 703/476–3486; FAX. 703/476–9527; Dr. Dong Ja Yang, President

L

Leading Age, 2519 Connecticut Avenue, NW, Washington, DC 20008–1520; tel. 202/783–2242; FAX. 202/783–2255; William L. Minnix, Jr., D. Min., President and Chief Executive Officer

Learning Ally, 20 Roszel Road, Princeton, NJ 08540; tel. 800/221–4792; FAX. 609/987–8116; Jim Maloney, Vice President, Marketing

Lupus Foundation of America, Inc., 2000 L Street, NW, Suite 410, Washington, DC 20036; tel. 202/349–1155; FAX. 202/349–1156; Dawn Isherwood, Health Educator

M

March of Dimes Foundation, 1275 Mamaroneck Avenue, White Plains, NY 10605; tel. 914/428–7100; FAX. 914/428–8203; Jennifer L. Howse, PhD, President

Medical Fitness Association (MFA), 1905 Huguenot Road, Suite 203, Richmond, VA 23235; tel. 804/897–5701; FAX. 804/897–5704; Robert Boone, President and Chief Executive Officer

Medical Library Association, 65 East Wacker Place, Suite 1900, Chicago, IL 60601–7298; tel. 312/419–9094; FAX. 312/419–8950; Carla J. Funk, Executive Director

MedicAlert Foundation, 2323 Colorado Avenue, Turlock, CA 95382; tel. 800/432–5378; FAX. 209/669–2495; Melanie Ripley, Director of Member Engagement and Experience

Men's Health Network, PO Box 75972, Washington, DC 20013; tel. 202/543–6461; FAX. 202/543–2727; Ana Fadich, MPH, CHES, Vice President

Mental Health America, (formerly known as the National Mental Health Association), 2000 N. Beauregard Street, 6th Floor, Alexandria, VA 22311; tel. 703/684–7722; FAX. 703/684–5968; Wayne W Lindstrom, Ph.D., President and Chief Executive Officer

MGMA, 104 Inverness Terrace, E., Englewood, CO 80112–5306; tel. 877/275–6462; FAX. 303/784–6108; Susan L. Turney, MD, MS, FACP, FACMPE, President and Chief Executive Officer

Midwives Alliance of North America, P.O. Box 373, Montvale, NJ 07645; tel. 844/626–2674; Marinah Farrell, President

Muscular Dystrophy Association, 3300 East Sunrise Drive, Tucson, AZ 85718; tel. 520/529–2000; FAX. 520/529–5300; Steven M. Derks, MD, President and Chief Executive Officer

N

National Academy of Sciences, Division on Earth and Life Studies, 500 Fifth Street, NW, Keck 654, Washington, DC 20001; tel. 202/334–2500; FAX. 202/334–3362; Gregory H. Symmes, PhD, Executive Director

National Accreditation Council for Blind and Low Vision Services (NAC), P.O. Box 15368, Chattanooga, TN 37415; tel. 423/875–2033; FAX. 423/875–2220; William A. Robinson, III, CPA, Executive Director

National Accrediting Agency for Clinical Laboratory Sciences, 5600 N. River Road, Suite 720, Rosemont, IL 60018; tel. 773/714–8880; FAX. 773/714–8886; Dianne M. Cearlock, Chief Executive Officer

National Alliance for Hispanic Health, 1501 16th Street, NW, Washington, DC 20036; tel. 202/387–5000; FAX. 202/797–4353; Mr. Adolph Falcón, Senior Vice President

National Alliance on Mental Illness, 3803 N. Fairfax Drive, Ste 100, Arlington, VA 22203; tel. 703/524–7600; FAX. 703/524–9094; Michael J. Fitzpatrick, MSW, Executive Director

National Association for Home Care & Hospice, 228 Seventh Street, SE, Washington, DC 20003; tel. 202/547–7424; FAX. 202/547–3540; Val J. Halamandaris, President

National Association for Practical Nurse Education and Service, Mail Processing, 1940 Duke Street, Alexandria, VA 22314; tel. 703/933–1003; FAX. 703/940–4089; Helen Larsen, JD, Executive Director

National Association Medical Staff Services, 2025 M Street, NW, Suite 800, Washington, DC 20036; tel. 202/367–1196; FAX. 202/367–2196; Lynn Boyd, Executive Director

National Association of ACO's, 310 81st Street W, Ste 100, Bradenton, FL 34209; tel. 202/640–1985; Clif Gaus, President and CEO

National Association of Boards of Pharmacy, 1600 Feehanville Drive, Mt. Prospect, IL 60056; tel. 847/391–4406; FAX. 847/391–4502; Carmen A. Catizone, MS, R.Ph., D.Ph., Executive Director/ Secretary

National Association of County and City Health Officials, 1100 17th Street, NW, 7th Floor, Washington, DC 20036; tel. 202/783–5550; FAX. 202/783–1583; Robert M. Pestronk, Executive Director

National Association of Dental Assistants, 900 South Washington Street, Suite G13, Falls Church, VA 22046; tel. 703/237–8616; FAX. 703/533–1153; S. Young, Director

National Association of Dental Laboratories, (Includes National Board for Certification in Dental Laboratory Technology), 325 John Knox Rd, #L 103, Tallahassee, FL 32303; tel. 800/950–1150; FAX. 850/222–0053; Bennett Napier, CAE, Co-Executive Director

National Association of Health Services Executives, 1050 Connecticut Avenue, NW, 10th Floor, Washington, DC 20036; tel. 202/772–1030; FAX. 202/772–1072; Beverly Glover, Association Manager

National Association of Psychiatric Health Systems, 900 17th Street, NW, Suite 420, Washington, DC 20006–2507; tel. 202/393–6700; FAX. 202/783–6041; Mark J. Covall, President and Chief Executive Officer

National Association of Social Workers, 750 First Street, NE, Suite 700, Washington, DC 20002; tel. 202/336–8200; FAX. 202/336–8313; Elizabeth Clark, PhD, ACSW, MPH, Executive Director

National Association of State Mental Health Program Directors, 66 Canal Center Plaza, Suite 302, Alexandria, VA 22314; tel. 703/739–9333; FAX. 703/548–9517; Robert W. Glover, PhD, Executive Director

National Board for Respiratory Care, NBRC Executive Office, 18000 W 105th Street, Olathe, KS 66061–7543; tel. 913/895–4900; FAX. 913/895–4650; Gary A. Smith, Executive Director

National Board of Anesthesiology, Inc., 11817 Summit, Kansas, MO 64114; tel. 785/842–7067; FAX. 816/836–8953; R. Scott Richart, JD, Executive Director

National Board of Medical Examiners, 3750 Market Street, Philadelphia, PA 19104; tel. 215/590–9500; FAX. 215/590–9430; Donald E. Melnick, MD, President

National Board of Public Health Examiners, 1900 M Street, NW #710, Washington, DC 20036; tel. 866/514–7569; Molly M. Eggleston, Executive Director

National Council of State Boards of Nursing, 111 E. Wacker Drive, Suite 2900, Chicago, IL 60601; tel. 312/525–3600; FAX. 312/279–1032; Kathy Apple, Chief Executive Officer

National Council on Aging, Inc., NCOA Headquarters, 1901 L Street, NW, 4th Floor, Washington, DC 20024; tel. 202/479–1200; FAX. 202/479–0735; James P. Firman, Ed.D., President and Chief Executive Officer

National Council on Alcoholism and Drug Dependence, Inc., NCADD, 217 Broadway, Suite 712, New York, NY 10007; tel. 212/269–7797; FAX. 212/269–7510; William H. Foster, Ph.D., President and Chief Executive Officer

National Council on Radiation Protection and Measurements, 7910 Woodmont Avenue, Suite 400, Bethesda, MD 20814; tel. 301/657–2652; FAX. 301/907–8768; David A. Schauer, Executive Director Emeritus

National Dental Association, 3517 16th Street, NW, Washington, DC 20010; tel. 202/588–1697; FAX. 202/588–1244; Robert S. Johns, Executive Director

National Environmental Health Association, 720 South Colorado Boulevard, North Tower, Suite 1000-N, Denver, CO 80246–1926; tel. 303/756–9090; FAX. 303/691–9490; Nelson Fabian, Executive Director

National Federation of Licensed Practical Nurses, 111 West Main Street, #100, Garner, NC 27529; tel. 919/779–0046; FAX. 919/779–5642

National Fire Protection Association, PO Box 9101, One Batterymarck Park, Quincy, MA 02269–9101; tel. 617/770–3000; FAX. 617/770–7110; Jonathan R. Hart, Fire Protection Engineer

National Gaucher Foundation, Inc., 2227 Idlewood Road, Suite 6, Tucker, GA 30084; tel. 800/504–3189; FAX. 770/934–2911; Rhonda Buyers, Chief Executive Officer

National Headache Foundation, 820 N. Orleans, Suite 411, Chicago, IL 60610–3132; tel. 888/643–5552; FAX. 312/640–9049; Mary Franklin, Director of Operations

National Health Council, Inc., 1730 M Street, NW, Suite 500, Washington, DC 20036; tel. 202/785–3910; FAX. 202/785–5923; Myrl Weinberg, FASAE, CAE, Chief Executive Officer

National Hemophilia Foundation, 116 West 32nd Street, 11th Floor, New York, NY 10001; tel. 212/328–3700; FAX. 212/328–3799; Val Bias, Chief Executive Officer

National Institute for Jewish Hospice, Central Telephone Network, PO Box 48025, Los Angeles, CA 90048; tel. 800/446–4448; FAX. 516/791–6999; Shirley Lamm, Executive Director

National Institute for Occupational Safety and Health, 395 E Street, SW, Suite 9200, Washington, DC 20201; tel. 202/245–0625; John Howard, MD, Director

National Kidney Foundation, 30 East 33rd Street, New York, NY 10016; tel. 800/622–9010; FAX. 212/779–0068; Bruce Skyer, Chief Executive Officer

National League for Nursing, 2600 Virginia Ave. NW, 8th Floor, Washington, DC 20037; tel. 202/909–2500; FAX. 202/944–8523; Beverly Malone, PhD, RN, FAAN, Chief Executive Officer

National Multiple Sclerosis Society, 733 Third Avenue, New York, NY 10017; tel. 212/986–3240; FAX. 212/986–7981; Cynthia Zagieboylo, President and Chief Executive Officer

National Organization for Rare Disorders, 55 Kenosia Avenue, Danbury, CT 06813–1968; tel. 203/744–0100; FAX. 203/798–2291; Names Peter L. Saltonstall, President and Chief Executive Officer

National Parkinson Foundation, Inc., 200 SE 1st Street, Suite 800, Miami, FL 33131; tel. 800/473–4636; FAX. 305/537–9901; Jill Davidson, Vice President, Finance and Administration

National Perinatal Association, 457 State Street, Binghampton, NY 13901; tel. 888/971–3295; FAX. 607/772–0468; Bernadette Hoppe, MA, JD, MPH, President

National Registry of Emergency Medical Technicians, 6610 Busch Boulevard, PO Box 29233, Columbus, OH 43229; tel. 614/888–4484; FAX. 614/888–8920; Severo Rodriguez, Executive Director

National Rehabilitation Association, (Includes Nine National Divisions and 58 Affiliate Chapters), PO Box 150235, Alexandria, VA 22315; tel. 703/836–0850; FAX. 703/836–0848; Patricia Leahy, Interim Executive Director

National Resident Matching Program, 2121 K Street, NW, Washington, DC 20037–1127; tel. 202/828–0676; FAX. 202/828–4797; Mona M. Signer, Executive Director

National Rural Health Association, 1025 Vermont Ave NW, Suite 1100, Washington, DC 20005; tel. 202/639–0550; FAX. 202/639–0559; Alan Morgan, Chief Executive Officer

National Safety Council, 1121 Spring Lake Drive, Itasca, IL 60143–3201; tel. 800/621–7615; FAX. 630/285–1315; Janet Froetscher, President and Chief Executive Officer

National Stroke Association, 9707 E Easter Lane, Building B, Centennial, CO 80112; tel. 800/787–6537; FAX. 303/649–1328; Maria Rentzios, Customer Relations Coordinator

National Student Nurses' Association, Inc., 45 Main Street, Suite 606, Brooklyn, NY 11201; tel. 718/210–0705; FAX. 718/797–1186; Diane J. Mancino, Ed.D., RN, CAE, FAAN, Executive Director

National Tay-Sachs and Allied Diseases Association, 2001 Beacon Street, Suite 204, Brighton, MA 02135; tel. 800/906–8723; FAX. 617/277–0134; Susan R. Kahn, Executive Director

National Women's Health Network, 1413 K Street, NW, Fourth Floor, Washington, DC 20005; tel. 202/682–2640; FAX. 202/682–2648; Cynthia Pearson, Executive Director

New England Gerontological Association, One Cutts Road, Durham, NH 03824–3102; tel. 603/868–5757; Eugene E. Tillock, Ed.D., Executive Director

New York State Nurses Association, NYSNA, 11 Cornell Road, Latham, NY 12110; tel. 518/782–9400; FAX. 518/782–9530; Jill Furillo, Executive Director

NSF International, 789 N.Dixboro Road, Ann Arbor, MI 48105; tel. 734/769–8010; FAX. 313/769–0109; Kevan Lawlor, President and Chief Executive Officer

O

Office of Radiation and Indoor Air, Environmental Protection Agency, 1200 Pennsylvania Avenue, NW, Mail Code 6601J, Washington, DC 20460; tel. 202/343–9213; Dennis O'Connor, Senior Policy Advisor

Osteogenesis Imperfecta Foundation, Inc., 804 West Diamond Avenue, Suite 210, Gaithersburg, MD 20878; tel. 301/947–0083; FAX. 301/947–0456; Tracy Smith Hart, Chief Executive Officer

P

Pan American Health Organization, Pan American Sanitary Bureau, Regional Office of the World Health Organization, 525 23rd Street, NW, Washington, DC 20037; tel. 202/974–3000; FAX. 202/974–3663; Dr. Carissa F. Etienne, Director

Parkinson's Disease Foundation, Inc., (Formerly United Parkinson Foundation), 1359 Broadway, Suite 1509, New York, NY 10018; tel. 800/457–6676; FAX. 212/923–4778; Yasnahia Cortorreal, Vice President of Administration

Partnership for Food Safety Education, 2345 Crystal Drive, Suite 800, Arlington, VA 22202; tel. 202/220–0651; FAX. 202/220–0873; Shelley Feist, Executive Director

Partnership for Prevention, 1015 18th Street, NW, Suite 300, Washington, DC 20036; tel. 202/833–0009; FAX. 202/833–0113; Elissa Matulis Myers, President and Chief Executive Officer

Physician Executive Leadership Center, 3403 West Fletcher Avenue, Tampa, FL 33618–2813; tel. 813/963–1800; Jennifer R. Grebenschikoff, Executive Vice President

Pilot Dogs, Inc., 625 West Town Street, Columbus, OH 43215; tel. 614/221–6367; FAX. 614/221–1577; J. Jay Gray, Executive Director

Practice Greenhealth, 12355 Sunrise Valley Drive, Suite 680, Reston, VA 20191; tel. 888/688–3332; FAX. 866/379–8705; Sherry MacDonald, Director of Marketing and Communications

Prevent Blindness, 211 W. Wacker Drive, Suite 1700, Chicago, IL 60606; tel. 800/331–2020; FAX. 312/363–6052; Hugh Parry, President and Chief Executive Officer

Public Health Foundation, 1300 L Street NW, Suite 800, Washington, DC 20005–4208; tel. 202/218–4400; FAX. 202/218–4409; Sue Madden, Deputy Executive Director

Public Relations Society of America, 33 Maiden Lane 11th Floor, New York, NY 10038–5150; tel. 212/460–1400; FAX. 212/995–0757; Catherine A. Bolton, Executive Director and Chief Operating Officer

R

Radiological Society of North America, Inc., 820 Jorie Boulevard, Oak Brook, IL 60523–2251; tel. 630/571–2670; FAX. 630/571–7837; Jennifer Divelbiss, Director of Marketing

Renal Physicians Association, 1700 Rockville Pike, Suite 220, Rockville, MD 20852; tel. 301/468–3515; FAX. 301/468–3511; Dale Singer, MHA, Executive Director

Robert Wood Johnson Foundation, PO Box 2316, Route One and College Road East, Princeton, NJ 08543–2316; tel. 877/843–7953; FAX. 609/927–7582; Lydia Ryba, Manager, Office of Proposal Management

Section C

S

Safe Kids Worldwide, 1301 Pennsylvania Avenue, NW, Suite 1000, Washington, DC 20004; tel. 202/662–0600; FAX. 202/393–2072; Kate Carr, President and Chief Executive Officer

School-Based Health Alliance, 1010 Vermont Avenue, NW, Suite 600, Washington, DC 20005; tel. 202/638–5872; FAX. 202/638–5879; Linda Juszczak, President

Shriners Hospitals for Children, PO Box 31356, Tampa, FL 33631–3356; tel. 813/281–8111; FAX. 813/281–8174; John P. McCabe, Executive Vice President

SNMTS, Society of Nuclear Medicine Technologist Section, 1850 Samuel Morse Drive, Reston, VA 20190; tel. 703/708–9000; FAX. 703/708–9015; Nikki Wenzel-Lamb, MBA, Administrator and Director of Leadership Services

Society for Academic Emergency Medicine, 2340 S. River Road, Suite 208, Des Plaines, IL 60018; tel. 847/813–9823; FAX. 847/813–5450; Ronald S. Moen, Chief Executive Officer

Society for Adolescent Health and Medicine (SAHM), 111 Deer Lake Road, Suite 100, Deerfield, IL 60015; tel. 847/753–5226; FAX. 847/480–9282; Debbie Trueblood, Executive Director

Society for Healthcare Consumer Advocacy (SHCA), 155 N. Wacker Drive, Suite 400, Chicago, IL 60606; tel. 312/422–3700; FAX. 312/278–0881; Carol Santalucia, MBA, President, Vice President

Society for Healthcare Strategy and Market Development (SHSMD), 155 N. Wacker Drive, Suite 400, Chicago, IL 60606; tel. 312/422–3888; FAX. 312/278–0883; Diane Webber, Executive Director

Society for Occupational and Environmental Health, 6728 Old McLean Village Drive, McLean, VA 22101; tel. 703/556–9222; FAX. 703/556–8729; Connie MacKay, Account Manager

Society for Pediatric Pathology, 3643 Walton Way Extension, Augusta, GA 30909; tel. 706/364–3375; FAX. 706/733–8033; Kerry Crockett, Director of Operations and Meetings

Society for Social Work Leadership in Health Care (SSWLHC), 100 North 20th Street, Suite 400, Philadelphia, PA 19103; tel. 866/237–9542; FAX. 215/564–2175; Kyle Fernley, Account Manager

Society of Cardiac Monitoring, Inc., PO Box 3219, Spring Hill, FL 34611; tel. 813/394–4968; Jonni Cooper, Chief Executive Officer

Society of Cardiovascular Patient Care, 6161 Riverside Drive, Dublin, OH 43017; tel. 614/442–5950; FAX. 614/442–5953; Wilbert D. Mick, Chief Executive Officer

Society of Critical Care Medicine, 500 Midway Drive, Mount Prospect, IL 60056; tel. 847/827–6869; FAX. 847/827–6886; David J. Martin, CAE, Chief Executive Officer and EVP

Society of Neurological Surgeons, 355 W. 16th St., Suite 5100, Indianapolis, IN 46202; tel. 317/396–1234; FAX. 317/396–1268; Nicholas M. Barbaro, MD, Secretary

Society of University Otolaryngologists-Head and Neck Surgeons, USC School of Medicine, Department of Otolaryngology, Los Angeles, CA 90033; tel. 323/226–7315; FAX. 323/226–2780; Donna Hoffman, M.A., Executive Director

Special Care Dentistry Association, 401 N. Michigan Avenue, 22nd Floor, Chicago, IL 60611; tel. 312/527–6764; FAX. 312/673–6663; Kaye Englebrecht

Spina Bifida Association, 4590 MacArthur Boulevard, NW, Suite 250, Washington, DC 20007; tel. 800/621–3141; FAX. 202/944–3295; Sara Struwe, Interim President and Chief Executive Officer

Susan G. Komen Breast Cancer Foundation, 5005 LBJ Freeway, Suite 250, Dallas, TX 75244; tel. 800/465–6636; Kimberly Simpson, Chief Operating Officer

T

The Academy of Nutrition and Dietetics, 120 South Riverside Plaza, Suite 2000, Chicago, IL 60606–6995; tel. 312/899–0040; FAX. 312/899–4765; Patricia M. Babjak, Chief Executive Officer

The American Association of Immunologists, Inc., 9650 Rockville Pike, Bethesda, MD 20814; tel. 301/634–7178; FAX. 301/634–7887; M. Michele Hogan, PhD, Executive Director

The American Board of Anesthesiology, Inc., 4208 Six Forks Road, Suite 1500, Raleigh, NC 27609–5765; tel. 919/745–2200; FAX. 919/745–2201; Mary E. Post, MBA, CAE, Executive Director, Administrative Affairs

The American Board of Disability Analysts (ABDA), Belle Meade Office Park, 4525 Harding Road, Nashville, TN 37205; tel. 615/327–2984; FAX. 615/327–9235; Alexander Horowitz, MD, Executive Officer Emeritus

The American Board of Obstetrics and Gynecology, Inc., 2915 Vine Street, Dallas, TX 75204; tel. 214/871–1619; FAX. 214/871–1943; Larry Gilstrap, MD, Executive Director

The American Board of Pediatric Dentistry, 325 E. Washington Street, Suite 208, Iowa City, IA 52240–3960; tel. 319/341–8488; FAX. 319/341–9499; Jeffrey A. Dean, Executive Director

The American Board of Plastic Surgery, Inc., Seven Penn Center, Suite 400, 1635 Market Street, Philadelphia, PA 19103–2204; tel. 215/587–9322; FAX. 215/587–9622; Terry M. Cullison, RN, MSN, Administrator

The American Board of Urology, Inc., 600 Peter Jefferson Pkwy, Suite 150, Charlottesville, VA 22911; tel. 434/979–0059; FAX. 434/979–0266; Gerald H. Jordan, MD, Executive Secretary

The American Orthopaedic Association, 6300 North River Road, Suite 505, Rosemont, IL 60018–4263; tel. 847/318–7330; FAX. 847/318–7339; Kristin Olds Glavin, Executive Director

The Arc of the United States, 1825 K Street, NW, Suite 1200, Washington, DC 20006; tel. 202/534–3700; FAX. 202/534–3731; Peter V. Berns, Chief Executive Officer

The Association for Research in Vision and Ophthalmology, 1801 Rockville Pike, Ste 400, Rockville, MD 20852–5622; tel. 240/221–2900; FAX. 240/221–0370; Iris M. Rush, CAE, Interim Executive Director

The Association of Medical Illustrators, 201 E Main Street, Suite 1405, Lexington, KY 40507; tel. 866/393–4264; FAX. 859/514–9166; Melanie Bowzer, Executive Director

The Association of Women's Health, Obstetric and Neonatal Nurses, 2000 L. Street, NW, Suite 740, Washington, DC 20036; tel. 202/261–2400; FAX. 202/728–0575; Lynn Erdman, MN, RN, FAAN, Chief Executive Officer

The Christopher and Dana Reeve Foundation, Paralysis Resource Center, Short Hills Plaza, 636 Morris Turnpike, Suite #3A, Short Hills, NJ 07078–7503; tel. 800/539–7309; Angela Cantillon, Director-Operations

The Duke Endowment, 100 North Tryon Street, Suite 3500, Charlotte, NC 28202; tel. 704/376–0291; FAX. 704/376–9336; Mary L. Piepenbring, Vice President

The Endocrine Society, 8401 Connecticut Avenue, Suite 900, Chevy Chase, MD 20815; tel. 301/941–0200; FAX. 301/941–0259; Janet Kreizman, Deputy Executive Director & Chief Policy Officer

The Foundation Fighting Blindness, Inc., 7168 Columbia Gateway Drive, Suite 100, Columbia, MD 21046; tel. 410/423–0600; FAX. 410/872–0438; William T. Schmidt, Chief Executive Officer

The Foundation for Ichthyosis and Related Skin Types, Inc. (FIRST), 2616 N. Broad Street, Colmar, PA 18915; tel. 215/997–9400; FAX. 215/997–9403; Jean Pickford, Executive Director

The Gerontological Society of America, 1220 L Street, NW, Suite 901, Washington, DC 20005–4018; tel. 202/842–1275; FAX. 202/842–1150; James Appleby, Executive Director and Chief Executive Officer

The Histochemical Society, 9650 Rockville Pike, Bethesda, MD 20814; tel. 301/634–7026; FAX. 301/634–7099; W.L. Stahl, PhD, Executive Director

The International Dyslexia Association, 40 York Road, 4th Floor, Baltimore, MD 21204; tel. 410/296–0232; FAX. 410/321–5069; Elisabeth Liptak, Director of Professional Development

The Joint Commission, One Renaissance Boulevard, Oakbrook Terrace, IL 60181; tel. 630/792–5650; FAX. 630/792–4650; Mark R. Chassin, MD, MPP, MPH, President

The Leukemia & Lymphoma Society, 1311 Mamaroneck Avenue, White Plains, NY 10650; tel. 914/949–5213; FAX. 914/949–6691; John E. Walter, President and Chief Executive Officer

The Mended Hearts, Inc., 8150 N. Central Expy., M2075, Dallas, TX 75206; tel. 888/432–7899; FAX. 214/295–9552; Karen Caruth, Executive Director

The National Commission for Health Education Credentialing, Inc., 1541 Alta Drive, Suite 303, Whitehall, PA 18052–5642; tel. 484/223–0770; FAX. 800/813–0727; Linda Lysoby, MS, MCHES, CAE, Executive Director

The Seeing Eye, Inc., PO Box 375, Morristown, NJ 07963–0375; tel. 973/539–4425; FAX. 973/539–0922; Jim Kutsch, President and Chief Executive Officer

The Southwestern Surgical Congress, 5019 W 147th St, Leawood, KS 66224; tel. 913/402–7102; FAX. 913/273–9940; James A. Edney, MD, Executive Director

The Vision Council, 225 Reinekers Lane, Suite 700, Alexandria, VA 22314; tel. 703/548–4560; FAX. 703/548–4580; Ed Greene, Chief Executive Officer

U

UCLA Medical Center, Neurosurgery, Box 956901, Los Angeles, CA 90095–6901; tel. 301/267–9449; FAX. 310/825–7245; Neil A. Martin, MD

United Cerebral Palsy Association, 1825 K Street NW, Suite 600, Washington, DC 20006; tel. 800/872–5827; FAX. 202/776–0414; Stephen Bennett, President and Chief Executive Officer

United Methodist Association of Health and Welfare Ministries, 2800 W Main Street, Tupelo, MS 38801–3027; tel. 662/269–2955; FAX. 662/269–2956; Stephen L. Vinson, President and Chief Executive Officer

United Way Worldwide, 701 North Fairfax Street, Alexandria, VA 22314–2045; tel. 703/836–7100; FAX. 703/683–7846; Brian A. Gallagher, President and Chief Executive Officer

USP, United States Pharmacopeia Convention, 12601 Twinbrook Parkway, Rockville, MD 20852; tel. 301/816–8368; FAX. 301/816–8511; Arline M. Bilbo, Senior Director, Member and Professional Relations

W

Western Orthopedic Association, 154-A W. Foothill Boulevard, # 107, Upland, CA 91786; tel. 866/962–1388; FAX. 410/494–0515; Chuck Freitag, Executive Director

Wound, Ostomy and Continence Nursing Certification Board (WOCNCB), 555 E. Wells Street, Suite 1100, Milwaukee, WI 53202; tel. 888/496–2622; FAX. 414/276–2146; Anniekay Erby, Executive Director

International Organizations

ARGENTINA

Cámara Argentina De Empresas De Salud, (Argentina Hospital Association), Tucuman 1668, 2 Piso, C.P. 1050, Buenos Aires; tel. 541143725915; FAX. 541143723229; Norberto Larroca-President

AUSTRALIA

Australian Healthcare and Hospitals Association, Unit 8, 2 Phipps Close, Deakin ACT, 2600; tel. +61 2 6162 0780; FAX. +61 2 6162 0779; Prue Power, Executive Director

CANADA

Canadian Blood Services, Head Office, 1800 Alta Vista Drive, Ottawa, ON K1G 4J5; tel. 613/739–2300; FAX. 613/731–1411; Dr. Graham D. Sher, CEO

Canadian Healthcare Association, 17 York Street, Suite 100, 3rd Floor, Ottawa, ON K1N 9J6; tel. 613/241–8005; FAX. 613/241–5055; Phil Dresch, Interim President and Chief Executive Officer

Canadian Medical Association, 1867 Alta Vista Drive, Ottawa, ON K1G 5W8; tel. 613/236–8864; FAX. 613/731–7314; Paul-Emile Cloutier, Secretary General and Chief Executive Officer

Canadian Medical Engineering Consultants, 594 Bush Street, Belfountain, ON L7K 0E8; tel. 519/927–3286; FAX. 519/927–9440; A. M. Dolan, President

Canadian Orthopaedic Association, 4150 Street Catherine Street West, Suite 450, Westmount, PQ H3Z 2Y5; tel. 514/874–9003; FAX. 514/874–0464; Douglas C. Thomson, Chief Executive Officer

Canadian Public Health Association, 1525 Carling Avenue, Suite 404, Ottawa, ON K1Z 8R9; tel. 613/725–3769; FAX. 613/725–9826; Ian Culbert, Executive Director

Catholic Health Alliance of Canada, Annex C, Saint-Vincent Hospital, 60 Cambridge Street North, Ottawa, ON K1R 7A5; tel. 613/562–6262; FAX. 613/782–2857; Michael Shea, President

COSTA RICA

Asociacion Costarricense de Hospitales, (Costa Rica Hospital Association), Avenida 8, Calle 16, San Jose 267-1005, San Jose; tel. 5062214919; FAX. 5062550363; Dr. Fernando Quiros Madrigal, Presidente

ENGLAND

British Medical Association (BMA), BMA House, Tavistock Square, London, WCIH 9JP; tel. 02073874499; FAX. 02073836400; Mr. Tony Bourne, Chief Executive and Secretary

FRANCE

Fédération Hospitalière De France, (France Hospital Association), 1 bis, Rue Cabanis, Paris, 75014; Gerard Vincent, Delegue General

World Medical Association, CS 5001, 13-A Chemin Du Levant, Ferney-Voltaire, 01210; tel. 33450407575; FAX. 33450405937; Dr. Otmar Kloiber, Secretary General

GERMANY

Deutsche Krankenhausgesellschaft, (German Hospital Federation), Wegelystrae 3, 10623, Berlin; tel. +49 (0)30 39801–1030; FAX. +49 (0)30 39801–3310; Advocate Marc Schreiner, LL.M., Director, EU-Policies/International Affairs

HUNGARY

Magyar Korhazszovetseg, (Hungarian Hospital Association), 1113 Budapest, Ibrahim u. 19., Hungary; tel. (1) 2145159; Dr. Zoltan Ajkay, President

INDIA

Indian Hospital Association, B-401 Sarita Vihar, New Delhi, 110 044; FAX. 91–11–694126; P.Ghez, MD, Secretary General

INDONESIA

Indonesian Hospital Association, Jl. Boulevard Artha Gading Blok, A-7A No. 28, Jakarta, Utara, 14240; tel. 2145845303; FAX. 2144587832; Muki Reksoprodjo

ITALY

Federazione Italiana delle Aziende Sanitarie e Ospedaliere (FIASO), (Italy Hospital Association), Corso Vi Horis Emmanuele II n. 24, Roma, 00186; tel. 06 69924145; FAX. 06 6780907; Dott. Francesco Ripa di Meana, Presidente

KOREA

Korean Hospital Association, 13-15F Hyundai Building, 15 Mapodaero, Seoul, 121-737; tel. 8227059200; FAX. 8227059209; International Affairs Officer

MEXICO

Asociación Mexicana De Hospitales AC. (Mexico Hospital Association), Queretaro 210, Mexico City, 06700; tel. 55740135; FAX. 55841882; LIC. Francisco Spindola Salazar, Manager

MONGOLIA

Mongolian Hospital Association, PO Box 48/54, Enkhtaivan Street 13b, Ulaanbaatar, 210648; tel. 9769999020; FAX. 9769996070; Jambaljav Lkhamsuren, MD, President

PANAMA

Asociación Panamena de Hospitales Privados, (Panama Hospital Association), Apartado 07503, Panama, Panama; tel. 5072690615; FAX. 5079664223; Rodrigo A. Moreno, President

PERÚ

Asociación de Clinicas Particulares del Perú, Av. Dos De Mayo 1502, Oficina 202, San Isidro, Lima, 27; tel. 5114224024; FAX. 5114419546; Dr. Clodoaldo Barreda Dominguez, Administrator

PHILIPPINES

Philippine Hospital Association, 14 Kamias Road, Quezon City-1, Metro Manila, 1102; tel. 6329227674; FAX. 6329212219

SOUTH AFRICA

Provincial Administration, Health Services Branch, P.O. Box 227, South Africa, 9300; tel. 0514081107; FAX. 0514081058; Dr. S. Kabane

South Africa Department of Health, Private Bag X828, Pretoria, 0001; tel. 012 395 8086; FAX. 012 395 9165; Dr Pakishe Aaron Motsoaledi, Minister of Health

SWITZERLAND

H+ Die Spitaeler der Schweiz, (Swiss Hospital Association), Lorrainestrasse 4 A, Bern; M. Bernhard Wegmueller, Director

International Hospital Federation, P.A. Hôpital de Loëx, Route de Loëx 151, 1233 BERNEX; tel. 41228509420; FAX. 41227571016; Kwang Tae Kim, M.D., Ph.D, President

World Federation of Public Health Associations, c/o Institute for Social and Preventative Medicine, University of Geneva, CMU, Genve, CH-1211; Bettina Borisch, MD, PBH, FRCPath, Director of the Office of the Secretariat

UGANDA

International Council on Social Welfare, P.O. Box 28957, Kampala; tel. +256 (0) 414–32 11 50; Sergei Zelenev, Executive Director

UNITED STATES

International Association of Healthcare Central Service Materiel Management, 55 W. Wacker Dr., Suite 501, Chicago, IL 60601; tel. 312/440–0078; FAX. 312/440–9474; Susan Adams, Executive Director, Executive Director

Rehabilitation International, 41 Madison Ave., Office 3141, New York, NY 10010; tel. 212/420–1500; FAX. 855/600–6054; Jan A. Monsbakken, President

The following information is based on data available as of May, 2014.
For more information about U.S. government agencies, consult the U.S. Government Manual. *Additional assistance may be obtained by contacting the American Hospital Association's Washington office, 800 10th Street, N.W., TwoCity Center, Suite 400, Washington, DC 20001.*

Executive Office of the President, The White House
1600 Pennsylvania Avenue NW
Washington, DC 20500
202/456-1414
Barack H. Obama, President of the United States
www.whitehouse.gov

Office of the Vice President of the United States
The White House
1600 Pennsylvania Avenue NW
Washington, DC 20501
202/456-1414
Joseph R. Biden, Vice President of the United States
www.whitehouse.gov/administration/vice-president-biden

Centers for Disease Control and Prevention
1600 Clifton Road
Atlanta, GA 30333
404/639-3311
Dr. Thomas Frieden, MD, MPH, Director
www.cdc.gov

Centers for Medicare & Medicaid Services
7500 Security Blvd
Baltimore, MD 21244
877/267-2323
Marilyn Tavenner, Acting Administrator and Chief Operating Officer
www.cms.gov

Council of Economic Advisors
Eisenhower Executive Office Building
Washington, DC 20502
202/395-5109
Alan Krueger, Chairman
www.whitehouse.gov/administration/eop/cea/

Council on Environmental Quality
722 Jackson Place NW
Washington, DC 20503
202/395-5750
Nancy Sutley, Chair
www.whitehouse.gov/administration/eop/ceq

Department of Agriculture
1400 Independence Avenue SW
Washington, DC 20250
202/720-3631
Thomas J. Vilsack, Secretary of Agriculture
www.usda.gov

Department of Commerce
1401 Constitution Avenue NW
Washington, DC 20230
202/482-2000
Rebecca M. Blank, Deputy Secretary of Commerce.
www.commerce.gov

Department of Defense
Office of the Secretary
The Pentagon
Washington, DC 20301-1400
703/545-6700
Chuck Hagel, Secretary of Defense
www.defenselink.mil

Department of Education
400 Maryland Avenue SW
Washington, DC 20202
800/872-5327
Arne Duncan, Secretary of Education
www.ed.gov

Department of Energy
1000 Independence Avenue SW
Washington, DC 20585
202/586-5000
Ernest Moniz, Secretary of Energy
www.energy.gov

Department of Health and Human Services
200 Independence Avenue SW
Washington, DC 20201
877/696-6775
Sylvia Matthews Burwell, Secretary of Health and Human Services
www.hhs.gov

Department of Justice
950 Pennsylvania Ave NW
Washington, DC 20530-0001
202/514-2000
Eric H. Holder, Jr., The Attorney General
www.usdoj.gov

Department of Labor
Frances Perkins Building
200 Constitution Avenue NW
Washington, DC 20210
202/693-6000
Seth Harris, Acting Secretary of Labor
www.dol.gov

Department of State
2201 C Street NW
Washington, DC 20520
202/647-4000
John Kerry, Secretary of State
www.state.gov

Department of the Air Force
1670 Air Force Pentagon
Washington, DC 20330-1670
703/695-9664
Michael B. Donley, Secretary of the Air Force
www.af.mil/main/welcome.asp

Department of the ARMY
1400 Defense Pentagon
Washington, DC 20301-1400
703/695-4311
John McHugh, Secretary of the ARMY
www.army.mil

Department of the NAVY
2000 Navy Pentagon
Washington, DC 20350-2000
703/545-6700
Ray Mabus, Secretary of the NAVY
www.navy.mil

Department of the Treasury
1500 Pennsylvania NW
Washington, DC 20220
202/622-2000
Jacob Lew, Secretary of the Treasury
www.treasury.gov

Department of Veterans Affairs
810 Vermont Avenue NW
Washington, DC 20420
202/273-5400
Eric K. Shineski, Secretary of Veterans Affairs
www.va.gov

Drug Enforcement Administration
8701 Morrissette Drive
Springfield, VA 22102
202/307-1000
Michele Leonhart, Administrator
www.justice.gov/dea/index.htm

Environmental Protection Agency
Ariel Rios Building
1200 Pennsylvania Avenue NW
Washington, DC 20460
202/564-4700
Bob Perciasepe, Acting Administrator and Deputy Administrator
www.epa.gov

Equal Employment Opportunity Commission
131 M Street NE
Washington, DC 20507
202/663-4191
Jacqueline Berrien, Chair
www.eeoc.gov

Food and Drug Administration
10903 New Hampshire Ave
Silver Spring, MD 20903
888/463-6332
Margaret Hamburg, Commissioner
www.fda.gov

Health Resources and Services Administration
5600 Fishers Lane
Room 14-71
Rockville, MD 20857
301/443-2216
Mary K. Wakefield, PhD, RN, Administrator
www.hrsa.gov

Office of Management and Budget
725 17th Street NW
Washington, DC 20503
202/395-3080
Jeffrey Zients, Acting Director
www.whitehouse.gov/omb/

Office of National Drug Control Policy
750 17th Street NW
Washington, DC 20503
202/395-6700
R. Gil Kerlikowske, Director
www.whitehousedrugpolicy.gov

Social Security Administration, Office of Public Inquiries
Windsor Park Building
6401 Security Blvd.
Baltimore, MD 21235
800/772-1213
Carolyn W. Colvin, Acting Commissioner of Social Security
www.ssa.gov

Substance Abuse and Mental Health Services Administration
One Choke Cherry Road
Rockville, MD 20857
240/276-2000
Pamela Hyde, Administrator
www.samhsa.gov

State and Provincial Government Agencies

The following list includes state departments of health and welfare, and their subagencies. The information was obtained directly from the agencies.

United States

ALABAMA
The Honorable Robert Bentley, Governor, 334/242-7100

Facility Licensure Agencies

Alabama Department of Public Health, Health Provider Standards, 201 Monroe Street, Suite 710, Montgomery, AL 36130-3017; tel. 334/206-5175; FAX. 334/206-5219; Walter T. Geary, MD, Bureau Director and Medical Director

Health Agencies

Department of Public Health, The RSA Tower, Suite 1552, PO Box 303017, Montgomery, AL 36130-3017; tel. 334/206-5200; FAX. 334/206-2008; Donald E. Williamson, MD, State Health Officer

State Health Planning and Development Agency, 100 North Union Street, Suite 870, Montgomery, AL 36103-3025; tel. 334/242-4103; FAX. 334/242-4113; Alva Lambert, Executive Director

Managed Care Agencies

Department of Insurance, 201 Monroe Street, Suite 502, Montgomery, AL 36130-3351; tel. 334/269-3550; FAX. 334/241-4192; Jim Ridling, Commissioner

Medical & Nursing Licensure Agencies

Alabama Board of Nursing, 770 Washington Avenue, Suite 250, RSA Plaza, Montgomery, AL 36130-3900; tel. 800/656-5318; FAX. 334/293-5201; N. Genell Lee, RN, MSN, JD, Executive Officer

Alabama State Board of Medical Examiners, 848 Washington Avenue, PO Box 946, Montgomery, AL 36101-0946; tel. 334/242-4116; FAX. 334/242-4155; Larry D. Dixon, Executive Director

ALASKA
The Honorable Sean Parnell, Governor, 907/465-3500

Facility Licensure Agencies

Facilities Section, Department of Health and Social Services, PO Box 110650, Juneau, AK 99811-0650; tel. 907/465-3037; FAX. 907/465-2607; Jennifer Klein, Section Chief

Health Agencies

Department of Health and Social Services, 350 Main Street, Room 404, PO Box 110601, Juneau, AK 99811-0601; tel. 907/465-3030; FAX. 907/465-3068; William J. Streur, Commissioner

Managed Care Agencies

Alaska Division of Insurance, 333 Willoughby Avenue, Ninth Floor, State Office Building, Juneau, AK 99811-0805; tel. 907/465-2515; FAX. 907/465-3422; Lori Wing-Heier, Director

Medical & Nursing Licensure Agencies

Alaska Board of Nursing, Division of Corporations, Business, and Professional Licensing, 550 W. Seventh Avenue, Suite 1500, Anchorage, AK 99501; tel. 907/269-8161; FAX. 907/269-8196; Nancy Sanders, Executive Administrator

Alaska State Medical Board, 550 W. Seventh Avenue, Suite 1500, Anchorage, AK 99501; tel. 907/269-8163; FAX. 907/269-8196; Debora J. Stovern, Executive Administrator

ARIZONA
The Honorable Janice K. Brewer, Governor, 602/542-4331

Facility Licensure Agencies

Arizona Department of Health Services, Medical Facilities Licensing Bureau, 150 N. 18th Avenue, Suite 450, Phoenix, AZ 85007; tel. 602/364-3030; FAX. 602/792-0466; Connie Belden, Bureau Chief

Health Agencies

Arizona Department of Health Services, 150 N. 18th Avenue, Suite 500, Phoenix, AZ 85007; tel. 602/542-1027; FAX. 602/542-1062; Will Humble, Director

Managed Care Agencies

Arizona Department of Insurance, 2910 N. 44th Street, Suite 210 (2nd Floor), Phoenix, AZ 85018-7269; tel. 602/364-2499; FAX. 602/364-2175; Germaine L. Marks, Director of Insurance

Medical & Nursing Licensure Agencies

Arizona Board of Osteopathic Examiners in Medicine and Surgery, 9535 E. Doubletree Ranch Road, Scottsdale, AZ 85258; tel. 480/657-7703; FAX. 480/657-7715; Jenna Jones, Executive Director

Arizona Department of Health Services, Division of Licensing Services, 150 N 18th Avenue, Suite 400, Phoenix, AZ 85007; tel. 602/364-3031; FAX. 602/364-4764; Colby Dower, Assistant Director

Arizona Medical Board, 9545 E. Doubletree Ranch Road, Scottsdale, AZ 85258; tel. 480/551-2791; FAX. 480/551-2828; C. Lloyd Vest, II, Executive Director

Arizona State Board of Nursing, 4747 N. Seventh Street, Suite 200, Phoenix, AZ 85014-3653; tel. 602/771-7800; FAX. 602/771-7888; Joey Ridenour, RN, MN, FAAN, Executive Director

ARKANSAS
The Honorable Michael Beebe, Governor, 501/682-2345

Facility Licensure Agencies

Health Facility Services, Arkansas Department of Health, 5800 West 10th Street, Suite 400, Little Rock, AR 72204-1704; tel. 501/661-2201; FAX. 501/661-2165; Connie Melton, Section Chief

Health Agencies

Arkansas Department of Health, 4815 West Markham, Little Rock, AR 72205; tel. 501/661-2000; FAX. 501/661-2388; Nathaniel Smith, MD, Director and State Health Officer

Managed Care Agencies

Arkansas Insurance Department, 1200 West Third Street, Little Rock, AR 72201-1904; tel. 501/371-2600; FAX. 501/371-2618; Jay Bradford, Insurance Commissioner

Medical & Nursing Licensure Agencies

Arkansas State Board of Nursing, University Tower Building, 1123 South University Avenue, Little Rock, AR 72204; tel. 501/686-2700; FAX. 501/686-2714; Sue A. Tedford, ASBN Executive Director

Arkansas State Medical Board, 1401 W. Capitol, Suite 340, Little Rock, AR 72201; tel. 501/296-1802; FAX. 501/603-3555; Joseph M. Beck, MD, Chairman

CALIFORNIA
The Honorable Edmund Brown, Jr., Governor, 916/445-2841

Facility Licensure Agencies

Department of Public Health – Center for Health Care Quality, 1615 Capitol Avenue, Stop 0512, PO Box 997413, Sacramento, CA 95899-7377; tel. 916/324-6630; FAX. 916/324-4820; Jean Iacino, Interim Deputy Director

Health Agencies

California Department of Public Health, PO Box 997377, MS 0500, Sacramento, CA 95899-7377; tel. 916/558-1700; FAX. 916/558-1762; Dr. Ron Chapman, Director

Department of Health Care Services, P.O. Box 997413, Mail Stop 000, Sacramento, CA 95899-7413; tel. 916/440-7400; Toby Douglas, Director

Healthcare Workforce Development Division, 400 R Street, Room 330, Sacramento, CA 95811; tel. 916/326-3700; FAX. 916/322-2588; Lupe Alonzo-Diaz, MPA,Deputy Director

Managed Care Agencies

California Department of Managed Health Care, 980 9th St., Suite 500, Sacramento, CA 95814-2725; tel. 888/466-2219; FAX. 916/255-5241; Brent A. Barnhart, Director

Ombudsman's Office, California Department of Insurance, 300 Capitol Mall, Suite 1600, Sacramento, CA 95814; tel. 916/492-3545; Dave Jones, Insurance Commissioner

Medical & Nursing Licensure Agencies

Board of Vocational Nursing and Psychiatric Technicians, 2535 Capitol Oaks Drive, Suite 205, Sacramento, CA 95833; tel. 916/263-7800; FAX. 916/263-7859; Cheryl Anderson, MSN, RN, Supervising Nursing Education Consultant

California Board of Registered Nursing, 1747 N. Market Boulevard, Suite 150, Sacramento, CA 95834-1924; tel. 916/322-3350; FAX. 916/574-7700; Louise Bailey, M.Ed, RN, Executive Director

Medical Board of California, 2005 Evergreen Street, Suite 1200, Sacramento, CA 95815; tel. 916/263-2382; FAX. 916/263-2387; Kimberly Kirchmeyer, Executive Director

COLORADO
The Honorable John Hickenlooper, Governor, 303/866-2471

Facility Licensure Agencies

Health Facilities Division, Colorado Department of Public Health and Environment, 4300 Cherry Creek Drive South, Building A, Second Floor, Denver, CO 80246-1530; tel. 303/692-2800; FAX. 303/753-6214; Howard Roitman, Director

Health Agencies

Colorado Department of Public Health and Environment, Business Office, 4300 Cherry Creek Drive, S., Denver, CO 80246-1530; tel. 303/692-2016; FAX. 303/751-3043; Christopher E. Urbina, Executive Director and Chief Medical Officer

Managed Care Agencies

Department of Regulatory Agencies, Colorado Division of Insurance, 1560 Broadway, Suite 850, Denver, CO 80202; tel. 303/894-7499; FAX. 303/894-7455; Margaret Salazar, Commissioner

Medical & Nursing Licensure Agencies

Colorado Medical Board, 1560 Broadway, Suite 1350, Denver, CO 80202-5140; tel. 303/894-7690; FAX. 303/894-7692; Karen M. McGovern, Program Director

Colorado State Board of NursingDepartment of Regulatory Agencies, 1560 Broadway, Suite 1350, Denver, CO 80202; tel. 303/894-2430; FAX. 303/894-7693; Georgia Roberts, Program Director

Department of Regulatory Agencies, 1560 Broadway, Suite 1550, Denver, CO 80202; tel. 303/894-7855; FAX. 303/894-7885; Barbara Kelley, Executive Director

CONNECTICUT
The Honorable Daniel Malloy, Governor, 800/406-1527

Facility Licensure Agencies

Department of Public Health, Healthcare Quality and Safety Branch, 410 Capitol Avenue, MS 12HCS, P.O. Box 340308, Hartford, CT 06134-0308; tel. 860/509-7406; FAX. 860/509-7539; Wendy Furniss, RNC, MS, Branch Chief

Health Agencies

Department of Public Health, 410 Capitol Avenue, Mail Stop 12APP, Hartford, CT 06134-0308; tel. 860/509-7590; FAX. 860/707-1931; Jennifer Filippone, Chief Practitioner, Licensing and Investigations

Managed Care Agencies

State of Connecticut, Insurance Department, Life & Health Division, PO Box 816, 153 Market St., Hartford, CT 06142-0816; tel. 860/297-3901; FAX. 860/297-3941; Mary Ellen Breault, Director

Medical & Nursing Licensure Agencies

Connecticut Board of Examiners for Nursing, Department of Public Health, 410 Capitol Avenue, MS #13PHO, PO Box 340308, Hartford, CT 06134-0308; tel. 860/509-7603; FAX. 860/509-7553; Janice Wojick, Board Liaison

Connecticut Department of Public Health, 410 Capitol Avenue, MS #12 APP, PO Box 340308, Hartford, CT 06134-0308; tel. 860/509-7590; FAX. 860/707-1984; Jewel Mullen, MD, Commissioner

Section C

DELAWARE
The Honorable Jack Markell, Governor, 302/744–4101

Facility Licensure Agencies

Department of Health and Social Services – Division of Public Health, Office of Health Facilities Licensing and Certification, 258 Chapman Road, Suite 101, Chopin Building, Newark, DE 19702; tel. 302/283–7220; FAX. 302/283–7221; Roseann Sapp, Office Manager

Health Agencies

Delaware Health and Social Services, 1901 North DuPont Highway, Main Administration Building, New Castle, DE 19720; tel. 302/255–9040; FAX. 302/255–4429; Rita M. Landgraf, Cabinet Secretary

Division of Public Health, Jesse Cooper Building, 417 Federal Street, Dover, DE 19901; tel. 302/744–4700; FAX. 302/739–6659; Karyl Thomas Rattay, MD, MS, Director

Managed Care Agencies

Delaware Department of Insurance, Consumer Department, 841 Silver Lake Boulevard, Dover, DE 19904; tel. 302/674–7300; FAX. 302/739–6278; Michael Gould, Director of Consumer Services

Medical & Nursing Licensure Agencies

Delaware Board of Medical Licensure and Discipline Delaware Division of Professional Regulation, Cannon Building, 861 Silver Lake Boulevard, Suite 203, Dover, DE 19904; tel. 302/744–4500; FAX. 302/739–2711; David C. Mangler, Director

Delaware Board of Nursing, 861 Silver Lake Boulevard, Suite 203, Dover, DE 19904; tel. 302/744–4500; FAX. 302/739–2712; Pamela C. Zickafoose, Ed.D., MSN, RN, Executive Director

DISTRICT OF COLUMBIA
Governor Switchboard, 202/624–5300

Facility Licensure Agencies

District of Columbia Department of Health, Health Regulation Licensing Administration, 899 N Capitol Street, NE, 2nd Floor, Washington, DC 20002; tel. 202/724–8800; FAX. 202/724–8677; Rikin S. Mehta, PharmD, JD, LLM, Senior Deputy Director

Health Agencies

Department of Health, Government of the District of Columbia, 899 North Capitol Street NE, Washington, DC 20002; tel. 202/442–5955; FAX. 202/442–4795; Saul M. Levin, MD, MPA, Interim Director

Managed Care Agencies

District of Columbia Department of Insurance, Securities and Banking, Union Center Plaza, 810 First Street NE, Washington, DC 20002; tel. 202/727–8000; FAX. 202/535–1196; Chester A. McPherson, Interim Commissioner

Medical & Nursing Licensure Agencies

DC Board of Nursing, Department of Health, 899 North Capitol Street, NE, First Floor, Washington, DC 20002; tel. 202/724–8800; FAX. 202/724–8677; Karen Skinner, Executive Director

District of Columbia Board of Medicine, 899 North Capital Street NE, 2nd Floor, Washington, DC 20002; tel. 202/724–8800; FAX. 202/724–8677; Jacqueline Watson, DO, MBA, Executive Director

FLORIDA
The Honorable Rick Scott, Governor, 850/488–2272

Facility Licensure Agencies

Agency for Health Care Administration, Bureau of Health Facility Regulation, Hospital and Outpatient Services Unit, 2727 Mahan Drive, Mail Stop 31, Tallahassee, FL 32308; tel. 850/412–4549; FAX. 850/922–4351; Molly McKinstry, Deputy Secretary, Unit Manager

Health Agencies

Department of Health, State Surgeon General, 4052 Bald Cypress Way, Bin #A00, Tallahassee, FL 32399–1701; tel. 850/245–4321; FAX. 850/922–9453; John Armstrong, MD, FACS, State Surgeon General

Managed Care Agencies

Office of Insurance Regulation, 200 East Gaines Street, Tallahassee, FL 32399; tel. 850/413–3140; FAX. 850/488–3334; Kevin M. McCarty, Commissioner

Medical & Nursing Licensure Agencies

Florida Board of Medicine, 4052 Bald Cypress Way, Bin #C03, Tallahassee, FL 32399–3253; tel. 850/245–4131; FAX. 850/488–0596; Allison M. Dudley, J.D., Executive Director

Florida Board of Nursing, Department of Health, 4052 Bald Cypress Way, Bin C–02, Tallahassee, FL 32399–3252; tel. 850/245–4125; FAX. 850/245–4179; Joe Baker, Jr., Executive Director

Florida Board of Osteopathic Medicine, 4052 Bald Cypress Way, Bin C–06, Tallahassee, FL 32399–3257; tel. 850/245–4161; FAX. 850/921–6184; Christy Robinson, Program Operations Administrator

GEORGIA
The Honorable Nathan Deal, Governor, 404/656–1776

Facility Licensure Agencies

Department of Community Health, Healthcare Facility Regulation Division, Two Peachtree Street, NW, Room 31–447, Atlanta, GA 30303–3142; tel. 404/657–5850; FAX. 404/651–7295; Victoria Walter, Director, Licensing and Certification

Health Agencies

Department of Public Health, 2 Peachtree Street, NW, Suite 15–470, Atlanta, GA 30303–3682; tel. 404/657–2700; FAX. 404/657–2715; Brenda Fitzgerald, MD, Commissioner

Managed Care Agencies

Office of Commissioner of Insurance, State of Georgia, Two Martin Luther King, Jr. Drive, Suite 704, West Tower, Atlanta, GA 30334; tel. 404/656–2070; Ralph T. Hudgens, Commissioner of Insurance

Medical & Nursing Licensure Agencies

Georgia Board of Nursing, 237 Coliseum Drive, Macon, GA 31217–3858; tel. 478/207–2440; FAX. 877/371–5712; Jim Cleghorn, Executive Director

Georgia Composite Medical Board, Two Peachtree Street, NW, 36th Floor, Atlanta, GA 30303; tel. 404/656–3913; FAX. 404/656–9723; LaSharn Hughes, MBA, Executive Director

HAWAII
The Honorable Neil Abercrombie, Governor, 808/586–0034

Facility Licensure Agencies

Hawaii State Department of Health, Office of Health Care Assurance, 601 Kamokila Blvd, Room 395, Kapolei, HI 96707; tel. 808/692–7420; FAX. 808/692–7447; Keith Ridley, Chief

Health Agencies

Hawaii State Department of Health, PO Box 3378, 1250 Punchbowl Street, Honolulu, HI 96801; tel. 808/586–4410; FAX. 808/586–4368; Linda Rosen, MD, MPH, Director of Health

Hawaii State Health Planning and Development Agency, 1177 Alakea Street, Suite 402, Honolulu, HI 96813; tel. 808/587–0788; FAX. 808/587–0783; Romala Sue Radcliffe, Administrator

Managed Care Agencies

State of Hawaii Department of Labor and Industrial Relations, Disability Compensation Division, PO Box 3769, 830 Punchbowl St., Honolulu, HI 96812; tel. 808/586–9151; FAX. 808/586–9219; Walter B. Kawamura, Administrator

Medical & Nursing Licensure Agencies

Hawaii Board of Nursing, Professional and Vocational Licensing Division, PO Box 3469, Honolulu, HI 96801; tel. 808/586–2695; FAX. 808/586–2689; Lee Ann Teshima, Executive Officer

Hawaii Medical Board, Department of Commerce and Consumer Affairs, 335 Merchant Street, Room 301, Honolulu, HI 96801; tel. 808/586–3000; Constance Cabral, Executive Officer

IDAHO
The Honorable C.L. "Butch" Otter, Governor, 208/334–2100

Facility Licensure Agencies

Bureau of Facility Standards, Department of Health and Welfare, PO Box 83720, 3232 Elder Street, Boise, ID 83720; tel. 208/334–6626; FAX. 208/364–1888; Sylvia Creswell, Co–Supervisor NLTC

Health Agencies

Department of Health and Welfare, Division of Public Health, 450 West State, Fourth Floor, PO Box 83720, Boise, ID 83720–0036; tel. 208/334–6996; FAX. 208/334–6581; Elke Shaw–Tulloch, Administrator

Managed Care Agencies

Idaho Department of Insurance, 700 West State Street, Third Floor, P.O. Box 83720, Boise, ID 83720–0043; tel. 208/334–4250; FAX. 208/334–4398; Bill Deal, Director

Medical & Nursing Licensure Agencies

Idaho State Board of Medicine, PO Box 83720, Boise, ID 83720–0058; tel. 208/327–7000; FAX. 208/327–7005; Nancy Kerr, Executive Director

Idaho State Board of Nursing, 280 North 8th Street, Suite 210, PO Box 83720, Boise, ID 83720–0061; tel. 208/577–2476; FAX. 208/334–3262; Sandra Evans, MAEd., RN Executive Director

ILLINOIS
The Honorable Pat Quinn, Governor, 217/782–6830

Facility Licensure Agencies

Division of Health Care Facilities and Programs, Illinois Department of Public Health, 525 West Jefferson Street, Fourth Floor, Springfield, IL 62761–0001; tel. 217/782–7412; FAX. 217/782–0382; William A. Bell, Division Chief

Health Agencies

Illinois Department of Public Health, 535 West Jefferson Street, Springfield, IL 62761; tel. 217/557–2556; FAX. 217/557–3497; LaMar Hasbrouck, MD, MPH, Director

Managed Care Agencies

Illinois Department of Insurance, 320 West Washington Street, Springfield, IL 62767–0001; tel. 217/782–4515; FAX. 217/782–5020; Andrew Boron, Director

Medical & Nursing Licensure Agencies

Illinois Department of Financial & Professional Regulation, James R. Thompson Center, 100 West Randolph Street, Chicago, IL 60601; tel. 800/560–6420; FAX. 312/814–5392; Michele Bromberg, MSN, APN, Nursing Coordinator

Illinois Department of Financial and Professional Regulation, Division of Professional Regulation, 320 West Washington Street, Third Floor, Springfield, IL 62786; tel. 217/785–0820; FAX. 217/557–7662; Jay Stewart, Division Director

INDIANA
The Honorable Mike Pence, Governor, 317/232–4567

Facility Licensure Agencies

Division of Acute Care, Indiana State Department of Health, Two North Meridian Street, Suite 4A, Indianapolis, IN 46204; tel. 317/233–7472; FAX. 317/233–7157; Randy Snyder, Division Director

Health Agencies

Indiana State Department of Health, Two North Meridian Street, Indianapolis, IN 46204; tel. 317/233–7400; FAX. 317/233–7387; William C. VanNess II, MD, Commissioner

Managed Care Agencies

Indiana Department of Insurance Company Compliance Division, 311 West Washington Street, Suite 300, Indianapolis, IN 46204; tel. 317/232–2385; FAX. 317/232–5251

Medical & Nursing Licensure Agencies

Indiana Professional Licensing Agency, Indiana State Board of Nursing, 402 West Washington, Room W072, Indianapolis, IN 46204; tel. 317/234–2043; FAX. 317/233–4236; Elizabeth Kiefner Crawford, Board Director

Indiana Professional Licensing Agency, Medical Licensing Board of Indiana, 402 West Washington, Room W072, Indianapolis, IN 46204; tel. 317/234–2060; FAX. 317/233–4236; Kristen Kelley, Director

IOWA
The Honorable Terry Branstad, Governor, 515/281–5211

Facility Licensure Agencies

Iowa Department of Inspections and Appeals, Health Facilities Division, Lucas State Office Building, 321 East 12th Street, Des Moines, IA 50319–0083; tel. 515/281–4115; FAX. 515/242–5022; Mary Spracklin, Bureau Chief

Health Agencies

Iowa Department of Public Health, Lucas State Office Building, 321 E. 12th Street, Des Moines, IA 50319–0075; tel. 515/281–8474; FAX. 515/281–4958; Gerd W. Clabaugh, MPA, Interim Director

Managed Care Agencies

Iowa Department of Commerce, Insurance Division, 330 Maple, Des Moines, IA 50319–0065; tel. 515/281–5705; FAX. 515/281–3059; Nick Gerhart, Commissioner

Medical & Nursing Licensure Agencies

Iowa Board of Medicine, 400 SW 8th Street, Suite C, Des Moines, IA 50309–4686; tel. 515/281–6641; FAX. 515/242–5908; Mark Bowden, Executive Director

Iowa Board of Nursing, 400 SW 8th Street, Suite B, Des Moines, IA 50309; tel. 515/281–3255; FAX. 515/281–4825; Kathleen R. Weinberg, RN, MSN, Executive Director

KANSAS

The Honorable Sam Brownback, Governor, 785/296–3232

Facility Licensure Agencies

Kansas Department of Health and Environment, Division of Public Health, 1000 Southwest Jackson, Suite 340, Topeka, KS 66612–1365; tel. 785/296–1200; FAX. 785/296–1231; Mindee Reece, Administrator, Division of Public Health, Director of Medical Facilities and Support

Health Agencies

Kansas Department of Health and Environment, Curtis Building, 1000 SW Jackson, Topeka, KS 66612–1368; tel. 785/296–0461; FAX. 785/368–6368; Robert Moser, MD, Secretary, Kansas Health and Environment

Managed Care Agencies

Kansas Insurance Department, 420 Southwest Ninth Street, Topeka, KS 66612; tel. 785/296–7850; FAX. 785/296–2537; Linda Sheppard, Accident and Health Supervisor

Medical & Nursing Licensure Agencies

Kansas State Board of Healing Arts, 800 SW Jackson, Lower Level–Suite A, Topeka, KS 66612; tel. 785/296–7413; FAX. 785/296–0852; Kathleen Selzler Lippert, Executive Director

Kansas State Board of Nursing, Landon State Office Building, 900 SW Jackson, Topeka, KS 66612–1230; tel. 785/296–4929; FAX. 785/296–3929; Mary Blubaugh MSN, RN, Executive Administrator

KENTUCKY

The Honorable Steven L. Beshear, Governor, 502/564–2611

Facility Licensure Agencies

Office of Inspector General, Division of Healthcare, Cabinet for Health and Family Services, 275 East Main Street, 5E–A, Frankfort, KY 40621; tel. 502/564–7963; FAX. 502/564–6546; Connie Payne, Executive Director

Health Agencies

Department for Public Health, Cabinet for Health & Family Services, 275 East Main Street, Mail Stop HS1WA, Frankfort, KY 40621; tel. 502/564–3970; FAX. 502/564–9377; Stephanie Mayfield–Gibson, MD, FCAP, Commissioner

Managed Care Agencies

Department of Insurance, Health and Life Division, 215 West Main Street, PO Box 517, Frankfort, KY 40602; tel. 502/564–6088; FAX. 502/564–2728; Maggie Woods, Director

Medical & Nursing Licensure Agencies

Kentucky Board of Medical Licensure, 310 Whittington Parkway, Suite 1B, Louisville, KY 40222; tel. 502/429–7150; FAX. 502/429–7158; Michael S. Rodman, Executive Director

Kentucky Board of Nursing, 312 Whittington Parkway, Suite 300, Louisville, KY 40222; tel. 502/429–3300; FAX. 502/429–3311; Paula S. Schenk, Executive Director

LOUISIANA

The Honorable Bobby Jindal, Governor, 225/342–7015

Facility Licensure Agencies

Department of Health and Hospitals, Bureau of Health Services, Ambulatory Surgery Centers, 602 N. Fifth Street, 2nd Floor, Baton Rouge, LA 70802; tel. 225/342–9348; FAX. 225/342–0157; Hedra Dubea, RN, Program Manager, Ambulatory Surgery Centers

Department of Health and Hospitals, Office of Management and Finance, Health Standards Section, 602 N. Fifth Street, 2nd Floor, Baton Rouge, LA 70821–3767; tel. 225/342–0138; FAX. 225/342–0157; Dora Kane, Non–Long Term Care Supervisor

Health Agencies

Louisiana Department of Health and Hospitals, 628 North 4th Street, Baton Rouge, LA 70802; tel. 225/342–9500; FAX. 225/342–5568; Kathy Kliebert, DHH Secretary

Managed Care Agencies

Louisiana Department of Insurance, 1702 North Third Street, Baton Rouge, LA 70802; tel. 225/342–0800; FAX. 225/342–7401; Mike Boutwell, Asst. Commissioner, Licensing & Compliance

Medical & Nursing Licensure Agencies

Louisiana State Board of Medical Examiners, 630 Camp Street, New Orleans, LA 70130; tel. 504/568–6820; FAX. 504/568–5754; Cecilia Mouton, MD, MHA, FACP, Executive Director

Louisiana State Board of Nursing, 17373 Perkins Road, Baton Rouge, LA 70810; tel. 225/755–7500; FAX. 225/755–7584; Karen Lyon, PhD, APRN, ACNS, NEA, Executive Director

Louisiana State Board of Practical Nurse Examiners, 3421 N. Causeway Blvd., Suite 505, Metairie, LA 70002; tel. 504/838–5791; FAX. 504/838–5279; Lynn Ansardi, RN, Executive Director

MAINE

The Honorable Paul LePage, Governor, 207/287–3531

Facility Licensure Agencies

Division of Licensing and Regulatory Services, Department of Health and Human Services, 41 Anthony Avenue, 11 State House Station, Augusta, ME 04333; tel. 207/287–9300; FAX. 207/287–5807; Kenneth Albert, RN, Esq., Director

Health Agencies

Department of Health and Human Services, 11 State House Station, Augusta, ME 04333–0011; tel. 207/287–4223; FAX. 207/287–3005; Mary C. Mayhew, Commissioner

Managed Care Agencies

Department of Professional and Financial Regulation, Bureau of Insurance, #34 State House Station, Augusta, ME 04333–0334; tel. 207/624–8494; FAX. 207/624–8599; Glenn Griswold, Director, Consumer Health Care Division

Medical & Nursing Licensure Agencies

Maine Board of Licensure in Medicine, 137 State House Station, Augusta, ME 04333–0137; tel. 207/287–3601; FAX. 207/287–6590; Randal C. Manning, Executive Director

Maine Board of Osteopathic Licensure, 142 State House Station, 161 Capitol Street, Augusta, ME 04333–0142; tel. 207/287–2480; FAX. 207/287–3015; Susan E. Strout, Executive Secretary

Maine State Board of Nursing, 161 Capitol Street, 158 State House Station, Augusta, ME 04333–0158; tel. 207/287–1133; FAX. 207/287–1149; Myra A. Broadway, JD, MS, RN, Executive Director

MARYLAND

The Honorable Martin O'Malley, Governor, 410/974–3901

Facility Licensure Agencies

Maryland Department of Health and Mental Hygiene, Freestanding Ambulatory Surgery Centers and Hospices, Spring Grove Hospital Center, 55 Wade Avenue, Cantonville, MD 21288; tel. 410/402–8040; FAX. 410/402–8277; Barbara Fagan, Manager and Coordinator

Maryland Office of Health Care Quality, Department of Health & Mental Hygiene, Spring Grove Hospital Center, 55 Wade Avenue, Cantonville, MD 21228; tel. 410/402–8002; FAX. 410/402–8218; Tricia Nay, MD, Acting Director

Health Agencies

Department of Health and Mental Hygiene, 201 West Preston Street, Baltimore, MD 21201; tel. 410/767–6500; FAX. 410/767–6489; Joshua M. Sharfstein, MD, Secretary

Managed Care Agencies

Maryland Insurance Administration, Life & Health Complaints and Investigations, 200 St. Paul Place, Suite 2700, Baltimore, MD 21202; tel. 410/468–2000; FAX. 410/468–2258; Therese M. Goldsmith, Insurance Commissioner

Medical & Nursing Licensure Agencies

Maryland Board of Nursing, 4140 Patterson Avenue, Baltimore, MD 21215–2254; tel. 410/585–1900; FAX. 410/358–3530; Patricia A. Noble, MSN, RN, Executive Director

Maryland Board of Physicians, 4201 Patterson Avenue, 4th Floor, Baltimore, MD 21215–0095; tel. 800/492–6836; FAX. 410/358–2252; Christine A. Farrelly, Acting Executive Director

MASSACHUSETTS

The Honorable Deval Patrick, Governor, 617/725–4000

Facility Licensure Agencies

Massachusetts Department of Public Health, Bureau of Health Care Safety and Quality, 99 Chauncy Street, 11th Floor, Boston, MA 02111; tel. 617/753–8000; FAX. 617/753–8125; Deborah Allwes, Bureau Director

Health Agencies

Massachusetts Department of Public Health, 250 Washington Street, 2nd Floor, Boston, MA 02108; tel. 617/624–6000; FAX. 617/624–5185; Cheryl Bartlett, RN, CommissionerLauren Smith, MD, MPH, Interim Commissioner

Managed Care Agencies

Commonwealth of Massachusetts, Division of Insurance, 1000 Washington St, Suite 810, Boston, MA 02118–2208; tel. 617/521–7794; FAX. 617/753–6380; Joseph G. Murphy, Commissioner

Medical & Nursing Licensure Agencies

Commonwealth of Massachusetts, Board of Registration in Medicine, 200 Harvard Mill Square, Suite 330, Wakefield, MA 01880; tel. 781/876–8200; FAX. 781/876–8384; Barbara A. Piselli, JD, Interim Executive Director

MICHIGAN

The Honorable Rick Snyder, Governor, 517/373–3400

Facility Licensure Agencies

Health Facilities Division, Michigan Department of Licensing and Regulatory Affairs, Bureau of Health Care Services, PO Box 30664, 611 West Ottawa, Lansing, MI 48909; tel. 517/241–4160; FAX. 517/241–3354; Larry Horvath, Director

Health Agencies

Michigan Department of Community Health, Public Health Administration, 201 Townsend Street, Lansing, MI 48913; tel. 517/335–8024; FAX. 517/335–9032; Melanie Brim, Senior Deputy Director, Public Health Administration

Managed Care Agencies

Department of Insurance and Financial Services, PO Box 30220, 611 West Ottawa, Lansing, MI 48909–7979; tel. 517/373–0220; FAX. 517/335–4978; Annette E. Flood, Director

Medical & Nursing Licensure Agencies

Michigan Board of Medicine, 611 West Ottawa Street, First Floor, Lansing, MI 48909; tel. 517/335–0918; FAX. 517/241–2895; Carol Moultine, Director of Health Professions Licensing Division

Michigan Board of Nursing, Bureau of Health Professions, 611 West Ottawa Street, First Floor, Lansing, MI 48909; tel. 517/335–0918; FAX. 517/373–2179; Rae Ramsdell, Director of Health Licensing Division

Michigan Board of Osteopathic Medicine and Surgery, 611 West Ottawa Street, First Floor, PO Box 30670, Lansing, MI 48909; tel. 517/335–0918; FAX. 517/373–2179; Carol Moultine, Director of Health Professions Licensing Division

MINNESOTA

The Honorable Mark Dayton, Governor, 651/201–3400

Facility Licensure Agencies

Minnesota Department of Health, Compliance Monitoring Division, Licensing and Certification Program, PO Box 64900, St. Paul, MN 55164–0900; tel. 651/201–4100; FAX. 651/215–9697; Mary Absolon, Program Manager

Health Agencies

Minnesota Department of Health, 625 Robert Street N, P.O. Box 64975, St. Paul, MN 55164–0975; tel. 651/201–5000; Edward Ehlinger, MD, Commissioner

Managed Care Agencies

Minnesota Department of Health, Managed Care Systems, PO Box 64882, 85 E. Seventh Place, St. Paul, MN 55164–0882; tel. 651/201–5166; FAX. 651/201–5186; Irene Goldman, Manager

Medical & Nursing Licensure Agencies

Minnesota Board of Medical Practice, 2829 University Avenue, SE, Suite 500, Minneapolis, MN 55414–3246; tel. 612/617–2149; FAX. 612/617–2166; Robert A. Leach, Executive Director

Minnesota Board of Nursing, 2829 University Avenue SE, Suite 200, Minneapolis, MN 55414-3253; tel. 612/317-3000; FAX. 612/617-2190; Shirley A. Brekken, RN, MS, Executive Director

MISSISSIPPI
The Honorable Phil Bryant, Governor, 601/359-3150

Facility Licensure Agencies
Bureau of Health Facilities Licensure and Certification, Mississippi State Department of Health, PO Box 1700, 143 B Lefleur's Square, Jackson, MS 39215; tel. 601/364-1100; FAX. 601/364-5054; Marilynn Winborne, Bureau Director of Long Term Care

Health Agencies
Mississippi State Department of Health, Office of Health Policy and Planning, 570 East Woodrow Wilson, P.O. Box 1700, Jackson, MS 39215-1700; tel. 601/576-7874; FAX. 601/576-7530; Donald E. Eicher, III, Director

Managed Care Agencies
Mississippi Department of Insurance, PO Box 79, 501 North West Street, Jackson, MS 39205; tel. 601/359-3569; FAX. 601/359-2474; Bob Williams, Director, Life and Health Actuarial

Medical & Nursing Licensure Agencies
Mississippi Board of Nursing, 713 S. Pear Orchard Rd, Suite 300, Ridgeland, MS 39157; tel. 601/957-6300; FAX. 601/957-6301; Dr. Lynn Langley, DNP, FNP, ANP, CPHQ, Interim Executive Director
Mississippi State Board of Medical Licensure, 1867 Crane Ridge Drive, Suite 200-B, Jackson, MS 39216; tel. 601/987-3079; FAX. 601/987-4159; H. Vann Craig, MD, Executive Director

MISSOURI
The Honorable Jeremiah W. (Jay) Nixon, Governor, 573/751-3222

Facility Licensure Agencies
Bureau of Home Care and Rehabilitative Standards, PO Box 570, Jefferson City, MO 65012; tel. 573/751-6336; FAX. 573/751-6315; Lisa Coots, RN, Bureau Chief
Bureau of Hospital Standards, Missouri Department of Health and Senior Services, PO Box 570, Jefferson City, MO 65102; tel. 573/751-6303; FAX. 573/526-3621; Donya Lowrie, Bureau Chief

Health Agencies
Department of Health and Senior Services, PO Box 570, 912 Wildwood, Jefferson City, MO 65102; tel. 573/751-6001; FAX. 573/751-6041; Gail Vasterling, Director

Managed Care Agencies
Department of Insurance, Division of Market Regulation, Life and Healthcare Section, PO Box 690, Jefferson City, MO 65102-0690; tel. 573/751-4126; FAX. 573/526-1165; Angela Nelson, Insurance Market Regulatory Director

Medical & Nursing Licensure Agencies
Missouri State Board of Nursing, 3605 Missouri Boulevard, PO Box 656, Jefferson City, MO 65102; tel. 573/751-0681; FAX. 573/751-0075; Lori Scheidt, Executive Director
Missouri State Board of Registration for the Healing Arts, 3605 Missouri Boulevard, PO Box 4, Jefferson City, MO 65102; tel. 573/751-0098; FAX. 573/751-3166; Connie Clarkston, Executive Director

MONTANA
The Honorable Steve Bullock, Governor, 406/444-3111

Facility Licensure Agencies
Department of Public Health and Human Services, Quality Assurance Division, 2401 Colonial Drive, Second Floor, P.O. Box 202953, Helena, MT 59620-2953; tel. 406/444-2037; FAX. 406/444-1742; Jeff Buska, Administrator

Health Agencies
Montana Department of Public Health and Human Services, 111 North Sanders, P.O. Box 4210, Helena, MT 59604; tel. 406/444-5622; FAX. 406/444-1970; Richard Opper, Director

Managed Care Agencies
Office of the Commissioner of Securities and Insurance, Montana State Auditor, 840 Helena Avenue, Helena, MT 59601; tel. 406/444-2040; FAX. 406/444-3497; Steve Matthews, Chief Financial Examiner

Medical & Nursing Licensure Agencies
Montana Board of Medical Examiners, 301 S. Park Avenue, 4th Floor, PO Box 200513, Helena, MT 59620-0513; tel. 406/841-2360; FAX. 406/841-2305; Ian Marquand, Executive Director
Montana State Board of Nursing, 301 S. Park Avenue, 4th Floor, PO Box 200513, Helena, MT 59620-0513; tel. 406/841-2300; FAX. 406/841-2305; Cynthia Gustafson, PhD, RN, Executive Director

NEBRASKA
The Honorable Dave Heineman, Governor, 402/471-2244

Facility Licensure Agencies
Nebraska Department of Health and Human Services, Division of Public Health – Licensure Unit, 301 Centennial Mall South, Nebraska State Office Bldg., 3rd Floor, Lincoln, NE 68509-4986; tel. 402/471-2115; FAX. 402/471-3577; Helen L. Meeks, Licensure Unit Administrator

Health Agencies
Nebraska Department of Health and Human Services, 301 Centennial Mall South, PO Box 95026, Lincoln, NE 68509-5026; tel. 402/471-3121; FAX. 402/471-9449; Kerry T. Winterer, Chief Executive Officer

Managed Care Agencies
Nebraska Department of Insurance, Life & Health Division, 941 O Street, Suite 400, Lincoln, NE 68508-3639; tel. 402/471-2201; FAX. 402/471-4610; Bruce Ramge, Director

Medical & Nursing Licensure Agencies
Nebraska Board of Medicine and Surgery, Licensure Unit, 301 Centennial Mall South, PO Box 94986, Lincoln, NE 68509-4986; tel. 402/471-2118; FAX. 402/471-8614; Helen Meeks, Administrator
Office of Community & Rural Health, 301 Centennial Mall, South, PO Box 95026, Lincoln, NE 68509; tel. 402/471-2353; FAX. 402/471-8259; David Palm, PhD, Administrator

NEVADA
The Honorable Brian Sandoval, Governor, 775/684-5670

Facility Licensure Agencies
Bureau of Health Care Quality and Compliance, Division of Public and Behavorial Health, 727 Fairview Drive, Suite E, Carson City, NV 89701-5493; tel. 775/684-1030; FAX. 775/684-1073; Kyle Devine, MSW Bureau Chief

Health Agencies
Department of Health and Human Services, 4126 Technology Way, Suite 100, Carson City, NV 89706-2009; tel. 775/684-4000; FAX. 775/684-4010; Michael J. Willden, Director
Nevada Division of Public and Behavorial Health, 4150 Technology Way, Suite 300, Carson City, NV 89706; tel. 775/684-4200; FAX. 775/684-4211; Richard Whitley, Administrator

Managed Care Agencies
Nevada Division of Insurance, 1818 E. College Pkwy, Suite 103, Carson City, NV 89706; tel. 775/687-0700; FAX. 775/687-0787; Scott J. Kipper, Insurance Commissioner

Medical & Nursing Licensure Agencies
Nevada State Board of Medical Examiners, Licensing Division, PO Box 7238, 1105 Terminal Way, Reno, NV 89502-2144; tel. 775/688-2559; FAX. 775/688-2321; Lynnette L. Daniels, Chief of Licensing
Nevada State Board of Nursing, 5011 Meadowood Mall Way, Suite 300, Reno, NV 89502; tel. 775/687-7700; FAX. 775/687-7707; Debra Scott, Executive Director
Nevada State Board of Osteopathic Medicine, 901 American Pacific Dr, Unit 180, Henderson, NV 89014; tel. 702/732-2147; FAX. 702/732-2079; Barbara Longo, Executive Director

NEW HAMPSHIRE
The Honorable Maggie Hassan, Governor, 603/271-2121

Facility Licensure Agencies
Bureau of Health Facilities Administration, Office of Operations Support, Licensure and Regulation, 129 Pleasant Street, Concord, NH 03301; tel. 603/271-9011; FAX. 603/271-8716; Michael Fleming, Bureau Chief
Health Facilities Administration – Licensing, 129 Pleasant Street, Concord, NH 03256; tel. 603/271-9305; FAX. 603/271-4968; Rodney Bascom, Chief of HFA–Licensing

Health Agencies
Office of Health Services Planning and Review, 29 Hazen Drive, Concord, NH 03301-6527; tel. 603/271-4606; FAX. 603/271-4141; Cindy Carrier, Managing Analyst

Managed Care Agencies
Department of Health and Human Services, Division of Public Health Services, 29 Hazen Drive, Concord, NH 03301-6521; tel. 603/271-4501; FAX. 603/271-4827; Dr. José T. Montero, Director

Medical & Nursing Licensure Agencies
New Hampshire Board of Medicine, 121 South Fruit Street, Suite 301, Concord, NH 03301; tel. 603/271-1203; FAX. 603/271-6702; Penny Taylor, Administrator
New Hampshire Board of Nursing, 121 South Fruit Street, Concord, NH 03301; tel. 603/271-2323; FAX. 603/271-6605; Denise M. Nies, MSN, RN, BC, Executive Director

NEW JERSEY
The Honorable Christopher Christie, Governor, 609/292-6000

Facility Licensure Agencies
New Jersey Department of Health, Certificate of Need and Healthcare Facility Licensure, PO Box 358, Trenton, NJ 08625-0358; tel. 609/292-8773; FAX. 609/292-3780; John A. Calabria, Director

Health Agencies
New Jersey Department of Health, Office of the Commissioner, PO Box 360, Trenton, NJ 08625-0360; tel. 609/292-7837; FAX. 609/292-0053; Mary E. O'Dowd, MPH, State Commissioner of Health

Managed Care Agencies
Division of Medical Assistance and Health Services, Office of Managed Health Care, PO Box 712, Trenton, NJ 08625-0712; tel. 609/588-2705; FAX. 609/588-6290; Karen Brodsky, Chief of Managed Care Contracting

Medical & Nursing Licensure Agencies
New Jersey Board of Nursing, 124 Halsey St, PO Box 45010, Newark, NJ 07101; tel. 973/504-6430; FAX. 973/648-3481; George Hebert, RN, MA, Executive Director
New Jersey State Board of Medical Examiners, PO Box 183, Trenton, NJ 08625-0183; tel. 609/826-7100; FAX. 609/826-7117; William V. Roeder, JD, Executive Director

NEW MEXICO
The Honorable Susana Martinez, Governor, 505/476-2200

Facility Licensure Agencies
New Mexico Department of Health, Health Facility Licensing and Certification Bureau, 2040 S. Pacheco Street, 2nd Floor, Room 413, Santa Fe, NM 87505; tel. 505/476-9093; FAX. 505/476-9075; Judy Parks, Acting Director

Health Agencies
New Mexico Department of Health, 1190 S. Street Francis Drive, PO Box 26110, Santa Fe, NM 87502-6110; tel. 505/827-2613; FAX. 505/827-2530; Retta Ward, Cabinet Secretary

Managed Care Agencies
Public Regulation Commission, Insurance Division, PO Box 1269, 1120 Paseo de Peralta, Santa Fe, NM 87504-1269; tel. 505/827-4297; FAX. 505/476-0326; John G. Franchini, Superintendent of Insurance

Medical & Nursing Licensure Agencies
New Mexico Board of Osteopathic Medical Examiners, 2550 Cerrillos Road, Second Floor, Santa Fe, NM 87505; tel. 505/476-4622; FAX. 505/476-4665; Roxann Ortiz, Licensing Specialist
New Mexico Medical Board, 2055 S. Pacheco, Building 400, Santa Fe, NM 87505; tel. 505/476-7220; FAX. 505/476-7237; Lynn S. Hart, Executive Director
State of New Mexico Board of Nursing, 6301 Indian School NE, Suite 710, Albuquerque, NM 87110; tel. 505/841-8340; FAX. 505/841-8347; Nancy Darbro, PhD, APRN, RN, CNS, Executive Director

NEW YORK
The Honorable Andrew Cuomo, Governor,
518/474–7516

Facility Licensure Agencies
Center for Health Care Quality & Surveillance, New York State Department of Health, Corning Tower, 14th Floor, Albany, NY 12237; tel. 518/402–5673; FAX. 518/486–2564; Mark L. Kissinger, Director

Division of Hospitals and Diagnostic & Treatment Centers, 875 Central Avenue, Albany, NY 12206; tel. 518/402–1004; FAX. 518/402–0784; Ruth Leslie, Director

New York State Department of Health, Office of Health Systems Management, Corning Tower, Empire State Plaza, Albany, NY 12237; tel. 518/474–7028; FAX. 518/486–2564; Lora K. Lefebvre, Deputy Director

Health Agencies
New York State Department of Health, Empire State Plaza, Corning Tower, Room 1495, Albany, NY 12237; tel. 518/474–2011; FAX. 518/474–5450; Howard A. Zucker, MD, JD, Acting Commissioner

Managed Care Agencies
NYS DOH, Bureau of Managed Care Certification and Surveillance, Room 2019, Corning Tower, Empire State Plaza, Albany, NY 12237; tel. 518/474–5515; FAX. 518/473–3583; Vallencia Lloyd, Director, Division of Health Contracting and Oversight

Medical & Nursing Licensure Agencies
New York State Board for NursingNY State Education Department, Office of the Professions, 89 Washington Avenue, Albany, NY 12234–1000; tel. 518/474–3817; FAX. 518/474–3706; Suzanne Sullivan, RN, Executive Secretary

New York State Board of Medicine, 89 Washington Avenue, East Wing, Second Floor, Albany, NY 12234; tel. 518/474–3817; FAX. 518/486–4846; Suzanne Sullivan, Interim Executive Secretary

New York State Education Department, Office of the Professions, State Education Building, 2nd Floor, Albany, NY 12234; tel. 518/474–3817; FAX. 518/474–1449; Susan Naccarato, Acting Director of Professional Licensing

NORTH CAROLINA
The Honorable Pat McCrory, Governor,
919/733–4240

Facility Licensure Agencies
Department of Health and Human Services, Division of Health Service Regulation, 2711 Mail Service Center, 1205 Umstead Drive, Raleigh, NC 27699; tel. 919/855–4620; FAX. 919/715–8476; Azzie Y. Conley, Chief, Acute and Home Care Licensure and Certification

Health Agencies
NC Department of Health and Human Services, 2001 Mail Service Center, Raleigh, NC 27699–2001; tel. 919/855–4800; FAX. 919/715–4645; Aldona Zofia Wos, MD, Secretary

Managed Care Agencies
North Carolina Department of Insurance, Financial Evaluation Division, 1203 Mail Service Center, 430 N. Salisbury Street, Raleigh, NC 27699–1203; tel. 919/807–6166; FAX. 919/807–6636; Jackie Obusek, Chief Financial Analyst

Medical & Nursing Licensure Agencies
North Carolina Board of Nursing, PO Box 2129, 4516 Lake Boone Trail, Raleigh, NC 27602–2129; tel. 919/782–3211; FAX. 919/781–9461; Julia L. George, RN, MSN, FRE, Executive Director

North Carolina Medical Board, 1203 Front Street, Raleigh, NC 27609; tel. 919/326–1100; FAX. 919/326–1130; David Henderson, Executive Director

NORTH DAKOTA
The Honorable Jack Dalrymple, Governor,
701/328–2200

Facility Licensure Agencies
North Dakota Department of Health, Division of Health Facilities, 600 East Boulevard Avenue, Department 301, Bismarck, ND 58505–0200; tel. 701/328–2352; FAX. 701/328–1890; Darleen Bartz, PhD, Chief – Health Resources Section

Health Agencies
State Department of Health, 600 East Boulevard Avenue, Bismarck, ND 58505–0200; tel. 701/328–2372; FAX. 701/328–4727; Londa Rodahl, Administrative Assistant

Managed Care Agencies
North Dakota Insurance Department, 600 East Boulevard Avenue, Bismarck, ND 58505–0320; tel. 701/328–2440; FAX. 701/328–4880; Adam Hamm, Commissioner

Medical & Nursing Licensure Agencies
North Dakota Board of Nursing, 919 South Seventh Street, Suite 504, Bismarck, ND 58504–5881; tel. 701/328–9777; FAX. 701/328–9785; Constance Kalanek, PhD, RN, Executive Director

North Dakota State Board of Medical Examiners, 418 East Broadway Avenue, Suite 12, Bismarck, ND 58501; tel. 701/328–6500; FAX. 701/328–6505; Duane Houdek, JD, Executive Secretary

OHIO
The Honorable John Kasich, Governor,
614/466–3555

Facility Licensure Agencies
Ohio Department of Health, Division of Quality Assurance, 246 North High Street, Third Floor, Columbus, OH 43215; tel. 614/466–7857; FAX. 614/644–0208; Rebecca Maust, Chief, Division of Quality Assurance

Health Agencies
Ohio Department of Health, 246 North High Street, Columbus, OH 43215; tel. 614/466–3543; FAX. 614/644–0085; Lance D. Himes, Interim Director of Health

Managed Care Agencies
The Ohio Department of Insurance, 50 W. Town Street, Third Floor, Suite 300, Columbus, OH 43215; tel. 614/644–2658; William Preston, Life and Health Division

Medical & Nursing Licensure Agencies
Ohio Board of Nursing, 17 South High Street, Suite 400, Columbus, OH 43215–7410; tel. 614/466–3947; FAX. 614/466–0388; Betsy J. Houchen, JD, RN, MS, Executive Director

State Medical Board of Ohio, 30 E. Broad Street, Third Floor, Columbus, OH 43215–6127; tel. 614/466–3934; FAX. 614/728–5946; Kimberly C. Anderson, Esq., Interim Executive Director

OKLAHOMA
The Honorable Mary Fallin, Governor,
405/521–2342

Facility Licensure Agencies
Oklahoma State Department of Health, Protective Health Services, Medical Facilities Service, 1000 Northeast 10th Street, Oklahoma City, OK 73117–1299; tel. 405/271–6576; FAX. 405/271–1308; Lee Martin, Director

Health Agencies
State Department of Health, 1000 Northeast 10th St, Room 1114, Oklahoma City, OK 73117–1299; tel. 405/271–6576; FAX. 405/271–1308; Terry Cline, PhD, Commissioner

Managed Care Agencies
Oklahoma State Department of Health, Managed Care Systems – Health Resources Development Service, 1000 Northeast 10th Street, Room 1011, Oklahoma City, OK 73117–1299; tel. 405/271–6868; FAX. 405/271–7360; James Joslin, Director

Medical & Nursing Licensure Agencies
Oklahoma Board of Nursing, 2915 N. Classen Boulevard, Suite 524, Oklahoma City, OK 73106; tel. 405/962–1800; FAX. 405/962–1821; Kimberly Glazier, M.Ed., RN, Executive Director

Oklahoma State Board of Medical Licensure and Supervision, 101 NE 51st Street, PO Box 18256, Oklahoma City, OK 73154–0256; tel. 405/962–1400; FAX. 405/962–1499; Lyle Kelsey, MBA, CMBE, Executive Director

Oklahoma State Board of Osteopathic Examiners, 4848 North Lincoln Boulevard, Suite 100, Oklahoma City, OK 73105–3321; tel. 405/528–8625; FAX. 405/557–0653; Deborah J. Bruce, Executive Director

OREGON
The Honorable John Kitzhaber, Governor,
503/373–1027

Facility Licensure Agencies
Health Care Regulation and Quality Improvement, 800 Northeast Oregon Street, Suite 305, Portland, OR 97232; tel. 971/673–0540; FAX. 971/673–0556; Dana Selover, MD MPH

Health Agencies
Oregon Health Authority–Public Health Division, Health Care Regulation and Quality Improvement, 800 NE Oregon Street, Suite 305, Portland, OR 97232; tel. 971/673–0540; FAX. 971/673–0556; Dana Selover, Section Manager

Managed Care Agencies
Department of Consumer and Business Services, insurance Division, PO Box 14480, 350 Winter Street NE, Salem, OR 97309–0405; tel. 503/947–7980; FAX. 503/378–4351; Louis Savage, Commissioner

Medical & Nursing Licensure Agencies
Oregon Medical Board, 1500 SW First Avenue, Suite 620, Portland, OR 97201–5847; tel. 971/673–2700; FAX. 971/673–2670; Kathleen Haley, JD, Executive Director

Oregon State Board of Nursing, 17938 SW Upper Boones Ferry Road, Portland, OR 97224–7012; tel. 971/673–0685; FAX. 971/673–0684; Ruby R. Jason, Executive Director

PENNSYLVANIA
The Honorable Tom Corbett, Governor,
717/787–2500

Facility Licensure Agencies
Bureau of Facility Licensure and Certification, 625 Forster Street, Room 528, Harrisburg, PA 17120; tel. 717/787–8015; FAX. 717/772–2163; Ann Chronister, Bureau Director

Department of Health, Division of Home Health, 132 Kline Plaza, Suite A, Harrisburg, PA 17104; tel. 717/783–1379; FAX. 717/772–0232; Linda Chamberlain, MS, BSN, RN, Division Director

Division of Acute and Ambulatory Care, Pennsylvania Department of Health, Health & Welfare Building, Room 532, Harrisburg, PA 17120; tel. 717/783–8980; FAX. 717/705–6663; Joanne Salsgiver, Director

Health Agencies
Pennsylvania Department of Health, Health & Welfare Building, Suite 802, 625 Forster Street, Harrisburg, PA 17120; tel. 717/787–6436; FAX. 717/787–0191; Michael Wolf, Secretary

Managed Care Agencies
Pennsylvania Insurance Department, Office of Corporate and Financial Regulation, Company Licensing Division, 1345 Strawberry Square, Harrisburg, PA 17120; tel. 717/787–2317; FAX. 717/787–8585; Robert E. Brackbill, Chief of Company Licensing Division

Medical & Nursing Licensure Agencies
Pennsylvania Department of Health, Quality Assurance, 625 Forster Street, Eighth Floor West, Harrisburg, PA 17120; tel. 717/783–1078; FAX. 717/525–5506; Anna Marie Sossong, Deputy Secretary

Pennsylvania State Board of Medicine, PO Box 2649, Harrisburg, PA 17105–2649; tel. 717/783–1400; FAX. 717/787–7769; Michael Coates, Administrator

Pennsylvania State Board of Nursing, PO Box 2649, Harrisburg, PA 17105–2649; tel. 717/783–7142; FAX. 717/783–0822; Laurette Keiser, Executive Secretary

Pennsylvania State Board of Osteopathic Medicine, PO Box 2649, Harrisburg, PA 17105–2649; tel. 717/783–4858; FAX. 717/787–7769; Suzanne Smith, Administrator

RHODE ISLAND
The Honorable Lincoln Chafee, Governor,
401/222–2080

Facility Licensure Agencies
Rhode Island Department of Health, Division of Facilities Regulation, Three Capitol Hill, Room 306, Providence, RI 02908–5097; tel. 401/222–2566; FAX. 401/222–3999; Raymond Rusin, Chief of Facilities Regulation

Health Agencies
Department of Health, Three Capitol Hill, Providence, RI 02908–5097; tel. 401/222–5960; FAX. 401/277–6548; Michael Fine, MD, Director

Managed Care Agencies
Department of Business Regulation, Insurance Regulation Division, 1511 Pontiac Avenue, Cranston, RI 02920; tel. 401/462–9520; FAX. 401/462–9602; Paul McGreevy, Director

Medical & Nursing Licensure Agencies
Division of Professional Regulation, Rhode Island Department of Health, Three Capitol Hill, Suite 104, Providence, RI 02908–5097; tel. 401/222–2827; FAX. 401/222–1272; Michael Simoli, Supervisor

Section C

Rhode Island Board of Medical Licensure & Discipline, Three Capitol Hill, Room 205, Providence, RI 02908-5097; tel. 401/222-3855; FAX. 401/222-2158; James McDonald, MD, MPH, Chief Administrative Officer

Rhode Island Board of Nurse Registration and Nursing Education, 3 Capitol Hill, Room 105, Providence, RI 02908-5097; tel. 401/222-5700; FAX. 401/222-3352; Twila McInnis, MPA, MS, RN, Director of Nurse Registration and Nursing Education

SOUTH CAROLINA
The Honorable Nikki Haley, Governor, 803/734-2100

Facility Licensure Agencies

SC Department of Health & Environmental Control, Bureau of Health Facilities Licensing, 2600 Bull Street, Columbia, SC 29201; tel. 803/545-4370; FAX. 803/545-4212; Gwendolyn C. Thopmson, Director

Health Agencies

Department of Health and Human Services, 1801 Main Street, P.O. Box 8206, Columbia, SC 29202-8206; tel. 888/549-0820; FAX. 803/255-8235; Anthony E. Keck, Director

Medical & Nursing Licensure Agencies

Department of Labor, Licensing and Regulation, State Board of Nursing for South Carolina, PO Box 12367, 110 Centerview Drive, Columbia, SC 29211-2367; tel. 803/896-4550; FAX. 803/896-4515; Nancy Murphy, Administrator

South Carolina Board of Medical Examiners, Synergy Business Park, Kingstree Building, 110 Centerview Drive, Columbia, SC 29211; tel. 803/896-4500; FAX. 803/896-4515; April Koon, Administrator

SOUTH DAKOTA
The Honorable Dennis Daugaard, Governor, 605/773-3212

Facility Licensure Agencies

Office of Health Care Facilities Licensure and Certification, State Department of Health, 615 E. Fourth Street, Pierre, SD 57501-1700; tel. 605/773-3356; FAX. 605/773-6667; Vickie Anderson, Interim Administrator

Health Agencies

South Dakota Department of Health, 600 East Capitol, Pierre, SD 57501-2536; tel. 605/773-3361; FAX. 605/773-5683; Doneen B. Hollingsworth, Secretary of Health

Managed Care Agencies

South Dakota Division of Insurance, 445 E. Capitol Avenue, Pierre, SD 57501; tel. 605/773-3563; FAX. 605/773-5369; Melissa Klemann, Senior Policy Analyst

Medical & Nursing Licensure Agencies

South Dakota Board of Medical and Osteopathic Examiners, 101 N. Main Avenue, Suite 301, Sioux Falls, SD 57104; tel. 605/367-7781; FAX. 605/367-7786; Margaret B. Hansen, PA-C, MPAS, Executive Director

South Dakota Board of Nursing, 4305 South Louise Avenue, Suite 201, Sioux Falls, SD 57106; tel. 605/362-2760; FAX. 605/362-2768; Gloria Damgaard, RN, MS, Executive Director

TENNESSEE
The Honorable Bill Haslam, Governor, 615/741-2001

Facility Licensure Agencies

Division of Health Licensure and Regulation, Office of Health Care Facilities, 665 Mainstream Drive, Second Floor, Nashville, TN 37243; tel. 615/741-7221; FAX. 615/253-8798; Ann Rutherford Reed, RN, BSN, MBA, Director of Licensure

Health Agencies

Department of Health, Andrew Johnson Tower, 5th Floor, 710 James Robertson Parkway, Nashville, TN 37243; tel. 615/741-3111; FAX. 615/741-2491; John J. Dreyzehner, MD, MPH, FACOEM, Commissioner

Managed Care Agencies

Department of Commerce and Insurance, Insurance Division, 500 James Robertson Parkway, Nashville, TN 37243-0565; tel. 615/741-2241; FAX. 615/532-2788; Mark Jaquish, Insurance Analysis Director

Medical & Nursing Licensure Agencies

Department of HealthDivision of Health Licensure and Regulation, 665 Mainstream Drive, 2nd Floor, Nashville, TN 37243; tel. 615/741-8402; FAX. 615/741-5542; Michelle J. Long, JD, Assistant Commissioner

Tennessee Board of Medical Examiners, 665 Mainstream Dr., Nashville, TN 37243; tel. 800/778-4123; FAX. 615/253-4484; Michael Zanolli, MD, President

Tennessee Board of Nursing, 665 Mainstream Drive, Nashville, TN 37243; tel. 800/778-4123; FAX. 615/741-7899; Elizabeth J. Lund, MSN, RN, Executive Director

Tennessee Medical Laboratory Board, 665 Mainstream Drive, Metro Center Complex, 2nd Floor, Nashville, TN 37247; tel. 615/532-5128; FAX. 615/253-8724; Lynda S. England, Director

Tennessee State Board of Osteopathic Examination, Office of Health, Licensure and Regulation, 227 French Landing, Suite 300, Nashville, TN 37243; tel. 800/778-4123; FAX. 615/253-4484; Jill Robinson, DO, President

TEXAS
The Honorable Rick Perry, Governor, 512/463-2000

Facility Licensure Agencies

Texas Department of Aging and Disability Services, 701 W. 51st Street, PO Box 149030, Austin, TX 78714-9030; tel. 512/438-3030; FAX. 512/438-4220; Jon Weizenbaum, Commissioner

Texas Department of State Health Services, Facility Licensing Group, Mail Code: 2835, P.O. Box 149347, Austin, TX 78714-9347; tel. 512/834-6648; FAX. 512/834-4514; Ellen Cooper, MSW, RN, MSN, Manager

Health Agencies

Texas Department of State Health Services, P.O. Box 149347, Austin, TX 78714-9347; tel. 512/776-7363; FAX. 512/776-7477; David L. Lakey, MD, Commissioner

Managed Care Agencies

Texas Department of Insurance, 333 Guadalupe, P.O. Box 149104, Austin, TX 78714-9104; tel. 512/322-6464; FAX. 512/490-1013; Eleanor Kitzman, Commissioner of Insurance

Medical & Nursing Licensure Agencies

Texas Board of Nursing, 333 Guadalupe, Suite 3-460, Austin, TX 78701; tel. 512/305-7400; FAX. 512/305-7401; Katherine A. Thomas, MN, RN, FAAN, Executive Director

Texas Medical Board, 333 Guadalupe, Tower Three, Suite 610, PO Box 2018, Austin, TX 78768-2018; tel. 512/305-7010; FAX. 512/305-7008; Mari Robinson, JD, Executive Director

UTAH
The Honorable Gary R. Herbert, Governor, 801/538-1000

Facility Licensure Agencies

Utah Department of Health, Health Facility Licensing and Certification, PO Box 144103, 288 North 1460 West, Salt Lake City, UT 84114-4103; tel. 801/538-6158; FAX. 801/538-6163; Joel Hoffman, Director

Health Agencies

Utah Department of Health, PO Box 141000, Salt Lake City, UT 84114-1000; tel. 801/538-6111; FAX. 801/538-6306; W. David Patton, Executive Director

Managed Care Agencies

Utah Insurance Department, 3110 State Office Building, Salt Lake City, UT 84114-6901; tel. 801/538-3800; FAX. 801/538-3829; Todd E. Kiser, Commissioner

Medical & Nursing Licensure Agencies

Utah Physicians Licensing Board, Division of Occupational and Professional Licensure, Heber M. Wells Building, First Floor, 160 East 300 South, Salt Lake City, UT 84114-6741; tel. 801/530-6621; FAX. 801/530-6511; Noel Taxin, Bureau Manager

Utah State Board of Nursing, 160 East 300 South, Box 146741, Salt Lake City, UT 84114-6741; tel. 801/530-6628; FAX. 801/530-6511; Dr. Debra F. Hobbins, APRN, Executive Administrator

VERMONT
The Honorable Peter Shumlin, Governor, 802/828-3333

Facility Licensure Agencies

Hospice & Palliative Care Council of Vermont, 137 Elm Street #3, Montpelier, VT 05602; tel. 802/229-0579; FAX. 802/223-6218; Virginia L. Fry, MA, Director

Vermont Board of Medical Practice, Vermont Department of Health, 108 Cherry Street, Second Floor, PO Box 70, Burlington, VT 05402; tel. 802/657-4220; FAX. 802/657-4227; David Herlihy, Executive Director

Health Agencies

Vermont Department of Health, 108 Cherry Street, P.O. Box 70, Burlington, VT 05402; tel. 802/863-7280; FAX. 802/951-1275; Harry L. Chen, MD, Commissioner

Managed Care Agencies

Green Mountain Care Board, 89 Main Street, 3rd Floor, Montpelier, VT 05620; tel. 802/828-2919; Susan Barrett, Executive Director

Medical & Nursing Licensure Agencies

Vermont Board of Nursing, National Life Building, North Floor 2, Montpelier, VT 05620-3402; tel. 802/828-2396; FAX. 802/828-2484; Nancy Morin, Administrator

Vermont Board of Osteopathic Physicians and Surgeons, Office of Professional Regulation, National Life Building, North Floor 2, Montpelier, VT 05620-3402; tel. 802/828-2373; FAX. 802/828-2465; Aprille Morrison, Licensing Board Specialist

Vermont Department of Disabilities Aging and Independent Living, Division of Licensing and Protection, Ladd Hall, 103 South Main Street, Waterbury, VT 05671-2306; tel. 802/871-3317; FAX. 802/871-3318; Suzanne Leavitt, Director

VIRGINIA
The Honorable Robert McDonnell, Governor, 804/786-2211

Facility Licensure Agencies

Office of Licensure and Certification, Virginia Department of Health, 9960 Mayland Drive, Suite 401, Henrico, VA 23230; tel. 804/367-2102; FAX. 804/527-4502; Erik O. Bodin, Director

Health Agencies

Virginia Department of Health, PO Box 2448, 109 Governor Street, Richmond, VA 23218; tel. 804/864-7001; FAX. 804/864-7022; Marissa J. Levine, MD, MPH, FAAFP, State Health Commissioner

Virginia Department of Health, Division of Certificate of Public Need, 9960 Mayland Drive, Suite 401, Henrico, VA 23233; tel. 804/367-2126; FAX. 804/527-4501; Peter Boswell, Director, Director

Managed Care Agencies

State Corporation Commission, Bureau of Insurance, PO Box 1157, 1300 East Main St., Richmond, VA 23218; tel. 804/371-9741; FAX. 804/371-9511; Connie Doung, Senior Financial Analyst

Medical & Nursing Licensure Agencies

Virginia Board of Medicine, Perimeter Center, 9960 Mayland Drive, Richmond, VA 23233-1463; tel. 804/367-4600; FAX. 804/527-4426; William L. Harp, MD, Executive Director

Virginia Board of Nursing, Perimeter Center, 9960 Mayland Drive, Henrico, VA 23233-1463; tel. 804/367-4515; FAX. 804/527-4455; Jay P. Douglas, MSM, RN, CSAC, FRE, Executive Director

WASHINGTON
The Honorable Jay Inslee, Governor, 360/902-4111

Facility Licensure Agencies

Credentialing, Washington Department of Health, PO Box 47877, 310 Israel Road, SE, Olympia, WA 98504-7852; tel. 360/236-4900; FAX. 360/236-4909; Diane Young, Credentialing Manager

State Department of Health, Investigations and Inspections Office, PO Box 47874, Olympia, WA 98504-7874; tel. 360/236-4732; FAX. 360/586-0123; Linda Foss, Executive Manager of Clinical Care Facilities

Health Agencies

Washington State Department of Health, PO Box 47890, Olympia, WA 98504-7890; tel. 360/236-4030; John Weisman, DrPH, MPH, Secretary of Health

Managed Care Agencies

Office of the Insurance Commissioner, Rates & Forms, Healthcare, Life, Disability, PO Box 40255, Olympia, WA 98504-0255; tel. 360/725-7111; FAX. 360/586-0759; Molly Nollette, Deputy Insurance Commissioner

Medical & Nursing Licensure Agencies

Health Systems Quality Assurance, Department of Health, 111 Israel Road, SE, Mail Stop 47850, Tumwater, WA 98504–7850; tel. 360/236–4600; FAX. 360/236–4626; Karen Jensen, Assistant Secretary

Washington State Board of Osteopathic Medicine and Surgery, Department of Health, PO Box 47852, Olympia, WA 98504–7852; tel. 360/236–4700; FAX. 360/236–2901; Blake Maresh, Executive Director

Washington State Department of Health, Medical Quality Assurance Commission, PO Box 47866, Olympia, WA 98504–7866; tel. 360/236–2750; FAX. 360/236–2795; Julie Kitten, Operations Manager

Washington State Nursing Care Quality Assurance Commission, Department of Health, 111 Israel Rd S.E., PO Box 47864, Olympia, WA 98504–7864; tel. 360/236–4700; FAX. 360/236–4818; Paula Meyer, RN, MSN, Executive Director

WEST VIRGINIA
The Honorable Earl Ray Tomblin, Governor, 304/558–2000
Facility Licensure Agencies

Office of Health Facility Licensure and Certification, Office of Inspector General, 408 Leon Sullivan Way, Charleston, WV 25301–3718; tel. 304/558–0050; FAX. 304/558–2515; Will Wright, Program Manager II

Health Agencies

Department of Health and Human Resources, One Davis Square, Suite 100–East, Charleston, WV 25301; tel. 304/558–0684; FAX. 304/558–1130; Karen L. Bowling, Cabinet Secretary

West Virginia Health Care Authority, 100 Dee Drive, Charleston, WV 25311–1600; tel. 304/558–7000; FAX. 304/558–7001; James L. Pitrolo, Chair

Managed Care Agencies

West Virginia Offices of the Insurance Commissioner, PO Box 50540, 1124 Smith Street, Charleston, WV 25301; tel. 304/558–3354; FAX. 304/558–3869; Janice Hemmelgarn, Commissioner's Secretary

Medical & Nursing Licensure Agencies

Office of Chief Medical Examiner, 619 Virginia Street West, Charleston, WV 25302; tel. 304/558–6920; FAX. 304/558–7886; Allen R. Mock, MD, MSc, DABP, FCAP, Chief Medical Examiner

West Virginia Board of Examiners for Registered Professional Nurses, 101 Dee Drive, Suite 102, Charleston, WV 25311–1620; tel. 304/558–3596; FAX. 304/558–3666; Laura S. Rhodes, RN, MSN, Executive Director

West Virginia Board of Osteopathic Medicine, 405 Capitol Street, Suite 402, Charleston, WV 25301; tel. 304/558–6095; FAX. 304/558–6096; Diana Shepard, Executive Director

West Virginia State Board of Examiners for Licensed Practical Nurses, 101 Dee Drive, Suite 100, Charleston, WV 25311; tel. 304/558–3572; FAX. 304/558–4367; Lanette Anderson, MSN, JD, RN, Executive Director

WISCONSIN
The Honorable Scott Walker, Governor, 608/266–1212
Facility Licensure Agencies

Division of Quality Assurance, Department of Health Services, One West Wilson Street, PO Box 2969, Madison, WI 53701–2969; tel. 608/267–7185; FAX. 608/267–0352; Otis Woods, Administrator

Health Agencies

Department of Health Services, PO Box 7850, Madison, WI 53707–7850; tel. 608/266–9622; FAX. 608/266–7882; Kitty Rhoades

Managed Care Agencies

Office of the Commissioner of Insurance, 125 S. Webster Street, P.O. Box 7873, Madison, WI 53707–7873; tel. 608/266–3585; FAX. 608/266–9935; Theodore Nickel, Commissioner

Medical & Nursing Licensure Agencies

Wisconsin Department of Saftey and Professional Services, 1400 East Washington Avenue, PO Box 8935, Madison, WI 53708–8935; tel. 608/266–2112; FAX. 608/267–3816

Wisconsin Medical Examining Board, 1400 East Washington Avenue, PO Box 8935, Madison, WI 53708; tel. 608/261–2378; FAX. 608/267–3816; Tom Ryan, Executive Director

WYOMING
The Honorable Matthew Mead, Governor, 307/777–7434
Facility Licensure Agencies

Wyoming Department of Health, Healthcare Licensing and Surveys, 6101 Yellowstone Road, Suite 186C, Cheyenne, WY 82002; tel. 307/777–7123; FAX. 307/777–7127; Ron Pearson, Administrator

Health Agencies

Department of Health, 401 Hathaway Building, Cheyenne, WY 82002; tel. 307/777–7656; FAX. 307/777–7439; Thomas O. Forslund, Director

Managed Care Agencies

State of Wyoming Department of Insurance, 106 E. Sixth Avenue, Cheyenne, WY 82002; tel. 307/777–7401; FAX. 307/777–2446; Tom C. Hirsig, Commissioner

Medical & Nursing Licensure Agencies

Wyoming Board of Medicine, 130 Hobbs Ave., Suite A, Cheyenne, WY 82002; tel. 307/778–7053; FAX. 307/778–2069; Kevin Bohnenblust, Executive Director

Wyoming State Board of Nursing, 130 Hobbs Avenue, Suite B, Cheyenne, WY 82002; tel. 307/777–7601; FAX. 307/777–3519; Cynthia LaBonde, MN, RN, Executive Director

U.S. Associated Areas

GUAM
The Honorable Eddie Baza Calvo, Governor, 671/472–8931
Health Agencies

Department of Public Health and Social Services, 123 Chalan Kareta, Mangilao, GU 96913–6304; tel. 671/735–7173; FAX. 671/734–5910; James W. Gillan, Director, DPHSS

Managed Care Agencies

Department of Public Health and Social Services, Government of Guam, 123 Chalan Kareta Route 10, Mangilao, GU 96913; tel. 671/735–7102; FAX. 671/734–5910; James W. Gillan, Director

Medical & Nursing Licensure Agencies

Guam Board of Medical Examiners, Health Professional Licensing Office, 651 Legacy Square Commerical Complex S., Rte. 10, Suite 9, Mangilao, GU 96913; tel. 671/735–7406; FAX. 671/735–7413; MaryLou Loualhati, Acting Administrator

Guam Board of Nurse Examiners Department of Public Health and Social Services, 651 Legacy Square Commercial Complex S., Route 10, Suite 9, Mangilao, GU 96913; tel. 671/733–7408; FAX. 671/477–4733; Margaret Guerrero

PUERTO RICO
The Honorable Alejandro Garca Padilla, Governor, 787/721–7000
Facility Licensure Agencies

Department of Health Commonwealth of Puerto Rico, Departamento de Salud, PO Box 70184, Calle Maga, Edifico E Altos, San Juan, PR 00936–0184; tel. 787/765–2929; FAX. 787/250–6547; Francisco Joglar, MD, Secretary of Health

Puerto Rico Department of Health, P.O. Box 70184, San Juan, PR 00936–8184; tel. 787/765–2929; FAX. 787/767–8341; Lorenzo Gonzalez Feliciano, MD, MBA, Secretary of Health

Health Agencies

Puerto Rico Department of Health, Building A – Medical Center, Call Box 70184, San Juan, PR 00936–8184; tel. 787/274–6822; FAX. 787/767–8341; Lorenzo Gonzalez Feliciano, MD, MBA, Secretary of Health

Managed Care Agencies

Office of the Commissioner of Insurance, B5 Calle Tabonuco, Suite 216, PMB 356, Guaynabo, PR 00968–3029; tel. 787/304–8686; FAX. 787/273–6365; Sol Gisela Marrero, Health Insurance Supervisor, Actuarial Analysis Division

Medical & Nursing Licensure Agencies

Junta de Licenciatmiento y Disciplina Médica, PO Box 13969, San Juan, PR 00908; tel. 787/999–8989; Gladys N. Tomes Diaz, Executive Director

Puerto Rico Board of Medical Examiners, PO Box 13969, San Juan, PR 00908; tel. 787/999–8989; FAX. 787/792–4436; Gladys N. Tomes Diaz, Executive Director

VIRGIN ISLANDS
The Honorable John deJongh, Jr., Governor, 340/774–0001
Health Agencies

Virgin Islands Department of Health, Charles Harwood Complex, 3500 Richmond Est, St. Croix, VI 00820–4370; tel. 340/773–6551; FAX. 340/773–1376; Fern P. Clarke, Territorial Asst. Commissioner

Canada

ALBERTA
Medical & Nursing Licensure Agencies

College of Physicians & Surgeons of Alberta, 10020 100th Street, NW, Suite 2700, Edmonton, AB T5J 0N3; tel. 780/423–4764; FAX. 780/420–0651; Dr. Trevor Theman, Registrar

MANITOBA
Health Agencies

Department of Health, 302 Legislative Building, 450 Broadway, Winnipeg, MB R3C 0V8; tel. 204/945–3731; FAX. 204/945–0441; Honourable Erin Selby, Health Minister

Medical & Nursing Licensure Agencies

College of Physicians and Surgeons of Manitoba, 1000–1661 Portage Avenue, Winnipeg, MB R3J 3T7; tel. 204/774–4344; FAX. 204/774–0750; William D.B. Pope, MD, Registrar

NEW BRUNSWICK
Medical & Nursing Licensure Agencies

College of Physicians and Surgeons of New Brunswick, One Hampton Road, Suite 300, Rothesay, NB E2E 5K8; tel. 506/849–5050; FAX. 506/849–5069; Dr. Ed Schollenberg, Registrar

NEWFOUNDLAND
Health Agencies

Department of Health and Community Services, Confederation Building (West Block), P.O. Box 8700, St. John's, NF A1B 4J6; tel. 709/729–3124; FAX. 709/729–0121; Paul Davis, Minister, Health and Community Services

NOVA SCOTIA
Health Agencies

Department of Health and Wellness, PO Box 488, Halifax, NS B3J 2R8; tel. 902/424–3377; FAX. 902/424–0559; Leo A. Glavine, Minister of Health & Wellness/Seniors

Medical & Nursing Licensure Agencies

College of Physicians and Surgeons of Nova Scotia, Office of the Registrar, 7071 Bayers Road, Suite 5005, Halifax, NS B3L 2C2; tel. 902/422–5823; FAX. 902/422–5035; Gus Grant, MD, Registrar and Chief Executive Officer

PRINCE EDWARD ISLAND
Medical & Nursing Licensure Agencies

College of Physicians and Surgeons of Prince Edward Island, 14 Paramount Drive, Charlottetown, PE C1E 0C7; tel. 902/566–3861; FAX. 902/566–3986; C. Moyse, MD, Registrar

QUEBEC
Health Agencies

Ministère de la Santé et des Services Sociaux, 1075 Chemin Sainte–Foy, Quebec, PQ G1S 2M1; tel. 4182667171; Gaétan Barrette, Minister

Medical & Nursing Licensure Agencies

Collège des médecins du Québec, 2170 boul. René–Levesque Ouest, Montreal, PQ H3H 2T8; tel. 5149334441; FAX. 5149333112; Charles Bernard, President and Chief Executive Officer

SASKATCHEWAN
Health Agencies

Ministry of Health, 3475 Albert Street, Third Floor, Regina, SK S4S 6X6; tel. 306/787–3696; FAX. 306/787–8310; The Hon. Dustin Duncan, Minister

Medical & Nursing Licensure Agencies

College of Physicians and Surgeons of Saskatchewan, 500 321A 21st Street, E., Saskatoon, SK S7K 0C1; tel. 3062447355; FAX. 3062440090; Karen Shaw, MD, Registrar

Organizations and Agencies

Hospital Associations

The following list of state and metropolitan hospital associations is derived from the American Hospital Association. For additional information visit the American Hospital Association website: www.aha.org.

United States

ALABAMA: Alabama Hospital Association, 500 North East Boulevard, Montgomery, AL 36117; tel. 334/272–8781; FAX. 334/270–9527; J. Michael Horsley, President and Chief Executive Officer

ALASKA: Alaska State Hospital and Nursing Home Association, 1049 W. Fifth Avenue, Suite 100, Anchorage, AK 99501; tel. 907/646–1444; FAX. 907/646–3964; Karen Perdue, President and Chief Executive Officer

ARIZONA: Arizona Hospital and Healthcare Association, 2800 North Central Avenue, Suite 1450, Phoenix, AZ 85004-1054; tel. 602/445–4300; FAX. 602/445–4299; Greg Vigdor, President and Chief Executive Officer

ARKANSAS: Arkansas Hospital Association, 419 Natural Resources Drive, Little Rock, AR 72205-1539; tel. 501/224–7878; FAX. 501/224–0519; Robert "Bo" Ryall, President and Chief Executive Officer

CALIFORNIA: California Hospital Association, 1215 K Street, Suite 800, Sacramento, CA 95814; tel. 916/552–7547; FAX. 916/552–7680; C. Duane Dauner, President and Chief Executive Officer

  Hospital Association of San Diego and Imperial Counties, 5575 Ruffin Road, Suite 225, San Diego, CA 92123; tel. 858/614–0200; FAX. 858/614–0201; Steven A. Escoboza, President and Chief Executive Officer

  Hospital Association of Southern California, 515 South Figueroa Street, Suite 1300, Los Angeles, CA 90071-3322; tel. 213/538–0700; FAX. 213/629–4272; James D. Barber, President and Chief Executive Officer

  Hospital Council of Northern and Central California, 1215 K Street, Suite 730, Sacramento, CA 95814; tel. 916/552–7608; FAX. 916/554–2286; Arthur A. Sponseller, President and Chief Executive Officer

COLORADO: Colorado Hospital Association, 7335 East Orchard Road, Greenwood Village, CO 80111; tel. 720/489–1630; FAX. 720/489–9400; Steven J. Summer, President and Chief Executive Officer

CONNECTICUT: Connecticut Hospital Association, 110 Barnes Road, PO Box 90, Wallingford, CT 06492-0090; tel. 203/265–7611; FAX. 203/284–9318; Jennifer Jackson, President and Chief Executive Officer

DELAWARE: Delaware Healthcare Association, 1280 South Governors Avenue, Dover, DE 19904-4802; tel. 302/674–2853; FAX. 302/734–2731; Wayne A. Smith, President and Chief Executive Officer

DISTRICT OF COLUMBIA: District of Columbia Hospital Association, 1152 15th Street, NW, Suite 900, Washington, DC 20005-1723; tel. 202/682–1581; FAX. 202/371–8151; Robert A. Malson, President

FLORIDA: Florida Hospital Association, 306 East College Avenue, Tallahassee, FL 32301; tel. 850/222–9800; FAX. 850/561–6230; Bruce Rueben, President

  South Florida Hospital and Healthcare Association, Inc., 1855 Griffin Rd, Suite A415, Dania Beach, FL 33004; tel. 954/964–1660; FAX. 954/920–4595; Linda S. Quick, President

GEORGIA: Georgia Hospital Association (GHA), 1675 Terrell Mill Road, Marietta, GA 30067; tel. 770/249–4500; FAX. 770/955–5801; Earl Rogers, President

HAWAII: Healthcare Association of Hawaii, 707 Richards Street, PH2, Honolulu, HI 96813; tel. 808/521–8961; FAX. 808/599–2879; George W. Greene, President and Chief Executive Officer

IDAHO: Idaho Hospital Association, 615 N. Seventh Street, Boise, ID 83701-1278; tel. 208/338–5100; FAX. 208/338–7800; Steven A. Millard, President and Chief Executive Officer

ILLINOIS: Illinois Hospital Association, 1151 East Warrenville Road, P.O. Box 3015, Naperville, IL 60566-7015; tel. 630/276–5400; FAX. 630/276–5431; Maryjane A. Wurth, President and Chief Executive Officer

  Metropolitan Chicago Healthcare Council, 222 South Riverside Plaza, Suite 1900, Chicago, IL 60606; tel. 312/906–6000; FAX. 312/993–4500; Kevin Scanlan, President and Chief Executive Officer

INDIANA: Indiana Hospital Association, 1 American Square, Suite 1900, Indianapolis, IN 46282; tel. 317/633–4870; FAX. 317/633–4875; Douglas J. Leonard, FACHE, President

IOWA: Iowa Hospital Association, 100 East Grand Avenue, Suite 100, Des Moines, IA 50309-1835; tel. 515/288–1955; FAX. 515/283–9366; Kirk Norris, President and Chief Executive Officer

KANSAS: Kansas Hospital Association, 215 SE 8th Ave., Topeka, KS 66603; tel. 785/233–7436; FAX. 785/233–6955; Thomas L. Bell, President and Chief Executive Officer

  Health Alliance of MidAmerica, 7015 College Boulevard, Suite 150, Overland Park, KS 66211; tel. 913/327–7200; FAX. 913/327–7210; Michael R. Dunaway, President

KENTUCKY: Kentucky Hospital Association, 2501 Nelson Miller Parkway, P.O. Box 436629, Louisville, KY 40253; tel. 502/426–6220; FAX. 502/426–6226; Michael T. Rust, FACHE, President and Chief Executive Officer

LOUISIANA: Louisiana Hospital Association, 9521 Brookline Avenue, Baton Rouge, LA 70809-1431; tel. 225/928–0026; FAX. 225/923–1004; Paul A. Salles, President and Chief Executive Officer

  Metropolitan Hospital Council of New Orleans, 2450 Severn Avenue, Suite 210, Metairie, LA 70001; tel. 504/837–1171; FAX. 504/837–1174; Jennifer McMahon, Executive Director

MAINE: Maine Hospital Association, 33 Fuller Road, Augusta, ME 04330; tel. 207/622–4794; FAX. 207/622–3073; Steven R. Michaud, President

MARYLAND: Maryland Hospital Association, 6820 Deerpath Road, Elkridge, MD 21075-6234; tel. 410/379–6200; FAX. 410/379–8239; Carmela Coyle, President and Chief Executive Officer

  Healthcare Council of the National Capital Area, 4061 Powder Mill Rd, Suite 100, Calverton, MD 20705; tel. 301/731–4700; FAX. 301/731–8286; Leslie "Les" H. Pitton, Jr., President and Chief Executive Officer

MASSACHUSETTS: Massachusetts Hospital Association, 5 New England Executive Park, Burlington, MA 01803; tel. 781/262–6000; FAX. 781/272–1524; Lynn Nicholas, FACHE, President and Chief Executive Officer

MICHIGAN: Michigan Health & Hospital Association, 2112 University Park Drive, Okemos, MI 48864; tel. 517/323–3443; FAX. 517/323–0946; Spencer C. Johnson, President

  Hospital Council of East Central Michigan, 315 Mullholland Avenue, Bay City, MI 48708; tel. 989/891–8810; FAX. 989/891–8161; Elizabeth S. Schnettler, President

  Upper Peninsula Hospital Council, 110 W. Michigan Ave., Suite 1200, Lansing, MI 48933; tel. 517/323–3443; FAX. 517/323–0946; Clark R. Ballard, Regional Liason

MINNESOTA: Minnesota Hospital Association, 2550 University Avenue W, Suite 350-S, St. Paul, MN 55114-1900; tel. 651/641–1121; FAX. 651/659–1477; Lawrence J. Massa, President and Chief Executive Officer

MISSISSIPPI: Mississippi Hospital Association, 116 Woodgreen Crossing, PO Box 1909, Madison, MS 39130; tel. 800/289–8884; FAX. 601/368–3200; Timothy H. Moore, President and Chief Executive Officer

MISSOURI: Missouri Hospital Association, PO Box 60, 4712 Country Club Drive, Jefferson City, MO 65102-0060; tel. 573/893–3700; FAX. 573/893–2809; Herb Kuhn, President and Chief Executive Officer

MONTANA: MHA...An Association of Montana Health Care Providers, 1720 Ninth Avenue, PO Box 5119, Helena, MT 59601; tel. 406/442–1911; FAX. 406/443–3894; Dick Brown, President and Chief Executive Officer

NEBRASKA: Nebraska Hospital Association, 3255 Salt Creek Circle, Suite 100, Lincoln, NE 68504; tel. 402/742–8140; FAX. 402/742–8191; Laura J. Redoutey, FACHE, President

NEVADA: Nevada Hospital Association, 5190 Neil Road, Suite 400, Reno, NV 89502; tel. 775/827–0184; FAX. 775/827–0190; Bill M. Welch, President and Chief Executive Officer

NEW HAMPSHIRE: New Hampshire Hospital Association, Foundation for Healthy Communities, 125 Airport Road, Concord, NH 03301-7300; tel. 603/225–0900; FAX. 603/225–4346; Stephen Ahnen, President

NEW JERSEY: New Jersey Hospital Association, 760 Alexander Rd., P.O. Box 1, Princeton, NJ 08543-0001; tel. 609/275–4000; FAX. 609/452–8097; Elizabeth A. Ryan, Esq., President and Chief Executive Officer

  Hospital Alliance of New Jersey, 50 West State Street, Suite 1008, Trenton, NJ 08608; tel. 609/989–8200; FAX. 609/989–7768; Suzanne Ianni, President & Chief Executive Officer

NEW MEXICO: New Mexico Hospital Association, 7471 Pan American Freeway, NE, Albuquerque, NM 87109; tel. 505/343–0010; FAX. 505/343–0012; Jeff Dye, President and Chief Executive Officer

NEW YORK: Healthcare Association of New York State, One Empire Drive, Rensselaer, NY 12144; tel. 518/431–7600; FAX. 518/431–7915; Dennis Whalen, President

  Greater New York Hospital Association, 555 West 57 Street, 15th Floor, New York, NY 10019; tel. 212/246–7100; FAX. 212/262–6350; Kenneth E. Raske, President and Chief Executive Officer

  Iroquois Healthcare Alliance, 15 Executive Park Drive, Clifton Park, NY 12065; tel. 518/383–5060; FAX. 518/383–2616; Gary J. Fitzgerald, President

  Nassau-Suffolk Hospital Council, Inc., 1383 Veterans Memorial Highway, Suite 26, Hauppauge, NY 11788; tel. 631/435–3000; FAX. 631/435–2343; Kevin W. Dahill, President and Chief Executive Officer

  New York City Health & Hospitals Corporation, 125 Worth Street, New York, NY 10013; tel. 212/788–3321; Ram Raju, MD, President and Chief Executive Officer

  Northern Metropolitan Hospital Association, 400 Stony Brook Court, Newburgh, NY 12550; tel. 845/562–7520; FAX. 845/562–0187; Kevin W. Dahill, President and Chief Executive officer

  Rochester Regional Healthcare Association, Rochester Regional Healthcare Advocates, 3445 Winton Place, Suite 222, Rochester, NY 14623; tel. 585/273–8180; FAX. 585/475–0266; Diane H. Ashley, President and Chief Executive Officer

  Western New York Healthcare Association, 1876 Niagara Falls Boulevard, Tonawanda, NY 14150-6439; tel. 716/695–0843; FAX. 716/695–0073; John E. Bartimole, President

NORTH CAROLINA: North Carolina Hospital Association, PO Box 4449, Cary, NC 27519-4449; tel. 919/677–2400; FAX. 919/677–4200; William A. Pully, President

NORTH DAKOTA: North Dakota Hospital Association, 1622 E. Interstate Avenue, PO Box 7340, Bismarck, ND 58507; tel. 701/224–9732; FAX. 701/224–9529; Jerry E. Jurena, President

OHIO: Ohio Hospital Association, 155 East Broad Street, Suite 301, Columbus, OH 43215; tel. 614/221–7614; FAX. 614/221–4771; Michael D. Abrams, President and Chief Executive Officer

  Akron Regional Hospital Association, 3200 West Market Street, Suite 200, Akron, OH 44333; tel. 330/873–1500; FAX. 330/873–1501; Sarah Metzger, Director

  Central Ohio Hospital Council, 155 East Broad Street, 23rd Floor, Columbus, OH 43215; tel. 614/358–2710; FAX. 614/358–2725; Jeff Klingler, President & Chief Executive Officer

  Greater Cincinnati Health Council, 2100 Sherman Avenue, Suite 100, Cincinnati, OH 45212-2775; tel. 513/531–0200; FAX. 513/531–0278; Craig Brammer, Chief Executive Officer

Greater Dayton Area Hospital Association, 2 Riverplace, Suite 400, Dayton, OH 45405; tel. 937/228–1000; FAX. 937/228–1035; Bryan J. Bucklew, President and Chief Executive Officer

Hospital Council of Northwest Ohio, 3231 Central Park West Drive, Suite 200, Toledo, OH 43617; tel. 419/842–0800; FAX. 419/843–8889; W. Scott Fry, President and Chief Executive Officer

The Center for Health Affairs, 1226 Huron Road East, Cleveland, OH 44115; tel. 216/696–6900; FAX. 216/696–1875; William T. (Bill) Ryan, President and Chief Executive Officer

OKLAHOMA: Oklahoma Hospital Association, 4000 Lincoln Boulevard, Oklahoma City, OK 73105; tel. 405/427–9537; FAX. 405/424–4507; Craig W. Jones, FACHE, President

OREGON: Oregon Association of Hospitals and Health Systems, 4000 Kruse Way Place, Building 2, Suite 100, Lake Oswego, OR 97035-2543; tel. 503/636–2204; FAX. 503/636–8310; Andy Davidson, President and Chief Executive Officer

PENNSYLVANIA: The Hospital & Healthsystem Association of Pennsylvania, 4750 Lindle Road, P.O. Box 8600, Harrisburg, PA 17105-8600; tel. 717/564–9200; FAX. 717/561–5334; Andy Carter, President and Chief Executive Officer

Hospital Council of Western Pennsylvania, 500 Commonwealth Drive, Warrendale, PA 15086; tel. 724/772–7206; FAX. 724/772–8339; A.J. Harper, President

RHODE ISLAND: Hospital Association of Rhode Island, 100 Midway Road, Suite 21, Cranston, RI 02920; tel. 401/946–7887; FAX. 401/946–8188; Michael R. Souza, Acting President

SOUTH CAROLINA: South Carolina Hospital Association, 1000 Center Point Road, Columbia, SC 29210-5802; tel. 803/796–3080; FAX. 803/796–2938; Thorton Kirby, FACHE, President and Chief Executive Officer

SOUTH DAKOTA: South Dakota Association of Healthcare Organizations (SDAHO), 3708 West Brooks Place, Sioux Falls, SD 57106; tel. 605/361–2281; FAX. 605/361–5175; David R. Hewett, President and Chief Executive Officer

TENNESSEE: Tennessee Hospital Association, 5201 Virginia Way, Brentwood, TN 37027; tel. 615/256–8240; FAX. 615/242–4803; Craig A. Becker, President

TEXAS: Texas Hospital Association, 1108 Lavaca, Suite 700, Austin, TX 78701-2180; tel. 512/465–1000; FAX. 512/465–1090; Ted Shaw, President and Chief Executive Officer

Dallas-Fort Worth Hospital Council, 250 Decker Drive, Irving, TX 75062; tel. 972/719–4900; FAX. 972/719–4009; W. Stephen Love, President and Chief Executive Officer

UTAH: UHA, Utah Hospital Association, 2180 South 1300 East, Suite 440, Salt Lake City, UT 84106-2843; tel. 801/486–9915; FAX. 801/486–0882; Gregory S. Bell, President and Chief Executive Officer

VERMONT: Vermont Association of Hospitals and Health Systems, 148 Main Street, Montpelier, VT 05602; tel. 802/223–3461; FAX. 802/223–0364; Marie Beatrice Grause, President and Chief Executive Officer

VIRGINIA: Virginia Hospital & Healthcare Association, 4200 Inslake Drive, Suite 203, Glen Allen, VA 23060; tel. 804/965–1227; FAX. 804/965–0475; Laurens Sartoris, President

WASHINGTON: Washington State Hospital Association, 300 Elliott Avenue West, Suite 300, Seattle, WA 98119-4118; tel. 206/281–7211; FAX. 206/283–6122; C. Scott Bond, President and Chief Executive Officer

WEST VIRGINIA: West Virginia Hospital Association, 100 Association Drive, Charleston, WV 25311-1571; tel. 304/344–9744; FAX. 304/414–0210; Joseph M. Letnaunchyn, President and Chief Executive Officer

WISCONSIN: Wisconsin Hospital Association, 5510 Research Park Drive, P.O.Box 259038, Madison, WI 53725-9038; tel. 608/274–1820; FAX. 608/274–8554; Eric Borgerding, President

WYOMING: Wyoming Hospital Association, 2005 Warren Avenue, Cheyenne, WY 82001; tel. 307/632–9344; FAX. 307/632–9347; Dan Perdue, President

U.S. Associated Areas

PUERTO RICO: Puerto Rico Hospital Association, Villa Nevarez Professional Center, Suite 101, San Juan, PR 00927; tel. 787/764–0290; FAX. 787/753–9748; Ruby Rodriguez, Vice President

Canada

NOVA SCOTIA: Health Association Nova Scotia, 2 Dartmouth Road, Bedford, NS B4A 2K7; tel. 902/832–8500; FAX. 902/832–8505; Mary Lee, President and Chief Executive Officer

ONTARIO: Catholic Health Alliance of Canada, Annex C, Saint-Vincent Hospital, 60 Cambridge Street North, Ottawa, ON K1R 7A5; tel. 613/562–6262; FAX. 613/782–2857; Michael Shea, President and Chief Executive Officer

Ontario Hospital Association, 200 Front Street, West, Suite 2800, Toronto, ON M5V-3L1; tel. 416/205–1300; FAX. 416/205–1301; Anthony Dale, President and Chief Executive Officer

SASKATCHEWAN: Health Shared Services Saskatchewan (3sHealth), 800–2002 Victoria Avenue, Regina, SK S4P 0R7; tel. 306/347–5500; FAX. 306/525–1960; Andrew Will, President and Chief Executive Officer

Section C

Group Purchasing Organizations

The following list of Group Purchasing Organizations is derived from the AHA Annual Survey of Hospitals and the organizations themselves. It reflects Group Purchasing Organizations serving hospitals. Inclusion or omission of any organization's name indicates neither approval nor disapproval by Health Forum LLC, an American Hospital Association company.

A

Advantage/Amerinet
see HSI Group Purchasing Division

Adventist Health, 2100 Douglas Boulevard, Roseville, CA 95661; tel. 916/781–2000; Lowell G. Church, Vice President, Materiel Management; President, Supply Chain and Affiliated Services; www.adventisthealth.org

Alegent Health
see Prairie Health Ventures

All Health
see Amerinet, Inc.

Alliant Purchasing Group
see Alliant Purchasing, LLC

Alliant Purchasing, LLC, 2650 Eastpoint Parkway, Suite 201, Louisville, KY 40223; tel. 800/446–8760; FAX. 502/992–3526; Joe Broyles, Senior Vice President, Operations; www.alliantpurchasing.com

Ameribergen
see AmerisourceBergen Drug Corporation

Amerinet Intermountain Healthcare
see Intermountain Healthcare Supply Chain Organization

Amerinet, Inc., Two CityPlace Drive, Suite 400, St. Louis, MO 63141; tel. 877/711–5700; Todd C. Ebert, President and Chief Executive Officer; www.amerinet-gpo.com/Pages/Home.aspx

Amerinet/Advantage
see HSI Group Purchasing Division

Amerinet/Shared Health
see Shared Purchasing Solutions

AmerisourceBergen Drug Corporation, 1300 Morris Drive, Chesterbrook, PA 19087; tel. 610/727–7000; David W. Neu, Senior Vice President and President, AmerisourceBergan Drug Corporation; www.amerisourcebergendrug.com

APS, 7015 College Boulevard, Suite 150, Overland Park, KS 66211; tel. 888/941–2771; FAX. 913/327–7210; Dennis George, Chief Executive Officer; www.apskc.org/content/home

APS/MedAssets
see APS

ArchCare, 205 Lexington Avenue, 3rd Floor, New York, NY 10016; tel. 646/633–4717; Terence Gallagher, Vice President, Supply Chain; www.archcare.org

Ascension Health
see The Resource Group, LLC

Associated Purchasing
see APS

Associated Purchasing Group
see APS

Association Purchasing Services
see APS

Avera PACE, 3900 West Avera Drive, Suite 200, Sioux Falls, SD 57108; tel. 800/657–8095; FAX. 605/322–4666; Lili Shim, Director; www.avera.org/pace

Avera PACE - Premier
see Avera PACE

B

Baptist Health Services Group
see Novation, LLC

Barnabas Health
see MedAssets, Inc.

Baycare Purchasing Partners, LLC, c/o Baycare Health System, Inc., 2985 Drew Street, Clearwater, FL 33759; tel. 877/692–2922; Stephen R. Mason, President and Chief Executive Officer; www.baycare.org/default.cfm

BJC HealthCare, 4901 Forest Park Avenue, St. Louis, MO 63108; tel. 314/747–9322; www.bjc.org/Default.aspx

Bon Secours
see Premier, Inc.

Boone Hospital Center, 1600 East Broadway, Columbia, MO 65201-5844; tel. 573/815–8000; FAX. 573/815–2492; James J. Sinek, FACHE, President; www.boone.org

Broadlane Group
see MedAssets, Inc.

C

California Department of General Services, Procurement Division, 707 Third Street, 2nd Floor, West Sacramento, CA 95605; tel. 916/375–4400; FAX. 916/375–4613; Jim Butler, Procurement Division Deputy Director; www.dgs.ca.gov/Default.aspx?alias=www.dgs.ca.gov/dgs

Cape Girardeau
see MedAssets, Inc.

Capella Healthcare
see HealthTrust Purchasing Group, LP

Cardinal Health, Inc., 7000 Cardinal Place, Dublin, OH 43017; tel. 614/757–5000; George S. Barrett, Chairman and Chief Executive Officer; www.cardinalhealth.com

Care New England, 45 Willard Avenue, Providence, RI 02905; tel. 401/453–7900; www.carenewengland.org

Carilion Clinic, P.O. Box 13367, Roanoke, VA 24033; tel. 800/422–8482; Nancy Howell Agee, President and Chief Executive Officer; www.carilionclinic.org

Carolinas HealthCare System
see Carolinas Shared Services

Carolinas Shared Services, P.O. Box 35126, Charlotte, NC 28235; tel. 704/512–7271; FAX. 704/512–7037; James Olsen, Senior Vice President and Chief Operating Officer; www.carolinassharedservices.org

Catholic Health East, 3805 West Chester Pike, Suite 100, Newtown Square, PA 19073; tel. 610/355–2000; Florence Doyle, Vice President, Supply Chain; www.che.org/services/materiels.php

Catholic Health Initiatives
see HealthTrust Purchasing Group, LP

Catholic Health Services
see Catholic Health Services of Long Island

Catholic Health Services of Long Island, 992 North Village Avenue, Rockville Centre, NY 11570; tel. 855/247–4500; Alan Guerci, MD, President and Chief Executive Officer; www.chsli.org

Centura Health
see HealthTrust Purchasing Group, LP

Champs
see CHAMPS Group Purchasing

CHAMPS Group Purchasing, 1226 Huron Road East, Cleveland, OH 44115; tel. 800/362–2628; FAX. 216/696–1875; Yolandi Myers, Vice President, CHAMPS Group Purchasing; champshealthcare.com/GroupPurchasing.aspx

Child Health Corp of America
see Children's Hospital Association

Children's Hospital Association, 6803 West 64th Street, Shawnee Mission, KS 66202; tel. 913/262–1436; FAX. 913/262–1575; Tim Rezash, Group Vice President, Purchasing Services; www.chca.com

CHRISTUS Health
see MedAssets, Inc.

Coalition Health Services
see Coalition of Health Services, Inc.

Coalition of Health Services, Inc., 301 South Polk, Suite 740, Amarillo, TX 79101; tel. 888/892–2273; FAX. 806/337–1704; Carolyn Witherspoon, Executive Director; www.cohs.net

Coastal Cooperative of New Jersey, LLC, 1350 Campus Parkway, Wall, NJ 07753; tel. 732/751–3404; www.coastalcoop.com

Colonial Health Alliance, LLC, 1800 Dual Highway, Suite 304, Hagerstown, MD 21740; tel. 240/347–4920; FAX. 240/347–4921; Mike Ewing, Executive Director; www.colonialregional.com

Colonial Regional Alliance, LLC
see Colonial Health Alliance, LLC

Commonwealth of Massachusetts
see Massachusetts Executive Office for Administration and Finance

Commonwealth of Virginia
see Virginia Department of General Services, Division of Purchases and Supply

Community Health Systems
see HealthTrust Purchasing Group, LP

Connecticut Department of Administrative Services, State Procurement Marketplace, 165 Capitol Avenue, Hartford, CT 06106; tel. 860/713–5095; Carol Wilson, Director; das.ct.gov/cr1.aspx?page=8

Consolidated Supply Chain Services, LLC
Warrendale, PA

Consorta, Inc.
see HealthTrust Purchasing Group, LP

Cooperative Services
see Cooperative Services of Florida, Inc.

Cooperative Services of Florida, Inc., 2727 Winkler Avenue, Fort Myers, FL 33901; tel. 239/939–8771; FAX. 239/939–8877; Robert Simpson, President and Chief Executive Officer; www.csofl.com

CRC Health Group Inc., 20400 Stevens Creek Boulevard, 6th Floor, Cupertino, CA 95014; tel. 877/637–6237; Jerome E. Rhodes, Chief Executive Officer; www.crchealth.com

D

Defense Logistics Agency, Andrew T. McNamara Building, 8725 John J. Kingman Road, Fort Belvoir, VA 22060-6221; tel. 877/352–2255; Mark D. Harnitchek, Vice Admiral, SC, USN, Director; www.dla.mil/Pages/default.aspx

Department of Central Management Services
see Illinois Department of Central Management Services

Department of General Services State Office of Procurement
see California Department of General Services, Procurement Division

Department of Veterans Affairs
see U.S. Department of Veterans Affairs VISN listings

Dignity Health Purchasing Network, LLC, 3030 North 3rd Avenue, Phoenix, AZ 85013; Keith Callahan, Director; purchasingnetwork.dignityhealth.org

Division of Purchasing
see Missouri Office of Administration, Division of Purchasing & Materials Management

DSSI, LLC, 40 Oak Hollow Street, Suite 225, Southfield, MI 48033; tel. 248/208–8375; Bhagwan P. Thacker, President, Founder and Chief Executive Officer; www.directsourcing.com

E

East Florida Supply Chain Center
see HealthTrust Purchasing Group, LP

ETMC Regional Healthcare System
see FirstChoice Cooperative

F

Fairview Premier
see Fairview Purchasing Network

Fairview Purchasing Network, 400 Stinson Boulevard., N.E., Minneapolis, MN 55413; tel. 612/672–4409; FAX. 612/672–4440; Laurel Sampson, Manager; www.fairview.org/About/PurchasingNetwork/index.htm

First Choice Cooperative
see FirstChoice Cooperative

FirstChoice Cooperative, 4815 Troup Highway, Tyler, TX 75703; tel. 800/250–3457; Ron Kethan; www.fccoop.org:8080/web/guest

FMOL Health System
see ROi

Forum Sparks, MD

G

GNYHA Services, Inc., 555 West 57th Street, 15th floor, New York, NY 10019; tel. 212/246–7100; FAX. 212/262–6350; Lee H. Perlman, FACHE, President; www.gnyhaservices.com/1/Default.aspx

Great Lakes Healthcare
see VHA Inc. - Great Lakes Healthcare Purchasing Network (supply network)

Greater New York Hospital Association
see GNYHA Services, Inc.

GSA
see U.S. General Services Administration

Gulf South Medical Supply, 4345 Southpoint Boulevard, Jacksonville, FL 32216; tel. 800/347–2456; FAX. 800/827–2002; www.pssworldmedical.com/gs/#

H

Hartford Hospital, 80 Seymour Street, Hartford, CT 06102; tel. 860/545–5000; FAX. 860/545–5066; Stuart K. Markowitz, MD, FACR, President; www.harthosp.org/default.aspx

Hawaii Health Systems Corporation, 3675 Kilauea Avenue, Honolulu, HI 96816; tel. 808/733–4168; Joseph Evanoff, Corporate Director of Contract and Materials Management; www.hhsc.org/procurement/default.aspx

HCA
see HealthTrust Purchasing Group, LP

Health Affiliated Services
see Alliant Purchasing, LLC

Health Care Purchasing
see HealthTrust Purchasing Group, LP

Health Enterprises
see Health Enterprises Cooperative

Health Enterprises Cooperative, 5825 Dry Creek Lane, N.E., Cedar Rapids, IA 52402; tel. 319/368–3621; FAX. 319/368–3626; Jeanie Brown, Vice President; www.healthenterprises.org/aboutHec.html

Health Enterprises of Iowa
see Health Enterprises Cooperative

Health Future, LLC, 916 Town Centre Drive, Medford, OR 97504; tel. 541/772–3062; Leslie A. Flick, Executive Director; www.healthfuture.org

Health Purchasing Alliance, Inc.
see Healthcare Purchasing Alliance, Inc.

Health Purchasing Group
see HealthTrust Purchasing Group, LP

Health Trust
see HealthTrust Purchasing Group, LP

Health Trust Purchasing
see HealthTrust Purchasing Group, LP

Healthcare Coalition of Texas
see Texas Purchasing Coalition

Healthcare Purchasing Alliance, LLC, 8529 Southpark Circle, Suite 250, Orlando, FL 32819; tel. 321/841–4724; FAX. 321/843–4724; Rick Schooler, President; www.hpallc.org

Healthcare Purchasing Group
see HealthTrust Purchasing Group, LP

HealthGroup of Alabama, Huntsville Hospital, 101 Sivley Road, Huntsville, AL 35801; tel. 256/922–6683; Rob Smith, Chief Executive Officer; www.huntsvillehospital.org/services/hga

HealthSouth Corporation
see MedAssets, Inc.

HealthTrust
see HealthTrust Purchasing Group, LP

HealthTrust Partners Group
see HealthTrust Purchasing Group, LP

HealthTrust Purchasing Group (HPG)
see HealthTrust Purchasing Group, LP

HealthTrust Purchasing Group, LP, 155 Franklin Road, Suite 400, Brentwood, TN 37027; tel. 615/344–3000; Ed Jones, President and Chief Executive Officer; www.healthtrustpg.com

Hospital Group Purchasing
see HealthTrust Purchasing Group, LP

Hospital Purchasing Services
see HPS MI, Inc.

Hospital Shared SVS Amerinet
see Amerinet, Inc.

HPG
see HealthTrust Purchasing Group, LP

HPPI/Innovation
see Provista

HPS MI, Inc., 3275 North M-37 Highway, P.O. Box 247, Middleville, MI 49333-0247; tel. 800/632–4572; FAX. 269/795–9788; Tom LaPres, President and Chief Executive Officer; www.hpsnet.net

HPSI, 1 Ada, Suite 150, Irvine, CA 92618; tel. 800/223–4774; David Lindahl, Managing Director, Sales and Marketing; www.hpsionline.com

HSCA
see MedAssets, Inc.

HSI Group Purchasing Division, P.O. Box 7340, Bismarck, ND 58507-7340; tel. 701/224–9732; FAX. 701/224–9529; Jerry Jurena, President; www.advantage-healthcare.net

HSS/Amerinet
see Amerinet, Inc.

HTPG
see HealthTrust Purchasing Group, LP

Huntsville Hospital
see HealthGroup of Alabama

HVA
see Novation, LLC

I

IHC/Amerinet
see intermountain Healthcare Supply Chain Organization

Illinois Department of Central Management Services, JRTC Suite 4-500, 100 West Randolph, Chicago, IL 60601-3219; tel. 312/814–2141; Malcolm Weems, Director; www2.illinois.gov/cms/Pages/default.aspx

Illinois Purchasing Collaborative
see IPC Group Purchasing

Indian Health Service, Division of Acquisition and Policy, 12300 Twinbrook Parkway, Suite 605, Rockville, MD 20852; tel. 301/443–5774; FAX. 301/443–1329; Dale Burson, Director; www.ihs.gov/DAP/index.cfm?module=home

Indiana University Health
see IU Health Supply Chain Operations

Innovatix, LLC, 555 West 57th Street, 12th floor, New York, NY 10019; tel. 888/258–3273; FAX. 646/638–2641; John P. Sganga, FACHE, President and Chief Executive Officer; www.innovatix.com

Intermountain Healthcare
see Intermountain Healthcare Supply Chain Organization

Intermountain Healthcare Supply Chain Organization, 7302 South Bingham Junction Boulevard, Midvale, UT 84047-4804; tel. 800/442–9023; Brent Johnson, Vice President, Supply Chain & Support Services, Chief Purchasing Officer; intermountainhealthcare.org/about/contactus/Pages/supply-chain.aspx

Iowa Health System
see UnityPoint Health

IPC Group Purchasing, 1151 East Warrenville Road, Naperville, IL 60563; tel. 630/276–5400; Patrick Sonin, Managing Executive; www.ipcgrouppurchasing.com

Iroquois Health Alliance
see United Iroquois Shared Services, Inc.

IU Health Supply Chain Operations; tel. 317/962–3556; iuhealth.org/about-iu-health/vendor-relations

J

JHHU
see Johns Hopkins Health System Purchasing Department

Johns Hopkins Health System Purchasing Department, Supply Chain Shared Service Center, 3910 Keswick Road, Baltimore, MD 21211; tel. 443/997–4900; FAX. 443/997–5630; Kenneth Grant, Vice President, General Services and Supply Chain; www.hopkinsmedicine.org/purchasing

K

Kaiser National Purchasing Organization
see Kaiser Permanente

Kaiser Permanente, One Kaiser Plaza, Oakland, CA 94612-3600; tel. 510/271–5910; Laurel Junk, Vice President, Supply Chain; https://healthy.kaiserpermanente.org/html/kaiser/index.shtml

Kansas Department of Administration, Office of Procurement and Contracts, 800 S.W. Jackson, Suite 600, Topeka, KS 66612; tel. 785/296–2376; FAX. 785/296–7240; Mark J. McGivern, Director; www.da.ks.gov/purch

Kindred Healthcare, Inc., 680 South Fourth Street, Louisville, KY 40202; tel. 800/545–0749; Paul J. Diaz, Chief Executive Officer; www.kindredhealthcare.com

Section C

M

MaineHealth, 110 Free Street, Portland, ME 04101; tel. 207/661-7001; FAX. 207/661-7029; William L. Caron, Jr., President; www.mainehealth.org

Managed Health Care Associates, Inc., 25-A Vreeland Road, Suite 200, Florham Park, NJ 07932-0789; tel. 800/642-3020; FAX. 973/966-5529; Michael J. Sicilian, President; www.mhainc.com/default.aspx

Managed Healthcare Association
see Managed Health Care Associates, Inc.

Marianna CBOC
see U.S. Department of Veterans Affairs, VISN 8: VA Sunshine Healthcare Network

Massachusetts Executive Office for Administration and Finance, State House, Room 373, Boston, MA 02133; tel. 617/727-2040; FAX. 617/727-2779; Glen Shor, Secretary; www.mass.gov/anf

McKesson Corporation, One Post Street, San Francisco, CA 94104; tel. 415/983-8300; John H. Hammergren, Chairman, President and Chief Executive Officer; www.mckesson.com

Med Assets
see MedAssets, Inc.

Med Assets Prime
see PRIME

Med-Op, Inc., 205 East 7th Street, Suite 133, Hays, KS 67601; tel. 785/621-4510; FAX. 785/621-4511; David Brittain, Executive Director; www.medopinc.com

MedAssets, Inc., 100 North Point Center East, Suite 200, Alpharetta, GA 30022; tel. 888/883-6332; John A. Bardis, Founder, Chairman, President and Chief Executive Officer; www.medassets.com

MedCenter Direct, 3350 Peachtree Road, N.E., Suite 1610, Atlanta, GA 30326; tel. 404/233-2563

Medi-Sota, 1280 Locust Street, Suite 16, Dawson, MN 56232; tel. 320/769-2269; FAX. 320/769-2298; Deb Ranallo, Director; www.medi-sota.org/main

Medical Assets
see MedAssets, Inc.

Medline Industries, Inc., One Medline Place, Mundelein, IL 60060; tel. 800/633-5463; FAX. 800/351-1512; Charlie Mills, Chief Executive Officer; www.medline.com

Mercy Health Network-North Iowa
see ROi

Mercy ROi
see ROi

MHA Ventures, Inc., P. O. Box 5119, Helena, MT 59604; tel. 406/442-1911; FAX. 406/443-3894; Kristyn Hansard, Group Purchasing Program Coordinator; www.mtha.org/ventures1.htm

Mid-America Service Solutions
see VHA, Inc. - Mid-America Service Solutions CSC, LLC (supply network)

Mid-Atlantic Health Care Network
see U.S. Department of Veterans Affairs, VISN 6: Mid-Atlantic Health Care Network

Minnesota Multi-State Contract Purchasing
see Minnesota Multistate Contracting Alliance for Pharmacy

Minnesota Multistate Contracting Alliance for Pharmacy, (MMCAP), State of Minnesota, Department of Administration, 50 Sherburne Avenue, St. Paul, MN 55155; tel. 651/201-2420; Alan Dahlgren, Managing Director; www.mmd.admin.state.mn.us/mmcap

Minnesota Rural Health Alliance
see Rural Health Alliance

Missouri Division of Purchasing
see Missouri Office of Administration, Division of Purchasing & Materials Management

Missouri Office of Administration, Division of Purchasing & Materials Management, Harry S Truman Building, 301 West High Street, Jefferson City, MO 65101; tel. 573/751-2387; FAX. 573/526-9815; Karen Boeger, CPPB, Director; www.oa.mo.gov/purch

Morris & Dickenson Co. LLC
see Morris and Dickson Co., L.L.C.

Morris and Dickson Co., L.L.C., 410 Kay Lane, Shreveport, LA 71115; tel. 800/388-3833; FAX. 318/798-6007; www.morrisdickson.com/default.aspx

MSS
see VHA Inc. - Mid-America Service Solutions CSC, LLC (supply network)

N

National Acquisition Center
see U.S. Department of Veterans Affairs, National Acquisition Center

National Service Supply Center
see Indian Health Service, Division of Acquisition and Policy

Nebraska Purchasing Group LLC
see Prairie Health Ventures

Network Logistics Office
see U.S. Department of Veterans Affairs, VISN 22: Desert Pacific Healthcare Network

Nevada Healthcare Cooperative, 1000 Ryland Street, Suite 403, Reno, NV 89502; Gary Michealree, President

New England Alliance for Health, One Medical Center Drive, Lebanon, NH 03756; tel. 603/650-5000; Stephen J. LeBlanc, Executive Director; www.neahllc.org

New England Regional Health Care Cooperative, 575 Beech Street, Holyoke, MA 01040; tel. 413/534-2824; FAX. 413/534-2650; Richard M. Buzzee, Executive Director; www.nerhcc.org

New Jersey Hospital Association, 782 Alexander Road, Princeton, NJ 08543; tel. 972/910-6676; Susan Revell; www.njha.com/business-services/purchasing-solutions-provista

New York City Health and Hospitals Corporation, Office of Materials Management, 346 Broadway, 5th floor West, New York, NY 10013; tel. 212/442-3933; Richard Olah, Acting Senior Director; www.nyc.gov/html/hhc/html/contact/Contact-DoingBizWithHHC.shtml

New York State Office of General Services, New York State Procurement, Corning Tower, 38th Floor, Albany, NY 12242; tel. 518/474-6717; RoAnn M. Destito, Commissioner; ogs.ny.gov/BU/PC

New York State Office of Mental Health, 44 Holland Avenue, Albany, NY 12229; tel. 800/597-8481; Ann Marie T. Sullivan, MD, Acting Commissioner; www.omh.ny.gov/index.html

North Carolina Department of Administration, Division of Purchase & Contract, 116 West Jones Street, 4th Floor (Receptionist Office 4062), Raleigh, NC 27603-8002; tel. 919/807-4500; FAX. 919/807-4511; Patti Bowers, State Purchasing Officer; www.pandc.nc.gov/index.htm

Northeast Purchasing Coalition
see VHA Inc. - New England (regional office)

Northern Michigan Supply Alliance, LLC, 2651 Aero Park Drive, Traverse City, MI 49686; tel. 231/935-8233; Mark Deponio, Vice President; www.nmsa-mi.org/?id=865&sid=11

Northwest Ohio Shared Services, 3231 Central Park West Drive, Suite 200, Toledo, OH 43617; tel. 419/842-0800; FAX. 419/843-8886; John Pilewski, Vice President; www.hcno.org/noss/noss.html

Novation PHCD
see Novation, LLC

Novation UHC
see Novation, LLC

Novation VHA
see Novation, LLC

Novation, LLC, 290 East John Carpenter Freeway, Irving, TX 75062; tel. 888/766-8283; Jody Hatcher, President and Chief Executive Officer; www.novationco.com/default.asp

Novation/Provista
see Novaton, LLC

Novation/WVHN
see Wisconsin Valley Health Network, LLC

NYC Health and Hospitals Corporation
see New York City Health and Hospitals Corporation, Office of Materials Management

O

Office of General Services (NY)
see New York State Office of General Services, New York State Procurement

Office of General Services (OH)
see Ohio Department of Administrative Services, Office of Procurement Services

Ohio Department of Administrative Services, Office of Procurement Services, 4200 Surface Road, Columbus, OH 43228; tel. 614/466-5090; FAX. 614/485-1056; Gretchen Adkins, Chief Procurement Officer; das.ohio.gov/Divisions/GeneralServices/ProcurementServices.aspx

Ohio Health Corporation
see OhioHealth Corporation

Ohio State Health Network, 660 Ackerman Road, Columbus, OH 43202; tel. 888/722-6746; FAX. 614/293-3768; Tom Blincoe, Executive Director; oshn.osu.edu/services/grouppurchase

OhioHealth Corporation, 180 East Broad Street, Columbus, OH 43215; tel. 614/544-4455; Bob Boswell, Vice President, Supply Chain; www.ohiohealth.com

OUHSC
see University of Oklahoma, Purchasing Department

Owens & Minor, Inc., 9120 Lockwood Boulevard, Mechanicsville, VA 23116; tel. 804/723-7000; FAX. 804/723-7100; Craig R. Smith, Chairman and Chief Executive Officer; www.owens-minor.com/Pages/default.aspx

P

Pace Premier
see Avera PACE

Partners Cooperative, Inc., 3625 Cumberland Boulevard, S.E., Suite 1425, Atlanta, GA 30339; tel. 678/842-7300; FAX. 678/842-7329; Karen Becker; pcgpo.org

Partners HealthCare, Materials Management, 529 Main Street, Charlestown, MA 02129; tel. 617/726-2142; www.partners.org/About/Vendor-Information/Default.aspx

PeaceHealth Oregon Region
see Premier, Inc.

Pennsylvania Department of General Services, 515 North Office Building, Harrisburg, PA 17125; tel. 717/787-5996; FAX. 717/772-2026; Sheri L. Phillips, Secretary; www.dgs.state.pa.us/portal/server.pt/community/department_of_general_services/1230

PR Hospital Association
see Puerto Rico Hospital Association

Prairie Health Ventures, 421 South 9th Street, Suite 102, Lincoln, NE 68508-2245; tel. 800/409-4990; FAX. 402/476-7422; David Christensen, Chief Executive Officer; www.phvne.com

Premier Purchasing
see Premier, Inc.

Premier, Inc., 13034 Ballantyne Corporate Place, Charlotte, NC 28277; tel. 877/777-1552; Durral R. Gilbert, President, Supply Chain Services; www.premierinc.com

Premier/CCG
see Premier, Inc.

Premier/Fairview
see Fairview Purchasing Network

Premier/GNYHA
see GNYHA Services, Inc.

Premier/IPC
see IPC Group Purchasing

Premier/Medline
see Medline Industries, Inc.

Premier/Seagate
see Seagate Alliance, LLC

Premier/Yankee
see Yankee Alliance

PRIME, 6820 Deerpath Road, Elkridge, MD 21075-6200; tel. 800/899–2199; FAX. 410/379–8239; Nancy Davenport, Senior Vice President; www.mhaprime.org

Prime Med Assets
see PRIME

Providence Health & Services, 1801 Lind Avenue, S.W., Suite 9016, Renton, WA 98057; tel. 425/525–3355; Dave Hunter, Vice President, Supply Chain Management; www2.providence.org/Pages/default.aspx

Provider Supply Chain Partners, Fifth Avenue Place - 25th Floor, 120 Fifth Avenue, Pittsburgh, PA 15222; tel. 412/544–0271; Michael Monahan, Vice President, Supply Chain Operations; www.providerscp.com/index.shtml

Provista, 290 East John Carpenter Freeway, Irving, TX 75062; tel. 888/538–4662; Dan Thomas, President; www.provistaco.com/Pages/default.aspx

Puerto Rico Hospital Association, Villa Nevarez Professional Center, Suite 101, San Juan, PR 00927; tel. 787/764–0290; FAX. 787/753–9748; Domingo Cruz, President; hospitalespr.org

Q

QHR
see HealthTrust Purchasing Group, LP

Quorum Health Resources
see HealthTrust Purchasing Group, LP

R

Rapid City Regional Hospital
see Regional Health

Regional Health, 353 Fairmont Boulevard, Rapid City, SD 57701; tel. 605/755–1000; Charles E. Hart, MD, MS, President and Chief Executive Officer; www.regionalhealth.com

Resource Optimization & Innovation
see ROi

RHS Materials Management
see Riverside Health System

Riverside Health System, Fountain Plaza One, Suite 1000, Newport News, VA 23606; tel. 757/534–7000; William B. Downey, President and Chief Executive Officer; www.riversideonline.com/index.cfm

ROi, 645 Maryville Centre Drive, Suite 200, St. Louis, MO 63141; tel. 314/364–6400; Gene Kirtser, President and Chief Executive Officer; www.roiscs.com

Rural Health Alliance, 1210 South Broadway, Suite 240, Alexandria, MN 56308; tel. 320/762–8602; Erik Malchow, President; myrha.com

S

Sanford Health
see Sanford Supply Chain Management

Sanford Supply Chain Management, 1305 West 18th Street, P.O. Box 5039, Sioux Falls, SD 57117-5039; tel. 605/333–6490; www.sanfordhealth.org/About/SupplyChain

SCM Alliance, Inc.; tel. 904/543–8799; John J. Little, Executive Vice President; www.coalescoinc.com/218-client-scm-alliance,-inc.html

SCMA Alliance, Inc.
see SCM Alliance, Inc.

Seagate Alliance, LLC, 3445 Winton Place, Suite 222, Rochester, NY 14623-2950; tel. 888/732–4282; FAX. 585/273–8189; Diane H. Ashley, President and Chief Executive Officer; www.seagatealliance.com

Seneca Medical, 85 Shaffer Park Drive, P.O. Box 399, Tiffin, OH 44883; tel. 800/447–0225; FAX. 419/447–7201; Roger Benz, President and Chief Executive Officer; www.senecamedical.com/wps/portal/aboutUs

Servi-Share
see ServiShare

ServiShare, 100 East Grand Avenue, Suite 100, Des Moines, IA 50309; tel. 800/240–1046; FAX. 515/283–9366; Dennis White, Senior Vice President, ServiShare; www.ihaonline.org/iMIS15/IHAOnline/Members_Groups/ServiShare_home.aspx

Shared Health
see Shared Purchasing Solutions

Shared Health Services
see Shared Purchasing Solutions

Shared Purchasing Solutions, 2635 Hemstock Street, La Crosse, WI 54603-2395; tel. 800/657–4445; FAX. 608/781–4412; Wade E. Turner, Executive Director; www.sps-gpo.com

Shared Service Systems, 1725 South 20th Street, Omaha, NE 68108; tel. 800/228–9976; www.sharedomaha.com/default.asp

Shared Services
see Shared Service Systems

Sisters of Charity of Leavenworth Health System Buying Department, 2420 West 26th Avenue, Suite D-100, Denver, CO 80211; tel. 303/813–5190; Michael Slubowski, FACHE, FACMPE, President and Chief Executive Officer; www.sclhealthsystem.org/vendors

Sisters of Mercy Health System
see ROi

Spectrum Health
see VHA Inc.

SSMC-Premier
see Premier, Inc.

St. Mary's Medical Center, 2900 First Avenue, Huntington, WV 25702; tel. 304/526–1234; Michael G. Sellards, President and Chief Executive Officer; www.st-marys.org

St. Vincent Health
see The Resource Group, LLC

State of California State Purchasing
see California Department of General Services

State of Connecticut Procurement Services
see Connecticut Department of Administrative Services, State Procurement Marketplace

State of Kansas State Purchasing
see Kansas Department of Administration, Office of Procurement and Contracts

State of Missouri State Purchasing
see Missouri Office of Administration, Division of Purchasing & Materials Management

State of North Carolina State Purchasing
see North Carolina Department of Administration, Division of Purchase & Contract

State of Texas State Purchasing
see Texas Facilities Commission

State of West Virginia Purchasing
see West Virginia Purchasing Division

T

Tehachapi Family Health Center - Mojave
see Tehachapi Valley Healthcare District

Tehachapi Valley Healthcare District, 115 West E Street, P.O. Box 1900, Tehachapi, CA 93581-1900; tel. 661/823–3000; Evan J. Rayner, Interim Chief Executive Officer; www.tvhd.org/getpage.php?name=index

Tenet Health/Broadlane
see MedAssets, Inc.

Tenet Health/MedAssets
see MedAssets, Inc.

Texas Children's Hospital
see Novation, LLC

Texas Facilities Commission, 1711 San Jacinto, Austin, TX 78701; tel. 512/463–3446; Terry Keel, Executive Director; www.tfc.state.tx.us

Texas Health Resources, Supply Chain Management, 612 East Lamar Boulevard, Suite 1100, Arlington, TX 76011; tel. 682/236–7517; John Gaida, Senior Vice President, Supply Chain Management; www.texashealth.org/vendorcompliance

Texas Purchasing Coalition, 7160 Dallas Parkway, Suite 600, Plano, TX 75024; tel. 469/366–2100; FAX. 469/366–2101; Geoff Brenner, President and Chief Executive Officer; www.texaspurchasingcoalition.com/content/home/?id=1390

THA Solutions Group, 5201 Virginia Way, Brentwood, TN 37027; tel. 615/256–8240; FAX. 615/242–4803; Jim Goodloe, Senior Vice President; www.tha.com/Default.aspx?pid=12

The Resource Group, LLC, 4600 Edmundson Road, St. Louis, MO 63134; tel. 314/733–8000; Scott Caldwell, Chief Executive Officer; www.ascensionhealth.org/index.php?option=com_content&view=article&id=365&Itemid=289

TN Hospital Association Group
see THA Solutions Group

Trinity Health, Supply Chain Management, 20555 Victor Parkway, Livonia, MI 48152; tel. 734/343–1000; Louis J. Fierens, II, Senior Vice President, Supply Chain and Capital Projects Management; www.trinity-health.org/supply-chain-management

U

U.S. Department of Veterans Affairs, National Acquisition Center, 1st Avenue, North of Cermack Road, P.O. Box 76, Hines, IL 60141; tel. 708/786–5157; FAX. 708/786–5148; Craig Robinson, Associate Deputy Assistant Secretary for National Healthcare Acquisitions; www.va.gov/oal/about/nac.asp

U.S. Department of Veterans Affairs, VISN 1: VA New England Healthcare System, 200 Springs Road, Building 61, Bedford, MA 01730; tel. 781/687–4821; FAX. 781/687–3470; Michael F. Mayo-Smith, MD, MPH, Network Director; www.newengland.va.gov

U.S. Department of Veterans Affairs, VISN 2: VA Health Care Upstate New York, 113 Holland Avenue, Building 67, Albany, NY 12208; tel. 518/626–7327; Darlene Delancey, MT ASCP, MS, Interim Network Director; www.visn2.va.gov

U.S. Department of Veterans Affairs, VISN 3: VA NY/NJ Veterans Healthcare Network, 130 West Kingsbridge Road, Bronx, NY 10468; tel. 718/584–9000; FAX. 718/741–4269; Michael A. Sabo, MBA, FACHE, Network Director; www.nynj.va.gov

U.S. Department of Veterans Affairs, VISN 5: VA Capitol Health Care Network, 849 International Drive, Suite 275, Linthicum, MD 21090; tel. 410/691–1131; Fernando O. Rivera, MBA, FACHE, Network Director; www.va.gov/visn5

U.S. Department of Veterans Affairs, VISN 6: Mid-Atlantic Health Care Network, 300 West Morgan Street, Suite 700, Durham, NC 27701; tel. 919/956–5541; FAX. 919/956–7152; Daniel F. Hoffmann, FACHE, Network Director; www.visn6.va.gov

U.S. Department of Veterans Affairs, VISN 7: VA Southeast Network, 3700 Crestwood Parkway, Suite 500, Duluth, GA 30096; tel. 678/924–5700; FAX. 678/924–5757; Charles Sepich, FACHE, Network Director; www.southeast.va.gov

Section C

U.S. Department of Veterans Affairs, VISN 8: VA Sunshine Healthcare Network, 140 Fountain Parkway, Suite 600, St. Petersburg, FL 33716; tel. 727/575–8069; FAX. 727/575–8093; Jolene Clark, MBA, FACHE, Network Director; www.visn8.va.gov/VISN8/index.asp

U.S. Department of Veterans Affairs, VISN 9: VA MidSouth Healthcare Network, 1801 West End Avenue, Suite 600, Nashville, TN 37203; tel. 615/695–2200; FAX. 615/321–2721; John E. Patrick, Network Director; www.visn9.va.gov/about/index.asp

U.S. Department of Veterans Affairs, VISN 10: VA Healthcare System of Ohio, 11500 Northlake Drive, Suite 200, Cincinnati, OH 45249; Jack Hetrick, Network Director; www.visn10.va.gov

U.S. Department of Veterans Affairs, VISN 11: Veterans in Partnership, P. O. Box 134002, Ann Arbor, MI 48113-4002; tel. 734/222–4300; FAX. 734/222–4340; Paul Bockelman, Network Director; www.visn11.va.gov

U.S. Department of Veterans Affairs, VISN 12: VA Great Lakes Health Care System, Four Westbrook Corporate Tower, 11301 West Cermak Road, Westchester, IL 60154; tel. 708/492–3900; FAX. 708/492–3948; Jeffrey A. Murawsky, MD, Network Director; www.visn12.va.gov

U.S. Department of Veterans Affairs, VISN 15: VA Heartland Network, 1201 Walnut Street, Suite 800, Kansas City, MO 64106; tel. 816/701–3000; William P. Patterson, MD, Network Director; www.visn15.va.gov

U.S. Department of Veterans Affairs, VISN 16: South Central VA Health Care Network, 715 South Pear Orchard Road, Plaza 1, Ridgeland, MS 39157; tel. 601/206–6900; FAX. 601/206–7018; Rica Lewis-Peyton, Network Director; www.visn16.va.gov

U.S. Department of Veterans Affairs, VISN 17: VA Heart of Texas Health Care Network, 2301 East Lamar Boulevard, Suite 650, Arlington, TX 76006; tel. 817/652–1111; FAX. 817/385–3700; Joe Dalpiaz, Network Director; www.heartoftexas.va.gov

U.S. Department of Veterans Affairs, VISN 18: VA Southwest Health Care Network, 335 East Germann Road, Suite 201, Gilbert, AZ 85297; tel. 480/397–2700; Susan P. Bowers, Network Director; www.southwest.va.gov

U.S. Department of Veterans Affairs, VISN 19: Rocky Mountain Network, 4100 East Mississippi Avenue, Suite 1100, Glendale, CO 80246; tel. 303/756–9279; FAX. 303/756–9243; Ralph T. Gigliotti, Network Director; www.visn19.va.gov

U.S. Department of Veterans Affairs, VISN 20: Northwest Health Network, P. O. Box 1035, Portland, OR 97207; tel. 360/619–5925; FAX. 360/690–0868; Lawrence H. Carroll, Network Director; www.visn20.med.va.gov

U.S. Department of Veterans Affairs, VISN 21: Sierra Pacific Network, 201 Walnut Avenue, Mare Island, CA 94592; tel. 707/562–8350; FAX. 707/562–8369; Sheila M. Cullen, Network Director; www.visn21.va.gov/index.asp

U.S. Department of Veterans Affairs, VISN 22: Desert Pacific Healthcare Network CA; www.desertpacific.va.gov

U.S. Department of Veterans Affairs, VISN 23: VA Midwest Health Care Network, 2805 Dodd Road, Suite 250, Eagan, MN 55121; tel. 651/405–5600; FAX. 651/452–0399; Janet P. Murphy, Network Director; www.visn23.va.gov

U.S. Department of Veterans Affairs, VISN 4, 323 North Shore Drive, Suite 400, Pittsburgh, PA 15212; tel. 412/822–3316; FAX. 412/822–3275; Gary W. Devansky, Interim Network Director; www.visn4.va.gov

U.S. General Services Administration, 1800 F Street, N.W., Washington, DC 20405; tel. 202/501–0800; Dan M. Tangherlini, Administrator; www.gsa.gov/portal/category/100000

UH Supply Chain Services
see Owens & Minor, Inc.

UHC, 155 North Wacker Drive, Chicago, IL 60606; tel. 312/775–4100; Jake J. Groenewold, MBA, Senior Vice President, Supply Chain; www.uhc.edu/1408.htm

UHC/Novation
see UHC

UHN/Novation
see UHC

UHS Consortium
see Universal Health Services, Inc., Supply Chain

UMCSC
see VHA Inc. - Upper Midwest Consolidated Services Center, LLC (supply network)

United Iroquois Shared Services, Inc., 5740 Commons Park, East Syracuse, NY 13057; tel. 800/772-4090; FAX. 315/445–2293; Terry A. Field, Manager, Supply Chain Strategies; www.iroquois.org/uiss

UnityPoint Health, 1776 West Lakes Parkway, Suite 400, West Des Moines, IA 50266; tel. 515/241–6161; Katie Marchik, Vice President, Supply Chain Management; www.unitypoint.org

Universal Health Services, Inc., Supply Chain, 367 South Gulph Road, P.O. Box 61558, King of Prussia, PA 19406; tel. 610/768–3300; Alan B. Miller, Chief Executive Officer and Chairman of the Board; www.uhsinc.com/about-us/uhs-supply-chain

University HealthSystem Consortium
see UHC

University of Iowa, Accounts Payable, Purchasing and Travel Department, 202 Plaza Centre One, Iowa City, IA 52242; tel. 319/335–0115; FAX. 319/335–2443; Deborah Zumbach, Senior Associate Director - Business Services and Director of Purchasing; www.uiowa.edu/purchasing/p_index.htm

University of Oklahoma, Purchasing Department, 2750 Venture Drive, Norman, OK 73069-8279; tel. 405/325–2811; FAX. 405/329–8394; Jan Duke, Associate Director - Purchasing/Property Control; www.ou.edu/purchasing/index.html

UP Health Care Network
see Upper Peninsula Health Care Network

UPHCN
see Upper Peninsula Health Care Network

UPMC Supply Chain Management, 200 Lothrop Street, Pittsburgh, PA 15213-2582; tel. 800/533–8762; Jeffrey A. Romoff, President and Chief Executive Officer; www.upmc.com/about/partners/supply-chain/Pages/default.aspx

Upper Midwest Consolidated Services Center
see VHA Inc. - Upper Midwest Consolidated Services Center, LLC (supply network)

Upper Midwest CSC/Novation
see VHA Inc. - Upper Midwest Consolidated Services Center, LLC (supply network)

Upper Peninsula Health Care Network, 228 West Washington Street, Suite 2, Marquette, MI 49855; tel. 906/225–3146; FAX. 906/225–7868; Dennis H. Smith, Executive Director; www.uphcn.org

V

Vantage Purchasing Partners, 1305 South Main Street, Meadville, PA 16335; tel. 814/337–0000; Anne Poux, Director; www.vantagevpp.com

Vantage/Premier
see Vantage Purchasing Partners

VHA AROK
see VHA Inc. - AROK Purchasing Coalition, LLC (supply network)

VHA BJC
see BJC HealthCare

VHA Central
see VHA Inc. - Central (regional office)

VHA Gulf States
see VHA Inc. - Gulf States, Inc. (regional office)

VHA Inc., 290 East John Carpenter Freeway, Irving, TX 75062; tel. 800/842–5146; Curt Nonomaque, President and Chief Executive Officer; www.vha.com

VHA Inc. - AROK Purchasing Coalition, LLC (supply network); Scott Snider; https://www.vha.com/Networking/SupplyNetworks/Documents/Profile_AROK.pdf

VHA Inc. - Central (regional office), 8900 Keystone Crossing, Suite 480, Indianapolis, IN 46240; tel. 317/818–8000; https://www.vha.com/AboutVHA/Offices/Central/Pages/Default.aspx

VHA Inc. - Central Atlantic (regional office); https://www.vha.com/AboutVHA/Offices/CentralAtlantic/Pages/Default.aspx

VHA Inc. - Central Atlantic Health Network, LLC (supply network); Jerri Phillips; https://www.vha.com/Networking/SupplyNetworks/Documents/Profile_CentralAtlanticHeatlthNetwork.pdf

VHA Inc. - Friendship 7 Sourcing Collaborative (supply network); Robyn Retterer; https://www.vha.com/Networking/SupplyNetworks/Documents/Profile_Friendship.pdf

VHA Inc. - Georgia (regional office), 900 Circle 75 Parkway, Suite 1450, Atlanta, GA 30339; tel. 770/850–7400; https://www.vha.com/AboutVHA/Offices/Georgia/Pages/Default.aspx

VHA Inc. - Great Lakes Healthcare Purchasing Network (supply network); Linda Avery; https://www.vha.com/Networking/SupplyNetworks/Documents/Profile_GreatLakesHCPurchasingNetwork.pdf

VHA Inc. - Gulf States Purchasing Coalition (supply network); Kristin Allen; https://www.vha.com/Networking/SupplyNetworks/Documents/Profile_GulfStatesPC.pdf

VHA Inc. - Gulf States, Inc. (regional office), 8940 Bluebonnet Boulevard, Suite 200, Baton Rouge, LA 70810; tel. 225/761–1568; Kathy Christensen, President; https://www.vha.com/AboutVHA/Offices/GulfStates/Pages/Default.aspx

VHA Inc. - Healthcare Service Center, Inc. (supply network); David Matthews; https://www.vha.com/Networking/SupplyNetworks/Documents/Profile_HealthcareServiceCtr.pdf

VHA Inc. - Heartland Sourcing Collaborative (supply network); Dawn Smith; https://www.vha.com/Networking/SupplyNetworks/Documents/Profile_Heartland.pdf

VHA Inc. - Michigan Purchasing Coalition (supply network); Linda Avery; https://www.vha.com/Networking/SupplyNetworks/Documents/Profile_MichiganPC.pdf

VHA Inc. - Mid-America (regional office); https://www.vha.com/AboutVHA/Offices/MidAmerica/Pages/Default.aspx

VHA Inc. - Mid-America Service Solutions CSC, LLC (supply network): Janie Ott; https://www.vha.com/Networking/SupplyNetworks/Documents/Profile_MSS.pdf

VHA Inc. - Mid-Atlantic (regional office), Park West Two, 2000 Cliff Mine Road, Pittsburgh, PA 15275; tel. 412/494–4915; https://www.vha.com/AboutVHA/Offices/Midatlantic/Pages/default.aspx

VHA Inc. - Mid-Atlantic Purchasing Coalition, LLC (supply network); Lyndia Schwab; https://www.vha.com/Networking/SupplyNetworks/Documents/Profile_Mid-AtlanticPC.pdf

VHA Inc. - Midwest Purchasing Coalition (supply network); Mike Eurich; https://www.vha.com/Networking/SupplyNetworks/Documents/Profile_MidwestPurchasingCoalition.pdf

VHA Inc. - MNS Supply Chain Network, LLC (supply network); Krista Marshall; https://www.vha.com/Networking/SupplyNetworks/Documents/Profile_MNS.pdf

VHA Inc. - New England (regional office), 350 Granite Street, Suite 2304, Braintree, MA 02184; tel. 781/794–6500; FAX. 781/794–6529; https://www.vha.com/AboutVHA/Offices/NewEngland/Pages/Default.aspx

VHA Inc. - Northeast Purchasing Coalition (supply network); Steve Roll; https://www.vha.com/Networking/SupplyNetworks/Documents/Profile_NortheastPurchasingCoalition.pdf

VHA Inc. - Oklahoma/Arkansas (regional office), 4013 Northwest Expressway, Oklahoma City, OK 73116; https://www.vha.com/AboutVHA/Offices/OKAR/Pages/Default.aspx

VHA Inc. - Pacific Northwest (regional office), 1600 Lind Avenue, S.W., Suite 180 (The Landmark), Renton, WA 98057; tel. 425/277–3902; https://www.vha.com/AboutVHA/Offices/PacificNW/Pages/default.aspx

VHA Inc. - Southeast Supply Solutions, LLC (supply network); Robert Grady; https://www.vha.com/Networking/SupplyNetworks/Documents/Profile_NortheastPurchasingCoalition.pdf

VHA Inc. - Southeast, Inc. (regional office), 4211 West Boy Scout Boulevard, Suite 750, Tampa, FL 33607; tel. 813/350–8300; FAX. 813/350–8383; https://www.vha.com/AboutVHA/Offices/Southeast/Pages/Default.aspx

VHA Inc. - Upper Midwest (regional office), 7601 France Avenue South, Suite 500, Edina, MN 55435; tel. 952/837–4700; https://www.vha.com/AboutVHA/Offices/UpperMidwest/Pages/Default.aspx

VHA Inc. - Upper Midwest Consolidated Services Center, LLC (supply network); Brad Kaisersatt; https://www.vha.com/Networking/SupplyNetworks/Documents/Profile_UpperMidwestConsolidatedServicesCenterLLC.pdf

VHA Inc. - VHA Pacific Northwest Supply Network (supply network); Bridget Bonning; https://www.vha.com/Networking/SupplyNetworks/Documents/Profile_PacificNorthwestSupplyNetwork.pdf

VHA Inc. - West Coast (regional office), 4900 Hopyard Road, Suite 320, Pleasanton, CA 94588; tel. 888/619–1900; https://www.vha.com/AboutVHA/Offices/WestCoast/Pages/Default.aspx

VHA Inc. - West Coast Purchasing Coalition (supply network); Don Stutsman; https://www.vha.com/Networking/SupplyNetworks/Documents/Profile_WestCoastPC.pdf

VHA Inc. - Western Purchasing Coalition (supply network); Robyn Retterer; https://www.vha.com/Networking/SupplyNetworks/Documents/Profile_WesternPurchasingCoalition.pdf

VHA Mid-America
see VHA Inc. - Mid-America (regional office)

VHA Mid-Atlantic
see VHA Inc. - Mid-Atlantic (regional office)

VHA Mountain States
see VHA Inc. - Mid-America Service Solutions CSC, LLC (supply network)

VHA New England
see VHA Inc. - New England (regional office)

VHA Novation
see Novation, LLC

VHA OK AR
see VHA Inc. - AROK Purchasing Coalition, LLC (supply network)

VHA Pacific Northwest Supply Network
see VHA Inc. - VHA Pacific Northwest Supply Network (supply network)

Via Christi Health, 929 North St. Francis Street, Wichita, KS 67214-3882; tel. 316/268–5000; Jeff Korsmo, President and Chief Executive Officer; www.via-christi.org

Vidant Health, 2100 Stantonsburg Road, P.O. Box 6028, Greenville, NC 27835-6028; tel. 800/472–8500; David C. Herman, MD, President and Chief Executive Officer; https://www.vidanthealth.com/ForVendors

Virginia Department of General Services, Division of Purchases and Supply, 1111 East Broad Street, P.O. Box 1199, Richmond, VA 23218-1199; tel. 804/786–3842; FAX. 804/225–3707; Robert Gleason, Director; dgs.virginia.gov/DivisionofPurchasesandSupply/tabid/418/Default.aspx

VISN
see U.S. Department of Veterans Affairs listings

Voluntary Hospitals of America
see VHA Inc.

Volunteer Hospital Association
see VHA Inc.

W

West Virginia Purchasing Division, 2019 Washington Street, East, Charleston, WV 25305; tel. 304/558–2306; FAX. 304/558–6026; David Tincher, Purchasing Director; www.state.wv.us/admin/purchase/default.html

Wisconsin Valley Health Network, LLC, Aspirus, Inc., 425 Pine Ridge Boulevard, Wausau, WI 54401; tel. 800/283–2881; www.aspirus.org/hospitalsClinics/index.cfm?catID=2&subCatID=16&pageID=681#

WNC Health Network, 1200 Ridgefield Boulevard, Suite 200, Asheville, NC 28806; tel. 877/667–8220; FAX. 828/667–8228; Tim Bugg, President and Chief Executive Officer; www.wnchn.org

WNCHN
see WNC Health Network

WSCA-NASPO Cooperative Purchasing Organization, LLC, 201 East Main Street, Suite 1405, Lexington, KY 40507; tel. 859/402–9774; FAX. 859/514–9166; Lee Ann Pope, WSCA-NASPO Program Manager; www.aboutwsca.org

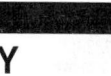

Y

Yankee Alliance, 138 River Road, Andover, MA 01810-1083; tel. 978/470–2000; FAX. 978/681–6100; James W. Oliver, President and Chief Executive Officer; www.yankeealliance.com

Quality Improvement Organizations

The following list of QIOs was obtained from the agencies themselves and the Centers for Medicare and Medicaid Services, Quality Improvement Organization programs.

United States

ALABAMA: Alabama Quality Assurance Foundation, Two Perimeter Park, S., Suite 200 West, Birmingham, AL 35243-2337; tel. 205/970–1600; FAX. 205/970–1616; Wesley Smith, Chief Executive Officer

ALASKA: Mountain-Pacific Quality Health-Alaska QIO, 4241 B Street, Suite 101, Anchorage, AK 99503; tel. 907/561–3202; FAX. 907/561–3204; Sharon C. Scudder, Office Director

ARIZONA: Health Services Advisory Group, Inc., 3133 E. Camelback, Suite 300, Phoenix, AZ 85016; tel. 602/801–6600; FAX. 602/241–0757; Mary Ellen Dalton, PhD, MBA, RN, Chief Executive Officer

ARKANSAS: Arkansas Foundation for Medical Care, Inc., 1020 W 4th Street, Suite 300, Little Rock, AR 72201; tel. 501/212–8660; FAX. 501/374–2826; Ray Hanley, President and Chief Executive Officer

CALIFORNIA: Health Services Advisory Group of California, 700 N. Brand Boulevard, Suite 370, Glendale, CA 91203; tel. 818/409–9229; FAX. 818/409–0835; Rick Potter, Chief Executive Officer

COLORADO: Colorado Foundation for Medical Care (CFMC), 61 Inverness Drive East, Suite 210, Englewood, CO 80112; tel. 720/460–4154; John Bozin, Executive Director
Telligen, 23 Inverness Way East, Suite 100, Englewood, CO 80112; tel. 303/695–3300; FAX. 303/695–3343; Jeff Chungath, Chief Executive Officer

CONNECTICUT: Qualidigm, 1290 Silas Deane Highway, Suite 4A, Wethersfield, CT 06109; tel. 860/632–2008; FAX. 860/632–5865; Timothy Elwell, President and Chief Executive Officer

DELAWARE: Quality Insights of Delaware, Baynard Building Suite 100, 3411 Silverside Rd, Wilmington, DE 19810; tel. 302/478-3600; FAX. 302/478–4109; John C. Wiesendanger, Chief Executive Officer

DISTRICT OF COLUMBIA: Delmarva Foundation of the District of Columbia, 2029 K Street N.W., Suite 700, Washington, DC 20006-1004; tel. 800/937–3362; FAX. 202/293–9650; Fredia S. Wadley, MD, Chief Executive Officer
Delmarva Foundation of the District of Columbia, 2175 K Street, NW, Suite 250, Washington, DC 20037; tel. 800/937–3362; FAX. 202/293–9650; Fredia S. Wadley, MD, MSHPA, Chief Executive Officer

FLORIDA: Florida Medical Quality Assurance. Inc., 5201 W. Kennedy Boulevard, Suite 900, Tampa, FL 33609; tel. 813/354–9111; FAX. 813/354–1319; James Zachary Henshaw, MHA, MPH, MLIS, Chief Executive Officer

GEORGIA: Alliant Georgia Meidical Care Foundation, 1455 Lincoln Parkway, Suite 800, Atlanta, GA 30346; tel. 678/527–3000; FAX. 404/982–7591; Dennis White, President and Chief Executive Officer

HAWAII: Hawaii Health Information Corp. (HHIC), 733 Bishop Street, Suite 1870, Makai Tower, Honolulu, HI 96813-4002; tel. 808/534–0288; FAX. 808/534–0292; Deborah Higashi, Office Manager
Mountain-Pacific Quality Health - Hawaii, 1360 South Beretania Street, Suite 501, Honolulu, HI 96814; tel. 808/545–2550; FAX. 808/440–6030; Dee Dee Nelson, Director of Hawaii Office

ILLINOIS: Telligen, 711 Jorie Blvd, Oak Brook, IL 60523-4425; tel. 630/928–5821; FAX. 630/928–5865; Pat Merryweather, Executive Director

INDIANA: Health Care Excel, 2601 Metropolis Parkway, Suite 200, Plainfield, IN 46168-2299; tel. 317/754-5400; FAX. 317/347-4567; Joy Casterton, Chief Executive Officer

IOWA: Telligen, 1776 West Lakes Parkway, West Des Moines, IA 50266; tel. 515/223–2900; FAX. 515/222–2407; Jeff Chungath, Chief Executive Officer

KANSAS: Kansas Foundation for Medical Care, Inc., 2947 Southwest Wanamaker Drive, Topeka, KS 66614; tel. 785/273–2552; FAX. 785/273–0737; Kenneth Mishler, President and Chief Executive Officer

KENTUCKY: Health Care Excel of Kentucky, Incorporated, 1941 Bishop Lane, Suite 400, Louisville, KY 40218; tel. 502/454–5112; FAX. 502/454–5113; Joy Casterton, Chief Executive Officer

LOUISIANA: eQHealth Solutions, 8591 United Plaza Blvd, Suite 270, Baton Rouge, LA 70809; tel. 225/248–7003; FAX. 225/923–0957; Edie Castello, President and Chief Executive Officer

MASSACHUSETTS: Masspro, 245 Winter Street, Waltham, MA 02451-1231; tel. 781/890–0011; FAX. 781/487–0083; Laura Moore, MPA, President and Chief Executive Officer

MICHIGAN: MPRO, 22670 Haggerty Rd, Suite 100, Farmington Hills, MI 48335-2611; tel. 248/465–7300; FAX. 248/465–7428; Robert J. Yellan, President and Chief Executive Officer

MINNESOTA: Stratis Health, 2901 Metro Drive, Suite 400, Bloomington, MN 55425; tel. 952/854–3306; FAX. 952/853–8503; Jennifer Lundblad, PhD, MBA, Chief Executive Officer

MISSISSIPPI: Information & Quality Healthcare, 385 B Highland Colony Parkway, Suite 504, Ridgeland, MS 39157; tel. 601/957–1575; FAX. 601/956–1713; James McIlwain, MD, President of Medical Affairs

MISSOURI: Primaris, 200 N. Keene Street, Suite 101, Columbia, MO 65201; tel. 573/817–8300; FAX. 573/777–9039; Richard A. Royer, Chief Executive Officer

MONTANA: Mountain-Pacific Quality Health-Montana-Wyoming-Hawaii and Alaska, 3404 Cooney Drive, Helena, MT 59602; tel. 406/443–4020; FAX. 406/513–1920; Sara Medley, Chief Executive Officer

NEBRASKA: CIMRO of Nebraska, 1230 O Street, Suite 120, Lincoln, NE 68508; tel. 402/476–1399; FAX. 402/476–1335; Tina Georgy, Chief Executive Officer

NEW HAMPSHIRE: Northeast Health Care Quality Foundation, 15 Old Rollinsford Road, Suite 302, Dover, NH 03820-2830; tel. 603/749–1641; FAX. 603/749–1195; Robert A. Aurilio, FACHE, President and Chief Executive Officer
Northeast Health Care Quality Foundation - Maine, 15 Old Rollinsford Road, Suite 302, Dover, NH 03820; tel. 603/749–1641; FAX. 603/749–1195; Robert A. Aurilio, FACHE, President and Chief Executive Officer
Northeast Health Care Quality Foundation - Vermont, 15 Old Rollinsford Road, Suite 302, Dover, NH 03820; tel. 603/749–1641; FAX. 603/749–1195; Robert A. Aurilio, FACHE, President and Chief Executive Officer

NEW JERSEY: Healthcare Quality Strategies, Inc., 557 Cranbury Road, Suite 21, East Brunswick, NJ 08816; tel. 732/238–5570; FAX. 732/432–5647; Mary Jane Brubaker, Chief Operating OfficerMary Jane Brubaker, Chief Operating Officer

NEW MEXICO: HealthInsight New Mexico, 5801 Osuna Rd NE, Suite 200, Albuquerque, NM 87109; tel. 505/998–9898; FAX. 505/998–9899; Richard Kozoll, MD, MPH, President, Board of Directors

NEW YORK: IPRO, 1979 Marcus Avenue, Lake Success, NY 11042-1002; tel. 516/326–7767; FAX. 516/328–2310; Theodore O. Will, Chief Executive Officer

NORTH CAROLINA: The Carolinas Center for Medical Excellence, 100 Regency Forest Dr., Suite 200, Cary, NC 27518; tel. 919/461–5500; FAX. 919/461–5700; Melinda Postal, Director of Communications

The Carolinas Center for Medical Excellence, 100 Regency Forest Drive, Suite 200, Cary, NC 27518-8598; tel. 919/461–5500; FAX. 919/461–5700; Joy Hogan Rozman, Chief Executive Officer

NORTH DAKOTA: North Dakota Health Care Review Inc. (NDHCRI), 3520 North Broadway, Minot, ND 58703; tel. 701/852–4231; FAX. 701/857–9755; Barbara Groutt, Chief Executive Officer

OHIO: Ohio KEPRO, Rock Run Center, Suite 100, 5700 Lombardo Center Drive, Seven Hills, OH 44131; tel. 216/447–9604; FAX. 216/447–7925; Rita Bowling, RN, MSN, MBA, CPHQ, Project Director

OKLAHOMA: Oklahoma Foundation for Medical Quality, 14000 Quail Springs Parkway, Suite 400, Oklahoma City, OK 73134; tel. 405/840–2891; FAX. 405/840–1343; Gregg Koehn, CPA, President and Chief Executive Officer

OREGON: Acumentra Health, 2020 SW Fourth Avenue, Suite 520, Portland, OR 97201-4960; tel. 503/279–0100; FAX. 503/279–0190; Jon Mitchell, FACHE, President and Chief Executive Officer

PENNSYLVANIA: Quality Insights of Pennsylvania, 2601 Market Place Street, Suite 320, Harrisburg, PA 17110; tel. 717/671–5425; FAX. 717/671–5970; John C. Wiesendanger, Chief Executive Officer

RHODE ISLAND: Healthcentric Advisors, formerly Quality Partners of Rhode Island, 235 Promenade Street, Suite 500, Providence, RI 02908; tel. 401/528–3200; FAX. 401/528–3210; H. John Keimig, MHA, FACHE, President and Chief Executive Officer

SOUTH DAKOTA: South Dakota Foundation for Medical Care, 2600 West 49th Street, Suite 300, Sioux Falls, SD 57105; tel. 605/336–3505; FAX. 605/373–0580; Jay Lewis, Chief Executive Officer

TENNESSEE: Qsource, 3340 Players Club Pkwy, Suite 300, Memphis, TN 38125; tel. 800/528–2655; FAX. 901/761–3786; Dawn FitzGerald, Chief Operating Officer

TEXAS: TMF, Health Quality Institute, Bridgepoint 1, Suite 300, 5918 West Courtyard Drive, Austin, TX 78730-5036; tel. 512/329–6610; FAX. 512/327–7159; Thomas Manley, President and Chief Executive Officer

UTAH: HealthInsight, 756 E. Winchester St., Suite 200, Salt Lake City, UT 84107; tel. 801/892–0155; FAX. 801/892–0160; Marc Bennett, MA, President and Chief Executive Officer
HealthInsight Utah, 756 East Winchester Street, Suite 200, Salt Lake City, UT 84107; tel. 801/892–0155; FAX. 801/892–0160; Marc Bennett, President and Chief Executive Officer

VIRGINIA: VHQC, 9830 Mayland Drive, Suite J, Richmond, VA 23233; tel. 804/289–5320; FAX. 804/289–5324; Donald A. Glozer, MHA, FACHE, President and Chief Executive Officer

WASHINGTON: Qualis Health, 10700 Meridian Avenue, N., Suite 100, Seattle, WA 98133-9075; tel. 206/364–9700; FAX. 206/368–2419; Jonathan Sugarman, President and Chief Executive Officer
Qualis Health, 10700 Meridian Ave. N, Suite 100, Seattle, WA 98133; tel. 800/949–7536; FAX. 206/368–2419

WEST VIRGINIA: WVMI & Quality Insights, 3001 Chesterfield Avenue, Charleston, WV 25304; tel. 304/346–9864; FAX. 304/346–9863; John Wiesendanger, MHA, Chief Executive Officer

WISCONSIN: MetaStar, Inc., 2909 Landmark Place, Madison, WI 53713; tel. 608/274–1940; FAX. 608/274–5008; Greg E. Simmons, President and Chief Executive Officer

WYOMING: Mountain-Pacific Quality Health - Wyoming, 145 S. Durbin, Suite 105, Casper, WY 82601; tel. 307/472–0507; FAX. 307/472–1791; Deborah Fleming, Office Director

U.S. Associated Areas

PUERTO RICO: Quality Improvement Professional Research Organization, City View Plaza, Torre I Suite 412, Guaynabo, PR 00968; tel. 787/641–1240; FAX. 787/641–1248; Jose Robles, Chief Executive Officer

VIRGIN ISLANDS: Virgin Islands Medical Institute, Inc., 1AD Estate Diamond Ruby, PO Box 5989, Christiansted, VI 00823-5989; tel. 340/712–2400; FAX. 340/712–2449; M. "Rikki" Nelthropp, Chief Executive Officer

The following list of Health Information Exchanges (HIEs) is based on information provided by the exchanges themselves. Inclusion or omission of any organization's name indicates neither approval nor disapproval by Health Forum, LLC, an American Hospital Association company.

United States

ALABAMA: Alabama Health Information Exchange, Alabama Medicaid Agency, PO Box 5624, 501 Dexter Avenue, Montgomery, AL 36103-5624; tel. 334/242–5011; FAX. 334/353–4818; Kim Davis-Allen, Director of Transformation Initiatives

ALASKA: Alaska eHealth Network, 4000 Old Seward Hwy, Suite 203, Anchorage, AK 99503; tel. 866/966–9030; Rebecca Madison, Executive Director; ak-ehealth.org

ARIZONA: Arizona Health-e Connection, 3877 N. 7th Street, Suite 130, Phoenix, AZ 85014; tel. 602/688–7200; FAX. 602/264–8823; Melissa Kotrys, Chief Executive Officer; www.azhec.org
Health Information Network of Arizona, 3877 N. 7th St., Suite 130, Phoenix, AZ 85014; tel. 602/688–7200; FAX. 602/264–8823; Melissa Kotrys, Chief Executive Officer; www.hinaz.org

ARKANSAS: Arkansas Office of Health Information Technology (OHIT), 1501 N. University Ave., Prospect Building, Suite 420, Little Rock, AR 72207; tel. 501/410–1999; Shirley Tyson, Chief Operations and Technical Officer; ohit.arkansas.gov
HITArkansas, Arkansas Foundation for Medical Care, 1020 West 4th Street, Suite 420, Little Rock, AR 72201; tel. 501/212–8616; FAX. 501/212–8689; Jonathan M. Fuchs, FACHE, Chief Operating Officer; www.hitarkansas.com

CALIFORNIA: California eHealth Collaborative, 1966 Tice Valley Boulevard #144, Walnut Creek, CA 94595; tel. 415/260–6277; Lori Hack, MBA, Chief Executive Officer; caehc.org
State of California Office of Health Information Integrity, 1600 9th Street, Room 460, Sacramento, CA 95814; tel. 916/654–3454; FAX. 916/653–9588; Pamela Lane, Deputy Secretary for HIE; www.ohii.ca.gov

COLORADO: CORHIO, Colorado Regional Health Information Organization, 4500 Cherry Creek South Drive, Suite 820, Denver, CO 80246; tel. 720/285–3200; FAX. 720/285–3205; Brian Braun, Chief Financial and Corporate Operations Officer; www.corhio.org

CONNECTICUT: eHealth Connecticut, 1290 Silas Deane Highway, Suite 4A, Wethersfield, CT 06109; tel. 860/240–5617; FAX. 860/278–2400; Scott Cleary, Program Manager; www.ehealthconnecticut. org
Health Information Exchange Program, Connecticut Department of Public Health, 410 Capitol Avenue, MS#13PLN, Hartford, CT 06134; tel. 860/509–8000; Vanessa Kapral, Chief, Information Technology

DELAWARE: Delaware Health Information Network, 107 Wolf Creek Boulevard, Suite 2, Dover, DE 19901; tel. 302/678–0220; FAX. 302/645–0398; Dr. Jan Lee, Executive Director; www.dhin.org

FLORIDA: Big Bend Regional Healthcare Information Organization (BBRHIO), 3411 Capital Medical Boulevard, Tallahassee, FL 32308; tel. 850/702–0365; Allen Byington, Executive Director; www.bigbendhealth.com
Central Florida RHIO, 3208-C East Colonial Dr., Suite 301, Orlando, FL 32806; tel. 407/425–9500; FAX. 407/425–9559; Michael Kovner, Project Director; www.centralfloridarhio.org
Florida Health Information Network, Agency for Health Care Administration, 2727 Mahan Drive, Tallahassee, FL 32308; tel. 850/922–7036; FAX. 850/414–7831; Christine Nye, Director; www.fhin. net
North East Florida Regional Health Organization, Inc., 6484 Ft. Caroline Road, Jacksonville, FL 32277; tel. 904/731–0221; William Carriere, MD; www.nefrho.org
SunCoast RHIO, 5020 Clark Road, #127, Sarasota, FL 34233; tel. 941/426–6093; Lee S. Gross, MD, Consultant; www.suncoastrhio.org

GEORGIA: GA Health Information Exchange, 2 Peachtree Street, Atlanta, GA 30303; tel. 404/656–7282; FAX. 770/344–4035; Archie Banks, Director Office of Information Technology and Transparency; www.dch.georgia.gov

HAWAII: Hawaii Health Information Exchange, 900 Fort Street Mall, Suite 1305, Honolulu, HI 96813; tel. 808/441–1346; FAX. 808/441–1472; Gregory Suenaga, State HIE Project Director; www. hawaiihie.org

IDAHO: Idaho Health Data Exchange, 450 W. State Street, PO Box 6978, Boise, ID 83707; tel. 208/332–7253; FAX. 208/332–7217; Scott Carrell, Executive Director; www.idahohde.org

ILLINOIS: Illinois Health Information Exchange Authority, JRTC 100 W. Randolph, Suite 4-750, Chicago, IL 60601; tel. 312/814–3534; Raul Recarey, ILHIE Authority Executive Director; www2. illinois.gov/gov/HIE
Illinois Office of Health Information Technology, 100 W. Randolph Street, 2-201, Chicago, IL 60601; tel. 312/814–1600; FAX. 312/814–1468; Laura Zaremba, Director/State HIT Coordinator; www.hie.illinois.gov

INDIANA: Indiana Health Information Exchange, 846 N. Senate Ave., Suite 110, Indianapolis, IN 46202; tel. 317/644–1750; John Kansky, Executive Director; www.ihie.org
Indiana Health Information Exchange, 846 N. Senate Avenue, Suite 110, Indianapolis, IN 46202; tel. 317/644–1750; FAX. 317/644–1751; Harold Apple, Chief Executive Officer; www.ihie.org
Michiana Health Information Network, 220 W. Colfax, Suite 300, South Bend, IN 46601; tel. 574/968–1001; FAX. 574/968–1020; Tim Roberts, Executive Director; www.mhin.org

IOWA: Iowa e-Health, Iowa Department of Public Health, Lucas Building, 321 E. 12th Street, Des Moines, IA 50319; tel. 866/924–4636; FAX. 515/281–4958; Kim Norby, Executive Director; www.iowaehealth.org

LOUISIANA: Louisiana Health Care Quality Forum, 8550 United Plaza Blvd, Suite 500, Baton Rouge, LA 70809; tel. 225/334–9299; FAX. 225/334–9847; Nadine Robin, HIT Program Manager; www.lhcqf.org

MAINE: HealthInfoNet, 125 Presumpscot Street, Box 8, Portland, ME 04103; tel. 207/541–9250; FAX. 207/541–9258; Devore Culver, Executive Director and Chief Executive Officer; www.hinfonet.org
Office for Health Information Technology, 242 State Street, Augusta, ME 04333; tel. 207/287–4532; James Leonard, Deputy Director; www.maine.gov/hit

MARYLAND: Chesapeake Regional Information System for Our Patients, CRISP, 7160 Columbia Gateway Drive, Suite 230, Columbia, MD 21046; tel. 877/952–7477; FAX. 443/817–9587; David Horrocks, President; www.crisphealth.org

MASSACHUSETTS: Massachusetts eHealth Institute, 2 Center Plaza, Suite 200, Boston, MA 02108-19046; tel. 617/371–3999; FAX. 617/725–8938; Laurance Stuntz, Director; www.mehi.masstech.org
Massachusetts Health Data Consortium, 460 Totten Pond Rd., Suite 690, Waltham, MA 02451; tel. 781/419–7800; FAX. 781/795–0155; Denny Brennan, Executive Director and Chief Executive Officer; www.mahealthdata.org

MINNESOTA: MN e-Health Initiative, Minnesota Department of Health, 85 E. Seventh Place, Suite 220, St. Paul, MN 55164; tel. 651/201–4856; FAX. 651/201–3830; Bob Johnson, Senior Planner; www.health.state.mn.us/e-health

MISSISSIPPI: Mississippi Health Information Network (MS-HIN), MS; tel. 601/977–8192; Candice Whitfield, HIT Coordinator; www.ms-hin.ms.gov

MISSOURI: Missouri Health Connection, PMB 270, 2000 E. Broadway, Columbia, MO 65201; tel. 573/777–4550; Mark Pasquale, Chief Executive Officer; missourihealthconnection.org

MONTANA: HealthShare Montana, 2475 Village Lane, Suite 302, Billings, MT 59102; tel. 406/794–0170; FAX. 406/248–9373; Brad Putnam, Executive Director; www.healthsharemontana.org

NEBRASKA: eHealth Council, Nebraska Information Technology Commission, 501 S. 14th Street, 4th Floor, P.O. Box 95045, Lincoln, NE 68509-5045; tel. 402/471–3805; Anne Byers, Community and eHealth Manager; www.nitc.nebraska.gov

NEW HAMPSHIRE: Health Information Exchange, NH Health Information Organization (NHHIO), 125 Airport Road, Concord, NH 03301; tel. 603/219–0184; FAX. 603/218–6216; Jeff Loughlin, Acting Executive Director; www.nhhio.org

NEW JERSEY: New Jersey Health Information Technology Commission, New Jersey Department of Health & Senior Services, PO Box 360, Trenton, NJ 08625-0360; Emmanouil Skoufos, Executive Director; www.state.nj.us/ health/bc/hitc.shtml

NEW MEXICO: LCF Research, 2309 Renard Place SE, Suite 103, Albuquerque, NM 87106; tel. 505/938–9900; FAX. 505/938–9940; Mark Butler, IT Manager; www.lcfresearch.org

NEW YORK: Healthcare Information Xchange of New York (HIXNY), 15 Cornell Road, Latham, NY 12110; tel. 518/783–0518; FAX. 518/785–3101; Mark McKinney, Chief Executive Officer; www.hixny. org
New York eHealth Collaborative (NYeC), 40 Worth Street, 5th Floor, New York, NY 10013; tel. 646/619–6400; Dave Whitlinger, Executive Director; nyehealth.org

NORTH CAROLINA: NC Health Information Exchange, 2300 Rexwoods Drive, Suite 390, Raleigh, NC 27607; tel. 919/926–1042; Chris Scarboro, President; nchie.org
NC Healthcare Information and Communications Alliance, Inc. (NCHICA), 3200 NC Highway 54, Cape Fear Building, Suite 200, Research Triangle Park, NC 27709-3048; tel. 919/558–9258; FAX. 919/558–2198; W. Holt Anderson, Executive Director; www.nchica.org

NORTH DAKOTA: North Dakota Health Information Network, 600 E. Boulevard Avenue, Dept. 112, Bismark, ND 58505-0100; tel. 701/328–1991; FAX. 701/328–3000; Sheldon H. Wolf, North Dakota Health Information Technology Director; www.ndhin.org

OHIO: CliniSync, Ohio Health Information Partnership, 3455 Mill Run Drive, Suite 315, Hilliard, OH 43026; tel. 614/664–2600; FAX. 888/390–7274; Dan Paoletti, Chief Executive Officer; www.clinisync.org

OREGON: Oregon Health Information Technology Oversight Council (HITOC), 500 Summer Street Ste E52, Salem, OR 97301; tel. 503/373–7859; FAX. 503/378–5511; Carol Robinson, Director; www.oregon.gov/OHPPR/HITOC/index.shtml

PENNSYLVANIA: Pennsylvania eHealth Initiative, c/o The Hospital & Healthsystem Association of Pennsylvania, 4750 Lindle Road, Suite 228, Harrisburg, PA 17105; tel. 717/561–5216; Kathleen Moyer; www.paehi.org

SOUTH DAKOTA: South Dakota Health Link, South Dakota Department of Health, 820 N. Washington Ave., Madison, SD 57042; tel. 605/256–5555; Kevin DeWald, State Health IT Coordinator; www.sdhealthlink.org

TENNESSEE: Office of eHealth Initiatives, 310 Great Circle Road, Fourth Floor, East, Nashville, TN 37243; tel. 615/507–6406; FAX. 615/532–2849; George Beckett, HIT Coordinator; www.tn.gov/ehealth

TEXAS: Greater Houston Healthconnect, 1213 Hermann Dr., Suite 135, Houston, TX 77004; tel. 832/564–2599; FAX. 832/490–1318; www.ghhconnect.org
SOPHIE (SETHS Operated Provider Health Information Exchange), Southeast Texas Health System, PO Box 947, Goliad, TX 77963-0947; tel. 361/645–1762; FAX. 361/645–1743; Shannon Calhoun, Executive Director; www.seths.info, www.seths.info/index.php/sophie

Statewide Health Coordinating Council, Texas State Health Plan, Department of State Health Services, 1100 W. 49th Street MC-1898, PO Box 149347, Austin, TX 78714-9347; tel. 512/776–6541; FAX. 512/776–7344; Matt Turner, DSHS Coordinator; www.dshs.state.tx.us/chs/shcc

Texas Health Services Authority, Texas Health Information Exchange, 5900 Southwest Parkway, Building 2, Suite 201, Austin, TX 78735; tel. 512/814–0321; FAX. 512/814–0322; Tony Gilman, Chief Executive Officer; hietexas.org

UTAH: Utah Health Information Network, 6056 Fashion Square Dr., Suite 210, Murray, UT 84107; tel. 801/466–7705; FAX. 801/466–7169; Levy Woodruff, Communications Coordinator; www.uhin.org

VERMONT: Vermont Information Technology Leaders (VITL), 144 Main Street, Suite 1, Montpelier, VT 05602; tel. 802/223–4100; FAX. 802/651–4208; John K. Evans, President and Chief Executive Officer; www.vitl.net

VIRGINIA: Health Information Technology Spotlight (HITS), 109 Governor Street, Richmond, VA 23219; tel. 804/864–7661; Kim Barnes, Director of Health IT; www.hits.virginia.gov

WASHINGTON: OneHealthPort, 2003 Western Ave, Suite 600, Seattle, WA 98121; tel. 206/624–3128; FAX. 206/624–3168; Rick Rubin, Chief Executive Officer; onehealthport.com

WEST VIRGINIA: WV Health Information Network (WVHIN), 100 Dee Drive, Charleston, WV 25311; tel. 304/558–4503; FAX. 304/558–2734; Phil Weikle, Chief Operations Officer; www.wvhin.org

WISCONSIN: Wisconsin Statewide Health Information Network (WISHIN), PO Box 259038, Madison, WI 53725; tel. 608/274–1820; FAX. 608/274–8554; Joseph Kachelski, Chief Executive Officer; www.wishin.org

WYOMING: Wyoming Health Information Organization (WyHIO), 109 E. 17th Street, Cheyenne, WY 82001; tel. 307/432–4025; Larry Biggio, Executive Director; www.wyhio.org

Wyoming Health Information Technology, 2001 Capitol Avenue, Emerson Building #237, Cheyenne, WY 82002; tel. 307/777–5282; Dallas Lain, HIT Coordinator; www.wyominghit.org

Section C

Other Health Care Providers

Freestanding Ambulatory Surgery Centers

The following list of freestanding ambulatory surgery centers was developed with the assistance of state government agencies and the individual facilities listed.

The AHA Guide contains two types of ambulatory surgery center listings; those that are hospital based and those that are freestanding. Hospital based ambulatory surgery centers are listed in section A of the AHA Guide and are identified by Facility Code F8 and F71.

We present this list simply as a convenient directory. Inclusion or omission of any organization's name indicates neither approval nor disapproval by Health Forum LLC, an American Hospital Association company.

United States

ALABAMA

Birmingham Surgery Center, Inc., 2621 19th Street, South, Homewood, AL 35209; tel. 205/271–8200; Kathy Sands, RN, Administrator

Dothan Surgery Center, 1450 Ross Clark Circle, SE, Suite 4, Dothan, AL 36301; tel. 334/793–3442; FAX. 334/793–3318; W. Berry Sowell, Chief Executive Officer and Administrator

Florence Surgery Center, L.P., 103 Helton Court, Florence, AL 35630; tel. 256/760–0672; FAX. 256/766–4547; Jennifer Lathram, Administrator

Gadsden Surgery Center, 418 South Fifth Street, Gadsden, AL 35901; tel. 256/543–1253; FAX. 256/543–1260; Harriet Willoughby, Administrator

Huntsville Endoscopy Center, Inc., 119 Longwood Drive, Huntsville, AL 35801; tel. 256/533–6488; FAX. 256/532–2238; Dalia Biggerstaff, RN, Clinical Director

Montgomery Eye Surgery Center, 2752 Zelda Road, Montgomery, AL 36106; tel. 334/270–9677; FAX. 334/213–0622; Deborah Cauthen, Administrator

Montgomery Surgical Center, 470 Taylor Road, Montgomery, AL 36117; tel. 334/284–9600; FAX. 334/284–4233; Linda Westhoff, Interim Administrator

Outpatient Services East, Inc., 52 Medical Park Drive, E., Suite 401, Birmingham, AL 35235; tel. 205/838–3888; FAX. 205/314–2469; H. Alan Perry, President, Chairman of the Board

The Kirklin Clinic of UAB Hospital, 2000 Sixth Avenue, S., Birmingham, AL 35233; tel. 205/801–8000; Reid F. Jones, Chief Operating Officer, UAB Health System

The Surgery Center of Huntsville, 721 Madison Street, Huntsville, AL 35801; tel. 256/533–4888; FAX. 256/532–9510; William Sammons, Chief Executive Officer

Tuscaloosa Endoscopy Center, 100 Rice Mine Road, N, Suite E, Tuscaloosa, AL 35406; tel. 205/345–0010; FAX. 205/752–1175; A. B. Reddy, MD, Medical Director

Tuscaloosa Surgical Center, 1400 McFarland Boulevard, N., Tuscaloosa, AL 35406; tel. 205/345–5500; Jeff Hayes, Administrator

ALASKA

Alaska Women's Health P.C., 3260 Providence Dr, Suite 322, Anchorage, AK 99508; tel. 907/563–7228; FAX. 907/563–6278; Carol Mitchell-Springer, MD, President

Geneva Woods Surgical Center, 3730 Rhone Circle, Suite 100, Anchorage, AK 99508; tel. 907/562–4764; FAX. 907/561–8519; Barbara Cope, Administrator

Pacific Cataract & Laser Institute, 1600 "A" Street, Suite 200, Anchorage, AK 99501; tel. 907/272–2423; FAX. 907/272–2428

ARIZONA

Adobe Surgery Center, 2585 North Wyatt Drive, Tucson, AZ 85712; tel. 520/721–2728; FAX. 520/720–0719; Sam E. Moussa, MD, Administrator

Arizona Outpatient Surgery Center, 6245 N. 16th Street, Phoenix, AZ 85016; tel. 602/274–1705; FAX. 602/419–3070

Arizona Surgical Arts, Inc., 1245 North Wilmot Road, Tucson, AZ 85712; tel. 520/296–7550; FAX. 520/722–6937; Robert M. Dryden, MD

Banner Canyon Springs Surgery Center, 2940 E. Banner Gateway Drive, #100, Gilbert, AZ 85234; tel. 480/641–9292; Christine Casto, RN, Administrator

Banner Desert Surgery Center, 1500 South Dobson Road, Suite 101, Mesa, AZ 85202; tel. 480/412–3590; FAX. 480/412–8774; Karl Klungreseter, Administrator

Barnet Dulaney Perkin Eye Center, 4800 N 22nd Street, Phoenix, AZ 85016; tel. 602/508–4721; FAX. 602/759–1336; Amber Gearhart, Director of Nursing

CIGNA Healthplan of Arizona, Outpatient Surgery, 755 East McDowell Road, Phoenix, AZ 85006; tel. 602/271–3020; Katie Rousey, RN Manager

Cochise Eye and Laser, PC, 2445 East Wilcox Drive, Sierra Vista, AZ 85635; tel. 520/458–8131; FAX. 520/458–0422; Sheree H. Christian, Administrator

Cottonwood Day Surgery Center, Inc., 55 South Sixth Street, Cottonwood, AZ 86326; tel. 928/634–5118; FAX. 928/634–8522; Linda Davis, Administrator

Desert Mountain Surgicenter, 895 S. Dobson Rd., Ste 1, Chandler, AZ 85224-5721; tel. 480/899–3737; FAX. 480/899–6262; David M. Creech, MD

Eye Institute at Boswell, 10541 West Thunderbird Boulevard, Sun City, AZ 85351; tel. 602/933–3402; FAX. 602/972–5014; Jan Zellmann, Administrator

Fifty-Ninth Avenue Surgical Facility, Ltd., 8608 North 59th Avenue, Glendale, AZ 85302; tel. 623/934–3211; FAX. 623/930–1891; Mark Gorman, Administrator

Fishkind Bakewell Maltzman Eye Care and Surgery Center, 5599 North Oracle Road, Tucson, AZ 85704; tel. 520/293–6740; FAX. 520/293–6771; Kathleen A. Brown, Surgery Center Supervisor

Flagstaff Foot Doctors, 421 North Humphries Street, Flagstaff, AZ 86001; tel. 928/774–4825; FAX. 888/464–1135; Anthony Rosales, MD, President

Good Samaritan Surgicenter, 1111 B East McDowell Road, Phoenix, AZ 85006; tel. 602/239–2776; FAX. 602/239–5352; Brenda Mastopietro, Administrator

Havasu Foot and Ankle Surgi-Center, 90 Riviera Drive, Lake Havasu, AZ 86403; tel. 928/855–7800; FAX. 928/855–5392; Robert Novack, DPM, Director

Hodges Eye Care & Surgery Center, 1502 North Tucson Boulevard, Tucson, AZ 85716; tel. 520/326–4321; FAX. 520/326–4736; Dr. Timothy L. Hodges, MD

Kokopelli Eye Care, P.C., 2820 North Glassford Hill Road, Suite 101, Prescott Valley, AZ 86314; tel. 928/775–5606; FAX. 928/759–9902; Laura Crain, Office Manager

Kokopelli Eye Care, P.C., 412 Whipple Street, Prescott, AZ 86301; tel. 928/771–9000; FAX. 928/759–9902; Laura Crain, Office Manager

Metro Surgery Center, LLC, 6790 W. Thunderbird Rd., Peoria, AZ 85381; tel. 623/979–1717; FAX. 623/979–1707; Diane Elmore, Administrator

Outpatient Surgical Care, Ltd., 1530 West Glendale, Suite 105, Phoenix, AZ 85021; tel. 602/995–3395; FAX. 602/995–1853; Gabriel Perry, DO, Medical Director

Phoenix Eye Surgical Center, LLC, 5133 North Central Avenue, Suite 100, Phoenix, AZ 85012; tel. 602/279–0044; FAX. 602/279–0088; Don Baca, Administrator

Physicians Surgery Center of Tempe, LLC, 1940 East Southern Avenue, Tempe, AZ 85282; tel. 480/820–7101; FAX. 480/820–9291; Susan Vitort, Administrator

Prescott Outpatient Surgery Center, LLP, 815 Ainsworth Drive, Prescott, AZ 86301; tel. 602/778–9770; Derron DeRouin, Administrative Director

Prescott Urocenter, Ltd., 811 Ainsworth, Suite 101, Prescott, AZ 86301; tel. 928/771–5282; FAX. 928/771–5283; Shannon Leek, Office Manager

Scottsdale Eye Surgery Center, P.C., 3320 North Miller Road, Scottsdale, AZ 85251; tel. 480/429–0700; FAX. 480/429–1700; Joyce Schweikert, Administrator

Southwester Eye Center, 2005 Injo, Suite 102, Lake Havasu City, AZ 86403-5874; tel. 928/505–3696; FAX. 928/505–6129; Gary Dillon, Director, Contract Services

Southwestern Eye Center, 2610 E. University Drive, Mesa, AZ 85213; tel. 480/892–8400; FAX. 480/892–9533; Gary Dillon, Director, Contract Services

Southwestern Eye Center, 1919 Florence Avenue, Kingman, AZ 86401; tel. 928/753–5454; FAX. 928/753–7790; Richard Hinton, Administrator

Southwestern Eye Center, 3321 E. Bell Road, Suite B12, Phoenix, AZ 85032-2755; tel. 602/787–9100; FAX. 602/787–9101; Sarah Mumford, Contract Services

Southwestern Eye Center, 3003 Highway 95 Ste 63, Bullhead City, AZ 86442-7860; tel. 928/763–7555; FAX. 928/763–7565; Gary Dillon, Director, Contract Services

Southwestern Eye Center, 270 S. Candy Lane, Cottonwood, AZ 86326-4164; tel. 928/634–4202; FAX. 928/634–5693; Gary Dillon, Director, Contract Services

Southwestern Eye Center, 2650 E. Show Low Lake Rd, Suite 2, Show Low, AZ 85901-7955; tel. 928/537–4240; FAX. 928/537–3892; Gary Dillon, Director, Contract Services

Southwestern Eye Center, 1600 Willow Creek Rd., Prescott, AZ 86301-1108; tel. 928/776–7477; FAX. 928/776–0693; Southwestern Eye Center Administration

Southwestern Eye Center, 2242 W. 16th Street, Safford, AZ 85546-4081; tel. 928/428–0068; FAX. 928/428–0713; Gary Dillon, Director, Contract Services

Southwestern Eye Center, 1055 S. Stapley Drive, Mesa, AZ 85204-5013; tel. 480/833–9100; FAX. 480/833–6000; Gary Dillon, Director, Contract Services

Southwestern Eye Center, 10615 W. Thunderbird Bldg., A100, Sun City, AZ 85351-3018; tel. 623/977–9600; FAX. 623/977–9602

Southwestern Eye Center, 75 Colonia De Salud A-100, Sierra Vista, AZ 85635-2487; tel. 520/459–6860; FAX. 520/459–6858; Gary Dillon, Director, Contract Services

Southwestern Eye Center, 2149 W. 24th Street, Yuma, AZ 85364-6163; tel. 928/726–4120; FAX. 928/341–0315; Gary Dillon, Director, Contract Services

Southwestern Eye Center-Casa Grande, 560 N. Camino Mercado, Suite 1, Casa Grande, AZ 85222; tel. 520/426–9224; FAX. 520/426–1554; Ellen Lopez, RN, Director of Surgical Services

Southwestern Eye Surgicenter-Nogales, 1815 North Mastick Way, Nogales, AZ 85621; tel. 520/761–3533; FAX. 520/281–1950; Gary Dillon, Director, Contract Services

Summit Surgery & Recovery Care Center, 1485 N. Turquoise Drive, #100, Flagstaff, AZ 86001; tel. 928/214–3211; FAX. 928/214–3219; Jantina Wilson, Administrator

Sun City Endoscopy Center, Inc., 13640 North 99th Avenue, Suite 700, Sun City, AZ 85351; tel. 623/972–5083; FAX. 623/523–0505; Jagdish Patel, MD

Surgery Center of Peoria, 13260 North 94th Drive, Suite 200, Peoria, AZ 85381; tel. 623/933–2900; FAX. 623/933–0017; Kolette Al-Jamal, Administrator

Surgi-Care, 5115 North Central Avenue, Phoenix, AZ 85012; tel. 602/264–1818; FAX. 602/264–2172; Ellison F. Herro, MD, Administrator

Swagel Wootton Eye Center, 220 South 63rd Street, Mesa, AZ 85206; tel. 602/641–3937; FAX. 602/924–5096; S. Joyce Graham

T.A.S.I. Surgery Center, 5585 North Oracle Road, Suite B, Tucson, AZ 85704; tel. 520/293–7077; FAX. 520/293–7561; John A. Pierce, MD, Medical Director

Tempe New Day Surgery Center LP, 2000 East Southern Avenue, Suite 106, Tempe, AZ 85282; tel. 480/838–9313; FAX. 480/491–8802; John L. Titus, President

The PAIN MDS ASC, 2525 W Carefree Hwy, Suite 134, Phoenix, AZ 85085; tel. 623/580–4357; FAX. 623/580–5249; Paul A. Pannozzo, MD

Thunderbird Samaritan Surgicenter, 5555 B West Thunderbird Road, Glendale, AZ 85306-4622; tel. 602/588-5475; FAX. 602/588–5472; Diane Elmore, RN, Administrator

Valley Outpatient Surgery Center, 160 West University Drive #1, Mesa, AZ 85201; tel. 602/835-7373; FAX. 602/969–7981; Craig R. Cassidy, DO, President

Vital Sight P.C., 5632 East Fifth Street, Tucson, AZ 85711; tel. 520/790–8888; FAX. 520/790–1427; Elaine Jones, Administrator

Warner Park Surgery Center, 604 West Warner Road, Building A, Chandler, AZ 85225; tel. 480/899–2571; FAX. 480/899–4263; Dale Holmes

White Mountain Ambulatory Surgery Center, 2650 East Show Low Lake Road, Suite Two, Show Low, AZ 85901; tel. 908/537-4240; William J. Waldo

ARKANSAS

Arkansas Endoscopy Center, P.A., 9501 Baptist Health Drive, Suite 100, Little Rock, AR 72205; tel. 501/224-9100; FAX. 501/224–0420; Ronald D. Hardin, MD

Arkansas Surgery and Endoscopy Center, 4800 Hazel Street, Pine Bluff, AR 71603; tel. 870/536-4800; FAX. 870/534-5535; Syed Samad, MD, FACP, FACG

Arkansas Surgery Center, 10 Hospital Circle, Batesville, AR 72501; tel. 870/793-4040; FAX. 870/793–5649; Ronald L. Lowery, MD, Administrator

Boozman-Hof Eye Surgery and Laser Center, LLC, 3737 West Walnut Street, P.O. Box 1353, Rogers, AR 72757-1353; tel. 501/246–1751; FAX. 501/631–2702; Donna R. Acord, Director

Doctors Surgery Center PA, 303 West Polk Ave, Suite B, West Memphis, AR 72301; tel. 870/732-2100; FAX. 870/732–3027; Lois Meyers, RN

Endoscopy Center of Hot Springs, 151 McGowan Court, Hot Springs, AR 71913; tel. 501/623–4101; FAX. 501/623–0103; Barbara Hulsey, Administrator

H. Lewis Pearson Eye Institute, 3211 Surger Hill Road, Texarkana, AR 71854-9265; tel. 870/772-4440; FAX. 870/772–7190; Glen Wile, Comptroller

James Trice, M.D., P.A., dba Digestive Disease Center, 7005 South Hazel Street, Pine Bluff, AR 71603; tel. 870/536-3070; FAX. 870/536-3171; Louis Trice, Administrator

Little Rock Surgery Center, 8820 Knoedl Court, Little Rock, AR 72205; tel. 501/224–6767; FAX. 501/224-8203; Kim Hamma, RN, Administrator

Lowery Medical/Surgical Eye Center, P.A., 105 Central Avenue, Searcy, AR 72143; tel. 501/268-7154; FAX. 501/268–9071; Robert D. Lowery, MD, Administrator

North Hills Gastroenterology Endoscopy Center, Inc., 3344 North Futrall Drive, Fayetteville, AR 72703; tel. 501/582-7280; FAX. 510/582-7279; William C. Martin, MD

Novamed Surgery Center of Jonesboro, dba Eye Surgery Center of Arkansas, 601 East Matthews, Jonesboro, AR 72401; tel. 870/935-6396; FAX. 870/935-4063; Tracy Gholson, Director

Ozark Eye Center, 360 Highway Five North, Mountain Home, AR 72653; tel. 870/425-2277; Cheryl Pearman, Administrator

Physicians' Surgery Center of Fayetteville, 3873 North Parkview Drive, Suite One, Fayetteville, AR 72703; tel. 479/527–0050; FAX. 479/582-1338; Russ Greene RN Administrator

South Arkansas Surgery Center, 4310 South Mulberry, Pine Bluff, AR 71603; tel. 870/535-5719; FAX. 870/536–1963; Heather Walters, Business Manager

The Gastro-Intestinal Center, 405 North University, Little Rock, AR 72205; tel. 501/663-1074; FAX. 501/663-0906; Brett Kirkman, Administrator

CALIFORNIA

Advanced Surgery Center, 5771 North Fresno Street, Suite 101, Fresno, CA 93710; tel. 559/448-9900; FAX. 559/448-9546; B. David Singh MD, Administrator

Aestheticare Outpatient Surgery Center, 30260 Rancho Viejo Road, San Juan Capistrano, CA 92675; tel. 949/661-1700; FAX. 949/661-4321; Ronald E. Moser, MD

Ambulatory Surgical Center of Southern California, Gastroenterology Diagnostic Center, 880 South Atlantic Boulevard G-10, Monterey Park, CA 91754; tel. 626/293–8851; FAX. 626/293–1606; Zelman Weingaren, MD

Ambulatory Surgical Center, Inc., 14400 Bear Valley Road, Suite 201, Victorville, CA 92392; tel. 760/951-5162; FAX. 818/985–0055; Garey L. Weber, DPM, Administrator

Antelope Valley Surgery Center, 44301 North Lorimer Avenue, Lancaster, CA 93534; tel. 661/940–1112; FAX. 661/940–6856; Lorie Hibler, Administrator

Bakersfield Endoscopy Center, 1408 Commercial Way, Bakersfield, CA 93309; tel. 661/327–4455; FAX. 661/633–5484; Ramesh Gupta, MD, Medical Director

Bascom Surgery Center, 3803 S. Bascom Avenue, Suite 106, Campbell, CA 95008; tel. 408/369–9535; FAX. 408/369–9106

Bedford Surgery Center, 100 UCLA Medical Plaza, Suite 310, Los Angeles, CA 90024-6999; tel. 310/777–8820; FAX. 310/777–8890; Patricia Adams, RN,PHD, Director of Nursing

Beverly Hills Sunset Surgery Center, Inc., 9201 Sunset Boulevard, Suite 405, Los Angeles, CA 90069; tel. 310/887–1730; FAX. 310/887–1734; Sue Kim, Nursing Administrator

Bolsa Outpatient Surgery Center, 10362 Bolsa Avenue, Suite 100, Westminster, CA 92683; tel. 714/775–5690; FAX. 714/775–7405; Van Kychuong, MD, Medical Director

Brockton Surgery Center, 6958 Brockton Avenue, Riverside, CA 92506-3832; tel. 951/788–4400; Michael N. Durrant, DPM, MPH

Camden Surgery Center of Beverly Hills, 414 North Camden Drive, Suite 800, Beverly Hills, CA 90210; tel. 310/859–3991; FAX. 310/859–7126; Yvette L. Lee Administrator

Campus Surgery Center, LP, 901 Campus Drive, Suite 102, Daly City, CA 94015; tel. 650/991–2000; FAX. 650/755–8638

Center for Surgery of Encinitas, 477 North El Camino Real, Suite C-100, Encinitas, CA 92024; tel. 760/942–8800; FAX. 760/942–0106; Chris Clinton, RN, CASC Administrator

Crown Valley Outpatient Surgical Center, 26921 Crown Valley Parkway, Suite 110, Mission Viejo, CA 92691; tel. 949/367–1006; FAX. 949/612–0857; Jeff Shad, DC, Chief Executive Officer

Cypress Outpatient Surgical Center, Inc., 1665 Dominican Way, Suite 120, Santa Cruz, CA 95065; tel. 831/476–6943; FAX. 831/476–1473; Nicole Rojas, RN, Administrator

Digestive Disease Center, 24411 Health Center Drive, Suite 450, Laguna Hills, CA 92653; tel. 949/586–9386; FAX. 949/586–0864; Robert Dyer, Medical Director

E N T Facial Surgery Center, 1351 East Spruce, Fresno, CA 93720; tel. 559/432–3724; FAX. 559/432–8579; JoAnn LoForti, RN, MS, Division of Nursing

El Mirador Surgical Center, 1180 North Indian Canyon Drive, Suite 110, Palm Springs, CA 92262; tel. 760/416–4600; FAX. 760/416–4668; David Wiche, Director

Endoscopy Center of Chula Vista, 681 Third Avenue, Suite B, Chula Vista, CA 91910; tel. 619/425–2150; FAX. 619/425–2848; Robert Penner, MD, Administrator

Endoscopy Center of Southern California, 2336 Santa Monica Boulevard, Suite 204, Santa Monica, CA 90404; tel. 310/453–4477; FAX. 310/453–4811; Richard F. Corlin MD

Endoscopy Center of the Central Coast, 77 Casa Street, Suite 106, San Luis Obis, CA 93405; tel. 805/541–1021; FAX. 805/541–3142; Jill Quinn, RN, Center Director

Escondido Surgery Center, 555 E. Valley Pkwy., Escondido, CA 92025; tel. 760/480–6606; FAX. 760/480–6671; L. Richard Greenstein, MD, Medical Director

Eye Center of Northern California, 6500 Fairmount Avenue, Suite Two, El Cerrito, CA 94530; tel. 510/525–2600; FAX. 510/524–1887; William Ellis

Eye Life Institute, 6283 Clark Road, Suite 11, Paradise, CA 95969; tel. 530/877–2020; FAX. 530/877–4641; Almary Hivale, RN, Director of ASC

Eye Surgery Center of Southern California, Inc./ Med. Group, dba Tri-City Surgery Center, 2023 West Vista Way, Suite E, Vista, CA 92083; tel. 760/941–8152; FAX. 760/941–8967; Anui Gupta, MD, Medical Director

Eye Surgery Center of the Desert, 72301 Country Club Dr., Suite 101, Rancho Mirage, CA 92270; tel. 760/340–3937; FAX. 760/773–3823; Timothy D. Milauskas, Administrator

Feather River Surgery Center, 370 Del Norte Avenue, Yuba City, CA 95991; tel. 530/751–4800; FAX. 530/751–4884; Ann Perry, Administrator

Foothill Ambulatory Surgery Center, 1030 East Foothill Boulevard, Suite 101B, Upland, CA 91786; tel. 909/981–5859; FAX. 909/981–8293; Natee Poopat, MD, Office Director

Fremont Surgery Center, 2675 Stevenson Boulevard-South, Fremont, CA 94538; tel. 510/793–4987; FAX. 510/793–5084; Debi Ford, RN, Director of Nursing

GastroDiagnostics, A Medical Group, 1140 West La Veta, Suite 550, Orange, CA 92868; tel. 714/835–3636; FAX. 714/835–5567; Vicki Kersey, Administrator

Glendale Eye Surgery Center, 607 North Central, Suite 103, Glendale, CA 91203; tel. 818/956–1010; FAX. 818/543–6083; Richard Weise, MD

Golden Triangle Surgicenter, 25405 Hancock Avenue, Suite 103, Murrieta, CA 92562; tel. 909/698-4670; FAX. 909/698–4675; Ella Stockstill, Administrator

Greater Sacramento Surgery Center, 2288 Auburn Boulevard, Suite 201, Sacramento, CA 95821; tel. 916/929–7229; FAX. 916/929–2590; Susan Brunone, MHS, Administrator

Grossmont Plaza Surgery Center, 5525 Grossmont Center Drive, La Mesa, CA 91942; tel. 619/644–4561; Chris Ekern, Manager

Halcyon Laser and Surgery Center, Inc., 303 South Halcyon Road, Arroyo Grande, CA 93420; tel. 805/489-8254; FAX. 805/474–1997; Sanja Brewer, Administrator

HealthSouth Arcadia Outpatient Surgery, Inc., 614 West Duarte Road, Arcadia, CA 91007; tel. 626/445–4714; FAX. 626/445–1701; Sara Lamm, Administrator

HealthSouth Forest Surgery Center, 2110 Forest Avenue, San Jose, CA 95128; tel. 408/297–3432; FAX. 408/298–3338; Camille Magamon RN

HealthSouth Grossmont Surgery Center, 8881 Fletcher Parkway, Suite 100, La Mesa, CA 91942; tel. 619/698–0930; FAX. 619/698–3093; Administrator

HealthSouth North Coast Surgery Center, 3903 Waring Road, Oceanside, CA 92056; tel. 760/940–0997; FAX. 760/940–0407; Donna Danley, Administrator

HealthSouth Surgery Center, 75 Scripts Drive, Sacramento, CA 95825; tel. 916/929–9431; FAX. 916/929–0132; Deanne Conner, Administrator

HealthSouth Surgery Center-Scripps, 75 Scripps Drive, Sacramento, CA 95825; tel. 916/929–9431; FAX. 916/929–0132; Jodean Lake, Administrator

Hemet Endoscopy Center, 1003 East Florida Avenue, Suite 104, Hemet, CA 92543; tel. 951/652–2252; FAX. 951/925–9252; Milan S. Chakrabarty, MD

Hemet Healthcare Surgicenter, 301 North San Jacinto Avenue, Hemet, CA 92543; tel. 909/765–1717; FAX. 909/765–1716; Josh Hoffner, Business Office Manager

High Desert Endoscopy, 18523 Corwin Road, Suite H2, Apple Valley, CA 92307; tel. 760/242–3000; FAX. 760/242–1802; Raman S. Poola, MD, Administrator

Hope Square Surgical Center, 39700 Bob Hope Drive, Suite 301, Rancho Mirage, CA 92270; tel. 760/346–7696; FAX. 760/776–1069; BJ Clarke, RN, MPA, Administrator

Huntington Outpatient Surgery Center, 797 South Fair Oaks Avenue, Pasadena, CA 91105; tel. 626/535–2434; FAX. 626/535–2430; Robin Waldvogel, Medical Director

Inland Endoscopy Center, Inc., dba Mountain View Surgery Center, 10408 Industrial Circle, Redlands, CA 92374; tel. 909/796–7803; FAX. 909/796–0614; Khushal Stanisai

Inland Surgery Center, 1620 Laurel Avenue, Redlands, CA 92373; tel. 909/793–4701; FAX. 909/792–6397; Jacquelin Belcher, Facility Administrator

Inland Surgery Center, 1620 Laurel Ave, Redlands, CA 92373; tel. 909/793–4701; FAX. 951/658–3953; James Watson, MD, Medical Director

Irvine Multi-Specialty Surgical Care, 4900 Barranca Parkway, Suite 104, Irvine, CA 92604-8603; tel. 949/726–0677; FAX. 949/726–0678; Lauren Parrott, BS, Administrator

Section C

Kaiser Ambulatory Surgical Center, 2025 Morse Avenue, Sacramento, CA 95825; tel. 916/973–7786; FAX. 916/973–5530; Brian J. Brosnahan, RN, BSN, ASU Manager

Kaiser Ambulatory Surgical Center, 10725 International Drive, Rancho Cordov, CA 95670; tel. 916/631–2000; FAX. 916/631–2013; Steven Metzger, RN, Manager

La Jolla Endoscopy Center, 9850 Genesee Avenue, Suite 980, La Jolla, CA 92037; tel. 858/453–7525; FAX. 858/453–5753; Dr. Andrew Mayer

La Veta Surgical Center, an Affiliate of SCA, 681 South Parker Street, Suite 150, Orange, CA 92868; tel. 714/744–0900; FAX. 714/744–0283; Kelly Ruiz, Administrator

Laser Surgery Center, Ltd., 2021 Ygnacio Valley Road, Building H-102, Walnut Creek, CA 94598; tel. 925/944–9400; FAX. 925/947–2160; Michele McKinley, Administrator

Lassen Surgery Center, 103 Fair Drive, PO Box 1150, Susanville, CA 96130; tel. 530/257–7772; FAX. 530/257–2939; Rebecca Donlon, Medical Staff Coordinator

Lodi Outpatient Surgical Center, 521 South Ham Lane, Suite F, Lodi, CA 95242; tel. 209/333–0905; FAX. 209/333–0219; Kippy Pogue, Administrator

Loma Linda Ambulatory Surgical Center, Podiatry Corp, 11332 Mountain View Avenue, Suite A, Loma Linda, CA 92354; tel. 909/796–3707; FAX. 909/796–3709; Mariam Amiri, DPM, Administrator

Los Altos Surgery Center, 795 Altos Oaks Drive, Los Altos, CA 94024; tel. 650/209–1100; Harry Mittelman, MD

Los Gatos Surgical Center, 15195 National Avenue, Suite 100, Los Gatos, CA 95032; tel. 408/356–0454; FAX. 408/358–3924; David Hokeness, Administrator

M/S Surgery Center, LLC, 3510 Martin Luther King Boulevard, Lynwood, CA 90262; tel. 310/635–7550; FAX. 310/603–8749; John H. Shammas, MD, Medical Director

Marin Ophthalmic Surgery Center, 901 E Street, Suite 270, San Rafael, CA 94901; tel. 415/454–2112; FAX. 415/454–6542; Minda Soria, RN Clinical Director

Martel Eye Institute, LLC, 11216 Trinity River, Rancho Cordova, CA 95670; tel. 916/631–7868; FAX. 916/631–3788; Joseph Martel, MD

Medical Arts Ambulatory Surgery Center, 205 South West Street, Suite B, Visalia, CA 93291; tel. 209/625–9601; FAX. 209/625–9025; Judy Van Ness, Manager

Medical Plaza Orthopedic Surgery Center, 1301 20th Street, Suite 140, Santa Monica, CA 90404; tel. 310/315–0333; FAX. 310/315–0341; Trish Fowler, Director Surgical Services

Merced Ambulatory Endoscopy Center, 750 West Olive Avenue, Suite 107A, Merced, CA 95348; tel. 209/384–3116; FAX. 209/384–0878; Vijaya Tangella, Administrator

Mission Ambulatory Surgicenter, 26730 Crown Valley Parkway, First Floor, Mission Viejo, CA 92691; tel. 949/364–2201; FAX. 949/364–5372; Mary Parker, Administrator

Mission Valley Surgery Center, 39263 Mission Boulevard, Fremont, CA 94539; tel. 510/796–4500; FAX. 510/796–4573; Sarb S. Hundal, MD

Modesto Surgery Center, Inc., 400 East Orangeburg Avenue, Suite One, Modesto, CA 95350; tel. 209/526–3000; FAX. 209/526–3133; Dr. Greg Tesluk, Administrator

Monterey Peninsula Surgery Center, LLC, 966 Cass Street, Suite 210, Monterey, CA 93940; tel. 831/372–2169; FAX. 408/372–6323; David J. Ogimachi, Administrator

Napa Surgery Center, 3444 Valle Verde Drive, Napa, CA 94558; tel. 707/252–9669; FAX. 707/257–3328; Eric Grigsby, MD, Owner

Newport Beach Orange Coast Endoscopy Center, 1525 Superior Avenue, Suite 114, Newport Beach, CA 92663; tel. 949/646–6999; FAX. 949/646–9699; Donald Abraham

Newport Surgery Institute, 360 San Miguel Drive, Suite 406, Newport Beach, CA 92660; tel. 949/759–0995; Suzanne Tavenner, Office Manager

North Anaheim Surgicenter, 1154 North Euclid, Anaheim, CA 92801; tel. 714/635–6272; FAX. 714/635–0943; Jeanette Rasmussen, Administrator

North Bay Eye Associates, Inc., Ambulatory Surgery Center, 380 Tesconi Court, Santa Rosa, CA 95401; tel. 707/544–3375; FAX. 707/544–0808; William H. Bartlett, Medical Director

Optima Ophthalmic Medical Associates, Inc., 1237 B Street, Hayward, CA 94541-2977; tel. 510/886–3937; FAX. 510/886–6304; Kelly Best, Office Manager

Orange County Institute of Gastroenterology and Endoscopy, 26732 Crown Valley Parkway, Suite 241, Mission Viejo, CA 92691; tel. 949/364–2611; FAX. 949/364–0226; Dina Moatazedi, Office Manager

Pacific Eye Institute, 555 North 13th Avenue, Upland, CA 91786; tel. 909/982–8846; FAX. 909/982–4007; Robert Fabricant, MD, FACS, Medical Director

Pacific Hills Surgery Center, LLC, 24022 Calle De La Plata, Suite 180, Laguna Hills, CA 92653; tel. 949/458–3551; FAX. 949/951–9478; Kristi Morse, RN, Nurse Manager, Compliance

Pacific Surgicenter, Inc., 1301 20th Street, Suite 470, Santa Monica, CA 90404; tel. 310/315–0222; FAX. 310/828–8852; Randi Ogilvie- Manager

Petaluma Surgicenter, 1400 Professional Drive, Suite 102, Petaluma, CA 94954; tel. 707/763–9325; FAX. 707/769–0751; Ronald M. La Vigna, DPM Manager

Physicians Plaza Surgical Center, 6000 Physicians Boulevard, Bakersfield, CA 93301; tel. 661/322–4744; FAX. 661/322–2938; Terri Waller, Administrator

Plastic and Reconstructive Surgery Center, 1387 Santa Rita Road, Pleasanton, CA 94566; tel. 925/462–3700; FAX. 510/462–4681; Ronald Iverson, Administrator

Podiatric Surgery Center, 255 North Gilbert, Suite B-1, Hemet, CA 92543; tel. 951/925–2186; FAX. 951/925–4947; Robert Drake, DPM, Administrator

Premiere Surgery Center, Inc., 700 West El Norte Parkway, Escondido, CA 92026; tel. 760/738–7830; FAX. 760/738–7834; R. K. Massengill, MD, President

Providence Ambulatory Surgical Center, 1310 West Stewart Drive, Suite 310, Orange, CA 92668; tel. 714/771–6363; FAX. 714/771–0754; Harrell E. Robinson, MD, President

Providence Holy Cross Surgery Center, 11550 Indian Hills Road, Suite 160, Mission Hills, CA 91345; tel. 818/256–2100; FAX. 818/256–2156; Dale Bowman, Administrator

Redlands Dental Surgery Center, 1180 Nevada Street, Suite 100, Redlands, CA 92374; tel. 909/335–0474; FAX. 909/335–0477; Russell O. Seheult, DDS

Richburg Valley Eye Institute Ambulatory Surgical Center, 1680 East Herndon Avenue, Fresno, CA 93720; tel. 209/432–4200; FAX. 209/432–0147; Frederick Richburg, MD, Administrator

Riverside Medical Clinic Surgery Center, 7160 Brockton Avenue, Riverside, CA 92506; tel. 951/782–3801; FAX. 951/328–9742; Judy Carpenter, President and Chief Operating Officer

Sacramento Eye Surgicenter, 3150 J Street, Sacramento, CA 95816; tel. 916/444–7052; FAX. 916/446–1145; Yvonne Jones, ASC Director

Sacramento Midtown Endoscopy Center, 3941 J Street, Suite 460, Sacramento, CA 95819; tel. 916/733–6940; FAX. 916/733–6934; Gautam Gandhi, MD

Saddleback Eye Center, 23161 Moulton Parkway, Laguna Hills, CA 92653; tel. 949/951–4641; FAX. 949/951–4601; Linda Riley, Administrator

Salinas Surgery Center, 955-A Blanco Circle, Salinas, CA 93901; tel. 831/753–5800; FAX. 831/753–5808; Christine Gallagher, Vice President

San Francisco Surgery Center, 1635 Divisidero Street, Suite 200, San Francisco, CA 94115; tel. 415/346–1218; FAX. 415/346–2930; Judith Mulligan, Administrator

San Gabriel Valley Surgical Center, 1250 South Sunset Avenue, Suite 100, West Covina, CA 91790; tel. 626/960–6623; FAX. 626/962–4341; Susan Raub, Administrator

San Joaquin Laser Surgery Center, 1805 North California Street, # 101A, Stockton, CA 95204; tel. 209/948–3241; FAX. 209/948–8009; Susan Ford, Administrator

San Leandro Surgery Center, 15035 East 14th Street, San Leandro, CA 94578; tel. 510/276–2800; FAX. 510/276–2890; JoAnn Peterson

Sani Eye Surgery Center, 1315 Las Tablas Road, Templeton, CA 93465; tel. 805/434–2533; FAX. 805/434–3037; Karim Rasheed, MD, Director

Santa Cruz Surgery Center, 3003 Paul Sweet Road, Santa Cruz, CA 95065; tel. 408/462–5512; FAX. 408/462–2451; Mary Ann Dunlap, RN

Sequoia Surgery Center, LLC, 842 South Akers Street, Visalia, CA 93277; tel. 559/740–4094; FAX. 559/740–4100; Gina Mayo, RN, BSN, Clinical Director

Shepard Surgical Center, 1418 East Main Street, Suite 110, Santa Maria, CA 93454-4806; tel. 805/614–7005; FAX. 805/614–7006; Dennis D. Shepard, MD

Silicon Valley Surgery Center, LP, 14601 S. Bascom Avenue, Suite 100, Los Gatos, CA 95032; tel. 408/402–0663; FAX. 408/402–7055

Sonora Eye Surgery Center, 940 Sylva Lane, Suite G, Sonora, CA 95370; tel. 209/532–2020; FAX. 209/532–1687; Desiree Torres, RN, Surgery Administrator

South Coast Laser Center, 3420 Bristol Street, Suite 701, Costa Mesa, CA 92626; tel. 714/957–0272; FAX. 714/641–2020; Marc R. Rose, MD, Medical Director

Southern California Surgery Center, 7305 Pacific Boulevard, Huntington Pa, CA 90255; tel. 323/584–8222; FAX. 323/584–8606; Ruth Huezo, Administrator

Southland Endoscopy Center, 949 East Calhoun Place, Suite B, Hemet, CA 92543; tel. 951/929–1177; FAX. 951/765–9111; Sreenivasa R. Nakka, MD, FACP, FACG

Southwest Surgical Center, Health South, 201 New Stine Road, Suite 130, Bakersfield, CA 93309; tel. 661/396–8900; FAX. 661/397–2929; Linda Bloomquist, Administrator

St. Joseph Surgery and Laser Center, Inc., dba St. Mary and Joseph Surgery and Laser Center, Inc., 436 South Glassell Street, Orange, CA 92866; tel. 714/633–9566; FAX. 714/633–5193; Kathleen Rupert, Administrator

Starpoint Health Foundation, PO Box 7459, Newport Beach, CA 92658-7459; tel. 949/705–5100; FAX. 949/985–0055; Eric D. Friedlander, Chief Executive Officer

Surgecenter of Palo Alto, 795 El Camino Real, Palo Alto, CA 94301; tel. 650/324–1832; FAX. 650/330–4520; Margo Mynderse-Isola, Chief Executive Officer

Surgery Center of San Buena Ventura, 3525 Loma Vista Road, Suite B, Ventura, CA 93003; tel. 805/641–6434; FAX. 805/641–6437; Chris Behm, Administrator

Surgery Center of Santa Monica, 2121 Wilshire Boulevard, Suite 201, Santa Monica, CA 90403; tel. 310/264–7300; FAX. 310/828–8626

Surgical Center at Saddleback, 24411 Health Center Dr., Laguna Hills, CA 92653; tel. 949/472–0244; FAX. 949/472–0380; Brian Fitzgerald, Administrator

Surgitek Outpatient Center, Inc., 460 North Greenfield Avenue, Suite Eight, Hanford, CA 93230; tel. 559/582–0238; FAX. 559/582–9341; Wiley Elick, Owner, Administrator

Sutter Alhambra Surgery Center, 1201 Alhambra Boulevard, Suite 110, Sacramento, CA 95816; tel. 916/733–8222; FAX. 916/733–8224; Ken Schwam, Administrator

Sutter Auburn Surgery Center, 3123 Professional Drive, Suite 100, Auburn, CA 95603; tel. 530/888–8899; FAX. 530/888–1464; Toni Angle, MBA, Administrator

Sutter North Procedure Center, 550 B Street, Yuba City, CA 95991; tel. 530/749–3653; FAX. 530/749–3493; Deborah Smith, Ancillary Services Director

The Center for Endoscopy, 3921 Waring Road, Suite B, Oceanside, CA 92056; tel. 760/940–6300; FAX. 760/940–8074; Barbara Bockover, RN, Administrator

The Centre for Plastic Surgery, 1869 N Waterman Avenue, San Bernardino, CA 92404; tel. 909/883–8686; FAX. 909/881–6537; David Nguyen, MD

The Endoscopy Center, 870 Shasta Street, Suite 200, Yuba City, CA 95991; tel. 530/671–3636; Rose Wood, Office Manager

The Endoscopy Center of the South Bay, 23560 Madison Street, Suite 109, Torrance, CA 90505; tel. 310/325–6331; FAX. 310/325–6335; Gloria Sze, MD, Medical Director

The Eye Surgery Center (Colton), 1900 East Washington Street, Colton, CA 92324; tel. 909/825–8002; FAX. 909/424–1662; Melissa Goins, RN, Director

The Eye Surgery Center of Northern California, 5959 Greenback Lane Suite 310, Citrus Height, CA 95621; tel. 916/723-7400; FAX. 916/723-4449; Scott George, Clinic Director

The Montebello Surgery Center, 229 East Beverly Boulevard, Montebello, CA 90640; tel. 323/728-7998; FAX. 323/728-5041; Millie Kelly, Administrator

The Palos Verdes Ambulatory Surgery Medical Center, 3400 West Lomita Boulevard, Suite 307A, Torrance, CA 90505; tel. 310/539-5888; FAX. 310/517-9916; Christine Petti, MD, Medical Director

The Plastic Surgery Center, 95 Scripps Drive, Sacramento, CA 95825; tel. 916/929-1833; FAX. 916/929-6730; Marlin Schriock, Administrator

The San Luis Obispo Surgery Center, 1304 Ella Street, Suite C, San Luis Obis, CA 93401; tel. 805/544-7874; FAX. 866/384-2036; Judy Shapazian, RN, Administrator

The Surgery Center of Alta Bates Summit Medical Center, 3875 Telegraph Avenue, Oakland, CA 94609; tel. 510/547-2244; FAX. 510/653-5242; Kim D'Ambrosia, Administrator

The Surgery Center of Riverside, Inc., 8990 Garfield, Suite One, Riverside, CA 92503; tel. 951/785-5421; FAX. 951/785-0130

The Surgery Center of Santa Rosa, 1111 Sonoma Avenue, Lower Level, Santa Rosa, CA 95405; tel. 707/578-4100; FAX. 707/578-7997; Ken Alban, Administrator

Third Street Surgery Center, 420 East Third Street, Suite 110, Los Angeles, CA 90013; tel. 213/617-9194; FAX. 213/617-0605; Tomoko Okuda, RN, Clinical Coordinator

Time Surgical Facility, 720 North Tustin Avenue, Suite 202, Santa Ana, CA 92705; tel. 714/972-1811; FAX. 714/972-0986; Tracey Mora, RN, Nurse Manager

Torrance Surgicenter, 22410 Hawthorne Boulevard, Suite Three, Torrance, CA 90505; tel. 310/373-2238; FAX. 310/373-8238; Lindon Kawahara, MD, Administrator

Truxtun Surgery Center, Inc., 4260 Truxtun Avenue, Suite 120, Bakersfield, CA 93309; tel. 661/327-3636; Mary Moeder, AOM

Twin Cities Surgicenter, Inc., 812 Fourth Street, Suite A, Marysville, CA 95901; tel. 530/741-3937; FAX. 530/743-0427; Karen M. Wasilenko, CASC Administrator

University Ambuiatory Surgery Center, 8929 University Center Lane, Suite 103, San Diego, CA 92122; tel. 858/554-0220; FAX. 858/554-0458; Eileen Smith, Administrator

Upland Outpatient Surgical Center, Inc., 1330 San Bernardino Road #F, Upland, CA 91786; tel. 909/981-8755; FAX. 909/981-9462; Brian Olson, Administrator

Valencia Outpatient Surgical Center Partners, L.P., dba Valencia Surgical Center, 24355 Lyons Avenue, Suite 120, Santa Clarita, CA 91321; tel. 661/255-6644; FAX. 661/255-7653; Pat Monolias, RN, Director of Nursing

Valley Endoscopy Center, 18425 Burbank Boulevard, Suite 525, Tarzana, CA 91356; tel. 818/708-6050; FAX. 818/708-6055; Christine Scoggins, RN, Clinical Director

Ventura Out-Patient Surgery, Inc., 3555 Loma Vista Road, Suite 204, Ventura, CA 93003; tel. 805/653-5460; FAX. 805/653-1470; Brian D. Brantner, MD

Washington Outpatient Surgery Center, 2299 Mowry Avenue, First Floor, Fremont, CA 94538; tel. 510/791-5374; FAX. 510/790-8916; Dr. Jeffery Stuart, Medical Director

Waverley Surgery Center, LP, 400 Forest Avenue, Palo Alto, CA 94301; tel. 650/324-0600; FAX. 650/269-1620

West Hills Surgical Center, 7240 Medical Center Drive, West Hills, CA 91307; tel. 818/226-9151; FAX. 818/226-0947

Westlake Eye Surgery Center, 2900 Townsgate Road, Suite 201, Westlake Village, CA 91361; tel. 805/496-6789; FAX. 805/494-8392; John Darin, MD, Medical Director

Zeiter Eye Surgical Center, Inc., 1801 E. March Lane, Suite C360, Stockton, CA 95210; tel. 209/337-2020; FAX. 209/337-2021; Theresa Slaton, RN, Surgical Administrator

COLORADO

Avista Surgery Center, 2525 Fourth Street, Lower Level, Boulder, CO 80304; tel. 303/443-3672; John Sackett, Administrator

Boulder Medical Center, P C, 2750 Broadway, Boulder, CO 80304; tel. 303/440-3000; Mr. Bradford McKane, Chief Executive Officer

Centennial Medical Plaza, 14200 East Arapahoe Road, Centennial, CO 80112; tel. 303/699-3000; FAX. 303/699-3152; Mary Beth Savory, Director of Operations

Centrum Surgical Center, 8200 East Belleview, Suite 300, East Tower, Greenwood Village, CO 80111; tel. 303/290-0600; FAX. 303/290-6359; Ken Kolb, Administrator

Colorado Center for Reproductive Medicine, 10290 Ridgegate Circle, Lone Tree, CO 80124-5331; tel. 303/788-8300; FAX. 303/788-8310; Dr. William Schoolcraft, Administrator

Colorado Outpatient Eye Surgical Center, 2480 South Downing, Suite G-20, Denver, CO 80210; tel. 303/777-7303; FAX. 303/282-0266; Diane Nelson, RN, ASC Administrator

Colorado Springs Eye Surgery Center, 2920 North Cascade Avenue, Colorado Springs, CO 80907; tel. 719/636-5054; FAX. 719/520-3576; Dr. Robert Foerster, Medical Director

Colorado Springs Health Partners Ambulatory Surgery Center, 1615 Medical Center Point, Colorado Springs, CO 80907; tel. 719/636-3555; FAX. 719/538-2999; Ms. Joan Compton, VP Operations

Colorado Springs Surgery Center An Affiliate of SCA, 1615 Medical Center Point, Colorado Springs, CO 80907; tel. 719/635-7740; FAX. 719/635-7750; Jenny (Jen) Knellinger, Administrator

Day Surgery of Grand Junction, Inc., 1000 Wellington Avenue, Grand Junction, CO 81501; tel. 970/245-5989; FAX. 970/243-9023; Karen Higuera, RN, Surgery Center Administrator

Denver Eye Surgery Center, Inc., 13772 Denver West Parkway, Building 55, Suite 120, Lakewood, CO 80401; tel. 303/273-8770; FAX. 303/273-8775; Jacqueline Paller, Clinical Director

Denver Midtown Surgery Center, 1919 East 18th Avenue, Denver, CO 80206; tel. 303/322-3993; FAX. 303/322-7329; Lisa Cross, Administrator

Dishler Laser Institute, 8400 East Prentice Avenue, Suite 1200, Greenwood Village, CO 80111; tel. 303/793-3000; FAX. 303/793-3008; Jon Dishler, MD, President

Durango Surgicenter, LLC, 316 Sawyer Drive, Durango, CO 81303; tel. 970/259-3818; FAX. 970/259-9553; D.J. Winder, MD, Administrator

Eye Center of Northern Colorado Surgery Center, 1725 E. Prospect Avenue, Fort Collins, CO 80525; tel. 970/221-2222; FAX. 970/221-2223; Carol Wittmer, Administrator

Eye Surgery Center of Colorado, P.C., 8403 Bryant Street, Westminster, CO 80031; tel. 303/426-4810; FAX. 303/426-8708; William G. Self, Jr., MD, Administrator

Foot Surgery Center of Northern Colorado, 1355 Riverside Avenue, #B, Fort Collins, CO 80524; tel. 970/484-4620; FAX. 970/407-1194; Adriann Anderson, Administrator

Kaiser Permanente Ambulatory Surgery Center, 2045 Franklin Street, Denver, CO 80205; tel. 303/764-4444; Renee Paul, Director KASC

Littleton Day Surgery Center, 8381 South Park Lane, Littleton, CO 80120; tel. 303/795-2244; FAX. 303/795-5965; Cindy Richardson, RN, BS, CLNC, Clinical Director/Administrator

North Denver Endoscopy Center, 10001 North Washington St., Thornton, CO 80229; tel. 303/205-1090; FAX. 303/205-1091; Lance Goudzwaard, Chief Executive Officier

Orthopaedic & Spine Center of the Rockies Ambulatory Surgery Center, 2500 East Prospect Road, Fort Collins, CO 80525; tel. 970/493-4010; FAX. 970/419-7151; Barb Hardes, RN, BSN, CNOR, Director/Administrator of Surgical Operations

Park Meadows Outpatient Surgery, 7430 Park Meadows Drive #300, Lone Tree, CO 80124; tel. 303/706-1100; FAX. 303/790-7322; Charlene A. Sherwood, Administrator

Peak One Surgery Center, LLC, 350 Peak One Drive, P.O. Box 4460, Frisco, CO 80443; tel. 970/668-1458; FAX. 970/668-6677; Diane Lampron, Administrator

Pikes Peak Endoscopy & Surgery Center, 1699 Medical Center Pt., Colorado Springs, CO 80907; tel. 719/632-7101; FAX. 719/632-4468; Tricia Tappan, Chief Executive Officer

Pueblo Surgery Center, 25 Montebello Road, Pueblo, CO 81001; tel. 719/544-1600; FAX. 719/544-2599; Jennifer Arellano, Administrator

South Denver Endoscopy Center, Inc., 499 East Hampden Avenue, Suite 430, Englewood, CO 80110; tel. 303/874-0350; Dr. Dan Hruza, Medical Director

Surgery Center of Fort Collins, 1100 East Prospect Road, Fort Collins, CO 80525; tel. 970/494-4800; FAX. 970/493-2380; Ross Alexander, Administrator

U.S. Air Force Academy Clinic, 10 MDG/CC, 4102 Pinion Drive, USAF Academy, CO 80840-4000; tel. 719/333-5660; FAX. 719/333-5670

CONNECTICUT

Connecticut Foot Surgery Center, 318 New Haven Avenue, Milford, CT 06460; tel. 203/882-0065; FAX. 203/882-0248; Martin Pressman, DPM, Administrator

HealthSouth Surgery Center of Hartford, 100 Retreat Avenue, Hartford, CT 06106; tel. 860/549-7970; FAX. 860/247-4121; Theresa Klimczak, Administrative Director

Stamford Surgical Center, 32 Strawberry Hill Court, Stamford, CT 06902; tel. 203/276-6196; FAX. 203/276-4921; Patrice Kelly, Executive Director of Perioperative Services

DELAWARE

Bayview Endoscopy Center, Inc., 1539 Savannah Road, Lewes, DE 19958; tel. 302/644-0455; FAX. 302/645-5214; Harry J. Anagnostakos, DO, President

Cataract and Laser Center, LLC, 4102 Ogletown/ Stanton Road, Suite 1, Newark, DE 19713; tel. 302/454-8802; FAX. 302/454-8801; Alexandra Meyer, Center Administrator

Central Delaware Endoscopy Unit, 644 South Queen Street, Suite 105, Dover, DE 19904; tel. 302/677-1617; FAX. 302/677-1669; William M. Kaplan, MD, Medical Director

Limestone Medical Center, Inc., 1941 Limestone Road, Suite 113, Wilmington, DE 19808; tel. 302/633-9873; FAX. 302/992-0563; Thomas E. Mulhern, MBA, CASC Executive Director

DISTRICT OF COLUMBIA

MedStar Surgery Center, 1145 19th Street, NW, Suite 850, Washington, DC 20036; tel. 202/223-9040; FAX. 202/223-9047; William Heron, MD, Medical Director

Planned Parenthood of Metropolitan Washington, D.C., 1108 16th Street, NW, Washington, DC 20036; tel. 202/347-8512; FAX. 202/347-0267; Takina Wilson, Director of Patient Services

Premier Surgery Center of D.C., 6323 Georgia Avenue, NW, Suite 200, Washington, DC 20011; tel. 202/291-0126; FAX. 202/291-0126; Lenora Hollaway, RN, Administrative Director

The Endoscopy Center of Washington, DC, L.P., 2021 K Street, NW, Suite T-115, Washington, DC 20006; tel. 202/775-8692; FAX. 202/463-1165; Debra Jay RN, Center Director

FLORIDA

Aker Kasten Eye Center, 1445 Northwest Boca Raton Boulevard, Boca Raton, FL 33432; tel. 561/338-7722; FAX. 561/338-7785; Kim Harrington, Administrator

All Saints Surgery Center, 11377 Cortez Boulevard, Brooksville, FL 34613; tel. 352/597-3060; FAX. 352/597-3077; Julie Curky, RN, Administrator and Clinical Director

Alpha Ambulatory Surgery, Inc., 2160 Capital Circle, NE, Tallahassee, FL 32308; tel. 850/385-0033; FAX. 850/422-0201; Juanita Legree, RN, Administrator

Ambulatory Surgery Center, 4500 East Fletcher Avenue, Tampa, FL 33613; tel. 813/977-8550; FAX. 813/977-7941; Edward J. Tennant, CASC, Administrator

Ambulatory Surgery Center of Brevard, 719 East New Haven Avenue, Melbourne, FL 32901; tel. 321/726-4106; FAX. 321/728-3001; Norm Gagnon, General Manager

Ambulatory Surgical Care, 1045 North Courtenay Parkway, Merritt Island, FL 32953; tel. 321/452-4448; FAX. 321/452-4533; Robyn Allard, RN, Administrator

Atlantic Surgery Center, 541 Health Boulevard, Daytona Beach, FL 32114; tel. 386/239-0021; FAX. 386/248-8226; Shirley A. Hines, RN, CASC, Administrator

Atlantic Surgical Center, Inc., 150 Southwest 12th Avenue, Suite 450, Pompano Beach, FL 33069; tel. 954/941-3369; FAX. 954/941-8470; Andrew Byers, Administrator

Barkley Surgicenter, 63 Barkley Circle, Suite 104, Fort Myers, FL 33907; tel. 239/275-8452; FAX. 239/275-1969; Kerri Gantt LHRM, CMM, Administrative Director

Bayfront Same Day Surgery Center, LLC, 603 Seventh Street South, St. Petersburg, FL 33701; tel. 727/553-7906; FAX. 727/553-7880; Michaela Hames, Administrator

Section C

Belleair Surgery Center, 1130 Ponce de Leon Boulevard, Clearwater, FL 33756; tel. 727/581–4800; FAX. 813/585–0319; Ed Callahan, Administrator

Beraja Healthcare Corp., 2550 Douglas Road, Coral Gables, FL 33134; tel. 305/443–7070; FAX. 305/357–1701; Margarita Caffe, RN, DON

Bethesda Outpatient Surgery Center, LLC, 10301 Hagen Ranch Road, Suite 520, Boynton Beach, FL 33437; tel. 561/374–5550; FAX. 561/374–9977; Maddie Linder, RN, Director of Surgical Services

Boynton Beach ASC, LLC, 1717-1799 Woolbright Road, Boynton Beach, FL 33426; tel. 516/737–8031; FAX. 561/736–5062; Lily Lee, Administrator

Brandon Surgery Center, 711 South Parsons, Brandon, FL 33511; tel. 813/654–7771; FAX. 813/654–3347; Edward J. Tennant, CASC, Administrator and Chief Executive Officer

Brevard Surgery Center, 665 Apollo Boulevard, Melbourne, FL 32901; tel. 321/984–3200; FAX. 321/984–0032; Gary R. Hardey, MBA, Administrator

Cape Surgery Center, 1941 Waldemere Street, Sarasota, FL 34239-3555; tel. 941/917–1900; FAX. 941/917–2356; Sharon Tolhurst, RN, MBA, Administrator

Center for Digestive Health and Pain Management, 12700 Creekside Lane, Suite 202, P.O. Box 33906, Fort Myers, FL 33919; tel. 941/489–4454; FAX. 941/489–2114; Vivian DiCarlo, RN, Nursing Director

Center for Special Surgery, 4650 Fourth Street, N., St. Petersburg, FL 33703; tel. 727/527–1919; FAX. 727/527–0714; Paula Russo, Administrator

Central Florida Eye Institute, 3133 Southwest 32nd Avenue, Ocala, FL 34474; tel. 352/237–8400; FAX. 352/237–7190; Thomas L. Croley, MD

Citrus Endoscopy and Surgery Center, 6412 West Gulf to Lake Highway, Crystal River, FL 34429; tel. 352/563–0223; FAX. 352/563–2961

Citrus Surgery Center, 110 North Lecanto Highway, Lecanto, FL 34461; tel. 352/527–1825; FAX. 352/527–1827; Richard Rice, Facility Administrator

Clearwater Endoscopy Center, 401 Corbett Street, Suite 220, Clearwater, FL 33756; tel. 727/443–0100; FAX. 727/461–4893; Nancy Wheeling RN, LHRM Administrator

Coral View Surgery Center, 8390 West Flager, Suite 216, Miami, FL 33144; tel. 305/226–5574; Ruben Paradela, Chief Executive Officer

Cortez Foot Surgery Center, PA, 1800 Cortez Road W, Suite 8, Bradenton, FL 34207; tel. 941/758–4608; FAX. 941/758–4438; Connie Belculfine, Administrator

Countryside Surgery Center, 3291 North McMullen Booth Road, Clearwater, FL 33761; tel. 727/725–5800; FAX. 727/797–4002; Cathy Buscema, RN, MSN, CNOR, Administrator

Doctors Surgery Center, 921 North Main Street, Kissimmee, FL 34744; tel. 407/933–7800; FAX. 407/933–8657; Helen Rivera

Emerald Coast Surgery Center, 995 Northwest Mar Walt Drive, Fort Walton Beach, FL 32547; tel. 850/863–7887; FAX. 850/863–4955; Lynda Wright, Business Office Manager

Endoscopy Center of Ocala, Inc., 1901 SE 18th Avenue, #400, Ocala, FL 34471; tel. 352/732–8905; FAX. 352/732–2661; Bill Emerson, Administrator

Endoscopy Center of Sarasota, 1435 Osprey Avenue, Suite 100, Sarasota, FL 34239; tel. 941/366–4475; FAX. 941/366–4390; Pam Copeland, RN, Administrator

Eye Care and Surgery Center of Ft. Lauderdale, 2540 Northeast Ninth Street, Ft. Lauderdale, FL 33304; tel. 954/561–3533; FAX. 954/565–9706; Jane M. Beatly, Administrator

Eye Surgery and Laser Center, 4120 Del Prado Boulevard, Cape Coral, FL 33904; tel. 239/542–4068; FAX. 239/542–0704; Latosha Underwood, RN, BSN, Risk Manager Designee

Eye Surgery and Laser Center, LLC, 409 Avenue K, SE, Winter Haven, FL 33880; tel. 863/299–8574; FAX. 863/294–8305; Eileen T. Beltramba, RN, BS, Center Director

Eye Surgicenter, 2521 Northwest 41st Street, Gainesville, FL 32606; tel. 352/377–7733; FAX. 352/377–9577; William A. Newsome, MD

Florida Eye Clinic Ambulatory Surgical Center, 160 Boston Avenue, Altamonte Springs, FL 32701; tel. 407/834–7776; FAX. 407/834–2478; Sondra Hoffman, Chief Executive Officer/Administrator

Florida Eye Institute Surgicenter, LLC, 2750 Indian River Boulevard, Vero Beach, FL 32960; tel. 772/569–9500; FAX. 772/569–9507; Lyn M. Lane, Administrator

Florida Medical Clinic Special Procedures Center, 38135 Market Square, Zephyrhills, FL 33542; tel. 813/780–8266; FAX. 813/715–4150; Melissa LoParco, RN, Manager

Florida Surgery Center, 180 Boston Avenue, Altamonte Springs, FL 32701; tel. 407/830–0573; FAX. 407/830–4373; Patricia Rustin, Administrator

Foundation for Advanced Eye Care, 3737 N. Pine Island Rd, Sunrise, FL 33351; tel. 954/572–5888; Wayne Bizer, DO Medical Director

Gaskins Eye Care and Surgery Center, 2335 Ninth Street, N., Suite 304, Naples, FL 34103; tel. 239/263–7750; William Darrell Gaskins, MD

Gulf Coast Surgery Center, 411 Second Street, E., Bradenton, FL 34208; tel. 941/746–1121; FAX. 941/746–7816; Diana Williford, MBA/HA, Administrator

Gulfcoast Surgery Center, 12132 Cortez Boulevard, Brooksville, FL 34613; tel. 352/596–0744; Fawzi Soliman, MD

HealthPark Surgery Center, 1283 Jacaranda Boulevard, Venice, FL 34292; tel. 941/497–5660; FAX. 941/492–3942; Kermit Knight, CASC Administrator

HealthSouth Orlando Center for Outpatient Surgery, 1405 South Orange Avenue, Suite 400, Orlando, FL 32806; tel. 407/426–8331; FAX. 407/425–9582

Hillmoor Eye Surgery Center, LLC dba One Day Surgery, 1715 Southeast Tiffany Avenue, Port St. Lucie, FL 34952; tel. 772/335–7005; FAX. 772/398–9195; Diane DelRosario, Administrator

Holiday Surgery Center, 1109 U.S. Highway 19, Suite B, Holiday, FL 34691; tel. 727/934–5705; FAX. 727/937–3756; David Wall, Practice Administrator

Jacksonville Surgery Center, 7021 A.C. Skinner Parkway, Jacksonville, FL 32256; tel. 904/281–0021; FAX. 904/281–0988; Katherine Anderson, RN, BSN, Administrator

Kissimmee Surgery Center, 2275 North Central Avenue, Kissimmee, FL 34741; tel. 407/870–0573; FAX. 407/870–1859; James Caudill, Administrator

Lake Surgery and Endoscopy Center, 8100 Country Road 44 LEG A, Leesburg, FL 34788; tel. 352/323–1995; FAX. 352/326–9990; Ismail A. Ismail, RPH, Chief Financial Officer

Lee County Center for Foot and Ankle Surgery, Inc., 12734 Kenwood Lane, Suite 44, Fort Myers, FL 33907; tel. 941/936–2454; FAX. 941/936–1974; Sandra Desai, DPM

Martin Memorial SurgiCenter, 509 Riverside Drive, Suite 100, Stuart, FL 34994; tel. 772/223–5920; FAX. 772/288–5820

Mayo Clinic Jacksonville Ambulatory Surgery Center for G.I., 4500 San Pablo Road, Jacksonville, FL 32224; tel. 904/223–2000; Christopher Hasse, Manager of Clinical Operations

Medical Development Corporation of Pasco County, 7315 Hudson Avenue, Hudson, FL 34667; tel. 727/868–9563; FAX. 727/869–2773; Dawn M. Ernst, Director, Nursing

Melbourne Surgery Center, 1340 Medical Park Drive, Suite 101, Melbourne, FL 32901; tel. 321/729–9493; FAX. 321/768–6043; Brian Rye, Administrator

Merritt Island Surgery Center, 220 North Sykes Creek Parkway, Suite 101, Merritt Island, FL 32953; tel. 321/459–0015; FAX. 321/459–2291; Cynthia Johnson, Administrator

Mid Florida Surgery Center, 17564 West Highway 441, Mt. Dora, FL 32757; tel. 352/735–4100; FAX. 352/735–2444; Sonya Troxell, RN, Administrative Director

Montgomery Eye Center, 700 Neapolitan Way, Naples, FL 34103; tel. 239/261–8383; FAX. 239/261–8443; Jay E. Montgomery, Administrator

Mullis Eye Institute, Inc., 1600 Jenks Avenue, Panama City, FL 32405; tel. 904/763–6666; FAX. 904/763–6665; Colette Smith, RN, Director

Naples Day Surgery North, 11161 Health Park Boulevard, Naples, FL 34110; tel. 239/598–3111; FAX. 239/598–1707; Thomas C. Buckley, Executive Director

New Port Richey Surgery Center at Trinity, 9332 State Road 54, Suite 100, Trinity, FL 34655; tel. 727/848–0446; FAX. 727/842–3166; Linda Bedwell, RN, Administrator

Newgate Surgery Center, Inc., 5200 Tamiami Trail, Suite 202, Naples, FL 34103; tel. 239/263–6766; FAX. 239/263–3320; Dr. R. Crane

North County Surgicenter, 4000 Burns Road, Palm Beach Gardens, FL 33410; tel. 561/626–6446; FAX. 561/626–7244; Lucas Buchholz, Business Manager

North Florida Surgery Center, 256 Professional Glen, Lake City, FL 32025; tel. 386/758–8937; FAX. 386/755–2169; Vivian Douberly, Administrator

North Florida Surgical Pavilion, 6705 Northwest 10th Place, Gainesville, FL 32605; tel. 352/333–4555; FAX. 352/333–4569; Susan Roland, Administrative Director

North Tampa Outpatient Surgical Facility, 5329 Primrose Lake Circle, Tampa, FL 33647; tel. 813/463–9762; FAX. 813/463–9764; Deanna Sorerns, Administrator

Northwest Florida Surgery Center, 767 Airport Road, Panama City, FL 32405; tel. 850/747–0400; FAX. 850/913–9744; Ron Samuelian, Chief Executive Officer

Novamed Surgery Center of Sebring, 3601 South Highlands Avenue, Sebring, FL 33870; tel. 863/382–7500; FAX. 863/385–7332; Dana G. Cowart, ASC Director

Ocala Eye Surgery Center, 3330 Southwest 33rd Road, Ocala, FL 34474; tel. 352/873–9311; FAX. 352/873–9652; Ann Hotaling, Director

Orange Park Surgery Center, 2050 Professional Center Drive, Orange Park, FL 32073; tel. 904/272–2550; FAX. 904/272–7911; Alisa Fischer-Hurst, RN, Administrator

Outpatient Surgical Services, Ltd., 301 Northwest 82nd Avenue, Plantation, FL 33324; tel. 954/693–8600; FAX. 954/424–1966; Wayne C. Jones, FACHE, Administrator

Palm Beach Eye Clinic, 130 Butler Street, West Palm Beach, FL 33407; tel. 561/832–6113; FAX. 561/833–3003; Andre J. Golino, MD

Palm Beach Lakes Surgery Center, 2047 Palm Beach Lakes Boulevard, West Palm Beach, FL 33409; tel. 561/296–1330; FAX. 561/296–1350; Jonathan Cutler DPM, Manager

Palm Beach Outpatient Surgery Center, 2889 10th Ave. N, Suite 203, Palm Springs, FL 33461; tel. 561/747–1111; FAX. 560/747–6682; Tom M. Coffman, MD, Medical Director

Parkside Surgery Center, 2731 Park Street, Jacksonville, FL 32205; tel. 904/389–1077; FAX. 904/338–9016; David Manning, Administrator

Physician's Surgical Care Center, 2056 Aloma Avenue, Winter Park, FL 32792; tel. 407/647–5100; FAX. 407/647–1966

Physicians Ambulatory Surgery Center, 300 Clyde Morris Boulevard, Suite B, Ormond Beach, FL 32174; tel. 386/672–1080; FAX. 386/672–8628; Lee Baylor, Administrator

Physicians Surgery Center, Ltd., dba Lee Island Coast Surgery Center, 4035 Evans Avenue, Fort Myers, FL 33901; tel. 941/939–7375; FAX. 941/275–5248; Jacquelyn Paul, RN, Administrator

Port Orange Endoscopy & Surgery Center, 1185 Dunlawton Avenue, Suite 100, Port Orange, FL 32127; tel. 386/672–0017; FAX. 386/672–6732; Susan K. Amon, RN, DON LHCRM

Rand Surgical Pavilion Corp., Five West Sample Road, Deerfield Beach, FL 33064; tel. 954/782–1700; FAX. 954/782–7490; Deborah Rand, Administrator

Same Day Surgicenter of Orlando, 88 West Kaley Street, Orlando, FL 32806; tel. 407/423–0573; FAX. 407/841–3872; Bob Bashore, Administrator

Samuel Wells Surgicenter, Inc., 3599 University Boulevard, S., Suite 604, Jacksonville, FL 32216; tel. 904/399–0905; FAX. 904/346–0757; Faye T. Evans, Risk Manager

Seven Springs Surgery Center, Inc., 2024 Seven Springs Boulevard, New Port Richey, FL 34655; tel. 727/376–7000; FAX. 727/375–8944; Kathleen M. Geiger, RN, Surgery Director

Southwest Florida Endoscopy Center, 5050 Mason Corbin Court, Ft. Myers, FL 33907; tel. 239/275–6678; FAX. 239/275–5216; Jansi Prabakaran, MD, Administrator

Southwest Florida Institute of Ambulatory Surgery, 3700 Central Avenue, Suite Two, Ft. Myers, FL 33901; tel. 239/275–0665; FAX. 239/275–0503; Susan Hanzevack, Executive Director

Specialty Surgery Of Ocala, LLC, 3201 Southwest 34th Street, Ocala, FL 34474; tel. 352/237–6162; FAX. 352/509–9409; DeeDee Burroughs, RN, LHRM, Nurse Administrator

St. Augustine Endoscopy Center, 212 Southpark Circle, East, St. Augustine, FL 32086; tel. 904/824–6108; FAX. 904/823–9613; Santiago A. Rosado, MD, FACP, FACG, President

St. Lucy's Outpatient Surgery Center, 21275 Olean Boulevard, Port Charlotte, FL 33952; tel. 941/625-1325; FAX. 941/255-6985; Barb Vivas, RN, DON, Clinical Administrator

St. Luke's Outpatient Surgery Center - Satellite, 4500 San Pablo Road, Jacksonville, FL 32224; tel. 904/953-0100; FAX. 904/953-0019; Carla Pats, Manager

St. Luke's Surgical Center, 43309 U.S. Highway 19, N., Tarpon Spring, FL 34689; tel. 727/938-2020; FAX. 727/938-5606; Gustavo Gamero, MD, Medical Director

Suncoast Eye Center, Eye Surgery Institute, 14003 Lakeshore Boulevard, Hudson, FL 34667; tel. 727/868-9442; FAX. 727/862-6210; Lawrence A. Seigel, MD, PA, Medical Director

Surgery Center at Coral Springs, 967 University Drive, Coral Springs, FL 33071; tel. 954341-5553; FAX. 954/344-7054; Jeff Rosenberg, Administrator

Surgery Center at St. Andrews, Inc., 1350 East Venice Avenue, Venice, FL 34285; tel. 941/488-2030; FAX. 941/484-2010; Carol Carr, Administrator

Surgery Center of North Florida, Inc., 6520 Northwest Ninth Boulevard, Gainsville, FL 32615; tel. 352/331-7987; FAX. 352/331-2787; Joy Ingram, Administrator

Surgery Center of Stuart, 2096 Southeast Ocean Boulevard, Stuart, FL 34996; tel. 772/223-0174; FAX. 772/223-0946; Matt Berke, Administrator

Surgical Licensed Ward, dba Underwood Surgery Center, 110 West Underwood Street, Suite B, Orlando, FL 32806; tel. 407/648-9151; FAX. 407/426-7017; Doug Oakley, Administrator

Surgical Park Center, Ltd., 9100 Southwest 87th Avenue, Miami, FL 33176; tel. 305/271-9100; FAX. 305/598-5509; Lionel Lima

Surgicare Center, Inc., 4101 Evans Avenue, Ft. Myers, FL 33901; tel. 239/939-3456; FAX. 239/335-1962; Mary E. Blackwell, RN, BS, Director of Nursing

Tallahassee Endoscopy Center, 2400 Miccosukee Road, Tallahassee, FL 32308; tel. 850/877-2105; FAX. 850/942-1761; Noel Withers, Administrator

Tallahassee Outpatient Surgery Center, 3334 Capital Medical Boulevard, Suite 500, Tallahassee, FL 32308; tel. 850/877-4688; FAX. 850/877-0368; Bonnie Goodwin, Administrator

Tampa Bay Surgery Center, 11811 North Dale Mabry Hwy, Tampa, FL 33618; tel. 813/961-8500; FAX. 813/265-2564; Jay L. Rosen, MD, Chief Executive Officer

Tampa Bay Surgery Center, 2727 MLK Blvd, Tampa, FL 33607; tel. 813/961-8500; FAX. 813/265-2564; Jay L. Rosen, MD, Chief Executive Officer

Tampa Eye Surgery Center, 4302 North Gomez, Tampa, FL 33607; tel. 813/870-6330; FAX. 813/871-3956; Beverly Martin, Administrator

Tampa Outpatient Surgical Facility, 5013 North Armenia Avenue, Tampa, FL 33603; tel. 813/875-0562; FAX. 813/871-5236; Christina McDonald, Administrator

The Aesthetic Plastic Surgery Center, 135 San Marco Drive, Venice, FL 34285; tel. 941/484-6836; FAX. 941/484-9690; Linda Martin, Administrative Director

The Endoscopy Center, 4810 North Davis Highway, Pensacola, FL 32503; tel. 850/474-8988; FAX. 850/478-9903; Steve Dunn, Administrator

The Endoscopy Center, Inc., 5101 Southwest 8th Street, Miami, FL 33134; tel. 305/461-1881; FAX. 305/445-2406; Carla Guerrero, Administration

The Eye Associates Surgery Center, 6002 Pointe West Boulevard, Bradenton, FL 34209; tel. 941/792-2020; FAX. 941/792-2832; Pamela Morgan, RN, ASC Director

The Gastrointestinal Center of Hialeah, Inc., 135 West 49th Street, Hialeah, FL 33012; tel. 305/825-1487; FAX. 305/825-9731; Maria T. Pineda, Administrator

The Sarasota Ophthalmology, ASC, LLC, dba Center for Advanced Eye Surgery, 3920 Bee Ridge Road Building F, Suite C, Sarasota, FL 34233; tel. 941/925-0000; FAX. 941/927-2726; Darice Downs, RN, LHRM,Center Director

The Sheridan Surgery Center, 95 Bulldog Boulevard, Suite 104, Melbourne, FL 32901; tel. 321/952-9800; FAX. 321/952-7889; Anne Latorra, Director

The Surgery Center of Coral Gables, LLC, 1097 SW Le Jeune Road, Miami, FL 33134; tel. 305/461-1300; Laura Lilburn, RN, CNOR, Center Director

Total Surgery Center, 130 Tamiami Trail, Suite 210, Naples, FL 34102; tel. 239/434-4118; FAX. 239/434-6343; Margaret M. Kiefer, RN

Treasure Coast Center for Surgery, 1411 East Ocean Boulevard, Stuart, FL 34996; tel. 772/286-8028; FAX. 772/283-6628; Andrea Day, Business Office Manager

University Surgical Center, 7251 University Boulevard, Suite 100, Winter Park, FL 32792; tel. 407/677-0066; FAX. 407/677-4199; Carol Cavanagh, Administrator

Urological Ambulatory Surgery Center, Inc., 1812 North Mills Avenue, Orlando, FL 32803; tel. 407/992-2640; FAX. 407/897-2290; William Hamiger, Administrator

Venture Ambulatory Surgery Center, 16853 Northeast Second Avenue, Suite 400, North Miami Beach, FL 33162; tel. 305/652-2999; FAX. 305/652-8156; Lali Perez, RN, BSN, Center Director

Vero Eye Center, 70 Royal Palm Pointe, Vero Beach, FL 32960; tel. 772/569-6600; FAX. 772/569-5341; E.S. Branigan, III, MD

Volusia Endoscopy & Surgery Center, Inc., 550 Memorial Circle, Suite G, Ormond Beach, FL 32174; tel. 386/672-0017; FAX. 386/672-6732; Susan K. Amon, RN, DON LHCRM

Waterside Ambulatory Surgical Center, Inc., 2001 North Flagler Drive, West Palm Beach, FL 33407; tel. 561/721-8755; FAX. 561/659-7802; Lisa Bolognini, Administrative Director

GEORGIA

Advanced Surgery Center of Georgia, 220 Hospital Road, Canton, GA 30114; tel. 770/479-2202; FAX. 770/479-6666; Marguerite Cammarata, Administrator

Aesthetic Laser & Surgery Facility, 416 Gordon Avenue, Thomasville, GA 31792-6644; tel. 229/228-7200; FAX. 229/228-5193; G. Courtney Houston, MD, Medical Director

Affinity Outpatient Services, 2224 US Highway 41 North, Tifton, GA 31794; tel. 912/391-4299; FAX. 912/391-4291; Barry L. Cutts, Administrator

Albany Surgery Center, LLP, 531 Seventh Avenue, Albany, GA 31701; tel. 229/883-3535; FAX. 229/883-3783; Stephen M. Wilder, DPM, Medical Director

Ambulatory Foot and Leg Surgical Center, 1650 Mulkey Road, Austell, GA 30106; tel. 770/941-3633; FAX. 770/944-9038; Douglas Elleby, DPM, Chief Executive Officer

Ambulatory Laser and Surgery Center, 425 Forest Parkway, Suite 103, Forest Park, GA 30297-2135; tel. 404/363-1087; FAX. 404/363-9951; Dr. Paul A. Colon, Medical Director

Athens Plastic Surgery Center, 2325 Prince Avenue, Athens, GA 30606; tel. 706/546-0280; FAX. 404/548-0258; Stephen B. Lober, MD, Administrator

Atlanta Center for Women's Choice, Inc., 1874 Piedmont Ave NE, Ste 585 E, Atlanta, GA 30324; tel. 404/602-4495; FAX. 404/607-0728; Toni P. Hawkins, Administrator

Atlanta Endoscopy Center, Ltd., 2665 North Decatur Road, Suite 545, Decatur, GA 30033; tel. 404/297-5000; FAX. 404/296-9890; Patrick Light, Practice Administrator

Atlanta Gastroenterology Associates, 301 Philip Blvd, Suite A, Lawrenceville, GA 30046; tel. 770/822-5560; Diane Wilkins, Office Manager

Atlanta Outpatient Peachtree Dunwoody Center, 5505 Peachtree-Dunwoody Road, Suite 150, Atlanta, GA 30342; tel. 404/847-0893; FAX. 404/843-8664; Kim Ashe, Chief Executive Officer, Director

Atlanta Women's Medical Center, Inc., 235 West Wieuca Road, Atlanta, GA 30342; tel. 404/257-0057; FAX. 404/257-1245; Golda Melnik, Administrator

Atlantic Foot and Ankle Specialists, 95 Bel-Air Drive, Statesboro, GA 30461-6879; tel. 912/489-3668; Luke Renfroe, Practice Administrator

Augusta Plastic Surgery Center, Inc., 1348 Walton Way, Suite 6300, Augusta, GA 30901-2772; tel. 706/724-5611; FAX. 706/724-5435

Augusta Surgical Center, 915 Russell Street, Augusta, GA 30904-4115; tel. 706/738-4925; FAX. 706/738-7224; Jeff Simless, Administrator

Brunswick Endoscopy Center, 3217 4th Street, Brunswick, GA 31520-3759; tel. 912/267-1802; FAX. 912/267-0061; Rita Warren, Administrator

Center for Plastic Surgery, Inc., 365 East Paces Ferry Road, Atlanta, GA 30305; tel. 404/814-0868; FAX. 404/814-0869; Dr. Vincent Zubowicz, Medical Director

Clayton Outpatient Surgical Center, Inc., 6911 Tara Boulevard, Jonesboro, GA 30236; tel. 770/477-9535; FAX. 770/471-7826; Renee Grimsley, Administrator

Cobb Foot and Leg Surgical Center, 165 Vann Street, Marietta, GA 30060; tel. 770/422-9856; FAX. 770/984-0303; Glyn Lewis, Administrator

Coliseum Same Day Surgery, 340 Hospital Drive, P.O. Box 6154, Macon, GA 31208; tel. 912/742-1403; FAX. 912/742-1671; Lenore Sell, Administrator

Columbus Women's Health Organization, Inc., 3850 Rosemont Drive, Columbus, GA 31901; tel. 706/323-8363

DBA Atlanta Ambulatory Surgery Center, Atlanta Aesthetic Surgery Center, LLC, 4200 Northside Parkway, Building Eight, Atlanta, GA 30327; tel. 404/233-3833; FAX. 404/233-8447; Debbie Clotfelter, Administrator

DeKalb Gastroenterology Associates II, LLC, dba DeKalb Endoscopy Center, 2675 North Decatur Road, Suite 506, Decatur, GA 30033; tel. 404/299-1679; FAX. 404/508-7558; Mark A. Stern, MD

Dennis Surgery Center, Inc., 3193 Howell Mill Road, Suite 215, Atlanta, GA 30327; tel. 404/355-1312; FAX. 404/352-2798; Valerie Garrett, Administrator

Endoscopy Center of Columbus, LLC, 1130 Talbotton Road, Columbus, GA 31904-8745; tel. 706/641-6900; FAX. 706/327-0757; Jean Patterson, RN, Administrator

Endoscopy Center of Southeast Georgia, Inc., 200 Maple Drive, P.O. Box 1367, Vidalia, GA 30474; tel. 912/538-1003; FAX. 912/537-9843; Dixie Calhoun, RN, Administrator

Evans Surgery Center, 635 Ronald Reagan Drive, Evans, GA 30809; tel. 706/868-3110; FAX. 706/868-3156; Sharon Gelinas, Administrator

Fayette Plastic Surgery Center LLC, 874 Lanier Avenue West, One Prestige Park, Fayetteville, GA 30124; tel. 770/461-4000; FAX. 770/603-7064; Paul D. Feldman, President

Feminist Women's Health Center, 1924 Cliff Valley Way, Atlanta, GA 30329; tel. 404/728-7900; FAX. 404/728-7907; Erin Mabile, Clinical Director

G.I. Endoscopy Center, 6555 Professional Place, Suite B, Riverdale, GA 30274; tel. 770/692-0100; FAX. 770/692-6190; Aruna Prakash, BSc, Administrator

Gainesville Surgery Center, 1945 Beverly Road, Gainesville, GA 30501-2034; tel. 770/287-1500; Karen Fankhauser, Administrator

Georgia Surgical Centers - South, 541 Forest Parkway, Suite 14, Forest Park, GA 30297-6110; tel. 404/366-5652; Trudy Hunley, Administrator

Gwinnett Endoscopy Center, 301 Philip Blvd, NW, Suite B, Lawrenceville, GA 30046; tel. 770/682-7220; FAX. 770/338-0510; Kerry H. King, MD, Medical Director

HealthSouth Surgery Center of Gwinnett, 2131 Fountain Drive, Snellville, GA 30078; tel. 770/979-8200; FAX. 770/979-1327; Holly Kouts, Administrator

Kramer Professional Building, 215 Clairemont Avenue, Decatur, GA 30030; tel. 404/373-2529; FAX. 404/373-1655; Jerald N. Kramer, DPM, President

Marietta Surgical Center, 780 Canton Road, Suite 100, Marietta, GA 30060; tel. 770/422-1579; FAX. 770/428-4861; Faith Wheeler, RNCNOR, QA and Risk Manager

Medical Eye Associates, Inc., 1429 Oglethorpe Street, Macon, GA 31201; tel. 478/743-7061; FAX. 478/743-6296; Diane Vaughn, Practice Manager

North Atlanta Head and Neck Surgery Center, LLC, 980 Johnson Ferry Road, Northside Doctors Centre, Atlanta, GA 30342; tel. 404/843-9171; FAX. 404/250-1881; Pradeep K. Snha, MD, PhD

North Georgia Endoscopy Center, Inc., 320 Hospital Road, Canton, GA 30114; tel. 770/479-5535; FAX. 770/479-8821; Kevin V. Kellogg, Administrator

North Georgia Outpatient Surgery Center, 795 Red Bud Road, Calhoun, GA 30701; tel. 706/629-1852; FAX. 706/629-8004; Herbert E. Kosmahl, President

North Oak Ambulatory Surgery Center, LLC, 2718 North Oak Street, Valdosta, GA 31602; tel. 229/242-3668; FAX. 229/253-8666; T.E. Pitts, DPM

Northeast Endoscopy Center, LLC, 721 Wellness Way, Suite 110, Lawrenceville, GA 30045; tel. 770/995-7989; FAX. 770/339-8646; Patricia F. Ellington, Practice Manager

Section C

Northeast Georgia Plastic Surgery Center, 1296 Sims Street, Gainesville, GA 30501; tel. 770/534–1856; FAX. 770/531–0355; D.J. Campbell, M.D., Medical Director

Northlake Endoscopy Center, 1459 Montreal Road, Suite 204, Tucker, GA 30084; tel. 770/939–4721; FAX. 770/939–1187; R. Robert Beton, M.D.

Northside Foot and Ankle Outpatient Surgical Center, 3415 Holcomb Bridge Road, Norcross, GA 30092; tel. 770/449–1122; FAX. 770/242–8709; Steven T. Arminio, DPM, Administrator

Northside Women's Clinic, Inc., 3543 Chamblee-Dunwoody Road, Atlanta, GA 30341; tel. 770/455–4210; FAX. 770/451–9529; James W. Gay, MD, Administrator

Outpatient Center for Foot Surgery, Inc., 730 South Eighth Street, Suite B, Griffin, GA 30224; tel. 770/228–6644; FAX. 770/228–5769; Mark Henson, Administrator

Paces Plastic Surgery Center, Inc., 3200 Downwood Circle, Suite 640, Atlanta, GA 30327; tel. 404/351–0051; FAX. 404/351–0632; Delene Graham, Office Manager

Perimeter Surgery Center of Atlanta, 1140 Hammond Drive, Building F, Suite 6100, Atlanta, GA 30328; tel. 770/551–9944; FAX. 770/551–8826; Cindy Smith, Administrator

Planned Parenthood of Reproductive Health Services, 1289 Broad Street, Augusta, GA 30911; tel. 706/724–5557; FAX. 706/724–5293; Vanetta D. King, Center Manager

Pulliam Ambulatory Surgical Center, 4167 Hospital Drive, P.O. Box 469, Covington, GA 30015; tel. 770/786–1234; M.M. Pulliam, PC, Medical Director

Resurgens Surgical Center, 5671 Peachtree Dunwoody Road, Suite 800, Atlanta, GA 30342; tel. 404/531–8532; Leslie Mattson, RN Administrator

Savannah Foot and Ankle Surgery Center, 310 Eisenhower Drive, Savannah, GA 31406; tel. 912/356–8440; FAX. 912/356–8439; Kay J. West, Administrator

Savannah Medical Clinic, 120 East 34th Street, Savannah, GA 31401; tel. 912/236–1603; FAX. 912/236–1605; William Knorr, MD, Administrator

Savannah Plastic Surgicenter, 7208 Hodgson Memorial, Savannah, GA 31406; tel. 912/351–5050; FAX. 912/351–5051; Scott W. Vann MD

The Emory Clinic Ambulatory Surgery Center, 1365 Clifton Road, NE, Atlanta, GA 30322; tel. 404/778–5000; W. Mike Mason, Administrator

The Foot Surgery Center, 2520 Windy Hill Road, Suite 105, Marietta, GA 30067; tel. 770/952–0868; FAX. 770/952–4833; Donna L. Cowan, Nurse Administrator

The Rome Surgery Center, 16 John Maddox Drive, Rome, GA 30165; tel. 706/802–3727; FAX. 706/802–3883; Neal Jochimsen, Administrator

The Surgery Center, LLC, 2548 Weems Rd, Columbus, GA 31909-6248; tel. 706/323–8803; FAX. 706/323–9101; Jennifer Winters, Administrator

Tifton Endoscopy Center, Inc., 1111 E. 20th Street, Tifton, GA 31794-3668; tel. 229/382–9338; FAX. 229/382–4282; Linda Moran, RN, Nursing Administrator

Village Podiatry, 1350 Upper Hembree Road, Suite 100, Roswell, GA 30076; tel. 770/663–8011; FAX. 770/754–9820; Dr. Mitch Hilsen, Administrator

HAWAII

Aloha Surgical Center, 239 Hoohana Street, Kahului, HI 96732; tel. 808/893–0578; FAX. 808/893–0580; R. Ezra Erb, Administrator/Chief Executive Officer

Big Island Endoscopy Center, LLC, 64-5188 Kinohou Street, Kamuela, HI 96743; tel. 808/887–0600; FAX. 808/887–6699; Aulii Delenia, Administrator

Cataract and Vision Center of Hawaii, 1712 Liliha Street, Suite 400, Honolulu, HI 96817; tel. 808/524–1010; FAX. 808/531–1030; Worldster Lee, MD, Director

Hawaii Endoscopy Center, LLC, 2226 Liliha Street, Suite 307, Honolulu, HI 96817; tel. 808/531–5828; FAX. 808/531–5819; Linda Oshiro, Administrator

Hawaiian Eye Surgicenter, 606 Kilani Avenue, Wahiawa, HI 96786; tel. 808/621–8448; FAX. 808/621–3177; Christopher M. Tortora, MD, Surgeon, Director

Hilo Community Surgery Center, 82 Pu'uhonu Place, Suite 100, Hilo, HI 96720; tel. 808/969–9669; FAX. 808/969–9608; Allan S. Takase, MD, Administrator

Kaiser Honolulu Clinic, 1010 Pensacola Street, Honolulu, HI 96814; tel. 808/432–2000; FAX. 808/597–2249; Jonathan Ganz, Administrator

Kaiser Wailuku Clinic, 80 Mahalani Street, Wailuku, HI 96793; tel. 808/243–6618; FAX. 808/243–6609; Mary Hew, Administrator

The Endoscopy Center, 134 Puuhonu Way, Hilo, HI 96720; tel. 808/935–1956; FAX. 808/935–7657; Jody Montell, Administrator

The Surgical Suites, LLC, 1100 Ward Avenue, Suite 1001, Honolulu, HI 96814; tel. 808/531–0127; FAX. 808/531–0455; Carlos Omphroy, MD, President

IDAHO

Addison Surgery Center, 191 Addison Avenue, Twin Falls, ID 83301; tel. 208/734–5993; FAX. 208/734–5993; David A. Blackmer, DPM, President

Boise Gastroenterology Associates, P.A., Idaho Endoscopy Center, 6259 W. Emerald Street, Boise, ID 83704; tel. 208/489–1900; FAX. 208/375–5286; Robb F. Gibson, MD, President

Coeur D'Alene Foot and Ankle Surgery Center, 101 Ironwood Drive, Suite 131, Coeur D'Alene, ID 83814; tel. 208/666–0814; FAX. 208/666–0916; Stephen A. Isham, DPM, Chief Executive Officer

Emerald Surgical Center, 811 North Liberty, Boise, ID 83704; tel. 208/323–4522; FAX. 208/321–9585; Camille Miley, Nurse Director

Idaho Ambucare Center, Inc., 4400 Flamingo Avenue, Nampa, ID 83686; tel. 208/288–4750; FAX. 208/288–4765; Gary Botimer, Administrator

Idaho Eye Surgicenter, 2025 East 17th Street, Idaho Falls, ID 83404; tel. 208/524–2025; FAX. 208/529–1924; Bradley P. Garnder, MD

Idaho Foot Surgery Center, 1540 Elk Creek Drive, Idaho Falls, ID 83404; tel. 208/529–8393; FAX. 208/529–8398; Kylin T. Kovac, DPM, Facility Director

Jefferson Day Surgery Center, 220 West Jefferson, Boise, ID 83702; tel. 208/343–3802; FAX. 208/343–9161; William Stano, President

Millennium Surgery Center, 1828 S. Millenium Way, Suite 100, Meridian, ID 83642; tel. 208/381–0262; FAX. 208/429–8575; Shane Ricks, Administrator

North Idaho Cataract and Laser Center, Inc., 1814 Lincoln Way, Coeur D'Alene, ID 83814; tel. 208/667–2531; FAX. 208/765–9385; Karen Sines, Administrator

Pacific Cataract and Laser Institute, 2822 South Vista Avenue, Boise, ID 83705; tel. 208/385–7576; FAX. 208/385–0050; Earl Callahan, Site Manager

St. Luke's Clinic, Gastroenterology, 775 Pole Line Rd West, Suite 203, Twin Falls, ID 83301; tel. 208/732–3000; FAX. 208/733–8970; Karen R. Butler, Clinical Manager

Surgicare Center of Idaho, LLC, 360 East Mallard Drive, Suite 125, Boise, ID 83706; tel. 208/336–8700; FAX. 208/386–3239; Mark Hollingshead, Medical Director

ILLINOIS

25 East Same Day Surgery, 25 East Washington, Suite 300, Chicago, IL 60602; tel. 312/726–3329; FAX. 312/726–3823; Kimberly Zidonis, RN, Administrator

Aanchor Health Center, Ltd., 1186 Roosevelt Rd., Glen Ellyn, IL 60137; tel. 630/495–4400; FAX. 630/629–5892; Aimee Dillard, Assistant Administrator

Able Health Center, Ltd., 1640 Arlington Heights Road, Suite 110, Arlington Heights, IL 60004; tel. 847/255–7400; FAX. 847/398–4585

Access Health Center, Ltd., 1700 75th Street, Downers Grove, IL 60516; tel. 630/964–0000; FAX. 630/964–0047; Jenny Mitchell, Assistant Administrator

ACU Health Center, Ltd., 736 N. York Rd., Hinsdale, IL 60521; tel. 630/794–0645; FAX. 630/794–0169; Aimee Dillard, Assistant Administrator

Advantage Health Care, Ltd., 203 E. Irving Park Rd, Wood Dale, IL 60191; tel. 630/595–1515; FAX. 630/595–9907; Aimee Dillard, Assistant Administrator

Ambulatory Surgicenter of Downers Grove, Ltd., 4333 Main Street, Downers Grove, IL 60515; tel. 630/322–9451; FAX. 630/322–9455; Inga Ferdkoff, MD, Administrator

Bel-Clair Ambulatory Surgical Treatment Center, 325 West Lincoln, Belleville, IL 62220; tel. 618/235–2299; FAX. 618/235–2556; David Horace, Administrator

Belleville Surgical Center, 28 North 64th Street, Belleville, IL 62223; tel. 618/398–5705; FAX. 618/398–5764; Diana Geoghegan, Administrator

Belmont & Harlem Surgery Center, 3101 North Harlem Avenue, Chicago, IL 60634; tel. 773/889–2000; FAX. 773/745–5522; Sandra Ankebrant, Executive Director

Carle Surgicenter, 1702 South Mattis Avenue, Champaign, IL 61821; tel. 217/326–2030; Administrator

Children's Pediatric Specialty Services In Westchester, 2301 Enterprise Drive, Westchester, IL 60154; tel. 708/836–4800; FAX. 708/836–4805; Kristen DiCicco, Administrator

Community Health and Emergency Services, 13245 Kessler Road, P.O. Box 233, Cairo, IL 62914; tel. 618/734–4400; FAX. 618/734–9046; Frederick L. Bernstein, Chief Executive Officer

Dreyer Ambulatory Surgery Center, 1221 North Highland Avenue, Aurora, IL 60506; tel. 630/264–8400; FAX. 630/264–8402; Amanda Smith, RN, BSN, Administrative Director

Eastland Medical Plaza SurgiCenter, LLC, 1505 Eastland Drive, Suite 180, Bloomington, IL 61701; tel. 309/662–2500; FAX. 309/662–7143; Brenda Cyrulik, Manager

Edwardsville Ambulatory Surgical Center, LLC, 12 Ginger Creek Parkway, Glen Carbon, IL 62034; tel. 618/656–8200; FAX. 618/656–8204; Michelle Looney, Director of Operations

Elmwood Park Same Day Surgery Center, 1614 North Harlem Avenue, Elmwood Park, IL 60607; tel. 847/869–9700; FAX. 847/556–6449; Scott Borre

Foot and Ankle Surgical Center, Ltd./dba Regenerative Surgery Center, 1455 Golf Road, Suite 131, Des Plaines, IL 60016; tel. 847/390–7666; Lowell S. Weil, DPM, FACFAS, Medical Director

Forestview Medical Center, Ltd., 2750 S. River Road, Des Plaines, IL 60018; tel. 847/375–1000; FAX. 847/827–5977; Nancy Nelson, Administrator

Fullerton Kimball Medical & Surgical Center, 3412 West Fullerton Avenue, Chicago, IL 60647; tel. 773/235–8000; FAX. 773/235–7018; Renlin Xia, MD, Medical Director

Golf Surgical Center, 8901 Golf Road, Des Plaines, IL 60016; tel. 847/299–2273; FAX. 847/299–2297; Mark Mayo, Executive Director

Hawthorn Surgery Center, 1900 Hollister Drive, Suite 100, Libertyville, IL 60048; tel. 847/367–8100; FAX. 847/367–8335; Dr. Gary Rippberger, Administrator

Hinsdale Surgical Center, LLC, 908 North Elm Street, Suite 401, Hinsdale, IL 60521; tel. 630/325–5035; FAX. 630/325–5134; Henry DeVries, Jr., Administrator

Hope Clinic for Women, Ltd., 1602 21st Street, Granite City, IL 62040; tel. 618/451–5722; FAX. 615/451–9092; Sally Burgess, MBA, Executive Director

Illinois Eye Surgeons Cataract Surgery, 3990 North Illinois Street, Belleville, IL 62221; tel. 618/235–3100; Nancy Mueth, Administrator

Loyola Ambulatory Surgery Center at Oakbrook, One South 224 Summit Avenue, Suite 201, Oakbrook Terrace, IL 60181; tel. 630/916–7088; Samantha Lee, Administrator

Magna Surgical Center, 7456 State Road, Suite 300, Bedford Park, IL 60638; tel. 773/445–9696; FAX. 773/445–9590; Patty Wamsley, Director of ASC Operations

Michigan Avenue Center for Health, Ltd., 2415 S. Michigan Avenue, Chicago, IL 60616; tel. 312/328–1200; FAX. 312/328–1240; Aimee Dillard, Assistant Administrator

Midwest Center for Day Surgery, 3811 Highland Avenue, Downers Grove, IL 60515; tel. 630/852–9300; FAX. 630/852–7773; Ronald P. Ladniak, Administrator

Midwest Eye Center, S.C., 1700 East West Road, Calumet City, IL 60409; tel. 708/891–3330; FAX. 708/891–0904; Afzal Ahmad, MD, Medical Director

Naperville Surgical Centre, 1263 Rickert Drive, Naperville, IL 60540; tel. 630/305–3300; FAX. 630/305–3301; Ronald P. Ladniak

North Shore Endoscopy Center, 101 South Waukegan Road, Suite 980, Lake Bluff, IL 60044; tel. 847/604–8700; FAX. 847/604–8711; Erik Hamnes, Vice President

North Shore Surgicenter, 3725 West Touhy Avenue, Lincolnwood, IL 60712-2603; tel. 847/324–7770; FAX. 847/324–7762; Gary Rippberger, MD, Administrator

Northwest Community Day Surgery Center, 675 West Kirchoff Road, Arlington Heights, IL 60005; tel. 874/618–7004; FAX. 874/618–7069; Roxanne Matias, Director

Northwest Surgicare, 1100 West Central Road, Arlington Heights, IL 60005; tel. 847/259–3080; FAX. 847/259–3190; Pat Jepsen, Administrator

Nova Med Eye Surgery Center of Maryville, LLC, 12 Maryville Professional Park Drive, Maryville, IL 62062; tel. 618/288–7483; Sarah Davis, Administrator

Novamed Center for Reconstructive Surgery–Oak Lawn, 6311 West 95th Street, Oak Lawn, IL 60453; tel. 708/499–3355; FAX. 708/425–5654; Carmen Hollimon, Administrator

Novamed Surgery Center of Chicago - Northshore, 3034 West Peterson Avenue, Chicago, IL 60659; tel. 773/973–7432; FAX. 773/973–4134

NovaMed Surgery Center River Forest, LLC, 7427 Lake Street, River Forest, IL 60305; tel. 708/488–1300; FAX. 708/771–7321; Kelly Spillane, RN, ASC Director

Oak Brook Surgical Centre, Inc., 2425 West 22nd Street, Suite 101, Oak Brook, IL 60523; tel. 630/990–2212; FAX. 630/990–3130; Ali Nili, Chief Operating Officer

Oak Park Eye Center, SC, 7638 W North Avenue, Elmwood Park, IL 60707; tel. 708/452–4257; FAX. 708/452–4283; Manuel Santiago, MD, Administrator

Palos Surgicenter, 7340 West College Drive, Palos Heights, IL 60463; tel. 708/361–3233; FAX. 708/361–4876; Thomas Holecek, Administrator

Peoria Ambulatory Surgery Center, 4909 North Glen Park Place, Peoria, IL 61614; tel. 309/691–9069; FAX. 309/690–9005; Cynthia J. Leisinger, MBA,CASC, Director of Surgical Services

Peoria Day Surgery Center, 7309 North Knoxville, Peoria, IL 61614; tel. 309/692–9210; FAX. 309/693–6472; Rita Hancock, Administrator

Physicians' Surgery Center, 2601 West Main Street, Carbondale, IL 62901; tel. 618/351–7300; FAX. 618/457–7890; Stephen Renfro, Administrator

Physicians' Surgical Center, LLC, 311 West Lincoln, Suite 300, Belleville, IL 62220; tel. 618/233–7077; FAX. 618/233–2814; Michelle Colbert, Administrator

Planned Parenthood of East Central Illinois, 302 East Stoughton Street, Champaign, IL 61820; tel. 217/359–8022; FAX. 217/359–2683; Robin Beach, Vice President and Chief Operating Officer

Premier Dermatology, 2051 Plainfield Road, Crest Hill, IL 60403; tel. 815/741–4343; FAX. 815/741–8660; Corky Bellile, Chief Operating Officer

Quad City Ambulatory Surgery Center, 520 Valley View Drive, Suite 300, Moline, IL 61265; tel. 309/762–1952; FAX. 309/762–3642; Gloria Catlett, RN, Manager

Regional Surgicenter, 545 Valley View Drive, Moline, IL 61265; tel. 309/762–5560; FAX. 309/762–7351; Sadie Kostka, Administrator

River North Same Day Surgery, One East Erie, Suite 300, Chicago, IL 60611; tel. 312/649–3939; FAX. 312/649–5747; Jonette Marino, RN, MBA, Administrator

Rockford Ambulatory Surgery Center, 1016 Featherstone Drive, Rockford, IL 61107; tel. 815/226–3300; FAX. 815/226–9990; Dr. Steven Gunderson, Chief Executive Officer/Medical Director

Rockford Endoscopy Center, 401 Roxbury Road, Rockford, IL 61107; tel. 815/397–7340; FAX. 815/397–7388; Nancy Garry, Administrator

Rogers Park One Day Surgery Center, 7616 North Paulina, Chicago, IL 60626; tel. 773/761–0500; FAX. 773/761–1355; Mira Pekic, Credentialing Dept. Manager

Springfield Clinic Ambulatory Surgery and Endoscopy Center, 1025 South Seventh Street, Springfield, IL 62794-9248; tel. 217/528–7541; FAX. 217/527–8956; Ginny Timke

Surgery Center of Southern Illinois, PO Box 1729, 806 N. Treas, Marion, IL 62959; tel. 618/993–2113; FAX. 618/993–2041; Linda Bickers, RN, Administrator

Surgicare Center, Inc., 333 Dixie Highway, Chicago Heights, IL 60411; tel. 708/754–4890; FAX. 708/709–6242; Dolores Stam, RN - Supervisor

Surgicore, Inc., 10547 South Ewing Avenue, Chicago, IL 60617; tel. 773/221–1690; FAX. 773/221–1675; Michael A. Wood, DPM, Medical Director

The Center for Orthopedic Medicine, LLC, dba The Center For Outpatient Medicine, 2502-B East Empire Street, Bloomington, IL 61704; tel. 309/662–6120; FAX. 309/661–0060; Sarah Gardner, Business Director

The Center for Surgery, 475 East Diehl Road, Naperville, IL 60563-1253; tel. 630/505–7733; FAX. 630/505–0656; Eric Myers, Administrator

The Surgery Center of Centralia, 1045 Martin Luther King Jr. Drive, Centralia, IL 62801; tel. 618/532–3110; FAX. 618/532–7226; Mark Murfin, MD, Medical Director

Valley Ambulatory Surgery Center and Valley Medical Inn, 2210 Dean Street, St. Charles, IL 60175; tel. 630/584–9800; FAX. 630/584–9805; Deborah Lee Crook, RN, Administrator

Women's Aid Clinic, 4801 W Peterson Ave, Suite 609, Chicago, IL 60646; tel. 847/676–2428

INDIANA

Aesthetic Surgery Center, 13590 N. Meridian, Carmel, IN 46032; tel. 317/846–0846; FAX. 317/846–0722; William H. Beeson, MD, Medical Director

Broadwest Specialty Surgical Center, LLC, 315 West 89th Avenue, Merrillville, IN 46410-2904; tel. 219/757–5275; FAX. 219/757–5292; Angela Leach, Business Administrator

Central Indiana Surgery Center, 9002 North Meridian, Lower Level, Indianapolis, IN 46260; tel. 317/848–1763; FAX. 317/848–1895; Francis Price, Jr., MD, Medical Director

Columbus Surgery Center, 940 North Marr Road, Suite B, Columbus, IN 47201; tel. 812/372–1370; FAX. 812/373–9526; Marcy Ross, RN, Director

Digestive Health Center, 1120 AAA Way, Suite A, Carmel, IN 46032-3210; tel. 317/848–5494; FAX. 317/575–0390; Daniel J. Stout, MD, President

Evansville Surgery Center, 520 Mary Street, Evansville, IN 47710; tel. 812/250–0100; FAX. 812/250–0151; Cathy Head RN, BS, MHA, CASA Administrator

Eye Specialists Surgery Centers, LLC, 200 North Tillotson Avenue, Muncie, IN 47304-3988; tel. 765/286–8888; FAX. 765/747–7962; Rita Singh, MD, Chief Executive Officer

Foot and Ankle Surgery Center, Inc., 8651 Township Line Road, Indianapolis, IN 46260-1578; tel. 317/334–0232; FAX. 317/334–0268; Anthony E. Miller, DPM, Owner

Franciscan Physicians Hospital, 701 Superior Avenue, Munster, IN 46321; tel. 219/924–1300; FAX. 219/922–4810; Barb Greene, President

Gastrointestinal Endoscopy Center, 801 Street Mary's Drive, Suite 110 West, Evansville, IN 47714; tel. 812/477–6103; FAX. 812/477–4897; Butch Moors, CPA, Administrator

Grand Park Surgical Center, 1479 East 84th Place, Merrillville, IN 46410; tel. 219/738–2828; FAX. 219/756–3349; Chris Macarthy, Administrator

Grossnickle Eye Surgery Center, Inc., 2251 DuBois Drive, Warsaw, IN 46580-3212; tel. 574/269–3777; FAX. 574/371–4697; Diana Ostrom, RN, Administrator

IMA Endoscopy Surgicenter, P.C., 8895 Broadway, Merrillville, IN 46410; tel. 219/736–4660; FAX. 219/736–4663; Dawn Bailey, Administrator

Indiana Endoscopy Center, 1801 North Senate, Suite 410, Indianapolis, IN 46202; tel. 317/962–5660; FAX. 317/963–5255; David B. Thomas, Medical Director

Indiana Eye Clinic, 30 North Emerson Avenue, Greenwood, IN 46143-9760; tel. 317/881–3937; FAX. 317/887–4008; Ken Dyar, RN, BSN, MBA, Executive Director

Indiana Surgery Center, 1550 East County Line Road, Suite 100, Indianapolis, IN 46227; tel. 317/621–7600; FAX. 317/621–7606; Peggy Davidson, Administrator

Indiana Surgery Center - North, 8040 Clearvista Parkway, Suite 150, Indianapolis, IN 46256; tel. 317/621–2000; FAX. 317/621–2069; Shannon Arrendale, RN, MBA, Executive Director

Indianapolis Endoscopy Center, 8315 E. 56th Street, Suite 100, Indianapolis, IN 46216; tel. 317/621–2232; FAX. 317/621–3232; Kathy Anderson, Executive Director

Meridian Plastic Surgery Center, 170 West 106th Street, Indianapolis, IN 46290-1004; tel. 317/575–0336; FAX. 317/571–8667; Joann Jones, RN, Director

Michiana Endoscopy Center, LLC, 53830 Generation Drive, South Bend, IN 46635; tel. 574/271–0893; FAX. 574/271–1285; Pankaj Patel, MD, Medical Director

North Meridian Surgery Center, 13225 N. Meridian Street, Carmel, IN 46032; tel. 317/574–5400; FAX. 317/575–0173; Julie Berzins, Director and Chief Executive Officer

Northeast Indiana Endoscopy Center, 7900 West Jefferson Boulevard, Suite 200, Fort Wayne, IN 46804; tel. 206/969–7181; FAX. 260/969–7182; Jerry Steele, Administrator

Oakview Surgical Center, Inc., 120 E. 18th Street, Rochester, IN 46975; tel. 574/224–7500; FAX. 574/223–3057; Laurence C. Rogers, DPM, Administrator

Outpatient Surgery Center of Indiana, LLP, 711 Gardner Drive, Marion, IN 46952; tel. 317/664–2000; FAX. 317/668–6797; Dixie Hewitt, RN, Director

Premier Surgery Center, 11141 Parkview Plaza Drive, Fort Wayne, IN 46845-1714; tel. 260/266–9070; FAX. 260/266–9071; Nora Bass, NP, MSN, MBA, Senior Vice President Surgery Services

Riverpointe Surgery Center, 500 Arcade Avenue, Suite 100, Elkhart, IN 46514-2459; tel. 574/522–9505; FAX. 574/296–6484; John Cloyd, PhD, Executive Director

Sagamore Surgical Services, Inc., 2320 Concord Road, Suite B, Lafayette, IN 47909; tel. 765/474–7854; FAX. 765/474–1317; Carol Blanar, Administrator

South Bend Clinic Surgicenter, 211 North Eddy Street, P.O. Box 1755, South Bend, IN 46634-4061; tel. 574/237–9366; FAX. 574/237–9363; Paul J. Meyer, Chief Executive Officer

Southern Indiana Surgery Center, 2800 Rex Grossman Boulevard, Bloomington, IN 47403; tel. 812/333–8969; FAX. 812/335–2309; Elizabeth Smith, RN, Administrative Director

Surgery Center of Merrillville, LLC, 8514 Broadway, Merrillville, IN 46410; tel. 219/756–5010; FAX. 219/736–5106; Tina Jackson, Director

Surgery ONE, 5052 North Clinton, Fort Wayne, IN 46825-5822; tel. 219/482–5194; FAX. 219/482–5686; Debra McCarter, Director

Surgical Care Center, Inc., 8103 Clearvista Parkway, Indianapolis, IN 46256-4600; tel. 317/842–5173; FAX. 317/570–7429; Janelle Gray, RN, Director

Surgical Center of New Albany, 2201 Green Valley Road, New Albany, IN 47150-4648; tel. 812/949–1223; FAX. 812/945–4765; Tamara E. Jones, BSN, Administrator

Surgicare, 2907 McIntire Drive, Suite C, Bloomington, IN 47403; tel. 812/339–8000; FAX. 812/339–2524; Susan Bower, RN, Administrator

Surgicare of Jeffersonville, 1305 Wall Street, Suite 101, Jeffersonville, IN 47130-3898; tel. 812/288–9674; FAX. 812/283–6955; Marsha Parker, Administrator

The Endoscopy Center at St. Francis, 8051 South Emerson, Suite 150, Indianapolis, IN 46237; tel. 317/865–2955; FAX. 317/865–2952; James Turner, Chief Executive Officer

The Eye Surgical Center of Fort Wayne, 321 East Wayne Street, Ft. Wayne, IN 46802-2713; tel. 260/422–5976; FAX. 260/969–1041; Amy Thiele, RN

The Indiana Hand to Shoulder Center, 8501 Harcourt Road, P.O. Box 80434, Indianapolis, IN 46260-0434; tel. 317/875–9105; FAX. 317/872–1423; Valeria M. Wareham, DON, Chief Operating Officer

Valley Cataract and Laser Institute, Inc., dba Valley Surgery Center, 220 East Virginia, Evansville, IN 47711; tel. 812/435–1600; FAX. 812/435–1603; Lisa J. Gossman-Werner, Facility Administrator

Whitewater Surgery Center, 1900 Chester Boulevard, Richmond, IN 47374; tel. 765/966–1776; FAX. 765/962–1191; Mary Pordifio, RN, Nurse Manager

Williams Eye Surgery Center, 6836 Hohman Avenue, Hammond, IN 46324; tel. 219/937–5063; FAX. 219/937–5068; Renee Peters, Administrator

IOWA

Iowa Digestive Disease Center, Iowa Endoscopy Center, 1378 NW 124th Street, Suite 100, Clive, IA 50325; tel. 515/288–6097; FAX. 515/288–0384; Jean Shelton, Chief Executive Officer

Jones Eye Clinic, 4405 Hamilton Boulevard, Sioux City, IA 51104-1140; tel. 712/239–3937; FAX. 712/239–4946; Charles E. Jones, MD, Medical Director

Mississippi Valley Surgery Center, L.C., 3400 Dexter Court, Suite 200, Davenport, IA 52807; tel. 563/344–6600; FAX. 563/344–6699; Michael Patterson, Chief Executive Officer

Spencer Surgery and Laser Center, LLC, 1721 West 18th Street, P.O. Box 420, Spencer, IA 51301; tel. 712/580-3278; FAX. 712/580-3279; Dennis D. Gordy, MD, Administrator

Spring Park Surgery Center, LLC, 3319 Spring Street, Suite 202-A, Davenport, IA 52807; tel. 563/355-6236; FAX. 563/359-6347; Heather Hilgendorf-Cooley, MBA, Administrator

Surgery Center of Des Moines, 717 Lyon Street, Des Moines, IA 50312; tel. 515/266-3140; FAX. 515/266-3073; Marsha Schultz, Director of Nursing

KANSAS

Cotton-O'Neil Clinic Endoscopy Center, 720 SW Lane St, Topeka, KS 66606-1539; tel. 785/270-4800; FAX. 785/270-4801; Mark Davis, Director

Emporia Ambulatory Surgery Center, 2528 West 15th Avenue, Emporia, KS 66801-6102; tel. 602/343-2233; J. E. Bosiljevac, MD, Administrator

Endoscopic Services, P.A., 1431 South Bluffview Street, Suite 215, Wichita, KS 67218-3000; tel. 316/687-0234; FAX. 316/687-0360; Jace Hyder, MD

Endoscopy and Surgery Center of Topeka, L.P., 2200 Southwest Sixth Avenue, Suite 103, Topeka, KS 66606-1707; tel. 913/354-1254; FAX. 913/354-1255; Ashraf M. Sufi, MD, Medical Director

Eye Surgical Center, 1100 North Topeka Street, Wichita, KS 67214-2810; tel. 316/263-6273; FAX. 316/263-5568; David A. Kingrey, Medical Director

Hutchinson Clinic Ambulatory Surgery Center, 2205 North Waldron, Hutchinson, KS 67502; tel. 620/728-2700; FAX. 620/694-4418; Mary Wood, Director

Surgicare of Wichita, Inc., 2818 N. Greenwich Rd., Wichita, KS 67226; tel. 316/685-2207; FAX. 316/685-2861; Tracie Johanek, RN, Administrator

Team Vision Surgery Center, 6100 East Central Street, Suite Six, Wichita, KS 67208-4237; tel. 316/681-2020; FAX. 316/684-4939; Stacey Linn, Administrator

Team Vision Surgery Center, 6100 East Central, Suite 6, Wichita, KS 67208; tel. 316/681-2020; FAX. 316/684-4939; Patricia Kusnerus, Administrator

Via Christi Surgery Center, 1947 Founders' Circle, Wichita, KS 67206; tel. 316/613-4607; FAX. 316/613-4725; Penny Freeman, RN, BSN, CNOR, Manager

KENTUCKY

Ambulatory Surgery Center, 2831 Lone Oak Road, Paducah, KY 42003; tel. 270/554-8373; FAX. 270/554-8987; Laxmaiah Manchikanti, MD

Asethetic Plastic Surgery Institute of Louisville, LLC, dba Louisville Surgery Center, 444 S. First Street, Suite 201, Louisville, KY 40202; tel. 502/238-2861; FAX. 502/238-2897; Amy McKiernan, Director of Nursing

Baptist-Physicians' Surgery Center, 1720 Nicholasville Rd, Suite 101, Louisville, KY 40503; tel. 859/260-7000; FAX. 859/260-7010; Evan Long, Administrator

Bluegrass Surgery & Laser Center, 1400 Poplar Level Road, Suite 1, Louisville, KY 40217; tel. 502/637-4800; FAX. 502/637-1550; Don E. Lenz, RN, Administrator

Center For Surgical Care, 7575 U.S. 42, Florence, KY 41042; tel. 606/283-6050; FAX. 606/283-6060; Jenny Brallier, RN, Director

Commonwealth Eye Surgery Center, 2353 Alexandria Drive, Suite 350, Lexington, KY 40504; tel. 859/224-2655; FAX. 859/296-1565; Jenny Lackey, Chief Operations Officer

Cumberland Valley Surgical Center, 275 Hwy 770, Corbin, KY 40729; tel. 606/526-7874; FAX. 606/526-7836; Kim Turner, Administrator

Dermatology Associates Of KY, PSC, 250 Fountain Court, Lexington, KY 40509; tel. 859/263-4444; Joy Hayes, Administrator

Dupont Surgery Center, 4004 Dupont Circle, Louisville, KY 40207; tel. 502/896-6428; FAX. 502/893-5270; Sherry Oeswein, Administrator

E.M.W. Women's Surgical Center, 138 West Market Street, Louisville, KY 40202; tel. 502/589-2124; FAX. 502/589-1588; Anne Ahola, Executive Director

Eyecare Network, Ltd., 1360 Medical Park Dr, Maysville, KY 41056; tel. 606/759-5341; Bryan Prater, Administrator

Healthsouth Lexington Surgery Center, 1451 Harrodsburg Rd, Suite 102, Lexington, KY 40504; tel. 859/276-2525; Dianna Bennett, Administrator

Healthsouth Louisville Surgery Center, 614 E Chestnut St, Louisville, KY 40202; tel. 502/589-9488; Vanessa McDermott, Administrator

Jewish Hospital Medical Center East, 3920 Dutchman's Lane, Louisville, KY 40207; tel. 502/259-6003; FAX. 502/259-6111; Shelley Neal, Administrator

Kentucky Surgery Center, 240 Fountain Court, Lexington, KY 40509; tel. 859/278-1460; FAX. 859/514-5107; Glenda Satterly, RN, Administrative Director

Lake Cumberland Surgery Center, 301 Langdon Street, Somerset, KY 42501; tel. 606/678-9688; FAX. 606/679-7479; Michael Everett, Administrative Director

Louisville Endoscopy Center, 1400 Poplar Level Road, Suite 2, Louisville, KY 40217; tel. 502/636-2003; FAX. 502/636-4032; Rosemary Gentry, RN, BSN, CGRN, Center Director

Mangat-KUY-Holzapfel Plastic Surgery Center, 133 Barnwood Drive, Edgewood, KY 41017; tel. 859/331-9600; FAX. 859/578-3321; Linda Robinson, Administrator

McPeak Surgery Center, 108 Bravo Boulevard, Glasgow, KY 42141; tel. 270/651-2181; FAX. 270/651-2183; Sheila Dishman, Administrator

Muhlenberg Surgery Center, 1008 Medical Center Dr, Suite B, Powderly, KY 42367; tel. 270/338-9929; FAX. 270/338-9282; Susan Hust, Administrator

New Lexington Clinic, PSC, dba Lexington Clinic Ambulatory Surgery Center, 1225 South Broadway, Suite 100, Lexington, KY 40504; tel. 859/258-4600; FAX. 859/258-4664; Ashley Karathanasis, ASC Administrator

Patient First Digestive Disease Center, 340 Thomas More Parkway, Suite 160B, Crestview, KY 41017; tel. 859/331-6466; FAX. 859/331-1932; Gail Hynko, Site Manager

Premier Surgery Center of Louisville, 2511 Terra Crossing Blvd., Louisville, KY 40245; tel. 502/589-9488; FAX. 502/589-9928; Stephanie Perna, Administrator, RN, MSN, CCRN

Somerset Surgery Center, 30 Medpark Drive, Somerset, KY 42503-2797; tel. 606/679-9322; FAX. 606/678-2666; Kathy Turner, Administrator

Stone Road Surgery Center, 280 Pasadena Dr, Lexington, KY 40503; tel. 859/278-1316; FAX. 859/260-2470; Heather C. Wright, Administrator

Surgical Center of Elizabethtown, Hardin Memorial Hospital, 108 Financial Drive, Elizabethtown, KY 42701; tel. 270/737-5200; FAX. 270/737-2422; Joe Saltsman, Manager

Surgicare Lourdes Ambulatory Surgery Center, 225 Medical Center Drive, Suite 105, Paducah, KY 42003; tel. 270/441-4500; FAX. 270/441-4577; Nancy Edwards, Director

The Pain Treatment Center Inc. dba Stone Road Surgery Center, 280 Pasadena Drive, Lexington, KY 40503; tel. 859/278-1316; FAX. 859/276-3847; Heather C. Wright, Chief Executive Officer

Tri-State Digestive Disorder Center Ambulatory Surgery Center, 425 Centre View Blvd, Crestview Hills, KY 41017; tel. 859/341-3575; FAX. 859/341-5701; Ross McHenry, MD

LOUISIANA

Acadiana Surgery Center, Inc., 2309 East Main Street, Suite 102, New Iberia, LA 70560; tel. 337/364-9680; FAX. 337/364-9689; Dana W. Stokes, RN. Director of Nurses

Alexandria Laser and Surgery Center, 4100 Parliament Drive, Alexandria, LA 71303; tel. 318/487-8342; FAX. 318/487-9942; Martina Anders, RN., Center Director

Ambulatory Eye Surgery Center of Louisiana, 3900 Veterans Boulevard, Suite 100, Metairie, LA 70002; tel. 504/455-1550; FAX. 504/455-2011; Judy Dufrechou RN, Director

Brass Surgery Center, 5328 Didesse Drive, Baton Rouge, LA 70808; tel. 225/766-1718; FAX. 225/766-1225; Derald W. Smith, Administrator

Colonnade Endoscopy Center, 555 Dr. Michael DeBakey Drive, Suite 102, Lake Charles, LA 70601; tel. 337/439-6226; FAX. 337/436-6223; Nellie Rideaux, Administrative Assistant

Foot Surgery Center of Shreveport, 9308 Mansfield Road, Suite 300, Shreveport, LA 71118; tel. 318/686-9622; Richard Havens, DPM, Administrator

Houma Outpatient Surgery Center, Ltd., 3717 Houma Boulevard, Suite 300, Metairie, LA 70006; tel. 504/456-1515; FAX. 504/454-3810; Landon Tucker, Administrator

Houma Surgi Center, Inc., 1020 School Street, Houma, LA 70360; tel. 985/868-4320; FAX. 985/868-3617; Pat Hitt, RN Assistant Administrator

LaHaye Eye and Ambulatory Surgical Center, 4313 I-49 S. Service Rd., Opelousas, LA 70570; tel. 337/942-2024; FAX. 337/948-6216; Bridget Ray, Administrator

LaHaye Total Eye Care, 201 Rue Iberville, Suite 800, Lafayette, LA 70508; tel. 337/235-2149; FAX. 337/231-4012; Bridget Ray

Lake Charles Medical-Surgical Clinic, 501 Dr. Michael DeBakey Drive, Lake Charles, LA 70601; tel. 337/433-8400; FAX. 337/433-7350; Karen Guillory, RN, Administrator

Laser and Surgery Center of Acadiana, 514 Street Landry Street, Lafayette, LA 70506; tel. 337/234-2020; FAX. 318/234-8230; Jackie Ipson, Office Manager

Louisiana Endoscopy Center, Inc., 9103 Jefferson Highway, Baton Rouge, LA 70809; tel. 225/927-0970; FAX. 225/706-0160; Albert Hart, IV, Administrator

LSU Eye Surgery Center, 2020 Gravier Street, Suite B, New Orleans, LA 70112; tel. 504/412-1590; FAX. 504/472-1268; W. L. Blackwell, Chief Executive Officer

MGA-GI Diagnostic and Therapeutic Center, 1111 Medical Center Boulevard, Suite 450, Marrero, LA 70072; tel. 504/349-6310; FAX. 504/349-6444; Thomas D. McCaffery, Jr., President

MGA-GI Diagnostic and Therapeutic Center, 2820 Napolean Ave, Suite 700, New Orleans, LA 70115; tel. 504/896-8680; FAX. 504/896-8699; Thomas D. McCaffery, Jr., President

Ochsner Outpatient Surgery Center, 103 Medical Center Drive, Slidell, LA 70461; tel. 985/646-4466; FAX. 985/646-5699; Allison F. Maestri, RN

Omega Hospital, LLC, 2525 Severn Avenue, Metairie, LA 70001; tel. 504/832-4200; FAX. 504/832-4209; Deborah Scnenck, Administrator

Outpatient Eye Surgery Center, 4324 Veterans Boulevard #101, Metairie, LA 70006; tel. 504/455-4046; FAX. 504/455-9890; Cheryl Crouse, RN, Administrator

Shreveport Endoscopy Center, AMC, 3217 Mabel Street, PO Box 37045, Shreveport, LA 71133-7045; tel. 318/631-0072; FAX. 318/631-9688; Randy Rossi, Administrator

Shreveport Surgery Center, 745 Olive Street, Suite 100, Shreveport, LA 71104; tel. 318/227-1163; FAX. 318/227-0413; Mary Jones, Administrator

Surgery Center, Inc., 1101 South College Road, Suite 100, Lafayette, LA 70503; tel. 337/233-8603; FAX. 337/234-0341; Russell J. Arceneaux, Administrator

Surginet Outpatient Surgery, LLC, 101 La Rue France, Suite 400, Lafayette, LA 70508; tel. 318/269-9828; FAX. 318/269-9823; Millissa R. Coco, Administrator

Thibodaux Laser & Surgery Center, LLC, 1101 Audubon Avenue, Suite S-Four, Thibodaux, LA 70301; tel. 985/447-7258; FAX. 985/448-1521; Nate Graff, Administrator

Urology Specialty and Surgery Center, 234 Dr. Michael DeBakey Drive, Lake Charles, LA 70601; tel. 337/433-5282; FAX. 337/433-1159; Shari Davis, Administrator

West Monroe Endoscopy Center, 102 Thomas Road, Suite 506, West Monroe, LA 71291; tel. 318/388-8878; FAX. 318/388-8870; J.B. Duke McHugh, MD

MAINE

Acadia Medical Arts Ambulatory Surgical Suite, 404 State Street, Bangor, ME 04401; tel. 207/990-0928; FAX. 207/945-4354; Paulette Blue, RN, Administrator

Eyecare Medical Group, 53 Sewall Street, Portland, ME 04102; tel. 207/828-2020; FAX. 207/773-0754; Clement Berry, Chief Executive Officer

Maine Eye Center, P.A., 15 Lowell Street, Portland, ME 04102; tel. 207/774-8277; FAX. 207/871-1415; Curtis M. Libby, MD, Director

Northern Maine Ambulatory Endoscopy Center, 11 Martin Street, P.O. Box 748, Presque Isle, ME 04769-0151; tel. 207/764-2482; FAX. 207/764-1569; Devin McHalten, Administrator

OA Centers for Orthopaedics, 33 Sewall Street, Portland, ME 04102; tel. 207/828-2100; FAX. 207/828-2190; Linda M. Ruterbories, ASU Director

Vision Care of Maine-Ardostook, LLC, 173 Academy Street, Presque Isle, ME 04769; tel. 207/764-0376; FAX. 207/764-7612; Craig W. Young, MD, Director

MARYLAND

Ambulatory Endoscopy Center of Maryland, Inc., 7350 Van Dusen Road, Suite 230, Laurel, MD 20707; tel. 301/498-5500; FAX. 301/604-5956; Kim Wilson RN, Center Director

Ambulatory Plastic Surgery Center Associates, CHTD, 15245 Shady Grove Road, Suite 155, Rockville, MD 20850; tel. 240/912-4708; FAX. 240/912-6992; Mary Vincent, Office Manager

Anne Arundel Gastroenterology Associates, Bestgate Medical Clinic, 820 Bestgate Road, Annapolis, MD 21401; tel. 410/224-2116; Gary M. Evans, Administrator

Baltimore Ambulatory Center for Endoscopy, 19 Fontana Lane, Suite 104, Rosedale, MD 21237; tel. 410/574-7776; FAX. 410/574-9038; Dr. J. Khan, Medical Director

Baltimore Podiatry Group, 5205 East Drive, Suite I, Arbutus, MD 21227; tel. 410/247-5333; Neil Scheffler, DPM, President

Baltimore Washington Eye Center, 200 Hospital Drive, Suite 600, Glen Burnie, MD 21061; tel. 410/766-3937; FAX. 410/766-2904; Lisa Haynes, RN, ASC Coordinator

Bayside Surgical Center, Inc., 8023 Ritchie Highway, Pasadena, MD 21122; tel. 410/761-4190; FAX. 410/761-0265; Sheila Freeze, Office Manager

Beitler, Samuel D., DPM Ambulatory Surgery Center, Glen Burnie Podiatric Surgery Center, 795 Aquahart Road, Suite 125, Glen Burnie, MD 21061; tel. 410/768-0702; FAX. 410/768-0649; Samuel D. Beitler, DPM

Bel Air Ambulatory Surgical Center, LLC, 2007 Rock Spring Road, Lower Level, Forest Hill, MD 21050; tel. 410/879-2474; FAX. 410/879-8194; Karen Carey, RN, Administrator

Belcrest Surgery Center, 6505 Belcrest Road, Suite One, Hyattsville, MD 20782; tel. 301/699-5900; FAX. 301/699-9297; Johnny J. Motran, DPM, Medical Director

Bethesda Ambulatory Surgical Center, 5620 Shields Drive, Bethesda, MD 20817; tel. 301/530-4181; FAX. 301/530-4373; John Lydon, DPM, Administrator

Bethesda Endoscopy Center, LLC, 10215 Fernwood Road, Suite 260, Bethesda, MD 20817; tel. 301/530-2800; FAX. 301/530-9560

Bethesda Surgery Center, LLC, 10215 Fernwood Road, Suite 412, Bethesda, MD 20817; tel. 301/530-6100; FAX. 301/530-6104; Janet Scanlon

Center for Oral & Maxillofacial Surgery, 1212 York Road, Suite A201, Lutherville, MD 21093; tel. 410/337-7755; FAX. 410/337-7922; Laurie Kolmer, Office Manager

Chesapeake Ambulatory Surgery Center, LLC, 8028 Governor Ritchie Highway, Suite 100, Pasadena, MD 21122; tel. 410/768-5800; FAX. 410/768-5806; Ira J. Gottlieb, DPM, Owner, Administrator

Chesapeake Plastic Surgery, 802 Bestgate Rd., Annapolis, MD 21401; tel. 410/646-3226; FAX. 443/949-7508; Haven Barlow, MD, Director

Cumberland Valley Surgical Center, LLC, 1110 Professional Court, Hagerstown, MD 21740; tel. 240/420-5559; Stacey Taylor, RN, BSN, Administrator, CASC

De Leonibus and Palmer, LLC, ASC, MedSurg Foot Center, 2086 Generals Highway, Suite 101, Annapolis, MD 21401; tel. 410/266-7666; FAX. 410/266-7703; John DeLeonibus, DPM, Owner

Dimensions Surgery Center, 14999 Health Center Drive, Ste 103, Bowie, MD 20716; tel. 301/809-2000; FAX. 301/464-3572; Joan McHale, Director of Operations

Drs. Liss & Mirkin PA T-A Foot & Ankle Associates dba Foot and Ankle Associates, dba Kensington Surgery Center, 10901 Connecticut Avenue, Suite 200 B, Kensington, MD 20895; tel. 301/949-2000; FAX. 301/949-2002; Dr. Gene Mirkin

Dulaney Eye Institute, 901 Dulaney Valley Road, Suite 220, Towson, MD 21204; tel. 410/583-1000; FAX. 410/583-5700; Andrea Hyatt, CASC, Administrator

Dundalk Ambulatory Surgery Center, 1123 Merritt Boulevard, Baltimore, MD 21222; tel. 410/282-6666; FAX. 410/282-0357; Pam Green, Office Manager

Ellicott City Ambulatory Surgery Center, 2850 North Ridge Road, Ellicott City, MD 21043; tel. 410/461-1600; FAX. 410/750-7615; Beth H. Davis, Administrator

Facial Plastic Surgicenter, Ltd., 1838 Greene Tree Road, Baltimore, MD 21208; tel. 410/486-3400; FAX. 410/486-0092; Ira D. Papel, MD, President

Flaum, Martin/Rockville Ambulatory Surgical Center, LLC, 50 West Edmonston Drive, Suite 306, Rockville, MD 20852; tel. 301/340-8666; FAX. 301/340-7448; Martin C. Flaum, Owner

Foot Care Associates Ambulatory Care Center at Joppa Foot Care, 2316 East Joppa Road, Baltimore, MD 21234; tel. 410/882-5100

Four Corners Ambulatory Surgical Center, LLC, Dr. Gary A. Lieberman, PA, ASC, 10101 Lorain Avenue, Silver Spring, MD 20901; tel. 301/681-8400; FAX. 301/681-3339; Gayle Rickert, Administrator

Frederick Surgical Center, LLC, 45 Thomas Johnson Drive, Ste 207, Frederick, MD 21702; tel. 301/694-3400; FAX. 301/694-3620; Tracey Tylicki, BSN, RN, CASC, Administrator and Director of Surgical Services

Giardina and Glubo, P.A., 4660 Wilkens Avenue, Baltimore, MD 21229; tel. 410/242-7066; FAX. 410/242-4126; Eileen Giardina, RN

Gynemed Surgi-Center, 17 Fontana Lane, Suite 201, Baltimore, MD 21237; tel. 410/686-8220; FAX. 410/391-0943; David O'Neil, MD

Harford County Ambulatory Surgery Center, 1952-A Pulaski Highway, Edgewood, MD 21040; tel. 410/538-7000; FAX. 410/679-4291; Ms. Kim Merrill, RN, BN, Nurse Administrator

Harford Endoscopy Center, LLC, Two North Avenue, Suite 102, Belair, MD 21014; tel. 410/838-6345; FAX. 410/838-1595; Sherry Adkins, Center Director

Johns Hopkins Plastic Surgery Associates, JHOC 8, 601 North Caroline Street, Baltimore, MD 21287; tel. 443/997-9466; FAX. 410/614-1296; Anu Mullick, Administrator

Kaiser-Permanente-Kensington, 10810 Connecticut Avenue, Kensington, MD 20895; tel. 301/929-7275; FAX. 301/929-7577; Wanda McCulley, RN, Administrator

Lake Forest Ambulatory Surgical Center, 702 Russell Avenue, Gaithersburg, MD 20877; tel. 301/948-3668; FAX. 301/926-7787; Fatimah, Office Manager

Laser Surgery Center, Inc., 484A Ritchie Highway, Severna Park, MD 21146; tel. 410/544-4600; FAX. 410/544-0997; Barbara Stein, Office Manager

Laurel Foot and Ankle Surgery Center Inc., 14440 Cherry Lane Court, Suite 104, Laurel, MD 20707; tel. 301/953-3668; Dr. Frank Smith, Administrator

Maple Springs Ambulatory Surgery Center, 10810 Darnstown Road, Suite 101, Gaithersburg, MD 20878; tel. 301/762-3338; FAX. 301/762-1585; Dr. Stuart Snyder, PA, President

Maryland Endoscopy Center, LLC, 100 West Road, Suite 115, Towson, MD 21204; tel. 410/494-0144; FAX. 410/494-0147; Irma Haak, RN, Center Director

Metropolitan Ambulatory Urologic Institute LLC, 7759 Belle Point Drive, Greenbelt, MD 20770; tel. 301/474-5583; FAX. 301/474-5742; Bernie Schwartz, Manager

Michetti, Michael, Dr. of District Heights, 6400 Marlboro Pike, District Heights., MD 20747; tel. 301/736-6900

Mid Shore Surgical Eye Center, 8420 Ocean Gateway, Suite One, Easton, MD 21601; tel. 410/822-0424; FAX. 410/822-2283; Cheryl Schmitt, RN

Montgomery Endoscopy Center P.A., Montgomery Gastroenterology P.A., 12012 Veirs Mill Road, Silver Spring, MD 20906; tel. 301/942-3550; FAX. 301/933-3621; Sindu Stephen, MD, ASC Director

Montgomery Surgical Center, 46 West Gude Drive, Rockville, MD 20850; tel. 301/424-6901; FAX. 301/294-7847; Charlie Gallagher, Administrator

Parris-Castoro Eye & Laser Center, 620 Boulton Street, Bel Air, MD 21014; tel. 410/399-8427; FAX. 410/399-8427; Mary Ripley, RN, Nurse Manager

Plastic Surgery Specialists, 2448 Holly Avenue, Suite 400, Annapolis, MD 21401; tel. 410/841-5355; FAX. 410/841-6589; Amanada Freeland, Administrator

Plastic Surgery Specialists, 2448 Holly Ave., Suite 400, Annapolis, MD 21401; tel. 410/841-5355; FAX. 410/841-6589; Amanda Freeland, Administrator

Plaza Ambulatory Surgical Center, 6506 Reisterstown Road, Suite 501, Baltimore, MD 21215; tel. 410/764-7044; FAX. 410/764-8637; Dr. Brian Kashan, Administrator

Podiatry Associates, P.A., One North Main Street, Bel Air, MD 21014; tel. 410/879-1212; FAX. 410/893-1081

Podiatry Associates, P.A., 6569 North Charles Street, Suite 702, Towson, MD 21204; tel. 410/828-5420; FAX. 410/828-1663; Stan Book, Billing Manager

Podiatry Associates, P.A., Charter Professional Center, 10700 Charter Drive, Suite 300, Columbia, MD 21044; tel. 410/730-0970; FAX. 410/730-0161; Dr. Boyd, Capello, Ritter, Podiatrist

Prince George's Multi-Specialty Surgery Centre, Inc., 8700 Central Avenue, Suite 105, Landover, MD 20785; tel. 301/499-3338; FAX. 301/499-1266; John Bubser, Administrator

River Reach Outpatient Surgery Center, 790 Governor Ritchie Highway, Suite E-35, Severna Park, MD 21146; tel. 410/544-2487; FAX. 410/544-1872; Pat Hofmeier, Administrator

Riverside Ambulatory Surgery Center, 560 Riverside Drive, Suite A-101, Salisbury, MD 21801; tel. 410/749-0121; FAX. 410/749-6807; Patricia Timmons, PMAC, Administrator

Robinwood Surgery Center, LLC, 11110 Medical Campus Road, Suite 200, Hagerstown, MD 21742; tel. 301/714-4300; FAX. 301/714-4324; Michael Reyka, Executive Director

Saint Mary's Multispecialty Surgery Center, Inc., Route 235 and Chancellors Run Road, Suite 15, PO Box 1310, California, MD 20619; tel. 301/862-3338; FAX. 301/862-3335; Douglas H. Hallgren, Administrator

Spector, Adam, DPM, Ambulatory Surgery Center/ Silver Spring Podiatry Center, 2730 University Boulevard W., Suite 1000, Wheaton, MD 20902; tel. 301/949-3668; FAX. 301/949-8833; Adam Spector, DPM, Administrator

Summit Ambulatory Surgery Center, Ambulatory Surgery Center, 1001 Pine Heights Avenue, Suite 104, Baltimore, MD 21229; tel. 410/644-0929; Narang Ashok, Administrator

SurgiCenter of Baltimore, LLP, 23 Crossroads Drive, Suite 100, Owings Mills, MD 21117; tel. 410/356-0300; FAX. 410/356-7507; Rosemary L. Lambie, RN, Administrator

The Adult and Pediatric Urology Surgery Center of MD, 3455 Wilkens Avenue, Suite 100, Baltimore, MD 21229; tel. 410/646-0330; FAX. 410/644-6182; Bridget Mastrounni, Practice Administrator

The Ambulatory Urosurgical Center, 401 East Jefferson Street, Suite 105, Rockville, MD 20850; tel. 301/309-8219; FAX. 301/309-9370; Bernadette Noel, RN, Administrative Director

The ASC at Waugh Chapel, 2401 Brandermill Blvd, Suite 340, Gambrills, MD 21054; tel. 410/451-3206; FAX. 410/451-3207; Lance Caffiero, Administrator and Owner

The Endoscopy Center, 7402 York Road, Suite 101, Towson, MD 21204; tel. 410/494-0156; FAX. 410/828-1706; Barry Gendason, General Manager

The Friendship Ambulatory Surgery Center, PC, 5550 Friendship Boulevard, Suite 270, Chevy Chase, MD 20815; tel. 301/215-7347; FAX. 301/215-7345; Anthony Ruffin, Administrator

The Surgery Center of Ophthalmology Associates, LLC, 10755 Falls Road, Suite 110B, Lutherville, MD 21093; tel. 410/583-2811; FAX. 410/583-2814; Lynne Young, Administrator

Total Foot Care Surgery Center, Inc., 7525 Greenway Center Drive, Suite 112, Greenbelt, MD 20770; tel. 301/345-4087; FAX. 301/345-0482; Kathi Reinhart, Office Manager

Towson South Surgical Center, LLC, 7505 Osler Drive, Suite 508, Towson, MD 21204; tel. 410/296-5333; FAX. 410/828-7275; Denise S. Lewis, CMC, Finance Manager

Waldorf Endoscopy Center, 11340 Pembroke Square, Suite 202, Waldorf, MD 20603; tel. 301/638-5354; FAX. 301/843-5184; Center Director

Western Maryland Eye Surgical Center, 1003 West Seventh Street, Suite 400, Frederick, MD 21701; tel. 301/662-3721; FAX. 301/698-8164

MASSACHUSETTS

Andover Surgery Center, LP, 138 Haverhill Street, Andover, MA 01810; tel. 508/475-2880; FAX. 508/475-9562; Nancy Aucoin, Executive Director

Boston Center for Ambulatory Surgery, Inc., 170 Commonwealth Avenue, Boston, MA 02116; tel. 617/267-0710; FAX. 617/236-8704; Phiiip J. Gaven, MBA, Administrator

Boston Eye Surgery & Laser Center, P.C., 50 Stanford Street, Boston, MA 02114; tel. 617/723-2015; FAX. 617/723-7787; Sheila M. Harney, Business Manager

Boston University Eye Assoc., Inc., 90 New State Highway, Raynham, MA 02767; tel. 508/822-8839; FAX. 508/880-3616; Judith A. Orsie, RNBSN, Director of Surgical Services

Cataract and Laser Center West, LLC, 171 Interstate Drive, West Springfield, MA 01089; tel. 413/737-5500; FAX. 413/732-3514; C. Michael Duca, Administrator

Cataract and Laser Center, Inc., 333 Elm Street, Dedham, MA 02026; tel. 781/326-3800; FAX. 728/326-2120; Kathleen Carey, RN, Administrator

HealthSouth Maple Surgery Center, 298 Carew Street, Springfield, MA 01104; tel. 413/739-9668; FAX. 413/781-3652; Kathleen S. Loomis, RN, Facility Administrator

New England Eye Surgery Center, 696 Main Street, Weymouth, MA 02190; tei. 617/331-3820; FAX. 617/331-1076; Kenneth Camerota

Northeast Ambulatory Center, Three Woodland Road, Suite 321, Stoneham, MA 02180; tel. 781/665-5233; FAX. 781/662-4878; Anil Kumar, MD, Medical Director

Plymouth Laser and Surgical Center, 40 Industrial Park Road, Plymouth, MA 02360; tel. 508/746-8600; FAX. 508/747-0824; Kathleen Murphy, Administrator

Same Day SurgiClinic, 272 Stanley Street, Fall River, MA 02720; tel. 508/672-2290; FAX. 508/679-3766; Steven Pimental, Administrator

Surgery Center of Waltham, 130 2nd Avenue, Waltham, MA 02451; tel. 781/434-6400; FAX. 781/434-6501; Sharon Edwards, Chief Operating Officer

The Cosmetic Surgery Center, 68 Camp Street, Hyannis, MA 02601; tel. 508/775-7026; FAX. 508/771-0499; Zara Borgoff, RN

Worcester Surgical Center, Inc., 300 Grove Street, Worcester, MA 01650; tel. 508/754-0700; FAX. 508/831-9989; Andy H. Poritz, MD, Professional Services Director

MICHIGAN

Balian Eye Center, 432 West University Drive, Rochester, MI 48307; tel. 248/651-6122; FAX. 248/651-4825; E. Mike Raphtis, MD

Centre for Plastic Surgery, 2060 East Paris Ave. SE, Suite 150, Grand Rapids, MI 49546; tel. 616/454-1256; FAX. 616/454-0308; Patty Bakker, Administrator

East Michigan Surgery Center, 701 South Ballenger, Flint, MI 48532; tel. 810/238-3603; FAX. 810/767-5194; Destiny Hahn, Administrator

Eastside Endoscopy Center, 28963 Little Mack, Suite 103, St. Clair Shores, MI 48081; tel. 586/447-5110; FAX. 586/774-6091; Beth Miller, Administrator

Eastside Endoscopy Center, 17700 23 Mile Road, Suite 250, Macomb Township, MI 48044; tel. 586/416-7501; FAX. 586/416-7506; Beth Miller, Administrator

Endoscopy and Surgery Center at Woodbridge Hills, 7901 Angling Road, Portage, MI 49024; tel. 269/324-8406; FAX. 269/324-8476; Renee Langeland, MSN, RN, Administrator

Health Care Midwest Surgery Center, 125 West Walnut, Kalamazoo, MI 49007; tel. 616/343-1381; Gregor W. Blix, MD, Medical Director

Hemorrhoid Clinics of America, 22000 Greenfield Road, Oak Park, MI 48237; tel. 248/967-4140; FAX. 248/967-0745; Max Ali, MD, President

Henry Ford Medical Center, 6777 West Maple Road, West Bloomfield, MI 48322; tel. 248/661-4100; FAX. 248/661-6494; Sally Bertonia, Administrative Manager

Henry Ford Medical Center-Lakeside Ambulatory Surgery, 14500 Hall Road, Sterling Heights, MI 48313; tel. 586/247-2680; FAX. 586/247-2682; Peter Tate, Group Practice Director

John Michael Garrett, MD, 1301 Carpenter Avenue, Iron Mountain, MI 49801; tel. 906/774-1404; FAX. 906/774-8132; Teri Mulka, RN, ASC Director

Lakeshore Eye Surgery Center, 21711 Greater Mack Avenue, St. Clair Shores, MI 48080; tel. 586/774-4080; FAX. 586/541-3399; Mariann Pomaville, Center Director

Lansing Surgery Center, 1707 Lake Lansing Road, Lansing, MI 48912; tel. 517/708-3333; FAX. 517/267-0430; Richard Smith, Chief Executive Officer

M.D. Surgicenter, 375 Barclay Circle, Rochester Hill, MI 48307; tel. 248/852-3636; FAX. 248/852-3631; David Boberg, Administrator

Michigan Center for Outpatient Ocular Surgery, 33080 Utica Road, P.O. Box 26010, Fraser, MI 48026; tel. 810/296-7250; FAX. 810/296-0276; Norbert P. Czajkowski, MD, Director

Midwest Medical Center, 4700 Schaefer Road, Dearborn, MI 48126; tel. 313/581-5500; FAX. 313/581-6013; Mark B. Saffer, MD, President and Chief Executive Officer

North Oakland ASC, iLLC, 1305 North Oakland Boulevard, Waterford, MI 48327; tel. 248/666-5552; FAX. 248/666-5508; Bonnie Kalous, Charge Nurse

Oakland Surgi Center, Inc., 2820 Crooks Road, Suite 200, Rochester Hills, MI 48309; tel. 248/852-7484; Marisel Estrada, RN, BSN, Administrator

Planned Parenthood Mid and South Michigan, 3100 Professional Drive, P.O. Box 3673, Ann Arbor, MI 48106-3673; tel. 734/973-0710; FAX. 734/973-0595; Danielle Terry

Planned Parenthood of South Central Michigan, 4201 West Michigan Avenue, Kalamazoo, MI 49006-5833; tel. 269/372-1205; FAX. 269/372-1279; Amy Steward, MSN, FNP, Associate Medical Director

Southgate Surgery Center, 14050 Dix-Toledo Road, Southgate, MI 48195; tel. 734/281-0100; FAX. 734/281-7447; Linda Phillips, RN, Administrator

Spectrum Health Surgical Center, 1000 East Paris SE, Suite 100, Grand Rapids, MI 49546; tel. 616/285-1822; FAX. 616/285-1820; Deb Williams, Nurse Manager

St. John Surgery Center, 21000 12 Mile Road, St. Clair Shores, MI 48081; tel. 810/447-5015; FAX. 810/447-5012; Cheri Dendy, Administrator

St. Mary's Ambulatory Care Center, 4599 Towne Centre, Saginaw, MI 48604; tel. 517/797-3000; FAX. 517/797-3010; Lori Jurgens, Director

Superior Endoscopy Center/U P Digestive Disease Associates, P.C., 1414 West Fair Avenue, Suite 135, Marquette, MI 49855; tel. 906/226-6025; FAX. 906/226-5366; Jessica Jones, RN, Director of Nursing

Surgery Center of Michigan, 44650 Delco Boulevard, Sterling Heights, MI 48313; tel. 586/254-3391; FAX. 586/254-3344; Jay Novetsky, MD, Medical Director

Surgical Care Center of Michigan, 750 East Beltline, NE, Grand Rapids, MI 49525; tel. 616/940-3600; FAX. 616/954-0216; Kris Kilgore, RN, BSN, Administrative Director

The Berry Surgery Center, 28500 Orchard Lake Road, Suite100, Farmington Hills, MI 48334; tel. 248/851-6767; FAX. 248/851-2077; Aaron Betel, Medical Director

MINNESOTA

Abbott Northwestern - WestHealth, 2855 Campus Drive, Plymouth, MN 55441; tel. 763/577-7000; Jason Gaines, Vice President, WestHealth & Regional Specialty Services

Centennial Lakes Surgery Center, 7373 France Avenue, S., Suite 404, Edina, MN 55435; tel. 952/832-9360; FAX. 952/832-5079; Pamela Spohn, Administrator

Children's - Minnetonka, 6050 Clearwater Drive, Minnetonka, MN 55343; tel. 612/930-8600; FAX. 612/930-8650; Brent Lindstrom, Periop Business Development Manager

Landmark Surgery Center, 17 West Exchange Street, Suite 222, St. Paul, MN 55102; tel. 651/968-5468; FAX. 651/968-5493; Beckie Hines, Nurse Director

Midwest Surgery Centers, 2080 Woodwinds Drive, Woodbury, MN 55125; tel. 651/642-1106; FAX. 651/642-9837; H. Joseph Drannen, Administrator

Willmar Surgery Center, 1320 South First Street, Willmar, MN 56201; tel. 320/235-6506; FAX. 320/235-7069; John Seifert, Medical Director

MISSISSIPPI

Better Living Clinic Endoscopy Center, 3000 Halls Ferry Road, Vicksburg, MS 39180; tel. 601/638-9800; FAX. 601/638-9808; Barbara Neal, Office Manager

Cedar Lake Surgery Center, 1720 B Medical Park Drive, Biloxi, MS 39532; tel. 228/702-2000; FAX. 228/702-2019; Michael T. Gossman, Administrator

Columbus Endoscopy Center, Inc., 600 Leigh Drive, Columbus, MS 39705; tel. 662/327-7525; FAX. 662/243-2252; Julie Rawson, Administrator

East Mississippi Endoscopic Center, LLC, 1926 23rd Ave, Meridian, MS 39302; tel. 601/485-1131; FAX. 601/485-1336; Crystal Boler, Director

Endoscopy Center of North Mississippi, 1206 Office Park Drive, Oxford, MS 38655; tel. 662/234-9888; FAX. 662/234-9872; Roger Franck, Administrator

ENT and Facial Plastic Surgery, PA, dba Head & Neck Surgery Center, LLC, 107 Millsaps Drive, P.O. Box 17829, Hattiesburg, MS 39402; tel. 601/268-5131; FAX. 601/268-5138; Jean Lincoln, Business Manager

Eye Surgical Center of Mississippi, LLC, 1053 River Oaks Drive, Flowood, MS 39232; tel. 601/969-1430; FAX. 601/709-2117; Dr. Brannon Aden, Medical Director

Gastrointestinal Association Endoscopy, 1405 North State Street, Third Floor, Jackson, MS 39205; tel. 601/354-1234; FAX. 601/352-4882; Diane Winsner, Administrator

Gulf Coast Outpatient Surgery Center, 2781 C T Switzer Sr Drive, Suite 101, Biloxi, MS 39531; tel. 228/594-2900; FAX. 228/594-2901; Diane Farris, Administrator

Gulf South Surgery Center, 1206 31st Avenue, P.O. Box 1778, Gulfport, MS 39501; tel. 228/864-0008; FAX. 228/864-0742; Warren Hiatt, Jr., MD, President

Gulfport Surgery Center, 1300 Broad Ave, Gulfport, MS 39501; tel. 228/575-2200; FAX. 228/575-2249; William Hertzog, Administrator

Jackson Eye Institute & ASC, 2500 Lakeland Drive, Suite B, Flowood, MS 39208; tel. 601/933-1197; FAX. 601/939-6823; Dr. James Bruce, Administrator

Laurel Surgery and Endoscopy Center, LLC, 1710 West 12th Street, Laurel, MS 39440; tel. 601/369-2021; FAX. 601/369-2022; Meredith Baker, Administrator

Lowery A. Woodall Outpatient Surgery Facility, 105 South 28th Avenue, Hattiesburg, MS 39401; tel. 601/579-3400; FAX. 601/264-2025; Tommy Thornton, Administrator

MAE Physicians Surgery Center, LLC, 1190 North State Street, Suite 102, Jackson, MS 39202; tel. 601/968-1790; FAX. 601/292-4531; Carla Glaze, Administrator

Magnolia Regional Health Center Surgery Center, 401 Alcorn Drive, Corinth, MS 38834; tel. 662/293-2000; FAX. 662/287-3562; Angela Jackson, Administrator

Meridian Surgery Center, 2100 13 Street, Meridian, MS 39301; tel. 601/485-4443; FAX. 601/485-9060; Brett Hawkins, Administrator

Mississippi Coast Endoscopy & ASC, 2406 Catalpa Ave, Pascagoula, MS 39567; tel. 228/696-0818; FAX. 228/696-0893; Mary Lynn, Administrator

Mississippi Surgical Center, 1421 North State Street, Suite 101, Jackson, MS 39202; tel. 601/353-8000; FAX. 601/948-2507; Cindy Seal, Administrator

New Gulf Coast Surgery Center, LLC, 3882 Bienville Blvd, Ocean Springs, MS 39564; tel. 228/872-6290; FAX. 228/818-5538; Donna Griggs, CNO, Administrator

North Mississippi Ambulatory Surgery Center, LLC, 589 Garfield, Tupelo, MS 38801; tel. 662/377-4700; FAX. 662/377-3101; Scott Edwards, Administrator

Ocean Springs Surgical & Endoscopy Center, 3301 Bienville Blvd, Ocean Springs, MS 39564; tel. 228/872-8854; FAX. 228/872-0265; Mary Lynn, Administrator

Oxford Surgery Center, 499 Azalea Drive, Oxford, MS 38655; tel. 662/234-7979; FAX. 662/234-7079; Margaret Tatum, Administrator

Pain Treatment Center, LLC, 106 Asbury Circle, Hattiesburg, MS 39402; tel. 601/268-8698; FAX. 601/296-3049; Tracey Oden, Administrator

Scuthern Eye Surgery Center, LLC, 1420 South 28th Avenue, Hattiesburg, MS 39402; tel. 601/264-3937; FAX. 601/264-5930; Cameron S. Griffith, MD, Medical Staff President

Surgicare of Jackson, 760 Lakeland Drive, Jackson, MS 39216; tel. 601/362-8700; FAX. 601/362-6439; Dawn Thomas, Administrator

MISSOURI

Auburn Surgery Center, Inc., 300 South Mount Auburn Road, Suite 200, Cape Girardeau, MO 63703; tel. 573/332-7881; FAX. 573/332-7176; Lanna Kelley, Administrator

Cataract and Glaucoma Outpatient Surgicenter, 7220 Watson Road, St. Louis, MO 63119; tel. 314/352-5500; Stanley C. Becker, MD

CMMP Surgical Center, 1705 Christy Drive, Suite 100, Jefferson City, MO 65101; tel. 573/635-7022; FAX. 573/635-7209; Angela R. Erosenko, Administrator

Section C

Creekwood Surgery Center, 211 Northeast 54th Street, Suite 100, Kansas City, MO 64118; tel. 816/455–4214; FAX. 816/455–4216; Diana J. Carr, Regional Vice President

Creve Coeur Surgery Center, LLC, dba City Place Surgery Center, LLC, 845 N. New Ballas Ct., Suite 100, Creve Coeur, MO 63141; tel. 314/872–7100; FAX. 314/872–9176; Sandi Baber, RN, MHA, Regional Vice President

Doctors' Park Surgery, Inc., 30 Doctors' Park, Cape Girardeau, MO 63703; tel. 573/334–9606; FAX. 573/334–9608; Darin Roberts, Chief Executive Officer/Administrator

Eye Surgery Center-The Cliffs, 4801 Cliff Avenue, Suite 101, Independence, MO 64055; tel. 816/478–4400; FAX. 816/478–8240; Jacki Wyrick, RN, BSN, Direct of Nursing

NovaMed Eye Surgery Center of North County, dba Cataract Surgery Center, 900 North Highway 67 (Lindbergh), Florissant, MO 63031; tel. 314/838–0321; FAX. 314/838–6532; Karen L. Bell, RN, ASC Director

Saint Luke's — G.I. Diagnostics, Inc., 4321 Washington, Suite 5700, Kansas City, MO 64111; tel. 816/561–2000; FAX. 816/931–7559; Craig B. Reeves, Administrator

South County Surgical Center, LLC, 12345 West Bend Drive, Suite 201, St. Louis, MO 63128; tel. 314/722–2530; FAX. 314/525–0198; Ellen Kluesner, Administrator

Surgery Center of St. Joseph, 3201 Ashland Avenue, Suite C & D, St. Joseph, MO 64506; tel. 816/279–0079; FAX. 816/364–1100; Samantha Long, Administrator

Surgicenter of Kansas City, LLC, 1800 East Meyer Boulevard, Kansas City, MO 64132; tel. 816/523–0100; FAX. 816/995–3190; Rita Gooding, Administrator

The Endoscopy Center, 3800 South Whitney, Independence, MO 64055; tel. 816/478–4887; FAX. 816/478–7140; Andrea L. Wyatt, MBA, CMPE, Chief Executive Officer

The Endoscopy Center, 9601 NE 79th Street, Kansas City, MO 64158; tel. 816/478–4887; FAX. 816/478–7140; Andrea L. Wyatt, MBA, CMPE, Chief Executive Officer

The Endoscopy Center, 5330 North Oak Traffic Way #100, Kansas City, MO 64118; tel. 816/478–4887; FAX. 816/478–7140; Andrea L. Wyatt, MBA, CMPE, Chief Executive Officer

The Endoscopy Center, 5330 N. Oak Trafficway, Kansas City, MO 64118; tel. 816/478–4887; FAX. 816/478–7140; Andrea L. Wyatt, MBA, CMPE, Chief Executive Officer

The Endoscopy Center, 9601 NE 79th Street, Kansas City, MO 64158; tel. 816/478–4887; FAX. 816/478–7140; Jean Hansen, MBA, FACMPE, Chief Executive Officer

The Endoscopy Center II, 5330 North Oak Trafficway, Suite 100, Kansas City, MO 64118; tel. 816/478–4887; FAX. 816/478–7140; Jean Thompson, Chief Executive Officer

The Tobin Eye Institute, 3902 Sherman Avenue, St. Joseph, MO 64506; tel. 816/279–1363; FAX. 816/233–8936; Lindsey Williams, RN, Director of Nursing and Operations

Tri-County Surgery Center, LP, 1111 East Sixth Street, Washington, MO 63090; tel. 636/239–1766; FAX. 636/239–2964; Candy Garofalo, Administrator

MONTANA

Billings Cataract and Laser Surgicenter, 1221 North 26th Street, Billings, MT 59101; tel. 406/252–5681; FAX. 406/252–5025; George F. Hatch, Jr., MD, Director

Northern Rockies Surgery Center, 940 North 30th Street, Billings, MT 59101; tel. 406/248–7186; FAX. 406/248–6889; Debbie Howe, RN, MSN, Administrator

Same Day Surgery Center, LLC, 300 North Wilson, Suite 600F, Bozeman, MT 59715; tel. 406/586–1956; Suellen Bradley, Clinical Director

The Eye Surgicenter, 2475 Village Lane, Suite 202, Billings, MT 59102; tel. 406/252–6608; FAX. 406/252–2600; Cheri Salthe, Office Manager

NEBRASKA

Aesthetic Surgical Images, P.C., 8900 West Dodge Road, Omaha, NE 68114; tel. 402/390–0100; FAX. 402/390–2711; Rita Petersen, Administrator

Bergan Mercy Surgery Center, Health Inventures, 7500 Mercy Road, Suite 4300, Omaha, NE 68124; tel. 402/398–5665, FAX. 402/398–6606; Leslie Voigt

Lincoln Eye and Laser Institute, 1500 South 48th Street, Suite 610, Lincoln, NE 68506; tel. 402/483–4448; FAX. 402/483–4750; Rhonda Assmus, Manager

Lincoln Surgical Center, 1710 South 70th, Suite 200, Lincoln, NE 68506; tel. 402/484–9090; FAX. 402/483–0476; Robin Linnafelter, Chief Executive Officer

Omaha Ambulatory Surgery Center, 825 North 90th Street, Omaha, NE 68114; tel. 402/397–1180; FAX. 402/408–1783; Jeff Bierle, Executive Director

Omega Surgery Center, LLC, 1500 S. 48th Street, Suite 612, Lincoln, NE 68506; tel. 402/483–4448; FAX. 402/483–4750; Ann Perl, RN, ASC Administrator

Omega Surgery Centers, LLC, 11606 Nicholas Street, Suite 200, Omaha, NE 68154; tel. 402/493–2020; FAX. 402/431–8569; Kellie Johnson, RN, ASC Manager

The Urology Center, P.C., 111 1/2 South 90th Street, Omaha, NE 68114; tel. 402/397–9800; Laura Forehead, Administrator

NEVADA

Carson Endoscopy Center, 1385 Vista Lane, Carson City, NV 89703; tel. 775/884–4567; FAX. 775/884–4569; Autumn Uyechi, RN, Director of Center Operations

Digestive Disease Center, 2136 East Desert Inn Road, Suite B, Las Vegas, NV 89109; tel. 702/734–0075; FAX. 702/734–3912; Osama Haikal, MD, Administrator

Digestive Health Center, 5250 Kietzke Lane, Reno, NV 89511; tel. 775/829–8855; FAX. 775/770–2717; Laura Kennedy, RN, Center Director

Ford Center for Foot Surgery, 2321 Pyramid Way, Sparks, NV 89431; tel. 702/331–1919; FAX. 702/331–2008; Dr. L. Bruce Ford, Administrator

Las Vegas Surgicare, Ltd., 870 South Rancho Drive, Las Vegas, NV 89106; tel. 702/870–2090; FAX. 702/870–5468; Kelly Marcum, Administrator

Shepherd Eye Surgicenter, 3575 Pecos McLeod, Las Vegas, NV 89121; tel. 702/731–2088; FAX. 702/734–7836; Christina Kennelley, Administrator

Sierra Center for Foot Surgery, 1801 North Carson, Suite B, Carson City, NV 89701; tel. 775/882–1441; FAX. 775/882–6844; Dr. Jeffrey Bean, DPM, Administrator

SMA Surgery Center, 2450 West Charleston, Las Vegas, NV 89102; tel. 702/877–8660; FAX. 702/877–5180; Steve Evans, MD, Medical Director

NEW HAMPSHIRE

Bedford Ambulatory Surgical Center, 11 Washington Place, Bedford, NH 03110; tel. 603/622–3670; FAX. 603/626–9750; Suzanna Majewski, Chief Operating Officer

Dartmouth Ambulatory Surgery Center, 100 Hitchcock Way, Manchester, NH 03104; tel. 603/695–1800; FAX. 603/629–1730; Sean E. Hunt, MD, Medical Director, ASC

Dr. O'Connell's Pain Care Centers, Inc., Pinewood Medical Center, 255 Route 108, Somersworth, NH 03878; tel. 603/692–3166; FAX. 603/692–3168; Tom Barnes, Administrator

Elliot One Day Surgery Center, One Elliot Way, Manchester, NH 03103; tel. 603/663–5932; FAX. 603/626–4300; William J. Oifederico, MHA, Administrative Director

Nashua Eye Surgery Center, Inc., Five Coliseum Avenue, Nashua, NH 03063; tel. 603/882–9800; FAX. 603/882–0556; Paul O'Leary, Administrator

Orthopaedic Surgery Center, 264 Pleasant Street, Concord, NH 03301; tel. 603/228–7211; FAX. 603/228–7192; Donna Quinn, Administrator

Salem Surgery Center, 32 Stiles Road, Salem, NH 03079; tel. 603/898–3610; FAX. 603/890–3313; Cynthia C. Fortune, Director

NEW JERSEY

Advanced Gastroenterology of Bergen County, PA, AGBC Endoscopy Center, 140 Sylvan Avenue, Suite 101A/101B, Englewood Cliffs, NJ 07632-2554; tel. 201/945–6564; FAX. 201/461–9038; Michael Gailie, Practice Administrator

Arthur W. Perry, M.D., FACS Plastic Surgery Center, 3055 Route 27, Franklin Park, NJ 08823; tel. 732/422–9600; Arthur W. Perry, MD, Director

Atlantic Surgery Center, LLC, 279 Third Avenue, Suite 105, Long Branch, NJ 07740; tel. 732/222–7373; FAX. 732/571–9212; Daniel B. Goldberg, MD, President

Atrium Surgery Center, Inc., 195 Route 46, Suite 202, Mine Hill, NJ 07803; tel. 973/989–5185; FAX. 973/328–4097; Jennifer Rand, RN, CNOR, Director of Nursing

Bergen-Passaic Cataract Surgery and Laser Center, Inc., 18-01 Pollitt Drive, Suite 4, Fair Lawn, NJ 07410-2815; tel. 201/414–5649; FAX. 201/398–9132; Caroline B. Ivanovski-Hauser, Administrator

Berkeley Heights Eye Group, PA, Summit Eye Group, 369 Springfield Avenue, Berkeley Heights, NJ 07922; tel. 908/464–4600; FAX. 908/464–4737; Elizabeth Way, RN, Administrator

Campus Eye Group Ambulatory Surgery Center, Inc., 1700 Whitehorse Hamilton Square Road, Suite A, Hamilton, NJ 08690; tel. 609/587–2020; FAX. 609/588–9545; Denise Agness, OD, Office Manager

Center for Special Surgery, 104 Lincoln Avenue, Hawthorne, NJ 07506; tel. 973/427–6800; FAX. 973/427–9602; John Tauber, Business Administrator

Clifton Surgery Center, 1117 Route 46 East Suite 303, Clifton, NJ 07013; tel. 973/779–7210; FAX. 973/779–7387; Daniel Rice, MD, President and Medical Director

East Brunswick Surgery Center, dba University Surgi Center, 561 Cranbury Road, East Brunswick, NJ 08816; tel. 732/390–4300; FAX. 732/390–0556; Paula Zuckerman, Clinical Director

Endo-Surgi Center, 1201 Morris Avenue, Union, NJ 07083; tel. 908/686–0066; FAX. 908/686–5388; Sharon DeMato, Administrator

Endo-Surgi Center of Old Bridge, 42 Throckmorton Lane, Old Bridge, NJ 08857; tel. 732/679–8808; FAX. 732/679–7280; Sharon DeMato, Executive Director

Endo/Surgical Center of North Jersey, 999 Clifton Avenue, Clifton, NJ 07013; tel. 973/777–3938; FAX. 973/591–0178; Ellen Tummillo RN, CGRN, Director of Nursing

Englewood Endoscopic Associates, 420 Grand Avenue, Suite 101, Englewood, NJ 07631; tel. 201/569–7044; FAX. 201/569–1999; Carmen Rivera, Office Manager

Essex Surgical, LLC, 776 Northfield Avenue, West Orange, NJ 07052; tel. 973/324–2300; FAX. 973/324–1421; George C. Peck, Jr., MD

Eye Institute of Essex Surgeye Center, 50 Newark Avenue, Belleville, NJ 07109; tel. 973/751–6060; FAX. 973/450–1464; Eileen Beltramba, Administrator

Eye Physician of Sussex County Surgical Center, 183 High Street, Newton, NJ 07860; tel. 973/383–6345; FAX. 973/383–0032; Patricia Fowler, RN

Eye Surgery Princeton, 419 North Harrison Street, Princeton, NJ 08540; tel. 609/921–9437; FAX. 609/921–0277; Richard H. Wong, MD, Medical Director

Gastroenterology Diagnosis Northern New Jersey, 205 Browertown Road, Suite 102, West Paterson, NJ 07424; tel. 973/890–4780; FAX. 973/890–1097; Ann Kalafsky, RN, Administrative Director

Hand Surgery and Rehabilitation Center of New Jersey, P.A., 5000 Sagemore Drive, Suite 106, Marlton, NJ 08053; tel. 856/983–4263; FAX. 856/983–3894; Sheila McAteer, RN, BSN, Administrator of Surgical Center

Hunterdon Center for Surgery, LLC T/A Surgery Today, 9100 Wescott Drive, Suite 201, Flemington, NJ 08822; tel. 908/806–7017; FAX. 908/806–2838; Lisa York, Executive Director

James Street Surgical Suite, 261 James Street, Suite 3E, Morristown, NJ 07960; tel. 973/267–7181; FAX. 973/267–3656; Patricia D'Amico, RN, Director of Nursing

Mediplex Surgery Center, 98 James Street, Suite 108, Edison, NJ 08820-3998; tel. 732/632–1600; FAX. 732/632–1678; Janet Kovacs, Director

Mid Atlantic Eye Center, 70 East Front Street, Red Bank, NJ 07701; tel. 732/741–0858; FAX. 732/219–0180; Walter J. Kahn, MD and Mark Friedberg, MD

Northern New Jersey Eye Institute, 71 Second Street, South Orange, NJ 07079; tel. 973/763–2203; FAX. 973/763–5207; Shirley Vitale, Practice Administrator

Northwest Jersey Ambulatory Surgery Center, 350 Sparta Avenue, Building A, Sparta, NJ 07871; tel. 973/729–8580; FAX. 973/729–2344; Mary Ulanet, Administrator

Ocean Surgical Pavilion, Inc., 1907 Highway 35, Suite Nine, Oakhurst, NJ 07755; tel. 732/517–8885; FAX. 732/517–0304; Barbara DeMaria, RN, CNOR, Center Director

Pavonia Surgery Center, PC, 600 Pavonia Avenue, Fourth Floor, Jersey City, NJ 07306; tel. 201/216–1700; FAX. 201/216–1800; William H. Constad, MD, President

Penn Cardiology at Willingboro, 200 Campbell Drive, Suite 115, Willingboro, NJ 08046; tel. 609/871–7070; FAX. 609/835–4510; Constance G. Matarese, Senior Practice Manager

Physicians of Monmouth, LLC, 733 North Beers Street, Holmdel, NJ 07733; tel. 732/739–0707; FAX. 732/739–8533; Renee Sharkey, RN, Surgical Coordinator

Princeton Orthopaedic Associates, P.A., 727 State Road, Princeton, NJ 08540; tel. 609/924–8131; FAX. 609/924–8532; William G. Hyncik, Jr., Executive Director

Retina Consultants Surgery Center, 39 Sycamore Avenue, Little Silver, NJ 07739; tel. 732/530–7730; FAX. 732/530–3837

Ridgedale Surgery Center, 14 Ridgedale Avenue, Suite 120, Cedar Knolls, NJ 07927; tel. 973/605–5151; FAX. 973/605–1208; Diana Ruccio, Office Manager

Ridgewood Ambulatory Surgery Center, 1200 Ridgewood Avenue, Ridgewood, NJ 07450; tel. 201/444–9002; FAX. 201/612–8114; Kristine Williams, RN

Saddle Brook Surgicenter, Inc., 289 Market Street, Saddle Brook, NJ 07663; tel. 201/843–4444; FAX. 201/368–2817; Dr. Ronald Sollitto, President and Chief Executive Officer

Seashore Ambulatory Surgery Center, 1907 New Road, Northfield, NJ 08225; tel. 609/645–8884; FAX. 609/645–9780; Kathleen Clark, Administrator

Somerset Eye Institute, P.C., 562 Easton Avenue, Somerset, NJ 08873; tel. 732/828–5900; FAX. 732/828–3327; Bernadette Santana, RN, BSN, Nursing Administrator

Somerset Surgical Center, PA, 1081 Route 22 West, Suite 201, Bridgewater, NJ 08807; tel. 908/575–0020; FAX. 908/575–1515; Joan McKibben, Administrator

South Jersey Endoscopy Center, 26 East Red Bank Avenue, Woodbury, NJ 08096; tel. 856/848–4464; FAX. 856/848–8706; Barbara Fargnoli, Billing Manager

South Jersey Surgicenter, 2835 South Delsea Drive, Vineland, NJ 08360; tel. 856/696–0020; FAX. 856/205–0300; Susy Olmeda, Administrative Coordinator and Debra Gaffney, Clinical Coordinator

Summit Surgical Center, LLC, 200 Bowman Drive, Suite D–160, Voorhees, NJ 08043; tel. 856/247–7800; FAX. 856/247–7858; Anthonia Schmidt, Administrator

Surgical Center of South Jersey, an SCA affiliate, 130 Gaither Drive, Suite 160, Mount Laurel, NJ 08054; tel. 856/722–7000; FAX. 856/722–8962; Eleanor O. Peschko, Administrator

Surgicare of Central Jersey, Inc., 40 Stirling Road, Watchung, NJ 07060; tel. 908/769–8000; FAX. 908/769–4139; Linda Kollar, Executive Director

Surgicare Surgical Associates of Fair Lawn, LLC, 1501 Broadway, Route 4 West, Suite One and Three, Fair Lawn, NJ 07410; tel. 201/703–8487; FAX. 201/791–6585; John H. Hajjar, MD, Member

Teaneck Gastroenterology and Endoscopy Center, 1086 Teaneck Road, Suite Three B, Teaneck, NJ 07666; tel. 201/837–9636; FAX. 201/837–9544; Mia D. Oliver, Manager

The Endoscopy Center of Red Bank, 365 Broad Street, Red Bank, NJ 07701; tel. 732/842–4294; FAX. 732/842–3854; Donna D. Spring, Director of Operations

The New Jersey Eye Center, 1 North Washington Avenue, Bergenfield, NJ 07621; tel. 201/384–7333; FAX. 201/384–9915; James Dello Russo, OD

The Surgical Center at South Jersey Eye Physicians, P.A., 509 South Lenola Road, Suite 11B, Moorestown, NJ 08057; tel. 856/234–0258; FAX. 609/727–0064; Elizabeth Hanley, RN

Wills Eye Surgery Center of Cherry Hill, 408 Route 70 East, Cherry Hill, NJ 08034; tel. 856/354–1600; FAX. 856/429–7555; Deborah M. O'Donnell, RN, Administrator

NEW MEXICO

Alamogordo Eye Clinic and Surgical Center, 1124 10th Street, Alamogordo, NM 88310; tel. 505/434–1200; FAX. 505/437–3947; Cindy Buttram, RN

HealthSouth Albuquerque Surgery Center, 1720 Wyoming Boulevard, NE, Albuquerque, NM 87112; tel. 505/292–9200; FAX. 505/292–1398; Terry Sanchez, Administrator

Northside Presbyterian, PO Box 26666, 5901 Harper Drive, NE, Albuquerque, NM 87125; tel. 505/291–2114; FAX. 505/291–2983; Karin Vantiunen

The Endoscopy Center of Santa Fe, 1630 Hospital Dr., Suite A, Santa Fe, NM 87505; tel. 505/988–3373; FAX. 505/984–1858; Betsy Libowitz, RN, Center Director

NEW YORK

Ambulatory Surgery Center of Brooklyn, 313 43rd Street, Brooklyn, NY 11232; tel. 718/369–1900; FAX. 718/965–4157; Frank A. Mazzagatti, PhD, Vice President of Operations and Administrator

Ambulatory Surgery Center of Greater New York, LLC, 1101 Pelham Parkway, N., Bronx, NY 10469; tel. 718/515–3500; Erin Duffy, RN, Administrator

Boulevard Surgical Center, 46-04 31st Avenue, Long Island C, NY 11103; tel. 718/545–5050; FAX. 718/545–0032; Linda M. Smith, RN, Consultant

Brook Plaza Ambulatory Surgical Center, 1901 Utica Avenue, Brooklyn, NY 11234; tel. 718/629–5590; FAX. 347/587–4770; Steven Ackerman, Chief Executive Officer

Brooklyn Eye Surgery Center, LLC, 1301 Avenue J, Brooklyn, NY 11230; tel. 718/688–3937; FAX. 718/692–4456; Jay Raifman, Administrator

Buffalo Ambulatory Surgery Center, 3095 Harlem Road, Cheektowaga, NY 14225; tel. 716/896–3815; FAX. 716/896–3015; Todd Everhart, RN, Administrator

Camillus Surgery Center, 5700 Genesee Street, Suite 11, Camillus, NY 13031; tel. 315/701–9378; FAX. 315/701–0871; Stephanie Foody, Administrator

Central New York Eye Center, 22 Green Street, Poughkeepsie, NY 12601; tel. 845/471–3977; FAX. 845/483–0574; Kim M. Quick, RN, COE

Day-Op Center of Long Island, Inc., 110 Willis Avenue, Mineola, NY 11501; tel. 516/294–0030; FAX. 516/294–0228; Juliette LaRegina, Administrator

Fifth Avenue Surgery Center, 1049 Fifth Avenue, New York, NY 10028; tel. 212/772–6667; FAX. 212/988–8018; Charles J. Raab, Chief Executive Officer

Garden City SurgiCenter., 400 Endo Boulevard, Garden City, NY 11530; tel. 516/832–8504; FAX. 516/228–9429; Kelly Fitzpatrick, Administrator

Harrison Center Outpatient Surgery, dba Holdings, LLC, 550 Harrison Street, Suite 230, Syracuse, NY 13202; tel. 315/472–4424; FAX. 315/475–8056; Margaret M. Alteri, Administrator and Chief Executive Officer

Kingston Ambulatory Surgical Center, LLC, 40 Hurley Avenue, Suite 13, Kingston, NY 12401; tel. 845/338–4777; FAX. 845/339–7339; Kathleen Keily, Administrator

Lattimore Community Surgicenter, 125 Lattimore Road, Rochester, NY 14620; tel. 585/473–9000; FAX. 585/697–3519; Peter G. Varlan, Administrator

North Shore Surgi Center, Inc., 989 West Jericho Turnpike, Smithtown, NY 11787; tel. 631/864–7100; FAX. 631/864–7129; Michael Guarino, Administrator

Queens Surgi-Center, 83-40 Woodhaven Boulevard, Glendale, NY 11385; tel. 718/849–8700; FAX. 718/849–6523; Adce Abadir, Administrator

The Mackool Eye Institute, 31-27 41st Street, Astoria, NY 11103; tel. 718/728–3400; FAX. 718/721–7562

Westfall Surgery Center, LLP, 1065 Senator Keating Boulevard, Rochester, NY 14618; tel. 585/256–1330; FAX. 585/256–3823; Gary J. Scott, Administrative Director

NORTH CAROLINA

Asheboro Endoscopy Center of Randolph Specialty Group, 700 Sunset Avenue, PO Box 4830, Asheboro, NC 27203; tel. 336/625–0305; FAX. 336/625–9941; Vickie Whitaker, RN, Clinical Director

Blue Ridge Day Surgery Center, 2308 Wesvill Court, Raleigh, NC 27607; tel. 919/781–4311; FAX. 919/781–0625; Kathy Leibl Administrator

Carolina East Surgery Center, 630 McCarthy Blvd, New Bern, NC 28562; tel. 252/633–2000; FAX. 252/633–9045; Robin Schaefer, Director of Perioperative Services

Caromont Specialty Surgery, 2511 Court Drive, Gastonia, NC 28054; tel. 704/671–5600; FAX. 704/671–5650; Lisa Lineberger, Manager

Carteret Surgery Center, 3714 Guardian Avenue, Morehead City, NC 28557; tel. 252/247–0314; FAX. 252/247–2031; Kim Blaine, Business Manager

Chapel Hill Surgical Center, 109 Conner Drive, Suite 1201, Chapel Hill, NC 27514; tel. 919/968–0611; FAX. 919/967–8637; Gary S. Berger, MD, President

Charlotte Surgery Center, 2825 Randolph Road, Charlotte, NC 28211; tel. 704/377–1647; FAX. 704/358–8267; Connie M. Wilson, Administrator

Cleveland Ambulatory Services, 1100 North Lafayette Street, Shelby, NC 28150; tel. 704/482–1331; FAX. 704/482–4833; John Reynolds, MD, Clinical Director

Eye Surgery and Laser Clinic, 500 Lake Concord Road, NE, Concord, NC 28025; tel. 704/782–1127; FAX. 704/782–1207; Administrator

Eye Surgery Center of Shelby, 1622 East Marion Street, Shelby, NC 28150; tel. 704/482–2020; FAX. 704/482–2707; Frank T. Hannah, MD, Medical Director

Fayetteville Ambulatory Surgery Center, 1781 Metromedical Drive, Fayetteville, NC 28304; tel. 910/323–1647; FAX. 910/323–4142; John T. Henley, Jr., MD, Medical Director

Goldsboro Endoscopy Center, Inc., 2705 Medical Office Place, Goldsboro, NC 27534; tel. 919/580–9111; FAX. 919/580–0988; Venkata C. Motaparthy, MD, Chief Executive Officer

High Point Surgery Center, 600 Lindsay Street, P.O. Box 2476, High Point, NC 27261; tel. 336/878–6068; FAX. 336/878–6111; Joan D. White, Administrative Director

Iredell Head, Neck and Ear Ambulatory Surgery Center, Inc., 707 Bryant Street, Statesville, NC 28677; tel. 704/873–5224; FAX. 704/873–5984; Angie Kerr, Office Manager

Iredell Surgical Center, 1720 Davie Avenue, Statesville, NC 28677; tel. 704/871–0081; FAX. 704/871–0086; Glenda Tallent, MBA, Administrator

Plastic Surgery Center of North Carolina, Inc., 2901 Maplewood Avenue, Winston-Salem, NC 27103; tel. 336/768–6210; FAX. 336/768–6236; John A. Fagg, MD

Raleigh Plastic Surgery Center, Inc., 1112 Dresser Court, Raleigh, NC 27609; tel. 919/872–2616; FAX. 919/872–2771; Nancy Nicoll O'Neil, Administrator

Regional Medical Services Surgery Center, 5200 North Croatan Highway, Kitty Hawk, NC 27949; tel. 252/255–6000; FAX. 252/255–6018; Janet Jarrett, Executive Director

Southern Eye Associates, P.A., Ophthalmic Surgery Center, 2801 Blue Ridge Road, Suite 200, Raleigh, NC 27607; tel. 919/571–0081; Kathryn O'Neill, Director of Clinical Services

Surgical Eye Center, 3312 Battleground Avenue, Greensboro, NC 27410; tel. 336/282–8330; FAX. 336/282–2625; Trudy Wester, Center Director

SurgiCare of Jacksonville, 166 Memorial Court, Jacksonville, NC 28546; tel. 910/353–9565; FAX. 919/353–5497; Takey Crist, Medical Director

Vidant SurgiCenter, 102 Bethesda Drive, Greenville, NC 27834; tel. 252/847–7700; FAX. 252/847–7784; Stephen W. Tripp, RPh, President

WHA Medical Clinic, PLLC, 1202 Medical Center Drive, Wilmington, NC 28401; tel. 910/341–3433; Diane A. Atkinson, Executive Director

Wilmington SurgCare, 1801 South 17th Street, Wilmington, NC 28401; tel. 910/763–4555; FAX. 910/332–8920; James Shafer, Facility Administrator

NORTH DAKOTA

Bismarck Surgical Associates, 600 N. 9th Street, Bismarck, ND 58501; tel. 701/221–2299; FAX. 701/323–3370; Scott Osadchuk, Director

Dakota Surgery & Laser Center, 430 E. Sweet Avenue, Bismarck, ND 58504; tel. 701/222–4900; FAX. 701/222–4999; Charles R. Volk, Administrator

Day Surgery-Wahpeton, 275 South 11th Street, Wahpeton, ND 58075; tel. 701/642–2000; FAX. 701/671–4106; Mark Waldera, Administrator

FM Endoscopy Center, 300 Main Ave, Suite 205, Fargo, ND 58103; tel. 701/200–4150; FAX. 701/476–0000; Rodney Ludwig, Administrator

Great Plains Clinic Surgery Center, 33 Ninth Street, W., Dickinson, ND 58601; tel. 701/483–6017; FAX. 701/483–5018; Mark Grove, Administrator

Innovis Health, 1702 S. University Drive, Fargo, ND 58103; tel. 701/364–8900; FAX. 701/364–8990; Dennis Furman, Chief Operating Officer

Institute For Lower Back Care, 300 Main Ave, Suite 212, Fargo, ND 58103; tel. 701/297–0817; Panjin Sivanna, MD, Administrator

Institute for Special Surgery, 2301 25th Street, Fargo, ND 58103; tel. 702/271–1045; FAX. 702/271–1044; Timothy Haugen, Administrator

Lamb Plastic Surgery Center, 1507 S University Dr, Fargo, ND 58103; tel. 701/237-9592; Donald Lamb, MD, Administrator

Laser and Surgery Center, 4344 20th Ave S, Fargo, ND 58103; tel. 701/277-7200; Steve Bagan, MD, Administrator

Mid Dakota Clinic Surgicenter, 401 N 9th Street, Bismarck, ND 58501; tel. 701/530-6010; FAX. 701/530-5996; Robert Winandy, Nursing Manager, Administrator

North Dakota Surgery Center, 3035 Demers Avenue, Grand Forks, ND 58201; tel. 701/775-4240; FAX. 701/775-4255; Kristen Vik, RN, BSN, Nursing Manager

Northern Plains Surgery Center, 44 4th St S, Fargo, ND 58103; tel. 701/232-9200; Sarah Ouse, RN, ASC Coordinator

St. Alexius Same Day Surgery Center, 810 East Rosser, Bismarck, ND 58501; tel. 701/530-5000; Sandy Gerving, Director

Trinity Community Clinic-Western Dakota, 1321 W. Dakota Pkwy., Williston, ND 58801; tel. 701/572-7711; FAX. 701/572-2283; Mary E. Banta, Administrator

OHIO

Amend Center for Eye Surgery, 5939 Colerain Avenue, Cincinnati, OH 45239; tel. 513/923-3900; FAX. 513/923-3012

Bloomberg Eye Center, 1651 West Main Street, Newark, OH 43055; tel. 740/522-3937; FAX. 740/522-0063; Judy Mackey, Director of Corp. Services

Central Ohio Endoscopy Center, LLC, Dublin Center, 6670 Perimeter Drive, Suite 200, Dublin, OH 43016; tel. 614/754-5500; FAX. 614/707-4204; Debbie Sauls, RN, Nurse Manager

Central Ohio Endoscopy Center, LLC, East Center, 85 McNaughten Road, Suite 320, Columbus, OH 43213; tel. 614/754-5500; FAX. 614/864-2062; Debbie Sauls, RN, Nurse Manager

Central Ohio Endoscopy Center, LLC, North Center, 3800 Olentangy River Road, Columbus, OH 43214; tel. 614/754-5500; FAX. 614/754-5501; Debbie Sauls, RN, Nurse Manager

Central Ohio Endoscopy Center, LLC, West Center, 815 W. Broad Street, Suite 220, Columbus, OH 43222; tel. 614/754-5500; FAX. 614/707-4204; Debbie Sauls, RN, Nurse Manager

Cincinnati Eye Institute and Ambulatory Surgery Center, 1945 CEI Drive, Cincinnati, OH 45242; tel. 513/984-5133; FAX. 513/984-4240; Clyde Bell, Chief Executive Officer

Cincinnati Foot Clinic, Inc., 8111 Cheviot Road, Cincinnati, OH 45247; tel. 513/385-6946; Robert Hayman, MD, President

Columbus Eye Surgery Center, 5965 East Broad Street, Suite 460, Columbus, OH 43213; tel. 614/751-4080; FAX. 614/751-4092; Janie Norman, RN, Center Director

Consultants in Gastroenterology, Inc., 5900 Landerbrook Drive, Suite 195, Mayfield Heights, OH 44124; tel. 440/461-3596; FAX. 440/460-0130; Wendy Callahanl, RN, Manager

Consultants in Gastroenterology, Inc., 7530 Fredle Drive, Concord, OH 44077; tel. 440/386-2250; FAX. 440/386-2251; Wendy Callahan, RN, Nurse Manager

Crystal Clinic Surgery Center, 3975 Embassy Parkway, Suite 202, Akron, OH 44313; tel. 330/668-4085; FAX. 330/668-2624; Katherine L. McNeal, RN, Administrator

Digestivecare Endoscopy Unit, 75 Sylvania Drive, Beavercreek, OH 45440; tel. 937/320-5050; FAX. 937/320-5060; Craig Penno, Administrator

Endoscopy Center of Dayton Ltd., 4200 Indian Ripple Road, Beavercreek, OH 45440; tel. 937/427-2078; FAX. 937/427-9081; Jennette Papalios, RN, Nurse Manager

Endoscopy Center West, 3654 Werk Road, Cincinnati, OH 45248; tel. 513/451-6001; FAX. 513/451-7310; Angela Tiemann, Administrator

Eye Institute of Northwestern Ohio, Inc., 3509 Briarfield Blvd, Maumee, OH 43537; tel. 419/865-3866; FAX. 419/865-3451; Carol R. Kollarits, MD, President

Facial Surgery Center, 1130 Congress Avenue, Glendale, OH 45246; tel. 513/772-2442; FAX. 513/772-2844; Joseph J. Moravec, MD, Medical Director

Fairview Hospital Surgery Center, 850 Columbia Road, Westlake, OH 44145; tel. 216/808-4000; FAX. 216/808-4010; Michelle Padden, RN, Administrator

Firas Atassi, M.D. Outpatient Surgery Center, 34500 Center Ridge Road, North Ridgeville, OH 33039; tel. 216/327-2414

Gastroenterology Associates, Inc., 4665 Belpar Street, NW, PO Box 36329, Canton, OH 44735; tel. 330/493-1480; FAX. 330/493-6805; Stacy Daugherty, RN, Endoscopy Nurse Manager

Gastroenterology Specialists, Inc., 2726 Fulton Drive, NW, Canton, OH 44718; tel. 330/455-5011; FAX. 330/588-7127; Connie M. Kowalski, RN

Kunesh Eye Surgery Center, 2601 Far Hills Avenue, Dayton, OH 45419-1665; tel. 937/298-1093; FAX. 937/298-6344; Lucy Helmers, Administrator

Midwest Eye Surgery Center, 4452 Eastgate Boulevard, Suite 305, Cincinnati, OH 45245; tel. 513/752-5700; FAX. 513/752-5716; Holly Schwab, RN, Surgery Manager

North Coast Endoscopy, Inc., 9500 Mentor Avenue, Suite 380, Mentor, OH 44060; tel. 440/352-9400; FAX. 440/352-9407; Ahmad Ascha, MD

North Shore Endoscopy Center, 850 Columbia Road, Suite 200, Westlake, OH 44145; tel. 440/808-1212; FAX. 440/808-0321; Christine St.George-Gray, RN, BSN, Operations Manager

Ohio Eye Associates, Eye Surgery & Laser Center, 466 South Trimble Road, Mansfield, OH 44906; tel. 419/756-8000; FAX. 419/756-7100; Thomas F. Marquardt, Administrator

Optivue Vision, 2740 Navarre Avenue, Oregon, OH 43616; tel. 419/697-3616; FAX. 419/697-3655; Karen R. Hess, RN, LMT, OR Manager

Parkway Surgery Center, Ltd., 3500 Executive Parkway, Toledo, OH 43606; tel. 419/531-8349; FAX. 419/531-6833; Richard I. Tapper, MD, Medical Executive Director

Sidney Foot and Ankle Center, 1000 Michigan, Sidney, OH 45365; tel. 937/492-1211; FAX. 937/492-6557; Norma Polasky, Administrative Director

Surgery Alliance Ltd., 975 Sawburg Avenue, Alliance, OH 44601; tel. 330/821-7997; FAX. 330/821-7295; Hazel Thomas, Administrator

Taylor Station Surgery Center, 275 Taylor Station Road, Columbus, OH 43213; tel. 614/751-4466; FAX. 614/751-4474; Linda Meikle, Administrator

The Endoscopy Center, 3439 Granite Circle, Toledo, OH 43617; tel. 419/843-7993; FAX. 419/841-7789; Alice Horner, RN Nurse Manager

The Surgery Center, 19250 East Bagley Road, Middleburg Heights, OH 44130; tel. 440/826-3240; FAX. 440/826-3250; Barb Draves, CASC, Administrator

Toledo Clinic, Inc., 4235 Secor Road, Toledo, OH 43623; tel. 419/479-5650; FAX. 419/479-3982; Scott Porterfield, Administrator

Tri-State Centers, For Sight Surgery Center, 8044 Montgomery Road, Suite 155, Cincinnati, OH 45236; tel. 513/791-7967; FAX. 513/791-1473; Jo Slocum RN, BSN, Administrator

University Suburban Health Center, Wright Surgery Center Department, 1611 South Green Road, Suite 124, South Euclid, OH 44121; tel. 216/382-1868; FAX. 216/382-0584; Thomas Stellato, MD, Medical Director

Western Reserve Surgery Center, 1930 State Route 59, Kent, OH 44240; tel. 330/677-3292; FAX. 330/677-3624; Laurie Simon, Administrator

Zeeba Ambulatory Surgery Center, 29017 Cedar Road, Lyndhurst, OH 44124; tel. 440/460-8000; FAX. 440/460-4225; Franklin Keathley, Administrator

OKLAHOMA

Ambulatory Surgery Associates, 6160 South Yale Avenue, Tulsa, OK 74136; tel. 918/495-2625; FAX. 918/497-3259; Kathy Helberg, RN, Director

Central Oklahoma Ambulatory Surgical Center, Inc., 3301 Northwest 63rd Street, Oklahoma City, OK 73116; tel. 405/842-9732; FAX. 405/842-9771; W. Edward Dalton, MD, Administrator

Eastern Oklahoma Surgery Center, LLC, 5020 East 68th Street, Tulsa, OK 74136; tel. 918/492-1539; FAX. 918/494-8683; Linda Taylor, RN Supervisor

Great Plains Ambulatory Surgery Center, 5404 West Lee Boulevard, Suite 100, Lawton, OK 73505; tel. 580/536-7533; FAX. 580/536-7535; Richard Wedig, Administrator

Heritage Eye Surgery Center, LLC, dba Precision Vision Surgery Center, 6922 South Western Avenue, Suite 102, Oklahoma City, OK 73139; tel. 405/636-1508; FAX. 405/636-1239; Ray Z. Pasion, RN, Administrator

McGee Eye Surgery Center, 1000 North Lincoln, Suite 150, Oklahoma City, OK 73104; tel. 405/232-8696; FAX. 405/235-4423; Glenda Woodside, Administrator

Medical Plaza Endoscopy Unit, 1125 North Porter, Suite 304, Norman, OK 73071; tel. 405/360-2799; FAX. 405/447-0321; Philip C. Bird, MD

Oklahoma Surgicare, 4317 W. Memorial Road, Oklahoma City, OK 73134; tel. 405/755-6240; FAX. 405/752-1819; Lindie Slater, Administrator

Orthopedic Associates Ambulatory Surgery Center, Inc., 3301 Northwest 50th Street, Oklahoma City, OK 73112; tel. 405/947-5610; FAX. 405/948-5166; Carolyn Moles, RN, Director

Physicians Surgical Center, 3121 S. Telephone Rd., Moore, OK 73160; tel. 405/364-9789; FAX. 405/366-8081; Sandra Vaughn, RN, Administrator

Southern Oklahoma Surgical Center, Inc., 2412 North Commerce, Ardmore, OK 73401; tel. 580/226-5000; FAX. 580/226-5035; Christy Morris, RN, BSN, Administrator

Southern Plains Medical Center, Inc., 2222 Iowa Avenue, PO Box 1069, Chickasha, OK 73023; tel. 405/224-8111; FAX. 405/222-5359; Steven Browning, Administrator

Southwest Ambulatory Surgery Center, LLC, 8125 South Walker Avenue, Oklahoma City, OK 73139; tel. 405/606-8890; FAX. 405/604-2885; Anthony L. Cruse, DO, Medical Director

Surgery Center of South Oklahoma City, 9500 N. Broadway Extension, Oklahoma City, OK 73114; tel. 405/475-0678; FAX. 405/634-8300; Larry Smith, Administrator

Tower Day Surgery, 1044 Southwest 44th Street, Suite 100, Oklahoma City, OK 73109; tel. 405/636-1701; FAX. 405/636-4314; Teresa Carter, RN, Director of Patient Services

Triad Eye Medical Clinic and Cataract Institute, 6140 South Memorial, Tulsa, OK 74133; tel. 918/252-2020; FAX. 918/252-7466; Marc L. Abel, DO, Medical Director

OREGON

Aesthetic Breast and Cosmetic Surgery Center, 10201 Southeast Main, Suite 20, Portland, OR 97216; tel. 503/253-3458; FAX. 503/253-0856; Ronald V. DeMars, MD, Administrator

Center for Cosmetic and Plastic Surgery, 1353 East McAndrews Road, Medford, OR 97504; tel. 541/770-6776; FAX. 541/770-5791; Robert M. Jensen, MD, Administrator

Eye Surgery Center, 1408 E. Barnett Road, Medford, OR 97504-8279; tel. 541/779-2020; FAX. 541/770-6838; Loren R. Barrus, MD, Administrator

Futures Outpatient Surgical Center, Inc., 1849 Northwest Kearney, Suite 302, Portland, OR 97209; tel. 503/553-3653; FAX. 503/224-0722; Bryce E. Potter, MD, Principal

Lovejoy Surgicenter, Inc., 933 Northwest 25th Avenue, Portland, OR 97210; tel. 503/221-1870; FAX. 503/221-1488; Joy Staples, Administrator

McKenzie Surgery Center, 940 Country Club Road, Eugene. OR 97401; tel. 541/344-2600; FAX. 541/344-3317; Lynn M. Stapes, RN, Administrator

North Bend Medical Center, Inc., 1900 Woodland Drive, Coos Bay, OR 97420; tel. 541/267-5151; FAX. 541/266-4522; William H. Murray, Chief Executive Officer

Ontario Surgery Center, 251 SW 19th Street, Ontario, OR 97914; tel. 541/889-3198; FAX. 541/889-3904; Jeffrey C. Pitts, MD, Director

Oregon Eye Surgery Center, Inc., 1550 Oak Street, Suite 8, Eugene, OR 97401; tel. 541/683-8771; FAX. 541/434-0995; Virginia Pecora, RN, Administrator

Orion Eye/Eye Surgery Institute, 1775 SW Umatilla Ave., Redmond, OR 97756; tel. 541/548-7170; FAX. 541/548-3842; Lilly Uriz, ASC Facilitator

The Oregon Clinic Portland Gastroenterology ASC, 1111 NE 99th Street, Suite 302, Portland, OR 97220; tel. 503/963-2707; FAX. 503/963-2802; David Neale, Administrator

The Portland Clinic, Roger E. Alberty, MD Surgery Center, 9100 S.W. Oleson Rd., Tigard, OR 97223; tel. 503/445-9066; FAX. 503/445-9067; J. Michael Schwab, Chief Executive Officer

The Portland Clinic Surgical Center, 800 Southwest 13th Avenue, Portland, OR 97205; tel. 503/221-0161; FAX. 503/221-4451; J. Michael Schwab, Chief Executive Officer

Westside Surgery Center, 13240 Southwest Pacific Highway, Suite 200, Tigard, OR 97223; tel. 503/639-9951; FAX. 503/624-6037; Julie Solso, RN, ASC Director

Willamette Valley Eye SurgiCenter, 2001 Commercial Street, SE, Salem, OR 97302; tel. 503/363-1500; FAX. 503/588-2028; Gordon Miller, MD, Administrator

Section C

PENNSYLVANIA

Abington Surgical Center, 2701 Blair Mill Road, Suite 35, Willow Grove, PA 19090; tel. 215/443–8505; FAX. 215/957–0565; Stanley E. Grissinger, MBA, CHE, Executive Director

Aestique Ambulatory Surgical Center, One Aesthetic Way, Greensburg, PA 15601; tel. 724/832–7555; FAX. 724/832–7568; Theodore A. Lazzaro, MD, Medical Director

Delaware Valley Laser Surgery Institute, (Nevyas Eye Associates), Two Bala Plaza, Pl 33, Bala Cynwd, PA 19004; tel. 215/668–2847; FAX. 215/668–1509; Herbert J. Nevyas, MD, Medical Director

Dermatologic SurgiCenter, 1200 Locust Street, Philadelphia, PA 19107; tel. 215/546–3666; FAX. 215/546–6060; Anthony V. Benedetto, DO, FACP, Medical Director

Dermatologic SurgiCenter, 2221 Garrett Rd., Drexel Hill, PA 19026; tel. 610/623–5885; FAX. 610/623–7276; Anthony V. Benedetto, DO, FACP, Medical Director

Digestive Disease Institute, 899 Poplar Church Road, Camp Hill, PA 17011; tel. 717/763–1239; FAX. 717/763–9854; Iris Garman, Administrator

Fairgrounds Surgical Center/Lehigh Valley Hospital, 400 North 17th Street, Suite 300, Allentown, PA 18104; tel. 610/969–3100; FAX. 610/969–3199; Darlene G. Hinkle, Director, Perioperative Services

Kremer Eye Center, 200 Mall Boulevard, King of Prussia, PA 19406; tel. 610/337–1580; FAX. 610/337–3184; Mary Fitzgerald

Lebanon Outpatient Surgical Center, L.P., 830 Tuck Street, Lebanon, PA 17042; tel. 717/228–1620; FAX. 717/228–1642; Anita Gingrich Fuhrman, RN, BS, CASC, Director

Memorial Hospital, Outpatient Surgery Center, 1750 Fifth Ave., York, PA 17405; tel. 717/843–7613; FAX. 717/849–5662; Pam Neiderer, Director of Surgical Services

Mt. Lebanon Surgical Center, Professional Office Building, 1050 Bower Hill Road, Suite 102, Pittsburgh, PA 15243; tel. 412/942–5770; FAX. 412/942–5780; Cynthia Fabus, Supervisor

Mt. Pleasant Surgery Center, 200 Bessemer Road, Mt. Pleasant, PA 15666; tel. 724/547–5432; FAX. 724/547–2435; Brian Konieczny, Administrative Director

NEI Ambulatory Surgery Center Inc., PC, 204 Mifflin Avenue, Scranton, PA 18503; tel. 570/340–8090; FAX. 570/342–3136; Mary Ann Labas, RN, Director of Nursing

Northwood Surgery Center, 3729 Easton-Nazareth Highway, Easton, PA 18045; tel. 610/559–7110; FAX. 610/559–7317; Chitu Patel, Administrator

Ophthalmology Laser and Surgery Center, Inc., 92 Tuscarora Street, Harrisburg, PA 17104; tel. 717/233–2020; FAX. 717/233–0825

Paoli Surgery Center, One Industrial Boulevard, Paoli, PA 19301; tel. 610/408–0822; FAX. 610/408–9933; Caryl Berlin, Facility Manager

Pennsylvania Eye Surgery Center, 4100 Linglestown Road, Harrisburg, PA 17112; tel. 717/657–2020; FAX. 717/657–2071; Kimberly Myers, RN, Director, Surgical Services

Pocono Ambulatory Surgery Center, One Storm Street, Stroudsburg, PA 18360; tel. 570/421–4978; Mary P. Hayden RN, BS,CASC, Administrative Director

Shadyside Surgi-Center, Inc., 5727 Centre Avenue, Pittsburgh, PA 15206; tel. 412/363–6626; FAX. 412/363–7008; Susan M. Katch, RN, Director

Southwestern Ambulatory Surgery Center, 500 Lewis Run Road, Suite 202, Pittsburgh, PA 15122; tel. 412/469–6964; FAX. 412/469–6948; Pamela Wroblewski, CRNA, MPM, CASC Administrator

Southwestern Pennsylvania Eye Surgery Center, 750 East Beau Street, Washington, PA 15301; tel. 412/228–7477; FAX. 412/228–6271; Jennifer Cross, RN, Clinical Director

The Surgery Center of Chester County, 460 Creamery Way, Oaklands Corporate Center, Exton, PA 19341-2533; tel. 610/594–8900; FAX. 610/594–8907; Dean Daringer, MBA, Administrator

UPMC Monroeville Surgery Center, 125 Daugherty Drive, Monroeville, PA 15146-2749; tel. 412/374–9385; FAX. 412/374–9490; Carol Fiske Boumbouras, CMSC, Administrative Assistant, Medical Staff Manager

Valley Surgery Center, 1130 Highway 315, Wilkes-Barre, PA 18702; tel. 570/821–2830; FAX. 570/823–7921; Patricia Williams, Administrator

West Shore Endoscopy Center, 423 North 21st Street, Camp Hill, PA 17011; tel. 717/975–2430; FAX. 717/730–2158; James Bohenick, Chief Operating Officer

Wills Surgery Center of Bucks County, 401 North York Road, Warminster, PA 18974; tel. 215/443–3022; FAX. 215/443–5859; Patricia Cobb, RN, Administrator

Zitelli & Brodland, Ambulatory Surgery Facility, 5200 Centre Avenue, Suite 303, Pittsburgh, PA 15232; tel. 412/681–9400; FAX. 412/681–5240; John A. Zitelli, MD

RHODE ISLAND

Bayside Endoscopy Center, LLC, 33 Staniford Street, Providence, RI 02905; tel. 401/274–1810; FAX. 401/273–9689; Kathryn Abiri, RN, MSN, Administrator

Ocean State Endoscopy Center, 148 West River Street, Providence, RI 02904; tel. 401/274–1260; Cynthia Del Sesto, Administrator

St. James Surgery Center, 444 Quaker Lane, Warwick, RI 02886; tel. 401/384–6537; FAX. 401/384–6541; Valerie Martin, MSN, RN, Director

Women's Medical Center, 1725 Broad Street, Cranston, RI 02905; tel. 401/467–9111; FAX. 401/461–1390; Angelyn Sotirakos, Administrator

SOUTH CAROLINA

Ambulatory Eye Surgery and Laser Center, Inc., 9297 Medical Plaza Drive, Charleston, SC 29406; tel. 803/572–2888; Margaret A. Thompson

AnMed Health Medicus Surgery Center, LLC, 107 Professional Court, P.O. Box 1886, Anderson, SC 29622-1886; tel. 864/225–1933; FAX. 864/716–7965; Angela Kay, RN, Administrator

Bay Microsurgical Unit, Inc., 1200 Highmarket Street, Georgetown, SC 29440; tel. 843/546–8421; FAX. 843/546–1173; Janet Spring, Director of Nursing

Bearwood Ambulatory Surgery Center, 3031 Highway 81, N., Anderson, SC 29621; tel. 864/226–7371; FAX. 864/226–8367; Meryle Martin, Office Manager

Charleston Plastic Surgery Center, Inc., 261 Calhoun Street, Suite 200, Charleston, SC 29401; tel. 843/722–1985; FAX. 843/722–4840; Linda Crosby, Office Manager

Columbia Gastrointestinal Endoscopy Center, 2739 Laurel Street, Suite One-B, Columbia, SC 29240; tel. 803/254–9588; FAX. 803/931–8085; Cindy Sease, RN, Administrator

Columbia Surgery Center, Inc., 238 Shuler RD, Columbia, SC 29212-8048; tel. 803/732–6180; FAX. 803/732–6563; Vickie H. Ott, Administrator

Cross Creek Surgery Center of Greenville Hospital System, Nine Doctors Drive, Crosscreek Medical Park, Greenville, SC 29605; tel. 803/455–8400; Barbara Callahan, Administrator

Greenville Endoscopy Center, 317 Street Francis Drive, Suite 150, Greenville, SC 29601; tel. 864/232–7338; FAX. 864/240–8140; Rebecca K. Swoyer, Administrator

Greenville Endoscopy Center, 200 Patewood Drive, Ste 100B, Greenville, SC 29615; tel. 864/232–7338; FAX. 864/240–8140; Rebecca K. Swoyer, Administrator

Greenville Surgery Center, Five Memorial Medical Court, Greenville, SC 29605; tel. 864/272–3409; FAX. 864/272–3460; Denise Stills, Administrator

HealthSouth Surgery Center of Charleston, 2690 Lake Park Drive, North Charles, SC 29406; tel. 803/764–0992; FAX. 803/764–3187; Rosina Feagin, RN, MSN, Administrator

Roper West Ashley Surgery Center, 325 Folly Rd, Ste 200, Charleston, SC 29412-2507; tel. 843/763–3763; FAX. 843/763–3721; Maria I. Sample, Administrator

Spartanburg Surgery Center, 391 Serpentine Drive, Suite 200, Spartanburg, SC 29303; tel. 864/585–2002; FAX. 864/585–3300; Rick Sizemore, RN, Administrator

Upstate Surgery Center, LLC, 10 Enterprise Boulevard, Suite 109, Greenville, SC 29615; tel. 864/458–7141; FAX. 864/676–9116; Geoffrey Hibbert, Interim Director

SOUTH DAKOTA

Avera Medical Group - Pierre, 100 Mac Lane, Pierre, SD 57501; tel. 605/945–5210; FAX. 605/945–5084; Patti Lynn Trapp, RN, Director Operative Services

Black Hills Regional Eye Surgery Center, 2800 Third Street, Rapid City, SD 57701-7394; tel. 605/341–2000; FAX. 605/719–3211; Joyce Hatch, Human Resource Manager

Mallard Pointe Surgical Center, 1201 Mickelson Drive, Watertown, SD 57201-7100; tel. 605/882–4743; FAX. 605/882–6064; Mary Petersen, Administrative Director

TENNESSEE

Bristol Surgery Center, 350 Blountville Highway, Suite 108, Bristol, TN 37620; tel. 423/844–6120; FAX. 423/844–6119; Karen Williams, GCHC, MPH, NHA, CHES Administrator

Chattanooga Surgery Center, 400 North Holtzclaw Avenue, Chattanooga, TN 37404; tel. 423/698–6871; FAX. 423/622–8993; K.D. Ratchford, Administrator

Clarksville Endoscopy Center, 132 Hillcrest Drive, Clarksville, TN 37043; tel. 931/552–0180; FAX. 931/572–0915; Deborah Glassell, Clinical Director

DDC Surgery Center, Nine Physicians Drive, Jackson, TN 38305; tel. 731/661–0086; FAX. 731/661–9783; Audrey Hardee, RN, Clinical Director

East Memphis Surgery Center, 80 Humphreys Center Drive, Suite 101, Memphis, TN 38120; tel. 901/747–3233; FAX. 901/747–3230; Cathy Gilland, RN, Facility Administrator

Endoscopy Center of Kingsport, dba Sullivan Digestive Center, 2204 Pavilion Drive, Kingsport, TN 37660; tel. 423/392–6100; FAX. 423/392–6159; Penny Vaughn, Administrator

Eye Surgery Center of East Tennessee, 1124 Weisgarber Road, Suite 110, Knoxville, TN 37909; tel. 865/588–1037; FAX. 865/909–9104; Ashley Archer, RN, CNOR, Center Director

Eye Surgery Center of Middle Tennessee, Parkview Tower, Suite 900, 210 25th Avenue, N., Nashville, TN 37203; tel. 615/964–5912; FAX. 615/964–5913; Deborah MacDonald, Administrator

Fort Sanders West Outpatient Surgery Center, LLC, 210 Fort Sanders West Boulevard, Knoxville, TN 37922; tel. 865/531–5200; FAX. 865/531–5770; Erma Morgan, Director

Germantown Ambulatory Surgical Center, L.L.C., 7499 Poplar Pike, Germantown, TN 38138; tel. 901/755–6465

HealthSouth Nashville Surgery Center, 1717 Patterson Street, Nashville, TN 37203; tel. 615/329–1888; FAX. 615/329–0179; Lori Seymore, Administrator

Knoxville Center for Reproductive Health, 1547 West Clinch Avenue, Knoxville, TN 37916; tel. 865/637–3861; FAX. 865/637–0222; Kim Denison, Director

Lebanon HMA Surgical Center, 1414 Baddour Parkway, Lebanon, TN 37087; tel. 615/453–8252; FAX. 615/444–8994; Sylvia Black, Nurse Manager

LeBonheur East Surgery Center, L.P., 786 Estate Place, Memphis, TN 38120; tel. 901/287–4100; FAX. 901/287–4140; Sherrye Crone, Administrative Director, Lisa Burress, Clinical Director

Lisa Ross Birth & Women's Center, Inc., Maternity Center of East Tennessee (formerly), 1925-B Ailor Avenue, Knoxville, TN 37921; tel. 865/524–4422; FAX. 865/523–3687; Linda Cole, CNM Executive Director

Mays & Schnapp Pain Clinic and Rehabilitation Center, 55 Humphreys Center Drive, Suite 200, Memphis, TN 38120; tel. 901/747–0040; FAX. 901/747–0042; Ray Saunders, Practice Administrator

Memphis Center for Reproductive Health, 1726 Poplar Avenue, Memphis, TN 38104; tel. 901/274–3550; FAX. 901/274–3551; Rebecca L. Terrell, Executive Director

Memphis Eye and Cataract Ambulatory Surgery Center, 6485 Poplar Avenue, Memphis, TN 38119; tel. 901/767–3937; FAX. 901/767–1695; Ramona Jackson, Nurse Manager

Memphis Gastroenterology Endoscopy Center, 8000 Wolf River Blvd, #200, Germantown, TN 38138-1727; tel. 901/747–3630; FAX. 901/747–4039; Sylvia Hawkins, RN, Compliance Manager

Memphis Regional Gamma Knife Center, 1211 Union Ave, Ste 220, Memphis, TN 38104; tel. 901/726–6444; FAX. 901/726–6145; Betsy Smith, Administrator

Memphis Surgery Center, 1044 Cresthaven Road, Memphis, TN 38119; tel. 901/682–1516; FAX. 901/682–1545; Jason Young, RN, Facility Administrator

Mid-State Endoscopy Center, 2010 Church Street, Suite 420, Nashville, TN 37203; tel. 615/321–2141; FAX. 615/321–0522; Allan H. Bailey, MD, Medical Director

Nashville Endosurgery Center, 300 20th N, Eighth Floor, Nashville, TN 37203; tel. 615/284–1335; FAX. 615/284–1316

Nashville Gastrointestinal Endoscopy Center, 4230 Harding Road, Suite 309, Nashville, TN 37205; tel. 615/383–0165; FAX. 615/321–9292; Ron E. Pruitt, MD

Northridge Surgery Center, 647 Myatt Drive, Madison, TN 37115; tel. 615/868–8942; FAX. 615/868–1134; Tim Shannon, Administrator

Oral Facial Surgery Center, 322 22nd Avenue, N., Nashville, TN 37203; tel. 615/321–6160; FAX. 615/321–6175; Joey Cupit, RN, MSN, Clinical Administrator

Planned Parenthood - Greater Memphis Region, 2430 Poplar Avenue, Suite 100, Memphis, TN 38112; tel. 901/725–1717; FAX. 901/274–4790; Ellen Ruby - Markie, Chief Executive Officer

Ridge Lake Ambulatory Surgery Center, 825 Ridge Lake Boulevard, Memphis, TN 38119; tel. 901/685–2200; Kimberly Thorpe, ASC Administrator

Shea Ear Clinic, 6133 Poplar Pike, Memphis, TN 38119; tel. 901/761–9720; FAX. 901/763–4400; John J. Shea Jr., MD, President

Southern Endoscopy Center, 330 Wallace Road, Suite 103, Nashville, TN 37211; tel. 615/832–5530; FAX. 615/832–5713; Robert W. Herring, Jr., MD, Medical Director

St. Thomas Medical Group Endoscopy Center, 4230 Harding Road, Suite 400, Nashville, TN 37205; tel. 615/250–4108; Jeff May RN, Center Director

Surgery Center of Clarksville, 121 Hillcrest Drive, Clarksville, TN 37043; tel. 931/552–9992; FAX. 931/648–1816; Angela Farmer, Administrator

Surgical Services, P.C., 604 South Main Street, Sweetwater, TN 37874; tel. 423/337–4508; FAX. 423/337–4588; Linda Villanueva, Administrator

Surgicenter Of Murfreesboro Medical Clinic, P.A., 1272 Garrison Drive, Murfreesboro, TN 37129; tel. 615/867–8160; FAX. 615/876–7876; Sandy Gordon, Coordinator

Tennessee Endoscopy Center, 1706 East Lamar Alexander Parkway, Maryville, TN 37804; tel. 615/983–0073; FAX. 615/984–1731; Craig Jarvis, MD, Administrator

The Cookeville Surgery Center, 100 West Fourth Street, Suite 100, Cookeville, TN 38501; tel. 931/526–8115; FAX. 931/526–7619; Jeanie McGinnis, RN Administrator

The Endoscopy Center of Centennial, L.P., 2400 Patterson Street, Suite 515, Nashville, TN 37203; tel. 615/327–2111; FAX. 615/327–9292; Donna Crumley, RN, BS, MBA, Endoscopy Administrator

The Eye Surgery Center of Oak Ridge, 90 Vermont Avenue, Oak Ridge, TN 37830; tel. 865/482–8894; FAX. 865/481–8349; Regina Harkleroad, Director of Nursing

Urology Surgery Center, L.P., 2801 Charlotte Avenue, Nashville, TN 37209; tel. 615/250–9202; FAX. 615/250–9251; Mary Ellen, Danielson, RN, CNOR, CASC, Director

Volunteer Women's Medical Clinic, 313 Concord Street, Knoxville, TN 37919; tel. 865/522–5173; FAX. 865/522–9907; Elizabeth Fraley-Dumas, Clinical Director

Wesley Ophthalmic Plastic Surgery Center, 1800 Church Street, Suite 100, Nashville, TN 37203; tel. 615/329–3624; Janie Stucker, RN, Director

TEXAS

Abilene Cataract and Refractive Surgery Center, 2120 Antilley Road, Abilene, TX 79606; tel. 325/695–2020; FAX. 325/695–2326; Paul B. Thames MD Medical Director

Abilene Endoscopy Center, 1249 Ambler Avenue, Abilene, TX 79601; tel. 325/677–2626; FAX. 325/677–6835; Steve Johnson, MD, Medical Director

Amarillo Cataract and Eye Surgery Center, Inc., 7310 Fleming Avenue, Amarillo, TX 79106; tel. 806/354–8891; FAX. 806/354–2591; Carol A. Pearson, Director

Ambulatory Urological Surgery Center, Inc., 1149 Ambler, Abilene, TX 79601; tel. 915/676–3557; FAX. 915/673–2143; Angela X. Young, RN, Manager

American Surgery Centers of South Texas, LTD, 7810 Louis Pasteur, Suite 100, San Antonio, TX 78229; tel. 210/692–0218; FAX. 210/692–7980; Laura Rodriguez, Office Manager

Arlington Day Surgery Center, 918 North Davis Street, Arlington, TX 76012; tel. 817/860–9933; FAX. 817/860–2314; Dan Chambers, Administrator

Bailey Square Surgical Center, Ltd., 1111 West 34th Street, Austin, TX 78705; tel. 512/454–6753; FAX. 512/454–4314; Randy Humphrey, Administrator

Bay Area Endoscopy Center, 444 FM 1959, Suite B, Houston, TX 77034; tel. 281/481–9400; FAX. 281/481–9490; N.S. Bala, Medical Director

Bay Area Surgicare Center, 502 Medical Center Boulevard, Webster, TX 77598; tel. 281/332–2433; FAX. 281/332–0619; Carol Simons, Administrator

Baylor SurgiCare, 3920 Worth Street, Dallas, TX 75246; tel. 214/820–2581; FAX. 214/820–7484; Robin Shaw, Administrative Director

Baylor Surgicare at Valley View, 5744 LBJ Freeway, Suite 200, Dallas, TX 75240; tel. 972/490–4333; FAX. 972/991–1649; Gina Schilthuis, RN, Administrator

Brazosport Eye Institute, 103 Parking Way, P.O. Box 369, Lake Jackson, TX 77566; tel. 979/297–2961; FAX. 979/297–2395; Frank J. Grady, MD, PhD, FACS, Director

Coastal Bend Ambulatory Surgical Center, 900 Morgan, Corpus Christ, TX 78404; tel. 361/888–4288; FAX. 361/888–4786; Barbara VandenBout, Administrator

Columbia Physicians DaySurgery Center, 3930 Crutcher Street, Dallas, TX 75246; tel. 214/827–0760; FAX. 214/827–0944; Robin Shaw, RN, Administrator

Conroe Surgery Center, 1501 River Pointe Drive, Suite 200, Conroe, TX 77304; tel. 936/760–3443; FAX. 936/760–1322; Kathy Schutz, RN, BSN, CASC, Facility Administrator

Covenant Surgicenter, Ltd., 2301 Quaker Avenue, Lubbock, TX 79410; tel. 806/725–8801; FAX. 806/725–8820; Elizabeth Hawronsky, Director

Crystal Outpatient Surgery Center, Inc., 215 Oak Drive, S., Suite J, Lake Jackson, TX 77566; tel. 409/299–6118; FAX. 409/299–1007; R. Scott Yarish, MD, Administrator

Cy-Fair Surgery Center, 11250 Fallbrook Drive, Houston, TX 77065; tel. 713/955–7194; FAX. 713/890–0895; Sonja Christmas, Administrator

Dallas DaySurgery of Texas North, Ltd., 9101 North Central Expressway, Suite 650, Dallas, TX 75231; tel. 214/821–8613; FAX. 214/821–4958; Elizabeth Toony, RN, BSN, CASC, Administrator

Dallas Ophthalmology Center, Inc., 4633 North Central Expressway, Suite 310, Dallas, TX 75205; tel. 214/520–7600; FAX. 214/528–6522; Susan Points, RN, Administrator

DeHaven Surgical Center, 1424 East Front Street, Tyler, TX 75702; tel. 903/595–4144; FAX. 903/595–0236; Terri McDougal, RN, Administrator

Doctors' Surgery Center, Inc., 5300 North Street, Nacogdoches, TX 75965; tel. 936/569–8278; FAX. 936/569–0275; Robert P. Lehmann, MD, Director

East El Paso Surgery Center, 7835 Corral Drive, El Paso, TX 79915; tel. 915/595–3353; FAX. 915/595–6796; Laura Ice, Administrator

East Side Surgery Center, Inc., 10918 East Freeway, Houston, TX 77029; tel. 713/451–4299; FAX. 713/451–4383; Vicky Mizell, Administrator

East Texas Eye Associates Surgery Center, 1306 Frank Avenue, Lufkin, TX 75904; tel. 409/634–8381; Jo Ann O'Neill, COT, Administrator

Elm Place Ambulatory Surgical Center, 2217 South Danville Drive, Abilene, TX 79605; tel. 325/695–0600; FAX. 325/695–3908; Rebecca Laird, RN

Endoscopy Center of Dallas, Ambulatory Endoscopy Clinic of Dallas, 6390 LBJ Freeway, Suite 200, Dallas, TX 75240; tel. 972/934–3691; FAX. 972/934–3694; Jeane Suggs, Administrator

Facial Plastic and Cosmetic Surgical Center, 6300 Regional Plaza, Suite 475, Abilene, TX 79606; tel. 325/695–3630; FAX. 325/695–3633; Howard A. Tobin, MD, FACS, Medical Director

Fort Worth Endoscopy Center, 900 W. Magnolia Street, Suite 101, Fort Worth, TX 76104; tel. 817/332–6500; Jenny Hunter, Administrator

Forth Worth Surgery Center, 2001 West Rosedale, Fort Worth, TX 76104; tel. 817/877–4777; David Yodge, Administrator

Foundation Surgery Center of Dickinson, 3810 Hughes Court, Dickinson, TX 77539; tel. 713/337–7001; FAX. 713/337–7091; Theresa Mitcham, Administrator Assistant

Gastroenterology Consultants Outpatient Surgical Center, 8214 Wurzbach, San Antonio, TX 78229; tel. 210/614–1234; FAX. 210/614–7749; Robert Rosso, Chief Executive Officer

Good Shepard Ambulatory Surgical Center, Ltd., 703 East Marshall Avenue, Suite 2000, Longview, TX 75601-5563; tel. 903/315–5300; FAX. 903/315–5301; Dewayne Hodges, Executive Director

Gramercy Outpatient Surgery Center, Ltd., 2727 Gramercy, Houston, TX 77025; tel. 713/666–6900; FAX. 713/660–0704; Hamel Patel, Administrator

Greenville Surgery Center, 7150 Greenville Avenue, Suite 200, Dallas, TX 75231; tel. 214/891–0466; FAX. 214/739–4702; Christine Locke, Administrator

Heart of Texas Outpatient Cataract Center, 100 South Park Drive, Brownwood, TX 76801; tel. 325/643–3561; Larry Smith, CRNA, Administrator

Heritage Surgery Center, 1501 Redbud Boulevard, McKinney, TX 75069; tel. 972/548–0771; FAX. 972/562–2300; Rudolf Churner, MD, Administrator

Howerton Surgical Center, 2610 I.H. 35 South, Austin, TX 78704-5703; tel. 512/443–9715; FAX. 512/443–9845; Lisa Williams, RN, Director of Nursing

Key Whitman Surgery Center, 2801 Lemmon Avenue, Suite 400, Dallas, TX 75204; tel. 214/754–0000; FAX. 214/754–0079; Jeffrey Whitman, MD

Knapp Medical Center ASC, 1402 East Sixth Street, Weslaco, TX 78596; tel. 956/968–6155; FAX. 956/968–8291; Paul Giles, Administrator

Las Colinas Surgery Center, 4255 North Macarthur Boulevard, Irving, TX 75038; tel. 214/257–0144; FAX. 214/258–0436; Michael Scott, Administrator

Lufkin Endoscopy Center, 317 Gaslight Boulevard, Lufkin, TX 75904; tel. 936/634–3713; FAX. 936/634–8136; Bhagvan R. Malladi, MD, Administrator

Medical City Dallas Ambulatory Surgery Center, 7777 Forest Lane, Suite C-150, Dallas, TX 75231; tel. 972/566–6171; FAX. 972/566–2502; Vickie Roberts, Administrator

Memorial Hermann Surgery Center Woodlands Parkway, 1441 Woodstead Court, Suite 100, The Woodlands, TX 77380; tel. 281/363–0058; FAX. 281/363–0450; Susan Olis, Administrator

Metroplex Ambulatory Surgical Center, 2717 Osler Drive, Suite 102, Grand Prairie, TX 75051; tel. 972/647–6272; FAX. 972/660–1822; Glenda Daniels, RN, Director

Metroplex Surgicare Partners, Ltd., dba Baylor Surgicare at Bedford, 1600 Central Drive, Suite 180, Bedford, TX 76022; tel. 817/571–1999; FAX. 817/571–1220; Brandon Shows, Administrator

Mid-Town Surgical Center, LLP, 2105 Jackson Street, Suite 200, Houston, TX 77003; tel. 713/571–8141; FAX. 713/571–8184; Louis Varela, MD

North Carrier Surgicenter, 517 North Carrier Parkway, Suite A, Grand Prairie, TX 75050-5494; tel. 972/264–1645; FAX. 972/262–5974; Abraham F. Syrquin, MD, Medical Director

North Dallas Surgicare, 375 Municipal Drive, Suite 214, Richardson, TX 75080; tel. 972/918–9400; FAX. 972/918–9749

Park Central Surgical Center, 12200 Park Central Drive, Third Floor, Dallas, TX 75251; tel. 972/661–0505; FAX. 972/661–5511; Molly Paulose, Administrator

Physicians SurgiCenter of Houston True Results, 7515 South Main Street, Suite 800, Houston, TX 77030; tel. 713/799–9990; FAX. 713/796–1142; Jeff Young, MBA, Administrator

Plano Ambulatory Surgery Associates, L.P., dba Surgery Center of Plano, 1620 Coit Road, Plano, TX 75075-7799; tel. 972/519–1100; DeWayne Hodges, Administrator

Plaza Day Surgery, 909 Ninth Avenue, Fort Worth, TX 76104-3986; tel. 817/339–2300; FAX. 817/339–2329; Gina Basham, RN, Administrator

Port Arthur Day Surgery Center, 2555 Jimmy Johnson Boulevard, Port Arthur, TX 77640-2007; tel. 409/983–6144; Vicki Clark, Administrative Director

Premier Ambulatory Surgery of Austin, dba South Austin Surgery Center, 4207 James Casey, Suite 203, Austin, TX 78745; tel. 512/440–7894; FAX. 512/440–1932; Tammy Smittle, RN, CASC, Administrator

Q Plus Outpatient Surgery Center, 2507 Medical Row, Suite 101, Grand Prairie, TX 75051; tel. 972/647–8520; FAX. 972/336–0488; James L. Grace Administrator

Rio Grande Surgery Center, 1809 South Cynthia, McAllen, TX 78503; tel. 956/618–4402; FAX. 956/618–4174; Jill Finke, CNOR Administrator

San Antonio Digestive Disease Endoscopy Center, 1804 Northeast Loop 410, Suite 101, San Antonio, TX 78217; tel. 210/828–8400; FAX. 210/804–4454; Ricardo Hernandez, MD, Medical Director

San Antonio Gastroenterology Endoscopy Center, 520 Euclid Avenue, San Antonio, TX 78212; tel. 210/271–0606; FAX. 210/271–0180; Ernesto Guerra, MD

San Antonio Surgery Center, Inc., dba The Center for Special Surgery, 21 Spurs Lane, Sub-Level 100, San Antonio, TX 78240; tel. 210/614–0187; FAX. 210/692–7757; Tyla Blom, Administrator

Southwest Endoscopy & Surgery Center, 701 East Rendon Crowley Rd., Burleson, TX 76028; tel. 817/568–5188; FAX. 817/568–1568; J. Leslie Hill

Surgery Center of Northeast Texas, 1902 Moores Ln, Suite B, Texarkana, TX 75503; tel. 903/792–2108; FAX. 903/792–0606; Robin Walter, Administrator

Surgery Center of Texas, 155 East Loop 338, Suite 500, Odessa, TX 79762; tel. 432/367–3906; FAX. 432/367–3895; Libby Palma, Administrator

SurgEyeCare, GP, 5421 La Sierra Drive, Dallas, TX 75231; tel. 214/361–1443; FAX. 214/691–3299; Leah Padgett, R.N., Administrator

Surgical and Diagnostic Center, LP., 729 Bedford Euless Road West, Suite 100, Hurst, TX 76053; tel. 817/282–1001; FAX. 817/282–4040; Bart Steele, Administrator

Surgical Center of El Paso, 1815 North Stanton, El Paso, TX 79902; tel. 915/533–8412; FAX. 915/542–0367; Raymond Sainz, Administrator

Texarkana Surgery Center, 5404 Summerhill Road, Texarkana, TX 75503; tel. 903/793–4872; FAX. 903/794–6300; Kimble Hatridge, Administrator

Texoma Outpatient Surgery Center, Inc., 1712 Eleventh Street, Wichita Falls, TX 76301; tel. 940/723–2499; FAX. 940/923–2497; Tracy Youngblood, Administrator

The Cataract Center of East Texas, dba Novamed Surgery Center of Tyler, 802 Turtle Creek Drive, Tyler, TX 75701; tel. 903/595–4333; FAX. 903/535–9845; S. Stephens, RN, Clinical Administrator

The Center for Sight, P.A., 2 Medical Center Boulevard, Lufkin, TX 75904-3175; tel. 936/634–8434; FAX. 936/639–2581; Ashley Hooks, Office Manager

The Endoscopy Center of Southeast Texas, 950 North 14th Street,#200, Beaumont, TX 77702; tel. 409/833–5555; FAX. 409/833–9911; JoAnn Hughes, RNBC, Center Director

The Ocular Surgery Center, Inc., 1100 North Main Avenue, San Antonio, TX 78212; tel. 210/222–2154; FAX. 512/222–0706; Jane Wilson, Administrator

Urological Surgery Center of Fort Worth, 418 South Henderson, Fort Worth, TX 76104; tel. 817/870–9165; FAX. 817/335–5421; Charles Bamberger, MD

Valley Endoscopy Center, LLP, 3101 South 77 Sunshine Strip, Suite B, Harlingen, TX 78550; tel. 956/421–2324; FAX. 956/421–5791; Stephanie V. Gonzalez, RN, Director of Nursing

Vista Surgical Center West, 2500 Fondren, Suite 350, Houston, TX 77063; tel. 713/782–8279; FAX. 713/782–3139; Diana Hastings, RN, CNOR - Clinical Director

West Houston Surgicare, 970 Campbell Road, Houston, TX 77024-2804; tel. 713/461–3547; FAX. 713/722–8921; Bradley Cardenas, Administrator

Wilson Surgicenter, 4315 28th Street, Lubbock, TX 79410; tel. 806/792–2104; Bill W. Wilson, MD, Chief Executive Officer

UTAH

Central Utah Surgical Center, 1067 North 500 West, Provo, UT 84604; tel. 801/374–0354; FAX. 801/717–2364; Jill Andrews, RN, BSN, CNOR, Administrator

Institute of Facial and Cosmetic Surgery, 5929 Fashion Boulevard, Salt Lake City, UT 84107; tel. 801/261–3637; FAX. 801/261–4096; Dr. Brent D. Kennedy, Director

Salt Lake Endoscopy Center, 24 South 1100 East, Salt Lake City, UT 84102; tel. 801/355–2987; FAX. 801/531–9704

Salt Lake Surgical Center, 617 East 3900 South, Salt Lake City, UT 84107; tel. 801/261–3141; FAX. 801/268–2599; Robyn Archer, Administrator

St. George Surgical Center, 676 South Bluff Street, St. George, UT 84770; tel. 435/673–8080; FAX. 435/673–0096; Ty Tippets, Administrator

St. Mark's Outpatient Surgery Center, 1250 East 3900 South, Suite 100, Salt Lake City, UT 84124; tel. 801/262–0358; FAX. 801/262–0901; Diana McPherson, MBA, CASC, Administrator

The SurgiCare Center of Utah, 755 East 3900 South, Salt Lake City, UT 84107; tel. 801/266–2283; FAX. 801/268–6151; Helen Cionni, Administrator

Wasatch Endoscopy, 1220 East 3900 South, Suite 1B, Salt Lake City, UT 84124; tel. 801/281–3657; FAX. 801/281–4258; Jeri Fowles, Administrator

Wasatch Surgery Center, 555 South Foothill Boulevard, Salt Lake City, UT 84112; tel. 801/581–7782; FAX. 801/581–8962; Karen Ipson, Administrator, Manager

VIRGINIA

Blue Ridge Surgery Center, 1802 Braeburn Drive, Salem, VA 24153; tel. 540/772–3600; FAX. 540/725–4543; Shawna Hall, RN, CASC, Administrator

Cataract and Refractive Surgery Center, LLC, 2010 Bremo Road, Suite 132, Richmond, VA 23226; tel. 804/673–5272; FAX. 804/673–5279; Patricia Lampman, Director

Fredericksburg Ambulatory Surgery Center, 1201 Sam Perry Boulevard, Suite 101, Fredericksburg, VA 22401; tel. 540/741–7000; FAX. 540/899–6893; Jeane Bullock, Administrator

Kaiser Permanente Falls Church Ambulatory Surgery Center, 201 North Washington Street, Falls Church, VA 22046; tel. 703/531–1623; FAX. 703/536–1400; Eileen Field, Director, ASC

Lakeview Medical Center, Inc., 2000 Meade Parkway, Suffolk, VA 23424; tel. 757/539–0251; FAX. 757/923–9632; Laura E. Joyner, Chief Operations Officer

Parham Surgery Center, 7640 E Parham Road, Henrico, VA 23294; tel. 804/591–2202; FAX. 804/591–2237; Louise M. Smith, Interim Administrator or Ryan Duffy, Interim Administrator

Piedmont Day Surgery Center, Inc., 1040 Main Street, P.O. Box 1360, Danville, VA 24543-1360; tel. 434/792–1433; FAX. 434/797–2807; Edward Wright, MD, President

Riverside Hampton Surgery Center, 850 Enterprise Parkway, Suite 1000, Hampton, VA 23666-6255; tel. 757/251–7700; FAX. 757/251–7799; Sheila Rilee, RN, Administrator

Surgi Center of Central Virginia, Inc., 1500 Dixon St., Suite 101, Fredericksburg, VA 22401; tel. 703/371–5349; FAX. 703/373–1745; Kenny Ellinger, RN, Facility Administrator

Surgi-Center at Winchester Medical Center, 1860 Amherst Street, Winchester, VA 22601; tel. 540/536–8934; FAX. 540/536–8936; David J. Kliewer, MD, Medical Director

Urosurgical Center of Richmond, 9105 Stony Point Dr, Richmond, VA 23235; tel. 804/330–9105; FAX. 804/560–0914; Terry W. Coffey, Administrator

Urosurgical Center of Richmond-North, 8228 Meadowbridge Road, Mechanicsville, VA 23116; tel. 804/730–5023; FAX. 804/746–4015; Terry W. Coffey, Administrator

Virginia Ambulatory Surgery, Inc., 337-15th Street, SW, Charlottesville, VA 22903; tel. 434/951–4600; FAX. 434/817–8465; Gerry Dobrasz, Administrator

Virginia Beach Ambulatory Surgery Center, 1700 Will-o-Wisp Drive, Virginia Beach, VA 23454; tel. 757/496–6400; FAX. 757/496–3137; Martha R. Colen, Administrator

Virginia Eye Institute/Eye Surgeons of Richmond, Inc., 400 Westhampton Station, Richmond, VA 23226; tel. 804/287–4244; FAX. 804/287–4207; Margaret Benson, Marketing and Communications Director

Woodburn Surgery Center, 3289 Woodburn Road, Suite 100, Annandale, VA 22003; tel. 703/207–7520; Jolene Tornabeni, Senior Vice President, Administrator

WASHINGTON

Allure Laser Center, 625 4th Avenue, Suite 301, Kirkland, WA 98033; tel. 425/216–7200; FAX. 425/216–7272; Janet Jordan, Administrator

Bel-Red Ambulatory Surgical Facility, 1260 116th Avenue, NE, #110, Bellevue, WA 98004; tel. 425/455–7225; FAX. 425/455–0045; Jan Zemplenyi, MD, Director

Cascade Ear Nose & Throat, A Division of Proliance Surgeons, 111 S. 13th Street, Mount Vernon, WA 98274; tel. 360/336–2178; FAX. 360/336–1674; Christine Brewder, Administrator

Cascade Valley Arlington Surgery Center, 875 Wesley Street, Suite 160, Arlington, WA 98223; tel. 360/435–6969; FAX. 360/435–1068; Jola Barnett, Assistant Administrator

Edmonds Surgery Center, 21229 84th Avenue W., Edmonds, WA 98026; tel. 206/775–1505; FAX. 206/775–9078; Mark A. Kuzel, DPM, F.A.C.F.S

Evergreen Endoscopy Center, 11800 NE 128th Street, Suite 100, Kirkland, WA 98034; tel. 425/899–4500; FAX. 425/899–4510; Stacy Gordon, Rn, Endoscopy Manager

Evergreen Eye Center, 34719 Sixth Avenue South, Federal Way, WA 98003; tel. 800/340–3595; FAX. 206/212–2194; Richard A. Boudreau, Administrator

Eye Surgery Center Northwest, 842 South Cowley, Suite 3, Spokane, WA 99202; tel. 509/747–6358; FAX. 509/321–5020; Michael H. Cunningham, MD, President

First Hill Surgery Center, 515 Minor Avenue, Suite 130, Seattle, WA 98104; tel. 206/682–6103; FAX. 206/682–3511; Debbie Perdue, Director

Foot Care Associates Ambulatory Surgery Center, Admin Center, 8105 166th Ave. NE, Suite 104, Redmond, WA 98052; tel. 425/885–7004; Dr. Brunsman, Medical Director

GH TASC, 209 Martin Luther King Jr. Way, Tacoma, WA 98405; tel. 253/596–3590; Nancy Sowers, RN, MBA, CNOR, Manager

Minor & James Medical, PLLC, 515 Minor Avenue, Suite 200, Seattle, WA 98104; tel. 206/386–9500; FAX. 206/576–3807; Patricia Creed, RN, ASC Manager

Moses Lake Clinic ASC, 840 E. Hill Avenue, Moses Lake, WA 98837; tel. 509/764–6400; FAX. 509/764–6434; Jeanette Wood, Vice President

North Kitsap Ambulatory Surgical Center Inc., dba Pacific Surgery Center, 20669 Bond Road, NE, Suite 200, Poulsbo, WA 98370; tel. 360/779–6527; FAX. 360/697–2743; Susan Simons, RN, BSN, CASC, Administrator

Northwest Center for Plastic and Reconstructive Surgery, 16259 Sylvester Road, SW, Suite 302, Seattle, WA 98166; tel. 206/241–5400; FAX. 206/241–8591; Sindi Tracey, Office Manager

Northwest Gastroenterology, dba Northwest Endoscopy, 2930 Squalicum Parkway, Suite 202, Bellingham, WA 98225; tel. 360/734–1420; FAX. 360/734–8748; Sandra Vander Yacht, Manager

Northwest Nasal Sinus Center, 3100 Carillon Point, Kirkland, WA 98033; tel. 425/576–1700; FAX. 425/827–7725; Rick Fischer, Business Administrator

Northwest Surgery Center, 1920 100th Street, SE, Everett, WA 98208; tel. 425/316–3700; FAX. 425/316–6881; Chris Vance, President

Northwest Surgery Center, Inc., West 123 Francis, Spokane, WA 99205; tel. 509/483–9363; FAX. 509/483–0355; Renee Batt, Office Manager

Olympic Plastic Surgery Suite, 2600 Cherry Avenue, Suite 201, Bremerton, WA 98310; tel. 360/415–0762; Suzanne Fletcher, Administrator

Pacific Cataract and Laser Institute, 2517 Northeast Kresky, Chehalis, WA 98532; tel. 206/748–8632; FAX. 360/748–4007; Debbie Eldredge, Vice President and Chief Operating Officer

Pacific Cataract and Laser Institute, 10500 Northeast Eighth Street, Suite 1650, Bellevue, WA 98004-4332; tel. 425/462–7664; FAX. 425/462–6429; Maynard Pohl, OD, Clinical Director

Pacific Cataract and Laser Institute, 6695 W. Rio Grand Ave., Kennewick, WA 99336; FAX. 360/748–4007; Debbie Eldredge, Vice President and Chief Operating Officer

Pacific NW Facial Plastic Ambulatory Surgery Center, 600 Broadway, Suite 280, Seattle, WA 98122; tel. 206/386–3550; FAX. 206/386–3553; Sherry Gizewski, Practice Manager

Parkway Surgical Center, 2940 Squalicum Parkway, Suite 204, Bellingham, WA 98225; tel. 206/676–8350; FAX. 206/676–8351; Dr. Keith VanderGriend

PeaceHealth St. Joseph Medical Center, PeaceHealth Medical Group, 4545 Cordata Parkway, Bellingham, WA 98226; tel. 360/738–2200; FAX. 360/752–5681; Debra L. Taylor, Dir Operations PHMG

Phillip C. Kierney, M.D., Cosmetic and Plastic Surgery, 105 27th Avenue, SE, Puyallup, WA 98374; tel. 253/848–8110; FAX. 253/845–3561; P. Kierney, Owner

Physicians Eye Surgical Center, 3930 Hoyt Avenue, Everett, WA 98201; tel. 206/259–2020; Ms. Mello Johnson, Administrator

Premier Orthopedic Group Surgery Center, 21401 72nd Ave W., Edmonds, WA 98026; tel. 425/774–2636; FAX. 425/774–2688; Jerry Hawley, Director

Rockwood Clinic, dba Gastrointestinal Endoscopy Unit, 400 East 5th Avenue, Spokane, WA 99202; tel. 509/838–2531; FAX. 509/755–6580; Craig Whiting, MD, Administrator

Seattle Endoscopy Center, 11027 Meridian Avenue, N., Suite 100, Seattle, WA 98133; tel. 206/365–4492; FAX. 206/368–3456; Mary Beth Philips, BSN, RN, CGRN, Manager

Seattle Hand Surgery Group, P.C., 600 Broadway, Suite 440, Seattle, WA 98122; tel. 206/292–6252; FAX. 206/292–7893

Seattle Plastic Surgery Center, 600 Broadway, Suite 320, Seattle, WA 98122; tel. 206/324–1120; FAX. 206/720–0800; Gail Boren, Manager

Seattle Surgery Center, Columbus Pavilion, 900 Terry Avenue, Third Floor, Seattle, WA 98104-1240; tel. 206/382–1021; FAX. 206/332–9369; Jim Sapienza, FACHE, Chief Executive Officer

Sequim Same Day Surgery, 777 North Fifth Avenue, Sequim, WA 98382; tel. 360/582–2632; FAX. 360/582–2631; Tammy Paolini, Operational Manager

South Hill Ambulatory Surgical Center, 3707 S. Grand Blvd., Suite A, Spokane, WA 99203; tel. 509/747–0279; FAX. 509/747–3220; Borys Markewych, President

Spokane Digestive Disease Center, P.S., 105 West Eighth Avenue, Suite 6010, Spokane, WA 99204-2341; tel. 509/838–5950; FAX. 509/838–5961; Michelle Avenger, RN, CGRN, Director

Spokane Surgery Center, North 1120 Pines Road, Spokane, WA 99206; tel. 509/928–1990; FAX. 509/928–2933; Stewart P. Brim, DPM

Surgery Center Of Spokane, 205 N. University #4, Spokane, WA 99206; tel. 509/922–3199; FAX. 509/463–8656; Dr. Jacqueline Babol

The Eastside Endoscopy Center, LLC, A Physicians Endoscopy Partnered Facility, 1135 116th Ave NE Suite 570, Bellevue, WA 98004-3049; tel. 425/451–7335; FAX. 425/451–1226; Michelle Steele, CGRN, Nurse Administrator

The Plastic SurgiCentre, Inc., 535 South Pine Street, Spokane, WA 99202; tel. 509/623–2160; FAX. 509/623–1135; Vern Myrick, RN, Nurse Manager

The Polyclinic, Inc., 1145 Broadway, Seattle, WA 98122; tel. 206/329–1760

Virginia Mason-Issaquah, 100 Northeast Gilman Boulevard, Issaquah, WA 98027; tel. 425/557–8000; Bobbie Eatmon, Director Ambulatory Services

Washington Centre for Reproductive Medicine, ASC, 1370 116th Avenue, NE, Suite 202, Bellevue, WA 98004; tel. 425/462–6100; FAX. 425/635–0742; Dr. James Kustin, Medical Director

Washington Orthopedic Center, Inc., PS, 1900 Cooks Hill Road, Centralia, WA 98531; tel. 360/736–2889; Dondi Sahlinger, OR Manager

Whidbey SurgiCare, PO Box 11782, Suite A Two, Olympia, WA 98508-1782; tel. 360/679–3117; FAX. 360/679–3118; Stephen T. Miller, DPM, Medical Director

WEST VIRGINIA

Anwar Eye Center, 1500 Lafayette Avenue, Moundsville, WV 26041; tel. 304/845–0908; FAX. 304/845–1250; M. F. Anwar, MD

Cabell Huntington Hospital Surgery Center, 1201 Hal Greer Boulevard, Huntington, WV 25701; tel. 304/523–1885; FAX. 304/523–8942; Lexa Woodyard, Director

Day Surgery Center, Chesterfield Medical Plaza, 2335 Chesterfield Ave. #400, Charleston, WV 25304; tel. 304/925–9300; FAX. 304/925–2924; Olivia Garton, Administrator

Greenbrier Clinic Surgery Center, LLC, 320 W. Main Street, White Sulphur Spring, WV 24986; tel. 304/536–4870; FAX. 304/536–1325; Thomas O. Dotson, MD, Medical Director

Jerry N. Black, M.D., Surgical Suite, 10 Amalia Drive, Suite 3C, Buckhannon, WV 26201; tel. 304/472–2100; FAX. 304/472–2118; Jerry N. Black, MD, Medical Director

Surgical Eye Center of Morgantown, 1299 Pineview Drive, 5th Floor, Morgantown, WV 26505; tel. 304/598–5755; Heather Huffman, RN, Administrator

Tri State Surgical Center, LLC, 1006 Tavern Road, Martinsburg, WV 25401; tel. 304/267–0556; Stacey Ferguson, Administrator

WISCONSIN

BayCare Surgery Center, 2253 West Mason, P.O. Box 33227, Green Bay, WI 54303-0102; tel. 920/592–9100; FAX. 920/497–8056; Tammy Kruegger, Executive Director

Children's Hospital of Wisconsin - Surgicenter, 3223 South 103rd Street, Milwaukee, WI 53227; tel. 414/328–5800; FAX. 414/328–5805; Suzan Buchaklian, Director

Green Bay Surgical Center, Ltd., 704 South Webster Avenue, Ste 301, Green Bay, WI 54301; tel. 920/432–7433; FAX. 920/432–6003

Menomonee Falls Ambulatory Surgery Center, W180 N8045 Town Hall Road, Menomonee Falls, WI 53051; tel. 262/250–0950; FAX. 262/250–0955; Dianne Appleby, Executive Director

North Shore Surgical Center, 7007 North Range Line Road, Milwaukee, WI 53209; tel. 414/352–3341; FAX. 414/247–4588; Helen Kowalski, Executive Director

Northwest Surgery Center, 2300 North Mayfair Road, Suite 295, Wauwatosa, WI 53226; tel. 414/257–3322; FAX. 414/257–3364; Gail Wuestoff, Administrator

Riverview Surgery Center, 616 North Washington Street, Janesville, WI 53545; tel. 608/758–7300; FAX. 608/758–1050; Lynn Jenkins, Director

St. Mary's Dean Ventures Surgery Centers, PO Box 259630, Madison, WI 53725-9630; tel. 608/259–3510; FAX. 608/255–1272; Jane Hrdlicka, Interim Vice President

Surgicenter of Racine, Ltd., 5802 Washington Avenue, Racine, WI 53406; tel. 262/886–9100; FAX. 262/886–9130; Dennis J. Kontra, Administrator

Wauwatosa Surgery Center, 10900 West Potter Road, Wauwatosa, WI 53226-3424; tel. 414/774–9227; FAX. 414/774–0957; Dan Cresco, Administrator

WYOMING

Wyoming Outpatient Services, 5050 Powderhouse Road, Cheyenne, WY 82009; tel. 307/634–1311; FAX. 307/432–7550; Laura Jean Davis, RN, Nurse Manager

Yellowstone Surgery Center, LLC, 5201 Yellowstone Road, Cheyenne, WY 82009; tel. 307/635–7070; FAX. 307/632–9920; Deborah Wright, Office Administrator

U.S. Associated Areas

PUERTO RICO

ASC Espanola Clinic, Box 490, La Quinta, Mayaguez, PR 00681; tel. 787/832–2094

Clinica de Cirugia Ambulatoria de Puerto Rico, Box 3748, Mayaguez, PR 00681; tel. 787/833–4400; FAX. 787/265–6621; Roberto Ruiz, Administrator

Instituto Cirugia Plastica Del Oeste, 165 Este Mendez Vigo Street, Mayaguez, PR 00680; tel. 787/833–3248; FAX. 787/831–4400; Oscar Vargas, MD, Medical Director

Instituto Quirurgico De Un Dia - Dr. Pila, PO Box 331910, Ponce, PR 00733-1910; tel. 787/848–5600; FAX. 787/841–1085; Mrs. Joselyn Irizarry RN, Supervisor

OJOS, Eye Surgery Specialists of P.R.LLC, Hipodromo Street 809, Santurce, PR 00909; tel. 787/721–8330; FAX. 787/722–3222; Maria Delos A. Tirado, Administrator

San Juan Health Centre Ambulatory Clinic, 150 De Diego Avenue, Badorioty Corner, San Juan, PR 00907; tel. 787/977–7575; FAX. 787/977–7587; Pedro Rivera-Archilla, Executive Director

The Joint Commission Accredited Freestanding Long–Term Care Organizations

The accredited freestanding long–term care organizations listed have been accredited as of May 2014 by The Joint Commission on Accreditation of Healthcare Organizations by decision of the Accreditation Committee of the Board of Commissioners.

The organizations listed here have been found to be in compliance with The Joint Commission standards for long–term care organizations, as found in the Comprehensive Accreditation Manual for the Long–Term Care Organizations.

Please refer to section A of the AHA Guide for information on hospitals with Long–Term Care services. These hospitals are identified by Facility Code F128. In section A, those hospitals identified by Approval Code 1 are Joint Commission accredited.

We present this list simply as a convenient directory. Inclusion or omission of any organization's name indicates neither approval nor disapproval by Health Forum LLC, an American Hospital Association company.

United States

ALABAMA
Central Alabama Veterans Health Care System, 215 Perry Hill Road, Montgomery, AL 36109; tel. 334/272–4670
Tuscaloosa VA Medical Center, 3701 Loop Road East, Tuscaloosa, AL 35404; tel. 205/554–2000

ALASKA
Norton Sound Regional Hospital, PO Box 966, Nome, AK 99762; tel. 907/443–3311

ARIZONA
Citadel Care Center, 5121 East Broadway Road, Mesa, AZ 85206; tel. 480/832–5555
Desert Cove Nursing Center, 1750 West Frye Road, Chandler, AZ 85224; tel. 480/899–0641
Globe Medical Investors, LLC, 1300 South Street, Globe, AZ 85501; tel. 928/425–3118
La Canada Care Center, 7970 North LaCanada Drive, Tucson, AZ 85704; tel. 520/797–1191
Las Fuentes Care Center, 1045 Scott Drive, Prescott, AZ 86301; tel. 928/778–9603
Life Care Center at South Mountain, 8008 South Jesse Owens Parkway, Phoenix, AZ 85040; tel. 602/243–2780
Life Care Center of North Glendale, 13620 North 55th Avenue, Glendale, AZ 85304; tel. 602/843–8433
Life Care Center of Paradise Valley, 4065 East Bell Road, Phoenix, AZ 85032; tel. 602/867–0212
Life Care Center of Scottsdale, 9494 East Becker Lane, Scottsdale, AZ 85260; tel. 480/860–6396
Life Care Center of Sierra Vista, 2305 East Wilcox Drive, Sierra Vista, AZ 85635; tel. 520/458–1050
Life Care Center of Tucson, 6211 North LaCholla Boulevard, Tucson, AZ 85741; tel. 520/575–0900
Life Care Center of Yuma, 2450 South 19th Avenue, Yuma, AZ 85364; tel. 928/344–0425
Mi Casa Nursing Center, 330 South Pinnule Circle, Mesa, AZ 85206; tel. 480/981–0687
Mountain View Care Center, 1313 West Magee Road, Tucson, AZ 85704; tel. 520/797–2600
Northern Arizona VA Health Care System, 500 Highway 89 North, Prescott, AZ 86313; tel. 928/445–4860
Payson Care Center, 107 East Lone Pine Drive, Payson, AZ 85541; tel. 928/474–6896
Phoenix VA Health Care System, 650 East Indian School Road, Phoenix, AZ 85012-1892; tel. 602/277–5551
Scottsdale Heritage Court, 3339 North Drinkwater Boulevard, Scottsdale, AZ 85251; tel. 480/949–5400
Southern Arizona VA Health Care System, 3601 South Sixth Avenue, Tucson, AZ 85723; tel. 520/629–1821
Sun Grove Village Care Center, 20625 North Lake Pleasant Road, Peoria, AZ 85382; tel. 623/566–0642

ARKANSAS
Central Arkansas Veterans Healthcare System, 4300 West Seventh Street (00/LR), Little Rock, AR 72205; tel. 501/257–5314

CALIFORNIA
Bel Tooren Villa Convalescent Hospital, 16910 Woodruff Avenue, Bellflower, CA 90706; tel. 562/867–1761
California Special Care Center, Inc., 8787 Center Drive, La Mesa, CA 91942; tel. 619/460–4444
Care Meridian, 12461 Springdale Street, Garden Grove, CA 92845; tel. 949/263–6630

Care Meridian - Phoenix, 18A Journey, Aliso Viejo, CA 92656; tel. 949/263–6630
CareMeridian, 18A Journey, Suite 200, Aliso Viejo, CA 92656; tel. 949/263–6630
CareMeridian - San Fernando Valley, 10318 Laramie Street, Chatsworth, CA 91311; tel. 818/882–2903
CareMeridian-Las Vegas, 18A Journey, Suite 200, Aliso Viejo, CA 92656; tel. 949/263–6630
Community Hospital of the Monterey Peninsula, PO Box HH, Monterey, CA 93942; tel. 831/625–4553
Department of State Hospitals-Metropolitan, 11401 South Bloomfield Avenue, Norwalk, CA 90650; tel. 562/863–7011
East Los Angeles Doctors Hospital, 4060 East Whittier Boulevard, Los Angeles, CA 90023; tel. 323/268–5514
Encino Hospital Medical Center, 16237 Ventura Boulevard, Encino, CA 91436; tel. 818/995–5002
Fallbrook Hospital Corporation, 624 East Elder Street, Fallbrook, CA 92028-3099; tel. 760/728–1191
Fresno Community Hospital and Medical Center, PO Box 1232, Fresno, CA 93715; tel. 559/459–6000
Goleta Valley Cottage Hospital, PO Box 6306, Santa Barbara, CA 93160-6306; tel. 805/967–3411
Hemet Valley Medical Center, 1117 East Devonshire Avenue, Hemet, CA 92543; tel. 951/652–2811
Hollywood Presbyterian Medical Center, 1300 North Vermont Avenue, Los Angeles, CA 90027; tel. 323/413–3000
Imperial Convalescent Center, 11926 La Mirada Boulevard, La Mirada, CA 90638; tel. 562/943–7156
Kaiser Foundation Hospital - Manteca/Modesto, 4601 Dale Road, Modesto, CA 95356; tel. 209/735–3000
La Habra Convalescent Hospital, 1233 West La Habra Boulevard, La Habra, CA 90631; tel. 562/691–0781
Lake Forest Nursing Center, 25652 Old Trabuco Road, Lake Forest, CA 92630; tel. 949/380–9380
Life Care Center of Escondido, 1980 Felicita Road, Escondido, CA 92025; tel. 760/741–6109
Life Care Center of Menifee, 27600 Encanto Drive, Menifee, CA 92586; tel. 951/679–6858
Life Care Center of Vista, 304 North Melrose Drive, Vista, CA 92083; tel. 760/724–8222
Los Robles Hospital and Medical Center, 215 West Janss Road, Thousand Oaks, CA 91360; tel. 805/370–4421
Magnolia Special Care Center, 635 South Magnolia, El Cajon, CA 92020; tel. 619/442–8826
Marian Regional Medical Center, 1400 East Church Street, Santa Maria, CA 93454; tel. 805/739–3000
Methodist Hospital of Sacramento, 7500 Hospital Drive, Sacramento, CA 95823; tel. 916/423–3000
Mirada Hills Rehabilitation and Convalescent Hospital, 12200 La Mirada Boulevard, La Mirada, CA 90638; tel. 562/947–8691
North Walk Villa Convalescent Hospital, 12350 Rosecrans Avenue, Norwalk, CA 90650; tel. 562/921–6624
Oak Valley Hospital District, 350 South Oak Avenue, Oakdale, CA 95361; tel. 209/847–3011
Orangegrove Rehabilitation Hospital, 12332 Garden Grove Boulevard, Garden Grove, CA 92843; tel. 714/534–1041
Pacifica Nursing and Rehab Center, 385 Esplanade Avenue, Pacifica, CA 94044; tel. 650/993–5576
Rady Children's Hospital San Diego, 3020 Children's Way, MC 5069, San Diego, CA 92123-4282; tel. 858/576–1700

Reche Canyon Rehabilitation and Health Care Center, 1350 Reche Canyon Road, Colton, CA 92324; tel. 909/370–4411
Rimrock Villa Convalescent Hospital, 27555 Rimrock Road, Barstow, CA 92311; tel. 760/252–2515
San Francisco General Hospital and Trauma Center, 1001 Potrero Avenue, Second Floor, Room 2A 5, San Francisco, CA 94110; tel. 415/206–3455
San Francisco VA Medical Center, 4150 Clement Street, San Francisco, CA 94121; tel. 415/221–4810
Sharp Chula Vista Medical Center, 751 Medical Center Court, Chula Vista, CA 91911-6699; tel. 619/502–3664
St. Jude Medical Center, 101 East Valencia Mesa Drive, Fullerton, CA 92835; tel. 714/992–3000
The Cloisters of La Jolla, 7160 Fay Avenue, La Jolla, CA 92037; tel. 858/459–4361
The Cloisters of Mission Hills, 3680 Reynard Way, San Diego, CA 92103; tel. 619/297–4484
Totally Kids Rehabilitation Hospital, 1720 Mountain View Avenue, Loma Linda, CA 92354; tel. 909/796–6915
VA Central California Health Care System, 2615 East Clinton Avenue, Fresno, CA 93703; tel. 559/225–6100
VA Greater Los Angeles Healthcare System, 11301 Wilshire Boulevard, Los Angeles, CA 90073; tel. 310/268–3132
VA Loma Linda Healthcare System, 11201 Benton Street, Loma Linda, CA 92357; tel. 909/583–6002
VA Long Beach Health Care System, 5901 East Seventh Street, Long Beach, CA 90822; tel. 562/826–5400
VA Northern California Health Care System, 10535 Hospital Way, Mather, CA 95655; tel. 916/843–7000
VA Palo Alto Health Care System, 3801 Miranda Avenue, Palo Alto, CA 94304; tel. 650/493–5000
VA San Diego Healthcare System, 3350 La Jolla Village Drive, San Diego, CA 92161; tel. 858/552–8585
Whittier Hospital Medical Center, 9080 Colima Road, Whittier, CA 90605-1898; tel. 562/945–3561

COLORADO
Arkansas Valley Regional Medical Center, 1100 Carson Avenue, La Junta, CO 81050; tel. 719/383–6001
Berkley Medical Investors, LLC, 735 South Locust Street, Denver, CO 80224; tel. 303/320–4377
Briarwood Health Care Center, 1440 Vine Street, Denver, CO 80206; tel. 303/399–0350
Caremeridian-Littleton, 5945 South Wright Street, Littleton, CO 80127; tel. 303/390–3000
Colorado Medical Investors, 905 Harding Avenue, Canon City, CO 81212; tel. 719/275–4106
Columbine Manor Care Center, 530 West 16th Street, Salida, CO 81201; tel. 719/539–6112
Evergreen Nursing Home, 1991 Carroll Avenue, Alamosa, CO 81101; tel. 719/589–4951
Garden Terrace Alzheimer's Center of Excellence, 1600 South Potomac Street, Aurora, CO 80012; tel. 303/750–8418
Grand Junction Veterans Affairs Medical Center, 2121 North Avenue, Grand Junction, CO 81501; tel. 970/242–0731
Hallmark Nursing Center, 3701 West Radcliff Avenue, Denver, CO 80236; tel. 303/794–6484
Heritage Park Care Center, 1200 Village Road, Carbondale, CO 81623; tel. 970/963–1500
Life Care Center of Aurora, 14101 East Evans Avenue, Aurora, CO 80014; tel. 303/751–2000

Life Care Center of Colorado Springs, 2490 International Circle, Colorado Springs, CO 80910; tel. 719/630-8888

Life Care Center of Evergreen, 2987 Bergen Peak Drive, Evergreen, CO 80439; tel. 303/674-4500

Life Care Center of Greeley, 4800 25th Street, Greeley, CO 80634; tel. 970/330-6400

Life Care Center of Littleton, 1500 West Mineral Avenue, Littleton, CO 80120; tel. 303/795-7300

Life Care Center of Longmont, 2451 Pratt Street, Longmont, CO 80501; tel. 303/776-5000

Life Care Center of Pueblo, 2118 Chatelet Lane, Pueblo, CO 81005; tel. 719/564-2000

San Luis Care Center, 240 Craft Drive, Alamosa, CO 81101; tel. 719/589-9081

University Park Care Center, 945 Desert Flower Boulevard, Pueblo, CO 81001; tel. 719/545-5321

VA Eastern Colorado Healthcare System, 1055 Clermont Street, Denver, CO 80220; tel. 303/399-8020

Valley View Villa, 815 Fremont Avenue, Fort Morgan, CO 80701; tel. 970/867-8261

Villa Manor Care Center, 7950 West Mississippi Avenue, Lakewood, CO 80226; tel. 303/986-4511

Western Hills Health Care Center, 1625 Carr Street, Lakewood, CO 80214; tel. 303/232-6881

Westminster Medical Investors, LLC, 7751 Zenobia Court, Westminster, CO 80030; tel. 303/412-9121

CONNECTICUT

4 Hazel Avenue Operations, LLC of Naugatuck, CT, 4 Hazel Avenue, Naugatuck, CT 06770; tel. 203/723-1456

Hughes Health and Rehabilitation, Inc., 29 Highland Street, West Hartford, CT 06119; tel. 860/236-5623

Montowese Health and Rehabilitation Center, Inc., 163 Quinnipiac Avenue, North Haven, CT 06473; tel. 203/624-3303

Salmon Brook Center, 72 Salmon Brook Drive, Glastonbury, CT 06033; tel. 860/633-5244

VA Connecticut Healthcare System, 950 Campbell Avenue, West Haven, CT 06516; tel. 203/932-5711

Village Green of Wallingford, 55 Kondracki Lane, Wallingford, CT 06492; tel. 203/265-6771

Village Green of Waterbury, 128 Cedar Avenue, Waterbury, CT 06705; tel. 203/757-9271

Yale Health, PO Box 208237, New Haven, CT 06520; tel. 203/432-4096

DELAWARE

VA Medical Center, 1601 Kirkwood Highway, Wilmington, DE 19805; tel. 302/994-2511

DISTRICT OF COLUMBIA

Providence Hospital, 1150 Varnum Street, Northeast, Washington, DC 20017; tel. 202/269-7000

Sibley Memorial Hospital, 5255 Loughboro Road, Northwest, Washington, DC 20016; tel. 202/537-4000

VA Medical Center, 50 Irving Street, Northwest, Washington, DC 20422; tel. 202/745-8000

FLORIDA

Bay Pines VA Healthcare System, 10000 Bay Pines Boulevard, Bay Pines, FL 33744; tel. 727/398-6661

Bon Secours Maria Manor Nursing & Rehabilitation Center, 10300 4th Street North, Saint Petersburg, FL 33716; tel. 727/576-1025

Darcy Hall of Life Care, 2170 Palm Beach Lakes Boulevard, West Palm Beach, FL 33409; tel. 561/683-3333

Escambia Medical Investors, LLC, 3291 East Olive Road, Pensacola, FL 32507; tel. 850/494-2327

Florida Institute for Neurologic Rehabilitation, Inc., PO Box 1348, Wauchula, FL 33873; tel. 863/773-2857

Gardens Court Medical Investors, LLC, 3803 PGA Boulevard, Palm Beach Gardens, FL 33410; tel. 561/626-1125

Inverrary Medical Investors, LLC, 4300 Rock Island Road, Lauderhill, FL 33319; tel. 954/485-6144

James A. Haley Veterans' Hospital, 13000 Bruce B. Downs Boulevard, Tampa, FL 33612; tel. 813/972-2000

Lakeside Health Center, 2501 Australian Avenue, West Palm Beach, FL 33407; tel. 561/655-7780

Life Care Center of Jacksonville, 4813 Lenoir Avenue, Jacksonville, FL 32216; tel. 904/332-4546

Life Care Center at Wells Crossing, 355 Crossing Boulevard, Orange Park, FL 32073; tel. 904/264-1950

Life Care Center of Altamonte Springs, 989 Orienta Avenue, Altamonte Springs, FL 32701; tel. 407/831-3446

Life Care Center of Citrus County, 3325 Jerwayne Lane, Lecanto, FL 34461; tel. 352/746-4434

Life Care Center of Estero, 3850 Williams Road, Estero, FL 33928; tel. 239/495-4000

Life Care Center of Hilliard, 3756 West 3rd Street, Hilliard, FL 32046; tel. 904/845-3988

Life Care Center of Melbourne, 606 East Sheridan Road, Melbourne, FL 32901; tel. 321/727-0984

Life Care Center of New Port Richey, 7400 Trouble Creek Road, New Port Richey, FL 34653; tel. 727/375-2999

Life Care Center of Ocala, 2800 Southwest 41st Street, Ocala, FL 34474; tel. 352/873-7570

Life Care Center of Orange Park, 2145 Kingsely Avenue, Orange Park, FL 32073; tel. 904/272-2424

Life Care Center of Orlando, 3211 Rouse Road, Orlando, FL 32817; tel. 407/281-1070

Life Care Center of Palm Bay, 175 Villa Nueva Avenue, Palm Bay, FL 32907; tel. 321/952-1818

Life Care Center of Port St. Lucie, 3720 Southeast Jennings Road, Port Saint Lucie, FL 34952; tel. 772/398-8080

Life Care Center of Sarasota, 8104 Tuttle Avenue, Sarasota, FL 34243; tel. 941/360-6411

Life Care Center of Winter Haven, 1510 Cypress Gardens Boulevard, Winter Haven, FL 33884; tel. 863/318-8646

Miami Jewish Health Systems, Inc., 5200 Northeast 2nd Ave, Miami, FL 33137; tel. 305/751-8626

Miami VA Healthcare System, 1201 Northwest 16th Street, Miami, FL 33125; tel. 305/575-7000

North Florida/South Georgia Veterans Health System, 1601 Southwest Archer Road, Gainesville, FL 32608-1197; tel. 352/376-1611

Orlando VA Medical Center, 5201 Raymond Street, Orlando, FL 32803; tel. 407/629-1599

Punta Gorda Medical Investors Limited Partnership, 450 Shreve Street, Punta Gorda, FL 33950; tel. 941/639-8771

Shands Jacksonville Medical Center, Inc., 580 West Eighth Street (Mailbox # T-33), Jacksonville, FL 32209; tel. 904/244-4000

St. Anne's Nursing Center, St. Anne's Residence, Inc., 11855 Quail Roost Drive, Miami, FL 33177; tel. 305/252-4000

St. Catherine's Rehab Hospital/Villa Maria Nursing Center, 1050 Northeast 125th Street, Miami, FL 33161; tel. 305/891-8850

St. John's Rehabilitation Hospital and Nursing Center, 3487 Northwest 30th Street, Lauderdale Lakes, FL 33311; tel. 954/739-6233

Sunrise Health and Rehabilitation Center, 4800 Nob Hill Road, Sunrise, FL 33351; tel. 954/577-3600

VA Medical Center - West Palm Beach, Florida, 7305 North Military Trail, West Palm Beach, FL 33410-6400; tel. 516/422-8262

GEORGIA

Camellia Gardens of Life Care, 804 South Broad Street, Thomasville, GA 31792; tel. 229/226-0076

Central State Hospital, 620 Broad Street, Milledgeville, GA 31062; tel. 478/445-4128

Charlie Norwood VA Medical Center, 1 Freedom Way, Augusta, GA 30904; tel. 706/733-0188

East Central Regional Hospital, 100 Myrtle Boulevard, Gracewood, GA 30812; tel. 706/790-2030

Effingham Hospital, PO Box 386, Springfield, GA 31329; tel. 912/754-6451

Family Life Enrichment Center, Inc., PO Box 10, High Shoals, GA 30645; tel. 706/769-7738

Georgia Regional Hospital at Atlanta, PO Box 37047, Decatur, GA 30034-0407; tel. 404/243-2100

Georgia War Veterans Home, 2249 Vinson Highway, Milledgeville, GA 31061; tel. 478/445-4516

Georgia War Veterans Nursing Home, 1101 15th Street, Augusta, GA 30901; tel. 706/721-2531

Gwinnett Medical Center, 1000 Medical Center Boulevard, Lawrenceville, GA 30046; tel. 678/312-4321

Heritage Healthcare of Macon, 2255 Anthony Road, Macon, GA 31204; tel. 478/784-7900

Hospital Authority of Lowndes County and Valdosta, Georgia, 116 West Thigpen Avenue, Lakeland, GA 31635; tel. 229/482-3110

Irwin County Hospital, 710 North Irwin Avenue, Ocilla, GA 31774; tel. 229/468-3800

Liberty Regional Medical Center, PO Box 919, Hinesville, GA 31310; tel. 912/369-9400

Life Care Center of Gwinnett, 3850 Safehaven Drive, Lawrenceville, GA 30044; tel. 770/923-0005

Life Care Center of Lawrenceville, 210 Collins Industrial Way, Lawrenceville, GA 30043; tel. 678/442-0777

Mayo Clinic Health System in Waycross, 1900 Tebeau Street, Waycross, GA 31501; tel. 912/283-3030

North Georgia Medical Center, 1362 South Main Street, Ellijay, GA 30540; tel. 706/276-4741

Pruitt Health-Brookhaven, 3535 Ashton Woods Drive, Atlanta, GA 30319; tel. 770/451-0236

PruittHealth Fairburn, 7560 Butner Road, Fairburn, GA 30213; tel. 770/306-7878

Sadie G. Mays Health and Rehabilitation Center, 1821 Anderson Avenue, Northwest, Atlanta, GA 30314; tel. 404/794-2477

The Hospital Authority of Habersham County, PO Box 37, Demorest, GA 30535; tel. 706/754-2161

Tift Regional Medical Center, 706 North Parrish Avenue, Adel, GA 31620; tel. 229/896-8000

Unihealth Post Acute Care Austell, 1700 Mulkey Road, Austell, GA 30106; tel. 770/941-5753

VA Medical Center - Atlanta, 1670 Clairmont Road, Decatur, GA 30033; tel. 404/728-7601

VA Medical Center - Carl Vinson, 1826 Veterans Boulevard, Dublin, GA 31021; tel. 478/277-2701

HAWAII

Hale Anuenue Restorative Care Center, 1333 Waianuenue Avenue, Hilo, HI 96720; tel. 808/961-6644

Ka Punawai Ola, 91-575 Farrington Highway, Kapolei, HI 96707; tel. 808/674-9262

Life Care Center of Hilo, 944 West Kawailani Street, Hilo, HI 96720; tel. 808/959-9151

Life Care Center of Kona, 78-6957 Kamehameha III Road, Kailua Kona, HI 96740; tel. 808/322-2790

VA Pacific Islands Health Care System, 459 Patterson Road, Honolulu, HI 96819-1522; tel. 808/433-0683

IDAHO

Boise VA Medical Center, 500 West Fort Street, Boise, ID 83702-4598; tel. 208/422-1000

Bridgeview Estates, 1828 Bridgeview Boulevard, Twin Falls, ID 83301; tel. 208/736-3933

Life Care Center of Coeur d'Alene, 500 West Aqua Avenue, Coeur d Alene, ID 83815; tel. 208/762-1122

Life Care Center of Boise, 808 North Curtis Road, Boise, ID 83706; tel. 208/376-5273

Life Care Center of Idaho Falls, 2725 East 17th Street, Idaho Falls, ID 83406; tel. 208/529-4567

Life Care Center of Lewiston, 325 Warner Drive, Lewiston, ID 83501; tel. 208/798-8500

Life Care Center of Post Falls, 460 North Garden Plaza, Post Falls, ID 83854; tel. 208/755-9522

Life Care Center of Sandpoint, 1125 North Division Street, Sandpoint, ID 83864; tel. 208/265-9299

Life Care Center of Treasure Valley, 502 North Kimball Place, Boise, ID 83704; tel. 208/377-1900

Life Care Center of Valley View, 1130 North Allumbaugh Street, Boise, ID 83704; tel. 208/854-8500

State Hospital South, PO Box 400, Blackfoot, ID 83221; tel. 208/785-1200

ILLINOIS

Alden - Des Plaines Skilled Nursing and Rehabilitation, 1221 East Golf Road, Des Plaines, IL 60016; tel. 847/768-1300

Alden Estates of Barrington, Inc., 1420 South Barrington Road, Barrington, IL 60010; tel. 847/382-6664

Alden Estates of Evanston, 2520 Gross Point Road, Evanston, IL 60201; tel. 847/328-6000

Alden Estates of Naperville, Inc., 1525 Oxford Lane, Naperville, IL 60565; tel. 630/983-0300

Alden Estates of Shorewood, Inc., 710 West Black Road, Shorewood, IL 60404; tel. 815/230-8700

Alden Estates of Skokie, Inc., 4626 Old Orchard Road, Skokie, IL 60076; tel. 847/676-4800

Alden North Shore Rehab & HCC, 5050 West Touhy Avenue, Skokie, IL 60077; tel. 847/679-6100

Alden Northmoor Rehabilitation and Health Care Center, Inc., 5831 North Northwest Highway, Chicago, IL 60631-2642; tel. 773/775-8080

Alden of Waterford, LLC., 2021 Randi Drive, Aurora, IL 60504; tel. 630/851-7266

Alden Poplar Creek Rehabilitation and Health Care Center, Inc., 1545 Barrington Road, Hoffman Estates, IL 60169-1018; tel. 847/884-0011

Alden Rehabilitation and Health Care Center/ Orland Park, 16450 South 97th Avenue, Orland Park, IL 60467; tel. 708/403-6500

Alden Valley Ridge Rehabilitation and Health Care Center, Inc., 275 East Army Trail Road, Bloomingdale, IL 60108-2198; tel. 630/893-9616

Anna Hospital Corporation, 517 North Main, Anna, IL 62906; tel. 618/833-4511

Applewood Rehabilitation Center, 21020 Kostner Avenue, Matteson, IL 60443-2000; tel. 708/747-1300

Aria Post Acute Care, LLC, 4600 North Frontage Road, Hillside, IL 60162; tel. 708/544-9933

Astoria Place Living and Rehabilitation Center, LLC, 6300 North California Avenue, Chicago, IL 60659; tel. 773/973-1900

Beecher Manor Nursing and Rehabilitation, LLC, 1201 Dixie Highway, Beecher, IL 60401; tel. 708/946-2600

Berkshire Nursing and Rehab, 8200 West Roosevelt Road, Forest Park, IL 60130; tel. 708/488-9850

Brentwood North Health Care and Rehabilitation Centre, 3705 Deerfield Road, Riverwoods, IL 60015; tel. 847/947-9000

Brightview Care Center, Inc., 4538 North Beacon Street, Chicago, IL 60640-5519; tel. 773/275-7200

Bronzeville Park Skilled Nursing and Living Center, 3400 South Indiana Avenue, Chicago, IL 60616; tel. 312/842-5000

Burgess Square Healthcare and Rehabilitation Centre, 5801 South Cass Avenue, Westmont, IL 60559; tel. 630/971-2645

Butterfield Healthcare II, Inc., 720 Raymond Drive, Naperville, IL 60563; tel. 630/355-0220

Butterfield Healthcare VII, LLC, 339 South 9th Avenue, La Grange, IL 60525; tel. 708/354-4660

Butterfield Healthcare, Inc., 431 Remington Boulevard, Bolingbrook, IL 60440; tel. 630/759-1112

Capitol HealthCare and Rehabilitation Centre, LLC, 555 West Carpenter, Springfield, IL 62702; tel. 217/525-1880

CAPT James A. Lovell Federal Health Care Center, 3001 Green Bay Road, North Chicago, IL 60064; tel. 224/610-3700

Chateau Nursing and Rehabilitation Center, 7050 Madison Street, Willowbrook, IL 60527; tel. 630/323-6380

Claremont of Hanover Park, 2000 West Lake Street, Hanover Park, IL 60133; tel. 630/556-2000

Columbus Park Nursing and Rehabilitation Center, 901 South Austin Boulevard, Chicago, IL 60644; tel. 773/287-5959

Concord Nursing and Rehab, 9401 South Ridgeland Avenue, Oak Lawn, IL 60453; tel. 708/599-6700

Countryside Care Centre, 2330 West Galena Boulevard, Aurora, IL 60506-4299; tel. 630/896-4686

East Bank Center, LLC, 6131 Park Ridge Road, Loves Park, IL 61111; tel. 815/633-6810

Edward Hines Jr. VA Hospital, 5000 South 5th Avenue, Hines, IL 60141-5000; tel. 708/202-5652

Elmbrook Nursing, LLC, 127 West Diversey Avenue, Elmhurst, IL 60126; tel. 630/530-5225

Elmwood Care, 7733 West Grand Avenue, Elmwood Park, IL 60707; tel. 708/452-9200

Elston Nursing and Rehabilitation Centre, 4340 North Keystone, Chicago, IL 60641; tel. 773/545-8700

Evergreen Living & Rehab Center, LLC, 10124 South Kedzie Avenue, Evergreen Park, IL 60805; tel. 847/440-2650

Forest Villa Nursing and Rehabilitation Center, LLC, 6840 West Touhy Avenue, Niles, IL 60714; tel. 847/647-6400

Franciscan Communities, Inc., 4021 West Belmont Avenue, Chicago, IL 60641; tel. 773/328-5500

Franciscan Communities, Inc., 1055 East Grand Avenue, Lindenhurst, IL 60046; tel. 847/356-4600

Franciscan Communities, Inc., 555 McHenry Road, Wheeling, IL 60090; tel. 847/537-2900

Galesburg Cottage Hospital, 695 North Kellogg Street, Galesburg, IL 61401; tel. 309/343-8131

Glen Oaks Nursing and Rehabilitation Centre, 270 Skokie Boulevard, Northbrook, IL 60062-1683; tel. 847/498-9320

GlenBridge Nursing and Rehabilitation Centre, Ltd, 8333 West Golf Road, Niles, IL 60714; tel. 847/966-9190

Glencrest Nursing and Rehabilitation Centre, 2451 West Touhy Avenue, Chicago, IL 60645; tel. 773/338-6800

GlenLake Terrace Nursing And Rehabilitation Center, 2222 West 14th Street, Waukegan, IL 60085; tel. 847/249-2400

GlenShire Nursing and Rehabilitation Centre, Ltd., 22660 South Cicero Avenue, Richton Park, IL 60471; tel. 708/747-6120

Glenview Terrace Nursing Center, 1511 Greenwood Road, Glenview, IL 60026; tel. 847/729-9090

Glenwood HealthCare and Rehab Center, Inc., 3856 Oakton Street, Suite 200, Skokie, IL 60076; tel. 708/758-6200

Graham Hospital Assoc., 210 West Walnut Street, Canton, IL 61520; tel. 309/647-5240

Greek American Rehabilitation and Care Centre, 220 North 1st Street, Wheeling, IL 60090; tel. 847/459-8700

Harmony Healthcare & Rehabilitation Center, 3919 West Foster Avenue, Chicago, IL 60625; tel. 773/588-9500

Helia Healthcare of Yorkville, LLC, 1308 Game Farm Road, Yorkville, IL 60560; tel. 630/553-5811

Highland Park Nursing & Rehab, 50 Pleasant Avenue, Highwood, IL 60040-1813; tel. 847/432-9142

International Nursing and Rehab, 4815 South Western Boulevard, Chicago, IL 60609; tel. 773/927-4200

Jackson Square Nursing and Rehabilitation Center, 5130 West Jackson Boulevard, Chicago, IL 60644; tel. 773/921-8000

Jesse Brown VA Medical Center, 820 South Damen Avenue, Chicago, IL 60612; tel. 312/569-6101

Lake Shore HealthCare & Rehabilitation Centre, LLC, 7200 North Sheridan Road, Chicago, IL 60626; tel. 773/973-7200

Lakeview Rehabilitation & Nursing Center, LLC, 735 West Diversey Parkway, Chicago, IL 60614; tel. 773/348-4055

Lakewood Nursing and Rehabilitation Center, 14716 South Eastern Avenue, Plainfield, IL 60544; tel. 815/436-3400

Lemont Center Nursing and Rehabilitation, 12450 Walker Road, Lemont, IL 60439-9301; tel. 630/243-0400

Lexington Health Care Center of Chicago Ridge, Inc., 10300 Southwest Highway, Chicago Ridge, IL 60415-1426; tel. 708/425-1100

Lexington Health Care Center of La Grange, Inc., 4735 Willow Springs Road, La Grange, IL 60525-6130; tel. 708/352-6900

Lexington Health Care Center of Lake Zurich, Inc., 900 South Rand Road, Lake Zurich, IL 60047-2450; tel. 847/726-1200

Lexington Health Care Center of Lombard, 2100 South Finley Road, Lombard, IL 60148-4893; tel. 630/495-4000

Lexington Health Care Center of Streamwood, Inc., 815 East Irving Park Road, Streamwood, IL 60107-3083; tel. 630/837-5300

Lexington Healthcare - Schaumburg, 675 South Roselle Road, Schaumburg, IL 60193-3100; tel. 847/352-5500

Lexington Healthcare Center of Bloomingdale, Inc., 165 South Bloomingdale, Bloomingdale, IL 60108-1434; tel. 630/980-8700

Lexington Healthcare Center of Elmhurst, Inc., 420 West Butterfield Road, Elmhurst, IL 60126-4980; tel. 630/832-2300

Lexington Healthcare Center of Orland Park, Inc., 14601 South John Humphrey Drive, Orland Park, IL 60462-2641; tel. 708/349-8300

Lexington Healthcare Center of Wheeling, Inc., 730 West Hintz Road, Wheeling, IL 60090-5501; tel. 847/537-7474

Lutheran Home for the Aged, Inc., 800 West Oakton Street, Arlington Heights, IL 60004-4600; tel. 847/368-7400

Manor Care Health Services - Naperville, 200 Martin Avenue, Naperville, IL 60540; tel. 630/355-4111

Manor Care of Oak Lawn (East) IL, LLC, 9401 South Kostner Avenue, Oak Lawn, IL 60453; tel. 708/423-7882

Manor Care of Oak Lawn (West) IL, LLC, 6300 West 95th Street, Oak Lawn, IL 60453-2256; tel. 708/599-8800

Manor Care of Palos Heights (West) IL, LLC, 11860 Southwest Highway, Palos Heights, IL 60463; tel. 708/361-4555

Manor Care of Palos Heights, IL, LLC, 7850 West College Drive, Palos Heights, IL 60463-1010; tel. 708/361-6990

ManorCare Health Services - Arlington Heights, 715 West Central Road, Arlington Heights, IL 60005; tel. 847/392-2020

ManorCare Health Services - Elgin, 180 South State Street, Elgin, IL 60123; tel. 847/742-3310

ManorCare Health Services - Elk Grove Village, 1920 Nerge Road, Elk Grove Village, IL 60007; tel. 847/301-0550

ManorCare Health Services - Highland Park, 2773 Skokie Valley Road, Highland Park, IL 60035-1042; tel. 847/266-9266

ManorCare Health Services - Northbrook, 3300 Milwaukee Avenue, Northbrook, IL 60062; tel. 847/795-9700

ManorCare Health Services- Libertyville, 1500 South Milwaukee Avenue, Libertyville, IL 60048; tel. 847/816-3200

ManorCare Health Services-Westmont, 512 East Ogden Avenue, Westmont, IL 60559; tel. 630/323-4400

Manorcare of Homewood, IL, LLC, 940 Maple Avenue, Homewood, IL 60430-2061; tel. 708/799-0244

ManorCare of Rolling Meadows, IL, LLC, 4225 Kirchoff Road, Rolling Meadows, IL 60008; tel. 847/397-2400

ManorCare of South Holland IL, LLC, 2145 East 170th Street, South Holland, IL 60473; tel. 708/895-3255

ManorCare of Wilmette IL, LLC, 432 Poplar Drive, Wilmette, IL 60091; tel. 847/256-5000

Maplewood Care Center, 50 North Jane Drirve, Elgin, IL 60123-5196; tel. 847/697-3750

Maryhaven Nursing and Rehabilitation Center, 1700 East Lake Avenue, Glenview, IL 60025; tel. 847/729-1300

Mayfield Care Center, Inc., 5905 West Washington Boulevard, Chicago, IL 60644-2845; tel. 773/261-7074

Mercy Harvard Hospital, Inc., PO Box 850, Harvard, IL 60033; tel. 815/943-5431

Mid America Care Center, LLC, 4920 North Kenmore Avenue, Chicago, IL 60640; tel. 773/769-2700

Neighbors Nursing and Rehabilitation Center, 811 West 2nd Street, Byron, IL 61010-0585; tel. 815/234-2511

Northwestern Lake Forest Hospital, 660 North Westmoreland Road, Lake Forest, IL 60045; tel. 847/234-5600

Northwoods Care Center, 2250 Pearl Street, Belvidere, IL 61008-6099; tel. 815/544-0358

Oak Brook HealthCare & Rehabilitation Centre, LTD, 2013 Midwest Road, Oak Brook, IL 60523; tel. 630/495-0220

Oakton Pavillion Health Care Facility, 1660 Oakton Place, Des Plaines, IL 60018; tel. 847/299-5588

Park Place Christian Community of Elmhurst, 1150 Euclid Avenue, Elmhurst, IL 60126; tel. 630/936-4106

Park Villa Nursing and Rehabilitation Center, LLC, 12550 South Ridgeland Avenue, Palos Heights, IL 60463; tel. 708/597-9300

Peterson Park Associates, LLC, 6141 North Pulaski Road, Chicago, IL 60646; tel. 773/478-2000

Pine Crest Health Care, LLC, 3300 West 175th Street, Hazel Crest, IL 60429; tel. 708/335-2400

Prairie Manor Nursing and Rehab, 345 Dixie Highway, Chicago Heights, IL 60411-1757; tel. 708/754-7601

Presence Ballard Nursing Center, 9300 Ballard Road, Des Plaines, IL 60016; tel. 847/294-2300

Presence Cor Mariae Center, 3330 Maria Linden Drive, Rockford, IL 61114; tel. 815/986-7522

Presence Heritage Village, 901 North Entrance Avenue, Kankakee, IL 60901; tel. 815/939-4506

Presence Life Connections, 659 East Jefferson Street, Freeport, IL 61032; tel. 815/232-6181

Presence McAuley Manor, 400 West Sullivan Road, Aurora, IL 60506; tel. 630/859-3700

Presence Our Lady of Victory, 20 Briarcliff Lane, Bourbonnais, IL 60914; tel. 815/937-2022

Presence Pine View Care Center, 611 Allen Lane, St Charles, IL 60174; tel. 630/377-2211

Presence Resurrection Life Center, 7370 West Talcott Avenue, Chicago, IL 60631; tel. 773/594-7804

Presence Resurrection Nursing and Rehabilitation Center, 1001 North Greenwood Avenue, Park Ridge, IL 60068; tel. 847/692-5600

Presence Saint Anne Center, 4405 Highcrest Road, Rockford, IL 61107; tel. 815/229-1999

Presence Saint Benedict Nursing and Rehabilitation Center, 6930 West Touhy Avenue, Niles, IL 60714; tel. 847/647-0003

Presence Villa Franciscan, 210 North Springfield Avenue, Joliet, IL 60435; tel. 815/725-3400

Presence Villa Scalabrini Nursing and Rehabilitation Center, 480 North Wolf Road, Northlake, IL 60164; tel. 708/562-5180

Providence Healthcare & Rehabilitation Center Downers Grove, 3450 Saratoga Avenue, Downers Grove, IL 60515; tel. 630/969–2900

Providence Healthcare and Rehabilitation of Palos Heights, 13259 South Central Avenue, Palos Heights, IL 60463; tel. 708/597–1000

Red Bud Regional Hospital, LLC, 325 Spring Street, Red Bud, IL 62278; tel. 618/282–3831

Regency Healthcare and Rehabilitation Center, 6631 North Milwaukee Avenue, Niles, IL 60714; tel. 847/647–7444

Renaissance at Midway, 4437 South Cicero Avenue, Chicago, IL 60632; tel. 773/884–0484

Renaissance At South Shore, Inc., 2425 East 71st Street, Chicago, IL 60649; tel. 773/721–5000

Renaissance Park South, 10923 South Halsted Street, Chicago, IL 60628; tel. 773/928–2000

Rock Island Nursing and Rehabilitation Center, 2545 24th Street, Rock Island, IL 61201; tel. 309/788–0458

Rolling Hills Manor, 3521 16th Street, Zion, IL 60099; tel. 847/746–8382

Salem Village Nursing & Rehabilitation Center, LLC, 1314 Rowell Avenue, Joliet, IL 60433; tel. 815/727–5451

Seneca Nursing Home, Inc., 1301 Lee Street, Des Plaines, IL 60018; tel. 847/635–4000

Sherman West Court, 1950 Larkin Avenue, Elgin, IL 60123; tel. 847/742–7070

St. Matthew Center for Health, 1601 North Western Avenue, Park Ridge, IL 60068-1233; tel. 847/825–5531

St. Paul's House - Health Care Ctr., 3800 North California Avenue, Chicago, IL 60618-3606; tel. 773/478–4222

Symphony Crestwood, LLC, 14255 Cicero Avenue, Crestwood, IL 60445; tel. 708/371–0400

Symphony Deerbrook, LLC, 306 North Larkin Avenue, Joliet, IL 60435-6681; tel. 815/744–5560

Symphony Maple Ridge, 2202 North Kickapoo Street, Lincoln, IL 62656-1386; tel. 217/735–1538

Symphony McKinley, LLC, 500 West McKinley Avenue, Decatur, IL 62526-3281; tel. 217/875–0020

The Abington of Glenview, 3901 Glenview Road, Glenview, IL 60025; tel. 847/729–0000

The Carlton at the Lake, Inc., 725 West Montrose Avenue, Chicago, IL 60613; tel. 773/929–1700

The Chalet Living and Rehabilitation Center, LLC, 7350 North Sheridan Road, Chicago, IL 60626; tel. 773/274–1000

The Claremont Rehab and Living Center, 150 North Weiland Road, Buffalo Grove, IL 60089; tel. 847/465–0200

The Grove at Lincoln Park Living and Rehab Center, LLC, 2732 North Hampton Court, Chicago, IL 60614; tel. 773/248–6000

The Grove at the Lake Living and Rehabilitation Center, LLC, 2534 Elim Avenue, Zion, IL 60099; tel. 847/746–8435

The Grove of Evanston, 500 Ashbury Avenue, Evanston, IL 60202; tel. 847/637–0722

The Grove of LaGrange Park, 701 North LaGrange Road, La Grange Park, IL 60526; tel. 708/752–6602

The Grove of Northbrook Living and Rehabilitation Center, LLC, 263 Skokie Boulevard, Northbrook, IL 60062; tel. 847/564–0505

The Grove of Skokie Living and Rehabilitation Center, LLC, 9000 North Lavergne Ave, Skokie, IL 60077; tel. 847/679–2322

The Heights HealthCare and Rehabilitation Centre, LLC, 1629 East Gardner Lane, Peoria Heights, IL 61616; tel. 309/685–1545

The Imperial Grove Pavilion, 1366 West Fullerton Avenue, Chicago, IL 60613; tel. 773/248–9300

The Renaissance at 87th Street, 2940 West 87th Street, Chicago, IL 60652; tel. 773/434–8787

The Villa at South Holland, 16300 South Wausau Avenue, South Holland, IL 60473; tel. 708/596–5500

The Villa at Windsor Park Nursing and Rehab Center, LLC, 2649 East 75th Street, Chicago, IL 60649; tel. 773/356–9300

The Wealshire Limited Partnership, 150 Jamestown Lane, Lincolnshire, IL 60069-2119; tel. 224/543–7100

THI of Illinois at Brentwood, LLC, 5400 West 87th Street, Burbank, IL 60459; tel. 708/423–1200

VA - Illiana Health Care System, 1900 East Main Street, Danville, IL 61832; tel. 217/554–3000

VA Medical Center, 2401 West Main Street, Marion, IL 62959; tel. 618/997–5311

Vanguard Health Systems of Illinois, 3249 South Oak Park Avenue, Berwyn, IL 60402; tel. 708/783–9100

Warren Barr Living & Rehab Center, LLC, 66 West Oak Street, Chicago, IL 60610; tel. 312/705–5100

Washington County Hospital District, 705 South Grand Avenue, Nashville, IL 62263; tel. 618/327–8236

Wauconda HealthCare & Rehabilitation Centre, LLC, 176 Thomas Court, Wauconda, IL 60084; tel. 847/526–5551

Whitehall North, LLC, 300 Waukegan Road, Deerfield, IL 60015-4988; tel. 847/945–4600

Willowcrest Nursing Pavilion, 515 North Main Street, Sandwich, IL 60548; tel. 815/786–8426

INDIANA

Franciscan Communities, Inc., 203 Franciscan Drive, Crown Point, IN 46307; tel. 219/661–5100

Gibson General Hospital, Inc., 1808 Sherman Drive, Princeton, IN 47670; tel. 812/385–3401

Green Valley Care Center, 3118 Green Valley Road, New Albany, IN 47150; tel. 812/945–2341

Hammond Whiting Care Center, 1000 114th Street, Whiting, IN 46394; tel. 219/659–2770

Indiana University Health La Porte Hospital, Inc., PO Box 250, La Porte, IN 46350; tel. 219/326–1234

Lafayette Medical Investors, 3401 Soldiers Home Road, West Lafayette, IN 47906; tel. 765/463–1541

Life Care Center of Fort Wayne, 1649 Spy Run Avenue, Fort Wayne, IN 46805; tel. 260/422–8520

Life Care Center of LaGrange, 0770 North 075 East, Lagrange, IN 46761; tel. 260/463–7445

Life Care Center of Michigan City, 802 US Highway 20 East, Michigan City, IN 46360; tel. 219/872–7251

Life Care Center of Rochester, 827 West 13th Street, Rochester, IN 46975; tel. 574/223–4331

Life Care Center of Valparaiso, 3405 Campbell Road, Valparaiso, IN 46385; tel. 219/462–1023

Life Care Center of Willows, 1000 Elizabeth Street, Valparaiso, IN 46383; tel. 219/464–4858

Mitchell Manor, PO Box 338, Mitchell, IN 47446; tel. 812/849–2221

Parkview Care Center, 2819 North St. Joseph Avenue, Evansville, IN 47720; tel. 812/424–2941

Presence Sacred Heart Home, 515 North Main, Avilla, IN 46710; tel. 260/897–2841

Rensselaer Medical Investors, 1309 East Grace Street, Rensselaer, IN 47978; tel. 219/866–4181

The Arbors Operator, LLC, 1101 East Cool Springs Avenue, Michigan City, IN 46360; tel. 219/874–5211

The Lane House, 1000 Lane Avenue, Crawfordsville, IN 47933; tel. 765/362–0007

The Woodlands, 3820 West Jackson Street, Muncie, IN 47304; tel. 765/289–3451

VA Northern Indiana Health Care System, 2121 Lake Avenue, Fort Wayne, IN 46805; tel. 260/460–1310

Westside Limited Partnership, 8616 West 10th Street, Indianapolis, IN 46234; tel. 317/209–2800

IOWA

Mercy Health Services - Iowa, 250 Mercy Drive, Dubuque, IA 52001; tel. 563/589–8000

VA Central Iowa Health Care System, 3600 30th Street, Des Moines, IA 50310-5774; tel. 515/699–5999

KANSAS

Garden Terrace at Overland Park, 7541 Switzer Road, Overland Park, KS 66214; tel. 913/631–2273

Life Care Center of Andover, 621 West 21st Street, Andover, KS 67002; tel. 316/733–1349

Life Care Center of Burlington, 601 Cross Street, Burlington, KS 66839; tel. 620/364–2117

Life Care Center of Kansas City, 3231 North 61st Street, Kansas City, KS 66104; tel. 913/299–1770

Life Care Center of Osawatomie, 1615 Parker Street - Box 159, Osawatomie, KS 66064; tel. 913/755–4165

Life Care Center of Seneca, 512 Community Drive, Seneca, KS 66538; tel. 785/336–3528

Life Care Center of Wichita, 622 North Edgemoor, Wichita, KS 67208; tel. 316/686–5100

Robert J. Dole VA Medical Center, 5500 East Kellogg, Wichita, KS 67218; tel. 316/651–3601

The Congregational Home, 1001 Southwest 29th Street, Topeka, KS 66611; tel. 785/274–3304

VA Eastern Kansas Health Care System, 2200 Southwest Gage, Topeka, KS 66622; tel. 785/350–3111

KENTUCKY

Appalachian Regional Healthcare, 260 Hospital Drive, South Williamson, KY 41503; tel. 606/237–1700

Bureau of Prisons - FMC Lexington, 3301 Leestown Road, Lexington, KY 40511-8799; tel. 859/255–6812

Christian Care Center of Kuttawa, 1253 Lake Barkley Drive, Kuttawa, KY 42055; tel. 270/388–2291

Highlandspring of Ft. Thomas, 960 Highland Avenue, Fort Thomas, KY 41075; tel. 859/572–0660

Lancaster Medical Investors, LLC, 308 West Maple Avenue, Lancaster, KY 40444; tel. 859/792–6844

Laurel Creek Health Care Center, 1033 North Highway 11, Manchester, KY 40962; tel. 606/598–6163

Lexington VA Medical Center, 1101 Veterans Drive, Lexington, KY 40502-2236; tel. 859/233–4511

Life Care Center of Bardstown, 120 Life Care Way, Bardstown, KY 40004; tel. 502/348–4220

Life Care Center of LaCenter, 252 West 5th Street, La Center, KY 42056; tel. 270/665–5681

Life Care Center of Morehead, PO Box 884, Morehead, KY 40351; tel. 606/784–7518

Madonna Manor, Inc., 2344 Amsterdam Road, Villa Hills, KY 41017; tel. 859/341–3981

Mountain View Health Care, PO Box 650, Elkhorn City, KY 41522; tel. 606/754–4134

Murray-Calloway County Hospital, 803 Poplar Street, Murray, KY 42071-2432; tel. 270/762–1102

Parkview Nursing and Rehabilitation Center, 544 Lone Oak Road, Paducah, KY 42003; tel. 270/443–6543

Rockcastle Regional Hospital and Respiratory Care Center, 145 Newcomb Avenue, PO Box 1310, Mount Vernon, KY 40456; tel. 606/256–2195

The Medical Center, PO Box 90010, Bowling Green, KY 42102-9010; tel. 270/745–1000

Villaspring Health Care Center, Inc., 630 Viox Drive, Erlanger, KY 41018; tel. 859/727–6700

LOUISIANA

Alexandria VA Health Care System, PO Box 69004, Alexandria, LA 71306; tel. 318/473–0010

East Jefferson General Hospital, 4200 Houma Boulevard, Metairie, LA 70006; tel. 504/454–4000

Lane Regional Medical Center, 6300 Main Street, Zachary, LA 70791; tel. 225/658–4303

Trinity Neurologic Rehabilitation Center, LLC, 1400 Lindberg Drive, Slidell, LA 70458; tel. 985/641–4985

MAINE

VA Maine Healthcare System, 1 VA Center, Augusta, ME 04330; tel. 207/623–8411

MARYLAND

Calvert Memorial Hospital, 100 Hospital Road, Prince Frederick, MD 20678; tel. 410/535–4000

Deer's Head Center, PO Box 2018, Salisbury, MD 21802-2018; tel. 410/543–4000

Potomac Valley Nursing Facilities, Inc., 1235 Potomac Valley Road, Rockville, MD 20850; tel. 301/762–0700

VA Maryland Health Care System, 10 North Greene Street, Baltimore, MD 21201; tel. 410/605–7000

Western Maryland Hospital Center, 1500 Pennsylvania Avenue, Hagerstown, MD 21742-3194; tel. 301/745–4200

MASSACHUSETTS

137 Nichols St., Inc., 137 Nichols Street, Norwood, MA 02062-2009; tel. 781/762–0858

140 Prescott Street Operations, LLC, 140 Prescott Street, North Andover, MA 01845; tel. 978/685–8086

140 Webb St., Inc., 140 Webb Street, Weymouth, MA 02188-2799; tel. 781/335–4352

16 Pleasant St., Inc., 16 Pleasant Street, Bridgewater, MA 02324-2498; tel. 508/697–4616

1801 Turnpike Street Operations, LLC, 1801 Turnpike Street, North Andover, MA 01845; tel. 978/688–1212

184 Main, LLC, 184 Main Street, Fairhaven, MA 02719; tel. 508/997–3193

249 Corey Rd, Inc., 249 Corey Road, Brighton, MA 02135-8396; tel. 617/734–7138

30 Princeton Boulevard Operations, LLC, 30 Princeton Boulevard, Lowell, MA 01851; tel. 978/454–8086

30 Webster Street Operations, LLC, 30 Webster Street, Brookline, MA 02446; tel. 617/734–2300

34 Lincoln St., Inc., 34 South Lincoln Street, Natick, MA 01760-5939; tel. 508/653–8330

40 Parkhurst Road Operations, LLC, 40 Parkhurst Road, Chelmsford, MA 01824; tel. 978/256–3151

400 Groton Road Operations, LLC, 400 Groton Road, Ayer, MA 01432; tel. 978/772–1704

519 Main St., Inc., 80 Access Road, Norwood, MA 02062; tel. 508/359–6050

65 Cooper Street Operations, LLC, 65 Cooper Street, Agawam, MA 01001; tel. 413/786–8000

750 Woburn Street Operating Company, LLC, 750 Woburn Street, Wilmington, MA 01887; tel. 978/988–0888

8 Butler St., Inc., 8 Butler Street, Blackstone, MA 01504-1598; tel. 508/883–5818

84 Elm St., Inc., 84 Elm Street, Holliston, MA 01746-2138; tel. 508/429–4566

841 Merrimack Street Operations, LLC, 841 Merrimack Street, Lowell, MA 01854; tel. 978/459–0546

Abbott House, 28 Essex Street, Lynn, MA 01902; tel. 781/595–5500

Academy Nursing Home, 89 Morton Street, Andover, MA 01810; tel. 978/475–0944

Alliance Health of Massachusetts, Inc., 39 Lafayette Street, Marblehead, MA 01945-1997; tel. 781/631–6120

Alliance Health of Massachusetts, Inc., 22 Johnson Street, Peabody, MA 01960; tel. 978/535–8700

Alliance Healthcare of Southeastern Mass, Inc., 175 Grove Street, Braintree, MA 02184; tel. 781/848–2050

Arbetter Corporation, 9 Arbetter Drive, Framingham, MA 01701; tel. 508/877–3300

Beacon Rehabilitation and Nursing, LLC, 170 Corey Road, Brighton, MA 02135; tel. 617/731–0515

Bear Hill Nursing Center at Wakefield, 11 North Street, Stoneham, MA 02180; tel. 781/438–8515

Beaumont at University Campus, LLC, 378 Plantation Street, Worcester, MA 01605; tel. 508/755–7300

Beaumont Nursing Home, Inc., PO Box 940, Northbridge, MA 01534-0935; tel. 508/234–9771

Beaumont/Whitney Place Northboro, LLC, 238 West Main Street, Northborough, MA 01532; tel. 508/393–2368

Belmont Manor Nursing Home, Inc., 34 Agassiz Avenue, Belmont, MA 02478; tel. 617/489–1200

Bentley Saint Francis, LLC, 101 Plantation Street, Worcester, MA 01604; tel. 508/755–8605

Berkshire Extended Care Services, Inc., 40 Sunset Avenue, Lenox, MA 01240; tel. 413/637–5011

Bourne Manor Extended Care Facility, 146 MacArthur Boulevard, Bourne, MA 02532; tel. 508/759–8880

Braemoor Rehabilitation and Nursing Center, Inc., 34 North Pearl Street, Brockton, MA 02301; tel. 508/586–3696

Brentwood Operating, LLC, 56 Liberty Street, Danvers, MA 01923; tel. 978/777–2700

Briarwood Healthcare Nursing Center, 150 Lincoln Street, Needham, MA 02492; tel. 781/449–4040

Brighton Health Group, 10 Bellamy Street, Brighton, MA 02135; tel. 617/782–8113

Calvin Coolidge Nursing & Rehabilitation Center, 548 Elm Street, Northampton, MA 01060; tel. 413/586–3150

Cape Heritage MA SNF LLS, 37 Route 6A, Sandwich, MA 02563; tel. 508/888–8222

Cape Regency MA SNF, LLC, 120 South Main Street, Centerville, MA 02632; tel. 508/778–1835

Catholic Memorial Home, Inc., 2446 Highland Avenue, Fall River, MA 02720-4599; tel. 508/679–0011

Cedar Hill Health Care Center, 49 Thomas Patten Drive, Randolph, MA 02368; tel. 781/961–1160

CFM Buckley North, LLC, 95 Laurel Street, Greenfield, MA 01301; tel. 413/774–3143

Charlwell Healthcare, LLC, 305 Walpole Street, Norwood, MA 02062; tel. 781/762–7700

Chelsea Jewish Foundation, 17 Lafayette Avenue, Chelsea, MA 02150; tel. 617/884–6766

Christopher House of Worcester, Inc., 10 Mary Scano Drive, Worcester, MA 01605; tel. 508/754–3800

Claflin Hill Corporation, 20 Claflin Street, Milford, MA 01757; tel. 508/473–1272

Clifton Rehabilitative Nursing Center, 500 Wilbur Avenue, Somerset, MA 02725; tel. 508/675–7589

Colonial Health Group-TCU, LLC, 340 Thompson Road, Webster, MA 01570; tel. 508/949–8420

Colonial Rehabilitation and Nursing Center, 125 Broad Street, Weymouth, MA 02188; tel. 781/337–3121

Concord Health Care Center, 57 Old Road to Nine Acre Corner, Concord, MA 01742; tel. 978/371–3400

Copley at Stoughton Nursing Care Center, 380 Sumner Street, Stoughton, MA 02072; tel. 781/341–2300

Countryside Health Care of Milford, 1 Countryside Drive, Milford, MA 01757; tel. 508/473–0435

Courtyard Nursing Care Center, 200 Governors Avenue, Medford, MA 02155; tel. 781/391–5400

CPL (Cabot), LLC, 279 Cabot Street, Holyoke, MA 01040; tel. 413/536–3435

CPL (Glen Ridge), LLC, 120 Murray Street, Medford, MA 02155; tel. 781/391–0800

D'Youville Transitional Care, Inc., 1071 Varnum Avenue, Lowell, MA 01854; tel. 978/569–1000

Dartmouth House Nursing Home, Inc., 567 Dartmouth Street, South Dartmouth, MA 02748; tel. 508/997–7787

Den Mar Rehabilitation and Nursing Center, 44 South Street, Rockport, MA 01966; tel. 978/546–6311

Deutsches Altenheim, Inc., 2222 Centre Street, West Roxbury, MA 02132; tel. 617/325–1230

Duxbury Healthcare Partnership, 308 Kingstown Way, Duxbury, MA 02332; tel. 781/585–5561

East Longmeadow Skilled Nursing Center, 305 Maple Street, East Longmeadow, MA 01028; tel. 413/525–6361

Eastpointe Nursing Home, Inc., 255 Central Avenue, Chelsea, MA 02150; tel. 617/884–5700

Edgar P. Benjamin Healthcare Center, 120 Fisher Avenue, Boston, MA 02120; tel. 617/738–1500

Edith Nourse Rogers Memorial Veterans Hospital, 200 Springs Road, Bedford, MA 01730; tel. 781/687–3080

EPOCH Senior Healthcare of Brewster, 873 Harwich Road, Brewster, MA 02631; tel. 508/896–7046

EPOCH Senior Healthcare of Harwich, LLC, 111 Headwaters Drive, Harwich, MA 02645-1726; tel. 508/430–1717

EPOCH Senior Healthcare of Melrose, 15 Green Street, Melrose, MA 02176; tel. 781/665–3950

EPOCH Senior Healthcare of Norton, LLC, 184 Mansfield Avenue, Norton, MA 02766; tel. 508/285–7745

EPOCH Senior Healthcare of Sharon, 259 Norwood Street, Sharon, MA 02067; tel. 781/784–6781

EPOCH Senior Healthcare of Weston, LLC, 75 Norumbega Road, Weston, MA 02493; tel. 781/891–6100

EPOCH Senior Living, Inc., LLC, 615 Heath Street, Chestnut Hill, MA 02467; tel. 781/891–0777

Erlin Manor Nursing Home, Inc., 10 Erlin Terrace, Tewksbury, MA 01876; tel. 978/851–3121

Essex Park Rehabilitation & Nursing Center, 265 Essex Street, Beverly, MA 01915; tel. 978/927–3260

Essex Pavilion, LLC, 876 Falmouth Road, Hyannis, MA 02601; tel. 508/775–6663

Everett Nursing and Rehabilitation Center, 289 Elm Street, Everett, MA 02149; tel. 617/387–6560

Fairhaven Healthcare Center, Inc., 476 Varnum Avenue, Lowell, MA 01854; tel. 978/458–3388

Fairview Commons Nursing & Rehabilitation Center, 151 Christian Hill Road, Great Barrington, MA 01230; tel. 413/528–4560

Fall River Jewish Home, Inc., 538 Robeson Street, Fall River, MA 02720; tel. 508/679–6172

Federal Bureau of Prisons Federal Medical Center Devens, P.O. Box 880, Ayer, MA 01432; tel. 978/796–1443

Fox Hill Village Partnership, 30 Longwood Drive, Westwood, MA 02090; tel. 781/326–5652

FRC, Inc., 1245 Centre Street, West Roxbury, MA 02132; tel. 617/325–5400

Genesis Healthcare, LLC, 1 Bathol Street, Wakefield, MA 01880; tel. 781/245–7600

Geriatric Authority of Holyoke, 45 Lower Westfield Road, Holyoke, MA 01040; tel. 413/536–8110

GGNSC, 25 Armory Street, West Newton, MA 02465; tel. 617/969–2300

GGNSC Attleboro Pleasant Manor, LLC, 195 Pleasant Street, Attleboro, MA 02703; tel. 508/222–4950

GGNSC Chestnut Hill, LLC, 188 Florence Street, Chestnut Hill, MA 02467; tel. 617/332–4730

GGNSC Cohasset, LLC, 1 Chief Justice Cushing Highway, Cohasset, MA 02025; tel. 781/383–9060

GGNSC Gloucester, LLC, 272 Washington Street, Gloucester, MA 01930; tel. 978/281–0333

GGNSC Lexington, LLC, 840 Emerson Gardens Road, Lexington, MA 02420; tel. 781/861–8630

GGNSC Newton, LLC, 1650 Washington Street, West Newton, MA 02465; tel. 617/244–5407

GGNSC Norwood, LLC, 460 Washington Street, Norwood, MA 02062; tel. 781/769–2200

GGNSC Plymouth, LLC, 19 Obery Street, Plymouth, MA 02360; tel. 508/747–4790

Golden Living Center - Fitchburg, 1199 John Fitch Highway, Fitchburg, MA 01420; tel. 978/345–0146

Golden LivingCenter - Attleboro, 27 George Street, Attleboro, MA 02703; tel. 508/226–1650

Golden LivingCenter - The Hermitage, 383 Mill Street, Worcester, MA 01602; tel. 508/791–8131

Great Barrington Rehab & Nursing Center, 148 Maple Avenue, Great Barrington, MA 01230; tel. 413/528–3320

Greenfield Management Systems, 130 Colrain Road, Greenfield, MA 01301; tel. 413/774–3724

Guardian Center, Inc., 888 North Main Street, Brockton, MA 02301; tel. 508/587–6556

Hancock Park Rehabilitation and Nursing Center, 164 Parkingway, Quincy, MA 02169; tel. 617/773–4222

Harbor House Rehabilitation and Nursing Center, 11 Condito Road, Hingham, MA 02043; tel. 781/749–4774

Harborside Massachusetts, LP, 15 Kirkbride Drive, Danvers, MA 01923; tel. 978/716–3600

Harborside Massachusetts, LP, 63 Locust Street, Danvers, MA 01923; tel. 978/777–0011

Hathaway Manor, ECF, 863 Hathaway Road, New Bedford, MA 02740; tel. 508/996–6763

Hellenic Womens Benevolent Association, Inc., 601 Sherman Street, Canton, MA 02021-2053; tel. 781/828–7450

Heritage Hall East Center, 464 Main Street, Agawam, MA 01001; tel. 413/821–0753

Heritage Hall West - Genesis HealthCare, 61 Cooper Street, Agawam, MA 01001; tel. 413/786–8000

Highgate Nursing, LLC, 10 CareMatrix Drive, Dedham, MA 02026; tel. 781/461–9663

Highlander Nursing, LLC, 1748 Highland Avenue, Fall River, MA 02720; tel. 508/730–1070

Hillcrest Commons, 169 Valentine Road, Pittsfield, MA 01201; tel. 413/445–2300

Hillcrest Nursing and Rehabilitation Center, 94 Summer Street, Fitchburg, MA 01420; tel. 978/343–3530

Holden Nursing Home, 32 Mayo Drive, Holden, MA 01520; tel. 508/829–5555

Holyoke HealthCare Center, LLC, 282 Cabot Street, Holyoke, MA 01040; tel. 413/538–7470

Holyoke Rehabilitation Center, 260 Easthampton Road, Holyoke, MA 01040; tel. 413/538–9733

Hunt Nursing and Rehabilitation Center, 90 Lindall Street, Danvers, MA 01923; tel. 978/777–3740

J&B Partnership, LLP, 209 County Road, North Falmouth, MA 02556; tel. 508/563–5913

Jewish Geriatric Services, Inc., 770 Converse Street, Longmeadow, MA 01106; tel. 413/567–6211

Jewish Healthcare Center, Inc., 629 Salisbury Street, Worcester, MA 01609; tel. 508/798–8653

Jewish Rehabilitation Center for Aged of the North Shore, 240 Lynnfield Street, Peabody, MA 01960; tel. 978/471–5100

JML Care Center, Inc., 184 Ter Heun Drive, Falmouth, MA 02540-2503; tel. 508/457–4621

John Adams Nursing Home, LLC, 211 Franklin Street, Quincy, MA 02169; tel. 617/479–0837

John Scott House Nursing Home, Inc. (The), 233 Middle Street, Braintree, MA 02184; tel. 781/843–1860

Kathleen Daniel Healthcare, 485 Franklin Street, Framingham, MA 01702; tel. 508/872–8801

Kindred Nursing and Rehabilitation - Harborlights, 804 East 7th Street, South Boston, MA 02127; tel. 617/268–8968

Kindred Nursing and Rehabilitation Hallmark, 1123 Rockdale Avenue, New Bedford, MA 02740; tel. 508/997–7448

Kindred Nursing and Rehabilitation-Braintree, 1102 Washington Street, Braintree, MA 02184; tel. 781/848–3100

Kindred Nursing and Rehabilitation-Walden, 785 Main Street, Concord, MA 01742; tel. 978/369–6889

Kindred Nursing Centers East, LLC, 11 McGrath Highway, Quincy, MA 02169-5311; tel. 617/479–2820

Kindred Nursing Centers East, LLC, 11 Pontiac Avenue, Webster, MA 01570; tel. 508/943–3889

Kindred Transitional Care & Rehabilitation - Crawford, 273 Oak Grove Avenue, Fall River, MA 02723; tel. 508/679–4866

Kindred Transitional Care and Rehabilitation - Avery, 100 West Street, Needham Heights, MA 02494; tel. 781/234–6300

Kindred Transitional Care and Rehabilitation - Franklin, 130 Chestnut Street, Franklin, MA 02038; tel. 508/528–4600

Kindred Transitional Care and Rehabilitation - Hammersmith, 73 Chestnut Street, Saugus, MA 01906; tel. 781/233–8123

Kindred Transitional Care and Rehabilitation Harrington, 160 Main Street, Walpole, MA 02081; tel. 508/660-3080

Kindred Transitional Care and Rehabilitation Westborough, 8 Colonial Drive, Westborough, MA 01581; tel. 508/366-9131

Kindred Transitional Care and Rehabilitation-Blueberry Hill, 75 Brimbal Avenue, Beverly, MA 01915; tel. 978/927-2020

Kindred Transitional Care and Rehabilitation-Eagle Pond, PO Box 208, South Dennis, MA 02660; tel. 508/385-6034

Kindred Transitional Care and Rehabilitation-Eliot, 168 West Central Street, Natick, MA 01760; tel. 508/655-1000

Kindred Transitional Care and Rehabilitation-Forestview, 50 Indian Neck Road, Wareham, MA 02571; tel. 508/295-6264

Kindred Transitional Care and Rehabilitation-Marlborough, 400 Bolton Street, Marlborough, MA 01752; tel. 508/481-6123

Knollwood Nursing Center, 87 Briarwood Circle, Worcester, MA 01606; tel. 508/853-6910

Lanessa Extended Care Facility, Inc., 751 School Street, Webster, MA 01570; tel. 508/949-1334

Laurel Lake Health and Rehabilitation, LLC, 620 Laurel Street, Lee, MA 01238; tel. 413/243-2010

Ledgewood Healthcare Corporation, 87 Herrick Street, Beverly, MA 01915; tel. 978/921-1392

Legend Center for Rehabilitation and Nursing, 59 Eastwood Circle, Gardner, MA 01440; tel. 978/632-8776

Lexington Health Care Center, 178 Lowell Street, Lexington, MA 02420; tel. 781/862-7400

Life Care Center of Acton, One Great Road, Acton, MA 01720; tel. 978/263-9101

Life Care Center of Attleboro, 969 Park Street, Attleboro, MA 02703; tel. 508/222-4182

Life Care Center of Auburn, 14 Masonic Circle, Auburn, MA 01501; tel. 508/832-4800

Life Care Center of Leominster, 370 West Street, Leominster, MA 01453; tel. 978/537-0771

Life Care Center of Merrimack Valley, 80 Boston Road, North Billerica, MA 01862; tel. 978/667-2166

Life Care Center of Stoneham, 25 Woodland Road, Stoneham, MA 02180; tel. 781/662-2545

Life Care Center of the South Shore, PO Box 830, Scituate, MA 02066; tel. 781/545-1370

Life Care Center of West Bridgewater, 765 West Center Street, West Bridgewater, MA 02379; tel. 508/580-4400

Life Care Center of Wilbraham, 2399 Boston Road, Wilbraham, MA 01095; tel. 413/596-3111

Life Care Centers of America, 191 Foster Street, Littleton, MA 01460; tel. 978/486-3512

Linda Manor Extended Care Facility, 349 Haydenville Road, Leeds, MA 01053; tel. 413/586-7700

Linden Ponds, Inc., 400 Linden Ponds Way, Hingham, MA 02043; tel. 781/534-7171

LNF Corporation, 123 High Street, Topsfield, MA 01983-1926; tel. 978/887-7002

Lowell Health Care Center, 19 Varnum Street, Lowell, MA 01850; tel. 978/454-5644

Lydia Taft House, 60 Quaker Highway, Uxbridge, MA 01569; tel. 508/278-9500

Lynn Medical Investors, LLP, 111 Birch Street, Lynn, MA 01902; tel. 781/592-9667

Madonna Manor, Inc., 85 North Washington Street, North Attleboro, MA 02760; tel. 508/699-2740

Marian Manor, Inc., 33 Summer Street, Taunton, MA 02780; tel. 508/822-4885

Marina Bay Skilled Nursing and Rehabilitation Center, 2 Seaport Drive, Quincy, MA 02171; tel. 617/769-5100

Maristhill Nursing & Rehabilitation Center, 66 Newton Street, Waltham, MA 02453; tel. 781/893-0240

Marlborough Hills Healthcare Center, 121 Northboro Road, East, Marlborough, MA 01752; tel. 508/485-4040

Mary Ann Healthcare Corp., 45 Union Street, Natick, MA 01760; tel. 508/433-4400

Mayflower Place Nursing Center, Inc., 579 Buck Island Road, West Yarmouth, MA 02673; tel. 508/957-7007

MBO Corporation, 314 Marion Road, Middleboro, MA 02346; tel. 508/947-8632

Meadow Green Nursing Home, Inc., 45 Woburn Street, Waltham, MA 02452; tel. 781/899-8600

Medway Country Manor, Inc., 115 Holliston Street, Medway, MA 02053; tel. 508/533-6634

Metro Health Foundation of Massachusetts, Inc., 389 Alden Road, Fairhaven, MA 02719; tel. 508/991-8600

Metro Health Foundation, Inc., 337 Neponset Avenue, Dorchester, MA 02122; tel. 617/265-2350

Metrowest Rehab Corp, 150 Flanders Road, Westborough, MA 01581; tel. 508/870-2222

Millbury Health Care Center, 312 Millbury Avenue, Millbury, MA 01527; tel. 508/793-0088

Milton Health Care, 1200 Brush Hill Road, Milton, MA 02186; tel. 617/333-0600

Mount Saint Vincent Care Center, 35 Holy Family Road, Holyoke, MA 01040; tel. 413/532-3246

MRN Corporation, 15 Mill Street, Marion, MA 02738; tel. 508/748-3830

Mt. Greylock Extended Care Facility, 1000 North Street, Pittsfield, MA 01201; tel. 413/499-7186

Neville Center at Fresh Pond for Nursing and Rehabilitation, 640 Concord Avenue, Cambridge, MA 02138; tel. 617/497-0600

New Bedford Health Care Center, 221 Fitzgerald Drive, New Bedford, MA 02745; tel. 508/996-4600

New Bedford Jewish Convalescent Home, Inc., 200 Hawthorn Street, New Bedford, MA 02740; tel. 508/997-9314

New Bedford Medical Investors, LLC, 4525 Acushnet Avenue, New Bedford, MA 02745; tel. 508/998-7807

New England Pediatric Care, 78 Boston Road, North Billerica, MA 01862; tel. 978/667-5123

Newton Health Care Center, 2101 Washington Street, Newton Lower Falls, MA 02462; tel. 617/969-4660

North Adams Commons, 175 Franklin Street, North Adams, MA 01247; tel. 413/664-4041

Northwood MA SNF, LLC, 1010 Varnum Avenue, Lowell, MA 01854; tel. 978/458-8773

Notre Dame Long Term Care Center, 559 Plantation Street, Worcester, MA 01605-2350; tel. 508/852-3011

Odd Fellows Home of MA, 104 Randolph Road, Worcester, MA 01606-2493; tel. 508/853-6687

Our Lady's Haven of Fairhaven, Inc., 71 Center Street, Fairhaven, MA 02719; tel. 508/999-4561

Overlook Masonic Health Center, PO Box 1000, Charlton, MA 01507-0189; tel. 508/248-7344

Park Marion Avenue Nursing & Rehabilitation Center, 146 Park Avenue, Arlington, MA 02476-5896; tel. 781/648-9530

Park Marion & Vernon Streets Operating Company, LLC, 99 Park Street, Brookline, MA 02446; tel. 617/731-1050

Peabody Glen Health Care Center, 199 Andover Street, Peabody, MA 01960; tel. 978/531-0772

Penacook Place, Inc., 150 Water Street, Haverhill, MA 01830-6298; tel. 978/374-0707

Pilgrim Rehabilitation and Skilled Nursing Center, 96 Forest Street, Peabody, MA 01960-3907; tel. 978/532-0303

Plymouth MA SNF, LLC, 123 South Street, Plymouth, MA 02360; tel. 508/746-4343

Plymouth Medical Investors, 94 Obery Street, Plymouth, MA 02360; tel. 508/747-9800

Poet's Seat Health Care Center, 359 High Street, Greenfield, MA 01301; tel. 413/774-6318

Quabbin Valley Healthcare, 821 Daniel Shays Highway, Athol, MA 01331; tel. 978/249-3717

Queen Anne Nursing Home, Inc., 50 Recreation Park Drive, Hingham, MA 02043; tel. 781/749-4982

Raynham Medical Investors, LP, 546 South Street East, Raynham, MA 02767; tel. 508/821-5700

Renaissance Manor of Westfield, 37 Feeding Hills Road, Westfield, MA 01085; tel. 413/568-2341

River Terrace Healthcare, 1675 Main Street, Lancaster, MA 01523; tel. 978/365-4537

Royal Braintree Nursing and Rehabilitation Center, 95 Commercial Street, Braintree, MA 02184; tel. 781/848-3678

Royal Cape Cod Nursing & Rehabilitation Center, 8 Lewis Point Road, Buzzards Bay, MA 02532; tel. 508/759-5752

Royal Nursing Center, LLC, 545 Main Street, Falmouth, MA 02540; tel. 508/548-3800

Royal Taber Street Nursing & Rehabilitation Center, 19 Taber Street, New Bedford, MA 02740; tel. 508/997-0791

Sacred Heart Home, Inc., 359 Summer Street, New Bedford, MA 02740; tel. 508/996-6751

Sancta Maria Hospital, Inc., 799 Concord Avenue, Cambridge, MA 02138; tel. 617/868-2200

Sarah S. Brayton Nursing Care Center, 4901 North Main Street, Fall River, MA 02720; tel. 508/675-1001

Seacoast Nursing and Rehabilitation Center, 292 Washington Street, Gloucester, MA 01930; tel. 978/283-0300

Senior Residential Care/Kingston, Inc., 17 Chipman Way, Kingston, MA 02364; tel. 781/585-4100

Senior Residential Care/South Hadley, LLC, 573 Granby Road, South Hadley, MA 01075; tel. 413/532-2200

Shaughnessy-Kaplan Rehabilitation Hospital, Inc., Dove Avenue, Salem, MA 01970; tel. 978/825-8500

Sheehan Debt Acquisition, 47 East Main Street, West Brookfield, MA 01585; tel. 508/867-7716

Sherrill House, Inc., 135 South Huntington Avenue, Boston, MA 02130; tel. 617/731-2400

SNR Residential Care Worcester, Inc., 59 Acton Street, Worcester, MA 01604; tel. 508/791-3147

Soldiers' Home in Holyoke, 110 Cherry Street, Holyoke, MA 01040; tel. 413/532-9475

Soldiers' Home in Massachusetts, 91 Crest Avenue, Chelsea, MA 02150; tel. 617/884-5660

Somerset Ridge Nursing Center, 455 Brayton Avenue, Somerset, MA 02725; tel. 508/679-2240

Southbridge MA SNF, LLC, 84 Chapin Street, Southbridge, MA 01550; tel. 508/765-9133

Southeast Rehabilitation and Skilled Nursing Center, 184 Lincoln Street, North Easton, MA 02356; tel. 508/238-7053

Southpointe Rehabilitation and Skilled Care Center, 100 Amity Street, Fall River, MA 02721; tel. 508/675-2500

Southwood at Norwell Nursing Center, 501 Cordwainer Drive, Norwell, MA 02061; tel. 781/982-7450

SRC Springfield, Inc., 215 Bicentennial Highway, Springfield, MA 01118; tel. 413/796-7511

SSC Methuen Operating Company, LLC, 480 Jackson Street, Methuen, MA 01844; tel. 978/686-3906

SSC New Bedford Operating Company, LLC, 4586 Acushnet Avenue, New Bedford, MA 02745; tel. 508/998-1188

St. Camillus Health Center, 447 Hill Street, Whitinsville, MA 01588; tel. 508/234-7306

St. Joseph Rehabilitation and Nursing Care Center, 321 Centre Street, Dorchester, MA 02122; tel. 617/825-6320

Sterling Village, LLC, 18 Dana Hill Road, Sterling, MA 01564; tel. 978/422-5111

Sudbury Pines Extended Care Facility, 642 Boston Post Road, Sudbury, MA 01776; tel. 978/443-9000

Sunbridge Healthcare, LLC, PO Box 720, 20 North Maple Street, Hadley, MA 01035; tel. 413/584-5057

Sunny Acres Nursing Home, Inc., 254 Billerica Road, Chelmsford, MA 01824; tel. 978/256-1616

Sweet Brook Transitional Care and Living Centers, 1561 Cold Spring Road, Williamstown, MA 01267; tel. 413/458-8127

Synergy Health Centers, LLC, 59 Coolidge Hill Road, Watertown, MA 02472-2884; tel. 617/924-1130

The Ellis Nursing and Rehabilitation Center, 135 Ellis Avenue, Norwood, MA 02062; tel. 781/762-6880

The Highlands Medical Investors, LLC, 335 Nichols Road, Fitchburg, MA 01420; tel. 978/343-4411

The Lafayette Rehabilitation and Skilled Nursing Facility, 25 Lafayette Street, Marblehead, MA 01945; tel. 781/631-4535

VA Boston Healthcare System, 1400 VFW Parkway, West Roxbury, MA 02132; tel. 508/583-4500

VA Central Western Massachusetts Healthcare System, 421 North Main Street, Leeds, MA 01053-9764; tel. 413/584-4040

Vibra Hospital of Western Massachusetts, LLC, 111 Huntoon Memorial Highway, Rochdale, MA 01542; tel. 508/892-6800

VK East Bridgewater, LLC, 66 Central Street, East Bridgewater, MA 02333; tel. 508/378-7227

Waban Health and Rehabilitation Center, 20 Kinmonth Road, Waban, MA 02468; tel. 617/332-8481

We Do Care, Inc. dba Carlyle House, 342 Winter Street, Framingham, MA 01702; tel. 508/879-6100

Webster Manor Healthcare Center, 745 School Street, Webster, MA 01570; tel. 508/949-0644

Webster Operator, LLC, 56 Webster Street, Rockland, MA 02370-1737; tel. 781/871-0555

West Boylston Nursing Home, Inc., 76 North Main Street, West Boylston, MA 01583-1130; tel. 508/835-6076

Westfield Healthcare, LLC, 60 East Silver Street, Westfield, MA 01085; tel. 413/562-5121

Westford House, 3 Park Drive, Westford, MA 01886; tel. 978/392-1144

Weymouth Health Care Center, 64 Performance Drive, Weymouth, MA 02189; tel. 781/340-9800

Section C

WHC - Haverhill, 190 North Avenue, Haverhill, MA 01830; tel. 978/372-7700

Whitney Place at Natick, LP, 3 Vision Drive, Route 9 West, Natick, MA 01760; tel. 508/655-3344

Willowood of Williamstown, 25 Adams Road, Williamstown, MA 01267; tel. 413/458-2111

Windsor Skilled Nursing and Rehabilitation Center, 265 North Main Street, South Yarmouth, MA 02664; tel. 508/394-3514

Wingate at Andover, Inc., 80 Andover Street, Andover, MA 01810; tel. 978/470-3434

Wingate at Belvidere, 500 Wentworth Avenue, Lowell, MA 01852; tel. 978/458-1271

Wingate at Brighton, 100 North Beacon Street, Boston, MA 02134; tel. 617/787-2300

Wingate at East Longmeadow Rehabilitative & Skilled Nursing, 32 Chestnut Street, East Longmeadow, MA 01028; tel. 413/525-1893

Wingate at Hampden, 34 Main Street, Hampden, MA 01036; tel. 413/566-5511

Wingate at Reading, 1364 Main Street, Reading, MA 01867; tel. 781/942-1210

Wingate at Sudbury, Inc., 136 Boston Post Road, Sudbury, MA 01776; tel. 978/443-2722

Wingate at Wilbraham, Inc., 9 Maple Street, Wilbraham, MA 01095; tel. 413/596-2411

Wingate SRC West Springfield, 42 Prospect Avenue, West Springfield, MA 01089; tel. 413/733-3151

Woodbriar of Wilmington Rehab and Skilled Nursing Center, 90 West Street, Wilmington, MA 01887; tel. 978/658-2700

Worcester Health Care, LLC, 25 Oriol Drive, Worcester, MA 01605; tel. 508/852-3330

Worcester Rehabilitation and Health Care Center, 119 Providence Street, Worcester, MA 01604; tel. 508/860-5000

MICHIGAN

Aleda E. Lutz VA Medical Ctr., 1500 Weiss Street, Saginaw, MI 48602; tel. 989/497-2500

Battle Creek VA Medical Center, 5500 Armstrong Road, Battle Creek, MI 49037; tel. 269/966-5600

John D. Dingell VA Medical Center, 4646 John R, Detroit, MI 48201; tel. 313/576-1000

Life Care Center of Plainwell, 320 Brigham Street, Plainwell, MI 49080; tel. 269/688-9805

Oscar G. Johnson VA Medical Center, 325 East H Street, Iron Mountain, MI 49801; tel. 906/774-3300

Rivergate Terrace, 14141 Pennsylvania Road, Riverview, MI 48193; tel. 734/284-8000

Special Tree NeuroCare Center, 10909 Hannan Road, Romulus, MI 48174; tel. 734/893-1044

VA Ann Arbor Healthcare System, 2215 Fuller Road, Ann Arbor, MI 48105; tel. 734/769-7100

MINNESOTA

Bureau of Prisons - FMC Rochester, PO Box 4600, Rochester, MN 55903; tel. 507/287-0674

Mayo Clinic Health System in Fairmont, 800 Medical Center Drive, Fairmont, MN 56031; tel. 507/238-8100

St. Cloud VA Health Care System, 4801 Veterans Drive, Saint Cloud, MN 56303; tel. 320/255-6480

VA Health Care System - Minneapolis, One Veterans Drive, Minneapolis, MN 55417; tel. 612/725-2000

MISSISSIPPI

East Mississippi State Hospital, PO Box 4128 West Station, Meridian, MS 39304; tel. 601/581-7600

Mississippi State Hospital, PO Box 157-A, Whitfield, MS 39193-0157; tel. 601/351-8190

North Mississippi Medical Center, Inc., 830 South Gloster Street, Tupelo, MS 38801; tel. 662/377-3847

VA Gulf Coast Veterans Health Care System, 400 Veterans Avenue, Biloxi, MS 39531; tel. 228/523-5000

VA Medical Center - G. V. (Sonny) Montgomery, 1500 East Woodrow Wilson Avenue, Jackson, MS 39216; tel. 601/364-1201

Webster Health Services, Inc., 70 Medical Plaza, Eupora, MS 39744; tel. 662/258-6221

MISSOURI

Barnes-Jewish Hospital, 1 Barnes Jewish Hospital Plaza, Saint Louis, MO 63110; tel. 314/747-3000

Bethesda Health Group, Inc. Bethesda Southgate, 1630 Des Peres Road, Saint Louis, MO 63131; tel. 314/846-2000

Bravo Care of Northbrook, Inc., 11701 Borman Drive, Suite 315, Saint Louis, MO 63146; tel. 314/994-9070

Florissant Medical Investors, LLC, 1201 Garden Plaza Drive, Florissant, MO 63033; tel. 314/831-3752

Harry S. Truman Memorial Veterans' Hospital, 800 Hospital Drive, Columbia, MO 65201; tel. 573/814-6000

John J. Pershing VA Medical Center, 1500 North Westwood Boulevard, Poplar Bluff, MO 63901; tel. 573/686-4151

Lester E. Cox Medical Centers, 1423 North Jefferson Avenue, Springfield, MO 65802; tel. 417/269-3000

Life Care Center of Waynesville, 700 Birch Lane, Waynesville, MO 65583; tel. 573/774-6456

Life Care Center of Bridgeton, 12145 Bridge Square Drive, Bridgeton, MO 63044; tel. 314/298-7444

Life Care Center of Brookfield, 315 Hunt Street, Brookfield, MO 64628; tel. 660/258-3367

Life Care Center of Cape Girardeau, 365 South Broadview Street, Cape Girardeau, MO 63703; tel. 573/335-2086

Life Care Center of Carrollton, 300 Life Care Lane, Carrollton, MO 64633; tel. 660/542-0155

Life Care Center of Grandview, 6301 East 125th Street, Grandview, MO 64030; tel. 816/765-7714

Life Care Center of Saint Louis, 3520 Chouteau Avenue, Saint Louis, MO 63129; tel. 314/771-2100

Life Care Center of Sullivan, 875 Dunsford Drive, Sullivan, MO 63080; tel. 573/468-3128

Northwood Hills Care Center, LLC, PO Box 187, Humansville, MO 65674; tel. 417/754-2208

St. Louis VA Healthcare System, 915 North Grand Boulevard, Saint Louis, MO 63106; tel. 314/289-7020

The Westchester House, 550 White Road, Chesterfield, MO 63017; tel. 314/469-1200

U.S. Medical Center for Federal Prisoners, 1900 West Sunshine Street, Springfield, MO 65807; tel. 417/862-7041

MONTANA

VA Montana Healthcare System, 3687 Veterans Drive, Fort Harrison, MT 59636-1500; tel. 406/447-7900

NEBRASKA

Life Care Center of Elkhorn, 20275 Hopper Street, Elkhorn, NE 68022; tel. 402/289-2572

Life Care Center of Omaha, 6032 Ville De Sante Drive, Omaha, NE 68104; tel. 402/571-6770

VA Nebraska-Western Iowa Health Care System, 4101 Woolworth Avenue, Omaha, NE 68105; tel. 402/449-0600

NEVADA

Life Care Center of Las Vegas, 6151 Vegas Drive, Las Vegas, NV 89108; tel. 702/648-4900

Life Care Center of Paradise Valley, 2325 East Harmon, Las Vegas, NV 89119; tel. 702/798-7990

Life Care Center of Reno, 445 Holcomb Ranch Lane, Reno, NV 89511; tel. 775/851-0123

VA Sierra Nevada Health Care System, 975 Kirman Avenue, Reno, NV 89502-2597; tel. 775/786-7200

NEW HAMPSHIRE

Rochester Manor, 40 Whitehall Road, Rochester, NH 03867; tel. 603/332-7711

VA Medical Center, 718 Smyth Road, Manchester, NH 03104-4098; tel. 603/624-4366

NEW JERSEY

Absecon Manor Nursing and Rehabilitation Center, 1020 Pitney Road, Absecon, NJ 08201; tel. 609/646-5400

Bacharach Institute for Rehabilitation, PO Box 723, Pomona, NJ 08240-0723; tel. 609/652-7000

Bartley Healthcare Nursing and Rehabilitation, 175 Bartley Road, Jackson, NJ 08527; tel. 732/370-4700

Bergen Regional Medical Center, 230 East Ridgewood Avenue, Paramus, NJ 07652; tel. 201/967-4000

Care One At Hamilton, 1660 WhiteHorse Hamilton Square Road, Trenton, NJ 08619; tel. 609/586-4600

CentraState Healthcare Affiliates, Inc., 689 West Main Street, Freehold, NJ 07728; tel. 732/431-5200

Daughters of Miriam Center, 155 Hazel Street, Clifton, NJ 07011; tel. 973/772-3700

Forest Hill Healthcare Center, Inc., 497 Mount Prospect Avenue, Newark, NJ 07104; tel. 973/482-3600

Forkidcare, LLC, 1304 Laurel Oak Road, Voorhees, NJ 08043; tel. 856/346-3300

Franklin Care Center, 3371 Route 27, Franklin Park, NJ 08823; tel. 732/821-8000

Linwood Care Center, New Road and Central Avenue, Linwood, NJ 08221; tel. 609/927-6131

Mainland Manor Nursing and Rehabilitation Center, PO Box 1309, Pleasantville, NJ 08232; tel. 609/646-6900

Medford Care Center, 185 Tuckerton Road, Medford, NJ 08055; tel. 856/983-8500

Meridian Nursing & Rehabilitation at Brick, 415 Jack Martin Boulevard, Brick, NJ 08724; tel. 732/206-8000

Prospect Heights Care Center, 336 Prospect Avenue, Hackensack, NJ 07601; tel. 201/678-1800

Regent Care Center, 50 Polifly Road, Hackensack, NJ 07601; tel. 201/646-1166

Robert Wood Johnson University Hospital at Rahway, 865 Stone Street, Rahway, NJ 07065; tel. 732/499-6050

South Mountain Healthcare and Rehabilitation Center, 2385 Springfield Avenue, Vauxhall, NJ 07088-1046; tel. 908/688-3400

St. Lawrence Rehabilitation Center, 2381 Lawrenceville Road, Lawrenceville, NJ 08648; tel. 609/896-9500

VA New Jersey Health Care System, 385 Tremont Avenue, Director's Office (00), East Orange, NJ 07018; tel. 973/676-1000

Virtua - Memorial Hospital Burlington County, Inc., 175 Madison Avenue, Mount Holly, NJ 08060; tel. 609/914-6000

Virtua-West Jersey Health System, Inc.(Voorhees), 100 Bowman Drive, Voorhees New Jersey, Voorhees, NJ 08043; tel. 856/247-3000

West Caldwell Care Center, 165 Fairfield Avenue, West Caldwell, NJ 07006; tel. 973/226-1100

Whiting Healthcare Center, 3000 Hilltop Road, Whiting, NJ 08759; tel. 732/849-4400

NEW MEXICO

Deming Hospital Corporation, 900 West Ash Street, Deming, NM 88030; tel. 575/546-5800

Life Care Center of Farmington, 1101 West Murray Drive, Farmington, NM 87401; tel. 505/326-1600

New Mexico Behavioral Health Institute at Las Vegas, 3695 Hot Springs Boulevard, Las Vegas, NM 87701; tel. 505/454-2266

New Mexico State Veteran's Home, 992 South Broadway, Truth Or Consequences, NM 87901; tel. 575/894-4200

New Mexico VA Health Care System, 1501 San Pedro, Drive Souteast, Albuquerque, NM 87108; tel. 505/265-1711

NEW YORK

Alice Hyde Medical Center, PO Box 729, Malone, NY 12953; tel. 518/483-3000

Coler-Goldwater Specialty Hosp. and NF - Coler Campus, 900 Main Street, New York, NY 10044-0052; tel. 212/848-6956

Dr. Susan Smith McKinney Nursing/Rehabilitation Center, 594 Albany Avenue, Brooklyn, NY 11203; tel. 718/245-7170

Good Samaritan Hospital Medical Center, 1000 Montauk Highway, West Islip, NY 11795; tel. 631/376-4001

Gouverneur Skilled Nursing Facility, 227 Madison Street, New York, NY 10002; tel. 212/441-5017

Helen Hayes Hospital, 51-55 Route 9, West, West Haverstraw, NY 10993; tel. 845/786-4000

Henry J. Carter Specialty Hospital and Nursing Facility, 1752 Park Avenue, New York, NY 10035; tel. 646/686-0051

James J Peters Bronx VA Medical Center, 130 West Kingsbridge Road, Bronx, NY 10468; tel. 718/584-9000

Jewish Home Lifecare - Manhattan, 120 West 106 Street, New York, NY 10025; tel. 212/870-5000

Jewish Home Lifecare, Sarah Neuman Center, Westchester, 845 Palmer Avenue, Mamaroneck, NY 10543; tel. 914/698-6005

Jewish Home LifeCare,Harry & Jeanette Weinberg Campus,Bronx, 100 West Kingsbridge Road, Bronx, NY 10468; tel. 718/410-1280

Kingsbrook Jewish Medical Center, 585 Schenectady Avenue, Brooklyn, NY 11203; tel. 718/604-5000

Nassau Health Care Corporation, 2201 Hempstead Turnpike, East Meadow, NY 11554; tel. 516/572-0123

No Shore Univ Hosp Stern Family Center for Rehabilitation, 330 Community Drive, Manhasset, NY 11030; tel. 516/562-8070

Orzac Center for Rehabilitation, 900 Franklin Avenue, Valley Stream, NY 11580; tel. 516/256-6502

Our Lady of Consolation Nursing & Rehabilitative Care Center, 111 Beach Drive, West Islip, NY 11795; tel. 631/587-1600

Providence Rest, 3304 Waterbury Avenue, Bronx, NY 10465; tel. 718/931-3000

Queens Boulevard Extended Care Facility, 61-11 Queens Boulevard, Woodside, NY 11377; tel. 718/205-0287

Samuel S. Stratton VA Medical Center, 113 Holland Avenue, Albany, NY 12208; tel. 518/626-5000

Sea View Hospital Rehabilitation Center and Home, 460 Brielle Avenue, Staten Island, NY 10314; tel. 718/317-3000

St. James Healthcare Center, 275 Moriches Road, Saint James, NY 11780; tel. 631/862-8000

Unity Hospital, 1555 Long Pond Road, Rochester, NY 14626; tel. 585/723-7000

Upstate New York VA Health Care Network at Canandaigua, 400 Fort Hill Avenue, Canandaigua, NY 14424; tel. 585/394-2000

VA Healthcare Network Upstate New York at Bath, 76 Veterans Avenue, Bath, NY 14810; tel. 607/664-4722

VA Healthcare Network Upstate New York at Syracuse, 800 Irving Avenue, Syracuse, NY 13210; tel. 315/425-4400

VA Hudson Valley Health Care System, 2094 Albany Post Road, Route 9A, Montrose, NY 10548; tel. 914/737-4400

VA Medical Center Northport, 79 Middleville Road, Northport, NY 11768; tel. 631/261-4400

VA New York Harbor Healthcare System, 800 Poly Place, Brooklyn, NY 11209; tel. 718/630-3521

VA Western New York Health Care System, 3495 Bailey Avenue, Buffalo, NY 14215; tel. 716/862-8529

NORTH CAROLINA

Alamance Regional Medical Center, Inc., PO Box 202, Burlington, NC 27216-0202; tel. 336/538-7450

Charles George VA Medical Center at Asheville, 1100 Tunnel Road, Asheville, NC 28805; tel. 828/298-7911

Granville Health System, College Street PO 947, Oxford, NC 27565; tel. 919/690-3419

Highlands - Cashiers Hospital, Inc., PO Drawer 190, Highlands, NC 28741-0190; tel. 828/526-1200

Life Care Center of Banner Elk, PO Box 2199, Banner Elk, NC 28604; tel. 828/898-5136

Life Care Center of Hendersonville, 400 Thompson Street, Hendersonville, NC 28792; tel. 828/697-4348

Person Memorial Hospital, 615 Ridge Road, Roxboro, NC 27573; tel. 336/599-2121

PruittHealth Raleigh, 2420 Lake Wheeler Road, Raleigh, NC 27603; tel. 919/755-0226

Southeastern Regional Medical Center, PO Box 1408, Lumberton, NC 28359; tel. 910/671-5000

United Veteran Services of North Carolina, 214 Cochran Avenue, Fayetteville, NC 28301; tel. 910/482-4131

United Veteran Services of North Carolina, PO Box 599, Salisbury, NC 28145; tel. 704/638-4200

VA Medical Center, 508 Fulton Street, Durham, NC 27705; tel. 919/286-0411

VA Medical Center, 2300 Ramsey Street, Fayetteville, NC 28301; tel. 910/822-7091

Vidant Chowan Hospital, 211 Virginia Road, Edenton, NC 27932; tel. 252/482-8451

W. G. (Bill) Hefner VA Medical Center, 1601 Brenner Avenue, Salisbury, NC 28144; tel. 704/638-9000

NORTH DAKOTA

Fargo VA Health Care System, 2101 Elm Street North, Fargo, ND 58102; tel. 701/232-3241

OHIO

Broadview Nursing Home, Inc., 5520 Broadview Road, Parma, OH 44134; tel. 216/749-4010

Daniel Drake Center for Post-Acute Care, LLC, 151 West Galbraith Road, Cincinnati, OH 45216; tel. 513/418-2500

DaySpring of Miami Valley Health Care Center and Rehab, 8001 Dayton-Springfield Road, Fairborn, OH 45324; tel. 937/864-5800

Department of Veterans Affairs Medical Center, Dayton, Ohio, 4100 West 3rd Street, Dayton, OH 45428; tel. 937/268-6511

Eastgatespring Health Care Center and Rehabilitation, 4400 Gleneste Withamsville Road, Cincinnati, OH 45245; tel. 513/752-3710

Euclid Hospital, 18901 Lake Shore Boulevard, Euclid, OH 44119; tel. 216/531-9000

Franciscan Care Center, 4111 North Holland Sylvania Road, Toledo, OH 43623; tel. 419/882-6582

Fulton County Health Center, 725 South Shoop Avenue, Wauseon, OH 43567; tel. 419/335-2015

Heritagespring Health Care and Rehabilitation Center, 7235 Heritagespring Drive, West Chester, OH 45069; tel. 513/759-5777

Hillspring Healthcare & Rehab Center, 325 East Central Avenue Route 73, Springboro, OH 45066; tel. 937/748-1100

Hospitality Homes Center for Rehabilitation and Healing, 1301 North Monroe Drive, Xenia, OH 45385; tel. 937/372-4495

Life Care Center of Elyria, 1212 South Abbe Road, Elyria, OH 44035; tel. 440/365-5200

Life Care Center of Medina, 2400 Columbia Road, Medina, OH 44256; tel. 330/483-3131

Life Care Center of Westlake, 26520 Center Ridge Road, Westlake, OH 44145; tel. 440/871-3030

Louis Stokes, Cleveland VA Medical Center, 10701 East Boulevard, Cleveland, OH 44106; tel. 216/231-3456

Mayfair Village Nursing Care Center, 3000 Bethel Road, Columbus, OH 43220; tel. 614/889-6320

Oregon Health Investors Co., 2841 Munding Drive, Oregon, OH 43616; tel. 419/697-4100

Providence Care Center, 2025 Hayes Avenue, Sandusky, OH 44870; tel. 419/627-2273

Rosary Care Center, 6832 Convent Boulevard, Sylvania, OH 43560; tel. 419/824-3600

Shawneespring Health Care and Rehabilitation Center, 10111 Simonson Road, Harrison, OH 45030; tel. 513/367-7780

St. Leonard, 8100 Clyo Road, Centerville, OH 45458; tel. 937/433-0480

The Ohio Eastern Star Home, 1451 Gambier Road, Mount Vernon, OH 43050; tel. 740/397-1706

The Village at St. Edward Nursing Care, 3131 Smith Road, Fairlawn, OH 44333-2697; tel. 330/666-1183

Trinity Health System, 380 Summit Avenue, Steubenville, OH 43952; tel. 740/283-7212

VA Healthcare System of Ohio - Cincinnati Campus, 3200 Vine Street, Cincinnati, OH 45220; tel. 513/861-3100

VA Medical Center - Chillicothe, 17273 State Route 104, Chillicothe, OH 45601; tel. 740/773-1141

OKLAHOMA

Department of Veterans Affairs Medical Center, 921 Northeast 13th Street, Oklahoma City, OK 73104; tel. 405/456-3312

OREGON

Life Care Center of Coos Bay, 2890 Ocean Boulevard, Coos Bay, OR 97420; tel. 541/267-5433

Life Care Center of McMinnville, 1309 East 27th Street, McMinnville, OR 97128; tel. 503/472-4678

Life Care Center Valley West Health Care Center, 2300 Warren Street, Eugene, OR 97405; tel. 541/686-2828

Portland VA Medical Center, PO Box 1034, Portland, OR 97207; tel. 503/273-5267

VA Roseburg Healthcare System, 913 Northwest Garden Valley Boulevard, Roseburg, OR 97471; tel. 541/440-1000

PENNSYLVANIA

Albert Einstein Medical Center, 5501 Old York Road, Philadelphia, PA 19141; tel. 215/456-7890

Angela Jane Pavilion, 8410 Roosevelt Boulevard, Philadelphia, PA 19152; tel. 215/708-1200

Barclay Friends, 700 North Franklin Street, West Chester, PA 19380; tel. 610/696-5211

Berwick Hospital Center, 701 East 16th Street, Berwick, PA 18603; tel. 570/759-5000

Bible Fellowship Church Homes, Inc., 3000 Fellowship Drive, Whitehall, PA 18052; tel. 610/799-3000

Charles Cole Memorial Hospital, 1001 East Second Street, Coudersport, PA 16915; tel. 814/274-5347

Erie VA Medical Center, 135 East 38th Street, Erie, PA 16504; tel. 814/868-8661

Gnaden Huetten Memorial Hospital, 211 North 12th Street, Lehighton, PA 18235-1195; tel. 610/377-1300

Good Shepherd Rehabilitation Hospital, 850 South Fifth Street, Allentown, PA 18103-3295; tel. 610/776-3133

Hickory House Nursing Home, 3120 Horseshoe Pike, Honey Brook, PA 19344; tel. 610/273-2915

Lebanon VA Medical Center, 1700 South Lincoln Avenue, Lebanon, PA 17042; tel. 717/272-6621

Main Line Hospital Lankenau, 100 East Lancaster Avenue, Wynnewood, PA 19096; tel. 484/476-2000

Nazareth Hospital, 2601 Holme Avenue, Philadelphia, PA 19152-2096; tel. 215/335-6000

Philadelphia VA Medical Center, University and Woodland Avenues, Philadelphia, PA 19104; tel. 215/823-5857

Presbyterian Medical Center of the UPHS, 51 North 39th Street, Philadelphia, PA 19104; tel. 215/662-8260

River's Edge Nursing and Rehabilitation Center, 9501 State Road, Philadelphia, PA 19114; tel. 215/632-5700

Squirrel Hill Operating Center, LLC, 2025 Wightman Street, Pittsburgh, PA 15217; tel. 412/421-8443

UPMC Horizon, 110 North Main Street, Greenville, PA 16125; tel. 724/588-2100

VA Butler Healthcare, 325 New Castle Road, Butler, PA 16001-2480; tel. 724/287-4781

VA Medical Center, 1400 Black Horse Hill Road, Coatesville, PA 19320-2097; tel. 610/384-7711

VA Medical Center - James E. Van Zandt, 2907 Pleasant Valley Boulevard, Altoona, PA 16602-4377; tel. 814/943-8164

VA Medical Center Wilkes-Barre, 1111 East End Boulevard, Wilkes Barre, PA 18711; tel. 570/821-7204

VA Pittsburgh Healthcare System, University Drive C, Pittsburgh, PA 15240; tel. 412/360-6391

RHODE ISLAND

Cedar Crest Nursing Centre, 125 Scituate Avenue, Cranston, RI 02921; tel. 401/944-8500

Cherry Hill Manor, 2 Cherry Hill Road, Johnston, RI 02919; tel. 401/231-3102

Chestnut Terrace Nursing & Rehabilitation Center, 100 Wompanoag Trail, Riverside, RI 02915; tel. 401/438-4275

EPOCH Senior Healthcare on Blackstone Blvd, LLC, 353 Blackstone Boulevard, Providence, RI 02906; tel. 401/273-6565

Evergreen House Health Center, One Evergreen Drive, East Providence, RI 02914; tel. 401/438-3250

Harken, Inc., PO Box 152, Pascoag, RI 02859; tel. 401/568-2549

Kent Regency Genesis Health Care, 660 Commonwealth Avenue, Warwick, RI 02886; tel. 401/739-4241

Kindred Transitional Care and Rehabilitation - Oak Hill, 544 Pleasant Street, Pawtucket, RI 02860; tel. 401/725-8888

Pezzelli Nursing Home, Inc., 100 Smithfield Road, North Providence, RI 02904; tel. 401/353-1710

Roger Williams Medical Center, 825 Chalkstone Avenue, Providence, RI 02908; tel. 401/456-2043

Ryan Health Center, Inc., 80 Morgan Avenue, Johnston, RI 02919; tel. 401/944-7800

South County Nursing and Rehabilitation Center, 740 Oak Hill Road, North Kingstown, RI 02852; tel. 401/294-4545

Westerly Health Center, 280 High Street, Westerly, RI 02891; tel. 401/348-0020

Woonsocket Health and Rehabilitation Centre, 262 Poplar Street, Woonsocket, RI 02895; tel. 401/765-2100

SOUTH CAROLINA

C. M. Tucker, Jr. Nursing Care Center, 2200 Harden Street, Columbia, SC 29203; tel. 803/737-5301

Life Care Center of Charleston, 2600 Elms Plantation Boulevard, North Charleston, SC 29406; tel. 843/764-3500

Life Care Center of Columbia, 2514 Faraway Drive, Columbia, SC 29223; tel. 803/865-1999

Life Care Center of Hilton Head, 120 Lamotte Drive, Hilton Head Island, SC 29926; tel. 843/681-6006

Pepper Hill Nursing and Rehab Center, 3525 Augustus Road, Aiken, SC 29802-3188; tel. 803/642-8376

PruittHealth- Rock Hill, LLC, 261 South Herlong Avenue, Rock Hill, SC 29732; tel. 803/366-7133

QHG of South Carolina, INC, PO Box 1150, Marion, SC 29571; tel. 843/431-2000

Ralph H. Johnson VA Medical Center, 109 Bee Street, Charleston, SC 29401-5799; tel. 843/577-5011

UniHealth Post Acute Care North Augusta, 1200 Talisman Drive, North Augusta, SC 29841; tel. 803/278-2170

William Jennings Bryan Dorn VA Medical Center, 6439 Garners Ferry Road, Columbia, SC 29209; tel. 803/776-4000

SOUTH DAKOTA

Sioux Falls VA Health Care System, PO Box 5046, Sioux Falls, SD 57117; tel. 605/336-3230

VA Black Hills Health Care System-Fort Meade-Hot Springs, SD, 113 Comanche Road, Fort Meade, SD 57741; tel. 605/720-7170

TENNESSEE

Christian Care Center of Bedford County, 835 Union Street, Shelbyville, TN 37160; tel. 931/680-2300

Section C

Christian Care Center of Cheatham County, 2501 River Road, Ashland City, TN 37015; tel. 615/792–4948

Christian Care Center of Johnson City, Inc., 140 Technology Lane, Johnson City, TN 37604; tel. 423/434–2016

Christian Care Center of Rutherford County, 202 Enon Springs Road East, Smyrna, TN 37167; tel. 423/975–5455

Christian Care Center of Springfield, LLC, 704 5th Avenue East, Springfield, TN 37172; tel. 615/384–7977

Crossville Medical Investors, LLC, 80 Justice Street, Crossville, TN 38555; tel. 931/484–4782

Fort Sanders Regional Medical Center, 1901 Clinch Avenue, Knoxville, TN 37916; tel. 865/541–1100

Ivy Hall Nursing Home, Inc., 301 Watauga Avenue, Elizabethton, TN 37643; tel. 423/542–6512

KDM, Inc., 55 Nursing Home Road, Chuckey, TN 37641; tel. 423/257–6761

Lakebridge Medical Investors, LLC, 115 Woodlawn Drive, Johnson City, TN 37604; tel. 423/975–0095

Life Care Center of Elizabethton, 1641 Highway 19E Bypass, Elizabethton, TN 37643; tel. 423/542–4133

Life Care Center of Athens, PO Box 786, Athens, TN 37371-0786; tel. 423/754–8181

Life Care Center of Centerville, 112 Old Dickson Road, Centerville, TN 37033; tel. 931/729–4236

Life Care Center of Cleveland, 3530 Keith Street Northwest, Cleveland, TN 37312; tel. 423/476–3254

Life Care Center of Collegedale, PO Box 658, Collegedale, TN 37315; tel. 423/396–2182

Life Care Center of Columbia, 841 West James Campbell Boulevard, Columbia, TN 38401; tel. 931/388–5035

Life Care Center of Copper Basin, PO Box 518, Ducktown, TN 37326; tel. 423/496–3245

Life Care Center of East Ridge, 1500 Fincher Avenue, East Ridge, TN 37412; tel. 423/894–1254

Life Care Center of Gray, 791 Old Gray Station Road, Gray, TN 37615; tel. 423/477–7146

Life Care Center of Greeneville, 725 Crum Street, Greeneville, TN 37743; tel. 423/639–8131

Life Care Center of Morgan County, 419 South Kingston Street, Wartburg, TN 37887; tel. 423/346–6691

Life Care Center of Morristown, 501 West Economy Road, Morristown, TN 37814; tel. 423/581–5435

Life Care Center of Red Bank, 1020 Runyan Drive, Chattanooga, TN 37405; tel. 423/877–1155

Life Care Center of Sparta, 508 Mose Drive, Sparta, TN 38583; tel. 931/738–9430

Life Care Center of Tullahoma, 1715 North Jackson Street, Tullahoma, TN 37388; tel. 931/455–8557

Life Care Centers of America, Inc., 336 W Old Andrew Johnson Highway, Jefferson City, TN 37760; tel. 865/475–6097

Lynchburg Nursing Center, 40 Nursing Home Road, Lynchburg, TN 37352; tel. 931/759–6000

Milford Medical Investors, LP, PO Box 137, Bruceton, TN 38317; tel. 731/586–2061

Ridgeview Terrace of Life Care, PO Box 26, Rutledge, TN 37861; tel. 865/828–5295

Roan Highlands Nursing Center, 146 Buck Creek Road, Roan Mountain, TN 37687; tel. 423/772–0161

Saint Thomas Hickman Hospital, 135 East Swan Street, Centerville, TN 37033; tel. 931/729–4271

Sweetwater Nursing Center, Inc., 978 Highway 11 South, Sweetwater, TN 37874; tel. 423/337–6631

The Heritage Center, 1026 McFarland Street, Morristown, TN 37814; tel. 423/581–5100

The Wexford House, 2421 John B. Dennis Highway, Kingsport, TN 37660-5896; tel. 423/288–3988

VA Medical Center - James H. Quillen, PO Box 4000, Mountain Home, TN 37684; tel. 423/926–1171

VA Tennessee Valley Healthcare System, 1310 24th Avenue South, Nashville, TN 37212-2637; tel. 615/327–4751

TEXAS

Alameda Oaks Nursing Center, 1101 South Alameda, Corpus Christi, TX 78404; tel. 361/882–2711

Amarillo VA Health Care System, 6010 Amarillo Boulevard, West, Amarillo, TX 79106; tel. 806/355–9703

Bureau of Prisons - FCI Fort Worth, 3150 Horton Road, Fort Worth, TX 76119; tel. 817/534–8400

Burleson St. Joseph Manor, 1022 Presidential Corridor, Highway 21 East, Caldwell, TX 77836; tel. 979/567–0920

Central Texas Veterans Health Care System, 1901 Veterans Memorial Drive, Temple, TX 76504; tel. 254/743–2306

Garden Terrace Alzheimer's Center of Excellence, 7500 Oakmont Boulevard, Fort Worth, TX 76132; tel. 817/346–8080

Garden Terrace Alzheimer's Center of Excellence, 7887 Cambridge Street, Houston, TX 77054; tel. 713/796–2777

Life Care Center of Haltom, 2936 Markum Drive, Haltom City, TX 76117; tel. 817/831–0545

Life Care Center of Plano, 3800 West Park Boulevard, Plano, TX 75075; tel. 972/612–1700

Michael E. DeBakey VA Medical Center, 2002 Holcombe Boulevard, Houston, TX 77030; tel. 713/794–7931

Moore County Hospital District, 224 East Second Street, Dumas, TX 79029; tel. 806/935–7171

Renaissance Park Multi-Care Center, 4252 Bryant Irvin Road, Fort Worth, TX 76109; tel. 817/738–2975

Scott & White Memorial Hospital, 2401 South 31st Street, Temple, TX 76508; tel. 254/724–6583

South Texas Veterans Health Care System, 7400 Merton Minter Boulevard, San Antonio, TX 78229-4404; tel. 210/617–5205

St. Joseph Manor, 2333 Manor Drive, Bryan, TX 77802; tel. 979/821–7330

The Vosswood Nursing Center, 815 South Voss Road, Houston, TX 77057; tel. 713/827–0883

VA North Texas Health Care System, 4500 South Lancaster Road, Dallas, TX 75216; tel. 202/329–8673

West Texas VA Health Care System, 300 Veterans Boulevard, Big Spring, TX 79720; tel. 432/263–7361

Wooldridge Place Nursing Center, 7352 Wooldridge Road, Corpus Christi, TX 78414; tel. 361/991–9633

UTAH

Garden Terrace Alzheimer's Center of Excellence, 1201 East 4500 South, Salt Lake City, UT 84117; tel. 801/261–3664

Life Care Center of Bountiful, 460 West 2600 South, Bountiful, UT 84010; tel. 801/295–3135

VERMONT

Bennington Health and Rehabilitation Center, 2 Blackberry Lane, Bennington, VT 05201; tel. 802/442–8525

St. Johnsbury Health and Rehab Center, 1248 Hospital Drive, Saint Johnsbury, VT 05819; tel. 802/748–8757

SVHC Centers for Living and Rehabilitation, 160 Hospital Drive, Bennington, VT 05201; tel. 802/447–1547

VIRGINIA

Augusta Health, Inc., PO Box 1000, Fishersville, VA 22939; tel. 540/332–4800

Community Memorial Healthcenter, PO Box 90, South Hill, VA 23970-0090; tel. 434/447–3151

CPL (Iliff), LLC, 8000 Iliff Drive, Dunn Loring, VA 22027; tel. 703/560–1000

Eastern State Hospital, 4601 Ironbound Road, Williamsburg, VA 23188; tel. 757/253–5161

Hiram W. Davis Medical Center, PO Box 4030, Petersburg, VA 23803; tel. 804/524–7112

Inova Loudoun Hospital, 44045 Riverside Parkway, Leesburg, VA 20176; tel. 703/858–6000

James River Convalescent & Rehabilitation Center, 540 Aberthaw Avenue, Newport News, VA 23601; tel. 757/595–2273

Life Care Center of New Market, 315 East Lee Highway, New Market, VA 22844; tel. 540/740–8041

Lonesome Pine Hospital, PO Drawer I, Big Stone Gap, VA 24219-0230; tel. 276/523–3111

Salem VA Medical Center, 1970 Roanoke Boulevard, Salem, VA 24153; tel. 540/982–2463

Southampton Memorial Hospital, 100 Fairview Drive, Franklin, VA 23851; tel. 757/569–6100

VA Medical Center - Hunter Holmes McGuire, 1201 Broad Rock Boulevard, Richmond, VA 23249; tel. 804/675–5000

VA Medical Center-Hampton, 100 Emancipation Drive, Hampton, VA 23667; tel. 757/722–9961

WASHINGTON

Alderwood Manor, 3600 East Hartson Avenue, Spokane, WA 99202; tel. 509/535–2071

Cascade Park Care Center, 801 Southeast Park Crest Avenue, Vancouver, WA 98683; tel. 360/260–2200

Cottesmore of Life Care, 2909 14th Avenue Northwest, Gig Harbor, WA 98335; tel. 253/851–5433

Garden Terrace Alzheimer's Center of Excellence, 491 South 338th Street, Federal Way, WA 98003; tel. 253/661–2226

Hallmark Manor, 32300 1st Avenue South, Federal Way, WA 98003; tel. 253/874–3580

Life Care Center of Mount Vernon, 2120 East Division Street, Mount Vernon, WA 98274; tel. 360/424–4258

Life Care Center of Federal Way, 1045 S. 308th Street, Federal Way, WA 98003; tel. 253/946–2273

Life Care Center of Kennewick, 1508 West Seventh Avenue, Kennewick, WA 99336; tel. 509/586–9185

Life Care Center of Kirkland, 10101 Northeast 120th Street, Kirkland, WA 98034; tel. 425/823–2323

Life Care Center of Port Orchard, 2031 Pottery Avenue, Port Orchard, WA 98366; tel. 360/876–8035

Life Care Center of Port Townsend, 751 Kearney Street, Port Townsend, WA 98368; tel. 360/385–3555

Life Care Center of Puyallup, 511 10th Avenue Southeast, Puyallup, WA 98372; tel. 253/845–7566

Life Care Center of Richland, 44 Goethals Drive, Richland, WA 99352; tel. 509/943–1117

Life Care Center of Skagit Valley, 1462 West SR 20, Sedro Woolley, WA 98284; tel. 360/856–6867

Life Care Center of the San Juan Islands, 660 Spring Street, Friday Harbor, WA 98250; tel. 360/378–2117

Marysville Care Center, 1821 Grove Street, Marysville, WA 98270; tel. 360/659–3926

Ritzville Medical Investors, Inc., 506 South Jackson Street, Ritzville, WA 99169; tel. 509/659–1600

Sea-Mar Community Health Center, 1040 South Henderson Street, Seattle, WA 98108; tel. 206/763–5277

VA Medical Center, North 4815 Assembly Street, Spokane, WA 99205; tel. 509/434–7000

VA Puget Sound Health Care System, 1660 South Columbian Way (S-002-Ql), Seattle, WA 98108-1597; tel. 206/764–2731

WEST VIRGINIA

CamdenClark Medical Center, PO Box 718, Parkersburg, WV 26102; tel. 304/424–2111

Pleasant Valley Hospital, 2520 Valley Drive, Point Pleasant, WV 25550; tel. 304/675–4340

VA Medical Center, 200 Veterans Avenue, Beckley, WV 25801; tel. 304/255–2121

VA Medical Center, 510 Butler Avenue, Martinsburg, WV 25405; tel. 304/263–0811

VA Medical Center - Louis A. Johnson, 1 Medical Center Drive, Clarksburg, WV 26301; tel. 304/623–3461

WISCONSIN

Alden Estates of Countryside, Inc., 1130 Collins Road, Jefferson, WI 53549; tel. 920/674–3170

Clement J. Zablocki VA Medical Center, 5000 West National Avenue, Milwaukee, WI 53295-1000; tel. 414/384–2000

Divine Savior Healthcare, Inc., PO Box 387, Portage, WI 53901; tel. 608/742–4131

VA Medical Center - Great Lakes Health Care System, 500 East Veterans Street, Tomah, WI 54660; tel. 608/372–1777

William S. Middleton Memorial Veterans Hospital, 2500 Overlook Terrace, Madison, WI 53705; tel. 608/256–1901

WYOMING

Life Care Center of Casper, 4041 South Poplar Street, Casper, WY 82601; tel. 307/266–0000

Life Care Center of Cheyenne, 1330 Prairie Avenue, Cheyenne, WY 82009; tel. 307/778–8997

Sheridan VA Health Care System, 1898 Fort Road, Sheridan, WY 82801; tel. 307/675–3530

St. John's Medical Center, PO Box 428, Jackson, WY 83001; tel. 307/733–3636

VA Medical Center, 2360 East Pershing Boulevard, Cheyenne, WY 82001; tel. 307/778–7550

Westview Health Care Center, 1990 West Loucks, Sheridan, WY 82801; tel. 307/672–9789

U.S. Associated Areas

PUERTO RICO

VA Caribbean Healthcare System, 10 Casia Street, San Juan, PR 00921-3201; tel. 787/641–7582

The Joint Commission Accredited Freestanding Behavioral Health Care Organizations

The accredited freestanding mental health care organizations listed have been accredited as of May 2014 by The Joint Commission on Accreditation of Healthcare Organizations by decision of the Accreditation Committee of the Board of Commissioners.

The organizations listed here have been found to be in compliance with The Joint Commissions standards for Accreditation Manual for Mental Health, Chemical Dependency, and Mental Retardation/Development Disabilities Services.

Please refer to section A of the AHA Guide for information on hospitals with inpatient and/or outpatient services. These hospitals are identified by Facility Codes F96, F97, F98, F99, F100, F101, F102, and F103. In section A, those hospitals identified by Approval Code 1 are Joint Commission accredited.

We present this list simply as a convenient directory. Inclusion or omission of any organization's name indicates neither approval nor disapproval by Health Forum LLC, an American Hospital Association company.

United States

ALABAMA

*Alabama Center for Eating Disorders, PO Box 55901, Birmingham, AL 35255; tel. 205/933-0041

Alabama Clinical Schools, Inc., 1221 Alton Drive, Birmingham, AL 35210; tel. 205/836-9923

*AltaPointe Health Systems, Inc., 5750-A Southland Drive, Mobile, AL 36693; tel. 251/450-5901

*Bradford Health Services - Huntsville Lodge, 1600 Browns Ferry Road, Madison, AL 35758; tel. 256/461-7272

*Bradford Health Services - Warrior, PO Box 129, Warrior, AL 35180; tel. 205/647-1945

Brookwood Medical Center, 2010 Brookwood Medical Center Drive, Birmingham, AL 35209; tel. 205/877-1000

Carlorene House, Inc., 2308 Highway 82 West, Prattville, AL 36067; tel. 334/365-1260

Central Alabama Veterans Health Care System, 215 Perry Hill Road, Montgomery, AL 36109; tel. 334/272-4670

*Fox Army Health Center US Army Medical Dept Activity, 4100 Goss Road, Huntsville, AL 35809-7000; tel. 256/955-8888

*Franklin Primary Health Center, Inc., 1303 Dr. Martin Luther King Jr. Avenue, Mobile, AL 36603; tel. 251/434-8188

Glenwood, Inc., 150 Glenwood Lane, Birmingham, AL 35242; tel. 205/969-2880

Highlands Treatment Center, LLC, 2807 Greystone Commercial Blvd, Suite 36, Birmingham, AL 35242; tel. 205/552-0417

Hill Crest Behavioral Health Services, 6869 Fifth Avenue South, Birmingham, AL 35212; tel. 205/833-9000

Laurel Oaks Behavioral Health Center, 700 East Cottonwood Road, Dothan, AL 36301; tel. 334/794-7373

*Lyster Army Health Clinic, 301 Andrews Avenue, Fort Rucker, AL 36362-5333; tel. 334/255-7609

Magnolia Creek, LLC, 645 Crenshaw Road, Columbiana, AL 35051; tel. 205/678-4373

Mountain View Hospital, PO Box 8406, Gadsden, AL 35902-8406; tel. 256/546-9265

Southeast Alabama Medical Center, PO Drawer 6987, Dothan, AL 36302-6987; tel. 334/793-8111

The Pinnacle Schools, Inc., 500 Governors Drive, Huntsville, AL 35801; tel. 256/518-9998

*Tuscaloosa VA Medical Center, 3701 Loop Road East, Tuscaloosa, AL 35404; tel. 205/554-2000

*University of Alabama at Birmingham, 619 19th Street South, Birmingham, AL 35249-1900; tel. 205/934-4444

*VA Medical Center, 700 19th Street South, Birmingham, AL 35233; tel. 205/933-8101

Walker Baptist Medical Center, PO Box 3400, 3400 Highway 78E, Jasper, AL 35502-3547; tel. 205/387-4000

ALASKA

*Akeela, Inc., 360 West Benson Boulevard, Anchorage, AK 99503; tel. 907/565-1200

Alaska Children's Services, Inc., 4600 Abbott Road, Anchorage, AK 99507-4314; tel. 907/346-2101

*Alaska VA Healthcare System, 1201 North Muldoon Road, Anchorage, AK 99504; tel. 907/257-5460

Boys and Girls Home of Alaska, Inc., 3101 Lathrop Street, Fairbanks, AK 99701; tel. 907/459-4700

*Bristol Bay Area Health Corporation, PO Box 130, Dillingham, AK 99576; tel. 907/842-5201

*Eastern Aleutian Tribes, 3380 C Street, Suite 100, Anchorage, AK 99503; tel. 907/277-1440

Frontline Hospital, 2530 DeBarr Road, Anchorage, AK 99508-2948; tel. 907/258-7575

Iliuliuk Family Health Services, Inc., 34 Lavelle Court, Unalaska, AK 99685; tel. 907/581-1202

Providence Adolescent Residential Treatment Program, 3210 West 62nd Avenue, Anchorage, AK 99502; tel. 907/212-2040

*SouthEast Alaska Regional Health Consortium, 222 Tongass Drive, Sitka, AK 99835; tel. 907/966-2411

*Yukon Kuskokwim Delta Regional Hospital, PO Box 287, Bethel, AK 99559; tel. 907/543-6300

ARIZONA

*A Better Today Recovery Services, 10609 North Hayden Road, Suite E106, Scottsdale, AZ 85260; tel. 480/315-1141

*A New Leaf, Inc., 868 East University Drive, Mesa, AZ 85203; tel. 480/969-4024

ANASAZI Foundation, 1424 South Stapley Drive, Mesa, AZ 85204; tel. 480/892-7403

Aurora Behavioral Health Systems, LLC, 6015 West Peoria Avenue, Glendale, AZ 85302; tel. 623/344-4400

*Banner Behavioral Health Hospital, 7575 East Earll Drive, Scottsdale, AZ 85251; tel. 480/941-7500

*Banner Thunderbird Medical Center, 5555 West Thunderbird Road, Glendale, AZ 85306; tel. 602/865-5555

*Chandler Valley Hope, PO Box 1839, Chandler, AZ 85244-1839; tel. 602/899-3335

*Community Counseling Centers, Inc., 105 North Fifth Avenue, Holbrook, AZ 86025; tel. 928/524-6701

*Compass Health Care, Inc., 2475 North Jackrabbit Avenue, Tucson, AZ 85745-1208; tel. 520/407-5900

Crisis Response Network of Southern Arizona, Inc., 2802 East District Street, Tucson, AZ 85714; tel. 520/284-3501

*Desert Visions Youth Wellness Center, PO Box 458, Sacaton, AZ 85147; tel. 520/562-3801

Devereux/Arizona - Richard L. Raskin Treatment Network, 11000 North Scottsdale Road, Suite 260, Scottsdale, AZ 85254; tel. 480/998-2920

*EBH Southwest Services, Inc., 12816 East Turquoise Avenue, Scottsdale, AZ 85259; tel. 480/773-7900

*Helping Associates, Inc., 1901 North Trekell Road, Suite A, Casa Grande, AZ 85122; tel. 520/836-1029

*Horizon Human Services, Inc., 210 East Cottonwood Lane, Casa Grande, AZ 85122; tel. 520/836-1688

*Little Colorado Behavioral Health Centers, PO Box 579, Saint Johns, AZ 85936; tel. 928/337-4301

Mingus Mountain Estate Residential Center, Inc., PO Box 26485, Prescott Valley, AZ 86312; tel. 602/335-2000

*Mohave Mental Health Clinic, Inc., 1743 Sycamore Avenue, Kingman, AZ 86409; tel. 928/757-8111

Northern Arizona VA Health Care System, 500 Highway 89 North, Prescott, AZ 86313; tel. 928/445-4860

*Phoenix VA Health Care System, 650 East Indian School Road, Phoenix, AZ 85012-1892; tel. 602/277-5551

*Pinal Hispanic Council, 107 East 4th Street, Eloy, AZ 85131; tel. 520/466-7765

*Raymond W. Bliss Army Health Center, 2240 East Winrow Avenue, Fort Huachuca, AZ 85613-7079; tel. 520/533-9026

Recovery Innovations, Inc., 2701 North 16th Street, Suite 316, Phoenix, AZ 85006; tel. 602/650-1212

Remuda Ranch, One East Apache Street, Wickenburg, AZ 85390; tel. 928/684-3913

Rosewood Ranch L.P., 36075 South Rincon Road, Wickenburg, AZ 85390; tel. 928/684-9594

*Sierra Tucson, Inc., 39580 South Lago del Oro Parkway, Tucson, AZ 85739; tel. 520/624-4000

*Southern Arizona VA Health Care System, 3601 South Sixth Avenue, Tucson, AZ 85723; tel. 520/629-1821

Southwestern Children's Health Services, Inc., 2190 North Grace Boulevard, Chandler, AZ 85225; tel. 480/917-9301

St. Luke's Behavioral Hospital L.P., 1800 East Van Buren, Phoenix, AZ 85006; tel. 602/251-8808

*The Guidance Center, Inc., 2187 North Vickey Street, Flagstaff, AZ 86004; tel. 928/527-1899

The Meadows of Wickenburg, Inc., 1655 North Tegner, Wickenburg, AZ 85390; tel. 928/684-3926

The New Foundation, 1200 North 77th Street, Scottsdale, AZ 85257; tel. 480/945-3302

*The River Source Treatment Center, 950 North Arizola Road, Suite 3, Casa Grande, AZ 85122; tel. 480/321-9091

Touchstone Behavioral Health, 15648 North 35th Avenue, Phoenix, AZ 85053; tel. 623/930-8705

*UBH of Phoenix, LLC, 3550 East Pinchot, Phoenix, AZ 85018; tel. 940/320-8994

Urgent Psychiatric Center, 903 North 2nd Street, Phoenix, AZ 85004-1906; tel. 602/416-7600

*Verde Valley Guidance Clinic, Inc., 8 East Cottonwood Street, Cottonwood, AZ 86326; tel. 928/634-2236

*West Yavapai Guidance Clinic, 3343 Windsong Drive, Prescott Valley, AZ 86314; tel. 928/583-6411

Youth Development Institute, 1830 East Roosevelt Street, Phoenix, AZ 85006; tel. 602/256-5300

ARKANSAS

BHC Pinnacle Pointe Hospital, Inc., 11501 Financial Centre Parkway, Little Rock, AR 72211; tel. 501/223-3322

Bokker Enterprises, PO Box 176, Cherokee Village, AR 72525; tel. 870/257-3336

*Central Arkansas Veterans Healthcare System, 4300 West Seventh Street (OO/LR), Little Rock, AR 72205; tel. 501/257-5314

Community Counseling Services, Inc., 125 Dons Way, Hot Springs National Park, AR 71913; tel. 501/624-7111

Cornerstone Community Counseling Corp., 609 West 3rd Street, Imboden, AR 72434; tel. 870/869-1500

Counseling and Education Center, Inc., 406 Pecan Street, Helena, AR 72342; tel. 870/338-8447

Delta Counseling Associates, Inc., 790 Roberts Drive, Monticello, AR 71655; tel. 870/367-9732

---

*Indicates organization is a Joint Commission accredited Chemical Dependency organization.

Delta Family Health and Fitness Center for Children, Inc., 815 East St. Louis Street, Hamburg, AR 71646; tel. 870/853-4224

Families, Inc. of Arkansas, 1815 Pleasant Grove Road, Jonesboro, AR 72401; tel. 870/933-6886

Habilitation Centers, Inc., PO Box 727, Fordyce, AR 71742; tel. 870/352-8203

Hometown Behavioral Health Services of Arkansas, Inc., PO Box 299, Hoxie, AR 72433; tel. 870/886-1333

Inspiration Day Treatment, Inc., 1014 Autumn Road, Suite 4, Little Rock, AR 72211; tel. 501/221-1941

***Life Strategies Counseling, Inc.,** 1217 Stone Street, Jonesboro, AR 72401; tel. 870/972-1268

Life Strategies of Arkansas, LLC, 703 Calvin Avery Drive, West Memphis, AR 72301; tel. 870/732-1878

Living Hope Southeast, LLC, 10025 West Markham, Suite 210, Little Rock, AR 72205; tel. 501/663-5473

Maxus, Inc., 1033 Old Burr Road, Warm Springs, AR 72478; tel. 870/647-1400

NeuroRestorative Timber Ridge, PO Box 208, Benton, AR 72018; tel. 501/594-5211

***Ozark Guidance Center, Inc.,** PO Box 6430, Springdale, AR 72766-6430; tel. 479/750-2020

Piney Ridge Treatment Center, LLC, 4253 Crossover Road, Fayetteville, AR 72703; tel. 479/587-1408

Riverview Behavioral Health, 701 Arkansas Boulevard, Suite 300, Texarkana, AR 71854; tel. 870/772-5028

Texarkana Behavioral Associates, LLC, 4253 Crossover Road, Fayetteville, AR 72703; tel. 479/521-5731

***The BridgeWay, Inc.,** 21 BridgeWay Road, North Little Rock, AR 72113; tel. 501/771-1500

***The Centers for Youth and Families,** PO Box 251970, Little Rock, AR 72225-1970; tel. 501/666-8686

The Logan Centers, Inc., 1766 Killough Road, Wynne, AR 72396; tel. 870/494-4600

Trinity Behavioral Health Care System, Inc., 1033 Old Burr Road, Warm Springs, AR 72478; tel. 870/647-1400

United Methodist Behavioral Health System, Inc., 1601 Murphy Drive, Maumelle, AR 72113; tel. 501/803-3388

***United Methodist Children's Home, Inc.,** PO Box 56050, Little Rock, AR 72215; tel. 501/661-0720

***University of Arkansas for Medical Sciences,** 4301 West Markham, Slot 554, Little Rock, AR 72205; tel. 501/526-8100

Valley Behavioral Health System, LLC, 10301 Mayo Drive, Barling, AR 72923; tel. 479/494-5700

***Veterans Health Care System of the Ozarks,** 1100 North College Avenue, Fayetteville, AR 72703; tel. 479/444-5000

Woodridge Behavioral Care, 603 Kittle Road, Forrest City, AR 72335; tel. 870/633-3200

Youth Home, Inc., 20400 Colonel Glenn Road, Little Rock, AR 72210-5323; tel. 501/821-5500

CALIFORNIA

***Action Family Counseling, Inc.,** 26893 Bouquet Canyon Road, Suite C-134, Santa Clarita, CA 91350; tel. 661/297-6644

***Adolescent Growth, Inc.,** 6323 Zindell Avenue, Commerce, CA 90040; tel. 323/948-9998

Alameda County Medical Center, 1411 East 31 Street, Oakland, CA 94602; tel. 510/437-4943

AltaMed Health Services Corporation, 2040 Camfield Avenue, Los Angeles, CA 90040; tel. 323/725-8751

Aspiranet, 400 Oyster Point Boulevard, Suite 501, South San Francisco, CA 94080; tel. 650/866-4080

***AToN Center,** 3250 Country Rose Circle, Encinitas, CA 92024; tel. 858/759-5017

***Aurora Behavioral Health Care / San Diego,** 11878 Avenue of Industry, San Diego, CA 92128; tel. 858/487-3200

Aurora Behavioral Healthcare-Santa Rosa, LLC, 1287 Fulton Road, Santa Rosa, CA 95401; tel. 707/800-7700

***Aurora Charter Oak - Los Angeles, LLC,** 1161 East Covina Boulevard, Covina, CA 91724; tel. 626/966-1632

Aurora Las Encinas, LLC, 2900 East Del Mar Boulevard, Pasadena, CA 91107; tel. 626/795-9901

***Avalon Malibu Cottage,** 32430 Pacific Coast Highway, Malibu, CA 90265; tel. 310/457-9111

***Axis Residential Treatment - East,** 75450 Fairway Drive, Indian Wells, CA 92210; tel. 760/409-1287

Balance Treatment Corporation, 26039 Mulholland Highway, Calabasas, CA 91302; tel. 818/880-0800

Berkeley Addiction Treatment Services, Inc., 2975 Sacramento Street, Berkeley, CA 94702; tel. 510/644-0200

***BHC Alhambra Hospital,** 4619 North Rosemead Boulevard, Rosemead, CA 91770; tel. 626/286-1191

***BHC Fremont Hospital,** 39001 Sundale Drive, Fremont, CA 94538; tel. 510/796-1100

***BHC Heritage Oaks Hospital,** 4250 Auburn Boulevard, Sacramento, CA 95841; tel. 916/489-3336

***BHC Sierra Vista Hospital,** 8001 Bruceville Road, Sacramento, CA 95823; tel. 916/288-0300

California Department of Corrections - CIW 45 Bed PIP, 16756 Chino-Corona Road, Corona, CA 92880; tel. 909/597-1771

California Department of State Hospitals, 7707 South Austin Road, Stockton, CA 95215; tel. 209/467-2516

California Institution for Women, PO Box 6000, Corona, CA 92878-6000; tel. 909/597-1771

Canyon Ridge Hospital, Inc., 5353 G Street, Chino, CA 91710; tel. 909/590-3700

***Casa Palmera Care Center, Inc.,** 14750 El Camino Real, Del Mar, CA 92014; tel. 858/481-4411

Castlewood West LLC dba Monarch Cove, 213 Seventeen Mile Drive, Pacific Grove, CA 93950; tel. 831/718-9595

CHCM, Inc., 301 Victoria Street, Costa Mesa, CA 92627; tel. 949/642-2734

***Children's Hospital Los Angeles,** 4650 West Sunset Boulevard, MS 1, Los Angeles, CA 90027; tel. 323/660-2450

***Cliffside Malibu,** 30060 Andromeda Lane, Malibu, CA 90265; tel. 310/589-2800

***Clinica Sierra Vista,** PO Box 1559, Bakersfield, CA 93302-1559; tel. 661/635-3050

College Hospital, Inc., 10802 College Place, Cerritos, CA 90703; tel. 562/924-9581

Community Hospital of San Bernardino, 1805 Medical Center Drive, San Bernardino, CA 92411-1288; tel. 909/887-6333

***Community Recovery, Inc.,** 6708 Melrose, Los Angeles, CA 90038; tel. 818/635-9380

Corona Regional Medical Center, Inc., 800 South Main Street, Corona, CA 92882; tel. 951/737-4343

Del Amo Hospital, 23700 Camino Del Sol, Torrance, CA 90505; tel. 310/530-1151

***Design for Living Behavior Health, Inc.,** 43858 Beech Avenue, Lancaster, CA 93534; tel. 661/729-8155

***Dual Diagnosis Treatment Center, Inc.,** 1211 Puerta Del Sol, San Clemente, CA 92673; tel. 949/369-1300

***El Camino Hospital,** 2500 Grant Ave, Mountain View, CA 94040; tel. 650/940-7300

Fred Finch Youth Center, 3800 Coolidge Avenue, Oakland, CA 94602; tel. 510/485-5260

***Glendale Adventist Medical Center,** 1509 Wilson Terrace, Glendale, CA 91206; tel. 818/409-8000

GOALS For Women: African American Family Counseling Center, 1331 Garden Highway, Sacramento, CA 95833; tel. 510/334-0003

***Good Samaritan Hospital,** 901 Olive Drive, Bakersfield, CA 93308; tel. 661/215-7500

***Good Samaritan Hospital, LP,** 2425 Samaritan Drive, San Jose, CA 95124; tel. 408/559-2011

HAART- Oakland, 10850 MacArthur Boulevard, Suite 200, Oakland, CA 94605; tel. 510/875-2300

Hathaway-Sycamores Child and Family Services, 210 South De Lacey Avenue, Suite 110, Pasadena, CA 91105; tel. 626/395-7100

Hazelden Betty Ford Foundation, 39000 Bob Hope Drive, Rancho Mirage, CA 92270; tel. 760/773-4100

***Helix Healthcare, Inc.,** 7050 Parkway Drive, La Mesa, CA 91942; tel. 619/465-4411

Humanistic Alternatives to Addiction Research and Treatment, 20094 Mission Boulevard, Hayward, CA 94541; tel. 510/727-9755

***Huntington Memorial Hospital,** PO Box 7013, Pasadena, CA 91109-7013; tel. 626/397-5555

***John Muir Behavioral Health,** 2740 Grant Street, Concord, CA 94520; tel. 925/674-4100

***K'ima:w Medical Center,** PO Box 1288, Hoopa, CA 95546; tel. 530/625-4261

Kaiser Foundation Hospital - Los Angeles Medical Center, 4733 Sunset Boulevard, Los Angeles, CA 90027; tel. 323/783-8101

La Palma Intercommunity Hospital, 7901 Walker Street, La Palma, CA 90623; tel. 714/670-7400

***La Ventana Treatment Programs,** 275 East Hillcrest Drive, Thousand Oaks, CA 91360; tel. 415/345-1238

Langley Porter Psychiatric Hospital and Clinics - UCSF, 401 Parnassus Avenue, HOS 0984, San Francisco, CA 94143-0984; tel. 415/476-7000

Lionrock Behavioral Health, Inc., 925 Lakeville Street, Suite 322, Petaluma, CA 94952; tel. 760/994-4990

***Loma Linda University Behavioral Medicine Center,** 1710 Barton Road, Redlands, CA 92373; tel. 909/558-9204

Marin General Hospital, 250 Bon Air Road, Greenbrae, CA 94904; tel. 415/925-7000

***Mills-Peninsula Health Services,** 1501 Trousdale Drive, Burlingame, CA 94010; tel. 650/696-5270

Mission Community Hospital, 14850 Roscoe Boulevard, Panorama City, CA 91402; tel. 818/904-3685

***Mission Hospital Regional Medical Center,** 27700 Medical Center Road, Mission Viejo, CA 92691; tel. 949/365-2248

Monte Nido Residential Center, Inc., 514 Live Oak Circle, Calabasas, CA 91302; tel. 310/457-9958

MU'EED Incorporated, PO Box 276372, Sacramento, CA 95827; tel. 916/486-1737

***Naval Medical Center San Diego,** 34800 Bob Wilson Drive, San Diego, CA 92134-5000; tel. 619/532-9160

Northridge Hospital Medical Center, 18300 Roscoe Boulevard, Northridge, CA 91328; tel. 818/885-5321

Oak Grove Institute Foundation, Inc., 24275 Jefferson Avenue, Murrieta, CA 92562; tel. 951/677-5599

Opioid Replacement Treatment Prog., Dept. of Veterans Affairs, 525 21st Street, Oakland, CA 94612; tel. 510/587-3434

***Optimum Performance Institute,** 3080 Eucalyptus Hill Road, Santa Barbara, CA 93108; tel. 818/610-3956

OTP Los Angeles Ambulatory Care Center, 11301 Wilshire Boullevard, Building 500, Room 6404, Los Angeles, CA 90073; tel. 310/268-3132

***Pacifica Recovery Services,** PO Box 2041, Upland, CA 91785; tel. 909/447-5081

Palomar Medical Center, 2185 Citracado Parkway, Escondido, CA 92029; tel. 442/281-1006

***Paradigm Treatment Centers, Inc.,** 6323 Via Escondido Drive, Malibu, CA 90265; tel. 310/457-6300

***Passages,** 241 Market Street, Port Hueneme, CA 93041; tel. 805/283-4737

Penny Lane Centers, 15305 Rayen Street, North Hills, CA 91343; tel. 818/892-3423

Positive Option Family Service, 2400 Glendale Lane, Suite G, Sacramento, CA 95825; tel. 916/973-2838

Prime Healthcare Paradise Valley, LLC, 2400 East Fourth Street, National City, CA 91950-2099; tel. 619/470-4115

***Principles Inc.,** PO Box 93607, Pasadena, CA 91103; tel. 626/798-0884

Puente de Vida, PO Box 86020, San Diego, CA 92138; tel. 858/452-3915

***Recovery Homes of America,** 13682 Yorba Street, Tustin, CA 92780; tel. 714/730-5399

Redlands Community Hospital, 350 Terracina Boulevard, Redlands, CA 92373; tel. 909/335-5500

River Oak Center for Children, 5030 El Camino Avenue, Carmichael, CA 95608; tel. 916/609-5100

***San Diego Center for Children,** 3002 Armstrong Street, San Diego, CA 92111; tel. 858/277-9550

San Francisco VA Medical Center, 4150 Clement Street, San Francisco, CA 94121; tel. 415/221-4810

***Santa Barbara Cottage Hospital,** PO Box 689, Santa Barbara, CA 93102; tel. 805/569-7404

Santa Rosa Memorial Hospital, 1165 Montgomery Drive, Santa Rosa, CA 95405; tel. 707/522-1520

Scripps Mercy Hospital, 4077 Fifth Avenue- MER 1, San Diego, CA 92103; tel. 619/294-8111

Seneca Family of Agencies, 2275 Arlington Drive, San Leandro, CA 94578; tel. 510/654-4004

***Sharp McDonald Center,** 7850 Vista Hill Avenue, San Diego, CA 92123; tel. 858/637-6920

*Indicates organization is a Joint Commission accredited Chemical Dependency organization.

Section C

Silver Lake Medical Center, 1711 West Temple Street, Los Angeles, CA 90026; tel. 213/989–6100

*Soba Living, LLC, 22669 Pacific Coast Highway, Malibu, CA 90265; tel. 310/924–2053

*Sober Sanctuaries, Inc., 234 East 17th Street, Suite 209, Costa Mesa, CA 92627; tel. 855/447–8733

St. Helena Hospital Center for Behavioral Health, 525 Oregon Street, Vallejo, CA 94590; tel. 707/648–2200

St. Joseph Hospital, 1100 West Stewart Drive, Orange, CA 92863-5600; tel. 714/771–8000

St. Mary Medical Center, 1050 Linden Avenue, Long Beach, CA 90813; tel. 562/491–9000

St. Mary's Medical Center, 450 Stanyan Street, San Francisco, CA 94117; tel. 415/668–1000

Stars Behavioral Health Group, 1501 Hughes Way, Suite 150, Long Beach, CA 90810; tel. 310/221–6336

Stewart & Lynda Resnick Neuropsychiatric Hospital at UCLA, 150 Medical Plaza 4230C, MC 746330, Los Angeles, CA 90095; tel. 310/267–9092

*Summit BHC Sacramento, LLC, 2221 Fair Oaks Boulevard, Sacramento, CA 95825; tel. 916/514–8500

Summit Psychotherapy Associates, PC, 3610 American River Drive, Suite 140, Sacramento, CA 95864; tel. 916/574–1000

Sutter Center for Psychiatry, 7700 Folsom Boulevard, Sacramento, CA 95826; tel. 916/386–3000

Sutter East Bay Hospitals, 2450 Ashby Avenue, Berkeley, CA 94705; tel. 510/204–2606

Tarzana Treatment Centers (OTP-Maintenance), 18646 Oxnard Street, Tarzana, CA 91356; tel. 818/996–1051

Tessie Cleveland Community Services Corp., 8019 South Compton Avenue, Los Angeles, CA 90001; tel. 323/586–7333

*The Discovery House Residential Treatment, 847 Barton Avenue, Camarillo, CA 93010; tel. 805/228–2826

The Discovery Practice Management, Inc., 4281 Katella, Suite 111, Los Alamitos, CA 90720; tel. 714/828–1800

The Family Care Network, Inc., 1255 Kendall Road, San Luis Obispo, CA 93401; tel. 805/781–3535

The Huntington Beach Hospital, 17772 Beach Boulevard, Huntington Beach, CA 92647; tel. 714/843–5000

The Pathway Home, Inc., 100 California Drive, Yountville, CA 94599; tel. 707/948–3028

*Therapeutic Solutions, 3255 Esplanade, Chico, CA 95973; tel. 530/899–3150

TLC Child & Family Services, PO Box 2079, Sebastopol, CA 95473-2079; tel. 707/823–7300

*Twin Town Corp., 4388 East Katella Avenue, Los Alamitos, CA 90720; tel. 562/594–8844

*VA Central California Health Care System, 2615 East Clinton Avenue, Fresno, CA 93703; tel. 559/225–6100

*VA Greater Los Angeles Healthcare System, 11301 Wilshire Boulevard, Los Angeles, CA 90073; tel. 310/268–3132

*VA Loma Linda Healthcare System, 11201 Benton Street, Loma Linda, CA 92357; tel. 909/583–6002

*VA Long Beach Health Care System, 5901 East Seventh Street, Long Beach, CA 90822; tel. 562/826–5400

*VA Northern California Health Care System, 10535 Hospital Way, Mather, CA 95655; tel. 916/843–7000

*VA Palo Alto Health Care System, 3801 Miranda Avenue, Palo Alto, CA 94304; tel. 650/493–5000

*VA San Diego Healthcare System, 3350 La Jolla Village Drive, San Diego, CA 92161; tel. 858/552–8585

VAMC-San Francisco Substance Abuse Treatment Clinic, 4150 Clement Street, Building 1, San Francisco, CA 94121; tel. 415/750–2050

*Vista Behavioral Hospital, LLC, 5900 Brockton Avenue, Riverside, CA 92506; tel. 951/275–8400

Vista Del Mar Child and Family Services, 3200 Motor Avenue, Los Angeles, CA 90034; tel. 310/836–1223

West Anaheim Medical Center, 3033 West Orange Avenue, Anaheim, CA 92804; tel. 714/229–4000

West Oakland Health Council, 700 Adeline Street, Oakland, CA 94607; tel. 510/835–9610

Western Medical Center Anaheim, 1025 South Anaheim Boulevard, Anaheim, CA 92805-0880; tel. 714/533–6220

Westside Community Mental Health, Inc., 1153 Oak Street, San Francisco, CA 94117; tel. 415/563–8200

Wynspring Family Resource Center, 2755 Cottage Way, Suite 16, Sacramento, CA 95825; tel. 916/480–0280

COLORADO

AspenPointe Health Services, 525 North Cascade Avenue, Suite 100, Colorado Springs, CO 80903; tel. 719/572–6100

*Cedar Springs Hospital, Inc., 2135 Southgate Road, Colorado Springs, CO 80906; tel. 719/633–4114

*Centura Health-Porter Adventist Hospital, 2525 S Downing Street, Denver, CO 80210; tel. 303/778–1955

Children's Hospital Colorado, 13123 East 16th Avenue, Aurora, CO 80045; tel. 720/777–1234

Comprehensive Addiction Treatment Services, 2222 East 18th Avenue, Unit C, Denver, CO 80206; tel. 303/394–2714

Denver Health and Hospital Authority, 777 Bannock Street, Denver, CO 80204; tel. 303/436–5690

Devereux Cleo Wallace, 8405 Church Ranch Boulevard, Westminster, CO 80021; tel. 303/466–7391

Eating Recovery Center, LLC, 1830 Franklin Street, Suite 405, Denver, CO 80218; tel. 303/825–8584

EDC - Denver, LLC, 950 South Cherry, Suite 1010, Denver, CO 80246; tel. 303/771–0861

El Pueblo Boys' & Girls' Ranch, Inc., One El Pueblo Ranch Way, Pueblo, CO 81006; tel. 719/544–7496

*Evans Army Community Hospital, 1650 Cochrane Circle, Building 7500, Fort Carson, CO 80913-4604; tel. 719/526–7500

Forest Heights Lodge, PO Box 789, Evergreen, CO 80437-0789; tel. 303/674–6681

*Grand Junction Veterans Affairs Medical Center, 2121 North Avenue, Grand Junction, CO 81501; tel. 970/242–0731

*Parker Valley Hope, PO Box 670, Parker, CO 80134; tel. 303/841–7857

*Parkview Medical Center, Medical Staff Services, 400 West 16th Street, Pueblo, CO 81003; tel. 719/584–4000

Poudre Valley Hospital, 1024 South Lemay Avenue, Fort Collins, CO 80524-3998; tel. 970/495–7000

SBH Colorado, LLC, 7353 Sisters Grove, Colorado Springs, CO 80923; tel. 719/444–8484

Southern Peaks Regional Treatment Center, 700 Four Mile Parkway, Canon City, CO 81212; tel. 719/276–7500

*University of Colorado Hospital Authority, 12401 East 17th Avenue, F448, Suite 1000, Aurora, CO 80045; tel. 720/848–7800

*VA Eastern Colorado Healthcare System, 1055 Clermont Street, Denver, CO 80220; tel. 303/399–8020

VCPHCS X, LLC dba BHG Boulder Treatment Center, 850 23rd Avenue, Longmont, CO 80501; tel. 303/245–0123

VCPHCS XI, LLC dba BHG Westminster Treatment Center, 8407 North Bryant Street, Westminster, CO 80031; tel. 303/487–7776

CONNECTICUT

Albert J. Solnit Children's Center - South Campus, 915 River Road, Middletown, CT 06457; tel. 860/704–4000

Blue Hills Substance Abuse Services, 500 Vine Street, Hartford, CT 06112-1639; tel. 860/666–7665

Bridgeport Hospital, 267 Grant Street, Bridgeport, CT 06610; tel. 203/384–3000

*Bristol Hospital, Inc., PO Box 977, Bristol, CT 06011-0977; tel. 860/585–3222

Capitol Region Mental Health Center, 500 Vine Street, Hartford, CT 06112; tel. 860/297–0903

Center for Discovery New England, 1320 Mill Hill Road, Southport, CT 06890; tel. 562/631–7938

Community Health Center, Inc., 635 Main Street, Middletown, CT 06457; tel. 860/347–6971

*Community Health Resources, Inc., 995 Day Hill Road, Windsor, CT 06095; tel. 860/731–5522

Community Health Resources: Pathways OTP Program, 391 Pomfret Street, Putnam, CT 06260; tel. 860/731–5522

*Community Mental Health Affiliates, Inc., 270 John Downey Drive, New Britain, CT 06051; tel. 860/826–1358

*Community Renewal Team, 555 Windsor Street, Hartford, CT 06120; tel. 860/761–7904

*Connecticut Mental Health Center, 34 Park Street, New Haven, CT 06519; tel. 203/974–7300

Connecticut Valley Hospital-Addiction Services Div.-Merritt, PO Box 351, Middletown, CT 06457-7023; tel. 860/262–5887

Cornell Scott-Hill Health Corporation, 400 Columbus Avenue, New Haven, CT 06519; tel. 203/503–3000

*Griffin Hospital, 130 Division Street, Derby, CT 06418; tel. 203/732–7500

*Hartford Community Mental Health Center, Inc., 2550 Main Street, Hartford, CT 06120; tel. 860/548–0101

*Hartford Hospital, 80 Seymour Street, Hartford, CT 06102-5037; tel. 860/545–2100

InterCommunity, Inc., 281 Main Street, East Hartford, CT 06118; tel. 860/569–5900

John Dempsey Hospital, 263 Farmington Avenue, Farmington, CT 06030-3802; tel. 860/679–2233

Klingberg Family Centers, Inc., 370 Linwood Street, New Britain, CT 06052; tel. 860/224–9113

Lawrence & Memorial Hospital, 365 Montauk Avenue, New London, CT 06320; tel. 860/442–0711

Manchester Memorial Hospital, 71 Haynes Street, Manchester, CT 06040; tel. 860/646–1222

*Middlesex Hospital, 28 Crescent Street, Middletown, CT 06457; tel. 860/358–6000

*Natchaug Hospital, Inc., 189 Storrs Road, Mansfield Center, CT 06250; tel. 860/456–1311

New Era Rehabilitation Center, 3851 Main Street, 2nd floor, Bridgeport, CT 06606; tel. 203/372–3333

Opiate Treatment Program, VA Connecticut Healthcare System, 950 Campbell Avenue, Building 36, West Haven, CT 06516; tel. 203/932–5711

*Perception Programs, Inc., PO Box 407, Willimantic, CT 06226; tel. 860/450–7122

River Valley Services, PO Box 351, Middletown, CT 06457; tel. 860/262–5200

*Rushford Center, Inc., 883 Paddock Avenue, Meriden, CT 06450; tel. 203/235–1792

Saint Francis Hospital & Medical Center - 8 West Unit, 500 Blue Hills Avenue, Hartford, CT 06112; tel. 860/714–2333

*Silver Hill Hospital, 208 Valley Road, New Canaan, CT 06840; tel. 203/801–2297

South Central Rehabilitation Center, 232 Cedar Street, New Haven, CT 06519; tel. 203/503–3356

*Southwest Community Health Center, Inc., 46 Albion Street, Bridgeport, CT 06605; tel. 203/332–3501

Southwest Connecticut Mental Health System, 1635 Central Avenue, Bridgeport, CT 06610; tel. 203/551–7461

St. Vincent's Medical Center, 2800 Main Street, Bridgeport, CT 06606; tel. 203/576–5476

State of CT DMHAS - Southeastern Mental Health Authority, 401 West Thames Street, Building 301, Norwich, CT 06360; tel. 860/859–4734

*Stonington Behavioral Health, Inc., 75 Swantown Hill Road, North Stonington, CT 06359; tel. 860/535–1010

The Charlotte Hungerford Hospital, PO Box 988, Torrington, CT 06790; tel. 860/496–6666

*The Children's Center of Hamden, Inc., 1400 Whitney Avenue, Hamden, CT 06517; tel. 203/248–2225

*The Hospital of Central Connecticut, PO Box 100, New Britain, CT 06050-0100; tel. 860/224–5666

The Wellspring Foundation, Inc., 21 Arch Bridge Road, Bethlehem, CT 06751; tel. 203/266–8000

*The Wheeler Clinic, 91 Northwest Drive, Plainville, CT 06062; tel. 860/793–3500

The William W. Backus Hospital, 326 Washington Street, Norwich, CT 06360; tel. 860/823–6399

*United Services, Inc., 1007 North Main Street, Dayville, CT 06241; tel. 860/774–2020

*Waterbury Hospital, 64 Robbins Street, Waterbury, CT 06708; tel. 203/573–6000

Western Connecticut Mental Health Network, 55 West Main Street, Suite 410, Waterbury, CT 06702; tel. 203/805–6400

Yale - New Haven Hospital, 20 York Street, New Haven, CT 06510-3203; tel. 203/688–4242

DELAWARE

*Brandywine Counseling & Community Services, 2500 West Fourth Street, Wilmington, DE 19805; tel. 302/472–0381

Brandywine Counseling & Community Services, South Chapel, 24 Brookhill Drive, Newark, DE 19702; tel. 302/454–3020

---

*Indicates organization is a Joint Commission accredited Chemical Dependency organization.

Section C

Brandywine Counseling & Community Services, Lancaster, 2713 Lancaster Avenue, Wilmington, DE 19805; tel. 302/656-2347

Christiana Care -Christiana Hospital, 4755 Ogletown-Stanton Road, Newark, DE 19718; tel. 302/733-1580

Delaware Guidance Services for Children and Youth, Inc., 1213 Delaware Avenue, Wilmington, DE 19806; tel. 302/652-3948

***Gateway Foundation Delaware City Treatment Center,** PO Box 547, Delaware City, DE 19706; tel. 312/663-1130

Meadow Wood Behavioral Health System, 575 South DuPont Highway, New Castle, DE 19720; tel. 302/328-3330

Rockford Center, 100 Rockford Drive, Newark, DE 19713; tel. 302/996-5480

***SODAT - Delaware, Inc.,** 625 North Orange Street, Wilmington, DE 19801; tel. 302/656-4044

***Thresholds, Inc.,** 20505 DuPont Boulevard, Suite 1, Georgetown, DE 19947; tel. 302/856-1835

***UHS of Dover, LLC,** 725 Horsepond Road, Dover, DE 19901; tel. 302/741-0140

***VA Medical Center,** 1601 Kirkwood Highway, Wilmington, DE 19805; tel. 302/994-2511

DISTRICT OF COLUMBIA

Department of Veterans Affairs, Substance Abuse Rehab Prog, 50 Irving Street, Northwest, Washington, DC 20422; tel. 202/745-8564

McClendon Center, 1313 New York Avenue, Northwest, Washington, DC 20005; tel. 202/737-6191

***MedStar Washington Hospital Center,** 110 Irving Street, Northwest, Washington, DC 20010; tel. 202/877-7000

The Episcopal Center for Children, 5901 Utah Avenue, Northwest, Washington, DC 20015-1616; tel. 202/363-1333

The HSC Pediatric Center, 1731 Bunker Hill Road, Northeast, Washington, DC 20017; tel. 202/832-4400

The Psychiatric Institute of Washington - OTP, 4228 Wisconsin Avenue, Northwest, Washington, DC 20016; tel. 202/885-5600

FLORIDA

ABC's for Success, LLC, 1550 South Dixie Highway, Suite 203, Coral Gables, FL 33146; tel. 786/536-9714

Alpha Health Care Clinic, Inc., 1990 Northeast 163rd Street, Suite 102, North Miami Beach, FL 33162; tel. 305/945-9906

***Alternative Treatment International, Inc.,** 2120 Range Road, Clearwater, FL 33765; tel. 727/798-3719

Alzheimer's Community Care, Inc., 800 Northpoint Parkway, Suite 101B, West Palm Beach, FL 33407; tel. 561/683-2700

***Ambrosia Treatment Center,** 5220 Hood Road, Suite 101, Palm Beach Gardens, FL 33418; tel. 561/578-8600

***Apalachee Center, Inc.,** 2634-J Capital Circle Northeast, Tallahassee, FL 32308; tel. 850/523-3333

Aspire Health Partners, 1800 Mercy Drive, Orlando, FL 32808; tel. 407/875-3700

***Atlantic Shores Hospital,** 4545 North Federal Highway, Fort Lauderdale, FL 33308; tel. 954/771-2711

***Bay Pines VA Healthcare System,** 10000 Bay Pines Boulevard, Bay Pines, FL 33744; tel. 727/398-6661

***Beachcomber Rehab, Inc.,** 4493 North Ocean Boulevard, Delray Beach, FL 33483; tel. 561/276-6226

Behavioral Support Services, Inc., 801 Douglas Avenue, Suite 208, Altamonte Springs, FL 32714; tel. 407/830-6412

Blue Horizon Eating Disorders Services, LLC, 1155 Louisiana Avenue, Suite 210, Winter Park, FL 32789; tel. 407/960-2651

***Broward Addiction Recovery Center (BARC) Division,** 1011 Southwest 2nd Court, Fort Lauderdale, FL 33312; tel. 954/357-4860

Carrousel Therapy Services, Corp., 4898 East Erlo Bronson Highway, 2nd Floor, Saint Cloud, FL 34771; tel. 407/891-3054

***Center for Alcohol & Drug Studies, Inc.,** 631 US Highway 1, North Palm Beach, FL 33408; tel. 561/615-6664

Central Florida Behavioral Hospital, 6601 Central Florida Parkway, Orlando, FL 32821; tel. 407/370-0111

Central Florida Treatment Center - Ft. Pierce Clinic, 1302 Lawnwood Circle, Suite B, Fort Pierce, FL 34950; tel. 772/468-6800

CFSATC, Inc., 1800 West Colonial Drive, Orlando, FL 32804; tel. 407/843-0041

CFSATC, Inc. - Palm Bay, 2198 Harris Avenue, Palm Bay, FL 32905; tel. 321/951-9750

CFSATC, Inc. Cocoa, 7 North Cocoa Boulevard, Cocoa, FL 32922; tel. 321/631-4578

CFSATC-Lake Worth, Inc., 3155 Lake Worth Road, Suite 2, Lake Worth, FL 33461; tel. 561/439-8440

***Circles of Care, Inc.,** 400 East Sheridan Road, Melbourne, FL 32901-3184; tel. 321/984-4900

***Citrus Health Network, Inc.,** 4175 West 20th Avenue, Hialeah, FL 33012; tel. 305/424-3100

***Coastal Behavioral Healthcare, Inc.,** 1565 State Street, Sarasota, FL 34236; tel. 941/927-8900

Coastal Mental Health Services, Inc., 2750 Enterprise Road, Orange City, FL 32763; tel. 800/614-4124

***Community Health of South Florida, Inc.,** 10300 Southwest 216 Street, Miami, FL 33190; tel. 305/252-4853

Comprehensive Psychiatric Center, 9735 East Fern Street, Miami, FL 33157; tel. 305/238-5121

Comprehensive Psychiatric Center North, 240 Northwest 183rd Street, Miami, FL 33169; tel. 305/651-2332

Comprehensive Psychiatric Center-Central, 4790 Northwest 7th Street, Suites 101 & 102, Miami, FL 33126; tel. 305/529-5810

***Dade Family Counseling Community Mental Health Center,** 4343 West Flagler Street, Suite 100, Miami, FL 33134; tel. 305/774-9570

***David Lawrence Center,** 6075 Bathey Lane, Naples, FL 34116; tel. 239/455-8500

***Destination Hope, Inc.,** 6555 Northwest 9th Avenue, Suite 112, Fort Lauderdale, FL 33309; tel. 954/771-2091

***EBH Acquisition Subsidiary, Inc.,** 3100 East Commercial Boulevard, Fort Lauderdale, FL 33308; tel. 954/200-8308

***Elan Healthcare Corporation, Inc.,** 18814 South Dixie Hwy, Cutler Bay, FL 33157; tel. 305/281-6898

***Empathic Recovery,** 1408 Killian Drive, Suite 201, Lake Park, FL 33403; tel. 561/318-5954

ESP Case Management Professionals, Inc., 345 Beville Road, Suite 106, Daytona Beach, FL 32119-2147; tel. 386/760-7533

Fair Oaks Pavilion at Delray Medical Center, 5352 Linton Boulevard, Delray Beach, FL 33484; tel. 561/495-3278

***Fairwinds Treatment Center,** 1569 South Fort Harrison Avenue, Clearwater, FL 33756; tel. 727/449-0300

***Family Resource Center of South Florida, Inc.,** 155 South Miami Avenue, Suite 400, Miami, FL 33130-1617; tel. 305/374-6006

Flagler Hospital, Inc., 400 Health Park Boulevard, Saint Augustine, FL 32086; tel. 904/819-5155

***Florida Center for Recovery,** 3451 West Midway Road, Fort Pierce, FL 34981; tel. 772/460-2777

Florida Institute for Neurologic Rehabilitation, Inc., PO Box 1348, Wauchula, FL 33873; tel. 863/773-2857

Florida Palms Academy, Inc./Alternate Group Care, Inc., 10001 West Oakland Park Boulevard, Suite 200, Sunrise, FL 33351; tel. 954/746-5200

Fort Lauderdale Hospital - OTP, 1601 East Las Olas Boulevard, Fort Lauderdale, FL 33301; tel. 954/463-4321

***Ft. Lauderdale Addiction Treatment Center, LLC,** 307 Southwest 5th Street, Fort Lauderdale, FL 33315; tel. 954/764-6556

***G&G Healthcare Services, LLC,** 1590 Northeast 162nd Street, Suite 200, North Miami Beach, FL 33162; tel. 305/945-8384

Geo Care, Inc. / Treasure Coast Forensic Treatment Center, 96 Southwest Allapattah Road, Indiantown, FL 34956; tel. 772/597-9400

Gulf Coast Treatment Center, 1015 Mar Walt Drive, Fort Walton Beach, FL 32547; tel. 850/863-4160

Halifax Health, PO Box 2830, Daytona Beach, FL 32120-9718; tel. 386/425-4773

Hanley Center, 933 45th Street, West Palm Beach, FL 33407-2374; tel. 561/841-1000

***Hazelden Betty Ford Foundation,** 950 Sixth Avenue North, Naples, FL 34102; tel. 888/257-7800

***HealthCare Connection of Tampa, Inc.,** 825 West Linebaugh Avenue, Tampa, FL 33612; tel. 813/931-5560

***Healthy Living Detox, LLC,** 250 Thelma Avenue, Jupiter, FL 33458; tel. 561/575-2020

***Hendry Glades Mental Health Clinic, Inc.,** 601 West Alverdez Avenue, Clewiston, FL 33440; tel. 863/983-1423

HHC Focus Florida, Inc. - OTP, 5960 Southwest 106th Avenue, Cooper City, FL 33328; tel. 954/680-2700

Homestead Behavioral Health Clinic, 654 Northeast 9th Place, Homestead, FL 33030; tel. 305/248-3488

***Jackson Memorial Hospital,** 1611 Northwest 12th Avenue, Miami, FL 33136-1094; tel. 305/585-1111

***Jackson North Community Mental Health Center,** 20201 Northwest 37th Avenue, Opa Locka, FL 33056; tel. 786/466-2700

***James A. Haley Veterans' Hospital,** 13000 Bruce B. Downs Boulevard, Tampa, FL 33612; tel. 813/972-2000

***Jessie Trice Community Health Center, Inc.,** 5607 Northwest 27th Avenue, Miami, FL 33142; tel. 305/805-1700

***John's Place, Inc.,** 315 Southeast 11th Street, Fort Lauderdale, FL 33316; tel. 954/463-9590

***La Amistad Residential Treatment Center, LLC,** 1650 Park Avenue North, Maitland, FL 32751; tel. 407/647-0660

***Lakeview Health Systems, LLC,** 1900 Corporate Square Boulevard, Jacksonville, FL 32216; tel. 904/727-6455

Larkin Community Hospital, Inc., 7031 Southwest 62nd Avenue, South Miami, FL 33143; tel. 305/284-7700

***Manatee Glens,** PO Box 9478, Bradenton, FL 34206-9478; tel. 941/782-4299

Memorial Hospital of Tampa, 2901 Swann Avenue, Tampa, FL 33609; tel. 813/873-6400

***Mental Health Care, Inc.,** 5707 North 22nd Street, Tampa, FL 33610; tel. 813/272-2244

***Miami VA Healthcare System,** 1201 Northwest 16th Street, Miami, FL 33125; tel. 305/575-7000

Milestones In Recovery, Inc., 2525 Embassy Drive, Suite 10, Hollywood, FL 33026; tel. 800/347-2364

Multicultural Community Mental Health Center, 2112 South Congress Avenue, Suite 104, West Palm Beach, FL 33406; tel. 561/653-6292

National Deaf Academy, LLC, 19650 US Highway 441, Mount Dora, FL 32757; tel. 352/735-9500

New Directions Community Mental Health Center, 28870 South Dixie Highway, Homestead, FL 33033; tel. 305/247-4009

***New Era Health Center, Inc.,** 9600 Southwest 8th Street, Suite 1, Miami, FL 33174; tel. 305/559-8838

***New Horizons Community Mental Health Center, Inc.,** 1469 Northwest 36th Street, 2nd Floor, Miami, FL 33142; tel. 305/635-0366

***New Objectives, LLC,** 8144 Okeechobee Boulevard, West Palm Beach, FL 33411; tel. 561/223-3269

***North Florida/South Georgia Veterans Health System,** 1601 Southwest Archer Road, Gainesville, FL 32608-1197; tel. 352/376-1611

Northside Mental Health Center, 12512 Bruce B. Downs Boulevard, Tampa, FL 33612-9209; tel. 813/977-8700

***Novus Medical Detox of Pasco County, LLC,** 9261 Royal Palm Avenue, New Port Richey, FL 34654; tel. 727/232-8356

Nueva America, Inc., 2682 Southwest 87th Avenue, Miami, FL 33165; tel. 305/480-5680

***Ocala Behavioral Health,** 3130 Southwest 27th Avenue, Ocala, FL 34471; tel. 352/671-3130

***Ocean Breeze Recovery LLC,** 2413 East Atlantic Boulevard, Pompano Beach, FL 33062; tel. 954/946-7121

Oglethorpe, Port St. Lucie Hospital, LLC, 2550 Southeast Walton Road, Port Saint Lucie, FL 34952; tel. 772/335-0400

Oliver-Pyatt Centers, LLC, 6150 Southwest 76 Street, Miami, FL 33143; tel. 305/663-1738

***Orlando VA Medical Center,** 5201 Raymond Street, Orlando, FL 32803; tel. 407/629-1599

***Palm Partners, LLC,** 1177 George Bush Boulevard, Suite 400, Delray Beach, FL 33483; tel. 561/921-6121

Palm Shores Behavioral Health Center, 1324 37th Avenue East, Bradenton, FL 34208; tel. 941/792-2222

Parent's Information and Resource Center, Inc., 817 North Dixie Highway, Pompano Beach, FL 33060; tel. 954/785-8285

---

*Indicates organization is a Joint Commission accredited Chemical Dependency organization.

*PB Institute Partners Limited Partnership, 1017 North Olive Avenue, West Palm Beach, FL 33401; tel. 800/433-5098

*Peace River Center for Personal Development, Inc., PO Box 1559, Bartow, FL 33831-1559; tel. 863/519-0575

*Personal Enrichment through Mental Health Services, Inc., 11254 58th Street North, Pinellas Park, FL 33782; tel. 727/545-6477

*Professional Training Association Corporation, 321 Northlake Boulevard, Suite 102, North Palm Beach, FL 33408; tel. 561/494-0866

*RBHS & MHRC & MHCJ, PO Box 19249, Jacksonville, FL 32245-9249; tel. 904/743-1883

*Reawakening Wellness Center, 3600 Red Road, Miramar, FL 33025; tel. 954/738-1369

Recapturing the Vision International, Inc., 9780 East Indigo Street, Suite 302, Palmetto Bay, FL 33157; tel. 305/232-6003

*Recovery First, Inc., 4110 Davie Road Extension, Hollywood, FL 33024; tel. 954/981-4545

*Recovery Resources Enterprises, Inc., 120 State Market Road, Pahokee, FL 33476; tel. 561/285-9112

*Recovery Road, LLC, 4362 Northlake Boulevard, Suite 109, Palm Beach Gardens, FL 33410; tel. 561/899-4388

*Reflections Wellness Center of Broward, Inc., 6848 Stirling Road, Hollywood, FL 33024; tel. 954/362-0104

*Renaissance Healthcare Group, LLC, 625 Virginia Drive, Orlando, FL 32803; tel. 407/896-2636

*Serenity House Detox, LLC, 1780 Northwest 52nd Avenue, Lauderhill, FL 33313; tel. 954/805-0177

*Serenity Now CMHC, Inc., 2724 North Australian Avenue, Building 1, West Palm Beach, FL 33407; tel. 561/802-4211

South County Mental Health Center, Inc., 16158 South Military Trail, Delray Beach, FL 33484; tel. 561/637-1000

SP Behavioral, LLC, 11301 Southeast Tequesta Terrace, Tequesta, FL 33469; tel. 561/744-0211

*Springbrook Hospital, 7007 Grove Road, Brooksville, FL 34609; tel. 352/596-4306

*Stepping Stone Center for Recovery, 2701 Gateway Drive, Pompano Beach, FL 33069; tel. 954/489-2588

Stepping Stone Center for Recovery - OTP, 8889 Corporate Square Court, Jacksonville, FL 32216; tel. 954/489-2580

Suncoast Mental Health Center, Inc., 2814 South US Highway 1, Suite D - 4, Fort Pierce, FL 34982; tel. 772/489-4726

*Sunrise Detox III, 2331 Northeast 53rd Street, Fort Lauderdale, FL 33308; tel. 954/491-9700

*Sunrise Detoxification Center, LLC, 3185 Boutwell Road, Lake Worth, FL 33461; tel. 561/533-0074

*TBJ Behavioral Center, LLC, PO Box 17128, Jacksonville, FL 32245-7128; tel. 904/724-9202

*The Centers, 5664 Southwest 60th Avenue, Ocala, FL 34474; tel. 352/291-5456

*The Centre for Women, Inc., 305 South Hyde Park Avenue, Tampa, FL 33606; tel. 813/251-8437

The Devereux Foundation, Inc., 5850 T. G. Lee Boulevard, Suite 400, Orlando, FL 32822; tel. 407/362-9210

*The Jerome Golden Center for Behavioral Health, Inc., 1041 45th Street, West Palm Beach, FL 33407; tel. 561/383-8000

The Pavilion at Healthpark, LLC, 9241 Park Royal Drive, Fort Myers, FL 33908; tel. 615/861-7345

*The Recovery Village, 633 Umatilla Boulevard, Umatilla, FL 32784; tel. 352/669-8000

The Renfrew Center of Florida, 7700 Renfrew Lane, Coconut Creek, FL 33073; tel. 215/482-5353

*The Transition House, Inc., 3800 5th Street, Saint Cloud, FL 34769; tel. 407/892-5700

*The Treatment Center of the Palm Beaches, LLC, 4905 Lantana Road, Lake Worth, FL 33463; tel. 561/253-6790

*The Village South, Inc., 169 East Flagler Street, Suite 1300, Miami, FL 33131; tel. 305/573-3784

The Watershed Treatment Programs - OTP, 200 Congress Park Drive, Suite 100, Delray Beach, FL 33445; tel. 561/361-6608

*The Willough at Naples, 9001 Tamiami Trail East, Naples, FL 34113; tel. 239/775-4500

*Transitions Recovery Program, 1928 Northeast 154th Street, Miami, FL 33162; tel. 305/949-9001

*Treatment Alternatives, 7000 North Federal Highway, Boca Raton, FL 33487; tel. 561/637-4766

*Treatment Solutions of South Florida, Inc., 6278 North Federal Highway, PMB 392, Fort Lauderdale, FL 33308; tel. 954/627-6157

*Turning Point of Tampa, Inc., 6227 Sheldon Road, Tampa, FL 33615; tel. 813/882-3003

*Tykes & Teens, 3577 Southwest Corporate Parkway, Palm City, FL 34990; tel. 772/220-3439

*Unity Recovery Center, Inc., 1240 US Highway 1, Suite 200, North Palm Beach, FL 33408; tel. 561/855-6000

University Behavioral, LLC, 2500 Discovery Drive, Orlando, FL 32826; tel. 407/281-7000

*VA Medical Center - West Palm Beach, Florida, 7305 North Military Trail, West Palm Beach, FL 33410-6400; tel. 516/422-8262

Volunteers of America of Florida, Inc., 405 Central Avenue, Suite 100, Saint Petersburg, FL 33701; tel. 727/369-8500

*Wekiva Springs Center, LLC, 3947 Salisbury Road, Jacksonville, FL 32216; tel. 904/296-3533

West Palm Hospital, 2201 45th Street, West Palm Beach, FL 33407; tel. 561/863-3104

*Windmoor Healthcare of Clearwater, Inc., 11300 US 19 North, Clearwater, FL 33764; tel. 727/541-2646

GEORGIA

Central State Hospital, 620 Broad Street, Milledgeville, GA 31062; tel. 478/445-4128

Chanan Foundation, Inc., 3136 Golf Ridge Boulevard, Douglasville, GA 30135; tel. 678/715-8891

*Charlie Norwood VA Medical Center, 1 Freedom Way, Augusta, GA 30904; tel. 706/733-0188

*Coastal Harbor Health Systems, 1150 Cornell Avenue, Savannah, GA 31406; tel. 912/354-3911

*Coliseum Psychiatric Center, LLC, 340 Hospital Drive, Macon, GA 31217-8002; tel. 478/741-1355

Connecting Generations, Inc., PO Box 962783, Riverdale, GA 30296; tel. 770/331-6576

*Cord of Three Counseling Services, 204 South Crawford Street, Waycross, GA 31503; tel. 912/288-7480

DeRiche Agency, Inc., 3175 Cherokee Street, Kennesaw, GA 30144; tel. 678/490-3761

Devereux Georgia Treatment Network, 1291 Stanley Road, Kennesaw, GA 30152-4359; tel. 770/427-0147

DM & ADR, Inc., 1710 Commerce Road, Athens, GA 30607; tel. 706/552-0688

*Dwight David Eisenhower Army Medical Center, Dwight David Eisenhower Army Medical Center, Attn: MCHF-QM, Fort Gordon, GA 30905-5650; tel. 706/787-2801

East Central Regional Hospital, 100 Myrtle Boulevard, Gracewood, GA 30812; tel. 706/790-2030

*Familys Matter Counseling and Psychological Services, 4568 Lawrenceville Highway, Suite 201, Lilburn, GA 30047; tel. 404/602-0182

*Foundations Recovery Network Outpatient, LLC, 114 Sloan Street, Roswell, GA 30075; tel. 770/594-3060

*Fulton County Dept. of BHDD, 99 Jesse Hill Jr Drive, Suite 408, Atlanta, GA 30303; tel. 404/613-1202

*Georgia Pines Community Service Board, 1102 Smith Avenue, Suite K, Thomasville, GA 31792; tel. 229/225-4335

Georgia Regional Hospital at Atlanta, PO Box 37047, Decatur, GA 30034-0407; tel. 404/243-2100

Grady Memorial Hospital Corporation, 80 Jesse Hill Jr. Drive, Southeast, Atlanta, GA 30303; tel. 404/616-4252

Greenleaf Center, 2209 Pineview Drive, Valdosta, GA 31602; tel. 229/671-6611

Hopes of Honorable Youth, LLC, 4470 Chamblee Dunwoody Road, Suite 430, Atlanta, GA 30338; tel. 404/797-7126

KidsPeace National Centers of Georgia, Inc., 101 KidsPeace Drive, Bowdon, GA 30108; tel. 770/437-7200

Laurel Heights Hospital, 934 Briarcliff Road, Northeast, Atlanta, GA 30306; tel. 404/888-7860

Magnolia Behavioral Health, Inc., 3350 Northlake Parkway, Suite B, Atlanta, GA 30345; tel. 770/724-8093

*Martin Army Community Hospital, 7950 Martin Loop, Fort Benning, GA 31905-5637; tel. 706/544-4762

*Metro Atlanta Recovery Residences, Inc., 2815 Clearview Place, Atlanta, GA 30340; tel. 678/805-5100

Murphy Harpst Children's Centers, Inc., 740 Fletcher Street, Cedartown, GA 30125; tel. 770/748-1500

*Newport Integrated Behavioral Healthcare, Inc., 1810 Moseri Road, Decatur, GA 30032; tel. 404/289-8223

*Northside Hospital, Inc., 1000 Johnson Ferry Road, Atlanta, GA 30342-1611; tel. 404/851-8000

*Ogeechee Behavioral Health Services, PO Box 1259, Swainsboro, GA 30401; tel. 478/289-2522

One Community Behavioral Services, LLC, 3783 Presidential Parkway, Suite 125, Atlanta, GA 30340; tel. 202/735-7595

*Peachford Behavioral Health System of Atlanta, 2151 Peachford Road, Atlanta, GA 30338; tel. 770/455-3200

Ramsey Youth Services, 3500 Riverside Drive, Macon, GA 31210; tel. 478/477-3829

Reunited Counseling & Training, 3590 Covington Highway, Decatur, GA 30032; tel. 404/687-9188

*Ridgeview Institute, Inc., 3995 South Cobb Drive, Smyrna, GA 30080; tel. 770/434-4567

*RiverWoods Behavioral Health System, LLC, 223 Medical Center Drive, Riverdale, GA 30274; tel. 770/991-8500

RTS Services Unlimited, Inc., 6018 Craftsman Street, Johns Creek, GA 30097; tel. 404/767-7737

Skyland Trail, 1961 North Druid Hills Road, Atlanta, GA 30329; tel. 404/315-8333

Southside Behavioral Lifestyle Enrichment Center, 1100 Cleveland Avenue, East Point, GA 30344; tel. 404/627-1385

Southside Medical Center, Inc., 1046 Ridge Avenue, Atlanta, GA 30315; tel. 404/688-1350

St. Francis Hospital, Inc., PO Box 7000, Columbus, GA 31908-7000; tel. 706/596-4000

*Talbott Recovery Campus, 5448 Yorktowne Drive, Atlanta, GA 30349; tel. 770/994-0185

Tanner Medical Center / Villa Rica, 601 Dallas Highway, Villa Rica, GA 30180; tel. 770/456-3000

Tanner Medical Center, Inc., 705 Dixie Street, Carrollton, GA 30117; tel. 770/836-9580

The Renfrew Center of Georgia, LLC, 50 Glenlake Parkway, Suite 120, Atlanta, GA 30328; tel. 954/698-9222

*Turning Point Hospital, LLC, PO Box 1177, Moultrie, GA 31776; tel. 229/985-4815

*UHS of Anchor, LP, 5454 Yorktowne Drive, Atlanta, GA 30349; tel. 770/991-6044

*UHS of Summit Ridge, 250 Scenic Highway, Lawrenceville, GA 30046; tel. 678/442-5800

*VA Medical Center - Atlanta, 1670 Clairmont Road, Decatur, GA 30033; tel. 404/728-7601

*VA Medical Center - Carl Vinson, 1826 Veterans Boulevard, Dublin, GA 31021; tel. 478/277-2701

Visions of New Hope, 5300 Memorial Drive, Stone Mountain, GA 30083; tel. 919/801-0014

We Speak For Oursleves, LLC, 2020 Oakcreek Drive, Lithia Springs, GA 30122; tel. 678/438-8310

*WellStar Cobb Hospital, 3950 Austell Road, Southwest, Austell, GA 30106-1121; tel. 470/732-4000

Wesley Woods Center of Emory University, 1821 Clifton Road, Northeast, Atlanta, GA 30329; tel. 404/728-6200

West Central Georgia Regional Hospital, PO Box 12435, Columbus, GA 31917-2435; tel. 706/568-5203

*Willingway, Inc., 311 Jones Mill Road, Statesboro, GA 30458; tel. 912/764-6236

Youth Villages of Florida/Georgia/Alabama, 4685 Dorsett Shoals Road, Douglasville, GA 30135; tel. 770/852-6300

HAWAII

*Access Capabilities, Inc., 74-5583 Pawai Pl B-125, Kailua Kona, HI 96740-2123; tel. 808/334-0979

Benchmark Behavioral Health System - Pearl City, PO Box 1196, Pearl City, HI 96782; tel. 808/454-1411

Hawaii State Hospital, 45 710 Keaahala Road, Kaneohe, HI 96744; tel. 808/247-2191

*Naval Health Clinic Hawaii, 480 Central Avenue, Pearl Harbor, HI 96860-4908; tel. 808/471-3025

Sutter Health Pacific, 91-2301 Old Fort Weaver Road, Ewa Beach, HI 96706; tel. 808/671-8511

The Queen's Medical Center, 1301 Punchbowl Street, Honolulu, HI 96813; tel. 808/538-9011

*VA Pacific Islands Health Care System, 459 Patterson Road, Honolulu, HI 96819-1522; tel. 808/433-0683

*Indicates organization is a Joint Commission accredited Chemical Dependency organization.

IDAHO

*BHC Intermountain Hospital, 303 North Allumbaugh Street, Boise, ID 83704; tel. 208/377-8400
*Boise VA Medical Center, 500 West Fort Street, Boise, ID 83702-4598; tel. 208/422-1000
CenterPointe, Inc., 915 Park Centre Way, Suite 7, Nampa, ID 83651; tel. 208/442-7791
*Community Health Clinics, Inc., 211 16th Avenue, North, Nampa, ID 83653; tel. 208/465-7643
Eastern Idaho Regional Medical Center, PO Box 2077, Idaho Falls, ID 83404; tel. 208/529-6210
Project Patch, PO Box 450, Garden Valley, ID 83622; tel. 360/690-8495

ILLINOIS

*Adventist Hinsdale Hospital, 120 North Oak Street, Hinsdale, IL 60521; tel. 630/856-9000
*Advocate Addiction Treatment Program, 701 Lee Street, Suite 800, Des Plaines, IL 60016; tel. 847/795-3900
*Advocate Illinois Masonic Medical Center, 836 West Wellington Avenue, Chicago, IL 60657; tel. 773/975-1600
*Alexian Brothers Behavioral Health Hospital, 1650 Moon Lake Boulevard, Hoffman Estates, IL 60169; tel. 847/882-1600
Alexian Brothers Center for Mental Health, 3436 North Kennicott Avenue, Arlington Heights, IL 60004; tel. 847/952-7460
Allendale Association, PO Box 1088, Lake Villa, IL 60046; tel. 847/356-2351
Alton Memorial Hospital, One Memorial Drive, Alton, IL 62002; tel. 618/463-7300
*Aunt Martha's Youth Service Center, Inc., 19990 Governors Highway, Olympia Fields, IL 60461; tel. 708/747-7100
*Aurora Chicago Lakeshore Hospital, 4840 North Marine Drive, Chicago, IL 60640; tel. 773/878-9700
Beacon Therapeutic Diagnostic and Treatment Center, 1912 West 103rd Street, Chicago, IL 60643; tel. 773/298-1243
*Ben Gordon Center, 12 Health Services Drive, DeKalb, IL 60115; tel. 815/756-4875
CAP of Downers Grove, 4954 South Main Street, Downers Grove, IL 60515; tel. 630/810-0186
*CAPT James A. Lovell Federal Health Care Center, 3001 Green Bay Road, North Chicago, IL 60064; tel. 224/610-3700
Center for Addictive Problems, 609 North Wells Street, Chicago, IL 60654; tel. 312/266-0404
Center for Discovery, Chicago, 3737 Lawson Road, Glenview, IL 60026; tel. 224/235-4373
*Center for Outpatient Alcoholism Treatment (Project COAT), 9730 South Western Ave, Suite 204, Evergreen Park, IL 60805; tel. 708/425-3000
Center on Deafness, 3444 Dundee Road, Northbrook, IL 60062; tel. 847/559-0110
*Central DuPage Hospital Association, 25 North Winfield Road, Winfield, IL 60190; tel. 630/933-1600
Central Illinois Center for the Treatment of Addictions, 3420 North Rochelle, Peoria, IL 61604; tel. 309/671-8005
*Chestnut Health Systems, 1003 Martin Luther King Drive, Bloomington, IL 61701; tel. 309/827-6026
Coles County Mental Health Association, Inc., 750 Broadway Avenue East, Mattoon, IL 61938; tel. 217/238-5700
*Community Counseling Centers of Chicago, 4740 North Clark Street, Chicago, IL 60640; tel. 773/769-0205
Comprehensive Behavioral Health Center - OTP, 505 South 8th Street, East Saint Louis, IL 62201; tel. 618/482-7330
*Cornell Interventions, Inc., 5701 South Wood, Chicago, IL 60636; tel. 773/737-4600
DuPage County Health Dept./ Behavioral Health Services, 111 North County Farm Road, Wheaton, IL 60187; tel. 630/682-7400
*DuPage Interventions, 11 South 250 Route 83, Willowbrook, IL 60527; tel. 630/325-5050
Ecker Center for Mental Health, 1845 Grandstand Place, Elgin, IL 60123; tel. 847/695-0484
Edward Hines Jr VA Hospital / Drug Dependency Treatment Ct, PO Box 5000, Hines, IL 60141; tel. 708/202-8387
*Edward Hines Jr. VA Hospital, 5000 South 5th Avenue, Hines, IL 60141-5000; tel. 708/202-5652
*Edward-Elmhurst Healthcare, 155 East Brush Hill Road, Elmhurst, IL 60126; tel. 331/221-1000
Family Alliance, Inc., 2028 North Seminary Avenue, Woodstock, IL 60098-2828; tel. 815/338-3590

Family Guidance Centers - Joliet, 1611 Jefferson Street, Joliet, IL 60435; tel. 815/730-7521
Family Guidance Centers - Springfield, 2618 Patriot Boulevard, Glenview, IL 60026; tel. 217/544-9858
Family Guidance Centers, Inc., 751 Aurora Avenue, Aurora, IL 60505; tel. 630/801-0017
Family Guidance Centers, Inc., 310 West Chicago Avenue, Chicago, IL 60654; tel. 312/943-6545
Family Guidance Centers, Inc., 484 Lee Street, Des Plaines, IL 60016; tel. 847/827-7517
FHN Family Counseling Center, 421 West Exchange Street, Freeport, IL 61032; tel. 815/599-7300
Garfield Counseling Center, Inc., 4132 West Madison, Chicago, IL 60624; tel. 773/533-0433
*Gateway Foundation, Inc., 55 East Jackson Boulevard, Suite 1500, Chicago, IL 60604; tel. 312/663-1130
Hartgrove Hospital, 5730 West Roosevelt Road, Chicago, IL 60644; tel. 773/413-1700
*Heartland Human Services, PO Box 1047, Effingham, IL 62401; tel. 217/347-7179
*Human Service Center, PO Box 1346, Peoria, IL 61654-1346; tel. 309/671-8005
Insight Behavioral Health Centers, 333 North Michigan Avenue, Suite 1900, Chicago, IL 60601; tel. 312/540-9955
Jackson Park Hospital and Medical Center, 7531 South Stony Island Avenue, Chicago, IL 60649; tel. 773/947-7500
Jesse Brown Opioid Addiction Treatment Program (OTP) VA, 820 South Damen Avenue (Independence Hall), Chicago, IL 60612; tel. 312/569-6101
Kenneth Young Center, 1001 Rohlwing Road, Elk Grove Village, IL 60007; tel. 847/524-8800
Lake County Health Department, 3004 Grand Avenue, Waukegan, IL 60085; tel. 847/377-8120
*Lake County Health Department / Behavioral Health Services, 3010 Grand Avenue, Waukegan, IL 60085; tel. 847/377-8299
*Leyden Family Service and Mental Health Center, 10001 West Grand Avenue, Franklin Park, IL 60131; tel. 847/451-0330
*Linden Oaks Hospital, 801 South Washington Street, Naperville, IL 60540-6400; tel. 630/305-5500
*Little Company of Mary Hospital, 2800 West 95th Street, Evergreen Park, IL 60805; tel. 708/422-6200
*Memorial Medical Center, 385 Millennium Drive, Crystal Lake, IL 60012; tel. 815/788-5800
Memorial Medical Center, 701 North First Street, Springfield, IL 62781-0001; tel. 217/788-3000
Mental Health and Deafness Resources, Inc., 614 Anthony Trail, Northbrook, IL 60062; tel. 847/509-8260
Near North Health Service Corporation, 1276 North Clybourn Avenue, Chicago, IL 60610; tel. 312/337-1073
*North Central Behavioral Health Systems, Inc., PO Box 1488, La Salle, IL 61301; tel. 815/224-1610
*NorthShore University HealthSystem, 1301 Central Street, Suite 300, Evanston, IL 60201; tel. 847/570-5005
*Northwest Community Hospital Youth Center, 901 Kirchoff Road, Arlington Heights, IL 60005; tel. 847/618-1000
*Palos Community Hospital, 12251 South 80th Avenue, Palos Heights, IL 60463; tel. 708/923-4000
*PEER Services, Inc., 906 Davis Street, Evanston, IL 60201; tel. 847/492-1778
*Presence Mercy Medical Center, 1325 North Highland Avenue, Aurora, IL 60506; tel. 630/859-2222
*Presence Saint Joseph Hospital, 2900 North Lake Shore Drive, Chicago, IL 60657; tel. 773/665-3000
*ProCare Centers, 1820 South 25th Avenue, Broadview, IL 60153; tel. 708/338-3806
*Remedies Renewing Lives, 516 Green Street, Rockford, IL 61102; tel. 815/966-1285
Riveredge Hospital, 8311 West Roosevelt Road, Forest Park, IL 60130; tel. 708/771-7000
*Riverside Medical Center, 350 North Wall Street, Kankakee, IL 60901; tel. 815/933-1671
Rock River Academy and Residential Center, 344 Elmwood Road, Rockford, IL 61101; tel. 815/877-3440
*Rosecrance, Inc., 1021 North Mulford Road, Rockford, IL 61107; tel. 815/387-5600
Rush University Medical Center, 1653 West Congress Parkway, Chicago, IL 60612; tel. 312/942-5000

Saint Anthony Hospital, 2875 West 19th Street, Chicago, IL 60623; tel. 773/484-4015
Sequel Schools, LLC, 998 Corporate Blvd, Aurora, IL 60502; tel. 847/391-8000
*Sinnissippi Centers, Inc., 325 Illinois Route 2, Dixon, IL 61021; tel. 815/284-6611
*Southeastern Illinois Counseling Centers, Inc., Drawer M, Olney, IL 62450; tel. 618/395-4306
St. Joseph's Hospital, PO Box 99, Breese, IL 62230; tel. 618/526-4511
*Tazwood Mental Health Center, Inc., 3248 Vandever Avenue, Pekin, IL 61554; tel. 309/347-5579
*The Child, Adolescent and Family Recovery Center, LLC, 900 North Shore Drive, Suite 140, Lake Bluff, IL 60044; tel. 847/457-6730
*The Pavilion Foundation, 809 West Church Street, Champaign, IL 61820; tel. 217/373-1700
*The South Suburban Council on Alcoholism and Substance Abuse, 1909 Cheker Square, Hazel Crest, IL 60429; tel. 708/647-3333
*The Women's Treatment Center, 140 North Ashland Avenue, Chicago, IL 60607; tel. 312/850-0050
*TK Behavioral, LLC, 40 Timberline Drive, Lemont, IL 60439; tel. 630/257-9600
Touchette Regional Hospital, 5900 Bond Avenue, Centreville, IL 62207; tel. 618/332-5400
*VA - Illiana Health Care System, 1900 East Main Street, Danville, IL 61832; tel. 217/554-3000
*VA Medical Center, 2401 West Main Street, Marion, IL 62959; tel. 618/997-5311
Waukegan IL Hospital Company, LLC, 2615 Washington Street, Waukegan, IL 60085; tel. 847/249-3900
Westlake Hospital, 1225 West Lake Street, Melrose Park, IL 60160; tel. 708/938-4000
*Woodridge Interventions, 2221 64th Street, Woodridge, IL 60517; tel. 630/968-6477

INDIANA

Adult and Child Mental Health Center, Inc., 222 East Ohio Street, Suite 600, Indianapolis, IN 46204; tel. 317/882-5122
Anchor Homes, Inc., 420 South Main Street, New Castle, IN 47362; tel. 765/521-2630
*Aspire Indiana, 9516 East 148th Street, Suite 1, Noblesville, IN 46060; tel. 317/587-0500
Bloomington Meadows Hospital, 3600 North Prow Road, Bloomington, IN 47404; tel. 812/331-8000
Brentwood Meadows, LLC, 4488 Roslin Road, Newburgh, IN 47630; tel. 812/858-7200
Columbus Hospital LLC, 2223 Poshard Drive, Columbus, IN 47203; tel. 812/376-1711
*Community Health Network, Inc., 1500 North Ritter Avenue, Indianapolis, IN 46219; tel. 317/355-5520
*Community Howard Regional Health, PO Box 9011, Kokomo, IN 46904; tel. 765/453-8547
Crossroad Child & Family Services, Inc., 2525 Lake Avenue, Fort Wayne, IN 46805-5457; tel. 260/484-4153
*Cummins Behavioral Health Systems, Inc., 6655 East US 36, Avon, IN 46123; tel. 317/272-3330
Eskenazi Health, Eskenazi Avenue, Indianapolis, IN 46202; tel. 317/880-8000
Evansville Psychiatric Children's Center, 3300 East Morgan Avenue, Evansville, IN 47715; tel. 812/477-6436
*Fairbanks Hospital, Inc., 8102 Clearvista Parkway, Indianapolis, IN 46256-4698; tel. 317/849-8222
*Four County Comprehensive Mental Health Center, Inc., 1015 Michigan Avenue, Logansport, IN 46947; tel. 574/722-5151
*Good Samaritan Hospital, 520 South Seventh Street, Vincennes, IN 47591; tel. 812/885-3335
*Grant-Blackford Mental Health, Inc., 505 North Wabash Avenue, Marion, IN 46952; tel. 765/662-3971
Health and Hospital Corporation, 720 Eskenazi Avenue, Indianapolis, IN 46202; tel. 317/880-8000
HHC Indiana, Inc., 1800 North Oak Drive, Plymouth, IN 46563; tel. 574/936-3784
*Indiana University Health, Inc., PO Box 1367, Fairbanks Hall, Suite 6100, Indianapolis, IN 46206; tel. 317/963-0235
John H. Boner Community Center, 2236 East 10th Street, Indianapolis, IN 46201-2006; tel. 317/633-3104
*LifeSpring, Inc., 460 Spring Street, Jeffersonville, IN 47130; tel. 812/280-2080
Logansport State Hospital, 1098 South State Road 25, Logansport, IN 46947; tel. 574/722-4141

*Indicates organization is a Joint Commission accredited Chemical Dependency organization.

*Meridian Health Services, 240 North Tillotson Avenue, Muncie, IN 47304; tel. 765/288–1928

*Oaklawn Psychiatric Center, Inc., PO Box 809, 330 Lakeview Drive, Goshen, IN 46527-0809; tel. 574/533–1234

Options Treatment Center, 5602 Caito Drive, Indianapolis, IN 46226; tel. 317/544–4340

Person First Consulting, Inc., 6002 Morning Dove Drive, Indianapolis, IN 46228; tel. 317/750–0222

Persons Centered Value Partners, LLC, 4459 Peggy Hollow Road, Shoals, IN 47581; tel. 812/936–3543

Premier Care of Indiana, Inc., 317 South Norton Avenue, Marion, IN 46952; tel. 765/664–0101

R.T.C. Resource Acquisition Corporation, 1404 South State, Indianapolis, IN 46203; tel. 317/783–4003

Resolute Acquisition Corporation, 320 North Tibbs, Indianapolis, IN 46222; tel. 317/630–5215

Richard L. Roudebush VAMC Opioid Substitution Clinic, 1481 West 10th Street, Building 1, Indianapolis, IN 46202; tel. 317/988–2121

Riverview Adult Day Center, 2715 East Jackson Boulevard, Elkhart, IN 46516-5053; tel. 574/293–6886

Samlind of Indiana, Inc., 50770 SR 933, South Bend, IN 46637; tel. 574/855–1810

Sequel TSI of Indiana, LLC, 2426 Parker Lane, Lexington, IN 47138; tel. 812/889–3992

*Southlake Mental Health Center, 8555 Taft Street, Merrillville, IN 46410-6199; tel. 219/769–4005

*Southwestern Behavioral Healthcare, Inc., 415 Mulberry Street, Evansville, IN 47713-1298; tel. 812/423–7791

*St. Vincent Anderson Regional Hospital, Inc., 2015 Jackson Street, Anderson, IN 46016; tel. 765/646–8373

Starline Community Services, Inc., PO Box 1576, South Bend, IN 46634; tel. 574/323–8707

*Tara Treatment Center, Inc., 6231 South US 31, Franklin, IN 46131; tel. 812/526–2611

The Midwest Center for Youth and Families, PO Box 669, Kouts, IN 46347; tel. 219/766–2999

*The Otis R. Bowen Center for Human Services, Inc., PO Box 497, Warsaw, IN 46581-0497; tel. 574/267–7169

*VA Northern Indiana Health Care System, 2121 Lake Avenue, Fort Wayne, IN 46805; tel. 260/460–1310

*Valle Vista Hospital, LLC, 898 East Main Street, Greenwood, IN 46143; tel. 317/887–1348

*Wabash Valley Alliance, Inc., 415 North 26th Street, Lafayette, IN 47904; tel. 765/446–6537

*Wellstone Regional Hospital Acquisition, LLC, 2700 Vissing Park Road, Jeffersonville, IN 47130; tel. 812/284–8000

Willowgien Academy - Indiana, Inc., 308 East 21st Avenue, Gary, IN 46407; tel. 219/886–1320

Youth Villages of Indiana, 130 Demaree Drive, Madison, IN 47250; tel. 901/251–4944

IOWA

Boys and Girls Home and Family Services, Inc., PO Box 1197, Sioux City, IA 51102; tel. 712/293–4700

*Broadlawns Medical Center, 1801 Hickman Road, Des Moines, IA 50314; tel. 515/282–2200

Central Iowa In Home Counseling, 2317 Rick Collins Way, Eldora, IA 50627; tel. 641/858–3852

Clarinda Youth Corporation, 1820 North 16th Street, Clarinda, IA 51632; tel. 712/542–3103

Family Empowerment Services, Inc., 505 North Mississippi Street, Blue Grass, IA 52726; tel. 563/579–7790

Healthy Homes Family Services, Inc., 118 North Elm Street, Avoca, IA 51521; tel. 712/307–6014

Hillcrest Family Services, 2005 Asbury Road, Dubuque, IA 52001; tel. 563/583–7357

Integrative Health Services, Inc., PO Box 118, Williamsburg, IA 52361-0118; tel. 319/668–2050

*Iowa City VA Health Care System, 601 Highway 6 West, Iowa City, IA 52246; tel. 319/338–0581

Mental Health Institute, 2277 Iowa Avenue, Independence, IA 50644; tel. 319/334–2583

*Mercy Medical Center, 1111 6th Avenue, Des Moines, IA 50314; tel. 515/247–3121

Mercy Medical Center - Sioux City, PO Box 3168, Sioux City, IA 51101; tel. 712/279–2010

*Orchard Place, 925 Porter Avenue, Des Moines, IA 50315; tel. 515/285–6781

*St. Luke's Methodist Hospital, 1026 A Avenue Northeast, Cedar Rapids, IA 52402; tel. 319/369–7211

*The University of Iowa Hospitals and Clinics, 200 Hawkins Drive, Iowa City, IA 52242; tel. 319/384–5897

*VA Central Iowa Health Care System, 3600 30th Street, Des Moines, IA 50310-5774; tel. 515/699–5999

Woodward Academy, 1251 334th Street, Woodward, IA 50276; tel. 515/438–3481

KANSAS

*Atchison Valley Hope, PO Box 312, Atchison, KS 66002; tel. 913/367–1618

*EmberHope, Inc., 4505 East 47th Street South, Wichita, KS 67210; tel. 316/529–9100

*Haskell Indian Health Center, 2415 Massachusetts, Lawrence, KS 66046; tel. 785/843–4824

Kansas City Metro Methadone Program, MS 4015, 3901 Rainbow Boulevard, Kansas City, KS 66160-7341; tel. 913/588–6493

KVC Behavioral HealthCare, Inc., 7940 Marshall Drive, Lenexa, KS 66214; tel. 913/499–8100

KVC Hospitals, Inc., 21350 West 153rd Street, Olathe, KS 66061; tel. 913/322–4900

*Marillac Center, Inc., 8000 West 127th Street, Overland Park, KS 66213; tel. 913/951–4300

*Moundridge Valley Hope, PO Box 956, Moundridge, KS 67107; tel. 620/345–4673

*Munson Army Health Center, 550 Pope Avenue, Building 343, Fort Leavenworth, KS 66027-2332; tel. 913/684–6420

*Norton Valley Hope, PO Box 510, Norton, KS 67654; tel. 785/877–5101

*Prairie View, Inc., PO Box 467, Newton, KS 67114; tel. 316/284–6400

*Robert J. Dole VA Medical Center, 5500 East Kellogg, Wichita, KS 67218; tel. 316/651–3601

*Saint Francis Community Services, Inc., 509 East Elm Street, Salina, KS 67401; tel. 785/825–0541

Sequel of Kansas, LLC, 2050 West 11th Street, Wichita, KS 67203; tel. 316/267–5710

*Shawnee Mission Medical Center, 9100 West 74th Street, Shawnee Mission, KS 66204; tel. 913/676–2000

The Children's Mercy Hospital, 5808 West 110th, Overland Park, KS 66211; tel. 913/696–8000

*VA Eastern Kansas Health Care System, 2200 Southwest Gage, Topeka, KS 66622; tel. 785/350–3111

VCPHCS XIV, LLC dba BHG Overland Park Treatment Center, 6331 West 110th Street, Overland Park, KS 66211; tel. 936/524–2140

KENTUCKY

BHG XXIV, LLC d/b/a BHG Paintsville Treatment Center, 628 Jefferson Avenue, Paintsville, KY 41240; tel. 606/789–6966

BHG XXV, LLC/dba BHG Pikeville Treatment Center, 368 South Mayo Trail, Pikeville, KY 41501; tel. 606/437–0047

BHG XXVI, LLC d/b/a BHG Hazard Treatment Center, 48 Independence Drive, Hazard, KY 41701; tel. 606/487–1646

*Blanchfield Army Community Hospital, MCXD-DCMCC, 650 Joel Drive, Fort Campbell, KY 42223-5349; tel. 270/798–8512

Bluegrass Regional / Narcotics Addiction Program, 1351 Newtown Pike, Building 1, Lexington, KY 40511; tel. 859/253–1686

*Cumberland River Regional MH/MR Board, Inc., PO Box 568, Corbin, KY 40702; tel. 606/528–7010

*Ireland Army Community Hospital, 289 Ireland Avenue, Building 851, Fort Knox, KY 40121-5520; tel. 502/624–0251

*Jewish Hospital and St. Mary's Healthcare, 200 Abraham Flexner Way, Louisville, KY 40202-1886; tel. 502/587–4011

*KMI Acquisition, LLC, 8521 LaGrange Road, Louisville, KY 40242; tel. 502/426–6380

*Lexington VA Medical Center, 1101 Veterans Drive, Lexington, KY 40502-2236; tel. 859/233–4511

*Lincoln Trail Behavioral Health System, PO Box 369, Radcliff, KY 40160; tel. 270/351–9444

*NorthKey Community Care, PO Box 2680, Covington, KY 41012; tel. 859/578–3233

*Robley Rex Medical Center, 800 Zorn Avenue, Louisville, KY 40206; tel. 502/287–4000

*Seven Counties Services, Inc., 101 West Muhammad Ali Boulevard, Louisville, KY 40202; tel. 502/589–8600

Spectrum Care Academy, Inc., PO Box 911, Columbia, KY 42728; tel. 270/384–6444

Sunrise Children's Services, PO Box 1429, Mount Washington, KY 40047-1429; tel. 502/538–1000

*TBD Acquisition, LLC, 1405 Browns Lane, Louisville, KY 40207; tel. 502/896–0495

*UHS of Bowling Green, LLC, 1035 Porter Pike Road, Bowling Green, KY 42103; tel. 270/843–1199

LOUISIANA

Absolute Health, Inc., 560 Belle Terre Boulevard, La Place, LA 70068; tel. 985/652–0078

Abundant Health, Inc., 2053 Gause Boulevard East, Suite 150, Slidell, LA 70461; tel. 985/649–1001

*Acadia Vermilion Hospital, LLC, 2520 North University Avenue, Lafayette, LA 70507; tel. 337/234–5614

Acceptable Health Services, LLC, 5640 Rad Boulevard, Suite 740, New Orleans, LA 70126; tel. 504/245–2440

*Alexandria VA Health Care System, PO Box 69004, Alexandria, LA 71306; tel. 318/473–0010

ANIOMA, Inc., 10001 Lake Forest Boulevard, Suite 616, New Orleans, LA 70127; tel. 504/240–3056

Bayou Mental Health Services, LLC, 818 Main Street, Suite A, Pineville, LA 71360; tel. 337/353–2129

Beacon Behavioral Hospital, Inc., 9938 Airline Highway, Suite 200, Baton Rouge, LA 70816; tel. 225/258–6103

Beacon Behavioral Hospital-New Orleans, 14500 Hayne Boulevard, Suite 200, New Orleans, LA 70128; tel. 225/810–4040

*Brentwood Acquisition-Shreveport, Inc., 1006 Highland Avenue, Shreveport, LA 71101; tel. 318/678–7500

CHRISTUS Health Southwestern Louisiana, 524 Dr. Michael DeBakey Drive, Lake Charles, LA 70601; tel. 337/491–7766

Community Care Hospital, 1421 General Taylor Street, New Orleans, LA 70115; tel. 504/899–2500

Community Empowerment Services, 11726 Bricksome Avenue, Baton Rouge, LA 70816; tel. 919/332–5425

Crossroads Hospital, 44 Versailles Boulevard, Alexandria, LA 71303; tel. 318/445–5111

DRD Management, Inc., 417 South Johnson Street, New Orleans, LA 70112; tel. 504/524–7205

Eastern Louisiana Mental Health System, PO Box 498, Jackson, LA 70748-0498; tel. 225/634–0216

Ekems Healthcare, 8470 Morrison Road, Suite A, New Orleans, LA 70127; tel. 504/248–1581

Greenbrier Hospital, 201 Greenbrier Boulevard, Covington, LA 70433; tel. 985/893–2970

Lake Charles Memorial Hospital, PO Drawer M, Lake Charles, LA 70601; tel. 337/494–3000

Lane Regional Medical Center, 6300 Main Street, Zachary, LA 70791; tel. 225/658–4303

Liberty HealthCare Systems, LLC, 4673 Eugene Ware Boulevard, Bastrop, LA 71220; tel. 318/281–2448

MBH of Louisiana, LLC, 23515 Highway 190, Mandeville, LA 70448; tel. 985/626–6300

Natchitoches Regional Medical Center, PO Box 2009, Natchitoches, LA 71457; tel. 318/214–4200

Oceans Behavioral Hospital of Greater New Orleans, 716 Village Road, Kenner, LA 70065; tel. 504/464–8895

*Oceans Behavioral Hospital of Lafayette, LLC, 420 Albertson Parkway, Broussard, LA 70518; tel. 337/839–9008

*Overton Brooks VA Medical Center, 510 East Stoner Avenue, Shreveport, LA 71101-4295; tel. 318/990–5113

Phoenix Behavioral Hospital of Eunice, 2021 Crowley-Rayne Highway, Rayne, LA 70578; tel. 337/788–0091

Positive Choices Counseling Services, Inc., PO Box 614, Vidalia, LA 71373; tel. 318/336–4700

Premier Rehab of Southwest Louisiana, LLC, 840 West Bayou Pines, Suite B, Lake Charles, LA 70601; tel. 337/491–1740

Provision Rehab, LLC, 113 Bienville Square, Suite 6, Natchitoches, LA 71457; tel. 318/238–4030

River Oaks, Inc., 1525 River Oaks Road West, New Orleans, LA 70123; tel. 504/734–1740

Sahara Health Systems, LLC, 1530 Highway 90 West, Jennings, LA 70546; tel. 337/616–8122

Seaside Health System, LLC, 4363 Convention Street, Baton Rouge, LA 70806; tel. 225/522–4076

Section C

---

*Southeast Louisiana Veterans Healthcare System, PO Box 61011, New Orleans, LA 70161-1011; tel. 504/565-4836

St. Francis Medical Center, PO Box 1901, Monroe, LA 71210-1901; tel. 318/966-4000

St. James Behavioral Health Hospital, Inc., PO Box 2069, Gonzales, LA 70707; tel. 225/647-7524

Success Counseling Services-North, 1504 Barksdale Boulevard, Bossier City, LA 71111; tel. 318/222-4299

Therapeutic Health Care Concepts LLC dba Journey Rehab, 1403 Metro Drive Suite East, Alexandria, LA 71303; tel. 318/445-9019

VCPHCS V, LLC d.b.a. BHG New Orleans Westbank Treatment Cent, 1141 Whitney Avenue, Building 4, Gretna, LA 70056; tel. 504/347-1120

VCPHCS VI, LLC d.b.a. BHG Lake Charles Treatment Center, 2829 4th Avenue, Suite 200, Lake Charles, LA 70601; tel. 337/433-8281

MAINE

Acadia Hospital - Narcotic Treatment Program, PO Box 422, Bangor, ME 04402-0422; tel. 207/973-6100

CAP Quality Care, Inc., 1 Delta Drive, Suite A, Westbrook, ME 04092; tel. 207/856-7227

Cary Medical Center, 163 Van Buren Road, Caribou, ME 04736; tel. 207/498-3111

Maine Medical Center, 22 Bramhall Street, Portland, ME 04102; tel. 207/662-0111

*MaineGeneral Medical Center, 35 Medical Center Parkway, Augusta, ME 04330; tel. 207/626-1000

Mercy Recovery Center, 40 Park Road, Westbrook, ME 04092; tel. 207/857-8085

Riverview Psychiatric Center, 11 State House Station, Augusta, ME 04333-0011; tel. 207/624-4683

SequelCare of Maine, LLC, 500 US Route 1, Suite 102, Yarmouth, ME 04096; tel. 207/847-2273

*Southern Maine Health Care, PO Box 626, Biddeford, ME 04005-0626; tel. 207/283-7000

*St. Mary's Regional Medical Center, PO Box 291, Campus Avenue, Lewiston, ME 04243-0291; tel. 207/777-8100

*The Acadia Hospital, PO Box 422, Bangor, ME 04402-0422; tel. 207/973-6100

*VA Maine Healthcare System, 1 VA Center, Augusta, ME 04330; tel. 207/623-8411

MARYLAND

Addiction Treatment Services of Hopkins Bayview, 5510 Nathan Shock Drive, Suite 1500, Baltimore, MD 21224; tel. 410/550-0100

Adventist Behavioral Health Eastern Shore, 821 Fieldcrest Road, Cambridge, MD 21613; tel. 410/221-0288

*Adventist Health Care, Inc., 14901 Broschart Road, Rockville, MD 20850; tel. 301/251-4500

All Walks of Life, LLC, 2510 St. Paul Street, Baltimore, MD 21218; tel. 410/558-0019

*Ashley, Inc., 800 Tydings Lane, Havre De Grace, MD 21078; tel. 410/273-6600

Aspen Day Treatment, LLC, 1634 Sulphur Spring Road, Halethorpe, MD 21227; tel. 410/242-0920

Bon Secours New Hope Treatment Center, 2401 West Baltimore Street, Baltimore, MD 21223; tel. 410/945-7706

Bon Secours' ADAPT Cares, 2000 West Baltimore Street, Baltimore, MD 21223; tel. 410/362-3011

Brook Lane Health Services, PO Box 1945, Hagerstown, MD 21742-1945; tel. 301/733-0330

*Carroll Hospital Center, Inc., 200 Memorial Avenue, Westminster, MD 21157; tel. 410/871-6221

Catholic Charities Child and Family Services, 2300 Dulaney Valley Road, Timonium, MD 21093; tel. 410/252-4700

*Center for Addiction Medicine, 827 Linden Ave, Baltimore, MD 21201; tel. 410/225-6249

*Chase Brexton Health Services, Inc., 1111 North Charles Street, Baltimore, MD 21201; tel. 410/837-2050

*Crossroads Center of Frederick, LLC, 511 West South Street, Frederick, MD 21701; tel. 301/696-1950

Daybreak Rehabilitation Center, 2490 Giles Road, Baltimore, MD 21225; tel. 410/396-1646

Eastern Shore Hospital Center, PO Box 800, Cambridge, MD 21613; tel. 410/221-2525

*Family Health Centers of Baltimore, Inc., 631 Cherry Hill Road, Baltimore, MD 21225; tel. 410/354-2000

*Fort Meade USA MEDDAC, 2480 Llewellyn Avenue, Fort George G Meade, MD 20755-5129; tel. 301/677-8174

Frederick County Health Dept. /Behavior Health Services, 300-B Scholl's Lane, Frederick, MD 21701; tel. 301/600-1775

Glass Substance Abuse Program, Inc., 3635 Old Court Road, Pikesville, MD 21208; tel. 410/484-2700

*Health Care for the Homeless, Inc., 421 Fallsway, Baltimore, MD 21202; tel. 410/837-5533

Hope Health Systems, Inc., 6707 Whitestone Road, Suite 106, Woodlawn, MD 21207; tel. 410/265-8737

House of the Good Shepherd of the City of Baltimore, 4100 Maple Avenue, Baltimore, MD 21227; tel. 410/247-2770

*Hudson Health Services, Inc., PO Box 1096, Salisbury, MD 21802-1096; tel. 410/219-9000

John L. Gildner Regional Institute for Children& Adolescents, 15000 Broschart Road, Rockville, MD 20850; tel. 301/251-6800

*Johns Hopkins Bayview Medical Center, 4940 Eastern Avenue, Baltimore, MD 21224-2780; tel. 410/550-0120

*JR Healthcare Associates, 200 South Arlington Avenue, Baltimore, MD 21223; tel. 410/962-7180

Levindale Hebrew Geriatric Center and Hospital, 2434 West Belvedere Avenue, Baltimore, MD 21215; tel. 410/466-8700

Maple Shade Youth & Family Services, Inc., 23704 Ocean Gateway, Mardela Springs, MD 21837; tel. 410/742-7400

*Maryland IOP Partners, 21 West Courtland Street, Bel Air, MD 21014; tel. 877/762-3766

*Maryland Treatment Centers, Inc., PO Box 136, Emmitsburg, MD 21727; tel. 301/447-2361

MBA Southeast Baltimore County, 8860 Citation Road, Suite B, Essex, MD 21221; tel. 410/486-2500

*MedStar Montgomery Medical Center, 18101 Prince Philip Drive, Olney, MD 20832; tel. 301/774-8770

MedStar St. Mary's Hospital, PO Box 527, Leonardtown, MD 20650; tel. 301/475-8981

Medstar Union Memorial Hospital, 201 East University Parkway, Baltimore, MD 21218; tel. 410/554-2000

Methadone for Business Achievers (MBA), 821 North Eutaw Street, Baltimore, MD 21201; tel. 410/225-9185

Methadone for Business Achievers - Timonium, 2 West Aylesbury Road, Timonium, MD 21093; tel. 410/561-9591

Nalty & Associates, Inc., 6819 Timberlane Road, Baltimore, MD 21209; tel. 410/366-1151

*Naval Health Clinic Annapolis, 250 Wood Road, Annapolis, MD 21402-5050; tel. 410/293-1330

*Naval Health Clinic, Patuxent River, 47149 Buse Road, Building 1370, Patuxent River, MD 20670-5370; tel. 301/342-1418

*Park West Health System, Inc., 3319 West Belvedere Avenue, Baltimore, MD 21215; tel. 410/542-7800

*Pathways, 2620 Riva Road, Annapolis, MD 21401; tel. 410/573-5400

*People's Community Health Center, Inc., 1734 Maryland Avenue, Baltimore, MD 21201; tel. 410/467-6040

*Prince George's County Health Department, 1701 McCormick Drive, Suite 230, Largo, MD 20774; tel. 301/883-7853

Reflective Treatment Center, 301 North Gay Street, Baltimore, MD 21202; tel. 410/752-3500

Regional Institute for Children and Adolescents-Baltimore, 605 South Chapel Gate Lane, Baltimore, MD 21229; tel. 410/368-7800

Saint Luke Institute, 8901 New Hampshire Avenue, Silver Spring, MD 20903; tel. 301/445-7970

Sheppard Pratt Health System, Inc., PO Box 6815, Baltimore, MD 21285-6815; tel. 410/938-3000

*Shore Health System of Maryland, Inc., 219 South Washington Street, Easton, MD 21601; tel. 410/822-1000

Sinai Hospital Addictions Recovery Program, 2401 West Belvedere Avenue, Baltimore, MD 21215; tel. 410/601-5355

*Suburban Hospital Incorporated, 8600 Old Georgetown Road, Bethesda, MD 20814; tel. 301/896-3107

The Johns Hopkins Hospital Drug Abuse Program, 600 North Wolfe Street, Baltimore, MD 21287; tel. 410/955-5000

Thomas B. Finan Center, PO Box 1722 Country Club Road, Cumberland, MD 21501-1722; tel. 301/777-2405

*Tuerk House, Inc., 730 Ashburton Street, Baltimore, MD 21216-6116; tel. 410/233-0684

*University of Maryland Medical Center, 22 South Greene Street, Baltimore, MD 21201-1595; tel. 410/328-6027

VA Maryland Health Care System Opioid Treatment Program, 10 North Greene Street, Baltimore, MD 21201; tel. 410/605-7000

*Walter Reed National Military Medical Center, Bethesda, 8901 Wisconsin Avenue, Bethesda, MD 20889-5600; tel. 301/319-4618

Wicomico County Health Department, 108 East Main Street, Salisbury, MD 21801; tel. 410/742-3784

Woodbourne Center, Inc., 1301 Woodbourne Avenue, Baltimore, MD 21239; tel. 410/433-1000

*Worcester County Health Department, PO Box 249, Snow Hill, MD 21863; tel. 410/632-1100

Zenith Healthcare Services, Inc., 800 N Charles Street, Baltimore, MD 21201; tel. 410/244-5599

MASSACHUSETTS

AdCare Hospital of Worcester, Inc., 107 Lincoln Street, Worcester, MA 01605; tel. 508/799-9000

Arbour - Fuller Hospital, 200 May Street, South Attleboro, MA 02703; tel. 508/761-8500

Arbour Hospital, Inc., 49 Robinwood Avenue, Jamaica Plain, MA 02130; tel. 617/522-4400

*Arbour-HRI Hospital, 227 Babcock Street, Brookline, MA 02446; tel. 617/731-3200

Austen Riggs Center, 25 Main Street, Stockbridge, MA 01262-0962; tel. 413/298-5511

Baldpate Hospital - OTP, 83 Baldpate Road, Georgetown, MA 01833; tel. 978/352-2131

Baystate Franklin Medical Center, 164 High Street, Greenfield, MA 01301; tel. 413/773-0211

Baystate Medical Center, 759 Chestnut Street, Springfield, MA 01199; tel. 413/794-5960

*Berkshire Medical Center, 725 North Street, Pittsfield, MA 01201; tel. 413/447-2000

Bridgewater State Hospital, 20 Administration Road, Bridgewater, MA 02324; tel. 508/279-4500

Brockton Multi Service Center, 165 Quincy Street, Brockton, MA 02302; tel. 508/897-2000

Cambridge Eating Disorder Center, 3 Bow Street, Cambridge, MA 02138; tel. 617/547-2255

Cape Cod and Islands Community Mental Health Center, 830 County Road, Pocasset, MA 02559; tel. 508/564-9600

Cohannet Academy, 60 Hodges Avenue, Cain 2, Taunton, MA 02780; tel. 508/977-3730

*Counseling & Assessment Clinic of Worcester, LLC, 38 Front Street, 5th Floor, Worcester, MA 01608; tel. 508/756-5400

Dimock Community Foundation, Inc. - OTP, 55 Dimock Street, Roxbury, MA 02119; tel. 617/442-8800

Doctor Franklin Perkins School, 971 Main Street, Lancaster, MA 01523; tel. 978/365-7376

Dr. John C. Corrigan Mental Health Center, 49 Hillside Street, Fall River, MA 02720; tel. 508/235-7200

Dr. Solomon Carter Fuller Mental Health Center, 85 East Newton Street, Boston, MA 02118; tel. 617/626-8861

Edith Nourse Rogers Memorial Veterans Hospital, 200 Springs Road, Bedford, MA 01730; tel. 781/687-3080

Federal Bureau of Prisons Federal Medical Center Devens, PO Box 880, Ayer, MA 01432; tel. 978/796-1443

*Fenway Community Health Center, Inc., 1340 Boylston Street, Boston, MA 02215; tel. 617/267-0900

*First Psychiatric Planners, 300 South Street, Chestnut Hill, MA 02467; tel. 617/469-0300

Franciscan Hospital for Children, Inc., 30 Warren Street, Boston, MA 02135-3680; tel. 617/254-3800

*Gosnold, Inc., 200 Ter Heun Drive, Falmouth, MA 02540; tel. 508/540-6550

High Point Treatment Center - OTP, 10 Meadowbrook Road, Brockton, MA 02301; tel. 508/742-4400

High Point Treatment Center - OTP (Outpatient), 30 Meadowbrook Road, Brockton, MA 02301; tel. 508/408-6190

*High Point Treatment Center, Inc., 98 North Front Street, 3rd Floor, New Bedford, MA 02740; tel. 774/628-1095

High Point Treatment Center, Inc., 1233 State Road, Plymouth, MA 02360-5133; tel. 508/224-7701

---

*Indicates organization is a Joint Commission accredited Chemical Dependency organization.

High Point Treatment Center, Inc. (OTP), 108 North Front Street, New Bedford, MA 02740; tel. 774/628–1000

Hillcrest Educational Centers, Inc., 788 South Street, Pittsfield, MA 01201; tel. 413/499–7924

HVL Corporation, 76 Summer Street, Haverhill, MA 01830; tel. 978/373–8222

JRI Intensive Residential Treatment Programs, PO Box 374, Tewksbury, MA 01876; tel. 978/858–3776

Justice Resource Institute — The Meadowridge Schools, 160 Gould Street, Suite 300, Needham Heights, MA 02494; tel. 781/559–4900

Justice Resource Institute Behavioral Health Centers, 380 Massachusetts Avenue, Acton, MA 01720; tel. 978/264–3500

Laurel Hill Inn, LTD, 121 Mystic Street, Medford, MA 02155; tel. 781/391–8000

*Lowell Community Health Center, 161 Jackson Street, Lowell, MA 01852; tel. 978/937–9700

Luminosity Behavioral Health Services, 810 Washington Street, Stoughton, MA 02072; tel. 781/344–0102

*Lynn Community Health Center, PO Box 526, Lynn, MA 01903; tel. 781/596–2502

*McLean Hospital, 115 Mill Street, Belmont, MA 02478; tel. 617/855–3450

*Mercy Hospital, Inc., 271 Carew Street, Springfield, MA 01104; tel. 413/748–9000

Mercy Hospital, Inc. - MMTP, 227 Mill Street, Springfield, MA 01102; tel. 413/539–2400

Mercy Hospital, Inc. MMTP, 1233 Main Street, Holyoke, MA 01040; tel. 413/539–2950

MetroWest Medical Center, 115 Lincoln Street, Framingham, MA 01702; tel. 508/383–1000

Multicultural Wellness Center, Inc., 250 Commercial Street, Suite 330, Worcester, MA 01608; tel. 508/752–4665

NFI Massachusetts IRTP, 309 Belmont Street, Adolescent Wing D2, Worcester, MA 01604; tel. 508/368–3734

North End Community Health Committee, Inc., 332 Hanover Street, Boston, MA 02113; tel. 617/643–8000

North Shore Medical Center, Inc., 81 Highland Avenue, Salem, MA 01970; tel. 978/741–1200

Northeast Hospital Corporation, 85 Herrick Street, Beverly, MA 01915-1777; tel. 978/922–3000

Osiris Family Institute, LLC, 184 Dudley Street, Suite 107 LL, Roxbury, MA 02119; tel. 617/442–2002

Priority Professional Care, LLC, 1613 Blue Hill Avenue, Suite 302, Mattapan, MA 02126; tel. 857/598–4774

Pyramid Builders Counseling Services, Inc., 11 Roxbury Street, Roxbury, MA 02119; tel. 617/516–0280

SSTAR, 1010 South Main Street, Fall River, MA 02724; tel. 508/235–5010

SSTAR DETOX, 386 Stanley Street, Fall River, MA 02720; tel. 508/324–3500

Steward Saint Anne's Hospital, 795 Middle Street, Fall River, MA 02721-1798; tel. 508/674–5600

The Renfrew Center of Massachusetts, LLC, 870 R Commonwealth Avenue, Boston, MA 02215; tel. 954/698–9222

The Three Rivers Treatment Program, 26 Ridgewood Terrace, Springfield, MA 01105; tel. 413/733–4032

The Whitney Academy, Inc., PO Box 619, East Freetown, MA 02717; tel. 508/763–3737

UHS of Westwood Pembroke, 45 Clapboardtree Street, Westwood, MA 02090; tel. 781/762–7764

VA Boston Healthcare System Drug Dependence Treatment Center, 1400 VFW Parkway, West Roxbury, MA 02132; tel. 617/323–7700

*VA Central Western Massachusetts Healthcare System, 421 North Main Street, Leeds, MA 01053-9764; tel. 413/584–4040

Valley Psychiatric Service, Inc., 511 East Columbus Avenue, Springfield, MA 01105; tel. 413/523–7126

Walden Behavioral Care, 9 Hope Avenue, Suite 500, Waltham, MA 02453; tel. 781/647–6767

*Whittier Street Health Center, 1290 Tremont Street, Roxbury, MA 02120; tel. 617/427–1000

Wild Acre Inns, Inc., 108 Pleasant Street, Arlington, MA 02476; tel. 781/643–0643

MICHIGAN
*ACAC, Inc., 3949 Sparks Drive Southeast, Suite 103, Grand Rapids, MI 49546; tel. 616/957–5850

*Access Behavioral Healthcare, LLC, 42189 East Ann Arbor Road, Plymouth, MI 48170; tel. 734/453–5603

*Aleda E. Lutz VA Medical Ctr., 1500 Weiss Street, Saginaw, MI 48602; tel. 989/497–2500

*Apex Behavioral Health - Dearborn, 6 Parklane Boulevard, Suite 695, Dearborn, MI 48126; tel. 313/271–8170

*Apex Behavioral Health Western Wayne, PLLC, 1547 South Wayne Road, Westland, MI 48186; tel. 734/729–3133

*Apex Downriver Behavioral Health, 19366 Allen Road, Suite C, Brownstown, MI 48183; tel. 734/479–0949

*Arbor Circle Corporation, 1115 Ball Avenue, Grand Rapids, MI 49505; tel. 616/456–7775

*Battle Creek VA Medical Center, 5500 Armstrong Road, Battle Creek, MI 49037; tel. 269/966–5600

*Bay Mills Indian Community, 12124 West Lake Shore Drive, Brimley, MI 49715; tel. 906/248–5527

Beacon Specialized Living Services, Inc., 555 Railroad Street, PO Box 69, Bangor, MI 49013; tel. 269/427–8400

*Brighton Hospital, 12851 Grand River Road, Brighton, MI 48116; tel. 810/227–1211

C.W. Enterprises LLC, 50630 Chesterfield Road, Chesterfield, MI 48051; tel. 586/949–7680

*Community Care Services, 26184 West Outer Drive, Lincoln Park, MI 48146; tel. 313/389–7525

Community Mental Health for Central Michigan, 301 South Crapo, Suite 100, Mount Pleasant, MI 48858; tel. 989/772–5938

Cruz Clinic, 17177 North Laurel Park Drive, Suite 131, Livonia, MI 48152; tel. 734/462–3210

Delta Family Clinic South, 4413 Corunna Road, Flint, MI 48532; tel. 810/630–1152

Forest View Psychiatric Hospital, 1055 Medical Park Drive Southeast, Grand Rapids, MI 49546; tel. 616/942–9610

Genesys Practice Partners, Inc., 8435 Holly Road, Grand Blanc, MI 48439; tel. 810/424–2400

*Growth Works Incorporated, PO Box 6115, Plymouth, MI 48170-6115; tel. 734/455–4095

Havenwyck Hospital, 1525 University Drive, Auburn Hills, MI 48326; tel. 248/373–9200

*Hegira Programs, Inc., 8623 North Wayne Road, Suite 200, Westland, MI 48185; tel. 734/458–4601

Henry Ford Macomb Hospital, 15855 Nineteen Mile Road, Clinton Township, MI 48038; tel. 586/263–2700

*Horizon Treatment Services, LLC, 24681 Northwestern Highway, Suite 306, Southfield, MI 48075-2302; tel. 248/423–1728

Huron Valley Consultation Center, Inc., 2750 South State Street, Ann Arbor, MI 48104; tel. 734/662–6300

Integro, LLC, 1200 North West Avenue, Suite 300, Jackson, MI 49202; tel. 517/789–1234

*Ionia County Substance Abuse, 175 East Adams, Ionia, MI 48846; tel. 616/527–5341

John D. Dingell VA Medical Center, 4646 John R Street, Detroit, MI 48201; tel. 313/576–1000

*Jump Start Consulting, LLC D.B.A. Inner Door Center, 317 East Eleven Mile Road, Royal Oak, MI 48067; tel. 248/336–2868

*Karalee & Associates, P.C., 1308 South Main Street, Plymouth, MI 48170; tel. 734/451–3440

Lakeside Academy, 3921 Oakland Drive, Kalamazoo, MI 49008; tel. 269/381–4760

*Latino Family Services, Inc., 3815 West Fort Street, Detroit, MI 48216; tel. 313/279–3232

Lenawee Community Mental Health Authority, 1040 South Winter Street, Suite 1022, Adrian, MI 49221; tel. 517/263–8905

*Life Challenge of Michigan, 2220 Spring Road, Hillsdale, MI 49242; tel. 517/437–4454

Livingston County Community Mental Health Authority, 622 East Grand River, Howell, MI 48843; tel. 517/548–0081

McLaren Flint Medical Center, 401 South Ballenger Highway, Flint, MI 48532; tel. 810/342–2000

*Meridian Professional Psychological Consultants, PC, 5031 Park Lake Road, East Lansing, MI 48823; tel. 517/332–0811

Metro East Substance Abuse Treatment Corporation, PO Box 13408, Detroit, MI 48213; tel. 313/371–0055

Michigan Access Center, Inc., 2722 East Michigan Avenue, Suite 104, Lansing, MI 48912; tel. 517/332–9000

*Michigan Behavior Medicine, 2525 Crooks Road, Suite 100, Troy, MI 48084; tel. 248/740–9360

Monroe Community Mental Health Authority, PO Box 726, Monroe, MI 48161-0726; tel. 734/243–7340

Nardin Park Recovery Center, 9605 Grand River Avenue, Detroit, MI 48204; tel. 313/834–5930

New Center Community Services, 2051 West Grand Boulevard, Detroit, MI 48208; tel. 313/961–3200

*Oakland Psychological Clinic, P.C., 2550 South Telegraph Road, Suite 250, Bloomfield Hills, MI 48302; tel. 248/322–0003

Oakwood Hospital - Taylor, 10000 Telegraph Road, Taylor, MI 48180; tel. 313/295–5000

Oscar G. Johnson VA Medical Center, 325 East H Street, Iron Mountain, MI 49801; tel. 906/774–3300

*PHC of MI, Inc., 35031 23 Mile Road, New Baltimore, MI 48047; tel. 586/725–5777

Rainbow Center of Michigan (Monroe), 14733 South Telegraph Road, Monroe, MI 48161; tel. 734/243–8707

Rainbow Center of Michigan, Inc., PO Box 725098, Berkley, MI 48072; tel. 313/865–1580

Rainbow Center of Michigan, Inc., 20724 Eureka Road, Taylor, MI 48180; tel. 734/759–0510

*Recovery Pathways, LLC, 717 East Midland Street, Bay City, MI 48706; tel. 989/928–3566

*Redford Counseling Center, 25945 West Seven Mile Road, Redford, MI 48240; tel. 313/535–6560

*River's Bend, P.C., 800 Stephenson Highway, Suite 250, Troy, MI 48083; tel. 248/585–3239

Rose Hill Center, Inc., 5130 Rose Hill Boulevard, Holly, MI 48442; tel. 248/634–5530

Safehaus, Inc., 21056 Dean Street, Warren, MI 48091; tel. 586/806–4678

*Salvation Army Turning Point Programs, 72 Sheldon Boulevard, Southeast, Grand Rapids, MI 49503; tel. 616/742–0351

St. John Macomb-Oakland Hospital, 11800 East Twelve Mile Road, Warren, MI 48093; tel. 586/573–5000

*St. Joseph Mercy Hospital, 5333 McAuley Drive, Office 6104, Ypsilanti, MI 48197; tel. 734/712–3456

St. Mary's of Michigan Medical Center, 800 South Washington Avenue, Saginaw, MI 48601; tel. 989/907–8000

Star Center, Inc., 13575 Lesure, Detroit, MI 48227; tel. 313/493–4410

*Sterling Area Health Center, PO Box 740, Sterling, MI 48659; tel. 989/654–2491

*Summit Pointe, 140 West Michigan Avenue, Battle Creek, MI 49017; tel. 269/966–1460

Sunshine Treatment Institute, PO Box 690, Southfield, MI 48037; tel. 313/368–4800

Taylor Psychological Clinic, PC, 1172 Robert T Longway Blvd, Flint, MI 48503; tel. 810/232–8466

TBCI, PC, 1059 Owendale, Troy, MI 48083; tel. 248/526–0110

*The Guidance Center, 13101 Allen Road, Southgate, MI 48195; tel. 734/785–7700

Trinity Health - Michigan, 200 Jefferson Avenue Southeast, Grand Rapids, MI 49503; tel. 616/685–5000

Ultimate Solutions, 29240 Buckingham, Suite 11, Livonia, MI 48154; tel. 734/513–2800

*University of Michigan Health System, 1500 East Medical Center Drive, Med Inn Building, Room C201, SPC 5825, Ann Arbor, MI 48109; tel. 734/647–2478

*VA Ann Arbor Healthcare System, 2215 Fuller Road, Ann Arbor, MI 48105; tel. 734/769–7100

*Washtenaw County Community Supports and Treatment Services, 2140 East Ellsworth Road, Ann Arbor, MI 48108; tel. 734/544–3000

MINNESOTA
Abbott Northwestern Hospital, 800 East 28th Street, Minneapolis, MN 55407; tel. 612/863–4875

Andrew Residence, 1215 South 9th Street, Minneapolis, MN 55404; tel. 612/333–0111

Anoka-Metro Regional Treatment Center, 3301 7th Avenue North, Anoka, MN 55303; tel. 651/431–5000

Bureau of Prisons - FMC Rochester, PO Box 4600, Rochester, MN 55903; tel. 507/287–0674

*Community Addiction Recovery Enterprise, 3301 Seventh Avenue North, Anoka, MN 55303; tel. 218/736–1886

Community Addiction Recovery Enterprise - Willmar OTP, 1801 Technology Drive Northeast, Willmar, MN 56201; tel. 320/231–5468

---

*Indicates organization is a Joint Commission accredited Chemical Dependency organization.

Section C

*Hazelden Betty Ford Foundation, PO Box 11, Center City, MN 55012; tel. 651/213-4200

*Hazelden New York, 15251 Pleasant Valley Road, PO Box 11 BC-5, Center City, MN 55012; tel. 800/258-7810

Hennepin Healthcare System, Inc., 701 Park Avenue, Minneapolis, MN 55415; tel. 612/873-2338

Hennepin Healthcare System, Inc., 914 South Eighth Street, Suite 131, Minneapolis, MN 55404; tel. 612/873-2338

*Mayo Clinic Health System - Albert Lea and Austin, 404 West Fountain Street, Albert Lea, MN 56007; tel. 507/373-2384

Mercy Hospital, 4050 Coon Rapids Boulevard, Coon Rapids, MN 55433; tel. 763/236-6000

Minnesota Security Hospital, 100 Freeman Drive, Saint Peter, MN 56082; tel. 507/985-3128

Minnesota Specialty Health System-Brainerd, 11615 State Avenue, Brainerd, MN 56401; tel. 218/828-6123

Minnesota Specialty Health Systems - Wadena, 240 Shady Lane Drive, Wadena, MN 56482; tel. 218/319-6001

Minnesota Specialty Health Systems - Willmar, 1208 Olena Avenue Southeast, Willmar, MN 56201; tel. 320/235-0018

*New Beginnings at Waverly, LLC, 109 North Shore Drive, Waverly, MN 55390-9743; tel. 763/658-5800

Park Nicollet Health Services, PO Box 650, Minneapolis, MN 55440; tel. 952/993-5000

PrairieCare, 12915 63rd Avenue North, Maple Grove, MN 55369; tel. 952/838-5800

*Saint Cloud Hospital, 1406 Sixth Avenue North, Saint Cloud, MN 56303; tel. 320/251-2700

SMDC Medical Center, 502 East Second Street, Duluth, MN 55805; tel. 218/727-8762

*St. Cloud VA Health Care System, 4801 Veterans Drive, Saint Cloud, MN 56303; tel. 320/255-6480

St. Joseph's Hospital Chemical Dependency Unit, 45 West 10th Street, Saint Paul, MN 55102; tel. 651/232-3256

United Hospital, 333 North Smith Avenue, Saint Paul, MN 55102; tel. 651/241-8802

*University of Minnesota Medical Center, Fairview, 2450 Riverside Avenue, Minneapolis, MN 55455; tel. 612/273-3000

*VA Health Care System - Minneapolis, One Veterans Drive, Minneapolis, MN 55417; tel. 612/725-2000

MISSISSIPPI

Adams County Correctional Center, PO Box 850, Washington, MS 39190; tel. 601/304-2500

Biloxi HMA, LLC, PO Box 128, Biloxi, MS 39533; tel. 228/436-1104

Brentwood Behavioral Healthcare of Mississippi, LLC, 3531 East Lakeland Drive, Flowood, MS 39232; tel. 601/936-2024

CARES Center, Inc. and Mississippi Children's Home Society, 1465 Lakeland Drive, Jackson, MS 39216; tel. 601/352-7784

*COPAC, Inc., 3949 Highway 43 North, Brandon, MS 39047; tel. 601/829-2500

Diamond Grove Center for Children and Adolescents, PO Box 848, Louisville, MS 39339; tel. 662/779-0119

*East Mississippi State Hospital, PO Box 4128 West Station, Meridian, MS 39304; tel. 601/581-7600

Millcreek of Pontotoc, PO Box 619, Pontotoc, MS 38863; tel. 662/488-8878

*Mississippi State Hospital, PO Box 157-A, Whitfield, MS 39193-0157; tel. 601/351-8190

Natchez Community Hospital, PO Box 1203, Natchez, MS 39121; tel. 601/445-6205

North Oak Regional Medical Center, PO Box 648, Senatobia, MS 38668-0648; tel. 662/562-3100

*Parkwood Behavioral Health System, 8135 Goodman Road, Olive Branch, MS 38654; tel. 662/895-4900

PSI Crossings, 5000 Highway 39 North, Meridian, MS 39301; tel. 601/483-5452

Rehabilitation Centers, Inc., PO Box 1160, Magee, MS 39111; tel. 601/849-4221

Specialized Treatment Facility, 14426 James Bond Road, Gulfport, MS 39503; tel. 228/328-6000

*VA Gulf Coast Veterans Health Care System, 400 Veterans Avenue, Biloxi, MS 39531; tel. 228/523-5000

*VA Medical Center - G. V. (Sonny) Montgomery, 1500 East Woodrow Wilson Avenue, Jackson, MS 39216; tel. 601/364-1201

Youth Villages of Mississippi, The Atrium Building, Ridgeland, MS 39157; tel. 901/251-4944

MISSOURI

*Alternative Behavioral Care, 255 Spencer Road, Suite 101, Saint Peters, MO 63376; tel. 636/477-6111

Barnes-Jewish Hospital, 1 Barnes Jewish Hospital Plaza, Saint Louis, MO 63110; tel. 314/747-3000

BJC Behavioral Health, 1430 Olive Street, Suite 400, Saint Louis, MO 63103; tel. 314/206-3712

*Boonville Valley Hope, 1415 Ashley Road, Boonville, MO 65233; tel. 660/882-6547

Castlewood Treatment Center for Eating Disorders, LLC, 1260 St. Paul Road, Ballwin, MO 63021; tel. 636/386-6611

Center for Behavioral Medicine, 1000 East 24th Street, Kansas City, MO 64108-2620; tel. 816/512-7000

*CenterPointe Behavioral Health Kansas City, 763 South New Ballas Road, Suite 300, Saint Louis, MO 63141; tel. 816/795-1445

*CenterPointe Hospital, 4801 Weldon Spring Parkway, Saint Charles, MO 63304; tel. 636/441-7300

*Centrec Care, Inc., 1224 Fern Ridge Parkway, Suite 305, Saint Louis, MO 63141; tel. 314/205-8068

Change Academy Lake of the Ozarks (CALO), 130 Calo Lane, Lake Ozark, MO 65049; tel. 573/365-2221

Child Advocacy Services Center, Inc., 2 East 59th Street, Kansas City, MO 64113-2116; tel. 816/363-1898

*Christian Hospital Northeast - Northwest, 11133 Dunn Road, Saint Louis, MO 63136; tel. 314/653-5616

Cottonwood Residential Treatment Center, 1025 North Sprigg, Cape Girardeau, MO 63701; tel. 573/290-5888

*Crittenton, 10918 Elm Avenue, Kansas City, MO 64134-4199; tel. 816/765-6600

DRD Columbia Treatment Clinic, 1301 Vandiver, Suite Y, Columbia, MO 65202; tel. 573/449-8338

DRD Kansas City Medical Clinic, 723 East 18th Street, Kansas City, MO 64108; tel. 816/283-3877

DRD Springfield Medical Clinic, 404 East Battlefield Street, Springfield, MO 65807; tel. 417/865-8045

Epworth Children & Family Services, 110 North Elm Avenue, Saint Louis, MO 63119; tel. 314/961-5718

Great Circle, PO Box 189, Saint James, MO 65559; tel. 573/265-3251

Great Plains Hospital, Inc., 1500 West Ashland, Nevada, MO 64772; tel. 417/667-2666

*Harry S. Truman Memorial Veterans' Hospital, 800 Hospital Drive, Columbia, MO 65201; tel. 573/814-6000

Hawthorn Children's Psychiatric Hospital, 1901 Pennsylvania Avenue, Saint Louis, MO 63133; tel. 314/512-7800

*John J. Pershing VA Medical Center, 1500 North Westwood Boulevard, Poplar Bluff, MO 63901; tel. 573/686-4151

*Kansas City Veterans Affairs Medical Center, 4801 Linwood Boulevard, Kansas City, MO 64128; tel. 816/861-4700

Lakeland Hospital Acquisition Corporation, 440 South Market Avenue, Springfield, MO 65806; tel. 417/865-5581

McCallum Place Eating Disorders Treatment, 231 West Lockwood Avenue, Suite 201, Saint Louis, MO 63119; tel. 314/968-1900

*Menzies Institute of Recovery from Addiction (MIRA), 5351 Delmar Boulevard, Saint Louis, MO 63112; tel. 314/300-2057

Ozarks Medical Center, PO Box 1100, West Plains, MO 65775; tel. 417/256-9111

*Provident, Inc., 2650 Olive Street, Saint Louis, MO 63103; tel. 314/371-6500

Southeast Missouri Mental Health Center, 1010 West Columbia Street, Farmington, MO 63640-2997; tel. 573/218-6792

*SSM DePaul Health Center, 12303 DePaul Drive, Bridgeton, MO 63044-2588; tel. 314/344-6000

SSM St. Joseph Health Center, 300 First Capitol Drive, Saint Charles, MO 63301; tel. 636/947-5000

SSM St. Mary's Health Center, 6420 Clayton Road, Richmond Heights, MO 63117; tel. 314/768-8000

St. Alexius Hospital Corporation # 1, 3933 South Broadway, Saint Louis, MO 63118; tel. 314/865-7902

*St. Anthony's Medical Center, 10010 Kennerly Road, Saint Louis, MO 63128; tel. 314/525-1000

St. Louis Psychiatric Rehabilitation Center, 5300 Arsenal Street, Saint Louis, MO 63139; tel. 314/877-6500

*St. Louis VA Healthcare System, 915 North Grand Boulevard, Saint Louis, MO 63106; tel. 314/289-7020

*Swope Health Services, 3801 Blue Parkway, Kansas City, MO 64130; tel. 816/923-5800

The Salvation Army, 101 West Linwood Boulevard, Kansas City, MO 64111; tel. 816/285-2480

*Truman Medical Center, 2301 Holmes Street, Kansas City, MO 64108; tel. 816/404-0905

*Truman Medical Center- Lakewood, 7900 Lees Summit Road, Kansas City, MO 64139; tel. 816/404-0905

Two Rivers Psychiatric Hospital, 5121 Raytown Road, Kansas City, MO 64133; tel. 816/382-6360

U.S. Medical Center for Federal Prisoners, 1900 West Sunshine Street, Springfield, MO 65807; tel. 417/862-7041

VCPHCS XV, LLC, PO Box 4692, Joplin, MO 64803; tel. 214/365-6111

Woodridge of Missouri, LLC, PO Box 4067, Waynesville, MO 65583; tel. 573/774-5353

MONTANA

Billings Clinic, PO Box 37000, Billings, MT 59107-7000; tel. 406/657-4000

Intermountain Children's Home, 500 South Lamborn, Helena, MT 59601; tel. 406/442-7920

Kid's Behavioral Health of Montana, 55 Basin Creek Road, Butte, MT 59701; tel. 406/494-4183

Montana Academy, 9705 Lost Prairie Road, Marion, MT 59925; tel. 406/858-2339

Montana Children's Home and Hospital, PO Box 5539, Helena, MT 59604; tel. 406/444-7500

*Rocky Mountain Treatment Center, 920 Fourth Avenue North, Great Falls, MT 59401; tel. 406/727-8832

*VA Montana Healthcare System, 3687 Veterans Drive, Fort Harrison, MT 59636-1500; tel. 406/447-7900

NEBRASKA

*Alegent Creighton Health Immanuel Medical Center, 6901 North 72nd Street, Omaha, NE 68122; tel. 402/572-2291

*Behavioral Health Specialists, Inc., 900 W Norfolk Avenue, Suite 200, Norfolk, NE 68701; tel. 402/370-3140

*Blue Valley Behavioral Health, Inc., 1123 North 9th Street, Beatrice, NE 68310; tel. 402/228-3386

*Bryan Medical Center, 1600 South 48th Street, Lincoln, NE 68506; tel. 402/481-1111

*East Central District Health Department, 2282 East 32nd Avenue, Columbus, NE 68601; tel. 402/562-8950

Epworth Village, Inc., PO Box 503, York, NE 68467-0503; tel. 402/362-3353

Father Flanagan's Boys Home, 555 North 30th Street, Omaha, NE 68131; tel. 402/498-6525

*Hastings Regional Center, PO Box 579, Hastings, NE 68902-0579; tel. 402/462-1971

Lincoln Lancaster County Child Guidance Center, 2444 'O' Street, Lincoln, NE 68510; tel. 402/475-7666

Lincoln Regional Center, PO Box 94949, Lincoln, NE 68509-4949; tel. 402/471-4444

*O'Neill Valley Hope, 1421 North 10th Street, Oneill, NE 68763; tel. 402/336-3747

OMNI Behavioral Health, 5115 F Street, Omaha, NE 68117; tel. 402/397-9866

*VA Nebraska-Western Iowa Health Care System, 4101 Woolworth Avenue, Omaha, NE 68105; tel. 402/449-0600

NEVADA

*Desert Parkway Behavioral Healthcare Hospital, LLC, 3247 South Maryland Parkway, Las Vegas, NV 89109; tel. 702/776-3500

Desert Willow Treatment Center, 6171 West Charleston Boulevard, Building 17, Las Vegas, NV 89146; tel. 702/486-8900

*Las Vegas Recovery Center, 3371 North Buffalo Drive, Las Vegas, NV 89129; tel. 702/515-1374

New Beginnings Counseling Center, 3376 South Eastern Avenue, Suite 148, Las Vegas, NV 89169; tel. 702/538-7412

*New Frontier Treatment Center, PO Box 1240, Fallon, NV 89407; tel. 775/423-1412

---

*Indicates organization is a Joint Commission accredited Chemical Dependency organization.

© 2014 AHA Guide

Northern Nevada Adult Mental Health Services, 480 Galletti Way, Sparks, NV 89431; tel. 775/688-2001

Northern Nevada Medical Center, 2375 East Prater Way, Sparks, NV 89434; tel. 775/331-7000

*SBH-Montevista Hospital, 5900 West Rochelle Avenue, Las Vegas, NV 89103-3327; tel. 702/364-1111

*Seven Hills Hospital, Inc., 3021 West Horizon Ridge Parkway, Henderson, NV 89052; tel. 702/646-5000

*VA Sierra Nevada Health Care System, 975 Kirman Avenue, Reno, NV 89502-2597; tel. 775/786-7200

VA Southern Nevada Healthcare System, 6900 North Pecos Road, North Las Vegas, NV 89086; tel. 702/791-9000

Willow Springs Center, 690 Edison Way, Reno, NV 89502; tel. 775/858-3303

NEW HAMPSHIRE

*Community Council of Nashua, NH, 7 Prospect Street, Nashua, NH 03060; tel. 603/889-6147

Lakeview NeuroRehabilitation Center, 244 Highwatch Road, Effingham, NH 03882; tel. 603/539-7451

NFI North, Inc., 40 Park Lane, Contoocook, NH 03229; tel. 603/746-7550

*VA Medical Center, 718 Smyth Road, Manchester, NH 03104-4098; tel. 603/624-4366

NEW JERSEY

*AtlantiCare Behavioral Health, 6550 Delilah Road, Building 300, Egg Harbor Township, NJ 08234; tel. 609/645-7600

AtlantiCare Regional Medical Center, 1925 Pacific Avenue, Atlantic City, NJ 08401; tel. 609/345-4000

Bancroft Rehabilitation Services, 425 Kings Highway East, Haddonfield, NJ 08033; tel. 856/429-5637

*Bergen Regional Medical Center, 230 East Ridgewood Avenue, Paramus, NJ 07652; tel. 201/967-4000

*Bonnie Brae, 3415 Valley Road, PO Box 825, Liberty Corner, NJ 07938-0825; tel. 908/647-0800

*Cape Counseling Services, 1129 Route 9, Cape May Court House, NJ 08210; tel. 609/778-6100

*Care Plus NJ, Inc., 610 Valley Health Plaza, Paramus, NJ 07652; tel. 201/265-8200

*Carrier Clinic, PO Box 147, Belle Mead, NJ 08502-0147; tel. 908/281-1000

*Catholic Charities - Diocese of Metuchen, 319 Maple Street, Perth Amboy, NJ 08861; tel. 732/324-8200

Christian Health Care Center, 301 Sicomac Avenue, Wyckoff, NJ 07481; tel. 201/848-5200

CPC Behavioral Healthcare, Inc., 10 Industrial Way East, Eatontown, NJ 07724; tel. 732/935-2220

East Orange General Hospital, 300 Central Avenue, East Orange, NJ 07018; tel. 973/672-8400

Hampton Behavioral Health Center, 650 Rancocas Road, Westampton, NJ 08060; tel. 609/267-7000

*High Focus Centers, 47 Maple Street, Suite 401, Summit, NJ 07901; tel. 908/363-1023

*Hoboken University Medical Center, 308 Willow Avenue, Hoboken, NJ 07030; tel. 201/418-1000

Hunterdon Medical Center, 2100 Wescott Drive, Flemington, NJ 08822; tel. 908/788-6151

Inspira Medical Center Woodbury, 509 North Broad Street, Woodbury, NJ 08096; tel. 856/845-0100

*Jersey Shore University Medical Center, 1945 Route 33, Neptune, NJ 07754-0397; tel. 732/776-4900

*Kennedy University Hospital-Stratford Division, 18 East Laurel Road, Stratford, NJ 08084; tel. 856/566-5243

Khaleidoscope Health Care, Inc., Jones and Associates, 111 Wayne Street, Jersey City, NJ 07302; tel. 201/451-5425

Monmouth Medical Center, 300 Second Avenue, Long Branch, NJ 07740; tel. 732/222-5200

Montclair Health Systems, LLC, 1 Bay Avenue, Montclair, NJ 07042; tel. 973/429-6000

*Morristown Medical Center, 100 Madison Avenue, Morristown, NJ 07960; tel. 973/971-5450

Newark Beth Israel Medical Center, 201 Lyons Avenue, Newark, NJ 07112; tel. 973/926-7000

Newton Medical Center, 175 High Street, Newton, NJ 07860; tel. 973/383-2121

*North Hudson Community Action Corporation Union City, 800-31st Street, Union City, NJ 07087; tel. 201/866-2727

*Overlook Medical Center, PO Box 220, Summit, NJ 07902-0220; tel. 908/522-4912

*Princeton HealthCare System, 1 Plainsboro Road, Plainsboro, NJ 08536; tel. 609/853-6500

*Recovery Services of New Jersey, Inc., 5034 Atlantic Avenue, Mays Landing, NJ 08330; tel. 609/625-4900

Richard Hall Community Mental Health Center, 500 North Bridge Street, Bridgewater, NJ 08807; tel. 908/725-2800

*Riverview Medical Center, One Riverview Plaza, Red Bank, NJ 07701; tel. 732/741-2700

Rutgers University Behavioral Health Care, PO Box 1392, Piscataway, NJ 08855-1392; tel. 732/235-5500

Saint Barnabas Behavioral Health Center, Inc., 1691 US Highway 9, CN 2025, Toms River, NJ 08754; tel. 732/914-1688

*Saint Clare's Health System, 25 Pocono Road, Denville, NJ 07834; tel. 973/983-5588

Saint Peter's University Hospital, 254 Easton Avenue, New Brunswick, NJ 08901; tel. 732/745-8600

Sequel of New Jersey, Inc., 1770 Mt Ephraim Avenue, Camden, NJ 08104; tel. 856/635-0200

Somerset Medical Center, 110 Rehill Avenue, Somerville, NJ 08876-2598; tel. 908/685-2200

South Jersey Drug Treatment, PO Box 867, Bridgeton, NJ 08302; tel. 856/455-5441

St. Francis Medical Center, 601 Hamilton Avenue, Trenton, NJ 08629; tel. 609/599-5000

St. Mary's Hospital, 350 Boulevard, Passaic, NJ 07055; tel. 973/365-4300

Stepping Forward Counseling Center, 26 Main Street, Chatham, NJ 07928; tel. 973/635-6550

Stress Care of New Jersey, LLC, 4122 Route 516, Matawan, NJ 07747; tel. 732/679-4500

*Summit Oaks Hospital, 19 Prospect Street, Summit, NJ 07901; tel. 908/522-7000

*Sunrise Detox II, LLC, 1272 Long Hill Road, Stirling, NJ 07980; tel. 908/504-2700

*The Counseling Center at Freehold, 4345 Highway Rt. 9, Freehold, NJ 07728; tel. 732/431-5300

*The Lester A. Drenk Behavioral Health Center, Inc., 1289 Route 38 West, Suite 203, Hainesport, NJ 08036; tel. 609/267-5656

*Trinitas Regional Medical Center, 225 Williamson Street, Elizabeth, NJ 07207; tel. 908/994-5754

*VA New Jersey Health Care System, 385 Tremont Avenue, Director's Office (00), East Orange, NJ 07018; tel. 973/676-1000

Virtua-West Jersey Health System, Inc.(Voorhees), 100 Bowman Drive, Voorhees New Jersey, Voorhees, NJ 08043; tel. 856/247-3000

VisionQuest - New Jersey, PO Box 370, New Lisbon, NJ 08064; tel. 609/894-4856

Willowglen Academy New Jersey, Inc., 8 Wilson Drive, Sparta, NJ 07871; tel. 973/579-3700

Youth Consultation Service, 284 Broadway, Newark, NJ 07104; tel. 973/482-8411

NEW MEXICO

*Mesilla Valley Hospital, 3751 Del Rey Boulevard, Las Cruces, NM 88012; tel. 575/382-3500

New Mexico Behavioral Health Institute at Las Vegas, 3695 Hot Springs Boulevard, Las Vegas, NM 87701; tel. 505/454-2266

*New Mexico VA Health Care System, 1501 San Pedro Drive Southeast, Albuquerque, NM 87108; tel. 505/265-1711

*Presbyterian Medical Services, 1422 Paseo de Peralta, Santa Fe, NM 87501-2267; tel. 505/982-5565

Sequel of New Mexico, LLC, 5400 Gibson Boulevard, Albuquerque, NM 87108; tel. 505/924-6330

Sequoyah Adolescent Treatment Center, 3405 W Pan American Freeway Northeast, Albuquerque, NM 87107; tel. 505/222-0302

Strategic Behavioral Health El Paso, LLC, 5045 McNutt Road, Santa Teresa, NM 88008; tel. 575/589-3000

University of New Mexico Health Sciences Center, 2211 Lomas Blvd Northeast, Albuquerque, NM 87106; tel. 505/272-0140

Youth and Family Centered Services of New Mexico, Inc., 5310 Sequoia Northwest, Albuquerque, NM 87120; tel. 505/836-7330

NEW YORK

*A.R.E.B.A.- Casriel, Inc., 500 West 57th Street, New York, NY 10019; tel. 212/376-1810

Acute Chemical Dependency Detox Unit - Kings County, 410 Winthrop Street, Brooklyn, NY 11203; tel. 718/245-3901

Allynwood Academy, 431 Chapel Hill Road, Hancock, NY 13783; tel. 607/637-8200

*Arms Acres, Inc., 75 Seminary Hill Road, Carmel, NY 10512; tel. 845/225-3400

Astor Services for Children & Families, PO Box 5005, Rhinebeck, NY 12572-5005; tel. 845/871-1000

August Aichhorn R.T.F., 23 West 106th Street, New York, NY 10025; tel. 212/316-9353

Baker Victory Services, Inc., 780 Ridge Road, Lackawanna, NY 14218; tel. 716/828-9515

Bellevue Hospital Center Chemi Dependency Medically Detox, 462 First Avenue, New York, NY 10016; tel. 212/788-3339

Beth Israel Medical Center MMTP - Gouverneur Clinic, 109-11 Delancey Street, New York, NY 10002; tel. 212/420-2086

Beth Israel Medical Center MMTP - Harlem 6/7, 103 East 125th Street, 2nd Floor, New York, NY 10035; tel. 212/774-3260

Beth Israel Medical Center MMTP - Vincent P Dole, 25 - 12th Street, Brooklyn, NY 11215; tel. 718/965-7900

Beth Israel Medical Center MMTP Clinic 1E, 429 Second Avenue, New York, NY 10010; tel. 212/844-1929

Beth Israel Medical Center MMTP Clinic 3C, 435 Second Avenue, 3rd Floor, New York, NY 10010; tel. 212/726-6824

Beth Israel Medical Center MMTP Cumberland Clinic, 100 Flatbush Avenue, Brooklyn, NY 11217; tel. 718/237-9600

Beth Israel Medical Center MMTP Harlem Clinic 1, First Avenue @ 16th Street, New York, NY 10003; tel. 212/774-3210

Beth Israel Medical Center MMTP Harlem Clinic 8, 140 West 125th Street, 6th Floor, New York, NY 10027; tel. 212/864-8177

Beth Israel Medical Center MMTP, Avenue A Clinic, 26 Avenue A, New York, NY 10009; tel. 212/420-2078

Bon Secours Community Hospital - OTP, 160 East Main Street, Port Jervis, NY 12771; tel. 845/858-7000

Bronx Psychiatric Center, 1500 Waters Place, Bronx, NY 10461; tel. 718/862-3300

*Bronx-Lebanon Hospital Center, 1650 Grand Concourse, Bronx, NY 10457; tel. 718/590-1800

Bronx-Lebanon Hospital Center - MMTP, 1650 Selwyn Avenue, Suite 3A, Bronx, NY 10457; tel. 718/590-1800

Buffalo Psychiatric Center, 400 Forest Avenue, Buffalo, NY 14213; tel. 716/885-2261

Canton-Potsdam Hospital - Opioid Treatment Program, 50 Leroy Street, Potsdam, NY 13676; tel. 315/265-3300

Carnegie Hill Institute, 116 East 92nd Street, New York, NY 10128; tel. 212/289-7166

Central New York Psychiatric Center, PO Box 300, Marcy, NY 13403-0300; tel. 315/765-3660

*Coney Island Hospital - Acute Care Addictions Program, 2601 Ocean Parkway, Brooklyn, NY 11235; tel. 718/616-3000

Conifer Park, Inc., 79 Glenridge Road, Glenville, NY 12302; tel. 518/399-6446

Creedmoor Psychiatric Center, 79-25 Winchester Boulevard, Queens Village, NY 11427; tel. 718/264-3600

Crouse Hospital Methadone Maintenance Treatment Program, 410 South Crouse Avenue, Syracuse, NY 13210; tel. 315/470-8300

Eastern Long Island Hospital Association, Inc., 201 Manor Place, Greenport, NY 11944; tel. 631/477-1000

Ellis Hospital, 1101 Nott Street, Schenectady, NY 12308; tel. 518/243-4000

*Elmhurst Hospital Center, 79-01 Broadway, Elmhurst, NY 11373; tel. 718/334-4000

Elmira Psychiatric Center, 100 Washington Street, Elmira, NY 14901-2898; tel. 607/737-4739

Erie County Medical Center, 462 Grider Street, Buffalo, NY 14215; tel. 716/898-3000

Flushing Hospital Medical Ctr / Chemical Dependency Unit, 45th Avenue at Parsons Blvd, Flushing, NY 11355; tel. 718/670-5918

Four Winds - Saratoga, 30 Crescent Avenue, Saratoga Springs, NY 12866; tel. 518/584-3600

Four Winds, Inc., 800 Cross River Road, Katonah, NY 10536; tel. 914/763-8151

*Glens Falls Hospital, 100 Park Street, Glens Falls, NY 12801; tel. 518/926-1000

Good Samaritan Hospital - OTP, 255 Lafayette Avenue, Suffern, NY 10901; tel. 845/368-5153

Section C

*Indicates organization is a Joint Commission accredited Chemical Dependency organization.

Gracie Square Hospital - OTP, 420 East 76th Street, New York, NY 10021; tel. 212/434–5322

Greater Binghamton Health Center, 425 Robinson Street, Binghamton, NY 13904; tel. 607/773–4082

*****Guthrie Ambulatory Health Care Clinic,** 11050 Mt. Belvedere Boulevard, Fort Drum, NY 13602-5004; tel. 315/772–4024

Harlem Hospital Center Chemical Dependence Detoxification Unit, 506 Lenox Avenue, New York, NY 10037; tel. 212/939–1340

HealthAlliance Hospital Broadway Methadone Treatment Program, 2 Barbarossa Lane, Kingston, NY 12401; tel. 845/943–6022

HealthAlliance of the Hudson Valley, Mary's Avenue Campus, 105 Mary's Avenue, Kingston, NY 12401; tel. 845/334–2500

*****Hudson River HealthCare, Inc.,** 1037 Main Street, Peekskill, NY 10566; tel. 914/734–8800

Interfaith Medical Center Substance Abuse Detoxification, 1545 Atlantic Avenue, Brooklyn, NY 11213; tel. 718/613–4001

Jacobi Medical Center, 1400 Pelham Parkway, Bronx, NY 10461; tel. 718/918–5322

*****James J Peters Bronx VA Medical Center,** 130 West Kingsbridge Road, Bronx, NY 10468; tel. 718/584–9000

*****John T. Mather Memorial Hospital,** 75 North Country Road, Port Jefferson, NY 11777-2190; tel. 631/473–1320

*****Keller Army Community Hospital,** 900 Washington Road, West Point, NY 10996; tel. 845/938–3305

*****Kings County Hospital,** 451 Clarkson Avenue, Brooklyn, NY 11203; tel. 718/245–5315

*****Long Island Center for Recovery, Inc.,** 320 West Montauk Highway, Hampton Bays, NY 11946; tel. 631/728–3100

*****Long Island Jewish Medical Center,** 270-05 76th Avenue, New Hyde Park, NY 11040; tel. 516/470–7000

Long Island Jewish Medical Center - M.M.T.P., 75-59 263rd Street, Glen Oaks, NY 11004; tel. 718/470–8285

Loyola Recovery Foundation, Inc., 113 Holland Avenue, Albany, NY 12208; tel. 518/626–5300

*****Loyola Recovery Foundation, Inc. - BHC,** 1159 Pittsford Victor Road, Pittsford, NY 14534; tel. 585/203–1005

Manhattan Psychiatric Center, 600 East 125th Street - Ward's Island, New York, NY 10035; tel. 646/672–6000

Methadone Treatment Program - Kings County / Clinic 3, 648 Albany Avenue, Brooklyn, NY 11203; tel. 718/245–3901

Metropolitan Correctional Center - New York / OTP, 150 Park Row, New York, NY 10007; tel. 646/836–6300

*****Metropolitan Hospital Center,** 1901 First Avenue, New York, NY 10029; tel. 212/423–7588

*****Metropolitan Hospital Methadone Treatment Program,** 1900 First Ave, Room 2M29, New York, NY 10029; tel. 212/423–6501

Mohawk Valley Psychiatric Center, 1400 Noyes Street, Utica, NY 13502; tel. 315/738–3800

Montefiore Medical Center - SATP, 111 East 210th Street, Bronx, NY 10467; tel. 718/920–2001

Montefiore Medical Center - SATP - OTP - Unit III, 2005 Jerome Avenue, 1st Floor, Bronx, NY 10467; tel. 718/920–2001

Montefiore Mount Vernon, 12 North Seventh Avenue, Mount Vernon, NY 10550; tel. 914/361–6100

Mount Sinai Hospital, One Gustave L. Levy Place, Box 1051, New York, NY 10029-6574; tel. 212/241–8108

Narco Freedom, Inc., Grand Concourse MMTP, 250 Grand Concourse, Bronx, NY 10451; tel. 718/292–2240

Narco Freedom, Inc.-Bridge Plaza MMTP, 37-18 34th Street, Long Island City, NY 11101; tel. 718/292–2240

Nassau County Dept. Methadone Maintenance Treatment Program, NUMC, 2201 Hempstead Turnpike, Building K, East Meadow, NY 11554; tel. 516/572–5906

Nassau Health Care Corporation, 2201 Hempstead Turnpike, East Meadow, NY 11554; tel. 516/572–4876

New York City Children's Center, 74-03 Commonwealth Boulevard, Bellerose, NY 11426-1839; tel. 718/264–4500

New York State Psychiatric Institute, 1051 Riverside Drive, New York, NY 10032; tel. 212/543–5000

North Central Bronx Hospital, 3424 Kossuth Avenue, Bronx, NY 10467; tel. 718/519–3500

Oswego Hospital, 110 West Sixth Street, Oswego, NY 13126; tel. 315/349–5566

*****Pathways, Sisters of Charity Hospital,** 158 Holden Street, Buffalo, NY 14214; tel. 716/862–1000

*****Phelps Memorial Hospital Association,** 701 North Broadway, Sleepy Hollow, NY 10591; tel. 914/366–1000

Pilgrim Psychiatric Center, 998 Crooked Hill Road, West Brentwood, NY 11717; tel. 631/761–3500

PROMESA Methadone Treatment Program, 1776 Clay Ave, Bronx, NY 10457; tel. 718/960–7601

*****Queens Hospital Center,** 82-68 164th Street, Jamaica, NY 11432; tel. 718/883–2351

*****Richmond Medical Center,** 355 Bard Avenue, Staten Island, NY 10310; tel. 718/818–1234

Rochester Mental Health Center (BHN, Inc.), 490 East Ridge Road, Rochester, NY 14621; tel. 585/922–2500

Rochester Pathways, Sisters of Charity Hospital, 435 East Henrietta Road, Rochester, NY 14607; tel. 585/424–6580

Rockland Children's Psychiatric Center, 2 First Avenue, Orangeburg, NY 10962; tel. 845/450–4040

Rockland Psychiatric Center, 140 Old Orangeburg Road, Orangeburg, NY 10962; tel. 845/359–1000

Sagamore Children's Psychiatric Center, 197 Half Hollow Road, Dix Hills, NY 11746; tel. 631/370–1701

Saint Joseph's Hospital Yonkers, 211 Powell Street, Brooklyn, NY 11212; tel. 718/485–6000

*****Seafield Center, Inc.,** 7 Seafield Lane, Westhampton Beach, NY 11978; tel. 631/288–1122

South Beach Psychiatric Center, 777 Seaview Avenue, Staten Island, NY 10305; tel. 718/667–2300

South Nassau Communities Hospital, 1 Healthy Way, Oceanside, NY 11572; tel. 516/632–3999

South Oaks Hospital, 400 Sunrise Highway, Amityville, NY 11701; tel. 631/608–5725

St. Baranabas Hospital, 183rd Street and Third Avenue, Bronx, NY 10457; tel. 718/960–6170

*****St. Barnabas Hospital,** 4422 Third Avenue, Bronx, NY 10457; tel. 718/960–6108

*****St. John's Episcopal Hospital - South Shore,** 327 Beach 19th Street, Far Rockaway, NY 11691; tel. 718/869–7000

St. Johns Riverside Hospital M.M.T.P., 2 Park Avenue, Yonkers, NY 10703; tel. 914/964–4000

St. Joseph's Hospital - MMTP, 317 South Broadway, Yonkers, NY 10701; tel. 914/378–7000

St. Joseph's Hospital Yonkers, 147-18 Archer Avenue, Jamaica, NY 11435; tel. 718/291–1888

St. Joseph's Hospital Yonkers, 127 South Broadway, Yonkers, NY 10701; tel. 718/953–2302

St. Lawrence Psychiatric Center, One Chimney Point Drive, Ogdensburg, NY 13669; tel. 315/541–2279

St. Luke's-Roosevelt Hospital Center - MMTP, 1000 Tenth Avenue, New York, NY 10019; tel. 212/523–6881

St. Mary's Hospital at Amsterdam - OTP, 427 Guy Park Avenue, Amsterdam, NY 12010; tel. 518/841–7101

Staten Island Univ Hospital (Coney Island M.M.T.P. Clinic), 450 Seaview Avenue, Staten Island, NY 10305; tel. 718/226–6939

Staten Island Univ Hospital Inpatient Chem Dep Detox Unit, 375 Seguine Avenue, Staten Island, NY 10309; tel. 718/226–6939

*****Staten Island University Hospital,** 475 Seaview Avenue, Staten Island, NY 10305; tel. 718/226–9000

Stony Brook University Hospital, Nicolls Road, Stony Brook, NY 11794-8503; tel. 631/444–2721

*****Strong Memorial Hospital,** 601 Elmwood Avenue, Rochester, NY 14642; tel. 585/275–2644

Stuyvesant Square Chemical Dependency Outpatient Detox, 1-9 Nathan Perlman Place, New York, NY 10003; tel. 212/420–4220

Suffolk County Department of Health - East End Clinic, 300 Center Drive, Riverhead, NY 11901; tel. 631/852–2680

Suffolk County Dept. of Health Services, Huntington MMTP, PO Box 6100, Building C-928, North County Complex, Hauppauge, NY 11788; tel. 631/854–4400

*****Syracuse Community Health Center, Inc.,** 819 South Salina Street, Syracuse, NY 13202; tel. 315/476–7921

The Brooklyn Hospital Center Parkside Drug Detox Program, 121 DeKalb Avenue, Brooklyn, NY 11201; tel. 718/250–8005

The Children's Home RTF, Inc., 638 Squirrel Hill Road, Chenango Forks, NY 13746; tel. 607/656–9004

The Greater Hudson Valley Family Health Center - OTP, 3 Commercial Place, Newburgh, NY 12550; tel. 845/220–2146

The Guidance Center Chemical Dependency Treatment Center, 256 Washington Street, Mount Vernon, NY 10553; tel. 914/613–0700

The House of the Good Shepherd, 1550 Champlin Avenue, Utica, NY 13502; tel. 315/235–7600

The Institute for Family Health, 16 East 16th Street, New York, NY 10003; tel. 212/633–0800

*****The Long Island Home,** 400 Sunrise Highway, Amityville, NY 11701; tel. 631/264–4000

United Health Services Hospitals, 10-42 Mitchell Avenue, Binghamton, NY 13903; tel. 607/762–2263

*****Upstate New York VA Health Care Network at Canandaigua,** 400 Fort Hill Avenue, Canandaigua, NY 14424; tel. 585/394–2000

*****VA Healthcare Network Upstate New York at Bath,** 76 Veterans Avenue, Bath, NY 14810; tel. 607/664–4722

*****VA Healthcare Network Upstate New York at Syracuse,** 800 Irving Avenue, Syracuse, NY 13210; tel. 315/425–4400

*****VA Hudson Valley Health Care System,** 2094 Albany Post Road, Route 9A, Montrose, NY 10548; tel. 914/737–4400

*****VA Medical Center Northport,** 79 Middleville Road, Northport, NY 11768; tel. 631/261–4400

*****VA New York Harbor Healthcare System,** 800 Poly Place, Brooklyn, NY 11209; tel. 718/630–3521

VA New York Harbor Healthcare System - OTP, 423 East 23rd Street, New York, NY 10010; tel. 212/686–7500

*****VA Western New York Health Care System,** 3495 Bailey Avenue, Buffalo, NY 14215; tel. 716/862–8529

*****Villa of Hope,** 3300 Dewey Avenue, Rochester, NY 14616; tel. 585/865–1550

Vincent P. Dole Treatment Program, 525 East 68th Street, Box 437, New York, NY 10065; tel. 212/746–5454

West Midtown Medical Group - OTP, 505 Eighth Avenue, 10th Floor, New York, NY 10018; tel. 212/736–5900

Westchester Health Care Corporation, 100 Woods Road, Taylor Pavilion, Valhalla, NY 10595; tel. 914/493–7000

Western New York Children's Psychiatric Center, 1010 East and West Road, West Seneca, NY 14224; tel. 716/677–7000

Whitney M. Young, Jr. Health Services, Inc., 10 Dewitt Street, Albany, NY 12207; tel. 518/463–3882

Woodhull Medical & Mental Health Medically Managed Detoxific, 760 Broadway, Unit 9-300, Brooklyn, NY 11206; tel. 718/963–8101

NORTH CAROLINA

A Caring Home, Inc., 8616 Nations Ford Road, Charlotte, NC 28217-5126; tel. 704/525–2840

A Day of Distinction, 1106 East Market Street, Greensboro, NC 27401; tel. 336/317–9226

A Plus Life Skills North Carolina, 201 West Walnut Street, Goldsboro, NC 27530; tel. 919/288–1139

AbleCare Corporation, 305 South Westgate Drive, Greensboro, NC 27407; tel. 336/218–7008

Alexander Youth Network, PO Box 220632, Charlotte, NC 28222-9979; tel. 704/366–8712

AssistedCare Management Group, Inc., 1003 Old Waterford Way, Suite 2C, Leland, NC 28451; tel. 910/332–2346

Autumn Halls of Unaka, 14949 Joe Brown Highway, Murphy, NC 28906; tel. 828/835–8103

Bethesda Care dba Keston Care, 11312 US 15/501 N, Chatham Crossing, Suite 400, Chapel Hill, NC 27517; tel. 919/967–0507

Beyond Challenges Community Services, LLC, 515 Yadkin Street, Henderson, NC 27536; tel. 252/572–2167

Blessed Aims, PO Box 16527, Greensboro, NC 27416; tel. 336/379–1314

Brynn Marr Hospital, 192 Village Drive, Jacksonville, NC 28546; tel. 910/577–1400

Canaan Care Home, LLC, 2804 Stirrup Court, Wake Forest, NC 27587; tel. 919/274–0596

*Indicates organization is a Joint Commission accredited Chemical Dependency organization.

Cantor LLC dba: Family United, 1801 North Tryon Street, Suite 336, Charlotte, NC 28206; tel. 336/471–8130

Caring Hands and Supplementary Enrichment Education, LLC, 2216 South Miami Boulevard, Suite 101, Durham, NC 27703; tel. 919/479–6806

Caring Touch Home Health Care, LLC, 799 James Lynn Drive, Pembroke, NC 28372; tel. 910/521–9175

*** Carolinas Medical Center,** PO Box 32861, Charlotte, NC 28232; tel. 704/355–7359

*** Carter's Circle of Care, Inc.,** 2031 Martin Luther King Jr. Drive, Suite E,D, Greensboro, NC 27406; tel. 336/271–5888

*** Charles George VA Medical Center at Asheville,** 1100 Tunnel Road, Asheville, NC 28805; tel. 828/298–7911

Citizens Choice, LLC, 3300 Sunset Avenue, Suite F, Rocky Mount, NC 27804; tel. 252/557–9797

Community CarePartners, Inc., 68 Sweeten Creek Road, Asheville, NC 28803; tel. 828/277–4800

Community Treatment Alternatives, Inc., 4901 Rosena Drive, Charlotte, NC 28227; tel. 704/323–9266

*** Continuum Care Services, Inc.,** PO Box 6331, Concord, NC 28027; tel. 704/784–0753

Crystal E. Nickerson, LLC, 2302 West Meadowview Road, Suite 228, Box 24, Greensboro, NC 27407; tel. 336/218–5176

Eagle Healthcare Services, Inc., 4428 Louisburg Road, Suite 109, Raleigh, NC 27604; tel. 919/872–7686

Extended Reach Day Treatment, 919 Ramsey Street, Fayetteville, NC 28301; tel. 910/484–0095

*** Fellowship Hall, Inc.,** PO Box 13890, Greensboro, NC 27415; tel. 336/621–3381

First Genesis Group Home, Inc., 1903 Delmar Drive, Greensboro, NC 27406; tel. 336/274–4447

FirstHealth of the Carolinas, Inc., PO Box 3000, Pinehurst, NC 28374; tel. 910/715–1442

Grandfather Home for Children, PO Box 98, Banner Elk, NC 28604; tel. 828/898–5465

Greater Image Healthcare Corporation, Inc., 401 Robeson Street, Fayetteville, NC 28301; tel. 910/321–0069

I Innovations, Inc., 176 Sandollar Court, Sanford, NC 27332; tel. 919/770–2617

JMJ Enterprise LLC d/b/a Fresh Start Home for Children, 2020 Textile Drive, Greensboro, NC 27405; tel. 336/271–6982

*** Julian F. Keith Alcohol and Drug Abuse Treatment Center,** 201 Tabernacle Road, Black Mountain, NC 28711; tel. 828/257–6200

Kids Health Services, Inc., PO Box 429, Fayetteville, NC 28301; tel. 910/829–7184

KidsPeace National Centers of North America, Inc., 3109 Poplarwood Court, Suite 310, Raleigh, NC 27604; tel. 919/872–6447

McLaurin Vocational Training Center, Inc., PO Box 413, Hamlet, NC 28345; tel. 910/582–0934

Miss Daisy's Gentlemen of Future, Inc., PO Box 1991, Wilson, NC 27894-1991; tel. 252/363–5446

Naval Hospital Camp Lejeune, 100 Brewster Boulevard, Camp Lejeune, NC 28547-2538; tel. 910/450–4007

*** New Beginning Youth Facility,** 525 Greenbriar Farm Trail, Siler City, NC 27344; tel. 336/302–0801

New Directions Group Care Management, PO Box 1442, Whiteville, NC 28472; tel. 910/640–1737

Noir Enterprises, LLC, PO Box 1794, Arden, NC 28704; tel. 828/654–9452

Old Vineyard Behavioral Health Services, 3637 Old Vineyard Road, Winston Salem, NC 27104-4842; tel. 336/794–3550

*** Open Arms Treatment Center,** 3911 Jack Pine Court, Greensboro, NC 27406; tel. 336/617–0469

Patterson Home, Inc., PO Box 64013, Fayetteville, NC 28306; tel. 910/527–8427

Phoenix Supported Living, Inc., 2996 NC 69 S, Suite 6, Hayesville, NC 28904; tel. 828/389–1795

*** Quality Home Care Services, inc.,** 3552 Beatties Ford Road, Charlotte, NC 28216; tel. 704/394–8968

Recovery Innovations, 300 Parkview Drive West, Henderson, NC 27536; tel. 252/438–4145

Renewed Services, Inc., 625 South Lafayette Street, Shelby, NC 28150; tel. 704/487–4440

Residential Services, Inc., 111 Providence Road, Chapel Hill, NC 27514; tel. 919/942–7391

*** Robeson Health Care Corporation,** 60 Commerce Drive, Pembroke, NC 28372; tel. 910/521–2900

SBH Raleigh, LLC, 3200 Waterfield Drive, Garner, NC 27529; tel. 919/800–4400

SBH-Wilmington, LLC, 2050 Mercantile Drive, Leland, NC 28451; tel. 910/371–2500

The Renfrew Center of North Carolina, 6633 Fairview Road, Charlotte, NC 28210; tel. 704/366–1264

*** The Ringer Centers, Inc.,** 213 East Bessemer Ave, Greensboro, NC 27401; tel. 336/379–7144

Timber Ridge Treatment Center, PO Box 259, Gold Hill, NC 28071; tel. 704/279–1199

Total Care & Concern, Inc., 1428 Orchard Lake Drive, Charlotte, NC 28270; tel. 704/321–1635

*** Tri-County Community Health Council, Inc.,** PO Box 227, Newton Grove, NC 28366; tel. 910/567–6194

Trinity House, Inc., 1803 Lochwood Drive, Greensboro, NC 27427; tel. 336/965–1305

Unique Home Care, Inc., PO Box 835, Jefferson, NC 28640; tel. 336/246–6991

*** United Quest Care Services, LLC,** 806 Summit Avenue, Suite 210A, Greensboro, NC 27405-7861; tel. 336/279–1227

*** Unity Healing Center,** PO Box C-201, Cherokee, NC 28719; tel. 828/497–3958

Unity Home Care, Inc., 211 Fairway Drive, Suite A, Fayetteville, NC 28305; tel. 910/864–1799

*** University of North Carolina Hospitals,** 101 Manning Drive, Chapel Hill, NC 27514; tel. 919/966–2016

*** VA Medical Center,** 508 Fulton Street, Durham, NC 27705; tel. 919/286–0411

*** VA Medical Center,** 2300 Ramsey Street, Fayetteville, NC 28301; tel. 910/822–7091

Veritas Collaborative, LLC, 615 Douglas Street, Suite 500, Durham, NC 27705; tel. 919/908–9730

*** W & B Health Care, Inc.,** PO Box 168, Red Springs, NC 28377; tel. 910/843–1997

*** W. G. (Bill) Hefner VA Medical Center,** 1601 Brenner Avenue, Salisbury, NC 28144; tel. 704/638–9000

*** Walter B. Jones Alcohol & Drug Abuse Treatment Center,** 2577 West 5th Street, Greenville, NC 27834; tel. 252/830–3426

Well Care, LLC, 6752 Parker Farm Drive, Wilmington, NC 28405; tel. 910/362–9405

Whitaker PRTF, 1003 12th Street, Butner, NC 27509; tel. 919/575–7927

*** Wilmington Treatment Center, Inc.,** 2520 Troy Drive, Wilmington, NC 28401; tel. 910/762–2727

*** Womack Army Medical Center,** Building 4-2817, Reilly Road, Fort Bragg, NC 28310; tel. 910/907–8917

Youth Villages of North Carolina and DC, 100 Capitola Drive, Suite 310, Durham, NC 27713; tel. 919/474–6400

NORTH DAKOTA

Altru Health System, PO Box 6002, Grand Forks, ND 58206-6002; tel. 701/780–5000

Fargo VA Health Care System, 2101 Elm Street North, Fargo, ND 58102; tel. 701/232–3241

*** Heartview Foundation,** 101 East Broadway Avenue, Bismarck, ND 58501; tel. 701/222–0386

*** North Dakota State Hospital,** 2605 Circle Drive, Jamestown, ND 58401-6905; tel. 701/253–3964

*** Prairie St. John's,** PO Box 2027, Fargo, ND 58107-2027; tel. 701/476–7200

Sanford Medical Center Fargo, 801 Broadway North, Fargo, ND 58122; tel. 701/234–2000

*** Trinity Hospitals,** PO Box 5020, Minot, ND 58702-5020; tel. 701/857–5000

OHIO

*** Abraxas Counseling Center,** 899 East Broad Street, Columbus, OH 43205; tel. 614/220–8655

Access Ohio, LLC, 99 North Brice Road, Suite 360, Columbus, OH 43213; tel. 614/367–7700

Akron Drug Abuse Clinic - Community Health Center, 725 East Market Street, Akron, OH 44305; tel. 330/434–4141

*** Akron-Urban Minority Alcoholism Drug Abuse Outreach,** 665 W Market Street, Akron, OH 44303; tel. 330/379–3467

Appalachian Behavioral Healthcare, 100 Hospital Drive, Athens, OH 45701; tel. 740/594–5000

Applewood Centers, Inc., 10427 Detroit Avenue, Cleveland, OH 44102-1645; tel. 216/696–5800

*** Beech Brook,** 3737 Lander Road, Cleveland, OH 44124; tel. 216/831–2255

*** Behavioral Connections of Wood County, Inc.,** Post Office Box 29, Bowling Green, OH 43402; tel. 419/352–5387

*** Bellefaire Jewish Children's Bureau,** 22001 Fairmount Boulevard, Shaker Heights, OH 44118; tel. 216/932–2800

Belmont Pines Hospital, 615 Churchhill-Hubbard Road, Youngstown, OH 44505; tel. 330/759–2700

BHC Fox Run Hospital, 67670 Traco Drive, Saint Clairsville, OH 43950; tel. 740/695–2131

*** Center for Chemical Addictions Treatment,** 830 Ezzard Charles Drive, Cincinnati, OH 45214; tel. 513/381–6672

*** Chalmers P. Wylie Ambulatory Care Center,** 420 North James Road, Columbus, OH 43219; tel. 614/257–5200

Child Guidance & Family Solutions, 18 N. Forge Street, Akron, OH 44304; tel. 330/762–0591

Children's Hospital Medical Center of Akron, One Perkins Square, Akron, OH 44308-1082; tel. 330/543–1000

Cincinnati Children's Hospital Medical Center, 3333 Burnet Avenue, Cincinnati, OH 45229-3039; tel. 513/636–3333

Cleveland Clinic Children's Hospital for Rehabilitation, 2801 Martin Luther King, Jr. Drive, Cleveland, OH 44104; tel. 216/448–6400

Community Behavioral Health Center, 3355 Richmond Road, 225-A, Beachwood, OH 44122; tel. 216/831–1494

*** Community Behavioral Health, Inc.,** 520 Eaton Avenue, Hamilton, OH 45013; tel. 513/785–4782

Comprehensive Psychiatry Group, Inc., 955 Windham Court, Boardman, OH 44512; tel. 330/726–9570

*** Cornell Abraxas,** 2775 State Route 39, Shelby, OH 44875; tel. 419/747–3322

*** Craig and Frances Lindner Center of HOPE,** 4075 Old Western Row Road, Mason, OH 45040; tel. 513/536–4673

*** Crisis Intervention and Recovery Center, Inc.,** 832 McKinley Avenue Northwest, Canton, OH 44703; tel. 330/452–9812

*** Crossroads: Lake County Adolescent Counseling Service,** 8445 Munson Road, Mentor, OH 44060; tel. 440/255–1700

*** Department of Veterans Affairs Medical Center, Dayton, Ohio,** 4100 West 3rd Street, Dayton, OH 45428; tel. 937/268–6511

Far West Center, 29133 Health Campus Drive, Westlake, OH 44145; tel. 440/835–6212

*** Glenbeigh,** PO Box 298, Rock Creek, OH 44084-0298; tel. 440/563–3400

*** Ironton-Lawrence County Community Action Organization,** 305 North Fifth Street, Ironton, OH 45638; tel. 740/532–3534

Lake Health, 7590 Auburn Road, Painesville, OH 44077; tel. 440/375–8100

*** Lorain County Alcohol & Drug Abuse Services, Inc.,** 2115 West Park Drive, Lorain, OH 44053-1138; tel. 440/989–4900

*** Louis Stokes, Cleveland VA Medical Center,** 10701 East Boulevard, Cleveland, OH 44106; tel. 216/231–3456

Lutheran Hospital, 1730 West 25th Street, Cleveland, OH 44113; tel. 216/696–4300

Marymount Hospital, 12300 McCracken Road, Garfield Heights, OH 44125; tel. 216/581–0500

Maumee Valley Guidance Center, 211 Biede Avenue, Defiance, OH 43512; tel. 419/782–8856

Medical University of Ohio at Toledo, 3000 Arlington Avenue, MS 1096, Toledo, OH 43614; tel. 419/383–4977

*** Mental Health Services for Clark and Madison Counties, Inc.,** 474 North Yellow Springs Street, Springfield, OH 45504; tel. 937/399–9500

*** Nationwide Children's Hospital, Inc.,** 700 Children's Drive, Columbus, OH 43205; tel. 614/722–5950

*** Neil Kennedy Recovery Clinic,** 2151 Rush Boulevard, Youngstown, OH 44507; tel. 330/744–1181

Neurobehavioral Medicine Consultants PC, Inc., 302 West Main Street, Saint Clairsville, OH 43950; tel. 740/968–7006

New Albany Home Health Solutions, LLC, 2525 Tiller Lane, Columbus, OH 43231; tel. 614/305–5151

New Day Counseling & Wellness, Inc., PO Box 27, Girard, OH 44420; tel. 330/727–8949

*** New Directions, Inc.,** 30800 Chagrin Boulevard, Cleveland, OH 44124; tel. 216/591–0324

Northcoast Behavioral Healthcare, 1756 Sagamore Road, Northfield, OH 44067; tel. 330/467–7131

---

*Indicates organization is a Joint Commission accredited Chemical Dependency organization.

Section C

*Northland/The Ridge, 50 West Techne Center Drive, Suite B5, Milford, OH 45150; tel. 513/753–9964

Ohio Hospital for Psychiatry, 880 Greenlawn Avenue, Columbus, OH 43223; tel. 614/449–9664

Paramount Development Association, 1818 West Third Street, Dayton, OH 45417; tel. 937/263–8176

Phoenix Rising Behavioral Healthcare And Recovery, Inc., 4974 Higbee Avenue, Suite 209, Canton, OH 44718; tel. 330/493–4553

Pomegranate Health Systems of Central Ohio, 765 Pierce Drive, Columbus, OH 43223; tel. 614/223–1650

Portage Path Behavioral Health, 340 South Broadway, Akron, OH 44308; tel. 330/253–3100

PsyCare, Inc., 2980 Belmont Avenue, Youngstown, OH 44505; tel. 330/759–2310

Psychological and Behavioral Consultants, 25101 Chagrin Boulevard, Beachwood, OH 44122; tel. 216/456–8103

*Rakesh Ranjan MD and Associates, Inc., 801 East Washington Street, Medina, OH 44256; tel. 330/722–1069

*Ravenwood Mental Health Center, 401 South Street, Building 2A, Chardon, OH 44024; tel. 440/285–2170

*Rescue Incorporated, 3350 Collingwood Boulevard, Toledo, OH 43610; tel. 419/255–9585

Rocking Horse Children's Health Center, 651 South Limestone Street, Springfield, OH 45505; tel. 937/324–1111

Shaker Clinic, LLC, 20600 Chagrin Boulevard, Suite 620, Shaker Heights, OH 44122; tel. 216/751–4762

*Southeast, Inc., 16 West Long Street, Columbus, OH 43215; tel. 614/225–0980

*Southwest General Health Center, 18697 Bagley Road, Middleburg Heights, OH 44130; tel. 440/816–8000

Specialty Care Counseling Services, Ltd, 2000 East Market Street, Warren, OH 44483; tel. 330/399–1221

*St. Vincent Charity Medical Center, 2351 East 22nd Street, Cleveland, OH 44115; tel. 216/861–6200

*Stella Maris, Inc., 1320 Washington Avenue, Cleveland, OH 44113; tel. 216/781–0550

Ten Lakes Center, LLC, 819 North First Street, Dennison, OH 44621; tel. 740/922–5121

*The Buckeye Ranch, Inc., 5665 Hoover Road, Grove City, OH 43123; tel. 614/875–2371

The Centers for Families and Children, 4500 Euclid Avenue, Cleveland, OH 44103; tel. 216/432–7200

*The Crossroads Center, 311 Martin Luther King Drive, Cincinnati, OH 45219; tel. 513/475–5300

The MetroHealth System, 2500 MetroHealth Drive, Cleveland, OH 44109-1998; tel. 216/778–7800

*The Ohio State University Hospital, 410 West Tenth Avenue, DN 168, Columbus, OH 43210; tel. 614/293–9700

*The Toledo Hospital, 2142 North Cove Boulevard, Toledo, OH 43606; tel. 419/291–7460

*The Woods at Parkside, 349 Olde Ridenour Road, Columbus, OH 43230; tel. 614/471–2552

Twin Valley Behavioral Healthcare, 2200 West Broad Street, Columbus, OH 43223; tel. 614/752–0333

*Unison Behavioral Health Group, PO Box 10015, Toledo, OH 43699-0015; tel. 419/693–0631

*VA Healthcare System of Ohio - Cincinnati Campus, 3200 Vine Street, Cincinnati, OH 45220; tel. 513/861–3100

*VA Medical Center - Chillicothe, 17273 State Route 104, Chillicothe, OH 45601; tel. 740/773–1141

Visiting Nurse Association Healthcare Partners of Ohio, 2500 East 22nd Street, Cleveland, OH 44115; tel. 216/931–1300

*Windsor Laurelwood Center for Behavioral Medicine, 35900 Euclid Avenue, Willoughby, OH 44094; tel. 440/953–3000

Wood County Children's Services Association, PO Box 738, Bowling Green, OH 43402; tel. 419/352–7588

OKLAHOMA
*Advantage Community Resources, LLC, 5929 North May Avenue, Suite 310, Oklahoma City, OK 73112; tel. 405/206–0177

*Alpha II, Inc., 1608 North Main Street, Tonkawa, OK 74653; tel. 580/628–2539

BetterLife Counseling Services, Inc., 9700 South Pennsylvania Avenue, Oklahoma City, OK 73159; tel. 405/735–9732

*Brookhaven Hospital, 201 South Garnett Road, Tulsa, OK 74128-1800; tel. 918/438–4257

Carl Albert Community Mental Health Center, PO Box 579, McAlester, OK 74502; tel. 918/426–7800

Cedar Ridge, 6505 Northeast 50th Street, Oklahoma City, OK 73141; tel. 405/605–6111

*Central Oklahoma Family Medical Center, Inc., PO Box 358, Konawa, OK 74849; tel. 580/925–3286

Child & Family Wellness Center, 355004 East 750 Road, Cushing, OK 74023; tel. 918/225–0750

*Children's Recovery Center of Oklahoma, 320 12th Avenue Northeast, Norman, OK 73071; tel. 405/364–9004

Choices Institute, 529 North Grand, Enid, OK 73701; tel. 580/234–8880

Cornerstone Clinical Services, Inc., 1919 West Elk Avenue, Duncan, OK 73533; tel. 580/595–7000

*Counseling Works, Inc., 1601 West Okmulgee, Muskogee, OK 74401; tel. 918/681–4944

*Cushing Valley Hope, PO Box 472, Cushing, OK 74023-0472; tel. 918/225–1736

Daybreak Family Services, 1516 South Boston Avenue, Suite 1, Tulsa, OK 74119; tel. 918/561–0400

*Department of Veterans Affairs Medical Center, 921 Northeast 13th Street, Oklahoma City, OK 73104; tel. 405/456–3312

Discovery Uttuwah, LLC, 118 South Main, Wagoner, OK 74467; tel. 918/485–1573

Duncan Regional Hospital, Inc., 1407 Whisenant Drive, Duncan, OK 73533; tel. 580/252–5300

*Dynasty Care Services, 4337 Southeast 15th Street, Del City, OK 73115; tel. 405/609–1760

Elite Counseling, LLC, 717 B Highway 70 East, Kingston, OK 73439; tel. 580/564–7308

Family Options Community Based Counseling Services, 2905 Harr Drive, Suite 203, Midwest City, OK 73110; tel. 405/610–2859

Full Circle Youth And Family Services, PLLC, 1212 South Air Depot, Suite 19B, Midwest City, OK 73110; tel. 405/455–7244

Generations Family Counseling, 206 East Blue Starr Drive, Claremore, OK 74017; tel. 918/341–8100

*Health Concepts Family Services Outpatient Behavioral Health, 1843 East 15th Street, Tulsa, OK 74104; tel. 918/872–6135

Hillcrest Medical Center Behavioral Health Services, 1120 South Utica, Tulsa, OK 74104-4090; tel. 918/579–1000

IMPACT (University of Oklahoma - Tulsa), 4502 East 41st Street, Room 2G07, Tulsa, OK 74135; tel. 918/660–3150

Improving Lives Counseling Services, Inc., 6216 South Lewis Avenue, Suite 180, Tulsa, OK 74136-1044; tel. 918/812–6010

*Inspiration Family Counseling, LLC, 3601 North Classen Ste. 107, Oklahoma City, OK 73118; tel. 405/315–1357

INTEGRIS Baptist Medical Center, 3300 Northwest Expressway, Oklahoma City, OK 73112-4481; tel. 405/951–8065

Jack C. Montgomery VA Medical Center, 1011 Honor Heights Drive, Muskogee, OK 74401; tel. 918/577–3000

*Jim Taliaferro Community Mental Health Center, 602 Southwest 38th Street, Lawton, OK 73505; tel. 580/248–5780

Land of Hope, Inc., 57533 MoccasinTrail Road, Prague, OK 74864; tel. 405/567–0054

*Laureate Psychiatric Clinic and Hospital, 6655 South Yale Avenue, Tulsa, OK 74136; tel. 918/481–4000

Lifeworks Counseling Solutions, LLC, PO Box 281, Canton, OK 73724; tel. 580/515–1010

Making A Difference, Inc., 210 East Maple, Enid, OK 73701; tel. 580/233–5900

New Opportunities Waiting, LLC, 419 West Broadway, Suite 203, Muskogee, OK 74401; tel. 918/686–6005

Next Step Counseling, Inc., 3923 North Pennsylvania Avenue, Oklahoma City, OK 73112; tel. 405/424–0007

Norman Regional Health System, PO Box 1308, Norman, OK 73070-1308; tel. 405/307–1000

*Northwest Center for Behavioral Health (NCBH), 1222 10th Street, Suite 211, Woodward, OK 73801; tel. 580/256–8615

Oklahoma Forensic Center, PO Box 69, Vinita, OK 74301-0069; tel. 918/256–7841

Omega Plans LLC, 3324 Ozark Drive, Edmond, OK 73034; tel. 405/228–0898

Parkside, Inc., 1620 East 12th Street, Tulsa, OK 74120; tel. 918/582–2131

Pennington Creek Lifehouse, 801 East Main, Tishomingo, OK 73460; tel. 580/310–4164

Positive Changes, LLC, 744 Southeast 25th Street, Oklahoma City, OK 73129; tel. 405/636–1463

*Professional Counseling Solutions, PLLC, 1500 North Main, Frederick, OK 73542; tel. 580/335–3320

Promise Family Center, PLLC, 5350 South Western, Suite 305, Oklahoma City, OK 73109; tel. 405/431–0232

Quality Counseling and Intervention Services, Inc., 1330 Clasen Boulevard, Suite 311, Oklahoma City, OK 73106; tel. 405/702–0502

Resolutions Counseling Group, 126 South Main, Perkins, OK 74059; tel. 405/547–2743

Sequel of Oklahoma, LLC, 3301 North Martin Luther King Avenue, Oklahoma City, OK 73111; tel. 405/548–1280

Shadow Mountain Behavioral Health, 6262 South Sheridan Road, Tulsa, OK 74133; tel. 918/492–8200

Solutions for Life Counseling Services, 1202 West Willow, Suite D, Enid, OK 73703; tel. 580/234–4700

Southeastern Psychiatric Services, PLLC, PO Box 1589, McAlester, OK 74502; tel. 918/423–3700

Southwest Oklahoma Counseling, PO Box 691, Clinton, OK 73601; tel. 580/323–9800

SPUR, 4801 North Classen Boulevard, Suite 135, Oklahoma City, OK 73118; tel. 405/848–0011

*St. Anthony Hospital, 1000 North Lee Street, Oklahoma City, OK 73101; tel. 405/272–7000

The Agency at Zoe, LLC, 729 East Maine Avenue, Enid, OK 73701; tel. 580/237–7703

Tulsa Center for Behavioral Health, 2323 South Harvard, Tulsa, OK 74114; tel. 918/293–2140

Unified Dimensions, LLC, 1330 North Classen Boulevard, Suite 302, Oklahoma City, OK 73106; tel. 405/514–0727

VCPHCS IV, LLC, 5401 Southwest 29th, Oklahoma City, OK 73128; tel. 405/681–2003

Willow Crest Hospital, Inc., 130 A Street South West, Miami, OK 74354; tel. 918/542–1836

*YCO TFC, Inc., PO Box 95207, Oklahoma City, OK 73143; tel. 866/926–6552

*YCO OKC, Inc., 222 East Sheridan Street, Suite 2, Oklahoma City, OK 73104; tel. 405/200–0131

OREGON
Albertina Kerr Centers, 424 Northeast 22nd Avenue, Portland, OR 97232; tel. 503/255–4205

CODA, Inc., 1027 East Burnside, Portland, OR 97214-1328; tel. 503/239–8400

*Hazelden Betty Ford Foundation, 1901 Esther Street, Newberg, OR 97132; tel. 503/554–4300

Kairos, 715 Southwest Ramsey Avenue, Grants Pass, OR 97527; tel. 541/956–4943

Northwest Behavioral Healthcare Services, 18000 Southeast Webster Road, Gladstone, OR 97027; tel. 503/722–4470

Northwest Human Services, 681 Center Street, Northeast, Salem, OR 97301; tel. 503/588–5828

Oregon State Hospital, 2600 Center Street, Northeast, Salem, OR 97301-2682; tel. 503/945–2870

*Portland VA Medical Center, PO Box 1034, Portland, OR 97207; tel. 503/273–5267

Portland VA Medical Center Opiate Treatment Program, 3710 SW US Veteran's Hospital Road, PO Box 1034, (P3OTP), Portland, OR 97239; tel. 503/220–8262

*Providence Portland Medical Center, 4805 Northeast Glisan Street, Portland, OR 97213; tel. 503/215–2349

*Providence St.Vincent Medical Center, 9205 Southwest Barnes Road, Portland, OR 97225; tel. 503/216–1234

Rainrock Treatment Center, 1863 Pioneer Parkway East, Suite 304, Springfield, OR 97477; tel. 541/896–9300

*Serenity Lane, 2133 Centennial Plaza, Eugene, OR 97401; tel. 541/284–8611

Trillium Family Services, Inc., 3415 Southast Powell Boulevard, Portland, OR 97202; tel. 503/234–9591

*UBH of Oregon, LLC, 10300 Southwest Eastridge Street, Portland, OR 97225; tel. 503/944–5000

*Indicates organization is a Joint Commission accredited Chemical Dependency organization.

*VA Roseburg Healthcare System, 913 Northwest Garden Valley Boulevard, Roseburg, OR 97471; tel. 541/440-1000

*VA Southern Oregon Rehabilitation Center and Clinics, 8495 Crater Lake Highway, White City, OR 97503; tel. 541/826-2111

Youth Villages Oregon, PO Box 368, Marylhurst, OR 97036; tel. 503/635-3416

PENNSYLVANIA

Abraxas Academy, 1000 Academy Drive, Morgantown, PA 19543; tel. 610/913-8000

*Abraxas I, PO Box 59, Marienville, PA 16239; tel. 814/927-6615

Adaptive Behavioral Services, 6031 Broad Street, Suite 201, Pittsburgh, PA 15206; tel. 412/661-7790

*Adelphoi Village, Inc., 1119 Village Way, Latrobe, PA 15650; tel. 724/804-7000

Albert Einstein Medical Center, 5501 Old York Road, Philadelphia, PA 19141; tel. 215/456-7890

Associates in Counseling & Child Guidance, 272 East Connelly Boulevard, Sharon, PA 16146; tel. 724/983-1381

Belmont Center for Comprehensive Treatment, 4200 Monument Road, Philadelphia, PA 19131; tel. 215/877-2000

Bethesda Children's Home, 15667 State Highway 86, Meadville, PA 16335; tel. 814/724-7510

Child Guidance Resource Centers, 2000 Old West Chester Pike, Havertown, PA 19083; tel. 484/454-8700

Children's Behavioral Health, Inc., 203 College Park Plaza, Johnstown, PA 15904; tel. 814/262-0768

Children's Home of Bradford, 800 East Main Street, Bradford, PA 16701; tel. 814/817-1400

Children's Service Center of Wyoming Valley, Inc., 335 South Franklin Street, Wilkes Barre, PA 18702; tel. 570/825-6425

Choices Program of Wyoming Valley, 307 Laird Street, Plains, PA 18705; tel. 570/552-3700

CHOR Youth & Family Services, Inc., 1010 Centre Avenue, Reading, PA 19601-1498; tel. 610/478-8266

*Clear Brook, Inc., 37 North River Street, Second Floor, Wilkes Barre, PA 18702; tel. 570/822-0800

*Conewago Snyder, 800 West Fourth Street, Williamsport, PA 17701; tel. 570/601-0877

CPP Behavioral Health, Inc., 253 South Mount Vernon Ave, Second Floor, Uniontown, PA 15401; tel. 724/787-4117

Crozer Chester Medical Center, One Medical Center Boulevard, Chester, PA 19013; tel. 610/447-2000

Devereux Children's Behavioral Health Services, 655 Sugartown Road, PO Box 297, Malvern, PA 19355-0297; tel. 484/595-6733

Diversified Treatment Alternatives, Inc., 148 Fairfield Road, Lewisburg, PA 17837; tel. 570/523-3457

Eagleville Hospital, 100 Eagleville Road, Eagleville, PA 19408; tel. 610/539-6000

EIHAB Human Services, Inc., 1200 SR 92 South, Tunkhannock, PA 18657; tel. 570/388-6155

*Erie VA Medical Center, 135 East 38th Street, Erie, PA 16504; tel. 814/868-8661

*Fairmount Behavioral Health System, 561 Fairthorne Avenue, Philadelphia, PA 19128; tel. 215/487-4000

Foundations Medical Services, LLC, 124 Hollywood Dr- Bantam Commons, Building 2, Butler, PA 16001; tel. 724/431-2006

Friends Behavioral Health System, LP, 4641 Roosevelt Boulevard, Philadelphia, PA 19124-2399; tel. 215/831-4600

*Gateway Rehabilitation Center / Genesis Division, 311 Rouser Road, Moon Township, PA 15108; tel. 412/604-8900

Glade Run Lutheran Services, PO Box 70, Zelienople, PA 16063-0070; tel. 724/452-4453

*Greater Philadelphia Health Action, Inc. (GPHA), 432 North 6th Street, Philadelphia, PA 19123; tel. 215/925-2400

Haven Behavioral Services of Reading, LLC, 145 North 6th Street, Reading, PA 19601; tel. 610/406-4340

Hoffman Homes, Inc., 815 Orphanage Road, Littlestown, PA 17340; tel. 717/359-7148

*Holcomb Associates, Inc., 467 Creamery Way, Exton, PA 19341; tel. 610/363-1488

Holy Spirit Hospital, 503 North 21st Street, Camp Hill, PA 17011-2288; tel. 717/763-2100

Kensington Hospital Outpatient Treatment Program, 136 West Diamond Street, Philadelphia, PA 19122; tel. 215/426-8100

KidsPeace National Centers, Inc./KidsPeace Children's Hosp, 4085 Independence Drive, Schnecksville, PA 18078; tel. 610/799-8000

Kirkbride Center, 111 North 49th Street, Philadelphia, PA 19139; tel. 215/471-2600

Lakeview Neurocare Pennsylvania, Inc., 65 Woods Lane, Lewistown, PA 17044; tel. 813/440-9974

*Lebanon VA Medical Center, 1700 South Lincoln Avenue, Lebanon, PA 17042; tel. 717/272-6621

Lehigh Valley Hospital, PO Box 689, Cedar Crest & I-78, Allentown, PA 18105-1556; tel. 610/402-8000

Lehigh Valley Hospital - Muhlenberg, 2545 Schoenersville Road, Bethlehem, PA 18017-7384; tel. 484/884-2200

*Live Well Services, Inc., 203 Floral Vale Boulevard, Yardley, PA 19067; tel. 215/968-7600

*Livengrin Foundation, Inc., 4833 Hulmeville Road, Bensalem, PA 19020-3099; tel. 215/638-5200

Main Line Hospital Paoli, 255 West Lancaster Avenue, Paoli, PA 19301; tel. 610/648-1000

*Marworth, PO Box 36, Waverly, PA 18471; tel. 570/563-1112

Mercy Catholic Medical Center/Mercy Philadelphia Hospital, 501 South 54th Street, Philadelphia, PA 19143; tel. 215/748-9300

*Mirmont Treatment Center, 100 Yearsley Mill Road, Media, PA 19063-5593; tel. 484/227-1400

*Montgomery County Emergency Service, Inc., 50 Beech Drive, Norristown, PA 19403-5421; tel. 610/279-6100

Narcotic Addict Rehabilitation Program of Thomas Jefferson U, 1020 South 21st Street (Northeast Corner of 21st & Washington Avenue, Philadelphia, PA 19146; tel. 215/735-5979

New Vitae, Inc. Partial Hospital Program & Outpatient Clinic, 16 South Main Street, Quakertown, PA 18951; tel. 215/538-3403

Nulton Diagnostic and Treatment Center, PC, 214 College Park Plaza, Johnstown, PA 15904; tel. 814/262-0025

Omni Health Services, Inc., PO Box 454, Montgomeryville, PA 18936; tel. 215/997-2000

Paoletta Counseling Services, 456 North Pitt Street, Mercer, PA 16137; tel. 724/662-7202

Penn State Hershey Medical Center, PO Box 850, Hershey, PA 17033; tel. 717/531-8521

Pennsylvania Psychiatric Institute, 2501 Third Street, Harrisburg, PA 17110; tel. 717/782-4742

Perseus House, Inc., 1511 Peach Street, Erie, PA 16501; tel. 814/480-5900

Philadelphia VA Medical Center Opioid Treatment Program, University and Woodland Avenues, Building 3, Philadelphia, PA 19104; tel. 215/823-5857

Philhaven, PO Box 550, Mount Gretna, PA 17064; tel. 717/273-8871

*Phoenix-Washington, Inc., 800 Manor Drive, Washington, PA 15301; tel. 724/225-9700

Presbyterian Children's Village Services, 452 South Roberts Road, Bryn Mawr, PA 19010; tel. 610/525-5400

Progressive Medical Specialists, Inc., 2453 West Pike Road, Houston, PA 15342; tel. 724/873-5655

Progressive Medical Specialists, Inc., 2900 Smallman Street, Pittsburgh, PA 15201; tel. 412/391-6384

Psychiatric Care Systems, PC, 110 Hidden Valley Road, McMurray, PA 15317; tel. 724/941-4070

Pyramid Healthcare Inc., Dolminis Methadone Clinic, 2 Sellers Drive, Altoona, PA 16601; tel. 814/204-0059

*Pyramid Healthcare, Inc., PO Box 967, Duncansville, PA 16635; tel. 814/940-0407

Pyramid Healthcare, Inc. - York, OTP, 104 Davies Drive, York, PA 17402; tel. 717/840-2300

*Reading Hospital, PO Box 16052, Reading, PA 19612-6052; tel. 484/628-8000

RHJ Medical Center, Inc., 1005 Old State Route 119, Hunker, PA 15639; tel. 724/696-9600

RHJ Medical Center, Inc./Vandergrift, LLC, 2994 River Road, Vandergrift, PA 15690; tel. 724/842-0357

*Roxbury Treatment Center, 601 Roxbury Road, Shippensburg, PA 17257; tel. 717/532-4217

Saint John Vianney Center, 151 Woodbine Road, Downingtown, PA 19335; tel. 610/269-2600

Sarah A. Reed Children's Center, 2445 West 34th Street, Erie, PA 16506; tel. 814/838-1954

*Sharon Pennsylvania Hospital Company, 740 East State Street, Sharon, PA 16146; tel. 615/465-7000

Silver Springs - Martin Luther School, 512 West Township Line Road, Plymouth Meeting, PA 19462-1001; tel. 610/825-4440

Southwood Psychiatric Hospital, 2575 Boyce Plaza Road, Pittsburgh, PA 15241; tel. 412/257-2290

St. Clair Memorial Hospital, 1000 Bower Hill Road, Pittsburgh, PA 15243; tel. 412/942-4000

Stairways Behavioral Health, 2185 West 8th Street, Erie, PA 16505; tel. 814/453-5806

The Bradley Center, Inc., 5180 Campbells Run Road, Pittsburgh, PA 15205; tel. 412/788-8219

The Bridge, 1100 Adams Avenue, Philadelphia, PA 19124; tel. 215/342-5000

The Children's Hospital of Philadelphia, 34th Street and Civic Center Boulevard, Philadelphia, PA 19104; tel. 215/590-1000

The Horsham Clinic, 722 East Butler Pike, Ambler, PA 19002; tel. 215/643-7800

*The Meadows Psychiatric Center, 132 The Meadows Drive, Centre Hall, PA 16828; tel. 814/364-2161

The Renfrew Centers, Inc., 475 Spring Lane, Philadelphia, PA 19128; tel. 215/482-5353

Thomas Jefferson University - Family Center, 1233 Locust Street, 2nd Floor, Philadelphia, PA 19107; tel. 215/955-8577

*TODAY, Inc., PO Box 908, Newtown, PA 18940; tel. 215/968-4713

Tree of Life Professional Behavioral Services, 7040-7048 Castor Avenue, Philadelphia, PA 19149; tel. 215/533-5433

UHS of Doylestown, LLC, 833 East Butler Avenue, Doylestown, PA 18901; tel. 215/345-0444

*Universal Recovery Foundation, 2001 Providence Avenue, Chester, PA 19013; tel. 610/876-9000

*UPMC Presbyterian Shadyside, 200 Lothrop Street, Pittsburgh, PA 15213; tel. 412/647-8788

*VA Butler Healthcare, 325 New Castle Road, Butler, PA 16001-2480; tel. 724/287-4781

*VA Medical Center, 1400 Black Horse Hill Road, Coatesville, PA 19320-2097; tel. 610/384-7711

*VA Medical Center - James E. Van Zandt, 2907 Pleasant Valley Boulevard, Altoona, PA 16602-4377; tel. 814/943-8164

*VA Medical Center Wilkes-Barre, 1111 East End Boulevard, Wilkes Barre, PA 18711; tel. 570/821-7204

*VA Pittsburgh Healthcare System, University Drive C, Pittsburgh, PA 15240; tel. 412/360-6391

Valley Forge Medical Center & Hospital/OTP, 1033 West Germantown Pike, Norristown, PA 19403; tel. 610/539-8500

Warwick House, Inc., 1460 Meetinghouse Road, Warminster, PA 18974; tel. 215/491-7404

Western Pennsylvania PsyCare, 1607 3rd Street, Beaver, PA 15009; tel. 724/728-8400

Wordsworth, 3905 Ford Road, Philadelphia, PA 19131; tel. 215/643-5400

WPIC Narcotic Addiction Program (of UPMC), 6714 Kelly Street, Pittsburgh, PA 15208; tel. 412/864-5300

Y.A.P.A. Apartment Living Program, Inc., One Highland Drive, Chalfont, PA 18914; tel. 215/997-9959

RHODE ISLAND

*Butler Hospital, 345 Blackstone Boulevard, Providence, RI 02906; tel. 401/455-6200

*Comprehensive Community Action, Inc., 311 Doric Avenue, Cranston, RI 02910; tel. 401/467-9610

*East Bay Center, 610 Wampanoag Trail, Riverside, RI 02915; tel. 401/431-9870

Emma Pendleton Bradley Hospital, 1011 Veterans Memorial Parkway, Riverside, RI 02915; tel. 401/432-1000

*Gateway Healthcare, Inc., 249 Roosevelt Avenue, Pawtucket, RI 02860; tel. 401/724-8400

*Naval Health Clinic New England, 43 Smith Road, Newport, RI 02841-1002; tel. 401/841-3236

Newport County Community Mental Health Center, Inc., 127 Johnnycake Hill Road, Middletown, RI 02842; tel. 401/846-1213

Providence VA Opioid Treatment Program, 830 Chalkstone Avenue, Building 1, Providence, RI 02908; tel. 401/273-7100

Rhode Island Hospital, 593 Eddy Street, Providence, RI 02903; tel. 401/444-5131

Roger Williams Medical Center - OTP, 825 Chalkstone Avenue, Providence, RI 02908; tel. 401/456-2257

SSTAR of Rhode Island, 1950 Tower Hill Road, North Kingstown, RI 02852; tel. 401/294-6160

---

*Indicates organization is a Joint Commission accredited Chemical Dependency organization.

Section C

*Women & Infants Hospital of Rhode Island, 101 Dudley Street, Providence, RI 02905-2499; tel. 401/274-1122

SOUTH CAROLINA
*Aiken Regional Medical Centers LLC, 302 University Parkway, Aiken, SC 29801; tel. 803/641-5600

Carolina Children's Home, 1154 Sunnyside Drive, Columbia, SC 29240; tel. 803/787-2306

Children's Place, 310 Barnwell Ave Northeast, Aiken, SC 29801; tel. 803/641-4144

G. Werber Bryan Psychiatric Hospital, 220 Faison Drive, Columbia, SC 29203; tel. 803/935-5761

Greenville Hospital System University Medical Center, 701 Grove Road, Greenville, SC 29605; tel. 864/455-7000

*HHC South Carolina, Inc., 152 Waccamaw Medical Park Drive, Conway, SC 29526; tel. 843/347-8871

*Medical University of South Carolina Medical Center, PO Box 250332, Charleston, SC 29425; tel. 843/792-4000

*Moncrief Army Community Hospital, 4500 Stuart Street, Columbia, SC 29207; tel. 803/751-7812

*Naval Health Clinic Charleston, 110 NNPTC Circle, Goose Creek, SC 29445-6314; tel. 843/794-6200

Naval Hospital Beaufort, 1 Pinckney Boulevard, Beaufort, SC 29902-6148; tel. 843/228-5200

New Hope Treatment Centers, 7515 Northside Drive, Suite 200, North Charleston, SC 29420; tel. 843/572-3498

*Palmetto Health Baptist, 1330 Taylor Street, Columbia, SC 29201; tel. 803/296-5678

*Palmetto Lowcountry Behavioral Health, LLC, 2777 Speissegger Drive, Charleston, SC 29405-8299; tel. 843/747-5830

Palmetto Pee Dee Behavioral Health, LLC, 601B Gregg Avenue, Florence, SC 29502; tel. 843/667-0644

*Ralph H. Johnson VA Medical Center, 109 Bee Street, Charleston, SC 29401-5799; tel. 843/577-5011

SpringBrook Behavioral Health System, PO Box 1005, Travelers Rest, SC 29690; tel. 864/834-8013

The Nurturing Center, 1332 Pickens Street, Columbia, SC 29201; tel. 803/771-4160

The Pines Residential Treatment Center-Charleston Campus, 225 Midland Parkway, Summerville, SC 29485; tel. 843/851-5015

*Three Rivers Behavioral Health, LLC, 2900 Sunset Boulevard, West Columbia, SC 29169; tel. 803/796-9911

Three Rivers Residential Treatment | Midlands Campus, 200 Ermine Road, West Columbia, SC 29170; tel. 803/791-9918

*UHS of Greenville, LLC, 2700 East Phillips Road, Greer, SC 29650; tel. 864/235-2335

*William Jennings Bryan Dorn VA Medical Center, 6439 Garners Ferry Road, Columbia, SC 29209; tel. 803/776-4000

*William S. Hall Psychiatric Institute, 1800 Colonial Drive, Columbia, SC 29203; tel. 803/898-1593

SOUTH DAKOTA
Black Hills Children's Home, 24100 South Rockerville Road, Rapid City, SD 57702; tel. 605/343-5422

Sioux Falls Children's Home, PO Box 1749, Sioux Falls, SD 57101-1749; tel. 605/334-6004

*Sioux Falls VA Health Care System, PO Box 5046, Sioux Falls, SD 57117; tel. 605/336-3230

*VA Black Hills Health Care System-Fort Meade-Hot Springs, SD, 113 Comanche Road, Fort Meade, SD 57741; tel. 605/720-7170

*Wellspring, Inc., PO Box 1087, Rapid City, SD 57709; tel. 605/718-4870

TENNESSEE
*Blount Memorial Hospital, Inc., 907 East Lamar Alexander Parkway, Maryville, TN 37804-5016; tel. 865/983-7211

*Brookhaven Retreat, LLC, 1016 I.C. King Road, Seymour, TN 37865; tel. 865/573-3656

*Buffalo Valley, Inc., PO Box 879, Hohenwald, TN 38462; tel. 931/796-5427

*Cornerstone of Recovery, Inc., 1214 Topside Road, Louisville, TN 37777; tel. 865/970-7747

*Council for Alcohol and Drug Abuse Services, Inc., PO Box 4797, Chattanooga, TN 37405; tel. 423/756-7644

Counseling and Consultation Services, Inc., PO Box 278, Limestone, TN 37681; tel. 423/257-6054

*Cumberland Heights Foundation, Inc., PO Box 90727, Nashville, TN 37209; tel. 615/352-1757

DRD Knoxville Medical Clinic, 626 Bernard Street, Knoxville, TN 37921; tel. 865/522-0161

DRD Management, Inc., 412 Citico Street, Knoxville, TN 37921; tel. 865/522-0661

*Focus Healthcare of Tennessee, 7429 Shallowford Road, Chattanooga, TN 37421; tel. 423/308-2560

Foothills Care, Inc., 404 North Kentucky Street, Kingston, TN 37763; tel. 865/376-3464

*Foundations Recovery Network, Nashville, 101 Lea Avenue, Nashville, TN 37210; tel. 615/372-8935

*Homeless Health Care Center, PO Box 1746, Chattanooga, TN 37401; tel. 423/265-5708

*Johnson City Medical Center, 400 North State of Franklin Road, Johnson City, TN 37604; tel. 423/431-6111

Keystone Memphis, LLC, 7900 Lowrance Road, Memphis, TN 38125; tel. 901/758-2002

*La Paloma Treatment Center, 2009 Lamar Ave, Memphis, TN 38114; tel. 901/969-5524

*Lakeside Behavioral Health System, LLC, 2911 Brunswick Road, Memphis, TN 38133; tel. 901/377-4700

*Memphis VA Medical Center, 1030 Jefferson Avenue, Memphis, TN 38104; tel. 901/577-7200

*Oak Plains Academy of Tennessee, Inc., 1751 Oak Plains Road, Ashland City, TN 37015; tel. 931/362-4723

*Parkridge Medical Center, Inc., 2333 McCallie Avenue, Chattanooga, TN 37404; tel. 423/493-6970

Parkwest Medical Center, 9352 Park West Boulevard, Knoxville, TN 37923; tel. 865/373-1000

Partial Hospital Systems, Inc., 2262 Germantown Road South, Germantown, TN 38138; tel. 901/753-4300

*Pathways of Tennessee, Inc., 238 Summar Drive, Jackson, TN 38301; tel. 731/541-8200

Ridgeview Psychiatric Hospital and Center, Inc., 240 West Tyrone Road, Oak Ridge, TN 37830; tel. 865/482-1076

Sequel Schools, LLC, PO Box 1647, Norris, TN 37828; tel. 865/494-5554

*Tennova Healthcare-Physicians Regional Medical Center, 900 East Oak Hill Avenue, Knoxville, TN 37917; tel. 865/545-8000

The Renfrew Center of Tennessee, 1624 Westgate Circle, Suite 100, Brentwood, TN 37027; tel. 215/482-5353

The Summits at HealthQuest, 8130 Country Village Drive, Suite 103, Cordova, TN 38016-2087; tel. 901/308-2915

The Transformation Center For Women, LLC, 1088 Rogers Road, Cordova, TN 38018; tel. 901/755-1396

*TriStar Skyline Medical Center, 3441 Dickerson Pike, Nashville, TN 37207; tel. 615/769-7100

*VA Medical Center - James H. Quillen, PO. Box 4000, Mountain Home, TN 37684; tel. 423/926-1171

*VA Tennessee Valley Healthcare System, 1310 24th Avenue South, Nashville, TN 37212-2637; tel. 615/327-4751

*Vanderbilt University Hospital and The Vanderbilt Clinic, AA 1204 MCN, 1161 21st Avenue South, Nashville, TN 37232-2101; tel. 615/322-1117

Varangon Academy, 3030 Brunswick Road, Bartlett, TN 38133; tel. 901/531-1950

VCPHCS I LLC dba ADC Recovery Counseling Center, 3041 Getwell Road, Building A, Suite 101, Memphis, TN 38118; tel. 901/375-1050

VCPHCS IX, LLC dba/Middle Tennessee Treatment Center, 2410 Charlotte Avenue, Nashville, TN 37203; tel. 615/321-2575

VCPHCS VIII, LLC, 1734 Madison Avenue, Memphis, TN 38104; tel. 901/722-9429

VCPHCS XIX, LLC, 1869 Highway 45 Bypass, Jackson, TN 38305; tel. 731/660-0880

VCPHCS XVII, LLC d/b/a BHG Columbia, TN Treatment Center, 1202 S. James Campbell Boulevard, Suite 7A, Columbia, TN 38401; tel. 931/381-0020

VCPHCS XX, LLC, 2555 East Wood Street, Paris, TN 38242; tel. 731/641-4545

VCPHCS XXI, LLC, 2960-B Austin Peay Highway, Memphis, TN 38128; tel. 901/372-7878

Village Behavioral Health, 2431 Jones Bend Road, Louisville, TN 37777; tel. 865/970-1263

Youth Villages, 3320 Brother Boulevard, Memphis, TN 38133; tel. 901/251-5000

TEXAS
*Access Counseling Group, Inc., 2600 K Ave, Ste 102, Plano, TX 75074; tel. 972/423-8727

Aeschbach & Associates, Incorporated, 2824 South Congress Avenue, Austin, TX 78704; tel. 512/444-5092

*Amarillo VA Health Care System, 6010 Amarillo Boulevard, West, Amarillo, TX 79106; tel. 806/355-9703

*Aspire Hospital, LLC, 2006 South Loop 336 West, Suite 500, Conroe, TX 77304; tel. 936/647-3500

Audubon Behavioral Healthcare of Longview, LLC, 615 Clinic Drive, Longview, TX 75605; tel. 903/212-3105

Austin Child Guidance Center, 810 West 45th Street, Austin, TX 78751; tel. 512/451-2242

Austin Counseling Connection, PLLC, 3355 Bee Caves Road, Austin, TX 78746; tel. 512/329-9455

*Austin Travis County Mental Health Mental Retardation Center, 1430 Collier Street, Austin, TX 78704; tel. 512/447-4141

Austin Travis County MHMR Narcotic Treatment Program, 1631 A East 2nd Street, Austin, TX 78702; tel. 512/804-3380

Baylor All Saints Medical Centers, PO Box 31, Fort Worth, TX 76101; tel. 817/926-2544

Big Spring State Hospital, 1901 North Highway 87, Big Spring, TX 79720; tel. 432/268-7386

Burke Center, 2001 South Medford Drive, Lufkin, TX 75901; tel. 936/639-1141

C & I Holdings, LLC, 16303 Grant Road, Cypress, TX 77429; tel. 281/516-6200

*Cambridge Hospital, 7601 Fannin, Houston, TX 77054; tel. 713/790-1155

*Carl R. Darnall Army Medical Center, 36000 Darnall Loop, Room 2417, Fort Hood, TX 76544-5063; tel. 254/288-8627

CDHS, Inc., 214 Billings, Suite 240, Arlington, TX 76010; tel. 817/652-1004

*Central Texas Veterans Health Care System, 1901 Veterans Memorial Drive, Temple, TX 76504; tel. 254/743-2306

Children's Hope Residential Services, Inc. - Lubbock, 2402 Canyon Lake Drive, Lubbock, TX 79415; tel. 806/897-9735

Clarity Child Guidance Center, 8535 Tom Slick Drive, San Antonio, TX 78229; tel. 210/616-0300

Continuum Integrated, 3003 South Loop West, Suite 475, Houston, TX 77054-1301; tel. 713/383-0888

Cross Roads Recovery Center, Inc., 5552 S. Hampton Road, Dallas, TX 75232; tel. 214/339-3181

DebLin Health Concepts and Associates, Inc., PO Box 550769, Houston, TX 77255-0769; tel. 713/686-9194

Devereux Texas Treatment Network, 1150 Devereux Drive, League City, TX 77573; tel. 281/335-1000

East Texas Clinic, PO Box 9486, Longview, TX 75608; tel. 903/759-4966

*East Texas Medical Center Tyler, PO Box 6400, Tyler, TX 75711; tel. 903/597-0351

EDCASA (Eating Disorder Center at San Antonio), 515 Busby Drive, San Antonio, TX 78209-1116; tel. 210/826-7447

*El Paso Psychiatric Assoc., PA, 7760 Alabama Street, El Paso, TX 79904; tel. 915/757-7999

*El Paso VA Health Care System, 5001 North Piedras Street, El Paso, TX 79930-4210; tel. 915/564-7910

Family Services of Greater Houston, 2700 Southwest Freeway, Suite 209, Houston, TX 77098-4612; tel. 713/861-4849

Fulshear Ranch Academy, 10514 Oberrender Road, Needville, TX 77461; tel. 979/793-3011

*Grapevine Valley Hope, 2300 William D. Tate Avenue, Grapevine, TX 76051; tel. 817/424-1305

*Green Oaks Hospital Subsidiary, LP, 7808 Clodus Fields Drive, Dallas, TX 75251; tel. 972/770-0840

*Guadalupe Regional Medical Center, 1215 East Court Street, Seguin, TX 78155; tel. 830/401-7202

Hector Garza Center, 620 East Afton Oaks, San Antonio, TX 78232; tel. 210/568-8600

*Hickory Trail Hospital, 2000 North Old Hickory Trail, Desoto, TX 75115; tel. 972/298-7323

HMIH Cedar Crest, LLC, 3500 South IH- 35, Belton, TX 76513; tel. 254/939-2100

Horizon Health, 1025 East 32nd Street, Austin, TX 78705-2714; tel. 512/544-5253

---

*Indicates organization is a Joint Commission accredited Chemical Dependency organization.

*Houston Area Community Services, Inc. (HACS), 2150 W. 18th Street, Suite 300, Houston, TX 77008; tel. 713/426-0027

Houston Maintenance Clinic, Inc., 4608 Main Street, Suite A, Houston, TX 77002; tel. 713/527-0064

Huntsville Clinic, Inc., 829 10th Street, Huntsville, TX 77320; tel. 936/291-9172

Huntsville Clinic, Inc. d/b/a Conroe Treatment & Recovery Ctr, 501 Everett Street, Conroe, TX 77301; tel. 936/441-9172

InnerWisdom, Inc., 10777 Stella Link Road, Houston, TX 77025; tel. 713/592-9292

*Innovative Psychiatric Solutions, Inc., 621 SW Johnson Avenue, Suite C, Burleson, TX 76028; tel. 325/829-4371

IntraCare Hospital North, 1120 Cypress Station Drive, Houston, TX 77090; tel. 281/893-7200

Johnnie M. Hawkins LAMP Clinic, 2201 Southeast Loop 820, Fort Worth, TX 76119; tel. 817/730-0703

*La Hacienda Treatment Center, PO Box 1, Hunt, TX 78024; tel. 830/238-4222

*Life Management Resources, 2301 Ohio Drive, Suite 150, Plano, TX 75093; tel. 972/985-7565

*Memorial Hermann Prevention and Recovery Center, 3043 Gessner Drive, Houston, TX 77080; tel. 713/329-7300

Meridell Achievement Center, PO Box 87, Liberty Hill, TX 78642; tel. 512/528-2100

Meth-Laam, 3204 Ennis Street, Houston, TX 77004; tel. 713/526-2441

Methodist Hospital, 8109 Fredericksburg Road, San Antonio, TX 78229; tel. 210/575-4000

Metroplex Adventist Hospital, Inc., 2201 South Clear Creek Road, Killeen, TX 76549; tel. 254/526-7523

Michael E. DeBakey VA MC Opioid Treatment Program, 2002 Holcombe Boulevard, Building 100, Houston, TX 77030; tel. 713/794-7931

*Millwood Hospital LP, 1011 North Cooper Street, Arlington, TX 76011; tel. 817/261-3121

*Montrose Counseling Center, Inc., 401 Branard, 2nd Floor, Houston, TX 77006; tel. 713/800-0900

*Naval Health Clinic Corpus Christi, Naval Air Station 10651 East Street, Suite 100, Corpus Christi, TX 78419; tel. 361/961-2688

*Neuro Institute of Austin, LP, 1106 West Dittmar Road, Austin, TX 78745; tel. 512/444-4835

*New Dimensions Day Hospital LP, 1345 Space Park, Suite C, Houston, TX 77058; tel. 281/333-2284

*Nexus Recovery Center Incorporated, 8733 La Prada, Dallas, TX 75228; tel. 214/321-0156

Northshore Treatment Center, 176 Uvalde Road, Houston, TX 77015; tel. 713/455-7008

Northwest Texas Healthcare System, Inc., 1501 Coulter Road, Amarillo, TX 79106; tel. 806/354-1000

Nueces County MHMR Community Center, 1630 South Brownlee Street, Corpus Christi, TX 78404; tel. 361/886-1037

Pasadena Substance Abuse Clinic, 1645 Pasadena Boulevard, Pasadena, TX 77502; tel. 713/473-1405

Rio Grande State Center, PO Box 2668, Harlingen, TX 78551-2668; tel. 956/364-8000

*RR Recovery, LLC, 2501 Taylor Street, Wichita Falls, TX 76309; tel. 940/761-3034

Rusk State Hospital, 805 North Dickinson, Rusk, TX 75785-0318; tel. 903/683-3421

*Sabine Valley Regional MHMR Center, PO Box 6800, Longview, TX 75601; tel. 903/758-2471

San Antonio State Hospital, 6711 South New Braunfels Avenue, Suite 100, San Antonio, TX 78223-3006; tel. 210/532-8811

*SAS Healthcare, Inc., 7000 US, Highway 287, Arlington, TX 76001; tel. 817/583-8080

*Serenity Foundation of Texas, 150 Orange Street, Abilene, TX 79601; tel. 325/673-6489

*Seton Shoal Creek Hospital, 3501 Mills Avenue, Austin, TX 78731; tel. 512/324-2000

Shiloh Treatment Center, Inc., 3926 Bahler Avenue, Manvel, TX 77578; tel. 281/489-1290

*Shoreline, Inc., PO Box 68, Taft, TX 78390; tel. 361/528-3356

*South Texas Rural Health Services, Inc., PO Box 599, Cotulla, TX 78014; tel. 830/879-3047

*South Texas Veterans Health Care System, 7400 Merton Minter Boulevard, San Antonio, TX 78229-4404; tel. 210/617-5205

*Spindletop Center, PO Box 3846, Beaumont, TX 77704-3846; tel. 409/839-1000

*Summer Sky, Inc., 1100 McCart Street, Stephenville, TX 76401; tel. 254/968-2907

*Sundown Ranch, Inc., 3120 Van Zandt County Road, Suite 2318, Canton, TX 75103; tel. 903/479-3933

Tarrant County Hospital District, 1500 South Main Street, Fort Worth, TX 76104; tel. 817/921-3431

Texas Clinic Fulton, 6311 Fulton Street, Houston, TX 77022; tel. 713/694-8100

Texas Clinic Westview, 9320 Westview Drive, Suite 10, Houston, TX 77055; tel. 713/468-0536

*Texas Cypress Creek Hospital, 17750 Cali Drive, Houston, TX 77090; tel. 281/586-7000

*Texas Health Harris Methodist Hospital Hurst Euless Bedford, 1600 Hospital Parkway, Bedford, TX 76022; tel. 817/848-4600

*Texas Health Presbyterian Hospital Dallas, 8200 Walnut Hill Lane - J7, Dallas, TX 75231-4496; tel. 214/345-6789

*Texas Laurel Ridge Hospital, LP, 17720 Corporate Woods Drive, San Antonio, TX 78259; tel. 210/491-3551

Texas San Marcos Treatment Center, LP, 120 Bert Brown Road, San Marcos, TX 78666; tel. 512/396-8500

The Renfrew Center of Texas, LLC, 9400 North Central Expressway, Suite 150, Dallas, TX 75231; tel. 215/482-5353

*TRS Behavioral Care, Inc., 902 West Alabama Street, Houston, TX 77006; tel. 713/933-1391

*UHS of Timberlawn, 4600 Samuell Boulevard, Dallas, TX 75228; tel. 214/381-7181

*University Behavioral Health of Denton, 2026 West University, Denton, TX 76201; tel. 940/320-8100

*University Behavioral Health of El Paso, LLC, 1900 Denver Avenue, El Paso, TX 79902; tel. 915/544-4000

VA North TX Health Care System / Opioid Replacement Clinic, 4500 S. Lancaster Road, Dallas, TX 75216; tel. 214/857-7000

*VA Texas Valley Coastal Bend Health Care System, 2701 South 77 Sunshine Strip, Harlingen, TX 78550; tel. 956/430-9200

VCPHCS II, LLC, 1105 Memorial Drive, Denison, TX 75020; tel. 903/464-0727

VCPHCS III, LLC, 207 Broad Street, Wichita Falls, TX 76301; tel. 940/322-9355

VCPHCS VII, LLC dba BHG-San Antonio, 519 East Quincy, San Antonio, TX 78212; tel. 210/299-1614

VCPHCS XVI, LLC, 19333 Highway 59 North, Ste 280, Humble, TX 77338; tel. 281/540-0331

VCPHCS XVIII, LLC d/b/a BHG Center Treatment Center, 1110 Tenaha Street, Suite 5, Center, TX 75935; tel. 936/524-2140

VCPHCS XXII, LLC d/b/a BHG Lufkin Treatment Center, 216 North John Redditt Drive, Lufkin, TX 75904; tel. 936/637-2223

Volunteers at the Creek, 4110 Guadalupe, Building 635, Austin, TX 78751; tel. 512/458-7686

Waco Center for Youth, 3501 North 19th Street, Waco, TX 76708; tel. 254/756-2171

*West Oaks Hospital, Inc., 6500 Hornwood Drive, Houston, TX 77074; tel. 713/995-0909

*West Texas VA Health Care System, 300 Veterans Boulevard, Big Spring, TX 79720; tel. 432/263-7361

Whispering Hills Achievement Center, 4110 FM 609, Flatonia, TX 78941; tel. 361/865-3083

Wise Regional Health System, 609 Medical Center Drive, Decatur, TX 76234; tel. 940/627-5921

UTAH

*Ascend Recovery (Illume Center, LLC), 6280 West 9600 North, Highland, UT 84003; tel. 801/216-4800

Ashcreek Ranch Academy, Inc., PO Box 39, Toquerville, UT 84774; tel. 435/215-0500

Avalon Hills Health Care, Inc., PO Box 3412, Logan, UT 84323; tel. 435/938-6060

Benchmark Behavioral Health Systems, 592 West 1350 South, Woods Cross, UT 84087; tel. 801/299-5300

Cinnamon Hills Youth Crisis Center, 770 East St. George Boulevard, Saint George, UT 84770; tel. 435/674-0984

*Cirque Lodge, Inc., 777 North Palisade Dr, Orem, UT 84097; tel. 801/222-9200

Copper Hills Youth Center, 5899 West Rivendell Drive, West Jordan, UT 84081; tel. 801/561-3377

*EBH Southwest Services, Inc., 8072 South Highland Drive, Salt Lake City, UT 84121; tel. 801/839-7262

Elevations RTC, 2650 West 2700 South, Syracuse, UT 84075; tel. 801/773-0200

*George E. Wahlen VA Salt Lake City Health Care System, 500 Foothill Boulevard, Salt Lake City, UT 84148; tel. 801/582-1565

*Havenwood Academy, Inc., PO Box 21, Cedar City, UT 84721; tel. 435/586-2500

Heritage Schools, Inc., 5600 North Heritage School Drive, Provo, UT 84604; tel. 801/226-4600

Life-Line, Inc., 1130 West Center Street, North Salt Lake, UT 84054; tel. 801/936-4000

New Roads Treatment Center, 230 West Towne Ridge Parkway, Suite 225, Sandy, UT 84070; tel. 801/669-5888

*Nexstep Medical Detox, LLC, 1371 East 750 North, Orem, UT 84097; tel. 801/607-1189

*Odyssey House, Inc. - Utah, 344 East 100 South, Suite 301, Salt Lake City, UT 84111; tel. 801/322-4257

*Primary Children's Medical Center, 100 North Mario Capecchi Drive, Salt Lake City, UT 84113; tel. 801/662-1000

Recovery Help, LLC, PO Box 57940, Salt Lake City, UT 84157; tel. 800/705-5850

*Recovery Ways, LLC, 2815 East 3300 South, Salt Lake City, UT 84109; tel. 801/326-5161

*Red Rock Canyon School, 747 East St. George Boulevard, Saint George, UT 84770; tel. 435/673-6111

Salt Lake Behavioral Health, 3802 South 700 East, Salt Lake City, UT 84106; tel. 801/264-6000

Solacium - New Haven, 2172 East 7200 South, Spanish Fork, UT 84660; tel. 801/794-1218

Sorenson's Ranch School, Inc., Box 440219, Koosharem, UT 84744; tel. 435/638-7318

*Steps Recovery Center, LLC, 984 South 930 West, Payson, UT 84651; tel. 801/465-5111

*Sunrise Residential Treatment Center, 65 North 1150 West, Hurricane, UT 84737; tel. 435/635-1185

Telos Residential Treatment, 870 West Center Street, Orem, UT 84057; tel. 801/426-8800

Tranquility Place of Utah, LLC, 160 East 800 South, Suite B, Salt Lake City, UT 84111; tel. 801/924-9240

*Turning Point Centers, LLC, 10658 South Dimple Dell Road, Sandy, UT 84092; tel. 801/576-0745

Turning Point Family Care, Inc., 115 North 300 West, B200, Washington, UT 84780; tel. 435/674-7421

UHS of Provo Canyon, Inc., 763 North 1650 West, Springville, UT 84663; tel. 801/491-3910

UHS of Salt Lake City, LLC, 1110 West 3300 South, South Salt Lake, UT 84119; tel. 801/433-2900

UHS of Timpanogos, Inc., 1790 North State Street, Orem, UT 84057; tel. 801/224-8255

*Wasatch Recovery Treatment Center, 8420 S. Wasatch Boulevard, Cottonwood Heights, UT 84121; tel. 801/901-0024

WayPoint Academy, WayPoint Academy, PO Box 488, Huntsville, UT 84317; tel. 801/899-0726

*Willow Tree Recovery, LLC, 145 South 1300 West, Pleasant Grove, UT 84062; tel. 801/785-9400

Youth Care of Utah, PO Box 909, Draper, UT 84020; tel. 801/572-6989

Youthtrack, Inc., PO Box 887, Brigham City, UT 84302; tel. 435/723-1799

VERMONT

*Brattleboro Retreat, 1 Anna Marsh Lane, Brattleboro, VT 05302; tel. 802/257-7785

*Health Care & Rehabilitation Services of Southeastern VT, 390 River Street, Springfield, VT 05156; tel. 802/886-4500

VA Medical Center, 215 North Main Street, White River Junction, VT 05009; tel. 802/295-9363

VIRGINIA

Alice C. Tyler Village of Childhelp, 23164 Dragoon Road, Lignum, VA 22726; tel. 540/399-1926

*Centra Health, Inc., 1901 Tate Springs Road, Lynchburg, VA 24501-1167; tel. 434/200-4705

Commonwealth Center for Children and Adolescents, PO Box 4000, Staunton, VA 24402-4000; tel. 540/332-2100

Cumberland Hospital for Children and Adolescents, 9407 Cumberland Road, New Kent, VA 23124; tel. 804/966-2242

Dominion Hospital, 2960 Sleepy Hollow Road, Falls Church, VA 22044; tel. 703/538-2882

Ed Murphy & Associates, 181 Kings Highway, Suite 127, Fredericksburg, VA 22405; tel. 540/368-3098

*Indicates organization is a Joint Commission accredited Chemical Dependency organization.

Section C

Family Counseling Center for Recovery, 4906 Radford Avenue, Richmond, VA 23230; tel. 804/354-1996

Family Counseling Centers for Recovery - Fredericksburg, 11720 Main Street, Suite 108, Fredericksburg, VA 22408; tel. 540/735-9350

FCCR - Southlake, 905 C Southlake Boulevard, Richmond, VA 23236; tel. 804/419-0492

*Fort Belvoir Community Hospital, 9300 DeWitt Loop, Fort Belvoir, VA 22060; tel. 571/231-4121

*Galax Treatment Center, Inc., PO Box 27, Galax, VA 24333; tel. 540/236-2994

Galax Treatment Center, Inc. dba: New River Treatment Center, 140 Larkspur Lane, Galax, VA 24333; tel. 276/236-6341

Galax Treatment Center, Inc. dba:Clinch Valley Treatment Ctr, 111 Town Hollow Road, Cedar Bluff, VA 24609; tel. 540/963-3554

Hallmark Youthcare - Richmond, 12800 West Creek Parkway, Richmond, VA 23238; tel. 804/784-2200

Harbor Point Behavioral Health Center, Inc., 301 Fort Lane, Portsmouth, VA 23704; tel. 757/393-0061

*Inova Fairfax Hospital, 3300 Gallows Road, Falls Church, VA 22042; tel. 703/776-3445

*Inova Kellar Center, 11204 Waples Mill Road, Fairfax, VA 22030-2522; tel. 703/218-8500

Kempsville Center for Behavioral Health, 860 Kempsville Road, Norfolk, VA 23502; tel. 757/461-4565

Kenner Army Health Clinic, 700 24th Street, Fort Lee, VA 23801-1716; tel. 804/734-9277

Liberty Point Behavioral Healthcare, LLC, 1110 Montgomery Avenue, Staunton, VA 24401; tel. 540/213-0450

Marion Correctional Treatment Center, 110 Wright Street, Marion, VA 24354; tel. 276/783-7154

*Mary Washington Hospital, Inc., 1001 Sam Perry Boulevard, Fredericksburg, VA 22401; tel. 540/741-1100

MBHS of Kenbridge, LLC, 231 Hickory Road, Kenbridge, VA 23944; tel. 434/676-1378

*McDonald Army Health Center, Building 576, Jefferson Avenue, Fort Eustis, VA 23604-5548; tel. 757/314-7523

*Naval Health Clinic Quantico, 3259 Catlin Avenue, Quantico, VA 22134-6050; tel. 703/784-1500

Newport News Behavioral Health Center, 17579 Warwick Boulevard, Newport News, VA 23603; tel. 757/888-0400

North Spring Behavioral Healthcare, 42009 Victory Lane, Leesburg, VA 20176; tel. 703/777-0800

*PHC of VA, Inc., 405 Kimball Avenue, Salem, VA 24153; tel. 540/389-4761

*Poplar Springs Hospital, 350 Poplar Drive, Petersburg, VA 23805; tel. 804/733-6874

*Riverside Behavioral Health Center, 2244 Executive Drive, Hampton, VA 23666; tel. 757/827-1001

*Salem VA Medical Center, 1970 Roanoke Boulevard, Salem, VA 24153; tel. 540/982-2463

The Barry Robinson Center, 443 Kempsville Road, Norfolk, VA 23502; tel. 757/455-6100

VA Medical Center - Methadone Maintenance Program, 1201 Broad Rock Boulevard, Richmond, VA 23249; tel. 804/675-5000

*VA Medical Center-Hampton, 100 Emancipation Drive, Hampton, VA 23667; tel. 757/722-9961

Virginia Treatment Center, Inc., 3208 Hershberger Road, Roanoke, VA 24017; tel. 540/336-5248

*Williamsburg Place/The Farley Center, 5477 Mooretown Road, Williamsburg, VA 23188; tel. 757/565-0106

WASHINGTON

American Lake Opioid Treatment Program, 9600 Veterans Drive, Building 8, Tacoma, WA 98493; tel. 253/583-1759

Central Washington Comprehensive Mental Health, 402 South Fourth Avenue, Yakima, WA 98902; tel. 509/575-4084

*Central Washington Comprehensive Mental Health, PO Box 959, Yakima, WA 98907; tel. 509/575-4084

*Jonathan M. Wainwright Memorial VA Medical Center, 77 Wainwright Drive, Walla Walla, WA 99362; tel. 509/525-5200

Lourdes Health Network, PO Box 2568, Pasco, WA 99302; tel. 509/547-7704

Navos, 2600 Southwest Holden Street, Seattle, WA 98126; tel. 206/933-7299

Pearl Street Center / Comprehensive Mental Health, 815 South Pearl Street, Tacoma, WA 98445; tel. 253/396-5930

*Providence St. Peter Hospital, 413 Lilly Road Northeast, Olympia, WA 98506-5166; tel. 360/491-9480

*Sea-Mar Community Health Center, 1040 South Henderson Street, Seattle, WA 98108; tel. 206/763-5277

Tamarack Center, 2901 West Ft. George Wright Drive, Spokane, WA 99224; tel. 509/326-8100

The Moore Center for Eating Disorders, 1601 114th Ave Southeast, Bellevue, WA 98004; tel. 425/451-1134

*VA Medical Center, North 4815 Assembly Street, Spokane, WA 99205; tel. 509/434-7000

*VA Puget Sound Health Care System, 1660 South Columbian Way (S-002-QI), Seattle, WA 98108-1597; tel. 206/764-2731

*Valley Cities Counseling & Consultation, 325 West Gowe Street, Kent, WA 98032; tel. 253/833-7444

*Yakima Valley Farm Workers Clinic, 604 West 1st Avenue, Toppenish, WA 98948; tel. 509/865-5898

WEST VIRGINIA

Elkins Mountain Schools, 100 Bell Street, Elkins, WV 26241; tel. 304/637-8000

*Olympia Center Preston, Inc., PO Box 158, Kingwood, WV 26537; tel. 304/329-2400

River Park Hospital, PO Box 1875, Huntington, WV 25719-1875; tel. 304/526-9111

*Shenandoah Valley Medical System, Inc., PO Box 1146, Martinsburg, WV 25402; tel. 304/263-4999

*Thomas Memorial Hospital, 4605 MacCorkle Avenue Southwest, South Charleston, WV 25309; tel. 304/766-4529

*VA Medical Center, 200 Veterans Avenue, Beckley, WV 25801; tel. 304/255-2121

*VA Medical Center, 1540 Spring Valley Drive, Huntington, WV 25704; tel. 304/429-6741

*VA Medical Center, 510 Butler Avenue, Martinsburg, WV 25405; tel. 304/263-0811

*VA Medical Center - Louis A. Johnson, 1 Medical Center Drive, Clarksburg, WV 26301; tel. 304/623-3461

West Virginia University Hospitals, Inc., PO Box 8242, Morgantown, WV 26506-8242; tel. 304/598-4200

William R. Sharpe, Jr. Hospital, 936 Sharpe Hospital Road, Weston, WV 26452; tel. 304/269-1210

WISCONSIN

*Aurora Psychiatric Hospital, 1220 Dewey Avenue, Wauwatosa, WI 53213; tel. 414/454-6600

*Clement J. Zablocki VA Medical Center, 5000 West National Avenue, Milwaukee, WI 53295-1000; tel. 414/384-2000

*Columbia St. Mary's Hospital Milwaukee, Inc., PO Box 503, Milwaukee, WI 53201-0503; tel. 414/291-1000

*Gundersen Lutheran Medical Center, Inc., 1900 South Avenue, La Crosse, WI 54601-5467; tel. 608/782-7300

Lakeview NeuroRehab Center Midwest, 1701 Sharp Road, Waterford, WI 53185; tel. 262/534-7297

*Rogers Memorial Hospital, Inc., 34700 Valley Road, Oconomowoc, WI 53066; tel. 262/646-4411

*St. Agnes Hospital, 430 East Division Street, Fond Du Lac, WI 54935; tel. 920/929-2300

*St. Joseph Hospital, An Affiliate of Hospital Sisters Health System, 1701 Dousman Street, Green Bay, WI 54303; tel. 920/498-8600

*St. Joseph's Hospital, 2661 County Highway I, Chippewa Falls, WI 54729; tel. 715/717-7200

Theda Care Hospitals, 130 Second Street, Neenah, WI 54956; tel. 920/729-3100

*VA Medical Center - Great Lakes Health Care System, 500 East Veterans Street, Tomah, WI 54660; tel. 608/372-1777

Waukesha Memorial Hospital, Inc., 725 American Avenue, Waukesha, WI 53188-5099; tel. 262/928-1000

*Wheaton Franciscan Healthcare-All Saints, Inc., 3801 Spring Street, Racine, WI 53405; tel. 262/687-4011

*Wheaton Franciscan, Inc., 5000 West Chambers Street, Milwaukee, WI 53210; tel. 414/447-2000

*William S. Middleton Memorial Veterans Hospital, 2500 Overlook Terrace, Madison, WI 53705; tel. 608/256-1901

WYOMING

Cathedral Home for Children, 4989 North 3rd Street, Laramie, WY 82072; tel. 307/745-8997

Normative Services, Inc., 5 Lane Lane, Sheridan, WY 82801; tel. 307/674-6878

*Sheridan VA Health Care System, 1898 Fort Road, Sheridan, WY 82801; tel. 307/675-3530

St. Joseph's Children's Home, PO Box 1117, Torrington, WY 82240; tel. 307/532-4197

UHS of Wyoming, Inc., 2521 East 15th Street, Casper, WY 82609; tel. 307/237-7444

*VA Medical Center, 2360 East Pershing Boulevard, Cheyenne, WY 82001; tel. 307/778-7550

*Wyoming Recovery, LLC, 231 South Wilson, Casper, WY 82601; tel. 307/265-3791

U.S. Associated Areas

APO/AE

31st Medical Group - Aviano Air Base, Italy, 31 MDG/SGQ - Unit 6180, Box 245, APO, AE 09604-0245; tel. 043-430-5073

48th Medical Group RAF Lakenheath, Unit 5210, Box 230, APO, AE 09464-0230; tel. 163-855-8493

Installation Management Command - Europe, IMEU-HR (Attn: Amanda Frederick) Unit 23103, APO, AE 09136; tel. 011-.49-.611

Landstuhl Regional Medical Center, CMR #402, APO, AE 09180-3460; tel. 637-186-7895

U.S Naval Hospital Sigonella, PSC 836 Box 2670, FPO, AE 09636; tel. 011/390-9556

U.S. Naval Hospital Rota, PSC 819 Box 18, FPO, AE 09645; tel. 011/349-5682

US Naval Hospital - Naples, Italy, PSC 827, Box 1000, APO, AE 09617-1000; tel. +39-081-8116

USAMEDDAC Bavaria, Unit 28038 CMR 411, APO, AE 09112; tel. +49- 96-6283

GUAM

Latte Treatment Center, LLC, HC1 Box 17500, Inarajan, GU 96915; tel. 671/727-7665

PUERTO RICO

A.P. Community Mental Services, Corp., PO Box 1231, Las Piedras, PR 00771-1231; tel. 787/733-6699

Advanced Behavioral Center, Inc., 3181 Marbella Street, Ponce, PR 00716-4809; tel. 787/841-8855

Centro Ambulatorio Para Tu Salud Emocional Niños y Adolescen, Psiquiatria RCM-50, PO Box 29134, San Juan, PR 00929-0134; tel. 787/758-2525

Centro De Orientacion Y Ayuda Psiquiatrica, Inc., Loiza Valley Shopping Center/Local AA-6, Canovanas, PR 00729; tel. 787/256-0273

Centro de Salud Conductual Menonita CIMA, PO Box 871, Aibonito, PR 00705; tel. 787/714-2462

Clinica Interdisciplinaria de Psiquiatria Avanzada, 650 Lloveras Street Cond Centro Plaza, Suite 101, San Juan, PR 00909-2113; tel. 787/721-4020

Clinica Medicina Conductual, Inc., Urbanizacion Belisa Calle Bori 1542, San Juan, PR 00927; tel. 787/274-9494

First Hospital Panamericano, PO Box 1400, Cidra, PR 00739; tel. 787/739-5555

Instituto Psicoterapéutico de Puerto Rico (Inspira), PO Box 9809, Caguas, PR 00726-9809; tel. 787/704-0705

San Juan Capestrano Hospital, Inc., Rural Route 2, Box 11, Rio Piedras, PR 00926; tel. 787/760-0222

Servicios Salud Mental Carolina, CSP, Plaza Carolina Station PO Box 9067, Carolina, PR 00988-9067; tel. 787/752-1979

VA Caribbean Healthcare System, 10 Casia Street, San Juan, PR 00921-3201; tel. 787/641-7582

---

*Indicates organization is a Joint Commission accredited Chemical Dependency organization.

Abbreviations Used in the AHA Guide

AB, Army Base
ACSW, Academy of Certified Social Workers
AEC, Atomic Energy Commission
AFB, Air Force Base
AHA, American Hospital Association
AK, Alaska
AL, Alabama
AODA, Alcohol and Other Drug Abuse
APO, Army Post Office
AR, Arkansas
A.R.T., Accredited Record Technician
A.S.C., Ambulatory Surgical Center
A.T.C., Alcoholism Treatment Center
Ave., Avenue
AZ, Arizona

B.A., Bachelor of Arts
B.B.A., Bachelor of Business Administration
B.C., British Columbia
Blvd., Boulevard
B.S., Bachelor of Science
B.S.Ed., Bachelor of Science in Education
B.S.H.S., Bachelor of Science in Health Studies
B.S.N., Bachelor of Science in Nursing
B.S.W., Bachelor of Science and Social Worker
CA, California; Controller of Accounts

C.A.A.D.A.C., Certified Alcohol and Drug Abuse Counselor
CAC, Certified Alcoholism Counselor
CAE, Certified Association Executive
CAP, College of American Pathologists
CAPA, Certified Ambulatory Post Anesthesia
C.A.S., Certificate of Advanced Study
CCDC, Certified Chemical Dependency Counselor
C.D., Commander of the Order of Distinction
CDR, Commander
CDS, Chemical Dependency Specialist
CFACHE, Certified Fellow American College of Healthcare Executives
CFRE, Certified Fund Raising Executive
C.G., Certified Gastroenterology
CHC, Certified Health Consultant
CHE, Certified Healthcare Executive
C.L.D., Clinical Laboratory Director
CLU, Certified Life Underwriter, Chartered Life Underwriter
CMA, Certified Medical Assistant
C.M.H.A., Certified Mental Health Administrator
CNHA, Certified Nursing Home Administrator
CNM, Certified Nurse Midwife
CNOR, Certified Operating Room Nurse
C.N.S., Clinical Nurse Specialist
CO, Colorado; Commanding Officer
COA, Certified Ophthalmic Assistant
COMT, Commandant
C.O.M.T., Certified Ophthalmic Medical Technician
Conv., Conventions
Corp., Corporation; Corporate
C.O.T., Certified Ophthalmic Technician
CPA, Certified Public Accountant
C.P.H.Q., Certified Professional in Health Care Quality
CPM, Certified Public Manager
CRNA, Certified Registered Nurse Anesthetist
CRNH, Certified Registered Nurse Hospice
C.S.J.B, Catholic Saint John the Baptist
CSW, Certified Social Worker
CT, Connecticut
CWO, Chief Warrant Officer

D.B.A., Doctor of Business Administration
DC, District of Columbia
D.D., Doctor of Divinity
D.D.S., Doctor of Dental Surgery
DE, Delaware
Diet, Dietitian; Dietary; Dietetics
D.M.D., Doctor of Dental Medicine
D.MIN., Doctor of Ministry
D.O., Doctor of Osteopathic Medicine and Surgery, Doctor of Osteopathy
DPA, Doctorate Public Administration
D.P.M., Doctor of Podiatric Medicine
Dr., Drive
Dr.P.h., Doctor of Public Health
D.Sc., Doctor of Science
D.S.W., Doctor of Social Welfare
D.V.M., Doctor of Veterinary Medicine

E., East
Ed.D., Doctor of Education
Ed.S., Specialist in Education
ENS, Ensign
Esq., Esquire
Expwy., Expressway
ext., extension

FAAN, Fellow of the American Academy of Nursing
FACATA, Fellow of the American College of Addiction Treatment Administrators
FACHE, Fellow of the American College of Healthcare Executives
FACMGA, Fellow of the American College of Medical Group Administrators
FACP, Fellow of the American College of Physicians
FACS, Fellow of the American College of Surgeons
FAX, Facsimile
FL, Florida
FPO, Fleet Post Office
FRCPSC, Fellow of the Royal College of Physicians and Surgeons of Canada
FT, Full-time

GA, Georgia
Govt., Government; Governmental

HHS, Department of Health and Human Services
HI, Hawaii
HM, Helmsman
HMO, Health Maintenance Organization
Hon., Honorable; Honorary
H.S.A., Health System Administrator
Hts., Heights
Hwy., Highway

IA, Iowa
ID, Idaho
IL, Illinois
IN, Indiana
Inc., Incorporated

J.D., Doctor of Law
J.P., Justice of the Peace
Jr., Junior

KS, Kansas
KY, Kentucky

LA, Louisiana
LCDR, Lieutenant Commander
LCSW, Licensed Certified Social Worker
L.H.D., Doctor of Humanities

L.I.S.W., Licensed independent Social Worker
LL.D., Doctor of Laws
L.L.P., Limited Licensed Practitioner
L.M.H.C., Licensed Master of Health Care
L.M.S.W., Licensed Master of Social Work
L.N.H.A., Licensed Nursing Home Administrator
L.P.C., Licensed Professional Counselor
LPN, Licensed Practical Nurse
L.P.N., Licensed Practical Nurse
L.S.W., Licensed Social Worker
Lt., Lieutenant
LTC, Lieutenant Colonel
Ltd., Limited
LT.GEN., Lieutenant General
LTJG, Lieutenant (junior grade)

MA, Massachusetts
M.A., Master of Arts
Maj., Major
M.B., Bachelor of Medicine
M.B.A., Masters of Business Administration
MC, Medical Corps; Marine Corps
M.C., Member of Congress
MD, Maryland
M.D., Doctor of Medicine
ME, Maine
M.Ed., Master of Education
MFCC, Marriage/Family/Child Counselor
MHA, Mental Health Association
M.H.S., Masters in Health Science; Masters in Human Service
MI, Michigan
MM, Masters of Management
MN, Minnesota
M.N., Master of Nursing
MO, Missouri
M.P.A., Master of Public Administration; Master Public Affairs
M.P.H., Master of Public Health
M.P.S., Master of Professional Studies; Master of Public Science
MS, Mississippi
M.S., Master of Science
MSC, Medical Service Corps
M.S.D., Doctor of Medical Science
MSHSA, Master of Science Health Service Administration
M.S.N., Master of Science in Nursing
M.S.P.H., Master of Science in Public Health
M.S.S.W., Master of Science in Social Work
M.S.W., Master of Social Work
MT, Montana
Mt., Mount

N., North
NC, North Carolina
N.C.A.D.C., National Certification of Alcohol and Drug Counselors
ND, North Dakota
NE, Nebraska
NH, New Hampshire
NHA, National Hearing Association; Nursing Home Administrator
NJ, New Jersey
NM, New Mexico
NPA, National Perinatal Association
NV, Nevada
NY, New York

OCN, Oncology Certified Nurse
O.D., Doctor of Optometry
O.F.M., Order Franciscan Monks, Order of Friars Minor
OH, Ohio
OK, Oklahoma
OR, Oregon
O.R., Operating Room

O.R.S., Operating Room Supervisor
OSF, Order of St. Francis

PA, Pennsylvania
P.A., Professional Association
P.C., Professional Corporation
Pharm.D., Doctor of Pharmacy
Ph.B., Bachelor of Philosophy
Ph.D., Doctor of Philosophy
PHS, Public Health Service
Pkwy., Parkway
Pl., Place
PR, Puerto Rico
PS, Professional Services
PSRO, Professional Standards Review Organization

RADM, Rear Admiral
RD, Rural Delivery
Rd., Road
R.F.D., Rural Free Delivery
RI, Rhode Island
R.M., Risk Manager
R.N., Registered Nurse
RNC, Republican National Committee; Registered Nurse or Board Certified
R.Ph., Registered Pharmacist
RRA, Registered Record Administrator
R.S.M., Religious Sisters of Mercy
Rte., Route

S., South
SC, South Carolina
S.C., Surgery Center
SCAC, Senior Certified Addiction Counselor
Sc.D., Doctor of Science
Sci., Science, Scientific
SD, South Dakota
SHCC, Statewide Health Coordinating Council
Sgt., Sergeant
SNA, Surgical Nursing Assistant
SNF, Skilled Nursing Facility
Sq., Square
Sr., Senior, Sister
St., Saint, Street
Sta., Station
Ste., Saint; Suite

Tel., Telephone
Terr., Terrace
TN, Tennessee
Tpke, Turnpike
Twp., Township
TX, Texas

USA, United States Army
USAF, United States Air Force
USMC, United States Marine Corps
USN, United States Navy
USPHS, United States Public Health Service
UT, Utah

VA, Virginia
VADM, Vice Admiral
VI, Virgin Islands
Vlg., Village
VT, Vermont

W., West
WA, Washington
WI, Wisconsin
WV, West Virginia
WY, Wyoming

Abbreviations

Index

Notes

Notes